D1632909

Stanley Gibbons
Simplified Catalogue

Stamps of the World

Essex County Council
3013021716332 7

Stanley Gibbons Simplified Catalogue

Stamps of the World 4

2019 Edition

Countries **Jersey – New Republic**

Stanley Gibbons Ltd
London and Ringwood

By Appointment to
Her Majesty The Queen
Philatelists
Stanley Gibbons Ltd
London

81st Edition
Published in Great Britain by
Stanley Gibbons Ltd
Publications Editorial, Sales Offices and Distribution Centre
7, Parkside, Christchurch Road,
Ringwood, Hampshire BH24 3SH
Telephone +44 (0) 1425 472363

British Library Cataloguing in
Publication Data.
A catalogue record for this book is available
from the British Library.

Volume 4
ISBN 978-1-911304-07-4

Boxed Set
ISBN 978-1-911304-31-9

Published as Stanley Gibbons Simplified Catalogue from 1934 to 1970, renamed Stamps of the World in 1971, and produced in two (1982-88), three (1989-2001), four (2002-2005) five (2006-2010) and six from 2011 volumes as Stanley Gibbons Simplified Catalogue of Stamps of the World.

© Stanley Gibbons Ltd 2018

The contents of this catalogue, including the numbering system and illustrations, are fully protected by copyright. No part of this publication may be reproduced, stored in a retrieval system, or transmitted, in any form or by any means, electronic, mechanical, photocopying, recording or otherwise, without the prior permission of Stanley Gibbons Limited. Requests for such permission should be addressed to the Catalogue Editor at Ringwood.

This catalogue is sold on condition that it is not, by way of trade or otherwise lent, re-sold, hired out, circulated or otherwise disposed of other than in its complete, original and unaltered form and without a similar condition including this condition being imposed on the subsequent purchaser.

Errors and omissions excepted. The colour reproduction of stamps in this catalogue is only as accurate as the printing process allows.

Item No. R2881 Set–19

Printed and bound in Wales by Stephens & George

Contents – Volume 4

Introduction vii
Information for users viii
Guide to Entries x
Key-Types xii

Jersey **1**
(a) War Occupation Issues **1**
(b) Independent Postal Administration **1**
Jhalawar **23**
Jind **23**
Johore **23**
Jordan **24**
Jordanian Occupation of Palestine **47**
Jubaland **47**
Kampuchea **48**
Karelia **53**
Katanga **53**
Kathiri State of Seiyun **53**
Kazakhstan **54**
Kedah **68**
Kelantan **69**
Kenya **71**
Kenya, Uganda and Tanganyika (Tanzania) **80**
Khmer Republic **83**
Khor Fakkan **84**
Kiautschou (Kiaochow) **84**
King Edward VII Land **84**
Kionga **84**
Kiribati **84**
Kishangarh **91**
Korea **92**
Korean Empire **92**
Korea (South Korea) **92**
A. United States Military Government **92**
B. Republic of Korea **93**
C. North Korean Occupation **145**
Korea (North Korea) **145**
A. Russian Occupation **145**
B. Korean People's Democratic Republic **145**
Kosovo Republic **213**
Kouang Tcheou (Kwangchow) **217**
Kuwait **217**
Kyrgyzstan **240**
Kyrgyzstan Express Post **249**
La Aguera **251**
Labuan **251**
Lagos **251**
Laos **251**
Las Bela **274**
Latakia **274**
Latvia **275**
Lebanon **288**
Leeward Islands **305**
Lesotho **305**
Liberia **320**
Libya **335**
A. Italian Colony **335**
B. Independent **335**
Liechtenstein **364**
Lithuania **387**
Lombardy and Venetia **403**
Lourenco Marques **403**
Lubeck **404**
Luxembourg **404**
Macao **433**
Macedonia **453**
A. German Occupation **453**
B. Independent Republic **453**
Madagascar **470**
A. French Post Offices **470**
B. French Colony of Madagascar and Dependencies **470**
Madeira **477**
Mafeking **480**
Mahra Sultanate of Qishn and Socotra **480**
Malacca **480**
Malagasy Republic **481**
Malawi **495**
Malaya (British Military Adminstration) **504**
Malaya (Japanese Occupation) **504**
(a) Johore **504**
(b) Kedah **504**
(c) Kelantan **504**
(d) Penang **504**
(e) Selangor **504**
(f) Singapore **504**
(g) Trengganu **504**
Malay (Thai Occupation) **505**
Malayan Federation **505**
Malayan Postal Union **506**
Malaysia **506**
A. National Series **506**
B. Federal Territory Issues **530**
Maldive Islands **530**
Mali **562**
A. Federation **562**
B. Republic **562**
Malta **584**
Manama **604**
Manchukuo **604**
Mariana Islands **605**
Marienwerder **605**
Marshall Islands **605**
A. German Protectorate **606**
B. Republic **606**
Martinique **633**
Mauritania **634**
Mauritius **648**
Mayotte **659**
Mecklenburg-Schwerin **665**
Mecklenburg-Strelitz **665**
Memel **665**
Lithuanian Occupation **665**
Mexico **666**
Revolutionary Provisionals **666**
Constitutionalist General Issues **666**
Conventionist Issues **667**
Constitutionalist Provisional Issues **667**
General Issues **667**
Micronesia **721**
Middle Congo **740**
Modena **740**
Moheli **740**
Moldova **740**
Monaco **752**
Mongolia **805**
Mong-Tseu (Mengtsz) **841**
Montenegro **841**
Italian Occupation **846**
German Occupation **846**
Montserrat **846**
Morocco **861**
A. Northern Zone **861**
B. Southern Zone **861**
C. Issues for the whole of Morocco **862**
Morocco Agencies **889**
I. Gibraltar Issues Overprinted **889**
II. British Currency **889**
III. Spanish Currency **889**
IV. French Currency **889**
V. Tangier International Zone **889**
Morvi **890**
Mosul **890**
Mozambique **890**
Mozambique Company **908**
Muscat **909**
Muscat and Oman **909**
Myanmar **909**
Nabha **912**
Nagorno-Karabakh **912**
Nakhichevan **912**
Namibia **912**
Nandgaon **922**
Naples **922**
Natal **922**
Nauru **922**
Nawanagar **929**
Neapolitan Provinces **930**
Negri Sembilan **930**
Nepal **930**
Netherlands **949**
International Court of Justice **984**
Provincial Stamps **984**
Netherlands Antilles **984**
Netherlands Indies **1002**
Netherlands New Guinea **1004**
Nevis **1005**
New Brunswick **1028**
New Caledonia **1028**
Newfoundland **1056**
New Guinea **1057**
New Hebrides **1058**
British Administration **1058**
French Administration **1060**
New Republic **1062**

Index **1063**

Gibbons Stamp Monthly

The first choice for stamp collectors since 1890

Subscribe TODAY!

Gibbons Stamp Monthly offers you:

- Great value, usually 20-30% more pages than other stamp magazines
- More on Great Britain and Commonwealth
- A magazine written by stamp collectors for stamp collectors
- Comprehensive catalogue supplement every month
- More news · More articles

By subscribing you will also receive:

- Monthly subscriber letters offering big discounts off SG products
- Savings on the latest Stanley Gibbons catalogues
- Free access to GSM online with paper subscription

"The premier philatelic magazine available anywhere – it's difficult to improve on perfection"
– Everett L. Parker, Global Stamp News

3 easy ways to read Gibbons Stamp Monthly

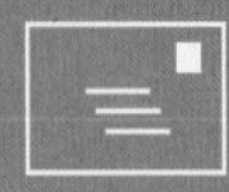

POST

Call our Subscription Hotline or complete the form facing this page to receive your monthly issue straight to your door:

0800 611 622 (UK)
+44 1425 472 363 (Overseas)

ONLINE

Subscribe and view online:
stanleygibbons.com/gsm-sub

APP

View via our APP and view anytime or anywhere:
stanleygibbons.com/app

www.stanleygibbons.com

Stanley Gibbons Limited
7 Parkside, Christchurch Road,
Ringwood, Hants, BH24 3SH
+44 (0)1425 472 363

Introduction

The ultimate reference work for all stamps issued around the world since the very first Penny Black of 1840, now with an improved layout.

Stamps of the World provides a comprehensive, illustrated, priced guide to postage stamps, and is the standard reference tool for every collector. It will help you to identify those elusive stamps, to value your collection, and to learn more about the background to issues. *Stamps of the World* was first published in 1934 and has been updated every year since 1950.

Included is a guide to stamp identification so that you can easily discover which country issued your stamp.

Re-designed to provide more colourful, clearer, and easy-to-navigate listings, these volumes continue to present you with a wealth of information to enhance your enjoyment of stamp collecting.

Features:

- Current values for every stamp in the world
- Easy-to-use simplified listings
- World-recognised Stanley Gibbons catalogue numbers
- A wealth of historical, geographical and currency information
- Indexing and cross-referencing throughout the volumes
- Miniature sheets listed and priced
- Thousands of new issues since the last edition

For this edition, prices have been thoroughly reviewed for Great Britain, and all Commonwealth countries up to 1970, with further updates for Commonwealth countries which have appeared in our recently published or forthcoming comprehensive catalogues, under the *India & Indian States*, *East Africa*, *Australia* as well as *Belize*, *Guyana* and *Trinidad & Tobago*.

Other countries with complete price updates from the following comprehensive catalogues are: *North-East Africa*, *Denmark & Norway*, *Germany* and *Middle East*.

The first *Gibbons Stamp Monthly* Catalogue Supplement to this edition is September 2018.

Clare de la Feuillade, Editor

Sue Price and Lesley Brine, New Issue Listings
Barbara Hawkins, Pricing Assistant
Leslie Fuller, Proof Reader

Information for users

Scope of the Catalogue

Stamps of the World contains listings of postage stamps only. Apart from the ordinary definitive, commemorative and air-mail stamps of each country there are sections for the following, where appropriate. Noted below are the Prefixes used for each section (see Guide to Entries for further information):

- postage due stamps – Prefix in listing D
- parcel post or postcard stamps – Prefix P
- official stamps – Prefix O
- express and special delivery stamps - Prefix E
- frank stamps – Prefix F
- charity tax stamps – Prefix J
- newspaper and journal stamps – Prefix N
- printed matter stamps – Prefix P
- registration stamps - Prefix R
- acknowledgement of receipt stamps – Prefix AR
- late fee and too late stamps – Prefix L
- military post stamps- Prefix M
- recorded message stamps – Prefix RM
- personal delivery stamps – Prefix P
- concessional letter post – Prefix CL
- concessional parcel post – Prefix CP
- pneumatic post stamps – Prefix PE
- publicity envelope stamps – Prefix B
- bulk mail stamps – Prefix BP
- telegraph stamps used for postage – Prefix PT
- telegraph stamps (Commonwealth Countries) – Prefix T
- obligatory tax – Prefix T

As this is a simplified listing, the following are NOT included:

Fiscal or revenue stamps: stamps used solely in collecting taxes or fees for non-postal purposes. For example, stamps which pay a tax on a receipt, represent the stamp duty on a contract, or frank a customs document. Common inscriptions found include: Documentary, Proprietary, Internal Revenue and Contract Note.

Local stamps: postage stamps whose validity and use are limited in area to a prescribed district, town or country, or on certain routes where there is no government postal service. They may be issued by private carriers and freight companies, municipal authorities or private individuals.

Local carriage labels and Private local issues: many labels exist ostensibly to cover the cost of ferrying mail from one of Great Britain's offshore islands to the nearest mainland post office. They are not recognised as valid for national or international mail. Examples: Calf of Man, Davaar, Herm, Lundy, Pabay, Stroma.

Telegraph stamps: stamps intended solely for the prepayment of telegraphic communication.

Bogus or "phantom" stamps: labels from mythical places or non-existent administrations. Examples in the classical period were Sedang, Counani, Clipperton Island and in modern times Thomond and Monte Bello Islands. Numerous labels have also appeared since the War from dissident groups as propaganda for their claims and without authority from the home governments. Common examples are the numerous issues for Nagaland.

Railway letter fee stamps: special stamps issued by railway companies for the conveyance of letters by rail. Example: Talyllyn Railway. Similar services are now offered by some bus companies and the labels they issue likewise do not qualify for inclusion in the catalogue.

Perfins ("perforated initials"): stamps perforated with the initials or emblems of firms as a security measure to prevent pilferage by office staff.

Labels: Slips of paper with an adhesive backing. Collectors tend to make a distinction between stamps, which have postal validity and anything else, which has not.

Cut-outs: Embossed or impressed stamps found on postal stationery, which are cut out if the stationery has been ruined and re-used as adhesives.

Further information on a wealth of terms is in *Philatelic Terms Illustrated*, published by Stanley Gibbons, details are listed under Stanley Gibbons Publications. There is also a priced listing of the postal fiscals of Great Britain in our *Commonwealth & British Empire Stamps 1840-1970* Catalogue and in Volume 1 of the *Great Britain Specialised Catalogue* (5th and later editions). A full list of our current publications is given on page xxiii.

Organisation of the Catalogue

The catalogue lists countries in alphabetical order with country headers on each page and extra introductory information such as philatelic historical background at the beginning of each section. The Contents list provides a detailed guide to each volume, and the Index has full cross-referencing to locate each country in each volume.

Each country lists postage stamps in order of date of issue, from earliest to most recent, followed by separate sections for categories such as postage due stamps, express stamps, official stamps, and so on (see above for a complete listing).

"Appendix" Countries

Since 1968 Stanley Gibbons has listed in an appendix stamps which are judged to be in excess of true postal needs. The appendix also contains stamps which have not fulfilled all the normal conditions for full catalogue listing. Full catalogue listing requires a stamp to be:

- issued by a legitimate postal authority
- recognised by the government concerned
- adhesive
- valid for proper postal use in the class of service for which they are inscribed
- available to the general public at face value with no artificial restrictions being imposed on their distribution (with the exception of categories such as postage dues and officials)

Only stamps issued from component parts of otherwise united territories which represent a genuine political, historical or postal division within the country concerned have a full catalogue listing. Any such issues which do not fulfil this stipulation will be recorded in the Catalogue Appendix only.

Stamps listed in the Appendix are constantly under review in light of newly acquired information about them. If we are satisfied that a stamp qualifies for proper listing in the body of the catalogue it will be moved in the next edition.

"Undesirable Issues"

The rules governing many competitive exhibitions are set by the Federation Internationale de Philatelie and stipulate a downgrading of marks for stamps classed as "undesirable issues".

This catalogue can be taken as a guide to status. All stamps in the main listings are acceptable. Stamps in the Appendix are considered, "undesirable issues" and should not be entered for competition. Correspondence

We welcome information and suggestions but we must ask correspondents to include the cost of postage for the return of any materials, plus registration where appropriate. Letters and emails should be addressed to Lorraine Holcombe, 7 Parkside, Christchurch Road, Ringwood, Hampshire BH24 3SH, UK. lholcombe@stanleygibbons.co.uk. Where information is solicited purely for the benefit of the enquirer we regret we are seldom able to reply.

Identification of Stamps

We regret we do not give opinion on the authenticity of stamps, nor do we identify stamps or number them by our Catalogue.

Thematic Collectors

Stanley Gibbons publishes a range of thematic catalogues (see page xxiii for details) and *Stamps of the World* is ideal to use with these titles, as it supplements those listings with extra information.

Type numbers

Type numbers (in bold) refer to illustrations, and are not the Stanley Gibbons Catalogue numbers.

A brief description of the stamp design subject is given below or beside the illustrations, or close by in the entry, where needed. Where a design is not illustrated, it is usually the same shape and size as a related design, unless otherwise indicated.

Watermarks

Watermarks are not covered in this catalogue. Stamps of the same issue with differing watermarks are not listed separately.

Perforations

Perforations – all stamps are perforated unless otherwise stated. No distinction is made between the various gauges of perforation but early stamp issues which exist both imperforate and perforated are usually listed separately. Where a heading states, "Imperf or perf"or "Perf. or rouletted" this does not necessarily mean that all values of the issue are found in both conditions

Se-tenant Pairs

Se-tenant Pairs – Many modern issues are printed in sheets containing different designs or face values. Such pairs, blocks, strips or sheets are described as being "*se-tenant*" and they are outside the scope of this catalogue, although reference to them may occur in instances where they form a composite design.

Miniature Sheets are now fully listed.

Guide to Entries

A **Country of Issue**

B **Part Number** – shows where to find more detailed listings in the Stanley Gibbons Comprehensive Catalogue. Part 6 refers to France and so on – see p. li for further information on the breakdown of the Catalogue.

C **Country Information** – Brief geographical and historical details for the issuing country.

D **Currency** – Details of the currency, and dates of earliest use where applicable, on the face value of the stamps. Where a Colony has the same currency as the Mother Country, see the details given in that country.

E **Year Date** – When a set of definitive stamps has been issued over several years the Year Date given is for the earliest issue, commeorative sets are listed in chronological order. As stamps of the same design or issue are usually grouped together, a list of King George VI stamps, for example, headed "1938" may include stamps issued from 1938 to the end of the reign.

F **Stanley Gibbons Catalogue number** – This is a unique number for each stamp to help the collector identify stamps in the listing. The Stanley Gibbons numbering system is universally recognized as definitive. The majority of listings are in chronological order, but where a definitive set of stamps has been re-issued with a new watermark, perforation change or imprint date, the cheapest example is given; in such cases catalogue numbers may not be in numerical order.

Where insufficient numbers have been left to provide for additional stamps to a listing, some stamps will have a suffix letter after the catalogue number. If numbers have been left for additions to a set and not used they will be left vacant.

The separate type numbers (in bold) refer to illustrations (see M).

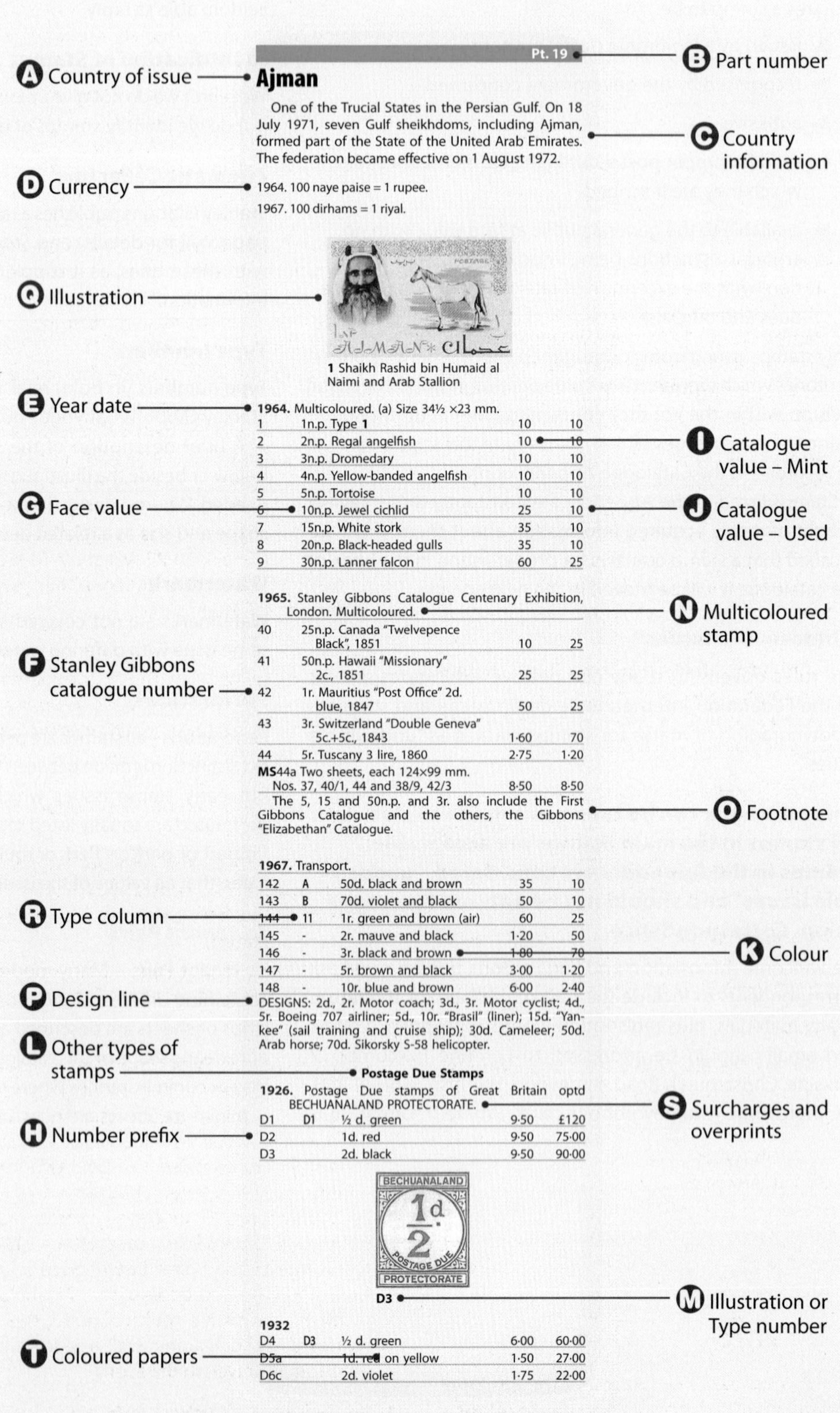

Pt. 19

Ajman

One of the Trucial States in the Persian Gulf. On 18 July 1971, seven Gulf sheikhdoms, including Ajman, formed part of the State of the United Arab Emirates. The federation became effective on 1 August 1972.

1964. 100 naye paise = 1 rupee.
1967. 100 dirhams = 1 riyal.

1 Shaikh Rashid bin Humaid al Naimi and Arab Stallion

1964. Multicoloured. (a) Size 34½ ×23 mm.

1	1n.p. Type **1**	10	10
2	2n.p. Regal angelfish	10	10
3	3n.p. Dromedary	10	10
4	4n.p. Yellow-banded angelfish	10	10
5	5n.p. Tortoise	10	10
6	10n.p. Jewel cichlid	25	10
7	15n.p. White stork	35	10
8	20n.p. Black-headed gulls	35	10
9	30n.p. Lanner falcon	60	25

1965. Stanley Gibbons Catalogue Centenary Exhibition, London. Multicoloured.

40	25n.p. Canada "Twelvepence Black", 1851	10	25
41	50n.p. Hawaii "Missionary" 2c., 1851	25	25
42	1r. Mauritius "Post Office" 2d. blue, 1847	50	25
43	3r. Switzerland "Double Geneva" 5c.+5c., 1843	1·60	70
44	5r. Tuscany 3 lire, 1860	2·75	1·20
MS44a	Two sheets, each 124x99 mm. Nos. 37, 40/1, 44 and 38/9, 42/3	8·50	8·50

The 5, 15 and 50n.p. and 3r. also include the First Gibbons Catalogue and the others, the Gibbons "Elizabethan" Catalogue.

1967. Transport.

142	A	50d. black and brown	35	10
143	B	70d. violet and black	50	10
144	11	1r. green and brown (air)	60	25
145	-	2r. mauve and black	1·20	50
146	-	3r. black and brown	1·80	70
147	-	5r. brown and black	3·00	1·20
148	-	10r. blue and brown	6·00	2·40

DESIGNS: 2d., 2r. Motor coach; 3d., 3r. Motor cyclist; 4d., 5r. Boeing 707 airliner; 5d., 10r. "Brasil" (liner); 15d. "Yankee" (sail training and cruise ship); 30d. Cameleer; 50d. Arab horse; 70d. Sikorsky S-58 helicopter.

Postage Due Stamps

1926. Postage Due stamps of Great Britain optd BECHUANALAND PROTECTORATE.

D1	D1	½ d. green	9·50	£120
D2		1d. red	9·50	75·00
D3		2d. black	9·50	90·00

BECHUANALAND ½d POSTAGE DUE PROTECTORATE

D3

1932

D4	D3	½ d. green	6·00	60·00
D5a		1d. red on yellow	1·50	27·00
D6c		2d. violet	1·75	22·00

462 Canadian Maple Leaf Emblem

1981
1030a **462** A (30c.) red 20 40
No. 1030a was printed before a new first class domestic letter rate had been agreed, "A" representing the face value of the stamp, later decided to be 30c.

G Face value – This refers to the value of each stamp and is the price it was sold for at the Post Office when issued. Some modern stamps do not have their values in figures but instead shown as a letter, see for example the entry above for Canada 1030a/Illustration 462.

H Number Prefix – Stamps other than definitives and commemoratives have a prefix letter before the catalogue number. Such stamps may be found at the end of the normal listing for each country. (See Scope of the Catalogue p.viii for a list of other types of stamps covered, together with the list of the main abbreviations used in the Catalogue).

Other prefixes are also used in the Catalogue. Their use is explained in the text: some examples are A for airmail, E for East Germany or Express Delivery stamps.

I Catalogue Value – Mint/Unused. Prices quoted for pre-1945 stamps are for lightly hinged examples. Prices quoted of unused King Edward VIII to Queen Elizabeth II issues are for unmounted mint.

J Catalogue Value – Used. Prices generally refer to fine postally used examples. For certain issues they are for cancelled-to-order.

Prices

Prices are given in pence and pounds. Stamps worth £100 and over are shown in whole pounds:

Shown in Catalogue as	
10	**10 pence**
1.75	**£1.75**
15.00	**£15**
£150	**£150**
£2300	**£2300**

Prices assume stamps are in 'fine condition'; we may ask more for superb and less for those of lower quality. The minimum catalogue price quoted is 10p and is intended as a guide for catalogue users. The lowest price for individual stamps purchased from Stanley Gibbons is £1.

Prices quoted are for the cheapest variety of that particular stamp. Differences of watermark, perforation, or other details, outside the scope of this catalogue, often increase the value. Prices quoted for mint issues are for single examples. Those in *se-tenant* pairs, strips, blocks or sheets may be worth more. Where no prices are listed it is either because the stamps are not known to exist in that particular condition, or, more usually, because there is no reliable information on which to base their value.

All prices are subject to change without prior notice and we cannot guarantee to supply all stamps as priced. Prices quoted in advertisements are also subject to change without prior notice. Due to differing production schedules it is possible that new editions of Parts 2 to 22 will show revised prices which are not included in that year's Stamps of the World.

K Colour – Colour of stamp (if fewer than four colours, otherwise noted as "multicoloured" – see N below). Colour descriptions are simple in this catalogue, and only expanded to aid identification – see other more comprehensive Stanley Gibbons catalogues for more detailed colour descriptions (see p.xxxix).

Where stamps are printed in two or more colours, the central portion of the design is the first colour given, unless otherwise stated.

L Other Types of Stamps – See Scope of the Catalogue p.viii for a list of the types of stamps included.

M Illustration or Type Number – These numbers are used to help identify stamps, either in the listing, type column, design line or footnote, usually the first value in a set. These type numbers are in a bold type face – **123**; when bracketed (**123**) an overprint or a surcharge is indicated. Some type numbers include a lower-case letter – **123a**, this indicates they have been added to an existing set. N Multicoloured – Nearly all modern stamps are multicoloured; this is indicated in the heading, with a description of the stamp given in the listing.

O Footnote – further information on background or key facts on issues

P Design line – Further details on design variations

Q Illustration – Generally, the first stamp in the set. Stamp illustrations are reduced to 60%, with overprints and surcharges shown actual size.

R Key Type – indicates a design type (see p. xii for further details) on which the stamp is based. These are the bold figures found below each illustration. The type numbers are also given in bold in the second column of figures alongside the stamp description to indicate the design of each stamp. Where an issue comprises stamps of similar design, the corresponding type number should be taken as indicating the general design. Where there are blanks in the type number column it means that the type of the corresponding stamp is that shown by the number in the type column of the same issue. A dash (–) in the type column means that the stamp is not illustrated. Where type numbers refer to stamps of another country, e.g. where stamps of one country are overprinted for use in another, this is always made clear in the text.

S Surcharges and Overprints – usually described in the headings. Any actual wordings are shown in bold type. Descriptions clarify words and figures used in the overprint. Stamps with the same overprints in different colours are not listed separately. Numbers in brackets after the descriptions are the catalogue numbers of the non-overprinted stamps. The words "inscribed" or "inscription" refer to the wording incorporated in the design of a stamp and not surcharges or overprints.

T Coloured Papers – stamps printed on coloured paper are shown – e.g. "brn on yell" indicates brown printed on yellow paper. No information on the texture of paper, e.g. laid or wove, is provided in this catalogue.

Key-Types

Standard designs frequently occuring on the stamps of the French, German, Portuguese and Spanish colonies are illustrated below together with the descriptive names and letters by which they are referred to in the lists to avoid repetition. Please see the Guide to Entries for further information.

French Group

A "Blanc" **B** "Mouchon" **C** "Merson" **D** "Tablet"

INTERNATIONAL COLONIAL EXHIBITION

E **F** " **G** **H**

I "Faidherbe" **J** "Palms" **K** "Balay" **L** "Natives" **M** "Figure"

German Group

N "Yacht" **O** "Yacht"

Spanish Group

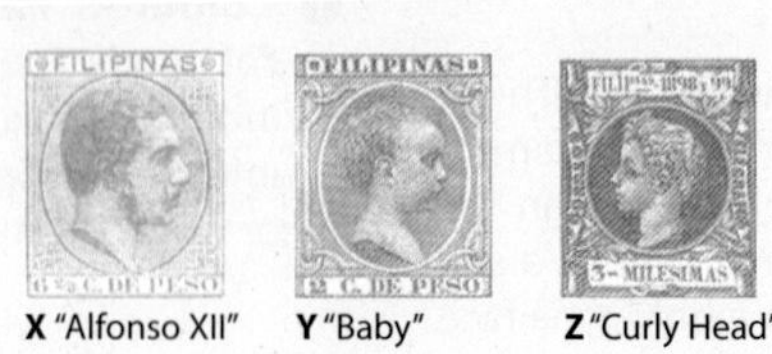

X "Alfonso XII" **Y** "Baby" **Z** "Curly Head"

Portuguese Group

P "Crown"

Q "Embossed"

R "Figures"

S "Carlos"

T "Manoel"

U Ceres"

V "Newspaper"

W "Due"

ANDREW PROMOTING PHILATELY ON THE ALAN TITCHMARSH SHOW ITV

Selling Your Stamps?

Summary Tip #21:
5 Different Ways to Sell your Stamps: Selling via Auction

by Andrew McGavin

Dear Collector,

In Part 3 (Volume 3) of 'Selling your Stamps' we discussed the importance of selecting the right dealers/organisations to approach and ensuring the choice of those with transparent modus operandi.

Here in Part 4 of 'Selling your Stamps' we'll discuss the potential advantages and disadvantages of selling through auction on your own account.

Remember we previously discussed the importance of knowing the strength of your collection. This is never more important than when making the decision to consign your stamps to auction. We have touched upon this in previous 'Stamp Tips of the Trade'. The most important thing to remember – is 'who buys complete stamp collections at auction?'

Collectors want to buy stamps that are missing from their collections: Dealers want to buy complete collections to break out individual stamps/sets to supply to collectors. By breaking collections into individual parts dealers add value/profi t. When you consign your collection as one lot to auction – 9 times out of 10 .... it is a dealer that will be buying it. Unless you are a collector that purchases collections, extract the stamps you need, and sell on the rest – you will be looking to buy specifi c stamps, sets or small 'runs'.

So what is wrong with consigning stamps to auction? Nothing, if it is the right kind of stamps. For example – you need to 'quiz' the auctioneer selected as to what he/she is actually going to do with your stamps. Let's give you an example. A few weeks ago we purchased a 'Birds' thematic collection from public auction. We paid the auctioneer exactly £1011.50= ... but the actual price the stamps were 'knocked down' to us was exactly £800=. The buyer's premium was 26.4375% - and that was before the increase in VAT. If we purchased the same collection today – the buyer's premium would be 27%!

Unless your collection includes valuable stamps/sets that the auctioneer agrees to extract and offer individually ... you are paying an enormous percentage of the value of your stamps for that auction to sell to dealers.

And did the collector realise £800=? NO. Even if the collector was charged just 12% + VAT selling commission – at today's rate the collector would receive £685=. Imagine, this collection has been sold to a dealer for £1011- by an auction who has put no money on the table and yet made a gross profit of £326= on the transaction. The dealer that paid £1,011.50 expects to make a profit. It follows that if you can approach the right dealers in the right way – then you can expect to eliminate much of the money that you pay for that auction to offer your stamps to dealers. Please refer to 'Selling your Stamps?' Tip 19 (Volume 2) for suggestions as to how this may be achieved for more valuable collections.

The 'funniest' thing of all was that the auction does not even pack your purchases .... we had to pay another £35 for a company to collect the stamps, package them and deliver them to us by parcel delivery!

To read the rest of this series 'SELLING YOUR STAMPS?' see the relevant pages in each volume:

Summary Tip 18 – Volume 1 (opposite Key Types)
Summary Tip 19 – Volume 2 (opposite Key Types)
Summary Tip 20 – Volume 3 (opposite Key Types)
Summary Tip 21 – Volume 4 (opposite Key Types)
Summary Tip 22 – Volume 5 (opposite Key Types)

Please go to Volume 6 (opposite Key Types) to see how UPA can pay you up to 36% more for your collection.

The point is that unless your collection includes valuable stamps/sets that the auctioneer agrees to extract and offer individually ... you are paying an enormous percentage of the value of your stamps for that auction to sell to dealers.

BUT, if your collection is one basically comprised of rarities – then an argument can be made for offering your collection individually lotted. In this way you are going to reach collectors + if yours is a 'named' collection often there is a 'kudos' value/premium that stamps with provenance achieve.

However – so large are the major auctions selling and buyer's premiums today – that even with collections of rarities – leading dealers can often offer to pay in excess of a fair auction estimate immediately – without risk, uncertainty of unsold lots, and immediately. The simple answer is get the auction to underwrite the minimum NET amount that they will guarantee you receive ... and then see by how much the 'trade' will improve upon this. Then you make a fully informed decision.

In Part 5 (Volume 5) of 'Selling your Stamps?' we'll discuss the merits and obstacles of selling your stamps on-line via eBay and other on-line auctions.

Happy collecting from us all,

PS. If you find this 'tip' interesting please forward it to a philatelic friend.

Andrew McGavin
Philatelic Author, Managing Director:
Universal Philatelic Auctions,
Omniphil & Avon Approvals,
Avon Mixtures,
Universal Philatelic (Ebay)

STAMPS! WE LOVE THEM! Buying or selling your stamps? Collectors – we have four different departments that can help you fi nd all the stamps you want. **REQUEST Your FREE Catalogue** and yes it's true – we do give collectors your 1st £55 Auction Winnings **FREE** if you are new to U P A, aged 18+ and live in the UK, U S A, West Europe, Australia, Canada, New Zealand **so You CAN TEST U P A**

Visit **www.upastampauctions.co.uk** when you want to buy or sell stamps.

If you'd like to receive the rest of the series, why not sign up for our FREE Stamp Tips of The Trade via our website

If you'd like to discuss the sale of your collection please contact Elaine or Andrew on 01451 861111

UNIVERSAL PHILATELIC AUCTIONS,
(Dept. SOTW) 4 The Old Coalyard, West End
Northleach, Glos. GL54 3HE UK
Tel: 01451 861111 • Fax: 01451 861297
www.upastampauctions.co.uk • Info@upastampauctions.co.uk

START NOW

if YOU BUY STAMPS need **MASSIVE PHILATELIC CHOICE?**

I'll GIVE You **3 FREE** Catalogues, **WORTH £45**
900+ pages, **10,000** colour illustrations
of 60,000+ Different Lots to choose from ***PLUS***
YOUR 1ST £55 FREE ***YES Your 1st £55 FREE***
to get you started – REQUEST in any way
Your 3 FREE AUCTION CATALOGUES NOW

Looking for that
Elusive Stamp?

Get in touch with our team

Great Britain Department: email gb@stanleygibbons.com or phone 020 7557 4464
Commonwealth Department: email amansi@stanleygibbons.com or phone 020 7557 4455

STANLEY GIBBONS
LONDON 1856

STANLEY GIBBONS 399 STRAND LONDON WC2R 0LX | WWW.STANLEYGIBBONS.COM

JERSEY

Island in the English Channel off N.W. coast of France. Occupied by German forces from June 1940 to May 1945 with separate stamp issues.

The general issue of 1948 for Channel Islands and the regional issues of 1958 are listed at end of GREAT BRITAIN.

Jersey had its own postal administration from 1969.

1941. 12 pence = 1 shilling; 20 shillings = 1 pound.
1971. 100 (new) pence = 1 pound sterling.

(a) War Occupation Issues

5

1941

1	**5**	½d. green	8·00	6·00
2	**5**	1d. red	8·00	5·00

6 Old Jersey Farm

1943

3	**6**	½d. green	12·00	12·00
4	-	1d. red	3·00	50
5	-	1½d. brown	8·00	5·75
6	-	2d. yellow	7·50	2·00
7a	-	2½d. blue	1·00	1·75
8	-	3d. violet	3·00	2·75

Designs: 1d. Portelet Bay; 1½d. Corbiere Lighthouse; 2d. Elizabeth Castle; 2½d. Mont Orgueil Castle; 3d. Gathering vraic (seaweed).

(b) Independent Postal Administration

14 Elizabeth Castle

1969. Multicoloured.

15	½d. Type **14**	10	60
16	1d. La Hougue Bie (prehistoric tomb)	10	10
17	2d. Portelet Bay	10	10
18	3d. La Corbiere Lighthouse	10	10
19	4d. Mont Orgueil Castle by night	10	10
20	5d. Arms and Royal Mace	10	10
21	6d. Jersey cow	10	10
22	9d. Chart of the English Channel	10	20
23	1s. Mont Orgueil Castle by day	25	25
24	1s.6d. Chart of the English Channel	80	80
25	1s.9d. Queen Elizabeth II (after Cecil Beaton) (vert)	1·00	1·00
26	2s.6d. Jersey Airport	1·60	1·60
27	5s. Legislative Chamber	6·50	6·50
28	10s. The Royal Court	14·00	14·00
29	£1 Queen Elizabeth II (after Cecil Beaton) (vert)	1·90	1·90

28 First Day Cover

1969. Inauguration of Post Office.

30	**28**	4d. multicoloured	10	10
31	**28**	5d. multicoloured	10	10
32	**28**	1s.6d. multicoloured	30	40
33	**28**	1s.9d. multicoloured	60	80

29 Lord Coutanche, former Bailiff of Jersey (Sir James Gunn)

1970. 25th Anniversary of Liberation. Multicoloured.

34	4d. Type **29**	20	20
35	5d. Sir Winston Churchill (Van Praag)	20	20
36	1s.6d. *Liberation* (Edmund Blampied) (horiz)	60	60
37	1s.9d. SS *Vega* (horiz)	80	80

33 'A Tribute to Enid Blyton'

1970. Battle of Flowers Parade. Multicoloured.

38	4d. Type **33**	20	10
39	5d. 'Rags to Riches'	20	20
40	1s.6d. 'Gourmet's Delight'	2·00	1·75
41	1s.9d. 'We're the Greatest'	2·00	1·75

37 Jersey Airport

1970. Decimal Currency. Nos. 15, etc, but with new colours, new design (6p.) and decimal values, as T **37**.

42	½p. multicoloured (as No. 15)	10	10
43	1p. multicoloured (as No. 18)	10	10
44	1½p. multicoloured (as No. 21)	10	10
45	2p. multicoloured (as No. 19)	10	10
46	2½p. multicoloured (as No. 20)	10	10
47	3p. multicoloured (as No. 16)	10	10
48	3½p. multicoloured (as No. 17)	10	10
49	4p. multicoloured (as No. 22)	10	10
49a	4½p. multicoloured (as No. 20)	75	75
50	5p. multicoloured (as No. 23)	10	10
50a	5½p. multicoloured (as No. 21)	75	75
51	6p. multicoloured (Martello Tower, Archirondel, 23×22 mm)	20	10
52	7½p. multicoloured (as No. 24)	20	10
52a	8p. multicoloured (as No. 19)	75	75
53	9p. multicoloured (as No. 25)	70	70
54	10p. multicoloured (as No. 26)	40	30
55	20p. multicoloured (as No. 27)	90	80
56	50p. multicoloured (as No. 28)	1·00	1·00

38 White Eared-pheasant ('White-eared Pheasant')

1971. Wildlife Preservation Trust (1st series). Multicoloured.

57	2p. Type **38**	20	10
58	2½p. Thick-billed parrot (vert)	20	15
59	7½p. Western black-and-white colobus monkey (vert)	1·75	1·75
60	9p. Ring-tailed lemur	2·50	2·50

See also Nos. 73/76, 217/221, 324/329, 447/451 and 824/829.

43 Poppy Emblem and Field

1971. 50th Anniversary of Royal British Legion. Multicoloured.

61	2p. Royal British Legion Badge	20	10
62	2½p. Type **43**	20	10
63	7½p. Jack Counter VC, and Victoria Cross	1·00	1·10
64	9p. Crossed Tricolour and Union Jack	1·00	1·10

46 *Tante Elizabeth* (E. Blampied)

1971. Paintings. Multicoloured.

65	2p. Type **46**	15	10
66	2½p. *English Fleet in the Channel* (P. Monamy) (horiz)	20	10
67	7½p. *The Boyhood of Raleigh* (Millais) (horiz)	95	95
68	9p. *The Blind Beggar* (W. W. Ouless)	1·10	1·10

See also Nos. 115/118 and 213/216.

50 Jersey Fern

1972. Wild Flowers of Jersey. Multicoloured.

69	3p. Type **50**	20	10
70	5p. Jersey thrift	30	20
71	7½p. Jersey orchid	95	95
72	9p. Jersey viper's bugloss	1·00	1·00

1972. Wildlife Preservation Trust (2nd series). As T **38**. Multicoloured.

73	2½p. Cheetah	30	10
74	3p. Rothschild's mynah (vert)	25	20
75	7½p. Spectacled bear	50	70
76	9p. Tuatara	80	90

58 Artillery Shako

1972. Royal Jersey Militia (1st issue). Multicoloured.

77	2½p. Type **58**	10	10
78	3p. Shako (2nd North Regt.)	10	10
79	7½p. Shako (5th South-West Regt.)	30	30
80	9p. Helmet (3rd Jersey Light Infantry)	50	60

See also Nos. 1253/1257.

62 Princess Anne

1972. Royal Silver Wedding. Multicoloured.

81	2½p. Type **62**	10	10
82	3p. Queen Elizabeth and Prince Philip (horiz)	10	10
83	7½p. Prince Charles	35	35
84	20p. The Royal Family (horiz)	35	35

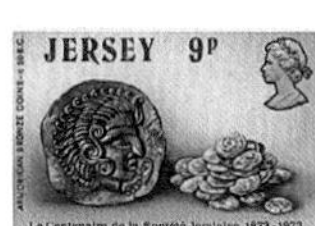

69 Armorican Bronze Coins

1973. Centenary of La Societe Jersiaise. Multicoloured.

85	2½p. Silver cups	10	10
86	3p. Gold torque (vert)	10	10
87	7½p. Royal Seal of Charles II (vert)	25	25
88	9p. Type **69**	30	30

70 Balloon *L'Armee de la Loire* and Letter, Paris, 1870

1973. Jersey Aviation History (1st series). Multicoloured.

89	3p. Type **70**	10	10
90	5p. Astra seaplane, 1912	10	10
91	7½p. Supermarine Sea Eagle amphibian G-EBFK	35	35
92	9p. de Havilland DH.86 Dragon Express G-ACYF *Giffard Bay*	45	45

See also Nos. 340/343, 409/413, 530/534, 618/623, 807/812, 962/967, 1074/**MS**1080, 1326/**MS**1332, 1410/**MS**1416 and 1643/**MS**1649.

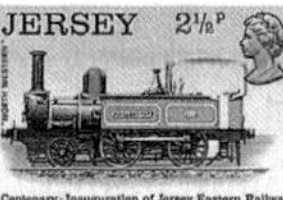

74 *North Western*, 1870

1973. Jersey Railway History (1st series). Centenary of Jersey Eastern Railway. Early Locomotives. Multicoloured.

93	2½p. Type **74**	10	10
94	3p. *Calvados*, 1873	10	10
95	7½p. *Carteret* at Grouville station, 1893	35	35
96	9p. *Caesarea*, 1873, and route map	45	45

See also Nos. 365/369 and 1433/**MS**1439.

78 Princess Anne and Capt. Mark Phillips

1973. Royal Wedding.

97	**78**	3p. multicoloured	10	10
98	**78**	20p. multicoloured	50	50

79 Spider Crab

1973. Marine Life. Multicoloured.

99	2½p. Type **79**	10	10
100	3p. Conger eel	10	10
101	7½p. Lobster	30	35
102	20p. Tuberculate ormer	40	45

83 Freesias

1974. Spring Flowers. Multicoloured.

103	3p. Type **83**	10	10
104	5½p. Anemones	15	15
105	8p. Carnations and Gladioli	25	30
106	10p. Daffodils and Iris	30	35

87 First UK Pillarbox and Contemporary Cover

1974. Centenary of UPU. Multicoloured.

107	2½p. Type **87**	10	10
108	3p. Jersey postmen, 1862 and 1969	10	15
109	5½p. Modern pillarbox and cover, 1974	25	25
110	20p. RMS *Aquila* (1874) and BAC One Eleven 200 (1974)	35	40

91 John Wesley

1974. Anniversaries.

111	**91**	3p. black and brown	10	10
112	-	3½p. violet and blue	10	10
113	-	8p. black and lilac	20	25
114	-	20p. black and stone	45	50

Portraits and Events: 3p. (Bicentenary of Methodism in Jersey); 3½p. Sir William Hillary, founder (150th anniversary of RNLI); 8p. Canon Wace (poet and historian) (800th death anniversary); 20p. Sir Winston Churchill (Birth centenary).

95 *Catherine* and *Mary* (Royal yachts)

1974. Marine Paintings by Peter Monamy. Multicoloured.

115	3½p. Type **95**	10	10
116	5½p. French two-decker	15	10
117	8p. Dutch vessel (horiz)	25	30
118	25p. Battle of Cap La Hague, 1692 (55×27 mm)	55	60

99 Potato Digger

1975. 19th-century Farming. Multicoloured.

119	3p. Type **99**	10	10
120	3½p. Cider crusher	10	10
121	8p. Six-horse plough	20	25
122	10p. Hay cart	35	40

103 HM Queen Elizabeth, the Queen Mother (photograph by Cecil Beaton)

1975. Royal Visit.

123	**103** 20p. multicoloured	50	50

104 Nautilus Shell

1975. Jersey Tourism. Multicoloured.

124	5p. Type **104**	10	10
125	8p. Parasol	15	15
126	10p. Deckchair	30	30
127	12p. Sandcastle with flags of Jersey and the UK	40	40
MS128	146×68 mm. Nos. 124/127	90	1·10

108 Common Tern

1975. Sea Birds. Multicoloured.

129	4p. Type **108**	10	10
130	5p. British storm petrel ('Storm-Petrel')	15	10
131	8p. Brent geese	40	30
132	25p. Shag	70	70

112 Armstrong Whitworth Siskin IIIA

1975. 50th Anniversary of Royal Air Force Association, Jersey Branch. Multicoloured.

133	4p. Type **112**	10	10
134	5p. Supermarine Southampton I flying boat	15	15
135	10p. Supermarine Spitfire Mk 1	40	30
136	25p. Folland Fo-141 Gnat T1	70	60

116 Map of Jersey Parishes

1976. Multicoloured. (a) Parish Arms and Views.

137	½p. Type **116**	10	10
138	1p. Zoological Park	10	10
139	5p. St Mary's Church	10	10
140	6p. Seymour Tower	10	10
141	7p. La Corbiere Lighthouse	10	10
142	8p. St Saviour's Church	15	10
143	9p. Elizabeth Castle	15	10
144	10p. Gorey Harbour	20	10
145	11p. Jersey Airport	25	25
146	12p. Grosnez Castle	25	20
147	13p. Bonne Nuit Harbour	25	20
148	14p. Le Hocq Tower	30	20
149	15p. Morel Farm	30	25

129 Parish Arms and Island Scene

(b) Emblems.

150	20p. Type **129**	45	45
151	30p. Flag and map	55	50
152	40p. Postal HQ and badge	80	80
153	50p. Parliament, Royal Court and Arms	1·00	1·00
154	£1 Lieutenant-Governor's flag and Government House	3·00	3·00
155	£2 Queen Elizabeth II (vert)	4·00	4·00

135 Sir Walter Raleigh and Map of Virginia

1976. Bicentenary of American Independence. Multicoloured.

160	5p. Type **135**	10	10
161	7p. Sir George Carteret and map of New Jersey	15	10
162	11p. Philippe d'Auvergne and Long Island landing	40	40
163	13p. John Copley and sketch	50	50

139 Dr. Grandin and Map of China

1976. Birth Centenary of Dr. Lilian Grandin (medical missionary).

164	**139** 5p. multicoloured	10	10
165	- 7p. yellow, brown and black	10	10
166	- 11p. multicoloured	35	30
167	- 13p. multicoloured	50	50

Designs: 7p. Sampan on the Yangtze; 11p. Overland trek; 13p. Dr. Grandin at work.

143 Coronation, 1953 (photographed by Cecil Beaton)

1977. Silver Jubilee. Multicoloured.

168	5p. Type **143**	15	10
169	7p. Visit to Jersey, 1957	20	15
170	25p. Queen Elizabeth II (photo by Peter Grugeon)	40	55

146 Coins of 1871 and 1877

1977. Centenary of Currency Reform. Multicoloured.

171	5p. Type **146**	10	10
172	7p. One-twelfth shilling, 1949	15	10
173	11p. Silver crown, 1966	30	30
174	13p. £2 piece, 1972	40	40

150 Sir William Weston and *Santa Anna*, 1530

1977. Centenary of St John Ambulance. Multicoloured.

175	5p. Type **150**	10	10
176	7p. Sir William Drogo and ambulance, 1877	10	10
177	11p. Duke of Connaught and ambulance, 1917	25	25
178	13p. Duke of Gloucester and stretcher-team, 1977	40	40

154 Arrival of Queen Victoria, 1846

1977. 125th Anniversary of Victoria College. Multicoloured.

179	7p. Type **154**	15	10
180	10½p. Victoria College, 1852	20	15
181	11p. Sir Galahad Statue, 1924 (vert)	25	25
182	13p. College Hall (vert)	40	40

158 Harry Vardon Statuette and Map of Royal Jersey Course

1978. Centenary of Royal Jersey Golf Club. Multicoloured.

183	6p. Type **158**	10	10
184	8p. Harry Vardon's grip and swing	15	10
185	11p. Harry Vardon's putt	35	35
186	13p. Golf trophies and book by Harry Vardon	40	40

162 Mont Orgueil Castle

1978. Europa. Castles from Paintings by Thomas Phillips. Multicoloured.

187	6p. Type **162**	10	10
188	8p. St. Aubin's Fort	15	15
189	10½p. Elizabeth Castle	35	40

165 *Gaspé Basin* (P. J. Ouless)

1978. Links with Canada. Multicoloured.

190	6p. Type **165**	10	10
191	8p. Map of Gaspé Peninsula	15	10
192	10½p. *Century* (brigantine)	20	20
193	11p. Early map of Jersey	40	35
194	13p. St Aubin's Bay, town and harbour	45	45

170 Queen Elizabeth and Prince Philip

1978. 25th Anniversary of Coronation.

195	**170** 8p. silver, black and red	20	10
196	- 25p. silver, black and blue	50	60

Design: 25p. Hallmarks of 1953 and 1977.

172 Mail Cutter, 1778–1827

1978. Bicentenary of England–Jersey Government Mail Packet Service.

197	**172** 6p. black, brown and yellow	10	10
198	- 8p. black, green and yellow	15	10
199	- 10½p. black, ultram & bl	30	25
200	- 11p. black, purple and lilac	35	35
201	- 13p. black, red and pink	40	45

Designs: Ships—8p. *Flamer*, 1831–7; 10½p. *Diana*, 1877–1890; 11p. *Ibex*, 1891–1925; 13p. *Caesarea*, 1960–1975.

177 Jersey Calf

1979. Ninth Conference of World Jersey Cattle Bureau. Multicoloured.

202	6p. Type **177**	10	10
203	25p. Ansom Designette (calf presented to the Queen, 1978) (46×29 mm)	50	60

179 Jersey Pillarbox, *c.* 1860

1979. Europa. Communications. Multicoloured.

204	8p. Type **179**	15	15
205	8p. Clearing modern postbox	15	15
206	10½p. Telephone switchboard, *c.* 1900	15	15
207	10½p. Modern SPC telephone system	15	15

183 Percival Mew Gull G-AEXF *Golden City*

1979. 25th — International Air Rally. Multicoloured.

208	6p. Type **183**	10	10
209	8p. de Havilland Canada DHC-1 Chipmunk trainer OO-PHS	25	20
210	10½p. Druine D.31 Turbulent	25	30
211	11p. de Havilland DH.82A Tiger Moth	30	30
212	13p. North American AT-6 Harvard F-BRGB	40	40

188 *My First Sermon*

1979. International Year of the Child and 150th Birth Anniversary of Sir John Millais (painter). Paintings. Multicoloured.

213	8p. Type **188**	20	15
214	10½p. *Orphans*	30	30
215	11p. *The Princes in the Tower*	30	30
216	25p. *Christ in the House of his Parents* (50×32 mm)	50	60

1979. Wildlife Preservation Trust (3rd series). As T **38**. Multicoloured.

217	6p. Pink pigeon (vert)	10	10
218	8p. Orangutan (vert)	20	15
219	11½p. Waldrapp ('Waldrapp Ibis')	30	30
220	13p. Lowland gorilla (vert)	45	40
221	15p. Rodriguez flying fox (vert)	45	40

197 Plan of Mont Orgueil

1980. Jersey Fortresses. Drawings by Thomas Phillips. Multicoloured.

222	8p. Type **197**	20	15
223	11½p. Plan of La Tour de St Aubin	30	30
224	13p. Plan of Elizabeth Castle	30	30
225	25p. Map of Jersey showing fortresses (38×27 mm)	50	60

201 Sir Walter Raleigh

1980. Europa. Links with Britain. Multicoloured.

226	9p. Type **201**	20	15
227	9p. Paul Ivy (engineer) discussing Elizabeth Castle	20	15
228	13½p. Sir George Carteret receiving deeds to Smith's Island, Virginia from Charles II	30	30
229	13½p. Lady Carteret, maid and Jean Chevalier	30	30

Nos. 226/227 and 228/229 were issued together, *se-tenant*, forming composite designs.

205 Planting

1980. Centenary of Jersey Royal Potato. Multicoloured.

230	7p. Type **205**	20	20
231	15p. Digging	30	30
232	17½p. Weighbridge	40	40

208 Three Lap Event

1980. 60th Anniversary of Jersey Motorcycle and Light Car Club. Multicoloured.

233	7p. Type **208**	15	15
234	9p. Jersey International Road Race	20	15
235	13½p. Scrambling	30	30
236	15p. Sand racing (saloon cars)	30	35
237	17½p. National Hill Climb	35	40

213 *Eye of the Wind*

1980. Operation Drake and 150th Anniversary of Royal Geographical Society (14p). Multicoloured.

238	7p. Type **213**	15	15
239	9p. Diving from inflatable raft	20	20
240	13½p. Exploration of Papua New Guinea	30	30
241	14p. *Discovery*	30	35
242	15p. Aerial walkway, conservation project, Sulawesi	35	40
243	17½p. *Eye of the Wind* and Goodyear Aerospace airship *Europa*	40	40

219 Detail of *The Death of Major Peirson*

1981. Bicentenary of Battle of Jersey. Details of J. S. Copley's painting.

244	**219**	7p. multicoloured	15	15
245	-	10p. multicoloured	25	25
246	-	15p. multicoloured	35	40
247	-	17½p. multicoloured	40	40
MS248		144×97 mm. Nos. 244/247	1·40	1·60

Stamps from No. **MS**248 are without white margins.

223 De Bagot

250 *Queen Elizabeth II* (Norman Hepple)

1981. Arms of Jersey Families.

249	**223**	½p. black, silver and green	20	20
250	-	1p. multicoloured	10	10
251	-	2p. multicoloured	10	10
252	-	3p. multicoloured	10	15
253	-	4p. silver, black and mauve	15	15
254	-	5p. multicoloured	15	15
255	-	6p. multicoloured	20	20
256	-	7p. multicoloured	25	25
257	-	8p. multicoloured	30	30
258	-	9p. multicoloured	30	25
259	-	10p. multicoloured	25	25
260	-	11p. multicoloured	30	30
261	-	12p. multicoloured	35	30
262	-	13p. multicoloured	35	35
263	-	14p. multicoloured	40	40
264	-	15p. multicoloured	40	40
265	-	16p. multicoloured	35	35
266	-	17p. multicoloured	45	45
266a	-	18p. multicoloured	50	50
266b	-	19p. multicoloured	60	60
267	-	20p. black, silver and yellow	50	50
268	-	25p. black and blue	45	45
268a	-	26p. black, silver and red	50	50
269	-	30p. multicoloured	50	60
270	-	40p. multicoloured	80	80
271	-	50p. multicoloured	1·00	1·00
272	-	75p. multicoloured	1·50	1·50
273	-	£1 multicoloured	2·00	2·00
274	**250**	£5 multicoloured	8·00	8·00

Designs: As T **223**—1p. De Carteret; 2p. La Cloche; 3p. Dumaresq; 4p. Payn; 5p. Janvrin; 6p. Poingdestre; 7p. Pipon; 8p. Marett; 9p. Le Breton; 10p. Le Maistre; 11p. Bisson; 12p. Robin; 13p. Herault; 14p. Messervy; 15p. Fiott; 16p. Malet; 17p. Mabon; 18p. De St Martin; 19p. Hamptonne; 20p. Badier; 25p. L'Arbalestier; 30p. Journeaulx; 40p. Lempriere; 50p. Auvergne; 75p. Remon. 38×22 mm—£1 Jersey crest and map of Channel.

251 Knight of Hambye slaying Dragon

1981. Europa. Folklore. Multicoloured.

275	10p. Type **251**	25	15
276	10p. Servant slaying Knight of Hambye and awaiting execution	25	15
277	18p. St Brelade celebrating Easter on island	30	30
278	18p. Island revealing itself as a huge fish	30	30

Legends: 10p. (both) Slaying of the Dragon of Lawrence by the Knight of Hambye; 18p. (both) Voyages of St Brelade.

255 The Harbour by Gaslight

1981. 150th Anniversary of Gas Lighting in Jersey. Multicoloured.

279	7p. Type **255**	20	15
280	10p. The Quay	25	25
281	18p. Royal Square	40	40
282	22p. Halkett Place	45	45
283	25p. Central Market	60	60

260 Prince Charles and Lady Diana Spencer

1981. Royal Wedding.

284	**260**	10p. multicoloured	20	20
285	**260**	25p. multicoloured	70	80

261 Christmas Tree in Royal Square

1981. Christmas. Multicoloured.

286	7p. Type **261**	25	20
287	10p. East window, Parish Church, St. Helier	35	30
288	18p. Boxing Day meet of Jersey Drag Hunt	50	50

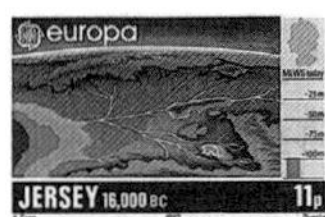

264 Jersey, 16,000 BC

1982. Europa. Formation of Jersey. Multicoloured.

289	11p. Type **264**	20	20
290	11p. In 10,000 BC (vert)	20	20
291	19½p. In 7,000 BC (vert)	50	50
292	19½p. In 4,000 BC	50	50

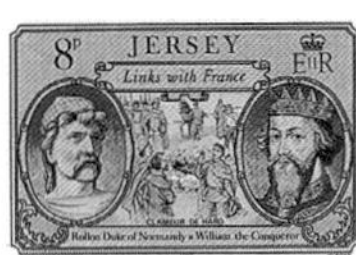

268 Duke Rollo of Normandy, William the Conqueror and 'Clameur de Haro' (traditional procedure for obtaining justice)

1982. Links with France. Multicoloured.

293	8p. Type **268**	20	15
294	8p. John of England, Philippe Auguste of France, and Siege of Rouen	20	15
295	11p. Jean Martell (brandy merchant), early still and view of Cognac	30	20
296	11p. Victor Hugo, Le Rocher des Proscrits (rock where he used to meditate) and Marine Terrace	30	20
297	19½p. Pierre Teilhard de Chardin (philosopher) and Maison Saint Louis (science institute)	45	30
298	19½p. Pere Charles Rey (scientist), anemotachymeter and The Observatory, St Louis	45	30

274 Sir William Smith and Proclamation of King George V, Jersey, 1910

1982. Youth Organisations. Multicoloured.

299	8p. Type **274**	20	20
300	11p. Boys' Brigade band, Liberation Parade, 1945 (vert)	20	20
301	24p. Sir William Smith and Lord Baden-Powell at Boys' Brigade Display, 1903	45	50
302	26p. Lord and Lady Baden-Powell, St Helier, 1924 (vert)	60	60
303	29p. Scouts in summer camp, Jersey	75	70

Nos. 299/301 were issued on the occasion of the 75th anniversary of the Boy Scout Movement, the 125th birth anniversary of Lord Baden-Powell and centenary of the Boys' Brigade (1983).

279 HMS *Tamar* and HMS *Dolphin* at Port Egmont

1983. Jersey Adventurers (1st series). 250th Birth anniversary of Philippe de Carteret. Multicoloured.

304	8p. Type **279**	20	15
305	11p. HMS *Dolphin* and HMS *Swallow* off Magellan Strait	25	15
306	19½p. Discovering Pitcairn Island	40	40
307	24p. Carteret taking possession of English Cove, New Zealand	45	50
308	26p. HMS *Swallow* sinking a pirate, Macassar Strait	50	50
309	29p. HMS *Endymion* leading convoy from West Indies	65	65

See also Nos. 417/421 and 573/578.

285 1969 5s. Legislative Chamber Definitive

1983. Europa. Multicoloured.

310	11p. Type **285**	25	30
311	11p. Royal Mace (23×32 mm)	25	30
312	19½p. 1969 10s. Royal Court definitive showing green border error	35	40
313	19½p. Bailiff's Seal (23×32 mm)	35	40

289 Charles Le Geyt and Battle of Minden (1759)

1983. World Communications Year and 250th Birth Anniversary of Charles Le Geyt (First Jersey postmaster). Multicoloured.

314	8p. Type **289**	20	20
315	11p. London to Weymouth mail coach	30	30
316	24p. PO Mail Packet *Chesterfield* attacked by French privateer	55	55
317	26p. Mary Godfray and the Hue Street Post Office	65	65
318	29p. Mail steamer leaving St Helier harbour	80	80

294 Assembly Emblem

1983. 13th General Assembly of the AIPLF (Association Internationale des Parlementaires de Langue Francaise) Jersey.

319	**294**	19½p. multicoloured	75	75

295 *Cardinal Newman*

1983. 50th Death Anniversary of Walter Ouless (artist). Multicoloured.

320	8p. Type **295**	30	30
321	11p. *Incident in the French Revolution*	50	50
322	20½p. *Thomas Hardy*	75	75
323	31p. *David with the head of Goliath* (38×32 mm)	1·00	1·00

299 Golden Lion Tamarin

1984. Wildlife Preservation Trust (4th series). Multicoloured.

324	9p. Type **299**	25	25
325	12p. Snow leopard	25	25
326	20½p. Jamaican boa	60	60
327	26p. Round island gecko	75	75
328	28p. Coscoroba swan	80	80
329	31p. St Lucia amazon ('St Lucia Parrot')	1·00	1·00

305 CEPT 25th Anniversary Logo

1984. Europa.

330	**305**	9p. light blue, blue and black	40	40
331	**305**	12p. lt green, green and black	50	50
332	**305**	20½p. lilac, purple and black	90	90

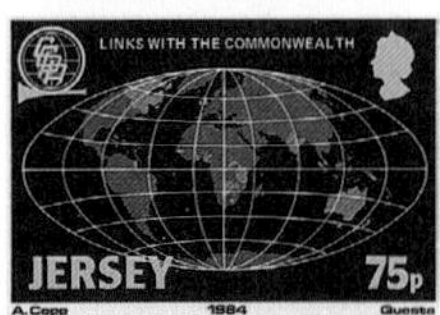

306 Map showing Commonwealth

1984. Links with the Commonwealth. Sheet 108×74 mm.

MS333 **306** 75p. multicoloured		2·00	2·00

307 *Sarah Bloomshoft* at Demie de Pas Light, 1906

1984. Centenary of Jersey RNLI Lifeboat Station. Multicoloured.

334	9p. Type **307**	25	20
335	9p. *Hearts of Oak* and *Maurice Georges*, 1949	25	20
336	12p. *Elizabeth Rippon* and *Hanna*, 1949	35	35
337	12p. *Elizabeth Rippon* and *Santa Maria*, 1951	35	35
338	20½p. *Elizabeth Rippon* and *Bacchus*, 1973	60	70
339	20½p. *Thomas James King* and *Cythara*, 1983	60	70

313 Bristol Type 170 Freighter Mk 32 G-ANWM

1984. Jersey Aviation History (2nd series). 40th Anniversary of ICAO. Multicoloured.

340	9p. Type **313**	20	15
341	12p. Airspeed A.S.57 Ambassador 2 G-ALZO	35	35
342	26p. de Havilland DH.114 Heron 1B G-AMYU	75	75
343	31p. de Havilland DH.89A Dragon Rapide G-AGPH	1·00	1·00

317 *Robinson Crusoe leaves the Wreck*

1984. Links with Australia. Paintings by John Alexander Gilfillan. Multicoloured.

344	9p. Type **317**	25	20
345	12p. *Edinburgh Castle*	30	20
346	20½p. *Maori Village*	60	60
347	26p. *Australian Landscape*	70	70
348	28p. *Waterhouse's Corner, Adelaide*	80	80
349	31p. *Captain Cook at Botany Bay*	80	80

325 *Hebe* off Corbiere, 1874

1984. Death Centenary of Philip John Ouless (artist). Multicoloured.

352	9p. Type **325**	25	20
353	12p. *The Gaspe engaging the Diomede*	30	30
354	22p. *The Paddle-steamer London entering Naples, 1856*	65	65
355	31p. *The Rambler entering Cape Town, 1840*	1·00	1·00
356	34p. *St Aubin's Bay from Mount Bingham, 1871*	1·20	1·20

330 John Ireland (composer) and Faldouet Dolmen

1985. Europa. European Music Year. Multicoloured.

357	10p. Type **330**	30	30
358	13p. Ivy Saint Helier (actress) and His Majesty's Theatre, London	40	40
359	22p. Claude Debussy (composer) and Elizabeth Castle	70	70

333 Girls' Brigade

1985. International Youth Year. Multicoloured.

360	10p. Type **333**	30	30
361	13p. Girl Guides (75th anniversary)	40	40
362	29p. Prince Charles and Jersey Youth Service Activities Base	80	80
363	31p. Sea Cadet Corps	90	90
364	34p. Air Training Corps	1·10	1·10

338 *Duke of Normandy* at Cheapside

1985. Jersey Railway History (2nd series). Jersey Western Railway. Multicoloured.

365	10p. Type **338**	35	35
366	13p. Saddletank at First Tower	40	40
367	22p. *La Moye* at Millbrook	80	80
368	29p. *St Heliers* at St Aubin	95	95
369	34p. *St Aubyns* at Corbiere	1·00	1·00

343 Memorial Window to Revd. James Hemery (former Dean) and St Helier Parish Church

1985. 300th Anniversary of Huguenot Immigration. Multicoloured.

370	10p. Type **343**	30	30
371	10p. Judge Francis Jeune, Baron St Helier, and Houses of Parliament	30	30
372	13p. Silverware by Pierre Amiraux	40	40
373	13p. Francis Voisin (merchant) and Russian port	40	40
374	22p. Robert Brohier, Schweppes carbonation plant and bottles	55	50
375	22p. George Ingouville, VC, RN and attack on Viborg	55	50

349 Howard Davis Hall, Victoria College

1985. Thomas Davis (philanthropist) Commemoration. Multicoloured.

376	10p. Type **349**	35	35
377	13p. Racing schooner *Westward*	50	50
378	31p. Howard Davis Park, St Helier	80	80
379	34p. Howard Davis Experimental Farm, Trinity	90	90

353 *Amaryllis belladonna* (Pandora Sellars)

1986. Jersey Lilies. Multicoloured.

380	13p. Type **353**	45	45
381	34p. *A Jersey Lily* (Lily Langtry) (Sir John Millais) (30×48 mm)	1·00	1·10
MS382	140×96 mm. Nos. 380×4 and 381	2·75	3·00

355 King Harold, William of Normandy and Halley's Comet, 1066 (from Bayeux Tapestry)

1986. Appearance of Halley's Comet. Multicoloured.

383	10p. Type **355**	35	35
384	22p. Lady Carteret, Edmond Halley, map and Comet	75	75
385	31p. Aspects of communications in 1910 and 1986 on TV screens	90	1·10

358 Dwarf Pansy

1986. Europa. Environmental Conservation. Multicoloured.

386	10p. Type **358**	35	35
387	14p. Sea stock	45	45
388	22p. Sand crocus	70	70

361 Queen Elizabeth II (from photo by Karsh)

1986. 60th Birthday of Queen Elizabeth II.

389	**361**	£1 multicoloured	2·50	2·75

See also No. 491b.

362 Le Rât Cottage

1986. 50th Anniversary of National Trust for Jersey. Multicoloured.

390	10p. Type **362**	25	20
391	14p. The Elms (Trust headquarters)	35	30
392	22p. Morel Farm	65	65
393	29p. Quétivel Mill	80	80
394	31p. La Vallette	90	90

367 Prince Andrew and Miss Sarah Ferguson

1986. Royal Wedding.

395	**367**	14p. multicoloured	35	35
396	**367**	40p. multicoloured	1·10	1·10

368 *Gathering Vraic*

1986. Birth Centenary of Edmund Blampied (artist).

397	**368**	10p. multicoloured	25	25
398	-	14p. black, blue and grey	40	40
399	-	29p. multicoloured	75	75
400	-	31p. black, orange and grey	90	90
401	-	34p. multicoloured	95	95

Designs: 14p. *Driving Home in the Rain*; 29p. *The Miller*; 31p. *The Joy Ride*; 34p. *Tante Elizabeth*.

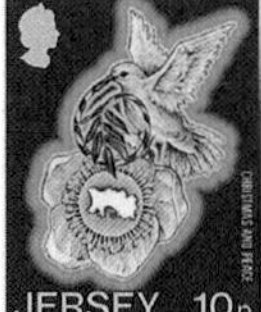

373 Island Map on Jersey Lily, and Dove holding Olive Branch

1986. Christmas. International Peace Year. Multicoloured.

402	10p. Type **373**	30	25
403	14p. Mistletoe wreath encircling European robin and dove	50	40
404	34p. Christmas cracker releasing dove	1·10	90

376 *Westward* under Full Sail

1987. Racing Schooner *Westward*. Multicoloured.

405	10p. Type **376**	40	35
406	14p. T. B. Davis at the helm	50	55
407	31p. *Westward* overhauling *Britannia*	95	95
408	34p. *Westward* fitting-out at St Helier	95	95

380 de Havilland DH.86 Dragon Express G-ACZP *Belcroute Bay*

1987. Jersey Aviation History (3rd series). 50th Anniversary of Jersey Airport. Multicoloured.

409	10p. Type **380**	30	30
410	14p. Boeing 757 and Douglas DC-9-15	45	45
411	22p. Britten-Norman BN-2A Mk III 'long nose' Trislander and Islander aircraft	55	50
412	29p. Shorts 330 G-OJUK and Vickers Viscount 800	90	90
413	31p. BAC One Eleven 500 and Handley Page H.P.R.7 Dart Herald	95	95

385 St Mary and St Peter's Roman Catholic Church

1987. Europa. Modern Architecture. Multicoloured.

414	11p. Type **385**	30	30
415	15p. Villa Devereux, St Brelade	45	45
416	22p. Fort Regent Leisure Centre, St Helier (57×29 mm)	70	75

388 HMS *Racehorse* and HMS *Carcass* (bomb ketches) trapped in Arctic

1987. Jersey Adventurers (2nd series). Philippe d'Auvergne. Multicoloured.

417	11p. Type **388**	30	30
418	15p. HMS *Alarm* on fire, Rhode Island	40	45
419	29p. HMS *Arethusa* wrecked off Ushant	70	75
420	31p. HMS *Rattlesnake* stranded on Isle de Trinidad	80	90
421	34p. Mont Orgueil Castle and fishing boats	85	95

See also Nos. 501/506 and 539/544.

393 Grant of Lands to Normandy, 911 and 933

1987. 900th Death Anniversary of William the Conqueror. Multicoloured.

422 11p. Type **393** 30 30
423 15p. Edward the Confessor and Duke Robert I of Normandy landing on Jersey, 1030 35 35
424 22p. King William's Coronation, 1066 and fatal fall, 1087 70 65
425 29p. Death of William Rufus, 1100 and Battle of Tinchebrai, 1106 75 75
426 31p. Civil war between Matilda and Stephen, 1135–1141 85 85
427 34p. Henry inherits Normandy, 1151; John asserts Ducal Rights in Jersey, 1213 95 95

399 *Grosnez Castle*

1987. Christmas. Paintings by John Le Capelain. Multicoloured.

428 11p. Type **399** 35 30
429 15p. *St Aubin's Bay* 50 50
430 22p. *Mont Orgueil Castle* 65 65
431 31p. *Town Fort and Harbour, St Helier* 90 80
432 34p. *The Hermitage* 1·00 1·00

404 *Cymbidium pontac*

1988. Jersey Orchids (2nd series). Multicoloured.

433 11p. Type **404** 30 35
434 15p. *Odontioda* 'Eric Young' (vert) 45 45
435 29p. *Lycaste auburn*, 'Seaford' and 'Ditchling' 75 75
436 31p. *Odontoglossum* 'St Brelade' (vert) 80 80
437 34p. *Cymbidium mavourneen* 'Jester' 95 95

409 Labrador Retriever

1988. Centenary of Jersey Dog Club. Multicoloured.

438 11p. Type **409** 35 40
439 15p. Wire-haired dachshund 45 60
440 22p. Pekingese 70 80
441 31p. Cavalier King Charles spaniel 90 1·00
442 34p. Dalmatian 1·00 1·00

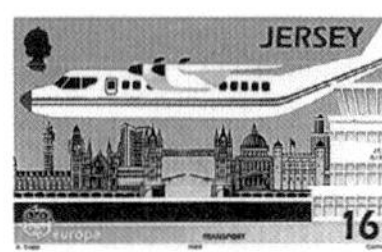

414 de Havilland Canada DHC-7 Dash Seven, London Landmarks and Jersey Control Tower

1988. Europa. Transport and Communications. Multicoloured.

443 16p. Type **414** 40 45
444 16p. Weather radar and Jersey airport landing system (vert) 40 45
445 22p. Hydrofoil, St Malo and Elizabeth Castle, St Helier 75 75
446 22p. Port control tower and Jersey Radio maritime communication centre, La Moye (vert) 75 75

418 Rodriguez Fody ('Rodrigues Fody')

1988. Wildlife Preservation Trust (5th series). Multicoloured.

447 12p. Type **418** 40 45
448 16p. Volcano rabbit (horiz) 50 50
449 29p. White-faced marmoset 90 1·00
450 31p. Ploughshare tortoise (horiz) 1·00 1·10
451 34p. Mauritius kestrel 1·10 1·20

423 Rain Forest Leaf Frog, Costa Rica

1988. Operation Raleigh. Multicoloured.

452 12p. Type **423** 35 25
453 16p. Archaeological survey, Peru 40 40
454 22p. Climbing glacier, Chile 60 60
455 29p. Red Cross Centre, Solomon Islands 75 75
456 31p. Underwater exploration, Australia 80 90
457 34p. *Zebu* (brigantine) returning to St Helier 1·00 1·00

429 St Clement Parish Church

1988. Christmas. Jersey Parish Churches (1st series). Multicoloured.

458 12p. Type **429** 30 15
459 16p. St Ouen 45 30
460 31p. St Brelade 90 90
461 34p. St Lawrence 95 95

See also Nos. 535/538 and 597/600.

433 Talbot Type 4 CT Tourer, 1912

1989. Vintage Cars (1st series). Multicoloured.

462 12p. Type **433** 35 30
463 16p. De Dion Bouton Type 1-D, 1920 50 45
464 23p. Austin 7 Chummy, 1926 65 55
465 30p. Ford Model T, 1926 90 80
466 32p. Bentley 8 litre, 1930 90 1·00
467 35p. Cadillac 452A–V16 Fleetwood Sports Phaeton, 1931 1·00 1·00

See also Nos. 591/596, 905/910 and 1532/1536.

439 Belcroute Bay

464 Arms of King George VI

1989. Jersey Scenes. Multicoloured.

468 1p. Type **439** 10 10
469 2p. High Street, St Aubin 10 10
470 4p. Royal Jersey Golf Course 10 10
471 5p. Portelet Bay 10 15
472 10p. Les Charrieres D'Anneport 30 30
473 13p. St Helier Marina 40 45
474 14p. Sand yacht racing, St Ouen's Bay 40 45
475 15p. Rozel Harbour 45 50
476 16p. St Aubin's Harbour 50 55
477 17p. Jersey Airport 50 55
478 18p. Corbiére Lighthouse 55 60
479 19p. Val de la Mare 55 60
480 20p. Elizabeth Castle 45 45
481 21p. Greve de Lecq 50 55
482 22p. Samarés Manor 45 50
483 23p. Bonne Nuit Harbour 75 55
484 24p. Grosnez Castle 60 60
485 25p. Augrés Manor 70 75
486 26p. Central Market 75 80
487 27p. St Brelade's Bay 80 90
488 30p. St Ouen's Manor 85 90
489 40p. La Hougue Bie 1·00 1·00
490 50p. Mont Orgueil Castle 1·20 1·40
491 75p. Royal Square, St Heller 2·00 1·50
491b £2 Queen Elizabeth II (from photo by Karsh) 4·00 3·25
491c £4 Type **464** 7·00 6·75

Nos. 469/491 are as T **439**.

465 Agile Frog

1989. Endangered Jersey Fauna. Multicoloured.

492 13p. Type **465** 60 65
493 13p. *Heteropterus morpheus* (butterfly) (vert) 60 65
494 17p. Barn owl (vert) 80 85
495 17p. Green lizard 80 85

469 Toddlers' Toys

1989. Europa. Children's Toys and Games. Designs showing clay plaques. Multicoloured.

496 17p. Type **469** 50 50
497 17p. Playground games 50 50
498 23p. Party games 75 75
499 23p. Teenage sports 75 75

473 Queen Elizabeth II and Royal Yacht *Britannia* in Elizabeth Harbour

1989. Royal Visit.

500 **473** £1 multicoloured 2·75 2·75

474 Philippe d'Auvergne presented to Louis XVI, 1786

1989. Bicentenary of the French Revolution. Philippe d'Auvergne. Multicoloured.

501 13p. Type **474** 40 30
502 17p. Storming the Bastille, 1789 50 40
503 23p. Marie de Bouillon and revolutionaries, 1790 60 50
504 30p. D'Auvergne's headquarters at Mont Orgueil, 1795 95 1·00
505 32p. Landing arms for Chouan rebels, 1796 1·00 1·10
506 35p. The last Chouan revolt, 1799 1·20 1·30

See also Nos. 539/544.

480 *St. Helier* off Elizabeth Castle

1989. Centenary of Great Western Railway Steamer Service to Channel Islands. Multicoloured.

507 13p. Type **480** 30 30
508 17p. *Caesarea II* off Corbière Lighthouse 35 35
509 27p. *Reindeer* in St Helier harbour 80 80
510 32p. *Ibex* racing *Frederica* off Portelet 95 95
511 35p. *Lynx* off Noirmont 1·10 1·10

485 *Gorey Harbour*

1989. 150th Birth Anniversary of Sarah Louisa Kilpack (artist). Multicoloured.

512 13p. Type **485** 25 25
513 17p. *La Corbière* 30 30
514 23p. *Grève de Lecq* 80 75
515 32p. *Bouley Bay* 85 85
516 35p. *Mont Orgueil* 90 1·00

490 Head Post Office, Broad Street, 1969

1990. Europa. Post Office Buildings. Multicoloured.

517 18p. Type **490** 50 50
518 18p. Postal Headquarters, Mont Millais, 1990 50 50
519 24p. Hue Street Post Office, 1815 (horiz) 65 65
520 24p. Head Post Office, Halkett Place, 1890 (horiz) 65 65

494 Battle of Flowers Parade

1990. Festival of Tourism. Multicoloured.

521 18p. Type **494** 55 55
522 24p. Sports 70 70
523 29p. Mont Orgueil Castle and German Underground Hospital Museum 85 85
524 32p. Salon Culinaire 90 90
MS525 151×100 mm. Nos. 521/524 2·75 3·00

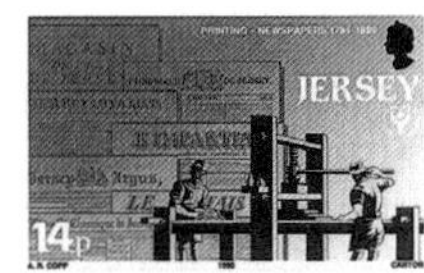

498 Early Printing Press and Jersey Newspaper Mastheads

1990. International Literacy Year. Jersey News Media. Multicoloured.

526 14p. Type **498** 45 45
527 18p. Modern press, and offices of *Jersey Evening Post* in 1890 and 1990 45 45
528 34p. Radio Jersey broadcaster 90 90
529 37p. Channel Television studio cameraman 95 95

502 British Aerospace Hawk T.1

1990. Jersey Aviation History (4th series). 50th Anniv of Battle of Britain. Multicoloured.

530 14p. Type **502** 40 45
531 18p. Supermarine Spitfire 55 60
532 24p. Hawker Hurricane Mk I 85 85
533 34p. Vickers-Armstrong Wellington 1·50 1·60
534 37p. Avro Type 683 Lancaster 1·60 1·60

1990. Christmas. Jersey Parish Churches (2nd series). As T **429**. Multicoloured.

535 14p. St Helier 45 40
536 18p. Grouville 45 40
537 34p. St Saviour 1·00 1·00
538 37p. St John 1·20 1·20

1991. 175th Death Anniversary of Philippe d'Auvergne. As T **474**. Multicoloured.

539 15p. Prince's Tower, La Hougue Bie 45 40
540 20p. D'Auvergne's arrest in Paris 55 55
541 26p. D'Auvergne plotting against Napoleon 70 75
542 31p. Execution of George Cadoudal 90 90
543 37p. HMS *Surly* (cutter) attacking French convoy 1·10 1·10
544 44p. D'Auvergne's last days in London 1·20 1·20

517 *Landsat 5* and Thematic Mapper Image over Jersey

1991. Europa. Europe in Space. Multicoloured.

545	20p. Type **517**	50	50
546	20p. *ERS-1* earth resources remote sensing satellite	50	50
547	26p. *Meteosat* weather satellite	80	85
548	26p. *Olympus* direct broadcasting satellite	80	85

521 1941 1d. Stamp (50th anniversary of first Jersey postage stamp)

1991. Anniversaries. Multicoloured.

549	15p. Type **521**	30	30
550	20p. Steam train (centenary of Jersey Eastern Railway extension to Gorey Pier)	50	55
551	26p. Jersey cow and Herd Book (125th anniversary of Jersey Herd Book)	60	70
552	31p. Stone-laying ceremony (from painting by P. J. Ouless) (150th anniversary of Victoria Harbour)	75	80
553	53p. Marie Bartlett and hospital (250th anniversary of Marie Bartlett's hospital bequest)	1·70	1·70

526 *Melitaea cinxia*

1991. Butterflies and Moths (1st series). Multicoloured.

554	15p. Type **526**	35	35
555	20p. *Euplagia quadripunctaria*	45	30
556	37p. *Deilephilia porcellus*	1·40	1·50
557	57p. *Inachis io*	1·70	1·90

See also Nos. 1279/**MS**1285 and 1651/**MS**1657.

530 Drilling for Water, Ethiopia

1991. Overseas Aid. Multicoloured.

558	15p. Type **530**	45	40
559	20p. Building construction, Rwanda	50	45
560	26p. Village polytechnic, Kenya	70	70
561	31p. Treating leprosy, Tanzania	85	90
562	37p. Ploughing, Zambia	1·10	1·10
563	44p. Immunisation clinic, Lesotho	1·20	1·40

536 *This is the Place for Me*

1991. Christmas. Illustrations by Edmund Blampied for J. M. Barrie's *Peter Pan*. Multicoloured.

564	15p. Type **536**	40	40
565	20p. *The Island Come True*	65	65
566	37p. *The Never Bird*	1·20	1·20
567	53p. *The Great White Father*	1·60	1·60

540 Pied Wagtail

1992. Winter Birds. Multicoloured.

568	16p. Type **540**	50	25
569	22p. Firecrest	70	55
570	28p. Common snipe ('Snipe')	80	85
571	39p. Northern lapwing ('Lapwing')	1·20	1·20
572	57p. Fieldfare	1·70	1·70

See also Nos. 635/639.

545 Shipping at Shanghai, 1860

1992. Jersey Adventurers (3rd series). 150th Birth Anniversary of William Mesny. Multicoloured.

573	16p. Type **545**	40	45
574	16p. Mesny's junk running Taiping blockade, 1862	40	45
575	22p. General Mesny outside river gate, 1874	65	65
576	22p. Mesny in Burma, 1877	65	65
577	33p. Mesny and Governor Chang, 1882	90	95
578	33p. Mesny in mandarin's sedan chair, 1886	90	95

551 *Tickler* (brigantine)

1992. Jersey Shipbuilding. Multicoloured.

579	16p. Type **551**	45	40
580	22p. *Hebe* (brig)	70	75
581	50p. *Gemini* (barque)	1·40	1·50
582	57p. *Percy Douglas* (full-rigged ship)	1·60	1·70
MS583	148×98 mm. Nos. 579/582	4·00	4·25

555 John Bertram (ship owner) and Columbus

1992. Europa. 500th Anniversary of Discovery of America by Columbus. Multicoloured.

584	22p. Type **555**	65	50
585	28p. Sir George Carteret (founder of New Jersey)	75	80
586	39p. Sir Walter Raleigh (founder of Virginia)	1·10	1·40

558 *Snow Leopards* (Allison Griffiths)

1992. Batik Designs. Multicoloured.

587	16p. Type **558**	45	40
588	22p. *Three Elements* (Nataly Miorin)	65	45
589	39p. *Three Men in a Tub* (Amanda Crocker)	1·10	1·20
590	57p. *Cockatoos* (Michelle Millard)	1·50	1·70

1992. Vintage Cars (2nd series). As T **433**. Multicoloured.

591	16p. Morris Cowley Bullnose, 1925	30	30
592	22p. Rolls Royce 20/25, 1932	45	45
593	28p. Chenard and Walcker T5, 1924	70	75
594	33p. Packard 900 series Light Eight, 1932	90	95
595	39p. Lanchester 21, 1927	1·00	1·10
596	50p. Buick 30 Roadster, 1913	1·50	1·70

1992. Christmas. Jersey Parish Churches (3rd series). As T **429**. Multicoloured.

597	16p. Trinity	40	30
598	22p. St Mary	55	50
599	39p. St Martin	1·10	1·10
600	57p. St Peter	1·50	1·50

572 Farmhouse

1993. Multicoloured.

601	(–) Type **572**	60	70
602	(–) Trinity Church	60	70
603	(–) Daffodils and cows	60	70
604	(–) Jersey cows	60	70
605	(–) Sunbathing	70	60
606	(–) Windsurfing	70	60
607	(–) Crab (Queen's head at left)	70	60
608	(–) Crab (Queen's head at right)	70	60
609	(–) 'Singin' in the Rain' float	85	80
610	(–) 'Dragon Dance' float	85	80
611	(–) 'Bali, Morning of the World' float	85	80
612	(–) 'Zulu Fantasy' float	85	80

The above do not show face values, but are inscribed 'BAILIWICK POSTAGE PAID' (Nos. 601/604), 'U.K. MINIMUM POSTAGE PAID' (Nos. 605/608) or 'EUROPE POSTAGE PAID' (Nos. 609/612). They were initially sold at 17p., 23p. or 28p., but it is intended that these face values will be increased to reflect postage rate changes in the future.

584 *Phragmipedium* Eric Young 'Jersey'

1993. Jersey Orchids (3rd series). Multicoloured.

613	17p. Type **584**	45	35
614	23p. *Odontoglossum* Augres 'Trinity'	70	65
615	28p. *Miltonia* St Helier 'Colomberie'	80	75
616	39p. *Phragmipedium pearcei*	1·20	1·40
617	57p. *Calanthe* Grouville 'Gorey'	1·70	1·90

589 Douglas DC-3 Dakota

1993. Jersey Aviation History (5th series). 75th Anniversary of Royal Air Force. Multicoloured.

618	17p. Type **589**	45	30
619	23p. Wight seaplane	60	65
620	28p. Avro Shackleton A.E.W.2	70	70
621	33p. Gloster Meteor Mk III and de Havilland Vampire FB.5	80	85
622	39p. Hawker Siddeley Harrier GR.1A	1·00	1·10
623	57p. Panavia Tornado F.3	1·50	1·60
MS624	147×98 mm. Nos. 619 and 623	4·50	4·75

Nos. 618/624 also commemorate the 50th anniversary of the Royal Air Force Association and the 40th anniversary of the first air display on Jersey.

595 *Jersey's Opera House* (Ian Rolls)

1993. Europa. Contemporary Art. Multicoloured.

625	23p. Type **595**	60	60
626	28p. *The Ham and Tomato Bap* (Jonathan Hubbard)	70	70
627	39p. *Vase of Flowers* (Neil MacKenzie)	1·10	1·10

598 1943 ½d. Occupation Stamp

1993. 50th Anniversary of Edmund Blampied's Occupation Stamps. Designs showing stamps from the 1943 issue.

628	**598**	17p. green, light green and black	35	35
629	-	23p. red, pink and black	50	50
630	-	28p. brown, cinnamon and black	70	70
631	-	33p. orange, salmon and black	85	85
632	-	39p. blue, cobalt and black	1·20	1·20
633	-	50p. mauve, light mauve and black	1·40	1·40

Designs: 23p. 1d. value; 28p. 1½d. value; 33p. 2d. value; 39p. 2½d. value; 50p. 3d. value.

604 Queen Elizabeth II (from painting by Mara McGregor)

1993. 40th Anniversary of Coronation.

634	**604**	£1 multicoloured	2·75	2·75

605 Short-toed Treecreeper

1993. Summer Birds. Multicoloured.

635	17p. Type **605**	45	50
636	23p. Dartford warbler	70	75
637	28p. Northern wheatear ('Wheatear')	80	85
638	39p. Cirl bunting	1·20	1·20
639	57p. Jay	1·70	1·70

610 Two Angels holding *Hark the Herald Angels Sing* Banner

1993. Christmas. Stained Glass Windows by Henry Bosdet from St Aubin on the Hill Church. Multicoloured.

640	17p. Type **610**	40	35
641	23p. Two Angels playing harps	60	60
642	39p. Two Angels playing violins	1·10	1·20
643	57p. Two Angels holding *Once in Royal David's City* banner	1·70	1·90

614 *Coprinus comatus*

1994. Fungi (1st series). Multicoloured.

644	18p. Type **614**	45	40
645	23p. *Amanita muscaria*	65	70
646	30p. *Cantharellus cibarius*	80	85
647	41p. *Macrolepiota procera*	1·20	1·20
648	60p. *Clathrus ruber*	1·60	1·60

See also Nos. 1240/**MS**1246 and 1464/1469.

619 Pekingese (image scaled to 44% of original size)

1994. Hong Kong '94 International Stamp Exhibition. Chinese Year of the Dog. Sheet 110×75 mm.

MS649	**619** £1 multicoloured	2·50	2·75

620 Maine Coon

1994. 21st Anniversary of Jersey Cat Club. Multicoloured.

650	18p. Type **620**	40	30
651	23p. British shorthair (horiz)	60	50
652	35p. Persian	80	80
653	41p. Siamese (horiz)	1·20	1·20
654	60p. Non-pedigree	1·20	1·50

625 Mammoth Hunt, La Cotte de St Brelade

1994. Europa. Archaeological Discoveries. Multicoloured.

655	23p. Type **625**	50	55
656	23p. Stone Age hunters pulling mammoth into cave	50	55
657	30p. Chambered passage, La Hougue Bie	75	85
658	30p. Transporting stones	75	85

629 Airspeed AS 51 Horsa Gliders and Douglas C-47 Tow Aerolanes approaching France

1994. 50th Anniversary of D-Day. Multicoloured.

659	18p. Type **629**	55	50
660	18p. Landing craft approaching beaches	55	50
661	23p. Disembarking from landing craft on Gold Beach	75	70
662	23p. British troops on Sword Beach	75	70
663	30p. Spitfires over beaches	80	75
664	30p. Invasion map	80	75

635 Sailing

1994. Centenary of International Olympic Committee. Multicoloured.

665	18p. Type **635**	40	35
666	23p. Rifle-shooting	55	55
667	30p. Hurdling	75	75
668	41p. Swimming	1·10	1·10
669	60p. Hockey	1·50	1·60

640 Strawberry Anemone

1994. Marine Life. Multicoloured.

670	18p. Type **640**	40	45
671	23p. Hermit crab and parasitic anemone	60	65
672	41p. Velvet swimming crab	1·20	1·40
673	60p. Common jellyfish	1·60	1·60

644 *Condor 10* (catamaran)

1994. 25th Anniversary of Jersey Postal Administration. Multicoloured.

674	18p. Type **644**	50	45
675	23p. Map of Jersey and pillarbox	60	50
676	35p. Vickers Type 953 Vanguard of BEA	85	85
677	41p. Short 360 of Aurigny Air Services	1·10	1·00
678	60p. *Caesarea* (Sealink ferry)	1·60	1·50
MS679	150×100 mm. Nos. 674/678	4·50	4·50

649 *Away in a Manger*

1994. Christmas. Carols. Multicoloured.

680	18p. Type **649**	40	40
681	23p. *Hark! the Herald Angels Sing*	50	50
682	41p. *While Shepherds Watched*	1·20	1·20
683	60p. *We Three Kings of Orient Are*	1·50	1·50

653 Dog and 'GOOD LUCK'

1995. Greetings Stamps. Multicoloured.

684	18p. Type **653**	30	20
685	18p. Rose and 'WITH LOVE'	30	20
686	18p. Chick and 'CONGRATULATIONS'	30	20
687	18p. Bouquet of flowers and 'THANK YOU'	30	20
688	23p. Dove with letter and 'WITH LOVE'	45	25
689	23p. Cat and 'GOOD LUCK'	45	25
690	23p. Carnations and 'THANK YOU'	45	25
691	23p. Parrot and 'CONGRATULATIONS'	45	25
692	60p. Pig and 'HAPPY NEW YEAR' (25×63 mm)	45	25

No. 692 commemorates the Chinese New Year of the Pig.

662 Camellia 'Captain Rawes'

1994. Camellias. Multicoloured.

693	18p. Type **662**	55	50
694	23p. 'Brigadoon'	80	70
695	30p. 'Elsie Jury'	90	85
696	35p. 'Augusto L'Gouveia Pinto'	1·10	1·20
697	41p. 'Bella Romana'	1·20	1·30

667 *Liberation* (sculpture, Philip Jackson)

1995. Europa. Peace and Freedom.

698	**667**	23p. black and blue	55	55
699	**667**	30p. black and pink	70	95

668 Bailiff and Crown Officers in Launch

1995. 50th Anniversary of Liberation. Multicoloured.

700	18p. Type **668**	40	40
701	18p. *Vega* (Red Cross supply ship)	40	40
702	23p. HMS *Beagle* (destroyer)	60	60
703	23p. British troops in Ordnance Yard, St Helier	60	60
704	60p. King George VI and Queen Elizabeth in Jersey	1·50	1·50
705	60p. Unloading supplies from landing craft, St Aubin's	1·50	1·50
MS706	110×75 mm. £1 Royal Family with Winston Churchill on Buckingham Palace balcony, VE Day (80×39 mm)	2·75	2·75

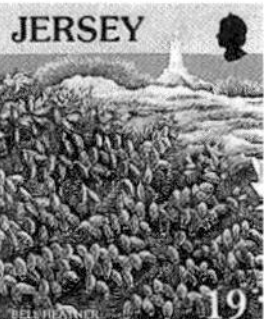

675 Bell Heather

1995. European Nature Conservation Year. Wild Flowers. Multicoloured.

707	19p. Type **675**	40	20
708	19p. Sea campion	40	20
709	19p. Spotted rock-rose	40	20
710	19p. Thrift	40	20
711	19p. Sheep's-bit scabious	40	20
712	23p. Field bind-weed	50	25
713	23p. Common bird's-foot trefoil	50	25
714	23p. Sea-holly	50	25
715	23p. Common centaury	50	25
716	23p. Dwarf pansy	50	25

Nos. 707/711 and 712/716 respectively were printed together, *se-tenant*, forming composite designs.

685 *Precis almana*

1995. Butterflies. Multicoloured.

717	19p. Type **685**	50	55
718	23p. *Papilio palinurus*	55	60
719	30p. *Catopsilia scylla*	80	85
720	41p. *Papilio rumanzovia*	1·00	1·10
721	60p. *Troides helena*	1·60	1·70
MS722	150×100 mm. Nos. 720/721	2·40	2·50

No. **MS**722 includes the Singapore '95 International Stamp Exhibition logo on the sheet margin and shows the two stamp designs without frames.

690 Peace Doves and United Nations Anniversary Emblem

1995. 50th Anniversary of United Nations.

723	**690**	19p. cobalt and blue	60	50
724	-	23p. turquoise and green	70	70
725	-	41p. green and turquoise	1·20	1·20
726	**690**	60p. blue and cobalt	1·50	1·50

Design: 23p., 41p. Symbolic wheat and anniversary emblem.

692 *Puss in Boots*

1995. Christmas. Pantomimes. Multicoloured.

727	19p. Type **692**	50	40
728	23p. *Cinderella*	55	45
729	41p. *Sleeping Beauty*	1·00	1·00
730	60p. *Aladdin*	1·60	1·50

696 Rat with Top Hat (image scaled to 44% of original size)

1996. Chinese New Year. Year of the Rat. Sheet 110×75 mm.

MS731	**696** £1 multicoloured	2·50	2·50

697 African Child and Map

1996. 50th Anniversary of UNICEF. Multicoloured.

732	19p. Type **697**	45	40
733	23p. Children and globe	55	45
734	30p. European child and map	70	65
735	35p. South American child and map	90	95
736	41p. Asian child and map	1·00	1·10
737	60p. South Pacific child and map	1·50	1·60

703 Queen Elizabeth II (from photo by T. O'Neill)

1996. 70th Birthday of Queen Elizabeth II.

738	**703**	£5 multicoloured	10·00	10·00

704 Elizabeth Garrett (first British woman doctor)

1996. Europa. Famous Women. Multicoloured.

739	23p. Type **704**	60	60
740	30p. Emmeline Pankhurst (suffragette)	90	90

706 Player shooting at Goal

1996. European Football Championship, England. Multicoloured.

741	19p. Type **706**	50	40
742	23p. Two players chasing ball	60	50
743	35p. Player avoiding tackle	95	90
744	41p. Two players competing for ball	1·00	1·00
745	60p. Players heading ball	1·60	1·60

711 Rowing

1996. Sporting Anniversaries. Multicoloured.

746	19p. Type **711**	50	40
747	23p. Judo	60	50
748	35p. Fencing	95	95
749	41p. Boxing	1·00	1·00
750	60p. Basketball	1·60	1·60
MS751	150×100 mm. £1 Olympic torch (50×37 mm)	2·50	2·50

Anniversaries: Nos. 746/748, 750/751, Centenary of modern Olympic Games; No. 749, 50th anniversary of International Amateur Boxing Association.

No. **MS**751 also includes the CAPEX '96 International Stamp Exhibition logo.

717 Bay on North Coast

1996. Tourism. Beaches. Multicoloured.

752	19p. Type **717**	50	50
753	23p. Portelet Bay	60	60
754	30p. Greve de Lecq Bay	80	80
755	35p. Beauport Beach	95	95
756	41p. Plemont Bay	1·10	1·10
757	60p. St Brelade's Bay	1·60	1·60

723 Drag Hunt

1996. Horses. Multicoloured.

758	19p. Type **723**	50	50
759	23p. Pony and trap	60	60
760	30p. Training racehorses on beach	80	80
761	35p. Show-jumping	95	95
762	41p. Pony Club event	1·10	1·10
763	60p. Shire mare and foal	1·60	1·60

729 The Journey to Bethlehem

1996. Christmas. Multicoloured.

764	19p. Type **729**	50	50
765	23p. The Shepherds	60	70
766	30p. The Nativity	90	95
767	60p. The Three Kings	1·40	1·50

733 Jersey Cow wearing Scarf

1997. Chinese New Year. Year of the Ox. Sheet 110×74 mm.

MS768	**733** £1 multicoloured	3·25	3·75

1997. HONG KONG '97 International Stamp Exhibition. No. **MS**768 optd with exhibition emblem in black and **JERSEY AT HONG KONG '97** in red, both on sheet margin.

MS769	**733** £1 multicoloured	3·75	4·00

734 Lillie the Cow on the Beach

1997. Tourism. Lillie the Cow. Multicoloured. Self-adhesive.

770	(23p.) Type **734**	80	85
771	(23p.) Lillie taking photograph	80	85
772	(23p.) Carrying bucket and spade	80	85
773	(23p.) Eating meal at Mont Orgueil	80	85

738 Red-breasted Merganser

1997. Seabirds and Waders. Multicoloured.

774	1p. Type **738**	10	10
775	2p. Sanderling	10	10
776	4p. Northern gannet ('Gannet')	10	10
777	5p. Great crested grebe	10	15
778	10p. Common tern	20	25
779	15p. Black-headed gull	30	35
780a	20p. Dunlin	40	45
781	21p. Sandwich tern	40	45
782	22p. Ringed plover	45	50
783	23p. Bar-tailed godwit	45	50
784a	24p. Atlantic puffin ('Puffin')	45	50
785	25p. Brent goose	50	55
786	26p. Grey plover	50	55
787	27p. Black scoter ('Common Scoter')	55	60
788	28p. Lesser black-backed gull	60	65
789	29p. Little egret	60	65
790	30p. Fulmar	60	65
791	31p. Golden plover	60	65
792	32p. Common greenshank ('Greenshank')	65	70
793	33p. Little grebe	65	70
794	34p. Great cormorant ('Common Cormorant')	70	75
795	35p. Western curlew ('Curlew')	70	75
796	37p. Oystercatcher	75	80
797	40p. Ruddy turnstone ('Turnstone')	80	85
798	44p. Herring gull	90	95
799	45p. Rock pipit	90	95
800	50p. Great black-backed gull	1·00	1·10
801	60p. Pied avocet ('Avocet')	1·20	1·40
802	65p. Grey heron	1·20	1·40
803	75p. Common redshank ('Redshank')	2·00	2·10
804	£1 Razorbill	2·50	2·50
805	£2 Shag	5·00	5·25
MS806	Four sheets, each 136×130 mm. (a) Nos. 774, 778/780, 784, 796, 803 and 805. (b) Nos. 775, 777, 781, 785, 790, 797, 801 and 804. (c) Nos. 776, 782, 786, 791/792, 795, 798 and 800. (d) Nos. 783, 787/789, 793/794, 799 and 802 Set of 4 sheets	25·00	25·00

770 de Havilland DH.95 Flamingo

1997. Jersey Aviation History (6th series). 60th Anniversary of Jersey Airport. Multicoloured.

807	20p. Type **770**	45	40
808	24p. Handley Page H.P.R. 5 Marathon	55	40
809	31p. de Havilland DH.114 Heron	65	65
810	37p. Boeing 737-236	95	95
811	43p. Britten-Norman BN-2A Mk III Trislander	1·10	1·10
812	63p. BAe 146-200	1·70	1·70

776 *The Bull of St Clement*

1997. Europa. Tales and Legends. Multicoloured.

813	20p. Type **776**	65	60
814	24p. *The Black Horse of St Ouen*	75	70
815	31p. *The Black Dog of Bouley Bay*	1·00	1·10
816	63p. *Les Fontaines des Mittes*	1·25	1·80

Nos. 814/815 include the EUROPA emblem.

1997. Pacific 97 International Stamp Exhibition, San Francisco. No. **MS**806a optd with exhibition emblem on sheet margin.

MS817	136×130 mm. Nos. 774, 778/80, 784, 796, 803 and 805	7·50	8·50

780 Cycling

1997. Seventh Island Games, Jersey. Multicoloured.

818	20p. Type **780**	55	55
819	24p. Archery	65	65
820	31p. Windsurfing	80	80
821	37p. Gymnastics	1·00	1·00
822	43p. Volleyball	1·10	1·10
823	63p. Running	1·70	1·70

786 Mallorcan Midwife Toad

1997. Wildlife Preservation Trust (6th series). Multicoloured.

824	20p. Type **786**	50	45
825	24p. Aye-aye	60	50
826	31p. Mauritius parakeet ('Echo Parakeet')	90	90
827	37p. Pigmy hog	1·00	1·10
828	43p. St Lucia whip-tail	1·10	1·20
829	63p. Madagascar teal	1·70	1·80

792 Ash

1997. Trees. Multicoloured.

830	20p. Type **792**	50	45
831	24p. Elder	60	50
832	31p. Beech	90	90
833	37p. Sweet chestnut	1·00	1·10
834	43p. Hawthorn	1·10	1·20
835	63p. Common oak	1·70	1·80

798 Father Christmas and Reindeer outside Jersey Airport

1997. Christmas. Multicoloured.

836	20p. Type **798**	60	60
837	24p. Father Christmas with presents, St Aubin's Harbour	70	70
838	31p. Father Christmas in sleigh, Mont Orgueil Castle	1·00	1·00
839	63p. Father Christmas with children, Royal Square, St Helier	1·90	1·90

802 Wedding Photograph, 1947

1997. Golden Wedding of Queen Elizabeth and Prince Philip. Multicoloured.

840	50p. Type **802**	1·00	60
841	50p. Queen Elizabeth and Prince Philip, 1997	1·00	60
MS842	150×100 mm. £1·50 Full-length Wedding photograph, 1947 (38×50 mm)	4·50	4·50

805 Tiger wearing Scarf (image scaled to 44% of original size)

1998. Chinese New Year. Year of the Tiger. Sheet 110×75 mm.

MS843	**805** £1 multicoloured	2·50	2·75

806 JMT Bristol 4 Tonner, 1923

1998. 75th Anniversary of Jersey Motor Transport Company. Buses. (1st series). Multicoloured.

844	20p. Type **806**	55	50
845	24p. Safety Coach Service Regent double decker, 1934	65	50
846	31p. Slade's Dennis Lancet, *c.* 1936	75	70
847	37p. Tantivy Leyland PLSC Lion, 1947	1·00	1·00
848	43p. JBS Morris, *c.* 1958	1·10	1·10
849	63p. JMT Titan TD4 double decker, *c.* 1961	1·50	1·60

See also Nos. 1364/**MS**1370, 1553/1558 and 1736/1741.

812 Creative Arts Festival

1998. Europa. National Festivals. Multicoloured.

850	20p. Type **812**	65	45
851	24p. Jazz Festival	70	55
852	31p. Good Food Festival	90	1·00
853	63p. Floral Festival	1·70	1·90

Nos. 851/852 include the EUROPA emblem.

816 Hobie Cat and *Duke of Normandy* (launch)

1998. Jersey Yachting (1st series). Opening of Elizabeth Marina, St Helier. Multicoloured.

854	20p. Type **816**	40	20
855	20p. Hobie Cat with white, yellow, red and green sails	40	20
856	20p. Hobie Cats with pink, purple and orange sails	40	20
857	20p. Bow of Hobie Cat with yellow, blue and purple sail	40	20
858	20p. Hobie Cat heeling	40	20
859	24p. Yacht with red, white and blue spinnaker	45	25
860	24p. Yacht with pink spinnaker	45	25
861	24p. Yacht with two white sails	45	25
862	24p. Trimaran	45	25
863	24p. Yacht with blue, white and yellow spinnaker in foreground	45	25

Nos. 854/858 and 859/863 respectively were printed together, *se-tenant*, forming composite designs of yacht races.

See also No. **MS**1319.

826 Bass

1998. International Year of the Ocean. Fish. Multicoloured.

864	20p. Type **826**	50	50
865	24p. Red gurnard	65	65
866	31p. Skate	80	80
867	37p. Mackerel	1·00	1·00
868	43p. Tope	1·10	1·10
869	63p. Cuckoo wrasse	1·50	1·50

832 Cider-making

1998. Days Gone By. Multicoloured. Self-adhesive.

870	(20p.) Type **832**	90	90
871	(20p.) Potato barrels on cart	90	90
872	(20p.) Collecting seaweed for fertiliser	90	90
873	(20p.) Milking Jersey cows	90	90

836 Irises

1998. Flowers. Multicoloured.

874	20p. Type **836**	50	40
875	24p. Carnations	60	50
876	31p. Chrysanthemums	75	70
877	37p. Pinks	90	90
878	43p. Roses	1·00	1·10
879	63p. Lilies	1·40	1·50
MS880	150×100 mm. £1·50 *Lilium* 'Star Gazer' (50×37 mm)	3·25	3·75

No. **MS**880 includes the ITALIA '98 stamp exhibition emblem on the margin.

843 Central Market Crib

1998. Christmas. Cribs. Multicoloured.

881	20p. Type **843**	40	40
882	24p. St Thomas's Church crib	50	55
883	31p. Trinity Parish Church crib	65	65
884	63p. Royal Square crib	1·60	1·60

847 Rabbit (image scaled to 44% of original size)

1999. Chinese New Year. Year of the Rabbit. Sheet 110×75 mm.

MS885	**847** £1 multicoloured	2·50	2·75

848 Jersey Eastern Railway Mail Train

1999. 125th Anniversary of UPU. Multicoloured.

886	20p. Type **848**	55	50
887	24p. *Brighton* (paddle-steamer)	65	60
888	43p. de Havilland DH.86 Dragon Express at Jersey Airport	95	1·10
889	63p. Jersey Postal Service Morris Minor van	1·40	1·70

852 *Jessie Eliza*, St Catherine

1999. 175th Anniversary of Royal National Lifeboat Institution. Multicoloured.

890	75p. Type **852**	2·00	80
891	£1 *Alexander Coutanche*, St Helier	2·50	1·00

854 *Cymbidium Maufant* 'Jersey'

1999. Jersey Orchids (4th series). Multicoloured.

892	21p. Type **854**	55	50
893	25p. *Miltonia Millbrook* 'Jersey'	55	50
894	31p. *Paphiopedilum* 'Transvaal'	75	70
895	37p. *Paphiopedilum* 'Elizabeth Castle'	85	80
896	43p. *Calanthe* 'Five Oaks'	90	90
897	63p. *Cymbidium* Icho Tower 'Trinity'	2·00	2·00
MS898	150×100 mm. £1·50 *Miltonia* "Portelet"	4·00	4·50

No. **MS**898 also includes the Australia '99 World Stamp Exhibition, Melbourne, emblem on the margin at top left.

861 Howard Davis Park

1999. Europa. Parks and Gardens. Multicoloured.

899	21p. Type **861**	50	50
900	25p. Sir Winston Churchill Memorial Park	70	70
901	31p. Coronation Park	1·00	1·00
902	63p. La Collette Gardens	2·00	2·00

Nos. 900/901 include the EUROPA logo at top left and all four values show the iBRA '99 International Stamp Exhibition, Nuremberg, emblem at top right.

865 Prince Edward and Miss Sophie Rhys-Jones

1999. Royal Wedding.

903	**865**	35p. multicoloured (yellow background)	75	75
904	**865**	35p. multicoloured (blue background)	75	75

866 Jersey-built Benz, 1899

1999. Vintage Cars (3rd series). Centenary of Motoring in Jersey. Multicoloured.

905	21p. Type **866**	45	45
906	25p. Star Tourer, 1910	55	55
907	31p. Citroen Traction Avant, 1938	65	65
908	37p. Talbot BG110 Tourer, 1937	1·00	1·00
909	43p. Morris Cowley Six Special Coupe, 1934	1·20	1·20
910	63p. Ford Anglia Saloon, 1946	1·50	1·50

872 West European Hedgehog

1999. Small Mammals. Multicoloured.

911	21p. Type **872**	45	45
912	25p. Eurasian red squirrel	55	55
913	31p. Nathusius pipistrelle	65	65
914	37p. Jersey bank vole	1·00	1·10
915	43p. Lesser white-toothed shrew	1·00	1·10
916	63p. Common mole	2·00	2·20

878 Gorey Pierhead Light

1999. 150th Anniversary of First Lighthouse on Jersey (1st series). Multicoloured.

917	21p. Type **878**	45	45
918	25p. La Corbiere	55	55
919	34p. Noirmont Point	75	75
920	38p. Demie de Pas	1·00	1·00
921	44p. Greve d'Azette	1·20	1·20
922	64p. Sorel Point	2·00	2·00

See also Nos. 1086/1091.

884 Mistletoe

1999. Christmas. Festive Foliage. Multicoloured.

923	21p. Type **884**	45	45
924	25p. Holly	55	55
925	34p. Ivy	1·10	75
926	64p. Christmas Rose	1·60	2·00

888 Jersey Crest

2000. New Millennium.

927	**888**	£10 gold, red and carmine	20·00	22·00

889 Dragon (image scaled to 44% of original size)

2000. Chinese New Year. Year of the Dragon. Sheet 110×75 mm.

MS928	**889** £1 multicoloured	3·00	3·00

890 *Ocean Adventure* (Gemma Carré)

2000. Stampin' the Future (children's stamp design competition) Winners. Multicoloured.

929	22p. Type **890**	65	65
930	22p. *Solar Power* (Chantal Varley-Best)	65	65
931	22p. *Floating City and Space Cars* (Nicola Singleton)	65	65
932	22p. *Conservation* (Carly Logan)	65	65
MS933	150×100 mm. Nos. 929/932	3·00	3·50

894 Jersey in Europe

2000. Europa. Multicoloured.

934	26p. Type **894**	2·00	2·00
935	34p. Building Europe (29×39 mm)	3·00	3·50

896 Roman Merchant Ship

2000. The Stamp Show 2000 International Stamp Exhibition, London. Maritime Heritage. Multicoloured.

936	22p. Type **896**	45	25
937	22p. Viking longship	45	25
938	22p. 13th-century warship	45	25
939	22p. 14th/15th-century merchant ship	45	25
940	22p. Tudor warship	45	25
941	26p. 17th-century warship	50	30
942	26p. 18th-century naval cutter	50	30
943	26p. 19th-century barque	50	30
944	26p. 19th-century oyster cutter	50	30
945	26p. 20th-century ketch	50	30
MS946	174×104 mm. Nos. 936/945	6·00	6·00

906 Bottle-nosed Dolphins

2000. World Environment Day. Marine Mammals. Multicoloured.

947	22p. Type **906**	50	55
948	26p. Long-finned pilot whales	55	60
949	34p. Common porpoises	80	85
950	38p. Grey seals	1·00	1·10
951	44p. Risso's dolphins	1·10	1·20
952	64p. White-beaked dolphin	1·50	1·70
MS953	150×100 mm. £1·50 Common dolphins (80×29 mm)	4·00	4·50

913 Prince William and Alps

2000. 18th Birthday of Prince William. Multicoloured.

954	75p. Type **913**	1·75	1·50
955	75p. Prince William and polo player	1·75	1·50
956	75p. Prince William and Beaumaris Castle	1·75	1·50
957	75p. Prince William and fireworks	1·75	1·50

2000. World Stamp Expo 2000, Anaheim, USA. As No. **MS**953, but with multicoloured exhibition logo added to top left corner of sheet margin.

MS958	150×100 mm. £1·50 Common dolphins (80×29 mm)	4·00	4·00

917 Queen Elizabeth the Queen Mother with Roses

2000. Queen Elizabeth the Queen Mother's 100th Birthday. Multicoloured.

959	50p. Type **917**	1·20	1·20
960	50p. Queen Elizabeth the Queen Mother with daisies	1·20	1·20
MS961	150×100 mm. Nos. 959/960	2·50	3·00

919 Supermarine Spitfire Mk Ia

2000. Jersey Aviation History (7th series). 60th Anniversary of Battle of Britain. Multicoloured.

962	22p. Type **919**	50	55
963	26p. Hawker Hurricane Mk I	60	65
964	36p. Bristol Blenheim Mk IV	80	85
965	40p. Vickers Wellington Mk Ic	90	95
966	45p. Boulton Paul P.82 Defiant Mk I	1·00	1·10
967	65p. Short S.25 Sunderland Mk I	1·50	1·60

925 Virgin Mary

2000. Christmas. Children's Nativity Play. Multicoloured.

968	22p. Type **925**	55	55
969	26p. Shepherd	65	65
970	36p. Angel	1·00	1·00
971	65p. Magi with gift	1·60	1·60

929 Snake (image scaled to 44% of original size)

2001. Chinese New Year. Year of the Snake. Sheet 110×75 mm.

MS972	**929** £1 multicoloured	2·75	3·00

930 *Rose* (1851–1861)

2001. Maritime Links with France. Mail Packet Ships. Multicoloured.

973	22p. Type **930**	50	55
974	26p. *Comete* (1856–1867)	60	65
975	36p. *Cygne* (1894–1912)	80	85
976	40p. *Victoria* (1896–1918)	90	95
977	45p. *Attala* (1920–1925)	1·20	1·30
978	65p. *Brittany* (1933–1962)	1·70	1·80

936 HMS *Jersey* (4th Rate), 1654–1691

2001. Jersey Naval Connections (1st series). Royal Navy Ships named after Jersey. Multicoloured.

979	23p. Type **936**	50	55
980	26p. HMS *Jersey* (6th Rate), 1694–1698	60	65
981	37p. HMS *Jersey* (4th Rate), 1698–1731	80	85
982	41p. HMS *Jersey* (4th Rate), 1736–1783	1·00	95
983	46p. HMS *Jersey* (cutter), 1860–1873	1·20	1·10
984	66p. HMS *Jersey* (destroyer), 1938–1941	1·50	1·60

See also Nos. 1380/**MS**1386 and 1470/1475.

942 Jersey Cows

2001. Jersey Agriculture. Multicoloured. Self-adhesive.

985	(26p.) Type **942**	1·50	1·50
986	(26p.) Potatoes	1·50	1·50
987	(26p.) Tomatoes	1·50	1·50

988 (26p.) Cauliflower and purple-sprouting broccoli 1·50 1·50
989 (26p.) Peppers and courgettes 1·50 1·50

Nos. 985/989, which are inscribed 'UK MINIMUM POSTAGE PAID', were initially sold at 26p each.

947 Queen Elizabeth II

2001. 75th Birthday of Queen Elizabeth II.
990 **947** £3 multicoloured 6·00 6·50

948 Agile Frog

2001. Europa. Pond Life. Multicoloured.
991 23p. Type **948** 60 65
992 26p. Trout 70 75
993 37p. White water-lily 1·00 1·10
994 41p. Common blue damselfly 1·10 1·20
995 46p. Palmate newt 1·20 1·40
996 66p. Tufted duck 2·00 2·20
MS997 150×100 mm. £1.50 Common kingfisher (36×50 mm) 5·00 5·00

The 26 and 37p. values include EUROPA emblem.

2001. Belgica 2001 International Stamp Exhibition, Brussels. No. **MS**997 optd **JERSEY AT BELGICA 2001** on sheet margin.
MS998 150×100 mm. £1·50 Common kingfisher (36×50 mm) 5·00 4·50

955 Long-eared Owl

2001. Birds of Prey. Multicoloured.
999 23p. Type **955** 50 55
1000 26p. Peregrine falcon 60 65
1001 37p. Short-eared owl 80 85
1002 41p. Western marsh harrier ('Marsh Harrier') 1·00 95
1003 46p. Northern sparrow hawk ('Sparrowhawk') 1·20 1·10
1004 66p. Tawny owl 1·50 1·60
MS1005 110×75 mm. £1·50 Barn owl (30×47 mm) 5·00 5·00

962 *Jersey Clipper* (yacht) (image scaled to 32% of original size)

2001. The Times Clipper 2000 Round the World Yacht Race. Sheet 150×100 mm.
MS1006 **962** £1·50 multicoloured 4·00 5·00

963 Tilley 26 Manual Fire Engine, *c.* 1845

2001. Centenary of Jersey Fire and Rescue Service. Fire Engines. Multicoloured.
1007 23p. Type **963** 50 55
1008 26p. Albion Merryweather, *c.* 1935 60 65
1009 37p. Dennis Ace, *c.* 1940 80 85
1010 41p. Dennis F8 Pump Escape, *c.* 1952 90 95
1011 46p. Land Rover Merryweather, *c.* 1968 1·00 1·10
1012 66p. Dennis Carmichael, *c.* 1989 1·50 1·60

2001. Hafnia 01 International Stamp Exhibition, Copenhagen. As No. **MS**1005, but with brown-red exhibition logo added to bottom left corner of sheet margin and additionally inscr 'Jersey visits Hafnia 01 Denmark'.
MS1013 £1·50 Barn owl (30×47 mm) 4·00 4·00

969 Nativity

2001. Christmas. Bells. Multicoloured. Self-adhesive.
1014 (23p.) Type **969** 1·00 70
1015 (23p.) Street decorations 1·00 70
1016 (23p.) Carol singers with hand bells 1·00 70
1017 (23p.) Father Christmas 1·00 70
1018 (23p.) Christmas tree decorations 1·00 70
1019 (26p.) Adoration of the shepherds 1·00 70
1020 (26p.) Carol singers and Father Christmas in sleigh 1·00 70
1021 (26p.) Paper bell, chains and Christmas tree 1·00 70
1022 (26p.) Church bells ringing 1·00 70
1023 (26p.) Christmas cracker 1·00 70

Nos. 1014/1018, which are inscribed 'JERSEY MINIMUM POSTAGE PAID', were initially sold for 23p., and Nos. 1019/1023, inscribed 'U.K. MINIMUM POSTAGE PAID', were sold for 26p.

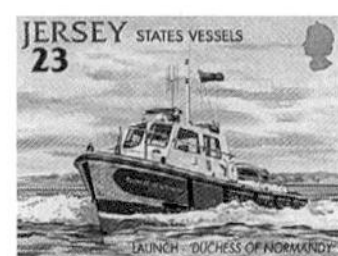

979 *Duchess of Normandy* (launch)

2002. States Vessels. Multicoloured.
1024 23p. Type **979** 50 55
1025 29p. *Duke of Normandy* (tug) 65 70
1026 38p. *Challenger* (customs patrol boat) 80 85
1027 47p. *Le Fret* (pilot boat) 1·20 1·30
1028 68p. *Norman le Brocq* (fisheries protection vessel) 1·70 1·90

984 Queen Elizabeth in Coronation Robes (after Cecil Beaton)

2002. Golden Jubilee.
1029 **984** £3 multicoloured 6·25 6·25

985 Horse (image scaled to 44% of original size)

2002. Chinese New Year. Year of the Horse. Sheet 110×75 mm.
MS1030 **985** £1 multicoloured 2·50 2·50

986 Elephant Float, Parish of St John, 1980

2002. Europa. Circus. Designs showing carnival floats. Multicoloured.
1031 23p. Type **986** 50 55
1032 29p. Clown with red hair, Grouville, 1996 65 70
1033 38p. Clown with white hat, Optimists, 1988 1·00 1·10
1034 68p. Performing seal, Grouville, 1996 1·70 2·00

The 29p. and 38p. values include the EUROPA emblem.

990 Aubrey Boomer

2002. Centenary of La Moye Golf Club. Multicoloured.
1035 23p. Type **990** 55 55
1036 29p. Harry Vardon 70 70
1037 38p. Sir Henry Cotton 85 85
1038 47p. Diagram of golf swing 1·10 1·10
1039 68p. Putting 1·75 1·75

995 Vauxhall 12, 1952

2002. 50th Anniversary of States of Jersey Police. Patrol Vehicles. Multicoloured.
1040 23p. Type **995** 55 55
1041 29p. Jaguar 2.4 MkII, 1959–1960 70 70
1042 38p. Austin 1800, 1972–1973 95 85
1043 40p. Ford Cortina MkIV, 1978 1·00 90
1044 47p. Honda ST 1100 motorcycle, 1995–2000 1·10 1·10
1045 68p. Vauxhall Vectra, 1998–2000 1·75 1·75

1001 Honey Bee

2002. Insects (1st series). Multicoloured.
1046 23p. Type **1001** 55 55
1047 29p. Seven-spot ladybird 70 70
1048 38p. Great green bush-cricket 85 85
1049 40p. Greater horn-tail 90 90
1050 47p. Emperor dragonfly 1·25 1·25
1051 68p. Hawthorn shield bug 1·75 1·75

See also Nos. 1393/1398.

1007 Queen Elizabeth the Queen Mother in 1910, 1923 and 2002

2002. Queen Elizabeth the Queen Mother Commemoration.
1052 **1007** £2 multicoloured 4·25 4·50

1008 Hydrangeas

2002. Centenary of Battle of Flowers Parade. Multicoloured.
1053 23p. Type **1008** 55 55
1054 29p. Chrysanthemums 70 70
1055 38p. Hare's tails and pampas grasses 95 85
1056 40p. Asters 1·90 90
1057 47p. Carnations 1·10 1·10
1058 68p. Gladioli 1·75 1·75
MS1059 150×100 mm. £2 'Zanzibar' float (winner of Prix d'Honneur, 1999) (75×38 mm) 4·25 4·50

1015 British Dilute Tortoiseshell

2002. 25th Anniversary of Caesarea Cat Club. Multicoloured.
1060 23p. Type **1015** 55 55
1061 29p. Cream Persian 70 70
1062 38p. Blue exotic shorthair 95 85
1063 40p. Black smoke Devon rex 1·00 90
1064 47p. British silver tabby 1·10 1·10
1065 68p. Usual Abyssinian 1·75 1·75
MS1066 110×75 mm. £2 British cream/white bi-colour cross (38×51 mm) 4·25 4·50

1022 Victorian Pillarbox in Central Market

2002. Jersey Postal History (1st series). 150th Anniversary of the First Pillarbox. Multicoloured.
1067 23p. Type **1022** 55 55
1068 29p. Edward VII wall box, Colomberie 70 70
1069 38p. George V wall box, St Clement's Inner Road 95 85
1070 40p. George V 'Boite Mobile' ship box 1·00 90
1071 47p. Elizabeth II pillarbox, Parade 1·10 1·10
1072 68p. Modern pillarboxes, La Collette 1·75 1·60
MS1073 150×100 mm. £2 Posting letter in first pillarbox, David Place (40×77 mm) 4·25 4·50

See also Nos. 1286/**MS**1292, **MS**1442, 1503/**MS**1510 and 1511/**MS**1517.

1029 Sanchez-Besa Hydroplane

2003. Jersey Aviation History (8th series). Centenary of Powered Flight. Multicoloured.
1074 23p. Type **1029** 55 55
1075 29p. Supermarine S.6B seaplane 70 70
1076 38p. de Havilland DH.84 Dragon 95 85
1077 40p. de Havilland DH.89a Rapide 1·00 90
1078 47p. Vickers 701 Viscount 1·10 1·10
1079 68p. BAC One Eleven 1·75 1·60
MS1080 112×76 mm. £2 Jacob Ellehammer's Biplane, 1906 (60×40 mm) 4·25 4·50

1036 Ram (image scaled to 44% of original size)

2003. Chinese New Year. Year of the Ram. Sheet 110×75 mm.
MS1081 **1036** £1 multicoloured 2·50 2·75

1037 *Portelet* (Adrian Allinson)

2003. Europa. Travel Posters. Multicoloured.
1082 23p. Type **1037** 50 55
1083 29p. *Jersey* (Lander) (vert) 80 80
1084 38p. *Channel Islands Map* (vert) 1·25 1·50
1085 68p. *Jersey, the Sunny Channel Island* (A. Allinson) 1·75 2·00

The 29p. and 38p. values include the EUROPA emblem.

2003. Jersey Lighthouses (2nd series). T **878**. Multicoloured.
1086 29p. Violet Channel light buoy 50 30
1087 29p. St Catherine's Breakwater Light 50 30
1088 30p. Frouquie Aubert light buoy 55 35
1089 30p. Mont Ube Lighthouse 55 35
1090 48p. Banc des Ormes light buoy 85 50
1091 48p. Gronez Point Lighthouse 85 50

1047 Southern-marsh Orchid

2003. Wild Orchids. Multicoloured.

1092	29p. Type **1047**	70	65
1093	30p. Loose-flowered orchid	75	65
1094	39p. Spotted orchid	95	85
1095	50p. Autumn ladies tresses	1·25	1·10
1096	53p. Green-winged orchid	1·25	1·25
1097	69p. Pyramidal orchid	1·75	1·50
MS1098	110×75 mm. £2 Loose-flowered orchid (different)	4·00	4·25

1054 Sovereign's Orb

2003. 50th Anniversary of Coronation. Coronation Regalia. Multicoloured.

1099	29p. Type **1054**	70	65
1100	30p. St Edward's Crown	75	65
1101	39p. Sceptre with Cross	95	85
1102	50p. Ampulla and Spoon	1·25	1·10
1103	53p. Sovereign's Ring	1·25	1·10
1104	69p. Armills	1·75	1·50
MS1105	150×100 mm. Nos. 1099/1104	6·00	5·75

1060 Prince William, Prince Charles and Queen Elizabeth (image scaled to 44% of original size)

2003. Royal Links. Sheet 110×75 mm.

MS1106	**1060** £2 multicoloured	5·00	4·25

1061 Rock Samphire and Paternosters

2003. Offshore Reefs. Multicoloured. Self-adhesive.

1107	(29p.) Type **1061**	1·10	1·25
1108	(29p.) Bluebells and Les Ecrehous	1·10	1·25
1109	(29p.) Tree-mallow and Les Ecrehous	1·10	1·25
1110	(29p.) Smooth Sow-thistle and Les Minquiers	1·10	1·25
1111	(29p.) Thrift and Les Minquiers	1·10	1·25

Nos. 1107/1111 are inscribed 'JERSEY MINIMUM POSTAGE PAID' and were initially sold at 29p.

1066 Albino Rex Rabbit

2003. Pets. Multicoloured.

1112	29p. Type **1066**	95	95
1113	30p. Black labrador puppy	95	95
1114	38p. Canary and budgerigar	1·20	1·20
1115	53p. Hamster	1·70	1·70
1116	69p. Guinea pig	2·20	2·20
MS1117	150×100 mm. £2 Border collie (39×51 mm)	5·50	5·50

2003. Bangkok 2003 International Stamp Exhibition. No. **MS**1098 optd **Jersey at Bangkok 2003** and emblem on sheet margin.

MS1118	110×75 mm. £2 Loose-flowered orchid	5·50	5·50

2003. Winter Flowers. As T **836**. Multicoloured.

1119	29p. Japanese quince	70	65
1120	30p. Winter jasmine	75	65
1121	39p. Snowdrop	95	85
1122	48p. Winter heath	1·10	1·00
1123	53p. Chinese witch-hazel	1·25	1·10
1124	69p. Winter daphne	1·75	1·50

1078 Rook

2004. Jersey Festivals (1st issue). Festival of Chess. Multicoloured.

1125	29p. Type **1078**	95	95
1126	30p. Knight	1·00	1·00
1127	39p. Bishop	1·30	1·30
1128	48p. Pawn	1·60	1·60
1129	53p. Queen	1·70	1·70
1130	69p. King	2·20	2·20

See also Nos. 1204/1209 and 1359/13563.

1084 Monkey (image scaled to 44% of original size)

2004. Chinese New Year. Year of the Monkey. Sheet 110×75 mm.

MS1131	**1084** £1 multicoloured	3·25	3·25

1085 St Aubin's Harbour

2004. Europa. Holidays. Multicoloured.

1132	29p. Type **1085**	95	95
1133	30p. Mont Orgueil Castle	95	95
1134	39p. Corbiere Lighthouse	1·30	1·30
1135	69p. Rozel Harbour	2·30	2·30

The 30p. and 39p. values include the EUROPA emblem.

1089 Green-winged Teal ('Eurasian Teal')

2004. Ducks and Swans. Multicoloured.

1136	32p. Type **1089**	1·00	1·00
1137	33p. Mute swan	1·10	1·10
1138	40p. Northern shoveler	1·30	1·30
1139	49p. Common pochard	1·60	1·60
1140	62p. Black swan	2·00	2·00
1141	70p. European Wigeon ('Eurasian Wigeon')	2·30	2·30
MS1142	150×100 mm. £2 Mallard (38×50 mm)	6·50	6·50

1096 *Cymbidium lowianum* 'Concolor'

2004. Jersey Orchids (5th series). Multicoloured.

1143	32p. Type **1096**	1·00	1·00
1144	33p. *Phragmipedium besseae* var. *flavum*	1·10	1·10
1145	40p. *Peristeria elata*	1·30	1·30
1146	54p. *Cymbidium tracyanum*	1·80	1·80
1147	62p. *Paphiopedilum* Victoria Village 'Isle of Jersey'	2·00	2·00
1148	70p. *Paphiopedilum hirsutissimum*	2·30	2·30
MS1149	110×75 mm. £2 *Phragmipedium* 'Jason Fischer'	6·50	6·50

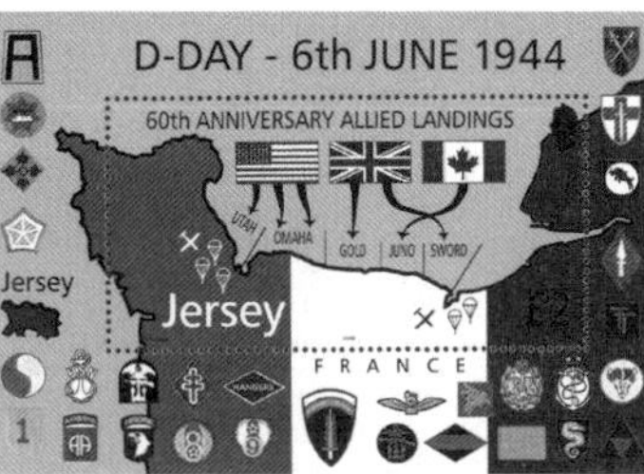

1103 Invasion Map (image scaled to 44% of original size)

2004. 60th Anniversary of D-Day. Sheet 110×75 mm.

MS1150	**1103** £2 multicoloured	6·50	6·50

1104 Mont Orgueil Castle in 13th-century

2004. Jersey. 'A Peculiar of the Crown'. Multicoloured.

1151	32p. Type **1104**	60	35
1152	32p. King John, *c.* 1204 (23×31 mm)	60	35
1153	33p. Mont Orgueil Castle in 17th-century	60	35
1154	33p. King Charles II, *c.* 1684 (23×31 mm)	60	35
1155	40p. Mont Orgueil Castle, 2004	80	45
1156	40p. Queen Elizabeth II, 2002 (23×31 mm)	80	45

2004. Salon du Timbre Stamp Exhibition, Paris. As No. **MS**1149, but optd **Jersey at Le Salon du Timbre 2004** at top left corner of sheet margin.

MS1157	110×75 mm. £2 *Phragmipedium* (Jason Fischer)	6·50	6·50

1110 Wall Lizard

2004. Endangered Species. Multicoloured.

1158	32p. Type **1110**	1·00	1·00
1159	33p. Ant lion	1·10	1·10
1160	49p. Field cricket	1·60	1·60
1161	70p. Dartford warbler	2·30	2·30
MS1162	141×174 mm. Nos. 1158/1161 each×2	12·00	12·00

1114 Dead Man's Fingers

2004. Corals. Multicoloured.

1163	32p. Type **1114**	1·00	1·00
1164	33p. Devonshire cup	1·10	1·10
1165	40p. White sea fan	1·30	1·30
1166	54p. Pink sea fan	1·80	1·80
1167	62p. Sunset cup	2·00	2·00
1168	70p. Red fingers	2·30	2·30
MS1169	150×100 mm. Nos. 1166/1168	6·00	6·00

1120 Nativity Scene

2004. Christmas. Illuminations. Multicoloured. Self-adhesive.

1170	(32p.) Type **1120**	1·00	1·00
1171	(32p.) Fairy lights over busy street	1·00	1·00
1172	(32p.) Santa Claus, children and Christmas tree	1·00	1·00
1173	(32p.) Candles in church	1·00	1·00
1174	(32p.) Three candles and holly	1·00	1·00
1175	(33p.) Mary and Jesus	1·10	1·10
1176	(33p.) Stockings and candle on mantelpiece	1·10	1·10
1177	(33p.) Five candles	1·10	1·10
1178	(33p.) Angel and candle	1·10	1·10
1179	(33p.) Candles in window	1·10	1·10

Nos. 1170/1174 are inscribed 'JERSEY MINIMUM POSTAGE PAID' and were sold for 32p., and Nos. 1175/1179 are inscribed 'U.K. MINIMUM POSTAGE PAID' and were sold for 33p.

2004. Designs as Nos. 1107/1111. Self-adhesive.

1180	(32p.) Type **1061**	1·25	1·50
1181	(32p). Bluebells and Les Ecrehous	1·25	1·50
1182	(32p.) Tree-mallow and Les Ecrehous	1·25	1·50
1183	(32p.) Smooth Sow-thistle and Les Minquiers	1·25	1·50
1184	(32p.) Thrift and Les Minquiers	1·25	1·50

Nos. 1180/1184, which are inscribed 'JERSEY MINIMUM POSTAGE PAID' and were initially sold at 32p each. Nos. 1180/1184 are inscribed '2004' with copyright symbol after date.

1130 Britten-Norman BN-2 Islander C 1 Air Search Aircraft

2005. Rescue Craft. Multicoloured.

1185	32p. Type **1130**	65	70
1186	33p. Eurocopter AS355 Ecurevil II	65	70
1187	40p. Beach lifeguard service	80	85
1188	49p. Fire rescue inflatable	1·50	1·50
1189	70p. RAF Westland Sea King helicopter	1·75	1·75

1135a Rooster

2005. Chinese New Year. Year of the Rooster. Sheet 110×75 mm.

MS1190	**1135a** £1 multicoloured	2·50	2·75

1136 Conger Eel Soup

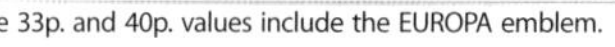

2005. Europa. Gastronomy. Multicoloured.

1191	32p. Type **1136**	65	70
1192	33p. Oysters	65	70
1193	40p. Bean crock	80	85
1194	70p. Bourdélots with black butter	1·40	1·50

The 33p. and 40p. values include the EUROPA emblem.

1140 *Little Red Riding Hood*

2005. Fairy Tales. Multicoloured.

1195	33p. Type **1140**	65	70
1196	34p. *The Little Mermaid*	70	75
1197	41p. *Beauty and the Beast*	80	85
1198	50p. *Rumpelstiltskin*	1·50	1·50
1199	73p. *Goose that laid the Golden Egg*	2·00	2·00
MS1200	110×75 mm. £2 *The Ugly Duckling* (50×37 mm)	4·50	4·75

Nos. 1195/**MS**1200 commemorate the birth bicentenary of Hans Christian Andersen.

1146 Muratti Vase Medal (image scaled to 44% of original size)

2005. Centenary of Jersey Football Association and Muratti Vase. Sheet 110×75 mm.

MS1201	**1146** £2 ochre, black and brown	4·50	4·50

1147 Peace Dove

2005. 60th Anniversary of Liberation of Channel Islands. Peace and Reconciliation. Sheet 110×75 mm.

MS1202	**1147** £2 multicoloured	4·50	4·50

2005. Nordia 2005 Stamp Exhibition, Goteborg, Sweden. No. **MS**1200 optd **Jersey at Nordia 2005** and **Goteborg 26-29 mai SVENSKA FRIMARKET 150 AR.**

MS1203	110×75 mm. £2 *The Ugly Duckling* (50×37 mm)	4·00	4·25

1148 MGB GT

2005. Jersey Festivals (2nd issue). Motor Festival. Classic Cars. Multicoloured.

1204	33p. Type **1148**	65	70
1205	34p. Mini Cooper	70	75
1206	41p. Citroen DS	80	85
1207	50p. Jaguar E Type	1·00	1·10
1208	56p. Volkswagen Beetle	1·10	1·20
1209	73p. Aston Martin DB5	1·50	1·60

1155 Scarlet Pimpernel

2005. Wild Flowers. Multicoloured.

1210	1p. Yellow bartsia	10	10
1211	2p. Type **1155**	10	10
1212	3p. Wild angelica	10	10
1213	4p. Common knapweed	10	10
1214	5p. Marsh St Johnswort	10	15
1215	10p. Black bryony	30	30
1216	15p. Bog pimpernel	30	35
1217	20p. Greater stitchwort	40	45
1218	25p. Horseshoe vetch	75	75
1219	30p. Common mallow	60	65
1220	35p. English stone crop	1·00	1·00
1221	40p. White campion	80	85
1222	45p. Tutsan	1·30	1·30
1223	50p. Common dog-violet	1·00	1·10
1224	55p. Oxeye daisy	1·60	1·60
1225	60p. Rook sea spurrey	1·80	1·80
1226	65p. Herb-Robert	1·30	1·40
1227	70p. Ragged robin	1·40	1·50
1228	75p. Brooklime	1·50	1·60
1229	80p. Mouse ear hawkweed	2·30	2·30
1230	85p. Cuckoo flower	1·70	1·80
1231	90p. Yellow iris	1·80	1·90
1232	£1 Three-cornered garlic	2·00	2·10
1233	£1·50 Devil's-bit scabious	4·50	4·50
MS1234	Three sheets, each 150×100 mm. (a) Nos. 1211, 1213, 1217, 1219, 1221, 1223, 1226 and 1232. (b) Nos. 1210, 1212, 1214, 1216, 1227/1228 and 1230/1231. (c) Nos. 1215, 1218, 1220, 1222, 1224/1225, 1229 and 1223 Set of 3 sheets	26·00	27·00

1178 Le Hocq Tower

2005. Coastal Towers (1st series). Multicoloured.

1235	33p. Type **1178**	65	70
1236	34p. Seymour Tower	70	75
1237	41p. Archirondel Tower	1·00	85
1238	56p. Kempt Tower	1·50	1·75
1239	73p. Le Rocco Tower	2·00	2·25

See also Nos. 1694/1699.

1183 *Hygrocybe calyptriformis*

2005. Fungi (2nd series). Multicoloured.

1240	33p. Type **1183**	65	70
1241	34p. *Boletus erythropus*	70	75
1242	41p. *Inocybe godeyi*	80	85
1243	50p. *Myriostoma coliforme*	1·00	1·10
1244	56p. *Helvella crispa*	1·10	1·20
1245	73p. *Hygrocybe coccinea*	1·50	1·60
MS1246	150×100 mm. £2 *Marasmius oreades* (50×38 mm)	4·50	4·75

1190 HMS *Belleisle*

2005. Bicentenary of the Battle of Trafalgar. Multicoloured.

1247	33p. Type **1190**	65	70
1248	34p. HMS *Royal Sovereign*	70	75
1249	41p. HMS *Neptune*	80	95
1250	50p. HMS *Euryalus*	1·50	1·50
1251	73p. HMS *Mars*	2·00	2·00
MS1252	110×75 mm. £2 HMS *Victory* (50×38 mm)	5·00	5·00

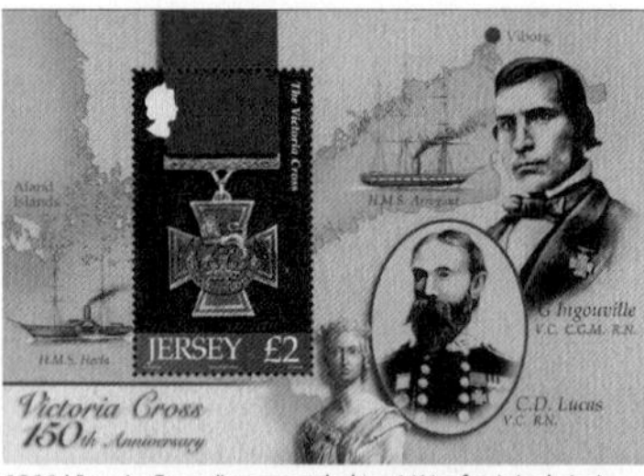

1196 Royal Jersey Regiment, *c.* 1830

2006. Royal Jersey Militia (2nd series). Uniforms and Badges. Multicoloured.

1253	33p. Type **1196**	65	70
1254	34p. Royal Jersey Regiment, *c.* 1844	70	75
1255	41p. Royal Jersey Artillery, *c.* 1881	80	85
1256	50p. Royal Jersey Light Infantry, *c.* 1890	1·50	1·50
1257	73p. Royal Engineers (modern)	2·00	2·00

1201 Victoria Cross (image scaled to 44% of original size)

2006. 150th Anniversary of the Victoria Cross. Sheet 110×75 mm.

MS1258	**1201** £2 multicoloured	5·00	5·00

1202 Dog

2005. Chinese New Year. Year of the Dog. Sheet 110×75 mm.

MS1259	**1202** £1 multicoloured	3·50	3·75

1203 Chinese National Costumes and Mask (Elliott Grimes)

2006. Europa. Winning Entries in Children's Stamp Design Competition. Multicoloured.

1260	33p. Type **1203**	65	70
1261	34p. Portuguese Fado Music Festival (Liam Reynolds)	70	75
1262	41p. Polish Pisanki painted Easter egg design (Kelly Reynolds)	1·75	1·50
1263	73p. Indian national costumes (Olivia Grimes)	2·25	2·25

1207 Flat Periwinkle

2006. Sea Shells. Multicoloured.

1264	34p. Type **1207**	70	75
1265	37p. Painted top shell	75	80
1266	42p. Dog cockle	85	90
1267	51p. Variegated scallop	1·00	1·10
1268	57p. Blue rayed limpet	1·10	1·20
1269	74p. European cowrie	1·50	1·60
MS1270	150×100 mm. £2 Ormer shell (oval, 45×30 mm)	4·50	4·50

1214 Wedding Photograph

2006. First Wedding Anniversary of Prince Charles and Duchess of Cornwall.

1271	**1214** £2 multicoloured	4·50	4·50

1215 Queen Elizabeth II

2006. 80th Birthday of Queen Elizabeth II. Multicoloured.

1272	£5 Type **1215**	10·00	10·50
MS1273	150×100 mm. £5 Type **1215**; No. 2874 of New Zealand (sold at £7)	15·00	15·00

No. **MS**1273 is identical to **MS**2875 of New Zealand.

1217 Football and World Cup Trophy

2006. World Cup Football Championship, Germany. Sheet 110×75 mm.

MS1274	**1217** £2 multicoloured	4·75	5·00

1218 Greve de Lecq

2006. Island Views. Multicoloured. Self-adhesive.

1275	(37p.) Type **1218**	1·50	1·50
1276	(37p.) La Rocque	1·50	1·50
1277	(37p.) Portelet	1·50	1·50
1278	(37p.) St Brelade's Bay	1·50	1·50

Nos. 1275/1278, which are inscribed 'UK MINIMUM POSTAGE PAID' and were initially sold at 37p.

1222 Red Underwing Moth

2006. Butterflies and Moths (2nd series). Multicoloured.

1279	34p. Type **1222**	70	75
1280	37p. Comma butterfly	75	80
1281	42p. Black arches moth	85	90
1282	51p. Small copper butterfly	1·00	1·10
1283	57p. Holly blue butterfly	1·10	1·20
1284	74p. Orange-tip butterfly	1·50	1·60
MS1285	150×100 mm. Nos. 1282/1284	4·50	4·50

Stamps from **MS**1285 have no white borders.

1228 LDV Luton Van, *c.* 2004

2006. Jersey Postal History (2nd series). Postal Vehicles. Multicoloured.

1286	34p. Type **1228**	70	75
1287	37p. Renault Kangoo, 1999–2004	75	80
1288	42p. LDV Pilot, 1994–2004	85	90
1289	51p. Ford Transit, Luton body, 1988–1996	1·00	1·10
1290	57p. Morris Marina, 440/575, *c.* 1978	1·10	1·20
1291	74p. Morris Minor, *c.* 1969	1·50	1·60
MS1292	150×100 mm. Nos. 1289/1291	4·50	4·75

2006. Belgica '06 International Stamp Exhibition, Brussels. No. **MS**1270 optd **Jersey at and Belgica** emblem on bottom left sheet margin.

MS1293	150×100 mm. £2 Ormer shell (oval, 45×30 mm)	5·00	5·50

1234 Molybdenite

2007. Mineralogy. Multicoloured.

1294	34p. Type **1234**	1·00	1·00
1295	37p. Muscovite in pegmatite vein, feldspar+quartz	1·10	1·10
1296	42p. Orthoclase and plagioclase	1·20	1·20
1297	51p. Quartz coated with manganese oxide	1·50	1·50
1298	74p. Smoky quartz	2·20	2·20

1239a Pig

2007. Chinese New Year. Year of the Pig. Sheet 110×75 mm.

MS1299	**1239** £1 multicoloured	3·25	3·50

1240 Windsurfing, canoeing and land yachting (Adventure)

2007. Europa. Centenary of Scouting. Multicoloured.

1300	34p. Type **1240**	1·00	1·00
1301	37p. Scouts playing trumpets and National Flags (International Friendship)	1·10	1·10
1302	42p. Climbing and go-karting (Developing Young People)	1·20	1·20
1303	74p. Scouts and badges (Changing the World for Good)	2·20	2·20

1244 Long-tailed Field Mouse

2007. Countryside Animals. Multicoloured.

1304	34p. Type **1244**	1·00	1·00
1305	37p. Rabbits	1·10	1·10
1306	42p. Polecat	1·30	1·30
1307	51p. Common shrew	1·50	1·50
1308	57p. Stoat	1·70	1·70
1309	74p. Brown rat	2·20	2·20
MS1310	150×100 mm. As Nos. 1307/1309	5·50	5·50

Stamps from **MS**1310 have no white borders.

1250 House Sparrow

2007. Jersey Birdlife (1st series). Garden Birds. Multicoloured.

1311	34p. Type **1250**	1·00	1·00

1312	37p. Chaffinch	1·10	1·10
1313	42p. Blue tit	1·30	1·30
1314	51p. Blackbirds (pair)	1·50	1·50
1315	57p. Magpie	1·70	1·70
1316	74p. Great tit	2·20	2·20
MS1317	150×100 mm. Nos. 1314/1316	5·25	5·25
MS1318	150×100 mm. Nos. 1311/1316	8·75	8·75

Stamps from **MS**1317 have no white borders.

See also Nos. 1400/**MS**1407, 1450/**MS**1457, 1495/**MS**1502, 1584/**MS**1591 and 1681/**MS**1688.

1256 Gorey Regatta

2007. Jersey Yachting (2nd issue). 150th Anniversary of Gorey Regatta. Sheet 110×75 mm.

MS1319	**1256** £2 multicoloured	6·00	6·00

1257 Clematis Nelly Moser and The President

2007. Summer Flowers. Multicoloured.

1320	34p. Type **1257**	1·00	1·00
1321	37p. Rose Just Joey	1·10	1·10
1322	42p. Honeysuckle *Lonicera x Americana*	1·30	1·30
1323	51p. Fuchsia Swingtime	1·50	1·50
1324	57p. Sweet peas	1·70	1·70
1325	74p. Lilac	2·20	2·20

1263 Dornier Do-24 ATT

2007. Jersey Aviation History (9th series). 60th Anniversary of Jersey International Air Display. Multicoloured.

1326	34p. Type **1263**	1·00	1·00
1327	37p. Avro Type 698 Vulcan B.2	1·10	1·10
1328	42p. Junkers Ju 52/3m	1·30	1·30
1329	51p. Sukhoi Su-27 Flanker	1·50	1·50
1330	57p. Boeing B-52 Stratofortress	1·70	1·70
1331	74p. Anglo French Concorde	2·20	2·20
MS1332	110×75 mm. £2·50 BAe Hawk T1s of the Red Arrows (60×40 mm)	7·25	7·25

1270 Queen's Valley Reservoir

2007. Jersey Scenery (1st series). Multicoloured.

1333	34p. Type **1270**	1·00	1·00
1334	37p. Mont Orgueil Castle	1·10	1·10
1335	42p. Bonne Nuit Harbour	1·30	1·30
1336	51p. La Hougue Bie	1·50	1·50
1337	57p. Bouley Bay	1·70	1·70
1338	74p. La Corbiere Lighthouse	2·20	2·20

See also Nos. 1458/1463 and 1612/1617.

1276 *Minuit Chretiens*

2007. Christmas Carols. Multicoloured. Self-adhesive.

1339	(35p.) Type **1276**	1·00	1·00
1340	(35p.) *While Shepherds Watched*	1·00	1·00
1341	(35p.) *O Come All Ye Faithful*	1·00	1·00
1342	(35p.) *O Christmas Tree*	1·00	1·00
1343	(35p.) *Jingle Bells*	1·00	1·00
1344	(39p.) *Hark the Herald Angels Sing*	1·20	1·20
1345	(39p.) *We Three Kings*	1·20	1·20
1346	(39p.) *Ding Dong Merrily on High*	1·20	1·20
1347	(39p.) *Holly and the Ivy*	1·20	1·20
1348	(39p.) *Good King Wenceslas*	1·20	1·20

Nos. 1339/1343 which are inscribed 'JERSEY MINIMUM POSTAGE PAID' were sold for 35p., and Nos. 1344/1348 which are inscribed 'U.K. MINIMUM POSTAGE PAID' were sold for 39p.

1286 Queen Elizabeth II and Duke of Edinburgh

2007. Diamond Wedding of Queen Elizabeth II and Duke of Edinburgh.

1349	**1286** £3 multicoloured	8·75	8·75

1287 Sunshine

2008. 300th Anniversary of Jersey Signal Station. Multicoloured.

1350	35p. Type **1287**	1·00	1·00
1351	39p. Strong wind signals	1·20	1·20
1352	43p. Weather signals	1·30	1·30
1353	58p. Temperature	1·70	1·70
1354	76p. Tides and wave signals	2·30	2·30

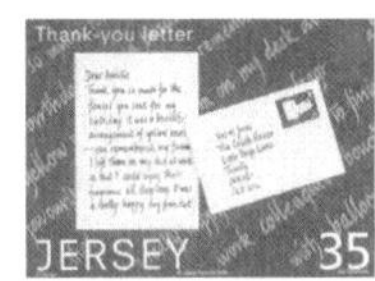

1292 Thank You Letter

2008. Europa. The Letter. Multicoloured.

1355	35p. Type **1292**	1·00	1·00
1356	39p. Love letter	1·20	1·20
1357	43p. Letter to Santa Claus	1·30	1·30
1358	76p. Family letter	2·30	2·30

The 39p. and 43p. values include the EUROPA emblem.

1296 Arts and Crafts

2008. Jersey Festivals (3rd issue). Centenary of Jersey Eisteddfod. Multicoloured.

1359	35p. Type **1296**	1·00	1·00
1360	39p. Dance and drama	1·20	1·20
1361	43p. Speech	1·30	1·30
1362	58p. Films and photography	1·70	1·70
1363	76p. Music	2·30	2·30

1301 Grey Bus Services Daimler CB, *c.* 1920

2008. Jersey Transport. Buses (2nd series). Multicoloured.

1364	35p. Type **1301**	85	85
1365	39p. SCS Ex LGOC 'K' single decker, *c.* 1930	95	95
1366	43p. JMT Town Bus Service, *c.* 1941	1·00	1·00
1367	52p. JMT Leyland Lion Charcoal Burner, *c.* 1941	1·30	1·30
1368	58p. JBS Bedford WLB, *c.* 1956	1·40	1·40
1369	76p. JMT Commer Commando, *c.* 1963	1·80	1·80
MS1370	110×75 mm. £2·50 JMT Ford Willowbrook, *c.* 1977 (74×30 mm)	7·25	7·25

1308 Jersey Bull Mermaid's Warrior Count

2008. 18th World Jersey Cattle Bureau Conference, Jersey. Sheet 110×75 mm.

MS1371	**1308** £2 multicoloured	5·75	5·75

1309 *Cymbidium* Averanches 'Victoria Village'

2008. Jersey Orchids (6th series). Multicoloured.

1372	35p. Type **1309**	1·00	1·00
1373	39p. *Miltonia* 'Tesson Mill'	1·20	1·20
1374	43p. *Anguloa* Victoire 'Trinity'	1·30	1·30
1375	52p. *Phragmipedium* 'La Hougette'	1·50	1·50
1376	58p. *Phragmipedium* Havre des Pas 'Jersey'	1·70	1·70
1377	76p. *Paphiopedilum* Rolfei 'Trinity'	2·30	2·30
MS1378	110×75 mm. £2·50 *Paphiopedilum* 'Rocco Tower'	7·25	7·25

1316 Jersey Cricket Board, Ball hitting Stumps

2008. World Cricket League Division 5 Tournament, Jersey. Sheet 110×75 mm.

MS1379	**1316** £2 multicoloured	5·75	5·75

1317 HMS *Roebuck*

2008. Jersey Naval Connections (2nd series). Visiting Naval Vessels. Multicoloured.

1380	35p. Type **1317**	1·00	1·00
1381	39p. HMS *Monmouth*	1·20	1·20
1382	43p. HMS *Edinburgh*	1·30	1·30
1383	52p. HMS *Express*	1·50	1·50
1384	58p. HMS *Severn*	1·70	1·70
1385	76p. HMS *Cottesmore*	2·30	2·30
MS1386	110×75 mm. £2·50 HMY *Britannia* (60×40 mm)	7·00	7·00

1324 Daimler Dart

2008. Jersey Festival of Speed. Sheet 110×75 mm.

MS1387	**1324** £2·50 multicoloured	7·25	7·25

1325 Cockerel, Hen and Chicks

2008. Farm Animals. Multicoloured. Self-adhesive.

1388	(35p.) Type **1325**	1·00	1·00
1389	(35p.) Ewe and lambs	1·00	1·00
1390	(35p.) Sow and piglets	1·00	1·00
1391	(35p.) Geese and goslings	1·00	1·00
1392	(35p.) Jersey cows and calf	1·00	1·00

Nos. 1388/1392 are inscribed 'JERSEY MINIMUM POSTAGE PAID' and were sold for 35p. each.

Nos. 1388/1392 commemorate the 175th anniversary of the Royal Jersey Agricultural and Horticultural Society.

Nos. 1388/1392 were initially released with '2008' imprint dates. They were re-issued on 2nd April 2010 with '2010' imprint dates.

1330 Carpenter Bee

2008. Insects (2nd series). Multicoloured.

1393	35p. Type **1330**	1·00	1·00
1394	39p. Buff-tailed bumblebee	1·20	1·20
1395	43p. Clown-faced bug	1·30	1·30
1396	52p. Large migrant hoverfly	1·50	1·50
1397	58p. Ruby-tailed wasp	1·70	1·70
1398	76p. 22-spot ladybird	2·30	2·30

2008. Wipa 08 International Stamp Exhibition, Vienna. No. **MS**1370 optd **Jersey at WIPA08** on bottom right sheet margin.

MS1399	110×75 mm. £2·50 JMT Ford Willowbrook, *c.* 1977 (74×30 mm)	7·25	7·25

2008. Jersey Birdlife (2nd series). Migrating Birds. As T **1250**. Multicoloured.

1400	35p. Northern wheatear	1·00	1·00
1401	39p. Whinchat	1·20	1·20
1402	43p. Pied flycatcher	1·30	1·30
1403	52p. Yellow wagtail	1·50	1·50
1404	58p. Ring ouzel	1·70	1·70
1405	76p. Common redstart	2·30	2·30
MS1406	150×100 mm. Nos. 1400/1405	9·00	9·00
MS1407	150×100 mm. Nos. 1403/1405	5·50	5·50

1342 Prince Charles

2008. 60th Birthday of Prince Charles.

1408	**1342** £4 multicoloured	12·00	12·00
MS1409	150×100 mm. No. 1408	12·00	12·00

1343 Douglas C-47 Dakota 3 Pionair

2009. Jersey Aviation History (10th series). 75th Anniversary of the First Flight from Jersey to Southampton. Multicoloured.

1410	35p. Type **1343**	1·00	1·00
1411	39p. Vickers Viscount 833	1·25	1·25
1412	43p. Handley Page HPR7 Dart-Herald	1·25	1·25
1413	52p. Bristol Superfreighter 32	1·50	1·50
1414	58p. Fokker F-27 Friendship	1·75	1·75
1415	76p. Bombardier Q400 Dash 8	2·25	2·25
MS1416	110×75 mm. £3 de Havilland DH.84 Dragon 2	9·00	9·00

1350 Io, Ursa Major and Cassiopeia

2009. Europa. Astronomy. Satellites of Jupiter and Constellations. Multicoloured.

1417	35p. Type **1350**	1·00	1·00
1418	39p. Europa, Bootes and Corona Borealis	1·25	1·25
1419	43p. Ganymede, Cygnus and Pegasus	1·25	1·25
1420	76p. Callisto, Perseus and Orion	2·25	2·25

1354 Blue Iguana (*Cyclura lewisi*)

2009. Endangered Species (1st series). 50th Anniversary of the Durrell Wildlife Conservation Trust. Multicoloured.

1421	35p. Type **1354**	1·00	1·00
1422	39p. Madagascan giant jumping rat (*Hypogeomys antimena*)	1·25	1·25
1423	43p. Mountain chicken frog (*Leptodactylus fallax*)	1·25	1·25
1424	52p. Livingstone's fruit bat (*Pteropus livingstonii*)	1·50	1·50
1425	58p. Andean bear (*Tremarctos ornatus*)	1·75	1·75
1426	76p. Western lowland gorilla (*Gorilla g. gorilla*)	2·25	2·25

1360 Crocus and Grape Hyacinths

2009. Spring Flowers. Multicoloured.

1427	35p. Type **1360**	1·00	1·00
1428	39p. Daffodils	1·25	1·25
1429	43p. Anemones de Caen	1·25	1·25
1430	52p. Tulips	1·50	1·50
1431	58p. Hyacinths	1·75	1·75
1432	76p. Polyanthus and Primulas	2·25	2·25

1366 *Mont Orgueil*

1372 Locomotive No. 5 *La Moye* awaits Departure from St Aubin (image scaled to 44% of original size)

2009. Jersey Railway History (3rd series). Jersey Railways. Multicoloured.

1433	37p. Type **1366**	1·10	1·10
1434	42p. *Corbiere*	1·25	1·25
1435	45p. *Carteret*	1·40	1·40
1436	55p. Railcar *Pioneer*	1·60	1·60
1437	61p. *La Moye*	1·75	1·75
1438	80p. *St Brelades*	2·40	2·40
MS1439	110×75 mm. **1372** £3 multicoloured	9·25	9·25

2009. IBRA International Stamp Exhibition, Essen, Germany. No. **MS**1439 optd **JERSEY AT iBRA** on upper left sheet margin.

MS1440	110×75 mm. **1372** £3 multicoloured	9·00	9·00

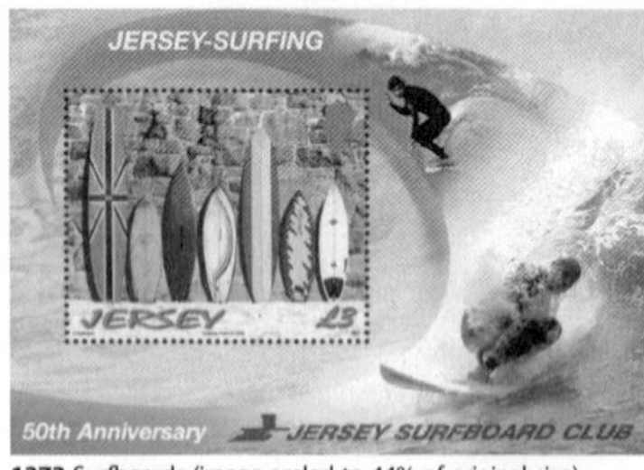

1373 Surfboards (image scaled to 44% of original size)

2009. 50th Anniversary of Jersey Surfboard Club. Sheet 110×75 mm.

MS1441	**1373** £3 multicoloured	9·00	9·00

1374 Post Office, Broad Street, St Helier, 1909 (image scaled to 44% of original size)

2009. Jersey Postal History (3rd series). Post Office Buildings. Sheet 110×75 mm.

MS1442	**1374** £3 multicoloured	9·00	9·00

No. **MS**1442 commemorates the centenary of Jersey's Head Post Office at Broad Street, St Helier.

1375 Investiture of the Prince of Wales at Caernarfon Castle, 1969 (image scaled to 44% of original size)

2009. 40th Anniversary of the Investiture of Prince Charles as the Prince of Wales. Sheet 110×75 mm.

MS1443	**1375** £3 multicoloured	8·75	8·75

1376 *Ascophyllum nodosum* (egg wrack)

2009. Seaweed. Multicoloured.

1444	37p. Type **1376**	1·00	1·00
1445	42p. *Enteromorpha* sp. (gutweed)	1·25	1·25
1446	45p. *Dilsea carnosa* (red rags)	1·40	1·40
1447	55p. *Ulva lactuca* (sea lettuce)	1·50	1·50
1448	64p. *Laminaria hyperborea*	2·00	2·00
1449	80p. *Codium tomentosum* (velvet horn)	2·40	2·40

1382 Dunnock

2009. Jersey Birdlife (3rd series). Songbirds. Multicoloured.

1450	37p. Type **1382**	1·00	1·00
1451	42p. Song thrush	1·25	1·25
1452	45p. Wren	1·40	1·40
1453	55p. Blackcap	1·50	1·50
1454	61p. Mistle thrush	2·00	2·00
1455	80p. Robin	2·40	2·40
MS1456	150×100 mm. Nos. 1450/1455	9·50	9·50
MS1457	150×100 mm. Nos. 1453/1455	5·75	5·75

Stamps from **MS**1457 have no white borders.

1388 Green Island

2009. Jersey Scenery (2nd series). Multicoloured.

1458	37p. Type **1388**	1·00	1·00
1459	42p. Gorey Castle at night	1·25	1·25
1460	45p. St Aubin's Harbour	1·40	1·40
1461	55p. St Peter's Valley	1·50	1·50
1462	61p. La Rocque Harbour	2·00	2·00
1463	80p. Greve de Lecq	2·40	2·40

1394 Parrot Wax-cap (*Hygrocybe psittacina*)

2009. Fungi (3rd series). Multicoloured.

1464	**1394**	37p. Type **1394**	1·10	1·10
1465	**1394**	42p. *Russula sardonia*	1·25	1·25
1466	**1394**	45p. Velvet foot (*Flammulina velutipes*)	1·25	1·25
1467	**1394**	55p. Honey fungus (*Armillaria mellea*)	1·60	1·60
1468	**1394**	61p. Orange peel fungus (*Aleuria aurantia*)	1·75	1·75
1469	**1394**	80p. Jewelled deathcap (*Amanita gemmata*)	2·25	2·25

1400 HMS *Garland*

2009. Jersey Naval Connections (3rd series). 400th Birth Anniversary of Sir George Carteret. Multicoloured.

1470	37p. Type **1400**	1·10	1·10
1471	42p. HMS *Eighth Lion's Whelp*	1·25	1·25
1472	45p. HMS *Unicorn*	1·25	1·25
1473	55p. HMS *Mary Rose*	1·60	1·60
1474	61p. HMS *Antelope*	1·75	1·75
1475	80p. HMS *Rainbow*	2·25	2·25

1406 Gymnast and Cyclist (Healthy Lifestyles)

2010. Centenary of the Girl Guide Association. Multicoloured.

1476	37p. Type **1406**	1·00	1·00
1477	42p. Broken globe, tap and young child drinking (global awareness)	1·25	1·25
1478	45p. Guide salute and handshake (Skills and Relationships)	1·25	1·25
1479	61p. Guides holding hands around globe (Celebrating Diversity)	1·75	1·75
1480	80p. Guides doing handicrafts and on climbing wall (Discovery)	2·25	2·25

1411 A Pushmi-Pullyu (*The Story of Doctor Dolittle* by Hugh Lofting)

2010. Europa. Children's Books. Multicoloured.

1481	37p. Type **1411**	1·50	1·50
1482	42p. *How the Elephant got his Trunk* (Rudyard Kipling)	1·60	1·60
1483	45p. The Mad Hatter's Tea Party (*Alice's Adventures in Wonderland* by Lewis Carroll)	1·75	1·75
1484	80p. *The Dong with a Luminous Nose* (Edward Lear)	3·25	3·25

The 42p. and 45p. values are inscr 'EUROPA'.

1415 Map, *c.* 1685

2010. Maps. Multicoloured. Self-adhesive.

1485	(42p.) Type **1415**	1·25	1·25
1486	(42p.) Map, *c.* 1844	1·25	1·25
1487	(42p.) Map, *c.* 1980s	1·25	1·25
1488	(42p.) Map, *c.* 2000	1·25	1·25
1489	(42p.) Satellite view	1·25	1·25

Nos. 1485/1489 were inscribed 'UK LETTER' and originally sold for 42p. each.

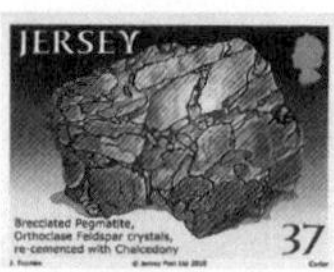

1420 Brecciated Pegmatite, Orthoclase Feldspar Crystals, re-cemented with Chalcedony

2010. Petrology. Multicoloured.

1490	37p. Type **1420**	1·10	1·10
1491	42p. Diorite with Incipient Orbicular Structure	1·25	1·25
1492	45p. Granite	1·25	1·25
1493	61p. Jasper in Andesite	1·75	1·75
1494	80p. Pebbles of Granite, Andesite and Shale in Rozel Conglomerate	2·40	2·40

1425 Jay

2010. Jersey Birdlife (4th series). Woodland Birds. Multicoloured.

1495	37p. Type **1425**	1·10	1·10
1496	42p. Great spotted woodpecker	1·25	1·25
1497	45p. Short-toed treecreeper	1·40	1·40
1498	55p. Chiffchaff	1·60	1·60
1499	61p. Long-tailed tit	1·75	1·75
1500	80p. Turtle dove	2·40	2·40
MS1501	150×100 mm. Nos. 1495/1500	9·50	9·50

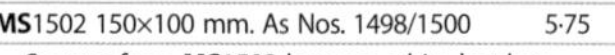

MS1502	150×100 mm. As Nos. 1498/1500	5·75	5·75

Stamps from **MS**1502 have no white borders.

1431 *Royal Charlotte*

2010. Jersey Postal History (4th series). Mail Ships. Multicoloured.

1503	39p. Type **1431**	1·10	1·10
1504	45p. *Dispatch*	1·40	1·40
1505	55p. *Diana*	1·60	1·60
1506	60p. *Reindeer*	1·75	1·75
1507	72p. *Caesarea* (II)	2·25	2·25
1508	80p. *St Patrick* (III)	2·40	2·40
MS1509	150×100 mm. Nos. 1503/1508	10·50	10·50
MS1510	110×75 mm. £3 *Watersprite* *c.* 1827	8·50	8·50

1438 1958 3d. Deep Lilac Stamp

2010. Jersey Postal History (5th series). British Regional Definitive Stamps for Jersey 1958–1969. Multicoloured.

1511	36p. Type **1438**	1·10	1·10
1512	39p. 1964 2½d. carmine-red stamp	1·10	1·10
1513	45p. 1966 4d. ultramarine stamp	1·40	1·40
1514	55p. 1968 4d. olive-sepia stamp	1·60	1·60
1515	60p. 1968 5d. royal blue stamp	1·75	1·75
1516	72p. 1969 4d. bright vermilion stamp	2·25	2·25
MS1517	150×100 mm. Nos. 1511/1516	9·25	9·25

1444 'Nostalgia'

2010. Roses. Multicoloured.

1518	36p. Type **1444**	1·10	1·10
1519	39p. 'Mountbatten'	1·10	1·10
1520	45p. 'Royal William'	1·40	1·40
1521	55p. 'Elina'	1·60	1·60
1522	60p. 'New Dawn'	1·75	1·75
1523	72p. 'Lovers Meeting'	2·25	2·25
MS1524	£3 'Pride of England'	8·50	8·50

2010. Planete Timbres National Stamp Exhibition, Paris. No. **MS**1524 inscr with emblem on top left margin

MS1524a	£3 multicoloured	8·75	8·75

1451 Strawberry Anemone (*Actinia fragacea*)

1457 Dahlia Anemone (*Urticina felina*) (image scaled to 44% of original size)

2010. Sea Anemones. Multicoloured.

1525	36p. Type **1451**	1·10	1·10
1526	39p. Snakelocks Anemone (*Anemonia viridis*)	1·10	1·10
1527	45p. Jewel Anemone (*Corynactis viridis*)	1·40	1·40
1528	55p. Parasitic Anemone (*Sagartia parasitica*)	1·60	1·60
1529	60p. Tube Anemone (*Pachycerianthus* 'Dorothy')	1·75	1·75
1530	72p. Beadlet Anemone (*Actinia equina*)	2·25	2·25
MS1531	**1457** £3 multicoloured	9·00	9·00

1458 Rolls Royce Silver Ghost, 1912

2010. Vintage Cars (4th series). Multicoloured.
1532 39p. Type **1458** 1·10 1·10
1533 45p. Bugatti Type 37, 1926 1·10 1·10
1534 55p. Austin Seven, 1933 1·40 1·40
1535 60p. Citroën Light 15, 1938 1·60 1·60
1536 72p. Morris 10, 1946 1·75 1·75
1537 80p. Rover 75 Sports Saloon, 1949 2·25 2·25

1464 Perch (*Perca fluviatilis*)

2010. Freshwater Fish. Multicoloured.
1538 36p. Type **1464** 1·10 1·10
1539 39p. Tench (*Tinca tinca*) 1·10 1·10
1540 45p. Roach (*Rutilus rutilus*) 1·40 1·40
1541 55p. Rudd (*Scardinius erythrophthalmus*) 1·60 1·60
1542 60p. Mirror Carp (*Cyprinus carpio*) 1·75 1·75
1543 72p. Common Bream (*Abramis brama*) 2·25 2·25
MS1544 110×75 mm. £3 Brown Trout (*Salmo trutta*) 9·00 9·00

Nos. 1538/1543 commemorate the 50th anniversary of the Jersey Freshwater Angling Association.

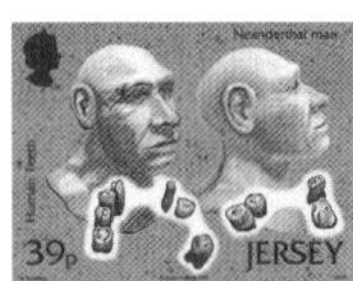

1471 Neanderthal Man and Teeth

2010. Archaeology (1st series). La Cotte de St Brelade. Multicoloured.
1545 39p. Type **1471** 1·10 1·10
1546 45p. Woolly Rhinoceros and Skull 1·40 1·40
1547 55p. Woolly Mammoth, Tusks and Teeth 1·60 1·60
1548 60p. Flint Tools 1·75 1·75
1549 80p. Giant Deer and Antler 2·25 2·25

See also Nos. 1605/1610 and 1700/1704.

1476

2010. Jersey Map with Lions from Crest of Jersey.
1550 (36p.) Type **1476** 1·10 1·10
1551 (39p.) multicoloured 1·10 1·10
1552 (45p.) multicoloured 1·40 1·40

No. 1550 was inscribed 'STANDARD LETTER' and originally sold for 36p. each.
No. 1551 was inscribed 'PRIORITY LETTER' and originally sold for 39p. each.
No. 1552 was inscribed 'UK LETTER' and originally sold for 45p. each.

1479 Paragon C10 AEC B, *c.* 1926

2011. Jersey Transport (3rd series). Coaches. Multicoloured.
1553 36p. Type **1479** 1·10 1·10
1554 45p. Rambler Tours Chevrolet, *c.* 1935 1·40 1·40
1555 55p. JMT Leyland Lioness C14, *c.* 1938 1·60 1·60
1556 60p. JMT Leyland PLSC1 Lion, *c.* 1939 1·70 1·70
1557 72p. Mascot Motors Morris CVF 13/5, *c.* 1948 2·25 2·25
1558 80p. Mascot Motors AEC Regal 4, *c.* 1961 2·40 2·40

1485 Silver Birch (*Betula pendula*)

2011. Europa. Forests. Multicoloured.
1559 39p. Type **1485** 1·10 1·10
1560 45p. English Oak (*Quercus robur*) 1·40 1·40
1561 55p. Beech (*Fagus sylvatica*) 1·60 1·60
1562 80p. Lime (*Tilia cordata*) 2·40 2·40

1489 Dame Margot Fonteyn

2011. Women of Achievement. Multicoloured.
1563 36p. Type **1489** 1·10 1·10
1564 45p. Florence Nightingale 1·40 1·40
1565 60p. Marie Curie 1·75 1·75
1566 72p. Mother Teresa 2·25 2·25

1493 Gooseberry Sea Squirt (*Dendrodoa grossularia*)

2011. Sea Squirts and Sponges. Multicoloured.
1567 (36p.) Type **1493** 1·10 1·10
1568 (39p.) Finger Sponge (*Axinella dissimilis*) 1·10 1·10
1569 (45p.) Purse Sponge (*Scypha ciliata*) 1·40 1·40
1570 60p. Star Squirt (*Botryllus schlosseri*) 1·75 1·75
1571 72p. Light Bulb Sea Squirt (*Clavelina lepadiformis*) 2·25 2·25
1572 80p. Red Sea Squirt (*Polysyncraton lacazei*) 2·40 2·40
MS1573 150×100 mm. As Nos. 1570/1572 10·00 10·00

No. 1567 was inscr 'LOCAL STANDARD LETTER' and originally sold for 36p.
No. 1568 was inscr 'LOCAL PRIORITY LETTER' and originally sold for 39p.
No. 1569 was inscr 'UK LETTER' and originally sold for 45p.

1499 Queen Elizabeth II in Jersey, 2005

2011. 85th Birthday of Queen Elizabeth II.
1574 **1499** £3 multicoloured 7·00 7·00
MS1575 150×100 mm. No. 1574 7·00 7·00

1500 Prince William and Miss Catherine Middleton

2011. Royal Wedding.
1576 **1500** £3.50 multicoloured 8·00 7·00

1501 *Paphiopedilum* La Garenne 'St John'

2011. Jersey Orchids (7th series). Multicoloured.
1577 (36p.) Type **1501** 1·10 1·10
1578 (39p.) *Odontioda* Les Brayes 'Pontac' 1·10 1·10
1579 (45p.) *Phragmipedium* Don Wimber 1·40 1·40
1580 55p. *Kriegerara* Kemp Tower 'Trinity' 1·60 1·60
1581 60p. *Angulocaste* Noirmont 'Isle of Jersey' 1·75 1·75
1582 72p. *Calanthe* Beresford 'Victoria Village' 2·25 2·25
MS1583 110×75 mm. £3 *Miltonia* Point des Pas 'Jersey' 7·00 7·00

No. 1577 was inscr 'LOCAL STANDARD LETTER' and originally sold for 36p.
No. 1578 was inscr 'LOCAL PRIORITY LETTER' and originally sold for 39p.
No. 1579 was inscr 'UK LETTER' and originally sold for 45p.

1508 Barn Swallow (*Hirundo rustica*)

2011. Jersey Birdlife (5th series). Summer Visiting Birds. Multicoloured.
1584 42p. Type **1508** 1·25 1·25
1585 50p. Spotted Flycatcher (*Muscicapa striata*) 1·50 1·50
1586 59p. Cuckoo (*Cuculus canorus*) 1·75 1·75
1587 64p. Whitethroat (*Sylvia communis*) 1·90 1·90
1588 79p. Linnet (*Carduelis cannabina*) 2·40 2·40
1589 86p. Swift (*Apus apus*) 2·60 2·60
MS1590 150×100 mm. Nos. 1584/1589 11·50 11·50
MS1591 150×100 mm. Nos. 1587/1589 7·00 7·00

1514 *Princess Ena*, 1935

2011. Shipwrecks. Multicoloured.
1592 37p. Type **1514** 1·10 1·10
1593 49p. *Caledonia*, 1881 1·50 1·50
1594 59p. *Ibex*, 1897 1·75 1·75
1595 64p. *Schokland*, 1943 1·90 1·90
1596 79p. USS *PT 509*, 1944 2·40 2·40
1597 86p. *Superb*, 1850 2·50 2·50
MS1598 110×75 mm. £3 *Roebuck*, 1911 9·00 9·00

1521 Marsh Harrier (*Circus aeruginosus*) and La Caumine à Marie Best

2011. 75th Anniversary of the National Trust for Jersey. Multicoloured.
1599 42p. Type **1521** 1·25 1·25
1600 50p. Swallowtail Butterfly (*Papilio machaon*) and Victoria Tower 1·50 1·50
1601 59p. Dartford Warbler (*Sylvia undata*) and La Cotte Battery 1·75 1·75
1602 64p. Red Squirrel (*Sciurus vulgaris*) and La Moulin de Quétivel 1·90 1·90
1603 75p. Marsh Harrier (*Circus aeruginosus*) and La Caumine à Marie Best painted Green 2·25 2·25
1604 79p. Puffin (*Fratercula arctica*) and North Coast Sea Cliffs 2·40 2·40

1527 Billion Stater of the XN Series (*c.* 55-50 BC)

2011. Archaeology (2nd series). Buried Treasure. Celtic Coins. Multicoloured.
1605 37p. Type **1527** 1·10 1·10
1606 49p. Durotriges Base Gold Quarter Stater (*c.* 50-30 BC) 1·50 1·50
1607 59p. Baiocasses Gold Stater (*c.* 50 BC) 1·75 1·75
1608 64p. Gold Chute Type Stater (*c.* 50 BC) 1·90 1·90
1609 79p. Southern British Silver Unit (*c.* 50-30 BC) 2·40 2·40
1610 86p. Billion Stater of the Coriosolites Tribe (*c.* 55-50 BC) 2·50 2·50

1533 1960 Fourth of a Shilling Coin, Jersey Lilies and Crest (image scaled to 44% of original size)

2011. 50th Anniversary of Jersey's Finance Industry. Sheet 110×75 mm.
MS1611 **1533** £3 multicoloured 7·00 7·00

1534 Beauport

2011. Jersey Scenery (3rd series). Multicoloured.
1612 42p. Type **1534** 1·25 1·25
1613 49p. St Ouen's Bay 1·50 1·50
1614 50p. Ouaisné 1·50 1·50
1615 64p. St Brelade's Bay 1·90 1·90
1616 79p. Mont Orgueil 2·40 2·40
1617 86p. Portelet 2·50 2·50

1540 Rozel Mill, *c.* 1880

2011. Jersey Architecture (1st series). Mills. Multicoloured.
1618 37p. Type **1540** 1·10 1·10
1619 42p. Tesson Mill, *c.* 1880 1·25 1·25
1620 49p. St. Peter's Mill, *c.* 1905 1·50 1·50
1621 50p. Ponterrin Mill, 19th-century 1·50 1·50
1622 59p. Quétivel Mill, 20th-century 1·75 1·75
1623 79p. Gréve De Lecq Mill, 20th-century 2·40 2·40

See also Nos. 1807/1812.

1546 Santa, Baubles and 1970s Light

2011. Christmas. Multicoloured.
1624 37p. Type **1546** 1·10 1·10
1625 42p. Bauble, Bells and Gold Glass Beaded Garland 1·25 1·25
1626 49p. Baubles enclosing Nativity Scenes and Gold Beads 1·50 1·50
1627 50p. Glass Baubles enclosing Santa scenes and 1980s Candle Lights 1·50 1·50
1628 79p. Angel, Bauble and Glass Bead Garland 2·40 2·40
1629 86p. Nativity Bauble and Silver Bead Garland 2·50 2·50

1552 Violin and *Hark! The Herald Angels Sing* (Mendelssohn)

2011. 25th Anniversary of Jersey Symphony Orchestra. Multicoloured.
1630 37p. Type **1552** 1·10 1·10
1631 50p. Trumpets and *Pomp and Circumstance* (Elgar) 1·50 1·50
1632 59p. Harp and *Pini di Roma* (Respighi) 1·75 1·75
1633 64p. Timpani and *La Gazza Ladra* (Rossini) 1·90 1·90
1634 79p. Bassoons and *Slavonic Dances–Op. 46 No. 1* (Dvorak) 2·40 2·40
1635 86p. French Horn and *Slavonic Dances–Op. 46 No. 3* (Dvorak) 2·50 2·50

1558 Jersey Produce

2012. Europa. Visit Jersey. Multicoloured.

1636	42p. Type **1558**	1·25	1·25
1637	49p. Surfer, Dinghies and Sand Yachts	1·50	1·50
1638	59p. Cyclist, Family walking and Hikers	1·75	1·75
1639	86p. Re-enactment of 1781 Jersey Militia, Elizabeth Castle and La Hougue Bie	2·50	2·50

1562 Queen Elizabeth II, 1954 **1563** King George VI

2012. Diamond Jubilee (1st issue)

1640	**1562** £2 black and new blue	5·00	5·00
1641	**1563** £2 black and new blue	5·00	5·00
MS1642	126×85 mm. Nos. 1640/1641	10·00	10·00

See also No. 1662.

1564 de Havilland DH.86, *c.* 1937

1570 Fairchild Dornier 328-110, *c.* 2009 (image scaled to 44% of original size)

2012. Jersey Aviation History (11th series). 75th Anniversary of Jersey Airport. Multicoloured.

1643	37p. Type **1564**	1·10	1·10
1644	49p. Bristol 170 Wayfarer, *c.* 1946	1·50	1·50
1645	50p. Airspeed Ambassador, *c.* 1953	1·50	1·50
1646	64p. Hawker Siddeley Trident, *c.* 1966	1·75	1·75
1647	79p. Britten-Norman Trislander, *c.* 1977	2·25	2·25
1648	86p. Vickers VC10, *c.* 1987	2·50	2·50
MS1649	110×75 mm. **1570** £3 multicoloured	6·50	6·50

1571 Titanic (image scaled to 32% of original size)

2012. Centenary of the Sinking of the *Titanic*. Sheet 150×100 mm.

MS1650	**1571** £3 multicoloured	7·00	7·00

1572 Broad-bordered Yellow Underwing (moth) (*Noctua fimbriata*)

2012. Butterflies and Moths (3rd series). Multicoloured.

1651	(45p.) Type **1572**	1·25	1·25
1652	(55p.) Painted Lady (*Vanessa cardui*)	1·50	1·50
1653	(60p.) Merveille du Jour (moth) (*Dichonia aprilina*)	1·75	1·75
1654	(68p.) Queen of Spain Fritillary (*Issoria lathonia*)	1·90	1·90
1655	(70p.) Large Emerald (moth) (*Geometra papilionaria*)	2·00	2·00
1656	(88p.) Red Admiral (*Vanessa atalanta*)	2·50	2·50
MS1657	150×100 mm. Nos. 1654/1656	6·25	6·25

Nos. 1651/1656 were inscr 'Local Letter', 'UK Letter', 'Europe', 'Local Large', 'International' and 'UK Large' and were originally sold for 45p., 55p., 60p., 68p., 70p. and 88p respectively.

Stamps from **MS**1657 have no white borders.

1578 Archirondel Tower

2012. Simply Jersey. Landmarks. Multicoloured.

1658	(45p.) Type **1578**	1·25	1·25
1659	(45p.) Mont Orgueil	1·25	1·25
1660	(55p.) Corbiere Lighthouse	1·50	1·50
1661	(55p.) Clasped Hands Sculpture	1·50	1·50

1582 *Equanimity* (official holographic portrait)

2012. Diamond Jubilee (2nd issue).

1662	**1582** £10 black and new blue	23·00	23·00

1583 Prince William

2012. 30th Birthday of Prince William. Multicoloured.

1663	45p. Type **1583**	1·25	1·25
1664	68p. Prince William in RAF Uniform	1·90	1·90
1665	70p. Prince William in Irish Guards Uniform	2·00	2·00
1666	88p. Prince William in Royal Navy Uniform	2·50	2·50

1587 *Magnolia campbellii*

2012. 75th Anniversary of Jersey Trees for Life (formerly Jersey branch of the Men of the Trees). Multicoloured.

1667	45p. Type **1587**	1·25	1·25
1668	55p. Swamp Cypress (*Taxodium distichum*)	1·50	1·50
1669	60p. Flowering Cherry (*Prunus* 'Pink Perfection')	1·75	1·75
1670	68p. Maidenhair (*Ginkgo biloba*)	1·90	1·90
1671	70p. Hill Cherry (*Prunus jamasakura*)	2·00	2·00
1672	88p. London Plane (*Platanus* × *hispanica*)	2·50	2·50

1593 Champagne Glasses

2012. Jersey Moments. Multicoloured.

1673	(45p.) Type **1593**	1·25	1·25
1674	(45p.) Flower	1·25	1·25
1675	(45p.) Coloured Ribbons	1·25	1·25
1676	(45p.) Teddy Bear	1·25	1·25
1677	(55p.) Balloons	1·25	1·25
1678	(55p.) Candles on Birthday Cake	1·25	1·25
1679	(55p.) Rosette of Gold Ribbon	1·25	1·25
1680	(55p.) Red Ribbon Heart	1·25	1·25

1601 Lesser spotted Woodpecker (*Dendrocopos minor*)

2012. Jersey Birdlife (6th series). Threatened Birds. Multicoloured.

1681	45p. Type **1601**	1·25	1·25
1682	55p. Stonechat (*Saxicola torquata*)	1·50	1·50
1683	60p. Yellowhammer (*Emberiza citronella*)	1·75	1·75
1684	68p. Serin (*Serinus serinus*)	1·90	1·90
1685	70p. Bullfinch (*Pyrrhula pyrrhula*)	2·00	2·00
1686	88p. Cirl Bunting (*Emberiza cirlus*)	2·50	2·50
MS1687	150×100 mm. Nos. 1684/1686	6·25	6·25
MS1688	150×100 mm. Nos. 1681/1686	10·50	10·50

1607 Jambo the Gorilla

1611 Jambo and his Family (image scaled to 44% of original size)

2012. Jambo the Gorilla 1961-1992. Multicoloured.

1689	45p. Type **1607**	1·25	1·25
1690	60p. Jambo sitting in Tree	1·75	1·75
1691	80p. Jambo with Female and Baby	2·40	2·40
1692	88p. Close-up of Jambo	2·50	2·50
MS1693	110×75 mm. **1611** £1 multicoloured	2·50	2·50

1612 Flicquet Tower

2012. Coastal Towers (2nd series). Multicoloured.

1694	45p. Type **1612**	1·25	1·25
1695	55p. Portelet Tower	1·50	1·50
1696	60p. Ouaisné Tower	1·75	1·75
1697	68p. Lewis Tower	1·90	1·90
1698	70p. Noirmont Tower	2·00	2·00
1699	80p. St Catherine's Tower	2·40	2·40

1618 Mont Ubé

2012. Archaeology (3rd series). Dolmens. Multicoloured.

1700	45p. Type **1618**	1·25	1·25
1701	55p. Le Couperon	1·50	1·50
1702	60p. Ville és Nouaux	1·75	1·75
1703	68p. Les Mont Grantez	1·90	1·90
1704	88p. La Pouquelaye de Faldouet	2·50	2·50

1623 Reformed Scrooge ('A Merry Christmas one and all!')

2012. Christmas. *A Christmas Carol* by Charles Dickens. Multicoloured.

1705	40p. Type **1623**	1·10	1·10
1706	45p. Ebenezer Scrooge ('Bah Humbug!')	1·25	1·25
1707	50p. Scrooge, Bob Cratchit and his Family ('The End of It')	1·50	1·50
1708	55p. Charles Dickens and Scrooge with Marley's Ghost	1·50	1·50
1709	60p. Charles Dickens and Scrooge with the Ghost of Christmas Past	1·75	1·75
1710	68p. Charles Dickens and Scrooge with the Ghost of Christmas Present	1·90	1·90
1711	80p. Charles Dickens, Scrooge and the Ghost of Christmas Future	2·40	2·40
1712	88p. Charles Dickens and Bob Cratchit and Tiny Tim	2·50	2·50

1631 *Camellia sasanqua* 'Paradise Belinda'

2013. Frosts and Nature. Multicoloured.

1713	45p. Type **1631**	1·25	1·25
1714	55p. Butcher's Broom (*Ruscus aculeatus*)	1·50	1·50
1715	60p. Snowdrop (*Galanthus nivalis*)	1·75	1·75
1716	68p. Mistletoe (*Viscum album*)	1·90	1·90
1717	80p. Bramble (*Rubus fruticosus*)	2·40	2·40
1718	88p. Hawthorn (*Craetagus monogyna*)	2·50	2·50

1637 Statue of King Edward VII, Liverpool

1643 Statue of King Edward VII, Queen's Park, Toronto (image scaled to 44% of original size)

2013. The Royal Legacy of Queen Victoria (1st issue). King Edward VII. Multicoloured.

1719	45p. Type **1637**	1·25	1·25
1720	55p. Statue of King Edward VII, Aberdeen	1·50	1·50
1721	60p. Statue of King Edward VII, Birmingham	1·75	1·75
1722	68p. Statue of King Edward VII, Reading	1·90	1·90
1723	80p. Statue of King Edward VII, Bristol	2·40	2·40
1724	88p. Statue of King Edward VII, London	2·50	2·50
MS1725	110×75 mm. **1643** £2 multicoloured	4·50	4·50

See also Nos. 2034/**MS**2040, **MS**2128 and 2148/**MS**2154.

1644 Boxer

2013. 125th Anniversary of the Kennel Club of Jersey. Multicoloured.

1726	45p. Type **1644**	1·25	1·25
1727	55p. Lhasa Apso	1·50	1·50
1728	60p. Irish Setter	1·75	1·75
1729	68p. Kerry Blue Terrier	1·90	1·90
1730	80p. Pomeranian	2·40	2·40
1731	88p. Afghan Hound	2·50	2·50

1650 Postman's Bicycle, Mailbag and Trolley

2013. Europa. Postal Vehicles. Multicoloured.

1732	45p. Type **1650**	1·25	1·25
1733	55p. Jersey Post Lorry and Vans	1·50	1·50
1734	60p. Jersey Post Van, Lorry and Ferry	1·75	1·75
1735	80p. Loading Air Mail	2·40	2·40

1654 Leyland, *c.* 1948

2013. 90th Anniversary of Jersey Motor Transport Company. Buses (4th series). Multicoloured.

1736	45p. Type **1654**	1·25	1·25
1737	55p. Leyland, *c.* 1955	1·50	1·50
1738	60p. Karrier Bantam, *c.* 1960	1·75	1·75
1739	68p. Leyland Tiger Cub, *c.* 1962	1·90	1·90
1740	80p. Leyland, *c.* 1963	2·40	2·40
1741	88p. Dennis Triton, *c.* 1963	2·50	2·50

1660 Corbiere lining up at Start of Race

1664 Corbiere and Corbiere Lighthouse (image scaled to 51% of original size)

2013. Corbiere, Grand National Winner, 1983. Multicoloured.

1742	55p. Type **1660**	1·50	1·50
1743	60p. Corbiere leading Field in Race	1·75	1·75
1744	68p. Corbiere jumping	1·90	1·90
1745	80p. Corbiere winning Grand National	2·40	2·40
MS1746	95×97 mm. **1664** £2 multicoloured	5·00	5·00

1665 Tracing and Messaging (to reunite separated families)

1671 Red Cross Ship SS *Vega* arriving in Jersey, 1940-1945 (image scaled to 42% of original size)

2013. 150th Anniversary of the International Red Cross and Red Crescent. Multicoloured.

1747	(45p.) Type **1665**	1·25	1·25
1748	(55p.) Red Cross Staff and Volunteers unloading Emergency Supplies	1·50	1·50
1749	(60p.) Villagers drawing Water (Water, shelter and food)	1·75	1·75
1750	(68p.) First Aid Training	1·90	1·90
1751	(80p.) South African Red Cross Helicopter (Emergency response)	2·40	2·40
1752	(88p.) Princess Diana visiting HALO Trust (landmine clearance organisation), Angola, 1997	2·50	2·50
MS1753	115×80 mm. **1671** £2 multicoloured	4·50	4·50

No. 1747 was inscr 'LOCAL LETTER', No. 1748 'UK LETTER', No. 1749 'EUROPE', No. 1750 'LOCAL LARGE', No. 1751 'INTERNATIONAL' and No. 1752 'UK LARGE' and they were originally sold for 45p., 55p., 60p., 68p., 80p. and 88p. respectively.

1672 Queen Elizabeth II

2013. 60th Anniversary of the Coronation. Multicoloured.

1754	£2 Type **1672**	5·00	5·00
1755	£2 Queen Elizabeth II (Cecil Beaton) on 1971 9p. Stamp	5·00	5·00
MS1756	125×85 mm. Nos. 1754/1755	10·00	10·00

1674 Henry Cavill as Man of Steel

1680 Man of Steel flying (image scaled to 44% of original size)

2013. *Man of Steel* (film). Multicoloured.

1757	45p. Type **1674**	1·25	1·25
1758	55p. Henry Cavill as Man of Steel	1·50	1·50
1759	60p. Henry Cavill as Man of Steel	1·75	1·75
1760	68p. Man of Steel flying above Earth	1·90	1·90
1761	80p. Man of Steel walking on Beauport Bay Pebbles	2·40	2·40
1762	88p. Henry Cavill as Man of Steel	2·50	2·50
MS1763	110×75 mm. **1680** £3 multicoloured	7·50	7·50

1681 Beautiful Demoiselle (*Calopteryx virgo*)

2013. Dragonflies and Damselflies. Multicoloured.

1764	45p. Type **1681**	1·25	1·25
1765	55p. Golden-ringed Dragonfly (*Cordulegaster boltonii*)	1·50	1·50
1766	60p. Dainty Damselfly (*Coenagrion scitulum*)	1·75	1·75
1767	68p. Large Red Damselfly (*Pyrrhosoma nymphula*)	1·90	1·90
1768	80p. Scarlet Darter (*Crocothemis erythraea*)	2·40	2·40
1769	88p. Willow Emerald Damselfly (*Lestes viridis*)	2·50	2·50

1687 *Stavros S. Niarchos*

2013. Visiting Tall Ships. Multicoloured.

1770	45p. Type **1687**	1·25	1·25
1771	55p. HM Bark *Endeavour*	1·50	1·50
1772	60p. STS *Tenacious*	1·75	1·75
1773	68p. *Eye of the Wind*	1·90	1·90
1774	80p. *Prince William*	2·40	2·40
1775	88p. Sk/S *Christian Radich*	2·50	2·50
MS1776	150×100 mm. Nos. 1770/1775	11·00	11·00

1693 Stoewer R200 Radio Car

2013. Military Vehicles. Multicoloured.

1777	45p. Type **1693**	1·25	1·25
1778	55p. Kettenkrad NSU HK 101 (1944)	1·50	1·50
1779	60p. HMMWV M998	1·75	1·75
1780	68p. Kubelwagen Type 82 (1944)	1·90	1·90
1781	80p. Sd.Kfz 251-Ausf C Half Track	2·40	2·40
1782	88p. Ford Willys Jeep GPW	2·50	2·50

1699 *Clover*

2013. Jersey Cows. Paintings by Kathy Rondel. Multicoloured.

1783	(45p.) Type **1699**	1·25	1·25
1784	(55p.) *Daisy*	1·50	1·50
1785	(60p.) *Butterfly*	1·75	1·75
1786	(68p.) *Florence*	1·90	1·90
1787	(80p.) *Dolly Maud*	2·40	2·40
1788	(88p.) *Buttercup*	2·50	2·50

No. 1783 was inscr 'LOCAL LETTER', No. 1784 'UK LETTER', No. 1785 'EUROPE', No. 1786 'LOCAL LARGE', No. 1787 'INTERNATIONAL' and No. 1788 'UK LARGE' and they were originally sold for 45p., 55p., 60p., 68p., 80p. and 88p. respectively.

1705 First Pole Position, Lotus 95T, US Grand Prix, 1984

2013. Legacy of a Formula One Champion. Nigel Mansell. Multicoloured.

1789	45p. Type **1705**	1·25	1·25
1790	55p. First Formula 1 Win, Williams Honda, European Grand Prix, 1985	1·50	1·50
1791	60p. Winning Debut with Ferrari, Brazilian Grand Prix, 1989	1·75	1·75
1792	68p. F1 World Champion, Williams Renault, Hungarian Grand Prix, 1992	1·90	1·90
1793	80p. IndyCar Champion, Newman/Haas Lola Ford, Nazareth Speedway, 1993	2·40	2·40
1794	88p. The 'Mansell Taxi' giving Ayrton Senna a lift during Victory Lap, British Grand Prix, 1991	2·50	2·50
MS1795	150×100 mm. Nos. 1789/1794	11·00	11·00

1711 Prince of Wales in Welsh Guards Uniform

2013. 65th Birthday of the Prince of Wales.

1796	**1711** £4 multicoloured	9·50	9·50
MS1797	100×100 mm. As No. 1796 (without white border)	9·50	9·50

1712 Jersey Royal Mace

2013. 350th Anniversary of the Jersey Royal Mace. Multicoloured.

MS1798	70×155 mm. **1712** £1 multicoloured	2·25	2·25

1713 Christmas Pudding

2013. Christmas. Christmas Fayre. Multicoloured.

1799	40p. Type **1713**	1·10	1·10
1800	45p. Mulled Wine and Mince Pies	1·25	1·25
1801	50p. Gingerbread	1·50	1·50
1802	55p. Christmas Cake	1·50	1·50
1803	60p. Stollen	1·75	1·75
1804	68p. Mixed Nuts	1·90	1·90
1805	88p. Gingerbread House	2·50	2·50
1806	95p. Chocolate Yule Log	2·50	2·50

1721 Trinity Manor

2014. Jersey Architecture (2nd series). Manor Houses. Multicoloured.

1807	45p. Type **1721**	1·25	1·25
1808	55p. Longueville Manor	1·50	1·50
1809	60p. Rosel Manor	1·75	1·75
1810	68p. St John's Manor	1·90	1·90
1811	80p. St Ouen's Manor	2·40	2·40
1812	88p. Millbrook Manor	2·50	2·50

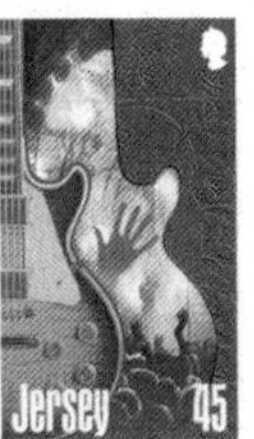

1727 Guitar and Audience at Rock Concert

2014. Europa. Musical Instruments. Multicoloured.

1813	45p. Type **1727**	1·25	1·25
1814	55p. Piano and Concert Hall (Classical)	1·50	1·50
1815	60p. Trumpet and Jazz Musicians	1·75	1·75
1816	80p. Banjo and Jersey Landscape (Folk)	2·40	2·40

1731 *Romeo and Juliet*

1737 William Shakespeare

2014. 450th Birth Anniversary of William Shakespeare. Multicoloured.

1817	46p. Type **1731**	1·25	1·25
1818	56p. *Hamlet*	1·50	1·50
1819	62p. *Macbeth*	1·75	1·75
1820	70p. *Othello*	1·90	1·90
1821	82p. *Twelfth Night*	2·40	2·40
1822	91p. *Midsummer Night's Dream*	2·50	2·50
MS1823	65×90 mm. **1737** £3 multicoloured	7·50	7·50

1738 Poppies and Soldiers

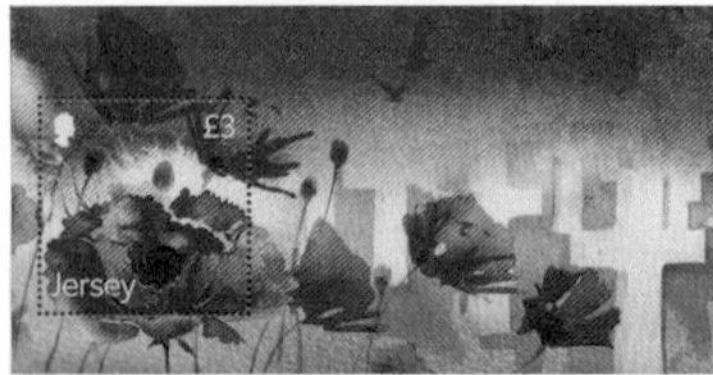

1744 *In Flanders Fields* (poem by John McCrae) (image scaled to 36% of original size)

2014. Remembrance 2014. Centenary of the First World War. Multicoloured.

1824	46p. Type **1738**	1·25	1·25
1825	56p. Poppy Flower	1·50	1·50
1826	62p. Eternal Flame in Poppy Flower	1·75	1·75
1827	70p. Poppy Flower and Soldier	1·90	1·90
1828	82p. Poppy Flower	2·40	2·40
1829	91p. Poppy Flowers and Soldiers	2·50	2·50
MS1830	136×70 mm. **1744** £3 multicoloured	7·50	7·50

Nos. 1824/1825 each had field poppy seeds affixed to them.

1745 Sword Beach, Normandy

1751 Piper Bill, Pegasus Bridge, Normandy (image scaled to 43% of original size)

2014. 70th Anniversary of D-Day. Multicoloured.

1831	46p. Type **1745**	1·25	1·25
1832	56p. Ste.-Mère-Eglise, Normandy	1·50	1·50
1833	62p. Gold Beach, Normandy	1·75	1·75
1834	70p. Pegasus Bridge, Normandy	1·90	1·90
1835	82p. Approaching Carentan, Normandy	2·40	2·40
1836	91p. Off Gold Beach, Normandy	2·50	2·50
MS1837	112×80 mm. **1751** £2 multicoloured	4·50	4·50

1752 Boat at Belcroute Bay

2014. Jersey Seasons (1st series). Summer. Multicoloured.

1838	46p. Type **1752**	1·25	1·25
1839	56p. Seymour Tower at High Tide	1·50	1·50
1840	62p. Summer Calm at Beauport	1·75	1·75
1841	69p. Fisherman's Chapel, St Brelade's Bay	1·90	1·90
1842	70p. The White House at Sunrise	1·90	1·90
1843	82p. South Coast Rocks	2·40	2·40
1844	91p. Reflections of Archirondel Tower	2·50	2·50
1845	£1·20 A View Underwater at Les Ecréhous	3·25	3·25

See also Nos. 1999/2206 and 2109/2116.

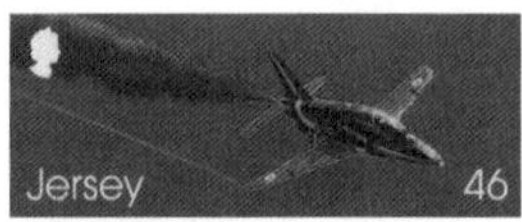

1760 Red Arrows Jet

2014. 50th Display Season of Red Arrows. Multicoloured.

1846	46p. Type **1760**	1·25	1·25
1847	56p. Four Red Arrows	1·60	1·60
1848	62p. Red Arrows flying in Arrow Formation	1·75	1·75
1849	70p. Seven Red Arrows	2·00	2·00
1850	82p. Red Arrows Jet	2·40	2·40
1851	91p. Two Red Arrows	2·50	2·50
MS1852	170×90 mm. Nos. 1846/1851	11·50	11·50

1766 Jersey MIlitiaman

1772 'Are YOU in this?' Poster by Lt. Gen. Sir R. S. S. Baden-Powell

2014. Centenary of the Great War (1st issue). Participation. Multicoloured.

1853	46p. Type **1766**	1·25	1·25
1854	56p. VAD Nurse	1·60	1·60
1855	62p. French Reservist	1·75	1·75
1856	70p. Land Worker	2·00	2·00
1857	82p. Flag Seller	2·40	2·40
1858	91p. Royal Navy Officer	2·50	2·50
MS1859	125×98 mm. Nos. 1853/1858	11·50	11·50
MS1860	66×98 mm. **1772** £1 multicoloured (50×36 mm)	3·00	3·00

See also Nos. 1977/**MS**1984 and 2087/**MS**2094.

1773 Roman Invasion

1779 Elephant ridden into Battle (image scaled to 46% of original size)

2014. Jersey's Roman Connections. Multicoloured.

1861	46p. Type **1773**	1·25	1·25
1862	56p. Traders and Roman Temple	1·60	1·60
1863	62p. Emperor Hadrian and Building of Hadrian's Wall	1·75	1·75
1864	70p. Conversion to Christianity	2·00	2·00
1865	82p. Family and Roman Soldiers	2·40	2·40
1866	91p. War Chariot	2·50	2·50
MS1867	105×75 mm. **1779** £2 multicoloured	5·75	5·75

1780 Barnegat Lighthouse, New Jersey

2014. 350th Anniversary of Founding of the US State of New Jersey. Multicoloured.

1868	46p. Type **1780**	1·25	1·25
1869	56p. Elizabeth Castle, Jersey	1·60	1·60
1870	62p. Corbière Lighthouse, Jersey	1·75	1·75
1871	70p. Seymour Tower, Jersey	2·00	2·00
1872	82p. Statue of Liberty, New York/ New Jersey	2·40	2·40
1873	91p. George Washington Bridge, New Jersey	2·50	2·50
MS1874	124×97 mm. As Nos. 1868/1873	11·50	11·50

1786 19th-century Oyster Fishing Boat

1792 Basket of Oysters (image scaled to 32% of original size)

2014. Oyster Fishing. Multicoloured.

1875	46p. Type **1786**	1·25	1·25
1876	56p. 19th-century Shore Workers	1·60	1·60
1877	62p. 19th-century Oyster Fishermen with Dredges	1·75	1·75
1878	70p. Tending Modern Oyster Beds	2·00	2·00
1879	82p. Tending Oyster Beds at Low Tide with Tractor and Trailer	2·40	2·40
1880	91p. *La Duchesse de Normandie* (20th-century transport)	2·50	2·50
MS1881	151×100 mm. **1792** £2 multicoloured	5·75	5·75

1793 Galleons

2014. Pirates and Privateering. Multicoloured.

1882	46p. Type **1793**	1·25	1·25
1883	56p. Pirates on board Ship	1·60	1·60
1884	69p. In Longboat	2·00	2·00
1885	£1·20 Galleons	3·50	3·50
MS1886	114×98 mm. Nos. 1882/1885	8·25	8·25

1797 White Teddy Bear

2014. Greetings Stamps. My Moments. Multicoloured.

1887	(46p.) As Type **1797**	1·25	1·25
1888	(46p.) Red and Yellow Balloons	1·25	1·25
1889	(46p.) Hands forming Heart	1·25	1·25
1890	(46p.) Wrapped Present	1·25	1·25
1891	(46p.) Arms	1·25	1·25
1892	(46p.) Fireworks	1·25	1·25
1893	(56p.) White Teddy Bear	1·60	1·60
1894	(56p.) 'hello' in Sand	1·60	1·60
1895	(56p.) Heart-shaped Stone and Ribbon	1·60	1·60
1896	(56p.) Champagne Glasses	1·60	1·60
1897	(56p.) Flag	1·60	1·60
1898	(56p.) Globe showing Western Europe	1·60	1·60

1809 Father Christmas talking with Child

2014. Christmas. The Story of Father Christmas. Multicoloured.

1899	41p. Type **1809**	1·10	1·10
1900	46p. Carrying Tree	1·25	1·25
1901	51p. Wrapping Presents	1·50	1·50
1902	56p. On Top of Roof	1·60	1·60
1903	62p. Eating Mince Pie	1·75	1·75
1904	70p. Writing Christmas Letter	2·00	2·00
1905	91p. With Child carrying Tree	2·50	2·50
1906	£1·10 Filling Sack with Presents	3·25	3·25

1817 The Beowulf Dragon

2015. Dragons. Multicoloured.

1907	46p. Type **1817**	1·25	1·25
1908	56p. St George and the Dragon	1·60	1·60
1909	62p. The Bakunawa	1·75	1·75
1910	70p. The Colchian Dragon	2·00	2·00
1911	82p. The Chinese Dragons	2·40	2·40
1912	91p. The Welsh Dragon	2·50	2·50
MS1913	150×98 mm. Nos. 1907/1912	11·50	11·50

1823 Crest of Jersey

1824 Crest of Jersey

2015. Crest of Jersey.

1914	**1823**	1p. bright reddish violet	10	10
1915		2p. bistre	10	10
1916		3p. ultramarine	10	10
1917		4p. deep bluish-green	10	10
1918		5p. brown-purple	15	15
1919		10p. bright magenta	30	30
1920		20p. bright orange	60	60
1921		40p. greenish blue	1·10	1·10
1921*a*		48p. bright magenta and dull claret (2.2.17)	1·40	1·40
1922		50p. bright green	1·50	1·50
1922*a*		60p. violet-blue and dull claret (2.2.17)	1·75	1·75
1922*b*		66p. turquoise-green and dull claret (2.2.17)	1·90	1·90
1922*c*		76p. bright reddish violet and dull claret (2.2.17)	2·25	2·25
1922*d*		88p. yellow (2.2.17)	2·50	2·50
1923		£1 vermilion	3·00	3·00

1923*a*	£1 dull claret (2.2.17)	3·00	3·00
1924	**1824** £5 silver	14·50	14·50

Nos. 1914/1924 have the names of all 12 Jersey parishes printed in micro text in the background waves on the stamps.

No. 1924 contains a hologram which has been embossed.

1825 British Pullman

2015. Europa. Traditional Toys. Hornby Model Trains. Multicoloured.

1925	46p. Type **1825**	1·25	1·25
1926	56p. GWR Passenger Freight	1·60	1·60
1927	62p. *Flying Scotsman*	1·75	1·75
1928	70p. *The Cornishman*	2·00	2·00
1929	82p. Mixed Freight	2·40	2·40
1930	91p. *Caledonian Belle*	2·50	2·50

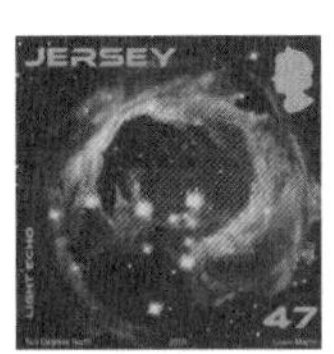

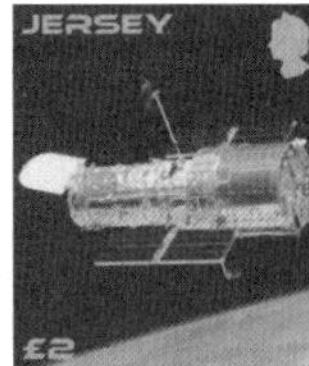

1831 Light Echo **1839** Hubble Telescope

2015. 25th Anniversary of Launch of Hubble Space Telescope. Multicoloured.

1931	47p. Type **1831**	1·25	1·25
1932	57p. Spiral Galaxy	1·60	1·60
1933	64p. Mystic Mountain	1·75	1·75
1934	71p. Jupiter's New Red Spot, 2006	2·00	2·00
1935	73p. Cat's Eye Nebula	2·00	2·00
1936	85p. Mars	2·40	2·40
1937	95p. A Rose of Galaxies	2·50	2·50
1938	£1·25 The Pistol Star	3·50	3·50
MS1939	110×75 mm. **1839** £2 multicoloured	5·75	5·75

1840 '9TH MAY 1945' (THE CHANNEL ISLANDS WERE LIBERATED ON THIS DAY)

1846 Winston Churchill, 30 December 1941 (image scaled to 36% of original size)

2015. 50th Death Anniversary of Sir Winston Churchill (1st issue). 70th Anniversary of Victory and Liberation. Multicoloured.

1940	47p. Type **1840**	1·25	1·25
1941	57p. HMS *Beagle* (THE GERMAN OCCUPYING FORCES ON JERSEY SIGNED THE TERMS OF SURRENDER ABOARD HMS *BEAGLE*)	1·60	1·60
1942	64p. Arms and Outline Map of Jersey (TASK FORCE 135 SAILED INTO ST HELIER TO LIBERATE THE ISLAND)	1·75	1·75
1943	73p. SS *Vega* and Map of its Voyage (INTERNATIONAL RED CROSS SHIP SS *VEGA* FIRST ARRIVED IN JERSEY FROM LISBON 31 DECEMBER 1944)	2·00	2·00
1944	85p. Royal Square, St Helier (V FOR VICTORY WAS DEFIANTLY SET IN THE PAVING STONES OF ST HELIER'S ROYAL SQUARE)	2·40	2·40
1945	95p. "THIS IS YOUR VICTORY" (Winston Churchill) and Radio (CHURCHILL ADDRESSED THE NATION ON THE DAY OF VICTORY)	2·50	2·50
MS1946	150×100 mm. Nos. 1940/1945	11·00	11·00
MS1947	131×94 mm. **1846** £3 multicoloured	8·50	8·50

See also Nos. 1969/**MS**1976.

1847 Scales ('800 YEARS OF JUSTICE')

1853 '800 YEARS OF *MAGNA CARTA* 1215-2015' (image scaled to 38% of original size)

2015. 800th Anniversary of *Magna Carta*. Multicoloured.

1948	47p. Type **1847**	1·25	1·25
1949	57p. Key ('800 YEARS OF FREEDOM')	1·60	1·60
1950	64p. Fist ('800 YEARS OF HUMAN RIGHTS')	1·75	1·75
1951	73p. Dove ('800 YEARS OF LIBERTY')	2·00	2·00
1952	85p. Outline Map of Jersey ('800 YEARS OF CITIZENSHIP')	2·40	2·40
1953	95p. Cross on Ballot Paper ('800 YEARS OF DEMOCRACY')	2·50	2·50
MS1954	125×85 mm. **1853** £1·50 black and gold	4·50	4·50

1854 Table Tennis

2015. Island Games, Jersey. Multicoloured.

1955	(62p.) Type **1854**	1·75	1·75
1956	(62p.) Archery	1·75	1·75
1957	(62p.) Athletics	1·75	1·75
1958	(62p.) Sailing	1·75	1·75
1959	(62p.) Beach Volleyball	1·75	1·75
1960	(62p.) Swimming	1·75	1·75
1961	(62p.) Golf	1·75	1·75
1962	(62p.) Shooting	1·75	1·75
1963	(62p.) Triathlon	1·75	1·75
1964	(62p.) Football	1·75	1·75
1965	(62p.) Basketball	1·75	1·75
1966	(62p.) Tennis	1·75	1·75
1967	(62p.) Badminton	1·75	1·75
1968	(62p.) Cycling	1·75	1·75

Nos. 1955/1968 were all inscr 'POSTCARD' and were originally sold for 62p. each.

1868 Mk I Spitfire

1874 Winston Churchill (image scaled to 37% of original size)

2015. 50th Death Anniversary of Sir Winston Churchill (2nd issue). 75th Anniversary of the Battle of Britain. Multicoloured.

1969	47p. Type **1868**	1·25	1·25
1970	57p. Radar	1·60	1·60
1971	64p. RAF Wings and 'THE FEW	1·75	1·75
1972	73p. Target and 'AROUND 1,000 RAF PLANES WERE LOST DURING THE BATTLE OF BRITAIN. LUFTWAFFE LOSSES EXCEEDED 1.800.'	2·00	2·00
1973	85p. Barrage Balloons and Dome of St. Paul's Cathedral, London	2·40	2·40
1974	95p. Hawker Hurricane Fighter Planes	2·50	2·50
MS1975	150×100 mm. Nos. 1969/1974	11·00	11·00
MS1976	131×94 mm. **1874** £3 multicoloured	8·50	8·50

1875 Tank and Cavalryman (Mechanisation)

1881 Flt Lt Charles Stanley Mossop and Wight Seaplane (first sinking of enemy submarine from the air, 1917) (image scaled to 37% of original size)

2015. Centenary of the Great War (2nd issue). Change. Multicoloured.

1977	47p. Type **1875**	1·25	1·25
1978	57p. Military Field Telephone and Signals with Flags (Communication)	1·60	1·60
1979	64p. Ship painted with Dazzle Pattern (Camouflage and Deception)	1·75	1·75
1980	73p. Uniforms	2·00	2·00
1981	85p. Aeroplane and Observation Balloon (Observation)	2·40	2·40
1982	95p. Helmet and Barbed Wire (Tactics of War)	2·50	2·50
MS1983	165×98 mm. Nos. 1977/1982	11·00	11·00
MS1984	131×70 mm. **1881** £1 multicoloured	3·00	3·00

1882 De Carteret Coat of Arms and St Ouen's Manor, Jersey (image scaled to 32% of original size)

2015. 450th Anniversary of Island of Sark as a Fief to the Crown. Sheet 150×100 mm.

MS1985	**1882** £1·50 multicoloured	4·50	4·50

1883 Coronation Portrait (Cecil Beaton)

1887 *The Coronation Theatre, Westminster Abbey: A Portrait of Her Majesty Queen Elizabeth II* (Ralph Heimans) (image scaled to 39% of original size)

2015. Queen Elizabeth II. Longest Reigning British Monarch. Multicoloured.

1986	47p. Type **1883**	1·25	1·25
1987	57p. Silver Jubilee Portrait (Peter Grugeon)	1·60	1·60
1988	71p. Golden Jubilee Portrait (John Swannell)	2·00	2·00
1989	£1·25 Diamond Jubilee Portrait (John Swannell)	3·50	3·50
MS1990	148×85 mm. Nos. 1986/1989	8·25	8·25
MS1991	122×84 mm. **1887** £3 multicoloured	8·50	8·50

1888 Magnolia

2015. Links with China (1st series). Garden Flowers. Multicoloured.

1992	47p. Type **1888**	1·25	1·25
1993	47p. Camellia	1·25	1·25
1994	47p. Azalea	1·25	1·25
1995	47p. hydrangea	1·25	1·25
1996	47p. Chrysanthemum	1·25	1·25
1997	47p. Peony	1·25	1·25
MS1998	125×96 mm. Nos. 1996/1997	2·50	2·50

1894 Country Lane near St John's Village

2015. Jersey Seasons (2nd series). Autumn. Photographs by Andy Le Gresley. Multicoloured.

1999	47p. Type **1894**	1·25	1·25
2000	57p. Sun through the Clouds at Corbière	1·60	1·60
2001	64p. Autumn in the Sand Dune	1·75	1·75
2002	71p. Stormy Day at Noirmont Point	2·00	2·00
2003	73p. High Tide Shore Break at St Catherine's Bay	2·00	2·00
2004	85p. Sunset at the Radio Tower, St Brelade	2·40	2·40
2005	95p. Woodland Path through St Peter's Valley	2·50	2·50
2006	£1·25 Kempt Tower through the Beach Grass, St Ouen	3·50	3·50

1902 Jersey Cow (Millie Foley)

2015. Greetings Stamps. My Jersey. Winning Designs from Design a Stamp Competition. Multicoloured.

2007	(47p.) Type **1902**	1·25	1·25
2008	(47p.) White House, St Ouen's Bay, and Flowers (Jennifer Crocker)	1·25	1·25
2009	(47p.) Sun, Surfboard and Sailing Boat (Matthew Brown)	1·25	1·25
2010	(47p.) Girl and Boy Rock Pooling (Leah O'Brien)	1·25	1·25
2011	(47p.) Seymour Tower (Anna Le Moine Gray)	1·25	1·25
2012	(57p.) Puffin (Sophie Dixon)	1·60	1·60
2013	(57p.) Jersey Royal Potato Farming (Ciaran Britton)	1·60	1·60
2014	(57p.) Jersey Cow and Calf at Seaside (Allan Giles McCartney)	1·60	1·60
2015	(57p.) Corbiere Lighthouse at Sunset (Skye Leather)	1·60	1·60
2016	(57p.) Crest of Jersey, Liberation Sculpture, Mont Orgueil Castle and Corbiere Lighthouse (Claudia Dixon)	1·60	1·60

Nos. 2007/2011 were inscr 'Local Letter' and originally sold for 47p. each. Nos. 2012/2016 were inscr 'UK Priority Letter' and originally sold for 57p. each.

1912 Virgin Mary

2015. Christmas. Stained Glass Windows by Henry Thomas Bosdet depicting the Annunciation. Multicoloured.

2017	42p. Type **1912**	1·10	1·10
2018	47p. Archangel Gabriel	1·25	1·25
2019	52p. Archangel Gabriel	1·50	1·50
2020	57p. Virgin Mary	1·60	1·60
2021	64p. Archangel Gabriel	1·75	1·75
2022	73p. Virgin Mary	2·00	2·00
2023	95p. Archangel Gabriel	2·50	2·50
2024	£1·15 Virgin Mary	3·00	3·00

1920 Monkey holding Peach

1921 Monkey picking Peach (image scaled to 39% of original size)

2016. Chinese New Year. Year of the Monkey.

2025	**1920** 47p. multicoloured	1·25	1·25
MS2026	125×95 mm. **1921** £1 multicoloured	3·00	3·00

1922 Pilot in Dinghy and Lockheed Hudson Aircraft responding to Distress Flare

2016. 75th Anniversary of RAF Search and Rescue. Multicoloured.

2027	47p. Type **1922**	1·25	1·25
2028	57p. Air Sea Rescue High Speed Launch	1·60	1·60
2029	71p. Supermarine Walrus Seaplane rescuing Two Pilots in Dinghy	2·00	2·00
2030	73p. Westland Whirlwind Helicopter carrying out Winch Rescue from Sinking Boat	2·00	2·00
2031	95p. Westland Wessex Helicopter	2·50	2·50
2032	£1·25 Westland Sea King Helicopter carrying out Cliff Rescue	3·50	3·50
MS2033	138×98 mm. Nos. 2027/2032	12·50	12·50

1928 King George V, 1911

1934 King George V, 1934

2016. The Royal Legacy of Queen Victoria (2nd issue). King George V. Multicoloured.

2034	47p. Type **1928**	1·25	1·25
2035	57p. King George V, 1914	1·60	1·60
2036	64p. King George V, 1922	1·75	1·75
2037	73p. King George V, 1926	2·00	2·00
2038	85p. King George V, 1933	2·40	2·40
2039	95p. King George V, 1934	2·50	2·50
MS2040	116×81 mm. **1934** £2 multicoloured	5·75	5·75

1935 Princess Elizabeth aged Two

2016. 90th Birthday of Queen Elizabeth II. Multicoloured.

2041	48p. Type **1935**	1·25	1·25
2042	48p. King George VI, Queen Elizabeth and Princesses Elizabeth and Margaret	1·25	1·25
2043	60p. Princess Elizabeth and Duke of Edinburgh, *c.* 1949	1·75	1·75
2044	60p. Queen Elizabeth II, Duke of Edinburgh, Prince Charles and Princess Anne, *c.* 1953	1·75	1·75
2045	66p. Queen Elizabeth II, Prince Charles and Princess Anne, *c.* 1953	1·75	1·75
2046	74p. Queen Elizabeth II, Duke of Edinburgh, Prince Charles, Princess Anne, Prince Andrew and Prince Edward	2·00	2·00
2047	76p. Queen Elizabeth the Queen Mother, Queen Elizabeth II and Princess Margaret	2·00	2·00
2048	88p. Queen Elizabeth and Queen Elizabeth the Queen Mother	2·40	2·40
2049	£1 Queen Elizabeth II and Duke of Edinburgh	3·00	3·00
2050	£1·29 Queen Elizabeth II, Duke and Duchess of Cambridge and Prince Harry	3·50	3·50

1945 Wedding of Duke and Duchess of Cambridge (image scaled to NaN% of original size)

1950 Christening of Princess Charlotte, July 2015 (image scaled to 44% of original size)

2016. Fifth Wedding Anniversary of Duke and Duchess of Cambridge. Multicoloured.

2051	48p. Type **1945**	1·25	1·25
2052	60p. Duke and Duchess of Cambridge	1·75	1·75
2053	74p. Duke and Duchess of Cambridge with Prince George, August 2013	2·00	2·00
2054	£1 Duke and Duchess of Cambridge with Prince George	3·00	3·00
2055	£1·29 Duke and Duchess of Cambridge with Princess Charlotte, 2015	3·50	3·50
MS2056	110×75 mm. **1950** £2 multicoloured	5·75	5·75

1951 Profile ('Sustainable')

2016. Europa. 'Think Green'. Multicoloured.

2057	74p. Type **1951**	2·00	2·00
2058	76p. Map of Jersey ('Recycle')	2·00	2·00
2059	£1 Globe ('effect')	3·00	3·00
2060	£1·29 Polluted and Clean Environments	3·50	3·50

1955 Albert Einstein reading

1961 Albert Einstein, *c.* 1950 (image scaled to 37% of original size)

2016. Centenary of Albert Einstein's Theory of General Relativity. Each black and greenish yellow.

2061	48p. Type **1955**	1·25	1·25
2062	60p. Young Albert Einstein and Earth	1·75	1·75
2063	66p. Albert Einstein writing Equation on Blackboard	1·75	1·75
2064	76p. Albert Einstein, *c.* 1950	2·00	2·00
2065	88p. Albert Einstein	2·40	2·40
2066	£1 Albert Einstein, *c.* 1921	3·00	3·00
MS2067	140×100 mm. Nos. 2061/2066	11·00	11·00
MS2068	131×94 mm. **1961** £2 black, greenish yellow and silver	5·75	5·75

1962 MG TC, 1948

1970 Michael Wilcock and John Sweeny in 1912 Talbot, Boxing Day Run, 1969 (image scaled to 44% of original size)

2016. 50th Anniversary of Jersey Old Motor Club. Multicoloured.

2070	48p. Type **1962**	1·25	1·25
2071	60p. Rolls-Royce 20, 1928	1·75	1·75
2072	66p. 60HP Mercedes, 1903	1·75	1·75
2073	74p. Daimler 15, 1934	2·00	2·00
2074	76p. Morgan Aero Three Wheeler, 1929	2·00	2·00
2075	88p. 3½ Litre Bentley, 1934	2·40	2·40
2076	£1 Austin 7 Chummy, 1929	3·00	3·00
2077	£1·29 Gladiator Tonneau, 1902	3·50	3·50
MS2078	110×75 mm. **1970** £2 multicoloured	5·75	5·75

1971 'Daddy-o' (1950s language) (image scaled to NaN% of original size)

1977 A Jersey Street, 1950s (1950s popular culture. Street life) (image scaled to 37% of original size)

2016. Popular Culture (1st series). The 1950s. Multicoloured.

2079	48p. Type **1971**	1·40	
2080	60p. Dancers (1950s music, rock & roll)	1·75	1·75
2081	66p. Pink and White Spotted Dress (1950s fashion, full skirt)	1·90	1·90
2082	76p. Couple watching Coronation on Television (1950s event, Elizabeth II coronation)	2·25	2·25
2083	88p. Mother and Son (1950s food, jelly)	2·50	2·50
2084	£1 Boy with Model Car (1950s leisure, model cars)	3·00	3·00
MS2085	140×99 mm. Nos. 2079/2084	12·50	12·50
MS2086	130×94 mm. **1977** £2 multicoloured	5·75	5·75

1978 First Battle of Ypres, 1914

1984 Cambrai, 1917 (image scaled to 37% of original size)

2016. Centenary of the Great War (3rd issue). Battles. Multicoloured.

2087	48p. Type **1978**	1·40	1·40
2088	60p. Gallipoli, 1915-1916	1·75	1·75
2089	66p. Battle of Jutland, 1916	1·90	1·90
2090	76p. The Somme Offensive, 1916	2·25	2·25
2091	88p. Battle of Aqaba, 1917	2·50	2·50
2092	£1 Passchendaele, 1917	3·00	3·00
MS2093	164×97 mm. Nos. 2087/2092	12·50	12·50
MS2094	130×70 mm. **1984** £2 multicoloured	5·75	5·75

2016. New York 2016 World Stamp Show. No. **MS**2068 inscr with emblem on lower right sheet margin

MS2069	131×94 mm. **1961** £2 black, greenish yellow and silver	5·75	5·75

1985 Tufted Duck

2016. Links with China (2nd series). Waterfowl. Multicoloured.

2095	48p. Type **1985**	1·40	1·40
2096	48p. Northern Pintail	1·40	1·40
2097	48p. Mandarin	1·40	1·40
2098	48p. Common Shelduck	1·40	1·40
2099	48p. Smew	1·40	1·40
2100	48p. Mallard	1·40	1·40
MS2101	130×90 mm. Nos. 2097/2098	2·75	2·75

1991 The Fairies of St Brelade's Church

2016. Jersey Myths and Legends. Multicoloured.

2102	48p. Type **1991**	1·40	1·40
2103	60p. William and the Sea Sprite	1·75	1·75
2104	74p. The Witches of Rocqueberg	2·10	2·10
2105	76p. The Dragon of St Lawrence	2·25	2·25
2106	£1 The Black Dog of Bouley Bay	3·00	3·00
2107	£1·29 The Ghostly Bride of Waterworks Valley	3·75	3·75
MS2108	135×94 mm. Nos. 2102/2107	14·00	14·00

1997 Corbière Lighthouse surrounded by Stormy Winter Seas

2016. Jersey Seasons (3rd series). Winter. Photographs by Andy Le Gresley. Multicoloured.

2109	48p. Type **1997**	1·40	1·40
2110	60p. Snow at St Catherine's Woods	1·75	1·75
2111	66p. Cold Water at Noirmont Tower	1·90	1·90
2112	74p. Snow at Mont Orgueil Castle	2·10	2·10
2113	76p. Night Skies at Les Écréhous	2·25	2·25
2114	88p. Hail Showers at La Moye Golf Course	2·50	2·50
2115	£1 Winter Woodland at Noirmont	3·00	3·00
2116	£1·29 Gales blow into the Headland at Corbière	3·75	3·75

2005 Father Christmas and Corbière Lighthouse

2013 Father Christmas emerging from Farmhouse Fireplace

2016. Father Christmas in Jersey. Multicoloured.

2117	43p. Type **2005**	1·25	1·25
2118	48p. Father Christmas and his Sleigh at St Ouen's Manor	1·40	1·40
2119	55p. Father Christmas in Royal Square	1·60	1·60
2120	60p. Father Christmas and his Sleigh above Trinity Church	1·75	1·75
2121	66p. Father Christmas and his Sleigh near Elizabeth Castle	1·90	1·90
2122	76p. Father Christmas and his Sleigh outside Jersey Post Headquarters	2·25	2·25
2123	£1 Father Christmas and his Sleigh outside Samarès Farmhouse	3·00	3·00
2124	£1·19 Father Christmas on Rooftop near St Thomas' Church	3·50	3·50
MS2125	127×97 mm. **2013** £2·92 multicoloured	8·50	8·50

2014 Rooster and Cockscomb (*Celosia cristata*)

2015 Hen and Chicks (image scaled to 39% of original size)

2017. Chinese New Year. Year of the Rooster.

2126	**2014** 48p. multicoloured	1·40	1·40
MS2127	125×95 mm. **2015** £1 multicoloured	3·00	3·00

2017. Crest of Jersey. As T **1823.**

2129	48p. bright magenta and dull claret	1·40	1·40
2130	60p. violet-blue and dull claret	1·75	1·75
2131	66p. turquoise-green and dull claret	1·90	1·90
2132	76p. bright reddish violet and dull claret	2·25	2·25
2133	88p. yellow	2·50	2·50
2134	£1 dull claret	3·00	3·00

2016 King Edward VIII in Naval Uniform (image scaled to 41% of original size)

2017. The Royal Legacy of Queen Victoria (3rd issue). King Edward VIII.

MS2128	116×81 mm. **2016** £2 multicoloured	5·75	5·75

2017 Grosnez Castle

2017. Jersey Castles and Forts. Multicoloured.

2135	74p. Type **2017**	2·10	2·10
2136	76p. Elizabeth Castle	2·25	2·25
2137	£1 St Aubin's Fort	3·00	3·00
2138	£1·29 Mont Orgueil Castle	3·75	3·75
MS2139	90×90 mm. Nos. 2135 and 2138	6·00	6·00

Nos. 2135 and 2138 include the EUROPA emblem.

2021 Golden Torque, 1st-century BC, from Le Câtillon II Hoard

2017. Ancient Artefacts. Multicoloured.

2140	49p. Type **2021**	1·40	1·40
2141	63p. Rotary Quern, 1st-century BC, found near La Hougue Bie	1·75	1·75
2142	73p. St Lawrence Pillar, 800 AD, from St Lawrence Parish Church	2·10	2·10
2143	79p. Bronze Dagger, 1st-century BC, Le Câtel De Rozel	2·25	2·25
2144	90p. Flint Arrowhead, 2850-2250 BC, from Le Pinacle, made with stone from Le Grand-Pressigny, France	2·50	2·50
2145	£1·07 Silver and Gilt Brooch, 14th-century AD, from Les Ecréhous Priory	3·00	3·00
2146	£1·32 Bronze Statue, possibly Hercules or Mercury, 2nd-century BC	3·75	3·75
2147	£2·52 Bronze Age Axe Head, 1500-800 BC	7·25	7·25

2029 King George VI, 1937

2035 King George VI making Radio Broadcast, 1939 (image scaled to 41% of original size)

2017. The Royal Legacy of Queen Victoria (4th issue). King George VI.. Multicoloured.

2148	49p. Type **2029**	1·40	1·40
2149	63p. King George VI making Speech inaugurating Empire Exhibition, 1938	1·75	1·75
2150	73p. King George VI, 1941	2·10	2·10
2151	79p. King George VI, 1943	2·25	2·25
2152	90p. King George VI with his Stamp Collection, 1944	2·50	2·50
2153	£1·07 King George VI with Corgi, 1948	3·00	3·00
MS2154	116×81 mm. **2035** £2 multicoloured	5·75	5·75

2036 Jersey Fund Raising Swimarathon (image scaled to NaN% of original size)

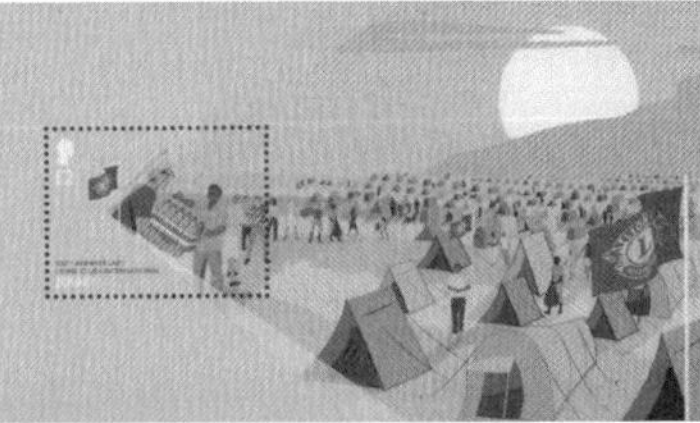

2042 Refugee Camp ('Worldwide Disaster Relief') (image scaled to 37% of original size)

2017. Centenary of Lions Clubs International.. Multicoloured.

2155	49p. Type **2036**	1·40	1·40
2156	63p. Treating Eye Disease and Recycling Glasses	1·75	1·75
2157	73p. Flood Rescue ('Worldwide Disaster Relief')	2·10	2·10
2158	79p. Tackling Environmental Issues	2·25	2·25
2159	90p. Hearing Tests and Recycled Hearing Aids	2·50	2·50
2160	£1·07 Holidays for the Disabled	3·00	3·00
MS2161	130×75 mm. **2042** £2 multicoloured	5·75	5·75

2043 Mangrove Finch (*Camarhynchus heliobates*)

2049 Charles Darwin

2017. Durrell and Darwin. 25 Years of the Darwin Initiative.. Multicoloured.

(a) Ordinary gum

2162	49p. Type **2043**	1·40	1·40
2163	63p. Livingtone's Fruit Bat (*Pteropus livingstonii*)	1·75	1·75
2164	73p. Telfair's Skink (*Leiolopisma telfairii*)	2·10	2·10
2165	79p. Mountain Chicken (*Leptodactylus fallax*)	2·25	2·25
2166	90p. Hispaniolan Solenodon (*Solenodon paradoxus*)	2·50	2·50
2167	£1·07 Pygmy Hog (*Porcula salvania*)	3·00	3·00

(b) Self-adhesive

MS2168	120×90 mm. **2049** £3 multicoloured	8·75	8·75

No. **MS**2168 was printed on sycamore wood.

2050 Shells and Anemones Kaleidoscope

2017. Bicentenary of Kaleidoscopes. Multicoloured.

2169	49p. Type **2050**	1·40	1·40
2170	63p. Feathers and Eggs Kaleidoscope	1·75	1·75
2171	73p. Woodlands Kaleidoscope	2·10	2·10
2172	79p. Wildflowers Kaleidoscope	2·25	2·25
2173	90p. Minibeasts Kaleidoscope	2·50	2·50
2174	£1·07 Marine Life Kaleidoscope	3·00	3·00
MS2175	145×99 mm. Nos. 2169/2174	13·50	13·50

2056 Sopwith Camel (image scaled to NaN% of original size)

2062 Airco DH.2 of Royal Flying Corps 32 Squadron at Vert Galand Aerodrome, northern France (image scaled to 29% of original size)

2017. Centenary of the Great War (4th issue). War in the Air. Multicoloured.

2176	49p. Type **2056**	1·40	1·40
2177	63p. Airco DH.2 and Albatros DJI	1·75	1·75
2178	73p. Nieuport 16 and and Fokker Eindecker	2·10	2·10
2179	79p. Fokker DR.I	2·25	2·25
2180	90p. Sopwith Triplane	2·50	2·50
2181	£1·07 Nieuport 28	3·00	3·00
MS2182	151×86 mm. Nos. 2176/2181	13·50	13·50
MS2183	166×75 mm. **2062** £2 multicoloured	5·75	5·75

2063 Black-veined White (*Aporia crataegi*)

2017. Links with China (3rd series). Butterflies. Multicoloured.

2184	49p. Type **2063**	1·40	1·40
2185	49p. Small Tortoiseshell (*Aglais urticae*)	1·40	1·40
2186	49p. Swallowtail (*Papilio machaon*)	1·40	1·40
2187	49p. Purple Emperor (*Apatura iris*)	1·40	1·40
2188	49p. White Admiral (*Limenitis camilla*)	1·40	1·40
2189	49p. Camberwell Beauty (*Nymphalis antiopa*)	1·40	1·40
MS2190	125×86 mm. Nos. 2184 and 2186	3·25	3·25
MS2191	134×98 mm. Nos. 2184/2189	8·50	8·50

2069 Kate Hardcastle (*She Stoops to Conquer*)

2077 Cleopatra (*Antony and Cleopatra*) (image scaled to 38% of original size)

2017. Lillie Langtry (1853-1929, actress) Commemoration. Multicoloured.

(a) Ordinary gum

2192	49p. Type **2069**	1·40	1·40
2193	49p. Blanche Hayes (*Ours*)	1·40	1·40
2194	63p. Rosalind (*As You Like It*)	1·75	1·75
2195	63p. Hester Grazebrook (*An Unequal Match*)	1·75	1·75
2196	73p. Mademoiselle Mars (*Mademoiselle Mars*)	2·10	2·10
2197	79p. Lena Despard (*As in a looking-Glass*)	2·10	2·10
2198	90p. Lady Macbeth (*Macbeth*)	2·50	2·50
2199	£1·07 Pauline (*The Lady of Lyons*)	3·00	3·00

(b) Self-adhesive

MS2200	125×92 mm. **2077** £2 multicoloured	5·75	5·75

2078 Honey Bee on Flower, collecting Nectar

2017. Centenary of the Jersey Beekeepers Association. Multicoloured.

2201	49p. Type **2078**	1·40	1·40
2202	63p. Queen Bee, Worker Bees and Cells containing Larvae	1·75	1·75
2203	73p. Beekeeper using Smoker to pacify Bees	2·10	2·10
2204	79p. Beekeeper removing Brood Frame containing Raw Honeycomb from Hive	2·25	2·25
2205	90p. Using Blade to scrape Beeswax Seal from Brood Frame	2·50	2·50
2206	£1·07 Jar of Honey and Honey Dipper	3·00	3·00
MS2207	110×80 mm. **2084** £2 multicoloured	5·75	5·75

2085 Engagement of Princess Elizabeth and Lt. Philip Mountbatten, 1947

2091 Queen Elizabeth II and Prince Philip at State Opening of Parliament, May 2016 (image scaled to 43% of original size)

2017. Platinum Wedding Anniversary of Queen Elizabeth II and Prince Philip, Duke of Edinburgh. Multicoloured.

2208	49p. Type **2085**	1·40	1·40
2209	63p. Wedding of Princess Elizabeth and Prince Philip, 1947	1·75	1·75
2210	73p. Princess Elizabeth and Prince Philip on Honeymoon at Broadlands, Hampshire, 1947	2·10	2·10
2211	79p. Queen Elizabeth II and Prince Philip on their Silver Wedding Anniversary, 1972	2·25	2·25
2212	90p. Queen Elizabeth II and Prince Philip on their Golden Wedding Anniversary, 1997	2·50	2·50
2213	£1·07 Queen Elizabeth II and Prince Philip on their Diamond Wedding Anniversary, Broadlands, Hampshire, 2007	3·00	3·00
MS2214	150×98 mm. Nos. 2208/2213	13·50	13·50
MS2215	110×75 mm. **2091** £2 multicoloured	5·75	5·75

2092 Bringing Home the Christmas Tree

2017. A Traditional Christmas. Multicoloured.

2216	43p. Type **2092**	1·25	1·25
2217	49p. Decorating the Christmas Tree	1·40	1·40
2218	55p. Leaving Mince Pie for Santa	1·60	1·60
2219	63p. Carol Singing	1·75	1·75
2220	73p. Making Christmas Cake	2·10	2·10
2221	79p. Building Snowman	2·25	2·25
2222	90p. Opening Christmas Presents	2·50	2·50
2223	£1·07 Nativity Play	3·00	3·00

2100 Dog

2101 Dog and Puppies (image scaled to 39% of original size)

2018. Chinese New Year. Year of the Dog.

2224	**2100** 49p. multicoloured	1·40	1·40
MS2225	125×95 mm. **2101** £1 multicoloured	3·00	3·00

2102 Flower Power Emblem (1960s language) (image scaled to NaN% of original size)

2108 1960s Street (image scaled to 37% of original size)

2018. Popular Culture (2nd series). The 1960s. Multicoloured.

2226	49p. Type **2102**	1·40	1·40
2227	63p. Guitarist (1960s music, psychedelic rock)	1·75	1·75
2228	73p. Young Women (1960s fashion, mini skirt)	2·10	2·10
2229	79p. Moon and Rocket (1960s event, Moon landing)	2·25	2·25
2230	90p. Reaching Hand (1960s food, cheese and pineapple sticks)	2·50	2·50
2231	£1·07 Girl (1960s leisure, dolls houses)	3·00	3·00
MS2232	140×100 mm. Nos. 2226/2231	13·50	13·50
MS2233	131×94 mm. **2108** £2 multicoloured	5·75	5·75

2109 Sunset from the Walkway at Devil's Hole

2018. Jersey Seasons (4th series). Spring. Photographs by Andy Le Gresley. Multicoloured.

2234	49p. Type **2109**	1·40	1·40
2235	49p. Waves breaking at Quaisné	1·40	1·40
2236	63p. Daffodils in Rozel Woods	1·75	1·75
2237	73p. Calm Seas at Portelet Bay	2·10	2·10
2238	79p. Grosnez Castle at Dusk	2·25	2·25
2239	90p. A St Lawrence Valley View in Springtime	2·50	2·50
2240	£1·07 The Headland overlooking St Brelade's Bay	3·00	3·00
2241	£1·32 Sun shining through the Trees at Grantez	3·75	3·75

The 73p. value includes the sepac emblem.

2117 Havre des Pas Bridge

2018. Europa. Bridges and Causeways. Multicoloured.

2242	73p. Type **2117**	2·10	2·10
2243	79p. La Corbière Causeway	2·25	2·25
2244	90p. Queen's Valley Reservoir	2·50	2·50
2245	£1·07 Elizabeth Castle Causeway	3·00	3·00
MS2246	120×80 mm. Nos. 2242 and 2244	4·75	4·75

2121 Royal Aircraft Factory SE5A

2018. Centenary of the RAF (Royal Air Force). Multicoloured.

2247	50p. Type **2121**	1·50	1·50
2248	65p. Hawker Fury Mk.I	1·90	1·90
2249	76p. Short Stirling B.III	2·25	2·25
2250	82p. Supermarine Spitfire PR.XIX	2·40	2·40
2251	94p. English Electric Lightning F6	2·75	2·75
2252	£1·12 Eurofighter Typhoon	3·25	3·25
MS2253	155×95 mm. Nos. 2248 and 2251	4·50	4·50

2018. Stampex 2018, London. No. **MS**2233 overprinted with emblem and **STAMPEX 14 - 17 February 2018** on white margin at right.

MS2233*a*	131×94 mm. **2108** £2 multicoloured		

2127 Crew and Avro Lancaster Bomber

2133 Wing Commander Guy Gibson, VC (1918-1944) at RAF Scampton, 27 May 1943

2018. 75th Anniversary of The Dam Busters Raid (Operation Chastise).. Multicoloured.

2254	50p. Type **2127**	1·50	1·50
2255	65p. Pilot and Avro Lancaster B Mk III	1·90	1·90
2256	76p. Targeting and Bomb Aiming	2·25	2·25
2257	82p. Releasing Bouncing Bomb	2·40	2·40
2258	94p. Bomb exploding and rupturing Dam	2·75	2·75
2259	£1·12 Sir Barnes Wallis (1887-1979, inventor of bouncing bomb)	3·25	3·25
MS2260	105×80 mm. **2133** £2 multicoloured	5·75	5·75

2134 Puppy (24 Hour Ambulance)

2018. 150th Anniversary of the JSPCA (Jersey Society for the Prevention of Cruelty to Animals).

2261	50p. Type **2134**	1·50	1·50
2262	65p. Dog (Welfare Investigation)	1·90	1·90
2263	76p. Snake (Education)	2·25	2·25
2264	82p. Cat (Boarding)	2·40	2·40
2265	94p. Dog (Lost and Found)	2·75	2·75
2266	£1·12 Dog (Re-homing)	3·25	3·25
2267	£1·38 Guinea Pig (Volunteers)	4·00	4·00
2268	£2·64 Owl Chick (Wildlife)	7·75	7·75
MS2269	85×85 mm. Nos. 2264/2265	5·50	5·50

2142 'I began the CREATION of a HUMAN being'

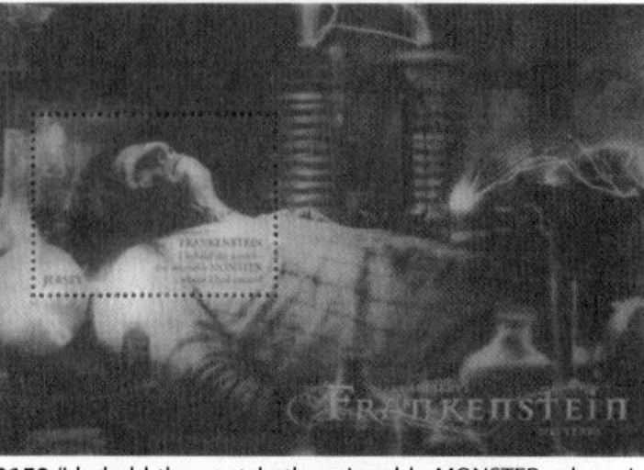

2150 'I beheld the wretch–the miserable MONSTER, whom I had created' (image scaled to 44% of original size)

2018. Bicentenary of Publication of *Frankenstein* (novel by Mary Shelley, 1797-1851). Multicoloured.

2270	50p. Type **2142**	1·50	1·50
2271	65p. 'I BEHELD the accomplishment of my TOILS'	1·90	1·90
2272	76p. 'his EYES, if eyes they *may* be called, were FIXED on me'	2·25	2·25
2273	82p. 'I was a poor, *helpless* miserable, WRETCH'	2·40	2·40
2274	94p. 'My heart YEARNED to be known and LOVED by these amiable CREATURES'	2·75	2·75
2275	£1.12 'REMEMBER' that I am *thy* CREATURE'	3·25	3·25
2276	£1.38 'You are my CREATOR, *but* I am your master;–OBEY!'	4·00	4·00
2277	£2.64 '*where* can I find rest but in DEATH?'	7·75	7·75
MS2278	175×80 mm. Nos. 2270/7	26·00	26·00
MS2279	110×75 mm. **2150** £3 multicoloured	8·75	8·75

2151 Rwanda: Jersey Cow Programme

2018. 50th Anniversary of Jersey Overseas Aid (JOA). Multicoloured.

2280	50p. Type **2151**	1·50	1·50
2281	65p. South Sudan: Famine Relief	1·90	1·90
2282	76p. Uganda: Tropical Diseases	2·25	2·25
2283	82p. Nepal: Economic Development	2·40	2·40
2284	94p. Madagascar: Rural Livelihoods	2·75	2·75
2285	£1.12 Kenya: Sand Dam Construction	3·25	3·25

POSTAGE DUE STAMPS

D1

1969

D1	**D1**	1d. violet	65	1·10
D2	**D1**	2d. sepia	90	1·10
D3	**D1**	3d. mauve	1·00	1·10
D4	-	1s. green	5·50	5·00
D5	-	2s.6d. grey	10·00	12·00
D6	-	5s. red	13·00	15·00

Designs: 1s., 2s.6d., 5s. Map.

1971. Decimal Currency. Design as Nos. D4/D6, but values in new currency.

D7	½p. black	10	10
D8	1p. blue	10	10
D9	2p. brown	10	10
D10	3p. purple	10	10
D11	4p. red	10	10
D12	5p. green	10	10
D13	6p. orange	10	10
D14	7p. yellow	10	10
D15	8p. blue	15	20
D16	10p. green	15	20
D17	11p. brown	30	35
D18	14p. violet	40	50
D19	25p. green	45	90
D20	50p. purple	1·10	1·70

D4 Arms of St Clement and Dovecote at Samares

1978. Parish Arms and Views.

D21	**D4**	1p. black and green	10	10
D22	-	2p. black and yellow	10	10
D23	-	3p. black and brown	10	10
D24	-	4p. black and red	10	10
D25	-	5p. black and blue	10	10
D26	-	10p. black and olive	10	10
D27	-	12p. black and blue	15	10
D28	-	14p. black and orange	20	15
D29	-	15p. black and mauve	25	30
D30	-	20p. black and green	30	40
D31	-	50p. black and brown	90	80
D32	-	£1 black and blue	1·40	1·40

Designs: 2p. Arms of St Lawrence and Handois Reservoir; 3p. Arms of St John and Sorel Point; 4p. Arms of St Ouen and Pinnacle Rock; 5p. Arms of St Peter and Quetivel Mill; 10p. Arms of St Martin and St Catherine's Breakwater; 12p. Arms of St Helier and Harbour; 14p. Arms of St Saviour and Highlands College; 15p. Arms of St Brelade and Beauport Bay; 20p. Arms of Grouville and La Hougue Bie; 50p. Arms of St Mary and Perry Farm; £1 Arms of Trinity and Bouley Bay.

D16 St Brelade

1982. Jersey Harbours. Black, and colour given below

D33	**D16**	1p. green	10	10
D34	-	2p. yellow	10	10
D35	-	3p. brown	10	10
D36	-	4p. red	10	10
D37	-	5p. blue	10	10
D38	-	6p. green	10	15
D39	-	7p. mauve	15	20
D40	-	8p. red	15	20
D41	-	9p. green	20	20
D42	-	10p. blue	20	20
D43	-	20p. green	40	40
D44	-	30p. purple	60	60
D45	-	40p. orange	80	80
D46	-	£1 violet	2·00	2·00

Designs: 2p. St Aubin; 3p. Rozel; 4p. Greve de Lecq; 5p. Bouley Bay; 6p. St Catherine; 7p. Gorey; 8p. Bonne Nuit; 9p. La Rocque; 10p. St Helier; 20p. Ronez; 30p. La Collette; 40p. Elizabeth Castle; £1 Upper Harbour Marina.

JHALAWAR

A state of Rajasthan, India. Now uses Indian stamps.

4 paisa = 1 anna.

1 Apsara (dancing nymph of Hindu Paradise) (1 paisa)

1886. Imperf.

1	**1**	1p. green	6·50	24·00
2	-	¼a. green	2·25	3·25

The ¼a. is larger and has a different frame.

JIND

A "convention" state of the Punjab, India, which now uses Indian stamps.

12 pies = 1 anna; 16 annas = 1 rupee.

J1 (½a.)

1874. Imperf

J8	**J1**	½a. blue	1·75	7·50
J9	**J1**	1a. purple	4·75	20·00
J3	**J1**	2a. bistre	2·75	8·50
J11	**J1**	4a. green	4·25	25·00
J12	**J1**	8a. purple	11·00	13·00

J6 (¼a.)

1882. Various designs and sizes. Imperf or perf

J16	**J6**	¼a. brown	50	1·50
J19	**J6**	½a. bistre	2·25	75
J20	**J6**	1a. brown	2·25	3·25
J22	**J6**	2a. blue	4·75	3·50
J23	**J6**	4a. green	4·25	3·00
J25	**J6**	8a. red	9·50	5·00

Stamps of India (Queen Victoria) overprinted

1885. Optd **JHIND STATE** vert (curved).

1	**23**	½a. turquoise	12·00	10·00
2	-	1a. purple	80·00	£110
3	-	2a. blue	42·00	30·00
4	-	4a. green (No. 71)	£120	£140
5	-	8a. mauve	£700	
6	-	1r. grey (No. 101)	£700	

1885. Optd **JEEND STATE**.

7	**23**	½a. turquoise	£200	
8	-	1a. purple	£200	
9	-	2a. blue	£225	
10	-	4a. green (No. 71)	£300	
11	-	8a. mauve	£300	
12	-	1r. grey (No. 101)	£325	

1886. Optd **JHIND STATE** horiz.

17	**23**	½a. turquoise	1·25	10
18	-	1a. purple	6·00	30
20	-	1a.6p. brown	5·50	6·00
21	-	2a. blue	5·50	50
23	-	3a. orange	7·50	1·75
15		4a. green (No. 71)	90·00	
24	-	4a. green (No. 96)	8·50	4·75
27	-	6a. brown	10·00	35·00
28	-	8a. mauve	20·00	42·00
30	-	12a. purple on red	14·00	45·00
31	-	1r. grey (No. 101)	20·00	85·00
32	**37**	1r. green and red	21·00	85·00
33	**38**	2r. red and orange	£550	£2250
34	**38**	3r. brown and green	£850	£1800
35	**38**	5r. blue and violet	£900	£1500

1900. Optd **JHIND STATE** horiz.

36	**40**	3p. red	1·10	3·50
37	**40**	3p. grey	40	5·00
38	**23**	½a. green	8·00	10·00
40	-	1a. red	3·25	14·00

Stamps of India optd JHIND STATE

1903. King Edward VII

41	**41**	3p. grey	60	20
43	-	½a. green (No. 121)	4·25	3·00
44	-	1a. red (No. 123)	3·25	2·50
46	-	2a. lilac	6·00	1·75
47	-	2½a. blue	3·00	11·00
48	-	3a. orange	7·50	1·25
50	-	4a. olive	17·00	20·00
51	-	6a. bistre	14·00	45·00
52	-	8a. mauve	10·00	32·00
54	-	12a. purple on red	7·50	25·00
55	-	1r. green and red	10·00	42·00

1907. King Edward VII (inscr 'INDIA POSTAGE and REVENUE').

56		½a. green (No. 149)	1·75	30
57		1a. red (No. 150)	3·75	70

1913. King George V

58	**55**	3p. grey	10	2·50
59	**56**	½a. green	10	75
60	**57**	1a. red	10	60
61	**59**	2a. purple	15	4·75
62	**62**	3a. orange	1·50	17·00
63	**64**	6a. bistre	14·00	50·00

1914. Stamps of India (King George V) optd **JIND STATE** in two lines.

64	**55**	3p. grey	2·75	1·25
65	**56**	½a. green	4·25	15
66	**57**	1a. red	3·00	15
80	**57**	1a. brown	6·50	3·75
67	**58**	1½a. brown (A. No. 163)	7·00	9·50
68	**58**	1½a. brown (B. No. 165)	1·60	2·50
81	**58**	1½a. red (B.)	30	2·75
69	**59**	2a. purple	4·50	2·00
70	**61**	2a.6p. blue	75	7·00
82	**61**	2a.6p. orange	2·00	12·00
71	**62**	3a. orange	75	7·50
83	**62**	3a. blue	4·00	9·00
72	**63**	4a. olive	3·25	13·00
73	**64**	6a. brown	8·50	32·00
74	**65**	8a. mauve	8·00	32·00
75	**66**	12a. red	6·00	40·00
76	**67**	1r. brown and green	18·00	48·00
77	**67**	2r. red and brown	20·00	£200
78	**67**	5r. blue and violet	80·00	£600

1922. No. 192 of India optd **JIND**.

79	**57**	9p. on 1a. red	1·25	17·00

Stamps of India optd JIND STATE in one line

1927. King George V.

84	**55**	3p. grey	10	10
85	**56**	½a. green	50	35
86	**80**	9p. green	2·25	40
87	**57**	1a. brown	15	10
88	**82**	1a.3p. mauve	25	30
89	**58**	1½a. red	1·25	5·50
90	**70**	2a. lilac	6·50	1·25
91w	**61**	2a.6p. orange	1·25	18·00
92	**62**	3a. blue	10·00	29·00
93w	**83**	3a.6p. blue	75	28·00
95	**64**	6a. bistre	75	28·00
96	**65**	8a. mauve	13·00	4·00
97w	**66**	12a. red	13·00	35·00
98	**67**	1r. brown and green	14·00	16·00
99	**67**	2r. red and orange	80·00	£225
100	**67**	5r. blue and violet	20·00	55·00
101	**67**	10r. green and red	25·00	18·00
102	**67**	15r. blue and olive	£190	£1500
103	**67**	25r. orange and blue	£350	£2000

1934. King George V.

104	**79**	½a. green	30	25
105	**81**	1a. brown	2·00	30
106	**59**	2a. orange	7·00	70
107	**62**	3a. red	3·25	40
108	**63**	4a. olive	3·25	1·75

1937. King George VI.

109	**91**	3p. slate	10·00	3·50
110	**91**	½a. brown	1·00	7·00
111	**91**	9p. green	1·00	4·00
112	**91**	1a. red	75	75
113	**92**	2a. red	3·50	30·00
114	-	2a.6p. violet	1·50	40·00
115	-	3a. green	7·00	38·00
116	-	3a.6p. blue	8·00	40·00
117	-	4a. brown	17·00	32·00
118	-	6a. green	10·00	60·00
119	-	8a. violet	14·00	45·00
120	-	12a. red	5·00	55·00
121	**100**	1r. slate and brown	13·00	65·00
122	**100**	2r. purple and brown	15·00	£250
123	**100**	5r. green and blue	32·00	£150
124	**100**	10r. purple and red	60·00	£130
125	**100**	15r. brown and green	£110	£1600
126	**100**	25r. slate and purple	£1100	£2250

1941. Stamps of India (King George VI) optd **JIND**. (a) On issue of 1937.

127	**91**	3p. slate	20·00	27·00
128	**91**	½a. brown	1·25	3·75
129	**91**	9p. green	17·00	32·00
130	**91**	1a. red	1·00	8·00
131	**100**	1r. slate and brown	11·00	40·00
132	**100**	2r. purple and brown	20·00	55·00
133	**100**	5r. green and blue	45·00	£180
134	**100**	10r. purple and red	60·00	£130
135	**100**	15r. brown and green	£200	£300
136	**100**	25r. slate and purple	60·00	£500

(b) On issue of 1940.

137	**100a**	3p. slate	50	2·00
138	**100a**	½a. mauve	50	2·50
139	**100a**	9p. green	75	4·50
140	**100a**	1a. red	1·00	1·50
141	**101**	1a.3p. yellow-brown	1·00	6·50
142	**101**	1½a. violet	10·00	7·00
143	**101**	2a. red	1·00	7·00
144	**101**	3a. violet	10·00	9·00
145	**101**	3½a. blue	9·00	17·00
146	**102**	4a. brown	2·75	8·50
147	**102**	6a. green	9·00	22·00
148	**102**	8a. violet	7·00	20·00
149	**102**	12a. purple	14·00	25·00

OFFICIAL STAMPS

Postage stamps of Jind optd SERVICE

1885. Nos. 1/3 (Queen Victoria).

O1	**O23**	½a. green	4·50	60
O2	-	1a. purple	1·00	10
O3	-	2a. blue	55·00	55·00

1886. Nos. 17/32 and No. 38 (Queen Victoria).

O12	**23**	½a. turquoise	6·00	10
O22	**23**	½a. green (No. 38)	5·00	40
O14	-	1a. purple	24·00	1·75
O16	-	2a. blue	5·50	40
O17	-	4a. green (No. 24)	8·00	4·50
O19	-	8a. mauve	12·00	9·00
O21	**37**	1r. green and red	12·00	75·00

1903. Nos. 42/55 (King Edward VII).

O23	**41**	3p. grey	1·75	10
O25	-	½a. green (No. 43)	6·00	10
O26	-	1a. red (No. 44)	6·50	10
O28	-	2a. lilac	3·75	10
O29	-	4a. olive	4·50	45
O31	-	8a. mauve	13·00	1·50
O32	-	1r. green and red	3·25	2·25

1907. Nos. 56/57 (King Edward VII).

O33		½a. green	2·25	10
O34		1a. red	3·50	10

1914. Official stamps of India. Nos. O75/O96 (King George V) optd **JIND STATE**.

O35	**55**	3p. grey	10	10
O36	**56**	½a. green	10	10
O37	**57**	1a. red	75	10
O46	**57**	1a. brown	60	10
O39	**59**	2a. purple	40	30
O40	**63**	4a. olive	2·00	20
O41	**64**	6a. bistre	3·50	2·50
O42	**65**	8a. mauve	1·25	1·50
O43	**67**	1r. brown and green	8·00	2·25
O44	**67**	2r. red and brown	21·00	75·00
O45	**67**	5r. blue and violet	45·00	£500

Stamps of India optd JIND STATE SERVICE

1927. King George V.

O50	**57**	1a. brown	10	10
O47	**55**	3p. grey	10	20
O48	**56**	½a. green	10	1·00
O49	**80**	9p. green	1·00	15
O51	**82**	1a.3p. mauve	40	15
O52	**70**	2a. lilac	25	15
O64	**59**	2a. orange	30	15
O53	**61**	2a.6p. orange	2·00	23·00
O54	**71**	4a. green	35	25
O55	**64**	6a. bistre	6·50	30·00
O56w	**65**	8a. mauve	75	1·75
O57	**66**	12a. red	2·75	27·00
O58	**67**	1r. brown and green	9·00	11·00
O59	**67**	2r. red and orange	85·00	65·00
O60	**67**	5r. blue and purple	14·00	£425
O61	**67**	10r. green and red	60·00	£190

1934. King George V.

O62	**79**	½a. green	20	15
O63	**81**	1a. brown	20	15
O65	**63**	4a. olive	10·00	30

1937. King George VI.

O66	**91**	½a. brown	85·00	30
O67	**91**	9p. green	6·50	28·00
O68	**91**	1a. red	6·00	30
O69	**100**	1r. slate and brown	75·00	85·00
O70	**100**	2r. purple and brown	85·00	£550
O71	**100**	5r. green and blue	£150	£700
O72	**100**	10r. purple and red	£700	£2000

1939

Official stamps of India optd **JIND**

O73	**O20**	3p. slate	60	2·00
O74	**O20**	½a. brown	4·50	1·25
O75	**O20**	½a. purple	60	30
O76	**O20**	9p. green	3·00	16·00
O77	**O20**	1a. red	3·75	15
O78	**O20**	1½a. violet	9·00	3·00
O79	**O20**	2a. orange	8·50	30
O80	**O20**	2½a. violet	5·00	13·00
O81	**O20**	4a. brown	8·50	8·50
O82	**O20**	8a. violet	12·00	14·00

Stamps of India (King George VI) optd **JIND SERVICE**

O83	**100**	1r. slate and brown	18·00	80·00
O84	**100**	2r. purple and brown	42·00	£325
O85	**100**	5r. green and blue	70·00	£800
O86	**100**	10r. purple and red	£225	£1300

JOHORE

A state of the Federation of Malaya, incorporated in Malaysia in 1963.

100 cents = 1 dollar (Straits or Malayan).
1996. 100 sen = 1 ringgit

Queen Victoria stamps of Straits Settlements overprinted

1876. Optd with Crescent and Star.

1	**5**	2c. brown	£25000	£8500

1882. Optd **JOHORE**.

6	**5**	2c. pink (with full point)	£225	£225
8	**5**	2c. pink (no full point)	£130	£140

1884. Optd **JOHOR**.

10	**5**	2c. pink (no full point)	27·00	12·00
14	**5**	2c. pink (with full point)	£225	75·00

1891. Surch **JOHOR Two CENTS**.

17	**5**	2c. on 24c. green	28·00	40·00

21 Sultan Aboubakar

1891

21	**21**	1c. purple	1·00	50
22	**21**	2c. purple and yellow	60	1·50
23	**21**	3c. purple and red	60	60
24	**21**	4c. purple and black	2·75	21·00
25	**21**	5c. purple and green	7·00	21·00
26	**21**	6c. purple and blue	8·00	21·00
27	**21**	$1 green and red	85·00	£170

1892. Surch **3 cents**.

28	**21**	3c. on 4c. purple and black	2·50	50
29	**21**	3c. on 5c. purple and green	2·00	5·00
30	**21**	3c. on 6c. purple and blue	3·50	9·00
31	**21**	3c. on $1 green and red	12·00	75·00

1896. Sultan's Coronation. Optd **KEMAHKOTAAN**.

32	**21**	1c. purple	50	1·00
33	**21**	2c. purple and yellow	50	1·00
34	**21**	3c. purple and red	55	1·00
35	**21**	4c. purple and black	80	2·25
36	**21**	5c. purple and green	5·50	7·50
37	**21**	6c. purple and blue	3·50	6·50
38	**21**	$1 green and red	65·00	£130

24 Sultan Ibrahim

1896

39	**24**	1c. green	80	3·25
40	**24**	2c. green and blue	50	1·50
41	**24**	3c. green and purple	4·00	5·50
42	**24**	4c. green and red	1·00	4·00
43	**24**	4c. yellow and red	1·50	2·25
44	**24**	5c. green and brown	2·00	5·00
45	**24**	6c. green and yellow	2·00	7·50
46	**24**	10c. green and black	7·00	50·00
47	**24**	25c. green and mauve	9·00	50·00
48	**24**	50c. green and red	16·00	50·00
49	**24**	$1 purple and green	32·00	75·00
50	**24**	$2 purple and red	55·00	80·00
51	**24**	$3 purple and blue	50·00	£120
52	**24**	$4 purple and brown	50·00	85·00
53	**24**	$5 purple and yellow	£100	£130

1903. Surch in figures and words.

54	**24**	3c. on 4c. yellow and red	60	1·10
55	**24**	10c. on 4c. green & red (A)	3·75	18·00
58	**24**	10c. on 4c. yellow & red (B)	20·00	40·00
59	**24**	10c. on 4c. green & red (B)	9·50	70·00
56	**24**	50c. 50c. on $3 purple and blue	30·00	85·00
60	**24**	50c. on $5 purple and yellow	80·00	£170
57	**24**	$1 on $2 purple and red	65·00	£120

10c. on 4c. Type A, cents in small letters. Type B, CENTS in capitals.

33 Sultan Sir Ibrahim

1904

78	**33**	1c. purple and green	1·25	15
90	**33**	2c. purple and orange	1·00	8·50
63	**33**	3c. purple and black	4·75	60
91	**33**	4c. purple and red	1·75	70
109	**33**	5c. purple and green	50	30
83	**33**	8c. purple and blue	4·00	16·00
84	**33**	10c. purple and black	60·00	3·00
116	**33**	25c. purple and green	6·50	1·00
119	**33**	50c. purple and red	4·00	1·60
120	**33**	$1 green and mauve	3·75	1·25
121	**33**	$2 green and red	10·00	4·75
72	**33**	$3 green and blue	48·00	85·00
73	**33**	$4 green and brown	48·00	£120
124	**33**	$5 green and orange	70·00	50·00
75	**33**	$10 green and black	£140	£200
76	**33**	$50 green and blue	£475	£650
77	**33**	$100 green and red	£650	£1000
128	**33**	$500 blue and red	£24000	

1912. Surch **3 CENTS.** and bars.

88	**33**	3c. on 8c. purple and blue	18·00	15·00

1918

103	**33**	1c. purple and black	30	20
89	**33**	2c. purple and green	50	3·00
104	**33**	2c. purple and sepia	1·25	4·25
105	**33**	2c. green	60	40
106	**33**	3c. green	2·00	8·00
107	**33**	3c. purple and sepia	1·40	2·00
110	**33**	6c. purple and red	50	50
93	**33**	10c. purple and blue	2·00	1·40
112	**33**	10c. purple and yellow	50	25
113	**33**	12c. purple and blue	1·00	1·25
114	**33**	12c. blue	55·00	1·75
115	**33**	21c. purple and orange	2·00	3·00
117	**33**	30c. purple and orange	11·00	18·00
118	**33**	40c. purple and brown	12·00	19·00

37 Sultan Sir Ibrahim and Sultana

1935

129	**37**	8c. violet and grey	7·00	3·25

38 Sultan Sir Ibrahim

1940

130	**38**	8c. black and blue	25·00	1·75

1948. Silver Wedding. As T **61/62** of Jamaica.

131		10c. violet	20	75
132		$5 green	26·00	50·00

39 Sultan Sir Ibrahim

1949

133	**39**	1c. black	1·00	10
134	**39**	2c. orange	50	20
135	**39**	3c. green	2·75	1·00
136	**39**	4c. brown	2·25	10
136a	**39**	5c. purple	3·00	30
137	**39**	6c. grey	2·25	20
138	**39**	8c. red	7·00	1·25
138a	**39**	8c. green	11·00	2·25
139	**39**	10c. mauve	1·50	10
139a	**39**	12c. red	13·00	9·00
140	**39**	15c. blue	6·00	10
141	**39**	20c. black and green	5·00	1·00
141a	**39**	20c. blue	2·00	10
142	**39**	25c. purple and orange	3·75	10
142a	**39**	30c. red and purple	3·25	2·75
142b	**39**	35c. red and purple	13·00	1·75
143	**39**	40c. red and purple	10·00	18·00
144	**39**	50c. black and blue	6·00	10
145	**39**	$1 blue and purple	14·00	2·00
146	**39**	$2 green and red	32·00	13·00
147	**39**	$5 green and brown	50·00	17·00

1949. UPU. As T **63/66** of Jamaica.

148		10c. purple	30	40
149		15c. blue	2·00	2·00
150		25c. orange	65	4·25
151		50c. black	1·25	4·50

1953. Coronation. As T **71** of Jamaica.

152		10c. black and purple	1·25	10

40 Sultan Sir Ibrahim

1955. Diamond Jubilee of Sultan.

153	**40**	10c. red	10	10

41 Sultan Sir Ismail and Johore Coat of Arms

1960. Coronation of Sultan.

154	**41**	10c. multicoloured	20	20

1960. As Nos. 92/102 of Kedah but with inset portrait of Sultan Sir Ismail.

155	1c. black	10	1·25
156	2c. red	10	2·25
157	4c. sepia	10	10
158	5c. lake	10	10
159	8c. green	4·25	5·50
160	10c. purple	30	10
161	20c. blue	2·00	1·00
162	50c. black and blue	50	20
163	$1 blue and purple	8·50	8·50
164	$2 green and red	21·00	27·00
165	$5 brown and green	42·00	48·00

42 *Vanda hookeriana*

1965. Inset portrait of Sultan Ismail. Multicoloured.

166	1c. Type **42**	10	30
167	2c. *Arundina graminifolia*	10	1·00
168	5c. *Paphiopedilum niveum*	10	10
169	6c. *Spathoglottis plicata*	40	30
170	10c. *Arachnis flos-aeris*	40	20
171	15c. *Rhyncostylis retusa*	1·50	10
172	20c. *Phalaenopsis violacea*	1·75	75

The higher values used in Johore were Nos. 20/27 of Malaysia (National Issues).

44 *Delias ninus*

1971. Butterflies. Inset portrait of Sultan Ismail. Multicoloured.

175	1c. Type **44**	50	2·50
176	2c. *Danaus melanippus*	1·50	3·25
177	5c. *Parthenos sylvia*	1·50	50
178	6c. *Papilio demoleus*	1·50	2·50
179	10c. *Hebomoia glaucippe*	1·50	20
180	15c. *Precis orithya*	1·75	10
181	20c. *Valeria valeria*	1·75	50

The higher values in use with this issue were Nos. 64/71 of Malaysia (National Issues).

45 *Rafflesia hasseltii* (inset portrait of Sultan Ismail)

1979. Flowers. Multicoloured.

188	1c. Type **45**	10	1·00
189	2c. *Pterocarpus indicus*	10	1·00
190	5c. *Lagerstroemia speciosa*	10	60
191	10c. *Durio zibethinus*	15	10
192	15c. *Hibiscus rosa-sinensis*	15	10
193	20c. *Rhododendron scortechinii*	20	25
194	25c. *Etlingera elatior* (inscr 'Phaeomeria speciosa')	40	25

46 Coconuts (inset portrait of Sultan Mahmood)

1986. Agricultural Products of Malaysia. Multicoloured.

202	1c. Coffee	10	75
203	2c. Type **46**	10	75
204	5c. Cocoa	15	10
205	10c. Black pepper	20	10
206	15c. Rubber	40	10
207	20c. Oil palm	40	15
208	30c. Rice	40	15

2003. As T **46** but renominated in sen. Multicoloured.

209	30s. Rice	1·75	10

47 *Nelumbium nelumbo* (sacred lotus) (Inset portrait of Sultan Mahmud Iskandar)

2007. Garden Flowers. Multicoloured.

210	5s. Type **47**	10	10
211	10s. *Hydrangea macrophylla*	15	10
212	20s. *Hippeastrum reticulatum*	25	15
213	30s. *Bougainvillea*	40	20
214	40s. *Ipomoea indica*	50	30
215	50s. *Hibiscus rosa-sinensis*	65	35
MS216	100×85 mm. Nos. 210/215	2·25	2·25

48 *Nelumbium nelumbo* (Sacred Lotus) (inset portrait of Sultan Ibrahim Ismail Iskandar)

2016. As Nos. 210/**MS**216 but with portrait of Sultan Ibrahim Ismail Iskandar as in T **48** and new face values. Multicoloured.

217	10s. Type **48**	20	30
218	20s. *Hydrangea macrophylla*	30	25
219	30s. *Hippeastrum reticulatum*	45	25
220	40s. Bougainvillea	60	30
221	50s. *Ipomoea indica*	75	45
222	60s. *Hibiscus rosa-sinensis*	90	60
MS223	100×85 mm. Nos. 217/222	7·00	7·50

POSTAGE DUE STAMPS

D1

1938

D1	**D1**	1c. red	22·00	50·00
D2	**D1**	4c. green	45·00	40·00
D3	**D1**	8c. orange	50·00	£160
D4	**D1**	10c. brown	50·00	50·00
D5	**D1**	12c. purple	55·00	£140

JORDAN

A territory to the E. of Israel, formerly called Transjordan; under British mandate from 1918 to 1946. Independent kingdom since 1946.

1920. 1000 milliemes = 100 piastres = £1 Egyptian.
1927. 1000 milliemes = £1 Palestinian.
1950. 1000 fils = 1 Jordan dinar.
2004. 1 dinar =100 qirsh/piastre=1000 fils.

(1) East of Jordan

1920. Stamps of Palestine optd with T **1**.

1	**3**	1m. brown	3·75	6·50
10	**3**	2m. green	3·50	6·00
3	**3**	3m. brown	4·50	4·75
4	**3**	4m. red	4·25	4·50
5	**3**	5m. orange	11·00	3·75
14	**3**	1p. blue	3·75	4·75
15	**3**	2p. olive	15·00	15·00
16	**3**	5p. purple	7·50	18·00
17	**3**	9p. ochre	7·50	55·00
18	**3**	10p. blue	18·00	55·00
19	**3**	20p. grey	20·00	90·00

(2) Tenth of a piastre

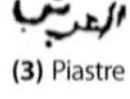
(3) Piastre

1922. Handstamped with T **2** or **3** (piastre values). (a) 1920 issue of Jordan (No. 1 etc).

28	**2**	1/10p. on 1m. brown	25·00	30·00
29	**2**	2/10p. on 2m. green	29·00	29·00
22	**2**	3/10p. on 3m. brown	15·00	15·00
23	**2**	4/10p. on 4m. red	60·00	65·00
24	**2**	5/10p. on 5m. orange	£180	£100
31	**3**	1p. on 1p. blue	£200	60·00
25	**3**	2p. on 2p. olive	£250	75·00
26	**3**	5p. on 5p. purple	65·00	80·00
27a	**3**	9p. on 9p. ochre	£130	£140
33	**3**	10p. on 10p. blue	£850	£1000
34	**3**	20p. on 20p. grey	£650	£850

(b) T **3** of Palestine.

35		10p. on 10p. blue	£1800	£2500
36		20p. on 20p. grey	£2500	£3000

(4) Arab Government of the East, April, 1921

1922. Stamps of Jordan handstamped with T **4**.

No.	Description	Unused	Used
45	1m. brown	16·00	20·00
46a	2m. green	10·00	10·00
39b	3m. brown	9·00	9·00
40	4m. red	60·00	65·00
41a	5m. orange	19·00	12·00
48a	1p. blue	22·00	11·00
42c	2p. olive	17·00	12·00
43b	5p. purple	65·00	85·00
44b	9p. ochre	70·00	85·00
52a	10p. blue	£1100	£1600
53a	20p. grey	£1100	£1800

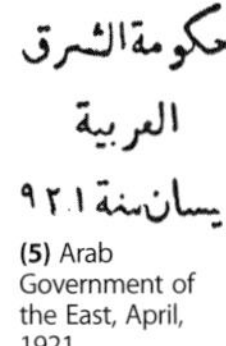

(5) Arab Government of the East, April, 1921

1923. Stamps of Jordan optd with T **5**.

No.	Description	Unused	Used
62	1m. brown	19·00	32·00
63	2m. green	18·00	21·00
56	3m. brown	18·00	19·00
57	4m. red	20·00	19·00
64	5m. orange	14·00	14·00
65	1p. blue	14·00	18·00
59	2p. olive	23·00	21·00
60	5p. purple	75·00	£100
66	9p. ochre	90·00	£130
67	10p. blue	85·00	£130
68	20p. grey	85·00	£130

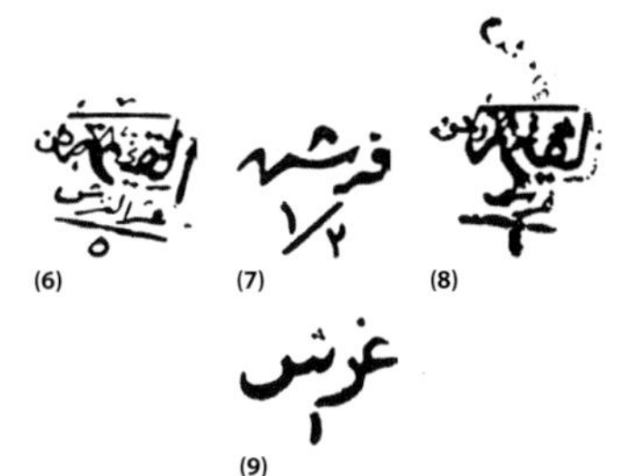

(6) (7) (8)

(9)

1923. Various stamps surch as T **6/9**. (a) 1920 issue of Jordan (No. 1 etc).

No.	Type	Description	Unused	Used
70	-	2 1/2/10thsp. on 5m.	£170	£170
70c	6	5/10p. on 3m.	†	£5000
70d	6	5/10p. on 5m.	£2500	
70e	9	2p. on 20p.		

(b) No. 7 of Palestine.

No.	Type	Description	Unused	Used
71	6	5/10p. on 3m.	£3000	

(c) 1922 issue of Jordan (Nos. 22 etc).

No.	Type	Description	Unused	Used
72		5/10p. on 3m.	£7000	
73		5/10p. on 5p.	75·00	85·00
73b		5/10p. on 9p.	£1300	
74	7	1/2p. on 5p.	75·00	85·00
75a	7	1/2p. on 9p.	£350	£400
77	8	1p. on 5p.	85·00	£110

(d) 1922 issue of Jordan (Nos. 39b etc).

No.	Type	Description	Unused	Used
78b	6	5/10p. on 3m.	50·00	60·00
79	6	5/10p. on 5p.	10·00	19·00
79d	6	5/10p. on 9p.		£1200
80c	7	1/2p. on 2p.	60·00	£110
81a	7	1/2p. on 5p.	£1000	
83b	8	1p. on 5p.	£2000	£2250

(e) 1923 issue of Jordan (Nos. 56 etc).

No.	Type	Description	Unused	Used
84	6	5/10p. on 3m.	29·00	45·00
85	7	1/2p. on 9p.	95·00	£160
87	9	1p. on 10p.	£2250	£2500
88	9	2p. on 20p.	65·00	85·00

حكومة

الشرق العربية

٩ شعبان ١٣٤١

(10) Arab Government of the East, 9 Sha'ban, 1341

1923. Stamps of Saudi Arabia optd with T **10**.

No.	Type	Description	Unused	Used
89	11	1/8p. brown	5·50	4·25
96	11	1/4 on 1/8p. brown (47)	16·00	8·00
90	11	1/2p. red	5·50	4·25
91	11	1p. blue	4·25	1·25
92	11	1 1/2p. lilac	4·50	2·50
93	11	2p. orange	5·50	8·00
94	11	3p. brown	14·00	20·00
95	11	5p. green	32·00	45·00
97	11	10 on 5p. green (49)	35·00	40·00

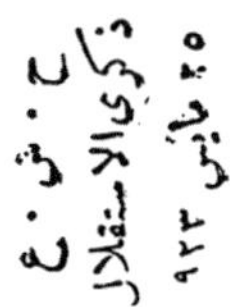

(11) Arab Government of the East, Commemoration of Independence, 25 May, 1923

1923. Stamps of Palestine optd with T **11**.

No.	Type	Description	Unused	Used
98A	3	1m. brown	23·00	23·00
99A	3	2m. green	42·00	50·00
100A	3	3m. brown	14·00	18·00
101A	3	4m. red	15·00	18·00
102A	3	5m. orange	70·00	80·00
103B	3	1p. blue	70·00	85·00
104A	3	2p. olive	70·00	90·00
105A	3	5p. purple	80·00	90·00
106B	3	9p. ochre	70·00	85·00
107A	3	10p. blue	80·00	£100
108B	3	20p. grey	85·00	£110

1923. No. 107 surch with T **9**.

No.	Type	Description	Unused	Used
109	11	1p. on 10p. blue	£6000	

نصف قرش

(12)

1923. No. 92 surch with T **12**.

No.	Type	Description	Unused	Used
110	11	1/2p. on 1 1/2p. lilac	12·00	14·00

حكومة

الشرق العربية

٩ شعبان ١٣٤١

(13a) Arab Government of the East, 9 Sha'ban, 1341

1923. Stamp of Saudi Arabia handstamped as T **13a**.

No.	Type	Description	Unused	Used
112	11	1/2p. red	15·00	16·00

حكومة الشرق العربية

(15) Arab Government of the East

1924. Stamps of Saudi Arabia optd with T **15**.

No.	Type	Description	Unused	Used
114	11	1/2p. red	22·00	16·00
115	11	1p. blue	£300	£200
116	11	1 1/2p. violet	£350	

د · ق · ج

ملك العرب

١ اج · ث ٣٤٢

(16) Commemorating the coming of His Majesty the King of the Arabs and date

1924. Stamps of Saudi Arabia optd with T **15** and **16**.

No.	Type	Description	Unused	Used
117	11	1/2p. red	3·25	3·25
118	11	1p. blue	4·00	3·50
119	11	1 1/2p. violet	4·25	4·50
120	11	2p. orange	13·00	13·00

حكومة الشرق

العربي

١٣٤٢

(17) Government of the Arab East, 1342

1924. Stamps of Saudi Arabia optd with T **17**.

No.	Type	Description	Unused	Used
125	11	1/8p. brown	1·50	1·25
126	11	1/4p. green	1·50	70
127	11	1/2p. red	1·50	70
129	11	1p. blue	10·00	1·50
130	11	1 1/2p. lilac	6·50	6·50
131	11	2p. orange	4·75	3·50
132	11	3p. red	4·75	4·75
133	11	5p. green	6·50	6·50
134	-	10p. purple and mauve	15·00	16·00

(18) Government of the Arab East, 1343

1925. Stamps of Saudi Arabia optd with T **18**.

No.	Type	Description	Unused	Used
135	11	1/8p. brown	1·00	1·50
136	11	1/4p. blue	2·00	3·00
137	11	1/2p. red	1·50	60
138	11	1p. green	1·50	1·50
139	11	1 1/2p. orange	3·50	4·00
140	11	2p. blue	4·50	6·00
141	11	3p. green	5·00	8·00
142	11	5p. brown	7·50	15·00

(19) East of the Jordan

1925. Stamps of Palestine (without Palestine opt) optd with T **19**.

No.	Type	Description	Unused	Used
143	3	1m. brown	55	3·50
144	3	2m. yellow	1·00	75
145	3	3m. blue	2·75	2·00
146	3	4m. red	2·75	4·25
147	3	5m. orange	3·25	50
148	3	6m. green	2·75	2·50
149	3	7m. brown	2·75	2·50
150	3	8m. red	2·75	1·25
151	3	1p. grey	2·75	70
152	3	13m. blue	3·25	3·00
153	3	2p. olive	4·25	4·75
154	3	5p. purple	9·50	11·00
155	3	9p. ochre	14·00	28·00
156	3	10p. blue	29·00	42·00
157	3	20p. violet	48·00	85·00

22 Emir Abdullah

23 Emir Abdullah

1927. Figures at left and right.

No.	Type	Description	Unused	Used
159	22	2m. blue	3·50	1·75
160	22	3m. red	4·75	4·25
161	22	4m. green	6·50	8·50
162	22	5m. orange	3·25	30
163	22	10m. red	5·50	8·50
164	22	15m. blue	4·50	1·00
165	22	20m. olive	4·50	4·75
166	23	50m. purple	4·50	15·00
167	23	90m. brown	7·50	38·00
168	23	100m. blue	8·50	27·00
169	23	200m. violet	17·00	50·00
170	23	500m. brown	60·00	85·00
171	23	1000m. grey	£100	£150

(24) Constitution

1928. Optd with T **24**.

No.	Type	Description	Unused	Used
172	22	2m. blue	7·00	7·50
173	22	3m. red	8·00	13·00
174	22	4m. green	8·00	16·00
175	22	5m. orange	8·00	4·50
176	22	10m. red	8·00	17·00
177	22	15m. blue	8·00	5·00
178	22	20m. olive	16·00	27·00
179	23	50m. purple	21·00	30·00
180	23	90m. brown	25·00	£100
181	23	100m. blue	25·00	£100
182	23	200m. violet	90·00	£180

1930. Locust campaign. Optd **LOCUST CAMPAIGN** in English and Arabic.

No.	Type	Description	Unused	Used
183	22	2m. blue	3·25	7·50
184	22	3m. red	2·50	6·50
185	22	4m. green	3·75	19·00
186	22	5m. orange	23·00	14·00
187	22	10m. red	2·25	4·25
188	22	15m. blue	2·25	4·00
189	22	20m. olive	4·00	4·00
190	23	50m. purple	5·00	11·00
191	23	90m. brown	10·00	48·00
192	23	100m. blue	12·00	50·00
193	23	200m. violet	32·00	85·00
194	23	500m. brown	75·00	£200

28 Emir

29 Emir

1930

No.	Type	Description	Unused	Used
230	28	1m. brown	30	75
195	28	2m. green	2·25	50
196a	28	3m. green	11·00	85
258	28	3m. pink	45	40
233	28	4m. pink	1·75	3·75
259	28	4m. green	45	40
198	28	5m. orange	3·75	40
199	28	10m. red	4·75	15
260	28	10m. violet	45	40
261	28	12m. red	1·10	1·00
200	28	15m. blue	4·75	20
262	28	15m. green	1·40	1·30
201	28	20m. green	5·00	35
263	28	20m. blue	1·50	1·40
202	29	50m. purple	6·50	1·25
203	29	90m. bistre	3·75	4·25
240	29	100m. blue	5·50	1·75
241	29	200m. violet	13·00	16·00
242	29	500m. brown	15·00	12·00
243	29	£P1 grey	27·00	22·00

30 Mushetta

31a The Khazneh at Petra

1933

No.	Type	Description	Unused	Used
208	30	1m. black and purple	1·75	1·40
209	-	2m. black and red	5·00	1·25
210	-	3m. green	5·50	1·60
211	-	4m. black and brown	12·00	7·00
212	-	5m. black and orange	7·00	1·40
213	-	10m. red	15·00	4·75
214	31a	15m. blue	8·50	1·40
215	-	20m. black and olive	8·50	5·50
216	-	50m. black and purple	35·00	21·00
217	-	90m. black and yellow	35·00	60·00
218	-	100m. black and blue	35·00	60·00
219	-	200m. black and violet	65·00	£130
220	31a	500m. red and brown	£225	£450
221	-	$P1 black and green	£500	£1000

Designs: Horiz—2m. Nymphaeum, Jerash; 3, 90m. Kasr Kharana; 4m. Kerak Castle; 5, 100m. Temple of Artemis, Jerash; 10, 200m. Ajlun Castle; 20m. Allenby Bridge over Jordan; 50m. Threshing. Vert: £P1, Emir Abdullah.

Nos. 216 to 221 are larger (33 1/2×24 mm or 24×33 1/2 mm).

35 Map of Jordan

1946. Installation of King Abdullah and National Independence.

No.	Type	Description	Unused	Used
249	35	1m. purple	30	30
250	35	2m. orange	30	30
251	35	3m. green	30	30
252	35	4m. violet	30	30
253	35	10m. brown	30	30
254	35	12m. red	30	30
255	35	20m. blue	45	40
256	35	50m. blue	1·10	1·00
257	35	200m. green	4·50	4·25

39 Parliament Building

1947. Inauguration of First National Parliament.

No.	Type	Description	Unused	Used
276	39	1m. violet	30	30
277	39	3m. red	30	30
278	39	4m. green	30	30
279	39	10m. purple	30	30
280	39	12m. red	30	30
281	39	20m. blue	30	30
282	39	50m. red	45	40
283	39	100m. pink	90	85
284	39	200m. green	2·00	1·80

40 Globe and Forms of Transport

1949. 75th Anniversary of UPU.

285	**40**	1m. brown	60	55
286	**40**	4m. green	1·10	1·00
287	**40**	10m. red	1·40	1·30
288	**40**	20m. blue	2·30	2·10
289	-	50m. green	3·75	3·50

Design: 50m. King Abdullah.

44 Lockheed Constellation Airliner and Globe

1950. Air.

295	**44**	5f. purple and yellow	1·50	1·00
296	**44**	10f. brown and violet	1·50	1·00
297	**44**	15f. red and olive	1·50	1·00
298	**44**	20f. black and blue	2·10	1·70
299	**44**	50f. green and mauve	3·50	1·70
300	**44**	100f. brown and blue	6·00	4·00
301	**44**	150f. orange and black	9·00	5·50

1952. Optd **FILS** and bars or **J.D.** (on 1d.).

313	**28**	1f. on 1m. brown	75	70
314	**28**	2f. on 2m. green	75	70
315	**28**	3f. on 3m. green	45·00	†
316	**28**	3f. on 3m. pink	75	70
310	**28**	4f. on 4m. pink	11·00	5·25
318	**28**	4f. on 4m. green	75	70
319	**28**	5f. on 5m. orange	1·10	1·00
320	**28**	10f. on 10m. red	45·00	†
321	**28**	10f. on 10m. violet	1·40	1·30
322	**28**	12f. on 12m. red	1·40	1·30
312	**28**	15f. on 15m. blue	48·00	24·00
325	**28**	15f. on 15m. green	1·80	1·00
326	**28**	20f. on 20m. green	47·00	†
327	**28**	20f. on 20m. blue	3·25	1·40
328	**29**	50f. on 50m. purple	3·25	2·20
329	**29**	90f. on 90m. bistre	24·00	15·00
330	**29**	100f. on 100m. blue	15·00	5·00
331	**29**	200f. on 200m. violet	21·00	6·25
332	**29**	500f. on 500m. brown	48·00	20·00
333	**29**	1d. on £P1 grey	£110	25·00

48 Dome of the Rock and Khazneh at Petra

1952. Unification of Jordan and Palestine.

355	**48**	1f. green and brown	60	55
356	**48**	2f. red and green	60	55
357	**48**	3f. black and red	60	55
358	**48**	4f. orange and green	60	55
359	**48**	5f. purple and brown	75	70
360	**48**	10f. brown and violet	75	70
361	**48**	20f. black and blue	1·80	1·00
362	**48**	100f. sepia and brown	6·50	4·50
363	**48**	200f. orange and violet	17·00	8·50

49 King Abdullah

1952. (a) Size 18×21½ mm.

364	**49**	5f. orange	60	55
365	**49**	10f. lilac	60	55
366	**49**	12f. red	2·40	1·70
367	**49**	15f. olive	1·50	55
368	**49**	20f. blue	1·50	70

(b) Size 20×24½ mm.

369		50f. purple	3·75	1·40
370		90f. brown	10·50	5·00
371		100f. blue	11·50	3·25

1953. Optd with two horiz bars across Arabic commemorative inscription.

378A	**48**	1f. green and brown	60	55
379A	**48**	2f. red and green	60	55
380A	**48**	3f. black and red	60	55
381A	**48**	4f. orange and green	60	55
382A	**48**	5f. purple and brown	60	55
383A	**48**	10f. brown and violet	1·80	1·00
384A	**48**	20f. black and blue	1·80	1·30
385A	**48**	100f. brown and blue	10·50	2·75
386A	**48**	200f. orange and violet	14·50	8·50

(51)

1953. Obligatory Tax stamps optd for postal use as in T **51**. (a) Inscr 'MILS'.

387	**T36**	1m. blue	60	55
388	**T36**	3m. green	60	55
389	**T36**	5m. purple	£200	£200
390	-	10m. red	85·00	65·00
391	-	15m. black	5·25	2·75
392	-	20m. brown	£180	£130
393	-	50m. violet	1·50	1·30
394	-	100m. red	17·00	12·50

(b) Inscr 'MILS' and optd **PALESTINE**.

395	**T36**	1m. blue	£110	65·00
396	**T36**	3m. green	£110	65·00
397	**T36**	5m. purple	£110	65·00
398	-	10m. red	£110	65·00
399	-	15m. black	£110	65·00
400	-	20m. brown	£110	65·00
400a	-	50m. violet	†	†
401	-	100m. red	£110	65·00

(c) Inscr "MILS', optd **FILS** (No. T334, etc).

402	**T36**	1f. on 1m. blue	£100	75·00
403	**T36**	3f. on 3m. green	£100	75·00
404	-	10f. on 10m. red	£100	75·00
405	-	15f. on 15m. black	£100	75·00
406	-	20f. on 20m. brown	£100	75·00
407	-	100f. on 100m. red	£110	£100

(d) Inscr 'FILS'.

408	**T36**	5f. purple	60	30
409	-	10f. red	75	30
410	-	15f. black	1·80	1·40
411	-	20f. brown	3·50	2·20
412	-	100f. orange	9·00	4·50

51a King Hussein

1953. Enthronement of King Hussein.

413	**51a**	1f. black and green	30	30
414	**51a**	4f. black and red	45	40
415	**51a**	15f. black and blue	2·75	55
416	**51a**	20f. black and lilac	4·75	55
417	**51a**	50f. black and green	10·50	4·50
418	**51a**	100f. black and blue	21·00	13·50

52 El-Deir Temple, Petra

54a Temple of Artemis Jerash

1954

445	**52**	1f. brown & grn (postage)	30	20
446	-	2f. black and red	30	20
447	**52**	3f. violet and purple	30	20
448	-	4f. green and brown	30	20
449	**52**	5f. green and violet	60	30
470	**54a**	5f. orange and blue (air)	40	30
433	**54a**	10f. red and brown	1·10	1·00
450	-	10f. green and purple	5·50	3·50
451	-	12f. sepia and red	2·30	30
452	-	15f. red and brown	1·40	30
453	-	20f. green and blue	1·10	30
434	**54a**	25f. blue and green	1·50	1·00
435	**54a**	35f. blue and mauve	1·80	1·00
436	**54a**	40f. slate and red	2·30	1·00
437	**54a**	50f. orange and blue	3·00	1·40
454	-	50f. red and blue	2·30	30
428	-	100f. blue and green	5·50	1·70
438	**54a**	100f. brown and blue	3·50	2·50
439	**54a**	150f. lake and turquoise	6·00	3·25
456	-	200f. blue and lake	13·50	3·50
457	-	500f. purple and brown	48·00	18·00
458	-	1d. lake and olive	85·00	27·00

Designs: Vert—2f., 4f., 500f., 1d. King Hussein. Horiz—10f., 15f., 20f. Dome of the Rock, Jerusalem; 12f., 50f., 100f., 200f. Facade of Mosque of El Aqsa.

1955. Arab Postal Union. As Nos. 502/504 of Egypt but inscr 'H. K. JORDAN' at top and 'ARAB POSTAL UNION' at foot.

440		15f. green	1·10	55
441		20f. violet	1·10	55
442		25f. brown	1·40	1·00

56 King Hussein and Queen Dina

1955. Royal Wedding.

443	**56**	15f. blue	3·25	1·30
444	**56**	100f. lake	12·00	5·00

58 Envelope with Postmarks in English and Arabic

1956. First Arab Postal Congress, Amman.

459	**58**	1f. brown and black	45	40
460	**58**	4f. red and black	45	40
461	**58**	15f. blue and black	45	40
462	**58**	20f. bistre and black	45	40
463	**58**	50f. blue and black	1·10	40
464	**58**	100f. orange and black	1·70	1·00

59 'Flame of Freedom'

1958. Tenth Anniversary of Declaration of Human Rights.

476	**59**	5f. red and blue	15	15
477	**59**	15f. black and brown	45	40
478	**59**	35f. purple and green	90	85
479	**59**	45f. black and red	1·20	1·10

60 King Hussein

1959. Centres in black.

480	**60**	1f. green	25	15
481	**60**	2f. violet	30	15
482	**60**	3f. red	60	15
483	**60**	4f. purple	75	15
484	**60**	7f. green	90	20
485	**60**	12f. red	1·10	20
486	**60**	15f. red	1·20	30
487	**60**	21f. green	1·50	30
488	**60**	25f. brown	1·80	30
489	**60**	35f. blue	2·75	30
490	**60**	40f. green	3·75	30
491	**60**	50f. red	4·50	30
492	**60**	100f. green	6·00	1·00
493	**60**	200f. purple	17·00	4·25
494	**60**	500f. blue	38·00	17·00
495	**60**	1d. purple	70·00	42·00

61 Arab League Centre, Cairo

1960. Inaug of Arab League Centre, Cairo.

496	**61**	15f. black and green	55	30

62 'Care of Refugees'

1960. World Refugee Year.

497	**62**	15f. red and blue	45	30
498	**62**	35f. blue and bistre	90	70

63 Shah of Iran and King Hussein

1960. Visit of Shah of Iran.

499	**63**	15f. multicoloured	75	70
500	**63**	35f. multicoloured	1·10	1·00
501	**63**	50f. multicoloured	1·50	1·40

64 Petroleum Refinery, Zarka

1961. Inauguration of Jordanian Petroleum Refinery.

502	**64**	15f. blue and violet	45	30
503	**64**	35f. brown and violet	75	55

65 Jordanian Families and Graph

1961. First Jordanian Census Commemoration.

504	**65**	15f. brown	45	30

1961. Dag Hammarskjold Memorial Issue. Optd **IN MEMORIAL OF DAG HAMMARSKJOELD 1904–1961** in English and Arabic and laurel leaves at top and bottom.

505	**62**	15f. red and blue	8·25	7·75
506	**62**	35f. blue and bistre	8·25	7·75

67 Campaign Emblem

1962. Malaria Eradication.

507	**67**	15f. mauve	45	40
508	**67**	35f. blue	90	55
MS509		75×76 mm. Nos. 507/508	11·50	11·00

68 Telephone Exchange, Amman

1962. Inauguration of Amman's Automatic Telephone Exchange.

510	**68**	15f. blue and purple	30	35
511	**68**	35f. purple and green	90	85

69 Aqaba Port and King Hussein

1962. Opening of Aqaba Port.

512	**69**	15f. black and purple	1·10	30
513	**69**	35f. black and blue	2·00	70
MS514		80×93 mm. Nos. 512/513	7·50	7·25

70 Dag Hammarskjold and UN Headquarters

1963. 17th Anniversary of UN.

515	**70**	15f. red, olive and blue	75	30
516	**70**	35f. blue, red and olive	1·80	85
517	**70**	50f. olive, blue and red	3·00	1·70
MS518		135×95 mm. Nos. 515/517. Imperf	20·00	19·00

71 Church of Holy Virgin's Tomb, Jerusalem

1963. Holy Places. Multicoloured.

519		50f. Type **71**	2·30	2·10
520		50f. Basilica of the Agony, Gethsemane	2·30	2·10
521		50f. Holy Sepulchre, Jerusalem	2·30	2·10
522		50f. Nativity Church. Bethlehem	2·30	2·10
523		50f. Haram of Ibrahim, Hebron	2·30	2·10
524		50f. Dome of the Rock, Jerusalem	2·30	2·10
525		50f. Omer-el-Khetab Mosque, Jerusalem	2·30	2·10
526		50f. El-Aqsa Mosque, Jerusalem	2·30	2·10

72 League Centre, Cairo and Emblem

1963. Arab League.

527	**72**	15f. blue	45	30
528	**72**	35f. red	1·50	55

73 Wheat and FAO Emblem

1963. Freedom from Hunger.

529	**73**	15f. green, black and blue	60	30
530	**73**	35f. green, black and apple	90	55
MS531		98×85 mm. Nos. 529/530	3·00	2·40

74 Canal and Symbols

1963. East Ghor Canal Project.

532	**74**	1f. black and bistre	30	15
533	**74**	4f. black and blue	30	15
534	**74**	5f. black and purple	30	15
535	**74**	10f. black and green	60	15
536	**74**	35f. black and orange	3·25	2·20

75 Scales of Justice and Globe

1963. 15th Anniversary of Declaration of Human Rights.

537	**75**	50f. red and blue	1·50	1·40
538	**75**	50f. blue and red	1·50	1·40

1963. Surch in English and Arabic.

539	**60**	1f. on 21f. black and green	45	40
540	**60**	2f. on 21f. black and green	45	40
541	**60**	4f. on 12f. black and red	27·00	42·00
542	-	4f. on 12f. sepia and red (No. 451)	60	55
543	**60**	5f. on 21f. black and green	1·20	85
544	**60**	25f. on 35f. blue	4·50	1·80

77 King Hussein and Red Crescent

1963. Red Crescent Commemoration.

545	**77**	1f. purple and red	30	30
546	**77**	2f. turquoise and red	30	30
547	**77**	3f. blue and red	30	30
548	**77**	4f. turquoise and red	30	30
549	**77**	5f. sepia and red	30	30
550	**77**	85f. green and red	4·00	3·00
MS551		90×65 mm. 100f. purple and red (larger). Imperf	48·00	46·00

78 Red Cross Emblem

1963. Centenary of Red Cross.

552	**78**	1f. purple and red	45	40
553	**78**	2f. turquoise and red	45	40
554	**78**	3f. blue and red	45	40
555	**78**	4f. turquoise and red	45	40
556	**78**	5f. sepia and red	45	40
557	**78**	85f. green and red	6·25	4·25
MS558		90×65 mm. 100f. purple and red (larger). Imperf	45·00	43·00

79 Kings Hussein of Hejaz and Hussein of Jordan

1963. Arab Renaissance Day.

559	**79**	15f. multicoloured	1·20	55
560	**79**	25f. multicoloured	1·70	85
561	**79**	35f. multicoloured	3·00	1·80
562	**79**	50f. multicoloured	6·25	5·00
MS563		112×93 mm. Nos. 559/562	13·50	13·00

80 Al Aqsa Mosque, Pope Paul and King Hussein

1964. Pope Paul's Visit to the Holy Land.

564	**80**	15f. green and black	60	40
565	-	35f. mauve and black	90	55
566	-	50f. brown and black	1·80	1·30
567	-	80f. blue and black	3·25	2·20
MS567a		138×108 mm. Nos. 564/567. Imperf	39·00	37·00

Designs: 35f. Dome of the Rock (Mosque of Omar), Jerusalem; 50f. Church of the Holy Sepulchre, Jerusalem; 80f. Church of the Nativity, Bethlehem.

81 Prince Abdullah

1964. Second Birthday of Prince Abdullah. Multicoloured.

568		5f. Prince standing by wall	75	30
569		10f. Head of Prince and roses	90	70
570		35f. Type **81**	2·00	1·40

Sizes: 5f. as T **81** but vert; 10f. diamond (63×63 mm).

NOTE.—A set of ten triangular 20f. stamps showing astronauts and rockets was issued, but very few were put on sale at the Post Office and we are not listing them unless we receive satisfactory evidence as to their status.

82 Basketball

1964. Olympic Games, Tokyo (1st issue).

571	**82**	1f. red	30	30
572	-	2f. blue	30	30
573	-	3f. green	30	30
574	-	4f. buff	30	30
575	-	5f. violet	30	30
576	-	35f. red	3·25	1·40
577	-	50f. green	6·00	2·75
578	-	100f. brown	9·00	5·00
MS579		88×64 mm. 200f. blue (as 100f. but larger). Imperf	70·00	65·00

Designs: Vert—2f. Volleyball; 3f. Football; 5f. Running. Horiz—4f. Table tennis; 35f. Cycling; 50f. Fencing; 100f. Pole vaulting.

See also Nos. 610/**MS**618 and 641/**MS**647.

83 Woman and Child

1964. Fourth Session of Social Studies Seminar, Amman.

580	**83**	5f. multicoloured	75	70
581	**83**	10f. multicoloured	75	70
582	**83**	25f. multicoloured	75	70

84 King Hussein Sports Stadium, Amman

1964. Air. Inauguration of Hussein Sports City.

583	**84**	1f. multicoloured	45	40
584	**84**	4f. multicoloured	45	40
585	**84**	10f. multicoloured	45	40
586	**84**	35f. multicoloured	90	85
MS587		120×94 mm. Nos. 583/586	4·50	4·25

85 President Kennedy

1964. President Kennedy Memorial Issue.

588	**85**	1f. violet	60	55
589	**85**	2f. red	60	55
590	**85**	3f. blue	60	55
591	**85**	4f. brown	60	55
592	**85**	5f. green	60	55
593	**85**	85f. red	30·00	17·00
MS594		110×77 mm. **85** 100f. sepia (larger). Imperf	33·00	32·00

86 Statues at Abu Simbel

1964. Nubian Monuments Preservation.

595	**86**	4f. black and blue	75	70
596	**86**	15f. violet and yellow	75	70
597	**86**	25f. red and green	75	70

87 King Hussein and Map of Palestine in 1920

1964. Arab Summit Conference.

598	**87**	10f. multicoloured	30	15
599	**87**	15f. multicoloured	45	20
600	**87**	25f. multicoloured	60	30
601	**87**	50f. multicoloured	1·40	40
602	**87**	80f. multicoloured	2·50	2·00
MS603		110×90 mm. Nos. 598/602. Imperf. No gum	8·25	8·00

88 Pope Paul VI, King Hussein and Ecumenical Patriarch

1964. Meeting of Pope, King and Patriarch, Jerusalem. Multicoloured, background colour given.

604	**88**	10f. green	30	30
605	**88**	15f. purple	45	40
606	**88**	25f. brown	60	55
607	**88**	50f. blue	1·40	1·30
608	**88**	80f. green	2·50	2·40
MS609		130×100 mm. Nos. 604/608. Imperf. No gum	13·50	13·00

89 Olympic Flame

1964. Olympic Games, Tokyo (2nd issue).

610	**89**	1f. red	15	15
611	**89**	2f. violet	25	20
612	**89**	3f. green	30	30
613	**89**	4f. brown	40	35
614	**89**	5f. red	45	40
615	**89**	35f. blue	1·50	1·40
616	**89**	50f. olive	2·30	2·10
617	**89**	100f. blue	5·25	5·00
MS618		108×76 mm. **89** 100f. rose (larger). Imperf	33·00	32·00

90 Scouts crossing River

1964. Jordanian Scouts.

619	**90**	1f. brown	25	20
620	-	2f. violet	25	20
621	-	3f. ochre	30	30
622	-	4f. lake	30	30
623	-	5f. green	30	30
624	-	35f. blue	8·25	3·00
625	-	50f. green	9·00	4·75
MS626		108×76 mm. 100f. blue (as 50f. but larger). Imperf	39·00	19·00

Designs: 2f. First aid; 3f. Exercising; 4f. Practising knots; 5f. Cooking meal; 35f. Sailing; 50f. Around camp-fire.

91 Four-coloured Bush Shrike

1964. Air. Birds. Multicoloured.

627		150f. Type **91**	45·00	21·00
628		500f. Ornate hawk eagle (vert)	£120	55·00
629		1000f. Grey-headed kingfisher (vert)	£200	£100

92 Bykovsky

1965. Russian Astronauts.

630		40f. brown and green (Type **92**)	2·10	1·40
631		40f. violet & brown (Gagarin)	2·10	1·40
632		40f. maroon & bl (Nikolaev)	2·10	1·40
633		40f. lilac and bistre (Popovich)	2·10	1·40
634		40f. sepia & blue (Tereshkova)	2·10	1·40
635		40f. green and pink (Titov)	2·10	1·40
MS636		115×83 mm. 100f. blue and black (space ship and the six cosmonauts). Imperf	38·00	36·00
MS637		As above opt **VOSKHOD 12/10/64/VLADIMIR KOMATOV/ KONSTANTIN FEOKTISTOV/BORIS YEGEROV**	38·00	36·00

93 UN Headquarters and Emblem

1965. 19th Anniversary (1964) of UN.

638	**93**	30f. violet, turquoise and brown	90	70
639	**93**	70f. brown, blue and violet	1·80	1·00
MS640		76×102 mm. Nos. 638/639. Imperf	30·00	29·00

94 Olympic Flame

1965. Air. Olympic Games, Tokyo (3rd issue).

641	**94**	10f. red	60	55
642	**94**	15f. violet	60	55
643	**94**	20f. blue	60	55
644	**94**	30f. green	60	55
645	**94**	40f. brown	90	85
646	**94**	60f. mauve	1·20	1·10
MS647 102×102 mm. **94** 100f. blue (larger). Imperf			29·00	27·00

95 Dagger on Deir Yassin, Palestine

1965. Deir Yassin Massacre.

648	**95**	25f. red and olive	6·50	3·50

96 Horse-jumping

1965. Army Day.

649	**96**	5f. green	30	15
650	-	10f. blue	60	30
651	-	35f. brown	2·00	70

Designs: 10f. Tank; 35f. King Hussein making inspection in army car.

97 Volleyball Player and Cup

1965. Arab Volleyball Championships.

652	**97**	15f. olive	1·70	55
653	**97**	35f. lake	3·25	1·40
654	**97**	50f. blue	5·25	3·00
MS655 63×89 mm. **97** 100f. brown (larger). Imperf			42·00	40·00

98 President J. F. Kennedy

1965. First Death Anniversary of President Kennedy.

656	**98**	10f. black and green	75	70
657	**98**	15f. violet and orange	1·10	70
658	**98**	25f. brown and blue	1·70	1·00
659	**98**	50f. purple and green	3·25	1·80
MS660 114×90 mm. **98** 50f. salmon and blue. Imperf			30·00	29·00

99 Pope Paul, King Hussein and Dome of the Rock

1965. First Anniversary of Pope Paul's Visit to the Holy Land.

661	**99**	5f. brown and mauve	75	15
662	**99**	10f. lake and green	1·50	55
663	**99**	15f. blue and flesh	2·10	70
664	**99**	50f. grey and pink	5·50	2·40
MS665 102×76 mm. **99** 50f. blue and violet. Imperf			42·00	40·00

100 Cathedral Steps

1965. Air. Jerash Antiquities. Multicoloured.

666	55f. Type **100**	2·50	2·40
667	55f. Artemis Temple Gate	2·50	2·40
668	55f. Street of Columns	2·50	2·40
669	55f. Columns of South Theatre	2·50	2·40
670	55f. Forum (horiz)	2·50	2·40
671	55f. South Theatre (horiz)	2·50	2·40
672	55f. Triumphal Arch (horiz)	2·50	2·40
673	55f. Temple of Artemis (horiz)	2·50	2·40

101 Jordan Pavilion at Fair

1965. New York World's Fair.

674	**101**	15f. multicoloured	30	30
675	**101**	25f. multicoloured	75	40
676	**101**	50f. multicoloured	1·70	1·00
MS677 113×75 mm. **101** 100f. multicoloured			5·75	5·50

102 Lamp and Burning Library

1965. Burning of Algiers Library.

678	**102**	25f. green, red and black	75	40

103 ITU Emblem and Symbols

1965. Centenary of ITU.

679	**103**	25f. blue and light blue	75	30
680	**103**	45f. black and green	1·20	70
MS681 40×32 mm. **103** 100f. lake and red (larger). Imperf			4·50	4·25

104 *Syncom* Satellite and Pagoda

1965. Space Achievements. Multicoloured.

682	5f. Type **104**	60	55
683	10f. North American X-15 rocket aeroplane	60	55
684	15f. Astronauts	90	70
685	20f. As 10f.	1·20	85
686	50f. Type **104**	2·75	2·00
MS687 101×76 mm. 50f. *Syncom* Satellite and Earth's sphere. Imperf		29·00	27·00

105 Dead Sea

1986. Dead Sea. Multicoloured.

688	35f. Type **105**	1·40	85
689	35f. Boats and palms	1·40	85
690	35f. Qumran Caves	1·40	85
691	35f. Dead Sea Scrolls	1·40	85

1965. Air. Space Flight of McDivitt and White. Nos. 641/**MS**647 optd **James McDivitt Edward White 2-6-1965** in English and Arabic and rocket.

692	**94**	10f. red	2·30	2·10
693	**94**	15f. violet	3·00	2·75
694	**94**	20f. blue	4·25	4·00
695	**94**	30f. green	6·25	6·00
696	**94**	40f. brown	8·25	7·75
697	**94**	60f. mauve	12·00	11·00
MS698 102×102 mm. **94** 100f. blue (larger). Imperf			45·00	43·00

107 King Hussein, UN Emblem and Headquarters

1965. King Hussein's Visit to France and the USA.

699	**107**	5f. sepia, blue and pink	60	55
700	-	10f. sepia, green and grey	60	55
701	-	20f. agate, brown and blue	1·10	1·00
702	**107**	50f. lilac, brown and blue	2·50	2·40
MS703 102×102 mm. **107** 50f. lilac, brown and blue. Imperf			18·00	17·00

Designs: 10f. King Hussein, President de Gaulle and Eiffel Tower; 20f. King Hussein, President Johnson and Statue of Liberty.

108 ICY Emblem

1965. International Co-operation Year.

704	**108**	5f. red and orange	45	30
705	**108**	10f. violet and blue	1·10	40
706	**108**	45f. purple and green	4·00	2·75

109 APU Emblem

1965. Tenth Anniversary (1964) of Arab Postal Union's Permanent Office at Cairo.

707	**109**	15f. black and blue	30	30
708	**109**	25f. black and green	1·10	40

110 Dome of the Rock

1965. Inauguration (1964) of Dome of the Rock.

709	**110**	15f. multicoloured	1·70	55
710	**110**	25f. multicoloured	2·75	1·70

111 King Hussein

1966. (a) Postage. Portraits in blue (1f. to 15f.) or purple (21f. to 150f.); background colours given.

711	**111**	1f. orange	15	15
712	**111**	2f. blue	15	15
713	**111**	3f. violet	15	15
714	**111**	4f. purple	15	15
715	**111**	7f. brown	45	15
716	**111**	12f. mauve	45	15
717	**111**	15f. brown	60	15
718	**111**	21f. green	90	20
719	**111**	25f. blue	1·10	20
720	**111**	35f. stone	1·40	30
721	**111**	40f. yellow	1·50	40
722	**111**	50f. green	1·70	70
723	**111**	100f. green	2·75	1·50
724	**111**	150f. violet	6·25	2·40

(b) Air. Portraits in brown; background colours given.

725	200f. turquoise	9·75	2·75
726	500f. green	17·00	10·50
727	1d. blue	29·00	17·00

1966. Space Flights of Belyaev and Leonov. Nos. 630/**MS**637 optd **Alexei Leonov Pavel Belyaev 18 3-1965** in English and Arabic and spacecraft motif.

728	**92**	40f. brown and green	9·00	8·50
729	-	40f. violet and brown	9·00	8·50
730	-	40f. purple and blue	9·00	8·50
731	-	40f. lilac and bistre	9·00	8·50
732	-	40f. sepia and blue	9·00	8·50
733	-	40f. green and pink	9·00	8·50
MS734 115×83 mm. 100f. blue and black (No. **MS**636)			90·00	85·00
MS735 115×83 mm. 100f. blue and black (No. **MS**637)			90·00	85·00

1966. Pope Paul's Visit to UN (1965). Nos. 604/608 optd **PAPA PAULUS VI WORLD PEACE VISIT TO UNITED NATIONS 1965** in English and Arabic.

736	**88**	10f. green	45	15
737	**88**	15f. purple	1·10	40
738	**88**	25f. brown	1·10	55
739	**88**	50f. blue	2·00	1·00
740	**88**	80f. green	3·25	1·50
MS740a 130×100 mm. Nos. 736/740. Imperf. No gum			20·00	19·00

114 Agricultural Symbols

1966. Anti-TB Campaign. (a) Unissued Freedom from Hunger stamps optd as in T **114**.

741	**114**	15f. multicoloured	75	55
742	**114**	35f. multicoloured	2·00	1·30
743	**114**	50f. multicoloured	3·00	2·75
MS744 108×76 mm. Nos. 741/743. Gold background			23·00	22·00
MS744a 108×76 mm. Nos. 741/742. White background. Imperf			23·00	22·00

(b) As Nos. 741/743 but with additional premium obliterated by bars.

745	15f. multicoloured	75	55
746	35f. multicoloured	2·00	1·30
747	50f. multicoloured	3·00	2·75

115 First Station of the Cross

1966. Christ's Passion. The Stations of the Cross.

749	**115**	1f. multicoloured	30	15
750	-	2f. multicoloured	30	15
751	-	3f. multicoloured	45	30
752	-	4f. multicoloured	45	30
753	-	5f. multicoloured	75	40
754	-	6f. multicoloured	1·10	55
755	-	7f. multicoloured	1·50	85
756	-	8f. multicoloured	1·70	90

757	-	9f. multicoloured	2·00	1·00
758	-	10f. multicoloured	2·10	1·30
759	-	11f. multicoloured	2·50	1·50
760	-	12f. multicoloured	2·50	1·50
761	-	13f. multicoloured	2·75	1·70
762	-	14f. multicoloured	2·75	1·80
MS763		101×76 mm. **115** 100f. multicoloured	55·00	50·00

Designs: The 14 Stations. The denominations, expressed in Roman numerals, correspond to the numbers of the stations.

116 Schirra and *Gemini 6*

1966. Space Achievements.

764	**116**	1f. blue, violet and green	30	30
765	-	2f. green, violet and blue	30	30
766	-	3f. violet, blue and green	30	30
767	-	4f. violet, green and ochre	45	30
768	-	30f. turquoise, brn & vio	3·00	2·00
769	-	60f. brown, turq & vio	4·00	2·75
MS770		114×88 mm. 100f. multicoloured (The six astronauts etc). Imperf	36·00	34·00

Designs: 2f. Stafford and *Gemini 6* 3f. Borman and *Gemini 7*; 4f. Lovell and *Gemini 7*; 30f. Armstrong and *Gemini 8*; 60f. Scott and *Gemini 8*.

117 The Three Kings

1966. Christmas. Multicoloured.

771		5f. Type **117**	45	15
772		10f. The Magi presenting gifts to the infant Christ	60	30
773		35f. The flight to Egypt (vert)	5·75	1·80
MS774		115×90 mm. 50f. As 10f. Imperf	42·00	40·00

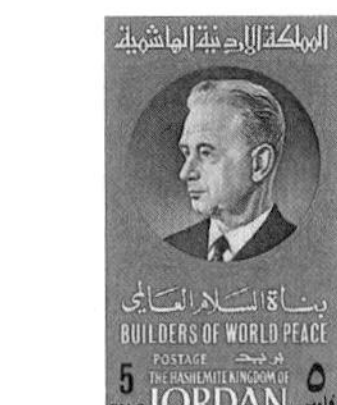

118 Dag Hammarskjold

1967. Builders of World Peace. Multicoloured. (a) (1st issue).

775		5f. Type **118**	30	30
776		10f. Pandit Nehru	45	30
777		35f. President Kennedy	1·70	85
778		50f. Pope John XXIII	4·00	1·10
779		100f. King Abdullah (of Jordan)	4·50	3·25
MS780		99×64 mm. 100f. The above five portraits. Imperf	36·00	34·00

(b) (2nd issue).

781		5f. U. Thant	30	30
782		10f. President De Gaulle	45	30
783		35f. President Johnson	1·70	85
784		50f. Pope Paul VI	4·00	1·10
785		100f. King Hussein	4·50	3·25
MS786		99×64 mm. 100f. The above five portraits	36·00	34·00

119 King Hussein

1967. Gold Coins. Circular designs, centre and rim embossed on gold foil. Imperf. (a) As T **119**. (i) Diameter 41 mm.

787	**119**	5f. orange and blue	1·10	1·00
788	**119**	10f. orange and violet	1·10	1·00

(ii) Diameter 47 mm.

789		50f. lilac and brown	5·75	5·25
790		100f. pink and green	7·25	6·75

(iii) Diameter 54 mm.

791		200f. blue and deep blue	17·00	15·00

(b) Crown Prince Hassan of Jordan. (i) Diameter 41 mm.

792		5f. black and green	1·10	1·00
793		10f. black and lilac	1·10	1·00

(ii) Diameter 47 mm.

794		50f. black and blue	5·75	5·25
795		100f. black and brown	7·25	6·75

(iii) Diameter 54 mm.

796		200f. black and mauve	17·00	15·00

A similar set was also issued in the same values and sizes but different colours with portrait of John F. Kennedy.

120 University City, Statue and Olympic Torch

1967. Preparation for Olympic Games in Mexico (1968).

797	**120**	1f. red, black and violet	45	40
798	-	2f. black, violet and red	45	40
799	-	3f. violet, red and black	45	40
800	-	4f. blue, brown and green	45	40
801	-	30f. green, blue and brown	1·10	1·00
802	-	60f. brown, green and blue	2·10	2·00
MS803		115×90 mm. 100f. brown, green and ultramarine (as 60f.). Imperf	36·00	34·00

Designs (each with Olympic torch): 2f. Fishermen on Lake Patzcuaro; 3f. University City and skyscraper, Mexico City; 4f. Avenida de la Reforma, Mexico City; 30f. Guadalajara Cathedral; 60f. Fine Arts Theatre, Mexico City.

121 Decade Emblem

1967. International Hydrological Decade.

804	**121**	10f. black and red	45	15
805	**121**	15f. black and turquoise	90	40
806	**121**	25f. black and purple	1·70	1·00

122 UNESCO Emblem

1967. 20th Anniversary of UNESCO.

807	**122**	100f. multicoloured	2·30	2·10

123 Dromedary

1967. Animals. Multicoloured.

808		1f. Type **123** (postage)	3·50	55
809		2f. Karakul sheep	3·50	55
810		3f. Angora goat	3·50	55
811		4f. Striped hyena (air)	3·50	55
812		30f. Arab horses	4·75	1·10
813		60f. Goitred gazelle	8·25	2·10
MS814		115×89 mm. 100f. (as 30f.). Imperf	50·00	48·00

124 WHO Building

1967. Inauguration of WHO Headquarters, Geneva.

815	**124**	5f. black and green	30	30
816	**124**	45f. black and orange	1·20	55

125 Arab League Emblem, Open Book and Reaching Hands

1968. Literacy Campaign.

817	**125**	20f. green and orange	1·20	40
818	**125**	20f. blue and mauve	90	40

126 WHO Emblem and '20'

1968. 20th Anniversary of WHO.

819	**126**	30f. multicoloured	1·20	40
820	**126**	100f. multicoloured	3·50	1·80

127 Eurasian Goldfinch ('Goldfinch')

1968. Game Protection. Multicoloured.

821		5f. Type **127** (postage)	5·00	2·10
822		10f. Chukar partridge ('Rock Partridge') (vert)	9·00	2·10
823		15f. Ostriches (vert)	13·00	2·75
824		20f. Sand partridge	13·00	3·00
825		30f. Mountain gazelle	8·25	2·40
826		40f. Arabian oryx	11·50	2·75
827		50f. Houbara bustard ('Bustard')	18·00	6·00
828		60f. Ibex (vert) (air)	14·50	7·00
829		100f. Flock of mallard ('Duck')	23·00	13·50

128 Human Rights Emblem

1968. Human Rights Year.

830	**128**	20f. black, buff and brown	45	30
831	**128**	60f. black, blue and green	1·80	1·40

129 ILO Emblem

1969. 50th Anniversary of ILO.

832	**129**	10f. black and blue	45	15
833	**129**	20f. black and brown	45	30
834	**129**	25f. black and green	60	40
835	**129**	45f. black and mauve	1·10	70
836	**129**	60f. black and orange	1·50	1·00

130 Horses in Pasture

1969. Arab Horses. Multicoloured.

837		10f. Type **130**	2·30	40
838		20f. White horse	6·25	1·50
839		45f. Black mare and foal	11·50	4·75

131 Kaaba, Mecca, and Dome of the Rock, Jerusalem

1969. Multicoloured

840		5f. As Type **131**	60	15
841		10f. Dome of the Rock (30×36 mm)	1·10	70
842		20f. As 10f.	2·00	1·00
843		45f. As 5f.	4·75	1·10

132 Oranges

1969. Fruits. Multicoloured.

844		10f. Type **132**	45	15
845		20f. Gooseberry	75	40
846		30f. Lemons	1·70	50
847		40f. Grapes	2·40	55
848		50f. Olives	3·25	1·50
849		100f. Apples	5·25	2·75

133 Prince Hassan and Bride

1969. Wedding of Prince Hassan (1968).

850	-	20f. multicoloured	90	85
851	-	60f. multicoloured	2·10	1·70
852	**133**	100f. multicoloured	3·50	3·25

Nos. 850/851 show a similar design to T **133**.

134 Wrecked Houses

1969. Tragedy of the Refugees. Various vert designs as T **134**. Multicoloured.

853-882		1f. to 30f. inclusive	55·00	55·00

135 Bombed Mosque

1969. Tragedy in the Holy Lands. Various vert designs as T **135**. Multicoloured.

883-912		1f. to 30f. inclusive	55·00	55·00

136 Pomegranate

1970. Flowers. Multicoloured.

913		5f. Type **136**	75	30
914		15f. Wattle	1·20	30
915		25f. Caper	2·00	30
916		35f. Convolvulus	2·75	40
917		45f. Desert scabious	3·75	1·30
918		75f. Black iris	6·00	4·75

Nos. 913/915 and 917 are wrongly inscribed on the stamps.

137 Football

1970. Sports. Multicoloured.

919		5f. Type **137**	30	15
920		10f. Diving	45	30
921		15f. Boxing	75	30
922		50f. Running	2·30	1·00
923		100f. Cycling (vert)	5·50	1·80
924		150f. Basketball (vert)	8·25	4·25

138 Arab Children

1970. Children's Day. Multicoloured.

925		5f. Type **138**	45	15
926		10f. Refugee boy with kettle (vert)	45	20
927		15f. Refugee girl in camp (vert)	1·10	30
928		20f. Refugee child in tent (vert)	1·50	40

139 White-crowned Black Wheatear ('Black Chat')

1970. Birds.

929	**139**	120f. black and orange	21·00	4·25
930	-	180f. brown, black & lilac	26·00	9·00
931	-	200f. multicoloured	33·00	12·50

Designs: 180f. Masked shrike; 200f. Palestine sunbird.

140 Grotto of the Nativity, Bethlehem

1970. Christmas. Church of the Nativity, Bethlehem. Multicoloured.

932		5f. Type **140**	60	30
933		10f. Christmas crib	1·10	35
934		20f. Crypt Altar	1·40	55
935		25f. Nave, Church of the Nativity	1·80	70

141 Arab League Flag, Emblem and Map

1971. 25th Anniversary (1970) of Arab League.

936	**141**	10f. green, violet and orange	30	20
937	**141**	20f. green, brown and blue	75	30
938	**141**	30f. green, blue and olive	1·10	40

142 Heads of Four Races and Emblem

1971. Racial Equality Year. Multicoloured.

939		5f. Type **142**	45	40
940		10f. "Plant" and emblem	45	40
941		15f. Doves and emblem (horiz)	60	40

No. 939 is inscribed 'KINIGDOM' in error.

143 Shore of the Dead Sea

1971. Tourism. Multicoloured.

942		5f. Type **143**	60	40
943		30f. Ed Deir, Petra	2·10	85
944		45f. Via Dolorosa, Jerusalem (vert)	3·00	1·10
945		60f. River Jordan	5·00	2·40
946		100f. Christmas Bell, Bethlehem (vert)	7·25	4·75

144 Ibn Sinai (Avicenna)

1971. Famous Arab Scholars. Multicoloured.

947		5f. Type **144**	45	15
948		10f. Ibn Rushd	60	15
949		20f. Ibn Khaldun	90	30
950		25f. Ibn Tufail	1·50	30
951		30f. Ibn El Haytham	2·30	1·00

145 New UPU HQ Building

1971. Inauguration of New UPU Headquarters Building, Berne.

952	**145**	10f. brown, green and yellow	1·10	40
953	**145**	20f. purple, green and yellow	1·40	40

146 Young Pupil

1972. International Education Year.

954	**146**	5f. multicoloured	15	15
955	**146**	15f. multicoloured	45	15
956	**146**	20f. multicoloured	75	30
957	**146**	30f. multicoloured	1·70	85

147 Mothers and Children

1972. Mothers Day. Multicoloured.

958		10f. Type **147**	90	40
959		20f. Mother and child (vert)	90	40
960		30f. Bedouin mother and child (vert)	1·10	40

148 Pope Paul VI leaving Holy Sepulchre, Jerusalem

1972. Easter. Multicoloured.

961		30f. Type **148** (postage)	1·10	30
962		60f. The Calvary, Church of the Holy Sepulchre (air)	2·10	70
963		100f. *Washing of the Feet*, Jerusalem	3·75	1·40

149 Children and UNICEF Emblem

1972. 25th Anniversary of UNICEF.

964	**149**	10f. turquoise, blue and brown	90	40
965	-	20f. brown, green and pur	1·10	40
966	-	30f. brown, mauve and blue	1·40	40

Designs: Vert—20f. Child with toy bricks. Horiz—30f. Nurse holding baby.

150 Dove of Peace

1972. 25th Anniversary (1970) of United Nations.

967	**150**	5f. green, violet and yellow	30	30
968	**150**	10f. green, red and yellow	45	30
969	**150**	15f. blue, black and yellow	1·10	35
970	**150**	20f. blue, green and yellow	1·40	40
971	**150**	30f. green, brown & yell	2·50	1·10

151 Al Aqsa Mosque and Pilgrims

1972. Burning of Al Aqsa Mosque (1970). Multicoloured.

972		30f. Type **151**	3·25	40
973		60f. Mosque in flames	8·25	2·10
974		100f. Mosque interior	11·50	4·25

152 Arab with Kestrel

1972. Jordanian Desert Life. Multicoloured.

975		5f. Type **152**	90	40
976		10f. Desert bungalow (horiz)	90	40
977		15f. Camel trooper, Arab Legion (horiz)	90	40
978		20f. Boring operations (horiz)	1·40	50
979		25f. Shepherd (horiz)	1·40	50
980		30f. Dromedaries at water-trough (horiz)	2·40	70
981		35f. Chicken farm (horiz)	2·50	1·30
982		45f. Irrigation scheme (horiz)	4·00	2·20

153 Wasfi el Tell and Dome of the Rock, Jerusalem

1972. Wasfi el Tell (assassinated statesman) Memorial Issue. Multicoloured.

983		5f. Type **153**	45	15
984		10f. Wasfi el Tell, map and flag	60	30
985		20f. Type **153**	1·40	30
986		30f. As 10f.	1·50	1·10

154 Clay-pigeon shooting

1972. World Clay-pigeon Shooting Championships. Multicoloured.

987		25f. Type **154**	1·10	40
988		75f. Marksman on range (horiz)	2·10	1·70
989		120f. Marksman taking aim (horiz)	4·00	2·50

155 Aero Club Emblem

1973. Royal Jordanian Aero Club.

990	**155**	5f. black, blue and yellow (postage)	1·10	40
991	**155**	10f. black, blue and yellow	1·10	40
992	-	15f. multicoloured (air)	1·10	40
993	-	20f. multicoloured	1·20	50
994	-	40f. multicoloured	2·40	1·00

Designs: 15f. Piper Cherokee 140 aircraft; 20f. Beech B55 Baron aeroplane; 40f. Winged horse emblem.

156 Dove and Flag

1973. 50th Anniversary of Hashemite Kingdom of Jordan. Multicoloured.

995		5f. Type **156**	15	15
996		10f. Anniversary emblem	45	20
997		15f. King Hussein	1·10	30
998		30f. Map and emblems	2·30	1·80

157 Map and Jordanian Advance

1973. Fifth Anniversary of Battle of Karama. Multicoloured.

999		5f. Type **157**	45	30
1000		10f. Jordanian attack, and map	90	40
1001		15f. Map, and King Hussein on tank	2·30	1·40

158 Father and Son

1973. Fathers' Day. Multicoloured.

1002		10f. Type **158**	30	30
1003		20f. Father and daughter	1·10	30
1004		30f. Family group	1·70	70

159 Phosphate Mines

1973. Development Projects. Multicoloured.

1005		5f. Type **159**	60	15
1006		10f. Cement factories	1·10	30
1007		15f. Sharhabil Dam	1·50	30
1008		20f. Kafrein Dam	2·00	70

160 Racing Camel

1973. Camel Racing. Multicoloured.

1009		5f. Type **160**	1·40	40
1010		10f. Camels in paddock	1·40	40
1011		15f. Start of race	1·40	40
1012		20f. Camel racing	1·40	55

161 Book Year Emblem

1973. International Book Year (1972).

1013	**161**	30f. multicoloured	90	40
1014	**161**	60f. multicoloured	2·10	55

162 Family Group

1973. Family Day.

1015	**162**	20f. multicoloured	90	40
1016	-	30f. multicoloured	90	40
1017	-	60f. multicoloured	1·70	55

Designs: 30, 60f. Different family groups.

163 Shah of Iran, King Hussein, Cyrus's Tomb and Mosque of Omar

1973. 2500th Anniversary of Iranian Monarchy.

1018	**163**	5f. multicoloured	90	30
1019	**163**	10f. multicoloured	1·20	35
1020	**163**	15f. multicoloured	1·40	40

1021	**163**	30f. multicoloured	3·25	1·00

164 Emblem of Palestine Week

1973. Palestine Week. Multicoloured.

1022	5f. Type **164**	75	40
1023	10f. Torch and emblem	1·10	50
1024	15f. Refugees (26×47 mm)	1·20	55
1025	30f. Children and map on Globe	2·75	85

165 Traditional Harvesting

1973. Ancient and Modern Agriculture. Multicoloured.

1026	5f. Type **165** (postage)	30	30
1027	10f. Modern harvesting	45	30
1028	15f. Traditional seeding	90	35
1029	20f. Modern seeding	1·40	35
1030	30f. Traditional ploughing	1·50	40
1031	35f. Modern ploughing	1·80	40
1032	45f. Pest control	2·30	50
1033	60f. Horticulture	4·00	1·80
1034	100f. Agricultural landscape (air)	4·50	2·10

166 Long-nosed Butterflyfish

1974. Red Sea Fish. Multicoloured.

1035	5f. Type **166**	75	30
1036	10f. Monocle bream	90	30
1037	15f. As No. 1036	1·10	30
1038	20f. Slender-spined mojarra	1·40	40
1039	25f. As No. 1038	1·90	75
1040	30f. Russell's snapper	3·00	85
1041	35f. As No. 1040	3·50	1·40
1042	40f. Blue-barred orange parrotfish	4·25	1·50
1043	45f. As No. 1042	4·50	1·70
1044	50f. Type **166**	7·50	1·80
1045	60f. Yellow-edged lyretail	9·50	2·40

167 Battle of Muta

1974. Islamic Battles against the Crusaders. Multicoloured.

1046	10f. Type **167**	90	30
1047	20f. Battle of Yarmouk	2·30	55
1048	30f. Battle of Hattin	3·75	1·50

168 *The Club-footed Boy* (Murillo)

1974. Famous Paintings. Multicoloured.

1049	5f. Type **168**	2·00	55
1050	10f. *Praying Hands* (Durer)	2·00	55
1051	15f. *St. George and the Dragon* (Uccello)	2·00	55
1052	20f. *The Mona Lisa* (L. da Vinci)	2·00	55
1053	30f. *Hope* (F. Watts)	2·00	55
1054	40f. *The Angelus* (Jean Millet) (horiz)	2·40	65
1055	50f. *The Artist and her Daughter* (Angelica Kauffmann)	3·00	70
1056	60f. *Whistler's Mother* (J. Whistler) (horiz)	4·50	1·50
1057	100f. *Master Hare* (Sir J. Reynolds)	6·25	2·50

المؤتمر الدولي لتاريخ بلاد الشام
٢٠ - ١٩٧٤/٤/٢٥
الجامعة الاردنية

(169)

1974. International Conference for Damascus History. Nos. 1013/1014 optd with T **169**.

1058	**161**	30f. multicoloured	90	55
1059	**161**	60f. multicoloured	2·10	1·30

170 UPU Emblem

1974. Centenary of Universal Postal Union.

1060	**170**	10f. multicoloured	60	55
1061	**170**	30f. multicoloured	90	65
1062	**170**	60f. multicoloured	1·70	70

171 Camel Caravan

1974. The Dead Sea. Multicoloured.

1063	2f. Type **171**	30	15
1064	3f. Palm and shore	45	15
1065	4f. Hotel on coast	60	15
1066	5f. Jars from Qumram Caves	1·10	55
1067	6f. Copper scrolls (vert)	1·20	55
1068	10f. Cistern steps, Qumram (vert)	1·40	55
1069	20f. Type **171**	1·50	30
1070	30f. As 3f.	2·10	40
1071	40f. As 4f.	2·30	85
1072	50f. As 5f.	3·00	70
1073	60f. As 6f.	3·75	85
1074	100f. As 10f.	6·00	1·30

172 WPY Emblem

1974. World Population Year.

1075	**172**	5f. purple, green & black	30	15
1076	**172**	10f. red, green and black	45	30
1077	**172**	20f. orange, green & blk	1·10	40

173 Water-skier

1974. Water-skiing. Multicoloured.

1078	5f. Type **173**	60	55
1079	10f. Water-skier (side view) (horiz)	60	55
1080	20f. Skier turning (horiz)	60	55
1081	50f. Type **173**	1·20	70
1082	100f. As 10f.	2·10	1·00
1083	200f. As 20f.	4·50	2·00

174 Kaaba, Mecca, and Pilgrims

1974. Pilgrimage Season.

1084	**174**	10f. multicoloured	45	30
1085	**174**	20f. multicoloured	1·40	85

175 Amrah Palace

1974. Desert Ruins. Multicoloured.

1086	10f. Type **175**	45	30
1087	20f. Hisham Palace	1·10	85
1088	30f. Kharana Castle	2·75	1·30

176 King Hussein at Wheel of Car

1975. Air. Royal Jordanian Automobile Club.

1089	**176**	30f. multicoloured	90	30
1090	**176**	60f. multicoloured	2·75	1·40

177 Woman in Costume

1975. Jordanian Women's Costumes.

1091	**177**	5f. multicoloured	30	15
1092	-	10f. multicoloured	45	20
1093	-	15f. multicoloured	90	30
1094	-	20f. multicoloured	1·40	40
1095	-	25f. multicoloured	1·80	1·00

Designs: 10f. to 25f. Various costumes as T **177**.

178 Treasury, Petra

1975. Tourism. Multicoloured.

1096	15f. Type **178** (postage)	1·50	55
1097	20f. Omayyad Palace, Amman (horiz)	1·50	55
1098	30f. Dome of the Rock, Jerusalem (horiz)	2·10	65
1099	40f. Forum columns, Jerash (horiz)	2·75	70
1100	50f. Palms, Aqaba (air)	2·10	70
1101	60f. Obelisk Tomb, Petra (horiz)	3·25	85
1102	80f. Fort of Wadi Rum (horiz)	3·50	90

179 King Hussein

1975

1103	**179**	5f. blue and green	45	15
1104	**179**	10f. blue and violet	45	15
1105	**179**	15f. blue and pink	15	15
1106	**179**	20f. blue and brown	90	30
1107	**179**	25f. blue and ultramarine	90	30
1108	**179**	30f. blue and brown	30	30
1109	**179**	35f. blue and violet	45	30
1110	**179**	40f. blue and red	1·10	40
1111	**179**	45f. blue and mauve	60	40
1112	**179**	50f. blue and green	60	40
1113	**179**	60f. brown and green	2·00	70
1114	**179**	100f. brown & lt brown	3·25	85
1115	**179**	120f. brown and blue	1·70	1·30
1116	**179**	180f. brown and mauve	2·75	1·80
1117	**179**	200f. brown and blue	3·25	2·50
1118	**179**	400f. brown and purple	5·50	4·25
1119	**179**	500f. brown and red	7·00	6·25

Nos. 1113/1119 are larger, 22×27 mm.

180 Globe and Desert

1975. Tenth Anniversary of ALIA (Royal Jordanian Airlines). Multicoloured.

1120	10f. Type **180**	45	15
1121	30f. Boeing 707 linking globe and map of Jordan (horiz)	1·50	55
1122	60f. Globe and ALIA logo	3·00	1·30

181 Satellite and Earth Station

1975. Satellite Earth Station Opening.

1123	**181**	20f. multicoloured	1·20	30
1124	**181**	30f. multicoloured	2·10	1·00

182 Emblem of Chamber of Commerce

1975. 50th Anniversary of Amman Chamber of Commerce.

1125	**182**	10f. multicoloured	30	30
1126	**182**	15f. multicoloured	60	30
1127	**182**	20f. multicoloured	90	55

183 Emblem and Hand with Spanner

1975. Completion of Three Year Development Plan.

1128	**183**	5f. black, red and green	30	30
1129	**183**	10f. black, red and green	45	40
1130	**183**	20f. black, red and green	1·10	55

184 Jordanian Family

1976. International Women's Year (1975). Multicoloured.

1131	5f. Type **184**	15	15
1132	25f. Woman scientist	90	40
1133	60f. Woman graduate	2·40	1·30

185 ALO Emblem and Salt Mine

1976. Arab Labour Organisation. Multicoloured.

1134	10f. Type **185**	75	55
1135	30f. Welding	75	55
1136	60f. Quayside, Aqaba	1·50	70

1976. Nos. 853-882 surch in English and Arabic.

1137-1146	25f. on 1f. to 10f.
1147-1151	40f. on 11f. to 15f.
1152-1156	50f. on 16f. to 20f.
1157-1161	75f. on 21f. to 25f.
1162-1166	125f. on 26f. to 30f.

1976. Nos. 883-912 surch in English and Arabic.

1167-1176	25f. on 1f. to 10f.
1177-1182	40f. on 11f. to 15f.
1183-1187	50f. on 16f. to 20f.
1188-1192	75f. on 21f. to 25f.
1193-1196	125f. on 26f. to 30f.

187 Tennis

1976. Sports and Youth. Multicoloured.

1197	5f. Type **187**	30	15

No.	Type	Description	Unused	Used
1198		10f. Body-building	45	20
1199		15f. Football	60	30
1200		20f. Show jumping	90	35
1201		30f. Weightlifting	1·50	55
1202		100f. Stadium, Amman	6·00	3·00

188 Schu'aib Dam

1976. Dams. Multicoloured.

No.	Description	Unused	Used
1203	30f. Type **188**	1·20	55
1204	60f. Al-Kafrein Dam	2·40	70
1205	100f. Ziqlab Dam	4·00	1·30

189 Early and Modern Telephones

1977. Telephone Centenary. Multicoloured.

No.	Description	Unused	Used
1206	75f. Type **189**	2·30	1·30
1207	125f. Early telephone and modern receiver	3·75	2·10

190 Road Crossing and Traffic Lights

1977. International Traffic Day. Multicoloured.

No.	Description	Unused	Used
1208	5f. Type **190**	1·10	40
1209	75f. Roundabout and traffic lights	3·25	1·50
1210	125f. Motorcycle policemen, road signs and traffic lights	5·00	2·10

191 Airliner over Ship

1977. Silver Jubilee of King Hussein. Multicoloured.

No.	Description	Unused	Used
1211	10f. Type **191**	30	15
1212	25f. Pylons and factories	60	30
1213	40f. Fertiliser plant	90	35
1214	50f. Ground-to-air missile	1·20	55
1215	75f. Mosque	2·10	1·00
1216	125f. Ground satellite receiving aerial	3·25	2·00
MS1217	100×70 mm. 100f. Silver Jubilee emblem. Imperf	15·00	14·50

192 Child, Toys and Moneybox

1977. Postal Savings Bank. Multicoloured.

No.	Description	Unused	Used
1218	10f. Type **192**	15	15
1219	25f. Child with piggy bank	60	30
1220	50f. Savings Bank emblem	1·40	55
1221	75f. Boy and bank teller	2·75	1·30

193 King Hussein and Queen Alia

1977

No.	Type	Description	Unused	Used
1222	**193**	10f. multicoloured	30	30
1223	**193**	25f. multicoloured	60	30
1224	**193**	40f. multicoloured	1·10	40
1225	**193**	50f. multicoloured	1·40	85

194 Queen Alia

1977. Queen Alia Commemoration.

No.	Type	Description	Unused	Used
1226	**194**	10f. multicoloured	30	30
1227	**194**	25f. multicoloured	60	30
1228	**194**	40f. multicoloured	1·10	40
1229	**194**	50f. multicoloured	1·40	85

195 Mohammed Ali Jinnah

1977. Birth Centenary of Mohammed Ali Jinnah (First Governor-General of Pakistan).

No.	Type	Description	Unused	Used
1230	**195**	25f. multicoloured	1·10	40
1231	**195**	75f. multicoloured	3·00	1·10

196 APU Emblem and Flags

1978. 25th Anniversary (1977) of Arab Postal Union.

No.	Type	Description	Unused	Used
1232	**196**	25f. multicoloured	1·20	70
1233	**196**	40f. multicoloured	2·00	1·30

197 Coffee Pots and Cups

1978. Handicrafts. Multicoloured.

No.	Description	Unused	Used
1234	25f. Type **197**	60	30
1235	40f. Porcelain plate and ashtray	90	35
1236	75f. Vase, necklace and chains	2·10	85
1237	125f. Containers holding pipes	3·25	2·10

198 Roman Amphitheatre, Jerash

1978. Tourism. Multicoloured.

No.	Description	Unused	Used
1238	5f. Type **198**	90	40
1239	20f. Roman columns, Jerash	90	40
1240	40f. Roman mosaic, Madaba	1·20	55
1241	75f. Rock formations, Rum	2·75	1·10

199 King Hussein and Pres. Sadat of Egypt

1978. Visits of Arab Leaders to Jordan. Multicoloured.

No.	Description	Unused	Used
1242	40f. Type **199**	90	30
1243	40f. King Hussein and Pres. Assad (horiz)	90	30
1244	40f. King Hussein and King Khalid (horiz)	90	30

200 Cement Works

1978. Industrial Development. Multicoloured.

No.	Description	Unused	Used
1245	5f. Type **200**	15	15
1246	10f. Science laboratory	60	30
1247	25f. Printing press	1·50	40
1248	75f. Fertilizer plant	3·75	1·40

201 UNESCO Emblem

1978. 30th Anniversary of UNESCO.

No.	Type	Description	Unused	Used
1249	**201**	40f. multicoloured	1·20	85
1250	**201**	75f. multicoloured	2·75	1·80

202 King Hussein

1979. Dated 1979.

No.	Type	Description	Unused	Used
1251	**202**	25f. brown, flesh and blue	90	30
1252	**202**	40f. brown, flesh & pur	1·50	35

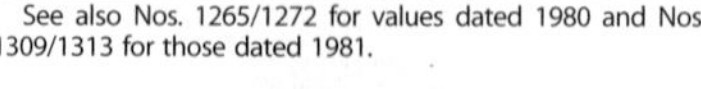
See also Nos. 1265/1272 for values dated 1980 and Nos. 1309/1313 for those dated 1981.

203 Emblems within Cogwheels

1979. Five Year Development Plan.

No.	Type	Description	Unused	Used
1253	**203**	25f. multicoloured	75	30
1254	**203**	40f. multicoloured	1·10	35
1255	**203**	50f. multicoloured	1·20	70

204 IYC Emblem and Flag of Jordan

1979. International Year of the Child.

No.	Type	Description	Unused	Used
1256	**204**	25f. multicoloured	90	40
1257	**204**	40f. multicoloured	1·40	50
1258	**204**	50f. multicoloured	2·10	55

205 Census Emblem

1979. Population and Housing Census.

No.	Type	Description	Unused	Used
1259	**205**	25f. multicoloured	60	30
1260	**205**	40f. multicoloured	1·10	35
1261	**205**	50f. multicoloured	1·50	70

206 Nurse holding Baby

1980. International Nursing Day.

No.	Type	Description	Unused	Used
1262	**206**	25f. multicoloured	90	30
1263	**206**	40f. multicoloured	1·50	55
1264	**206**	50f. multicoloured	1·80	1·00

1980

No.	Type	Description	Unused	Used
1265	**202**	5f. brown, pink and green	30	30
1266	**202**	10f. brown, pink & violet	30	30
1267	**202**	20f. brown and pink	30	30
1268	**202**	25f. brown, pink and blue	45	40
1269	**202**	40f. brown and mauve	1·10	50
1270	**202**	50f. brown, pink & green	1·20	1·00
1271	**202**	75f. brown, pink and grey	1·20	70
1272	**202**	125f. brown, pink and red	3·75	1·10

Nos. 1265/1272 are similar to Nos. 1251/1252 but are inscr '1980'.

207 El Deir Temple, Petra

1980. World Tourism Conference, Manila.

No.	Type	Description	Unused	Used
1273	**207**	25f. black, grey and green	90	40
1274	**207**	40f. black, grey and blue	1·70	55
1275	**207**	50f. black, grey & purple	2·10	70

208 Mosque and Kaaba, Mecca

1980. 1400th Anniversary of Hegira.

No.	Type	Description	Unused	Used
1276	**208**	25f. multicoloured	45	40
1277	**208**	40f. multicoloured	1·10	55
1278	**208**	50f. multicoloured	1·40	70
1279	**208**	75f. multicoloured	2·40	1·10
1280	**208**	100f. multicoloured	2·40	1·50
MS1281		127×89 mm. Nos. 1276/1280. Imperf	11·50	11·00

209 Conference Emblem

1980. 11th Arab Summit Conference, Amman.

No.	Type	Description	Unused	Used
1282	**209**	25f. multicoloured	45	40
1283	**209**	40f. multicoloured	90	55
1284	**209**	50f. multicoloured	1·20	70
1285	**209**	75f. multicoloured	2·00	1·10
1286	**209**	100f. multicoloured	2·40	1·50
MS1287		100×100 mm. Nos. 1282/1286. Imperf	11·50	11·00

210 Picking Crops, examining Patients and Flag-raising Ceremony

1981. Red Crescent.

No.	Type	Description	Unused	Used
1288	**210**	25f. multicoloured	1·10	40
1289	**210**	40f. multicoloured	1·40	70
1290	**210**	50f. multicoloured	1·50	85

211 ITU and WHO Emblems and Ribbons forming Caduceus

1981. World Telecommunications Day.

No.	Type	Description	Unused	Used
1291	**211**	25f. multicoloured	1·10	40
1292	**211**	40f. multicoloured	1·80	70
1293	**211**	50f. multicoloured	2·40	1·30

212 Jordan Stamps of 1930 and 1975

1981. Opening of Postal Museum. Multicoloured.

No.	Description	Unused	Used
1294	25f. Type **212**	1·10	30
1295	40f. Jordan stamps of 1933 and 1954 (vert)	1·50	55
1296	50f. Jordan stamps of 1946 and 1952	2·10	1·00

213 Khawla Bint el-Azwar

1981. Arab Women in History. Multicoloured.

No.	Description	Unused	Used
1297	25f. Type **213**	1·50	40
1298	40f. El-Khansa (writer)	2·50	70
1299	50f. Rabia el-Adawiyeh (Sufi religious leader)	4·25	2·00

214 FAO Emblem and Olive Branches

1981. World Food Day.

1300 **214** 25f. multicoloured 75 40
1301 **214** 40f. multicoloured 1·40 70
1302 **214** 50f. multicoloured 1·70 70

215 IYDP Emblem

1981. International Year of Disabled Persons.

1303 **215** 25f. multicoloured 75 40
1304 **215** 40f. multicoloured 1·70 55
1305 **215** 50f. multicoloured 2·10 70

216 Hands reading Braille

1981. The Blind.

1306 **216** 25f. multicoloured 75 40
1307 **216** 40f. multicoloured 1·70 55
1308 **216** 50f. multicoloured 2·10 70

1982

1309 **202** 5f. brown, pink and green 40 30
1310 **202** 10f. brown, pink & violet 45 30
1311 **202** 20f. brown and pink 55 30
1312 **202** 25f. brown, pink and blue 60 30
1313 **202** 40f. brown, pink & pur 90 40

Nos. 1309/1313 are similar to Nos. 1251/1252, but are inscr '1981'.

217 Hand holding Jug and Stone Tablets

1982. Jordan Monuments.

1314 **217** 25f. multicoloured 1·10 30
1315 **217** 40f. multicoloured 1·70 40
1316 **217** 50f. multicoloured 2·10 1·00

218 APU Emblem

1982. 30th Anniversary of Arab Postal Union.

1317 **218** 10f. multicoloured 90 40
1318 **218** 25f. multicoloured 1·20 50
1319 **218** 40f. multicoloured 1·70 55
1320 **218** 50f. multicoloured 2·10 70
1321 **218** 100f. multicoloured 4·25 1·40

219 King Hussein and Dassault Mirage F1C

1982. Independence, Army Day and 30th Anniversary of King's Accession to Throne. Multicoloured.

1322 10f. King Hussein and rockets 45 30
1323 25f. King Hussein and tanks 90 35
1324 40f. Type **219** 1·70 55
1325 50f. King Hussein and tanks (different) 2·10 1·00
1326 100f. King Hussein and flag being hoisted by armed forces 4·25 2·75

220 Salt Secondary School

1982. Salt Secondary School.

1327 **220** 10f. multicoloured 75 40
1328 **220** 25f. multicoloured 1·10 50
1329 **220** 40f. multicoloured 1·70 55
1330 **220** 50f. multicoloured 1·80 85
1331 **220** 100f. multicoloured 3·50 1·40

221 City Gate, Jerusalem

1982. Jerusalem. Multicoloured.

1332 10f. Type **221** 45 40
1333 25f. Minaret 1·50 70
1334 40f. Mosque 2·40 1·30
1335 50f. Mosque (different) 2·75 1·40
1336 100f. Dome of the Rock 6·00 3·00

222 Soldiers, Flags and Badge

1982. Yarmouk Forces.

1337 **222** 10f. multicoloured 45 15
1338 **222** 25f. multicoloured 90 30
1339 **222** 40f. multicoloured 1·50 55
1340 **222** 50f. multicoloured 1·80 1·00
1341 **222** 100f. multicoloured 3·25 2·20
MS1342 71×51 mm. 100f. multicoloured (Forces badge). Imperf 26·00 25·00

223 Dish Aerial, Earth and UN Emblem

1982. Second UN Conference on the Exploration and Peaceful Uses of Outer Space, Vienna.

1343 **223** 10f. multicoloured 45 15
1344 **223** 25f. multicoloured 90 30
1345 **223** 40f. multicoloured 1·50 55
1346 **223** 50f. multicoloured 1·80 1·00
1347 **223** 100f. multicoloured 3·25 2·50

224 King Abdullah and Dome of the Rock

1982. Birth Centenary of King Abdullah.

1348 **224** 10f. multicoloured 45 15
1349 **224** 25f. multicoloured 90 30
1350 **224** 40f. multicoloured 1·50 55
1351 **224** 50f. multicoloured 1·80 1·00
1352 **224** 100f. multicoloured 3·25 2·50

225 King Hussein and Temple Colonnade

1982. Roman Ruins at Jerash. Multicoloured.

1353 10f. Type **225** 1·20 55
1354 25f. Archway 1·50 55
1355 40f. Temple of Artemis 2·10 70
1356 50f. Amphitheatre 2·75 70
1357 100f. Hippodrome 5·50 1·50

226 King Hussein

1983

1358 **226** 10f. multicoloured 45 40
1359 **226** 25f. multicoloured 45 40
1360 **226** 40f. multicoloured 75 55
1361 **226** 60f. multicoloured 1·20 70
1362 **226** 100f. multicoloured 1·80 1·10
1363 **226** 125f. multicoloured 2·40 1·30

227 Massacre Victims

1983. Massacre of Palestinian Refugees in Sabra and Shatila Camps. Multicoloured.

1364 10f. Type **227** 45 30
1365 25f. Covered bodies 1·40 35
1366 40f. Orphans 2·00 55
1367 50f. Massacre victims in street 2·75 1·10
1368 100f. Massacre victims (different) 4·50 2·75
MS1369 80×59 mm. 100f. Wounded child in hospital (sold at 1500f.) 30·00 29·00

228 Control Tower and Airport Buildings

1983. Opening of Queen Alia International Airport. Multicoloured.

1370 10f. Type **228** 45 15
1371 25f. Tower and terminal building 1·20 30
1372 40f. Tower and hangar 2·00 55
1373 50f. Tower and aerial view of airport 2·40 1·10
1374 100f. Tower and embarkation bridge 4·50 2·75

229 King Hussein with Radio Equipment

1983. Royal Jordanian Radio Amateurs Society.

1375 **229** 10f. multicoloured 45 15
1376 **229** 25f. multicoloured 1·20 30
1377 **229** 40f. multicoloured 1·80 55
1378 **229** 50f. multicoloured 2·00 1·10
1379 **229** 100f. multicoloured 4·00 2·75

230 Academy Building, Amman

1983. Establishment of Royal Academy for Islamic Civilisation Research. Multicoloured.

1380 10f. Type **230** 60 55
1381 25f. Silk rug 1·20 70
1382 40f. View of Amman 1·80 1·10
1383 50f. Panorama of Jerusalem 2·10 1·40
1384 100f. Holy sites of Islam 4·75 2·75
MS1385 80×60 mm. 100f. Letter from Mohammed to Heraclius. Imperf 26·00 25·00

231 Irrigation Canal

1983. Food Security. Multicoloured.

1386 10f. Type **231** 45 30
1387 25f. Growing crops under glass 1·20 30
1388 40f. Battery hens 2·00 55
1389 50f. Harvesting 2·30 1·00
1390 100f. Flock of sheep 4·00 2·75

232 Switchboard and Emblem

1983. World Communications Year. Multicoloured.

1391 10f. Type **232** 90 50
1392 25f. Aerial view of satellite receiving station 1·40 55
1393 40f. Microwave antenna and emblems of communication 2·00 65
1394 50f. WCY emblems 2·50 70
1395 100f. Airmail letter 5·25 1·70

233 Dome of the Rock, Jerusalem

1983. Palestinian Solidarity.

1396 **233** 5f. multicoloured 90 55
1397 **233** 10f. multicoloured 1·80 70

234 Human Rights Emblems

1983. 35th Anniversary of Declaration of Human Rights.

1398 **234** 10f. multicoloured 45 15
1399 **234** 25f. multicoloured 1·20 30
1400 **234** 40f. multicoloured 1·80 55
1401 **234** 50f. multicoloured 2·00 1·10
1402 **234** 100f. multicoloured 3·75 2·75

235 Stop Polio Campaign Emblem

1984. Anti-poliomyelitis Campaign.

1403 **235** 40f. orange, black & blue 1·70 40
1404 **235** 60f. silver, black and red 2·75 1·10
1405 **235** 100f. green, black & yell 4·50 2·40

236 Bomb and Cogwheel

1984. Israel's Attack on Iraqi Nuclear Reactor. Multicoloured.

1406 40f. Type **236** 2·30 70
1407 60f. Hand with dagger attacking nuclear symbol 3·00 85
1408 100f. Aircraft bombing nuclear symbol 4·50 1·50

237 King Hussein and Tanks

1984. Independence and Army Day. Multicoloured.

1409 10f. Type **237** 45 30
1410 25f. King Hussein and naval patrol boat 1·20 35
1411 40f. King Hussein and Camel Corps 2·00 55
1412 60f. King Hussein and soldiers at Independence Monument 3·00 1·10
1413 100f. Parading soldiers 4·00 2·75

238 Sports Pictogram

1984. Olympic Games. Los Angeles. Multicoloured.

1414 25f. Type **238** 1·20 55
1415 40f. Swimming 2·00 70
1416 60f. Shooting and archery pictograms 3·00 1·40
1417 100f. Gymnastics (floor exercises) 5·50 2·20
MS1418 90×70 mm. 100f. Pole vaulting. Imperf 23·00 22·00

239 Amman Power Station

1984. Water and Electricity Year. Multicoloured.

1419	25f. Power lines and factories	75	30
1420	40f. Type **239**	1·40	40
1421	60f. Reservoirs and water pipe	2·00	1·10
1422	100f. Telephone lines, street light, water tap and pipeline	3·00	1·80

240 Omayyid Coins

1984. Coins. Multicoloured.

1423	40f. Type **240**	1·70	70
1424	60f. Abbasid coins	2·40	1·00
1425	125f. Hashemite coins	5·00	2·40

241 Shield and Antelope

1984. Release of Antelope in Jordan. Multicoloured.

1426	25f. Type **241**	1·10	30
1427	40f. Four antelope	1·80	55
1428	60f. Three antelope	2·75	1·30
1429	100f. Duke of Edinburgh, King Hussein and Queen Alia	4·75	2·00

242 Mu'ta Military University, Karak City

1984. Jordanian Universities. Multicoloured.

1430	40f. Type **242**	1·20	40
1431	60f. Yarmouk University, Irbid City	1·80	85
1432	125f. Jordan University, Amman	3·00	1·80

243 Tombs of El-Hareth bin Omier el-Azdi and Derar bin el-Azwar

1984. Al Sahaba Tombs. Multicoloured.

1433	10f. Type **243**	45	15
1434	25f. Tombs of Sharhabil bin Hasna and Abu Obaidah Amer bin el-Jarrah	1·10	30
1435	40f. Muath bin Jabal's tomb	1·50	40
1436	50f. Tombs of Zaid bin Haretha and Abdullah bin Rawaha	1·70	70
1437	60f. Tomb of Amer bin Abi Waqqas	2·00	1·10
1438	100f. Jafar bin Abi Taleb's tomb	3·25	1·80

244 Soldier descending Mountain and King Hussein

1985. Independence and Army Day. Multicoloured.

1439	25f. Type **244**	90	30
1440	40f. Flags on map, King Abdullah and King Hussein	1·50	40
1441	60f. Flag, monument and Arms	2·30	1·10
1442	100f. King Hussein, flag, King Abdullah and Arms	4·00	2·75

245 Sir Rowland Hill (instigator of first stamps)

1985. Postal Celebrities. Multicoloured.

1443	40f. Type **245**	1·40	40
1444	60f. Heinrich von Stephan (founder of Universal Postal Union)	2·00	1·10
1445	125f. Yacoub Sukker (first Jordanian stamp designer)	4·00	2·75

246 Emblem and Delegates round Table

1985. First Jordanians Abroad Conference. Multicoloured.

1446	40f. Type **246**	1·40	40
1447	60f. Conference emblem and globe and hand over torch	2·00	1·10
1448	125f. Globe encircled by Jordanian flags	4·00	2·75

247 IYY Emblem

1985. International Youth Year. Multicoloured.

1449	10f. Type **247**	45	30
1450	25f. Arab couple on map, flag and emblem	1·10	40
1451	40f. Stylised figures flanking globe, flag and emblem	1·50	50
1452	60f. Part of cogwheel, laurel branch and ribbons in jug decorated with emblem	2·30	1·10
1453	125f. Stylised figures and emblem	4·00	2·75

248 El-Deir Temple, Petra

1985. Tenth Anniversary of World Tourist Organisation. Multicoloured.

1454	10f. Type **248**	45	30
1455	25f. Temple of Artemis (ruins), Jerash	1·10	40
1456	40f. Amrah Palace	1·50	50
1457	50f. Hill town, Jordan valley	1·80	70
1458	60f. Sailing in Aqaba bay	2·30	1·40
1459	125f. Roman amphitheatre, Amman and city arms	4·00	3·00
MS1460	90×70 mm. 100f. Flower with emblem as vase and flag. Imperf	11·50	11·00

249 Mother and Baby and Hospital

1985. UNICEF Child Survival Campaign. Multicoloured.

1461	25f. Type **249**	1·10	40
1462	40f. Child being weighed	1·50	55
1463	60f. Childrens' heads as balloons	2·30	1·40
1464	125f. Mother feeding baby	4·00	3·00
MS1465	90×70 mm. 100f. Hands cradling children's heads. Imperf	20·00	19·00

250 Dancers

1985. Fifth Anniversary of Jerash Festival. Multicoloured.

1466	10f. Opening ceremony, 1980	45	30
1467	25f. Type **250**	1·10	40
1468	40f. Dancers (different)	1·50	55
1469	60f. Male choir at Roman theatre	2·30	1·40
1470	100f. King Hussein and his wife	4·00	2·75

251 Flag and Emblem forming '40'

1985. 40th Anniversary of UNO.

1471	**251**	60f. multicoloured	2·50	1·50
1472	**251**	125f. multicoloured	4·00	2·75

252 Hussein comforting Boy

1985. 50th Birthday of King Hussein. Multicoloured.

1473	10f. Type **252**	45	15
1474	25f. Hussein in Arab robes	1·10	55
1475	40f. Hussein piloting aircraft	1·50	85
1476	60f. Hussein in army uniform	2·30	1·40
1477	100f. Hussein in Arab headdress	4·00	2·75
MS1478	90×70 mm. 200f. Hussein in uniform, flags and Dome of the Rock, Jerusalem. Imperf	26·00	25·00

253 El Aqsa Mosque

1985. Compulsory Tax. Restoration of El Aqsa Mosque, Jerusalem.

1479	**253**	5f. multicoloured	1·80	1·70
1480	**253**	10f. multicoloured	4·00	2·75

254 Policeman beside Car

1985. The Police. Multicoloured.

1481	40f. Type **254**	1·70	55
1482	60f. Policeman and crowd of children	2·30	85
1483	125f. Policeman taking oath	5·00	1·50

255 Satellite over Map of Arab Countries

1986. First Anniversary of Launch of *Arabsat I* Communications Satellite. Multicoloured.

1484	60f. Satellite	1·40	55
1485	100f. Type **255**	2·50	85

256 King presenting Colours

1986. 30th Anniversary of Arabisation of Jordanian Army. Multicoloured.

1486	40f. Type **256**	1·20	30
1487	60f. King Hussein shaking hands with soldier	1·70	55
1488	100f. King Hussein addressing Army	2·75	1·50
MS1489	90×70 mm. 100f. Text and Hussein addressing Army. Imperf	18·00	17·00

257 King Abdullah decorating Soldier

1986. 40th Anniversary of Independence.

1490	**257**	160f. multicoloured	4·50	2·40

258 King Hussein of Hejaz and Sons

1986. 70th Anniversary of Arab Revolt. Multicoloured.

1491	40f. Type **258**	1·20	30
1492	60f. King Abdullah with armed men	2·10	70
1493	160f. King leading soldiers on horseback	4·00	2·75
MS1494	90×70 mm. King Abdullah and Independence declaration. Imperf	15·00	14·50

259 Emblem

1986. International Peace Year.

1495	**259**	160f. multicoloured	4·00	2·40
1496	**259**	240f. black, orange & grn	5·25	3·25

260 Cardiac Centre Building

1986. King Hussein Medical City. Multicoloured.

1497	40f. Type **260**	1·20	40
1498	60f. Patient undergoing operation	2·10	1·00
1499	100f. View of operating theatre during operation	3·00	1·70

261 Extract of King Hussein's Speech in Arabic

1986. 40th Anniversary of UNO. Multicoloured.

1500	40f. Type **261**	1·20	30
1501	80f. Extract of speech in Arabic (different)	2·00	1·10
1502	100f. Extract of speech in English	2·75	1·50
MS1503	90×70 mm. 200f. Extracts of speech in Arabic and English and King Hussein making speech. Imperf	14·50	14·00

262 Head Post Office, Amman

1987. 35th Anniversary of Arab Postal Union. Multicoloured.

1504	80f. Type **262**	1·70	85
1505	160f. Ministry of Communications, Amman	3·00	2·10

263 Jaber ibn Hayyan al-Azdi

1987. Arab and Muslim Pharmacists. Multicoloured.

1506	60f. Type **263**	1·40	55
1507	80f. Abu-al-Qasem al-Majreeti	1·70	85
1508	240f. Abu-Bakr al-Razi	4·50	3·75

264 Village

1987. SOS Childrens' Village, Amman. Multicoloured.

1509	80f. Type **264**	2·75	1·30
1510	240f. Child and mural	4·75	3·75

265 Soldiers on Wall

1987. 40th Anniversary of 4th Army Brigade. Multicoloured.

1511	60f. Type **265**	2·10	1·00
1512	80f. Mortar crew	3·00	1·30
MS1513	70×90 mm. 160f. Soldiers on parade	13·50	13·00

266 Black-headed Bunting

1987. Birds. Multicoloured.

1514	10f. Hoopoe	1·70	70
1515	40f. Palestine sunbird	2·75	1·10
1516	50f. Type **266**	3·25	1·40
1517	60f. Spur-winged plover	4·25	1·50
1518	80f. Western greenfinch ('Greenfinch')	5·50	2·75
1519	100f. Black-winged stilt	6·50	3·00

267 King Hussein

1987

1520	**267**	60f. multicoloured	90	70
1521	**267**	80f. multicoloured	1·40	1·00
1522	**267**	160f. multicoloured	3·00	2·10
1523	**267**	240f. multicoloured	4·25	2·75

268 Horsemen Charging

1987. 800th Anniversary of Battle of Hattin. Multicoloured.

1524	60f. Type **268**	2·00	85
1525	80f. Horseman and Dome of the Rock	2·50	1·40
1526	100f. Saladin, horsemen and Dome of the Rock	3·00	2·00
MS1527	90×70 mm. 100f. Saladin (29×44 mm). Perf or imperf	13·50	13·00

269 Arms

1987

1528	**269**	80f. multicoloured	1·70	1·10
1529	**269**	160f. multicoloured	3·50	2·10

270 Amman Industrial Estate, Sahab

1987

1530	**270**	80f. multicoloured	1·70	40

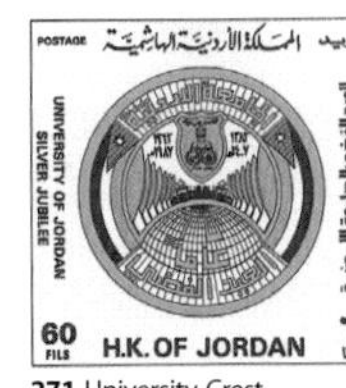

271 University Crest

1987. 25th Anniversary of Jordan University. Multicoloured.

1531	60f. Type **271**	1·70	40
1532	80f. Entrance to campus (47×32 mm)	2·00	85

272 Child's Head in Droplet

1987. UNICEF Child Survival Campaign. Multicoloured.

1533	60f. Type **272**	1·40	70
1534	80f. Hands reaching towards child and flag as 'J'	2·50	1·50
1535	160f. Baby on scales and children reading	3·50	2·40

273 Parliament in Session, 1987

1987. 40th Anniversary of Jordanian Parliament.

1536	-	60f. mauve and gold	1·70	1·10
1537	**273**	80f. multicoloured	3·00	2·40

Design: 60f. 1947 opening ceremony.

274 Emblem

1987. Extraordinary Arab Summit Conference, Amman.

1538	**274**	60f. multicoloured	1·40	40
1539	**274**	80f. multicoloured	1·80	70
1540	**274**	160f. multicoloured	3·00	1·80
1541	**274**	240f. multicoloured	4·50	2·75
MS1542		90×66 mm. 100f. Emblem, King Hussein and map. Imperf	13·00	12·50

275 King Hussein receiving Cape

1988. Award of 1987 Dag Hammarskjold Peace Prize to King Hussein. Multicoloured.

1543	80f. Type **275**	1·80	70
1544	160f. King Hussein receiving Prize	3·00	1·80

276 Golden Sword

1988. Jordanian Victory in 1987 Arab Military Basketball Championship. Multicoloured.

1545	60f. Type **276**	1·40	40
1546	80f. King Hussein congratulating winners	1·80	1·00
1547	160f. Match scene	3·75	2·75

277 Anniversary Emblem and National Flag

1988. 40th Anniversary of WHO.

1548	**277**	60f. multicoloured	1·70	55
1549	**277**	80f. multicoloured	2·10	1·00

278 Emblems and Globe

1988. 75th Anniversary of Arab Scout Movement.

1550	**278**	60f. multicoloured	1·70	55
1551	**278**	80f. multicoloured	2·10	1·00

279 Crested Lark

1988. Birds. Multicoloured.

1552	10f. Type **279**	3·50	55
1553	20f. Stone-curlew	3·50	55
1554	30f. Common redstart ('Redstart')	3·50	55
1555	40f. Blackbird	5·25	70
1556	50f. Feral rock pigeon ('Rock Dove')	6·25	85
1557	160f. White-throated kingfisher ('Smyrna Kingfisher')	20·00	2·75
MS1558	70×90 mm. 310f. Birds as in Nos. 1552/1557. Imperf	26·00	25·00

280 City cupped in Hands

1988. Restoration of Sana'a, Yemen Arab Republic.

1559	**280**	80f. multicoloured	1·50	1·10
1560	**280**	160f. multicoloured	3·25	2·20

281 Um al-Rasas

1988. Historic Sites. Multicoloured.

1561	60f. Type **281**	1·20	85
1562	80f. Umm Qais	1·70	1·10
1563	160f. Iraq al-Amir	3·25	2·20
MS1564	100×70 mm. Nos. 1561/1563. Imperf	9·00	8·75

282 Tennis

1988. Olympic Games, Seoul. Multicoloured.

1565	10f. Type **282**	60	40
1566	60f. Mascot	1·50	85
1567	80f. Running and swimming	2·00	1·10
1568	120f. Basketball	3·00	1·70
1569	160f. Football	4·25	2·20
MS1570	70×90 mm. 100f. Games emblem. Imperf	26·00	25·00

283 Flame and Figures

1988. 40th Anniversary of Declaration of Human Rights.

1571	**283**	80f. multicoloured	1·70	85
1572	**283**	160f. multicoloured	2·50	1·40

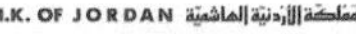

284 El-Deir Temple, Petra

1988. 25th Anniversary of Royal Jordanian Airline. Multicoloured.

1573	60f. Type **284**	1·70	1·10
1574	80f. Boeing 737 airliner and map of world	2·40	1·30

285 Dome of the Rock, Jerusalem

1989. Palestinian Welfare.

1575	**285**	5f. multicoloured	45	30
1576	**285**	10f. multicoloured	45	30

286 Treasury, Petra, Flags and King Hussein

1989. Formation of Arab Co-operation Council (economic grouping of four states). Multicoloured.

1577	10f. Type **286**	15	15
1578	30f. Sana'a, Yemen	60	30
1579	40f. Spiral Tower of Samarra, Iraq	75	40
1580	60f. Pyramids, Egypt	1·20	55

287 Jordanian Parliament Building

1989. Centenary of Interparliamentary Union.

1581	**287**	40f. multicoloured	45	30
1582	**287**	60f. multicoloured	1·10	55

288 Modern Flats and Emblems

1989. Arab Housing Day and World Refugee Day. Multicoloured.

1583	5f. Type **288**	90	30
1584	40f. Hand supporting refugee family (horiz)	1·70	40
1585	60f. Modern blocks of flats (horiz)	3·00	55

289 King Abdullah, Mosque and King Hussein

1989. Inauguration of King Abdullah Ibn al-Hussein Mosque, Amman.

1586	**289**	40f. multicoloured	75	30
1587	**289**	60f. multicoloured	1·20	40
MS1588 90×70 mm. **289** 100f. multicoloured. Imperf			11·50	11·00

290 Horse's Head

1989. Arabian Horse Festival. Multicoloured.

1589	5f. Horse in paddock and emblem of Royal Stables (horiz)	1·10	30
1590	40f. Horse rearing and Treasury, Petra (horiz)	1·80	35
1591	60f. Type **290**	3·50	40
MS1592 90×70 mm. 100f. Mare and foal. Imperf		45·00	43·00

291 Trees

1989. 50th Anniversary of Ministry of Agriculture. Multicoloured.

1593	5f. Type **291**	1·40	40
1594	40f. Tree and '50'	1·50	50
1595	60f. Orange trees and hives	1·80	55

292 Open Book, Globe and Flags

1989. Jordan Library Association.

1596	**292**	40f. multicoloured	90	30
1597	**292**	60f. multicoloured	1·20	40

293 Man carrying Basket

1989. Mosaics. Multicoloured.

1598	5f. Type **293**	1·10	40
1599	10f. Philadelphia (modern Amman)	1·20	50
1600	40f. Deer	2·30	70
1601	60f. Man with stick	3·25	1·00
1602	80f. Jerusalem (horiz)	4·50	1·40
MS1603 90×70 mm. 100f. As No. 1602. Imperf		26·00	25·00

294 Flags and Map

1990. First Anniversary of Arab Co-operation Council.

1604	**294**	5f. multicoloured	45	40
1605	**294**	20f. multicoloured	55	50
1606	**294**	60f. multicoloured	1·20	70
1607	**294**	80f. multicoloured	1·50	1·00

295 Wild Asses at Oasis

1990. Nature Conservation. Multicoloured.

1608	40f. Type **295**	90	40
1609	60f. Rock formation, Rum	1·40	50
1610	80f. Desert palm trees	1·80	55

296 Horsemen and Building

1990. 70th Anniversary of Arrival of Prince Abdullah in Ma'an.

1611	**296**	40f. multicoloured	45	40
1612	**296**	60f. multicoloured	60	50
MS1613 90×73 mm. 200f. multicoloured. Imperf			10·50	10·00

Design: 200f. King Abdullah, Flags and horseman.

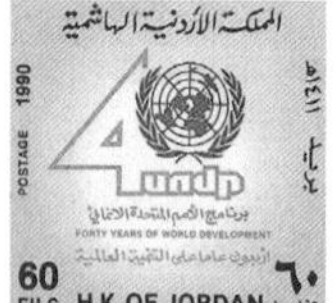

297 Emblem

1990. 40th Anniversary of United Nations Development Programme.

1614	**297**	60f. multicoloured	60	40
1615	**297**	80f. multicoloured	75	50

298 King Hussein

1990. Multicoloured, frame colour given.

1616	**298**	5f. yellow	45	40
1617	**298**	60f. blue	75	40
1620	**298**	20f. green	45	40
1621	**298**	40f. red	45	40
1622a	**298**	80f. mauve	1·20	40
1623	**298**	240f. brown	2·30	85
1624	**298**	320f. purple	3·00	1·10
1625	**298**	1d. green	4·50	3·25

299 Nubian Ibex

1991. Endangered Animals. Multicoloured.

1631	5f. Type **299**	30	30
1632	40f. Onager	90	40
1633	80f. Arabian gazelles	1·80	70
1634	160f. Arabian oryx	3·75	1·50

300 Electric Light Bulbs

1991. Energy Rationalisation. Multicoloured.

1635	5f. Type **300**	45	40
1636	40f. Solar energy (vert)	55	40
1637	80f. Angle-poise lamp by window (vert)	90	40

301 Grain

1991. Grain Production. Multicoloured.

1638	5f. Type **301**	45	40
1639	40f. Ear of wheat and leaves	55	40
1640	80f. Ear of wheat and field	90	40

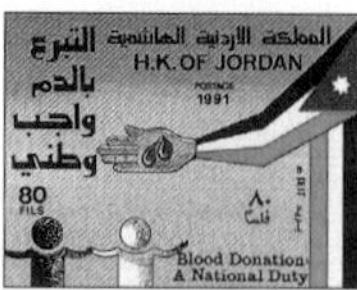

302 Drops of Blood on Hand

1991. National Blood Donation Campaign.

1641	**302**	80f. multicoloured	1·40	70
1642	**302**	160f. multicoloured	2·40	1·00

303 Jerusalem and Map

1991. Palestinian Intifida Movement.

1643	**303**	20f. multicoloured	1·80	85

304 Emblem

1992. Expo '92 World's Fair, Seville.

1644	**304**	80f. multicoloured	75	40
1645	**304**	320f. multicoloured	3·00	1·80

305 Man and Woman balancing Scales

1992. World Health Day. 'Heartbeat–the Rhythm of Health'.

1646	80f. Type **305**	1·10	40
1647	125f. Man and heart in balance and cardiograph (horiz)	1·50	70

306 Children

1992. SOS Children's Village, Aqaba. Multicoloured.

1648	80f. Type **306**	1·10	40
1649	125f. Village	1·50	70

307 Judo and Olympic Flame

1992. Olympic Games, Barcelona. Multicoloured.

1650	5f. Type **307**	45	40
1651	40f. Runners and track (vert)	55	40
1652	80f. Gymnast	90	40
1653	125f. Mascot (vert)	1·70	70
1654	160f. Table tennis	2·00	85
MS1655 70×90 mm. 100f. Motifs as Nos. 1650/1654. Imperf		26·00	25·00

308 King Hussein

1992. 40th Anniversary of King Hussein's Accession. Multicoloured.

1656	40f. Type **308**	45	40
1657	80f. National Colours, crown and King (horiz)	75	55
1658	125f. King and flags (horiz)	1·40	65
1659	160f. King, crown and anniversary emblem (horiz)	1·70	85
MS1660 90×70 mm. 200f. King Hussein and flame. Imperf		12·00	11·50

309 African Monarch

1992. Butterflies. Multicoloured.

1661	5f. Type **309**	45	30
1662	40f. Black-veined white	90	40
1663	80f. Swallowtail	2·30	70
1664	160f. *Pseudochazara telephassa*	4·25	1·50
MS1665 90×70 mm. 200f. Butterflies as in Nos. 1661/1664. Imperf		24·00	23·00

310 Hadrian's Triumphal Arch, Jerash

1993. Variously dated 1992 to 1996.

1666	**310**	5f. brown, blue and black	15	15
1788	**310**	25f. brown, purple & blk	30	30
1718	**310**	40f. brown, green & blk	30	30
1798	**310**	50f. brown, yellow & blk	45	40
1799	**310**	75f. brown, cinn & blk	75	70
1667	**310**	80f. brown, green & blk	45	30
1668	**310**	100f. brown, red & black	60	30
1800	**310**	100f. brown, green & blk	90	85
1801	**310**	120f. brown, green & blk	1·20	1·10
1669	**310**	125f. brown, pink & blk	75	30
1721	**310**	125f. brown, blue & blk	1·10	1·00
1802	**310**	150f. brown, pink & blk	1·70	1·50
1670	**310**	160f. brown, yell & blk	90	30
1803	**310**	200f. brown, grey & blk	2·00	1·80
1671	**310**	240f. brown, pur & blk	1·20	40
1804	**310**	300f. brown, pink & blk	3·25	3·00
1672	**310**	320f. brown, chest & blk	1·70	40
1805	**310**	400f. brown, blue & blk	4·50	4·25
1793	**310**	500f. brown, ochre & blk	3·75	1·40
1674	**310**	1d. brown, yellow & blk	4·50	4·25

311 Customs Co-operation Council Emblem, Flag and Laurel

1993. International Customs Day.

1680	**311**	80f. multicoloured	1·10	40
1681	**311**	125f. multicoloured	1·50	70

312 King Hussein and Military Equipment

1993. Army Day and 77th Anniversary of Arab Revolt. Multicoloured.

1682	5f. Type **312**	30	30
1683	40f. King Hussein, soldier, surgeons and tank	45	35
1684	80f. King Abdullah and Dome of the Rock	90	40
1685	125f. King Hussein of Hejaz, Dome of the Rock and horsemen	1·40	50

MS1686		90×70 mm. 100f. King Hussein, flags of Jordan and Palestine and army emblem. Imperf	9·75	9·50

313 Society Emblem and Natural Energy Resources

1993. 23rd Anniversary of Royal Scientific Society.

1687	**313**	80f. multicoloured	90	55

314 Courtyard

1993. Centenary of Salt Municipality.

1688	**314**	80f. multicoloured	1·10	40
1689	**314**	125f. multicoloured	1·50	70
MS1690		90×71 mm. Nos. 1688/1689. Imperf (sold at 200f.)	10·50	10·00

315 Long-tailed Blue

1993. Butterflies. Multicoloured.

1691		5f. Type **315**	75	30
1692		40f. *Melanargria titea*	1·20	55
1693		80f. *Allancastria deyrollei*	1·70	70
1694		160f. *Gonepteryx cleopatra*	4·00	1·70
MS1695		91×72 mm. 100f. Butterflies as in Nos. 1691/1694. Imperf	38·00	36·00

316 Eyes, Candle and White Cane

1993. White Cane Day. Multicoloured.

1696		80f. Type **316**	1·10	40
1697		125f. Globe, white cane and eye (vert)	1·50	70

317 King Hussein in Army Uniform

1993. 40th Anniversary of King Hussein's Enthronement. Multicoloured.

1698		40f. Type **317**	45	40
1699		80f. King wearing Bedouin costume	90	55
1700		125f. King wearing suit	1·40	65
1701		160f. King with Queen Noor (horiz)	1·80	85
MS1702		90×71 mm. 100f. As No. 1701. Imperf	13·50	13·00

318 Saladin and Dome of the Rock, Jerusalem

1993. 800th Death Anniversary of Saladin.

1703	**318**	40f. multicoloured	45	40
1704	**318**	80f. multicoloured	75	50
1705	**318**	125f. multicoloured	1·40	70

319 King Hussein and Crowd

1993. King Hussein's Return from Surgery in USA (1992). Multicoloured.

1706		80f. Type **319**	90	40
1707		125f. King waving at crowd	1·40	70
1708		160f. King embracing his mother	1·80	85
MS1709		90×70 mm. 100f. King Hussein at top of steps. Imperf	9·00	8·75

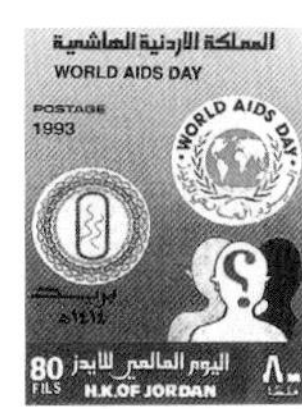

320 Virus, Emblem and Silhouettes

1993. World AIDS Day.

1710	**320**	80f. multicoloured	90	55
1711	**320**	125f. multicoloured	1·40	85
MS1712		91×71 mm. Nos. 1710/1711. Imperf (sold at 200f.)	10·50	10·00

321 Emblems and Flag

1993. 45th Anniversary of United Nations Declaration of Human Rights.

1713	**321**	40f. multicoloured	45	40
1714	**321**	160f. multicoloured	1·80	85

322 Loading Aeroplane

1994. Jordan Hashemite Charity Organisation. Multicoloured.

1715		80f. Type **322**	90	55
1716		125f. Transport aeroplane	1·40	85

323 Mosque and King Hussein

1994. Refurbishment of El Aqsa Mosque and Dome of the Rock.

1726		80f. Type **323**	90	40
1727		125f. Dome of the Rock and King Hussein	1·20	70
1728		240f. Dome of the Rock and King Hussein (different)	2·50	1·10
MS1729		90×70 mm. 100f. King Hussein and interior and exterior view of dome. Imperf	13·50	13·00

324 Emblems on Doves

1994. 75th Anniversary of International Red Cross and Red Crescent Societies. Multicoloured.

1730		80f. Child and emblems (horiz)	1·50	40
1731		160f. Type **324**	2·30	85
MS1732		70×90 mm. As Nos. 1721/1722 but smaller (sold at 200f.)	21·00	20·00

325 Globe, Emblem and '75'

1994. 75th Anniversary of ILO.

1733	**325**	80f. multicoloured	75	40
1734	**325**	125f. multicoloured	1·20	55

326 Sports Pictograms and Olympic Rings

1994. Centenary of International Olympic Committee. Multicoloured.

1735		80f. Type **326**	75	40
1736		125f. Sports pictograms, flame and '100'	1·40	65
1737		160f. Olympic rings, track and athlete (horiz)	1·70	70
1738		240f. Olympic rings and hand holding torch (horiz)	2·50	1·50
MS1739		90×70 mm. 100f. Olympic rings and Jordanian flag forming 'J'. Imperf	14·50	14·00

327 King Hussein greeting Soldiers

1994. Jordanian Participation in United Nations Peace-keeping Forces. Multicoloured.

1740		80f. Type **327**	75	40
1741		125f. King Hussein inspecting troops	1·20	65
1742		160f. UN checkpoint	1·40	70

328 Flag, Emblem, Globe, Wheat and Family

1994. International Year of the Family.

1743	**328**	80f. multicoloured	75	40
1744	**328**	125f. multicoloured	1·40	65
1745	**328**	160f. multicoloured	1·70	70

329 Douglas DC-3, Boeing 737 and Emblem

1994. 50th Anniversary of ICAO.

1746	**329**	80f. multicoloured	90	70
1747	**329**	125f. multicoloured	1·20	1·00
1748	**329**	160f. multicoloured	1·70	1·40

330 Hands around Water Droplet

1994. Water Conservation Campaign. Multicoloured.

1749		80f. Type **330**	1·20	50
1750		125f. Glass beneath running tap, foodstuffs and industry	1·80	70
1751		160f. Water droplets and boy on lush hillside	2·30	70

331 Crown Prince Hassan

1994. Tenth Anniversary of Crown Prince's Award.

1752	**331**	80f. multicoloured	1·20	55
1753	**331**	125f. multicoloured	1·80	65
1754	**331**	160f. multicoloured	2·30	70

332 University Emblem

1995. Inauguration of Al al-Bayt University.

1755	**332**	80f. gold, blue and black	75	55
1756	**332**	125f. gold, green & black	1·50	65
MS1757		89×70 mm. Nos. 1755/1756 (sold at 200f.)	6·25	6·00

333 UN Emblem and '50'

1995. 50th Anniversary of UNO.

1758	**333**	80f. multicoloured	1·10	55
1759	**333**	125f. multicoloured	1·70	70

334 Labour Emblem and Crowd with Flag

1995. Labour Day. Multicoloured.

1760		80f. Type **334**	75	70
1761		125f. Emblem, world map and miner's head	1·10	1·00
1762		160f. Hands holding spanner and torch	1·50	1·40

335 Flags and Globe

1995. Jordan Week in Japan. Multicoloured.

1763		80f. Type **335**	1·10	70
1764		125f. Hemispheres and flags	1·70	85
1765		160f. Flags, brick wall and globe	2·00	1·00

336 Artefacts

1995. Petra, 'The Rose City'. Multicoloured.

1766		50f. Amphitheatre	1·20	50
1767		75f. Type **336**	1·50	55
1768		80f. Treasury seen through cleft in rocks (vert)	1·80	65
1769		160f. Treasury (vert)	3·00	70
MS1770		90×70 mm. 200f. El-Deir Temple. Imperf	30·00	29·00

337 Emblem

1995. 50th Anniversary of Arab League.

1771	**337**	80f. multicoloured	75	70

1772	**337**	125f. multicoloured	1·10	1·00
1773	**337**	160f. multicoloured	1·50	1·40

338 Leaves and Emblem

1995. 50th Anniversary of FAO. Multicoloured.

1774		80f. Type **338**	75	55
1775		125f. Ears of wheat and '50' incorporating FAO emblem	1·40	65
1776		160f. United Nations emblem and '50' incorporating FAO emblem	1·80	70

339 Knotted Ropes, Summit Emblem and National Flags

1995. Middle Eastern and North African Economic Summit, Amman.

1777	**339**	80f. multicoloured	75	55
1778	**339**	125f. multicoloured	1·40	65

340 King Hussein

1995. 60th Birthday of King Hussein. Multicoloured.

1779		25f. Type **340**	60	55
1780		40f. Hussein within shield	60	55
1781		80f. Dove incorporating '60', El-Deir Temple (Petra) and Hussein	75	55
1782		100f. Hussein in military uniform and anniversary emblem	1·10	65
1783		125f. King Hussein	1·40	70
1784		160f. Hussein, National Flag and '60 60 60'	1·80	70
MS1785		90×70 mm. 200f. Dome of the Rock and King Hussein within '60'. Imperf	10·50	10·00

341 Hands and Hard of Hearing Emblem

1995. The Deaf. Multicoloured.

1786		80f. Type **341**	75	55
1787		125f. Emblems, sign language and hard of hearing emblem	1·40	65

342 Anniversary Emblem and Map of Jordan

1996. 50th Anniversary of Independence. Multicoloured.

1794		100f. Type **342**	1·10	55
1795		200f. King Hussein, map of Jordan and King Abdullah	2·00	1·00
1796		300f. King Hussein	2·75	1·50
MS1797		85×66 mm. 200f. King Hussein in military uniform. Imperf	11·50	11·00

343 Games Emblem, Olympic Rings and Pictograms

1996. Olympic Games, Atlanta. Multicoloured.

1806		50f. Type **343**	90	55
1807		100f. Games emblem and pictograms	1·50	65
1808		200f. Games emblem forming torch and figure	2·75	85
1809		300f. Games emblem, torch and national flag	3·75	1·30

344 Hand protecting Animals and Plants

1996. Protection of the Ozone Layer.

1810	**344**	100f. multicoloured	3·00	1·00

345 Anniversary Emblem

1996. 50th Anniversary of UNICEF Fund.

1811	**345**	100f. multicoloured	1·40	70
1812	**345**	200f. multicoloured	2·40	1·00

346 Playing Polo

1997. 50th Birthday of Crown Prince Hassan. Multicoloured.

1813		50f. Type **346**	75	70
1814		100f. Wearing western dress (vert)	1·10	75
1815		200f. In military uniform	2·30	1·00
MS1816		90×69 mm. 200f. Wearing graduation robes. Imperf	13·00	12·50

347 Karak

1997. Centenary of Discovery of Madaba Mosaic Map. Multicoloured.

1817		100f. Type **347**	1·40	70
1818		200f. River Jordan (horiz)	2·75	1·00
1819		300f. Jerusalem	4·25	1·70
MS1820		90×70 mm. 100f. Remains of map. Imperf	23·00	22·00

348 Von Stephan

1997. Death Centenary of Heinrich von Stephan (founder of UPU).

1821	**348**	100f. multicoloured	2·10	70
1822	**348**	200f. multicoloured	4·00	1·00

349 Sinai Rosefinch ('Rosefinch')

1997. Sinai Rosefinch (The Jordanian Rosefinch).

1823	**349**	50f. multicoloured	75	40
1824	**349**	100f. multicoloured	1·50	1·00
1825	**349**	150f. multicoloured	2·30	1·50
1826	**349**	200f. multicoloured	3·00	2·10

350 Performers and Hadrian's Triumphal Arch

1997. 15th Anniversary of Jerash Festival. Multicoloured.

1827		50f. Type **350**	45	40
1828		100f. Orchestra, Festival emblem and Jerash ruins	1·10	1·00
1829		150f. Temple of Artemis and marching band	1·70	1·50
1830		200f. Women dancers and audience at performance	2·30	2·10
MS1831		90×70 mm. 200f. Torch-lighting ceremony. Imperf	14·50	14·00

351 Current and Previous Parliament Buildings

1997. 50th Anniversary of First National Parliament. Multicoloured.

1832		100f. Type **351**	1·10	1·00
1833		200f. King Hussein addressing, and view of, Chamber of Deputies	2·10	2·00

352 Meeting Emblem

1997. 53rd International Air Transport Association Annual General Meeting, Amman.

1834	**352**	100f. multicoloured	1·10	1·00
1835	**352**	200f. multicoloured	2·10	2·00
1836	**352**	300f. multicoloured	3·25	3·00

353 King Hussein and Queen Noor

1997. 62nd Birthday of King Hussein.

1837	**353**	100f. multicoloured	1·10	1·00
1838	**353**	200f. multicoloured	2·10	2·00
1839	**353**	300f. multicoloured	3·25	3·00
MS1840		70×90 mm. 200f. As No. 1838 but 44×61 mm.	13·00	12·50

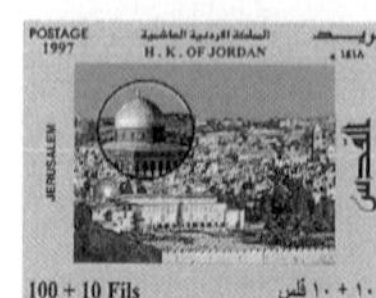

354 Jerusalem and Dome of the Rock

1997. Jerusalem.

1841	**354**	100f.+10f. multicoloured	1·10	1·00
1842	**354**	200f.+20f. multicoloured	2·40	2·20
1843	**354**	300f.+30f. multicoloured	3·50	3·25

355 Opening Ceremony

1997. Jordan, Arab Football Champion, 1997. Multicoloured.

1844		50f. Type **355**	60	55
1845		75f. Team saluting National Anthem	75	70
1846		100f. Posing for team photograph and police officers patrolling crowd	1·10	1·00
MS1847		91×71 mm. 200f. King Hussein and Queen Noor among dignitaries and motorcade. Imperf	18·00	17·00

356 Women

1997. National Women's Forum. Multicoloured.

1848		50f. Type **356**	60	55
1849		100f. National Flag, women's profiles and emblems (horiz)	1·10	1·00
1850		150f. Forum meeting and emblem (horiz)	1·80	1·70

357 Air Pollution by Factories and Cars

1998. Earth Day. Children's Paintings. Multicoloured.

1851		50f. Polluted air, land and water	90	55
1852		100f. Type **357**	1·50	1·00
1853		150f. 'Earth' being strangled by pollution (vert)	2·30	1·70

358 King Abdullah and Camel in Desert

1998. 75th Anniversary of Recognition of Transjordan as Autonomous State. Multicoloured.

1864		100f. Type **358**	1·20	1·00
1865		200f. King Hussein and camel in desert	2·40	2·10
1866		300f. King Abdullah, King Hussein and May 1923 9p. stamp	4·00	3·25
MS1867		89×74 mm. 300f. As No. 1866 but 78×70 mm. Imperf	13·00	12·50

359 Thistle

1998. Flowers. Multicoloured.

1868		50f. Type **359**	1·10	70
1869		100f. Poppy	1·50	1·30
1870		150f. Carnation	2·50	2·00
MS1871		70×90 mm. 200f. Iris. Imperf	13·00	12·50

360 Animals and Trees

1998. Mosaics from Um ar-Rasas. Multicoloured.

1872		100f. Type **360**	1·20	1·00
1873		200f. City buildings	2·40	2·10
1874		300f. Mosiac panel	4·00	3·25

361 Honey Bee and Honeycomb

1998. Second Arab Bee-keeping Conference. Multicoloured.

1875	50f. Type **361**	75	70
1876	100f. Bee on flower (vert)	1·40	1·30
1877	150f. Bee, flower and honeycomb	2·10	2·00
MS1878	90×70 mm. 200f. Bees on flowers. Imperf	13·00	12·50

362 Dove with Stamp

1998. International Stamp Day. Multicoloured.

1879	50f. Type **362**	1·10	65
1880	100f. World map and UPU emblem	1·80	1·10
1881	150f. Stamps encircling globe	3·00	1·80

363 King Hussein and Map of Jordan

1998. 63rd Birthday of King Hussein.

1882	**363**	100f. multicoloured	1·10	1·00
1883	**363**	200f. multicoloured	2·30	2·10
1884	**363**	300f. multicoloured	3·50	3·25
MS1885		90×70 mm. 300f. King Hussein and map of Jordan (different). Imperf	13·00	12·50

364 King Hussein and Emblem

1998. 25th Anniversary of Arab Police and Security Chiefs' Meeting. Multicoloured.

1886	100f. Type **364**	1·10	1·00
1887	200f. Flags of member countries of Arab League (vert)	2·30	2·10
1888	300f. Police beret and map of Jordan	3·50	3·25

365 Family and Anniversary Emblem

1998. 50th Anniversary of Universal Declaration of Human Rights. Multicoloured.

1889	100f. Type **365**	1·10	1·00
1890	200f. Silhouettes of people and United Nations emblem	2·30	2·10

366 Wahbi al Tal

1999. Birth Centenary and 50th Death Anniversary of Mustafa Wahbi al Tal (poet).

1891	**366**	100f. multicoloured	2·10	1·30

367 Mascot and Sports Pictograms

1999. Ninth Arab Sports Tournament. Multicoloured.

1892	50f. Type **367**	75	40
1893	100f. Emblem, mascot and torch	1·10	70
1894	200f. Sportsmen, emblem and '9' (vert)	2·40	1·40
1895	300f. Jordanian flag, mascot and emblem	3·25	2·10
MS1896	90×70 mm. 200f. Mascot and sports pictograms. Imperf	5·25	5·00

368 Railway Map, Station and Train

1999. Hijazi Railway Museum. Multicoloured.

1897	100f. Type **368**	1·50	1·40
1898	200f. Type **368**	3·00	2·75
1899	300f. Train and station building	4·50	4·25

369 *Pachyseris speciosa*

1999. Marine Life in the Gulf of Aqaba. Corals. Multicoloured.

1900	50f. Type **369**	75	55
1901	100f. *Acropora digitfera*	1·50	1·30
1902	200f. *Oxypora lacera*	2·50	2·20
1903	300f. *Fungia echinata*	4·00	3·25
MS1904	90×70 mm. 200f. *Gorgonia*. Imperf	12·00	11·50

370 '125' and Emblem on Envelope

1999. 125th Anniversary of Universal Postal Union. Multicoloured.

1905	100f. Type **370**	1·10	1·00
1906	200f. UPU emblem on envelope, target and post emblem	2·40	2·20
MS1907	90×70 mm. 200f. As No. 1906. Imperf	2·40	2·30

371 Children helping Sick Globe

1999. Environmental Protection. Multicoloured.

1908	100f. Type **371**	1·10	1·00
1909	200f. Hands holding globe as apple	1·90	1·70

372 Aerial View of Temple

1999. Cradle of Civilisations. Multicoloured. (a) Petra.

1910	100f. Type **372**	1·10	1·00
1911	200f. Front view of temple	2·10	1·80
1912	300f. Building in cliffs	3·25	2·75

(b) Jerash.

1913	100f. Path between columns	1·10	1·00
1914	200f. Columns	2·10	1·80
1915	300f. Columns and ruined building	3·25	2·75

(c) Amman.

1916	100f. Auditorium	1·10	1·00
1917	200f. Columns	2·10	1·80
1918	300f. Statues	3·25	2·75

(d) Aqaba.

1919	100f. Camels, Wadi Rum	1·10	1·00
1920	200f. Building with wooden door	2·10	1·80
1921	300f. Fort	3·25	2·75

(e) Baptism Site.

1922	100f. Rushes at water's edge	1·10	1·00
1923	200f. Aerial view of site	2·10	1·80
1924	300f. Archaeological site	3·25	2·75

(f) Madaba.

1925	100f. Mosaic of man	1·10	1·00
1926	200f. Temple	2·10	1·80
1927	300f. Mosaic of town	3·25	2·75

(g) Pella.

1928	100f. Columns and steps	1·10	1·00
1929	200f. Columns and wall	2·10	1·80
1930	300f. Columns and sheep	3·25	2·75

(h) Ajloun.

1931	100f. Castle	1·10	1·00
1932	200f. Castle from below	2·10	1·80
1933	300f. Hill top castle	3·25	2·75

(i) Um Quais.

1934	100f. Arches and columns	1·10	1·00
1935	200f. Amphitheatre	2·10	1·80
1936	300f. Columns and rubble	3·25	2·75

(j) Desert Palaces.

1937	100f. Mushatta	1·10	1·00
1938	200f. Kharaneh	2·10	1·80
1939	300f. Amra	3·25	2·75

373 Jordanian Stamps

1999. 20th Anniversary of Jordan Philatelic Club. Multicoloured.

1940	100f. Type **373**	1·10	1·00
1941	200f. Jordanian stamps (different)	2·10	1·80

374 Assembly Room

1999. Museum of Political History. Multicoloured.

1942	100f. Type **374**	1·10	1·00
1943	200f. Courtyard	2·10	1·80
1944	300f. Entrance	3·25	2·75

375 Jordanian Flag and Emblems

1999. 50th Anniversary of SOS Children's Villages. Multicoloured.

1945	100f. Type **375**	1·10	1·00
1946	200f. Woman and children	2·10	1·80

376 King Abdullah II

1999. Coronation of King Abdullah II Bin Al-Hussein.

1947	**376**	100f. multicoloured	1·10	1·00
1948	**376**	200f. multicoloured	2·10	1·80
1949	**376**	300f. multicoloured	3·25	2·75
MS1950		70×89 mm. 200f. No. 1948 but with gold border	3·25	3·00

377 King Abdullah II and Queen Rania

1999. Coronation of King Abdullah II Bin Al-Hussein and Queen Rania al-Abdullah.

1951	**377**	100f. multicoloured	1·10	1·00
1952	**377**	200f. multicoloured	2·10	1·80
1953	**377**	300f. multicoloured	3·25	2·75
MS1954		70×89 mm. 200f. No. 1952 but with gold border	3·25	3·00

378 Crowned Portrait

2000. 38th Birth Anniversary of King Abdullah II. Multicoloured.

1955	100f. Type **378**	1·10	1·00
1956	200f. King Abdullah II (horiz)	2·10	1·80
1957	300f. King Abdullah II and flag (horiz)	3·25	2·75
MS1958	90×74 mm. 200f. As No. 1956. Imperf	3·25	3·00

379 Red Cross Emblem and Jordanian Flag

2000. 50th Anniversary of Geneva Red Cross Conventions. Multicoloured.

1959	**379**	100f. multicoloured	1·10	1·00
1960	**379**	200f. multicoloured	2·20	2·00
1961	**379**	300f. multicoloured	3·50	3·00

380 Flag and '2000 A.D.'

2000. New Millennium. Multicoloured.

1962	100f. Type **380**	1·10	1·00
1963	200f. Palms, sand and fish swimming	2·20	2·00
1964	300f. As No. 1962 but inscription in Arabic	3·50	3·00

381 King Abdullah II, Roofs and Pope John Paul II

2000. 36th Anniversary of Pope Paul VI's Visit to Jordan.

1965	**381**	100f. multicoloured	1·10	1·00
1966	**381**	200f. multicoloured	2·20	2·00
1967	**381**	300f. multicoloured	3·50	3·00

382 Pope John Paul II, Trees and King Abdullah II

2000. Pope John Paul II's Visit to Jordan. Multicoloured.

1968	100f. Type **382**	1·10	1·00
1969	200f. Pope John Paul II, river and King Abdullah II	2·20	2·00
1970	300f. Pope John Paul II, flags and King Abdullah II	3·50	3·00
MS1971	70×90 mm. 200f. Pope John Paul II. Imperf	8·00	7·25

383 Globe and Organisation Emblem

2000. 50th Anniversary of World Meteorological Organisation. Multicoloured.

1972	100f. Type **383**	1·60	1·40
1973	200f. Globe and emblem (different)	3·25	2·75

384 Emblem, Flag and '90'

2000. 90th Anniversary of Jordan Boy Scouts. Multicoloured.

1974	100f. Type **384**	1·80	1·50
1975	200f. Pyramids	3·50	3·00
1976	300f. '90', flag and pyramids	5·00	4·50
MS1977	90×70 mm. 200f. As No. 1974 but with design enlarged. Imperf	6·50	6·00

385 Clinic Building and Emblem

2000. Al-Amal Cancer Centre. Multicoloured.

1978	200f. Type **385**	2·75	2·40
1979	300f. Emblem and family	4·25	3·75

387 Scales enclosing Palace of Justice

2000. Palace of Justice, Amman. Multicoloured.

1980	100f. Type **387**	1·40	1·30
1981	200f. Building façade	2·75	2·40

388 Dove

2000. Endangered Species. Multicoloured.

1982	50f. Type **388**	65	55
1983	100f. Oryx	1·40	1·30
1984	150f. Caracal	2·20	2·00
1985	200f. Red fox	3·00	2·50
1986	300f. Iris	4·50	4·00
1987	400f. White broom	5·75	5·00

389 Iris

2000. World Conservation Union Conference, Amman.

1988	**389**	200f. multicoloured	3·00	2·50
1989	**389**	300f. multicoloured	4·50	4·00

390 Petra

2000. Tourism. Multicoloured.

1990	50f. Type **390**	65	40
1991	100f. Jerash	1·30	1·00
1992	150f. Mount Nebo	1·90	1·50
1993	200f. Dead Sea	2·50	2·00
1994	300f. Aqaba	3·75	3·00
1995	400f. Wadi Rum	4·75	4·00

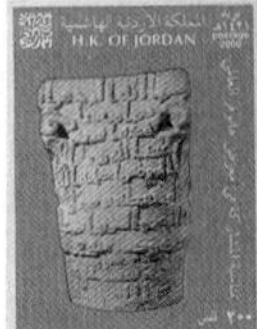

391 Column Capital

2000. Expo 2000, Hanover. Multicoloured.

1996	200f. Type **391**	3·00	2·50
1997	300f. Statuette	4·50	4·00
MS1998	90×70 mm. 200f. King Abdullah, Queen Rania Al-Abdullah and Expo 2000 buildings	6·50	6·00

392 King Hussein

2000. First Death Anniversary of King Hussein. Multicoloured.

1999	50f. Type **392**	65	55
2000	150f. King Hussein enclosed in wreath (horiz)	2·20	2·00
2001	200f. Symbols of industry and King Hussein (horiz)	3·00	2·50
MS2002	90×70 mm. 200f. As No. 2000 but with design enlarged	4·00	3·75

393 Women and Child

2000. 50th Anniversary of United Nations High Commissioner for Refugees (2001).

2003	200f. multicoloured	3·00	2·50
2004	300f. green, blue and black	4·50	4·00

Design: 200f. T **393**; 300f. UNHCR emblem.

394 Conference Emblem and Jordanian Flag

2001. 13th Arab Summit Conference, Amman.

2005	50f. Type **394**	65	55
2006	200f. Flags, emblem and map of Arab countries	2·40	2·10
2007	250f. King Abdullah II and emblem	3·25	2·75

395 Muhammad al-Durrah, his Father and Dome

2001. First Death Anniversary of Muhammad al-Durrah. Multicoloured.

2008	200f. Type **395**	2·40	2·10
2009	300f. Muhammad al-Durrah and father	3·75	3·25

396 Dome of the Rock with Arms

2001. Al Aqsa Intifada. Multicoloured.

2010	200f. Type **396**	2·40	2·10
2011	300f. Dome of the Rock and protesters	3·75	3·25

397 Wheelchair User

2001. Sports for Special Needs. Multicoloured.

2012	200f. Type **397**	2·40	2·10
2013	300f. Woman holding medal	3·75	3·25

398 School Children and No-Smoking Sign

2001. Campaign to stop Smoking amongst Young People. Multicoloured.

2014	200f. Type **398**	2·40	2·10
2015	300f. Stylised student holding no-smoking sign (vert)	3·75	3·25

399 Olive Branches and Map of Jordan

2001. Olive Cultivation. Multicoloured.

2016	200f. Type **399**	2·40	2·10
2017	300f. Girl holding olives (vert)	3·75	3·25

400 Family and World Map

2001. United Nations Year of Dialogue among Civilisations. Multicoloured.

2018	200f. Type **400**	2·40	2·10
2019	300f. Emblem, clasped hands and olive tree	3·75	3·25

401 Sheik Hussein Bridge and Japanese and Jordanian Flags

2001. Japan–Jordan Co-operation. Multicoloured.

2020	200f. Type **401**	2·40	2·10
2021	300f. King Hussein bridge and clasped hands	3·75	3·25

402 Emblem, Star and National Colours

2002. Amman, Arab Cultural Capital, 2002. Multicoloured.

2022	100f. Type **402**	1·10	1·00
2023	200f. Flame and pen	1·90	1·70
2024	300f. Emblem and amphitheatre	3·00	2·75

403 Buildings

2002. Jordanian Artists. Multicoloured.

2025	100f. Type **403**	1·10	1·00
2026	150f. Abstract (Mahmoud Taha) (horiz)	1·40	1·30
2027	200f. Woman (Mohanna Durra)	1·90	1·70
2028	300f. Hilltop castle (Wijdan) (horiz)	3·00	2·75

404 Bird carrying Envelope

2002. 25th Anniversary of Jordan–China Diplomatic Relations. Multicoloured.

2029	200f. Type **404**	1·90	1·70
2030	300f. King Abdullah II and President Jiang Zemin	3·00	2·75

405 Goldfinch

2002. Birds. Multicoloured.

2031	100f. Type **405**	1·40	1·30
2032	200f. Rufous scrub robin (inscr 'rufous bush robin')	2·50	2·20
2033	300f. Stork	4·00	3·50
MS2034	70×90 mm. 200f. Golden oriole, goshawk, bunting and hoopoe	18·00	17·00

406 Symbols of Industry

2002. Jordan Vision 2002 (campaign for economic development). Multicoloured.

2035	200f. Type **406**	1·90	1·70
2036	300f. Hand and computer circuit board	3·00	2·75

2003. Hadrian's Triumphal Arch, Jerash. Dated '2003'. Multicoloured.

2036a	25f. As Type **310**		
2036b	50f. As Type **310**		

407 Building Facade

2003. Archaeological Museum. Multicoloured.

2037	150f. Type **407**	1·40	1·30
2038	250f. Building from below	2·50	2·20

408 Sherif Hussein bin Ali

2003. Hashemite Dynasty. Sheet 230×90 mm containing T **408** and similar vert designs. Multicoloured.

MS2039	200f.×5 Type **408**; King Abdullah; King Talal bin Abdullah; King Hussein bin Talal; King Abdullah II	9·50	9·00

409 *Cistanche tubulosa*

2003. Flora. Multicoloured.

2040	50f. Type **409**	65	55
2041	100f. *Ophioglossum polyphyllum* (vert)	1·40	1·30
2042	150f. *Narcissus tazetta*	1·90	1·70
2043	200f. *Gynandriris sisyrinchium* (vert)	2·50	2·20

410 Italian Cypress (*Cupressus sempervirens*)

2003. Trees. Multicoloured.

2044	50f. Type **410**	1·10	1·00
2045	100f. *Pistacia atlantica*	1·40	1·30
2046	200f. *Quercus aegilops*	1·90	1·70

411 Short-toed Eagle (*Ciraetus gallicus*)

2003. Trees. Multicoloured.

2047	100f. Type **411**	1·40	1·30
2048	200f. Peregrine falcon (*Falco peregrinus*)	2·50	2·20
2049	300f. Northern sparrow hawk (*Accipter nisus*)	4·00	3·50
MS2050	70×90 mm 200f. *Ciraetus gallicus* (different). Imperf	13·00	12·50

412 Company Emblem, Colours and Arch

2003. Jordan Post Company. Multicoloured.

2051	50f. Type **412**	65	55
2052	100f. Columns, stamp outline and emblem	1·40	1·30

413 Ferrari F40 (1989)

2003. Royal Car Museum, Amman. Multicoloured.

2053	100f. Type **413**	1·40	1·30
2054	150f. Rolls Royce Phantom V (1968)	1·90	1·70
2055	300f. Mercedes Benz Cabriolet D (1961)	3·75	3·25
MS2056	90×70 mm. 200f. Panther J72 convertible (1972), Mercedes Benz 300sc roadster (1956) and Cadillac 53 (1916). Imperf	12·00	11·00

414 Grey

2004. Arabian Horses. Multicoloured.

2057	5pt. Type **414**	50	40
2058	7pt.50 Light bay, red bridle	80	70
2059	12pt.50 Dark bay	1·30	1·10
2060	15pt. Grey, long mane	1·60	1·40
2061	25pt. Chestnut	2·50	2·20
MS2062	90×70 mm. 10pt. Two horses. Imperf	13·50	12·50

415 Camels

2004. Children's Paintings. Multicoloured.

2063	5pt. Type **415**	50	40
2064	7pt.50 Valley	65	55
2065	12pt.50 Sun	1·10	1·00
2066	15pt. Sea and buildings	1·30	1·10
2067	25pt. Buildings and tree	2·20	2·00
MS2068	90×70 mm. 10pt. Collage of Nos. 2063/2067 (detail). Imperf	12·00	11·00

416 Piper and Grapes

2004. Mosaics, Church of the Holy Martyrs, Mount Nebo. Sheet 205×110 mm containing T **416** and similar vert designs. Multicoloured.

MS2069	10pt. Type **416**; 10pt. Man using sickle (68×90 mm); 15pt. House; 25pt. Man carrying basket	13·00	12·00

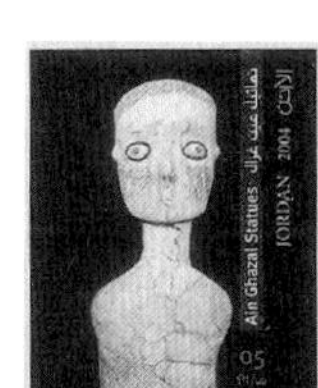
417 Statue

2004. Statues from Ain Ghazal (Neolithic site). Multicoloured.

2070	5pt. Type **417**	50	40
2071	7pt.50 Female statue	65	55
2072	12pt.50 Armless statue	1·10	1·00
2073	15pt. Statue with arms	1·30	1·10
2074	25pt. Two-headed statue	2·20	2·00
MS2075	70×90 mm. 10pt. Two statues. Imperf	12·00	11·00

418 Nazareth Iris

2004. Nazareth Iris (*Iris bismarkiana*). Sheet 224×167 mm containing T **418** and similar vert designs. Multicoloured.

MS2076	5pt. Type **418**; 7pt.50 Speckled petals; 10pt. Iris and bud (70×90 mm); 12pt.50 Lined petals; 15pt. Speckled petals below, striped petal above; 25pt. Throat of iris flower	13·00	12·00

419 Salt Deposit

2005. EXPO 2005, Aichi, Japan. Sheet 321×111 mm containing T **419** and similar vert designs. Multicoloured.

MS2077	5pt. Type **419**; 7pt.50 Encrusted salt deposit; 12pt.50 Layered salt deposit; 20pt. Cliffs and Dead Sea (70×90 mm)	8·00	7·75

420 Twoband Anemonefish

2005. Red Sea Fish. Multicoloured.

2078	5pt. Type **420**	30	30
2079	5pt. Emperor angelfish	80	70
2080	7pt.50 Blue-masked butterflyfish	1·30	1·10
2081	12pt.50 Pufferfish	2·20	2·00
MS2082	90×70 mm. 20pt. Ragged-finned firefish	9·50	9·00

421 Tennis

2005. Children's Drawings. International Year of Sports and Sports Education. Multicoloured.

2083	1pt. Type **421**	30	30
2084	10pt. Medal winner	1·10	1·00
2085	15pt. Football (horiz)	1·80	1·50
2086	20pt. Swimmer (horiz)	2·40	2·10
MS2087	70×90 mm. 20pt. Boy. Imperf	8·75	8·50

422 Oryx

2005. Arabian Oryx (*Oryx leucoryx*). Multicoloured.

2088	1pt.50 Type **422**	50	40
2089	5pt. Mother and calf	1·30	1·10
2090	7pt.50 Calf and adults (horiz)	1·80	1·50
2091	12pt.50 Two adults (horiz)	3·00	2·50
MS2092	90×70 mm. 20pt. Head and shoulders	19·00	18·00

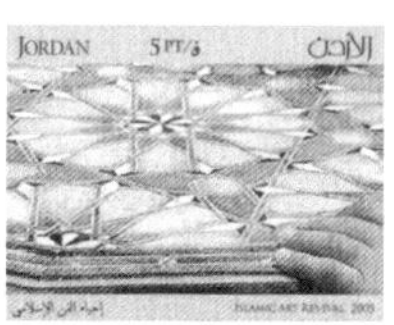
423 Mosaic

2005. Islamic Art Revival. Multicoloured.

2093	5pt. Type **423**	80	70
2094	7pt.50 Metalwork	1·10	1·00
2095	10pt. Calligraphy	1·40	1·30
2096	15pt. Wood carving	2·10	1·80
MS2097	90×70 mm. 20pt. Circular calligraphy. Imperf	9·50	9·00

424 Adult Hand holding Child's Hand

2005. Child Protection.

2098	**424**	7pt.50 silver and blue	1·10	1·00
2099	-	10pt. silver and orange	1·60	1·40
2100	-	12pt.50 silver and carmine	2·10	1·80
MS2101		70×90 mm. 20pt. silver and gold. Imperf	9·50	9·00

Designs: 7pt.50 T **424**; 10pt. Child enclosed in adult arms; 12pt.50 Adult arms holding toddler; 20pt. Boy with head on hand.

425 Japanese Calligraphy

2005. Jordan–Japan Friendship. Multicoloured.

2102	7pt.50 Type **425**	95	85
2103	12pt.50 Floodlit buildings	1·60	1·40
2104	15pt. Museum by day	1·90	1·70
MS2105	70×90 mm. 20pt. Museum exhibits. Imperf	10·50	9·75

426 Umayyad Coin

2006. Coins. Showing early coins. Multicoloured.

2106	5pt. Type **426**	80	70
2107	7pt.50 Hisham (obverse)	1·10	1·00
2108	10pt. Abbasid	1·60	1·40
2109	12pt.50 Umayyad	2·10	1·80
2110	15pt. Hisham (reverse)	2·40	2·10
MS2111	90×70 mm. 30pt. Umayyad. Imperf	9·50	9·00

427 '2006 FIFA World Cup Germany'

2006. World Cup Football Championship, Germany. Multicoloured.

2112	5pt. Type **427**	80	70
2113	7pt.50 As Type **427**	1·10	1·00
2114	10pt. Championship emblem	1·60	1·40
2115	12pt.50 As No. 2114	2·10	1·80
2116	15pt. As No. 2114	2·40	2·10
MS2117	90×70 mm. 30pt. Championship emblem. Imperf	9·50	9·00

428 Waterfront Development

2006. Contemporary Architecture. Multicoloured.

2118	7pt.50 Type **428**	1·10	1·00
2119	10pt. Interior (horiz)	1·60	1·40
2120	12pt.50 Garden (horiz)	2·10	1·80
MS2121	90×70 mm. 20pt. Curved facade. Imperf	8·00	7·75

429 Police Vehicle

2006. Public Service Vehicles. Multicoloured.

2122	10pt. Type **429**	1·10	1·00
2123	12pt.50 Fire engine	1·60	1·40
2124	17pt.50 Waste disposal truck	2·10	1·80
2125	20pt. Support vans	2·50	2·20
MS2126	90×70 mm. 20pt. Ambulance. Imperf	7·75	7·25

430 Blue Lizard

2006. Desert Reptiles. Multicoloured.

2127	5pt. Type **430**	70	65
2128	7pt.50 Snake	1·10	95
2129	10pt. Two lizards	1·40	1·30
2130	12pt.50 Lizard	1·80	1·60
2131	15pt. Small lizard (horiz)	2·20	1·90
2132	20pt. Viper	3·00	2·50
MS2133	90×70 mm. 20pt. Monitor lizard. Imperf	9·00	8·75

431 Hearts

2006. Art. Multicoloured.

2134	5pt. Type **431**	70	65
2135	10pt. Dancers	1·40	1·30
2136	15pt. Buildings	2·20	1·90
2137	20pt. Abstract	3·00	2·50
MS2138	90×70 mm. 20pt. Four paintings. Imperf	9·00	8·75

432 King Abdullah II

2006. National Celebration. Multicoloured.

2139	5pt. Type **432**	70	65
2140	7pt.50 King Abdullah II wearing suit	1·10	95
2141	10pt. Armed forces (horiz)	1·40	1·30
2142	12pt.50 King Abdullah II wearing army uniform	1·80	1·60
2143	15pt. National Flag (horiz)	2·20	1·90
2144	20pt. Sharif Hussein bin Ali during a visit to Amman, 1924 (horiz)	3·00	2·50
2145	25pt. Army tanks in parade (horiz)	3·50	3·25
2146	30pt. Rose on flag (horiz)	4·25	3·75

433 Laptop User

2006. ICT in Education. Multicoloured.

2147	7pt.50 Type **433**	1·10	95
2148	12pt.50 Woman using touch screen	1·80	1·60
2149	15pt. Man using touch screen	2·20	1·90
2150	20pt. Woman using mobile telephone	3·00	2·50
MS2151	70×90 mm. 20pt. Hand and key pad. Imperf	9·00	8·75

Nos. 2152/2153 are vacant.

434 Orange

2007. Fruit. Multicoloured.

2154	10p. Type **434**	1·40	1·30
2155	15p. Cherries	2·10	1·90
2156	20p. Figs	2·75	2·50
2157	25p. Pomegranate	3·50	3·25
2158	30p. Grapes	4·25	3·75

435 Mafraq

2007. Traditional Women's Clothes. Multicoloured.

2159	10p. Type **435**	1·40	1·30
2160	15p. Ma'an	2·10	1·90
2161	20p. Amman	2·75	2·50
2162	25p. Jerash	3·50	3·25
2163	30p. Salt	4·25	3·75

436 Sculpture

2007. Petra. Multicoloured.

2164	10p. Type **436**	1·40	1·30
2165	15p. Ceramic plate	2·10	1·90
2166	20p. Carved leaves	2·75	2·50
2167	25p. Siq al Barid	3·50	3·25
2168	30p. Rock formation	4·25	3·75
MS2168a	87×105 mm 40p. Treasury	11·50	11·00
MS2168b	71×91 mm. As **MS**2181a. Imperf	12·50	12·00

437 Doorway

2007. Aqaba. Multicoloured.

2169	10p. Type **437**	1·40	1·30
2170	15p. Scuba diver	2·10	1·90
2171	20p. Marina	2·75	2·50
2172	30p. Yacht	4·25	3·75

438 Butterfly

2007. Butterflies. Multicoloured.

2173	10pt. Type **438**	1·40	1·30
2174	15p. Brimstone	2·10	1·90
2175	20pt. Large white	2·75	2·50
2176	25pt. White admiral (horiz)	3·50	3·25
2177	30pt. Orange tip (horiz)	4·25	3·75
MS2178	90×70 mm. 40pt. Clouded yellow. Imperf	9·25	9·00

439 Metal Jug

2007. Islamic Art. Multicoloured.

2179	10pt. Type **439**	1·40	1·30
2180	20pt. Iron jug with legs and animal head spout	2·75	2·50
2181	30pt. Octagonal incised jug	4·25	3·75
MS2182	90×70 mm. 25pt. Jug with tall spout. Imperf	8·00	7·50

440 Pile of Books

2007. Culture and Identity. Multicoloured.

2183	10pt. Type **440**	1·10	1·10
2184	20pt. Lute	1·40	1·30
2185	25pt. Desert scene enclosed in bottle	2·75	2·50
2186	30pt. Script	3·50	3·25
MS2186a	70×90 mm. 20pt. Details of designs from Nos. 2182/2185 and paint brushes. Imperf	7·00	6·50

441 Suspension Bridge

2008. 50th Anniversary of Engineers' Association. Multicoloured.

2187	15p. Type **441**	2·10	1·90
2188	20p. 50	2·75	2·50
2189	25p. Pylons	3·50	3·25

442 Taekwondo

2008. Olympic Games, Beijing. Multicoloured.

2190	20p. Type **442**	2·75	2·50
2191	30p. Equestrian	4·25	3·75
2192	40p. Table Tennis	5·50	5·00
2193	50p. Athletics	7·00	6·25

443 Oud

2007. Musical Instruments. Multicoloured.

2194	20p. Type **443**	1·80	1·70
2195	40p. Rababah	3·75	3·25
2196	60p. Kanoun	5·50	5·00
2197	80p. Flute	7·25	6·75
2198	100p. Drum	9·25	8·50
MS2199	90×70 mm. 50p. Instruments	7·00	6·50

444 *Silene aegyptiaca* (inscr 'Egyptian Catchfly')

2008. Flowers. Multicoloured.

2200	5pt. Type **444**	45	40
2201	10pt. Inscr 'Lupin'	90	85
2202	15pt. Judean viper's bugloss (*Echium judaeum*)	1·40	1·30
2203	20pt. Blue pimpernel	1·80	1·70
2204	30pt. Inscr 'Asiatic Crowfoot'	2·75	2·50
2205	40pt. Grape hyacinth	3·75	3·25
2206	50pt. Large flowered sage	4·50	4·25
2207	60pt. Star of Bethlehem	5·50	5·00
2208	80pt. *Orchid pyramidalis*	7·25	6·75
2209	100pt. *Calotropis* (inscr 'calotrpis')	9·25	8·50
MS2210	90×70 mm. 50pt. Cyclamen. Imperf	7·00	6·50

445 Fresco

2008. World Heritage Site. Quseir Amra (early 8th-century castle, one of the most important examples of early Islamic art). Designs showing frescoes. Multicoloured.

2211	40pt. Type **445**	3·75	3·25
2212	60pt. Grapes and vine	5·50	5·00
2213	80pt. Games	7·25	6·75
2214	100pt. Face	9·25	8·50
MS2215	90×70 mm. 50pt. Quseir Amra	7·00	6·50

2009. Centenary of Hejaz Railway. Multicoloured.

2216	20pt. Steam train crossing bridge	20	20
2217	30pt. Steam locomotive	80	80
2218	50pt. Railway station	1·20	1·20

2009. Birds. Multicoloured.

2219	10pt. *Anas platyrhynchos* (Mallard)	1·00	1·00
2220	15pt. *Falco cherrug* (Saker Falcon)	1·00	1·00
2221	20pt. *Cursorius cursor* (Cream-coloured Courser)	1·00	1·00
2222	30pt. Starling (Inscr 'Cursorius cursor')	1·80	1·80
2223	40pt. *Upupa epops* (Hoopoe)	1·80	1·80
2224	50pt. *Francolinus francolinus* (Black Francolin)	1·80	1·80
2225	60pt. *Merops orientalis* (Green Bee-eater)	2·75	2·75
2226	80pt. *Carpodacus synoicus* (Sinai Rosefinch)	2·75	2·75

448 Coffee Grinder

2009. Coffee Drinking. Multicoloured.

2228	40pt. Type **448**	3·75	3·25
2229	60pt. Coffee pots and coffee roasting over embers	5·50	5·00
2230	80pt. Coffee pot and cups	7·25	6·75
2231	100pt. Coffee and coffee roasting implements	9·25	8·50
MS2232	70×90 mm. 50pt. Coffee making equipment. Imperf	7·00	6·50

449 Woman wearing Dress with Embroidered Bodice

2009. Traditional Clothes. Multicoloured.

2233	40pt. Type **449**	3·75	3·25
2234	60pt. Woman wearing brown dress and white veil	5·50	5·00
2235	80pt. Woman wearing red headdress and coin jewellery	7·25	6·75
2236	100pt. Couple	9·25	8·50
MS2237	70×90 mm. 50pt. As Type **449** (enlarged detail). Imperf	7·00	6·50

450 Pope Benedict XVI and King Abdullah II

2009. Visit of Pope Benedict XVI. Multicoloured.

2238	20pt. Type **450**	1·80	1·70
2239	30pt. Pope Benedict XVI	2·75	2·50
2240	40pt. Pope Benedict XVI and King Abdullah II (*different*)	3·75	3·25
MS2241	90×70 mm. 50pt. As No. 2240 (enlarged detail). Imperf	8·00	7·50

451 King Abdullah II

2009. Tenth Anniversary of Accession of King Abdullah II.

2242	**451**	10pt. multicoloured	90	85
2243	**451**	15pt. multicoloured	1·40	1·30
2244	**451**	20pt. multicoloured	1·80	1·70
2245	**451**	25pt. multicoloured	2·30	2·10
2246	**451**	30pt. multicoloured	2·75	2·50
2247	**451**	35pt. multicoloured	3·25	3·00
2248	**451**	40pt. multicoloured	3·75	3·25
2249	**451**	45pt. multicoloured	4·25	3·75
2250	**451**	50pt. multicoloured	4·50	4·25
2251	**451**	1d. multicoloured	9·25	8·50

452 Diana, the Huntress (As T **2342** of USA)

2009. Breast Cancer Awareness Campaign.

2252	**452**	30pt.+50pt. multicoloured	7·25	6·75

453 Horse

2009. Fauna. Multicoloured.

2253	10pt. Type **453**	90	85
2254	20pt. Rabbits	1·80	1·70
2255	30pt. Fox	2·75	2·50
2256	40pt. Oryx (inscr 'Maha Gazelle')	3·75	3·25
2257	50pt. Gazelle	4·50	4·25
MS2258	90×70 mm. 60pt. Camel. Imperf	7·00	6·50

No. 2259 is vacant.

454 Cables

2009. e-Government Programme. Multicoloured.

2260	20pt. Type **454**	1·80	1·70
2261	30pt. Emblem	2·75	2·50
2262	40pt. 'www.jordan.gov.jo'	3·75	3·25
2263	50pt. Symbols of communication	4·50	4·25

455 Spring-fed Waterfalls

2009. Hammamat Ma'een Hot Springs. Multicoloured.

2264	10pt. Type **455**	90	85
2265	20pt. Resort	1·80	1·70
2266	30pt. Waterfall and pool	2·75	2·50
2267	40pt. Waterfalls (*different*)	3·75	3·25
2268	50pt. Springs and dam	4·50	4·25
MS2269	70×90mm. 60pt. Single waterfall	7·00	6·50

456 **457**

458 **459**

460 **461**

462 **463**

464 **465**

2009. Jordanian Universities.

2270	**456**	20pt. multicoloured	1·80	1·70
2271	**457**	20pt. multicoloured	1·80	1·70
2272	**458**	20pt. multicoloured	1·80	1·70
2273	**459**	20pt. multicoloured	1·80	1·70
2274	**460**	20pt. multicoloured	1·80	1·70
2275	**461**	20pt. multicoloured	1·80	1·70
2276	**462**	20pt. multicoloured	1·80	1·70
2277	**463**	20pt. multicoloured	1·80	1·70
2278	**464**	20pt. multicoloured	1·80	1·70
2279	**465**	20pt. multicoloured	1·80	1·70

466 Sweetcorn

2009. Vegetables. Multicoloured.

2280	20pt. Type **466**	1·80	1·70
2281	20pt. Garlic and onions	1·80	1·70
2282	20pt. Peas, beans and okra	1·80	1·70
2283	20pt. Cabbages	1·80	1·70
2284	20pt. Aubergines	1·80	1·70
2285	20pt. Squash	1·80	1·70
2286	20pt. Sweet peppers	1·80	1·70
2287	20pt. Chilli peppers	1·80	1·70
2288	20pt. Turnips, swedes and radishes	1·80	1·70
2289	20pt Tomatoes and courgettes	1·80	1·70

467 Distressed Tree and Litter

2009. Environmental Protection. Multicoloured.

2290	20pt. Type **467**	1·80	1·70
2291	30pt. Litter on fire and children running	2·75	2·50
2292	40pt. Farm animals eating litter	3·75	3·25
2293	50pt. Litter in stream and recycling bins	4·50	4·25

No. 2294 is vacant.

468 Emblem

2009. al-Quds 2009. Arab Capital of Culture.

2295	**468**	20pt.+25pt. multicoloured	4·25	3·75
2296	**468**	30pt.+25pt. multicoloured	5·00	4·50
2297	**468**	40pt.+25pt. multicoloured	6·00	5·50
2298	**468**	50pt.+25pt. multicoloured	7·00	6·25

469 Stag Beetle

2009. Insects. Multicoloured.

2299	10pt. Type **469**	90	85
2300	15pt. Butterfly	1·40	1·30
2301	20pt. Ladybird	1·80	1·70
2302	25pt. Honey Bee	2·30	2·10
2303	30pt. Mantis	2·75	2·50
2304	40pt. Moth	3·75	3·25
2305	50pt. Dragon Fly	4·50	4·25
2306	60pt. Fly	5·50	5·00
2307	80pt. Grasshopper	7·25	6·75
2308	100pt. Dragon Fly and Damsel Fly	9·25	8·50

(470)

2009. Nos. 929/931 surch as T **470.**

2309	80pt. on 120f. black and salmon (Type **139**)	7·25	6·75
2310	80pt. on 180f. black, deep brown and lilac (No. 930)	7·25	6·75
2311	80pt. on 200f. multicoloured (No. 931)	7·25	6·75

80 pt

(470a)

2009. Un-listed Stamp 25f. of 2003 (as No. 1788) surch T **470a.**

2311a	80pt. on 25f. chestnut, pale reddish purple and black (Type **310**)	7·25	6·75

471 Ajlun

2010. Tourism. Multicoloured.

2312	10pt. Type **471**	90	85
2313	20pt. Column and capital, Amman	1·80	1·70
2314	30pt. Stone corridor, Karak	2·75	2·50
2315	40pt. Stone staircase, Showbak	3·75	3·25
MS2316	90×70 mm. 50pt. Partial façade, Jerash. Imperf	4·50	4·25

472 *Cortinarius balteatus*

2010. Fungi. Multicoloured.

2317	20pt. Type **472**	1·80	1·70
2318	20pt. *Russula bicolor*	1·80	1·70
2319	20pt. Fly agaric (inscr 'Red Fly Agaric')	1·80	1·70
2320	20pt. Inscr 'Amanita muscaria'	1·80	1·70
2321	20pt. *Boletus edulis*	1·80	1·70
2322	20pt. *Amanita ocreata* (inscr 'Amanita albocreata')	1·80	1·70
2323	20pt. Inscr 'Agaricus Anderwij'	1·80	1·70
2324	20pt. *Agaricus bisporus*	1·80	1·70

473 Jordan University Mosque

2010. Mosques. Multicoloured.

2325	10pt. Type **473**	90	85
2326	20pt. Abu-Darwiesh	1·80	1·70
2327	30pt. Al-Hussainy	2·75	2·50
2328	40pt. King Abdullah Mosque	3·75	3·25
2329	50pt. King Hussain Bin Talal Mosque	4·50	4·25

474 Skydiving

2010. Sports. Multicoloured.

2330	10pt. Type **474**	90	85
2331	20pt. Swimming	1·80	1·70
2332	30pt. Air ballooning	2·75	2·50
2333	40pt Yacht racing	3·75	3·25
MS2334	70×90mm. 50pt. Rallying. Imperf	4·50	4·25

475 Ma'an Development Area

2011. Developmental Zones. Multicoloured.

2335	20pt. Type **475**	1·80	1·70
2336	20pt. King Hussain Bin Talal Development Area	1·80	1·70
2337	20pt. Dead Sea Development Zone	1·80	1·70
2338	20pt. Jabal Ajloun Development Area	1·80	1·70
2339	20pt. Irbid Development Area	1·80	1·70

476 *Ocimum basilicum*

2011. Wild Herbs. Multicoloured.

2340	20pt. Type **472**	1·80	1·70
2341	20pt. *Matricaria chamomilia*	1·80	1·70
2342	20pt. *Salvia officinalis*	1·80	1·70
2343	20pt. *Thymus serpyllum* (inscr 'Thymus seryvllum')	1·80	1·70
2344	20pt. Lavender (inscr 'Lavandulaivera')	1·80	1·70
2345	20pt. *Artemisia herba alba*	1·80	1·70
2346	20pt. *Capparis spinsa* (inscr 'Capparis spinsa')	1·80	1·70
2347	20pt. *Trignella foenum-graecum*	1·80	1·70

477 Millstone

2011. Antique Tools. Multicoloured.

2348	20pt. Type **477**	1·80	1·70
2349	20pt. Horse drawn flail	2·75	2·50
2350	20pt. Pitchfork	3·75	3·25
2351	20pt. Donkey powered olive crusher	4·50	4·25

478 Dam

479 Dam

480 Dam

481 Dam

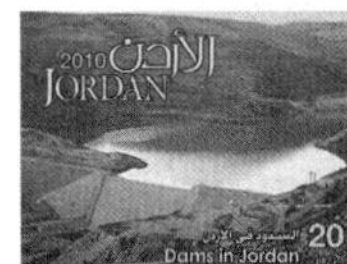

482 Dam

483 Dam

484 Dam

485 Dam

486 Dam

487 Dam

2011. Dams.

2352	**478**	20pt. multicoloured	1·80	1·70
2353	**479**	20pt. multicoloured	1·80	1·70
2354	**480**	20pt. multicoloured	1·80	1·70
2355	**481**	20pt. multicoloured	1·80	1·70
2356	**482**	20pt. multicoloured	1·80	1·70
2357	**483**	20pt. multicoloured	1·80	1·70
2358	**484**	20pt. multicoloured	1·80	1·70
2359	**485**	20pt. multicoloured	1·80	1·70
2360	**486**	20pt. multicoloured	1·80	1·70
2361	**487**	20pt. multicoloured	1·80	1·70
MS2362		90×70 mm. 30pt. As Type **480.** Imperf	5·75	5·25

488 Necklace

2011. Traditional Jewellery. Multicoloured.

2363	20pt Type **488**	1·80	1·70
2364	30pt. Turquoise and gold 'doughnut', Hand of Fatima pendant and gold chain with decorative inserts	2·75	2·50
2365	40pt. Large decorated gold ring	3·75	3·25
2366	50pt. Necklace with several pendants	4·50	4·25
MS2367	77×76mm. 30pt. Pierced work bangle. Imperf	5·75	5·50

489 Fencers

2011. Fencing Championship. Multicoloured.

2368	10pt. Type **489**	90	85
2369	20pt. Hit (purple)	1·80	1·70
2370	30pt. Attack (green)	2·75	2·50
2371	40pt. Lunge (bistre)	3·75	3·25
2372	50pt. Lunge and parry (grey)	4·50	4·25
MS2373	75×94mm. 50pt. Lunge and leap. Imperf	7·00	6·50

490 Red Bull Citroen Rally Car

2011. FIA World Rally Championship (WRC), Jordan. Multicoloured.

2374	10pt. Type **490**	90	85
2375	20pt. Sports Academy Racing Team Mitsubishi race car	1·80	1·70
2376	30pt. BP Ford Abu Dhabi race car	2·75	2·50
2377	40pt. Rally Jordan P-WRC winner Patrik Flodin (No. 48)	3·75	3·25
2378	50pt. Red Mitsubishi race car	4·50	4·25
MS2379	93×74mm. 50pt. Subaru race car (No. 3) Imperf	7·00	6·50

491 *Diploria strigose*

2011. Marine Life. Red Sea Coral Reefs. Multicoloured.

2380	20pt. Type **491**	1·80	1·70
2381	30pt. Coral and fish	2·75	2·50
2382	40pt. *Diploastrea heliopora*	3·75	3·25
2383	50pt. *Acropora hyacinthus*	4·50	4·25
2384	60pt. *Pectinia lactuca*	5·50	5·00
MS2385	90×70mm. 40pt. Coral bed and fish. Imperf	5·75	5·50

492 Tall Jug and Head

2011. Ceramics. Multicoloured.

2386	10pt. Type **492**	90	85
2387	20pt. Complex plaque with raised fortified decoration	1·80	1·70
2388	30pt. Circular jug with script decoration	2·75	2·50
2389	40pt. Flat circular tile with lower left extrusion	3·75	3·25
2390	50pt. Flat circular tile with lower right eroded	4·50	4·25
2391	60pt. Circular vessel on stand	5·50	5·00
MS2392	70×90mm. 30pt. Tiles. Imperf	3·50	3·25

493 King Abdullah II

2011. Historical Path. Multicoloured.

2393	20pt. Type **493**	1·80	1·70
2394	20pt. Harpist, carving	1·80	1·70
2395	20pt. White buildings on hillside (*horiz*)	1·80	1·70
2396	20pt. Assyrian bas-relief with figures and tree (*horiz*)	1·80	1·70
2397	20pt. Antelopes and figues, carving (*horiz*)	1·80	1·70
2398	20pt. Damaged fresco showing ships (*horiz*)	1·80	1·70
2399	20pt. Stylised multicoloured decorative buildings (*horiz*)	1·80	1·70
2400	20pt. Building (*horiz*)	1·80	1·70
2401	20pt. Circular plaque with woman's head (*horiz*)	1·80	1·70
2402	20pt. Ceres, bas-relief (*horiz*)	1·80	1·70

494 Astrolabe

2012. Old Astronomical Instruments. Multicoloured.

2403	10pt. Type **494**	90	85
2404	20pt. Telescope	1·80	1·70
2405	30pt. Sextant	2·75	2·50
2406	40pt Sundial	3·75	3·25

495 Crown Prince Hussein

2012. Crown Prince Hussein bin Abdullah.

2407	**495**	20pt. multicoloured	1·80	1·70
2408	**495**	30pt. multicoloured	2·75	2·50
2409	**495**	50pt. multicoloured	4·50	4·25

496 Penguins

2012. Preserve the Polar Regions and Glaciers. Multicoloured.

MS2410	80pt. Type **496**; 1d. Stranded Polar Bear	17·00	16·00

497 Royal Jordanian Falcons

2012. Royal Jordanian Falcons. Multicoloured.

2411	10pt. Type **497**	90	85
2412	20pt. Lead pilot	1·80	1·70
2413	30pt. Flying over wadi	2·75	2·50
2414	40pt Flying over river	3·75	3·25
MS2415	90×70mm. 50pt. Falcons and flag. Imperf	4·75	4·50

498 Raised Fists

2012. International Labour Day.

2416	20pt. orange-yellow and black	1·80	1·70
2417	30pt. Indian red	2·75	2·50
2418	40pt. agate	3·75	3·25
2419	50pt. multicoloured	4·50	4·25

Designs: 20 pt. Type **498**; 30pt. Miners; 40pt. Family; 50pt. Construction worker

499 Hands holding Globe

2012. World Telecommunication Day. Multicoloured.

2420	30pt. Type **499**	2·75	2·50
2421	40pt. Satellite dish	3·75	3·25
2422	50pt. Laptop computer	4·50	4·25

500 King Abdullah II and Khazne al-Firaun, Petra

2012. 50th Birthday of King Abdullah II ibn al-Hussein. Multicoloured.

2423	20pt. Type **500**	1·80	1·70
2424	20pt. Mosque, Amman	1·80	1·70
2425	20pt. Palace of Justice, Amman	1·80	1·70
2426	20pt. Oil refinery	1·80	1·70
2427	20pt. *Zhen Hua 16* freighter with containers	1·80	1·70
2428	20pt. Abdoun suspension bridge	1·80	1·70
MS2429	90×70 mm. 50pt. King Abdullah. Imperf	4·75	4·50

501 Dressage

2012. Olympic Games, London. Multicoloured.

2430	20pt. Type **501**	1·80	1·70
2431	30pt. Football	2·75	2·50
2432	40pt. Tennis	3·75	3·25
2433	50pt. Canoeing	4·50	4·25

502 King and Queen

2013. Chess. Multicoloured.

2434	20pt. Type **502**	1·80	1·70
2435	20pt. Chess board	1·80	1·70
2436	20pt. Rook and pawn	1·80	1·70

503 Kumquats

2013. Fruit. Multicoloured.

2437	10pt. Type **503**	90	85
2438	20pt. Mandarines	1·80	1·70
2439	30pt. Lemons	2·75	2·50
2440	40pt. Oranges	3·75	3·25
2441	50pt. Pomelos	4·50	4·25

504 Tyrannosaurus Rex

2013. Prehistoric Animals. Multicoloured.

MS2442	133×133mm. 20pt.×4, Type **504**; Brachiosaurus; Raptors; Triceratops	8·00	7·50
MS2443	133×93mm. 20pt.×4, Archaeopteryx; Tyrannosaurus; Triceratops and Stegosaurus; Two-horned dinosaur	8·00	7·50

505 Book surmounting Globe

2013. 50th Anniversary of Jordan Library and Information Association. Multicoloured.

2444	40pt. Type **505**	3·75	3·25
2445	50pt. Anniversary emblem	4·50	4·25

506 Mare and Foal

2013. Horses. Multicoloured.

2446	10pt. Type **506**	90	85
2447	20pt. Chestnut with white blaze galloping (*horiz*)	1·80	1·70
2448	30pt. Chestnut Mare and foal (*horiz*)	2·75	2·50
2449	40pt. Head of Bright Bay with black mane (*horiz*)	3·75	3·50
2450	50pt. Bay galloping through sea (*horiz*)	4·50	4·25
MS2451	90×70mm. 50pt. Herd. Imperf	4·75	4·50

507 Tawfiq Nimri

508 Hassan Ibrahim

509 Moses

510 Mahmoud Saymeh

511 Jordanian Artist

512 Jordanian Artist

513 Jordanian Artist

514 Jordanian Artist

2013. Jordanian Artists.

2452 **507**	20pt. multicoloured	1·80	1·70
2453 **508**	20pt. multicoloured	1·80	1·70
2454 **509**	20pt. multicoloured	1·80	1·70
2455 **510**	20pt. multicoloured	1·80	1·70
2456 **511**	20pt. multicoloured	1·80	1·70
2457 **512**	20pt. multicoloured	1·80	1·70
2458 **513**	20pt. multicoloured	1·80	1·70
2459 **514**	20pt. multicoloured	1·80	1·70

515 Full Sail

2013. Sailing Ships. Multicoloured.

2460	20pt. Type **515**	1·80	1·70
2461	30pt. In harbour	2·75	2·50
2462	40pt. On stormy sea	3·75	3·50
2463	50pt. Partially rigged	4·50	4·25
MS2464	90×70mm. 50pt. Armada of ships. Imperf	4·75	4·50

516 *Landscape with Rainbow* (Peter Paul Rubens)

2013. Paintings. Masterpieces of Art. Multicoloured.

2465	20pt. Type **516**	1·80	1·70
2466	20pt. *The Milkmaid* (Johannes Vermeer) (*vert*)	1·80	1·70
2467	20pt. *Slavers throwing overboard the Dead and Dying-Typhoon coming on* (J M W Turner)	1·80	1·70
2468	20pt. *Women in the Garden* (Claude Monet) (*vert*)	1·80	1·70
2469	20pt. *Impression. Soleil Levant* (Claude Monet)	1·80	1·70
2470	20pt. *Les Meules à Giverny* (Claude Monet)	1·80	1·70
2471	20pt. *The Red Vineyard* (Vincent van Gogh)	1·80	1·70
2472	20pt. *Strolling along the Seashore* (Joaquin Sorolla y Bastida)	1·80	1·70

517 Amethyst

2013. Precious Stones. Multicoloured.

2473	20pt. Type **517**	1·80	1·70
2474	20pt. Red Diamond	1·80	1·70
2475	20pt. Emerald	1·80	1·70
2476	20pt. Black Opal	1·80	1·70
2477	20pt. Pearl	1·80	1·70
2478	20pt. Ruby	1·80	1·70

518 Mountain Pass

2014. Nature Reserves in Jordan. Dana Nature Reserve. Multicoloured.

2479	10pt. Type **518**	90	85
2480	20pt. Succulent flower (*horiz*)	1·80	1·70
2481	30pt. Lake (*horiz*)	2·75	2·50
2482	40pt. Hillside (*horiz*)	3·75	3·50
2483	50pt. Oryx (*horiz*)	4·50	4·25
MS2484	90×70mm. 50pt. Cliffs and valley. Imperf	4·75	4·50

519 Grey-crowned Crane

2014. Migratory Birds. Multicoloured.

2485	20pt. Type **519**	1·80	1·70
2486	20pt. Great White Pelican	1·80	1·70
2487	20pt. Mallard (Duck)	1·80	1·70
2488	20pt. Collared Flycatcher	1·80	1·70
2489	20pt. Common Buzzard	1·80	1·70
2490	20pt. Female Eurasian Blackcap	1·80	1·70
2491	20pt. European Bee-eater (*vert*)	1·80	1·70
2492	20pt. Glossy Ibis (*vert*)	1·80	1·70

520 1933 500m. Stamp (As No. 220), Map and Ruins of Petra (image scaled to 42% of original size)

2014. 80th Anniversary of Petra Stamps. Multicoloured.

MS2493	80pt. Type **520**	7·50	7·25
MS2494	80pt. 1933 15m. Stamp (As No. 214), map and ruins of Petra	7·50	7·25

521 Pope Francis

2014. 50th Anniversary of First Papal Visit to Jordan. Multicoloured.

2495	20pt. Type **521**	1·80	1·70
2496	30pt. Pope Francis and HM King Abdulla II	2·75	2·50
2497	40pt. Pope Francis releasing dove (vert)	3·75	3·50
MS2498	90×70mm. 50pt. Images of Papal visits, 1964, 2000, 2009 and 2014. Imperf	4·00	3·75

522 Cartoon by Osama Hajjaj

523 Cartoon by Osama Hajjaj

524 Cartoon by Osama Hajjaj

525 Abu Mohammad (cartoon by Emad Hajjaj)

526 Abu Mohammad and Abu Mahjoob (cartoon by Emad Hajjaj)

527 Abu Mahjoob (cartoon by Emad Hajjaj)

2014. Cartoonists.

2499 **522**	20pt. multicoloured	1·80	1·70
2500 **523**	20pt. multicoloured	1·80	1·70
2501 **524**	20pt. multicoloured	1·80	1·70
2502 **525**	20pt. multicoloured	1·80	1·70
2503 **526**	20pt. multicoloured	1·80	1·70
2504 **527**	20pt. multicoloured	1·80	1·70

528 Doorway, Justice Palace

2014. Architecture. Doors and Windows. Multicoloured.

2505	20pt. Type **528**	1·80	1·70
2506	20pt. Circular window, Al-Salt	1·80	1·70
2507	20pt. Glazed door, Alt-Salt School	1·80	1·70
2508	20pt. Arched window, Raghadan Palace	1·80	1·70
2509	20pt. Doorway, Royal Hashemite Court	1·80	1·70
2510	20pt. Doorway, King Hussein's Mosque (horiz)	1·80	1·70
2511	20pt. Doorway, Umayyad Palace (horiz)	1·80	1·70

529 Mediterranean

2014. EUROMED. Euromed 2014 Postal Conference.

2513 **529**	80pt. multicoloured	7·25	7·00

530 Emblem

2015. 90th Anniversary of Amman Chamber of Commerce.

2514 **530**	40pt. multicoloured	3·75	3·50

531 Statue of Soldier and Emblem

2015. Economic and Social Foundation for Military Retirees and Veterans.

2515 **531**	40pt. multicoloured	3·75	3·50

532 Scales

2015. Arab Lawyers' Union.

2516 **532**	40pt. multicoloured	3·75	3·50

533 Signing

2015. Jordanian Deaf Women's Association.

2517 **533**	40pt. multicoloured	3·75	3·50

534 1dinar Banknote

2015. Jordanian Currency. Multicoloured.

2518	10pt. Type **534**	90	85
2519	20pt. 5d. banknote	1·80	1·70
2520	40pt. 10d. banknote	3·75	3·50
2521	60pt. 15d. banknote	5·50	5·25
2522	80pt. 50d. banknote	7·25	7·00

535 Order of Independence

2015. Royal Medals. Multicoloured.

2523	50pt. Type **535**	4·50	4·25
2524	50pt. Order of Renaissance (green 'leaves', red circle, crossed flags)	4·50	4·25
2525	50pt. Al-Hussein Order of Military Merit–Second Class (white star, red centre, crown and wreath)	4·50	4·25
2526	50pt. Order of Renaissance (green 'leaves', red circle, crossed flags) (*different*)	4·50	4·25
2527	50pt. Al-Hussein Decoration for Distinguished Service–First Class (gold circle and central profile)	4·50	4·25
2528	50pt. The Order of Hussein ibn Ali (gold, oval, surmounted by crown) (*vert*)	4·50	4·25
2529	50pt. Order of Military Gallantry (head of King Abdullah ibn Hussein facing left) (*vert*)	4·50	4·25
2530	50pt. Medal of Honour (gold medal and bar) (*vert*)	4·50	4·25
2531	50pt. Order of the Star of Jordan (seven gold stars, green circle)	4·50	4·25
2532	50pt. Order of the Hashemite Star (white star, central profile, surmounted by crown) (*vert*)	4·50	4·25

2015. 70th Anniversary of United Nations. Multicoloured.

2533	80pt. '70' and 'Strong UN Better World'	7·25	7·00

2015. Traditional Costumes. Multicoloured.

2534	20pt. Salt	1·80	1·70
2535	20pt. Um Qais	1·80	1·70
2536	20pt. Jerash	1·80	1·70
2537	20pt. Karak	1·80	1·70
2538	20pt. Tafilah	1·80	1·70
2539	20pt. Wadi Rum	1·80	1·70
2540	20pt. Amman	1·80	1·70
2541	20pt. Ma'an	1·80	1·70
2542	20pt. Badawi	1·80	1·70
2543	20pt. Ajloun	1·80	1·70
2544	20pt. Mafraq	1·80	1·70
2545	20pt. Madaba	1·80	1·70

2015. The Four Seasons. Multicoloured.

MS2546	30pt.×4, Tips of bough in Spring time; Boughs and trunk in Summer; Upper and lower bough in Autumn; Tips of boughs in winter	11·00	10·50

2015. Jordanian Mosaics. Multicoloured.

2547	30pt. Male figure	2·75	2·50
2548	30pt. Horse	2·75	2·50
2549	30pt. City	2·75	2·50
2550	30pt. Ox in a roundel	2·75	2·50
MS2551	90×70mm. 60pt. Woman and fish. Imperf	5·75	5·50

540 Decorated Bottles

2015. Jordanian Handicrafts. Multicoloured.

2552	30pt. Type **540**	2·75	2·50
2553	30pt. Mosaic box	2·75	2·50
2554	30pt. Coloured sand in bottles	2·75	2·50
2555	30pt. Decorated pot	2·75	2·50
2556	30pt. Jewellery	2·75	2·50
MS2557	90×70mm. 60pt. Coloured sand in bottles (*different*). Imperf	5·75	5·50

541 Umm Aljemal

2015. Decapolis. Multicoloured.

2558	50pt. Type **541**	4·50	4·25
2559	50pt. Um Gals	4·50	4·25
2560	50pt. Beit Ras	4·50	4·25
2561	50pt. Quwayliba	4·50	4·25
2562	50pt. Gerasa	4·50	4·25

542 Camel Riders

2016. Centenary of Great Arab Revolt. Multicoloured.

2563	10pt. Type **542**	90	85
2564	20pt. Horseman	1·80	1·70
2565	30pt. Leaders	2·75	2·50
2566	50pt. King Abdullah II	4·50	4·25
2567	100pt. Sherif Hussein bin Ali and emblem	9·00	8·75
MS2568	70×90mm. 60pt. Emblem (*different*). Imperf	5·75	5·50

543 Scorpionfish

2016. Fish of the Mediterranean Sea. Multicoloured.

2569	40pt. Type **543**	3·75	3·50
2570	40pt. Axillary Wrasse	3·75	3·50
2571	40pt. Lionfish	3·75	3·50
2572	40pt. Black Back Butterflyfish	3·75	3·50
2573	40pt. Butterfly Blenny	3·75	3·50

544 Emblem

2016. First Amman International Numismatic and Philatelic Fair.

2574	**544**	30pt. multicoloured	2·75	2·50
2575	**544**	50pt. multicoloured	4·50	4·25

545 Wadi Rum

2016. Tourism. Hiking Destinations in Jordan. Multicoloured.

2576	40pt. Type **545**	3·75	3·50
2577	40pt. Madaba	3·75	3·50
2578	40pt. Karak	3·75	3·50
2579	40pt. Ajlun (*vert*)	3·75	3·50
2580	40pt. Wadi Al Dab (*vert*)	3·75	3·50
2581	40pt. Ma'in (*vert*)	3·75	3·50
2582	40pt. Madaba (*different*)	3·75	3·50

546 Emblem

2016. Arab Post Day. Multicoloured.

2583	40pt. Type **546**	3·75	3·50
2584	40pt. As Type **546** but with design reversed	3·75	3·50

547 Player

2016. Football. FIFA U-17 Women's World Cup. Multicoloured.

2585	40pt. Type **547**	3·75	3·50
2586	50pt. Two players	4·50	4·25
2587	60pt. Player (*different*)	5·50	5·25
2588	70pt. Player kicking ball	6·25	6·00

548 Ajlun Castle

2016. Ancient Castles in Jordan. Multicoloured.

2589	30pt. Type **548**	2·75	2·50
2590	30pt. Al-Azraq	2·75	2·50
2591	30pt. Umayyad Palace	2·75	2·50
2592	40pt. Shobak Castle	3·75	3·50
2593	40pt. Karak Castle	3·75	3·50
2594	40pt. Aqaba Castle	3·75	3·50

549 Emblem

2016. Museum of Parliamentary Life. Multicoloured.

2595	20pt. Type **549**	1·80	1·70
2596	30pt. Gateway	2·75	2·50
2597	40pt. Meeting room	3·75	3·50
2598	50pt. Dias and chamber	4·50	4·25
2599	60pt. King Abdullah II	5·50	5·25

550 Map and Flags of Participants

2017. 28th Arab League Summit, Amman, Jordan. Multicoloured.

2600	10pt. Type **550**	90	85
2601	20pt. Amman	1·80	1·70
2602	30pt. Mosque	2·75	2·50
2603	40pt. '28'	3·75	3·50
MS2604	95×80mm. 50pt. King Abdullah II bin Al-Hussein. Imperf	4·75	4·50

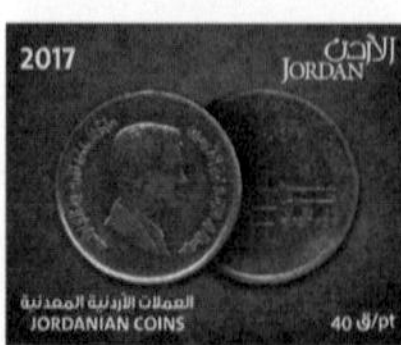

551 Coins

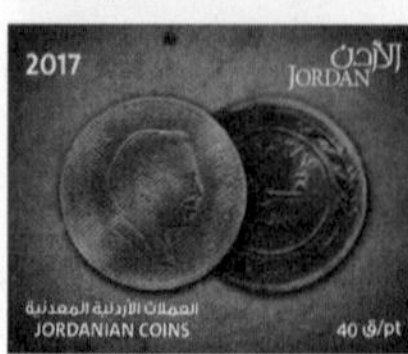

552 Coins

553 Coins

554 Coins

555 Coins

556 Coins

2017. Coins. Multicoloured.

2605	**551**	40pt. multicoloured	3·75	3·50
2606	**552**	40pt. multicoloured	3·75	3·50
2607	**553**	40pt. multicoloured	3·75	3·50
2608	**554**	40pt. multicoloured	3·75	3·50
2609	**555**	40pt. multicoloured	3·75	3·50
2610	**556**	40pt. multicoloured	3·75	3·50

557 Spanish Fir

2017. EUROMED - Mediterranean Trees. Multicoloured.

2611	30pt. Type **557**	2·75	2·50
2612	50pt. Turkey Oak	4·50	4·25

10pt ١٠ قروش

(558)

2017. No. 2036b (Hadrian's Triumphal Arch, Jerash - 2003) surch as T **558**

2613	10pt. on 50f. multicoloured	90	85
2614	15pt. on 50f. multicoloured	85	85
2615	20pt. on 50f. multicoloured	1·80	1·70
2616	25pt. on 50f. multicoloured	2·30	2·20
2617	30pt. on 50f. multicoloured	2·75	2·50
2618	35pt. on 50f. multicoloured	3·25	3·00
2619	40pt. on 50f. multicoloured	3·75	3·50
2620	45pt. on 50f. multicoloured	4·25	3·75
2621	50pt. on 50f. multicoloured	4·50	4·25
2622	60pt. on 50f. multicoloured	5·50	5·25

559 Strawberries

2017. Fruit. Multicoloured.

2623	20pt. Type **559**	1·80	1·70
2624	20pt. Pomegranates	1·80	1·70
2625	20pt. Figs	1·80	1·70
2626	20pt. Mulberries	1·80	1·70
2627	20pt. Grapes	1·80	1·70
2628	20pt. Prickly Pears	1·80	1·70
2629	20pt. Peaches	1·80	1·70
2630	20pt. Cantaloupe Melon	1·80	1·70
2631	20pt. Plums	1·80	1·70
2632	20pt. Watermelon	1·80	1·70

20 pt

(560)

2017. Various stamps (Cradle of Civilization) surch in red as T **560**

2633	20pt. on 100f. multicoloured (No. 1910) (Temple, Petra)	1·80	1·70
2634	20pt. on 100f. multicoloured (No. 1913) (Path between columns, Jerash)	1·80	1·70
2635	20pt. on 100f. multicoloured (No. 1919) (Camels, Wadi Rum)	1·80	1·70
2636	20pt. on 100f. multicoloured (No. 1928) (Columns and steps, Pella)	1·80	1·70
2637	20pt. on 100f. multicoloured (No. 1931) (Castle, Ajloun)	1·80	1·70
2638	20pt. on 100f. multicoloured (No. 1934) (Arches and columns, um Quais)	1·80	1·70
2639	20pt. on 100f. multicoloured (No. 1937) (Mushatta Palace)	1·80	1·70

30pt

(561)

2017. No. 1918 (Statues (Cradle of Civilization)) surch in red as T **561**

2640	30pt. on 300f. multicoloured	2·75	2·50
2641	50pt. on 300f. multicoloured	4·50	4·25

562 Rock Dove (inscr 'Carrier Pigeon')

2017. Birds. Multicoloured.

MS2642	30pt.×6, Type **562;** Goldfinch; Long-legged Buzzard (Inscr '*Buteo rufinus*'); Blackbird; Chukar Partridge (Inscr 'Shunnarbird'); Rose Finch	17·00	16·00

563 Armed Forces Badge and Personnel

564 Armed Forces Badge and Personnel

565 Armed Forces Badge and Personnel

566 Armed Forces Badge and Personnel

567 Armed Forces Badge and Personnel

568 Armed Forces Badge and Personnel

569 Armed Forces Badge and Personnel

2017. Jordanian Armed Forces

2643	**563**	30pt. multicoloured	2·75	2·50
2644	**564**	30pt. multicoloured	2·75	2·50
2645	**565**	30pt. multicoloured	2·75	2·50
2646	**566**	30pt. multicoloured	2·75	2·50
2647	**567**	30pt. multicoloured	2·75	2·50
2648	**568**	30pt. multicoloured	2·75	2·50
2649	**569**	30pt. multicoloured	2·75	2·50

570 Afra Baths

2017. Medical Tourism in Jordan. Multicoloured.

2650	40pt. Type **570**	3·75	3·50
2651	40pt. Maeen Baths	3·75	3·50
2652	40pt. Dead Sea	3·75	3·50
2653	40pt. Jordan's natural springs	3·75	3·50

571 Um Er-Rasas

2017. World Heritage Sites in Jordan. Multicoloured.

2654	40pt. Type **571**	3·75	3·50
2655	40pt. Wadi Rum	3·75	3·50
2656	40pt. Petra	3·75	3·50
2657	40pt. Qusayr Amra	3·75	3·50
2658	40pt. Inscr 'Baptism'	3·75	3·50

OBLIGATORY TAX

T36 Mosque in Hebron

1947

T264	**T36**	1m. blue	90	50
T265	**T36**	2m. red	1·10	65
T266	**T36**	3m. green	1·20	85
T267	**T36**	5m. red	1·50	1·00
T268	-	10m. red	1·70	1·40
T269	-	15m. grey	2·40	1·50
T270	-	20m. brown	3·50	2·00
T271	-	50m. violet	6·00	4·00
T272	-	100m. red	18·00	12·00
T273	-	200m. blue	55·00	28·00
T274	-	500m. green	£110	85·00
T275	-	£P1 brown	£225	£180

Designs: Nos. T268/T271, Dome of the Rock; Nos. T272/T275, Acre.

1950. Optd **Aid** in English and Arabic.

T290	**T28**	5m. orange	29·00	27·00
T291	**T28**	10m. violet	38·00	35·00
T292	**T28**	15m. green	45·00	42·00

T43 Ruins at Palmyra, Syria

1950. Revenue stamps optd **Aid** in English and Arabic.

T296	**T43**	5m. orange	33·00	24·00
T297	**T43**	10m. violet	33·00	28·00

1951. Values in FILS.

T302	**T36**	5f. red	1·10	1·00
T303	-	10f. red	1·10	1·00
T304	-	15f. black	1·20	1·10
T305	-	20f. brown	1·50	1·40
T306	-	100f. orange	7·50	7·00

Designs: Nos. T303/T305, Dome of the Rock; No. T306, Acre.

1952. Nos. T264/T275 optd **J.D.** (T344) or **FILS** (others).

T334	**T36**	1f. on 1m. blue	60	55
T335	**T36**	2f. on 2m. red	£140	†
T336	**T36**	3f. on 3m. green	90	55
T337	-	10f. on 10m. red	1·10	55
T338	-	15f. on 15m. grey	2·10	1·40
T339	-	20f. on 20m. brown	2·40	2·20
T340	-	50f. on 50m. violet	4·50	4·25
T341	-	100f. on 100m. orange	26·00	13·50
T342	-	200f. on 200m. blue	65·00	36·00
T343	-	500f. on 500m. green	£140	£100
T344	-	1d. on £P1 brown	£250	£200

OFFICIAL STAMPS

(حكومة)
الشرق العربي
١٣٤٢

(O16) Arab Government of the East, 1342

1924. Type **11** of Saudi Arabia optd with Type **O16**.

O117	½p. red	35·00	£110

POSTAGE DUE STAMPS

حكومة
مستحق
الشرق العربية
مستحق ٩ شعبان ١٣٤١

(D12) Due **(D13)**

1923. Issue of 1923 (with opt **T 10**) further optd. (a) With Type **D12** (the 3p. also surch as **T 12**).

D112	**11**	½p. on 3p. brown	42·00	45·00
D113	**11**	1p. blue	25·00	27·00
D114	**11**	1½p. lilac	38·00	40·00
D115	**11**	2p. orange	40·00	42·00

(b) With Type **D13** and surch as T **12**.

D116	½p. on 3p. brown	55·00	60·00

POSTAGE DUE STAMPS

(D14)

1923. Stamps of Saudi Arabia handstamped with Type **D14**.

D117	**11**	½p. red	4·50	10·00
D118	**11**	1p. blue	9·00	9·00
D119	**11**	1½p. violet	6·50	10·00
D120	**11**	2p. orange	9·00	11·00
D121	**11**	3p. brown	22·00	28·00
D122	**11**	5p. olive	24·00	45·00

(D20) Due East of the Jordan

1925. Stamps of Palestine (without Palestine opt) optd with Type **D20**.

D159	**3**	1m. brown	2·75	16·00
D160	**3**	2m. yellow	5·00	10·00
D161	**3**	4m. red	5·00	23·00
D162	**3**	8m. red	7·50	24·00
D163	**3**	13m. blue	12·00	25·00
D164	**3**	5p. purple	14·00	42·00

مستحق

١ مليم

(D21)

1926. Stamps of Palestine as last surch as Type **D21** (DUE and new value in Arabic).

D165	**3**	1m. on 1m. brown	14·00	40·00
D166	**3**	2m. on 1m. brown	13·00	40·00
D167	**3**	4m. on 3m. blue	14·00	42·00
D168	**3**	8m. on 3m. blue	14·00	42·00
D169	**3**	13m. on 13m. blue	19·00	48·00
D170	**3**	5p. on 13m. blue	23·00	70·00

The lower line of the surcharge differs for each value.

(D25)

1928. Surch as Type **D25** or optd only.

D183	**22**	1m. on 3m. red	1·75	8·00
D184	**22**	2m. blue	4·50	7·50
D185	**22**	4m. on 15m. blue	5·00	20·00
D186	**22**	10m. red	9·50	9·50
D187	**23**	20m. on 100m. blue	8·00	32·00
D188	**23**	50m. purple	6·00	27·00

(D26)

1929

D244	**D26**	1m. brown	1·50	9·00
D245	**D26**	2m. yellow	2·75	9·00
D246	**D26**	4m. green	2·75	15·00
D247	**D26**	10m. red	8·00	17·00
D193	**D26**	20m. olive	17·00	28·00
D194	**D26**	50m. blue	20·00	38·00

1952. Optd **FILS FILS** in English and Arabic.

D350	**D26**	1f. on 1m. brown	1·50	1·80
D351	**D26**	2f. on 2m. yellow	1·50	1·80
D352	**D26**	4f. on 4m. green	2·30	2·75
D353	**D26**	10f. on 10m. red	6·00	6·75
D354	**D26**	20f. on 20m. olive	12·50	11·50
D346	**D26**	50f. on 50m. blue	13·00	12·00

(D50)

1952. Inscr 'THE HASHEMITE KINGDOM OF THE JORDAN'.

D372	**D50**	1f. brown	90	1·10
D373	**D50**	2f. yellow	90	1·10
D374	**D50**	4f. green	90	1·10
D375	**D50**	10f. red	1·80	2·00
D376	**D50**	20f. brown	1·80	2·20
D377	**D50**	50f. blue	5·00	5·25

1957. As Type **D50**, but inscr 'THE HASHEMITE KINGDOM OF JORDAN'.

D465	1f. brown	1·50	1·80
D466	2f. yellow	1·50	1·80
D467	4f. green	1·50	2·50
D468	10f. red	2·30	2·50
D469	20f. brown	4·00	5·00

JORDANIAN OCCUPATION OF PALESTINE

1948. Stamps of Jordan optd **PALESTINE** in English and Arabic.

P1	**28**	1m. brown	1·10	95
P2	**28**	2m. green	1·10	95
P3	**28**	3m. green	1·10	1·10
P4	**28**	3m. pink	65	65
P5	**28**	4m. green	65	65
P6	**28**	5m. orange	65	65
P7	**28**	10m. violet	1·90	1·80
P8	**28**	12m. red	1·80	1·10
P9	**28**	15m. green	2·50	2·50
P10	**28**	20m. blue	3·50	1·90
P11	**29**	50m. purple	3·75	3·75
P12	**29**	90m. bistre	19·00	4·00
P13	**29**	100m. blue	22·00	12·00
P14	**29**	200m. violet	10·00	18·00
P15	**29**	500m. brown	75·00	33·00
P16	**29**	£P1 grey	£150	80·00

1949. 75th Anniversary of UPU. Stamps of Jordan optd **PALESTINE** in English and Arabic.

P30	**40**	1m. brown	90	90
P31	**40**	4m. green	90	90
P32	**40**	10m. red	1·40	1·40
P33	**40**	20m. blue	1·40	1·40
P34	-	50m. green (No. 289)	3·50	3·50

OBLIGATORY TAX

1950. Nos. T264/T275 of Jordan optd **PALESTINE** in English and Arabic.

PT35	**T36**	1m. blue	40	90
PT36	**T36**	2m. red	40	90
PT37	**T36**	3m. green	90	1·00
PT38	**T36**	5m. purple	1·10	90
PT39	-	10m. red	1·30	90
PT40	-	15m. black	3·50	1·10
PT41	-	20m. brown	5·50	1·90
PT42	-	50m. violet	8·25	3·75
PT43	-	100m. red	14·00	6·00
PT44	-	200m. blue	35·00	18·00
PT45	-	500m. green	£100	55·00
PT46	-	£P1 brown	£190	£100

POSTAGE DUE STAMPS

1948. Postage Due stamps of Jordan optd **PALESTINE** in English and Arabic.

PD25	**D26**	1m. brown	4·50	6·00
PD26	**D26**	2m. yellow	5·00	7·00
PD18	**D26**	4m. green	5·00	7·00
PD28	**D26**	10m. red	5·00	6·25
PD20	**D26**	20m. olive	4·50	5·50
PD21	**D26**	50m. blue	5·25	7·00

After a time the stamps of Jordan were used in the occupied areas.

JUBALAND

A district in E. Africa, formerly part of Kenya, ceded by Gt. Britain to Italy in 1925, and incorporated in Italian Somaliland.

100 centesimi = 1 lira.

1925. Stamps of Italy optd **OLTRE GIUBA**.

1	**30**	1c. brown	4·50	17·00
2	**31**	2c. brown	4·50	17·00
3	**37**	5c. green	3·00	11·50
4	**37**	10c. pink	3·00	11·50
5	**37**	15c. grey	3·00	14·00
6	**41**	20c. orange	3·00	14·00
39	**39**	20c. green	11·50	18·00
7	**39**	25c. blue	3·50	14·00
8	**39**	30c. brown	5·75	17·00
40	**39**	30c. grey	11·50	23·00
9	**39**	40c. brown	8·75	14·00
10	**39**	50c. mauve	8·75	14·00
11	**39**	60c. red	8·75	17·00
41	**34**	75c. red and carmine	70·00	70·00
12	**34**	1l. brown and green	17·00	23·00
42	**34**	1l.25 blue and ultramarine	85·00	£100
13	**34**	2l. green and orange	85·00	50·00
43	**34**	2l.50 green and orange	£120	£180
14	**34**	5l. blue and pink	£170	80·00
15	**34**	10l. green and pink	23·00	90·00

1925. Royal Jubilee stamps of Italy optd **OLTRE GIUBA**.

44B	**82**	60c. red	2·30	11·50
45B	**82**	1l. blue	2·30	23·00
46B	**82**	1l.25 blue	5·75	29·00

1926. St Francis of Assisi stamps of Italy, as Nos. 191/196, optd **OLTRE GIUBA**.

47	**83**	20c. green	3·50	25·00
48	-	40c. violet	3·50	25·00
49	-	60c. red	3·50	40·00
50	-	1l.25 blue	3·50	60·00
51	-	5l.+2l.50 olive	8·00	85·00

8 Map of Jubaland

1926. First Anniversary of Acquisition of Jubaland.

54	**8**	5c. orange	1·50	14·00
55	**8**	20c. green	1·50	14·00
56	**8**	25c. brown	1·50	14·00
57	**8**	40c. red	1·50	14·00
58	**8**	60c. purple	1·50	14·00
59	**8**	1l. blue	1·50	14·00
60	**8**	2l. grey	1·50	17·00

1926. As Colonial Propaganda T **6** of Cyrenaica, but inscr 'OLTRE GIUBA'.

61	5c.+5c. brown	1·20	8·00
62	10c.+5c. olive	1·20	8·00
63	20c.+5c. green	1·20	8·00
64	40c.+5c. red	1·20	8·00
65	60c.+5c. orange	1·20	8·00
66	1l.+5c. blue	1·20	14·00

EXPRESS LETTER STAMPS

1926. Express Letter stamps of Italy optd **OLTRE GUIBA**.

E52	**E35**	70c. red	35·00	46·00
E53	**E41**	2l.50 blue and pink	50·00	£120

PARCEL POST STAMPS

1925. Parcel Post stamps of Italy optd **OLTRE GIUBA**.

P16	**P53**	5c. brown	9·75	29·00

P17	**P53**	10c. blue	7·00	29·00
P18	**P53**	20c. black	7·00	29·00
P19	**P53**	25c. red	7·00	29·00
P20	**P53**	50c. orange	10·50	29·00
P21	**P53**	1l. violet	8·00	70·00
P22	**P53**	2l. green	12·50	70·00
P23	**P53**	3l. yellow	35·00	85·00
P24	**P53**	4l. grey	14·00	85·00
P25	**P53**	10l. purple	80·00	£130
P26	**P53**	12l. brown	£170	£225
P27	**P53**	15l. olive	£160	£300
P28	**P53**	20l. purple	£160	£300

Unused prices are for complete stamps, used prices for half-stamps.

POSTAGE DUE STAMPS

1925. Postage Due stamps of Italy optd **OLTRE GIUBA**.

D29	**D12**	5c. purple and orange	17·00	17·00
D30	**D12**	10c. purple and orange	17·00	17·00
D31	**D12**	20c. purple and orange	17·00	23·00
D32	**D12**	30c. purple and orange	17·00	23·00
D33	**D12**	40c. purple and orange	23·00	25·00
D34	**D12**	50c. purple and orange	23·00	35·00
D35	**D12**	60c. brown and orange	7·00	46·00
D36	**D12**	1l. purple and blue	30·00	60·00
D37	**D12**	2l. purple and blue	£150	£250
D38	**D12**	5l. purple and blue	£180	£250

KAMPUCHEA

Following the fall of the Khmer Rouge government which had terminated the Khmer Republic, the People's Republic of Kampuchea was proclaimed on 10 January 1979.

Kampuchea was renamed Cambodia in 1989.

100 cents = 1 riel.

105 Soldiers with Flag and Independence Monument, Phnom Penh

1980. Multicoloured. Without gum.

402	0.1r. Type **105**	9·25	9·00
403	0.2r. Khmer people and flag	14·00	13·50
404	0.5r. Fisherman pulling in nets	23·00	22·00
405	1r. Armed forces and Kampuchean flag	43·00	42·00

106 Moscow Kremlin and Globe

1982. 60th Anniversary of USSR. Multicoloured.

406	50c. Type **106**	80	40
407	1r. Industrial complex and map of USSR	1·50	55

107 Arms of Kampuchea

1983. Fourth Anniversary of People's Republic of Kampuchea. Multicoloured.

408	50c. Type **107**	95	25
409	1r. Open book illustrating National Flag and Arms (horiz)	1·60	40
410	3r. Stylised figures and map	4·50	1·30
MS411 90×109 mm. 6r. Temple, Phnom Penh (28×35 mm)		8·75	3·00

108 Runner with Olympic Torch

1983. Olympic Games, Los Angeles (1984) (1st issue). Multicoloured.

412	20c. Type **108**	45	15
413	50c. Javelin throwing	60	20
414	80c. Pole vaulting	80	25
415	1r. Discus throwing	95	35
416	1r.50 Relay (horiz)	1·60	40
417	2r. Swimming (horiz)	2·30	55
418	3r. Basketball	3·50	65
MS419 92×64 mm. 6r. Football (31×39 mm)		7·50	4·00

See also Nos. 526/**MS**533.

109 Orange Tiger

1983. Butterflies. Multicoloured.

420	20c. Type **109**	35	15
421	50c. *Euploea althaea*	45	20
422	80c. *Byasa polyeuctes* (horiz)	70	25
423	1r. *Stichophthalma howqua* (horiz)	1·40	35
424	1r.50 Leaf butterfly	2·30	40
425	2r. Blue argus	3·00	55
426	3r. Lemon migrant	4·75	65

110 Srah Srang

1983. Khmer Culture. Multicoloured.

427	20c. Type **110**	35	15
428	50c. Bakong	45	20
429	80c. Ta Som (vert)	55	25
430	1r. North gate, Angkor Thom (vert)	90	40
431	1r.50 Kennora (winged figures) (vert)	2·00	55
432	2r. Apsara (carved figures), Angkor (vert)	2·30	65
433	3r. Banteai Srei (goddess), Tevoda (vert)	3·50	95

111 Dancers with Castanets

1983. Folklore. Multicoloured.

434	50c. Type **111**	45	25
435	1r. Dancers with grass headdresses	1·60	55
436	3r. Dancers with scarves	3·50	1·30
MS437 94×63 mm. 6r. Warrior with blowpipe (31×39 mm)		6·75	2·75

112 Detail of Fresco

1983. 500th Birth Anniversary of Raphael (artist).

438	**112**	20c. multicoloured	35	15
439	-	50c. multicoloured	45	20
440	-	80c. multicoloured	55	25
441	-	1r. multicoloured	1·00	40
442	-	1r.50 multicoloured	1·70	55
443	-	2r. multicoloured	2·30	65
444	-	3r. multicoloured	2·75	95
MS445 97×75 mm. 6r. multicoloured (39×31 mm)			10·00	4·00

Designs: Nos. 439/444, different details of frescoes by Raphael.

113 Montgolfier Balloon

1983. Bicentenary of Manned Flight. Multicoloured.

446	20c. Type **113**	35	15
447	30c. *La Ville d'Orleans*, 1870	45	20
448	50c. Charles's hydrogen balloon	55	25
449	1r. Blanchard and Jeffries crossing Channel, 1785	1·10	40
450	1r.50 Salomon Andree's balloon flight over Arctic	1·60	55
451	2r. Auguste Piccard's stratosphere balloon *F.N.R.S.*	2·30	65
452	3r. Hot-air balloon race	3·25	95
MS453 75×67 mm. 6r. Balloons over European town (vert)		10·00	3·25

114 Cobra

1983. Reptiles. Multicoloured.

454	20c. Crested lizard (horiz)	35	20
455	30c. Type **114**	45	25
456	80c. Trionyx turtle (horiz)	80	35
457	1r. Chameleon	1·20	40
458	1r.50 Boa constrictor	2·30	65
459	2r. Crocodile (horiz)	2·75	95
460	3r. Turtle (horiz)	3·50	1·30

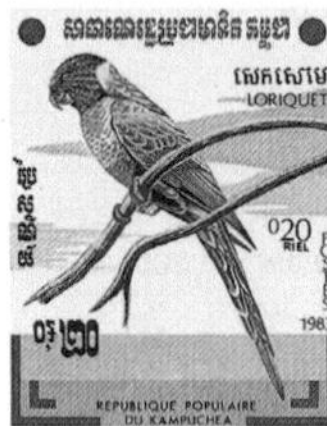

115 Rainbow Lory

1983. Birds. Multicoloured.

461	20c. Type **115**	35	15
462	50c. Barn swallow	45	25
463	80c. Golden eagle (horiz)	80	40
464	1r. Griffon vulture (horiz)	1·60	65
465	1r.50 Javanese collared dove (horiz)	2·75	95
466	2r. Black-billed magpie	3·50	1·30
467	3r. Great Indian hornbill	6·25	2·00

116 Sunflower

1983. Flowers. Multicoloured.

468	20c. Type **116**	35	15
469	50c. *Caprifoliaceae*	45	20
470	80c. *Bougainvillea*	55	75
471	1r. *Ranunculaceae*	1·10	1·00
472	1r.50 *Nyctagynaeceae*	2·30	55
473	2r. Cockscomb	2·75	65
474	3r. Roses	3·50	95

117 Luge

1983. Winter Olympic Games, Sarajevo (1984) (1st issue). Multicoloured.

475	1r. Type **117**	1·10	40
476	2r. Biathlon	2·50	65
477	4r. Ski-jumping	4·75	95
478	5r. Two-man bobsleigh	5·75	1·10
479	7r. Ice hockey	8·50	1·30
MS480 81×68 mm. 6r. Skiing (35×28 mm)		9·00	2·75

See also Nos. 496/**MS**503.

118 Cyprinid

1983. Fish. Multicoloured.

481	20c. Type **118**	35	15
482	50c. Loach	45	20
483	80c. Bubblebee catfish	55	25
484	1r. Spiny eel	1·20	40
485	1r.50 Cyprinid (different)	2·30	55
486	2r. Cyprinid (different)	3·25	65
487	3r. Aberrant fish	3·75	95

119 Factory and Gearwheel

1983. Festival of Rebirth. Multicoloured.

488	50c. Type **119**	45	25
489	1r. Tractor and cow (horiz)	1·60	55
490	3r. Bulk carrier, diesel locomotive, car and bridge	3·25	1·10
MS491 65×85 mm. 6r. Radio signal (31×39 mm)		8·00	2·75

120 Red Cross and Sailing Ship

1984. Fifth Anniversary of Liberation. Multicoloured.

492	50c. Type **120**	45	25
493	1r. Three soldiers, flags and temple	1·10	40
494	3r. Crowd surrounding temple	3·25	1·10
MS495 91×60 mm. 6r. Man carrying containers (31×39 mm)		8·00	2·75

121 Speed Skating

1984. Winter Olympic Games, Sarajevo (2nd issue). Multicoloured.

496	20c. Type **121**	35	15
497	50c. Ice hockey	45	20
498	80c. Skiing	55	25
499	1r. Ski jumping	1·10	40
500	1r.50 Skiing (different)	2·30	55
501	2r. Cross-country skiing	2·75	65
502	3r. Ice skating (pairs)	3·50	95
MS503 120×80 mm. 6r. Ice skating (individual) (31×29 mm)		8·00	2·75

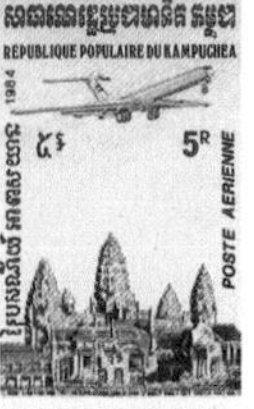

122 Ilyushin Il-62M Jet over Angkor Vat

1984. Air.

504	**122**	5r. multicoloured	6·25	1·3
505	**122**	10r. multicoloured	11·50	2·7
506	**122**	15r. multicoloured	16·00	4·0
507	**122**	25r. multicoloured	27·00	6·7

For design as T **122** but inscribed 'R.P. DU KAMPUCHEA', see Nos. 695/698.

123 Cattle Egret

1984. Birds. Multicoloured.

508	10c. Type **123**	35	15
509	40c. Black-headed shrike	1·10	20
510	80c. Slaty-headed parakeet	2·00	30
511	1r. Golden-fronted leafbird	2·75	45
512	1r.20 Red-winged crested cuckoo	3·25	60
513	2r. Grey wagtail	5·75	75
514	2r.50 Forest wagtail	6·25	90

124 Doves and Globe

1984. International Peace in South-East Asia Forum, Phnom Penh. Mult, background colour given.

515	**124** 50c. green	45	30
516	**124** 1r. blue	1·10	35
517	**124** 3r. violet	3·25	90

125 *Luna 2*

1984. Space Research. Multicoloured.

518	10c. *Luna 1*	35	10
519	40c. Type **125**	45	10
520	80c. *Luna 3*	55	15
521	1r. *Soyuz 6* and cosmonauts (vert)	1·10	20
522	1r.20 *Soyuz 7* and cosmonauts (vert)	1·60	30
523	2r. *Soyuz 8* and cosmonauts (vert)	2·30	35
524	2r.50 Book, rocket and S. P. Korolev (Russian spaceship designer) (vert)	3·25	45
MS525	81× 80 mm. 6r. Soyuz-Salyut space complex and Earth (39×31 mm)	9·00	2·00

126 Throwing the Discus

1984. Olympic Games, Los Angeles (2nd issue). Multicoloured.

526	20c. Type **126**	35	10
527	50c. Long jumping	45	15
528	80c. Hurdling	55	20
529	1r. Relay	1·50	30
530	1r.50 Pole vaulting	2·00	35
531	2r. Throwing the javelin	2·40	45
532	3r. High jumping	3·25	75
MS533	79×59 mm. 76r. Sprinting	8·75	2·20

127 Hispano-Suiza "K6", 1933

1984. Espana 84 International Stamp Exhibition, Madrid. Sheet 71×58 mm.

MS534	**127** 5r. multicoloured	8·75	4·00

128 Coyote

1984. Dog Family. Multicoloured.

535	10c. Type **128**	35	10
536	40c. Dingo	45	15
537	80c. Hunting dog	75	20
538	1r. Golden jackal	1·50	30
539	1r.20 Red fox	1·80	35
540	2r. Maned wolf (vert)	3·25	45
541	2r.50 Wolf	4·25	60

129 Class BB 1002 Diesel Locomotive, 1966, France

1984. Railway Locomotives. Multicoloured.

542	10c. Type **129**	30	10
543	40c. Class BB 1052 diesel locomotive, 1966, France	35	15
544	80c. Franco-Belgian-built steam locomotive, 1945, France	45	20
545	1r. Steam locomotive No. 231-505, 1929, France	1·10	30
546	1r.20 Class 803 diesel railcar, 1968, Germany	1·80	35
547	2r. Class BDE-405 diesel locomotive, 1957, France	2·30	45
548	2r.50 Class DS-01 diesel railcar, 1925, France	3·75	50

130 Magnolia

1984. Flowers. Multicoloured.

549	10c. Type **130**	30	10
550	40c. *Plumeria* sp.	35	15
551	80c. *Himenoballis* sp.	65	20
552	1r. *Peltophorum roxburghii*	1·60	30
553	1r.20 *Couroupita guianensis*	1·80	35
554	2r. *Lagerstroemia* sp.	3·00	45
555	2r.50 *Thevetia perubiana*	4·25	50

131 Mercedes Benz

1984. Cars. Multicoloured.

556	20c. Type **131**	30	15
557	50c. Bugatti	35	30
558	80c. Alfa Romeo	65	35
559	1r. Franklin	1·40	45
560	1r.50 Hispano-Suiza	2·00	60
561	2r. Rolls Royce	2·75	75
562	3r. Tatra	3·75	1·20
MS563	68×70 mm. 6r. Mercedes Benz (39×31 mm)	8·25	2·50

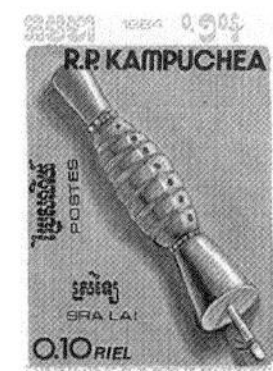

132 Sra Lai (Rattle)

1984. Musical Instruments. Multicoloured.

564	10c. Type **132**	25	15
565	40c. Skor drum (horiz)	35	30
566	80c. Skor drums (different)	40	45
567	1r. Thro khmer (stringed instrument) (horiz)	85	50
568	1r.20 Raneat ek (xylophone) (horiz)	1·70	60
569	2r. Raneat kong (bells) (horiz)	1·80	75
570	2r.50 Thro khe (stringed instrument) (horiz)	2·75	1·00

133 Gazelle

1984. Mammals. Multicoloured.

571	10c. Type **133**	25	10
572	40c. Roe deer	35	15
573	80c. Hare (horiz)	40	25
574	1r. Red deer	85	30
575	1r.20 Indian elephant	1·70	40
576	2r. Genet (horiz)	1·80	45
577	2r.50 Kouprey (horiz)	2·75	55

134 *Madonna and Child*

1984. 450th Death Anniversary of Correggio (artist). Multicoloured.

578	20c. Type **134**	20	10
579	50c. Detail showing man striking monk	30	15
580	80c. *Madonna and Child* (different)	45	25
581	1r. *Madonna and Child* (different)	85	30
582	1r.50 *Mystical Marriage of St. Catherine*	1·40	40
583	2r. *Pieta*	1·70	45
584	3r. Detail showing man descending ladder	2·10	55
MS585	91×64 mm. 6r. *Coronation of the Virgin* (39×31 mm)	7·00	2·00

135 Bullock Cart

1985. National Festival (Sixth Anniversary of People's Republic). Multicoloured.

586	50c. Type **135**	55	30
587	1r. Horse-drawn passenger cart	1·20	45
588	3r. Elephants	3·50	75
MS589	85×64 mm. 6r. Bullock-drawn passenger cart (31×39 mm)	7·25	2·00

136 Footballers

1985. World Cup Football Championship, Mexico (1986) (1st issue). Designs showing footballers.

590	**136** 20c. multicoloured	20	10
591	- 50c. multicoloured	30	15
592	- 80c. multicoloured	45	20
593	- 1r. multicoloured (horiz)	75	25
594	- 1r.50 mult (horiz)	1·20	30
595	- 2r. multicoloured	1·50	40
596	- 3r. multicoloured	2·20	45
MS597	94×57 mm. 6r. multicoloured (39×31 mm)	7·00	2·00

See also Nos. 680/**MS**687.

137 Eska-Mofa Motor Cycle, 1939

1985. Centenary of Motorcycle. Multicoloured.

598	20c. Type **137**	30	10
599	50c. Wanderer, 1939	35	15
600	80c. Premier, 1929	45	30
601	1r. Ardie, 1939	85	45
602	1r.50 Jawa, 1932	1·40	75
603	2r. Simson, 1983	1·70	1·20
604	3r. CZ 125, 1984	2·30	1·50
MS605	100×85 mm. 6r. MBA, 1984 (39×31 mm)	7·25	2·00

138 Glistening Ink Cap

1985. Fungi. Multicoloured.

606	20c. *Gymnophilus spectabilis* (horiz)	20	10
607	50c. Type **138**	35	15
608	80c. Panther cap	75	20
609	1r. Fairy cake mushroom	1·00	25
610	1r.50 Fly agaric	2·00	30
611	2r. Shaggy ink cap	2·75	40
612	3r. Caesar's mushroom	3·00	45

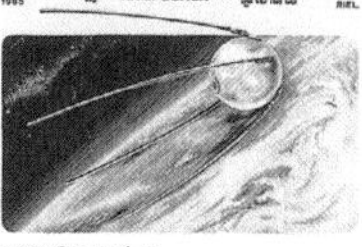

139 *Sputnik 1*

1985. Space Exploration. Multicoloured.

613	20c. Type **139**	20	10
614	50c. Soyuz rocket on transporter and Yuri Gagarin (first man in space)	30	25
615	80c. *Vostok 6* and Valentina Tereshkova (first woman in space)	40	30
616	1r. Space walker	75	45
617	1r.50 Salyut–Soyuz link	1·20	60
618	2r. *Lunokhod 1* (lunar vehicle)	1·50	75
619	3r. *Venera* (Venus probe)	2·30	1·20
MS620	94×59 mm. 6r. Soyuz preparing to dock with Salyut space station (39×31 mm)	7·25	2·75

140 Absara Dancer

1985. Traditional Dances. Multicoloured.

621	50c. Absara group (horiz)	95	30
622	1r. Tepmonorom dance (horiz)	1·40	45
623	3r. Type **140**	3·00	1·50

140a Captured Nazi Standards, Red Square, Moscow

1985. 40th Anniversary of End of Second World War. Multicoloured.

623a	50c. Rejoicing soldiers in Berlin	95	30
623b	1r. Type **140a**	1·40	45
623c	3r. Tank battle	3·25	1·70

141 Tortoiseshell Cat

1985. Domestic Cats. Multicoloured.

624	20c. Type **141**	20	10
625	50c. Tortoiseshell (different)	30	25
626	80c. Tabby	50	30
627	1r. Long-haired Siamese	1·10	45

628	1t.50 Sealpoint Siamese	1·50	60
629	2r. Grey cat	2·10	75
630	3r. Black cat	3·00	1·20

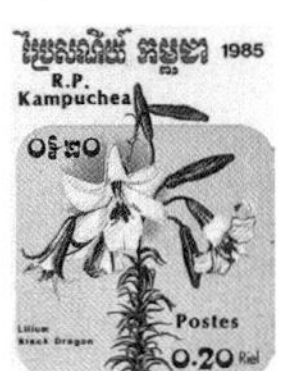
142 'Black Dragon' Lily

1985. Flowers. Multicoloured.

631	20c. Type **142**	20	10
632	50c. *Iris delavayi*	30	15
633	80c. *Crocus aureus*	50	25
634	1r. *Cyclamen persicum*	85	30
635	1r.50 Fairy primrose	1·70	45
636	2r. Pansy 'Ullswater'	2·10	55
637	3r. *Crocus purpureus grandiflorus*	2·75	75

143 *Per Italiani* (Antoine Watteau)

1985. International Music Year. Multicoloured.

638	20c. Type **143**	20	10
639	50c. *St Cecilia* (Carlos Saraceni)	30	15
640	80c. *Still Life with Violin* (Jean Baptiste Oudry) (horiz)	40	25
641	1r. *Three Musicians* (Fernand Leger)	85	30
642	1r.50 Orchestra	1·10	45
643	2r. *St Cecilia* (Bartholomeo Schedoni)	1·60	60
644	3r. *Harlequin with Violin* (Christian Caillard)	2·30	90
MS645	55×89 mm. 6r. *The Fifer* (Edouard Manet) (31×39 mm)	9·50	2·75

144 Lenin and Arms

1985. 115th Birth Anniversary of Lenin. Multicoloured.

646	1r. Type **144**	1·60	75
647	3r. Lenin on balcony and map	3·25	1·50

145 Saffron-cowled Blackbird

1985. Argentina '85 International Stamp Exhibition, Buenos Aires. Birds. Multicoloured.

648	20c. Type **145**	20	10
649	50c. Saffron finch (vert)	40	15
650	80c. Blue and yellow tanager (vert)	65	25
651	1r. Scarlet-headed blackbird	1·30	30
652	1r.50 Amazon kingfisher (vert)	2·30	45
653	2r. Toco toucan (vert)	3·25	70
654	3r. Rufous-bellied thrush	3·75	90

146 River Launch, Cambodia, 1942

1985. Water Craft. Multicoloured.

655	10c. Type **146**	20	10
656	40c. River launch, Cambodia, 1948	30	15
657	80c. Tug, Japan, 1913	40	25
658	1r. Dredger, Holland	85	30
659	1r.20 Tug, USA	1·10	45
660	2r. River freighter	1·60	60
661	2r.50 River tanker, Panama	2·30	90

147 *The Flood* (Michelangelo)

1985. Italia '85 International Stamp Exhibition, Rome. Paintings. Multicoloured.

662	20r. Type **147**	20	10
663	50r. *The Virgin of St Marguerite* (Mazzola)	30	15
664	80r. *The Martyrdom of St Peter* (Zampieri Domenichino)	40	25
665	1r. *Allegory of Spring* (detail) (Sandro Botticelli)	85	30
666	1r.50 *The Sacrifice of Abraham* (Caliari)	1·60	45
667	2r. *The Meeting of Joachim and Anne* (Giotto)	2·10	60
668	3r. *Bacchus* (Michel Angelo Carraraggio)	2·40	90
MS669	94×64 mm. 6r. Early steam locomotive, Berlin (31×39 mm)	9·50	2·75

148 Son Ngoc Minh

1985. Festival of Rebirth.

670	**148**	50c. multicoloured	1·00	30
671	**148**	1r. multicoloured	2·10	45
672	**148**	3r. multicoloured	4·25	90

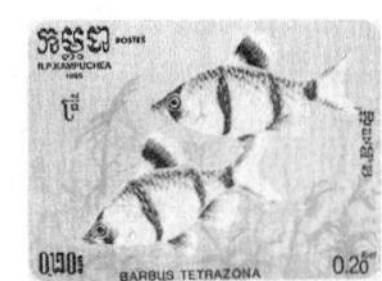
149 Tiger Barbs

1985. Fish. Multicoloured.

673	20c. Type **149**	20	10
674	50c. Giant snakehead	30	15
675	80c. Veil-tailed goldfish	50	25
676	1r. Pearl gourami	95	30
677	1r.50 Six-banded tiger barbs	1·60	45
678	2r. Siamese fighting fish	1·90	60
679	3r. Siamese tigerfish	3·00	90

150 Footballers

1986. World Cup Football Championship, Mexico (2nd issue).

680	**150**	20c. multicoloured	20	10
681	-	50c. multicoloured	30	15
682	-	80c. multicoloured	40	25
683	-	1r. multicoloured	75	30
684	-	1r.50 multicoloured	1·00	45
685	-	2r. multicoloured	1·50	60
686	-	3r. multicoloured	2·10	90
MS687		95×92 mm. 6r. multicoloured (31×39 mm)	7·75	2·00

Designs: 50c. to 6r. Various footballing scenes.

151 Cob

1986. Horses. Multicoloured.

688	20c. Type **151**	20	10
689	50c. Arab	30	15
690	80c. Australian pony	40	25
691	1r. Appaloosa	85	30
692	1r.50 Quarter horse	1·50	45
693	2r. Vladimir heavy draught horse	1·80	60
694	3r. Andalusian	2·30	90

152 *Mir* Space Station and Spacecraft

1986. 27th Russian Communist Party Congress. Multicoloured.

694a	50c. Type **152**	30	30
694b	1r. Lenin	1·10	75
694c	5r. Statue and launch of space rocket	4·50	1·40

1986. Air. As Nos. 504/507 but inscr 'R.P. DU KAMPUCHEA'.

695	**122**	5r. multicoloured	4·25	60
696	**122**	10r. multicoloured	8·25	1·20
697	**122**	15r. multicoloured	10·50	1·50
698	**122**	25r. multicoloured	19·00	2·75

153 Edaphosaurus (²/₃-size illustration)

1986. Prehistoric Animals. Multicoloured.

699	20c. Type **153**	40	10
700	50c. Sauroctonus	50	15
701	80c. Mastodonsaurus	1·00	25
702	1r. Rhamphorhynchus (vert)	1·90	30
703	1r.50 Brachiosaurus brancai (vert)	3·00	45
704	2r. Tarbosaurus bataar (vert)	3·75	60
705	3r. Indricotherium (vert)	4·75	1·20

154 *Luna 16*

1986. 25th Anniversary of First Man in Space. Multicoloured.

706	10c. Type **154**	20	10
707	40c. *Luna 3*	35	15
708	80c. *Vostok*	45	25
709	1r. Cosmonaut Leonov on space walk	80	30
710	1r.20 Apollo and Soyuz preparing to dock	1·40	45
711	2r. Soyuz docking with Salyut space station	1·70	60
712	2r.50 Yuri Gagarin (first man in space) and spacecraft	2·50	90

155 Baksei Chamkrong Temple, 920

1986. Khmer Culture. Multicoloured.

713	20c. Type **155**	25	10
714	50c. Buddha's head	35	15
715	80c. Prea Vihear monastery, Dangrek	55	25
716	1r. Fan with design of man and woman	70	30
717	1r.50 Fan with design of men fighting	90	45
718	2r. Fan with design of dancer	1·50	60
719	3r. Fan with design of dragon-drawn chariot	2·00	1·20

156 Tricar, 1885

1986. Centenary (1985) of Motor Car. Mercedes Benz Models. Multicoloured.

720	20c. Type **156**	25	10
721	50c. Limousine, 1935	35	15
722	80c. Open tourer, 1907	45	25
723	1r. Light touring car, 1920	80	30
724	1r.50 Cabriolet, 1932	1·40	45
725	2r. SKK tourer, 1938	1·70	60
726	3r. 190, 1985	2·50	1·20

157 Orange Tiger

1986. Butterflies. Multicoloured.

727	20c. Type **157**	35	10
728	50c. Five-bar swallowtail	45	15
729	80c. Chequered swallowtail	55	25
730	1r. Chestnut tiger	1·10	30
731	1r.50 *Idea blanchardi*	2·10	45
732	2r. Common mormon	2·50	60
733	3r. *Dabasa payeni*	3·00	1·20

158 English Kogge of Richard II's Reign

1986. Medieval Ships.. Multicoloured.

734	20c. Type **158**	25	10
735	50c. Kogge	35	15
736	80c. Knarr	45	25
737	1r. Galley	80	30
738	1r.50 Norman ship	1·10	45
739	2r. Mediterranean usciere	1·60	60
740	3r. French kogge	2·30	90

159 Solar System, Copernicus, Galileo and Tycho Brahe (astronomers)

1986. Appearance of Halley's Comet. Multicoloured.

741	10c. Type **159**	25	10
742	20c. *Nativity* (Giotto) and comet from Bayeux Tapestry	30	15
743	50c. Comet, 1910, and Mt. Palomar observatory, USA	35	25
744	80c. Edmond Halley and *Planet A* space probe	55	30
745	1r.20 Diagram of comet's trajectory and *Giotto* space probe	90	45
746	1r.50 *Vega* space probe and camera	1·10	60
747	2r. Thermal pictures of comet	1·70	90
MS748	87×56 mm. 6r. *Vega* space probe (31×39 mm)	6·25	2·30

160 Ruy Lopez

1986. Stockholmia 86 International Stamp Exhibition Chess. Multicoloured.

749	20c. Type **160**	25	1
750	50c. Francois-Andre Philidor	35	1
751	80c. Karl Anderssen and Houses of Parliament, London	55	2
752	1r. Wilhelm Steinitz and Charles Bridge, Prague	1·00	3
753	1r.50 Emanuel Lasker and medieval knight	1·80	4
754	2r. Jose Raul Capablanca and Morro Castle, Cuba	2·30	6
755	3r. Aleksandr Alekhine	2·75	1·2
MS756	62×72 mm. 6r. Chess pieces (39×31 mm)	9·00	2·7

No. 751 is wrongly inscribed 'Andersen'.

161 *Parodia maassii*

1986. Cacti. Multicoloured.

757	20c. Type **161**	25	10
758	50c. *Rebutia marsoneri*	35	15
759	80c. *Melocactus evae*	45	25
760	1r. *Gymnocalycium valnicekianum*	90	30
761	1r.50 *Discocactus silichromus*	1·60	45
762	2r. *Neochilenia simulans*	1·90	60
763	3r. *Weingartia chiquichuquensis*	2·50	90

162 Bananas

1986. Fruit. Multicoloured.

764	10c. Type **162**	25	10
765	40c. Papaya	35	25
766	80c. Mangoes	55	30
767	1r. Breadfruit	70	40
768	1r.20 Lychees	90	60
769	2r. Pineapple	1·50	90
770	2r.50 Grapefruit (horiz)	2·00	1·20

163 Concorde

1986. Aircraft. Multicoloured.

771	20c. Type **163** (wrongly inscr 'Concord')	25	10
772	50c. Douglas DC-10	35	25
773	80c. Boeing 747SP	55	30
774	1r. Ilyushin Il-62M	80	40
775	1r.50 Ilyushin Il-86	1·20	60
776	2r. Antonov An-24 (wrongly inscr 'AN-124')	1·70	90
777	3r. Airbus Industrie A300	2·50	1·20

164 Elephant and Silver Containers on Tray

1986. Festival of Rebirth. Silverware. Multicoloured.

778	50c. Type **164**	55	45
779	1r. Tureen	1·10	60
780	3r. Dish on stand	3·50	1·20

165 Kouprey

1986. Endangered Animals. Cattle. Multicoloured.

781	20c. Type **165**	1·70	45
782	20c. Gaur	2·75	75
783	80c. Bateng cow and calf	6·75	1·50
784	1r.50 Asiatic water buffalo	11·50	3·00

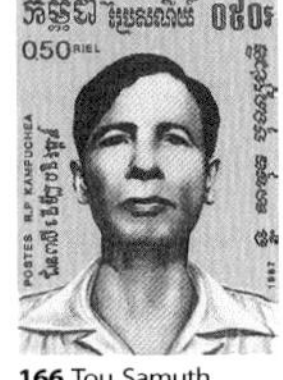

166 Tou Samuth (revolutionary)

1987. National Festival. Eighth Anniversary of People's Republic.

785	**166**	50c. multicoloured	55	45
786	**166**	1r. multicoloured	1·10	60
787	**166**	3r. multicoloured	2·30	90

167 Biathlon

1987. Winter Olympic Games, Calgary (1988) (1st issue). Multicoloured.

788	20c. Type **167**	25	10
789	50c. Figure skating	35	25
790	80c. Speed skating	45	30
791	1r. Ice hockey	80	40
792	1r.50 Two-man luge	1·10	60
793	2r. Two-man bobsleigh	1·60	90
794	3r. Cross-country skiing	2·30	1·20
MS795	91×65 mm. 6r. Skiing (39×31 mm)	6·75	2·30

See also Nos. 864/**MS**871.

168 Weightlifting

1987. Olympic Games, Seoul (1988) (1st issue). Designs showing ancient Greek and modern athletes. Multicoloured.

796	20c. Type **168**	25	10
797	50c. Archery (horiz)	35	15
798	80c. Fencing (horiz)	45	25
799	1r. Gymnastics	80	30
800	1r.50 Throwing the discus (horiz)	1·10	45
801	2r. Throwing the javelin	1·60	60
802	3r. Hurdling	2·30	75
MS803	93×63 mm. 6r. Wrestling (39×31 mm)	6·75	2·30

See also Nos. 875/**MS**882.

169 Papillon

1987. Dogs. Multicoloured.

804	20c. Type **169**	35	10
805	50c. Greyhound	45	15
806	80c. Great Dane	55	25
807	1r. Dobermann	1·10	30
808	1r.50 Samoyed	2·00	45
809	2r. Borzoi	2·50	75
810	3r. Rough collie	3·25	1·20

170 *Sputnik 1*

1987. Space Exploration. Multicoloured.

811	20c. Type **170**	25	10
812	50c. *Soyuz 10*	35	15
813	80c. *Proton*	45	25
814	1r. *Vostok 1*	80	30
815	1r.50 *Elektron 2*	1·10	45
816	2r. *Kosmos*	1·60	75
817	3r. *Luna 2*	2·30	1·20
MS818	71×48 mm. 6r. *Elektron 4* (39×31 mm)	6·75	2·30

171 Flask

1987. Metalwork. Multicoloured.

819	50c. Type **171**	35	30
820	1r. Repousse box (horiz)	90	45
821	1r.50 Teapot and cups on tray (horiz)	1·40	60
822	3r. Ornamental sword	2·50	90

172 Carmine Bee-eater

1987. Capex '87 International Stamp Exhibition, Toronto. Birds. Multicoloured.

823	20c. Type **172**	25	10
824	50c. Hoopoe (vert)	35	15
825	80c. South African crowned crane (vert)	45	25
826	1r. Barn owl (vert)	80	30
827	1r.50 Grey-headed kingfisher (vert)	1·40	40
828	2r. Red-whiskered bulbul	1·70	45
829	3r. Purple heron (vert)	2·50	60
MS830	70×94 mm. 6r. Asiatic paradise flycatcher (28×39 mm)	6·50	90

173 Horatio Phillip's 'multiplane' Model, 1893

1987. Experimental Aircraft Designs. Multicoloured.

831	20c. Type **173**	25	10
832	50c. John Stringfellow's steam-powered model, 1848	35	15
833	80c. Thomas Moy's model *Aerial Steamer*, 1875	45	25
834	1r. Leonardo da Vinci's 'ornithopter', 1490	80	30
835	1r.50 Sir George Cayley's 'convertiplane', 1843	1·40	40
836	2r. Sir Hiram Maxim's *Flying Test Rig*, 1894	1·70	45
837	3r. William Henson's *Aerial Steam Carriage*, 1842	2·50	60
MS838	98×83 mm. 6r. Leonardo da Vinci's drawing of *Flying Man* (31×39 mm)	6·75	2·00

No. 835 is wrongly dated 1840.

174 Giant Tortoise

1987. Reptiles. Multicoloured.

839	20c. Type **174**	25	10
840	50c. African spiny-tailed lizard	35	15
841	80c. Iguana	45	25
842	1r. Coast horned lizard	80	30
843	1r.50 Northern chuckwalla	1·10	45
844	2r. Glass lizard	1·60	60
845	3r. Common garter snake	2·30	90

175 Kamov Ka-15

1987. Hafnia 87 International Stamp Exhibition, Copenhagen. Helicopters. Multicoloured.

846	20c. Type **175**	25	10
847	50c. Kamov Ka-18	35	15
848	80c. Westland WG-13 Lynx	45	25
849	1r. Sud Aviation SA 341 Gazelle	80	30
850	1r.50 Sud Aviation SA 330E Puma	1·10	45
851	2r. Boeing-Vertol CH-47 Chinook	1·60	60
852	3r. Boeing UTTAS	2·30	90
MS853	65×85 mm. 6r. Fairey rotodyne	6·75	2·30

176 Revolutionaries

1987. 70th Anniversary of Russian October Revolution. Multicoloured.

853a	2r. Revolutionaries on street corner (horiz)	1·70	45
853b	3r. Type **176**	2·00	90
853c	5r. Lenin receiving ticker-tape message (horiz)	4·75	1·50

177 Magirus-Deutz No. 21

1987. Fire Engines. Multicoloured.

854	20c. Type **177**	25	10
855	50c. SIL-131 rescue vehicle	35	15
856	80c. Cas-25 fire pump	45	25
857	1r. Sirmac Saab 424	90	30
858	1r.50 Rosenbaum-Falcon	1·70	45
859	2r. Tatra 815-PRZ	2·30	60
860	3r. Chubbfire C-44-20	2·50	90

178 Earth Station Dish Aerial

1987. Telecommunications. Multicoloured.

861	50c. Type **178**	55	45
862	1r. Technological building with radio microwave aerial (27×44 mm)	1·10	60
863	3r. Intersputnik programme earth station (44×27 mm)	2·50	1·10

179 Speed Skating

1988. Winter Olympic Games, Calgary (2nd issue). Multicoloured.

864	20c. Type **179**	25	10
865	50c. Ice hockey	35	15
866	80c. Slalom	45	25
867	1r. Ski jumping	80	30
868	1r.50 Biathlon	1·10	45
869	2r. Ice dancing	1·60	60
870	3r. Cross-country skiing	2·30	90
MS871	66×89 mm. 6r. Four-man bobsleigh (31×39 mm)	6·75	2·00

180 Irrigation Canal Bed

1988. Irrigation Projects. Multicoloured.

872	50c. Type **180**	55	45
873	1r. Dam construction	1·10	60
874	3r. Dam and bridge	2·50	90

181 Beam Exercise

1988. Olympic Games, Seoul (2nd issue). Women's Gymnastics. Multicoloured.

875	20c. Type **181**	25	10
876	50c. Bar exercise (horiz)	35	15
877	80c. Ribbon exercise	45	25
878	1r. Hoop exercise	70	30
879	1r.50 Baton exercise	1·00	45
880	2r. Ball exercise (horiz)	1·50	60
881	3r. Floor exercise (horiz)	2·00	90
MS882	84×59 mm. 6r. Ball exercise (different) (28×36 mm)	6·75	2·00

182 Abyssinian

1988. Juvalux 88 Ninth Youth Philately Exhibition, Luxembourg. Cats. Multicoloured.

No.	Description	Mint	Used
883	20c. White long-haired (horiz)	25	10
884	50c. Type **182**	35	15
885	80c. Ginger and white long-haired	45	25
886	1r. Tortoiseshell queen and kitten (horiz)	80	30
887	1r.50 Brown cat	1·40	45
888	2r. Black long-haired cat	1·70	60
889	3r. Grey cat	2·50	90
MS890	61×50 mm. 6r. Kittens (39×31 mm)	9·00	2·00

183 *Emerald Seas* (liner)

1988. Essen 88 International Stamp Fair. Ships. Multicoloured.

No.	Description	Mint	Used
891	20c. Type **183**	35	10
892	50c. Car ferry	45	15
893	80c. *Mutsu* (nuclear-powered freighter)	55	25
894	1r. *Kosmonavt Yury Gagarin* (research ship)	1·00	30
895	1r.50 Tanker	1·70	45
896	2r. Hydrofoil	2·00	60
897	3r. Hovercraft	3·25	90
MS898	95×70 mm. 6r. Hydrofoil (different) (39×31 mm)	7·25	2·00

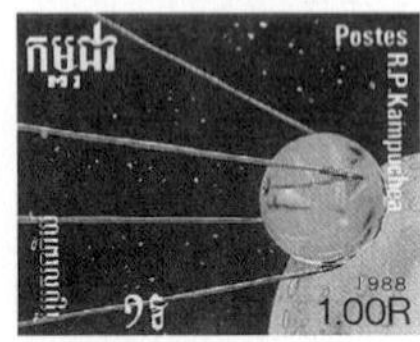

184 Satellite

1988. Space Exploration. Designs showing different satellites.

No.	Type	Description	Mint	Used
899	-	20c. multicoloured (vert)	25	10
900	-	50c. multicoloured (vert)	35	15
901	-	80c. multicoloured (vert)	45	25
902	**184**	1r. multicoloured	70	30
903	-	1r.50 multicoloured	1·00	45
904	-	2r. multicoloured	1·50	60
905	-	3r. multicoloured	2·00	90
MS906		103×63 mm. 6r. multicoloured (39×31 mm)	6·75	2·00

185 Swordtail

1988. Finlandia 88 International Stamp Exhibition, Helsinki. Tropical Fish. Multicoloured.

No.	Description	Mint	Used
907	20c. Type **185**	35	10
908	50c. Head-and-taillight tetra	45	15
909	80c. Paradise fish	55	25
910	1r. Black moor goldfish	1·00	30
911	1r.50 Cardinal tetra	1·70	45
912	2r. Sword-tailed characin	2·00	60
913	3r. Sail-finned molly	2·75	90
MS914	62×72 mm. 6r. Angelfish (31×39 mm)	7·25	2·10

186 Flowery Helicostyla

1988. Sea Shells. Multicoloured.

No.	Description	Mint	Used
915	20c. Type **186**	25	10
916	50c. Changing helicostyla	35	15
917	80c. Shining helicostyla	45	25
918	1r. Marinduque helicostyla	80	30
919	1r.50 Siren chlorena	1·40	45
920	2r. Miraculous helicostyla	1·70	60
921	3r. *Helicostyla limansauensis*	2·50	90

187 Seven-spotted Ladybird

1988. Insects. Multicoloured.

No.	Description	Mint	Used
922	20c. Type **187**	35	10
923	50c. *Zonabride geminata* (blister beetle)	45	15
924	80c. *Carabus auronitens* (ground beetle)	55	25
925	1r. Honey bee	1·00	30
926	1r.50 Praying mantis	1·70	45
927	2r. Dragonfly	2·00	60
928	3r. Soft-winged flower beetle	3·25	90

188 *Cattleya aclandiae*

1988. Orchids. Multicoloured.

No.	Description	Mint	Used
929	20c. Type **188**	25	10
930	50c. *Odontoglossum* 'Royal Sovereign'	35	15
931	80c. *Cattleya labiata*	45	25
932	1r. Bee orchid	80	30
933	1r.50 *Laelia anceps*	1·10	45
934	2r. *Laelia pumila*	1·60	60
935	3r. *Stanhopea tigrina* (horiz)	2·30	90

189 Egyptian Banded Cobra

1988. Reptiles. Multicoloured.

No.	Description	Mint	Used
936	20c. Type **189**	35	10
937	50c. Common iguana	45	15
938	80c. Long-nosed vine snake (horiz)	55	25
939	1r. Common box turtle (horiz)	1·00	30
940	1r.50 Iguana (horiz)	1·70	45
941	2r. Viper (horiz)	2·00	60
942	3r. Common cobra	3·25	90

190 Walking Dance

1988. Festival of Rebirth. Khmer Culture. Multicoloured.

No.	Description	Mint	Used
943	50c. Type **190**	55	45
944	1r. Peacock dance (horiz)	1·20	60
945	3r. Kantere dance (horiz)	3·25	1·40

191 Bridge

1989. National Structures. Multicoloured.

No.	Description	Mint	Used
946	50c. Type **191**	55	30
947	1r. More distant view of bridge	1·10	75
948	3r. Closer view of bridge	2·75	2·00

192 Cement Works

1989. National Festival. Tenth Anniversary of People's Republic of Kampuchea. Multicoloured.

No.	Description	Mint	Used
949	3r. Bayon Earth Station (horiz)	45	30
950	12r. Electricity generating station 4 (horiz)	1·10	75
951	30r. Type **192**	3·25	2·30

193 Footballers

1989. World Cup Football Championship, Italy (1990).

No.	Type	Description	Mint	Used
952	**193**	2r. multicoloured	25	10
953	-	3r. multicoloured	35	15
954	-	5r. multicoloured	45	25
955	-	10r. multicoloured	1·00	30
956	-	15r. multicoloured	1·50	45
957	-	20r. multicoloured	2·00	60
958	-	35r. multicoloured	3·50	90
MS959		92×54 mm. 45r. multicoloured (goalkeeper) (31×39 mm)	6·75	2·00

Designs: 3r. to 45r. Various footballing scenes. See also Nos. 1042/**MS**1049.

194 Tram

1989. Trams and Trains. Multicoloured.

No.	Description	Mint	Used
960	2r. Type **194**	35	10
961	3r. ETR 401 Pendolino express train, 1976, Italy	45	15
962	5r. High speed train, Germany	55	25
963	10r. Theme park monorail train	1·00	30
964	15r. German Trans Europe Express (TEE) train	1·50	45
965	20r. Hikari express train, Sanyo Shinkansenline, Japan	2·00	60
966	35r. TGV express train, France	3·75	90
MS967	85×55 mm. 45r. multicoloured (39×31 mm)	8·50	2·30

195 Fidel Castro

1989. 30th Anniversary of Cuban Revolution.

No.	Type	Description	Mint	Used
968	**195**	12r. multicoloured	1·70	1·20

196 Scarlet Macaw

1989. Parrots. Multicoloured.

No.	Description	Mint	Used
969	20c. Type **196**	35	10
970	80c. Sulphur-crested cockatoo	45	15
971	3r. Rose-ringed parakeet	55	25
972	6r. Blue and yellow macaw	1·10	30
973	10r. Brown-necked parrot	1·50	45
974	15r. Blue-fronted amazon	2·30	60
975	25r. White-capped parrot (horiz)	3·50	90
MS976	65×75 mm. 45r. Red-fronted parakeet (31×39 mm)	8·50	2·30

197 Skiing

1989. Winter Olympic Games, Albertville (1992). Multicoloured.

No.	Description	Mint	Used
977	2r. Type **197**	25	10
978	3r. Biathlon	35	15
979	5r. Cross-country skiing	45	25
980	10r. Ski jumping	1·00	30
981	15r. Speed skating	1·40	45
982	20r. Ice hockey	1·70	60
983	35r. Two-man bobsleighing	3·50	90
MS984	75×89 mm. 45r. Figure skating (31×39 mm)	6·75	2·00

See also Nos. 1069/**MS**1076 and 1152/**MS**1159 of Cambodia.

198 *Nymphaea capensis* (pink)

1989. Water Lilies. Multicoloured.

No.	Description	Mint	Used
985	20c. Type **198**	25	10
986	80c. *Nymphaea capensis* (mauve)	30	15
987	3r. *Nymphaea lotus dentata*	35	25
988	6r. 'Dir. Geo. T. Moore'	55	30
989	10r. 'Sunrise'	80	45
990	15r. *Escarboncle*	1·60	60
991	25r. *Cladstoniana*	2·50	90
MS992	59×79 mm. 45r. 'Paul Hariot' (31×39 mm)	6·75	1·80

199 Wrestling

1989. Olympic Games, Barcelona (1992). Multicoloured.

No.	Description	Mint	Used
993	2r. Type **199**	25	10
994	3r. Gymnastics (vert)	35	15
995	5r. Putting the shot	45	25
996	10r. Running (vert)	1·00	30
997	15r. Fencing	1·40	45
998	20r. Canoeing (vert)	1·70	60
999	35r. Hurdling (vert)	3·50	90
MS1000	62×87 mm. 45r. Weightlifting (31×39 mm)	6·75	1·80

See also Nos. 1061/**MS**1068, 1163/**MS**1170, 1208/**MS**1213 and 1241/**MS**1246 of Cambodia.

200 Downy Boletus

1989. Fungi. Multicoloured.

No.	Description	Mint	Used
1001	20c. Type **200**	25	10
1002	80c. Red-staining inocybe	35	15
1003	3r. Honey fungus	45	25
1004	6r. Field mushroom	90	30
1005	10r. Brown roll-rim	1·10	45
1006	15r. Shaggy ink cap	1·80	60
1007	25r. Parasol mushroom	2·50	90

201 Shire Horse

1989. Horses. Multicoloured.

No.	Description	Mint	Used
1008	2r. Type **201**	25	10
1009	3r. Brabant	35	15
1010	5r. Boulonais	45	25
1011	10r. Breton	1·00	30
1012	15r. Vladimir heavy draught horse	1·50	45
1013	20r. Italian heavy draught horse	2·00	60
1014	35r. Freiberger	3·50	90
MS1015	77×56 mm. 45r. Team of four white horses (39×31 mm)	7·25	2·30

KARELIA

Northern Karelia, on the border of Finalnd, declared its independence from Russia on 1 October 1921 and issued the following stamps.

100 pennia = 1 markka.

1 Arms of Karelia

1922

1	**1**	5p. grey	20·00	55·00
2	**1**	10p. blue	20·00	55·00
3	**1**	20p. rose	20·00	55·00
4	**1**	25p. brown	20·00	55·00
5	**1**	40p. violet	20·00	55·00
6	**1**	50p. olive	20·00	55·00
7	**1**	75p. yellow	20·00	55·00
8	**1**	1m. black and rose	20·00	55·00
9	**1**	2m. black and green	50·00	£130
10	**1**	3m. black and blue	50·00	£140
11	**1**	5m. black and violet	50·00	£170
12	**1**	10m. black and brown	50·00	£275
13	**1**	15m. carmine and green	50·00	£275
14	**1**	20m. green and mauve	50·00	£275
15	**1**	25m. blue and yellow	50·00	£275

Stamps inscribed 'ITA-KARJALA' (Eastern Karelia) are listed under Finnish Occupation of Eastern Karelia.

KATANGA

The following stamps were issued by Mr. Tshombe's Government for independent Katanga. In 1963 Katanga was reunited with the Central Government of Congo.

1960. Various stamps of Belgian Congo optd **KATANGA** and bar or surch also. (a) Masks issue of 1948.

1	1f.50 on 1f.25 mauve and blue	80	20
2	3f.50 on 2f.50 green and brown	80	25
3	20f. purple and red	2·75	85
4	50f. black and brown	6·50	3·00
5	100f. black and red	48·00	21·00

(b) Flowers issue of 1952. Flowers in natural colours; colours given are of backgrounds and inscriptions.

6	10c. yellow and purple	20	20
7	15c. green and red	20	20
8	20c. grey and green	35	25
9	25c. orange and green	35	25
10	40c. salmon and green	35	25
11	50c. turquoise and red	45	35
12	60c. purple and green	35	25
13	75c. grey and lake	45	35
14	1f. lemon and red	55	45
15	2f. buff and olive	65	55
16	3f. pink and green	90	65
17	4f. lavender and sepia	1·25	95
18	5f. green and purple	1·25	95
19	6f.50 lilac and red	1·25	85
20	7f. brown and green	1·75	1·25
21	8f. yellow and green	1·75	1·25
22	10f. olive and purple	28·00	17·00

(c) Wild animals issue of 1959.

23	10c. brown, sepia and blue	20	10
24	20c. blue and red	1·60	80
25	40c. brown and blue	20	10
26	50c. multicoloured	20	10
27	1f. black, green and brown	6·75	4·00
28	1f.50 black and yellow	11·00	7·50
29	2f. black, brown and red	50	10
30	3f. black, purple and slate	4·25	3·00
31	5f. brown, green and sepia	75	30
32	6f.50 brown, yellow and blue	95	30
33	8f. bistre, violet and brown	1·40	35
34	10f. multicoloured	2·10	50

(d) Madonna.

35	**102**	50c. brown, ochre and chestnut	15	15
36	**102**	1f. brown, violet and blue	15	15
37	**102**	2f. brown, blue and slate	20	20

(e) African Technical Co-operation Commission. Inscr in French or Flemish.

38	**103**	3f. salmon and slate	7·00	7·00
39	**103**	3f.50 on 3f. salmon and slate	2·10	2·10

1960. Independence. Independence issue of Congo optd **11 JUILLET DE L'ETAT DU KATANGA**.

40	**106**	20c. bistre	10	10
41	**106**	50c. red	10	10
42	**106**	1f. green	10	10
43	**106**	1f.50 brown	10	10
44	**106**	2f. mauve	10	10
45	**106**	3f.50 violet	15	10
46	**106**	5f. blue	15	10
47	**106**	6f.50 black	15	10
48	**106**	10f. orange	25	20
49	**106**	20f. blue	45	30

5

1961. Katanga Art.

50	**5**	10c. green	10	10
51	**5**	20c. violet	10	10
52	**5**	50c. blue	10	10
53	**5**	1f.50 green	10	10
54	**5**	2f. brown	10	10
55	-	3f.50 blue	10	10
56	-	5f. turquoise	10	10
57	-	6f. brown	10	10
58	-	6f.50 blue	10	10
59	-	8f. purple	15	10
60	-	10f. brown	15	10
61	-	20f. myrtle	25	20
62	-	50f. brown	50	40
63	-	100f. turquoise	85	70

Designs: 3f.50 to 8f. Preparing food; 10f. to 100f. Family circle.

6 Pres. Tshombe

1961. First Anniversary of Independence. Portrait in brown.

64	**6**	6f.50+5f. red, green & gold	1·25	1·00
65	**6**	8f.+5f. red, green and gold	1·25	1·00
66	**6**	10f.+5f. red, green and gold	1·25	1·00

7 'Tree'

1961. Katanga International Fair. Vert symbolic designs as T **7**.

67	**7**	50c. red, green and black	10	10
68	-	1f. black and blue	10	10
69	-	2f.50 black and yellow	15	15
70	**7**	3f.50 red, brown and black	15	15
71	-	5f. black and violet	25	25
72	-	6f.50 black and yellow	30	30

8 Farman H.F.III Biplane, Steam Train and Safari

1961. Air.

73	**8**	3f.50 multicoloured	3·00	3·25
74	-	6f.50 multicoloured	65	65
75	**8**	8f. multicoloured	3·00	3·25
76	-	10f. multicoloured	65	65

Designs: 6f.50, 10f. Tail of Boeing 707.

9 Gendarme in armoured Vehicle

1962. Katanga Gendarmerie.

77	**9**	6f. multicoloured	2·25	2·25
78	**9**	8f. multicoloured	35	35
79	**9**	10f. multicoloured	45	45

POSTAGE DUE STAMPS

1960. Postage Due stamps of Belgian Congo handstamped **KATANGA**. (a) On Nos. D270/D274.

D50	**D86**	10c. olive	80	80
D51	**D86**	20c. blue	80	80
D52	**D86**	50c. green	1·00	1·00
D53	**D86**	1f. brown		
D54	**D86**	2f. orange		

(b) On Nos. D330/D336.

D55	**D99**	10c. brown	3·25	3·25
D56	**D99**	20c. purple	3·25	3·25
D57	**D99**	50c. green	3·25	3·25
D58	**D99**	1f. blue	1·00	1·00
D59	**D99**	2f. red	2·00	2·00
D60	**D99**	4f. violet	2·75	2·75
D61	**D99**	6f. blue	3·25	3·25

KATHIRI STATE OF SEIYUN

The stamps of Aden were used in Kathiri State of Seiyun from 22 May 1937 until 1942.

1937. 16 annas = 1 rupee.
1951. 100 cents = 1 shilling.
1966. 1000 fils = 1 dinar.

1 Sultan of Seiyun

2 Seiyun

1942

1	**1**	$^1/_2$a. green	20	2·00
2	**1**	$^3/_4$a. brown	60	4·50
3	**1**	1a. blue	70	2·25
4	**2**	$1^1/_2$a. red	70	2·75
5	-	2a. brown	50	2·75
6	-	$2^1/_2$a. blue	1·25	2·75
7	-	3a. brown and red	1·75	4·50
8	-	8a. red	3·25	1·50
9	-	1r. green	7·50	5·00
10	-	2r. blue and purple	16·00	27·00
11	-	5r. brown and green	38·00	35·00

Designs: Vert—2a. Tarim; $2^1/_2$a. Mosque at Seiyun; 1r. South Gate, Tarim; 5r. Mosque entrance, Tarim. Horiz—3a. Fortress at Tarim; 8a. Mosque at Seiyun; 2r. A Kathiri house.

1946. Victory. Optd **VICTORY ISSUE 8TH JUNE 1946**.

12	**2**	$1^1/_2$a. red	20	65
13	-	$2^1/_2$a. blue (No. 6)	20	35

1949. Royal Silver Wedding. As T **59b/59c** of Jamaica.

14	$1^1/_2$a. red	30	4·50
15	5r. green	18·00	17·00

1949. 75th Anniversary of UPU. As T **59d/59g** of Jamaica, surch with new values.

16	$2^1/_2$a. on 20c. blue	15	2·00
17	3a. on 30c. red	1·25	3·50
18	8a. on 50c. orange	25	6·50
19	1r. on 1s. blue	30	2·50

1951. 1942 stamps surch in cents or shillings.

20	**1**	5c. on 1a. blue	15	2·75
21	-	10c. on 2a. brown	30	2·25
22	-	15c. on $2^1/_2$a. blue	20	3·00
23	-	20c. on 3a. brown and red	25	3·00
24	-	50c. on 8a. red	1·25	2·25
25	-	1s. on 1r. green	3·25	4·75
26	-	2s. on 2r. blue and purple	14·00	42·00
27	-	5s. on 5r. brown and green	38·00	65·00

1953. Coronation. As T **61a** of Jamaica.

28	15c. black and green	60	2·00

14 Sultan Hussein

1954. As 1942 issue and new designs, but with portrait of Sultan Hussein as in T **14**.

29	**14**	5c. brown	10	25
30	**14**	10c. blue	15	25
31	**2**	15c. green	20	25
32	-	25c. red	20	25
33	-	35c. blue	20	25
34	-	50c. brown and red	20	20
39	-	70c. black	4·25	2·50
35	-	1s. orange	20	20
40	-	1s.25 green	4·50	11·00
41	-	1s.50 violet	4·50	11·00
36	-	2s. green	5·00	3·50
37	-	5s. blue and violet	11·00	15·00
38	-	10s. brown and violet	13·00	15·00

Designs: Vert—35c. Mosque at Seiyun; 70c. Qarn Adh Dhabi; 2s. South Gate, Tarim; 10s. Mosque entrance, Tarim. Horiz—50c. Fortress at Tarim; 1s. Mosque at Seiyun; 1s.25, Seiyun; 1s.50, Gheil Omer; 5s. Kathiri house.

1966. Nos. 29 etc surch **SOUTH ARABIA** in English and Arabic, with value and bar.

42	**14**	5f. on 5c.	30	60
43	**14**	5f. on 10c.	30	1·75
44	**2**	10f. on 15c.	30	2·25
45	-	15f. on 25c.	1·25	1·25
46	-	20f. on 35c.	40	1·50
47	-	25f. on 50c.	1·25	1·50
61	-	35f. on 70c.	2·50	75
49	-	50f. on 1s.	50	1·00
50	-	65f. on 1s.25	50	35
51	-	75f. on 1s.50	2·00	1·00
65	-	100f. on 2s.	6·50	2·50
53	-	250f. on 5s.	2·50	4·00
54	-	500f. on 10s.	2·50	4·00

Each value has two similar surcharges.

1966. Nos. 57, 59, 61/67 variously optd as given below, together with Olympic rings.

68	10f. on 15c. (**LOS ANGELES 1932**)	30	70
69	20f. on 35c. (**BERLIN 1936**)	40	75
70	35f. on 70c. (**INTERNATIONAL COOPERATION**, etc)	40	75
71	50f. on 1s. (**LONDON 1948**)	40	1·00
72	65f. on 1s.25 (**HELSINKI 1952**)	40	1·00
73	75f. on 1s.50 (**MELBOURNE 1956**)	50	1·50
74	100f. on 2s. (**ROME 1960**)	60	1·75
75	250f. on 5s. (**TOKYO 1964**)	80	3·75
76	500f. on 10s. (**MEXICO CITY 1968**)	1·00	4·50

1966. World Cup Football Championship. Nos. 57, 59, 61/62, 65/67 optd **CHAMPIONS ENGLAND** (10f., 50f. and 250f.) or **FOOTBALL 1966** (others). Both with football symbol.

77	10f. on 15c.	60	14·00
78	20f. on 35c.	80	1·00
79	35f. on 70c.	1·00	1·00
80	50f. on 1s.	1·10	1·00
81	100f. on 2s.	2·00	2·75
82	250f. on 5s.	4·50	9·50
83	500f. on 10s.	5·50	13·00

29 *Telstar*

1966. Centenary of ITU (1965).

84	**29**	5f. green, black and violet	2·50	15
85	-	10f. purple, black and green	2·75	20
86	-	15f. blue, black and orange	3·25	20
87	**29**	25f. green, black and red	3·75	20
88	-	35f. purple, black and yellow	3·75	20
89	-	50f. blue, black and brown	3·75	25
90	**29**	65f. green, black and yellow	4·00	30

Designs: 10, 35f. *"Relay*; 15, 50f. *Ranger*.

32 Churchill at Easel

1966. Sir Winston Churchill's Paintings. Multicoloured.

91	5f. Type **32**	1·75	15
92	10f. *Antibes*	2·00	15
93	15f. *Flowers* (vert)	2·00	20
94	20f. *Tapestries*	2·00	35
95	25f. *Village, Lake Lugano*	2·00	35
96	35f. *Church, Lake Como* (vert)	2·00	40
97	50f. *Flowers at Chartwell* (vert)	2·25	65
98	65f. Type **32**	2·75	90

1967. World Peace. Nos. 57, 59, 61/67 optd **WORLD PEACE** and names as given below.

99	10f. on 15c. (**PANDIT NEHRU**)	5·00	2·00
100	20f. on 35c. (**WINSTON CHURCHILL**)	7·00	2·75
101	35f. on 70c. (**DAG HAMMARSKJOLD**)	50	80
102	50f. on 1s. (**JOHN F. KENNEDY**)	60	90
103	65f. on 1s.25 (**LUDWIG ERHARD**)	70	1·10
104	75f. on 1s.50 (**LYNDON JOHNSON**)	80	1·25
105	100f. on 2s. (**ELEANOR ROOSEVELT**)	1·00	2·25
106	250f. on 5s. (**WINSTON CHURCHILL**)	18·00	12·00
107	500f. on 10s. (**JOHN F. KENNEDY**)	5·00	13·00

40 *Master Crewe as Henry VIII* (Sir Joshua Reynolds)

1967. Paintings. Multicoloured.

108	5f. Type **40**	40	25
109	10f. *The Dancer* (Degas)	45	30
110	15f. *The Fifer* (Manet)	50	35
111	20f. *Stag at Sharkey's* (boxing match, G. Bellows)	55	40
112	25f. *Don Manuel Osorio* (Goya)	60	45
113	35f. *St Martin distributing his Cloak* (A. van Dyck)	60	65
114	50f. *The Blue Boy* (Gainsborough)	70	75
115	65f. *The White Horse* (Gauguin)	80	1·00
116	75f. *Mona Lisa* (Da Vinci) (45×62 mm)	90	1·25

1967. American Astronauts. Nos. 57, 59, 61/62 and 65/66 optd as below, all with space capsule.

117	10f. on 15c. (**ALAN SHEPARD JR.**)	55	1·25
118	20f. on 35c. (**VIRGIL GRISSOM**)	70	1·25
119	35f. on 70c. (**JOHN GLENN JR.**)	95	1·50
120	50f. on 1s. (**SCOTT CARPENTER**)	95	1·50
121	100f. on 2s. (**WALTER SCHIRRA JR.**)	1·75	3·50
122	250f. on 5s. (**GORDON COOPER JR.**)	2·50	8·00

50 Churchill Crown

1967. Churchill Commemoration.

123	**50**	75f. multicoloured	8·00	7·50

APPENDIX

The following stamps have either been issued in excess of postal needs or have not been made available to the public in reasonable quantities at face value.

1967

Hunting. 20f.
Olympic Games, Grenoble. Postage 10, 25, 35, 50, 75f.; Air 100, 200f.
Scout Jamboree, Idaho. Air 150f.
Paintings. Renoir. Postage 10, 35, 50, 65, 75f.; Air 100, 200, 250f.
Paintings. Toulouse-Lautrec. Postage 10, 35, 50, 65, 75f.; Air 100, 200, 250f.

The National Liberation Front is said to have taken control of Kathiri State of Seiyun on 1 October 1967.

KAZAKHSTAN

Formerly a constituent republic of the Soviet Union, Kazakhstan declared its independence on 16 December 1991.

1992. 100 kopeks = 1 rouble.
1994. 100 tyin (ty.) = 1 tenge (t.).

1 Golden Warrior

1992. Golden Warrior (from 5th-century BC tomb).

1	**1**	50k. multicoloured	50	40

ҚАЗАҚСТАН
(2)

1992. Nos. 6079/6080 of Russia optd as T **2**, in Cyrillic (2, 4) or English (3, 5) capitals.

2	12k. purple	5·00	5·50
3	12k. purple	5·00	5·50
4	13k. violet	5·00	5·50
5	13k. violet	5·00	5·50

(3)

1992. Russian–French Space Flight. Nos. 6072/6074 of Russia surch as T **3**.

6	30k. on 2k. brown	3·25	3·00
7	75k. on 3k. green	3·25	3·00
8	1r. on 1k. brown	3·50	3·25

4 Saiga

1992

9	**4**	75k. multicoloured	75	50

5 *Turksib* (E. K. Kasteev)

1992. Kazakh Art.

10	**5**	1r. multicoloured	65	50

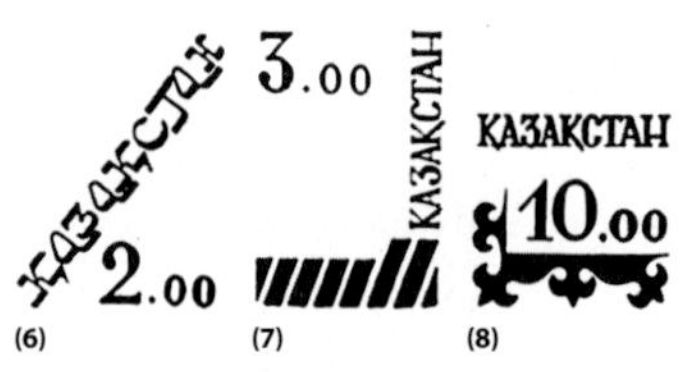
(6) **(7)** **(8)**

1992. Various stamps of Russia surch as T **6** (11/12), **7** (13/14) or **8** (15/16).

11	1r.50 on 1k. brown (No. 6072)	90	85
12	2r. on 2k. brown (No. 6073)	1·00	95
13	3r. on 6k. blue (No. 4673)	1·00	95
14	5r. on 6k. blue (No. 4673)	1·00	95
15	10r. on 1k. brown (No. 6072)	1·00	95
16	24r.50 on 1k. brown (No. 6072)	2·30	2·20

9 National Flag and Arms

1992. Republic Day.

17	**9**	5r. multicoloured	3·75	3·50

10 Rocket Launch

11 National Flag

1993

18	**10**	1r. green	15	10
19	**10**	3r. red	15	10
20	**10**	10r. bistre	50	50
21	**10**	25r. violet	1·30	1·20
22	**11**	50r. yellow, blue and deep blue	2·50	2·40

See also Nos. 45 etc.

12 Rocket and Earth

1993. Space Mail.

23	**12**	100r. multicoloured	3·00	2·75

13 Cock

1993. Chinese New Year. Year of the Cock.

24	**13**	60r. black, red and yellow	2·00	1·90

14 Space Station

1993. Cosmonautics Day.

25	**14**	90r. multicoloured	3·00	2·75

15 Nazarbaev and Flag on Map

1993. President Nursultan Nazarbaev (1st series).

26	**15**	50r. multicoloured	1·50	1·50

See also No. 28.

16 Kalkaman-Uly

1993. 325th Birth Anniversary of Bukar Zhyrau Kalkaman-Uly (poet).

27	**16**	15r. multicoloured	75	65

17 Arms, Flag on Map and Nazarbaev

1993. President Nursultan Nazarbaev (2nd series).

28	**17**	100r. multicoloured	2·75	2·40

18 Desert Dormouse

1993. Mammals. Multicoloured.

29	5r. Type **18**	40	35
30	10r. Porcupine	50	45
31	15r. Marbled polecat	65	55
32	20r. Asiatic wild ass	90	75
33	25r. Mouflon	1·00	90
34	30r. Cheetah	1·10	1·00

19 Ice Hockey

1994. Winter Olympic Games, Lillehammer, Norway (1st issue). Multicoloured.

35	15t. Type **19**	40	35
36	25t. Skiing	65	55
37	90t. Ski jumping	2·50	2·20
38	150t. Speed skating	4·00	3·50

20 Skiers

1994. Winter Olympic Games, Lillehammer, Norway (2nd issue). Multicoloured.

39	2t. Type **20**	60	50
40	6t.80 Vladimir Smirnov (Kazakh skier)	1·10	90

See also No. 42.

21 Dog

1994. Chinese New Year. Year of the Dog.

41	**21**	30t. black, blue and green	1·80	1·60

22 Smirnov

1994. Vladimir Smirnov, Winter Olympic Games Medals Winner. As No. 40 but face value changed and with additional inscription in Kazakh.

42	**22**	12t. multicoloured	2·30	2·00

23 Launch of *Soyuz TM16* at Baikonur

1994. Cosmonautics Day.

43	**23**	2t. multicoloured	1·10	90

24 Space Shuttle *Buran* on Baikonur Launch Pad and Toktar Aubakrirov

1994. First Space Flight of Kazakh Cosmonaut. Sheet 107×66 mm.

MS44	**24** 4 ×6t.80 multicoloured	7·00	6·00

1994

45	**10**	15ty. blue	1·80	1·60
46	**10**	80ty. purple	4·25	3·75
76	**10**	20ty. orange	20	15
77	**10**	25ty. yellow	25	25
78	**10**	50ty. grey	35	30
79	**10**	1t. green	45	40
80	**10**	2t. blue	90	80
81	**10**	4t. mauve	1·40	1·30
82	**10**	6t. green	1·80	1·60
83	**10**	12t. mauve	3·50	3·25

25 Mt. Abay

1994. Fifth Asia Dauysy International Music Festival, Almaty. Multicoloured.

47	10t. Type 25	1·60	1·40
48	15t. Medeo Ice Stadium, Almaty	2·10	1·80

26 Horsfield's Tortoises

1994. Reptiles. Multicoloured.

49	1t. Type **26**	25	20
50	1t.20 Toad-headed agamas	45	40
51	2t. Halys vipers	60	50
52	3t. Turkestan plate-tailed geckos	70	60
53	5t. Steppe agamas	90	80
54	7t. Glass lizards	1·20	1·00
MS55	93×73 mm. 10t. Transcaspian desert monitor (*Varanus griseus*)	3·50	3·25

27 National Arms

1994. Republic Day.

56	**27**	2t. multicoloured	90	80

28 *Why does the Swallow have a Forked Tail?* (dir. Amen Khaidorov)

1994. Children's Fund. Kazakh Children's Films. Multicoloured.

57	1t.+30ty. Type **28**	55	50
58	1t.+30ty. *The Calf and Hare seek a Better Life* (E. Abdrakhmanov)	55	50
59	1t.+30ty. Asses (*Lame Kulan* dir. Amen Khaidarov)	55	50

29 Entelodon

1994. Prehistoric Animals. Multicoloured.

60	1t. Type **29**	20	15
61	1t.20 Saurolophus	35	30
62	2t. Plesiosaurus	45	40
63	3t. Sordes pilosus	55	50
64	5t. Mosasaurus	70	65
65	7t. Megaloceros giganteum	90	80
MS66	92×72 mm. 10t. Koelodonta antiquitatis	2·75	2·50

1995. Nos. 45/46 surch.

67	**24**	1t. on 15ty. blue	20	15
68	**24**	2t. on 15ty. blue	55	50
69	**24**	3t. on 80ty. purple	70	65
70	**24**	4t. on 80ty. purple	90	80
71	**24**	6t. on 80ty. purple	1·10	95
72	**24**	8t. on 80ty. purple	1·40	1·30
73	**24**	12t. on 80ty. purple	1·60	1·40
74	**24**	20t. on 80ty. purple	2·10	1·90

31 Pig

1995. Chinese New Year. Year of the Pig.

75	**31**	10t. blue, black and light blue	2·30	2·10

32 Kunanbaev

1995. 150th Birth Anniversary of Abai Kunanbaev (writer). Multicoloured.

86	4t. Type **32**	55	50
87	9t. Kunanbaev holding pen and book	1·10	95

33 Flight Path of Soyuz Spacecraft

1995. Cosmonautics Day. Multicoloured.

88	2t. Type **33**	7·00	6·50
89	10t. Yuri Malenchenko, Talgat Musabaev and Ulf Merbold (cosmonauts)	26·00	24·00

34 Manshuk Mametova and Battle Scene

1995. 50th Anniversary of End of Second World War. Multicoloured.

90	1t. Type **34**	1·80	1·60
91	3t. Aliya Moldafulova and tank	4·50	4·00
92	5t. Wheat field, dove and eternal flame	7·50	6·75

35 *Spring* (S. Membeev)

1995. Paintings. Multicoloured.

93	4t. Type **35**	90	85
94	9t. *Mountains* (Zh. Shardenov)	1·80	1·70
95	15t. *Kulash Baiseitova in role of Kyz Zhibek* (G. Ismailova) (vert)	3·50	3·25
96	28t. *Kokpar* (K. Telzhanov)	6·00	5·50

1995. Asia Dauysy International Music Festival, Almaty. Nos. 47/48 optd **KAZAKSTAN '95 1995**.

97	10t. multicoloured	1·80	1·70
98	15t. multicoloured	2·75	2·50

37 Dauletkerei

1995. 175th Birth Anniversary of Dauletkerei (composer and poet).

99	**37**	2t. multicoloured	75	70
100	**37**	28t. multicoloured	9·75	9·00

38 Gandhi, Temple and Spinning Wheel

1995. 125th Birth Anniversary (1994) of Mahatma Gandhi.

101	**38**	9t. red and black	3·00	2·75
102	**38**	22t. red and black	7·50	7·00

39 Anniversary Emblem

1995. 50th Anniversary of UNO.

103	**39**	10t. gold and blue	2·75	2·50
104	**39**	36t. gold and blue	7·50	7·00

40 Cathedral of the Ascension

1995. Buildings in Almaty.

105	**40**	1t. green	75	70
106	-	2t. blue	1·20	1·10
107	-	3t. red	1·50	1·40
108	-	48t. brown	11·50	11·00

Designs: 2t. Culture Palace; 3t. Opera and Ballet House; 48t. Theatre.

See also Nos. 124/125.

41 White-tailed Sea Eagle

1995. Birds of Prey. Multicoloured.

109	1t. Type **41**	30	30
110	3t. Osprey	45	40
111	5t. Lammergeier	60	55
112	6t. Himalayan griffon	75	70
113	30t. Saker falcon	3·00	2·75
114	50t. Golden eagle	5·25	5·00

42 Rat and Lunar Cycle

1996. Chinese New Year. Year of the Rat.

115	**42**	25t. red, black and lilac	3·75	3·50

43 Baikonur Launch Pad highlighted on Globe

1996. Cosmonautics Day. Multicoloured.

116	6t. Type **43**	2·50	2·40
117	15t. Yuri Gagarin	5·75	5·25
118	20t. Proposed 'Alpha' space station	8·25	7·75

44 Caracal (*Felis caracal*)

1996. Save the Aral Sea. Sheet 128×108 mm containing T **44** and similar horiz designs. Multicoloured.

MS119	20t. Type **44**; 20t. Aral trout (*Salmo trutta aralensis*); 20t. Striped hyena (*Hyaena hyaena*); 20t. Kaufmann's shovelnose (*Pseudoscaphirhynchus kaufmanni*); 20t. Pike asp (*Aspiolucius esocinus*)	7·50	7·25

45 Cycling

1996. Olympic Games, Atlanta. Multicoloured.

120	4t. Type **45**	1·50	1·40
121	6t. Wrestling	2·30	2·10
122	30t. Boxing	9·75	9·00
MS123	92×69 mm. 50t. Hurdling (45×27 *mm*)	6·00	5·75

1996. As T **40** but smaller, size 24×19 mm.

124	1t. green	40	35
125	6t. green	85	75

Designs: 1t. Circus; 6t. Academy of Sciences (50th anniversary).

46 Zhabaev (after embroidery by G. Atknin)

1996. 150th Birth Anniversary of Zhambil Zhabaev (writer).

126	**46**	12t. multicoloured	2·75	2·50

47 Tomb, Dombauyl

1996. Ancient Buildings. Multicoloured.

127	1t. Type **47**	75	70
128	3t. Mausoleum, Aisha Biy	2·30	2·10
129	6t. Mausoleum, Syrly Tam	4·75	4·50
MS130	90×60 mm. 30t. Kozha Ahmet Yasavi Mausoleum, Turkestan	4·50	4·25

48 *Soyuz TM-13* docked with *Mir* Space Station

1996. Fifth Anniversary of Toktar Aubakirov's (cosmonaut) Service on *Mir*. Multicoloured.

131	46t. Type **48**	5·75	5·50
132	46t. Aubakirov	5·75	5·50

Nos. 131/132 were issued together, *se-tenant*, forming a composite design.

49 Map of Kazakhstan and Dove with Letter

1996. World Post Day.

133	**49**	9t. blue	1·50	1·40
134	-	40t. orange	5·25	5·00

Design: 40t. Dove with letter and Universal Postal Union emblem.

1996. Republic Day. No. 56 surch **KAZAKSTAN 1. 1996**.

135	**27**	21t. on 2t. multicoloured	2·30	2·10

51 *Saturnia schenki*

1996. Butterflies. Multicoloured.

136	4t. Type **51**	45	40
137	6t. *Parnassius patricius*	60	55
138	12t. *Parnasssius ariadne*	90	85
139	46t. *Colias draconis*	3·00	2·75

52 Borzois giving Chase

1996. Hunting Dogs.

140	**52**	5t. multicoloured	1·20	1·10
MS141		95×70 mm. **52** 100t. multicoloured	7·25	7·00

53 Bride before Yurt

1996. Traditional Costumes and Dwelling. Multicoloured.

142	10t. Type **53**	1·20	1·10
143	16t. Bridegroom before yurt	2·10	2·00
144	45t. Yurt interior	5·75	5·25

Nos. 142/144 were issued together, *se-tenant*, Nos. 142/143 forming a composite design.

54 Writing Materials and Books

1996. Bicentenary of National Archive.

145	**54**	4t. brown	60	55
146	-	68t. violet	4·50	4·25

Design: 68t. Book and documents.

55 Scene from *Angel with Tyubetejka* by Shaken Aimanov

1996. Centenary (1995) of Motion Pictures. Sheet 135×148 mm containing T **55** and similar horiz designs. Multicoloured.

MS147	24t. Type **55**; 24t. *The Zhibek Girl* (S. Kozhykov); 24t. *His Time will Come* (M. Begalin); 24t. *My Name is Kozha* (A. Karsakbaev)	15·00	14·50

56 Head

1997. The Marbled Polecat. Multicoloured.

148	6t. Type **56**	90	85
149	10t. Adult with tail down	1·10	1·00
150	32t. Two polecats	3·00	2·75
151	46t. Adult with tail raised	4·00	3·75

57 Ox

1997. Chinese New Year. Year of the Ox.

152	**57**	40t. brown, black and green	4·25	4·00

58 Aries

1997. Star Signs. Each violet and purple.

153	1t. Type **58**	15	15
154	2t. Taurus	25	20
155	3t. Gemini	30	30
156	4t. Cancer	40	35
157	5t. Leo	45	40
158	6t. Virgo	55	50
159	7t. Libra	60	55
160	8t. Scorpio	70	65
161	9t. Sagittarius	75	70
162	10t. Capricorn	85	75
163	12t. Aquarius	90	85
164	20t. Pisces	1·20	1·10
MS165	109×164 mm. Nos. 153/164	7·50	7·00

59 Saturn and Automatic Transfer Vehicle

1997. Cosmonautics Day. Multicoloured.

166	10t. Type **59**	1·70	1·50
167	10t. Space shuttle and *Mir* space station	1·70	1·50
168	10t. *Sputnik 1* and Earth	1·70	1·50

Nos. 166/168 were issued together, *se-tenant*, forming a composite design.

60 Emblem

1997. World Book and Copyright Day.

169	**60**	15t. yellow and green	85	80
170	**60**	60t. yellow and green	3·50	3·25

61 Auezov Museum, Almaty

1997. Birth Centenary of Mukhtar Auezov (philologist). Multicoloured.

171	25t. Type **61**	1·90	1·80
172	40t. Auezov at table (after Shcherkassky)	3·00	3·00

62 Order of Bravery

1997. Orders and Medals. Multicoloured.

173	15t. Type **62**	1·00	95
174	15t. Medal of Honour	1·00	95
175	20t. Order of Victory	1·40	1·30
176	30t. National Order of Merit	1·70	1·60

63 *Tulipa alberti*

1997. Tulips. Multicoloured.

177	15t. *Tulipa regelii*	1·40	1·30
178	35t. Type **63**	2·75	2·50
179	35t. *Tulipa greigii*	2·75	2·50

64 *Shepherd* (Sh. Sariev)

1997. Paintings. Multicoloured.

180	25t. Type **64**	2·00	1·90
181	25t. *Fantastic Still Life* (S. Kalmykov)	2·00	1·90
182	25t. *Capturing Horse* (M. Kenbaev) (horiz)	2·00	1·90

65 Moss Agate

1997. Minerals. Multicoloured.

183	15t. Type **65**	1·90	1·80
184	15t. Chalcedony	1·90	1·80
185	20t. Azurite	2·40	2·20
186	20t. Malachite	2·40	2·20
MS187	110×99 mm. Nos. 182/185	8·50	8·25

66 *Gylippus rickmersi*

1997. Arachnidae. Multicoloured.

188	30t. Type **66**	2·00	1·90
189	30t. *Latrodectus pallidus*	2·00	1·90
190	30t. *Oculicosa supermirabilis*	2·00	1·90
191	30t. *Anomalobuthus rickmersi*	2·00	1·90

67 Argali

1997. Karkaraly Nature Park. Sheet 114×148 mm containing T **67** and similar vert designs. Multicoloured.

MS192	30t. Type **67**; 30t. Common juniper; 30t. Cudgel stone	13·00	12·50

68 Horse Race

1997. National Sports. Multicoloured.

193	20t. Type **68**	2·50	2·40
194	20t. Tearing goatskin (Koknar)	2·50	2·40
195	20t. Wrestling	2·50	2·40
196	20t. Two-horse race	2·50	2·40

69 Ice Dancing

1998. Winter Sports. Multicoloured.

197	15t. Type **69**	1·20	1·10
198	30t. Biathlon	2·20	2·10

70 *Little Girl* (A. Ashkiyazara)

1998. Children's Paintings. Multicoloured.

199	15t. Type **70**	1·00	95
200	15t. *My House* (M. Tarakara) (horiz)	1·00	95

71 Tiger and Lunar Cycle

1998. Chinese New Year. Year of the Tiger.

201	**71**	30t. brown, black and yellow	4·25	4·00

72 Kurmangazy

1998. 175th Birth Anniversary of Kurmangazy (composer).

202	**72**	30t. yellow, brown and black	1·90	1·80

73 Baitursynov

1998. 125th Birth Anniversary of Akhmet Baitursynov (writer).

203	**73**	30t. light brown, brown and black	1·90	1·80

74 Winged and Horned Beasts, Issyk Kurgan

1998. Archaeological Finds. Multicoloured.

204	15t. Type **74**	1·30	1·20
205	30t. Pendants, Aktasty (vert)	2·50	2·40
206	40t. Gold and jewel-studded open-work ornament depicting animals, Kargaly	3·50	3·25

75 *Apollo 8* Spacecraft and Moon

1998. Cosmonautics Day. Multicoloured.

207	30t. Type **75**	1·70	1·60
208	30t. *Apollo 8*, Earth and Moon	1·70	1·60
209	50t. *Vostok 6* orbiting Earth	2·50	2·40

Nos. 207/208 were issued together, *se-tenant*, forming a composite design.

76 Mosque

1998. Astana. New Capital of Kazakhstan.

210	**76**	10t. brown	1·00	95
211	-	15t. blue (inscr 'Akmola')	1·20	1·10
212	-	15t. blue (inscr 'Astana')	1·20	1·10
213	-	20t. blue	1·50	1·40
214	-	25t. violet	1·70	1·60
MS215		99×73 mm. 100t. multicoloured	6·00	5·75

Designs: Vert—15t. Petroleum Ministry; 20t. Parliament. Horiz—25k. Presidents Palace. 43×25 mm—100t. Presidents Palace.

77 State Arms

1998

216	**77**	1t. green	15	15
217	**77**	2t. blue	25	25
218	**77**	3t. red	35	30
219	**77**	4t. purple	45	40
220	**77**	5t. yellow	50	50
221	**77**	8t. orange	85	80
222	**77**	20t. orange	1·40	1·30
223	**77**	50t. blue	3·25	3·00

78 Climber fixing Tent

1998. Kazakhstan Expedition to Mt. Everest. Sheet 85×67 mm.

MS230	**78** 100t. multicoloured	8·50	8·25

79 Black Stork

1998. Birds. Multicoloured.

231	15t. Type **79**	1·20	1·10
232	30t. Greater flamingoes	2·50	2·40
233	50t. Great white crane	4·25	4·00

80 Lynx

1998. Wild Cats. Multicoloured.

234	15t. Type **80**	1·20	1·10
235	30t. Sand dune cat	2·50	2·40
236	50t. Snow leopard	4·25	4·00

81 Dove and Emblem

1998. Admission of Kazakhstan to Universal Postal Union (1st issue). Sheet 104×84 mm.

MS237	**81** 50t. multicoloured	4·50	4·25

See also No. **MS**278.

82 Stamp and UPU Emblem

1998. World Post Day.

238	**82**	30t. bistre	2·00	1·90

83 Anniversary Emblem

1998. Fifth Anniversary of the Tenge (currency unit).

239	**83**	40t. orange	2·75	2·50

84 Warrior with Sword

1998. Kazakh Horsemen. Multicoloured.

240	20t. Type **84**	1·90	1·80
241	30t. Using bow and arrow	3·00	2·75
242	40t. With spear and shield	4·00	3·75

85 Rock Formation in Lake

1998. Environmental Protection. Buradai National Park. Sheet 110×98 mm containing T **85** and similar vert design. Multicoloured.

MS243	30t. Type **85**; 30t. View over lake	6·00	5·75

86 Family (census)

1999

244	**86**	1t. green	35	30
245	-	3t. red	50	50
246	-	9t. green	85	80
247	-	15t. red	1·00	95
248	-	20t. brown	1·20	1·10
249	-	30t. brown	1·70	1·60

Designs: Horiz—15t. Kanyish Sambaev (geologist and President of Academy of Sciences, birth centenary) and book; 20t. Sambaev and Academy of Sciences. Vert—3, 9, 30t. Dish aerial and *Intelsat* satellite.

87 Rabbit and Lunar Cycle

1999. Chinese New Year. Year of the Rabbit.

250	**87**	40t. green, black and yellow	4·75	4·50

88 Steam Locomotive and Railway Route Map

1999. Railway Locomotives. Multicoloured.

251	40t. Type **88**	3·50	3·25
252	50t. Electric locomotive	4·00	3·75
253	60t. Diesel railcar	4·75	4·50
254	80t. Electric locomotive (different)	6·50	6·00

89 Satellite

1999. Cosmonautics Day. Multicoloured.

255	50t. Type **89**	9·75	9·25
256	90t. Astronaut on Moon (30th anniversary of first manned Moon landing) (horiz)	20·00	19·00

90 *Pseudoeremostachys severzowii*

1999. Flowers. Multicoloured.

257	20t. Type **90**	2·10	2·00
258	30t. *Rhaphidophyton regelii*	3·00	2·75
259	90t. *Niedzwedzkia semiretschenskia*	7·75	7·25

91 Scene from *Turksib* (1929)

1999. 70th Anniversary of Kazak Cinema. Multicoloured.

260	15t. Type **91**	85	80
261	20t. M. Berkovich (director) and scenes from *Jambul's Youth* (1997) and *Wolf Cub among People* (1998)	1·00	95
262	30t. Scenes from *The Devil Paths* (1935), *Our Dear Doctor* (1957) and *Amangeldy* (1938)	1·50	1·40
263	35t. Scenes from *Zama-ay* (1997), *Biography of a Young Accordionist* (1994) and *Who are you Rider?* (1989)	1·70	1·60
264	50t. Alfred Hitchcock (director) and scene from *The Birds*	3·50	3·25
265	60t. Sergei Eisenstein (director)	5·00	4·75

92 Red Fox

1999. Endangered Species. Foxes. Multicoloured.

266	20t. Type **92**	2·50	2·40
267	30t. Dhole	4·25	4·00
268	90t. Corsac fox	11·00	10·50

93 Magnifying Glass and Stamps

1999. 125th Anniversary of Universal Postal Union.

269	**93**	10t. violet	85	80

94 Mushroom Cloud

1999. Environmental Protection Sheet 130×108, containing T **94** and similar horiz designs. Multicoloured.

MS270	15t. Type **94** (tenth Anniversary of cessation of nuclear testing at Semipalatinsk); 45t. Emblem (International Day for Protection of the Ozone Layer); 60t. Butterflies and landscape	10·00	9·75

95 Flower

1999. Endangered Flora (1st series).

271	**95**	4t. mauve	35	30
272	**95**	30t. green	1·90	1·80

See also Nos. 296/298, 310/311 and 357/363.

96 T. Musabayev

1999. Cosmonauts. Multicoloured.

273	40t. Type **96**	2·50	2·40
274	50t. T. Aubakirov (first Kazakhstan cosmonaut) (vert)	3·50	3·25

97 Ice Hockey Match

1999. Sports. Multicoloured.

275	20t. Type **97**	1·70	1·60
276	30t. Ice hockey team	2·50	2·40
277	40t. G. Kosanov (athlete)	3·50	3·25

98 Globe and Horse-drawn Carriage

1999. 125th Anniversary of UPU (2nd issue). Sheet 120×85 mm.

MS278	**98** 20t. multicoloured	4·50	4·25

99 Oil Rig

2000. Centenary of Oil Extraction in Kazakhstan.

279	**99**	7t. red	50	50

100 Yurt, Horse racing and Artifacts

2000. Navruz Bayram Festival. Imperf.

280	**100**	20t. multicoloured	3·50	3·25

101 Millennium Emblem

2000. New Millennium.

281	**101**	30t. blue, deep blue and orange	3·25	3·00

102 28th Guardsman-Panfilovs Memorial and Eternal Flame, Alma-Ata

2000. 55th Anniversary of End of Second World War.

282	**102**	3t. brown and red	50	50

103 *Stride into the Bright Future* (painting, Kostya Balakirev)

2000. International Children's Day. New Millennium. Sheet 127×106 mm.

MS283	**103** 70t. multicoloured	6·75	6·50

104 Koumiss (fermented mare's milk) Flask

2000. Joint issue with People's Republic of China. Pots. Multicoloured.

284	15t. Type **104**	1·70	1·60
285	50t. He-pot (Chinese wine vessel)	4·25	4·00

105 Mukanov

2000. Birth Centenary of Sabit Mukanov (writer).

286	**105**	1t. green	70	65

106 Dulati

2000. 500th Birth Anniversary of Mukhammed Khaidar Dulti (historian) (1999).

287	**106**	8t. blue	50	50

107 Canoeing

2000. Olympics Games, Sydney. Multicoloured.

288	35t. Type **107**	2·40	1·90
289	40t. Gymnastics	2·75	2·20
290	40t. Taekwondo	2·75	2·20
291	50t. Triathlon	3·25	2·75

108 *Echo* Telecommunications Satellite

2000

292	**108**	5t. orange	45	40
293	**108**	15t. blue	1·10	1·00
294	**108**	20t. blue	1·20	1·10

109 Arystan Bab's Mausoleum

2000. 1500th Anniversary of Turkestan (town). Sheet 160×140 mm containing T **109** and similar horiz designs. Multicoloured.

MS295	50t. Type **109**; 50t. Rabiy Sultan Begim's and Karashash Ana's mausolea; 70t. Kozhah Akhmet Yassauy's mausoleum	10·50	10·00

Stamps of a similar design were issued by Turkey.

110 Flower

2000. Endangered Flora (2nd series).

296	**110**	1t. green	15	15
297	**110**	2t. blue	30	30
298	**110**	50t. blue	2·75	2·50

111 Momysh-Uly and Gold Star of Hero of Soviet Union Medal

2000. 90th Birth Anniversary of Baurdzhan Momyush-Uly (Soviet military leader).

299	**111**	4t. brown and black	45	40

2001. Nos. 57/59 surch **2001 10.00**.

300	10t. on 1t. +30ty. multicoloured	55	50
301	10t. on 1t. +30ty. multicoloured	55	50
302	10t. on 1t. +30ty. multicoloured	55	50

113 Snail and Lunar Cycle

2001. Chinese New Year. Year of the Snail.

303	**113**	40t. black, blue and yellow	2·40	2·20

114 Rocket, Yuri Gagarin and Dogs

2001. Cosmonautics Day (2000). Multicoloured.

304	40t. Type **114** (40th anniversary of space flight by Belka and Strelka (dogs))	2·10	2·00
305	70t. Rocket launch (45th anniversary of Baikonur cosmodrome) (vert)	3·50	3·25

115 Snake and Lunar Cycle

2001. Chinese New Year. Year of the Snake.

306	**115**	40t. black, brown and green	2·40	2·20

116 Dove, Globe and Transport

2001. Tenth Anniversary of Ministry of Transportation and Communication. Sheet 100×70 mm.
MS307 **116** 100t. multicoloured 12·00 11·50

117 *Soyuz-II* Spacecraft and Salyut Space Station

2001. Cosmonautics Day. Multicoloured.

308	45t. Type **117**	2·40	2·20
309	70t. Yuri Gagarin and earth (40th anniversary of first manned space flight)	3·25	3·00

118 *Aquilegia karatavica*

2001. Endangered Flora (3rd series).

310	**118**	3t. green	15	15
311	**118**	10t. green	60	55

119 Abulkhair-Khan (1693–1748)

2001. Khans (feudal rulers). Multicoloured.

312	50t. Type **119**	2·75	2·50
313	60t. Abylai-Khan (1711–1781)	3·25	3·00

120 Roborovski Hamster (*Phodopus roborovskii*)

2001. Fauna (1st series).

314	**120**	8t. orange	30	30
315	**120**	15t. blue	75	70
316	**120**	20t. blue	1·10	1·00
317	**120**	50t. brown	2·75	2·50

See also 351/354, 386/392 and 397.

121 Northern Eagle Owl (*Bubo bubo*)

2001. Owls. Multicoloured.

318	30t. Type **121**	2·75	2·75
319	40t. Long-eared owl (*Asio otis*)	3·75	3·50
320	50t. Hawk owl (*Surnia ulula*)	4·75	4·50

122 Winged Lion and Fibre Optic Cable

2001. National Development Plan. Communications.

321	**122**	40t. multicoloured	2·10	2·00

123 Red Deer (*Cervus elaphus*)

2001. Fauna of Lake Markakol (national park). Sheet 110×98 mm containing T **123** and similar vert designs. Multicoloured.
MS322 Type **123**; 30t. Brown bear (*Ursus arctos*); 30t. Lenok (*Brachymystax lenok*) 13·50 13·00

124 Bobak Marmot (*Marmota bobak*)

2001. Flora and Fauna. Sheet 215×102 mm containing T **124** and similar horiz designs. Multicoloured.
MS323 Type **124**; 12t. Great bustard (*Otis tarda*); 25t. Relict gull (*Larus relictus*); 60t. African wildcat (*Felis silvestris libyca*); 90t. Water lily (*Nymphaea alba*); 100t. Dalmatian pelican (*Pelecanus crispus*) 18·00 17·00

125 Druzhba Station Facade

2001. Anniversaries. Sheet 105×74 mm containing T **125** and similar horiz designs. Multicoloured.
MS324 Type **125** (Tenth anniversary of Kazakhstan–China railway); 20t. Steam locomotive (70th anniversary of Turkestan–Siberia railway); 50t. Workmen (opening of Aksu–Delegen railway) 13·50 13·00

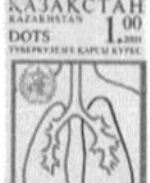
126 Lungs and United Nations Emblem

2001. Health.

325	**126**	1t. green, blue and black	30	30
326	-	5t. red, grey and black	45	40

Designs: 1t. T **126** (tuberculosis prevention campaign); 5t. Ribbon and book (AIDS prevention campaign).

127 River Charyn Cliffs

2001. International Year of Mountains. Multicoloured.

327	35t. Type **127**	1·70	1·50
328	60t. Mt. Khan Tegri	2·75	2·75

128 Alexej Leonov

2001. Space Anniversaries. Multicoloured.

329	50t. Type **128** (35th anniversary of First space walk)	6·00	5·50
330	70t. Soyuz and Apollo space craft (25th anniversary of joint USSR–USA space flight) (horiz)	8·25	7·75

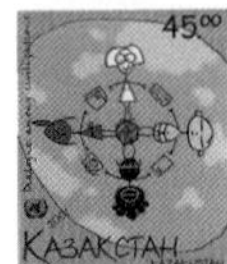
129 Children encircling Globe

2001. United Nations Year of Dialogue among Civilisations.

331	**129**	45t. multicoloured	3·00	2·75

130 Wild Ass

2001. Endangered Species. Asiatic Wild Ass (*Equus heminus kulan*). Multicoloured.

332	9t. Type **130**	75	70
333	12t. Galloping	1·10	1·00
334	25t. Fighting	2·00	1·80
335	50t. Mare and foal	3·75	3·50

131 School Palace, Alma Ata

2001. Architecture.

336	**131**	7t. mauve	45	40
337	-	30t. green	1·80	1·70

Design: 30t. School Palace, Alma Ata (different).

132 Union Emblem

2001. Tenth Anniversary of Union of Independent States.

338	**132**	40t. multicoloured	2·30	2·10

133 President Nursultan Nazarbaev and Pope John Paul II

2001. Visit of Pope John Paul II to Kazakhstan. Multicoloured.

339	20t. Type **133**	1·70	1·50
340	50t. President Nazarbaev and Pope John Paul II (different)	4·00	3·75

134 Independence Monument, Almaty

2001. Tenth Anniversary of Independence (1st issue). Sheet 110×96 mm containing T **134** and similar vert designs. Multicoloured.
MS341 Type **134**; 25t. Parliament House, Astana; 35t. Pres. Nursultan Nazarbaev 8·25 8·00

135 Celebration Emblem and Map

2001. Tenth Anniversary of Independence (2nd issue).

342	**135**	40t. yellow, blue and black	2·10	2·00

136 Man's Costume

2001. Traditional Costumes. Multicoloured.

343	25t. Type **136**	1·50	1·40
344	35t. Woman's costume	2·30	2·10

Nos. 343/344 were issued together, *se-tenant*, forming a composite design.

137 Women Ice Hockey Players

2002. Winter Olympic Games, Salt Lake City, USA. Multicoloured.

345	50t. Type **137**	3·75	3·50
346	150t. Freestyle ski jump	9·00	8·50

138 Horse and Lunar Cycle

2002. Chinese New Year. Year of the Horse.

347	**138**	50t. black, ochre and stone	3·00	2·75

139 Chestnut Horse

2002. Horses. Multicoloured.

348	9t. Type **139**	1·10	1·00
349	25t. Dark chestnut, two legs raised	2·00	1·80
350	60t. Grey	3·75	3·50

140 Pallid Pygmy Jerboa (*Salpingotus pallidus*)

2002. Fauna (2nd series).

351	**140**	5t. purple	15	15
352	**140**	15t. blue	60	55
353	**140**	40t. brown	1·80	1·70
354	**140**	50t. sepia	2·30	2·10

141 Denis Tito (passenger), Talgat Musabaev and Yury Baturin (crew of *Soyuz TM-32*)

2002. Cosmonautics Day. Multicoloured.

355		30t. Type **141**	1·50	1·40
356		70t. Flags of USA, Kazakhstan and Russia	3·25	3·00

142 *Pterygostemon spathulatus*

2002. Endangered Flora (4th series).

357	**142**	1t. green	45	40
358	**142**	2t. blue	60	55
359	**142**	3t. green	75	70
360	**142**	10t. violet	1·10	1·00
361	**142**	12t. mauve	1·20	1·10
362	**142**	25t. violet	1·50	1·40
363	**142**	35t. olive	2·00	1·80

143 Two Players

2002. World Cup Football Championship, Japan and South Korea. Multicoloured.

364		10t. Type **143**	1·50	1·40
365		10t. Player heading ball	1·50	1·40

144 Globe

2002. TRANSEURASIA 2002 International Conference.

366	**144**	30t. blue, black and yellow	1·40	1·30

145 *Leontopodium fedtschenkoanum* (flower)

2002. Alatau National Park. Sheet 115×110 mm containing T **145** and similar vert designs. Multicoloured.

MS367 30t.×3, Type **145**; Ermine (*Mustela erminea*); Aport Alexander apples — 4·50 — 4·25

146 Trading House

2002. 250th Anniversary of Petropavlovsk.

368	**146**	6t. red	15	15
369	-	7t. purple	30	30
370	-	8t. orange (vert)	45	40
371	-	23t. blue (vert)	1·10	1·00

Designs: 7t. No. 368; 8t. Karasai and Agyntai (heroes) monument; 23t. No. 370.

147 *Kazakh Composition* (E. Sidorkin)

2002. Art.

372	**147**	8t. brown, bistre and black	60	55
373	-	9t. black and drab	75	70
374	-	60t. sepia, bistre and black	4·25	4·00

Designs: 9t. *Makhambet* (M. Kisametdinov); 60t. *Batyr* (E. Sidorkin).

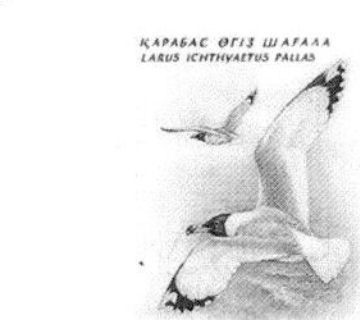

148 Great Black-headed Gull (Pallas' Gull) (*Larus ichthyaetus Pallas*)

2002. Endangered Species. Birds. Multicoloured.

375		10t. Type **148**	60	55
376		15t. Demoiselle crane (*Anthropoides virgo*)	90	85

Stamps of the same design were issued by Russia.

149 *Huso huso ponticus* (fish)

2002. Endangered Species. Marine Animals. Multicoloured.

377		20t. Type **149**	1·20	1·10
378		35t. Caspian seal (*Phoca caspica*)	1·70	1·50

Stamps of the same design were issued by Ukraine.

150 Mosque

2002. Bimillenary of Taraz. Sheet 115×80 mm.

MS379 **150** 70t. multicoloured — 3·75 — 3·50

151 Altau Mountains

2002. International Year of Mountains. Sheet 90×70 mm.

MS380 **151** 50t. multicoloured — 2·75 — 2·50

152 Gabiden Mustaphin

2002. Birth Centenary of Gabiden Mustaphin (writer).

381	**152**	10t. blue	45	40

153 Gani Muratbaev

2002. Birth Centenary of Gani Muratbaev (politician).

382	**153**	3t. brown	30	30

154 Gabit Musrepov

2002. Birth Centenary of Gabit Musrepov (writer).

383	**154**	20t. multicoloured	90	85

155 Ilyushin IL-86 over Almaty Airport

2002. Aircraft. Multicoloured.

384		20t. Type **155**	1·20	1·10
385		40t. Tupelov TU-144 (25th Anniversary of flight from Russia to Almaty)	2·30	2·10

156 Desert Dormouse (*Selevinia betpakdalensis*)

2003. Fauna (3rd series).

386	**156**	4t. brown	25	20
387	**156**	5t. brown	30	30
388	**156**	6t. olive	40	35
389	**156**	7t. green	45	40
390	**156**	10t. blue	75	70
391	**156**	63t. red	3·00	2·75
392	**156**	150t. purple	6·75	6·25

157 Argali-Merino Ram

2003. Sheep. Multicoloured.

393		20t. Type **157**	90	85
394		40t. Ram (different)	1·80	1·70
395		50t. Argali ram	2·30	2·10

158 Sheep and Lunar Cycle

2003. Chinese New Year. Year of the Sheep.

396	**158**	50t. black, blue and light blue	2·75	2·50

2003. Fauna. Roborovski Hamster (*Phodopus roborovskii*) (4th issue).

397	**120**	35t. green	2·30	2·10

159 *Pioner-10*

2003. Cosmonautics Day. Multicoloured.

398		40t. Type **159**	1·80	1·70
399		70t. *Mir* space station (vert)	3·00	2·75

160 Memorial to Victims of Political Repression

2003. Tenth Anniversary of Rehabilitation of Victims of Political Repression Law.

400	**160**	1t. magenta	15	15
401	**160**	8t. brown	30	30

161 IAAS Emblem

2003. Tenth Anniversary of the International Association of Academies of Sciences.

402	**161**	50t. multicoloured	2·30	2·10

162 Couple wearing Kazakhstan Costumes

2003. Traditional Costumes. Sheet 115×97 mm containing T **162** and similar vert designs (1st series). Multicoloured.

MS403 35t.×3, Type **162**; Russian; Ukrainian — 4·75 — 4·50

See also No. **MS**453.

163 Dombra

2003. Traditional Instruments. Multicoloured.

404		25t. Type **163**	1·10	1·10
405		50t. Kobyz	2·20	2·10

164 *Intelsat* Satellite

2003

406	**164**	3t. red	50	45
407	**164**	9t. blue	65	60
408	**164**	84t. orange	3·75	3·50
409	**164**	100t. purple	4·25	4·00

165 Aldar Kose and Alasha Khan

2003. Fairy Tale Characters. Multicoloured.

410		30t. Type **165**	1·30	1·20
411		40t. Aldar Kose and Karynbaj	1·80	1·70

166 *Game of a Chess* (A. Richchi)

2003. Museum of Arts Exhibits. Multicoloured.

412		20t. Type **166**	1·30	1·20
413		35t. *Portrait of a Shepherd* (sculpture, H. Nauryzbaev)	2·20	2·10
414		45t. *Drinking Koumiss* (A. Galimbaeva)	3·00	2·75

167 Aiteke Bi Baibekuly (1689–1766)

2003. Judges. Multicoloured.

415		60t. Type **167**	2·75	2·50
416		60t. Kazibek Bi Keldibekuly (1667–1763)	2·75	2·50
417		60t. Tole Bi Alibekuly (1663–1756)	2·75	2·50

168 Anniversary Emblem

2003. Tenth Anniversary of Halyk Bank.

418	**168**	23t. multicoloured	95	90

169 Conference and UN Emblems

2003. International Ministerial Transport Co-operation Conference.

419	**169**	40t. multicoloured	1·90	1·80

170 Globe and UPU emblems

2003. World Post Day.

420	**170**	23t. violet and blue	95	90

171 Central Mosque, Almaty

2003. Religious Buildings. Multicoloured.

421		50t. Type **171**	1·90	1·80
422		50t. Almaty Cathedral	1·90	1·80

172 Anniversary Emblem

2003. Tenth Anniversary of Kazakhstan Currency (tenge).

423	**172**	25t. lemon and blue	1·10	1·10

173 *Happiness* (S. Aitbaev) (1966)

2003. Paintings. Multicoloured.

424	100t. Type **173**	3·75	3·50
425	100t. *Morning Motherhood* (R. Ahmedov) (1962)	3·75	3·50

Stamps of similar designs were issued by Uzbekistan.

174 *Populus diversifolia*

2003. Endangered Species. Asiatic Poplar.

426	**174**	100t. multicoloured	3·75	3·50

175 Cow

2003. Tamalgy. UNESCO World Heritage Site. Petroglyphs (carvings). Multicoloured.

427	25t. Type **175**	1·30	1·20
428	30t. Sun and bull (vert)	1·40	1·40

2004. No. 45 surch **200t.**

429	200t. on 80t. claret	11·00	10·50

177 Abylhan Kasteev

2004. Birth Centenary of Abylhan Kasteev (artist).

430	**177**	115t. multicoloured	4·75	4·50

178 Monkey and Lunar Cycle

2004. Chinese New Year. Year of the Monkey.

431	**178**	35t. blue, ultramarine and ochre	1·60	1·50

179 Spacecraft *Mariner-10*

2004. Cosmonautics Day. Multicoloured.

432	40t. Type **179**	1·80	1·70
433	50t. *Luna-3* space station (horiz)	2·20	2·10

180 Kazakhstan Arms

2004

434	**180**	1t. green	15	15
435	**180**	2t. blue	25	25
436	**180**	4t. purple	30	30
437	**180**	5t. yellow	40	40
438	**180**	10t. olive	65	60
439	**180**	16t. mauve	80	75
440	**180**	20t. mauve	95	90
441	**180**	35t. yellow	1·60	1·50
442	**180**	50t. emerald	2·20	2·10
443	**180**	72t. orange	3·00	2·75
444	**180**	100t. turquoise	4·00	3·75
445	**180**	200t. vermilion	8·00	7·50

181 National Flag

2004

451	**181**	25t. blue and lemon	1·10	1·10

182 Electric Locomotive

2004. Centenary of Kazakhstan Railway. Sheet 101×71 mm.

MS452	**182** 150t. multicoloured	6·50	6·25

2004. Traditional Costumes (2nd series). Sheet 110×96 mm containing vert designs as T **162**. Multicoloured.

MS453	65t.×2, Uzbekistan; German	5·00	4·75

183 Player and Emblem

2004. Centenary of FIFA (Federation Internationale de Football Association). Multicoloured.

454	100t. Type **183**	4·00	3·75
455	100t. Player facing right and emblem	4·00	3·75

184 Bayan Sulu (fairy tale)

2004. Children's Drawings. Multicoloured.

456	45t. Type **184** (D. Ishanova)	1·90	1·80
457	45t. Mountains, yurts and sheep (A. Sadykov) (horiz)	1·90	1·80

185 Boxing

2004. Olympic Games, Athens. Sheet 100×90 mm containing T **185** and similar horiz design. Multicoloured.

MS458	70t. Type **185**; 115t. Rifle shooting	7·25	7·00

186 Cinereous Vulture (*Aegypius monachus*) (inscr 'Acgypius')

2004. Altyn Yemel National Park. Sheet 80×110 mm containing T **186** and similar horiz designs. Multicoloured.

MS459	50t.×3 T **186**; Siberian ibex (*Capra sibirica*); Persian gazelle (*Gazella subgutturosa*)	6·50	6·25

187 Emblem

2004. Tenth Anniversary of Kazakhtelecom Company. Sheet 100×70 mm.

MS460	**187** 70t. multicoloured	4·00	3·75

188 Alkei Margulan

2004. Birth Centenary of Alkei Hakanovich Margulan (archaeologist).

461	**188**	115t. multicoloured	4·75	4·50

189 Flowers

2004. Greetings Stamp.

462	**189**	25t. multicoloured	1·40	1·40

2004. World Post Day.

463	**170**	3t. violet and blue	50	45
464	**170**	30t. lemon and blue	1·30	1·20

190 Bauble

2004. Happy New Year.

465	**190**	65t. multicoloured	2·40	2·30

191 Adyrna

2004. Traditional Musical Instruments. Multicoloured.

466	100t. Type **191**	4·00	3·75
467	100t. Gizhak	4·00	3·75

Stamps of the same design were issued by Tadjikistan.

192 Saken Seifullin

2004. 110th Birth Anniversary of Saken Seifullin (writer).

468	**192**	35t. multicoloured	1·40	1·40

193 Kazakh Woman's Headdress

2004. Women's Headdress. Multicoloured.

469	72t. Type **193**	3·00	2·75
470	72t. Mongolian woman's headdress	3·00	2·75

Stamps of the same design were issued by Mongolia.

194 Emblem

2005. Centenary of Research Institute of Veterinary Science.

471	**194**	7t. vermilion, blue and ultramarine	50	45

195 Arms and Book

2005. Tenth Anniversary of Constitution.

472	**195**	1t. blue and brown	15	15
473	**195**	2t. mauve and brown	25	25
474	**195**	3t. green and brown	30	30
475	**195**	8t. blue and -brown	50	45
476	**195**	10t. carmine and brown	65	60
477	**195**	A (25t.) purple and brown	95	90
478	**195**	50t. bistre and brown	1·60	1·50
479	**195**	65t. blue and brown	2·10	2·00

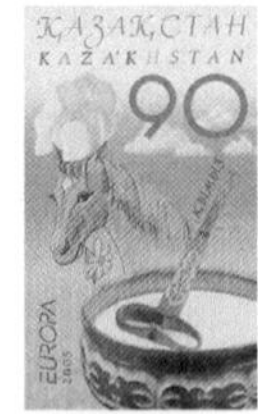

196 Horse and Bowl of Kumis

2005. Europa. Gastronomy.

480	**196**	90t. multicoloured	6·00	5·75

197 *Rodina-mat* (statue)

2005. 60th Anniversary of End of World War II.

481	**197**	72t. multicoloured	3·00	2·75

198 Soyuz Spacecraft

2005. 50th Anniversary of Baikonur Cosmodrome. Sheet 111×71 mm containing T **198** and similar horiz designs. Multicoloured.

MS482	72t.×3 Type **198**; *Buran* spacecraft; Parachute and space capsule	7·75	7·50

199 Building Plan of Project

2005. Peace and Harmony Palace Project (designed by Norman Foster).

483	**199**	65t. multicoloured	2·40	2·30

200 Inscr 'Ashirite'

2005. Minerals. Multicoloured.

484	50t. Type **200**	1·80	1·70
485	70t. Tubular agate	2·50	2·40

201 Aldar Kose and Rich Musician

2005. Fairy Tale Characters. Multicoloured.

486	35t. Type **201**	1·30	1·20
487	45t. *How Aldar Kose taught the rich man to grow donkeys*	1·60	1·50

202 Anniversary Emblem

2005. Tenth Anniversary of Constitution.
488 **202** 72t. multicoloured 2·50 2·40

203 Zhaksylyk Ushkempirov (Graeco-Roman wrestling, Moscow, 1980)

2005. Sport. Olympic Champions. Sheet 139×84 mm containing T **203** and similar horiz designs.
MS489 100t.×4, Type **203**; Vitaly Savin (4×100 metres men's relay, Seoul, 1988); Vasily Zhirov (boxing light heavyweight, Atlanta, 1996); Bekzat Sattarkhanov (boxing featherweight, Sydney, 2000) 14·50 14·00

2005

204

2005. No. 203 optd T **204**.
490 **73** 30t. multicoloured 1·10 1·10

205 UPU Emblem

2005. World Post Day.
491 **205** 35t. blue and lilac 1·30 1·20
492 **205** 40t. violet and claret 1·40 1·40

206 Kazak Tazi (hound)

2005. Hunting Dogs. Multicoloured.
493 138t. Type **206** 5·50 5·25
494 138t. Estonia hound 5·50 5·25
Stamps of similar design were issued by Estonia.

207 '60' and UN Emblem

2005. 60th Anniversary of United Nations.
495 **207** 150t. blue, orange and black 5·00 4·75

208 Baiterek Monument, Clock Face and Tree

2005. New Year.
496 **208** 65t. multicoloured 2·40 2·30

209 Evgeny Brusilovsky

2005. Birth Centenary of Evgeny Grigorevich Brusilovsky (composer).
497 **209** 150t. multicoloured 5·00 4·75

210 Flag

2005. State Symbols. Sheet 135×80 mm containing T **210** and similar vert designs. Multicoloured.
MS498 70t. Type **210**; 70t. Words to hymn and statue; 300t. State arms 16·00 15·00

211 Turgen Waterfall

2005. Mountain Landscapes. Multicoloured.
499 12t. Type **211** 95 90
500 100t. Mountain lake (horiz) 4·75 4·50

212 Hans Christian Andersen and Characters from Stories

2005. Birth Bicentenary of Hans Christian Andersen (writer).
501 **212** 200t. multicoloured 7·25 6·75

213 Emblem

2006. Tenth Anniversary of Parliament.
502 **213** 50t. multicoloured 1·90 1·80

214 *Ablai Khan* (Aubakir Ismailov)

2006. Art.
503 **214** 94t. multicoloured 3·75 3·50

215 Curling

2006. Winter Olympic Games, Turin.
504 **215** 138t. multicoloured 4·75 4·50

216 *Cosmonauts* (P. M. Popov) (1966)

2006. Cosmonautics Day. Paintings. Multicoloured.
505 100t. Type **216** 3·50 3·25
506 120t. *Cosmonaut* (A. M. Stepanov) (1970) 5·25 5·00

217 Cuff

2006. Jewellery. Multicoloured.
507 110t. Type **217** 4·00 3·75
508 110t. Brooch 4·00 3·75
Stamps of the same design were issued by Latvia.

218 *Haloxylon aphyllum*

2006
509 **218** 25t. multicoloured 95 90

219 Hands of Many Nations

2006. Europa. Integration.
510 **219** 210t. multicoloured 8·25 7·75

220 *Turksib* (painting) (Abylhan Kasteev)

2006. 75th Anniversary of Turkestan–Siberian Railway.
511 **220** 200t. multicoloured 7·25 6·75

221 Football and Emblem

2006. World Cup Football Championship, Germany.
512 **221** 150t. multicoloured 6·50 6·00

222 Emblem

2006. International Year of Deserts and Desertification.
513 **222** 110t. multicoloured 4·00 3·75

223 Astana Mosque

2006

514	**223**	5t. green	55	50
515	**223**	8t. blue	70	70
516	**223**	10t. green	90	85
517	**223**	A (25t.) purple	1·60	1·50
517a	**223**	100t. blue	4·00	3·75
518	**223**	110t. brown	4·50	4·25
519	**223**	120t. magenta	5·00	4·75
520	**223**	200t. green	8·00	7·75

224 Akzhan Mashani

2006. Birth Centenary of Akzhan Mashani (geologist).
521 **224** 85t. multicoloured 3·50 3·50

225 Holy Trinity Cathedral Church, Almaty

2006. Places of Worship. Multicoloured.
522 25t. Type **225** 1·10 1·00
523 25t. Chabad Lubavich Synagogue, Almaty 1·10 1·00

226 Chokan Valikhanov (scientist-historian), 1835–1865

2006. Personalities. Sheet 84×100 mm containing T **226** and similar horiz designs. Multicoloured.
MS524 90t.×4, Type **226**; Saken Sejfullin (writer), 1894–1938; Nazir Tjurjakulov, 1893–1937; Kanysh Satpaev (geologist), 1899–1964 13·50 13·00

227 Flags of Participating Countries and Map

2006. Third Meeting of ECO Postal Authorities.
525 **227** 210t. multicoloured 9·00 8·50

АНКАРА

(228)

2006. Third Meeting of ECO Postal Authorities. No. 525 overprinted with T **228**. Multicoloured.
526 210t. As No. 525 9·00 8·50

229 Ahmet Zhubanov

2006. Birth Centenary of Ahmet Zhubanov (composer).
527 **229** 85t. multicoloured 3·50 3·50

229a Almaty

2006. Town Arms. Multicoloured.
528 17t. Type **229a** 70 70
529 80t. Astana 3·25 3·00

230 Snowman

2006. Happy New Year.
530 **230** 25t. multicoloured 1·10 1·00

232 Manash Kozybaev

2006. 75th (2005) Birth Anniversary of Manash Kozybaev (historian).
532 **232** 20t. brown 70 70
533 **232** 30t. claret 90 85

233 Mukagali Makataev

2006. 75th (2005) Birth Anniversary of Mukagali Makataev (writer).

534	**233**	1t. ultramarine	20	15
535	**233**	4t. olive	25	25
536	**233**	7t. claret	35	35
537	**233**	15t. chestnut	55	50

234 18th-century Helmet

2006. Ancient Armour and Weapons.
538 **234** 85t. multicoloured 4·00 3·75

235 *The Silk Girl* (opera)

2006. Theatre Art.
539 **235** 80t. multicoloured 3·75 3·50

236 Nikolai Repinsky

2006. Birth Centenary of Nikolai Repinsky (architect).
540 **236** 2t. ultramarine 35 30
541 **236** 3t. brown 45 40
542 **236** 105t. olive 4·75 4·50
543 **236** 150t. blue 7·50 7·25
544 **236** 500t. purple 22·00 21·00

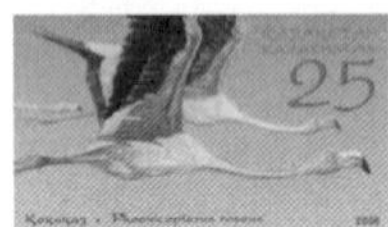
237 *Phoenicopterus roseus*

2006. Kurgalzhinsky Nature Reserve. Sheet 80×110 mm containing T **237** and similar horiz designs. Multicoloured.
MS545 25t. Type **237**; 100t. *Cygnus cygnus*; 120t. *Meles meles* 11·50 11·00

238 Anniversary Emblem

2007. Tenth Anniversary of KazTransOil.
546 **238** 25t. multicoloured 1·50 1·50

239 Konstantin Tsiolkovski (physicist and rocket pioneer) (150th birth anniversary)

2007. Cosmonautics Day. Anniversaries. Multicoloured.
547 80t. Type **239** 5·50 5·25
548 110t. Sergei Korolev (rocket engineer and designer) (birth centenary) 6·50 6·25

240 Scout (Danagul Orazymbetova)

2007. Europa. Centenary of Scouting. Children's Drawings. Multicoloured.
549 25t. Type **240** 2·00 1·90
550 65t. Scouts wearing packs (Tamara Turta) 4·25 4·00

241 Anniversary Emblem

2007. 60th Anniversary of UN ESCAP (United Nations Economic and Social Commission for Asia and the Pacific)
551 **241** 25t. multicoloured 1·30 1·30

242 Gali Ormanov

2007. Birth Centenary of Gali Ormanov (writer).
552 **242** 25t. multicoloured 1·30 1·30

243 Emblem

2007. 15th Anniversary of Conference on Interaction and Confidence Building in Asia (CICA).
553 **243** 80t. multicoloured 4·00 3·75

244 Maulen Balakaev

2007. Birth Centenary of Maulen Balakaev (writer).
554 **244** 1t. brown 35 30
555 **244** 4t. green 55 55
556 **244** 5t. brown 65 65

245 Zebra

2007. 70th Anniversary of Almaty Zoo. Multicoloured.
557 25t. Type **245** 1·50 1·50
558 110t. Elephant 5·25 5·00

246 Swallow

2007. Swallow (*Hirundo rustica*).
559 **246** 20t. black and vermilion 1·40 1·30
560 **246** 25t. black and vermilion 1·60 1·50
561 **246** 50t. black and vermilion 3·00 2·75
562 **246** 100t. black and vermilion 5·75 5·50

247 Kazakhstan Saddle

2007
563 **247** 80t. multicoloured 4·25 4·00

248 *Sputnik I*

2007. 50th Anniversary of Space Exploration.
564 **248** 500t. multicoloured 25·00 24·00

2007. Town Arms. As T **229a**. Multicoloured.
565 10t. Pavlodar 1·10 1·10
566 10t. Karaganda 1·10 1·10

249 Bauble

2007. New Year.
567 **249** 25t. multicoloured 1·60 1·50

250 Uigur Couple

2007. Traditional Costumes. Sheet 110×96 mm containing T **250** and similar vert designs. Multicoloured.
MS568 105t.×2, Type **250**; Tatar couple 10·50 10·00

251 Vladimir Smirnov

2007. Olympic Gold Medallists. Sheet 138×83 mm containing T **251** and similar horiz designs. Multicoloured.
MS569 150t.×4, Type **251** (skier) (Lillehammer 1994); Yuri Melinichenko (wrestling) (Atlanta 1996); Olga Shishigina (hurdler) (Sydney 2000); Ermahan Ibraimov (boxer) (Sydney 2000) 33·00 32·00

252 Tulip

2008. Women's Day. Flowers. Sheet 144×144 mm containing T **252** and similar square designs. Multicoloured.
MS570 25t.×6, Type **252**; Tulip, white and yellow flowers; Large yellow and small white chrysanthemums; Part of large orange and several small yellow and white chrysanthemums; Part of large yellow and small white and yellow chrysanthemums; Part of large orange and yellow and white chrysanthemums 11·00 10·50

The stamps, gutter and margins of **MS**570 form a composite design of a bouquet of flowers.

253 Flowers and Couple on Swing

2008. Nauryz (Spring) Festival.
571 **253** 25t. multicoloured 1·10 1·10

254 Torch Relay in Alma-Ata

2008. Olympic Games, Beijing.
572 **254** 25t. multicoloured 1·40 1·30

255 Main Post Office

2008. 15th Anniversary of Kazakhstan Posts.
573 **255** 25t. multicoloured 1·40 1·30

256 Space Station *Mir*

2008. Cosmonautics Day. Tenth Anniversary of International Space Station. Multicoloured.
574 100t. Type **256** 4·50 4·25
575 150t. Space station 6·75 6·25

257 Dove and Label

2008. Europa. The Letter. Multicoloured.
576 150t. Type **257** 6·75 6·25
577 150t. Label and dove 6·75 6·25

Nos. 576/577 were issued together, *se-tenant*, forming a composite design.

258 Judo

2008. Olympic Games, Beijing. Multicoloured.
578 100t. Type **258** 4·50 4·25
579 100t. Handball 4·50 4·25
580 100t. As Type **258** (grey background) 4·50 4·25
581 100t. As No. 579 (grey background) 4·50 4·25

Nos. 578/579 and 580/581 were issued together, *se-tenant*, each pair forming a composite design.

259 *Cervus elphas*

2008. Fauna. Multicoloured.
582 110t. Type **259** 5·50 5·00
583 110t. *Cervus nippon* 5·50 5·00

Stamps of a similar design were issued by Moldova

260 4th/5th-century Gold Buckle, Kazakhstan

2008. Jewellery. Multicoloured.
584 25t. Type **260** 1·40 1·30
585 150t. 17th-century gold medallion, Iran 8·00 7·50

Stamps of a similar design were issued by Iran.

261 Anniversary Emblem

2008. 60th Anniversary of Declaration of Human Rights.
586 **261** 25t. multicoloured 1·40 1·30

262 Tair Zharokov

2008. Birth Centenary of Tair Zharokov (writer).
587 **262** · 25t. multicoloured 1·40 1·30

263 Shakarim Kudaiberdyuly

2008. 150th Birth Anniversary of Shakarim Kudaiberdyuly (writer).
588 **263** 25t. multicoloured 1·40 1·30

264 Executive Committee Meeting Record (fragment)

2008. 90th (2007) Anniversary of Alash (movement for independence).
589 **264** 25t. multicoloured 1·40 1·30

265 Zhelbuaz

2008. Musical Instruments. Multicoloured.
590 25t. Type **265** 1·40 1·30
591 100t. Dauylpaz 5·50 5·00

266 *Portrait of Kenesary* (Abylkhan Kasteev)

2008. Art. Multicoloured.

592		25t. Type **266**	1·40	1·30
593		100t. *Guest has arrived* (Salihitdin Aitbaev)	5·50	5·00

267 *Callisthenes semenovi*

2008. Beetles. Multicoloured.

594		25t. Type **267**	1·40	1·30
595		100t. Inscr 'Dorcadion acharlense'	5·50	5·00

268 Petr Aravin

2008. Birth Centenary of Petr Aravin (musical critic and historian).

596	**268**	10t. multicoloured	55	55

269 Eagle

2008

597	**269**	20t. multicoloured	1·10	1·10

270 Atyrau

2008. Arms. Multicoloured.

598		A Type **270**	1·10	1·10
599		A Taraz	1·10	1·10

270a Polar Bear

2009. Preserve Polar Regions and Glaciers.

599a	**270a**	230t. multicoloured	8·25	7·75

271 Musician and Dancers

2009. Nauryz (Spring) Festival.

600	**271**	25t. multicoloured	1·40	1·30

272 Louis Braille

2009. Birth Bicentenary of Louis Braille (inventor of Braille writing for the blind).

601	**272**	230t. multicoloured	9·00	8·50

273 Constellation, Star Gazers and Telescope

2009. Europa. Astronomy. Multicoloured.

602		230t. Type **273**	8·00	7·25
603		230t. Galileo Galilei	8·00	7·25

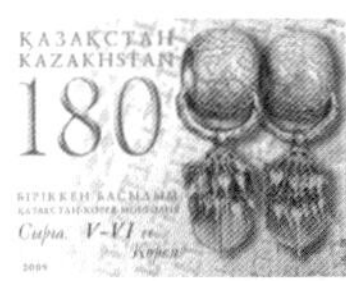
274 5th/6th-Century Korean Earrings

2009. Earrings. Multicoloured.

604		180t. Type **274**	6·00	5·75
605		180t. 17th/19th-century Mongolian	6·00	5·75
606		180t. 1st/2nd-century BC Kazakhstan	6·00	5·75

275 Telescope

2009. Astronomy and Space. Multicoloured.

607		180t. Type **275**	6·00	5·75
608		230t. Observatory	8·00	7·25

276 18th-Century Shield

2009. Armour.

609	**276**	190t. multicoloured	6·50	6·00

277 Marija Lizogub

2009. Birth Centenary of Marija Lizogub (artist).

610	**277**	180t. multicoloured	6·00	5·75

278 Kenen Azerbaev

2009. 125th Birth Anniversary of Kenen Azerbaev (singer and composer).

611	**278**	180t. multicoloured	6·00	5·75

279 Garifolla Kurmangaliev

2009. Birth Centenary of Garifolla Kurmangaliev (singer).

612	**279**	180t. multicoloured	6·00	5·75

280 Emblem

2009. UNWTO (United Nations world tourist organisation) General Assembly, Astana, Kazakhstan 2009.

613	**280**	140t new blue, dull ultramarine and magenta	5·25	4·75

281 *Giselle*

2009. National Ballet. Multicoloured.

MS614 180t. Type **281**; 180t. *Don Quixote*; 180t. *Swan Lake*; 180t. *Tlep and Sarkyzy*; 230t. *Legend about Love*; 230t. *Bahchisarayskiy Fountain* 40·00 39·00

282 Tymak uru

2009. National Sports. Multicoloured.

615		140t. Type **282**	4·75	4·50
616		180t. At omyraulastyru (two horses)	6·00	5·75

283 Abdilda Tazhibaev

2009. Birth Centenary of Abdildy Tazhibaev (poet).

617	**283**	180t. multicoloured	6·00	5·75

284 *Crataegus ambigua*

2009. Flora and Fauna. Multicoloured.

618		180t. Type **284**	6·00	5·75
619		180t. *Mellivora capensis* (honey badger)	6·00	5·75

285 Iskander Tynyshpaev

2009. Birth Centenary of Iskander Tynyshpaev (actor and cameraman).

620	**285**	25t. multicoloured	1·10	1·10

286 Tuleu Basenov

2009. Birth Centenary of Tuleu Basenov (architect).

621	**286**	25t. multicoloured	1·10	1·10

287 Birzhan sal Kozhagululy

2009. 175th Birth Anniversary of Birzhan sal Kozhagululy (composer).

622	**287**	25t. multicoloured	1·10	1·10

288 Symbols of Kazakhstan and Map of Route

2009. Construction of Gas Main through Central Asia.

623	**288**	25t. multicolored	1·10	1·10

289 Emblem

2010. Kazakhstan's Chairmanship of OSCE.

624	**289**	230t multicoloured	8·00	7·50

290 Symbols of Conflict

2010. 65th Anniversary of End of World War II.

625	**290**	32st. multicoloured	1·10	1·10

290a Horse Race

2010. Nowruz Festival.

625a	**290a**	32t. multicoloured	1·10	1·10

291 Ski Jumper

2010. Winter Olympic Games, Vancouver. Multicoloured.

626		32t. Type **291**	1·10	1·10
627		190t. Alpine skier	7·00	6·50

292 Cat, Wolf and Characters from Children's Fiction

2010. Europa 2010. Children's Books.

628	**292**	240t. multicoloured	8·00	7·50

293 Anniversary Emblem

2010. 50th Anniversary of Temirtau.

629	**293**	32t. multicoloured	1·40	1·30

294 Khan Shatyr Entertainment Centre, Astana (designed by Norman Foster)

2010. Modern Architecture.

630	**294**	32t. multicoloured	1·40	1·30

295 Championship Emblem

2010. World Cup Football Championship, South Africa.

631	**295**	240t. multicoloured	8·50	8·00

296 Aktyubinsk

2010. Arms.

632	**296**	10t. multicoloured	70	65

297 Chimkent

2010. Arms.

633	**297**	5t. multicoloured	45	40

298 Constitution

2010. 15th Anniversary of Constitution.

634	**298**	32t. mutlcoloured	1·40	1·30

299 Musa Baijanuly

2010. 175th Birth Anniversary of Musa Baijanuly (composer).

635	**299**	A multicoloured	1·40	1·30

300 Rocket as Dove and Globe

2010. 55th Anniversary of Scientific Research Test Range N.5, Baikonur.

636	**300**	190t. multicoloured	7·00	6·50

301 Mukhamedjan Karataev

2010. Birth Centenary of Mukhamedjan Karataev (academician).

637	**301**	20t. multicoloured	1·10	1·10

302 Baurjan Momyasuhly

2010. Birth Centenary of Baurjan Momysuhly (World War II hero).

MS638 **302**	140t. multicoloured	5·75	5·50

303 Shokan Valikhanov

2010. 175th Birth Anniversary of Chokan Chingisovich Valikhanov (scholar, ethnographer and historian).

639	**303**	140t. multicoloured	5·50	5·00

304 Frédéric Chopin

2010. Birth Bicentenary of Fryderyk Franciszek (Frédéric) Chopin (composer).

640	**304**	240t. multicoloured	9·00	8·50

305 Sun over Lake

2010. Tenth Anniversary of Kazakhstan–Kyrgyzstan Water Agreement.

641	**305**	32t. multicoloured	1·40	1·30

306 Ak Orda Monument

2010. Organisation on Safety and Co-operation in Europe Summit, Astana.

MS642 32t. Type **306**; 140t. Palace of Independence (right); 190t. Palace of Independence (left) and Palace of World and Consent 13·50 13·00

307 *Phoenicopterus roseus* (greater flamingo)

2010. Ecology of Caspian Sea. Multicoloured.

643	140t. Type **307**	5·25	4·75
644	140t. *Ardeola ralloides* (Squacco heron)	5·25	4·75

Stamps of the same design were issued by Azerbaijan

308 Irbi, Games Mascot

2010. 2011 Asian Winter Games, Astana and Almaty. Multicoloured.

645	190t. Type **308**	7·00	6·50
646	190t. Games emblem	7·00	6·50
647	240t. Irbi skating	8·25	7·75
648	240t. Irbi ski jumping	8·25	7·75

309 Mirzhakyp Dulatov

2010. 175th Birth Anniversary of Mirzhakyp Dulatov (writer).

649	**309**	50t. multicoloured	1·60	1·50

310 *Tadorna ferruginea* (ruddy shelduck)

2010. Bayanaul Nature Reserve. Fauna. Multicoloured.

MS650 32t. Type **310**; 140t. *Mustela nivalis* (weasel); 190t. *Capreolus pygargus* (Siberian roe deer) 23·00 22·00

The stamps of **MS**650 have a printing error, which shows 'H' instead of 'N' (KAZAKHSTAH) at the end of the country name

311 *Rhinecanthus aculeatus* (Picasso triggerfish)

2010. Astana Oceanarium. Multicoloured.

651	32t. Type **311**	1·10	1·10
652	190t. *Zebrasoma veliferum* (Pacific sailfin tang)	7·00	6·50

312 Korean Couple

2010. Traditional Costumes. Multicoloured.

MS653 32t. Type **312**; 190t. Belorusian couple 8·00 7·75

313 Yuri Gagarin

2011. 50th Anniversary of First Manned Space Flight.

654	**313**	190t. multicoloured	6·75	6·25

314 Forest under Magnifying Glass

2011. Europa 2011. Forests.

655	**314**	250t. multicoloured	8·25	8·00

315

2011. Tenth Anniversary of Shanghai Organisation of Co-operation.

656	**315**	210t. multicoloured	6·75	6·25

316 AIDS Ribbon

2011. 30th Anniversary of AIDS Prevention Campaign.

657	**316**	32t. multicoloured	1·10	1·10

317 Emblem

2011. Tenth Anniversary of Eurasian Economic Community (EAEC).

658	**317**	32t. multicoloured	1·10	1·10

318 Kasym Amanzholov

2011. Birth Centenary of Kasym Amanzholov (poet).

659	**318**	32t multicoloured	1·10	1·10

319 Coin

320 Coin

321 Coin

322 Coin

2011. Coins. Multicoloured.

660	**319**	32t. multicoloured	1·10	1·10
661	**320**	32t. multicoloured	1·10	1·10
662	**321**	32t. multicoloured	1·10	1·10
663	**322**	32t. multicoloured	1·10	1·10

323 Orymbek Zhautykov

2011. Birth Centenary of Orymbek Akhmetbekovich Zhautykov (scientist).

664	**323**	32t. multicoloured	1·10	1·10

324 Emblem (note different inscription)

2011. Customs Union of EAEC.

665	**324**	32t. multicoloured	1·10	1·10

325 Anniversary Emblem

2011. 20th Anniversary of Regional Communication Community (RCC).

666	**325**	150t. multicoloured	5·50	5·00

326 G. Slanov

2011. Birth Centenary of Gabdol Slanov (writer).

667	**326**	32t. multicoloured	1·10	1·10

327 Coat of Arms of Kazakhstan

2011. Arms.

668	**327**	A (32t.) multicoloured	1·10	1·10
669	**327**	50t. multicoloured	1·80	1·70
670	**327**	80t. multicoloured	3·00	2·75
671	**327**	100t. multicoloured	3·50	3·25
672	**327**	200t. multicoloured	7·25	6·75
673	**327**	500t. multicoloured	18·00	17·00

328 U. Sultangazin

2011. 75th Birth Anniversary of Umirzak Sultangazin (scientist).

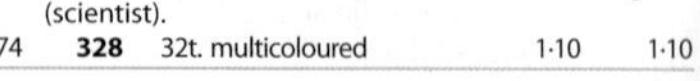

674	**328**	32t. multicoloured	1·10	1·10

329 Dina Nurpeisova

2011. 150th Birth Anniversary of Dina Nurpeisova (composer and musician).
675 **329** 32t. multicoloured 1·10 1·10

330 Anniversary Emblem

2011. 20th Anniversary of Community of Independent States (CIS).
676 **330** 150t. multicoloured 5·50 5·00

331 Anniversary Emblem

2011. 20th Anniversary of Independence (1st issue).
677 **331** 32t. multicoloured 1·10 1·10
See also No. 680.

332 Isatai Isabayev

2011. 75th Birth Anniversary of Isatai Isabayev (artist).
678 **332** 32t. multicoloured 1·10 1·10

333 *Turdus merula* (Blackbird)

2011. Birds. Multicoloured.
MS679 250t.×8, Type **333**; *Acridotheris tristis* (Common Myna); *Parus major* (Great Tit); *Corvus frugilegus* (Rook); *Pica pica* (Magpie); *Columba livia* (Rock Dove); *Corvus cornix* (Hooded Crow); *Passer domesticus* (House Sparrow) 70·00 65·00

334 Nursultan Nazarbayev

2011. 20th Anniversary of Independence (2nd issue).
680 **334** 20t. multicoloured 80 75

335 Vehicle and Kazakh Flag on Map of South Pole

2011. First Kazakh Expedition to South Pole.
681 **335** 190t. multicoloured 7·50 7·00

336 Oil Well

2011. 25th Anniversary of Petro Kazakhstan Kumkol Resources.
682 **336** 150t. multicoloured 5·50 5·00

337 'e gov'

2011. Electronic Government of Kazakhstan.
683 **337** 32t. multicoloured 1·10 1·10

338 Dinmukhamed Kunayev

2012. Birth Centenary of Dinmukhamed Kunayev (scientist).
684 **338** 100t. multicoloured 3·50 3·25

339 Mountains and Forest

2012. Katynkaragay National Nature Reserve.
685 **339** 110t. multicoloured 3·75 3·50

(340)

2012. 20th Anniversary of First Kazkhstan Stamp. No. 1 surch as T **340.**
686 50t. on 50k. multicoloured 1·80 1·70

341 Walkers and Mountain

2012. Europa 2012. Visit Kazakhstan.
687 **341** 250t. multicoloured 8·25 7·75

342 *Erinaceus europaeus*

2012. Hedgehogs. Multicoloured.
688 190t. Type **342** 3·25 3·00
689 190t. *Hemiechinus auritus* 3·25 3·00
Numbers left for stamps not yet received.

343 Musician and Woman riding Horses

2012. Nowruz Festival.
692 **343** 190t. multicoloured 6·50 6·00

344 Space Probe

2012. Space.
693 **344** 250t. multicoloured 8·25 7·75

345 Ufa Ahmedsafin

2012. Birth Centenary of Ufa Mendbayevich Ahmedsafin (scientist and leader in the establishment of methods to map underground water resources). UNESCO Anniversaries.
694 **345** 150t. multicoloured 5·00 4·50

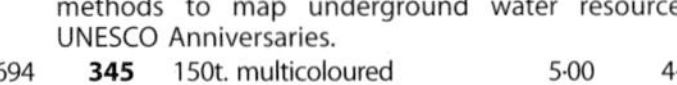

346 Dove and Globe

2012. Conference for a Nuclear Free World, Astana.
695 **346** 50t. bright new blue, dull ultramarine and black 1·70 1·60

347 Mezhit Begalin

2012. 90th Birth Numbers left for stamps not yet received. of Mezhit Begalin (film director).
696 **347** 90t. multicoloured 3·00 2·75

348 Lev Gumilev

2012. Birth Centenary of Lev Gumilev (scientist).
697 **348** 100t. multicolloured 3·50 3·25

349 Dmitry Snegin

2012. Birth Centenaries. Multicoloured.
698 80t. Type **349** (writer) 2·75 2·50
699 100t. Shara Zhienkulova (dancer) 3·50 3·25

350 *Warriors* (P. Zaltsman)

2012. Art of Kazakhstan. Multicoloured.
700 250t. Type **350** 8·25 7·75
701 250t. *Milking Red Camel* (A. Sadykhanov) 8·25 7·75

351 Emblem

2012. 20th Anniversary of Broadcasting Company MIR
702 **351** 10t. multicoloured 45 40

352 Emblem

2012. Tenth Anniversary of Contract of Collective Safety.
703 **352** 80t. multicoloured 2·75 2·50

353 Kulyash Baisetova

2012. Birth Centenary of Kulyash Baisetova (singer and actress).
704 **353** 2t. multicoloured 25 20
705 50t. multicoloured 1·40 1·30
706 A (60t.) multicoloured 1·60 1·50

354 Zein Shashkin

2012. Birth Centenaries. Multicoloured.
707 5t. Type **354** (writer) 35 30
708 10t. Zhamal Omarova (actress) 45 40
709 20t. Zhumagali Sain (writer) 70 65

355 Arms and Flag

2012. 20th Anniversary of Kazakhstan Flag and Coat of Arms.
710 **355** 190t. multicoloured 6·25 6·00

356 Anniversary Emblem

2012. 25th Anniversary of Union of Designers.
711 **356** 80t. multicoloured 2·75 2·50

357 Two Gold Deer linked by Bird (7th/8th-century buckle) (Kazakhstan)

2012. 20th Anniversary of Kazakhstan–Bulgaria Diplomatic Relations. Multicoloured.
712 250t. Type **357** 8·25 7·75
713 250t. Thracian Gold Rhyton (4th-century BC) (Bulgaria) 8·25 7·75

358 Raoul Wallenberg

2012. Birth Centenary of Raoul Wallenberg (saviour of thousands of Budapest Jews during WWII).
714 **358** 250t. multicoloured 8·25 7·75

359 Mangylik El Triumphal Arch

2012. Architecture of Astana. Multicoloured.
715 100t. Type **359** 3·50 3·25
716 100t. School Children's Palace 3·50 3·25
717 100t. L.N. Gumilyov Eurasian National University 3·50 3·25

360 Older Couple

2013. National Costumes. Multicoloured.

718	150t. Bridal couple	5·25	4·75
719	250t. Type **360**	8·25	7·75

361 Iliya Ilyin (weightlifter)

2013. Olympic Champions of Kazakhstan. Gold Medallists, Olympic Games, London 2012. Multicoloured.

MS720 150t.×7, Type **361**; Serik Sapiev (boxer); Olga Rypakova (long jump); Alexander Vinokurov (cyclist); Svetlana Podobedova (weightlifter); Zulfiya Chinshanlo (weightlifter); Maiya Maneza (weightlifter) 36·00 35·00

362 Rat (Year of the Rat)

2013. Oriental Lunar Calendar. Multicoloured.

721	100t. Type **362**	3·50	3·25
722	100t. Calf (Year of the Ox)	3·50	3·25
723	100t. Snow Leopard (Year of the Tiger)	3·50	3·25
724	100t. Rabbit (Year of the Rabbit)	3·50	3·25
725	100t. Snail (Year of the Dragon)	3·50	3·25
726	100t. Snake (Year of the Snake)	3·50	3·25
727	100t. Foal (Year of the Horse)	3·50	3·25
728	100t. Lamb (Year of the Sheep)	3·50	3·25
729	100t. Monkey (Year of the Monkey)	3·50	3·25
730	100t. Chicks (Year of the Rooster)	3·50	3·25
731	100t. Puppy (Year of the Dog)	3·50	3·25
732	100t. Piglet (Year of the Pig)	3·50	3·25

363 *Messenger* (Nikolai Khludov)

2013. Europa 2013. Postal Transport.

733	**363**	200t. multicoloured	6·75	6·25

364 Rocket, Parachute and Seagull

2013. 50th Anniversary of First Woman in Space. Multicoloured.

734	150t. Type **364**	5·25	4·75
735	200t. Valentina Tereshkova	6·75	6·25

365 Map of Kazakhstan and President Nazarbaev

2013. 20th Anniversary of Establishment Diplomatic Relations. Multicoloured.

MS736	250t. Type **365**	8·50	8·25
MS737	900t. As Type **365**	32·00	31·00

366 President Nazarbaev

2013. 15th Anniversary of Astana. Multicoloured.

MS738 100t.×4, Type **366**; Anniversary emblem; Arms of Astana; EXPO 2017 Exhibition emblem 13·50 13·00

MS739 100t.×4, 'Ak Orda' Presidential Palace; 'Tauelsyzdyk' Independence Palace; 'Baiterek' Monument; 'Kazakh Eli' Independence Monument 13·50 13·00

367 People's Assembly Emblem

2013. Nowruz Festival. Multicoloured.

MS740 150t.×4, Type **367**; President Nazarbaev with children; President Nazarbaev holding dombra and Sara Nazarbaev (his wife); World Leaders Congress emblem 20·00 19·00

368 President Nazarbaev at Twenty-Eight Panfilov Guardsmen Memorial, Almaty

2013. Victory Day. Multicoloured.

MS741 90t.×4, Type **368**; President Nazarbaev laying wreath at Eternal Flame Memorial (left); President Nazarbaev laying wreath at Eternal Flame Memorial (right); President Nazarbaev greeting WW II veterans 12·50 12·00

369 Bakhtiyar Artaev (boxer, Athens, 2004)

2013. Olympic Champions of Kazakhstan. Gold Medallists. Multicoloured.

MS742 150t.×3, Type **369**; Aleksander Parygin (pentathalon, Atlanta, 1996); Bakhyt Sarsekbaev (boxer, Beijing, 2008) 15·00 14·00

370 President Nazarbayev

2013. International Day Against Nuclear Testing. Multicoloured.

MS743 150t.×2, Type **370**; President Obama (USA), President Nazarbayev (Kazakhstan) and Prime Minister Medvedev (Russia) 10·00 9·00

371 *Tulipa behmiana*

2013. Flowers of Kazakhstan. Multicoloured.

MS744 60t. Type **371**; 60t. *Tulipa ostrowskiana*; 100t. *Papaver tianschanicum*; 100t. *Papaver pavoninum* 10·00 10·00

372 Symbols of Postal Service

2013. 20th Anniversary of Kazakhstan Postal Service. Sheet 110×99 mm.

MS745 **372** 200t. multicoloured 4·00 4·00

373 100,000 Tenge Gold Coin

2013. 20th Anniversary of Introduction of Tenge (National Currency). Multicoloured.

MS746 60t.×4, Type **373**; Reverse of 100,000t. coin; 500t. coin; Reverse of 500t. coin 8·50 8·50

374 *Chetusia gregaria* (Sociable Plover)

2013. Birds of the Steppe. Multicoloured.

MS747 150t.×6, Type **374**; *Tetrax tetrax* (Little Bustard); *Aquila nipalensis* (Steppe Eagle); *Numenius arquata* (Eurasian Curlew); *Oxyura leucocephala* (White-headed Duck); *Melanocorypha yeltoniensis* (Black Lark) 15·00 15·00

375 *Acinonyx jubatus* (Cheetah)

2013. Ustyurt. Natural Game Reserve. Multicoloured.

MS748 60t. Type **375**; 150t. *Saga pedo pallas* (Grasshopper); 190t. *Circaetus gallicus* (Short-toed Eagle) 5·50 5·50

376 Mukan Tolebayev (birth centenary)

2013. Personalities and Fauna.

749	1t. pale lemon and black	20	20
750	3t. pale light green and black	40	40
751	5t. new blue and black	60	60
752	10t. pale ochre and black (horiz)	90	90

Designs: 1t. T **376**; 3t. Amire Kashaubayev (125th birth anniversary); 5t. Valentina Tereshkova (50th anniversary of first woman in space); 10t. *Saiga tatarica*

377 'Tep' (seating for guests)

2014. Traditional Yurt Interior. Multicoloured.

MS753 200t.×3, Type **377**; 'Owak' (table and hearth); 'Солжак' (sleeping area) 10·00 10·00

378 Symbols of Communication

2014. Regional Commonwealth in Field of Communications. Sheet 110×90 mm.

MS754 **378** 200t. multicoloured 4·00 4·00

379 Sabira Maikanova

2014. Birth Centenaries. Yellow and black.

707	100t. Type **354** (actress)	3·00	3·00
708	100t. Iliyas Djansugurov (writer)	3·00	3·00

380 Emblem

2014. World Weightlifting Championship, Almaty.

757	**380**	200t. cerise and black	6·00	6·00

381 Kulahmet Kodjikov

2014. Birth Centenary of Kulahmet Kodjikov.

758	**381**	50t. azure and black	1·50	1·50

382 Headdress

2015. Kimeshek National Headdresses. Muulticoloured.

MS759 50t.×4, Type **382**; Jewelled and highly decorated; Simple gold surround; Gold surround with pyramidal chest piece 8·00 8·00

383 M. Y. Lermontov

2015. Birth Bicentenary (2014) of Mikhail Yuryevich Lermontov (writer and artist).

760	**383**	60t. multicoloured	1·75	1·75

384 Anna Akhmatova

2015. 125th Birth Anniversary (2014) of Anna Akhmatova (poet).

761	**384**	60t. multicoloured	1·75	1·75

385 Talgat Musabayev

2015. 20th Anniversary (2014) of First Space Flight of Talgat Musabayev

762	**385**	150t. multicoloured	4·50	4·50

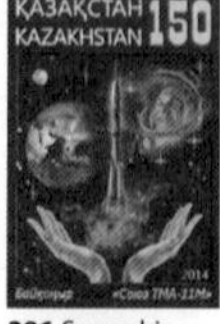

386 Spaceship delivering Olympic Torch into Space

2015. The Olympic Torch in Space.

763	**386**	150t. multicoloured	4·50	4·50

387 *Voskhod 1*

2015. 50th Anniversary (2014) of First Multimanned Spaceship Flight.
764 **387** 150t. multicoloured 4·50 4·50

388 Emblem

2015. Employment Roadmap 2020.
765 **388** 150t. multicoloured 4·50 4·50

389 Foal

2015. Chinese New Year. Year of the Horse (2014). Sheet 80×80 mm.
MS766 **389** 200t. multicoloured 8·00 8·00

390 Short Track Speed Skating

2015. Winter Olympic and Paralympic Games, Sochi, 2014. Multicoloured.
MS767 Olympic Games. 120×84 mm. 200t.×4, Type **390**; Figure skating; Snowboarding; Skeleton 20·00 20·00
MS768 Paralympic Games. 111×78 mm. 205t.×4, Alpine skiing; Cross country skiing; Sledge hockey; Curling 22·00 22·00

391 White Waterlily (*Nymphaea candida*)

2015. Naurzum Nature Reserve. Multicoloured.
MS769 200t.×3, Type **391**; White-tailed Eagle (*Haliaetus albicilla*); Elk (*Alces alces*) 17·00 17·00

392 Shaken Aimanov

2015. Birth Centenary (2014) of Shaken Aimanov (actor). Sheet 74×104 mm.
MS770 **392** 200t. multicoloured 8·00 8·00

393 Monument to Zhanibek Berdauletuly

2015. 300th Birth Anniversary (2014) of Zhanibek Berdauletuly. Sheet 74×104 mm.
MS771 **393** 200t. multicoloured 8·00 8·00

394 Satellite and Ground Control Complex and Spacecraft

2015. Tenth Anniversary (2014) of Kazakhstan Space Communications. Sheet 104×74 mm.
MS772 **394** 300t. multicoloured 8·00 8·00

395 *Beauty Kunekey* (Vasilenko Raisa)

2015. Children's Drawings of Kazakh Fairy Tales. Multicoloured.
773 50t. Type **395** 1·50 1·50
774 50t. *Alpamys Batyr* (Talipov Dmitry) 1·50 1·50
775 50t. *Maktakyz and Cat* (Mushtubayeva Elvira) 1·50 1·50
776 50t. *Aldar-Koze. Wonderful Fur Coat* (Sidorov Aleksander) 1·50 1·50

396 Emblem

2015. Centenary of Disease Prevention using Vaccination in Kazakhstan.
776 **396** 60t. multicoloured 1·75 1·75

397 Scene from *The Kid*

2015. 125th Birth Anniversary (2014) of Charlie Chaplin.
MS777 60t. Type **397**; 100t. Scene from *The Tramp* (37×26 mm); Behind the camera (37×52 mm) 5·00 5·00

398 Figures and The Atom Project Emblem

2015. International Day (2014) Against Nuclear Testing. Multicoloured.
MS778 100t.×2, Type **398**; Landscape and The Atom Project emblem 8·00 8·00

399 Ice Hockey Players

2015. Regional Commonwealth in Field of Communications. Winter Sports (2014).
779 **399** 100t. multicoloured 3·00 3·00

400 Flag and Conference Emblem

2015. Kazakhstan Chairs Energy Charter Conference, Astana 2014.
780 **400** 100t. multicoloured 3·00 3·00

401 Emblem

2015. Nowruz Festival, 2014.
781 **401** 190t. multicoloured 6·00 6·00

402 Interior of Mausoleum Roof

2015. Zhoshy Khan Mausoleum. Multicoloured.
MS782 200t.×4, Type **402**; Mausoleum, roofs; Mausoleum, left elevation; Mausoleum, from a distance 22·00 22·00

403 Dombra

2015. Europa 2014. Musical Instruments. Multicoloured.
783 200t. Type **403** 6·00 6·00
784 200t. Kobyz 6·00 6·00

404 Rakymzhan Kashkarbayev

2015. 70th Anniversary of End of World War II. Multicoloured.
MS785 200t.×3, Type **404**; Menshuk Mametova; Ivan Panfilov 20·00 20·00

405 Emblem

2015. Eurasian Economic Union.
786 **405** 100t. multiloured 3·00 3·00

406 Emblem

2015. Expo 2017, Astana (1st issue).
787 **406** 20t. pink and black 75 75

See also Noss. 803, 824 and **MS**827.

407 People and Map

2015. 20th Anniversary of People of Kazakhstan's Assembly. Sheet 104×72 mm.
MS791 **407** 200t. multicoloured 6·00 6·00

408 Anniversary Emblem

2015. 20th Anniversary of Constitution.
792 **408** A (112t.) multicoloured 3·00 3·00

409 *Battle of Anyrakai* (A. Shakhmardan)

2015. 550th Anniversary of Kazakh Khanate.
793 **409** 550t. multicoloured 15·50 15·50

410 Bones

2015. Europa 2015 Old Toys. Multicoloured.
794 200t. Type **410** 6·00 6·00
795 300t. Playing Asyk atu 9·00 9·00

411 Sheikh Halifa ben Zaid Al Nahayan

2015. Development of UAE–Kazakhstan Diplomatic Relations. Multicoloured.
796 200t. Type **411** 6·00 6·00
797 200t. Nursultan Nazarbayev 6·00 6·00

412 Stylised Tulip

2015. Nowruz Festival, 2015.
798 **412** 140t. multicoloured 4·25 4·25

413 'Happy Postcrossing'

2015. Postcrossing.
799 **413** N (140t.) multicoloured 3·50 3·50

413a Lamb

2015. Chinese New Year. Year of the Sheep. Sheet 80×80 mm.
MS799a **413a** 300t. multicoloured 8·00 8·00

414 Aidyn Aimbetov

2015. Aidyn Aimbetov, Kazakh Cosmonaut.
800 **414** 300t. multicoloured 9·00 9·00

415 A.A. Leonov (first to leave spacecraft whilst in orbit)

2015. 50th Anniversary of First Spacewalk. Multicoloured.
801 200t. Type **415** 6·00 6·00
802 B (200t.) *Voskhod 2* and space walk 6·00 6·00

416 Exhibition Emblem

2015. Expo 2017, Astana (2nd issue).
803 **416** 300t. multicoloured 9·00 9·00

417 Kuubrin's Store

2015. Regional Commonwealth in Field of Communications. Architecture. Multicoloured.
804 200t. Type **417** 6·00 6·00
805 B (200t.) Astana Supermarket on Kenesary Street, now 6·00 6·00

418 Kobylandy Batyr Memorial Complex

2015. Aktobe Region. Multicoloured.
MS806 140t. Type **418**; 200t. Aliya Moldagulova Mausoleum 9·50 9·50

419 Kazhymukan Munaitpasov

2016. Kazhymukan Munaitpasov (Qajymuqan Munaitpasuly) (World Champion wrestler) Commemoration. Multicoloured.
807 60t. Type **419** 1·60 1·60
808 200t. Letter from Joseph Stalin 6·00 6·00

420 *Tulipa greigii*

2016. Aksu-Zhabagly Nature Reserve. Multicoloured.
MS809 200t.×3, Type **420**; Siberian Ibex (*Capra sibirica*); Bearded Vulture (*Gypaetus barbatus*) 15·00 15·00

421 Two Puppies

2016. Tobet (Molosser) Dogs
MS810 60t. Type **421**; 140t. Tri-colour dog facing left (34×26 mm); 200t. Three light-coloured adult dogs (34×26 mm); 400t. Seated light-coloured dog (37×52 mm) 20·00 20·00

422 Anniversary Emblem

2016. 25th Anniversary of Regional Communication Community (RCC).
811 **422** 60t. multicoloured 1·60 1·60

423 University Building

2016. 20th Anniversary of L. N. Gumilev Eurasian National University.
812 **423** 60t. multicoloured 1·60 1·60

424 Cossack Khans

2016. *Mangilik El* (paintings dedicated to the 550th Anniversary of the Kazakh Khanate) by Yerbolat Tolepbai. Multicoloured.
MS813 250t. Type **424**; 250t. 'Zheti Zhargy' (Seven Rules); 500t. Nursultan Nazarbayev (28×40 mm) 20·00 20·00

425 President Nursultan Nazarbayev

2016. National Patriotic Idea.Mangilik El. Sheet 72×104mm.
MS814 **425** A (121t.) multicoloured 3·00 3·00

426 Order of the Fatherland

2016. Orders of Kazakhstan. Multicoloured.
MS815 100t.×9, Type **426**; Order of First President of Kazakhstan; Order of Bars; Order of Glory; Order of Valour; Order of Nobility; Order of Friendship; Order of Honour 32·00 32·00

427 Lake and Mountains

2016. Akmola Region. Multicoloured.
MS816 140t. Type **427**; 200t. Mosque 7·25 7·25

428 Rocket Launch

2016. 50th Anniversary of General de Gaulle's Visit to Baikonur. Multicoloured.
817 C (218t.) Type **428** 6·00 6·00
818 C (218t.) General de Gaulle's visit to Baikonur Cosmodrome 6·00 6·00

429 Gennady Golovkin

2016. Kazakhstan Champions. Boxing. Gennady Golovkin. Multicoloured.
MS819 A (121t.) Type **429**; B (200t.) With fists raised, black gloves (34×26 mm); 200t. Wearing winner's robe (37×26 mm); 200t. Fists together, blue and orange gloves (37×26 mm); C (218t.) In boxing ring, wearing white gloves (34×26 mm) 21·00 21·00

430 Alikhan Bokeikhanov

2016. Personalities.
820 5t. azure and black 30 30
821 50t. new blue and black (22.7) 1·50 1·50
822 A (121t.) blue and scarlet 3·00 3·00
823 C (218t.) violet and black 6·00 6·00

Designs: 5t. T **430** (birth bicentenary); 50t. M. Shamenov (birth centenary); A (121t.) Ibrai Altynsarin (175th birth anniversary); C (218t.) Kayum Mukhmedhanov (birth centenary)

431 Emblem

2016. Expo 2017, Astana (3rd issue).
824 **431** 200t. bright pink and black 6·00 6·00

432 Emblem

2016. The 100 Concrete Steps (reforms).
825 **432** 100t. multicoloured 3·00 3·00

433 Design Pattern

2016. Kazakh Ornament. Multicoloured.
MS826 60t.×4, Type **433**×4 7·25 7·00

434 Emblem

2016. Expo 2017, Astana (4th issue) Sheet 100×90 mm.
MS827 **434** 300t. multicoloured 7·50 7·50

435 Local Foods

2016. Regional Commonwealth in Field of Communications. Gastronomy.
828 **435** 200t. multicoloured 6·00 6·00

KEDAH

A state of the Federation of Malaya, incorporated in Malaysia in 1963.

100 cents = 1 dollar (Straits or Malayan).

1 Sheaf of Rice

2 Malay ploughing

1912

1 **1** 1c. black and green 60 25
26 **1** 1c. brown 1·50 20
52 **1** 1c. black 1·00 10
27 **1** 2c. green 1·50 20
2 **1** 3c. black and red 4·50 30
19 **1** 3c. purple 65 4·50
53 **1** 3c. green 2·25 90
3 **1** 4c. red and grey 10·00 25
20 **1** 4c. red 12·00 2·25
54 **1** 4c. violet 1·00 10
4 **1** 5c. green and brown 2·25 3·00
55 **1** 5c. yellow 3·50 10
56 **1** 6c. red 3·25 65
5 **1** 8c. black and blue 4·00 5·00
57 **1** 8c. black 24·00 10
58 **2** 12c. black and blue 12·00 3·50
6 **2** 10c. blue and brown 2·25 1·00
31 **2** 20c. black and green 11·00 2·00
32 **2** 21c. mauve and purple 2·25 13·00
33 **2** 25c. blue and purple 2·25 9·00
34 **2** 30c. black and pink 4·00 11·00
59 **2** 35c. purple 25·00 48·00
9 **2** 40c. black and purple 3·50 26·00
36 **2** 50c. brown and blue 6·00 28·00
37w - $1 black and red on blue £141 8·50
38 - $2 green and brown 13·00 £100
39 - $3 black and blue on blue 80·00 £100
40 - $5 black and red £110 £160

Design: As Type **2**—$1 to $5, Council Chamber.

1919. Surch in words.
24 50c. on $2 green and brown 70·00 80·00
25 $1 on $3 black and blue on blue 20·00 95·00

1922. Optd **MALAYA-BORNEO EXHIBITION**.
45 **1** 1c. brown 7·50 35·00
41 **1** 2c. green 5·50 29·00
46 **1** 3c. purple 6·00 50·00
47 **1** 4c. red 6·50 25·00
48 **2** 10c. blue and sepia 15·00 50·00
42 **2** 21c. purple 45·00 85·00
43 **2** 25c. blue and purple 45·00 85·00
44 **2** 50c. brown and blue 45·00 £100

6 Sultan Abdul Hamid Halimshah

1937

60 **6** 10c. blue and brown 8·00 2·25
61 **6** 12c. black and violet 70·00 3·25
62 **6** 25c. blue and purple 16·00 5·00
63 **6** 30c. green and red 16·00 10·00
64 **6** 40c. black and purple 9·00 19·00
65 **6** 50c. brown and blue 16·00 6·00
66 **6** $1 black and green 8·00 10·00
67 **6** $2 green and brown £130 75·00
68 **6** $5 black and red 42·00 £180

1948. Silver Wedding. As T **59b/59c** of Jamaica.
70 10c. violet 20 40
71 $5 red 28·00 50·00

1949. UPU. As T **59d/59g** of Jamaica.
72 10c. purple 25 1·25
73 15c. blue 2·00 1·50
74 25c. orange 65 5·00
75 50c. black 1·00 6·50

7 Sheaf of Rice

8 Sultan Badlishah

1950

76 **7** 1c. black 1·00 30
77 **7** 2c. orange 50 15
78 **7** 3c. green 2·00 1·00
79 **7** 4c. brown 75 10
79*aab* **7** 5c. purple 6·00 1·00
80 **7** 6c. grey 70 15
81 **7** 8c. red 4·00 5·00
81a **7** 8c. green 7·50 4·00
82 **7** 10c. mauve 70 10
82a **7** 12c. red 7·50 3·00
83 **7** 15c. blue 6·50 35
84 **7** 20c. black and green 6·50 2·50
84a **7** 20c. blue 2·75 10
85 **8** 25c. purple and orange 1·50 30
85a **8** 30c. red and purple 6·00 1·25
85b **8** 35c. red and purple 8·00 1·50
86 **8** 40c. red and purple 9·00 10·00
87 **8** 50c. black and blue 6·50 35
88 **8** $1 blue and purple 9·00 11·00
89 **8** $2 green and red 30·00 60·00
90 **8** $5 green and brown 70·00 £100

1953. Coronation. As T **61a** of Jamaica.
91 10c. black and purple 2·50 60

15 Fishing Craft

1957. Inset portrait of Sultan Badlishah.

92	-	1c. black	10	60
93	-	2c. red	1·00	3·00
94	-	4c. sepia	30	1·50
95	-	5c. lake	30	1·50
96	-	8c. green	2·50	8·00
97	-	10c. sepia	80	40
98	**15**	20c. blue	2·75	3·25
99	-	50c. black and blue	3·75	4·25
100	-	$1 blue and purple	16·00	26·00
101	-	$2 green and red	45·00	55·00
102	-	$5 brown and green	60·00	60·00

Designs: Horiz—1c. Copra; 2c. Pineapples; 4c. Ricefield; 5c. Masjid Alwi Mosque, Kangar; 8c. East Coast Railway Golden Blowpipe Express; $1 Govt Offices; $2 Bersilat (form of wrestling); $5 Weaving. Vert—10c. Tiger; 50c. Aborigines with blowpipe.

20 Sultan Abdul Halim Mu' Adzam Shah

1959. Installation of Sultan.

103	**20**	10c. yellow, brown and blue	1·00	10

21 Sultan Abdul Halim Shah

1959. As Nos. 92/102 but with inset portrait of Sultan Abdul Halim Shah as in T **21**.

104	1c. black	10	75
105	2c. red	10	2·00
106	4c. sepia	10	75
107	5c. lake	10	10
108	8c. green	3·50	3·50
109	10c. sepia	1·00	10
109a	10c. purple	18·00	1·50
110	20c. blue	1·00	1·00
111a	50c. black and blue	30	60
112	$1 blue and purple	6·00	2·25
113	$2 green and red	13·00	25·00
114	$5 brown and green	16·00	21·00

22 *Vanda hookeriana*

1965. Flowers. Multicoloured.

115	1c. Type **22**	10	2·25
116	2c. *Arundina graminifolia*	10	2·50
117	5c. *Paphiopedilum niveum*	10	55
118	6c. *Spathoglottis plicata*	15	60
119	10c. *Arachnis flos-aeris*	30	50
120	15c. *Rhyncostylis retusa*	1·50	10
121	20c. *Phalaenopsis violacea*	2·00	2·00

The higher values used in Kedah were Nos. 20/27 of Malaysia.

23 *Danaus melanippus*

1971. Butterflies. Multicoloured.

124	1c. *Delias ninus*	30	2·50
125	2c. Type **23**	50	2·50
126	5c. *Parthenos sylvia*	1·25	1·00
127	6c. *Papilio demoleus*	1·25	2·50
128	10c. *Hebomoia glaucippe*	1·25	10
129	15c. *Precis orithya*	1·25	10
130	20c. *Valeria valeria*	1·50	70

The higher values in use with this issue were Nos. 64/71 of Malaysia.

24 *Pterocarpus indicus*

1979. Flowers. Multicoloured.

135	1c. *Rafflesia hasseltii*	10	90
136	2c. Type **24**	10	90
137	5c. *Lagerstroemia speciosa*	10	60
138	10c. *Durio zibethinus*	15	10
139	15c. *Hibiscus rosa-sinensis*	15	10
140	20c. *Rhododendron scortechinii*	20	10
141	25c. *Etlingera elatior* (inscr 'Phaeomeria speciosa')	40	20

25 Sultan Abdul Halim Shah

1983. Silver Jubilee of Sultan's Installation. Multicoloured.

142	20c. Type **25**	70	30
143	40c. Paddy fields (horiz)	1·75	1·75
144	60c. Paddy fields and Mount Jerai (horiz)	2·50	5·25

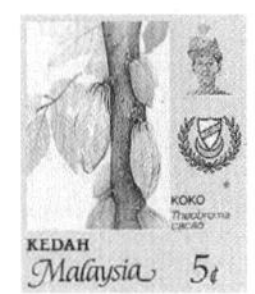

26 Cocoa

1986. Agricultural Products of Malaysia. Multicoloured.

152	1c. Coffee	10	50
153	2c. Coconuts	10	50
154	5c. Type **26**	15	10
155	10c. Black pepper	20	10
156	15c. Rubber	40	10
157	20c. Oil palm	40	15
158	30c. Rice	40	15

2003. As T **26** but redenominated in 'sen'. Multicoloured.

159	30s. Rice	1·40	10

27 *Nelumbium nelumbo* (sacred lotus)

2007. Garden Flowers. As Nos. 210/215 of Johore, but with portrait of Sultan Abdul Halim Shah and Arms of Kedah as in T **27**. Multicoloured.

160	5s. Type **27**	10	10
161	10s. *Hydrangea macrophylla*	15	10
162	20s. *Hippeastrum reticulatum*	25	15
163	30s. *Bougainvillea*	40	20
164	40s. *Ipomoea indica*	50	30
165	50s. *Hibiscus rosa-sinensis*	65	35
MS166	110×85 mm. Nos. 160/165	2·25	2·25

KELANTAN

A state of the Federation of Malaya, incorporated in Malaysia in 1963.

100 cents = 1 dollar (Straits or Malayan).

1

1911

1*a*	**1**	1c. green	6·00	30
15	**1**	1c. black	1·00	50
16	**1**	2c. brown	7·50	3·75
16a	**1**	2c. green	5·50	40
2	**1**	3c. red	4·25	15
16b	**1**	3c. brown	5·00	1·00
17	**1**	4c. black and red	3·50	10
18	**1**	5c. green and red on yellow	1·75	10
19	**1**	6c. purple	3·50	1·00
19a	**1**	6c. red	4·00	1·25
5	**1**	8c. blue	5·50	1·00
20	**1**	10c. black and mauve	3·00	10
21	**1**	30c. purple and red	4·00	4·00
8	**1**	50c. black and orange	8·50	2·00
9	**1**	$1 green	50·00	35·00
9a	**1**	$1 green and brown	75·00	2·00
10	**1**	$2 green and red	1·50	2·25
11	**1**	$5 green and blue	4·00	2·50
12	**1**	$25 green and orange	50·00	£120

1922. Optd **MALAYA BORNEO EXHIBITION**.

37	1c. green	4·50	55·00
30	4c. black and red	7·00	50·00
31	5c. green and red on yellow	7·00	50·00
38	10c. black and mauve	7·00	75·00
32	30c. purple and red	7·00	80·00
33	50c. black and orange	10·00	85·00
34	$1 green and brown	32·00	£110
35	$2 green and red	£110	£275
36	$5 green and blue	£275	£500

3 Sultan Ismail

1928

40	**3**	1c. olive and yellow	2·75	55
41	**3**	2c. green	9·00	20
42	**3**	4c. red	9·00	1·00
43	**3**	5c. brown	4·75	10
44	**3**	6c. lake	27·00	16·00
45	**3**	8c. olive	4·75	10
46	**3**	10c. purple	42·00	2·75
47	**3**	12c. blue	8·50	8·00
48	**3**	25c. red and purple	9·00	4·25
49	**3**	30c. violet and red	65·00	26·00
50	**3**	40c. orange and green	12·00	48·00
51	**3**	50c. olive and orange	90·00	10·00
39	**3**	$1 blue	15·00	90·00
52	**3**	$1 violet and green	65·00	16·00
53	**3**	$2 brown and red	£400	£250
54	**3**	$5 red and lake	£1000	£1000

All except No. 39 are larger than T **3**.

1948. Silver Wedding. As T **59b/59c** of Jamaica.

55	10c. violet	75	2·75
56	$5 red	30·00	50·00

1949. UPU. As T **59d/59g** of Jamaica.

57	10c. purple	25	30
58	15c. blue	2·25	4·50
59	25c. orange	40	8·50
60	50c. black	70	3·75

5 Sultan Ibrahim

1951

61	**5**	1c. black	50	30
62	**5**	2c. orange	1·25	35
63	**5**	3c. green	6·50	1·50
64	**5**	4c. brown	2·00	15
65	**5**	5c. mauve	1·50	50
66	**5**	6c. grey	75	20
67	**5**	8c. red	6·00	5·00
68	**5**	8c. green	7·00	1·75
69	**5**	10c. purple	65	10
70	**5**	12c. red	7·00	4·50
71	**5**	15c. blue	9·00	60
72	**5**	20c. black and green	7·00	15·00
73	**5**	20c. blue	2·00	25
74	**5**	25c. purple and orange	2·00	55
75	**5**	30c. red and purple	1·50	6·50
76	**5**	35c. red and purple	2·25	1·50
77	**5**	40c. red and purple	17·00	27·00
78	**5**	50c. black and blue	8·00	40
79	**5**	$1 blue and purple	9·50	18·00
80	**5**	$2 green and red	50·00	70·00
81	**5**	$5 green and brown	75·00	85·00

1953. Coronation. As T **61a** of Jamaica.

82	10c. black and purple	1·75	1·40

1957. As Nos. 92/102 of Kedah but inset portrait of Sultan Ibrahim.

83	1c. black	10	30
84	2c. red	75	1·50
85	4c. sepia	40	10
86	5c. lake	40	10
87	8c. green	4·00	4·50
88	10c. sepia	3·00	10
89	10c. purple	22·00	16·00
90	20c. blue	2·50	30
91	50c. black and blue	50	2·50
92	$1 blue and purple	13·00	1·50
93	$2 green and red	22·00	13·00
94	$5 brown and green	30·00	12·00

6 Sultan Yahya Petra and Arms of Kelantan

1961. Coronation of the Sultan.

95	**6**	10c. multicoloured	60	1·50

7 Sultan Yahya Petra

1961. As Nos. 83, etc, but with inset portrait of Sultan Yahya Petra as in T **7**.

96	1c. black	25	3·00
97	2c. red	2·25	4·25
98	4c. sepia	3·00	3·50
99	5c. lake	3·00	1·25
100	8c. green	20·00	17·00
101	10c. purple	1·75	75
102	20c. blue	12·00	3·25

8 *Vanda hookeriana*

1965. As Nos. 115/121 of Kedah but with inset portrait of Sultan Yahya Petra as in T **8**.

103	**8**	1c. multicoloured	10	1·75
104	-	2c. multicoloured	10	1·75
105	-	5c. multicoloured	15	30
106	-	6c. multicoloured	70	3·00
107	-	10c. multicoloured	30	25
108	-	15c. multicoloured	1·50	25
109	-	20c. multicoloured	2·75	3·50

The higher values used in Kelantan were Nos. 20/27 of Malaysia (National Issues).

9 *Parthenos sylvia*

1971. Butterflies. As Nos. 124/130 of Kedah but with portrait of Sultan Yahya Petra as in T **9**.

112		1c. multicoloured	30	2·75
113		2c. multicoloured	50	2·75
114	**9**	5c. multicoloured	1·50	60
115	-	6c. multicoloured	1·50	2·75
116	-	10c. multicoloured	1·50	30
117	-	15c. multicoloured	1·50	10
118	-	20c. multicoloured	2·00	2·00

The higher values in use with this series were Nos. 64/71 of Malaysia (National Issues).

10 *Lagerstroemia speciosa*

1979. Flowers. As Nos. 135/141 of Kedah but with portrait of Sultan Yahya Petra as in T **10**.

123	1c. *Rafflesia hasseltii*	10	1·00
124	2c. *Pterocarpus indicus*	10	1·00
125	5c. Type **10**	10	80
126	10c. *Durio zibethinus*	15	10
127	15c. *Hibiscus rosa-sinensis*	15	10
128	20c. *Rhododendron scortechinii*	20	10
129	25c. *Etlingera elatior* (inscr 'Phaeomeria speciosa')	40	50

11 Sultan Tengku Ismail Petra

1980. Coronation of Sultan Tengku Ismail Petra.

130	**11**	10c. multicoloured	40	75
131	**11**	15c. multicoloured	40	15
132	**11**	50c. multicoloured	90	2·75

12 Black Pepper

1986. Agricultural Products of Malaysia. Multicoloured.

140	1c. Coffee	10	60
141	2c. Coconuts	10	60
142	5c. Cocoa	50	20
143	10c. Type **12**	20	10
144	15c. Rubber	50	10
145	20c. Oil palm	40	15
146	30c. Rice	45	15

13 *Nelumbium nelumbo* (sacred lotus)

2007. Garden Flowers. As Nos. 210/215 of Johore, but with portrait of Sultan Ismail Petra and Arms of Kelantan as in T **13**. Multicoloured.

147	5s. Type **13**	10	10
148	10s. *Hydrangea macrophylla*	15	10
149	20s. *Hippeastrum reticulatum*	25	15
150	30s. *Bougainvillea*	40	20
151	40s. *Ipomoea indica*	50	30
152	50s. *Hibiscus rosa-sinensis*	65	35
MS153	100×85 mm. Nos. 147/152	2·25	2·25

STANLEY GIBBONS

LONDON 1856

STOCKBOOKS

Deluxe - available in a range of four colours.

A deluxe A4 stock book with padded leather cover. Black pages with 9 clear strips and clear interleaving.

Luxury Leather 64 Page - £49.95

• R2672BLK • R2672BLU • R2672GRN • R2672MAR

Standard (A4 size)

16 Page (black) with 9 glassine strips and double glassine interleaving

• R2680BLK • R2680BLU • R2680GRN

To order, call **01425 472 363**

email **orders@stanleygibbons.com** or visit **stanleygibbons.com**

KENYA

Formerly part of Kenya, Uganda and Tanganyika (q.v.). Became independent in 1963 and a Republic in 1964.

100 cents = 1 shilling.

1 Cattle Ranching

3 National Assembly

1963. Independence.

No.	Type	Description	Unused	Used
1	**1**	5c. multicoloured	10	55
2	-	10c. brown	10	10
3	-	15c. mauve	1·00	10
4	-	20c. black and green	15	10
5	-	30c. black and yellow	15	10
6	-	40c. brown and blue	15	30
7	-	50c. red, black and green	60	10
8	-	65c. turquoise and yellow	55	65
9	**3**	1s. multicoloured	20	10
10	-	1s.30 brown, black and green	5·00	30
11	-	2s. multicoloured	1·25	40
12	-	5s. brown, blue and green	1·25	1·50
13	-	10s. brown and blue	9·00	3·00
14	-	20s. black and red	4·00	11·00

Designs: As T **1**—10c. Wood-carving; 15c. Heavy industry; 20c. Timber industry; 30c. Jomo Kenyatta facing Mt. Kenya; 40c. Fishing industry; 50c. Kenya flag; 65c. Pyrethrum industry. As T **3**—1s.30, Tourism (Treetops hotel); 2s. Coffee industry; 5s. Tea industry; 10s. Mombasa Port; 20s. Royal College, Nairobi.

4 Cockerel

1964. Inauguration of Republic. Multicoloured.

No.	Description	Unused	Used
15	15c. Type **4**	15	15
16	30c. President Kenyatta	15	10
17	50c. African lion	15	10
18	1s.30 Hartlaub's turaco	2·00	50
19	2s.50 Nandi flame	20	4·75

5 Thomson's Gazelle

7 Greater Kudu

1966

No.	Type	Description	Unused	Used
20	**5**	5c. orange, black and sepia	20	20
21	-	10c. black and green	10	10
22	-	15c. black and orange	10	10
23	-	20c. ochre, black and blue	10	15
24	-	30c. indigo, blue and black	20	10
25	-	40c. black and brown	60	30
26	-	50c. black and orange	60	10
27	-	65c. black and green	1·25	2·00
28	-	70c. black and purple	4·00	1·75
29	**7**	1s. brown, black and blue	30	10
30	-	1s.30 blue, green and black	4·00	20
31	-	1s.50 black, brown and green	1·50	3·00
32	-	2s.50 yellow, black and brown	3·50	1·25
33	-	5s. yellow, black and green	75	70
34	-	10s. ochre, black and brown	3·50	3·00
35	-	20s. multicoloured	8·00	13·00

Designs: As T **5**—10c. Sable antelope; 15c. Aardvark (Ant Bear); 20c. Lesser bushbaby; 30c. Warthog; 40c. Common zebra; 50c. African buffalo; 65c. Black rhinoceros; 70c. Ostrich. As T **7**—1s.30, African elephant; 1s.50, Bat-eared fox; 2s.50, Cheetah; 5s. Savanna monkey (Vervet Monkey); 10s. Giant ground pangolin; 20s. Lion.

8 Perna Tellin (*Tellina perna* - inscr '*Pharaonella perna*')

9 Ramose Murex (*Murex ramosus* - inscr '*Chicoreus ramosus*')

1971. Sea Shells. Multicoloured.

(a) As T **8**

No.	Description	Unused	Used
36	5c. Type **8**	10	30
37	10c. Episcopal mitre	15	10
38	15c. Purplish clanculus	15	20
39	20c. Humpback cowrie	15	20
40	30c. Variable abalone	20	10
41	40c. Flame top shell	20	10
42	50c. Common purple janthina	20	20
43	50c. Common purple janthina	13·00	3·00
44	60c. Bullmouth helmet	20	1·75
45	70c. Chambered or pearly nautilus	35	1·50
46	70c. Chambered or pearly nautilus	13·00	6·50

(b) As Type **9**

No.	Description	Unused	Used
47*a*	1s. Type **9**	20	10
48	1s.50 Trumpet triton	1·00	10
49	2s.50 Trapezium horse conch	1·00	10
50*a*	5s. Great green turban	1·00	10
51	10s. Textile or cloth of gold cone	1·00	15
52*a*	20s. Scorpion conch	1·50	25

Inscriptions: No. 42, *Janthina globosa*; No. 43, *Janthina janthina*; No. 45, *Nautilus pompileus*; No. 46, *Nautilus pompilius*.

Nos. 47/52 are larger, as Type **9**.

1975. Nos. 48/49 and 52a surch.

No.	Description	Unused	Used
53	2s. on 1s.50 Trumpet triton	5·00	6·00
54	3s. on 2s.50 Trapezium horse conch	8·50	23·00
55	40s. on 20s. Scorpion conch	4·50	15·00

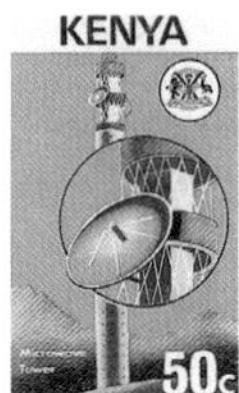

11 Microwave Tower

1976. Telecommunications Development. Multicoloured.

No.	Description	Unused	Used
56	50c. Type **11**	10	10
57	1s. Cordless switchboard (horiz)	10	10
58	2s. Telephones	20	30
59	3s. Message switching centre (horiz)	75	45
MS60	120×120 mm. Nos. 56/59. Imperf	1·10	2·50

12 Akii Bua, Ugandan Hurdler

1976. Olympic Games, Montreal. Multicoloured.

No.	Description	Unused	Used
61	50c. Type **12**	10	10
62	1s. Filbert Bayi, Tanzanian runner	15	10
63	2s. Steve Muchoki, Kenyan boxer	30	35
64	3s. Olympic flame and East African flags	70	50
MS65	129×154 mm. Nos. 61/64	5·00	7·50

13 Diesel-hydraulic Train, Tanzania–Zambia Railway

1976. Railway Transport. Multicoloured.

No.	Description	Unused	Used
66	50c. Type **13**	30	10
67	1s. Nile Bridge, Uganda	50	15
68	2s. Nakuru Station, Kenya	1·00	80
69	3s. Uganda Railway Class A steam locomotive, 1896	1·00	1·00
MS70	154×103 mm. Nos. 66/69	7·00	8·00

14 Nile Perch

1977. Game Fish of East Africa. Multicoloured.

No.	Description	Unused	Used
71	50c. Type **14**	25	10
72	1s. Nile mouthbrooder ('Tilapia')	30	10
73	3s. Sailfish	60	60
74	5s. Black marlin	80	80
MS75	153×129 mm. Nos. 71/74	7·50	4·00

15 Maasai Manyatta (village), Kenya

1977. Second World Black and African Festival of Arts and Culture, Nigeria. Multicoloured.

No.	Description	Unused	Used
76	50c. Type **15**	15	10
77	1s. 'Heartbeat of Africa' (Ugandan dancers)	15	10
78	2s. Makonde sculpture, Tanzania	60	1·25
79	3s. 'Early man and technology' (skinning hippopotamus)	75	2·00
MS80	132×109 mm. Nos. 76/79	3·50	5·50

16 Rally Car and Villagers

1977. 25th Anniversary of Safari Rally. Multicoloured.

No.	Description	Unused	Used
81	50c. Type **16**	15	10
82	1s. President Kenyatta starting rally	15	10
83	2s. Car fording river	40	60
84	5s. Car and elephants	1·25	1·50
MS85	126×93 mm. Nos. 81/84	2·50	6·50

17 Canon Kivebulaya

1977. Centenary of Ugandan Church. Multicoloured.

No.	Description	Unused	Used
86	50c. Type **17**	10	10
87	1s. Modern Namirembe Cathedral	10	10
88	2s. The first Cathedral	30	55
89	5s. Early congregation, Kigezi	50	1·25
MS90	126×94 mm. Nos. 86/89	1·00	2·50

18 Sagana Royal Lodge, Nyeri, 1952

1977. Silver Jubilee. Multicoloured.

No.	Description	Unused	Used
91	2s. Type **18**	15	15
92	5s. Treetops Hotel (vert)	20	35
93	10s. Queen Elizabeth and President Kenyatta	30	60
94	15s. Royal visit, 1972	45	1·00
MS95	Two sheets. (a) 140×60 mm. No. 94. (b) 152×127 mm. 50s. Queen and Prince Philip in Treetops Hotel Set of 2 sheets	2·00	1·40

19 Pancake Tortoise

1977. Endangered Species. Multicoloured.

No.	Description	Unused	Used
96	50c. Type **19**	25	10
97	1s. Nile crocodile	35	10
98	2s. Hunter's hartebeest	75	40
99	3s. Red colobus monkey	80	50
100	5s. Dugong	1·00	75
MS101	127×101 mm. Nos. 97/100	4·50	3·00

20 Kenya–Ethiopia Border Point

1977. Nairobi–Addis Ababa Highway. Multicoloured.

No.	Description	Unused	Used
102	50c. Type **20**	15	10
103	1s. Archer's Post	15	10
104	2s. Thika Flyover	30	25
105	5s. Marsabit Game Lodge	50	75
MS106	144×91 mm. Nos. 102/105	1·75	3·50

21 Gypsum

22 Amethyst

1977. Minerals. Multicoloured.

(a) As Type **21**

No.	Description	Unused	Used
107	10c. Type **21**	1·25	20
108	20c. Trona	2·00	20
109	30c. Kyanite	2·00	20
110	40c. Amazonite	1·40	10
111	50c. Galena	1·40	10
112	70c. Silicified wood	7·50	1·00
113	80c. Fluorite	7·50	60

(b) As Type **22**

No.	Description	Unused	Used
114	1s. Type **22**	1·40	10
115	1s.50 Agate	1·50	30
116	2s. Tourmaline	1·50	20
117	3s. Aquamarine	1·75	55
118	5s. Rhodolite garnet	1·75	1·10
119	10s. Sapphire	1·75	1·50
120	20s. Ruby	4·50	2·50
121	40s. Green grossular garnet	20·00	20·00

23 Joe Kadenge (Kenya) and Forwards

1978. World Cup Football Championship, Argentina. Multicoloured.

No.	Description	Unused	Used
122	50c. Type **23**	10	10
123	1s. Mohamed Chuma (Tanzania) and cup presentation	10	10
124	2s. Omari Kidevu (Zanzibar) and goalmouth scene	30	70
125	3s. Polly Ouma (Uganda) and three forwards	40	95
MS126	136×81 mm. Nos. 122/125	2·75	3·50

24 Boxing

1978. Commonwealth Games, Edmonton. Multicoloured.

No.	Description	Unused	Used
127	50c. Type **24**	15	10
128	1s. Welcoming the Olympic Games Team, 1968	15	10
129	3s. Javelin throwing	50	1·00
130	5s. Pres. Kenyatta admiring boxer's trophy	60	1·60

25 'Overloading is Dangerous'

1978. Road Safety. Multicoloured.

No.	Description	Unused	Used
131	50c. Type **25**	40	10
132	1s. 'Speed does not pay'	50	10
133	1s.50 'Ignoring Traffic Signs may cause death'	60	45
134	2s. 'Slow down at School Crossing'	80	65
135	3s. 'Never cross a continuous line'	90	1·50
136	5s. 'Approach Railway Level Crossing with extreme caution'	1·50	3·25

26 President Kenyatta at Mass Rally, 1963

1978. Kenyatta Day. Multicoloured.

137	50c. Harambee Water Project	10	10
138	1s. Handing over of Independence Instruments, 1963	15	10
139	2s. Type **26**	25	25
140	3s. Harambee, 15 Great Years	40	70
141	5s. Struggle for Independence, 1952	60	1·50

27 Freedom Fighters, Namibia

1978. International Anti-Apartheid Year.

142	**27**	50c. multicoloured	10	10
143	-	1s. black and blue	15	10
144	-	2s. multicoloured	20	30
145	-	3s. multicoloured	35	65
146	-	5s. multicoloured	45	1·00

Designs: 1s. International seminar on apartheid; 2s. Steve Biko's tombstone; 3s. Nelson Mandela; 5s. Bishop Lamont.

28 Children Playing

1979. International Year of the Child. Multicoloured.

147	50c. Type **28**	10	10
148	2s. Boy fishing	20	50
149	3s. Children singing and dancing	35	90
150	5s. Children with camels	60	2·00

29 *The Lion and the Jewel*

1979. Kenya National Theatre. Multicoloured.

151	50c. Type **29**	10	10
152	1s. *Utisi*	15	10
153	2s. Theatre programmes	20	30
154	3s. Kenya National Theatre	30	45
155	5s. *Genesis*	40	75

30 Blind Telephone Operator

1979. 50th Anniversary of Salvation Army Social Services.

156	50c. Type **30**	20	10
157	1s. Care for the aged	20	10
158	3s. Village polytechnic (horiz)	40	1·00
159	5s. Vocational training (horiz)	70	2·00

31 'Father of the Nation' (Kenyatta's funeral procession)

1979. First Death Anniversary of President Kenyatta. Multicoloured.

160	50c. Type **31**	10	10
161	1s. 'First President of Kenya' (Kenyatta receiving independence)	10	10
162	3s. 'Kenyatta the politician' (speaking at rally)	30	50
163	5s. 'A true son of Kenya' (Kenyatta as a boy carpenter)	40	95

32 British East Africa Company 1890 1a. Stamp

1979. Death Centenary of Sir Rowland Hill.

164	**32**	50c. multicoloured	15	10
165	-	1s. multicoloured	15	10
166	-	2s. black, red and brown	20	40
167	-	5s. multicoloured	35	1·00

Designs: 1s. Kenya, Uganda and Tanganyika 1935 1s. stamp; 2s. Penny Black; 5s. 1964 2s.50 Inauguration of Republic commemorative.

33 Roads, Globe and Conference Emblem

1980. International Road Federation. African Highway Conference, Nairobi. Multicoloured.

168	50c. Type **33**	15	10
169	1s. New weighbridge, Athi River	15	10
170	3s. New Nyali Bridge, Mombasa	40	85
171	5s. Highway to Jomo Kenyatta International Airport	50	2·00

34 Mobile Unit in action in Masailand

1980. Flying Doctor Service. Multicoloured.

172	50c. Type **34**	15	10
173	1s. Donkey transport to Turkana airstrip (vert)	20	10
174	3s. Surgical team in action at outstation (vert)	65	1·00
175	5s. Emergency airlift from North Eastern Province	90	1·60
MS176	146×133 mm. Nos. 172/175	2·00	2·75

35 Statue of Sir Rowland Hill

1980. London 1980 International Stamp Exhibition.

177	**35**	25s. multicoloured	1·00	2·50
MS178		114×101 mm. No. 177	1·00	2·75

36 Pope John Paul II

1980. Papal Visit. Multicoloured.

179	50c. Type **36**	25	10
180	1s. Pope, Arms and cathedral (vert)	25	10
181	5s. Pope, flags and dove (vert)	40	65
182	10s. Pope, President Moi and map of Africa	75	1·50

37 Blue-spotted Stingray

1980. Marine Life. Multicoloured.

183	50c. Type **37**	20	10
184	2s. Allard's anemonefish	60	65
185	3s. Four-coloured nudibranch	70	1·40
186	5s. *Eretmochelys imbricata*	1·25	2·25

38 National Archives

1980. Historic Buildings. Multicoloured.

187	50c. Type **38**	10	10
188	1s. Provincial Commissioner's Office, Nairobi	10	10
189	1s.50 Nairobi House	15	20
190	2s. Norfolk Hotel	20	50
191	3s. McMillan Library	25	95
192	5s. Kipande House	40	1·60

39 'Disabled enjoys Affection'

1981. International Year for Disabled Persons. Multicoloured.

193	50c. Type **39**	15	10
194	1s. President Moi presenting flag to Disabled Olympic Games team captain	15	10
195	3s. Blind people climbing Mount Kenya, 1975	55	65
196	5s. Disabled artist at work	70	1·00

40 Longonot Complex

1981. Satellite Communications. Multicoloured.

197	50c. Type **40**	15	10
198	2s. *Intelsat V*	40	35
199	3s. *Longonot I*	45	55
200	5s. *Longonot II*	60	85

41 Kenyatta Conference Centre

1981. OAU (Organisation of African Unity) Summit Conference, Nairobi.

201	**41**	50c. multicoloured	15	10
202	-	1s. black, yellow and blue	15	10
203	-	3s. multicoloured	25	40
204	-	5s. multicoloured	50	65
205	-	10s. multicoloured	60	1·00
MS206		110×110 mm. No. 205	1·10	1·50

Designs: 1s. Panaftel earth stations; 3s. Parliament Building; 5s. Jomo Kenyatta International Airport; 10s. OAU flag.

42 St. Paul's Cathedral

1981. Royal Wedding. Multicoloured.

207	50c. Prince Charles and President Daniel Arap Moi	10	10
208	3s. Type **42**	15	20
209	5s. Royal Yacht *Britannia*	25	30
210	10s. Prince Charles on safari in Kenya	40	55
MS211	85×102 mm. 25s. Prince Charles and Lady Diana Spencer	75	80

43 Giraffe

1981. Rare Animals. Multicoloured.

212	50c. Type **43**	15	10
213	2s. Bongo	25	25
214	5s. Roan antelope	40	1·00
215	10s. Agile mangabey	60	2·25

44 'Technical Development'

1981. World Food Day. Multicoloured.

216	50c. Type **44**	10	10
217	1s. 'Mwea rice projects'	15	10
218	2s. 'Irrigation schemes'	30	55
219	5s. 'Breeding livestock'	60	1·75

45 Kamba

1981. Ceremonial Costumes (1st series). Multicoloured.

220	50c. Type **45**	40	10
221	1s. Turkana	45	10
222	2s. Giriama	1·00	85
223	3s. Masai	1·25	2·50
224	5s. Luo	1·50	4·25

See also Nos. 329/333, 413/417 and 515/519.

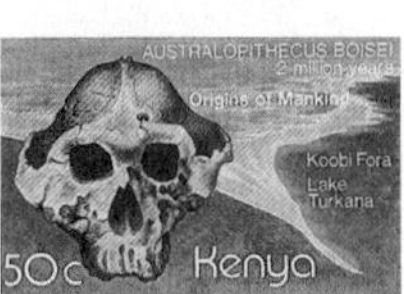

46 *Australopithecus boisei*

1982. Origins of Mankind. Skulls. Multicoloured.

225	50c. Type **46**	2·00	30
226	2s. *Homo erectus*	3·50	1·50
227	3s. *Homo habilis*	3·50	3·75
228	5s. *Proconsul africanus*	4·25	5·50

47 Tree-planting

1982. 75th Anniversary of Boy Scout Movement (Nos. 229, 231, 233 and 235) and 60th Anniversary of Girl Guide Movement (Nos. 230, 232, 234 and 236). Multicoloured.

229	70c. Type **47**	30	80
230	70c. Paying homage	30	80
231	3s.50 'Be Prepared'	80	1·75
232	3s.50 'International Friendship'	80	1·75
233	5s. Helping disabled	1·00	2·25
234	5s. Community service	1·00	2·25
235	6s.50 Paxtu Cottage (Lord Baden-Powell's home)	1·00	2·50
236	6s.50 Lady Baden-Powell	1·00	2·50
MS237	112×112 mm. Nos. 229, 231, 233 and 235	3·75	3·00

48 Footballer displaying Shooting Skill

1982. World Cup Football Championship, Spain. Footballers silhouetted against Map of World. Multicoloured.

238	70c. Type **48**	75	50
239	3s.50 Heading	1·50	2·25
240	5s. Goalkeeping	1·75	3·75
241	10s. Dribbling	2·75	7·00
MS242	101×76 mm. 20s. Tackling	5·50	4·00

49 Cattle Judging

1982. 80th Anniversary of Agricultural Society of Kenya. Multicoloured.

243	70c. Type **49**	40	10
244	2s.50 Farm machinery	1·00	1·00
245	3s.50 Musical ride	1·25	2·00
246	6s.50 Agricultural Society emblem	1·50	4·25

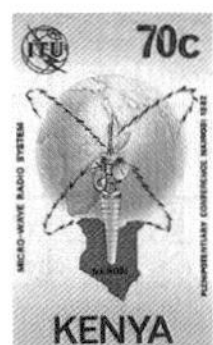

50 Micro-wave Radio System

1982. ITU Plenipotentiary Conference, Nairobi. Multicoloured.

247	70c. Type **50**	40	10
248	3s.50 Sea-to-shore service link	1·50	1·25
249	5s. Rural telecommunications system	1·75	3·25
250	6s.50 ITU emblem	2·00	4·25

1982. No. 113 surch **70c.**

251	70c. on 80c. Fluorite	1·00	1·25

52 Container Cranes

1983. Fifth Anniversary of Kenya Ports Authority. Multicoloured.

252	70c. Type **52**	85	10
253	2s. Port by night	1·75	1·90
254	3s.50 Container cranes (different)	2·50	3·50
255	5s. Map of Mombasa Port	3·25	4·50
MS256	125×85 mm. Nos. 252/255	7·50	9·50

53 Shada Zambarau

54 Waridi Kikuba

1983. Flowers. Multicoloured.

(a) As Type **53**

257	10c. Type **53**	40	40
258	20c. Kilua Kingulima	55	40
259	30c. Mwalika Mwiya	55	40
260	40c. Ziyungi Buluu	55	40
261	50c. Kilua Habashia	55	30
262	70c. Chanuo Kato	60	20
262a	80c. As 40c.	4·50	5·50
262b	1s. Waridi Kikuba	4·50	80

(b) As Type **54**

263	1s. Type **54**	65	20
264	1s.50 Mshomoro Mtambazi	1·75	60
265	2s. Papatuo Boti	1·75	60
266	2s.50 Tumba Mboni	1·75	60
266a	3s. Mkuku Mrembo	14·00	12·00
267	3s.50 Mtongo Mbeja	1·50	1·50
267b	4s. Mnukia Muuma	4·75	8·00
268	5s. Nyungu Chepuo	1·25	1·50
268a	7s. Mlua Miba	6·50	11·00
269	10s. Muafunili	1·25	1·50
270	20s. Mbake Nyanza	1·25	2·50
271	40s. Njuga Pagwa	2·00	8·00

The 1s.50 to 40s. are in the same format as T **54**.

55 Coffee Plucking

1983. Commonwealth Day. Multicoloured.

272	70c. Type **55**	10	10
273	2s. President Daniel Arap Moi	15	20
274	5s. Satellite view of Earth (horiz)	35	45
275	10s. Masai dance (horiz)	65	1·00

56 Examining Parcels

1983. 30th Anniversary of Customs Co-operation Council. Multicoloured.

276	70c. Type **56**	25	10
277	2s.50 Customs Headquarters, Mombasa	65	30
278	3s.50 Customs Council Headquarters, Brussels	75	40
279	10s. Customs patrol boat	2·40	2·50

57 Communications via Satellite

1983. World Communications Year. Multicoloured.

280	70c. Type **57**	60	10
281	2s.50 Telephone and Postal Services	1·50	1·75
282	3s.50 Communications by sea and air (horiz)	2·00	3·00
283	5s. Road and rail communications (horiz)	2·50	4·00

58 *Craftsman* (freighter) in Kilindini Harbour

1983. 25th Anniversary of Intergovernmental Maritime Organisation. Multicoloured.

284	70c. Type **58**	1·40	10
285	2s.50 Life-saving devices	2·50	1·40
286	3s.50 Mombasa container terminal	3·00	2·50
287	10s. Marine park	4·25	8·50

59 President Moi signing Visitors' Book

1983. 29th Commonwealth Parliamentary Conference. Multicoloured.

288	70c. Type **59**	25	10
289	2s.50 Parliament building, Nairobi (vert)	90	1·25
290	5s. State opening of Parliament (vert)	1·60	3·00
MS291	122×141 mm. Nos. 288/290	2·75	6·50

60 Kenyan and British Flags

1983. Royal Visit. Multicoloured.

292	70c. Type **60**	50	10
293	3s.50 Sagana State Lodge	2·00	1·50
294	5s. Treetops Hotel	2·25	2·75
295	10s. Queen Elizabeth II and President Moi	3·50	7·00
MS296	126×100 mm. 25s. Designs as Nos. 292/295, but without face values. Imperf	4·50	7·50

61 President Moi

1983. 20th Anniversary of Independence. Multicoloured.

297	70c. Type **61**	10	10
298	2s. President Moi planting tree	15	20
299	3s.50 Kenyan flag and emblem	25	35
300	5s. School milk scheme	40	50
301	10s. People of Kenya	75	1·10
MS302	126×93 mm. 25s. Designs as Nos. 297 and 299/301, but without face values. Imperf	1·50	2·75

62 White-backed Night Heron

1984. Rare Birds of Kenya. Multicoloured.

303	70c. Type **62**	1·50	30
304	2s.50 Quail plover	2·50	2·50
305	3s.50 Taita olive thrush	3·25	3·75
306	5s. Mufumbiri shrike	3·75	4·25
307	10s. White-winged apalis	4·50	7·00

63 Radar Tower

1984. 40th Anniversary of International Civil Aviation Organisation. Multicoloured.

308	70c. Type **63**	30	10
309	2s.50 Kenya School of Aviation (horiz)	75	70
310	3s.50 Boeing 707 taking off from Moi airport (horiz)	1·10	1·50
311	5s. Air traffic control centre	1·50	2·50

64 Running

1984. Olympic Games, Los Angeles.

312	**64**	70c. black, green and deep green	25	10
313	-	2s.50 black, purple and violet	50	55
314	-	5s. black, blue and deep blue	1·00	2·25
315	-	10s. black, yellow and brown	3·75	6·00
MS316		130×121 mm. 25s. Designs as Nos. 312/15, but without face values. Imperf	3·25	3·25

Designs: 2s.50, Hurdling; 5s. Boxing; 10s. Hockey.

65 Conference and Kenya Library Association Logos

1984. 50th Conference of the International Federation of Library Associations. Multicoloured.

317	70c. Type **65**	10	10
318	3s.50 Mobile library	50	60
319	5s. Adult library	65	1·25
320	10s. Children's library	1·00	3·25

66 Doves and Cross

1984. Fourth World Conference on Religion and Peace. As T **66**, each design showing a different central symbol. Multicoloured.

321	70c. Type **66**	20	10
322	2s.50 Arabic inscription	80	1·10
323	3s.50 Peace emblem	1·25	1·75
324	6s.50 Star and Crescent	1·75	4·00

67 Export Year Logo

1984. Kenya Export Year. Multicoloured.

325	70c. Type **67**	30	10
326	3s.50 Forklift truck with air cargo (horiz)	1·75	2·00
327	5s. Loading ship's cargo	2·50	3·00
328	10s. Kenyan products (horiz)	3·75	6·50

1984. Ceremonial Costumes (2nd series). As T **45**. Multicoloured.

329	70c. Luhya	80	15
330	2s. Kikuyu	2·00	1·75
331	3s.50 Pokomo	2·50	2·25
332	5s. Nandi	3·00	3·00
333	10s. Rendile	4·00	6·50

68 Staunton Knight and Nyayo National Stadium

1984. 60th Anniversary of International Chess Federation. Multicoloured.

334	70c. Type **68**	2·25	40
335	2s.50 Staunton rook and Fort Jesus	3·25	1·75
336	3s.50 Staunton bishop and National Monument	3·75	2·00
337	5s. Staunton queen and Parliament Building	4·00	3·75
338	10s. Staunton king and Nyayo Fountain	6·00	8·00

69 Cooking with Wood-burning Stove and Charcoal Fire

1985. Energy Conservation. Multicoloured.

339	70c. Type **69**	20	10
340	2s. Solar energy panel on roof	65	75
341	3s.50 Production of gas from cow dung	75	1·25
342	10s. Ploughing with oxen	2·25	6·00
MS343	110×85 mm. 20s. Designs as Nos. 339/342, but without face values	2·50	2·50

70 Disabled Girl Guide making Table-mat

1985. 75th Anniversary of Girl Guide Movement. Multicoloured.

344	1s. Type **70**	45	15
345	3s. Girl Guides doing community service	1·00	75
346	5s. Lady Olave Baden-Powell (founder)	1·40	2·00
347	7s. Girl Guides gardening	2·25	6·00

71 Stylised Figures and Globe

1985. World Red Cross Day.

348	**71**	1s. black and red	80	15
349	-	4s. multicoloured	3·00	3·00
350	-	5s. multicoloured	3·25	3·50
351	-	7s. multicoloured	4·50	6·00

Designs: 4s. First Aid Team; 5s. Hearts containing crosses ('Blood Donation'); 7s. Cornucopia ('Famine Relief').

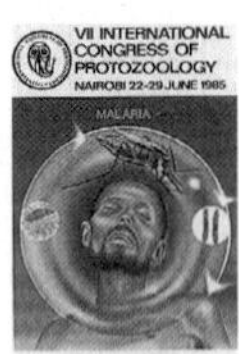

72 Man with Malaria

1985. Seventh International Congress of Protozoology, Nairobi. Multicoloured.

352	1s. Type **72**	2·00	25
353	3s. Child with Leishmaniasis	4·00	2·75
354	5s. Cow with Trypanosomiasis	4·50	4·25
355	7s. Dog with Babesiosis	7·50	8·50

73 Repairing Water Pipes

1985. United Nations Women's Decade Conference. Multicoloured.

356	1s. Type **73**	20	10
357	3s. Traditional food preparation	60	70
358	5s. Basket-weaving	75	1·25
359	7s. Dressmaking	1·00	3·00

74 The Last Supper

1985. 43rd International Eucharistic Congress, Nairobi. Multicoloured.

360	1s. Type **74**	50	10
361	3s. Village family ('The Eucharist and the Christian Family')	2·00	1·50
362	5s. Congress altar, Uhuru Park	2·25	2·75
363	7s. St Peter Claver's Church, Nairobi	2·50	5·50
MS364	117×80 mm. 25s. Pope John Paul II	8·50	7·00

75 Black Rhinoceros

1985. Endangered Animals. Multicoloured.

365	1s. Type **75**	2·75	40
366	3s. Cheetah	3·50	2·75
367	5s. De Brazza's monkey	3·75	4·00
368	10s. Grevy's zebra	7·50	9·00
MS369	129×122 mm. 25s. Endangered species (122×114 mm). Imperf	10·00	7·00

76 *Borassus aethiopum*

1986. Indigenous Trees. Multicoloured.

370	1s. Type **76**	1·25	15
371	3s. *Acacia xanthophloea*	3·50	2·50
372	5s. *Ficus natalensis*	4·50	4·50
373	7s. *Spathodea nilotica*	6·00	9·50
MS374	117×96 mm. 25s. Landscape with trees (109×90 mm). Imperf	4·00	4·50

77 Dove and UN Logo (from poster)

1986. International Peace Year. Multicoloured.

375	1s. Type **77**	30	10
376	3s. UN General Assembly (horiz)	60	50
377	7s. Nuclear explosion	1·50	2·75
378	10s. Quotation from Wall of Isaiah, UN Building, New York (horiz)	2·25	3·50

78 Dribbling the Ball

1986. World Cup Football Championship, Mexico. Multicoloured.

379	1s. Type **78**	65	15
380	3s. Scoring from a penalty	2·00	1·25
381	5s. Tackling	2·50	2·00
382	7s. Cup winners	3·00	3·50
383	10s. Heading the ball	4·00	4·25
MS384	110×86 mm. 30s. Harambee Stars football team (102×78 mm). Imperf	3·75	3·75

79 Rural Post Office and Telephone

1986. Expo '86 World Fair, Vancouver. Multicoloured.

385	1s. Type **79**	50	15
386	3s. Container depot, Embakasi	2·50	1·75
387	5s. Piper PA-30B Twin Commanche aeroplane landing at game park airstrip	4·00	2·75
388	7s. Container ship	4·25	4·50
389	10s. Transporting produce to market	4·50	5·25

80 Telephone, Computer and Dish Aerial

1986. African Telecommunications. Multicoloured.

390	1s. Type **80**	35	10
391	3s. Telephones of 1876, 1936 and 1986	1·00	85
392	5s. Dish aerial, satellite, telephones and map of Africa	1·25	1·25
393	7s. Kenyan manufacture of telecommunications equipment	1·75	2·25

81 Mashua

1986. Dhows of Kenya. Multicoloured.

394	1s. Type **81**	1·25	20
395	3s. Mtepe	2·75	1·50
396	5s. Dau La Mwao	3·25	3·00
397	10s. Jahazi	6·00	7·00
MS398	118×80 mm. 25s. Lamu dhow and map of Indian Ocean	6·00	6·00

82 Nativity

1986. Christmas. Multicoloured.

399	1s. Type **82**	60	10
400	3s. Shepherd and sheep	1·50	55
401	5s. Angel and slogan 'LOVE PEACE UNITY' (horiz)	2·25	1·60
402	7s. The Magi riding camels (horiz)	3·00	3·00

83 Immunisation

1987. 40th Anniversary of UNICEF. Multicoloured.

403	1s. Type **83**	45	10
404	3s. Food and nutrition	1·00	70
405	4s. Oral rehydration therapy	1·50	1·50
406	5s. Family planning	1·50	1·50
407	10s. Female literacy	2·25	4·00

84 Akamba Woodcarvers

1987. Tourism. Multicoloured.

408	1s. Type **84**	55	10
409	3s. Tourism on beach	3·25	1·75
410	5s. Tourist and guide at view point	4·00	4·00
411	7s. Pride of lions	6·00	7·00
MS412	118×81 mm. 30s. Geysers	11·00	12·00

1987. Ceremonial Costumes (3rd series). As T **45**. Multicoloured.

413	1s. Embu	1·00	10
414	3s. Kisii	2·75	70
415	5s. Samburu	3·25	1·75
416	7s. Taita	4·00	4·25
417	10s. Boran	4·25	4·75

85 Telecommunications by Satellite

1987. Tenth Anniversary of Kenya Posts and Telecommunications Corporation. Multicoloured.

418	1s. Type **85**	85	30
419	3s. Rural post office, Kajiado	1·90	2·00
420	4s. Awarding trophy, Welfare Sports	2·00	3·00
421	5s. Village and telephone box	2·50	3·00
422	7s. Speedpost labels and outline map of Kenya	3·50	6·00
MS423	110×80 mm. 25s. Corporation flag	2·50	2·75

86 Volleyball

1987. Fourth All-Africa Games, Nairobi. Multicoloured.

424	1s. Type **86**	20	10
425	3s. Cycling	85	65
426	4s. Boxing	35	1·25
427	5s. Swimming	40	1·25
428	7s. Steeplechasing	60	2·25
MS429	117×80 mm. 30s. Kasarani Sports Complex (horiz)	2·50	2·75

87 *Aloe volkensii*

1987. Medicinal Herbs. Multicoloured.

430	1s. Type **87**	1·00	10
431	3s. *Cassia didymobotrya*	2·50	1·25
432	5s. *Erythrina abyssinica*	3·25	3·00
433	7s. *Adenium obesum*	4·00	5·50
434	10s. Herbalist's clinic	4·75	7·00

88 *Epamera sidus*

89 *Papilio rex*

1988. Butterflies. Multicoloured.

(a) As Type **88**

434a	10c. *Cyrestis camillus*	1·50	2·25
435	20c. Type **88**	30	70
436	40c. *Cynthia cardui*	50	70
437	50c. *Colotis euippe*	50	70
438	70c. *Precis westermanni*	50	70
439	80c. *Colias electo*	50	70
440	1s. *Eronia leda*	50	30
440a	1s.50 *Papilio dardanus*	5·50	30

(b) As Type **89**

441	2s. Type **89**	70	40
442	2s.50 *Colotis phisadia*	75	90
443	3s. *Papilio desmondi*	1·00	90
444	3s.50 *Papilio demodocus*	1·00	60
445	4s. *Papilio phorcas*	1·25	1·00
446	5s. *Charaxes druceanus*	1·25	70
447	7s. *Cymothoe teita*	1·25	2·50
448	10s. *Charaxes zoolina*	1·25	1·75
449	20s. *Papilio dardanus*	1·25	4·50
450	40s. *Charaxes cithaeron*	2·00	9·00

The 10c. to 1s.50 are in the same format as T **88**.

90 Samburu Lodge and Crocodiles

1988. Kenyan Game Lodges. Multicoloured.

451	1s. Type **90**	70	10
452	3s. Naro Moru River Lodge and rock climbing	1·00	60
453	4s. Mara Serena Lodge and zebra with foal	1·25	1·40
454	5s. Voi Safari Lodge and buffalo	1·25	1·40
455	7s. Kilimanjaro Buffalo Lodge and giraffes	2·50	2·75
456	10s. Meru Mulika Lodge and rhinoceroses	2·75	3·25

91 Athletes and Stadium, Commonwealth Games, Brisbane, 1982

1988. Expo '88 World Fair, Brisbane, and Bicentenary of Australian Settlement. Multicoloured.

457	1s. Type **91**	40	10
458	3s. Flying Doctor Service de Havilland Drover 3 and Piper PA-30B Twin Commanche aircraft	2·75	1·25
459	4s. HMS *Sirius* (frigate), 1788	3·00	2·25
460	5s. Ostrich and emu	3·25	2·50
461	7s. Queen Elizabeth II, President Arap Moi of Kenya and Prime Minister Hawke of Australia	3·00	4·25
MS462	117×80 mm. 30s. Entrance to Kenya Pavilion	2·50	2·25

92 WHO Logo and Slogan

1988. 40th Anniversary of WHO.

463	**92**	1s. blue, gold and deep blue	30	10
464	-	3s. multicoloured	1·00	70
465	-	5s. multicoloured	1·40	1·50
466	-	7s. multicoloured	1·75	2·50

Designs: 3s. Mother with young son and nutritious food; 5s. Giving oral vaccine to baby; 7s. Village women drawing clean water from pump.

93 Handball

1988. Olympic Games, Seoul. Multicoloured.

467	1s. Type **93**	45	10
468	3s. Judo	75	55
469	5s. Weightlifting	1·00	1·00
470	7s. Javelin	1·00	2·00
471	10s. Relay racing	1·50	3·00
MS472	110×78 mm. 30s. Tennis	2·50	3·00

94 Calabashes

1988. Kenyan Material Culture (1st issue). Multicoloured.

473	1s. Type **94**	30	10
474	3s. Milk gourds	75	55
475	5s. Cooking pots (horiz)	85	85
476	7s. Winnowing trays (horiz)	1·25	1·75
477	10s. Reed baskets (horiz)	1·60	2·50
MS478	118×80 mm. 25s. Gourds, calabash and horn (horiz)	1·75	1·75

See also Nos. 646/650.

95 President Arap Moi taking Oath, 1978

1988. Tenth Anniversary of Nyayo Era. Multicoloured.

479	1s. Type **95**	30	10
480	3s. Building soil conservation barrier	1·00	70
481	3s.50 Passengers boarding bus	3·00	1·40
482	4s. Metalwork shop	1·25	1·50
483	5s. Moi University, Eldoret	1·25	1·50
484	7s. Aerial view of hospital	3·00	3·50
485	10s. President Arap Moi and Mrs. Thatcher at Kapsabet Telephone Exchange	8·00	7·00

96 Kenya Flag

1988. 25th Anniversary of Independence. Multicoloured.

486	1s. Type **96**	75	10
487	3s. Coffee picking	80	50
488	5s. Proposed Kenya Posts and Telecommunications Headquarters building	1·00	1·10
489	7s. Kenya Airways Airbus Industrie A310-300 *Harambee Star*	5·50	4·00
490	10s. New diesel locomotive No. 9401	7·50	6·00

97 Gedi Ruins, Malindi

1989. Historic Monuments. Multicoloured.

491	1s.20 Type **97**	60	10
492	3s.40 Vasco Da Gama Pillar, Malindi (vert)	1·40	1·75
493	4s.40 Ishiakani Monument, Kiunga	1·50	2·50
494	5s.50 Fort Jesus, Mombasa	1·75	2·50
495	7s.70 She Burnan Omwe, Lamu (vert)	2·50	4·50

98 125th Anniversary and Kenya Red Cross Logos

1989. 125th Anniversary of International Red Cross. Multicoloured.

496	1s.20 Type **98**	50	10
497	3s.40 Red Cross workers with car crash victim	1·25	90
498	4s.40 Disaster relief team distributing blankets	1·40	1·60
499	5s.50 Henri Dunant (founder)	1·50	2·25
500	7s.70 Blood donor	1·75	3·50

99 Female Giraffe and Calf

1989. Reticulated Giraffe. Multicoloured.

501	1s.20 Type **99**	1·75	30
502	3s.40 Giraffe drinking	3·25	3·00
503	4s.40 Two giraffes	3·75	4·00
504	5s.50 Giraffe feeding	4·50	5·50
MS505	80×110 mm. 30s. Designs as Nos. 501/504, but without face values	5·50	7·00

Designs from No. **MS**505 are without the Worldwide Fund for Nature logo.

100 *Lentinus sajor-caju*

1989. Mushrooms. Multicoloured.

506	1s.20 Type **100**	1·50	30
507	3s.40 *Agaricus bisporus*	2·50	2·00
508	4s.40 *Agaricus bisporus* (different)	2·75	2·50
509	5s.50 *Termitomyces schimperi*	3·50	3·50
510	7s.70 *Lentinus edodes*	4·25	5·50

101 Independence Monuments

1989. Birth Centenary of Jawaharlal Nehru (Indian statesman). Multicoloured.

511	1s.20 Type **101**	1·50	30
512	3s.40 Nehru with graduates and open book	3·50	1·75
513	5s.50 Jawaharlal Nehru	4·50	4·00
514	7s.70 Industrial complex and cogwheels	4·75	6·50

1989. Ceremonial Costumes (4th series). As T **45**. Multicoloured.

515	1s.20 Kipsigis	1·50	20
516	3s.40 Rabai	2·50	1·60
517	5s.50 Duruma	3·00	2·75
518	7s.70 Kuria	4·00	4·25
519	10s. Bajuni	4·25	6·00

102 EMS Speedpost Letters and Parcel

1990. Tenth Anniversary of Pan African Postal Union. Multicoloured.

520	1s.20 Type **102**	25	10
521	3s.40 Mail runner	60	40
522	5s.50 Mandera Post Office	80	90
523	7s.70 EMS Speedpost letters and globe (vert)	1·00	1·75
524	10s. PAPU logo (vert)	1·00	1·75

103 'Stamp King' with Tweezers and Magnifying Glass

1990. Stamp World London '90 International Stamp Exhibition.

525	**103**	1s.50 multicoloured	45	10
526	-	4s.50 multicoloured	1·50	1·25
527	-	6s.50 black, red and blue	1·60	2·00
528	-	9s. multicoloured	2·00	4·00
MS529		113×77 mm. Nos. 525/8	5·00	7·00

Designs: 4s.50, Penny Black and Kenya Stamp Bureau postmark; 6s.50, Early British cancellations; 9s. Ronald Ngala Street Post Office, Nairobi.

104 Moi Golden Cup

1990. World Cup Football Championship, Italy. Trophies. Multicoloured.

530	1s.50 Type **104**	75	10
531	4s.50 East and Central Africa Challenge Cup	2·25	1·75
532	6s.50 East and Central Africa Club Championship Cup	3·25	3·75
533	9s. World Cup	3·50	7·00

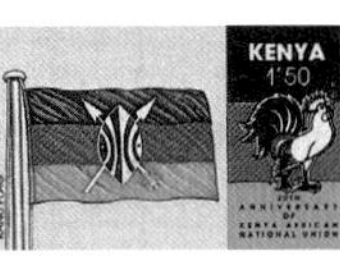

105 KANU Flag

1990. 30th Anniversary of Kenya African National Union. Multicoloured.

534	1s.50 Type **105**	20	10
535	2s.50 Nyayo Monument	20	15
536	4s.50 Party Headquarters	45	35
537	5s. Jomo Kenyatta (Party founder)	50	40
538	6s.50 President Arap Moi	70	1·00
539	9s. President Moi addressing rally	1·00	2·25
540	10s. Queue of voters	1·00	2·25

106 Desktop Computer

1990. 125th Anniversary of ITU. Multicoloured.

541	1s.50 Type **106**	15	10
542	4s.50 Telephone switchboard assembly, Gilgil	35	50
543	6s.50 '125 YEARS'	45	1·00
544	9s. Urban and rural telecommunications	70	2·25

107 Queen Mother at British Museum, 1988

108 Queen Elizabeth at Hospital Garden Party, 1947

1990. 90th Birthday of Queen Elizabeth the Queen Mother.

545	**107**	10s. multicoloured	75	1·00
546	**108**	40s. black and green	2·00	4·00

109 Kenya 1988 2s. Definitive

1990. Centenary of Postage Stamps in Kenya. Multicoloured.

547	1s.50 Type **109**	1·40	10
548	4s.50 East Africa and Uganda 1903 1a.	2·75	90
549	6s.50 British East Africa Co 1890 $^{1}/_{2}$a. optd on GB 1d.	3·25	2·00
550	9s. Kenya and Uganda 1922 20c.	3·75	3·50
551	20s. Kenya, Uganda, Tanzania 1971 2s.50 railway commemorative	6·75	9·50

110 Adult Literacy Class

1990. International Literacy Year. Multicoloured.

552	1s.50 Type **110**	30	10
553	4s.50 Teaching by radio	1·00	1·10
554	6s.50 Technical training	1·25	2·00
555	9s. International Literacy Year logo	2·00	3·50

111 National Flag

1991. Olympic Games, Barcelona (1992) (1st issue). Multicoloured.

556	2s. Type **111**	1·10	10
557	6s. Basketball	2·75	1·40
558	7s. Hockey	2·75	2·25
559	8s.50 Table tennis	2·50	3·75
560	11s. Boxing	2·50	4·25

See also Nos. 580/584.

112 Symbolic Man and Pointing Finger

1992. AIDS Day. Multicoloured.

561	2s. Type **112**	1·00	15
562	6s. Victim and drugs	2·50	1·25
563	8s.50 Male and female symbols	3·00	4·00
564	11s. Symbolic figure and hypodermic syringe	4·50	6·00

113 Queen and Prince Philip with Pres. Moi

1992. 40th Anniversary of Queen Elizabeth II's Accession.

565	3s. Type **113**	50	10
566	8s. Marabou storks in tree	2·00	75
567	11s. Treetops Hotel	1·00	85
568	14s. Three portraits of Queen Elizabeth	1·00	1·00
569	40s. Queen Elizabeth II	2·00	4·50

114 Leopard

1992. Kenya Wildlife. Multicoloured.

570	3s. Type **114**	2·50	45
571	8s. Lion	3·25	2·00
572	10s. Elephant	8·50	3·75
573	11s. Buffalo	3·25	4·00
574	14s. Black rhinoceros	11·00	8·00

115 Fiat 509, 1924

1992. Vintage Cars. Multicoloured.

575	3s. International Harvester Safari Truck, 1926	2·25	30
576	8s. Type **115**	3·50	2·00
577	10s. Hupmobile, 1923	3·75	3·50
578	11s. Chevrolet Box Body, 1928	3·75	3·75
579	14s. Bentley/Parkward, 1934	4·25	7·00

116 Kenyan Athlete winning Race

1992. Olympic Games, Barcelona (2nd issue). Multicoloured.

580	3s. Type **116**	1·00	10
581	8s. Men's judo	2·00	1·25
582	10s. Kenyan women's volleyball players	2·50	2·50
583	11s. Kenyan men's 4×100 m relay runners	2·50	2·75
584	14s. Men's 10,000 m	2·75	5·50

117 Holy Child, Joseph and Animals

1992. Christmas. Multicoloured.

585	3s. Type **117**	30	10
586	8s. Mary with Holy Child	75	50
587	11s. Christmas tree	1·00	80
588	14s. Adoration of the Magi	1·25	2·25

118 Asembo Bay Lighthouse, Lake Victoria

1993. Lighthouses. Multicoloured.

589	3s. Type **118**	2·75	55
590	8s. Old Ras Serani lighthouse, Mombasa	4·00	2·50
591	11s. New Ras Serani lighthouse, Mombasa	4·25	4·25
592	14s. Gingira, Lake Victoria	5·00	7·00

119 Superb Starling

120 Yellow-billed Hornbill

1993. Birds. Multicoloured

(a) As T **119**

593	50c. Type **119**	15	1·25
594	1s. Red and yellow barbet	25	80
594a	1s.50 Lady Ross's turaco	65	1·25
595	3s. Black-throated honeyguide ('Greater honeyguide')	50	20
595a	5s. African fish eagle	80	1·00
595b	6s. Vulturine guineafowl	8·00	1·75
596	7s. Malachite kingfisher	70	30
597	8s. Speckled pigeon	70	20
598	10s. Cinnamon-chested bee-eater	70	20
599	11s. Scarlet-chested sunbird	70	25
600	14s. Bagalafecht weaver ('Reichenow's weaver')	75	30

(b) As T **120**.

601	50s. Type **120**	1·25	2·00
602	80s. Lesser flamingo	1·60	3·00
603	100s. Hadada ibis	1·90	3·50

121 Nurse bandaging Boy's Legs

1993. 17th World Congress of Rehabilitation International.

611	**121**	3s. multicoloured	70	10
612	-	8s. multicoloured	1·10	70
613	-	10s. multicoloured	1·25	1·40
614	-	11s. multicoloured	1·25	1·60
615	-	14s. black, blue and orange	1·50	2·50

Designs: Horiz—8s. Singing group on crutches; 10s. Vocational training; 11s. Wheelchair race. Vert: 14s. Congress emblem.

122 Maendeleo House, Nairobi

1994. 40th Anniversary of Maendeleo Ya Wanawake Organisation. Multicoloured.

616	3s.50 Type **122**	80	20
617	9s. Planting saplings	1·10	70
618	11s. Rural family planning clinic (vert)	1·25	1·60
619	12s.50 Women carrying water	1·60	2·75
620	15s.50 Improved wood-burning cooking stove (vert)	1·90	3·50

123 *Ansellia africana*

1994. Orchids. Multicoloured.

621	3s.50 Type **123**	2·00	30
622	9s. *Aerangis luteoalba* var *rhodosticta*	2·50	85
623	12s.50 *Polystachya bella*	2·75	2·50
624	15s.50 *Brachycorythis kalbreyeri*	3·25	3·75
625	20s. *Eulophia guineensis*	4·00	5·50

124 Emblem and KICC Building, Nairobi

1994. 30th Anniversary of African Development Bank. Multicoloured.

626	6s. Type **124**	1·00	25
627	25s. Isinya-Kajiado project	3·50	5·00

125 Kenyan Family

1994. International Year of the Family. Multicoloured.

628	6s. Type **125**	70	10
629	14s.50 Nurse with mother and baby	1·60	1·40
630	20s. School children and teacher (horiz)	2·50	3·75
631	25s. Emblem (horiz)	2·50	4·25

126 Paul Harris (founder of Rotary)

1994. 50th Anniversary of Rotary Club of Mombasa. Multicoloured.

632	6s. Type **126**	40	10
633	14s.50 Anniversary logo	1·00	70
634	17s.50 Administering polio vaccine	1·40	2·25
635	20s. Women at stand pipe	1·50	2·50
636	25s. Rotary emblem	1·60	2·75

127 Donkey

1995. Kenya Society for Prevention of Cruelty to Animals. Multicoloured.

637	6s. Type **127**	50	10
638	14s.50 Cow	60	45
639	17s.50 Sheep	65	1·00
640	20s. Dog	2·25	2·50
641	25s. Cat	2·25	2·50

128 Male Golfer in Bunker

1995. Golf. Multicoloured.

642	6s. Type **128**	1·50	20
643	17s.50 Female golfer on fairway	2·75	1·75
644	20s. Male golfer teeing-off	2·75	3·00
645	25s. Head of golf club	3·00	3·25

129 Perfume Containers

1995. Kenyan Material Culture (2nd issue). Multicoloured.

646	6s. Type **129**	30	10
647	14s.50 Basketry	75	75
648	17s.50 Preserving pots	85	1·25
649	20s. Gourds	1·10	1·75
650	25s. Wooden containers	1·25	2·00

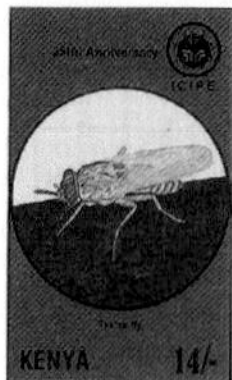

130 Tsetse Fly

1995. 25th Anniversary of ICIPE. Insect Pests. Multicoloured.

651	14s. Type **130**	80	30
652	26s. Tick	1·25	80
653	32s. Wild silkmoth	1·40	1·25
654	33s. Maize borer	1·50	2·00
655	40s. Locust	2·25	3·00

131 Maize

1995. 50th Anniversary of FAO. Multicoloured.

656	14s. Type **131**	1·25	30
657	28s. Cattle	1·75	80
658	32s. Chickens	2·25	1·75
659	33s. Fisherman with catch	2·25	3·00
660	40s. Fruit	3·00	4·75

132 Kenyan and United Nations Flags over Headquarters, Nairobi

1995. 50th Anniversary of United Nations.

661	**132**	23s. multicoloured	85	70
662	-	26s. multicoloured	95	95
663	-	32s. multicoloured	1·25	1·40
664	-	40s. blue, red and black	1·75	2·50

Designs: 26s. Multi-racial group with emblem; 32s. United Nations helmet; 40s. 50th anniversary emblem.

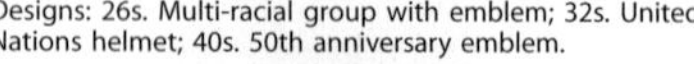

133 Swimming

1996. Olympic Games, Atlanta (1st issue). Events and Gold Medal Winners. Multicoloured.

665	14s. Type **133**	1·00	1·10
666	20s. Archery	1·00	1·10
667	20s. Weightlifting	1·00	1·10
668	20s. Pole vault (vert)	1·00	1·10
669	20s. Equestrian (vert)	1·00	1·10
670	20s. Diving (vert)	1·00	1·10
671	20s. Sprinting (vert)	1·00	1·10
672	20s. Athlete carrying Olympic Torch (vert)	1·00	1·10
673	20s. Hurdling (vert)	1·00	1·10
674	20s. Kayak (vert)	1·00	1·10
675	20s. Boxing (vert)	1·00	1·10
676	20s. Gymnastics (vert)	1·00	1·10
677	25s. Greg Louganis (USA) (diving, 1984 and 1988) (vert)	1·25	1·40
678	25s. Cassius Clay (USA) (boxing, 1960) (vert)	1·25	1·40
679	25s. Nadia Comaneci (Rumania) (gymnastics, 1980) (vert)	1·25	1·40
680	25s. Daley Thompson (Great Britain) (decathlon, 1980 and 1984) (vert)	1·25	1·40
681	25s. Kipchoge Keino (Kenya) (running, 1968) (vert)	1·25	1·40
682	25s. Kornelia Enders (Germany) (swimming, 1976) (vert)	1·25	1·40
683	25s. Jackie Joyner-Kersee (USA) (long jump, 1988) (vert)	1·25	1·40
684	25s. Michael Jordan (USA) (basketball, 1984) (vert)	1·25	1·40
685	25s. Shun Fujimoto (Japan) (gymnastics, 1972) (vert)	1·25	1·40
686	32s. Javelin	1·25	1·40
687	40s. Fencing	1·25	1·40
688	50s. Discus	1·50	1·75
MS689	Two sheets, each 79×109 mm. (a) 100s. Athlete with medal (vert). (b) 100s. Athlete carrying Olympic Torch (different) (vert) Set of 2 sheets	7·50	10·00

Nos. 665/667 with 686/688, 668/676 and 677/685 respectively were printed together, *se-tenant*, forming composite designs.

See also Nos. 702/706.

134 Lions

135 Water Buck

1996. Tourism. Multicoloured

(a) Designs as T **134**

690	6s. Type **134**	30	10
691	14s. Mt. Kenya	35	30
692	20s. Sail boards	55	70
693	25s. Hippopotami	1·25	1·50
694	40s. Couple in traditional dress	1·25	2·50
MS695	100×80 mm. 50s. Female giraffe and calf (vert)	4·50	4·50

(b) Horiz designs as T **135**.

696	20s. Type **135**	7·50	8·00

697 20s. Pair of rhinoceroses 7·50 8·00
698 20s. Cheetah 7·50 8·00
699 20s. Group of oryx 7·50 8·00
700 20s. Pair of giraffes 7·50 8·00
701 20s. Monkey and bongo 7·50 8·00

136 Women's 10,000 Metres

1996. Olympic Games, Atlanta (2nd issue). Multicoloured.
702 6s. Type **136** 35 10
703 14s. Steeple-chasing 55 30
704 20s. Victorious athletes with flag 80 80
705 25s. Boxing 80 1·00
706 40s. Men's 1500 m 1·40 2·50

137 Red Cross Emblem

1996. Kenya Red Cross Society.
707 **137** 6s. red and black 35 10
708 - 14s. multicoloured 65 35
709 - 20s. multicoloured 85 80
710 - 25s. multicoloured 95 95
711 - 40s. multicoloured 1·60 2·25

Designs: 14s. Giving blood; 20s. Immunisation; 25s. Refugee child with food; 40s. Cleaning the environment.

138 Impala

1996. East African Wildlife Society. Multicoloured.
712 6s. Type **138** 30 10
713 20s. Colobus monkey 80 70
714 25s. African elephant 2·25 1·50
715 40s. Black rhinoceros 3·25 3·75

139 Kenya Lions Club Logo

1996. Work of Lions Club International in Kenya. Multicoloured.
716 6s. Type **139** 15 10
717 14s. Eye operation 55 45
718 20s. Two disabled children in wheelchair 70 1·25
719 25s. Modern ambulance 1·00 1·50

140 COMESA Logo

1997. Inauguration of Common Market for Eastern and Southern Africa. Multicoloured.
720 6s. Type **140** 15 15
721 20s. Kenyan flag and logo 85 1·10

141 *Haplochromis cinctus*

1997. Endangered Fish. Lake Victoria Cichlid Fish. Multicoloured.
722 25s. Type **141** 90 1·00
723 25s. *Haplochromis* 'Orange Rock Hunter' 90 1·00
724 25s. *Haplochromis chilotes* 90 1·00
725 25s. *Haplochromis nigricans* 90 1·00

142 Class 94 Diesel-electric Locomotive No. 9401, 1981

1997. Kenya Railway Locomotives. Multicoloured.
726 6s. Type **142** 70 15
727 14s. Class 87 diesel-electric No. 8721, 1964 1·10 40
728 20s. Class 59 Garratt steam No. 5905, 1955 1·50 65
729 25s. Class 57 Garratt steam No. 5701, 1939 1·50 1·10
730 30s. Class 23 steam No. 2305, 1923 1·75 2·50
731 40s. Class 10 steam No. 1001, 1914 1·90 3·00

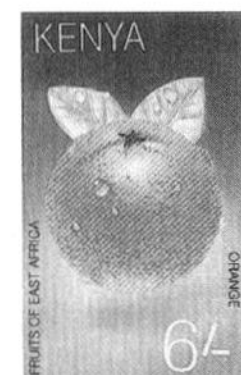

143 Orange

1997. Fruits of East Africa. Multicoloured.
732 6s. Type **143** 75 60
733 14s. Pineapple 1·50 1·00
734 20s. Mango 2·25 2·25
735 25s. Pawpaw 2·50 2·50

144 Crocodile

1997. Local Tourist Attractions. Multicoloured.
736 10s. Type **144** 1·25 25
737 27s. Lake Bogoria hot springs 2·00 1·50
738 30s. Warthogs 2·00 1·75
739 33s. Windsurfing 2·00 2·25
740 42s. Traditional huts 3·25 3·25

145 Girl Guides Anniversary Logo

1997. 75th Anniversary of Kenyan Girl Guides Anniversary. Multicoloured.
741 10s. Type **145** 55 70
742 10s. Lord Baden-Powell 55 70
743 27s. Girl guides hiking 90 1·10
744 27s. Rangers in camp 90 1·10
745 33s. Girl guides planting seedlings 1·00 1·25
746 33s. Boy scouts giving first aid 1·00 1·25
747 42s. Boy scouts in camp 1·25 1·25
748 42s. Brownies entertaining the elderly 1·25 1·25

146 Portuguese Ships arriving at Malindi

1998. 500th Anniversary of Vasco da Gama's Arrival at Malindi. Multicoloured.
749 10s. Type **146** 65 25
750 24s. Portuguese ships 1·40 80
751 33s. Map of Africa 1·75 2·00
752 42s. Vasco da Gama Pillar and harbour 2·00 2·50

147 Lion

1998. 18th Anniversary of Pan African Postal Union. Wildlife. Multicoloured.
753 10s. Type **147** 1·50 25
754 24s. Buffalo 2·00 80
755 33s. Grant's gazelle 2·25 2·50
756 42s. Cheetah 3·25 4·50
MS757 94×76 mm. 50s. Hirola gazelle 5·50 5·50

148 President Arap Moi taking Oath, 1998

1998. Daniel Arap Moi's Fifth Presidential Term.
758 **148** 14s. multicoloured 1·50 80

149 Leatherback Turtle

2000. Turtles. Multicoloured.
759 17s. Type **149** 1·10 35
760 20s. Green sea turtle 1·40 40
761 30s. Hawksbill turtle 1·75 1·25
762 47s. Olive Ridley turtle 2·50 3·50
763 59s. Loggerhead turtle 3·00 4·50

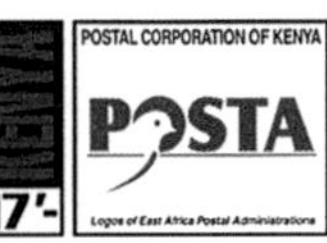

150 Kenya Postal Corporation Logo

2000. East Africa Postal Administrations' Co-operation. Multicoloured (except 17s.).
764 17s. Type **150** (red, blue and black) 1·00 35
765 35s. Uganda Post Ltd logo 1·75 1·75
766 50s. Tanzania Posts Corporation logo 2·00 3·00
MS767 100×80 mm. 70s. As 50s. 4·00 4·75

151 Cotton **152** Tea

2001. Crops. Multicoloured

(a) Vert designs as T **151**
768 2s. Type **151** 10 30
769 4s. Bananas 15 30
770 5s. Avocado 15 30
771 6s. Cassava 15 30
772 8s. Arrowroot 25 30
773 10s. Pawpaw 25 30
774 19s. Orange 50 35
775 20s. Pyrethrum 50 35
776 30s. Groundnuts 80 55
777 35s. Coconut 1·00 60
778 40s. Sisal 1·25 70
779 50s. Cashew nuts 1·40 85

(b) Vert designs as T **152**.
780 60s. Type **152** 1·50 1·00
781 80s. Maize 2·00 1·40
782 100s. Coffee 4·50 1·75
783 200s. Finger millet 4·25 3·75
784 400s. Sorghum 7·50 8·00
785 500s. Sugar cane 9·00 9·50

153 Source of the Nile, Jinja, Uganda

2002. Historical Sites of East Africa. Multicoloured.
786 19s. Type **153** 1·00 35
787 35s. Kamu Fort, Kenya (35×35 mm) 1·50 1·10
788 40s. Olduvai Gorge, Tanzania 2·75 2·75
789 50s. Thimlich Ohinga (ancient settlement), Kenya (35×35 mm) 2·75 3·50

154 Section of Mombasa Road

2003. 40th Anniversary of Kenya–China Diplomatic Relations. Multicoloured.
790 21s. Type **154** 2·00 40
791 66s. Kasarani Stadium 4·00 4·50

155 Lioness and Baby Oryx

2004. Tourism. Multicoloured.
792 21s. Type **155** 1·25 35
793 60s. Leopard and cub 2·25 1·75
794 66s. Zebra and calf 2·25 2·00
795 88s. Bongo and calf 3·50 5·00

156 Risen Christ

2005. Easter. Showing bronze bas-reliefs, each black, brown and yellow.
796 25s. Type **156** 70 45
797 65s. Christ brought before Pilate 1·75 1·60
798 75s. Crucifixion 2·00 2·00
799 95s. Christ praying in Gethsemane 3·00 4·25

157 Polio Vaccination

2005. Centenary of Rotary International. Multicoloured.
800 25s. Type **157** 70 45
801 65s. Donation of Jaipur feet (prosthetics) 1·75 1·75
802 75s. Don Bosco Centre (Nairobi) 2·00 2·25
803 95s. Donation of sewing machine 3·25 4·25

158 Gabbra

2005. Traditional Costumes of East Africa (1st series). Multicoloured.
804 21s. Type **158** 1·25 35
805 60s. Pokot 2·50 2·00
806 66s. Meru 2·75 2·50
807 88s. Digo 3·75 5·00

See also Nos. 830/833.

159 Elephant Snout Fish

2006. Fish of Lake Victoria. Multicoloured.

808	25s. Type **159**	£130	1·50
809	55s. Sudan catfish	4·00	2·50
810	75s. Nile perch	5·50	6·00
811	95s. Redbreast tilapia	7·00	8·00

160 Emblem

2006. 24th UPU Congress, Nairobi (1st issue).

812	**160**	25s. multicoloured	1·00	1·25

The UPU Congress was moved to Geneva, Switzerland, due to political unrest in Kenya.

See also Nos. 838/841.

161 Owen and Mzee, 2005 (Illustration reduced. Actual size 60×31 mm)

2006. Owen and Mzee (baby hippopotamus and giant tortoise), Haller Park, Mombasa.

813	**161**	25s. multicoloured	2·50	2·50

162 Roan Antelope

2006. Tourism. 'Kenya The Land of Opportunity'. Multicoloured.

814	25s. Type **162**	7·00	7·00
815	25s. Weaver bird at nest	7·00	7·00
816	25s. Monkey	7·00	7·00
817	25s. Turkana hut	7·00	7·00
818	25s. Athletes in steeplechase	7·00	7·00
819	25s. Golf course	7·00	7·00
820	25s. Waterfalls, Abadares	7·00	7·00
821	25s. Balloon safari	7·00	7·00
822	25s. Bullfight	7·00	7·00
823	25s. Chimpanzee	7·00	7·00
824	25s. Maasai	7·00	7·00
825	25s. Kit Makaye (rock formation)	7·00	7·00

163 Mt. Kenya

2007. Mountains of East Africa. Multicoloured.

826	25s. Type **163**	1·00	35
827	75s. Mt. Ruwenzori, Uganda	3·00	3·50
828	95s. Mt. Kilimanjaro, Tanzania	3·50	4·50

164 African Woman

2007. Breast Cancer Research.

829	**164**	25s. multicoloured	3·00	1·75

165 Oglek

2007. Traditional Costumes of East Africa (2nd series). Multicoloured.

830	25s. Type **165**	1·00	35
831	65s. Sabaot	2·25	1·50
832	75s. Ribe	2·50	2·50
833	95s. Elmolo	3·50	4·00

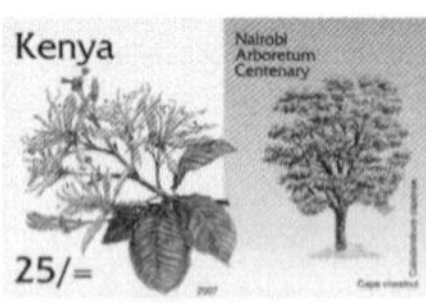

166 *Calodendrum capense* (Cape chestnut)

2007. Centenary of Nairobi Arboretum. Multicoloured.

834	25s. Type **166**	75	35
835	65s. Tree Centre and *Cupressus torulosa* (Bhutan cypress)	2·00	1·50
836	75s. *Spathodea campanulata* (Nandi flame)	2·25	2·50
837	95s. *Monodora myristica* (calabash nutmeg)	3·25	4·00

167 Sitatunga Gazelle in Saiwa Swamp

2008. 24th UPU Congress, Nairobi (2nd issue). Multicoloured.

838	25s. Type **167**	75	25
839	65s. Jackson's hartebeest at Ruma Park	2·00	1·50
840	75s. Athlete in steeplechase	2·25	2·50
841	95s. Kenyatta International Conference Centre, Nairobi	3·25	4·00

The UPU Congress was moved to Geneva, Switzerland, due to political unrest in Kenya.

168 Athletes parading with Kenyan Flag

2008. Olympic Games, Beijing. Multicoloured.

842	25s. Type **168**	1·25	50
843	65s. Women's volleyball	3·00	2·25
844	75s. Five women athletes in race	3·75	4·00
845	95s. Boxing match	4·75	5·50

169 Oginga Odinga, Pio Gama Pinto, Tom Mboya and Ronald Ngala (politicians) (Post Independence)

2008. Heroes of Kenya. Multicoloured.

846	25s. Type **169**	70	40
847	65s. Bildad Kaggia, Kung'u Karumba, Jomo Kenyatta, Fred Kubai, Paul Ngei and Achieng' Oneko (The Kapenguria Six)	1·75	1·75
848	75s. Dedan Kimathi (Mau Mau rebellion leader), Elijah Masinde (political and religious leader), Mekatilili Wa Menza (anti colonial leader) and Koitalel Samoei (Nandi rebellion leader) (Pre Independence)	2·25	2·50
849	95s. Kenya Army Peacekeeping Force	2·50	3·25

170 Woman loading Donkey with Water Cans

2008. Centenary of Theosophical Order of Service. Provision of Wells and Boreholes.

850	**170**	25s. multicoloured	1·25	1·00

171 Madrasa Programme

2008. Golden Jubilee of the Aga Khan. Multicoloured.

851	25s. Type **171**	1·25	40
852	65s. Workers in field (Coastal Rural Support Programme)	2·50	2·00
853	75s. Aga Khan Academy, Mombasa (44×29 mm)	3·25	3·00
854	95s. Aga Khan University Hospital, Nairobi (44×29 mm)	4·00	4·00

172 Blind Man

2009. Birth Bicentenary of Louis Braille (inventor of Braille writing for the blind).

855	**172**	25s. multicoloured	1·50	1·00

173 Market Stallholder ('Financial Services')

2009. Tenth Anniversary of Postal Corporation of Kenya. Multicoloured.

856	25s. Type **173**	1·25	1·25
857	25s. Parcels ('We Deliver Peace of Mind!')	1·25	1·25
858	25s. Courier and Posta Dispatch vans ('Pick-up Services')	1·25	1·25
859	25s. Boy and stamps ('Say it with Stamps!')	1·25	1·25
860	25s. Brochures in postbox ('Direct Mail Marketing')	1·25	1·25
861	25s. 'Utility Bills Retail Services Salaries' ('Agency Services')	1·25	1·25
862	25s. Woman reading letter ('We Deliver Emotions!')	1·25	1·25
863	25s. Postman and private letter boxes	1·25	1·25
864	25s. 'Financial Services'	1·25	1·25
865	65s. Unloading parcels from aeroplane ('Expedited Mail Service')	2·00	2·00
866	75s. Narok Post Office	2·50	2·50
867	95s. Water standpipe ('Corporate Social Responsibility')	4·00	4·00

174 Taita African Violet and Amegilla Bee, Taita Hills

2010. Centenary (2009) of the East Africa Natural History Society. Multicoloured.

868	25s. Type **174**	1·00	30
869	65s. Reed frog, Shimba Hills	2·50	2·00
870	75s. Great blue turaco, Kakamega Forest	3·50	2·50
871	95s. Golden-rumped sengi, Arabuko-Sokoke Forest	3·25	3·50

175 Elephant

2010. 30th Anniversary of PAPU (Pan African Postal Union).

872	**175**	25s. multicoloured	1·50	1·00

176 President Mwai Kibaki holding New Constitution

2011. Promulgation of New Constitution.

873	**176**	25s. multicoloured	1·00	1·00

177 *Oplostomus haroldi* (large hive beetle)

2011. 40th Anniversary of ICIPE (International Centre of Insect Physiology and Ecology). Insects. Multicoloured.

874	25s. African Monarch butterfly (*Danaus chrysippus*)	6·50	6·50
875	25s. *Pontia helice*	6·50	6·50
876	25s. Yellow Pansy butterfly (*Junonia hierta*)	6·50	6·50
877	25s. *Chiasmia subcurvaria*	6·50	6·50
878	25s. African Migrant butterfly (*Catopsilia florella*)	6·50	6·50
879	25s. False Dotted Border (*Belenois thysa*)	6·50	6·50
880	25s. *Leucinodes orbonalis* sp.	6·50	6·50
881	25s. *Gelechioidea* sp.	6·50	6·50
882	25s. *Eupithecia* sp. cf. *festiva*	6·50	6·50
883	25s. *Nymphalidae*	6·50	6·50
884	25s. *Paraccra mimesa*	6·50	6·50
885	25s. *Hodebertia testalis*	6·50	6·50
886	25s. *Alucitidae* sp.	6·50	6·50
887	25s. *Anthozela* sp.	6·50	6·50
888	25s. *Eucosmini* gen. n. sp. n.	6·50	6·50
889	25s. *Eucosmini* sp.	6·50	6·50
890	25s. *Zalaca snelleni*	6·50	6·50
891	25s. *Yponomeuta strigillata*	6·50	6·50
892	25s. *Tortrix dinota*	6·50	6·50
893	25s. *Parotis* sp. nr. *prasinalis*	6·50	6·50
894	25s. *Precis hierta*	6·50	6·50
895	25s. *Colotis antevippe*	6·50	6·50
896	25s. *Cryptophlebia semilunana*	6·50	6·50
897	25s. *Hypolimnas misippus*	6·50	6·50
898	25s. *Yponomeuta fumigatus*	6·50	6·50
899	65s. Type **177**	2·00	2·00
900	65s. *Cartoblatta* sp. (cockroach)	2·00	2·00
901	65s. *Mormotomyia hirsuta*	2·00	2·00
902	65s. *Cicindellidae*	2·00	2·00
903	65s. *Nosognatha ruficollis*	2·00	2·00
904	65s. *Hetrodinae* sp.	2·00	2·00
905	65s. *Helopeltis schoutedeni* (and damaged leaves)	2·00	2·00
906	65s. Blister Beetle (*Ceroctis* sp.)	2·00	2·00
907	65s. *Bagrada cruciferarum*	2·00	2·00
908	65s. *Popillia aeneipennis* (chafer)	2·00	2·00
909	65s. Jewel Beetle (*Lampetis* sp.)	2·00	2·00
910	65s. *Oryctes* sp. (Rhinoceros beetle)	2·00	2·00
911	65s. *Homoderus mellyi*	2·00	2·00
912	65s. *Zonocerus variegatus*	2·00	2·00
913	65s. *Leucospidae*	2·00	2·00
914	65s. *Agnoscelis versicolor*	2·00	2·00
915	65s. Tortoise Beetle (*Hispinae*)	2·00	2·00
916	65s. *Curculionidae*	2·00	2·00
917	65s. *Cypholoba perspicillaris*	2·00	2·00
918	65s. *Lycidae*	2·00	2·00
919	65s. Milkweed bugs	2·00	2·00
920	65s. *Mylabris tristigma*	2·00	2·00
921	65s. *Paederus* sp.	2·00	2·00
922	65s. *Pyrops turritus*	2·00	2·00
923	65s. *Tenebrionidae*	2·00	2·00
924	75s. Fig Wasp (perched)	2·00	2·00
925	75s. Rain Tree Bug (*Ptyelus flavescens*)	2·00	2·00
926	75s. *Phlebotomus* feeding	2·00	2·00
927	75s. Fig Wasp (with ovipositor extended)	2·00	2·00
928	75s. Dragonfly (*Trithemis annulata*)	2·00	2·00
929	75s. Braconid Wasp	2·00	2·00
930	75s. Paper Wasp (*Polistes* sp.)	2·00	2·00
931	75s. *Helopeltis schoutedeni* (in close-up)	2·00	2·00
932	75s. Dragonfly (*Trithemis* sp.)	2·00	2·00
933	75s. Cicada	2·00	2·00
934	75s. Silverfish	2·00	2·00
935	75s. Stingless Bee	2·00	2·00
936	75s. *Lipotriches* sp.	2·00	2·00
937	75s. *Bombyliidae*	2·00	2·00

938 75s. *Bromophila caffra* 2·00 2·00
939 75s. *Schistocerca gregaria* 2·00 2·00
940 75s. *Plagiotryptus hippiscus* 2·00 2·00
941 75s. *Reduviidae* 2·00 2·00
942 75s. Stalk-eyed Fly (*Diopsidae*) 2·00 2·00
943 75s. *Lamyra gulo* and wasp prey 2·00 2·00
944 75s. *Dictyopharidae* 2·00 2·00
945 75s. *Rhiniidae* cf. *Fainia* sp. 2·00 2·00
946 75s. Locust 2·00 2·00
947 75s. *Megastigmus* sp. 2·00 2·00
948 75s. *Glossina morsitans* feeding 2·00 2·00
949 95s. *Bactrocera invadens* (facing upwards) 3·00 3·00
950 95s. *Trirhithrum culcasiae* 3·00 3·00
951 95s. *Trirhithrum coffeae* 3·00 3·00
952 95s. *Bactrocera invadens* (facing downwards) 3·00 3·00
953 95s. *Bactrocera munroi* 3·00 3·00
954 95s. *Caprophthoromyla dimidiata* 3·00 3·00
955 95s. *Celidodacus obnubilus* 3·00 3·00
956 95s. *Ceratitis caetrata* 3·00 3·00
957 95s. *Ceratitis captiata* 3·00 3·00
958 95s. *Ceratitis copelandi* 3·00 3·00
959 95s. *Ceratitis cosyra* 3·00 3·00
960 95s. *Ceratitis cuthbertsoni* 3·00 3·00
961 95s. *Ceratitis rosa* 3·00 3·00
962 95s. *Ceratitis stictica* 3·00 3·00
963 95s. *Ceratitis whartoni* 3·00 3·00
964 95s. *Conradtina acroleuca* 3·00 3·00
965 95s. *Dacus apostata* 3·00 3·00
966 95s. *Dacus frontalis* 3·00 3·00
967 95s. *Dacus sphaeristicus* 3·00 3·00
968 95s. *Dacus telfairae* 3·00 3·00
969 95s. *Munromyia whartoni* 3·00 3·00
970 95s. *Craspedoxantha* sp. 3·00 3·00
971 95s. *Taomyia marshalli* 3·00 3·00
972 95s. *Themarictera laticeps* 3·00 3·00
973 95s. *Trirhithrum albomaculatum* 3·00 3·00

178 Flags at UNEP Regional Office, Nairobi

2012. 40th Anniversary of UNEP (United Nations Environment Programme) (1st issue). Multicoloured.
974 30s. Type **178** 1·25 70
975 90s. City of Stockholm, Sweden 3·25 3·50
976 110s. Christ the Redeemer statue, Rio de Janeiro 3·75 4·00

179 Fauna and Flora (CITES–Convention on International Trade in Endangered Species of Wild Fauna and Flora)

2012. 40th Anniversary of UNEP (United Nations Environment Programme) (2nd issue). Multicoloured.
977 30s. Type **179** 1·25 70
978 90s. Globe encircled by human figures (Montreal Protocol on substances that deplete the ozone layer) 3·25 3·50
979 110s. Symbolic globe with green shoots, sun, wind farm and water tap (GREEN economy) 3·75 4·00

180 United Nations Energy-neutral Offices, Nairobi

2012. 40th Anniversary of UNEP (United Nations Environment Programme) (3rd issue). World Environment Day. Multicoloured.
980 30s. Type **180** 1·25 70
981 90s. Olkaria Geothermal Station 3·25 3·50
982 110s. Turkana Wind Farm 3·75 4·00

181 Prof. Wangari Muta Maathai (founder of Green Belt Movement)

2012. Professor Wangari Muta Maathai's Nobel Peace Prize, 2004.
983 **181** 30s. multicoloured 1·50 1·00

183 First Plane to Land in Kenya, 1920

2013. 50th Anniversary of Independence. Multicoloured.
993 30s. Type **183** 85 85
994 30s. Locomotive, 1904 85 85
995 30s. East Africa Railway and Harbour 85 85
996 30s. Jamhuri High School 85 85
997 30s. Prince of Wales School 85 85
998 30s. Machakos Girls School 85 85
999 30s. Royal Technical College, University of Nairobi 85 85
1000 30s. Kenyatta University 85 85
1001 30s. Jomo Kenyatta University of Agriculture and Technology 85 85
1002 30s. Nairobi City 85 85
1003 30s. King George VI Hospital 85 85
1004 30s. Kenyatta National Hospital 85 85
1005 30s. Jomo Kenyatta International Airport 85 85
1006 30s. Mobile Library 85 85
1007 30s. Kenya National Library, Nairobi 85 85
1008 30s. Horticulture 85 85
1009 30s. Poultry farming 85 85
1010 30s. Maize farming 85 85
1011 30s. Beef farming 85 85
1012 30s. Dairy farming 85 85
1013 30s. Compulsory Free Primary Education 85 85
1014 30s. Kenya National Adult Literacy Survey 85 85
1015 30s. Murang'a Road Junction 85 85
1016 30s. Globe Cinema Complex 85 85
1017 30s. Oil prospecting 85 85
1018 75s. President Ururu Kenyatta and Deputy President William Ruto 1·75 1·75
1019 75s. Queen Elizabeth II and Prince Philip (Coronation, 1953) 1·75 1·75
1020 75s. Lancaster House Conference 1·75 1·75
1021 75s. Dedan Kimathi 1·75 1·75
1022 75s. Mau Mau movement 1·75 1·75
1023 75s. The Kapenguria Six 1·75 1·75
1024 75s. The Kapenguria cells 1·75 1·75
1025 75s. The Lowering of the Union Jack 1·75 1·75
1026 75s. Munyao Lisoi hoisting of the Kenya Flag on Mt. Kenya, 1963 1·75 1·75
1027 75s. Promulgation of the New Constitution 1·75 1·75
1028 75s. First Transition 1·75 1·75
1029 75s. Second Transition 1·75 1·75
1030 75s. Third Transition 1·75 1·75
1031 75s. Fourth Transition 1·75 1·75
1032 75s. Parliament Building 1·75 1·75
1033 75s. First Cabinet, 1963 1·75 1·75
1034 75s. Colonial and current Coat of Arms 1·75 1·75
1035 75s. Colonial flag and Kenya national flag 1·75 1·75
1036 75s. Colonial provincial boundaries and modern county boundaries 1·75 1·75
1037 75s. The Judiciary 1·75 1·75
1038 75s. Kenyatta Mausoleum 1·75 1·75
1039 75s. Old Provincial Commissioner's Office, 1913 1·75 1·75
1040 75s. Nyayo House, Nairobi 1·75 1·75
1041 75s. First Governor of Nairobi Delamere 1·75 1·75
1042 75s. Kenya Defence Force in Somalia 1·75 1·75
1043 90s. Fort Jesus, built 1565 2·00 2·00
1044 90s. Kenya–Uganda Railway Line, 1896 2·00 2·00
1045 90s. Nyali Bridge, 1900 2·00 2·00
1046 90s. 13th-century Gedi ruins 2·00 2·00
1047 90s. First Post Office in Mombasa 2·00 2·00
1048 90s. First GPO in Mombasa, 1920 2·00 2·00
1049 90s. First GPO in Nairobi, 1944 2·00 2·00
1050 90s. Kenya National Archives, 1944 2·00 2·00
1051 90s. Macmillan Library, 1925 2·00 2·00
1052 90s. Nairobi National Museum, 1890 2·00 2·00
1053 90s. Mombasa coins, 1885 2·00 2·00
1054 90s. Maasai morans 2·00 2·00
1055 90s. Luo traditional homestead 2·00 2·00
1056 90s. Karen Blixen Museum 2·00 2·00
1057 90s. Kipande House, Nairobi, 1913 2·00 2·00
1058 90s. Laikipia Camel Caravan 2·00 2·00
1059 90s. East Africa and Uganda Protectorates 1912–21 5r. blue and dull purple stamp and 1963 65c. pyrethrum industry stamp from Independence set 2·00 2·00
1060 90s. Chuka Drummers 2·00 2·00
1061 90s. Obokono (musical instrument) 2·00 2·00
1062 90s. Vasco Da Gama Pillar, Malindi 2·00 2·00
1063 90s. Naftali Temu winning Olympic gold medal in men's 10000 metres, Mexico City, 1968 2·00 2·00
1064 90s. Athletes Pamela Jelimo and Janeth Jepkosgel with Kenyan flag 2·00 2·00
1065 90s. Ezekial Kemboi winning Olympic gold medal in 3000 metres steeplechase, Athens, 2004 2·00 2·00
1066 90s. David Rudisha winning Olympic gold medal in 800 metres, London, 2012 2·00 2·00
1067 90s. Kenya Rugby Union national team 2·00 2·00
1068 110s. Lion 3·50 3·50
1069 110s. Elephant 3·50 3·50
1070 110s. Leopard 3·50 3·50
1071 110s. Rhinoceros with calf 3·50 3·50
1072 110s. Buffalo 3·50 3·50
1073 110s. Hippopotamus 3·50 3·50
1074 110s. Cheetah 3·50 3·50
1075 110s. Giraffe 3·50 3·50
1076 110s. Zebra 3·50 3·50
1077 110s. Warthog 3·50 3·50
1078 110s. Wildebeest migration 3·50 3·50
1079 110s. Bongo 3·50 3·50
1080 110s. Impala 3·50 3·50
1081 110s. Hyena 3·50 3·50
1082 110s. Jackal 3·50 3·50
1083 110s. Crocodiles, River Tana 3·50 3·50
1084 110s. Flamingoes, Lake Nakuru 3·50 3·50
1085 110s. Two ostriches 3·50 3·50
1086 110s. Colobus Monkey 3·50 3·50
1087 110s. Falcon 3·50 3·50
1088 110s. Longonot Crater 3·50 3·50
1089 110s. Thompson Falls, Nyahururu 3·50 3·50
1090 110s. Mt. Kenya 3·50 3·50
1091 110s. Lake Turkana 3·50 3·50
1092 110s. Solar Eclipse 3·50 3·50
MS1093 110×105 mm. 30s.×4 East African coins, 1910–65; Kenya coins, 1966–2010; East African notes; Kenyan notes 7·50 7·50
MS1094 110×105 mm. 30s.×6 Mail runner, 1880; Postman delivering letters at a marketplace, 1902; Street posting box, 1920; Modern delivery van; Letter boxes; Modern posting box 10·00 10·00
MS1095 90×125 mm. 150s. Jomo Kenyatta (President 1963–75), Daniel Arap Moi (President 1978–2002), Mwai Kibaki (President 2002–13) and Uhuru Kenyatta (President 2013–). Imperf 5·00 5·00

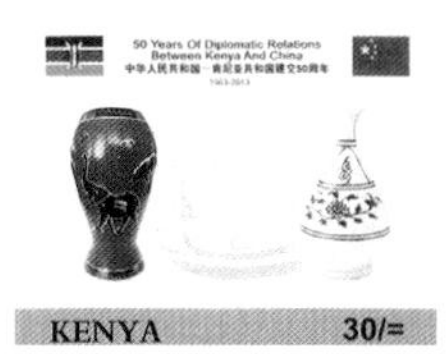

184 Kenyan and Chinese Flower Vases

2013. 50th Anniversary of Diplomatic Relations between Kenya and People's Republic of China. Multicoloured.
1096 30s. Type **184** 1·25 75
1097 110s. President Uhuru Kenyatta and Xi Jingping of China 3·00 3·00
MS1098 110×80 mm. 150s. As No. 1096 5·00 5·00

182 Red and Yellow Barbet (*Trachyphonus erythrocephalus*)

2013. Birds. Multicoloured.
984 30s. Type **182** 70 20
985 35s. Scarlet-chested Sunbird (*Nectarinia senegalensis*) 75 25
986 50s. Yellow-billed Hornbill (*Tockus flavirostris*) 1·25 75
987 55s. Greater Honeyguide (*Indicator indicator*) 1·40 1·00
988 65s. Superb Starling (*Spreo superbus*) 1·75 1·40
989 70s. African Fish Eagle (*Haliaeetus vocifer*) 1·75 1·75
990 80s. Lesser Flamingo (*Phoeniconaias minor*) 1·90 1·90
991 100s. Hadada Ibis (*Bostrychia hagedash*) 2·25 2·25
992 110s. Ross's Turaco (*Musophaga rossae*) 2·50 2·50

Nos. 984/992 have three punched holes at lower left.

185 Don Bosco

2015. Birth Bicentenary of Don Bosco (St John Bosco). Multicoloured.
1099 35s. Type **185** 1·00 70
MS1100 135×84 mm. 100s. Painting of Don Bosco with boys and shepherd with sheep (70×30 mm) 2·00 2·00

186 Emblem

2015. 70th Anniversary of United Nations.
1101 **186** 35s. multicoloured 1·00 70

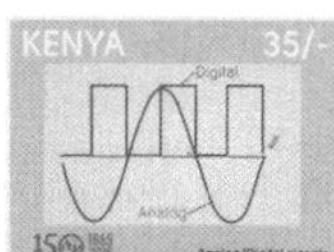

187 Analog and Digital Signals

2015. 150th Anniversary of ITU (International Telecommunications Union). Multicoloured.
1102 35s. Type **187** 75 25
1103 90s. Terrestrial Services 1·75 1·40
1104 105s. Anniversary logo 2·00 2·00
1105 130s. Satellite (Space services) 2·50 3·00

188 Elephant

2017. The Big Five. Multicoloured.
1106 35s. Type **188** 75 25
1107 80s. Lion (horiz) 1·60 1·25
1108 90s. Buffalo (horiz) 1·75 1·40
1109 105s. Leopard (horiz) 2·00 2·00
1110 130s. Rhinoceros 2·50 3·00
MS1111 110×80 mm. 175s. Lion, buffalo, elephant, leopard and rhinoceros. Imperf 3·50 4·00

189 Mombasa Terminus

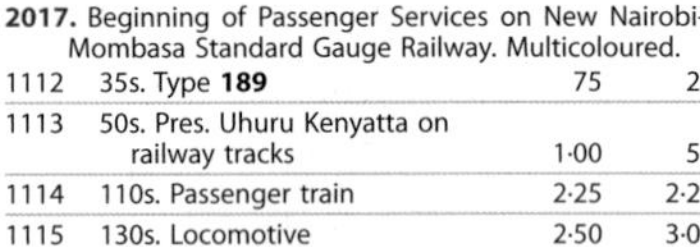

2017. Beginning of Passenger Services on New Nairobi--Mombasa Standard Gauge Railway. Multicoloured.

1112	35s. Type **189**	75	25
1113	50s. Pres. Uhuru Kenyatta on railway tracks	1·00	50
1114	110s. Passenger train	2·25	2·25
1115	130s. Locomotive	2·50	3·00
1116	150s. Nairobi Terminus	3·00	3·50
MS1117	140×101 mm. 200s. As No. 1113	4·00	3·50

190 Sun ('7 AFFORDABLE AND CLEAN ENERGY')

2017. United Nations 17 Sustainable Development Goals. Multicoloured.

1118	50s. Type **190**	1·00	50
1119	90s. Fish ('14 LIFE BELOW WATER')	1·75	1·40
1120	105s. Globe emblem ('13 CLIMATE ACTION')	2·00	2·00
1121	130s. Tree ('15 LIFE ON LAND')	2·50	3·00

191 US Pres. Barack Obama and Kenyan Pres. Uhuru Kenyatta, July 2015

2017. Pres. Barack Obama's State Visit to Kenya, July 2015

1122	**191**	50s. multicoloured	1·00	50

OFFICIAL STAMPS

Intended for use on official correspondence of the Kenya Government only, but there is no evidence that they were so used.

1964. Stamps of 1963 optd **OFFICIAL**.

O21	**1**	5c. multicoloured	10
O22	-	10c. brown	10
O23	-	15c. mauve	1·25
O24	-	20c. black and green	20
O25	-	30c. black and yellow	30
O26	-	50c. red, black and green	2·75

POSTAGE DUE STAMPS

D3

1967

D13	**D3**	5c. red	15	2·75
D41	**D3**	10c. green	40	1·75
D42	**D3**	20c. blue	40	1·75
D44	**D3**	30c. brown	1·00	2·00
D45	**D3**	40c. purple	1·00	2·00
D46	**D3**	80c. red	1·50	2·25
D49	**D3**	50c. green	10	10
D50	**D3**	1s. orange	10	10
D51	**D3**	2s. violet	10	10
D52	**D3**	3s. blue	10	10
D53	**D3**	5s. red	10	10

KENYA, UGANDA AND TANGANYIKA (TANZANIA)

From 1903 joint issues were made for British East Africa (later Kenya) and Uganda. In 1933 the postal administrations of Kenya, Uganda and Tanganyika were combined.

On independence of the constituent territories in the 1960s the postal administration became the East African Posts and Telecommunications Corporation. As well as separate issues for each state (q.v.), joint commemorative issues (which however were not valid in Zanzibar) were made until the dissolution of the Corporation in 1977.

1903. 16 annas = 100 cents = 1 rupee.
1922. 100 cents = 1 shilling.

1

2

1903

17	**1**	½a. green	8·50	3·00
2	**1**	1a. grey and red	2·75	2·00
19a	**1**	2a. purple	3·50	2·75
21	**1**	2½a. blue	7·50	17·00
22a	**1**	3a. purple and green	6·00	48·00
23	**1**	4a. green and black	7·50	18·00
24	**1**	5a. grey and brown	8·00	15·00
25	**1**	8a. grey and blue	7·00	8·50
9	**2**	1r. green	27·00	65·00
27	**2**	2r. purple	55·00	75·00
28	**2**	3r. green and black	£100	£150
29	**2**	4r. grey and green	£130	£200
30	**2**	5r. grey and red	£170	£225
31	**2**	10r. grey and blue	£375	£425
15	**2**	20r. grey and stone	£800	£1900
16	**2**	50r. grey and brown	£2500	£4500

1907

34	**1**	1c. brown	2·50	15
35	**1**	3c. green	21·00	70
36	**1**	6c. red	3·00	10
37	**1**	10c. lilac and olive	13·00	8·50
38	**1**	12c. purple	10·00	2·75
39	**1**	15c. blue	32·00	8·50
40	**1**	25c. green and black	25·00	7·00
41	**1**	50c. green and brown	19·00	17·00
42	**1**	75c. grey and blue	4·75	45·00

1912. As T **1/2** but portraits of King George V.

44	1c. black	30	1·75
45	3c. green	2·00	60
46	6c. red	1·25	40
47	10c. orange	2·00	50
48	12c. grey	2·75	50
49	15c. blue	2·75	80
50	25c. black and red on yellow	50	1·25
51	50c. black and lilac	1·50	1·75
52b	75c. black and green	11·00	7·50
53	1r. black and green	2·75	4·25
54	2r. red and black on blue	26·00	45·00
55	3r. violet and green	32·00	£130
56	4r. red and green on yellow	60·00	£110
57	5r. blue and purple	65·00	£160
58	10r. red and green on green	£250	£350
59	20r. black and purple on red	£475	£450
60	20r. purple and blue on blue	£550	£850
61	50r. red and green	£900	£950
62	100r. purple and black on red	£9500	£3750
63	500r. green and red on green	£40000	

1919. No. 46 surch **4 cents**.

64	4c. on 6c. red	1·25	15

6

7

1922

76	**6**	1c. brown	1·00	4·76
77	**6**	5c. violet	7·50	75
78	**6**	5c. green	2·00	30
79	**6**	10c. green	1·50	30
80	**6**	10c. black	4·00	20
81*a*	**6**	12c. black	15·00	26·00
82	**6**	15c. red	1·25	10
83	**6**	20c. orange	3·25	10
84	**6**	30c. blue	4·25	50
85	**6**	50c. grey	2·50	10
86	**6**	75c. olive	11·00	9·00
87	**7**	1s. green	7·00	2·50
88	**7**	2s. purple	9·00	21·00
89	**7**	2s.50 brown	19·00	£120
90	**7**	3s. grey	19·00	6·50
91	**7**	4s. grey	42·00	£130
92	**7**	5s. red	24·00	22·00
93	**7**	7s.50 orange	£130	£350
94	**7**	10s. blue	80·00	75·00
95	**7**	£1 black and orange	£225	£325
96	**7**	£2 green and purple	£1100	£2000
97	**7**	£3 purple and yellow	£1800	
98	**7**	£4 black and mauve	£3000	
99	**7**	£5 black and blue	£3250	
100	**7**	£10 black and green	£14000	
101	**7**	£20 red and green	£29000	
102	**7**	£25 black and red	£38000	
103	**7**	£50 black and brown	£50000	
104	**7**	£75 purple and grey	£150000	
105	**7**	£100 red and black	£160000	

8 South African Crowned Cranes

9 Dhow on Lake Victoria

1935. King George V.

110	**8**	1c. black and brown	1·00	1·50
111	**9**	5c. black and green	4·00	20
112	-	10c. black and yellow	7·50	60
113	-	15c. black and red	4·50	10
114	**8**	20c. black and orange	3·50	20
115	-	30c. black and blue	5·00	1·00
116	**9**	50c. purple and black	7·00	10
117	-	65c. black and brown	9·00	2·00
118	-	1s. black and green	5·50	1·50
119	-	2s. red and purple	12·00	4·50
120	-	3s. blue and black	20·00	15·00
121	-	5s. black and red	25·00	27·00
122	**8**	10s. purple and blue	£100	£130
123	-	£1 black and red	£325	£425

Designs: Vert—10c., £1 Lion; 30c., 5s. Nile Railway Bridge, Ripon Falls. Horiz—15c., 2s. Kilimanjaro; 65c. Mt. Kenya; 1s., 3s. Lake Naivasha.

14a Windsor Castle

1935. Silver Jubilee.

124	**14a**	20c. blue and olive	2·75	10
125	**14a**	30c. brown and blue	3·50	3·00
126	**14a**	65c. green and blue	2·00	3·00
127	**14a**	1s. grey and purple	2·25	5·50

14b King George VI and Queen Elizabeth

1937. Coronation.

128	**14b**	5c. green	20	10
129	**14b**	20c. orange	40	30
130	**14b**	30c. blue	60	1·75

15 Dhow on Lake Victoria

1938. As 1935 (except 10c.) but with portrait of King George VI as in T **15**.

131a	**8**	1c. black and brown	30	50
132	**15**	5c. black and green	7·00	50
133	**15**	5c. brown and orange	2·75	8·50
134	-	10c. brown and orange	2·25	10
135	-	10c. black and green	30	2·00
136	-	10c. brown and grey	1·75	55
137a	-	15c. black and red	8·00	4·00
138	-	15c. black and green	3·00	6·00
139b	**8**	20c. black and orange	9·50	10
140	**15**	25c. black and red	2·25	2·25
141b	-	30c. black and blue	3·25	10
142	-	30c. purple and brown	1·75	40
143	**8**	40c. black and blue	2·25	4·25
144e	**15**	50c. purple and black	14·00	55
145*a*	-	1s. black and brown	23·00	30
146b	-	2s. red and purple	50·00	30
147ac	-	3s. blue and black	50·00	9·00
148b	-	5s. black and red	50·00	2·00
149b	**8**	10s. purple and blue	55·00	8·50
150a	-	£1 black and red	42·00	25·00

Design: Horiz—10c. Lake Naivasha.

1941. Stamps of South Africa surch **KENYA TANGANYIKA UGANDA** and value. Alternate stamps inscr in English or Afrikaans.

151	**7**	5c. on 1d. black and red	1·75	1·75
152	**12**	10c. on 3d. blue	6·00	9·00
153	**8**	20c. on 6d. green and red	4·00	3·50
154	-	70c. on 1s. brown and blue (No. 120)	22·00	5·00

Prices for Nos. 151/154 are for unused pairs and used singles.

1946. Victory. As T **59a** of Jamaica.

155	20c. orange	50	10
156	30c. blue	50	75

1948. Silver Wedding. As T **59b/59c** of Jamaica.

157	20c. orange	1·00	50
158	£1 red	50·00	70·00

1949. UPU. As T **59d/59g** of Jamaica.

159	20c. orange	15	10
160	30c. blue	1·75	2·25
161	50c. grey	45	1·00
162	1s. brown	50	60

1952. Visit of Queen Elizabeth II (as Princess) and Duke of Edinburgh. As Nos. 135 and 145ba but inscr 'ROYAL VISIT 1952'.

163	10c. black and green	30	1·50
164	1s. black and brown	1·75	2·75

1953. Coronation. As T **61a** of Jamaica.

165	20c. black and orange	30	10

1954. Royal Visit. As No. 171 but inscr 'ROYAL VISIT 1954'.

166	**18**	30c. black and blue	1·00	70

18 Owen Falls Dam

20 Royal Lodge, Sagana

21 Queen Elizabeth II

1954

167		5c. black and brown	1·75	50
168	-	10c. red	2·75	10
169a	-	15c. black and blue	1·75	1·25
170	-	20c. black and orange	2·00	10
171	**18**	30c. black and blue	1·50	10
172	-	40c. brown	1·50	1·00
173	-	50c. purple	3·50	10
174	-	65c. green and purple	2·75	1·50
175	-	1s. black and purple	3·75	10
176	-	1s.30 lilac and orange	18·00	10
177	-	2s. black and green	16·00	1·50
178	-	5s. black and orange	45·00	3·50
179	**20**	10s. black and blue	48·00	5·50
180	**21**	£1 red and black	19·00	22·00

Designs: Vert (Size as T **18**)—10, 50c. Giraffe; 20, 40c., 1s. Lion. Horiz—15c., 1s.30, 5s. Elephants; 65c., 2s. Mt. Kilimanjaro.

25 Map of E. Africa showing Lakes

1958. Centenary of Discovery of Lakes Tanganyika and Victoria by Burton and Speke.

181	**25**	40c. blue and green	1·00	40
182	**25**	1s.30 green and purple	1·00	1·60

26 Sisal

28 Mt. Kenya and Giant Plants

29 Queen Elizabeth II

1960

183	**26**	5c. blue	10	15
184	-	10c. green	10	10
185	-	15c. purple	30	10
186	-	20c. mauve	20	10
187	-	25c. green	3·25	1·25
188	-	30c. red	15	10
189	-	40c. blue	15	20
190	-	50c. violet	15	10
191	-	65c. olive	30	2·00
192	**28**	1s. violet and purple	2·50	10
193	-	1s.30 brown and red	7·00	15

194	-	2s. indigo and blue	10·00	40
195	-	2s.50 olive and turquoise	11·00	2·75
196	-	5s. red and purple	5·00	60
197	-	10s. myrtle and green	16·00	9·00
198	**29**	20s. blue and lake	30·00	30·00

Designs: As T **26**—10c. Cotton; 15c. Coffee; 20c. Blue wildebeest; 25c. Ostrich; 30c. Thomson's gazelle; 40c. Manta; 50c. Common zebra; 65c. Cheetah. As T **28**—1s.30, Murchison Falls and hippopotamus; 2s. Mt. Kilimanjaro and giraffe; 2s.50, Candelabra tree and black rhinoceros; 5s. Crater Lake and Mountains of the Moon; 10s. Ngorongoro Crater and African buffalo.

30 Land Tillage

1963. Freedom from Hunger.

199	**30**	15c. blue and olive	50	10
200	-	30c. brown and yellow	65	10
201	**30**	50c. blue and orange	85	10
202	-	1s.30 brown and blue	1·40	1·75

Design: 30c., 1s.30, African with corncob.

31 Scholars and Open Book

1963. Founding of East African University.

203	**31**	30c. multicoloured	10	10
204	**31**	1s.30 multicoloured	20	30

32 Red Cross Emblem

1963. Centenary of Red Cross.

205	**32**	30c. red and blue	1·75	30
206	**32**	50c. red and brown	2·25	1·25

35 East African 'Flags'

1964. Olympic Games, Tokyo.

207	-	30c. yellow and purple	15	10
208	-	50c. purple and yellow	20	10
209	**35**	1s.30 yellow, green and blue	50	10
210	**35**	2s.50 mauve, violet and blue	60	3·00

Design: Vert—30, 50c. Chrysanthemum emblem.

36 Rally Badge

1965. 13th East African Safari Rally.

211	**36**	30c. black, yellow & turq	10	10
212	**36**	50c. black, yellow and brown	10	10
213	-	1s.30 green, ochre and blue	35	10
214	-	2s.50 green, red and blue	60	3·00

Design: 1s.30, 2s.50, Cars en route.

38 ITU Emblem and Symbols

1965. Centenary of ITU. 'ITU' and symbols in gold.

215	**38**	30c. brown and mauve	30	10
216	**38**	50c. brown and grey	45	10
217	**38**	1s.30 brown and blue	1·00	10
218	**38**	2s.50 brown and turquoise	1·25	2·50

39 ICY Emblem

1965. International Co-operation Year.

219	**39**	30c. green and gold	20	10
220	**39**	50c. black and gold	25	10
221	**39**	1s.30 blue and gold	50	10
222	**39**	2s.50 red and gold	1·00	3·75

40 Game Park Lodge, Tanzania

1966. Tourism. Multicoloured.

223	30c. Type **40**	90	10
224	50c. Murchison Falls, Uganda	1·00	10
225	1s.30 Lesser flamingoes, Lake Nakuru, Kenya	3·25	30
226	2s.50 Deep sea fishing, Tanzania	2·00	2·25

41 Games Emblem

1966. Eighth British Empire and Commonwealth Games, Jamaica.

227	**41**	30c. multicoloured	10	10
228	**41**	50c. multicoloured	15	10
229	**41**	1s.30 multicoloured	20	10
230	**41**	2s.50 multicoloured	35	1·50

42 UNESCO Emblem

1966. 20th Anniversary of UNESCO.

231	**42**	30c. black, green and red	80	10
232	**42**	50c. black, green and brown	90	10
233	**42**	1s.30 black, green and grey	2·25	20
234	**42**	2s.50 black, green and yellow	2·75	6·50

43 de Havilland DH.89 Dragon Rapide

1967. 21st Anniversary of East African Airways.

235	**43**	30c. violet, blue and green	30	10
236	-	50c. multicoloured	40	10
237	-	1s.30 multicoloured	85	30
238	-	2s.50 multicoloured	1·25	3·00

Designs: 50c. Vickers Super VC-10; 1s.30, Hawker Siddeley Comet 4B; 2s.50, Fokker F.27 Friendship.

44 Pillar Tomb

1967. Archaeological Relics.

239	**44**	30c. ochre, black and purple	15	10
240	-	50c. red, black and brown	65	10
241	-	1s.30 black, yellow and green	85	15
242	-	2s.50 black, ochre and red	1·40	2·50

Designs: 50c. Rock painting; 1s.30, Clay head; 2s.50, Proconsul skull.

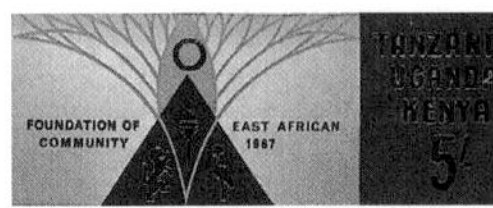

48 Unified Symbols of Kenya, Tanzania and Uganda

1967. Foundation of East African Community.

243	**48**	5s. gold, black and grey	40	1·50

49 Mountaineering

1968. Mountains of East Africa. Multicoloured.

244	30c. Type **49**	15	10
245	50c. Mt. Kenya	25	10
246	1s.30 Mt. Kilimanjaro	40	10
247	2s.50 Ruwenzori Mountains	60	2·25

50 Family and Rural Hospital

1968. World Health Organisation.

248	**50**	30c. green, lilac and brown	10	10
249	-	50c. slate, lilac and black	15	10
250	-	1s.30 brown, lilac and light brown	20	15
251	-	2s.50 grey, black and lilac	30	1·90

Designs: 50c. Family and nurse; 1s.30, Family and microscope; 2s.50, Family and hypodermic syringe.

51 Olympic Stadium, Mexico City

1968. Olympic Games, Mexico.

252	**51**	30c. green and black	10	10
253	-	50c. green and black	15	10
254	-	1s.30 red, black and grey	25	15
255	-	2s.50 sepia and brown	35	1·50

Designs: Horiz—50c. High-diving boards; 1s.30, Running tracks. Vert: 2s.50, Boxing ring.

52 *Umoja* (railway ferry)

1969. Water Transport.

256	**52**	30c. blue and grey	50	10
257	-	50c. multicoloured	60	10
258	-	1s.30 green and blue	1·00	20
259	-	2s.50 orange and blue	1·50	3·25

Designs: 50c. SS *Harambee*; 1s.30, MV *Victoria*; 2s.50, *St Michael*.

53 ILO Emblem and Agriculture

1969. 50th Anniversary of Int Labour Organisation.

260	**53**	30c. black, green and yellow	10	10
261	-	50c. multicoloured	10	10
262	-	1s.30 black, brown and orange	10	10
263	-	2s.50 black, blue & turq	20	90

Designs: ILO emblem and—50c. Building-work; 1s.30, Factory-workers; 2s.50, Shipping.

54 Pope Paul VI and Ruwenzori Mountains

1969. Visit of Pope Paul VI to Uganda.

264	**54**	30c. black, gold and blue	15	10
265	**54**	70c. black, gold and red	20	10
266	**54**	1s.50 black, gold and blue	25	20
267	**54**	2s.50 black, gold and violet	30	1·40

55 Euphorbia Tree shaped as Africa, and Emblem

1969. Fifth — of African Development Bank.

268	**55**	30c. green and gold	10	10
269	**55**	70c. green, gold and violet	15	10
270	**55**	1s.50 green, gold and blue	30	10
271	**55**	2s.50 green, gold and brown	35	2·00

56 Marimba

1970. Musical Instruments.

272	**56**	30c. buff and brown	15	10
273	-	70c. green, brown and yellow	25	10
274	-	1s.50 brown and yellow	40	10
275	-	2s.50 orange, yellow and brown	60	2·50

Designs: 70c. Amadinda; 1s.50, Nzomari; 2s.50, Adeudeu.

57 Satellite Earth Station

1970. Inauguration of Satellite Earth Station.

276	**57**	30c. multicoloured	10	10
277	-	70c. multicoloured	15	10
278	-	1s.50 black, violet & orge	30	10
279	-	2s.50 multicoloured	60	2·50

Designs: 70c. Transmitter daytime; 1s.50, Transmitter night; 2s. 50, Earth and satellite.

58 Athlete

1970. Ninth Commonwealth Games.

280	**58**	30c. brown and black	10	10
281	**58**	70c. green, brown and black	10	10
282	**58**	1s.50 lilac, brown and black	15	10
283	**58**	2s.50 blue, brown and black	20	1·25

59 '25' and UN Emblem

1970. 25th Anniversary of United Nations.

284	**59**	30c. multicoloured	10	10
285	**59**	70c. multicoloured	10	10
286	**59**	1s.50 multicoloured	20	10
287	**59**	2s.50 multicoloured	45	2·25

60 Balance and Weight Equivalents

1971. Conversion to Metric System. Multicoloured.

288	30c. Type **60**	10	10

289		70c. Fahrenheit and Centigrade thermometers	10	10
290		1s.50 Petrol pump and liquid capacities	15	10
291		2s.50 Surveyors and land measures	35	2·00

61 Class 11 Tank Locomotive

1971. Railway Transport. Multicoloured.

292		30c. Type **61**	15	10
293		70c. Class 90 diesel-electric locomotive	25	10
294		1s.50 Class 59 steam locomotive	50	20
295		2s.50 Class 30 steam locomotive	90	2·25
MS296		120×88 mm. Nos. 292/295	5·50	10·00

62 Syringe and Cow

1971. OAU Rinderpest Campaign.

297	**62**	30c. black, brown and green	10	10
298	-	70c. black, blue and brown	10	10
299	**62**	1s.50 black, purple & brn	15	10
300	-	2s.50 black, red and brown	25	70

Design: 70c., 2s.50, as T **62** but with bull facing right.

63 Livingstone meets Stanley

1971. Centenary of Livingstone and Stanley meeting at Ujiji.

301	**63**	5s. multicoloured	30	75

64 President Nyerere and Supporters

1971. Tenth Anniversary of Tanzanian Independence. Multicoloured.

302		30c. Type **64**	10	10
303		70c. Ujamaa village	15	10
304		1s.50 Dar es Salaam University	30	25
305		2s.50 Kilimanjaro International Airport	1·25	3·25

65 Flags and Trade Fair Emblem

1972. All-Africa Trade Fair.

306	**65**	30c. multicoloured	10	10
307	**65**	70c. multicoloured	10	10
308	**65**	1s.50 multicoloured	20	10
309	**65**	2s.50 multicoloured	30	80

66 Child with Cup

1972. 25th Anniversary of UNICEF. Multicoloured.

310		30c. Type **66**	10	10
311		70c. Children with ball	10	10
312		1s.50 Child at blackboard	10	10
313		2s.50 Child and tractor	25	80

67 Hurdling

1972. Olympic Games, Munich. Multicoloured.

314		40c. Type **67**	10	10
315		70c. Running	10	10
316		1s.50 Boxing	20	15
317		2s.50 Hockey	45	1·75
MS318		131×98 mm. Nos. 314/317	3·75	7·00

68 Ugandan Kobs

1972. Tenth Anniversary of Ugandan Independence. Multicoloured.

319		40c. Type **68**	30	10
320		70c. Conference Centre	30	10
321		1s.50 Makerere University	65	30
322		2s.50 Coat of Arms	1·00	3·50
MS323		132×120 mm. Nos. 319/322	3·50	3·50

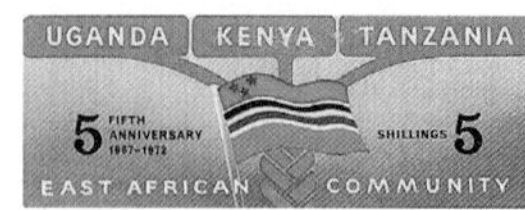

69 Community Flag

1972. Fifth Anniversary of East African Community.

324	**69**	5s. multicoloured	55	1·90

70 Run-of-the-wind Anemometer

1972. Centenary of IMO/WMO. Multicoloured.

325		40c. Type **70**	10	10
326		70c. Weather balloon (vert)	20	10
327		1s.50 Meteorological rocket	30	15
328		2s.50 Satellite receiving aerial	55	2·25

71 Learning by Serving

1973. 24th World Scouting Conference, Nairobi.

329	**71**	40c. multicoloured	10	10
330	-	70c. red, violet and black	15	10
331	-	1s.50 blue, violet and black	30	10
332	-	2s.50 multicoloured	60	1·50

Designs: 70c. Baden-Powell's grave, Nyeri; 1s.50, World Scout emblem; 2s.50, Lord Baden-Powell.

72 Kenyatta Conference Centre

1973. IMF/World Bank Conference.

333	**72**	40c. green, grey and black	10	10
334	-	70c. brown, grey and black	10	10
335	-	1s.50 multicoloured	25	35
336	-	2s.50 orange, grey and black	35	1·75
MS337		166×141 mm. Nos. 333/6. Imperf	1·40	4·75

Designs: Nos. 334/336 show different arrangements of Bank emblems and the Conference Centre, the 1s.50 being vertical.

73 Police Dog-handler

1973. 50th Anniversary of Interpol.

338	**73**	40c. yellow, blue and black	55	15
339	-	70c. green, yellow and black	90	15
340	-	1s.50 violet, yellow and black	1·50	90
341	-	2s.50 green, orange and black	3·75	7·00
342	-	2s.50 green, orange and black	3·75	7·00

Designs: 70c. East African policemen; 1s.50, Interpol emblem; 2s.50 (2), Interpol H.Q.

No. 341 is inscribed 'St Clans' and 342 'St Cloud'.

74 Tea Factory

1973. Tenth Anniversary of Kenya's Independence. Multicoloured.

343		40c. Type **74**	10	10
344		70c. Kenyatta Hospital	20	10
345		1s.50 Nairobi Airport	65	20
346		2s.50 Kindaruma hydro-electric scheme	70	2·25

75 Party HQ

1973. Tenth Anniversary of Zanzibar's Revolution. Multicoloured.

347		40c. Type **75**	10	10
348		70c. Housing scheme	15	10
349		1s.50 Colour TV	35	35
350		2s.50 Amaan Stadium	70	3·25

76 Symbol of Union

1974. Tenth Anniversary of Tanganyika–Zanzibar Union. Multicoloured.

351		40c. Type **76**	10	10
352		70c. Handclasp and map	15	10
353		1s.50 Communications	35	30
354		2s.50 Flags of Tanu, Tanzania and Afro-Shirazi Party	70	3·00

77 East African Family (Stability of the Home)

1974. 17th Social Welfare Conference, Nairobi.

355	**77**	40c. yellow, brown and black	10	10
356	-	70c. multicoloured	10	10
357	-	1s.50 yellow, green and black	20	30
358	-	2s.50 red, violet and black	1·00	2·00

Designs: 70c. Dawn and drummer (UN Second Development Plan); 1s.50, Agricultural scene (Rural Development Plan); 2s.50, Transport and telephone (Communications).

78 New Postal HQ, Kampala

1974. Centenary of UPU. Multicoloured.

359		40c. Type **78**	10	10
360		70c. Mail-train and post-van	20	10
361		1s.50 UPU Building, Berne	15	20
362		2s.50 Loading mail into Vickers Super VC-10	55	1·50

79 Family-planning Clinic

1974. World Population Year.

363	**79**	40c. multicoloured	10	10
364	-	70c. mauve and red	10	10
365	-	1s.50 multicoloured	15	20
366	-	2s.50 blue, emerald and green	30	1·90

Designs: 70c. Tug of War; 1s.50, Population scales; 2s.50, WPY emblem.

80 Seronera Wildlife Lodge, Tanzania

1975. East African Game Lodges. Multicoloured.

367		40c. Type **80**	15	10
368		70c. Mweya Safari Lodge, Uganda	20	10
369		1s.50 'Ark' Aberdare Forest Lodge, Kenya	35	35
370		2s.50 Paraa Safari Lodge, Uganda	60	2·50

81 Kitana (wooden comb), Bajun of Kenya

1975. African Arts. Multicoloured.

371		50c. Type **81**	10	10
372		1s. Earring, Chaga of Tanzania	15	10
373		2s. Okoco (armlet), Acholi of Uganda	35	75
374		3s. Kitete, Kamba gourd, Kenya	85	1·75

82 International Airport, Entebbe

1975. OAU Summit Conference, Kampala. Multicoloured.

375		50c. Type **82**	30	10
376		1s. Map of Africa and flag (vert)	30	10
377		2s. Nile Hotel, Kampala	30	90
378		3s. Martyrs' Shrine, Namugongo (vert)	40	1·90

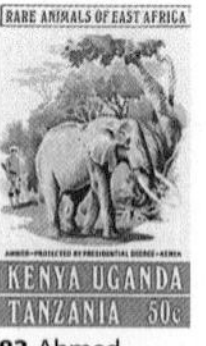

83 Ahmed (Presidential Elephant)

1975. Rare Animals. Multicoloured.

379		50c. Type **83**	40	10
380		1s. Albino buffalo	40	10
381		2s. Ahmed in grounds of National Museum	1·25	1·50
382		3s. Abbott's duiker	1·25	3·00

84 Maasai Manyatta (village), Kenya

1975. Second World Black and African Festival of Arts and Culture, Nigeria (1977). Multicoloured.

383		50c. Type **84**	15	10
384		1s. Heartbeat of Africa (Ugandan Dancers)	15	10
385		2s. Makonde sculpture, Tanzania	50	85
386		3s. Early Man and Technology (skinning animal)	75	1·40

85 Fokker F.27 Friendship at Nairobi Airport

1975. 30th Anniversary of East African Airways. Multicoloured.

387	50c. Type **85**	1·00	30
388	1s. Douglas DC-9 at Kilimanjaro Airport	1·10	30
389	2s. Vickers Super VC-10 at Entebbe Airport	3·50	3·50
390	3s. East African Airways crest	3·75	4·25

Further commemorative sets were released during 1976–1978 using common designs, but each inscribed for one republic only. See Kenya, Tanzania and Uganda.

Co-operation between the postal services of the three member countries virtually ceased after 30 June 1977. The postal services of Kenya, Uganda and Uganda then operated independently.

OFFICIAL STAMPS

For use on official correspondence of the Tanganyika Government only.

1959. Stamps of 1954 optd **OFFICIAL**.

O1	**18**	5c. black and brown	10	1·25
O2	-	10c. red	30	1·25
O3	-	15c. black and blue	75	1·25
O4	-	20c. black and orange	20	20
O5	**18**	30c. black and blue	15	80
O6	-	50c. purple	1·75	20
O7	-	1s. black and red	20	75
O8	-	1s.30 orange and lilac	10·00	3·00
O9	-	2s. black and green	1·25	1·00
O10	-	5s. black and orange	14·00	4·00
O11	**20**	10s. black and blue	3·25	7·50
O12	**21**	£1 red and black	7·00	25·00

1960. Stamps of 1960 optd **OFFICIAL**.

O13	**26**	5c. blue	10	3·75
O14	-	10c. green	10	3·00
O15	-	15c. purple	10	3·75
O16	-	20c. mauve	10	75
O17	-	30c. red	10	10
O18	-	50c. violet	30	1·00
O19	**28**	1s. violet and purple	30	10
O20	-	5s. red and purple	22·00	65

POSTAGE DUE STAMPS

D1

1923

D1	**D1**	5c. violet	2·50	1·00
D2	**D1**	10c. red	2·50	15
D3	**D1**	20c. green	4·00	4·25
D4	**D1**	30c. brown	28·00	19·00
D5	**D1**	40c. blue	6·50	14·00
D6	**D1**	1s. green	70·00	£140

D2

1935

D7	**D2**	5c. violet	2·75	1·75
D8	**D2**	10c. red	30	50
D9	**D2**	20c. green	40	50
D10	**D2**	30c. brown	1·50	50
D11	**D2**	40c. blue	1·50	3·00
D12	**D2**	1s. grey	19·00	19·00

KHMER REPUBLIC

Cambodia was renamed Khmer Republic on 9 October 1970.

Following the fall of the Khmer Republic, the People's Republic of Kampuchea was proclaimed on 10 January 1979.

100 cents = 1 riel.

78 'Attack'

1971. Defence of Khmer Territory.

285	**78**	1r. multicoloured	70	60
286	**78**	3r. multicoloured	1·00	80
287	**78**	10r. multicoloured	2·50	1·20

79 World Races and UN Emblem

1971. Racial Equality Year.

288	**79**	3r. multicoloured	45	25
289	**79**	7r. multicoloured	70	45
290	**79**	8r. multicoloured	1·20	70

80 General Post Office, Phnom Penh

1971

291	**80**	3r. multicoloured	25	10
292	**80**	9r. multicoloured	80	60
293	**80**	10r. multicoloured	1·00	70

81 Global Emblem

1971. World Telecommunications Day.

294	**81**	3r. multicoloured	35	20
295	**81**	4r. multicoloured	45	25
296	-	7r. multicoloured	55	30
297	-	8r. red, black and orange	70	35

Design: 7, 8r. ITU emblem.

82 Indian Coral Bean

1971. Wild Flowers. Multicoloured.

298	2r. Type **82**	60	55
299	3r. Orchid tree	75	65
300	6r. Flame-of-the-forest	1·60	1·30
301	10r. Malayan crape myrtle (vert)	2·00	1·60

83 Arms of the Republic

84 Monument and Flag

1971. First Anniversary of Republic.

302	**83**	3r. bistre and green	35	10
303	**84**	3r. multicoloured	45	20
304	**84**	4r. multicoloured	50	25
305	**83**	8r. bistre and orange	55	30
306	**83**	10r. bistre and brown	80	35
307	**84**	10r. multicoloured	90	45
MS308		Two sheets, each 130×100 mm. (a) Nos. 302 and 305/306 (sold for 25r.); (b) Nos. 303/304 and 307 (sold for 20r.)	8·00	7·00

85 UNICEF Emblem

1971. 25th Anniversary of UNICEF.

309	**85**	3r. purple	45	25
310	**85**	5r. blue	55	45
311	**85**	9r. red and violet	1·10	70

86 Book Year Emblem

1972. International Book Year.

312	**86**	3r. green, purple and blue	45	25
313	**86**	8r. blue, green and purple	70	45
314	**86**	9r. bistre, blue and green	1·10	70
MS315		160×100 mm. Nos. 312/314 (sold at 25r.)	3·50	3·25

87 Lion of St Mark's

1972. UNESCO Save Venice Campaign.

316	**87**	3r. brown, buff and purple	55	25
317	-	5r. brown, buff and green	1·00	45
318	-	10r. brown, blue and green	1·50	70
MS319		160×100 mm. Nos. 316/18 (sold at 23r.)	5·00	4·75

Designs: Horiz—5r. St Mark's Basilica. Vert—10r. Bridge of Sighs.

88 UN Emblem

1972. 25th Anniversary of Economic Commission for Asia and the Far East (CEAEO).

320	**88**	3r. red	45	25
321	**88**	6r. blue	70	45
322	**88**	9r. red	1·00	70
MS323		141×101 mm. Nos. 320/323 (sold at 23r.)	3·25	3·00

89 Dancing Apsaras (relief), Angkor

1972

324	**89**	1r. brown	35	20
325	**89**	3r. violet	40	20
326	**89**	7r. purple	55	25
327	**89**	8r. brown	70	30
328	**89**	9r. green	80	35
329	**89**	10r. blue	1·20	40
330	**89**	12r. purple	1·60	45
331	**89**	14r. blue	2·00	60

90 'UIT' on TV Screen

1972. World Telecommunications Day.

332	**90**	3r. black, blue and yellow	45	25
333	**90**	9r. black, blue and mauve	85	45
334	**90**	14r. black, blue and brown	1·20	70

91 Conference Emblem

1972. United Nations Environmental Conservation Conference, Stockholm.

335	**91**	3r. green, brown and violet	55	25
336	**91**	12r. violet and green	80	45
337	**91**	15r. green and violet	1·10	70
MS338		131×100 mm. Nos. 335/337 (sold at 35r.)	4·50	4·00

92 Javan Rhinoceros

1972. Wild Animals.

339	**92**	3r. black, red and violet	70	30
340	-	4r. violet, bistre and purple	80	35
341	-	6r. brown, green and blue	1·60	60
342	-	7r. ochre, green and brown	2·30	70
343	-	8r. black, green and blue	2·75	80
344	-	10r. black, blue and green	3·75	1·20

Designs: 4r. Mainland serow; 6r. Thamin; 7r. Banteng; 8r. Water buffalo; 10r. Gaur.

1972. Olympic Games, Munich. Nos. 164 of Cambodia and 302, 306 and 336/337 of Khmer Republic optd **XXe JEUX OLYMPIQUES MUNICH 1972**, Olympic rings and emblem.

345	**83**	3r. bistre and green	90	45
346	**83**	10r. bistre and brown	1·70	95
347	-	12r. green and brown	2·00	1·20
348	**91**	12r. violet and green	2·10	1·30
349	**91**	15r. green and violet	2·40	1·50

94 Hoisting Flag

1972. Second Anniversary of Republic.

350	**94**	3r. multicoloured	35	25
351	**94**	5r. multicoloured	55	35
352	**94**	9r. multicoloured	1·10	70

1972. Red Cross Aid for War Victims. No. 164 of Cambodia and 302, 306 and 336/337 of Khmer Republic surch **SECOURS AUX VICTIMES DE GUERRE**, red cross and value.

353	**83**	3r.+2r. bistre and green	45	35
354	**83**	10r.+6r. bistre and brown	1·00	95
355	-	12r.+7r. green and brown	1·10	1·10
356	**91**	12r.+7r. violet and green	1·10	1·10
357	**91**	15r.+8r. green and violet	1·90	1·90

96 Garuda

1973. Air.

358	**96**	3r. red	40	25
359	**96**	30r. blue	2·50	1·40
360	**96**	50r. lilac	4·50	2·50
361	**96**	100r. green	6·25	4·00

97 Crest and Temple

1973. New Constitution.

362	**97**	3r. multicoloured	40	10
363	**97**	12r. multicoloured	45	20
364	**97**	14r. multicoloured	70	60
MS365		130×100 mm. Nos. 362/364 (sold at 34r.)	3·50	3·25

98 Apsara

1973. Angkor Sculptures.

366	**98**	3r. black	70	30
367	-	8r. blue	1·10	45
368	-	10r. brown	1·70	70
MS369		130×100 mm. Nos. 366/368 (sold at 25r.)	3·50	3·25

Designs: 8r. Devata (12th-century); 10f. Devata (10th-century).

99 Interpol Emblem

1973. 50th Anniversary of International Criminal Police Organisation (Interpol).

370	**99**	3r. green and turquoise	50	25
371	**99**	7r. green and red	60	45
372	**99**	10r. green and brown	85	70
MS373		130×100 mm. Nos. 370/372 (sold at 30r.)	4·50	4·25

100 Marshal Lon Nol

1973. Honouring Marshal Lon Nol, First President of Republic.

374	**100**	3r. black, brown and green	45	25
375	**100**	8r. black, brown and green	70	35
376	**100**	14r. black, brown and agate	1·10	45
MS377		130×100 mm. Nos. 374/376 but background colours changed (sold at 50r.)	6·75	6·50

102 Copernicus and Space Rocket

1974. 500th Birth Anniversary of Nicolas Copernicus (astronomer). Multicoloured.

382	1r. Type **102** (postage)	45	35
383	5r. Copernicus and *Mariner II*	55	40
384	10r. Copernicus and Apollo command module	90	45
385	25r. Copernicus and *Telstar*	2·00	95
386	50r. Copernicus and space-walker	4·00	1·80
387	100r. Copernicus and spaceship landing on Moon	8·50	4·50
388	150r. Copernicus and Moon-landing craft leaving Apollo command module	12·50	7·00
389	200r. Copernicus and *Skylab III* (air)	16·00	8·25
390	250r. Copernicus and Concorde	25·00	13·00

1974. Fourth Anniversary of Republic. Various stamps optd **4E ANNIVERSAIRE DE LA REPUBLIQUE.**

391	**78**	10r. multicoloured	3·50	1·20
392	**77**	50r. on 3r. multicoloured	8·00	3·00
393	**94**	100r. on 5r. multicoloured	16·00	7·50

No. 392 is additionally optd **REPUBLIQUE KHMERE** in French and Cambodian.

104 Xylophone

1975. Unissued stamps of Cambodia showing musical instruments, surch **REPUBLIQUE KHMERE** in French and Cambodian and new value. Multicoloured.

394	5r. on 8r. Type **104**		
395	20r. on 1r. So (two-stringed violin)		
396	160r. on 7r. Khoung vong (bronze gongs)		
397	180r. on 14r. Two drums		
398	235r. on 12r. Barrel-shaped drum		
399	500r. on 9r. Xylophone (different)		
400	1000r. on 10r. Boat-shaped xylophone		
401	2000r. on 3r. Twenty-stringed guitar on legs		

POSTAGE DUE STAMPS

D101 Frieze, Angkor Vat

1974

D378	**D101**	2r. brown	40	35
D379	**D101**	6r. green	50	45
D380	**D101**	8r. red	80	70
D381	**D101**	10r. blue	1·20	1·10

APPENDIX

The following stamps have either been issued in excess of postal needs or have not been available to the public in reasonable quantities at face value. Such stamps may later be given full listing if there is evidence of regular postal use.

1972

Moon Landing of *Apollo 16*. Embossed on gold foil. Air 900r.×2.
Visit of President Nixon to China. Embossed on gold foil. Air 900r.×2.
Olympic Games, Munich. Embossed on gold foil. Air 900r.×2.

1973

Gold Medal Winners, Munich Olympics. Embossed on gold foil. Air 900r.×2.
World Cup Football Championship, West Germany (1974). Embossed on gold foil. Air 900r.×4.

1974

President Kennedy and *Apollo 11*. Embossed on gold foil. Air 1100r.×2.
500th Birth Anniversary of Nicolas Copernicus (astronomer). Embossed on gold foil. Air 1200r.
Centenary of UPU (1st issue). Postage 10, 60r.; Air 700; 1200r. embossed on gold foil.

1975

Olympic Games, Montreal (1976). Postage 5, 10, 15, 25r.; Air 50, 100, 150, 200, 250r.; 1200r. embossed on gold foil.
World Cup Football Championship, West Germany (1974). Postage 1, 5, 10, 25r.; Air 50, 100, 150, 200, 250, 1200r. embossed on gold foil.
Centenary of UPU (2nd issue). Postage 15, 20, 70, 160, 180, 235r.; Air 500, 1000, 2000, 2000r. embossed on gold foil.

KHOR FAKKAN

From 1965 various issues were produced for this dependency, some being overprinted on, or in the same designs as, issues for Sharjah.

APPENDIX

The following stamps have either been issued in excess of postal needs or have not been available to the public in reasonable quantities at face value. Such stamps may later be given full listing if there is evidence of regular postal use.

1965

Views. Nos. 75/80 of Sharjah optd. Air 10, 20, 30, 40, 75, 100n.p.
Boy and Girl Scouts. Nos. 74 and 89 of Sharjah optd. 2, 2r.
Birds. Nos. 101/6 of Sharjah optd. Air 30, 40, 75, 150n.p., 2, 3r.
Olympic Games, Tokyo 1964. Nos. 95/97 of Sharjah optd. 40, 50n.p., 2r.
New York World's Fair. Nos. 81/83 of Sharjah optd. Air 20, 40n.p., 1r.
President Kennedy Commemoration Nos. 98/100 of Sharjah optd. Air 40, 60, 100n.p.
Centenary of ITU Postage 1, 2, 3, 4, 5, 50n.p., 1r., 120n.p.
Pan-Arab Games, Cairo. 50p.×5.

1966

International Co-operation Year. 50n.p.×8.
Churchill Commemoration. 2, 3, 4, 5r.
Roses. 20, 35, 60, 80n.p., 1r., 125n.p.
Fish. 1, 2, 3, 4, 5, 15, 20, 30, 40, 50, 75n.p., 1, 2, 3, 4, 5, 10r.
International Stamp Exhibition, Washington DC (SIPEX). 80, 120n.p., 2r.

New Currency Surcharges in Rials and Piastres.
(a) 1965 ITU Centenary issue. 10p. on 50n.p., 16p. on 120n.p., 1r. on 1r.
(b) Churchill issue. 1r. on 2r., 2r. on 3r., 3r. on 4r., 4r. on 5r.
(c) Roses issue. 1p. on 20n.p., 2p. on 35n.p., 4p. on 60n.p., 6p. on 80n.p., 10p. on 125n.p., 12p. on 1r.

New Currency Surcharges in Dirhams and Riyals.
(a) 1965 Pan-Arab Games issue. 20d. on 50p.×5.
(b) Fish issue. 1d. on 1n.p., 2d. on 2n.p., 3d. on 3n.p., 4d. on 4n.p., 5d. on 5n.p., 15d. on 15n.p., 20d. on 20n.p., 30d. on 30n.p., 40d. on 40n.p., 50d. on 50n.p., 75d. on 75n.p., 1r. on 1r., 2r. on 2r., 3r. on 3r., 4r. on 4r., 5r. on 5r., 10r. on 10r.
Third Death Anniversary of President J. Kennedy. Optd on International Stamp Exhibition, Washington issue. 80d. on 80n.p., 120d. on 120n.p., 2r. on 2r.
World Football Cup Championship, England. ½r.×7.

1967

Fourth Death Anniversary of President J. Kennedy. Optd on 1966 International Stamp Exhibition issue. 80d. on 80n.p., 120d. on 120n.p., 2r. on 2r.

1968

Famous Paintings. Optd on Sharjah. Postage 1, 2, 3, 4, 5, 30, 40, 60, 75d.; Air 1, 2, 3, 4, 5r.
Winter Olympic Games, Grenoble. Optd on Sharjah. Postage 1, 2, 3, 4, 5d.; Air 1, 2, 3r.
Previous Olympic Games. Optd on Sharjah. Air 25, 50, 75d., 1r.50, 3, 4r.
Olympic Games, Mexico. Optd on Sharjah. 10, 20, 30d., 2, 2r.40, 5r.

1969

12th World Jamboree. Optd on 1968 issue of Sharjah. Postage 1, 2, 3, 4, 5, 10d.; Air 30, 50, 60d., 1r.50.
Martyrs of Liberty. Optd on 1968 issue of Sharjah. Air 35d.×4, 60d.×4, 1r.×4
Sportsmen and Women. Optd on 1968 issue of Sharjah. Postage 20, 30, 40, 60d., 1r.50, 2r.50; Air 35, 50d., 1, 2, 3r.25, 4, 4r.

A number of issues on gold or silver foil also exist, but it is understood that these were mainly for presentation purposes, although valid for postage.

In common with the other states of the United Arab Emirates the Khor Fakkan stamp contract was terminated on 1 August 1972, and any further new issues released after that date were unauthorised.

KIAUTSCHOU (KIAOCHOW)

A port in Shantung, China, leased by Germany from China in 1898. It was occupied by Japan in 1914, but reverted to China in 1922.

1900. 100 pfennige = 1 mark.
1905. 100 cents = 1 dollar (Chinese).

1900. No. 9 of German Post Offices in China surch **5 Pfg.**

3	5pf. on 10pf. red	65·00	75·00

1901. Yacht key-types inscr 'KIAUTSCHOU'.

11	**N**	3pf. brown	2·75	2·50
12	**N**	5pf. green	2·75	2·20
13	**N**	10pf. red	3·25	2·75
14	**N**	20pf. blue	10·00	11·00
15	**N**	25pf. black and red on yellow	18·00	22·00
16	**N**	30pf. black and orange on buff	18·00	22·00
17	**N**	40pf. black and red	21·00	26·00
18	**N**	50pf. black and purple on buff	21·00	31·00
19	**N**	80pf. black and red on pink	39·00	70·00
20	**O**	1m. red	65·00	£120
21	**O**	2m. blue	£110	£140
22	**O**	3m. black	£110	£275
23	**O**	5m. red and black	£300	£900

1905. Chinese currency. Yacht key-types inscr 'KIAUTSCHOU'.

34	**N**	1c. brown	1·70	2·20
35	**N**	2c. green	1·50	1·80
36	**N**	4c. red	1·30	1·70
37	**N**	10c. blue	1·40	5·00
38	**N**	20c. black and red	3·75	22·00
39	**N**	40c. black and red on pink	4·25	70·00
40	**O**	½d. red	13·00	90·00
41	**O**	1d. blue	17·00	£110
42	**O**	1½d. black	28·00	£275
43	**O**	2½d. red and black	65·00	£650

KING EDWARD VII LAND

Stamp issued in connection with the Shackleton Antarctic Expedition in 1908. The expedition landed at Cape Royds in Victoria Land, instead of King Edward VII Land, the intended destination.

1908. Stamp of New Zealand optd **KING EDWARD VII LAND.**

A1	**42**	1d. red	£475	42·00

KIONGA

Part of German E. Africa, occupied by the Portuguese during the 1914/18 war, and now incorporated in Mozambique.

1916. King Carlos key-type of Lourenco Marques optd **REPUBLICA** and surch **KIONGA** and new value.

1	**S**	½c. on 100r. blue on blue	17·00	13·50
2	**S**	1c. on 100r. blue on blue	17·00	13·50
3	**S**	2½c. on 100r. blue on blue	17·00	13·50
4	**S**	5c. on 100r. blue on blue	17·00	13·50

KIRIBATI

This group of islands in the Pacific, formerly known as the Gilbert Islands, achieved independence on 12 July 1979 and was renamed Kiribati.

100 cents = 1 dollar.

15 National Flag

1979. Independence. Multicoloured.

84	10c. Type **15**	10	35
85	45c. Houses of Parliament and Maneaba ni Maungatabu (House of Assembly)	20	65

16 *Teraaka* (training ship)

1979. Multicoloured

86	1c. Type **16**	10	1·00
122	3c. *Tautunu* (inter-island freighter)	15	30
123	5c. Hibiscus	10	15
124	7c. Catholic Cathedral, Tarawa	10	15
125	10c. Maneaba, Bikenibeu	10	15
91	12c. Betio Harbour	15	20
92	15c. Reef heron	35	25
93	20c. Flamboyant tree	20	25
129	25c. Moorish idol (fish)	30	30
95	30c. Frangipani	25	30
96	35c. GIPC Chapel, Tangintebu	25	30
97	50c. *Hypolimnas bolina* (butterfly)	75	55
133	$1 *Tabakea* (Tarawa Lagoon ferry)	50	75
134	$2 Evening scene	50	75
135	$5 National Flag	1·00	2·00

17 Gilbert and Ellice Islands 1911 ½d. Stamp

1979. Death Centenary of Sir Rowland Hill. Multicoloured.

100	10c. Type **17**	10	10
101	20c. Gilbert & Ellice Islands 1956 2s.6d. definitive	15	20
102	25c. GB Edward VII 2s.6d.	15	20
103	45c. Gilbert and Ellice Islands 1924 10s.	25	35
MS104	113×110 mm. Nos. 100/103	70	1·00

18 Boy with Giant Clam Shell

1979. International Year of the Child. Multicoloured.

105	10c. Type **18**	10	10
106	20c. Child climbing coconut palm (horiz)	10	10
107	45c. Girl reading	15	20
108	$1 Child in traditional costume	30	50

19 Downrange Station, Christmas Island

1980. Satellite Tracking. Multicoloured.

109	25c. Type **19**	10	10
110	45c. Map showing satellite trajectory	15	15
111	$1 Rocket launch, Tanegashima, Japan (vert)	30	35

20 TS *Teraaka*

1980. London 1980 International Stamp Exhibition. Multicoloured.

112	12c. Type **20**	15	10
113	25c. Loading Air Tungaru Britten-Norman BN-2 Islander, Bonriki Airport	15	10
114	30c. Radio operator	15	10
115	$1 Bairiki Post Office	20	35
MS116	139×116 mm. Nos. 112/115	60	85

21 *Achaea janata*

1980. Moths. Multicoloured.

117	12c. Type **21**	10	10
118	25c. *Ethmia nigroapicella*	15	15
119	30c. *Utetheisa pulchelloides*	15	15
120	50c. *Anua coronata*	25	25

22 Captain Cook Hotel

1980. Development. Multicoloured.

136	10c. Type **22**	10	10
137	20c. Sports stadium	10	10
138	25c. International Airport, Bonriki	15	10
139	35c. National Library and Archives, Bairiki	15	10
140	$1 Otintai Hotel, Bikenibeu	20	40

23 *Acalypha godseffiana*

1981. Flowers. Multicoloured.

141	12c. Type **23**	10	10
142	30c. *Hibiscus schizopetalus*	15	15
143	35c. *Calotropis gigantea*	15	15
144	50c. *Euphorbia pulcherrima*	20	20

25 Maps of Abaiang and Marakei, and String Figures

1981. Island Maps (1st series). Multicoloured.

145	12c. Type **25**	15	10
146	30c. Maps of Little Makin and Butaritari, and village house	20	10
147	35c. Map of Maiana and coral road	25	15
148	$1 Map of Christmas Island, and Captain Cook's HMS *Resolution*	70	75

See also Nos. 201/204, 215/218, 237/240, 256/260 and 270/273.

26 *Katherine*

27 Prince Charles and Lady Diana Spencer (image scaled to 59% of original size)

1981. Royal Wedding. Royal Yachts. Multicoloured.

149	12c. Type **26**	10	15
150	12c. Type **27**	20	30
151	50c. *Osborne*	25	40
152	50c. Type **27**	50	75
153	$2 *Britannia*	35	80
154	$2 Type **27**	1·50	2·50
MS155	120×109 mm. $1.20 Type **27**	75	1·00

28 Tuna Bait Breeding Centre, Bonriki Fish Farm

1981. Tuna Fishing Industry. Multicoloured.

158	12c. Type **28**	15	10
159	30c. Tuna fishing	20	20
160	35c. Cold storage, Betio	20	25
161	50c. Government Tuna Fishing Vessel *Nei Manganibuka*	30	50
MS162	134×99 mm. Nos. 158/161	1·00	1·40

29 Pomarine Skua

1982. Birds. Multicoloured.

163	1c. Type **29**	15	15
164	2c. Mallard	15	15
165	4c. Collared petrel	20	20
166	5c. Blue-faced booby	20	20
167	7c. Friendly quail dove	20	20
168	8c. Common shoveler ('Shoveler')	20	20
169	12c. Polynesian reed warbler	20	20
170	15c. Pacific golden plover ('Pacific Plover')	25	25
171	20c. Reef heron	30	30
171a	25c. Common noddy ('Brown Noddy')	1·75	1·50
172	30c. Brown booby	30	30
173	35c. Audubon's shearwater	1·00	35
174	40c. White-throated storm petrel (vert)	35	40
175	50c. Bristle-thighed curlew (vert)	40	45
175a	55c. White tern ('Fairy Tern') (vert)	9·00	16·00
176	$1 Kuhl's lory ('Scarlet-breasted Lorikeet') (vert)	1·25	40
177	$2 Long-tailed koel ('Long-tailed Cuckoo') (vert)	1·25	55
178	$5 Great frigatebird (vert)	1·50	1·25

30 Riley Turbo Skyliner

1982. Air. Inauguration of Tungaru Airline. Multicoloured.

179	12c. Type **30**	15	10
180	30c. Britten-Norman BN-2A Mk III 'short nose' Trislander	20	20
181	35c. Casa-212 Aviocar	20	25
182	50c. Boeing 727-200	30	35

No. 179 is inscr 'de Havilland DH114 Heron' in error.

31 Mary of Teck, Princess of Wales, 1893

1982. 21st Birthday of Princess of Wales. Multicoloured.

183	12c. Type **31**	10	10
184	50c. Coat of Arms of Mary of Teck	20	35
185	$1 Diana, Princess of Wales	30	70

1982. Birth of Prince William of Wales. Nos. 183/185 optd **ROYAL BABY.**

186	12c. Type **31**	10	15
187	50c. Coat of Arms of Mary of Teck	25	50
188	$1 Diana, Princess of Wales	40	70

32 First Aid Practice

1982. 75th Anniversary of Boy Scout Movement. Multicoloured.

189	12c. Type **32**	20	15
190	25c. Boat repairs	20	30
191	30c. On parade	25	35
192	50c. Gilbert Islands 1977 8c. Scouting stamp and '75'	25	60

33 Queen and Duke of Edinburgh with Local Dancer

1982. Royal Visit. Multicoloured.

193	12c. Type **33**	15	15
194	25c. Queen, Duke of Edinburgh and outrigger canoe	20	20
195	35c. New Philatelic Bureau building	30	30
MS196	88×76 mm. 50c. Queen Elizabeth II	60	60

On No. **MS**196 the captions on the map for the islands of Teraina and Tabuaeran have been transposed.

34 *Obaia, The Feathered* (Kiribati legend)

1983. Commonwealth Day. Multicoloured.

197	12c. Type **34**	10	10
198	30c. Robert Louis Stevenson Hotel, Abemama	15	10
199	50c. Container ship off Betio	15	25
200	$1 Map of Kiribati	20	50

1983. Island Maps (2nd series). As T **25**. Multicoloured.

201	12c. Beru, Nikunau and canoe	25	15
202	25c. Abemama, Aranuka, Kuria and fish	25	20
203	35c. Nonouti and reef fishing (vert)	30	35
204	50c. Tarawa and House of Assembly (vert)	30	50

35 Collecting Coconuts

1983. Copra Industry. Multicoloured.

205	12c. Type **35**	15	15
206	25c. Selecting coconuts for copra	25	25
207	30c. Removing husks	25	30
208	35c. Drying copra	25	35
209	50c. Loading copra at Betio	30	45

36 War Memorials

1983. 40th Anniversary of Battle of Tarawa. Multicoloured.

210	12c. Type **36**	15	15
211	30c. Maps of Tarawa and Pacific Ocean	20	30
212	35c. Gun emplacement	20	35
213	50c. Modern and wartime landscapes	25	55
214	$1 Aircraft carrier USS *Tarawa*	40	75

1983. Island Maps (3rd series). As T **25**. Multicoloured.

215	12c. Teraina and Captain Fanning's ship *Betsey*, 1798	25	15
216	30c. Nikumaroro and hawksbill turtle	30	35
217	35c. Kanton and local postmark	35	40
218	50c. Banaba and flying fish	40	55

37 Tug *Riki*

1984. Kiribati Shipping Corporation. Multicoloured.

219	12c. Type **37**	30	15
220	35c. Ferry *Nei Nimanoa*	55	35
221	50c. Ferry *Nei Tebaa*	70	60
222	$1 Cargo ship *Nei Momi*	1·00	1·10
MS223	115×98 mm. Nos. 219/222	2·75	5·50

38 Water and Sewage Schemes

1984. Ausipex International Stamp Exhibition, Melbourne. Multicoloured.

224	12c. Type **38**	15	15
225	30c. *Nouamake* (game fishing boat)	20	30
226	35c. Overseas training schemes	20	40
227	50c. International communications link	25	55

39 *Tabakea supporting Banaba*

1984. Kiribati Legends (1st series). Multicoloured.

228	12c. Type **39**	15	20
229	30c. *Nakaa, Judge of the Dead*	15	35
230	35c. *Naareau and Dragonfly*	15	45
231	50c. *Whistling Ghosts*	20	55

See also Nos. 245/248.

40 Sail-finned Tang

1985. Reef Fish. Multicoloured.

232	12c. Type **40**	60	25
233	25c. Picasso triggerfish	1·00	65
234	35c. Clown surgeonfish	1·25	85
235	80c. Red squirrelfish	2·00	2·50
MS236	140×107 mm. Nos. 232/235	4·25	4·75

1985. Island Maps (4th series). As T **25**. Multicoloured.

237	12c. Tabuaeran and great frigatebird ('Frigate Bird')	1·75	25
238	35c. Rawaki and germinating coconuts	2·25	40
239	50c. Arorae and xanthid crab	2·50	65
240	$1 Tamana and fish hook	3·00	1·50

41 Youths playing Football on Beach

1985. International Youth Year. Multicoloured.

241	15c. Type **41**	55	60
242	35c. Logos of IYY and Kiribati Youth Year	80	1·10
243	40c. Girl preparing food (vert)	85	1·40
244	55c. Map illustrating Kiribati's youth exchange links	1·25	2·00

1985. Kiribati Legends (2nd series). As T **39**. Multicoloured.

245	15c. *Nang Kineia and the Tickling Ghosts*	35	35
246	35c. *Auriaria and Tituabine*	60	80
247	40c. *The first coming of Babai at Arorae*	70	1·25
248	55c. *Riiki and the Milky Way*	90	1·60

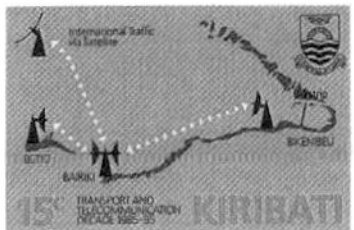

42 Map showing Telecommunications Satellite Link

1985. Transport and Telecommunications Decade (1st issue). Multicoloured.

249	15c. Type **42**	1·50	1·00
250	40c. MV *Moanaraoi* (Tarawa–Suva service)	2·75	3·00

See also Nos. 268/269, 293/294 and 314/315.

1986. 60th Birthday of Queen Elizabeth II. As T **230a** of Jamaica. Multicoloured.

251	15c. Princess Elizabeth in Girl Guide uniform, Windsor Castle, 1938	15	15
252	35c. At Trooping the Colour, 1980	20	30
253	40c. With Duke of Edinburgh in Kiribati, 1982	20	35
254	55c. At banquet, Austrian Embassy, London, 1966	25	50
255	$1 At Crown Agents Head Office, London, 1983	45	1·25

1986. Island Maps (5th series). As T **25**. Multicoloured.

256	15c. Manra and coconut crab	2·75	1·50
257	30c. Birnie and McKean Islands and cowrie shells	3·50	2·75
258	35c. Orona and red-footed booby	4·25	2·75
259	40c. Malden Island and whaling ship, 1844	4·25	3·75
260	55c. Vostok, Flint and Caroline Islands and Bellingshausen's *Vostok*, 1820	4·25	4·25

43 *Lepidodactylus lugubris*

1986. Geckos. Multicoloured.

261	15c. Type **43**	1·50	70
262	35c. *Gehyra mutilata*	1·75	1·50
263	40c. *Hemidactylus frenatus*	1·90	1·75
264	55c. *Gehyra oceanica*	2·25	2·50

See also Nos. 274/**MS**278.

44 Maps of Australia and Kiribati

1986. America's Cup Yachting Championship. Multicoloured.

265	15c. Type **44**	20	65
266	55c. America's Cup and map of course	50	1·00
267	$1.50 *Australia II* (1983 winner)	70	1·25

45 Freighter *Moamoa*

1987. Transport and Telecommunications Decade (2nd issue). Multicoloured.

268	30c. Type **45**	2·75	2·50
269	55c. Telephone switchboard and automatic exchange	3·75	3·50

1987. Island Maps (6th series). As T **25**. Multicoloured.

270	15c. Starbuck and red-tailed tropicbird ('Red-tailed Tropicbird')	60	80
271	30c. Enderbury and white tern	70	85
272	55c. Tabiteuea and pandanus tree	70	90
273	$1 Onotoa and okai (house)	80	2·50

1987. Skinks. As T **43**. Multicoloured.

274	15c. *Emoia nigra*	30	45
275	35c. *Cryptoblepharus* sp.	30	50
276	40c. *Emoia cyanura*	30	55
277	$1 *Lipinia noctua*	45	1·50
MS278	130×114 mm. Nos. 274/277	1·10	3·25

1987. Royal Ruby Wedding. Nos. 251/255 optd **40TH WEDDING ANNIVERSARY**.

279	15c. Princess Elizabeth in Girl Guide uniform, Windsor Castle, 1938	15	25
280	35c. At Trooping the Colour, 1980	20	30
281	40c. With Duke of Edinburgh in Kiribati, 1982	25	35
282	55c. At banquet, Austrian Embassy, London, 1966	30	45
283	$1 At Crown Agents Head Office, London, 1983	50	1·25

46 Henri Dunant (founder)

1988. 125th Anniversary of International Red Cross. Multicoloured.

284	15c. Type **46**	80	65
285	35c. Red Cross workers in Independence parade, 1979	1·25	1·50
286	40c. Red Cross workers with patient	1·25	1·60
287	55c. Gilbert & Ellice Islands 1970 British Red Cross Centenary 10c. stamp	1·60	1·75

47 Causeway built by Australia

1988. Bicentenary of Australian Settlement and Sydpex '88 National Stamp Exhibition, Sydney. Multicoloured.

288	15c. Type **47**	25	20
289	35c. Capt. Cook and Pacific map	60	60
290	$1 Obverse of Australian $10 Bicentenary banknote	1·00	1·75
291	$1 Reverse of $10 Bicentenary banknote	1·00	1·75
MS292	95×76 mm. $2 *Logistic Ace* (container ship) (37×26 mm)	4·75	5·00

No. **MS**292 also commemorates the 150th anniversary of the first screw-driven steamship.

48 Manual Telephone Exchange and Map of Kiritimati

1988. Transport and Telecommunications Decade (3rd issue). Multicoloured.

293	35c. Type **48**	75	75
294	45c. Betio-Bairiki Causeway	1·00	1·00

49 *Hound* (brigantine), 1835

1989. Nautical History (1st series). Multicoloured.

295	15c. Type **49**	90	55
296	30c. *Phantom* (brig), 1854	1·50	1·10
297	40c. HMS *Alacrity* (schooner), 1873	1·60	1·60
298	$1 *Charles W. Morgan* (whaling ship), 1851	3·00	3·75

See also Nos. 343/**MS**347 and 523/526.

50 Reef Heron ('Eastern Reef Heron')

1989. Birds with Young. Multicoloured.

299	15c. Type **50**	1·25	1·50
300	15c. Reef heron ('Eastern Reef Heron') chicks in nest	1·25	1·50
301	$1 White-tailed tropicbird	2·50	3·25
302	$1 Young white-tailed tropicbird	2·50	3·25

Nos. 299/300 and 301/302 were each printed together, *se-tenant*, each pair forming a composite design.

51 House of Assembly

1989. Tenth Anniversary of Independence. Multicoloured.

303	15c. Type **51**	25	25
304	$1 Constitution	1·25	1·75

51a *Apollo 10* on Launch Gantry

1989. 20th Anniversary of First Manned Landing on Moon. Multicoloured.

305	20c. Type **51a**	30	30
306	50c. Crew of *Apollo 10* (30×30 mm)	70	90
307	60c. *Apollo 10* emblem (30×30 mm)	80	1·00
308	75c. *Apollo 10* splashdown, Hawaii	95	1·25
MS309	82×100 mm. $2.50 *Apollo 11* command module in lunar orbit	6·50	7·50

51b Gilbert and Ellice Islands, 1949 75th Anniversary of UPU 3d. Stamp

1989. Philexfrance 89 International Stamp Exhibition, Paris, and World Stamp Expo '89, Washington (1st issue). Sheet 104×86 mm.

MS310	**51b** $2 multicoloured	3·50	5·00

51c Examining Fragment of Statue

1989. Philexfrance 89 International Stamp Exhibition, Paris, and World Stamp Expo '89, Washington (2nd issue). Designs showing Statue of Liberty. Multicoloured.

311	35c. Type **51c**	1·10	1·40
312	35c. Workman drilling Statue	1·10	1·40
313	35c. Surveyor with drawing	1·10	1·40

52 Telecommunications Centre

1989. Transport and Telecommunications Decade (4th issue). Multicoloured.

314	30c. Type **52**	1·50	1·25
315	75c. *Mataburo* (inter-island freighter)	4·00	4·25

1989. Melbourne Stampshow '89. Nos. 301/302 optd with Exhibition emblem showing tram.

316	$1 White-tailed tropicbird	3·00	3·50
317	$1 Young white-tailed tropicbird	3·00	3·50

54 Virgin and Child (detail, *The Adoration of the Holy Child* (Denys Calvert))

1989. Christmas. Paintings. Multicoloured.

318	10c. Type **54**	1·00	55
319	15c. *The Adoration of the Holy Child* (Denys Calvert)	1·25	70
320	55c. *The Holy Family and St Elizabeth* (Rubens)	3·00	1·25
321	$1 *Madonna with Child and Maria Magdalena* (School of Correggio)	4·50	7·00

55 Gilbert and Ellice Islands 1912 1d. and GB Twopence Blue Stamps

1990. 150th Anniversary of the Penny Black and Stamp World London 90 International Stamp Exhibition. Multicoloured.

322	15c. Type **55**	1·00	1·00
323	50c. Gilbert and Ellice Islands 1911 ½d. and GB Penny Black	2·50	2·75
324	60c. Kiribati 1982 1c. bird and GB 1870 ½d.	2·50	2·75
325	$1 Gilbert Islands 1976 1c. ship and GB 1841 1d. brown	2·75	3·50

56 Blue-barred Orange Parrotfish

1990. Fish. Multicoloured.

326	1c. Type **56**	30	75
327	5c. Honeycomb grouper	45	75
328	10c. Blue-finned trevally	55	85
329	15c. Hump-backed snapper	70	50
330	20c. Variegated emperor	75	70
356	23c. Bennett's pufferfish	1·00	1·00
331	25c. Rainbow runner	80	65
332	30c. Black-saddled coral grouper	90	65
333	35c. Great barracuda	1·00	75
334	40c. Convict tang	1·00	80
335	50c. Violet squirrelfish	1·25	90
336	60c. Stocky hawkfish	1·75	1·40
337	75c. Pennant coralfish	1·90	1·60
338	$1 Common blue-striped snapper ('Yellow and blue sea perch')	2·25	1·90
339	$2 Sailfish	3·25	4·75
340	$5 White-tipped reef shark	6·50	10·00

1990. 90th Birthday of Queen Elizabeth the Queen Mother. As T **107** (75c.) or **108** ($2) of Kenya.

341	75c. multicoloured	1·00	1·50
342	$2 black and green	1·75	3·00

Designs: 21×36 mm—75c. Queen Elizabeth the Queen Mother. 29×37 mm—$2 King George VI and Queen Elizabeth with air raid victim, London, 1940.

1990. Nautical History (2nd series). As T **49**. Multicoloured.

343	15c. *Herald* (whaling ship), 1851	1·00	70
344	50c. *Belle* (barque), 1849	1·75	1·75
345	60c. *Supply* (schooner), 1851	2·00	2·50
346	75c. *Triton* (whaling ship), 1848	2·00	2·50
MS347	95×75 mm. $2 *Charlotte* (convict transport), 1789	7·50	8·50

57 Manta

1991. Endangered Species. Fish. Multicoloured.

348	15c. Type **57**	80	55
349	20c. Manta (different)	1·00	90
350	30c. Whale shark	1·50	2·00
351	35c. Whale shark (different)	1·75	2·25

58 Queen Elizabeth II

1991. 65th Birthday of Queen Elizabeth II and 70th Birthday of Prince Philip. Multicoloured.

366	65c. Type **58**	1·25	1·50
367	70c. Prince Philip in RAF uniform	1·25	1·50

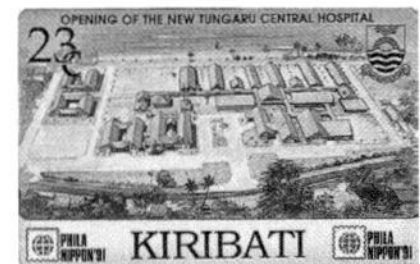

59 Aerial View of Hospital

1991. Phila Nippon '91 International Stamp Exhibition, Tokyo, and Opening of Tungaru Central Hospital. Multicoloured.

368	23c. Type **59**	30	30
369	50c. Traditional dancers	60	75
370	60c. Hospital entrance	65	85
371	75c. Foundation stone and plaques	85	1·25
MS372	125×83 mm. $5 Casualty on trolley and ambulance	7·00	8·00

60 Mother and Child

1991. Christmas. Multicoloured.

373	23c. Type **60**	60	40
374	50c. The Holy Family in Pacific setting	1·10	90
375	60c. The Holy Family in traditional setting	1·25	1·50
376	75c. Adoration of the Shepherds	1·50	2·00

1992. 40th Anniv of Queen Elizabeth II's Accession. As T **214** of Lesotho. Multicoloured.

377	23c. Kiribati village	30	30
378	30c. Lagoon at sunset	40	45
379	50c. Tarawa waterfront	60	70
380	60c. Three portraits of Queen Elizabeth	70	90
381	75c. Queen Elizabeth II	90	1·10

1992. EXPO '92 World's Fair, Seville. Nos. 356, 336/337 and 339 optd **EXPO'92 SEVILLA**.

382	23c. Bennett's pufferfish	55	40
383	60c. Stocky hawkfish	1·25	1·50
384	75c. Pennant coralfish	1·40	1·60
385	$2 Sailfish	3·00	4·00

62 Marine Training Centre Sign

1992. 25th Anniversary of Marine Training Centre. Multicoloured.

386	23c. Type **62**	45	40
387	50c. Cadets on parade	80	1·00
388	60c. Fire school	80	1·00
389	75c. Lifeboat training	1·10	1·40

63 Healthy Children

1992. United Nations World Health and Food and Agriculture Organisations. Multicoloured.

390	23c. Type **63**	55	50
391	50c. Fishing at night	1·00	1·00
392	60c. Fruit	1·25	1·50
393	75c. *Papuan Chief* (container ship)	3·25	2·50

64 Phoenix Petrel

1993. Birds. Multicoloured.

394	23c. Type **64**	40	70
395	23c. Cook's petrel	40	70
396	60c. Pintail ('Northern Pintail')	90	1·25
397	60c. European wigeon ('Eurasian Wigeon')	90	1·25
398	75c. Spectacled tern	1·00	1·25
399	75c. Black-naped tern	1·00	1·25
400	$1 Australian stilt ('Stilt Wader')	1·25	1·40
401	$1 Wandering tattler	1·25	1·40

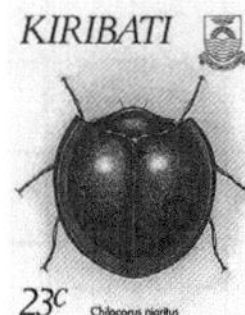

65 *Chilocorus nigritus*

1993. Insects. Multicoloured.

402	23c. Type **65**	1·00	55
403	60c. *Rodolia pumila* (ladybird)	1·50	2·00
404	75c. *Rodolia cardinalis* (ladybird)	1·60	2·50
405	$1 *Cryptolaemus montrouzieri*	1·75	3·00

66 US Air Reconnaissance Consolidated B-24 Liberator

1993. 50th Anniversary of Battle of Tarawa. Multicoloured.

406	23c. Type **66**	1·00	1·00
407	23c. USS *Nautilus* (submarine)	1·00	1·00
408	23c. USS *Indianapolis* (cruiser)	1·00	1·00
409	23c. USS *Pursuit* (destroyer)	1·00	1·00
410	23c. Vought Sikorsky OS2U Kingfisher spotter seaplane	1·00	1·00
411	23c. USS *Ringgold* and *Dashiell* (destroyers)	1·00	1·00
412	23c. Sherman tank on seabed	1·00	1·00
413	23c. Grumman F6F Hellcat fighter aircraft in lagoon	1·00	1·00
414	23c. Naval wreck on seabed	1·00	1·00
415	23c. First US aircraft to land on Betio	1·00	1·00
416	75c. Landing craft leaving transports	1·40	1·40
417	75c. Marines landing on Betio	1·40	1·40
418	75c. Landing craft approaching beach	1·40	1·40
419	75c. Marines pinned down in surf	1·40	1·40
420	75c. USS *Maryland* (battleship)	1·40	1·40
421	75c. Aerial view of Betio Island	1·40	1·40
422	75c. US Navy memorial	1·40	1·40
423	75c. Memorial to expatriates	1·40	1·40
424	75c. Japanese memorial	1·40	1·40
425	75c. Plan of Betio Island	1·40	1·40

67 Shepherds and Angels

1993. Christmas. Pacific Nativity Scenes. Multicoloured.

426	23c. Type **67**	30	30
427	40c. Three Kings	50	60
428	60c. Holy Family	70	1·00
429	75c. Virgin and Child	80	1·25
MS430	100×81 mm. $3 Virgin and Child (different)	2·75	5·00

68 Group of Dogs

1994. Hong Kong '94 International Stamp Exhibition. Chinese New Year. Year of the Dog. Sheet 120×90 mm.

MS431	**68** $3 multicoloured	3·25	4·75

69 Bryde's Whale and Calf

1994. Whales. Multicoloured.

432	23c. Type **69**	1·00	1·25
433	23c. Bryde's whale with two calves	1·00	1·25
434	40c. Blue whale and calf (face value at left)	1·25	1·40
435	40c. Blue whales and calf (face value at right)	1·25	1·40
436	60c. Humpback whale and calf (face value at left)	1·90	2·25
437	60c. Humpback whale and calf (face value at right)	1·90	2·25
438	75c. Killer whale and calf	1·90	2·25
439	75c. Killer whale and two calves	1·90	2·25

70 Family silhouetted on Beach

1994. 15th Anniversary of Independence. Protecting the Environment. Multicoloured.

440	40c. Type **70**	45	60
441	60c. Fish and coral	70	1·25
442	75c. Great frigate birds in flight	1·25	1·50

71 *Diaphania indica*

1994. Butterflies and Moths. Multicoloured.

443	1c. Type **71**	10	30
444	5c. *Herpetogramma licarsisalis*	15	50
445	10c. *Parotis suralis*	25	50
446	12c. *Sufetula sunidesalis*	25	50
447	20c. *Aedia sericea*	35	50
448	23c. *Anomis vitiensis*	35	25
449	30c. *Anticarsia irrorata*	45	30
450	35c. *Spodoptera litura*	55	40
451	40c. *Mocis frugalis*	65	50
452	45c. *Agrius convolvuli*	70	50
453	50c. *Cephonodes picus*	75	55
454	55c. *Gnathothlibus erotus*	80	60
455	60c. *Macroglossum hirundo*	80	60
456	75c. *Badamia exclamationis*	1·00	75
457	$1 *Precis villida*	1·40	1·40
458	$2 *Danaus plexippus*	2·25	2·50
459	$3 *Hypolimnas bolina* (male)	2·75	3·50
460	$5 *Hypolimnas bolina* (female)	3·75	5·00

See also No. **MS**527.

72 *Nerium oleander*

1994. Seasonal Flowers. Multicoloured.

461	23c. Type **72**	30	30
462	60c. *Catharanthus roseus*	80	1·25
463	75c. *Ipomea pes-caprae*	1·00	1·40
464	$1 *Calophyllum inophyllum*	1·40	2·00

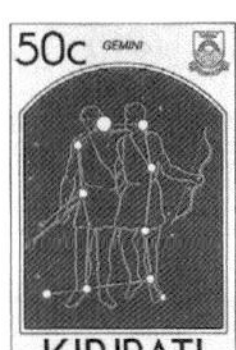

73 Gemini (The Twins)

1995. Night Sky over Kiribati. Multicoloured.

465	50c. Type **73**	75	75
466	60c. Cancer (The Crab)	85	1·00
467	75c. Cassiopeia (The Queen of Ethiopia)	1·00	1·40
468	$1 Southern Cross	1·25	1·75

74 Church and Traditional Meeting Hut

1995. Tourism. Multicoloured.

469	30c. Type **74**	85	95
470	30c. Fishermen and outrigger canoes	85	95
471	30c. Gun emplacement and map	85	95
472	30c. Children with marine creatures	85	95
473	30c. Sports	85	95
474	40c. Local girls in traditional costume	85	95
475	40c. Windsurfing	85	95
476	40c. Fishermen and wood carver	85	95
477	40c. Underwater sport	85	95
478	40c. Women weaving	85	95

75 Grumman TBF Avenger

1995. 50th Anniversary of End of Second World War. American Aircraft. Multicoloured.

489	23c. Type **75**	60	45
490	40c. Curtiss SOC.3-1 Seagull seaplane	80	70
491	50c. Consolidated B-24 Liberator bomber	90	90
492	60c. Grumman G-21 Goose amphibian	1·10	1·10
493	75c. Martin B-26 Marauder bomber	1·40	1·50
494	$1 Northrop P-61 Black Widow bomber	1·60	1·75
MS495	75×85 mm. $2 Reverse of 1939–1945 War Medal (vert)	2·00	3·00

76 Eclectus Parrots, Great Frigate Bird and Coconut Crabs

1995. Protecting the Environment. Multicoloured.

496	60c. Type **76**	85	1·10
497	60c. Red-tailed tropicbirds, common dolphin and pantropical spotted dolphin	85	1·10
498	60c. Blue-striped snapper ('Yellow and blue sea perch'), blue-barred orange parrotfish and green turtle	85	1·10
499	60c. Red-breasted wrasse, pennant coralfish and violet squirrelfish	85	1·10

1995. Jakarta '95 Stamp Exhibition, Indonesia. Nos. 496/499 optd **JAKARTA 95** within emblem.

500	60c. Type **76**	2·25	2·50
501	60c. Red-tailed tropicbirds, common dolphin and pantropical spotted dolphin	2·25	2·50
502	60c. Blue-striped snapper, blue-barred orange parrotfish and green turtle	2·25	2·50
503	60c. Red-breasted wrasse, pennant coralfish and violet squirrelfish	2·25	2·50

78 Sow feeding Piglets

1995. Singapore '95 International Stamp Exhibition and Beijing International Coin and Stamp Expo '95. Two sheets, each 113×85 mm, containing T **78**.

MS504	$2 multicoloured (Singapore '95)	2·00	3·00
MS505	$2 multicoloured (Beijing '95)	2·75	3·50

Nos. **MS**504/5 show the exhibition logos on the sheet margins.

79 *Teanoai* (police patrol boat)

1995. Police Maritime Unit. Multicoloured.

506	75c. Type **79**	1·40	1·75
507	75c. *Teanoai* at sea	1·40	1·75

80 Pantropical Spotted Dolphins

1996. Dolphins. Multicoloured.

508	23c. Type **80**	75	55
509	60c. Spinner dolphins	1·50	1·25
510	75c. Fraser's dolphins	1·60	1·75

511	$1 Rough-toothed dolphins	1·75	2·25

81 Tap and Top Left Segment of UNICEF Emblem

1996. 50th Anniversary of UNICEF. Multicoloured.

512	30c. Type **81**	50	70
513	30c. Documents and top right segment	50	70
514	30c. Syringe and bottom left segment	50	70
515	30c. Open book and bottom right segment	50	70

Nos. 512/515 were printed together, *se-tenant*, with each block of four showing the complete emblem.

82 Chinese Dragon

1996. CHINA '96 Ninth Asian International Stamp Exhibition, Peking. Sheet 110×86 mm.

MS516	**82** 50c. multicoloured	1·00	1·50

83 LMS No. 5609 *Gilbert and Ellice Islands* Locomotive

1996. CAPEX '96 International Stamp Exhibition, Toronto. Sheet 111×80 mm.

MS517	**83** $2 multicoloured	2·40	3·00

84 Rathbun Red Crab

1996. Sea Crabs. Multicoloured.

518	23c. Type **84**	35	40
519	60c. Red and white painted crab	65	70
520	75c. Red-spotted crab	75	85
521	$1 Red-spotted white crab	1·00	2·00

85 Kiribati Canoe

1996. Taipei '96 International Stamp Exhibition, Taiwan. Sheet 110×86 mm.

MS522	**85** $1.50 multicoloured	2·50	3·25

1996. Nautical History (3rd series). As T **49**. Multicoloured.

523	23c. *Potomac* (whaling ship), 1843	60	40
524	50c. *Southern Cross IV* (missionary ship), 1891	90	90
525	60c. *John Williams III* (missionary sailing ship), 1890	1·10	1·10
526	$1 HMS *Dolphin* (frigate), 1765	1·60	2·00

1997. HONG KONG '97 International Stamp Exhibition. Sheet 130×90 mm, containing No. 457. Multicoloured.

MS527	$1 *Precis villida*	1·10	1·60

1997. Pacific '97 International Stamp Exhibition, San Francisco. Nos. 489/494 optd **PACIFIC 97 World Philatelic Exhibition San Francisco, California 29 May - 8 June**.

528	23c. Type **75**	40	35
529	40c. Curtiss SOC.3-1 Seagull seaplane	60	55
530	50c. Consolidated B-24 Liberator bomber	70	70
531	60c. Grumman G-21 Goose amphibian	80	90
532	75c. Martin B-26 Marauder bomber	90	1·10
533	$1 Northrop P-61 Black Widow bomber	1·10	1·40
MS534	75×85 mm. $2 Reverse of 1939–1945 War Medal (vert)	1·75	2·50

87 Queen Elizabeth II in 1996

1997. Golden Wedding of Queen Elizabeth and Prince Philip. Multicoloured.

535	50c. Type **87**	1·00	1·40
536	50c. Prince Philip carriage-driving at Windsor Horse Show	1·00	1·40
537	60c. Queen in phaeton at Trooping the Colour	1·00	1·40
538	60c. Prince Philip on Montserrat, 1993	1·00	1·40
539	75c. Queen Elizabeth and Prince Philip, 1989	1·00	1·40
540	75c. Prince Edward on horseback	1·00	1·40
MS541	110×70 mm. $2 Queen Elizabeth and Prince Philip in Landau (horiz)	3·00	4·00

Nos. 535/536, 537/538 and 539/540 respectively were printed together, *se-tenant*, with the backgrounds forming composite designs.

88 Young Rock Dove

1997. Birds. Multicoloured.

542	50c. Type **88**	1·25	1·40
543	50c. Adult rock dove	1·25	1·40
544	60c. Adult Pacific pigeon	1·25	1·40
545	60c. Young Pacific pigeon	1·25	1·40
546	75c. Adult Micronesian pigeon	1·25	1·40
547	75c. Young Micronesian pigeon	1·25	1·40

1997. ASIA '97 Stamp Exhibition, Bangkok. Nos. 542/543 and 546/547 optd **ASIA '97 KIRIBATI 5 - 14 OCTOBER** and elephant.

548	50c. Type **88**	85	1·25
549	50c. Adult rock dove	85	1·25
550	75c. Adult Micronesian pigeon	1·00	1·40
551	75c. Young Micronesian pigeon	1·00	1·40

90 Spiny Lobster

1998. Endangered Species. Spiny Lobster. Multicoloured.

552	25c. Type **90**	40	60
553	25c. Facing right	40	60
554	25c. With coral in foreground	40	60
555	25c. On sponge	40	60
MS556	69×49 mm. $1.50 Spiny Lobster	1·90	2·50

No. **MS**556 does not show the WWF panda emblem.

91 Diana, Princess of Wales, 1992

1998. Diana, Princess of Wales Commemoration.

557	**91** 25c. multicoloured	50	60
MS558	145×70 mm. 25c. Type **91**; 50c. Wearing black evening dress, 1981; 60c. With scarf over head, 1992; 75c. Wearing brown jacket, 1993 (sold at $2.10+50c. charity premium)	1·25	2·25

92 Children and Smiling Sun

1998. Towards the Millennium (1st issue). Sheet 102×69 mm.

MS559	**92** $1 multicoloured	1·25	2·00

See also Nos. 580/**MS**584 and 594/598.

93 Indo-Pacific Humpbacked Dolphin

1998. Whales and Dolphins. Multicoloured.

560	25c. Type **93**	55	65
561	25c. Bottlenose dolphin	55	65
562	60c. Short-snouted spinner dolphin	80	1·00
563	60c. Risso's dolphin	80	1·00
564	75c. Striped dolphin	1·00	1·10
565	75c. Sei whale	1·00	1·10
566	$1 Fin whale	1·25	1·40
567	$1 Minke whale	1·25	1·40

94 Reuben K. Uatioa Stadium, Kiribati

1998. Italia '98 International Stamp Exhibition, Milan. Sheet 110×85 mm.

MS568	**94** $2 multicoloured	2·00	2·75

95 Pollutants and Harmful Emissions

1998. The Greenhouse Effect. Multicoloured.

569	25c. Type **95**	30	30
570	50c. Diagram of greenhouse effect	50	50
571	60c. Diagram of rising sea levels on Tarawa	60	65
572	75c. Diagram of rising sea levels on Kiritimati	70	85
MS573	103×69 mm. $1.50 Outrigger canoe	3·50	4·00

96 HMS *Resolution* (Cook) at Christmas Island, 1777

1999. Australia '99 World Stamp Exhibition, Melbourne. Sheet 136×56 mm.

MS574	**96** $2 multicoloured	2·25	2·75

97 Northern Shoveler (male)

1999. iBRA '99 International Stamp Exhibition, Nuremberg. Ducks. Multicoloured.

575	25c. Type **97**	60	50
576	50c. Northern Shoveler (female) and ducklings	75	65
577	60c. Green-winged teal (male)	80	80
578	75c. Green-winged teal (female) and ducklings	90	1·00
MS579	100×70 mm. $3 Green-winged teal (male) and duckling	3·25	4·25

98 Map of Millennium Island

1999. Towards the Millennium (2nd issue). 20th Anniversary of Independence. Multicoloured.

580	25c. Type **98**	1·00	80
581	60c. Map of Kiribati	1·50	1·25
582	75c. Map of Nikumaroro	1·50	1·25
583	$1 Amelia Earhart (aviator) and Lockheed Model 10 Electra	2·00	2·00
MS584	100×80 mm. Nos. 582/3	2·75	3·50

No. 581 shows Tarawa as 'TAROWA' in error.

98a Buzz Aldrin (astronaut)

1999. 30th Anniversary of First Manned Landing on Moon. Multicoloured.

585	25c. Type **98a**	35	35
586	60c. Service module docking with lunar module	65	75
587	75c. *Apollo 11* on Moon's surface	75	85
588	$1 Command module separating from service section	95	1·10
MS589	90×80 mm. $2 Kiribati as seen from Moon (circular, 40 mm diam)	1·90	2·50

99 Santa Claus in Sailing Canoe

1999. Christmas and 125th Anniversary of Universal Postal Union. Multicoloured.

590	25c. Type **99**	35	35
591	60c. Santa and unloading freighter	65	65
592	75c. Santa in sleigh passing aircraft	80	90
593	$1 Santa using computer	1·00	1·50

100 Open Hands around Globe ('FAITH')

2000. Towards the Millennium (3rd issue). A Region of Peace. Multicoloured.

594	25c. Type **100**	30	40
595	40c. Solar eclipse ('HARMONY')	45	60
596	60c. Stars and Sun over Earth ('HOPE')	60	80
597	75c. Sun over Earth ('ENLIGHTENMENT')	75	1·00
598	$1 Dove over Earth ('PEACE')	90	1·25

101 Bert feeding Pigeons

2000. *Sesame Street* (children's TV programme). Multicoloured.

599	20c. Type **101**	20	30
600	20c. Little Bear flying kite	20	30
601	20c. Grover calling	20	30
602	20c. Elmo and Cookie Monster	20	30
603	20c. Telly leaning out of window	20	30
604	20c. Zoe painting house	20	30
605	20c. Ernie with bird	20	30
606	20c. Big Bird and Rosita reading	20	30
607	20c. Oscar the Grouch and Slimey in dustbin	20	30
MS608	139×86 mm. $1.50 Grover as postman	1·40	1·75

Nos. 599/607 were printed together, *se-tenant*, with the backgrounds forming a composite design.

102 Queen Elizabeth II in Kiribati, 1982

2000. The Stamp Show 2000 International Stamp Exhibition, London. Sheet 80×70 mm.

MS609	**102** $5 multicoloured	4·25	5·50

2000. EXPO 2000 World's Fair, Hanover. Nos. 444/445, 447, 457 and 459 optd **KIRIBATI AT EXPO 2000 1.06-31.10.2000**.

610	5c. *Herpetogramma licarsisalis*	15	25
611	10c. *Parotis suralis*	15	25
612	20c. *Aedia sericea*	25	30
613	$1 *Precis villida*	1·00	1·25
614	$3 *Hypolimnas bolina* (male)	2·75	3·25

104 Prince William as a Baby with Prince Charles

2000. 18th Birthday of Prince William. Each showing Prince William with Prince Charles. Multicoloured.

615	25c. Type **104**	60	45
616	60c. In Italy, 1985	95	95
617	75c. At Sandringham, Christmas, 1992	1·10	1·10
618	$1 At Balmoral, 1997	1·25	1·75

105 Wandering Whistling Duck

2001. Ducks. Multicoloured.

619	25c. Type **105**	1·40	1·25
620	25c. Green-winged teal	1·40	1·25
621	25c. Mallard	1·40	1·25
622	25c. Northern shoveler	1·40	1·25
623	25c. Pacific black duck	1·40	1·25
624	25c. Mountain duck ('Blue Duck')	1·40	1·25
MS625	85×75 mm. $1 Grey teal	7·00	7·00

106 Man with Tap (Tiare Hongkai)

2001. Water Conservation. Children's Drawings. Multicoloured.

626	25c. Type **106**	45	40
627	50c. Cooking pot on fire and house in rain (Gilbert Tluanga)	60	50
628	60c. Map in raindrop and cup (Mantokataake Tebaiuea) (vert)	70	55
629	75c. Hand holding drop (Tokaman Karanebo) (vert)	80	70
630	$2 Water management system (Taom Simon)	1·90	3·00

107 Betio Port

2001. Philanippon '01 International Stamp Exhibition, Tokyo. Development Projects. Multicoloured.

631	75c. Type **107**	1·00	75
632	$2 New Parliament House complex	2·00	2·75

108 Norwegian Cruise Liner and Map of Route

2001. Tourism. Fanning Island. Multicoloured.

633	75c. Type **108**	1·75	1·00
634	$3 *Betsey* (full-rigged sealer) and map of Fanning Island	4·50	5·00

109 *Paracanthrus hepatus*

2002. Tropical Fish. Multicoloured.

635	5c. Type **109**	35	60
636	10c. *Centropyge flavissimus*	45	60
637	15c. *Anthias squamipinnis*	55	65
638	20c. *Centropyge loriculus*	60	60
639	25c. *Acanthurus lineatus*	70	25
640	30c. *Oxycirrhites typus*	75	40
641	40c. *Dascyllus trimaculatus*	80	50
642	50c. *Acanthurus achilles*	1·00	55
643	60c. *Pomacentrus caeruleus*	1·25	70
644	75c. *Acanthurus glaucopareius*	1·40	90
645	80c. *Thalassoma lunare*	1·50	1·00
646	90c. *Arothron meleagris*	1·60	1·50
647	$1 *Odonus niger*	2·00	1·50
648	$2 *Cephalopholis miniatus*	3·25	3·25
649	$5 *Pomacanthus imperator*	7·50	8·50
650	$10 *Balistoides conspicillum*	12·00	14·00

The 60c. is inscribed 'coeruleus' in error.

110 Admiral Bellinghausen and *Vostok*, 1820

2002. Pacific Explorers. Multicoloured.

651	25c. Type **110**	85	45
652	40c. Captain Wilkes and the USS *Vincennes* (sail frigate), 1838–1842	95	65
653	60c. Captain Fanning and *Betsey* (full-rigged sealer), 1798	1·10	80
654	75c. Captain Coffin and *Transit* (full-rigged ship), 1823	1·25	85
655	$1 Commodore Byron and HMS *Dolphin* (frigate), 1765	1·60	1·10
656	$3 Captain Broughton and HMS *Providence* (sloop), 1795	3·50	5·00
MS657	92×63 mm. $5 Captain Cook (vert)	7·00	7·50

111 Statue of Liberty with US and Kiribati Flags

2002. In Remembrance. Victims of Terrorist Attacks on USA (11 September 2001).

658	**111**	25c. multicoloured	1·00	1·00
659	**111**	$2 multicoloured	2·25	2·75

112 Queen Elizabeth in 1953

2002. Golden Jubilee. Featuring photographs by Dorothy Wilding. Multicoloured.

660	25c. Type **112**	1·00	80
MS661	135×110 mm. $2 Queen Elizabeth wearing Garter sash; $2 Queen Elizabeth in evening dress	5·50	6·00

113 Woven 'Parcel'

2002. Christmas.

662	**113**	25c. multicoloured	45	25
663	-	60c. multicoloured	65	50
664	-	75c. multicoloured	75	65
665	-	$1 multicoloured	80	85
666	-	$2.50 multicoloured	2·25	3·25

Designs: 60c. to $2.50 show different weave patterns.

114 *Cypraea mappa*

2003. Cowrie Shells of Kiribati. Multicoloured.

667	25c. Type **114**	35	35
668	50c. *Cypraea eglantine*	50	45
669	60c. *Cypraea mauritiana*	60	55
670	75c. *Cypraea cribraria*	75	75
671	$1 *Cypraea talpa*	80	85
672	$2.50 *Cypraea depressa*	2·25	3·00
MS673	130×95 mm. Nos. 667/672	5·25	6·50

115 Queen Elizabeth II and Duke of Edinburgh waving from Palace Balcony

2003. 50th Anniversary of Coronation. Multicoloured.

674	25c. Type **115**	40	25
675	$3 Newly crowned Queen in Coronation ceremony	2·00	2·75
MS676	95×115 mm. $2 As Type **115**; $5 As $3	4·00	5·00

116 Sopwith Camel

2003. Centenary of Powered Flight. Multicoloured.

677	25c. Type **116**	70	55
678	30c. Northrop Alpha	90	70
679	60c. de Havilland DH.106 Comet	1·10	80
680	75c. Boeing 727	1·10	85
681	$1 English Electric Canberra	1·75	1·25
682	$2.50 Lockheed Martin F22 Raptor	4·00	5·00
MS683	115×65 mm. 40c. Mitsubishi A6M-5 Zero; 60c. Grumman F6F Hellcat	2·50	2·50

No. **MS**683 also commemorates the 60th anniversary of the Battle of Tarawa.

117 Teareba Teomeka, Tabwakea

2003. Christmas. Churches of Christmas Island. Multicoloured.

684	25c. Type **117**	35	25
685	40c. Seventh-Day Adventist Church, London (Port Camp)	45	40
686	50c. St Teresa Catholic Church, Tabakea Village	50	45
687	60c. Betaera Fou, London	60	55
688	75c. Children standing by church bells, London	80	80
689	$1.50 Emanuira Church, London	1·50	2·00
690	$2.50 Church of Christ (Ana Ekaretia Kristo) (58×22 mm)	2·50	3·50
MS691	144×82 mm. Nos. 684/690	6·00	7·00

118 Road Sign showing Car Accident

2004. World Health Day. Road Safety. Multicoloured.

692	30c. Type **118**	1·60	1·75
693	40c. Road sign showing speeding car	1·75	1·90
694	50c. Road sign showing cigarette and alcohol	1·90	2·00
695	60c. Road sign showing children	2·00	2·25
MS696	165×58 mm. As Nos. 692/695	6·50	7·00

119 Pacific Golden Plover

2004. Bird Life International. Shore Birds. Multicoloured.

697	25c. Type **119**	65	55
698	40c. Whimbrel	85	70
699	50c. Wandering tattler (*Heteroscelus incanus*)	95	75
700	60c. Sanderling	1·10	85
701	75c. Bar-tailed godwit	1·25	90
702	$2.50 Ruddy turnstone	3·50	4·50
MS703	175×80 mm. $1 Head of Bristle-thighed curlew; $1 Front of Bristle-thighed curlew (vert); $1 Back of Bristle-thighed curlew (vert); $1 Two Bristle-thighed curlews; $1 Bristle-thighed curlews and tree	10·00	11·00

See also No. **MS**741.

120 Athletes

2004. Olympic Games, Athens. Multicoloured.

704	25c. Type **120**	50	50
705	50c. Taekwondo	75	70
706	60c. Weight-lifting	85	90
707	75c. Sprinting	90	1·25
MS708	98×74 mm. $2.50 Athletes in training; $2.50 Athletes in front of Parliament House	6·00	7·00

121 *Dendrobium anosmum*

2004. Orchids. Multicoloured.

709	$1 Type **121**	1·50	1·50
710	$1 *Dendrobium chrysotoxum*	1·50	1·50
711	$1 *Dendrobium laevifolium*	1·50	1·50
712	$1 *Dendrobium mohlianum*	1·50	1·50
713	$1 *Dendrobium pseudoglomeratum*	1·50	1·50
714	$1 *Dendrobium purpureum*	1·50	1·50
715	$1 *Grammatophyllum speciosum*	1·50	1·50
716	$1 *Dendrobium williamsianum*	1·50	1·50
717	$1 *Spathoglottis plicata*	1·50	1·50
718	$1 *Vanda hindsii*	1·50	1·50

Nos. 709/718 were printed together, *se-tenant*, with the backgrounds forming composite designs.

122 MV *Montelucia*

2004. Merchant Ships. Multicoloured.

719	50c. Type **122**	1·25	60
720	75c. MS *Pacific Princess*	1·50	70
721	$2.50 MS *Prinsendam*	3·75	4·00
722	$5 MS *Norwegian Wind*	6·50	7·50

123 French 36 Pounder Cannon

2005. Bicentenary of the Battle of Trafalgar (1st issue). Multicoloured.

No.	Description	Unused	Used
723	25c. Type **123**	80	55
724	50c. *San Indefonso* and HMS *Defence* in battle	1·25	70
725	75c. HMS Victory lashed to *Redoubtable*	1·75	1·00
726	$1 Emperor Napoleon Bonaparte (vert)	1·75	1·25
727	$1.50 HMS *Victory*	2·50	2·75
728	$2.50 Vice-Admiral Sir Horatio Nelson (vert)	3·50	4·25
MS729	120×79 mm. $2.50 Admiral Federico Gravina; $2.50 *Santissima Trinidad*	8·00	8·00

No. 727 contains traces of powdered wood from HMS *Victory*.

See also Nos. 743/745.

124 Japanese Type 95 Ha-Go Tank

2005. 60th Anniversary of the End of World War II. The Route to Victory. Multicoloured.

No.	Description	Unused	Used
730	75c. Type **124**	1·40	1·50
731	75c. Japanese A6M Zero fighter aircraft on Gilbert Islands	1·40	1·50
732	75c. US Marines from USS *Argonaut* and *Nautilus* coming ashore at Butaritari, 6.8.1942 ('Carlson Raid')	1·40	1·50
733	75c. Admiral of Pacific Fleet Chester Nimitz	1·40	1·50
734	75c. USS *Liscome Bay* (sunk by Japanese 24.11.1943)	1·40	1·50
735	75c. US Forces Higgins Landing Craft approaching Tarawa Red Beach, 20.11.1943	1·40	1·50
736	75c. F6F-3 Hellcats providing air cover, Tarawa Red Beach, November 1943	1·40	1·50
737	75c. LVT's reaching shore, Tarawa Red Beach, 20.11.1943	1·40	1·50
738	75c. Sherman tank of C Company, Tarawa Red Beach, 20.11.1943	1·40	1·50
739	75c. US Marines taking cover on Tarawa Red Beach, 20.11.1943	1·40	1·50
MS740	90×60 mm. $5 John Curtin (Australian Prime Minister) and Winston Churchill, London, 1944	10·00	10·00

125 Lesser Frigatebird

2005. Bird Life International (Part II Breeding Birds (**MS**741a) and Part III Seabirds (**MS**741b)). Multicoloured.

No.	Description	Unused	Used
MS741	Two sheets, each 170×85 mm. (a) 25c.×6, Type **125**; Red-tailed tropicbird; Blue-grey noddy; Christmas Island shearwater; Sooty tern; Blue-faced (Masked) booby. (b) $2×6, White-tailed tropicbird; White-capped (Black) noddy; Red-footed booby; Wedge-tailed shearwater; White tern; Great frigatebird	20·00	24·00

2005. Pope John Paul II Commemoration. As T **338** of Jamaica.

No.	Description	Unused	Used
742	$1 multicoloured	2·50	2·25

2005. Bicentenary of the Battle of Trafalgar (2nd issue). Multicoloured As T **339** of Jamaica.

No.	Description	Unused	Used
743	25c. HMS *Victory*	1·00	60
744	50c. Ships engaged in battle (horiz)	1·25	70
745	$5 Admiral Lord Nelson	7·50	8·50

126 Harlequin Shrimp

2005. Endangered Species. Harlequin Shrimp (*Hymenocera picta*). Multicoloured.

No.	Description	Unused	Used
746	50c. Type **126**	85	55
747	60c. Shrimp on yellow rocks	95	65
748	75c. Two shrimp	1·25	80
749	$5 Shrimp on red rocks	7·50	8·50

127 Princess Elizabeth

2006. 80th Birthday of Queen Elizabeth II. Multicoloured.

No.	Description	Unused	Used
750	50c. Type **127**	1·00	65
751	75c. Queen wearing tiara (looking left)	1·40	85
752	$1 Wearing tiara (facing forward)	1·75	1·40
753	$2 Wearing pink hat and jacket	3·25	4·00
MS754	144×75 mm. $1.50 As No. 752; $2.50 As No. 751	6·50	7·50

128 Kiribati and EU Flags

2006. 50th Anniversary of First Europa Stamps. Multicoloured, background colour given.

No.	Type	Description	Unused	Used
755	**128**	$2 grey	2·25	2·50
756	**128**	$2.50 lilac	2·25	2·50
757	**128**	$3 brown and yellow	3·00	3·75
758	**128**	$5 blue	5·00	7·50
MS759		77×122 mm. Nos. 755/758	10·00	15·00

129 Charles Darwin (originator of *Theory of Evolution*) and Corals

2006. Exploration and Innovation. Anniversaries. Multicoloured.

No.	Description	Unused	Used
760	25c. Type **129** (175th anniversary of voyage on *Beagle*)	1·25	1·25
761	25c. Fish and coral reef	1·25	1·25
762	50c. Isambard Kingdom Brunel (engineer) (birth bicentenary)	1·50	1·50
763	50c. Foundry	1·50	1·50
764	75c. Christopher Columbus (discoverer of New World) (500th death anniversary)	2·25	2·25
765	75c. *Santa Maria*	2·25	2·25
766	$1 Thomas Edison (inventor and physicist) (75th death anniversary)	2·25	2·25
767	$1 'Tin foil' phonograph	2·25	2·25
768	$1.25 Wolfgang Amadeus Mozart (composer) (250th birth anniversary)	3·50	3·50
769	$1.25 Violin and score	3·50	3·50
770	$1.50 Concorde (30th anniversary of inaugural flight)	4·00	4·00
771	$1.50 Concorde on runway and in flight	4·00	4·00

Nos. 760/761, 762/763, 764/765, 766/767, 768/769 and 770/771 were each printed together, *se-tenant*, each pair forming a composite design.

130 Ultrasaurus

2006. Dinosaurs. Multicoloured.

No.	Description	Unused	Used
772	25c. Type **130**	85	70
773	50c. Rhamphorhynchus	1·40	1·10
774	60c. Dilophosaurus	1·60	1·60
775	75c. Brachiosaurus	1·75	1·75
776	$1 Minmi paravertebra	2·00	2·00
777	$1 Eoraptor	2·00	2·00
778	$1.25 Stegosaurus	2·25	2·25
779	$1.50 Giganotosaurus	2·50	2·75

131 Troop Sgt. Major John Berryman refusing to leave Capt. Webb, Balaclava

2006. 150th Anniversary of the Victoria Cross. Multicoloured.

No.	Description	Unused	Used
780	$1.50 Type **131**	3·00	2·75
781	$1.50 Private W. Norman bringing in single-handed two Russian prisoners	3·00	2·75
782	$1.50 Sgt. Major John Grieve saving officer at Balaclava	3·00	2·75
783	$1.50 Private Thomas Beach rescuing Col. Carpenter, Inkerman	3·00	2·75
784	$1.50 Brevet-Major C. H. Lumley engaged with three Russian gunners in the Redan	3·00	2·75
785	$1.50 Major F. C. Elton working in trenches under heavy fire	3·00	2·75

132 Princess Elizabeth and Lt. Philip Mountbatten, 1947

2007. Diamond Wedding of Queen Elizabeth II and Prince Philip. Multicoloured.

No.	Description	Unused	Used
786	50c. Type **132**	1·75	1·25
787	75c. Wedding procession down the aisle	2·00	1·75
788	$1 Waving from balcony on wedding day	2·25	2·25
789	$1.50 At Broadlands, Romsey, Hampshire, 1947	2·75	2·75
MS790	125×85 mm. $5 Wedding photograph (42×56 mm)	7·00	7·50

2007. Centenary of Scouting. As T **348** of Jamaica. Multicoloured.

No.	Description	Unused	Used
791	25c. Kiribati scouts with their flag	60	45
792	50c. AIDS awareness	1·00	75
793	75c. Scout leaders	1·50	1·10
794	$2 Scout shelter, Kiribati, 1962	2·50	3·50
MS795	90×65 mm. $1 Kiribati Scouts emblem (vert); $1.50 Lord Baden-Powell (founder) (vert)	4·00	4·25

133 Diana, Princess of Wales

2007. Tenth Death Anniversary of Diana, Princess of Wales. Multicoloured.

No.	Description	Unused	Used
796	25c. Type **133**	65	60
797	25c. In profile	65	60
798	50c. Wearing cream jacket	1·10	65
799	75c. Wearing black and white check dress	1·40	1·25
800	75c. In close up, wearing earrings and emerald choker	1·40	1·25
801	$1 Wearing red dress	1·60	1·50

134 Royal Engineers

2007. Military Uniforms. Multicoloured.

No.	Description	Unused	Used
802	25c. Type **134**	75	55
803	40c. 95th Rifles	1·25	80
804	50c. 24th Regiment of Foot	1·40	80
805	60c. New Zealand soldiers	1·50	1·00
806	75c. 93rd Sutherland Highlanders	1·60	1·25
807	90c. Irish Guards	1·75	1·50
808	$1 Japanese soldiers	2·00	2·00
809	$1.50 United States Marine Corps	2·50	3·00

135 Great Crested Terns

2008. Birds. Multicoloured.

No.	Description	Unused	Used
810	5c. Type **135**	35	65
811	10c. Eurasian teal	50	75
812	15c. Laughing gulls	70	75
813	20c. Black-tailed godwit	75	75
814	25c. Pectoral sandpipers	75	60
815	50c. Band-rumped storm-petrel	1·25	65
816	60c. Sharp-tailed sandpiper	1·40	80
817	75c. Grey-tailed tattler	1·40	85
818	90c. Red phalarope	1·50	1·25
819	$1 Pink-footed shearwater	1·60	1·25
820	$2 Ring-billed gull	2·50	2·75
821	$5 Bonin petrel	5·50	7·00
MS822	Two sheets, each 120×90 mm. (a) Nos. 810/811, 813/815 and 821. (b) Nos. 812 and 816/820	17·00	18·00

136 Avro Type 696 Shackleton

2008. 90th Anniversary of the Royal Air Force. Multicoloured.

No.	Description	Unused	Used
823	25c. Type **136**	75	60
824	50c. Hawker Siddeley (BAe) Harrier	1·25	1·00
825	75c. Eurofighter EF-2000 Typhoon	1·50	1·40
826	$1 Vickers Valiant	1·75	1·75
MS826a	110×70 mm. $2.50 Dambusters Raid	3·75	4·00

137 Traditional Hut

2008. Phoenix Islands Protected Area (1st issue). Multicoloured.

No.	Description	Unused	Used
827	40c. Type **137**	75	55
828	75c. Outline map of Kanton Island	1·00	80
829	80c. Map of protected area	1·00	1·10
830	85c. Phoenix petrel with chick	1·50	1·25
831	$1.25 *Acropora nobilis* (coral)	1·50	1·75
832	$1.75 Blacktip reef shark	2·00	3·00
MS833	170×85 mm. Nos. 827/832	8·25	8·50

See also No. **MS**885.

138 Weightlifting

2008. Olympic Games, Beijing. Multicoloured.

No.	Description	Unused	Used
834	25c. Type **138**	45	40
835	50c. Running	60	50
836	60c. Cycling	1·00	90
837	75c. Javelin-thrower	1·50	1·50

139 Lady Sacred Heart, Bairiki

2008. Churches of Tarawa, Kiribati. Multicoloured.

No.	Description	Unused	Used
838	25c. Type **139**	70	70
839	25c. Kiribati Protestant Church, Bikenibeu	70	70
840	40c. Kaotitaeka RCC, Betio	1·00	1·00
841	40c. Mormon Church, Iesu Kristo	1·00	1·00
842	50c. Moaningaina	1·00	1·00
843	50c. Sacred Heart Cathedral	1·00	1·00

844 75c. St Paul's Millennium Church 1·50 1·50
845 75c. Kainkatikun Kristo, Naninimo, Tarawa 1·50 1·50
MS846 165×92 mm. Nos. 838/845 8·25 8·50

140 Ernest Shackleton

2009. Seafaring and Exploration. Multicoloured.
847 25c. Type **140** 1·50 1·25
848 40c. Robert Falcon Scott 1·75 1·50
849 50c. Captain James Cook 2·25 1·50
850 75c. Marco Polo 2·50 2·25
851 $1.50 Matthew Flinders 3·75 4·00
852 $1.75 John Cabot 3·75 4·00

141 Grumman Avenger

2009. Centenary of Naval Aviation. Multicoloured.
853 40c. Type **141** 1·75 1·50
854 50c. Chance Vought Corsair 2·00 1·50
855 75c. Westland Whirlwind helicopter 2·50 2·00
856 $1.25 McDonnell Douglas Phantom 3·50 3·50
MS857 110×70 mm. $3 Helicopter on deck of HMS *Ark Royal* 8·00 8·00

142 Mars Science Laboratory

2009. International Year of Astronomy. 40th Anniversary of First Moon Landing. Multicoloured.
858 40c. Type **142** 1·00 1·00
859 50c. International Space Station 1·25 1·25
860 75c. *Endeavour* and Boeing Transporter, 2008 1·50 1·50
861 $1.25 *Apollo 12* launch, 1969 2·00 2·00
862 $3 *Luna 16*, 1970 5·00 6·00
MS863 100×80 mm. $3 *Tradition* (*Apollo 11* crew erecting US flag on Moon) (Alan Bean) (39×59 mm). Wmk upright 5·00 6·00

143 Aircraft Servicing

2010. 70th Anniversary of the Battle of Britain. Multicoloured.
864 25c. Type **143** 1·00 70
865 40c. Pikeman with England standard 1·60 1·00
866 50c. Parachute packing 1·75 1·00
867 75c. Ground control 2·25 1·60
868 $1 Rescue services 2·75 2·25
869 $1.50 RAF badge 3·75 4·50
MS870 110×70 mm. $3 Sir Douglas Bader 6·50 6·50

Nos. 864/869 show stained glass windows from St George's RAF Chapel of Remembrance, Biggin Hill, Kent.

2011. Royal Wedding. Sheet 118×90 mm containing vert design as T **71** of British Indian Ocean Territory. Multicoloured.
MS871 $5 Prince William and Miss Catherine Middleton 12·00 11·00

Beatified
1 May 2011
(144)

2011. Beatification of Pope John Paul II. No. 742 optd with Type **144.**
872 $1 Pope John Paul II 2·50 2·25

1911 - 2011
100 Years of stamps
25c XXX
(145)

2011. Centenary of First Gilbert and Ellice Islands Stamps. Nos. 810/813 surch as T **145** and Nos. 641, 648 and 650 optd only.
873 25c. on 5c. Type **135** 1·00 75
874 30c. on 10c. Eurasian Teal 1·25 1·00
875 40c. *Dascyllus trimaculatus* 1·25 1·00
876 50c. on 20c. Black-tailed Godwit 1·75 1·25
877 75c. on 15c. Laughing Gulls 2·00 1·50
878 $2 *Cephalopholis miniatus* 2·75 3·00
879 $10 *Balistoides conspicillum* 14·00 17·00

1952 • DIAMOND JUBILEE • 2012
(146)

2012. Diamond Jubilee. Nos. 750/753 die-stamped with holographic text and diamond in silver (T **146).**
880 50c. Type **127** 1·25 1·25
881 75c. Queen wearing tiara (looking left) 1·40 1·40
882 $1 Wearing tiara (facing forward) 1·75 1·75
883 $2 Wearing pink hat and jacket 2·75 3·00

147 School of Giant Trevally

2012. Endangered Species. Giant Trevally (*Caranx ignobilis*). Multicoloured.
MS884 200×141 mm. 80c. Type **147**×2; $1 Four giant trevally×2; $1.50 Giant trevally×2; $2 Giant trevally (mouth open)×2 14·00 15·00

148 Manta Ray (*Manta birostris*)

2012. Phoenix Islands Protected Area (2nd issue). Multicoloured.
MS885 40c. Type **148**; 50c. Napoleon wrasse (*Cheilinus undulatus*); 60c. School of yellow and blueback fusilier (*Caesio teres*); 75c. School of rainbow runner (*Elagatis bipinnulata*); $1 Green turtle (*Chelonia mydas*); $1.50 School of ornate butterflyfish (*Chaetodon ornatissimus*); $2 *Chrysiptera albata*; $2.50 Small giant clam (*Tridacna maxima*) 12·00 13·00

149 Christmas Island Outrigger

2013. Water Transportation. Multicoloured.
886 5c. Type **149** 35 40
887 10c. Ferry to shore 50 50
888 15c. Inter-island ferries anchored near Betio harbour, Tarawa 70 50
889 20c. Fishing boats 75 50
890 25c. Inter-island ferry at sea 75 50
891 30c. *Te Tia Akawa* and cargo boat 85 55
892 35c. *Bwaan Tetangira II* 95 55
893 40c. Te Okarsi outrigger diving, Kiritimati 1·00 60
894 45c. *Akenraoi* in Abaiang Lagoon 1·10 60
895 50c. Native house with outrigger 1·25 65
896 55c. *Moamoa* 1·25 70
897 60c. *Kiribati Chief* (container ship) 1·40 80
898 75c. *Pride of Aloha* (cruise liner) 1·40 85
899 $1 Modern yacht Type Kiribati 36 1·60 1·25
900 $2 *Teeitei* (Tarawa pilot boat) 2·50 2·75
901 $5 Historic traditional outrigger 5·50 6·00
MS902 160×190 mm. Nos. 886/901 21·00 17·00

150 Mangroves and Village

2014. Mangroves. Multicoloured.
903 45c. Type **150** 1·00 60
904 75c. Man, two boys and shoreline with newly planted mangroves 1·60 1·25
905 $1 Villagers in mangroves and newly planted mangroves 1·75 1·60
906 $3 President Anote Tong of Kiribati and local youths planting mangroves 4·50 5·00

151 David Katoatau Weightlifting

2014. Commonwealth Games, Glasgow, Scotland. Multicoloured.
907 25c. Type **151** 60 50
908 75c. David Katoatau with gold medal for men's weightlifting 105kg event (Kiribati's first Commonwealth Games medal) 1·60 1·75
MS909 122×78 mm. $2.50 Kiribati team marching into stadium behind Kiribati flag (horiz); $2.50 Scottish terrier Games mascot wearing 'KIRIBATI' jacket (horiz) 6·50 7·00

152 Meadow Argus (*Junonia villida*)

2015. Butterflies of Kiribati. Multicoloured.
MS910 $2 Type **152**; $3 Blue Moon (*Hypolimnas bolina*) 7·00 7·00

The upper and right-hand portions of **MS**910 were cut in the shape of a Monarch butterfly.

SINGAPORE 2015

40C 
(153)

2015. Singapore 2015 International Stamp Exhibition. Nos. 818 and 821 surch as T **153** and Nos. 819/820 optd only.
911 40c. on 90c. Red Phalarope 1·00 80
912 60c. on $5 Bonin Petrel 1·50 1·25
913 $1 Pink-footed Shearwater 2·25 2·00
914 $2 Ring-billed Gull 4·00 4·50

154 Queen Elizabeth II

2016. 90th Birthday of Queen Elizabeth II. Multicoloured.
915 25c. Type **154** 60 40
916 75c. Queen Elizabeth II (wearing beige) 1·60 1·10
917 $1 Queen Elizabeth II (wearing floral pattern dress and white hat with blue feather decoration) 1·75 1·50
918 $2.50 Queen Elizabeth II (wearing beige and black) 3·25 3·50
919 $3.75 Queen Elizabeth II (wearing bright blue) 4·75 5·50
MS920 78×94 mm. $5 Queen Elizabeth II and Duke of Edinburgh on visit to Kiribati, 1982 7·00 7·00

155 Independence Celebrations

2016. NY 2016 World Stamp Show, New York. Multicoloured.
921 25c. Type **155** 60 40
922 75c. Parading with banner, Independence Celebrations 1·60 1·10
923 $1.25 Boat on beach ('PASSPORT STAMP') 2·00 1·90
924 $3 Betio Memorial, Tarawa ('REMEMBERING ARMED FORCES') 4·00 4·75

OFFICIAL STAMPS

1981. Nos. 86/135 optd **O.K.G.S.**
O11 1c. Type **16** 10 50
O12 3c. MV *Tautunu* (inter-island freighter) 10 30
O13 5c. Hibiscus 10 20
O14 7c. Catholic Cathedral, Tarawa 10 20
O15 10c. Maneaba, Bikenibeu 10 20
O16 12c. Betio Harbour 30 30
O17 15c. Reef heron 1·75 30
O18 20c. Flamboyant tree 20 30
O19 25c. Moorish idol (fish) 30 30
O20 30c. Frangipani 30 35
O21 35c. GIPC Chapel, Tangintebu 35 40
O22 50c. *Hypolimnas bolina* (butterfly) 1·00 55
O23 $1 *Tabakea* (Tarawa Lagoon ferry) 65 50
O24 $2 Evening scene 70 70
O25 $5 National Flag 1·25 1·75

1983. Nos. 169, 172/173, 175 and 177 optd **O.K.G.S.**
O36 12c. Polynesian reed warbler 40 30
O37 30c. Brown booby 70 50
O38 35c. Audubon's shearwater 80 60
O39 50c. Bristle-thighed curlew 1·00 80
O40 $2 Long-tailed koel 3·00 2·75

POSTAGE DUE STAMPS

D1 Kiribati Coat of Arms

1981
D1 **D1** 1c. black and mauve 10 10
D2 **D1** 2c. black and blue 10 10
D3 **D1** 5c. black and green 10 10
D4 **D1** 10c. black and brown 10 15
D5 **D1** 20c. black and blue 15 25
D6 **D1** 30c. black and brown 15 35
D7 **D1** 40c. black and purple 20 45
D8 **D1** 50c. black and green 20 50
D9 **D1** $1 black and red 30 75

KISHANGARH

A state of Rajasthan, India. Now uses Indian stamps.

1

1899. Imperf or perf
1 **1** 1a. green 25·00 85·00
3 **1** 1a. blue £900

2 (¼a.)

5 (2a.) Maharaja Sardul Singh

1899. Various arms designs. Perf or imperf
22*a* **2** ¼a. red 25 50
26*a* **2** ½a. blue 2·00 50
21 **2** ¼a. green £550 £850
7 **2** ½a. lilac £350 £600
8 **2** ½a. red £5500 £2500
25 **2** ½a. green 13·00 16·00
12*b* **2** 1a. pink £150 £450
27 **2** 1a. grey 8·00 6·00

29	2	1a. mauve	1·50	1·25
15	5	2a. orange	9·00	5·00
31	2	4a. brown	3·50	9·00
17	2	1r. lilac	32·00	48·00
32	2	1r. green	11·00	15·00
33	2	1r. yellow	£1500	
34	2	2r. red	35·00	55·00
35	2	5r. mauve	35·00	70·00

11 (½a.)

12 Maharaja Sardul Singh

1903. Imperf or perf

39	11	½a. pink	20·00	3·00
40	12	2a. orange	3·50	8·00
41	2	8a. grey	5·00	9·00

13 Maharaja Madan Singh

1904

42	13	¼a. red	60	1·00
43a	13	½a. brown	1·25	30
44a	13	1a. blue	4·00	2·75
45	13	2a. orange	15·00	8·50
46a	13	4a. brown	15·00	22·00
47	13	8a. violet	32·00	65·00
48	13	1r. green	30·00	£100
49	13	2r. yellow	50·00	£325
50	13	5r. brown	28·00	£250

14 Maharaja Madan Singh

1912

63	14	¼a. blue	30	45
64	14	½a. green	30	1·75
65	14	1a. red	2·25	3·25
67	14	4a. blue	6·00	8·00
68	14	8a. brown	7·00	65·00
69	14	1r. mauve	27·00	£275
70	14	2r. green	£160	£700
71	14	5r. brown	35·00	£700

15

1913

59	15	¼a. blue	30	90
60	15	2a. purple	16·00	35·00

16 Maharaja Yagyanarayan Singh

1928

72	16	¼a. blue	1·75	2·00
73	16	½a. green	4·00	2·50
74	-	1a. red	2·00	2·00
75	-	2a. purple	3·00	8·50
76	16	4a. brown	2·75	2·00
77	16	8a. violet	7·00	40·00
78	16	1r. green	21·00	95·00
79	16	2r. yellow	35·00	£475
80	16	5r. red	70·00	£500

Nos. 74/5 are larger.

OFFICIAL STAMPS

1918. Optd **ON K S D.**

O5	2	¼a. green	—	£250
O6	2	¼a. pink	2·75	60
O7	2	½a. blue	£800	80·00
O9	2	1a. mauve	90·00	3·75
O10	5	2a. orange	—	£225
O11	2	4a. brown	£130	16·00
O16	2	8a. grey	£160	30·00
O12	2	1r. green	£275	£200
O13	2	2r. brown	—	£1400
O14	2	5r. mauve	—	£4000

1918. Optd **ON K S D.**

O15	12	2a. orange	£170	5·00

1918. Optd **ON K S D.**

O17	13	¼a. red	—	£500
O18	13	½a. brown	3·25	1·75
O19	13	1a. blue	18·00	4·00
O20	13	2a. orange	—	£1500
O21	13	4a. brown	90·00	18·00
O22	13	8a. violet	£550	£375
O23	13	1r. green	£1700	£1500
O24	13	5r. brown		

1918. Optd **ON K S D.**

O28	14	¼a. blue	3·50	1·50
O29	14	½a. green	2·50	75
O30a	14	1a. red	1·50	1·00
O31	14	2a. purple	24·00	12·00
O32	14	4a. blue	55·00	24·00
O33	14	8a. brown	£250	85·00
O34	14	1r. mauve	£600	£500
O35	14	2r. green		
O36	14	5r. brown	£2500	

1918. Optd **ON K S D.**

O25	15	¼a. blue	15·00	
O26	15	2a. purple	—	£150

For later issues see **RAJASTHAN**.

KOREA

A peninsula to the S. of Manchuria in E. Asia. Formerly an empire under Chinese suzerainty, it was annexed by Japan in 1910 and used Japanese stamps. After the defeat of Japan in 1945, Russian and United States Military administrations were set up in Korea to the north and south of the 38th Parallel respectively; in 1948 South Korea and North Korea became independent republics.

Korean Empire.
1884. 100 mon = 1 tempo.
1895. 5 poon = 1 cheun.
1900. 10 re (or rin) = 1 cheun;
100 cheun = 1 weun.

South Korea.
1946. 100 cheun = 1 weun.
1953. 100 weun = 1 hwan.
1962. 100 chon = 1 won.

North Korea.
100 cheun = 1 won.

KOREAN EMPIRE

1

1894

1	1	5m. pink	£110	£6000
2	-	10m. blue	29·00	£4250

Design: 10m. Central motif as in Type **1** but different frame and inscribed 'COREAN POST POST'.

3 Korean Flag

1895

7	3	5p. green	32·00	19·00
8	3	10p. blue	70·00	22·00
9	3	25p. red	75·00	30·00
10a	3	50p. lilac	18·00	11·00

(4)

1897. Optd with T **4**.

12A		5p. green	95·00	35·00
13A		10p. blue	£100	47·00
14A		25p. red	£110	48·00
16A		50p. lilac	95·00	45·00

1899. Surch in Korean characters.

17	3	1(p.) on 5p. green (No. 7)	£2250	£900
20	3	1(p.) on 5p. green (No. 12)	£950	£250
18	3	1(p.) on 25p. red (No. 9)	£500	£160
21	3	1(p.) on 25p. red (No. 14)	90·00	55·00

6

7 National Emblems

8

1900. T **6**, **7** (2ch.), **8** (2ch.) and similar designs.

22Aa		2r. grey	6·00	2·20
23B		1ch. green	11·00	5·25
24A		2ch. blue (Type **7**)	55·00	37·00
25B		2ch. blue (Type **8**)	8·75	7·50
26B		3ch. orange	13·50	8·00
27B		4ch. red	34·00	15·00
28B		5ch. pink	18·00	11·00
29B		6ch. blue	19·00	12·50
30B		10ch. purple	24·00	18·00
31Ba		15ch. purple	37·00	28·00
32B		20ch. red	55·00	41·00
33C		50ch. green and pink	£275	£150
34C		1wn. multicoloured	£800	£225
35C		2wn. green and purple	£1300	£300

9 Imperial Crown

1902. 40th Anniversary of Emperor's Accession as King.

36	9	3ch. orange	65·00	33·00

T **10** to **12** are in two parts, the horizontal strokes (one, two or three) representing the value figures and the bottom part being the character for cheun.

Some variation can be found in these woodblock overprints.

(10)

(11)

(12)

(16)

1902. (a) Surch as T **10** to **12**.

37B	3	1ch. on 25p. red (No. 9)	22·00	7·50
38A	3	1ch. on 25p. red (No. 14)	£150	80·00
39B	3	2ch. on 25p. red (No. 9)	26·00	8·75
40A	3	2ch. on 25p. red (No. 14)	95·00	75·00
42A	3	2ch. on 50p. lilac (No 10a)		£475
43B	3	3ch. on 25p. red (No. 9)	65·00	£110
44A	3	3ch. on 25p. red (No. 14)		
46B	3	3ch. on 50p. lilac (No. 10a)	27·00	15·00
47A	3	3ch. on 50p. lilac (No. 16)	75·00	55·00

(b) Surch as T **16** (Japanese sen character) and strokes.

49		3ch. on 50p. lilac	£1300	£650

17 Falcon, Sceptre and Orb

1903

50	17	2r. grey	12·50	5·00
51	17	1ch. purple	13·00	6·50
52	17	2ch. green	13·50	6·50
53	17	3ch. orange	15·00	6·50
54	17	4ch. pink	22·00	7·25
55	17	5ch. brown	23·00	8·50
56	17	6ch. lilac	27·00	10·00
57	17	10ch. blue	31·00	13·50
58	17	15ch. red on yellow	50·00	24·00
59	17	20ch. purple on yellow	65·00	29·00
60	17	50ch. red on green	£190	£100
61	17	1wn. lilac on lilac	£350	£225
62	17	2wn. purple on orange	£450	£300

SOUTH KOREA

A. UNITED STATES MILITARY GOVERNMENT

(31)

1946. Stamps of Japan surch as T **31**.

69		5ch. on 5s. purple (No. 396)	13·50	12·00
70		5ch. on 14s. red & brn (No. 324)	2·50	3·00
71		10ch. on 40s. purple (No. 407)	2·50	3·00
72		20ch. on 6s. blue (No. 397)	2·50	3·00
73		30ch. on 27s. red (No. 404)	2·50	3·00
74		5w. on 17s. violet (No. 402)	13·50	12·00

33 National Emblem

1946. Liberation from Japanese Rule.

75	-	3ch. orange	1·50	1·00
76	-	5ch. green	1·50	1·00
77	-	10ch. red	1·50	1·00
78	-	20ch. blue	1·50	1·00
79	33	50ch. purple	3·00	1·20
80	33	1w. brown	5·25	1·60

Design: 3ch. to 20ch. Family and flag.

34 Dove of Peace and Map of Korea

1946. First Anniversary of Liberation.

81	34	50ch. violet	10·00	4·00

35 US and Korean Flags

1946. Resumption of Postal Service between Korea and USA.

82	35	10w. red	8·50	3·25

36 Kyongju Observatory

39 Golden Crown of Silla

40 Admiral Li Sun Sin

1946

83	36	50ch. blue	1·80	1·50
84	-	1w. brown	2·20	1·90
85	-	2w. blue	2·40	1·90
86	39	5w. mauve	22·00	11·00
87	40	10w. green	24·00	17·00

Designs: As T **36**—1w. Hibiscus; 2w. Map of Korea.

41 Korean Alphabet

1946. 500th Anniversary of Creation of Korean Alphabet.

88	41	50ch. blue	8·75	4·50

42 Li Jun, patriot

44 16th-century 'Turtle' Ship

1947

89	42	5w. green	11·00	7·00
90	-	10w. blue	11·00	7·00
91	-	20w. red	7·50	3·75
92	44	50w. brown	£130	37·00

Designs: 10w. Admiral Li Sun Sin; 20w. Independence Arch, Seoul.

45 Letters Surrounding Globe

1947. Resumption of International Postal Service.

93	**45**	10w. blue	17·00	7·25

46 Douglas DC-4 Airliner

1947. Air. Inauguration of Air Mail Service.

94	**46**	50w. red	13·50	3·75
126	**46**	150w. blue	3·75	1·50
127	**46**	150w. green	22·00	13·00

47 Hand and Ballot Slip

48 Casting Votes

1948. South Korea Election.

95	**47**	2w. orange	20·00	6·50
96	**47**	5w. mauve	33·00	10·00
97	**47**	10w. violet	47·00	16·00
98	**48**	20w. red	65·00	24·00
99	**48**	50w. blue	47·00	21·00

49 Korean Flag and Laurel Wreath

1948. Olympic Games.

100	**49**	5w. green	£150	55·00
101	-	10w. violet	65·00	20·00

Design: Vert—10w. Runner with torch.

50 Capitol and Ears of Rice

1948. Meeting of First National Assembly.

102	**50**	4w. brown	27·00	10·50

MINIATURE SHEETS. Many of the stamps from 1948 to 1956 exist in miniature sheets from limited printings which were presented to postal and government officials.

51 Korean Family

1948. Promulgation of Constitution.

103	**51**	4w. green	£120	30·00
104	-	10w. brown	50·00	19·00

Design: Horiz—10w. Flag of Korea.

52 Dr. Syngman Rhee (First President)

1948. Election of First President.

105	**52**	5w. blue	£400	£130

B. REPUBLIC OF KOREA

53 Hibiscus

1948. Proclamation of Republic.

106	-	4w. blue	50·00	24·00
107	**53**	5w. mauve	90·00	30·00

Design: 4w. Dove and olive branch.

54 Li Jun

55 Kyongju Observatory

1948

108	**54**	4w. red	1·50	1·10
109	**55**	14w. blue	1·50	1·10

56 Doves and UN Emblem

1949. Arrival of UN Commission.

110	**56**	10w. blue	60·00	18·00

57 Citizen and Date

1949. National Census.

111	**57**	15w. violet	75·00	21·00

58 Children and Plant

1949. 20th Anniversary of Children's Day.

112	**58**	15w. violet	44·00	11·00

59 Hibiscus

61 Dove and Globe

60 Map of Korea and Black-billed Magpies

62 Admiral Li Sun Sin

1949

113	-	1w. red	7·75	3·25
114	-	2w. grey	6·75	2·75
115	-	5w. green	27·00	7·50
116	-	10w. green	3·00	1·10
117	**59**	15w. red	1·10	1·00
118	-	20w. brown	1·50	1·00
119	-	30w. green	1·50	1·00
120	-	50w. blue	1·50	1·00
121	**60**	65w. blue	2·50	1·90
122	-	100w. green	1·50	1·00
123	**61**	200w. green	1·10	1·00
124	-	400w. brown	1·10	1·00
125	**62**	500w. blue	1·10	1·00

Designs: As T **59**—1w. Postman; 2w. Worker and factory; 5w. Harvesting rice; 10w. Manchurian cranes; 20w. Diamond Mountains; 30w. Ginseng plant; 50w. South Gate, Seoul; 100w. Tabo Pogoda, Kyongju. As T **61**—400w. Diamond Mountains.

63 Symbol and Phoenix

1949. First Anniversary of Independence.

128	**63**	15w. blue	60·00	13·50

64 Steam Train

1949. 50th Anniversary of Korean Railways.

129	**64**	15w. blue	£160	37·00

65 Korean Flag

1949. 75th Anniversary of UPU.

130	**65**	15w. multicoloured	33·00	15·00

66 Post-horse Warrant

1950. 50th Anniversary of Membership of UPU.

131	**66**	15w. green	50·00	15·00
132	**66**	65w. brown	22·00	7·50

67 Douglas DC-2 Aeroplane and Globe

1950. Air. Opening of Internal Air Mail Service.

133	**67**	60w. blue	37·00	7·50

68 Demonstrators

1950. 31st Anniversary of Abortive Proclamation of Independence.

134	**68**	15w. green	48·00	15·00
135	**68**	65w. violet	22·00	6·00

69 Capitol, Seoul

1950. Second South Korean Election.

136	**69**	30w. multicoloured	30·00	6·75

70 Dr. Syngman Rhee

71 Flag and Mountains

1950. Unification of Korea.

137	**70**	100w. blue	7·50	3·00
138	**71**	100w. green	9·50	3·00
139	-	200w. green	6·75	2·20

Design: 35×24 mm—200w. Map of Korea and flags of UN and Korea.

73 Manchurian Crane

76 Post-horse Warrant

77 Fairy (8th-century painting)

1951. Perf or roul.

140	**73**	5w. brown	3·25	2·20
181	-	20w. violet	3·75	3·00
187	-	50w. green	5·50	2·50
183	**76**	100w. blue	4·50	1·50
193	**77**	1000w. green	11·00	75

Designs: Horiz—20w. Astrological Tiger (ancient painting); 50w. Dove and Korean flag.

1951. Surch with new value.

145	**54**	100w. on 4w. red	6·25	3·75
146	**59**	200w. on 15w. red	12·00	5·75
147	**54**	300w. on 4w. red	4·75	3·75
149	**55**	300w. on 14w. blue	9·50	3·75
150	**59**	300w. on 15w. red	4·75	3·75
151	-	300w. on 20w. brown (No. 118)	6·00	4·50
152	-	300w. on 30w. green (No. 119)	4·75	3·75
153	-	300w. on 50w. blue (No. 120)	4·50	3·25
154	**60**	300w. on 65w. blue	5·00	3·75
155	-	300w. on 100w. green (No. 122)	4·75	3·00
156	-	300w. on 10w. green (No. 116)	14·00	5·25

80 Statue of Liberty and Flags

1951. Participation in Korean War. Flags in National Colours. A. As T **80** in green. B. As T **80** but showing UN Emblem and doves in blue.

158A	500w. Australia	12·00	12·00
158B	500w. Australia	10·50	10·50
159A	500w. Belgium	12·00	12·00
159B	500w. Belgium	10·50	10·50
160A	500w. Britain	12·00	12·00
160B	500w. Britain	10·50	10·50
161A	500w. Canada	12·00	12·00
161B	500w. Canada	10·50	10·50
162A	500w. Colombia	12·00	12·00
162B	500w. Colombia	10·50	10·50
163A	500w. Denmark	60·00	60·00
163B	500w. Denmark	37·00	37·00
164A	500w. Ethiopia	12·00	12·00
164B	500w. Ethiopia	10·50	10·50
165A	500w. France	12·00	12·00
165B	500w. France	10·50	10·50
166A	500w. Greece	12·00	12·00
166B	500w. Greece	10·50	10·50
167A	500w. India	50·00	50·00
167B	500w. India	37·00	37·00
168A	500w. Italy (with crown)	60·00	60·00
168B	500w. Italy (with crown)	44·00	44·00
169A	500w. Italy (without crown)	13·50	13·50
169B	500w. Italy (without crown)	22·00	22·00
170A	500w. Luxembourg	50·00	50·00
170B	500w. Luxembourg	37·00	37·00
171A	500w. Netherlands	12·00	12·00
171B	500w. Netherlands	10·50	10·50
172A	500w. New Zealand	12·00	12·00
172B	500w. New Zealand	10·50	10·50
173A	500w. Norway	50·00	50·00
173B	500w. Norway	37·00	37·00
174A	500w. Philippines	12·00	12·00
174B	500w. Philippines	10·50	10·50
175A	500w. Sweden	12·00	12·00
175B	500w. Sweden	10·50	10·50
176A	500w. Thailand	12·00	12·00
176B	500w. Thailand	10·50	10·50
177A	500w. Turkey	12·00	12·00
177B	500w. Turkey	10·50	10·50
178A	500w. Union of South Africa	12·00	12·00
178B	500w. Union of South Africa	10·50	10·50
179A	500w. USA	10·50	10·50
179B	500w. USA	8·75	8·75

1951. Air. No. 126 surch **500 WON**.

180	**46**	500w. on 150w. blue	10·50	3·75

82 Buddha of Sokkuram

83 Pulguksa Temple, Kyongju

84 Monument to King Muryol, Kyongju

85 Shrine of Admiral Li Sun Sin, Tongyong

1952. Inscr 'KOREA'.

184	**82**	200w. red	3·75	1·50
185	**83**	300w. green	3·00	75
191	**84**	500w. red	5·25	1·50
192	**84**	500w. blue	44·00	£150
194	**85**	2000w. blue	3·75	75

See also Nos. 200/201 and 205.

86 President Syngman Rhee

1952. President's Election to Second Term of Office.

195	**86**	1000w. green	13·50	7·50

87 Douglas DC-3 over Freighter

1952. Air.

196	**87**	1200w. brown	2·50	75
197	**87**	1800w. blue	2·50	75
198	**87**	4200w. violet	6·50	1·00

For stamps in new currency, see Nos. 210/212.

88 Tree-planting

89 Monument to King Muryol, Kyongju

91 Pagoda Park, Seoul

92 Sika Deer

93 Sika Deer

1953. New currency. With character hwan after figure of value.

244	**88**	1h. blue	70	45
200	**84**	2h. blue	1·90	40
201	**84**	5h. green	2·30	40
202	**89**	5h. green	2·75	1·20
203	**88**	10h. green	7·00	1·40
204	-	10h. brown	11·00	1·90
205	**85**	20h. brown	8·00	1·50
206	**91**	30h. blue	2·30	1·40
242	**92**	100h. brown	75·00	6·25
243	**91**	200h. violet	15·00	2·30
208	**93**	500h. orange	85·00	5·50
209	**93**	1000h. brown	£200	6·25

Design: No. 204, *Metopta rectifasciata* (moth) and Korean flag.

For designs without character after figure of value, see 1955 issue (No. 273 etc).

1953. Air. Colours changed and new Currency.

210	**87**	12h. blue	3·00	65
211	**87**	18h. violet	3·75	75
212	**87**	42h. green	4·50	1·20

94 Field Hospital

1953. Red Cross Fund. Crosses in red.

213	**94**	10h.+5h. green	17·00	4·75
214	-	10h.+5h. blue	17·00	4·75

Design: Vert—No. 214, Nurses supporting wounded soldier.

95 YMCA Badge and Map

1953. 50th Anniversary of Korean Young Men's Christian Association.

215	**95**	10h. red and black	11·00	3·75

96 Douglas DC-6 over East Gate, Seoul

1954. Air.

216	**96**	25h. brown	6·25	1·40
217	**96**	35h. purple	6·25	1·60
218	**96**	38h. green	6·25	1·80
219	**96**	58h. blue	6·25	2·00
220	**96**	71h. blue	15·00	2·40
258	**96**	70h. green	11·50	3·75
259	**96**	110h. brown	11·50	3·75
260	**96**	205h. mauve	19·00	3·75

98 Tokto Island

1954

221	-	2h. purple	3·75	2·30
222	-	5h. blue	8·25	2·30
223	**98**	10h. green	12·00	2·30

Design: 2, 5h. Rocks off Tokto Island.

99 Erosion Control

1954. Fourth World Forestry Congress, Dehru Dun.

224	**99**	10h. light green and green	7·00	1·20
225	**99**	19h. light green and green	7·00	1·90

100 Presidents Syngman Rhee and Eisenhower

1954. Korea–United States Mutual Defence Treaty.

226	**100**	10h. blue	5·00	1·50
227	**100**	19h. brown	5·50	1·50
228	**100**	71h. green	9·25	2·30

101 Rebirth of Industry

1955. Reconstruction.

229A	**101**	10h. brown	5·50	2·75
230B	**101**	15h. violet	5·00	90
231B	**101**	20h. blue	5·00	95
232B	**101**	50h. mauve	9·50	1·30
269	**101**	50h. red	9·25	1·90

102 Rotary Emblem

1955. 50th Anniversary of Rotary International.

236	**102**	20h. violet	9·25	2·75
237	**102**	25h. green	4·75	1·50

238	**102**	71h. purple	4·75	1·50

103 President Syngman Rhee

1955. 80th Birthday of President.

239	**103**	20h. blue	27·00	7·75

104 Independence Arch, Seoul

1955. Tenth Anniversary of Liberation.

240	**104**	40h. green	11·50	1·90
241	**104**	100h. brown	11·50	2·75

105 Hibiscus

106 King Sejong

107 Kyongju Observatory

1955. Without character after figure of value.

273	**88**	2h. blue	75	40
309	**89**	4h. blue	1·20	40
310	**89**	5h. green	1·20	40
247	**105**	10h. mauve	1·80	70
277	-	10h. green	1·30	10
248	**106**	20h. purple	3·50	70
279	**105**	20h. mauve	1·50	40
280	-	30h. violet	1·50	40
281	**106**	40h. purple	1·70	30
249	**107**	50h. violet	4·00	70
315	-	55h. purple	3·25	75
250	**92**	100h. purple	28·00	4·00
284	**107**	100h. violet	4·25	45
285	**92**	200h. purple	5·00	45
286	**91**	400h. violet	75·00	4·75
251	**93**	500h. brown	70·00	4·75
288	**93**	1000h. brown	£150	11·50
MS289		Set of 10 sheets (110×83 mm) each with one of Nos. 273, 277, 279/281, 283/286, 309	£1100	

Designs: Horiz—No. 277, South Gate, Seoul; No. 280, Tiger. Vert—No. 315, Haegumgang (cliff face).

108 Runners and Torch

1955. 36th National Athletic Meeting.

252	**108**	20h. purple	7·00	1·90
253	**108**	55h. green	7·00	1·90

109 UN Emblem

1955. Tenth Anniversary of UN.

254	**109**	20h. green	5·50	1·50
255	**109**	55h. blue	5·50	1·50

110 Admiral Li Sun Sin and 16th-century 'Turtle' Ship

1955. Tenth Anniversary of Korean Navy.

256	**110**	20h. blue	10·50	2·50

111 Admiration Pagoda

1956. 81st Birthday of President.

257	**111**	20h. green	7·75	2·20

112 President Syngman Rhee

1956. President's Election to Third Term of Office.

261	**112**	20h. brown	£120	27·00
262	**112**	55h. blue	55·00	11·50

113 Torch and Olympic Rings

1956. Olympic Games.

263	**113**	20h. brown	6·25	2·30
264	**113**	55h. green	6·25	2·30

114 Central PO, Seoul

1956. Stamp Day. Inscr '4289.12.4'.

265	**114**	20h. turquoise	15·00	2·75
266	-	50h. red	23·00	4·75
267	-	55h. green	11·50	1·90

Designs: Vert—50h. Stamp of 1884. Horiz—55h. Man leading post-pony.

MINIATURE SHEETS. Beginning in 1957 miniature sheets were put on sale at post offices. Miniature sheets of earlier issues were intended only for presentation purposes.

119 ITU Emblem and Radio Mast

1957. Fifth Anniversary of Korea's Admission to ITU.

290	**119**	40h. blue	3·00	1·30
291	**119**	55h. green	3·00	1·30
MS292		110×3 mm. Nos. 290/291. Imperf. No gum.	£950	

120 Korean Scout and Badge

1957. 50th Anniversary of Boy Scout Movement.

293	**120**	40h. purple	2·75	1·30
294	**120**	55h. purple	2·75	1·30
MS295		110×83 mm. Nos. 293/294. Imperf	£3250	

1957. Flood Relief Fund. As No. 281 but Korean inscr and premium added and colour changed.

299	**121**	40h.+10h. green	11·50	2·30
MS300		110×84 mm. No. 299	£250	

123 Mercury, Flags and Freighters

1957. Korean–American Friendship Treaty.

301	**123**	40h. orange	2·30	85
302	**123**	205h. green	4·75	1·70
MS303 110×84 mm. Nos. 301/302. Imperf. No gum			£1700	

124 Star of Bethlehem and Pine Cone

1957. Christmas and New Year Issue.

304	**124**	15h. brown, green and orange	11·00	1·90
305	-	25h. green, red and yellow	11·00	1·90
306	-	30h. blue, green and yellow	22·00	2·75
MS307 Three sheets, each 90×60 mm. Nos. 304/306. Imperf			£3750	

Designs: 25h. Christmas tree and tassels; 30h. Christmas tree and dog by window.

125 Winged Letter

1958. Postal Week.

321	**125**	40h. blue and red	2·30	75
MS322 90×60 mm. No. 321. Imperf			£2250	

126 Korean Children regarding future

1958. Tenth Anniversary of Republic of Korea.

323	**126**	20h. grey	1·90	60
324	-	40h. red	2·75	85
MS325 110×84 mm. Nos. 323/324. Imperf			£550	£500

Design: 40h. Hibiscus flowers forming figure '10'.

127 UNESCO Headquarters, Paris

1958. Inauguration of UNESCO Building, Paris.

326	**127**	40h. orange and green	1·50	55
MS327 90×60 mm. No. 326. Imperf			£225	£200

128 Children flying Kites

1958. Christmas and New Year.

330	**128**	15h. green	2·30	75
331	-	25h. red, yellow and blue	2·30	75
332	-	30h. red, blue and yellow	3·75	1·20
MS333 Three sheets each 90×60 mm. Nos. 330/332. Imperf			£250	£250

Designs: Vert—25h. Christmas tree, tassels and wicker basket (cooking sieve); 30h. Children in traditional festive costume.

129 Rejoicing Crowds in Pagoda Park, Flag and Torch

1959. 40th Anniversary of Abortive Proclamation of Independence.

334	**129**	40h. purple and brown	1·50	60
MS335 90×60 mm. No. 334			£140	£130

130 Marines going ashore from Landing-craft

1959. Tenth Anniversary of Korean Marine Corps.

336	**130**	40h. bronze green	1·50	60
MS337 90×60 mm. No. 336. Imperf			15·00	12·50

1959. Third Postal Week. Sheet containing Nos. 311/314.

MS338 70×105 mm		11·50	10·50

131

1959. Tenth Anniversary of Korea's Admission to WHO.

339	**131**	40h. purple and pink	1·50	60
MS340 90×60 mm. No. 339. Imperf			13·00	10·50

132 Diesel Train

1959. 60th Anniversary of Korean Railways.

341	**132**	40h. sepia and brown	2·50	1·00
MS342 90×60 mm. No. 341. Imperf			31·00	25·00

133 Runners in Relay Race

1959. 40th Korean National Games.

343	**133**	40h. brown and blue	1·70	70
MS344 90×60 mm. No. 343. Imperf			19·00	17·00

134 Red Cross and Korea

1959. Red Cross. Inscr '1959 4292.10.27'.

345	**134**	40h. red and green	1·50	45
346	-	55h. red and mauve	1·50	45
MS347 110×60 mm. Nos. 345/346. Imperf			42·00	38·00

Design: 55h. Red Cross on globe.

135 Korean Postal Flags Old and New

1959. 75th Anniversary of Korean Postal Service.

348	**135**	40h. red and blue	1·50	55
MS349 90×60 mm. No. 348. Imperf			23·00	21·00

136 Mice in Korean Costume and New Year Emblem

1959. Christmas and New Year.

350	**136**	15h. pink, blue and grey	1·50	35
351	-	25h. red, green and blue	1·50	40
352	-	30h. red, black and mauve	3·00	50
MS353 Three sheets each 90×60 mm. Nos. 350/352. Imperf			95·00	85·00

Designs: 25h. Carol singers; 30h. Crane.

137 UPU Monument

1960. 60th Anniversary of Admission of Korea to UPU.

354	**137**	40h. chocolate and blue	1·90	75
MS355 90×60 mm. No. 354. Imperf			39·00	35·00

138 Honey Bee and Clover

1960. Children's Savings Campaign.

356	**138**	10h. yellow, brown and green	1·50	75
357	-	20h. brown, blue and pink	1·90	75

Design: 20h. Snail and Korean money-bag.

For these stamps in new currency, see Nos. 452 etc.

139 'Uprooted Tree'

1960. World Refugee Year.

358	**139**	40h. red, blue and green	1·50	55
MS359 90×60 mm. No. 358. Imperf			60·00	55·00

140 President Eisenhower

1960. Visit of President Eisenhower of United States.

360	**140**	40h. ultramarine, vermillion and green	4·75	1·90
MS361 90×60 mm. No. 360. Imperf			39·00	38·00

141 Schoolchildren

1960. 75th Anniversary of Educational System.

362	**141**	40h. purple, chestnut and olive	1·50	45
MS363 90×60 mm. No. 362. Imperf			9·25	8·50

142 Assembly

1960. Inauguration of House of Councillors.

364	**143**	40h. grey	1·50	45
MS365 90×60 mm. No. 364. Imperf			9·25	8·50

143 Liberation

1960. 15th Anniversary of Liberation.

366	**143**	40h. lake, blue and ochre	1·90	55
MS367 90×60 mm. No. 366. Imperf			9·25	8·50

144 Weightlifting

1960. Olympic Games.

368	**144**	20h. brown, flesh & turq	1·70	75
369	-	40h. brown, blue & turq	1·70	75
MS370 90×60 mm. Nos. 368/369. Imperf			29·00	26·00

Design: 40h. South Gate, Seoul.

145 Barn Swallow and Insulators

1960. 75th Anniversary of Korean Telegraph Service.

371	**145**	40h. violet, grey and blue	1·70	75
MS372 90×60 mm. No. 371. Imperf			8·50	7·50

146 Rebirth of Republic

1960. Establishment of New Government.

373	**146**	40h. green, blue and orange	1·50	45
MS374 90×60 mm. No. 373. Imperf			7·75	7·00

1960. Postal Week and International Correspondence Week. Sheet containing Nos. 356/357. Imperf.

MS375 90×60 mm		5·50	5·00

147 'Torch of Culture'

1960. Cultural Month.

376	**147**	40h. yellow, light blue and blue	1·50	45
MS377 90×60 mm. No. 376. Imperf			7·75	6·75

148 UN Flag

1960. 15th Anniversary of UN.

378	**148**	40h. blue, green and mauve	1·50	45
MS379 90×60 mm. No. 378. Imperf			7·75	6·75

149 UN Emblem and Gravestones

1960. Establishment of UN Memorial Cemetery.

380	**149**	40h. brown and orange	1·50	45
MS381 90×60 mm. No. 380. Imperf			7·75	6·75

150 National Stocktaking

1960. Census of Population and Resources.

382	**150**	40h. carmine, drab and blue	1·50	45
MS383 90×60 mm. No. 382. Imperf			7·75	6·75

151 Festival Stocking

1960. Christmas and New Year Issue.

384	-	15h. brown, yellow and grey	2·30	40
385	**151**	25h. red, green and blue	3·00	40
386	-	30h. red, yellow and blue	3·75	75
MS387 Three sheets, each 90×60 mm. Nos. 384/386. Imperf			32·00	27·00

Designs: 15h. Ox's head; 30h. Girl bowing in New Year's greeting.

152 Wind-sock and Ancient Rain-gauge

1961. World Meteorological Day.

388	**152**	40h. ultramarine and blue	1·50	45
MS389 90×60 mm. No. 388. Imperf			4·75	4·25

153 Family, Sun and Globe

1961. World Health Day.

390	**153**	40h. brown and orange	1·50	45
MS391 90×60 mm. No. 390. Imperf			4·75	4·25

154 Students' Demonstration

1961. First Anniversary of April Revolution (Overthrow of President Syngman Rhee).

392	**154**	40h. green, red and blue	1·90	75
MS393 90×60 mm. No. 392. Imperf			11·50	10·50

155 Workers and Conference Emblem

1961. International Community Development Conference, Seoul.

394	**155**	40h. green	1·50	55
MS395 90×60 mm. No. 394. Imperf			7·00	6·25

156 Girl Guide, Camp and Badge

1961. 15th Anniversary of Korean Girl Guide Movement.

396	**156**	40h. green	1·90	55
MS397 90×60 mm. No. 396. Imperf			15·00	14·00

157 Soldier's Grave

1961. Memorial Day.

398	**157**	40h. black and drab	3·00	1·30
MS399 90×60 mm. No. 398. Imperf			11·50	10·50

158 Soldier with Torch

1961. Revolution of 16 May (Seizure of Power by General Pak Chung Hi).

400	**158**	40h. brown and yellow	3·00	1·30
MS401 90×60 mm. No. 400. Imperf			11·00	9·75

159 Three Liberations

1961. Liberation Day.

402	**159**	40h. multicoloured	3·00	1·30
MS403 90×60 mm. No. 402. Imperf			6·25	5·50

160 Korean Forces, Flag and Destroyer

1961. Armed Forces Day.

404	**160**	40h. multicoloured	3·00	1·20
MS405 90×60 mm. No. 404. Imperf			5·50	4·75

161 'Korean Art' (Kyongbok Palace Art Gallery)

1961. Tenth Korean Art Exhibition.

406	**161**	40h. chocolate and brown	1·90	55
MS407 90×60 mm. No. 406. Imperf			4·75	4·25

162 Birthday Candle

1961. 15th Anniversary of UNESCO.

408	**162**	40h. blue and green	1·90	55
MS409 90×60 mm. No. 408. Imperf			4·75	4·25

163 Mobile X-Ray Unit

1961. Tuberculosis Vaccination Week.

410	**163**	40h. brown, black and light brown	1·50	55
MS411 90×60 mm. No. 410. Imperf			4·75	4·25

164 Ginseng

166 White-bellied Black Woodpecker

165 King Sejong

167 Rice Harvester

168 Korean Drum

1961

412	**164**	20h. red	2·30	60
413	**165**	30h. purple	6·25	60
414	**166**	40h. blue and red	5·50	60
415	**167**	40h. green	9·25	75
416	**168**	100h. brown	12·50	1·50

See also 1962 issue (No. 537 etc), and for stamps inscribed 'REPUBLIC OF KOREA', see Nos. 641 etc.

169 Douglas DC-8 Jetliner over Pagoda

1961. Air.

417	**169**	50h. violet and blue	23·00	6·25
418	-	100h. brown and blue	31·00	10·00
419	-	200h. brown and blue	46·00	12·50
420	-	400h. green and blue	55·00	13·00

Designs: Aeroplane over—100h. West Gate, Suwon; 200h. Gateway and wall of Toksu Palace, Seoul; 400h. Pavilion, Kyongbok Palace, Seoul.

See also Nos. 454 etc.

170 ITU Emblem as Satellite

1962. Tenth Anniversary of Admission to ITU.

421	**170**	40h. red and blue	2·30	1·00
MS422 90×59 mm. No. 421. Imperf			14·00	12·50

171 Triga Mark II Reactor

1962. First Korean Atomic Reactor.

423	**171**	40h. green, drab and blue	2·30	55

172 Mosquito and Emblem

1962. Malaria Eradication.

424	**172**	40h. red and green	1·50	75
MS425 90×60 mm. No. 424			3·75	3·25

173 Girl and YWCA Emblem

1962. 40th Anniversary of Korean Young Women's Christian Association.

426	**173**	40h. blue and orange	2·30	55

174 Emblem of Asian Film Producers' Federation

1962. Ninth Asian Film Festival, Seoul.

427	**174**	40h. violet, red and turquoise	3·00	55

175 Soldiers crossing Han River Bridge

1962. First Anniversary of 16th May Revolution.

428	-	30h. green and brown	3·00	1·10
429	**175**	40h. brown, green & turq	3·00	1·10
430	-	200h. yellow, red and blue	34·00	8·50
MS431 Three sheets, each 90×140 mm. Nos. 428/30. Imperf. Inscr in Korean			£120	£110
MS432 As last but sheets inscr in English			£250	£225

Designs: Horiz—30h. 'Industrial Progress' (men moving cogwheel up slope); 200h. 'Egg' containing Korean badge and industrial skyline.

176 20-oared 'Turtle' Ship

1962. 370th Anniversary of Hansan Naval Victory over Japanese.

433	**176**	2w. blue and light blue	19·00	1·50
434	-	4w. black, violet & turq	24·00	2·30

Design: 4w. 16-oared 'turtle' ship.

177 Chindo Dog

178 *Hanabusaya asiatica*

179 Statue of Goddess Mikuk Besal

180 Farmers' Dance

181 12th-century Wine-jug

182 Mison

183 13th-century Printing-block and Impression used for *Tripitaka Koreana*

191 Sika Deer

192 Bell of King Kyongdok

213 Longhorn Beetle

214 Factory, Fish and Corn

215 Boddhisatva, Sokkuram Shrine

216 Tile, Silla Dynasty

217 *Azure Dragon*, Koguryo period

1962. New Currency.

537	**177**	20ch. brown	75	25
436	**178**	40ch. blue	1·50	40
785	-	40ch. green	1·50	40
539	**179**	50ch. brown	75	25
540	**213**	60ch. brown	95	30
541	**180**	1w. blue	2·30	25
542	**179**	1w.50 grey	75	30
543	**164**	2w. red	3·75	25
472	**165**	3w. purple	14·50	30
545	**167**	4w. green	75	25
442	**181**	5w. blue	6·25	85
547	**214**	7w. mauve	3·00	75
548	**168**	10w. brown	4·75	25
549	**182**	20w. mauve	4·75	40
550	**183**	40w. purple	7·75	1·50
551	**191**	50w. brown	19·00	1·50
552	**192**	100w. green	70·00	2·30
553	**215**	200w. deep green and green	27·00	3·00
554	**216**	300w. green and brown	55·00	3·75
555	**217**	500w. blue and light blue	27·00	3·75

Design: 18×72 mm—No. 785, motif as T **178** but inscriptions differently arranged.

See also Nos. 607, 609 and 641/649.

184 Scout Badge and Korean Flag

1962. 40th Anniversary of Korean Scout Movement.

446	**184**	4w. brown, red and blue	1·90	75
447	**184**	4w. green, red and blue	1·90	75
MS448 Two sheets, each 90×60 mm. (a) As No. 446; (b) As No. 447			15·00	14·00

185 Chub Mackerel, Trawler and Nets

1962. Tenth Indo-Pacific Fishery Council Meeting, Seoul.

449	**185**	4w. ultramarine and blue	5·00	75

186 ICAO Emblem

1962. Tenth Anniversary of Korea's Entry into ICAO.

450	**186**	4w. blue and brown	2·30	75
MS451 90×60 mm. No. 450. Imperf			10·00	9·00

1962. Children's Savings Campaign. As Nos. 356/357 but new currency.

452	1w. yellow, brown and green	7·00	1·20
453	2w. brown, blue and pink	11·50	1·50

1962. Air. New Currency.

454	**169**	5w. blue and violet	95·00	17·00
512	-	10w. brown and green (As No. 418)	15·00	4·75
513	-	20w. brown and green (As No. 419)	55·00	7·75
563	**169**	39w. drab and blue	11·50	2·30
514	-	40w. green and blue (As No. 420)	29·00	6·25
564	-	64w. green and blue (As No. 418)	10·00	2·75
565	-	78w. blue and green (As No. 419)	27·00	4·75
566	-	112w. green and blue (As No. 420)	13·00	2·75

187 Electric Power Plant

1962. Inauguration of First Korean Economic Five Year Plan.

458	**187**	4w. violet and orange	21·00	2·30
459	-	4w. ultramarine and blue	21·00	2·30

Design: No. 459, Irrigation Dam.

See also Nos. 482/483, 528/529, 593/594 and 634/635.

188 Campaign Emblem

1963. Freedom from Hunger.

460	**188**	4w. green, buff and blue	1·50	55
MS461 90×60 mm. No. 460. Imperf			4·75	4·00

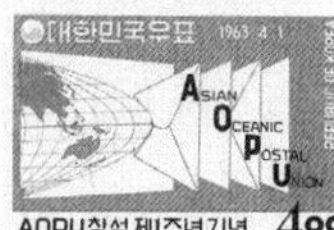

189 Globe and Letters

1963. First Anniversary of Asian–Oceanic Postal Union.

462	**189**	4w. purple, green and blue	2·30	55
MS463 90×60 mm. No. 462. Imperf			4·75	4·25

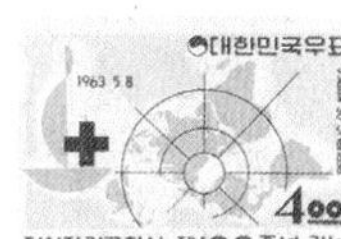

190 Centenary Emblem and Map

1963. Centenary of Red Cross.

464	**190**	4w. red, grey and blue	1·50	55
465	**190**	4w. red, grey and orange	1·50	55
MS466 140×90 mm. Nos. 464/465. Imperf			14·00	12·50

1963. Flood Relief. As No. 545, but new colour and inscr with premium.

479	4w.+1w. blue	9·25	1·20

193 '15' and Hibiscus

1963. 15th Anniversary of Republic.

480	**193**	4w. red, violet and blue	3·00	1·10

194 Nurse and Emblem

1963. 15th Anniversary of Korean Army Nursing Corps.

481	**194**	4w. black, turquoise and green	2·30	95

1963. Five Year Plan. Dated 1963. As T **187**.

482	4w. violet and blue	16·00	1·50
483	4w. chocolate and brown	16·00	1·50

Designs: No. 482, Cement Factory, Mun'gyong, and bag of cement; No. 483, Miner and coal train, Samch'ok region.

195/196 Rock Temples of Abu Simbel

1963. Nubian Monuments Preservation.

484	**195**	3w. green and drab	5·50	2·20
485	**196**	4w. green and drab	5·50	2·20
MS486 90×60 mm. Nos. 484/485. Imperf			8·50	7·50

Nos. 484/485 were issued together, *se-tenant*, forming the composite design illustrated.

197 Rugby Football and Athlete

1963. 44th National Games.

487	**197**	4w. green, brown and blue	3·75	1·30

198 Nurse and Motor Clinic

1963. Tenth Anniversary of Korean Tuberculosis Prevention Society.

488	**198**	4w. blue and red	1·90	75

199 Eleanor Roosevelt

1963. 15th Anniversary of Declaration of Human Rights.

489	**199**	3w. brown and blue	1·50	55
490	-	4w. blue, green and buff	1·50	55
MS491 90×60 mm. Nos. 489/90. Imperf			6·25	5·50

Design: 4w. Freedom torch and globe.

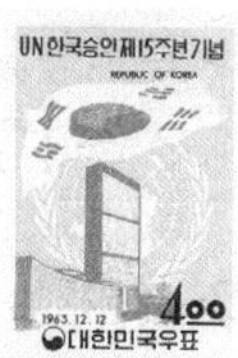

200 UN Headquarters

1963. 15th Anniversary of UN Recognition of Korea.

492	**200**	4w. green, blue and black	1·50	45
MS493 90×60 mm. No. 492			5·00	4·50

201 President Pak Chong Hi and Capitol

1963. Inauguration of President Pak Chong Hi.

494	**201**	4w. blue, turquoise and black	60·00	15·00

202 Tai-Keum (Bamboo Flute)

1963. Musical Instruments and Players. As T **202**.

495	4w. green, brown and drab	5·25	1·30
496	4w. black, blue and light blue	5·25	1·30
497	4w. green, mauve and pink	5·25	1·30
498	4w. brown, violet and grey	5·25	1·30
499	4w. blue, brown and pink	5·25	1·30
500	4w. turquoise, black and blue	5·25	1·30
501	4w. violet, bistre and yellow	5·25	1·30
502	4w. blue, brown and mauve	5·25	1·30
503	4w. black, blue and purple	5·25	1·30
504	4w. black, brown and pink	5·25	1·30

Musical Instruments (and players): Vert—No. 495, T **202**; No. 496, Wul-keum (banjo); No. 497, Tang-piri (flageolet); No. 498, Na-bal (trumpet); No. 499, Hyang-pipa (lute); No. 500, Pyenkyeng jade chimes; No. 501, Taipyeng-so (clarinet); No. 502, Chang-ko (double-ended drum). Horiz—No. 503, Wa-kong-hu (harp); No. 504, Kaya-ko (zither).

203 Symbols of Metric System

1964. Introduction of Metric System in Korea.

505	**203**	4w. multicoloured	1·50	45

204 'UNESCO'

1964. Tenth Anniversary of Korean UNESCO Committee.

506	**204**	4w. ultramarine, red & blue	1·90	70

205 Symbols of Industry and Census

1964. National Industrial Census (1963).

507	**205**	4w. brown, black and grey	1·90	70

206 YMCA Emblem and Profile of Young Man

1964. 50th Anniversary of Korean Young Men's Christian Association.

508	**206**	4w. red, blue and green	1·50	45

207 Fair Emblem, Ginseng Root and Freighter

1964. New York World's Fair.

509	**207**	40w. brown, green and yellow	3·75	1·30
510	-	100w. ultramarine, brown and blue	35·00	7·75
MS511 90×60 mm. Nos. 509/510. Imperf			80·00	75·00

Design: 100w. Korean pavilion at Fair.

208 Secret Garden

1964. Background in light blue.

517	**208**	1w. green	1·50	45
518	-	2w. green	1·50	45
519	-	3w. green	1·50	45
520	-	4w. green	3·00	95
521	-	5w. violet	5·50	1·50
522	-	6w. blue	7·00	1·90
523	-	7w. brown	10·00	2·75
524	-	8w. brown	10·50	2·75
525	-	9w. violet	10·50	2·75
526	-	10w. green	15·00	3·00
MS527 Five sheets each 90×60 mm. 1w. and 10w.; 2w. and 9w.; 3w. and 8w.; 4w. and 7w.; 5w. and 6w. Imperf			95·00	85·00

Designs: 2w. Whahong Gate; 3w. Uisang Pavilion; 4w. Mt. Songni; 5w. Paekma River; 6w. Anab Pond; 7w. Choksok Pavilion; 8w. Kwanghan Pavilion; 9w. Whaom Temple; 10w. Chonjeyon Falls.

1964. Five Year Plan. Dated 1964. As T **187**.

528	4w. black and blue	5·50	1·20
529	4w. blue and yellow	5·50	1·20

Designs: No. 528, Trawlers and fish; 529, Oil refinery and barrels.

209 Wheel and Globe

1964. Colombo Plan Day.

530	**209**	4w. light brown, brown and green	1·50	55
MS531 90×60 mm. No. 530. Imperf			5·50	4·75

210 'Helping Hand'

1964. 15th Anniversary of Korea's Admission to WHO.

532	**210**	4w. black, green and light green	1·50	55
MS533 90×60 mm. No. 532. Imperf			5·50	4·75

211 Running

1964. 45th National Games, Inchon.

534	**211**	4w. pink, green and purple	3·75	1·30

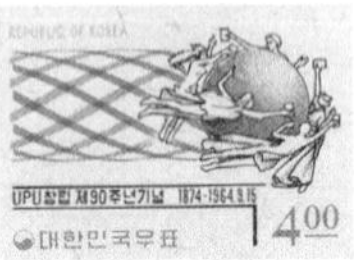

212 UPU Monument, Berne, and Ribbons

1964. 90th Anniversary of UPU.

535	**212**	4w. brown, blue and pink	1·50	55
MS536 90×60 mm. No. 535. Imperf			5·75	5·00

218 Federation Emblem

1964. Fifth Meeting of Int Federation of Asian and Western Pacific Contractors' Associations.

556	**218**	4w. green, light green and brown	1·50	55

219 Olympic 'V' Emblem

1964. Olympic Games, Tokyo.

557	**219**	4w. blue, turquoise and brown	3·00	1·00
558	-	4w. mauve, blue and green	3·00	1·00
559	-	4w. brown, ultramarine and blue	3·00	1·00
560	-	4w. red, brown and blue	3·00	1·00
561	-	4w. brown, purple and blue	3·00	1·00
MS562 Five sheets each 90×60 mm. As Nos. 557/561. Imperf			23·00	21·00

Designs: Horiz—No. 558, Running; No. 559, Rowing; No. 560, Horse-jumping; No. 561, Gymnastics.

220 Unissued 1884 100m. Stamp

1964. 80th Anniversary of Korean Postal Services.

567	**220**	3w. blue, violet and mauve	3·75	95
568	-	4w. black, violet and green	5·50	1·20

Design: 4w. Hong Yong Sik, First Korean Postmaster-general.

221 Pine Cone

1965. Korean Plants. Plants multicoloured, background colours given.

571	**221**	4w. green	2·30	75
572	-	4w. brown (Plum blossom)	2·30	75
573	-	4w. blue (Forsythia)	2·30	75
574	-	4w. green (Azalea)	2·30	75
575	-	4w. pink (Lilac)	2·30	75
576	-	4w. grey (Wild rose)	2·30	75
577	-	4w. green (Balsam)	2·30	75
578	-	4w. grey (Hibiscus)	2·30	75
579	-	4w. flesh (Crepe myrtle)	2·30	75
580	-	4w. blue (Ullung chrysanthemum)	2·30	75
581	-	4w. buff (Paulownia, tree)	2·30	75
582	-	4w. blue (Bamboo)	2·30	75
MS583 12 sheets each 90×60 mm. Nos. 571/582. Imperf			37·00	30·00

222 Folk Dancing

1965. Pacific Area Travel Association Conference, Seoul.

584	**222**	4w. violet, brown and green	1·40	45
MS585 90×60 mm. No. 584. Imperf			3·75	3·25

223 Flag and Doves

1965. Military Aid for Vietnam.

586	**223**	4w. brown, blue and yellow	1·40	45
MS587 90×60 mm. No. 586. Imperf			3·75	3·25

224 Food Production

1965. Agricultural Seven Year Plan.

588	**224**	4w. brown, green and black	1·40	45

225 Family Scales

1965. Family Planning Month.

589	**225**	4w. green, drab and light green	1·40	45
MS590 90×60 mm. No. 589. Imperf			3·50	3·25

226 ITU Emblem and Symbols

1965. Centenary of ITU.

591	**226**	4w. black, red and blue	1·40	45
MS592 90×60 mm. No. 591. Imperf			3·50	3·25

1965. Five Year Plan. Dated 1965. As T **187**.

593	4w. blue and pink	2·30	1·20
594	4w. sepia and brown	2·30	1·20

Designs: No. 593, *Korea* (freighter) at quayside and crates; No. 594, Fertiliser plant and wheat.

227 Flags of Australia, Belgium, Great Britain, Canada and Colombia

1965. 15th Anniversary of Outbreak of Korean War.

595	**227**	4w. multicoloured	1·50	70
596	-	4w. multicoloured	1·50	70
597	-	4w. multicoloured	1·50	70
598	-	4w. multicoloured	1·50	70
599	-	10w. multicoloured	5·50	1·50
MS600 Five sheets each 90×60 mm. Nos. 595/9. Imperf			11·50	10·50

Designs: UN Emblem and flags of—No. 596, Denmark, Ethiopia, France, Greece and India; No. 597, Italy, Luxembourg, Netherlands, New Zealand and Norway; No. 598, Philippines, Sweden, Thailand, Turkey and South Africa; No. 599, General MacArthur and flags of Korea, UN and USA.

228 Flag and Sky-writing ('20')

1965. 20th Anniversary of Liberation.

601	**228**	4w. red, violet and blue	3·00	55
602	-	10w. red, blue and violet	3·75	75

Design: 10w. South Gate and fireworks.

229 Ants and Leaf

1965. Savings Campaign.

603	**229**	4w. brown, ochre and green	1·40	45

230 Hoisting Flag

1965. 15th Anniversary of Recapture of Seoul.

604	**230**	3w. green, blue and orange	3·00	1·20

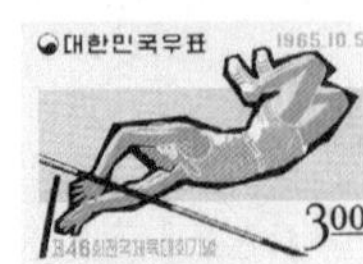

231 Radio Aerial

1965. 80th Anniversary of Korean Telecommunications.

605	**231**	3w. green, black and blue	2·30	45
606	-	10w. black, blue and yellow	4·75	75

Design: 10w. Telegraphist of 1885.

1965. Flood Relief. As No. 545 (1962 issue), but colour changed and inscr with premium.

607	4w.+2w. blue	4·75	1·20

232 Pole Vaulting

1965. National Athletic Meeting, Kwangju.

608	**232**	3w. multicoloured	2·30	95

1965. Aid for Children. As No. 545 (1962 issue), but colour changed and inscr with premium.

609	4w.+2w. purple	4·75	1·20

233 ICY Emblem

1965. International Co-operation Year and 20th Anniversary of United Nations.

610	**233**	3w. red, green and deep green	1·20	45
611	-	10w. ultramarine, green and blue	2·30	75
MS612 Two sheets each 90×60 mm. (a) No. 610; (b) No. 611			7·75	7·00

Design: Vert—10w. UN flag and headquarters, New York.

234 Child posting Letter

1965. Tenth Communications Day.

613	**234**	3w. multicoloured	3·00	95
614	-	10w. red, blue and green	6·25	1·70

Design: 10w. Airmail envelope and telephone receiver.

235 Children with Toboggan

1965. Christmas and New Year.

615	**235**	3w. blue, red and green	2·30	55
616	-	4w. blue, red and green	3·75	55
MS617 90×60 mm. Nos. 615/616. Imperf			4·75	4·00

Design: 4w. Boy and girl in traditional costume.

236 Freedom House

1966. Opening of Freedom House, Panmunjom.

618	**236**	7w. black, emerald & grn	2·30	75
619	**236**	39w. black, lilac and green	13·00	3·00
MS620 90×60 mm. Nos. 618/619. Imperf			23·00	19·00

237 Mandarins

1966. Korean Birds. Multicoloured.

621	3w. Type **237**	2·30	1·30
622	5w. Manchurian crane	2·50	1·30
623	7w. Common pheasant	3·75	1·30
MS624 Three sheets each 90×60 mm. Nos. 621/623. Imperf		14·00	12·00

238 Pine Forest

1966. Reafforestation Campaign.

625	**238**	7w. brown, green and light green	1·50	55

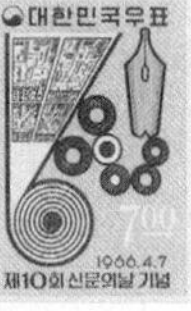

239 Printing Press and Pen

1966. Tenth Newspaper Day.

626	**239**	7w. purple, yellow and green	1·30	55

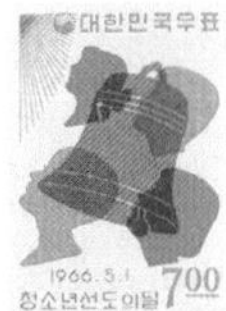
240 Curfew Bell and Young Koreans

1966. Youth Guidance Month.
627 **240** 7w. orange, green and blue 1·30 55

241 WHO Building

1966. Inauguration of WHO Headquarters, Geneva.
628 **241** 7w. black, blue and yellow 1·50 60
629 **241** 39w. red, grey and yellow 11·50 3·50
MS630 90×60 mm. No. 628. Imperf 4·75 3·50

242 President Pak, Handclasp and Flags

1966. President Pak Chung Hi's State Tour of South-East Asia.
631 **242** 7w. multicoloured 7·75 2·50

243 Girl Scout and Flag

1966. 20th Anniversary of Korean Girl Scouts.
632 **243** 7w. black, green and yellow 2·30 85

244 Student and Ehwa Women's University

1966. 80th Anniversary of Korean Women's Education.
633 **244** 7w. multicoloured 1·30 55

1966. 5-Year Plan. Dated 1966. As T **187**.
634 7w. ultramarine and blue 3·75 1·20
635 7w. black and yellow 3·75 1·20
Designs: No. 634, Map and transport; No. 635, Radar aerials and telephone.

245 Carrier Pigeons

1966. International Correspondence Week. Unissued sheet (90×60 mm) surch as shown in T **245** and optd **6, 1966.6.13—19** with bars obliterating old inscr.
MS636 7(w.) on 40(h.) deep green, green and red 3·75 3·50

246 Wall-eyed Pollack

1966. Korean Fish. Multicoloured.
637 3w. Type **246** 3·00 85
638 5w. Lenok 3·75 85
639 7w. Manchurian croaker 4·75 1·00
MS640 Three sheets each 90×60 mm. Nos. 637/639. Imperf 11·50 10·00

247 Incense-burner

249 Buddha, Kwanchok Temple

1966. As previous issues (some redrawn) and new designs, all inscr 'REPUBLIC OF KOREA'.
641 **213** 60ch. green 40 10
642 **180** 1w. green 4·25 40
643 **164** 2w. green 40 10
644 **165** 3w. brown 40 10
645 **181** 5w. blue 5·00 75
646 **214** 7w. blue 5·50 30
789 **168** 10w. blue (22×18 mm) 31·00 70
647 **247** 13w. blue 5·50 75
709 **182** 20w. green and light green 70·00 1·50
710 **183** 40w. green and olive 42·00 1·50
793 **183** 40w. blue and pink (18×22 mm) 46·00 2·30
711 **191** 50w. brown and bistre 8·50 1·50
648 - 60w. green 31·00 1·50
649 **249** 80w. green 11·50 1·50
Design: As T **247**—60w. 12th-century porcelain vessel.

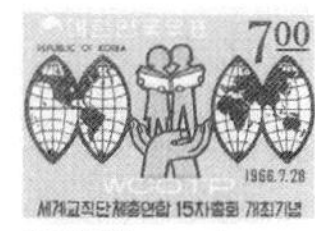
250 Children and Hemispheres

1966. 15th Assembly of World Conference of Teaching Profession (WCOTP), Seoul.
650 **250** 7w. violet, brown and blue 1·50 55
MS651 90×60 mm. No. 650. Imperf 3·75 3·50

251 Factory within Pouch

1966. Savings Campaign.
652 **251** 7w. multicoloured 1·30 55

252 People on Map of Korea

1966. National Census.
653 **252** 7w. multicoloured 1·30 55

253 *Lucida lateralis*

1966. Insects. Multicoloured.
654 3w. Type **253** 2·30 85
655 5w. *Hexacentrus japonicus* (grasshopper) 2·30 85
656 7w. *Sericinus montela* (butterfly) 3·00 1·00
MS657 Three sheets each 90×60 mm. (a) No. 654; (b) No. 655; (c) No. 656 11·00 10·00

254 CISM Emblem and Round Table Meeting

1966. 21st General Assembly of International Military Sports Council (CISM), Seoul.
658 **254** 7w. multicoloured 1·30 55
MS659 90×60 mm. No. 658. Imperf 3·75 3·50

255 Soldiers and Flags

1966. First Anniversary of Korean Troops in Vietnam.
660 **255** 7w. multicoloured 9·25 2·30

256 Wrestling

1966. 47th Athletic Meeting, Seoul.
661 **256** 7w. multicoloured 2·50 1·20

257 Lions Emblem and Map

1966. Fifth Orient and South-East Asian Lions Convention, Seoul.
662 **257** 7w. multicoloured 1·50 55
MS663 90×60 mm. No. 662. Imperf 3·75 3·50

258 University Emblem, '20' and Shields

1966. 20th Anniversary of Seoul University.
664 **258** 7w. multicoloured 1·50 55

259 APACL Emblem

1966. 12th Conference of Asian People's Anti-Communist League (APACL), Seoul.
665 **259** 7w. multicoloured 1·50 55
MS666 90×60 mm. No. 665. Imperf 3·50 3·25

260 Presidents Pak and Johnson

1966. President Johnson's Visit to Korea.
667 **260** 7w. multicoloured 2·30 75
668 **260** 83w. multicoloured 13·00 3·75
MS669 90×60 mm. Nos. 667/668. Imperf 15·00 14·00

261 UNESCO Symbols and Emblem

1966. 20th Anniversary of UNESCO.
670 **261** 7w. multicoloured 1·50 45
MS671 90×60 mm. No. 670. Imperf 3·75 3·50

1966. Hurricane Relief. As No. 646 but colour changed and premium added.
672 **214** 7w.+2w. red 6·25 1·50

262 'Lucky Bag'

1966. Christmas and New Year. Multicoloured.
673 5w. Type **262** 2·30 40
674 7w. Sheep (vert) 3·75 40
MS675 Two sheets each 90×60 mm. Nos. 673/674. Imperf 7·75 7·00

263 Eurasian Badger

1966. Korean Fauna. Multicoloured.
676 3w. Type **263** 3·00 1·10
677 5w. Asiatic black bear 3·00 1·10
678 7w. Tiger 3·75 1·10
MS679 Three sheets each 90×60 mm. Nos. 676/678. Imperf 14·50 13·50

264 *Syncom* Satellite

1967. 15th Anniversary of Korea's Admission to ITU.
680 **264** 7w. multicoloured 1·50 70
MS681 90×60 mm. No. 680. Imperf 4·25 3·75

265 Presidents Pak and Lubke

1967. Visit of President Lubke of West Germany to Korea.
682 **265** 7w. multicoloured 2·50 1·20
MS683 90×60 mm. No. 682. Imperf 4·75 4·25

266 Coin, Factories and Houses

1967. First Anniversary of Korean Revenue Office.
684 **266** 7w. sepia and green 1·50 55

267 Okwangdae Mask

1967. Folklore. Multicoloured.
685 4w. Type **267** 2·30 70
686 5w. Sandi mask (horiz) 2·30 75
687 7w. Mafoe mask 3·00 1·00
MS688 Three sheets each 90×60 mm. Nos. 685/687. Imperf 11·00 9·75

268 JCI Emblem and Pavilion

1967. International Junior Chamber of Commerce Conference, Seoul.
689 **268** 7w. multicoloured 1·40 45
MS690 90×60 mm. No. 689. Imperf 3·75 3·50

269 Map Emblem

1967. Fifth Asian Pacific Dental Congress, Seoul.
691 **269** 7w. multicoloured 1·40 45
MS692 90×60 mm. No. 691. Imperf 3·75 3·50

270 Korean Pavilion

1967. World Fair, Montreal.
693 **270** 7w. black, red and yellow 3·75 75
694 **270** 83w. black, red and blue 23·00 5·50
MS695 90×60 mm. Nos. 693/694 19·00 18·00

271 Worker and Soldier

1967. Veterans' Day.

696	**271**	7w. multicoloured	1·50	45

272 Railway Wheel and Rail

1967. Second Five Year Plan. Dated 1967.

697	**272**	7w. black, yellow and brown	7·00	1·20
698	-	7w. orange, brown and black	7·00	1·20

Design: No. 698, Nut and bolt.
See also Nos. 773/774, 833/834, 895/896 and 981/982.

273 Sword Dance

1967. Folklore. Multicoloured.

699	4w. Type **273**	2·30	70
700	5w. Peace dance (vert)	2·30	75
701	7w. Buddhist dance (vert)	3·00	1·00
MS702	Three sheets each 90×60 mm. Nos. 699/701. Imperf	11·00	10·00

274 Soldier and Family

1967. Fund for Korean Troops Serving in Vietnam.

703	**274**	7w.+3w. black and purple	7·75	1·20

275 President Pak and Phoenix

1967. Inauguration of President Pak for Second Term.

704	**275**	7w. multicoloured	23·00	3·75
MS705		90×60 mm. No. 704. Imperf	65·00	60·00

276 Scout, Badge and Camp

1967. Third Korean Scout Jamboree. Multicoloured.

706	7w. Type **276**	1·50	70
707	20w. Scout badge, bridge and tent	5·50	2·20
MS708	Two sheets each 90×60 mm. Nos. 706/707. Imperf	11·00	10·00

280 Girls on Swing

1967. Folklore. Multicoloured.

712	4w. Type **280**	3·75	75
713	5w. Girls on seesaw (vert)	3·75	95
714	7w. Girls dancing (vert)	6·25	1·10
MS715	Three sheet each 90×60 mm. Nos. 712/714. Imperf	20·00	19·00

281 Freedom Centre

1967. First World Anti-Communist League Conference, Taipei. Multicoloured.

716	5w. Type **281**	1·50	45
717	7w. Hand grasping chain (vert)	1·50	45
MS718	Two sheets each 90×60 mm. Nos. 716/717. Imperf	11·00	10·00

282 Boxing

1967. National Athletic Meeting, Seoul. Multicoloured.

719	5w. Type **282**	2·30	75
720	7w. Basketball	3·00	75

283 Students' Memorial, Kwangjoo

1967. Students' Day.

721	**283**	7w. multicoloured	1·50	45

284 Decade Emblem

1967. International Hydrological Decade.

722	**284**	7w. multicoloured	1·50	45

285 Children spinning Top

1967. Christmas and New Year.

723	**285**	5w. blue, red and pink	3·00	40
724	-	7w. brown, blue and bistre	3·75	30
MS725		Two sheets each 90×60 mm. Nos. 723/724. Imperf	7·75	7·00

Design: 7w. Monkey and Signs of the Zodiac.

286 Playing Shuttlecock

1967. Folklore. Multicoloured.

726	4w. Type **286**	3·00	1·00
727	5w. 'Dalmaji' (horiz)	3·00	1·00
728	7w. Archery	3·00	1·00
MS729	Three sheets each 90×60 mm. Nos. 726/728. Imperf	12·50	11·50

287 Microwave Transmitter

1967. Inauguration of Microwave Telecommunications Service.

730	**287**	7w. black, green and blue	1·50	70
MS731		90×60 mm. No. 730. Imperf	3·75	3·50

288 Carving, King Songdok's Bell

289 5th/6th-century Earrings

290 Korean Flag

1968

732	**288**	1w. brown and yellow	40	10
733	**289**	5w. yellow and green	3·00	55
734	**290**	7w. red and blue	1·50	25
787	**290**	7w. blue	3·75	40
788	**290**	7w. blue*	1·50	30
790	**290**	10w. blue*	1·50	25

*Nos. 788 and 790 have their face values shown as '7' or '10' only, omitting the noughts shown on Nos. 734 and 787.
For designs similar to T **290** see Nos. 771, 780 and 827.

291 WHO Emblem

1968. 20th Anniversary of WHO.

735	**291**	7w. multicoloured	1·50	45
MS736		90×60 mm. No. 735. Imperf	3·75	3·50

292 EATA Emblem and Korean Motif

1968. Second East Asia Travel Association Conference, Seoul.

737	**292**	7w. multicoloured	1·50	45
MS738		90×60 mm. No. 737. Imperf	4·75	4·25

293 CACCI Emblem, Korean Doorknocker and Factories

1968. Second Conference of Confederation of Asian Chambers of Commerce and Industry (CACCI), Seoul.

739	**293**	7w. multicoloured	1·50	45
MS740		90×60 mm. No. 739. Imperf	4·25	3·75

294 President Pak and Emperor Haile Selassie

1968. Visit of Emperor of Ethiopia.

741	**294**	7w. multicoloured	3·75	1·50
MS742		90×60 mm. No. 741. Imperf	7·75	7·00

295 Post bag

1968. Postman's Day. Multicoloured.

743	5w. Type **295**	1·50	70
744	7w. Postman	1·50	70

296 Atomic and Development Symbols

1968. Promotion of Science and Technology.

745	**296**	7w. blue, green and red	1·50	45

297 Kyung Hi University and Conference Emblem

1968. Second Conference of International Association of University Presidents.

746	**297**	7w. multicoloured	1·50	45
MS747		90×60 mm. No. 746. Imperf	5·50	5·00

298 Liberation

1968. Liberation of Suppressed Peoples' Campaign.

748	**298**	7w. multicoloured	1·50	45

299 Reservist

1968. Army Reservists' Fund.

749	**299**	7w.+3w. black & green	13·00	1·50

300 Stylised Peacock

1968. 20th Anniversary of Republic.

750	**300**	7w. multicoloured	1·50	45

301 Fair Entrance

1968. First Korean Trade Fair, Seoul.

751	**301**	7w. multicoloured	1·50	45

302 Assembly Emblem

1968. Third General Assembly of Asian Pharmaceutical Association Federation.

752	**302**	7w. multicoloured	1·50	45

303 Scout Badge

1968. Sixth Far East Scout Conference, Seoul.

753	**303**	7w. multicoloured	2·30	75

304 Soldier and Battle Scene

1968. 20th Anniversary of Korean Armed Forces.

754	**304**	7w. orange and green	7·75	2·30
755	-	7w. blue and light blue	7·75	2·30
756	-	7w. blue and orange	7·75	2·30
757	-	7w. light blue and blue	7·75	2·30
758	-	7w. green and orange	7·75	2·30

Designs: No. 755, Sailor and naval guns; No. 756, Servicemen and flags; No. 757, Pilot and Northrop F-5A Freedom Fighters; No. 758, Marine and landings.

305 Colombo Plan Emblem and Globe

1968. 19th Meeting of Colombo Plan Consultative Committee, Seoul.

759	**305**	7w. multicoloured	1·50	40

306 (I) Olympic Emblems

307 (II) Olympic Emblems

1968. Olympic Games, Mexico. Multicoloured.

760	7w. Type **306**	14·50	4·75
761	7w. Type **307**	14·50	4·75
762	7w. Cycling (I)	14·50	4·75
763	7w. Cycling (II)	14·50	4·75
764	7w. Boxing (I)	14·50	4·75
765	7w. Boxing (II)	14·50	4·75
766	7w. Wrestling (I)	14·50	4·75
767	7w. Wrestling (II)	14·50	4·75
MS768	Four sheets each 90×60 mm. Imperf (a) Nos. 760/761; (b) Nos. 762/763; (c) Nos. 764/765; (d) Nos. 766/767	46·00	42·00

The two types of each design may be identified by the position of the country name at the foot of the design. Ranged right in types I, and left in types II. On three of the designs (excluding Cycling) the figures of value are on left and right respectively. Types I and II of each design were issued together horizontally *se-tenant* within the sheets of 50 stamps.

308 Statue of Woman

1968. 60th Anniversary of Women's Secondary Education.

769	**308**	7w. multicoloured	1·50	40

309 Coin and Symbols

1968. National Wealth Survey.

770	**309**	7w. multicoloured	1·50	40

1968. Disaster Relief Fund. As No. 734, but with additional inscr and premium added.

771	**290**	7w.+3w. red and blue	42·00	7·75

The face value on No. 771 is expressed as 7 00+3 00, see also Nos. 780 and 827.

310 Shin Eui Ju Memorial

1968. Anniversary of Student Uprising, Shin Eui Ju (1945).

772	**310**	7w. multicoloured	1·90	55

1968. Second Five Year Plan. As T **272**. Dated 1968. Multicoloured.

773	7w. Express motorway	13·00	1·20
774	7w. Clover-leaf road junction	7·75	1·20

311 Demonstrators

1968. Human Rights Year.

775	**311**	7w. multicoloured	1·50	40

312 Christmas Lanterns

1968. Christmas and New Year. Multicoloured.

776	5w. Type **312**	11·50	55
777	7w. Cockerel	11·50	55
MS778	Two sheets each 90×60 mm. Nos. 776/777. Imperf	15·00	14·00

314 Korean House and UN Emblems

1968. 20th Anniversary of South Korea's Admission to UN.

779	**314**	7w. multicoloured	1·50	40

1969. Military Helicopter Fund. As No. 734 but colours changed and inscr with premium added.

780	**290**	7w.+3w. red, blue & grn	11·50	1·30

315 Torch and Monument, Pagoda Park, Seoul

1969. 50th Anniversary of Samil (Independence) Movement.

781	**315**	7w. multicoloured	1·50	45

316 Hyun Choong Sa and 'Turtle' Ships

1969. Dedication of Rebuilt Hyun Choong Sa (Shrine of Admiral Li Sun Sin).

782	**316**	7w. multicoloured	1·50	45

317 President Pak and Yang di-Pertuan Agong

1969. Visit of Yang di-Pertuan Agong (Malaysian Head-of-State).

783	**317**	7w. multicoloured	3·75	1·20
MS784		90×60 mm. No. 783. Imperf	65·00	60·00

318 Stone Temple Lamp

1969

786	**318**	5w. purple	1·10	25
791	-	20w. green	2·30	40
792	-	30w. green	3·75	75
794	-	40w. mauve and blue	2·75	75
795	-	100w. brown and purple	95·00	2·30

Designs: As T **318**. Vert—20w. Wine jug; 40w. Porcelain Jar, Yi Dynasty; 100w. Seated Buddha (bronze). Horiz—30w. 'Duck' vase.

323 'Red Cross' between Faces

1969. 50th Anniversary of League of Red Cross Societies.

796	**323**	7w. multicoloured	1·90	45
MS797		90×60 mm. No. 796. Imperf	5·50	5·00

324 Building the Nation's Economy

1969. Second Economy Drive.

798	**324**	7w. multicoloured	1·50	45

325 Presidents Pak and Nguyen van Thieu

1969. Visit of President Nguyen van Thieu of South Vietnam.

799	**325**	7w. multicoloured	3·00	1·20
MS800		90×60 mm. No. 799. Imperf	8·50	6·75

326 Reafforestation and Flooded Fields

1969. Flood and Drought Damage Prevention Campaign. Multicoloured.

801	7w. Type **326**	1·50	40
802	7w. Withered and flourishing plants	1·50	40

327 Ignition of Second-stage Rocket

1969. First Man on the Moon.

803	**327**	10w. blue, black and red	3·75	1·10
804	-	10w. blue, black and red	3·75	1·10
805	-	20w. multicoloured	3·75	1·10
806	-	20w. multicoloured	3·75	1·10
807	-	40w. blue, red and black	3·75	1·10
MS808		160×110 mm. Nos. 803/807. Imperf	35·00	31·00

Designs: No. 804, Separation of modules from rocket; No. 805, Diagram of lunar orbit; No. 806, Astronauts on Moon; No. 807, Splashdown of *Apollo 11*.

328 Stepmother admonishing Kongji

1969. Korean Fairy Tales (1st series). *Kongji and Patji*. Multicoloured.

809	5w. Type **328**	3·75	95
810	7w. Kongji and sparrows	3·75	95
811	10w. Kongji and ox	6·25	1·30
812	20w. Kongji in sedan-chair	6·25	1·30
MS813	Four sheets each 90×60 mm. Imperf. (a) No. 809; (b) No. 810; (c) No. 811; (d) No. 812	25·00	22·00

See also Nos. 828/**MS**832, 839/**MS**843, 844/**MS**848 and 853/**MS**857.

332 Steam Locomotive of 1899

1969. 70th Anniversary of Korean Railways. Multicoloured.

814	7w. Type **332**	1·90	70
815	7w. Early steam and modern diesel locomotives	1·90	70

333 Northrop F-5A Freedom Jet Fighters

1969. 20th Anniversary of Korean Air Force. Multicoloured.

816	10w. Type **333**	5·50	75
817	10w. McDonnell-Douglas F-4D Phantom II jet fighter	7·00	75

334 Game of Cha-jun

1969. Tenth Korean Traditional Arts Contest, Taegu.

818	**334**	7w. multicoloured	1·20	40

335 Molecule and Institute Building

1969. Completion of Korean Institute of Science and Technology.

819	**335**	7w. multicoloured	1·20	40

336 Presidents Pak and Hamani

1969. Visit of President Hamani of Niger Republic.

820	**336**	7w. multicoloured	2·30	1·00
MS821		90×60 mm. No. 820. Imperf	14·00	12·50

337 Football

1969. 50th Anniversary of National Athletic Meeting. Multicoloured.

822	10w. Type **337**	3·00	75
823	10w. Volleyball	3·00	75
824	10w. Korean wrestling (horiz)	3·00	75
825	10w. Fencing (horiz)	3·00	75
826	10w. Taekwondo (karate) (horiz)	3·00	75

1969. Searchlight Fund. As T **290** but with additional inscr and premium. Face value expressed as 7+3.

827	7w.+3w. red and blue	39·00	1·70

1969. Korean Fairy Tales (2nd series). *The Hare's Liver*. As T **328**. Multicoloured.

828	5w. Princess and Doctors	2·30	70
829	7w. Hare arriving at Palace	2·30	70
830	10w. Preparing to remove the Hare's liver	2·30	95
831	20w. Escape of the Hare	3·75	95
MS832	Four sheets each 90×60 mm. Imperf. (a) No. 828; (b) No. 829; (c) No. 830; (d) No. 831	22·00	20·00

1969. Second Five-year Plan. As T **272**. Dated 1969. Multicoloured.

833	7w. 'Agriculture and Fisheries'	1·50	45
834	7w. Industrial emblems	1·50	45

342 Students ringing 'Education'

1969. First Anniversary of National Education Charter.

835	**342**	7w. multicoloured	1·20	3·75

343 Toy Dogs

1969. Lunar New Year. Year of the Dog. Multicoloured.
836 5w. Type **343** 1·50 45
837 7w. Candle and lattice doorway 1·50 45

344 Woman with Letter and UPU Monument, Berne

1970. 70th Anniversary of Korea's Admission to UPU.
838 **344** 10w. multicoloured 11·50 3·75

1970. Korean Fairy Tales (3rd series). *The Sun and the Moon*. As T **328**. Multicoloured.
839 5w. Mother meets the tiger 2·30 70
840 7w. Tiger in disguise 2·30 70
841 10w. Children chased up a tree 2·30 95
842 20w. Children escape to Heaven 3·75 1·20
MS843 Four sheets each 90×60 mm. Imperf. (a) No. 839; (b) No. 840; (c) No. 841; (d) No. 842 22·00 20·00

1970. Korean Fairy Tales (4th series). *The Woodcutter and the Fairy*. As T **328**. Multicoloured.
844 10w. Woodcutter hiding Fairy's dress 2·75 1·00
845 10w. Fairy as Woodcutter's Wife 2·75 1·00
846 10w. Fairy and children fly to Heaven 2·75 1·00
847 10w. Happy reunion 2·75 1·00
MS848 Four sheets each 90×60 mm. Imperf. (a) No. 844; (b) No. 845; (c) No. 846; (d) No. 847 22·00 20·00

353 IEY Emblem on Open Book

1970. International Education Year.
849 **353** 10w. multicoloured 6·25 2·30

354 Seated Buddha and Korean Pavilion

1970. EXPO 70 World Fair, Osaka, Japan.
850 **354** 10w. multicoloured 6·25 1·60

355 '4-11' Club Emblem

1970. 15th '4-11' Club (young farmers' organisation) Central Contest, Suwon.
851 **355** 10w. multicoloured 1·90 75

356 Bank Emblem and Cash

1970. Third General Meeting of Asian Development Bank, Seoul.
852 **356** 10w. multicoloured 1·90 75

1970. Korean Fairy Tales (5th series). *Heungbu and Nolbu*. As T **328**. Multicoloured.
853 10w. Heungbu tending swallow 6·25 1·20
854 10w. Heungbu finds treasure in pumpkin 6·25 1·20
855 10w. Nolbu with pumpkin 6·25 1·20
856 10w. Nolbu chased by devil 6·25 1·20
MS857 Four sheets each 90×60 mm. Imperf. (a) No. 853; (b) No. 854; (c) No. 855; (d) No. 856 60·00 55·00

361 Royal Palanquin (Yi Dynasty)

1970. Early Korean Transport.
858 **361** 10w. multicoloured 2·75 95
859 - 10w. multicoloured 2·75 95
860 - 10w. multicoloured 2·75 95
861 - 10w. black, stone and blue 2·75 95
Designs: Horiz—No. 859, Tramcar, 1899; No. 860, Emperor Sunjong's cadillac, 1903; No. 861, Nieuport 28 biplane, 1922.

362 New Headquarters Building

1970. Opening of New UPU Headquarters Building, Berne.
862 **362** 10w. multicoloured 1·50 40

363 Dish Aerial and Hemispheres

1970. Inauguration of Satellite Communications Station, Kum San.
863 **363** 10w. multicoloured 1·90 75

364 'PEN' and Quill Pen

1970. 37th International PEN (literary organisation) Congress, Seoul.
864 **364** 10w. multicoloured 1·50 40

365 Section of Motorway

1970. Opening of Seoul–Pusan Motorway.
865 **365** 10w. multicoloured 1·90 75

366 Postal Code Symbol

1970. Introduction of Postal Codes.
866 **366** 10w. multicoloured 1·50 40

367 Parcel Sorting Area

1970. Inauguration of Postal Mechanisation.
867 **367** 10w. multicoloured 1·50 40
MS868 130×90 mm. Nos. 866/867×2 £100 90·00

368 Children's Hall and Boy

1970. Opening of Children's Hall, Seoul.
869 **368** 10w. multicoloured 1·50 40

369 *Mountain and River* (Yi In Moon)

1970. Korean Paintings of Yi Dynasty (1st series). Multicoloured.
870 10w. Type **369** 2·75 75
871 10w. *Jongyangsa Temple* (Chong Son) 2·75 75
872 10w. *Mountain and River by Moonlight* (Kim Doo Ryang) (vert) 2·75 75
MS873 Three sheets each 130×90 mm. Nos. 870/872×2 14·00 12·50
See also Nos. 887/**MS**890, 897/**MS**900, 947/**MS**953, 956/**MS**959 and 961/**MS**966.

370 PTTI Emblem

1970. Councillors' Meeting, Asian Chapter of Postal, Telegraph and Telephone International (Post Office Trade Union Federation).
874 **370** 10w. multicoloured 1·50 45

371 WAC and Corps Badge

1970. 20th Anniversary of Korean Women's Army Corps.
875 **371** 10w. multicoloured 1·50 45

372 President Pak and Flag

1970
876 **372** 10w. multicoloured 9·25 3·75
877 - 10w. black, green and blue 14·00 3·75
Design: Vert—No. 877, President Pak and industrial complex.

373 Presidents Pak and Sanchez Hernandez

1970. Visit of President Sanchez Hernandez of El Salvador.
878 **373** 10w. multicoloured 3·00 1·50
MS879 90×60 mm. No. 878. Imperf (inscr 'SOLVADOL') 39·00 38·00

374 People and Houses

1970. National Census.
880 **374** 10w. multicoloured 1·50 40

375 Diving

1970. 51st National Athletic Games, Seoul.
881 10w. Type **375** 4·75 1·20
882 10w. Hockey 4·75 1·20
883 10w. Baseball 4·75 1·20
MS884 Three sheets each 91×87 mm. Nos. 881/883×2. Imperf 30·00 29·00

376 Police Badge and Activities

1970. National Police Day.
885 **376** 10w. multicoloured 1·50 55

377 Bell and Globe

1970. 25th Anniversary of United Nations.
886 **377** 10w. multicoloured 1·50 45

1970. Korean Paintings of the Yi Dynasty (2nd series). Vert designs as T **369**, showing animals. Multicoloured.
887 30w. *Fierce Tiger* (Shim Sa Yung) 12·50 1·90
888 30w. *Cats and Sparrows* (Pyun Sang Byuk) 12·50 1·90
889 30w. *Dog with Puppies* (Yi Am) 12·50 1·90
MS890 Three sheets each 130×90 mm. Nos. 887/889×2 £170 £160

378 Kite and Reel

1970. Lunar New Year. Year of the Pig. Multicoloured.
891 10w. Type **378** 1·50 40
892 10w. Toy pig 1·50 40
MS893 Two sheets each 90×60 mm. Nos. 891/892×3 15·00 14·00

379 Quotation and Emblems on Globe

1970. 15th Communications Day.
894 **379** 10w. multicoloured 1·50 55

1970. Second Five Year Plan. As T **272**. Dated 1970. Multicoloured.
895 10w. Port Development 1·50 40
896 10w. House Construction 1·50 40

1970. Korean Paintings of the Yi Dynasty (3rd series). Vert designs as T **369**. Multicoloured.
897 10w. *Chokpyokdo* (river cliff) (Kim Hong Do) 2·75 75
898 10w. *Hen and Chicks* (Pyn Sang Byuk) 2·75 75
899 10w. *The Flute-player* (Shin Yun Bok) 2·75 75
MS900 Three sheets each 90×60 mm. Nos. 897/899×2. Perf or imperf 28·00 25·00

380 Fields (Food Production)

1971. Economic Development (1st series). Multicoloured.
901 10w. Type **380** 1·90 55
902 10w. Dam (Electric Power) (horiz) 1·90 55
903 10w. Map on crate (Exports) (horiz) 1·90 55

MS904 Three sheets each 90×60 mm. Nos. 901/903. Imperf 21·00 19·00

See also Nos. 905/**MS**908 and 910/**MS**913.

381 Coal-mining

1971. Economic Development (2nd series). Multicoloured.

905	10w. Type **381**	1·50	40
906	10w. Cement works (vert)	1·50	40
907	10w. Fertilizer plant	1·50	40

MS908 Three sheets each 90×60 mm. Nos. 905/907×2. Imperf 21·00 19·00

382 Globe, Torch and Spider

1971. Anti-espionage Month.

909 **382** 10w. multicoloured 1·50 45

383 Motorway Junction

1971. Economic Develepment (3rd series). Multicoloured.

910	10w. Type **383**	1·50	40
911	10w. Scales (Gross National Income) (horiz)	1·50	40
912	10w. Bee and coins (Increased Savings) (horiz)	1·50	40

MS913 Three sheets each 90×60 mm. Nos. 910/912×2. Imperf 16·00 14·50

384 Reservist and Badge

1971. Third Home Reserve Forces Day.

914 **384** 10w. multicoloured 1·50 45

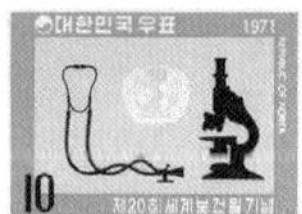

385 WHO Emblem, Stethoscope and Microscope

1971. 20th World Health Day.

915 **385** 10w. multicoloured 1·40 55

386 Underground Train

1971. Construction of Seoul Underground Railway System.

916 **386** 10w. multicoloured 1·40 40

387 Footballer

1971. First Asian Soccer Games, Seoul.

917 **387** 10w. multicoloured 1·90 75

388 Veteran and Association Flag

1971. 20th Korean Veterans' Day.

918 **388** 10w. multicoloured 1·40 45

389 Girl Scouts

1971. 25th Anniversary of Korean Girl Scouts Federation.

919 **389** 10w. multicoloured 1·40 30

390 Torch and Economic Symbols

1971. Tenth Anniversary of May 16th Revolution.

920 **390** 10w. multicoloured 1·40 40

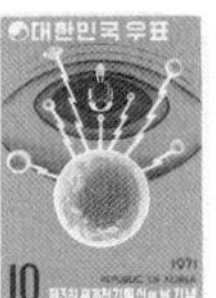

391 Telecommunications

1971. Third World Telecommunications Day.

921 **391** 10w. multicoloured 1·40 45

392 FAO Emblem

1971. The Work of the United Nations Organisation.

922	-	10w. mauve, black and green	3·75	1·20
923	**392**	10w. blue, black and mauve	3·75	1·20
924	-	10w. multicoloured	3·75	1·20
925	-	10w. blue, black and mauve	3·75	1·20
926	-	10w. mauve, black and green	3·75	1·20
927	-	10w. blue, black and mauve	3·75	1·20
928	-	10w. mauve, black and blue	3·75	1·20
929	-	10w. black, green and mauve	3·75	1·20
930	-	10w. mauve, black and blue	3·75	1·20
931	-	10w. blue, black and mauve	3·75	1·20
932	-	10w. mauve, black and blue	3·75	1·20
933	-	10w. black, mauve and green	3·75	1·20
934	-	10w. mauve, blue and black	3·75	1·20
935	-	10w. black, mauve and green	3·75	1·20
936	-	10w. mauve, black and blue	3·75	1·20
937	-	10w. blue, black and mauve	3·75	1·20
938	-	10w. mauve, black and blue	3·75	1·20
939	-	10w. black, mauve and green	3·75	1·20
940	-	10w. mauve, black and blue	3·75	1·20
941	-	10w. blue, black and mauve	3·75	1·20
942	-	10w. mauve, black and green	3·75	1·20
943	-	10w. black, blue and mauve	3·75	1·20
944	-	10w. multicoloured	3·75	1·20
945	-	10w. black, blue and mauve	3·75	1·20
946	-	10w. black, mauve and green	3·75	1·20

Emblems: No. 992, ILO; No. 924, General Assembly and New York Headquarters; No. 925, UNESCO; No. 926, WHO; No. 927, World Bank; No. 928, International Development Association; No. 929, Security Council; No. 930, International Finance Corporation; No. 931, International Monetary Fund; No. 932, International Civil Aviation Organisation; No. 933, Economic and Social Council; No. 934, South Korean flag; No. 935, Trusteeship Council; No. 936, UPU; No. 937, ITU; No. 938, World Meteorological Organisation; No. 939, International Court of Justice; No. 940, IMCO; No. 941, UNICEF; No. 942, International Atomic Energy Agency; No. 943, United Nations Industrial Development Organisation; No. 944, United Nations Commission for the Unification and Rehabilitation of Korea; No. 945, United Nations Development Programme; No. 946, United Nations Conference on Trade and Development.

393 *Boating* (Shin Yun Bok)

1971. Korean Paintings of the Yi Dynasty (4th series). Multicoloured.

947	10w. Type **393**	6·25	1·90
948	10w. *Greeting Travellers*	6·25	1·90
949	10w. *Tea Ceremony*	6·25	1·90
950	10w. *Lady and Servants on Country Road*	6·25	1·90
951	10w. *Couple Walking*	6·25	1·90
952	10w. *Fairy and Boy beneath Pine Tree* (Li Chae Kwan) (vert)	6·25	1·90

MS953 Six sheets each 130×90 mm. Nos. 947/952×2 75·00 65·00

Nos. 947/951 show Folk Customs paintings by Shin Yun Bok.

394 President Pak, Emblem and Motorway

1971. Re-election of President Pak for Third Term.

954 **394** 10w. multicoloured 23·00 2·30

MS955 90×60 mm. No. 954×2 75·00 70·00

1971. Korean Paintings of the Yi Dynasty (5th series). As T **393**. Multicoloured.

956	10w. *Chasing the Cat* (Kim Deuk Shin)	3·00	1·30
957	10w. *Valley Family* (Li Chae Kwan) (vert)	3·00	1·30
958	10w. *Man Reading* (Li Chae Kwan) (vert)	3·00	1·30

MS959 Three sheets each 130×90 mm. Nos. 956/958×2 25·00 23·00

395 Campfire and Badge

1971. 13th World Scout Jamboree, Asagiri, Japan.

960 **395** 10w. multicoloured 1·40 40

1971. Korean Paintings of the Yi Dynasty (6th series). As T **393** but vert. Multicoloured.

961	10w. *Classroom*	5·50	2·75
962	10w. *Wrestling Match*	5·50	2·75
963	10w. *Dancer with Musicians*	5·50	2·75
964	10w. *Weavers*	5·50	2·75
965	10w. *Drawing Water at the Well*	5·50	2·75

MS966 Five sheets each 130×90 mm. Nos. 961/965×2 60·00 55·00

Nos. 961/965 depict genre paintings by Kim Hong Do.

396 Cogwheel and Asian Map

1971. Third Asian Labour Minister's Conference, Seoul.

967 **396** 10w. multicoloured 1·40 45

MS968 90×60 mm. No. 967×2 50·00 45·00

397 Judo

1971. 52nd National Athletic Meeting, Seoul. Multicoloured.

969	10w. Type **397**	2·30	75
970	10w. Archery	2·30	75

MS971 Two sheets each 91×87 mm. Nos. 969/970×3 70·00 65·00

398 Korean Symbol on Palette

1971. 20th National Fine Art Exhibition.

972 **398** 10w. multicoloured 1·40 30

399 Doctor and Globe

1971. Seventh Congress of Medical Associations from Asia and Oceania.

973 **399** 10w. multicoloured 1·40 30

400 Emblems and Vocational Skills

1971. Second National Vocational Skill Contest for High School Students.

974 **400** 10w. multicoloured 1·40 30

MS975 90×60 mm. No. 974×2 42·00 38·00

401 Callipers and 'K' Emblem

1971. Tenth Anniversary of Industrial Standardisation.

976 **401** 10w. multicoloured 1·40 30

402 Fairy Tale Rats

1971. Lunar New Year. Year of the Rat. Multicoloured.

977	10w. Type **402**	1·90	40
978	10w. Flying crane	1·90	40

MS979 Two sheets each 90×60 mm. Nos. 977/978×3 55·00 49·00

403 Emblem and Hangul Alphabet

1971. 50th Anniversary of Hangul Hakhoe (Korean Language Research Society).

980 **403** 10w. multicoloured 1·40 30

1971. Second Five Year Plan. As T **272**. Dated 1971. Multicoloured.

981	10w. Atomic power plant	1·50	40
982	10w. Hydro-electric power project	1·50	40

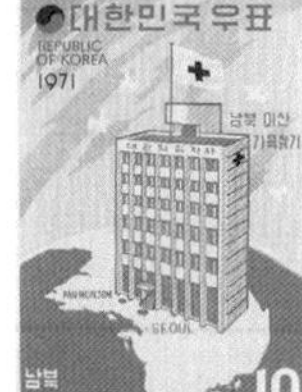

404 Korean Red Cross Building on Map

1971. South–North Korean Red Cross Conference, Panmunjom.
983 **404** 10w. multicoloured 1·50 60
MS984 125×90 mm. No. 983×2 12·50 11·00

405 Globe and Open Book

1971. International Book Year.
985 **405** 10w. multicoloured 1·20 30
MS986 90×60 mm. No. 985×2 11·50 10·50

406 *Intelsat 4* and Korean Earth Station

1971. 20th Anniversary of Korea's Membership of ITU.
987 **406** 10w. multicoloured 1·20 40

407 Speed Skating

1972. Winter Olympic Games, Sapporo, Japan. Multicoloured.
988 10w. Type **407** 1·50 60
989 10w. Figure-skating 1·50 60
MS990 90×60 mm. Nos. 988/989 11·50 10·50

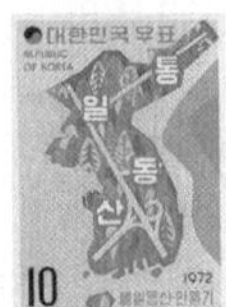
408 Forestry Map

1972. Trees for Unity Campaign.
991 **408** 10w. multicoloured 1·20 40

409 Scarab Beetles and Emblem

1972. 20th Anniversary of Korean Junior Chamber of Commerce.
992 **409** 10w. multicoloured 1·20 40

410 ECAFE Emblem and Industrial Symbols

1972. 25th Anniversary of UN Economic Commission for Asia and the Far East.
993 **410** 10w. multicoloured 1·20 40

411 Flags of Member Countries

1972. Tenth Anniversary of Asian and Oceanic Postal Union.
994 **411** 10w. multicoloured 1·20 40

412 Reserve Forces' Flag

1972. Home Reserve Forces Day.
995 **412** 10w. multicoloured 1·50 45

413 Emblem and *Terias harina*

1972. 50th Anniversary of Korean Young Women's Christian Association.
996 **413** 10w. multicoloured 1·70 45

414 Rural Activities

1972. New Community (rural development) Movement.
997 **414** 10w. multicoloured 1·20 40

415 'Anti-Espionage' and Korean Flag

1972. Anti-Espionage Month.
998 **415** 10w. multicoloured 1·20 40

416 Children with Balloons

1972. 50th Children's Day.
999 **416** 10w. multicoloured 1·20 40

417 Leaf Ornament from Gold Crown

1972. Treasures from King Munyong's Tomb. Multicoloured.
1000 10w. Type **417** 1·20 40
1001 10w. Gold earrings (horiz) 1·20 40

418 Lake Paengnokdam, Mt. Halla Park

419 Kalkot, Koje Island, Hanryo Straits Park

1972. National Parks (1st series).
1002 **418** 10w. multicoloured 3·00 45
1003 **419** 10w. multicoloured 3·00 45
See also Nos. 1018/1019 and 1026/1027.

420 Marguerite and Conference Emblem

1972. UN Environmental Conservation Conference, Stockholm.
1004 **420** 10w. multicoloured 1·20 40
MS1005 90×60 mm. No. 1004×2 7·75 7·00

421 Gwanghwa Gate and National Flags

1972. Seventh Asian and Pacific Council (ASPAC) Ministerial Meeting, Seoul.
1006 **421** 10w. multicoloured 1·20 40

422 Pasture (Development of Rural Economy)

1972. Third Five Year Plan. Dated 1972. Multicoloured.
1007 10w. Type **422** 1·90 55
1008 10w. Foundry ladle (Heavy Industries) 1·90 55
1009 10w. Crate and Globe (Increased Exports) 1·90 55

423 'Love Pin'

1972. Disaster Relief Fund.
1010 **423** 10w.+5w. red and blue 1·90 75

424 Judo

1972. Olympic Games, Munich. Multicoloured.
1011 20w. Type **424** 1·20 55
1012 20w. Weightlifting 1·20 55
1013 20w. Wrestling 1·20 55
1014 20w. Boxing 1·20 55
MS1015 Two sheets each 90×60 mm. (a) Nos. 1011/1012; (b) Nos. 1013/1014 12·50 11·00

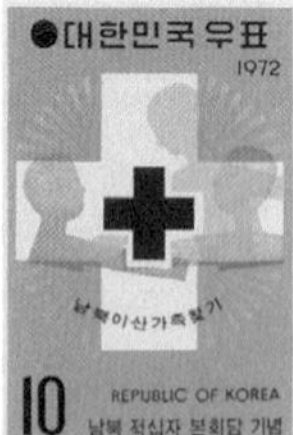
425 Family Reunion through Red Cross

1972. First Plenary Meeting of South–North Korean Red Cross Conference, Pyongyang.
1016 **425** 10w. multicoloured 1·90 75
MS1017 125×90 mm. No. 1016×2 27·00 26·00

426 Bulkuk Temple, Kyongju Park

427 Statue and Bopju Temple, Mt. Sokri Park

1972. National Parks (2nd series).
1018 **426** 10w. multicoloured 1·40 45
1019 **427** 10w. multicoloured 1·40 45

428 Conference Emblem within '5'

1972. Fifth Asian Judicial Conference, Seoul.
1020 **428** 10w. multicoloured 1·20 40

429 Lions Badge between Korean Emblems

1972. 11th Orient and South-East Asian Lions Convention, Seoul.
1021 **429** 10w. multicoloured 1·20 40

430 Scout taking Oath

1972. 50th Anniversary of Korean Boy Scouts Movement.
1022 **430** 10w. multicoloured 1·50 45

431 Dolls and Ox's Head

1972. Lunar New Year. Year of the Ox. Multicoloured.
1023 10w. Type **431** 1·20 40
1024 10w. Revellers in balloon 1·20 40
MS1025 Two sheets each 90×60 mm. Nos. 1023/1024×2 9·25 8·50

432 Temple, Mt. Naejang Park

433 Madeungryong Pass, Mt. Sorak Park

1972. National Parks (3rd series).
1026 **432** 10w. multicoloured 1·20 40
1027 **433** 10w. multicoloured 1·20 40

434 President Pak, Flag and 'Development'

1972. Re-election of President Pak.
1028 **434** 10w. multicoloured 7·75 1·50
MS1029 130×90 mm. Nos. 1028×2 65·00 60·00

435 National Central Museum, Kyongbok Palace

436 Temple, Mt. Sorak

1973. Korean Tourist Attractions (1st series).
1030 **435** 10w. multicoloured 1·20 40
1031 **436** 10w. multicoloured 1·20 40
See also Nos. 1042/1043, 1048/1049, 1057/1058 and 1075/1076.

437 Korean Family

1973. Korean Unification Campaign.
1032 **437** 10w. multicoloured 1·20 30

438 'V' Sign and Flags

1973. Return of Korean Forces from South Vietnam.
1033 **438** 10w. multicoloured 1·20 30

439 Construction Workers and Cogwheel

1973. Tenth Workers' Day.
1034 **439** 10w. multicoloured 85 30

440 WMO Emblem and Satellite

1973. Centenary of World Meteorological Organisation.
1035 **440** 10w. multicoloured 85 30
MS1036 90×60 mm. No. 1035×2 4·75 4·25

442 Wonsam Costume (woman's ceremonial)

1973. Korean Court Costumes of the Yi Dynasty (1st series). Multicoloured. Background colours given.
1037 - 10w. orange 3·75 70
1038 **442** 10w. orange 3·75 70
MS1039 Two sheets each 125×90 mm. Nos. 1037/1038×2 16·00 15·00

Design: No. 1037, Kujangbok (king's ceremonial costume).
See also Nos. 1045/**MS**1047, 1053/**MS**1055, 1060/**MS**1062 and 1078/**MS**1080.

443 Nurse with Lamp

1973. 50th Anniversary of Korean Nurses' Association.
1040 **443** 10w. multicoloured 95 25

444 Reservists and Flag

1973. Home Reserve Forces Day.
1041 **444** 10w. multicoloured 1·20 40

445 Palmi Island

446 Sain-am Rock, Mt. Dokjol

1973. Korean Tourist Attractions (2nd series).
1042 **445** 10w. multicoloured 1·20 30
1043 **446** 10w. multicoloured 1·20 30

447 Table Tennis Player

1973. Victory of South Korean Women's Team in World Table Tennis Championships, Sarajevo.
1044 **447** 10w. multicoloured 1·90 70

1973. Korean Court Costumes of the Yi Dynasty (2nd series). As T **442**. Multicoloured. Background colours given.
1045 10w. purple 3·50 60
1046 10w. green 3·50 60
MS1047 Two sheets each 125×90 mm. Nos. 1045/6×2 14·00 13·00

Designs: No. 1045, Konryongpo (king's costume); No. 1046, Jokui (queen's ceremonial costume).

450 Admiral Li Sun Sin's Shrine, Asan

451 Limestone Cavern, Kusan-ni

1973. Korean Tourist Attractions (3rd series).
1048 **450** 10w. multicoloured 1·50 40
1049 **451** 10w. multicoloured 1·50 40

452 Children's Choir

1973. 20th Anniversary of World Vision Int.
1050 **452** 10w. multicoloured 1·20 30

453 Love Pin and Disasters

1973. Disaster Relief Fund.
1051 **453** 10w.+5w. mult 1·20 45

454 Steel Converter

1973. Inauguration of Pohang Steel Works.
1052 **454** 10w. multicoloured 95 30

1973. Korean Court Costumes of the Yi Dynasty (3rd series). As T **442**. Multicoloured. Background colours given.
1053 10w. blue 3·00 60
1054 10w. pink 3·00 60
MS1055 Two sheets each 125×90 mm. Nos. 1053/1054×2 10·50 8·50

Designs: No. 1053, Kangsapo (crown prince's) costume; No. 1054, Tangui (princess's) costume.

457 Table Tennis Bat and Ball

1973. Table Tennis Gymnasium Construction Fund.
1056 **457** 10w.+5w. mauve and green 1·20 30

458 Namhae Suspension Bridge

459 Hongdo Island

1973. Korean Tourist Attractions (4th series).
1057 **458** 10w. multicoloured 1·20 30
1058 **459** 10w. multicoloured 1·20 30

460 Interpol and Korean Police Emblems

1973. 50th Anniversary of International Criminal Police Organisation (Interpol).
1059 **460** 10w. multicoloured 85 20

1973. Korean Court Costumes of the Yi Dynasty (4th series). As T **442**. Multicoloured. Background colours given.
1060 10w. yellow 1·50 55
1061 10w. blue 1·50 55
MS1062 Two sheets each 125×90 mm. Nos. 1060/1061×2 8·50 8·00

Designs: No. 1060, Kumkwanchobok (court official's) costume; No. 1061, Hwalot (queen's wedding) costume.

465 Manchurian Cranes

466 Sommal Lily

467 Motorway and Farm

1973
1063 - 1w. brown 45 15
1063a - 3w. black and blue 75 25
1064 - 5w. brown 40 15
1064a - 6w. turquoise and green 45 15
1065 **465** 10w. ultramarine & blue 1·20 25
1066 **466** 10w. red, black & green 1·50 40
1067 **467** 10w. green and red 75 15
1068 - 30w. brown and yellow 85 15
1068a - 50w. green and brown 75 25
1068b - 60w. brown and yellow 75 25
1068c - 80w. black and brown 1·50 30
1069 - 100w. yellow and brown 39·00 2·30
1069a - 100w. red 1·90 25
1069b - 200w. brown and pink 1·90 30
1069c - 300w. red and lilac 2·75 70
1069d - 500w. multicoloured 23·00 1·50
1069e - 500w. purple and brown 11·50 1·20
1069f - 1000w. green 10·00 1·50

Designs: Vert—1w. Mask of old man; 5w. Siberian chipmunk; 6w. Lily; 30w. Honey bee; 50w. Pot with lid; 60w. Jar; 100w. (No. 1069) Gold Crown, Silla dynasty; 100w. (No. 1069a) Admiral Yi Soon Shin; 300w. Pobjusa Temple; 500w. (No. 1069d) Gold Crown; 500w. (No. 1069e) Carved dragon (tile, Backje Dynasty). Larger 24×33 mm—100w. Flying deities (relief from bronze bell, Sangweon Temple). Horiz—3w. Black-billed magpie; 80w. Ceramic horseman; 200w. Muryangsujeon Hall, Busok Temple.
For designs similar to Type **465** but with frame, see Type **703**.

470 Tennis

1973. 54th National Athletic Meeting, Pusan. Multicoloured.
1070 10w. Type **470** 95 30
1071 10w. Hurdling 95 30

471 Children with Stamp Albums

1973. Philatelic Week.
1072 **471** 10w. multicoloured 75 30
MS1073 90×60 mm. No. 1072×2 15·00 14·00

472 Soyang River Dam

1973. Inauguration of Soyang River Dam.
1074 **472** 10w. multicoloured 55 15

473 Mt. Mai, Chinan

474 Tangerine Grove, Cheju Island

1973. Korean Tourist Attractions (5th series).
1075 **473** 10w. multicoloured 75 25
1076 **474** 10w. multicoloured 75 25

475 Match, Cigarette and Flames

1973. Tenth Fire Prevention Day.
1077 **475** 10w. multicoloured 55 15

1973. Korean Court Costumes of the Yi Dynasty (5th series). As T **442**. Multicoloured. Background colours given.
1078 10w. orange 1·50 45
1079 10w. pink 1·50 45
MS1080 Two sheets each 125×90 mm. Nos. 1078/1079×2 8·50 8·00

Designs: No. 1078, Pyongsangbok (official's wife) costume; No. 1079, Kokunbok (military officer's) costume.

478 Tiger and Candles

1973. Lunar New Year. Year of the Tiger. Multicoloured.
1081 10w. Type **478** 75 30
1082 10w. Decorated top 75 30
MS1083 Two sheets each 90×60 mm. Nos. 1081/1082×2 9·25 7·75

479 Korean Girl and Flame Emblem

1973. 25th Anniversary of Declaration of Human Rights.
1084 **479** 10w. multicoloured 60 15

480 Boeing 747-200 Jetliner and Polar Zone

1973. Air.
1085 **480** 110w. blue and pink 10·00 3·75
1086 - 135w. red and green 11·00 3·75
1087 - 145w. red and blue 14·00 4·75
1088 - 180w. yellow and lilac 35·00 7·00

Designs: Boeing 747-200 jetliner and postal zones on map—135w. South-east Asia; 145w. India, Australasia and North America; 180w. Europe, Africa and South America.

481 Komunko (zither)

1974. Traditional Musical Instruments (1st series). Multicoloured. Background colours given.
1089 **481** 10w. blue 1·20 30
1090 - 30w. orange 3·00 60
MS1091 Two sheets each 125×90 mm. (a) No. 1089×2; (b) No. 1090×2 13·00 12·00

Design: 30w. Nagak (trumpet triton).
See also Nos. 1098/**MS**1100, 1108/**MS**1110, 1117/**MS**1119 and 1132/**MS**1134.

483 Apricots

1974. Fruits (1st series). Multicoloured.

1092 10w. Type **483** 75 30
1093 30w. Strawberries 2·30 45
MS1094 Two sheets each 90×60 mm. (a) No. 1092×2; (b) No. 1093×2 11·00 10·00

See also Nos. 1104/**MS**1106, 1111/**MS**1113, 1120/**MS**1122 and 1143/**MS**1145.

485 Reservist and Factory

1974. Home Reserve Forces Day.

1095 **485** 10w. multicoloured 55 15

486 WPY Emblem

1974. World Population Year.

1096 **486** 10w. multicoloured 45 15
MS1097 90×60 mm. No. 1096×2 4·75 4·25

1974. Traditional Musical Instruments (2nd series). As T **481**. Multicoloured. Background colours given.

1098 10w. blue 1·00 25
1099 30w. green 2·30 55
MS1100 Two sheets each 125×90 mm. (a) No. 1098×2; (b) No. 1099×2 9·25 8·50

Designs: 10w. Tchouk; 30w. Eu.

489 Diesel Mail Train and Communications Emblem

1974. Communications Day.

1101 **489** 10w. multicoloured 95 25

490 CAFEA-ICC Emblem on Globe

1974. 22nd Session of International Chamber of Commerce's Commission on Asian and Far Eastern Affairs, Seoul.

1102 **490** 10w. multicoloured 45 10

491 Port Installations

1974. Inauguration of New Port Facilities, Inchon.

1103 **491** 10w. multicoloured 55 10

1974. Fruits (2nd series). As T **483**. Multicoloured.

1104 10w. Peaches 75 30
1105 30w. Grapes 2·30 45
MS1106 Two sheets each 90×60 mm. No. 1104/1105×2 10·50 9·50

494 UNESCO Emblem and Extended Fan

1974. 20th Anniversary of South Korean UNESCO Commission.

1107 **494** 10w. multicoloured 45 10

1974. Traditional Musical Instruments (3rd series). As T **481**. Multicoloured. Background colours given.

1108 10w. orange 95 15
1109 30w. pink 1·90 40
MS1110 Two sheets each 125×90 mm. Nos. 1108/1109×2 8·50 7·75

Designs: 10w. A-chaing (stringed instrument); 30w. Kyobang-ko (drum).

1974. Fruits (3rd series). As T **483**. Multicoloured.

1111 10w. Pears 60 15
1112 30w. Apples 2·30 45
MS1113 Two sheets each 91×61 mm. Nos. 1111/1112×2 11·00 9·75

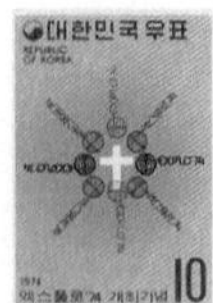
499 Cross and Emblems

1974. Explo 74 Second International Training Congress on Evangelism. Multicoloured.

1114 10w. Type **499** 40 10
1115 10w. Emblem and Korean map on Globe 40 10

501 Underground Train

1974. Opening of Seoul Underground Railway.

1116 **501** 10w. multicoloured 1·00 25

1974. Traditional Musical Instruments (4th series). As T **481**. Multicoloured. Background colours given.

1117 10w. blue 95 30
1118 30w. pink 1·90 45
MS1119 Two sheets each 125×90 mm. Nos. 1117/1118×2 7·75 7·00

Designs: No. 1117, So (Pan pipes); No. 1118, Haikem (Two-stringed fiddle).

1974. Fruits (4th series). As T **483**. Multicoloured.

1120 10w. Cherries 70 25
1121 30w. Persimmons 1·50 45
MS1122 Two sheets each 91×61 mm. Nos. 1120/1121×2 5·50 5·00

506 Rifle Shooting

1974. 55th National Athletic Meeting, Seoul. Multicoloured.

1123 10w. Type **506** 45 15
1124 30w. Rowing 1·30 40

508 UPU Emblem

1974. Centenary of UPU.

1125 **508** 10w. multicoloured (postage) 45 15
1126 **508** 110w. multicoloured (air) 2·30 1·00
MS1127 Two sheets each 90×60 mm. Nos. 1125/1126×2 20·00 18·00

509 Symbols of Member Countries

1974. First World Conference of People-to-People International.

1128 **509** 10w. multicoloured 45 10

510 Korean Stamps of 1884

1974. Philatelic Week and 90th Anniversary of First Korean Stamps.

1129 **510** 10w. multicoloured 55 10
MS1130 91×61 mm. No. 1129×2 8·50 7·75

511 Taekwondo Contestants

1974. First Asian Taekwondo Championships, Seoul.

1131 **511** 10w. multicoloured 55 10

1974. Traditional Musical Instruments (5th series). As T **481**. Multicoloured. Background colours given.

1132 10w. pink 95 25
1133 30w. ochre 1·90 45
MS1134 Two sheets each 125×90 mm. Nos. 1132/1133×2 7·75 7·00

Designs: 10w. Pak (clappers); 30w. Pyenchong (chimes).

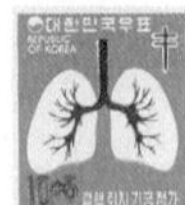
514 Lungs

1974. Tuberculosis Control Fund.

1135 **514** 10w.+5w. red & green 95 25

515 Presidents Pak and Ford

1974. State Visit of President Ford of United States.

1136 **515** 10w. multicoloured 85 30
MS1137 89×59 mm. No. 1136×2 7·75 7·00

516 Yook Young Soo (wife of Pres. Pak)

1974. Yook Young Soo Memorial Issue.

1138 **516** 10w. green 85 30
1139 **516** 10w. orange 85 30
1140 **516** 10w. violet 85 30
1141 **516** 10w. blue 85 30
MS1142 91×125 mm. No. 1138/1141 35·00 31·00

1974. Fruits (5th series). As T **483**. Multicoloured.

1143 10w. Tangerines 55 15
1144 30w. Chestnuts 1·30 40
MS1145 Two sheets each 91×61 mm. Nos. 1143/1144×2 5·75 5·25

519 'Good Luck' Purse

1974. Lunar New Year. Year of the Rabbit. Multicoloured.

1146 10w. Type **519** 60 20
1147 10w. Toy rabbits 60 20
MS1148 Two sheets each 91×61 mm. Nos. 1146/7×2 7·75 7·00

521 UPU Emblem and '75'

1975. 75th Anniversary of Korea's Membership of UPU. Multicoloured.

1149 10w. Type **521** 45 10
1150 10w. UPU emblem and paper dart 45 10

523 Dove with 'Good Luck' Card

1975. Inauguration of National Welfare Insurance System.

1151 **523** 10w. multicoloured 40 10

524 Dr. Schweitzer, Map and Syringe

1975. Birth Centenary of Dr. Albert Schweitzer.

1152 **524** 10w. bistre 95 40
1153 **524** 10w. mauve 95 40
1154 **524** 10w. orange 95 40
1155 **524** 10w. green 95 40

525 Salpuli Dancer

1975. Korean Folk Dances (1st series). Multicoloured. Background colour given.

1156 **525** 10w. green 70 25
1157 - 10w. blue 70 25
MS1158 Two sheets each 90×60 mm. Nos. 1156/1157×2 3·75 3·50

Design: No. 1157, Exorcism in dance.

See also Nos. 1168/**MS**1170, 1175/**MS**1177, 1193/**MS**1195 and 1208/**MS**1210.

527 Globe and Rotary Emblem

1975. 70th Anniversary of Rotary International.

1159 **527** 10w. multicoloured 40 10

528 Women and IWY Emblem

1975. International Women's Year.

1160 **528** 10w. multicoloured 40 10

529 Violets

1975. Flowers (1st series). Multicoloured.

1161 10w. Type **529** 75 25
1162 10w. Anemones 75 25

See also Nos. 1171/1172, 1184/1185, 1199/1200 and 1213/1214.

531 Saemaeul Township

1975. National Afforestation Campaign. Multicoloured.

1163 10w. Type **531** 75 30
1164 10w. Lake and trees 75 30
1165 10w. 'Green' forest 75 30
1166 10w. Felling timber 75 30

Nos. 1163/1166 were issued together, *se-tenant*, forming a composite design.

535 HRF Emblem on Map of Korea

1975. Homeland Reserve Forces Day.

1167	**535**	10w. multicoloured	60	10

536 Butterfly Dance

1975. Folk Dances (2nd series). Multicoloured. Background colour given.

1168	**536**	10w. green	75	25
1169	-	10w. yellow	75	25

MS1170 Two sheets each 90×60 mm. Nos. 1168/1169×2 3·50 3·00

Design: No. 1169, Victory dance.

538 Rhododendron

1975. Flowers (2nd series). Multicoloured.

1171	10w. Type **538**	75	25
1172	10w. Clematis	75	25

540 Metric Symbols

1975. Centenary of Metric Convention.

1173	**540**	10w. multicoloured	40	10

541 Soldier and Incense Pot

1975. 20th Memorial Day.

1174	**541**	10w. multicoloured	40	10

542 Mokjoong Dance

1975. Folk Dances (3rd series). Multicoloured.

1175	**542**	10w. blue	75	25
1176	-	10w. pink	75	25

MS1177 Two sheets each 90×60 mm. Nos. 1175/1176×2 3·50 3·00

Design: No. 1176, Malttungi dancer.

544 Flags of South Korea, UN and US

1975. 25th Anniversary of Korean War. Multicoloured.

1178	10w. Type **544**	75	30
1179	10w. Flags of Ethiopia, France, Greece, Canada and South Africa	75	30
1180	10w. Flags of Luxembourg, Australia, UK, Colombia and Turkey	75	30
1181	10w. Flags of Netherlands, Belgium, Philippines, New Zealand and Thailand	75	30

548 Presidents Pak and Bongo

1975. State Visit of President Bongo of Gabon.

1182	**548**	10w. multicoloured	55	10

MS1183 90×60 mm. No. 1182×2 2·75 2·40

549 Iris

1975. Flowers (3rd series). Multicoloured.

1184	10w. Type **549**	75	25
1185	10w. Thistle	75	25

551 Scout Scarf

1975. Nordjamb 75 World Scout Jamboree, Norway. Multicoloured.

1186	10w. Type **551**	75	30
1187	10w. Scout oath	75	30
1188	10w. Scout camp	75	30
1189	10w. Axe and rope	75	30
1190	10w. Camp fire	75	30

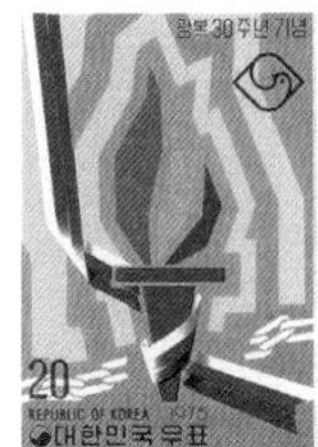
552 Freedom Flame

1975. 30th Anniversary of Liberation. Multicoloured.

1191	20w. Type **552**	70	25
1192	20w. Balloon emblems	70	25

554 Drum Dance

1975. Folk Dances (4th series). Multicoloured. Background colour given.

1193	**554**	20w. yellow	1·00	45
1194	-	20w. orange	1·00	45

MS1195 Two sheets each 90×60 mm. Nos. 1193/1194×2 5·50 5·00

Design: No. 1194, Bara dance.

556 Taekwondo Contestant

1975. Second World Taekwondo Championships, Seoul.

1196	**556**	20w. multicoloured	45	10

557 Assembly Hall

1975. Completion of National Assembly Hall.

1197	**557**	20w. multicoloured	45	10

558 Dumper Truck and Emblem

1975. Contractors' Association Convention, Seoul.

1198	**558**	20w. multicoloured	45	10

559 Broad-bell Flower

1975. Flowers (4th series). Multicoloured.

1199	20w. Type **559**	1·20	30
1200	20w. Bush clover	1·20	30

561 Morse Key and Dish Aerial

1975. 90th Anniversary of Korean Telecommunications.

1201	**561**	20w. black, orange & pur	45	10

562 Yeongweol Caves

1975. International Tourism Day. Multicoloured.

1202	20w. Type **562**	45	10
1203	20w. Mount Sorak	45	10

564 Flag and Missiles

1975. Korean Armed Forces Day.

1204	**564**	20w. multicoloured	40	10

565 'Gymnastics'

1975. 56th National Athletic Meeting. Multicoloured.

1205	20w. Type **565**	40	10
1206	20w. 'Handball'	40	10

567 'Kangaroo' Collector

1975. Philatelic Week.

1207	**567**	20w. multicoloured	40	10

568 Sogo Dance

1975. Folk Dances (5th series). Multicoloured. Background colour given.

1208	**568**	20w. blue	1·10	45
1209	-	20w. yellow	1·10	45

MS1210 Two sheets each 90×60 mm. Nos. 1208/1209×2 4·75 4·25

Design: No. 1209, Bupo Nori dance.

570 UN Emblem and Handclasps

1975. 30th Anniversary of United Nations.

1211	**570**	20w. multicoloured	40	10

571 Red Cross and Emblems

1975. 70th Anniversary of Korean Red Cross.

1212	**571**	20w. multicoloured	45	10

572 Camellia

1975. Flowers (5th series). Multicoloured.

1213	20w. Type **572**	1·70	55
1214	20w. Gentian	1·70	55

574 Union Emblem

1975. Tenth Anniversary of Asian Parliamentary Union.

1215	**574**	20w. multicoloured	40	10

575 Children Playing

1975. Lunar New Year. Multicoloured.

1216	20w. Type **575**	55	15
1217	20w. Dragon. Year of the Dragon	55	15

MS1218 Two sheets each 90×60 mm. Nos. 1216/1217×2 3·75 3·50

577 Electric Train

1975. Opening of Cross-country Electric Railway.

1219	**577**	20w. multicoloured	75	15

578 *Dilipa fenestra*

1976. Butterflies (1st series). Multicoloured, background colour given.

1220	**578**	20w. red	1·50	30
1221	-	20w. blue	1·50	30

Design: No. 1221, *Luehdorfia puziloi*.

See also Nos. 1226/1227, 1246/1247, 1254/1255 and 1264/1265.

580 Institute Emblem and Science Emblems

1976. Tenth Anniversary of Korean Institute of Science and Technology.

1222	**580**	20w. multicoloured	40	10

581 Japanese White-naped Crane

1976. Birds (1st series). Multicoloured.

1223	20w. Type **581**	1·50	40
1224	20w. Great bustard	1·50	40

See also Nos. 1243/1244, 1251/1252, 1257/1258 and 1266/1267.

583 Globe and Telephones

1976. Telephone Centenary.

1225	**583**	20w. multicoloured	40	10

584 *Papilio xuthus*

1976. Butterflies (2nd series). Multicoloured, background colour given.

1226	**584**	20w. yellow	1·50	30
1227	-	20w. green	1·50	30

Design: No. 1227, *Parnassius bremeri*.

586 National Development

1976. Homeland Reserve Forces Day.

1228	**586**	20w. multicoloured	40	10

587 Eye and People

1976. World Health Day. Prevention of Blindness.

1229	**587**	20w. multicoloured	40	10

588 President Pak and Flag

1976. Sixth Anniversary of Saemaul Movement (community self-help programme). Multicoloured.

1230	20w. Type **588**	1·50	45
1231	20w. People (Intellectual edification)	1·50	45
1232	20w. Village (Welfare)	1·50	45
1233	20w. Produce and fields (Production)	1·50	45
1234	20w. Produce and factory (Increase of Income)	1·50	45

589 Ruins of Moenjodaro

1976. Moenjodaro (Pakistan) Preservation Campaign.

1235	**589**	20w. multicoloured	45	10

590 US Flags of 1776 and 1976

1976. Bicentenary of American Revolution. Each black, blue and red.

1236	100w. Type **590**	3·00	1·20
1237	100w. Statue of Liberty	3·00	1·20
1238	100w. Map of United States	3·00	1·20
1239	100w. Liberty Bell	3·00	1·20
1240	100w. American astronaut	3·00	1·20
MS1241	91×61 mm. No. 1236	6·25	5·50

591 Camp Scene on Emblem

1976. 30th Anniversary of Korean Girl Scouts Federation.

1242	**591**	20w. multicoloured	95	15

592 Blue-winged Pitta

1976. Birds (2nd series). Multicoloured.

1243	20w. Type **592**	1·50	40
1244	20w. White-bellied black woodpecker	1·50	40

594 Buddha and Temple

1976. UNESCO Campaign for Preservation of Borobudur Temple (in Indonesia).

1245	**594**	20w. multicoloured	40	10

595 Chinese Windmill

1976. Butterflies (3rd series). Multicoloured, background colour given.

1246	**595**	20w. olive	1·50	30
1247	-	20w. violet	1·50	30

Design: No. 1247, Eastern Pale Clouded Yellow.

597 Protected Family

1976. National Life Insurance.

1248	**597**	20w. multicoloured	40	10

598 Volleyball

1976. Olympic Games, Montreal. Multicoloured.

1249	20w. Type **598**	45	10
1250	20w. Boxing	45	10

600 Black Wood Pigeon

1976. Birds (3rd series). Multicoloured.

1251	20w. Type **600**	1·50	40
1252	20w. Oystercatcher	1·50	40

602 Children and Books

1976. Books for Children.

1253	**602**	20w. multicoloured	40	10

603 *Hestina assimilis*

1976. Butterflies (4th series). Multicoloured, background colour given.

1254	**603**	20w. brown	2·20	85
1255	-	20w. drab	2·20	85

Design: No. 1255, Blue triangle.

604a Corps Members and Flag

1976. First Anniversary of Korean Civil Defence Corps.

1256	**604a**	20w. multicoloured	40	10

605 Black-faced Spoonbill

1976. Birds (4th series). Multicoloured.

1257	20w. Type **605**	1·50	40
1258	20w. Black stork	1·50	40

607 Chamsungdan, Mani Mountain

1976. International Tourism Day. Multicoloured.

1259	20w. Type **607**	75	25
1260	20w. Ilchumun Gate, Tongdosa	75	25

609 Cadet and Parade

1976. 30th Anniversary of Korean Military Academy.

1261	**609**	20w. multicoloured	45	15

610 *Musa basjoo* (flower arrangement, Cheong Jo the Great)

1976. Philatelic Week.

1262	**610**	20w. black, red and drab	45	10
MS1263		91×61 mm. No. 1262×2	3·75	3·50

611 Yellow-legged Tortoiseshell

1976. Butterflies (5th series). Multicoloured, background colour given.

1264	**611**	20w. light green	2·30	95
1265	-	20w. purple	2·30	95

Design: No. 1265, *Fabriciana nerippe*.

613 Cinereous Vulture

1976. Birds (5th series). Multicoloured.

1266	20w. Type **613**	3·75	1·40
1267	20w. Tundra swan	3·75	1·40

615 Snake (bas-relief, Kim Yu Shin's tomb)

1976. Lunar New Year. Year of the Snake. Multicoloured.

1268	20w. Type **615**	55	25
1269	20w. Door knocker with Manchurian cranes	55	25
MS1270	Two sheets each 90×60 mm. Nos. 1268/1269×2	3·75	3·50

617 Training Technicians

1977. Fourth Five Year Economic Development Plan. Multicoloured.

1271	20w. Type **617**	60	15
1272	20w. Tanker (Heavy Industries)	60	15

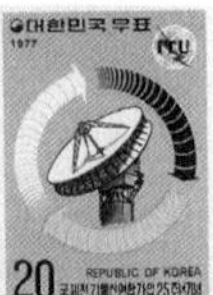

619 Dish Aerial

1977. 25th Anniversary of Korea's ITU Membership.

1273	**619**	20w. multicoloured	45	15

620 Korean Broadcasting Centre

1977. 50th Anniversary of Broadcasting in Korea.

1274	**620**	20w. multicoloured	45	15

621 Jar with Grape Design

1977. Korean Ceramics (1st series). Multicoloured, background colours given.

1275	20w. Type **621** (brown)	1·90	30
1276	20w. Celadon vase (grey)	1·90	30

See also Nos. 1285/1286, 1287/1288, 1290/1291 and 1300/1301.

623 'Two-children' Family

1977. Family Planning.
1277 **623** 20w. green, turq & orge 1·90 25

624 Reserve Soldier

1977. Ninth Homeland Reserve Forces Day.
1278 **624** 20w. multicoloured 40 10

625 Diagram of Brain

1977. Tenth Anniversary of Science Day.
1279 **625** 20w. multicoloured 40 10

626 Medical Book and Equipment

1977. 35th International Military Medicine Meeting.
1280 **626** 20w. multicoloured 55 10

627 Child with Flowers

1977. 20th Anniversary of Children's Charter.
1281 **627** 20w. multicoloured 40 10

628 Veterans' Flag and Emblem

1977. 25th Anniversary of Korean Veterans' Day.
1282 **628** 20w. multicoloured 55 10

629 Statue of Buddha, Sokkulam Grotto

1977. 2600th Birth Anniversary of Buddha.
1283 **629** 20w. green and brown 55 10
MS1284 90×60 mm. No. 1283×2 4·75 4·25

630 Celadon Jar

1977. Korean Ceramics (2nd series). Multicoloured, background colours given.
1285 20w. Type **630** (pink) 75 30
1286 20w. Porcelain vase (blue) (vert) 75 30

632 Buddha Celadon Wine Jar

1977. Korean Ceramics (3rd series). Multicoloured, background colours given.
1287 20w. Type **632** (mauve) 75 25
1288 20w. Celadon vase (pale blue) 75 25

수해구제
+10
(634)

1977. Flood Relief. No. 791 surch with T **634**.
1289 20w.+10w. green 7·75 6·75

635 Celadon Vase, Black Koryo Ware

1977. Korean Ceramics (4th series). Multicoloured, background colours given.
1290 20w. Type **635** (stone) 75 25
1291 20w. White porcelain bowl (green) (horiz) 75 25

637 Ulleung-do Island

1977. World Tourism Day. Multicoloured.
1292 20w. Type **637** 45 10
1293 20w. Haeundae Beach 45 10

639 Servicemen

1977. Armed Forces Day.
1294 **639** 20w. multicoloured 40 10

640/641 *Mount Inwang Clearing-up after the Rain* (detail from drawing by Chung Seon)

1977. Philatelic Week.
1295 **640** 20w. multicoloured 95 25
1296 **641** 20w. multicoloured 95 25
MS1297 90×60 mm. Nos. 1295/1296 7·00 6·25

Nos. 1295/1296 were issued together, *se-tenant*, forming the composite design illustrated.

642 Rotary Emblem and Koryo Dynasty Bronze Bell

1977. 50th Anniversary of Korean Rotary Club.
1298 **642** 20w. multicoloured 70 15

643 South Korean Flag over Everest

1977. South Korean Conquest of Mount Everest.
1299 **643** 20w. multicoloured 70 15

644 Punch'ong Bottle

1977. Korean Ceramics (5th series). Multicoloured, background colours given.
1300 20w. Type **644** (brown) 75 25
1301 20w. Celadon cylindrical bottle (pale brown) 75 25

646 Hands preserving Nature

1977. Nature Conservation.
1302 **646** 20w. blue, green and brown 75 15

647 Children with Kites

1977. Lunar New Year. Year of the Horse. Multicoloured.
1303 20w. Type **647** 45 15
1304 20w. Horse (bas-relief, Kim Yu Shin's tomb) 45 15
MS1305 Two sheets each 90×60 mm. (a) No. 1303×2; (b) No. 1304×2 4·25 4·00

649 Clay Pigeon Shooting

1977. 42nd World Shooting Championships, Seoul. Multicoloured.
1306 20w. Type **649** 55 10
1307 20w. Air pistol shooting 55 10
1308 20w. Air rifle shooting 55 10
MS1309 Three sheets each 90×60 mm. (a) No. 1306×2; (b) No. 1307×2; (c) No. 1308×2 11·50 10·50

652 Korean Airlines Boeing 747-200

1977. 25th Anniversary of Korean Membership of ICAO.
1310 **652** 20w. multicoloured 60 15

653 Exports

1977. Korean Exports.
1311 **653** 20w. multicoloured 45 10

654 Ships and World Map

1978. National Maritime Day.
1312 **654** 20w. multicoloured 40 10

655 Three-storey Pagoda, Hwaom Temple

656 Seven-storey Pagoda, T'app'yong-ri

1978. Stone Pagodas (1st series).
1313 **655** 20w. multicoloured 1·20 30
1314 **656** 20w. multicoloured 1·20 30

See also Nos. 1319/1320, 1322/1323, 1324/1325 and 1340/1341.

657 Ants with Coins

1978. Savings Encouragement.
1315 **657** 20w. multicoloured 55 10

658 Seoul Sejong Cultural Centre, Hahoe Mask and Violin

1978. Opening of Seoul Sejong Cultural Centre.
1316 **658** 20w. multicoloured 70 15

659 Standard Bearer

1978. Tenth Homeland Reserve Forces Day.
1317 **659** 20w. multicoloured 40 10

660 Pigeon and Young

1978. Family Planning.
1318 **660** 20w. black and green 1·00 30

661 Pagoda, Punhwang Temple

662 Pagoda, Miruk Temple

1978. Stone Pagodas (2nd series).
1319 **661** 20w. multicoloured 1·20 30
1320 **662** 20w. multicoloured 1·20 30

663 National Assembly

1978. 30th Anniversary of National Assembly.
1321 **663** 20w. multicoloured 40 10

664 Tabo Pagoda, Pulguk Temple

665 Three-storey Pagoda, Pulguk Temple

1978. Stone Pagodas (3rd series).
1322 **664** 20w. multicoloured 75 25
1323 **665** 20w. multicoloured 75 25

666 Ten-storey Pagoda, Kyongch'on Temple

667 Nine-storey Octagonal Pagoda, Wolchong Temple

1978. Stone Pagodas (4th series).

1324	**666**	20w. multicoloured	1·20	30
1325	**667**	20w. multicoloured	1·20	30

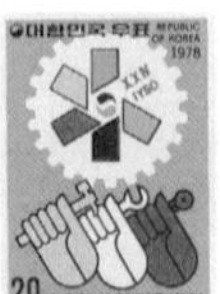

668 Emblem and Hands with Tools

1978. 24th International Youth Skill Olympics, Pusan.

1326	**668**	20w. multicoloured	40	10
MS1327 90×60 mm. No. 1326×1			3·00	2·75

669 Crater Lake, Mt. Baeguda and Bell of Joy

1978. 30th Anniversary of Republic of Korea.

1328	**669**	20w. multicoloured	40	10

670 Army Nursing Officer

1978. 30th Anniversary of Army Nursing Corps.

1329	**670**	20w. multicoloured	40	10

671 Sobaeksan Observatory and Telescope

1978. Opening of Sobaeksan Observatory.

1330	**671**	20w. multicoloured	45	10

672 Kyonghoeru Pavilion, Kyonbok Palace

673 Baeg-do Island

1978. World Tourism Day.

1331	**672**	20w. multicoloured	40	10
1332	**673**	20w. multicoloured	40	10

674 Customs Officers and Flag

1978. Centenary of Custom House.

1333	**674**	20w. multicoloured	40	10

675 Armed Forces

1978. 30th Anniversary of Korean Armed Forces.

1334	**675**	20w. multicoloured	40	10

676 Earthenware Figures, Silla Dynasty

1978. Culture Month.

1335	**676**	20w. black and green	40	10

677 *Painting of a Lady* (Shin Yoon-bok)

1978. Philatelic Week.

1336	**677**	20w. multicoloured	45	10
MS1337 91×60 mm. No. 1336×2			3·75	3·50

678 Young Men and YMCA Emblem

1978. 75th Anniversary of Korean YMCA.

1338	**678**	20w. multicoloured	40	10

679 Hand smothering Fire

1978. Fire Prevention Campaign.

1339	**679**	20w. multicoloured	30	10

680 Thirteen-storey Pagoda, Jeonghye Temple

681 Three-storey Pagoda, Jinjeon Temple

1978. Stone Pagodas (5th series).

1340	**680**	20w. multicoloured	55	10
1341	**681**	20w. multicoloured	55	10

682 Snow Scene

1978. Lunar New Year. Year of the Sheep. Multicoloured.

1342	20w. Type **682**	45	10
1343	20w. Sheep (bas-relief, Kim Yu Shin's tomb)	45	10
MS1344 Two sheets each 90×60 mm. Nos. 1342/1343×2		3·50	3·00

684 People within Hibiscus

1978. Tenth Anniversary of National Education Charter.

1345	**684**	20w. multicoloured	40	10

685 President Pak

1978. Re-election of President Pak.

1346	**685**	20w. multicoloured	85	30
MS1347 90×60 mm. No. 1346×2			12·50	11·00

686 Golden Mandarinfish

687 Lace Bark Pine

1979. Nature Conservation.

1348	**686**	20w. multicoloured	1·50	15
1349	**687**	20w. multicoloured	1·50	15

688 Samil Monument

1979. 60th Anniversary of Samil Independence Movement.

1350	**688**	20w. multicoloured	40	10

689 Worker and Bulldozer

1979. Labour Day.

1351	**689**	20w. multicoloured	40	10

690 Tabo Pagoda, Pulgak Temple

1979. Korean Art. Multicoloured.

1352	20w. Type **690**	45	15
1353	20w. Gilt-bronze Maitreya	45	15
1354	20w. Gold crown of Silla	45	15
1355	20w. Celadon vase	45	15
1356	60w. *Tano Day Activities* (silk screen) (50×33 mm)	85	30
MS1357 90×126 mm. No. 1356×2		3·25	3·00

695 Hand holding Symbols of Security

1979. Strengthening National Security.

1358	**695**	20w. multicoloured	40	10

696 Pulguk Temple and PATA Emblem

1979. 28th Pacific Area Travel Association Conference, Seoul.

1359	**696**	20w. multicoloured	40	10

697 Presidents Pak and Senghor

1979. Visit of President Senghor of Senegal.

1360	**697**	20w. multicoloured	40	10
MS1361 90×60 mm. No. 1360×2			1·50	1·40

698 Basketball

1979. Eighth World Women's Basketball Championships, Seoul.

1362	**698**	20w. multicoloured	55	10

699 Children playing

1979. International Year of the Child.

1363	**699**	20w. multicoloured	40	10
MS1363a 90×60 mm. No. 1363×2			1·50	1·40

700 Children on Swing

1979. Family Planning.

1364	**700**	20w. multicoloured	75	30

701 Mandarins

702 *Neofinettia falcata* (orchid)

1979. Nature Conservation.

1365	**701**	20w. multicoloured	1·50	25
1366	**702**	20w. multicoloured	1·50	25

703 Manchurian Cranes

1979

1367	**703**	10w. black and green	70	25
1368	-	15w. deep green and green	40	10
1369	-	20w. bistre, black & blue	40	10
1370	-	30w. multicoloured	45	10
1371	-	40w. multicoloured	55	10
1372	-	50w. brown, red & orge	40	10
1373	-	60w. grey, purple & mve	45	10
1374	-	70w. multicoloured	75	15
1375	-	80w. yellow, black & red	85	25
1376	-	90w. buff, green and orange	1·10	25
1377	-	100w. purple and mauve	95	25
1377a	-	100w. black	2·75	25
1378	-	150w. black, bistre and blue	1·00	25
1379	-	200w. brown and green	1·50	30
1380	-	300w. blue	2·30	30
1381a	-	400w. blue, ochre, brown and grey	3·50	40
1382	-	450w. brown	2·75	40

1383	-	500w. dp green & green	2·75	40
1384	-	600w. multicoloured	3·00	75
1385	-	700w. multicoloured	4·25	75
1386	-	800w. multicoloured	3·75	1·20
1387	-	1000w. lt brown & brn	4·25	45
1388	-	1000w. lt brown & brn	4·25	45
1389	-	5000w. multicoloured	27·00	5·50

Designs: As T **703** Horiz—15w. Mt. Sorak; 50w. Earthenware model of wagon; 90w. Paikryung Island; 1000w. Duck earthenware vessels (No. 1387 facing right; No. 1388 facing left). Vert—20w. Tolharubang (stone grandfather); 30w. National Flag; 40w. *Hibiscus syriacus*; 60w. Porcelain jar, Yi Dynasty; 70w. Kyongju Observatory; 80w. Mounted warrior (pottery vessel); 100w. (No. 1377) Ryu Kwan Soon; 100w. (No. 1377a) Chung Yak Yong (writer); 150w. Porcelain jar, Chosun Dynasty; 200w. Ahn Joong Geun; 300w. Ahn Chang Ho; 400w. Koryo celadon incense burner; 450, 550w. Kim Ku (organiser of Korean Independence Party); 500w. Brick with mountain landscape; 600w. Hong Yung Sik (postal reformer); 700w. Duck (lid of incense burner). 29×41 mm: 800w. Dragon's head flagpole finial; 5000w. Tiger.

See also No. 1065.

725 People suffering from Traffic Pollution

1979. Environmental Protection.

1390	**725**	20w. brown and green	75	25

726 Common Goral

727 *Convallaria leiskei* Miquel

1979. Nature Conservation.

1391	**726**	20w. multicoloured	1·50	15
1392	**727**	20w. multicoloured	1·50	15

728 Presidents Pak and Carter

1979. Visit of President Carter of United States.

1393	**728**	20w. multicoloured	40	10
MS1394 90×60 mm. No. 1393×2			1·50	1·40

729 Exhibition Building and Emblem

1979. Opening of Korea Exhibition Centre.

1395	**729**	20w. multicoloured	30	10

730 Boeing 747-200 Jetliner and Globe

1979. Tenth Anniversary of Korean Air Lines.

1396	**730**	20w. multicoloured	40	10

731 *The Courtesans' Sword Dance* (Shin Yun-bok)

1979. United States 5000 Years of Korean Art Exhibition (1st issue).

1397	**731**	60w. multicoloured	85	30
MS1398 89×125 mm. No. 1397×2			4·25	3·75

See also Nos. 1402/1403, 1406/1407, 1420/**MS**1422, 1426/1427, 1433/1434, 1441/1442 and 1457/1458.

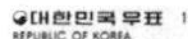

732 Mount Mai, North Cholla Province

733 Dragon's Head Rock, Cheju Island

1979. World Tourism Day.

1399	**732**	20w. multicoloured	40	10
1400	**733**	20w. multicoloured	40	10

734 Heart, Donors and Blood Drop

1979. Blood Donors.

1401	**734**	20w. red and green	75	15

735 White Porcelain Jar with Grape Design

736 Mounted Warrior (pottery vessel)

1979. 5000 Years of Korean Art Exhibition (2nd issue).

1402	**735**	20w. multicoloured	60	15
1403	**736**	20w. multicoloured	60	15

737 *Moon Travel* (Park Chung Jae)

1979. Philatelic Week.

1404	**737**	20w. multicoloured	30	10
MS1405 90×66 mm. No. 1404×2			1·40	1·30

738 Hahoe Mask

739 Golden Amitabha with Halo

1979. 5000 Years of Korean Art Exhibition (3rd issue).

1406	**738**	20w. multicoloured	55	15
1407	**739**	20w. multicoloured	55	15

740 Rain Frog

741 Asian Polypody

1979. Nature Conservation.

1408	**740**	20w. multicoloured	1·60	15
1409	**741**	20w. multicoloured	1·60	15

742 Monkey (bas-relief, Kim Yun Shin's tomb)

743 Children playing Yut

1979. Lunar New Year. Year of the Monkey.

1410	**742**	20w. multicoloured	40	10
1411	**743**	20w. multicoloured	40	10
MS1412 Two sheets each 90×60 mm. (a) No. 1410×2; (b) No. 1411×2			1·40	1·20

744 President Choi Kyu Hah

1979. Presidential Inauguration.

1413	**744**	20w. multicoloured	50	10
MS1414 91×61 mm. No. 1413×2			5·75	5·50

745 Firefly

746 Meesun Tree

1980. Nature Conservation (5th series).

1415	**745**	30w. multicoloured	1·60	15
1416	**746**	30w. multicoloured	1·60	15

747 President Pak

1980. President Pak Commemoration.

1417	**747**	30w. red	50	15
1418	**747**	30w. purple	50	15
MS1419 90×60 mm. Nos. 1417/1418			4·50	4·25

748 Earthenware Kettle

749 *Landscape* (Kim Hong Do)

1980. 5000 Years of Korean Art Exhibition (4th issue).

1420	**748**	30w. multicoloured	65	15
1421	**749**	60w. multicoloured	1·00	30
MS1422 90×128 mm. No. 1421×2			3·50	3·50

750 *Lotus*

751 *Magpie and Tiger*

1980. Folk Paintings (1st series).

1423	**750**	30w. multicoloured	65	15
1424	**751**	60w. multicoloured	1·60	55

See also Nos. 1429/**MS**1432, 1437/1438, 1439/1440 and 1453/1456.

752 Merchant Ships

1980. Korean Merchant Navy.

1425	**752**	30w. multicoloured	40	10

753 *Heavenly Horse* (tomb painting)

754 Banner Staff with Dragonhead Finial

1980. 5000 Years of Korean Art Exhibition (5th series).

1426	**753**	30w. multicoloured	65	15
1427	**754**	30w. multicoloured	65	15

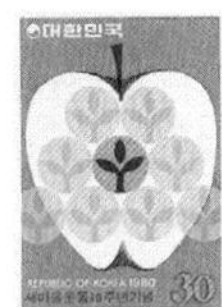

755 Fruition

1980. Tenth Anniversary of Saemaul Movement (community self-help programme).

1428	**755**	30w. multicoloured	40	10

756 *Red Phoenix*

757/758 *Sun and Moon over Mt. Konryun* (image scaled to 47% of original size)

1980. Folk Paintings (2nd series).

1429	**756**	30w. multicoloured	55	15
1430	**757**	60w. multicoloured	1·60	45
1431	**758**	60w. multicoloured	1·60	45
MS1432 127×91 mm. Nos. 1430/1431			5·75	5·50

Nos. 1430/1431 were issued together, *se-tenant*, forming a composite design.

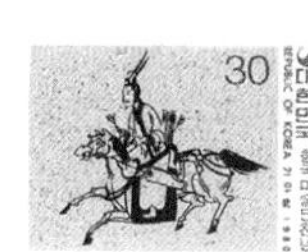

759 *Man on a Horse* (mural, Koguryo period)

760 *Tiger* (granite sculpture)

1980. 5000 Years of Korean Art Exhibition (6th issue).

1433	**759**	30w. multicoloured	65	15
1434	**760**	30w. multicoloured	65	15

761 UN Flag and Rifle

1980. 30th Anniversary of Intervention of UN Forces in Korean War.

1435	**761**	30w. multicoloured	40	10

762 *Venus de Milo* and Contestants

1980. Miss Universe Beauty Contest, Seoul.

1436	**762**	30w. multicoloured	40	10

763 *Rabbits pounding Grain in a Mortar* **764** *Dragon in Cloud*

1980. Folk Paintings (3rd series).

1437	**763**	30w. multicoloured	65	25
1438	**764**	30w. multicoloured	65	25

765 *Pine Tree* **766** *Flowers and Manchurian Cranes (detail, folding screen)*

1980. Folk Paintings (4th series).

1439	**765**	30w. multicoloured	65	25
1440	**766**	30w. multicoloured	1·20	30

767 Human faced Roof Tile **768** *White Tiger* (mural)

1980. 5000 Years of Korean Art Exhibition (7th issue).

1441	**767**	30w. multicoloured	55	15
1442	**768**	30w. multicoloured	55	15

769 Football

1980. Tenth President's Cup Football Tournament.

1443	**769**	30w. multicoloured	40	10

770 President Chun Doo Hwan

1980. Presidential Inauguration.

1444	**770**	30w. multicoloured	50	15
MS1445		90×60 mm. No. 1444×2	3·25	2·75

771 Woman Soldier and Emblem

1980. 30th Anniversary of Women's Army Corps.

1446	**771**	30w. multicoloured	40	10

772 River Baegma **773** Three Peaks of Dodam

1980. World Tourism Day.

1447	**772**	30w. pink and purple	40	10
1448	**773**	30w. yellow, green and blue	40	10

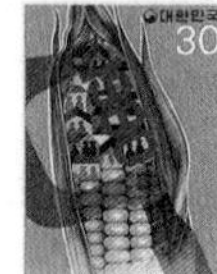
774 Corn-cob and Micrometer

1980. Population and Housing Census.

1449	**774**	30w. multicoloured	40	10

775 Tree

1980. 75th Anniversary of Korean Red Cross.

1450	**775**	30w. multicoloured	50	10

776 *Angels delivering Mail* (Kim Ki Chul)

1980. Philatelic Week.

1451	**776**	30w. multicoloured	40	10
MS1452		91×60 mm. No. 1451×2	1·50	1·30

777 *Ten Long-life Symbols*

1980. Folk Paintings (5th series). Multicoloured.

1453	30w. Type **777**	1·50	25
1454	30w. 'Herb of eternal youth' and deer	1·50	25
1455	30w. Pine and deer eating herb	1·50	25
1456	30w. Pine, water and rock	1·50	25

Nos. 1453/1456 were issued together, *se-tenant*, forming a composite design.

781 Deva King (sculpture)

1980. 5000 Years of Korean Art Exhibition (8th series).

1457	**781**	30w. black	65	15
1458	**781**	30w. red	65	15

782 *Cable Enterprise* (cable ship) and Cross-section of Cable

1980. Inauguration of Korea–Japan Submarine Cable.

1459	**782**	30w. multicoloured	50	10

783 Cock (bas-relief, Kim Yu Shin's tomb) **784** Cranes

1980. Lunar New Year. Year of the Cock.

1460	**783**	30w. multicoloured	50	10
1461	**784**	30w. multicoloured	50	10
MS1462		Two sheets each 90×60 mm. (a) No. 1460×2; (b) No. 1461×2	3·00	2·75

785 President Chun Doo Hwan and Factory within *Hibiscus syriacus*

1981. Presidential Inauguration.

1463	**785**	30w. multicoloured	40	10
MS1464		90×60 mm. No. 1463×2	1·40	1·30

786 *Korea Sun* (tanker) **787** *Asia Yukho* (freighter)

1981. Ships (1st series).

1465	**786**	30w. multicoloured	60	10
1466	**787**	90w. multicoloured	90	25

See also Nos. 1470/1471, 1482/1483, 1484/1485 and 1501/1502.

788 National Assembly Building

1981. Inaugural Session of 11th National Assembly.

1467	**788**	30w. brown and gold	40	10

789 Symbols of Disability and IYDP Emblem **790** Disabled Person in Wheelchair at Foot of Steps

1981. International Year of Disabled Persons.

1468	**789**	30w. multicoloured	40	10
1469	**790**	90w. multicoloured	85	40

791 *Saturn* (bulk-carrier) **792** *Hanjin Seoul* (container ship)

1981. Ships (2nd series).

1470	**791**	30w. deep purple, purple and blue	60	10
1471	**792**	90w. grey, blue and red	1·00	30

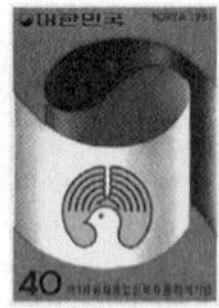
793 Council Emblem on Ribbon

1981. Advisory Council on Peaceful Unification Policy.

1472	**793**	40w. multicoloured	40	10

794 'Clean Rivers and Air' **795** White Storks visiting Breeding Grounds

1981. World Environment Day.

1473	**794**	30w. multicoloured	40	10
1474	**795**	90w. multicoloured	90	25

796 Presidents Chun and Suharto of Indonesia

1981. Presidential Visit to ASEAN Countries. Multicoloured.

1475	40w. Type **796**	65	10
1476	40w. President Chun and Sultan of Malaysia	65	10
1477	40w. Handshake and flags of South Korea and Singapore	65	10
1478	40w. President Chun and King of Thailand	65	10
1479	40w. Presidents Chun and Marcos of Philippines	65	10
1480	40w. President Chun and flags of Korea, Singapore, Malaysia and Philippines (39×43 mm)	65	10
MS1481	Two sheets each 126×90 mm. (a) Nos. 1475/1479; (b) No. 1480×2	5·50	5·00

802 *Chung Ryong No. 3* (tug) **803** *Soo Gong No. 71* (trawler)

1981. Ships (3rd series).

1482	**802**	40w. multicoloured	75	15
1483	**803**	100w. multicoloured	1·30	40

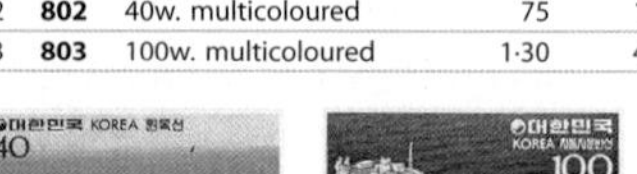

804 *Aldebaran* (log carrier) **805** *Hyundai No. 1* (car carrier)

1981. Ships (4th series).

1484	**804**	40w. multicoloured	75	15
1485	**805**	100w. multicoloured	1·30	30

806 Korean with Flag and Dates on Graph

1981. 36th Anniversary of Liberation.

1486	**806**	40w. multicoloured	40	10

807 Glider

1981. Third Model Aeronautic Competition. Multicoloured.

1487	10w. Type **807**	60	10
1488	20w. Elastic-powered aeroplane	60	10
1489	40w. Line-controlled aeroplane	60	20
1490	50w. Radio-controlled aeroplane	75	30
1491	80w. Radio-controlled helicopter	1·00	40

812 WHO Emblem and Citizens

1981. 32nd Session of WHO Regional Committee for the Western Pacific, Seoul.

1492	**812**	40w. multicoloured	40	10

813 Seoul Communications Tower **814** Ulreung Island

1981. World Tourism Day.

1493	**813**	40w. multicoloured	40	10
1494	**814**	40w. multicoloured	40	10

815 Cycling

816 Swimming

1981. 62nd National Sports Meeting, Seoul.

1495	**815**	40w. multicoloured	50	10
1496	**816**	40w. multicoloured	50	10

817 Presidents Chun and Carazo Odio

1981. Visit of President Carazo Odio of Costa Rica.

1497	**817**	40w. multicoloured	45	10

818 Hand holding Plate with FAO Emblem

1981. World Food Day.

1498	**818**	40w. multicoloured	45	10

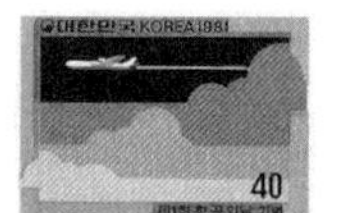

819 Airliner and Clouds

1981. National Aviation Day.

1499	**819**	40w. orange, brown and silver	50	10

820 South Gate of Seoul and Olympic Rings

1981. Choice of Seoul as 1988 Olympic Host City.

1500	**820**	40w. multicoloured	65	15

821 *Stolt Hawk* (chemical carrier)

822 Passenger Ferry

981. Ships (5th series).

501	**821**	40w. black	65	15
502	**822**	100w. blue	1·20	30

823 *Hang-gliding* (Kim Kyung Jun)

981. Philatelic Week.

503	**823**	40w. multicoloured	40	10
S1504		90×60 mm. No. 1503×2	1·80	1·70

824 Camellia and Dog

825 Children flying Kite

1981. Lunar New Year. Year of the Dog.

1505	**824**	40w. multicoloured	40	10
1506	**825**	40w. multicoloured	40	10
MS1507		Two sheets each 90×60 mm. (a) No. 1505×2; (b) No. 1506×2	3·75	3·50

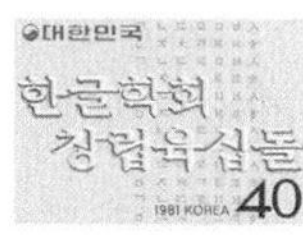

826 Hangul Hakhoe

1981. 60th Anniversary of Hangul Hakhoe (Korean Language Society).

1508	**826**	40w. multicoloured	50	10

827 Telephone and Dish Aerial

1982. Inauguration of Korea Telecommunication Authority.

1509	**827**	60w. multicoloured	60	10

828 Scout Emblem and Logs forming '75'

1982. 75th Anniversary of Boy Scout Movement.

1510	**828**	60w. multicoloured	65	15

829 Young Woman

1982. 60th Anniversary of Korean Young Women's Christian Association.

1511	**829**	60w. multicoloured	50	10

830 Dividers and World Map

1982. Centenary of International Polar Year.

1512	**830**	60w. multicoloured	65	15

831 Music and *Hibiscus syriacus*

1982. Children's Day.

1513	**831**	60w. multicoloured	50	10

832 President Chun and Samuel Doe

1982. Visit of Samuel Doe (Liberian Head of State).

1514	**832**	60w. multicoloured	60	15
MS1515		100×60 mm. No. 1514×2	1·80	1·70

833 Centenary Emblem

1982. Centenary of Korea–United States Friendship Treaty.

1516	**833**	60w. multicoloured	50	15
1517	-	60w. multicoloured	50	15
MS1518		90×60 mm. Nos. 1516/1517	3·75	3·50

Design: No. 1517, Statue of Liberty and Seoul South Gate.

835 Presidents Chun and Mobutu

1982. Visit of President Mobutu of Zaire.

1519	**835**	60w. multicoloured	50	15
MS1520		100×60 mm. No. 1519×2. Imperf	1·80	1·70

836 *Territorial Expansion by Kwanggaeto the Great* (Lee Chong Sang)

837 *General Euljimunduck's Great Victory at Salsoo* (Park Kak Soon)

1982. Documentary Paintings (1st series).

1521	**836**	60w. multicoloured	85	40
1522	**837**	60w. multicoloured	1·30	45

See also Nos. 1523/1524, 1537/1538 and 1548/1549.

838 *Shilla's Repulse of Invading Tang Army* (Oh Seung Woo)

839 *General Kang Kam Chan's Great Victory at Kyiju* (Lee Yong Hwan)

1982. Documentary Paintings (2nd series).

1523	**838**	60w. multicoloured	75	30
1524	**839**	60w. multicoloured	75	30

840 Convention Emblem and Globe

1982. 55th International Y's Men's Club Convention, Seoul.

1525	**840**	60w. multicoloured	40	10

841 Presidents Chun and Moi of Kenya

1982. Presidential Visits to Africa and Canada. Multicoloured.

1526	60w. Type **841**	50	10
1527	60w. Presidents Chun and Shagari of Nigeria	50	10
1528	60w. Presidents Chun and Bongo of Gabon	50	10
1529	60w. Presidents Chun and Diouf of Senegal	50	10
1530	60w. Flags of South Korea and Canada	50	10
MS1531	Five sheets each 90×60 mm. (a) No. 1526×2; (b) No. 1527×2; (c) No. 1528×2; (d) No. 1529×2; (e) No. 1530×2	12·50	11·50

846 National Flag

1982. Centenary of National Flag.

1532	**846**	60w. multicoloured	50	10
MS1533		90×60 mm. No. 1532×2	2·50	2·30

847 Emblem and Player

1982. Second Seoul Table Tennis Championships.

1534	**847**	60w. multicoloured	60	10

848 Baseball Player

1982. 27th World Baseball Championship Series, Seoul.

1535	**848**	60w. brown	60	15

849 Exhibition Centre

1982. Seoul International Trade Fair.

1536	**849**	60w. multicoloured	40	10

850 *Admiral Yi Sun Sin's Great Victory at Hansan* (Kim Hyung Ku)

851 *General Kim Chwa Jin's Chungsanri Battle* (Sohn Soo Kwang)

1982. Documentary Paintings (3rd series).

1537	**850**	60w. multicoloured	1·10	40
1538	**851**	60w. multicoloured	1·10	40

852 *Miners reading Consolatory Letters* (Um Soon Keun)

1982. Philatelic Week.

1539	**852**	60w. multicoloured	40	10
MS1540		90×60 mm. No. 1539×2	1·70	1·50

853 Presidents Chun and Suharto

1982. Visit of President Suharto of Indonesia.
1541 **853** 60w. multicoloured 40 10
MS1542 100×60 mm. No. 1541. Imperf×2 1·50 1·40

854 JCI Emblem over World Map

1982. 37th Junior Chamber International World Congress, Seoul.
1543 **854** 60w. multicoloured 40 10

855 *Intelsat 5* and *4-A* orbiting Globe

1982. Second UN Conference on the Exploration and Peaceful Uses of Outer Space, Vienna.
1544 **855** 60w. multicoloured 50 10

856 Pig (bas-relief, Kim Yu Shin's tomb)

1982. Lunar New Year. Year of the Pig.
1545 60w. Type **856** 50 10
1546 60w. Black-billed magpies and Korean moneybag 50 10
MS1547 Two sheets each 90×60 mm. (a) No. 1545×2; (b) No. 1546×2 4·25 3·75

858 *General Kwon Yul's Great Victory at Haengju* (Oh Seung Woo)

859 *Kim Chong Suh's Exploitation of Yukin* (Kim Tae)

1982. Documentary Paintings (4th series).
1548 **858** 60w. multicoloured 1·30 40
1549 **859** 60w. multicoloured 1·30 40

860 Flags of South Korea and Turkey

1982. Visit of President Evran of Turkey.
1550 **860** 60w. multicoloured 50 10
MS1551 100×60 mm. No. 1550×2. Imperf 1·70 1·50

861 Hand writing Letter

1982. Letter Writing Campaign.
1552 **861** 60w. multicoloured 40 10

862 Emblem, Airliner, Container Ship and Cranes

1983. International Customs Day.
1553 **862** 60w. multicoloured 60 10

863 Hyundai Pony 2

1983. Korean-made Vehicles (1st series). Multicoloured.
1554 60w. Type **863** 85 25
1555 60w. Keohwa Jeep 85 25
See also Nos. 1558/1559, 1564/1565, 1572/1573 and 1576/1577.

865 President Chun and Sultan of Malaysia

1983. Visit of King of Malaysia.
1556 **865** 60w. multicoloured 40 10
MS1557 90×60 mm. No. 1556×2 1·40 1·30

866 Daewoo Maepsy

867 Kia Bongo Minibus

1983. Korean-made Vehicles (2nd series).
1558 **866** 60w. multicoloured 85 25
1559 **867** 60w. multicoloured 85 25

868 Former General Bureau of Postal Administration

869 Central Post Office, Seoul

1983. Philakorea 84 International Stamp Exhibition, Seoul. Centenary of Korean Postal Service (1st series).
1560 **868** 60w. multicoloured 65 15
1561 **869** 60w. multicoloured 65 15
See also Nos. 1566/1567, 1574/1575 and 1603/1604, 1605/1606.

870 Old Village Schoolroom

1983. Teachers' Day.
1562 **870** 60w. multicoloured 50 10
MS1563 90×60 mm. No. 1562×2 2·10 1·90

871 Asia Motor Co. Bus

872 Kia Super Titan Truck

1983. Korean-made Vehicles (3rd series).
1564 **871** 60w. multicoloured 85 25
1565 **872** 60w. multicoloured 85 25

873 Early Postman

1983. Philakorea 84 International Stamp Exhibition, Seoul. Centenary of Korean Postal Service (2nd series).
1566 **873** 70w. multicoloured 85 25
1567 - 70w. multicoloured 85 25
Design: No. 1567, Modern postman on motorcycle.

875 *Communications in Outer Space* (Chun Ja Eun)

1983. World Communications Year.
1568 **875** 70w. multicoloured 40 10
MS1569 90×60 mm. No. 1568×2 1·50 1·40

876 Whooper Swans at Sunrise

1983. Inauguration of Communications Insurance.
1570 **876** 70w. multicoloured 85 15

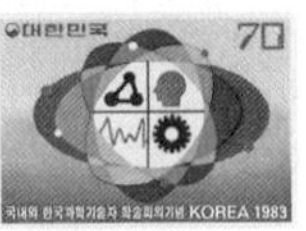
877 Emblems of Science and Engineering

1983. Korean Symposium on Science and Technology, Seoul.
1571 **877** 70w. multicoloured 60 15

878 Daewoo Dump Truck
879 Hyundai Cargo Lorry

1983. Korean-made Vehicles (4th series).
1572 **878** 70w. multicoloured 95 25
1573 **879** 70w. multicoloured 95 25

880 Mail carried by Horse

1983. Philakorea 84 International Stamp Exhibition, Seoul. Centenary of Korean Postal Service (3rd series). Multicoloured.
1574 70w. Type **880** 1·00 25
1575 70w. Mail truck and Douglas DC-8-60 Super Sixty jetliner 1·00 25

882 Dong-A Concrete Mixer Truck
883 Dong-A Tanker

1983. Korean-made Vehicles (5th series).
1576 **882** 70w. multicoloured 95 25
1577 **883** 70w. multicoloured 95 25

884 President Chun and King Hussein

1983. Visit of King Hussein of Jordan.
1578 **884** 70w. multicoloured 50 10
MS1579 100×60 mm. No. 1578×2. Imperf 1·60 1·40

885 Woman with Fan

1983. 53rd American Society of Travel Agents World Congress, Seoul.
1580 **885** 70w. multicoloured 50 10

886 IPU Emblem and Flags

1983. 70th Inter-Parliamentary Union Conference, Seoul.
1581 **886** 70w. multicoloured 50 10
MS1582 90×60 mm. No. 1581×2 1·60 1·40

887 Gymnastics

888 Football

1983. 64th National Sports Meeting, Inchon.
1583 **887** 70w. multicoloured 70 15
1584 **888** 70w. multicoloured 70 15

889 Presidents Chun and U San Yu of Burma

1983. Presidential Visits. Multicoloured.
1585 70w. Type **889** 1·60 7
1586 70w. Presidents Chun and Giani Zail Singh of India 1·60 7
1587 70w. Presidents Chun and Jayewardene of Sri Lanka 1·60 7
1588 70w. Flags of South Korea and Australia 1·60 7
1589 70w. Flags of South Korea and New Zealand 1·60 7
MS1590 Five sheets each 90×60 mm. (a) No. 1585×2; (b) No. 1586×2; (c) No. 1587×2; (d) No. 1588×2; (e) No. 1589×2 28·00 25·0

894 Rain Drops containing Symbols of Industry, Light and Food

1983. Development of Water Resources and Tent Anniversary of Soyang-gang Dam.
1591 **894** 70w. multicoloured 50 1

895 Centenary Dates

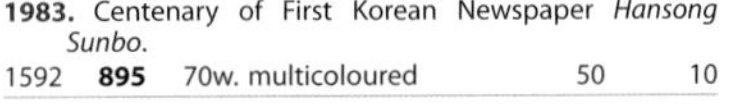

1983. Centenary of First Korean Newspaper *Hansong Sunbo*.

1592 **895** 70w. multicoloured 50 10

896 Tree with Lungs and Cross of Lorraine

1983. 30th Anniversary of Korean National Tuberculosis Association.

1593 **896** 70w. multicoloured 50 10

897 Presidents Chun and Reagan

1983. Visit of President Reagan of United States of America.

1594 **897** 70w. multicoloured 50 10

MS1595 90×60 mm. No. 1594×2 2·50 2·30

898 Child collecting Stamps

1983. Philatelic Week.

1596 **898** 70w. multicoloured 50 10

MS1597 90×60 mm. No. 1596×2 2·50 2·30

899 Rat (bas-relief, Kim Yu Shin's tomb)

1983. Lunar New Year. Year of the Rat. Multicoloured.

1598 70w. Type **899** 50 10

1599 70w. Manchurian cranes and pine 50 10

MS1600 Two sheets each 90×60 mm. (a) No. 1598×2; (b) No. 1599×2 5·25 4·75

901 Bicentenary Emblem

1984. Bicentenary of Catholic Church in Korea.

1601 **901** 70w. red, violet and silver 50 10

MS1602 90×60 mm. No. 1601×2 3·25 3·00

902 5m. and 10m. Stamps, 1884

1984. Philakorea 84 International Stamp Exhibition, Seoul. Centenary of Korean Postal Service (4th series). Multicoloured.

1603 70w. Type **902** 70 15

1604 70w. 5000w. stamp of 1983 70 15

904 Old Postal Emblem and Post Box

1984. Philakorea 84 International Stamp Exhibition, Seoul. Centenary of Korean Postal Service (5th series). Multicoloured.

1605 70w. Type **904** 70 15

1606 70w. Modern postal emblem and post box 70 15

906 President Chun and Sultan

1984. Visit of Sultan of Brunei.

1607 **906** 70w. multicoloured 50 10

MS1608 100×60 mm. No. 1607×2 1·70 1·50

907 President Chun and Sheikh Khalifa

1984. Visit of Sheikh Khalifa of Qatar.

1609 **907** 70w. multicoloured 50 10

MS1610 100×60 mm. No. 1609×2 1·70 1·50

908 Child posting Letter

1984. Centenary of Korean Postal Administration. Multicoloured.

1611 70w. Type **908** 50 10

1612 70w. Postman in city 50 10

MS1613 Two sheets each 90×60 mm. (a) No. 1611×2; (b) No. 1612×2 3·25 2·75

910 Pope John Paul II

1984. Visit of Pope John Paul II.

1614 **910** 70w. black 60 10

1615 **910** 70w. multicoloured 60 10

MS1616 100×60 mm. Nos. 1614/1615 2·50 2·30

911 Cogwheel, Worker's Tools and Flowers

1984. Labour Festival.

1617 **911** 70w. multicoloured 45 10

912 Globe, Jetliner, Container Ship and Emblem

1984. 63rd/64th Sessions of Customs Co-operation Council, Seoul.

1618 **912** 70w. multicoloured 70 10

913 Map and Flags of S. Korea and Sri Lanka

1984. Visit of President Jayewardene of Sri Lanka.

1619 **913** 70w. multicoloured 50 10

MS1620 90×60 mm. No. 1619×2 1·60 1·40

914 Symbols and Punctuation Marks

1984. 14th Asian Advertising Congress, Seoul.

1621 **914** 70w. multicoloured 50 10

915 Expressway

1984. Opening of 88 Olympic Expressway.

1622 **915** 70w. multicoloured 70 15

916 Laurel, 'Victory' and Olympic Rings

1984. 90th Anniversary of International Olympic Committee.

1623 **916** 70w. multicoloured 50 15

917 ABU Emblem and Microphone

1984. 20th Anniversary of Asia-Pacific Broadcasting Union.

1624 **917** 70w. multicoloured 50 10

918 Flags of South Korea and Senegal

1984. Visit of President Abdou Diouf of Senegal.

1625 **918** 70w. multicoloured 50 15

MS1626 100×60 mm. No. 1625×2. Imperf 2·30 2·00

919 Archery

1984. Olympic Games, Los Angeles. Multicoloured.

1627 70w. Type **919** 80 30

1628 440w. Fencing 3·00 75

921 Crucifixion

1984. Centenary of Korean Protestant Church. Multicoloured.

1629 70w. Type **921** 80 30

1630 70w. Cross, vine and dove 80 30

MS1631 80×100 mm. Nos. 1629/1630 6·00 5·50

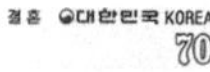

923 Man carrying Silk-covered Lantern

1984. Folk Customs (1st series). Wedding (Kim Kyo Man). Multicoloured.

1632 70w. Type **923** 80 30

1633 70w. Bridegroom on horse 80 30

1634 70w. Man playing clarinet 80 30

1635 70w. Bride in sedan chair (51×35 mm) 80 30

MS1636 90×61 mm. No. 1635 2·50 2·30

See also Nos. 1657/1658, 1683/1684, 1734/1738, 1808/1811, 1840/3, 1858/61 and 1915/18.

927 President Chun and Mt. Fuji

1984. President Chun's Visit to Japan.

1637 **927** 70w. multicoloured 60 15

MS1638 100×60 mm. No. 1637×2. Imperf 2·20 1·90

928 Flags of South Korea and Gambia

1984. Visit of President Sir Dawada Kairaba Jawara of Gambia.

1639 **928** 70w. multicoloured 60 15

MS1640 100×60 mm. No. 1639×2. Imperf 2·20 1·90

929 Symbols of International Trade

1984. Sitra '84 International Trade Fair, Seoul.

1641 **929** 70w. multicoloured 50 10

930 Namsan Tower and National Flags

1984. Visit of President El Hadj Omar Bongo of Gabon.

1642 **930** 70w. multicoloured 60 10

MS1643 100×60 mm. No. 1642×2. Imperf 1·90 1·70

931 Badminton

1984. 65th National Sports Meeting, Taegu. Multicoloured.

1644	70w. Type **931**	50	10
1645	70w. Wrestling	50	10

932 Magnifying Glass and Exhibition Emblem

1984. Philakorea 1984 International Stamp Exhibition, Seoul. Multicoloured.

1646	70w. Type **932**	50	10
1647	70w. South Gate, Seoul, and stamps (horiz)	50	10
MS1648	Two sheets each 124×90 mm. (a) Nos. 1646×2; (b) No. 1647×4	7·75	7·00
MS1649	124×90 mm. 5000w. No. 1389	37·00	32·00

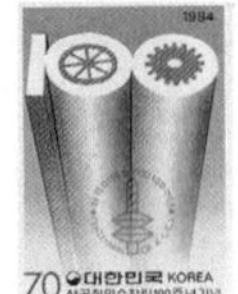
934 Presidents Chun and Gayoom

1984. Visit of President Maumoon Abdul Gayoom of the Maldives.

1650	**934**	70w. multicoloured	50	10
MS1651		100×60 mm. No. 1650×2. Imperf	2·20	1·90

935 '100' and Industrial Symbols

1984. Centenary of Korean Chamber of Commerce and Industry.

1652	**935**	70w. multicoloured	50	10

936 Children playing Jaegi-chagi

937 Ox (bas-relief, Kim Yu Shin's tomb)

1984. Lunar New Year. Year of the Ox.

1653	**936**	70w. multicoloured	60	15
1654	**937**	70w. multicoloured	60	15
MS1655		Two sheets each 90×60 mm. (a) No. 1653×2; (b) No. 1654×2	3·75	3·50

938 IYY Emblem

1985. International Youth Year.

1656	**938**	70w. multicoloured	50	10

939 Pounding Rice for New Year Rice Cake

940 Welcoming Year's First Full Moon

1985. Folk Customs (2nd series).

1657	**939**	70w. multicoloured	80	25
1658	**940**	70w. multicoloured	80	25

941 Seoul Olympic Emblem

1985. Olympic Games, Seoul (1988) (1st issue). Multicoloured.

1659	70w.+30w. Type **941**	80	30
1660	70w.+30w. Hodori (mascot)	80	30
MS1661	90×60 mm. Nos. 1659/60	2·20	1·90

See also Nos. 1673/**MS**1675, 1687/**MS**1689, 1694/**MS**1996, 1703/1710, 1747/1750, 1752/1755, 1784/**MS**1788, 1814/**MS**1818, 1826/**MS**1828, 1835/**MS**1837, 1844/**MS**1848 and **MS**1857.

943 *Still Life with Doll* (Lee Chong Woo)

944 *Rocky Mountain in Early Spring Morning* (Ahn Jung Shik)

1985. Modern Art (1st series).

1662	**943**	70w. multicoloured	80	30
1663	**944**	70w. multicoloured	80	30

See also Nos. 1680/1681, 1757/1760, 1791/1794 and 1875/1878.

945 Flags, Statue of Liberty and President Chun

1985. Presidential Visit to United States.

1664	**945**	70w. multicoloured	50	10
MS1665		100×60 mm. No. 1664×2	2·20	1·90

946 Flags, Seoul South Gate and National Flower

1985. Visit of President Mohammed Zia-ul-Haq of Pakistan.

1666	**946**	70w. multicoloured	60	15
MS1667		90×60 mm. No. 1666×2	2·30	2·00

947 Underwood Hall

1985. Centenary of Yonsei University.

1668	**947**	70w. black, buff and green	50	10

948 Flags and Map

1985. Visit of President Luis Alberto Monge of Costa Rica.

1669	**948**	70w. multicoloured	60	15
MS1670		90×60 mm. No. 1669×2	2·10	1·90

949 Rasbora

950 Sailfish

1985. Fish (1st series).

1671	**949**	70w. multicoloured	80	25
1672	**950**	70w. multicoloured	80	25

See also Nos. 1730/1733, 1797/1800, 1881/1884, 1903/1906 and 1951/1954.

951 Rowing

1985. Olympic Games, Seoul (1988) (2nd issue). Multicoloured.

1673	70w.+30w. Type **951**	80	30
1674	70w.+30w. Hurdling	80	30
MS1675	90×60 mm. Nos. 1673/1674	2·20	1·90

For designs similar to T **951** see Nos. 1687/**MS**1689 and 1694/**MS**1696.

952 National Flags

1985. Visit of President Hussain Muhammed Ershad of Bangladesh.

1676	**952**	70w. multicoloured	60	15
MS1677		90×60 mm. No. 1676×2. Imperf	1·70	1·50

953 National Flags

1985. Visit of President Joao Bernardo Vieira of Guinea-Bissau.

1678	**953**	70w. multicoloured	70	15
MS1679		90×60 mm. No. 1678×2. Imperf	1·70	1·50

954 *Spring Day on the Farm* (Huh Paik Ryun)

955 *The Exorcist* (Kim Chung Hyun)

1985. Modern Art (2nd issue).

1680	**954**	70w. multicoloured	80	30
1681	**955**	70w. multicoloured	80	30

956 Heavenly Lake, Paekdu and National Flower

1985. 40th Anniversary of Liberation.

1682	**956**	70w. multicoloured	60	15

957 Wrestling

958 Janggi

1985. Folk Customs (3rd series).

1683	**957**	70w. multicoloured	80	25
1684	**958**	70w. multicoloured	80	25

959 *The Spring of My Home* (Lee Won Su and Hong Nan Pa)

960 *A Leaf Boat* (Park Hong Keun and Yun Yong Ha)

1985. Korean Music (1st series).

1685	**959**	70w. multicoloured	80	25
1686	**960**	70w. multicoloured	80	25

See also Nos. 1728/1729, 1776/1777, 1854/1855, 1862/1863, 1893/1894, 1935/1936, 1996/1997 and 2064/2065.

1985. Olympic Games, Seoul (1988) (3rd issue). As T **951**. Multicoloured.

1687	70w.+30w. Basketball	80	30
1688	70w.+30w. Boxing	80	30
MS1689	90×60 mm. Nos. 1687/1688	2·20	1·90

961 Satellite, '100' and Dish Aerial

1985. Centenary of First Korean Telegraph Service.

1690	**961**	70w. multicoloured	60	15

962 Meetings Emblem

1985. World Bank and International Monetary Fund Meetings, Seoul.

1691	**962**	70w. multicoloured	60	15

963 UN Emblem and Doves

1985. 40th Anniversary of UNO.

1692	**963**	70w. multicoloured	60	15

964 Red Cross and Hands (detail *Creation of Adam*, Michelangelo)

1985. 80th Anniversary of Korea Red Cross.

1693	**964**	70w. black, red and blue	70	25

1985. Olympic Games, Seoul (1988) (4th issue). As T **951**. Multicoloured.

1694	70w.+30w. Cycling	80	30
1695	70w.+30w. Canoeing	80	30
MS1696	90×60 mm. Nos. 1694/1695	2·20	1·90

965 Cancelled Stamp on Envelope

1985. Philatelic Week.

1697	**965**	70w. multicoloured	60	15

966 Tiger (bas-relief, Kim Yu Shin's tomb)

1985. Lunar New Year. Year of the Tiger.

1698	**966**	70w. multicoloured	70	30

967 Mount Fuji and Boeing 747 Jetliner

1985. 20th Anniversary of Korea–Japan Treaty on Basic Relations.

1699	**967**	70w. mult (postage)	80	30
1700	**967**	370w. multicoloured (air)	3·00	95

968 Doves and Globe

1986. International Peace Year.

1701	**968**	70w. multicoloured	60	15
1702	**968**	400w. multicoloured	4·25	1·50

1986. Olympic Games, Seoul (1988) (5th series). As T **951**. Multicoloured.

1703	70w.+30w. Show jumping (postage)	85	40
1704	70w.+30w. Fencing	85	40
1705	70w.+30w. Football	85	40
1706	70w.+30w. Gymnastics	85	40
1707	370w.+100w. As No. 1703 (air)	2·50	1·20
1708	400w.+100w. As No. 1704	3·00	1·40
1709	440w.+100w. As No. 1705	3·50	1·50
1710	470w.+100w. As No. 1706	4·00	1·70

970 President Chun, Big Ben and Korean and British Flags

1986. Presidential Visit to Europe. Multicoloured.

1711	70w. Type **970**	85	30
1712	70w. President Chun, Eiffel Tower and Korean and French flags	85	30
1713	70w. President Chun, Belgian Parliament and Korean and Belgian flags	85	30
1714	70w. President Chun, Cologne Cathedral and Korean and West German flags	85	30
MS1715	4 sheets each 100×60 mm. (a) No. 1711×2; (b) No. 1712×2; (c) No. 1713×2; (d) No. 1714×2	14·00	12·50

974/975 Kyongju and Kwanchon Observatories

1986. Science (1st series). Appearance of Halley's Comet.

1716	**974**	70w. multicoloured	2·50	85
1717	**975**	70w. multicoloured	2·50	85

See also Nos. 1781/1782, 1833/1834, 1864/1865 and 1898/1899.

976 General Assembly Emblem

1986. Fifth Association of National Olympic Committees General Assembly, Seoul.

1718	**976**	70w. multicoloured	70	15

977 Swallowtail and Flowers

1986. Ameripex '86 International Stamp Exhibition, Chicago. Multicoloured.

1719	70w. Type **977**	3·50	1·50
1720	370w. *Papilio bianor*	3·50	1·50
1721	400w. Swallowtails	3·50	1·50
1722	440w. Swallowtail and frog	3·50	1·50
1723	450w. Swallowtail	3·50	1·50
1724	470w. *Papilio bianor*	3·50	1·50

Nos. 1719/1924 were printed together, *se-tenant*, forming a composite design.

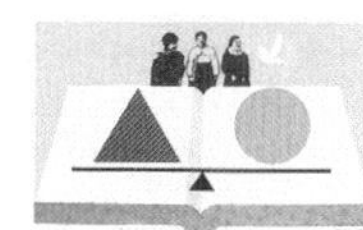

983 Male and Female Symbols in Balance

1986. Centenary of Korean Women's Education.

1725	**983**	70w. multicoloured	60	10

984 National Flags

1986. Visit of President Andre Kolingba of Central African Republic.

1726	**984**	70w. multicoloured	60	10
MS1727		100×60 mm. No. 1726×2. Imperf	1·60	1·40

985 *Half Moon* (Yun Keuk Young)

986 *Let's Go and Pick the Moon* (Yun Seok Jung and Park Tae Hyun)

1986. Korean Music (2nd series).

1728	**985**	70w. multicoloured	1·00	30
1729	**986**	70w. multicoloured	1·60	55

987 Cyprinid Fish

988 Ayu

989 Black-spotted Sardine

990 Hammerheads

1986. Fish (2nd series).

1730	**987**	70w. multicoloured	1·70	55
1731	**988**	70w. multicoloured	1·70	55
1732	**989**	70w. multicoloured	1·70	55
1733	**990**	70w. multicoloured	1·70	55

991 Flag Carrier and Gong Player

1986. Folk Customs (4th series). Farm Music. Multicoloured.

1734	70w. Type **991**	1·30	30
1735	70w. Drummer and piper	1·30	30
1736	70w. Drummer and gong player	1·30	30
1737	70w. Men with ribbons	1·30	30
1738	70w. Man and woman with child	1·30	30

Nos. 1734/1738 were printed together, *se-tenant*, forming a composite design.

996 Child

1986. Family Planning.

1739	**996**	80w. multicoloured	1·00	25

997 Bridge and '63' Building, Seoul

1986. Completion of Han River Development. Multicoloured.

1740	30w. Type **997**	1·30	30
1741	60w. Buildings and excursion boat	1·30	30
1742	80w. Rowing boat and Seoul Tower	1·30	30

Nos. 1740/1742 were printed together, *se-tenant*, forming a composite design.

1000 Emblem

1986. Tenth Asian Games, Seoul. (1st issue). Multicoloured.

1743	80w. Type **1000**	80	30
1744	80w. Firework display	80	30
MS1745	Two sheets each 90×60 mm. (a) No. 1743×2; (b) No. 1744×2	14·00	12·50

See also No. **MS**1751.

1002 '5', Delegates and Juan Antonio Samaranch (President of International Olympic Committee)

1986. Fifth Anniversary of Choice of Seoul as 1988 Olympic Games Host City.

1746	**1002**	80w. multicoloured	1·00	40

1986. Olympic Games, Seoul (1988) (6th issue). As T **951**. Multicoloured.

1747	80w.+50w. Weightlifting (postage)	1·70	85
1748	80w.+50w. Handball	1·70	85
1749	370w.+100w. As No. 1747 (air)	3·00	1·40
1750	400w.+100w. As No. 1748	3·00	1·40

1003 Main Stadium

1986. Tenth Asian Games, Seoul (2nd issue). Sheet 130×90 mm.

MS1751	**100**	3550w. multicoloured	24·00	22·00

1986. Olympic Games, Seoul (1988) (7th issue). As T **951**. Multicoloured.

1752	80w.+50w. Judo (postage)	1·70	85
1753	80w.+50w. Hockey	1·70	85
1754	440w.+100w. As No. 1752 (air)	3·50	1·50
1755	470w.+100w. As No. 1753	4·00	1·70

1004 Boy fishing for Stamp

1986. Philatelic Week.

1756	**1004**	80w. multicoloured	70	25

1005 *Chunhyang-do* (Kim Un Ho)

1006 *Flowers* (Lee Sang Bum)

1007 *Portrait of a Friend* (Ku Bon Wung)

1008 *Woman in a Ski Suit* (Son Ung Seng)

1986. Modern Art (3rd series).

1757	**1005**	80w. multicoloured	1·30	40
1758	**1006**	80w. multicoloured	1·30	40
1759	**1007**	80w. multicoloured	1·30	40
1760	**1008**	80w. multicoloured	1·30	40

1009 Rabbit

1986. Lunar New Year. Year of the Rabbit.

1761	**1009**	80w. multicoloured	85	30

1010 Eastern Broad-billed Roller ('Roller')

1986. Birds. Multicoloured.

1762A	80w. Type **1010**	1·30	40
1763A	80w. Japanese waxwing ('Waxwing')	1·30	40
1764A	80w. Black-naped oriole ('Oriole')	1·30	40
1765A	80w. Black-capped kingfisher ('Kingfisher')	1·30	40
1766A	80w. Hoopoe	1·30	40

1011 Siberian Tiger

1987. Endangered Animals. Multicoloured.

1767	80w. Type **1011**	2·20	70
1768	80w. Leopard cat	2·20	70
1769	80w. Red fox	2·20	70
1770	80w. Wild boar	2·20	70

1012 Bleeding Heart (*Dicentra spectabilis*)

1987. Flowers. Multicoloured.

1771A	550w. Type **1012**	2·50	60
1772A	550w. Diamond bluebell (*Hanabusaya asiatica*)	2·50	60
1773A	550w. *Erythronium japonicum*	2·50	60
1774A	550w. Pinks (*Dianthus chinensis*)	2·50	60
1775A	550w. *Chrysanthemum zawadskii*	2·50	60

1013 *Barley Field* (Park Wha Mok and Yun Yong Ha)

1014 *Magnolia* (Cho Young Shik and Kim Dong Jin)

1987. Korean Music (3rd series).

1776 **1013** 80w. multicoloured 3·00 1·00

1777 **1014** 80w. multicoloured 3·00 1·00

1015 National Flags and Korean National Flower

1987. Visit of President Ahmed Abdallah Abderemane of Comoros.

1778 **1015** 80w. multicoloured 60 10

MS1779 90×60 mm. No. 1778×2 2·20 1·90

1016 '100', Light Bulb and Hyang Woen Jeong

1987. Centenary of Electric Light in Korea.

1780 **1016** 80w. multicoloured 60 10

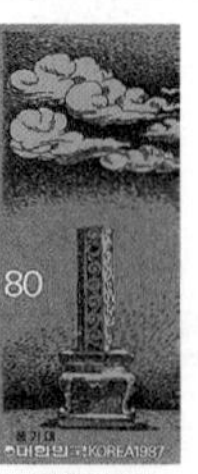
1017 Punggi Wind Observatory

1987. Science (2nd series).

1781 **1017** 80w. dp brown & brown 3·00 1·00

1782 - 80w. brown & dp brown 3·00 1·00

Design: No. 1782, Rain gauge.

1019 Globes, Crane and Ship

1987. 15th International Association of Ports and Harbours General Session, Seoul.

1783 **1019** 80w. multicoloured 60 10

1987. Olympic Games, Seoul (1988) (8th issue). As T **951**. Multicoloured.

1784 80w.+50w. Wrestling 1·20 40

1785 80w.+50w. Tennis 1·20 40

1786 80w.+50w. Diving 1·20 40

1787 80w.+50w. Show jumping 1·20 40

MS1788 Four sheets each 90×60 mm. (a) No. 1784×2; (b) No. 1785×2; (c) No. 1786×2; (d) No. 1787×2 11·00 10·00

1020 Flags and Doves

1987. Visit of President U San Yu of Burma.

1789 **1020** 80w. multicoloured 60 10

MS1790 90×60 mm. No. 1789×2 1·90 1·70

1021 *Valley of Peach Blossoms* (Pyen Kwan Sik)

1022 *Rural Landscape* (Lee Yong Wu)

1023 *Man* (Lee Ma Dong)

1024 *Woman with Water Jar on Head* (sculpture, Yun Hyo Chung)

1987. Modern Art (4th series).

1791 **1021** 80w. multicoloured 2·50 95

1792 **1022** 80w. multicoloured 2·50 95

1793 **1023** 80w. multicoloured 2·50 95

1794 **1024** 80w. multicoloured 2·50 95

1025 Map and Digital Key Pad

1987. Completion of Automatic Telephone Network (1795) and Communications for Information Year (1796).

1795 80w. Type **1025** 70 25

1796 80w. Emblem 70 25

1027 Cyprinid Fish

1028 Russell's Oarfish

1029 Cyprinid Fish

1030 Spine-tailed Mobula

1987. Fish (3rd series).

1797 **1027** 80w. multicoloured 2·50 95

1798 **1028** 80w. multicoloured 2·50 95

1799 **1029** 80w. multicoloured 2·50 95

1800 **1030** 80w. multicoloured 2·50 95

1031 Statue of Indomitable Koreans (detail) and Flags

1987. Opening of Independence Hall. Multicoloured.

1801 80w. Type **1031** 1·10 30

1802 80w. Monument of the Nation and aerial view of Hall 1·10 30

MS1803 Two sheets each 125×90 mm. (a) No. 1801×2; (b) No. 1802×2 24·00 22·00

1033 Map and Pen within Profile

1987. 16th Pacific Science Congress, Seoul.

1804 **1033** 80w. multicoloured 70 15

MS1805 90×60 mm. No. 1804×2 3·00 2·75

1034 Flags and Seoul South Gate

1987. Visit of President Virgilio Barco of Colombia.

1806 **1034** 80w. multicoloured 70 15

MS1807 90×60 mm. No. 1806×2 2·20 1·90

1035/1038 Festivities (image scaled to 42% of original size)

1987. Folk Customs (5th series). Harvest Moon Day.

1808 **1035** 80w. multicoloured 3·50 1·00

1809 **1036** 80w. multicoloured 3·50 1·00

1810 **1037** 80w. multicoloured 3·50 1·00

1811 **1038** 80w. multicoloured 3·50 1·00

Nos. 1808/1811 were issued together, *se-tenant*, forming a composite design.

1039 Telephone Dials forming Number

1987. Installation of over 10,000,000 Telephone Lines.

1812 **1039** 80w. multicoloured 70 25

1040 Service Flags and Servicemen

1987. Armed Forces Day.

1813 **1040** 80w. multicoloured 70 25

1987. Olympic Games, Seoul (1988) (9th issue). As T **951**. Multicoloured.

1814 80w.+50w. Table tennis 1·20 40

1815 80w.+50w. Shooting 1·20 40

1816 80w.+50w. Archery 1·20 40

1817 80w.+50w. Volleyball 1·20 40

MS1818 4 sheets each 90×60 mm. (a) No. 1814×2; (b) No. 1815×2; (c) No. 1816×2; (d) No. 1817×2 11·00 10·00

1041 Stamps around Child playing Trumpet

1987. Philatelic Week.

1819 **1041** 80w. multicoloured 70 25

1042 Korean Scientist and Map

1987. First Anniversary of South Korea's Signing of Antarctic Treaty.

1820 **1042** 80w. multicoloured 1·30 40

1043 Dragon

1987. Lunar New Year. Year of the Dragon.

1821 **1043** 80w. multicoloured 1·00 30

1044 Scattered Sections of Apple

1988. Compulsory Pension Programme.

1822 **1044** 80w. multicoloured 70 25

1045 Base and Gentoo Penguins

1988. Completion of Antarctic Base.

1823 **1045** 80w. multicoloured 1·00 30

1046 Flag, Olympic Stadium and President Roh Tae Woo

1988. Presidential Inauguration.

1824 **1046** 80w. multicoloured 1·30 40

MS1825 90×60 mm. No. 1824×2 19·00 17·00

1047 Dinghy Racing

1988. Olympic Games, Seoul (1988) (10th issue). Multicoloured.

1826 80w.+20w. Type **1047** 85 40

1827 80w.+20w. Taekwondo 85 40

MS1828 Two sheets each 90×60 mm. (a) No. 1826×2; (b) No. 1827×2 8·75 7·75

1049 Crane

1988. Japanese White-naped Crane. Multicoloured.

1829 80w. Type **1049** 1·60 70

1830 80w. Crane taking off 1·60 70

1831 80w. Crane with wings spread 1·60 70

1832 80w. Two cranes in flight 1·60 70

1053 Water Clock

1988. Science (3rd series). Multicoloured.

1833 80w. Type **1053** 85 30

1834 80w. Sundial 85 30

Nos. 1833/1834 were issued together, *se-tenant*, forming a composite design.

1055 Torch Carrier

1988. Olympic Games, Seoul (1988) (11th issue). Multicoloured.

1835 80w.+20w. Type **1055** 85 40

1836 80w.+20w. Stadium 85 40

MS1837 Two sheets each 90×60 mm. (a) No. 1835×2; (b) No. 1836×2 6·00 5·50

1057 Globe and Red Cross as Candle

1988. 125th Anniversary of International Red Cross.

1838 **1057** 80w. multicoloured 70 25

1058 Computer Terminal

1988. First Anniversary of National Use of Telepress.

1839	**1058**	80w. multicoloured	70	25

1059 Woman sitting by Pool and Woman on Swing

1988. Folk Customs (6th series). Tano Day. Multicoloured.

1840	80w. Type **1059**	1·30	40
1841	80w. Women dressing their hair	1·30	40
1842	80w. Woman on swing and boy smelling flowers	1·30	40
1843	80w. Boys wrestling	1·30	40

Nos. 1840/1843 were issued together, *se-tenant*, forming a composite design.

1063 Olympic Flag and Pierre de Coubertin (founder of modern Games)

1988. Olympic Games, Seoul (1988) (12th issue). Multicoloured.

1844	80w. Type **1063**	85	30
1845	80w. Olympic monument	85	30
1846	80w. View of Seoul (vert)	85	30
1847	80w. Women in Korean costume (vert)	85	30
MS1848	Four sheets each 90×60 mm. (a) No. 1844×2; (b) No. 1845×2; (c) No. 1846×2; (d) No. 1847×2	8·75	7·75

1067 Stamps forming Torch Flame

1988. Olymphilex '88 Olympic Stamps Exhibition, Seoul.

1849	**1067**	80w. multicoloured	70	25
MS1850		90×60 mm. No. 1849×2	2·20	1·90

1068 Pouring Molten Metal from Crucible

1988. 22nd International Iron and Steel Institute Conference, Seoul.

1851	**1068**	80w. multicoloured	70	25

1069 Gomdoori (mascot)

1988. Paralympic Games, Seoul.

1852	80w. Type **1069**	1·10	60
1853	80w. Archery	80	30

1071 *Homesick* (Lee Eun Sang and Kim Dong Jin)

1072 *The Pioneer* (Yoon Hae Young and Cho Doo Nam)

1988. Korean Music (4th series).

1854	**1071**	80w. multicoloured	80	30
1855	**1072**	80w. multicoloured	80	30

1073 Girls on See-saw

1988. Lunar New Year. Year of the Snake.

1856	**1073**	80w. multicoloured	70	25

1074 Flags at Opening Ceremony

1988. Olympic Games, Seoul (13th issue). Sheet 130×90 mm.

MS1857	**1074**	550w. multicoloured	16·00	14·00

1075 Dancers

1989. Folk Customs (7th series). Mask Dance. Multicoloured.

1858	80w. Type **1075**	1·30	40
1859	80w. Dancer with fans	1·30	40
1860	80w. Dancer holding branch	1·30	40
1861	80w. Dancer with 'Lion'	1·30	40

Nos. 1858/1861 were issued together, *se-tenant*, forming a composite design.

1079 *Arirang*

1080 *Doraji-taryong*

1989. Korean Music (5th series).

1862	**1079**	80w. multicoloured	70	25
1863	**1080**	80w. multicoloured	70	25

1081/1082 Wooden and metal Type Printing

1989. Science (4th series).

1864	**1081**	80w. brown, bis & stone	1·70	40
1865	**1082**	80w. brown, bis & stone	1·70	40

Nos. 1864/1865 were issued together, *se-tenant*, forming a composite design.

1083 Teeth, Globe, Pencil and Book

1989. 14th Asian-Pacific Dental Congress.

1866	**1083**	80w. multicoloured	60	15

1084 Hand with Stick in Heart

1989. Respect for the Elderly.

1867	**1084**	80w. multicoloured	2·40	30

1085 Emblem

1989. Rotary International Convention, Seoul.

1868	**1085**	80w. multicoloured	60	15

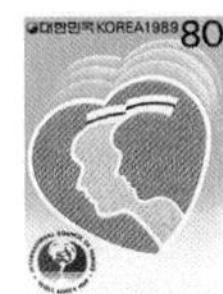
1086 Profiles within Heart

1989. 19th International Council of Nurses Congress, Seoul.

1869	**1086**	80w. multicoloured	60	15

1087 Communication

1989. National Information Technology Month.

1870	**1087**	80w. multicoloured	60	15

1088 Longevity

1989. World Environment Day.

1871	**1088**	80w. multicoloured	60	15

1089 Satellite, Globe and Dish Aerial

1989. Tenth Anniversary of Asia Pacific Telecommunity.

1872	**1089**	80w. multicoloured	60	15

1090 *Liberty guiding the People* (detail, Eugene Delacroix)

1989. Bicentenary of French Revolution.

1873	**1090**	80w. multicoloured	60	15

1091 Apple and Flask

1989. Fifth Asian and Oceanic Biochemists Federation Congress, Seoul.

1874	**1091**	80w. multicoloured	60	15

1092 *White Ox* (Lee Joong Sub)

1093 *Street Stall* (Park Lae Hyun)

1094 *Little Girl* (Lee Bong Sang)

1095 *Autumn Scene* (Oh Ji Ho)

1989. Modern Art (5th series).

1875	**1092**	80w. multicoloured	80	30
1876	**1093**	80w. multicoloured	80	30
1877	**1094**	80w. multicoloured	80	30
1878	**1095**	80w. multicoloured	80	30

1096 Hunting Scene

1989. Seoul Olympics Commemorative Festival and World Sports Festival for Ethnic Koreans.

1879	**1096**	80w. multicoloured	60	15

1097 Goddess of Law and Ancient Law Code

1989. First Anniversary of Constitutional Court.

1880	**1097**	80w. multicoloured	60	15

1098 Banded Knifejaw

1099 Banded Loach

1100 Torrent Catfish

1101 Japanese Pinecone Fish

1989. Fish (4th series).

1881	**1098**	80w. multicoloured	85	30
1882	**1099**	80w. multicoloured	85	30
1883	**1100**	80w. multicoloured	85	30
1884	**1101**	80w. multicoloured	85	30

1102 Emblem

1989. 44th International Eucharistic Congress, Seoul.

1885	**1102**	80w. multicoloured	60	15

1103 Control Tower and Boeing 747 Jetliner

1989. 29th International Civil Airports Association World Congress, Seoul.

1886	**1103**	80w. multicoloured	60	15

1104 Scissors cutting Burning Banner

1989. Fire Precautions Month.
1887 **1104** 80w. multicoloured 2·40 30

1105 Lantern

1989. Philatelic Week.
1888 **1105** 80w. multicoloured 70 25
MS1889 90×60 mm. No. 1888×2 2·20 1·90

1106 Cranes **1107** New Year Custom

1989. Lunar New Year. Year of the Horse.
1890 **1106** 80w. multicoloured 60 15
1891 **1107** 80w. multicoloured 60 15
MS1892 Two sheets each 90×60 mm. (a) No. 1890×2; (b) No. 1891×2 3·50 3·00

1108 *Pakyon Fall* **1109** *Chonan Samgori*

1990. Korean Music (6th series).
1893 **1108** 80w. multicoloured 70 25
1894 **1109** 80w. multicoloured 70 25

1110 Clouds, Umbrella and Satellite

1990. World Meteorological Day.
1895 **1110** 80w. multicoloured 60 15

1111 Child with Rose

1990. 40th Anniversary of UNICEF's Work in Korea.
1896 **1111** 80w. multicoloured 60 15

1112 Cable, Fish and Route Map

1990. Completion of Cheju Island–Kohung Optical Submarine Cable.
1897 **1112** 80w. multicoloured 60 15

1113/1114 Gilt-bronze Maitreya, Spear and Dagger Moulds

1990. Science (5th series). Metallurgy.
1898 **1113** 100w. multicoloured 70 25
1899 **1114** 100w. multicoloured 70 25
Nos. 1898/1899 were issued together, *se-tenant*, forming the composite design illustrated.

1115 Housing and '20'

1990. 20th Anniversary of Saemaul Movement (community self-help programme).
1900 **1115** 100w. multicoloured 60 15

1116 Youths

1990. Youth Month.
1901 **1116** 100w. multicoloured 60 15

1117 Butterfly Net catching Pollution

1990. World Environmental Day.
1902 **1117** 100w. multicoloured 4·75 30

1118 Belted Bearded Grunt **1119** Kusa Pufferfish

1120 Cherry Salmon **1121** Rosy Bitterling

1990. Fish (5th series).
1903 **1118** 100w. multicoloured 85 30
1904 **1119** 100w. multicoloured 85 30
1905 **1120** 100w. multicoloured 85 30
1906 **1121** 100w. multicoloured 85 30

1122 Automatic Sorting Machines

1990. Opening of Seoul Mail Centre.
1907 **1122** 100w. multicoloured 60 15
MS1908 90×60 mm. No. 1907×2 2·20 1·90

1123 Bandaged Teddy Bear in Hospital Bed

1990. Road Safety Campaign.
1909 **1123** 100w. multicoloured 1·60 30

1124 Campfire

1990. Eighth Korean Boy Scouts Jamboree, Kosong.
1910 **1124** 100w. multicoloured 60 15

1125 Lily

1990. Wild Flowers (1st series). Multicoloured.
1911 370w. Type **1125** 2·10 85
1912 400w. Asters 2·40 95
1913 440w. Pheasant's eye 2·50 1·00
1914 470w. Scabious 2·75 1·10
See also Nos. 1956/1959, 1992/1995, 2082/2085, 2133/2136, 2162/2165, 2191/2194 and 2244/2247.

1129 Washing Wool

1990. Folk Customs (8th series). Hand Weaving.
1915 **1129** 100w. red, yellow & blk 85 30
1916 - 100w. multicoloured 85 30
1917 - 100w. multicoloured 85 30
1918 - 100w. multicoloured 85 30
Designs: No. 1916, Spinning; No. 1917, Dyeing spun yarn; No. 1918, Weaving.

1133 Church

1990. Centenary of Anglican Church in Korea.
1919 **1133** 100w. multicoloured 60 15

1134 Top of Tower

1990. Tenth Anniversary of Seoul Communications Tower.
1920 **1134** 100w. black, blue and red 60 15

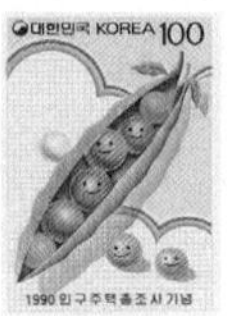
1135 Peas in Pod

1990. Census.
1921 **1135** 100w. multicoloured 60 15

1136 '40' and UN Emblem

1990. 40th Anniversary of UN Development Programme.
1922 **1136** 100w. multicoloured 60 15

1137 Inlaid Case with Mirror

1990. Philatelic Week.
1923 **1137** 100w. multicoloured 70 15
MS1924 90×60 mm. No. 1923×2 4·00 3·50

1138 Children feeding Ram

1990. Lunar New Year. Year of the Sheep. Multicoloured.
1925 100w. Type **1138** 60 15
1926 100w. Crane flying above mountains 60 15
MS1927 90×60 mm. Nos. 1925/1926 4·75 4·25

1140 Mascot

1990. Expo '93 World's Fair, Taejon (1st issue). Multicoloured.
1928 100w. Type **1140** 85 30
1929 440w. Yin and Yang (exhibition emblem) 2·20 95
MS1930 Two sheets each 90×60 mm. (a) No. 1928×2; (b) No. 1929×2 7·00 6·00
See also Nos. 1932/**MS**1934, 2000/**MS**2002 and 2058/**MS**2062.

1142 Books and Emblem

1991. 30th Anniversary of Saemaul Minilibrary.
1931 **1142** 100w. multicoloured 60 15

1143 Earth

1991. Expo '93 World's Fair, Taejon (2nd issue). Multicoloured.
1932 100w. Type **1143** 85 30
1933 100w. Expo Tower 85 30
MS1934 Two sheets each 90×60 mm. (a) No. 1932×2; (b) No. 1933×2 4·25 3·75

1145 *In a Flower Garden* (Uh Hyo Sun and Kwon Kil Sang) **1146** *Way to the Orchard* (Park Hwa Mok and Kim Kong Sun)

1991. Korean Music (7th series).
1935 **1145** 100w. multicoloured 80 30
1936 **1146** 100w. multicoloured 80 30

1147 Moth **1148** Beetle **1149** Butterfly

1150 Beetle **1151** Cicada **1152** Water Beetle

1153 Hornet **1154** Ladybirds **1155** Dragonfly

1156 Grasshopper

1991. Insects.
1937 **1147** 100w. multicoloured 1·00 25
1938 **1148** 100w. multicoloured 1·00 25
1939 **1149** 100w. multicoloured 1·00 25
1940 **1150** 100w. multicoloured 1·00 25
1941 **1151** 100w. multicoloured 1·00 25
1942 **1152** 100w. multicoloured 1·00 25
1943 **1153** 100w. multicoloured 1·00 25
1944 **1154** 100w. multicoloured 1·00 25
1945 **1155** 100w. multicoloured 1·00 25
1946 **1156** 100w. multicoloured 1·00 25

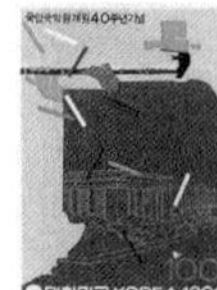

1157 Flautist and Centre

1991. 40th Anniversary of Korean Traditional Performing Arts Centre.

1947	**1157**	100w. multicoloured	60	20

1158 Flag and Provisional Government Building

1991. 72nd Anniversary of Establishment of Korean Provisional Government in Shanghai.

1948	**1158**	100w. multicoloured	60	20

1159 Urban Landscape and Emblem

1991. Employment for Disabled People.

1949	**1159**	100w. multicoloured	60	20

1160 Bouquet

1991. Teachers' Day.

1950	**1160**	100w. multicoloured	60	20

1161 Asian Minnow **1162** Majime Minnows

1163 Blotched Grunter **1164** Ijima's Left-eyed Flounder

1991. Fish (6th series).

1951	**1161**	100w. multicoloured	80	25
1952	**1162**	100w. multicoloured	80	25
1953	**1163**	100w. multicoloured	80	25
1954	**1164**	100w. multicoloured	80	25

1165 Animals waiting to Board Bus

1991. Waiting One's Turn Campaign.

1955	**1165**	100w. multicoloured	1·60	30

1166 *Aerides japonicum*

1991. Wild Flowers (2nd series). Multicoloured.

1956	100w. Type **1166**	70	25
1957	100w. *Heloniopsis orientalis*	70	25
1958	370w. *Aquilegia buergeriana*	1·80	70
1959	440w. *Gentiana zollingeri*	2·20	80

1167 Scout with Semaphore Flags

1991. 17th World Scout Jamboree.

1960	**1167**	100w. multicoloured	65	15
MS1961		90×60 mm. No. 1960×2	1·40	1·20

1168 'YMCA'

1991. Young Men's Christian Association World Assembly, Seoul.

1962	**1168**	100w. multicoloured	65	15

1169 Derelict Steam Locomotive and Family Members Reunited

1991. North–South Reunification.

1963	**1169**	100w. multicoloured	80	20

1170 Globe, Rainbow, Dove and UN Emblem

1991. Admission of South Korea to United Nations Organisation.

1964	**1170**	100w. multicoloured	65	15

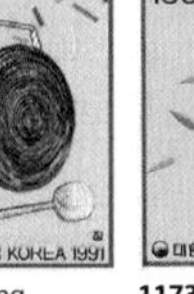

1171 Unra **1172** Jing **1173** Galgo

1174 Saeng-hwang

1991. Traditional Musical Instruments (1st series).

1965	**1171**	100w. multicoloured	70	30
1966	**1172**	100w. multicoloured	70	30
1967	**1173**	100w. multicoloured	70	30
1968	**1174**	100w. multicoloured	70	30

See also Nos. 1981/1984.

1175 Film and Theatrical Masks

1991. Culture Month.

1969	**1175**	100w. multicoloured	65	15

1176 Globe and Satellite

1991. Telecom 91 International Telecommunications Exhibition, Geneva.

1970	**1176**	100w. multicoloured	65	15

1177 Hexagonals **1178** Bamboo **1179** Geometric

1180 Tree

1991. Korean Beauty (1st series). Kottams (patterns on walls) from Jakyung Hall, Kyungbok Palace.

1971	**1177**	100w. multicoloured	1·00	30
1972	**1178**	100w. multicoloured	1·00	30
1973	**1179**	100w. multicoloured	1·00	30
1974	**1180**	100w. multicoloured	1·00	30

See also Nos. 2006/2009, 2068/2071, 2103/2106, 2157/2160, 2219/2222, 2257/2260, 2308/2315, 2349/2356 and 2437/2440.

1181 Light Bulb turning off Switch

1991. Energy Saving Campaign.

1975	**1181**	100w. multicoloured	1·60	30

1182 Longevity

1991. Lunar New Year. Year of the Monkey. Multicoloured.

1976	100w. Type **1182**	65	15
1977	100w. Flying kites	65	15
MS1978	Two sheets each 90×60 mm. (a) No. 1976×2; (b) No. 1977×2	3·50	3·25

1184 Stamps

1991. Philatelic Week.

1979	**1184**	100w. multicoloured	65	15
MS1980		90×60 mm. No. 1979×2	1·60	1·50

1185 Yonggo **1186** Chwago **1187** Kkwaenggwari

1188 T'ukchong

1992. Traditional Musical Instruments (2nd series).

1981	**1185**	100w. multicoloured	70	30
1982	**1186**	100w. multicoloured	70	30
1983	**1187**	100w. multicoloured	70	30
1984	**1188**	100w. multicoloured	70	30

1189 White Hibiscus

1992. *Hibiscus syriacus* (National Flower). Multicoloured.

1985	100w. Type **1189**	1·10	40
1986	100w. Pink hibiscus	1·10	40

1191 Satellite

1992. Science Day.

1987	**1191**	100w. multicoloured	55	15

1192 Yoon Pong Gil

1992. 60th Death Anniversary of Yoon Pong Gil (independence fighter).

1988	**1192**	100w. multicoloured	55	15

1193 Children and Heart

1992. Child Protection.

1989	**1193**	100w. multicoloured	1·60	25

1194 Japanese Warship attacking Korean Settlement

1992. 400th Anniversary of Start of Im-Jin War.

1990	**1194**	100w. multicoloured	55	15

1195 Farmer

1992. 60th International Fertiliser Industry Association Conference, Seoul.

1991	**1195**	100w. multicoloured	55	15

1992. Wild Flowers (3rd series). As T **1166**. Multicoloured.

1992	100w. *Lychnis wilfordii*	65	30
1993	100w. *Lycoris radiata*	65	30
1994	370w. *Commelina communis*	1·70	65
1995	440w. *Calanthe striata*	2·00	70

1196 *Longing for Mt. Keumkang* (Han Sang Ok and Choi Young Shurp)

1197 *The Swing* (Kim Mal Bong and Geum Su Hyeon)

1992. Korean Music (8th series).

1996	**1196**	100w. multicoloured	70	25
1997	**1197**	100w. multicoloured	70	25

1198 Gymnastics

1992. Olympic Games, Barcelona. Multicoloured.

1998 100w. Type **1198** 65 15
1999 100w. Pole vaulting 65 15

1199 Stylised View of Exhibition

1992. Expo '93 World's Fair, Taejon (3rd issue). Multicoloured.

2000 100w. Type **1199** 55 15
2001 100w. Expo 93 55 15
MS2002 Two sheets each 90×60 mm. (a) No. 2000×2; (b) No. 2001×2 3·50 3·00

1201 Korea Exhibition Centre and South Gate, Seoul

1992. 21st Universal Postal Union Congress, Seoul (1st issue). Multicoloured.

2003 100w. Type **1201** 55 15
2004 100w. Tolharubang (stone grandfather), Cheju 55 15
MS2005 Two sheets each 90×60 mm. (a) No. 2003×2; (b) No. 2004×2 3·25 3·00

See also Nos. 2075/**MS**2077, 2088/**MS**2089 and 2112/**MS**2117.

1203 Woven Pattern

1204 Fruit and Flower Decorations

1205 Carved Decorations

1206 Coral, Butterfly and Pine Resin Decorations

1992. Korean Beauty (2nd series). Maedeups (tassels).

2006 **1203** 100w. multicoloured 80 30
2007 **1204** 100w. multicoloured 80 30
2008 **1205** 100w. multicoloured 80 30
2009 **1206** 100w. multicoloured 80 30

1207 Lee Pong Chang

1992. 60th Death Anniversary of Lee Pong Chang (independence fighter).

2010 **1207** 100w. brown and orange 55 15

1208 Hwang Young Jo (Barcelona, 1992)

1992. Korean Winners of Olympic Marathon. Multicoloured.

2011 100w. Type **1208** 70 30
2012 100w. Shon Kee Chung (Berlin, 1936) 70 30
MS2013 90×60 mm. Nos. 2011/2012 4·50 4·00

1209 Sails on Map of Americas

1992. 500th Anniversary of Discovery of America by Columbus.

2014 **1209** 100w. multicoloured 55 15

1210 Heads and Speech Balloon

1992. Campaign for Purification of Language.

2015 **1210** 100w. multicoloured 1·60 30

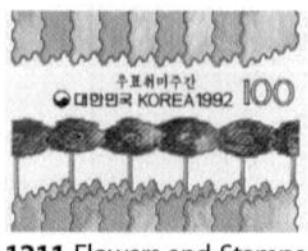

1211 Flowers and Stamps

1992. Philatelic Week.

2016 **1211** 100w. multicoloured 55 15
MS2017 60×90 mm. No. 2016×2 1·80 1·60

1212 Cockerels in Snow-covered Yard

1992. Lunar New Year. Year of the Cock. Multicoloured.

2018 100w. Type **1212** 60 15
2019 100w. Flying kites 60 15
MS2020 Two sheets each 90×60 mm. (a) No. 2018×2; (b) No. 2019×2 3·00 2·50

1214 Emblem, Globe and Woman holding Bowl

1992. International Nutrition Conference, Rome.

2021 **1214** 100w. multicoloured 55 15

1215 View of Centre and Logo

1993. Inauguration of Seoul Arts Centre's Opera House.

2022 **1215** 110w. multicoloured 65 25

1216 President Kim Young Sam, Flag and Mt. Paekdu Lake

1993. Inauguration of 14th President.

2023 **1216** 110w. multicoloured 90 30
MS2024 90×60 mm. No. 2023×2 7·25 6·50

1217 National Flag

1993. No. 2036a orange, black and pink, others multicoloured.

2025 10w. Type **1217** 35 15
2026 20w. White stork 25 15
2026a 20w. Black-crowned night heron 25 10
2027 30w. White magnolia 35 15
2027a 30w. *Vitis amurensis* 65 40
2028 40w. Korean white pine 45 15
2028a 40w. *Purpuricenus lituralus* (beetle) 35 30
2028b 50w. Water cock 35 15
2029 60w. Squirrel 55 15
2030 70w. Chinese lanterns (plant) 55 15
2030a 80w. Japanese white eye on japonica branch 35 15
2031 90w. Oriental scops owl 70 25
2031a 100w. Dishcloth gourd 55 15
2032 110w. *Hibiscus syriacus* (plant) 1·00 15
2033 120w. As 110w. 90 15
2034 130w. Narcissi 90 25
2034c 140w. As 130w. 1·00 15
2035 150w. Painted porcelain jar 1·40 80
2036 160w. Pine tree (horiz) 1·50 25
2036a 170w. Crayfish 1·30 30
2036c 170w. Far eastern curlew 55 25
2037 180w. Little tern (horiz) 1·40 25
2037a 190w. As 110w. 1·20 30
2038 200w. Turtle (horiz) 1·40 30
2038a 200w. Snow crab (horiz) 90 40
2038b 210w. As 180w. 1·40 25
2038c 260w. As 180w. 1·80 40
2039 300w. Eurasian skylark (horiz) 1·30 40
2040 370w. Drum and drum dance (horiz) 2·75 50
2041 400w. Celadon cockerel water dropper (horiz) 1·50 40
2042 420w. As 370w. 3·00 50
2043 440w. Haho'i mask and Ssirum wrestlers (horiz) 3·50 55
2044 480w. As 440w. 3·00 55
2045 500w. Celadon pomegranate water dropper 2·00 65
2045a 600w. Hong Yong-sik (first Postmaster General) 2·30 80
2046 700w. Gilt-bronze Bongnae-san incense burner (23×34 mm) 4·00 80
2046a 700w. Cloud and crane jade ornament, Koryo Dynasty 2·20 80
2046b 710w. King Sejong and alphabet 5·00 70
2046c 800w. Cheju ponies 2·75 65
2047 900w. Gilt-bronze buddha triad (23×34 mm) 6·00 95
2048 910w. As 710w. 6·00 90
2049 930w. Celadon pitcher (blue background) (23×31 mm) 2·75 50
2049a 930w. As No. 2049 (brown background) 3·25 2·40
2049b 1000w. Stone guardian animal (from tomb of King Muryong) (32×21 mm) 4·50 1·30
2050 1050w. As 930w. 5·50 95
2050a 1170w. Bronze incense burner 5·00 2·10
2050b 1190w. As 930w. 5·00 2·30
2050c 2000w. Crown from tomb of Shinch'on-ni 6·00 1·60

1243 Student and Computer

1993. Korean Student Inventions Exhibition.

2051 **1243** 110w. mauve and silver 60 15

1244 Emblem and Map

1993. International Human Rights Conference, Vienna, Austria.

2052 **1244** 110w. multicoloured 60 15

1245 Hand scooping Globe from Water

1993. Water is Life.

2053 **1245** 110w. multicoloured 1·20 25

1246 Matsu-take Mushroom (*Tricholoma matsutake*)

1993. Fungi (1st series). Multicoloured.

2054 110w. Type **1246** 70 25
2055 110w. *Ganoderma lucidum* 70 25
2056 110w. *Lentinula edodes* 70 25
2057 110w. Oyster fungus (*Pleurotus ostreatus*) 70 25

See also Nos. 2095/**MS**2099, 2146/**MS**2150, 2207/**MS**2211, 2249/**MS**2253 and 2293/**MS**2297.

1247 Government Pavilion

1248 International Pavilion and Mascot

1249 Recycling Art Pavilion

1250 Telecom Pavilion

1993. Expo '93 World's Fair, Taejon (4th issue).

2058 **1247** 110w. multicoloured 60 25
2059 **1248** 110w. multicoloured 60 25
2060 **1249** 110w. multicoloured 60 25
2061 **1250** 110w. multicoloured 60 25
MS2062 Four sheets each 90×60 mm. (a) No. 2058×2; (b) No. 2059×2; (c) No. 2060×2; (d) No. 2061×2 6·50 6·00

1251 Emblems

1993. 19th Congress of International Society of Orthopaedic and Trauma Surgery.

2063 **1251** 110w. multicoloured 60 15

1252 *O Dol Ddo Gi* (Cheju Island folk song)

1253 *Ong He Ya* (barley threshing song)

1993. Korean Music (9th series).

2064 **1252** 110w. multicoloured 70 25
2065 **1253** 110w. multicoloured 70 25

1254 Janggu Drum Dance

1255 Emblem

1993. Visit Korea Year (1994) (1st issue).

2066 **1254** 110w. multicoloured 60 15
2067 **1255** 110w. multicoloured 60 15

See also Nos. 2086/2087.

1256 Twin Tigers (military officials, 1st to 3rd rank)

1993. Korean Beauty (3rd series). Hyoongbae (embroidered insignia of the Chosun Dynasty). Multicoloured.

2068 110w. Type **1256** 70 25

2069 110w. Single Crane (civil officials, 4th to 9th rank) 70 25
2070 110w. Twin Cranes (civil officials, 1st to 3rd rank) 70 25
2071 110w. Dragon (King) 70 25

1260 Campaign Emblem

1993. Anti-litter Campaign.
2072 **1260** 110w. multicoloured 1·30 25

1261 *Eggplant and Oriental Long-nosed Locust* (Shin Saim Dang)

1993. Philatelic Week.
2073 **1261** 110w. multicoloured 60 25
MS2074 90×60 mm. No. 2073×2 1·60 1·40

1262 *Weaving*

1993. 21st UPU Congress, Seoul (2nd issue). Paintings by Kim Hong Do. Multicoloured.
2075 110w. Type **1262** 60 25
2076 110w. *Musicians and a Dancer* (vert) 60 25
MS2077 Two sheets each 90×60 mm. (a) No. 2075×2; (b) No. 2076×2 3·00 2·75

1263 Ribbon and Globe as '30', Freighter and Ilyushin Il-86 Airliner

1993. 30th Trade Day.
2078 **1263** 110w. multicoloured 60 25

1264 Sapsaree and Kite

1993. Lunar New Year. Year of the Dog. Multicoloured.
2079 110w. Type **1264** 60 25
2080 110w. Puppy with New Year's Greetings bow 60 25
MS2081 Two sheets each 90×60 mm. (a) No. 2079×2; (b) No. 2080×2 3·00 2·75

1993. Wild Flowers (4th series). As T **1166**.
2082 110w. *Weigela hortensis* 70 25
2083 110w. *Iris ruthenica* 70 25
2084 110w. *Aceriphyllum rosii* 70 25
2085 110w. Marsh marigold (*Caltha palustris*) 70 25

1266 Flautist on Cloud

1267 T'alch'um Mask Dance

1994. Visit Korea Year (2nd issue).
2086 **1266** 110w. multicoloured 60 15
2087 **1267** 110w. multicoloured 60 25

1268 Map'ae, Horse, Envelope and Emblem

1994. 21st UPU Congress, Seoul (3rd issue).
2088 **1268** 300w. multicoloured 1·40 55

MS2089 90×60 mm. No. 2088×2 3·50 3·00

1269 Monument

1994. 75th Anniversary of Samil (Independence) Movement.
2090 **1269** 110w. multicoloured 60 15

1270 Great Purple (*Sasakia charonda*)

1994. Protection of Wildlife and Plants (1st series). Multicoloured.
2091 110w. Type **1270** (butterfly) 70 30
2092 110w. *Allomyrina dichotoma* (beetle) 70 30
MS2093 Two sheets each 90×60 mm. (a) No. 2091×2; (b) No. 2092×2 3·50 3·00
See also Nos. 2143/**MS**2145, 2186/**MS**2188, 2241/**MS**2243, 2275/**MS**2279, 2326/**MS**2330, 2383/**MS**2387 and 2481/**MS**2485.

1271 Family of Mandarins

1994. International Year of the Family.
2094 **1271** 110w. multicoloured 60 15

1994. Fungi (2nd series). As T **1246**. Multicoloured.
2095 110w. Common morel (*Morchella esculenta*) 70 25
2096 110w. *Gomphus floccosus* 70 25
2097 110w. *Cortinarius purpurascens* 70 25
2098 110w. *Oudemansiella platyphylla* 70 25
MS2099 Four sheets each 90×60 mm. (a) No. 2095×2; (b) No. 2096×2; (c) No. 2097×2; (d) No. 2098×2 6·50 6·00

1272 Museum

1994. Inauguration of War Memorial Museum, Yongsan (Seoul).
2100 **1272** 110w. multicoloured 60 15

1273 Text and Dove

1994. Philakorea 1994 International Stamp Exhibition, Seoul (1st issue).
2101 **1273** 910w. multicoloured 4·00 1·60
MS2102 90×60 mm. No. 2101 4·75 4·25
See also Nos. 2107/**MS**2111.

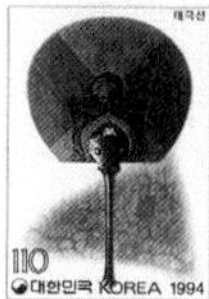
1274 Taeguk (Yin-Yang) Fan

1275 Crane Fan

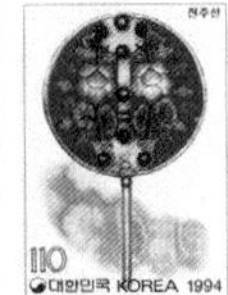
1276 Pearl Fan

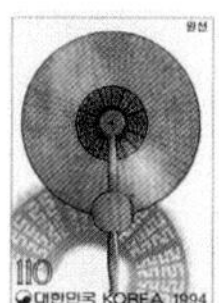
1277 Wheel Fan

1994. Korean Beauty (4th series). Fans.
2103 **1274** 110w. multicoloured 70 25
2104 **1275** 110w. multicoloured 70 25
2105 **1276** 110w. multicoloured 70 25
2106 **1277** 110w. multicoloured 70 25

1278 *Wintry Days* (Kim Chong Hui)

1994. Philakorea 1994 International Stamp Exhibition, Seoul (2nd issue). Multicoloured.
2107 130w. Type **1278** 60 15
2108 130w. *Grape* (Choe Sok Hwan) 60 15
2109 130w. *Riverside Scene* (Kim Duk Sin) 60 15
MS2110 Three sheets each 90×60 mm. (a) No. 2107×2; (b) No. 2108×2; (c) No. 2109×2 4·00 3·50
MS2111 130w. Manchurian crane and mountains; 300w. Manchurian cranes and sun; 370w. Manchurian cranes in treetops; 400w. Deer (vert); 440w. Turtle in stream (vert); 470w. Tree and stream (vert); 930w. Trees (vert) 10·50 9·75

1282 *Sword Dance* (Sin Yun Bok)

1994. 21st UPU Congress, Seoul (4th issue). Multicoloured.
2112 130w. Type **1282** 60 15
2113 130w. *Book Shelves* (detail of folk painting showing stamps) 60 15
2114 130w. Congress emblem 60 15
2115 130w. Hong Yung Sik (postal reformer) and Heinrich von Stephan (founder of UPU) (horiz) 60 15
MS2116 Four sheets each 90×60 mm. (a) No. 2112×2; (b) No. 2113×2; (c) No. 2114×2; (d) No. 2115×2 7·25 6·75
MS2117 125×86 mm. Nos. 2112/2115 4·00 3·50

1283 Old Map

1994. 600th Anniversary of Adoption of Seoul as Capital of Korea (1st issue).
2118 **1283** 130w. multicoloured 60 15
See also No. 2139.

1284 Mail Van

1994. Transport. Multicoloured.
2121 300w. Type **1284** 2·10 30
2122 330w. Boeing 747 2·10 40
2122a 340w. Boeing 747 facing left 2·10 50
2122b 380w. As 340w. 2·30 55
2123 390w. Boeing 747 (different) 3·00 50
2124 400w. As 330w. 2·10 40
2126 540w. Streamlined diesel train 3·50 55
2127 560w. As 330w. 3·50 65
2130 1190w. River cruiser 7·75 1·30
2131 1300w. As 330w. 6·75 1·20
2132 1340w. As 340w. 5·75 1·80
2132a 1380w. As 340w. 6·25 2·00

1994. Wild Flowers (5th series). As T **1166**. Multicoloured.
2133 130w. *Gentiana jamesii* 60 25
2134 130w. *Geranium eriostemon* var. *megalanthum* 60 25
2135 130w. *Leontopodium japonicum* 60 25
2136 130w. *Lycoris aurea* 60 25

1285 *Water Melon and Field Mice* (detail of folding screen, Shin Saimdang)

1994. Philatelic Week.
2137 **1285** 130w. multicoloured 60 25
MS2138 90×60 mm. No. 2137×2 1·50 1·30

1286 '600'

1994. 600th Anniversary of Seoul as Capital (2nd issue).
2139 **1286** 130w. multicoloured 60 10

1287 Pigs travelling in Snow

1994. Lunar New Year. Year of the Pig. Multicoloured.
2140 130w. Type **1287** 60 10
2141 130w. Family in forest 60 10
MS2142 Two sheets each 90×60 mm. (a) No. 2140×2; (b) No. 2141×2 3·00 2·75

1995. Protection of Wildlife and Plants (2nd series). As T **1270**. Multicoloured.
2143 130w. Plancy's green pond frog (*Rana plancyi*) 60 25
2144 130w. Common toad (*Bufo bufo*) 60 25
MS2145 Two sheets each 125×86 mm. (a) No. 2143×2; (b) No. 2144×2 3·25 3·00

1995. Fungi (3rd series). As T **1246**. Multicoloured.
2146 130w. Shaggy ink caps (*Coprinus comatus*) 70 25
2147 130w. Chicken mushroom (*Laetiporus sulphureus*) 70 25
2148 130w. *Lentinus lepideus* 70 25
2149 130w. Cracked green russula (*Russula virescens*) 70 25
MS2150 Four sheets each 90×60 mm. (a) No. 2146×2; (b) No. 2147×2; (c) No. 2148×2; (d) No. 2149×2 6·50 6·00

1290 Spheres around Reactor

1995. Completion of Hanaro Research Reactor.
2151 **1290** 130w. multicoloured 70 15

1291 Scales of Justice

1995. Centenary of Judicial System.
2152 **1291** 130w. multicoloured 70 15

1292 Tiger

1995. Centenary of Law Education.
2153 **1292** 130w. multicoloured 70 15

1293 *Dooly the Little Dinosaur* (Kim Soo Jeung)

1294 *Kochuboo* (Kim Yong Hwan)

1995. Cartoons (1st series). Multicoloured.
2154 **1293** 130w. multicoloured 70 25
2155 **1294** 440w. multicoloured 1·60 65
MS2156 Two sheets each 90×60 mm. (a) No. 2154; (b) No. 2155 4·75 4·50
See also Nos. 2196/**MS**2198, 2234/**MS**2236; 2280/**MS**2282; 2322/**MS**2325; 2402/**MS**2404; 2498/**MS**2500; 2594/**MS**2596; 2697/**MS**2699 and 2754/**MS**2756.

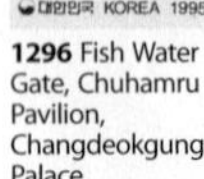

1295 Gate of Eternal Youth, Changdeokgung Palace

1296 Fish Water Gate, Chuhamru Pavilion, Changdeokgung Palace

1297 Pomosa Temple Gate, Pusan City

1298 Yangban Residence Gate, Hahoe Village

1995. Korean Beauty (5th series). Gates.
2157 **1295** 130w. multicoloured 75 25
2158 **1296** 130w. multicoloured 75 25
2159 **1297** 130w. multicoloured 75 25
2160 **1298** 130w. multicoloured 75 25

1299 Lion and Emblem

1995. 78th Convention of Lions Clubs International.
2161 **1299** 130w. multicoloured 65 15

1995. Wild Flowers (6th series). As T **1166**. Multicoloured.
2162 130w. *Halenia corniculata* 60 25
2163 130w. *Erythronium japonicum* 60 25
2164 130w. *Iris odaesanensis* 60 25
2165 130w. *Leontice microrrhyncha* 60 25

1300 National Flag

1995. 50th Anniversary of Liberation. Multicoloured.
2166 130w. Type **1300** 60 25
2167 440w. Anniversary emblem (96×19 mm) 1·90 55
MS2168 Two sheets each 125×85 mm. (a) No. 2166×2; (b) No. 2167 4·75 4·25

1301 Telescope

1995. Inauguration of Mt. Bohyun Optical Astronomy Observatory.
2169 **1301** 130w. multicoloured 65 15

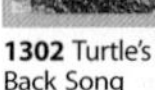

1302 Turtle's Back Song

1303 Song from *Standards of Musical Science*

1995. Literature (1st series).
2170 **1302** 130w. multicoloured 60 15
2171 **1303** 130w. multicoloured 60 15
MS2172 Two sheets each 90×60 mm. (a) No. 2170×2; (b) No. 2171×2 3·00 2·75

See also Nos. 2212/**MS**2214, 2269/**MS**2271, 2301/**MS**2303 and 2344/**MS**2348.

1304 '50Th' incorporating Man with Wheat

1995. 50th Anniversary of FAO.
2173 **1304** 150w. black and violet 75 25

1305 Open Bible

1995. Centenary of Korean Bible Society.
2174 **1305** 150w. multicoloured 75 25

1306 Families in Houses

1995. Population and Housing Census.
2175 **1306** 150w. multicoloured 75 25

1307 Dove of Flags

1995. 50th Anniversary of United Nations Organisation.
2176 **1307** 150w. multicoloured 75 25

1308 Rontgen

1995. Centenary of Discovery of X-Rays by Wilhelm Rontgen.
2177 **1308** 150w. multicoloured 75 25

1309 *Water Pepper and Mantis* (detail of folding screen, Shin Saim Dang)

1995. Philatelic Week.
2178 **1309** 150w. multicoloured 75 25
MS2179 90×60 mm. No. 2178×2 1·70 1·50

1310 Rat and Snowman

1995. Lunar New Year. Year of the Rat. Multicoloured.
2180 150w. Type **1310** 75 25
2181 150w. Cranes and pine trees (horiz) 75 25
MS2182 Two sheets each 90×60 mm. (a) No. 2180×2; (b) No. 2181×2 3·25 3·00

1312 Miroku Bosatsu, Koryu Temple, Kyoto

1995. 30th Anniversary of Resumption of Korea–Japan Diplomatic Relations.
2183 **1312** 420w. multicoloured 2·10 70

1313 Cable Route

1996. Inauguration of Korea–China Submarine Cable.
2184 **1313** 420w. multicoloured 2·10 70

1314 '30' and Molecule

1996. 30th Anniversary of Korea Institute of Science and Technology.
2185 **1314** 150w. multicoloured 75 25

1996. Protection of Wildlife and Plants (3rd series). As T **1270**. Multicoloured.
2186 150w. Black pond turtle (*Geoclemys reevesii*) 75 25
2187 150w. Ground skink (*Scincella laterale*) 75 25
MS2188 Two sheets each 125×86 mm. (a) No. 2186×2; (b) No. 2187×2 3·25 3·00

1315 Satellite and Launching Pad

1996. Launch of *Mugunghwa 2* Telecommunications Satellite.
2189 **1315** 150w. multicoloured 75 25

1316 So Chae P'il (founder) and Leader from First Issue

1996. Centenary of *Tongnip Shinmun* (first independent newspaper).
2190 **1316** 150w. multicoloured 75 25

1996. Wild Flowers (7th series). As T **1166**. Multicoloured.
2191 150w. *Cypripedium macranthum* 75 25
2192 150w. *Trilium tschonoskii* 75 25
2193 150w. *Viola variegata* 75 25
2194 150w. *Hypericum ascyron* 75 25

1317 Anniversary Emblem and Cadets

1996. 50th Anniversary of Korean Military Academy.
2195 **1317** 150w. multicoloured 75 25

1318 Gobau (Kim Song Hwan)

1319 Battle between Kkach'i and Caesarius (Lee Hyun Se) (from film *Armageddon*)

1996. Cartoons (2nd series).
2196 **1318** 150w. multicoloured 75 25
2197 **1319** 150w. multicoloured 75 25
MS2198 Two sheets each 90×60 mm. (a) No. 2196×2; (b) No. 2197 3·00 2·75

1320 Anniversary Emblem

1996. 50th Anniversary of Korean Girl Scouts.
2199 **1320** 150w. multicoloured 75 25

1321 Globe and Congress Emblem

1996. 35th World Congress of International Advertising Association, Seoul.
2200 **1321** 150w. multicoloured 75 25

1322 Syringes and Drugs

1996. International Anti-drug Day.
2201 **1322** 150w. multicoloured 75 25

1323 Skater

1996. World University Students' Games, Muju and Chonju (1st issue). Multicoloured.
2202 150w. Type **1323** 75 25
2203 150w. Games emblem (vert) 75 25

See also Nos. 2228/**MS**2230.

1324 Torch Bearer

1996. Olympic Games, Atlanta. Multicoloured.
2204 150w. Type **1324** 75 25
2205 150w. Games emblem 75 25

1325 Match Scene

1326 South Korean Team scoring Goal

1996. World Cup Football Championship (2002), South Korea and Japan. Two sheets each 134×78 mm. Multicoloured.
MS2206 Two sheets. (a) 400w.×4, Type **1325**; (b) 400w.×4, Type **1326** 21·00 18·00

1996. Fungi (4th series). As T **1246**. Multicoloured.
2207 150w. *Amanita inaurata* 75 25
2208 150w. *Paxillus atrotomentosus* 75 25
2209 150w. *Rhodophyllus crassipes* 75 25
2210 150w. *Sarcodon imbricatum* 75 25
MS2211 Four sheets each 90×60 mm. (a) No. 2207×2; (b) No. 2208×2; (c) No. 2209×2; (d) No. 2210×2 6·75 6·25

1327 *Requiem for a Deceased Sister*

1328 *Ode to Knight Kip'a*

1996. Literature (2nd series).
2212 **1327** 150w. multicoloured 75 25
2213 **1328** 150w. multicoloured 75 25
MS2214 Two sheets, each 90×61 mm. (a) No. 2212×2; (b) No. 2213×2 3·25 3·00

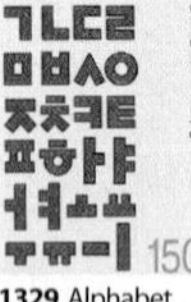

1329 Alphabet

1996. 550th Anniversary of Han-Gul (Korean alphabet created by King Sejong).
2215 **1329** 150w. black and grey 75 25
MS2216 90×60 mm. No. 2215×2 1·70 1·50

1330 Castle

1996. Bicentenary of Suwon Castle.
2217 **1330** 400w. multicoloured 2·10 80

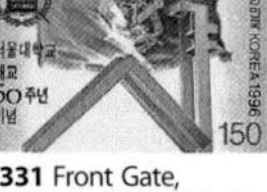

1331 Front Gate, University Flag and Emblem

1996. 50th Anniversary of Seoul National University.
2218 **1331** 150w. multicoloured 75 25

1332 Five-direction Pouch

1333 Chinese Phoenix Pouch (Queen's Court Pouch)

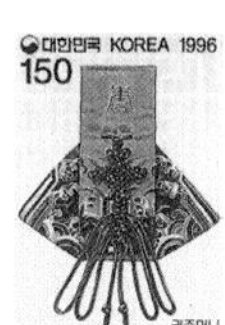
1334 Princess Pokon's Wedding Pouch

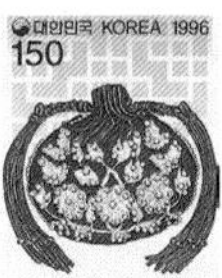
1335 Queen Yunbi's Pearl Pouch

1996. Korean Beauty (6th series). Pouches.
2219 **1332** 150w. multicoloured 75 25
2220 **1333** 150w. multicoloured 75 25
2221 **1334** 150w. multicoloured 75 25
2222 **1335** 150w. multicoloured 75 25

1336 *Poppy and Lizard* (detail of folding screen, Shin Saimdang)

1996. Philatelic Week.
2223 **1336** 150w. multicoloured 75 25
MS2224 90×60 mm. No. 2223×2 1·70 1·50

1337 Children riding Ox

1996. Lunar New Year. Year of the Ox. Multicoloured.
2225 150w. Type **1337** 75 25
2226 150w. Boy piper and resting ox 75 25
MS2227 Two sheets, each 90×60 mm. (a) No. 2225×2; (b) No. 2226×2 3·25 3·00

1339 Figure Skating

1997. World University Students' Games, Muju and Chonju (2nd issue). Multicoloured.
2228 150w. Type **1339** 65 25
2229 150w. Skiing 65 25
MS2230 Two sheets, each 60×90 mm. (a) No. 2228×2; (b) No. 2229×2 2·75 2·40

1340 Coins forming '100'

1997. Centenary of Foundation of Hansong Bank (first commercial bank in Korea).
2231 **1340** 150w. multicoloured 65 25

1341 *Auspicious Turtles*(painting)

1997. Interparliamentary Union Conference, Seoul.
2232 **1341** 150w. multicoloured 70 25

1342 Globe, Pen and open Book (Jeon Chong Kwan)

1997. World Book and Copyright Day.
2233 **1342** 150w. multicoloured 1·20 25

1343 A Long, Long Journey in Search of Mummy (Kim Chong Nae)
1344 Run, Run, Hannie (Lee Chin Ju)

1997. Cartoons (3rd series).
2234 **1343** 150w. multicoloured 70 25
2235 **1344** 150w. multicoloured 70 25
MS2236 Two sheets, each 90×60 mm. (a) No. 2234; (b) 2235 2·30 2·00

1345 Torch Bearer

1997. Second East Asian Games, Pusan.
2237 **1345** 150w. multicoloured 70 25

1346 Jules Rimet (founder)

1347 *Chukkuk* (Lee Chul Joo)

1997. World Cup Football Championship (2002), South Korea and Japan (1st issue).
2238 **1346** 150w. multicoloured 70 25
2239 **1347** 150w. multicoloured 70 25
MS2240 Two sheets, each 134×78 mm. (a) 2238×2; (b) 2242×2 5·25 4·75
See also Nos. 2284/**MS**2288.

1997. Protection of Wildlife and Plants (4th series). As T **1270**. Multicoloured.
2241 150w. Chinese nine-spined sticklebacks (*Pungitius sinensis*) 70 25
2242 150w. Spot-eared brook perch (*Coreoperca kawamebari*) 70 25
MS2243 Two sheets, each 125×86 mm. (a) 2241×2; (b) No. 2242×2 2·75 2·40

1997. Wild Flowers (8th series). As T **1166**. Multicoloured.
2244 150w. *Belamcanda chinensis* 70 25
2245 150w. *Hylomecon vernalis* 70 25
2246 150w. *Campanula takesimana* 70 25
2247 150w. *Magnolia sieboldii* 70 25

1348 Emblem and '97' forming Face

1997. Second Art Biennale, Kwangju.
2248 **1348** 150w. multicoloured 70 25

1997. Fungi (5th series). As T **1246**. Multicoloured.
2249 150w. *Inocybe fastigiata* 70 25
2250 150w. *Panaeolus papilionaceus* 70 25
2251 150w. *Ramaria flava* 70 25
2252 150w. Fly agaric (*Amanita muscaria*) 70 25
MS2253 Four sheets, each 90×60 mm. (a) No. 2249×2; (b) No. 2250×2; (c) No. 2251×2; (d) No. 2252×2 5·50 5·00

1349 Seoul South Gate and Emblem

1997. 85th World Dental Congress, Seoul.
2254 **1349** 170w. multicoloured 70 25

1350 Harbour and Score

1997. Centenary of Mokpo Port.
2255 **1350** 170w. multicoloured 70 25

1351 Main Building, Pyongyang

1997. Centenary of Founding of Soongsil Academy in Pyongyang (now situated in Seoul).
2256 **1351** 170w. multicoloured 70 25

1352 Concentric Squares

1353 Green Silk

1354 Pattern of Squares
1355 Pattern of Squares and Triangles

1997. Korean Beauty (7th series). Patchwork Pojagi (wrapping cloths).
2257 **1352** 170w. multicoloured 70 25
2258 **1353** 170w. multicoloured 70 25
2259 **1354** 170w. multicoloured 70 25
2260 **1355** 170w. multicoloured 70 25

1356 *Hollyhock and Frog* (detail of folding screen, Shin Saimdang)

1997. Philatelic Week.
2261 **1356** 170w. multicoloured 70 25
MS2262 90×60 mm. No. 2261×2 1·40 1·10

1357 Tiger's Head

1997. Lunar New Year. Year of the Tiger. Multicoloured.
2263 170w. Type **1357** 70 25
2264 170w. *Magpie and Tiger* (folk painting) 70 25
MS2265 Two sheets, each 90×60 mm. (a) No. 2263×2; (b) No. 2264×2 2·75 2·40

1359 Buddha, Sokkuram Shrine
1360 Pulguk Temple

1997. World Heritage Sites (1st series).
2266 **1359** 170w. multicoloured 1·30 90
2267 **1360** 380w. multicoloured 5·25 3·50
MS2268 144×88 mm. Nos. 2266/7 6·50 6·00
See also Nos. 2317/**MS**2319, 2365/**MS**2367, 2457/**MS**2459 and 2533/**MS**2535.

1361 *Poem to Sui General Yu Zhong Wen* (Ulchi Mundok)
1362 *Record of Travel to Five Indian Kingdoms* (Hye Ch'o)

1997. Literature (3rd series).
2269 **1361** 170w. multicoloured 65 25
2270 **1362** 170w. multicoloured 65 25
MS2271 Two sheets, each 90×60 mm. (a) No. 2269×2; (b) No. 2270×2 2·75 2·40

1363 Neon Lights on Globe and Nuclear Power Plant

1998. Centenary of Introduction of Electricity to Korea.
2272 **1363** 170w. multicoloured 65 15

1364 President Kim Dae Jung and Flag

1998. Inauguration of 15th President of South Korea.
2273 **1364** 170w. multicoloured 1·10 40
MS2274 120×110 mm. No. 2273 6·00 5·75

1998. Protection of Wildlife and Plants (5th series). Vert designs as T **1270**. Multicoloured.
2275 340w. Korean leopard (*Panthera pardus orientalis*) 2·00 30
2276 340w. Asiatic black bears (*Selenarctos thibetanus*) 2·00 30
2277 340w. European otters (*Lutra lutra*) 2·00 30
2278 340w. Siberian musk deers (*Moschus moschiferus*) 2·00 30
MS2279 129×123 mm. Nos. 2275/2278 8·25 7·00

1365 Aktong-i (Lee Hi Jae)

1366 Challenger (Park Ki Jong)

1998. Cartoons (4th series).
2280 **1365** 170w. multicoloured 80 25
2281 **1366** 340w. multicoloured 1·70 1·20
MS2282 Two sheets, each 90×60 mm. (a) No. 2280; (b) No. 2281 3·25 2·75

1367 Assembly Building and Firework Display

1998. 50th Anniversary of National Assembly.
2283 **1367** 170w. multicoloured 65 15

1368 Player with Ball

1998. World Cup Football Championship (2002), Korea and Japan (2nd issue). Multicoloured.
2284 170w. Type **1368** 90 25
2285 170w. Two players chasing ball 90 25

2286 170w. Players heading ball 90 25
2287 170w. Player kicking ball over head 90 25
MS2288 134×78 mm. No. 2284/2287 4·00 3·25

1369 Writing on Stone Tablets

1998. Information Technology. Multicoloured.

2289 170w. Type **1369** 80 25
2290 170w. Pony Express 80 25
2291 170w. Man using telephone and post box 80 25
2292 170w. Old and modern forms of communication (68×22 mm) 1·60 50

1998. Fungi (6th series). As T **1246**. Multicoloured.

2293 170w. *Pseudocolus schellenbergiae* 90 40
2294 170w. *Cyptotrama asprata* 90 40
2295 170w. *Laccaria vinaceoavellanea* 90 40
2296 170w. *Phallus rugulosus* 90 40
MS2297 114×144 mm. Nos. 2293/2296 5·00 4·50

1373 Flag and Runners

1998. 50th Anniversary of Proclamation of Republic.

2298 **1373** 170w. multicoloured 65 25

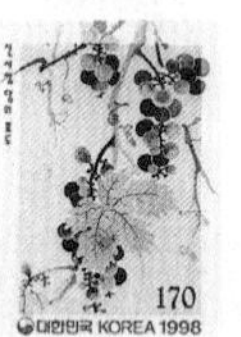

1374 *Grapes* (Lady Shin Saimdang)

1998. Philatelic Week.

2299 **1374** 170w. multicoloured 65 25
MS2300 90×60 mm. No. 2299×2 1·70 1·40

1375 *Thinking of Mother* **1376** *Would You Leave Me Now?*

1998. Literature (4th series). Sogyo Songs.

2301 **1375** 170w. multicoloured 65 25
2302 **1376** 170w. multicoloured 65 25
MS2303 Two sheets 90×20 mm. (a) No. 2301; (b) No. 2302 2·20 1·80

1377 Film Strips and Masks

1998. Third Pusan International Film Festival.

2304 **1377** 170w. multicoloured 65 25

1378 Myungnyundang Hall

1998. 600th Anniversary of Sungkyunkwan University.

2305 **1378** 170w. multicoloured 65 25

1379 National Constabulary, Badge and Lake Ch'onji

1998. 50th Anniversary of Korean Armed Forces.

2306 **1379** 170w. multicoloured 65 25

1380 Hot-air Balloon

1998. World Stamp Day.

2307 **1380** 170w. multicoloured 65 25

1381 Peach **1382** Double Crane **1383** Carp

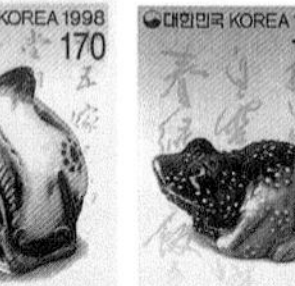

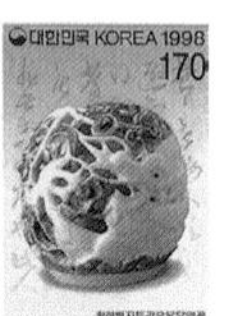

1384 Peach **1385** Toad **1386** Dragon and Cloud

1387 Monkey **1388** House

1998. Korean Beauty (8th series). Porcelain Water Droppers.

2308 **1381** 170w. multicoloured 1·10 40
2309 **1382** 170w. multicoloured 1·10 40
2310 **1383** 170w. multicoloured 1·10 40
2311 **1384** 170w. multicoloured 1·10 40
2312 **1385** 170w. multicoloured 1·10 40
2313 **1386** 170w. multicoloured 1·10 40
2314 **1387** 170w. multicoloured 1·10 40
2315 **1388** 170w. multicoloured 1·10 40

1389 Rabbits

1998. Lunar New Year. Year of the Rabbit.

2316 **1389** 170w. multicoloured 65 25

1390 *Tripitaka Koreana* (scriptures engraved on wooden blocks)

1391 Changgyong P'anjon (woodblock repository)

1998. World Heritage Sites (2nd series). Haein Temple.

2317 **1390** 170w. multicoloured 1·10 55
2318 **1391** 380w. multicoloured 3·25 1·60
MS2319 144×88 mm. Nos. 2317/2318 21·00 11·00

1392 Maize, Compass and Ship's Wheel

1999. Centenary of Kunsan Port.

2320 **1392** 170w. multicoloured 65 30

1393 Masan and Score of *I Want to Go* by Lee Eun Sang

1999. Centenary of Masan Port.

2321 **1393** 170w. multicoloured 65 30

1394 Rai-Fi (Kim San Ho)

1395 Tokgo T'ak (Lee Sang Mu)

1396 Im Kkuk Jung (Lee Du Ho)

1999. Cartoons (5th series).

2322 **1394** 170w. multicoloured 65 30
2323 **1395** 170w. multicoloured 65 30
2324 **1396** 170w. multicoloured 65 30
MS2325 Three sheets, each 88×58 mm. multicoloured. (a) 340w. Type **1394**; (b) 340w. Type **1395**; (c) 340w. Type **1396** 6·00 5·75

1999. Protection of Wildlife and Plants (6th series). Vert designs as T **1270**.

2326 170w. Peregrine falcon (*Falco peregrinus*) 1·30 30
2327 170w. Grey frog hawk (*Accipiter soloensis*) 1·30 30
2328 340w. Steller's sea eagle (*Haliaeetus pelagicus*) 2·75 65
2329 340w. Northern eagle owl (*Bubo bubo*) 2·75 65
MS2330 136×133 mm. Nos. 2326/2329 8·25 7·75

1397 Five clasped Hands

1999. 109th International Olympic Committee Congress, Seoul.

2331 **1397** 170w. multicoloured 65 30

1398 Goethe (after Joseph Stieler)

1999. 250th Birth Anniversary of Johann Wolfgang von Goethe (poet and playwright).

2332 **1398** 170w. multicoloured 80 30
MS2333 110×94 mm. **1398** 480w. multicoloured 2·75 2·40

1399 *Kumgang Mountain* (Kyomjae Chong Son)

1999. Philatelic Week.

2334 **1399** 170w. multicoloured 65 30
MS2335 120×90 mm. **1399** 340w. multicoloured 1·70 1·60

1400 Mogul Tank Locomotive No. 101 (first locomotive in Korea)

1999. Centenary of Railway in Korea.

2336 **1400** 170w. multicoloured 1·00 30

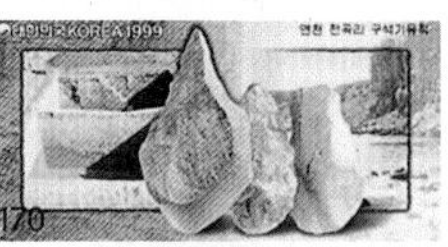

1401 Flint Tools and Paleolithic Ruins, Chungok-ri, Yonch'on

1999. New Millennium (1st series). Multicoloured.

2337 170w. Type **1401** 90 30
2338 170w. Comb-patterned pottery, burnt-out and reconstructed Neolithic dwellings, Amsa-dong, Seoul 90 30
2339 170w. Shell bracelets, bone spear heads and Neolithic shell mounds, Tongsam-dong, Pusan 90 30
2340 170w. Dolmen, Pukon-ri, Kanghwa-do Island 90 30
2341 170w. Bronze and stone daggers and Bronze-age earthenware, Son-gguk-ri, Puyo 90 30
2342 170w. Rock carvings, Pan'gudae 90 30

See also Nos. 2357/2362, 2374/2378, 2388/2392, 2397/2401, 2406/2410, 2420/2425, 2431/2436, 2460/2465, 2487/2491 and 2511/2515.

1402 Bird carrying Letter

1999. 125th Anniversary of Universal Postal Union.

2343 **1402** 170w. multicoloured 65 30

1403 *Little Odes on the Kwandong Area* (Chong Ch'ol)

1404 *Alas! How foolish I am!* (Hwang Jin-i)

1405 *Story of Hong Kil-dong* (Ho Kyun)

1406 *Story of Ch'unhyang*

1999. Literature (5th series).

2344 **1403** 170w. multicoloured 65 30
2345 **1404** 170w. multicoloured 65 30
2346 **1405** 170w. multicoloured 65 30
2347 **1406** 170w. multicoloured 65 30
MS2348 Four sheets, each 90×60 mm. (a) No. 2344; (b) 90×60 mm. No. 2345; (c) 60×90 mm. No. 2346; (d) 60×90 mm. No. 2347 5·50 5·00

1407 Chrysanthemum, Bird and Duck **1408** Birds in Tree and Snake on Korean Character **1409** Pot Plant with Butterfly on Korean Character

1410 Fish on Korean Character

1411 Plant behind Tub of Fish

1412 Crab on Korean Character

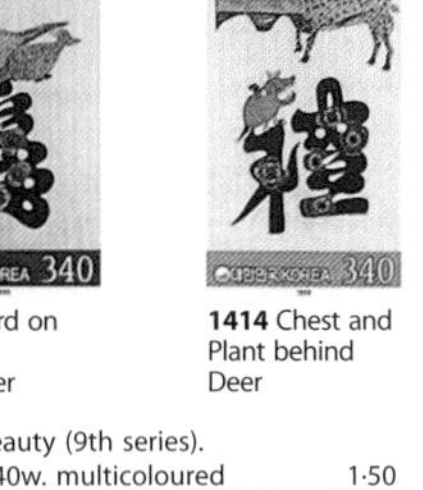

1413 Bird on Korean Character

1414 Chest and Plant behind Deer

1999. Korean Beauty (9th series).

2349	**1407**	340w. multicoloured	1·50	65
2350	**1408**	340w. multicoloured	1·50	65
2351	**1409**	340w. multicoloured	1·50	65
2352	**1410**	340w. multicoloured	1·50	65
2353	**1411**	340w. multicoloured	1·50	65
2354	**1412**	340w. multicoloured	1·50	65
2355	**1413**	340w. multicoloured	1·50	65
2356	**1414**	340w. multicoloured	1·50	65

1415 Ornament and Bird-shaped Vase

1416 Crown and Bowl

1417 Man on Horseback and Cave Paintings

1418 Gold Ornament and Jade Jewellery

1419 Stone Crafts

1420 Carved Stone Face

1999. New Millennium (2nd series).

2357	**1415**	170w. multicoloured	80	30
2358	**1416**	170w. multicoloured	80	30
2359	**1417**	170w. multicoloured	80	30
2360	**1418**	170w. multicoloured	80	30
2361	**1419**	170w. multicoloured	80	30
2362	**1420**	170w. multicoloured	80	30

1421 Dragon

1999. Lunar New Year. Year of the Dragon.

2363	**1421**	170w. multicoloured	60	30
MS2364		90×61 mm. No. 2363×2	1·50	1·20

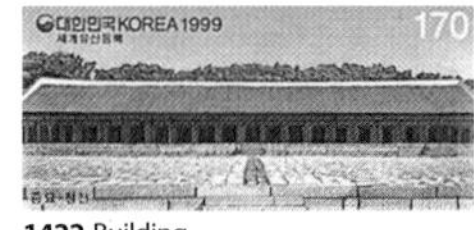

1422 Building

1423 Man and Musicians

1999. World Heritage Sites (3rd series).

2365	**1422**	170w. multicoloured	80	35
2366	**1423**	340w. multicoloured	2·00	70
MS2367		144×96 mm. Nos. 2365/2366	11·50	4·50

1424 Player

1999. World Cup Football Championship, Japan and Korea (2002). Multicoloured.

2368	170w. Type **1424**	70	35
2369	170w. Players tackling	70	35
2370	170w. Player receiving ball	70	35
2371	170w. Goalkeeper catching ball	70	35
MS2372	134×78 mm. Nos. 2368/2371	3·50	3·25

Nos. 2368/2371 were issued together, *se-tenant*, forming a composite design.

1425 Emblem

2000. Centenary of South Korea's Membership of Universal Postal Union.

2373	**1425**	170w. multicoloured	60	30

1426 Sunset, Altar and Tablet

2000. New Millennium (3rd series). Multicoloured.

2374	170w. Type **1426**	80	35
2375	170w. Cave painting of wrestlers	80	35
2376	170w. Inscribed bronze disc and warrior	80	35
2377	170w. Silhouettes of archers and inscribed standing stone	80	35
2378	170w. Junk and warrior	80	35

1427 Pashi Steam Locomotive

1428 Teho Steam Locomotive

1429 Mika Steam Locomotive

1430 Hyouki Steam Locomotive

2000. Railways (1st series).

2379	**1427**	170w. black, violet and mauve	80	30
2380	**1428**	170w. black, violet and mauve	80	30
2381	**1429**	170w. black, violet and grey	80	30
2382	**1430**	170w. black, violet and bistre	80	30

See also Nos. 2477/2480, 2585/2588; 2682/2685 and 2741/2744.

2000. Protection of Wildlife and Plants (7th series). As T **1270**. Multicoloured.

2383	170w. *Lilium cernum*	1·00	30
2384	170w. *Sedirea japonica*	1·00	30
2385	170w. *Hibiscus hamabo*	1·00	30
2386	170w. *Cypripedium japonicum*	1·00	30
MS2387	136×133 mm. Nos. 2383/6	4·25	4·00

Nos. 2383/**MS**2387 are impregnated with scent of flowers.

1431 State Civil Service Examination and Text

2000. New Millennium (4th series). Multicoloured.

2388	170w. Type **1431**	80	40
2389	170w. Man carving wood blocks	80	40
2390	170w. Pieces of metal type	80	40
2391	170w. An-Hyang (scholar) and Korean script	80	40
2392	170w. Mun Ik-jom (scholar), spinning wheel and cotton plant	80	40

1432 Children playing and House (Kim Chin Sook)

2000. World Water Day. Winning Design in Children's Painting Competition.

2393	**1432**	170w. multicoloured	60	40

1433 Globe and Satellite

2000. 50th Anniversary of World Meteorological Organization.

2394	**1433**	170w. multicoloured	60	40

1434 Hand holding Rose

2000. Share Love (good neighbour campaign).

2395	**1434**	170w. multicoloured	1·20	40

No. 2395 is impregnated with the scent of roses.

1435 '2000'

2000. CYBER KOREA 21.

2396	**1435**	170w. multicoloured	60	40

1436 King Sejong and Korean Script

2000. New Millennium (5th series). Multicoloured.

2397	170w. Type **1436**	80	50
2398	170w. Lady Shin Saimdang (caligrapher poet and painter) and detail of *Ch'ochung-do* (painting)	80	50
2399	170w. Yi Hwang and Yi I (founders of Confucian Academy)	80	50
2400	170w. Admiral Yi Sun-shin and model of 'turtle' ship	80	50
2401	170w. Sandae-nori (mask-dance drama)	80	50

1437 Park Soo Dong

1438 Bae Gum Taek

2000. Cartoons (6th series).

2402	**1437**	170w. multicoloured	60	50
2403	**1438**	170w. multicoloured	60	50
MS2404		Two sheets, each 90×60 mm. (a) No. 2402; (b) No. 2403	1·80	1·60

1439 Seedling on Map of Korean Peninsula

2000. Pyongyang, Korean Summit.

2405	**1439**	170w. multicoloured	80	65

1440 Anatomical Diagram from *Tonui Pogam* (medical treatise by Huh Joan)

2000. Millennium (6th series). Multicoloured.

2406	170w. Type **1440**	80	40
2407	170w. *Dancer with Musicians* (illustration by Kim Hong Do)	80	40
2408	170w. *Plum Blossoms and Bird* (painting, Chong Yak Yong) and house in Kangjin where he served his exile	80	40
2409	170w. Map of Korea by Kim Chong Ho and wheel chart	80	40
2410	170w. Chon Bong Joan (revolutionary) and Tonghak Peasant Uprising monument	80	40

1441 Numbers and Mathematical Symbols

2000. International Mathematical Olympiad (high school mathematics competition).

2411	**1441**	170w. multicoloured	60	40

1442 *Yolha Diary* (Park Ji Won)

1443 *Fisherman's Calender*

1444 *The Nine-Cloud Dream*

1445 *Tears of Blood*

1446 *From the Sea to a Child*

2000. Literature (6th series).

2412	**1442**	170w. multicoloured	70	40
2413	**1443**	170w. multicoloured	70	40
2414	**1444**	170w. multicoloured	70	40
2415	**1445**	170w. multicoloured	70	40
2416	**1446**	170w. multicoloured	70	40
MS2417		Five sheets. (a) 60×90 mm. No. 2414; (b) 60×90 mm. No. 2413; (c) 90×60 mm. No. 2414; (d) 90×60 mm. No. 2415; (e) 90×60 mm. No. 2416	5·00	4·50

1447 Mountain

2000. Philately Week.

2418	**1447**	340w. multicoloured	1·30	70
MS2419		120×90 mm. No. 2418	1·70	1·50

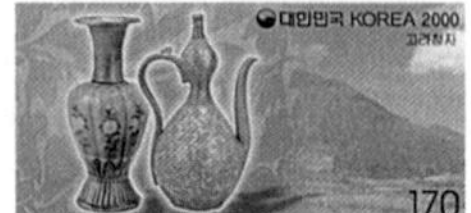
1448 Porcelain

2000. Millennium (7th series). Multicoloured.

2420	170w. Type **1448**	80	40
2421	170w. *Bongjongsa* Temple (Paradise Pavilion)	80	40
2422	170w. Hahoe Tal masks	80	40
2423	170w. Royal Palace	80	40
2424	170w. Landscape painting	80	40
2425	170w. Water clock	80	40

1454 Taekwondo

2000. Olympic Games, Sydney.

2426	**1454**	170w. multicoloured	75	50

1455 Former Kyunngi High School Building, Hwadong

2000. Centenary of Public Secondary Schools.

2427	**1455**	170w. multicoloured	75	50

1456 *Returning to the Retirement House (illustration from Album of the Gathering of Old Statesmen)*

2000. Third Asia-Europe Meeting, Seoul.

2428	**1456**	170w. multicoloured	75	50

1457 Emblem

2000. Icograde Millennium Congress, Seoul.

2429	**1457**	170w. black and yellow	75	50

1458 Mr. Gobau

2000. 50th Anniversary of Mr. Gobau (cartoon character).

2430	**1458**	170w. multicoloured	75	50

1459 18th-century Painting (Sin Yun Bok)

2000. Millennium (8th series). Multicoloured.

2431	170w. Type **1459**	80	40
2432	170w. Calligraphy by Kim Jeong Hui	80	40
2433	170w. Bongdon-Chiseong Hwaseong Fortress, Suwon	80	40
2434	170w. Myeongdong Cathedral	80	40
2435	170w. Wongaska theatre actors	80	40
2436	170w. The *KITSat* satellite	80	40

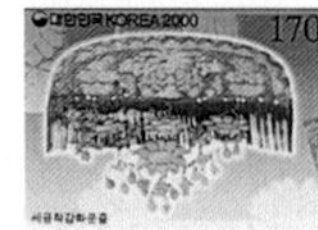
1460 Decorated Comb

2000. Korean Beauty (10th series). Multicoloured.

2437	170w. Type **1460**	75	40
2438	170w. Woman's ceremonial headdress	75	40
2439	170w. Butterfly-shaped hairpin	75	40
2440	170w. Hairpin with dragon decoration and jade hairpin with Chinese phoenix decoration	75	40

1461 Seoul World Cup Stadium

1462 Busan Sports Complex Main Stadium

1463 Daegu Sports Complex Stadium

1464 Incheon Munhak Stadium

1465 Gwangu World Cup Stadium

1466 Daejeon World Cup Stadium

1467 Ulsan Munsu Football Stadium

1468 Suwon World Cup Stadium

1469 Jeonju World Cup Stadium

1470 Jeju World Cup Stadium

2000. World Cup Football Championship (2002), South Korea and Japan.

2441	**1461**	170w. multicoloured	1·20	40
2442	**1462**	170w. multicoloured	1·20	40
2443	**1463**	170w. multicoloured	1·20	40
2444	**1464**	170w. multicoloured	1·20	40
2445	**1465**	170w. multicoloured	1·20	40
2446	**1466**	170w. multicoloured	1·20	40
2447	**1467**	170w. multicoloured	1·20	40
2448	**1468**	170w. multicoloured	1·20	40
2449	**1469**	170w. multicoloured	1·20	40
2450	**1470**	170w. multicoloured	1·20	40
MS2451		Five sheets each, 60×90 mm. (a) 170w. No. 2441/2442; (b) 170w. Nos. 2443/2444; (c) 170w. Nos. 2445/2446; (d) 170w. Nos. 2447/2448; (e) 170w. Nos. 2449/2450	15·00	14·50

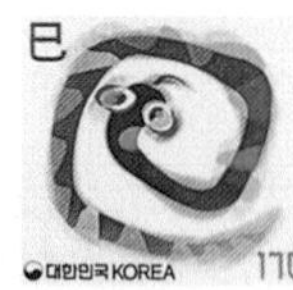
1471 Snake

2000. Lunar New Year. Year of the Snake. Ordinary or self-adhesive gum. (No. 2452).

2452	**1471**	170w. multicoloured	80	40
MS2453		170w. 107×69 mm. No. 2452×3	1·50	1·30

1472 President Kim Dae Jung and Children

2000. Award of Nobel Peace Prize to President Kim Dae Jung.

2455	**1472**	170w. multicoloured	80	40
MS2456		118×70 mm. No. 2455×2	2·50	2·20

1473 Repository, Jeongjok Mountain and Taejo Sillok (script)

2000. World Heritage Sites (4th series). Multicoloured.

2457	340w. Type **1473**	2·00	1·20
2458	340w. King Sejong and script	2·00	1·20
MS2459	143×89 mm. Nos. 2457/2458	5·00	3·00

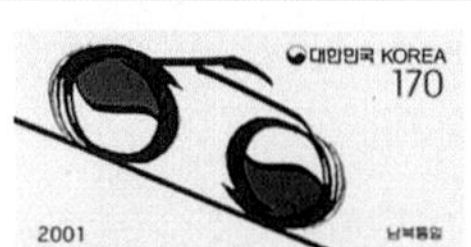
1474 Bicycle with coloured wheels (reunification of Korea)

2001. Millennium (9th series). Multicoloured.

2460	170w. Type **1474**	80	45
2461	170w. Rainbow (environmental protection)	80	45
2462	170w. Human DNA and figure (eradication of incurable diseases)	80	45
2463	170w. Satellite and mobile telephone (communications technology)	80	45
2464	170w. Space (space travel)	80	45
2465	170w. Solar panels, solar-powered car and windmills (alternative energy sources)	80	45

1475 *Oksunn Peaks* (Kim Hong Do)

2001. Visit Korea Year 2001.

2466	**1475**	170w. multicoloured	70	40

1476 Plough

2001. Agricultural Implements. Multicoloured.

2467	170w. Type **1476**	1·50	40
2468	170w. Harrow	1·50	40
2469	170w. Sowing basket and namtae	1·50	40
2470	170w. Short-handled hoes	1·50	40
2471	170w. Manure barrel and fertilizer ash container	1·50	40
2472	170w. Water dipper	1·50	40
2473	170w. Winnower and thresher	1·50	40
2474	170w. Square straw drying mat and wicker tray	1·50	40
2475	170w. Pestle, mortar and grinding stones	1·50	40
2476	170w. Rice basket and carrier	1·50	40

1486 2000 Series Diesel-electric Locomotive

1487 7000 Series Diesel-electric Locomotive

1488 Diesel Urban Commuter Train

1489 Diesel Saemaul Train

2001. Railways (2nd series).

2477	**1486**	170w. multicoloured	70	45
2478	**1487**	170w. multicoloured	70	45
2479	**1488**	170w. multicoloured	70	45
2480	**1489**	170w. multicoloured	70	45

2001. Protection of Wildlife and Plants (8th series). Vert designs as T **1270**. Multicoloured.

2481	170w. *Jeffersonia dubia*	90	55
2482	170w. *Diapensia lapponica*	90	55
2483	170w. *Rhododendron aureum*	90	55
2484	170w. *Sedum orbiculatum*	90	55
MS2485	170w. 125×108 mm. Nos. 2481/2484	3·75	3·50

Nos. 2481/2484 are impregnated with the scent of the Ume tree.

1490 Incheon Airport and Emblem

2001. Inauguration of Incheon Airport.

2486	**1490**	170w. multicoloured	70	40

1491 Kim Ku (leader of Independence Movement)

2001. Millennium (10th series). Multicoloured.

2487	170w. Type **1491**	80	40
2488	170w. Statue commemorating the March 1st Independence Movement	80	40
2489	170w. Interim Korean Government Headquarters, Shanghai and Members	80	40
2490	170w. Ahn Ik Tae (composer) and music score	80	40
2491	170w. Yun Dong Ju (poet) and *Seosi* (poem)	80	40

1492 Emblem

2001. International Olympic Fair, Seoul.

2492	**1492**	170w. multicoloured	70	40
MS2493		105×70 mm. No. 2492×2	2·00	1·80

1493 Bears hugging

2001. Greetings Stamps. Multicoloured.

2494	170w. Type **1493**	2·00	80
2495	170w. Flower	2·00	80
2496	170w. Trumpets (Congratulations)	2·00	80
2497	170w. Cake	2·00	80

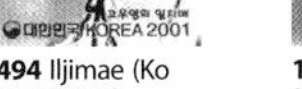

1494 Iljimae (Ko Woo Young)

1495 Kkeobeongi (Kil Chang Duk)

2001. Cartoons (7th series).

2498	**1494** 170w. multicoloured	70	40
2499	**1495** 170w. multicoloured	70	40
MS2500	Two sheets, each 90×60 mm. (a) No. 2498. (b) No. 2499 Price for 2 sheets	2·00	1·80

1496 Players and Mountains (Switzerland, 1954)

2001. World Cup Football Championship, Japan and South Korea. Multicoloured.

2501	170w. Type **1496**	90	40
2502	170w. Players and Ancient settlement (Mexico, 1986)	90	40
2503	170w. Players and Coliseum (Italy, 1990)	90	40
2504	170w. Players and buildings (United States of America, 1994)	90	40
2505	170w. Players and Eiffel Tower (France, 1998)	90	40
MS2506	Five sheets, each 60×90 mm. (a) No. 2501×2. (b) No. 2502×2. (c) No. 2503×2. (d) No. 2504×2. (e) No. 2505×2 Set for 5 sheets	10·00	9·75

1497 Baechu Kimchi (Chinese Cabbage)

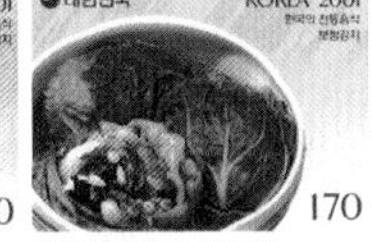

1498 Bossam Kimchi

1499 Dongchimi

1500 Klakdugi

2001. Korean Foods (1st series).

2507	**1497** 170w. multicoloured	80	40
2508	**1498** 170w. multicoloured	80	40
2509	**1499** 170w. multicoloured	80	40
2510	**1500** 170w. multicoloured	80	40

See also Nos. 2599/2602, 2705/2708, 2758/2761 and 2810/2813.

1501 Raising Flag (Liberation, 1945)

2001. Millennium (11th series). Multicoloured.

2511	170w. Type **1501**	80	40
2512	170w. Soldiers embracing (statue) (Korean War)	80	40
2513	170w. Seoul–Busan Expressway	80	40
2514	170w. Working in fields (Saemaul Undong movement)	80	40
2515	170w. Athletes forming emblem (Olympic Games, Seoul, 1988)	80	40

1502 Red Queen

1503 Pink Lady

2001. Philakorea 2002 International Stamp Exhibition, Seoul. (1st issue). Roses.

2516	**1502** 170w. multicoloured	70	40
2517	**1503** 170w. multicoloured	70	40
MS2518	Two sheets, each 115×73 mm. (a) No. 2516×2. (b) No. 2517×2 Set for 2 sheets	4·00	3·75

See also Nos. 2604/**MS**2606 and 2639/**MS**2640.

1504 Roses in Heart

2001. Philately Week.

2519	**1504** 170w. multicoloured	70	40
MS2520	108×69 mm. No. 2519×2	1·80	1·60

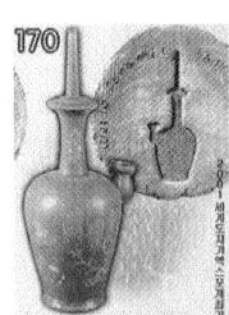

1505 Goryeo Dynasty Porcelain Vase and Exhibition Emblem

2001. World Ceramics Expo, Icheon, Yeoju, and Gwangju.

2521	**1505** 170w. multicoloured	70	40

1506 Conference Emblem

2001. International Statistical Institute (ISI) Conference, Seoul.

2522	**1506** 170w. multicoloured	70	40

1507 Joseon Coin and Stamping Machine

2001. 50th Anniversary of Korea Minting and Security Printing Corporation (KOMSEP).

2523	**1507** 170w. multicoloured	70	40

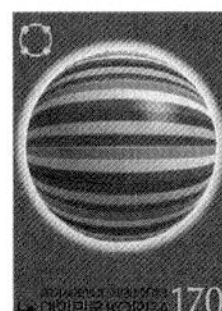

1508 Multicoloured Ball (Oullim Globe)

2001. International Council of Societies of Industrial Design (ICSID) Conference, Seoul.

2524	**1508** 170w. multicoloured	70	40

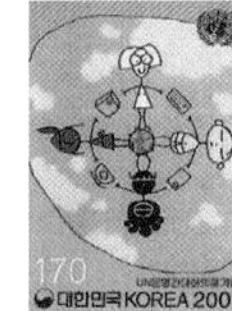

1509 Children encircling Globe

2001. United Nations Year of Dialogue among Civilisations.

2525	**1509** 170w. multicoloured	70	40

1510 Conference Emblem

2001. International Organisation of Supreme Audit Institutions (INTOSAI) Conference, Seoul.

2526	**1510** 170w. ultramarine and vermilion	70	40

1511 *Dendrobium moniliforme*

2001. Orchids (1st series). Multicoloured.

2527	170w. Type **1511**	80	40
2528	170w. *Gymnadenia camtschatica*	80	40
2529	170w. *Habenaria radiate*	80	40
2530	170w. *Orchis cyclochila*	80	40

Nos. 2527/2530 are impregnated with the scent of orchid.

See also Nos. 2670/2673; 2727/2730, 2789/2792 and 2836/2839.

1512 Snowflakes and Horse

2001. Lunar New Year. Year of the Horse.

2531	**1512** 170w. multicoloured	70	40
MS2532	90×60 mm. No. 2531×2	1·80	1·60

1513 Seonjeongjeon Conference Hall, Changdeokgung Palace

2001. World Heritage Sites (5th series). Multicoloured.

2533	170w. Type **1513**	1·00	40
2534	340w. Injeongjeon coronation hall, Changdeokgung Palace (52×36 mm)	2·00	80
MS2535	144×96 mm. Nos. 2533/2534	3·75	1·50

1514 *Limenitis populi*

2002. Fauna.

2536	60w. *Eophona migratoria*	80	40
2546	160w. Type **1514**	80	40
2547	210w. *Falco tinnunculus*	1·10	40
2548	280w. *Ficedula zanthopygia*	1·50	50

1515 Aeroplane, Locomotive and Lorry

2002. Transport.

2550	**1515** 280w. multicoloured	1·50	50
2551	**1515** 310w. multicoloured	1·60	55
2551a	**1515** 420w. multicoloured	1·40	95
2552	**1515** 1380w. multicoloured	4·50	2·50
2553	**1515** 1410w. multicoloured	4·75	2·75
2554	**1515** 1580w. multicoloured	5·00	4·00
2555	**1515** 1610w. multicoloured	5·00	4·00

1516 Kylin Roof Tile

2002. Roof Tiles. Multicoloured.

2565	1290w. Type **1516**	4·00	2·50
2566	1310w. Ridge-end tile	4·50	2·75
2567	1490w. As No. 2566 background colour altered	4·50	3·50
2568	1510w. As No. 2565 background colour altered	4·50	3·50

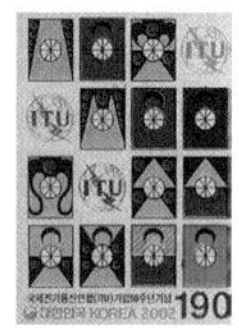

1518 Chungmu (signalling) Kites

2002. 50th Anniversary of Membership of International Telecommunications Union.

2584	**1518** 190w. multicoloured	80	40

1519 EL8000 Electric Locomotive

1520 EL8100 Electric Locomotive

1521 Express Rail Car

1522 Express Electric Rail Car

2002. Railways (3rd series).

2585	**1519** 190w. multicoloured	80	40
2586	**1520** 190w. multicoloured	80	40
2587	**1521** 190w. multicoloured	80	40
2588	**1522** 190w. multicoloured	80	40

1523 Safflower (*Carthamus tinctorius*)

2002. Traditional Dye Plants (1st series). Multicoloured.

2589	190w. Type **1523**	80	40
2590	190w. *Lithospermum erythrorhizon*	80	40
2591	190w. Ash tree (*Fraxinus rhynchophylla*)	80	40
2592	190w. Indigo plant (*Persicaria tinctoria*)	80	40

See also Nos. 2686/2689, 2745/2748 and 2801/2804.

1524 Flowers

2002. International Flower Exhibition, Anmyeondo.

2593	**1524** 190w. multicoloured	50	40

1525 *Mengkkong-i-Seodang Village School* (Yoon Seung-woon)

1526 *Wogdoggle Dugdoggle* (Hwang Mi-na)

2002. Cartoons (8th series).

2594	**1525**	190w. multicoloured	80	40
2595	**1526**	190w. multicoloured	80	40

MS2596 Two sheets, each 90×60 mm. (a) No. 2594; (b) No. 2595. Set of 2 sheets 2·40 2·10

1527 Campervan, Caravan and Tent

2002. 64th International Camping and Caravanning Rally.

2597	**1527**	190w. multicoloured	80	40

1528 Footballer (Europe)

2002. World Cup Football Championship, Japan and South Korea. Six sheets, each 60×90 mm containing T **1528**×2; Type **1528**×2; and similar circular designs. Multicoloured.

MS2598 (a) 190w.×2, Type **1528**×2; (b) 190w.×2, Central & North America×2; (c) 190w.×2, Asia×2; (d) 190w.×2, South America×2; (e) 190w.×2, Africa×2; (f) 170×240 mm. As Nos. **MS**2598a/e 20·00 20·00

1529 Jeolpyeon

1530 Sirutteok

1531 Injeolmi

1532 Songpyeon

2002. Korean Foods (2nd series).

2599	**1529**	190w. multicoloured	80	40
2600	**1530**	190w. multicoloured	80	40
2601	**1531**	190w. multicoloured	80	40
2602	**1532**	190w. multicoloured	80	40

1533 Woman's Face

2002. Women's Week.

2603	**1533**	190w. multicoloured	80	40

1534 Child holding Flags

2002. Philakorea 2002 International Stamp Exhibition, Seoul (2nd issue). Multicoloured.

2604	190w. Type **1534**	80	40
2605	190w. Children and globe	80	40

MS2606 Two sheets, each 115×73 mm. (a) No. 2604×2; (b) No. 2605. Set of 2 sheets 4·00 3·75

1535 Heung-injimun Fortress, Seoul

2002. Hometowns. Multicoloured.

2607	190w. Type **1535**	90	40
2608	190w. Two masked dancers, Seou	90	40
2609	190w. Basalt cliffs, Incheon	90	40
2610	190w. Dancers wearing white, Chamseongdan altar, Incheon	90	40
2611	190w. Freedom House, Paju, Gyeonggi	90	40
2612	190w. Yangjubyeol Sandaenori dancers one with raised arm, Gyeonggi	90	40
2613	190w. Ulsanbawi rock, Mt. Seoraksan, Gangwon	90	40
2614	190w. Two dancers one holding fan, Gangwon	90	40
2615	190w. Sail boat, Chungnam	90	40
2616	190w. Weaver, Chungnam	90	40
2617	190w. Tower, Expo Science Park, Daejeon	90	40
2618	190w. Scientist, Daedeok Science Town, Daejeon	90	40
2619	190w. Mt. Mai peaks, Jeonbuk	90	40
2620	190w. Iri folk band drummers, Jeonbuk	90	40
2621	190w. Odong island, Jeonnam	90	40
2622	190w. Ganggang Sullae circle dance, Jeonnam	90	40
2623	190w. May 18th monument, Gwangju	90	40
2624	190w. Gossaum Nori tug of war, Gwangju	90	40
2625	190w. Beopju temple, Mt. Songni, Chungbuk	90	40
2626	190w. Taekgyeon martial art, Chungbuk	90	40
2627	190w. Gwangbong Seokjoyeorae statue, Daegu	90	40
2628	190w. Dalseong forest, Daegu	90	40
2629	190w. Taejeondae cliffs, Busan	90	40
2630	190w. Three Dongnaeyaryu festival dancers, Busan	90	40
2631	190w. Dokdo islands, Gyeongbuk	90	40
2632	190w. Andongchajeon Nori log tying game, Gyeongbuk	90	40
2633	190w. Haegeumgang island, Gyeongnam	90	40
2634	190w. Goseong Ogwangdae clown dance, Gyeongnam	90	40
2635	190w. Cheonjeonnigakseok rock wall, Ulsan	90	40
2636	190w. Three Cheoyongmu masked dancers, Ulsan	90	40
2637	190w. Mt. Halla and Baeknokdam crater, Jeju	90	40
2638	190w. House, Jeju	90	40

1536 Exhibition Emblem and Talchum Masked Dancer

2002. Philakorea 2002 International Stamp Exhibition, Seoul (3rd issue).

2639	**1536**	190w. multicoloured	80	40

MS2640 90×60 mm. No. 2639×2. Imperf 2·00 1·50

1537 Children and Dog

2002. Philately Week.

2641	**1537**	190w. multicoloured	80	40

MS2642 108×69 mm. Nos. 2641×2 2·00 1·60

1538 Guus Hiddink (coach)

2002. South Korea. Semi-Finalists, World Cup Football Championship, Japan and South Korea. Showing team members. Multicoloured.

2643	190w. Type **1538**	90	40
2644	190w. No. 1 player	90	40
2645	190w. No. 2	90	40
2646	190w. No. 3	90	40
2647	190w. No. 4	90	40
2648	190w. No. 5	90	40
2649	190w. No. 6	90	40
2650	190w. No. 7	90	40
2651	190w. No. 8	90	40
2652	190w. No. 9	90	40
2653	190w. No. 10	90	40
2654	190w. No. 11	90	40
2655	190w. Goalkeeper	90	40
2656	190w. No. 13	90	40
2657	190w. No. 14	90	40
2658	190w. No. 15	90	40
2659	190w. No. 16	90	40
2660	190w. No. 17	90	40
2661	190w. No. 18	90	40
2662	190w. No. 19	90	40
2663	190w. No. 20	90	40
2664	190w. No. 21	90	40
2665	190w. No. 22	90	40
2666	190w. Goalkeeper (different)	90	40

1539 Stadium, Runner, Tower, Seagull and Diver

2002. 14th Asian Games, Busan.

2667	**1539**	190w. multicoloured	80	40

MS2668 120×70 mm. No. 2667×2 2·00 1·80

1540 Stylised Torch

2002. Eighth Far East and South Pacific Games for the Disabled (FESPIC), Busan.

2669	**1540**	190w. multicoloured	80	40

1541 *Cymbidium kanran*

2002. Orchids (2nd series). Multicoloured.

2670	190w. Type **1541**	80	40
2671	190w. *Gastrodia elata*	80	40
2672	190w. *Pogonia japonica*	80	40
2673	190w. *Cephalanthera falcate*	80	40

Each stamp impregnated with the scent of orchid.

1542 Taekwondo

2002. Tenth Anniversary of South Korea–China Diplomatic Relations. Martial Arts. Multicoloured.

2674	190w. Type **1542**	80	40
2675	190w. Wushu	80	40

1543 Sheep

2002. Lunar New Year. Year of the Sheep.

2676	**1543**	190w. multicoloured	80	40

MS2677 90×60 mm. No. 2676×2 1·80 1·60

1544 Gongsimdon Observatory Tower

2002. Hwaseong Fortress. UNESCO World Heritage Site. Sheet 145×232 mm containing T **1544** and similar horiz design. Multicoloured.

MS2678 190w.×5 Type **1544**; 280w. Banghwasuryu Pavilion (52×36 mm) 10·00 9·75

1545 Dabo Pagoda, Bulguk Temple, Gyeongju

2002. Tenth Anniversary of South Korea–Vietnam Diplomatic Relations. Multicoloured.

2679	190w. Type **1545**	80	40
2680	190w. One Pillar Pagoda, Hanoi	80	40

1546 American and Korean Flags Combined

2003. Centenary of Korean Emigration to United States of America.

2681	**1546**	190w. multicoloured	80	40

1547 Gondola Freight Car

1548 Box Car

1549 Tanker

1550 Hopper

2003. Railways (4th series).

2682	**1547**	190w. multicoloured	80	40

2683	**1548**	190w. multicoloured	80	40
2684	**1549**	190w. multicoloured	80	40
2685	**1550**	190w. multicoloured	80	40

1551 *Rubia akane*

2003. Traditional Dye Plants (2nd series). Multicoloured.

2686	190w. Type **1551**	80	40
2687	190w. *Rhus javanica*	80	40
2688	190w. *Sophora japonica*	80	40
2689	190w. *Isatis tinctoria*	80	40

1552 Roh Moo Hyun

2003. Inauguration of President Roh Moo Hyun. Sheet 115×70 mm.

2689a	**1522**	190w. multicoloured	80	40
MS2690	**1522**	190w. multicoloured	2·00	1·80

1553 Flag

2003

2691	**1553**	10w. multicoloured	20	10

1554 Unhye (embroidered shoes)

2003. Traditional Culture (1st issue). Each chocolate, brown and indigo.

2692	190w. Type **1554**	80	40
2693	190w. Mokhwa (ankle boots)	80	40
2694	190w. Jipsin (straw shoes)	80	40
2695	190w. Namaksin (wooden clogs)	80	40

See also Nos. 2700/2703, 2712/2715; 2720/2723; 2762/2765 and 2771/2774.

1555 Tortoise-shaped Celadon Jug

2003

2696	**1555**	400w. multicoloured	1·20	95

1556 *Goblin's Cap* (Shin Moon Soo)

1557 *Sword of Fire* (Kim Hye Rin)

2003. Cartoons (9th series).

2697	**1556**	190w. multicoloured	80	40
2698	**1557**	190w. multicoloured	80	40

MS2699 Two sheets, each 90×60 mm. (a) No. 2697; (b) No. 2698 Set of 2 sheets 3·00 2·75

2003. Traditional Culture (2nd issue). As T **1554**. Each black and brown.

2700	190w. Eoyeon (royal sedan chair)	80	40
2701	190w. Choheon (single-wheeled sedan chair)	80	40
2702	190w. Saingyo (wedding sedan chair)	80	40
2703	190w. Namyeo (small open sedan chair)	80	40

Nos. 2700/2703 were issued in horizontal *se-tenant* strips of four stamps within the sheet.

1558 Palmido Lighthouse

2003. Centenary of Lighthouse Building.

2704	**1558**	190w. multicoloured	80	40

1559 Yugwa

1560 Yeot Gangjeong

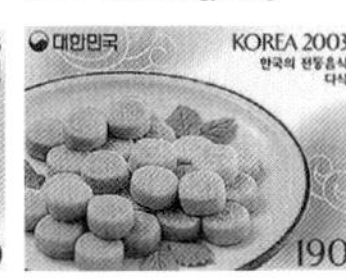

1561 Yakgwa

1562 Dasik

2003. Korean Foods (3rd series).

2705	**1559**	190w. multicoloured	80	40
2706	**1560**	190w. multicoloured	80	40
2707	**1561**	190w. multicoloured	80	40
2708	**1562**	190w. multicoloured	80	40

1563 *Malus asiatica*

2003. Fruit and Flower. Multicoloured. Self-adhesive.

2709	190w. Type **1563**	1·00	40
2710	190w. *Aquilegia flabellate* (horiz)	1·00	40

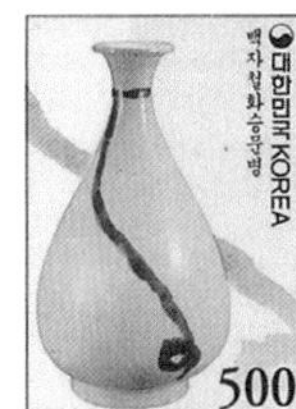

1564 Porcelain Vase

2003

2711	**1564**	500w. multicoloured	1·60	1·10

2003. Traditional Culture (3rd issue). As T **1554**. Each agate and chocolate.

2712	190w. Jojokdeung lantern	80	40
2713	190w. Deungjan (lamp-oil container)	80	40
2714	190w. Juchilmokje yukgakjedeung (hexagonal portable lantern)	80	40
2715	190w. Chot-dae (brass candlestick)	80	40

1565 Origami figure (Expression of Gratitude)

2003. Philately Week.

2716	**1565**	190w. multicoloured	80	40

MS2717 109×69 mm. Nos. 2716×2 Imperf 2·00 1·80

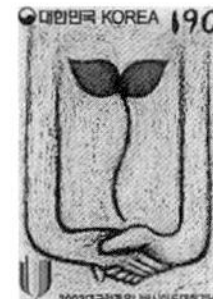

1566 Leaves and Clasped Hands

2003. Summer Universiade (games), Daegu.

2718	**1566**	190w. multicoloured	80	40
MS2719		91×60 mm. Nos. 2718×2	1·80	1·60

2003. Traditional Culture (4th issue). As T **1554**. Each indigo and claret.

2720	190w. Gujok-ban (table with decorated top)	80	40
2721	190w. Punghyeol-ban (tray table)	80	40
2722	190w. Ilju-ban (single stemmed table)	80	40
2723	190w. Haeju-ban (straight-sided table)	80	40

1567 Faces

2003. Centenary of Korean YMCA (Young Men's Christian Association) Movement.

2724	**1567**	190w. multicoloured	80	40

1568 Stylised Teacher and Pupil

2003. Centenary of Soong Eui Girl's School.

2725	**1568**	190w. multicoloured	80	40

1569 Hearts as TB Symbol

2003. 50th Anniversary of National Tuberculosis Association.

2726	**1569**	190w. vermilion, ultramarine and grey	80	40

1570 *Cremastra appendiculata*

2003. Orchids (3rd series). Multicoloured.

2727	190w. Type **1570**	80	40
2728	190w. *Cymbidium lancifolium*	80	40
2729	190w. *Orchis graminifolia*	80	40
2730	190w. *Bulbophyllum drymoglossum*	80	40

Each stamp is impregnated with the scent of orchid.

1571 Monkey

2003. Lunar New Year. Year of the Monkey.

2731	**1571**	190w. multicoloured	80	40
MS2732		90×60 mm. No. 2731×2	1·80	1·60

1572 Dolmen, Ganghwa

2003. Ganghwa, Hwasoon and Gochang. UNESCO World Heritage Sites. Sheet 145×232 mm containing T **1572** and similar horiz design. Multicoloured.

MS2733 190w.×5 Type **1572**; 280w.×5 Dolmen (52×36 mm) 10·00 9·75

1573 Cheomseongdae, Gyeongju

2003. 30th Anniversary of South Korea–India Diplomatic Relations. Observatories. Multicoloured.

2734	190w. Type **1573**	80	40
2735	190w. Jantar Mantar, Jaipur	80	40

1574 *Calystegia soldanella*

2004. Dokdo Island. Multicoloured.

2736	190w. Type **1574**	60	40
2737	190w. *Aster spathulifolius*	60	40
2738	190w. *Calonectris leucomelas* (inscr 'laucomelas')	60	40
2739	190w. *Larus crassirostris*	60	40

Nos. 2736/2739 were issued together, *se-tenant*, forming a composite design.

1575 Emblems

2004. 50th Anniversary of National UNESCO Commission.

2740	**1575**	190w. multicoloured	60	40

1576 Multiple Tie Tamper

1577 Ballast Regulator

1578 Track Inspection Car

1579 Ballast Cleaner

2004. Railways (5th series).

2741	**1576**	190w. multicoloured	60	40
2742	**1577**	190w. multicoloured	60	40
2743	**1578**	190w. multicoloured	60	40
2744	**1579**	190w. multicoloured	60	40

1580 *Juglans regia*

2004. Traditional Dye Plants (3rd series). Multicoloured.

2745	190w. Type **1580**	60	40
2746	190w. *Acer ginnala*	60	40
2747	190w. *Pinus densiflora*	60	40
2748	190w. *Punica granatum*	60	40

1581 Heart enclosing Water Droplet

2004. International Water Day.

2749	**1581**	190w. multicoloured	60	40

1582 Satellite, Dish and Weather Symbols

2004. Centenary of Meteorological Service.

2750	**1582**	190w. multicoloured	60	40

1583 Locomotive

2004. Inauguration of High Speed Trains.

2751	**1583**	190w. multicoloured	60	40

1584 *Space Exploration* (Radhika Kakrania)

2004. Science Day. Winning Entries in International Stamp Design Competition. Multicoloured.

2752	190w. Type **1584**	60	40
2753	190w. *Mysteries of Life* (Kim dong-min) (vert)	60	40

1585 *Wicked Boy Simsultong* (Lee Jeong-moon)

1586 *Nation of Winds* (Kim Jin)

2004. Cartoons (10th series).

2754	**1585**	190w. multicoloured	60	40
2755	**1586**	190w. multicoloured	60	40

MS2756 Two sheets, each 90×60 mm. (a) No. 2754; (b) No. 2755 1·20 1·10

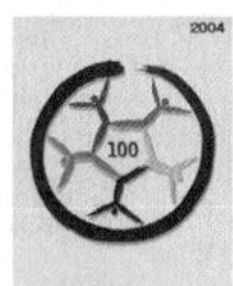
1587 Emblem

2004. Centenary of FIFA (Federation Internationale de Football).

2757	**1587**	190w. multicoloured	60	40

1588 Gujeolpan

1589 Hwayangjeok

1590 Bibimbap

1591 Sinsello

2004. Korean Foods (4th series).

2758	**1588**	190w. multicoloured	60	40
2759	**1589**	190w. multicoloured	60	40
2760	**1590**	190w. multicoloured	60	40
2761	**1591**	190w. multicoloured	60	40

2004. Traditional Culture (5th issue). As T **1554**. Each purple and green.

2762	190w. Work box	60	40
2763	190w. Thimble	60	40
2764	190w. Bobbin	60	40
2765	190w. Needle case	60	40

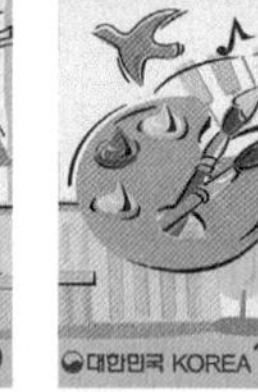
1592 Symbols of Science

1593 Symbols of Art

2004. 50th Anniversary of National Academies of Science and Art.

2766	**1592**	190w. multicoloured	60	40
2767	**1593**	190w. multicoloured	60	40

Nos. 2766/2767 were issued together, *se-tenant*, forming a composite design.

1594 Animals Celebrating

2004. Philately Week.

2768	**1594**	190w. multicoloured	60	40

MS2769 109×69 mm. Nos. 2768×2 1·00 95

1595 Acropolis

2004. Olympic Games, Athens.

2770	**1595**	190w. multicoloured	60	40

2004. Traditional Culture (6th issue). As T **1554**. Each maroon and blue.

2771	190w. Golden crown	60	40
2772	190w. Bamboo hat	60	40
2773	190w. Gauze hat	60	40
2774	190w. Horsehair hat	60	40

1596 Geumcheongyo Bridge

1596a Jeongotgyo

1596b Jincheon Nongdari

1596c Seungseongyo

2004. Bridges (1st series).

2775	**1596**	190w. multicoloured	60	40
2776	**1596a**	190w. multicoloured	60	40
2777	**1596b**	190w. multicoloured	60	40
2778	**1596c**	190w. multicoloured	60	40

See also Nos. 2826/2829, 2875/2878 and 2947/2950.

1597 Emblem

2004. International Council of Museums (ICOM) Conference, Seoul.

2779	**1597**	190w. multicoloured	60	40

1598 Obaegnahan Mountain

1598a Seonjakjiwat

1598b Baengnokdam

1598c Oreum

2004. Mountains (1st series).

2780	**1598**	190w. multicoloured	60	40
2781	**1598a**	190w. multicoloured	60	40
2782	**1598b**	190w. multicoloured	60	40
2783	**1598c**	190w. multicoloured	60	40

See also Nos. 2830/2833, 2895/2898, 2952/2955 and 3011/3014.

1599 White Hibiscus

2004. *Hibiscus syriacus.*

2784	190w. Type **1599**	50	40
2785	220w. Three white blooms and two buds	60	50
2786	240w. Red hibiscus	65	50
2787	310w. Five red blooms	80	65

1600 White Porcelain with Iron-painted Plum and Bamboo Design

2004

2788	**1600**	1520w. multicoloured	5·50	4·50

1601 *Goodyera maximowicziana*

2004. Orchids (4th series). Multicoloured.

2789	190w. Type **1601**	60	50
2790	190w. *Sarcanthus scolpendrifolius*	60	50
2791	190w. *Calanthe sieboldii*	60	50
2792	190w. *Bletilla striata*	60	50

Nos. 2789/2792 are impregnated with the scent of orchid.

1602 Hen and Chicks

2004. Lunar New Year. Year of the Rooster. Multicoloured.

MS2793 90×60 mm. 220w.×2, Type **1602**×2 1·20 1·00

1603 Daeneungwon Tumuli Park

2004. Gyenongju. UNESCO World Heritage Site. Sheet 145×232 mm containing T **1603** and similar horiz design. Multicoloured.

MS2794 310w.×10 Type **1603**×5; Anapjix5 (each, 52×36 mm) 8·00 7·25

1604 *Girella punctata*

2005. Marado Island. Multicoloured.

2795	190w. Type **1604**	60	50
2796	190w. *Epinephelus septemfasciatus*	60	50
2797	190w. *Chromis notata*	60	50
2798	190w. *Sebastiscus marmoratus*	60	50

Nos. 2795/2796 were issued together, *se-tenant*, forming composite design.

1605 Cells and Wheelchair User

2005. Stem Cell Research.

2799	**1605**	220w. multicoloured	70	50

1606 Emblem, Heart and Flying Figure

2005. Centenary of Rotary International.

2800	**1606**	220w. multicoloured	70	50

1607 *Clerodendron trichotomum*

2005. Traditional Dye Plants (4th series). Multicoloured.

2801	220w. Type **1607**	70	50
2802	220w. *Gardenia jasminoides*	70	50
2803	220w. *Taxus cuspidate*	70	50
2804	220w. *Smilax china*	70	50

1608 Vase, Mask and Dove

2005. Tourism. Visit Gyeonggi.

2805	**1608**	220w. multicoloured	70	50

1609 Children

2005. 50th Anniversary of Information and Communication Day. Multicoloured.

2806	220w. Type **1609**	70	50
2807	220w. Boy, computer screen and sheep (vert)	70	50

1610 Inchon Memorial Hall

2005. Centenary of Korea University.

2808	**1610**	220w. agate, silver and magenta	70	50

1611 *Eschrichtius robustus*

2005. International Whaling Commission Meeting, Ulsan.

2809	**1611**	220w. multicolourd	70	50

1612 Hwajeon (pan-fried rice with flower petals)

1613 Bindaetteok (pan-fried ground mung beans)

1614 Jeongol (casserole)

1615 Neobani (boiled beef)

2005. Korean Foods (5th series).

2810	**1612**	220w. multicoloured	70	50
2811	**1613**	220w. multicoloured	70	50
2812	**1614**	220w. multicoloured	70	50
2813	**1615**	220w. multicoloured	70	50

1616 Ancient Sword and Armoured Mounted Soldier

2005. Goguryeo (1st issue). Multicoloured.

2814	310w. Type **1616**	80	65
2815	310w. Oneyo fortress	80	65

See also Nos. 2869/2870 and 2936/2937.

1617 Girl icing Birthday Cake

2005. Philately Week.

2817	**1617**	220w. multicoloured	70	50

1618 Buncheong Jar

2005

2818	**1618**	1720w. multicoloured	6·00	5·75

1619 Provisional Government Building and Charter

2005. 60th Anniversary of Liberation. Multicoloured.

2819	480w. Type **1619**	1·00	80
2820	520w. Declaration of Independence	1·20	95
2821	580w. Freedom fighters taking oath of allegiance	1·40	1·10
2822	600w. Anniversary emblem	1·50	1·20

1620 Colours and Hand holding Cutlery

2005. Fusion Culture.

2824	**1620**	220w. multicoloured	70	50

1621 *Strix aluco*

2005

2825	**1621**	50w. multicoloured	50	40

1622 Hangang Bridge

1623 Expogyo Bridge

1624 Tongyeong Bridge

1625 Banghwa Bridge

2005. Bridges (2nd series).

2826	**1622**	220w. multicoloured	80	65
2827	**1623**	220w. multicoloured	80	65
2828	**1624**	220w. multicoloured	80	65
2829	**1625**	220w. multicoloured	80	65

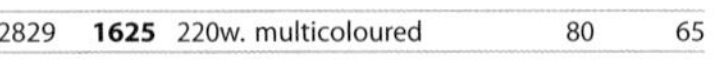

1626 Cheonwangbong Peak **1627** Baraebong Peak

1628 Ikki Falls

1629 Piagol Valley

2005. Mountains (2nd series). Mount Jirisan.

2830	**1626**	220w. multicoloured	80	65
2831	**1627**	220w. multicoloured	80	65
2832	**1628**	220w. multicoloured	80	65
2833	**1629**	220w. multicoloured	80	65

1630 Emblem

2005. Centenary of Korean Red Cross.

2834	**1630**	220w. multicoloured	80	65

1631 Buddha

2005. Relocation and Reopening of National Museum.

2835	**1631**	220w. multicoloured	80	65

1632 *Epipactis thunbergii*

2005. Orchids (5th series). Multicoloured.

2836	220w. Type **1632**	80	65
2837	220w. *Cymbidium goeringii*	80	65
2838	220w. *Cephalanthera erecta*	80	65
2839	220w. *Spiranthes sinensis*	80	65

1633 Nurimaru APEC House, Dongbaek Island

2005. APEC Economic Leaders' Meeting, Busan. Multicoloured.

2840	220w. Type **1633**	80	65
2841	220w. *The Sun, the Moon and Five Peaks* (traditional painting)	80	65

1634 Puppy

2005. Lunar New Year. Year of the Dog.

2842	**1634**	220w. multicoloured	80	65

1635 *Jikjisimcheyojeol* (oldest book created using moveable type)

2005. Registration of Korean Cultural Treasures as UNESCO World Heritage. Sheet 145×232 mm containing T **1635** and similar horiz design. Multicoloured.

MS2843	310w.×10, Type **1635**×5; *Seungjeongwon Ilgi* (Diaries of the Royal Secretariat)×5 (52×36 mm)	8·00	7·75

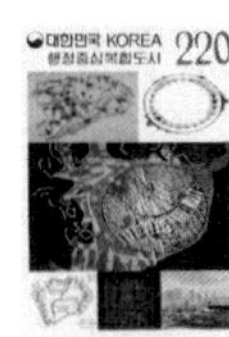

1636 Plans and Design Layout

2005. Construction of Multifunctional Administrative City, Chungcheong.

2844	**1636**	220w. multicoloured	80	65

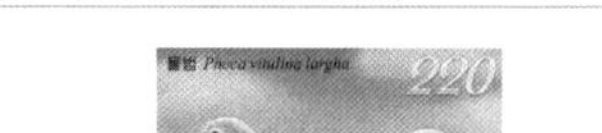

1637 *Phoca vitulina largha*

2006. Baengnyeongdo Island. Multicoloured.

2845	220w. Type **1637**	80	65
2846	220w. *Phalacrocorax pelagicus*	80	65
2847	220w. *Orithyia sinica*	80	65
2848	220w. *Ammodytes personatus*	80	65

Nos. 2845/2848 were issued in sheets with enlarged illustrated margins, the whole forming a composite design of the island.

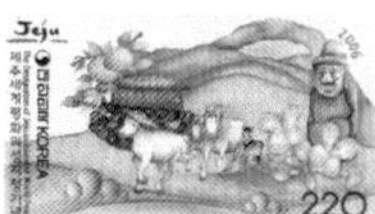

1638 Fruit, Horses, Flowers and Stone Grandfather

2006. First Anniversary of Jeju as Designated Island of World Peace.

2849	**1638**	220w. multicoloured	80	65

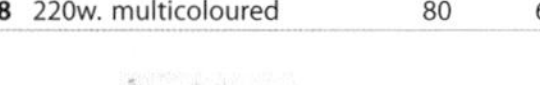

1639 *Crinum asiaticum*

2006

2850	**1639**	100w. multicoloured	80	65

1640 Car (automobile industries)

2006. Korean Industries. Multicoloured.

2851	220w. Type **1640**	80	65
2852	220w. Computer chips (semi-conductors)	80	65
2853	220w. Chemical symbols (petrochemical)	80	65
2854	220w. TV screen and mobile telephone (electronics)	80	65
2855	220w. Robotic arms (engineering)	80	65
2856	220w. Ships (ship building)	80	65
2857	220w. Rolls of steel (steel industry)	80	65
2858	220w. Fabric (textile industry)	80	65

1641 Rainbow, Children and Computer (Lee Annr Rulloda)

2006. Ubiquitous World (pervasive computing). Winning Designs in Children's Painting Competition. Multicoloured.

2859	220w. Type **1641**	80	65
2860	220w. Green IT (Kim Jeonghee) (horiz)	80	65

1642 Iguanodon

2006. Gyeongnam Goseong Dinosaurs World Expo. Multicoloured. Self-adhesive.

2861	220w. Type **1642**	80	65
2862	220w. Megaraptor	80	65

1643 Myeongjingwan Building

2006. Centenary of Dongguk University.

2863	**1643**	220w. multicoloured	80	65

1644 Second Foundation Campus

2006. Centenary of Sookmyung Women's University.

2864	**1644**	220w. multicoloured	80	65

No. 2865 and T **1645** are now vacant.

1646 *Parus major*

2006

2866	**1646**	90w. multicoloured	80	65

1647 Football, Emblem and Mascot

2006. World Cup Football Championship, Germany. Multicoloured.

2867	220w. Type **1647**	80	65
2868	220w. Players	80	65

2006. Goguryeo (2nd issue). As T **1616**. Multicoloured.

2869	480w. Janggunchong	1·50	1·20
2870	480w. Gods	1·50	1·20

1648 Fingerprints as Heart

2006. Philately Week. Marriage. Multicoloured.

2871	220w. Type **1648**	80	65
2872	220w. As No. 2871 but with country inscription and face value at top	80	65

1649 Tail Stole

2006. Extreme Sports (1st issue). Skateboarding. Sheet 75×106 mm containing T **1649** and similar vert designs. Multicoloured. Self-adhesive.

MS2873 220w.×4 Type **1649**; Drop in; Backside spin; Backside grab	3·50	3·25

The stamps of **MS**2873 form a composite background design.

See also Nos. 2942/2945 and 3003/3006.

1650 Ginseng Root

2006. World Ginseng Expo, Geumsan.

2874	**1650**	220w. multicoloured	80	65

1651 Olympic Bridge

1652 Seohae Bridge

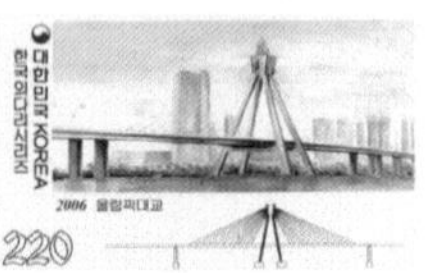
1653 Jindo Bridge

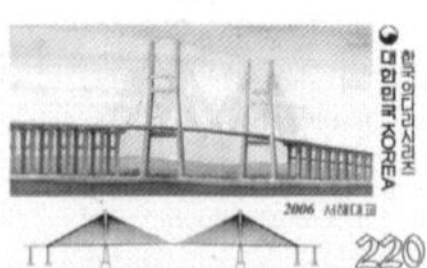
1654 Changseon-Samcheonpo Bridge

2006. Bridges (3rd series).

2875	**1651**	220w. multicoloured	80	65
2876	**1652**	220w. multicoloured	80	65
2877	**1653**	220w. multicoloured	80	65
2878	**1654**	220w. multicoloured	80	65

1655 Script

2006. 560th Anniversary of Hangeul (Korean script) Day.

2879	**1655**	220w. multicoloured	80	65

1656 Building Facade

2006. Centenary of Sahmyook University.

2880	**1656**	220w. multicoloured	80	65

1657 Flower

2006. My Own Stamp.

2881	**1657**	250w. multicoloured	1·00	80

1658 *Ninox scutulata*

2006

2882	**1658**	250w. multicoloured	1·00	80

1659 Swans

2006

2883	**1659**	340w. multicoloured	1·30	1·00

1660 Buncheong Ware Vase

2006

2884	**1660**	1750w. multicoloured	7·00	6·50

1661 *Lineage*

2006. Online Computer Games. Self adhesive.

2885	250w. Type **1661**	1·00	80
2886	250w. *Maple Story*	1·00	80
2887	250w. *Ragnarok*	1·00	80
2888	250w. *Gersang*	1·00	80
2889	250w. *Legend of Mir III*	1·00	80
2890	250w. *Kartrider*	1·00	80
2891	250w. *Mu*	1·00	80
2892	250w. *Pangya*	1·00	80
2893	250w. *Fortress 2 Blue*	1·00	80
2894	250w. *Mabinogi*	1·00	80

1662 Daecheongbong Peak

1663 Sibiseonnyeotang Valley

1664 Janggunbong Peak

1665 Ulsanbawi Rock

2006. Mountains (3rd series). Mount Seoraksan.

2895	**1662**	250w. multicoloured	1·00	80
2896	**1663**	250w. multicoloured	1·00	80
2897	**1664**	250w. multicoloured	1·00	80
2898	**1665**	250w. multicoloured	1·00	80

1666 Pig

2006. Lunar New Year. Year of the Pig.

2899	**1666**	250w. multicoloured	1·00	80

1667 Script, Singer and Drummer

2006. UNESCO Masterpiece of Oral and Intangible Heritage of Humanity. Pansori Songs and Singers. Multicoloured.

2900	480w. Type **1667**	2·00	1·60
2901	480w. Singer, musician and audience (51×35 mm)	2·00	1·60

1668 Faces and Hands holding Flowers (Kim Han-yun)

2006. Caring Neighbourhood and Donation Culture. Multicoloured.

2902	250w. Type **1668**	1·00	80
2903	250w. Man watering tree seedling	1·00	80

1669 Spring

1670 Summer

1671 Autumn

1672 Winter

2007. Rivers (1st issue). Nakdong River.

2904	**1669**	250w. multicoloured	1·10	90
2905	**1670**	250w. multicoloured	1·10	90
2906	**1671**	250w. multicoloured	1·10	90
2907	**1672**	250w. multicoloured	1·10	90

See also Nos. 2967/2970, 3026/3029 and 3107/3110.

1673 *Megatron/Matrix*

2007. First Death Anniversary of Nam June Paik (artist). Multicoloured.

2908	250w. Type **1673**	1·10	90
2909	250w. *TV Buddha*	1·10	90
2910	250w. *The More the Better*	1·10	90
2911	250w. *Oh-Mah (Mother)*	1·10	90

1674 Ring with National Flag

2007. Centenary of National Debt Repayment Movement.

2912	**1674**	250w. multicoloured	75	60

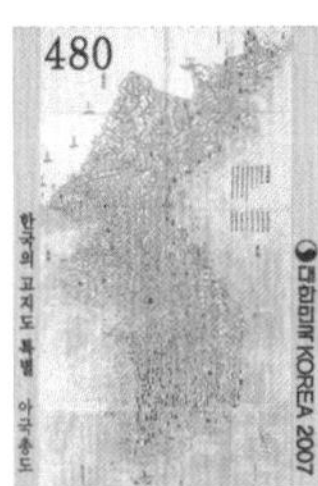
1675 Aguk Chong-do (map of Korea)

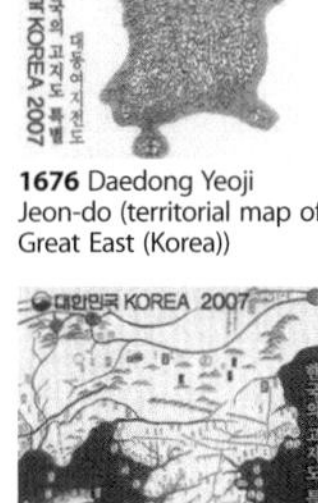
1676 Daedong Yeoji Jeon-do (territorial map of Great East (Korea))

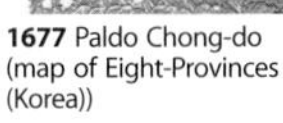
1677 Paldo Chong-do (map of Eight-Provinces (Korea))

1678 Honilgangni Yeokdae Gukdo-jido (early world map showing enlarged Korea)

2007. Ancient Maps. Multicoloured.

2913	**1675**	480w. multicoloured	2·00	1·60
2914	**1676**	520w. multicoloured	2·20	1·80
2915	**1677**	580w. multicoloured	2·30	1·90
2916	**1678**	600w. multicoloured	2·40	1·90

1679 Clock Tower

2007. Centenary of Daehan Hospital.

2917	**1679**	250w. multicoloured	1·10	90

1680 *Cypripedium agnicapitatum*

2007. Ninth Asia–Pacific Orchid Conference.

2918	**1680**	250w. multicoloured	1·10	90

1681 Chromosome

2007. Year of Biology.

2919	**1681**	250w. multicoloured	1·10	90

1682 Golden Piglet

2007. Personal Stamps (My Own Stamp). Multicoloured.

2920	250w. Type **1682**	1·10	90
2921	250w. Four-leaf clover	1·10	90
2922	250w. Sunflower	1·10	90

1683 Chinese Wedding Costume

2007. Wedding Costumes. Designs showing couples in wedding costumes. Multicoloured.

2923	250w. Type **1683**	1·10	90
2924	250w. Indian	1·10	90
2925	250w. Malay	1·10	90
2926	250w. Eurasian	1·10	90
2927	480w. Korean (sun, moon and five mountains backdrop)	2·00	1·60
2928	520w. Korean (peonies backdrop)	2·20	1·80
2929	580w. Korean (ducks and waterlily backdrop (bridegroom wearing dark blue robe))	2·30	1·90
2930	600w. Korean (mandarin ducks backdrop (bridegroom wearing pale blue robe))	2·40	1·90

1684 Sukjeonnmun Gate

2007. Opening of Fortress Wall, Mount Bugaksan, Seoul.

2931	**1684**	250w. multicoloured	1·10	90

1685 *The Internet Culture that Unites the World into One* (Choi Mi-Yeon) (Korea)

2007. Internet Culture. Ethics. Multicoloured.

2932	250w. Type **1685**	1·10	90
2933	250w. *The Internet Culture that Brightens Up the Future* (Daren Kaye C. Aquino) (Philippines)	1·10	90

1686 Child

2007. 50th Anniversary of National Children's Charter. Self-adhesive.

2934	**1686**	250w. multicoloured	1·10	90

1687 Lee Sang-sol, Lee Chun and Lee Wi-Jong

2007. Centenary of Special Envoys to Second Peace Conference, the Hague.

2935	**1687**	250w. multicoloured	1·10	90

2007. Goguryeo (3rd issue). As T **1616**. Multicoloured

2936	480w. Kitchen (mural, Anak Tomb No. 3, South Hwanghae Province, North Korea)	2·00	1·60
2937	480w. Host welcoming guest (mural, Muyong Tomb, Jian , China)	2·00	1·60

1688 *Arctous ruber*

2007

2938	**1688**	70w. multicoloured	55	45

1689 1884 5m. Stamp (As Type **1**)

2007. Philately Week. Multicoloured.

2939	250w. Type **1689**	1·10	90
2940	250w. 1884 10m. Stamp (As No. 2)	1·10	90
MS2941	140×70 mm. 250w.×2, Nos. 2917/2918	2·20	2·20

2007. Extreme Sports (2nd issue). Skateboarding. As T **1649**. Multicoloured. Self-adhesive.

2942	250w. Drop in	1·10	90
2943	250w. Flip	1·10	90
2944	250w. Spin	1·10	90
2945	250w. Grind	1·10	90

1690 Outline of Figure cradling Bird

2007. Centenary of Bar Association

2946	**1690**	250w. multicoloured	1·10	90

1691 Seongsan Bridge

1692 Yeongjong Bridge

1693 Gwangan Bridge

1694 Seongsu Bridge

2007. Bridges (4th issue).

2947	**1691**	250w. multicoloured	1·10	90
2948	**1692**	250w. multicoloured	1·10	90
2949	**1693**	250w. multicoloured	1·10	90
2950	**1694**	250w. multicoloured	1·10	90

1695 Dove

2007. Inter-Korean Summit, Pyongyang.

2951	**1695**	250w. multicoloured	1·10	90

1696 Hyeongje Falls

1697 Rimyeongsu Falls

1698 Lake Samjiyeon

1699 Lake Chonji

2007. Mountains (4th issue). Mount Baekdusan.

2952	**1696**	250w. multicoloured	1·10	90
2953	**1697**	250w. multicoloured	1·10	90
2954	**1698**	250w. multicoloured	1·10	90
2955	**1699**	250w. multicoloured	1·10	90

1700 *Arirang*

1701 *Looking for Love*

1702 *Ownerless Ferryboat*

1703 *Chunyangjeon*

2007. Korean Cinema (1st issue).

2956	**1700**	250w. multicoloured	1·10	90
2957	**1701**	250w. multicoloured	1·10	90
2958	**1702**	250w. multicoloured	1·10	90
2959	**1703**	250w. multicoloured	1·10	90

See also Nos. 3015/3018, 3075/3078 and 3128/3131.

1704 *Love for Eternity* (Roh Hye-rim (Korea))

2007. United Nations Convention on the Rights of the Child. Winning Designs in International Stamp Design Competition. Multicoloured.

2960	250w. Type **1704**	1·10	90
2961	250w. *Fathers Hands* (Robert Brun (Slovakia)) (horiz)	1·10	90

1705 Early and Modern Buildings

2007. Opening of New Central Post Office, Seoul. Multicoloured.

2962	250w. Type **1705**	1·10	90
2963	250w. New building (Post tower)	1·10	90

1706 Rat

2007. Chinese New Year. Year of the Rat.

2964	**1706**	250w. multicoloured	1·10	90

1707 Procession

2007. UNESCO Masterpiece of Oral and Intangible Heritage of Humanity. Gangneung Danoje Festival. Multicoloured.

2965 480w. Type **1707** 2·00 1·60
2966 480w. Masked players (51×35 mm) 2·00 1·60

1708 Spring

1709 Summer

1710 Autumn

1711 Winter

2008. Rivers (2nd issue). Seomjin River.

2967 **1708** 250w. multicoloured 1·10 90
2968 **1709** 250w. multicoloured 1·10 90
2969 **1710** 250w. multicoloured 1·10 90
2970 **1711** 250w. multicoloured 1·10 90

1712 Skidoos and Penguins

2008. King Sejong Antarctic Station. Multicoloured.

2971 250w. Type **1712** 1·10 90
2972 250w. Emperor penguins and station buildings 1·10 90

1713 Pres. Lee Myung Bak

2008. Inauguration of President Lee Myung Bak.

2973 **1713** 250w. multicoloured 1·10 90
MS2974 115×80 mm. 250w. As Type **1713** 1·10 1·10

1714 Mask

2008. African Savannah. Sheet 155×170 mm containing T **1714** and similar fan-shaped designs. Multicoloured. Self-adhesive.

MS2975 250w.×4, Type **1714**; Leopard; Elephant; Zebra 4·25 4·25

The stamps of **MS**2975 form a circular design enclosing a central circle showing a map of Africa.

1715 Buchaechum **1716** Salpurichum

1717 Seungmu **1718** Taepyeongmu

2008. PHILAKOREA 2009. Asian International Stamp Exhibition. Dance.

2976 **1715** 250w. multicoloured 1·10 90
2977 **1716** 250w. multicoloured 1·10 90
2978 **1717** 250w. multicoloured 1·10 90
2979 **1718** 250w. multicoloured 1·10 90
MS2979a 165×75 mm. Nos. 2976/2979 plus label 4·25 4·25

1719 *World in a Post Box* (Hamzah D. Marbella (Philippines))

2008. Mailbox of the Future. Winning designs in Children's Painting Competition. Multicoloured.

2980 250w. Type **1719** 1·10 90
2981 250w. *Spacecraft collecting and delivering post* (Lau Tsun Yin (Hong Kong)) 1·10 90

1720 *Mothers with Children/Mothers without Children* (Jazayeri Shirin (Iran))

2008. Nurturing Children. Winning Designs in International Stamp Design Competition. Multicoloured.

2982 250w. Type **1720** 1·10 90
2983 250w. *Mother and child* (Isaiah Otieno Nondoh (Kenya)) 1·10 90

1721 World Map and @

2008. OECD Ministerial Meeting on the Future of Internet Economy, Seoul.

2984 **1721** 250w. multicoloured 1·10 90

1722 Yun Bong-Gil

2008. Birth Centenary of Yun Bong-Gil (patriot).

2985 **1722** 250w. multicoloured 1·10 90

1723 *Euryale ferox*

2008. Self-adhesive.

2986 **1723** 250w. multicoloured 1·10 90

1724 Hwanung descending onto Siddansu on Taebaek Mountain

2008. Dangun Wanggeom (legend of founding of Korea). Multicoloured.

2987 250w. Type **1724** 1·10 90
2988 250w. Bear and tiger who desire to become human 1·10 90
2989 250w. Birth of Dangun Wanggeom 1·10 90
2990 250w. Dangun Wanggeom (founder of capital city) 1·10 90

1725 Plugs as Flowers (unplugging electronic equipment)

2008. Energy Conservation. Multicoloured.

2991 250w. Type **1725** 1·10 90
2992 250w. Thermometers (regulating temperature in the home) 1·10 90
2993 250w. Energy efficient products 1·10 90
2994 250w. Passenger straps growing leaves (using public transport) 1·10 90

1726 1902 3ch. Stamp (As Type **9**)

2008. Philately Week. Multicoloured.

2995 250w. Type **1726** 1·10 90
2996 250w. 1951 300w. on 14w. Stamp (As No. 149) 1·30 1·00
MS2997 140×70 mm. 250w.×2, Nos. 2995/2996 2·40 1·90

1727 Gymnast

2008. Olympic Games, Beijing.

2998 **1727** 250w. multicoloured 1·10 90

1728 '60'

2008. 60th Anniversary of Republic of Korea.

2999 **1728** 250w. multicoloured 1·10 90

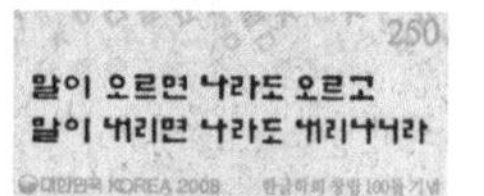
1729 *Hannara Mal* (Sigyeong Ju)

2008. Centenary of Korean Language Society.

3000 **1729** 250w. multicoloured 1·10 90

1730 Tap filling Glass

2008. Centenary of Seoul Waterworks.

3001 **1730** 250w. multicoloured 1·10 90

1731 Runner and Radio Waves

2008. 14th Amateur Radio Direction Finding (ARDF) Championships.

3002 **1731** 250w. multicoloured 1·10 90

2008. Extreme Sports (3rd issue). Snowboarding. As T **1649**. Multicoloured. Self-adhesive.

3003 250w. Carving turn 1·10 90
3004 250w. Indy grab 1·10 90
3005 250w. Nose grab 1·10 90
3006 250w. Air 1·10 90

1732 Charity Pot

2008. Centenary of Salvation Army in Korea.

3007 **1732** 250w. multicoloured 1·10 90

1733 '60th' Tag on Dove-shaped Chain

2008. 60th Anniversary of Armed Forces.

3008 **1733** 250w. multicoloured 1·10 90

1734 Grand Palace (Thailand)

2008. 50th Anniversary of Korea–Thailand Diplomatic Relations. Multicoloured.

3009 250w. Type **1734** 1·10 90
3010 250w. Changdeokgung Palace (Korea) 1·10 90

1735 Panorama

1736 Sangpaldam's Pools

1737 Manmulsang

1738 Gwimyeonam Rock

2008. Mountains (5th issue). Mount Geumgangsan.

3011 **1735** 250w. multicoloured 1·10 90
3012 **1736** 250w. multicoloured 1·10 90
3013 **1737** 250w. multicoloured 1·10 90
3014 **1738** 250w. multicoloured 1·10 90

1739 *A Coachman*

1739a *The Seashore Village*

1740 *Mother and a Guest*

1740a *The Wedding Day*

2008. Korean Cinema (2nd issue).

3015	**1739** 250w. multicoloured	1·10	90
3016	**1739a** 250w. multicoloured	1·10	90
3017	**1740** 250w. multicoloured	1·10	90
3018	**1740a** 250w. multicoloured	1·10	90

1741 Wetlands

2008. Tenth Meeting of Conference of the Contracting Parties to the Ramsar Convention on Wetlands

3019	**1741** 250w. multicoloured	1·10	90

1742 Big Head Buddha (Chinese Lion Dance)

2008. Masks. Multicoloured.

3020	250w. Type **1742**	1·10	90
3021	250w. Chwibari mask of Bongsan Mask Dance	1·10	90

Stamps of a similar design were issued by Hong Kong.

1743 Ox

2008. Chinese New Year. Year of the Ox.

3022	**1743** 250w. multicoloured	1·10	90

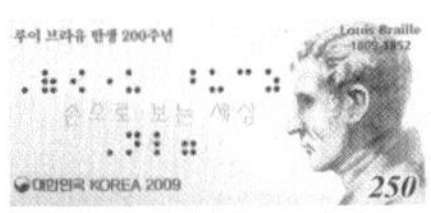
1744 Braille Script, Korean Script and Louis Braille

2009. Birth Bicentenary of Louis Braille (inventor of Braille writing for the blind).

3023	**1744** 250w. multicoloured	1·10	90

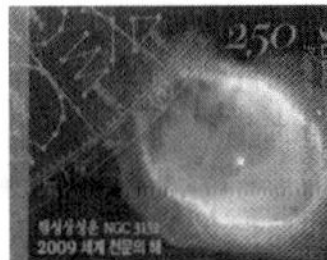
1745 Nebula NGC 3132

2009. International Year of Astronomy. Multicoloured.

3024	250w. Type **1745**	1·10	90
3025	250w. Whirlpool Galaxy M51	1·10	90

1746 Spring

1747 Summer

1748 Autumn

1749 Winter

2009. Rivers (3rd issue). Geum River.

3026	**1746** 250w. multicoloured	1·10	90
3027	**1747** 250w. multicoloured	1·10	90
3028	**1748** 250w. multicoloured	1·10	90
3029	**1749** 250w. multicoloured	1·10	90

1750 Hangawi Sonori (cow play), Korea

2009. 60th Anniversary of Philippines–South Korea Diplomatic Relations. Multicoloured.

3030	250w. Type **1750**	1·10	90
3031	250w. Panagbenga Flower Festival, Philippines	1·10	90

1751 Conifer, Cheonhwangsa Temple (Natural Monument No. 495)

1752 Zelkova Tree, Danjeon-ri (No. 478)

1753 Tree (called Seoksongnyeong), Cheonhyang (No. 294)

1754 Ginko Tree, Yongmunsa (No. 30)

2009. Ancient and Historic Trees of Korea.

3032	**1751** 250w. multicoloured	1·10	90
3033	**1752** 250w. multicoloured	1·10	90
3034	**1753** 250w. multicoloured	1·10	90
3035	**1754** 250w. multicoloured	1·10	90

1755 Tank, Ship and Helicopters

2009. 60th Anniversary of Marine Corps.

3036	**1755** 250w. multicoloured	1·10	90

1756 Envelopes and Post Box (Jaesong Yun)

2009. Asia becoming One Through Stamps. Winning Designs in Children's Design a Stamp Competition. Multicoloured.

3037	250w. Type **1756**	1·10	90
3038	250w. Envelope, flags in heart shape and children of many nations (Yu Hoi Dick Cherie) (vert)	1·10	90

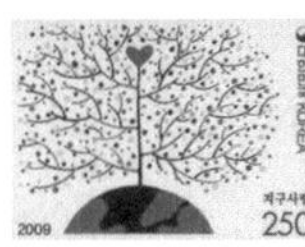
1757 Tree on Globe (Seo Hye Min)

2009. Love for the Earth. Winning Designs in Design a Stamp Competition. Multicoloured.

3039	250w. Type **1757**	1·10	90
3040	250w. Smiling globe (Cho Zaw Aung) (vert)	1·10	90

1757a Geumdongdaetap (gilt-bronze pagoda)

2009. Cultural Heritage.

3041	**1757a** 2000w. multicoloured	8·00	7·50

1758 *Mr. Gobau, Run Hany, Little Dino Dooly, Mengkkongi Village School* and *Robot Zzibba*

2009. Centenary of Korean Cartoons.

3042	**1758** 250w. multicoloured	1·10	90

1759 17th/19th-century Mongolian

2009. Earrings. Multicoloured.

3043	250w. Type **1759**	1·10	90
3044	250w. 1st/2nd-century BC Kazakhstan	1·10	90
3045	250w. 5th/6th-century Korean Earrings	1·10	90
MS3045a	87×137 mm. 250w.×3, Nos. 3043/3045	3·25	3·25

1760 Yongcheondonggul Lava Tube

2009. World Heritage Site. Jeju Volcanic Island. Multicoloured.

3046	250w. Type **1760**	1·10	90
3047	250w. Dangcheomuldonggul (52×36 mm)	1·10	90

1761 1900 3ch. Stamp (As No. 23A)

2009. Philately Week. Multicoloured.

3048	250w. Type **1761**	1·10	90
3049	250w. 1969 7w. Stamp (As No. 787)	1·10	90
MS3050	140×70 mm. 250w.×2, Nos. 3048/3049	4·25	4·25

1762 Cock Pheasant

2009. PHILAKOREA 2009. Asian International Stamp Exhibition, South Korea. Designs showing Yeongmohwa paintings. Multicoloured.

3051	250w. Type **1762**	1·10	90
3052	250w. Eagle leaning forward	1·10	90
3053	250w. Female duck	1·10	90
3054	250w. Crane with raised head	1·10	90
3055	250w. Hen pheasant	1·10	90
3056	250w. Eagle facing left	1·10	90
3057	250w. Male duck with head on back	1·10	90
3058	250w. Crane (different)	1·10	90

Nos. 3051 and 3055, 3052 and 3056, 3053 and 3057, 3054 and 3058, respectively, were printed together, *se-tenant*, forming composite designs.

1763 The God's Command moving Country's Capital

2009. Geumwawang of Buyeo Kingdom (from Samgukyusa (by Venerable Ilyeon)). Multicoloured.

3059	250w. Type **1763**	1·10	90
3060	250w. Horse riders (establishment of East Buyeo)	1·10	90
3061	250w. Birth of King Geumwawang	1·10	90
3062	250w. King Geumwawang's enthronement	1·10	90

Nos. 3059/3060 and 3061/3062 were printed, *se-tenant*, forming a composite design.

1764 House with Solar Thermal Roof Panels

2009. Green Energy. Multicoloured.

3063	250w. Type **1764**	1·10	90
3064	250w. Car with photo voltaic panels	1·10	90
3065	250w. Wind turbines	1·10	90
3066	250w. Tidal power generator	1·10	90

Nos. 3067/3073 and T **1765**/176**6** are vacant.

1767 World Map and Graph

2009. OECD World Forum, Busan, Korea.

3074	**1767** 250w. multicoloured	1·20	90

1768 *A Road to Sampo*

1769 *Never Never Forget Me*

1770 *Yalkae, A Joker In High School*

1771 *Chilsu and Mansu*

2009. Korean Cinema (3rd issue).

3075	**1768**	250w. multicoloured	1·20	90
3076	**1769**	250w. multicoloured	1·20	90
3077	**1770**	250w. multicoloured	1·20	90
3078	**1771**	250w. multicoloured	1·20	90

1772 ncheon Bridge, South Korea

1773 Octávio Frias de Oliveira bridge, Brazil

2009. Brazil–South Korea Diplomatic Relations.

3079	**1772**	250w. multicoloured	1·20	90
3080	**1773**	250w. multicoloured	1·20	90

Stamps of a similar design were issued by Brazil.

1773a Celadon Vase

2009. Cultural Heritage. Celadon Incense Burner.

3080*a*	**1773a**	1000w. multicoloured	4·00	3·75

1774 Tiger

2009. Chinese New Year. Year of the Tiger.

3081	**1774**	250w. multicoloured	1·20	90

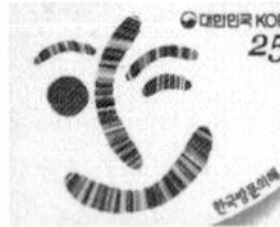

1775 Taegeukmaji (Jaekuk Jung)

1776 Saekdongeolgul (Yongsoon Na)

2010. Visit Korea.

3082	**1775**	250w. multicoloured	1·20	90
3083	**1776**	250w. multicoloured	1·20	90

1777 Figure Skating

2010. Winter Olympic Games, Vancouver. Multicoloured.

3084	250w. Type **1777**	1·20	90
3085	250w. Speed skating	1·20	90

1778 Malayan Tiger (*Panthera tigris jacksoni*)

2010. 50th Anniversary of Korea–Malaysia Diplomatic Relations. Multicoloured.

3086	250w. Type **1778**	1·20	90
3087	250w. Korean tiger (*Panthera tigris altaica*)	1·20	90

Stamps of a similar design were issued by Malaysia.

1779 Ahn Jung-geun, Script written on Stylised Taegeukgi (National Flag)

2010. Death Centenary of Ahn Jung-geun (independence activist, nationalist, and pan-Asianist). Multicoloured.

3088	250w. Type **1779**	1·20	90
3089	250w. Ahn Jung-geun's hand print with script inscribed on missing ring-finger	1·20	90

1780 National University of Technology, Seoul

2010. Centenary of National University of Technology, Seoul and Jinju National University.

3090	250w. Type **1780**	1·20	90
3091	250w. Jinju National University (vert)	1·20	90

1781 Old Buddha's Plum Tree at Baegyangsa Temple, Jangseong (Natural Monuments No. 486)

1782 Conifer, Samsong-ri, Goesan (No. 290)

1783 Two Chinese Junipers at Songgwangsa Temple (No. 88)

1784 *Thunbergii camphor*, Samsan-ri, Jangheung (No. 481)

2010. Ancient and Historic Trees of Korea.

3092	**1781**	250w. multicoloured	1·20	90
3093	**1782**	250w. multicoloured	1·20	90
3094	**1783**	250w. multicoloured	1·20	90
3095	**1784**	250w. multicoloured	1·20	90

1785 Mo Tae Bum (speed skater)

2010. Korea's Skating Victories at Winter Olympic Games, Vancouver. Background colour given. Multicoloured.

3096	250w. Type **1785**	1·20	90
3097	250w. Lee Sang Hwa (speed skater) (rose)	1·20	90
3098	250w. Lee Seung Hoon (speed skater) (dull yellow green)	1·20	90
3099	250w. Kim Yu Na (world champion figure skater) (deep mauve)	1·20	90
3100	250w. Kwak Yoon Gy (short track) (pale orange)	1·20	90
3101	250w. Kim Seoung Il (short track) (pale blue-green)	1·20	90
3102	250w. Park Seung Hi (short track) (pale slate-lilac)	1·20	90
3103	250w. Sung Si Bak (short track) (lavender)	1·20	90
3104	250w. Lee Eun Byul (short track) (bright lilac)	1·20	90
3105	250w. Lee Jung Su (short track) (violet-blue)	1·20	90
3106	250w. Lee Ho Suk (short track) (dark flesh)	1·20	90

1786 Autumn

1787 Winter

1788 Spring

1789 Summer

2010. Rivers (4th issue).

3107	**1786**	250w. multicoloured	1·20	90
3108	**1787**	250w. multicoloured	1·20	90
3109	**1788**	250w. multicoloured	1·20	90
3110	**1789**	250w. multicoloured	1·20	90

1790 Players and Championship Emblem

2010. World Cup Football Championship, South Africa.

3111	**1790**	250w. multicoloured	1·20	90

1791 Children and Women making 'Hands of Protection' (UNHCR emblem)

2010. Tenth Anniversary of World Refugee Day.

3112	**1791**	250w. multicoloured	1·20	90

1792 Chimney of Mt. Amisan in Gyeongbokgung Palace, Korea

1793 Traditional Air-conditioning Tower, UAE

2010. 30th Anniversary of Korea–United Arab Emirates Diplomatic Relations.

3113	**1792**	250w. multicoloured	1·20	90
3114	**1793**	250w. multicoloured	1·20	90

1794 Barbed Wire and Butterfly

2010. 60th Anniversary of Start of Korean War.

3115	**1794**	250w. multicoloured	1·20	90

1795 1980 30w. Stamp (As Type **781**)

2010. Philately Week.

3116	250w. black and vermilion	1·20	90
3117	250w. black, vermilion and new blue	1·20	90
MS3118	140×70 mm. 250w.×2, Nos. 3116/3117	2·40	2·40

Designs: No. 3116, T **1795**; No. 3117, 1980 30w. Stamp (As No. 1458)

1796 Herrerasaurus

2010. The Age of Dinosaurs (1st issue). Multicoloured.

3119	250w. Type **1796**	1·20	90
3120	250w. Coelophysis	1·20	90
3121	250w. Plateosaurus	1·60	1·10
3122	250w. Riojasaurus	1·60	1·10

See also Nos. 3166/3169 and 3219/3222.

1797 Stylised Trees and Symbols of Life

2010. IUFRO. Global Network for Forest Science Co-operation Congress, Seoul.

3123	**1797**	340w. multicoloured	1·60	1·10

1798 King Geumwa meeting Yuhwa

2010. Jumong of Goguryeo. Multicoloured.

3124	250w. Type **1798**	1·10	90
3125	250w. Jumong as a baby	1·10	90
3126	250w. Jumong and supporters crossing river on the backs of fish	1·10	90
3127	250w. Jumong defending Goguryeo	1·10	90

1799 *Seopyeonje*

1800 *Shiri* (Swiri)

1801 *The Brotherhood of War*

1802 *Take Off* (Gukga Daepyo)

2010. Korean Cinema (4th issue).

3128	**1799**	250w. multicoloured	1·10	90
3129	**1800**	250w. multicoloured	1·10	90
3130	**1801**	250w. multicoloured	1·10	90
3131	**1802**	250w. multicoloured	1·10	90

1803 Recycled Products as Flowers

2010. Reuse and Recycle Precious Resources. Multicoloured.

3136	250w. Type **1803**	1·10	90
3137	250w. Recycled goods being reprocessed	1·10	90

1804 Gwanghwamun

2010. G20 Summit, Seoul. Multicoloured.

3138	250w. Type **1804**	1·10	90
3139	250w. Emblem	1·10	90

1805 Rabbit

2010. Lunar New Year. Year of the Rabbit.

3140	**1805**	250w. multicoloured	1·10	90

1806 Eddy

2011. Korean-Made Characters. *Pororo The Little Penguin*. Multicoloured.

MS3141 250w.×10, Type **1806**; Crong; Pororo; Petty; Popo and Pipi; Poby; Harry; Loopy; Tong-tong; Rody 15·00 15·00

1807 Japanese Black Pines, Sancheondan, Jeju

1808 Ginkgo, Yogwang-ri, Geumsan

1809 Zelkov, Haksaru, Hamyang

1810 Rock Pine, Chukji-ri, Hadong

2011. Ancient and Historic Trees of Korea.

3142	**1807**	250w. multicoloured	1·10	90
3143	**1808**	250w. multicoloured	1·10	90
3144	**1809**	250w. multicoloured	1·10	90
3145	**1810**	250w. multicoloured	1·10	90

1811 Geobukseon (Turtle Ship), Korea

2011. 50th Anniversary of Korea–Portugal Diplomatic Relations. Multicoloured.

3146	250w. Type **1811**	1·10	90
3147	250w. Carrack, Portugal	1·10	90

1812 Family

2011. Family. Winning Designs in Design-a-Stamp Competition. Multicoloured.

3148	250w. Type **1812**	1·20	90
3149	250w. Stylised couple pushing baby	1·20	90

1813 Juknokwon, Damyang

1814 Green Tea growing, Boseong

1815 Upo Wetland

1816 Jusanji, Cheongsong

2011. Tourism.

3150	**1813**	250w. multicoloured	1·20	90
3151	**1814**	250w. multicoloured	1·20	90
3152	**1815**	250w. multicoloured	1·20	90
3153	**1816**	250w. multicoloured	1·20	90

1817 Two Penguins afloat on Shrunken Iceberg

2011. Preserve Polar Regions and Glaciers. Multicoloured.

3154	250w. Type **1817**	1·20	90
3155	250w. Polar bear and cub separated by polluting chimney	1·20	90

1818 School Song and Students

2011. Centenary of Shinheung Military Academy.

3156	**1818**	250w. multicoloured	1·20	90

1819 Tomb of King Taejo

1820 Tomb of King Sejong

2011. UNESCO World Heritage. Geonwolleung.

3157	**1819**	250w. multicoloured	1·20	90
3158	**1820**	250w. multicoloured	1·20	90

1821 Teddy Bear

2011. 50th Anniversary of Korea Disaster Relief Association.

3159	**1821**	250w. multicoloured	1·20	90

1822 *Sansui* (Jo Seok-Jin)

1823 *Jangsongnakii* (Ji Woon-Young)

1824 *Unnangjasang* (Chae Yong-Sin)

1825 *Gunmado* (Kim Ki-Chang)

2011. Philately Week.

3160	**1822**	250w. multicoloured	1·20	90
3161	**1823**	250w. multicoloured	1·20	90
3162	**1824**	250w. multicoloured	1·20	90
3163	**1825**	250w. multicoloured	1·20	90
MS3164		220×135 mm. Nos. 3160/3	6·00	6·00

1826 Skier

2011. Winter Olympic Games.- PyeongChang 2018

3165	**1826**	250w. multicoloured	1·20	90

1827 Scelidosaurus

2011. The Age of Dinosaurs (2nd issue). Multicoloured.

3166	250w. Type **1827**	1·20	90
3167	250w. Stegosaurus	1·20	90
3168	250w. Allosaurus	1·20	90
3169	250w. Diplohosaurus	1·20	90

1828 Stylised High Jump

2011. IAAF (International Athletics Federation) World Championships, Daegu. Multicoloured.

3170	250w. Type **1828**	1·20	90
3171	250w. Sprinter	1·20	90

1829 *Tripitaka Koreana*

2011. Millenary of Tripitaka Koreana (woodcut Buddhist text).

3172	**1829**	250w. multicoloured	1·20	90

1830 Taegeukgi (National Flag)

2011. National Flag.

3173	**1830**	270w. multicolured	1·20	90

1831 *Charonia sauliae*

2011. Shell. *Charonia sauliae.*

3174	**1831**	360w. multicoloured	1·75	1·50

1832 Jar with Figures

2011. Cultural Heritage.

3175	**1832**	1770w. multicoloured	6·00	5·50

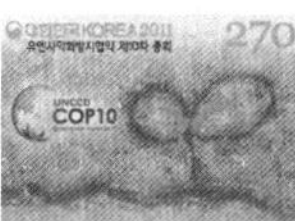
1833 Seedling ('The beginning of hope')

2011. Tenth Session of Parties to UNCCD (United Nations Convention to Combat Desertification) Conference, Changwon.

3176	**1833**	270w. multicoloured	1·20	90

1834 Ipo Weir, Han River

1835 Gongju Weir, Geum River

1836 Seungchon Weir, Yeongsan River

1837 Gangjeong-Goryeong Weir, Nakdong River

2011. Four Rivers Restoration.

3177	**1834**	270w. multicoloured	1·20	90
3178	**1835**	270w. multicoloured	1·20	90
3179	**1836**	270w. multicoloured	1·20	90
3180	**1837**	270w. multicoloured	1·20	90

1838 Woman playing Haegeum

2011. 50th Anniversary of Korea–Australia Diplomatic Relations. Multicoloured.

3181	270w. Type **1838**	1·20	90
3182	270w. Man playing didgeridoo	1·20	90

1839 Standing up to the Tang

1840 Defeating Tang Army

1841 Establishment of Balhae Kingdom

1842 Balhae as Haedongseongguk

2011. Daejoyeong of the Balhae Kingdom.

3183	**1839**	270w. multicoloured	1·20	90
3184	**1840**	270w. multicoloured	1·20	90
3185	**1841**	270w. multicoloured	1·20	90
3186	**1842**	270w. multicoloured	1·20	90
MS3186a		225×82 mm. As Nos. 3183/3186	6·00	5·50

1843 Dragon

2011. Lunar New Year. Year of the Dragon.

3187	**1843**	270w. multicoloured	1·20	90

1844 Symbols of Industry

2011. Korea's Achievement of One Trillion Dollars in Trade. Multicoloured.

3188	270w. Type **1844**	1·20	90
3189	270w. Taegeukgi	1·20	90

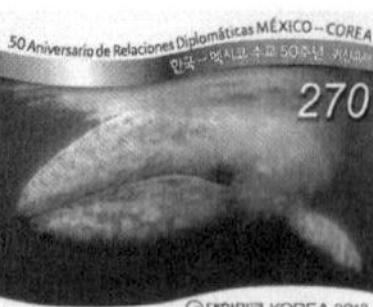

1845 Grey Whale

1846 Grey Whale

2012. 50th Anniversary of Korea–Mexico Diplomatic Relations.

3190	**1845**	270w. multicoloured	1·20	90
3191	**1846**	270w. multicoloured	1·20	90

1847 Ssoso

2012. Korean-Made Characters. *Pucca*. Multicoloured.

MS3192	270w.×10, Type **1847**; Abyo; Pucca; Garu; Ching; Bruce; Ho-Oh; Santa; Nini; Woo-Wuh	10·00	10·00

1848 Coffee

2013. 50th Anniversary of Korea–Colombia Diplomatic Relations. Multicoloured.

3193	270w. Type **1848**	1·20	90
3194	270w. Ginseng	1·20	90

1849 Conference Emblem

2012. Nuclear Security Summit, Seoul. Multicoloured.

3195	270w. Type **1849**	1·20	90
3196	270w. Dove	1·20	90

1850 Zelkova, Segan-ri, uiryeong

1851 Trifoliate Orange Tree, Gapgot-ri, Ganghwa

1852 Asian Fringe Tree in Grove, Gwangyang-eup

1853 Cherry Tree in Spring, Hwaeomsa Temple, Gurye

2011. Ancient and Historic Trees of Korea.

3197	**1850**	250w. multicoloured	1·20	90
3198	**1851**	250w. multicoloured	1·20	90
3199	**1852**	250w. multicoloured	1·20	90

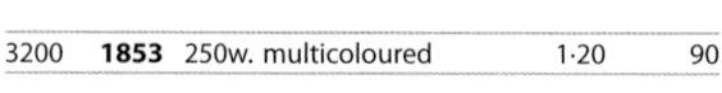

3200	**1853**	250w. multicoloured	1·20	90

1854 Fur Hat (Yeonju Chung)

2012. International Postage Stamp Design Contest. Winning Entries. Multicoloured.

202	270w. Children carrying rainbow (Glenn M Isaac)	1·20	90
3201	270w. Type **1854**	1·20	90

1855 Korea Pavilion and Suny (mascot)

2012. World EXPO 2012 Yesou, South Korea. Multicoloured.

3203	270w. Type **1855**	1·20	90
3204	270w. Theme Pavilion and Yeony (mascot)	1·20	90
3205	270w. The big-O and Suny	1·20	90
3206	270w. Sky Tower and Yeony	1·20	90
MS3207	165×80 mm. Nos. 3203/3206, each×2	10·00	10·00

1856 KOTRA Emblem

2012. 50th Anniversary of KOTRA. Korea Trade-Investment Promotion Agency. Multicoloured.

3208	270w. Type **1856**	1·20	90
3209	270w. KOTRA headquarters	1·20	90

1857 Gungnamji Pond, Buyeo

1858 Daegwallyeong Sheep Ranch

1859 Cheonjiyeon Waterfall, Jeju Island

1860 Dinosaur Ridge, Mt Seoraksan

2012. Tourism.

3210	**1857**	270w. multicoloured	1·20	90
3211	**1858**	270w. multicoloured	1·20	90
3212	**1859**	270w. multicoloured	1·20	90
3213	**1860**	270w. multicoloured	1·20	90

1861 Swimmer and Tower Bridge

2012. Olympic Games, London. Multicoloured.

3214	270w. Type **1861**	1·20	90
3215	270w. Archer and Big Ben (clock tower of Palace of Westminster)	1·20	90

1862 Ogyeon Jeongsa and Mask, Hahoe

2012. World Heritage Site. Hahoe and Yangdong Villages. Multicoloured.

3216	270w. Type **1862**	1·20	90
3217	270w. Yangdong (52×36 mm)	1·20	90
MS3218	145×100 mm. Nos. 3216/3217	3·00	3·00

1863 Pachycephalosaurus

2012. The Age of Dinosaurs (3rd issue). Multicoloured.

3219	360w. Type **1863**	1·50	1·00
3220	360w. Tyrannosaurus	1·50	1·00
3221	360w. Oviraptor	1·50	1·00
3222	360w. Protoceratops	1·50	1·00

1864 *The Back Alley* (Dong Jin Seo)

1865 *Namhyangjip* (Ji Ho Oh)

1866 *Tugye* (Joong Seop Lee)

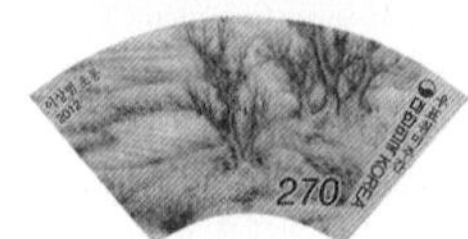

1867 *Chodong* (Sang Beom Lee)

2012. Philately Week.

3223	**1864**	270w. multicoloured	1·20	90
3224	**1865**	270w. multicoloured	1·20	90
3225	**1866**	270w. multicoloured	1·20	90
3226	**1867**	270w. multicoloured	1·20	90
MS3227		220×75 mm. Nos. 3223/3226	5·00	5·00

1868 Congress Emblem

2012. World Conservation Congress. Jeju.

3228	**1868**	270w. multicoloured	1·20	90

1869 Gathering of Village Leaders

1870 Horse bowing to Egg

1871 Birth of Park Hyekgeose from Egg

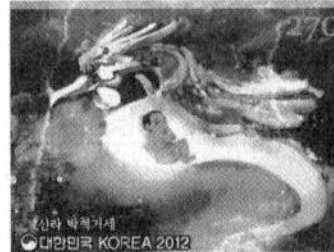
1872 Birth of Alyeong

1873 Founding of Silla Kingdom

2012. Park Hyeokgeose of the Silla Kingdom.

3229	**1869**	270w. multicoloured	1·20	90
3230	**1870**	270w. multicoloured	1·20	90
3231	**1871**	270w. multicoloured	1·20	90
3232	**1872**	270w. multicoloured	1·20	90
3233	**1873**	270w. multicoloured	1·20	90

1874 Snake

2012. Lunar New Year. Year of the Snake. Multicoloured.

3234	270w. Type **1874**	1·20	90
3235	270w. Child playing Jegichagi	1·20	90
MS3236	90×60 mm. Nos. 3234/3235	2·50	2·50

1875 Competitors

2013. Special Olympics World Winter Games. PyeongChang.

3237	**1875**	270w. multicoloured	1·20	90

1876 President Park Geun-hye

2013. Inauguration of President Park Geun-hye.

3238	**1876**	270w. multicoloured	1·20	90

1877 Roy

2013. Korean-Made Characters. *Robocar Poli*. Multicoloured.

MS3239	270w.×10, Type **1877**; Amber; Poli; Helly; Dumpoo; Cab; Posti; Spooki; Schoolbi; Cleani	10·00	10·00

1878 Jang Hyo-Jo

2013. Personalities. Baseball Legends. Multicoloured.

3240	25g. Type **1878**	1·20	90
3241	25g. Choi Dong-Won	1·20	90

1879 Seongsan Ilchulbong Peak, Korea

2013. 50th Anniversary of Korea–Peru Diplomatic Relations. Multicoloured.

3242	270w. Type **1879**	1·20	90
3243	270w. Machu Picchu, Peru	1·20	90

1880 Suncheon Bay

2013. Suncheon Bay Garden Expo 2013.

3244	**1880**	270w. multicoloured	1·20	90

1881 'Smart' Mobile Phone

2013. Information and Communication Day. Multicoloured.

3245	270w. Type **1881**	1·20	90
3246	270w. Post box and post	1·20	90
3247	270w. Television and satellite dish	1·20	90
3248	270w. Globe, rocket and symbols of science and technology	1·20	90

1882 Justice and Extract of the Constitution

2013. 50th Anniversary of Law Day.

3249	**1882**	270w. multicoloured	1·20	90

1883 Sungnyemun Gate

2013. Restoration of Sungnyemun.

3250	**1883**	270w. multicoloured	1·20	90

1884 Ahn Chang-Ho (founder) and Emblem

2013. Centenary of Young Korean Academy.

3251	**1884**	270w. multicoloured	1·20	90

1885 Pansori Epic Chant

2013. 20th Anniversary of Korea–Slovakia Diplomatic Relations. Multicoloured.

3252	270w. Type **1885**	1·20	90
3253	270w. Lucnica Dance Troop	1·20	90

1886 Hyangwonjeong Pavilion, Gyeongbokgung

2013. 130th Anniversary of Korea–Germany Diplomatic Relations. Multicoloured.

3254	270w. Type **1886**		90
3255	270w. Temple of the Sun, Bayreuth		90

1887 Chimneys producing Leaves (green industry)

2013. Energy Conservation. Winning Entries in Stamp Design Contest. Multicoloured.

3256	270w. Type **1887** (Ng Hio Wai (Macao))	1·20	90
3257	270w. Piggy bank with tail as plug saving coins (saving power/saving money) (Kim A-ram (Korea))	1·20	90
3258	270w. Icebergs on scale opposite CO_2 producing goods (saving icebergs) (Yu Jae-gyeol (Korea))	1·20	90
3259	270w. Bicycle with globe enclosed by flowers and sun enclosed by trees as wheels (Kim Eun-jeong (Korea))	1·20	90

1888 Girl writing Letter

2013. Philately Week. Multicoloured.

3260	300w. Type **1888**	1·25	1·00
3261	300w. Girl posting letter	1·25	1·00
3262	300w. Boy examing stamp	1·25	1·00
3263	300w. Boy putting stamp in album	1·25	1·00
MS3264	163×62 mm. 600w.×2, Design as Nos. 3260/3 but as one stamp (108×25 mm)×2	4·00	4·00

1889 *3005* Patrol Ship and Coastguard Emblem

2013. 60th Anniversary of Korean Coastguard.

3265	**1889**	300w. multicoloured	1·25	1·00

1890 Bukcheong Saja-nori (Lion Dance of Korea)

2013. 40th Anniversary of Diplomatic Relations with Indonesia. Multicoloured.

3266	300w. Type **1890**	1·25	1·00
3267	300w. Bantengan (bull) dance (Indonesia)	1·25	1·00

1891 Symbols of Cyberspace

2013. Conference on Cyberspace, Seoul.

3268	**1891**	300w. multicoloured	1·25	1·00

1892 Sungnyemun Gate

1893 Suwon Hwaseong Fortress

1894 Haeundae Dongbaek Island

1895 Dodamsambong Peaks

1896 Hingdo Island

1897 Cheomseongdae Observatory, Gyeongju

1898 Gwanghallu Pavilion, Namwon

1899 Gyeongpodae Pavilion,Gangeung

1900 Baengnokdam Lake on Mt Halla

1901 *Charonia sauliae* (As No. 3174)

1902 Jar with Figures (As No. 3175)

2013. Natural and Cultural Heritage. New Postal Rate.

3269	**1892**	300w. multicoloured	1·25	1·00
3270	**1893**	300w. multicoloured	1·25	1·00
3271	**1894**	300w. multicoloured	1·25	1·00
3272	**1895**	300w. multicoloured	1·25	1·00
3273	**1896**	300w. multicoloured	1·25	1·00
3274	**1897**	300w. multicoloured	1·25	1·00
3275	**1898**	300w. multicoloured	1·25	1·00
3276	**1899**	300w. multicoloured	1·25	1·00
3277	**1900**	300w. multicoloured	1·25	1·00
3278	**1901**	390w. multicoloured	1·75	1·50
3279	**1902**	1930w. multicoloured	5·00	5·00

1903 Jumong, His Wife and Biryu and Onjo

1904 Biryu and Onjo riding South

1905 Biryu riding to Michuhol

1906 Onjo's Capital, Wiryeseong

1907 Onjo ruling Baekje, the Kingdom United

2013. Onjo of the Baekje Kingdom.

3280	**1903**	300w. multicoloured	1·25	1·00
3281	**1904**	300w. multicoloured	1·25	1·00
3282	**1905**	300w. multicoloured	1·25	1·00
3283	**1906**	300w. multicoloured	1·25	1·00
3284	**1907**	300w. multicoloured	1·25	1·00

1908 Horse

2013. Lunar New Year. Year of the Horse. International Design a Stamp Competition. Multicoloured.

3285	300w. Type **1908**	1·25	1·00
3286	300w. Many horses	1·25	1·00
3287	300w. Outline horse on checkered background	1·25	1·00
3288	300w. Boy as pantomime horse	1·25	1·00

MS3289 132×158 mm. 630w.×4, Designs as Nos. 3283/3286 but as four different stamps (103×25 mm)×4 10·00 10·00

1909 Red

2014. Korean-Made Characters. *Larva*. Multicoloured.
MS3290 300w. Type **1909**; 300w. Pink; 300w. Brown; 300w. Black; 300w. Prussian; 390w. Yellow and Red; 390w. Red and Yellow; 390w. Yellow and Red with football on head; 400w. Red and Yellow holding ball; 1930w. Yellow 12·50 12·50

1911 Han Yongun

1912 Lee Yuksa

1913 Yun Dongju

2014. Personalities. Poets.
3293 **1911** 25g. multicoloured 1·25 1·00
3294 **1912** 25g. multicoloured 1·25 1·00
3295 **1913** 25g. multicoloured 1·25 1·00

1914 Birds and Flowers (Minhwa painting)

2014. PHILAKOREA 2014. Asian International Stamp Exhibition, South Korea. Designs showing Yeongmohwa paintings. Multicoloured.
3296 300w. Type **1914** 1·25 1·00
3297 300w. Hahoe mask 1·25 1·00
3298 300w. Hanbok (traditional dress) 1·25 1·00
3299 300w. Hangeul (alphabet) 1·25 1·00
3300 300w. Onggi pottery 1·25 1·00
3301 300w. Gayageum (stringed instrument) 1·25 1·00
3302 300w. Baekja (white porcelain jar) 1·25 1·00
3303 300w. Carved house eaves 1·25 1·00

1916 Pythagorean Theorem

2014. International Congress of Mathematicians. Seoul, South Korea. Multicoloured.
3306 300w. Type **1916** 1·50 1·00
3307 300w. Euler's Theorem 1·50 1·00
3308 540w. Pascal's Triangle 3·00 2·75

1917 Ten-pin Bowling

2014. 17th Asian Games, Incheon, South Korea. Multicoloured.
3309 300w. Type **1917** 1·25 1·00
3310 300w. Squash 1·25 1·00
3311 300w. Wrestling 1·25 1·00
3312 300w. Cricket 1·25 1·00
3313 540w. Rhythmic Gymnastics 3·00 2·75
3314 540w. Mascots 3·00 2·75

Nos. 3315/3316 and T **1918** are left for PHILAKOREA 2014, not yet received.

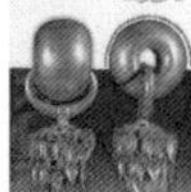
1919 Gold Earrings, Hwango-dong, Gyeongju

2014. Cultural Heritage. Multicoloured.
3317 1930w. Type **1919** 6·25 5·75
3318 3000w. *Lofty Scholar Contemplating Water* (painting by Hui An Kang) 10·00 9·50

1920 Tree containing Envelopes and Bird

2014. Philately Week. Multicoloured.
3319 300w. Type **1920** 1·25 1·00
3320 300w. Several generations of stamp collectors 1·25 1·00
3321 540w. Figure made up of stamps 3·00 2·75
3322 540w. Stamps as train 3·00 2·75
MS3323 120×98 mm. As Nos. 3319/3322 8·50 8·50

1921 Pope Francis

2014. Visit of Pope Francis. Multicoloured.
3324 300w. Type **1921** 1·25 1·00
3325 540w. Releasing dove 3·00 2·75

1922 Gold Earrings

2014. 60th Anniversary of Baekje Cultural Festival. Multicoloured.
3326 300w. Type **1922** 1·25 1·00
3327 540w. Great Gilt-bronze Incense Burner of Baekje (lower half) 3·00 2·75

1923 Diversity of Life

2014. 12th Meeting of the Conference of the Parties to the Convention on Biological Diversity.
3328 **1923** 300w. multicoloured 1·25 1·00

1924 Bongsudae Beacon Tower

2014. International Telecommunication Union (ITU) Plenipotentiary Conference, Busan. Multicoloured.
3329 300w. Type **1924** 1·50 1·00
3330 300w. Jeju Jeongnang (gate poles used for communication) 1·50 1·00
3331 300w. Gwangan Bridge 1·50 1·00
3332 540w. Conference emblem 3·00 2·75

1925 'Koreans around the World' and Nong-ak Emblem

2014. Korean Day.
3333 **1925** 300w. multicoloured 1·25 1·00

1926 Korean Musicians

2014. 50th Anniversary of Korea–Uruguay Diplomatic Relations. Multicoloured.
3334 300w. Type **1926** 1·25 1·00
3335 540w. Candombe (Uruguay) 3·00 2·75

1927 Hwangjejibo, National Seal of Korean Empire

2014. Cultural Heritage.
3336 **1927** 3550w. multicoloured 10·00 10·00

1928 *Pitta nympha* (Fairy Pitta)

2014. Birds.
3337 **1928** 400w. multicoloured 2·00 1·75

1929 Nine Leaders

2014. Kim Suro of Gayo Kingdom. The Period of Nine Leaders. Multicoloured.
3338 300w. Type **1929** 1·25 1·00
3339 300w. Dancing and singing 'Turtle turtle raise your head' 1·25 1·00
3340 300w. Six golden eggs in a golden box 1·25 1·00
3341 540w. Suro hatching from golden egg 3·00 2·75
3342 540w. Suro marrying princess Heo Hwang-ok 3·00 2·75

1930 Fish-dragon-shaped Celadon Ewer

2014. Cultural Heritage.
3343 **1930** 2000w. multicoloured 7·00 6·75

1931 Multicoloured Sheep

2014. Lunar New Year. Year of the Sheep. Multicoloured.
3344 300w. Type **1931** 1·25 1·00
3345 300w. Sheep's head surrounded by wool 1·25 1·00
3346 300w. Sheep with flowery wool 1·25 1·00
3347 300w. Cloud as sheep 1·25 1·00
MS3348 65×105 mm. 300w.×4, Nos. 3344/3347 10·00 10·00

1932 Gemini

1933 Constellations (image scaled to 28% of original size)

2015. Stories of the Constellations. Multicoloured.
MS3349 300w.×16, Type **1932**; Taurus; Aries; Pisces; Aquarius; Capricorn; Sagittarius; Scorpio; Libra; Virgo; Leo; Cancer; Canis Major; Cassiopeia; Cygnus; Azhari 16·00 16·00

1934 *Happy Art Class* (Kim Ga-Ram)

2015. Happy School Life. Multicoloured.

(a) Sheet Stamps. Ordinary gum
3350 300w. Type **1934** 1·25 1·00
3351 300w. *Our Happy School* (Faces and clock) (Cho Seul-gi) 1·25 1·00
3352 300w. *Friendship travels through Letters* (Two children forming heart) (Kim Seung-yeon) 1·25 1·00
3353 300w. *Variety, the More the Better* (Faces as jigsaw) (Kim Seon-hee) 1·25 1·00

(b) Self-adhesive
3354 300w. As Type **1934** 1·25 1·00
3355 300w. As No. 3351 1·25 1·00
3356 300w. As No. 3352 1·25 1·00
3357 300w. As No. 3353 1·25 1·00

1935 Globe, Butterfly and Child in Water Droplet

2015. World Water Forum, 2015, Daegu and Gyeongbuk.
3358 **1935** 300w. multicoloured 1·25 1·00

1936 Mother and Cubs

2015. Endangered Species. Wolf (*Canis lupus*). Multicoloured.
3359 300w. Type **1936** 1·25 1·00
3360 300w. Wolf, head and shoulders 1·25 1·00
MS3361 125×110 mm. As Nos. 3359/3360 4·00 4·00

1937 Benjamin W. Lee

2015. Science in Korea. Scientists. Multicoloured.

3362	25g. (300w.) Type **1937**	1·25	1·00
3363	25g. (300w.) Joo-myung Seok	1·25	1·00
3364	25g. (300w.) Man-chun Han	1·25	1·00

1938 *Mergus squamatus* (Scaly-sided Merganser)

2015. 50th Anniversary of Korea–Bolivia Diplomatic Relations. Multicoloured.

3365	25g. (300w.) Type **1938**	1·25	1·00
3366	25g. (300w.) *Phibalura flavirostris* (Swallow-tailed Cotinga)	1·25	1·00

1939 Flying Dragon

2015. Seals of the Joseon Dynasty. Multicoloured.

3367	25g. (300w.) Type **1939**	1·25	1·00
3368	25g. (300w.) Two entwined dragons (circular)	1·25	1·00
3369	25g. (300w.) Beast reclining (square)	1·25	1·00
3370	25g. (300w.) Crouching lion (mottled white)	1·25	1·00
MS3371	75×130 mm. As Nos. 3367/3370	6·00	6·00

1940 Major Sim Il

2015. Heroes. Heroes of the Korean War. Multicoloured.

3372	25g. (300w.) Type **1940**	1·25	1·00
3373	25g. (300w.) Captain Kim Gyosu	1·25	1·00
3374	25g. (300w.) Vice Admiral Son Won-Il	1·25	1·00
3375	25g. (300w.) Brigadier General Lee Geun-seok	1·25	1·00
3376	25g. (300w.) Police Inspector General Cha Il-hyeok	1·25	1·00
3377	25g. (300w.) General James Alward van Fleet	1·25	1·00
3378	25g. (300w.) Lieutenant Colonel James Power	1·25	1·00
3379	25g. (300w.) First Lieutenant Jin Du-tae	1·25	1·00
3380	25g. (300w.) Lieutenant Colonel Ralph Moncler	1·25	1·00
3381	25g. (300w.) Captain William Hamilton Shaw	1·25	1·00

1941 Confluence of Rivers (Yangyeong Dumulmeori)

2015. Tourism. Multicoloured.

3382	25g. (300w.) Type **1941**	1·25	1·00
3383	25g. (300w.) Rocks and temple, Goesan Hwanyang Gugok	1·25	1·00
3384	25g. (300w.) Chungjuho Lake	1·25	1·00
3385	25g. (300w.) Aerial view of Yeongwol Donggang River	1·25	1·00

1942 Nurubi (mascot)

2015. Universiade Gwangju Sports Festival. Multicoloured.

3386	25g. (300w.) Type **1942**	1·25	1·00
3387	25g. (300w.) Football	1·25	1·00
3388	25g. (300w.) Gymnastics	1·25	1·00
3389	25g. (300w.) Taekwondo	1·25	1·00
MS3390	140×75 mm. 25g.(300w.)×4, As Nos. 3386/3389	6·00	5·50

1943 Camel

2015. Silk Road Cultural Festival, Gyeongju 2015.

3391	**1943** 25g. (300w.) multicoloured	1·25	1·00

1944 Anniversary Emblem

2015. 70th Anniversary of Korean Liberation. Multicoloured.

3392	25g. (300w.) Type **1944**	1·25	1·00
3393	25g. (300w.) Kim Koo	1·25	1·00
MS3394	113×72 mm. 25g. (300w.)×2, As Nos. 3392/3393	4·00	4·00

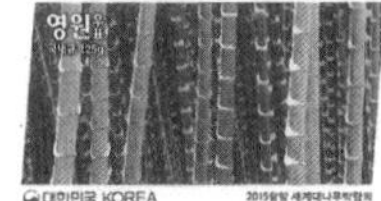

1945 Bamboo Grove

2015. World Bamboo Fair, Damyang, Korea 2015. Multicoloured.

3395	25g. (300w.) Type **1945**	1·25	1·00
3396	25g. (300w.) Single green stem	1·25	1·00
3397	25g. (300w.) Looking towards top of tall bamboos	1·25	1·00
3398	25g. (300w.) Buds breaking through ground	1·25	1·00

1946 Byung-Chu Lee (Samsung founder)

2015. Personalities. Business Leaders. Multicoloured.

3399	25g. (300w.) Type **1946**	1·25	1·00
3400	25g. (300w.) Chung Ju-Yung (Hyundai founder)	1·25	1·00

1947 Haeraon and Haeraoni (mascots)

2015. World CISM (International Military Sports Council) Games, Mungyeong, Korea. Multicoloured.

3401	25g. (300w.) Type **1947**	1·25	1·00
3402	25g. (300w.) Obstacle course	1·25	1·00
3403	25g. (300w.) Sky diving	1·25	1·00
3404	25g. (300w.) Shooting	1·25	1·00

1948 Dongmun Gate

2015. World Heritage Site. Namhansanseong Palace. Multicoloured.

3405	25g. (300w.) Type **1948**	1·25	1·00
3406	25g. (300w.) Aerial view of complex (52×36 mm)	1·25	1·00
MS3407	145×100 mm. 25g. (300w.)×2, Nos. 3405/3406	3·00	3·00

1949 'With Music Inside' (Yu-seon Yun)

2015. Post Culture Week. Winning Designs in Children's Drawing Competition. Multicoloured.

3408	25g. (300w.) Type **1949**	1·25	1·00
3409	25g. (300w.) Children riding on snail carrying envelope ('Slower speed for deeper love' (Jeong-hyeon Park))	1·25	1·00
3410	25g. (300w.) Postman cycling leaving trail of red hearts ('Sending it to you' (Yun-jeong Oh))	1·25	1·00
3411	25g. (300w.) Children and letterbox ('Letters from deep in the mountain' (Yeon-su Gang))	1·25	1·00

1950 Monkey in Snow

2015. Lunar New Year. Year of the Monkey. Multicoloured.

(a) Sheet Stamps. Self-adesive

3412	25g. (300w.) Type **1950**	1·25	1·00
3413	25g. (300w.) Monkeys partying	1·25	1·00

(b) Miniature sheet. Ordinary gum.

MS3414	107×97 mm. 25g. (300w.)×2, As Nos. 3412/3413	3·00	3·00

1951 Symbols of Science

2016. 50th Anniversary of KIST (Korean Institute of Science and Technology). Multicoloured.

3415	300w. Type **1951**	1·25	1·00
3416	300w. Monument	1·25	1·00

1952 Mother and Cubs

2016. Endangered Species. Otter (*Lutra lutra*). Multicoloured.

3417	390w. Type **1952**	2·00	2·00
3418	390w. Otter	2·00	2·00
MS3419	125×110 mm. 390w.×2 As Nos. 3417/3418	4·50	4·50

1953 Children painting Dove on Wall (Hun Juyeop)

2016. Postage Stamp Design Competition Winners. Peace and Safety. Multicoloured.

3420	300w. Type **1953**	1·25	1·00
3421	300w. Dove and rainbow (Kim Enok)	1·25	1·00
3422	300w. Multicoloured river of people (Kim Eunjeong)	1·25	1·00
3423	300w. Dove carrying globe containing children (Lee Juhyeok)	1·25	1·00
3424	300w. Wearing seatbelt making 'smiley' (Seo Eungyeong)	1·25	1·00
3425	300w. Mother shielding child from rain (Lee Minj)	1·25	1·00
3426	300w. Arms shielding smiling globe (Tsang Wing Tung)	1·25	1·00
3427	300w. Safety hat carrying workers (Jo Eunyeong)	1·25	1·00

1954 Jang Yeongsil (timepiece and astronomical engineer)

2016. Science in Korea. Inductees of Korea Science and Technology Hall of Fame. Multicoloured.

3428	300w. Type **1954**	1·25	1·00
3429	300w. Heo Jun (physician)	1·25	1·00
3430	300w. Ree Taikyue (theoretical chemist)	1·25	1·00

1955 'With this great opening of matter, let there be great opening of spirit'

2016. Centenary of Won-Buddhism.

3431	**1955** 300w. multicoloured	1·25	1·00

1956 Convention Emblem

2016. Rotary International Convention, Goyang KINTEX.

3432	**1956** 300w. multicoloured	1·25	1·00

1957 Early Building and Archangel Michael (statue)

2016. Centenary of Sorokdo National Hospital. Multicoloured.

3433	300w. Type **1957**	1·25	1·00
3434	300w. Hands and modern building	1·25	1·00

1958 Nam Ja-hyeon

2016. Heroes. National Independence Activists. Multicoloured.

3435	300w. Type **1958**	1·25	1·00
3436	300w. Ju Si-gyeong	1·25	1·00

1959 Celadon Incense Burner

2016. 130th Anniversary of France–Korea Diplomatic Relations. Cultural Heritage. Multicoloured.

3437	300w. Type **1959** (Korea)	1·25	1·00
3438	300w. Silver reliquary (France)	1·25	1·00

1960 Cardinal Stephen Kim Su-hwan

2016. Personalities. Religious Leaders. Multicoloured.

3439	300w. Type **1960**	1·25	1·00
3440	300w. Master Seongcheol (Buddhist)	1·25	1·00

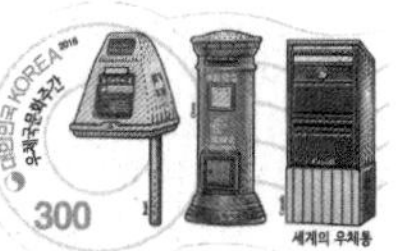

1961 Post Boxes

1962 Post Boxes

1963 Post Boxes

1964 Post Boxes

2016. Post Culture Week. Multicoloured.

3441	**1961**	300w. multicoloured	1·25	1·00
3442	**1962**	300w. multicoloured	1·25	1·00
3443	**1963**	300w. multicoloured	1·25	1·00
3444	**1964**	300w. multicoloured	1·25	1·00

1965 Hadong Simri Cherry Blossom Road

2016. Tourism. Multicoloured.

3445	300w. Type **1965**	1·25	1·00
3446	300w. Walkway over water	1·25	1·00
3447	300w. Coastal walk (Yeongdeok Blue Road)	1·25	1·00
3448	300w. Forest trail, Woljeongsa Jeonnamu	1·25	1·00

1966 Oryukdo Lighthouse

1967 Ulgi Lighthouse

1968 Somaemuldo Lighthouse

1969 Eocheongdo Lighthouse

2016. Lighthouses

3449	**1966**	300w. multicoloured	1·25	1·00
3450	**1967**	300w. multicoloured	1·25	1·00
3451	**1968**	300w. multicoloured	1·25	1·00
3452	**1969**	300w. multicoloured	1·25	1·00

STANLEY GIBBONS
LONDON 1856

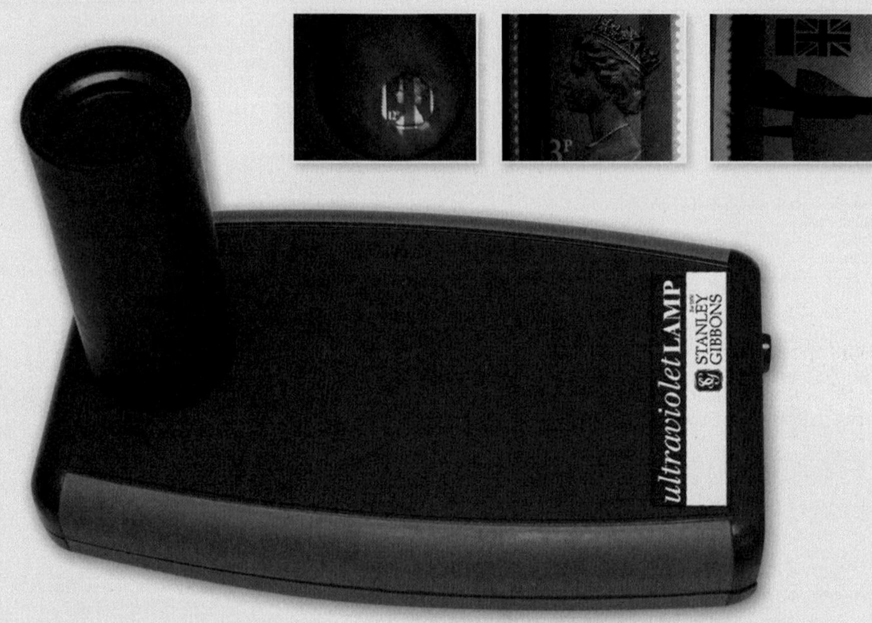

DUAL WAVE UV LAMP

Without question the most versatile ultraviolet lamp on the market, the Stanley Gibbons Dual Wave UV Lamp detects all fluorescent and phosphor bands, inks and paper coatings, making it the perfect accessory for collectors of any country whose modern issues display these features.

The main deficiencies with most lamps on the market are that they require total darkness for effective use and their unshielded light source presents a potential danger to the eyes.

The Dual Wave UV Lamp has been specially developed exclusively for Stanley Gibbons to overcome both these issues, with its 'hidden' bulb and separate eye-piece allowing safe and effective use at fairs and exhibitions as well as in the home.

R2573 £119

Broad wavelength covers both short-wave & long-wave phosphors

Detects fluorescent bands, papers & other devices

Detects cleaned pen cancellations & paper repairs

Powerful bulb gives much stronger reaction than other lamps

Safe to use: Ultraviolet bulb shielded from eye

To order, call **01425 472 363**
email **orders@stanleygibbons.com** or visit **stanleygibbons.com**

C. NORTH KOREAN OCCUPATION

1 Democratic People's Republic of Korea

1950. Nos. 116 and 118/119 optd with T **1**.

1		10w. green	65·00
2		20w. brown	25·00
3		30w. green	31·00

NORTH KOREA.

A. RUSSIAN OCCUPATION

GUM. All stamps of North Korea up to No. N1506 are without gum, except where otherwise stated.

1 Hibiscus

2 Diamond Mountains

1946. Perf, roul or imperf.

N1	**1**	20ch. red	75·00	50·00
N2	**2**	50ch. green	50·00	40·00
N4b	**2**	50ch. red	13·50	13·50
N5b	**2**	50ch. violet	12·50	14·50

4 General Kim Il Sung and Flag

1946. First Anniversary of Liberation from Japan.

N6	**4**	50ch. brown	£250	£190

5 Peasants

1947. Perf, roul or imperf.

N7	**5**	1wn. green	6·75	5·75
N8	**5**	1wn. violet	21·00	21·00
N9	**5**	1wn. blue on buff	8·50	6·75
N10	**5**	1wn. blue	4·25	3·25

6

1948. Second Anniversary of Labour Law.

N11	**6**	50ch. blue	£300	£300

7

1948. Third Anniversary of Liberation from Japan.

N12	**7**	50ch. red	£180	£600

8

1948. Promulgation of Constitution.

N13	**8**	50ch. blue and red	£225	£110

B. KOREAN PEOPLE'S DEMOCRATIC REPUBLIC

9 North Korean Flag

1948. Establishment of People's Republic. Roul.

N16	**9**	25ch. violet	4·50	4·50
N17	**9**	50ch. blue	8·00	7·75

10

1949. Roul or perf.

N18	**10**	6wn. red and blue	3·00	3·50

11 Kim Il Sung University, Pyongyang

11a Kim Il Sung University, Pyongyang

1949. Roul.

N19	**11**	1wn. violet	£110	60·00
N20	**11a**	1wn. blue	£150	41·00

12 North Korean Flags

1949. Fourth Anniversary of Liberation from Japan. Roul or perf.

N22	**12**	1wn. red, green and blue	£140	50·00

13 Order of the National Flag

1950. Perf, roul or imperf. Various sizes.

N24	**13**	1wn. green (A)	5·50	1·40
N25	**13**	1wn. orange (A)	70·00	55·00
N26	**13**	1wn. orange (B)	22·00	18·00
N27	**13**	1wn. green (C)	5·50	2·00
N28	**13**	1wn. olive (D)	9·25	5·75

Sizes: (A) $23\frac{1}{4}\times37\frac{1}{2}$ mm. (B) $20\times32\frac{1}{2}$ mm. (C) $22\times35\frac{1}{2}$ mm. (D) $22\frac{1}{2}\times36\frac{1}{2}$ mm.

14 Liberation Monument, Pyongyang

15 Soldier and Flags

16 Peasant and Worker

17 Tractor

1950. Fifth Anniversary of Liberation from Japan. Roul, perf or imperf. Various sizes.

N29	**14**	1wn. red, indigo and blue	1·60	1·10
N30	**14**	1wn. orange	9·25	8·75
N31	**15**	2wn. black, blue and red	1·60	1·20
N32	**16**	6wn. green (A)	2·20	1·60
N36	**16**	6wn. red (B)	17·00	13·50
N33	**17**	10wn. brown (C)	3·25	2·40
N37	**17**	10wn. brown (D)	25·00	16·00

Sizes: (A) 20×30 mm. (B) 22×33 mm. (C) 20×28 mm. (D) 22×30 mm.

18 Capitol, Seoul

1950. Capture of Seoul by North Korean Forces. Roul.

N38	**18**	1wn. red, blue and green	50·00	44·00

19

1951. Order of Admiral Li Sun Sin. Imperf or perf.

N39	**19**	6wn. orange	8·50	7·00

20 Kim Gi Ok and Aeroplane

1951. Air Force Hero Kim Gi Ok. Imperf.

N40	**20**	1wn. blue	10·50	6·75

21 Russian and North Korean Flags

22 Kim Ki U (hero)

23 North Korean and Chinese Soldiers

1951. Sixth Anniversary of Liberation from Japan. Roul or perf.

N41A	**21**	1wn. blue	4·50	3·25
N42A	**21**	1wn. red	4·50	3·25
N43A	**22**	1wn. blue	4·50	3·25
N44A	**22**	1wn. red	5·00	3·25
N45A	**23**	2wn. blue	9·25	6·50
N46A	**23**	2wn. red	13·50	11·50

All values exist on buff and on white paper.

24 Order of Soldier's Honour

1951. Imperf or perf.

N47	**24**	40wn. red	12·50	5·75

25

1951. Co-operation of Chinese People's Volunteers. Imperf or perf.

N49	**25**	10wn. blue	7·25	6·50

26 Woman Partisan, Li Su Dok

1952. Partisan Heroes. Imperf or perf.

N50	**26**	70wn. brown	5·50	1·60

27

1952. Peace Propaganda. Imperf or perf.

N51	**27**	20wn. blue, green and red	8·00	2·75

28 General P'eng Teh-huai

1952. Honouring Commander of Chinese People's Volunteers. Imperf.

N52	**28**	10wn. purple	16·00	6·50

29 Munition Worker

1952. Labour Day. Imperf or perf.

N53	**29**	10wn. red	42·00	40·00

30

1952. Sixth Anniversary of Labour Law. Imperf or perf.

N54a	**30**	10wn. blue	21·00	16·00

31

1952. Anti-US Imperialism Day. Imperf or perf.

N55	**31**	10wn. red	31·00	30·00

32

1952. North Korean and Chinese Friendship. Imperf or perf.

N56a	**32**	20wn. deep blue	14·00	13·50

33

34

1952. Seventh Anniversary of Liberation from Japan. Imperf or perf.

N57	**33**	10wn. red	31·00	30·00
N58	**34**	10wn. red	24·00	23·00

35

1952. International Youth Day. With gum. Imperf or perf.

N59	**35**	10wn. green	17·00	17·00

36

37

1953. Fifth Anniversary of People's Army. Imperf or perf.

N60	**36**	10wn. red	32·00	31·00
N61	**37**	40wn. purple	21·00	20·00

38

39

1953. International Women's Day. With gum. Imperf or perf.

N62	**38**	10wn. red	22·00	19·00
N63	**39**	40wn. green	24·00	21·00

40

41

1953. Labour Day. Imperf or perf.

N64	**40**	10wn. green	16·00	15·00
N65	**41**	40wn. orange	16·00	15·00

42

43

1953. Anti-US Imperialism Day. With gum. Imperf or perf.

N66	**42**	10wn. turquoise	31·00	30·00
N67	**43**	40wn. red	31·00	30·00

44

45

1953. Fourth World Youth Festival, Bucharest. With gum. Imperf or perf.

N68	**44**	10wn. blue and green	18·00	17·00
N69	**45**	20wn. green and pink	15·00	8·75

46

1953. Armistice and Victory Issue. With gum. Imperf or perf.

N70a	**46**	10wn. brown and yellow	90·00	85·00

47

1953. Eighth Anniversary of Liberation from Japan. Imperf.

N71	**47**	10wn. red	£400	£375

48

1953. Fifth Anniversary of People's Republic. Imperf or perf.

N72	**48**	10wn. blue and red	20·00	19·00

49 Liberation Monument, Pyongyang

1953. With gum. Imperf or perf.

N73	**49**	10wn. slate	19·00	9·75

(50)

1954. No. N18 optd **Fee Collected** in Korean characters, T **50**.

N74	**10**	6wn. red and blue	£250	£250

(51)

1954. Nos. N18 and N39 surch with T **51**.

N75	**10**	5wn. on 6wn. red and blue	29·00	19·00
N76	**19**	5wn. on 6wn. orange	75·00	55·00

52

1954. Post-war Economic Reconstruction. With gum. Imperf or perf.

N77	**52**	10wn. blue	31·00	18·00

53

1954. Sixth Anniversary of People's Army. With gum. Imperf or perf.

N78	**53**	10wn. red	£110	£110

54

1954. International Women's Day. With gum. Imperf or perf.

N79	**54**	10wn. red	25·00	24·00

55

1954. Labour Day. With gum. Imperf or perf.

N80	**55**	10wn. red	20·00	19·00

56

1954. Anti-US Imperialism Day. With gum. Imperf or perf.

N81	**56**	10wn. red	37·00	33·00

57 Taedong Gate, Pyongyang

1954. Imperf or perf.

N82	**57**	5wn. lake	4·25	1·50
N83	**57**	5wn. brown	4·25	1·50

58

1954. National Young Activists' Conference With gum. Imperf or perf.

N84	**58**	10wn. red, blue and slate	5·25	5·00

59 Soldier

1954. Ninth Anniversary of Liberation from Japan. With gum. Imperf or perf.

N85	**59**	10wn. red	12·00	11·50

60 North Korean Flag

1954. Sixth Anniversary of People's Republic. With gum. Imperf or perf.

N86	**60**	10wn. blue and red	9·75	9·25

61 Hwanghae Iron Works

62 Hwanghae Iron Works and Workers

1954. Economic Reconstruction. Imperf or perf.

N87	**61**	10wn. blue	8·75	1·20
N88	**62**	10wn. brown	8·75	1·20

63

1955. Seventh Anniversary of People's Army. With gum. Imperf or perf.

N89	**63**	10wn. red	11·50	9·75

64

1955. Internatonal Women's Day. With gum. Imperf or perf.

N90	**64**	10wn. deep blue	11·50	9·75

65

66

1955. Labour Day. With gum. Imperf or perf.

N91	**65**	10wn. green	8·25	7·75
N92	**66**	10wn. red	8·25	7·75

67 Admiral Li Sun Sin

1955. Imperf or perf.

N93	**67**	1wn. blue on green	4·75	60
N94	**67**	2wn. red on buff	5·25	60
N95	**67**	2wn. red	10·00	1·10

68

1955. Ninth Anniversary of Labour Law. With gum. Imperf or perf.

N96	**68**	10wn. red	12·50	11·50

69 Liberation Monument and Flags

1955. Tenth Anniversary of Liberation from Japan. Imperf or perf.

N97	**69**	10wn. green	4·25	3·75
N98	**69**	10wn. red, blue and brown (29½×42½ mm)	3·75	3·25

70

71

1955. Soviet Union Friendship Month. Imperf or perf.

N99	**70**	10wn. red	2·75	1·50
N100	**70**	10wn. red and blue	3·50	2·20
N101	**71**	20wn. red and slate	4·75	3·25
N102	**71**	20wn. red and blue	2·75	1·70

Sizes: No. N99, 22×32½ mm; No. N100, 29½×43 mm; No. N101, 18½×32 mm; No. N102, 25×43 mm.

72 Son Rock

1956. Haegeumgang Maritime Park. Imperf or perf.

N103	**72**	10wn. blue on blue	6·00	3·25

73

1956. Eighth Anniversary of People's Army. Imperf or perf.

N104	**73**	10wn. red on green	14·00	12·50

74

1956. Labour Day. Imperf or perf.

N105	**74**	10wn. blue	11·50	8·00

75 Machinist

76 Taedong Gate, Pyongyang

77 Woman Harvester

78 Moranbong Theatre, Pyongyang

1956. Imperf or perf.

N106	**75**	1wn. brown	2·00	95
N107	**76**	2wn. blue	8·50	1·90
N108	**77**	10wn. red	1·60	1·10
N109	**78**	40wn. green	11·00	5·50

79 Miner

1956. Tenth Anniversary of Labour Law. Imperf or perf.

N110	**79**	10wn. brown	3·25	1·40

80 Boy Bugler and Girl Drummer

1956. Tenth Anniversary of Children's Union. Imperf or perf.

N111	**80**	10wn. brown	5·50	3·50

81 Workers

1956. Tenth Anniversary of Sex Equality Law. Imperf or perf.

N112	**81**	10wn. brown	3·25	2·10

82 Industrial Plant

1956. Tenth Anniversary of Nationalisation of Industry. Imperf or perf.

N113	**82**	10wn. brown	50·00	33·00

83 Liberation Tower

1956. 11th Anniversary of Liberation from Japan. Imperf or perf.

N114	**83**	10wn. red	4·25	1·80

84 Kim Il Sung University

1956. Tenth Anniversary of Kim Il Sung University. Imperf or perf.

N115	**84**	10wn. brown	3·50	3·25

85 Boy and Girl

1956. Fourth Democratic Youth League Congress. Imperf or perf.

N116	**85**	10wn. brown	3·50	2·00

86 Pak Ji Won

1957. 220th Birth Anniversary of Pak Ji Won 'Yonam', (statesman). Imperf or perf.

N117	**86**	10wn. blue	2·00	1·00

87 Tabo Pagoda, Pulguksa

88 Ulmil Pavilion, Pyongyang

1957. Imperf, perf or roul.

N118	**87**	5wn. blue	1·80	1·20
N119	**88**	40wn. green	2·75	1·80

89 Furnaceman

1957. Production and Economy Campaign. With or without gum. Imperf or perf.

N121	**89**	10wn. blue	4·25	2·75

90 Furnaceman

91 Voters and Polling Booth

1957. Second General Election. Imperf or perf.

N122	**90**	1wn. orange	1·10	45
N123	**90**	2wn. brown	1·10	45
N124	**91**	10wn. red	6·50	1·80

92 Ryongwangjong, Pyongyang

1957. 1530th Anniversary of Pyongyang. Imperf or perf.

N125	**92**	10wn. green	1·30	35

93 Lenin and Flags

94 Kim Il Sung at Pochonbo

95 Lenin

96 Pouring Steel

1957. 40th Anniversary of Russian Revolution. Imperf or perf.

N126	**93**	10wn. green	1·00	55
N127	**94**	10wn. red	1·00	55
N128	**95**	10wn. blue	1·00	55
N129	**96**	10wn. orange	2·50	55

No. N126 exists with gum.

97 Congress Emblem

1957. Fourth World Trade Unions Federation Congress. Leipzig. Imperf (with or without gum) or perf.

N130	**97**	10wn. blue and green	1·60	65

98 Liberation Monument, Spassky Tower and Flags

1957. Russian Friendship Month. Imperf or perf.

N131	**98**	10wn. green	2·20	60

99 Weighing a Baby

100 Bandaging a Hand

1957. Red Cross. Imperf, perf or roul.

N132	**99**	1wn. red	7·50	1·20
N133	**99**	2wn. red	7·50	1·20
N134	**100**	10wn. red	20·00	3·50

No. N133 exists with and without gum.

101 Koryo Celadon Jug (12th-century)

102 Koryo Incense-burner (12th-century)

1958. Korean Antiquities. Imperf (with or without gum) or perf.

N135	**101**	10wn. blue	6·25	95
N136	**102**	10wn. green	6·25	95

103 Woljong Temple Pagoda

1958. With gum (5wn.), without gum (10wn.). Imperf or perf.

N137	**103**	5wn. green	1·50	80
N138	**103**	10wn. blue	2·50	1·40

104 Soldier

1958. Tenth Anniversary of People's Army. No gum (No. N139) with or without gum (No. N140). Imperf or perf.

N139	**104**	10wn. blue	3·25	60
N140	-	10wn. red	6·00	80

Design: Horiz (37½×26 mm)—No. N140, Soldier, flag and Hwanghae Iron Works.

106 Lisunov Li-2 Airliner over Pyongyang

1958. Air. Imperf or perf.

N141	**106**	20wn. blue	7·00	1·20

107 *Sputniks*

108 *Sputnik* encircling Globe

1958. IGY Inscr '1957–1958'. Imperf or perf.

N142	**107**	10wn. slate	5·25	3·25
N143	**108**	20wn. slate	5·25	3·25
N144	-	40wn. slate	5·25	3·25
N145	**107**	70wn. slate	11·50	9·75

Design: Horiz—40wn. *Sputnik* over Pyongyang Observatory.

Nos. N142/N144 exist with or without gum.

109 Furnaceman

1958. Young Socialist Constructors' Congress, Pyongyang. Imperf or perf.

N146	**109**	10wn. blue	3·75	70

110 Hwanghae Iron Works

1958. Opening of Hwanghae Iron Works. Imperf or perf.

N147	**110**	10wn. blue	5·50	80

111 Commemorative Badge

1958. Farewell to Chinese People's Volunteers (1st issue). Imperf or perf.

N148	**111**	10wn. purple and blue	2·75	70

See also No. N158.

112 Federation Emblem

1958. Fourth International Women's Federation Conference. Imperf or perf.

N149	**112**	10wn. blue	1·30	50

113 Conference Emblem

1958. First World Young Workers' Trade Union Federation Conference, Prague. Imperf or perf.

N150	**113**	10wn. brown and green	2·30	95

114 Flats, East Ward, Pyongyang

115 Workers' Flats, Pyongyang

1958. Rehousing Progress. Imperf or perf.

N151	**114**	10wn. blue	2·75	70
N152	**115**	10wn. green	2·75	70

117 Pyongyang Railway Station

119 Textile Worker

1958. Tenth Anniversary of Korean People's Republic. Imperf or perf.

N153	-	10wn. green	3·50	65
N154	**117**	10wn. green	12·50	2·00
N155	-	10wn. brown and buff	2·20	65
N156	**119**	10wn. brown	10·00	2·30
N157	-	10wn. brown	12·00	4·50

Designs: Horiz—No. N153, Hungnam Fertiliser Plant; No. N157, Yongp'ung Dam, Pyongyang. Vert—No. N155, Arms of People's Republic.

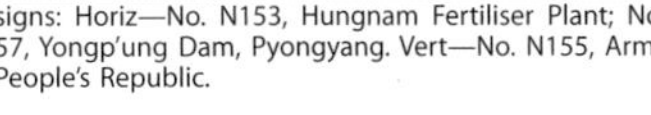

121 Volunteer and Steam Troop Train

1958. Farewell to Chinese People's Volunteers (2nd issue). Imperf or perf.

N158	**121**	10wn. sepia	30·00	9·75

122 Transplanting Rice

1958. Imperf or perf.

N159	**122**	10wn. sepia	1·10	30

123 Winged Horse of Chollima

1958. National Production Executives' Meeting, Pyongyang. With or without gum. Imperf or perf.

N160	**123**	10wn. red	1·90	30

124 North Korean and Chinese Flags

1958. North Korean–Chinese Friendship Month. With or without gum. Imperf or perf.

N161	**124**	10wn. red, blue green	1·60	40

125 Farm Workers

1959. National Co-operative Farming Congress, Pyongyang. With or without gum. Imperf or perf.

N162	**125**	10wn. blue	1·40	35

126 General Ulji Mun Dok

1959. Korean Celebrities. With gum. Imperf or perf.

N163	**126**	10wn. red and yellow	2·75	65

See also Nos. N165/N167 and N216/N219.

127 Women with Banner

1959. National Conference of Women Socialist Constructors, Pyongyang. With or without gum.

N164	**127**	10ch. brown and red	2·75	70

1959. Revalued currency. Portraits as T **126**. Imperf (with or without gum) or perf (with gum).

N165	-	2ch. blue on green	1·20	20
N166	-	5ch. purple on buff	1·40	25
N167	**126**	10ch. red on cream	2·40	30

Portraits: 2ch. General Kang Gam Chan; 5ch. General Chon Bong Jun.

128 Rocket and Moon

1959. Launch of Soviet Moon Rocket. With or without gum. Imperf or perf.

N168	**128**	2ch. purple on buff	8·50	3·00
N169	**128**	10ch. blue on green	16·00	4·00

129 Irrigation

1959. Land Irrigation Project. Imperf or perf.

N170	**129**	10ch. multicoloured	5·75	1·30

130 Inscribed Tree at Partisan HQ, Chongbong

131 Kim Il Sung Statue

132 Mt. Paekdu

1959. Partisan Successes against Japanese, 1937–1939. With gum (No. N172) or no gum (others). Perf (No. N172) or imperf or perf (others).

N171	**130**	5ch. multicoloured	3·75	70
N172	**131**	10ch. blue and turquoise	1·90	45
N173	**132**	10ch. violet	3·25	90

133 Flying Horse Tractor

1959. Great Perspectives (1st issue). Development of Industrial Mechanisation). With or without gum. Perf, roul or imperf.

N174	**133**	1ch. red, olive and green	1·70	25
N175	-	2ch. multicoloured	8·50	2·00
N176	-	2ch. red, pink and violet	1·60	30
N177	-	5ch. orange, brown and ochre	1·60	60
N178	-	10ch. blue, green & brn	2·00	50
N179	-	10ch. grn, lt grn & brn	3·75	65

Designs: No. N175, Electric mine locomotive; No. N176, Red Star 58 bulldozer; No. N177, Flying Horse excavator; No. N178, SU-50 universal lathe; No. N179, Victory 58 lorry.

See also Nos. N189a/N200 and N275/N279.

134 Armistice Building, Panmunjom

135 Protest Meeting

136 'Hoisting link between North and South Korea'

1959. Campaign for Withdrawal of US Forces from South Korea. With gum. Perf (20ch.) or imperf or perf (others).

N180	**134**	10ch. blue & ultramarine	1·20	30
N181	**135**	20ch. deep blue and blue	1·50	50
N182	**136**	70ch. brown, cream and purple	20·00	8·00

137 Emigration 'Pickets'

1959. Campaign Against Emigration of South Koreans. With gum.

N183	**137**	20ch. brown and sepia	4·50	1·30

138 Korean Type of 1234

139 Books breaking Chains

140 Emblems of Peace, Labour and Letters

141 Korean Alphabet of 1443

1959. International Book Exhibition, Leipzig. With gum (No. N184, N186) or no gum (others).

N184	**138**	5ch. sepia	20·00	6·50
N185	**139**	5ch. red and green	6·25	1·90
N186	**140**	10ch. blue	6·25	1·90
N187	**141**	10ch. violet and blue	9·25	3·25
MSN187a		152×122 mm. Nos. N184/N187	85·00	44·00

142 Pig Farm

1959. Animal Husbandry. With gum (5ch.) or no gum (2ch.).

N188	-	2ch. brown, green & buff	3·00	65
N189	**142**	5ch. cream, blue & brn	3·75	95

Design: Horiz—2ch. Cow girl with Cattle.

143 Rotary Cement Kiln

1959. Great Perspectives (2nd issue: Production Targets). With gum (Nos. N190 and N192) or no gum (others). Perf (Nos. N197/N198 and N200), perf or imperf (others).

N189a	**143**	1ch. cinnamon, brn & bl	40	25
N190	-	2ch. multicoloured	75	30
N191	-	5ch. multicoloured	70	35
N192	-	10ch. multicoloured	1·30	50
N193	-	10ch. purple, yell & bl	1·30	50
N194	-	10ch. yellow, grn & red	1·30	50
N195	-	10ch. multicoloured	1·30	50
N196	-	10ch. blue, light blue and green	1·30	50
N197	-	10ch. multicoloured	1·30	50
N198	-	10ch. green, buff and brown	1·30	50
N199	-	10ch. brown and orange	1·30	50
N200	-	10ch. multicoloured	1·30	50

Designs: Vert—No. N190, Electric power lines and dam; No. N191, Loading fertilisers into goods wagon. Horiz—No. N192, Factory, electric power lines and dam; No. N163, Harvesting; No. N194, Sugar-beet, factory and pieces of sugar; No. N195, Steel furnace; No. N196, Trawlers; No. N197, Pig-iron workers; No. N198, Coal miners; No. N199, Girl picking apples; No. N200, Textile worker.

144 Sika Deer

1959. Game Preservation. No gum (5ch.), with gum (10ch.).

N201		5ch. multicoloured	5·00	60
N202		5ch. yellow, brown & bl	5·00	60
N203		5ch. sepia, green & brn	5·00	60
N204		5ch. brown, black & blue	5·00	60
N205	**144**	10ch. multicoloured	5·00	65
N206	-	10ch. red, brown and green on cream	13·50	1·80

Designs: Horiz—No. N201, Chinese water deer; No. N202, Siberian weasel; No. N203, Steppe polecat; No. N204, European otter; No. N206, Common pheasant.

145 Congress Emblem

1960. Third Korean Trade Unions Federation Congress. With gum.

N207	**145**	5ch. multicoloured	70	25

146 *Chungnyon-ho* (freighter)

1959. Transport. With gum.

N208	-	5ch. purple	18·00	2·00
N209	**146**	10ch. green	4·50	1·30

Design: 5ch. Electric train.

147 Soldier, Tractor and Plough

1960. 12th Anniversary of Korean People's Army. With gum.

N210	**147**	5ch. violet and blue	70·00	55·00

148 Knife Dance

1960. Korean National Dances. Multicoloured.

N211	5ch. Type **148**	4·25	25
N212	5ch. Drum dance	4·25	25
N213	10ch. Farmers' dance	4·25	30

149 Women of Three Races

1960. 50th Anniversary of International Women's Day. With gum.

N214	**149**	5ch. mauve and blue	1·20	15
N215	-	10ch. green and orange	1·20	30

Design: Vert—10ch. Woman operating lathe.

150 Kim Jong Ho (geographer)

1960. Korean Celebrities. With gum.

N216	**150**	1ch. grey and green	1·30	10
N217	-	2ch. blue and yellow	1·60	10
N218	-	5ch. blue and yellow	5·75	25
N219	-	10ch. brown and ochre	1·60	15

Portraits: 2ch. Kim Hong Do (painter); 5ch. Pak Yon (musician); 10ch. Chong Da San (scholar).

151 Grapes

1960. Wild Fruits. Fruits in natural colours. With or without gum (Nos. N221/N222), with gum (others).

N220	5ch. olive and turquoise	2·75	65
N221	5ch. drab and blue	2·75	65
N222	5ch. olive and blue	2·75	65
N223	10ch. olive and orange	3·25	90
N224	10ch. green and pink	3·25	90

Fruits: No. N220, T **151**; No. N221, Fruit of *Actinidia arguta planch*; No. N222, Pine-cone; No. N223, Hawthorn berries; No. N224, Horse-chestnut.

152 Lenin

1960. 90th Birth Anniversary of Lenin. With gum.

N225	**152**	10ch. purple	90	20

153 Koreans and American Soldier (caricature)

1960. Campaign Day for Withdrawal of US Forces from South Korea. With gum.

N226	**153**	10ch. blue	4·50	50

154 Arch of Triumph Square, Pyongyang

1960. Views of Pyongyang.

N227	**154**	10ch. green	75	15
N228	-	20ch. slate	1·50	25
N229	-	40ch. green	2·50	55
N230	-	70ch. green	4·50	1·20
N231	-	1wn. blue	5·75	2·10

Views of Pyongyang: 20ch. River Taedong promenade; 40ch. Youth Street; 70ch. People's Army Street; 1wn. Sungri Street.

155 Russian Flag on Moon (14.9.59)

1960. Russian Cosmic Rocket Flights. With gum (5ch.) or no gum (10ch.).

N232		5ch. turquoise	7·50	7·25
N233	**155**	10ch. multicoloured	11·00	3·50

Design: 5ch. *Lunik 3* approaching Moon (4.10.59).

156 Mirror Rock

1960. Diamond Mountains Scenery (1st issue). Multicoloured.

N234	5ch. Type **156**	1·30	20
N235	5ch. Devil-faced Rock	1·30	20
N236	10ch. Dancing Dragon Bridge (horiz)	4·75	30
N237	10ch. Nine Dragon Falls	4·25	30
N238	10ch. Mt. Diamond on the Sea (horiz)	1·70	15

See also Nos. N569/N572, N599/N601 and N1180/N1184.

157 Lily

1960. Flowers. Multicoloured. With gum (No. N242), with or without gum (others).

N239	5ch. Type **157**	1·50	25
N240	5ch. Rhododendron	1·50	25
N241	10ch. Hibiscus	2·50	40
N242	10ch. Blue campanula	2·50	40
N243	10ch. Mauve campanula	2·50	40

158 Guerrillas in the Snow

1960. Revolutionary Leadership of Kim Il Sung.

N244	**158**	5ch. red	65	15
N245	-	10ch. blue	1·20	15
N246	-	10ch. red	1·20	15
N247	-	10ch. blue	1·20	15
N248	-	10ch. red	1·20	15

Designs: No. N245, Kim Il Sung talks to guerrillas; No. N246, Kim Il Sung at Pochonbo; No. N247, Kim Il Sung on bank of Amnok River; No. N248, Kim Il Sung returns to Pyongyang.

159 Korean and Soviet Flags

1960. 15th Anniversary of Liberation from Japan.

N249	**159**	10ch. red, blue & brown	1·00	20

160 "North Korean–Soviet Friendship"

1960. North Korean–Soviet Friendship Month.

N250	**160**	10ch. lake on cream	60	20

161 Okryu Bridge, Pyongyang

1960. Pyongyang Buildings.

N251	**161**	10ch. blue	3·25	30
N252	-	10ch. violet	2·75	15
N253	-	10ch. green	1·00	15

Designs: No. N252, Grand Theatre, Pyongyang; No. N253, Okryu Restaurant.

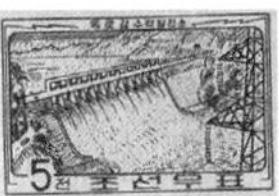
162 Tokro River Dam

1960. Inauguration of Tokro River Hydro-electric Power Station. With gum.

N254	**162**	5ch. blue	1·20	20

163

1960. 15th Anniversary of World Federation of Trade Unions.

N255	**163**	10ch. lt blue, ultram & bl	65	20

164 Quayside Welcome

1960. Repatriation of Korean Nationals from Japan.

N256	**164**	10ch. purple	3·25	25

165 Lenin and Workers

1960. Korea–Soviet Friendship. With gum.

N257	**165**	10ch. brown and flesh	70	20

166 Football

1960. Liberation Day Sports Meeting, Pyongyang. Multicoloured.

N258	5ch. Running (vert)	85	15
N259	5ch. Weightlifting (vert)	85	15
N260	5ch. Cycling (vert)	2·50	20
N261	5ch. Gymnastics (vert)	85	15
N262	5ch. Type **166**	1·30	20
N263	10ch. Swimming	1·00	50
N264	10ch. Moranbong Stadium, Pyongyang	85	50

167 Friendship Monument, Pyongyang

1960. Tenth Anniversary of Entry of Chinese Volunteers into Korean War. With gum.

N265	-	5ch. mauve	60	15
N266	**167**	10ch. blue	60	15

Design: Horiz—5ch. Chinese and Korean soldiers celebrating.

168 Federation Emblem

1960. 15th Anniversary of World Democratic Youth Federation.

N267	**168**	10ch. multicoloured	55	20

169 White-backed Woodpecker

1960. Birds.

N268	**169**	2ch. multicoloured	7·50	80
N268a	-	5ch. multicoloured	11·00	65
N269	-	5ch. brown, yellow & bl	13·50	1·80
N270	-	10ch. yellow, brn & grn	9·25	80

Designs: Horiz—5ch. (No. N268a), Mandarins; 10ch. Black-naped oriole. Vert—5ch. (No. N269), Oriental scops owl.

170 Korean Wrestling

1960. Sports and Games. Multicoloured.

N271	5ch. Type **170**	80	15
N272	5ch. Riding on swing (vert)	80	15
N273	5ch. Archery	3·25	40
N274	10ch. Jumping on see-saw (vert)	80	15

171 Cogwheel and Textiles

1961. Great Perspectives (3rd issue: Targets of Seven-Year Plan, 1961–1967. Inscr '1961'). Multicoloured.

N275	5ch. Type **171**	1·10	15
N276	5ch. Cogwheel and Corn (Mechanisation of Rural Economy)	2·10	15
N277	10ch. Hammer, sickle and torch on flag (vert)	55	15
N278	10ch. Cogwheels around power station	1·10	15
N279	10ch. Cogwheel and molten steel	80	15

172 Wild Ginseng (perennial herb)

1961. Multicoloured

N280	5ch. Type **172**	3·50	25
N281	10ch. Cultivated ginseng	3·50	25

173 Aldehyde Shop

1961. Construction of Vinalon Factory. With gum.

N282	**173**	5ch. red and yellow	1·00	15
N283	-	10ch. green and yellow	2·30	25
N284	-	10ch. blue and yellow	2·30	25
N285	-	20ch. purple and yellow	3·00	50

Designs: No. N283, Glacial acetic acid shop; No. N284, Polymerisation and saponification shop; No. N285, Spinning shop.

See also Nos. N338/N341.

174 Construction Work

1961. Construction of Children's Palace, Pyongyang. With gum.

N286	**174**	2ch. red on yellow	60	20

175 Museum Building

1961. Completion of Museum of Revolution, Pyongyang. With gum.

N287	**175**	10ch. red	50	20

176 Cosmic Rocket

1961. Launching of Soviet Venus Rocket.

N288	**176**	10ch. red, yellow & blue	6·25	25

177 Wheat Harvester

1961. Agricultural Mechanisation. With gum.

N289	-	5ch. violet	70	15
N290	-	5ch. green	70	15
N291	**177**	5ch. green	70	15
N292	-	10ch. blue	1·00	15
N293	-	10ch. purple	1·00	15

Designs: No. N289, Tractor-plough; No. N290, Disc-harrow; No. N292, Maize-harvester; No. N293, Tractors.

178

1961. Opening of Training Institute.

N294	**178**	10ch. brown on buff	90	20

179 Agriculture

1961. 15th Anniversary of Land Reform Law. With gum.

N295	**179**	10ch. green on yellow	85	20

180

1961. 15th Anniversary of National Programme. With gum.

N296	**180**	10ch. purple and yellow	50	20

181 Chub Mackerel

1961. Marine Life.

N297	**181**	5ch. multicoloured	2·75	25
N298	-	5ch. black and blue	6·50	80
N299	-	10ch. blue, black & lt bl	7·50	35
N300	-	10ch. multicoloured	2·75	25
N301	-	10ch. brown, yell & grn	2·75	25

Designs: No. N298, Common dolphin; No. N299, Whale sp; No. N300, Yellow-finned tuna; No. N301, Pacific cod.

182 Tractor-crane

1961. With gum.

N302	**182**	1ch. brown	1·30	15
N303	-	2ch. brown	1·30	15
N304	-	5ch. green	1·90	15
N305	-	10ch. violet	1·80	25

Designs: Horiz—2ch. Heavy-duty lorry; 5ch. Eight-metres turning lathe. Vert—10ch. 3000-ton press.

See also Nos. N378/N379c.

183 Tree-planting

1961. Re-afforestation Campaign. With gum.

N306	**183**	10ch. green	1·60	30

184 "Peaceful Unification" Banner

1961. Propaganda for Peaceful Reunification of Korea.

N307	**184**	10ch. multicoloured	20·00	2·00

185 Pioneers visiting Battlefield

1961. 15th Anniversary of Children's Union. Multicoloured.

N308	5ch. Pioneers bathing	1·30	25
N309	10ch. Pioneer bugler	3·25	50
N310	10ch. Type **185**	1·30	25

186 "Labour Law"

1961. 15th Anniversary of Labour Law. With gum.

N311	**186**	10ch. blue on yellow	85	25

187 Apples

1961. Fruit. Multicoloured.

N312	5ch. Peaches	1·10	15
N313	5ch. Plums	1·10	15

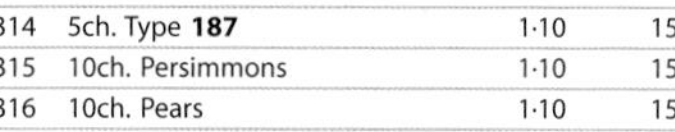

N314	5ch. Type **187**	1·10	15
N315	10ch. Persimmons	1·10	15
N316	10ch. Pears	1·10	15

188 Yuri Gagarin and *Vostok 1*

1961. World's First Manned Space Flight.

N317	**188**	10ch. ultramarine & blue	1·90	55
N318	**188**	10ch. violet and blue	1·90	55

189 Power Station

1961. 15th Anniversary of Nationalisation of Industries Law. With gum.

N319	**189**	10ch. brown	15·00	80

190 Women at Work

1961. 15th Anniversary of Sex Equality Law. With gum.

N320	**190**	10ch. red	60	20

191 Children planting Tree

1961. Children. Multicoloured.

N321	5ch. Type **191**	1·30	15
N322	5ch. Reading book	65	15
N323	10ch. Playing with ball	65	20
N324	10ch. Building a house	65	20
N325	10ch. Waving flag	65	20

192 Poultry and Stock-breeding

1961. Improvement in Living Standards. Multicoloured.

N326	5ch. Type **192**	1·00	15
N327	10ch. Fabrics and textile factory	1·60	25
N328	10ch. Trawler and fish (horiz)	1·50	25
N329	10ch. Grain-harvesting (horiz)	85	15

193 Soldiers on March (statue)

1961. 25th Anniversary of Fatherland Restoration Association. With gum.

N330	-	10ch. violet	65	30
N331	-	10ch. violet	65	30
N332	**193**	10ch. blue and buff	95	30

Designs: Marshal Kim Il Sung—No. N330, Seated under tree; No. N331, Working at desk.

194 Party Emblem and Members

1961. Fourth Korean Workers' Party Congress, Pyongyang. With gum.

N333	**194**	10ch. green	55	30
N334	-	10ch. purple	55	30
N335	-	10ch. red	55	30

Designs: Vert—No. N334, *Chollima* statue, Pyongyang. Horiz—No. N335, Marshal Kim Il Sung.

195 Miner

1961. Miners' Day. With gum.

N336	**195**	10ch. brown	11·00	80

196 Pak in Ro

1961. 400th Birth Anniversary of Pak in Ro (poet).

N337	**196**	10ch. indigo on blue	95	20

197 Aldehyde Shop

1961. Completion of Vinalon Factory. With gum.

N338	**197**	5ch. red and yellow	1·00	15
N339	-	10ch. brown and yellow	1·60	15
N340	-	10ch. blue and yellow	1·60	15
N341	-	20ch. purple and yellow	2·50	30

Designs: No. N339, Glacial-acetic shop; No. N340, Polymerisation and saponification shop; No. N341, Spinning shop.

198 Korean and Chinese Flags

1961. North Korean Friendship Treaties with China and the USSR.

N342		10ch. multicoloured	80	30
N343	**198**	10ch. red, blue & yellow	80	30

Design: No. N342, Korean and Soviet flags.

199 Basketball

1961. Physical Culture Day. With gum.

N344	-	2ch. grey	1·00	15
N345	-	5ch. blue	1·70	15
N346	**199**	10ch. blue	1·70	25
N347	-	10ch. blue	1·70	25
N348	-	10ch. purple	1·70	25
N349	-	20ch. purple	1·30	40

Designs: 2ch. Table tennis; 5ch. Flying model glider; 10ch. (N347) Rowing; 10ch. (No. N348) High jumping; 20ch. Sports emblem.

5전 대동여지도 100

(200)

1961. Centenary of Publication of Map *Taidong Yu Jido* by Kim Jung Ho. No. N216 surch with T **200**.

N350	**150**	5ch. on 1ch. grey and green	65·00	50·00

201 General Rock

1961. Mt. Chilbo Scenery. With gum.

N351	**201**	5ch. blue	90	15
N352	-	5ch. brown	90	15
N353	-	10ch. violet	1·70	25
N354	-	10ch. blue	1·70	25

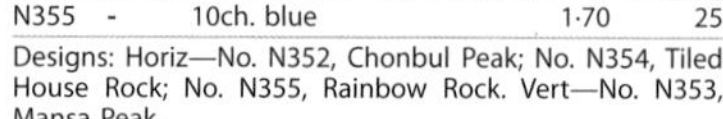

N355	-	10ch. blue	1·70	25

Designs: Horiz—No. N352, Chonbul Peak; No. N354, Tiled House Rock; No. N355, Rainbow Rock. Vert—No. N353, Mansa Peak.

202 Agriculture and Industry

1961. With gum.

N356	**202**	10ch. green	65	20

203 Winged Horse and Congress Emblem

1961. Fifth World Federation of Trade Unions Congress, Moscow. With gum.

N357	**203**	10ch. blue, purple and violet	40	20

204 Class Red Banner Electric Locomotive

1961. Railway Electrification. With gum.

N358	**204**	10ch. violet and yellow	18·00	2·10

205 Ice Hockey

1961. Winter Sports. With gum.

N359	-	10ch. brown and green	1·30	25
N360	-	10ch. brown and green	1·30	25
N361	**205**	10ch. brown and blue	1·30	25
N362	-	10ch. brown and blue	1·30	25

Designs: No. N359, Figure skating; No. N360, Speed skating; No. N362, Skiing.

206 Grain Harvest

1962. Six Heights of Production Targets (1st series). Inscr "1962". With gum.

N363	-	5ch. red, violet and grey	1·00	25
N364	-	5ch. brown and grey	6·75	65
N365	**206**	10ch. yellow, black & bl	1·00	25
N366	-	10ch. red, yellow & blue	3·25	25
N367	-	10ch. black and blue	3·00	30
N368	-	10ch. yellow, brown & bl	1·00	25

Designs: No. N363, Ladle and molten steel; No. N364, Electric mine train; No. N366, Fabrics and mill; No. N367, Trawler and catch; No. N368, Construction of flats.

See also Nos. N440/5.

207 Tiger

1962. Animals.

N369	**207**	2ch. multicoloured	3·75	25
N370	-	2ch. brown and green	2·75	15
N371	-	5ch. yellow and green	1·70	15
N372	-	10ch. brown and green	3·00	30

Animals: Horiz—2ch. (No. N370), Racoon-dog; 5ch. Chinese ferret-badger; 10ch. Asiatic black bear.

208 Kayagum Player

1962. Musical Instruments and Players (1st series). Multicoloured.

N373		10ch. Type **208**	2·75	30
N374		10ch. Man playing haegum (two-stringed bowed instrument)	2·75	30
N375		10ch. Woman playing wolgum (banjo)	2·75	30
N376		10ch. Man playing chotdae (flute)	2·75	30
N377		10ch. Woman playing wagonghu (harp)	2·75	30

See also Nos. N473/N477.

1962. As T **182**. Inscr '1962'. With gum (Nos. N379 and N379b), no gum (others).

N378		5ch. green	1·20	15
N379		10ch. blue	2·10	20
N379a		10ch. brown	—	12·50
N379b		5wn. brown	18·00	4·00
N379c		10wn. purple	23·00	8·00

Designs: Vert—5ch. Hydraulic press; 10ch. (2), Three-ton hammer; 10wn. Tunnel drill. Horiz—5wn. Hobbing machine.

209 *Leuhdorfia puziloi*

1962. Butterflies. Multicoloured.

N380		5ch. Type **209**	4·25	20
N381		10ch. *Sericinus telamon* (purple background)	4·25	20
N382		10ch. Keeled apollo (lilac background)	4·25	20
N383		10ch. Peacock (green background)	4·25	20

210 G. S. Titov and *Vostok 2*

1962. Second Soviet Manned Space Flight.

N384	**210**	10ch. multicoloured	3·00	30

211 Marshal Kim Il Sung and (inset) addressing Workers

1962. Marshal Kim Il Sung's 50th Birthday. With gum.

N385	**211**	10ch. red	65	25
N386	**211**	10ch. green	65	25
N387	-	10ch. blue	65	25

Design: No. N387, Kim Il Sung in fur hat and (inset) inspecting battle-front.

212 Kim Chaek

1962. Korean Revolutionaries (1st series). With gum.

N388	**212**	10ch. sepia	85	15
N389	-	10ch. blue	85	15
N390	-	10ch. red	85	15
N391	-	10ch. purple	85	15
N392	-	10ch. green	85	15
N393	-	10ch. blue	85	15
N394	-	10ch. brown	85	15

Portraits: No. N389, Kang Gon; No. N390, An Gil; No. N391, Ryu Gyong Su; Nos. N392/N393, Kim Jong Suk; No. N394, Choe Chun Guk.

See also Nos. N478/N482 and N733/N735.

213 Mother with Children

1962. National Mothers' Meeting, Pyongyang.

N395	**213**	10ch. multicoloured	65	20

214 Black-faced Spoonbill

1962. Birds. Inscr '1962'. Multicoloured.

N396		5ch. Type **214**	2·30	30
N397		5ch. Brown hawk owl	8·00	40
N398		10ch. Eastern broad-billed roller	4·75	50
N399		10ch. Black paradise flycatcher	4·75	50
N400		20ch. Tundra swan	5·75	80

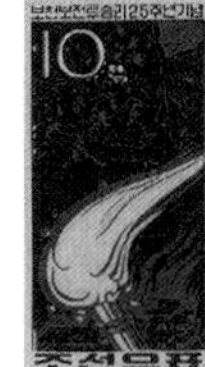
215 Victory Flame

1962. 25th Anniversary of Battle of Pochonbo.

N401	**215**	10ch. multicoloured	90	20

216 Japanese Croaker

1962. Fish. Multicoloured.

N402		5ch. Type **216**	2·10	15
N403		5ch. Hairtail	2·10	15
N404		10ch. Dotted gizzard shad (head pointing to right)	3·00	25
N405		10ch. Japanese spotted seabass (blue background)	3·00	25
N406		10ch. Japanese croaker (green background)	3·00	25

217 Waterdropper

1962. Antiques. With gum.

N407	-	4ch. black and blue	1·30	15
N408	**217**	5ch. black and ochre	1·30	15
N409	**A**	10ch. black and green	1·70	20
N410	**B**	10ch. black and orange	1·70	20
N411	**C**	10ch. black and purple	1·70	20
N412	**D**	10ch. black and brown	1·70	20
N413	**E**	10ch. black and yellow	1·70	20
N414	-	40ch. black and grey	5·00	50

Designs: Vert—4ch. Brush pot; 40ch. Porcelain decanter. Horiz—A, Inkstand; B, Brushstand; C, Turtle paperweight; D, Inkstone; E, Document case.

218 Radial Drill

1962. Double frame-line. With gum.

N415	-	2ch. green	45	10
N416	-	4ch. blue	3·00	10
N417	**218**	5ch. blue	85	10
N418	-	5ch. purple	95	10
N419	-	10ch. purple	1·30	10
N420	-	40ch. blue	6·50	25
N421	-	90ch. blue	2·75	40
N422	-	1wn. brown	8·25	65

Designs: Vert—2ch. Vertical milling machine; 5ch. (No. N418), Hydraulic hammer; 1wn. Spindle drill. Horiz—4ch. Victory April 15 motor car; 10ch. All-purpose excavator; 40ch. Trolley-bus; 90ch. Planing machine.

See also Nos. N513/N515 and N573.

219 Chong Da San

1962. Birth Bicentenary of Chong Da San (philosopher).

N423	**219**	10ch. purple	55	20

220 Voter

1962. Election of Deputies to National Assembly. Multicoloured.

N424		10ch. Type **220**	1·30	25
N425		10ch. Family going to poll	1·30	25

221 Pyongyang

1962. 1535th Anniversary of Pyongyang. With gum.

N426	**221**	10ch. black and blue	85	20

222 Globe and *Vostok 3* and *4*

1962. First Team Manned Space Flight.

N427	**222**	10ch. indigo, blue & red	3·00	65

223 Spiraea

1962. Korean Plants. Plants in natural colours; frame and inscr colours given.

N428	**223**	5ch. light green & green	1·50	15
N429	-	10ch. green and red	1·50	15
N430	-	10ch. blue and purple	1·50	15
N431	-	10ch. green and olive	1·50	15

Plants: No. N429, Ginseng; No. N430, Campanula; No. N431, *Rheumcoreanum makai* (Polyonaceae).

224 *Uibang Ryuchui*

1962. 485th Anniversary of Publication of *Uibang Ryuchui* (medical encyclopaedia).

N432	**224**	10ch. multicoloured	5·00	40

225 Science Academy

1962. Tenth Anniversary of Korean Science Academy.

N433	**225**	10ch. blue and turquoise	1·30	20

226 Fisherwomen

1962

N434	**226**	10ch. blue	1·30	20

227 European Mink

1962. Animals.

N435	**227**	4ch. brown and green	2·10	35
N436	-	5ch. blue, drab and green	2·10	35
N437	-	10ch. blue and yellow	2·50	35
N438	-	10ch. sepia and turquoise	2·50	35
N439	-	20ch. brown and blue	5·00	60

Animals: Horiz—No. N436, Chinese hare. Vert—No. N437, Eurasian red squirrel; No. N438, Common goral; No. N439, Siberian chipmunk.

228 Harvesting

1963. Six Heights of Production Targets (2nd issue). Inscr '1963'. Multicoloured.

N440		5ch. Miner	1·00	25
N441		10ch. Type **228**	75	15
N442		10ch. Furnaceman	75	15
N443		10ch. Construction worker	75	15
N444		10ch. Textiles loom operator	1·00	15
N445		40ch. Fisherman and trawler	2·50	55

229 Soldier

1963. 15th Anniversary of Korean People's Army. With gum.

N446	-	5ch. brown	50	10
N447	**229**	10ch. red	85	15
N448	-	10ch. blue	1·30	15

Designs: 5ch. Airman; 10ch. Sailor.

230 Peony

1963. Korean Flowers. Multicoloured.

N449		5ch. Type **230**	85	15
N450		10ch. Rugosa rose	1·30	15
N451		10ch. Azalea	1·30	15
N452		20ch. Campion	1·30	15
N453		40ch. Orchid	3·75	50

231 *Sadang-ch'um* (Korean folk dance)

1963. International Music and Dancing Contest, Pyongyang. Multicoloured.

N454		10ch. Type **231**	3·25	25
N455		10ch. Dancer with fan	3·25	25

232 Revolutionaries

1963. Third Anniversary of South Korean Rising of April, 1960.

N456	**232**	10ch. multicoloured	60	20

233 Karl Marx

1963. 145th Birth Anniversary of Karl Marx. With gum.

N457	**233**	10ch. blue	55	20

234 Children in Chemistry Class

1963. Child Care and Amenities. Multicoloured.

N458	2ch. Type **234**	1·10	25
N459	5ch. Children running	90	15
N460	10ch. Boy conducting choir	2·50	25
N461	10ch. Girl chasing butterfly	5·00	30

235 Armed Koreans and American Soldier (caricature)

1963. Campaign Month for Withdrawal of US Forces from South Korea.

N462	**235**	10ch. multicoloured	85	20

236 *Cyrtoclytus capra*

1963. Korean Beetles. Multicoloured designs. Colours of beetles given.

N463	5ch. Type **236**	1·70	25
N464	10ch. multicoloured	2·50	25
N465	10ch. red and blue	2·50	25
N466	10ch. indigo, blue and purple	2·50	25

Beetles: No. N464, *Cicindela chinensis* (tiger beetle); No. N465, *Purpuricenus lituratus*; No. N466, *Agapanthia pilicornis*.

237 Soldier with Flag

1963. Tenth Anniversary of Victory in Korean War.

N467	**237**	10ch. multicoloured	90	20

238 North Korean Flag

1963. 15th Anniversary of People's Republic. Multicoloured.

N468	10ch. Type **238**	50	25
N469	10ch. North Korean Badge	50	25

239 Namdae Gate, Kaesong

1963. Ancient Korean Buildings (1st series). With gum.

N470	**239**	5ch. black	40	15
N471	-	10ch. blue	70	20
N472	-	10ch. brown	70	20

Buildings: No. N471, Taedong Gate, Pyongyang; No. N472, Potong Gate, Pyongyang.

See also Nos. N537/N538.

240 Ajaeng (bowed zither)

1963. Musical Instruments and Players (2nd series). Multicoloured. Nos. N473 and N476 with gum.

N473	3ch. Type **240**	1·70	15
N474	5ch. Pyongyon (jade chimes)	1·70	15
N475	10ch. Saenap (brass bowl)	2·10	20
N476	10ch. Rogo (drums in frame)	2·10	20
N477	10ch. Piri (wooden pipe)	2·10	20

1963. Korean Revolutionaries (2nd issue). As T **212**. With gum.

N478	5ch. brown	35	10
N479	5ch. purple	35	10
N480	10ch. rose	40	15
N481	10ch. slate	40	15
N482	10ch. dull purple	40	15

Portraits: No. N478, Kwon Yong Byok; No. N479, Ma Dong Hui; No. N480, Li Je Sun; No. N481, Pak Dal; No. N482, Kim Yong Bom.

241 Nurse with Children

1963. Child Welfare. Multicoloured.

N483	10ch. Type **241**	50	20
N484	10ch. Children in playground	50	20

242 Hwajang Hall

1963. Mount Myohyang Resort. Multicoloured.

N485	5ch. Type **242**	65	15
N486	10c. Mountain stream and chalet	1·30	15
N487	10ch. Kwanum Pavilion and stone pagoda (horiz)	1·30	15
N488	10ch. Rope bridge across river (horiz)	3·25	15

243 Furnaceman

1963. Seven Year Plan. With gum.

N489	**243**	5ch. red	40	15
N490	-	10ch. grey	3·00	40
N491	-	10ch. red	3·00	40
N492	-	10ch. lilac	1·80	15

Designs: Vert—No. N490, Construction workers. Horiz—No. N491, Power technicians; No. N492, Miners.

244 Children hoeing

1963. *Hung Bo* (fairytale). Multicoloured.

N493	5ch. Type **244**	45	25
N494	10ch. Tying up broken leg of swallow	1·40	25
N495	10ch. Barn swallow dropping gourd seed	1·40	25
N496	10ch. Sawing through giant gourd	75	25
N497	10ch. Treasure inside gourd	75	25

245 Marksman

1963. Marksmanship. Multicoloured.

N498	5ch. Type **245**	50	15
N499	10ch. Marksman with small-bore rifle	75	15
N500	10ch. Marksman with standard rifle	75	15

246 Sinuiju Chemical Fibre Factory

1964. Chemical Fibres Factories. With gum.

N501	**246**	10ch. slate	1·00	15
N502	-	10ch. purple	1·00	15

Design: No. N502, Chongjin Chemical Fibre Factory.

247 Strikers

1964. 35th Anniversary of Wonsan General Strike. With gum.

N503	**247**	10ch. brown	85	20

248 Korean Alphabet

1964. 520th Anniversary of Korean Alphabet.

N504	**248**	10ch. green, buff & brn	85	25

249 Lenin

1964. 40th Death Anniversary of Lenin. With gum.

N505	**249**	10ch. red	55	20

250 Whale-catcher

1964. Fishing Industry. Multicoloured.

N506	5ch. Type **250**	85	15
N507	5ch. Trawler No. 051	85	15
N508	10ch. Trawler No. 397	1·70	40
N509	10ch. Trawler No. 738	1·70	40

251 Insurgents

1964. 45th Anniversary of Rising of 1st March. With gum.

N510	**251**	10ch. purple	45	20

252 Warring Peasants

1964. 70th Anniversary of Kabo Peasants' War. With gum.

N511	**252**	10ch. purple	45	20

253 Students' Palace, Pyongyang

1964. With gum.

N512	**253**	10ch. green	45	20

254 Changbaek Excavator

1964. Single frame-line. Dated 1964 or 1965 (No. N573). With gum.

N513	-	5ch. violet	1·10	15
N514	**254**	10ch. green	1·70	15
N515	-	10ch. blue	1·70	15
N573	-	10ch. violet	1·50	25

Designs: Vert—5ch. 200 metre drill; 10ch. (No. N573) Horning 500 machine. Horiz—10ch. (No. N515) 400 h.p. Diesel engine.

255 'On the March'

1964. Fifth Korean Democratic Youth League Congress, Pyongyang.

N516	**255**	10ch. multicoloured	45	20

256 Electric Train

1964. Inauguration of Pyongyang–Sinuiju Electric Railway.

N517	**256**	10ch. multicoloured	10·00	30

257 Rejoicing in Chongsan-ri Village

1964. Popular Movement at Chongsan-ri. With gum.

N517a	**257**	5ch. brown	£250	—

258 Drum Dance

1964. Korean Dances.

N518	**258**	2ch. mauve, buff & black	2·10	40
N519	-	5ch. red, black & yellow	2·50	40
N520	-	10ch. multicoloured	3·00	40

Designs: 5ch. 'Ecstasy' (solo); 10ch. Tabor.

259 'For the Sake of the Fatherland'

1964. Li Su Bok Commemorative. With gum.

N521	**259**	5ch. red	65	15

260 Nampo Smelting Works

1964. With gum.

N522	**260**	5ch. green	3·75	15
N523	-	10ch. slate	4·00	25

Design: 10ch. Hwanghae iron works.

261 Torch, Chollima Statue and Cogwheel

1964. Asian Economic Seminar, Pyongyang. Multicoloured.

N524	5ch. Type **261**	40	15
N525	10ch. Flags, statue and cogwheel	55	20

262 Korean People and Statue of Kang Ho Yong (war hero)

1964. Struggle for Reunification of Korea.

N526	**262**	10ch. multicoloured	70	15

263 Hawk Fowl

1964. Domestic Poultry. Multicoloured.

N527	2ch. Type **263**	85	15
N528	4ch. White fowl	85	15
N529	5ch. Ryongyon fowl	1·30	15
N530	5ch. Black fowl	1·30	15
N531	40ch. Helmet guineafowl	4·25	1·30

264 Skiing

1964. Winter Olympic Games, Innsbruck.

N532	**264**	5ch. red, blue and buff	65	10
N533	-	10ch. blue, green & buff	1·10	15
N534	-	10ch. blue, red and buff	1·10	15

Designs: No. N533, Ice skating; No. N534, Skiing (slalom).

265 *Tobolsk* (passenger ship) and Flags

1964. Fifth Anniversary of Agreement for Repatriation of Koreans in Japan.

N535	**265**	10ch. red, blue & lt blue	1·60	25
N536	-	30ch. multicoloured	1·60	15

Design: 30ch. Return of repatriates.

266 Tonggun Pavilion Uiju

1964. Ancient Korean Buildings (2nd series). With gum.

N537	**266**	5ch. purple	35	15
N538	-	10ch. green	40	15

Design: 10ch. Inpang Pavilion, Kanggye City.

267 Cycling

1964. Olympic Games, Tokyo.

N539	-	2ch. brown and blue	35	15
N540	**267**	5ch. brown and green	1·00	15
N541	-	10ch. orange and blue	40	15
N542	-	10ch. orange and green	40	15
N543	-	40ch. brown and blue	85	50

Designs: Horiz—2ch. Rifle-shooting; 10ch. blue, Running. Vert—10ch. green, Wrestling; 40ch. Volleyball.

268 Burning of the *General Sherman*

1964. The *General Sherman* Incident, 1866. With gum.

N544	**268**	30ch. brown	3·00	40

269 Organising Guerrillas

1964. Guerrilla Operations in the 1930s against the Japanese. With gum.

N545	**269**	2ch. violet	40	15
N546	-	5ch. blue	55	15
N547	-	10ch. black	65	15

Designs: 5ch. Kim Il Sung addressing guerillas; 10ch. Battle scene at Xiaowangqing.

270 Students attacking

1964. Kwangju Students Rising, 1929. With gum.

N548	**270**	10ch. violet	2·20	15

271 Weightlifting

1964. GANEFO Athletic Games, Djakarta, Indonesia (1963). Multicoloured.

N549	2ch. Type **271**	40	15
N550	5ch. Athlete breasting tape	40	15
N551	5ch. Boxing (horiz)	40	15
N552	10ch. Football (horiz)	75	15
N553	10ch. Globe emblem (horiz)	65	15

272 Lynx

1964. Animals. With gum.

N554	2ch. sepia (Type **272**)	1·50	25
N555	5ch. sepia (Leopard cat)	3·75	25
N556	10ch. brown (Leopard)	4·50	25
N557	10ch. sepia (Yellow-throated marten)	4·50	25

273 Vietnamese Attack

1964. Support for People of Vietnam.

N558	**273**	10ch. multicoloured	55	15

274 Professor Kim Bong Han and Emblems

1964. Kyongrak Biological Systems.

N559	**274**	2ch. purple and olive	90	15
N560	-	5ch. green, orange & bl	1·30	15
N561	-	10ch. red, yellow & blue	1·70	15

Designs: 33×23½ mm—5ch. Bonghan duct; 10ch. Bonghan corpuscle. Each include emblems as in T **274**.

275 Farmers, Tractor and Lorry

1964. Agrarian Programme. Multicoloured.

N562	5ch. Type **275**	25	10
N563	10ch. Peasants with scroll and book	40	15
N564	10ch. Peasants, one writing in book	40	15

276 Chung Jin gets a Pistol

1964. The Struggle to capture Japanese Arms. With gum.

N565	**276**	4ch. brown	60	15

277 Girl with Korean Products

1964. Economic 7 Year Plan. Multicoloured. With gum (5ch.) or no gum (others).

N566	5ch. Type **277**	75	10
N567	10ch. Farm girl	75	15
N568	10ch. Couple on winged horse (23½×23½ mm)	50	15

278 Three Fairies Rock

1964. Diamond Mountains Scenery (2nd issue). Inscr '1964'. Multicoloured. Without gum (2, 4ch.) or with gum (others).

N569	2ch. Type **278**	1·00	15
N570	4ch. Ryonju Falls	3·50	20
N571	10ch. The Ten Thousand Rocks, Manmulsang	1·00	15
N572	10ch. Chinju Falls	3·50	20

280 Soldiers Advancing, Fusong

1965. Guerrilla Operations against the Japanese, 1934–1940. With gum.

N574	**280**	10ch. violet	45	15
N575	-	10ch. violet	45	15
N576	-	10ch. green	45	15

Designs: No. N575, Soldiers descending hill, Hongqihe; No. N576, Soldiers attacking hill post, Luozigou.

281 Tuman River

1965. Korean Rivers. Multicoloured.

N577	2ch. Type **281**	60	10
N578	5ch. Taedong (vert)	2·10	15
N579	10ch. Amnok	85	15

282 Union Badge

1965. First Congress of Landworkers' Union, Pyongyang. With gum.

N580	**282**	10ch. multicoloured	70	15

283 Furnacemen and Workers

1965. 10 Major Tasks of 7 Year Plan. With gum.

N581	**283**	10ch. multicoloured	55	15

284 Miners' Strike, Sinhung Colliery

1965. 35th Anniversary of Strikes and Peasants' Revolt. With gum.

N582	**284**	10ch. olive	1·70	15
N583	-	10ch. brown	2·10	15
N584	-	40ch. purple	1·40	25

Designs: 10ch. Strikers at Pyongyang Rubber Factory; 40ch. Revolt of Tanchon peasants.

285 Embankment Construction

1965. Sunhwa River Works. With gum.

N585	**285**	10ch. multicoloured	40	15

286 Hand holding Torch

1965. Fifth Anniversary of South Korean Rising of April 19th. Multicoloured. With gum.

N586	10ch. Type **286**	35	15
N587	40ch. Student-hero, Kim Chio	70	15

287 Power Station under Construction

1965. Construction of Thermal Power Station, Pyongyang. With gum.

N588	**287**	5ch. brown and blue	75	15

288 African and Asian

1965. Tenth Anniversary of First Afro-Asian Conference, Bandung. With gum.

N589	**288**	10ch. multicoloured	50	15

289 Rejoicing of Koreans

1965. Tenth Anniversary of General Association of Koreans in Japan. With gum.

N590	**289**	10ch. blue and red	45	15
N591	-	40ch. indigo, blue & red	70	25

Design: 40ch. Patriot and flag.

290 Workers in Battle

1965. Second Afro-Asian Conference, Algiers. With gum.

N592	**290**	10ch. black, yellow red	1·10	15
N593	-	40ch. black, yellow red	1·80	40

Design: 40ch. Korean and African soldiers.
The Algiers Conference did not take place.

291 Victory 64 10-ton Lorry

1965. With gum.

N594	**291**	10ch. green	1·70	25

292 Kim Chang Gol

1965. War Heroes (1st series). With gum.

N595	**292**	10ch. green	40	15
N596	-	10ch. brown	40	15
N597	-	40ch. purple	1·30	50

Portraits: No. N596, Cho Gun Sil and machine-gun; No. N597, An Hak Ryong and machine-gun.

See also Nos. N781/N783 and N842/N843.

293 Marx and Lenin

1965. Postal Ministers' Congress, Peking. With gum.

N598	**293**	10ch. black, yellow red	2·00	30

294 Lake Samil

1965. Diamond Mountains Scenery (3rd issue). Multicoloured. With gum.

N599	2ch. Type **294**	85	15
N600	5ch. Chipson Peak	1·40	15
N601	10ch. Kwanum Falls	3·75	30

295 Amnok River, Kusimuldong

1965. Scenes of Japanese War. With gum.

N602	**295**	5ch. green and blue	50	15
N603	-	10ch. turquoise and blue	85	15

Design: 10ch. Lake Samji.

296 Footballer and Games' Emblem

1965. GANEFO Football Games, Pyongyang. Multicoloured. With gum.

N604	10ch. Type **296**	1·30	20
N605	10ch. Games emblem and Moranbong Stadium	1·30	20

297 Workers and Map

1965. 20th Anniversary of Liberation from Japan. With gum.

N606	**297**	10ch. multicoloured	40	15

298 Engels

1965. 145th Birth Anniversary of Engels. With gum.

N607	**298**	10ch. brown	40	15

299 Pole Vaulting

1965. Sports. Multicoloured. With gum.

N608	2ch. Type **299**	50	10
N609	4ch. Throwing the javelin	2·10	25
N610	10ch. Throwing the discus	60	15
N611	10ch. High jumping (horiz)	60	15
N612	10ch. Putting the shot (horiz)	60	15

301 Korean Fighters

1965. 20th Anniversary of Korean Workers' Party. Each black, yellow and red. With gum.

N613	10ch. Type **301**	1·10	40
N614	10ch. Party emblem	1·10	40
N615	10ch. Lenin and Marx	1·10	40
N616	10ch. Workers marching	1·10	40
N617	10ch. Fighters	1·10	40
N618	40ch. Workers	1·10	40
MSN619	191×99 mm. Nos. N613/N618	40·00	23·00

Nos. N613/N618 each have a red banner in the background and were issued together in blocks of six (3×2), forming a composite design, within the sheet.

302 Kim Chaek Iron Works

1965. With gum.

N620	**302**	10ch. purple	5·00	15
N621	-	10ch. brown	5·00	15

Design: No. N621, Chongjin Steel Works.

303 Grass Carp

1965. Freshwater Fish. Multicoloured. With gum.

N622	2ch. Rainbow trout	1·00	15
N623	4ch. Dolly Varden charr	1·10	15
N624	10ch. Brown trout (surfacing water)	2·10	15
N625	10ch. Common carp diving (date at left)	2·10	15
N626	10ch. Type **303**	2·10	15
N627	40ch. Crucian carp	3·25	40

304 Building House

1965. Kim Hong Do's Drawings. With gum.

N628	2ch. green (Type **304**)	60	15
N629	4ch. purple (Weaving)	1·30	15
N630	10ch. brown (Wrestling)	1·10	15
N631	10ch. blue (School class)	1·10	15
N632	10ch. red (Dancing)	1·70	15
N633	10ch. violet (Blacksmiths)	1·50	15

305 Children in Workshop

1965. Life at Pyongyang Children's and Students' Palace. Multicoloured. With gum.

N634	2ch. Type **305**	25	10
N635	4ch. Boxing	25	10
N636	10ch. Chemistry	1·00	20
N637	10ch. Playing violin and accordion	1·00	20

306 Whale-catcher

1965. Korean Fishing Boats. With gum.

N638	**306**	10ch. blue	1·70	35
N639	-	10ch. green	1·70	35

Design: No. N639, Fishing fleet service vessel.

307 Great Tit

1965. Korean Birds. Inscr '1965'. Multicoloured. With gum.

N640	4ch. Black-capped kingfisher (vert)	2·40	35
N641	10ch. Type **307**	3·25	55
N642	10ch. Pied wagtail (facing left)	3·25	55
N643	10ch. Azure-winged magpie (facing right)	3·25	55
N644	40ch. Black-tailed hawfinch	8·50	1·10

308 Silkworm Moth (*Bombyx mori*) and Cocoon

1965. Korean Sericulture. With gum.

N645	**308**	2ch. green	42·00	1·50
N646	-	10ch. brown	42·00	1·50
N647	-	10ch. purple	42·00	1·50

Moths and Cocoons: No. N646, Ailathus silk moth (*Samia cynthia*); No. N647, Chinese oak silk moth (*Antheraea pernyi*).

309 Hooded Crane

1965. Wading Birds. With gum.

N648	**309**	2ch. brown	4·50	40
N649	-	10ch. blue	5·00	65
N650	-	10ch. purple	5·00	65
N651	-	40ch. green	9·25	1·40

Birds: No. N649, Japanese white-naped crane; No. N650, Manchurian crane; No. N651, Grey heron.

310 Japanese Common Squid

1965. Korean Molluscs. Multicoloured. With gum.

N652	5ch. Type **310**	2·10	30
N653	10ch. Giant Pacific octopus	3·00	45

311 Spotbill Duck

1965. Korean Ducks. Multicoloured. With gum.

N654	2ch. Type **311**	3·25	40
N655	4ch. Ruddy shelduck	3·25	45
N656	10ch. Mallard	5·00	90
N657	40ch. Baikal teal	7·25	1·60

312 Circus Theatre, Pyongyang

1965. Korean Circus. With gum except No. N661.

N658	**312**	2ch. blue, black & brown	65	20
N659	-	10ch. blue, red and black	1·70	30
N660	-	10ch. red, black & green	1·70	30
N661	-	10ch. orange, sepia and green	1·70	30
N662	-	10ch. red, yellow & turq	1·70	30

Designs: Vert—No. N659, Trapeze artistes; No. N660, Performer with hoops on seesaw; No. N661, Tightrope dancers; No. N662, Performer with revolving cap on stick.

313 Marvel of Peru (*Mirabilis jalapa*)

1965. Korean Flowers. Multicoloured. With gum except No. N663.

N663	4ch. Type **313**	2·20	25
N664	10ch. Peony	3·50	40
N665	10ch. Moss rose	3·50	40
N666	10ch. Magnolia	3·50	40

314 Finn Class Dinghy

1965. Yachts. Multicoloured. With gum.

N667	2ch. Type **314**	75	25
N668	10ch. 5.5m class yacht	1·20	40
N669	10ch. Dragon class yacht	1·20	40
N670	40ch. Star class yacht	2·50	85

315 Cuban, Korean and African

1966. African, Asian and Latin American Friendship Conference, Havana. With gum.

N671	**315**	10ch. multicoloured	40	15

316 Hosta

1966. Wild Flowers. Mult. With gum. (a) 1st series.

N672	2ch. Type **316**	1·10	25
N673	4ch. Dandelion	1·10	25
N674	10ch. Pink convolvulus	1·60	25
N675	10ch. Lily-of-the-valley	1·60	25
N676	40ch. Catalpa blossom	4·75	65

(b) 2nd series.

N677	2ch. Polyanthus	1·10	25
N678	4ch. Lychnis	1·10	25
N679	10ch. Adonis	1·60	25
N680	10ch. Orange lily	1·60	25
N681	90ch. Rhododendron	7·50	80

Nos. N672/N676 exist imperf and without gum.

317 Farmer and Wife

1966. 20th Anniversary of Land Reform Law. With gum.

N682	**317**	10ch. multicoloured	40	15

318 Troops advancing, Dashahe

1966. Paintings of Guerrilla Battles, 1937–1939. With gum, except No. N684.

N683	**318**	10ch. red	50	15
N684	-	10ch. turquoise	50	15
N685	-	10ch. purple	50	15

Designs and Battles: No. N684, Troops firing from trees, Taehongdan; No. N685, Troops on hillside, Jiansanfeng.

319 Silla Bowl

1966. Art Treasures of Silla Dynasty. With gum.

N686	**319**	2ch. ochre	1·70	30
N687	-	5ch. black	1·70	30
N688	-	10ch. violet	1·70	30

Designs: 5ch. Earthenware jug. 10ch. Censer.

320 Hands holding Torch, Rifle and Hammer

1966. 80th Anniversary of Labour Day. With gum.

N689	**320**	10ch. multicoloured	45	15

321 Torch and Patriots

1966. 30th Anniversary of Association for Restoration of Fatherland.

N690	**321**	10ch. red and yellow	50	15

322 Harvester

1966. Aid for Agriculture. Multicoloured.

N691	5ch. Type **322**	35	15
N692	10ch. Labourer	45	15

323 Young Pioneers

1966. 20th Anniversary of Korean Children's Union. Without gum.

N693	**323**	10ch. multicoloured	45	15

324 Kangson Steel Works

1966. Korean Industries. With gum.

N694	**324**	10ch. grey	5·00	20
N695	-	10ch. red (Pongung Chemical Works)	5·00	20

325 Pacific Saury

1966. Korean Fish. With gum, except Nos. N699/N700.

N696	**325**	2ch. blue, green and purple	1·20	25
N697	-	5ch. purple, green & brn	1·50	25
N698	-	10ch. blue, buff & green	2·75	50
N699	-	10ch. purple and green	2·75	50
N700	-	40ch. green, buff & blue	6·25	85

Fish: 5ch. Pacific cod; 10ch. (No. N698), Chum salmon, (No. N699), Yellowfish; 40ch. Pink salmon.

326 Professor Kim Bong Han

1966. Kyungrak Biological System. With gum.

N701	**326**	2ch. blue, green and yellow	85	25
N702	-	4ch. multicoloured	85	25
N703	-	5ch. multicoloured	85	25
N704	-	10ch. multicoloured	85	25
N705	-	10ch. multicoloured	85	25
N706	-	10ch. multicoloured	85	25
N707	-	15ch. multicoloured	85	25
N708	-	40ch. multicoloured	85	25
MSN709		117×141 mm. Nos. N701/N708	24·00	23·00

Designs: No. N704, Kyongrak Institute; No. N708, Figure of Man; Nos. N702/N703, N705/N707, Diagram of system.

Nos. N701/N708 were issued together, *se-tenant*, forming a composite design.

327 Leonov in Space (*Voskhod 2*)

1966. Cosmonauts Day. Multicoloured.

N710	5ch. Type **327**	25	15
N711	10ch. *Luna 9*	85	40
N712	40ch. *Luna 10*	1·60	65

328 Footballers

1966. World Cup Football Championship. Multicoloured.

N713	10ch. Type **328**	1·70	40
N714	10ch. Jules Rimet Cup, football and boots	1·70	40
N715	10ch. Goalkeeper saving goal (vert)	1·70	40

329 Defence of Seoul

1966. Korean War of 1950–1953. With gum.

N716	**329**	10ch. green	65	15
N717	-	10ch. purple	65	15
N718	-	10ch. purple	65	15

Designs: No. N717, Battle on Mt. Napal; No. N718, Battle for Heigt 1211.

330 Women in Industry

1966. 20th Anniversary of Sex Equality Law.

N719	**330**	10ch. multicoloured	45	15

331 Industrial Workers

1966. 20th Anniversary of Industrial Nationalisation.

N720	**331**	10ch. multicoloured	1·30	20

332 Water-jar Dance

1966. Korean Dances. Multicoloured. 5, 40ch. with or without gum; others without.

N721	5ch. Type **332**	1·30	20
N722	10ch. Bell dance	2·10	35
N723	10ch. Dancer in a Mural Painting	2·10	35
N724	15ch. Sword dance	2·10	40
N725	40ch. Gold Cymbal dance	3·75	70

333 Korean attacking US Soldier

1966. Korean Reunification Campaign. With gum.

N726	**333**	10ch. green	85	20
N727	-	10ch. purple	85	20
N728	-	10ch. lilac	5·00	1·10

Designs: No. N727, Korean with young child; No. N728, Korean with shovel, industrial scene and electric train.

334 Yakovlev Yak-12M Crop-spraying

1966. Industrial Uses of Aircraft. With gum except 2 and 5ch.

N729	**334**	2ch. green and purple	50	10
N730	-	5ch. brown and green	7·25	80
N731	-	10ch. brown and blue	1·70	30
N732	-	40ch. brown and blue	1·70	30

Designs: 5ch. Yakovlev Yak-18U (forest-fire observation); 10ch. Lisunov Li-2 (geological survey); 40ch. Lisunov Li-2 (detection of fish shoals).

1966. Korean Revolutionaries (3rd issue). As T **212**. With gum.

N733	10ch. violet (O Jung Hub)	
N734	10ch. green (Kim Gyong Sok)	
N735	10ch. blue (Li Dong Gol)	

335 Kim Il Sung University

1966. 20th Anniversary of Kim Il Sung University. With gum.

N736	**335**	10ch. violet	65	15

336 Judo

1966. Ganefo Games, Phnom Penh.

N737	**336**	5ch. black, green and blue	60	20
N738	-	10ch. blk, grn & dp grn	60	20
N739	-	10ch. black and red	60	20

Designs: No. N738, Basketball; No. N739, Table tennis.

337 Hoopoe

1966. Korean Birds. Multicoloured. Inscr '1966'.

N740	2ch. Common rosefinch (horiz)	1·80	30
N741	5ch. Type **337**	2·10	35
N742	10ch. Black-breasted thrush (blue background) (horiz)	2·50	55
N743	10ch. Crested lark (green background) (horiz)	2·50	55
N744	40ch. White-bellied black woodpecker	5·75	1·10

338 Building Construction

1966. Increased Production with Economy. Multicoloured. Without gum (40ch.) or with gum (others).

N745	5ch. Type **338**	35	10
N746	10ch. Furnaceman and graph	60	15
N747	10ch. Machine-tool production	60	15
N748	40ch. Miners and pit-head	1·80	50

339 Parachuting

1966. National Defence Sports. With gum.

N749	**339**	2ch. brown	1·00	20
N750	-	5ch. red	65	15
N751	-	10ch. blue	3·50	60
N752	-	40ch. green	2·10	40

Designs: 5ch. Show jumping; 10ch. Motorcycle racing; 40ch. Radio receiving and transmitting competition.

340 *Samil Wolgan* (Association Magazine)

1966. 30th Anniversary of *Samil Wolgan* Magazine.

N753	**340**	10ch. multicoloured	1·20	20

341 Red Deer

1966. Korean Deer. Multicoloured.

N754	2ch. Type **341**	85	25
N755	5ch. Sika deer	1·30	25
N756	10ch. Indian muntjac (erect)	2·10	25
N757	10ch. Reindeer (grazing)	2·10	25
N758	70ch. Fallow deer	6·25	80

342 Blueberries

1966. Wild Fruit. Multicoloured.

N759	2ch. Type **342**	50	15
N760	5ch. Wild pears	75	20
N761	10ch. Wild raspberries	1·00	20
N762	10ch. Schizandra	1·00	20
N763	10ch. Wild plums	1·00	20
N764	40ch. Jujube	2·75	45

343 Onpo Rest Home

1966. Korean Rest Homes. With gum.

N765	**343**	2ch. violet	40	15
N766	-	5ch. turquoise	40	15
N767	-	10ch. green	65	20
N768	-	40ch. black	1·30	30

Rest Homes: 5ch. Mt. Myohyang; 10ch. Songdowon; 40ch. Hongwon.

344 Soldier

1967. 19th Anniversary of Army Day. Without gum.

N769	**344**	10ch. green, yellow and red	40	15

345 Sow

1967. Domestic Animals. Multicoloured. Without gum. 40ch. also with gum.

N770	5ch. Type **345**	1·30	40
N771	10ch. Goat	1·70	40
N772	40ch. Ox	4·25	1·00

346 Battle Scene

1967. 30th Anniversary of Battle of Pochonbo. With gum.

N773	**346**	10ch. orange, red and green	65	20

347 Students

1967. Compulsory Technical Education for Nine Years.

N774	**347**	10ch. multicoloured	40	15

348 Table Tennis Player

1967. 29th International Table Tennis Championships, Pyongyang. Designs showing players in action. 5ch. with or without gum.

N775	**348**	5ch. multicoloured	60	15
N776	-	10ch. multicoloured	1·00	20
N777	-	40ch. multicoloured	1·50	35

349 Anti-aircraft Defences

1967. Paintings of Guerrilla War against the Japanese. With gum.

N778	**349**	10ch. blue	40	15
N779	-	10ch. purple	3·75	40
N780	-	10ch. violet	40	15

Paintings: No. N779, Blowing-up railway bridge; No. N780, People helping guerrillas in Wangyugou.

1967. War Heroes (2nd series). As T **292**. Designs showing portraits and combat scenes. With gum.

N781	10ch. slate	50	15
N782	10ch. violet	50	15
N783	10ch. blue	1·30	20

Portraits: No. N781, Ri Dae Hun and grenade-throwing; No. N782, Choe Jong Un and soldiers charging; No. N783, Kim Hwa Ryong and Lavochkin La-11.

350 Workers

1967. Labour Day.

N784	**350**	10ch. multicoloured	40	15

351 Card Game

1967. Korean Children. Multicoloured.

N785	5ch. Type **351**	1·10	20
N786	10ch. Children modelling tractor	60	15
N787	40ch. Children playing with ball	1·20	30

352 Victory Monument

1967. Unveiling of Battle of Ponchonbo Monument.

N788	**352**	10ch. multicoloured	50	15

353 Attacking Tank

1967. Monuments to War of 1950–1953. 2ch. with or without gum.

N789	**353**	2ch. green and turquoise	25	10
N790	-	5ch. sepia and green	65	10
N791	-	10ch. brown and buff	50	15
N792	-	40ch. brown and blue	1·30	50

Monuments: 5ch. Soldier-musicians; 10ch. Soldier; 40ch. Soldier with children.

354 *Polygonatum japonicum*

1967. Medicinal Plants. Multicoloured; background colour of 10ch. values given to aid identification. Nos. N793/N795 and N797 with or without gum.

N793	2ch. Type **354**	1·20	20
N794	5ch. *Hibiscus manihot*	1·20	20
N795	10ch. *Scutellaria baicalensis* (turquoise)	1·40	25
N796	10ch. *Pulsatilla koreana* (blue)	1·40	25
N797	10ch. *Rehmannian glutinosa* (yellow)	1·40	25
N798	40ch. *Tanacetum boreale*	3·75	85

355 Servicemen

1967. People's Army. Multicoloured. 5ch. with or without gum.

N799	5ch. Type **355**	25	10
N800	10ch. Soldier and farmer	35	15
N801	10ch. Officer decorating soldier	35	15

356 Freighter *Chollima*

1967. With gum.

N802	**356**	10ch. green	1·50	30

357 *Reclamation of Tideland*

1967. *Heroic Struggle of the Chollima Riders.* Paintings. Without gum (5ch.) or with gum (others).

N803	-	5ch. brown	50	15
N804	**357**	10ch. grey	65	20
N805	-	10ch. green	1·10	20

Designs: Vert—5ch. *Drilling Rock Precipice*; 10ch. (No. N805), *Felling Trees*.

358 *Erimaculus isenbeckii*

1967. Crabs. Multicoloured.

N806	2ch. Type **358**	1·00	20
N807	5ch. *Neptunus trituberculatus*	1·30	20
N808	10ch. *Paralithodes camtschatica*	1·80	35
N809	40ch. *Chionoecetes opilio*	3·25	65

359 Electric Train and Hand switching Points

1967. Propaganda for Reunification of Korea.

N810	**359**	10ch. multicoloured	3·25	75

360 Tongrim Waterfall

1967. Korean Waterfalls. 2ch. with or without gum. Multicoloured.

N811	2ch. Type **360**	3·50	55
N812	10ch. Sanju waterfall, Mt. Myohyang	4·25	75
N813	40ch. Sambang waterfall, Mt. Chonak	6·75	1·40

361 Chollima Flying Horse and Banners

1967. The Revolutionary Surge Upwards. Various designs incorporating the Chollima Flying Horse.

N814	-	5ch. blue	4·25	35
N815	-	10ch. red	75	15
N816	-	10ch. green	75	15
N817	-	10ch. lilac	75	15
N818	**361**	10ch. red	65	15

Designs: Horiz—5ch. Ship, electric train and lorry (Transport); No. N815, Bulldozers (Building construction); No. N816, Tractors (Rural development); No. N817, Heavy presses (Machine-building industry).

362 Lenin

1967. 50th Anniversary of Russian October Revolution.

N819	**362**	10ch. brown, yell & red	50	15

363 Voters and Banner

1967. Korean Elections. Multicoloured.

N820	10ch. Type **363**	45	15
N821	10ch. Woman casting vote (vert)	45	15

364 Cinereous Black Vulture

1967. Birds of Prey. Multicoloured. With gum.

N822	2ch. Type **364**	3·00	60
N823	10ch. Booted eagle (horiz)	5·75	1·10
N824	40ch. White-bellied sea eagle	7·50	1·50

365 Chongjin

1967. North Korean Cities. With gum.

N825	**365**	5ch. green	90	20
N826	-	10ch. lilac	90	20
N827	-	10ch. violet	90	20

Designs: No. N826, Humhung; No. N827, Sinuiju.

366 Soldier brandishing Red Book

1967. 'Let us carry out the Decisions of the Workers' Party Conference!'. Multicoloured.

N828	10ch. Type **366**	40	15
N829	10ch. Militiaman holding bayonet	40	15
N830	10ch. Foundryman and bayonet	40	15

367 Whaler firing Harpoon

1967. With gum.

N831	**367**	10ch. blue	1·10	40

368 Airman, Soldier and Sailor

1968. 20th Anniversary of People's Army. Multicoloured. With gum.

N832	10ch. Type **368**	40	20
N833	10ch. Soldier below attack in snow	40	20
N834	10ch. Soldier below massed ranks	40	20
N835	10ch. Soldier holding flag	40	20
N836	10ch. Soldier holding book	40	20
N837	10ch. Soldiers and armed workers with flag	40	20
N838	10ch. Furnaceman and soldier	40	20
N839	10ch. Soldier saluting	40	20
N840	10ch. Charging soldiers	40	20
N841	10ch. Soldier, sailor and airman below flag	40	20

1968. War Heroes (3rd series). As T **292**. With gum.

N842	10ch. violet	40	15
N843	10ch. purple	40	15

Portraits: No. N842, Han Gye Ryol firing Bren gun; No. N843, Li Su Bok charging up hill.

369 Dredger *September 2*

370 Ten-storey Flats, East Pyongyang

371 Palace of Students and Children, Kaesong

1968. With gum.

N844	**369**	5ch. green	1·00	20
N845	**370**	10ch. blue	45	15
N846	**371**	10ch. blue	45	15

372 Marshal Kim Il Sung

1968. Marshal Kim Il Sung's 56th Birthday. With gum.

N847	**372**	40ch. multicoloured	85	50

373 Kim Il Sung with Mother

1968. Childhood of Kim Il Sung. Multicoloured.

N848	10ch. Type **373**	50	15
N849	10ch. Kim Il Sung with his father	50	15
N850	10ch. Setting out from home, aged 13	50	15
N851	10ch. Birthplace at Mangyongdae	50	15
N852	10ch. Mangyong Hill	50	15

374 Matsu-take Mushroom

1968. Mushrooms. With gum.

N853	**374**	5ch. brown and green	25·00	1·40
N854	-	10ch. ochre, brn & grn	42·00	1·50
N855	-	10ch. brown and green	42·00	1·50

Designs: No. N854, Black mushroom; No. N855, Cultivated mushroom.

375 Leaping Horseman

1968. 20th Anniversary of Korean People's Democratic Republic. Multicoloured. With gum.

N856	10ch. Type **375**	1·40	30
N857	10ch. Four servicemen	1·40	30
N858	10ch. Soldier with bayonet	1·40	30
N859	10ch. Advancing with banners	1·40	30
N860	10ch. Statue	1·40	30
N861	10ch. Korean flag	1·40	30
N862	10ch. Soldier and peasant with flag	1·40	30
N863	10ch. Machine-gunner with flag	1·40	30

376 Domestic Products

1968. Development of Light Industries. Multicoloured. With gum.

N864	2ch. Type **376**	35	15
N865	5ch. Textiles	1·40	15
N866	10ch. Tinned produce	50	15

377 Proclaiming the Ten Points

1968. Kim Il Sung's Ten Point Political Programme. Multicoloured.

N867	2ch. Type **377**	20	10
N868	5ch. Soldier and artisan (horiz)	30	10

378 Livestock

1968. Development of Agriculture. Multicoloured. With gum.

N869	5ch. Type **378**	35	10
N870	10ch. Fruit-growing	35	15
N871	10ch. Wheat-harvesting	35	15

379 Yesso Scallop

1968. Shellfish. Multicoloured. With gum.

N872	5ch. Type **379**	1·70	20
N873	5ch. *Meretrix chione* (venus clam)	1·70	20
N874	10ch. *Modiolus hanleyi* (mussel)	3·00	35

380 Kim Il Sung at Head of Columns

1968. Battle of Pochonbo Monument. Detail of Monument. Multicoloured.

N875	10ch. Type **380**	35	20
N876	10ch. Head of right-hand column	35	20
N877	10ch. Tail of right-hand column	35	20
N878	10ch. Head of left-hand column	35	20
N879	10ch. Tail of left-hand column	35	20
N880	10ch. Centre of right-hand column	35	20
N881	10ch. Centre of left-hand column	35	20

Sizes: Horiz—Nos. N876/N878, 43×28 mm. N880/N881, 56×28 mm.

The centrepiece of the Monument is flanked by two columns of soldiers, headed by Kim Il Sung.

381 Museum of the Revolution, Pochonbo

382 Grand Theatre, Pyongyang

1968

N883	**381**	2ch. green	30	10
N884	**382**	10ch. brown	90	20

383 Irrigation

1969. Rural Development. Multicoloured.

N885	3ch. Type **383**	25	10
N886	5ch. Agricultural mechanization	25	10
N887	10ch. Electrification	50	15
N888	40ch. Applying fertilisers and spraying trees	85	20

384 Grey Rabbits

1969. Rabbits. Multicoloured. With or without gum.

N889	2ch. Type **384**	1·50	25
N890	10ch. Black rabbits	1·70	25
N891	10ch. Brown rabbits	1·70	25
N892	10ch. White rabbits	1·70	25
N893	40ch. Doe and young	4·50	50

385 Age and Youth

1969. Public Health Service.

N894	**385**	2ch. brown and blue	50	10
N895	-	10ch. blue and red	1·00	20
N896	-	40ch. green and yellow	2·10	40

Designs: 10ch. Nurse with syringe; 40ch. Auscultation by woman doctor.

386 Sowing Rice Seed

1969. Agricultural Mechanisation.

N897	**386**	10ch. green	75	20
N898	-	10ch. orange	75	20
N899	-	10ch. black	75	20
N900	-	10ch. brown	75	20

Designs: No. N898, Rice harvester; No. N899, Weed-spraying machine; No. N900, Threshing machine.

387 Ponghwa

1969. Revolutionary Historical Sites. Multicoloured.

N901	10ch. Type **387**	55	15
N902	10ch. Mangyongdae, birthplace of Kim Il Sung	55	15

388 Kim crosses into Manchuria, 1926, aged 13

1969. Kim Il Sung in Manchuria. Multicoloured. No. N907 with gum.

N903	10ch. Type **388**	50	20
N904	10ch. Leading strike of Yuwen Middle School boys, 1927	50	20
N905	10ch. Leading anti-Japanese demonstration in Kirin, 1928	50	20
N906	10ch. Presiding at meeting of Young Communist League, 1930	50	20
N907	10ch. Meeting of young revolutionaries	50	20

389 Birthplace at Chilgol

1969. Commemoration of Mrs. Kang Ban Sok, mother of Kim Il Sung. Multicoloured.

N908	10ch. Type **389**	40	15
N909	10ch. With members of Women's Association	40	15
N910	10ch. Resisting Japanese police	3·50	75

390 Begaebong Bivouac

1969. Bivouac Sites in the Guerrilla War against the Japanese. Multicoloured.

N911	5ch. Type **390**	25	10
N912	10ch. Mupo site (horiz)	40	15
N913	10ch. Chongbong site	40	15
N914	40ch. Konchang site (horiz)	1·40	55

391 Chollima Statue

392 Museum of the Revolution, Pyongyang

1969

N915	**391**	10ch. blue	40	15
N916	**392**	10ch. green	40	15

393 Mangyong Chickens

1969. Korean Poultry.

N917	**393**	10ch. blue	1·30	25
N918	-	10ch. violet	3·75	45

Design: No. N918, Kwangpo ducks.

394 Marshal Kim Il Sung and Children

1969. Kim Il Sung's Educational System. Multicoloured.

N919	2ch. Type **394**	10	10
N920	10ch. Worker with books	25	15
N921	40ch. Students with books	1·00	55

395 Statue of Marshal Kim Il Sung

1969. Memorials on Pochonbo Battlefield. Inscr '1937.6.4'. Multicoloured.

N922	5ch. Machine-gun post	35	15
N923	10ch. Type **395**	35	15
N924	10ch. *Aspen-tree* monument	35	15
N925	10ch. Glade Konjang Hill	35	15

396 Teaching at Myongsin School

1969. Commemoration of Kim Hyong Jik, father of Kim Il Sung. Multicoloured.

N926	10ch. Type **396**	45	15
N927	10ch. Secret meeting with Korean National Association members	45	15

397 Relay Runner

1969. 20th Anniversary of Sports Day.

N928	**397**	10ch. multicoloured	55	15

398 President Nixon attacked by Pens

1969. Anti-US Imperialism Journalists' Conference, Pyongyang.

N929	**398**	10ch. multicoloured	1·20	15

399 Fighters and Battle

1969. Implementation of Ten-Point Programme of Kim Il Sung. Multicoloured.

N930	5ch. Type **399** (Reunification of Korea)	40	15
N931	10ch. Workers upholding slogan (vert)	40	15

400 Bayonet Attack over US Flag

1969. Anti-American Campaign.

N932	**400**	10ch. multicoloured	50	15

401 Armed Workers

1969. Struggle for the Reunification of Korea. Multicoloured.

N933	10ch. Workers stabbing US soldier (vert)	25	15
N934	10ch. Kim Il Sung and crowd with flags (vert)	25	15
N935	50ch. Type **401**	70	25

402 Buri

1969. Korean Fish. Multicoloured.

N936	5ch. Type **402**	85	15
N937	10ch. Eastern dace	1·30	20
N938	40ch. Flat-headed grey mullet	3·00	45

403 Freighter *Taesungsan*

1969

N939	**403**	10ch. purple	1·00	20

405 Dahwangwai (1935)

1970. Guerrilla Conference Places.

N940	**405**	2ch. blue and green	35	10
N941	-	5ch. brown and green	35	10
N942	-	10ch. lt green & green	35	10

Designs: 5ch. Yaoyinggou (barn) (1935); 10ch. Xiaohaerbaling (tent) (1940).

406 Lake Chon

1970. Mt. Paekdu, Home of Revolution (1st issue). Inscr '1970'.

N943	**406**	10ch. black, brown & grn	50	20
N944	-	10ch. black, green & yell	50	20
N945	-	10ch. purple, blue & yell	50	20
N946	-	10ch. black, blue and pink	50	20

Designs: No. N944, Piryu Peak; No. N945, Pyongsa (Soldier) Peak; No. N946, Changgun (General) Peak.

See also Nos. N979/N981.

407 Vietnamese Soldier and Furnaceman

1970. Help for the Vietnamese People.

N947	**407**	10ch. green, brown & red	40	15

408 Receiving his Father's Revolvers from his Mother

1970. Revolutionary Career of Kim Il Sung. Multicoloured.

N948	10ch. Type **408**	90	25
N949	10ch. Receiving smuggled weapons from his mother	90	25
N950	10ch. Talking to farm workers	90	25
N951	10ch. At Kalun meeting, 1930	90	25

409 Lenin

1970. Birth Centenary of Lenin.

N952	**409**	10ch. brown & cinnamon	45	15
N953	-	10ch. brown and green	45	15

Design: No. N953, Lenin making a speech.

410 March of Koreans

1970. 15th Anniversary of Association of Koreans in Japan.

N954	**410**	10ch. red	30	15
N955	**410**	10ch. purple	30	15

411 Uniformed Factory Worker

1970. Workers' Militia.

N956	**411**	10ch. green, brn & mve	30	10
N957	-	10ch. green, brown & bl	30	10

Design: Horiz—No. N957, Militiaman saluting.

412 Students and Newspapers

1970. Peasant Education. Multicoloured.

N958	2ch. Type **412**	50	10
N959	5ch. Peasant with book	25	10
N960	10ch. Students in class	25	10

413 Electricity Flows

1970. Commemoration of Army Electrical Engineers.

N961	**413**	10ch. brown	50	15

414 Soldier with Rifle

1970. Campaign Month for Withdrawal of US Troops from South Korea.

N962	**414**	5ch. violet	15	10
N963	-	10ch. purple	40	10

Design: 10ch. Soldier and partisan.

415 Rebel wielding Weapons

1970. Struggle in South Korea against US Imperialism.

N964	**415**	10ch. violet	30	15

416 Labourer (Fertilisers)

1970. Encouragement of Increased Productivity.

N965	**416**	10ch. green, pink & brn	50	15
N966	-	10ch. green, red & brn	1·00	20
N967	-	10ch. blue, green & brn	50	15
N968	-	10ch. bistre, brn & grn	50	15
N969	-	10ch. violet, green & brn	65	15

Designs: No. N966, Furnaceman (Steel); No. N967, Operative (Machines); No. N968, Labourer (Building Construction); No. N969, Miner (Mining).

417 Railway Guard

1970. Speed the Transport System.

N970	**417**	10ch. blue, orange & grn	1·70	35

418 Agriculture

1970. Executive Decisions of the Workers' Party Congress. Designs embodying book.

N971	**418**	5ch. red	35	10
N972	-	10ch. green	1·50	25
N973	-	40ch. green	1·50	25

Designs: 10ch. Industry; 40ch. The Armed Forces.

419 Chollima Statue and Workers' Party Banner

1970. 25th Anniversary of Korean Workers' Party.

N974	**419**	10ch. red, brown & buff	35	15

420 Kim Il Sung and the People

1970. Fifth Congress of Workers' Party. Miniature sheet (153×92 mm) comprising ten stamps as T **420** (10ch. values with symbols and inscr in panel at right).

MSN975	Multicoloured, comprising 40ch. T **420** and nine 10ch. stamps showing Family and new housing; Advance with Kim Il Sung's programme; People's army; Furnaceman and industry; Anti-US Imperialism; Peasants and agriculture; Students with books; Schoolgirl with book; Collaboration with Freedom Fighters	18·00	8·00

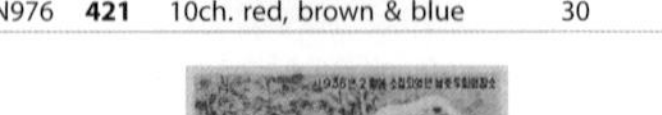
421 Emblem of League

1971. 25th Anniversary of League of Socialist Working Youth.

N976	**421**	10ch. red, brown & blue	30	15

422 Log Cabin, Nanhutou

1971. 35th Anniversary of Nanhutou Guerrilla Conference.

N977	**422**	10ch. multicoloured	30	15

423 Tractor Driver

1971. 25th Anniversary of Land Reform Law.

N978	**423**	2ch. red, green and black	30	15

1971. Mt. Paekdu, Home of Revolution (2nd issue). As T **406** but inscr '1971'.

N979	2ch. black, olive and green	50	15
N980	5ch. pink, black and slate	3·00	60
N981	10ch. black, red and grey	85	20

Designs: Horiz—2ch. General view; 10ch. Western peak. Vert—5ch. Waterfall.

424 Popyong Museum

1971. Museum of the Revolution.

N982	**424**	10ch. brown and yellow	25	15
N983	-	10ch. blue and orange	25	15
N984	-	10ch. green and orange	25	15

Designs: No. N983, Mangyongdae Museum; No. N984, Chunggang Museum.

425 Miner

1971. Six Year Plan for Coal Industry.

N985	**425**	10ch. multicoloured	65	25

426 Kim Il Sung

1971. Founding of Anti-Japanese Guerrilla Army. Multicoloured.

N986	10ch. Type **426**	50	20
N987	10ch. Kim Il Sung founding Anti-Japanese Guerrilla Army (horiz)	50	20
N988	10ch. Kim Il Sung addressing the people (horiz)	50	20
N989	10ch. Kim Il Sung and members of Children's Corps (horiz)	50	20

428 Hands holding Hammer and Rifle

1971. 85th Anniversary of Labour Day.
N990 **428** 1wn. red, brown and buff 3·00 55

429 Soldiers and Map

1971. 35th Anniversary of Association for Restoration of Fatherland.
N991 **429** 10ch. red, buff and black 50 20

430 Monument

1971. Battlefields in Musan Area, May 1939. Multicoloured.
N992 5ch. Type **430** 15 10
N993 10ch. Machine guns in perspex cases (horiz) 35 15
N994 40ch. Huts among birch trees (horiz) 90 55

431 Koreans Marching

1971. Solidarity of Koreans in Japan.
N995 **431** 10ch. brown 30 15

432 Flame Emblem

1971. 25th Anniversary of Korean Childrens' Union.
N996 **432** 10ch. red, yellow and blue 30 15

433 Marchers and Banners

1971. Sixth Congress of League of Socialist Working Youth.
N997 **433** 5ch. red, buff and black 25 10
N998 - 10ch. red, green & black 35 15
Design: 10c. Marchers and banner under globe.

434 Foundryman

1971. 25th Anniversary of Labour Law.
N999 **434** 5ch. black, purple & buff 30 15

435 Young Women

1971. 25th Anniversary of Sex Equality Law.
N1000 **435** 5ch. multicoloured 30 15

436 Schoolchildren

1971. 15th Anniversary of Compulsory Primary Education.
N1001 **436** 10ch. multicoloured 55 15

437 Choe Yong Do and Combat Scene

1971. Heroes of the Revolutionary Struggle in South Korea.
N1002 **437** 5ch. black and green 35 10
N1003 - 10ch. red and brown 35 10
N1004 - 10ch. black and red 35 10
Designs: No. N1003, Revolutionary with book; No. N1004, Kim Jong Tae and scene of triumph.

438 Two Foundrymen

1971. 25th Anniversary of Nationalisation of Industry Law.
N1005 **438** 5ch. black, green & brn 2·10 35

439 Struggle in Korea

1971. The Anti-Imperialist and Anti-US Imperialist Struggles.
N1006 **439** 10ch. red, black and brown 35 15
N1007 - 10ch. brown, black and blue 50 15
N1008 - 10ch. red, black and pink 65 15
N1009 - 10ch. black, olive and green 35 15
N1010 - 10ch. orange, black and red 65 15
N1011 - 40ch. green, black and pink 65 20
Designs: No. N1007, Struggle in Vietnam; No. N1008, Soldier with rifle and aeroplane marked 'E'; No. N1009, Struggle in Africa; No. N1010, Cuban soldier and Central America; No. N1011, Bayoneting US soldier.

440 Kim Il Sung University

1971. 25th Anniversary of Kim Il Sung University.
N1012 **440** 10ch. grey, red & yellow 30 10

441 Iron-ore Ladle (Mining)

1971. Tasks of Six Year Plan. Multicoloured.
N1013 10ch. Type **441** 2·10 35
N1014 10ch. Workers and text 40 15
N1015 10ch. Electric train and track (Transport) 2·10 35
N1016 10ch. Hand and wrench (Industry) 85 25
N1017 10ch. Mechanical scoop (Construction) 2·10 35
N1018 10ch. Manufactured goods (Trade) 40 15
N1019 10ch. Crate on hoists (Exports) 35 10
N1020 10ch. Lathe (Heavy Industries) 2·10 35
N1021 10ch. Freighter (Shipping) 85 25
N1022 10ch. Household equipment (Light Industries) 40 15
N1023 10ch. Corncob and wheat (Agriculture) 50 15

442 Technicians

1971. Cultural Revolution. Multicoloured.
N1024 2ch. Type **442** 25 10
N1025 5ch. Mechanic 35 10
N1026 10ch. Schoolchildren 40 10
N1027 10ch. Chemist 65 10
N1028 10ch. Composer at piano 1·10 10

443 Workers with Red Books

1971. Ideological Revolution. Multicoloured.
N1029 10ch. Type **443** 25 10
N1030 10ch. Workers reading book 25 10
N1031 10ch. Workers' lecture 25 10
N1032 10ch. Worker and pneumatic drill 25 10

444 Korean Family

1971. Improvement in Living Standards.
N1033 **444** 10ch. multicoloured 25 10

445 Furnaceman

1971. Implementation of Decisions of Fifth Workers' Party Conference.
N1034 **445** 10ch. multicoloured 1·40 25

446

1971. Solidarity with South Korean Revolutionaries.
N1036 **446** 10ch. brown, bl & blk 40 15
N1037 - 10ch. brn, flesh & red 40 15
N1038 - 10ch. multicoloured 40 15
N1039 - 10ch. multicoloured 40 15
Designs: Vert—No. N1037, US soldier attacked by poster boards; No. N1038, Hands holding rifles aloft. Horiz—No. N1039, Men advancing with rifles.

447 6000-ton Press

1971
N1040 **447** 2ch. brown 90 15
N1041 - 5ch. blue 1·30 25
N1042 - 10ch. green 1·50 25
N1043 - 10ch. green 1·50 25
Designs: No. N1041, Refrigerated freighter *Ponghwasan*; No. N1042, 300 h.p. bulldozer; No. N1043, Sungrisan lorry.

448 Title-page and Militants

1971. 35th Anniversary of *Samil Wolgan* Magazine.
N1044 **448** 10ch. red, green & black 60 15

452 Poultry Chicks

1972. Poultry Breeding.
N1051 **452** 5ch. yellow, black and brown 35 10
N1052 - 10ch. orange, bistre and brown 50 10
N1053 - 40ch. blue, orange and deep blue 85 50
Designs: 10ch. Chickens and battery egg house; 40ch. Eggs and fowls suspended from hooks.

453 Scene from *Village Shrine*

1972. Films of Guerrilla War.
N1054 **453** 10ch. grey and green 1·00 20
N1055 - 10ch. blue, pur & orge 1·00 20
N1056 - 10ch. purple, blue & yell 1·00 20
Designs: No. N1055, Patriot with pistol (*A Sea of Blood*); No. N1056, Guerrilla using bayonet (*The Lot of a Self-Defence Corps Member*).

454 Kim Il Sung acknowledging Greetings

1972. Kim Il Sung's 60th Birthday. Scenes in the life of Kim Il Sung, dated 1912–1972. Multicoloured.
N1057 5ch. Type **454** 25 10
N1058 5ch. In campaign HQ 25 10
N1059 5ch. Military conference (horiz) 25 10
N1060 10ch. In wheatfield (horiz) 40 10
N1061 10ch. Directing construction (horiz) 2·75 50
N1062 10ch. Talking to foundry workers (horiz) 25 10
N1063 10ch. Aboard whaler (horiz) 75 10
N1064 10ch. Visiting a hospital (horiz) 1·00 10
N1065 10ch. Viewing orchard (horiz) 25 10
N1066 10ch. With survey party on Haeju–Hasong railway line (horiz) 2·75 50
N1067 10ch. Meeting female workers at silk factory (horiz) 1·40 15
N1068 10ch. Village conference (horiz) 25 10
N1069 10ch. Touring chicken factory (horiz) 50 10
N1070 40ch. Relaxing with children 60 25
N1071 1wn. Giant portrait and marchers 90 50
MSN1072 100×79 mm. 3wn. Kim Il Sung by Lake Chon (horiz). Imperf 8·50 6·00

455 Bugler sounding 'Charge'

1972. 40th Anniversary of Guerrilla Army.
N1073 **455** 10ch. multicoloured 60 15

456 Pavilion of Ryongpo

1972. Historic Sites of the 1950–1953 War. Multicoloured.

N1074	2ch. Type **456**	20	10
N1075	5ch. Houses at Onjong	20	10
N1076	10ch. Headquarters, Kosanjin	20	10
N1077	40ch. Victory Museum, Chonsung-dong	40	15

457 Volleyball

1972. Olympic Games, Munich. Multicoloured.

N1078	2ch. Type **457**	35	10
N1079	5ch. Boxing (horiz)	40	10
N1080	10ch. Judo	50	15
N1081	10ch. Wrestling (horiz)	50	15
N1082	40ch. Rifle-shooting	1·30	55

458 Chollima Street, Pyongyang

1971. Chollima Street, Pyongyang.

N1083	-	5ch. orange and black	2·20	55
N1084	**458**	10ch. yellow and black	85	20
N1085	-	10ch. green and black	85	20

Designs: No. N1083, Bridge and skyscraper blocks; No. N1085, Another view looking up street.

459 Dredger

1972. Development of Natural Resources. Multicoloured.

N1086	5ch. Type **459**	50	10
N1087	10ch. Forestry	65	10
N1088	40ch. Reclaiming land from the sea	85	20

460 Ferrous Industry

1972. Tasks of the Six-Year Plan. The Metallurgical Industry. Inscr '1971–1976'. Multicoloured.

N1089	10ch. Type **460**	2·10	15
N1090	10ch. Non-ferrous Industry	60	15

461 Iron Ore Industry

1972. Tasks of the Six-Year Plan. The Mining Industry. Inscr '1971–1976'. Multicoloured.

N1091	10ch. Type **461**	85	15
N1092	10ch. Coal mining industry	3·25	45

462 Electronic and Automation Industry

1972. Tasks of the Six-Year Plan. The Engineering Industry. Inscr '1971–1976'. Multicoloured.

N1093	10ch. Type **462**	85	15
N1094	10ch. Single-purpose machines	60	15
N1095	10ch. Machine tools	60	15

463 Clearing Virgin Soil

1972. Tasks of the Six-Year Plan. Rural Economy. Multicoloured.

N1096	10ch. Type **463**	65	15
N1097	10ch. Irrigation	65	15
N1098	10ch. Harvesting	65	15

464 Automation

1972. Tasks of the Six-Year Plan. Inscr '1971–1976'. Multicoloured.

N1099	10ch. Type **464**	1·00	25
N1100	10ch. Agricultural mechanization	65	15
N1101	10ch. Lightening of household chores	65	15

465 Chemical Fibres and Materials

1972. Tasks of the Six-Year Plan. The Chemical Industry. Inscr '1971–1976'. Multicoloured.

N1102	10ch. Type **465**	85	15
N1103	10ch. Fertilizers, insecticides and weed killers	85	15

466 Textiles

1972. Tasks of the Six-Year Plan. Consumer Goods. Inscr '1971–1976'. Multicoloured.

N1104	10ch. Type **466**	90	20
N1105	10ch. Kitchen ware and overalls	65	15
N1106	10ch. Household goods	65	15

467 Fish, Fruit and Vegetables

1972. Tasks of the Six-Year Plan. The Food Industry. Multicoloured.

N1107	10ch. Type **467**	90	20
N1108	10ch. Tinned foods	90	20
N1109	10ch. Food packaging	90	20

468 Electrifying Railway Lines

1972. Tasks of the Six-Year Plan. Transport. Inscr '1971–1976'. Multicoloured.

N1110	10ch. Type **468**	65	15
N1111	10ch. Laying new railway track	65	15
N1112	10ch. Freighters	60	15

469 Soldier with Shell

1972. North Korean Armed Forces. Multicoloured.

N1113	10ch. Type **469**	50	15
N1114	10ch. Marine	50	15
N1115	10ch. Air Force pilot	50	15

470 'Revolution of 19 April 1960'

1972. The Struggle for Reunification of Korea. Multicoloured.

N1116	10ch. Type **470**	25	15
N1117	10ch. Marchers with banner	25	15
N1118	10ch. Insurgents with red banner	25	15
N1119	10ch. Attacking US and South Korean soldiers	25	15
N1120	10ch. Workers with posters	25	15
N1121	10ch. Workers acclaiming revolution	5·00	90
N1122	10ch. Workers and manifesto	25	15

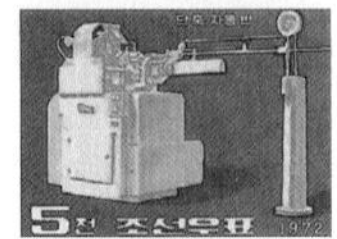

471 Single-spindle Automatic Lathe

1972. Machine Tools.

N1123	**471**	5ch. green and purple	35	15
N1124	-	10ch. blue and green	50	15
N1125	-	40ch. green and brown	1·20	20

Designs: Horiz—10ch. Kusong-3 lathe; Vert—40ch. 2,000 ton crank press.

472 Casting Vote

1972. National Elections. Multicoloured.

N1126	10ch. Type **472**	40	15
N1127	10ch. Election campaigner	40	15

475 Soldier

1973. 25th Anniversary of Founding of Korean People's Army. Multicoloured.

N1130	5ch. Type **475**	25	10
N1131	10ch. Sailor	40	10
N1132	40ch. Airman	1·00	65

476 Wrestling Site

1973. Scenes of Kim Il Sung's Childhood, Mangyongdae. Multicoloured.

N1133	2ch. Type **476**	15	15
N1134	5ch. Warship rock	15	15
N1135	10ch. Swinging site (vert)	25	15
N1136	10ch. Sliding rock	25	15
N1137	40ch. Fishing site	85	25

477 Monument to Socialist Revolution and Construction, Mansu Hill

1973. Museum of the Korean Revolution.

N1138	**477**	10ch. multicoloured	35	10
N1139	-	10ch. multicoloured	35	10
N1140	-	40ch. multicoloured	75	15
N1141	-	3wn. green and yellow	3·75	80

Designs: As T **477**—10ch. (No. N1139) Similar monument but men in military clothes; 40ch. Statue of Kim Il Sung. Horiz 60×29 mm—3wn. Museum building.

478 Karajibong Camp

1973. Secret Camps by Tuman-Gang in Guerrilla War, 1932. Multicoloured.

N1142	10ch. Type **478**	20	10
N1143	10ch. Soksaegol Camp	20	15

479

1973. Menace of Japanese Influence in South Korea.

N1144	**479**	10ch. multicoloured	30	10

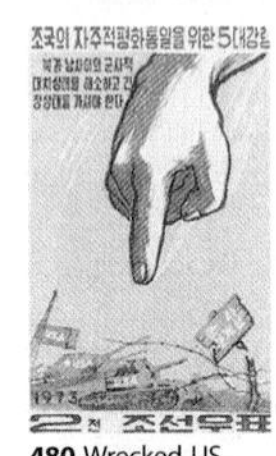

480 Wrecked US Tanks

1973. Five-point Programme for Reunification of Korea. Multicoloured.

N1145	2ch. Type **480**	60	10
N1146	5ch. Electric train and crane lifting tractor	3·75	50
N1147	10ch. Leaflets falling on crowd	25	10
N1148	10ch. Hand holding leaflet and map of Korea	60	10
N1149	40ch. Banner and globe	90	25

481 Lorries

1973. Lorries and Tractors. Multicoloured.

N1150	10ch. Type **481**	50	15
N1151	10ch. Tractors and earth-moving machine	50	15

482 Volleyball

1973. Socialist Countries' Junior Women's Volleyball Games, Pyongyang.

N1152	**482**	10ch. multicoloured	55	15

483 Battlefield

1973. 20th Anniversary of Victory in Korean War.

N1153	**483**	10ch. green, pur & blk	35	15
N1154	-	10ch. brown, bl & blk	35	15

Design: 10ch. Urban fighting.

484 *The Snow Falls*

1973. Mansudae Art Troupe. Dances. Multicoloured.

N1155	10ch. Type **484**	75	15
N1156	25ch. *A Bumper Harvest of Apples*	1·70	40
N1157	40ch. *Azalea of the Fatherland*	2·10	45

485 Schoolchildren

1973. Ten Years Compulsory Secondary Education.

N1158 **485**	10ch. multicoloured	40	15

486 *Fervour in the Revolution*

1973. The Works of Kim Il Sung (1st series).

N1159 **486**	10ch. brown, red and yellow	20	15
N1160 -	10ch. brown, green and yellow	20	15
N1161 -	10ch. lake, brown and yellow	20	15

Designs: No. N1160, Selected works; No. N1161, *Strengthen the Socialist System*.

See also Nos. N1217/N1218.

487 Celebrating Republic

1973. 25th Anniversary of People's Republic. Multicoloured.

N1162	5ch. Type **487**	20	10
N1163	10ch. Fighting in Korean War	20	10
N1164	40ch. Peace and reconstruction	2·20	60

488 Pobwang Peak

1973. Mt. Myohyang. Multicoloured.

N1165	2ch. Type **488**	30	10
N1166	5ch. Inhodae Pavilion	35	15
N1167	10ch. Taeha Falls (vert)	1·60	40
N1168	40ch. Rongyon Falls (vert)	4·50	70

489 Party Memorial Building

1973. Party Memorial Building.

N1169 **489**	1wn. brn, grey & buff	1·80	45

490 Football and Handball

1973. National People's Sports Meeting. Multicoloured.

N1170	2ch. Type **490**	75	15
N1171	5ch. High jumper and woman sprinter	35	10
N1172	10ch. Skaters and skiers	60	15
N1173	10ch. Wrestling and swinging	40	10
N1174	40ch. Parachutist and motor cyclists	4·25	70

491 Weightlifting

1973. Junior Weightlifting Championships of Socialist Countries.

N1175 **491**	10ch. blue, brn & grn	50	15

492 Chongryu Cliff

1973. Scenery of Moran Hill, Pyongyang. Multicoloured.

N1176	2ch. Type **492**	1·00	20
N1177	5ch. Moran Waterfall	4·25	80
N1178	10ch. Pubyok Pavilion	1·10	20
N1179	40ch. Ulmil Pavilion	1·30	25

493 Rainbow Bridge

1973. Diamond Mountains Scenery (4th issue). Multicoloured.

N1180	2ch. Type **493**	2·00	35
N1181	5ch. Suspension footbridge, Okryudong (horiz)	2·00	35
N1182	10ch. Chonnyo Peak	1·00	20
N1183	10ch. Chilchung Rock and Sonji Peak (horiz)	1·00	20
N1184	40ch. Sujong and Pari Peaks (horiz)	1·20	25

494 Magnolia Flower

1973

N1185 **494**	10ch. multicoloured	1·80	40

495 South Korean Revolutionaries

1973. South Korean Revolution. Multicoloured.

N1186	10ch. Type **495**	20	15
N1187	10ch. Marching revolutionaries	20	15

496 Cock sees Butterflies

1973. Scenes from *Cock Chasing Butterflies*. Fairy Tale. Multicoloured.

N1188	2ch. Type **496**	2·10	35
N1189	5ch. Butterflies discuss how to repel cock	2·10	35
N1190	10ch. Cock chasing butterflies with basket	3·00	40
N1191	10ch. Cock chasing butterfly up cliff	3·00	45
N1192	40ch. Cock chasing butterflies over cliff	3·25	55
N1193	90ch. Cock falls into sea and butterflies escape	5·00	60

497 Yonpung

1973. Historical Sites of War and Revolution (40ch.). Multicoloured.

N1196	2ch. Type **497**	15	10
N1197	5ch. Hyangha	15	10
N1198	10ch. Changgol	15	15
N1199	40ch. Paeksong	85	20

498 Science Library, Kim Il Sung University

1973. New Buildings in Pyongyang.

N1200 **498**	2ch. violet	75	15
N1201 -	5ch. green	25	15
N1202 -	10ch. brown	35	15
N1203 -	40ch. brown and buff	85	20
N1204 -	90ch. buff	1·40	40

Designs: Horiz—10ch. Victory Museum; 40ch. People's Palace of Culture; 90ch. Indoor stadium. Vert—5ch. Building No. 2, Kim Il Sung University.

499 *Red Book*

1973. Socialist Constitution of North Korea. Multicoloured.

N1205	10ch. Type **499**	35	15
N1206	10ch. Marchers with *Red Book* and banners	35	15
N1207	10ch. Marchers with *Red Book* and emblem	35	15

500 Oriental Great Reed Warbler

1973. Korean Songbirds. Multicoloured.

N1208	5ch. Type **500**	2·50	45
N1209	10ch. Grey starling (facing right)	3·75	70
N1210	10ch. Daurian starling (facing left)	3·75	70

503 Chollima Statue

1974. The Works of Kim Il Sung (2nd series). Multicoloured.

N1217	10ch. Type **503**	90	20
N1218	10ch. Bayonets threatening US soldier	15	15

504 Train in Station

1974. Opening of Pyongyang Metro. Multicoloured.

N1219	10ch. Type **504**	90	15
N1220	10ch. Escalators	90	15
N1221	10ch. Station hall	90	15

505 Capital Construction Front

1974. Five Fronts of Socialist Construction. Multicoloured.

N1222	10ch. Type **505**	20	15
N1223	10ch. Agricultural front	35	15
N1224	10ch. Transport front	1·80	35
N1225	10ch. Fisheries front	1·10	20
N1226	10ch. Industrial front (vert)	35	15

506 Marchers with Banners

1974. Tenth Anniversary of Publication of *Theses on the Socialist Rural Question in Our Country*. Multicoloured.

N1227	10ch. Type **506**	25	10
N1228	10ch. Book and rejoicing crowd	25	10
N1229	10ch. Tractor and banners	25	10

Nos. N1227/N1229 were issued together, *se-tenant*, forming a composite design.

507 Manure Spreader

1974. Farm Machinery.

N1230 **507**	2ch. green, black & red	60	15
N1231 -	5ch. red, black and blue	60	15
N1232 -	10ch. red, black and green	60	15

Designs: 5ch. Progress tractor; 10ch. Mount Taedoksan tractor.

508 Archery (Grenoble)

1974. North Korean Victories at International Sports Meetings. Multicoloured.

N1233	2ch. Type **508**	1·30	25
N1234	5ch. Gymnastics (Varna)	25	15
N1235	10ch. Boxing (Bucharest)	35	15
N1236	20ch. Volleyball (Pyongyang)	25	15
N1237	30ch. Rifle shooting (Sofia)	65	20
N1238	40ch. Judo (Tbilisi)	1·00	25
N1239	60ch. Model aircraft flying (Vienna) (horiz)	1·70	35
N1240	1wn. 50 Table tennis (Peking) (horiz)	3·00	65

509 Book and Rejoicing Crowd

1974. The First Country with No Taxes.

N1241 **509**	10ch. multicoloured	40	10

510 Drawing up Programme in Woods

1974. Kim Il Sung during the Anti-Japanese Struggle. Multicoloured.

N1242	10ch. Type **510**	35	15
N1243	10ch. Giving directions to Pak Dal	35	15
N1244	10ch. Presiding over Nanhutou Conference	35	15
N1245	10ch. Supervising creation of strongpoint	35	15

511 Sun Hui loses her Sight

1974. Scenes from *The Flower Girl* (revolutionary opera). Multicoloured.

N1246 2ch. Type **511**	1·00	20
N1247 5ch. Death of Ggot Bun's mother	1·00	20
N1248 10ch. Ggot Bun throws boiling water at landlord	2·10	35
N1249 40ch. Ggot Bun joins revolutionaries	2·75	45
MSN1250 111×62 mm. 50ch. Ggot Bun amid flowers of revolution. Imperf	3·75	1·50

512 Leopard Cat

1974. 15th Anniversary of Pyongyang Zoo. Multicoloured.

N1251 2ch. Type **512**	75	15
N1252 5ch. Lynx	75	15
N1253 10ch. Red fox	75	15
N1254 10ch. Wild boar	75	15
N1255 20ch. Dhole	75	15
N1256 40ch. Brown bear	85	40
N1257 60ch. Leopard	1·50	40
N1258 70ch. Tiger	2·10	45
N1259 90ch. Lion	2·75	55
MSN1260 140×100 mm. Diamond-shaped designs: 10ch. Wildcat; 30ch. Lynx; 50ch. Leopard; 60ch. Tiger. Imperf	29·00	8·00

513 *Rosa acucularis lindly*

1974. Roses. Multicoloured.

N1261 2ch. Type **513**	75	15
N1262 5ch. Yellow sweet briar	85	20
N1263 10ch. Pink aromatic rose	1·00	20
N1264 10ch. Aronia sweet briar (yellow centres)	1·00	20
N1265 40ch. Multi-petal sweet briar	2·50	35

514 Kim Il Sung greeted by Children

1974. 30th Anniversary of Korean Children's Union. Sheet 126×95 mm.

MSN1266 **514** 1w.20 multicoloured	4·50	3·25

515 Weigela

1974. Flowering Plants of Mt. Paekdu. Multicoloured.

N1267 2ch. Type **515**	60	15
N1268 5ch. Amaryllis	60	15
N1269 10ch. Red lily	60	15
N1270 20ch. Orange lily	85	20
N1271 40ch. Azalea	1·10	20
N1272 60ch. Yellow lily	1·80	35

516 Postwoman and Construction Site

1974. Centenary of UPU and Admission of North Korea to Union. Multicoloured.

N1273 10ch. Type **516**	1·80	30
N1274 25ch. *Chollima* monument	20	20
N1275 40ch. Globe and Antonov An-12 transport planes	1·30	30

517 Common Pond Frog

1974. Amphibians. Multicoloured.

N1276 2ch. Type **517**	3·00	30
N1277 5ch. Oriental fire-bellied toad	3·25	30
N1278 10ch. Bullfrog	3·75	45
N1279 40ch. Common toad	5·50	65

518 *Women of Namgang Village*

1974. Korean Paintings. Multicoloured.

N1281 2ch. Type **518**	75	15
N1282 5ch. *An Old Man on the Rakdong River* (60×49 mm)	85	20
N1283 10ch. *Morning in the Nae-kumgang* (bridge)	1·80	35
N1284 20ch. *Mt. Kumgang* (60×49 mm)	1·70	30
MSN1285 116×115 mm. 1wn.50 *Evening Glow in Kangson*. Imperf	6·25	4·50

519 *Elektron 1* and *Elektron 2*, 1964

1974. Cosmonauts Day. Multicoloured.

N1286 10ch. Type **519**	15	10
N1287 20ch. *Proton 1*, 1965	25	15
N1288 30ch. *Venera 3*, 1966	50	15
N1289 40ch. *Venera 5* and *Venera 6*, 1969	60	20
MSN1290 80×120 mm. 1wn. Dogs Belka and Strelka. Imperf	29·00	2·75

520 Satellite

1974. Fourth Anniversary of Launching of First Chinese Satellite. Sheet 80×120 mm. Imperf.

MSN1291 **520** 50ch. multicoloured	3·75	1·40

521 Antonov An-2 Biplane

1974. Civil Aviation. Multicoloured.

N1292 2ch. Type **521**	85	15
N1293 5ch. Lisunov Li-2	85	15
N1294 10ch. Ilyushin Il-14P	1·10	20
N1295 40ch. Antonov An-24	1·50	45
N1296 60ch. Ilyushin Il-18	2·75	70
MSN1297 96×68 mm. 90ch. Airliner. Imperf	6·25	4·75

522 *Rhododendron redowskianum*

1974. Plants of Mt. Paekdu. Multicoloured.

N1298 2ch. Type **522**	50	10
N1299 5ch. *Dryas octopetala*	50	15
N1300 10ch. *Potentilla fruticosa*	60	15
N1301 20ch. *Papaver somniferum*	75	15
N1302 40ch. *Phyllodoce caerulea*	1·00	30
N1303 60ch. *Oxytropis anertii*	2·20	55

523 *Sobaek River in the Morning*

1974. Modern Korean Paintings (1st series). Multicoloured.

N1304 10ch. Type **523**	1·30	20
N1305 20ch. *Combatants of Mt. Laohei* (60×40 mm)	1·50	25
N1306 30ch. *Spring in the Fields*	1·80	25
N1307 40ch. *Tideland Night*	5·75	85
N1308 60ch. *Daughter* (60×54 mm)	2·10	60

See also Nos. N1361/N1365, N1386/N1390, N1391/N1396 and N1485/N1489.

524

1974. Bologna Exhibition for 50th Anniversary of *L'Unita* (organ of the Italian communist party). Sheet 148×98 mm. Imperf.

MSN1309 **524** 1wn.50 multicoloured	6·25	2·10

525 Log Cabin, Unha Village

1974. Historic Sites of the Revolution. Multicoloured.

N1310 5ch. Munmyong	20	10
N1311 10ch. Type **525**	20	10

526 Sesame

1974. Oil-producing Plants. Multicoloured.

N1312 2ch. Type **526**	90	20
N1313 5ch. *Perilla frutescens*	1·00	20
N1314 10ch. Sunflower	1·20	25
N1315 40ch. Castor bean	1·70	55

527 Kim Il Sung as Guerrilla Leader

1974. Kim Il Sung. Multicoloured.

N1316 10ch. Type **527**	35	15
N1317 10ch. Commander of the People's Army (52×35 mm)	35	15
N1318 10ch. 'The commander is also a son of the people' (52×35 mm)	35	15
N1319 10ch. Negotiating with the Chinese anti-Japanese unit (52×35 mm)	35	15

528

1974. Grand Monument on Mansu Hill. Multicoloured.

N1320 10ch. Type **528**	25	15
N1321 10ch. As T **528** but men in civilian clothes	25	15
N1322 10ch. As T **528** but men facing left	25	15
N1323 10ch. As No. N1322 but men in civilian clothes	25	15

529 Factory Ship *Chilbosan*

1974. Deep-sea Fishing. Multicoloured.

N1324 2ch. Type **529**	1·20	30
N1325 5ch. Trawler support ship *Paekdusan*	1·20	30
N1326 10ch. Freighter *Moranbong*	1·20	30
N1327 20ch. Whale-catcher	1·20	30
N1328 30ch. Trawler	1·20	30
N1329 40ch. Stern trawler	1·20	30

539 Kim Il Sung crossing River Agrok

1975. 50th Anniversary of Kim Il Sung's crossing of River Agrok.

N1349 **539** 10ch. multicoloured	40	15

540 Pak Yong Sun 'World Table Tennis Queen'

1975. Pak Yong Sun, Winner of 33rd World Table Tennis Championships, Calcutta.

N1350 **540** 10ch. multicoloured	1·50	15
MSN1351 80×119 mm. 80ch. Table Tennis Crown. Imperf	2·75	80

541 Zebra

1975. Pyongyang Zoo. Multicoloured.

N1352 10ch. Type **541**	85	15
N1353 10ch. African buffalo	85	15
N1354 20ch. Giant panda (horiz)	2·10	25
N1355 25ch. Bactrian camel	1·70	40
N1356 30ch. Indian elephant	3·25	45

542 *Blue Dragon*

1975. 7th-century Mural Paintings from Koguryo Tombs, Kangso.

N1357	10ch. Type **542**	90	15
N1358	15ch. *White Tiger*	1·30	25
N1359	25ch. *Red Phoenix* (vert)	1·50	30
N1360	40ch. *Snake-turtle*	2·10	40

543 *Spring in the Guerrilla Base* (1968)

1975. Modern Korean Paintings (2nd series). Anti-Japanese struggle. Multicoloured.

N1361	10ch. Type **543**	50	15
N1362	10ch. *Revolutionary Army landing at Unggi* (1969)	50	15
N1363	15ch. *Sewing Team Members* (1961)	85	20
N1364	20ch. *Girl Watering Horse* (1969)	1·50	25
N1365	30ch. *Kim Jong Suk giving Guidance to Children's Corps* (1970)	1·20	25

544 Cosmonaut

1975. Cosmonauts' Day. Multicoloured.

N1366	10ch. Type **544**	15	10
N1367	30ch. *Lunokhod* moon vehicle (horiz)	65	15
N1368	40ch. Soyuz spacecraft and Salyut space laboratory (horiz)	90	25

545 Victory Monument

1975. Commemoration of Battle of Pochonbo. Sheet 140×98 mm. Imperf.

MSN1369	**545** 1wn. multicoloured	5·75	3·00

546 The Beacon lit at Pochonbo, 1937

1975. Kim Il Sung during the Guerrilla War against the Japanese. Multicoloured.

N1370	10ch. Type **546**	35	15
N1371	10ch. 'A Bowl of Parched-rice Powder', 1938	35	15
N1372	10ch. Guiding the Nanpaizi meeting, November, 1938	35	15
N1373	10ch. Welcoming helper	35	15
N1374	10ch. Lecturing the guerrillas	35	15
N1375	15ch. Advancing into the homeland, May 1939	40	15
N1376	25ch. By Lake Samji, May 1939	60	25
N1377	30ch. At Sinsadong, May 1939	75	30
N1378	40ch. Xiaohaerbaling meeting, 1940	1·10	40

547 Vase of Flowers and Kim Il Sung's Birthplace

1975. Kim Il Sung's 63rd Birthday. Multicoloured.

N1379	10ch. Type **547**	20	10
N1379a	40ch. Kim Il Sung's birthplace, Mangyongdae	65	15

548 South Korean Insurgent

1975. 15th Anniversary of April 19th Rising.

N1380	**548** 10ch. multicoloured	30	10

549 *Kingfisher at a Lotus Pond*

1975. Paintings of Li Dynasty. Multicoloured.

N1381	5ch. Type **549**	2·10	30
N1382	10ch. *Crabs*	1·30	25
N1383	15ch. *Rose of Sharon*	2·10	35
N1384	25ch. *Lotus and Water Cock*	3·00	50
N1385	30ch. *Tree Peony and Red Junglefowl*	4·25	75

1975. Modern Korean Paintings (3rd series). Fatherland Liberation War. Dated designs as T **543**. Multicoloured.

N1386	5ch. *On the Advance Southward* (1966) (vert)	25	15
N1387	10ch. *The Assigned Post* (girl sentry) (1968) (vert)	35	15
N1388	15ch. *The Heroism of Li Su Bok* (1965)	40	15
N1389	25ch. *Retaliation* (woman machine-gunner) (1970)	75	25
N1390	30ch. *The awaited Troops* (1970)	90	25

1975. Modern Korean Paintings (4th series). Socialist Construction. As T **543**. Multicoloured.

N1391	10ch. *Pine Tree* (1966) (vert)	1·00	20
N1392	10ch. *The Blue Signal Lamp* (1960) (vert)	3·75	55
N1393	15ch. *A Night of Snowfall* (1963)	1·10	20
N1394	20ch. *Smelters* (1968)	1·30	25
N1395	25ch. *Tideland Reclamation* (1961)	1·30	25
N1396	30ch. *Mount Paekgum* (1966)	1·30	25

550 Flag and Building

1975. 20th Anniversary of Chongryon Association of Koreans in Japan.

N1397	**550** 10ch. multicoloured	40	10
N1398	**550** 3wn. multicoloured	9·50	85

551 Marathon Runners

1975. Marathon Race of Socialist Countries. Sheet 105×74 mm. Imperf.

MSN1399	1wn. multicoloured	4·25	1·40

552 Feet first entry (man)

1975. Diving. Multicoloured.

N1400	10ch. Type **552**	15	10
N1401	25ch. Piked somersault (man)	65	30
N1402	40ch. Head first entry (woman)	1·30	40

553

1975. Campaign against US Imperialism.

N1403	**553** 10ch. multicoloured	40	15

554 Silver Carp

1975. Fresh-water Fish. Multicoloured.

N1404	10ch. Type **554**	85	15
N1405	10ch. Elongate ilisha (swimming to right)	85	15
N1406	15ch. Banded minnow	1·30	20
N1407	25ch. Bare-headed bagrid	1·80	30
N1408	30ch. Amur catfish (swimming to right)	2·50	40
N1409	30ch. Chevron snakehead (swimming to left)	2·50	40

555

1975. Tenth Socialist Countries' Football Tournament, Pyongyang.

N1410	**555** 5ch. multicoloured	50	10
N1411	- 10ch. multicoloured	50	15
N1412	- 15ch. multicoloured	60	15
N1413	- 20ch. multicoloured	75	25
N1414	- 50ch. multicoloured	1·40	50
MSN1415	112×80 mm. 1wn. multicoloured. Imperf	6·25	4·00

Designs: 10ch. to 1wn. Various footballers.

556 Blue and Yellow Macaw

1975. Birds. Multicoloured.

N1416	10ch. Type **556**	1·70	35
N1417	15ch. Sulphur-crested cockatoo	2·00	40
N1418	20ch. Blyth's parakeet	2·75	50
N1419	25ch. Rainbow lory	3·00	65
N1420	30ch. Budgerigar	3·25	70

557 Flats

1975. New Buildings in Pyongyang. Multicoloured.

N1421	90ch. Saesallim (formerly Sarguson) Street	5·00	90
N1422	1wn. Type **557**	5·00	95
N1423	2wn. Potonggang Hotel	10·00	2·00

558 White Peach Blossom

1975. Blossoms of Flowering Trees. Multicoloured.

N1424	10ch. Type **558**	60	15
N1425	15ch. Red peach blossom	60	15
N1426	20ch. Red plum blossom	1·00	25
N1427	25ch. Apricot blossom	1·20	25
N1428	30ch. Cherry blossom	1·70	40

559 Sejongbong

1975. Landscapes in the Diamond Mountains. Multicoloured.

N1429	5ch. Type **559**	50	10
N1430	10ch. Chonsondae	75	15
N1431	15ch. Pisamun	1·00	25
N1432	25ch. Manmulsang	1·30	30
N1433	30ch. Chaehabong	1·50	35

560 Azalea

1975. Flowers of the Azalea Family. Multicoloured.

N1434	5ch. Type **560**	65	15
N1435	10ch. White azalea	65	25
N1436	15ch. Wild rhododendron	1·00	25
N1437	20ch. White rhododendron	1·00	25
N1438	25ch. Rhododendron	1·30	30
N1439	30ch. Yellow rhododendron	1·70	40

561 Gliders

1975. Training for National Defence. Multicoloured.

N1440	5ch. Type **561**	60	10
N1441	5ch. Radio-controlled model aeroplane	60	10
N1442	10ch. Free fall parachutist (vert)	75	20
N1443	10ch. Parachutist landing on target (vert)	75	20
N1444	20ch. Parachutist with bouquet of flowers (vert)	1·30	30
MSN1445	90×68 mm. 50ch. Three parachutists in circle. Imperf	2·75	75

562 Wild Apple

1975. Fruit Tree Blossom. Multicoloured.

N1446	10ch. Type **562**	65	25
N1447	15ch. Wild pear	65	25
N1448	20ch. Hawthorn	1·00	30
N1449	25ch. Chinese quince	1·30	40
N1450	30ch. Flowering quince	1·40	50

563 Torch of Juche

1975. 30th Anniversary of Korean Workers' Party. Multicoloured.

N1451	2ch. 'Victory' and American graves	15	10
N1452	2ch. Sunrise over Mt. Paektu-san	15	10
N1453	5ch. Type **563**	15	10
N1454	5ch. *Chollima* Statue and sunset over Pyongyang	15	10
N1455	10ch. Korean with Red Book	15	10
N1456	10ch. *Chollima* Statue	15	10
N1457	25ch. Crowds and burning building	50	25
N1458	70ch. Flowers and map of Korea	1·60	80
MSN1459	Two sheets (a) 85×120 mm. 90ch. Kim Il Sung delivering speech; (b) 120×85 mm. 1wn. Kim Il Sung leading crowd	6·25	4·75

564 Welcoming Crowd

1975. 30th Anniversary of Kim Il Sung's Return to Pyongyang.

N1460	**564** 20ch. multicoloured	35	15

565 Workers holding 'Juche' Torch

1975. 30th Anniversary of *Rodong Simmun* (Journal of the Central Committee of the Worker's Party).

N1461	**565** 10ch. multicoloured	60	15
MSN1462	95×68 mm. **565** 1wn. multicoloured. Imperf	3·00	2·10

566 Hyonmu Gate

1975. Ancient Wall-Gates of Pyongyang. Multicoloured.

N1463	10ch. Type **566**	15	10
N1464	10ch. Taedong Gate	15	10
N1465	15ch. Potong Gate	25	15
N1466	20ch. Chongum Gate	40	25
N1467	30ch. Chilsong Gate (vert)	60	40

567

1975. Views of Mt. Chilbo.

N1468	**567** 10ch. multicoloured	50	15
N1469	- 10ch. multicoloured	50	20
N1470	- 15ch. multicoloured	75	25
N1471	- 20ch. multicoloured	90	30
N1472	- 30ch. multicoloured	1·00	35

Designs: Nos. N1468/N1472, Various views.

568 Right-hand Section of Monument

1975. Historic Site of Revolution in Wangjaesan. Multicoloured.

N1473	10ch. Type **568**	15	10
N1474	15ch. Left-hand section of monument	25	10
N1475	25ch. Centre section of monument (38×60 mm)	40	15
N1476	30ch. Centre section, close up (60×38 mm)	50	25

569 Marchers with Flags

1976. 30th Anniversary of Korean League of Socialist Working Youth. Multicoloured.

N1477	2ch. Flags and Emblem	20	15
N1478	70ch. Type **569**	1·30	65

570 Geese

1976. Ducks and Geese. Multicoloured.

N1479	10ch. Type **570**	85	15
N1480	20ch. 'Perennial' duck	1·80	25
N1481	40ch. Kwangpo duck	3·25	45

571 *Oath*

1976. Korean Peoples Army (sculptural works). Multicoloured.

N1482	5ch. Type **571**	25	10
N1483	10ch. *Union of Officers with Men* (horiz)	35	10
N1484	10ch. *This Flag to the Height*	35	10

572 *Rural Road at Evening*

1976. Modern Korean Paintings (5th series). Social Welfare. Multicoloured.

N1485	10ch. Type **572**	60	15
N1486	15ch. *Passing on Technique* (1970)	65	20
N1487	25ch. *Mother (and Child)* (1965)	90	20
N1488	30ch. *Medical Examination at School* (1970) (horiz)	1·70	35
N1489	40ch. *Lady Doctor of Village* (1970) (horiz)	2·00	45

573 Worker holding Text of Law

1976. 30th Anniversary of Agrarian Reform Law.

N1490	**573** 10ch. multicoloured	30	15

574 Telephones and Satellite

1976. Centenary of First Telephone Call. Multicoloured. With or without gum.

N1491	2ch. Type **574**	60	10
N1492	5ch. Satellite and antenna	60	10
N1493	10ch. Satellite and telecommunications systems	65	15
N1494	15ch. Telephone and linesman	1·40	35
N1495	25ch. Satellite and map of receiving stations	2·10	45
N1496	40ch. Satellite and cable-laying barge	3·25	60
MSN1497	94×70 mm. 50ch. Old telephone and satellite. Without gum	2·50	60

575 Cosmos

1976. Flowers. Multicoloured.

N1498	5ch. Type **575**	40	15
N1499	10ch. Dahlia	40	15
N1500	20ch. Zinnia	60	20
N1501	40ch. China aster	1·00	40

576 Fruit and Products

1976. Pukchong Meeting of Korean Workers' Party Presidium. Multicoloured.

N1502	5ch. Type **576**	85	20
N1503	10ch. Fruit and orchard scene	85	20

577 Pulgungi Electric Locomotive

1976. Railway Locomotives. Multicoloured.

N1504	5ch. Type **577**	50	15
N1505	10ch. Chaju underground train	1·00	20
N1506	15ch. Saebyol diesel locomotive	1·20	30

578 Satellite

1976. Space Flight. With or without gum.

N1507	**578** 2ch. multicoloured	15	10
N1508	- 5ch. multicoloured	15	10
N1509	- 10ch. multicoloured	25	15
N1510	- 15ch. multicoloured	40	15
N1511	- 25ch. multicoloured	60	25
N1512	- 40ch. multicoloured	1·00	30
MSN1513	77×98 mm. 50ch. Moon vehicle	1·30	55

Designs: 5ch. to 50ch. Various satellite and space craft.

579 Kim Il Sung beside Car

1976. Kim Il Sung's 64th Birthday.

N1514	**579** 10ch. multicoloured	50	20
MSN1515	120×80 mm. 40ch. Kim Il Sung and rejoicing crowd	4·50	1·30

580 Bat and Ribbon

1976. Third Asian Table Tennis Championships. Multicoloured. Without gum.

N1516	5ch. Type **580**	35	10
N1517	10ch. Three women players with flowers	35	15
N1518	20ch. Player defending	60	30
N1519	25ch. Player making attacking shot	1·00	40
MSN1520	74×99 mm. 50ch. Player making backhand shot. Imperf	2·50	80

581 Kim Il Sung announcing Establishment of Association

1976. 40th Anniversary of Association for the Restoration of the Fatherland. Without gum.

N1521	**581** 10ch. multicoloured	25	15

582 Golden Pheasant

1976. Pheasants. Multicoloured. With or without gum.

N1522	2ch. Type **582**	1·00	25
N1523	5ch. Lady Amherst's pheasant	1·10	25
N1524	10ch. Silver pheasant	1·30	30
N1525	15ch. Reeves's pheasant	1·50	40
N1526	25ch. Temminck's tragopan	2·00	60
N1527	40ch. Common pheasant (albino)	2·30	80
MSN1528	77×58 mm. 50ch. Ring-necked pheasant	5·00	2·10

583 Monument and Map of River

1976. Potong River Monument. Without gum.

N1529	**583** 10ch. brown and green	25	15

584 Running

1976. Olympic Games, Montreal. Multicoloured.

N1530	2ch. Type **584**	15	15
N1531	5ch. Diving	35	15
N1532	10ch. Judo	75	15
N1533	15ch. Gymnastics	1·30	25
N1534	25ch. Gymnastics	1·70	35
N1535	40ch. Fencing	3·50	85
MSN1536	109×85 mm. 50ch. Runner with torch and Olympic Stadium	4·25	2·10

585 Bronze Medal (Hockey, Pakistan)

1976. Olympic Medal Winners (1st issue). Multicoloured.

N1537	2ch. Type **585**	1·10	15
N1538	5ch. Bronze medal (shooting, Rudolf Dollinger)	35	10
N1539	10ch. Silver medal (boxing, Li Byong Uk)	35	15
N1540	15ch. Silver medal (cycling, Daniel Morelon)	3·00	45
N1541	25ch. Gold medal (marathon, Waldemar Cierpinski)	1·30	30
N1542	40ch. Gold medal (boxing, Ku Yong Jo)	1·70	35
MSN1543	109×84 mm. 50ch. Three medals	2·10	2·10

586 Boxing (Ku Yong Jo)

1976. Olympic Medal Winners (2nd issue). Multicoloured.

N1544	2ch. Type **586**	35	10
N1545	5ch. Gymnastics (Nadia Comaneci)	35	10
N1546	10ch. Pole vaulting (Tadeusz Slusarki)	35	15
N1547	15ch. Hurdling (Guy Drut)	40	15
N1548	25ch. Cycling (Bernt Johansson)	3·75	55
N1549	40ch. Football (East Germany)	2·20	40
MSN1550	104×84 mm. 50ch. Ku Yong Jo (boxing champion)	2·50	55

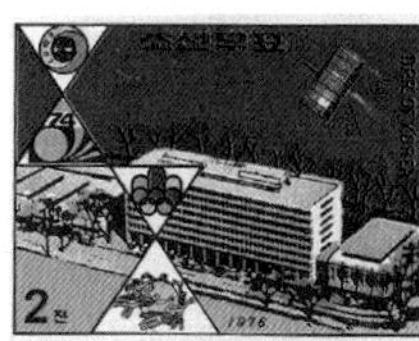
587 UPU Headquarters, Berne

1976. International Festivities. Multicoloured.

N1551	2ch. Type **587**	60	10
N1552	5ch. Footballers (World Cup)	60	10
N1553	10ch. Olympic Stadium	65	15
N1554	15ch. Olympic Village	1·40	25
N1555	25ch. Junk and satellite	1·20	35
N1556	40ch. Satellites	1·20	60
MSN1557	85×105 mm. 50ch. World map	2·10	1·40

588 Azure-winged Magpies

1976. Embroidery. Multicoloured. With or without gum.

N1558	2ch. Type **588**	2·00	40
N1559	5ch. White magpie	1·40	30
N1560	10ch. Roe deer	50	15
N1561	15ch. Black-naped oriole and magnolias	2·10	40
N1562	25ch. Fairy with flute (horiz)	1·20	25
N1563	40ch. Tiger	2·50	65
MSN1564	94×105 mm. 50ch. Tiger (52×82 mm)	10·00	90

589 Roman '5' and Flame

1976. Fifth Non-aligned States' Summit Conference, Colombo. Without gum.

N1565	**589**	10ch. multicoloured	25	15

590 Trophy and Certificate

1976. World Model Aeroplane Championships (1975). Multicoloured. Without gum.

N1566	5ch. Type **590**	25	10
N1567	10ch. Trophy and medals	40	10
N1568	20ch. Model aeroplane and emblem	60	20
N1569	40ch. Model glider and medals	1·00	50

591 Pulgungi Diesel Shunting Locomotive

1976. Locomotives. Multicoloured.

N1570	2ch. Type **591**	60	15
N1571	5ch. Saebyol diesel locomotive	85	20
N1572	10ch. Saebyol diesel shunting locomotive	90	20
N1573	15ch. Electric locomotive	1·10	25
N1574	25ch. Kumsong diesel locomotive	1·50	30
N1575	40ch. Pulgungi electric locomotive	1·80	35
MSN1576	100×68 mm. 50ch. Kumsong type diesel locomotive. Imperf	7·50	3·75

592 House of Culture

1976. House of Culture. Without gum.

N1577	**592**	10ch. brown and black	20	15

593 Kim Il Sung visiting Tosongrang

1976. Revolutionary Activities of Kim Il Sung. Multicoloured.

N1578	2ch. Type **593**	25	10
N1579	5ch. Kim Il Sung visits pheasants	25	10
N1580	10ch. Kim Il Sung on hilltop	35	10
N1581	15ch. Kim Il Sung giving house to farmhand	40	15
N1582	25ch. Kim Il Sung near front line	1·00	20
N1583	40ch. Kim Il Sung walking in rain	1·00	35
MSN1584	105×85 mm. 50ch. Kim Il Sung with child at roadside	1·80	1·40

594 Kim Il Sung with Union Members

1976. 50th Anniversary of Down-with-Imperialism Union. Without gum.

N1585	**594**	20ch. multicoloured	50	20

604 Searchlights and Kim Il Sung's Birthplace

1977. New Year. Without gum.

N1589	**604**	10ch. multicoloured	25	15

605 Spring Costume

1977. National Costumes of Li Dynasty. Multicoloured.

N1590	10ch. Type **605** (postage)	65	15
N1591	15ch. Summer costume	90	20
N1592	20ch. Autumn costume	1·00	25
N1593	40ch. Winter costume (air)	1·70	40

606 Two Deva Kings (Koguryo Dynasty)

1977. Korean Cultural Relics. Multicoloured.

N1594	2ch. Type **606** (postage)	60	15
N1595	5ch. Gold-copper decoration, Koguryo Dynasty	60	15
N1596	10ch. Copper Buddha, Koryo Dynasty	85	20
N1597	15ch. Gold-copper Buddha, Paekje Dynasty	1·00	20
N1598	25ch. Gold crown, Koguryo Dynasty	1·20	30
N1599	40ch. Gold-copper sun decoration, Koguryo Dynasty (horiz)	1·40	35
N1600	50ch. Gold crown, Silla Dynasty (air)	1·50	50

607 Worker with Five-point Programme

1977. Five-point Programme for Remaking Nature. Without gum.

N1601	**607**	10ch. multicoloured	30	15

608 Pine Branch and Map of Korea

1977. 60th Anniversary of Korean National Association. Without gum.

N1602	**608**	10ch. multicoloured	55	20

609 Championship Emblem and Trophy

1977. 34th World Table Tennis Championships. Multicoloured. Without gum.

N1603	10ch. Type **609** (postage)	25	10
N1604	15ch. Pak Yong Sun	40	15
N1605	20ch. Pak Yong Sun with trophy	65	20
N1606	40ch. Pak Yong Ok and Yang Ying (air)	1·30	40

610 Kim Il Sung founds Guerrilla Army at Mingyuegou

1977. Kim Il Sung's 65th Birthday. Multicoloured.

N1607	2ch. Type **610**	15	10
N1608	5ch. In command of army	15	10
N1609	10ch. Visiting steel workers in Kangson	35	10
N1610	15ch. Before battle	25	10
N1611	25ch. In schoolroom	35	15
N1612	40ch. Viewing bumper harvest	50	15
MSN1613	85×94 mm. 50ch. "Kim Il Sung among the Artists"	1·30	90

611 Chollima 72 Trolleybus

1977. Trolleybuses. Without gum.

N1614	**611**	5ch. blue, lilac and black	1·50	30
N1615	-	10ch. red, green & black	1·50	30

Design: 10ch. Chollima 74 trolleybus.

612 Red Flag and Hand holding Rifle

1977. 45th Anniversary of Korean People's Revolutionary Army. Without gum.

N1616	**612**	40ch. red, yellow & blk	85	25

613 Proclamation and Watchtower

1977. 40th Anniversary of Pochonbo Battle. Without gum.

N1617	**613**	10ch. multicoloured	25	15

614 Koryo White Ware Teapot

1977. Korean Porcelain. Multicoloured.

N1618 10ch. Type **614** (postage) 75 15
N1619 15ch. White vase, Li Dynasty 1·00 20
N1620 20ch. Celadon vase, Koryo Dynasty 1·30 30
N1621 40ch. Celadon vase with lotus decoration, Koryo Dynasty (air) 1·80 40

615 Postal Transport

1977. Postal Services. Multicoloured. Without gum.

N1623 2ch. Type **615** 1·50 30
N1624 10ch. Postwoman delivering letter 60 15
N1625 30ch. Mil Mi-8 helicopter 1·50 40
N1626 40ch. Ilyushin Il-18 airliner and world map 1·70 45

616 *Rapala arata*

1977. Butterflies and Dragonflies. Multicoloured.

N1627 2ch. Type **616** (postage) 65 10
N1628 5ch. *Colias aurora* 1·00 15
N1629 10ch. Poplar admiral 1·30 20
N1630 15ch. *Anax partherope* (dragonfly) 1·70 35
N1631 25ch. *Sympetrum pedemontanum* (dragonfly) 2·20 45
N1632 50ch. *Papilio maackii* (air) 2·75 60

617 Grey Cat

1977. Cats. Multicoloured.

N1634 2ch. Type **617** 1·70 30
N1635 10ch. Black and white cat 2·20 40
N1636 25ch. Ginger cat 3·75 55

618

1977. Dogs. Multicoloured.

N1638 5ch. Type **618** (postage) 1·30 25
N1639 15ch. Chow 1·50 25
N1640 50ch. Pungsang dog (air) 2·30 45

619 Kim Il Sung and President Tito

1977. Visit of President Tito.

N1642 **619** 10ch. multicoloured 15 10
N1643 **619** 15ch. multicoloured 15 10
N1644 **619** 20ch. multicoloured 25 15
N1645 **619** 40vh. multicoloured 40 25

620 Girl and Symbols of Education

1977. Fifth Anniversary of 11-year Compulsory Education. Without gum.

N1646 **620** 10ch. multicoloured 25 15

621 Chinese Mactra and Cobia

1977. Shellfish and Fish. Multicoloured.

N1647 2ch. Type **621** (postage) 50 10
N1648 5ch. Bladder moon 65 20
N1649 10ch. *Arca inflata* and pomfret 1·00 20
N1650 25ch. Thomas's rapa whelk and grouper 1·40 35
N1651 50ch. Thomas's rapa whelk and globefish (air) 2·30 65

622 Students and 'Theses'

1977. Kim Il Sung's *Theses on Socialist Education*. Multicoloured. Without gum.

N1653 10ch. Type **622** 25 10
N1654 20ch. Students, crowd and text 30 15

623 'Juche' Torch

1977. Seminar on the Juche Idea. Multicoloured. Without gum.

N1655 2ch. Type **623** 25 10
N1656 5ch. Crowd and red book 25 10
N1657 10ch. *Chollima* Statue and flags 25 10
N1658 15ch. Handclasp and red flag on world map 25 10
N1659 25ch. Map of Korea and anti-US slogans 35 15
N1660 40ch. Crowd and Mt. Paektu-san 40 15
MSN1661 117×78 mm. 50ch. Emblem of Juche seminar 1·30 55

624 Jubilant Crowd

1977. Election of Deputies to Supreme People's Assembly. Without gum.

N1662 **624** 10ch. multicoloured 25 15

625 Footballers

1977. World Cup Football Championship, Argentina. Without gum.

N1663 **625** 10ch. multicoloured 1·10 25
N1664 - 15ch. multicoloured 1·50 35
N1665 - 40ch. multicoloured 2·50 50
MSN1666 132×82 mm. 50ch. Footballers 2·20 55

Designs: 15ch. to 50ch. Different football scenes.

626 Kim Il Sung with Rejoicing Crowds

1977. Re-election of Kim Il Sung. Without gum.

N1667 **626** 10ch. multicoloured 30 15

627 Chollima Statue and Symbols of Communication

1977. 20th Anniversary of Socialist Countries' Communication Organization. Without gum.

N1668 **627** 10ch. multicoloured 30 15

Nos.N1669/N1686 T **628**/**637** are vacant.

638 Chollima Statue and City Skyline

1978. New Year. Without gum.

N1687 **638** 10ch. multicoloured 30 15

639 Skater in 19th-century Costume

1978. Winter Olympic Games, Sapporo and Innsbruck. Multicoloured.

N1688 2ch. Type **639** (postage) 60 15
N1689 5ch. Skier 60 15
N1690 10ch. Woman skater 60 15
N1691 15ch. Hunter on skis 65 20
N1692 20ch. Woman (in 19th-century costume) on skis 65 20
N1693 25ch. Viking with longbow 3·25 50
N1694 40ch. Skier (air) 1·80 35
MSN1695 Two sheets. (a) 78×97 mm. 50ch. Innsbruck skyline; (b) 97×78 mm. 60ch. Skater 3·00 1·30

640 Post-rider and 'Horse-ticket'

1978. Postal Progress. Multicoloured.

N1696 2ch. Type **640** (postage) 35 10
N1697 5ch. Postman on motorcycle 2·10 45
N1698 10ch. Electric train and post van 2·10 45
N1699 15ch. Mail steamer and Mil Mi-8 helicopter 1·20 25
N1700 25ch. Tupolev Tu-154 jetliner and satellite 1·10 25
N1701 40ch. Dove and UPU headquarters (air) 65 20
MSN1702 Two sheets each 97×79 mm. (a) 50ch. Dove and UPU symbol; (b) 60ch. Dove and UPU headquarters 6·25 3·25

641 Self-portrait

1978. 400th Birth Anniversary of Rubens.

N1703 **641** 2ch. multicoloured 35 15
N1704 **641** 5ch. multicoloured 35 15
N1705 **641** 40ch. multicoloured 2·10 45
MSN1706 96×79 mm. 50ch. multicoloured 2·50 1·70

642 Chungsong Tractor

1978. Farm Machines. Without gum.

N1707 **642** 10ch. red and black 65 20
N1708 - 10ch. brown and black 65 20

Design: No. N1708, Sprayer.

643 Show Jumping

1978. Olympic Games, Moscow (1980) (1st issue). Equestrian Events. Multicoloured.

N1709 2ch. Type **643** 35 10
N1710 5ch. Jumping bar 35 10
N1711 10ch. Cross-country 65 15
N1712 15ch. Dressage 65 25
N1713 25ch. Water splash 1·00 40
N1714 40ch. Dressage (different) 1·70 75
MSN1715 75×111 mm. 50ch. Jumping triple bar 2·50 55

See also Nos. N1861/**MS**N1866, N1873/**MS**N1880 and N1887/**MS**N1893.

644 Soldier

1978. Korean People's Army Day. Multicoloured. Without gum.
N1716 5ch. Type **644** 25 10
N1717 10ch. Servicemen saluting 25 10

645 *Mangyongbong* (Freighter)

1978. Korean Ships. Multicoloured.
N1718 2ch. Type **645** (postage) 2·10 50
N1719 5ch. *Hyoksin* (freighter) 35 15
N1720 10ch. *Chongchongang* (gas carrier) 65 15
N1721 30ch. *Sonbong* (tanker) 1·30 40
N1722 50ch. *Taedonggang* (freighter) (air) 1·50 85

646 Uruguayan Footballer

1978. World Cup Football Championship Winners. Multicoloured.
N1724 5ch. Type **646** (postage) 60 10
N1725 10ch. Italian player 60 10
N1726 15ch. West German player 60 15
N1727 25ch. Brazilian player 60 15
N1728 40ch. English player 1·00 35
N1729 50ch. Hands holding World Cup (vert) (air) 1·70 50
MSN1730 110×74 mm. 50ch. Italian and North Korean players (air) 3·75 1·00

647 Footballers (1930 Winners, Uruguay)

1978. History of World Cup Football Championship. Multicoloured.
N1731 20ch. Type **647** (postage) 1·00 35
N1732 20ch. Italy, 1934 1·00 35
N1733 20ch. France, 1938 1·00 35
N1734 20ch. Brazil, 1950 1·00 35
N1735 20ch. Switzerland, 1954 1·00 35
N1736 20ch. Sweden, 1958 1·00 35
N1737 20ch. Chile, 1962 1·00 35
N1738 20ch. England, 1966 1·00 35
N1739 20ch. Mexico, 1970 1·00 35
N1740 20ch. West Germany, 1974 1·00 35
N1741 20ch. Argentina, 1978 1·00 35
N1742 50ch. Footballers and emblem (air) 2·50 1·00
MSN1743 73×98 mm. 50ch. World Cup and championship emblem 2·10 60

648 *Sea of Blood* (opera)

1978. Art from the Period of Anti-Japanese Struggle. Multicoloured.
N1744 10ch. Type **648** 35 15
N1745 15ch. Floral kerchief embroidered with map of Korea 50 15
N1746 20ch. *Tansimjul* (maypole dance) 65 25
MSN1747 100×69 mm. 40ch. Notation of *Song of Korea* 1·60 60

649 Red Flag and '7', Electricity and Coal

1978. Second 7 Year Plan. Multicoloured. Without gum.
N1748 5ch. Type **649** 35 10
N1749 10ch. Steel and non-ferrous metal 35 10
N1750 15ch. Engineering and chemical fertilizer 50 15
N1751 30ch. Cement and fishing 75 25
N1752 50ch. Grain and tideland reclamation 1·00 50

650 Gymnastics (Alfred Flatow)

1978. Olympic Games History and Medal-winners. Multicoloured.
N1753 20ch. Type **650** 90 35
N1754 20ch. Runners (Michel Theato) 90 35
N1755 20ch. Runners (Wyndham Halswelle) 90 35
N1756 20ch. Rowing (William Kinnear) 90 35
N1757 20ch. Fencing (Paul Anspach) 1·70 50
N1758 20ch. Runners (Ugo Frigerio) 90 35
N1759 20ch. Runners (Ahmed El Quafi) 90 35
N1760 20ch. Cycling (Robert Charpentier) 2·10 50
N1761 20ch. Gymnastics (Josep Stalder) 90 35
N1762 20ch. Boxing (Lazio Papp) 1·20 40
N1763 20ch. Runners (Ronald Delany) 90 35
N1764 20ch. High jump (Jolanda Balas) 90 35
N1765 20ch. High jump (Valery Brumel) 90 35
N1766 20ch. Gymnastics (Vera Caslavska) 90 35
N1767 20ch. Rifle shooting (Li Ho Jun) 90 35
MSN1768 105×95 mm. 50ch. Boxing (Ku Yong Jo) 1·70 85

651 Douglas DC-8-63 and Comte AC-4 Gentleman

1978. Aircrafts. Multicoloured.
N1769 2ch. Type **651** 75 15
N1770 10ch. Ilyushin Il-62M and Avia BH-25 1·00 15
N1771 15ch. Douglas DC-8-63 and Savoia Marchetti S-71 1·10 25
N1772 20ch. Tupolev Tu-144 and Kalinin K-5 1·30 25
N1773 25ch. Tupolev Tu-154 and Antonov An-2 biplane 1·30 25
N1774 30ch. Ilyushin Il-18 1·30 25
N1775 40ch. Concorde and Wibault 283 trimotor 3·00 75
MSN1776 102×75 mm. 50ch. Airbus Industries A300B2 jetliner and Focke Wulf A-17 Mowe 2·75 60

652 White-bellied Black Woodpecker and Map

1978. White-bellied Black Woodpecker Preservation. Multicoloured.
N1777 5ch. Type **652** 1·10 40
N1778 10ch. Woodpecker and eggs 1·30 50
N1779 15ch. Woodpecker feeding young 1·70 65
N1780 25ch. Woodpecker feeding young (different) 2·10 85
N1781 50ch. Adult woodpecker on tree trunk 3·25 1·20

653 Demonstrators and Korean Map

1978. 30th Anniversary of Democratic People's Republic of Korea. Multicoloured. Without gum.
N1783 10ch. Type **653** 25 15
N1784 10ch. Flag and soldiers 25 15
N1785 10ch. Flag and 'Juche' 25 15
N1786 10ch. Red Flag 25 15
N1787 10ch. *Chollima* Statue and city skyline 25 15
N1788 10ch. 'Juche' torch and men of three races 25 15

654 *Cat and Pup*

1978. Animal Paintings by Li Am. Multicoloured.
N1789 10ch. Type **654** 3·00 65
N1790 15ch. *Cat up a tree* 3·00 65
N1791 40ch. *Wild geese* 3·00 65

655 Footballers

1978. Argentina's Victory in World Cup Football Championship. Without gum.
N1792 **655** 10ch. multicoloured 90 20
N1793 - 15ch. multicoloured 1·10 25
N1794 - 25ch. multicoloured 1·30 40
MSN1795 94×69 mm. 50ch. multicoloured 2·10 1·70
Designs: 15ch. to 50ch. Different football scenes.

Nos. N1796/N1811 T **656/667** are vacant.

668 Red Flag and Pine Branch

1979. New Year. Without gum.
N1812 **668** 10ch. multicoloured 30 15

669 Kim Il Sung with Children's Corps Members, Maanshan

1979. International Year of the Child (1st issue). Multicoloured. (a) Paintings of Kim Il Sung and children.
N1813 5ch. Type **669** 10 10
N1814 10ch. Kim Il Sung and Children's Corps members in classroom 25 10
N1815 15ch. New Year gathering 40 25
N1816 20ch. Kim Il Sung and children in snow 60 35
N1817 30ch. Kim Il Sung examines children's schoolbooks (vert) 85 40

(b) Designs showing children.
N1818 10ch. Tug-of-war 25 10
N1819 15ch. Dance *Growing up Fast* 40 15
N1820 20ch. Children of many races and globe 50 25
N1821 25ch. Children singing 85 40
N1822 30ch. Children in toy spaceships 85 40
MSN1823 Two sheets (a) 90×72 mm. 50ch. Kim Il Sung visits a kindergarten (vert); (b) 124×85 mm. 50ch. As No. N1820 5·00 4·25
See also Nos. N1907/**MS**N1915, N1916/**MS**N1918 and N2042/**MS**N2049.

670 Rose

1979. Roses. Multicoloured.
N1824 1wn. Red rose
N1825 3wn. White rose
N1826 5wn. Type **670**
N1827 10wn. Deep pink rose
See also Nos. N1837/N1842.

671 Warriors on Horseback

1979. *The Story of Two Generals*. Multicoloured. Without gum.
N1828 5ch. Type **671** 25 10
N1829 10ch. Farm labourer blowing feather 40 15
N1830 10ch. Generals fighting on foot 40 15
N1831 10ch. Generals on horseback 40 15

672 Red Guard and Industrial Skyline

1979. 20th Anniversary of Worker-Peasant Red Guards. Without gum.
N1832 **672** 10ch. multicoloured 30 15

673 Clement-Bayard Airship *Fleurus*

1979. Airships. Multicoloured. Without gum.
N1833 10ch. Type **673** 1·30 30
N1834 20ch. N.1 *Norge* 1·30 30
MSN1835 80×79 mm. 50ch. *Graf Zeppelin* 2·20 60

674 Crowd of Demonstrators

1979. 60th Anniversary of 1st March Popular Uprising. Without gum.
N1836 **674** 10ch. blue and red 30 15

1979. Roses. As Nos. N1824/N1827. Multicoloured.
N1837 5ch. As Type **670** (postage) 25 10

N1838	10ch. As No. N1827	35	10
N1839	15ch. As No. N1824	35	10
N1840	20ch. Yellow rose	60	15
N1841	30ch. As No. 1825	75	25
N1842	50ch. Deep pink rose (different) (air)	1·10	50

675 Table Tennis Trophy

1979. 35th World Table Tennis Championship, Pyongyang. Multicoloured. With or without gum.

N1843	5ch. Type **675**	25	10
N1844	10ch. Women's doubles	25	10
N1845	15ch. Women's singles	40	15
N1846	20ch. Men's doubles	65	15
N1847	30ch. Men's singles	1·00	35
MSN1848	84×108 mm. 50ch. Chollima Statue and championship emblem	2·50	1·70

676 Marchers with Red Flag

1979. Socialist Construction under Banner of 'Juche' Idea. Multicoloured. Without gum.

N1849	5ch. Type **676**	30	15
N1850	10ch. Map of Korea	30	15
N1851	10ch. 'Juche' torch	30	15

677 Badge

1979. Order of Honour of the Three Revolutions. Without gum.

N1852	**677**	10ch. blue	25	10

678 Emblem, Satellite orbiting Globe and Aerials

1979. World Telecommunications Day. Without gum.

N1853	**678**	10ch. multicoloured	40	15

679 Advancing Soldiers and Monument

1979. 40th Anniversary of Battle in Musan Area. Without gum.

N1854	**679**	10ch. mauve, light blue and blue	30	15

680 Exhibition Entrance

1979. International Friendship Exhibition. Without gum.

N1855	**680**	10ch. multicoloured	25	15

681 *Peonies*

1979. 450th Death Anniversary (1978) of Albrecht Durer (artist) (1st issue). Multicoloured.

N1856	15ch. Type **681**	85	25
N1857	20ch. *Columbines*	1·40	35
N1858	25ch. *A Great Tuft of Grass*	1·40	35
N1859	30ch. *Wing of a Bird*	2·10	55
MSN1860	92×67 mm. 50ch. As No. 1859	3·25	85

See also Nos. N2012/**MS**N2013.

682 Fencing

1979. Olympic Games, Moscow (2nd issue). Multicoloured. With gum (10, 40ch. only).

N1861	5ch. Type **682**	1·50	35
N1862	10ch. Gymnastics	60	15
N1863	20ch. Yachting	85	35
N1864	30ch. Athletics	1·00	40
N1865	40ch. Weightlifting	1·30	60
MSN1866	106×77 mm. 50ch. Equestrian event	3·25	1·70

683 Hunting

1979. Horse-riding (people of Koguryo Dynasty). Multicoloured.

N1867	5ch. Type **683**	85	35
N1868	10ch. Archery contest	85	35
N1869	15ch. Man beating drum on horseback	35	10
N1870	20ch. Man blowing horn	35	10
N1871	30ch. Man and horse, armoured with chainmail	40	15
N1872	50ch. Hawking (air)	2·75	55

684 Judo

1979. Olympic Games, Moscow (3rd issue). Multicoloured. With gum (5, 15, 20, 30ch. only).

N1873	5ch. Type **684**	40	10
N1874	10ch. Volleyball	40	10
N1875	15ch. Cycling	1·70	40
N1876	20ch. Basketball	65	25
N1877	25ch. Canoeing	65	25
N1878	30ch. Boxing	1·00	35
N1879	40ch. Shooting	90	35
MSN1880	79×108 mm. 50ch. Gymnastics	1·30	50

685 Warrior's Costume

1979. Warrior Costumes of Li Dynasty.

N1881	**685**	5ch. multicoloured	25	15
N1882	-	10ch. multicoloured	25	15
N1883	-	15ch. multicoloured	40	15
N1884	-	20ch. multicoloured	60	20
N1885	-	30ch. multicoloured	1·00	30
N1886	-	50ch. multicoloured (air)	1·30	50

Designs: 10ch. to 50ch. Different costumes.

686 Wrestling

1979. Olympic Games, Moscow (4th issue). Multicoloured.

N1887	10ch. Type **686**	40	15
N1888	15ch. Handball	40	15
N1889	20ch. Archery	2·10	50
N1890	25ch. Hockey	2·10	60
N1891	30ch. Rowing	1·00	35
N1892	40ch. Football	2·00	50
MSN1893	77×106 mm. 50ch. Equestrian events	3·25	1·40

687 Monument

1979. Chongbong Monument. Without gum.

N1894	**687**	10ch. multicoloured	30	15

688 Bottle-feeding Fawn

1979. Sika Deer. Multicoloured.

N1895	5ch. Type **688** (postage)	25	15
N1896	10ch. Doe and fawn	25	15
N1897	15ch. Stag drinking from stream	25	15
N1898	20ch. Stag	35	15
N1899	30ch. Stag and doe	40	35
N1900	50ch. Antlers and deer (air)	65	50

689 Moscovy Ducks

1979. Central Zoo, Pyongyang. Multicoloured.

N1901	5ch. Type **689** (postage)	35	15
N1902	10ch. Ostrich	65	25
N1903	15ch. Common turkey	90	35
N1904	20ch. Dalmatian pelican	1·10	40
N1905	30ch. Vulturine guineafowl	1·30	50
N1906	50ch. Mandarins (air)	2·00	85

690 Girl with Model Viking Ship

1979. International Year of the Child (2nd issue). Multicoloured.

N1907	20ch. Type **690**	1·50	40
N1908	20ch. Boys with model steam railway locomotive	3·25	40
N1909	20ch. Boy with model biplane	1·70	40
N1910	20ch. Boy with model spaceman	1·30	40
N1911	30ch. Boy with model speedboat	2·50	60
N1912	30ch. Boy sitting astride toy electric train	3·25	60
N1913	30ch. Boy and model aeroplane	2·50	60
N1914	30ch. Boy and flying spaceman	1·90	60
MSN1915	Four sheets, each 77×104 mm. (a) 80ch. Boy and Concorde; (b) 80ch. Girl and satellite; (c) Boy and model liner; (d) 80ch. Children with model train	29·00	6·75

691 Footballers

1979. International Year of the Child (3rd issue). Multicoloured.

N1916	20ch. Type **691**	1·30	50
N1917	30ch. Footballers (different)	2·10	75
MSN1918	104×78 mm. 80ch. Footballers (different)	6·75	2·10

692 Japanese Stonefish

1979. Marine Life. Multicoloured.

N1919	20ch. Type **692**	1·10	40
N1920	30ch. Schlegel's redfish	1·30	50
N1921	50ch. Northern sealion	2·20	85

693 Cross-country Skiing (Sergei Saveliev)

1979. Winter Olympic Games, Lake Placid. Multioloured.

N1922	10ch. Figure skating (Irina Rodnina and Aleksandr Zaitsev) (horiz)	60	20
N1923	20ch. Ice hockey (Russian team) (horiz)	1·00	30
N1924	30ch. Women's 5 km relay (horiz)	1·40	55
N1925	40ch. Type **693**	2·00	85
N1926	50ch. Women's speed skating (Tatiana Averina)	3·00	1·10
MSN1927	81×68 mm. 60ch. Ice dancing (Ludmila Pakhomova and Aleksandr Gorshkov)	6·25	4·75

694 The Honey Bee collecting Nectar

1979. The Honey Bee. Multicoloured.

N1928	20ch. Type **694**	1·70	35
N1929	30ch. Bee and flowers	2·00	40
N1930	50ch. Bee hovering over flower	2·20	50

695 Kim Jong Suk's Birthplace, Heoryong

1979. Historic Revolutionary Sites.

N1931	**695**	10ch. multicoloured	35	15
N1932	-	10ch. brown, blue & blk	35	15

Design: No. N1932, Sinpa Revolutionary Museum.

696 Mt. Paektu

1980. New Year.

N1933	**696**	10ch. multicoloured	75	15

697 Student and Books

1980. Studying.

N1934	**697**	10ch. multicoloured	35	15

698 Conveyor Belt

1980. Unryul Mine Conveyor Belt.

N1935	**698**	10ch. multicoloured	75	15

699 Children of Three Races

1980. International Day of the Child. Multicoloured.

N1936	10ch. Type **699**	40	15
N1937	10ch. Girl dancing to accordion	65	15
N1938	10ch. Children in fairground aeroplane	60	15
N1939	10ch. Children as astronauts	40	15
N1940	10ch. Children on tricycles	1·70	40
N1941	10ch. Children with toy diesel train	2·50	60
N1942	10ch. 'His loving care for the children, future of the fatherland' ($59^1/_2$×38 mm)	40	15
MSN1943	69×89 mm. 50ch. 'Father Marshal visiting Kindergarten' (52×44 mm)	3·00	1·40

700 Monument

1980. Chongsan-ri Historic Site. Multicoloured.

N1944	5ch. Type **700**	15	15
N1945	10ch. Meeting place of the General Membership	25	15

701 Monument

1980. Monument marking Kim Jong Suk's Return.

N1946	**701**	10ch. multicoloured	25	15

702 Vasco Nunez de Balboa

1980. Conquerors of the Earth. Multicoloured.

N1947	10ch. Type **702**	65	25
N1948	20ch. Francisco de Orellana	1·00	35
N1949	30ch. Haroun Tazieff	1·40	50
N1950	40ch. Edmund Hillary and Sherpa Tenzing	2·10	85
MSN1951	75×105 mm. 70ch. Ibn Battuta	3·50	1·70

703 Museum

1980. Ryongpo Revolutionary Museum.

N1952	**703**	10ch. blue and black	25	10

704 Rowland Hill and Stamps

1980. Death Centenary (1979) of Sir Rowland Hill. Multicoloured.

N1953	30ch. Type **704**	3·75	1·10
N1954	50ch. Rowland Hill and stamps (different)	5·50	1·40

705 North Korean Red Cross Flag

1980. World Red Cross Day. Multicoloured.

N1955	10ch. Type **705**	1·00	35
N1956	10ch. Henri Dunant (founder)	1·00	35
N1957	10ch. Nurse and child	1·00	35
N1958	10ch. Polikarpov Po-2 biplane and ship	1·30	50
N1959	10ch. Mil Mi-4 helicopter	1·50	50
N1960	10ch. Children playing at nurses	1·00	35
N1961	10ch. Red Cross map over Korea and forms of transport	3·50	1·30
MSN1962	83×93 mm. 50ch. Nurse with syringe	5·00	2·50

706 Fernando Magellan

1980. Conquerors of the Sea. Multicoloured.

N1963	10ch. Type **706**	2·10	75
N1964	20ch. Fridtjof Nansen	2·10	75
N1965	30ch. Auguste and Jacques Piccard	3·00	1·00
N1966	40ch. Jacques-Yves Cousteau	3·50	1·30
MSN1967	75×105 mm. 70ch. James Cook	6·75	1·80

707 Korean Stamps and Penny Black

1980. London 1980 International Stamp Exhibition. Multicoloured.

N1968	10ch. Type **707** (postage)	3·00	1·00
N1969	20ch. Korean cover and British Guiana 1c. black and red	3·00	1·00
N1970	30ch. Early Korean stamp and modern cover	2·10	75
N1971	50ch. Korean stamps	2·20	85
N1972	40ch. Korean stamp and miniature sheet (air)	3·50	1·30
MSN1973	110×138 mm. 20ch. Type **707**; 30ch. As No. N1969; 50ch. As No. N1970	9·25	3·25

708 Wright Brothers

1980. Conquerors of Sky and Space. Multicoloured.

N1974	10ch. Type **708**	85	30
N1975	20ch. Louis Bleriot	1·30	50
N1976	30ch. Anthony Fokker	1·70	65
N1977	40ch. Secondo Campini and Sir Frank Whittle	2·50	85
MSN1978	76×106 mm. 70ch. Count Ferdinand Zeppelin	3·25	1·00

709 Space Station on Planet

1980. Conquerors of the Universe. Multicoloured.

N1979	10ch. Orbiting space station	35	15
N1980	20ch. Type **709**	50	25
N1981	30ch. Prehistoric animals and spaceships	1·30	50
N1982	40ch. Prehistoric animals and birds and spaceship	1·70	60
MSN1983	77×105 mm. 70ch. Planetary scene	3·25	1·70

710 Flag and Banners

1980. 25th Anniversary of General Association of Korean Residents in Japan (Chongryon).

N1984	**710**	10ch. multicoloured	25	15

711 Hospital

1980. Pyongyang Maternity Hospital.

N1985	**711**	10ch. blue, purple & blk	60	20

712 Health Centre

1980. Changgangwon Health Centre, Pyongyang.

N1986	**712**	2ch. black and blue	35	15

713 Hand holding Rifle

1980. 50th Anniversary of Revolutionary Army.

N1987	**713**	10ch. multicoloured	35	15

714 Workers' Hostel, Samjiyon

1980

N1988	**714**	10ch. brown, blue & blk	40	15
N1989	-	10ch. black and green	65	25
N1990	-	10ch. black and red	65	25
N1991	-	10ch. black and yellow	65	25
N1992	-	10ch. multicoloured	40	15
N1993	-	10ch. multicoloured	40	15
N1994	-	10ch. multicoloured	1·70	50
N1995	-	10ch. green and black	1·30	40
N1996	-	10ch. grey, blue & black	5·00	85
N1997	-	10ch. multicoloured	5·75	85

Designs: No. N1989, Taedonggang rice transplanter; No. N1990, Chongsan-ri rice harvester; No. N1991, Maize harvester; No. N1992, Revolutionary building, Songmun-ri; No. N1993, Revolutionary building, Samhwa; No. N1994, Sundial of 1438; No. N1995, 16th-century 'turtle' ship; No. N1996, Pungsan dog; No. N1997, Japanese quail.

715 Party Emblem

1980. Sixth Korean Workers' Party Congress. Multicoloured.

N1998	10ch. Type **715**	25	15
N1999	10ch. Students and Laurel leaf on globe	25	15
N2000	10ch. Group with accordion	65	15
N2001	10ch. Group with banner, microscope, book and trophy	40	25
N2002	10ch. Worker with book and flag	1·30	40
N2003	10ch. Worker with spanner and flag	1·30	40
N2004	10ch. Marchers with torch and flags	25	15
N2005	10ch. Emblem, marchers and map	35	20
MSN2006	Two sheets each 94×77 mm. (a) 50ch. 'The great Leader inspires and encourages Colliers on the Spot' (41×50 mm); (b) 50ch. 'Leading the Van in the arduous March' (38×60 mm)	2·50	1·70

716 Dribbling Ball

1980. World Cup Football Championship, 1978–1982. Multicoloured.

N2007	20ch. Type **716**	3·50	1·30
N2008	30ch. Tackle	4·25	1·70
MSN2009	147×118 mm. 40ch. Tackling (different); 60ch. Moving in to tackle	7·25	2·75

717 Irina Rodnina and Aleksandr Zaitsev

1980. Winter Olympic Gold Winners. Multicoloured.

N2010	20ch. Type **717**	6·75	2·30
MSN2011	67×94 mm. 1wn. Natalia Linitshchnuk and Gennadi Karponosov	7·25	2·50

718 *Soldier with Horse*

1980. 450th Death Anniversary (1978) of Albrecht Durer (artist) (2nd issue). Multicoloured.

N2012	20ch. Type **718**	7·25	2·75
MSN2013	81×106 mm. 1wn. *Horse and Rider*	11·00	3·75

719 Kepler, Astrolabe and Satellites

1980. 350th Death Anniversary of Johannes Kepler (astronomer). Multicoloured.

N2014	20ch. Type **719**	3·75	1·70
MSN2015	93×75 mm. 1wn. Kepler astrolabe and satellites (different)	6·75	2·10

720 German 1m. and Russian 30k. Zeppelin Stamps

1980. Third International Stamp Fair, Essen. Multicoloured.

N2016	10ch. Type **720**	1·20	40
N2017	20ch. German 2m. and Russian 35k. Zeppelin stamps	2·50	90
N2018	30ch. German 4m. and Russian 1r. Zeppelin stamps	3·50	1·30
MSN2019	137×82 mm. 50ch. Russian 2r. Polar Flight stamp and Korean 50ch. IYC stamp	8·50	3·50

721 Shooting (Aleksandr Melentev)

1980. Olympic Medal Winners. Multicoloured.

N2020	10ch. Type **721**	40	15
N2021	20ch. Cycling (Robert Dill-Bundi)	4·50	1·60
N2022	25ch. Gymnastics (Stoyan Deltchev)	65	35
N2023	30ch. Wrestling (Chang Se Hong and Li Ho Pyong)	65	35
N2024	35ch. Weightlifting (Ho Bong Chol)	65	35
N2025	40ch. Running (Marita Koch)	70	40
N2026	50ch. Modern Pentathlon (Anatoli Starostin)	1·00	50
MSN2027	Two sheets. (a) 100×76 mm. 70ch. Boxing (Teofilo Stevenson); (b) 107×163 mm. 70ch. Ancient Greek rider on horse	5·75	3·75

722 Tito

1980. President Tito of Yugoslavia Commemoration.

N2028	**722**	20ch. multicoloured	50	15

723 Convair CV 340 Airliner

1980. 25th Anniversary of First Post-war Flight of Lufthansa. Multicoloured.

N2029	20ch. Type **723**	6·25	2·50
MSN2030	90×75 mm. 1wn. Airbus A 300	8·50	3·25

724 *The Rocket*

1980. 150th Anniversary of Liverpool–Manchester Railway. Multicoloured.

N2031	20ch. Type **724**	7·25	2·75
MSN2032	105×60 mm. 1wn. Locomotive drawing carriage and horsebox	8·50	3·25

725 Steam and Electric Locomotives

1980. Centenary of First Electric Train. Multicoloured.

N2033	20ch. Type **725**	7·25	2·50
MSN2084	106×86 mm. 1wn. Opening Ceremony of first electric railway	14·50	5·00

726 Hammarskjold

1980. 75th Birth Anniversary of Dag Hammarskjold (former Secretary General of United Nations). Multicoloured.

N2035	20ch. Type **726**	4·25	3·00
MSN2036	87×68 mm. 1wn. Hammarskjold (different)	5·50	3·25

727 Bobby Fischer and Boris Spassky

1980. World Chess Championship, Merano. Multicoloured.

N2037	20ch. Type **727**	8·00	2·50
MSN2038	84×84 mm. 1wn. Viktor Korchnoi and Anatoly Karpov	10·00	2·50

728 Stolz

1980. Birth Centenary of Robert Stolz (composer). Multicoloured.

N2039	20ch. Type **728**	3·75	1·30
MSN2040	94×76 mm. 1wn. Stolz examining stamp with magnifying glass	6·25	1·80

729 Chollima Statue

1981. New Year. Without gum.

N2041	**729**	10ch. multicoloured	40	15

730 Russian Fairy Tale

1981. International Year of the Child (1979) (4th issue). Fairy Tales. Multicoloured.

N2042	10ch. Type **730**	1·80	60
N2043	10ch. Icelandic tale	1·80	60
N2044	10ch. Swedish tale	1·80	60
N2045	10ch. Irish tale	1·80	60
N2046	10ch. Italian tale	1·80	60
N2047	10ch. Japanese tale	1·80	60
N2048	10ch. German tale	1·80	60
MSN2049	95×117 mm. 70ch. Korean tale	4·75	3·50

731 Changgwang Street

1981. Changgwang Street, Pyongyang.

N2050	**731**	10ch. multicoloured	40	15

732 Footballers

1981. World Cup Football Championship, Spain (1982) (1st issue). Multicoloured.

N2051	10ch. Type **732**	3·50	1·00
N2052	20ch. Hitting ball past defender	3·50	1·00
N2053	30ch. Disputing possession of ball	3·50	1·00
MSN2054	95×103 mm. 70ch. Three players	8·50	3·50

See also Nos. N2055/**MS**N2060 and N2201/**MS**N2207.

733 Map, Emblem and World Cup

1981. World Cup Football Championship, Spain (1982) (2nd issue). Multicoloured.

N2055	10ch. Type **733**	2·20	85
N2056	15ch. Footballers	2·20	85
N2057	20ch. Heading ball	2·20	85
N2058	25ch. Footballers (different)	2·20	85
N2059	30ch. Footballers (different)	2·20	85
MSN2060	96×92 mm. 70ch. Footballers (different)	8·50	3·50

734 Workers with Book and Marchers with Banner

1981. Implementation of Decision of the Sixth Koreans' Party Congress. Multicoloured.

N2061	2ch. Type **734**	15	10
N2062	10ch. Worker with book	20	10
N2063	10ch. Workers and industrial plant	35	15
N2064	10ch. Electricity and coal (horiz)	1·60	35
N2065	10ch. Steel and non-ferrous metals (horiz)	35	15
N2066	10ch. Cement and fertilizers (horiz)	35	15
N2067	30ch. Fishing and fabrics (horiz)	50	15
N2068	40ch. Grain and harbour (horiz)	65	25

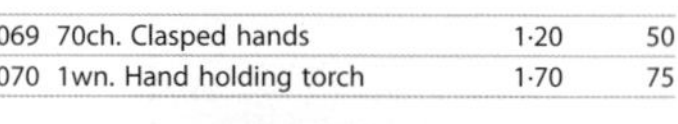

N2069	70ch. Clasped hands	1·20	50
N2070	1wn. Hand holding torch	1·70	75

735 Footballers

1981. Gold Cup Football Championship, Uruguay. Multicoloured.

N2071	20ch. Type **735**	3·75	1·50
MSN2072	99×84 mm. 1wn. Goalkeeper diving for ball	6·25	3·25

736 Dornier Do-X Flying Boat

1981. Naposta '81 International Stamp Exhibition, Stuttgart. Multicoloured.

N2073	10ch. Type **736**	3·50	65
N2074	20ch. Airship LZ-120 *Bodensee*	3·50	65
N2075	30ch. *Gotz von Berlichingen*	2·10	60
MSN2076	135×80 mm. 70ch. Mercedes-Benz W 196 car	6·25	3·00

737 Telecommunications Equipment

1981. World Telecommunications Day.

N2077	**737**	10ch. multicoloured	2·50	40

738 *Iris pseudacorus*

1981. Flowers. Multicoloured.

N2078	10ch. Type **738**	1·10	15
N2079	20ch. *Iris pallasii*	1·40	25
N2080	30ch. *Gladiolus gandavensis*	2·00	40

739 Austrian WIPA 1981 and Rudolf Kirchschlager Stamps

1981. WIPA 1981 International Stamp Exhibition, Vienna. Multicoloured.

N2081	20ch. Type **739**	2·50	75
N2082	30ch. Austrian Maria Theresa and Franz Joseph stamps	3·25	1·20
MSN2083	133×87 mm. 50ch. Kim Il Sung and choir (38×60 mm)	6·25	3·00

740 Rings Exercise

1981. Centenary of International Gymnastic Federation. Multicoloured.

N2084	10ch. Type **740**	50	25
N2085	15ch. Horse exercise	60	25
N2086	20ch. Backwards somersault	1·00	25
N2087	25ch. Floor exercise	1·10	35

N2088 30ch. Exercise with hoop 1·30 40
MSN2089 104×77 mm. 70ch. Exercise with wand (horiz) 2·50 1·10

741 Armed Workers

1981. 50th Anniversary of Mingyuehgou Meeting.
N2090 **741** 10ch. multicoloured 30 15

742 Farm Building, Sukchon

1981. 20th Anniversary of Agricultural Guidance System and Taean Work System.
N2091 **742** 10ch. green, black and gold 30 15
N2092 - 10ch. blue, black and gold 30 15
Design: No. N2092, Taean Revolutionary Museum.

743 Woman and Banner

1981. 55th Anniversary of Formation of Women's Anti-Japanese Association.
N2093 **743** 5wn. multicoloured 5·25 1·10

743a Scene from Opera

1981. Tenth Anniversary of *Sea of Blood* (opera).
N2094 **743a** 10wn. multicoloured 14·50 6·25

744 Joan of Arc

1981. 550th Death Anniversary of Joan of Arc. Multicoloured.
N2095 10ch. Type **744** 3·25 85
N2096 10ch. Archangel Michael 3·50 85
N2097 70ch. Joan of Arc in armour 3·50 85
MSN2098 96×124 mm. No. N2097 6·25 2·10

745 Torch, Mountains and Flag

1981. 55th Anniversary of Down with Imperialism Union.
N2099 **745** 1wn.50 multicoloured 1·60 75

746 Young Girl by the Window

1981. 375th Birth Anniversary of Rembrandt (artist). Multicoloured.
N2100 10ch. Type **746** 75 35
N2101 20ch. *Rembrandt's Mother* 1·70 60
N2102 30ch. *Saskia van Uylenburgh* 1·70 1·00
N2103 40ch. *Pallas Athene* 3·00 1·30
MSN2104 91×105 mm. 70ch. *Self-portrait* 6·25 3·25

747 Emblem and Banners over Pyongyang

1981. Symposium of Non-Aligned Countries on Food Self-Sufficiency, Pyongyang. Multicoloured.
N2105 10ch. Type **747** 25 15
N2106 50ch. Harvesting 65 35
N2107 90ch. Factories, tractors and marchers with banner 1·30 65

748 St Paul's Cathedral

1981. Wedding of Prince of Wales (1st issue). Multicoloured.
N2108 10ch. Type **748** 2·50 85
N2109 20ch. Great Britain Prince of Wales Investiture stamp 2·50 85
N2110 30ch. Lady Diana Spencer 2·50 85
N2111 40ch. Prince Charles in military uniform 2·50 85
MSN2112 93×96 mm. 70ch. Engagement day portrait of couple 10·50 6·25
See also Nos. N2120/**MS**2124.

749 Four Philosophers (detail)

1981. Paintings by Rubens. Multicoloured.
N2113 10ch. Type **749** 85 40
N2114 15ch. *Portrait of Helena Fourment* 1·30 60
N2115 20ch. *Portrait of Isabella Brandt* 1·70 65
N2116 25ch. *Education of Maria de Medici* 2·10 85
N2117 30ch. *Helena Fourment and her Child* 2·50 90
N2118 40ch. *Helena Fourment in her Wedding Dress* 3·00 1·30
MSN2119 92×110 mm. 70ch. *Portrait of Nikolaas Rubens* 6·25 3·00

750 Royal Couple

1981. Wedding of Prince of Wales (2nd issue). Multicoloured.
N2120 10ch. Type **750** 3·75 1·30
N2121 20ch. Couple on balcony after wedding 3·75 1·30
N2122 30ch. Couple outside St Paul's Cathedral 3·75 1·30
N2123 70ch. Full-length wedding portrait of couple 3·75 1·30
MSN2124 85×106 mm. 70ch. Royal couple and Queen Elizabeth on balcony 13·00 7·25

751 Rowland Hill and Stamps

1981. Philatokyo '81 International Stamp Exhibition. Multicoloured.
N2125 10ch. Korean 2ch. Seminar on Juche Idea stamp (41×29 mm) 1·30 35
N2126 10ch. Korean and 70ch. stamps (41×29 mm) 3·00 1·20
N2127 10ch. Type **751** 3·00 1·20
N2128 20ch. Korean Fairy Tale stamps 2·50 60
N2129 30ch. Japanese stamps 4·25 1·30
MSN2130 93×105 mm. 70ch. Medals, building and pigeon carrying letter 8·00 2·20

752 League Members and Flag

1981. Seventh League of Socialist Working Youth Congress, Pyongyang.
N2131 **752** 10ch. multicoloured 25 10
N2132 **752** 80ch. multicoloured 85 40

753 Government Palace, Sofia, Bulgarian Arms and Khan Asparuch

1981. 1300th Anniversary of Bulgarian State.
N2133 **753** 10ch. multicoloured 35 10

754 Dimitrov

1981. Birth Centenary of Georgi Dimitrov (Bulgarian statesman).
N2134 **754** 10ch. multicoloured 35 10

755 Emblem, Boeing 747-200, City Hall and Mercedes 500

1981. Philatelia '81 International Stamp Fair, Frankfurt-am-Main.
N2135 **755** 20ch. multicoloured 3·25 50

756 Concorde, Airship *Graf Zeppelin* and Count Ferdinand von Zeppelin

1981. Philexfrance 82 International Stamp Exhibition, Paris. Multicoloured. (a) As T **756**.
N2136 10ch. Type **756** 3·75 60
N2137 20ch. Concorde, Breguet Provence airliner and Santos-Dumont's biplane *14 bis* 4·50 1·10
N2138 30ch. *Mona Lisa* (Leonardo da Vinci) and stamps 2·50 40
MSN2139 99×105 mm. 60ch. French Rembrandt and Picasso stamps 8·00 2·50

(b) Size 32×53 mm.
N2140 10ch. Hotel des Invalides, Paris 1·40 60
N2141 20ch. President Mitterrand of France 1·40 60
N2142 30ch. International Friendship Exhibition building 1·40 60
N2143 70ch. Kim Il Sung 1·40 60

757 Rising Sun

1982. New Year.
N2144 **757** 10ch. multicoloured 40 10

758 Emblem and Flags

1982. Prospering Korea. Multicoloured.
N2145 2ch. Type **758** 15 10
N2146 10ch. Industry 35 15
N2147 10ch. Agriculture 35 15
N2148 10ch. Mining 60 15
N2149 10ch. Arts 35 15
N2150 10ch. Al Islet lighthouse, Uam-ri 3·50 60
N2151 40ch. Buildings 65 25

759 The Hair-do

1982. Birth Centenary of Pablo Picasso (artist). Multicoloured.
N2152 10ch. Type **759** 1·10 25
N2153 10ch. *Paulo on a donkey* 2·50 50
N2154 20ch. *Woman leaning on Arm* 1·30 35
N2155 20ch. *Harlequin* 2·50 50
N2156 25ch. *Child with Pigeon* 2·75 65
N2157 25ch. *Reading a Letter* 2·50 50
N2158 35ch. *Portrait of Gertrude Stein* 2·10 40
N2159 35ch. *Harlequin* (different) 2·50 50
N2160 80ch. *Minotaur* 2·50 50
N2161 90ch. *Mother with Child* 2·50 50
MSN2162 Two sheets each 78×96 mm. (a) No. N2160; (b) No. 2161 7·50 4·25

760 Fireworks over Pyongyang

1982. Kim Il Sung's 70th Birthday. Multicoloured.

N2163	10ch. Kim Il Sung's birthplace, Mangyongdae	25	10
N2164	10ch. Type **760**	25	10
N2165	10ch. 'The Day will dawn on downtrodden Korea' (horiz)	25	10
N2166	10ch. Signalling start of Pochonbo Battle (horiz)	25	10
N2167	10ch. Kim Il Sung starting Potong River project (horiz)	25	10
N2168	10ch. Embracing bereaved children (horiz)	25	10
N2169	10ch. Kim Il Sung as Supreme Commander (horiz)	25	10
N2170	10ch. 'On the Road of Advance' (horiz)	25	10
N2171	10ch. Kim Il Sung kindling flame of Chollima Movement, Kansong Steel Plant (horiz)	25	10
N2172	10ch. Kim Il Sung talking to peasants (horiz)	25	10
N2173	10ch. Kim Il Sung fixing site of reservoir (horiz)	25	10
N2174	20ch. Kim Il Sung visiting Komdok Valley (horiz)	25	10
N2175	20ch. Kim Il Sung visiting Red Flag Company (horiz)	25	10
N2176	20ch. Kim Il Sung teaching Juche farming methods (horiz)	25	10
N2177	20ch. Kim Il Sung visiting iron works (horiz)	25	10
N2178	20ch. Kim Il Sung talking with smelters (horiz)	25	10
N2179	20ch. Kim Il Sung at chemical plant (horiz)	25	10
N2180	20ch. Kim Il Sung with fishermen (horiz)	25	10
MSN2181	Two sheets. (a) 93×82 mm. 60ch. Kim Il Sung as a boy (35×47 mm); (b) 60ch. 'Long live Comrade Kim Il Sung' (35×46 mm)	4·25	2·10

761 Soldier saluting

1982. 50th Anniversary of People's Army.

N2182	**761**	10ch. multicoloured	35	10

762 *The Bagpiper* (Durer)

1982. Fourth Essen International Stamp Fair.

N2183	**762**	30ch. multicoloured	5·50	65

763 Surveyors

1982. Implementation of Four Nature-remaking Tasks.

N2184	**763**	10ch. multicoloured	60	10

764 Princess as Baby

1982. 21st Birthday of Princess of Wales.

N2185	**764**	10ch. multicoloured	65	25
N2186	-	20ch. multicoloured	1·50	40
N2187	-	30ch. multicoloured	1·80	60
N2188	-	50ch. multicoloured	1·90	1·00
N2189	-	60ch. multicoloured	1·90	1·00
N2190	-	70ch. multicoloured	1·90	1·00
N2191	-	80ch. multicoloured	1·90	1·00
MSN2192		Two sheets each 88×100 mm. (a) 40ch. Princess with her brother; (b) No. N2191	11·00	5·00

Designs: 20 to 80ch. Princess at various ages.

765 Tower of the 'Juche' Idea, Pyongyang

1982

N2193	**765**	2wn. multicoloured	2·75	85
N2194	-	3wn. orange and black	3·25	90

Design (26×38 mm): 3wn. Arch of Triumph.

766 Tiger

1982. Tigers.

N2195	**766**	20ch. multicoloured	2·20	65
N2196	-	30ch. multicoloured	3·00	65
N2197	-	30ch. mult (horiz)	3·75	1·10
N2198	-	40ch. mult (horiz)	3·75	1·10
N2199	-	80ch. mult (horiz)	3·75	1·10
MSN2200		105×54 mm. 80ch. multicoloured (horiz)	7·75	2·50

Designs: 30 to 80ch. Tigers.

767 Group 1 Countries

1982. World Cup Football Championship, Spain (3rd issue). Multicoloured.

N2201	10ch. Type **767**	75	25
N2202	20ch. Group 2 countries	1·50	60
N2203	30ch. Group 3 countries	2·20	90
N2204	40ch. Group 4 countries	2·50	1·10
N2205	50ch. Group 5 countries	3·00	1·30
N2206	60ch. Group 6 countries	3·75	1·40
MSN2207	133×92 mm. 1wn. World Cup, footballers and emblem	10·00	5·00

768 Rocket Launch

1982. The Universe. Multicoloured.

N2208	10ch. Type **768**	2·10	85
N2209	20ch. Spaceship over globe	2·10	85
N2210	80ch. Spaceship between globe and moon	2·50	85
MSN2211	71×103 mm. 80ch. Spaceship over crags	4·25	1·70

769 Charlotte von Stein

1982. 150th Death Anniversary of Johann von Goethe (writer). Multicoloured.

N2212	10ch. Type **769**	65	35
N2213	10ch. Goethe's mother	2·10	60
N2214	20ch. Goethe's sister	1·00	40
N2215	20ch. Angelika Kauffmann	2·10	60
N2216	25ch. Charlotte Buff	1·30	50
N2217	25ch. Anna Amalia	2·10	60
N2218	35ch. Lili Schonemann	1·70	55
N2219	35ch. Charlotte von Lengefeld	2·10	60
N2220	80ch. Goethe	2·10	60
MSN2221	126×84 mm. 80ch. Goethe (different)	5·00	2·10

770 Player holding aloft World Cup

1982. World Cup Football Championship Results. Multicoloured.

N2222	20ch. Type **770**	1·70	40
N2223	30ch. Group of players with World Cup	2·50	65
N2224	30ch. Type **770**	3·50	90
N2225	40ch. As No. N2203	3·50	90
N2226	80ch. King Juan Carlos of Spain and two players with World Cup	3·50	90
MSN2227	105×78 mm. No. N2226	5·75	2·75

771 Princess and Prince William of Wales

1982. First Wedding Anniv of Prince and Princess of Wales. Multicoloured.

N2228	30ch. Type **771**	6·50	3·25
MSN2229	135×102 mm. 80ch. Prince and Princess of Wales with Prince William	11·00	4·25

772 Royal Couple with Prince William

1982. Birth of Prince William of Wales. Multicoloured.

N2230	10ch. Couple with Prince William (different)	90	65
N2231	10ch. Princess of Wales holding bouquet	2·75	1·00
N2232	20ch. Couple with Prince William (different)	1·80	85
N2233	20ch. Prince Charles carrying baby, and Princess of Wales	2·75	1·00
N2234	30ch. Type **772**	3·00	1·30
N2235	30ch. Prince Charles carrying baby, and Princess of Wales (different)	2·75	1·00
N2236	40ch. Princess with baby	3·75	1·90
N2237	40ch. Prince and Princess of Wales (horiz)	3·25	1·50
N2238	50ch. Princess with baby (different)	4·75	2·10
N2239	50ch. Prince and Princess of Wales in evening dress (horiz)	3·25	1·50
N2240	80ch. Couple with Prince William (different)	2·75	1·00
N2241	80ch. Prince Charles holding baby, and Princess of Wales (horiz)	3·25	1·50
MSN2242	Two sheets each 115×90 mm. (a) 80ch. Princess of Wales holding Prince William and royal family; (b) 80ch. Princess of Wales holding Prince William and godparents	27·00	10·00

773 Airship *Nulli Secundus II*, 1908

1982. Bicentenary of Manned Flight (1st issue). Multicoloured.

N2243	10ch. Type **773**	1·50	50
N2244	10ch. Pauley and Durs Egg's dirigible balloon *The Dolphin*, 1818	2·75	85
N2245	20ch. Tissandier Brothers' airship, 1883	1·80	60
N2246	20ch. Guyton de Morveau's balloon with oars, 1784	2·75	85
N2247	30ch. Parseval airship PL-VII, 1912	2·50	65
N2248	30ch. Sir George Cayley's airship design, 1837	2·75	85
N2249	40ch. Count de Lennox's balloon *Eagle*, 1834	2·75	65
N2250	40ch. Camille Vert's balloon *Poisson Volant*, 1859	2·75	85
N2251	80ch. Dupuy de Lome's airship, 1872	2·75	85
MSN2252	71×100 mm. 80ch. Masse oar-powered balloon, 1784 (vert)	5·00	2·50

774 *Utopic Balloon Post* (Balthasar Antoine Dunker)

1982. Bicentenary of Manned Flight (2nd issue). Multicoloured.

N2253	10ch. Type **774**	1·30	50
N2254	10ch. Montgolfier balloon at Versailles, 1783	4·25	1·00
N2255	20ch. ... *and they fly into heaven and have no wings ...*	2·50	1·00
N2256	20ch. Montgolfier Brothers' balloon, 1783	4·25	1·00
N2257	30ch. Pierre Testu-Brissy's balloon ascent on horseback, 1798	3·75	1·70
N2258	30ch. Charles's hydrogen balloon landing at Nesle, 1783	4·25	1·00
N2259	40ch. Gaston Tissandier's test flight of *Zenith*, 1875	5·00	2·10
N2260	40ch. Blanchard and Jeffries' balloon flight over English Channel, 1785	4·25	1·00
N2261	80ch. Henri Giffard's balloon *Le Grand Ballon Captif* at World Fair, 1878	4·25	1·00
MSN2262	130×96 mm. 80ch. Night flight of balloon	5·00	2·50

775 Turtle with Scroll

1982. *Tale of the Hare*. Multicoloured.

N2263	10ch. Type **775**	1·10	25
N2264	20ch. Hare riding on turtle	1·50	35
N2265	30ch. Hare and turtle before Dragon King	1·80	50
N2266	40ch. Hare back on land	2·75	60

776 Flag, *Red Book* and City

1982. Tenth Anniversary of Socialist Constitution.
N2267 **776** 10ch. multicoloured 40 15

777 Tower of 'Juche' Idea

1983. New Year.
N2268 **777** 10ch. multicoloured 30 15

778 Children reading *Saenal*

1983. 55th Anniversary of *Saenal* Newspaper.
N2269 **778** 10ch. multicoloured 75 25

779 *Man in Oriental Costume*

1983. Paintings by Rembrandt. Multicoloured.
N2270 10ch. Type **779** 90 35
N2271 10ch. *Child with dead Peacocks* (detail) 2·50 85
N2272 20ch. *The Noble Slave* 1·80 50
N2273 20ch. *Old Man in Fur Hat* 2·50 85
N2274 30ch. *Dr. Tulp's Anatomy Lesson* (detail) 3·25 90
N2275 30ch. *Portrait of a fashionable Couple* 2·50 85
N2276 40ch. *Two Scholars disputing* 2·75 60
N2277 40ch. *Woman with Child* 2·50 85
N2278 80ch. *Woman holding an Ostrich Feather Fan* 2·50 85
MSN2279 102×69 mm. 80ch. *Self-portrait* 4·25 2·10

780 Airships *Gross Basenach II* and *Graf Zepplin* over Cologne

1983. Luposta International Air Mail Exhibition, Cologne. Multicoloured.
N2280 30ch. Type **780** 4·25 1·30
N2281 40ch. Parsevel airship PL-II over Cologne 4·25 1·30
MSN2282 86×95 mm. 80ch. *Virgin and Child* (Stephan Lochner) (vert) 4·25 2·10

781 Banner and Monument

1983. 50th Anniversary of Wangjaesan Meeting.
N2283 **781** 10ch. multicoloured 30 15

782 Karl Marx

1983. Death Centenary of Karl Marx.
N2284 **782** 10ch. multicoloured 1·10 40

783 Scholar, Marchers and Map of Journey

1983. 60th Anniversary of Thousand-ri Journey for Learning.
N2285 **783** 10ch. multicoloured 1·40 15

784 *Madonna of the Goldfinch*

1983. 500th Birth Anniversary of Raphael. Multicoloured.
N2286 10ch. Type **784** 1·80 50
N2287 20ch. *The School of Athens* (detail) 2·10 65
N2288 30ch. *Madonna of the Grand Duke* 3·00 75
N2289 50ch. *Madonna of the Chair* 3·50 85
N2290 50ch. *Madonna of the Lamb* 2·10 65
N2291 80ch. *The Beautiful Gardener* 2·10 65
MSN2292 80×106 mm. 80ch. *Sistine Madonna* 5·00 2·10

785 Department Store No. 1

1983. Pyongyang Buildings. Multicoloured.
N2293 2ch. Chongryu Restaurant 25 10
N2294 10ch. Part of Munsu Street 40 10
N2295 10ch. Ice Rink 50 15
N2296 40ch. Type **785** 95 55
N2297 70ch. Grand People's Study House 1·70 75

786 Emblem and Crowd

1983. Fifth Anniversary of International Institute of Juche Idea.
N2298 **786** 10ch. multicoloured 30 15

787 Judo

1983. Olympic Games, Los Angeles (1st issue). Multicoloured.
N2299 20ch. Type **787** 1·30 60
N2300 20ch. Wrestling 2·50 60
N2301 30ch. Judo (different) (value in gold) 1·30 60
N2302 30ch. Judo (different) (value in black) 2·50 60
N2303 40ch. Boxing 1·30 60
N2304 40ch. Li Ho Jun (1972 shooting gold medalist) 2·50 60
N2305 50ch. Weightlifting 1·30 60
N2306 50ch. Wrestling (different) 2·50 60
N2307 80ch. Boxing (different) 2·50 60
MSN2308 95×74 mm. 80ch. Judo (different) 5·00 1·80
See also Nos. N2359/**MS**N2365.

788 Satellite, Masts and Dish Aerial

1983. World Communications Year (1st issue).
N2309 **788** 10ch. multicoloured 2·10 40
See also Nos. N2349/**MS**N2354.

789 Emblem, Giant Panda and Stamp

1983. Tembal 83 International Thematic Stamp Exhibition, Basel. Multicoloured.
N2310 20ch. Type **789** 2·50 85
N2311 30ch. Emblem, flag and Basel Town Post stamp 2·75 90

790 *Colourful Cow* (kogge), 1402

1983. Old Ships. Multicoloured.
N2312 20ch. Type **790** 1·60 65
N2313 20ch. *Kwi-Sun* ('turtle' ship), 1592 3·75 1·10
N2314 35ch. *Great Harry* (warship), 1555 2·10 75
N2315 35ch. Admiral Li Sun Sin and 'turtle' ship 3·75 1·10
N2316 50ch. *Eagle of Lubeck* (galleon), 1567 3·00 1·00
N2317 50ch. *Merkur* (full-rigged sailing ship), 1847 3·75 1·10
N2318 80ch. *Herzogin Elisabeth* (cadet ship) 3·75 1·10
MSN2319 104×82 mm. 80ch. *Cristoforo Colombo* (cadet ship) 7·25 5·00

791 *Locomotion*, 1825, Great Britain

1983. Railway Locomotives. Multicoloured.
N2320 20ch. Type **791** 1·70 65
N2321 20ch. *Drache*, 1848, Germany 6·25 1·70
N2322 35ch. *Adler*, 1835, Germany 3·25 1·50
N2323 35ch. Korean steam locomotive 6·25 1·70
N2324 50ch. *Austria*, 1837, Austria 4·25 2·10
N2325 50ch. Bristol and Exeter Railway steam locomotive, 1853 6·25 1·70
N2326 80ch. Caledonian Railway locomotive, 1859 6·25 1·70
MSN2327 106×64 mm. 80ch. *Ilmarinen*, 1860 50·00 4·25

792 Map, Hand and Weapons

1983. Tenth Anniversary of Publication of Five-point Policy for Korea's Reunification.
N2328 **792** 10ch. multicoloured 60 15

793 Emblem, Tower of 'Juche' Idea and Fireworks

1983. World Conference on Journalists against Imperialism and for Friendship and Peace, Pyongyang. Multicoloured.
N2329 10ch. Type **793** 35 10
N2330 40ch. Emblem and rainbow and clasped hands 60 25
N2331 70ch. Emblem, map and hand with raised forefinger 90 40

794 Worker and Banners

1983. Let's Create the Speed of the 80s.
N2332 **794** 10ch. multicoloured 40 15

795 Soldier and Rejoicing Crowd

1983. 30th Anniversary of Victory in Liberation War.
N2333 **795** 10ch. multicoloured 35 10

796 *Gorch Fock* (cadet barque) and Korean 1978 2ch. Stamp

1983. Bangkok 1983 International Stamp Exhibition. Multicoloured.
N2334 40ch. Type **796** 4·25 1·70
MSN2335 195×71 mm. 80ch. Bangkok, Penny Black and Korean IYC stamp 6·75 3·25

797 Skiing

1983. Winter Olympic Games, Sarajevo (1984). Multicoloured.
N2336 10ch. Type **797** 90 40
N2337 20ch. Figure skating (vert) 3·25 85
N2338 30ch. Skating (pair) 2·50 1·30
N2339 50ch. Ski jumping 3·00 1·40
N2340 50ch. Ice hockey (vert) 3·25 85
N2341 80ch. Speed skating (vert) 3·25 85
MSN2342 74×87 mm. 80ch. Shooting (biathlon) (vert) 5·00 2·10

798 Workers and Soldier with Books

1983. 35th Anniversary of Korean People's Democratic Republic.

N2343	**798**	10ch. multicoloured	55	15

799 Archery

1983. Folk Games. Multicoloured.

N2344	10ch. Type **799**	3·75	60
N2345	10ch. Flying kites	90	35
N2346	40ch. See-sawing	90	35
N2347	40ch. Swinging	90	35

800 Girls holding Hands

1983. Korean–Chinese Friendship.

N2348	**800**	10ch. multicoloured	65	20

801 Envelopes and Forms of Transport

1983. World Communications Year (2nd issue). Multicoloured.

N2349	30ch. Mail van, motorcyclist and hand holding magazines	6·25	1·40
N2350	30ch. Satellite, globe and dish aerial	1·70	60
N2351	40ch. Type **801**	6·25	1·40
N2352	40ch. Television cameraman	1·70	60
N2353	80ch. Telephone and aerial	1·70	60
MSN2354	96×75 mm. 80ch. WCY emblem and satellite	4·50	2·10

802 Portrait

1983. Paintings by Rubens. Multicoloured.

N2355	40ch. Type **802**	1·80	75
N2356	40ch. Portrait (different) (horiz)	2·30	1·00
N2357	80ch. *The Sentencing of Midas* (horiz)	2·30	1·00
MSN2358	129×95 mm. 80ch. *The Bear Hunt*	3·25	1·20

803 Sprinting

1983. Olympic Games, Los Angeles (2nd issue). Multicoloured.

N2359	10ch. Type **803**	90	25
N2360	20ch. Show jumping	2·50	85
N2361	30ch. Cycling	3·75	85
N2362	50ch. Handball	2·50	85
N2363	50ch. Fencing	2·50	85
N2364	80ch. Gymnastics	2·50	85
MSN2365	109×75 mm. 80ch. Judo	4·25	1·80

804 *St Catherine*

1983. 450th Death Anniversary (1984) of Antonio Correggio (artist). Multicoloured.

N2366	20ch. Type **804**	2·10	65
N2367	20ch. *Morning* (detail)	2·50	85
N2368	35ch. *Madonna*	2·10	65
N2369	35ch. *Morning* (different)	2·50	85
N2370	50ch. *Madonna with St. John*	2·10	65
N2371	50ch. *St Catherine* (different)	2·50	85
N2372	80ch. *Madonna and Child*	2·50	85
MSN2373	58×73 mm. 80ch. *Madonna and Child with Music-making Angels*	5·50	2·10

804a Cat

1983. Cats. Multicoloured, frame colour given.

N2373a	**804a**	10ch. green	1·40	20
N2373b	-	10ch. gold	1·40	20
N2373c	-	10ch. blue	1·40	20
N2373d	-	10ch. red	1·40	20
N2373e	-	10ch. silver	1·40	20

Designs: Different cats' heads.

805 Kimilsung Flower

1983. New Year.

N2374	**805**	10ch. multicoloured	85	15

806 Worker and Workers' Party Flag

1984. Under the Leadership of the Workers' Party. Multicoloured.

N2375	10ch. Type **806**	35	10
N2376	10ch. Ore-dressing plant No. 3, Komdok General Mining Enterprise, and Party Flag	50	10

807 Farm Worker, Rice and Maize

1984. 20th Anniversary of Publication of *Theses of the Socialist Rural Question in Our Country*.

N2377	**807**	10ch. multicoloured	30	10

808 Changdok School, Chilgol

1984. Kim Il Sung's 72nd Birthday.

N2378	**808**	5ch. green, black & blue	40	15
N2379	-	10ch. multicoloured	40	15

Design: 10ch. Birthplace, Mangyongdae, and rejoicing crowd.

809 *Spanish Riding School* (Julius von Blaas)

1984. Espana 84 International Stamp Exhibition, Madrid. Multicoloured.

N2380	10ch. Type **809**	2·20	65
N2381	20ch. *Ferdinand of Austria* (Rubens)	2·20	65
MSN2382	73×96 mm. 80ch. *Spanish Riding School* (Julius von Blaas) (different)	5·75	2·50

810 *La Donna Velata*

1984. 500th Birth Anniversary (1983) of Raphael (artist). Multicoloured.

N2383	10ch. *Portrait of Agnolo Doni*	1·90	75
N2384	20ch. Type **810**	1·90	75
N2385	30ch. *Portrait of Jeanne d'Aragon*	1·90	75
MSN2386	79×105 mm. 80ch. *St. Sebastian*	5·25	2·50

811 Map and Second Stage Pumping Station

1984. 25th Anniversary of Kiyang Irrigation System.

N2387	**811**	10ch. multicoloured	65	20

812 Construction Site

1984. Construction on Five District Fronts.

N2388	**812**	10ch. red, black & yell	65	25

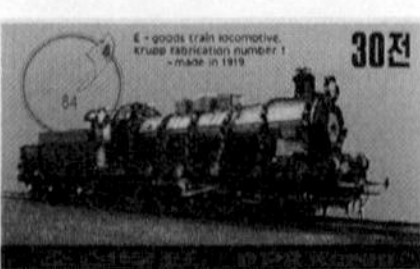

813 Bobsleighing (East Germany)

1984. Winter Olympic Games Medal Winners. Multicoloured.

N2389	10ch. Ski jumping (Matti Nykaenen)	3·00	65
N2390	20ch. Speed skating (Karin Enke)	2·10	60
N2391	20ch. Slalom (Max Julen)	3·00	65
N2392	30ch. Type **813**	2·10	60
N2393	30ch. Downhill skiing (Maria Walliser)	2·30	65
N2394	40ch. Cross-country skiing (Thomas Wassberg)	3·75	75
N2395	80ch. Cross-country skiing (Marja-Liisa Hamalainen)	3·75	75
MSN2396	106×86 mm. 80ch. Biathlon (Peter Angerer) (vert)	4·50	2·10

814 Steam Locomotive, 1919

1984. Essen International Stamp Fair. Multicoloured.

N2397	20ch. Streamlined steam locomotive, 1939	5·50	1·20
N2398	30ch. Type **814**	5·50	1·20
MSN2399	94×86 mm. 80ch. Type D locomotive	9·25	2·20

815 *Mlle. Fiocre in the Ballet 'La Source'*

1984. 150th Birth Anniversary of Edgar Degas (artist). Multicoloured.

N2400	10ch. Type **815**	2·00	50
N2401	20ch. *The Dance Foyer at the Rue le Peletier Opera*	3·00	55
N2402	30ch. *Race Meeting*	5·00	90
MSN2403	108×89 mm. 80ch. *Dancers at the Barre*	4·50	2·10

816 Map of Pyongnam Irrigation System and Reservoir

1984. Irrigation Experts Meeting, Pyongyang.

N2404	**816**	2ch. multicoloured	55	15

817 Korean Stamp and Building

1984. UPU Congress Stamp Exhibition, Hamburg.

N2405	**817**	20ch. multicoloured	3·75	65
MSN2406		106×76 mm. 80ch. *Gorch Fock* (cadet barque) and Koren 'turtle' stamp	6·25	3·25

818 Crowd and Banners

1984. Proposal for Tripartite Talks.

N2407	**818**	10ch. multicoloured	55	15

819 Nobel experimenting

1984. 150th Birth Anniv (1983) of Alfred Bernhard Nobel (inventor). Multicoloured.

N2408	20ch. Type **819**	3·75	65
N2409	30ch. Portrait of Nobel	4·25	65
MSN2410	109×99 mm. 80ch. Portrait of Nobel (different)	6·25	3·25

820 Drinks, Tinned Food, Clothes and Flats

1984. Improvements of Living Standards.

N2411	**820**	10ch. multicoloured	65	15

821 Sunhwa School, Mangyongdae

1984. School of Kim Hyong Jik (Kim Il Sung's Father).
N2412 **821** 10ch. multicoloured 60 15

822 Armed Crowd with Banners

1984. 65th Anniversary of Kuandian Conference.
N2413 **822** 10ch. multicoloured 65 15

823 *Thunia bracteata*

1984. Flowers. Multicoloured.
N2414 10ch. *Cattleya loddigesii* 90 10
N2415 20ch. Type **823** 1·40 35
N2416 30ch. *Phalaenopsis amabilis* 1·80 50
MSN2417 67×94 mm. Kimilsung flower 4·50 1·70

824 Swordfish and Trawler

1984. Fishing Industry. Multicoloured.
N2418 5ch. Type **824** 90 25
N2419 10ch. Blue marlin and trawler 1·30 40
N2420 40ch. Sailfish and game fishing launch 3·50 1·20

825 Revolutionary Museum, Chilgol

1984
N2421 **825** 10ch. multicoloured 55 15

826 Kim Hyok, Cha Gwang Su and Youth

1984. Let's All become the Kim Hyoks and Cha Gwang Sus of the '80s.
N2422 **826** 10ch. multicoloured 55 15

827 Inauguration of a French Railway Line, 1860

1984. Centenary (1983) of *Orient Express*. Multicoloured.
N2423 10ch. Type **827** 1·60 35
N2424 20ch. Opening of a British railway line, 1821 3·00 65
N2425 30ch. Inauguration of Paris–Rouen line, 1843 4·25 1·10
MSN2426 11×81 mm. Interiors of Wagons-lits Car, 1905 7·50 3·00

828 Clock Face

1984. Centenary of Greenwich Meridian. Multicoloured.
N2427 10ch. Type **828** 3·25 1·30
MSN2428 112×81 mm. 80ch. *Chollima* statue, buildings and clock 5·00 2·10

829 Grand Theatre, Hamburg

1984
N2429 **829** 10ch. blue 55 15

830 Turning on Machinery

1984. Automation of Industry.
N2430 **830** 40ch. multicoloured 75 40

831 *Dragon Angler*

1984. Paintings. Multicoloured.
N2431 10ch. Type **831** 1·10 20
N2432 20ch. *Ox Driver* (Kim Du Ryang) (47×35 mm) 1·40 40
N2433 30ch. *Bamboo* (Kim Jin U) (47×35 mm) 2·10 60
MSN2434 85×43 mm. 80ch. *Autumn Night* 5·50 5·50

832 Tsiolkovsky

1984. K. E. Tsiolkovsky (space scientist). Multicoloured.
N2435 20ch. Type **832** 1·10 35
N2436 30ch. *Sputnik* orbiting Earth 1·60 60
MSN2437 100×70 mm. 80ch. Rocket launch 5·00 1·30

833 *Pongdaesan*

1984. Container Ships. Multicoloured.
N2438 10ch. Type **833** 1·30 25
N2439 20ch. *Ryongnamsan* 1·40 50
N2440 30ch. *Rungrado* 1·80 75
MSN2441 97×107 mm. 80ch. *Kumgangsan* 6·25 1·90

834 Caracal

1984. Animals. Multicoloured.
N2442 10ch. Spotted hyenas 75 15
N2443 20ch. Type **834** 1·10 35
N2444 30ch. Black-backed jackals 1·60 60
N2445 40ch. Foxes 2·10 85
MSN2446 80×104 mm. 80ch. Lanner falcon (vert) 7·50 2·50

835 Marie Curie

1984. 50th Death Anniversary of Marie Curie (physicist). Multicoloured.
N2447 10ch. Type **835** 2·50 35
MSN2448 78×103 mm. 80ch. Portrait of Marie Curie 5·00 2·10

836 Chestnut-eared Aracari ('Toucan')

1984. Birds. Multicoloured.
N2449 10ch. Hoopoe 1·40 25
N2450 20ch. South African crowned cranes ('Crowned Crane') 1·80 50
N2451 30ch. Saddle-bill stork ('Stork') 2·50 65
N2452 40ch. Type **836** 3·50 90
MSN2453 104×74 mm 80ch. Black kite 9·25 2·50

837 Cosmonaut

1984. Space Exploration. Multicoloured.
N2454 10ch. Type **837** 65 15
N2455 20ch. Cosmonaut on space-walk 1·00 35
N2456 30ch. Cosmonaut (different) 1·40 50
MSN2457 77×90 mm. 80ch. Moon vehicle 4·50 1·70

838 *Arktika*

1984. Russian Ice-breakers. Multicoloured.
N2458 20ch. Type **838** 1·60 50
N2459 30ch. *Ermak* 2·20 65
MSN2460 97×67 mm. 80c. *Lenin* 6·25 2·10

839 Mendeleev

1984. 150th Birth Anniversary of Dmitri Mendeleev (chemist). Multicoloured.
N2461 10ch. Type **839** 1·20 25

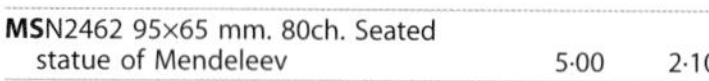

MSN2462 95×65 mm. 80ch. Seated statue of Mendeleev 5·00 2·10

840 Kim Il Sung in USSR

1984. Kim Il Sung's Visits to Eastern Europe. Multicoloured.
N2463 10ch. Type **840** 85 20
N2464 10ch. In Poland 85 20
N2465 10ch. In German Democratic Republic 85 20
N2466 10ch. In Czechoslovakia 85 20
N2467 10ch. In Hungary 85 20
N2468 10ch. In Bulgaria 85 20
N2469 10ch. In Rumania 85 20
MSN2470 80×105 mm. 10ch. In China 1·70 1·70

841 Freesia

1985. New Year.
N2471 **841** 10ch. multicoloured 90 25

842 Journey Route, Steam Locomotive and Memorials

1985. 60th Anniversary of 1000-ri Journey by Kim Il Sung. Multicoloured.
N2472 5ch. Type **842** 1·60 25
N2473 10ch. Boy trumpeter and schoolchildren following route 60 10
Nos. N2472/N2473 were issued together, *se-tenant*, forming a composite design.

843 Cugnot's Steam Car, 1769

1985. History of the Motor Car (1st series). Multicoloured.
N2474 10ch. Type **843** 1·60 20
N2475 15ch. Goldsworthy Gurney steam omnibus, 1825 1·60 25
N2476 20ch. Gottlieb Daimler diesel car, 1885 1·60 35
N2477 25ch. Benz three-wheeled diesel car, 1886 1·70 50
N2478 30ch. Peugeot diesel car, 1891 2·20 60
MSN2479 92×75 mm. 80c. black and gold (Wind car) 5·00 2·20
See also Nos. N2562/**MS**N2567.

844 Camp, Mt. Paekdu

1985. Korean Revolution Headquarters.
N2480 **844** 10ch. multicoloured 55 30

845 Taechodo Lighthouse

1985. Lighthouses. Multicoloured.

No.	Description	Mint	Used
N2481	10ch. Type **845**	2·20	20
N2482	20ch. Sodo	2·50	40
N2483	30ch. Pido	3·00	65
N2484	40ch. Suundo	3·50	1·00

846 Hedgehog challenges Tiger

1985. *The Hedgehog defeats the Tiger* (fable). Multicoloured.

No.	Description	Mint	Used
N2485	10ch. Type **846**	75	15
N2486	20ch. Tiger goes to stamp on rolled-up hedgehog	1·10	35
N2487	30ch. Hedgehog clings to tiger's nose	1·60	60
N2488	35ch. Tiger flees	1·70	65
N2489	40ch. Tiger crawls before hedgehog	2·00	85

847 *Pleurotus cornucopiae*

1985. Fungi. Multicoloured.

No.	Description	Mint	Used
N2490	10ch. Type **847**	1·40	20
N2491	20ch. Oyster fungus	1·70	40
N2492	30ch. *Catathelasma ventricosum*	2·50	65

848 West Germany v. Hungary, 1954

1985. World Cup Football Championship Finals.

No.	Type	Description	Mint	Used
N2493	**848**	10ch. black, buff & brn	75	20
N2494	-	10ch. multicoloured	75	20
N2495	-	20ch. black, buff & brn	1·10	35
N2496	-	20ch. multicoloured	1·10	35
N2497	-	30ch. black, buff & brn	1·60	60
N2498	-	30ch. multicoloured	1·60	60
N2499	-	40ch. black, buff & brn	2·00	85
N2500	-	40ch. multicoloured	2·00	85
MSN2501		Two sheets, (a) 105×75 mm. 80ch. black, cinnamon and gold; (b) 94×95 mm. 80ch.multicoloured	10·00	4·25

Designs: Vert—No. N2493, T **848**; No. N2496, West Germany v. Netherlands, 1974; No. N2499, England v. West Germany, No. **MS**N2501 (b), Azieca Stadium, Mexico (venue of 1966 final). Horiz—No. N2494, Brazil v. Italy, 1970; No. N2495, Brazil v. Sweden, 1958. No. N2497, Brazil v. Czechoslovakia, 1963; No. N2498 Argentina v Netherlands, 1968. No. N2500, Italy v West Germany, 1982; No. **MS**N2501 (a) North Korea's quarter-final place, 1966.

849 Date and Kim Il Sung's Birthplace

1985. 73rd Birthday of Kim Il Sung.

No.	Type	Description	Mint	Used
N2502	**849**	10ch. multicoloured	55	15

850 Horn Player

1985. 4th-century Musical Instruments. Multicoloured.

No.	Description	Mint	Used
N2503	10ch. Type **850**	1·70	20
N2504	20ch. So (pipes) player	1·70	35

851 Chongryon Hall, Tokyo

1985. 30th Anniversary of Chongryon (General Association of Korean Residents in Japan).

No.	Type	Description	Mint	Used
N2505	**851**	10ch. brown	55	15

852 Common Marmoset

1985. Mammals. Multicoloured.

No.	Description	Mint	Used
N2506	5ch. Type **852**	1·10	20
N2507	10ch. Ring-tailed lemur	1·10	20

853 National Emblem

1985. Sheet 51×70 mm.

No.	Type	Description	Mint	Used
MSN2508	**853**	80ch. multicoloured	1·90	65

854 Buenos Aires and Argentina 1982 Stamp

1985. Argentina '85 International Stamp Exhibition, Buenos Aires. Multicoloured.

No.	Description	Mint	Used
N2509	10ch. Type **854**	90	20
N2510	20ch. Iguacu Falls and Argentina 1984 and North Korea 1978 stamps (horiz)	3·00	35
MSN2511	73×100 mm. 80ch. Gaucho	6·25	5·00

855 Dancer and Gymnast

1985. 12th World Youth and Students' Festival, Moscow. Multicoloured.

No.	Description	Mint	Used
N2512	10ch. Type **855**	75	15
N2513	20ch. Spassky Tower, Moscow, and Festival emblem	1·10	35
N2514	40ch. Youths of different races	2·00	85

856 Peace Pavilion, Youth Park

1985. Pyongyang Buildings.

No.	Type	Description	Mint	Used
N2515	**856**	2ch. black and green	25	10
N2516	-	40ch. brown & lt brn	60	25

Design: 40ch. Multi-storey flats, Chollima Street.

857 Liberation Celebrations

1985. 40th Anniversary of Liberation.

No.	Type	Description	Mint	Used
N2517		5ch. red, black and blue	20	10
N2518		10ch. multicoloured	50	15
N2519		10ch. brown, blk & grn	50	15
N2520		10ch. multicoloured	50	15
N2521	**857**	10ch. yellow, blk & red	50	15
N2522	-	10ch. red, orange & blk	50	15
N2523	-	40ch. multicoloured	1·20	75
MSN2524		68×50 mm. 90ch. multicoloured	2·75	1·90

Designs: Horiz—No. N2517, Soldiers with rifles and flag; No. N2518, Crowd with banners and Flame of Juche; No. N2519, Korean and Soviet soldiers raising arms; No. N2520, Japanese soldiers laying down weapons; No. N2523, Students bearing banners. Vert—No. N2522, Liberation Tower, Moran Hill, Pyongyang; No. **MS**2524, Monument.

858 Halley and Comet

1985. Appearance of Halley's Comet. Multicoloured.

No.	Description	Mint	Used
N2525	10ch. Type **858**	90	15
N2526	20ch. Diagram of comet's flight and space probe	1·40	35
MSN2527	144×128 mm. 80ch. ultramarine and gold (Comet's trajectory)	5·00	2·20

859 *Camellia japonica*

1985. Flowers. Multicoloured.

No.	Description	Mint	Used
N2528	10ch. *Hippeastrum hybridum*	90	35
N2529	20ch. Type **859**	1·40	40
N2530	30ch. *Cyclamen persicum*	1·80	60

860 Hunting

1985. Koguryo Culture.. Multicoloured.

No.	Description	Mint	Used
N2531	10ch. Hero (vert)	75	15
N2532	15ch. Heroine (vert)	90	35
N2533	20ch. Flying Fairy	1·10	35
N2534	25ch. Type **860**	1·40	50
MSN2535	90×80 mm. 80ch. Pine Tree (28×48 mm)	4·25	1·30

861 Party Founding Museum

1985. 40th Anniversary of Korean Workers' Party. Multicoloured.

No.	Description	Mint	Used
N2536	5ch. Type **861**	20	10
N2537	10ch. Soldier with gun and workers	50	15
N2538	10ch. Soldiers and flag	50	15
N2539	40ch. Statue of worker, peasant and intellectual holding aloft party emblem	1·20	75
MSN2540	60×75 mm. 90ch. People with flowers	2·20	90

862 Arch of Triumph, Pyongyang

1985. 40th Anniversary of Kim Il Sung's Return.

No.	Type	Description	Mint	Used
N2541	**862**	10ch. brown and green	55	15

863 Colosseum, Rome, and North Korea 1975 10ch. Stamp

1985. Italia '85 International Stamp Exhibition, Rome. Multicoloured.

No.	Description	Mint	Used
N2542	10ch. Type **863**	75	25
N2543	20ch. *The Holy Family* (Raphael) (vert)	1·10	40
N2544	30ch. Head of *David* (statue, Michelangelo) (vert)	1·60	60
MSN2545	67×47 mm. 80ch. Pantheon, Rome	5·00	2·20

864 Mercedes Benz Type 300

1985. South-West German Stamp Fair, Sindelfingen. Multicoloured.

No.	Description	Mint	Used
N2546	10ch. Type **864**	1·10	15
N2547	15ch. Mercedes Benz Type 770	1·70	25
N2548	20ch. Mercedes Benz W 150	1·80	35
N2549	30ch. Mercedes Type 600	2·50	60
MSN2550	84×57 mm. 80ch. Mercedes Benz W31	5·50	1·50

865 Tackle

1985. World Cup Football Championship, Mexico (1st issue). Multicoloured.

No.	Description	Mint	Used
N2551	20ch. Type **865**	1·50	40
N2552	30ch. Three players	1·70	60
MSN2553	106×76 mm. 80ch. Goalkeeper and Mexican monuments	5·00	1·90

See also Nos. N2558/**MS**N2560 and N2577/**MS**N2583.

866 Dancers

1985. International Youth Year. Multicoloured.

No.	Description	Mint	Used
N2554	10ch. Type **866**	75	20
N2555	20ch. Sports activities	1·10	35
N2556	30ch. Technology	1·60	60
MSN2557	75×60 mm. 80ch. Young people	5·75	2·10

867 Players

1985. World Cup Football Championship, Mexico (2nd issue). Multicoloured.
N2558 20ch. Type **867** 1·50 40
N2559 30ch. Goalkeeper and players 1·70 60
MSN2560 102×80 mm. 80ch. Goalkeeper and bullfighter 5·00 2·10

868 'Juche' Torch

1986. New Year.
N2561 **868** 10ch. multicoloured 55 15

869 Amedee Bollee and Limousine, 1901

1986. History of the Motor Car (2nd series). Multicoloured.
N2562 10ch. Type **869** 90 15
N2563 20ch. Stewart Rolls, Henry Royce and Silver Ghost, 1906 1·60 35
N2564 25ch. Giovanni Agnelli and Fiat car, 1912 1·70 50
N2565 30ch. Ettore Bugatti and Royal coupe, 1928 2·00 60
N2566 40ch. Louis Renault and fiacre, 1906 3·00 85
MSN2567 75×80 mm. 80ch. Gottiebo Daimler, Karl Benz and Mercedes S, 1927 5·75 1·50

870 Gary Kasparov

1986. World Chess Championship, Moscow.
N2568 **870** 20ch. multicoloured 3·00 35
MSN2569 60×82 mm. 80ch. Anatoly Karpov and Kasparov 5·75 2·50

871 Cemetery Gate

1986. Revolutionary Martyrs' Cemetery, Pyongyang. Multicoloured.
N2570 5ch. Type **871** 25 10
N2571 10ch. Bronze sculpture (detail) 65 15

872 Tongdu Rock, Songgan

1986. 37th Anniversary of President Kim Il Sung's Visit to Songgan Revolutionary Site.
N2572 **872** 10ch. multicoloured 55 15

873 Buddhist Scriptures Museum

1986. Mt. Myohyang Buildings.
N2573 **873** 10ch. brown and green 50 15
N2574 - 20ch. violet and red 60 15
Design: 20ch. Taeung Hall.

874 Tomato Anemonefish

1986. Fish. Multicoloured.
N2575 10ch. Pennant coralfish 1·20 15
N2576 20ch. Type **874** 1·70 40

875 Footballers and Flags of Italy, Bulgaria and Argentina

1986. World Cup Football Championship, Mexico (3rd issue). Designs showing footballers and flags of participating countries. Multicoloured.
N2577 10ch. Type **875** 75 15
N2578 20ch. Mexico, Belgium, Paraguay and Iraq 1·10 35
N2579 25ch. France, Canada, USSR and Hungary 1·40 50
N2580 30ch. Brazil, Spain, Algeria and Northern Ireland 1·60 60
N2581 35ch. West Germany, Uruguay, Scotland and Denmark 1·70 65
N2582 40ch. Poland, Portugal, Morocco and England 2·00 85
MSN2583 100×70 80ch. Ball, boots, footballers and trophy 5·00 2·30

876 Singer, Pianist and Emblem

1986. Fourth Spring Friendship Art Festival, Pyongyang.
N2584 **876** 1wn. multicoloured 1·70 1·10

877 Daimler Motorwagen, 1886

1986. 60th Anniversary of Mercedes-Benz (car manufacturers). Multicoloured.
N2585 10ch. Type **877** 65 15
N2586 10ch. Benz velo, 1894 65 15
N2587 20ch. Mercedes car, 1901 1·00 35
N2588 20ch. Benz limousine, 1909 1·00 35
N2589 30ch. Mercedes tourenwagen, 1914 1·40 50
N2590 30ch. Mercedes-Benz 170 6-cylinder, 1931 1·40 50
N2591 40ch. Mercedes-Benz 380, 1933 1·80 90
N2592 40ch. Mercedes-Benz 540 K, 1936 1·80 90
MSN2593 75×60 mm. 80ch. Mercedes-Simplex phaeton, 1904 5·75 2·30

878 Mangyong Hill

1986. 74th Birthday of Kim Il Sung.
N2594 **878** 10ch. multicoloured 50 10

879 Crowd

1968. 50th Anniversary of Association for the Restoration of the Fatherland.
N2595 **879** 10ch. multicoloured 40 10

880 Dove carrying Letter

1986. International Peace Year. Multicoloured.
N2596 10ch. Type **880** 50 35
N2597 20ch. UN Headquarters, New York 1·00 65
N2598 30ch. Dove, globe and broken missiles 1·50 1·00
MSN2599 72×90 mm. 80ch. Sculpture 3·75 1·30

881 *Mona Lisa* (Leonardo da Vinci)

1986
N2600 **881** 20ch. multicoloured 1·20 40

882 Pink Iris

1986. Irises. Multicoloured.
N2601 20ch. Type **882** 1·50 40
N2602 30ch. Violet iris 1·70 60
MSN2603 84×64 80ch. Magenta iris 5·00 2·10

883 Kim Un Suk

1986. Tennis Players. Multicoloured.
N2604 10ch. Type **883** (postage) 2·20 50
N2605 20ch. Ivan Lendl 2·20 50
N2606 30ch. Steffi Graf 2·20 50
N2607 50ch. Boris Becker (air) 2·20 50

884 Sulphur-crested Cockatoo ('Cockatoo')

1986. Stampex '86 Stamp Exhibition, Adelaide, Australia. Multicoloured.
N2608 10ch. Type **884** 1·80 35
MSN2609 75×60 mm. 80ch. Kangaroo 5·00 2·10

885 First Issue of *L'Unita*

1986. National *L'Unita* (Italian Communist Party newspaper) Festival, Milan. Multicoloured.
N2610 10ch. Type **885** 70 40
N2611 20ch. Milan Cathedral 1·30 85
N2612 30ch. *Pieta* (Michelangelo) (vert) 1·80 1·30
MSN2613 85×65 mm. 80ch. Enrico Berlingoer (former General Secretary of Italian Communist Party) (vert) 2·50 1·00

886 *Express II* (icebreaker) and Sweden 1872 20 ore Stamp

1986. Stockholmia 86 International Stamp Exhibition, Stockholm.
N2614 10ch. multicoloured 2·50 25
MSN2615 86×60 mm. 80ch. UPU emblem, mail coach and Swedish stamps (horiz) 4·50 1·80

887 Reprint of First Stamp

1986. 40th Anniversary of First North Korean Stamps (1st issue). Multicoloured.
N2616 10ch. Type **887** (postage) 50 40
N2617 15ch. Imperforate reprint of first stamp 75 60
N2618 50ch. 1946 50ch. violet stamp (air) 2·50 1·70
See also Nos. N2619/N2621.

888 Postal Emblems and 1962 and 1985 Stamps

1986. 40th Anniversary of First North Korean Stamps (2nd issue). Multicoloured.
N2619 10ch. Type **888** (postage) 2·20 40
N2620 15ch. General Post Office and 1976 and 1978 stamps 1·20 25
N2621 50ch. Kim Il Sung, first stamp and reprint (vert) (air) 1·80 65

1986. World Cup Football Championship Results. Nos. N2577/N2582 optd **1st: ARG 2nd: FRG 3rd: FRA 4th: BEL.**
N2622 10ch. multicoloured 1·20 15
N2623 20ch. multicoloured 1·40 40
N2624 25ch. multicoloured 1·70 50
N2625 30ch. multicoloured 1·80 60
N2626 35ch. multicoloured 2·10 75
N2627 40ch. multicoloured 2·50 85
MSN2628 100×70 mm. 80ch. multicoloured 5·75 1·70

890 Flag and Man with raised Fist

1986. 60th Anniversary of Down-with-Imperialism Union.
N2629 **890** 10ch. multicoloured 40 25

891 Gift Animals House

1986. First Anniversary of Gift Animals House, Central Zoo, Pyongyang.
N2630 **891** 2wn. multicoloured 4·25 1·40

892 Schoolchildren

1986. 40th Anniversary of UNESCO. Multicoloured.
N2631 10ch. Type **892** 50 35

N2632	50ch. Anniversary emblem, Grand People's Study House and telecommunications (horiz)	2·50	1·70

893 Communications Satellite

1986. 15th Anniversary of Intersputnik.

N2633	**893**	5wn. multicoloured	9·25	4·25

894 Oil tanker leaving Lock

1986. West Sea Barrage.

N2634	**894**	10ch. multicoloured	65	15
N2635	-	40ch. grn, blk & gold	1·70	35
N2636	-	1wn. 20 multicoloured	3·50	85

Designs: 40ch. Aerial view of dam; 1wn.20, Aerial view of lock.

895 Common Morel

1986. Minerals and Fungi. Multicoloured.

N2637	10ch. Lengenbachite (postage)	2·10	40
N2638	10ch. Common funnel cap	2·10	40
N2639	15ch. Rhodochrosite	2·10	40
N2640	15ch. Type **895**	2·10	40
N2641	50ch. Annabergite (air)	2·10	40
N2642	50ch. Blue russula	2·10	40

896 Machu Picchu, Peru, and North Korea Taedong Gate Stamp

1986. North Korean Three-dimensional Photographs and Stamp Exhibition, Lima, Peru. Multicoloured.

N2643	10ch. Type **896**	1·70	35
MSN2644	110×75 mm. 80ch. Korean and Peruvian children	5·00	1·80

897 Pine Tree

1987. New Year. Multicoloured.

N2645	10ch. Type **897**	90	20
N2646	40ch. Hare	1·20	40

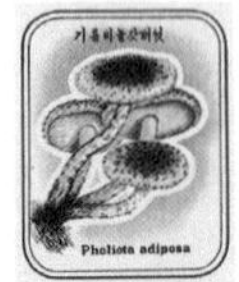

898 *Pholiota adiposa*

1987. Fungi. Multicoloured.

N2647	10ch. Type **898**	1·80	40
N2648	20ch. Chanterelle	1·90	40
N2649	30ch. *Boletus impolitus*	2·30	45
MSN2650	50×70 mm. 80ch. *Gomphidius rutilus*	5·75	2·30

899 Kim Ok Song (composer)

1987. Musicians' Death Anniversaries. Multicoloured.

N2651	10ch. Maurice Ravel (composer, 50th anniversary)	1·70	30
N2652	10ch. Type **899** (22nd anniversary)	1·70	30
N2653	20ch. Giovanni Lully (composer, 300th anniversary)	1·70	30
N2654	30ch. Franz Liszt (composer, centenary (1986))	1·70	30
N2655	40ch. Violins (250th anniversary of Antonio Stradivari (violin maker))	1·70	30
N2656	40ch. Christoph Gluck (composer, bicentenary)	1·70	30

900 Kim Jong Il

1997. Kim Jong Il's Birthday. Sheet 85×105 mm.

MSN2657	80ch. multicoloured	1·80	65

901 East Pyongyang Grand Theatre

1987. Buildings.

N2658	**901**	5ch. green	40	10
N2659	-	10ch. brown	50	15
N2660	-	3wn. blue	4·50	1·60

Designs: Vert—10ch. Pyongyang Koryo Hotel. Horiz—3wn. Rungnado Stadium.

902 *Gorch Fock* (German cadet barque)

1987. Sailing Ships. Multicoloured.

N2661	20ch. Type **902** (postage)	85	30
N2662	30ch. *Tovarishch* (Russian cadet barque) (vert)	1·20	40
N2663	50ch. *Belle Poule* (cadet schooner) (vert) (air)	1·70	65
N2664	50ch. *Sagres II* (Portuguese cadet barque) (vert)	1·70	65
N2665	1wn. Koryo period merchantman	3·75	1·30
N2666	1wn. *Dar Mlodziezy* (Polish cadet full-rigged ship) (vert)	3·75	1·30

903 Road Signs

1987. Road Safety.

N2667	**903**	10ch. blue, red and black (postage)	1·30	10
N2668	-	10ch. red and black	1·30	10
N2669	-	20ch. blue, red & black	1·70	30
N2670	-	50ch. red and black (air)	1·80	75

Designs: Nos. N2668/N2670, Different road signs.

904 Fire Engine

1987. Fire Engines.

N2671	**904**	10ch. mult (postage)	2·20	40
N2672	-	20ch. multicoloured	2·50	45
N2673	-	30ch. multicoloured	3·25	55
N2674	-	50ch. multicoloured (air)	4·25	75

Designs: N2672/N2674, 20ch. to 50ch. Different machines.

905 *Apatura ilia* and Spiraea

1987. Butterflies and Flowers. Multicoloured.

N2675	10ch. Type **905**	90	25
N2676	10ch. *Ypthima argus* and fuchsia	90	25
N2677	20ch. *Neptis philyra* and aquilegia	1·30	30
N2678	20ch. *Papilio protenor* and chrysanthemum	1·30	30
N2679	40ch. *Parantica sita* and celosia	2·10	65
N2680	40ch. *Vanessa indica* and hibiscus	2·10	65

906 Association Monument, Pyongyang

1987. 70th Anniversary of Korean National Association (independence movement).

N2681	**906**	10ch. red, silver & black	40	20

907 Doves, Emblem and Tree

1987. Fifth Spring Friendship Art Festival, Pyongyang.

N2682	**907**	10ch. multicoloured	40	20

908 Mangyong Hill

1987. 75th Birthday of Kim Il Sung. Multicoloured.

N2683	10ch. Type **908**	35	10
N2684	10ch. Kim Il Sung's birthplace, Mangyongdae (horiz)	35	10
N2685	10ch. 'A Bumper Crop of Pumpkins' (62×41 mm)	35	10
N2686	10ch. 'Profound Affection for the Working Class'	35	10

909 Bay

1987. Horses. Multicoloured.

N2687	10ch. Type **909**	40	20
N2688	10ch. Bay (different)	40	20
N2689	40ch. Grey rearing	1·70	1·20
N2690	40ch. Grey on beach	1·70	1·20

910 *Sputnik 1* (first artificial satellite)

1987. Transport. Multicoloured.

N2691	10ch. Juche class high speed train (horiz)	50	10
N2692	10ch. Electric locomotive Mangyongdae class (horiz)	50	10
N2693	10ch. Type **910** (30th anniversary of flight)	50	10
N2694	20ch. Laika (30th anniversary of first animal in space)	90	30
N2695	20ch. Tupolev Tu-144 supersonic airliner (horiz)	90	30
N2696	20ch. Concorde (11th anniversary of first commercial flight) (horiz)	90	30
N2697	30ch. Count Ferdinand von Zeppelin (70th death anniversary) and airship LZ-4 (horiz)	1·30	40
N2698	80ch. Zeppelin and diagrams and drawings of airships (horiz)	3·75	1·50

911 Musk Ox

1987. Capex '87 International Stamp Exhibition, Toronto. Multicoloured.

N2699	10ch. Type **911**	85	15
N2700	40ch. Jacques Cartier, his ship *Grande Hermine* and *Ierry Fox* (ice-breaker) (horiz)	2·20	55
N2701	60ch. Ice hockey (Winter Olympics, Calgary, 1988) (horiz)	2·20	85

912 Trapeze Artistes

1987. International Circus Festival, Monaco. Multicoloured.

N2702	10ch. Type **912**	50	15
N2703	10ch. 'Brave Sailors' (North Korean acrobatic act) (vert)	50	15
N2704	20ch. Clown and elephant (vert)	90	30
N2705	20ch. North Korean artiste receiving Golden Clown award	90	30
N2706	40ch. Performing horses and cat act	2·75	45
N2707	50ch. Prince Rainier and his children applauding	1·80	65

913 Attack on Watch Tower

1987. 50th Anniversary of Battle of Pochonbo.

N2708	**913**	10ch. brown, black and ochre	40	20

914 Sports

1987. Angol Sports Village.

N2709	**914**	5ch. brown and gold	15	1

N2710 -	10ch. blue and gold	25	10
N2711 -	40ch. brown and gold	85	30
N2712 -	70ch. blue and gold	1·40	45
N2713 -	1wn. red and gold	2·20	75
N2714 -	1wn.20 violet	2·75	1·10

Designs: Exteriors of—10ch. Indoor swimming pool; 40ch. Weightlifting gymnasium; 70ch. Table tennis gymnasium; 1wn. Football stadium; 1wn.20, Handball gymnasium.

915 Mandarins

1987. Mandarins. Multicoloured.

N2715	20ch. Type **915**	1·70	45
N2716	20ch. Mandarins on shore	1·70	45
N2717	20ch. Mandarins on branch	1·70	45
N2718	40ch. Mandarins in water	2·50	65

916 Exhibition Site and 1987 3wn. Stamp

1987. Olymphilex '87 Olympic Stamps Exhibition, Rome. Multicoloured.

N2719	10ch. Type **916**	1·30	20
MSN2720	95×80 mm. 80ch. Exhibition emblem and 5ch. and 1wn. Angol Sports Village stamps	4·25	1·60

917 Underground Station and Guard

1987. Railway Uniforms. Multicoloured.

N2721	10ch. Type **917**	50	10
N2722	10ch. Underground train and station supervisor	50	10
N2723	20ch. Guard and electric train	75	15
N2724	30ch. Guard with flag and electric train	1·10	30
N2725	40ch. *Orient Express* guard and steam locomotive	1·40	40
N2726	40ch. German ticket controller and diesel train	1·40	40

918 White Stork

1987. Hafnia 87 International Stamp Exhibition, Copenhagen. Multicoloured.

N2727	40ch. Type **918**	2·20	55
N2728	60ch. *Danmark* (cadet full-rigged ship) and *Little Mermaid*, Copenhagen	2·50	65

919 Ice Skating

1987. Winter Olympic Games, Calgary (1988). Multicoloured.

N2729	40ch. Type **919**	1·20	40
N2730	40ch. Ski jumping	1·20	40
N2731	40ch. Skiing (value on left) (horiz)	1·20	40
N2732	40ch. Skiing (value on right) (horiz)	1·20	40
MSN2733	73×100 mm. 80ch. Skiing	3·75	1·40

920 Victory Column

1987. 750th Anniversary of Berlin and Philatelia '87 International Stamp Exhibition, Cologne. Multicoloured.

N2734	10ch. Type **920**	50	10
N2735	20ch. Reichstag (horiz)	85	30
N2736	30ch. Pfaueninsel Castle	1·30	40
N2737	40ch. Charlottenburg Castle (horiz)	1·40	55
MSN2738	77×94 mm. 80ch. Olympic stadium (horiz)	3·75	1·40

921 Garros and Bleriot XI

1987. Birth Centenary of Roland Garros (aviator) and Tennis as an Olympic Sport. Multicoloured.

N2739	20ch. Type **921**	1·80	30
N2740	20ch. Ivan Lendl (tennis player)	3·00	40
N2741	40ch. Steffi Graf (tennis player)	3·75	55
MSN2742	80×102 mm. 80ch. Steffi Graf (different)	5·00	1·40

922 Kim Jong Suk

1987. 70th Birth Anniversary of Kim Jong Suk (revoloutionary). Sheet 80×100 mm.

MSN2743	**922** 80ch. multicoloured	1·60	75

923 Pyongyang Buildings

1988. New Year. Multicoloured.

N2744	10ch. Type **923**	25	10
N2745	40ch. Dragon	85	30

924 Banner and Newspaper

1988. 60th Anniversary of *Saenal* Newspaper.

N2746	**924** 10ch. multicoloured	60	20

925 Birthplace, Mt. Paekdu

1988. Kim Jong Il's Birthday. Multicoloured.

N2747	109×85 mm. 10ch. Type **925**	35	10
MSN2748	109×85 mm. Kim Jong Il (41×63 mm.)	1·80	65

926 Henry Dunant (founder)

1988. 125th Anniversary of International Red Cross. Multicoloured.

N2749	10ch. Type **926**	75	10
N2750	20ch. North Korean Red Cross emblem and map	1·20	30
N2751	20ch. International Committee headquarters, Geneva	1·20	30
N2752	40ch. Pyongyang Maternity Hospital, doctor and baby	1·20	40
MSN2753	70×100 mm. 80ch. Red Cross and Red Crescent flags and anniversary emblem	2·50	95

927 *Santa Maria*

1988. 500th Anniversary (1992) of Discovery of America by Christopher Columbus. Multicoloured.

N2754	10ch. Type **927**	1·70	20
N2755	20ch. *Pinta*	1·70	30
N2756	30ch. *Nina*	1·70	45
MSN2757	80×102 mm. 80ch. *Columbus on the deck of his Flagship* (detail, Karl von Piloty)	3·50	95

Nos. N2754/N2756 were issued together, *se-tenant*, forming a composite design of Columbus's ships leaving Palos.

928 Montgolfier Balloon and Modern Hot-air Balloons

1988. Juvalux '88 International Youth Stamp Exhibition, Luxembourg. Multicoloured.

N2758	40ch. Type **928**	1·10	40
N2759	60ch. Steam locomotive and railway map of Luxembourg, 1900	2·10	55

929 Dancers

1988. Sixth Spring Friendship Art Festival, Pyongyang. Multicoloured.

N2760	10ch. Singer (poster)	25	10
N2761	1wn.20 Type **929**	3·25	1·30

930 Inaugural Congress Emblem

1988. Tenth Anniversary of International Institute of the 'Juche' Idea.

N2762	**930** 10ch. multicoloured	40	10

931 Birthplace, Mangyongdae

1988. 76th Birthday of Kim Il Sung. Multicoloured.

N2763	10c. Type **931**	40	10
MSN2764	135×95 mm. 80ch. Kim Il Sung and schoolchildren (40×62 mm.)	1·40	65

932 *Urho* (ice-breaker)

1988. Finlandia 88 International Stamp Exhibition, Helsinki. Multicoloured.

N2765	40ch. Type **932**	1·80	40
N2766	60ch. Matti Nykaenen (Olympic Games ski-jumping medallist)	1·70	55

933 Postcard for 1934 Championship

1988. World Cup Football Championship, Italy (1st issue). Multicoloured.

N2767	10ch. Football match	65	15
N2768	20ch. Type **933**	1·10	30
N2769	30ch. Player tackling (horiz)	1·70	40
MSN2770	100×75 mm. 80ch. Winning Italian team, 1982 (horiz)	2·50	95

See also Nos. N2924/N2927.

934 Emblem

1988. 13th World Youth and Students' Festival, Pyongyang (1st issue). Multicoloured.

N2771	5ch. Type **934**	10	10
N2772	10ch. Dancer	50	10
N2773	10ch. Gymnast and gymnasium, Angol Sports Village	25	10
N2774	10ch. Map of Korea, globe and doves	35	10
N2775	10ch. Finger pointing at shattered nuclear rockets	90	20
N2776	1wn.20 Three differently coloured hands and dove	2·75	1·00

See also Nos. N2860/N2863 and N2879/N2880.

935 Fairy

1988. *Eight Fairies of Mt. Kumgang* (tale). Multicoloured.

N2777	10ch. Type **935**	25	10
N2778	15ch. Fairy at pool and fairies on rainbow	40	10
N2779	20ch. Fairy and woodman husband	60	20
N2780	25ch. Couple with baby	75	20
N2781	30ch. Couple with son and daughter	85	30

N2782 35ch. Family on rainbow 1·00 35

936 Mallards

1988. Praga '88 International Stamp Exhibition, Prague. Multicoloured.

N2783 20ch. Type **936** 1·50 30
N2784 40ch. Vladimir Remek (Czechoslovak cosmonaut) 1·10 40

937 Red Crossbill

1988. Birds. Multicoloured.

N2785 10ch. Type **937** 75 20
N2786 15ch. Common stonechat 1·00 30
N2787 20ch. Eurasian nuthatch 1·50 40
N2788 25ch. Great spotted woodpecker 1·70 45
N2789 30ch. River kingfisher 2·00 55
N2790 35ch. Bohemian waxwing 2·10 65

938 Fair Emblem

1988. 40th International Stamp Fair, Riccione. Multicoloured.

N2791 20ch. Type **938** 50 40
MSN2792 101×75 mm. 80ch. Drum dancer (vert) 2·10 75

939 Emu

1988. Bicentenary of Australian Settlement. Multicoloured.

N2793 10ch. Type **939** 85 20
N2794 15ch. Satin bowerbirds 1·10 30
N2795 25ch. Laughing kookaburra (vert) 1·80 45
MSN2796 101×73 mm. 80ch. HMS *Resolution* (Cook's ship) 3·00 1·00

940 Floating Crane *5-28*

1988. Ships. Multicoloured.

N2797 10ch. Type **940** 50 20
N2798 20ch. Freighter *Hwanggumsan* 85 30
N2799 30ch. Freighter *Changjasan Chongnyon-ho* 1·00 40
N2800 40ch. Liner *Samjiyon* 1·30 45

941 *Hansa*

1988. 150th Birth Anniversary of Count Ferdinand von Zeppelin (airship pioneer). Multicoloured.

N2801 10ch. Type **941** 35 10
N2802 20ch. *Schwaben* 65 30
N2803 30ch. *Viktoria Luise* 90 40
N2804 40ch. LZ-3 1·30 45
MSN2805 102×80 mm. 1wn. Portrait of Zeppelin (vert) 3·25 1·40

942 Kim Il Sung and Jambyn Batmunkh

1988. Kim Il Sung's Visit to Mongolia.

N2806 **942** 10ch. multicoloured 25 10

943 Hero and Labour Hero of the DPRK Medals

1988. National Heroes Congress.

N2807 **943** 10ch. multicoloured 25 10

944 Tower of 'Juche' Idea

1988. 40th Anniversary of Democratic Republic. Multicoloured.

N2808 5ch. Type **944** 15 10
N2809 10ch. Smelter and industrial buildings 25 10
N2810 10ch. Soldier and Mt. Paekdu 25 10
N2811 10ch. Map of Korea and globe 25 10
N2812 10ch. Hand holding banner, globe and doves 25 10
MSN2813 118×105 mm. 1wn.20 Kim Il Sung designing National Flag and emblem (41×63 mm) 3·00 1·10

945 *Sunflowers* (Vincent van Gogh)

1988. Filacept 88 Stamp Exhibition, The Hague. Multicoloured.

N2814 40ch. Type **945** 2·20 1·70
N2815 60ch. *The Chess Game* (Lucas van Leyden) (horiz) 3·25 2·40

946 Emblem

1988. 16th Session of Socialist Countries' Post and Telecommunications Conference, Pyongyang.

N2816 **946** 10ch. multicoloured 25 10

947 Chaju 82 10-ton Truck

1988. Tipper Trucks. Multicoloured.

N2817 20ch. Type **947** 50 40
N2818 40ch. Kumsusan-ho 40-ton truck 1·00 75

948 *Owl*

1988. Paintings by O Un Byol. Multicoloured.

N2819 10ch. Type **948** 2·20 30
N2820 15ch. *Dawn* (red junglefowl) 1·10 30
N2821 20ch. *Beautiful Rose received by Kim Il Sung* 85 25
N2822 25ch. *Sun and Bamboo* 1·00 25
N2823 30ch. *Autumn* (fruit tree) 1·20 30

949 Chunggi class Steam Locomotive No. 35

1988. Railway Locomotives. Multicoloured.

N2824 10ch. Type **949** 65 15
N2825 20ch. Chunggi class steam locomotive No. 22 90 20
N2826 30ch. Chongiha class electric locomotive No. 3 1·10 30
N2827 40ch. Chunggi class steam locomotive No. 307 1·30 40

950 Pirmen Zurbriggen (downhill skiing)

1988. Winter Olympic Games, Calgary, Medal Winners. Multicoloured.

N2828 10ch. Type **950** 25 10
N2829 20ch. Yvonne van Gennip (speed skating) 50 40
N2830 30ch. Marjo Matikainen (cross-country skiing) 75 55
N2831 40ch. USSR (ice hockey) (horiz) 1·00 75
MSN2832 Two sheets, each 105×95 mm. (a) 80ch. Katarina Witt (figure skating); (b) 80ch. As sheet (a) but with names of winners printed in margin 4·25 1·60

951 Yuri Gagarin

1988. First Man and Woman in Space. Multicoloured.

N2833 20ch. Type **951** 40 30
N2834 40ch. Valentina Tereshkova 90 65

952 Nehru

1988. Birth Centenary of Jawaharlal Nehru (Indian statesman) and India 89 International Stamp Exhibition, New Delhi.

N2835 **952** 20ch. purple, black and gold 85 20
MSN2836 90×74 mm. 60ch. multicoloured (Dancer) 1·70 55

953 Chollima Statue

1989. New Year. Multicoloured.

N2837 10ch. Type **953** 25 10
N2838 20ch. *The Dragon Angler* (17th-century painting) 85 20
N2839 40ch. *Tortoise and Serpent* (Kangso tomb painting) (horiz) 1·20 40

954 Archery

1989. National Defence Training. Multicoloured.

N2840 10ch. Type **954** 1·20 30
N2841 15ch. Rifle shooting 40 10
N2842 20ch. Pistol shooting 50 20
N2843 25ch. Parachuting 65 25
N2844 30ch. Launching model glider 75 30

955 Dobermann Pinscher

1989. Animals presented to Kim Il Sung. Multicoloured.

N2845 10ch. Type **955** 65 20
N2846 20ch. Labrador 90 25
N2847 25ch. German shepherd 1·20 30
N2848 30ch. Rough collies (horiz) 1·30 35
N2849 35ch. Serval (horiz) 1·70 40
MSN2850 95×75 mm. 80ch. *Felis libica* (horiz) 3·75 95

956 Begonia *Kimjongil*

1989. Kim Jong Il Birthday. Sheet 78×100 mm.

MSN2851 **956** 80ch. multicoloured 1·80 65

957 Agriculture

1989. 25th Anniversary of Publication of *Theses on the Socialist Rural Question in our Country* by Kim Il Sung.

N2852 **957** 10ch. multicoloured 50 15

958 The Gypsy and Grapes

1989. Fungi and Fruits. Multicoloured.

N2853 10ch. Type **958** 65 15
N2854 20ch. Caesar's mushroom and magnolia vine 1·10 30
N2855 25ch. *Lactarius hygrophoides* and *Eleagnus crispa* 1·50 35

N2856	30ch. *Agaricus placomyces* and Chinese gooseberries	1·70	40
N2857	35ch. Horse mushroom and *Lycium chinense*	2·10	40
N2858	40ch. Elegant boletus and *Juglans cordiformis*	2·20	45
MSN2859	100×78 mm. 1wn. *Gomphidius roseus* and Diospyros lotus" (48×30 mm)	4·50	1·40

959 Korean Girl

1989. 13th World Youth and Students' Festival, Pyongyang (2nd issue). Multicoloured.

N2860	10ch. Type **959**	25	10
N2861	20ch. Children of different races	45	30
N2862	30ch. Fairy and rainbow	65	45
N2863	40ch. Young peoples and Tower of 'Juche' Idea	90	65

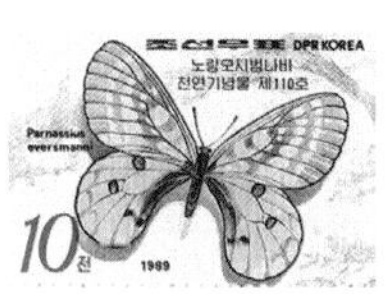

960 *Parnassius eversmanni*

1969. Insects. Multicoloured.

N2864	10ch. Type **960**	1·00	30
N2865	15ch. *Colias heos*	1·00	30
N2866	20ch. *Dilipa fenestra*	1·00	30
N2867	25ch. *Buthus martensis*	1·00	30
N2868	30ch. *Trichogramma ostriniae*	1·00	30
N2869	40ch. *Damaster constricticollis*	1·00	30
MSN2870	82×65 mm. 80ch. *Parnassius nomion*	3·25	1·10

961 Dancers (poster)

1989. Spring Friendship Art Festival, Pyongyang.

N2871 **961**	10ch. multicoloured	60	15

962 Birthplace, Mangyongdae

1989. 77th Birthday of Kim Il Sung.

N2872 **962**	10ch. multicoloured	35	10

963 Battle Plan and Monument to the Victory

1989. 50th Anniversary of Battle of the Musan Area.

N2873 **963**	10ch. blue, flesh and red	85	20

964 Modern Dance

1989. Chamo System of Dance Notation. Multicoloured.

N2874	10ch. Type **964**	60	20
N2875	20ch. Ballet	75	30
N2876	25ch. Modern dance (different)	1·00	35
N2877	30ch. Traditional dance	1·10	40
MSN2878	85×105 mm. 80ch. Dancers	3·00	75

965 Hands supporting Torch

1989. 13th World Youth and Students' Festival, Pyongyang (3rd issue).

N2879 **965**	5ch. blue	15	10
N2880 -	10ch. brown	25	10

Design: 10ch. Youth making speech.

966 Victorious Badger

1989. *Badger measures the Height* (cartoon film). Multicoloured.

N2881	10ch. Cat, bear and badger race to flag pole	1·10	20
N2882	40ch. Cat and bear climb pole while badger measures shadow	1·70	40
N2883	50ch. Typc **966**	2·00	45

967 Kyongju Observatory and Star Chart

1989. Astronomy.

N2884	20ch. multicoloured	1·30	25
MSN2885	102×85 mm. 80ch. Planet Saturn (horiz)	5·50	75

968 *Liberty guiding the People* (Eugene Delacroiz)

1989. Philexfrance 89 International Stamp Exhibition, Paris. Sheet 107×88 mm.

MSN2886 **968**	70ch. multicoloured	1·80	95

969 Pele (footballer) and 1978 25ch. Stamp

1989. Brasiliana 89 International Stamp Exhibition, Rio de Janeiro.

N2887 **969**	40ch. multicoloured	1·30	45

970 Nurse and Ambulance

1989. Emergency Services. Multicoloured.

N2888	10ch. Type **970**	25	10
N2889	20ch. Surgeon and ambulance	40	20
N2890	30ch. Fireman and fire engine	3·00	30
N2891	40ch. Fireman and engine (different)	3·00	40

971 Kaffir Lily

1989. Plants presented to Kim Il Sung. Multicoloured.

N2892	10ch. Type **971**	40	10
N2893	15ch. Tulips	50	15
N2894	20ch. Flamingo lily	75	20
N2895	25ch. *Rhododendron obtusum*	90	25
N2896	30ch. Daffodils	1·10	30
MSN2897	84×104 mm. 80ch. *Gerbera hybrida*	3·00	75

972 Air Mail Letter and Postal Transport

1989. 150th Anniversary of the Penny Black and Stamp World London 90 International Stamp Exhibition (1st issue). Multicoloured.

N2898	5ch. Type **972**	40	10
N2899	10ch. Post box and letters	60	15
N2900	20ch. Stamps, tweezers and magnifying glass	65	20
N2901	30ch. First North Korean stamps	85	30
N2902	40ch. Universal Postal Union emblem and headquarters, Berne	1·10	40
N2903	50ch. Sir Rowland Hill and Penny Black	1·50	55

See also No. N2956/**MS**N2957.

973 *Bistorta incana*

1989. Alpine Flowers. Multicoloured.

N2904	10ch. *Iris setosa*	50	15
N2905	15ch. *Aquilegia japonica*	65	20
N2906	20ch. Type **973**	85	25
N2907	25ch. *Rodiola elongata*	90	30
N2908	30ch. *Sanguisorba sitchensis*	1·00	35
MSN2909	62×49 mm. 80ch. *Trollius japonicus*	2·75	85

974 Tree, Mt. Paekdu

1989. Slogan-bearing Trees (1st series). Multicoloured.

N2910	10ch. Type **974**	25	10
N2911	3wn. Tree, Oun-dong, Pyongyang	8·50	6·50
N2912	5wn. Tree, Mt. Kanbaek	14·50	10·50

See also No. N2931.

975 Skipping

1989. Children's Games. Multicoloured.

N2913	10ch. Type **975**	25	10
N2914	20ch. Windmill	1·70	30
N2915	30ch. Kite	75	35
N2916	40ch. Whip and top	1·00	40

976 Marchers

1989. International March for Peace and Reunification of Korea. Sheet 100×77 mm.

MSN2917 **976**	80ch. multicoloured	2·10	1·40

977 Diesel Train and Sinpa Youth Station

1989. Railway Locomotives. Multicoloured.

N2918	10ch. Type **977**	50	10
N2919	20ch. *Pulgungi* electric locomotive	75	20
N2920	25ch. Diesel goods train	85	30
N2921	30ch. Diesel train	1·00	35
N2922	40ch. Steam locomotive	1·30	40
N2923	50ch. Steam locomotive (different)	1·30	45

978 Players and Map of Italy

1989. World Cup Football Championship, Italy (2nd issue). Multicoloured.

N2924	10ch. Type **978**	90	20
N2925	20ch. Free kick	50	20
N2926	30ch. Goal mouth scrimmage	75	30
N2927	40ch. Goalkeeper diving for ball	1·00	35

979 Magellan (navigator) and his Ship *Vitoria*

1989. Descobrex '89 International Stamp Exhibition, Portugal.

N2928 **979**	30ch. multicoloured	1·50	30

980 Mangyong Hill and Pine Branches

1990. New Year. Multicoloured.

N2929	10ch. Type **980**	25	10
N2930	20ch. Koguryo mounted archers	1·10	20

1990. Slogan-bearing Trees (2nd series). As T **974**. Multicoloured.

N2931	5ch. Tree, Mt. Paekdu	35	10

981 Ryukwoli

1990. Dogs. Multicoloured.

N2932	20ch. Type **981**	1·30	30
N2933	30ch. Palryuki	1·30	30
N2934	40ch. Komdungi	1·30	30
N2935	50ch. Oulruki	1·30	30

982 Birthplace, Mt. Paekdu

1990. Birthday of Kim Jong Il.

N2936 **982**	10ch. brown	35	10

983 Stone Instruments and Primitive Man

1990. Evolution of Man. Multicoloured.

N2937	10ch. Type **983**	2·50	20
N2938	40ch. Palaeolithic and Neolithic man	3·25	30

984 Rungna Bridge, Pyongyang

1990. Bridges. Multicoloured.

N2939	10ch. Type **984**	50	10
N2940	20ch. Potong bridge, Pyongyang	75	20
N2941	30ch. Sinuiji-Ryucho Island Bridge	1·00	30
N2942	40ch. Chungsongui Bridge, Pyongyang	1·30	40

985 Infantryman

1990. Warriors' Costumes. Multicoloured.

N2943	20ch. Type **985**	40	30
N2944	30ch. Archer	65	55
N2945	50ch. Military commander in armour	1·20	95
N2946	70ch. Officer's costume, 10th/14th-centuries	1·60	1·20

Nos. N2943/N2945 depict costumes from the 3rd-century BC to the 7th-century AD.

986 *Atergatis subdentatus* (poster)

1990. Crabs. Multicoloured.

N2947	20ch. Type **986**	50	20
N2948	30ch. *Platylambrus validus*	75	30
N2949	50ch. *Uca arcuata*	1·30	45

987 Dancers

1990. Spring Friendship Art Festival, Pyongyang.

N2950 **987**	10ch. multicoloured	35	10

988 Monument at Road Folk, Mangyongdae

1990. 78th Birthday of Kim Il Sung.

N2951 **988**	10ch. green and gold	35	10
MSN2952	85×105 mm. 80ch. multicoloured (Kim Il Sung) (38×60 mm)	2·10	75

989 *Gymnocalycium* sp.

1990. Cacti. Multicoloured.

N2953	10ch. Type **989**	50	10
N2954	30ch. *Pyllocactus hybridus*	90	30
N2955	50ch. *Epiphyllum truncatum*	1·50	45

990 Exhibition Emblem

1990. Stamp World London 90 International Stamp Exhibition (2nd issue).

N2956 **990**	20ch. red and black	60	20
MSN2957	49×66 mm. 70ch. grey, black and gold	2·00	1·90

Design: 70ch. Sir Rowland Hill.

991 Congo Peafowl

1990. Peafowl. Multicoloured.

N2958	10ch. Type **991**	1·00	20
N2959	20ch. Common peafowl	1·80	45
MSN2960	96×82 mm. 70ch. Common peafowl displaying tail	3·25	95

992 Dolphin and Submarine

1990. Bio-engineering. Multicoloured.

N2961	10ch. Type **992**	1·40	45
N2962	20ch. Bat and dish aerial	1·40	45
N2963	30ch. Owl and Tupolev Tu-154 jetliner	1·40	45
N2964	40ch. Squid, Soyuz rocket and Concorde supersonic jetliner	1·40	45

993 *Self-portrait* (Rembrandt)

1990. Belgica 90 International Stamp Exhibition, Brussels. Multicoloured.

N2965	10ch. Type **993**	35	10
N2966	20ch. *Self-portrait* (Raphael)	60	20
N2967	30ch. *Self-portrait* (Rubens)	75	30

994 K. H. Rummenigge (footballer)

1990. Dusseldorf '90 International Youth Stamp Exhibition. Multicoloured.

N2968	20ch. Steffi Graf (tennis player)	85	20
N2969	30ch. Exhibition emblem	75	30
N2970	70ch. Type **994**	1·70	65

995 Workers' Stadium, Peking, and Games Mascot

1990. 11th Asian Games, Peking (Nos. N2971/N2972) and Third Asian Winter Games, Samjiyon (N2973). Multicoloured.

N2971	10ch. Type **995**	25	10
N2972	30ch. *Chollima* Statue and sportsmen	75	40
N2973	40ch. Sportsmen and Games emblem	1·10	45

996 Ball

1990. West Germany, Winners of World Cup Football Championship. Multicoloured.

N2974	15ch. Emblem of FIFA (International Federation of Football Associations)	40	10
N2975	20ch. Jules Rimet	60	20
N2976	25ch. Type **996**	65	30
N2977	30ch. Olympic Stadium, Rome (venue of final)	75	35
N2978	35ch. Goalkeeper	90	40
N2979	40ch. Emblem of West German Football Association	1·10	45
MSN2980	106×92 mm. 80ch. German Football Association emblem and trophy (horiz)	2·10	1·40

997 Kakapo and Map of New Zealand

1990. New Zealand 1990 International Stamp Exhibition, Auckland.

N2981 **997**	30ch. multicoloured	1·50	55

998 'Summer at Chipson Peak'

1990. Europa 90 International Stamp Fair, Riccione. Sheet 90×70 mm.

MSN2982 **998**	80cn. multicoloured	2·10	75

999 Head of Procession

1990. Koguryo Wedding Procession. Multicoloured.

N2983	10ch. Type **999**	1·30	40
N2984	30ch. Bridegroom	1·30	40
N2985	50ch. Bride in carriage	1·30	40
N2986	1wn. Drummer on horse	1·30	40

Nos. N2983/N2986 were issued together, *se-tenant*, forming a composite design.

1000 Marchers descending Mt. Paekdu

1990. Rally for Peace and Reunification of Korea. Multicoloured.

N2987	10ch. Type **1000**	25	10
MSN2988	106×70 mm. 1wn. Crowd watching dancers	2·20	85

1001 Praying Mantis

1990. Insects. Multicoloured.

N2989	20ch. Type **1001**	50	20
N2990	30ch. Ladybird	75	30
N2991	40ch. *Pheropsophus jessoensis*	1·10	35
N2992	70ch. *Phyllium siccifolium*	1·70	55

1002 Footballers

1990. North–South Reunification Football Match, Pyongyang. Multicoloured.

N2993	10ch. Type **1002**	75	10
N2994	20ch. Footballers (different)	75	20
MSN2995	105×80 mm. 1wn. Teams parading	2·20	85

1003 Concert Emblem

1990. National Reunification Concert.

N2996 **1003**	10ch. multicoloured	35	10

1004 Ox

1990. Farm Animals.

N2997 **1004**	10ch. brown and green	25	10
N2998 -	20ch. lilac and yellow	45	20
N2999 -	30ch. grey and red	60	30
N3000 -	40ch. green and yellow	85	35
N3001 -	50ch. brown and blue	1·10	40

Designs: 20ch. Pig; 30ch. Goat; 40ch. Sheep; 50ch. Horse.

1005 Chinese and North Korean Soldiers

1990. 40th Anniversary of Participation of Chinese Volunteers in Korean War. Multicoloured.

N3002	10ch. Type **1005**	25	10
N3003	20ch. Populace welcoming volunteers (horiz)	45	20
N3004	30ch. Rejoicing soldiers and battle scene (horiz)	60	25
N3005	40ch. Post-war reconstruction (horiz)	85	30
MSN3006	95×75 mm. 80ch. Friendship Tower, Moran Hill, Pyongyang	1·70	70

1006 Anniversary Emblem

1990. 40th Anniversary of United Nations Development Programme.
N3007 **1006** 1wn. blue, silver & blk 3·00 2·10

1007 Mikado Sturgeon

1990. Fish.

N3008 **1007**	10ch. brown and green	25	10
N3009 -	20ch. green and blue	60	20
N3010 -	30ch. blue and purple	80	30
N3011 -	40ch. brown and blue	1·10	40
N3012 -	50ch. violet and green	1·40	50

Designs: 20ch. Large-headed sea bream; 30ch. Agoo flyingfish; 40ch. Fat greenling; 50ch. Tobij-ei eagle ray.

1008 Sheep

1990. New Year.
N3013 **1008** 40ch. multicoloured 85 30

1009 Moorhen

1990. Birds.

N3014 **1009**	10ch. blue, green & blk	50	10
N3015 -	20ch. brown, bistre and black	85	30
N3016 -	30ch. green, grey and black	1·10	50
N3017 -	40ch. brown, orange and black	1·60	60
N3018 -	50ch. ochre, brown and black	2·20	80

Designs: 20ch. Jay; 30ch. Three-toed woodpecker; 40ch. Whimbrel; 50ch. Water rail.

1010 Giant Panda

1991. Phila Nippon '91 International Stamp Exhibition, Tokyo. Multicoloured.

N3019	10ch. Type **1010**	25	10
N3020	20ch. Two giant pandas feeding	45	20
N3021	30ch. Giant panda clambering onto branch	60	25
N3022	40ch. Giant panda on rock	95	30
N3023	50ch. Two giant pandas	1·10	40
N3024	60ch. Giant panda in tree fork	1·30	50
MSN3025	115×85 mm. Giant panda	6·00	1·50

1011 Changsan

1991. Revolutionary Sites. Multicoloured.

N3026	5ch. Type **1011**	15	10
N3027	10ch. Oun	25	20

1012 Black-faced Spoonbills

1991. Endangered Birds. Multicoloured.

N3028	10ch. Type **1012**	25	10
N3029	20ch. Grey herons	60	20
N3030	30ch. Great egrets	85	30
N3031	40ch. Manchurian cranes	1·20	40
N3032	50ch. Japanese white-naped cranes	1·60	50
N3033	70ch. White storks	2·20	70

1013 *Clossiana angarensis*

1991. Alpine Butterflies. Multicoloured.

N3034	10ch. Type **1013**	15	10
N3035	20ch. *Erebia embla*	35	30
N3036	30ch. Camberwell beauty	50	40
N3037	40ch. Comma	70	50
N3038	50ch. Eastern pale clouded yellow	95	70
N3039	60ch. *Theela betulae*	1·20	80

1014 Hedgehog Fungus

1991. Fungi. Multicoloured.

N3040	10ch. Type **1014**	15	10
N3041	20ch. *Phylloporus rhodoxanthus*	45	20
N3042	30ch. *Calvatia craniiformis*	60	30
N3043	40ch. Cauliflower clavaria	80	40
N3044	50ch. *Russula integra*	1·00	50

1015 Kumchon

1991. Revolutionary Sites. Multicoloured.

N3045	10ch. Type **1015**	15	10
N3046	40ch. Samdung	70	50

1016 Dr. Kye Ung Sang (researcher)

1991. Silkworm Research. Multicoloured.

N3047	10ch. Type **1016**	15	10
N3048	20ch. Chinese oak silk moth	35	30
N3049	30ch. *Attacus ricini*	50	40
N3050	40ch. *Antheraea yamamai*	70	50
N3051	50ch. Silkworm moth	95	70
N3052	60ch. *Aetias artemis*	1·10	80

1017 Emblem and Venue

1991. Ninth Spring Friendship Art Festival, Pyongyang.
N3053 **1017** 10ch. multicoloured 20 10

1018 Emperor Penguins

1991. Antarctic Exploration. Multicoloured.

N3054	10ch. Type **1018**	45	20
N3055	20ch. Research station	45	20
N3056	30ch. Elephant seals	50	30
N3057	40ch. Research ship	95	40
N3058	50ch. Southern black-backed gulls	1·60	60
MSN3059	75×105 mm. 80ch. National Flag and map of Antarctica	1·60	90

1019 People's Palace of Culture (venue)

1991. 85th Interparliamentary Union Conference, Pyongyang.

N3060 **1019**	10ch. dp green, grn & sil	25	10
N3061 -	1wn.50 multicoloured	2·75	2·10

Design: 1wn.50, Conference emblem and azalea.

1020 Map and Kim Jong Ho

1991. 130th Anniversary of Publication of Kim Jong Ho's Map *Taidong Yu Jido*.
N3062 **1020** 90ch. black, brn & sil 1·90 1·30

1021 Cynognathus

1991. Dinosaurs. Multicoloured.

N3063	10ch. Type **1021**	35	10
N3064	20ch. Brontosaurus	70	40
N3065	30ch. Stegosaurus and allosaurus	1·00	50
N3066	40ch. Pterosauria	1·40	80
N3067	50ch. Ichthyosaurus	1·70	90

1022 Sprinting

1991. Olympic Games, Barcelona (1992) (1st issue). Multicoloured.

N3068	10ch. Type **1022**	15	10
N3069	10ch. Hurdling	15	10
N3070	20ch. Long jumping	45	20
N3071	20ch. Throwing the discus	45	20
N3072	30ch. Putting the shot	60	30
N3073	30ch. Pole vaulting	60	30
N3074	40ch. High jumping	95	50
N3075	40ch. Throwing the javelin	95	50
MSN3076	Two sheets, each 105×85 mm. (a) 80ch. Breasting the tape; (b) 80ch. Running	3·50	1·90

See also Nos. N3142/**MS**3148.

1023 Cats and Eurasian Tree Sparrows

1991. Cats. Multicoloured.

N3077	10ch. Type **1023**	50	40
N3078	20ch. Cat and rat	1·00	60
N3079	30ch. Cat and butterfly	1·60	80
N3080	40ch. Cats with ball	2·10	1·10
N3081	50ch. Cat and frog	2·75	1·30

1024 *Wisteria Flowers and Pups* (detail)

1991. Riccione '91 Stamp Fair and Exhibition, Italy. Sheet 116×80 mm. International.
MSN3082 **1024** 80ch. multicoloured 3·50 95

1025 Wild Horse

1991. Horses. Multicoloured.

N3083	10ch. Type **1025**	15	10
N3084	20ch. Hybrid of wild ass and wild horse	50	20
N3085	30ch. Przewalski's horse	70	30
N3086	40ch. Wild ass	95	50
N3087	50ch. Wild horse (different)	1·20	60

1026 Pennant Coralfish

1991. Fish. Multicoloured.

N3088	10ch. Type **1026** (postage)	15	10
N3089	20ch. Clown triggerfish	45	20
N3090	30ch. Tomato anemonefish	60	30
N3091	40ch. Palette surgeonfish	95	50
N3092	50ch. Freshwater angelfish (air)	1·30	70
MSN3093	88×60 mm. 80ch. Tetras (*Hyhessobrycon innesi*) (51×31 mm)	3·00	95

1027 Rhododendrons

1991. Flowers. Multicoloured.

N3094	10ch. Begonia	25	10
N3095	20ch. Gerbera	35	30
N3096	30ch. Type **1027**	50	40
N3097	40ch. Phalaenopsis	70	50
N3098	50ch. *Impatiens sultanii*	95	70
N3099	60ch. Streptocarpus	1·10	80

Nos. N3097/N3099 commemorate CANADA '92 international youth stamp exhibition, Montreal.

1028 Panmunjom

1991
N3100 **1028** 10ch. multicoloured 20 10

1029 Magnolia

1991. National Flower.

N3101	**1029** 10ch. multicoloured	20	10

1030 Players

1991. Women's World Football Championship, China. Multicoloured.

N3102	10ch. Type **1030**	25	10
N3103	20ch. Dribbling the ball	35	30
N3104	30ch. Heading the ball	50	40
N3105	40ch. Overhead kick	70	50
N3106	50ch. Tackling	95	70
N3107	60ch. Goalkeeper	1·10	80

1031 Squirrel Monkeys

1992. Monkeys. Multicoloured.

N3108	10ch. Type **1031**	45	20
N3109	20ch. Pygmy marmosets	80	40
N3110	30ch. Red-handed tamarins	1·40	50
MSN3111	65×91 mm. 80ch. Monkey leaping (33×51 mm)	2·30	1·70

1032 Eagle Owl

1992. Birds of Prey. Multicoloured.

N3112	10ch. Type **1032**	35	10
N3113	20ch. Common buzzard	80	40
N3114	30ch. African fish eagle	1·10	50
N3115	40ch. Steller's sea eagle	1·50	80
N3116	50ch. Golden eagle	1·90	90
MSN3117	78×59 mm. 80ch. Common kestrel (41×31 mm)	2·20	95

1033 Birthplace, Mt. Paekdu

1992. Birthday of Kim Jong Il. Mt. Paekdu. Multicoloured.

N3118	10ch. Type **1033**	15	10
N3119	20ch. Mountain summit	35	30
N3120	30ch. Lake Chon (crater lake)	50	40
N3121	40ch. Lake Sarryi	70	50
MSN3122	162×87 mm. 80ch. *Snowstorm on Mt. Paektu* (41×63 mm)	1·70	95

1034 Service Bus

1992. Transport.

N3123	**1034** 10ch. multicoloured	15	10
N3124	- 20ch. multicoloured	35	30
N3125	- 30ch. multicoloured	50	40
N3126	- 40ch. multicoloured	70	50
N3127	- 50ch. multicoloured	95	70
N3128	- 60ch. multicoloured	1·10	80

Designs: 20ch. to 60ch. Different buses and electric trams.

1035 Dancers and Emblem

1992. Spring Friendship Art Festival, Pyongyang.

N3129	**1035** 10ch. multicoloured	20	10

1036 Birthplace, Mangyongdae

1992. 80th Birthday of Kim Il Sung. Revolutionary Sites. Multicoloured.

N3130	10ch. Type **1036** (postage)	15	10
N3131	10ch. Party emblem and Turubong monument	15	10
N3132	10ch. Map and Ssuksom	15	10
N3133	10ch. Statue of soldier and Tongchang	15	10
N3134	40ch. Cogwheels and Taean	70	50
N3135	40ch. *Chollima* Statue and Kangson	70	50
N3136	1wn.20 Monument and West Sea Barrage (air)	2·40	1·90
MSN3137	160×160 mm. 80ch. *April spring Friendship Art Festival* (41×63 mm)	1·70	95

1037 Kang Ban Sok

1992. Birth Centenary of Kang Ban Sok (mother of Kim Il Sung). Sheet 80×103 mm.

MSN3138	**1037** 80ch. multicoloured	1·70	95

1038 Soldiers on Parade

1992. 60th Anniversary of People's Army. Multicoloured.

N3139	10ch. Type **1038**	15	10
N3140	10ch. Couple greeting soldier	15	10
N3141	10ch. Army, air force and navy personnel	15	10

1039 Hurdling

1992. Olympic Games, Barcelona (2nd issue). Multicoloured.

N3142	10ch. Type **1039**	15	10
N3143	20ch. High jumping	35	30
N3144	30ch. Putting the shot	50	40
N3145	40ch. Sprinting	70	50
N3146	50ch. Long jumping	95	70
N3147	60ch. Throwing the javelin	1·10	80
MSN3148	105×85 mm. 80ch. Running	1·70	95

1040 Planting Crops

1992. Evolution of Man. Designs showing life in the New Stone Age (10, 20ch.) and the Bronze Age (others). Multicoloured.

N3149	10ch. Type **1040** (postage)	45	10
N3150	20ch. Family around cooking pot	70	30
N3151	30ch. Ploughing fields	1·10	40
N3152	40ch. Performing domestic chores	1·40	50
N3153	50ch. Building a dolmen (air)	2·40	70

1041 White-bellied Black Woodpecker

1992. Birds. Multicoloured.

N3154	10ch. Type **1041**	15	10
N3155	20ch. Common pheasant	45	30
N3156	30ch. White stork	50	40
N3157	40ch. Blue-winged pitta	80	50
N3158	50ch. Pallas's sandgrouse	1·00	70
N3159	60ch. Black grouse	1·40	80
MSN3160	98×63 mm. 80ch. Daurian starling	1·70	1·50

1042 Map and Hands holding Text

1992. 20th Anniversary of Publication of North–South Korea Joint Agreement.

N3161	**1042** 1wn.50 multicoloured	2·75	2·10
MSN3162	112×76 mm. No. N3161×2	6·00	4·50

1043 *Bougainvillea spectabilis*

1992. Flowers. Multicoloured.

N3163	10ch. Type **1043**	15	10
N3164	20ch. *Ixora chinensis*	35	30
N3165	30ch. *Dendrobium taysuwie*	50	40
N3166	40ch. *Columnea gloriosa*	70	50
N3167	50ch. *Crinum*	95	70
N3168	60ch. *Ranunculus asiaticus*	1·10	80

1044 Venus, Earth, Mars and Satellite

1992. The Solar System. Multicoloured.

N3169	50ch. Type **1044**	95	70
N3170	50ch. Jupiter	95	70
N3171	50ch. Saturn	95	70
N3172	50ch. Uranus	95	70
N3173	50ch. Neptune and Pluto	95	70
MSN3174	90×71 mm. 80ch. Planet Earth	1·70	1·40

Nos. N3169/N3173 were issued together, *se-tenant*, forming a composite design.

1045 "470" Dinghy

1992. Riccione '92 Stamp Fair. Multicoloured.

N3175	10ch. Type **1045**	15	10
N3176	20ch. Sailboard	35	30
N3177	30ch. Sailing dinghy	50	40
N3178	40ch. Finn dinghy	70	50
N3179	50ch. 420 dinghy	95	70
N3180	60ch. Fair emblem	1·10	80

1046 Moreno Mannini (defender)

1992. Sampdoria, Italian Football Champion, 1991. Multicoloured.

N3181	20ch. Type **1046**	35	30
N3182	30ch. Gianluca Vialli (forward)	50	40
N3183	40ch. Pietro Vierchowod (defender)	70	50
N3184	50ch. Fausto Pari (defender)	95	70
N3185	60ch. Roberto Mancini (forward)	1·20	80
N3186	1wn. Paolo Mantovani (club president)	1·90	1·50
MSN3187	92×66 mm. 1wn. Vialli and Riccardo Garrone (president of club sponsor) (51×33 mm)	1·90	1·50

1047 Black-belts warming up

1992. Eighth World Taekwondo Championship, Pyongyang. Multicoloured.

N3188	10ch. Type **1047** (postage)	15	10
N3189	30ch. Roundhouse kick	50	40
N3190	50ch. High kick	95	70
N3191	70ch. Flying kick	1·30	95
N3192	90ch. Black-belt breaking tiles with fist	1·70	1·30
MSN3193	93×75 mm. 1wn.20 Flight scene (33×51 mm) (air)	2·30	1·70

1048 Common Toad (*Bufo bufo*)

1992. Frogs and Toads. Multicoloured.

N3194	40ch. Type **1048** (postage)	70	50
N3195	40ch. Moor frog (*Rana arvalis*)	70	50
N3196	40ch. *Rana chosenica*	70	50
N3197	70ch. Common pond frog (*Rana nigromaculata*)	1·40	95
N3198	70ch. Japanese tree toad (*Hyla japonica*)	1·40	95
N3199	70ch. *Rana coreana* (air)	1·40	95

1049 *Rhododendron mucronulatum*

1992. World Environment Day. Multicoloured.

N3200	10ch. Type **1049** (postage)	25	10
N3201	30ch. Barn swallow	50	40
N3202	40ch. *Stewartia koreana* (flower)	70	50
N3203	50ch. *Dictyoptera aurora* (beetle)	95	70
N3204	70ch. *Metasequoia glyptostroboides* (tree)	1·30	95
N3205	90ch. Chinese salamander	1·70	1·30
N3206	1wn. 20 *Ginkgo biloba* (tree) (air)	2·30	1·70
N3207	1wn. 40 Alpine bullhead	2·75	1·90

1050 Fin Whale (*Balaenoptera physalus*)

1992. Whales and Dolphins. Multicoloured.

N3208	50ch. Type **1050** (postage)	1·30	70
N3209	50ch. Common dolphin (*Delphinus delphis*)	1·30	70
N3210	50ch. Killer Whale (*Orcinus orca*)	1·30	70
N3211	50ch. Hump-backed whale (*Megaptera nodosa*)	1·30	70
N3212	50ch. Bottle-nosed whale (*Berardius bairdii*)	1·30	70
N3213	50ch. Sperm whale (*Physeter catadon*) (air)	1·30	70

1051 Mother and Chicks

1992. New Year. Roosters in various costumes. Multicoloured.

N3214	10ch. Type **1051**	15	10
N3215	20ch. Lady	35	30
N3216	30ch. Warrior	50	40
N3217	40ch. Courtier	70	50
N3218	50ch. Queen	95	70
N3219	60ch. King	1·10	80
MSN3220	112×80 mm. 1wn.20 Sultan	2·50	1·50

1052 Choe Chol Su (boxing)

1992. Gold Medal Winners at Barcelona Olympics. Multicoloured.

N3221	10ch. Type **1052**	15	10
N3222	20ch. Pae Kil Su (gymnastics)	35	30
N3223	50ch. Ri Hak Son (freestyle wrestling)	95	70
N3224	60ch. Kim Il (freestyle wrestling)	1·10	80
MSN3225	28×120 mm. Nos. N3221/N3224; 30ch. Flags of Spain and North Korea, flame, gold medal and archer; 40ch. Church of the Holy Family (Barcelona), games mascot and emblem	4·00	3·00

1053 Golden Mushroom

1993. Fungi. Multicoloured.

N3227	10ch. Type **1053**	15	10
N3228	20ch. Shaggy caps	35	30
N3229	30ch. *Ganoderma lucidum*	50	40
N3230	40ch. Brown mushroom	70	50
N3231	50ch. *Volvaria bombycina*	95	70
N3232	60ch. *Sarcodon aspratus*	1·10	80
MSN3233	59×60 mm. 1wn. Scarlet caterpillar fungus	2·20	1·50

1054 *Keumkangsania asiatica*

1993. Plants. Multicoloured.

N3234	10ch. Type **1054**	15	10
N3235	20ch. *Echinosophora koreensis*	35	30
N3236	30ch. *Abies koreana*	50	40
N3237	40ch. *Benzoin angustifolium*	70	50
N3238	50ch. *Abeliophyllum distichum*	95	70
N3239	60ch. *Abelia mosanensis*	1·10	80
MSN3240	73×93 mm. 1wn. *Pentactina rupicola* (27×38 mm)	1·90	1·50

1055 League Members and Flag

1993. Eighth League of Socialist Working Youth Congress. Multicoloured.

N3241	10ch. Type **1055**	15	10
N3242	40ch. Flame, League emblem and text	70	50

1056 Phophyong Revolutionary Site Tower and March Corps Emblem

1993. 70th Anniversary of 1000-ri Journey for Learning.

N3243	**1056** 10ch. multicoloured	20	10

1057 Tower of 'Juche' Idea and Grand Monument, Mt. Wangjae

1993. 60th Anniversary of Wangjaesan Meeting.

N3244	**1057** 5ch. multicoloured	10	10

1058 *Kimjomgil* (begonia)

1993. 51st Birthday if Kim Jong Il. Multicoloured.

N3245	10ch. Type **1058**	20	10
MSN3246	170×95 mm. 1wn. Kim Il Sung writing paean to Kim Jong Il on his 59th birthday (50×41 mm)	1·90	1·20

1059 Pilot Fish

1993. Fish. Multicoloured.

N3247	10ch. Type **1059**	15	10
N3248	20ch. Japanese stingray	35	30
N3249	30ch. Opah	50	40
N3250	40ch. Coelacanth	70	50
N3251	50ch. Moara grouper	1·00	70
MSN3252	96×70 mm. 1wn.20 Mako shark	2·75	1·50

1060/1064 *Spring on the Hill* (image scaled to 42% of original size)

1993. 18th-century Korean Painting.

N3253	**1060** 40ch. multicoloured	70	50
N3254	**1061** 40ch. multicoloured	70	50
N3255	**1062** 40ch. multicoloured	70	50
N3256	**1063** 40ch. multicoloured	70	50
N3257	**1064** 40ch. multicoloured	70	50

Nos. N3253/N3257 were issued together, *se-tenant*, forming the composite design illustrated.

1065 Violinist, Dancers and Emblem

1993. Spring Friendship Art Festival, Pyongyang.

N3258	**1065** 10ch. multicoloured	20	10

1066 Books

1993. 81st Birthday of Kim Li Sung and Publication of his Reminiscences *With the Country*. Multicoloured.

N3259	10ch. Type **1066**	20	10
MSN3260	140×105 mm. 1wn. Kim Il Sung writing (62×412 mm)	2·00	1·30

1067 Kwangbok Street

1993. Pyongyang. Multicoloured.

N3261	10ch. Type **1067**	15	10
N3262	20ch. Chollima Street	35	30
N3263	30ch. Munsu Street	50	40
N3264	40ch. Moranbong Street	70	50
N3265	50ch. Thongil Street	1·00	70
MSN3266	115×74 mm. 1wn. Changgwang street	1·90	1·50

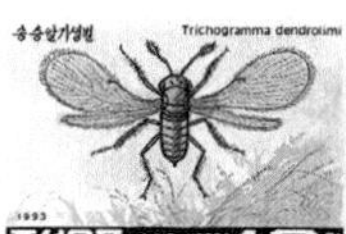
1068 *Trichogramma dendrolimi* (fly)

1993. Insects. Multicoloured.

N3267	10ch. Type **1068**	15	10
N3268	20ch. *Brachymeria obscurata* (fly)	35	30
N3269	30ch. *Metrioptera brachyptera* (cricket)	50	40
N3270	50ch. European field cricket	95	70
N3271	70ch. *Geocoris pallidipennis* (beetle)	1·40	95
N3272	90ch. *Cyphonony x dorsalis* (wasp) fighting spider	1·70	1·30

1069 Ri In Mo

1993. Return from Imprisonment of Ri in Mo (war correspondent). Multicoloured.

N3273	10ch. Type **1069**	20	10
MSN3274	110×80 mm. 1wn.20 Ri in Mo and flowers (47×35 mm)	2·50	1·50

1070 Footballers

1993. World Cup Football Championship, USA.

N3275	**1070** 10ch. multicoloured	15	10
N3276	- 20ch. multicoloured	35	30
N3277	- 30ch. multicoloured	50	40
N3278	- 50ch. multicoloured	1·00	70
N3279	- 70ch. multicoloured	1·40	95
N3280	- 90ch. multicoloured	1·70	1·30

Designs: 20ch. to 90ch. Various footballing scenes.

1071 Grey-headed Woodpecker

1993. Birds. Multicoloured.

N3281	10ch. Type **1071**	15	10
N3282	20ch. King bird of paradise	35	30
N3283	30ch. Lesser bird of paradise	50	40
N3284	40ch. Paradise whydah	70	50
N3285	50ch. Magnificent bird of paradise	1·00	70
N3286	60ch. Greater bird of paradise	1·10	80

Nos. N3283/N3284 also commemorate Indopex '93 international stamp exhibition, Surabaya.

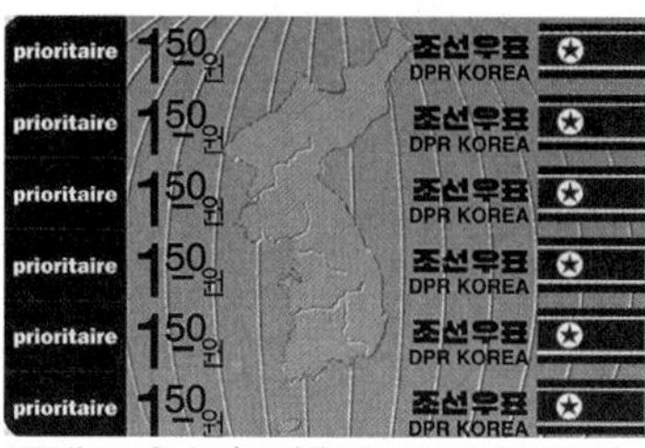

1072 Korean Peninsula and Flag (image scaled to 58% of original size)

1993. Self-adhesive. Roul.

N3287	**1072** 1wn.50 multicoloured	2·50	1·90

No. N3287 is for any one of the six stamps which together make up the design illustrated. They are peeled from a card backing.

1073 Kim Myong Nam (weightlifting, 1990)

1993. World Champions. Multicoloured.

N3293	10ch. Type **1073**	15	10
N3294	20ch. Kim Kwang Suk (gymnastics, 1991)	35	30
N3295	30ch. Pak Yong Sun (table tennis, 1975, 1977)	50	40
N3296	50ch. Kim Yong Ok (radio direction-finding, 1990)	1·00	70
N3297	70ch. Han Yun Ok (taekwondo, 1987, 1988, 1990)	1·40	95
N3298	90ch. Kim Yong Sik (free-style wrestling, 1986, 1989)	1·70	1·20

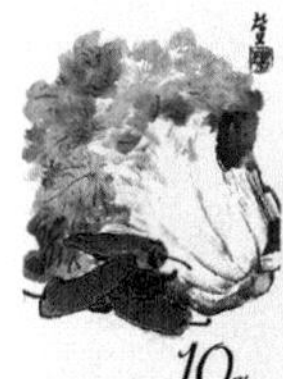
1074 Cabbage and Chilli Peppers

1993. Fruits and Vegetables. Multicoloured.

N3299	10ch. Type **1074**	15	10
N3300	20ch. Squirrels and horse chestnuts	35	30
N3301	30ch. Grapes and peach	50	40
N3302	40ch. Birds and persimmon	70	50
N3303	50ch. Tomatoes, aubergine and cherries	1·00	70
N3304	60ch. Radish, onion and garlic	1·10	80

1075 State Arms

1993

N3305	**1075** 10ch. red	20	10

1076 Soldiers and Civilians

1993. 40th Anniversary of Victory in Liberation War. Multicoloured.

N3306	10ch. Type **1076**	20	10
N3307	10ch. Officer and soldier	20	10
N3308	10ch. Guided missiles on low-loaders on parade	20	10
N3309	10ch. Anti-aircraft missiles on lorries on parade	20	10
N3310	10ch. Self-propelled missile launchers (tracked vehicles) on parade	20	10
N3311	10ch. Machine gun emplacement (30×48 mm)	20	10
N3312	10ch. Soldier holding flag (bronze statue) (30×48 mm)	20	10

N3313 40ch. Soldiers and flags ('Let us become Kim Jims and Ri Su Boks of the 90s') (30×48 mm) 80 50
N3314 10ch. Kim Il Sung at strategic policy meeting 20 10
N3315 10ch. Kim Il Sung directing battle for Height 1211 20 10
N3316 10ch. Kim Il Sung at munitions factory 20 10
N3317 10ch. Kim Il Sung with tank commanders 20 10
N3318 10ch. Kim Il Sung with triumphant soldiers 20 10
N3319 20ch. Kim Il Sung with artillery unit 40 30
N3320 20ch. Kim Il Sung encouraging machine gun crew 40 30
N3321 20ch. Kim Il Sung studying map of Second Front 40 30
N3322 20ch. Kim Il Sung with airmen 40 30
N3323 20ch. Musicians ('Alive is art of Korea') 40 30
MSN3324 Four sheets, (a) 150×90 mm; 80ch. Kim Il Sung beside tank (39×50 mm); (b) 131×75 mm. 80ch. Kim Il Sung and victory celebrations (33×51 mm); (c) 1wn. Kim Il Sung making speech (47×35 mm); (d) 190×93 mm. 1wn. Kim Il Sung taking salute (38×49 mm) 7·75 4·25

1077 Choe Yong Do

1993. National Reunification Prize Winners. Multicoloured.
N3325 10ch. Type **1077** 20 10
N3326 20ch. Kim Ku 40 30
N3327 30ch. Hong Myong Hui 60 40
N3328 40ch. Ryo Un Hyong 80 50
N3329 50ch. Kim Jong Thae 1·10 75
N3330 60ch. Kim Chaek 1·30 85

1078 *Robinia* sp.

1993. Taipei '93 International Stamp Exhibition, Taipeh. Multicoloured.
N3331 20ch. Type **1078** 40 30
N3332 30ch. *Hippeastrum* 60 40
MSN3333 75×105 mm. 1wn. Deer (33×51 mm) 2·10 1·60

1079 Newton

1993. 350th Birth Anniversary (1992) of Sir Isaac Newton (mathematician and scientist). Multicoloured.
N3334 10ch. Type **1079** 20 10
N3335 20ch. Apple tree and formula of law of gravitation 40 30
N3336 30ch. Satellite, reflecting telescope, dish aerial, globe and rocket 70 40
N3337 50ch. Formula of binomial theorem 1·10 75
N3338 70ch. Newton's works and statue 1·60 1·00

1080 King Tongmyong shooting Bow

1993. Restoration of King Tongmyong of Koguryo's Tomb. Multicoloured.
N3339 10ch. Type **1080** 20 10
N3340 20ch. King Tongmyong saluting crowd 40 30
N3341 30ch. Restoration monument 70 40
N3342 40ch. Temple of the Tomb of King Tongmyong (horiz) 90 60
N3343 50ch. Tomb (horiz) 1·10 75
MSN3344 95×105 mm. 80ch. Kim Il Sung visiting tomb (41×63 mm) 1·90 1·60

1081 First North Korea and Thailand Stamps

1993. Bangkok 1993 International stamp Exhibition, Thailand. Sheet 76×81 mm.
MSN3345 **1081** 1wn.20 multicoloured 2·50 2·10

1082 *Cyrtopodium andresoni*

1993. Orchids. Multicoloured.
N3346 10ch. Type **1082** 20 10
N3347 20ch. *Cattleya* 40 30
N3348 30ch. *Cattleya intermedia Oculata* 70 40
N3349 40ch. Potinaria *Maysedo godensia* 90 60
N3350 50ch. Kim Il Sung flower 1·10 75

모택동탄생100돐
毛泽东诞生100周年
1893-1993

(**1083**)

1993. Birth Centenary of Mao Tse-tung (1st issue). No. **MS**N3006 optd with T **1083**.
MSN3351 95×75 mm. 80ch. multicoloured 1·90 1·60

1084 Mao Tse-tung at Yanan, 1944

1993. Birth Centenary of Mao Tse-tung (2nd issue). Multicoloured.
N3352 10ch. Type **1084** 20 10
N3353 20ch. Seated portrait (Peking, 1960) 40 30
N3354 30ch. Casting a vote, 1953 70 40
N3355 40ch. With pupils at Shaoshan Secondary School, 1959 90 60
MSN3356 110×70 mm. 1wn. Mao Tse-tung and Pres. Kim Il Sung of North Korea (47×35 mm) 2·10 1·60
MSN3357 169×130 mm. Nos. N3352/**MS**N3356 25ch. Mao Tse-tung proclaiming foundation of Chinese People's Republic, 1949 (47×35 mm); 25ch. Mao Tse-tung with son Mao An-ying (47×35 mm) 5·25 4·25

1085 Phungsan

1994. New Year. Dogs. Multicoloured.
N3358 10ch. Type **1085** 20 10
N3359 20ch. Yorkshire terriers 40 30
N3360 30ch. Gordon setter 70 40
N3361 40ch. Pomeranian 80 60
N3362 50ch. Spaniel with pups 1·20 85
MSN3363 80×66 mm. 1wn. Pointer 2·10 1·60

1086 Purple Hyosong Flower

1994. 52nd Birthday of Kim Jong Il (2nd issue). Multicoloured.
N3364 10ch. Type **1086** 20 10
N3365 40ch. Yellow hyosong flower 90 60
MSN3366 156×82 mm. 1wn. Kim Il Sung and Kim Jong surrounded by flowers (44×53 mm) 2·10 1·60

1087 Red and Black Dragon-eyed

1994. Goldfish. Multicoloured.
N3367 10ch. Type **1087** 20 10
N3368 30ch. Red and white bubble-eyed 70 40
N3369 50ch. Red and white veil-tailed wenyu 1·10 75
N3370 70ch. Red and white fringe-tailed 1·60 1·00

1088 Crowd with Banners

1994. 20th Anniversary of Publication of *Programme for Modelling the Whole Society on the Juche Idea* by Kim Jong Il. Multicoloured.
N3371 20ch. Type **1088** 25 10
MSN3372 145×95 mm. 1wn.20 Kim Jong Il making speech (41×63 mm) 2·50 1·60

1089 Wheat, Banner and Woman writing

1994. 30th Anniversary of Publication of *Theses on the Socialist Rural Question in Our Country* by Kim Il Sung. Multicoloured.
N3373 10ch. Type **1089** 20 10
N3374 10ch. Electricity generating systems and pylon 20 10
N3375 10ch. Lush fields, grain and tractor 20 10
N3376 40ch. Modern housing, books, food crops and laboratory technician 90 60
N3377 40ch. Revellers 90 60
MSN3378 Two sheets, each 134×111 mm. (a) 1wn. Kimll Sung in field (38×59 mm); (b) 1wn. Peasants with Kim Il Sung (41×63 mm) 4·50 3·00

1090 *Mangyongbong-92* (ferry)

1994. Ships. Multicoloured.
N3379 20ch. Type **1090** 40 30
N3380 30ch. *Osandok* (freighter) 80 40
N3381 40ch. *Ryongaksan* (stern trawler) 90 60
N3382 50ch. Stern trawler 1·10 75
MSN3383 131×112 mm. Nos. N3379/N3382; 80ch.×2 *Maekjon-1* (passenger ship) 6·25 5·25

1091 National Flag

1994
N3384 **1091** 10ch. red and blue 25 10

1092 Birthplace and Magnolia (National Flower)

1994. 82nd Birthday of Kim Il Sung. Multicoloured.
N3385 10ch. Type **1092** 20 10
N3386 40ch. Birthplace, Manyongdae, and Kim Il Sung flower 90 60
MSN3387 162×103 mm. 40ch.×5 Composite design of Lake Chon (crater lake of Mt. Paektu) and score of *Song of General Kim Il Sung* 4·50 3·00

1093 *Chrysosplenium sphaerospermum*

1994. Alpine Plants on Mt. Paekdu. Multicoloured.
N3388 10ch. Type **1093** 20 10
N3389 20ch. *Campanula cephalotes* 40 30
N3390 40ch. *Trollius macropetalus* 90 60
N3391 40ch. *Gentiana algida* 90 60
N3392 50ch. *Sedum kamtschaticum* 1·10 75
MSN3393 78×64 mm. 1wn. *Dianthus repens* 2·10 1·60

1094 National Olympic Committee Emblem

1994. Centenary of International Olympic Committee. Multicoloured.
N3394 10ch. Type **1094** 20 10
N3395 20ch. Pierre de Coubertin (founder) 40 30
N3396 30ch. Olympic flag and flame 70 40
N3397 50ch. Emblem of Centennial Olympic Congress, Paris 1·10 75
MSN3398 Two sheets, each 75×105 mm. (a) 1wn. Torch carrier; (b) 1wn. Juan Antonio Samaranch (IOC President) and entrance headquarters 4·50 3·75

1095 Red Cross Launch ('Relief on the Sea')

1994. 75th Anniversary of International Red Cross and Red Crescent Federation. Multicoloured.
N3399 10ch. Electric tram, pedestrians on footbridge and traffic lights ('Prevention of Traffic Accident') 20 10
N3400 20ch. Type **1095** 40 30
N3401 30ch. Planting tree ('Protection of Environment') 70 40
N3402 40ch. Dam ('Prevention of Drought Damage') 90 60

1994. No. N3287 surch **160** in circle.
N3403 **1072** 1wn.60 on 1wn.50 multicoloured 4·50 3·75

1097 Northern Fur Seal

1994. Marine Mammals. Multicoloured.

N3404 10ch. Type **1097** 20 10
N3405 40ch. Southern elephant seal 90 60
N3406 60ch. Southern sealion 1·40 95
MSN3407 Two sheets, (a) 80×130 mm. 20ch. Californian sealion; 30ch. Ringed seal; 50ch. Walrus. (b) 80×88nn. 1wn. Harp seal 4·75 4·25

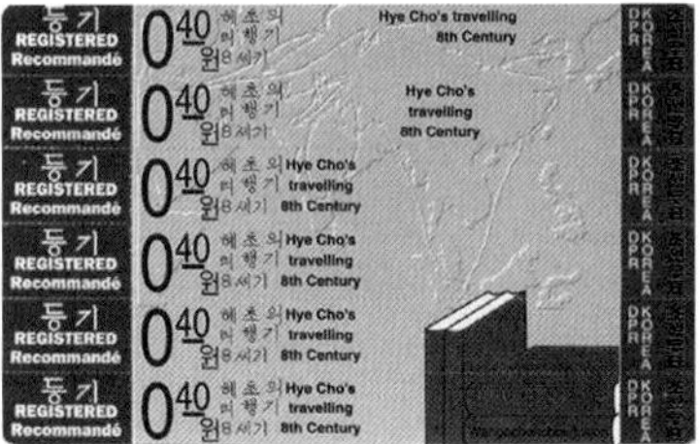
1098 Map of Asia and Books (image scaled to 57% of original size)

1994. 8th-century Travels of Hye Cho. Self-adhesive. Roul.

N3408 **1098** 40ch. multicoloured 70 50

No. N3408 is for any one of the six stamps which together make up the design illustrated. They are peeled from a card backing.

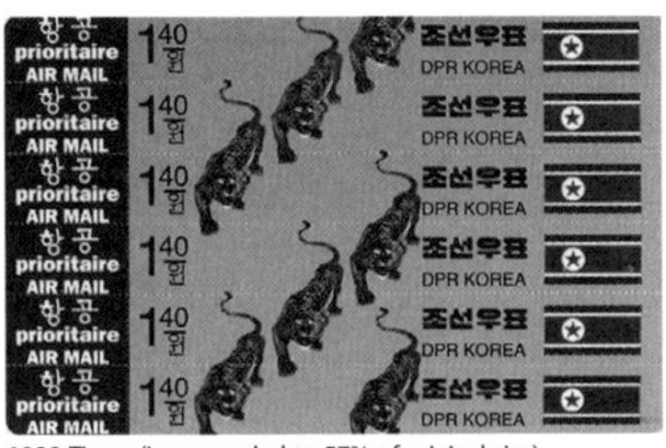
1099 Tigers (image scaled to 57% of original size)

1994. Self-adhesive. Roul.

N3409 **1099** 1wn.40 multicoloured 2·50 2·10

No. N3409 is for any one of the six stamps which together make up the design illustrated. They are peeled from a card backing.

1100 Kim Jong Il on Mt. Paektu

1994. 30th Anniversary of Kim Jong Il's Leadership of Korean Workers' Party. Two Sheets containing multicoloured designs as T **1100** showing various scenes featuring Kim Jong Il.

MSN3410 Two sheets. (a) 148×182 mm. 40ch. Type **1100**; 40ch With engineers surveying bay; 40ch. Visiting the set of *Star of Korea* (film); 40ch. Visiting Chongryu Restaurant; 40ch. Reviewing tank corps; 40k. Shaking hands with international figures. (b) 145×95 mm. 1wn. At desk (41×63 mm) 7·50 6·25

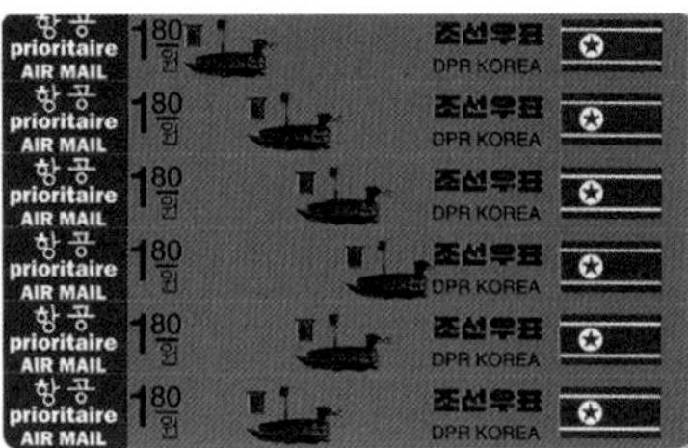
1101 'Turtle' Ships (image scaled to 57% of original size)

1994. Self-adhesive. Roul.

N3411 **1101** 1wn.80 multicoloured 3·00 2·50

No. N3411 is for any one of the six stamps which together make up the design illustrated. They are peeled from a card backing.

1102 Striped Bonnet

1994. Molluscs. Multicoloured.

N3412 30ch. Type **1102** 70 40
N3413 40ch. Equilateral venus 95 60
MSN3414 103×75 mm. 1wm.20 Bladder moon 2·75 2·10
MSN3415 Two sheets, each 127×73 mm. (a) Nos. N3413/**MS**N3414; 10ch. *Cardium muticum* (cockle). (b) Nos. N3412 and **MS**N3414; 20ch. *Buccinum bayani* (whelk) 7·25 6·25

1103 Trapeze

1994. Circus Acrobatics. Multicoloured.

N3416 10ch. Type **1103** 20 10
N3417 20ch. Reino (Swedish acrobat) performing rope dance 40 30
N3418 30ch. Seesaw performer 70 40
N3419 40ch. Unicycle juggler 90 60

1104 Korean Script and '100'

1994. Birth Centenary of Kim Hyong Jik (father of Kim Il Sung). Multicoloured.

N3420 10c. Type **1104** 80 10
MSN3421 61×85 mm. 1wn. Kim Hyong Jik (30×48 mm) 2·10 1·60

1105 Jon Pong Jun and Battle Scene

1994. Centenary of Kabo Peasant War.

N3422 **1105** 10ch. multicoloured 25 10

1106 Inoue Shuhachi

1994. Award of First International Kim Il Sung Prize to Inoue Shuhachi (Director Genaral to 'Juche' Idea International Institute). Sheet 103×78 mm.

MSN3423 **1106** 1wn.20 multicoloured 2·50 1·60

1107 Workers and Banner

1994. Revolutionary Economic Strategy.

N3424 **1107** 10ch. multicoloured 25 10

1108 Onsong Fish

1994. Fossils. Multicoloured.

N3425 40ch. Type **1108** 90 60
N3426 40ch. Metasequoia 90 60
N3427 40ch. Mammoth teeth 90 60
N3428 80ch. Archaeopteryx 1·80 1·20

1109 *Acorus calamus*

1994. Medicinal Plants. Multicoloured.

N3429 20ch. Type **1109** 40 30
N3430 30ch. *Arctium lappa* 70 40
MSN3431 Two sheet. (a) 133×86 mm. 80ch. *Lilium lancifolium*; 80ch. *Codonopsis lanceolata*. (b) 56×83 mm. 1wn. Ginseng (vert) 5·50 4·25

1110 Ribbon Exercise

1994. Callisthenics. Multicoloured.

N3432 10ch. Type **1110** 20 10
N3433 20ch. Ball exercise 40 30
N3434 30ch. Hoop exercise 70 40
N3435 40ch. Ribbon exercise (different) 90 60
N3436 50ch. Club exercise 1·10 75

1111 Chou En-lai at Tianjun, 1919

1994. 96th Birth Anniversary of Chou En-lai (Chinese statesman). Multicoloured.

N3437 10ch. Type **1111** 20 10
N3438 20ch. Arrival in Northern Shanxi from Long March 40 30
N3439 30ch. At Conference of Asian and African Countries, Bandung, Indonesia, 1955 70 40
N3440 40ch. Surrounded by children in Wulumuqi, Xinjiang Province 90 60
MSN3441 106×70 mm. 80ch. green, silver and black (Kim Il Sung proposing to Chou En-li during Korean visit, 1970) (46½×35 mm) 1·90 1·60
MSN3442 Two sheets, each 144×110 mm. (a) Nos. N3440/**MS**N3441; 20ch. Leading Nanchang Uprising, 1927 (46½×35 mm). (b) N3438/N3439 and **MS**3441; 20ch. At airport on return from foreign visit (46½×35 mm) 6·75 5·25

1113 Kim Il Sung as Youth, 1927

1994. Kim Il Sung Commemoration (1st issue). (a) As T **1113**. Each red, gold and black.

N3444 40ch. Type **1113** 90 60
N3445 40ch. Kim Il Sung and Kim Jong Suk 90 60
N3446 40ch. Kim Il Sung as young man 90 60

(b) Horiz designs as T **1115**. Each purple, gold and black.

N3447 40ch. Kim Il Sung making speech, Pyongyang, 1945 90 60
N3448 40ch. Kim Il Sung sitting at desk 90 60
N3449 40ch. Kim Il Sung at microphone 90 60

(c) Miniature sheet.

MSN3450 78×106 mm. 1wn. Kim Il Sung smiling (35×46 mm) 2·10 1·60

See also Nos. N3458/**MS**N3464.

1114 Player No. 4

1994. World Cup Football Championship, USA. Multicoloured.

N3451 10ch. Type **1114** 20 10
N3452 20ch. Player No. 5 40 30
N3453 30ch. Player No. 6 70 40
N3454 40ch. Player No. 7 90 60
N3455 1wn. Player No. 8 2·10 1·60
N3456 1wn.50 Player No. 9 3·50 2·30
MSN3457 Two sheets. (a) 79×112 mm. 2wn.50 Stadium, players and trophy (41×48 mm); (b) 200×223 mm. 1wn.×6, each depicting player, trophy and different view 18·00 11·50

1115 Kim Il Sung making Radio Broadcast, 1950

1994. Kim Il Sung Commemoration (2nd issue). (a) Each green, gold and black.

N3458 40ch. Type **1115** 90 60
N3459 40ch. Kim Il Sung with four soldiers, 1951 90 60
N3460 40ch. Kim Il Sung and crowd of soldiers, 1953 90 60

(b) Multicoloured (N3463) or lilac, gold and black (others).

N3461 40ch. Kim Il Sung with workers at Chongjin Steel Plant, 1959 90 60
N3462 40ch. Kim Il Sung on Onchon Plain 90 60
N3463 40ch. Kim Il Sung at desk using telephone 90 60

(c) Miniature sheet.

MSN3464 78×106 mm. 1wn. Kim Il Sung and Kim Jong Il (35×47 mm) 2·10 1·60

1116 National Flags and Flowers

1994. Korean–Chinese Friendship. Multicoloured.

N3465 10ch. Type **1116** 90 60
MSN3466 79×100 mm. 1wm.20 black, grey and gold (Mao Tse-tung and Kim Il Sung) (53×44 mm) 2·50 2·10

1117 Ri Myon Sang and Score of *Snow Falls*

1994. Composers. Multicoloured.

N3467 50ch. Type **1117** 1·10 75
N3468 50ch. Pak Han Kyu and score of *Nobody Knows* 1·10 75
N3469 50ch. Ludwig van Beethoven and score of *piano sonata No. 14* 1·10 75
N3470 50ch. Wolfgang Amadeus Mozart and score of *symphony No. 39* 1·10 75

1118 National Emblem

1994

N3471 **1118** 1wn. green 2·40 1·60
N3472 **1118** 3wn. brown 6·25 4·75

1119 P. Wiberg (Alpine combined skiing)

1994. Winter Olympic Games, Lillehammer, Gold Medal Winners. Multicoloured.

N3473 10ch. Type **1119** 20 10
N3474 20ch. D. Compagnoni (slalom) 40 30
N3475 30ch. O. Baiul (figure skating) 70 40
N3476 40ch. D. Jansen (speed skating) 90 60
N3477 1wn. L. Yegorova (cross-country sking) 2·10 1·60

N3478 1wn.50 B. Blair (speed skating) 3·25 2·30

MSN3479 Seven sheets, each 102×75 mm (a/f) or 131×895 mm (g). (a) 1wn. Norwegian skiing team and B. Daehile (Alpine combine); (b) 1wn. Gordeyeva and Grinkov (pairs figure skating); (c) 1wn. G. Hackl (luge); (e) 1wn. J. Weissflog (ski jumping); (f) 1wn. Kono, Ogiwara and Abe (cross-country skiing); (g.) 2wn.50 T. Moe (downhill) (50×35 mm) 18·00 11·50

1120 Pig Couple

1995. New Year. Year of the Pig. Multicoloured.

N3480 20ch. Type **1120** 40 30

N3481 40ch. Pigs carrying bucket and spade 90 60

MSN3482 40ch. Two sheets, each 72×70 mm. (a) 1wn. Adult pig greeting young pigs; (b) 1wn. Pig couple carrying pumpkin 4·75 4·25

See also No. **MS**3533.

1121 Pison Waterfalls, Mt. Myohyang

1995. 20th Anniversary of World Tourism Organisation. Multicoloured.

N3483 30ch. Tower of 'Juche' Idea, Pyongyang 70 40

N3484 30ch. Type **1121** 70 40

N3485 30ch. Myogilsang (cliff-face carving of Buddha), Mt. Kumgang 70 40

1122 Mangyongdae, Badaogou and Badge

1995. 70th Anniversary of 1000-ri (250 mile) Journey by Kim Il Sung to Restore Fatherland.

N3486 **1122** 40ch. multicoloured 90 60

1123 Monument bearing 50th Birthday Ode, Mt. Paekdu

1995. 53rd Birthday of Kim Jung Il. Multicoloured.

N3487 10ch. Type **1123** 20 10

MSN3488 Three sheets. (a) 75×90 mm. 20ch. Kim Il Sung and Kim Jong Il (horiz); 80ch, Kim Jong Il on balcony overlooking West Sea Barrage (horiz); (b) 90×75 mm. 40ch. Kim Jong Il in public park; 50ch. Kim Jong Il before memorial in Taesongsan Revolutionary Martyrs' Cemetery; (c) 96×75 mm. 1wn. Kim Jong Il on visit to Tyongsong Machine Complex, 1984 (31×50 mm) 6·25 5·25

1124 Reconstruction Monument

1995. Completion of Reconstruction of King Tangun's Tomb. Multicoloured.

N3489 10ch. Type **1124** 20 10

N3490 30ch. Bronze dagger on plinth 70 45

N3491 50ch. Monument inscribed with exploits of King Tangun 1·10 75

N3492 70ch. Gateway (horiz) 1·60 1·10

MSN3493 103×60 mm. 1wn.40 King Tangun 3·75 2·50

1125 Jamaedo Lighthouse

1995. Lighthouses. Multicoloured.

N3494 20ch. Type **1125** 40 20

N3495 1wn. Phido Lighthouse, West Sea Barrage 2·50 1·20

1126 Cracked Green Russula

1995. Fungi. Multicoloured.

N3496 20ch. Type **1126** 40 20

N3497 30ch. *Russula atropurpurea* 70 25

MSN3498 68×90 mm. 1wm. *Amanita caesarea* (29×41 mm) 2·10 1·50

1127 Couple planting Tree

1995. Tree Planting Day.

N3499 **1127** 10ch. multicoloured 20 10

1128 Birthplace, Mangyongdae

1995. 83rd Anniversary of Birth of Kim Il Sung (1912–1994)

N3500 10ch. Type **1128** 20 10

N3501 40ch. multicoloured 90 60

MSN3502 84×80 mm. 50ch. purple, gold and black 2·20 1·50

1129 Deng Xiaoping waving

1995. 20th Anniversary of Kim Il Sung's Visit to China. Multicoloured.

N3503 10ch. Type **1129** 20 10

N3504 20ch. Deng Xiaoping of China sitting in armchair (vert) 40 20

MSN3505 84×80 mm. 50ch. Kim Il Sung and Deng Xiaoping (60×38 mm) 1·10 65

1130 Venue

1995. 40th Anniversary of Asian–African Conference, Bandung.

N3506 **1130** 10ch. black, buff and red 20 10

N3507 - 50ch. brown, gold and black 1·10 45

MSN3508 88×85 mm. 1wn. brown and black 2·10 1·50

Designs: 50ch. Kim Il Sung receiving honorary Doctorate at Indonesia University. 1wn. Kim Il Sung and Kim Jong Il at conference tenth anniversary ceremony, Djakarta.

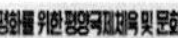

1131 Emblem

1995. International Sports and Cultural Festival for Peace, Pyongyang. Multicoloured.

N3509 20ch. Type **1131** 40 20

N3510 40ch. Dancer 90 40

N3511 40ch. Inoki Kanji (leader of Sports Peace Party of Japan) 90 40

MSN3512 87×70 mm. 1wn. Rikidozan (wrestler) 2·10 1·50

1132 Amethyst

1995. Minerals.

N3513 **1132** 20ch. multicoloured 40 20

1133 Eurasian Tree Sparrow

1995. White Animals. Multicoloured.

N3514 40ch. Type **1133** 90 40

N3515 40ch. *Stichopus japonicus* (sea slug) 90 40

1134 Ostrea

1995. Fossils. Multicoloured.

N3516 50ch. Type **1134** 1·10 45

N3517 1wn. Cladophlebis (fern) 2·10 1·00

1135 Chess

1995. Traditional Games. Multicoloured.

N3518 30ch. Type **1135** 70 25

N3519 60ch. Taekwondo 1·30 60

N3520 70ch. Yut 1·60 65

1136 National Flag and Korean Hall, Tokyo

1995. 40th Anniversary of Association of Koreans in Japan.

N3521 **1136** 1wn. multicoloured 2·10 1·00

1137 Weightlifting

1995. Olympic Games, Atlanta (1996). Multicoloured.

N3522 50ch. Type **1137** 1·10 45

N3523 50ch. Boxing 1·10 45

MSN3524 62×78 mm. 1wn. Clay-pigeon shooting 2·10 1·50

1138 *Russula citrina*

1995. Fungi. Multicoloured.

N3525 40ch. Type **1138** 90 40

N3526 60ch. Black trumpets 1·30 60

N3527 80ch. Shaggy caps 1·80 80

1139 Kim Il Sung greeting President Mugabe of Zimbabwe

1995. First Death Anniversary of Kim Il Sung. Four sheets containing designs as T **1139** inscriptions in black, frames in gold, centre colour listed.

MSN3528 Four sheets (a) 109×85 mm. 10ch. blue; 70ch. sepia. (b) 130×66 mm. 20ch. blue; 50ch. chocolate. (c) 129×66 mm. 30ch. blue; 40ch. purple. (d) 80×107 mm. 1wn. plum 7·00 4·75

Designs: Vert—70ch. With King Norodom Sihanouk of Cambodia. Horiz—Kim Il Sung being awarded title of Honorary Doctor of Algeria University, 1975; 30ch. With President Ho Chi Minh of Vietnam; 40ch. Greeting Che Cuevara; 50ch. With President Fidel Castro of Cuba; 1wm. Giving speech.

1140 Mt. Paektu and Revolutionaries

1995. 50th Anniversary of Liberation. Multicoloured.

N3529 10ch. Type **1140** 20 10

N3530 30ch. Map of Korea and family 70 25

N3531 60ch. Medal 1·30 60

MSN3532 Two sheets, each 120×110 mm. (a) 2×20ch. Revolutionary and crowd with banners; (b) No. N3530×2; 2×40ch. Revolutionaries 6·00 4·25

1995. Singapore '95 International Stamp Exibition. Sheet 139×90 mm. Multicoloured.

MSN3533 Nos. N3480/N3481, each×2 2·40 1·70

1141 Markswoman

1995. First Military World Games, Rome.

N3534 **1141** 40ch. multicoloured 90 40

1142 Kim Il Sung With Prime Minister Chou En-Lai of China, 1970

1995. Korean–Chinese Friendship, Three sheets containing designs as T **1142** inscriptions in black, frames in gold, centre colour listed below.

MSN3535 Three sheets. (a) 50ch. purple (Type **1142**); 50ch. green (With Deng Ying-chao of China, 1979). (b) 85×100 mm. 80ch. green (Greeting Mao Tse-tung of China, 1958) (vert). (c) 85×100 mm. 80ch. purple (In Hamburg with Prime Minister Chou En-lai of China) (vert) 5·75 4·00

1143 Emblem and Banner

1995. 50th Anniversary of Korean Workers' Party. Multicoloured.

N3536 10ch. Type **1143**	20	10
N3537 20ch. Statue of worker, peasant and intellectual	40	20
N3538 30ch. Party monument	70	25
MSN3539 108×75 mm. 1wn. Kim Il Sung (founder) (38×50 mm)	2·10	1·50

1144 Arch of Triumph, Pyongyang

1995. 50th Anniversary of Kim Il Sung's Return to Homeland.

N3540 **1144** 10ch. multicoloured	20	10

1145 Tuna

1995. Designs as T **1145**. Each brown and black. (a) Fish.

N3541 40ch. Type **1145**	95	40
N3542 50ch. Pennant coralfish (with two bands)	1·20	45
N3543 50ch. Needlefish	1·20	45
N3544 60ch. Seascorpion	1·40	60
N3545 5wn. Emperor angelfish	11·50	5·00

(b) Buildings on Kwangbok Street, Pyongyang.

N3546 60ch. Circus	1·40	65
N3547 70ch. Flats	1·60	65
N3548 80ch. Ryanggang Hotel	1·80	80
N3549 90ch. Tower apartment block (vert)	1·90	85
N3550 1wn. Sosan Hotel (vert)	2·10	1·00

(c) Machines.

N3551 10ch. Kamsusan tipper truck	30	10
N3552 20ch. Bulldozer	60	20
N3553 30ch. Excavator	80	25
N3554 40ch. Earth mover (vert)	1·30	40
N3555 10wn. Chollima 80 tractor (vert)	21·00	10·00

(d) Animals.

N3556 30ch. Giraffe (vert)	70	25
N3557 40ch. Ostrich (vert)	90	40
N3558 60ch. Bluebuck (vert)	1·30	60
N3559 70ch. Bactrian camel	1·60	65
N3560 3wn. Indian rhinoceros	6·25	3·00

(e) Sculptures of Children.

N3561 30ch. Boy holding bird (vert)	70	25
N3562 40ch. Boy with goose (vert)	90	40
N3563 60ch. Girl with geese (vert)	1·30	60
N3564 70ch. Boy and girl with football (vert)	1·60	75
N3565 2wn. Boy and girl arguing over football (vert)	4·50	2·00

1146 Kim Hyong Gwon

1995. 90th Birth Anniversary of Hyong Gwon (uncle of Kim Il Sung). Sheet 90×70 mm.

MSN3566 **1146** 1wn. black and gold	2·10	1·50

1147 Guinea Pig

1996. Rodents. Multicoloured.

N3567 20ch. Type **1147**	40	20
N3568 20ch. Squirrel	40	20
N3569 30ch. White rat	70	25

1148 Emblem, Badge and Flag

1996. 50th Anniversary of League of Socialist Working Youth.

N3570 **1148** 10ch. multicoloured	20	10

1149 Restoration Mounument

1996. Reconstruction of Tomb of King Wanggon. Multicoloured.

N3571 30ch. Type **1149**	70	25
N3572 40ch. Entrance gate	90	40
N3573 50ch. Tomb	1·10	45

1150 Teng Li-Chuang (singer)

1996. Sheet 130×86 mm.

MSN3574 **1150** 40ch. multicoloured	1·20	60

1151 Kim Song Sung

1996. Third Asian Games, Harbin, China (1st issue). Speed Skaters. Sheet 130×81 containing T **1151** and similar vert design. Multicoloured.

MSN3575 30ch. Type **1551**; 30ch. Ye Qiaobo	1·50	1·00

See also No. **MS**N3611.

1152 Jong Il Peak and Kim Jong Il Flower

1996. 54th Birthday of Kim Jong Il. Multicoloured.

N3576 10ch. Type **1152**	20	10
MSN3577 96×78 mm. 80ch. Kim Jong Il and servicemen in snow (35×78 mm)	1·80	1·20

1153 Pairs Skating

1996. Fifth Paektusan Prize Figure Skating Championships. Multicoloured.

N3578 10ch. Type **1153**	20	10
N3579 20ch. Pairs skating (different)	40	20
N3580 30ch. Pairs skating (different)	70	25
N3581 50ch. Women's individual skating	1·10	45
MSN3582 100×116 mm. No. N3578/N3581.	2·40	1·70

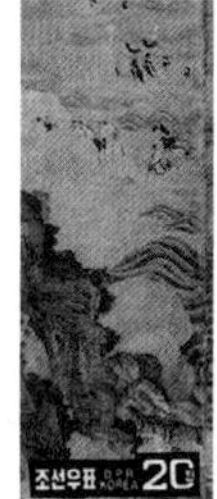
1154 Left-hand detail

1996. *Folk Tale* (screen painting) by Ryu Suk. Sheet 206×84 mm containing T **1154** and similar vert designs. Multicoloured.

MSN3583 8×20ch. Composite design of the painting	3·50	2·40

1155 Farm Worker

1996. 50th Anniversary of Agrarian Reform Law.

N3584 **1155** 10ch. multicoloured	20	10

1156 1946 20ch. Stamp and Tower of Juche Idea

1996. 50th Anniversary of First North Korean Stamps.

N3585 **1156** 1wn. multicoloured	2·10	1·00

1157 Yangzhou, China

1996. Centenary of founding of Chinese Imperial Post. Two sheets each 108×90 mm containing T **1157** or similar horiz designs. Multicoloured.

MSN3586 Two sheets (a) 50ch. Type **1157**; (b) 50ch. Taihu Lake, Jiangsu	4·50	3·00

1158 Birthplace, Mangyongdae

1996. 83rd Birthday of Kim Il Sung. Multicoloured.

N3587 10ch. Type **1158**	20	10
MSN3588 105×115 mm. 1wn. *Eternal Image* (portrait of Kim Il Sung) (41×62 mm)	2·10	1·50

1159 Gateway

1996. China '96 Asian International Stamp Exhibition, Peking. Landmarks in Zhejiang. Multicoloured.

N3589 10ch. Type **1159**	20	10
N3590 10ch. Haiyin Pool	20	10
MSN3591 105×80 mm. Pantuo Stone (60×38 mm)	1·30	85

1160 Hopscotch

1996. Children's Games. Multicoloured.

N3592 20ch. Type **1160**	40	20
N3593 40ch. Shuttlecock	90	40
N3594 50ch. Sledging	1·10	45

1161 Association Pamphlets

1996. 60th Anniversary of Association for Restoration of the Fatherland.

N3595 **1161** 10ch. multicoloured	20	10

1162 Ri Po Ik

1996. 120th Birth Anniversary of Ri Po Ik (grandmother of Kim Il Sung). Sheet 80×90 mm.

MSN3596 **1162** 1wn. grey, black and gold	2·10	1·50

1163 Arctic Fox

1996. Polar Animals. Multicoloured.

N3597 50ch. Type **1163**	1·20	50
N3598 50ch. Polar bear	1·20	50
N3599 50ch. Emperor penguins	1·20	50
N3600 50ch. Leopard seals	1·20	50

1164 Boy Saluting

1996. 50th Anniversary of Korean Children's Union. Multicoloured.

N3601 10ch. Type **1164**	20	10
MSN3602 83×98 mm. 1wn. *There's Nothing to envy in the World* (painting of Kim Il Sung with Union members) (33×51 mm)	2·10	1·50

1165 Steam Locomotive

1996. Railway Locomotives. Multicoloured.

N3603 50ch. Type **1165**	1·20	50
N3604 50ch. Electric locomotive (green livery)	1·20	50
N3605 50ch. Steam locomotive (facing right)	1·20	50
N3606 50ch. Diesel locomotive (red and yellow livery)	1·20	50

1166 Kim Chol Ju

1996. 80th Birth Anniversary of Kim Chol Ju (brother of Kim Il Sung). Sheet 58×77 mm.

MSN3607 **1166** 1wn.50 brown, gold black	3·75	2·50

1167 Open Book and Characters

1996. 760th Anniversary of Publication of *Complete Collection of Buddhist Scriptures printed from 80,000 Wooden Blocks.*

N3608 **1167** 40ch. multicoloured 95 45

1168 Worker using Microphone

1996. 50th Anniversary of Labour Law.

N3609 **1168** 50ch. multicoloured 30 15

1169 Eastern Broad-billed Roller

1996. Birds. (1st series). 110×92 mm containing T **1169** and similar horiz designs. Multicoloured.

MSN3610 Type **1169**; 40ch. Yellow-rumped flycatcher; 50ch. European cuckoo 3·25 2·30

See also Nos. **MS**N3622.

1170 Ye Qiaboo

1996. Third Asian Winter Games, Harbin, China (2nd issue). As No. **MS**N3575 but with right hand-stamp changed.

MSN3611 30ch. Type **1151**; 30ch. Type **1170** 1·50 1·10

1171 Kumsusan Memorial Palace

1996. Second Death Anniversary of Kim Il Sung. Multicoloured.

N3612 10ch. Type **1171** 20 10

MSN3613 Three sheets. (a) 116×71 mm. 1wn. Statue of Kim Il Sung, Kumsusan Memorial Palace (29×41 mm). (b) 80×106 mm. 1wn. Bars of *The Leader will always be with Us* (44×53 mm). (c) 115×105 mm. 1wn. Crowd visiting statue of Kim Il Sung, Manus Hill (34×51 mm) Set of 3 sheets 7·00 5·00

1172 Kim Il Sung meeting Jiang Zemin of China, 1991

1996. 35th Anniversary of Korean–Chinese Treaty for Friendship, Co-operation and Mutual Assistance.

N3614 **1172** 10ch. brown, gold and black 20 10

N3615 - 10ch. green, gold and black 20 10

MSN3616 70×80 mm. 80ch. ultramarine, gold and black 1·90 1·40

Designs: Vert—10ch. (No. N3615) Kim Il Sung meeting President Mao Zedong of China, 1954. Horiz—80ch. Kim Il Sung meeting Deng Xiaoping of China, 1982.

1173 Football and Ancient Greek Athletes

1996. Centenary of Modern Olympic Games and Olympic Games, Atlanta. Multicoloured.

N3617 50ch. Type **1173** 1·30 55

N3618 50ch. Tennis, Olympic Anthem and 1896 5l. Greek stamp 1·30 55

N3619 50ch. Throwing the hammer and advertisement poster for first modern olympics 1·30 55

N3620 50ch. Baseball and Olympic stadium, Atlanta 1·30 55

1174 Couple

1996. 50th Anniversary of Sex Equality Laws.

N3621 **1174** 10ch. multicoloured 35 15

1996. Birds (2nd series). Sheet 110×92 mm containing horiz design as T **1169**. Multicoloured.

MSN3622 10ch. crested shelduck; 40ch. Demoiselle crane; 50c. Mute Swan 3·25 2·30

1175 State Arms and Symbols of Industry and Communications

1996. 50th Anniversary of Nationalisation of Industries.

N3623 **1175** 10ch. bistre and brown 30 15

1176 Boy with Ball

1996. 50th Anniversary of UNICEF. Multicoloured.

N3624 10ch. Type **1176** 25 10

N3625 20ch. Boy with building blocks 45 25

N3626 50ch. Boy eating melon 1·30 55

N3627 60ch. Girl playing accordion 1·50 70

1177 Pae Kil Su (men's pommel) (North Korea)

1996. First Asian Gymnastics Championships, Changsha, China. Sheet 167×127 mm containing T **1177** and similar vert designs. Multicoloured.

MSN3628 15ch. Type **1177**; 15ch. Li Jing (China); 15ch. Chen Cui Ting on rings (China); 15ch. Kim Kwang Suk (asymmetrical bars) (N. Korea) 1·60 1·10

1178 University Buildings, Pyongyang

1996. 50th Anniversary of Kim Il Sung University.

N3629 **1178** 10ch. multicoloured 25 10

1179 Tiger

1996. World Conservation Union Congress, Montreal, Canada. Multicoloured.

N3630 50ch. Type **1179** 1·40 55

N3631 50ch. Royal spoonbill 1·40 55

MSN3632 80×66 mm. 80ch. Dove-hand protecting sapling growing from globe (horiz) 2·30 1·60

1180 Red Flag and Tower of 'Juche' Idea

1996. 70th Anniversary of Down-with-Imperialism Union.

N3633 **1180** 10ch. multicoloured 35 15

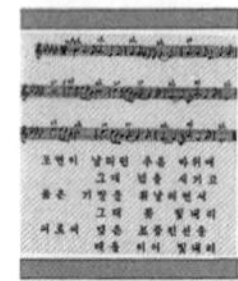

1181 Score of Theme Song from *Red Mountain Ridge* (film)

1996. 44th Death Anniversary of Huang Ji Guang (Chinese volunteer in Korean War).

MSN3634 142×80 mm. 10ch. multicoloured (Type **1181**); 30ch. brown, silver and black (Huang Ji Guang); 30ch. multicoloured Huang Ji Guang) (blocking gun muzzle with body) 1·80 1·30

1182 Archeozoic Era

1996. History of the Earth. Sheet 160×70 mm containing T **1182** and similar vert designs. Multicoloured.

MSN3635 50ch. Type **1182**; 50ch. Proterozoic era; 50ch. Palaeozoic era; 50ch. Mesozoic era; 50ch. Cainozoic era 6·25 4·50

1183 Japanese Eel

1996. Freshwater Fish. Multicoloured.

N3636 20ch. Type **1183** 65 25

N3637 20ch. Menada grey mullet (*Liza haematocheila*) 65 25

MSN3638 74×53 mm. 80ch. Silver carp 2·30 1·50

1184 Soldiers and Supreme Commander's Flag

1996. Fifth Anniversary of Appointment of Kim Jong Il as Supreme Commander of the People's Army.

N3639 **1184** 20ch. multicoloured 50 25

1185 *Ox Driver* (Kim Tu Ryang)

1997. New Year. Year of the Ox. Multicoloured.

N3640 70ch. Type **1185** 2·00 85

N3641 70ch. Bronze ritual plate of two bulls and a tiger 2·00 85

N3642 70ch. Boy with bull (ceramic) 2·00 85

N3643 70ch. Boy flautist sitting on bull (sculpture) 2·00 85

MSN3644 83×82 mm. 80ch. *People's support of the Front* (drawing, Jong Jong Yo) (60×38 mm) 2·20 1·60

1186 Left-hand Detail

1997. *Flowers and Butterflies* by Nam Kye U. Multicoloured.

N3645 50ch. Type **1186** 1·40 60

N3646 50ch. Centre detail 1·40 60

N3647 50ch. Right-hand detail 1·40 60

Nos. N3645/N3647 were issued together, *se-tenant*, forming a composite design of the painting.

1187 Kitten with Dogs in Basket

1997. Paintings of Cats and Dogs. Multicoloured.

N3648 50ch. Type **1187** 1·40 60

N3649 50ch. Pup in vine-wreathed basket, kitten and pumpkin 1·40 60

MSN3650 Two sheets, each 96×114 mm. (a) 50ch.×2, Kitten in basket of vegetables, pup, fruit and flowers; 50ch. Kitten in basket of flowers, pup and ball of wool; No. N3648. (b) 50ch.×2, Kittens, pup and vegetables (as in sheet a); No. N3649 Set of 2 sheets 6·75 4·00

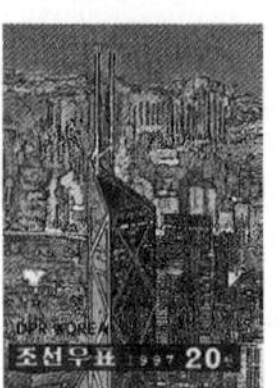

1188 Bank of China

1997. Return of Hong Kong to China. Sheet 145×100 mm containing T **1188** and similar vert designs. Multicoloured.

MSN3651 20ch. Type **1188**; 20ch. Building with spire; 20ch. High-rise buildings 3·75 3·00

1189 Birthplace, Mt. Paektu

1997. 55th Birthday of Kim Jong Il. Multicoloured.

N3652 10ch. Type **1189** 35 15

MSN3653 Two sheets, each 64×86 mm. (a) 1wn. Kim Jong Il inspecting farm equipment (47×53 mm); (b) 1wn. Kim Jong Il receiving flowers from soldier (47×35 mm) Set of 2 sheets 5·50 3·75

1190 Pair

1997. Sixth Paektusan Prize International Figure Skating Championships, Pyongyang. Multicoloured.

N3654 50ch. Type **1190** 1·40 60

N3655 50ch. Pair (mauve) 1·40 60

N3656 50ch. Pair (green) 1·40 60

1191 Kye Sun Hui

1997. North Korean Gold Medal in Women's Judo at Olympic Games, Atlanta. Sheet 90×100 mm.
MSN3657 **1191** 80ch. multicoloured 2·20 1·60

1192 Choe Un A

1997. Choe Un A (competitor in World Go championships at seven years). Sheet 90×110 mm.
MSN3658 **1192** 80ch. multicoloured 2·20 1·60

1193 *Prunus ansu*

1997. Apricots. Multicoloured.

N3659	50ch. Type **1193**	1·50	65
N3660	50ch. *Prunus mandshurica*	1·50	65
N3661	50ch. Hoeryong white apricot (*Prunus armeniaca*)	1·50	65
N3662	50ch. Puksan apricot (*Prunus sibirica*)	1·50	65

1194 Foundation Monument

1997. 80th Anniversary of Foundation of Korean National Association.
N3663 **1194** 10ch. brown and green 35 10

1195 Sapling

1997. 50th Anniversary of Reforestation Day. Multicoloured.

N3664	10ch. Type **1195**	35	15
MSN3665	90×100 mm. 1wn. Kim Il Sung planting sapling on Munsa Hill	2·20	1·50

1196 Birthplace, Mangyongdae

1997. 85th Birth Anniversary of Kim Il Sung. Multicoloured.

N3666	10ch. Type **1196**	25	10
N3667	20ch. Sliding Rock (horiz)	50	25
N3668	40ch. Warship Rock (horiz)	1·10	50
MSN3669	Two sheets. (a) 110×90 mm. 1wn. Kim Il Sung in crowd (50×41 mm). (b) 100×120 mm. 1wn. Kim Il Sung on flowered hill-top (33×51 mm) Set of 2 sheets	5·50	3·75

1197 Cap Badge and Modern Weapons

1997. 65th Anniversary of People's Army. Multicoloured.

N3670	10ch. Type **1197**	25	10
MSN3671	75×90 mm. 1wn. Soldier applauding Kin Il Sung and Kim Jong Il (35×49 mm)	2·75	1·90

1198 Map of Korea

1997. 25th Anniversary of Publication of North–South Korea joint Agreement.

N3672	10ch. Type **1198**	25	10
MSN3673	105×70 mm. 1wn. Kim Il Sung's Autograph Monument, Phammunjom (60×38 mm)	2·75	1·90

1199 Tower of 'Juche' Idea, People and Flag

1997. Posters reflecting Joint New Year Newspaper Editorials. Multicoloured.

N3674	10ch. Type **1199**	25	10
N3675	10ch. Man with flag	25	10
N3676	10ch. Soldier, miner, farmer, intellectual and bugler	25	10

1200 Exhibition Centre

1997. International Friendship Exhibition, Myohyang Mountains (1st series). Four sheets containing designs as T **1200**. Multicoloured.
MSN3677 Four sheets, each 105×120 mm. (a) 70ch. Type **1200**. (b) 70ch. Statue of Kim Il Sung in entrance hall; (c) 70ch. *Native Home in Mangyongdae* (ivory sculpture from China) (horiz); (d) 70ch. Stuffed crocodile holding cups on salver and wooden ash tray (from Nicaragua) Set of 4 sheets 7·50 5·25

See also Nos. N3752/**MS**N3755.

1201 Memorial Post and Blazing Fortress

1997. 60th Anniversary of Battle of Pochonbo.
N3678 **1201** 40ch. multicoloured 1·10 50

1202 Kim Il Sung transplanting Rice

1997. 50th Anniversary of Kim Il Sung's Visit to Mirin Plain Paddy-fields. Two sheets, each 75×105 mm, containing designs as T **1202**.
MSN3679 Two sheets. (a) 1wn. black and gold (Type **1202**); (b) 1wn. multicoloured (Kim Il Sung inspecting rice-transplanting machine) Set of 2 sheets 6·25 4·25

1203 Signing Nanjing Treaty, 1842

1997. Return of Hong Kong to China. Two sheets containing multicoloured designs as T **1203**.
MSN3680 Two sheets. (a) 124×117 mm. 20ch. Type **1203**; 20ch. Signing China–Britain Joint Statement, Peking, 1984; 20ch. Deng Xiaoping and Margaret Thatcher; 20ch. Jiang Zemin and Tong Jiahua (Mayor of Hong Kong), 1996. (b) 124×95 mm. 97 mm. Deng Xiaoping (circular, diameter 42 mm) (pair sold at 1wn.80) Set of 2 sheets 5·00 3·50

1204 Redlichia chinensis

1997. Fossils. Multicoloured.

N3681	50ch. Type **1204**	1·40	60
N3682	1wn. Ptychoparia coreanica	2·75	1·30

1205 Kim Il Sung at Kim Chaek Ironworks, June 1985

1997. Third Death Anniversary of Kim Il Sung. Multicoloured.

N3683	50ch. Kim Il Sung at microphones (party conference, October 1985)	1·40	60
N3684	50ch. Type **1205**	1·40	60
N3685	50ch. Kim Il Sung and farmers holding wheat (Songsin Co-operative Farm, Sadong District, 1993)	1·40	60
N3686	50ch. Performing artists applauding Kim Il Sung, 1986	1·40	60
N3687	50ch. Kim Il Sung at Jonchon Factory, Jagang Province, 1991	1·40	60
N3688	50ch. Kim Il Sung receiving flowers at People's Army Conference, 1989	1·40	60

1206 Blindman's Buff

1997. Children's Games. Multicoloured.

N3689	30ch. Type **1206**	85	35
N3690	60ch. Five stones	1·60	80
N3691	70ch. Arm wrestling	2·00	85

1207 Spring

1997. Women's National Costumes. Multicoloured.

N3692	10ch. Type **1207**	25	10
N3693	40ch. Summer	1·10	50
N3694	50ch. Autumn	1·40	60
N3695	60ch. Winter	1·60	80

1208 Aerial View

1997. Chongryu Bridge, Pyongyang. Multicoloured.

N3696	50ch. Type **1208**	1·40	60
N3697	50ch. Chongryu Bridge and birds	1·40	60

1209 Sun, Magnolias and Balloons

1997. 85th Anniversary of 'Juche' Era and Sun Day. Multicoloured.

N3698	10ch. Type **1209**	25	10
MSN3699	85×115 mm. 1wn. Kim Il Sung (circular, diameter 45 mm)	2·75	2·00

1210 Korean Text and Kim Il Sung University

1997. 20th Anniversary of Publication of *Theses on Socialist Education.*
N3700 **1210** 10ch. multicoloured 25 10

1211 Tupolev Tu-134

1997. 20th Anniversary of Korean Membership of International Civil Aviation Oraganisation. Three sheets, each 165×58 mm. containing designs as T **1211**. Multicoloured.
MSN3701 Three sheets. (a) 2×20ch. Type **1211**; (b) 2×30ch. Tupolev Tu-154; (c) 2×50ch. Illyushin IL-62 5·75 4·00

1212 Chonbul Peak

1997. Tenth Anniversary of Korean Membership of World Tourism Organization. Mt Chilbo. Multicoloured.

N3702	50ch. Type **1212**	1·40	60
N3703	50ch. Sea-Chilbo (coast)	1·40	60
N3704	50ch. Rojok Peak	1·40	60

1213 Podok Hermitage

1997. Kumgang Mountains. Multicoloured.

N3705	50ch. Type **1213**	1·40	60
N3706	50ch. Kumgang Gate	1·40	60

1214 School, Pupil and Mt. Paekdu

1997. 50th Anniversary of Mangyongdae Revolutionary School.
N3707 **1214** 40ch. multicoloured 1·10 50

1215 Lion

1997. Animals presented as Gifts to Kim Il Sung. Multicoloured.

N3708	20ch. Type **1215** (Ethiopia, 1987)	50	25
N3709	30ch. Jaguar (Japan, 1992)	85	35
N3710	50ch. Barbary sheep (Czechoslovakia, 1992)	1·40	60
N3711	80ch. Scarlet macaw (Austria, 1979)	2·20	1·00

1216 Bust

1997. 27th Anniversary of Participation in Korean War by Chinese People's Volunteers. Qu Shao Yun. Sheet 145×80 mm containing T **1216** and similar vert designs. Multicoloured.

MSN3712	10ch. Statue; 30ch. Type **1216**; 30ch. Qu Shao Yun on fire	2·00	1·40

1217 Ten-pin Bowling

1997. Sports. Multicoloured.

N3713	50ch. Type **1217**	1·40	60
N3714	50ch. Golf	1·40	60
N3715	50ch. Fencing	1·40	60

1218 Snails

1997. Snails. Multicoloured.

N3716	50ch. Type **1218**	1·50	60
N3717	50ch. Two snails on leaf	1·50	60
N3718	50ch. Snail laying eggs	1·50	60

1219 Shanghai

1997. International Stamp and Coin Exhibition, Shanghai. Sheet 145×199 mm containing T **1219** and similar vert design.

MSN3719	30ch. Type **1219**; 50ch. Shanghai (different)	2·20	1·60

1220 'Juche 87' and Temple

1997. New Year. Year of the Tiger. Multicoloured.

N3720	10ch. Type **1220**	25	10
N3721	50ch. Tiger in rocket (24×34 mm)	60	35
N3722	50ch. Tiger steering ship (24×34 mm)	60	35
MSN3723	(a) 112×75 mm. 80ch. Tiger driving train (24×34 mm). (b) 82×115 mm. Nos. N3721/N3722; 80ch. As No. **MS**3723a	4·50	3·25

1221 Birthplace, Hoeryong

1997. 80th Birth Anniversary of Kim Jong Suk (revolutionary). Multicoloured.

N3724	10ch. Type **1221**	25	10
MSN3725	85×115 mm. 1wn. Kim Jong Suk (41×50 mm)	2·75	1·90

1222 Skiing

1998. Winter Olympic Ganes, Nagano, Japan. Multicoloured.

N3726	20ch. Type **1222**	25	10
N3727	40ch. Speed skating	60	25

1223 Birthdate and Celebration Ribbon

1998. 50th Birth Anniversary of Kim Jong Il. Multicoloured.

N3728	10ch. Type **1223**	25	10
MSN3729	3wn. Log cabin (birthplace, Mt. Paektu)	4·25	3·00

1224 Korean Tigers

1998. Wildlife Paintings. Multicoloured.

N3730	50ch. Type **1224**	75	35
N3731	50ch. Manchurian cranes	75	35
MSN3732	102×157 mm. 50ch. Nos. N3730/N3731; 50ch. Bears; 50ch. Racoon dogs	3·00	2·10

1225 Route Map, Birthplace at Mangyongdae and Trail Followers

1998. 75th Anniversary of 1000-ri (250 mile) Journey by Kim Il Sung.

N3733	**1225** 10ch. multicoloured	25	10

1226 Soldiers and Balloons

1998. Fifth Anniversary of Appointment of Kim Jong Il as Chairman of National Defence Commission.

N3734	**1226** 10ch. multicoloured	25	10

1227 Flags and Birthplace, Mangyongdae

1228 Kim Il Sung as Child

1998. 86th Birth Anniversary of Kim Il Sung. Multicoloured.

N3735	**1227** 10ch. multicoloured	25	10
MSN3736	Eight sheets, each 84×155 mm. (a) 80ch. Type **1228**; (b) 80ch. As student (wearing cap with rectangular badge); (c) 80ch. Commander of revolutionary army (wearing cap with star badge); (d) 80ch. In jacket and tie (three-quarter face) 80ch. In army uniform; (f) 80ch. In Mao jacket; (g) 80ch. In jacket and tie (full-face); (h) 80ch. Wearing glasses Set of 8 sheets	9·00	6·25

1229 United Front Tower and Moranbong Theatre

1998. 50th Anniversary of North–South Conference, Pyongyang.

N3737	**1229** 10ch. brown, blue and black	25	10

1230 Players and Championship Emblem

1998. World Cup Football Championship, France. Multicoloured.

N3738	30ch. Type **1230**	35	15
N3739	50ch. Player winning ball and emblem	75	35
MSN3740	62×87 mm. 80ch. Tackling and emblem	1·10	80

1231 Cabbages

1998. Vegetables. Multicoloured.

N3741	10ch. Type **1231**	25	10
N3742	40ch. Radishes	50	25
N3743	50ch. Spring onions	60	35
N3744	60ch. Cucumbers	85	40
N3745	70ch. Pumpkins	1·00	45
N3746	80ch. Carrots	1·10	50
N3747	90ch. Garlic	1·20	60
N3748	1wn. Peppers	1·40	70

1232 *Countryside in May* (Jong Jong Yo)

1998. Paintings. Multicoloured.

N3749	60ch. Type **1232**	1·00	35
N3750	1wn.40 *Dance* (Kim Yong Jun)	2·20	85
MSN3751	80×80 mm. 3wn. *Heart to Heart talk with a Peasant* (Yu Yong Gwan) (59×58 mm.)	4·25	3·00

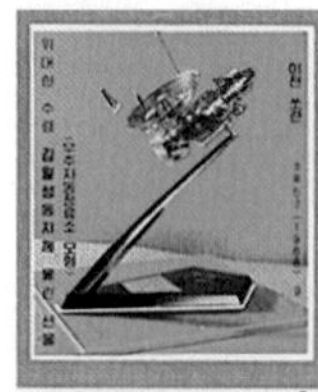

1233 Model of Automatic Space Station (from USSR)

1998. International Friendship Exhibition, Myohyang Mountains (2nd series). Multicoloured.

N3752	1wn. Type **1233**	1·40	60
N3753	1wn. Ceramic flower vase (from Egypt)	1·40	60
N3754	1wn. *Crane* (statuette, from Billy Graham (evangelist))	1·40	60
MSN3755	86×100 mm. 1wn. claret and black (Kim Il Sung) (35×56 mm)	1·40	95

1234 Research Ship, Buoy and Dolphins in Globe and Hydro-meteorological Headquarters

1998. International Year of the Ocean. Multicoloured.

N3756	10ch. Type **1234**	35	15
N3757	80ch. Sailing dinghies and mother with child	1·10	70
MSN3758	128×105 mm. 5wn. Vasco da Gama (vert)	6·75	4·75

1235 Stone Age Implement

1998. Korean Central History Museum, Pyongyang. Multicoloured.

N3759	10ch. Type **1235**	25	10
N3760	2wn.50 Fossil skull of monkey	3·50	1·70
MSN3761	80×75 mm. 4wn. claret, grey and black (Kim Il Sung visiting museum) (60×38 mm)	5·75	4·00

1236 Commander of Hedgehog Unit and Squirrel

1998. *Squirrels and Hedgehogs* (cartoon film). Multicoloured.

N3762	20ch. Type **1236**	25	10
N3763	30ch. Commander of hedgehog unit receiving invitation to banquet	35	15
N3764	60ch. Weasel ordering mouse to poison bear	85	45
N3765	1wn.20 Squirrel with poisoned bear	1·90	85
N3766	2wn. Weasel and mice invade Flower Village	2·75	1·30
N3767	2wn.50 Hedgehog scout rescues squirrel	3·50	1·70

1237 Ri Sung Gi and Molecular Model

1998. Second Death Anniversary of Ri Sung Gi (inventor of vinalon material). Multicoloured.

N3768	40ch. Type **1237**	60	25
MSN3769	80×65 mm. 80ch. Ri Sung Gi working in laboratory	1·10	80

1238 Tiger Cub

1998. Young Mammals. Multicoloured.

N3770	10ch. Type **1238**	25	10
N3771	50ch. Donkey foal	75	50
N3772	1wn.60 Elephant	2·40	1·70
N3773	2wn. Two lion cubs	2·75	2·00

1239 *Victory* (Liberation War Monument, Pyongyang) and Medal

1998. 45th Anniversary of Victory in Liberation War.

N3774	**1239** 10ch. brown and pink	25	15
MSN3775	Two sheets, each 62×87 mm. multicoloured. (a) 2w. Gaz-67 jeep and route map of Kim Il Sung's wartime inspections (30×48 mm). (b) 2wn. *Kim Il Sung inspecting Frontline* (painting) (48×30 mm) Set of 2 sheets	5·50	3·75

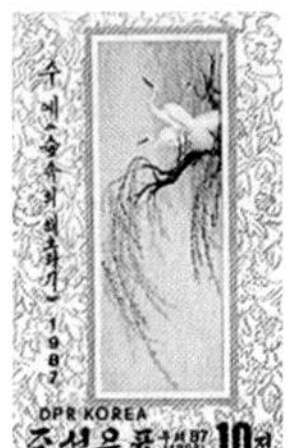
1240 *White Herons in Forest*

1998. Embroidery. Multicoloured.
N3776 10ch. Type **1240** 25 15
N3777 40ch. *Carp* 1·90 1·30
N3778 1wn.20 *Hollyhock* 1·90 1·30
N3779 1wn.50 *Cockscomb* 2·20 1·60
MSN3780 80×65 mm. 4wn. *Pine and Cranes* 5·75 4·00

1241 Pouch

1998. Traditional Costume Adornments. Multicoloured.
N3781 10ch. Type **1241** 25 10
N3782 50ch. Tassels 75 50
N3783 1wn.50 Hairpin 2·10 1·50
N3784 1wn.90 Silver knife 2·75 1·90

1242 Rocket and State Flag

1998. Launch of first Korean Artificial satellite *Kwangmyongsong 1*.
N3785 40ch. Type **1242** 60 45
MSN3786 81×115 mm. 1wn.50 Rocket and satellite orbit (41×63 mm) 2·40 1·70

1243 Kim Jong Il Flower

1998. Re-election of Kim Jung Il as Chairman of National dfence Commission. Multicoloured.
N3787 10ch. Type **1243** 25 15
MSN3788 69×94 mm. 1wn. Kim Jong Il (circular, diameter 42 mm) 1·40 95

1244 Tower of 'Juche' Idea, State Arms and Flag

1998. 50th Anniversary of Democratic Republic (1st issue). Multicoloured.
N3789 10ch. Type **1244** 25 15
N3790 1wn. Painting *The Founding of the Democratic People's Republic of Korea, Our Glorious Fatherland* (Kim Il Sung waving from balcony) (48×30 mm) 1·40 95
N3791 1wn. Painting *Square of Victory* (Kim Il Sung and crowd with banners) (48×30 mm) 1·40 95
N3792 1wn. Poster *The Sacred Marks of the Great Leader Kim Il Sung will shine on this Land of Socialism* (Kim Il Sung with produce against panoramic background of Korea) (48×30 mm) 1·40 95

See also No. **MS**N3794.

1245 'Let Us Push Ahead with the Forced March for Final Victory'

1998
N3793 **1245** 10ch. multicoloured 25 15

1246 State Flag and Arms forming '50'

1998. 50th Anniversary of Democratic Republic (2nd issue). Two sheets containing T **1246** or similar multicoloured design.
MSN3794 Two sheets. (a) 108×84 mm. 40ch. Type **1246**; (b) 108×125 mm. 1wn. Celebration Parade (31×38 mm) Set of 2 sheets 2·20 1·60

1247 Cycling

1998. Olympic Games, Sydney, Australia (2000). Multicoloured.
N3795 20ch. Type **1247** 25 15
N3796 50ch. Football 75 50
N3797 80ch. Show jumping 1·10 80
N3798 1wn.50 Throwing the javelin 2·20 1·60
MSN3799 57×80 mm. 2wn.50 Basketball 3·75 2·50

1248 *Cyclamen persicum*

1998. Plants presented as Gifts to Kim Jong Il. Multicoloured.
N3800 20ch. Type **1248** (France, 1994) 35 25
N3801 2wn. *Dianthus chinensis* var. *laciniatus* (Japan, 1994) 2·75 1·90

1249 Oral Vaccination

1998. National Vaccination Day.
N3802 **1249** 40ch. multicoloured 60 45

1250 Leopard

1998. The Leopard. Multicoloured.
N3803 1wn. Type **1250** 1·50 1·00
N3804 1wn. Leopard in snow 1·50 1·00
N3805 1wn. Leopard looking to left 1·50 1·00
N3806 1wn. Leopard's face 1·50 1·00

1251 Canal

1998. Land and Environment Conservation Day. Multicoloured.
N3807 10ch. Type **1251** 25 10
N3808 40ch. Motorway, tower blocks and lorry 65 45
MSN3809 85×71 mm. 1wn. Kim Il Sung shovelling earth to signal start of Pothong River improvement 1·50 1·00

1252 Emblem and Milan Cathedral

1998. Italia 98 International Stamp Exhibition, Milan, Italy. Sheet 108×90 mm.
MSN3810 2wn. multicoloured 3·00 2·10

1253 Peng Dehuai and Kim Il Sung

1998. Birth Centenary of Peng Dehuai (commander of Chinese People's Volunteers in Korea Liberation War). Sheet 131×112 mm containing T **1253** and similar multicoloured designs.
MSN3811 20ch. Type **1253**; 20ch. Mao Tse-tung (Chinese communist leader), Chou Enlai (Chinese statesman) and Peng Dehuai; 30ch. Peng Dehuai in marshal's uniform (27×38 mm); 30ch. *On the Front* ((painting), He Kong De) (27×38 mm) 1·60 1·10

1254 Liu Shaoqi

1998. Birth Centenary of Liu Shaoqi (Chairman of Chinese People's Republic, 1959–1968). Multicoloured.
N3812 10ch. Type **1254** 25 10
N3813 20ch. Liu Shaoqi and Mao Tse-tung 40 20
N3814 30ch. Liu Shaoqi and his daughter, Xiao Xiao 55 40
N3815 40ch. Liu Shaoqi and his wife, Wang Guangmei 65 45
MSN3816 100×70 mm. 1wn. Liu Shaoqi and Kim Il Sung (46½×35 mm.) 1·50 1·00

1255 Victory in Yonsong Monument, Yonan Fortress and Banners

1998. 400th Anniversary of Victory in Korean–Japanese War. Multicoloured.
N3817 10ch. Type **1255** 25 10
N3818 30ch. Naval Victory in Myongryang Monument, General Ri Sun Sin and 'turtle' ship 40 30
N3819 1wn.60 Monument to Hyujong in Kwangwon province, Hyujong (Buddhist priest), sword and helmet 2·40 1·70
MSN3820 12×68 mm. 10wn. *Sea Battle off Hansan Islet in 1592* (painting) 15·00 12·00

1256 Dish Aerial, Artificial Satellite, Globe and Relay Tower

1998. 15th Anniversary of North Korean Membership of Intersputnik.
N3821 **1256** 1wn. dp grn & grn 1·60 1·10

1257 Goat

1998
N3822 **1257** 10ch. black and green 30 20
N3823 **1257** 1wn. black and red 1·70 1·20

1258 *A Floral Carriage of Happiness* (sculpture) and Palace

1998. Mangyongdae School-children' palace. Multicoloured.
N3824 40ch. Type **1258** 70 50
MSN3825 85×64 mm. 1wn. Quotation of Kim Il Sung "Children are the treasure of our country. Korea of the future is theirs" 1·70 1·20

1259 Emblem

1998. 50th Anniv of Universal Declaration of Human Rights.
N3826 **1259** 20ch. multicoloured 30 20

1260 Reeves's Turtle

1998. Reptiles and Amphibians. Multicoloured.
N3827 10ch. Type **1260** 30 20
N3828 40ch. Skink 70 50
N3829 60ch. Loggerhead turtle 1·00 70
N3830 1wn.20 Leatherback turtle 2·00 1·40
Nos. N3827/N3830 were issued together, *se-tenant*, forming a composite design.

1261 Thajong Rock

1998. Mt. Chilbo. Multicoloured.
N3831 30ch. Type **1261** 40 30
N3832 50ch. Peasant Rock 85 60
N3833 1wn.70 Couple Rock 2·75 1·90

1262 Ri Mong Ryong marrying Song Chun Hyang

1998. Tale of Chun Hyang. Multicoloured.
N3834 40ch. Type **1262** 70 50
N3835 1wn.60 Pyon Hak Do watching Chun Hyang 2·50 1·90
N3836 2wn.50 Ri Mong Ryong and Chun Hyang 4·00 3·00
MSN3837 110×95 mm. Nos. N3834/N3836; 2wn. Chun Hyang in wedding veil 10·50 8·75

1263 Chollima Statue

1998. Pyongyang Monuments.
N3838 **1263** 10ch. red 20 15
N3839 **A** 10ch. red 20 15
N3840 **B** 10ch. red 20 15

N3841	**B**	20ch. orange	30	20
N3842	**1263**	30ch. orange	55	40
N3843	**A**	40ch. yellow	70	50
N3844	**B**	40ch. yellow	70	50
N3845	**1263**	70ch. green	1·10	85
N3846	**A**	70ch. green	1·10	85
N3847	**A**	1wn.20 green	2·00	1·50
N3848	**1263**	1wn.50 green	2·50	1·90
N3849	**B**	2wn. blue	3·50	2·50
N3850	**A**	3wn. blue	5·00	3·75
N3851	**1263**	5wn. blue	8·50	6·25
N3852	**B**	10wn. violet	17·00	12·50

Designs: A, Arch of Triumph; B, Tower of Juche Idea.

1264 Rabbit meeting Lion

1999. New Year. Year of the Rabbit. Multicoloured.
N3853 10ch. Type **1264** 30 20
N3854 1wn. Rabbit with mirror and lion 1·70 1·30
N3855 1wn.50 Lion in trap 2·50 1·90
N3856 2wn.50 Rabbit 4·00 3·00
MSN3857 160×70 mm. 10ch. Type **1264**; 1wn. No. N3854; 1wn.50 No. N3855; 2wn.50 No. N3856 8·50 6·50

1265 Automatic Rifle and Star

1999. 40th Anniversary of Worker-Peasant Red Guards.
N3858 **1265** 10ch. multicoloured 30 20

1266 Log Cabin (birthplace, Mt. Paektu)

1999. 57th Birth Anniversary of Kim Jong Il.
N3859 **1266** 40ch. multicoloured 70 55

1267 Cranes, Rice Sheaf and '35'

1999. 35th Anniversary of Publication of *Theses on the Socialist Rural Question in Our Country* by Kim Il Sung.
N3860 **1267** 10ch. multicoloured 30 20

1268 Korean Script and Crowd

1999. 80th Anniversary of 1st March Uprising.
N3861 **1268** 10ch. black and brown 30 20

1269 16th-century "Turtle" Ship

1999. Australia '99 International Stamp Exhibition, Melbourne.
N3862 **1269** 2wn. multicoloured 2·40 1·80
MSN3863 100×75 mm. **1269** 2wn. multicoloured 2·75 2·00

1270 Birthplace, Mangyondae

1999. 87th Birth Anniversary of Kim Il Sung.
N3864 **1270** 10ch. brown, flesh and grey 30 20
MSN3865 68×95 mm. 2wn. multicoloured (Kim Il Sung 94×62 mm) 2·75 2·00

1271 Player

1999. 45th Table Tennis Championship, Belgrade, Yugoslavia.
N3866 **1271** 1wn.50 multicoloured 2·00 1·50

1272 Korean Sports Stamps and Emblem

1999. iBRA '99 International Stamp Exhibition, Nuremberg, Germany.
N3867 **1272** 1wn. multicoloured 1·30 95

1273 *Benzoin obtus*

1999. 40th Anniversary of Central Botanical Garden, Mt. Taesong, Pyongyang. Multicoloured.
N3868 10ch. Type **1273** 30 20
N3869 30ch. *Styrax obassia* 40 30
N3870 70ch. *Petunia hybrida* 1·00 75
N3871 90ch. *Impatiens hybrida* 1·30 95
MSN3872 65×75 mm. 2wn. Kimilsung-flower and Kimjongil (begonia) 2·75 2·00

1274 Chimpanzee and Rhinoceros

1999. 40th Anniversary of Central Zoo, Mt. Taesong, Pyongyang. Multicoloured.
N3873 50ch. Type **1274** 70 55
N3874 60ch. Manchurian crane and deer 85 65
N3875 70ch. Common zebra and kangaroo 1·00 75
MSN3876 95×75 mm. 2wn. Tiger 2·75 2·00

1275 Light Industry Hall

1999. Three Revolutions Museum, Ryonmotdong, Pyongyang. Multicoloured.
N3877 60ch. Type **1275** 85 65
N3878 80ch. Heavy Industry Hall 1·10 85

1276 Methods of Communication, Satellite and Globe

1999. 20th Anniversary of Asia–Pacfic Telecommunications Union.
N3879 **1276** 1wn. multicoloured 1·40 1·10

1277 Monument

1999. 60th Anniversary of Victory in Battle of Musan.
N3880 **1277** 10ch. multicoloured 30 20

1278 Seagulls

1999. 190th Birth Anniversary of Charles Darwin (naturalist). Multicoloured.
N3881 30ch. Type **1278** 40 30
N3882 50ch. Bats 70 55
N3883 1wn. Dolphins 1·40 1·10
N3884 1wn.20 Man on horseback 1·70 1·30
N3885 1wn.50 Dancer 2·10 1·60
MSN3886 76×67 mm. 2wn. Charles Darwin (26×39 mm) 3·50 2·75

1279 *Princess Margarita in a White Dress*

1999. 400th Birth Anniversary of Diego Velazquez (artist). Multicoloured.
N3887 50ch. Type **1279** 70 55
N3888 50ch. *Men drawing Water from a Well* 70 55
N3889 3wn.50 *Self-portrait* 4·50 3·50
MSN3890 68×118 mm. No. N3889 4·75 3·75

1280 Rimyongsu Power Station

1999. Hydro-electric Power Stations. Multicoloured.
N3891 50ch. Type **1280** 70 55
N3892 1wn. Jangjasan Power Station 1·40 1·10

1281 Players tackling

1999. Third Women's World Football Championship, USA. Multicoloured.
N3893 1wn. Type **1281** 1·40 1·10
N3894 1wn.50 Player No. 3 and player wearing blue and white strip tackling 2·10 1·60
N3895 1wn.50 Player and goalkeeper 2·10 1·60
N3896 2wn. Player No. 7 and player wearing blue strip 2·75 2·10

1282 The Earth, Space Rocket and Mars

1999. Exploration of Planet Mars. Sheet 110×75 mm. containing T **1282** and similar vert designs. Multicoloured.
MSN3897 2wn. Type **1282**; 2wn. Satellite orbiting Mars; 2wn. Probe landing on Mars 8·50 6·50

1283 Man with Candlesticks

1999. *The Nation and Destiny* (Korean film). Scenes from the film. Multicoloured.
N3898 1wn. Type **1283** 1·30 95
N3899 1wn. Woman holding gun and man in white suit 1·30 95
N3900 1wn. Man behind bars 1·30 95
N3901 1wn. Man with protective goggles on head 1·30 95

1284 Samil Lagoon

1999. Mt. Kumgang. Multicoloured.
N3902 20ch. Type **1284** 30 20
N3903 40ch. Samson Rocks (vert) 55 45
N3904 60ch. Rock, Kumgang Sea 85 65
N3905 80ch. Kuryong Waterfall (vert) 1·00 75
N3906 1wn. Kwimyon Rock (vert) 1·30 95

1285 Emblem, Girl and Dove

1999. 125th Anniversary of Universal Postal Union. Sheet 87×67 mm.
MSN3907 **1285** 2wn. multicoloured 3·00 2·40

1286 France 1870 20c. Stamp and North Korea 20ch. 1946 Stamp

1999. Philexfrance99 International Stamp Exhibition, Paris. Sheet 102×77 mm.
MSN3908 **1286** 2wn.50 multicoloured 3·50 2·50

1287 Mercedes Motor Car

1999. Fifth Death Anniversary of Kim Il Sung. Multicoloured.
N3909 1wn. Type **1287** 1·70 1·30
N3910 1wn. Railway carriage 1·70 1·30

1288 Chinese Characters and Mangyong Hill

1999. 105th Birth Anniversary of Kim Hyong Jik (revolutionary).
N3911 **1288** 10ch. multicoloured 30 20

1289 Patterned Vessel

1999. Ceramics. Multicoloured.
N3912 70ch. Type **1289** 1·00 75
N3913 80ch. Wit and Beauty jar 1·10 85

N3914	1wn. Patterned vase	1·30	95
N3915	1wn.50 Celadon kettle	2·00	1·50
N3916	2wn.50 White china vase	3·25	2·50

1290 Silver Carp

1999. Fish Breeding. Multicoloured.

N3917	50ch. Type **1290**	70	55
N3918	1wn. Common carp	1·40	1·10
N3919	1wn.50 Spotted silver carp	2·10	1·60

1291 Map and Crowd

1999. Year of National Independence and Solidarity.

N3920	**1291** 40ch. multicoloured	55	45

1292 *Samjiyon* with Maps of Japan and Korea

1999. 40th Anniversary of Repatriation of Korean Nationals in Japan.

N3921	**1292** 1wn.50 multicoloured	2·50	1·90

1293 Symbols of Prosperity

1999

N3922	**1293** 40ch. multicoloured	55	45

1294 100 m Race

1999. World Athletics Championships, Seville, Spain. Multicoloured.

N3923	30ch. Type **1294**	45	35
N3924	40ch. Hurdles	60	45
N3925	80ch. Discus	1·20	80

1295 *Acalypha hispida*

1999. Plants presented to Kim Il Sung. Multicoloured.

N3926	40ch. Type **1295**	75	55
N3927	40ch. *Allamanda neriifolia*	75	55
N3928	40ch. *Begonia x hiemalis*	75	55
N3929	40ch. *Fatsia japonica*	75	55
N3930	40ch. *Streptocarpus hybrida*	75	55
N3931	40ch. *Streptocarpus rexii*	75	55

Nos. N3926/N3931 were issued together, *se-tenant*, forming a composite design.

1296 *Play a Flute to call the Phoenix*

1999. CHINA 1999 International Stamp Exhibition and 22nd UPU Congress, Beijing. T **1296** and similar vert designs. Multicoloured.

MSN3932	40ch. Type **1296**; 40ch. *Relics kept in Bamboo Field*; 40ch. *Six Friends in a Pine Forest*; 40ch. *Lady's Morning Dressing*	3·00	2·20

1297 *Grifola frondosa*

1999. Mushrooms. Multicoloured.

N3933	40ch. Type **1297**	75	55
N3934	60ch. *Lactarius volemus*	1·00	80
N3935	1wn. *Coriolus versicolor*	1·80	1·30

1298 *Aporocactus flagelliformis*

1999. Cacti. Multicoloured.

N3936	40ch. Type **1298**	75	55
N3937	50ch. *Astrophytum ornatum*	90	65
N3938	60ch. *Gymnocalycium michano vichii*	1·00	80

1299 Rat

1999. Animals of Eastern Zodiac. Two sheets, each 110×160 mm containing T **1299** and similar circular multicoloured designs.

MSN3942	Two sheets (a) 10ch. Type **1299**; 10ch. Ox; 10ch. Tiger; 10ch Rabbit; 10ch. Dragon; 10ch. Snake. (b) 10ch. Horse; 10ch. Sheep; 10ch. Monkey; 10ch. Cockerel; 10ch. Dog; Sow and piglets (each sold at 1wn.)	3·50	2·75

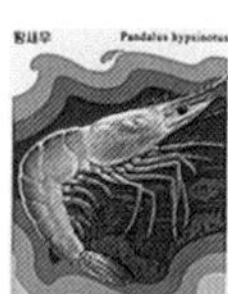
1300 Shrimp

1999. Crustacea. Multicoloured.

N3943	50ch. Type **1300**	90	65
N3944	70ch. Shrimp (different)	1·20	90
N3945	80ch. Lobster	1·50	1·10

1301 Jong Song Ok (marathon runner)

1999. Victory of Jong Song Ok at World Athletic Championship, Seville.

N3946	40ch. Type **1301**	75	55
MSN3947	90×70 mm. 2wn. Jong Song Ok (vert)	3·50	2·75

1302 Mt. Kumgang, North Korea

1999. 50th Anniversary of North Korean–China Diplomatic Relations. Multicoloured.

N3948	40ch. Type **1302**	75	55
N3949	60ch. Mt. Lushan, China	1·00	80
MSN3950	142×93 mm. Nos. N3948/N3949	2·10	1·70

1303 Deng Xiaoping

1999. Return of Macao to China. Four sheets containing T **1303** and similar multicoloured designs.

MSN3951	Four sheets. (a) 155×100m. 20ch. Type **1303** (green frame); 20ch. Jiang Zemin (President of People's Republic of China) and He Houba (mayor of Macao Special Administrative Region) (green frame); 80ch. Mao Tse-tung (green frame); (b) 155×100 mm. As No. **MS**N3951a but gold frames; (c) 90×122 mm. 1wn. Jiang Zemin (green frame) (circular design); (d) As **MS**N3951c but with gold frame	8·25	6·75

1304 Steel Worker holding Torch

2000. New Year. 40th Anniversary of 19 April Rising.

N3952	**1304** 10ch. multicoloured	30	20

1305 Yellow Dragon

2000. Koguryo Era Tomb Murals, Jian. Multicoloured.

N3953	70ch. Type **1305**	1·20	90
MSN3954	90×60 mm. 1wn.60 Blue dragon (51×33 mm)	3·00	2·20

1306 Weeding

2000. *Rural Life* (anon). Showing details from the painting. Multicoloured.

N3955	40ch. Type **1306**	75	55
N3956	40ch. Hemp cloth weaving	75	55
N3957	40ch. Threshing	75	55
N3958	40ch. Riverside market	75	55

1307 Views across Lake Chou

2000. Mt. Paektu. Multicoloured.

N3959	20ch. Type **1307**	45	35
N3960	20ch. Eagle-shaped rock formation	45	35
N3961	20ch. Owl-shaped rock formation	45	35

1308 Chuibari Mask Dance

2000. Pongsan Mask Dance. Depicting masks and characters from component dances. Multicoloured.

N3962	50ch. Type **1308**	90	65
N3963	80ch. Ryangban Mask Dance	1·50	1·10
N3964	1wn. Malttugi Mask Dance	2·10	1·60

1309 Cat

2000. Cats. Multicoloured.

N3965	50ch. Type **1309**	1·00	80
N3966	50ch. Three kittens	1·00	80
N3967	50ch. Mother and kittens	1·00	80

1310 Singapura Cat

2000. Fauna. Multicoloured.

N3968	2wn. Type **1310**	3·75	2·75
N3969	2wn. Blue Abyssinian cat	3·75	2·75
N3970	2wn. Oriental cat	3·75	2·75
N3971	2wn. Scottish fold tabby cat	3·75	2·75
N3972	2wn. Shiba inu	3·75	2·75
N3973	2wn. Yorkshire terrier	3·75	2·75
N3974	2wn. Japanese chin	3·75	2·75
N3975	2wn. Afghan hound	3·75	2·75
N3976	2wn. Przewalski's horse	3·75	2·75
N3977	2wn. Grey cob	3·75	2·75
N3978	2wn. White horse rearing	3·75	2·75
N3979	2wn. Donkeys	3·75	2·75
N3980	2wn. Panda in tree	3·75	2·75
N3981	2wn. Panda eating	3·75	2·75
N3982	2wn. Panda scratching against tree	3·75	2·75
N3983	2wn. Mother and cub	3·75	2·75
N3984	2wn. Two polar bears (*Ursus maritimus*)	3·75	2·75
N3985	2wn. Mother and cub	3·75	2·75
N3986	2wn. Standing bear	3·75	2·75
N3987	2wn. Bear lying down	3·75	2·75
N3988	2wn. Mexican lance-headed rattlesnake (*Crotalus polystictus*)	3·75	2·75
N3989	2wn. Scarlet king snake (*Lampropeltis triangulum elapsoides*)	3·75	2·75
N3990	2wn. Green tree python (*Chondropython viridis*)	3·75	2·75
N3991	2wn. Blood python (*Python curtus*)	3·75	2·75
N3992	2wn. Corythosaurus	3·75	2·75
N3993	2wn. Psittacosaurus	3·75	2·75
N3994	2wn. Megalosaurus	3·75	2·75
N3995	2wn. Muttaburrasaurus	3·75	2·75
N3996	2wn. Burmeister's porpoise (*Phocoena spinipinnis*)	3·75	2·75
N3997	2wn. Finless porpoise (*Neophocaena phocaenoides*)	3·75	2·75
N3998	2wn. Bottle-nosed dolphin (*Tursiops truncatus*)	3·75	2·75
N3999	2wn. Curvier's beaked whale (*Ziphius cavirostris*)	3·75	2·75
N4000	2wn. Port Jackson shark (*Heterodontus portusjacksoni*)	3·75	2·75
N4001	2wn. Great hammerhead shark (*Sphyrna mokarran*) (inscr 'mokkarran')	3·75	2·75
N4002	2wn. Zebra shark (*Stegostoma fasciatum*)	3·75	2·75
N4003	2wn. Ornate wobbegong (*Orectolobus ornatus*)	3·75	2·75
N4004	2wn. Ruddy shelduck (*Tadorna ferruginea*)	3·75	2·75
N4005	2wn. European widgeon (*Anas penelope*)	3·75	2·75
N4006	2wn. Mandarin drake (*Aix galericulata*)	3·75	2·75
N4007	2wn. Hottentot teal (*Anas hottentota*)	3·75	2·75
N4008	2wn. Little owl (*Athene noctua*)	3·75	2·75
N4009	2wn. Ural owl (*Strix uralensis*)	3·75	2·75
N4010	2wn. Great horned owl (*Bubo virginianus*)	3·75	2·75
N4011	2wn. Snowy owl (*Nyctea scandiaca*)	3·75	2·75
N4012	2wn. Slaty-headed parakeet (*Psittacula himalayana*)	3·75	2·75
N4013	2wn. Male eclectus parrot (*Eclectus roratus*)	3·75	2·75
N4014	2wn. Major Mitchell's cockatoo (*Cacatua leadbeateri*)	3·75	2·75
N4015	2wn. Female eclectus parrot (*Eclectus roratus*)	3·75	2·75
N4016	2wn. Indian leaf butterfly (*Kallima paralekta*)	3·75	2·75
N4017	2wn. Spanish festoon (*Zerynthia rumina*)	3·75	2·75

N4018 2wn. Male and female emerald swallowtails (*Papilio palinurus*) 3·75 2·75
N4019 2wn. *Bhutanitis lidderdalii* 3·75 2·75
N4020 2wn. Bumble bee 3·75 2·75
N4021 2wn. Bumble bee on flower 3·75 2·75
N4022 2wn. Honey bee (*Apis mellifera*) 3·75 2·75
N4023 2wn. Honey bee attacking spider 3·75 2·75
N4024 2wn. *Micrommata virescens* (spider) 3·75 2·75
N4025 2wn. *Araneus quadratus* (spider) 3·75 2·75
N4026 2wn. *Dolomedes fimbriatus* (spider) 3·75 2·75
N4027 2wn. *Aculepeira ceropegia* (spider) 3·75 2·75

Nos. N3980/N3983 are wrongly inscr 'Aculepeira ceropegia'.

1311 Log Cabin (birthplace, Mt. Paektu)

2000. 58th Birth Anniversary of Kim Jong Il.
N4028 **1311** 40ch. multicoloured 75 55

1312 Styracosaurus

2000. Dinosaurs. Sheet 120×80 mm, containing T **1312** and similar multicoloured designs.
MSN4029 1wn. Type **1312**; 1wn. Saltasaurus (29×41 mm); 1wn. Tyrannosaurus 6·25 5·00

1313 Peacock (*Inachis io*)

2000. Butterflies. Multicoloured.
N4030 40ch. Type **1313** 90 65
N4031 60ch. Swallowtail (*Papilio machaon*) 1·20 90
N4032 80ch. Mimic (*Hypolimnas misippus*) 1·50 1·10
N4033 1wn.20 *Papilio bianor Cramer* 2·40 1·80

1314 Patas Monkey (*Erythrocebus patas*)

2000. Primates. Multicoloured.
N4035 50ch. Type **1314** 1·00 80
N4036 50ch. Western tarsier (*Tarsius spectrm*) 1·00 80
MSN4037 Sheet 75×65 mm. 2wn. Mona monkey (*Cercopithecus mona*) 4·25 3·00

1315 Red Flag, Top of Chollima Statue and Emblem

2000. 55th Anniversary of Korean Worker's Party (1st issue).
N4038 **1315** 10ch. multicoloured 30 20

See also Nos. N4083/**MS**N4084.

1316 Demonstrators

2000. 40th Anniversary of 19 April Uprising, South Korea.
N4039 **1316** 10ch. multicoloured 30 20

1317 Kim Il Sun Flower

2000. 88th Birth Anniversary of Kim Il Sung.
N4040 **1317** 40ch. multicoloured 90 65

1318 Mun Ik Hwan

2000. Sixth Death Anniversary of Mun Ik Hwan (National Reunification Prize winner).
N4041 **1318** 50ch. multicoloured 1·00 80

1319 Symbols of Technology, Globe, Flag and Chollima Statue

2000. New Millennium. 55th Anniversary of Korean Worker's Party. Multicoloured.
N4042 40ch. Type **1319** 90 65
N4043 1wn.20 Dove with envelope, globe and satellites 2·40 1·80

1320 *Cattleya intermedia*

2000. Orchids. Multicoloured.
N4044 20ch. Type **1320** 45 35
N4045 50ch. *Dendrobium moschatum* 1·00 80
N4046 70ch. *Brassolaeliocattleya* 1·50 1·10
MSN4047 85×60 mm. 2wn. *Laeliocattleya* 4·25 3·00

1321 Okryu Bridge (River Taedong)

2000. Bridges.
N4048 20ch. Type **1321** 60 45
N4049 30ch. Ansan Bridge (River Pothong) 90 65
N4050 1wn. Rungna Bridge (River Taedong) 2·75 2·00

1322 Okryugum and Jaengggang Dancers

2000. Air. WIPA 2000 International Stamp Exhibition, Vienna. Traditional Instruments and Folk Dances. Sheet 150×84 mm, containing T **1322** and similar vert designs. Multicoloured.
MSN4051 1wn. Type **1322**; 1wn.50 Oungum and Full Moon Viewing; 1wn.50 Janggo (drum) and Trio 8·00 6·75

The 1wn. stamp does not carry an airmail inscription.

1323 *Half Moon* (Yun Kuk Yong)

2000. Children's Songs. Multicoloured.
N4052 40ch. Type **1323** 90 65
N4053 60ch. *Kangnam Nostalgia* (Kim Sok Song and An Ki Yong) 1·20 90
MSN4054 95×80 mm. 1.50wn. *Spring in Home Village* (Ri Won Su and Hong Ran Pha) 3·00 2·20

1324 Pearly Nautilus (*Nautilus pompilius*)

2000. Cephalopods. Multicoloured.
N4055 40ch. Type **1324** 90 65
N4056 60ch. Common octopus (*Octopus vulgaris*) 1·20 90
N4057 1wn.50 Squid (*Ommastrephes sloanei pacificus*) 3·00 2·20
MSN4058 60×70 mm. 1wn.50 No. N4057 3·00 2·20

1325 Drake and Duck

2000. Mandarin Ducks. Multicoloured.
N4059 50ch. Type **1325** 1·10 80
N4060 50ch. Drake with duck and couple on bridge 1·10 80
MSN4061 92×75 mm. 1wn. Duck, drake and ducklings 2·10 1·60

1326 Table Tennis

2000. World Expo 2000 International Stamp Exhibition, Anaheim, California. Sport. Multicoloured.
N4062 80ch. Type **1326** 1·70 1·30
N4063 1wn. Basketball 2·00 1·50
N4064 1wn.20 Baseball 2·40 1·90

1327 Sungri-61 NA

2000. Trucks. Multicoloured.
N4065 40ch. Type **1327** 90 70
N4066 70ch. Tipper truck 1·70 1·30
N4067 1wn.50 Konsol 25 ton dump truck 3·00 2·30

1328 Ri Tae Hun (artillery company commander) and 76 mm Field Gun

2000. Weaponry. Multicoloured.
N4068 60ch. Type **1328** 1·40 1·10
N4069 80ch. Ko Hyon Bin (tank commander) and T-34 tank 1·80 1·40
N4070 1wn. Squadron leader Paek Ki Rak and Yakovlev Yak-9P pursuit plane 2·10 1·60

1329 Fluorite

2000. Minerals. Multicoloured.
N4071 30ch. Type **1329** 60 45
N4072 60ch. Graphite 1·40 1·10
N4073 1wn.60 Magnesite 3·50 2·75
MSN4074 74×74 mm. 1wn.60 No. N4073 3·75 3·00

2000. Indonesia 2000 International Stamp Exhibition, Jakarta. Nos. N4059/**MS**N4061 optd **WORLD PHILATELIC EXHIBITION JAKARTA 15-21 AUGUST 2000** and emblem, No. **MS**N4061 optd in the margin.
N4075 50ch. multicoloured 1·10 90
N4076 50ch. multicoloured 1·10 90
MSN4077 1wn. multicoloured 2·30 1·90

1331 Swimming

2000. Olympic Games, Sydney. Triathlon. Sheet 78×110 mm, containing T **1331** and similar horiz designs. Multicoloured.
MSN4078 80ch. Type **1331**; 1wn.20 Cycling; 2wn. Running 9·00 7·75

1332 Sanju Falls

2000. Myohyang Mountain. Multicoloured.
N4079 40ch. Type **1332** 90 70
N4080 40ch. Inho rock 90 70
N4081 1wn.20 Sangwon valley 2·75 2·10

2000. Espana 2000 International Stamp Exhibition, Madrid. No. **MS**N4029 optd **Exposioion Mundial de Filatolia 2000. 0.6 - 14.** in the margin.
MSN4082 120×80 mm. 1wn. Type **1312**; 1wn. Saltasaurus; 1wn. Tyrannosaurus 6·25 5·00

1334 Anniversary Emblem and Party Museum

2000. 55th Anniversary of Korean Worker's Party (2nd issue). Multicoloured.
N4083 10ch. Type **1334** 30 25
MSN4084 120×85 mm. 50ch. Kim Il Sung (35×56 mm); 50ch. Kim Jong Il (35×56 mm); 50ch. Kim Jong Suk (35×56 mm) 3·50 2·75

1335 Flag, Bulldozer and Fields

2000. Land Re-organisation.
N4085 **1335** 10ch. multicoloured 30 25

1336 Potatoes, Pigs, Fields and Scientist

2000. Taehongdan (potato production centre). Multicoloured.
N4086 40ch. Type **1336** 90 70
MSN4087 110×92 mm. 2wn. Kim Il Sung with farmers in potato field (42×34 mm) 4·50 3·50

1337 Kim Jong Il and President Jiang Zemin

2000. Visit of Kim Jong Il to People's Republic of China. Sheet 110×80 mm.

MSN4088 **1337** 1wn.20 multicoloured 2·75 2·20

1338 Kim Jong Il and President Kim Dae Jung

2000. North Korea–South Korea Summit Meeting, Pyongyang. Sheet 85×110 mm.

MSN4089 **1338** 2wn. multicoloured 4·50 3·50

1339 Kim Jong Il and President Putin

2000. Visit of Pres. Vladimir Putin of Russian Federation. Sheet 94×108 mm.

MSN4090 **1339** 1wn.50 multicoloured 3·50 2·75

1340 Soldiers crossing River Amnok

2000. 50th Anniversary of Chinese People's Volunteers Participation in Korean War (1st issue). Sheet 139×164 mm, containing T **1340** and similar horiz designs. Multicoloured.

MSN4091 10ch. Type **1340**; 10ch. Battle; 50ch. Chinese and Korean soldiers; 50ch. Mao Tse-tung and Chinese leaders; 80ch. Soldiers and gun emplacement 4·50 3·50

1341 Chinese and Korean Soldiers

2000. 50th Anniversary of Chinese People's Volunteers Participation in Korean War (2nd issue).

N4092 **1341** 30ch. multicoloured 75 60

1342 *Aquilegia oxysepala*

2000. Alpine Flowers. Multicoloured.

N4093 30ch. Type **1342**	75	60
N4094 50ch. Brilliant campion (*Lychnis fulgens*)	1·20	95
N4095 70ch. Self-heal (*Prunela vulgaris*)	1·70	1·30

1343 Women presenting Prisoners with Flowers

2000. Repatriation of Long-term Prisoners of War. Sheets containing horiz designs as T **1343**. Multicoloured.

MSN4096 Two sheets. (a) 139×87 mm. 80ch. Type **1343**. (b) 165×120 mm. 1wn.20 Prisoners and crowd. Price for 2 sheets 4·50 3·75

1344 Flag, Factories and Trees

2001. New Year (1st issue).

N4097 **1344** 10ch. multicoloured 30 25

1345 White Snake meeting Xu Xian

2001. New Year (2nd issue). *Tale of the White Snake*. Multicoloured.

N4098 10ch. Type **1345**	30	25
N4099 40ch. Stealing the Immortal Grass	90	75
N4100 50ch. White and Green snakes and Xu Xian	1·10	90
N4101 80ch. Flooding of Jinshan Hill	1·70	1·40
MSN4102 105×80 mm. 1wn.20 White snake and Green snake (32×52 mm)	2·75	2·30

1346 E. Lasker and J-R. Capablanca

2001. World Chess Champions. 165th Birth Anniversary of Wilhelm Steinitz (19th-century champion) (**MS**N4109). Multicoloured.

N4103 10ch. Type **1346**	35	30
N4104 20ch. A. Alekhine and M. Euwe	65	55
N4105 30ch. M. Botvinnik and V. Smylov	80	70
N4106 40ch. T. Petrosian and M. Tal	1·00	85
N4107 50ch. B. Spassky and R. Fisher	1·20	95
N4108 1wn. A. Karpov and G. Kasparov	2·30	1·90
MSN4109 105×80 mm. 2wn.50 Wilhelm Steinitz (32×52 mm)	6·25	5·25

1347 White Suit and Black Hat

2001. Ri-Dynasty Men's Costumes. Multicoloured.

N4110 10ch. Type **1347**	35	30
N4111 40ch. White suit with blue waistcoat	1·00	85
N4112 50ch. White trousers, brown jacket and pagoda-shaped hat	1·20	95
N4113 70ch. Knee-length pale blue coat, black hat and stick	1·60	1·40
MSN4114 110×80 mm. 1wn.50 Blue knee-length coat with ornamental cummerbund and black boots	3·50	3·00

1348 Small Appliance (fire)

2001. Fire Engines. Designs showing engines and fire hazards. Multicoloured.

N4115 20ch. Type **1348**	50	40
N4116 30ch. Large engine with hydraulic ladder (oil can)	65	55
N4117 40ch. Small engine with two-door cab and closed back (match)	1·00	85
N4118 60ch. Small engine with ladder, spotlight and external hose reel (gas canister)	1·50	1·20
N4119 2wn. Older-style engine (cigarette)	5·00	4·25
MSN4120 95×90 mm. 2wn. As No. N4119 (32×52 mm)	5·25	4·50

1349 Black-naped Oriole (*Oriolus chinensis*)

2001. HONG KONG 2001 International Stamp Exhibition. Sheet 72×80 mm.

MSN4121 **1349** 1wn.40 multicoloured 3·25 2·75

1350 Jjong Il Peak and Flower

2001. 59th Birth Anniversary of Kim Jong Il.

N4122 **1350** 10ch. multicoloured 35 30

1351 Flag and Symbols of Industry and Agriculture

2001. New Millennium. *Rodong Sinmun*, *Josoninmingun* and *Chongnyonjonwi* Newspapers Joint Editorial.

N4123 **1351** 10ch. multicoloured 35 30

1352 Log Cabin (revolutionary headquarters, Mt. Paektu)

2001

N4124 **1352** 40ch. multicoloured 1·00 85

1353 Family Home, Mangyongdae

2001. 89th Birth Anniversary of Kim Il Sung. Multicoloured.

N4125 10ch. Type **1353**	50	30
MSN4126 170×103 mm. 80ch.×8, Eight different portraits of Kim Il Sung (vert)	16·00	14·00

1354 Kim Jong Il

2001. Army as Priority. Sheet 140×75 mm.

MSN4127 **1354** 1wn. multicoloured 2·50 2·10

1355 Pyongyang–Kaesong Motorway

2001. Roads. Multicoloured.

N4128 40ch. Type **1355**	1·00	85
N4129 70ch. Pyongyang–Hyanngsan expressway	1·60	1·40
N4130 1wn.20 Pyongyang–Nampo motorway	3·00	2·50
N4131 1wn.50 Pyongyang–Wonsan expressway	3·50	3·00

1356 Ryongwang Pavilion, Pyongyang

2001. Cultural Heritage. Pavilions. Multicoloured.

N4132 40ch. Type **1356**	1·00	85
N4133 80ch. Inphung, Kanggye	2·00	1·70
N4134 1wn.50 Paeksang, Anju	3·50	3·00
N4135 2wn. Thonggun, Uiju	5·00	4·25

1357 Man with raised Arm

2001

N4136 **1357** 10ch. Multicoloured 35 30

1358 Blue-throat (*Luscinia svecica*)

2001. Birds. Multicoloured.

N4137 10ch. Type **1358**	35	30
N4138 40ch. Grey lag goose (*Anser anser*)	1·00	85
N4139 80ch. Short-tailed albatross (*Diomedea albatrus*)	2·00	1·70
N4140 1wn. Little ring plover (*Charadrius dubius*)	2·50	2·10
N4141 1wn.20 Common guillemot (*Uria aalge*)	3·00	2·50
N4142 1wn.50 House martin (*Delichon urbica*)	3·50	3·00

1359 Mao Zedong

2001. 80th Anniversary of Chinese Communist Party. Three sheets, each 152×67 mm containing T **1359** and similar horiz designs. Multicoloured.

MSN4143 (a) 80ch. Type **1359**; (b) 80ch. Deng Xiaping; (c) 80ch. Jiang Zemin 6·00 5·00

1360 Woljong Temple, Mt. Kuwol

2001. Kumol Mountain. Multicoloured.

N4144 10ch. Type **1360**	35	30
N4145 40ch. Revolutionary building	1·00	85
N4146 70ch. Potnamu Pavilion	1·60	1·40
N4147 1wn.30 Tak Peak	3·25	2·75
N4148 1wn.50 Ryongyon Falls	3·50	3·00

1361 *Rheum coreanum*

2001. Endangered Species. Plants. Multicoloured.

N4149 10ch. Type **1361**	35	30
N4150 40ch. *Forsythia densiflora*	1·00	85
N4151 1wn. *Rhododendron yedoense*	2·50	2·10
N4152 2wn. *Iris setosa*	5·00	4·25

1362 *Eria pannea*

2001. Orchids. Multicoloured.

N4153 10ch. Type **1362**	35	30
N4154 40ch. *Cymbidium*	1·00	85
N4155 90ch. *Sophrolaeliocattleya*	2·10	1·80
N4156 1wn.60 *Cattleya trianae*	4·00	3·25
N4157 2wn. *Cypripedium macranthum*	5·00	4·25
MSN4158 142×96 mm. No. N4157	5·25	4·50

1363 Pibaldo Lighthouse

2001. Lighthouses. Multicoloured.

N4159 40ch. Type **1363**	1·00	85
N4160 70ch. Soho, Hamhung	1·60	1·40
N4161 90ch. Komalsan, Chongjin	2·10	1·80
N4162 1wn.50 Alsom, Rason	3·50	3·00
MSN4163 81×95 mm. No. N4162	3·75	3·25

1364 Kim Po Hyon

2001. 130th Birth Anniversary of Kim Po Hyon. Sheet 80×90 mm.

MSN4164 **1364** 1wn. black and bronze	2·50	2·10

1365 Black Stork (*Ciconia nigra*)

2001. Endangered Species. Fauna. Multicoloured.

N4165 10ch. Type **1365**	35	30
N4166 40ch. Cinereous vulture (*Aegypius monchus*)	1·00	85
N4167 70ch. Chinese water deer (*Hydropotes inermis*)	1·60	1·40
N4168 90ch. Goral (*Nemorhaedus goral*)	2·10	1·80
N4169 1wn.30 Northern eagle owl (*Bubo bubo*)	3·25	2·75
MSN4170 106×81 mm. No. N4169	3·50	3·00

1366 Deng Ya Ping receiving Gold Medal for Table Tennis from Juan Antonio Samaranch (Olympic president)

2001. Olympic Games 2008, Beijing. Sheet 152×115 mm containing T **1366** and similar circular designs. Multicoloured.

MSN4171 56ch.×5, Type **1366**; Jiang Zemin (pres. People's Republic of China); Wang Jun Xia (athletics); Li Ning (gymnast); Fu Ming Xia (diver)	7·50	6·25

1367 Cycle Football

2001. Cycling. Sheet 90×145 mm containing T **1367** and similar vert designs. Multicoloured.

MSN4172 10ch. Type **1367**; 40ch. Road racing; 1wn. Cyclocross; 2wn. Indoor racing	9·75	8·25

1368 Yuri Gagarin

2001. Space Exploration. Multicoloured.

N4173 10ch. Type **1368** (cosmonaut)	35	30
N4174 40ch. *Apollo 11* space ship	1·00	85
N4175 1wn.50 *Kwangmyongsong* satellite	3·50	3·00
N4176 2wn. Edmund Halley (astronomer). Halley's comet and Giotto satellite	5·00	4·25
MSN4177 140×197 mm. Nos. N4173/N4176	9·75	8·25

1369 Presidents Vladimir Putin and Kim Jong Il

2001. Visit of Kim Jong Il to Russia. Sheet 92×105 mm.

MSN4178 **1369** 1wn.50 mulicoloured	3·50	3·00

1370 Presidents Kim Jong Il and Jiang Zemin

2001. Meeting between President Kim Jong Il and Jiang Zemin (president People's Republic of China). Sheet 72×104 mm.

MSN4179 **1370** 1wn.50 multicoloured	3·50	3·00

1371 Kim Jong Suk protecting Kim Il Sung during Battle

2001. 84th Birth Anniversary of Kim Jong Suk (revolutionary fighter). Sheet 168×100 mm.

MSN4180 **1371** 1wn.60 multicoloured	4·00	3·25

1372 Kim Jong Il inspecting Troops

2001. Tenth Anniversary of Kim Jong Il's election as Supreme Commander of Korean People's Army. Sheet 90×110 mm.

MSN4181 1wn. multicoloured	2·50	2·10

1373 Chollima Statue

2002

N4182 **1373** 10ch. multicoloured	35	30

1374 Grey Horse

2002. New Year. Year of the Horse. *Ten Horses* (paintings by Wang Zhi Cheng) (Nos. N4183/N4186). Multicoloured.

N4183 10ch. Type **1374**	35	30
N4184 40ch. Bay	1·00	85
N4185 60ch. Skewbald	1·50	1·20
N4186 1wn.30 Piebald	3·25	2·75
MSN4187 (a) 106×80 mm. 1w.60. *Jiu Fang Gao* (painting by Xu Bei Hong) (36×57 mm); (b) 168×104 mm. Nos. N4183/N4186 and **MS**4187a	14·00	11·50

1375 Flower Basket

2002. 60th Birth Anniversary of Kim Jong Il. Multicoloured.

N4188 10ch. Type **1375**	35	30
MSN4189 (a) 124×94 mm. 1wn.20×3, Kim Il Sung (father) (32×52 mm); Kim Jong Il as child (32×52 mm); Kim Jong Suk (mother) (32×52 mm). (b) 105×85 mm. 1wn.50 Kim Jong Il with soldiers (45×34 mm). (c) 77×117 mm. 2wn. Kim Jong Il as young man (42×64 mm)	18·00	16·00

1376 Zeppelin LZ1

2002. Centenary of First Zeppelin Airship Flight. Multicoloured.

N4190 40ch. Type **1376**	80	70
N4191 80ch. LZ	1·60	1·40
N4192 1wn.20 Zeppelin NT	2·50	2·10
MSN4193 (a) 110×80 mm. 2wn.40 Zeppelin NT (different). (b) 132×110 mm. Nos. N4190/**MS**N4193a	15·00	13·00

1377 Banner, Torch and Soldiers

2002. *Rodong Sinmun*, *Josoninmingun* and *Chongnyonjonwi* Newspapers Joint Editorial.

N4194 **1377** 10ch. multicoloured	35	30

1378 *Collybia confluens*

2002. Fungi. Multicoloured.

N4195 10ch. Type **1378**	35	30
N4196 40ch. *Sparassis laminose*	80	70
N4197 80ch. Grisette (*Amanita vaginata*) (inscr 'Amanjta')	1·60	1·40
N4198 1wn.20 *Russla integra*	2·50	2·10
N4199 1wn.50 Scaly pholita (*Pholita squarrosa*)	3·00	2·50

1379 Family Home, Mangyongdae

2002. 90th Birth Anniversary of Kim Il Sung. Multicoloured.

N4200 10ch. Type **1379**	35	30
MSN4201 (a) 105×85 mm. 1wn.50 Kim Il Sung as young man (45×54 mm). (b) 105×85 mm. 1wn.50 With Kim Jong Suk (wife) (45×54 mm). (c) 105×85 mm. 1wn.50 With Kim Chaeck (revolutionary) (45×54 mm). (d) 76×117 mm. 2wn. Wearing black jacket (42×64 mm)	13·50	12·00

1380 Kang Pan Sok

2002. 110th Birth Anniversary of Kang Pan Sok (mother of Kim Il Sung). Sheet 70×100 mm.

MSN4202 **1380** 1wn. multicoloured	2·00	1·70

1381 Emblem, Doves, Dancers and Music

2002. 20th April Spring Friendship Art Festival.

N4203 **1381** 10ch. multicoloured	35	30

1382 Electric Locomotive

2002. 20th-century Locomotives. Multicoloured.

N4204 10ch. Type **1382**	35	30
N4205 40ch. Electric locomotive (different)	80	70
N4206 1wn.50 Steam locomotive	2·75	2·30
N4207 2wn. Steam locomotive (different)	3·50	3·00
MSN4208 65×55 mm. 2wn. Diesel locomotive	3·50	3·00

1383 Inscription

2002. Birth Centenary of He Baozhen (first wife of Liu Shaoqi (Chinese politician)). Sheet 150×110 mm containing T **1383** and similar multicoloured designs.
MSN4209 10ch. Type **1383**; 20ch. Arch; 30ch. Building; 40ch. Family (33×45 mm); 1wn. He Baozhen and Liu Shaoqi (33×45 mm) 4·00 3·50

1384 *Cristaria plicata*

2002. Shellfish. Multicoloured.

N4210	10ch. Type **1384**	35	30
N4211	40ch. *Lanceolaria cospidata*	65	55
N4212	1wn. *Schistodesmus lampreyanus*	1·60	1·40
N4213	1wn.50 *Lamprotula coreana*	2·50	2·10

1385 Soldiers

2002. 70th Anniversary of Korean People's Army. Multicoloured.
N4214 10ch. Type **1385** 35 30
MSN4215 60×85 mm. 1wn.60 Kim Il Sung and Kim Jong Il (39×51 mm). Perf or imperf 3·25 2·75

1386 Actors

2002. Arirang Festival. Multicoloured.

N4216	10ch. Type **1386**	35	30
N4217	20ch. Animation and cartoon characters	50	40
N4218	30ch. Dancer holding fan	65	55
N4219	40ch. Dancers	80	70

MSN4220 120×93 mm. 1wn. Woman holding tambourine (54×45 mm) 2·00 1·70

1387 Ri Rang and Song Bu

2002. Arirang Legend. Sheet 176×88 mm containing T **1387** and similar vert designs. Multicoloured.
MSN4221 10ch. Type **1387**; 40ch. As young adults; 50ch. Ri Rang killing landlord; 1wn.50 Song Bu 4·25 3·50

1388 Symbols of Modern Industry

2002. Science and Technology.
N4222 **1388** 10ch. multicoloured 35 30

1389 Squid-shaped Stalactite

2002. Ryongmun Cavern. Sheet 160×105 mm containing T **1389** and similar vert designs. Multicoloured.
MSN4223 10ch. Type **1389**; 20ch. Chandelier-shaped stalactite; 30ch. Hill-shaped stalagmite; 40ch. Stalagmite with rough surface 2·00 1·70

1390 Monument

2002. 30th Anniversary of Charter of Three Principles for Re-unification.
N4224 **1390** 10ch. multicoloured 35 30

1391 *Stauropus fagi*

2002. Butterflies and Moths. Multicoloured.

N4225	10ch. Type **1391**	35	30
N4226	40ch. *Agrias claudina*	65	55
N4227	1wn.50 *Catocala nupta*	2·50	2·10
N4228	2wn. Blue morpho (*Morpho rhetenor*)	3·25	2·75

조선우표 DPR KOREA 주체91(2002) 80전
(1392)

2002. 16th Chinese Communist Party Conference, Beijing. Nos. **MS**N4143a/**MS**N4143c optd in the margin with T **1392**.
MSN4229 (a) 80ch. Type **1359**. (b) 80ch. Deng Xiaping. (c) 80ch. Jiang Zemin 6·00 5·00

1393 Child and Old Man

2002. 50th Anniversary of Free Medical Care.
N4230 **1393** 10ch. multicoloured 35 30

1394 Kim Jong Suk as Child

2002. 85th Birth Anniversary of Kim Jong Suk (wife of Kim Il Sung). Sheet containing T **1394** and similar vert designs. Multicoloured.
MSN4231 10ch. Type **1394**; 40ch. As young woman; 1wn. Wearing uniform; 1wn.50 In middle age 5·00 4·25

1395 Workers, Soldiers and Symbols of Industry

2002. 30th Anniversary of Constitution.
N4232 **1395** 10ch. multicoloured 35 30

1396 Returnees

2002. Red Cross and Red Crescent (humanitarian organisations) Day. Multicoloured.

N4233	3wn. Type **1396**	35	30
N4234	12wn. Red Cross workers	80	70
N4235	80wn. Family (AIDS awareness)	1·60	1·40
N4236	150wn. Humanitarian aid to flood victims	3·00	2·50

MSN4237 (a) 150×115 mm. Nos. N4233/N4234 and N4326, each×2. (b) 85×113 mm. No. N4325 1·80 1·50

1397 Hong Chang Su

2002. Hong Chang Su. 2000 World Super-Flyweight Champion. Sheet 110×75 mm.
MSN4238 **1397** 75wn. multicoloured 1·60 1·40

1398 Kim Jong Il and President Vladimir Putin

2002. Kim Jong Il's Visit to Russia. Two sheets containing T **1398** and similar multicoloured design.
MSN4239 (a) 85×70 mm. 70wn. Type **1398**; (b) 120×100 mm. 120wn. President Putin and Kim Jong Il shaking hands (vert) 4·00 3·50

1399 Seal-point Shorthair Cat

2002. Cats and Dogs. Multicoloured.

N4240	3wn. Type **1399**	25	20
N4241	12wn. Pungsan dog	35	30
N4242	100wn. White shorthair cat	2·50	2·10
N4243	150wn. Black and white shorthair cat	3·50	3·00

MSN4244 57×70 mm. 150wn. Cavalier King Charles spaniel 3·75 3·25

1400 Iron Pyrite

2002. Minerals. Multicoloured.

N4245	3wn. Type **1400**	25	20
N4246	12wn. Magnetite	35	30
N4247	130wn. Calcite	3·00	2·50
N4248	150wn. Galena	3·50	3·00

1401 Prime Minister Koizumi Junichiro and Kim Jong Il signing Declaration

2002. Japan–Korea Bilateral Declaration. Two sheets containing T **1401** and similar horiz design. Multicoloured.
MSN4249 (a) 90×80 mm. 120wn. Type **1401**; (b) 75×65 mm. 150wn. Prime Minister Junichiro and Kim Jong Il shaking hands 5·75 5·25

1402 Family Home, Mangyongdae

2002. National Symbols.

N4250	**1402**	1wn. brown	15	15
N4251	-	3wn. green (vert)	15	15
N4252	-	5wn. agate	25	20
N4253	-	10wn. crimson (vert)	25	20
N4254	-	12wn. claret (17×26 mm)	35	30
N4255	-	20wn. scarlet and ultramarine (17×26 mm)	50	40
N4256	-	30wn. red (vert)	65	55
N4257	-	40wn. blue (vert)	1·00	85
N4258	-	50wn. brown (17×26 mm)	1·20	95
N4259	-	70wn. sepia (17×26 mm)	1·60	1·40
N4260	-	100wn. brown (17×26 mm)	2·50	2·10
N4261	-	200wn. crimson (17×26 mm)	5·00	4·25

Designs: 1w. T **1402**; 3w. Mount Paeku; 5w. Hoeryong; 10w. Kimilsungia; 12w. Torch (Tower of Juche Idea); 20w. Flag; 30w. Kimjongilia; 40w. Magnolia blossom; 50w. National emblem; 70w. Chollima statue; 100w. Victorious Fatherland monument; 200w. Workers Party monument.

1403 Workers and Soldiers

2003. New Year.
N4262 **1403** 3wn. multicoloured 25 20

1404 Bald Eagle steals Young Antelope

2003. Antelope defeats Bald Eagle (fairy tale). Multicoloured.

N4263	3wn. Type **1404**	25	20
N4264	50wn. Antelopes unite to defeat eagle	1·30	1·10
N4265	70wn. Eagle eating fish poisoned by antelopes	1·70	1·40
N4266	100wn. Mother antelope and rescued baby	2·50	2·10

MSN4267 110×80 mm. 150wn. Antelopes carrying fruit (54×45 mm) 3·25 2·75

1405 Greeting Full Moon (January 15th festival)

2003. Folk Festivals. Multicoloured.

N4268	3wn. Type **1405**	25	20
N4269	12wn. Dance greeting full moon (January 15th)	35	30
N4270	40wn. Swinging (Surinal festival)	1·00	85
N4271	70wn. Woman and child (Hangawi festival)	1·70	1·40
N4272	140wn. Peasant dance (Hangawi)	3·25	2·75

MSN4273 110×90 mm. 112wn. Wrestling (Surinal) 2·75 2·40

1406 Soldier

2003. *Rodong Sinmun*, *Josoninmingun* and *Chongnyonjonwi* Newspapers Joint Editorial.
N4274 **1406** 12wn. multicoloured 50 40

1407 Weapons

2003. Withdrawal from NPT.
N4275 **1407** 30wn. multicoloured 85 70

1408 Ode Monument

2003. 61st Birth Anniversary of Kim Jong Il. Multicoloured.
N4276 3wn. Type **1408** 25 20
MSN4277 90×60 mm. 75wn. Mt. Paektu (64×42 mm) 1·80 1·60

1409 *Paekmagang* (cargo ship)

2003. Ships. Multicoloured.
N4278 15wn. Type **1409** 40 35
N4279 50wn. *Konsol* (dredger) 1·20 1·00
N4280 70wn. *Undok No. 2* (passenger ship) 1·70 1·40
N4281 112wn. *Piryugang* (cargo ship) 2·75 2·40
MSN4282 78×52 mm. 150wn. *Pyongyang No. 1* (pleasure cruiser) 3·25 2·75

1410 Zis

2003. Kim Il Sung's Presidential Cars. Multicoloured.
N4283 3wn. Type **1410** 25 20
N4284 14wn. Gaz 40 35
N4285 70wn. Pobeda 1·70 1·40
N4286 90wn. Merceds Benz 2·20 1·80
MSN4287 100×80 mm. 150wn. *Delaying His Urgent Journey* (painting by Kim Sam Gon) (64×42 mm) 3·25 2·75

1411 Book Cover

2003. 30th Anniversary of Publication of *On the Art of the Cinema* by Kim Jong Il. Sheet 95×75 mm.
MSN4288 **1411** 120wn. multicoloured 3·00 2·50

1412 Trumpeter and Symbols of Journey

2003. 80th Anniversary of Kim Il Sung's 250 Mile Journey for Learning.
N4289 **1412** 15wn. multicoloured 50 40

1413 Soldier and Workers

2003. Korean People's Army.
N4290 **1413** 3wn. multicoloured 25 20

1414 Flags and Emblem

2003. Tenth Anniversary of Election of Kim Jong Il as Chairman of National Defence Commission. Multicoloured.
N4291 3wn. Type **1414** 25 20
MSN4292 175×75 mm. 12wn. Kim Jong Il with computers (51×49 mm); 70wn. With soldiers (51×49 mm); 112wn. With raised hand (51×49 mm) 5·75 5·00

1415 Birthplace, Mangyongdae and Kimilsungia

2003. 91st Birth Anniversary of Kim Il Sung.
N4293 **1415** 3wn. multicoloured 25 20

1416 Order of Suhbaatar (Mongolia)

2003. Kim Il Sung's Medals and Orders. Multicoloured.
N4294 12wn. Type **1416** 35 30
N4295 35wn. Order of Grand Cross (Madagascar) 1·00 85
N4296 70wn. Order of Lenin (USSR) 2·20 1·80
N4297 140wn. Order of Playa Giron (Cuba) 4·25 3·50
MSN4298 108×91 mm. 120wn. Fidel Castro (president of Cuba) and Kim Il Sung (horiz) 3·25 2·75

1417 *Pantala flavescens*

2003. Insects. Multicoloured.
N4299 15wn. Type **1417** 50 40
N4300 70wn. *Tibicen japonicus* 1·70 1·40
N4301 220wn. *Xylotrupes dichotomus* 5·75 5·00
N4302 300wn. *Lycaena dispar* 8·50 7·00
MSN4303 150×85 mm. Nos. N4299/N4302 17·00 16·00

1418 Glutinous Rice Cakes

2003. Traditional Food. Multicoloured.
N4304 3wn. Type **1418** 25 20
N4305 30wn. Tongkimchi 85 70
N4306 70wn. Sinsollo 2·00 1·70
MSN4307 100×83 mm. 120wn. Pyongyang raengmyon 3·25 2·75

1419 Victory Monument, Taechongdan Hill

2003. Sheet 98×71 mm.
MSN4308 **1419** 90wn. multicoloured 2·75 2·30

1420 Manse Pavilion

2003. Ryangchon Temple, Kowon, South Hamgyong Province. Multicoloured.
N4309 3wn. Type **1420** 25 20
N4310 12wn. Three statues 35 30
N4311 40wn. Buddha and two saints (painting) 1·20 1·00
N4312 50wn. Buddha and four saints (painting) 1·50 1·30
MSN4313 100×80 mm. 120wn. Taeung Hall 3·00 2·50

1421 Music Score

2003. *We are One* (song). Sheet 70×100 mm.
MSN4314 **1421** 60wn. multicoloured 1·50 1·30

1422 Tigers

2003. Animals. Sheet 157×72 mm containing T **1422** and similar vert designs. Multicoloured.
MSN4315 3wn. Type **1422**; 70wn. Bears; 150wn. Wild boar; 230wn. Deer 12·50 11·50

1423 Public Bonds

2003. Public Bond Purchase Campaign.
N4316 **1423** 140wn. multicoloured 3·75 3·00

1424 Distinguished Service Medal

2003. 50th Anniversary of Liberation. Multicoloured.
N4317 3wn. Type **1424** 25 20
MSN4318 Three sheets, all 146×106 mm. (a) 12wn. Kim Il Sung and radio microphone (38×31 mm); 35wn. Kim Il Sung with soldiers (38×31 mm); 70wn. Kim Il Sung signing document (38×31 mm); 140wn. Kim Il Sung (43×43 mm) (circular). (b) 12wn. Kim Il Sung with soldiers (38×31 mm); 35wn. Kim Il Sung inspecting soldier's weapons (38×31 mm); 70wn. Kim Il Sung and Kim Jong Il (38×31 mm); 140wn. Kim Il Sung (43×43 mm) (circular). (c) 12wn. Kim Jong Il receiving bouquet (38×31 mm); 35wn. Kim Jong Il with soldiers (38×31 mm); 70wn. Kim Jong Il with unit commander (38×31 mm); 140wn. Kim Jong Il (43×43 mm) (circular) 20·00 18·00
MSN4319 65×90 mm. 120wn. President Kim Il Sung 3·00 2·50

1425 *Minicattleya*

2003. Orchids. Multicoloured.
N4320 75wn. Type **1425** 2·00 1·70
N4321 100wn. *Phalaenopsis Aphrodite* (inscr 'Phalanopsis') 2·50 2·10
N4322 150wn. *Calanthe discolour* 3·75 3·25
N4323 200wn. *Dendrobium snowflake* (inscr 'Den.') 5·00 4·25

Nos. N4320/N4323 were issued together, *se-tenant*, forming a composite design.

1426 Japanese White-necked Crane (*Grus vipio*)

2003. Birds. Multicoloured.
N4324 12wn. Type **1426** 35 30
N4325 70wn. Black-crowned night heron (*Nycticorax nycticorax*) 2·10 1·80
N4326 100wn. Domestic pigeon (*Columba livia domestica*) 3·00 2·50
N4327 120wn. Cockatiel (*Nymphicus hollandicus*) 3·50 3·00
N4328 150wn. Tawny owl (*Strix aluco*) 4·25 3·75
MSN4329 70×90 mm. 225wn. Inscr 'Pseudogyps africanus' (39×51 mm) 6·75 6·00

1427 Adelie Penguin (*Pygoscelis adeliae*)

2003. Arctic and Antarctic Fauna. Sheet 160×114 mm containing T **1427** and similar horiz designs. Multicoloured.
MSN4330 15w. Type **1427**; 70wn. Walrus (*Odobenus rosmarus*); 140wn. Polar bear (*Thalarctos maritimus*); 150wn. Bowhead whale (*Balaena mysticetus*) (inscr 'mysticegus'); 220wn. Spotted seal (*Phoca largha*) 16·00 14·50

The stamps and margins of **MS**N4330 form a composite design.

1428 *Pholiota flammans*

2003. Fungi. Multicoloured.
N4331 3wn. Type **1428** 25 20
N4332 12wn. *Geastrum fimbriatum* 35 30
N4333 70wn. *Coprinus atramentarius* 1·90 1·60
N4334 130wn. *Pleurotus cornucopiae* 3·50 3·00
MSN4335 80×65 mm. 250wn. *Elfvingia applanata* 6·75 6·00

1429 Exhibition Hall

2003. National Stamp Exhibition. Multicoloured.

N4336	3wn. Type **1429**	25	20
N4337	60wn. Stamps and display stands (horiz)	1·70	1·50

1430 Emblem and Flag

2003. 55th Anniversary of Democratic Peoples' Republic of Korea. Multicoloured.

N4338	3wn. Type **1430**	25	20
MSN4339	Four sheets, each 65×120 mm. (a) 60wn. *The Birth of New Korea*; 60wn. *On the Road supporting Kim Il Sung*; (b) 60wn. *Braving Rain of Bullets*; 60wn. *Giving command for Counter Offensive*; (c) 60wn. *We Trust and Follow You*; 60wn. *Kim Il Sung at Power Plant*; (d) 60wn. *Victory Assured*; 60wn. *Keeping up Shongun Politics*	13·50	12·50
MSN4340	75×105 mm. 120wn. Kim Il Sung (43×43 mm) (circular)	3·50	3·00

1431

2003. Bangkok 2003 International Stamp Exhibition, Thailand. No. **MS**N4244 optd in the margin with T **1431**.

MSN4341	57×70 mm. 150wn. Cavalier King Charles spaniel	3·75	3·25

1432 Mao Zedong

2003. 110th Birth Anniversary of Mao Zedong (Chinese leader 1945–1976). Multicoloured. Imperf (140w.) or perf (others).

N4342	20wn. Type **1432**	70	60
N4343	20wn. During the 'Long March'	70	60
N4344	30wn. With female companion	85	75
N4345	30wn. Seated in room of men	85	75
N4346	30wn. Addressing partisans	85	75
N4347	30wn. With partisans wearing long coat	85	75
N4348	30wn. Addressing crowd in Beijing	85	75
N4349	30wn. With people from many nations	85	75

1433 Workers and Soldiers

2004. New Year.

N4351	**1433** 3wn. multicoloured	25	25

1434 *Cebus paella*

2004. Monkeys. Multicoloured.

N4352	3wn. Type **1434**	25	25
N4353	60wn. *Papio doguera*	1·70	1·50
N4354	70wn. *Cercopithecus aethiops*	2·10	1·80
N4355	100wn. *Saguinus Oedipus*	3·00	2·50
MSN4356	71×85 mm. 155wn. *Macaca mulatta*	4·25	3·75

1435 Children

2004. Lunar New Year.

N4357	**1435** 3wn. multicoloured	25	25

1436 Yong Liwei

2004. Yong Liwei. First Chinese Astronaut. Multicoloured.

N4358	91wn. Type **1436**	2·50	2·30
N4359	98wn. Returned space capsule (54×45 mm)	2·75	2·40
MSN4360	142×100 mm. Nos. N4358/N4359	5·50	4·75

1437

2004. Hong Kong 2004 International Stamp Exhibition. Nos. N4352/**MS**N4356 optd with T **1437**.

N4361	3wn. multicoloured	25	25
N4362	60wn. multicoloured	1·70	1·50
N4363	70wn. multicoloured	2·10	1·80
N4364	100wn. multicoloured	3·00	2·50
MSN4365	71×85 mm. 155wn. multicoloured	4·25	3·75

1438 Book, Weapons and Slogan

2004. *Rodong Sinmun*, *Josoninmingun* and *Chongnyonjonwi* Newspapers Joint Editorial.

N4366	**1438** 3wn. multicoloured	25	25

1440 Kim Jong Il

2004. 30th Anniversary of Publication of *Juche Idea Programme*. Sheet 151×80 mm.

MSN4372	**1440** 120wn. multicoloured	3·50	3·00

1441 Fields and Goat Herd

2004. 40th Anniversary of Publication of *Theses on Rural Socialist Question* by Kim Il Sung. Multicoloured.

N4373	3wn. Type **1441**	25	25
MSN4374	117×86 mm. 120wn. Kim Il Sung and farmer (49×51 mm)	3·25	2·75

1442 Sokgundo Lighthouse

2004. Lighthouses. Multicoloured.

N4375	3wn. Type **1442**	25	25
N4376	12wn. Yubundo	50	45
N4377	100wn. Jangdokdo	2·50	2·30
N4378	195wn. Amryongdan	5·25	4·50
MSN4379	131×121 mm. Nos. N4375/N4378	8·75	7·50

1443 Korean Chess

2004. Board Games. Multicoloured.

N4380	3wn. Type **1443**	25	25
N4381	12wn. Go	50	45
N4382	90wn. Yut	2·40	2·10
N4383	120wn. Koni	3·25	2·75
MSN4384	110×114 mm. Nos. N4380/N4383	6·75	6·00
MSN4385	97×81 mm. 98wn. Men and child playing chess (54×45 mm)	2·50	2·30

1444 Birthplace, Mangyongdae

2004. 92nd Birth Anniversary of Kim Il Sung. Multicoloured.

N4386	3wn. Type **1444**	25	25
MSN4387	94×76 mm. 120wn. Kim Il Sung (39×51 mm)	3·25	2·75

1445 18th-century Map of Korea

2004. Tok Islet. Multicoloured.

N4388	3wn. Type **1445**	25	25
N4389	12wn. Western islet	50	45
N4390	106wn. Eastern islet	3·00	2·50
N4391	116wn. Both islets (circular) (45×45 mm)	3·25	2·75
MSN4392	101×121 mm. Nos. N4388/N4390	3·75	3·25
MSN4393	160×81 mm. 116wn. No. N4391	3·50	3·00

1446 Calcinoplax antique

2004. Fossils. Multicoloured.

N4394	3wn. Type **1446**	25	25
N4395	12wn. Podozamites lanceolatus	50	45
N4396	70wn. Comptonia naumannii	1·90	1·70
N4397	120wn. Tingia carbonica	3·25	2·75
N4398	140wn. Clinocardium asagaiense	3·75	3·25
MSN4399	135×86 mm. Nos. N4394/N4396 and N4398	6·75	5·75
MSN4400	102×76 mm. 120wn. No. N4397	3·50	3·00

1447 *Notocactus leninghausii*

2004. Cacti. Multicoloured.

N4401	70wn. Type **1447**	1·70	1·50
N4402	90wn. *Echinocactus grusonii*	2·30	2·00
N4403	100wn. *Gymnocalycium baldianum*	2·50	2·30
N4404	140wn. *Mammillaria insularis*	3·75	3·25
MSN4405	148×93 mm. Nos. N4401/N4404	10·50	9·50

1448 Kim Jong Il and Hu Jintao

2004. Kim Jong Il's visit to China. Multicoloured

N4406	3wn. Type **1448**	25	25
N4407	3wn. With Wen Jiabao	25	25
N4408	12wn. With Jiang Zemin	35	30
N4409	12wn. With Jia Qinglin	35	30
N4410	40wn. With Wu Bangguo	1·00	90
N4411	40w. Seated with Zeng Qinghong	1·00	90
N4412	60wn. With Huang Guo and others	1·60	1·40
N4413	60wn. Inspecting Tianjin (new city)	1·60	1·40
N4414	74wn. With Hu Jintao (41×60 mm)	2·10	1·80
MSN4415	Two sheets, each 160×130 mm. (a) Nos. N4406, N4408, N4410 and N4412 (b) Nos. N4407, N4409, N4411 and N4413	6·50	5·50
MSN4416	90×120 mm. N4414 (41×60 mm)	2·30	2·00

1449 Flag

2004. 40th Anniversary of Kim Il Jong at WPK. Multicoloured.

N4417	3wn. Type **1449**	25	25
MSN4418	Three sheets, each 150×75 mm. (a) Size 54×45 mm. 12wn. Kim Il Jong at desk; 100wn. With paintings. (b) Size 54×45 mm. 12wn. Inspecting power station; 100wn. With soldiers. (c) Size 54×45 mm. 12wn. Wearing safety hat and glasses; 100wn. Kim Il Jong	9·00	7·75
MSN4419	84×100 mm. Size 42×60 mm. 130wn. Kim Il Sung and Kim Il Jong	2·10	1·80

1450 Monument and Kimilsungia

2004. Kim Il Sung Commemoration. Multicoloured.

N4420	3wn. Type **1450**	25	25
MSN4421	Four sheets, each 116×120 mm. (a) Size 51×39 mm. 12wn. Kim Il Sung with workers; 116wn. With farmers. (b) Size 51×39 mm. 12wn. With soldiers; 116wn. With children. (c) Size 51×39 mm. 12wn. With Kim Il Jong at Academy; 116wn. With Kim Il Jong on Mt. Paektu. (d) Size 51×39 mm. 12wn. With Mun Ik Hwan; 116wn. Holding telephone	12·50	11·00
MSN4422	70×90 mm. Size 39×51 mm. 112wn. Kim Il Sung	2·75	2·40

1451 Kim Hyong Jik and Kim Il Sung as a Child (statue)

2004. 110th Birth Anniversary of Kim Yong Jik (father of Kim Il Sung). Sheet 150×96 mm.

MSN4423 **1451** 112wn. multicoloured	2·75	2·40

1452 Deng Xiaoping as Young Man

2004. Birth Centenary of Deng Xiaoping (Chinese leader). Multicoloured.

N4424 3wn. Type **1452**	25	25
N4425 12wn. Wearing shorts	35	30
N4426 35wn. Wearing uniform	85	75
N4427 50wn. Giving speech	1·20	1·10
MSN4428 175×115 mm. Nos. N4424/N4427; 70w. Visiting shopping centre (51×39 mm)	5·25	4·50
MSN4429 100×70 mm. 80wn. Deng Xiaoping (51×39 mm)	2·10	1·80

1453 Boxing

2004. Olympic Games, Athens. Multicoloured.

N4430 3wn. Type **1453**	25	25
N4431 12wn. Football	35	30
N4432 85wn. High jump	2·30	2·00
N4433 140wn. Gymnastics	3·50	3·00

1454 *Carassius auratus*

2004. Fish. Sheet 110×140 mm containing T **1454** and similar horiz designs. Multicoloured.

MSN4434 3wn. Type **1454**; 12wn. *Tilapia nilotica*; 140wn. *Ophiocephalus argus*; 165wn. *Clarias gariepinus*	8·50	7·50

1455 Mercedes Benz Fire Appliance

2004. Fire Engines. Multicoloured.

N4435 3wn. Type **1455**	30	25
N4436 12wn. Fire truck	35	30
N4437 40wn. Jelcz fire appliance	1·00	90
N4438 105wn. Mercedes Benz without ladders, facing right	2·50	2·30
MSN4439 115×88 mm. Nos. N4435/N4438	4·25	3·50
MSN4440 85×75 mm. 97wn. Mercedes Benz with ladders, facing left	2·40	2·10

1456 Airbus A340–600

2004. Aircraft. Multicoloured.

N4441 3wn. Type **1456**	30	25
N4442 97wn. Concorde	2·50	2·30
N4443 104wn. *Graff Zeppelin II*	2·75	2·40
N4444 116wn. Junkers	3·00	2·50
MSN4445 126×1058 mm. Nos. N4441/N4444	8·75	7·50

Nos. N4441/N4442 and N4443/N4444 respectively each form a composite design. The two pairs combine with the margin in **MS**N4445 to form a composite design of an airfield.

1457 Kim Il Sung and Prime Minister Koizumi

2004. Kim Jong Il's Meeting with Japanese Prime Minister Junichiro Koizumi. Sheet 150×75 mm.

MSN4446 **1457** 220wn. multicoloured	5·25	4·50

1458 An Jung Gun

2004. 125th Birth Anniversary of An Jung Gun (revolutionary). Sheet 68×90 mm.

MSN4447 **1458** 112wn. multicoloured	2·50	2·30

1459 Kim Jong Suk's Pistol

2004. Kim Jong Suk (Kim Il Sung's wife and revolutionary fighter) Commemoration. Multicoloured.

N4448 3wn. Type **1459**	25	25
MSN4449 103×85 mm. 97wn. Kim Jong Suk (85×42 mm)	2·50	2·30

1460 *Anser cygnoides*

2004. Swan Goose (*Anser cygnoides*). Multicoloured.

N4450 3wn. Type **1460**	30	25
N4451 97wn. Facing left	2·75	2·30
N4452 104wn. Two geese	2·75	2·50
N4453 120wn. Two geese swimming	3·00	2·75

1461 Temple Building

2004. Simwon Temple. Multicoloured.

N4454 3wn. Type **1461**	30	25
MSN4455 120×80 mm. 97wn. Buddha (56×42 mm)	3·00	2·50

1462 Diesel Locomotive

2004. Railways. Multicoloured.

N4456 15wn. Type **1462**	55	45
N4457 40wn. Yellow locomotive	1·10	95
N4458 75wn. Electric locomotive	2·10	1·90
N4459 120wn. Older electric locomotive	3·50	3·00
N4460 150wn. Red locomotive	4·25	3·75
MSN4461 165×91 mm. Nos. N4456/N4458 and N4460	11·50	10·50
MSN4462 95×58 mm. 120wn. No. N4459	3·75	3·25

No. N4463 is vacant

1463 Kim Il Sung and Children

2004. 45th Anniversary of Repatriation. Sheet 85×77 mm.

MSN4464 **1463** 80wn. multicoloured	1·30	1·30

MARIO CESAR KINDELAND MESA (CUBA)

(1464)

2004. Olympic Games, Athens. Nos. N4430/N4433 optd as T **1464** with medal winners' names and country. Multicoloured.

N4465 3wn. Boxing (Mario Cesar Kindelan Mesa) (Cuba)	30	25
N4466 12wn. Football (Argentina)	35	30
N4467 85wn. High jump (Yelena Slesarenko) (Russia)	2·30	2·00
N4468 140wn. Gymnastics (Teng Haibin) (China)	3·50	3·00

1465 Soldier

2005. New Year.

N4469 **1465** 3wn. multicoloured	30	25

1466 Chick

2005. New Year. Year of the Rooster. Designs showing carved wooden fowl (N4470/**MS**4476). Multicoloured.

N4470 3wn. Type **1466**	30	25
N4471 12wn. Hen	35	30
N4472 30wn. Hen sitting on eggs	90	75
N4473 70wn. Hen pecking	2·00	1·70
N4474 100wn. Rooster	2·50	2·20
N4475 140wn. Basket of eggs	3·50	3·00
MSN4476 84×112 mm. Nos. N4470, N4473/N4475	8·50	7·50
MSN4477 80×130 mm. 97wn. Hen and chicks (painting) (50×60 mm)	2·50	2·20

1467 Kim Il Sung

2005. 80th Anniversary (2003) of Kim Il Sung's 250 Mile Journey for Learning. Sheet 125×90 mm.

MSN4478 **1467** 120wn. multicoloured	3·00	2·50

1468 Statue

2005. 45th Anniversary of Chongsanri Method. Sheet 136×95 mm.

MSN4479 **1468** 120wn. multicoloured	3·00	2·50

The stamps and margins of **MS**N4479 form a composite design.

1469 Sunset

2005. Landscapes. Sheet 136×95 mm containing T **1469** and similar horiz designs. Multicoloured.

MSN4480 3wn. Type **1469**; 12wn. Snow covered weapons; 40wn. Flowering trees and mountain; 50wn. Waterside town; 60wn. Waterfall in autumn; 70wn. Tractors working in fields; 80wn. Flower fields; 100wn. Paddy fields	9·50	8·50

1470 Flowers and Mount Paektu

2005. 63rd Birth Anniversary of Kim Jong Il. Multicoloured.

N4481 3wn. Type **1470**	30	25
MSN4482 Two sheets, each 192×60 mm. (a) 50wn.×3, Snow covered peaks, left; Snow covered main peak at sunrise; Snow covered peaks, right. (b) 50wn.×3, Peaks and clouds, left; Peaks and lake; Peaks and lake, right	30	7·75

The stamps of **MS**N4482a/**MS**N4482b, each form a composite design of a mountain range.

1471 Monuments

2005. *Rodong Sinmun*, *Josoninmingun* and *Chongnyonjonwi* Newspapers Joint Editorial.

N4483 **1471** 3wn. multicoloured	30	25

1472 Orchid

2005. 40th Anniversary of Orchid Festival. Multicoloured.

N4484 3wn. Type **1472**	30	25
MSN4485 107×80 mm. 120wn. Kim Il Sung and President Sukarno of Indonesia (54×45 mm)	3·00	2·50

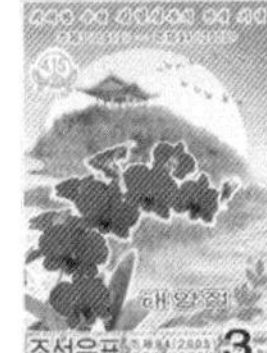
1473 Kimilsungii and Birthplace, Mangyongdae

2005. 93rd Birth Anniversary of Kim Il Sung. Multicoloured.

N4486 3wn. Type **1473** 30 25

MSN4487 105×78 mm. 112wn. Kim Il Sung (39×51 mm) 2·75 2·30

1474 Pack Yong Sun

2005. World Table Tennis Championship, Shanghai. Multicoloured.

N4488 3wn. Type **1474** 30 25
N4489 5wn. Mao Zedong 30 25
N4490 12wn. Wang Liqin 35 30
N4491 20wn. Jan-Ove Waldner 70 60
N4492 30wn. Zhang Yining 90 75
N4493 102wn. Werner Schlager 2·50 2·20

MSN4494 155×187 mm. Nos. N4488/N4493 5·25 4·75

1475 Panda

2005. Giant Panda (*Ailuropoda melanoleuca*). Multicoloured.

N4495 15wn. Type **1475** 55 45
N4496 45wn. Walking 1·20 1·00
N4497 70wn. Two pandas 2·00 1·70
N4498 120wn. Mother and cub 3·00 2·50
N4499 140wn. Eating bamboo 3·50 3·00

MSN4500 150×105 mm. Nos. N4495/N4499 10·50 9·25

MSN4501 80×130 mm. 120wn. Mother and cub 3·25 2·75

1477 Family

2005. 50th Anniversary of Korean Residents in Japan Association (Chongryon). Multicoloured.

N4507 3wn. Type **1477** 30 25

MSN4508 85×102 mm. 130wn. Kim Il Sung and Chongryon leader (45×54 mm) 3·25 2·75

1478 *Panthera tigris altaika*

2005. Far Eastern Animals. Multicoloured.

N4509 40wn. Type **1478** 1·10 95
N4510 40wn. *Martes zibellina* 1·10 95

Stamps of a similar design were issued by Russia.

1479 General's Tomb, Koguryo

2005. Relics and Remains of Koguryo Dynasty (277 BC–668 AD). Multicoloured.

N4511 3wn. Type **1479** 30 25
N4512 70wn. Hunting (tomb mural) 2·00 1·70
N4513 97wn. King Kwanggaetho's mausoleum (37×56 mm) 2·40 2·10
N4514 100wn. Fortress, Mt. Songsan 2·50 2·20
N4515 130wn. Gilded arrow heads 3·25 2·75

MSN4516 135×120 mm. Nos. N4511/N4512 and N4514/N4515 8·00 7·00

MSN4517 130×90 mm. 97wn. No. N4513 2·50 2·20

1480 Kim Chol Ju

2005. Kim Chol Ju (revolutionary) Commemoration. Sheet 75×100 mm.

MSN4518 **1480** 170wn. multicoloured 4·50 3·75

1481 Kim Jong Il and Kim Dae-jung (President South Korea 1998–2003)

2005. Fifth Anniversary of North–South Joint Declaration. Two sheets containing T **1481** and similar multicoloured designs showing Kim Il Jong and Kim Dae-jung.

MSN4519 120×125 mm. 112wn.×4, Type **1481**; Kim Jong Il and Kim Dae-jung (different); At banquet (horiz); At conference table (horiz) 13·50 12·50

MSN4520 90×110 mm. 167wn. Shaking hands (54×45 mm) 4·50 3·75

1482 White Tiger

2005. White Tiger (*Panthera tigris altaika*). Multicoloured.

N4521 3wn. Type **1482** 30 25
N4522 12wn. Snarling head 35 30
N4523 130wn. Head and shoulders 3·25 2·75
N4524 200wn. Snarling facing right 5·25 4·75

MSN4525 160×100 mm. Nos. N4521/N4524 9·50 8·50

MSN4526 131×105 mm. 150wn. Mother and cubs (42×64 mm) 4·00 3·50

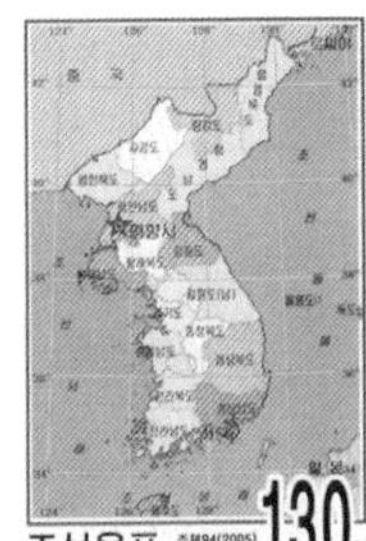
1483 Map of Korea

2005. Sheet 113×89 mm.

MSN4527 **1483** 130wn. multicoloured 3·25 2·75

1484 Soldier

2005. Period of Struggle.

N4528 **1484** 3wn. multicoloured 30 25

1485 Monument

2005. 60th Anniversary of National Liberation. Designs showing Kim Il Sung. Multicoloured.

N4529 3wn. Type **1485** 30 25

MSN4530 Two sheets, each 111×145 mm (a) 60wn.×4, Kim Il Sung at home (horiz); On horseback (horiz); With fighters in woodland (horiz); Planning strategy (horiz); 102wn. In uniform (44×44 mm. circular). (b) 60wn.×4, On board ship (horiz); With workers (horiz); Giving speech (horiz); With family (horiz); 102wn. At microphone (44×44 mm. circular) 20·00 19·00

MSN4531 98×126 mm. 128wn. Kim Il Sung (44×44 mm. circular) 3·25 2·75

(1486)

2005. Taipei 2005 International Stamp Exhibition. Nos. N4495/N4497, N4499 and **MS**N4501 overprinted as T **1486**.

N4532 15wn. As Type **1475** 55 45
N4533 45wn. Walking (As N4496) 1·20 1·00
N4534 70wn. Two pandas (As N4497) 2·10 1·90
N4535 140wn. Eating bamboo (As N4499) 3·50 3·00

MSN4536 80×80 mm. 120wn. Mother and cub (As **MS**N4501) 3·00 2·50

1487 Red Robes

2005. National Costume. Multicoloured.

N4537 3wn. Type **1487** 30 25
N4538 80wn. Blue and yellow robe 2·20 1·90
N4539 100wn. Green and cream robe with cranes 2·50 2·20
N4540 120wn. Brocade coat 3·00 2·50

MSN4541 140×80 mm. Nos. N4537/N4540 8·25 7·25

MSN4542 70×94 mm. 140wn. Children (39×51 mm) 3·50 3·00

1488 Marchers

2005. Joint Slogans.

N4543 **1488** 3wn. multicoloured 30 25

1489 Monument

2005. 60th Anniversary of Korean Workers Party. Multicoloured.

N4544 3wn. Type **1489** 30 25

MSN4545 Two sheets, each 153×125 mm. Horiz, size 51×39 mm. (a) 12wn. Kim Il Sung; 30wn. Kim Il Sung and Kim Jong Il; 60wn. Kim Il Sung with military leaders; 90wn. Kim Jong Il. (b) 12wn. Early discussions; 30wn. Joining together; 60wn. Planning; 90w. Giving speech 10·50 9·75

MSN4546 Two sheets, each 81×100 mm. Circular, size 46×46 mm. (a) 120wn. Kim Jong Il. (b) 120wn. Kim Il Sung 6·00 5·50

1490 Queen emerging

2005. Bees (*Apis mellifera*). Multicoloured.

N4547 3wn. Type **1490** 30 25
N4548 12wn. Two bees and grubs 35 30
N4549 128wn. Bee and honey 3·25 2·75
N4550 200wn. Bee in flight 5·25 4·75

MSN4551 140×80 mm. Nos. N4547/N4550 9·75 9·00

1491 '60' and Emblem

2005. 60th Anniversary of United Nations.

N4552 **1491** 15wn. multicoloured 30 25

1492 Pagoda

2005. Relics of Kaesong (1st issue). Two sheets, each 180×125 mm containing T **1492** and similar multicoloured designs.

MSN4553 (a) 35wn.×3, Type **1492**; Monument; Pagoda (different); 75wn. Buildings (64×42 mm). (b) 35wn.×3, Small building; Steps; Tablet (32×32 mm circular); 75wn. Gateway (64×42 mm) 5·75 5·00

See also Nos. **MS**N4556.

1493 Kim Hyong Gwon

2005. Birth Centenary of Kim Hyong Gwon (revolutionary). Sheet 75×110 mm.

MSN4554 **1493** 120wn. multicoloured 3·00 2·50

1494 Manuscript and 'X'

2005. Centenary of False Five Point Treaty.

N4555 **1494** 12wn. multicoloured 35 30

2005. Relics of Kaesong (2nd issue). Three sheets, each 180×125 mm containing multicoloured designs as T **1492**.

MSN4556 (a) 35wn.×2, Bridge; Statue; 75wn. Waterfall (42×64 mm). (b) 35wn.×2, Yeongjo of Joseon (32×32 mm circular); Gateway (45×33 mm); 75wn. Burial mound (64×42 mm). (c) 35wn.×6, Raised building and tunnel; Two burial mounds; Stone bridge; Steps and gateway; Buddha; Pillars and mound 14·00 13·00

The larger stamps in **MS**N4550a/**MS**N4550b merge with the margins to form composite background designs.

1495 President Hu Jintao and Kim Il Jong

2005. Visit of President Hu Jintao to Korea. Sheet 149×118 mm containing T **1495** and similar multicoloured designs.

MSN4557 35wn.×3, Type **1495**; With business men; Seated at flower strewn table; 102wn. Shaking hands (36×57 mm)	5·50	4·75

1496 Flowers and Mountain

2006. New Year.

N4558 **1496** 3wn. multicoloured	30	25

1497 Dog

2006. New Year. Year of the Dog (1st issue). Multicoloured.

N4559 3wn. Type **1497**	30	25
N4560 15wn. Hound	55	45
N4561 70wn. White and brown Spitz type	2·00	1·70
N4562 100wn. Black and white Spitz type	2·50	2·20
N4563 130wn. Spaniel	3·25	2·75
MSN4564 150×104 mm. Nos. N4559/N4563 plus stamp size label	9·00	8·00
MSN4565 80×80 mm. 130wn. No. N4563	3·50	3·00

See also Nos. N4568/**MS**N4569.

1498 Kim Jong Il

2006. 60th Anniversary of Kim Jong Il's Socialist Youth League. Two sheets containing T **1498** and similar vert designs. Multicoloured.

MSN4566 115×80 mm. 3wn. Type **1498**; 111wn. Kim Jong Il and young people; 150wn. Passing torch	7·00	6·50
MSN4567 130×115 mm. 128wn. With young socialists (42×64 mm)	3·25	2·75

The stamp and margins of **MS**N4567 form a composite design.

1499 Dog

2006. New Year. Year of the Dog (2nd issue). Multicoloured.

N4568 12wn. Type **1499**	35	30
MSN4569 80×130 mm. 70wn. Mastiff (painting) (50×60 mm)	2·00	1·80

1500 Revolutionary Tools

2006. *Rodong Sinmun, Josoninmingun and Chongnyonjonwi* Newspapers Joint Editorial.

N4570 **1500** 3wn. multicoloured	30	25

1501 Ice Dance

2006. Winter Olympic Games, Turin. Multicoloured.

N4571 15wn. Type **1501**	55	45
N4572 85wn. Ice hockey	2·30	2·00
N4573 110wn. Ski jump	2·75	2·30
N4574 135wn. Speed skating	3·50	3·00
MSN4575 140×112 mm. Nos. N4571/N4574	9·25	8·50

1502 Mount Paektu and Flowers

2006. 64th Birth Anniversary of Kim Jong Il. Multicoloured.

N4576 3wn. Type **1502**	30	25
MSN4577 140×76 mm. 12wn. *Polemorium racemosum*; 45wn. *Lilium concolor*; 100wn. *Taraxacum platycarpum*; 140wn. *Parnassia palustris*	9·00	8·00

1503 Crop Research Institute

2006. Kim Jong Il's Visit to China. Two sheets containing T **1503** and similar multicoloured designs showing Kim Jong Il.

MSN4578 170×120 mm. 3wn. Type **1503**; 12wn. Fibre optic production; 35wn. Outside at Three Gorges Dam; 70wn. Inside at Guangzhou International Conference and Exhibition Centre; 100wn. Inside at Gree Air-Conditioner Production Company; 120wn. Outside at Yandian Port	10·00	9·00
MSN4579 160×120 mm. 102wn. With President Hu Jintao (42×64 mm)	2·50	2·20

1504 Irrigation

2006. 60th Anniversary of Agrarian Reform Law. Multicoloured.

N4580 12wn. Type **1504**	35	30
MSN4581 96×72 mm. 150wn. Kim Il Sung and farmer (51×39 mm)	4·00	3·50

1505 As No. N4b

2006. 60th Anniversary of First Postage Stamps. Sheet 100×80 mm

MSN4582 **1505** 158wn. multicoloured	4·25	3·75

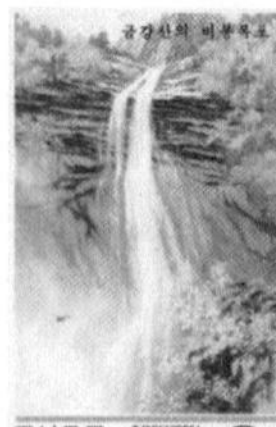

1506 Pibong Falls

2006. Mount Kumgang. Multicoloured designs.

N4583 3wn. Type **1506**	30	25
N4584 12wn. Podok Hermitage	35	30
N4585 35wn. Sokka Peak	1·00	85
N4586 50wn. Jipson Peak	1·30	1·20
N4587 70wn. Chongsok rocks (horiz)	2·00	1·70
N4588 100wn. Sejon Peak (horiz)	2·50	2·20
N4589 120wn. Chonhwa rock (horiz)	3·00	2·50
N4590 140wn. Piro Peak (horiz)	3·50	3·00

1507 Jules Verne (writer)

2006. Belgica 2006 International Stamp Exhibition. Multicoloured.

N4591 140wn. Type **1507**	3·50	3·00
N4592 140wn. *Tursiops truncates*	3·50	3·00
N4593 140wn. Alaskan malamute dog and Birman cat	3·50	3·00
N4594 140wn. *Australopithecus afarensis* heads	3·50	3·00
N4595 140wn. *Sunflowers* (Vincent Van Gogh)	3·50	3·00
N4596 140wn. *Nymphalidae* and *Disa grandiflora*	3·50	3·00
N4597 140wn. Football, chess piece, table tennis bat and ball	3·50	3·00
N4598 140wn. *Tyto alba*	3·50	3·00
N4599 140wn. Ernst Grube Type S 4000-1 fire appliance (1962) (horiz)	3·50	3·00
N4600 140wn. Maglev train (horiz)	3·50	3·00

1508 Kimilsungia

2006. 94th Birth Anniversary of Kim Il Sung.

N4601 **1508** 3wn. multicoloured	30	25

1509 Site of Donggang Meeting and Inaugural Declaration

2006. 70th Anniversary of Foundation for the Restoration of the Fatherland.

N4602 **1509** 3wn. multicoloured	30	25

1510 Pothong River Improvement Monument

2006. 60th Anniversary of Pothong River Improvement Project.

N4603 **1510** 12wn. multicoloured	35	30

1511 Necktie and Badge

2006. 60th Anniversary of Children's Union.

N4604 **1511** 3wn. multicoloured	30	25

1512 Chasing Ball

2006. World Cup Football Championship, Germany. Showing two players. Multicoloured.

N4605 3wn. Type **1512**	30	25
N4606 130wn. Tackling	3·25	2·75
N4607 160wn. Kicking ball into goal	4·25	3·75
N4608 210wn. Heading ball	5·75	5·00

1513 Kim Chol Ju and Zhang Weihua

2006. 90th Birth Anniversary of Kim Chol Ju (revolutionary). Sheet 65×83 mm.

MSN4609 **1513** 170wn. multicoloured	4·50	3·75

1514 Ri Su Bok

2006. Ri Su Bok (poet and soldier) Commemoration. Sheet 145×85 mm.

MSN4610 **1514** 120wn. multicoloured	3·00	2·50

The stamp and margin of **MS**N4610 form a composite design.

1515 Trapeze Artistes

2006. Circus. Sheet 125×150 mm containing T **1515** and similar multicoloured designs.

MSN4611 3wn. Type **1515**; 12wn. Four trapeze artistes; 130wn. Acrobat; 200wn. Blindfolded juggler (42×64 mm)	10·00	9·25

The stamps and margin of **MS**N4611 form a composite design.

1516 Kimchi

2006. Traditional Food. Multicoloured.

N4612 3wn. Type **1516**	30	25
N4613 12wn. Umegi	35	30
N4614 130wn. Rice cake dumplings	3·25	2·75
N4615 200wn. Sweet rice	5·25	4·75

1517 *Megaptera nodosa*

2006. Sea Mammals. Multicoloured.

N4616	3wn. Type **1517**	30	25
N4617	70wn. *Balaenoptera musculus*	2·00	1·70
N4618	160wn. *Physter catodon*	4·25	3·75
N4619	240wn. *Inia geoffrensis*	6·00	5·25

1518 Early Motorcycle

2006. Motorcycles. Multicoloured.

N4620	3wn. Type **1518**	30	25
N4621	102wn. Blue motorcycle with full faring	2·50	2·20
N4622	150wn. Early motorcycle	4·00	3·50
N4623	240wn. Red motorcycle with partial faring	6·50	5·50
MSN4624	175×100 mm. Nos. N4620/N4623, each×2	27·00	25·00

1519 *General Sherman* in Flames

2006. 140th Anniversary of Sinking of *General Sherman*.

N4625	**1519** 130wn. multicoloured	3·25	2·75

1520 *Tyto alba*

2006. Owls. Multicoloured.

N4626	12wn. Type **1520**	35	30
N4627	111wn. *Strix uralensis*	2·75	2·30
N4628	130wn. *Strix aluco*	3·25	2·75
N4629	160wn. *Nyctea scandiaca*	4·25	3·75

1521 Kim Il Sung (statue)

2006. 60th Anniversary of Kim Il Sung University. Sheet 90×115 mm.

MSN4630	**1521** 70wn. multicoloured	2·00	1·70

1522 Eulji Mundok

2006. Personalities. Multicoloured.

N4631	3wn. Type **1522**	30	25
N4632	12wn. So Hui	35	30
N4633	35wn. Kim Ung So	1·00	85
N4634	70wn. Kang Kam Chan	2·00	1·70
N4635	102wn. Yongae Somun	2·50	2·20
N4636	130wn. Ri Kyu Bo	3·25	2·75
N4637	160wn. Mun Ik Jom	4·25	3·75

1523 Flag

2006. 80th Anniversary of Anti-Imperialism Union. Multicoloured.

N4638	3wn. Type **1523**	30	25
MSN4639	160×100 mm. 70wn. Founder members in the countryside (51×40 mm); 102wn. Kim Il Sung as young man (46×46 mm) (circular); 120wn. Kim Il Sung and members on rail track	9·00	7·75

1524 Flag and Red Cross Vehicles

2006. 60th Anniversary of Red Cross Society.

N4640	**1524** 30wn. multicoloured	90	75

1525 Students (image scaled to 38% of original size)

2006. 60th Anniversary of Secondary Education Fund for Koreans in Japan. Sheet 150×95 mm.

MSN4641	**1525** 110wn. multicoloured	2·75	2·30

1526 Ruler

2006. 60th Anniversary of UNESCO. Tomb Murals, Anak. Sheet 165×112 mm containing T **1526** and similar multicoloured designs.

MSN4642	3wn. Type **1526**; 70wn. Consort; 130wn. Subak (martial art) (horiz); 135wn. Procession (horiz); 160wn. Kitchen (horiz)	13·50	12·00

1527 University Buildings

2006. 50th Anniversary of Joson University. Sheet 150×95 mm.

MSN4643	**1527** 110wn. multicoloured	2·75	2·30

(1528)

2006. Belgica 2006 International Stamp Exhibition. Owls. Nos. N4626/N4629 overprinted as T **1528**. Multicoloured.

N4644	12wn. As Type **1520**	35	30
N4645	111wn. As No. N4627	2·75	2·30
N4646	130wn. As No. N4628	3·25	2·75
N4647	160wn. As No. N4629	4·25	3·75

1529 Carving

2006. Army's Gift to Kim Jong Il. Sheet 90×130 mm.

MSN4648	**1529** 130wn. multicoloured	3·25	2·75

The stamp and margin of **MS**N4648 form a composite design.

1530 Bell and Snow-covered Pagoda

2007. New Year.

N4649	**1530** 3wn. multicoloured	30	25

1531 Pig

2007. New Year. Year of the Pig. Multicoloured.

N4650	3wn. Type **1531**	30	25
N4651	45wn. Pot-bellied pig	1·20	1·00
N4652	70wn. Saddle back	2·00	1·70
N4653	130wn. Large white	3·25	2·75
MSN4654	115×86 mm. Nos. N4650/N4653	7·00	6·50
MSN4655	80×57 mm. 70wn. No. N4652	2·00	1·80

1532 Begonia 'Kimjongilhwa'

2007. 65th Birth Anniversary of Kim Jong Il. Multicoloured.

N4656	3wn. Type **1532**	30	25
MSN4657	170×100 mm. Size 36×57 mm. 12wn. Score, mountains and lake (left); 70wn. Score, mountains (two peaks) and lake (centre); 100wn. Score, mountains and lake (larger); 140wn. Score, mountains and lake (right)	8·50	7·50

The stamps and margins of **MS**N4657 form a composite design of a lake ringed by mountains.

1533 Symbols of Industry and Agriculture

2007. *Rodong Sinmun*

N4658	**1533** 3wn. multicoloured	30	35

1534 *Callicore selima*

2007. Butterflies. Multicoloured.

N4659	15wn. Type **1534**	40	35
N4660	85wn. *Morpho rhetenor*	2·20	1·90
N4661	110wn. *Atrophaneura alcinous*	2·75	2·50
N4662	160wn. *Parnassius bremeri*	4·25	3·75

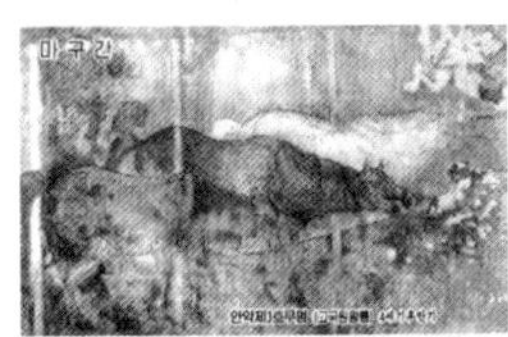

1535 Horses in Stable

2007. World Heritage Sites. Tomb Murals, Anak. Multicoloured.

N4663	3wn. Type **1535**	30	25
N4664	70wn. Well	2·00	1·70
N4665	130wn. Women milling (30×42 mm)	3·25	3·75
N4666	160wn. Horn (30×42 mm)	4·25	3·75
MSN4667	135×110 mm. 3wn. As Type **1535**; 70wn. As N4664; 130wn. As N4665 (*vert*); 160wn. As N4666 (*vert*)	13·50	12·00

1536 Building

2007. 90th Anniversary of Korean National Association.

N4668	**1536** 12wn. multicoloured	35	30

1537 Beethoven and Score

2007. 180th Death Anniversary of Ludwig van Beethoven (composer).

N4669	**1537** 80wn. multicoloured	2·10	1·80

1538 Mangyongdae (birthplace)

2007. 94th Birth Anniversary of Kim Il Sung. Multicoloured.

N4670	3wn. Type **1538**	30	25
MSN4671	92×112 mm. 130wn. Kim Il Sung and family (64×42 mm)	3·25	2·75
MSN4672	128×110 mm. Size 51×39 mm. 45wn. On '250 mile journey for learning'; 70wn. With soldiers; 100wn. On horseback; 160wn. With farmers	9·75	9·00

1539 *Sciurius vulgaris*

2007. Rodents. Sheet 145×85 mm containing T **1539** and similar triangular designs. Multicoloured.

MSN4673	3wn. Type **1539**; 12wn. *Muscardinus avellanarius*; 20wn. *Hypogeomys antimena*; 30wn. *Lemniscomys striatus*; 40wn. *Pedetes capensis*; 50wn. *Rattus norvegicus*; 80wn. *Eliomys quercinus*; 102wn. *Micromys minutes*	13·50	12·00

1540 Soldiers

2007. 75th Anniversary of National Army. Multicoloured.

N4674	12wn. Type **1540**	35	30
MSN4675	124×76 mm. Size 51×39 mm. 80wn. Kim Il Sung inspecting troops; 100wn. Kim Jong Il and soldiers	4·50	4·00
MSN4676	132×90 mm. Size 64×42 mm. 120wn. Kim Il Sung and Kim Jong Il on podium	3·00	2·40

1541 Spraying

2007. Avian Flu Prevention Campaign.

N4677	**1541** 85wn. multicoloured	2·20	1·90

1542 Banknote (1947)

2007. 60th Anniversary of National Currency. Sheet 118×160 mm containing T **1542** and similar horiz designs. Multicoloured.

MSN4678 3wn. Type **1542**; 12wn. Banknote (1947) (different); 35wn. Banknote (1959); 50wn. Banknote (1959) (different); 70wn. Banknote (1978); 110wn. Banknote (1978) (different); 130wn. Banknote (1992); 160wn. Banknote (1992) (different) 7·00 6·25

1543 Kim Il Sung

2007. 70th Anniversary of Pochonbo Battle. Sheet 140×102 mm.

MSN4679 **1543** 120wn. multicoloured 3·50 3·00

1544 *Naso lituratus*

2007. Fish. Multicoloured.

N4680	15wn. Type **1544**	15	10
N4681	50wn. *Carassius auratus*	1·30	1·10
N4682	110wn. Inscr 'A. citrinellus'	2·75	2·30
N4683	200wn. *Symphysodon discus*	5·25	4·75

1545 Ri Jun

2007. Death Centenary of Ri Jun (cultural activist).

N4684 **1545** 110wn. chocolate and green 2·75 2·30

1546 Tetracorallia

2007. Fossils. Multicoloured.

N4685	15wn. Type **1546**	15	10
N4686	70wn. Neuropteridium	2·00	1·70
N4687	130wn. Yoldia	3·25	2·75
N4688	200wn. Rhinoceros	5·25	4·75

1547 *Oncidium wyattianum*

2007. Orchids. Multicoloured.

N4689	3wn. Type **1547**	30	25
N4690	70wn. *Cymbidium* Red Beauty 'Carmen'	2·00	1·70
N4691	127wn. *Dendrobium thyrsiflorum*	3·00	2·50
N4692	140wn. *Dendrobium* Candy Stripe 'Kodama'	3·50	3·00

MSN4692a 192×91 mm. Nos. N4689/N4692

1548 Players

2007. Women's Football. Two sheets containing T **1548** and similar circular designs. Multicoloured.

MSN4693 152×110 mm. 12wn. Type **1548**; 40wn. Reverse kick; 70wn. Heading the ball; 110wn. Preparing to kick; 140wn. Tackle 9·75 9·00

MSN4694 96×65 mm. 130wn. Two players running for ball 3·25 2·75

1549 *Gladiolus gandavensis*

2007. Flowers. Multicoloured.

N4695	30wn. Type **1549**	30	25
N4696	30wn. *Iris ensata* Thumb	30	25
N4697	30wn. *Rosa hybrida*	30	25
N4698	30wn. *Nelumbo nucifera*	30	25

MSN4699 130×84 mm. N4695/N4698

Nos. N4695/N4698 were issued together, *se-tenant*, forming a composite design. The stamps and margins of **MS**N4699 form a composite design.

Stamps of a similar design were issued by Russia.

1550 Beibei

2007. Olympic Games, Beijing. Two sheets containing T **1550** and similar circular designs. Multicoloured.

MSN4700 152×110 mm. 3wn. Type **1550**; 12wn. Jingjing; 30wn. Huanhuan; 70wn. Yingying; 140wn. Nini 7·00 6·50

MSN4701 150x120mm. Size 44x44mm (circular). 3wn. Beibei; 12wn. Jungjing; 30wn. Huazhuan; 70wn. Yingying; 140wn. Niri

1551 Box

2007. Traditional Furniture. Multicoloured.

N4702	3wn. Type **1551**	30	25
N4703	12wn. Ornamental chest of drawers	35	30
N4704	40wn. Collapsible dressing tables	1·00	80
N4705	70wn. Wardrobe with perforated front	2·00	1·70
N4706	110wn. Triple chest of drawers inlaid with mother of pearl	2·75	2·30
N4707	130wn. Red lacquered triple chest of drawers	3·25	2·75

1552 Glutinous Potato Cake

2007. Traditional Food. Multicoloured.

N4708	12wn. Type **1552**	35	30
N4709	50wn. Yongchae kimchi	1·30	1·10
N4710	70wn. Fermented flatfish	2·00	1·70
N4711	110wn. Frozen potato cake	2·75	3·00

1553 Roo Moo Hyun (president of South Korea) and Kim Jong Il (leader of North Korea)

2007. North–South Summit Meeting. Sheet 110×80 mm.

MSN4712 **1553** 170wn. multicoloured 4·50 3·75

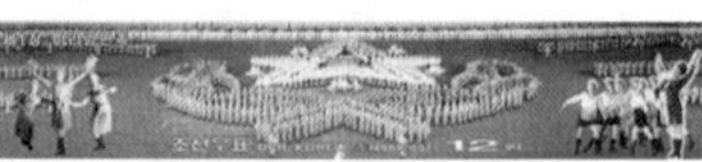

1554 Parade (image scaled to 29% of original size)

2007. Arirang Festival. Two sheets each 195×155 mm containing T **1554** and similar circular designs. Multicoloured.

MSN4713 (a) 12wn. Type **1554**; 50wn. Floodlit parade (93×35 mm); (b) 120wn. Two performers and massed performance; 155wn. Massed performance (93×35 mm) 7·75 6·50

1555 Ploughing

2007. Paintings by Kim Hong Do. Multicoloured.

N4714	13wn. Type **1555**	35	30
N4715	50wn. Weaving	1·30	1·10
N4716	70wn. Threshing	2·00	1·70
N4717	110wn. Archery	2·75	3·00

1555a Nong Duc Manh and Kim Jong Il

2007. Visit of Nong Duc Manh (General Secretary of the Communist Party of Vietnam) to Pyongyang. Sheet 98×76 mm.

MSN4718 **1555a** 120wn. multicoloured 3·00 2·50

1556 Kim Jong Suk's Home

2007. 90th Birth Anniversary of Kim Jong Suk (Kim Il Sung's wife and revolutionary fighter). Multicoloured.

N4719 3wn. Type **1556** 30 25

MSN4720 30wn. Kim Jong Suk and Kim Il Sung (53×44 mm); 70wn. Kim Jong Suk (circular (45×45 mm)); 110wn. With soldiers (53×44 mm) 5·00 4·25

1557 Flag and Skyline

2008. New Year.

N4721 **1557** 3wn. multicoloured 30 25

1558 Frontpage and Couple

2008. 80th Anniversary of Publication of *Saenal Sinmum* Newspaper.

N4722 **1558** 85wn. multicoloured 2·20 1·90

1559 Emblem

2008. *Rodong Sinmun*, *Josoninmingun* and *Chongnyonjonwi* Newspapers Joint Editorial. Multicoloured.

N4723	3wn. Type **1559**	30	25
N4724	3wn. Soldier leading crowd	30	25
N4725	12wn. Soldier with arm raised	35	30
N4726	12wn. Construction workers and soldiers (horiz)	35	30
N4727	30wn. Woman and food (horiz)	1·00	85
N4728	120wn. Musicians	3·00	2·50
N4729	135wn. Demonstrators from 6.15 Unification Alliance	3·25	2·75

1560 *Melopsittacus undulatus* (budgerigar)

2008. Cage Birds. Multicoloured.

N4730	15wn. Type **1560**	15	10
N4731	85wn. *Agapornis personata* (lovebird)	2·20	1·90
N4732	155wn. *Agapornis personata* (horiz)	4·00	3·50
N4733	170wn. *Melopsittacus undulatus* (horiz)	4·50	3·75

1561 Kim Il Sung and Kim Jong Il amongst Flowers

2008. 20th Anniversary of Dedication of Kimjongilia. Sheet 155×100 mm.

MSN4734 **1561** 85wn. multicoloured 2·20 2·20

1562 *Pyrethrum hybridum*

2008. 66th Birth Anniversary of Kim Jong Il. T **1562** and similar multicoloured designs.

N4735 3wn. Type **1562** 30 25

MSN4736 100×105 mm. 12wn. *Tulipa gesneriana*; 70wn. *Adonis amurensis*; 120wn. *Mathiola incana*; 155wn. *Begonia*× *tuberhybrida Voss* 'Kimjongilhwa' (43×43 mm (circular)) 9·25 9·25

No. N4737 and T **1563** have been left for Mangyongdae, issued on 15 March 2008, not yet received.

1564 Guitarist

2008. 35th Anniversary of Publication of *On the Art of Cinema*. Sheet 105×167 mm containing T **1564** and similar horiz designs. Multicoloured.

MSN4738 3wn. Type **1564**; 85wn. Fur-clad fighter; 135wn. Martial arts; 170wn. Family and young woman	10·00	10·00

1565 Map of Route

2008. 85th Anniversary of Kim Il Sung's 250 Mile Journey for Learning.

N4739 **1565** 15wn. multicoloured	20	15

1566 Football

2008. Olympic Games, Beijing. Multicoloured.

N4740 3wn. Type **1566**	10	10
N4741 12wn. Basketball	25	2·00
N4742 30wn. Tennis	35	30
N4743 70wn. Table tennis	1·00	85

1567 Choe Yong

2008. Personalities. Each brown.

N4744 85wn. Type **1567**	1·20	1·00
N4745 160wn. Ho Jun	2·30	2·00

1568 Flowers and Flags

2008. 15th Anniversary of Kim Jong Il's Chairmanship of National Defence Commission. Multicoloured.

N4746 12wn. Type **1568**	25	20
MSN4747 90×118 mm. 120wn. Kim Jong Il (42×64 mm)	1·70	1·50

1569 Jug

2008. International Friendship Exhibition, Mt. Myohyang. Multicoloured.

N4748 3wn. Type **1569**	10	10
N4749 85wn. Cockerel (painting)	1·20	1·00
N4750 155wn. Throne	2·00	1·90
MSN4751 101×80 mm. 135wn. Vase	2·00	2·00

1570 Mornabong Theatre (conference venue)

2008. 60th Anniversary of Joint North-South Conference.

N4752 **1570** 12wn. olive	25	20

1571 *Amanita muscaria*

2008. Fungi. Multicoloured.

N4753 12wn. Type**1571**	25	20
N4754 50wn. *Armillariella mellea*	75	65
N4755 135wn. *Macrolepiota procera*	2·00	1·70
N4756 155wn. *Tricholoma terreum*	2·20	1·90

1572 Building and Mountain

2008. Tourism. Mount Ryongak, Pyongyang. Multicoloured.

N4757 35wn. Type **1572**	40	35
N4758 155wn. Building and mountain (different)	2·20	1·90

1573 Hyangbipha

2008. Musical Instruments. Multicoloured.

N4759 15wn. Type**1573**	20	15
N4760 50wn. Phiri	75	65
N4761 120wn. Jangsaenap	1·70	1·50
N4762 160wn. Kayagum (horiz)	2·30	2·00

1574 Woman and Score (*Sea of Blood*)

2008. Five Revolutionary Operas. Designs showing images from the operas and scores. Multicoloured.

N4763 3wn. Type **1574**	10	10
N4764 12wn. Girl with basket of flowers (*Flower Girl*)	25	20
N4765 85wn. Woman in uniform (*True Daughter of the Party*)	1·20	1·00
N4766 120wn. Man in snow covered landscape (*Tell Oh Forest*)	1·70	1·50
N4767 155wn. Women (*The Song of Mt. Kumgang*)	2·20	1·90

1575 1946 20ch. Stamp (As Type **1**)

2008. EFIRO 2008. International Stamp Exhibition, Romania.

N4768 **1575** 85wn. multicoloured	1·30	1·10

1576 USS *Pueblo* (AGER-2) (US ship held in Pyongyang)

2008. Conflict.

N4769 **1576** 12wn. multicoloured	30	25

No. N4770 and T **1577** are left for Olympic Torch Relay, issued on 26 June 2008, not yet received.

1578 Serpentine (Magnesium Iron Silicate Hydroxide)

2008. Minerals. Multicoloured.

N4771 12wn. Type **1578**	30	25
N4772 75wn. Copper pyrites	1·10	90
N4773 135wn. Zinc blende (sphalerite)	2·10	1·80
N4774 155wn. Molybdenite (molybdenum disulfide)	2·30	2·00

1579 Kim Il Sung commanding Crossing of Han River

2008. 55th Anniversary of End of Korean War. Three sheets containing T **1579** and similar multicoloured designs.

MSN4775 90×130 mm. 3wn. Type **1579**; 120wn. Kim Il Sung, soldiers and villagers in snow	1·80	1·80
MSN4776 90×130 mm. 35wn. Kim Il Sung picnicking with soldiers; 155wn. Kim Il Sung and cheering crowd	2·75	2·50
MSN4777 144×95 mm. 85wn. Kim Il Sung and commanders (56×70 mm)	1·30	1·10

1580 Jong Il Peak

2008. 20th Anniversary of Naming of Jong Il Peak. Sheet 160×90 mm.

MSN4778 **1580** 120w. multicoloured	1·80	1·80

1581 Rice-Wormwood Cake

2008. Traditional Foods. Multicoloured.

N4779 3wn. Type **1581**	50	45
N4780 70wn. Nochi (rice cakes)	1·30	1·10
N4781 135wn. Green gram pancake	2·10	1·80
N4782 155wn. Young garlic preserved in soy	2·30	2·00

1582 Kim Jong Il

2008. Songun Revolutionary Leadership. Multicoloured.

N4782a 12wn. Soldiers	30	25
MSN4783 154×105 mm. 3wn. Type **1582**; 12wn. With factory workers; 120wn. In laboratory; 170wn. With cooks in kitchen	10·50	10·50
MSN4784 154×120 mm. 135wn. With soldiers in persimmon orchard (54×90 mm)	2·00	2·00

1583 Mask Dance

2008. World Heritage Sites. King Kogukwon's Tomb Murals, Anak. Sheet 135×112 containing T **1583** and similar multicoloured designs.

MSN4785 3wn. Type **1583**: 90wn. Janghadock (aide to the King) (30×42 mm); 120wn. Butchery; 155wn. Stable	5·25	5·25

1584 Flag

2008. National Flag.

N4786 **1584** 3wn. bright rosine and ultramarine	30	25
N4787 **1584** 155wn. bright rosine, ultramarine and new blue	2·20	1·90

1585 Chollima Statue and Flag

2008. 60th Anniversary of the Republic. Multicoloured.

N4788 3wn. Type **1585**	20	15
N4789 12wn. Workers and soldier	30	25
N4790 70wn. Soldiers	90	80
N4791 120wn. Workers and soldiers on flying horses	1·70	1·50
N4792 160wn. Hands	2·30	2·00
MSN4793 135×98 mm. 155wn. *When National Flag and Emblem were Born* (68×54 mm)	2·30	2·30

1586 Husky Sled Team

2008. Modes of Transport. Multicoloured.

N4794 680wn. Type **1586**	5·00	5·00
N4795 680wn. Cycling	5·00	5·00
N4796 680wn. Ferrari Enzo	5·00	5·00
N4797 680wn. Mercedes Benz LF 16 fire appliance	5·00	5·00
N4798 680wn. Steam locomotive (inscr 'Paravoz Y-127 1910 Russia')	5·00	5·00
N4799 680wn. LZ 129 *Hindenburg*	5·00	5·00
N4800 680wn. Concorde	5·00	5·00
N4801 680wn. *Sputnik 2* spacecraft and Laika (First animal in space)	5·00	5·00
N4802 680wn. Eurostar locomotive	5·00	5·00
N4803 680wn. *Nina* (Columbus' ship)	5·00	5·00

1587 *Salvelinus malma m. chonjiensis*

2008. Endangered Species. Sheet 100×70 mm.
MSN4804 **1587** 135w. multicoloured 2·10 1·80

1588 Choesung Pavilion

2008. Moran Hill. Sheet 188×128 mm containing T **1588** and similar horiz designs. Multicoloured.
MSN4805 3wn. Type **1588**: 45wn. Pagoda and stone pathway; 100wn. Shrubs and Pyongyang; 135wn. Pagoda, steps and gateway 4·25 4·25

1589 Children using Computers

2008. 50th Anniversary of Universal Compulsory Secondary Education.
N4806 **1589** 12wn. multicoloured 30 35

1590 Soldier

2008. Posters. Multicoloured.
N4807 12wn. Type **1590** 30 35
N4808 85wn. Woman holding bean halms 1·30 1·10

1591 Haeju Table

2008. Traditional Furniture. Multicoloured.
N4809 50wn. Type **1591** 75 65
N4810 70wn. Inkstone table with drawer and mother-of-pearl inlay 1·10 90
N4811 120wn. Red lacquer collapsible dressing table 1·00 85
N4812 170wn. Decorated cow horn trunk 2·30 2·00

1592 Pavilion

2008. Ulmil Pavilion, Pyongyang. Sheet 130×85 mm.
MSN4813 **1592** 85wn. multicoloured 1·30 1·20

1593 Snow Scene

2009. New Year.
N4814 **1593** 3wn. multicoloured 30 35

1594 Red Guards

2009. 50th Anniversary of Worker–Peasant Red Guards. Multicoloured.
N4815 12wn. Type **1594** 30 25
MSN4816 64×78 mm. 160wn. Kim Il Sung and Red Guards (51×39 mm) 1·20 2·10

1595 Tug of War

2009. Traditional Games. Multicoloured.
N4817 3wn. Type **1595** 40 35
N4818 120wn. Knee fighting 1·50 1·40

1596 *Crinum bracteatum*

2009. 67th Birth Anniversary of Kim Jong Il. Multicoloured.
N4819 3wn. Type **1596** 20 15
N4820 12wn. *Begonia* Irene Nuss 35 30
N4821 120wn. *Callistemon phoeniceus* 1·60 1·50
N4822 160wn. *Plumeria rubra* 2·20 2·00

1597 Kim Jong Il

2009. 35th Anniversary of Publication of *Juche Idea Programme*. Sheet 120×85 mm.
MSN4823 **1597** 170wn. multicoloured 2·40 2·20

1598 Torch and Chollima Statue

2009. *Rodong Sinmun, Josoninmingun* and *Chongnyonjonwi* Newspapers Joint Editorial. Four sheets, each 110×85 mm containing T **1598** and similar horiz designs. Multicoloured.
MSN4824 3wn. Type **1598**; 170wn. Symbols of industry 20 15
MSN4825 12wn. Wheat sheaf and other produce; 150wn. Musical instruments 2·20 2·20
MSN4826 30wn. Hand holding weapon; 120wn. Soldiers and flag 2·20 2·20
MSN4827 80wn. Emblem; 100wn. Hands on weapons 2·40 2·40

1599 Peonies and Butterflies

2009. China 2009 International Stamp Exhibition, Luoyang. Multicoloured.
N4827a 3wn. Type **1599** 20 15
N4827b 12wn. Tang horse and building 30 35
N4827c 90wn. Temple and statue 1·20 1·00
N4827d 100wn. Pink peonies 1·50 2·30
MSN4828 155×90 mm. 3wn. As Type **1599**; 100wn. As No. N4827d 1·50 1·50
MSN4829 155×90 mm. 12wn. As No. N4827b; 90wn. As No. N4827c 1·50 1·50

1600 Protestors

2009. 90th Anniversary of 1st March Uprising.
N4830 **1600** 90wn. multicoloured 1·20 1·00

1601 Mother and Child

2009. Centenary of Women's Day.
N4831 **1601** 35wn. multicoloured 45 40

1602 Horses (painting)

2009. 96th Birth Anniversary of Kim Il Sung. Gifts. Multicoloured.
N4832 3wn. Type **1602** 20 15
N4833 12wn. Fossil 45 40
N4834 140wn. Rifle 2·00 1·70
N4835 150wn. Bear skin 2·10 2·00

1603 *Anthropoides paradisea* (blue crane)

2009. 50th Anniversary of Central Zoo. Multicoloured.
N4836 12wn. Type **1603** 45 40
N4837 70wn. *Accipiter gentilis* (goshawk) 75 70
N4838 120wn. *Larus argentatus* (herring gull) 1·70 1·50
N4839 140wn. *Balearica pavonina* (black crowned crane) 1·90 1·70

1604 *Catalpa ovata* (Chinese catalpa)

2009. 50th Anniversary of Central Botanical Garden. Multicoloured.
N4840 3wn. Type **1604** 20 15
N4841 50wn. *Betula platyphylla* (Asian white birch) 75 60
N4842 120wn. *Juglans cordiformis* (Japanese walnut) 1·70 1·60
N4843 160wn. *Metasequoia glyptostroboides* (dawn redwood) 2·10 2·00

1605 Baseball

2009. Sports. Multicoloured.
N4844 12wn. Type **1605** 20 15
N4845 90wn. Tenpin bowling 1·20 1·10
N4846 160wn. Fencing 2·20 2·00
N4847 200wn. Golf 3·00 2·75

(1606)

2009. IBRA '09 International Stamp Exhibition. No. **MS**N4193b surch and overprinted in gold as T **1606**. Multicoloured.
MSN4848 20wn. on 40ch. Zeppelin LZ1; 40wn. on 80ch. LZ 120; 109wn. on 1wn.20 Zeppelin NT; 168wn. on 2wn.40 Zeppelin NT (different) 5·00 5·00

1607 Mountaineering

2009. Children's Union Camp. Multicoloured.
N4849 3wn. Type **1607** 20 15
N4850 80wn. Children with butterfly net 1·00 90
N4851 120wn. Cooking over camp fire 1·60 1·50
N4852 170wn. At the seaside 2·30 2·10

2009. 23rd Asian International Exhibition, Hong Kong. Sheet 130×42 mm containing horiz designs as T **1607**. Multicoloured.
MSN4853 3wn. As Type **1607**; 80wn. As N4850; 120wn. N4851; 170wn. N4852 5·25 5·25

1608 Kim Il Sung

2009. 70th Anniversary of Musan Battle. Sheet 130×45 mm.
MSN4854 **1608** 120wn. multicoloured 1·80 1·70

1609 UPU Emblem

2009. 135th Anniversary of Universal Postal Union.
N4855 **1609** 50wn. multicoloured 80 70

1610 *Vespa mandarinia*

2009. Insects. Multicoloured.
N4856 50wn. Type **1610** 70 65
N4857 90wn. *Cicindela japaonica* 1·30 1·40
N4858 120wn. *Locusta migratoria* 1·80 1·70
N4859 140wn. *Aphaenogaster famelica* 2·00 1·90

1611 Kim Chaek University of Technology Library

2009. Prominent Buildings in Pyongyang. Multicoloured.
N4860 12wn. Grand Theatre 35 30
MSN4861 145×97 mm. 3wn. Type **1611**; 70wn. Taedongmun Cinema; 90wn. Okyryu Restaurant (70×28 mm); 150wn. Chongryu Restaurant (70×28 mm) 4·75 4·50

1612 *Kim Il Sung drawing Party Emblem*

2009. 'Juche' Idea. Sheet 190×84 mm containing T **1612** and similar horiz designs showing paintings. Multicoloured.

MSN4862 12wn. Type **1612**; 50wn. *First Military Flags*; 70wn. *Birth*; 140wn. *Every Field with a Bumper Harvest*	4·00	4·00

1613 Nurse and Child

2009. Public Health. Multicoloured.

N4863 12wn. Type **1613**	45	40
N4864 150wn. Symbols of health care	2·20	2·00

1614 *Unha-2* Rocket

2009. Launch of Satellite. *Kwangmyongsong 2*. Sheet 127×100mm.

MSN4865 **1614** 120wn. multicoloured	1·80	1·80

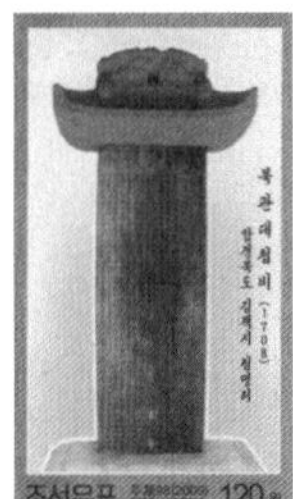
1615 Monument

2009. Re-erection of Victory Monument. Sheet 160×70mm.

MSN4866 **1615** 120wn. multicoloured	1·80	1·80

1616 Saenap

2009. Traditional Musical Instruments. Multicoloured.

N4867 12wn. Type **1616**	30	35
N4868 80wn. Drum	1·30	1·20
N4869 140wn. Songonghu	2·10	1·00
N4870 170wn. Flute	2·40	2·30

1617 Worker

2009. 150-Day Campaign for Innovation.

N4871 **1617** 12wn. multicoloured	45	40

1617a Dogs and Total Solar Eclipse

2009. International Year of Astronomy. Multicoloured.

N4871a 95wn. Type **1617a**	1·20	1·10
N4871b 95wn. *Cholima* statue	1·20	1·10
N4871c 95wn. Hares and partial solar eclipse	1·20	1·10
N4871d 95wn. Satellite, Gallilean telescope and Galileo Galilei	1·20	1·10
N4871e 95wn. Galaxy and planets	1·20	1·10
N4871f 95wn. Chomsongdae 7th-century observatory	1·20	1·10
MSN4871g 135×86 mm. 95wn. As Type **1617a**	2·40	2·40
MSN4871h 140×95 mm. 95wn.×2, Nos. N4871b and N4771d	2·40	2·40
MSN4871i 140×95 mm. 95wn.×2, Nos. N4871c and N4871e	2·40	2·40
MSN4871j 140×95 mm. 95wn.×2, As Type **1617a** and N4871f	2·40	2·40

1618 *Theragra chalcogramma*

2009. Fish. Multicoloured.

N4872 15wn. Type **1618**	50	40
N4873 60wn. *Cyprinus carpio*	80	75
N4874 140wn. *Euthynnus pelamis*	1·90	1·70
N4875 160wn. *Mugil cephalus*	2·20	2·00

1619 DPRK–China Friendship Stamps (image scaled to 34% of original size)

1620 DPRK–China Friendship Stamps (image scaled to 34% of original size)

2009. DPRK–China Friendship. Two sheets, each 140×110mm, containing T **1619** and similar horiz designs. Multicoloured.

MSN4876 60wn.×2, Type **1619**	1·40	1·40
MSN4877 60wn.×2, Type **1620**	1·40	1·40

1621 *Coturnicops exquistus* (Swinhoe's rail)

2009. Bird Pex. Multicoloured.

N4878 12wn. Type **1621**	45	40
N4879 90wn. *Porzana pusilla* (Baillon's crake)	1·40	1·20
N4880 170wn. *Porzana fusca* (ruddy-breasted crake)	2·40	2·20
MSN4880a 166×121 mm. 12wn.×2 As Type **1621**×2 (*Coturnicops exquistus* (Swinhoe's rail)): 90wn.×2, No. N4879×2, (*Porzana pusilla* (Baillon's crake)); 170wn. No. N4880 (*Porzana fusca* (ruddy-breasted crake))	6·25	6·25

1621a Henry Dunant

2009. Year of Red Cross and Red Crescent. 150th Anniversary of Battle of Solferino (witnessed by Henry Dunant who instigated campaign resulting in establishment of Geneva Conventions and Red Cross). Sheet 120×84 mm containing T **1621a** and similar vert designs. Multicoloured.

MSN4880b 75wn. Type **1621a**; 95wn. Trees and water (disaster risk reduction); 95wn. Red Cross workers and patient (first aid)	4·50	4·50

1622 Kim Jong Suk

2009. 60th Death Anniversary of Kim Jong Suk (Kim Il Sung's first wife and Kim Jong Il's mother). Sheet 93×106 mm containing T **1622** and similar multicoloured design.

MSN4881 90wn. Type **1622**; 100wn. With soldiers (57×36 mm)	5·00	5·00

1622a Hu Jintao and *In Praise of Harmony*

2009. 60th Anniversary of People's Republic of China. Sheet 160×133 mm containing T **1622a** and similar horiz designs. Multicoloured.

MS4881a 10wn. Type **1622a**; 67wn. Chinese cosmonauts; 67wn. National Stadium, China; 84wn. National Grand Theatre, China	3·00	3·00

1622b Spoonbill

2009. Endangered Species. Spoonbill (*Platalea minor*). Multicoloured.

N4881b 3wn. Type **1622b**	20	15
N4881c 12wn. Holding fish	45	40
N4881d 99wn. In flight	1·40	1·20
N4881e 266wn. With wings raised	4·00	4·00

1623 *Chamaeleo jacksonii* (Jackson's chameleon)

2009. Reptiles. Multicoloured.

N4882 15wn. Type **1623**	55	50
N4883 50wn. *Naja naja* (cobra)	80	75
N4884 110wn. *Caretta caretta* (loggerhead sea turtle) (horiz)	1·70	1·50
N4885 160wn. *Crocodylus niloticus* (Nile crocodile) (horiz)	2·40	2·20

1624 210wn. Stamp of 2006 (As No. N4608)

2009. Italia 2009. International Stamp Exhibition. Sheet 164×83 mm.

MSN4886 **1624** 210wn. multicoloured	3·25	3·25

Nos. N4887/N4891 and T **1625** are left for Lighthouses issued on 24 October 2009, not yet received.

1626 Kim Il Sung and Returnees

2009. Repatriation.

MSN4892 **1626** 160wn. multicoloured	2·20	1·90

1627 Rocket and Satellite (space)

2009. Year of Realising Ideals. Multicoloured.

MSN4893 159×125 mm. 10wn. Type **1627**; 20wn. Computer controlled machines (CNC); 20wn. Power plant, girders and transport; 30wn. Building site; 50wn. Refinery; 50wn. Cityscape; 57wn. Sturgeon, ostriches and farm animals; 70wn. Arable land; 80wn. Footballers and singer	3·50	3·50
MSN4894 162×113 mm. 100wn. Kim Jong Il and workmen (72×57 mm)	1·00	1·00

1628 Party Founding Monument, Mansu Hill

2010. New Year.

N4895 **1628** 10wn. multicoloured	30	25

1629 *Tiger* (painting by He Xiangning)

2010. Chinese New Year. Year of the Tiger. Multicoloured.

N4896 30wn. Type **1629**	40	35
N4897 67wn. Tiger (embroidery by Ri Won In)	90	85

1630 *Ailuropoda melanoleuca* (panda)

2010. Fauna. Multicoloured.

N4899 35wn. Type **1630**	40	35
N4900 60wn. *Aix galericulata* (Mandarin duck)	80	75·00
N4901 80wn. *Lagenorhynchus obliquidens* (Pacific white-sided dolphin)	95	90
N4902 110wn. *Panthera pardus* (leopard)	1·20	1·10

1631 Ice Hockey

2010. Winter Olympic Games, Vancouver. Multicoloured.

N4903 10wn. Type **1631**	35	30
N4904 40wn. Figure skating	45	40
N4905 50wn. Speed skating	60	55

N4906 70wn. Skiing 90 85

1632 *Impatiens sultani*

2010. 68th Birth Anniversary of Kim Jong Il. Multicoloured.

N4907 10wn. Type **1632** 30 25
N4908 50wn. *Gazania hybrida* 60 55
N4909 70wn. *Paeonia suffruticosa* 90 85
N4910 110wn. *Bougainvillea glabra* 1·20 1·10

1633 Workers, Soldier and Party Founding Monument

2010. *Rodong Sinmun, Josoninmingun* and *Chongnyonjonwi* Newspapers Joint Editorial. Multicoloured.

MSN4911 10wn. Type **1633**; 20wn. Woman factory worker and goods; 30wn. Woman carrying sheaf of corn; 57wn. Worker holding walkie-talkie, molten metal and symbols of development; 67wn. Two soldiers; 95wn. Two men and one woman with left arms raised; 125wn. Doves and globe 3·50 3·50

1634 Korean Soldiers

2010. Posters. Multicoloured.

N4912 76wn. Type **1634** 90 85
N4913 95wn. Japanese soldier and bayonet 1·10 1·00

1635 Kitten and Chicks

2010. Domestic Cats. Multicoloured.

N4914 10wn. Type **1635** 30 25
N4915 70wn. Two ginger and white cats 90 85
N4916 133wn. Tabby and white cat and mouse 1·10 1·00
N4917 170wn. Cat and kittens 1·20 1·10

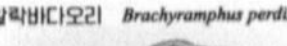

1636 *Brachyramphus perdix*

2010. BIRDPEX 2010 and ANTVERPIA 2010 International Stamp Exhibitions. Multicoloured.

MSN4918 30wn. Type **1636**; 125wn. *Gallinago solitaria*; 133wn. *Porzana paykullii* 2·75 2·75

1637 Ceramic Eagle

2010. 98th Birth Anniversary of Kim Il Sung. Multicoloured.

N4922 10wn. Type **1637** 30 25
N4923 30wn. Ceramic white crane 40 35
N4924 95wn. Embroidered tiger 1·10 1·00
N4925 152wn. Stuffed turtle (horiz) 1·20 1·10

1638 *Sophronitis brevipedunculata* (inscr 'Sophronitella brevipedunculata')

2010. Orchids. Multicoloured.

N4926 30wn. Type **1638** 40 35
N4927 80wn. *Epidendrum radiatum* 95 90
N4928 120wn. *Cymbidium* 1·10 1·00
N4929 152wn. *Dendrobium* 1·20 1·00

1639 Cholima Statue, Pyongyang

2010. Expo 2010, Shanghai (1st issue). Multicoloured.

MSN4930 10wn. Type **1639**; 80wn. Wind turbines, dolphins, children watering plant, skyline and animals 1·10 1·00

See also No. N4979.

1640 Forehand

2010. Table Tennis. Multicoloured.

N4931 10wn. Type **1640** 10 10
N4932 30wn. Serve 25 25
N4933 95wn. Backhand 80 80
N4934 152wn. Pushing ball 1·40 1·40
MSN4935 150×107 mm. Nos. N4931/N4934 2·50 2·50

1641 Worker with Megaphone and Soldiers

2010. 65th Anniversary of Workers' Party (1st issue).

N4936 **1641** 10wn. multicoloured 30 25

See also Nos. N4983/**MS**N4985.

No. N4937 is left for Winter Olympic Games Winners issued on 25 May 2010, not yet recieved.

1642 Two Players

2010. World Cup Football Championships, South Africa. Multicoloured.

N4938 20wn. Type **1642** 10 10
N4939 57wn. Players, No. 9 (yellow strip) and No. 4 (blue strip) 60 55
N4940 114wn. No. 5 (blue and yellow strip) player being tackled 1·20 1·10
N4941 190wn. No. 7 (red strip) and No. 9 player tackling 1·70 1·60
MSN4942 160×95 mm 20wn. As Type **1642**; 57wn. As No. N4939; 190wn. As No. N4941 1·90 1·90
MSN4943 85×61 mm. 114wn. As No. N4940 1·20 1·10

1643 Children in Carriage

2010. 60th Anniversary of Children's Day. Sheet 98×80 mm.

MSN4944 **1643** 95wn. multicoloured 1·10 1·10

1644 Symbols of Peace

2010. Tenth Anniversary of Publication of June 15 Joint Declaration.

N4945 **1644** 190wn. multicoloured 1·70 1·70

1645 Brontosaurus

2010. Dinosaurs. Multicoloured.

N4947 10wn. Type **1645** 30 25
N4948 125wn. Allosaurus 1·10 1·00
N4949 152wn. Pterodactylus 1·20 1·10
MSN4950 180×114 mm. 10wn. As Type **1645**; 125wn. As No. N4948; 152wn. As No. N4949 3·50 3·50

1645a Visiting Dalian Bingshan Group

2010. Unofficial Visit of Kim Jong Il to China (1st issue). Multicoloured.

MSN4950a 150×126 mm. 20wn. Type **1645a**; 35wn. Visiting Dalian Locomotive Company; 80wn. Visiting Liaoning Fishery Group 1·40 1·40
MSN4950b 150×126 mm. 20wn. Visiting Dalian Xuelong Group; 40wn. Visiting Tianjin Port; 67wn. Visiting Beiling Park 1·20 1·20
MSN4950c 170×129 mm. 30wn. Visiting Boao Biological Co.; 40wn. With President Hu Jintao; 70wn. Shaking hands with Pres. Jintao in farewell 1·30 1·30
MSN4950d 157×110 mm. 60wn. Pres. Jintao greeting Kim Jong Il (42×64 mm) 55 55

See also Nos. 4986/**MS**N4987 and **MS**N5067/**MS**N5069.

1646 *Butterfly and Cockerel*

2010. Children's Animated Films. Multicoloured.

MSN4951 10wn. Type **1646**; 30wn. *Clever Racoon Dog*; 95wn. *Hedgehog defeats Tiger*; 133wn. *Rabbit's Regret* 3·50 3·50

1647 *Rhododendron mucronulatum*

2010. Snow Azalea.

MSN4952 **1647** 85wn. multicoloured 1·10 1·00

1648 Score

2010. National Anthem, written by Pak Se Yong and composed by Kim Wyon Gyun.

MSN4953 **1648** 50wn. multicoloured 65 50

Nos. N4954/N4959 and T **1649** are left for Relics issued on 30 July 2010, not yet received.

Nos. N4960/N4961 and T **1650** are left for Singapore 2010 issued on 14 August 2010, not yet received.

1651 Kim Il Sung with Soldiers

2010. 65th Anniversary of End of Anti-Japanese War. Multicoloured.

MSN4962 155×102 mm. 10wn. Type **1651**; 15wn. Soldiers in snow; 20wn. Kim Il Sung and soldiers among azaleas; 40wn. Kim Il Sung wearing civilian dress with civilians and soldiers; 100wn. Kim Il Sung and Kim Jong Il as child seated with soldiers and peasants 2·50 2·50
MSN4963 138×98 mm. 60wn. Kim Il Sung, family and soldiers in snow (60×42 mm) 2·00 2·00

1652 Workers and Soldier

2010. 50th Anniversary of Songun Revolutionary Leadership. Multicoloured.

N4964 10wn. Type **1652** 15 10
MSN4965 167×112 mm. 15wn. Kim Jong Il and soldiers in snow (64×42 mm); 30wn. With soldiers and flags (51×39 mm); 55wn. Looking over valley (51×39 mm); 80wn. On roadway with jubilant soldiers (51×39 mm) 2·00 2·00
MSN4966 130×95 mm. 70wn. Kim Jong Il on snowy mountain top (78×51 mm) 90 90

1653 President Fidel Castro of Cuba and Kim Il Sung

2010. 50th Anniversary of North Korea–Cuba Diplomatic Relations

N4967 **1653** 85wn. multicoloured 1·00 1·00

1654 *Pine Tree and Hawk* (Sin Yun Bok)

2010. Korean Paintings. Multicoloured.

N4968 15wn. Type **1654** 10 10
N4969 35wn. *Waves of Ongchon* (Jong Son) 40 35
N4970 70wn. *Reeds and Wild Geese* (Jo Sok Jin) 65 60
N4971 100wn. *After picking Medicinal Herbs* (Kim Hong Do) 95 90

1655 Founding Guerrilla Army

2010. Sun of the Nation (1st issue). Birth Centenary of Kim Il Sung (2012). Multicoloured.

MSN4972 104×112 mm. 10wn. Type **1655**; 20wn. With crowd celebrating formation of revolutionary government; 35wn. With soldiers and flags during anti-Japanese war; 90wn. Addressing soldiers at founding of Association for the Restoration of Fatherland 1·10 1·10

MSN4973 166×100 mm.10wn. In snow during 250 mile Journey for Learning; 30wn. With workers in demonstration against railway; 40wn. Addressing meeting; 55wn. Receiving pistols from Kang Pan Sok, women's leader 1·10 1·10

MSN4974 140×87 mm. 20wn. Firing pistol into air; 30wn. Burning documents; 40wn. With children and soldiers in snow; 45wn. With soldiers, holding binoculars 95 95

MSN4975 150×68 mm. 20wn. As child with father; 55wn. As child writing, whilst mother sews 80 80

MSN4976 150×116 mm. 25wn. Kim Jong Suk defending Kim Il Sung (64×42 mm); 30wn. With Kim Jong Suk at Mt. Paektu camp; 45wn. With family and soldiers on horseback 1·00 1·00

MSN4977 158×101 mm. 50wn. Addressing crowd (39×51 mm) 60 60

MSN4978 147×83 mm. 60wn. With soldiers in snow, holding binoculars (39×51 mm) 65 65

See also Nos. N5040/**MS**N5066 and N5136/**MS**N5146.

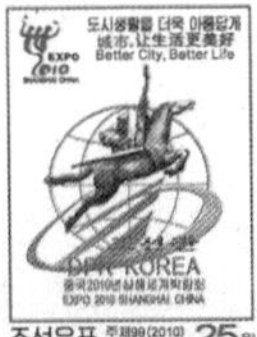
1656 Emblem of DPRK Pavilion, Expo 2010

2010. Expo 2010, Shanghai (2nd issue)

N4979 **1656** 25wn. multicoloured 15 10

1657 Chinese Soldier and Korean Woman

2010. 60th Anniversary of Chinese People's Volunteers' Entry into Korean War. Multicoloured.

N4980 25wn. Type **1657** 15 10

MSN4981 135×105 mm. 10wn. Chinese committee deciding to send volunteer force (60×42 mm); 15wn. Two soldiers (30×42 mm); 20wn. *For Peace* (bronze statue) (60×42 mm); 27wn. Children holding doves (30×42 mm) 75 75

(1657a)

2010. Europhila 2010 International Youth Stamp Collector's Exhibition, Stockholm. Multicoloured.

MSN4982 10wn. As Type **1645**; 125wn. As No. N4948; 152wn. As No. N4949 2·75 2·75

1658 Workers' Party Flag

2010. 65th Anniversary of Workers' Party (2nd issue). Multicoloured.

N4983 10wn. Type **1658** 10 10

MSN4984 165×106 mm. 10wn. As Type **1658**; 20wn. Kim Il Sung on military vessel; 25wn. Kim Il Sung and railway workers; 50wn. Kim Il Sung with scientists and equipment; 60wn. Kim Il Sung in fabric shop 1·20 1·20

MSN4985 145×97 mm. 70wn. Kim Il Sung examining party flag (45×54 mm) 80 80

1659 Kim Jong Il and President Hu Jintao of China

2010. Unofficial Visit of Kim Jong Il to China (2nd issue). Multicoloured.

N4986 70wn. Type **1659** 65 60

MSN4987 140×130 mm 30wn. Signing register at Jilin Yuwen Middle School (42×35 mm); 42wn. Examining railway carriage (42×35 mm); 70wn. Examining bottles at Harbin Huijiang Foodstuff Company (42×35 mm) 1·20 1·20

1660 WPK Flag and Kimjongilia

2010. Workers' Party of Korea Conference

N4988 **1660** 30wn. multicoloured 25 25

No. N4989 is vacant.

1662 Two Rabbits

2011. Chinese New Year. Year of the Rabbit. Multicoloured.

N4990 70wn. Type **1662** 60 60

N4991 140wn. Large white and small brown rabbits 1·10 1·10

MSN4992 115×85 mm. Nos. N4990/N4991 1·70 1·70

1663 DPRK National Flag and Air Koryo Airliner

2011. INDIPEX 2011 International Philatelic Exhibition, New Delhi. Sheet 100×72 mm

MSN4993 **1663** 70wn. multicoloured 60 60

1664 *Capra Hircus*

2011. 68th Birth Anniversary of Kim Jong Il. Animal Gifts from Kuwait. Multicoloured.

N4994 30wn. Type **1664** 25 25

N4995 42wn. *Ceropithecus aethiops* (green monkey) 30 30

N4996 112wn. *Cebuella pygmaea* (pygmy marmoset) 1·00 1·00

N4997 125wn. *Hystrix indica* (porcupine) (horiz) 1·10 1·10

No. N4998 and T **1665** are left for Martial Arts, not yet received.

1666 Celebrating Workers and Soldiers

2011. *Rodong Sinmun*, *Josoninmingun* and *Chongnyonjonwi* Newspapers Joint Editorial. Multicoloured.

N4999 10wn. Type **1666** 10 10

N5000 10wn. News vendor and symbols of productivity 10 10

N5001 30wn. Farmer carrying sheaf of corn and symbols of agriculture 25 25

N5002 70wn. Flags and service personnel 60 60

N5003 112wn. Map, three figures and broken missile (vert) 1·00 1·00

1667 *Paradisaea raggiana* (bird-of-paradise)

2011. Birds. Multicoloured.

N5004 30wn. Type **1667** 25 25

N5005 42wn. *Cygnus olor* (mute swan) 35 35

N5006 75wn. *Pulsatrix perspicillata* (spectacled owl) 65 65

N5007 133wn. *Goura victoria* (Victoria crowned pigeon) 1·20 1·20

1668 Flag, Flowers and 1946 50ch. Stamp (As T **2**)

2011. 65th Anniversary of First Postage Stamp

N5008 **1668** 30wn. multicoloured 25 25

1669 *Mao Zedong* (painting)

2011. 50th Anniversary of Treaty of Friendship, Co-operation and Mutual Assistance with China. Multicoloured.

MSN5009 10wn.×6, Type **1669**; Mao Zedong and Kim Il Sung (54×45 mm); Mao Zedong wearing blue; Mao Zedong addressing rally (painting) (56×39 mm); Mao Zedong wearing black (28×39 mm); Mao Zedong and Deng Xiaoping (56×39 mm) 55 55

MSN5010 10wn.×6, Mao Zedong and Peng Dehuai (45×33 mm); Kim Il Sung and Mao Zedong (36×45 mm); Mao Zedong and Chen Yi (45×33 mm); Mao Zedong and Liu Shaoqi wearing overcoats (56×39 mm); Mao Zedong and Zhou Enlai (28×39 mm); Zhu De and Mao Zedong applauding (56×39 mm) 55 55

1670 Young Couple (Disaster Risk Reduction)

2011. International Year of Volunteers. Multicoloured.

MSN5011 30wn. Type **1670**; 42wn. Red Cross worker (Promotion Activities); Rescue workers (Emergency Relief Activities) 65 65

1671 Apples

2011. 50th Anniversary of Pukchong Meeting of Presidium of WPK Central Committee. Multicoloured.

N5012 30wn. Type **1671** 65 65

MSN5013 114×79 mm. 70wn. Kim Il Sung (39×51 mm) 25 25

1672 Kimilsungia

2011. 99th Birth Anniversary of Kim Il Sung. Floral Gifts. Multicoloured.

N5014 30wn. Type **1672** 1·00 1·00

N5015 42wn. *Callistephus chinensis* 25 25

N5016 70wn. *Iris ensata* 35 35

N5017 98wn. *Rosa hybrida* 60 60

N5018 112wn. *Lilium* 80 80

MSN5019 165×97 mm. Nos. N5014/N5018 3·00 3·00

1673 Pyongyang Metro

2011. Tourism. Pyongyang. Multicoloured.

N5020 30wn. Type **1673** 25 25

N5021 42wn. Mangyongdae Children's Palace 35 35

N5022 56wn. May Day Stadium 45 45

N5023 70wn. People's Palace of Culture 60 60

N5024 84wn. Arch of Triumph 75 75

N5025 98wn. State Theatre 80 80

N5026 112wn. Party Museum 1·00 1·00

N5027 140wn. Kim Il Sung's Birthplace, Mangyongdae 1·10 1·10

1674 Kimilsungia

2011. International Horticultural Exposition in Xi'an, China. Multicoloured.

N5028 10wn. Type **1674** 95 95

N5029 30wn. *Magnolia sieboldi* 10 10

N5030 30wn. *Kimjongilia* (30×36 mm) 25 25

N5031 42wn. *Paeonia suffruticosa* 25 25

MSN5032 117×130 mm. 10wn. As Type **1674**; 30wn. As No. N5030; 42wn. As No. N5031 35 35

1675 Aerial Acrobat

2011. Circus. Multicoloured.

MSN5033 42wn. Type **1675**; 70wn. Aerial juggler; Highwire unicycle juggler; Skipping 95 95

1676 Chollima Statue

2011. Chollima Statue. Sheet 140×80mm.

MSN5034 **1676** 98wn. multicoloured 80 80

1677 Apples

2011. Taedonggang Combined Fruit Farm. Sheet 120×70 mm.

MSN5035 **1677** 70wn. multicoloured	60	60

1678 *Vanda hybrida*

2011. Orchids. Multicoloured.

N5036 10wn. Type **1678**	10	10
N5037 30wn. *Laeliocattlea*	35	25
N5038 70wn. *Laelia gouldiana*	60	60
N5039 142wn. *Phalaennnopsis*	1·10	1·10

1679 With Workers at Kangson Steel Works

2011. Sun of the Nation (2nd issue). Birth Centenary of Kim Il Sung (2012). Multicoloured.

N5040 10wn. Type **1679**	10	10
N5041 10wn. With his grandparents	10	10
N5042 10wn. At Pyongyang Railway Works	10	10
N5043 30wn. Digging at Pothong River Improvement Project	25	25
N5044 30wn. Land redistribution	25	25
N5045 30wn. On Ssuk Island	25	25
N5046 30wn. With bereaved children	25	25
N5047 30wn. Machine gun demonstration with Kim Jong Suk	25	25
N5048 30wn. Tank training	25	25
N5049 30wn. With airmen	25	25
N5050 30wn. Operational instruction to armed services	25	25
N5051 30wn. With tanks and soldiers	25	25
N5052 30wn. Outlining frontline strategy	35	35
N5053 42wn. With soldiers and musicians	35	35
N5054 42wn. With female soldier at frontline	35	35
N5055 42wn. With plough women	35	35
N5056 42wn. Party meeting at Rakwon Machine Plant	35	35
N5057 42wn. In soldiers' canteen	35	35
N5058 42wn. With railway engineers	35	35
N5059 42wn. With soldiers, tank and motorcycle	35	35
N5060 42wn. With returning soldiers	35	35
N5061 42wn. Directing Han River crossing	35	35
N5062 42wn. With soldiers and map	35	35
MSN5063 150×116 mm. 25wn. Holding papers in garden (64×42 mm); 30wn. Drawing party emblem; 45wn. Giving speech	90	90
MSN5064 159×86 mm. 40wn. Addressing crowd from balcony (36×45 mm)	35	35
MSN5065 159×86 mm. 50wn. With soldiers in snow (39×51 mm)	40	40
MSN5066 130×88 mm. 60wn. Seated with soldiers (39×51 mm)	55	55

1680 With Management Personnel

2011. Unofficial Visit of Kim Jong Il to China (3rd issue). Multicoloured.

MSN5067 90wn. Type **1680**	80	80
MSN5068 90wn. With President Jintao	80	80
MSN5069 90wn. Examining 3D display (horiz)	80	80

1681 Kim Jong Il and EU Delegation

2011. Tenth Anniversary of European Union–DPRK Diplomatic Relations. Sheet 122×92 mm

MSN5070 **1681** 140wn. multicoloured	1·10	1·10

1682 *Gymnocalycium schuetzianum*

2011. Cacti. Multicoloured.

N5071 30wn. Type **1682**	2·75	2·75
N5072 70wn. *Rebutia euanthema*	25	25
N5073 98wn. *Rebutia xanthocapa*	60	60
N5074 112wn. *Notocactus herteri*	80	80
MSN5075 95×105 mm. Nos. N5071/N5074	1·00	1·00

1683 Megalosaurus bucklandi

2011. Dinosaurs. Multicoloured.

N5076 42wn. Type **1683**	35	35
N5077 98wn. Staurikosaurus pricei	80	80
N5078 140wn. Chamosaurus belli	1·10	1·10

1684 ZIL Fire Appliance

2011. Fire Appliances. Multicoloured.

N5079 30wn. Type **1684**	25	25
N5080 70wn. Mercedes-Benz	60	60
N5081 98wn. ZIL with ladders	80	80
N5082 140wn. Mercedes-Benz with ladders	1·10	1·10
MSN5083 102×90 mm. Nos. N5079 and N5082	1·10	1·10
MSN5084 102×90 mm. Nos. N5080/N5081	1·40	1·40

1684a Pak Yon

2011. Korean Historic Personalities. Multicoloured.

N5085 10wn. Type **1684a**	30	25
N5086 30wn. Shin Saimdang	90	85
N5087 50wn. Jeong Yak-yong	1·10	1·00
N5088 70wn. Ryu Rin Sok	1·20	1·10

1685 Kim Jong Il with President Medvedev

2011. Kim Jong Il's Visit to Russia's Far Eastern Regions. Multicoloured.

MSN5089 110×85 mm. 70wn. Type **1685**	3·50	3·50
MSN5090 110×85 mm. 70wn. With leaders (45×35 mm)	3·50	3·50
MSN5091 110×85 mm. 70wn. Visiting factory (35×45 mm)	3·50	3·50

1686 Kim Jong Il with Chinese Leader

2011. Kim Jong Il's Visit to North East China. Sheet 135×90 mm

MSN5092 **1686** 70wn. multicoloured	3·50	3·50

1687 *Chairman Mao goes to Anyuan* (Liu Chunhua)

2011. Korea–China Friendship. Multicoloured.

MSN5093 120×135 mm. 10wn. Kim Il sung inspecting troops; 10wn. Mao Zedong writing; 10wn. Mao Zedong head and shoulders 30wn. Kim Il Sung; 30wn. Kim Il Sung and Mao Zedong shaking hands; 30wn. Kim Il Sung with Mao Zedong	3·50	3·50
MSN5094 120×135 mm. 10wn. Deng Xiaoping in car; 10wn. Deng Xiaoping wearing uniform; 10wn. Deng Xiaoping head and shoulders; 30wn. Kim Il Sung; 30wn. Kim Il Sung and Deng Xiaoping embracing; 30wn. Deng Xiaoping and Kim Il Sung wearing uniforms	3·50	3·50
MSN5095 120×135 mm. 10wn. Jiang Zemin in car; 10wn. People's Assemby; 10wn. Jiang Zemin head and shoulders; 30wn. Kim Jong Il; 30wn. Kim Jong Il and Jiang Zemin shaking hands; 30wn. Jiang Zemin and Kim Jong Il with clasped hands	3·50	3·50
MSN5096 120×135 mm. 10wn. Hu Jintao in car; 10wn. Hu Jintao; 10wn. Hu Jintao head and shoulders; 30wn. Kim Jong Il; 30wn. Hu Jintao and Kim Jong Il; 30wn. Kim Jong Il and Hu Jintao shaking hands	3·50	3·50

1688 Geographer Kim Jong Ho

2011. 50th Anniversary of First Korean National Map

N5097 **1688** 98wn. multicoloured	1·40	1·20

1689 Limonite

2011. Minerals. Multicoloured.

N5098 30wn. Type **1689**	40	35
N5099 42wn. Magnesium Borate (Inscr 'Mg3[BO3]2')	95	90
N5100 58wn. Wollastonite	1·10	1·00
N5101 98wn. Antimonite	1·20	1·00

1690 Kim Jong Il and Airmen

2011. 20th Anniversary of Kim Jong Il's Appointment to the Supreme Commander of the Army. Multicoloured.

MSN5102 150×90 mm. 10wn. Type **1690**; 30wn. With airmen in the snow; 70wn. Looking over valley; 80wn. On roadway with jubilant soldiers	2·00	2·00
MSN5103 160×85 mm. 98wn. Kim Jong Il standing in jeep (50×38 mm)	90	90

1691 Kim Jong Il

2011. Kim Jong Il Commemoration. Multicoloured.

MSN5104 70wn. Type **1691**	3·50	3·50
MSN5105 70wn. With Kim Jong-un	3·50	3·50

1692 Kimilsungia and 'Juche' Idea Tower

2012. New Year

N5106 **1692** 10wn. multicoloured	30	25

1693 Dragon

2012. Chinese New Year. Year of the Dragon. Multicoloured.

N5107 10wn. Type **1693**	60	60
N5108 30wn. Dragon circular	60	60
N5109 60wn. Dragon on hind legs	60	60

1694 Mount Paektu from Lake Samji

2012. Mount Paektu. Multicoloured.

N5110 20wn. Type **1694**	40	35
N5111 30wn. Lake Chon on Mount Paektu	95	90

1695 *Pachliopta coon*

2012. Butterflies. Multicoloured.

N5112 30wn. Type **1695**	30	25
N5113 70wn. *Agrias pericles*	90	85
N5114 90wn. *Bhutanitis lidderdalii*	1·10	1·00
N5115 120wn. *Cethosia biblis*	1·20	1·10

1696 Workers and Forces Personnel

2012. *Rodong Sinmun, Josoninmingun and Chongnyonjonwi* Newspapers Joint Editorial. Multicoloured.
N5116 10wn. Type **1696** 10 10
N5117 10wn. Symbols of food production (horiz) 10 10
N5118 30wn. Symbols of industry 25 25
N5119 30wn. Rifle 60 60
N5120 40wn. Fist 1·00 1·00
N5121 50wn. globe and dove 10 10

1697 Kopernik House, Moscow and Apartment House, Pyongyang

2012. Architecture of Pyongyang and Moscow. Multicoloured.
MSN5122 185×170 mm. 60wn. Type **1697**; 100wn. Inscr 'Patriarkh House', Moscow and East Pyongyang Theatre; 140wn. Inscr 'Patriarkh House in the Evening' and National Theatre; 140wn. Grand People's Study House and Gnezdikovskiy Palace; 190wn. Ultra High Apartment House, Pyongyang and Egg House, Moscow; 210wn. Hyangsan Hotel and Weber Villa 10·00 10·00
MSN5123 105×75 mm. 140wn. Inscr 'Patriarkh House in the Evening' and National Theatre in the Evening 2·00 2·00

1698 Worker with Raised Fist

2012. Workers' Party of Korea Conference
N5124 **1698** 10wn. multicoloured 30 25

1699 Kimjongilia

2012. 71st Birth Anniversary of Kim Jong Il. Multicoloured.
N5125 10wn. Type **1699** 30 25
MSN5126 150×100 mm. 40wn. At snow-covered gun emplacement; 70wn. With travellers in the snow 1·80 1·80
MSN5127 130×93 mm. 70wn. Kim Jong Il 1·50 1·50

1700 12th-century Ceramic Bottle with Lotus Flowers

2012. Ceramics. Multicoloured.
N5128 30wn. Type **1700** 9·00 85
N5129 70wn. 15th-century blue and white bottle with dragon decoration 1·20 1·10
N5130 70wn. 12th-century blue and green pitcher with handle and spout 1·20 1·10
MSN5131 70×85 mm. 70wn. As N5130 1·50 1·50

1701 Mount Paektu and Jong Il Peak

2012. Day of the Shining Star
N5132 **1701** 10wn. multicoloured 30 25

1702 Award

2012. Kim Jong Il's Posthumous Nomination of Generalissimo
N5133 **1702** 10wn. multicoloured 30 25

1703 Tulips

2012. Floriade 2012 World Horticultural Expo, Venlo, Netherlands
N5134 **1703** 30wn. multicoloured 90 85

1704 Emblem

2012. 90th Anniversary of Korean National Association
N5135 **1704** 30wn. olive-bistre 90 85

1705 Kim Il Sung with Foreign Leaders

2012. Sun of the Nation (3rd issue). Multicoloured.
N5136 30wn. Type **1705** 90 85
N5137 30wn. With workers, power plant in background 90 85
N5138 30wn. Seated picnicking with agricultural workers 90 85
N5139 30wn. Presenting awards 90 85
N5140 30wn. Comforting man in grey suit 90 85
N5141 30wn. With family 90 85
N5142 30wn. With young people 90 85
MSN5143 130×95 mm. 20wn.×4, Greeting families, wearing white suit; Addressing workers in snow, wearing black coat and hat; Seated, addressing meeting; With workers, wearing black coat 3·00 3·00
MSN5144 130×95 mm. 30wn.×4, Addressing workers in rail yard; With workers at cotton mill; With agricultural workers, wearing white shirt; With horticultural technicians wearing laboratory coat 3·50 3·50
MSN5145 130×95 mm. 40wn.×4, With airmen in snow; Addressing cadets; With women soldiers; With airmen and Kim Jong Il 4·00 4·00
MSN5146 70×85 mm. 70wn. Seated with women and children 1·50 1·50

1706 Birthplace and '100'

2012. Birth Centenary of Kim Il Sung. Multicoloured.
N5147 42wn. Type **1706** 90 85
MSN5148 165×85 mm. 70wn. With bereaved children; 100wn. Seated with girl on lapand families 3·00 3·00
MSN5149 80×115 mm. 100wn. With wife 3·00 3·00

1707 Stamps and National Emblems

2012. Opening of Korean Postal Museum, Pyongyang
N5150 **1707** 10wn. multicoloured 30 25

1708 Kang Pan Sok

2012. 120th Birth Anniversary of Kang Pan Sok. Sheet 110×70 mm
MSN5151 **1708** 70wn. multicoloured 1·50 1·50

APPENDIX

The following stamps have either been issued in excess of postal needs or have not been available to the public in reasonable quantities at face value. Such stamps may later be given full listing if there is evidence of regular postal use.

1976

Olympic Games, Montreal. Three-dimensional stamps showing Olympic events. 5, 10, 15, 20, 25, 40ch.

1977

Olympic Games, Montreal. Three-dimensional stamps showing medals. 5, 10, 15, 20, 25, 40ch.
Olympic Games, Montreal. 1976 Olympic Games issue optd with winners' names. 5, 10, 15, 20, 25, 40ch.

1979

XIII Winter Olympic Games, 1980. Nos. N1688/N1694 optd. 2, 5, 10, 15, 20, 25, 40ch.

1981

Nobel Prizes for Medicine. Nos. N1955/N1961 optd. 7×10ch.
World Cup Football Championship, Spain (1982). Nos. N1731/N1741 optd. 12×20ch.
World Cup Football Championship, Spain (1982). Three-dimensional stamps. Air 20, 30ch.

1982

21st Birthday of Princess of Wales. Nos. N2108/N2111 and N2120/N2123 optd. 10, 20, 30, 40ch.; 10, 20, 30, 70ch.
Birth of Prince William of Wales. Nos. N2185/N2191 optd. 10, 20, 30, 50, 60, 70, 80ch.
World Cup Football Championship, Spain, Results. Nos. N2201/N2206 optd. 10, 20, 30, 40, 50, 60ch.
Birth of Prince William of Wales. Three-dimensional stamps. 3×30ch.

1983

XXIII Olympic Games, Los Angeles, 1984. Nos. N2084/N2088 optd. 10, 15, 20, 25, 30ch.

1984

European Royal History. 81×10ch.

KOSOVO REPUBLIC

The Republic of Kosovo declared independence on the 17th February 2008.

100 cents = 1 euro.

41 William Walker (head of OSCE cease-fire verification mission)

2009. Tenth Anniversary of Racak Massacre. Multicoloured.
118 50c. Type **41** 2·30 2·30
119 70c. Broken stone inscribed RECAK 2·50 2·50

44 Monastery Building

2010. UNESCO World Heritage Site.
123 €1 Type **44** 5·50 5·50
124 €2 Early building 15·00 15·00
MS125 80×104 mm. Vert. €1 Window; €2 Head of Christ (fresco) 21·00 21·00

45 EU Stars, Man, Child and Telescope and Map

2009. Europa. Astronomy. Multicoloured.
126 €1 Type **45** 5·50 5·50
127 €2 Boy and rocket boosters 15·00 15·00
MS128 180×69 mm. €2 As No. 127 21·00 21·00
The stamp of **MS**128 has the design to the edge of the stamp and, with the margins, forms a composite design

46 Children

2009. Children's Day. Multicoloured.
129 20c. Type **46** 1·90 1·90
130 50c. Children holding balloon and kite 2·75 2·75
131 70c. Child's hand in adult's hand 3·25 3·25
132 €1 Child's silhouette 6·00 6·00

47 Flags of Kosovo and USA as Hands touching

2009. Kosovo–USA Friendship.
133 **47** €2 multicoloured 10·50 50

48 Lorenc Antoni and Piano

2009. Birth Centenary of Lorenc Antoni (composer).
134 **48** €1 multicoloured 5·50 5·50

49 Flags of Germany and Kosovo intertwined as Waves

2009. German Weeks.

1335	**49**	€1 multicoloured	5·50	5·50

50 Parchment and Script

2009. 320th Death Anniversary of Pjeter Bogdani (author of *Cuneus Prophetarum* (The Band of the Prophets), first prose work written in Albanian).

136	**50**	€1 multicoloured	5·50	5·50

51 *Head* (Teuta Beqiri)

2009. Visual Arts. Multicoloured.

137	30c. Type **51**	2·20	2·20
138	50c. *White horses* (I. Kodra)	2·75	2·75
139	70c. *Abstract* (G. J. G. Jokaj)	3·00	3·00
140	€1 *Back view of figure carrying rucksack* (M. Mulliqi)	5·00	5·00

52 Faruk Begolli (actor)

2010. Kosovo Cinema. Multicoloured.

141	30c. Type **52**	2·20	2·20
142	70c. Melihate Qena (actress)	3·25	3·25
143	€1 Abdurrahman Shala (producer and director)	5·50	5·50
MS144	81×105mm. 30c. Hadi Shehu (actor); 70c. Muharrem Qena (actor)	5·50	5·50

53 TMK (Protection Corps), SHPK (Police Force) and FSK (Security Force (replaced TMK)) Badges

2010. Independence Day. Multicoloured.

145	30c. Type **53**	2·20	2·20
146	50c. SHPK personnel	2·75	2·75
147	70c. FSK soldiers	3·25	3·25

54 Reading beneath Tree of Books

2010. Europa. Children's Books. Multicoloured.

148	€1 Type **54**	5·50	5·50
149	€2 Figure emerging from book pages carrying letter 'A'	10·50	10·50
MS150	80×69mm. €2 Boy reading	11·00	11·00

55 National Team Emblem and Map of Africa as Football Pitch

2010. World Cup Football Championships, South Africa. Multicoloured.

151	€1 Type **55**	5·50	5·50
152	€2 National Team emblem, globe and stream of colours	10·50	10·50
MS153	104×80mm. 50c.×2, Kosovo colours looped to football; Kosovo flag as football	5·50	5·50

56 Azem Galica, Shote Galica and Albanian Flag

2010. Personalities. Azem Galica (Azem Bejta) and his wife, Shote Galica (Qerime Radisheva) (nationalists) Commemoration.

154	**56**	€2 multicoloured	11·00	11·00

57 Waterfall, Mirusha Park

2010. National Parks. Multicoloured.

155	20c. Type **57**	1·90	1·90
156	50c. Lake and conifers, Rugova	2·50	2·50
157	70c. Lake and rocky hillside, Gjeravica	3·50	3·50
158	€1 Tree covered hillside and mountains, Sharri	5·50	5·50

58 Mother Teresa

2010. Personalities. Birth Centenary of Agnes Gonxha Bojaxhiu (Mother Teresa) (founder of Missionaries of Charity).

159	**58**	€1 multicoloured	5·50	5·50

59 Streaming towards EU Stars as '8'

2010. European Integration. Multicoloured.

160	70c. Type **59**	3·50	3·50
MS161	70×53mm. €1 Stars, streamers and '8' on map of Europe	5·50	5·50

60 Barn Swallows

2010. Birds. Multicoloured.

162	30c. Type **60**	2·20	2·20
163	50c. Tree swallow	2·75	2·75
164	70c. Redwing	3·50	3·50
165	€1 Red-rumped swallow	5·50	5·50
MS166	80×105 mm. 30c. Bluethroat; 30c. Dark barn swallow facing right; 70c. Barn swallow in flight; 70c. Barn swallow facing left	11·00	11·00

61 Beehive, Honeycomb and Honey Jars.

2010. Local Foods. Multicoloured.

167	70c. Type **61**	2·75	2·75
168	€1 Table with local dishes displayed	5·50	5·50

62 Symbols of Violence against Women

2010. Campaign to End Violence against Women.

169	**62**	€1 multicoloured	5·50	5·50

63 Shops

2010. Cultural Heritage. Multicoloured.

170	50c. Type **63**	2·20	2·20
171	70c. Village street	2·75	2·75
172	€1 Market place	5·50	5·50

64 Letters

2011. Third Anniversary of Independence. Multicoloured.

173	€1 Type **64**	5·50	5·50
174	€2 Fireworks over city	10·00	10·00

65 Elena Gjika

2011. Personalities. Elena Gjika (author) Commemoration.

175	**65**	€1 multicoloured	5·50	5·50

66 Houses

2011. Cities of Kosovo: Prizreni. Multicoloured.

176	20c. Type **66**	1·00	1·00
177	50c. Houses	2·20	2·20
178	70c. View over city	2·75	2·75

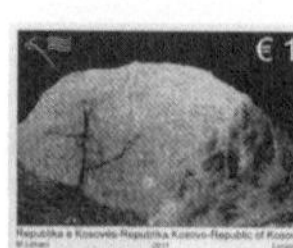

67 Forest

2011. Europa. Forests. Multicoloured.

179	€1 Type **67**	5·50	5·50
180	€2 Forest and mountains	10·00	10·00
MS181	69x53mm. €2 Forest clearing	10·00	10·00

68 Ancient Ruins

2011. Archaeology. Multicoloured.

182	10c. Type **68**	50	50
183	15c. Ancient ruins	75	75
184	€1 Relief	5·50	5·50

69 Decorated Socks

2011. National Costumes. Multicoloured.

185	30c. Type **69**	1·50	1·50
186	50c. National Dress	2·20	2·20
187	70c. Decorated bag	2·75	2·75
188	€1 Decorated dress	5·50	5·50
MS189	80x104mm €2 Headdress	10·00	10·00

70 Mill

2011. Old Mills. Multicoloured.

190	50c. Type **70**	2·20	2·20
191	70c. Brick mill	2·75	2·75
192	€1 Wooden water mill	5·50	5·50
MS193	61x85mm. €2 Mill	10·00	10·00

71 Interior, Cave of the Grand Canyon, Peja

2011. The Cave of the Grand Canyon, Peja. Multicoloured.

194	70c. Type **71**	2·75	2·75
195	€1 Cave interior	5·50	5·50

72 Rooster

2011. Roosters. Multicoloured.

196	70c. Type **72**	2·75	2·75
197	€1 Rooster	5·50	5·50

73 Esad Mekuli

2011. Personalities. Esad Mekuli (first president of Academy of Sciences and Arts of Kosovo) Commemoration.

198	**73**	€1 multicoloured	5·50	5·50

74 Znver Zymeri

2011. Personalities. Znver Zymeri (police officer) Commemoration.

199	**74**	€1 multicoloured	5·50	5·50

75 Scenes of Industry and Aerial View of City

2012. Cities of Kosovo: Mitrovica. Multicoloured.

200	€1 Type **75**	5·50	5·50
201	€2 Street scenes	10·00	10·00

76 Three Soldiers

2012. Beacons of Freedom. Multicoloured.

202	€1 Type **76**	5·50	5·50
203	€1 Three civilians	5·50	5·50

77 Rexho Mulliqi

2012. Personalities. Rexho Mulliqi (composer) Commemoration.

204	**77**	€1 multicoloured	5·50	5·50

78 Common Blue Butterfly

2012. Butterflies. Multicoloured.

205 10c. Type **78** 1·50 1·50
206 70c. Stylised blue butterfly 3·50 3·50
207 €1 Marbled White and Orange Swallowtail butterflies 5·50 5·50
MS208 86×63mm. €2 Scarlet Swallowtail and orchid 11·00 11·00

79 Mountains

2012. Europa. Forests. Multicoloured.

209 €1 Type **79** 5·50 5·50
210 €2 House with overhanging upper storey 10·00 10·00
MS211 63×86mm. €2 Wide plaza 11·00 11·00

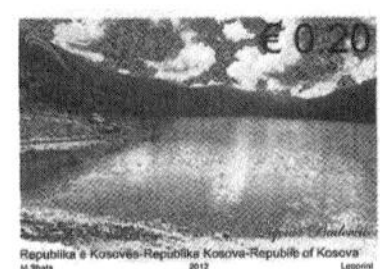

80 Lake Badovac

2012. Nature Protection. Multicoloured.

212 20c. Type **80** 1·00 1·00
213 50c. Lake Gazivoda 2·20 2·20
214 70c. Lake Lićenat 2·75 2·75

81 Isa Boletini

2012. Centenary of National Revolution. Multicoloured.

215 70c. Type **81** (freedom fighter) 2·75 2·75
216 €1 Hasan Prishtina (politician) 5·50 5·50

82 Bride with Head covered

2012. Local Traditions.

217 **82** €1 multicoloured 5·50 5·50

83 Majlinda Kelmendi

2012. Olympic Games, London. Majlinda Kelmendi (World and European under 52kg. champion). Multicoloured.

MS218 70c.×2, Type **83**×2; €1×2, With arms raised×2 12·00 12·00

84 Bridge building

2012. Myths and Legends. Multicoloured.

219 70c. Type **84** 3·00 3·00
220 €1 Warriors 5·50 5·50
MS221 86×61mm. €2 Bride and groom mounted on white horse (triangular) 12·00 12·00

85 Dancing Musicians

2012. Folk Dance. Multicoloured.

222 50c. Type **85** 2·75 2·75
223 70c. Female dance troop 4·00 4·00
224 €1 Seated musicians and black-coated dancers 5·50 5·50

86 Isa Boletini, Hasan Berisha and Bajram Curri

2012. Centenary of Albanian Independence.

225 €1 multicoloured 5·50 5·50

87 Marin Barleti

2012. Personalities. 500th Death Anniversary of Marin Barleti (historian and Catholic priest).

226 **87** €1 multicoloured 5·50 5·50

88 Emblem

2013. Fifth Anniversary of Independence.

227 **88** €2 multicoloured 9·00 9·00

89 Prishtina

2013. Cities of Kosovo: Prishtina. Multicoloured.

228 50c. Type **89** 3·00 3·00
229 70c. Houses 4·00 4·00
230 €1 View over city 5·50 5·50

90 Exterior of Museum

2013. Museum Exhibits. Multicoloured.

231 70c. Type **90** 3·00 3·00
232 €1 Room setting 5·50 5·50
MS233 92×86mm.Vert. €1×2, Room setting with low table (left); Room setting with low table (right) 12·00 12·00

91 Postman riding Bicycle, Map and Steam Train

2013. Europa. Postal Transport. Multicoloured.

234 €1 Type **91** 5·50 5·50
235 €2 Horse-drawn mail cart and modern postman riding scooter 9·00 9·00
MS236 92×86mm. Vert. €1×2, Horse-drawn mail cart; Modern postman riding scooter 12·00 12·00

92 Maja e Gjeravicës

2013. Mountains. Multicoloured.

237 50c. Type **92** 3·00 3·00
238 70c. Gryka e Rugovës 4·00 4·00
239 €1 Maja e Gjeravicës (different) 5·50 5·50

93 Stubilla e Epërme

2013. Villages of Kosovo. Multicoloured.

240 50c. Type **93** 3·00 3·00
241 70c. Opoja 4·00 4·00
242 €1 Lluka e Epërme 5·50 5·50

94 Hyrije Hana

2013. Famous Women. Multicoloured.

243 50c. Type **94** 3·00 3·00
244 70c. Xhevë Lladrovci 4·00 4·00
245 €1 Katarina Josipi 5·50 5·50

95 Baijram Curri

2013. Centenary of Baijram Curri Uprising.

246 **95** €1 multicoloured 5·50 5·50

96 Mountain Village

2013. Personalities. 80th Birth Anniversary of Adem Kastrati. Multicoloured.

247 70c. Type **96** 4·00 4·00
248 €1 Children and sheep 5·50 5·50
249 €2 Men and musicians seated around fire 11·00 11·00

97 University Façade

2013. 40th Anniversary of Prishtina University.

250 **97** €1 multicoloured 5·50 5·50

98 Qamili I Vogël

2013. Traditional Singers. Multicoloured.

251 20c. Type **98** 1·00 1·00
252 30c. Sali Krasniqi 2·20 2·20
253 50c. Dërvish Shaqa 3·00 3·00

99 Bekim Fehmiu

2013. Personalities. Bekim Fehmiu (actor) Commemoration.

254 **99** €1 multicoloured 5·50 5·50

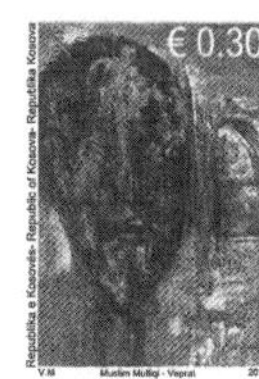

100 Blue Head

2014. Art. Paintings by Muslim Mulliqi. Multicoloured.

255 30c. Type **100** 2·20 2·20
256 60c. Building and woman's head 3·25 3·25
257 90c. Masks in frames and heads 5·00 5·00
258 €1 Heads in frames 5·50 5·50

101 Climbers

2014. Kosovo Sport. Alpinism.

259 €1 Type **101** 5·50 5·50
MS260 85×60 mm. €2 Climber ascending over-hang (horiz) 12·00 12·00

102 Square, Peja

2014. Cities of Kosovo: Peja. Multicoloured.

261 €1 Type **102** 5·50 5·50
262 €2 Street with awning over shop 11·00 11·00

103 Belts

2014. World Championship of Shotokan Karate. Multicoloured.

263 80c. Type **103** 4·50 4·50
264 90c. Competition emblem 5·00 5·00
MS265 85×60 mm. €2 Competition emblem (close up) 12·00 12·00

104 Flyover

2014. Ibrahim Rugova Highway. Multicoloured.

266 €1 Type **104** 5·50 5·50
267 €2 Highway and slip road 11·00 11·00

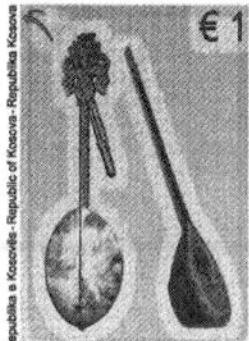

105 Lahuta and Sharkia

2014. Europa. Musical Instruments. Multicoloured.

268	€1 Type **105**	5·50	5·50
269	€2 Lahuta	11·00	11·00
MS270	85×60 mm. €2 Cifteli and flute (horiz)	12·00	12·00

106 Lilies

2014. Flowers. Multicoloured.

271	80c. Type **106**	4·50	4·50
272	90c. *Gladiolus illyricus*	5·00	5·00
273	€1 *Tulipa kosovarica*	5·50	5·50
MS273a	61×85 mm. €2 Peony	11·00	11·00

107 Jeronim de Rada

2014. Personalities. Birth Bicentenary of Geronimo de Rada (Jeronim de Rada) (writer).

274	**107**	€1 multicoloured	5·50	5·50

108 Woven Bag with Narrow Strap

2014. Handicrafts. Weaving. Multicoloured.

275	60c. Type **108**	3·25	3·25
276	80c. Multicoloured diamond design blanket	4·50	4·50
277	90c. Detail of rugs designs	5·00	5·00
278	€1 Two rugs	5·50	5·50

109 Fehmi and Xhevë Lladrovci

2014. Personalities. Fehmi and Xhevë Lladrovci (resistance fighters) Commemoration.

279	**109**	€2 multicoloured	11·00	11·00

110 Adrian Krasniqi

2014. Personalities. 17th Death Anniversary of Adrian Krasniqi (guerrilla fighter).

280	**110**	€1 multicoloured	5·50	5·50

111 Tringe Smalji

2014. Personalities. 97th Death Anniversary of Tringë Smajl Martini Ivezaj (guerrilla fighter).

281	**111**	€1 multicoloured	5·50	5·50

112 Iron Pyrites

2014. International Year of Crystallography. Multicoloured.

282	€1 Type **112**	5·50	5·50
283	€2 Quartz	11·00	11·00

113 Map and Emblems

2014. Kosovo in the International Olympic Committee.

284	**113**	€2 multicoloured	11·00	11·00

114 Street with Shops

2015. Cities of Kosovo: Gjakova. Multicoloured.

285	€1 Type **114**	5·50	5·50
286	€2 Street at dusk	11·00	11·00

115 Labyrinth

2015. Smira Circular Labyrinth.

287	**115**	€1 multicoloured	5·50	5·50

116 European Lynx

2015. Fauna. European Lynx. Multicoloured.

288	80c. Type **116**	4·50	4·50
289	90c. Head, facing left	5·00	5·00
290	€1 Head, facing front	5·50	5·50

117 Hashim Hajdini

2015. Personalities. Hashim Hajdini (patriot) Commemoration.

291	**117**	€1 multicoloured	5·50	5·50

118 Waterfall

2015. National Parks. Multicoloured.

292	30c. Type **118**	2·75	5·00
293	60c. River and bridge	3·25	3·25
294	80c. Stony river	4·50	4·50
295	90c. Tree leaning into turbulent river	5·00	5·00

119 Ilaz Kodra

2015. Personalities. Ilaz Kodra (Kosovo Liberation Army commander) Commemoration.

296	**119**	€2 multicoloured	11·00	11·00

120 Children's Games

2015. Europa. Old Toys. Multicoloured.

297	€1 Type **120**	5·50	5·50
298	€2 Home-made dolls	11·00	11·00
MS299	85×60mm. €2 Cradle	12·00	12·00

121 Ukshin Hoti

2015. Personalities. Ukshin Hoti (Kosovo Albanian philosopher and activist) Commemoration.

300	**121**	€1 multicoloured	5·50	5·50

122 Male Costume and Accessories

2015. National Costumes. Drenica. Multicoloured.

301	80c. Type **122**	4·50	4·50
302	90c. Woman, rear view	5·00	5·00
303	€1 Decorated bag	5·50	5·50
MS304	61×86mm. €2 Bodice	11·00	11·00

2015. Diaspora. Bright blue and gold.

305	€2 Blue hand holding golden globe	11·00	11·00

2015. Personalities. Family Lleshi (guerilla fighters).. Multicoloured.

306	€1 Mark (1926–1998), Prend (1964–1999), Kole (1967–1998) and Meme (1973–1999) Lleshi	5·50	5·50

2015. Gastronomy. Vineyards in Kosovo. Multicoloured.

307	60c. Mixed grapes in a basket	4·50	4·50
308	80c. Bottle of red wine and glass	5·00	5·00
309	90c. Vineyard and house	5·50	5·50
MS310	61×85 mm. €2 Woman picking grapes	11·00	11·00

126 Anton Çeta

2015. Personalities. 20th Death Anniversary of Anton Çeta (folklorist and academic).

311	**126**	€1 multicoloured	5·50	5·50

127 Qamili i Vogel

2015. Personalities. Qamili i Vogel (Kosovo Albanian singer, composer) Commemoration.

312	**127**	20c. multicoloured	1·50	1·50

128 Illyrian Potshards and Seated Figures

2015. Archaeology of Kosovo. Multicoloured.

MS313	€2×2, Type **128**×2	15·00	15·00

129 1950's Street Scene and Minaret

2016. Cities of Kosovo: Vushtrria (Vučitrn). Multicoloured.

314	€1 Type **129**	5·50	5·50
315	€2.10 Fortifications	11·00	11·00

130 Luan Haradinij

2016. Personalities. Guerilla Fighters. Multicoloured.

316	€1 Type **130**	5·50	5·50
317	€1 Skënder Rexhepi	5·50	5·50

131 Seated Woman

2016. Visual Art by Rexhep Ferri. Multicoloured.

318	40c. Type **131**	3·00	3·00
319	80c. Three male figures	4·50	4·50
320	90c. Abstract figure with purple bag	5·00	5·00

132 Ski-Lift and Skiers

2016. Mountain Tourism. Sheet 65×78 mm.

MS321	**132**	€2.10 multicoloured	11·50	11·50

133 Agim Ramadani

2016. Personalities. Battle of Koshare. Multicoloured.

322	€1 Type **133**	5·50	5·50
323	€1 Sali Çakaj	5·50	5·50

134 Map as Forest, with Hang-glider and Sunflowers

2016. Europa. Think Green. Multicoloured.

324	€1 Type **134**	5·50	5·50
325	€2.10 Blue water-filled profile, with landscape as hair	11·00	11·00
MS326	62×85mm. €2 House in a tree (vert)	12·00	12·00

135 Chess Pieces, Map and Flag

2016. European Individual Chess Championship. Gjakova, Kosovo. Multicoloured.

MS327	€1.80×2, Type **135**×2	14·00	14·00

136 *Boletus edulis* (inscr 'Boletus edilis')

2016. Fungi. Multicoloured.

MS328	60c. Type **136**; 80c. *Morchella* (inscr 'Marchella'); 90c. *Amanita muscaria*; €1.30 *Leccinum scabrum* (inscr 'Leccinum scarbum')	15·00	15·00

137 Emblem

2016. Olympic Games. Rio 2016. Multicoloured.

329	€1 Type **137**	5·50	5·50
330	€2.10 Celebrating	11·00	11·00
MS331	85×62 mm €2 Sprinter	11·50	11·50

138 Mother Teresa and Dove

2016. Canonisation of Mother Teresa.

332	**138**	€2.10 multicoloured	11·00	11·00

139 Dervish Rozhaja

2016. Personalities. 20th Death Anniversary of Dervish Rozhaja (academic).

333	**139**	€1.30 multicoloured	6·25	6·25

140 'Kosovo in UEFA'

2016. Football. Kosovo in UEFA and FIFA. Multicoloured.

334	€1.30 Type **140**	6·25	6·25
335	€2.10 'Kosovo in FIFA'	11·00	11·00

141 Apples

2016. Gastronomy. Fruit. Multicoloured.

336	40c. Type **141**	2·75	2·75
337	60c. Pears	3·25	3·25
338	80c. Blackberries	4·50	4·50

KOUANG TCHEOU (KWANGCHOW)

An area and port of S. China, leased by France from China in April 1898. It was returned to China in February 1943.

1906. 100 centimes = 1 franc.
1919. 100 cents = 1 piastre.

Unless otherwise stated the following are optd or surch on stamps of Indo-China.

1906. Surch **Kouang Tcheou-Wan** and value in Chinese.

1	**8**	1c. green	8·50	10·50
2	**8**	2c. red on yellow	7·75	7·75
3	**8**	4c. mauve on blue	7·50	9·50
4	**8**	5c. green	10·50	13·00
5	**8**	10c. red	12·00	10·50
6	**8**	15c. brown on blue	17·00	29·00
7	**8**	20c. red on green	10·00	13·50
8	**8**	25c. blue	7·75	10·00
9	**8**	30c. brown on cream	10·50	17·00
10	**8**	35c. black on yellow	19·00	26·00
11	**8**	40c. black on grey	10·50	17·00
12	**8**	50c. brown on cream	38·00	65·00
13	**D**	75c. brown on orange	65·00	70·00
14	**8**	1f. green	60·00	75·00
15	**8**	2f. brown on yellow	65·00	70·00
16	**D**	5f. mauve on lilac	£275	£250
17	**8**	10f. red on green	£350	£350

1908. Native types surch **KOUANG-TCHEOU** and value in Chinese.

18	**10**	1c. black and brown	1·90	1·80
19	**10**	2c. black and brown	2·00	1·90
20	**10**	4c. black and blue	2·10	2·30
21	**10**	5c. black and green	2·20	2·00
22	**10**	10c. black and red	2·75	3·00
23	**10**	15c. black and violet	5·00	7·25
24	**11**	20c. black and violet	8·50	12·50
25	**11**	25c. black and blue	10·50	14·00
26	**11**	30c. black and brown	14·00	27·00
27	**11**	35c. black and green	29·00	39·00
28	**11**	40c. black and brown	26·00	39·00
29	**11**	50c. black and red	30·00	46·00
30	**12**	75c. black and orange	23·00	46·00
31	-	1f. black and red	31·00	50·00
32	-	2f. black and green	65·00	75·00
33	-	5f. black and blue	£110	£120
34	-	10f. black and violet	£170	£170

1919. Nos. 18/34 surch in figures and words.

35	**10**	2/5c. on 1c. black and brown	1·40	6·75
36	**10**	4/5c. on 2c. black and brown	1·40	6·25
37	**10**	1 3/5c. on 4c. black and blue	1·50	6·25
38	**10**	2c. on 5c. black and green	7·00	9·00
39	**10**	4c. on 10c. black and red	5·75	4·50
40	**10**	6c. on 15c. black and violet	5·75	5·00
41	**11**	8c. on 20c. black and violet	13·00	13·00
42	**11**	10c. on 25c. black and blue	29·00	34·00
43	**11**	12c. on 30c. black & brown	9·00	10·00
44	**11**	14c. on 35c. black and green	6·50	10·00
45	**11**	16c. on 40c. black & brown	5·75	8·75
46	**11**	20c. on 50c. black and red	7·00	8·75
47	**12**	30c. on 75c. black & orange	13·00	23·00
48	-	40c. on 1f. black and red	22·00	21·00
49	-	80c. on 2f. black and green	16·00	30·00
50	-	2p. on 5f. black and blue	£225	£225
51	-	4p. on 10f. black and violet	41·00	65·00

1923. Native types optd **KOUANG-TCHEOU** only. (Value in cents and piastres).

52	**10**	1/10c. red and grey	50	7·75
53	**10**	1/5c. black and blue	50	7·75
54	**10**	2/5c. black and brown	55	7·25
55	**10**	4/5c. black and red	75	8·25
56	**10**	1c. black and brown	75	7·50
57	**10**	2c. black and green	1·30	9·00
58	**10**	3c. black and violet	1·30	9·50
59	**10**	4c. black and orange	1·60	7·75
60	**10**	5c. black and red	1·60	5·00
61	**11**	6c. black and red	1·50	10·00
62	**11**	7c. black and green	2·10	8·00
63	**11**	8c. black on lilac	3·25	9·25
64	**11**	9c. black and yellow on green	3·50	9·25
65	**11**	10c. black and blue	3·00	9·00
66	**11**	11c. black and violet	3·25	9·00
67	**11**	12c. black and brown	4·25	7·50
68	**11**	15c. black and orange	5·00	11·50
69	**11**	20c. black and blue on buff	5·50	10·00
70	**11**	40c. black and red	6·00	13·50
71	**11**	1p. black and green on green	11·50	34·00
72	**11**	2p. black and purple on pink	20·00	55·00

1927. Pictorial types optd **KOUANG-TCHEOU**.

73	**22**	1/10c. green	45	7·00
74	**22**	1/5c. yellow	45	7·00
75	**22**	2/5c. blue	65	7·75
76	**22**	4/5c. brown	65	5·25
77	**22**	1c. orange	1·10	8·00
78	**22**	2c. green	1·60	7·25
79	**22**	3c. blue	1·80	8·50
80	**22**	4c. pink	1·60	8·50
81	**22**	5c. violet	1·80	7·25
82	**23**	6c. red	1·80	5·75
83	**23**	7c. brown	2·00	9·25
84	**23**	8c. green	2·10	9·50
85	**23**	9c. purple	2·40	9·00
86	**23**	10c. blue	2·75	9·00
87	**23**	11c. orange	3·50	9·50
88	**23**	12c. grey	2·50	9·00
89	**24**	15c. brown and red	6·00	10·00
90	**24**	20c. grey and violet	4·75	11·00
91	-	25c. mauve and brown	4·50	11·00
92	-	30c. olive and blue	4·00	9·50
93	-	40c. blue and red	4·25	9·25
94	-	50c. grey and green	4·25	10·50
95	-	1p. black, yellow and blue	7·00	17·00
96	-	2p. blue, orange and red	10·00	18·00

1937. International Exhibition, Paris. As No. **MS**246a of Indo-China (Diane de Poitiers) but colour changed and optd **KOUANG-TCHEOU** in black.

MS97	30c. green	23·00	29·00

1937. 1931 issue optd **KOUANG-TCHEOU**.

98	**33**	1/10c. blue	40	7·75
99	**33**	1/5c. lake	40	8·25
100	**33**	2/5c. red	70	8·50
101	**33**	1/2c. brown	40	8·25
102	**33**	4/5c. violet	45	8·00
103	**33**	1c. brown	40	8·25
104	**33**	2c. green	40	7·75
105	-	3c. green	3·00	8·75
126	-	3c. brown	40	8·50
106	-	4c. blue	4·50	9·50
127	-	4c. green	65	7·75
128	-	4c. yellow	12·00	17·00
107	-	5c. purple	4·50	8·75
129	-	5c. green	90	8·50
108	-	6c. red	1·20	8·50
130	-	7c. black	90	8·50
131	-	8c. lake	1·00	8·75
132	-	9c. black on yellow	3·25	10·00
109	-	10c. blue	4·50	9·25
133	-	10c. blue on pink	1·70	9·25
110	-	15c. blue	1·30	8·75
134	-	18c. blue	1·40	9·25
111	-	20c. red	1·00	8·75
112	-	21c. green	90	8·75
135	-	22c. green	4·00	9·75
113	-	25c. purple	7·25	13·50
136	-	25c. blue	1·80	9·25
114	-	30c. brown	1·70	8·75
115	**36**	50c. brown	1·40	9·50
116	**36**	60c. purple	1·40	9·50
137	**36**	70c. blue	3·00	8·75
117	**36**	1p. green	2·75	11·00
118	**36**	2p. red	3·25	11·00

1939. New York World's Fair. As T **28** of Mauritania.

119	13c. red	1·60	9·50
120	23c. deep blue and blue	1·60	9·50

1939. 150th Anniversary of French Revolution. As T **29** of Mauritania.

121	6c.+2c. green	11·50	21·00
122	7c.+3c. brown	11·50	21·00
123	9c.+4c. orange	11·50	21·00
124	13c.+10c. red	11·50	21·00
125	23c.+20c. blue	11·50	21·00

KUWAIT

An independent Arab Sheikhdom on the N.W. coast of the Persian Gulf with Indian and later British postal administration. On 1 February 1959 the Kuwait Government assumed responsibility for running its own postal service. In special treaty relations with Great Britain until 19 June 1961 when Kuwait became completely independent.

1923. 12 pies = 1 anna; 16 annas = 1 rupee.
1957. 100 naye paise = 1 rupee.
1961. 1000 fils = 1 dinar.

1923. King George V.

16	**56**	1/2a. green	17·00	3·25
16b	**79**	1/2a. green	12·00	2·00
2	**57**	1a. brown	8·00	5·50
17b	**81**	1a. brown	18·00	1·50
3	**58**	1 1/2a. brown (No. 163)	6·50	14·00
4	**59**	2a. lilac	5·50	10·00
18	**70**	2a. lilac	10·00	2·25
19	**70**	2a. orange	20·00	95·00
19c	**59**	2a. orange	12·00	3·50
5	**61**	2a.6p. blue	4·25	8·50
6	**62**	3a. orange	4·25	27·00
20	**62**	3a. blue	3·50	3·50
21	**62**	3a. red	5·50	4·25
22	**71**	4a. green	25·00	£100
22a	**63**	4a. green	20·00	14·00
9	**64**	6a. bistre	8·50	13·00
23	**65**	8a. mauve	50·00	13·00
11	**66**	12a. red	14·00	60·00
12	**67**	1r. brown and green	48·00	60·00
26	**67**	2r. red and orange	26·00	70·00
27	**67**	5r. blue and violet	£140	£325
28	**67**	10r. green and red	£300	£550
29	**67**	15r. blue and olive	£950	£1300

1933. Air.

31	**72**	2a. green	25·00	27·00
32	**72**	3a. blue	5·50	3·25
33	**72**	4a. olive	£150	£225
34	**72**	6a. bistre	10·00	5·50

1939. King George VI.

36	**91**	1/2a. brown	7·00	4·75
38	**91**	1a. red	8·00	3·75
39	**92**	2a. orange	10·00	6·00
41	-	3a. green	14·00	3·75
43	-	4a. brown	45·00	32·00
44	-	6a. turquoise	27·00	24·00
45	-	8a. violet	29·00	40·00
46	-	12a. lake	20·00	95·00
47	**100**	1r. slate and brown	38·00	9·50
48	**100**	2r. purple and brown	10·00	30·00
49	**100**	5r. green and blue	19·00	35·00
50	**100**	10r. purple and red	85·00	£110
51	**100**	15r. brown and green	£375	£425

1942. King George VI stamps of 1940.

52	**100a**	3p. slate	4·00	13·00
53	**100a**	1/2a. purple	4·00	7·00
54	**100a**	9p. green	3·75	21·00
55	**100a**	1a. red	4·00	2·75
56	**101**	1 1/2a. violet	4·25	14·00
57	**101**	2a. red	5·00	10·00
58	**101**	3a. violet	6·00	19·00
59	**101**	3 1/2a. blue	6·50	20·00
60	**102**	4a. brown	6·50	5·50
60a	**102**	6a. turquoise	14·00	25·00
61	**102**	8a. violet	7·00	19·00
62	**102**	12a. lake	8·50	10·00
63	-	14a. purple (No. 277)	17·00	25·00

Stamps of Great Britain surch KUWAIT and new values in Indian currency

From 1948 onwards, for stamps with similar surcharges, but without name of country, see British Postal Agencies in Eastern Agencies

1948. King George VI.

64	**128**	1/2a. on 1/2d. green	3·75	4·25
84	**128**	1/2a. on 1/2d. orange	2·75	1·50
65	**128**	1a. on 1d. red	3·75	1·75
85	**128**	1a. on 1d. blue	2·75	1·60
66	**128**	1 1/2a. on 1 1/2d. brown	4·00	1·75
86	**128**	1 1/2a. on 1 1/2d. green	3·25	2·25
67	**128**	2a. on 2d. orange	3·75	1·75
87	**128**	2a. on 2d. brown	3·25	1·50
68	**128**	2 1/2a. on 2 1/2d. blue	4·00	1·00
88	**128**	2 1/2a. on 2 1/2d. red	3·25	2·75
69	**128**	3a. on 3d. violet	4·00	80
89	**129**	4a. on 4d. blue	2·75	1·50
70	**129**	6a. on 6d. purple	4·00	75
71	**130**	1r. on 1s. brown	8·50	2·00
72	**131**	2r. on 2s.6d. green	9·00	9·00
73	**131**	5r. on 5s. red	12·00	9·00
73a	-	10r. on 10s. blue (No. 478a)	60·00	11·00

From 1948 onwards, for stamps with similar surcharges, but without name of country, see British Postal Agencies in Eastern Arabia.

1948. Silver Wedding.

74	**137**	2 1/2a. on 2 1/2d. blue	2·25	2·50
75	**138**	15r. on £1 blue	38·00	50·00

1948. Olympic Games.

76	**139**	2 1/2a. on 2 1/2d. blue	1·75	5·00
77	**140**	3a. on 3d. violet	1·25	5·00
78	-	6a. on 5d. purple	1·50	4·50
79	-	1r. on 1s. brown	1·50	4·50

1949. UPU.

80	**143**	2 1/2a. on 2 1/2d. blue	1·50	3·50
81	**144**	3a. on 3d. violet	1·25	5·50

82	-	6a. on 6d. purple	1·25	3·75
83	-	1r. on 1s. brown	1·25	1·75

1951. Pictorial high values.

90	**147**	2r. on 2s.6d. green	26·00	9·00
91	-	5r. on 5s. red (No. 510)	32·00	11·00
92	-	10r. on 10s. blue (No. 511)	55·00	18·00

1952. Queen Elizabeth II.

93	**154**	½a. on ½d. orange	20	3·75
94	**154**	1a. on 1d. blue	20	10
95	**154**	1½a. on 1½d. green	15	2·00
96	**154**	2a. on 2d. brown	35	10
97	**155**	2½a. on 2½d. red	15	1·75
98	**155**	3a. on 3d. lilac	40	10
99	**155**	4a. on 4d. blue	1·25	1·00
100	**157**	6a. on 6d. purple	2·50	10
101	**159**	12a. on 1s.3d. green	7·50	2·50
102	**159**	1r. on 1s.6d. blue	6·00	10

1953. Coronation.

103	**161**	2½a. on 2½d. red	3·50	3·50
104	-	4a. on 4d. blue	4·50	3·50
105	**163**	12a. on 1s.3d. green	5·00	5·50
106	-	1r. on 1s.6d. blue	4·00	1·25

1955. Pictorials.

107	**166**	2r. on 2s.6d. brown	11·00	3·50
108	-	5r. on 5s. red	11·00	9·50
109	-	10r. on 10s. blue	11·00	6·00

1957. Queen Elizabeth II.

120	**157**	1n.p. on 5d. brown	10	70
121	**154**	3n.p. on ½d. orange	60	5·00
122	**154**	6n.p. on 1d. blue	60	1·25
123	**154**	9n.p. on 1½d. green	60	4·75
124	**154**	12n.p. on 2d. brown	60	5·50
125	**155**	15n.p. on 2½d. red	60	7·00
126	**155**	20n.p. on 3d. lilac	60	30
127	**155**	25n.p. on 4d. blue	2·75	3·25
128	**157**	40n.p. on 6d. purple	1·00	30
129	**158**	50n.p. on 9d. olive	5·50	4·00
130	**159**	75n.p. on 1s.3d. green	6·00	9·50

20 Sheikh Abdullah

21 Dhow

1958

131	**20**	5n.p. green	1·00	10
132	**20**	10n.p. red	75	10
133	**20**	15n.p. brown	60	25
134	**20**	20n.p. violet	60	25
135	**20**	25n.p. orange	1·20	25
136	**20**	40n.p. purple	4·75	1·25
137	**21**	40n.p. blue	1·20	25
138	-	50n.p. red	1·20	25
139	-	75n.p. green	1·20	55
140	-	1r. purple	1·50	65
141	-	2r. blue and brown	6·00	1·20
142	-	5r. green	11·00	3·25
143	-	10r. lilac	30·00	7·75

Designs: Horiz—As T **21**: 50n.p. Oil pipe-lines; 75n.p. Shuwaikh Power Station. 36×20 mm—1r. Oil rig; 2r. Single-masted dhow; 5r. Kuwait Mosque; 10r. Main Square, Kuwait Town.

22 Sheikh Abdullah and Flag

1960. Tenth Anniversary of Shaikh's Accession.

144	**22**	40n.p. red and green	1·10	25
145	**22**	60n.p. red and blue	1·90	35

1961. As 1958 issue but currency changed and new designs.

146	**20**	1f. green	10	10
147	**20**	2f. red	25	10
148	**20**	4f. brown	25	10
149	**20**	5f. violet	25	10
150	**20**	8f. red	35	20
151	**20**	15f. purple	50	20
152	-	20f. green (as No. 142)	60	25
153	-	25f. blue	70	35
154	-	30f. blue and brown (as No. 141)	85	35
155	-	35f. black and red	95	40
156	**21**	40f. blue (32×22 mm)	1·10	40
157	-	45f. brown	1·20	50
158	-	75f. brown & grn (as No. 141)	1·70	85
159	-	90f. brown and blue	1·80	70
160	-	100f. red	2·40	35
161	**21**	250f. green (32×22 mm)	14·50	1·80
162	-	1d. orange	24·00	6·00
163	-	3d. red (as No. 142)	55·00	36·00

New Designs: 37×20 mm—25, 100f. Vickers Viscount 700 airliner over South Pier, Mina al Ahmadi; 35, 90f. Shuwaikh Secondary School; 45f., 1d. Wara Hill.

23 Telegraph Pole

1962. Fourth Arab Telecommunications Union Conference.

164	**23**	8f. blue and black	70	15
165	**23**	20f. red and black	1·70	65

1962. Arab League Week. As T **76** of Libya.

166	20f. purple	70	25
167	45f. brown	1·70	75

25 Mubarakiya School, Sheikh Abdullah and Sheikh Mubarak

1962. Golden Jubilee of Mubarakiya School.

168	**25**	8f. multicoloured	95	15
169	**25**	20f. multicoloured	2·40	50

26 National Flag and Crest

1962. National Day.

170	**26**	8f. multicoloured	60	25
171	**26**	20f. multicoloured	1·20	40
172	**26**	45f. multicoloured	3·00	55
173	**26**	90f. multicoloured	4·25	1·40

27 Campaign Emblem

1962. Malaria Eradication.

174	**27**	4f. green and turquoise	50	15
175	**27**	25f. grey and green	1·90	90

28 'Industry and Progress'

1962. Bicentenary of Sabah Dynasty.

176	**28**	8f. multicoloured	50	15
177	**28**	20f. multicoloured	1·20	40
178	**28**	45f. multicoloured	1·60	75
179	**28**	75f. multicoloured	3·00	1·30

29 Mother and Child

1963. Mothers' Day. Centres black and green; value black; country name red.

180	**29**	8f. yellow	25	15
181	**29**	20f. blue	60	50
182	**29**	45f. olive	1·20	75
183	**29**	75f. grey	2·20	90

30 Campaign Emblem, Palm and Domestic Animals

1963. Freedom from Hunger. Design in brown and green. Background colours given.

184	**30**	4f. blue	35	25
185	**30**	8f. yellow	70	50
186	**30**	20f. lilac	1·30	90
187	**30**	45f. pink	3·00	2·10

31 'Education from Oil'

1963. Education Day.

188	**31**	4f. brown, blue and yellow	50	15
189	**31**	20f. green, blue and yellow	1·20	40
190	**31**	45f. purple, blue and yellow	1·90	75

32 Sheikh Abdullah and Flags

1963. Second Anniversary of National Day. Flags in green, black and red; values in black.

191	**32**	4f. blue	1·20	75
192	**32**	5f. ochre	1·80	1·30
193	**32**	20f. violet	9·00	5·75
194	**32**	50f. brown	18·00	9·50

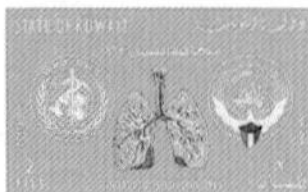
33 Human Lungs, and Emblems of WHO and Kuwait

1963. WHO Tuberculosis Control Campaign. Emblem yellow; Arms black, green and red.

195	**33**	2f. black and stone	35	20
196	**33**	4f. black and green	60	25
197	**33**	8f. black and blue	1·20	40
198	**33**	20f. black and red	3·50	1·00

34 Municipal Hall and Scroll

1963. New Constitution. Centres dull purple; Amir red.

199	**34**	4f. red	40	15
200	**34**	8f. green	55	20
201	**34**	20f. purple	1·00	40
202	**34**	45f. brown	1·50	80
203	**34**	75f. violet	2·30	1·50
204	**34**	90f. blue	3·25	1·90

35 Football

1963. Arab Schools Games. Multicoloured.

205	1f. Type **35**	40	15
206	4f. Basketball	50	20
207	5f. Swimming (horiz)	65	25
208	8f. Running	75	25
209	15f. Throwing the javelin (horiz)	1·30	45
210	20f. Pole vaulting (horiz)	1·50	50
211	35f. Gymnastics (horiz)	3·25	1·00
212	45f. Gymnastics	4·50	2·30

36 Scales of Justice and Globe

1963. 15th Anniversary of Declaration of Human Rights.

213	**36**	8f. black, green and violet	65	40
214	**36**	20f. black, yellow and grey	1·90	75
215	**36**	25f. black, brown and blue	2·50	1·10

37 Sheikh Abdullah

1964. Multicoloured, frame colours given.

216	**37**	1f. grey	20	15
217	**37**	2f. blue	25	15
218	**37**	4f. brown	30	15
219	**37**	5f. brown	40	15
220	**37**	8f. brown	50	15
221	**37**	10f. green	65	20
222	**37**	15f. green	75	20
223	**37**	20f. blue	90	25
224	**37**	25f. green	1·00	40
225	**37**	30f. green	1·10	40
226	**37**	40f. violet	1·50	50
227	**37**	45f. violet	1·80	65
228	**37**	50f. yellow	2·00	65
229	**37**	70f. purple	2·30	75
230	**37**	75f. red	2·75	90
231	**37**	90f. blue	4·50	90
232	**37**	100f. lilac	5·00	75
233	**37**	250f. brown (25×30 mm)	12·50	3·25
234	**37**	1d. purple (25×30 mm)	44·00	12·50

38 Rameses II in War Chariot

1964. Nubian Monuments Preservation.

235	**38**	8f. purple, blue and buff	55	15
236	**38**	20f. violet, blue and light blue	1·20	70
237	**38**	30f. violet, blue and turquoise	1·60	80

39 Mother and Child

1964. Mother's Day.

238	**39**	8f. blue, green and grey	25	15
239	**39**	20f. blue, green and red	80	25
240	**39**	30f. blue, green and bistre	1·10	50
241	**39**	45f. indigo, green and blue	1·40	80

40 Nurse giving BCG Vaccine to Patient, and Bones of Chest

1964. World Health Day.

242	**40**	8f. green and brown	80	15
243	**40**	20f. red and green	1·90	70

41 Dhow and Microscope

1964. Education Day.

244	**41**	8f. multicoloured	70	15
245	**41**	15f. multicoloured	95	25
246	**41**	20f. multicoloured	1·40	40
247	**41**	30f. multicoloured	2·00	80

42 Dhow and Doves

1964. Third Anniversary of National Day. Badge in blue, brown, black, red and green.

248	**42**	8f. black and brown	70	25
249	**42**	20f. black and green	1·10	40
250	**42**	30f. black and grey	1·60	70
251	**42**	45f. black and blue	2·00	95

43 APU Emblem

1964. Tenth Anniversary of Arab Postal Union's Permanent Office, Cairo.

252	**43**	8f. brown and blue	70	15
253	**43**	20f. blue and yellow	95	40
254	**43**	45f. brown and green	1·80	1·10

44 Hawker Siddeley Comet 4C and Douglas DC-3 Airliners

1964. Air. Tenth Anniversary of Kuwait Airways. Sky in blue; aircraft blue, red and black.

255	**44**	20f. black and bistre	2·00	40
256	**44**	25f. black and brown	2·40	45
257	**44**	30f. black and green	3·00	75
258	**44**	45f. black and brown	4·00	1·00

45 Conference Emblem

1965. First Arab Journalists' Conference, Kuwait.

259	**45**	8f. multicoloured	1·10	15
260	**45**	20f. multicoloured	2·30	40

46 Dhow, Doves and Oil-drilling Rig

1965. Fourth Anniversary of National Day.

261	**46**	10f. multicoloured	55	15
262	**46**	15f. multicoloured	1·20	30
263	**46**	20f. multicoloured	1·60	55

47 ICY Emblem

1965. International Co-operation Year.

264	**47**	8f. black and red	95	25
265	**47**	20f. black and blue	1·40	40
266	**47**	30f. black and green	2·40	70

The stamps are inscribed 'CO-OPERATIVE'.

48 Mother and Children

1965. Mothers' Day.

267	**48**	8f. multicoloured	70	15
268	**48**	15f. multicoloured	95	55
269	**48**	20f. multicoloured	1·90	80

49 Weather Kite

1965. World Meteorological Day.

270	**49**	4f. blue and yellow	70	15
271	**49**	5f. blue and orange	80	25
272	**49**	20f. blue and green	2·75	1·40

50 Census Graph

1965. Population Census.

273	**50**	8f. black, brown and blue	40	15
274	**50**	20f. black, pink and green	1·10	40
275	**50**	50f. black, green and red	2·50	1·10

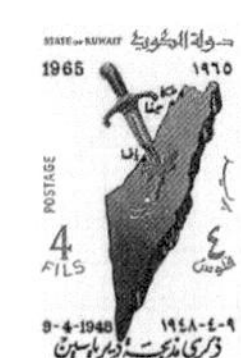
50a Dagger on Deir Yassin, Palestine

1965. Deir Yassin Massacre.

276	**50a**	4f. red and blue	2·20	45
277	**50a**	45f. red and green	6·00	1·60

51 Atomic Symbol and Tower of Shuwaikh Secondary School

1965. Education Day.

278	**51**	4f. multicoloured	70	15
279	**51**	20f. multicoloured	1·10	55
280	**51**	45f. multicoloured	2·30	1·40

52 ITU Emblem and Symbols

1965. ITU Centenary.

281	**52**	8f. red and blue	40	25
282	**52**	20f. red and green	1·60	45
283	**52**	45f. blue and red	4·00	1·70

52a Lamp and Burning Library

1965. Reconstitution of Burnt Algiers Library.

284	**52a**	8f. green, red and black	1·40	25
285	**52a**	15f. red, green and black	2·75	55

53 Saker Falcon

1965. Centre in brown.

286	**53**	8f. purple	2·75	40
287	**53**	15f. green	2·75	40
288	**53**	20f. blue	4·00	70
289	**53**	25f. red	4·25	95
290	**53**	30f. green	5·50	1·10
291	**53**	45f. blue	10·00	1·70
292	**53**	50f. purple	11·50	1·80
293	**53**	90f. red	19·00	3·50

54 Open Book

1966. Education Day.

294	**54**	8f. multicoloured	45	15
295	**54**	20f. multicoloured	1·20	55
296	**54**	30f. multicoloured	1·80	85

55 Sheikh Sabah

1966

297	**55**	4f. multicoloured	25	15
298	**55**	5f. multicoloured	40	20
299	**55**	20f. multicoloured	80	25
300	**55**	30f. multicoloured	1·10	35
301	**55**	40f. multicoloured	1·40	55
302	**55**	45f. multicoloured	1·60	70
303	**55**	70f. multicoloured	3·75	1·40
304	**55**	90f. multicoloured	4·25	2·00

56 Pomfrets and Ears of Wheat

1966. Freedom from Hunger.

305	**56**	20f. multicoloured	4·00	1·10
306	**56**	45f. multicoloured	5·50	2·00

57 Eagle and Scales of Justice

1966. Fifth Anniversary of National Day.

307	**57**	20f. multicoloured	1·90	45
308	**57**	25f. multicoloured	2·00	70
309	**57**	45f. multicoloured	4·00	1·70

58 Cogwheel and Map of Arab States

1966. Arab Countries Industrial Development Conference, Kuwait.

310	**58**	20f. green black and blue	1·20	40
311	**58**	50f. green, black and brown	2·20	1·00

59 Mother and Children

1966. Mothers' Day.

312	**59**	20f. multicoloured	1·20	40
313	**59**	45f. multicoloured	2·20	1·00

60 Red Crescent and Emblem of Medicine

1966. Fifth Arab Medical Conference, Kuwait.

314	**60**	15f. red and blue	80	1·10
315	**60**	30f. red, blue and pink	1·60	1·10

61 'Man and his Cities'

1966. World Health Day.

316	**61**	8f. multicoloured	1·00	25
317	**61**	10f. multicoloured	1·70	40

62 WHO Building

1966. Inauguration of WHO Headquarters, Geneva.

318	**62**	5f. green, blue and red	95	25
319	**62**	10f. green, blue and turquoise	1·80	25

62a Traffic Signals

1966. Traffic Day.

320	**62a**	10f. red, emerald and green	1·10	25
321	**62a**	20f. emerald, red and green	1·50	55

63 Symbol of Blood Donation

1966. Blood Bank Day.

322	**63**	4f. multicoloured	1·40	25
323	**63**	8f. multicoloured	2·75	80

64 Sheikh Ahmad and *British Fusilier* (tanker)

1966. 20th Anniversary of First Crude Oil Shipment.

324	**64**	20f. multicoloured	1·50	70
325	**64**	45f. multicoloured	3·25	1·40

65 Ministry Building

1966. Inauguration of Ministry of Guidance and Information Building.

326	**65**	4f. red and brown	45	15
327	**65**	5f. brown and green	55	15
328	**65**	8f. green and violet	70	20
329	**65**	20f. orange and blue	1·60	40

66 Dhow, Lobster, Fish and Crab

1966. FAO Near East Countries Fisheries Conference, Kuwait.

330	**66**	4f. multicoloured	1·20	25
331	**66**	20f. multicoloured	3·00	1·20

67 UN Flag

1966. UN Day.

332	**67**	20f. multicoloured	1·60	40
333	**67**	45f. multicoloured	3·50	1·70

68 UNESCO Emblem

1966. 20th Anniversary of UNESCO.

334	**68**	20f. multicoloured	1·40	25
335	**68**	45f. multicoloured	3·50	1·40

69 Ruler and University Shield

1966. Opening of Kuwait University.

336	**69**	8f. multicoloured	95	15
337	**69**	10f. multicoloured	1·10	20
338	**69**	20f. multicoloured	2·40	40
339	**69**	45f. multicoloured	5·25	1·80

70 Ruler and Heir-Apparent

1966. Appointment of Heir-Apparent.

340	**70**	8f. multicoloured	80	15
341	**70**	20f. multicoloured	2·00	40
342	**70**	45f. multicoloured	3·75	1·50

71 Scout Badge

1966. 30th Anniversary of Kuwait Scouts.

343	**71**	4f. brown and green	2·00	55
344	**71**	20f. green and brown	5·25	2·00

72 Symbols of Learning

1967. Education Day.

345	**72**	10f. multicoloured	1·50	25
346	**72**	45f. multicoloured	5·75	80

73 Fertiliser Plant

1967. Inauguration of Chemical Fertiliser Plant.

347	**73**	8f. multicoloured	1·50	15
348	**73**	20f. multicoloured	3·00	55

74 Ruler, Dove and Olive-branch

1967. Sixth Anniversary of National Day.

349	**74**	8f. multicoloured	1·50	15
350	**74**	20f. multicoloured	3·00	55

75 Map and Municipality Building

1967. First Arab Cities Organisation Conference, Kuwait.

351	**75**	20f. multicoloured	2·20	70
352	**75**	30f. multicoloured	3·75	1·80

76 Arab Family

1967. Family's Day.

353	**76**	20f. multicoloured	1·80	70
354	**76**	45f. multicoloured	3·50	1·80

77 Arab League Emblem

1967. Arab Cause Week.

355	**77**	8f. blue and grey	1·20	15
356	**77**	10f. green and yellow	2·30	25

78 Sabah Hospital

1967. World Health Day.

357	**78**	8f. multicoloured	1·60	15
358	**78**	20f. multicoloured	3·75	80

79 Nubian Statues

1967. Arab Week for Nubian Monuments Preservation.

359	**79**	15f. green, brown and yellow	1·50	25
360	**79**	20f. green, purple and blue	3·00	70

80 Traffic Policeman

1967. Traffic Day.

361	**80**	8f. multicoloured	2·20	45
362	**80**	20f. multicoloured	5·00	1·00

81 ITY Emblem

1967. International Tourist Year.

363	**81**	20f. black, blue & turquoise	1·50	30
364	**81**	45f. black, blue and mauve	3·00	1·50

82 'Reaching for Knowledge'

1967. Eliminate Illiteracy Campaign.

365	**82**	8f. multicoloured	2·20	15
366	**82**	20f. multicoloured	5·00	90

83 Map of Palestine

1967. UN Day.

367	**83**	20f. red and blue	2·20	35
368	**83**	45f. red and orange	5·00	1·20

84 Factory and Cogwheels

1967. Third Arab Labour Ministers' Conference.

369	**84**	20f. yellow and red	1·50	30
370	**84**	45f. yellow and grey	3·25	1·90

85 Open Book and Kuwaiti Flag

1968. Education Day.

371	**85**	20f. multicoloured	1·50	15
372	**85**	45f. multicoloured	3·75	1·60

86 Oil Rig and Map

1968. 30th Anniversary of Oil Discovery in Greater Burgan Field.

373	**86**	10f. multicoloured	2·20	30
374	**86**	20f. multicoloured	3·75	1·50

87 Ruler and Sun's Rays

1968. Seventh Anniversary of National Day.

375	**87**	8f. multicoloured	75	15
376	**87**	10f. multicoloured	85	20
377	**87**	15f. multicoloured	1·50	30
378	**87**	20f. multicoloured	2·20	40

88 Book, Eagle and Sun

1968. Teachers' Day.

379	**88**	8f. multicoloured	85	15
380	**88**	20f. multicoloured	1·70	30
381	**88**	45f. multicoloured	3·25	1·50

89 Family Picnicking

1968. Family Day.

382	**89**	8f. multicoloured	60	15
383	**89**	10f. multicoloured	85	15
384	**89**	15f. multicoloured	1·00	20
385	**89**	20f. multicoloured	1·30	30

90 Ruler, WHO and State Emblems

1968. World Health Day and 20th Anniversary of WHO.

386	**90**	20f. multicoloured	2·20	75
387	**90**	45f. multicoloured	5·00	1·80

91 Dagger on Deir Yassin, and Scroll

1968. 20th Anniversary of Deir Yassin Massacre.

388	**91**	20f. red and blue	3·25	80
389	**91**	45f. red and violet	7·50	1·60

92 Pedestrians on Road Crossing

1968. Traffic Day.

390	**92**	10f. multicoloured	1·50	60
391	**92**	15f. multicoloured	2·20	85
392	**92**	20f. multicoloured	4·25	1·20

93 Torch and Map

1968. Palestine Day.

393	**93**	10f. multicoloured	1·90	60
394	**93**	20f. multicoloured	3·50	75
395	**93**	45f. multicoloured	6·50	2·50

94 Palestine Refugees

1968. Human Rights Year.

396	**94**	20f. multicoloured	1·20	30
397	**94**	30f. multicoloured	1·50	60
398	**94**	45f. multicoloured	2·30	75
399	**94**	90f. multicoloured	4·75	3·00

95 National Museum

1968

400	**95**	1f. green and brown	45	15
401	**95**	2f. green and purple	75	15
402	**95**	5f. red and black	85	15
403	**95**	8f. green and brown	1·20	15
404	**95**	10f. purple and blue	1·50	20
405	**95**	20f. blue and brown	1·70	30
406	**95**	25f. orange and blue	2·30	35
407	**95**	30f. green and blue	3·00	45
408	**95**	45f. deep purple and purple	4·25	85
409	**95**	50f. red and green	5·75	1·70

96 Man reading Book

1968. International Literacy Day.

410	**96**	15f. multicoloured	85	15
411	**96**	20f. multicoloured	2·00	45

97 Refugee Children and UN Headquarters

1968. United Nations Day.

412	**97**	20f. multicoloured	75	15
413	**97**	30f. multicoloured	1·20	60
414	**97**	45f. multicoloured	1·70	75

98 Chamber of Commerce Building

1968. Inauguration of Kuwait Chamber of Commerce and Industry Building.

415	**98**	10f. purple and orange	75	15
416	**98**	15f. blue and mauve	1·20	30
417	**98**	20f. green and brown	1·50	60

99 Conference Emblem

1968. 14th Arab Chambers of Commerce, Industry and Agriculture Conference.

418	**99**	10f. multicoloured	75	15
419	**99**	15f. multicoloured	85	20
420	**99**	20f. multicoloured	1·30	60
421	**99**	30f. multicoloured	1·50	75

100 Refinery Plant

1968. Inauguration of Shuaiba Refinery.

422	**100**	10f. multicoloured	85	15
423	**100**	20f. multicoloured	1·50	30
424	**100**	30f. multicoloured	1·70	75
425	**100**	45f. multicoloured	3·25	1·50

101 Holy Koran, Scales and People

1968. 1,400th Anniversary of the Holy Koran.

426	**101**	8f. multicoloured	1·00	15
427	**101**	20f. multicoloured	1·70	60
428	**101**	30f. multicoloured	2·50	1·00
429	**101**	45f. multicoloured	3·50	1·60

102 Boeing 707 Airliner

1969. Inauguration of Boeing 707 Aircraft by Kuwait Airways.

430	**102**	10f. multicoloured	1·10	30
431	**102**	20f. multicoloured	1·70	65
432	**102**	25f. multicoloured	2·50	1·20
433	**102**	45f. multicoloured	3·75	1·60

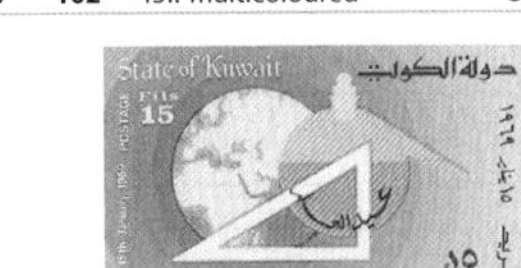

103 Globe and Symbols of Engineering and Science

1969. Education Day.

434	**103**	15f. multicoloured	1·50	30
435	**103**	20f. multicoloured	2·20	85

104 Hilton Hotel

1969. Inauguration of Kuwait Hilton Hotel.

436	**104**	10f. multicoloured	1·50	30
437	**104**	20f. multicoloured	2·20	45

105 Family and Teachers' Society Emblem

1969. Education Week.

438	**105**	10f. multicoloured	1·00	30
439	**105**	20f. multicoloured	1·90	50

106 Flags and Laurel

1969. Eighth Anniversary of National Day.

440	**106**	15f. multicoloured	75	30
441	**106**	20f. multicoloured	1·20	45
442	**106**	30f. multicoloured	1·70	75

107 Emblem, Teacher and Class

1969. Teachers' Day.

443	**107**	10f. multicoloured	1·00	30
444	**107**	20f. multicoloured	1·90	75

108 Kuwaiti Family

1969. Family Day.

445	**108**	10f. multicoloured	1·50	30
446	**108**	20f. multicoloured	3·00	45

109 Ibn Sina, Nurse with Patient and WHO Emblem

1969. World Health Day.

447	**109**	15f. multicoloured	1·60	30
448	**109**	20f. multicoloured	2·30	45

110 Motorcycle Police

1969. Traffic Day.

449	**110**	10f. multicoloured	3·00	30
450	**110**	20f. multicoloured	5·75	80

111 ILO Emblem

1969. 50th Anniversary of ILO.

451	**111**	10f. gold, black and red	1·00	30
452	**111**	20f. gold, black and green	1·90	45

112 Tanker *Al Sabahiah*

1969. Fourth Anniv of Kuwait Shipping Company.

453	**112**	20f. multicoloured	3·00	75
454	**112**	45f. multicoloured	5·75	2·10

113 Woman writing Letter

1969. International Literacy Day.

455	**113**	10f. multicoloured	1·00	15
456	**113**	20f. multicoloured	1·90	60

114 Amir Sheikh Sabah

1969. Portraits multicoloured; background colours given.

457	**114**	8f. blue	60	15
458	**114**	10f. pink	75	15
459	**114**	15f. grey	75	30
460	**114**	20f. yellow	85	30
461	**114**	25f. lilac	1·20	45
462	**114**	30f. orange	1·70	60
463	**114**	45f. grey	2·20	75
464	**114**	50f. green	2·50	85
465	**114**	70f. blue	2·50	1·00
466	**114**	75f. blue	3·75	1·20
467	**114**	90f. brown	4·00	1·50
468	**114**	250f. purple	12·50	3·75
469	**114**	500f. green	25·00	14·50
470	**114**	1d. purple	46·00	23·00

115 'Appeal to World Conscience'

1969. United Nations Day.

471	**115**	10f. blue, black and green	1·20	30
472	**115**	20f. blue, black and stone	2·50	45
473	**115**	45f. blue, black and red	5·00	1·50

116 Earth Station

1969. Inauguration of Kuwait Satellite Communications Station. Multicoloured.

474	20 Type **116**	2·50	30
475	45f. Dish aerial on Globe (vert)	4·75	1·50

117 Refugee Family

1969. Palestinian Refugee Week.

476	**117**	20f. multicoloured	4·25	85
477	**117**	45f. multicoloured	8·00	2·75

118 Globe, Symbols and IEY Emblem

1970. International Education Year.

478	**118**	20f. multicoloured	1·00	30
479	**118**	45f. multicoloured	2·50	1·30

119 Shoue

1970. Kuwait Sailing Dhows. Multicoloured.

480	8f. Type **119**	1·00	30
481	10f. Sambuk	1·20	45
482	15f. Baggala	1·70	60
483	20f. Battela	2·20	85
484	25f. Bum	2·50	1·00
485	45f. Baggala	4·75	1·90
486	50f. Dhow-building	5·50	2·20

120 Kuwaiti Flag

1970. Ninth Anniversary of National Day.

487	**120**	15f. multicoloured	1·50	45
488	**120**	20f. multicoloured	2·20	45

121 Young Commando and Dome of the Rock, Jerusalem

1970. Support for Palestinian Commandos. Multicoloured.

489	10f. Type **121**	3·00	1·20
490	20f. Commando in battledress	5·75	2·30
491	45f. Woman commando	10·00	5·25

122 Parents with 'Children'

1970. Family Day.

492	**122**	20f. multicoloured	1·50	30
493	**122**	30f. multicoloured	3·00	45

123 Arab League Flag, Emblem and Map

1970. 25th Anniversary of Arab League.

494	**123**	20f. brown, green and blue	1·50	30
495	**123**	45f. violet, green and orange	2·20	75

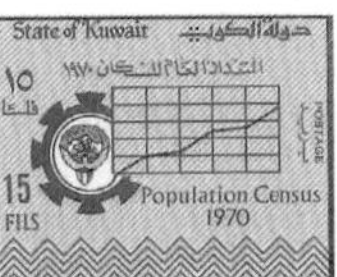

124 Census Emblem and Graph

1970. Population Census.

496	**124**	15f. multicoloured	75	15
497	**124**	20f. multicoloured	1·20	85
498	**124**	30f. multicoloured	1·70	75

125 Cancer the Crab in 'Pincers'

1970. World Health Day.

499	**125**	20f. multicoloured	1·50	75
500	**125**	30f. multicoloured	2·30	1·00

126 Traffic Lights and Road Signs

1970. Traffic Day.

501	**126**	20f. multicoloured	3·00	85
502	**126**	30f. multicoloured	4·25	1·50

127 Red Crescent

1970. International Red Cross and Crescent Day.

503	**127**	10f. multicoloured	1·30	20
504	**127**	15f. multicoloured	2·00	60
505	**127**	30f. multicoloured	4·00	1·00

128 New Headquarters Building

1970. Opening of New UPU Headquarters Building, Berne.

506	**128**	20f. multicoloured	1·50	45
507	**128**	30f. multicoloured	2·20	1·00

129 Amir Sheikh Sabah

1970

508	**129**	20f. multicoloured	1·30	30
509	**129**	45f. multicoloured	3·50	1·50
MS510		127×101 mm. Nos. 508/509. Imperf	14·50	10·00

130 UN Symbols

1970. 25th Anniversary of United Nations.

511	**130**	20f. multicoloured	1·80	30
512	**130**	45f. multicoloured	3·00	75

131 *Medora* (tanker) at Sea Island Jetty

1970. Oil Shipment Facilities, Kuwait.

513	**131**	20f. multicoloured	3·00	45
514	**131**	45f. multicoloured	4·25	1·50

132 Kuwaiti and UN Emblems and Hand writing

1970. International Literacy Day.

515	**132**	10f. multicoloured	1·90	30
516	**132**	15f. multicoloured	2·50	75

133 Guards and Badge

1970. First Graduation of National Guards.

517	**133**	10f. multicoloured	2·20	30
518	**133**	20f. multicoloured	3·25	75

134 Symbols and Flag

1971. Tenth Anniversary of National Day.

519	**134**	20f. multicoloured	3·00	60
520	**134**	30f. multicoloured	4·25	75

135 Dr. C. Best and Sir F. Banting (discoverers of insulin) and Syringe

1971. World Health Day, and 50th Anniversary of Discovery of Insulin.

521	**135**	20f. multicoloured	3·75	60
522	**135**	45f. multicoloured	6·50	1·00

136 Map of Palestine on Globe

1971. Palestine Week.

523	**136**	20f. multicoloured	3·75	30
524	**136**	45f. multicoloured	7·25	1·50

137 ITU Emblem

1971. World Telecommunications Day.

525	**137**	20f. black, brown and silver	2·20	45
526	**137**	45f. black, brown and gold	3·75	1·00

138 'Three Races'

1971. Racial Equality Year.

527	**138**	15f. multicoloured	1·50	30
528	**138**	30f. multicoloured	3·00	85

139 APU Emblem

1971. 25th Anniversary of Founding of Arab Postal Union at Sofar Conference.

529	**139**	20f. multicoloured	1·30	45
530	**139**	45f. multicoloured	2·50	1·00

140 Book, Pupils, Globes and Pen

1971. International Literacy Day.

531	**140**	25f. multicoloured	1·20	30
532	**140**	60f. multicoloured	3·00	1·50

141 Footballers

1971. Regional Sports Tournament, Kuwait. Multicoloured.

533	20f. Type **141**	2·00	75
534	30f. Footballer blocking attack	3·00	1·30

142 Emblems of UNICEF and Kuwait

1971. 25th Anniversary of UNICEF.

535	**142**	25f. multicoloured	3·00	45
536	**142**	60f. multicoloured	4·25	1·00

143 Book Year Emblem

1972. International Book Year.

537	**143**	20f. black and brown	1·20	60
538	**143**	45f. black and green	2·50	1·30

144 Crest and Laurel

1972. 11th Anniversary of National Day.

539	**144**	20f. multicoloured	1·50	20
540	**144**	45f. multicoloured	3·00	1·30

145 Telecommunications Centre

1972. Inauguration of Telecommunications Centre, Kuwait.

541	**145**	20f. multicoloured	2·00	45
542	**145**	45f. multicoloured	4·25	1·90

146 Human Heart

1972. World Health Day and World Heart Month.

543	**146**	20f. multicoloured	2·20	75
544	**146**	45f. multicoloured	6·50	2·20

147 Nurse and Child

1972. International Red Cross and Crescent Day.

545	**147**	8f. multicoloured	1·50	45
546	**147**	40f. multicoloured	5·75	1·70

148 Football

1972. Olympic Games, Munich. Multicoloured.

547	2f. Type **148**	45	15
548	4f. Running	75	15
549	5f. Swimming	85	15
550	8f. Gymnastics	1·00	15
551	10f. Throwing the discus	1·20	20
552	15f. Show jumping	1·70	30
553	20f. Basketball	2·00	35
554	25f. Volleyball	2·30	75

149 Produce and Fishing Boat

1972. 11th FAO Near East Regional Conference, Kuwait.

555	**149**	5f. multicoloured	75	60
556	**149**	10f. multicoloured	2·20	1·50
557	**149**	20f. multicoloured	4·25	3·00

150 Bank Emblem

1972. 20th Anniversary of National Bank of Kuwait.

558	**150**	10f. multicoloured	1·20	15
559	**150**	35f. multicoloured	4·75	1·20

151 Ancient Capitals

1972. Archaeological Excavations on Failaka Island. Multicoloured.

560	2f. Type **151**	45	20
561	5f. View of excavations	75	30
562	10f. 'Leaf' capital	1·60	40
563	15f. Excavated building	2·40	50

152 Floral Emblem

1973. 12th Anniversary of National Day.

564	**152**	10f. multicoloured	1·20	15
565	**152**	20f. multicoloured	2·30	50
566	**152**	30f. multicoloured	3·75	1·10

153 Interpol Emblem

1973. 50th Anniversary of International Criminal Police Organisation (Interpol).

567	**153**	10f. multicoloured	1·60	30
568	**153**	15f. multicoloured	2·30	60
569	**153**	20f. multicoloured	3·25	1·30

154 CISM Badge and Flags

1973. 25th Anniversary of International Military Sports Council (CISM).

570	**154**	30f. multicoloured	3·00	75
571	**154**	40f. multicoloured	4·25	1·00

155 Airways Building

1973. Opening of Kuwait Airways HQ Building.

572	**155**	10f. multicoloured	85	15
573	**155**	15f. multicoloured	1·20	30
574	**155**	20f. multicoloured	1·60	60

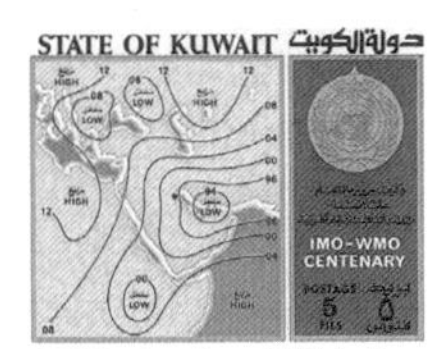

156 Weather Map of Middle East

1973. Centenary of World Meteorological Organisation.

575	**156**	5f. multicoloured	1·50	30
576	**156**	10f. multicoloured	2·20	45
577	**156**	15f. multicoloured	3·75	85

157 Sheikhs Ahmed and Sabah

1973. 50th Anniversary of First Kuwait Stamp Issue (overprints on India of 1923).

578	**157**	10f. multicoloured	1·20	15
579	**157**	20f. multicoloured	2·20	30
580	**157**	70f. multicoloured	5·50	2·00

158 Mourning Dove

1973. Birds and Hunting Equipment. Multicoloured. (a) Size 32×32 mm.

581	5f. Type **158**	1·00	30
582	5f. Hoopoe (*Upupa epops*)	1·00	30
583	5f. Feral rock pigeon (*Columba livia*)	1·00	30
584	5f. Stone-curlew (*Burhinus oedicnemus*)	1·00	30
585	8f. Great grey shrike (*Lanius excubitor*)	1·30	35
586	8f. Red-backed shrike (*Lanius collurio*)	1·30	35
587	8f. Black-headed shrike (*Lanius schach*)	1·30	35
588	8f. Golden oriole (*Orielus chinensis*)	1·30	35
589	10f. Willow warbler (*Phylloscopus trochilus*)	1·60	45
590	10f. Great reed warbler (*Acrocephalus arundinaceus*)	1·60	45
591	10f. Blackcap (*Sylvia atricapilla*)	1·60	45
592	10f. Barn swallow (*Hirundo rustica*)	1·60	45
593	15f. Rock thrush (*Monticola solitarius*)	2·30	60
594	15f. Common redstart (*Phoenicurus phoenicurus*)	2·30	60
595	15f. Northern wheatear (*Oenanthe oenanthe*)	2·30	60
596	15f. Bluethroat (*Luscinia svecica*)	2·30	60
597	20f. Houbara bustard (*Chlamydotis undulata*)	3·25	75
598	20f. Pin-tailed sandgrouse (*Pterocles alchata*)	3·25	75
599	20f. Greater wood rail (*Aramides ypecaha*)	3·25	75
600	20f. Spotted crake (*Porzana porzana*)	3·25	75

(b) Size 38×38 mm.

601	25f. American kestrel (*Falco sparverius*)	4·25	85
602	25f. Great black-backed gull (*Larus marinus*)	4·25	85
603	25f. Purple heron (*Ardea purpurea*)	4·25	85
604	25f. Wryneck (*Jynx torquilla*)	4·25	85
605	30f. European bee-eater (*Merops apiaster*)	4·75	1·00
606	30f. Saker falcon (*Accipiter*)	4·75	1·00
607	30f. Grey wagtail (*Motacilla cinerea*)	4·75	1·00
608	30f. Pied wagtail (*Motacilla alba*)	4·75	1·00
609	45f. Bird traps	6·75	2·20
610	45f. Driving great grey shrikes into net	6·75	2·20
611	45f. Stalking Feral rock pigeon with hand net	6·75	2·20
612	45f. Great grey shrike and disguised lure	6·75	2·20

159 Flame Emblem

1973. 25th Anniversary of Declaration of Human Rights.

613	**159**	10f. multicoloured	1·50	15
614	**159**	40f. multicoloured	3·00	75
615	**159**	75f. multicoloured	5·75	2·00

160 Congress Emblem

1974. Fourth Congress of Arab Veterinary Union, Kuwait.

616	**160**	30f. multicoloured	1·50	60
617	**160**	40f. multicoloured	2·20	1·30

161 Flag and Wheat Ear Symbol

1974. 13th Anniversary of National Day.

618	**161**	20f. multicoloured	60	30
619	**161**	30f. multicoloured	1·10	45
620	**161**	70f. multicoloured	2·40	2·20

162 AMU Emblem

1974. 12th Conference of Arab Medical Union and First Conference of Kuwait Medical Society.

621	**162**	30f. multicoloured	3·75	75
622	**162**	40f. multicoloured	5·00	1·50

163 Tournament Emblem

1974. Third Arabian Gulf Trophy Football Tournament, Kuwait.

623	**163**	25f. multicoloured	3·75	60
624	**163**	45f. multicoloured	5·00	1·50

164 Institute Buildings

1974. Inauguration of Kuwait Institute for Scientific Research.

625	**164**	15f. multicoloured	2·20	60
626	**164**	20f. multicoloured	3·75	85

165 Emblems of Kuwait, Arab Postal Union and UPU

1974. Centenary of UPU.

627	**165**	20f. multicoloured	1·50	30
628	**165**	30f. multicoloured	2·20	60
629	**165**	60f. multicoloured	3·75	1·00

166 Symbolic Telephone Dial

1974. World Telecommunications Day.

630	**166**	10f. multicoloured	85	30
631	**166**	30f. multicoloured	3·00	75
632	**166**	40f. multicoloured	3·75	85

167 Council Emblem and Flags of Member States

1974. 17th Anniversary of Signing Arab Economic Unity Agreement.

633	**167**	20f. green, black and red	1·50	60
634	**167**	30f. red, black and green	3·00	85

168 'Population Growth'

1974. World Population Year.

635	**168**	30f. multicoloured	2·20	30
636	**168**	70f. multicoloured	5·00	2·00

169 Fund Building

1974. Kuwait Fund for Arab Economic Development.

637	**169**	10f. multicoloured	1·20	30
638	**169**	20f. multicoloured	1·70	60

170 Shuaiba Emblem

1974. Tenth Anniversary of Shuaiba Industrial Area.

639	**170**	10f. multicoloured	1·50	30
640	**170**	20f. multicoloured	3·00	60
641	**170**	30f. multicoloured	4·25	1·30

171 Arms of Kuwait and '14'

1975. 14th Anniversary of National Day.

642	**171**	20f. multicoloured	1·50	20
643	**171**	70f. multicoloured	3·50	1·60
644	**171**	75f. multicoloured	3·75	2·00

172 Census Symbols

1975. Population Census.

645	**172**	8f. multicoloured	45	15
646	**172**	20f. multicoloured	1·00	30
647	**172**	30f. multicoloured	1·50	60
648	**172**	70f. multicoloured	3·75	1·50
649	**172**	100f. multicoloured	5·75	1·70

173 IWY and Kuwait Women's Union Emblems

1975. International Women's Year.

650	**173**	15f. multicoloured	1·30	30
651	**173**	20f. multicoloured	1·70	45
652	**173**	30f. multicoloured	2·75	85

174 Classroom within Open Book

1975. International Literacy Day.

653	**174**	20f. multicoloured	1·20	30
654	**174**	30f. multicoloured	2·50	85

175 ISO Emblem

1975. World Standards Day.

655	**175**	10f. multicoloured	1·50	30
656	**175**	20f. multicoloured	2·20	60

176 UN Flag, Rifle and Olive-branch

1975. 30th Anniversary of UNO.

657	**176**	20f. multicoloured	1·20	30
658	**176**	45f. multicoloured	2·50	1·00

177 Sheikh Sabah

1975

659	**177**	8f. multicoloured	1·00	15
660	**177**	20f. multicoloured	1·70	30
661	**177**	30f. multicoloured	3·00	60
662	**177**	50f. multicoloured	4·00	85
663	**177**	90f. multicoloured	7·25	1·60
664	**177**	100f. multicoloured	8·00	1·70

178 Kuwait 'Skyline'

1976. 15th Anniversary of National Day.

665	178	10f. multicoloured	1·00	30
666	178	20f. multicoloured	1·90	45

178a Emblem, Microscope and Operation

1976. Second Annual Conference of Kuwait Medical Association.

667	178a	5f. multicoloured	60	30
668	178a	10f. multicoloured	1·50	1·40
669	178a	30f. multicoloured	4·75	2·50

179 Early and Modern Telephones

1976. Telephone Centenary.

670	179	5f. black and orange	75	30
671	179	15f. black and blue	1·50	45

180 Eye

1976. World Health Day.

672	180	10f. multicoloured	85	30
673	180	20f. multicoloured	1·50	45
674	180	30f. multicoloured	2·75	1·20

181 Red Crescent Emblem

1976. Tenth Anniversary of Kuwait Red Crescent Society.

675	181	20f. multicoloured	75	30
676	181	30f. multicoloured	1·30	75
677	181	45f. multicoloured	2·50	1·20
678	181	75f. multicoloured	4·50	3·00

182 Suburb of Manama

1976. UN Human Settlements Conference.

679	182	10f. multicoloured	1·50	30
680	182	20f. multicoloured	2·20	45

183 Basketball

1976. Olympic Games, Montreal. Multicoloured.

681	4f. Type 183	30	15
682	8f. Running	60	15
683	10f. Judo	85	20
684	15f. Handball	1·20	30
685	20f. Figure-skating	1·50	45
686	30f. Volleyball	1·70	75
687	45f. Football	2·50	1·00
688	70f. Swimming	3·75	1·50

184 Ethnic Heads and Map of Sri Lanka

1976. Non-Aligned Countries' Congress, Colombo.

689	184	20f. multicoloured	85	30
690	184	30f. multicoloured	1·50	75
691	184	45f. multicoloured	2·00	1·20

185 Torch, UNESCO. Emblem and Kuwaiti Arms

1976. 30th Anniversary of UNESCO.

692	185	20f. multicoloured	1·00	30
693	185	45f. multicoloured	2·50	75

186 Pot-throwing

1977. Popular Games. Multicoloured.

694	5f. Type 186	45	15
695	5f. Kite-flying	45	15
696	5f. Balancing sticks	45	15
697	5f. Spinning tops	45	15
698	10f. Blind-man's-buff (horiz)	85	45
699	10f. Rowing (horiz)	85	45
700	10f. Rolling hoops (horiz)	85	45
701	10f. Rope game (horiz)	85	45
702	15f. Skipping	1·30	75
703	15f. Marbles	1·30	75
704	15f. Carting	1·30	75
705	15f. Teetotum (tops)	1·30	75
706	20f. Halma (horiz)	1·70	85
707	20f. Model boating (horiz)	1·70	85
708	20f. Pot and candle (horiz)	1·70	85
709	20f. Hide-and-seek (horiz)	1·70	85
710	30f. Knucklebones	2·50	1·30
711	30f. Hiding the stone	2·50	1·30
712	30f. Hopscotch	2·50	1·30
713	30f. Catch-as-catch-can	2·50	1·30
714	40f. Bowls (horiz)	3·50	1·70
715	40f. Hockey (horiz)	3·50	1·70
716	40f. Guessing which hand (horiz)	3·50	1·70
717	40f. Jacks (horiz)	3·50	1·70
718	60f. Hiding the cake (horiz)	5·25	2·75
719	60f. Chess (horiz)	5·25	2·75
720	60f. Story-telling (horiz)	5·25	2·75
721	60f. Treasure hunt (horiz)	5·25	2·75
722	70f. Hobby horses (horiz)	6·00	3·00
723	70f. Hide-and-seek (horiz)	6·00	3·00
724	70f. Catch shadow (horiz)	6·00	3·00
725	70f. Throwing game (horiz)	6·00	3·00

187 Diseased Knee

1977. World Rheumatism Year.

726	187	20f. multicoloured	1·00	30
727	187	30f. multicoloured	1·50	55
728	187	45f. multicoloured	2·00	85
729	187	75f. multicoloured	3·00	1·60

188 Sheikh Sabah

1977. 16th National Day.

730	188	10f. multicoloured	30	15
731	188	15f. multicoloured	60	30
732	188	30f. multicoloured	1·30	60
733	188	80f. multicoloured	3·00	1·40

189 Kuwait Tower

1977. Inauguration of Kuwait Tower.

734	189	30f. multicoloured	1·10	30
735	189	80f. multicoloured	3·00	1·50

190 APU Emblem and Flags

1977. 25th Anniversary of Arab Postal Union.

736	190	5f. multicoloured	30	15
737	190	15f. multicoloured	50	30
738	190	30f. multicoloured	95	45
739	190	80f. multicoloured	2·50	1·50

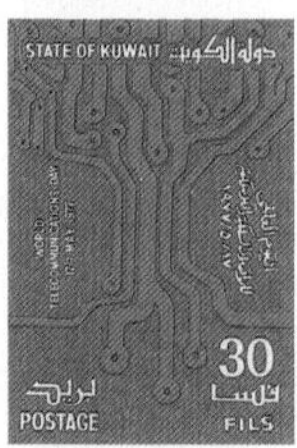
191 Printed Circuit

1977. World Telecommunications Day.

740	191	30f. orange and brown	1·50	30
741	191	80f. orange and green	3·00	2·00

192 Sheikh Sabah

1977

742	192	15f. brown, black and blue	1·60	1·00
743	192	25f. brown, black and yellow	2·50	1·10
744	192	30f. brown, black and red	3·25	1·50
745	192	80f. brown, black and lilac	7·75	2·50
746	192	100f. brown, black and orange	9·50	3·00
747	192	150f. brown, black and blue	14·00	4·75
748	192	200f. brown, black and green	19·00	6·00

192a Aerogramme stamp

1977. Aerogramme stamp. Imperf.

748a	192a	55f. red and blue	†	†

No. 748a was applied before sale to aerogrammes to uprate the imprinted 25f. stamp. It was not available separately.

193 Championship Emblem

1977. Fourth Asian Youth Basketball Championships.

749	193	30f. multicoloured	1·20	30
750	193	80f. multicoloured	2·50	1·50

194 *Popular Dancing* (O. Al-Nakeeb)

1977. Children's Paintings. Multicoloured.

751	15f. Type 194	60	15
752	15f. *Al Deirah* (A. M. al-Onizi)	60	15
753	30f. *Fishing* (M. al-Jasem)	1·20	30
754	30f. *Dugg al-Harees* (B. al-Sa'adooni) (vert)	1·20	30
755	80f. *Fraisa Dancing* (M. al-Mojaibel) (vert)	3·25	1·50
756	80f. *Kuwaiti Girl* (K. Ghazi) (vert)	3·25	1·50

195 Dome of the Rock and Palestinian Freedom Fighters

1978. Palestinian Freedom Fighters.

757	195	30f. multicoloured	3·00	1·50
758	195	80f. multicoloured	8·00	3·00

196 Dentist treating Patient

1978. Tenth Arab Dental Union Congress.

759	196	30f. multicoloured	1·50	30
760	196	80f. multicoloured	3·25	1·90

197 Carrying Water from Dhows

1978. Water Resources. Multicoloured.

761	5f. Type 197	30	15
762	5f. Camel	30	15
763	5f. Water carrier	30	15
764	5f. Pushing water in cart	30	15
765	10f. Irrigation with donkey	60	20
766	10f. Water troughs in desert	60	20
767	10f. Pool by a town	60	20
768	10f. Watering crops	60	20
769	15f. Bedouin watering sheep	85	30
770	15f. Bedouin women by pool	85	30
771	15f. Camels watered by pipeline	85	30
772	15f. Water skins in Bedouin tent	85	30
773	20f. Oasis with wells	1·20	45
774	20f. Washing and drinking at home	1·20	45
775	20f. Water urn	1·20	45
776	20f. Filling vessels from taps	1·20	45
777	25f. Desalination plant	1·50	50
778	25f. Water tanker	1·50	50
779	25f. Filling water tankers	1·50	50
780	25f. Modern water tanks	1·50	50
781	30f. Catching water during storm (vert)	1·70	60
782	30f. Water tank (vert)	1·70	60
783	30f. Sheet to catch rain (vert)	1·70	60
784	30f. Trees by water tanks (vert)	1·70	60
785	80f. Carrying water on donkey (vert)	4·75	1·60
786	80f. Woman carrying water-can (vert)	4·75	1·60
787	80f. Woman with water-skins (vert)	4·75	1·60
788	80f. Tanker delivering water to house (vert)	4·75	1·60
789	100f. Tanker delivering to courtyard tank (vert)	5·75	1·90
790	100f. Household cistern (vert)	5·75	1·90
791	100f. Filling cistern (vert)	5·75	1·90
792	100f. Drawing water from well (vert)	5·75	1·90

198 Symbols of Development

1978. 17th National Day.

793	**198**	30f. multicoloured	1·00	30
794	**198**	80f. multicoloured	2·50	1·00

199 Face of Smallpox Victim

1978. Global Eradication of Smallpox.

795	**199**	30f. multicoloured	1·50	30
796	**199**	80f. multicoloured	3·00	1·30

200 Microwave Antenna

1978. Tenth World Telecommunications Day.

797	**200**	30f. multicoloured	1·50	30
798	**200**	80f. multicoloured	3·75	1·20

201 Sheikh Jabir

1978. Portrait in brown; background colour given.

799	**201**	15f. green	75	45
800	**201**	30f. orange	1·50	75
801	**201**	80f. purple	3·00	1·70
802	**201**	100f. green	3·75	2·00
803	**201**	130f. brown	5·75	3·00
804	**201**	180f. violet	8·75	3·75
805	**201**	1d. red (24×29 mm)	22·00	17·00
806	**201**	4d. blue (24×29 mm)	90·00	44·00

202 Mount Arafat, Pilgrims and Kaaba

1978. Pilgrimage to Mecca.

807	**202**	30f. multicoloured	2·20	30
808	**202**	80f. multicoloured	5·00	1·50

203 UN and Anti-Apartheid Emblems

1978. International Anti-Apartheid Year.

809	**203**	30f. multicoloured	1·50	45
810	**203**	80f. multicoloured	3·00	1·50
811	**203**	180f. multicoloured	5·75	3·00

204 Refugees

1978. 30th Anniversary of Declaration of Human Rights.

812	**204**	30f. multicoloured	1·50	45
813	**204**	80f. multicoloured	3·00	1·00
814	**204**	100f. multicoloured	4·25	2·20

205 Information Centre

1978. Kuwait Information Centre.

815	**205**	5f. multicoloured	30	15
816	**205**	15f. multicoloured	75	30
817	**205**	30f. multicoloured	1·50	45
818	**205**	80f. multicoloured	3·50	1·30

206 Kindergarten

1979. International Year of the Child.

819	**206**	30f. multicoloured	1·00	30
820	**206**	80f. multicoloured	2·50	1·50

207 Kuwaiti Flag and Doves

1979. 18th National Day.

821	**207**	30f. multicoloured	1·20	60
822	**207**	80f. multicoloured	2·50	1·50

208 Crops and Greenhouse

1979. Fouth Arab Agriculture Ministers' Congress.

823	**208**	30f. multicoloured	75	30
824	**208**	80f. multicoloured	2·20	1·50

209 World Map, Koran and Symbols of Arab Achievements

1979. Arab Achievements

825	**209**	30f. multicoloured	1·00	30
826	**209**	80f. multicoloured	2·50	1·50

210 Children flying Kites

1979. Children's Paintings. Multicoloured.

827	30f. Type **210**	1·30	75
828	30f. Girl and doves	1·30	75
829	30f. Crowd and balloons	1·30	75
830	80f. Boys smiling (horiz)	3·00	1·70
831	80f. Children in landscape (horiz)	3·00	1·70
832	80f. Tug-of-war (horiz)	3·00	1·70

211 Wave Pattern and Television Screen

1979. World Telecommunications Day.

833	**211**	30f. multicoloured	1·20	30
834	**211**	80f. multicoloured	3·25	1·30

212 International Military Sports Council Emblem

1979. 29th International Military Football Championship.

835	**212**	30f. multicoloured	1·70	45
836	**212**	80f. multicoloured	4·00	1·70

213 Child and Industrial Landscape

1979. World Environment Day.

837	**213**	30f. multicoloured	2·20	75
838	**213**	80f. multicoloured	5·00	2·20

214 Children supporting Globe

1979. 50th Anniversary of International Bureau of Education.

839	**214**	30f. multicoloured	1·50	30
840	**214**	80f. multicoloured	3·00	1·30
841	**214**	130f. multicoloured	5·75	2·00

215 Children with Television

1979. 25th Anniversary of Kuwaiti Kindergartens. Children's Drawings. Multicoloured.

842	30f. Type **215**	1·50	30
843	80f. Children with flags	3·00	1·30

216 The Kaaba, Mecca

1979. Pilgrimage to Mecca.

844	**216**	30f. multicoloured	1·50	30
845	**216**	80f. multicoloured	3·75	1·30

217 Figure, with Dove and Torch, clothed in Palestinian Flag

1979. International Day of Solidarity with Palestinians.

846	**217**	30f. multicoloured	4·25	1·00
847	**217**	80f. multicoloured	10·00	2·50

218 Boeing 747 and Douglas DC-3 Airliners

1979. 25th Anniversary of Kuwait Airways.

848	**218**	30f. multicoloured	3·00	75
849	**218**	80f. multicoloured	7·25	2·20

219 *Pinctada* Shell bearing Map of Kuwait

1980. 19th National Day.

850	**219**	30f. multicoloured	1·50	30
851	**219**	80f. multicoloured	3·75	1·30

220 Graph with Human Figures

1980. Population Census.

852	**220**	30f. black, silver and blue	2·20	45
853	**220**	80f. black, gold and orange	5·00	1·30

221 Campaign Emblem

1980. World Health Day. Anti-smoking Campaign.

854	**221**	30f. multicoloured	3·00	30
855	**221**	80f. multicoloured	7·25	1·60

222 Municipality Building

1980. 50th Anniversary of Kuwait Municipality.

856	**222**	15f. multicoloured	1·50	15
857	**222**	30f. multicoloured	3·00	45
858	**222**	80f. multicoloured	5·75	1·60

223 *The Future*

1980. Children's Imagination of Future Kuwait. Multicoloured.

859	30f. Type **223**	3·00	60
860	80f. Motorways	7·25	1·60

224 Hand blotting out Factory

1980. World Environment Day.

861	**224**	30f. multicoloured	3·00	60
862	**224**	80f. multicoloured	7·25	1·20

225 Volleyball

1980. Olympic Games, Moscow. Multicoloured.

863	15f. Type **225**	85	30
864	15f. Tennis	85	30
865	30f. Swimming	1·50	45
866	30f. Weightlifting	1·50	45
867	30f. Basketball	1·50	45
868	30f. Judo	1·50	45
869	80f. Gymnastics	3·00	1·50
870	80f. Badminton	3·00	1·50
871	80f. Fencing	3·00	1·50
872	80f. Football	3·00	1·50

226 OPEC Emblem and Globe

1980. 20th Anniversary of Organisation of Petroleum Exporting Countries.

873	**226**	30f. multicoloured	1·50	45
874	**226**	80f. multicoloured	3·00	1·60

227 Mosque and Kaaba, Mecca

1980. 1400th Anniversary of Hegira.

875	**227**	15f. multicoloured	75	30
876	**227**	30f. multicoloured	1·50	60
877	**227**	80f. multicoloured	3·75	1·70

228 Dome of the Rock

1980. International Day of Solidarity with Palestinian People.

878	**228**	30f. multicoloured	2·50	1·20
879	**228**	80f. multicoloured	6·50	3·25

229 Ibn Sina (Avicenna)

1980. Birth Millenary of Ibn Sina (philosopher and physician).

880	**229**	30f. multicoloured	2·20	30
881	**229**	80f. multicoloured	5·00	1·60

230 Islamic Symbols

1981. First Islamic Medicine Conference, Kuwait.

882	**230**	30f. multicoloured	1·50	30
883	**230**	80f. multicoloured	3·00	2·00

231 Person in Wheelchair playing Snooker

1981. International Year of Disabled Persons. Multicoloured.

884	30f. Type **231**	3·00	45
885	80f. Girl in wheelchair	7·25	1·70

232 Symbols of Development and Progress

1981. 20th National Day.

886	**232**	30f. multicoloured	1·20	45
887	**232**	80f. multicoloured	3·25	1·70

233 Emblem of Kuwait Dental Association

1981. First Kuwait Dental Association Conference.

888	**233**	30f. multicoloured	3·75	1·00
889	**233**	80f. multicoloured	8·00	2·50

234 'Lamp'

1981. World Red Cross and Red Crescent Day.

890	**234**	30f. multicoloured	3·00	85
891	**234**	80f. multicoloured	7·25	2·30

235 Emblems of ITU and WHO and Ribbons forming Caduceus

1981. World Telecommunications Day.

892	**235**	30f. multicoloured	1·70	30
893	**235**	80f. multicoloured	4·00	2·30

236 Tanker polluting Sea and Car polluting Atmosphere

1981. World Environment Day.

894	**236**	30f. multicoloured	1·50	60
895	**236**	80f. multicoloured	4·25	2·30

237 Sief Palace

1981

896	**237**	5f. multicoloured	15	15
897	**237**	10f. multicoloured	20	15
898	**237**	15f. multicoloured	30	15
899	**237**	25f. multicoloured	45	15
900	**237**	30f. multicoloured	60	20
901	**237**	40f. multicoloured	75	30
902	**237**	60f. multicoloured	1·00	45
903	**237**	80f. multicoloured	1·50	45
904	**237**	100f. multicoloured	1·70	60
905	**237**	115f. multicoloured	2·00	75
906	**237**	130f. multicoloured	2·30	85
907	**237**	150f. multicoloured	2·50	1·00
908	**237**	180f. multicoloured	3·00	1·20
909	**237**	250f. multicoloured	4·00	1·60
910	**237**	500f. multicoloured	7·25	3·25
911	**237**	1d. multicoloured	14·50	6·50
912	**237**	2d. multicoloured	32·00	12·50
913	**237**	3d. multicoloured	50·00	19·00
914	**237**	4d. multicoloured	65·00	25·00

Nos. 911/914 are larger, 33×28 mm and have a different border.

238 Pilgrims

1981. Pilgrimage to Mecca.

915	**238**	30f. multicoloured	2·20	60
916	**238**	80f. multicoloured	5·00	1·70

239 Palm Trees, Sheep, Camel, Goat and FAO Emblem

1981. World Food Day.

917	**239**	30f. multicoloured	2·20	60
918	**239**	80f. multicoloured	5·00	1·70

240 Television Emblem

1981. 20th Anniversary of Kuwait Television.

919	**240**	30f. multicoloured	2·20	60
920	**240**	80f. multicoloured	5·00	1·70

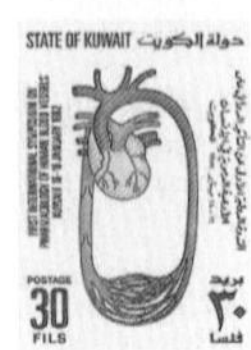

241 Blood Circulation Diagram

1982. First International Symposium on Pharmacology of Human Blood Vessels.

921	**241**	30f. multicoloured	2·20	1·60
922	**241**	80f. multicoloured	5·00	2·30

242 Symbols of Development, Progress and Peace

1982. 21st National Day.

923	**242**	30f. multicoloured	1·50	60
924	**242**	80f. multicoloured	3·75	1·60

243 Emblem of Kuwait Boy Scouts Association on Globe

1982. 75th Anniversary of Boy Scout Movement.

925	**243**	30f. multicoloured	3·00	85
926	**243**	80f. multicoloured	7·25	2·00

244 Emblem of Arab Pharmacists Union

1982. Arab Pharmacists Day.

927	**244**	30f. multicoloured	2·20	60
928	**244**	80f. multicoloured	5·00	2·00

245 Red Crescent, Arab and WHO Emblem

1982. World Health Day.

929	**245**	30f. multicoloured	2·20	1·30
930	**245**	80f. multicoloured	5·00	3·75

246 APU Emblem

1982. 30th Anniversary of Arab Postal Union.

931	**246**	30f. black, orange and green	2·20	60
932	**246**	80f. black, green and orange	5·00	2·00

247 Lungs and Microscope

1982. Centenary of Discovery of Tubercle Bacillus.

933	**247**	30f. multicoloured	4·25	1·20
934	**247**	80f. multicoloured	11·50	3·25

248 Crest and Emblems of Kuwait Football Association and Olympic Committee

1982. World Cup Football Championship, Spain.

935	**248**	30f. multicoloured	2·20	60
936	**248**	80f. multicoloured	5·00	2·00

249 Museum Exhibits

1982. Tenth Anniversary of Science and Natural History Museum.

937	**249**	30f. multicoloured	4·75	1·80
938	**249**	80f. multicoloured	11·00	5·25

250 *Al-Wattyah* (container ship)

1982. Sixth Anniversary of United Arab Shipping Company. Multicoloured.

939	30f. Type **250**	2·20	60
940	80f. *Al-Salimiah* (freighter)	5·00	1·70

251 Palm Trees

1982. Arab Palm Tree Day.

941	**251**	30f. multicoloured	2·20	60
942	**251**	80f. multicoloured	5·00	1·70

252 Pilgrims

1982. Pilgrimage to Mecca.

943	**252**	15f. multicoloured	85	15
944	**252**	30f. multicoloured	1·70	60
945	**252**	80f. multicoloured	4·75	1·70

253 Desert Flower

1983. Desert Plants. As T **253**. Multicoloured; background colours given. (a) Vert designs.

946	10f. green	20	15
947	10f. violet	20	15
948	10f. salmon	20	15
949	10f. pink (blue flowers)	20	15
950	10f. bistre	20	15

951	10f. green	20	15
952	10f. light orange	20	15
953	10f. red (poppy)	20	15
954	10f. brown	20	15
955	10f. blue	20	15
956	15f. green	35	30
957	15f. purple	35	30
958	15f. blue	35	30
959	15f. blue (iris)	35	30
960	15f. olive	35	30
961	15f. red	35	30
962	15f. brown	35	30
963	15f. blue (bellflowers)	35	30
964	15f. mauve	35	30
965	15f. pink	35	30
966	30f. brown	75	60
967	30f. mauve	75	60
968	30f. blue	75	60
969	30f. green	75	60
970	30f. pink	75	60
971	30f. blue	75	60
972	30f. green	75	60
973	30f. mauve	75	60
974	30f. bistre	75	60
975	30f. yellow	75	60

(b) Horiz designs.

976	40f. red (fungi)	1·00	75
977	40f. green (fungi)	1·00	75
978	40f. violet	1·00	75
979	40f. blue	1·00	75
980	40f. grey	1·00	75
981	40f. green	1·00	75
982	40f. mauve	1·00	75
983	40f. brown	1·00	75
984	40f. blue	1·00	75
985	40f. green (daisies)	1·00	75
986	80f. violet	2·20	1·20
987	80f. green	2·20	1·20
988	80f. yellow (yellow flowers)	2·20	1·20
989	80f. brown (green leaves)	2·20	1·20
990	80f. blue	2·20	1·20
991	80f. yellow	2·20	1·20
992	80f. green	2·20	1·20
993	80f. violet (red berries)	2·20	1·20
994	80f. brown (yellow flowers)	2·20	1·20
995	80f. yellow (red and blue flowers)	2·20	1·20

Designs: Various plants.

254 Peace Dove on Map of Kuwait

1983. 22nd National Day.

996	**254**	30f. multicoloured	2·20	45
997	**254**	80f. multicoloured	5·75	1·70

255 IMO Emblem

1983. 25th Anniversary of International Maritime Organisation.

998	**255**	30f. multicoloured	1·00	45
999	**255**	80f. multicoloured	3·25	1·20

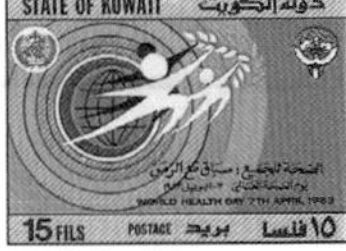
256 Virus and Map of Africa

1983. Third International Conference on Impact of Viral Diseases on Development of Middle East and African Countries.

1000	**256**	15f. multicoloured	60	30
1001	**256**	30f. multicoloured	1·20	60
1002	**256**	80f. multicoloured	3·00	2·00

257 Stylised Figures exercising

1983. World Health Day.

1003	**257**	15f. multicoloured	1·00	45
1004	**257**	30f. multicoloured	1·90	85
1005	**257**	80f. multicoloured	4·25	2·50

258 UPU, WCY and ITU Emblems

1983. World Communications Year.

1006	**258**	15f. multicoloured	1·00	45
1007	**258**	30f. multicoloured	1·90	85
1008	**258**	80f. multicoloured	4·25	2·50

259 Map of Kuwait and Dhow

1983. World Environment Day.

1009	**259**	15f. multicoloured	85	45
1010	**259**	30f. multicoloured	1·70	85
1011	**259**	80f. multicoloured	4·75	2·50

260 Walls of Jerusalem

1983. World Heritage Convention.

1012	**260**	15f. multicoloured	45	30
1013	**260**	30f. multicoloured	1·00	60
1014	**260**	80f. multicoloured	3·00	2·00

261 Pilgrims in Mozdalipha

1983. Pilgrimage to Mecca.

1015	**261**	15f. multicoloured	1·00	30
1016	**261**	30f. multicoloured	1·90	60
1017	**261**	80f. multicoloured	4·25	2·00

262 Arab within Dove

1983. International Day of Solidarity with Palestinian People.

1018	**262**	15f. multicoloured	85	45
1019	**262**	30f. multicoloured	1·70	85
1020	**262**	80f. multicoloured	4·75	2·30

263 Kuwait Medical Association and Congress Emblems

1984. 21st Pan-Arab Medical Congress.

1021	**263**	15f. multicoloured	85	45
1022	**263**	30f. multicoloured	1·70	85
1023	**263**	80f. multicoloured	4·25	3·00

264 State Arms within Key

1984. Inauguration of New Health Establishments.

1024	**264**	15f. multicoloured	75	30
1025	**264**	30f. multicoloured	1·50	60
1026	**264**	80f. multicoloured	3·75	2·00

265 Dove and Globe

1984. 23rd National Day.

1027	**265**	15f. multicoloured	60	30
1028	**265**	30f. multicoloured	1·30	60
1029	**265**	80f. multicoloured	3·25	2·00

266 Symbols of Medicine within Head

1984. Second International Medical Science Conference.

1030	**266**	15f. multicoloured	1·50	45
1031	**266**	30f. multicoloured	2·20	1·00
1032	**266**	80f. multicoloured	6·50	3·00

267 Douglas DC-3 Airliner

1984. 30th Anniversary of Kuwait Airways Corporation.

1033	**267**	30f. blue, dp blue & yell	3·00	1·50
1034	**267**	80f. blue, dp blue & mve	7·25	3·00

268 Magazine Covers

1984. 25th Anniversary of *Al-Arabi* (magazine).

1035	**268**	15f. multicoloured	1·00	30
1036	**268**	30f. multicoloured	2·20	60
1037	**268**	80f. multicoloured	5·50	2·00

269 Family and Emblems

1984. World Health Day.

1038	**269**	15f. multicoloured	1·10	30
1039	**269**	30f. multicoloured	1·90	60
1040	**269**	80f. multicoloured	4·25	2·00

270 Sudanese Orphan and Village

1984. Hanan Kuwaiti Village, Sudan.

1041	**270**	15f. multicoloured	1·00	30
1042	**270**	30f. multicoloured	1·90	60
1043	**270**	80f. multicoloured	4·25	2·00

271 ICAO, Kuwait Airport and Kuwait Airways Emblems

1984. 40th Anniversary of ICAO.

1044	**271**	15f. multicoloured	1·00	45
1045	**271**	30f. multicoloured	1·90	1·00
1046	**271**	80f. multicoloured	4·25	3·00

272 Map of Arab Countries and Youths

1984. Arab Youth Day.

1047	**272**	30f. multicoloured	2·20	1·00
1048	**272**	80f. multicoloured	5·00	2·50

273 Swimming

1984. Olympic Games, Los Angeles. Multicoloured.

1049	30f. Type **273**	1·50	75
1050	30f. Hurdling	1·50	75
1051	80f. Judo	4·25	2·20
1052	80f. Equestrian	4·25	2·20

274 Anniversary Emblem, Camera, Aeroplane, Al-Aujairy Observatory and Wind Tower

1984. Tenth Anniversary of Science Club.

1053	**274**	15f. multicoloured	1·50	45
1054	**274**	30f. multicoloured	3·75	1·00
1055	**274**	80f. multicoloured	9·50	3·00

275 Stoning the Devil

1984. Pilgrimage to Mecca.

1056	**275**	30f. multicoloured	1·70	1·00
1057	**275**	80f. multicoloured	4·00	2·75

276 Anniversary Emblem

1984. 20th Anniversary of International Telecommunications Satellite Consortium (Intelsat).

1058	**276**	30f. multicoloured	1·70	1·00
1059	**276**	80f. multicoloured	4·00	2·75

277 Council Emblem

1984. Fifth Supreme Council Session of Gulf Co-operation Council.

1060	**277**	30f. multicoloured	2·20	1·20
1061	**277**	80f. multicoloured	5·00	3·25

278 Hands breaking Star

1984. International Day of Solidarity with Palestinian People.

1062	**278**	30f. multicoloured	3·75	1·20
1063	**278**	80f. multicoloured	6·50	3·25

279 Company Emblem as Satellite

1984. 50th Anniversary of Kuwait Oil Company.

1064	**279**	30f. multicoloured	2·20	1·20
1065	**279**	80f. multicoloured	5·00	3·25

280 IYY Emblem

1985. International Youth Year.

1066	**280**	30f. multicoloured	3·00	45
1067	**280**	80f. multicoloured	7·25	1·70

281 '24', Hand holding Flame and Dove

1985. 24th National Day.

1068	**281**	30f. multicoloured	2·20	60
1069	**281**	80f. multicoloured	5·00	1·60

282 Programme Emblem

1985. International Programme for Communications Development.

1070	**282**	30f. multicoloured	1·70	75
1071	**282**	80f. multicoloured	4·00	2·20

283 Emblem

1985. First Arab Gulf Social Work Week.

1072	**283**	30f. multicoloured	2·20	75
1073	**283**	80f. multicoloured	5·00	2·20

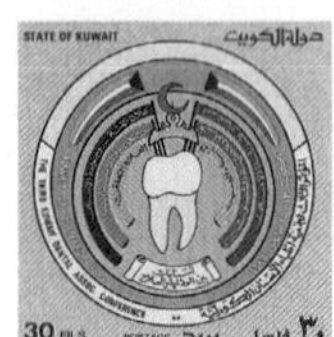
284 Molar

1985. Third Kuwait Dental Association Conference.

1074	**284**	30f. multicoloured	2·20	1·20
1075	**284**	80f. multicoloured	5·00	3·25

285 Emblem

1985. Population Census.

1076	**285**	30f. multicoloured	2·20	75
1077	**285**	80f. multicoloured	5·00	2·20

286 Globe and Figures

1985. World Health Day.

1078	**286**	30f. multicoloured	2·20	75
1079	**286**	80f. multicoloured	5·00	2·20

287 Arabic Script

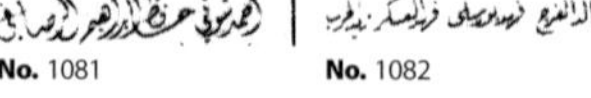
No. 1080

No. 1081

No. 1082

No. 1083

No. 1084

No. 1085

No. 1086

No. 1087

1985. 50th Anniversary of Central Library. Designs showing titles of books and names of authors in Arabic script (first line of text illustrated above).

1080	30f. gold	1·90	1·00
1081	30f. gold	1·90	1·00
1082	30f. gold	1·90	1·00
1083	30f. gold	1·90	1·00
1084	80f. black and gold	4·75	1·90
1085	80f. black and gold	4·75	1·90
1086	80f. black and gold	4·75	1·90
1087	80f. black and gold	4·75	1·90

288 Seascape

1985. World Environment Day.

1088	**288**	30f. multicoloured	3·00	1·20
1089	**288**	80f. multicoloured	7·25	3·25

289 Anniversary Emblem

1985. 25th Anniversary of Organisation of Petroleum Exporting Countries.

1090	**289**	30f. ultramarine, bl & mve	2·20	75
1091	**289**	80f. ultramarine, bl & brn	5·00	2·20

290 Emblem and Heads

1985. Introduction of Civilian Identity Cards.

1092	**290**	30f. multicoloured	2·20	75
1093	**290**	80f. multicoloured	5·00	2·20

291 Flag on Globe within Symbolic Design

1985. International Day of Solidarity with Palestinian People.

1094	**291**	15f. multicoloured	1·20	75
1095	**291**	30f. multicoloured	2·50	1·50
1096	**291**	80f. multicoloured	6·50	3·75

292 Birds

1986. 25th National Day.

1097	**292**	15f. multicoloured	1·50	45
1098	**292**	30f. multicoloured	2·20	1·00
1099	**292**	80f. multicoloured	5·75	3·00

293 Emblem

1986. 20th Anniversary of Kuwait Red Crescent.

1100	**293**	20f. multicoloured	1·50	45
1101	**293**	25f. multicoloured	2·20	75
1102	**293**	70f. multicoloured	5·00	2·50

294 WHO Emblem as Flower

1986. World Health Day.

1103	**294**	20f. multicoloured	2·20	1·00
1104	**294**	25f. multicoloured	3·00	1·20
1105	**294**	70f. multicoloured	6·50	3·75

295 IPY Emblem

1986. International Peace Year.

1106	**295**	20f. green, blue and black	2·20	45
1107	**295**	25f. blue, yellow and black	3·00	75
1108	**295**	70f. blue, mauve and black	5·75	2·50

296 *Al Mirqab*

1986. Tenth Anniversary of United Arab Shipping Company. Container Ships. Multicoloured.

1109	20f. Type **296**	3·00	75
1110	70f. *Al Mubarakiah*	7·25	3·00

297 Bank Emblem on Map

1986. 25th Anniversary of Gulf Bank.

1111	**297**	20f. multicoloured	2·00	75
1112	**297**	25f. multicoloured	2·30	1·00
1113	**297**	70f. multicoloured	5·75	2·50

298 Zig-zags and Diamonds

1986. Sadu Art. Multicoloured.

1114	20f. Type **298**	75	45
1115	70f. Triangles and symbols	3·00	1·70
1116	200f. Stripes and triangles	8·75	5·00

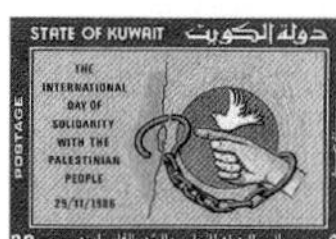
299 Dove on Manacled Hand pointing to Map

1986. International Day of Solidarity with Palestinian People.

1117	**299**	20f. multicoloured	2·00	75
1118	**299**	25f. multicoloured	2·50	1·00
1119	**299**	70f. multicoloured	7·00	2·50

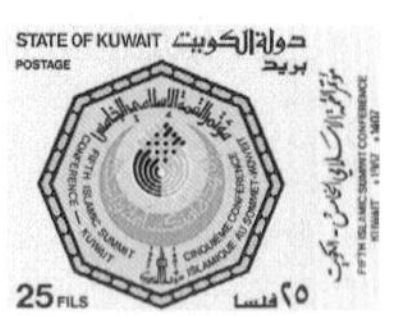
300 Conference Emblem

1987. Fifth Islamic Summit Conference.

1120	**300**	25f. multicoloured	1·50	45
1121	**300**	50f. multicoloured	3·00	1·00
1122	**300**	150f. multicoloured	8·75	3·00

301 Map in National Colours and Symbols of Development

1987. 26th National Day.

1123	**301**	50f. multicoloured	2·20	75
1124	**301**	150f. multicoloured	5·75	2·50

302 Health Science Centre

1987. Third Kuwait International Medical Sciences Conference: Infectious Diseases in Developing Countries.

1125	**302**	25f. multicoloured	1·50	45
1126	**302**	150f. multicoloured	6·50	2·50

303 Campaign Emblem

1987. World Health Day. Child Immunisation Campaign.

1127	**303**	25f. multicoloured	85	45
1128	**303**	50f. multicoloured	2·20	1·00
1129	**303**	150f. multicoloured	5·75	3·00

304 Jerusalem

1987. Jerusalem is an Arab City.

1130	**304**	25f. multicoloured	1·50	45
1131	**304**	50f. multicoloured	3·00	1·00
1132	**304**	150f. multicoloured	7·25	3·75

305 Pilgrims in Miqat Wadi Mihrim

1987. Pilgrimage to Mecca.

1133	**305**	25f. multicoloured	1·50	45
1134	**305**	50f. multicoloured	3·00	1·00
1135	**305**	150f. multicoloured	7·25	3·75

306 Emblem

1987. Arab Telecommunications Day.

1136	**306**	25f. multicoloured	1·50	45
1137	**306**	50f. multicoloured	3·00	1·00
1138	**306**	150f. multicoloured	7·25	3·75

307 Buoy and Container Ship

1987. World Maritime Day.

1139	**307**	25f. multicoloured	1·50	45
1140	**307**	50f. multicoloured	3·00	85
1141	**307**	150f. multicoloured	7·25	2·50

308 Project Monument and Site Plan

1987. Al-Qurain Housing Project.

1142	**308**	25f. multicoloured	1·50	30
1143	**308**	50f. multicoloured	3·00	75
1144	**308**	150f. multicoloured	7·25	1·90

309 Unloading Container Ship

1987. Tenth Anniversary of Ports Public Authority.

1145	**309**	25f. multicoloured	1·10	45
1146	**309**	50f. multicoloured	2·20	1·00
1147	**309**	150f. multicoloured	6·50	3·75

310 Symbolic Design

1987. International Day of Solidarity with Palestinian People.

1148	**310**	25f. multicoloured	1·50	45
1149	**310**	50f. multicoloured	3·00	1·00
1150	**310**	150f. multicoloured	8·75	3·00

311 Emblem

1988. 25th Anniversary of Women's Cultural and Social Society.

1151	**311**	25f. multicoloured	1·50	30
1152	**311**	50f. multicoloured	3·00	75
1153	**311**	150f. multicoloured	7·25	1·90

312 Emblem

1988. 27th National Day.

1154	**312**	25f. multicoloured	1·00	30
1155	**312**	50f. multicoloured	1·90	75
1156	**312**	150f. multicoloured	5·75	1·90

313 Hands holding WHO Emblem

1988. World Health Day. 40th Anniversary of WHO.

1157	**313**	25f. multicoloured	1·50	45
1158	**313**	50f. multicoloured	3·00	1·00
1159	**313**	150f. multicoloured	6·50	3·00

314 Regional Maritime Protection Organisation Symbol

1988. Tenth Anniversary of Kuwait Regional Convention for Protection of Marine Environment.

1160	**314**	35f. ultram, blue & brn	1·50	45
1161	**314**	50f. ultram, blue & grn	3·00	1·00
1162	**314**	150f. ultram, blue & pur	6·50	3·75

315 Society Emblem

1988. 25th Anniversary of Kuwait Teachers' Society.

1163	**315**	25f. multicoloured	1·50	30
1164	**315**	50f. multicoloured	3·00	85
1165	**315**	150f. multicoloured	6·50	2·50

316 Pilgrims at al-Sail al-Kabir Miqat

1988. Pilgrimage to Mecca.

1166	**316**	25f. multicoloured	1·50	30
1167	**316**	50f. multicoloured	3·00	85
1168	**316**	150f. multicoloured	6·50	2·50

317 Gang of Youths lying in wait for Soldiers

1988. Palestinian Intifida Movement.

1169	**317**	50f. multicoloured	5·75	75
1170	**317**	150f. multicoloured	13·00	2·20

318 Ring of Dwellings around Key

1988. Arab Housing Day.

1171	**318**	50f. multicoloured	2·20	75
1172	**318**	100f. multicoloured	3·75	1·50
1173	**318**	150f. multicoloured	5·75	2·20

319 Map of Palestine highlighted on Globe

1988. International Day of Solidarity with Palestinian People.

1174	**319**	50f. multicoloured	3·75	80
1175	**319**	100f. multicoloured	4·25	1·60
1176	**319**	150f. multicoloured	7·25	2·30

320 Volunteers embracing Globe

1988. International Volunteer Day.

1177	**320**	50f. multicoloured	3·00	80
1178	**320**	100f. multicoloured	4·25	1·60
1179	**320**	150f. multicoloured	7·25	2·30

321 Conference, Kuwait Society of Engineers and Arab Engineers Union Emblems

1989. 18th Arab Engineering Conference.

1180	**321**	50f. multicoloured	2·20	80
1181	**321**	100f. multicoloured	3·75	1·60
1182	**321**	150f. multicoloured	5·75	2·30

322 Flags as Figures supporting Map

1989. 28th National Day.

1183	**322**	50f. multicoloured	2·20	80
1184	**322**	100f. multicoloured	3·75	1·60
1185	**322**	150f. multicoloured	5·75	2·30

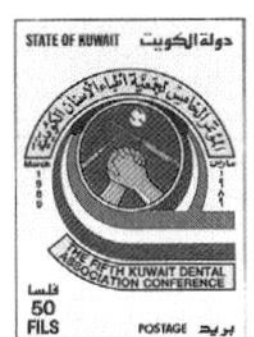

323 Conference Emblem

1989. Fifth Kuwait Dental Association Conference.

1186	**323**	50f. multicoloured	2·20	80
1187	**323**	150f. multicoloured	4·25	1·60
1188	**323**	250f. multicoloured	8·00	4·00

324 Emblems

1989. World Health Day.

1189	**324**	50f. multicoloured	3·00	60
1190	**324**	150f. multicoloured	4·25	1·90
1191	**324**	250f. multicoloured	6·50	3·00

325 Anniversary Emblem

1989. Tenth Anniversary of Arab Board for Medical Specialisations.

1192	**325**	50f. multicoloured	3·00	60
1193	**325**	150f. multicoloured	4·25	1·90

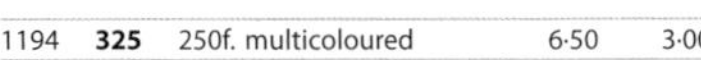

1194	**325**	250f. multicoloured	6·50	3·00

326 Torch, Pen and Flag

1989. 25th Anniversary of Kuwait Journalists' Association.

1195	**326**	50f. multicoloured	2·20	80
1196	**326**	200f. multicoloured	6·50	3·00
1197	**326**	250f. multicoloured	8·75	4·00

327 Attan'eem Miqat, Mecca

1989. Pilgrimage to Mecca.

1198	**327**	50f. multicoloured	3·00	80
1199	**327**	150f. multicoloured	6·50	2·30
1200	**327**	200f. multicoloured	9·50	3·00

328 Al-Qurain Housing Project

1989. Arab Housing Day.

1201	**328**	25f. multicoloured	2·20	30
1202	**328**	50f. multicoloured	4·25	80
1203	**328**	150f. multicoloured	9·50	2·30

329 Tree

1989. Greenery Week.

1204	**329**	25f. multicoloured	2·20	30
1205	**329**	50f. multicoloured	5·00	80
1206	**329**	150f. multicoloured	10·00	2·30

330 Dhow

1989. Coil Stamps.

1207	**330**	50f. gold and green	3·00	3·00
1208	**330**	100f. gold and blue	5·50	5·50
1209	**330**	200f. gold and red	11·50	11·50

331 Emblem and Map

1989. Fifth Anniversary of Gulf Investment Corporation.

1210	**331**	25f. multicoloured	1·20	30
1211	**331**	50f. multicoloured	2·50	80
1212	**331**	150f. multicoloured	7·25	2·30

332 Emblem

1989. First Anniversary of 'Declaration of Palestine State'.

1213	**332**	50f. multicoloured	2·20	80
1214	**332**	150f. multicoloured	5·75	2·30
1215	**332**	200f. multicoloured	8·75	3·00

333 Zakat House

1989. Orphanage Sponsorship Project.

1216	**333**	25f. multicoloured	1·50	45
1217	**333**	50f. multicoloured	3·00	1·10
1218	**333**	150f. multicoloured	7·25	3·00

334 Sheikh Sabah al-Salem as-Sabah (former Chief) and Officers

1989. 50th Anniversary (1988) of Kuwait Police.

1219	**334**	25f. multicoloured	1·70	45
1220	**334**	50f. multicoloured	3·25	1·10
1221	**334**	150f. multicoloured	9·50	3·00

335 Globe and Dove

1990. 29th National Day.

1222	**335**	25f. multicoloured	1·70	45
1223	**335**	50f. multicoloured	3·25	1·10
1224	**335**	150f. multicoloured	9·50	3·00

336 Earth, Clouds and Weather Balloon

1990. World Meteorological Day.

1225	**336**	50f. multicoloured	3·75	95
1226	**336**	100f. multicoloured	7·25	1·90
1227	**336**	150f. multicoloured	11·00	2·75

337 Map bordered by National Flag

1990. World Health Day.

1228	**337**	50f. multicoloured	3·75	95
1229	**337**	100f. multicoloured	7·25	1·90
1230	**337**	150f. multicoloured	11·00	2·75

338 Lanner Falcon

1990

1231	**338**	50f. gold and blue	9·50	11·00
1232	**338**	100f. gold and red	11·50	12·50
1233	**338**	150f. gold and green	14·00	14·50

339 Soldiers carrying Kuwait Flag

1991. Liberation (1st issue).

1234	**339**	25f. multicoloured	85	60
1235	**339**	50f. multicoloured	1·90	1·20
1236	**339**	150f. multicoloured	5·25	3·75

See also Nos. 1243/**MS**1285.

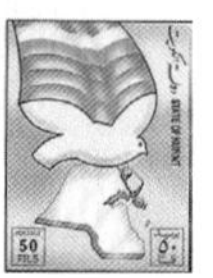
340 Dove and Map

1991. Peace.

1237	**340**	50f. multicoloured	1·90	1·10
1238	**340**	100f. multicoloured	3·75	2·50
1239	**340**	150f. multicoloured	5·25	3·50

341 Flag, Map, Kuwait Towers and Globe

1991. Reconstruction.

1240	**341**	50f. multicoloured	1·60	1·20
1241	**341**	150f. multicoloured	4·75	3·50
1242	**341**	200f. multicoloured	6·25	4·75

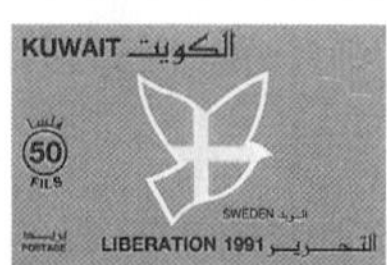

342 Sweden

1991. Liberation (2nd issue). Each showing a dove coloured with the flag of one of the assisting nations. Multicoloured.

1243	50f. Type **342**	1·90	1·60
1244	50f. Soviet Union	1·90	1·60
1245	50f. United States of America	1·90	1·60
1246	50f. Kuwait	1·90	1·60
1247	50f. Saudi Arabia	1·90	1·60
1248	50f. United Nations	1·90	1·60
1249	50f. Singapore	1·90	1·60
1250	50f. France	1·90	1·60
1251	50f. Italy	1·90	1·60
1252	50f. Egypt	1·90	1·60
1253	50f. Morocco	1·90	1·60
1254	50f. United Kingdom	1·90	1·60
1255	50f. Philippines	1·90	1·60
1256	50f. United Arab Emirates	1·90	1·60
1257	50f. Syria	1·90	1·60
1258	50f. Poland	1·90	1·60
1259	50f. Australia	1·90	1·60
1260	50f. Japan	1·90	1·60
1261	50f. Hungary	1·90	1·60
1262	50f. Netherlands	1·90	1·60
1263	50f. Denmark	1·90	1·60
1264	50f. New Zealand	1·90	1·60
1265	50f. Czechoslovakia	1·90	1·60
1266	50f. Bahrain	1·90	1·60
1267	50f. Honduras	1·90	1·60
1268	50f. Turkey	1·90	1·60
1269	50f. Greece	1·90	1·60
1270	50f. Oman	1·90	1·60
1271	50f. Qatar	1·90	1·60
1272	50f. Belgium	1·90	1·60
1273	50f. Sierra Leone	1·90	1·60
1274	50f. Argentina	1·90	1·60
1275	50f. Norway	1·90	1·60
1276	50f. Canada	1·90	1·60
1277	50f. Germany	1·90	1·60
1278	50f. South Korea	1·90	1·60
1279	50f. Bangladesh	1·90	1·60
1280	50f. Bulgaria	1·90	1·60
1281	50f. Senegal	1·90	1·60
1282	50f. Spain	1·90	1·60
1283	50f. Niger	1·90	1·60
1284	50f. Pakistan	1·90	1·60
MS1285	87×134 mm. 1d. Flag and dove. Imperf	28·00	28·00

343 'Human Terror'

1991. First Anniversary of Iraqi Invasion. Multicoloured.

1286	50f. Type **343**	2·30	1·20
1287	100f. 'Invasion of Kuwait'	4·00	2·30
1288	150f. 'Environmental Terrorism' (horiz)	6·25	3·50
MS1289	90×65 mm. 250f. 'Desert Storm' (liberation campaign). Imperf	12·50	12·50

344 Emblem

1991. 30th Anniversary (1990) of Organisation of Petroleum Exporting Countries.

1290	**344**	25f. multicoloured	80	60
1291	**344**	50f. multicoloured	1·90	1·20
1292	**344**	150f. multicoloured	5·50	3·75

345 National Flag, Arabic Script and Broken Chains

1991. Campaign to Free Kuwaiti Prisoners of War. Each black and yellow.

1293	50f. Type **345**	1·90	95
1294	150f. Prison bars, 'Don't Forget Our P.O.W.'s' and broken chains	5·75	3·00
MS1295	121×101 mm. No. 1293×2; No. 1294×2	17·00	17·00

346 Names of Member Countries forming Tree

1991. 12th Gulf Co-operation Council Summit Conference, Kuwait. Multicoloured.

1296	25f. Type **346**	95	80
1297	150f. National Flags as leaves of plant	4·50	3·00
MS1298	Two sheets, each 100×120 mm. (a) No. 1296×2, No. 1297×2; (b) No. 1297×2; 2×25f. Similar to No. 1296 but with tree multicoloured	27·00	27·00

347 ILY Emblem

1992. International Literacy Year (1990).

1299	**347**	50f. blue and brown	1·60	1·10
1300	**347**	100f. blue and yellow	3·25	2·20
1301	**347**	150f. blue and mauve	4·75	3·00

348 Doves and National Flag

1992. 31st National Day (1302) and First Anniversary of Liberation (No. 1303).

1302	**348**	50f. black, green and red	1·00	70
1303	-	150f. multicoloured	3·25	2·20
MS1304		120×99 mm. No. 1302×2; No. 1303×2	9·75	9·75

Design: 150f. Assisting nations' flags.

349 Dromedaries

1992

1305	**349**	25f. multicoloured	95	60
1306	**349**	50f. multicoloured	1·60	1·20
1307	**349**	150f. multicoloured	4·00	3·00
1308	**349**	200f. multicoloured	4·75	4·25
1309	**349**	350f. multicoloured	9·25	7·75

350 Paddle, La Giralda Tower and Kuwaiti Pavilion

1992. Expo '92 World's Fair, Seville. Multicoloured.

1310	50f. Type **350**	1·90	95
1311	50f. Dhows	1·90	95
1312	50f. Dhow	1·90	95
1313	50f. Kuwaiti Pavilion and dhow	1·90	95
1314	150f. Kuwaiti Pavilion on Spanish flag	5·00	2·75
1315	150f. Paddle and La Giralda Tower on hoist of Kuwaiti flag	5·00	2·75
1316	150f. Paddle, La Giralda Tower and dhow on Spanish flag	5·00	2·75
1317	150f. Kuwaiti Pavilion and dhow on fly of Kuwaiti flag	5·00	2·75
MS1318	120×169 mm. Nos. 1310/1317	26·00	26·00

351 Snake around Top of Palm Tree

1992. Second UN Conference on Environment and Development, Rio de Janeiro, Brazil. Multicoloured.

1319	150f. Type **351**	4·00	2·00
1320	150f. Snakes, Kuwait Colours on map and palm tree	4·00	2·00
1321	150f. Skull, snake around tree trunk and dead fish	4·00	2·00
1322	150f. Snake around camel's neck and bird	4·00	2·00
MS1323	121×101 mm. Nos. 1319/1322	20·00	20·00

Nos. 1319/1322 were issued together, *se-tenant*, forming a composite design of the painting *Environmental Terrorism*.

352 Palace of Justice

1992

1324	**352**	25f. multicoloured	95	30
1325	**352**	50f. multicoloured	2·20	60
1326	**352**	100f. multicoloured	4·00	1·60
1327	**352**	150f. multicoloured	6·25	2·30
1328	**352**	250f. multicoloured	10·00	3·00

353 Running and Handball

1992. Olympic Games, Barcelona. Multicoloured.

1329	50f. Swimming and football	2·30	95
1330	100f. Type **353**	4·00	2·30
1331	150f. Judo and show jumping	5·50	3·00

Each value also portrays the Olympic flag and Prince Fahed al-Ahmad al-Sabah, President of several sports organisations, who was killed in the Iraqi invasion.

354 Tanks, Demonstrators with Placards and Executed Civilians

1992. Second Anniversary of Iraqi Invasion. Children's Drawings. Multicoloured.

1332	50f. Type **354**	1·90	95
1333	50f. Soldiers rounding up civilians	1·90	95
1334	50f. Military vehicles and Kuwait Towers	1·90	95

1335		50f. Battle scene	1·90	95
1336		150f. Tanks, bleeding eye and soldiers	5·00	2·75
1337		150f. Battle scene around fortifications	5·00	2·75
1338		150f. Liberation	5·00	2·75
1339		150f. Soldiers and military vehicles	5·00	2·75
MS1340		121×171 mm. Nos. 1332/1339	28·00	28·00

355 Burning Well

1992. First Anniversary of Extinguishing of Oil Well Fires. Multicoloured.

1341		25f. Type **355**	80	45
1342		50f. Spraying dampener on fire	1·60	95
1343		150f. Close-up of spraying	5·50	3·00
1344		250f. Extinguished well (horiz)	7·75	5·00

356 Kuwait Towers

1993

1345	**356**	25f. multicoloured	95	45
1346	**356**	100f. multicoloured	3·50	1·70
1347	**356**	150f. multicoloured	5·00	2·75

357 Laying Bricks to form '32'

1993. 32nd National Day.

1348	**357**	25f. multicoloured	60	45
1349	**357**	50f. multicoloured	1·10	95
1350	**357**	150f. multicoloured	3·00	2·75

358 Symbols of Oppression and Freedom

1993. Second Anniversary of Liberation.

1351	**358**	25f. multicoloured	50	45
1352	**358**	50f. multicoloured	1·00	95
1353	**358**	150f. multicoloured	2·75	2·75

359 Hands Signing

1993. Deaf Child Week.

1354	**359**	25f. multicoloured	50	45
1355	**359**	50f. multicoloured	1·00	95
1356	**359**	150f. multicoloured	3·25	2·75
1357	**359**	350f. multicoloured	6·75	6·25

360 Chained Prisoner

1993. Campaign to Free Kuwaiti Prisoners of War. Multicoloured.

1358		50f. Type **360**	1·10	95
1359		150f. Chained hand, hoopoe and barred window (horiz)	2·75	2·75
1360		200f. Screaming face on wall of empty cell	4·00	3·50

361 Hand scratching Map

1993. Third Anniversary of Iraqi Invasion.

1361	**361**	50f. multicoloured	1·20	80
1362	**361**	150f. multicoloured	3·50	3·00

362 Emblem

1993. 40th Anniversary of Kuwait Air Force.

1363	**362**	50f. multicoloured	1·90	80
1364	**362**	150f. multicoloured	4·25	3·00

363 Flower and Dove

1994. 33rd National Day.

1365	**363**	25f. multicoloured	95	45
1366	**363**	50f. multicoloured	1·60	1·10
1367	**363**	150f. multicoloured	3·75	3·00

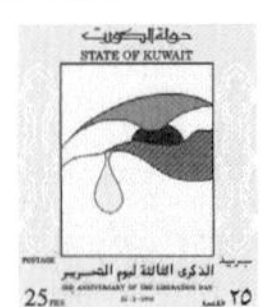

364 Anniversary Emblem

1994. Third Anniversary of Liberation.

1368	**364**	25f. multicoloured	80	45
1369	**364**	50f. multicoloured	1·60	1·10
1370	**364**	150f. multicoloured	5·50	3·00

365 Anniversary Emblem

1994. 25th Anniversary of Central Bank of Kuwait.

1371	**365**	25f. multicoloured	80	45
1372	**365**	50f. multicoloured	1·60	1·10
1373	**365**	150f. multicoloured	4·00	3·00

366 Stylised Emblems

1994. International Year of the Family. Multicoloured.

1374		50f. Type **366**	1·60	95
1375		150f. Three IYF emblems	4·00	3·00
1376		200f. Globe, emblem and spheres (horiz)	5·50	4·00

367 Emblem on Sky

1994. 20th Anniversary of Industrial Bank of Kuwait.

1377	**367**	50f. multicoloured	95	95
1378	**367**	100f. gold, blue and black	1·90	1·90
1379	**367**	150f. multicoloured	3·00	2·75

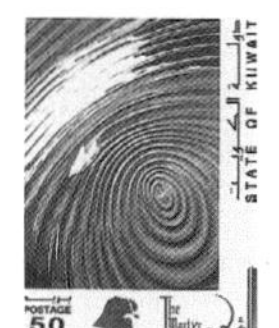

368 Fingerprint in Water

1994. Martyrs' Day. Multicoloured.

1380		50f. Type **368**	1·90	95
1381		100f. Fingerprint in sand	2·75	1·90
1382		150f. Fingerprint in National Colours	4·00	2·75
1383		250f. Fingerprint in clouds over Kuwait Towers	7·00	4·75
MS1384		91×111 mm. Nos. 1380/1383	16·00	16·00

369 Anniversary Emblem

1994. 75th Anniversary of ILO.

1385	**369**	50f. multicoloured	1·10	95
1386	**369**	150f. multicoloured	3·00	2·75
1387	**369**	350f. gold, blue and black	7·25	6·50

370 Free and Imprisoned Doves

1994. Fourth Anniversary of Iraqi Invasion.

1388	**370**	50f. multicoloured	1·60	95
1389	**370**	150f. multicoloured	4·00	2·75
1390	**370**	350f. multicoloured	11·50	6·50

371 Emblem

1994. Kuwait Ports Authority.

1391	**371**	50f. multicoloured	3·00	95
1392	**371**	150f. multicoloured	6·25	2·75
1393	**371**	350f. multicoloured	12·50	6·50

372 Anniversary Emblem

1994. 20th Anniversary of Kuwait Science Club.

1394	**372**	50f. multicoloured	1·10	95
1395	**372**	100f. multicoloured	2·20	1·90
1396	**372**	150f. multicoloured	3·00	2·75

373 Map and Building

1994. Inauguration of Arab Towns Organisation Permanent Headquarters. Multicoloured.

1397		50f. Type **373**	1·60	1·10
1398		100f. Close-up of arched facade	4·75	2·00
1399		150f. Door	6·25	3·00

374 ICAO and Kuwait International Airport Emblems

1994. 50th Anniversary of ICAO. Multicoloured.

1400		100f. Type **374**	3·00	2·00
1401		150f. Emblems and control tower	4·00	3·00
1402		350f. Aeroplane and '50 years'	8·50	6·75

375 Anniversary Emblem

1994. 40th Anniversary of Kuwait Airways.

1403	**375**	50f. multicoloured	1·60	1·10
1404	**375**	100f. multicoloured	4·00	2·00
1405	**375**	150f. multicoloured	5·50	3·00

376 Family

1995. Population Census.

1406	**376**	50f. multicoloured	1·10	95
1407	**376**	100f. multicoloured	2·00	1·90
1408	**376**	150f. multicoloured	3·50	2·75

377 Children waving Flags

1995. 34th National Day.

1409	**377**	25f. multicoloured	1·10	45
1410	**377**	50f. multicoloured	2·00	1·10
1411	**377**	150f. multicoloured	6·25	3·00

378 Falcon dragging Kuwaiti Flag from Snake's Grip

1995. Fourth Anniversary of Liberation.

1412	**378**	25f. multicoloured	1·60	45
1413	**378**	50f. multicoloured	2·30	1·10
1414	**378**	150f. multicoloured	7·00	3·00

379 Conference Venue

1995. International Medical Conference. Multicoloured.

1415		50f. Type **379**	1·90	1·10
1416		100f. Lecture	3·75	2·00
1417		150f. Emblem on map of Kuwait in National Colours	5·50	3·00

380 Anniversary Emblem and Flags

1995. 50th Anniversary of Arab League. Multicoloured.

1418		50f. Type **380**	1·90	1·10

1419	100f. Kuwaiti and League flags and League emblem (horiz)	3·75	2·00
1420	150f. Handshake and League emblem	5·50	3·00

381 Emblem

1995. World Health Day. 'A World without Polio'.

1421	**381**	50f. multicoloured	1·90	95
1422	**381**	150f. multicoloured	3·75	3·00
1423	**381**	200f. multicoloured	6·25	4·00

382 '100'

1995. Centenary of Volleyball.

1424	**382**	50f. multicoloured	1·10	95
1425	**382**	100f. multicoloured	2·20	2·00
1426	**382**	150f. multicoloured	3·25	3·00

383 Olive Branch falling from Wounded Dove's Beak

1995. Fifth Anniversary of Iraqi Invasion.

1427	**383**	50f. multicoloured	1·60	95
1428	**383**	100f. multicoloured	3·00	2·20
1429	**383**	150f. multicoloured	4·75	3·00

384 Doves and Anniversary Emblem

1995. 50th Anniversary of UNO.

1430	**384**	25f. multicoloured	95	80
1431	**384**	50f. multicoloured	2·00	1·60
1432	**384**	150f. multicoloured	4·00	3·00

385 Farmer with Animals

1995. 50th Anniversary of FAO. Multicoloured.

1433	50f. Type **385**	1·20	95
1434	100f. Fish market	2·00	1·60
1435	150f. Agriculture	3·25	3·00
MS1436	120×70 mm. Nos. 1433/1435	7·00	7·00

386 Emblems within Ruler

1995. World Standards Day. Multicoloured.

1437	50f. Type **386**	1·60	1·10
1438	100f. Emblems and aspects of industry (48×27 mm)	4·00	2·00
1439	150f. As No. 1438	7·00	3·00

387 *Onobrychis ptolemaica*

1995. Flowers. Multicoloured.

1440	5f. Type **387**	30	15
1441	15f. *Convolvulus oxyphyllus*	80	45
1442	25f. Corn poppy	1·20	95
1443	50f. *Moltkiopsis ciliata*	2·30	1·60
1444	150f. *Senecio desfontainei*	6·25	4·75

388 Coins forming Map of Kuwait

1996. Money Show.

1445	**388**	25f. multicoloured	80	45
1446	**388**	100f. multicoloured	3·50	1·90
1447	**388**	150f. multicoloured	5·00	3·00

389 Boy Scout in Watchtower

1996. 60th Anniversary of Scout Movement in Kuwait. Multicoloured.

1448	50f. Type **389**	1·60	1·20
1449	100f. Scout drawing water from well	3·00	2·75
1450	150f. Scouts planting sapling	4·75	4·00

390 Hands supporting Ear of Wheat

1996

1451	**390**	50f. multicoloured	1·10	95
1452	**390**	100f. multicoloured	2·00	1·90
1453	**390**	150f. multicoloured	3·25	2·75

391 Saker Falcon trailing National Colours, Falcon and City

1996. 35th National Day.

1454	**391**	25f. multicoloured	1·10	45
1455	**391**	50f. multicoloured	2·00	1·10
1456	**391**	150f. multicoloured	4·75	3·00

392 Horses

1996. Fifth Anniversary of Liberation.

1457	**392**	25f. multicoloured	1·20	45
1458	**392**	50f. multicoloured	2·30	1·10
1459	**392**	150f. multicoloured	5·75	3·00

393 View through Gateway

1996. Arab City Day.

1460	**393**	50f. multicoloured	1·60	1·10
1461	**393**	100f. multicoloured	4·00	2·00
1462	**393**	150f. multicoloured	5·50	3·00

394 Emblem

1996. Seventh Kuwait Dental Association Conference.

1463	**394**	25f. multicoloured	80	45
1464	**394**	50f. multicoloured	1·60	1·10
1465	**394**	150f. multicoloured	4·00	3·00

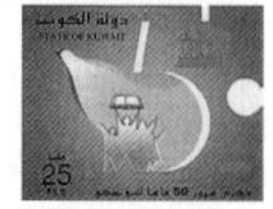

395 Figures holding Open Book within Bird

1996. 50th Anniversary of UNESCO.

1466	**395**	25f. multicoloured	55	45
1467	**395**	100f. multicoloured	2·00	1·90
1468	**395**	150f. multicoloured	3·00	2·75

396 Flags, Anniversary Emblem and Tanker

1996. 50th Anniversary of First Oil Shipment from Kuwait.

1469	**396**	25f. multicoloured	1·10	45
1470	**396**	100f. multicoloured	2·75	1·90
1471	**396**	150f. multicoloured	4·00	3·00

397 Sheikh Mubarak al-Sabah

1996. Centenary of Accession as Emir of Sheikh Mubarak al-Sabah. Multicoloured.

1472	25f. Type **397**	1·10	45
1473	50f. Sheikh Mubarak al-Sabah and ribbons	2·00	1·10
1474	150f. Type **397**	4·75	3·00

398 Rifle Shooting

1996. Olympic Games, Atlanta. Multicoloured.

1475	25f. Type **398**	95	45
1476	50f. Running	1·90	95
1477	100f. Weightlifting	3·75	1·90
1478	150f. Fencing	4·25	3·00

399 Festival Emblem

1996. National Council for Culture, Art and Letters. First Children's Cultural Festival.

1479	**399**	25f. multicoloured	1·10	45
1480	**399**	100f. multicoloured	2·75	1·90
1481	**399**	150f. multicoloured	4·00	3·00

400 Emblem

1996. Third Al-Qurain Cultural Festival.

1482	**400**	50f. multicoloured	1·60	95
1483	**400**	100f. multicoloured	2·30	2·00
1484	**400**	150f. multicoloured	4·00	3·00

401 University

1996. 30th Anniversary of Kuwait University.

1485	**401**	25f. multicoloured	80	45
1486	**401**	100f. multicoloured	2·30	1·90
1487	**401**	150f. multicoloured	3·25	3·00

402 Liberation Tower

1996

1488	**402**	5f. multicoloured	30	15
1489	**402**	10f. multicoloured	45	30
1490	**402**	15f. multicoloured	60	45
1491	**402**	25f. multicoloured	80	60
1492	**402**	50f. multicoloured	1·60	1·40
1493	**402**	100f. multicoloured	3·00	2·75
1494	**402**	150f. multicoloured	5·00	4·00
1495	**402**	200f. multicoloured	7·00	5·50
1496	**402**	250f. multicoloured	8·50	6·75
1497	**402**	350f. multicoloured	11·50	9·25

403 Sehel's Grey Mullet

1997. Marine Life. Multicoloured. (a) Fish.

1498	25f. Type **403**	80	45
1499	50f. Yellow-finned seabream	1·20	95
1500	100f. Greasy grouper	2·75	1·90
1501	150f. Silver-backed seabream	4·00	2·75
1502	200f. Silver grunt	5·50	3·75
1503	350f. Silver pomfret	9·25	6·50

(b) Shrimps.

1504	25f. Tail and body segments of shrimps	80	45
1505	25f. Head and body segments of shrimps	80	45
1506	25f. Underside of fish and body and legs of shrimp	80	45
1507	25f. Head of shrimp, fish and body and legs of shrimp	80	45
1508	50f. Tail and body segments of two shrimps	1·20	95
1509	50f. Legs and body segments of shrimp	1·20	95
1510	50f. Body segments of shrimp and fish	1·20	95
1511	50f. Head of shrimp, seaweed and body and legs of shrimp	1·20	95
1512	100f. Tail and body segments of two shrimps	2·30	1·90
1513	100f. Head, legs and body segments of shrimps	2·30	1·90
1514	100f. Body of shrimp	2·30	1·90
1515	100f. Part of head, legs, tail and body of three shrimps	2·30	1·90
1516	150f. Body segments of two shrimps and upper half of fish	4·00	3·00
1517	150f. Front part of bodies of two shrimps and tail of fish	4·00	3·00
1518	150f. Heads of two shrimps, complete shrimp and fish	4·00	3·00
1519	150f. Body segments of two shrimps and front part of shrimps head	4·00	3·00

Nos. 1504/1519 were issued together, *se-tenant*, forming a composite design of shrimps in a marine environment.

404 Flag, Cupped Hands and Sunflower

1997. 36th National Day.

1520	**404**	25f. multicoloured	80	45
1521	**404**	50f. multicoloured	1·60	95
1522	**404**	150f. multicoloured	4·00	2·75

405 Flag, rejoicing Crowd and Sheikh Jabir

1997. Sixth Anniversary of Liberation.

1523	**405**	25f. multicoloured	1·10	45
1524	**405**	50f. multicoloured	2·00	95
1525	**405**	150f. multicoloured	5·50	2·75

406 Emblem

1997. Tenth Anniversary of Montreal Protocol (on reduction of use of chlorofluorocarbons).

1526	**406**	25f. multicoloured	1·10	65
1527	**406**	50f. multicoloured	2·00	1·00
1528	**406**	150f. multicoloured	5·50	3·25

407 Emblem

1997. Kuwait Industries Exhibition.

1529	**407**	25f. multicoloured	1·10	65
1530	**407**	50f. multicoloured	2·00	1·00
1531	**407**	150f. multicoloured	5·50	3·25

408 Signs of Zodiac and Whale

1997. 25th Anniversary of Educational Science Museum.

1532		25f. Type **408**	1·60	65
1533		50f. Space shuttle orbiting Earth, whale, astronaut and dinosaur (horiz)	3·00	1·00
1534		150f. Symbols of past, present and future around whale	9·25	3·25
MS1535		100×75 mm. 150f. Coelacanth (horiz)	20·00	20·00

409 National Council for Culture, Arts and Letters Emblem

1997. 22nd Kuwait Arabic Book Exhbition.

1536	**409**	25f. multicoloured	1·10	65
1537	**409**	50f. multicoloured	2·00	1·00
1538	**409**	150f. multicoloured	5·50	3·25

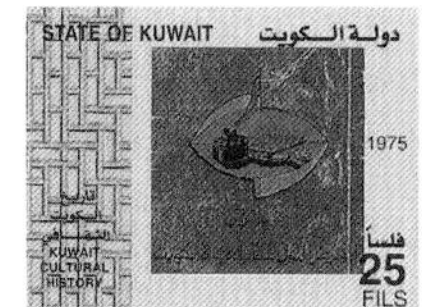

410 Ink-well and Book (first book fair, 1975)

1997. Kuwait Cultural History.

1539		25f. Type **410**	50	50
1540		25f. Front page of *Kuwait Magazine* (1928)	50	50
1541		25f. Front page *A'lam al-Fikr* (periodical) (1970)	50	50
1542		25f. Pyramids and dhow (*Al'Bitha* magazine, 1946)	50	50
1543		25f. Rising sun over open book and quill (*Al'am al Ma'rifa* (periodical), 1978)	50	50
1544		25f. Book with dhow on front cover (*Dalil Almohtar Fi Alaam Al-Bihar*, 1923)	50	50
1545		25f. Arabic script and 'brick' design (*Al-Arabi* magazine, 1958)	50	50
1546		25f. Open book (inauguration of first public library, 1923)	50	50
1547		25f. Two covers showing Arabic script in boxes and cosmic explosion (*Al Thaqafa Al-Alamiya* (periodical), 1981)	50	50
1548		25f. Actors and curtain (*The World Theatre* (periodical), 1969)	50	50
1549		50f. Entrance to Qibliya Girls' School (1937)	50	50
1550		50f. Scissors cutting ribbon (first Fine Arts Exhibition, 1959)	1·20	1·20
1551		50f. Mubarakiya School (1912)	1·20	1·20
1552		50f. Family entering Kuwait National Museum (1958)	1·20	1·20
1553		50f. Shuwaikh Secondary School (1953)	1·20	1·20
1554		50f. Door and three windows (Al-Marsam Al-Hor, 1959)	1·20	1·20
1555		50f. Decorated screen (Alma'had Aldini, 1947)	1·20	1·20
1556		50f. Courtyard of Folklore Centre (1956)	1·20	1·20
1557		50f. Three columns of Arabic script (Al Ma'arif printing press, 1947)	1·20	1·20
1558		50f. Class photograph (Literary Club, 1924)	1·20	1·20
1559		150f. Heads and curtains (Folk Theatre Group, 1956)	3·25	3·25
1560		150f. Musical instruments and notes (Academy of Music, 1972)	3·25	3·25
1561		150f. Film frames, audience and camera (opening of Al-Sharqiya cinema, 1955)	3·25	3·25
1562		150f. Curtains around couple at oasis (Theatrical Academy, 1967)	3·25	3·25
1563		150f. Marine views in film frame (*Bas Ya Bahar* (first Kuwaiti feature film), 1970)	3·25	3·25

411 Doves flying over Members' Flags

1997. 18th Gulf Co-operation Council Summit, Kuwait. Multicoloured.

1564		25f. Type **411**	1·70	85
1565		50f. Members' flags forming doves wheeling over map (horiz)	3·25	1·10
1566		150f. Doves perched atop wall of members' flags	10·00	3·50

412 State Flag

1998. 37th National Day.

1567	**412**	25f. multicoloured	1·20	65
1568	**412**	50f. multicoloured	2·10	1·30
1569	**412**	150f. multicoloured	5·75	4·00

413 Flag, Map and Dove

1998. Seventh Anniversary of Liberation.

1570	**413**	25f. multicoloured	1·70	85
1571	**413**	50f. multicoloured	3·25	1·70
1572	**413**	150f. multicoloured	10·00	4·25

414 Emblem

1998. Anti-drugs Campaign.

1573	**414**	25f. multicoloured	1·20	65
1574	**414**	50f. multicoloured	2·10	1·30
1575	**414**	150f. multicoloured	5·75	4·00

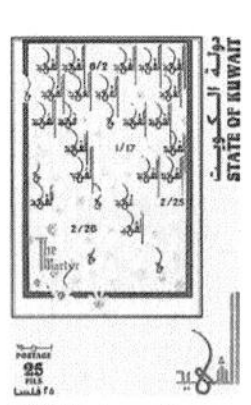

415 Text on Open Page with Flowers

1998. Martyrs' Day. Multicoloured.

1576		25f. Type **415**	1·20	65
1577		50f. Tree	2·10	1·30
1578		150f. Calligraphy	6·50	4·00
MS1579		60×54 mm. 500f. Sheikh Jabir; 500f. People of Kuwait	26·00	26·00

416 Woman selling Cooked Vegetables

1998. Life in Pre-Oil Kuwait (1st series). Multicoloured.

1580		25f. Type **416**	1·00	65
1581		50f. Ship-building	1·70	1·30
1582		100f. Sailor strapping his box	3·25	2·75
1583		150f. Pearl divers wading out to boat	5·00	4·25
1584		250f. Delivering fresh water	8·25	7·00
1585		350f. Pigeon trainer	12·50	9·00

See also Nos. 1599/1604.

417 Child's Face

1998. 12th Anniversary of Chernobyl Nuclear Disaster.

1586	**417**	25f. multicoloured	3·25	1·00
1587	**417**	50f. multicoloured	5·00	2·00
1588	**417**	150f. multicoloured	13·00	5·25

418 World Map and Emblem

1998. International Year of the Ocean. Multicoloured.

1589		25f. Type **418**	1·70	1·00
1590		50f. Motifs as in Type **418** but differently arranged in rectangle (27×37 mm)	2·50	1·50
1591		150f. Type **418**	7·50	5·00

419 Emblem

1998. 25th Anniversary of Union of Consumer Co-operative Societies. Multicoloured.

1592	**419**	25f. multicoloured	1·70	85
1593	**419**	50f. multicoloured	3·25	1·70
1594	**419**	150f. multicoloured	9·00	4·25

420 Men on Crutches

1998. Anti-landmine Campaign. Details from painting by Jafar Islah. Multicoloured.

1595		25f. Type **420**	1·70	85
1596		50f. Man on crutch	3·25	1·70
1597		150f. Man on crutches and woman helping child	8·25	4·25
MS1598		96×89 mm. 500f. Motifs of Nos. 1596/1597	17·00	17·00

1998. Life in Pre-Oil Kuwait (2nd series). As T **416**. Multicoloured.

1599		25f. Hairdresser	1·20	75
1600		50f. Hand-grinding	2·10	1·30
1601		100f. Tailor	4·25	2·50
1602		150f. Artist	5·00	3·75
1603		250f. Potter	9·00	6·50
1604		350f. Hand-spinning	11·50	9·25

421 New Postal Emblem

1998

1605	**421**	25f. multicoloured	90	55
1606	**421**	50f. multicoloured	2·10	1·30
1607	**421**	100f. multicoloured	3·75	2·40
1608	**421**	150f. multicoloured	6·00	3·75
1609	**421**	250f. multicoloured	9·75	6·00

422 Child's Painting

1998. Children's Cultural House.

1610	**422**	25f. multicoloured	1·10	55
1611	**422**	50f. multicoloured	2·00	1·30
1612	**422**	150f. multicoloured	4·50	3·75

423 Collage

1998. 50th Anniversary of Universal Declaration of Human Rights.

1613	**423**	25f. multicoloured	1·10	55
1614	**423**	50f. multicoloured	2·00	1·30
1615	**423**	150f. multicoloured	4·50	3·75

424 Falcon

1998

1616		25f. Type **424**	1·50	1·10
1617		50f. Young camels	3·00	2·20
1618		150f. Dhow	6·75	6·00

425 Emblem

1998. 25th Anniversary of Public Authority for Applied Education and Training.

1619	**425**	25f. multicoloured	1·50	55
1620	**425**	50f. multicoloured	3·00	1·30
1621	**425**	150f. multicoloured	6·00	3·75

426 Entrance and Palm Trees

1999. Seif Palace. Different views of the Palace. Multicoloured.

1622		25f. Type **426**	75	35
1623		50f. Palace buildings	1·80	95
1624		100f. Tower	3·50	1·90
1625		150f. Type **426**	4·50	3·00

1626	250f. As No. 1623	6·00	5·25
1627	350f. As No. 1624	9·00	7·50

427 '38'

1999. 38th National Day.

1628	**427**	50f. multicoloured	1·50	95
1629	**427**	150f. multicoloured	4·50	2·75

428 Building, Dove and '8'

1999. Eighth Anniversary of Liberation.

1630	**428**	50f. multicoloured	1·50	95
1631	**428**	150f. multicoloured	4·50	2·75

429 Liver and Kuwait Flag

1999. 20th Anniversary of Organ Transplantation in Kuwait. Multicoloured.

1632	50f. Type **429**	2·00	95
1633	150f. Heart and Kuwait flag	5·50	2·75

430 Emblem and Kuwait Flag

1999. 40th Anniversary of *Al-Arabi* (magazine).

1634	**430**	50f. multicoloured	2·00	95
1635	**430**	150f. multicoloured	5·50	2·75

431 Emblem

2000. 25th Anniversary (1999) of Kuwait Science Club.

1636	**431**	50f. multicoloured	2·30	1·10
1637	**431**	150f. multicoloured	6·00	3·50
1638	**431**	350f. multicoloured	13·00	8·25

432 Emblem

2000. International Civil Aviation Day.

1639	**432**	50f. multicoloured	1·50	1·10
1640	**432**	150f. multicoloured	3·75	3·50
1641	**432**	250f. multicoloured	7·50	5·50

433 '2000' and Emblem

2000. Kuwait International Airport.

1642	**433**	50f. multicoloured	1·50	1·10
1643	**433**	150f. multicoloured	3·75	3·50
1644	**433**	250f. multicoloured	6·00	5·50

434 Children, Globe and Jigsaw Pieces

2000. International Conference on Autism and Communication Deficiencies, Kuwait. Children's paintings. Multicoloured.

1645	25f. Type **434**	1·10	55
1646	50f. Globe and children	2·00	1·30
1647	150f. Children holding hands	4·50	3·75

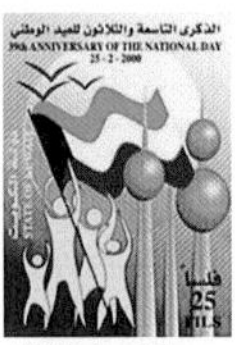
435 Stylised Figures and Flag

2000. 39th National Day.

1648	**435**	25f. multicoloured	1·10	55
1649	**435**	50f. multicoloured	2·00	1·30
1650	**435**	150f. multicoloured	4·50	3·75

436 State Flag

2000. Ninth Anniversary of Liberation.

1651	**436**	25f. multicoloured	1·50	1·20
1652	**436**	50f. multicoloured	4·25	3·25
1653	**436**	150f. multicoloured	6·25	5·25

437 Emblem

2000. International Investment Forum, Kuwait.

1654	**437**	25f. multicoloured	1·50	60
1655	**437**	50f. multicoloured	2·30	1·40
1656	**437**	150f. multicoloured	6·75	4·00

438 View over City

2000. Kuwait City.

1657	**438**	50f. multicoloured	1·50	1·00
1658	**438**	150f. multicoloured	4·50	2·75
1659	**438**	350f. multicoloured	9·00	6·50

439 Emblem and Hand holding Scroll

2000. Third Private Education Week.

1660	**439**	50f. multicoloured	1·50	1·00
1661	**439**	150f. multicoloured	4·50	2·75
1662	**439**	350f. multicoloured	9·00	6·50

440 Emblem and Stamps Encircling Globe

2000. 125th Anniversary of Universal Postal Union.

1663	**440**	50f. multicoloured	1·50	1·00
1664	**440**	150f. multicoloured	4·50	2·75
1665	**440**	350f. multicoloured	9·00	6·50

MS1666 100×75 mm. 1d. Stamps encircling globes 18·00 18·00

441 Hands and Emblem

2000. World Environment Day.

1667	**441**	50f. multicoloured	1·50	1·00
1668	**441**	150f. multicoloured	4·50	2·75
1669	**441**	350f. multicoloured	9·00	6·50

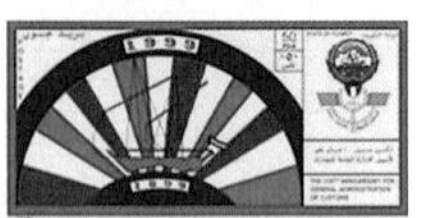
442 Galleon and Emblem

2000. Centenary of General Customs' Administration.

1670	**442**	50f. multicoloured	1·50	1·00
1671	**442**	150f. multicoloured	4·50	2·75
1672	**442**	350f. multicoloured	9·00	6·50

MS1673 100×5 mm. **442** 1d. multicoloured 18·00 18·00

443 Emblem

2000. Tenth Anniversary of Committee for Missing and Prisoners of War Affairs. Multicoloured.

1674	25f. Type **443**	1·50	40
1675	50f. Emblem and chains	3·00	1·00
1676	150f. Emblem forming '10'	6·00	2·50

444 Kick-boxing and Emblem

2000. Olympic Games, Sydney. Multicoloured.

1677	25f. Type **444**	75	40
1678	50f. Shooting	1·50	1·00
1679	150f. Swimming	4·50	2·75
1680	200f. Weight-lifting	6·00	3·75
1681	250f. Running	7·50	5·00
1682	350f. Football	9·75	7·00

A 1d. imperforate miniature sheet, the design consisting of the emblem and pictograms as depicted on the stamps, exists in a cover inscribed 'With the Compliments of Ministry of Communications–Post Sector'.

445 Emblem and Outline of Tooth

2000. 25th Anniversary of Kuwait Dental Association.

1683	**445**	50f. multicoloured	1·70	1·00
1684	**445**	150f. multicoloured	5·00	2·75
1685	**445**	350f. multicoloured	10·00	6·50

446 Emblem

2000. Sixth Gulf Co-operation Council (GCC) Joint Stamp Exhibition, Kuwait.

1686	**446**	25f. multicoloured	1·10	60
1687	**446**	50f. multicoloured	2·20	1·40
1688	**446**	150f. multicoloured	5·50	4·00

MS1689 146×111 mm. 1d. Emblems of current and previous exhibitions. Imperf 20·00 20·00

447 Building and '15' in Laurel Wreath

2000. 15th Anniversary of Gulf Investment Corporation and Inauguration of New Headquarters Building. Multicoloured.

1690	25f. Type **447**	1·10	60
1691	50f. Building in centre with '15' at left	2·20	1·40
1692	150f. Building at right with '15' in centre	5·50	4·00

448 Letters and Book

2000. National Council for Culture, Arts and Letters.

1693	**448**	25f. multicoloured	1·10	60
1694	**448**	50f. multicoloured	2·20	1·40
1695	**448**	150f. multicoloured	5·50	4·00

MS1695a **448** 500f. multicoloured (85×95 mm) 12·00 12·00

449 Map and Emblems

2001. Arab Cultural Capital.

1696	**449**	25f. multicoloured	1·10	70
1697	**449**	50f. multicoloured	2·50	1·60
1698	**449**	150f. multicoloured	7·00	4·50

450 Emblem

2001. Long Live February.

1699	**450**	25f. multicoloured	1·10	70
1700	**450**	50f. multicoloured	2·50	1·60
1701	**450**	150f. multicoloured	7·00	4·50

451 Anniversary Emblem

2001. 40th Anniversary of National Day.

1702	**451**	25f. multicoloured	1·10	70
1703	**451**	50f. multicoloured	2·50	1·60
1704	**451**	150f. multicoloured	7·00	4·50

452 Doves

2001. 10th Anniversary of Liberation Day.

1705	**452**	25f. multicoloured	1·10	70
1706	**452**	50f. multicoloured	2·50	1·60
1707	**452**	150f. multicoloured	7·00	4·50

453 Buildings

2001. 40th Anniversary of Kuwait Fund For Arab Economic Development.

1708	**453**	25f. multicoloured	1·10	70
1709	**453**	50f. multicoloured	2·50	1·60

454 Anniversary Emblem

2001. 50th Anniversary of United Nations Commissioner for Refugees. Multicoloured.

1710	25f. Type **454**	1·10	70
1711	50f. Anniversary emblem (vertical blue band)	2·50	1·60
1712	150f. Anniversary emblem (different)	7·00	4·50

455 Pierced Flag

2001. Prisoners.

1713	**455**	25f. multicoloured	1·10	70
1714	**455**	50f. multicoloured	2·50	1·60
1715	**455**	150f. multicoloured	7·00	4·50

456 Anniversary Emblem

2001. 50th Anniversary of Radio Kuwait.

1716	**456**	25f. multicoloured	1·10	70
1717	**456**	50f. multicoloured (vert)	2·50	1·60
1718	**456**	150f. multicoloured (vert)	7·00	4·50

457 Mosque and Colours

2001. Al Aqsa Uprising. Multicoloured.

1719	25f. Type **457**	1·10	70
1720	50f. Mosque dome and uprising	2·50	1·60
1721	150f. Mosque dome and uprising (different)	7·00	4·50

458 Children encircling Globe

2001. United Nations Year of Dialogue among Civilisations.

1722	**458**	25f. multicoloured	1·10	70
1723	**458**	50f. multicoloured	2·50	1·60
1724	**458**	150f. multicoloured	7·00	4·50

459 Script

2001. Heritage Management Foundation. Multicoloured.

1725	25f. Type **459**	1·10	70
1726	50f. Sheikh Abdulla	2·50	1·60
1727	150f. Sheikh Jabir	7·00	4·50

460 Stylised Tree with Nine Leaves

2001. 25th Anniversary of Tourism Enterprise. Multicoloured.

1728	25f. Type **460**	1·10	70
1729	50f. Twig with six long leaves	2·50	1·60
1730	100f. Many-branched tree with falling leaves	5·25	3·50
1731	150f. Tree with two branches	7·00	4·50
MS1732	60×80 mm. 250f. As Nos. 1728/1731. Imperf	18·00	18·00

461 Face covered by Hands

2001. Human Rights. Multicoloured.

1733	25f. Type **461**	1·10	70
1734	50f. Faces and barbed wire (horiz)	2·50	1·60
1735	150f. Chains, globe and child's face (horiz)	7·00	4·50

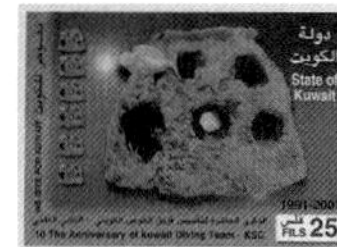
462 Metal Artefact

2001. Tenth Anniversary of Scientific Diving Team. Multicoloured.

1736	25f. Type **462**	1·10	70
1737	50f. Divers	2·50	1·60
1738	150f. Turtle (vert)	7·00	4·50

463 Original Building Facade

2002. 50th Anniversary of National Bank. Multicoloured.

1739	50f. Type **463**	1·10	70
1740	100f. Modern building	2·50	1·60
1741	150f. Anniversary emblem and camels	7·00	4·50

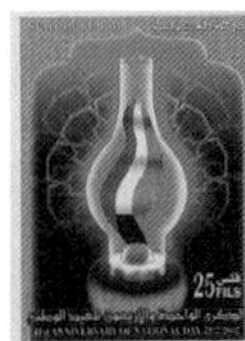
464 Flag enclosed Lamp

2002. 41st Anniversary of National Day. Multicoloured.

1742	**464**	25f. multicoloured	1·10	70
1743	**464**	50f. multicoloured	2·50	1·60
1744	**464**	150f. multicoloured	7·00	4·50

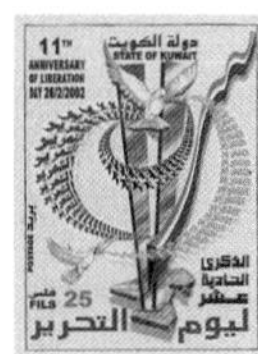
465 Monument, Doves, Flag and Map

2002. 11th Anniversary of Liberation Day. Multicoloured.

1745	**465**	25f. multicoloured	1·10	70
1746	**465**	50f. multicoloured	2·50	1·60
1747	**465**	150f. multicoloured	7·00	4·50

466 Camel Caravan

2002. Arab Nomads. Multicoloured.

1748	**466**	25f. multicoloured	1·10	70
1749	**466**	50f. multicoloured	2·50	1·60
1750	**466**	150f. multicoloured	7·00	4·50

467 Emblem and Gas Tower

2002. Rehabilitation of Al-Qurain Landfill Site. Multicoloured.

1751	**467**	25f. multicoloured	1·10	70
1752	**467**	50f. multicoloured	2·50	1·60
1753	**467**	150f. multicoloured	7·00	4·50

468 Northern Lapwing

2002. Kuwait Scientific Centre. Multicoloured.

1754	25f. Type **468**	1·80	1·80
1755	25f. Spur-winged plover	1·80	1·80
1756	25f. Otter	1·80	1·80
1757	25f. Crocodile	1·80	1·80
1758	25f. Fennec fox	1·80	1·80
1759	25f. Caracal	1·80	1·80
1760	25f. Protoreaster	1·80	1·80
1761	25f. Sepia	1·80	1·80
1762	25f. Nurse shark	1·80	1·80
1763	25f. Lionfish	1·80	1·80
1764	25f. Kestrel	1·80	1·80
1765	25f. Fruit bat	1·80	1·80
1766	50f. Centre building (45×27 mm)	3·50	3·50
MS1767	80×60 mm. 250f. Dock and building. Imperf	18·00	18·00

469 Adult and Child's Hands

2002. Tenth Anniversary of Social Development Office. Multicoloured.

1768	**469**	25f. multicoloured	1·10	70
1769	**469**	50f. multicoloured	2·50	1·60

470 Engineering Symbols

2002. 40th Anniversary of Society of Engineers. Multicoloured.

1770	**470**	25f. multicoloured	1·10	70
1771	**470**	50f. multicoloured	2·50	1·60
1772	**470**	150f. multicoloured	7·00	4·50

471 Anniversary Emblems

2002. 25th Anniversary of Science Foundation. Multicoloured.

1773	25f. Type **471**	1·10	70
1774	50f. Building	2·50	1·60
1775	150f. Map of Kuwait (vert)	7·00	4·50

472 Organisation Emblem

2002. International Year of Volunteers. KNPVC (welfare organisation).

1776	**472**	25f. multicoloured	1·10	70
1777	**472**	50f. multicoloured	2·50	1·60
1778	**472**	150f. multicoloured	7·00	4·50

473 Engineering Workers

2002. 20th Anniversary of Professional Education Programme. Multicoloured.

1779	25f. Type **473**	1·10	70
1780	50f. Theatre nurse	2·50	1·60
1781	100f. Man checking dials	4·50	3·00
1782	150f. Flag and '20'	7·00	4·50
1783	250f. Emblem	11·00	7·25

474 Traditional Boat

2003

1784	**474**	100f. multicoloured	4·25	2·75

475 Greek Ruins, Failaka Island

2003. 42nd Anniversary of National Day. Multicoloured.

1785	**475**	25f. multicoloured	1·40	90
1786	**475**	50f. multicoloured	2·50	1·60
1787	**475**	150f. multicoloured	7·25	4·75

476 Bureau Emblem and Boat

2003. The Martyrs' Bureau. Multicoloured.

1788	25f. Type **476**	85	70
1789	50f. National Flag on Qarow Island	1·40	1·40
1790	150f. Fingerprint on stone	4·00	3·50
1791	350f. '746' and map	11·00	9·00

477 Leafless Tree and Dunes

2003. International Day to Combat Desertification. Multicoloured.

1792	25f. Type **477**	1·10	70
1793	50f. Log in valley	2·00	1·30
1794	150f. Oasis	5·50	3·50

478 Statuette

2003. Kuwait Design. Multicoloured.

1795	25f. Type **478**	1·40	90
1796	100f. Statuette (different)	4·25	2·75
1797	150f. Group of statuettes	5·50	3·50

479 '43' and Star

2003. 43rd Anniversary of Commercial Bank. Multicoloured.

1798	25f. Type **479**	1·10	70
1799	50f. '43' and original building	2·00	1·30
1800	150f. '43' and modern building	5·50	3·50

480 Stylised Family

2004. Tenth Anniversary of Awqaf Public Foundation. Multicoloured.

1801	50f. Type **480**	2·00	1·30
1802	100f. Hand	4·00	2·50
1803	150f. Scholar and minaret	5·50	3·50

481 Palm Tree as Flag

2004. 43rd Anniversary of National Day. Multicoloured.

1804	25f. Type **481**	1·10	70
1805	50f. Pearl shell as flag and '43' as pearl	2·00	1·30
1806	150f. Flags flying above gateway	5·50	3·50
1807	350f. Boat and towers	12·50	8·00

482 Ground Crew and Boeing 727

2004. 50th Anniversary of Kuwait Airways. Multicoloured.

1808	25f. Type **482**	85	55
1809	50f. Aircraft and maintenance crew	1·40	90
1810	75f. Airbus A340 in flight	2·20	1·40
1811	100f. Airbus A340 on runway	2·75	1·80
1812	125f. Boeing 747 and support trucks	4·25	2·75
1813	150f. Passengers embarking	4·75	3·00

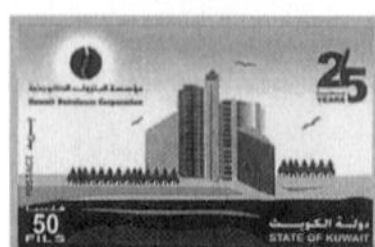

483 Building, Trees and Water

2005. 25th Anniversary of Petroleum Corporation. Multicoloured.

1814	50f. Type **483**	1·40	1·10
1815	75f. At sunset	2·20	1·70
1816	125f. At night	3·75	2·75

484 Flag and Sheikhs

2005. 14th Anniversary of Liberation. Multicoloured.

1817	50f. Type **484**	1·40	1·10
1818	150f. Flags and sheikhs (different)	4·25	3·25

485 Emblem and Sheikhs

2005. 44th Anniversary of National Day. Multicoloured.

1819	75f. Type **485**	2·20	1·70
1820	125f. Sheikhs (different)	3·75	2·75

486 Emblem

2005. 50th Anniversary of Technical Education.

1821	**486**	25f. multicoloured	85	65
1822	**486**	50f. multicoloured	1·40	1·10
1823	**486**	75f. multicoloured	2·20	1·70
1824	**486**	125f. multicoloured	3·75	2·75

487 Support Workers and Vehicles

2005. Civil Defence. Multicoloured.

1825	50f. Type **487**	1·10	1·00
1826	75f. Support workers and children	1·70	1·50
1827	125f. Support workers carrying stretcher	2·75	2·50

488 Flag

2005. Flags and Emblems. Multicoloured. (a) Ordinary gum. (i) 30×20 mm.

1828	200f. Type **488** (ships and harbour flag)	4·25	3·75
1829	250f. 1940 (official flag)	5·50	5·00

(ii) 40×30 mm.

1830	350f. 1903 (state emblems)	7·00	6·25
1831	500f. 1941–1950 (ruling family flag)	11·00	10·00

(iii) 60×30 mm.

1832	1d. Two flags (Sheikh Mubarak Al-Sabah (1914))	21·00	19·00
1833	1d. 1956–1962 and 1921–1940 (state emblems)	21·00	19·00

(b) Self-adhesive. (i) 39×34 mm.

1834	100f. 1956–1962 (official emblem)	3·75	3·25
1835	100f. 1921–1940 (official emblem)	3·75	3·25
1836	175f. Sheikh Mubarak Al-Sabah flag (1914)	6·50	5·75
1837	175f. Sheikh Mubarak Al-Sabah flag (1914) (different)	6·50	5·75
1838	175f. Sheikh Mubarak Al-Sabah flag (1914) (different)	6·50	5·75
1839	350f. 1866 (special event flag)	12·50	11·50
1840	350f. 1903 (special event flag)	12·50	11·50
1841	350f. 1921 (special event flag)	12·50	11·50
1842	500f. 1921–1940 (ruling family flag)	18·00	16·00
1843	500f. 1921–1940 (different)	18·00	16·00
1844	500f. 1941–1950 (different)	18·00	16·00

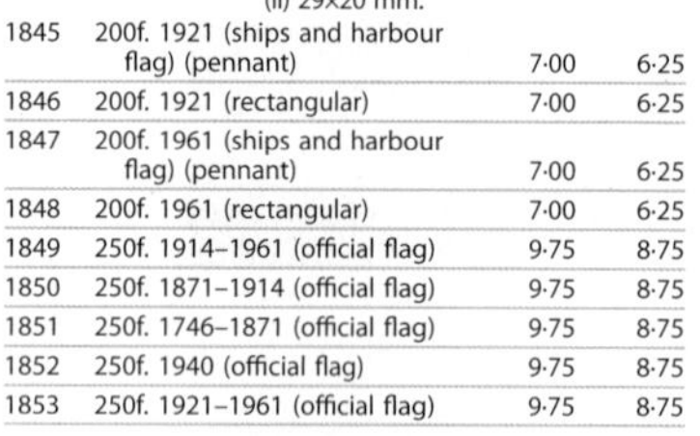

(ii) 29×20 mm.

1845	200f. 1921 (ships and harbour flag) (pennant)	7·00	6·25
1846	200f. 1921 (rectangular)	7·00	6·25
1847	200f. 1961 (ships and harbour flag) (pennant)	7·00	6·25
1848	200f. 1961 (rectangular)	7·00	6·25
1849	250f. 1914–1961 (official flag)	9·75	8·75
1850	250f. 1871–1914 (official flag)	9·75	8·75
1851	250f. 1746–1871 (official flag)	9·75	8·75
1852	250f. 1940 (official flag)	9·75	8·75
1853	250f. 1921–1961 (official flag)	9·75	8·75

489 Children riding Pegasus

2006. 20th Anniversary of *Al-Arabi Al Saghir* Children's Magazine. Multicoloured, background colour given.

1854	**489**	100f. blue	2·20	2·00
1855	**489**	200f. yellow	4·50	4·00
1856	**489**	350f. red	7·75	7·00

490 Heart Shape

2006. 45th Anniversary of National Day. Multicoloured, background colour given.

1857	**490**	75f. ultramarine	1·70	1·50
1858	**490**	200f. green	4·50	4·00

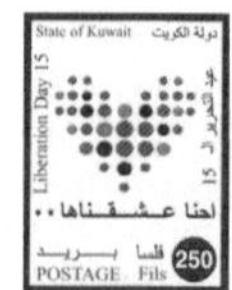

491 Heart Shape

2006. 15th Anniversary of Liberation. Multicoloured, background colour given.

1859	**491**	250f. black	5·50	5·00
1860	**491**	350f. red	7·75	7·00

No. 1861 and T **492** have been left for single stamp not yet received.

2006. 25th Anniversary of Gulf Co-operation Council. As T **166**. Multicoloured.

MS1862	165×105 mm. 500f. Flags of member states. Imperf	34·00	30·00

Stamps of similar designs were issued by Bahrain, Oman, Qatar, Saudi Arabia and United Arab Emirates.

493 Annual Meeting of the IDB Group

494 Coin

495 Coin

496 Coin

497 Coin

498 Coin

499 Coin

500 Coin

501 Coin

502 Coin

503 Coin

504 Coin

505 Coin

506 Coin

507 Coin

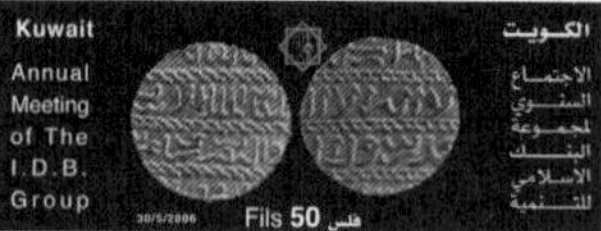

508 Coin

509 Coin

510 Coin

511 Coin

512 Coin

513 Coin

514 Coin

515 Annual Meeting of the IDB Group

516 Coin

517 Coin

518 Coin

519 Coin

520 Coin

521 Coin

522 Coin

523 Coin

524 Coin

525 Coin

526 Coin

527 Coin

528 Coin

529 Coin

530 Coin

531 Coin

2006. Islamic Development Meeting.

1863	**493**	50f. multicoloured	1·40	1·30
1864	**494**	50f. multicoloured	1·40	1·30
1865	**495**	50f. multicoloured	1·40	1·30
1866	**496**	50f. multicoloured	1·40	1·30
1867	**497**	50f. multicoloured	1·40	1·30
1868	**498**	50f. multicoloured	1·40	1·30
1869	**499**	50f. multicoloured	1·40	1·30
1870	**500**	50f. multicoloured	1·40	1·30
1871	**501**	50f. multicoloured	1·40	1·30
1872	**502**	50f. multicoloured	1·40	1·30
1873	**503**	50f. multicoloured	1·40	1·30
1874	**504**	50f. multicoloured	1·40	1·30
1875	**505**	50f. multicoloured	1·40	1·30
1876	**506**	50f. multicoloured	1·40	1·30
1877	**507**	50f. multicoloured	1·40	1·30
1878	**508**	50f. multicoloured	1·40	1·30
1879	**509**	50f. multicoloured	1·40	1·30
1880	**510**	50f. multicoloured	1·40	1·30
1881	**511**	50f. multicoloured	1·40	1·30
1882	**512**	50f. multicoloured	1·40	1·30
1883	**513**	50f. multicoloured	1·40	1·30
1884	**514**	50f. multicoloured	1·40	1·30
1885	**515**	150f. multicoloured	4·25	3·75
1886	**516**	150f. multicoloured	4·25	3·75
1887	**517**	150f. multicoloured	4·25	3·75
1888	**518**	150f. multicoloured	4·25	3·75
1889	**519**	150f. multicoloured	4·25	3·75
1890	**520**	150f. multicoloured	4·25	3·75
1891	**521**	150f. multicoloured	4·25	3·75
1892	**522**	150f. multicoloured	4·25	3·75
1893	**523**	150f. multicoloured	4·25	3·75
1894	**524**	150f. multicoloured	4·25	3·75
1895	**525**	150f. multicoloured	4·25	3·75
1896	**526**	150f. multicoloured	4·25	3·75
1897	**527**	150f. multicoloured	4·25	3·75
1898	**528**	150f. multicoloured	4·25	3·75
1899	**529**	150f. multicoloured	4·25	3·75
1900	**530**	150f. multicoloured	4·25	3·75
1901	**531**	150f. multicoloured	4·25	3·75
1902	-	150f. multicoloured	4·25	3·75
1903	-	150f. multicoloured	4·25	3·75
1904	-	150f. multicoloured	4·25	3·75
1905	-	150f. multicoloured	4·25	3·75
1906	-	150f. multicoloured	4·25	3·75

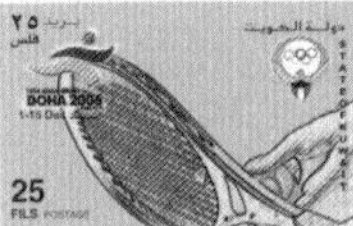
537 Tennis

2006. DOHA 2006. 15th Asian Games. Multicoloured.

1907	25f. Type **537**	85	75
1908	50f. Ten pin bowling	1·40	1·30
1909	150f. Shooting	4·00	3·50
1910	250f. Equestrian	6·50	5·75
1911	350f. Fencing	9·25	8·25

538 Emblem

2007. Campaign to Fight Hypertension. Multicoloured, background colour given.

1912	**538**	50f. green	1·40	1·30
1913	**538**	150f. vermilion	4·00	3·50
1914	**538**	350f. brown	9·25	8·25

539 Ship

2007. 46th Anniversary of National Day.

1915	**539**	25f. multicoloured	85	75
1916	**539**	50f. multicoloured	1·40	1·30
1917	**539**	150f. multicoloured	4·50	4·00

540 Flag and Doves

2007. 16th Anniversary of Liberation Day.

1918	**540**	25f. multicoloured	85	75
1919	**540**	50f. multicoloured	1·40	1·30
1920	**540**	150f. multicoloured	4·50	4·00

541 Emblem

2006. 40th Anniversary of Kuwait University. Multicoloured, background colour given.

1921	**541**	25f. lavender	85	75
1922	**541**	50f. yellow	1·40	1·30
1923	**541**	150f. green	4·00	3·50
1924	**541**	350f. rose	9·25	8·25

542 Anniversary Emblem

2007. 50th Anniversary of Kuwait Oil Tanker Company.

1925	**542**	25f. multicoloured	85	80
1926	**542**	50f. multicoloured	1·50	1·40
1927	**542**	150f. multicoloured	4·00	3·75

543 Early Coin

2007. First Anniversary of Philatelic and Numismatic Society. Multicoloured.

1928	25f. Type **543**	85	80
1929	50f. 1959 40n. stamp (As Type **21**)	1·50	1·40
1930	150f. Early coin and stamp (60×35 mm)	4·00	3·75

544 Women voting

2008. 47th National Day. Multicoloured.

1931	25f. Type **544**	85	80

1932	150f. Symbols of Kuwait (horiz)	4·75	4·25

545 '17' and Hand holding Map of Kuwait

2008. 17th Anniversary of Liberation Day.

1933	**545**	25f. multicoloured	85	80
1934	**545**	50f. multicoloured	1·70	1·60

546 Stylised Gymnasts and Games Emblem

2008. First GCC Women's Sports Tournament, Kuwait. Designs showing stylised women athletes. Multicoloured.

1935	25f. Type **546**	85	80
1936	25f. Runners	85	80
1937	25f. Rifle shooting	85	80
1938	25f. Basketball	85	80
1939	25f. Table tennis	85	80
1940	150f. Games emblem and stylised athletes, orange background (horiz)	5·00	4·50
1941	150f. As No. 1940, red background (horiz)	5·00	4·50
1942	150f. As No. 1940, violet background (horiz)	5·00	4·50
1943	150f. As No. 1940, green background (horiz)	5·00	4·50
1944	150f. As No. 1940, mauve background (horiz)	5·00	4·50

2008. 45th Anniversary of Diplomatic Relations with Romania

1945	150f. Anniversary emblem and man working on boat	7·25	6·75
1946	150f. Woman weaving and anniversary emblem	7·25	6·75
1946a	150f. Woman weaving and hand	7·25	6·75
1946b	150f. Hand and man working on boat	7·25	6·75
1946c	150f. Woman weaving and partial emblem	7·25	6·75
1946d	150f. Partial emblem and man working on boat	7·25	6·75
MS1946e	133×100 mm. 500f. Clasped hands (vert)	26·00	24·00

Type **547** is unavailable.

548 Drummer and Procession

2008. Old Kuwait. Designs showing paintings. Multicoloured.

1947	25f. Type **548**	60	55
1948	50f. Two drummers and men caulking boat	1·20	1·10
1949	100f. Covered street	2·40	2·20
1950	150f. Funfair	3·50	3·25
1951	200f. Minarets and male figure	4·75	4·50
1952	250f. Donkey riders and wooden gateway	6·00	5·50
1953	350f. Shoreline and boats disembarking	8·50	7·75
1954	500f. Stone gateway and male figures	12·00	11·00

549 Emir Sabah Al Ahmad Al Jabir Al Sabah and Flags

2009. 48th National Day.

1955	**549**	25f. multicoloured	1·10	1·00
1956	**549**	50f. multicoloured	2·10	2·00
1957	**549**	150f. multicoloured	6·25	6·00
MS1958		100×66 mm. 250f. As Type **549**. Imperf	11·50	10·50

550 Symbols of Liberation

2009. 18th Anniversary of Liberation Day.

1959	**550**	25f. multicoloured	1·10	1·00
1960	**550**	50f. multicoloured	2·10	2·00
1961	**550**	150f. multicoloured	6·25	8·00

2009. Kuwait Finance House. Multicoloured.

1962	25f. Globe and 'The World....is Your Home'	1·10	1·00
1963	50f. As No. 1962	2·10	2·00
1964	150f. As No. 1962	6·25	6·00

Type **551** is unavailable.

2009. 50th Anniversary Of Chamber of Commerce and Industry. Multicoloured.

1965	25f. Buildings and '50'	1·10	1·00
1966	50f. Dhow and '50'	2·10	2·00
1967	150f. Cogs and '50'	6·25	6·00

Type **552** is unavailable.

553 Falcon, Flowers and Buildings

2010. National Day. Multicoloured.

1968	25f. Type **553**	1·20	1·10
1969	50f. Sheikh Nawaf, Sheikh Sabah, falcon and flowers	2·30	2·20
1970	150f. Sheikh Nawaf, Sheikh Sabah and flag as rainbow	7·00	6·75

554 Celebratory Parade

2010. 19th Anniversary of Liberation Day. Children's Art. Multicoloured.

1971	25f. Type **554**	1·20	1·10
1972	50f. Girl wearing flag as dress	2·30	2·20
1973	150f. Two girls wearing dresses in National Colours	7·00	6·75

555 Emblem

2010. Jerusalem. Capital of Arab Culture 2009.

1974	**555**	25f. multicoloured	1·20	1·10
1975	**555**	50f. multicoloured	2·30	2·20

556 'KUWAIT e GATE'

2010. Kuwait E-Gate. 'Everything Kuwait' Smart 'Phone Application.

1976	**556**	25f. multicoloured	1·20	1·10
1977	**556**	50f. multicoloured	2·30	2·20
1978	**556**	150f. multicoloured	7·00	6·75

557 '50'

2010. 50th Anniversary of OPEC.

1979	**557**	25f. multicoloured	1·20	1·10
1980	**557**	50f. multicoloured	2·30	2·20
1981	**557**	150f. multicoloured	7·00	6·75

558 '20' enclosing Sheikh Nawaf

2011. 50th Anniversary of National Day and 20th Anniversary of Liberation Day. Multicoloured.

1982	25f. Type **558**	1·20	1·10
1983	25f. Sheikh Nawaf, Sheikh Sabah, dove, '20' and flag (41×26 mm)	1·20	1·10
1984	25f. '50' enclosing Sheikh Sabah	1·20	1·10
1985	25f. '50' enclosing Sheikh Sabah (41×26 mm)	1·20	1·10
MS1986	117×68 mm. 250f. Combined emblems (40×54 mm)	12·50	12·00

559 '50'

2011. 50th Anniversary of Commercial Bank of Kuwait. Multicoloured.

1987	50f. Type **559**	2·30	2·20
1988	50f. '50', building and silver background	2·30	2·20
1989	50f. '50', building (different) and gold background	2·30	2·20
1990	50f. '50' and Kuwait Towers	2·30	2·20
1991	50f. '50', skyline and trophy	2·30	2·20

560 Emblems

561 Emblems

562 Emblems

563 Emblems

564 Emblems

565 Emblems

566 Emblems

567 Emblems

568 Emblems

569 Emblems

2011. 15th General Assembly of Arab Towns Organisation. Cities of Knowledge and Future of Youth.

1992	**560**	50f. multicoloured	2·30	2·20
1993	**561**	50f. multicoloured	2·30	2·20
1994	**562**	50f. multicoloured	2·30	2·20
1995	**563**	50f. multicoloured	2·30	2·20
1996	**564**	50f. multicoloured	2·30	2·20
1997	**565**	50f. multicoloured	2·30	2·20
1998	**566**	50f. multicoloured	2·30	2·20
1999	**567**	50f. multicoloured	2·30	2·20
2000	**568**	50f. multicoloured	2·30	2·20
2001	**569**	50f. multicoloured	2·30	2·20
MS2002		110×70 mm. 250f. As Type **562** (54×40 mm)	12·50	12·00

570 Race Track

2011. 50th Anniversary of Kuwait Fund for Arab Economic Development. Multicoloured.

2003	150f. Type **570**	7·00	6·75
2004	150f. Kadhdhoo airport	7·00	6·75
2005	150f. Banjul International Airport	7·00	6·75
2006	150f. Oil pipeline	7·00	6·75
2007	150f. Oil platform	7·00	6·75
2008	150f. Sorting plants on conveyor belt	7·00	6·75
2009	150f. Vegetable garden	7·00	6·75
2010	150f. '50'	7·00	6·75
2011	150f. Water tank and irrigating plants	7·00	6·75
2012	150f. Hydro-electric dam	7·00	6·75
2013	150f. New roadway	7·00	6·75
2014	150f. Lake	7·00	6·75
2015	150f. As No. 2010	7·00	6·75
2016	150f. Petroleum installation	7·00	6·75
2017	150f. Cranes and port	7·00	6·75
2018	150f. Raised highway	7·00	6·75
2019	150f. Two highways intersecting by bridge	7·00	6·75
2020	150f. Highway on piles, through forested landscape	7·00	6·75
2021	150f. Dam (different)	7·00	6·75
2022	150f. Highway on viaduct	7·00	6·75

571 Mubarak bin Sabah Al-Sabah 1896–1915

2011. 51st Anniversary of National Day. Multicoloured.

MS2023	270×78 mm. 100f.×10, (From right to left in chronological order) Type **571**; Jaber II Al-Mubarak Al-Sabah, 1915–1917; Salim Al-Mubarak Al-Sabah, 1917–1921; Ahmad Al-Jaber Al-Sabah, 1921–1950; (Fom left to right in chronological order) Abdullah III Al-Salim Al-Sabah, 1950–1965; Sabah III Al-Salim Al-Sabah, 1965–1977; Jaber III al-Ahmad al-Jaber al-Sabah, 1977–2006; Saad Al-Abdullah Al-Salim Al-Sabah, 15–24 January 2006; Sheikh Nawaf Al-Ahmad Al-Jaber Al-Sabah, Crown Prince of Kuwait; Sabah IV Al-Ahmad Al-Jaber Al-Sabah, 2006–	48·00	46·00
MS2024	250×170 mm. 150f.×10, Mubarak bin Sabah Al-Sabah; Jaber II Al-Mubarak Al-Sabah; Abdullah III Al-Salim Al-Sabah (80×30 mm); Sabah III Al-Salim Al-Sabah; Jaber III al-Ahmad al-Jaber al-Sabah; Salim Al-Mubarak Al-Sabah; Ahmad Al-Jaber Al-Sabah; Sheikhs and Emirs of Kuwait (80×30 mm); Saad Al-Abdullah Al-Salim Al-Sabah; Sabah IV Al-Ahmad Al-Jaber Al-Sabah	75·00	70·00

572 Clock Tower, Amari Palace

2012. 21st Anniversary of Liberation Day. Multicoloured.

MS2025	50f.×10, Type **572**; Kuwait Towers; Liberation Tower; Kuwait National Assembly Building; Mother and child playing by lamplight; Girl and doll; Kuwait Chamber of Commerce; Liberation Tower (different); Water Reservoirs; Ship at dock	24·00	23·00

573 Emblems

574 Emblems

575 Emblems

576 Emblems

577 Emblems

578 Emblems

579 Emblems

580 Emblems

581 Emblems

582 Emblems

583 Emblems

584 Emblems

585 Emblems

586 Emblems

587 Emblems

588 Emblems

589 Emblems

590 Emblems

591 Emblems

592 Emblems

2012. 50th (2010) Anniversary of Kuwait in UNESCO.

2026	**573**	150f. multicoloured	7·00	6·75
2027	**574**	150f. multicoloured	7·00	6·75
2028	**575**	150f. multicoloured	7·00	6·75
2029	**576**	150f. multicoloured	7·00	6·75
2030	**577**	150f. multicoloured	7·00	6·75
2031	**578**	150f. multicoloured	7·00	6·75
2032	**579**	150f. multicoloured	7·00	6·75
2033	**580**	150f. multicoloured	7·00	6·75
2034	**581**	150f. multicoloured	7·00	6·75
2035	**582**	150f. multicoloured	7·00	6·75
2036	**583**	150f. multicoloured	7·00	6·75
2037	**584**	150f. multicoloured	7·00	6·75
2038	**585**	150f. multicoloured	7·00	6·75
2039	**586**	150f. multicoloured	7·00	6·75
2040	**587**	150f. multicoloured	7·00	6·75
2041	**588**	150f. multicoloured	7·00	6·75
2042	**589**	150f. multicoloured	7·00	6·75
2043	**590**	150f. multicoloured	7·00	6·75
2044	**591**	150f. multicoloured	7·00	6·75
2045	**592**	150f. multicoloured	7·00	6·75

593 Women and Coffee Pot

2012. Kuwait Society for the Disabled. Multicoloured.

2046	50f. Type **593**	2·30	2·20
2047	50f. Houses, women and children	2·30	2·20
2048	50f. Emir Sabah greeting child in wheechair	2·30	2·20
2049	50f. Teacher in wheelchair teaching art class	2·30	2·20
2050	50f. Girl with pigtails, two boys and boy wearing glasses	2·30	2·20
2051	50f. Children playing, sunshine and purple tree	2·30	2·20
2052	50f. Children and women on the beach	2·30	2·20
2053	50f. Watching parade	2·30	2·20
2054	50f. Child and 'star and crescent'	2·30	2·20
2055	50f. Couple under green flowers	2·30	2·20
2056	50f. Fish enclosing ship	2·30	2·20
2057	50f. Party with cake on table	2·30	2·20
2058	50f. Flags and dancers	2·30	2·20
2059	50f. Boy helping blind man to cross the road	2·30	2·20
2060	50f. Family at table	2·30	2·20
2061	50f. Fish and shells on blue background, insects on pink background	2·30	2·20
2062	50f. Women and water	2·30	2·20
2063	50f. Soldiers waving at car painted as flag	2·30	2·20
2064	50f. Woman carrying tray in doorway of room full of people	2·30	2·20
2065	50f. Ship, house, tree and people gardening	2·30	2·20

594 Sheikh Sabah Al-Ahmed Al-Jaber Al-Sabah and Ban Ki-Moon

2013. 50th Anniversary of Kuwait–UN Partnership. United Nations Day.

2066	50f. Type **594**	2·30	2·20
2067	50f. Anniversary emblem, UN and Kuwait emblems	2·30	2·20
2068	50f. Sheikh Sabah Al-Ahmed Al-Jaber Al-Sabah at UN	2·30	2·20
2069	50f. Sheikh Sabah Al-Ahmed Al-Jaber Al-Sabah speaking at UN	2·30	2·20
2070	50f. Building and anniversary emblem	2·30	2·20
2071	50f. Kuwait sail-boat	2·30	2·20
2072	50f. Kuwait Towers	2·30	2·20
2073	50f. Emblems	2·30	2·20
2074	50f. UN Building and flags (60×30 mm)	2·30	2·20
2075	50f. UN emblems (60×30 mm)	2·30	2·20

595 Emblem

2014. 53rd Anniversary of National Day. Multicoloured.

2076	35f. Emblem	1·60	1·50
2077	35f. Signing treaty	1·60	1·50
2078	35f. National Emblem	1·60	1·50
2079	35f. Clock tower	1·60	1·50
2080	35f. Landmarks	1·60	1·50
2081	35f. Building	1·60	1·50
2082	35f. Aerial view	1·60	1·50
2083	35f. '25'	1·60	1·50
2084	35f. Water towers	1·60	1·50
2085	35f. Dhow	1·60	1·50

596 Clouds and Emblem

2014. 23rd Anniversary of Liberation Day. Multicoloured.

2086	35f. Blue sky	1·60	1·50
2087	35f. Tanks and armoury	1·60	1·50
2088	35f. National Emblem	1·60	1·50
2089	35f. Fire	1·60	1·50
2090	35f. Liberation Tower	1·60	1·50
2091	35f. 'FREE KUWAIT'	1·60	1·50
2092	35f. Armoured vehicle	1·60	1·50
2093	35f. '26'	1·60	1·50
2094	35f. Helicopters	1·60	1·50
2095	35f. Burning oilfields	1·60	1·50

597 Anniversary Emblem

2014. 19th GCC Stamp Exhibition. Multicoloured.

MS2096 25f.×10, As Type **597**×10	1·20	1·10

598 Sheikh Abdullah Al Jabir Al Sabah and Students

2014. Sheikh Abdullah Al Jabir Al Sabah. Reformer of Culture and Education, UNESCO 2014–2015. Multicoloured.

2097	50f. Type **598**	2·30	2·20
2098	50f. Addressing seated children	2·30	2·20
2099	50f. Opening new school	2·30	2·20
2100	50f. Eating with children	2·30	2·20
2101	50f. Seated wearing formal clothes	2·30	2·20
2102	50f. Giving prizes	2·30	2·20
2103	50f. With female students	2·30	2·20
2104	50f. Leading parade with sword drawn	2·30	2·20
2105	50f. Greeting scout	2·30	2·20
2106	50f. Seated wearing formal clothes (different) (60×90 mm)	2·30	2·20

599 '20'

2014. 20th Anniversary of Kuwait Awqaf Public Foundation. Multicoloured.

2107	25f. Type **599**	1·20	1·10
2108	25f. Script	1·20	1·10
2109	25f. '20' (different)	1·20	1·10
2110	25f. Sheikh Nawaf Al-Ahmad Al-Jaber Al-Sabah	1·20	1·10
2111	25f. Sheikh Sabah Al-Ahmed Al-Jaber Al-Sabah	1·20	1·10
2112	25f. Symbols of charity	1·20	1·10
2113	25f. Gold ship, silver tray and glass awards	1·20	1·10
2114	25f. Al Tijaria Tower	1·20	1·10
2115	25f. Kuwait Centre for Autism	1·20	1·10
2116	25f. Script (different)	1·20	1·10

600 Children and Kuwait Towers

2014. International Autism Conference. Multicoloured.

2117	50f. Type **600**	2·30	2·20
2118	50f. 'AUTISM'	2·30	2·20
2119	50f. Kuwait Towers	2·30	2·20
2120	50f. Walls and tower	2·30	2·20
2121	50f. Stylised blue and white towers	2·30	2·20
2122	50f. Fishing from boat	2·30	2·20
2123	50f. Clock tower	2·30	2·20
2124	50f. Figures	2·30	2·20
2125	50f. Figures and Kuwait Towers (sketch)	2·30	2·20
2126	50f. Tent and camel	2·30	2·20

601 Post Tower

2014. Architecture. Multicoloured.

2127	1d. Type **601**	46·00	44·00
2128	1d. Liberation Tower	46·00	44·00

602 Staff Cars (image scaled to 55% of original size)

2014. 22nd Anniversary (2013) of Liberation Day. Multicoloured.

MS2129 50f.×10, Type **602**; Warships; Greeting soldiers (45×30 mm); Parade of tanks (45×30 mm); Marching soldiers (45×30 mm); Helicopter flying National Flag (45×30 mm); Soldiers on parade (45×30 mm); Fly Past (45×30 mm); Military motorcycles on parade (45×30 mm); Patrol boat (45×30 mm)	23·00	23·00

603 Debate

2014. 50th Anniversary of Kuwait Graduate Society. Multicoloured.

2130	50f. Type **603**	2·30	2·30

2131	50f. Anniversary emblem and different scripts	2·30	2·30
2132	50f. Orator wearing uniform (30×40 mm)	2·30	2·30
2133	50f. Emblem and symposium signage (30×40 mm)	2·30	2·30
2134	50f. Emblem and 'Kuwaitis for Jerusalem' (30×40 mm)	2·30	2·30
2135	50f. Emblem and script (30×40 mm)	2·30	2·30
2136	50f. Emblem and sun (30×40 mm)	2·30	2·30
2137	50f. Emblem and drawing of head (30×40 mm)	2·30	2·30
2138	50f. Emblem and publication (30×40 mm)	2·30	2·30
2139	50f. Emblem and jigsaw (30×40 mm)	2·30	2·30

604 Kuwait–Netherlands

2014. 50th Anniversary of Diplomatic Relations with Europe. Multicoloured.

2140	150f. Type **604**	7·00	6·75
2141	150f. Kuwait–Spain	7·00	6·75
2142	150f. Arms of Kuwait	7·00	6·75
2143	150f. Kuwait–Germany	7·00	6·75
2144	150f. Kuwait–Hungary	7·00	6·75
2145	150f. Kuwait–Denmark	7·00	6·75
2146	150f. Kuwait–Greece	7·00	6·75
2147	150f. Kuwait–Turkey	7·00	6·75
2148	150f. Kuwait–Belgium	7·00	6·75
2149	150f. Kuwait–Italy	7·00	6·75

605 Male Dancers

2014. 52nd Anniversary (2013) of Independence. Multicoloured.

MS2150 150f.×10, Type **605**; Greeting children; Male dancers with orange sashes (30×45 mm); Women dancers wearing black costumes with yellow edges (30×45 mm); Male dancers wearing decorated vests (30×45 mm); Women dancers wearing yellow and lilac (30×45 mm); Male dancers wearing yellow vests (30×45 mm); Girls wearing turquoise dresses (30×45 mm); Boys wearing blue (30×45 mm); Girls wearing pink, green and yellow dresses (30×45 mm) 75·00 75·00

606 Constitutional Assembly

2014. 50th Anniversary of Kuwait Constitution. Multicoloured.

2151	500f. Type **606**	16·00	16·00
2152	500f. Speakers	16·00	16·00
2153	500f. Sheikh Sabah Al-Ahmed Al-Jaber Al-Sabah	16·00	16·00
2154	500f. Emir Abdullah Al-Salem Al-Mubarak Al-Sabah	16·00	16·00
2155	500f. Emir Abdullah Al-Salem Al-Mubarak Al-Sabah and delegate	16·00	16·00
2156	500f. Two delgates	16·00	16·00
2157	500f. Emir Abdullah Al-Salem Al-Mubarak Al-Sabah seated	16·00	16·00
2158	500f. Delegates	16·00	16·00
2159	500f. Speakers (different)	16·00	16·00
2160	500f. Emir Abdullah Al-Salem Al-Mubarak Al-Sabah (65×90 mm)	16·00	16·00

607 Emir Sheikh Sabah Ahmed Al-Sabah

2014. Emir Sheikh Sabah Ahmed Al-Sabah

2161	**607**	1d. multicoloured	3·75	3·75
2162	**607**	350f. multicoloured	10·00	10·00
2163	**607**	500f. multicoloured	16·00	16·00
2164	**607**	750f. multicoloured	22·00	22·00

MS2165 140×110 mm. 250f. As Type **607** (120×90 mm) 12·50 12·50

608 Children

2015. 54th Anniversary of Independence. Multicoloured.

MS2166 150f.×4, Type **608**; Male dancers; Women dancers; Boy with National Flag painted on his face 25·00 25·00

609 Abdullah Alhamdan

2015. 24th Anniversary of Liberation Day. Martyrs of Kuwait. Multicoloured.

2167	25f. Type **609**	1·20	1·20
2168	25f. Bassam Sadeq	1·20	1·20
2169	25f. Nawaf Alhashan	1·20	1·20
2170	25f. Abdulhussain Albughbish	1·20	1·20
2171	25f. Muhammad Jaber	1·20	1·20
2172	25f. Jafar Taqi	1·20	1·20
2173	25f. Habib Alsheikh	1·20	1·20
2174	25f. Abdulrasoul Husain	1·20	1·20
2175	25f. Mansour Mansour	1·20	1·20
2176	25f. Faisal Albahar	1·20	1·20
2177	25f. Salem Alkanderi	1·20	1·20
2178	25f. Baqer Almousawi	1·20	1·20
2179	25f. Khalid Alsamhan	1·20	1·20
2180	25f. Nasser Aladwani	1·20	1·20
2181	25f. Mahmoud Aljasem	1·20	1·20
2182	25f. Mubarak Alnout	1·20	1·20
2183	25f. Bader Adulwahab	1·20	1·20
2184	25f. Ghazi Aloutaibi	1·20	1·20
2185	25f. Sabbar Alenezi	1·20	1·20
2186	25f. Saleh Saleh	1·20	1·20
2187	25f. Ahmad Kherallah	1·20	1·20
2188	25f. Ibrahim Meshael	1·20	1·20
2189	25f. Muhammad Attawash	1·20	1·20
2190	25f. Saad Alshammari	1·20	1·20
2191	25f. Hammad Alshammari	1·20	1·20
2192	25f. Khalid Ab'aijan	1·20	1·20
2193	25f. Hamdan Alenezi	1·20	1·20
2194	25f. Jamal Allengawi	1·20	1·20
2195	25f. Anwar Alrefai	1·20	1·20
2196	25f. Warid Jadran	1·20	1·20
2197	25f. Muhammad Alobaid	1·20	1·20
2198	25f. Majed Alkseli	1·20	1·20
2199	25f. Fahad Althaferi	1·20	1·20
2200	25f. Farhan Airuwaili	1·20	1·20
2201	25f. Sahmi Alsubaie	1·20	1·20
2202	25f. Adel Alhaie	1·20	1·20
2203	25f. Abdulaziz Kashaan	1·20	1·20
2204	25f. Mufreh Alenezi	1·20	1·20
2205	25f. Mansour Alkhseli	1·20	1·20
2206	25f. Matar Almadji	1·20	1·20
2207	25f. Sana Alfudari	1·20	1·20
2208	25f. Rashid Althaferi	1·20	1·20
2209	25f. Mussayer Alshammari	1·20	1·20
2210	25f. Abdulrahman Abdullah	1·20	1·20
2211	25f. Muhammad Alenezi	1·20	1·20
2212	25f. Ali Alraihan	1·20	1·20
2213	25f. Ibrahim Abdullah	1·20	1·20
2214	25f. Ali Alsa'baa	1·20	1·20
2215	25f. Wahid Safri	1·20	1·20
2216	25f. Musaed Alaskari	1·20	1·20
2217	25f. Ahmad S Alenezi	1·20	1·20
2218	25f. Ahmad K Alenezi	1·20	1·20
2219	25f. Edris Alshammari	1·20	1·20
2220	25f. Ebrahim Alsubaie	1·20	1·20
2221	25f. Ebrahim Naif	1·20	1·20
2222	25f. Hamed Alshammari	1·20	1·20
2223	25f. Jamal Alsalem	1·20	1·20
2224	25f. Jahal'aan Almutairi	1·20	1·20
2225	25f. Jasem Alfadhli	1·20	1·20
2226	25f. Ahmad Alenezi	1·20	1·20
2227	25f. Khalaf Alenezi	1·20	1·20
2228	25f. Humoud Rashdan	1·20	1·20
2229	25f. Hamad Alsultan	1·20	1·20
2230	25f. Hasan Alfadagh	1·20	1·20
2231	25f. Hasan Alshammari	1·20	1·20
2232	25f. Zakariya Bohamad	1·20	1·20
2233	25f. Refa'ie Almutairi	1·20	1·20
2234	25f. Rajaan Alazmi	1·20	1·20
2235	25f. Ra'ed Sabri	1·20	1·20
2236	25f. Daham Alshammari	1·20	1·20
2237	25f. Diaa Alsayegh	1·20	1·20
2238	25f. Safnan Althaferi	1·20	1·20
2239	25f. Sulaiman Sulaiman	1·20	1·20
2240	25f. Salman Alazmi	1·20	1·20
2241	25f. Salem Alenezi	1·20	1·20
2242	25f. Abdulrahman Abdulrahman	1·20	1·20
2243	25f. Abduljaleel Khaleel	1·20	1·20
2244	25f. Abbas Muhammad	1·20	1·20
2245	25f. Ayed Albraikan	1·20	1·20
2246	25f. Tariq Alfadhli	1·20	1·20
2247	25f. Faleh Althaferi	1·20	1·20
2248	25f. Ghazwan Hawas	1·20	1·20
2249	25f. Obaid Alshammari	1·20	1·20
2250	25f. Abdullah Saleh	1·20	1·20
2251	25f. Abdulkareem Ali	1·20	1·20
2252	25f. Kulaib Farhan	1·20	1·20
2253	25f. Kamil Jabr	1·20	1·20
2254	25f. Fahad Alsabah	1·20	1·20
2255	25f. Fraih Alshammari	1·20	1·20
2256	25f. Fayez Alrashidi	1·20	1·20
2257	25f. Muhammad Alenezi	1·20	1·20
2258	25f. Muhammad Muhammad	1·20	1·20
2259	25f. Muhammad Alaibany	1·20	1·20
2260	25f. Mohsen Alenezi	1·20	1·20
2261	25f. Mut'eb Alshammari	1·20	1·20
2262	25f. Mutlaq Almutairi	1·20	1·20
2263	25f. Mus'heb Mutlaq	1·20	1·20
2264	25f. Meshael Aladwani	1·20	1·20
2265	25f. Mur'ie Alenezi	1·20	1·20
2266	25f. Muhammad Althaydi	1·20	1·20

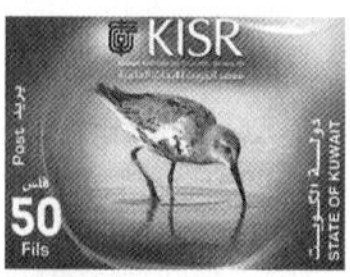

610 Sandpiper

2015. KISR. Kuwait Institute of Scientific Research. Multicoloured.

MS2267 50f.×10, Type **610**; Laboratory equipment; Workers in laboratory; Laboratory grown plants; Fish; Satellite dishes; Institute building; Bottles; Institute headquarters; Institute headquarters (different) 24·00 24·00

OFFICIAL STAMPS

1923. Stamps of India (King George V) optd **KUWAIT SERVICE**.

O1	**56**	½a. green	8·50	70·00
O2	**57**	1a. brown	7·50	29·00
O3	**58**	1½a. brown (No. 163)	5·50	80·00
O4	**59**	2a. lilac	15·00	65·00
O17	**70**	2a. lilac	70·00	£300
O5	**61**	2a.6p. blue	4·50	85·00
O6	**62**	3a. orange	6·50	90·00
O19	**62**	3a. blue	4·50	70·00
O8	**63**	4a. green	5·00	90·00
O20	**71**	4a. green	4·25	£110
O9	**65**	8a. mauve	6·00	£140
O22	**66**	12a. red	50·00	£275
O10	**67**	1r. brown and green	45·00	£225
O11	**67**	2r. red and orange	45·00	£325
O12	**67**	5r. blue and violet	£130	£500
O13	**67**	10r. green and red	£275	£450
O14	**67**	15r. blue	£425	£700

POSTAGE DUE STAMPS

D34

1963

D199	**D34**	1f. brown and black	40	40
D200	**D34**	2f. lilac and black	60	55
D201	**D34**	5f. blue and black	85	40
D202	**D34**	8f. green and black	1·40	65
D203	**D34**	10f. yellow and black	1·80	1·30
D204	**D34**	25f. red and black	3·50	4·00

The above stamps were not sold to the public unused until 1 July 1964.

D51

1965

D276	**D51**	4f. pink and yellow	45	4
D277	**D51**	15f. red and blue	1·70	7
D278	**D51**	40f. blue and green	3·00	1·6
D279	**D51**	50f. green and mauve	4·00	2·3
D280	**D51**	100f. blue and yellow	6·25	4·2

KYRGYZSTAN

Formerly Kirghizia, a constituent republic of th Soviet Union, Kyrgyzstan became independent i 1991. Its capital Frunze reverted to its previous nam of Bishkek.

1992. 100 kopeks = 1 rouble.
1993. 100 tyin = 1 som.

1 Sary-C'helek Nature Reserve

1992

1	**1**	15k. multicoloured	85	6

2 Golden Eagle

1992

2	**2**	50k. multicoloured	1·10	9

3 *Cattle at Issyk-Kule* (G. A. Aitiev)

1992

3	**3**	1r. multicoloured	70	6

4 Carpet and Samovar

1992

4	**4**	1r.50 multicoloured	70	6

5 Cave Paintings

1993. National Monuments. Multicoloured.

5	10k. Type **5**	15	1
6	50k. 11th-century tower, Burana (vert)	20	2
7	1r.+25k. Mausoleum of Manas, Talas (vert)	30	2
8	2r.+50k. Mausoleum, Uzgen	35	3
9	3r. Yurt	40	3
10	5r.+50k. Statue of Manas, Bishkek	70	6
11	9r. Cultural complex, Bishkek	1·10	9
MS12	61×91 mm. 10r. Cockle jewellery	2·75	2·5

The premium on Nos. 7/8 and 10 were used for the financing of a Manas museum.

КЫРГЫЗСТАН 1000

(6)

1993. Nos. 5940, 6073 and 4671 of Russia surch as T **6**.

13	10k. on 1k. brown	55	5
14	20k. on 2k. brown	85	7
15	30k. on 3k. red	1·30	1·1

(7)

1993. Nos. 4672/4673 of Russia surch as T **7**.

16	20t. on 4k. red	85	85
17	30t. on 6k. blue	1·10	1·20

8 Map

1993. Second Anniversary of Independence (No. 18) and First Anniversary of Admission to United Nations (No. 19). Multicoloured.

18	50t. Type **8**	1·40	1·20
19	60t. UN emblem, National Flag and Government Palace, Bishkek (vert)	1·50	1·30

See also No. **MS**35.

9 Komuz

1993. Music.

20	**9**	30t. multicoloured	1·30	1·10

MS21 84×67 mm. 140t. Similar design to Type **9** but with motifs reversed (51×39 mm) 21·00 20·00

10 Dog

1994. New Year. Year of the Dog.

22	**10**	60t. multicoloured	1·40	1·20

11 Adult and Cub

1994. The Snow Leopard. Multicoloured.

23	10t. Type **11**	40	35
24	20t. Lying curled-up	70	60
25	30t. Sitting	1·00	85
26	40t. Head	1·40	1·20

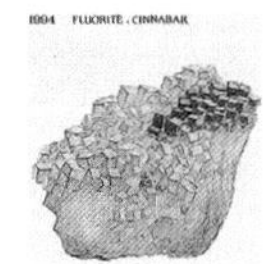

12 Mauve Flowers

1994. Flowers. Multicoloured.

27	1t. Type **12**	15	10
28	3t. Daisies (horiz)	30	25
29	10t. Tulip	70	60
30	16t. Narcissi	85	70
31	20t. Deep pink flower	1·00	85
32	30t. White flower	1·10	95
33	40t. Yellow flower	1·30	1·10

MS34 70×90 mm. 50t. *Trollius altaicum* 1·70 1·60

1994. Third Anniversary of Independence and Second Anniversary of Admission to United Nations. Sheet containing stamps as Nos. 18/19 but with face values changed. Multicoloured.

MS35 110×80 mm. 120t. Type **8**; 130t. As No. 19 9·75 9·50

13 Fluorite

1994. Minerals. Multicoloured.

36	80t. Type **13**	70	60
37	90t. Calcite	85	70
38	100t. Getchellite	1·00	85
39	110t. Barite	1·10	90
40	120t. Auripigment	1·10	95
41	140t. Antimonite	1·40	1·20

MS42 135×95 mm. 200t. Cinnabar 3·75 3·50

14 Turkestan Catfish

1994. Fish. Multicoloured.

43	110t. Type **14**	1·00	85
44	120t. Schmidt's dace	1·10	95
45	130t. Scaleless osman	1·30	1·10
46	140t. Spotted stone loach	1·40	1·20

MS47 82×57 mm. 200t. Common carp (*Cyprinus carpio*) 3·00 2·75

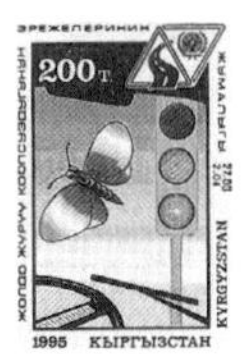

15 Woman with Rug

1995. Traditional Costumes. Multicoloured.

48	50t. Type **15**	70	50
49	50t. Musician	70	50
50	100t. Falconer	1·30	1·10
51	100t. Woman with long plaits	1·30	1·10

16 Butterfly, Traffic Lights and Emblem

1995. Road Safety Week.

52	**16**	200t. multicoloured	1·10	95

17 Brown Bear

1995. Animals. Multicoloured.

53	110t. Type **17**	40	35
54	120t. Snow leopard (horiz)	55	50
55	130t. Golden eagle	70	60
56	140t. Menzbier's marmot (horiz)	85	70
57	150t. Short-toed eagle (horiz)	1·00	85
58	160t. Golden eagle (different)	1·10	95
59	190t. Red fox (horiz)	1·30	1·10

MS60 90×70 mm. 130t. Golden eagle (different); 170t. Argali 2·10 2·00

18 Memorial Flame, Bishkek

1995. 50th Anniversary of End of Second World War. Sheet 90×70 mm.

MS61 **18** 150t. multicoloured 1·70 1·60

19 Aitschurek (wife of Manas)

1995. Millenary of *Manas* (epic poem). Each blue and gold.

62	10t.+5t. Type **19**	45	40
63	20t.+10t. Hoopoe on youth's wrist	60	55
64	30t.+10t. Birth of Semetey, son of Manas	80	70
65	30t.+10t. Woman carrying spear and leading horse	80	70
66	40t.+15t. Warrior astride dead dragon	95	80
67	50t.+15t. Jakyp, father of Manas	1·10	95
68	50t.+15t. Manas on horseback	1·10	95
69	50t.+15t. Seytek, grandson of Manas	1·10	95

MS70 Two sheets. (a) 166×107 mm. 2s.+50t. Saryakbai (Manas singer) cradling injured warrior (37×51 mm). (b) 148×131 mm. 2s.+50t. Sagymbai (Manas singer) (37×51 mm) 7·00 6·75

20 Osprey

1995. Birds. Multicoloured.

71	10t. Type **20**	30	25
72	50t. Tawny eagle	45	40
73	100t. Lammergeier	60	55
74	140t. Saker falcon	80	70
75	150t. Short-toed eagle	95	80
76	200t. Lammergeier	1·20	1·10
77	300t. Golden eagle	1·70	1·50

MS78 90×70 mm. 600t. White-tailed sea eagle (*Haliaeetus albicilla*) (29×40 mm) 3·50 3·00

21 Envelopes on Map and UPU Emblem

1995. Postage Stamp Week.

79	**21**	200t. multicoloured	1·60	1·40

22 State Arms

1995

80	**22**	20t. violet	30	25
81	**22**	50t. blue	60	55
82	**22**	100t. brown	1·10	95
83	**22**	500t. green	2·20	2·00

23 Mare and Foal Galloping

1995. Horses. Multicoloured.

89	10t. Type **23**	15	15
90	50t. Palamino mare and foal (vert)	30	25
91	100t. Brown mare and foal (vert)	60	55
92	140t. Chestnut mare and foal (vert)	80	70
93	150t. Chestnut mare and foal	95	80
94	200t. Grey mare and foal	1·20	1·10
95	300t. Pair of foals	1·60	1·40

MS96 91×71 mm. 600t. Brown and cream (Mongolian wild horses) (*Equus caballus*) (vert) 3·50 3·25

24 Headquarters, New York

1995. 50th Anniversary of United Nations Organisation. Sheet 71×91 mm containing T **24** and similar horiz design. Multicoloured.

MS97 100t. Type **24**; 100t. Rainbow and mountains 1·60 1·40

25 River Nile, Egypt

1995. Natural Wonders of the World. Multicoloured.

98	10t. Type **25**	15	15
99	50t. Mt. Kilimanjaro, Tanzania	30	25
100	100t. Sahara Desert, Algeria	60	55
101	140t. Amazon River, Brazil (vert)	85	70
102	150t. Grand Canyon, USA (vert)	1·10	95
103	200t. Victoria Falls, Zimbabwe (vert)	1·40	1·20
104	350t. Mt. Everest, Nepal	1·70	1·50
105	400t. Niagara Falls, Canada	2·00	1·80

MS106 Two sheets, each 90×70 mm. (a) Gull over Issyk-Kule lake, Kyrgyzstan; (b) Eagle over Issyk-Kule lake 7·75 7·50

No. 98 is wrongly inscribed 'Egipt'.

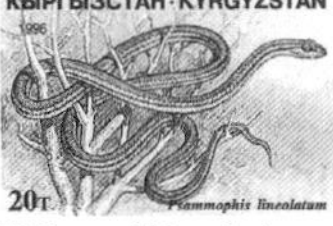

26 Steppe Ribbon Snake

1996. Reptiles. Multicoloured.

107	20t. Type **26**	30	25
108	50t. Fat-tailed panther gecko	45	40
109	50t. Tessellated water snake	45	40
110	100t. Central Asian viper	60	55
111	150t. Arguta	1·10	95
112	200t. Dione snake	1·40	1·20
113	250t. *Asyblepharus* sp. (wrongly inscr 'Asymblepharus')	1·70	1·50

MS114 91×71 mm. 500t. Sand lizard (*Lacerta agilis*) 4·00 3·75

27 Kaufmann's Shovelnose (*Pseudoscphirhyncus kafmanni*)

1996. Save the Aral Sea. Sheet 128×108 mm containing T **27** and similar horiz designs. Multicoloured.

MS115 100t. Caracal (*Felis caracal*); 100t. Aral trout (*Salmo trutta aralensis*); 100t. Striped hyena (*Hyaena hyaena*); 100t. Type **27**; 100t. Pike asp (*Aspiolucius esocinus*) 7·00 6·75

28 Show Jumping and Traditional Horse Race

1996. Olympic Games, Atlanta, USA. Multicoloured.

116	100t.+20t. Type **28**	60	55
117	140t.+30t. Boxing and traditional wrestling match	95	80
118	150t.+30t. Archer and mounted archer shooting at eagle	1·10	95
119	300t.+50t. Judo competitor, ballooning, yachting and water-skiing	1·90	1·60

29 Golden Eagle

1997. Animals. Multicoloured.

120	600t. Type **29**	1·80	1·70
121	600t. Markhor (*Capra falconeri*)	1·80	1·70
122	600t. Argali (*Ovis ammon*)	1·80	1·70

123	600t. Himalayan griffon (*Gyps himalayensis*)	1·80	1·70
124	600t. Asiatic wild ass (*Equus hemionus*)	1·80	1·70
125	600t. Wolf (*Canis lupus*)	1·80	1·70
126	600t. Brown bear (*Ursus arctos*) (wrongly inscr 'arctor')	1·80	1·70
127	600t. Saiga (*Saiga tatarica*)	1·80	1·70

30 Tiger

1998. New Year. Year of the Tiger.

128	**30**	600t. multicoloured	1·70	1·50

31 *Parnassius actius*

1998. Butterflies. Multicoloured.

129	600t. Type **31** (wrongly inscr 'Parnasius')	1·70	1·50
130	600t. *Colias christophi*	1·70	1·50
131	600t. Swallowtail (*Papilio machaon*)	1·70	1·50
132	600t. *Colias thisoa*	1·70	1·50
133	600t. *Parnassius delphius*	1·70	1·50
134	600t. *Parnassius tianschanicus*	1·70	1·50

32 Roe Deer

1998. Animals. Multicoloured.

135	600t. Type **32**	1·70	1·50
136	600t. Osprey (*Pandion haliaetus*)	1·70	1·50
137	600t. Hoopoe (*Upupa epops*)	1·70	1·50
138	600t. White stork (*Ciconia ciconia*)	1·70	1·50
139	1000t. Golden oriole (*Oriolus oriolus*)	2·75	2·40
140	1000t. Snow leopard	2·75	2·40
141	1000t. River kingfisher (*Alcedo althis*)	2·75	2·40
142	1000t. Common kestrel (*Falco tinnunculus*)	2·75	2·40

33 Andrei Dimitriyevich Sakharov (physicist)

1998. 50th Anniversary of Universal Declaration of Human Rights. Multicoloured.

143	10s. Type **33**	1·50	1·40
144	10s. Crowd cheering	1·50	1·40
145	10s. Martin Luther King (civil rights leader)	1·50	1·40
146	10s. Mahatma Gandhi (Indian leader)	1·50	1·40
147	10s. Eleanor Roosevelt (humanitarian)	1·50	1·40

34 Tyrannosaurus

1998. Prehistoric Animals. Multicoloured.

148	10s. Type **34**	1·70	1·50
149	10s. Saurolophus	1·70	1·50
150	10s. Gallimimus (horiz)	1·70	1·50
151	10s. Euoplocephalus (horiz)	1·70	1·50
152	10s. Protoceratops (horiz)	1·70	1·50
153	10s. Velociraptor (horiz)	1·70	1·50

35 Fish

1998. Fauna. Multicoloured.

154	600t. Type **35**	1·20	1·10
155	600t. Fish (with orange tail and fins)	1·20	1·10
156	1000t. Bar-headed goose	1·80	1·60
157	1000t. Chukar partridge	1·80	1·60
158	1000t. Goosander by water	1·80	1·60
159	1000t. Common shelduck swimming	1·80	1·60
160	1000t. Rodent	1·80	1·60
161	1000t. Himalayan snowcock standing on one leg	1·80	1·60

36 Map of Kyrgyzstan

1998. Fifth Anniversary of Constitution.

162	**36**	1000t. multicoloured	2·50	2·30

37 Fox

1999. iBRA'99 International Stamp Exhibition, Nuremberg, Germany. The Corsac Fox (*Vulpes corsac*). Multicoloured.

163	10s. Type **37**	2·00	1·80
164	10s. Fox sleeping	2·00	1·80
165	30s. Two foxes standing	4·50	4·00
166	50s. Mother and cubs	6·75	6·25

38 Fox

1999. The Corsac Fox (*Vulpes corsac*). Multicoloured.

167	10s. Type **38**	1·20	1·10
168	10s. Fox sleeping	1·20	1·10
169	30s. Two foxes standing	3·50	3·25
170	50s. Mother and cubs	5·75	5·25

39 *The Fisherman and the Golden Fish (poem)*

1999. Birth Bicentenary of Alexander Sergeevich Pushkin. Multicoloured.

171	36t. *Ruslan and Lyudmila* (poem)	40	35
172	6s. Type **39**	1·00	90
173	10s. *Tsar Saltan* (poem)	1·60	1·40
174	10s. *The Golden Cockerel* (fairy tale)	1·60	1·40
MS175	74×99 mm. 20s. Pushkin	6·25	6·00

40 State Arms

1999

176	**40**	20t. blue	1·60	1·40

41 Giant Panda (*Ailuropoda melanoleuca*)

1999. China '99 International Stamp Exhibition, Beijing, China. Sheet 90×90 mm containing T **41** and similar horiz design. Multicoloured.

MS180	10s. Type **41**; 15s. Brown wood owl (*Strix leptogrammica*)	5·00	4·75

42 State Flag and Emblem

1999. World Kick Boxing Championships, Bishkek. Multicoloured.

181	3s. Type **42**	1·00	90
182	3s. Emblem on blue background with Cyrillic championship title in red	1·00	90
183	3s. 'WORLD' in green across globe and emblem	1·00	90
MS184	121×62 mm. 6s. 'WORLD' in blue across globe and emblem (different); 6s. 'KICKBOXING' and emblem on yellow rectangle	4·00	3·75

43 Envelopes and Emblem

1999. 125th Anniversary of Universal Postal Union. Multicoloured.

185	3s. Type **43**	1·00	90
186	6s. Aeroplane, envelopes, horseman and emblem	1·80	1·60

44 Anniversary Emblem

2000. 3000th Anniversary of Osh. Sheet 139×109 mm. Multicoloured.

MS187	6s.+25t. Type **44**; 6s.+25t. Ravat Abdullakhan Mosque; 6s.+25t. Tahti Suleiman Mosque; 6s.+25t. Asaf ibn Burhia tower	7·50	7·25

45 Taigan

2000. Asian Dogs. Multicoloured.

188	3s. Type **45**	80	70
189	6s. Tasy	1·00	90
190	6s. Afghan hound	1·00	90
191	10s. Saluki	2·00	1·80
192	15s. Mid-Asian shepherd	2·75	2·50
193	15s. Akbash	2·75	2·50
194	20s. Chow Chow	3·75	3·25
195	25s. Akita-inu	4·75	4·25

46 Minjilkiev

2000. 60th Birth Anniversary of Bulat Minzhilkiev (opera singer).

196	**46**	5s. multicoloured	2·00	1·80

No. 196 is wrongly inscribed '1940–1998' instead of '1940–1997'.

47 Private Cholponbai Tuleberdiev and Medal

2000. 55th Anniversary of End of Second World War. Showing recipients of Gold Star of Hero of Soviet Union Medal. Multicoloured.

197	6s. Type **47**	1·60	1·40
198	6s. Major-General Ivan Vasilievich Panfilov (vert)	1·60	1·40
199	6s. Private Duishenkul Shopokov	1·60	1·40

2000. No. 27 surch **36t.**

200	36t. on 1t. multicoloured	1·20	1·10

49 Wrestling

2000. Olympic Games, Sydney. Multicoloured.

201	1s. Type **49**	40	35
202	3s. Hurdling (vert)	80	70
203	6s. Boxing	1·20	1·10
204	10s. Weightlifting (vert)	1·60	1·40

50 Atai Ogonbaev

2000. Birth Centenary of Atai Ogonbaev (musician).

205	**50**	6s. multicoloured	1·60	1·40

51 Dark Green Fritillary (*Argynnis aglaja*)

2000. Butterflies. Multicoloured.

206	3s. Type **51**	1·00	90
207	3s. Swallowtail (*Papilio machaon*)	1·00	90
208	3s. Peacock (*Inachis io*)	1·00	90
209	3s. Apollo (*Parnassius Apollo*)	1·00	90
210	3s. Small tortoiseshell (*Aglais urticae*)	1·00	90
211	3s. *Colias thisoa*	1·00	90

52 Khan-Tegri

2000. International Year of Mountains (1st series). Multicoloured.

212	10s. Type **52**	2·30	2·10
213	10s. Lenin Peak	2·30	2·10
214	10s. Victory Peak	2·30	2·10

See also Nos. 228/**MS**231.

53 Dank Medal (bravery)

2001. Orders and Medals. Multicoloured.

215	36t. Type **53**	15	15
216	48t. Baatyrene (women's medal)	20	20
217	1s. Manas 3rd class order	30	25
218	2s. Manas 2nd class order	40	35
219	3s. Manas 1st class order	60	55
220	6s. Danaker order (bravery)	1·20	1·10
221	10s. Ak Shumkar (Hero of Kyrgyz Republic)	2·00	1·80

54 Crying Child and Military Aircraft

2001. 50th Anniversary of United Nations High Commissioner for Refugees.

222	**54**	10s. multicoloured	1·80	1·60

55 Snake

2001. New Year. Year of the Snake.

223	**55**	6s. multicoloured	1·60	1·40

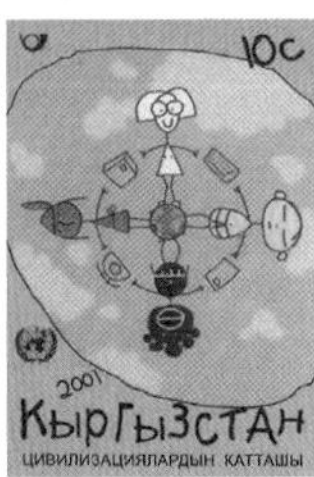
56 Children encircling Globe

2001. United Nations Year of Dialogue among Civilisations.

224	**56**	10s. multicoloured	1·80	1·60

57 Communication House

2001. Bishkek.

225	**57**	48t. green	40	35
226	-	1s. green	60	55
227	-	3s. brown	80	70

Designs: 1s. Government House; 3s. National Opera House.

58 Yaks in Pasture

2001. International Year of Mountains (2nd series). Multicoloured.

228	10s. Type **58**	1·90	1·80
229	10s. Horses crossing river	1·90	1·80
230	10s. Forested slopes	1·90	1·80
MS231	10×83 mm. Designs as Nos. 228/230	5·75	5·50

59 Yacht on Lake Issyk-Kul

2001. International Year of Eco-tourism. Multicoloured.

232	10s. Type **59**	1·90	1·80
233	10s. Lake Sary-Chelek	1·90	1·80
234	10s. Suusamyr Valley	1·90	1·80
MS235	119×89 mm. 10s. Mosque, Naryn (vert)	4·25	4·00

60 Ak-Shumkar (legendary bird) and Khan-Tengri Mountain

2001. Tenth Anniversary of Independence. Multicoloured.

236	1s.50 Type **60**	1·60	1·50
237	7s. Pres. Askar Akaev and National Flag	6·50	6·00
MS238	126×90 mm. 11s.50 Government House, Bishkek	8·00	7·75

61 Kurmanbek (statue), Djalal-Abad

2001. 500th Birth Anniversary of Kurmanbek Khan (military leader).

239	**61**	1s.50 multicoloured	1·40	1·40

2001. 40th Anniversary of Worldwide Fund for Nature. Nos. 163/166 overprinted **40th Anniversary 1961–2001** or surcharged.

240	25s. on 10s. Fox	3·25	3·00
241	25s. on 10s. Fox sleeping	3·25	3·00
242	30s. Two foxes standing	4·00	3·75
243	50s. Mother and cubs	5·50	5·25

Nos. 240/241 with both change of face value and celebratory inscription, and Nos. 242/243 with only celebratory inscription.

63 Kurmandjan Datka

2001. 190th Birth Anniversary of Kurmandjan Dakta (aka Alai Queen, female tribal leader).

244	**63**	10s.+70t. black	1·90	1·70

64 RCC and Kyrgyzstan Post

2001. Tenth Anniversary of Regional Communications Community.

245	**64**	7s. multicoloured	1·60	1·50

65 Union Emblem Office Emblems

2001. Tenth Anniversary of Union of Independent States.

246	**65**	6s. blue and yellow	1·40	1·30

66 Skating

2002. Olympic Games, Salt Lake City, USA. Multicoloured.

247	50t. Type **66**	15	15
248	1s.50 Biathlon	30	30
249	7s. Hockey	1·10	1·00
250	10s. Ski jumping	1·60	1·50
MS251	88×89 mm. 50s. Alpine skiing	8·00	7·75

67 Horse

2002. Chinese New Year. Year of the Horse.

252	**67**	1s. multicoloured	1·90	1·70

68 Two Players

2002. World Cup Football Championships, Japan and South Korea. Sheet 136×118 mm containing T **68** and similar vert designs. Multicoloured.

MS253	1s.50 Type **68**; 3s. Players tackling for ball; 7s.20 Player dribbling ball; 12s. Player defending; 24s. Players jumping for ball; 60s. Player chasing another	16·00	15·00

69 Kyrgyzstan and Pakistan Flags and Dove

2002. Tenth Anniversary of Kyrgyzstan–Pakistan Diplomatic Relations.

254	**69**	12s. multicoloured	1·90	1·70

2002. No. **MS**253 surch **Final BRAZIL 2 : 0 GREMANY Third Place TURKEY : KOREA** in either gold or silver.

MS255	(a) As No. **MS**253 (gold ovpt) (b) As No. **MS**253 (silver ovpt)	32·00	31·00

71 Greek Stamp and Discus Thrower (Athens, 1896)

2002. History of Summer Olympic Games. Four sheets, each 140×110 mm containing T **71** and similar horiz designs. Multicoloured.

MS256	(a) 1s. Type **71**; 2s. Boxer and French stamp (Paris 1900); 3s. Diver and American stamp (St. Louis 1904); 5s. Weightlifting and English stamp (London 1908); 7s. Rower and Swedish stamp (Stockholm 1912). 7s. Athlete and Belgian stamp (Antwerp 1920). (b) 1s. Gymnast and French stamp (Paris 1924); 2s. Diver and Dutch stamp (Amsterdam 1928); 3s. Table tennis and American stamp (Los Angeles 1932); 5s. Runner and German stamp (Berlin 1936); 7s. Fencing and English stamp (London 1948); 7s. Gymnast and Finnish stamp (Helsinki 1952). (c) 1s.50 Volleyball and Australian stamp (Melbourne 1956); 3s. Tennis and Italian stamp (Rome 1960); 5s. Swimmer and Japan stamp (Tokyo 1964); 5s. Wrestlers and Mexican stamp (Mexico 1968); 7s.20 Kayaker and German stamp (Munich 1972); 12s. Yacht and Canadian stamp (Montreal 1976). (d) 1s. Gymnast and USSR stamp (Moscow 1980); 3s. Synchronised swimmer and USA stamp (Los Angeles 1984); 5s. Cyclist and Korean stamp (Seoul 1988); 5s. High jumper and Spanish stamp (Barcelona 1992); 7s.20 Wind surfer and USA stamp (Atlanta 1996); 12s. Gymnast and Australian stamp (Sydney 2000)	30·00	29·00

72 Zhalal-Abad

2002. Regional Cities.

257	**72**	20t. purple	10	10
258	-	50t. purple	10	10
259	-	60t. purple	15	15
260	-	1s. blue	25	20
261	-	1s.50 blue	30	30
262	-	2s. slate	40	35
263	-	3s. slate	65	60
264	-	7s. slate	1·40	1·30
265	-	10s. blue	1·90	1·70

Designs: 20t. Zhalal-Abad; 50t. Talas; 60t. Osh; 1s. Zhalal-Abad; 1s.50 Talas; 2s. Osh; 3s. Zhalal-Abad; 7s. Talas; 10s. Osh.

2002. No. 27 surch **2000 1.50**.

266	1s.50 on 1t. multicoloured	65	60

2002. No. 28 surch **3.60**.

267	3s.60 on 3t. multicoloured	1·10	1·00

2002. No. 29 surch **7.00 2002**.

268	7s. on 10t. multicoloured	2·20	2·00

76 Olmoskhan Atabekova

2003. 80th (2002) Birth Anniversary of Olmoskhan Atabekova (war heroine).

269	**76**	7s.20 multicoloured	1·30	1·20

77 Atomic Symbol and Association Emblem

2003. Tenth Anniversary of the International Association of Academies of Sciences. Multicoloured.

270	1s.50 Type **77**	30	30
271	7s.20 Emblem	1·60	1·50

78 Figurines

2003. 2200th Anniversary of Nationhood (1st issue). Saki Tribal Gold and Bronze Artefacts. Two sheets containing T **78** and similar horiz designs. Multicoloured.

MS272	(a) 119×140 mm. 1s.50 Type **78**; 3s. Shield; 3s.60 Lion; 5s. Horned head; 7s. Bird; 10s. Two goat heads with joined horns; 20s.Coin; 42s. Animal headed staff.(b) 125×89 mm. 42s. Mask	26·00	25·00

See also No. **MS**277.

79 Aeroplane and Post Office Building, Bishkek

2003. 125th Anniversary of Bishkek Post Office. Multicoloured.

273	1s. Type **79**	30	30
274	3s. Wagon, jeep and building	65	60
275	7s. Building, dove and wagon	1·30	1·20
MS276	119×88 mm. 50s. Dove and building (different). Imperf	7·25	7·00

80 Barsbek

2003. 2200th Anniversary of Nationhood (2nd issue). Rulers. Sheet 99×160 mm containing T **80** and similar horiz designs. Multicoloured.

MS277	1s.50 Type **80** (7th-century leader); 3s. Alp Sol; 3s.60 Mukhammed; 5s. Manap; 7s.20 Zharban; 10s. Kubatbek; 18s. Azhy; 20s. Ormon; 25s. Alymbek; 30s. Shabdan	19·00	18·00

81 Rabat

2003. Tourism. Issyk Kul Resorts. Sheet 167×148 mm containing T **81** and similar horiz designs showing resorts. Multicoloured.

MS278	1s. Type **81**; 1s.50 Raduga; 2s. Teltoru; 3s. Kyrgyzskoe Vzmorije; 3s.60 Tamga; 5s. Solnyshko; 7s. Vityaz; 8s. AkBermet; 12s. Royal Beach; 20s. Inscr "Luchezarnoe poberejie"	9·50	9·25

82 Rat

2003. Chinese Lunar Calendar. Sheet 210×171 mm containing T **82** and similar horiz designs showing Chinese lunar animals. Multicoloured.

MS279	1.50 Year of the Rat; 3s. Year of the Ox; 5s. Year of the Tiger; 7s. Year of the Rabbit; 12s. Year of the Dragon; 12s. Year of the Snake; 15s. Year of the Horse; 15s. Year of the Sheep; 20s. Year of the Monkey; 20s. Year of the Cock; 25s. Year of the Dog; 25s. Year of the Pig	19·00	18·00

83 Flag

2003. National Symbols.

280	**83**	3s. vermilion, yellow and black	95	85
281	-	3s. black	95	85
282	-	5s. multicoloured	1·60	1·50

MS283 (a) 136×81 mm. Nos. 280/282 (b) 103×74 mm. 12s. multicoloured (52×37 mm) 3·50 3·25

Designs: 3s. (No. 281) Anthem; 5s. National Arms; 12s. 'Notes' (written by Syma Tsjan (Chinese historian).

84 Sheep

2003. New Year. Year of the Sheep.
284 **84** 1s.50 multicoloured 80 75

85 Buildings

2004. Tenth Anniversary of Meerim Welfare Fund. Multicoloured.
285 1s.50 Type **85** 30 30
286 7s. Buildings (different) 1·30 1·20
MS287 74×103 mm. 20s. Emblem (37×52 mm) 3·25 3·00

86 Monkey

2004. New Year. Year of the Monkey.
288 **86** 3s. multicoloured 1·30 1·20

87 Peugeot (1913)

2004. Cars. Sheet 123×108 mm containing T **87** and similar vert designs. Multicoloured.
MS289 3s.60 Type **87**; 3s.60 Mercedes Benz (1999); 10s. Volvo S40 (1996); 10s. Ford (1908); 15s. Alfa Romeo (1932); 15s. VAZ 2101 (1972); 25s. Nissan (1998); 25s. ZIS 110 (1950) 14·50 14·00

88 Winged Insect

2004. Singapore International Stamp Exhibition. Insects. Sheet 123×108 mm containing T **88** and similar vert designs. Multicoloured.
MS290 3s.60 Type **88**; 3s.60 Grasshopper; 10s. Cicada; 10s. Ladybirds; 15s. Dragonfly; 15s. Praying mantis; 25s. Moth; 25s. Bee 14·50 14·00

89 'FIFA' and Football

2004. Centenary of FIFA (Federation Internationale de Football Association). Multicoloured.
291 5s. Type **89** 65 60
292 6s. Anniversary emblem 80 75
293 7s. Player 95 85
294 10s. Player heading ball 1·30 1·20

2004

20.00

(90)

2004. Second International Festival of Arts. Peace and Respect. No. **MS**12 surch as T **90**.
MS295 20t. on 10r. multicoloured 3·50 3·25

91 Karakol Region

2004. Regions.
296 **91** 10t. blue 15 15
297 - 20t. green 15 15
298 - 50t. sepia 15 15
299 - 60t. ultramarine 20 15
300 - 1s. blue 25 25
301 - 2s. brown 35 35
302 - 3s. violet 55 50
303 - 5s. emerald 90 85
304 - 7s. brown 1·30 1·20

Designs: 20t. Monument, Naryn; 50t. Castle, Tokmok; 60t. Tower, Karakol; 1s. As No. 297; 2s. As No. 298; 3s. As No. 296; 5s. As No. 297; 7s. As No. 298.

92 Chynykei Biy

2004. Chynykei Biy Commemoration.
305 **92** 3s. chocolate and black 1·30 1·20

93 Original Academy Building

2004. 50th Anniversary of National Academy of Sciences. Multicoloured.
306 1s.50 Type **93** 35 35
307 3s.60 Modern Academy building 1·10 1·00

94 Nikolay Zvenchukov

2004. Basketball. Multicoloured.
308 1s.50 Type **94** 1·30 1·20
309 3s.60 Kubat Karabekov 2·50 2·30

95 Falcon

2004
310 **95** 10t. green 20 15
311 **95** 50t. blue 55 50
312 **95** 50t. blue 55 50
313 **95** 60t. violet 70 65
314 **95** 1s. brown 90 85
315 **95** 1s. claret 90 85
316 **95** 3s. brown 1·30 1·20

96 Rooster

2005. New Year. Year of the Rooster.
330 **96** 3s. multicoloured 1·80 1·70

97 Salizhan Sharipov

2005. Salizhan Sharipov (cosmonaut). Sheet 100×70 mm.
MS331 **97** 100s. multicoloured 27·00 26·00

98 Carpet

2005. National Museum of Graphic Arts. Multicoloured.
332 2s. Type **98** 20 15
333 3s.60 Carpet with border 35 35
334 7s. Cloth with orange border and red central design 90 85
335 12s. Black and white cloth 1·40 1·30
336 15s. Saddle 1·80 1·70
337 20s. Pots 2·30 2·10
MS338 70×100 mm. 40s. multicoloured cloth (detail) 6·25 6·00

99 Monuments and Doves

2005. 60th Anniversary of End of World War II.
339 **99** 5s. multicoloured 90 85

100 Horse Riders

2005. National Games (Kyz Kuumai).
340 **100** 3s. multicoloured 1·40 1·30

101 Paper Aeroplane, Globe and Kyrgyzstan Map

2005. World Information Society Summit, Tunis.
341 **101** 3s.60 multicoloured 1·60 1·50

102 Chatyrul Lake

2005. Lakes. Sheet 109×83 mm containing T **102** and similar horiz designs. Multicoloured.
MS342 7s. Type **102**; 20s. Sonkul; 25s. Sarychelek; 30s. Issykkul 12·50 12·00

103 Minaret, Uzgen

2005. 50th Anniversary of Europa Stamps. Multicoloured.
343 15s. Type **103** 1·80 1·70
344 20s. Acropolis, Athens 2·50 2·30
345 25s. Buran tower 3·00 2·75
346 60s. Tash Rabat 5·50 5·00
347 85s. St Mark's Basilica, Italy 7·25 6·50
MS348 134×130 mm. Nos. 343/347. Perf or imperf 29·00 28·00

104 Tugolbai Sydykbekov

2006. Tugolbai Sydykbekov (writer) Commemoration.
349 **104** 10s. multicoloured 1·60 1·50

105 Dog

2006. New Year. Year of the Dog.
350 **105** 3s. multicoloured 70 65

106 Skier

2006. Winter Olympic Games, Turin.
351 **106** 5s. multicoloured 1·40 1·30

107 Players

2006. World Cup Football Championship, Germany.
352 **107** 15s. multicoloured 2·75 2·50

108 100s. Gold Coin (Manas millenary) (2000)

2006. Commemorative Coins. Multicoloured.
353 1s.50 Type **108** 20 15
354 3s. 10s. silver coin (showing horseman (Manas millenary) (1995) 35 35
355 16s. 100s. coin showing Suleiman-Toho and the Davan Horses petroglyphs (3000th anniversary of Osh) (2001) 2·20 2·00
356 20s. 10s. coin showing mountains (Tenth anniversary of Independence and International Year of Mountains) 2·75 2·50
357 24s. 10s. coin showing edelweiss (International Year of Mountains) (2002) 3·50 3·25
358 28s. 10s. coin showing mountain arkhar (sheep) (International Year of Mountains) (2002) 4·00 3·75
359 30s. 10s. coin showing coins (Tenth anniversary of National Currency) (2003) 4·25 3·75
360 40s. 10s. coin showing head of a tiger, Turgesh coin and tower of Burana (statehood) (2003) 5·50 5·00
361 45s. 10s. coin showing woman, yurt and Victory Memorial (60th anniversary of end of World War II) (2005) 6·25 5·75
362 50s. 10s. coin showing Tashrabat (Great Silk road) (2005) 7·25 6·50

109 Symbols of Communications

2006. 15th Anniversary of RCC (Regional Commonwealth of Communications).
363 **109** 12s. multicoloured 2·00 1·80

110 Palace of Sport

2006. Architecture of Bishkek. Sheet 125×80 mm containing T **110** and similar horiz design. Each black on stone.
MS364 12s.×4, Type **110**; Theatre; Philharmonic Society building; Museum 7·25 7·00

111 Dancer

2006. International Telecommunication Union (ITU) Plenipotentiary Conference, Antalya, Turkey.

365	**111**	25s. multicoloured	4·25	4·00

112 Heroes of Panfilovtsy (bas relief)

2006. 65th Anniversary of Defence of Moscow.

366	**112**	7s. multicoloured	1·30	1·20

113 Suimenkul Chokmorov

2006. 65th Anniversary of National Cinema. T **113** and similar horiz designs showing actors. Each brown and flesh.

MS367 12s.×4, Type **113**; Bolot Bejshenaliev; Tattybyubyu Tursunbaeva; Baken Kydykeeva 7·25 7·00

114 Pig

2007. New Year. Year of the Pig.

368	**114**	3s. multicoloured	70	65

115 *Chingiz Aitmatov*

2007. Art. Sheet 130×70 mm containing Showing portraits. Multicoloured.

MS369 12s.×5, Type **115**; *Syimenkul Chokmorov; Kurmangazy Azykbaev; Omor Sultanov; Zhylkychy Zhakypov* 12·50 12·00

116 Archer

2007. National Sports (1st series).

370	**116**	7s. multicoloured	90	85

See also No. 387.

117 Tunnel

2007. 50th Anniversary of Bishkek–Osh Highway. Sheet 97×126 mm containing T **117** and similar horiz designs. Multicoloured.

MS371 25s.×4, Type **117**; Highway and lake; Highway and snow-capped mountains; Highway with hills on either side 14·50 14·00

118 Flowers

2007. Aigul (*Pentelium eduardi*).

372	1s. Type **118**		35	35

MS373 67×87 mm. 100s. As No. 372 (30×40 mm) 14·50 14·00

119 Kazakhstan

2007. Shanghai Co-operation Organisation Conference. Sheet 95×82 mm containing T **119** and similar horiz designs showing flags of member countries. Multicoloured.

MS374 12s.×6, Type **119**; Kyrgyzstan; China; Russia; Tajikistan; Uzbekistan 10·00 9·75

120 *Haliaeetus albicilla* (white-tailed eagle)

2007. Birds of Prey. Sheet 145×85 mm containing T **120** and similar horiz designs. Multicoloured.

MS375 25s.×6, Type **120**; *Falco rusticolus* (gyrfalcon); *Aquila chrysaetus* (golden eagle); *Accipiter gentilis* (goshawk); *Milvus migrans* (black kite); *Falco peregrinus* (peregrine falcon) 22·00 21·00

121 Santa Claus, Blue Birds and Letters

2007. Letters to Santa Claus.

376	**121**	3s. multicoloured	55	50

122 Rat

2008. New Year. Year of the Rat.

377	**122**	7s. multicoloured	1·40	1·20

123 *Ailuropoda melanoleuca* (giant panda)

2008. Fauna. Multicoloured.

378	7s. Type **123**	90	85
379	7s. *Uncia uncia* (snow leopard)	90	85
380	12s. *Ailurus fulgens* (red panda)	1·40	1·30
381	12s. *Panthera tigris* (tiger)	1·40	1·30
382	16s. *Pygathrix roxellana* (golden snub-nosed monkey)	1·80	1·70
383	16s. *Hystrix cristata* (porcupine)	1·80	1·70
384	25s. *Ovis ammon* (argali)	3·00	2·75
385	25s. *Felis manul* (Pallas' cat)	3·00	2·75
MS386	128×93 mm. Nos. 378/385	18·00	17·00

It is reported that Nos. 378/**MS**386 were also issued imperforate.

124 Horse Wrestlers

2008. National Sport (2nd series).

387	**124**	5s. multicoloured	90	85

125 Javelin

2008. Olympic Games, Beijing. Multicoloured.

388	20s. Type **125**	2·20	2·00
389	20s. Football	2·20	2·00
390	20s. Wrestling	2·20	2·00
391	20s. Basketball	2·20	2·00

126 Khan Tengri Peak, Kyrgyzstan

2008. Mountains. Sheet 110×56 mm containing T **126** and similar vert design. Multicoloured.

MS392 16s.×2, Type **126**; Sabalan peak, Iran 3·50 3·25

127 Stamp Outline, Mountains and Postal Emblem

2008. National Postal Service.

393	**127**	1s. multicoloured	20	20
394	**127**	3s. multicoloured	40	40

128 Sabira Kumushalieva

2008. Sabira Kumushalieva (actress) Commemoration.

395	**128**	10s. brown and black	1·40	1·30

129 Absamat Masaliev

2008. Absamat Masaliyevich Masaliyev (politician) Commemoration.

396	**129**	15s. sepia and black	2·00	1·90

2008. Postal Service. As T **127**.

397	**130**	50t. multicoloured	15	15
398	**130**	7s. multicoloured	80	75

131 Yakovlev Yak-12

2008. Aviation (1st issue). Sheet 130×115 mm containing T **131** and similar horiz designs. Multicoloured.

MS399 20s.×8, Type **131**; Mil Mi-2; Antonov An-2; Tupolev Tu-154; Ilyushin Il-14; Ilyushin Il-18; Antonov An-24; Mil Mi-4 17·00 16·00

See also Nos. **MS**409 and **MS**410.

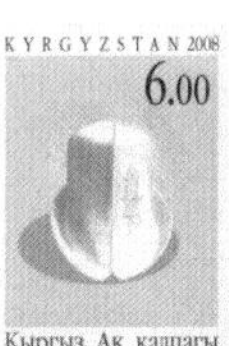

132 Hat

2008. Traditional Hats. Multicoloured.

400	**130**	6s. Type **132**	80	75
401	**130**	7s. With black embroidery and tassel	1·00	95
402	**130**	12s. With brown embroidery and blue tassel	1·20	1·10
403	**130**	50s. Quartered hat with black highlights	5·00	4·75

133 Yak

2008. Yaks. Multicoloured.

404	25s. Type **133**	2·40	2·30
405	25s. Black horned yak against mountains	2·40	2·30
406	25s. Brown horned yak against green valley	2·40	2·30
407	25s. Grey yak against mountains	2·40	2·30

134 Isa Akhunbaev

2008. Birth Centenary of Isa Akhunbaev (surgeon).

408	**134**	12s. multicoloured	2·20	2·10

2008. Civil Aviation (2nd issue). Sheet 130×115 mm containing horiz designs as T **131**. Multicoloured.

MS409 20s.×7, Antonov An-28; Yakovlev Yak-40; Antonov An-26;Tupolev Tu-134; Ilyushin Il-76; Airbus A320; Mil Mi-8 helicopter 15·00 14·50

2008. Aviation (3rd issue). Sheet 130×115 mm containing horiz designs as T **131**. Multicoloured.

MS410 20s.×8, Sopwith (Inscr 'Sopvich'); Yakovlev AIR-6; Inscr 'P-5'; Polikarpov Po-2;Junkers Ju 52 (inscr 'Yu-52/3'); Tupolev ANT-9; Mil Mi-17 (Inscr 'MI-1'); Lisunov Li-2. 17·00 16·00

Nos. 411/416 are vacant.

К. Бегалиев жана Р. Түмөнбаев–
XXIX ОлимпиаданЫн жеңүүчүлөрү

(135)

2008. Nos. 388/391 overprinted as T **135**

417	20s. Javelin (No. 388)	5·00	4·75
418	20s. Football (No. 389)	5·00	4·75
419	20s. Wrestling (No. 390)	5·00	4·75
420	20s. Basketball (No. 391)	5·00	4·75

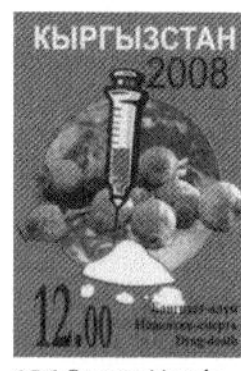

136 Poppy Heads, Syringe and Powder

2008. Drug Abuse Awareness Campaign.

421	**136**	12s. multicoloured	1·60	1·50

137 Ox

2008. Chinese New Year. Year of the Ox.

422	**137**	25s. multicoloured	3·25	3·00

138 Ishembay Abdraimov and Honored Pilot Medal

2009. Ishembay Abdraimov (test pilot) Commemoration.

423	**138**	10s. multicoloured	1·60	1·50

139 Horses and Riders

2009. National Sport (Kok-Boru).

424	**139**	25s. multicoloured	3·25	3·00

140 Bright Bay

2009. The Kyrgyz Horse. T **140** and similar horiz designs showing horses. Multicoloured.

425	16s. Type **140**	2·00	1·90
426	42s. Yellow dun	5·00	4·75
427	50s. Grey	6·00	5·75

428	60s. Bay with four white socks	7·00	6·75
MS429	130×101 mm. Nos. 425/428	20·00	19·00

141 Saker Falcon

2009. Endangered Species. Saker Falcon (*Falco cherrug*). Designs showing falcons. Multicoloured.

430	10s. Type **141**	80	75
431	15s. On nest	1·40	1·30
432	25s. In flight	2·00	1·90
433	50s. Adult and chicks	4·00	3·75

142 Woman (*Zhamiyla*)

2009. Chyngyz Aitmatov (writer) Commemoration. Sheet 131×116 mm containing T **142** and similar horiz designs showing scenes from his writing. Each slate-grey and scarlet-vermilion.

MS434 7s. Type **142**; 12s. Man and horse (*Gulsarat*); 16s. Woman and lorry (*Delbirim*); 21s. Woman and locomotive (*Samanchynyn Jolu*); 28s. Man carrying boy (*Birinchi Mughale*); 30s. Boy with binoculars and stag (*Ak-Keme*); 45s. Horseman and cranes (*Zrte Zhazdagy Turnalar*); 60s. Canoe in stormy weather 20·00 19·00

143 Barpy Alykulov

2009. 125th Birth Anniversary of Barpy Alykulov (poet).

435	**143** 16s. multicoloured	1·60	1·50

144 Building Facade

2009. 75th Anniversary of National Library.

436	**144** 12s. multicoloured	1·80	1·70

145 Ak-Sai Glacier

2009. Glaciers of Kyrgyzstan. Sheet 130×82 mm containing T **145** and similar horiz designs showing glaciers. Multicoloured.

MS437 12s. Type **145**; 16s. Kotur; 21s. Semenovsky; 28s. Zvezdochka; 45s. North Inylchek; 60s. South Inylchek 21·00 20·00

146 Railway Station

2009. Railways. Multicoloured.

438	16s. Type **146**	2·00	1·90
439	42s. Diesel train on bridge over river	5·00	4·75
440	50s. Locomotive emerging from covered way	6·00	5·75
441	60s. Diesel train on bridge over roadway	7·00	6·75

147 Children

2010. 50th Anniversary of United Nations Declaration of Rights of the Child.

442	**147** 21s. multicoloured	2·50	2·50

148 Tiger

2010. Chinese New Year. Year of the Tiger.

443	**148** 25s. multicoloured	3·00	2·75

149 Nordic Skiing

2010. Winter Olympic Games, Vancouver. Multicoloured.

444	21s. Type **149**	2·40	2·30
445	28s. Biathlon	3·25	3·00
446	45s. Skiing	5·50	5·25
447	60s. Snowboarding	7·00	6·75

150 Peonies

2010. Peonies. Multicoloured.

448	25s. Type **150**	3·00	2·75
449	30s. Single flower (double)	3·50	3·50
MS450	144×115 mm. As No. 449	5·00	4·75

151 Tank and Soldiers

2010. 65th Anniversary of End of World War II.

451	**151** 12s. multicoloured	1·60	1·50

152 *Portrait of Vengerov*, 1916 (I. E. Repin)

2010. 75th Anniversary of National Museum of Art. Multicoloured.

MS452 12s. Type **152**; 16s. *Field of Cabbage*, 1910 (R. R. Falk); 21s. *Still-life on Red Cloth*, 1916 (P. P. Konchalovsky); 24s. *Sea in Crimea*, 1866 (I. K. Aivazovsky); 28s. *Autumn in Jailoo* (autumn in summer pastures), 1945 (S. A. Chuikov); 30s. *Evening in South Kirgizia*, 1967 (G. A. Aitiev); 42s. *Autumn Garden*, 1989 (A. Ignatev); 45s. *By night*, 1971 (D. N. Deimant) 26·00 25·00

153 Games Emblem and Players

2010. World Cup Football Championships, South Africa. Multicoloured.

453	24s. Type **153**	3·00	2·75
454	30s. World Cup trophy and two players	4·00	3·75
455	42s. Games emblem and two players	5·00	4·75
456	60s. Trophy and goalkeeper	8·00	7·50

154 Earrings

2010. Jewellery. Multicoloured.

457	16s. Type **154**	2·00	1·90
458	24s. Six buttons	3·00	2·75
459	58s. Bangles	7·00	6·75
460	66s. Hair ornaments	8·00	7·50

155 Explosion

2010. Hydroelectric Power Station. Multicoloured.

MS461 28s. Type **155**; 42s. Power station in valley; 60s. Building work 16·00 15·00

156 Conference Emblem

2010. Plenipotentiary Conference in Mexico.

MS462	**156** 100s. multicoloured	12·50	12·00

157 Togolok Moldo

2010. 150th Birth Anniversaries. Multicoloured.

463	12s. Type **157** (akyn)	1·40	1·30
464	16s. Murataly Kurenkeev (composer)	1·80	1·70
465	21s. Zhenizhok Coco uulu (poet)	2·50	2·50

158 I. Razzakov

2010. Birth Centenary of Iskhak Razzakovich Razzakov (politician).

466	**158** 28s. multicoloured	3·50	3·25

159 *Agrionemys horsfieldi* (inscr 'Agrionemys horstieldi')

2010. Turtles and Tortoises. Multicoloured.

467	16s. Type **159**	1·80	1·70
468	24s. *Pseudemys scripta*	2·75	2·75
469	48s. *Geochelone elegans*	5·50	5·25
470	72s. *Testudo kleimanni*	8·50	8·00

160 Rabbit

2011. Chinese New Year. Year of the Rabbit.

471	**160** 24s. multicoloured	2·75	2·75

161 Eagle, Ala-Archa

2011. Nature Reserves of Kyrgyzstan. Multicoloured.

MS472 7s. Type **161**;12s. Bear, Chon-Kemin;16s. Deer, Naryn; 21s. Argali ram, Sary-Chelek; 24s. Fish and beach, Issyk-Kul; 28s. Bar-headed goose, Karatal-Zhapryk; 42s. Hobby (bird), Besh-Tash; 45s. Manul (wild cat), Sarychat-Ertash; 60s. Partridge, Padysha-Ata 30·00 29·00

162 *Vostok 1*

2011. 50th Anniversary of First Manned Space Flight. Multicoloured.

MS473	60s. Type **162**; 90s. Yuri Gagarin	17·00	16·00

163 Players in Goal

2011. World Hockey Championship, Slovakia. Multicoloured.

474	28s. Type **163**	3·50	3·25
475	42s. Players tackling	5·00	4·75

164 PAZ-672 and RAF-22038

2011. 30th Anniversary of Bus Terminal, Bishkek. Multicoloured.

MS476 12s. Type **164**; 16s. IKARUS-256 and GAZ-M24 Volga; 21s. LAZ-697R Tourist and UAZ-2206; 24s. FORD E series and VOLVO B12B; 30s. VOLKSWAGEN Transporter T4 and SETRA S 431 dt; 42s. MERECEDES Sprinter 313 and MITSUBUSHI Fuso Aero Queen Bus 17·00 16·00

~~30c~~
60c

50th Anniversary 1961–2011
(165)

50th Anniversary 1961–2011
(166)

2011. 50th Anniversary of WWF (Worldwide Fund for Nature). Nos. 165/166 surch as T **165.** Nos. 163/166 additionally overprinted as T **166.**

477	10s. As Type **37**	1·60	1·50
478	10s. As No. 164	1·60	1·50
479	60s. on 30s. multicoloured (No. 165)	10·00	9·50
480	90s. on 50s. multicoloured (No. 166)	15·00	14·00

167 Plum Blossom

2011. Plum Blossom. Multicoloured.

481	16s. Type **167**	2·00	1·90
482	60s. Plum blossom (different)	7·00	6·75

168 Monument to the Martyrs of Revolution

2011. 20th Anniversary of Independence. Sheet 101×81 mm.

MS483	**168** 100s. multicoloured	12·00	11·50

169 Satellite and RCC Emblem

2011. 20th Anniversary of Regional Communication Community (RCC).

484	**169**	28s. multicoloured	3·50	3·25

170 CIS Emblem, Tash Rabat and Caravan of Camels

2011. 20th Anniversary of Community of Independent States (CIS).

485	**170**	42s. multicoloured	5·00	4·75

171 *Agaricus*

2011. Fungi. Multicoloured.

486	16s. Type **171**	2·00	1·90
487	28s. *Pleurotus*	3·50	3·25
488	42s. *Marasmius oreades*	5·00	4·75
489	72s. *Lycoperdon*	8·50	8·25

172 Surnai (wind instrument)

2011. National Musical Instruments. Multicoloured.

490	16s. Type **172**	2·00	1·90
491	24s. Dobulbas (drum)	3·00	2·75
492	48s. Kyl kayak (stringed instrument)	6·00	5·75
493	60s. Ooz komuz (mouth harp)	7·00	6·75

173 Henri Giffard Dirigible. France, 1852

2011. Development of Dirigibles. Multicoloured.

494	12s. Type **173**	1·40	1·30
495	28s. LZ 127 *Graf Zeppelin* dirigible. Germany, 1928	3·50	3·25
496	45s. AU-30 *Argus* dirigible. Russia, 2006	5·50	5·25
497	48s. Dirigble of the future	6·00	5·75

174 Stylised Dragon

2012. Chinese New Year. Year of the Dragon.

498	**174**	36s. multicoloured	4·50	4·25

175 Dog

2012. Oriental Lunar Calendar. Multicoloured.
MS499 25s.×12, Type **175**; Boar; Rat; Ox; Rooster; Tiger; Monkey; Rabbit; Ram; Horse; Snake; Dragon 40·00 38·00

176 Woman's Headdress

2012. Traditional Women's Headdresses. Elechek. Multicoloured.

500	16s. Type **176** (Southern and South Western regions)	2·00	1·90
501	28s. Headdress with tassels (Northern region)	3·50	3·25
502	45s. White unadorned headdress (Northern region)	5·50	5·25
503	60s. Draped headdress with red under-cap (Southern region)	7·00	6·75

177 *Helianthus* (Sunflower)

2012. Flora. Sunflower.

504	**177**	42s. multicoloured	5·00	4·75

178 Bolot Beishenaliev

2012. Personalities. Multicoloured.

505	23s. Type **178** (actor) (75th birth anniversary)	3·25	3·00
506	49s. Gapar Aitiev (artist) (birth centenary)	5·75	5·50

179 Writing

2012. Greatest Inventions of Mankind. Multicoloured.
MS507 21s. Type **179**; 23s. Bread; 45s. Wheel; 49s. Money 17·00 16·00

180 *Turgon Gorge* (Torobekov Sujutbek)

2012. 40th Anniversary of United Nations Environment Programme.

508	**180**	45s. multicoloured	5·50	5·25

181 Mounted Archer

2012. National Horse Games.

509	**181**	28s. multicoloured	3·50	3·25

182 Monument, Borodino

2012. Bicentenary of Battle of Borodino (during Napoleonic Wars). Multicoloured.

510	12s. Type **182**	1·40	1·30
511	45s. Triumphal Arch	5·50	5·25

183 Snow Leopard

2012. Snow Leopard. Endangered Species. Multicoloured.

512	17s. Type **183**	2·00	1·90
513	20s. Snarling	2·40	2·30
514	23s. Head facing right	2·75	2·75
515	30s. Adult and cub	3·50	3·50

184 Couple

2012. National Costumes.

516	**184**	30s. multicoloured	3·50	3·50

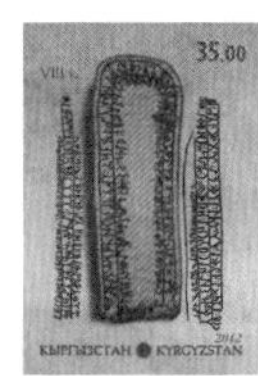
185 8th-century Inscribed Stone

2012. Written Heritage of Ancient Kyrgyz. Multicoloured.

517	35s. Type **185**	4·25	4·00
518	40s. 9th-century inscribed stone	4·75	4·50

186 Ysakbek Monuev

2012. Personalities. Multicoloured.

519	35s. Type **186** (general) (110th birth anniversary)	4·25	4·00
520	40s. Gapar Aitiev (Orman Niyazbek uulu Khan) (tribal leader) (220th birth anniversary)	4·75	4·50

187 Kyrgyzsaurus

2012. Prehistoric Fauna of Kyrgyzstan. Multicoloured.

521	23s. Type **187**	2·75	2·75
522	30s. Inscr 'Xenacanthidae'	3·25	3·00
523	40s. Longisguama	4·75	4·50
524	52s. Mammoth	6·25	6·00

188 Mayan Calendar

2012. Mayan Calendar. Multicoloured.
MS525 29s. Type **188**; 52s. Mayan pyramid, Chichen Itza 10·00 9·50

189 Snake

2013. Chinese New Year. Year of the Snake.

526	**189**	30s. multicoloured	4·00	3·75

190 Gold Medal Diploma

2013. Kyrgyzstan Gold Medal at UPU Congress, Doha 2012. Multicoloured.

527	28s. Type **190**	3·50	3·50
528	43s. Gold medal	5·50	5·25

191 Green Walnuts

2013. Wild Walnut Forest, Arstanbap. Multicoloured.
MS529 7s. Type **191**; 20s. Ripening fruits; 23s. Products of nut forest; 29s. Nut kernels; 35s. Basket of walnuts; 40s. Nut forest, Arstanbap 22·00 21·00

192 Pace Horse and Rider

2013. National Horse Games.

530	**192**	35s. multicoloured	4·50	4·25

193 Valentina Tereshkova

2013. 50th Anniversary of First Woman in Space.

531	**193**	50s. multicoloured	6·50	6·25

194 Symbols of Currency

2013. 20th Anniversary of Kyrgyzstan Currency.

532	**194**	28s. multicoloured	3·75	3·50

195 Argali Sheep

2013. Fauna of Kyrgyzstan. Argali, Mountain Sheep. Multicoloured.

533	29s. Type **195**	3·75	3·50
534	35s. Female with lambs	4·50	4·25
535	40s. Ram on mountain ledge	5·50	5·25
536	52s. Ram in snow	7·00	6·75
MS537	108×88 mm. Nos. 533/536	22·00	21·00

196 Kozhomkul and Monument

2013. 125th Birth Anniversary of Kaba uulu Kozhomkul (Kozhomkul) (wrestler and athlete).

538	**196**	30s. multicoloured	4·00	3·75

197 'Sulaiman Too'

2013. 'Sulaiman Too', Sacred Mountain.

539	**197**	45s. multicoloured	6·00	5·75

198 Snow Leopard

2013. International Forum on Snow Leopard Conservation. Multicoloured.
MS540 29s. Type **198**; 35s. Leaping (head and shoulders); 43s. On rocky outcrop, snarling; 52s. Kittens 22·00 21·00

199 Symbols of Communications

2013. History of National Communications.

541	**199**	36s. multicoloured	4·75	4·50

200 Arms of Kazakhstan

2013. 13th Meeting of Shanghai Co-operation Organisation. Multicoloured.
MS542 12s. Type **200**; 17s. Kyrgyzstan; 20s. China; 23s. Russia; 30s. Tadjikistan; 35s. Uzbekistan

201 Nasirdin Isanov

2013. 70th Birth Anniversary of Nasirdin Isanov (former prime minister).

543	**201**	17s. multicoloured		

202 Map of Territory

2013. 1170th Anniversary of Great Kyrgyz Kaganat. Multicoloured.

544	20s. Type **202**	2·20	2·20
545	23s. Cavalry	2·50	2·50
546	30s. Petroglyph	3·00	3·00

203 *Capparis spinosa*

2013. Flora. Medicinal Plants. Multicoloured.

547	20s. Type **203**	2·20	2·20
548	30s. *Aconitum leucostomum*	3·00	3·00
549	35s. *Hippophae rhamnoides*	3·50	3·50
550	52s. *Glycyrrhiza glabra*	5·50	5·50

204 Horse

2014. Chinese New Year. Year of the Horse.

551	**204**	35s. multicoloured		

206 Horsemen

2014. National Horse Games.

556	**206**	30s. multicoloured	3·00	3·00

207 Aikol Manas Monument

2014. Aikol Manas Monument.

557	**207**	20s. multicoloured	2·20	2·20
558	**207**	23s. multicoloured	2·50	2·50
559	**207**	30s. multicoloured	3·00	3·00
560	**207**	93s. multicoloured	9·00	9·00
561	**207**	100s. multicoloured	10·00	10·00

208 Sledging

2014. Winter Sports. Sledging ('Chana Tepmei').

562	**208**	40s. multicoloured	4·00	4·00

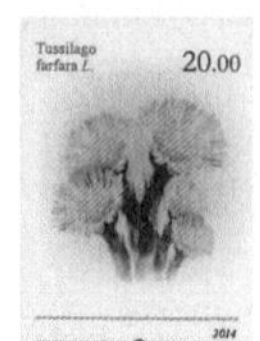
209 *Tussilago farfara*

2014. Flora. Medicinal Plants. Multicoloured.

563	20s. Type **209**	2·20	2·20
564	23s. *Ferula foetida*	2·50	2·50
565	35s. *Ziziphora clinopodioides*	3·50	3·50
566	40s. *Helichrysum maracandicum*	4·00	4·00

210 Black Vulture

2014. Black Vulture (*Aegypius monachus*). Multicoloured.

567	29s. Type **210**	3·00	3·00
568	35s. Flying	3·50	3·50
569	62s. On nest with chicks	6·40	6·40
570	74s. On ground displaying	8·25	8·25

211 Players

2014. Football. Multicoloured.
MS571 29s. Type **211**; 35s. Three players tackling for the ball; 40s. Two players running for the ball; 52s. Goalkeeper making a save 20·00 20·00

212 Dooronbek Sadyrbaev

2014. 75th Birth Anniversary of Dooronbek Sadyrbaev (film director and politician).

572	**212**	35s. multicoloured	3·50	3·50

213 Ala-kiyiz

2014. Cultural Heritage. Carpets. Multicoloured.

573	35s. Type **213**	3·50	3·50
574	45s. Shyrdak	4·80	4·80

214 Imanaly Aidarbekov

2014. Personalities. Multicoloured.

575	20s. Type **214** (120th birth anniversary)	2·20	2·20
576	29s. Abdykerim Sadykov (115th birth anniversary)	2·50	2·50
577	35s. Abdykadyr Orozbekov (115th birth anniversary)	3·50	3·50

215 Early University Building

2014. 60th Anniversary of State Technical University. Multicoloured.
MS578 52s. Type **215**; 62s. Modern building 12·00 12·00

216 Symbols of Communication

2014. ITU Conference, Korea. Sheet 90×90 mm.
MS579 **216** 30s. multicoloured 3·50 3·50

217 Toktogul Satylganov

2014. Personalities. Multicoloured.

580	35s. Type **217** (Kyrgyz Akyn (improvising poet and singer)) (150th birth anniversary)	3·50	3·50
581	40s. Suimenkul Chokmorov (film actor) (75th birth anniversary)	4·00	4·00

No. 582 and T **218** are left for 140th Anniversary of UPU, not yet received

Nos. 583/587 and T **219** are left for Fauna, not yet received.

220 Delegates

2014. Year of Strengthening the State of Kyrgyzstan.

588	**220**	30s. multicoloured	3·00	3·00

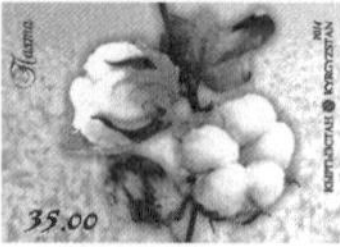
221 Cotton

2014. Cotton. White Gold of Kyrgyzstan. Multicoloured.
MS589 35s. Type **221**; 52s. Cotton (different) 9·00 9·00

222 *Ursus arctos* (Brown Bear)

2014. Fauna of Kyrgyzstan. *Red Book*. Multicoloured.

590	23s. Type **222**	2·50	2·50
591	30s. *Otocolobus mamul* (Pallas's Cat)	3·00	3·00
592	40s. *Cuon alpinus* (Dhole)	4·00	4·00
593	52s. *Lynx lynx* (inscr 'Linnaeus')	5·50	5·50

223 Ram

2015. Chinese New Year. Year of the Sheep.

594	**223**	40s. multicoloured	4·00	4·00

224 Fat-tailed (Aykol) Sheep

2015. Breeds of Sheep. Multicoloured.

595	35s. Type **224**	3·50	3·50
596	52s. Merino	5·50	5·50

225 Korgool Dosuev

2015. Personalities. Multicoloured.

597	29s. Type **225** (Kyrgyz Akyn (improvising poet and singer)) (125th birth anniversary)	3·00	3·00
598	35s. Zh. Sheraliev (musician) (birth centenary)	3·50	3·50
599	40s. M. Omurkanova (singer) (birth centenary)	4·00	4·00
600	52s. A. Osmonov (poet) (birth centenary)	5·50	5·50

226 Japanese Ainu

2015. Cats and Dogs. Multicoloured.

601	29s. Type **226**	3·00	3·00
602	35s. Persian Cat	3·50	3·50
603	62s. Siamese Cat	6·40	6·40
604	74s. Kyrgyz Taigan (dog)	8·25	8·25
MS605	100×77 mm. As Nos. 601/604	18·00	18·00

227 Taranchiev Ismailbek (fighter pilot)

2015. 70th Anniversary of End of World War II. Multicoloured.

606	30s. Type **227**	3·00	3·00
607	52s. Otorbaev Asanbek (machine gunner)	5·50	5·50
MS607a	75×70 mm. 40s.×2, Battlefield×2	9·00	9·00

228 Map of EAEU Countries and Flags (image scaled to 58% of original size)

2015. Eurasian Economic Union. Sheet 105×80 mm.
MS608 **228** 202s. multicoloured 16·00 16·00

2015. Paintings by Kyrgyz Artists. Multicoloured.
MS609 15s. *Poets* (G. Aytiev and D. Kozhakhmetov, 1956); 18s. *Labirinth* (D. Nurgaziev, 2001); 20s. *Street Scene, Osh City* (U. Ahynov, 1974); 30s. *Poppies* (E. Dogdurbek); 35s. *Mystic Night* (D. Umetov, 1974); 40s. *Touching Eternity* (S. Chuykov, 1974); 52s. *Holiday* (S. Chokmorov, 1987); 59s. *South Beach* (S. Torobekov, 1987) 22·00 22·00

T **229** is Unavailable.

2015. World Intangible Cultural Heritage of Humanity. *Epic of Manas* (epic poetic trilogy). Multicoloured.

610	20s. Horse riders, galloping (Manas)	2·20	2·20
611	35s. Horseman carrying sword, horse leaping (Semetey)	3·50	3·50
612	74s. Cavalry carrying spears (Seytek)	8·25	8·25

T **230** is unavailable.

2015. Regional Concord of Communication. Architecture of Capital Cities. Monument to Zhusup Balasagyn. Multicoloured.

613	52s. Zhusup Balsagyn	5·50	5·50

T **231** is unavailable.

232 Terrafugia Concept Flying Car

2015. Cars of the 21st-century. Multicoloured.

614		33s. Type **232**	3·00	3·00
615		36s. Mercedes-Benz FO15 hydrogen fuel car	3·50	3·50
616		39s. Tesla Model S electric car	4·00	4·00
617		83s. Toyoto Mirai, first production car using hydrogen	8·25	8·25

233 Whooper Swans in Flight

2015. Whooper Swans (*Cygnus cygnus*). Multicoloured.

618		36s. Type **233**	3·50	3·50
619		39s. Mother and cygnets swimming	4·00	4·00
620		48s. Adult swimming	5·00	5·00
621		117s. Adult with wings raised	10·50	10·50

234 Chess Pieces on Board

2015. Chess. Asian Junior Chess Championships, Kyrgyzstan. Multicoloured.

MS622 48s. Type **234**; Chess pieces (different) 5·00 5·00

235 Monkey

2016. Chinese New Year. Year of the Monkey.

623	**235**	76s. multicoloured	8·50	8·50

236 *Tulipa kolpakowskiana* (inscr 'Tulipa kolpakovskiana')

2013. Flora. Multicoloured.

624		36s. Type **236**	3·50	3·50
625		39s. Inscr 'Tulip Porto'	4·00	4·00
626		48s. Inscr 'Orchid Rio Bamba'	5·00	5·00
627		55s. *Cattleya* 'Queen Sirikit' (inscr 'Cattleya Queen Sirikhit')	5·50	5·50

MS628 85×110 mm Nos. 624/627 18·00 18·00

237 Symbols of Communication

2016. 25th Anniversary of Regional Concord of Communication (RCC).

629	**237**	55s. multicoloured	5·50	5·50

238 Boogachy Zhakypbek

2016. Personalities. Writers. Multicoloured.

630		48s. Type **238** (150th birth anniversary)	4·80	4·80
631		83s. Nasirdin Baytemirov (birth centenary)	8·50	8·50

239 Emblem

2016. 25th Anniversary of Community of Independent States (CIS).

632	**239**	83s. multicoloured	8·50	8·50

240 Lift-off of First Flight

2016. 55th Anniversary of First Manned Space Flight. Multicoloured.

MS633 22s. Type **240**; 117s. Alexei Leonov's space walk 17·00 16·00

241 Trolleybus BMZ-5298.01

2016. 65th Anniversary of First Bishkek Trolleybus. Multicoloured.

MS634 39s. Type **241**; 55s. Trolleybus MTB-82 (40×28 mm); 83s. Trolleybus MTB-82D (29×26 mm) 10·00 10·00

242 Monument to Manas Velikodushny, Moscow

2016. 25th Anniversary Kyrgyz Republic Independence. Sheet 90×50 mm.

MS635 **242** 100s. multicoloured 9·25 9·25

243 Tailak Baatyr

2016. 220th Birth Anniversary of Tailak Baatyr.

636	**243**	55s. multicoloured	5·50	5·50

244 Taekwondo

2016. Olympic Games. Rio 2016. Multicoloured.

637		22s. Type **244**	2·40	2·30
638		31s. Football	3·25	3·00
639		55s. Golf	5·50	5·25
640		117s. Wrestling	9·25	9·25

245 Beshbarmak

2016. Regional Concord of Communication (RCC). National Cuisine.

641	**245**	76s. multicoloured	8·25	8·25

246 *Lycosa singoriensis*

2016. Endangered Species. Spiders. Multicoloured.

642		20s. Type **246**	2·20	2·20
643		22s. *Eresus collari*	2·60	2·60
644		31s. *Solifugae*	3·20	3·20
645		117s. *Mesobuthus eupeus*	9·25	9·25

MS646 115×97 mm. 20s. As Type **246**; 22s. As No. 643; 31s. As No. 644; 117s. As No. 645 16·00 16·00

247 *Return from Red Army*

2016. Art. 125th Birth Anniversary of V.V. Obraztsov. Multicoloured.

647		20s. Type **247**	2·20	2·00
648		22s. *Near Globe*	2·40	2·20
649		31s. *Conspiracy*	3·50	3·00
650		39s. *The Guerrillas*	4·25	3·75
651		117s. *On the Way to China*	13·00	12·00

MS652 108×88 mm. As Nos. 647/651 26·00 25·00

248 Decorated Yurt

2016. Traditional Dwellings. Kurgyz Yurts. UNESCO Representative List of the Intangible Cultural Heritage of Humanity. Multicoloured.

653		22s. Type **248**	2·40	2·40
654		117s Group of yurts	13·00	12·00

249 General Panfilov, Monument and Detail of Battle

2016. 75th Death Anniversary of 28 Guardsmen of Panfilov Division (Feat of the 28 Panfilov Heroes) in the Defence of Moscow.

655	**249**	83s. multicoloured	9·25	8·75

250 Rooster

2017. Chinese New Year. Year of the Rooster.

656	**250**	76s. multicoloured	8·25	7·75

251 Pelican

2017. Endangered Species. Dalmatian Pelicans (*Pelicanus crispus*). Multicoloured.

657		22s. Type **251**	2·40	2·20
658		31s. Two in flight	3·50	3·00
659		39s. Swimming	4·25	3·75
660		117s. One standing, two swimming	13·00	12·00

MS661 120×168 mm. As Nos. 657/660, each×2 47·00 46·00

252 *Tulipa greigi*

2017. Fauna and Flora of Kyrgyzstan. Multicoloured.

662		39s. Type **252**	4·25	3·75
663		48s. *Ciconia nigra* (Black Stork)	5·25	4·75

MS664 100×75 mm As Nos. 662/663 9·50 9·00

253 National Horse Games, Chabysh

2017. National Horse Games.

665	**253**	83s. multicoloured	9·25	8·75

2017. UNESCO World Heritage. Protected Areas. Multicolouredt.

666		39s. Lake and mountains, Sary Chelek	4·25	3·75
667		48s. River valley amongst green mountains, Padysha-Ata	5·25	4·75
668		55s. Archway, wooded hillside and mountains, Besh-Aral	6·00	5·50

2017. Personalities. Singers. Multicoloured.

669		39s. Sagymbai Orozbakov (150th birth anniversary)	4·25	3·75
670		55s. Saira Kiyizbayeva (birth centenary)	6·00	5·50

256 Bolot Minzhylkiyev

2017. 75th Anniversary of Kyrgyz State Opera and Ballet Theatre. Multicoloured.

MS671 39s. Type **256**; 48s. Anniversary emblem; 55s. Dmitry Shostakovich (composer) 17·00 16·00

257 Baytik

2017. Birth Bicentenary of Baytik Kanat Uulu (Baytik Baatyr).

672	**257**	76s. multicoloured	8·25	7·75

258 Snow Leopard

2017. International Snow Leopard and Ecosystem Forum, Bishkek. Multicoloured.

MS673 39s. Type **258**; 117s. Snow Leopard crouched on rocky outcrop 18·00 17·00

259 Kyrgyz Family

2017. Year of Morality, Education and Culture.

674	**259**	76s. multicoloured	8·25	7·75

KYRGYZ EXPRESS POST

1 Air Bishkek

2014. 140th Anniversary of UPU. Postal Transport in Kyrgyzstan. Multicoloured.

1	**12**	500s. Type **1**	12·00

MS2 113×80 mm. 25s. Postman on horseback; 50s. Mail train; 250s. Modern post van; 500s. As Type **1** 20·00

MS3 134×134 mm. 700s. Dove carrying envelope (34×34 mm) 20·00

2 Snow Leopard (*Panthera uncia*)

2014. Fauna of Kyrgyzstan. Multicoloured.

4	250s. Type **2**	10·10	10·10
MS5	113×80 mm. 15s. Saker Falcon (*Falco cherrug*); 25s. Yak (*Bos grunniens*); 125s. Central Asian Ibex (*Capra sibirica alaiana*); 250s. As Type **2**	15·00	15·00

3 Eagle

2015. Salbuurun. Traditional Kyrgyz Hunting. Falconry. Multicoloured.

6	75s. Type **3**	8·25	8·25
7	75s. Falcon, in flight	8·25	8·25
8	75s. Falcon about to catch rabbit	8·25	8·25
MS9	134×134 mm. 75s.×3, Nos. 6/8	24·00	24·00

4 Alexey Leonov's Spacewalk, March 18, 1965

2015. Anniversaries. Multicoloured.

MS10	50s. Type **4**; 150s. Edward White's spacewalk, June 3, 1965 (50th anniversary of first spacewalk)	10·00	10·00
MS11	250s.'Penny Blac' (175th anniversary of first stamp) (30×40 mm)	10·50	10·50

5 Cotton Boll

2015. United Nations International Year of Light and Light-based Technologies and International Year of Soils. Multicoloured.

12	50s. Type **5**	5·00	5·00
13	75s. Electric discharge around stylized globe	8·25	8·25

6 *Dante and Beatrice* (Henry Holiday)

2015. Anniversaries. Dante Alighieri and Pyotr Ilyich Tchaikovsky. Multicoloured.

14	50s. Type **6** (750th birth anniversary)	5·00	5·00
15	100s. *P. I. Tchaikovsky* (T. Fiodorova) (175th birth anniversary)	9·25	9·25

7 Bright Bay

2015. Fauna of Kyrgyzstan. Horses. Multicoloured.

MS16	100s.×2, Type **7**; Horse with white blaze	9·50	9·50

8 Aragonite

2016. Minerals of Kyrgyzstan. Multicoloured.

17	50s. Type **8**	5·00	5·00
18	50s. Realgar	5·00	5·00
19	100s. Stibnite (antimonite, antimony)	9·25	9·25
20	100s. Kyanite (disthene)	9·25	9·25
MS21	113×108 mm. 50s. As Type **8**; 50s. As No. 18; 100s. As No. 19; 100s. As No.20	10·25	10·25

9 Yeti on Ski Slopes

2016. Legends of Kyrgyzstan. Yeti. Multicoloured.

22	C (150s.) Type **9**	9·50	9·50
23	P (250s.) Holding towel by lake with yachts	10·10	10·10

10 Formosan Black Bear

2016. Philatelic Exhibitions in 2016. PHILATAIPEI 2016. World Stamp Championship Exhibition (**MS**24). World Stamp Show NY2016, New York (**MS**25). Multicoloured.

MS24	90×66 mm. 150s. Type **10**		9·50
MS25	90×60 mm. 250s. Bald Eagle		10·10

11 Black Taigan

2016. Salbuurun. Traditional Kyrgyz Hunting. Taigans (Hunting Dogs). Multicoloured.

26	50s. Type **11**	5·00	5·00
27	100s. Smooth-coated tan and white Taigan	9·25	9·25
28	150s. Taigan and Wolf	9·50	9·50
MS29	134×134 mm. 50s. As No. 26; 100s. As No. 27; 150s. As No. 28	24·00	24·00

12 *Leontopodium ochroleucum*

2016. Flora of Kyrgyzstan. Multicoloured.

30	50s. Type **12**	5·00	5·00
31	50s. *Iris orchioides*	5·00	5·00
32	100s. *Primula turkestanica*	9·25	9·25
33	100s. *Tulipa greigii*	9·25	9·25
MS34	137×80 mm. 50s. As No. 30; 50s. As No. 31; 100s. As No. 32; 100s. As No. 33	24·00	24·00
MS35	108×65 mm. 200s. *Papaver rhoeas*	9·75	9·75

13 Cycling

2016. Olympic Games. Rio 2016. Multicoloured.

36	50s. Type **13**	5·00	5·00
37	150s. Tennis	9·50	9·50

14 Mounted Archery

2016. World Nomad Games. Kyrgyzstan 2016. Multicoloured.

38	50s. Type **14**	5·00	5·00
39	100s. Horseback wrestling	9·25	9·25
40	150s. 'Burning horseman'	9·50	9·50

15 Falcon and Flag

2016. 25th Anniversary of Independence of Kyrgyz Republic. Sheet 118×65 mm.

MS41	**15** 150s. multicoloured	9·50	9·50

16 Emblem and Chess Pieces

2016. 42nd Chess Olympiad.

42	**16** 150s. multicoloured	9·50	9·50

17 Sergei Prokofiev

2016. Great Musicians. Multicoloured.

43	50s. Type **17**	5·00	5·00
44	50s. Yehudi Menuhin	5·00	5·00
45	100s. Antonin Dvorak	9·50	9·50
46	100s. Wolfgang Amadeus Mozart	9·50	9·50
MS47	120×80 mm. 50s. As No. 43; 50s. As No. 44; 100s. As No. 45; 100s. As No. 46	24·00	24·00

18 *Issyk-Kul* (three-mast schooner)

2016. Navigation on Lake Issyk-Kul. Ships. Multicoloured.

48	50s. Type **18**	5·00	5·00
49	50s. *Progress of Kyrgyzstan*	5·00	5·00
50	100s. *Moscow* (luxury cruiser used by President)	9·25	9·25
51	100s. Torpedo boat (carrying out weapons testing on Lake Issyk-Ku)	9·25	9·25
MS52	113×108 mm. 50s. As Type **18**; 50s. As No. 49; 100s. As No. 50; 100s. As No.51	17·00	17·00

19 Christmas Tree

2017. Fungi. Multicoloured.

53	50s. Type **19**	4·80	4·80
54	100s. Rooster	9·25	9·25

20 *Pleurotus ostreatus*

2017. Edible Fungi of Kyrgyzstan. Multicoloured.

55	50s. Type **20**	5·50	5·00
56	50s. *Leccinum scabrum*	5·50	5·00
57	100s. *Morchella conica*	11·00	10·00
58	100s. *Pleurotus eryngii*	11·00	10·00
MS59	80×113 mm. As Nos. 55/58	34·00	32·00

21 Wrestling

2017. Fourth Islamic Solidarity Games, Baku, Azerbaijan. Multicoloured.

60	50s. Type **21**	5·50	5·00
61	50s. Weight lifting	5·50	5·00
62	75s. Table tennis	8·25	7·75
63	100s. Football	11·00	10·00
MS64	113×108 mm. 50s. As Type **21**; 50s. As No. 61; 75s. As No. 62; 100s. As No. 63	31·00	29·00

22 Li Bai

2017. 25th Anniversary of Kyrgyzstan–China Diplomatic Relations. Historical and Cultural Ties. Li Bai (Chinese poet, born in North Kyrgyzstan). Multicoloured.

MS65	50s. Type **22**; 100s. Illustration for *The Ching-Ting Mountain* (poem by Li Bai)	18·00	17·00

23 Trakehner Horse

2017. Horses. Multicoloured.

66	50s. Type **23**	5·50	5·00
67	100s. Novokyrgyz horse (bay)	11·00	10·00

24 Peony

2017. 19th International Botanical Congress in Shenzhen. Multicoloured.

68	50s. Type **24**	5·50	5·00
69	100s. Chrysanthemum	11·00	10·00

25 Archer on Horseback

2017. Salbuurun. Traditional Kyrgyz Hunting. Multicoloured.

70	50s. Type **25**	5·50	5·00
71	75s. Rider releasing hawk	8·25	7·75
72	100s. Taigan chasing fox	11·00	10·00
MS73	134×134 mm. 50s. As Type **25**; 75s. As No. 71; 100s. As No. 72	26·00	25·00

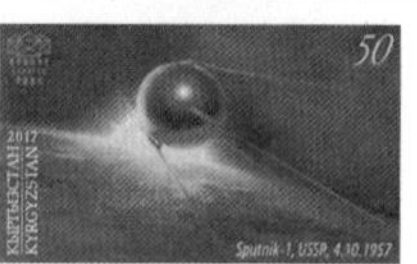

26 *Sputnik-1*, USSR, 4.10.1957

2017. 60th Anniversary of Space Exploration. Multicoloured.

74	50s. Type **26**	5·50	5·00
75	75s. Apollo Program, USA, 1961–1975	8·25	7·75
76	100s. Space Laboratory *Tiangong-2*, People's Republic of China, 2016	11·00	10·00
MS77	113×108 mm. 50s. As Type **26**; 75s. As No. 75; 100s. As No. 76	26·00	25·00

27 10s. *Gazella subgutturosa* (Goitered Gazelle) Collectors Coin (2013)

2017. 25th Anniversary of National Bank of Kyrgyz Republic.. Multicoloured.

MS78	50s. Type **27**; 100s. 10s. *Otis tardis* (Bustard) collectors coin (2015); 100s. 500s. banknote (2016), 1s., 3s., and 10s. coins (68×34 mm)	29·00	28·00

28 Manas Peak

2017. International Year of Tourism. Pearls of Kyrgyz Nature. Multicoloured.

MS79	50s. Type **28**; 150s. Kel-Suu Lake	23·00	22·00

29 Missile Launcher

2017. 25th Anniversary of Armed Forces of Kyrgyz Republic. Multicoloured.

80	50s. Type **29**	5·50	5·00
81	50s. Infantryman near an armoured troop-carrier	5·50	5·00
82	75s. Sappers mine-sweeping in the mountains	8·25	7·75
83	100s. Tank and military helicopter	11·00	10·00
MS84	113×108 mm. 50s. As Type **29**; 50s. As No. 81; 75s. As No. 82; 100s. As No. 83	31·00	30·00

30 Symbols of the Silk Road

2017. The Great Silk Road. Sheet 117×66 mm.

MS85	**30**	150s. multicoloured	18·00	17·00

31 Jonathon Swift

2017. Anniversaries. Multicoloured.

86	50s. Type **31** (writer) (350th birth anniversary)	5·50	5·00
87	50s. Arthur Charles Clarke (writer) (birth centenary)	5·50	5·00
88	75s. Marie Sklodowska-Curie (scientist) (150th birth anniversary)	8·25	7·75
89	100s. Gioachino Antonio Rossini (composer) (225th birth anniversary)	11·00	10·00
90	100s. John Ronald Reuel Tolkien (writer) (125th birth anniversary)	11·00	10·00
MS91	120×108 mm. 50s. As Type **31**; 50s. As No. 87; 75s. As No. 88; 100s. As No. 89; 100s. As No. 90	42·00	41·00

32 Year of the Earth Dog

2018. Chinese New Year. Year of the Dog

92	**32**	100s. multicoloured	11·00	10·00

LA AGUERA

An administrative district of Spanish Sahara, whose stamps it later used.

1920. Rio de Oro stamps optd **LA AGUERA**.

1	**15**	1c. green	2·75	2·75
2	**15**	2c. brown	2·75	2·75
3	**15**	5c. green	2·75	2·75
4	**15**	10c. red	2·75	2·75
5	**15**	15c. yellow	2·75	2·75
6	**15**	20c. violet	2·75	2·75
7	**15**	25c. blue	2·75	2·75
8	**15**	30c. brown	2·75	2·75
9	**15**	40c. pink	2·75	2·75
10	**15**	50c. blue	9·00	9·00
11	**15**	1p. red	18·00	18·00
12	**15**	4p. purple	50·00	50·00
13	**15**	10p. orange	£110	£110

2

1923

14	**2**	1c. blue	1·70	1·10
15	**2**	2c. green	1·70	1·10
16	**2**	5c. green	1·70	1·10
17	**2**	10c. red	1·70	1·10
18	**2**	15c. brown	1·70	1·10
19	**2**	20c. yellow	1·70	1·10
20	**2**	25c. blue	1·70	1·10
21	**2**	30c. brown	1·70	1·10
22	**2**	40c. red	2·40	1·60
23	**2**	50c. purple	6·75	5·00
24	**2**	1p. mauve	14·00	10·50
25	**2**	4p. violet	41·00	30·00
26	**2**	10p. orange	65·00	46·00

LABUAN

An Island off the N. coast of Borneo, ceded to Great Britain in 1846, and a Crown Colony from 1902. Incorporated with Straits Settlements in 1906, it used Straits stamps till it became part of N. Borneo in 1946.

100 cents = 1 dollar.

1

1879

17	**1**	2c. green	30·00	55·00
39	**1**	2c. red	6·50	3·50
6	**1**	6c. orange	£140	£150
40	**1**	6c. green	14·00	4·50
7	**1**	8c. red	£130	£130
41	**1**	8c. violet	13·00	19·00
43	**1**	10c. brown	32·00	8·00
9	**1**	12c. red	£300	£400
45	**1**	12c. blue	14·00	6·50
10	**1**	16c. blue	£100	£130
46	**1**	16c. grey	15·00	18·00
47	**1**	40c. orange	23·00	45·00

1880

(a) Surch **8**.

11	**1**	8c. on 12c. red	£1800	£850

(b) Surch **6 6** or **8 8**.

12	**1**	6c. on 16c. blue	£4000	£1300
13	**1**	8c. on 12c. red	£2250	£1200

1881. Surch **EIGHT CENTS**

14x	**1**	8c. on 12c. red	£425	£450

1881. Surch **Eight Cents**.

15	**1**	8c. on 12c. red	£150	£160

1883. Manuscript surch **one Dollar A.S.H.**

22	**1**	$1 on 16c. blue	£4500	

1885. Surch **2 CENTS** horiz.

23	**1**	2c. on 8c. red	£225	£550
24	**1**	2c. on 16c. blue	£950	£900

1885. Surch **2 Cents** horiz.

25	**1**	2c. on 16c. blue	£110	£160

1885. Surch with large **2 Cents** diag.

26	**1**	2c. on 8c. red	80·00	£130

1891. Surch **6 Cents**.

35	**1**	6c. on 8c. violet	16·00	16·00
37	**1**	6c. on 16c. blue	£2750	£2250
38	**1**	6c. on 40c. orange	£14000	£5000

1892. Surch as **Two CENTS** or **Six CENTS**.

49	**1**	2c. on 40c. orange	£170	£100
50	**1**	6c. on 16c. grey	£375	£150

1894. Types of North Borneo (different colours) optd **LABUAN**.

62	**24**	1c. black and mauve	1·50	14·00
63	**25**	2c. black and blue	2·50	15·00
64a	**26**	3c. black and yellow	18·00	9·00
65a	**27**	5c. black and green	50·00	25·00
67	**28**	6c. black and red	2·50	24·00
69	**29**	8c. black and pink	12·00	35·00
70	**30**	12c. black and orange	23·00	55·00
71	**31**	18c. black and brown	28·00	60·00
74a	**32**	24c. blue and mauve	22·00	55·00
80	-	25c. green (as No. 81)	42·00	50·00
81	-	50c. purple (as No. 82)	42·00	50·00
82	-	$1 blue (as No. 83)	80·00	75·00

1895. No. 83 of North Borneo surch **LABUAN** and value in cents.

75	4c. on $1 red	5·00	5·50
76	10c. on $1 red	11·00	1·40
77	20c. on $1 red	50·00	14·00
78	30c. on $1 red	55·00	65·00
79	40c. on $1 red	55·00	55·00

1896. Jubilee of Cession of Labuan to Great Britain. Nos. 62/68 optd **1846 JUBILEE 1896**.

83	**24**	1c. black and mauve	25·00	25·00
84d	**25**	2c. black and blue	50·00	24·00
85	**26**	3c. black and yellow	50·00	22·00
86	**27**	5c. black and green	70·00	16·00
87	**28**	6c. black and red	48·00	35·00
88b	**29**	8c. black and pink	55·00	15·00

Stamps of North Borneo. Nos. 92 to 106 (different colours), optd **LABUAN**. Opt at top of stamp.

89	1c. black and purple	8·00	4·75
90	2c. black and blue	28·00	6·00
91b	3c. black and yellow	9·00	7·00
92a	5c. black and green	65·00	60·00
93b	6c. black and red	15·00	21·00
94a	8c. black and pink	28·00	12·00
95a	12c. black and orange	32·00	55·00

1897. Stamps of North Borneo. Optd **LABUAN**. Overprint at foot of stamp

98a	12c. black and orange (as No. 106)	55·00	55·00

1897. Opt **LABUAN** at foot. Inscr 'POSTAL REVENUE'

96a	18c. black and bistre (as No. 108)	12·00	45·00

1897. Opt at foot. Inscr 'POSTAGE AND REVENUE'

99a	18c. black and bistre (as No. 110)	95·00	60·00

1897. Opt at top. Inscr 'POSTAGE AND REVENUE'

101b	18c. black and bistre (as No. 110)	55·00	60·00

1897. Opt at top. 'POSTAGE AND REVENUE' omitted

97a	24c. blue and lilac (as No. 109)	12·00	55·00

1897. Opt at top. Inscr 'POSTAGE AND REVENUE'

100	24c. blue and mauve (No. 111)	60·00	70·00

1899. Stamps of Labuan surch **4 CENTS**.

102	4c. on 5c. black & grn (No. 92a)	60·00	26·00
103	4c. on 6c. black & red (No. 93b)	32·00	19·00
104a	4c. on 8c. black and pink (No. 94a)	50·00	38·00
105	4c. on 12c. black and orange (No. 98a)	65·00	35·00
106	4c. on 18c. black and olive (No. 101b)	40·00	18·00
107a	4c. on 24c. blue and mauve (No. 100)	27·00	25·00
108	4c. on 25c. on 25c. green (No. 80)	6·00	7·50
109	4c. on 50c. on 50c. purple (No. 81)	8·50	7·50
110	4c. on $1 on $1 blue (No. 82)	8·50	7·50

1900. Stamps of North Borneo, as Nos. 95 to 107, optd **LABUAN**.

111	2c. black and green	3·75	2·50
112	4c. black and brown	8·50	75·00
113a	4c. black and red	5·00	18·00
114	5c. black and blue	20·00	23·00
115	10c. brown and grey	60·00	£100
116	16c. green and brown	50·00	£140

18

1902

117	**18**	1c. black and purple	7·00	7·50
118	**18**	2c. black and green	4·50	7·50
119	**18**	3c. black and brown	3·25	23·00
120	**18**	4c. black and red	3·25	4·00
121	**18**	8c. black and orange	14·00	9·00
122	**18**	10c. brown and blue	3·25	19·00
123	**18**	12c. black and yellow	16·00	26·00
124	**18**	16c. green and brown	4·75	38·00
125	**18**	18c. black and brown	3·25	38·00
126	**18**	25c. green and blue	7·50	29·00
127	**18**	50c. purple and lilac	11·00	50·00
128	**18**	$1 red and orange	10·00	50·00

1904. Surch **4 cents**.

129	4c. on 5c. black and green (No. 92a)	55·00	50·00
130	4c. on 6c. black and red (No. 93b)	12·00	50·00
131	4c. on 8c. black and pink (No. 94a)	25·00	55·00
132	4c. on 12c. black and orange (No. 98a)	50·00	50·00
133	4c. on 18c. black and olive (No. 101b)	23·00	50·00
134a	4c. on 24c. blue and mauve (No. 100)	42·00	42·00
135	4c. on 25c. green (No. 80)	8·50	40·00
136	4c. on 50c. purple (No. 81)	8·50	40·00
137	4c. on $1 blue (No. 82)	13·00	38·00

1904. Nos. 81, 83 and 84/86 of North Borneo optd **LABUAN**.

138	25c. indigo	£1200	†
139	$1 blue	†	†
140	$2 green	£3500	£3750
141	$5 purple	£6000	†
142	$10 brown	£55000	†

Dangerous forgeries exist.

POSTAGE DUE STAMPS

1901. Optd **POSTAGE DUE**.

D1	2c. black and green (No. 111)	28·00	45·00
D2	3c. black and yellow (No. 91)	38·00	£130
D3b	4c. black and red (No. 113)	50·00	£110
D4	5c. black and blue (No. 114)	55·00	£170
D5	6c. black and red (No. 93b)	45·00	£120
D6	8c. black and pink (No. 94a)	£120	£130
D7b	12c. black and orange (No. 98a)	£120	£170
D8	18c. black and olive (No. 101b)	42·00	£140
D9c	24c. blue and mauve (No. 100)	65·00	£130

LAGOS

A British colony on the southern coast of Nigeria. United with Southern Nigeria in 1906 to form the Colony and Protectorate of Southern Nigeria.

12 pence = 1 shilling;
20 shillings = 1 pound.

1

1874

21	**1**	½d. green	2·00	80
17	**1**	1d. mauve	42·00	30·00
22	**1**	1d. red	2·00	80
11	**1**	2d. blue	80·00	15·00
23	**1**	2d. grey	95·00	9·00
19	**1**	3d. brown	28·00	9·00
5	**1**	4d. red	£150	50·00
24	**1**	4d. violet	£160	13·00
25	**1**	6d. green	8·00	55·00
26	**1**	1s. orange	22·00	25·00
27	**1**	2s.6d. black	£350	£275
28	**1**	5s. blue	£700	£500
29	**1**	10s. brown	£1600	£1000

1887

30	**1**	2d. mauve and blue	8·50	2·00
31	**1**	2½d. blue	8·00	1·75
32	**1**	3d. mauve and brown	2·50	3·25
33	**1**	4d. mauve and black	2·25	1·75
34	**1**	5d. mauve and green	2·25	11·00
35	**1**	6d. mauve	4·75	3·00
36	**1**	7½d. mauve and red	4·50	38·00
37	**1**	10d. mauve and yellow	4·50	13·00
38	**1**	1s. green and black	5·50	29·00
39	**1**	2s.6d. green and red	23·00	80·00
40	**1**	5s. green and blue	48·00	£150
41	**1**	10s. green and brown	£120	£250

1893. Surch **HALF PENNY** and bars.

42	**1**	½d. on 4d. mauve and black	11·00	4·00

3

1904

44	**3**	½d. green	3·25	5·50
45	**3**	1d. purple and black on red	1·25	15
56	**3**	2d. purple and blue	6·00	3·25
47	**3**	2½d. purple and blue on blue	1·50	1·50
48	**3**	3d. purple and brown	3·50	1·75
59a	**3**	6d. purple and mauve	4·25	1·50
60a	**3**	1s. green and black	28·00	2·25
61	**3**	2s.6d. green and red	28·00	75·00
62	**3**	5s. green and blue	26·00	£110
63a	**3**	10s. green and brown	90·00	£250

LAOS

Previously part of French Indo-China, the Kingdom of Laos was proclaimed in 1947. In 1949 it became an Associated State within the French Union and in 1953 it became fully independent within the Union.

Laos left the French Union in 1956. In 1976 it became a Republic.

1951. 100 cents = 1 piastre.
1955. 100 cents = 1 kip.

1 River Mekong

2 King Sisavang Vong

1951

No.	Type	Description	Mint	Used
1	1	10c. green and turquoise	85	55
2	1	20c. red and purple	85	55
3	1	30c. blue and indigo	2·75	1·60
4	-	50c. brown and deep brown	65	55
5	-	60c. orange and red	65	55
6	-	70c. turquoise and blue	85	65
7	-	1p. violet and deep violet	1·60	1·10
8	2	1p.50 purple and brown	2·20	1·60
9	-	2p. green and turquoise	27·00	13·00
10	-	3p. red and purple	3·25	2·10
11	-	5p. blue and indigo	3·75	2·40
12	-	10p. purple and brown	4·25	2·50

Designs: As T **1**—50c. to 70c. Luang Prabang; 1p. and 2p. to 10p. Vientiane.

3 Laotian Woman

4 Laotian Woman Weaving

1952

No.	Type	Description	Mint	Used
13	3	30c. violet and blue (postage)	1·10	55
14	3	80c. turquoise and green	1·10	55
15	3	1p.10 red and crimson	1·10	1·10
16	3	1p.90 blue and indigo	1·70	1·60
17	3	3p. deep brown and brown	1·70	1·60
18	-	3p.30 violet and deep violet (air)	2·75	2·00
19	4	10p. green and blue	4·25	2·20
20	4	20p. red and crimson	7·00	4·25
21	4	30p. brown and black	11·00	8·25

Design: As T **4**—3p.30, Vat Pra Keo shrine.

1952. Anniversary of First Issue of Laos Stamps. Souvenir booklet containing 26 sheets inscr 'ROYAUME DU LASO' in French and Laotian. Nos. 1/2, 13/17, 19/21 and D22/D27.

MS21b 26 sheets each 130×90 mm £550

5 King Sisavang Vong and UPU Monument

1952. First Anniversary of Admission to UPU.

No.	Type	Description	Mint	Used
22	5	80c. violet, blue and indigo (postage)	2·20	1·60
23	5	1p. brown, red and lake	2·20	1·60
24	5	1p.20 blue and violet	2·20	1·60
25	5	1p.50 brown, emerald and green	2·20	1·60
26	5	1p.90 turquoise and sepia	2·20	1·60
27	5	25p. indigo and blue (air)	8·75	6·50
28	5	50p. sepia, purple and brown	8·75	6·50

6 Girl carrying her Brother

1953. Red Cross Fund. Cross in red.

No.	Type	Description	Mint	Used
29	6	1p.50+1p. purple and blue	4·25	3·75
30	6	3p.+1p.50 red and green	4·25	3·75
31	6	3p.90+2p.50 purple and brn	5·50	4·50

7 Court of Love

1953

No.	Type	Description	Mint	Used
32	7	4p.50 turquoise and blue	2·75	1·10
33	7	6p. brown and slate	3·25	1·10

8 Buddha

1953. Air. Statues of Buddha.

No.	Type	Description	Mint	Used
34	-	4p. green	2·75	1·10
35	-	6p.50 green	2·20	1·40
36	-	9p. green	2·75	2·00
37	8	11p.50 orange, brown and red	4·25	3·75
38	-	40p. purple	9·75	3·75
39	-	100p. green	22·00	14·00

Designs: Horiz—4p. Reclining. Vert—6p.50, Seated; 9p. Standing (full-face); 40p. Standing (facing right); 100p. Buddha and temple dancer.

9 Vientiane

1954. Golden Jubilee of King Sisavang Vong.

No.	Type	Description	Mint	Used
40	9	2p. violet and blue (postage)	80·00	80·00
41	9	3p. red and brown	80·00	80·00
42	9	50p. turquoise and blue (air)	£275	£275

10 Ravana

1955. Air. *Ramayana* (dramatic poem).

No.	Type	Description	Mint	Used
43	10	2k. blue, emerald and green	1·60	1·10
44	-	4k. red and brown	2·20	1·60
45	-	5k. green, brown and red	2·75	2·20
46	-	10k. black, orange and brown	5·50	4·25
47	-	20k. olive, green and violet	11·00	5·50
48	-	30k. black, brown and blue	15·00	7·50

Designs: Horiz—4k. Hanuman, the white monkey; 5k. Ninh Laphath, the black monkey. Vert—10k. Sita and Rama; 20k. Luci and Ravana's friend; 30k. Rama.

11 Buddha and Worshippers

1956. 2500th Anniversary of Buddhist Era.

No.	Type	Description	Mint	Used
49	11	2k. brown (postage)	6·50	3·25
50	11	3k. black	7·50	3·75
51	11	5k. sepia	8·75	4·50
52	11	20k. carmine and red (air)	43·00	39·00
53	11	30k. green and bistre	55·00	48·00

Nos. 49/53 were wrongly inscribed as commemorating the birth anniversary of Buddha.

12 UN Emblem

13 UN Emblem

1956. First Anniversary of Admission to UN.

No.	Type	Description	Mint	Used
54	12	1k. black (postage)	1·50	85
55	12	2k. blue	1·80	1·30
56	12	4k. red	2·20	1·40
57	12	6k. violet	2·75	1·80
58	13	15k. blue (air)	11·00	9·25
59	13	30k. red	14·00	13·00

14 Flute Player

1957. Native Musicians.

No.	Type	Description	Mint	Used
60	14	2k. multicoloured (postage)	2·75	1·80
61	-	4k. multicoloured	2·75	1·80
62	-	8k. blue, brown and orange	4·25	2·20
63	-	12k. multicoloured (air)	5·00	3·75
64	-	14k. multicoloured	5·50	4·50
65	-	20k. multicoloured	6·50	5·50

Designs: Vert—4k. Piper; 14k. Violinist; 20k. Drummer. Horiz—8k. Xylophonist; 12k. Bells player.

15 Harvesting Rice

1957. Rice Cultivation.

No.	Type	Description	Mint	Used
66	15	3k. multicoloured	2·20	85
67	-	5k. brown, red and green	2·20	1·10
68	-	16k. violet, olive and blue	3·75	2·00
69	-	26k. chocolate, brown and green	5·00	3·25

Designs: Vert—5k. Drying rice; 16k. Winnowing rice. Horiz—26k. Polishing rice.

16 The Offertory

1957. Air. Buddhism.

No.	Type	Description	Mint	Used
70	16	10k. multicoloured	2·00	1·30
71	-	15k. brown, yellow & choc	2·20	1·80
72	-	18k. yellow and green	3·75	2·40
73	-	24k. red, black and yellow	5·00	5·50

Designs: As T **16**: Horiz—15k. Meditation (children on river craft). 48×36½ mm—24k. The Great Renunciation (dancers with horse). Vert—18k. Serenity (head of Buddhist).

17 Carrier Elephants

1958. Laotian Elephants. Multicoloured.

No.	Description	Mint	Used
74	10c. Type **17**	1·10	55
75	20c. Elephant's head with headdress	1·10	55
76	30c. Elephant with howdah (vert)	1·30	55
77	2k. Elephant hauling log	1·60	55
78	5k. Elephant walking with calf (vert)	3·75	1·60
79	10k. Caparisoned elephant (vert)	6·00	1·60
80	13k. Elephant bearing throne (vert)	8·25	3·25

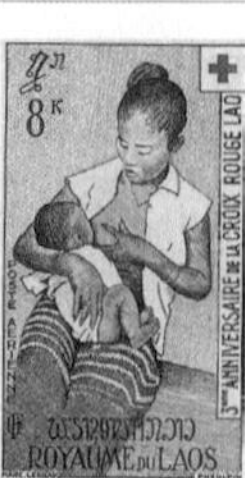
18 Mother and Child

1958. Air. Third Anniversary of Laotian Red Cross. Cross in red.

No.	Type	Description	Mint	Used
81	18	8k. black and grey	2·40	1·60
82	18	12k. olive and brown	2·50	1·60
83	18	15k. turquoise and green	2·75	1·80
84	18	20k. violet and bistre	3·25	2·20

19

1958. Inauguration of UNESCO Headquarters Building, Paris.

No.	Type	Description	Mint	Used
85	19	50c. blue, orange and red	65	35
86	-	60c. violet, brown and green	75	35
87	-	70c. blue, brown and red	75	35
88	-	1k. red, blue and bistre	1·10	65

Designs: Vert—60c. Woman, children and part of exterior of UNESCO building; 70c. Woman and children hailing UNESCO building superimposed on globe. Horiz—1k. General view of UNESCO building and Eiffel Tower.

20 King Sisavang Vong

1959

No.	Type	Description	Mint	Used
89	20	4k. lake	85	65
90	20	6k.50 red	1·00	75
91	20	9k. mauve	1·10	75
92	20	13k. green	1·60	1·10

21 Stage Performance

1959. Education and Fine Arts.

No.	Type	Description	Mint	Used
93	21	1k. multicoloured	75	45
94	-	2k. lake, violet and black	85	45
95	-	3k. black, green and purple	1·30	55
96	-	5k. green, yellow and violet	1·40	1·00

Designs: Vert—2k. Student and 'Lamp of Learning'; 5k. Stage performers and Buddhist temple. Horiz—3k. Teacher and children with 'Key to Education'.

22 Portal of Vat Phou Temple, Pakse

1959. Laotian Monuments. Multicoloured.

No.	Description	Mint	Used
97	50c. Type **22**	55	20
98	1k.50 That Ing Hang, Savannakhet (horiz)	85	35
99	2k.50 Vat Phou Temple, Pakse (horiz)	1·00	55
100	7k. That Luang, Vientiane	1·50	65
101	11k. As 7k., but different view (horiz)	1·60	1·00
102	12k.50 Phou-Si Temple, Luang Prabang	2·20	1·20

1960. World Refugee Year. Nos. 89 and 79 surch **ANNEE MONDIALE DU REFUGIE 1959–1960** and premium.

No.	Description	Mint	Used
103	4k.+1k. red	6·50	6·50
104	10k.+1k. multicoloured	9·75	9·75

24 Plain of Jars, Xieng Khouang

1960. Air. Tourism.

No.	Type	Description	Mint	Used
105	24	9k.50 red, bistre and blue	1·40	1·10
106	-	12k. brown, violet and green	1·50	1·40

107	-	15k. red, green and brown	2·10	1·70
108	-	19k. brown, orange and green	2·75	2·10

Designs: Horiz—12k. Phapheng Falls, Champassak; 15k. Pair of bullocks with cart. Vert—19k. Buddhist monk and village.

25 Funeral Urn

1961. Funeral of King Sisavang Vong.

109	**25**	4k. bistre, black and red	1·80	1·40
110	-	6k.50 brown and black	2·00	1·50
111	-	9k. brown and black	2·10	1·60
112	-	25k. black	6·00	4·50

Designs: 6k.50, Urn under canopy; 9k. Catafalque on dragon carriage; 25k. King Sisavang Vong.

26 Temples and Statues ('Pou Gneu Nha Gneu')

1962. Air. Festival of Makha Bousa.

113	**26**	11k. brown, red and green	1·60	1·10
114	-	14k. blue and orange	2·20	1·30
115	-	20k. green, yellow and mauve	2·75	2·00
116	-	25k. red, blue and green	3·25	2·40

Designs: As T **26**—14k. Bird (Garuda); 20k. Flying deities (Hanuman). 36×48 mm: 25k. Warriors (Nang Teng One).

27 King Savang Vatthana

1962

117	**27**	1k. brown, red and blue	55	25
118	**27**	2k. brown, red and mauve	1·00	35
119	**27**	5k. brown, red and blue	1·10	55
120	**27**	10k. brown, red and bistre	1·60	65

28 Laotian Boy

1962. Malaria Eradication.

121	**28**	4k. olive, black and green	75	20
122	-	9k. brown, black & turq	1·00	55
123	-	10k. red, yellow and green	1·50	65
MS123a		130×100 mm. Nos. 121/122. Imperf	£400	

Design: 9k. Laotian girl; 10k. Campaign emblem.

29 Royal Courier

1962. Philatelic Exhibition, Vientiane, and Stamp Day.

124	-	50c. multicoloured	1·00	85
125	-	70c. multicoloured	1·20	75
126	-	1k. black, green and red	2·00	1·60
127	**29**	1k.50 multicoloured	2·40	1·30
MS127a		Two sheets (each 129×100 mm) containing Nos. 124/125 and 126/127	£350	
MS127b		As above but imperf	£350	

Designs: Horiz—50c. Modern mail transport; 70c. Dancer and globe. Vert—1k. Royal courtier on elephant.

30 Fisherman

1963. Freedom from Hunger.

128	**30**	1k. bistre, violet and green	75	35
129	-	4k. blue, brown and green	1·00	55
130	-	5k. blue, bistre and green	1·10	65
131	-	9k. blue, green and brown	1·80	75
MS131a		220×100 mm. Nos. 128/131. Imperf	6·50	5·50

Designs: Vert—4k. Threshing rice; 9k. Harvesting rice. Horiz—5k. Ploughing paddy field.

31 Queen of Laos

1963. Red Cross Centenary.

132	**31**	4k. red, blue and brown	1·10	75
133	**31**	6k. multicoloured	1·30	85
134	**31**	10k. red, blue and brown	2·00	1·40
MS134a		140×100 mm. Nos. 132/134	11·00	7·50

32 Laotian supporting UN Emblem

1963. 15th Anniversary of Declaration of Human Rights.

135	**32**	4k. purple, blue and red	2·20	1·30

33 Temple, Map and Rameses II

1964. Nubian Monuments Preservation.

136	**33**	4k. multicoloured	65	55
137	**33**	6k. multicoloured	1·00	75
138	**33**	10k. multicoloured	1·30	1·10
MS138a		185×100 mm. Nos. 136/138 (sold at 25k.)	5·50	5·50

34 Offertory Vase and Horn

1964. Constitutional Monarchy. Multicoloured.

139		10k. Type **34**	75	35
140		15k. Seated Buddha of Vat Pra Keo	1·00	45
141		20k. Laotians walking across map	1·10	65
142		40k. Royal Palace, Luang Prabang	2·10	85
MS142a		140×140 mm. Nos. 139/142	7·50	6·50

35 Phra Vet and Wife

1964. Folklore. Phra Vet Legend. Multicoloured.

143		10k. Type **35**	75	65
144		32k. Benediction	1·10	1·00
145		45k. Phame and wife	1·60	1·40
146		55k. Arrest of Phame	2·00	1·80
MS146a		140×80 mm. Nos. 143/146. Imperf	13·00	9·25

36 Meo Warrior

1964. People of Laos.

147	-	25k. black, brown and green (postage)	2·00	1·10
148	**36**	5k. multicoloured (air)	75	20
149	-	10k. pink, grey and purple	1·10	35
150	-	50k. brown, drab and lilac	3·25	1·30
MS150a		150×115 mm. Nos. 147/150	8·25	6·50

Designs: 10k. Kha hunter; 25k. Girls of three races; 50k. Thai woman.

37 Red Lacewing

1965. Butterflies and Moths.

151	**37**	10k. chestnut, brown and green (postage)	3·25	2·75
152	-	25k. blue, black and yellow	6·50	3·25
153	-	40k. yellow, brown & green	13·00	6·50
154	-	20k. red and yellow (air)	7·50	4·25

Butterflies: As T **37**—25k. Yellow pansy. 48×27 mm—20k. Atlas moth; 40k. *Dysphania militaris* (moth).

38 Wattay Airport ('French Aid')

1965. Foreign Aid.

155	**38**	25k. mauve, brown & turq	75	55
156	-	45k. brown and green	1·10	75
157	-	55k. brown and blue	1·60	1·10
158	-	75k. multicoloured	2·50	1·60

Designs: Vert—45k. Mother bathing child (water resources: 'Japanese Aid'); 75k. School and plants (education and cultivation: 'American Aid'). Horiz: 55k. Studio of radio station ('British Aid').

39 Hophabang

1965

159	**39**	10k. multicoloured	1·00	65

40 Teleprinter Operator, Globe and Map

1965. ITU Centenary.

160	**40**	5k. brown, violet and purple	75	35
161	-	30k. brown, blue and green	1·00	65
162	-	50k. multicoloured	1·70	1·20
MS162a		150×100 mm. Nos. 160/2	6·50	5·50

Designs: 30k. Globe, map, telephonist and radio operator; 50k. Globe, radio receiver and mast.

1965. Nos. 89/90 surch.

163	**20**	1k. on 4k. lake	1·00	35
164	**20**	5k. on 6k.50 brown	1·10	45

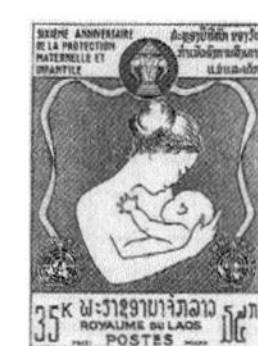
42 Mother and Baby

1965. Sixth Anniversary of UN. Protection of Mother and Child.

165	**42**	35k. ultramarine and red	2·00	1·50
MS165a		130×100 mm. No. 165	8·75	8·25

43 Leopard Cat

1965. Air. Laotian Fauna.

166	**43**	25k. yellow, brown & green	1·00	55
167	-	55k. brown, sepia and blue	1·40	1·00
168	-	75k. brown and green	1·60	1·20
169	-	100k. brown, black & yell	2·75	1·60
170	-	200k. black and red	7·50	5·00

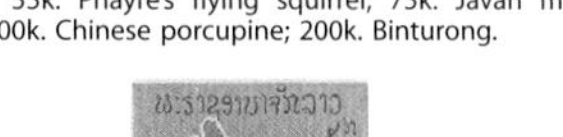
Designs: 55k. Phayre's flying squirrel; 75k. Javan mongoose; 100k. Chinese porcupine; 200k. Binturong.

44 UN Emblem on Map

1965. 20th Anniversary of UN.

171	**44**	5k. blue, grey and green	45	35
172	**44**	25k. blue, grey and mauve	75	55
173	**44**	40k. blue, grey and turquoise	1·10	1·00

45 Bulls in Combat

1965. Laotian Pastimes.

174	**45**	10k. brown, black and orange	65	35
175	-	20k. blue, red and green	75	45
176	-	25k. red, blue and green	85	55
177	-	50k. multicoloured	1·50	85

Designs: 20k. Tikhy (form of hockey); 25k. Pirogue race; 50k. Rocket festival.

46 Slaty-headed Parakeet

1966. Birds.

178	**46**	5k. green, brown and red	1·10	65
179	-	15k. brown, black & turq	1·60	75

180	-	20k. sepia, ochre and blue	2·75	1·30
181	-	45k. blue, sepia and violet	5·50	3·25

Birds: 15k. White-crested laughing thrush; 20k. Osprey; 45k. Indian roller (or 'blue jay').

47 WHO Building

1966. Inauguration of WHO Headquarters, Geneva.

182	**47**	10k. blue and turquoise	75	35
183	**47**	25k. green and red	85	45
184	**47**	50k. black and blue	1·30	85
MS185 150×100 mm. Nos. 182/184 (sold at 150k.)			30·00	28·00

48 Ordination of Priests

1966. Laotian Ceremonies. Multicoloured.

186	10k. Type **48**	75	35
187	25k. Sand-hills ceremony	85	55
188	30k. 'Wax pagoda' procession (vert)	1·30	65
189	40k. 'Sou-Khouan' ceremony (vert)	1·60	75

49 UNESCO Emblem

1966. 20th Anniversary of UNESCO.

190	**49**	20k. orange and black	45	35
191	**49**	30k. blue and black	65	55
192	**49**	40k. green and black	75	65
193	**49**	60k. red and black	1·10	1·00
MS194 140×140 mm. Nos. 190/193 (sold at 250k.)			7·50	6·50

50 Letter, Carrier Pigeon and Emblem

1966. International Correspondence Week.

195	**50**	5k. blue, brown and red	45	20
196	**50**	20k. purple, black and green	75	45
197	**50**	40k. brown, red and blue	85	55
198	**50**	45k. black, green and purple	1·30	85
MS199 130×100 mm. Nos. 195/198 (sold at 240k.)			6·50	5·50

51 Flooded Village

1967. Mekong Delta Flood Relief. Multicoloured.

200	20k.+5k. Type **51**	85	75
201	40k.+10k. Flooded market-place	1·30	1·20
202	60k.+15k. Flooded airport	2·10	2·00
MS203 150×100 mm. Nos. 200/202 (sold at 250k.)		8·75	8·25

52 Carving, Siprapouthbat Pagoda

1967. Buddhist Art.

204	**52**	5k. green and brown	35	20
205	-	20k. blue and sepia	65	35
206	-	50k. purple and sepia	1·40	85
207	-	70k. grey and brown	2·00	1·30

Designs: (carvings in temple pagodas, Luang Prabang): 30k. Visoun; 50k. Xiengthong; 70k. Visoun (different).

53 General Post Office

1967. Opening of New GPO Building, Vientiane.

208	**53**	25k. brown, green and purple	65	20
209	**53**	50k. blue, green and slate	85	55
210	**53**	70k. red, green and brown	1·30	85

54 Giant Snakehead

1967. Fish.

211	**54**	20k. black, bistre and blue	1·60	55
212	-	35k. slate, bistre and blue	2·00	65
213	-	45k. sepia, ochre and green	3·50	1·00
214	-	60k. black, bistre and green	5·00	1·10

Designs: 35k. Giant catfish; 45k. Tire-track spiny eel; 60k. Bronze knifefish.

55 *Cassia fistula*

1967. Flowers.

215	**55**	30k. yellow, green and mauve	85	55
216	-	55k. red, green and orange	1·30	65
217	-	75k. red, green and blue	1·60	1·20
218	-	80k. yellow, mauve and green	2·75	1·30

Designs: 55k. *Cucuma singulario*; 75k. *Poinciana regia*; 80k. *Plumeria acutifolia*.

56 Harvesting

1967. Tenth Anniversary of Laotian Red Cross.

219	**56**	20k.+5k. multicoloured	65	55
220	**56**	50k.+10k. multicoloured	1·30	1·10
221	**56**	60k.+15k. multicoloured	2·20	1·70
MS222 185×99 mm. Nos. 219/221 (sold at 250k.+30k.)			6·50	6·00

57 Banded Krait

1967. Reptiles.

223	**57**	5k. blue, yellow and green	1·10	55
224	-	40k. brown, bistre and green	2·20	85
225	-	100k. chocolate, brown and green	4·25	3·50
226	-	200k. black, brown and green	11·00	9·75

Designs: 40k. Marsh crocodile; 100k. Pit viper; 200k. Water monitor.

58 Human Rights Emblem

1968. Human Rights Year. Emblem in red and green.

227	**58**	20k. green	75	25
228	**58**	30k. brown	85	35
229	**58**	50k. blue	1·30	75
MS230 190×100 mm. Nos. 227/229 (sold at 250k.)			9·25	8·75

59 Military Parade

1968. Army Day. Multicoloured.

231	15k. Type **59** (postage)	55	45
232	20k. Soldiers and tank in battle	65	55
233	60k. Soldiers and Laotian flag	1·10	75
234	200k. Parade of colours before National Assembly building (air)	2·40	1·60
235	300k. As No. 234	3·50	2·20
MS236 80×110 mm. Nos. 231/235 (sold at 600k.)		11·50	11·00

60 WHO Emblem

1968. 20th Anniversary of WHO.

237	**60**	15k. brown, red and purple	35	25
238	**60**	30k. brown, green and blue	55	45
239	**60**	70k. brown, purple and red	85	55
240	**60**	110k. light brown, purple and brown	1·40	1·10
241	**60**	250k. brown, blue and green	3·25	2·40
MS242 130×115 mm. Nos. 237/241 (sold at 500k.)			11·50	11·00

61 *Chrysochroa mnizechi*

1968. Beetles.

243	**61**	30k. blue, yellow and green (postage)	1·10	55
244	-	50k. black, orange & purple	1·60	65
245	-	90k. blue, orange and ochre	2·75	1·20
246	-	120k. black and orange (air)	3·25	1·60
247	-	160k. multicoloured	4·25	2·75

Insects: Vert—50k. *Aristobia approximator*; 90k. *Eutaenia corbetti*. Horiz—120k. *Dorysthenes walkeri*; 160k. *Megaloxantha bicolor*.

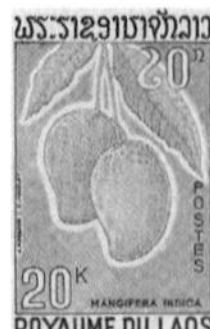
62 *Mangifera indica*

1968. Laotian Fruits.

248	**62**	20k. green, blue and black	65	45
249	-	50k. green, red and blue	85	55
250	-	180k. green, brown and orange	3·00	1·60
251	-	250k. green, brown and yellowl	4·25	2·40

Designs: Vert—50k. *Tamarindus indica*. Horiz—180k. *Artocarpus intregrifolia*; 250k. *Citrullus vulgaris*.

63 Hurdling

1968. Olympic Games, Mexico.

252	**63**	15k. green, blue and brown	55	35
253	-	80k. brown, turquoise and blue	1·10	65
254	-	100k. blue, brown and green	1·60	75
255	-	110k. brown, red and blue	2·20	85

Designs: 80k. Tennis; 100k. Football; 110k. High jumping.

64 Oriental Door, Wat Ong Tu (detail)

1969. Wat Ong Tu Temple.

256	**64**	150k. gold, black and red	3·25	1·60
257	-	200k. gold, black and red	4·25	2·40

Design: 200k. Central door, Wat Ong Tu.

65 Pharak praying to the Gods

1969. Laotian *Ballet Royal*. Designs showing dance characters. Multicoloured.

258	10k. Type **65** (postage)	85	35
259	15k. Soukhib ordered to attack	1·10	55
260	20k. Thotsakan reviewing troops	1·30	75
261	30k. Nang Sida awaiting punishment	1·60	85
262	40k. Pharam inspecting his troops	2·40	1·10
263	60k. Hanuman about to rescue Nang Sida	3·25	1·80
264	110k. Soudagnou battling with Thotsakan (air)	5·50	3·25
265	300k. Pharam dancing with Thotsakkan	11·00	6·00
MS266 Two sheets, each 106×106 mm. (a) Nos. 258/260, 265 (sold at 650k.); (b) Nos. 261/264 (sold at 480k.). Imperf		55·00	49·00

66 Handicrafts Workshop, Vientiane

1969. Tenth Anniversary of ILO.

267	**66**	30k. violet and purple (postage)	75	55
268	**66**	60k. brown and green	1·40	1·10
269	-	300k. black and brown (air)	8·75	6·50

Design: 300k. Elephants moving logs.

67 Chinese Pangolin

1969. Wild Animals (1st series). Multicoloured.

270	15k. Type **67** (postage)	85	45
271	30k. Type **67**	1·30	55

No.	Type	Description	Mint	Used
272		70k. Sun bear (air)	1·60	85
273		120k. Common gibbon (vert)	3·75	1·60
274		150k. Tiger	4·25	2·40

See also Nos. 300/303 and 331/335.

68 Royal Mausoleum, Luang Prabang

1969. Tenth Death Anniversary of King Sisavang Vong.

No.	Type	Description	Mint	Used
275	**68**	50k. ochre, blue and green	1·40	85
276	-	70k. ochre and lake	1·60	1·10

Design: 70k. King Sisavang Vong (medallion).

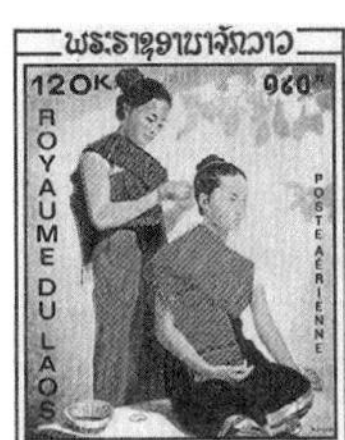

69 *Lao Woman being Groomed* (Leguay)

1969. Air. Paintings by Marc Leguay (1st series). Multicoloured.

No.	Description	Mint	Used
277	10k. Type **69**	2·75	1·60
278	150k. *Village Market* (horiz)	3·75	2·20

See also Nos. 285, 307/309 and 357/361.

70 Carved Capital, Wat Xieng Thong

1970. Laotian Pagodas. Multicoloured.

No.	Description	Mint	Used
279	70k. Type **70** (postage)	2·20	1·10
280	100k. Library, Wat Sisaket (air)	2·40	1·40
281	120k. Wat Xieng Thong (horiz)	2·75	1·60

71 Noon Drum

1970. Laotian Drums.

No.	Type	Description	Mint	Used
282	**71**	30k. mult (postage)	1·60	85
283	-	55k. black, green and brown	2·20	1·30
284	-	125k. brown, yellow and flesh (air)	4·25	2·20

Designs: Horiz—55k. Bronze drum. Vert—125k. Wooden drum.

1970. Air. Paintings by Marc Leguay (2nd series). As T **69**. Multicoloured.

No.	Description	Mint	Used
285	150k. *Banks of the Mekong* (horiz)	3·75	1·80

72 Franklin D. Roosevelt

1970. Air. 25th Death Anniversary of Franklin D. Roosevelt (American statesman).

No.	Type	Description	Mint	Used
286	**72**	120k. slate and green	3·25	1·60

73 *Lenin explaining Electrification Plan* (L. Shmatko)

1970. Birth Centenary of Lenin.

No.	Type	Description	Mint	Used
287	**73**	30k. multicoloured	1·80	65
288	**73**	70k. multicoloured	1·20	85

1970. Support for War Victims. Nos. 258/265 (*Ballet Royal*) surch **Soutien aux Victimes de la Guerre** and premium.

No.	Description	Mint	Used
289	10k.+5k. mult (postage)	85	65
290	15k.+5k. multicoloured	85	65
291	20k.+5k. multicoloured	85	65
292	30k.+5k. multicoloured	85	65
293	40k.+5k. multicoloured	1·70	1·30
294	60k.+5k. multicoloured	1·80	1·50
295	110k.+5k. multicoloured (air)	4·25	3·25
296	300k.+5k. multicoloured	6·00	5·00

75 Weaving Silk

1970. EXPO 70 World Fair, Osaka, Japan. Laotian Silk Industry.

No.	Type	Description	Mint	Used
297	**75**	30k. bl, brn & red (postage)	1·10	55
298	-	70k. multicoloured	1·60	1·10
299	-	125k. multicoloured (air)	2·75	2·20

Designs: 70k. Silk-spinning; 125k. Winding skeins.

76 Wild Boar

1970. Wild Animals (2nd series).

No.	Type	Description	Mint	Used
300	**76**	20k. brown and green (postage)	85	35
301	**76**	60k. brown and olive	1·60	65
302	-	210k. brown, red and yellow (air)	4·25	2·40
303	-	500k. green, brown and orange	7·50	4·25

Animals: 210k. Leopard; 500k. Gaur.

77 Buddha, UN Emblem and New York HQ

1970. 25th Anniversary of UNO.

No.	Type	Description	Mint	Used
304	**77**	30k. brown, mauve and blue (postage)	1·10	85
305	**77**	70k. brown, blue and green	2·20	1·10
306	-	125k. multicoloured (air)	3·75	2·75

Design: 26×36 mm—125k. Nang Thorani (Goddess of the Earth) and New York Headquarters.

1970. Air. Paintings by Marc Leguay (3rd series). As T **69**. Multicoloured.

No.	Description	Mint	Used
307	100k. *Village Track*	2·20	1·30
308	120k. *Paddy-field in the Rainy Season* (horiz)	2·75	2·00
309	150k. *Village Elder*	4·25	2·20

78 Nakhanet

1971. Laotian Mythology (1st series). Frescoes from Triumphal Arch, Vientiane. Multicoloured.

No.	Type	Description	Mint	Used
310	**78**	70k. orange, brown and red (postage)	1·60	1·10
311	-	85k. green, yellow and blue	2·20	1·30
312	-	125k. multicoloured (air)	3·75	2·75

Designs: As T **78**—85k. Rahu. 49×36 mm: 125k. Underwater duel between Nang Matsa and Hanuman.

See also Nos. 352/354 and 385/387.

79 Silversmiths

1971. Laotian Traditional Crafts. Multicoloured.

No.	Description	Mint	Used
313	30k. Type **79**	85	45
314	50k. Potters	1·10	55
315	70k. Pirogue-builder (49×36 mm)	1·30	1·10

80 Laotian and African Children

1971. Racial Equality Year.

No.	Type	Description	Mint	Used
316	**80**	30k. blue, red and green	65	35
317	-	60k. violet, red and yellow	1·20	45

Design: 60k. Laotian dancers and musicians.

81 Buddhist Monk at That Luang

1971. 50th Anniversary of Vientiane Rotary Club.

No.	Type	Description	Mint	Used
318	**81**	30k. violet, brown and blue	1·30	1·10
319	-	70k. grey, red and blue	2·00	1·70

Design: Vert—70k. Laotian girl on 'Dragon' staircase.

82 *Dendrobium agregatum*

1971. Laotian Orchids. Multicoloured.

No.	Description	Mint	Used
320	30k. Type **82** (postage)	1·50	75
321	40k. *Rynchostylis giganterum*	1·60	85
322	50k. *Ascocentrum miniatur* (horiz)	2·00	1·00
323	60k. *Paphiopedilum exul*	2·20	1·10
324	70k. *Trichoglottis fasciata* (horiz)	2·75	1·50
325	80k. Cattleya (horiz)	3·00	1·70
326	125k. Brazilian cattleya (horiz) (air)	6·50	3·25
327	150k. *Vanda teres* (horiz)	6·75	3·75

Nos. 321, 323 and 325 are smaller, 22×36 or 36×22 mm. Nos. 326/327 are larger, 48×27 mm.

83 Dancers from France and Laos

1971. Air. Twin Cities of St Astier (France) and Keng-Kok (Laos).

No.	Type	Description	Mint	Used
328	**83**	30k. brown and light brown	55	35
329	**83**	70k. purple and plum	1·60	85
330	**83**	100k. green and deep green	2·20	1·60

84 Common Palm Civet

1971. Wild Animals (3rd series).

No.	Type	Description	Mint	Used
331	**84**	25k. black, violet and blue (postage)	1·10	45
332	**84**	40k. black, green and olive	1·40	65
333	-	50k. orange and green	1·70	85
334	-	85k. brown, green and emerald	3·25	1·40
335	-	300k. brown and green (air)	8·25	3·50

Designs: 50k. Lesser Malay chevrotain; 85k. Sambar; 300k. Javan rhinoceros.

85 Laotian Woman (design from 1952 issue)

1971. 20th Anniversary of Laotian Stamps.

No.	Type	Description	Mint	Used
336	**85**	30k. chocolate, brown and violet (postage)	75	25
337	-	40k. multicoloured	1·10	35
338	-	50k. black, flesh and blue	1·40	55
339	-	125k. violet, brn & grn (air)	3·25	2·20
MS340		180×110 mm. **85** 30k. chocolate, brown and violet; 60k. red and brown; 85k. deep green, green and blue	8·25	7·50

Designs: 36×48 mm—40k. Violinist (1957 issue); 50k. Rama (1965 issue); 125k. The Offertory 1957 issue).

86 *Sunset on the Mekong*

1971. Air. Paintings by Chamnane Prisayane.

No.	Description	Mint	Used
341	125k. Type **86**	2·20	1·30
342	150k. *Quiet Morning at Ban Tane Pieo*	2·75	1·60

87 Children reading Book

1972. International Book Year.

No.	Type	Description	Mint	Used
343	**87**	30k. green (postage)	55	45
344	-	70k. brown	1·10	1·00
345	-	125k. violet (air)	2·75	2·20

Designs: 36×22 mm—70k. Laotian illustrating manuscript. 48×27 mm—125k. Father showing manuscripts to children.

88 Nam Ngum Dam and Obelisk

1972. 25th Anniversary of UN Economic Commission for Asia and the Far East (ECAFE). Multicoloured.

No.	Description	Mint	Used
346	40k. Type **88** (postage)	55	35
347	80k. Type **88**	1·10	55
348	145k. Lake and spill-way, Nam Ngum Dam (air)	2·20	1·10

89 *The Water-carrier*

1972. 25th Anniversary of UNICEF Drawings by Lao Schoolchildren. Multicoloured.

No.	Description	Mint	Used
349	50k. Type **89** (postage)	1·10	85

350		80k. *Teaching Bamboo-weaving*	1·60	1·00
351		120k. *Riding a Water-buffalo* (air)	2·20	1·40

90 Nakharath

1972. Air. Laotian Mythology (2nd series).

352	**90**	100k. turquoise	1·30	85
353	-	120k. lilac	1·60	1·10
354	-	150k. brown	2·20	1·30

Designs: 120k. Nang Kinnali; 150k. Norasing.

91 Festival Offerings

1972. Air. That Luang Religious Festival.

355	**91**	110k. brown	1·30	75
356	-	125k. purple	2·00	1·10

Design: 125k. Festival procession.

1972. Air. Paintings by Marc Leguay (4th series). As T **69**. Multicoloured.

357	50k. *In the Paddy Field* (detail)	85	55
358	50k. *In the Paddy Field* (different detail)	85	55
359	70k. *Village in the Rainy Season* (detail)	1·30	65
360	70k. *Village in the Rainy Season* (different detail)	1·30	65
361	120k. *Laotian Mother*	2·75	1·30

Nos. 357/358 and 359/360 when placed together form the complete painting in each case.

92 Attopeu Religious Costume

1973. Regional Costumes.

362	**92**	40k. yellow, mauve & brown (postage)	75	55
363	-	90k. black, red and brown	1·60	65
364	-	120k. brown, sepia and mauve (air)	2·20	1·30
365	-	150k. ochre, red and brown	2·75	1·40

Designs: 90k. Phongsaly festival costume; 120k. Luang Prabang wedding costume; 150k. Vientiane evening dress.

93 'Lion' Guardian, That Luang

1973. 55th Anniversary of Lions International.

366	**93**	40k. red, purple and bluel (postage)	1·10	55
367	**93**	80k. red, yellow and blue	1·60	85
368	-	150k. multicoloured (air)	2·75	1·60

Design: 48×27 mm—150k. Lions emblems and statue of King Saysetthathirath, Vientiane.

94 Satellite passing Rahu

1973. Traditional and Modern Aspects of Space. Multicoloured.

369	80k. Type **94**	1·00	55
370	150k. Landing module and Laotian festival rocket	2·00	75

95 Dr. Gerhard Hansen and Map of Laos

1973. Centenary of Identification of Leprosy Bacillus by Hansen.

371	**95**	40k. purple, deep purple and orange	85	55
372	**95**	80k. purple, brown and yellow& yell	1·80	65

96 Benediction

1973. 25th Anniversary of Laotian Boy Scouts Association.

373	**96**	70k. yellow and brown (postage)	1·30	65
374	-	110k. violet and orange (air)	1·60	85
375	-	150k. blue, drab and brown	2·00	1·10

Designs: 48×27 mm—110k. Campfire entertainment; 150k. Scouts helping flood victims, Vientiane, 1966.

97 Nang Mekhala. (Goddess of the Sea)

1973. Air. Centenary of World Meteorological Organisation.

376	**97**	90k. lilac, red and brown	1·30	1·10
377	-	150k. brown, red & lt brn	2·50	1·60

Design: Horiz—150k. Chariot of the Sun.

99 Interpol HQ, Paris

1973. 50th Anniversary of International Criminal Police Organisation (Interpol).

382	**99**	40k. blue (postage)	65	35
383	**99**	80k. brown and light brown	1·10	55
384	-	150k. violet, red and green (air)	2·10	1·10

Design:b 48×27 mm—150k. Woman in opium poppy field.

100 Phra Sratsvady

1974. Air. Laotian Mythology (3rd series).

385	**100**	100k. red, brown and lilac	1·80	1·00
386	-	110k. brown, lilac and red	2·00	1·10
387	-	150k. violet, brown and light brown	2·75	1·60

Designs: 110k. Phra Indra; 150k. Phra Phrom.

101 Boy and Postbox

1974. Centenary of UPU.

388	**101**	70k. brown, green and blue (postage)	1·10	55
389	**101**	80k. brown, blue and green	1·30	75
390	-	200k. brown and red (air)	4·00	2·20

Design: 48×36 mm—200k. Laotian girls with letters, and UPU Monument, Berne (T **105**).

102 *Eranthemum nervosum*

1974. Laotian Flora.

391	**102**	30k. violet & grn (postage)	75	55
392	-	50k. multicoloured	1·30	65
393	-	80k. red, green and brown	1·80	1·10
394	-	500k. green & brown (air)	8·25	5·00

Designs: As T **102** Horiz—50k. Water lily; 80k. Red silk-cotton. 36×36 mm—500k. Pitcher plant.

103 Mekong Ferry carrying Bus

1974. Laotian Transport.

395	**103**	25k. brown & orge (postage)	65	35
396	-	90k. brown and bistre	2·75	1·40
397	-	250k. brown & green (air)	4·25	1·70

Designs: Vert—90k. Bicycle rickshaw. Horiz—250k. Mekong house boat.

104 Marconi, and Laotians with Transistor Radio

1974. Birth Centenary of Guglielmo Marconi (radio pioneer).

398	**104**	60k. grey, green and brown (postage)	85	45
399	**104**	90k. grey, brown and green	2·20	1·10
400	-	200k. blue and brown (air)	2·75	1·70

Design: 200k. Communications methods.

105 UPU Monument and Laotian Girls

1974. Air Centenary of U.P.U.

401	**105**	500k. lilac and red	6·50	5·75
MS402		135×105 mm. No. 401	9·75	9·00

For 200k. as T **105** see No. 390.

106 *Diastocera wallichi*

1974. Beetles.

403	**106**	50k. brown, black and green (postage)	1·30	70
404	-	90k. black, turquoise and green	2·00	90
405	-	100k. black, orange and brown	2·50	1·40
406	-	110k. violet, red and green (air)	2·20	80

Designs: 90k. *Macrochenus isabellunus*; 100k. *Purpuricenus malaccensis*; 110k. *Sternocera multipunctata*.

107 Pagoda and Sapphire

1974. Mineral Riches.

407	**107**	100k. brown, green and blue	2·40	90
408	-	110k. brown, blue and yellow	2·75	1·10

Design: 110k. Gold-panning and necklace.

108 King Savang Vatthana, Prince Souvanna Phouma and Prince Souphanouvong

1975. First Anniversary (1974) of Laotian Peace Treaty (1st issue).

409	**108**	80k. brown, ochre and green	1·60	80
410	**108**	300k. brown, ochre and purple	2·75	2·00
411	**108**	420k. brown, ochre and turquoise	3·25	2·50

See also No. **MS**419.

109 Fortune-teller's Chart

1975. Chinese New Year. Year of the Rabbit.

413	**109**	40k. brown and green	1·10	55
414	-	200k. black, brown and green	2·75	1·10
415	-	350k. brown, green and blue	4·25	2·50

Designs: Horiz—200k. Fortune-teller. Vert—350k. Woman riding hare.

110 UN Emblem and Frieze

1975. International Women's Year.

416	**110**	100k. blue and turquoise	85	45
417	-	200k. orange and green	1·80	55
MS418		130×100 mm. Nos. 416/417	8·75	7·25

Design: 200k. IWY emblem.

111 King Savang Vatthana, Prince Souvanna Phouma and Prince Souvanouvong

1975. First Laotian Peace Treaty (2nd issue). Sheet 90×70 mm.

MS419	**111**	2000k. gold, red and green	17·00	16·00

112

1975. Pravet Sandone Religious Festival.

420	**112**	80k. multicoloured	85	70
421	-	110k. multicoloured	1·30	80
422	-	120k. multicoloured	1·60	90
423	-	130k. multicoloured	2·20	1·10

Designs: 110k. to 130k. Various legends.

113 Buddha and Stupas

1975. UNESCO Campaign for Preservation of Borobudur Temple (in Indonesia).

424	**113**	100k. green, blue and brown	1·30	55
425	-	200k. ochre, green and brown	2·50	1·20
MS426		130×100 mm. Nos. 424/425	6·00	5·75

Design: 200k. Temple sculptures.

114 Laotian Arms

1976. Multicoloured, background colour given.

427	**114**	1k. blue	35	20
428	**114**	2k. mauve	45	25
429	**114**	5k. green	55	35
430	**114**	10k. violet	75	55
431	**114**	200k. orange	5·50	3·50
MS432		165×70 mm. Nos. 427/431	20·00	18·00

115 Thathiang, Vien-Tran

1976. Pagodas. Multicoloured.

433	1k. Type **115**	45	20
434	2k. Phonsi, Luang Prabang	65	25
435	30k. Type **115**	1·30	80
436	80k. As 2k.	2·75	1·70
437	100k. As 2k.	3·75	2·30
438	300k. Type **115**	6·50	4·00
MS439	Two sheets, each 113×75 mm. (a) Nos. 433, 435 and 438; (b) Nos. 434 and 436/437	14·00	13·00

116 Silversmith

1977. Laotian Crafts. Multicoloured.

440	1k. Type **116**	20	10
441	2k. Weaver	35	15
442	20k. Potter	1·50	55
443	50k. Basket-weaver (vert)	2·75	1·10
MS444	Four sheets, 90×81 mm (d) or 81×90 mm (others). (a) No. 440×2; (b) No. 441×2; (c) No. 442×2; (d) No. 443×2	27·00	26·00

117 Gubarev, Grechko and Salyut Space Station

1977. 60th Anniversary of Russian Revolution. Multicoloured.

445	5k. Type **117**	35	10
446	20k. Lenin	65	25
447	50k. As 20k.	1·10	45
448	60k. Type **117**	1·40	70
449	100k. Government Palace, Vientiane, and Kremlin, Moscow (horiz)	2·20	1·10
450	250k. As 100k.	4·25	3·00
MS451	Two sheets, each 141×81 mm. (a) Nos. 445, 447 and 450; (b) Nos. 446 and 448/449	16·00	14·50

118 Laotian Arms

1978

452	**118**	5k. yellow and black	45	20
453	**118**	10k. sepia and black	55	25
454	**118**	50k. purple and black	85	35
455	**118**	100k. green and black	2·00	80
456	**118**	250k. violet and black	3·25	1·70

119 Soldiers with Flag

1978. Army Day. Multicoloured.

457	20k. Type **119**	45	25
458	40k. Soldiers attacking village (horiz)	85	55
459	300k. Anti-aircraft guns	3·25	2·30

120 Marchers with Banner

1978. National Day. Multicoloured.

460	20k. Type **120**	85	25
461	50k. Women with flag	1·10	45
462	400k. Dancer	3·25	2·30
MS463	Two sheets, each 160×105 mm, each containing Nos. 460/462, arranged from left (a) 20, 50, 400k.; (b) 400, 50, 20k. Imperf	16·00	14·50

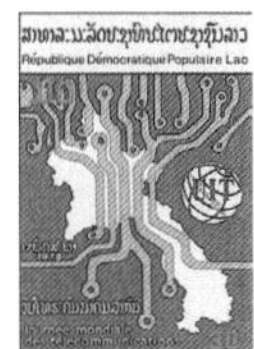

121 Printed Circuit and Map of Laos

1979. World Telecommunications Day.

464	**121**	30k. orange, brown and silver	45	10
465	-	250k. multicoloured	4·00	2·10

Design: 250k. Printed circuit, map of Laos and transmitter tower.

122 Woman posting Letter

1979. 15th Anniversary of Asian–Oceanic Postal Union. Multicoloured.

466	5k. Type **122**	20	10
467	10k. Post Office counter	35	15
468	80k. As 10k.	1·60	55
469	100k. Type **122**	2·20	80

123 Children playing Ball

1979. International Year of the Child (1st issue). Multicoloured. Without gum.

470	20k. Type **123**	35	25
471	50k. Children at school (horiz)	65	35
472	200k. Mother feeding child	3·25	1·20
473	500k. Nurse immunising child	9·25	2·75
MS474	215×110 mm. Nos. 470/473. Imperf	33·00	28·00

See also Nos. 479/**MS**482.

124 Elephant, Buffalo and Pirogues

1979. Transport. Multicoloured.

475	5k. Type **124**	35	25
476	10k. Buffalo carts	55	45
477	70k. As No. 476	1·10	90
478	500k. Type **124**	4·50	3·75

125 Dancing Child

1979. International Year of the Child (2nd issue). Multicoloured. Without gum.

479	100k. Children playing musical instruments (horiz)	1·60	55
480	200k. Child releasing dove	2·75	1·10
481	600k. Type **125**	6·50	4·00
MS482	189×109 mm. Nos. 479/481. Imperf	26·00	25·00

126 Forest and Paddy Field

1980. Fifth Anniversary of Republic (1st issue) and 25th Anniversary of People's Front. Multicoloured. Without gum.

483	30c. Type **126**	55	25
484	50c. Classroom and doctor examining baby (horiz)	1·00	35
485	1k. Three women	1·20	55
486	2k. Dam and electricity pylons (horiz)	2·75	1·70
MS487	170×99 mm. Nos. 483/486. Imperf	16·00	14·50

See also Nos. 493/**MS**497.

127 Lenin Reading

1980. 110th Birth Anniversary of Lenin. Multicoloured.

488	1k. Type **127**	45	25
489	2k. Lenin writing	75	35
490	3k. Lenin and Red Flag (vert)	1·00	55
491	4k. Lenin making speech (vert)	2·00	80
MS492	136×95 mm. Nos. 488/491. Imperf	8·75	8·00

128 Workers in Field

1980. Fifth Anniversary of Republic (2nd issue). Multicoloured. Without gum.

493	50c. Type **128**	45	25
494	1k.60 Loading logs on lorry and elephant hauling logs	1·10	55
495	4k.60 Veterinary workers tending animals	2·20	80
496	5k.40 Workers in paddy field	2·75	1·20
MS497	207×165 mm. Nos. 493/496. Imperf	20·00	18·00

129 Emblems of Industry, Technology, Transport, Sport and Art

1981. 26th PCUS (Communist Party) Congress. Multicoloured.

498	60c. Type **129**	55	25
499	4k.60 Communist star breaking manacles and globe	2·75	1·10
500	5k. Laurel branch and broken bomb	3·25	1·20
MS501	140×106 mm. Nos. 498/500 (sold at 15k.)	11·00	10·00

130 Giant Pandas

1981. Philatokyo 81 International Stamp Exhibition, Tokyo. Sheet 90×60 mm.

MS502	**130** 10k. multicoloured	9·25	8·00

131 Player heading Ball

1981. World Cup Football Championship, Spain (1982) (1st issue). Multicoloured.

503	1k. Type **131**	35	25
504	2k. Receiving ball	65	30
505	3k. Passing ball	85	35
506	4k. Goalkeeper diving for ball (horiz)	1·30	45
507	5k. Dribbling	2·40	90
508	6k. Kicking ball	2·50	1·10

See also Nos. 545/**MS**551.

132 Disabled Person on Telephone

1981. International Year of Disabled Persons. Multicoloured.

509	3k. Type **132**	2·20	55
510	5k. Disabled teacher	2·75	1·10
511	12k. Person in wheelchair mending net	5·50	2·75

133 Wild Cat

1981. Wild Cats. Multicoloured.

512	10c. Type **133**	35	25
513	20c. Fishing cat	45	30
514	30c. Caracal	55	35
515	40c. Clouded leopard	65	40
516	50c. Flat-headed cat	75	45
517	9k. Jungle cat	5·00	1·80

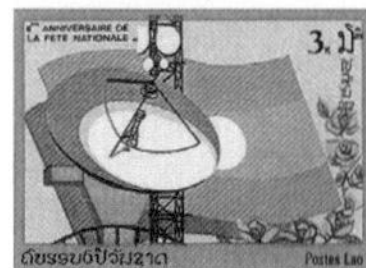
134 Dish Aerial and Flag

1981. Sixth National Day Festival. Multicoloured.

518 3k. Type **134** 1·10 45
519 4k. Soldier and flag 1·30 55
520 5k. Girls presenting flowers to soldier, flag and map of Laos 1·70 70

135 Indian Elephant

1982. Indian Elephant. Multicoloured.

521 1k. Type **135** 45 25
522 2k. Elephant carrying log 85 35
523 3k. Elephant with passengers 1·10 45
524 4k. Elephant in trap 1·50 55
525 5k. Elephant and young 2·00 80
526 5k.50 Herd of elephants 2·75 1·00

136 Laotian Wrestling

1982. Wrestling.

527 **136** 50c. multicoloured 20 15
528 - 1k.20 multicoloured 35 25
529 - 2k. multicoloured 65 30
530 - 2k.50 multicoloured 1·10 35
531 - 4k. multicoloured 1·60 55
532 - 5k. multicoloured 2·50 80

Designs: 1k.20 to 5k. Various wrestling scenes.

137 *Nymphaea zanzibariensis*

1982. Water Lilies. Multicoloured.

533 30c. Type **137** 20 15
534 40c. *Nelumbo nucifera* 'Gaertn Rose' 35 25
535 60c. *Nymphaea rosea* 45 30
536 3k. *Nymphaea nouchali* 1·10 45
537 4k. *Nymphaea* White 1·50 55
538 7k. *Nelumbo nucifera* 'Gaertn White' 3·00 80

138 Barn Swallow

1982. Birds. Multicoloured.

539 50c. Type **138** 20 15
540 1k. Hoopoe 35 25
541 2k. River kingfisher 75 35
542 3k. Black-naped blue monarch 1·10 45
543 4k. Grey wagtail (horiz) 1·50 55
544 10k. Long-tailed tailor bird (horiz) 3·75 1·10

139 Football

1982. World Cup Football Championship, Spain (2nd issue).

545 **139** 1k. multicoloured 45 25
546 - 2k. multicoloured 65 35
547 - 3k. multicoloured 85 45
548 - 4k. multicoloured 1·20 55
549 **139** 5k. multicoloured 1·50 70
550 - 6k. multicoloured 2·10 80
MS551 81×63 mm. 15k. multicoloured (footballer and flag) (36×28 mm) 6·00 5·75

Designs: 2, 3, 4, 6, 15k. Various football scenes.

140 *Herona marathus*

1982. Butterflies. Multicoloured.

552 1k. Type **140** 35 25
553 2k. *Neptis paraka* 75 35
554 3k. *Euripus halitherses* 1·20 45
555 4k. *Lebadea martha* 1·70 55
556 5k. *Iton semamora* (42×26 mm) 2·50 90
557 6k. Common palm fly (59×41 mm) 3·25 1·10

141 Buddhist Temple, Vientiane

1982. Philexfrance 82 International Stamp Exhibition, Paris. Sheet 86×64 mm.

MS558 **141** 10k. multicoloured 4·25 4·00

142 River Raft

1982. River Craft. Multicoloured.

559 50c. Type **142** 35 15
560 60c. River sampan 40 20
561 1k. River house boat 45 25
562 2k. River passenger steamer 85 35
563 3k. River ferry 1·10 55
564 8k. Self-propelled barge 2·50 1·10

143 Vat Chanh

1982. Pagodas. Multicoloured.

565 50c. Type **143** 35 15
566 60c. Vat Inpeng 45 25
567 1k. Vat Dong Mieng 55 30
568 2k. Ho Tay 1·00 35
569 3k. Vat Ho Pha Keo 1·30 45
570 8k. Vat Sisaket 2·50 90

1982. Various stamps optd **1982**.

571 **114** 1k. multicoloured 27·00 27·00
572 **116** 1k. multicoloured 11·00 11·00
573 - 2k. multicoloured (No. 441) 22·00 22·00
574 **117** 5k. multicoloured 27·00 27·00
575 **118** 5k. yellow and black 27·00 27·00
576 **122** 5k. multicoloured 27·00 27·00
577 **124** 5k. multicoloured 27·00 27·00
578 - 10k. multicoloured (No. 467) 49·00 49·00
579 - 10k. multicoloured (No. 476) 49·00 49·00
580 - 20k. multicoloured (No. 446) 55·00 55·00
581 **119** 20k. multicoloured 55·00 55·00
582 **121** 30k. orange, brown & sil 70·00 70·00
583 - 40k. multicoloured (No. 458) 80·00 80·00
584 - 50k. multicoloured (No. 443) 85·00 85·00
585 - 70k. multicoloured (No. 477) £120 £120
586 - 80k. multicoloured (No. 468) £130 £130
587 **122** 100k. multicoloured £180 £180
588 **114** 200k. multicoloured £300 £300
589 - 250k. multicoloured (No. 465) £375 £375

145 Poodle

1982. Dogs. Multicoloured.

591 50c. Type **145** 35 20
592 60c. Samoyed 45 25
593 1k. Boston terrier 55 30
594 2k. Cairn terrier 1·10 35
595 3k. Chihuahua 1·50 55
596 8k. Bulldog 3·75 90

146 Woman watering Crops

1982. World Food Day. Multicoloured.

597 7k. Type **146** 2·40 90
598 8k. Woman transplanting rice 3·00 1·10

147 Fiat, 1925

1982. Cars. Multicoloured.

599 50c. Type **147** 20 15
600 60c. Peugeot, 1925 35 20
601 1k. Berliet, 1925 55 25
602 2k. Ballot, 1925 1·10 35
603 3k. Renault, 1926 1·30 55
604 8k. Ford, 1925 2·75 90

148 Kaysone Phomvihane (prime minister)

1982. Seventh Anniversary of Republic. Multicoloured.

605 50c. Type **148** 20 15
606 1k. Tractors (horiz) 35 20
607 2k. Cow (horiz) 45 25
608 3k. Lorry passing dish aerial (horiz) 75 35
609 4k. Nurse examining child 1·10 45
610 5k. Classroom (horiz) 1·50 55
611 6k. Dancer 2·20 70

149 Dimitrov, Flag and Arms of Bulgaria

1982. Birth Centenary of Georgi Dimitrov (Bulgarian statesman).

612 **149** 10k. multicoloured 2·75 1·70

150 Kremlin and Arms of USSR

1982. 60th Anniversary of USSR. Multicoloured.

613 3k. Type **150** 1·10 55
614 4k. Doves and maps of USSR and Laos 1·70 80
MS615 96×92 mm. Nos. 613/614 5·50 3·50

151 Hurdling

1983. Olympic Games, Los Angeles (1984) (1st issue). Multicoloured.

616 50c. Type **151** 20 20
617 1k. Javelin 45 25
618 2k. Basketball 55 30
619 3k. Diving 1·00 35
620 4k. Gymnastics 1·30 55
621 10k. Weightlifting 3·75 1·10
MS622 91×62 mm. 15k. Football (31×39 mm) 5·50 3·50

See also Nos. 708/**MS**715.

152 Bucking Horse

1983. Horses. Multicoloured.

623 50c. Type **152** 35 20
624 1k. Rearing black horse 45 25
625 2k. Trotting brown horse 65 30
626 3k. Dappled grey horse 1·10 35
627 4k. Wild horse crossing snow 1·30 45
628 10k. Horse in paddock 4·00 1·10

153 *St Catherine of Alexandria*

1983. 500th Birth Anniversary of Raphael (artist). Multicoloured.

629 50c. Type **153** 45 20
630 1k. *Adoration of the Kings* 55 25
631 2k. *Madonna of the Grand Duke* 75 30
632 3k. *St. George and the Dragon* 1·20 35
633 4k. *The Vision of Ezekiel* 1·40 45
634 10k. *Adoration of the Kings* (different) 4·25 1·10
MS635 74×123 mm. 10k. *Coronation of the Virgin* (39×31 mm) 5·50 3·50

154 A. Gubarev (Soviet) and V. Remek (Czechoslovak)

1983. Cosmonauts. Multicoloured.

636 50c. Type **154** 35 20
637 50c. P. Klimuk (Soviet) and Miroslaw Hermaszewski (Polish) 35 20
638 1k. V. Bykovsky (Soviet) and Sigmund Jahn (East German) 45 25
639 1k. Nikolai Rukavishnikov (Soviet) and Georgi Ivanov (Bulgarian) 45 25
640 2k. V. Kubasov (Soviet) and Bertalan Farkas (Hungarian) 65 30
641 3k. V. Dzhanibekov (Soviet) and Gurragchaa (Mongolian) 1·00 35
642 4k. L. Popov (Soviet) and D. Prunariu (Rumanian) 1·30 40
643 6k. Soviet cosmonaut and Arnaldo Tamayo (Cuban) 2·00 55
644 10k. Soviet and French cosmonauts 4·00 1·10

MS645	92×90 mm. 10k. V. Gorbatko (Soviet) and Pham Tuan (Vietnamese) (28×35 mm)	5·50	4·00

155 Jacques Charles's Hydrogen Balloon, 1783

1983. Bicentenary of Manned Flight. Multicoloured.

646	50c. Type **155**	35	20
647	1k. Blanchard and Jeffries' balloon, 1785	45	25
648	2k. Vincenzo Lunardi's balloon (London–Ware flight), 1784	65	30
649	3k. Modern hot-air balloon over city	1·10	35
650	4k. Massed balloon ascent, 1890	1·30	55
651	10k. Auguste Piccard's stratosphere balloon *F.N.R.S.*, 1931	3·75	1·10
MS652	100×83 mm. 10k. Balloon *Double Eagle II* (312×39 mm)	4·25	3·75

156 German Maybach Car

1983. Tembal 83 Stamp Exhibition, Basle. Sheet 95×63 mm.

MS653	**156** 10k. multicoloured	5·00	3·50

157 *Dendrobium* sp.

1983. Flowers. Multicoloured.

654	1k. Type **157**	45	20
655	2k. *Aerides odoratum*	65	25
656	3k. *Dendrobium aggregatum*	1·00	35
657	4k. *Dendrobium*	1·20	40
658	5k. *Moschatum*	1·60	45
659	6k. *Dendrobium* sp. (different)	2·75	70

158 Downhill Skiing

1983. Winter Olympic Games, Sarajevo (1984) (1st issue). Multicoloured.

660	50c. Type **158**	35	15
661	1k. Slalom	45	20
662	2k. Ice hockey	65	25
663	3k. Speed skating	1·10	40
664	4k. Ski jumping	1·30	45
665	10k. Luge	3·75	1·10
MS666	91×57 mm. 15k. Bobsleigh (39×31 mm)	5·50	4·00

See also Nos. 696/**MS**703.

159 Boatman on Tachin River

1983. Bangkok 1983 International Stamp Exhibition. Sheet 93×72 mm.

MS667	**159** 10k. multicoloured	4·25	3·50

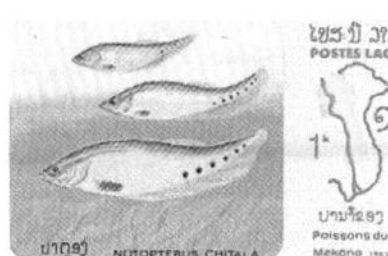
160 Clown Knifefish

1983. Fish of Mekong River. Multicoloured.

668	1k. Type **160**	35	20
669	2k. Common carp	55	25
670	3k. Lesser Mekong catfish	1·00	30
671	4k. Giant barb	1·30	35
672	5k. Black shark	2·00	55
673	6k. Nile mouthbrooder	3·00	90

161 Magellan and *Vitoria*

1983. Explorers and their Ships. Multicoloured.

674	1k. Type **161**	45	20
675	2k. Jacques Cartier and *Grande Hermine*	65	25
676	3k. Columbus and *Santa Maria*	1·30	30
677	4k. Pedro Alvares Cabral and *El Ray*	1·60	40
678	5k. Cook and HMS *Resolution*	2·00	50
679	6k. Charcot and *Pourquoi-pas?*	2·75	75

No. 679 is wrongly inscribed 'Cabot'.

162 Tabby Cat

1983. Domestic Cats. Multicoloured.

680	1k. Type **162**	45	20
681	2k. Long-haired Persian	1·10	25
682	3k. Siamese	1·20	30
683	4k. Burmese	1·30	40
684	5k. Persian	1·80	50
685	6k. Tortoiseshell	2·50	75

1983. Nos. 430 and 466 optd **1983**.

685a	**122**	5k. multicoloured	22·00	22·00
685b	**114**	10k. multicoloured	£140	£140

163 Marx, Book, Sun and Signature

1983. Death Centenary of Karl Marx. Multicoloured.

686	1k. Marx, dove, globe and flags	60	25
687	4k. Type **163**	1·80	40
688	6k. Marx and flags	3·00	90

164 Elephant dragging Log

1983. Eighth Anniversary of Republic. Multicoloured.

689	1k. Type **164**	60	25
690	4k. Cattle and pig (horiz)	1·80	40
691	6k. Crops	3·00	90

165 Carrier Pigeon and Telex Machine

1983. World Communications Year. Multicoloured.

692	50c. Type **165**	35	20
693	1k. Early telephone, handset and receiver	45	25
694	4k. Television tube and aerial	1·50	50
695	6k. Satellite and dish aerial	2·50	90

166 Ice Skating

1984. Winter Olympic Games, Sarajevo (2nd issue). Multicoloured.

696	50c. Type **166**	25	20
697	1k. Speed skating	35	25
698	2k. Biathlon	60	30
699	4k. Luge (horiz)	1·40	45
700	5k. Downhill skiing (horiz)	1·50	50
701	6k. Ski jumping	2·10	75
702	7k. Slalom	2·50	90
MS703	89×55 mm. 10k. Ice hockey (31×39 mm)	5·25	4·50

167 Tiger

1984. Endangered Animals. The Tiger. Multicoloured.

704	25c. Type **167**	90	40
705	25c. Tigers (horiz)	90	40
706	3k. Tiger and cubs (horiz)	8·25	1·90
707	4k. Tiger cubs	11·00	2·75

168 Diving

1984. Olympic Games, Los Angeles (2nd issue). Multicoloured.

708	50c. Type **168**	35	20
709	1k. Volleyball	60	25
710	2k. Running	1·10	30
711	4k. Basketball	2·00	40
712	5k. Judo	2·30	50
713	6k. Football	3·00	65
714	7k. Gymnastics	3·50	75
MS715	98×81 mm. 10k. Wrestling (31×39 mm)	5·25	4·50

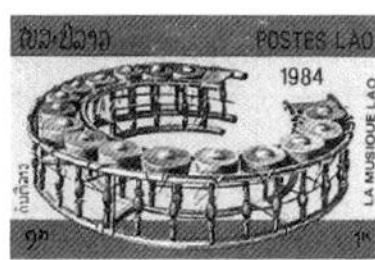
169 Tuned Drums

1984. Musical Instruments. Multicoloured.

716	1k. Type **169**	45	20
717	2k. Xylophone	95	25
718	3k. Pair of drums	1·40	40
719	4k. Hand drum	1·90	50
720	5k. Barrel drum	2·30	65
721	6k. Pipes and string instrument	3·50	90

170 National Flag

1984. National Day. Multicoloured.

722	60c. Type **170**	60	25
723	1k. National Arms	80	30
724	2k. As No. 723	1·30	40

171 Chess Game

1984. 60th Anniversary of World Chess Federation. Multicoloured.

725	50c. Type **171**	45	20
726	1k. Renaissance game from *The Three Ages of Man* (miniature attr. to Estienne Porchier)	80	25
727	2k. Woman teaching girls	1·20	30
728	2k. Margrave Otto IV of Brandenburg playing chess with his wife	1·20	30
729	3k. Four men at chessboard	1·50	40
730	4k. Two women playing	2·10	50
731	8k. Two men playing	4·75	1·30
MS732	87×70 mm. 10k. Human chess game (31×39 mm)	5·25	4·50

Nos. 725, 727 and 729/731 show illustrations from King Alfonso X's *Book of Chess, Dice and Tablings*.

172 *Cardinal Nino de Guevara* (El Greco)

1984. Espana 84 International Stamp Exhibition, Madrid. Multicoloured.

733	50c. Type **172**	45	20
734	1k. *Gaspar de Guzman, Duke of Olivares, on Horseback* (Velazquez)	60	25
735	2k. *The Annunciation* (Murillo)	95	30
736	2k. *Portrait of a Lady* (Zurbaran)	95	30
737	3k. *The Family of Charles IV* (Goya)	1·30	45
738	4k. *Two Harlequins* (Picasso)	1·80	50
739	8k. *Abstract* (Miro)	3·50	90
MS740	63×80 mm. 10k. *Burial of the Count of Orgaz* (El Gerco)	5·25	4·50

173 *Adonis aestivalis*

1984. Woodland Flowers. Multicoloured.

741	50c. Type **173**	35	20
742	1k. *Alpinia speciosa*	45	25
743	2k. *Cassia lechenaultiana*	80	30
744	2k. *Aeschynanthus speciosus*	80	30
745	3k. *Datura meteloides*	1·20	45
746	4k. *Quamoclit pennata*	1·60	50
747	8k. *Commelina benghalensis*	3·00	75

174 Nazzaro

1984. 19th Universal Postal Union Congress Philatelic Salon, Hamburg. Cars. Multicoloured.

748	50c. Type **174**	35	20
749	1k. Daimler	45	25
750	2k. Delage	80	30
751	2k. Fiat S 57/14B	80	30
752	3k. Bugatti	1·40	45
753	4k. Itala	2·10	50
754	8k. Blitzen Benz	4·00	95
MS755	79×52 mm. 10k. Winton Bullet	5·25	4·50

175 *Madonna and Child*

1984. 450th Death Anniversary of Correggio (artist). Multicoloured.

756	50c. Type **175**	25	20
757	1k. Detail showing horsemen resting	45	25
758	2k. *Madonna and Child* (different)	80	30
759	2k. *Mystical Marriage of St Catherine*	80	30
760	3k. *Four Saints*	1·20	45
761	4k. *Noli me Tangere*	1·80	50
762	8k. *Christ bids Farewell to the Virgin Mary*	3·50	1·00
MS763	80×107 mm. 10k. *Madonna and Child* (different) (31×39 mm)	6·50	5·75

176 *Luna 1*

1984. Space Exploration. Multicoloured.

764	50c. Type **176**	35	20
765	1k. *Luna 2*	45	25
766	2k. *Luna 3*	80	30
767	2k. Kepler and *Sputnik 2*	80	30
768	3k. Newton and *Lunokhod 2*	1·80	40
769	4k. Jules Verne and *Luna 13*	2·20	65
770	8k. Copernicus and space station	4·00	1·30

177 Malaclemys Terrapin

1984. Reptiles. Multicoloured.

771	50c. Type **177**	35	20
772	1k. Banded krait	45	25
773	2k. Indian python (vert)	80	30
774	2k. Reticulated python	80	30
775	3k. Tokay gecko	1·80	40
776	4k. *Natrix subminiata* (snake)	2·20	65
777	8k. Dappled ground gecko	4·00	1·30

178 Greater Glider

1984. Ausipex 84 International Stamp Exhibition, Melbourne. Marsupials. Multicoloured.

778	50c. Type **178**	35	20
779	1k. Platypus	60	25
780	2k. Southern hairy-nosed wombat (*Lasiorhinus latifrons*)	70	30
781	2k. Tasmanian devil (*Sarcophilus harrisii*)	70	30
782	3k. Thylacine	1·60	40
783	4k. Tiger cat	2·00	65
784	8k. Wallaby	3·50	1·00
MS785	95×58 mm. 10k. Red kangaroo (31×39 mm)	5·75	5·00

179 Nurse with Mother and Child

1984. Anti-poliomyelitis Campaign. Multicoloured.

786	5k. Type **179**	2·00	90
787	6k. Doctor inoculating child	2·30	1·00

180 Dragon Stair-rail

1984. Laotian Art. Multicoloured.

788	50c. Type **180**	35	20
789	1k. Capital of column	45	25
790	2k. Decorative panel depicting god	70	30
791	2k. Decorative panel depicting leaves	70	30
792	3k. Stylised leaves (horiz)	1·40	40
793	4k. Triangular flower decoration (horiz)	2·20	65
794	8k. Circular lotus flower decoration	4·00	1·00

181 River House Boats

1984. Ninth Anniversary of Republic. Multicoloured.

795	1k. Type **181**	80	25
796	2k. Passengers boarding Fokker Friendship airliner	1·20	40
797	4k. Building a bridge	2·00	1·00
798	10k. Building a road	4·50	2·00

182 Players with Ball

1985. World Cup Football Championship, Mexico (1986) (1st issue). Multicoloured.

799	50c. Type **182**	25	20
800	1k. Heading the ball	35	25
801	2k. Defending the ball	95	30
802	3k. Running with ball	1·40	40
803	4k. Taking possession of ball	2·10	50
804	5k. Heading the ball (different)	2·50	65
805	6k. Saving a goal	3·00	1·00
MS806	56×72 mm. 10k. Flag, player and ball (31×39 mm)	6·50	5·25

See also Nos. 868/**MS**875.

183 Motorcycle

1985. Centenary of Motorcycle. Multicoloured.

807	50c. Type **183**	25	20
808	1k. Gnome Rhone, 1920	45	25
809	2k. F.N. M67C, 1928	95	30
810	3k. Indian Chief, 1930	1·30	40
811	4k. Rudge Multi, 1914	1·90	50
812	5k. Honda Benly J, 1953	2·20	65
813	6k. CZ, 1938	2·75	1·00

1985. Various stamps optd **1985**.

813a	-	40k. multicoloured (No. 458)	42·00	42·00
813b	-	50k. multicoloured (No. 443)	48·00	48·00
813c	-	50k. multicoloured (No. 447)	48·00	48·00
813d	-	70k. multicoloured (No. 477)	48·00	48·00
813e	-	80k. multicoloured (No. 468)	48·00	48·00
813f	-	100k. multicoloured (No. 449)	85·00	85·00
813g	**122**	100k. multicoloured	85·00	85·00
813h	**114**	200k. multicoloured	£160	£160
813i	-	250k. multicoloured (No. 450)	£225	£225
813j	**118**	250k. violet and black	£225	£225
813k	-	250k. multicoloured (No. 465)	£225	£225
813m	-	300k. multicoloured (No. 459)	£250	£250

184 Fly Agaric

1985. Fungi. Multicoloured.

814	50c. Type **184**	35	20
815	1k. Cep	45	25
816	2k. Shaggy ink cap (*Coprinus comatus*)	95	30
817	2k. The blusher (*Amanita rubescens*)	95	30
818	3k. Downy boletus	1·60	50
819	4k. Parasol mushroom	2·75	65
820	8k. Brown roll-rim	4·75	1·30

184a Battle Plan, Kursk, and Tanks

1985. 40th Anniversary of End of Second World War. Multicoloured.

820a	1k. Type **184a**	1·40	40
820b	2k. Monument and military parade, Red Square, Moscow	2·50	50
820c	4k. Street battle and battle plan, Stalingrad	4·25	90
820d	5k. Battle plan and Reichstag, Berlin	5·25	1·30
820e	6k. Soviet Memorial, Berlin-Treptow, and military parade at Brandenburg Gate	6·00	1·50

185 Lenin reading *Pravda*

1985. 115th Birth Anniversary of Lenin. Multicoloured.

821	1k. Type **185**	60	25
822	2k. Lenin (vert)	2·10	1·00
823	10k. Lenin addressing meeting (vert)	3·50	1·30

186 *Cattleya percivaliana*

1985. Argentina '85 International Stamp Exhibition, Buenos Aires. Orchids. Multicoloured.

824	50c. Type **186**	25	20
825	1k. *Odontoglossum luteo-purpureum*	35	25
826	2k. *Cattleya lueddemanniana*	70	30
827	2k. *Maxillaria sanderiana*	70	30
828	3k. *Miltonia vexillaria*	1·20	40
829	4k. *Oncidium varicosum*	1·60	50
830	8k. *Cattleya dowiana*	3·50	1·00
MS831	82×63 mm. 10k. *Catasetum fimbriatum* (31×39 mm)	5·75	5·00

187 Rhesus Macaque

1985. Mammals. Multicoloured.

832	2k. Type **187**	60	25
833	3k. Kouprey	1·10	40
834	4k. Porcupine (horiz)	1·60	50
835	5k. Asiatic black bear (horiz)	2·00	55
836	10k. Chinese pangolin	4·00	1·00

188 Saturn Rocket on Launch Pad

1985. Tenth Anniversary of Apollo–Soyuz Space Link. Multicoloured.

837	50c. Type **188**	35	20
838	1k. Soviet rocket on launch pad	60	25
839	2k. Apollo approaching *Soyuz 19* (horiz)	80	30
840	2k. *Soyuz 19* approaching Apollo (horiz)	80	30
841	3k. Apollo and crew T. Stafford, V. Brand and D. Stayton (horiz)	1·20	40
842	4k. *Soyuz 19* and crew A. Leonov and V. Kubasov (horiz)	1·80	50
843	8k. Apollo and *Soyuz 19* docked (horiz)	3·25	1·00

189 Fiat Biplane

1985. Italia '85 International Stamp Exhibition, Rome. Multicoloured. (a) Aircraft. As T **189**.

844	50c. Type **189**	35	20
845	1k. Cant Z.501 Gabbiano flying boat	60	25
846	2k. Marina Fiat MF.5 flying boat	1·10	30
847	3k. Macchi Castoldi MC-100 flying boat	1·40	40
848	4k. Anzani biplane	1·60	50
849	5k. Ambrosini biplane	1·80	65
850	6k. Piaggio P-148	2·20	75
MS851	86×54 mm. 10k. Marina Fiat MF.4 flying boat (39×31 mm)	5·75	4·50

(b) Columbus and his Ships. Size 40×29 mm.

852	1k. *Pinta*	60	25
853	2k. *Nina*	95	30
854	3k. *Santa Maria*	1·30	40
855	4k. Christopher Columbus	1·60	50
856	5k. Map of Columbus's first voyage	2·20	65

190 UN and National Flags on Globe

1985. 40th Anniversary of UNO. Multicoloured.

857	2k. Type **190**	1·20	40
858	3k. UN emblem and Laotian Arms on globe	1·80	50
859	10k. Map on globe	4·75	1·60

191 Woman feeding Child

1985. Lao Health Services. Multicoloured.

860	1k. Type **191**	60	25
861	3k. Red Cross nurse injecting child (horiz)	1·50	40
862	4k. Red Cross nurse tending patient (horiz)	1·60	50
863	10k. Mother breast-feeding baby	3·50	1·30

192 Soldier, Workers and Symbols of Industry and Agriculture

1985. Tenth Anniversary of Republic. Multicoloured.

864	3k. Type **192**	1·20	40
865	10k. Soldier, workers and symbols of transport and communications	4·75	1·50

193 Soldier with Flag and Workers

1985. 30th Anniversary of Lao People's Revolutionary Party. Multicoloured.

866	2k. Type **193**	1·80	25
867	8k. Soldier with flag and workers (different)	4·75	1·00

194 Footballers

1986. World Cup Football Championship, Mexico (2nd issue).

868	**194**	50c. multicoloured	35	20
869	-	1k. multicoloured	45	25
870	-	2k. multicoloured	80	30
871	-	3k. multicoloured	1·20	40
872	-	4k. multicoloured	1·30	45
873	-	5k. multicoloured	1·50	50
874	-	6k. multicoloured	2·00	65
MS875		92×92 mm. 10k. multicoloured (39×31 mm)	5·75	3·25

Designs: 1k. to 10k. Various football scenes.

194a Cosmonaut, *Mir* Space Complex and Earth

1986. 17th Soviet Communist Party Congress. Multicoloured.

875a	4k. Type **194a**	4·75	50
875b	20k. Lenin and Red Flag	16·00	1·60

195 *Pelargonium grandiflorum*

1986. Flowers. Multicoloured.

876	50c. Type **195**	35	20
877	1k. Columbine	45	25
878	2k. *Fuchsia globosa*	80	30
879	3k. *Crocus aureus*	1·20	40
880	4k. Hollyhock	1·40	50
881	5k. *Gladiolus purpureo*	1·80	65
882	6k. *Hyacinthus orientalis*	2·20	90

196 *Aporia hippia*

1986. Butterflies. Multicoloured.

883	50c. Type **196**	35	20
884	1k. *Euthalia irrubescens*	45	25
885	2k. *Japonica lutea*	80	30
886	3k. *Pratapa ctesia*	1·20	40
887	4k. Leaf butterfly	1·40	50
888	5k. Yellow orange-tip	1·80	65
889	6k. Chestnut tiger	2·20	90

197 Rocket launch at Baikanur Space Centre

1986. 25th Anniversary of First Man in Space. Multicoloured.

890	50c. Type **197**	25	20
891	1k. *Molniya* communications satellite	45	25
892	2k. *Salyut* space station (horiz)	70	30
893	3k. Yuri Gagarin, *Sputnik 1* and rocket debris (horiz)	1·30	40
894	4k. *Luna 3* and Moon	1·80	45
895	5k. Vladimir Komarov on first space walk	2·50	65
896	6k. *Luna 16* lifting off from Moon	3·00	75
MS897	88×66 mm. 10k. Soyuz preparing to dock with Salyut space station (39×31 mm)	4·00	2·50

198 Giraffe

1986. Animals. Multicoloured.

898	50c. Type **198**	35	20
899	1k. Lion	45	25
900	2k. African elephant	80	30
901	3k. Red kangaroo	1·20	40
902	4k. Koala	1·50	45
903	5k. Greater flamingo	1·80	50
904	6k. Giant panda	3·25	90
MS905	80×60 mm. 10k. American bison (31×39 mm)	4·75	3·25

199 Boeing 747-100

1986. Air. Aircraft. Multicoloured.

906	20k. Type **199**	7·00	65
907	50k. Ilyushin Il-86	15·00	1·90

200 Great Argus Pheasant

1986. Pheasants. Multicoloured.

908	50c. Type **200**	35	20
909	1k. Silver pheasant	45	20
910	2k. Common pheasant	95	25
911	3k. Lady Amherst's pheasant	1·30	30
912	4k. Reeves's pheasant	1·40	40
913	5k. Golden pheasant	1·80	50
914	6k. Copper pheasant	2·30	65

201 Scarlet King Snake

1986. Snakes. Multicoloured.

915	50c. Corn snake	35	20
916	1k. Type **201**	45	20
917	1k. Richard's blind snake (vert)	95	25
918	2k. Western ring-necked snake	1·30	30
919	4k. Mangrove snake	1·40	40
920	5k. Indian python	1·80	50
921	6k. Common cobra (vert)	2·30	65

202 Bayeux Tapestry (detail) and Comet Head

1986. Appearance of Halley's Comet. Multicoloured.

922	50c. Comet over Athens (65×21 mm)	35	20
923	1k. Type **202**	45	20
924	2k. Edmond Halley (astronomer) and comet tail (20×21 mm)	80	25
925	3k. *Vega* space probe and comet head	1·20	30
926	4k. Galileo and comet tail (20×21 mm)	1·40	40
927	5k. Comet head (20×21 mm)	1·80	50
928	6k. *Giotto* space probe and comet tail	2·20	65
MS929	100×45 mm. 10k. Surface of Earth and comet head (39×31 mm)	4·75	3·75

Nos. 923/924, 925/926 and 927/928 resepctively were issued together, *se-tenant*, each pair forming a composite design.

203 Keeshond

1986. Stockholmia 86 International Stamp Exhibition. Dogs. Multicoloured.

930	50c. Type **203**	25	20
931	1k. Elkhound (horiz)	35	20
932	2k. Bernese (horiz)	80	25
933	3k. Pointing griffon (horiz)	1·20	30
934	4k. Collie (horiz)	1·40	40
935	5k. Irish water spaniel (horiz)	1·60	50
936	6k. Briard (horiz)	2·50	90
MS937	78×60 mm. 10k. Brittany spaniels chasing grey partridge (39×31 mm)	5·75	4·50

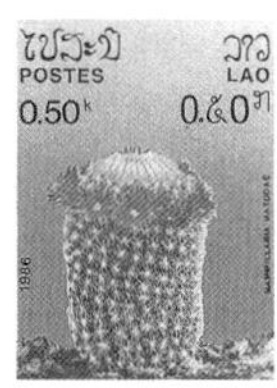

204 *Mammillaria matudae*

1986. Cacti. Multicoloured.

938	50c. Type **204**	35	20
939	1k. *Mammillaria theresae*	45	20
940	2k. *Ariocarpus trigonus*	80	25
941	3k. *Notocactus crassigibbus*	1·20	30
942	4k. *Astrophytum asterias* hybrid	1·40	40
943	5k. *Melocactus manzanus*	1·80	50
944	6k. *Astrophytum ornatum* hybrid	2·20	65

205 Arms and Dove on Globe

1986. International Peace Year.

945	**205**	3k. multicoloured	1·40	40
946	-	5k. black, blue and red	2·10	65
947	-	10k. multicoloured	4·75	1·50

Designs: 5k. Dove on smashed bomb; 10k. People supporting IPY emblem.

206 Vat Phu Champasak

1987. 40th Anniversary of UNESCO. Multicoloured.

948	3k. Type **206**	1·20	40
949	4k. Dish aerial and map of Laos on globe	1·80	50
950	9k. People reading books (horiz)	3·00	1·00

207 Speed Skating

1987. Winter Olympic Games, Calgary (1988) (1st issue). Multicoloured.

951	50c. Type **207**	35	20
952	1k. Biathlon	45	20
953	2k. Figure skating (pairs)	80	25
954	3k. Luge (horiz)	1·20	30
955	4k. Four-man bobsleigh (horiz)	1·40	40
956	5k. Ice hockey (horiz)	1·80	50
957	6k. Ski jumping (horiz)	2·20	65
MS958	78×58 mm. 10k. Skiing (31×39 mm)	4·75	3·75

See also Nos. 1046/**MS**1052.

208 Gymnast and Urn

1987. Olympic Games, Seoul (1988) (1st issue). Sports and Greek Pottery. Multicoloured.

959	50c. Type **208**	35	20
960	1k. Throwing the discus and vase (horiz)	45	20
961	2k. Running and urn	80	25
962	3k. Show jumping and bowl (horiz)	1·20	30
963	4k. Throwing the javelin and plate	1·40	40
964	5k. High jumping and bowl with handles (horiz)	1·80	50
965	6k. Wrestling and urn	2·20	65
MS966	82×55 mm. 10k. Runner leaving blocks (39×31 mm)	4·75	3·75

See also Nos. 1053/**MS**1060.

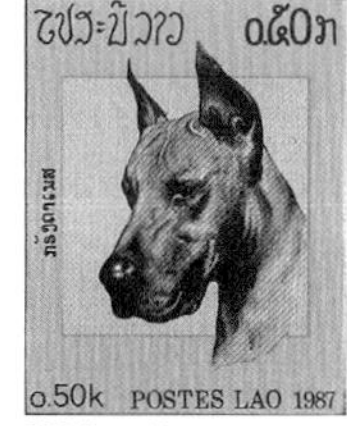

209 Great Dane

1987. Dogs. Multicoloured.

967	50c. Type **209**	25	20
968	1k. Black labrador	35	20
969	2k. St Bernard	70	25
970	3k. Tervuren shepherd dog	1·20	30
971	4k. German shepherd	1·30	40
972	5k. Beagle	2·10	50
973	6k. Golden retriever	2·30	90

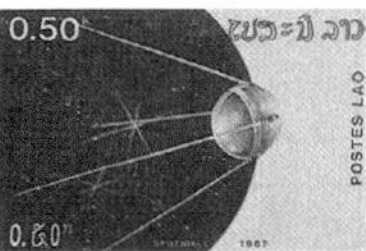

210 *Sputnik 1*

1987. 30th Anniversary of Launch of First Artificial Satellite. Multicoloured.

974	50c. Type **210**	35	20
975	1k. *Sputnik 2*	45	20
976	2k. *Cosmos 97*	80	25
977	3k. *Cosmos*	1·20	30
978	4k. *Mars*	1·40	40
979	5k. *Luna 1*	1·80	50
980	9k. *Luna 3* (vert)	2·20	75

211 'MONTREAL' Handstamp on Letter to Quebec and Schooner

1987. Capex 87 International Stamp Exhibition, Toronto. Ships and Covers. Multicoloured.

981	50c. Type **211**	35	20
982	1k. 'PAID MONTREAL' on letter and schooner	45	20
983	2k. Letter from Montreal to London and *William D. Lawrence* (full-rigged ship)	80	25
984	3k. 1840 letter to Williamsburgh and *Neptune* (steamer)	1·20	30
985	4k. 1844 letter to London and *Athabasca* (screw-steamer)	1·40	40
986	5k. 1848 letter and *Chicora* (paddle-steamer)	1·80	50
987	6k. 1861 letter and *Passport* (river paddle-steamer)	2·20	75
MS988 80×60 mm. 10k. 1949 4c. Canadian stamp (39×31 mm)		4·75	3·75

212 Horse

1987. Horses. Multicoloured.

989	50c. Type **212**	35	20
990	1k. Chestnut (vert)	45	20
991	2k. Black horse with sheepskin noseband (vert)	80	25
992	3k. Dark chestnut (vert)	1·20	30
993	4k. Black horse (vert)	1·40	40
994	5k. Chestnut with plaited mane (vert)	1·80	50
995	6k. Grey (vert)	2·20	75

213 Volvo 480

1987. Motor Cars. Multicoloured.

996	50c. Type **213**	35	20
997	1k. Alfa Romeo 33	45	20
998	2k. Ford Fiesta	80	25
999	3k. Ford Fiesta (different)	1·20	30
1000	4k. Ford Granada	1·40	40
1001	5k. Citroen AX	1·80	50
1002	6k. Renault 21	2·20	75
MS1003 65×52 mm. 10k. Skoda Estelle (39×31 mm)		4·75	3·75

214 *Vanda teres*

1987. Orchids. Multicoloured.

1004	3k. Type **214**	35	20
1005	7k. *Laeliocattleya* sp.	45	20
1006	10k. *Paphiopedilum* hybrid	80	25
1007	39k. *Sobralia* sp.	1·20	30
1008	44k. *Paphiopedilum* hybrid (different)	1·40	40
1009	47k. *Paphiopedilum* hybrid (different)	1·80	50
1010	50k. *Cattleya trianaei*	2·20	75
MS1011 52×75 mm. 95k. *Vanda tricolour* (31×39 mm)		4·75	3·75

215 Elephants

1987. Hafnia 87 International Stamp Exhibition, Copenhagen. Elephants. Multicoloured.

1012	50c. Type **215**	35	20
1013	1k. Three elephants	45	20
1014	2k. Elephant feeding	80	25
1015	3k. Elephant grazing on grass	1·20	30
1016	4k. Adult with calf	1·40	40
1017	5k. Elephant walking	1·80	50
1018	6k. Elephant (vert)	2·20	75
MS1019 64×44 mm. 10k. Adults and calf (39×31 mm)		4·75	3·75

216 Building Bamboo House

1987. International Year of Shelter for the Homeless. Multicoloured.

1020	1k. Type **216**	35	25
1021	27k. Building wooden house	1·20	40
1022	46k. House on stilts	2·30	50
1023	70k. Street of houses on stilts	3·00	1·00

217 Clown Loach

1987. Fish. Multicoloured.

1024	3k. Type **217**	35	20
1025	7k. Harlequin filefish	45	20
1026	10k. Silver-spotted squirrelfish	80	25
1027	39k. Mandarin fish	1·20	30
1028	44k. Coral hind	1·40	40
1029	47k. Zebra lionfish	1·80	50
1030	50k. Semicircle angelfish	2·20	75

218 Watering Seedlings

1987. World Food Day. Multicoloured.

1031	1k. Type **218**	25	20
1032	3k. Harvesting maize (vert)	35	25
1033	5k. Harvesting rice	45	30
1034	63k. Children with fish (vert)	2·30	75
1035	142k. Tending pigs and poultry	5·25	1·50

219 Wounded Soldiers on Battlefield

1987. 70th Anniversary of Russian Revolution. Multicoloured.

1036	1k. Type **219**	35	25
1037	2k. Mother and baby	70	30
1038	4k. Storming the Winter Palace	1·30	40
1039	8k. Lenin amongst soldiers and sailors	2·50	75
1040	10k. Lenin labouring in Red Square	3·50	1·00

220 Hoeing

1987. Rice Culture in Mountain Regions. Mult.

1041	64k. Type **220**	2·30	50
1042	100k. Working in paddy fields	4·00	1·30

221 Laotheung Costume

1987. Ethnic Costumes. Multicoloured.

1043	7k. Type **221**	60	25
1044	38k. Laoloum costume	1·80	40
1045	144k. Laosoun costume	5·25	1·80

222 Two-man Bobsleigh

1988. Winter Olympic Games, Calgary (2nd issue). Multicoloured.

1046	1k. Type **222**	35	20
1047	4k. Biathlon (shooting)	80	25
1048	20k. Cross-country skiing	1·20	30
1049	42k. Ice hockey	1·40	50
1050	63k. Speed skating	1·80	75
1051	70k. Slalom	2·20	90
MS1052 74×45 mm. 95k. Skiing (39×31 mm)		4·75	3·75

223 Throwing the Javelin

1988. Olympic Games, Seoul (2nd issue). Multicoloured.

1053	2k. Type **223**	25	15
1054	5k. Triple jumping	30	20
1055	10k. Men's gymnastics	35	25
1056	12k. Pirogue racing	60	30
1057	38k. Women's gymnastics	1·60	40
1058	46k. Fencing	2·10	50
1059	100k. Wrestling	4·25	1·10
MS1060 100×67 mm. 95k. Men's gymnastics (36×38 mm)		4·75	3·75

224 Tyrannosaurus

1988. Juvalux 88 Youth Philately Exhibition, Luxembourg. Prehistoric Animals. Multicoloured.

1061	3k. Type **224** (wrongly inscr 'Trachodon')	25	20
1062	7k. Ceratosaurus nasicornis (vert)	35	25
1063	39k. Iguanodon bernissartensis (vert)	1·80	40
1064	44k. Scolosaurus (vert)	1·90	45
1065	47k. Phororhacus sp. (vert)	2·10	50
1066	50k. Anatosaurus (wrongly inscr 'Tyrannosaurus')	2·30	65
MS1067 73×94 mm. 95k. Pteranodon (39×31 mm)		4·75	3·75

225 Adults in Hygiene Class

1988. 40th Anniversary of WHO. Multicoloured.

1068	5k. Type **225**	35	25
1069	27k. Fumigating houses	95	40
1070	164k. Woman pumping fresh water (vert)	5·75	2·00

226 *Sans Pareil*, 1829

1988. Essen 88 International Stamp Fair. Early Railway Locomotives. Multicoloured.

1071	6k. Type **226**	35	15
1072	15k. *Rocket*, 1829	70	20
1073	20k. *Royal George*, 1827 (horiz)	80	25
1074	25k. Trevithick's locomotive, 1803 (horiz)	1·20	40
1075	30k. *Novelty*, 1829 (horiz)	1·60	50
1076	100k. *Tom Thumb*, 1829 (horiz)	4·00	1·30
MS1077 82×70 mm. 95k. Stephenson's *Locomotion*, 1825 (34×28 mm)		5·25	4·00

227 Red Frangipani

1988. Finlandia 88 International Stamp Exhibition, Helsinki. Flowers. Multicoloured.

1078	8k. Type **227**	35	15
1079	9k. Hollyhock	45	20
1080	15k. Flame-of-the forest	60	25
1081	33k. Golden shower	1·20	40
1082	64k. *Dahlia coccinea* (red)	2·30	75
1083	69k. *Dahlia coccinea* (yellow)	3·00	90
MS1084 76×58 mm. 95k. Hollyhock, frangipani and flame-of-the-forest (31×39 mm)		5·75	3·75

228 Sash Pattern

1988. Decorative Stencil Patterns.

1085	**228**	1k. multicoloured	35	15
1086	-	2k. yellow, red and black	40	20
1087	-	3k. multicoloured	45	25
1088	-	25k. multicoloured	1·20	40
1089	-	163k. multicoloured	5·25	2·40

Designs: (stencils for) Vert—2k. Pagoda doors; 3k. Pagoda walls. Horiz—25k. Pagoda pillars; 163k. Skirts.

229 Dove and Figures

1988. 125th Anniversary of Red Cross Movement. Multicoloured.

1090	4k. Type **229**	35	25
1091	52k. Red Cross workers with disabled people	2·00	90
1092	144k. Red Cross worker vaccinating baby (horiz)	6·50	2·75

230 Stork-billed Kingfisher

1988. Birds. Multicoloured.

1093	6k. Type **230**	35	20
1094	10k. Japanese quail	60	25
1095	13k. Blossom-headed parakeet	70	30
1096	44k. Orange-breasted green pigeon	1·40	40
1097	63k. Black-crested bulbul	2·75	75
1098	64k. Mountain imperial pigeon	3·00	90

231 Red Cross Workers loading Supplies into Pirogue

1988. Completion of First Five Year Plan. Multicoloured.

1099	20k. Type **231**	95	40
1100	40k. Library	1·60	65
1101	50k. Irrigating fields	2·30	90
1102	100k. Improvement in communications	3·50	1·80

232 Ruy Lopez Segura

1988. Chess Masters. Multicoloured.

1103	1k. Type **232**	25	15
1104	2k. Karl Anderssen	30	20
1105	3k. Paul Morphy (wrongly inscr 'Murphy')	35	25
1106	6k. Wilhelm Steinitz	45	30
1107	7k. Emanuel Lasker	60	40
1108	12k. Jose Raul Capablanca	80	45
1109	172k. Aleksandr Alekhine	6·50	1·80

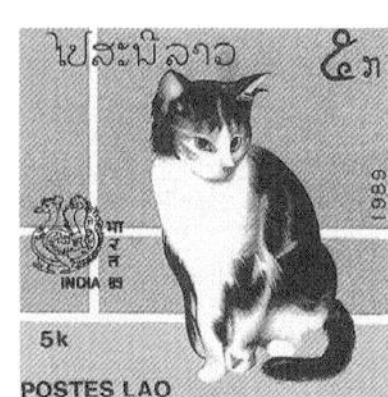

233 Tortoiseshell and White

1989. India 89 International Stamp Exhibition, New Delhi. Cats. Multicoloured.

1110	5k. Type **233**	25	15
1111	6k. Brown tabby	35	20
1112	10k. Black and white	70	25
1113	20k. Red tabby	1·10	30
1114	50k. Black	2·00	65
1115	172k. Silver tabby and white	6·50	1·50
MS1116	70×94 mm. 95k. Brown tabby and white (31×39 mm)	4·75	3·75

234 Gunboat, Tank, Soldiers and Flags

1989. 40th Anniversary of People's Army. Multicoloured.

1117	1k. Type **234**	25	15
1118	2k. Soldier teaching mathematics (vert)	35	20
1119	3k. Army medics vaccinating civilians	45	25
1120	250k. Peasant, revolutionary, worker and soldiers	10·50	1·60

235 Footballers

1989. World Cup Football Championship, Italy (1990) (1st issue). Multicoloured.

1121	10k. Type **235**	45	15
1122	15k. Footballer looking to pass ball	60	20
1123	20k. Ball hitting player on chest	80	25
1124	25k. Tackle	1·20	40
1125	45k. Dribbling ball	1·60	50
1126	105k. Kicking ball	4·00	1·30
MS1127	52×65 mm. 95k. Players and goalkeeper (38×29 mm)	4·75	3·75

See also Nos. 1168/**MS**1174.

236 Couple planting Sapling

1989. Preserve Forests Campaign. Multicoloured.

1128	4k. Type **236**	35	25
1129	10k. Burning and fallen trees	45	30
1130	12k. Man felling tree (vert)	60	40
1131	200k. Trees on map (vert)	7·50	1·50

237 Camilo Cienfuegos, Fidel Castro and Flag

1989. 30th Anniversary of Cuban Revolution. Multicoloured.

1132	45k. Type **237**	2·20	65
1133	50d. Cuban and Laotian flags	2·50	75

238 Skaters

1989. Winter Olympic Games, Albertville (1992) (1st issue). Figure Skating. Multicoloured.

1134	9k. Type **238**	45	20
1135	10k. Pair (horiz)	60	25
1136	15k. Ice dancing	80	30
1137	24k. Female skater	95	40
1138	29k. Pair	1·20	50
1139	114k. Male skater	4·25	1·50
MS1140	49×78 mm. 95k. Pair (different) (31×39 mm)	4·00	3·25

See also. Nos. 1196/**MS**1202, 1237/**MS**1242 and 1276/**MS**1281.

239 High Jumping

1989. Olympic Games, Barcelona (1992) (1st issue). Multicoloured.

1141	5k. Type **239**	35	20
1142	15k. Gymnastics	60	25
1143	20k. Cycling (horiz)	80	40
1144	25k. Boxing (horiz)	95	50
1145	70k. Archery	2·20	90
1146	120k. Swimming	4·75	1·00
MS1147	65×91 mm. 95k. Baseball (31×39 mm)	4·00	3·25

See also Nos. 1179/**MS**1185, 1231/**MS**1236 and 1282/**MS**1287.

240 *Poor on Seashore*

1989. Philexfrance '89 International Stamp Exhibition, Paris. Paintings by Picasso. Multicoloured.

1148	5k. Type **240**	25	15
1149	7k. *Motherhood*	35	20
1150	8k. *Portrait of Jaime S. le Bock*	45	25
1151	9k. *Harlequins*	80	40
1152	105k. *Boy with Dog*	4·25	1·00
1153	114k. *Girl on Ball*	4·50	1·30
MS1154	65×75 mm. 95k. *Woman in Hat* (31×39 mm)	4·75	3·75

241 Sapodillas

1989. Fruits. Multicoloured.

1155	5k. Type **241**	35	25
1156	20k. Sugar-apples	95	40
1157	20k. Guavas	95	40
1158	30k. Durians	1·40	50
1159	50k. Pomegranates	2·20	75
1160	172k. *Moridica charautia*	7·00	1·50

242 Sikhotabong Temple, Khammouane

1989. Temples. Multicoloured.

1161	5k. Type **242**	35	25
1162	15k. Dam Temple, Vientiane	60	40
1163	61k. Ing Hang Temple, Savannakhet	2·00	90
1164	161k. Ho Vay Phra Luang Temple, Vientiane	5·75	1·80

243 Nehru and Woman

1989. Birth Centenary of Jawaharlal Nehru (Indian statesman). Multicoloured.

1165	1k. Type **243**	60	25
1166	60k. Nehru and group of children (horiz)	2·30	75
1167	200k. Boy garlanding Nehru	7·50	1·80

244 Footballer

1990. World Cup Football Championship, Italy (2nd issue).

1168	**244**	10k. multicoloured	35	20
1169	-	15k. multicoloured	45	25
1170	-	20k. multicoloured	70	30
1171	-	25k. multicoloured	80	40
1172	-	45k. multicoloured	1·50	50
1173	-	105k. multicoloured	3·75	1·30
MS1174		90×67 mm. 95k. multicoloured (31×39 mm)	4·75	3·75

Designs: 15 to 95k. Different football scenes.

245 Teacher and Adult Class

1990. International Literacy Year. Multicoloured.

1175	10k. Type **245**	45	25
1176	50k. Woman teaching child (vert)	2·10	1·00
1177	60k. Monk teaching adults	2·30	1·10
1178	150k. Group reading and writing under tree	5·75	1·80

246 Basketball

1990. Olympic Games, Barcelona (1992) (2nd issue). Multicoloured.

1179	10k. Type **246**	45	25
1180	30k. Hurdling	1·10	30
1181	45k. High jumping	1·60	40
1182	50k. Cycling	2·00	50
1183	60k. Throwing the javelin	2·10	75
1184	90k. Tennis	3·50	1·30
MS1185	86×102 mm. 95k. Gymnastics (31×39 mm)	4·75	3·75

247 Great Britain 1840 Penny Black and Mail Coach

1990. Stamp World London 90 International Stamp Exhibition. Multicoloured.

1186	15k. Type **247**	60	25
1187	20k. US 1847 5c. stamp and early steam locomotive	95	30
1188	40k. France 1849 20c. stamp and mail balloons, Paris, 1870	1·60	40
1189	50k. Sardinia 1851 5c. stamp and post rider	1·90	50
1190	60k. Indo-China 1892 1c. stamp and elephant	2·30	75
1191	100k. Spain 1850 6c. stamp and Spanish galleon	4·50	1·10
MS1192	54×54 mm. 95k. Laos 1976 1k. stamp and Douglas DC-8 airliner (36×28 mm)	4·75	3·75

248 Ho Chi Minh addressing Crowd

1990. Birth Centenary of Ho Chi Minh. Multicoloured.

1193	40k. Type **248**	1·60	75
1194	60k. Ho Chi Minh and Laotian Prime Minister	2·50	1·00
1195	160k. Ho Chi Minh and Vietnamese flag (vert)	7·00	2·75

249 Speed Skating

1990. Winter Olympic Games, Albertville (1992) (2nd issue). Multicoloured.

1196	10k. Type **249**	45	20
1197	25k. Cross-country skiing (vert)	95	25
1198	30k. Downhill skiing	1·10	30
1199	35k. Tobogganing	1·60	40
1200	80k. Figure skating (pairs) (vert)	3·00	90
1201	90k. Biathlon	3·50	1·00
MS1202	97×83 mm. 95k. Ice hockey (31×39 mm)	4·75	3·75

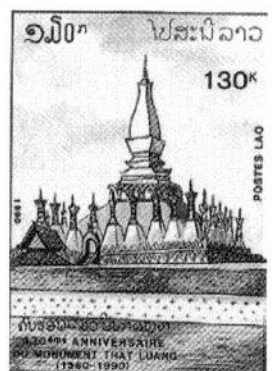

250 That Luang, 1990

1990. 430th Anniversary of That Luang. Multicoloured.

1203	60k. That Luang, 1867 (horiz)	3·00	75
1204	70k. That Luang, 1930 (horiz)	3·50	1·00
1205	130k. Type **250**	6·50	1·80

251 Parson Bird

1990. New Zealand 1990 International Stamp Exhibition, Auckland. Multicoloured.

1206	10k. Type **251**	35	20
1207	15k. Eurasian sky lark	45	25
1208	20k. Oystercatcher	70	40
1209	50k. Variable cormorant	2·00	50
1210	60k. Great Reef heron	2·30	75
1211	100k. Brown kiwi	4·25	1·30
MS1212	56×82 mm. 95k. Rough-faced cormorant (30×37 mm)	5·75	4·00

252 Brown-antlered Deer

1990. Mammals. Multicoloured.

1213	10k. Type **252**	45	20
1214	20k. Gaur	80	25
1215	40k. Wild water buffalo	1·60	40
1216	45k. Kouprey	1·90	50
1217	120k. Javan rhinoceros	4·75	1·50

253 Surgeons Operating

1990. 40th Anniversary of United Nations Development Programme. Multicoloured.

1218	30k. Type **253**	1·40	50
1219	45k. Fishermen inspecting catch	2·30	65
1220	80k. Air-traffic controller (vert)	3·50	1·50
1221	90k. Electricity plant workers	4·00	2·00

254 Rice Ceremony

1990. New Year. Multicoloured.

1222	5k. Type **254**	45	25
1223	10k. Elephant in carnival parade	60	30
1224	50k. Making offerings at temple	2·00	50
1225	150k. Family ceremony	5·75	1·90

255 Memorial, Wreath and Eternal Flame

1990. 15th National Day Festival. Multicoloured.

1226	15k. Type **255**	80	40
1227	20k. Celebration parade	1·20	75
1228	80k. Hospital visit	3·75	1·50
1229	120k. Girls parading with banner	5·75	2·00

256 West German World Cup Football Champion

1991. West Germany, World Cup Football Champion. Sheet 86×58 mm.

MS1230	**256** 95k. multicoloured	6·50	5·00

257 Two-man Kayak

1991. Olympic Games, Barcelona (1992) (3rd issue). Multicoloured.

1231	22k. Type **257**	35	20
1232	32k. Canoeing	45	25
1233	285k. Diving (vert)	1·60	40
1234	330k. Racing dinghies (vert)	2·00	50
1235	1000k. Swimming	4·50	1·50
MS1236	83×55 mm. 700k. Two-man canoeing (39×31 mm)	4·75	3·75

258 Bobsleighing

1991. Winter Olympic Games, Albertville (1992) (3rd issue). Multicoloured.

1237	32k. Type **258**	35	20
1238	135k. Cross-country skiing (horiz)	80	25
1239	250k. Ski jumping (horiz)	1·40	40
1240	275k. Biathlon (horiz)	1·60	50
1241	900k. Speed skating (horiz)	4·75	1·50
MS1242	80×63 mm. 700k. Skiing (31×39 mm)	4·75	3·75

259 Pha Pheng Falls, Champassak

1991. Tourism. Multicoloured.

1243	155k. Type **259**	95	40
1244	220k. Pha Tang mountains, Vangvieng	1·30	50
1245	235k. Tat Set waterfall, Saravane (vert)	1·50	90
1246	1000k. Plain of Jars, Xieng Khouang (vert)	5·50	1·90

260 Match Scene

1991. World Cup Football Championship, USA (1994) (1st issue). Multicoloured.

1247	32k. Type **260**	35	20
1248	330k. Goalkeeper catching ball	1·50	30
1249	340k. Player controlling ball (vert)	1·90	40
1250	400k. Player dribbling ball	2·30	50
1251	500k. Tackle	2·75	1·30
MS1252	75×57 mm. 700k. Player shooting at goal (31×39 mm)	4·75	3·75

See also Nos. 1292/**MS**1297, 1370/**MS**1375 and 1386/**MS**1391.

261 Planting Saplings

1991. National Tree Planting Day. Multicoloured.

1253	350k. Type **261**	1·20	50
1254	700k. Planting saplings (different)	3·50	1·30
1255	800k. Removing saplings from store	4·00	1·90

262 *Mallard*, 1938, Great Britain

1991. Espamer '91 Spain–Latin America Stamp Exhibition, Buenos Aires. Railway Locomotives. Multicoloured.

1256	25k. Type **262**	35	20
1257	32k. Class 4500 steam locomotive, France (inscr 'Pacific 231')	45	25
1258	285k. Streamlined steam locomotive, USA.	1·80	50
1259	650k. Canadian Pacific Class T1b steam locomotive, 1938	3·25	1·10
1260	750k. East African Railways Class 59 steam locomotive, 1955	4·75	1·60
MS1261	80×64 mm. 700k. Class VT601 diesel-hydraulic intercity express (39×31 mm)	4·75	3·75

263 Spindle Festival

1991. Traditional Music. Multicoloured.

1262	20k. Type **263**	25	15
1263	220k. Mong player (vert)	1·10	40
1264	275k. Siphandone singer (vert)	1·20	50
1265	545k. Khap ngum singer	2·75	1·10
1266	690k. Phouthaydam dance	3·50	1·50

264 Great Purple

1991. Phila Nippon '91 International Stamp Exhibition, Tokyo. Butterflies. Multicoloured.

1267	55k. Type **264**	60	20
1268	90k. *Luehdorfia puziloi* (wrongly inscr 'Luendorfia')	70	25
1269	255k. *Papilio bianor*	1·60	40
1270	285k. Swallowtail	1·80	50
1271	900k. Mikado swallowtail	5·25	1·50
MS1272	60×77 mm. 700k. Common map butterfly (39×31 mm)	5·75	4·00

265 Emblem and Pattern

1991. International Decade for Cultural Development (1988–1997). Multicoloured.

1273	285k. Type **265**	1·40	50
1274	330k. Emblem and drum	1·60	65
1275	1000k. Emblem and pipes	5·25	1·90

266 Bobsleighing

1992. Winter Olympic Games, Albertville (4th issue). Multicoloured.

1276	200k. Type **266**	80	25
1277	220k. Slalom skiing	1·10	40
1278	250k. Downhill skiing (horiz)	1·20	45
1279	500k. One-man luge	2·50	65
1280	600k. Figure skating	3·00	1·30
MS1281	77×61 mm. 700k. Speed skating (31×39 mm)	4·75	3·75

267 Running

1992. Olympic Games, Barcelona (4th issue). Multicoloured.

1282	32k. Type **267**	25	15
1283	245k. Baseball	1·10	40
1284	275k. Tennis	1·40	45
1285	285k. Basketball	1·50	50
1286	900k. Boxing (horiz)	4·75	1·30
MS1287	71×59 mm. 700k. Diving (39×31 mm)	4·75	3·75

268 Pest Control

1992. World Health Day. Multicoloured.

1288	200k. Type **268**	1·10	40
1289	255k. Anti-smoking campaign	1·30	50
1290	330k. Donating blood	1·60	1·00
1291	1000k. Vaccinating child (vert)	5·00	2·00

269 Argentinian and Italian Players and Flags

1992. World Cup Football Championship, USA (1994) (2nd issue). Multicoloured.

1292	260k. Type **269**	95	25
1293	305k. German and English players and flags	1·30	40
1294	310k. United States flag, ball and trophy	1·40	50
1295	350k. Italian and English players and flags	2·10	75
1296	800k. German and Argentinian players and flags	4·25	1·50
MS1297	60×88 mm. 700k. Goalkeeper catching ball (31×39 mm)	5·75	4·00

270 Monocled Cobra

1992. Snakes. Multicoloured.

1298	280k. Type **270**	1·40	40
1299	295k. Chinese cobra	1·50	45
1300	420k. Wagler's pit viper	2·10	50
1301	700k. King cobra (vert)	4·50	1·50

271 Doorway and Ruins

1992. Restoration of Wat Phou. Multicoloured.

1302	185k. Type **271**	95	55
1303	220k. Doorway (different)	1·10	65
1304	1200k. Doorway with collapsed porch (horiz)	6·50	2·75

272 *Pinta* and Juan Martinez's Map

1992. Genova '92 International Thematic Stamp Exhibition. Multicoloured.

1305	100k. Type **272**	35	25
1306	300k. Piri Reis's map and caravelle (vert)	1·40	40
1307	350k. Magellan's ship and Paolo del Pozo Toscanelli's world map	1·90	50
1308	400k. Gabriel de Vallesca's map and Vasco da Gama's flagship *Sao Gabriel*	2·00	75
1309	455k. Juan Martinez's map and Portuguese four-masted caravel	2·50	1·10
MS1310	94×63 mm. 700k. *Santa Maria* (39×31 mm)	4·75	3·75

273 Woman in Traditional Costume

1992. Traditional Costumes of Laotian Mountain Villages.

1311	**273**	25k. multicoloured	25	15
1312	-	55k. multicoloured	35	20
1313	-	400k. multicoloured	2·10	75
1314	-	1200k. multicoloured	6·50	2·00

Designs: 55 to 1200k. Different costumes.

274 Boy Drumming

1992. International Children's Day. Children at Play. Multicoloured.

1315	220k. Type **274**	1·10	40
1316	285k. Girls skipping (horiz)	1·50	45
1317	330k. Boys racing on stilts	2·10	65
1318	400k. Girls playing 'escape' game (horiz)	2·30	1·00

275 Praying before Buddha

1992. National Customs. Multicoloured.

1319	100k. Type **275**	45	25
1320	140k. Wedding (horiz)	70	40
1321	160k. Religious procession (horiz)	1·20	50
1322	1500k. Monks receiving alms (horiz)	7·50	3·75

276 Crested Gibbon

1992. Climbing Mammals. Multicoloured.

1323	10k. Type **276**	35	25
1324	100k. Variegated langur	45	40
1325	250k. Pileated gibbon	1·30	50
1326	430k. Francois's monkey	2·30	75
1327	800k. Lesser slow loris	4·75	1·40

277 New York

1993. 130th Anniversary of Underground Railway Systems. Multicoloured.

1328	15k. Type **277**	25	20
1329	50k. West Berlin	35	25
1330	100k. Paris	45	40
1331	200k. London	1·30	50
1332	900k. Moscow	5·00	2·00
MS1333	85×55 mm. 700k. Royal Mail underground system, London (31×39 mm)	5·75	4·50

278 Malayan Bullfrog

1993. Amphibians. Multicoloured.

1334	55k. Type **278**	35	25
1335	90k. Muller's clawed frog	45	30
1336	100k. Glass frog (vert)	70	40
1337	185k. Giant toad	1·10	50
1338	1200k. Common tree frog (vert)	6·50	2·00

279 Common Tree-shrew

1993. Mammals. Multicoloured.

1339	45k. Type **279**	25	20
1340	60k. Philippine flying lemur	35	25
1341	120k. Loris	70	40
1342	500k. Eastern tarsier	2·50	1·10
1343	600k. Giant gibbon	3·00	2·00

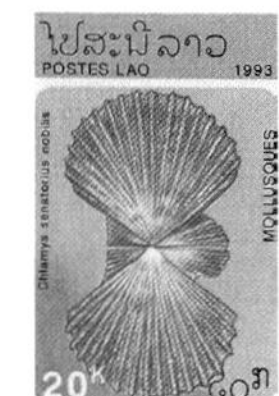
280 Noble Scallop

1993. Molluscs. Multicoloured.

1344	20k. Type **280**	25	20
1345	30k. Precious wentletrap	35	25
1346	70k. Spider conch	45	40
1347	500k. Aulicus cone	2·75	1·10
1348	1000k. Milleped spider conch	5·00	2·00

281 Drugs and Skull smoking

1993. Anti-drugs Campaign. Multicoloured.

1349	200k. Type **281**	1·10	50
1350	430k. Burning seized drugs	2·20	1·00
1351	900k. Instructing on dangers of drugs	5·00	2·00

282 House

1993. Traditional Houses. Multicoloured.

1352	32k. Type **282**	35	25
1353	200k. Thatched house with gable end (horiz)	1·40	40
1354	650k. Thatched house (horiz)	3·50	1·00
1355	750k. House with tiled roof (horiz)	4·00	2·00

283 Greater Spotted Eagle

1993. Birds of Prey. Multicoloured.

1356	10k. Type **283**	25	20
1357	100k. Spotted little owl	70	40
1358	330k. Pied harrier (horiz)	2·50	75
1359	1000k. Short-toed eagle	6·50	2·10

284 Fighting Forest Fire

1993. Environmental Protection. Multicoloured.

1360	32k. Type **284**	45	25
1361	40k. Wildlife on banks of River Mekong	60	30
1362	260k. Paddy fields	2·10	50
1363	1100k. Oxen in river	7·25	2·00

285 *Narathura atosia*

1993. Bangkok 1993 International Stamp Exhibition. Butterflies. Multicoloured.

1364	35k. Type **285**	35	25
1365	80k. *Parides philoxenus*	45	30
1366	150k. *Euploea harrisi*	80	40
1367	220k. Yellow orange-tip	1·40	50
1368	500k. Female common palm fly	3·50	1·40
MS1369	85×69 mm. 700k. *Stichophtlalma Louisa* (39×31 mm)	5·75	4·00

286 Footballer

1993. World Cup Football Championship, USA (3rd issue). Multicoloured.

1370	10k. Type **286**	20	15
1371	20k. Brazil player	25	20
1372	285k. Uruguay player	1·30	40
1373	400k. Germany player	2·20	75
1374	800k. Forward challenging goalkeeper	4·25	2·00
MS1375	99×72 mm. 700k. Ball on pitch (31×39 mm)	5·25	3·75

287 Hesperornis

1994. Prehistoric Birds. Multicoloured.

1376	10k. Type **287**	25	15
1377	20k. Mauritius dodo	30	20
1378	150k. Archaeopteryx	95	40
1379	600k. Phororhachos	3·00	75
1380	700k. Giant moa	4·00	1·50
MS1381	80×65 mm. 700k. Teratornis mirabilis (Teratornis) (39×31 mm)	5·75	4·00

288 Olympic Flag and Flame

1994. Centenary of International Olympic Committee. Multicoloured.

1382	100k. Type **288**	45	25
1383	250k. Ancient Greek athletes (horiz)	1·30	40
1384	1000k. Pierre de Coubertin (founder) and modern athlete	5·25	2·40

289 Bridge and National Flags

1994. Opening of Friendship Bridge between Laos and Thailand.

1385	**289**	500k. multicoloured	4·00	3·25

290 World Map and Players

1994. World Cup Football Championship, USA (4th issue).

1386	**290**	40k. multicoloured	25	15
1387	-	50k. multicoloured	30	20
1388	-	60k. multicoloured	35	25
1389	-	320k. multicoloured	1·90	75
1390	-	900k. multicoloured	5·25	2·00
MS1391		82×59 mm. 700k. multicoloured (31×39 mm)	5·25	3·25

Designs: 50 to 900k. Different players on world map.

291 Pagoda

1994. Pagodas.

1392	**291**	30k. multicoloured	35	25
1393	-	150k. multicoloured	95	40
1394	-	380k. multicoloured	2·20	65
1395	-	1100k. multicoloured	6·50	2·30

Designs: 150 to 1100k. Different gabled roofs.

292 Bear eating

1994. The Malay Bear. Multicoloured.

1396	50k. Type **292**	70	40
1397	90k. Bear's head	1·40	50
1398	200k. Adult and cub	3·00	65
1399	220k. Bear	3·25	1·00

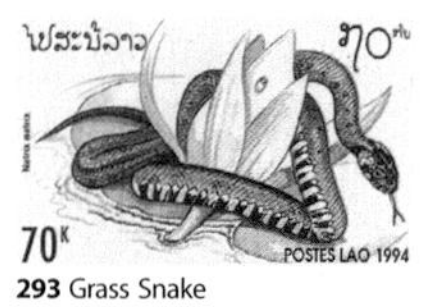
293 Grass Snake

1994. Amphibians and Reptiles. Multicoloured.

1400	70k. Type **293**	35	20
1401	80k. Tessellated snake	45	25
1402	90k. Fire salamander	60	30
1403	600k. Alpine newt	3·25	1·00
1404	800k. Green lizard (vert)	4·00	2·00
MS1405	79×50 mm. 700k. Great crested newt (39×31 mm)	4·75	3·75

294 Phra Xayavoraman 7

1994. Buddhas. Multicoloured.

1406	15k. Type **294**	45	25
1407	280k. Phra Thong Souk	2·20	50
1408	390k. Phra Manolom	3·00	75
1409	800k. Phra Ongtu	5·00	2·00

295 Family supporting Healthy Globe

1994. International Year of the Family. Multicoloured.

1410	200k. Type **295**	1·20	50
1411	500k. Mother taking child to school (horiz)	2·50	1·40
1412	700k. Mother and children	3·75	2·00
MS1413	50×70 mm. 700k. Family and flag	5·75	4·00

296 Kong Hang

1994. Traditional Laotian Drums. Multicoloured.

1414	370k. Type **296**	2·20	65
1415	440k. Kong Leng (portable drum)	2·75	70
1416	450k. Kong Toum (drum on stand)	2·75	75
1417	600k. Kong Phene (hanging drum)	3·50	1·10

297 Elephant in Procession

1994. Ceremonial Elephants. Multicoloured.

1418	140k. Type **297**	80	40
1419	400k. Elephant in pavilion	2·75	1·40
1420	890k. Elephant in street procession (vert)	4·50	2·10

298 Theropodes

1994. Prehistoric Animals. Multicoloured.

1421	50k. Type **298**	70	25
1422	380k. Iguanodontides	3·00	1·00
1423	420k. Sauropodes	3·75	1·30

299 Playing Musical Instruments

1995. 20th Anniversary of World Tourism Organisation. Multicoloured.

1424	60k. Type **299**	5·75	25
1425	250k. Women dancing	1·80	40
1426	400k. Giving alms to monks	2·30	75
1427	650k. Waterfall (vert)	3·50	1·40
MS1428	40×83 mm. 700k. Close-up view of waterfall in No. 1427 (31×39 mm)	5·75	4·00

300 Trachodon

1995. Prehistoric Animals. Multicoloured.

1429	50k. Type **300**	45	25
1430	70k. Protoceratops	70	30
1431	300k. Brontosaurus	1·80	50
1432	400k. Stegosaurus	2·30	75
1433	600k. Tyrannosaurus	3·50	1·10

301 Indian Jungle Mynah

1995. Birds. Multicoloured.

1434	50k. Type **301**	45	25
1435	150k. Jerdon's starling	1·10	30
1436	300k. Common mynah	2·00	65
1437	700k. Southern grackle	3·50	1·40

302 Children and Emblem

1995. 25th Anniversary of Francophonie. Multicoloured.

1438	50k. Type **302**	45	25
1439	380k. Golden roof decorations	2·10	1·00
1440	420k. Map	2·75	1·10

303 Pole Vaulting

1995. Olympic Games, Atlanta, USA (1st issue). Multicoloured.

1441	60k. Type **303**	35	25
1442	80k. Throwing the javelin	45	30
1443	200k. Throwing the hammer	1·30	40
1444	350k. Long jumping	2·10	65
1445	700k. High jumping	3·75	1·40
MS1446	90×60 mm. 700k. Baseball (39×31 mm)	5·75	4·50

See also Nos. 1484/**MS**1489.

304 Chalice

1995. Antique Vessels. Multicoloured.

1447	70k. Type **304**	35	25
1448	200k. Resin and silver bowl (horiz)	1·10	40
1449	450k. Geometrically decorated bowl (horiz)	2·30	90
1450	600k. Religious chalice (horiz)	3·25	1·10

305 Procession

1995. Rocket Festival. Multicoloured.

1451	80k. Launching rocket (vert)	60	25
1452	160k. Type **305**	1·10	40
1453	500k. Musicians in procession	2·75	90
1454	700k. Crowds and rockets	4·00	1·40

306 Red Tabby Longhair

1995. Cats. Multicoloured.

1455	40k. Type **306**	35	20
1456	50k. Siamese sealpoint	45	25
1457	250k. Red tabby longhair (different)	1·90	40
1458	400k. Tortoiseshell shorthair	2·75	50
1459	650k. Head of tortoiseshell shorthair (vert)	3·25	1·10
MS1460	49×70 mm. 700k. Tortoiseshell shorthair (different) (39×31 mm)	5·75	4·50

307 *Nepenthes villosa*

1995. Insectivorous Plants. Multicoloured.

1461	90k. Type **307**	45	20
1462	100k. *Dionaea muscipula*	60	25
1463	350k. *Sarracenia flava*	1·80	50
1464	450k. *Sarracenia purpurea*	2·30	65
1465	500k. *Nepenthes ampullaria*	3·00	1·00
MS1466	59×77 mm. 1000k. *Nepenthes gracillis* (31×39 mm)	6·50	5·00

308 Stag Beetle

1995. Insects. Multicoloured.

1467	40k. Type **308**	35	20
1468	50k. May beetle	45	25
1469	500k. Blue carpenter beetle	3·00	75
1470	800k. Great green grasshopper	4·50	1·40

309 Cattle grazing

1995. 50th Anniversary of FAO. Multicoloured.

1471	80k. Type **309**	45	25
1472	300k. Working paddy-field	1·60	75
1473	1000k. Agriculture	5·25	2·00

310 At Meeting

1995. 50th Anniversary of UNO. Peoples of Different Races. Multicoloured.

1474	290k. Type **310**	1·60	65
1475	310k. Playing draughts	1·80	75
1476	440k. Children playing	2·75	1·10

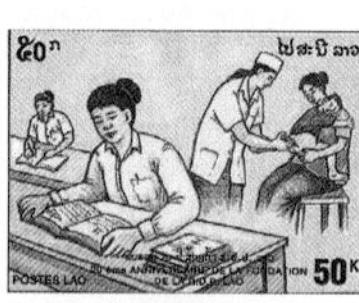

311 Students and Nurse vaccinating Child

1995. 20th Anniversary of Republic. Multicoloured.

1477	50k. Type **311**	35	20
1478	280k. Agricultural land	1·80	75
1479	600k. Bridge	3·75	1·50

312 Mong

1996. Traditional New Year Customs. Multicoloured.

1480	50k. Type **312**	45	25
1481	280k. Phouthai	2·10	50
1482	380k. Ten Xe	2·50	75
1483	420k. Lao Loum	2·75	90

313 Cycling

1996. Olympic Games, Atlanta, USA (2nd issue). Multicoloured.

1484	30k. Type **313**	35	20
1485	150k. Football	95	25
1486	200k. Basketball (vert)	1·30	40
1487	300k. Running (vert)	1·80	50
1488	500k. Shooting	2·75	1·00
MS1489	80×60 mm. 1000k. High jumping (38×30 mm)	5·75	4·50

314 Sun Bear

1996. Animals. Multicoloured.

1490	40k. Type **314**	45	25
1491	60k. Grey pelican	60	30
1492	200k. Leopard	1·10	40
1493	250k. Swallowtail	1·40	50
1494	700k. Indian python	3·50	1·40

315 Weaving

1996. International Women's Year. Multicoloured.

1495	20k. Type **315**	45	25
1496	290k. Physical training instructress	2·00	50
1497	1000k. Woman feeding child (vert)	5·25	1·90

316 Rat

1996. New Year. Year of the Rat.

1498	**316**	50k. multicoloured	45	25
1499	-	340k. multicoloured	2·75	90
1500	-	350k. multicoloured	2·75	1·00
1501	-	370k. multicoloured	3·00	1·10

Designs: 340k. to 370k. Different rats.

317 Players

1996. World Cup Football Championship, France (1998) (1st issue).

1502	**317**	20k. multicoloured	35	20
1503	-	50k. multicoloured	45	25
1504	-	300k. multicoloured	1·40	50
1505	-	400k. multicoloured	1·80	75
1506	-	500k. multicoloured	2·50	90
MS1507		63×92 mm. 1000k. multicoloured (30×37 mm)	5·75	4·50

Designs: 50k. to 1000k. Different football scenes.

See also Nos. 1589/**MS**1595.

318 Village Women grinding Rice

1996. Children's Drawings. Multicoloured.

1508	180k. Type **318**	1·90	50
1509	230k. Women picking fruit	2·50	65
1510	310k. Village women preparing food	3·25	90
1511	370k. Women tending vegetable crops	4·00	1·10

319 Morane Monoplane

1996. Capex '96 International Stamp Exhibition, Toronto, Canada. Aircraft. Multicoloured.

1512	25k. Type **319**	35	20
1513	60k. Sopwith Camel biplane	45	25
1514	150k. de Havilland D.H.4 biplane	95	30
1515	250k. Albatros biplane	1·50	50

1516	800k. Caudron biplane	3·75	1·50

320 Front View

1996. Ox-carts. Multicoloured.

1517	50k. Type **320**	60	25
1518	100k. Side view	1·10	40
1519	440k. Oxen pulling cart	3·00	1·00

321 *Dendrobium secundum*

1996. Orchids (1st series). Multicoloured.

1520	50k. Type **321**	45	25
1521	200k. *Ascocentrum miniatum*	1·40	40
1522	500k. *Aerides multiflorum*	2·50	1·00
1523	520k. *Dendrobium aggregatum*	2·75	1·10

See also Nos. 1563/**MS**1569, 1626/1629, 1685/**MS**1689 and 1836/1846.

322 White Horse

1996. Saddle Horses. Multicoloured.

1524	50k. Type **322**	35	20
1525	80k. Horse with red and black bridle	45	25
1526	200k. Bay horse with white bridle and reins	1·30	40
1527	400k. Horse with red and yellow cords braided into mane	1·90	75
1528	600k. Chestnut horse with white blaze	3·00	1·10
MS1529	89×69 mm. 1000k. Horse with ornate yellow and red bridle (28×36 mm)	5·75	4·50

323 Pupils displaying Slates to Teacher

1996. 50th Anniversary of UNICEF. Multicoloured.

1530	200k. Type **323**	1·30	50
1531	500k. Mother breastfeeding (vert)	3·25	1·40
1532	600k. Woman drawing water at public well	3·75	1·90

324 Leatherback Turtle

1996. 25th Anniversary of Greenpeace (environmental organisation). Turtles. Multicoloured.

1533	150k. Type **324**	1·20	50
1534	250k. Leatherback turtle at water's edge	1·80	75
1535	400k. Hawksbill turtle	3·00	1·30
1536	450k. *Chelonia agassizi*	3·50	1·60

325 Oral Vaccination

1997. National Vaccination Day. Multicoloured.

1537	50k. Type **325**	60	25
1538	340k. Nurse injecting child's leg	2·30	1·00
1539	370k. Nurse pushing child in wheelchair	3·00	1·10

326 George Stephenson and *Pioneer*, 1836

1997. Steam Railway Locomotives. Multicoloured.

1540	100k. *Kinnaird*, 1846 (44×27 mm)	60	25
1541	200k. Type **326**	95	40
1542	300k. Robert Stephenson and long-boiler express locomotive, 1848	1·40	50
1543	400k. Stephenson locomotive *Adler*, 1835, Germany	1·80	75
1544	500k. *Lord of the Isles*, 1851–84	2·30	1·00
1545	600k. *The Columbine*, 1845	3·00	1·30
MS1546	69×93 mm. 2000k. South Carolina Railroad locomotive *Best Friend of Charleston*, 1830 (39×31 mm)	10·00	8·25

The 200 and 300k. are wrongly inscr 'Stephesonʼ.

327 Pseudoryx lying down

1997. *Pseudoryx* (Saola). Multicoloured.

1547	350k. Type **327**	2·30	2·10
1548	380k. Grazing (vert)	3·00	2·40
1549	420k. Scratching with hind leg	3·50	2·50

328 Masked Lovebirds (*Agapornis personata*)

1997. Lovebirds. Multicoloured.

1550	50k. Type **328**	45	20
1551	150k. Grey-headed lovebird (*Agapornis cana*)	80	25
1552	200k. Nyasa lovebirds (*Agapornis lilianae*)	1·10	40
1553	400k. Fischer's lovebirds (*Agapornis fischeri*)	1·90	75
1554	500k. Black-cheeked lovebirds (*Agapornis nigregenis*)	2·20	1·00
1555	800k. Peach-faced lovebird (*Agapornis roseicollis*)	3·50	1·50
MS1556	91×74 mm. 2000k. Black-winged lovebirds (31×38 mm)	10·00	8·25

329 Signs of the Chinese Zodiac

1997. New Year. Year of the Ox. Multicoloured.

1557	50k. Type **329**	45	25
1558	300k. Woman riding ox (vert)	2·50	2·00
1559	440k. Ox on float in procession	3·25	2·75

330 Steaming Rice

1997. Food Preparation. Multicoloured.

1560	50k. Type **330**	80	40
1561	340k. Water containers (horiz)	2·10	90
1562	370k. Table laid with meal (horiz)	2·30	1·00

331 *Vanda roeblingiana*

1997. Orchids (2nd series). Multicoloured.

1563	50k. Type **331**	45	25
1564	100k. *Dendrobium findleyanum*	80	30
1565	150k. *Dendrobium crepidatum*	1·10	40
1566	250k. *Sarcanthus birmanicus*	1·40	50
1567	400k. *Cymbidium lowianum*	2·10	75
1568	1000k. *Dendrobium gratiosissimum*	4·00	1·90
MS1569	95×70 mm. 2000k. *Paphiopedilum chamberlainanum* (31×37 mm)	10·00	8·25

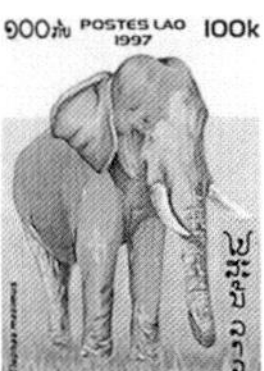

332 Indian Elephant (*Elephas maximus*)

1997. Elephants. Multicoloured.

1570	100k. Type **332**	70	25
1571	250k. Indian elephant carrying log (horiz)	1·40	50
1572	300k. Indian elephant with young (horiz)	1·50	55
1573	350k. African elephant (*Loxodonta africana*) (horiz)	1·60	65
1574	450k. African elephant in water (horiz)	2·00	90
1575	550k. African elephant with ears flapping	2·75	1·00
MS1576	117×74 mm. 2000k. Forequarter of African elephant (31×39 mm)	10·00	8·25

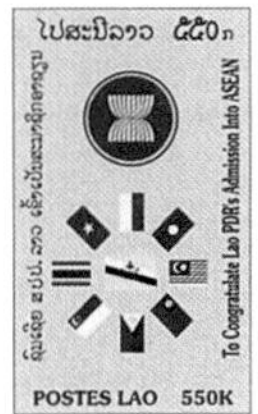

333 Emblem and Brunei Flag

1997. Admission of Laos into Association of South East Asian Nations. Members' flags, centre flag given.

1577	550k. Type **333**	1·80	1·40
1578	550k. Indonesia (red and white bands)	1·80	1·40
1579	550k. Laos (red, blue with white circle, red bands)	1·80	1·40
1580	550k. Malaysia (crescent and star on blue quarter, red and white stripes)	1·80	1·40
1581	550k. Myanmar (flower and stars on blue quarter, red)	1·80	1·40
1582	550k. Philippines (sun and stars on white triangle, blue and red bands)	1·80	1·40
1583	550k. Singapore (crescent and five stars on red band, white band)	1·80	1·40
1584	550k. Thailand (red, white, blue, red bands)	1·80	1·40
1585	550k. Vietnam (yellow star on red)	1·80	1·40
MS1586	Nine sheets, each 138×110 mm. (a) No. 1577; (b) No. 1578; (c) No. 1582; (d) No. 1580; (e) No. 1581; (f) No. 1582; (g) No. 1583; (h) No. 1584; (i) No. 1585	16·00	14·00

335 Headquarters, Djakarta, Indonesia

1997. 30th Anniversary of Association of South East Asian Nations. Multicoloured.

1587	150k. Type **335**	1·40	1·00
1588	600k. Map of Laos and state flag	4·25	3·75

336 Players

1997. World Cup Football Championship, France (1998) (2nd issue).

1589	**336**	100k. multicoloured	70	25
1590	-	200k. multicoloured	1·40	40
1591	-	250k. multicoloured	1·50	45
1592	-	300k. multicoloured	1·60	50
1593	-	350k. multicoloured	2·00	65
1594	-	700k. multicoloured	2·75	1·30
MS1595		111×84 mm. 2000k. multicoloured	10·00	8·25

Designs: 200k. to 2000k. Various football scenes.

337 Phoenician Nef

1997. Sailing Ships. Multicoloured.

1596	50k. Type **337**	45	20
1597	100k. 13th-century nef	80	25
1598	150k. 15th-century nef	1·10	30
1599	200k. 16th-century Portuguese caravel	1·20	40
1600	400k. 17th-century Dutch ship	2·30	75
1601	900k. HMS *Victory* (Nelson's flagship)	4·00	1·80
MS1602	80×60 mm. 2000k. *Great Harry* (sail warship), 1514	10·00	8·25

338 Headdress

1997. Headdresses and Masks. Multicoloured.

1603	50k. Type **338**	45	20
1604	100k. Headdress with flower at left	70	25
1605	150k. Mask with curved tusks (horiz)	95	30
1606	200k. Mask tipped with headdress decorated with two faces	1·20	40
1607	350k. Mask with green face	2·10	65

339 Two Pirogues

1997. Pirogue Race. Multicoloured.

1608	50k. Type **339**	45	25
1609	100k. Crowd cheering competitors from land	80	30
1610	300k. Side view of two competing pirogues	1·80	50
1611	500k. People cheering on spectator boat	2·30	90

340 Sunken Net

1998. Traditional Fishing Methods. Multicoloured.

1612	50k. Type **340**	60	30
1613	100k. Fisherman throwing net (horiz)	80	50
1614	450k. Funnel net	2·75	2·40
1615	650k. Lobster pots (horiz)	3·50	3·25

341 Man riding Tiger

1998. New Year. Year of the Tiger.

1616	**341**	150k. multicoloured	1·20	1·00
1617	**341**	350k. multicoloured	2·50	2·40
1618	**341**	400k. multicoloured	3·25	3·00

342 Wat Sisaket Shrine

1998. Temples. Multicoloured.

1619	10000k. Type **342**	18·00	15·00
1620	25000k. Wat Phou temple, Pakse (horiz)	35·00	31·00
1621	45000k. That Luang (royal mausoleum) (horiz)	55·00	50·00

343 Boat and Pole

1998. Water Transport. Multicoloured.

1622	1100k. Type **343**	4·50	2·75
1623	1200k. Covered canoe	4·75	3·25
1624	2500k. Motorised canoe	9·25	7·00

344 Buddha, Luang Phabang Temple

1998

1625	**344**	3000k. multicoloured	14·00	11·50

345 *Paphiopedilum callosum*

1998. Orchids (3rd series). Multicoloured.

1626	900k. Type **345**	4·50	3·25
1627	950k. *Paphiopedilum concolor*	4·75	3·50
1628	1000k. *Dendrobium thyrsiflorum* (vert)	5·00	3·75
1629	1050k. *Dendrobium lindleyi* (vert)	5·25	4·00

346 Children in Classroom

1998. 50th Anniversary of Universal Declaration of Human Rights. Multicoloured.

1630	300k. Type **346**	95	65
1631	1700k. Woman posting vote into ballot box	5·50	4·50

347 Gaeng

1998. Wind Instruments. Multicoloured.

1632	900k. Type **347**	4·75	3·25
1633	1200k. Khuoy (flute)	5·75	3·75
1634	1500k. Khaen (bamboo pipes of various lengths)	8·25	5·75

348 Military Personnel and Flag

1999. 50th Anniversary of People's Army. Multicoloured.

1635	1300k. Type **348**	3·50	2·10
1636	1500k. Soldier with upraised arm and jungle fighters (vert)	4·75	2·50

349 Inscribed Monument (world heritage)

1999. UNESCO World Heritage Site. Luang Prabang. Multicoloured.

1637	400k. Type **349**	1·40	1·00
1638	1150k. House with veranda and dovecote (horiz)	3·00	2·50
1639	1250k. Wat Xiengthong (horiz)	3·75	2·75

350 Yao Children celebrating New Year, Muong Sing

1999. Tourism Year (1st issue). Multicoloured.

1640	200k. Type **350**	1·20	65
1641	500k. Phadeang, Vangvieng district	1·80	90
1642	1050k. Wat That Makmo, Luang Prabang	3·00	1·80
1643	1300k. Patuxay (victory monument), Vientiane (vert)	4·00	2·40

See also No. **MS**1653 and 1713/1716.

351 Rabbit and Chinese Zodiac Animals

1999. New Year. Year of the Rabbit. Multicoloured.

1644	1500k. Type **351**	8·25	7·00
1645	1600k. White rabbit (horiz)	9·25	7·50

352 Iron Plough

1999. Traditional Farming Implements. Multicoloured.

1646	1500k. Type **352**	3·00	2·10
1647	2000k. Harrow	3·50	3·00
1648	3200k. Wooden plough	4·75	4·50

353 Collared Owlet (*Glaucidium brodiei*)

1999. Owls and Bat. Multicoloured.

1649	900k. Type **353**	1·80	1·30
1650	1600k. Collared scops owl (*Otus lempiji*)	3·50	2·50
1651	2100k. Barn owl (*Tyto alba*)	4·00	3·75
1652	2800k. Black capped fruit bat (*Chironax melanocephalus*)	5·75	5·00

354 Patuxay (victory monument), Vientiane

1999. Tourism (2nd issue). Sheet 135×100 mm containing T **354** and similar horiz designs.

MS1653	2500k. Type **354**; 4000k. Ho Phra Keo, Vientiane; 5500k. Wat Xieng Thong, Luang Prabang; 8000k. Pha That Luang, Vientiane	35·00	31·00

355 Envelope and Globe

1999. 125th Anniversary of Universal Postal Union. Multicoloured.

1654	2600k. Type **355**	5·75	5·25
1655	3400k. Postman delivering letter	8·25	7·00

356 Carved Tree Stump

1999. International Horticultural Exposition, Kunming, China. Exposition buildings. Multicoloured.

1656	300k. Type **356**	80	40
1657	900k. China Hall	1·90	75
1658	2300k. Science and Technology Hall	3·75	2·00
1659	2500k. Traditional Laotian house	5·25	2·40

357 Javan Rhino (*Rhinoceros sondaicus*)

1999. Animals. Multicoloured.

1660	700k. Type **357**	1·80	1·30
1661	900k. Water buffalo (*Bubalus bubalis*) (vert)	2·10	1·60
1662	1700k. Spotted linsang (*Prionodon pardicolor*)	3·50	3·00
1663	1800k. Sambar deer (*Cervus unicolor*)	3·75	3·25
1664	1900k. Lion (*Panthera leo*) (vert)	4·00	3·50

358 Airport and Hospital

2000. Millennium (1st issue). Multicoloured.

1665	2000k. Type **358**	2·30	1·50
1666	2000k. Temple	2·30	1·50
1667	2000k. Building with portico	2·30	1·50
1668	2000k. River and traditional buildings	2·30	1·50
MS1669	124×181 mm. Nos. 1665/1668	14·00	12·00

Nos. 1665/1668 were issued together, *se-tenant*, forming a composite design.

See also Nos. 1718/1719.

359 Kor Loma

2000. Women's Regional Costumes (1st series). Multicoloured.

1670	100k. Type **359**	35	25
1671	200k. Kor Pchor	45	30
1672	500k. Nhuan Krom	60	40
1673	900k. Taidam	95	65
1674	2300k. Yao	1·40	1·30
1675	2500k. Meuy	1·60	1·40
1676	2600k. Sila	1·80	1·50
1677	2700k. Hmong	1·90	1·60
1678	2800k. Yao (different)	2·00	1·80
1679	3100k. Kor Nukkuy	2·10	1·90
1680	3200k. Kor Pouxang	2·20	2·00
1681	3300k. Yao Lanten	2·30	2·10
1682	3400k. Khir	2·50	2·30
1683	3500k. Kor	2·75	2·40
1684	3900k. Hmong (different)	3·00	2·50

See also Nos. 1777/1787.

360 *Dendrobium draconis*

2000. Orchids (4th series). Bangkok 2000 International Stamp Exhibition (**MS**1689) Multicoloured.

1685	500k. Type **360**	1·20	40
1686	900k. *Paphiopedilum hirsutissimum*	1·80	65
1687	3000k. *Dendrobium sulcatum*	4·00	2·00
1688	3400k. *Rhynchostylis gigantean*	4·75	2·30
MS1689	111×145 mm. Nos. 1686/1690	18·00	16·00

361 Dragon and Chinese Zodiac

2000. Year of the Dragon. Multicoloured.

1690	1800k. Type **361**	2·30	1·00
1691	2300k. Dragon swimming	4·00	1·50

362 River, Deer and Trees

2000. Children's Paintings. Multicoloured.

1692	300k. Type **362**	1·20	25
1693	400k. Animals running from fire	1·40	40
1694	2300k. Animals and birds	3·00	2·00
1695	3200k. Animals and birds (vert)	3·50	2·75

363 Peacock

2000. The Peacock. Multicoloured.

1696	700k. Type **363**	60	40
1697	1000k. With tail displayed	80	65
1698	1800k. Peahen (horiz)	1·40	1·00
1699	3500k. Pair (horiz)	2·75	2·00
MS1700	146×110 mm. 10000k. Front showing tail displayed	8·75	6·25

364 Bridge

2000. Pakse Bridge over Mekong River. Multicoloured.

1701	900k. Type **364**	80	65
1702	2700k. Overview of bridge	2·20	1·90
1703	3200k. Bridge from right	2·75	2·10
MS1704	180×122 mm. 4000k. No. 1701; 7500k. No. 1702; 8500k. No. 1703	18·00	15·00

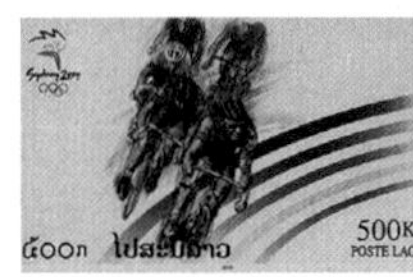

365 Cycling

2000. Olympic Games, Sydney. Multicoloured.

1705	500k. Type **365**	45	25
1706	900k. Boxing	1·10	65
1707	2600k. Kick boxing	2·20	1·80
1708	3600k. Canoeing	3·50	2·50
MS1709	124×180 mm. Nos. 1705/1708	11·50	10·00

366 Lao Theung

2000. Regional Wedding Costumes. Multicoloured.

1710	800k. Type **366**	70	50
1711	2300k. Lao Lum	1·60	1·30
1712	3400k. Lao Sung	3·00	2·00

367 Phousy Stupa, Luang Prabang

2000. Tourism (3rd issue). Multicoloured.

1713	300k. Type **367**	35	25
1714	600k. Tham Chang cave	60	40
1715	2800k. Inhang Stupa	2·50	2·00
1716	3300k. Buddha, Phiawal temple, Xiengkhuang	3·50	2·40

368 Building Facade

2000. 25th Anniversary of Republic of Laos.

1717	**368**	4000k. multicoloured	3·25	2·30

369 Satellites and Child writing

2001. Millennium (2nd issue). Multicoloured.

1718	3200k. Type **369**	2·10	1·80
1719	4000k. Electricity pylons and dam	2·50	2·30

370 Roadway

2001. Route 13 Highway Improvement Project. Sheet 120×190 mm containing T **370** and similar horiz designs. Multicoloured.

MS1720	4000k. Type **370**; 4000k. Bridge and mountains; 4000k. Bridge (different)	10·50	10·00

371 Yao mane Huaphanh

2001. Men's Regional Costumes. Multicoloured.

1721	100k. Type **371**	20	10
1722	200k. Gnaheun Champasak	25	15
1723	500k. Katou Sarvane	35	25
1724	2300k. Hmong Dam Oudomxay	1·40	1·30
1725	2500k. Harlak Xekong	1·50	1·40
1726	2600k. Kui Luangnamtha	1·60	1·50
1727	2700k. Krieng Xekong	1·80	1·60
1728	3100k. Khmu Nhuan Luangnamtha	1·90	1·80
1729	3200k. Ta Oy Saravane	2·00	1·90
1730	3300k. TaiTheng Bolihamxay	2·10	2·00
1731	3400k. Hmong Khao Huaphanh	2·20	2·10
1732	3500k. Gnor Khammouane	2·30	2·30
1733	3600k. Phouthai Na Gnom ZVK	2·50	2·40
1734	4000k. Yao Ventiane	2·75	2·50
1735	5000k. Hmong LPQ	3·25	3·00

372 Cocks

2001. Fighting Cocks. Multicoloured.

1736	500k. Type **372**	60	40
1737	900k. Pair with wings outstretched	80	65
1738	3200k. Pair, one in flight	2·50	2·30
1739	3500k. Pair resting	2·75	2·40
MS1740	140×111 mm. 10000k. Cock crowing (36×51 mm)	8·75	8·25

373 Pou Nyer and Nya Nyer

2001. Luang Prabang New Year Celebrations. Multicoloured.

1741	300k. Type **373**	35	25
1742	600k. Hae Nang Sangkhan	60	40
1743	1000k. Sand Stupa (horiz)	1·10	75
1744	2300k. Hae Prabang	2·00	1·60
1745	4000k. Takbat	3·75	3·00

374 Snake

2001. Year of the Snake. Multicoloured.

1746	900k. Type **374**	1·20	65
1747	3500k. Snake and Chinese zodiac symbols	3·50	2·10

375 The Gate of Heavenly Peace (Tian An Men)

2001. 40th Anniversary of Laos–China Diplomatic Relations.

1748	**375**	1000k. multicoloured	1·40	75

376 Nurse, Mother and Children

2001. Polio Eradication Campaign. Sheet 135×101 mm containing T **376** and similar horiz design.

MS1749	900k. Type **376**; 2500k. Family and map	4·00	3·75

377 Mekong River

2001. Mekong River at Twilight. Multicoloured.

1750	900k. Type **377**	80	65
1751	2700k. River with boats in foreground	2·30	1·90
1752	3400k. River (different)	3·50	2·30

378 Poppy Field

2001. Anti-Drug Campaign. Multicoloured.

1753	100k. Type **378**	1·10	75
1754	4000k. Burning seized drugs	3·00	2·30

379 Intermediate Egret (*Egretta intermedia*)

2001. Birds. Philanippon '01 International Stamp Exhibition. Multicoloured.

1755	700k. Type **379**	70	50
1756	800k. Bulbucus ibis (33×49 mm)	80	65
1757	3100k. Grey heron (*Ardea cinera*) (33×49 mm)	2·50	2·00
1758	3400k. Great egret (*Egretta alba*)	2·75	2·30
MS1759	200×146 mm. Nos. 1755/1758	7·75	6·50

380 Temple Door

2001. Buddhist Temple Doors.

1760	**380**	600k. multicoloured	60	40
1761	-	2300k. multicoloured	2·00	1·40
1762	-	2500k. multicoloured	2·10	1·50
1763	-	2600k. multicoloured	2·30	1·60

Designs: 2300k. to 2600k. Different temple doors.

381 White Frangipani

2001. The Frangipani. Multicoloured.

1764	1000k. Type **381**	1·10	65
1765	2500k. Pink frangipani (vert)	1·90	1·50
1766	3500k. Red frangipani	2·30	2·00
MS1767	145×111 mm. Nos. 1764/1766	7·00	6·25

382 Women using Pestles and Mortar

2001. Traditional Mortars. Multicoloured.

1768	900k. Type **382**	55	50
1769	2600k. Wheel driven pestle and mortar (horiz)	1·60	1·40
1770	3500k. Fulcrum and lever pestle and mortar	2·75	1·90

383 Himavanta

2001. *Vessantara* (Buddhist story illustrating charity). Multicoloured.

1771	200k. Type **383**	25	15
1772	900k. Vanapavesa	95	65
1773	3200k. Kumarakanda	2·75	2·30
1774	3600k. Sakkapabba	3·00	2·50
MS1775	120×151 mm. Nos. 1772/1774	8·25	7·50

384 People and Emblem

2001. International Year of Volunteers.

1776	**384**	1000k. multicoloured	1·20	75

2002. Women's Regional Costumes (2nd series). As T **359**. Multicoloured.

1777	200k. Meuy	20	15
1778	300k. Leu	25	20
1779	500k. Tai Kouane	40	25
1780	700k. Tai Dam	50	40
1781	1000k. Tai Man	65	50
1782	1500k. Lanten	90	75
1783	2500k. Hmong	1·70	1·40
1784	3000k. Phouxang	1·90	1·60
1785	3500k. Taitheng	2·20	1·90
1786	4000k. Tai O	2·50	2·10
1787	5000k. Tai Dam (different)	3·00	2·75

385 Phou Phamane

2002. International Year of Mountains. Multicoloured.

1788	1500k. Type **385**	1·60	1·00
1789	1500k. Pha Tang	1·60	1·00

386 Horse

2002. Chinese New Year. Year of the Horse. Multicoloured.

1790	1500k. Type **386**	1·30	1·00
1791	3500k. Galloping horse	2·50	2·00

387 Two Men carrying Parcels on Pole

2002. 50th Anniversary of Laos Admission to Universal Postal Union.

1792	**387**	3000k. black	2·50	2·30

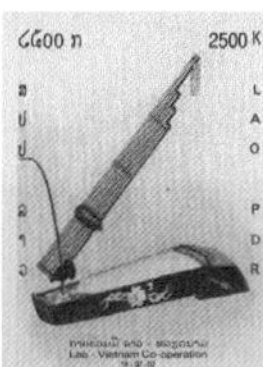

388 Laotian and Vietnamese Musical Instruments

2002. 40th Anniversary of Laos–Vietnam Diplomatic Relations. 25th Anniversary of Friendship Treaty.

1793	**388**	2500k. multicoloured	1·70	1·40
1794	-	3500k. black and orange (horiz)	2·50	1·90

Designs: 2500k. T **388**; 3500k. Prince Souvanna Vong and Ho Chi Minh (Vietnamese leader).

389 *Sagra femorata*

2002. Beetles. PhilaKorea 2002. Multicoloured.

No.	Description	Mint	Used
1795	1000k. Type **389**	65	50
1796	1000k. *Cerambycidae*	65	50
1797	1000k. *Chrysoxhroa mniszechii*	65	50
1798	1000k. *Anoplophora*	65	50
1799	1000k. *Chrysochroa saundersi*	65	50
1800	1000k. *Mouhotia batesi*	65	50
1801	1000k. *Megaloxantha assamensis*	65	50
1802	1000k. *Eupatorus gracillicornis*	65	50
MS1803	150×210 mm. 1000k.×8, *Sagra femorata* (different); *Cerambycidae* (different); *Chrysoxhroa mniszechii* (different); *Anoplophora* (different);*Chrysochroa saundersi* (different); *Mouhotia batesi* (different); *Megaloxantha assamensis* (different); *Eupatorus gracillicornis* (different)	6·50	5·75

390 Pearlscale Oranda

2002. Goldfish. Multicoloured.

No.	Description	Mint	Used
1804	1000k. Type **390**	65	50
1805	1000k. Moor	65	50
1806	1000k. Bubble eye	65	50
1807	1000k. Red-capped oranda	65	50
1808	1000k. Lionhead	65	50
1809	1000k. Pom pom	65	50
1810	1000k. Ranchu	65	50
1811	1000k. Fantail	65	50
1812	1000k. Celestial	65	50
1813	1000k. Ryukin	65	50
1814	1000k. Brown oranda	65	50
1815	1000k. Veiltail (inscr 'Veitail')	65	50

391 Buffalo

2002. Buffalo Fighting. Multicoloured.

No.	Description	Mint	Used
1816	200k. Type **391**	50	25
1817	300k. Two buffalos with raised heads	65	30
1818	3000k. Two with locked horns	2·30	1·60
1819	4000k. Two chasing one another	2·75	2·10

392 Roadway

2002. Route 9 Highway Improvement Project. Sheet 190×116 mm containing T **392** and similar horiz designs. Multicoloured.

No.	Description	Mint	Used
MS1820	1500k.×3, Type **392**; Road junction; Open road	5·25	4·50

393 Arched Doorway

2003. World Heritage Site. Wat Phou Temple, Champasak. Multicoloured.

No.	Description	Mint	Used
1821	1500k. Type **393**	1·20	75
1822	3000k. Wat Phou (horiz)	2·20	1·40
1823	4000k. Internal doorway and Buddha	2·75	2·10
MS1824	145×150 mm. 10000k. Carving showing three-headed elephant (96×30 mm)	7·75	7·00

394 Great Mormon (*Papillio memnon*)

2003. Butterflies. Multicoloured.

No.	Description	Mint	Used
1825	1000k. Type **394**	80	50
1826	1000k. *Pachliopta aristolochiae*	80	50
1827	1000k. Inscr 'Dalias pasithoe'	80	50
1828	1000k. *Castalius rosimon*	80	50
1829	1000k. *Polyura Schreiber*	80	50
1830	1000k. Blue triangle (*Graphium sarpedon*)	80	50
1831	1000k. *Spindasis lohita*	80	50
1832	1000k. *Hasora schoenherr*	80	50
MS1833	156×129 mm. 1000k. *Danaus genutia*	7·75	7·00

No. **MS**1833 was cut round in the shape of a butterfly.

395 Two Goats

2003. New Year. Year of the Goat. Multicoloured.

No.	Description	Mint	Used
1834	2500k. Type **395**	1·90	1·30
1835	5000k. Goat wearing bell and saddle cloth	4·00	2·50

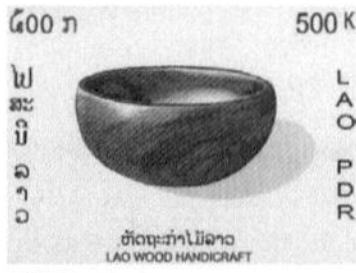
396 *Phalaenopsis paifang*

2003. Orchids (5th series). Multicoloured.

No.	Description	Mint	Used
1836	200k. Type **396**	40	15
1837	300k. *Coelogyne lentiginosa*	50	20
1838	500k. *Phalaenopsis sumatrana*	80	25
1839	1000k. *Phalaenopsis bellina*	90	50
1840	1500k. *Paphiopedilum appletonianum*	1·00	65
1841	2000k. *Vanda bensonii*	1·30	90
1842	2500k. *Dendrobium harveyanum*	1·60	1·10
1843	3000k. *Paphiopedilum glaucophyllum*	1·80	1·40
1844	3500k. *Paphiopedilum gratrixianum*	2·20	1·60
1845	4000k. *Vanda roeblingiana*	2·30	1·80
1846	5000k. *Phalaenopsis Lady Sakara*	2·75	2·30

397 Bowl

2003. Wooden Crafts. Multicoloured.

No.	Description	Mint	Used
1847	500k. Type **397**	50	25
1848	1500k. Drinks set	1·20	65
1849	2500k. Flower-shaped bowl	1·90	1·10
1850	3500k. Vase (vert)	2·50	1·60

398 Children using Coconut Feet Lifters

2003. Traditional Sports and Games. Multicoloured.

No.	Description	Mint	Used
1851	1000k. Type **398**	80	50
1852	3000k. Spinning tops	1·70	1·40
1853	4000k. Tee knee (hockey)	2·10	1·80

399 Deer and Stop Sign

2003. Stop Hunting Campaign. Multicoloured.

No.	Description	Mint	Used
1854	1500k. Type **399**	1·00	75
1855	2000k. Rifle and bow	1·30	1·00
1856	4500k. Prey animals	2·50	2·30

400 Mango

2003. Fruit. Multicoloured.

No.	Description	Mint	Used
1857	500k. Type **400**	65	25
1858	1500k. Water melon	1·00	65
1859	2500k. Custard apple	1·70	1·10
1860	4000k. Pineapple	2·50	1·80

401 Monk writing on Palm Leaf

2003. Palm Leaf Manuscripts. Multicoloured.

No.	Description	Mint	Used
1861	500k. Type **401**	40	25
1862	1500k. Manuscript book	1·20	75
1863	2500k. Manuscript casket	1·90	1·30
1864	3000k. Ho Tai temple archive	2·30	1·40

402 Buddha (Pha Sene Souk)

2003. Luang Prabang Statues. Statues of Buddha. Multicoloured.

No.	Description	Mint	Used
1865	500k. Type **402**	40	25
1866	1500k. Pha Gnai	1·20	75
1867	3000k. Pha Ong Luang	2·10	1·40
1868	3500k. Pha Ong Sene	2·75	1·80
MS1869	110×144 mm. 1000k. Pha Attharatsa (30×96 mm)	7·75	7·00

403 Traditional Cloth and Woman wearing Sin Mai (skirt) and Bieng Phae (scarf)

2003. Laotian Textiles. Showing cloth and woman. Multicoloured.

No.	Description	Mint	Used
1870	500k. Type **403**	65	25
1871	1000k. Woman at right and brown patterned cloth	1·20	65
1872	3000k. Woman at left and green patterned cloth	2·50	1·40
1873	4000k. Woman at right and block patterned cloth	3·25	2·00

404 Haw Pha Keaw (Installed Emerald Buddha), Vientiane

2004

No.	Type	Description	Mint	Used
1874	**404**	5500k. multicoloured	4·00	2·75

405 *Buceros bicornis*

2004. Birds. Multicoloured.

No.	Description	Mint	Used
1875	2000k. Type **405**	1·40	90
1876	2500k. *Pycnonotus jocosus*	1·90	1·10
1877	3000k. *Ploceus hypoxanthus*	2·20	1·40
1878	3500k. *Alcedo atthis*	2·50	1·50
1879	4000k. *Megalaima* (inscr 'Magalaima') *incognita*	2·50	1·60
1880	4500k. *Serilophus lunatus*	2·75	1·90
1881	5000k. *Eurylaimus ochromalus*	3·25	2·10
1882	5500k. *Lacedo pulchella*	4·00	2·40

406 Two Dolphins

2004. Endangered Species. Irrawaddy Dolphins. Multicoloured.

No.	Description	Mint	Used
1883	1500k. Type **406**	1·00	75
1884	2500k. Leaping	1·80	1·10
1885	3500k. With heads raised	2·50	1·60

407 Two Monkeys

2004. New Year. Year of the Monkey. Multicoloured.

No.	Description	Mint	Used
1886	500k. Type **407**	90	40
1887	4500k. Monkey king	3·25	2·00

409 Children

2004. Children's Day Multicoloured.

No.	Description	Mint	Used
1890	3500k. Type **409**	2·20	1·60
1891	4500k. Children (different)	3·00	2·10

412 Tangwai

2004. Dances. Multicoloured.

No.	Description	Mint	Used
1897	1000k. Type **412**	65	40
1898	1500k. Khabthoume Luangprabang	90	65
1899	2000k. Lao Lamvong	1·20	75
1900	2500k. Salavan	1·60	1·00

413 Marigold

2004. Marigold. Multicoloured.

No.	Description	Mint	Used
1901	3500k. Type **413**	2·20	1·40
1902	5000k. Marigold (different)	2·75	1·90
1903	5500k. Hats and marigold garlands	3·25	2·10

414 Demons

2004. Ramakian. Multicoloured.

No.	Description	Mint	Used
1904	3500k. Type **414**	2·20	1·40
1905	4500k. Hanuman, Rama and Lakshman	2·50	1·60
1906	5500k. Hanuman, Rama and Lakshman (different)	3·25	1·90
1907	6500k. Demon, Hanuman, Rama and Lakshman	3·50	2·10

415 Gods and Naga

2004. Naga Fire. Multicoloured.

1908	2000k. Type **415**	1·60	90
1909	3000k. Naga in kingdom beneath the water (horiz)	1·90	1·30
1910	3500k. Naga in river (horiz)	2·50	1·40
1911	4000k. Naga rearing out of water	3·00	1·50

416 Betel Nuts and Equipment

2004. Betel Tray. Multicoloured.

1912	2000k. Type **416**	1·30	90
1913	4000k. Leaf tray and wrappings	2·20	1·50
1914	6000k. Decorated tray and equipment	3·50	2·40

417 Elephant, Wat, Building and Reindeer

2004. 40th Anniversary of Laos–Sweden Diplomatic Relations.

1915	**417**	8500k. multicoloured	5·25	3·25

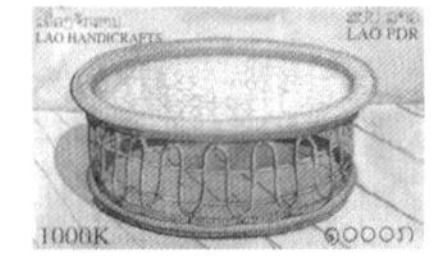
418 Woven Table

2005. Handicrafts. Multicoloured.

1916	1000k. Type **418**	90	50
1917	2000k. Paddle	1·40	90
1918	2500k. Basket (vert)	1·80	1·10
1919	5500k. Hanging lidded basket (vert)	3·00	2·50

419 Rooster, Hen and Chicks

2005. New Year. Year of the Rooster. Multicoloured.

1920	2000k. Type **419**	1·30	90
1921	7500k. Rooster	4·50	3·25

420 Sunday's Buddha

2005. Days of the Week. Designs showing Buddha. Multicoloured.

1922	500k. Type **420**	50	25
1923	1000k. Monday	65	50
1924	1500k. Tuesday (horiz)	90	65
1925	2000k. Wednesday	1·20	90
1926	2500k. Thursday	1·40	1·10
1927	3000k. Friday	1·70	1·40
1928	3500k. Saturday	2·10	1·60

421 Growing Rice

2005. Rice. Multicoloured.

1929	1500k. Type **421**	1·20	65
1930	3000k. Cooked rice on woven tray (horiz)	2·10	1·40
1931	6500k. Rice straw (horiz)	4·00	3·00

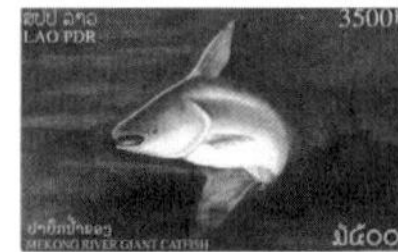
422 Catfish

2005. Mekong River Giant Catfish (*Pangasianodon giga*). Multicoloured.

1932	3500k. Type **422**	2·50	1·60
1933	6500k. Catfish (different)	4·00	3·00

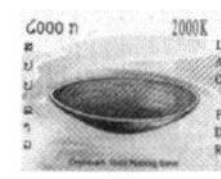
423 Gold Panning Sieve

2005. Tools. Multicoloured.

1934	2000k. Type **423**	1·30	90
1935	7500k. Woman using sieve (vert)	4·00	3·25

424 Musician and Singer

2005. Folk Music. Multicoloured.

1936	1000k. Type **424**	65	50
1937	3500k. Seated singer and musician	2·50	1·30
1938	5500k. Singer and three musicians (horiz)	4·00	2·00

425 Harvesting

2005. 50th Anniversary of Laos–United Nations Co-operation. Multicoloured.

1939	3000k. Type **425**	2·30	1·50
1940	3000k. Child immunization	2·30	1·50
1941	3000k. Education	2·30	1·50

426 Stonehenge, UK and Field of Jars, Laos

2005. 50th Anniversary of Europa Stamps. Multicoloured.

1943	6000k. Type **426**	2·50	1·60
1944	7000k. Knossos, Greece and Patuxay, Laos	3·00	1·90
1945	7000k. Coliseum, Rome and Wat Phu, Laos	3·00	1·90
1946	7500k. Lom Church, Norway and Wat Xieng Thong, Laos	3·25	2·30
1947	7500k. Notre Dame Cathedral, Paris and That Lauang, Laos	3·25	2·30
1948	8000k. Trier Cathedral, Germany	3·50	2·40
MS1949	142×90 mm. Nos. 1943/1948	39·00	35·00

427 Flag and Government Building

2005. 30th Anniversary of Laos People's Democratic Republic (1st issue). Multicoloured.

1950	500k. Type **427**	40	25
1951	1000k. Flag, map and figures	80	50
1952	2000k. State arms and flag	1·30	1·00
1953	5000k. '30' enclosing State Arms	3·00	2·50

428 Cement Works

2005. 30th Anniversary of Laos People's Democratic Republic (2nd issue). Multicoloured.

1954	15500k. Type **428**	11·50	7·50
MS1955	170×130 mm. 2000k. As No. 1954	14·00	12·50

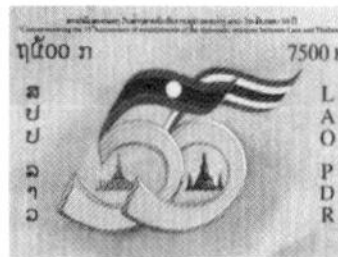
429 Flags and '55'

2005. 55th Anniversary of Laos–Thailand Diplomatic Relations.

1956	**429**	7500k. multicoloured	5·75	5·00

430 Cherry Blossom and Frangipani

2005. 50th Anniversary of Laos–Japan Diplomatic Relations.

1957	**430**	7000k. multicoloured	5·25	3·75

431 King Phangum Lenglathorany

2006. King Phangum Lenglathorany.

1958	**431**	8500k. multicoloured	6·50	5·75

No. 1958 was issued both in sheets and premium miniature sheets, 110×145 mm, which were on sale for 20000k.

No. 1959 is vacant.

432 Dog

2006. New Year. Year of the Dog. Multicoloured.

1960	2000k. Type **432**	2·50	1·00
1961	6500k. Dog surrounded by astrological animals	5·75	3·25

433 Laotian and Russian Women

2006. Vientiane–Moscow Friendship. Multicoloured.

1962	7500k. Type **433**	4·50	3·50
1963	87500k. Laotian and Russian statues and buildings	5·75	4·25
MS1964	130×170 mm. Nos. 1962/1963	13·00	12·00

434 Vehicles

2006. 15th Anniversary of Insurance Provision in Laos. Multicoloured.

1965	8000k. Type **434**	5·25	3·75
1966	8500k. Map showing provinces	5·75	4·25
1967	9500k. Family	6·50	4·75

435 Images of China and Laos

2006. 45th Anniversary of Laos–China Diplomatic Relations.

1968	**435**	8500k. multicoloured	6·50	6·25

436 Garden

2006. Wat Xieng Khouang (garden of Buddhas). Multicoloured.

1969	1000k. Type **436**	90	50
1970	2500k. Demon	1·90	1·30
1971	3000k. Centre of garden	2·30	1·50
1972	5000k. Reclining Buddha	3·25	2·50

437 Shrimps

2006. Shrimps. Multicoloured.

1973	1000k. Type **437**	80	50
1974	2000k. Facing left	1·60	1·00
1975	4000k. Facing right	2·50	2·00
1976	6000k. Amongst weeds	4·25	3·00

No. 1977 is vacant.

438 Leopold Senghor

2006. Birth Centenary of Leopold Senghor (poet and president of Senegal 1960–1980).

1978	**438**	8500k. multicoloured	5·75	4·50

439 Drum

2006. Drums. Multicoloured.

1978a	2000k. Type **439**	1·60	1·00
1978b	3500k. Drum with two handles	2·50	1·80
1978c	7500k. Waisted drum	5·00	3·75

No. 1979 is vacant.

440 Green Bananas

2006. Bananas. Multicoloured.

1980	1000k. Type **440**	90	65
1981	2000k. Double bunch	1·60	1·10
1982	4000k. Long bunch	2·50	2·00
1983	8000k. Long bunch with stalk	4·75	4·00

441 Bridge Over Mekong River and Japanese, Thai and Laotian Flags

2006. Friendship Bridge. Multicoloured.

1984	7500k. Type **441**	5·25	3·75
1985	7500k. Bridge at night	5·25	3·75

442 Pig and Signs of Chinese Zodiac

2007. New Year. Year of the Pig. Multicoloured.

1986	7500k. Type **442**	5·25	3·75
1987	7500k. Pig and piglets	5·25	3·75

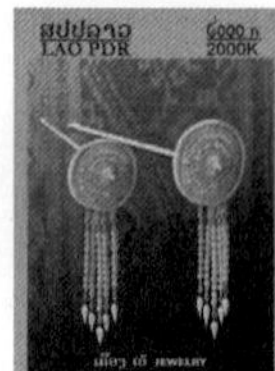

443 Earrings

2007. Jewellery. Multicoloured.

1988	2000k. Type **443**	1·90	90
1989	5000k. Bracelet	3·25	2·40
1990	7000k. Circular earrings	4·25	3·25
1991	7500k. Pendant	5·00	3·50
MS1992	127×170 mm. Nos. 1988/1991	18·00	16·00

444 Crab

2007. Crabs. Multicoloured.

1993	1000k. Type **444**	1·00	65
1994	2000k. Purple crab facing right	1·90	1·00
1995	7000k. Facing left	4·25	3·50
1996	7500k. With one enlarged pincer	4·50	3·75

No. 1997 is vacant.

444a Traditional House, Laos

2007. 40th Anniversary of ASEAN. Multicoloured.

1998	700k. Type **444a**	80	65
1999	700k. Secretariat Building, Bandar Seri Bagwan, Brunei	80	65
2000	700k. National Museum of Cambodia	80	65
2001	700k. Fatahillah Museum, Jakarta, Indonesia	80	65
2002	700k. Railway Headquarters Building, Kuala Lumpur, Malaysia	80	65
2003	700k. Post Office, Yangon, Myanmar	80	65
2004	700k. Malcanang Palace, Philippines	80	65
2005	700k. National Museum of Singapore	80	65
2006	700k. Vimanmek Mansion, Bangkok, thailand	80	65
2007	700k. Presidential Palace, Hanoi, Vietnam	80	65
2008	7000k. As Type **444a** with additional Laotian script	3·50	3·25

444b Elephant and Rider

2008. Elephant Festival. Multicoloured

2008a	1000k. Type **444b**	80	40
2008b	2000k. Two elephants and riders	1·20	75
2008c	3000k. Crowd, parasol and presentation	1·70	1·10
2008d	5000k. Elephant with rider wearing hat	2·30	1·80
2008e	7500k. Woman dressing elephant	3·25	2·75
2008f	8500k. Elephants moving logs	3·75	3·00
MS2008g	146×110 mm. 20000k. Two elephants with riders wearing red. Imperf	11·00	10·00

445 Monks and Women

2008. Tak Bat Dok Mai Floral Festival (giving alms to monks including Dok Khao Phansa flowers that only come into bloom during the Buddhist Lent). Multicoloured.

2009	2000k. Type **445**	1·30	90
2010	5000k. Monks receiving alms	3·25	2·40
2011	7500k. Women preparing alms	4·50	3·50

446 Aircraft

2008. Transport. Multicoloured.

2012	2000k. Type **446**	1·30	90
2013	5000k. Ferry	3·25	2·40
2014	7500k. Lorry convoy	4·50	3·50

447 Monks and Festival Goers

2008. That Luang Festival. Multicoloured.

2015	2000k. Type **447**	1·30	90
2016	5000k. Procession	3·25	2·40
2017	8000k. Illuminated temple	5·25	3·75

448 Sticky Rice cooked in Bamboo Tube

2008. Traditional Foods. Multicoloured.

2018	2000k. Type **448**	1·30	90
2019	5500k. Green papaya salad	4·00	2·75
2020	7500k. Grilled chicken	4·50	3·50

449 Gibbon

2008. Endangered Species. Lar Gibbon (white-handed gibbon) (*Hylobates lar*). Multicoloured.

2021	6000k. Type **449**	3·00	2·10
2022	7000k. Mother and baby	3·75	2·50
2023	8000k. Gibbon howling	4·25	3·00
2024	9000k. Two gibbons	4·50	3·25

450 Coffee Cup and Beans

2008. Coffee. Multicoloured.

2025	3000k. Type **450**	1·90	1·10
2026	5000k. Coffee berries	2·50	1·80
2027	6000k. Coffee beans	3·25	2·10

A minature sheet 110×141 mm, containing one example each of Nos. 2025/2027, was on sale for 18000k., 4000k. above face value.

451 Woman separating Seeds from Fibres

2008. Cotton. Multicoloured.

2028	1000k. Type **451**	65	40
2029	5000k. Cotton flower	2·50	1·80
2030	5500k. Cotton bolls	3·25	2·00

452 Judo

2008. Olympic Games, Beijing. Multicoloured.

2031	5000k. Type **452**	2·50	1·90
2032	5000k. Cycling	2·50	1·90
2033	5000k. Football	2·50	1·90
2034	5000k. High jump	2·50	1·90

453 Bees on Honeycomb

2008. Bees. Multicoloured.

2035	1000k. Type **453**	65	40
2036	4000k. Bees on flower	1·90	1·40
2037	6000k. Swarm	2·50	2·10
2038	8500k. Bee in flight	4·00	3·00

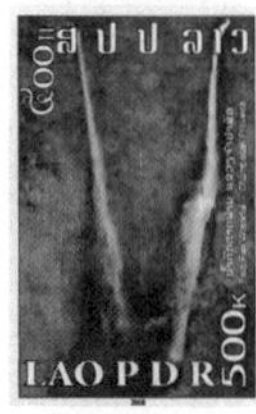

454 Taat Fan, Champasak

2008. Waterfalls. Multicoloured.

2039	500k. Type **454**	65	25
2040	2000k. Tad Sae, Luangprabang (horiz)	1·30	75
2041	5000k. Kuang Si, Luangprabang	1·90	1·80
2042	6500k. Khonphapheng, Champasak (horiz)	2·50	2·40

455 White Aubergines

2008. Aubergines. Multicoloured.

2043	2043 Type **455**	65	40
2044	2000k. Circular green	1·30	75
2045	4000k. Circular green striped	1·90	1·40
2046	5500k. Long thin purple	2·50	2·00

456 Humong Woman

2008. Humong New Year. Multicoloured.

2047	1000k. Type **456**	65	40
2048	5500k. Fighting bulls (horiz)	2·50	2·00
2049	6000k. Musician dancing	3·00	2·10
2050	7500k. Two actors wearing traditional dress (horiz)	4·25	2·75
MS2051	151×123 mm. Nos. 2047/2050	14·00	12·00

457 Haw Phra Kaew

2009. Antiquities. Multicoloured.

2052	1000k. Type **457**	70	40
2053	2000k. Plain of jars	1·40	80
2054	4000k. Phat That Luang	2·10	1·40
2055	7500k. Temple	3·50	2·75
MS2056	137×170 mm. Nos. 2052/2055	8·50	6·50

458 Early Soldiers

2009. 60th Anniversary of Lao People's Army. Multicoloured.

2057	2000k. Type **458**	1·10	80
2058	2000k. Soldiers on parade, marching right	1·10	80
2059	2000k. Soldiers, heads, facing left	1·10	80
2060	2000k. Soldiers wearing helmets, facing left	1·10	80

459 Locomotive and Train

2009. Opening of Laos–Thailand Rail Link. Multicoloured.

2061	3000k. Type **459**	2·75	1·20
2062	3000k. Train in station	2·75	1·20
2063	3000k. Rail link bridge	2·75	1·20

460 Kalachuchi

2009. China 2009. World Stamp Exhibition, Luoyang. Multicoloured.

2064	7500k. Type **460**	4·25	3·25
2065	7500k. Peony	4·25	3·25

461 Inscr 'Mari Flower'

2009. Flowers. Multicoloured.

2066	500k. Type **461**	55	25
2067	2000k. Ixora	1·00	80
2068	4000k. White crown flowers (inscr 'Vuddhish Flowers')	2·00	1·40
2069	7500k. Mauve crown flowers (inscr 'Vuddhish Flowers')	3·50	2·75

462 Pot with Straws

2009. Rice Alcohol. Multicoloured.

2070	1000k. Type **462**	70	40
2071	2000k. Drinking horn	1·00	80
2072	5500k. Drinking through straw from large pot	2·75	2·10

463 R. P. Vientiane

2009. Post Day. Each royal blue and black.

2073	2000k. Type **463**	1·10	80
2074	2000k. Centre de Tri	1·10	80
2075	2000k. Phongsaly	1·10	80
2076	2000k. Luangnamtha	1·10	80
2077	2000k. Oudomxay	1·10	80
2078	2000k. Bokeo	1·10	80
2079	2000k. Luangpabang	1·10	80
2080	2000k. Huaphan	1·10	80
2081	2000k. Sayaboury	1·10	80
2082	2000k. Xiengkhouang	1·10	80
2083	2000k. Vientiane	1·10	80
2084	2000k. Bolikhamxay	1·10	80
2085	2000k. Khammouane	1·10	80
2086	2000k. Savannakhet	1·10	80
2087	2000k. Saravan	1·10	80
2088	2000k. Sekong	1·10	80
2089	2000k. Champasack	1·10	80
2090	2000k. Attapeu	1·10	80

464 Champa and Champi, Games Mascots

2009. 25th Southeast Asian Games, Vientiane. Multicoloured.

2091	5000k. Type **464**	2·50	1·90
2092	7000k. Champa, Champi and Laotian flag	2·50	1·90

465 Female Statue

2009. Wat Si Muang (Wat Simuong). Multicoloured.

2093	4000k. Type **465**	2·00	1·60
2094	5000k. Stone ruin	2·50	1·90
2095	6000k. Temple	3·00	2·30

Nos. 2096/2098 and T **466** are left for Village Life, issued on 15 February 2010, not yet received.

Nos. 2099/2101 and T **467** are left for Architecture, issued on 15 March 2010, not yet received.

Nos. 2102/2105 and T **468** are left for Landscapes, issued on 1 April 2010, not yet received.

469 *Litsea cubeba*

2010. Flora. Multicoloured.

2106	1000k. Type **469**	65	50
2107	3000k. *Orthosiphon stamineus* (vert)	2·00	1·60
2108	4000k. *Strychnos nux vomica* (vert)	2·75	2·10
2109	5000k. *Zingiber*	3·25	2·50
2110	8000k. *Styrax tonkinensis* (vert)	5·25	4·25
2111	9000k. *Aquilaria crassna* (vert)	6·00	4·75

Nos. 2112/2114 and T **470** are left for Rice, not yet received.

Nos. 2115/2118 and T **471** are left for Fruit, not yet received.

472 The Golden Stupa, 1889

2010. 450th Anniversary of Vientiane as Capital of Laos. Pha That Luang Temple (The Golden Stupa).

2119	1000k. Type **472**	85	65
2120	3000k. Stupa, 1910	2·50	1·90
2121	5000k. Stupa, 1935	4·25	3·25
2122	6000k. Stupa, 2010	5·00	4·00
MS2123	110×142 mm. 20000k. Golden Stupa (48×60 mm)	17·00	13·00

473 The Golden Stupa, 1889

2010. 15th Anniversary of Luangprabang as UNESCO World Heritage Site. Multicoloured.

2124	2000k. Type **473**	1·70	1·30
2125	3000k. Women carrying gifts and monks	2·50	1·90
2126	5000k. Men carrying plaque	4·25	3·25
2127	10000k. Masked dancers, New Year Festival	8·25	6·50
MS2128	141×111 mm. Nos. 2124/2127	17·00	13·00

474 Officer giving Directions

2010. 35th Anniversary of Republic of Laos. Multicoloured.

2129	5000k. Type **474**	4·25	3·25
2130	6000k. Soldiers at gun emplacement	5·00	4·00
2131	10000k. Procession led by Prince Souphanouvong	8·25	6·50
MS2132	166×131 mm. 5000k. As Type **474**; 6000k. As No. 2130; 9000k. As No. 2131	17·00	13·00

475 Woman of Lolo Tribe

2011. Tribal Costumes. Multicoloured.

2133	1000k. Type **475**	85	65
2134	3000k. Mong Luangnamtha	2·20	1·70
2135	4000k. Lahu	2·75	2·20
2136	5000k. Hiumieng	3·50	2·75
2137	8000k. Katang	5·75	4·50

476 Potter

2011. Handicrafts. Pottery. Multicoloured.

2138	1000k. Type **476**	85	65
2139	3000k. Pot with wide base	2·20	1·70
2140	5000k. Decorated pot with elongated top	3·50	2·75
2141	6000k. Potter (different)	4·25	3·25

477 Peony

2011. Peonies. Multicoloured.

2142	7000k. Type **477**	4·00	3·00
2143	8000k. Single white peony	4·25	3·25
MS2144	98×65 mm. As No. 2143	5·00	5·00

478 Woman wearing Laotian Dress

2011. 60th Anniversary of Laos–Thailand Diplomatic Relations. Multicoloured.

2145	8000k. Type **478**	4·25	3·25
2146	8000k. Woman wearing Thai traditional dress	4·25	3·25
2147	8000k. Cassia (golden shower) flowers (Thailand)	4·25	3·25
2148	8000k. Plumeria (frangipani) flowers (Laos)	4·25	3·25
MS2149	145×152 mm. As Nos. 2145/2148	25·00	19·00

479 Masked Dancers

2011. 50th Anniversary of Laos–China Diplomatic Relations.

2150	**479**	9000k. multicoloured	6·75	5·25
MS2151		144×106 mm. As Type **479**	17·00	13·00

480 *Paphiopedilum barbigerum*

2011. Orchids. *Paphiopedilum barbigerum*. Multicoloured.

2152	1000k. Type **480**	85	65
2153	9000k. Three yellow and brownish striped flowers	5·75	4·50
2154	11000k. Orange flower and leaves	6·75	5·25

Nos. 2155/2156 are left for stamps not yet received.

481 Inscr 'Gomme laque' (Shellac)

2011. Non Timber Forest Products of Laos. Multicoloured.

2157	3000k. Type **481**	2·00	1·60
2158	4000k. Inscr 'Cannelle royale' (Cinnamon tree)	2·50	1·90
2159	5000k. Inscr 'Noix de malva' (Malva nut tree)	3·25	2·50
2160	6000k. Inscr 'Gurjum balsam' (Gurjum balsam essential oil)	4·25	3·25
2161	11000k. Inscr 'Gomme dammar' (Dammar gum)	7·00	5·50
2162	12000k. Wild bees' nest (inscr 'Cire d'abeille (beeswax)) (horiz)	7·75	6·00

482 Asian Elephant

2011. Endangered Species. Multicoloured.

2163	1000k. Type **482**	85	65
2164	3000k. Tiger	2·00	1·60
2165	5000k. Saola	3·25	2·50
2166	8000k. Red-shanked douc langur	4·25	3·25
MS2167	175×125 mm. Nos. 2163/2166	17·00	13·00

Nos. 2168/2169 and T **483** are left for Waterlilies, not yet received.

484 Carved Pillar

2011. Historic Landmarks of Vientiane. Multicoloured.

2170	9000k. Type **484**	5·75	4·50
2171	9000k. Inscribed stones found at Phia Vat village, Sisattanark district, Vientiane (horiz)	5·75	4·50
2172	9000k. Ancient incised stone pillar	5·75	4·50
MS2173	200×150 mm. Nos. 2170/2172	18·00	14·00

485 The Golden Stupa

2011. Vientiane–Moscow Co-operation. Multicoloured.

MS2174	6000k. Type **485**; 7000k. St Basil's Cathedral, Moscow; 8000k. Temple, Vientiane; 9000k. Rotunda, Moscow	17·00	17·00

486 Dragon

2012. Chinese New Year. Year of the Dragon.

2175	**486**	8000k. multicoloured	4·00	3·50

487 Kaysone Phomvihan and Ho Chi Minh

2012. Laos–Vietnam Co-operation. Multicoloured.

2176	4000k. Type **487**	2·00	1·75
2177	12000k. Laotian and Vietnamese pagodas	7·75	7·50

488 Pha That Luang

2012. Asia–Europe Meeting (ASEM) Summit, Laos. Multicoloured.

2178	9000k. Type **488**	4·75	4·00
2179	11000k. Map of member countries	7·00	6·50

489 Boiling Cocoons

2013. Mulberry Cultivation and Silk Production. Multicoloured.

2180	2000k. Type **489**	1·20	1·00
2181	3000k. Distibuting silkworms	1·75	1·50
2182	4000k. Collecting leaves	2·00	1·75
2183	5000k. Growing fruit and leaves	2·75	2·00

490 Pha That Luang

2013. Pha That Luang

2184	**490**	50000k. multicoloured	25·00	24·50
2185	**490**	100000k. multicoloured	35·00	34·50
2186	**490**	200000k. multicoloured	45·00	42·50

491 Patuaxy, Vientiane

2013. Laos–Russia Cultural Co-operation. Multicoloured.

MS2187	6000k. Type **491**; 7000k. Triumphal arch, Moscow; Pagoda; Watch tower	7·85	7·50

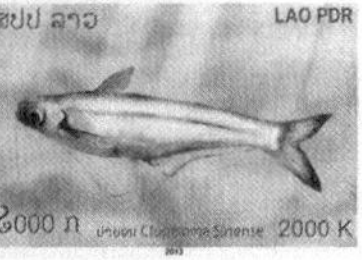

492 *Clupisoma sinense*

2013. Catfish of the Mekong River. Multicoloured.

2188	2000k. Type **492**	1·25	1·00
2189	4000k. *Hemibagrus filamentus*	2·00	1·75
2190	6000k. *Wallago attu* (inscr 'Great White')	3·25	2·50
2191	9000k. *Bagarius yarrelli*	4·75	4·00

494 Xiengkhoeng, Huaphanh

2013. Antiquities of Laos. Stupas. Multicoloured.

2193	1000k. Type **494**	1·10	85
2194	2000k. Wat That Luang, Luang Prabang	1·25	1·00
2195	3000k. That Makmo, Luang Prabang	1·75	1·50
2196	4000k. Phonphao, Luang Prabang	2·00	1·75
2197	10000k. Phousi, Luang Prabang	5·75	5·50

495 Bridge over Mekong River

2013. Opening of Fourth Thai-Lao Mekong Bridge. Multicoloured.

2198	8000k. Type **495**	4·00	3·50
2199	8000k. Border Clearance Building, Ban Houayxay	4·00	3·50

496 Buddha Procession and Songkran Festival

2014. 20th Anniversary of Lao-Thai Friendship Bridge (Vientiane-Nong Khai). Multicoloured.

2200	9000k. Type **496**	4·75	4·00
2201	9000k. Wat Pho Chai in Nong Khai and Wat Ong Teu Mahawihan in Laos	4·75	4·00
MS2203	205×135 mm. 9000k.×2, As Type **496**; As No. 2201. Perf and imperf. Sold at 20000k.	12·00	12·00

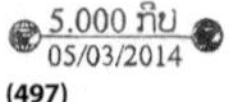

(497)

2014. Nos. 1036, 1037, 722, 723 and No. 724 surch as T **497.**

2204	5000k. on 1k. multicoloured	2·75	2·00
2205	8000k. on 2k.. multicoloured	4·00	3·50
2206	10000k. on 60c. multicoloured	5·75	5·50
2207	11000k. on 1k. multicoloured	7·00	6·50
2208	12000k. on 2k. multicoloured	7·75	7·50

498 Buddha subduing Mara

2014. Buddha.

2209	5000k. Type **498**	2·75	2·00
2210	5000k. Standing with hands raised	2·75	2·00
2211	5000k. Seated wearing red robe	2·75	2·00
2212	5000k. Reclining Buddha (horiz)	2·75	2·00
MS2213	185×145 mm. 5000k.×4, As Nos. 2209/2212. Perf and imperf. Sold at 25000k.	13·00	13·00

499 Wat Nonglamchanh, Savannakhet

2014. Antiquities of Laos. Multicoloured.

2214	5000k. Type **499**	2·75	2·50
2215	5000k. Tham Ting Cave, Luang Prabang	2·75	2·50
2216	5000k. Wat Sisakhet Tripitaka Hall, Vientiane	2·75	2·50
2217	5000k. Sikhottabong Stupa, Khammuan	2·75	2·50
2218	9000k. Wat Phiawat, Xiengkhuang	4·75	4·00
MS2219	140×110 mm. 5000k.×4, As Nos. 2214/2217 Perf and imperf. Sold at 25000k.	12·00	12·00

500 Saya Setthathirath (1534-1572)

2014. Early Kings of Laos. Multicoloured.

2220	5000k. Type **500**	2·75	2·00
2221	5000k. King Chao Anouvong (1767-1829)	2·75	2·00
2222	11000k. King Fa Ngum (1353–1372)	7·00	6·50
MS2223	185×145 mm. 5000k.×4, As Nos. 2220/2222. Perf and imperf. Sold at 25000k.	13·00	13·00

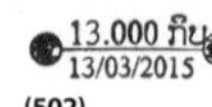

(502)

2015. Nos. 722, 723 and No. 1315 surch as T **502.**

2225	10000k. on 60c. multicoloured	5·75	5·50
2226	12000k. on 1k. multicoloured	7·75	7·50
2227	13000k. on 220k. multicoloured	8·00	7·75

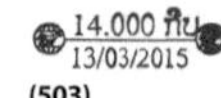

(503)

2015. Surcharges. Stamps of No. **MS**432 surch as T **503.**

MS2228	165×70 mm. 14000k. on 1k.; 14000k. on 2k.; 14000k. on 5k.; 14000k. on 10k.; 14000k. on 200k.	30·00	30·00

504 Telephone, Telegraph, Airmail and Postbox

2015. 50th Anniversary of National Posts and Telecommunication's Day. Multicoloured.

2229	10000k. Type **504**	5·75	5·50
2230	10000k. Digital mail and communications	5·75	5·50
MS2231	140×110 mm. 10000k.×2, As Nos. 2229/2230 Perf and imperf. Sold at 25000k.	13·00	13·00

POSTAGE DUE STAMPS

D5 Vat Sisaket Shrine

D6 Sampans

1952

D22	**D5**	10c. brown	65	20
D23	**D5**	20c. violet	65	20
D24	**D5**	50c. red	65	20
D25	**D5**	1p. green	1·20	35
D26	**D5**	2p. blue	1·40	35
D27	**D5**	5p. purple	2·30	1·10
D28	**D6**	10p. blue	3·50	1·60

D98 Serpent

1973

D378	**D98**	10k. black, brn & yell	85	35
D379	**D98**	15k. black, yell & grn	85	35
D380	**D98**	20k. black, green & bl	85	35
D381	**D98**	50k. black, blue & red	1·30	55

APPENDIX

The following stamps have either been issued in excess of postal needs or have not been available to the public in reasonable quantities at face value. Such stamps may later be given full listing if there is evidence of regular postal use.

1975

Centenary of UPU Postage 10, 15, 30, 40k.; Air 1000, 1500k. On gold foil 2500, 3000k.

Apollo-Soyuz Space Link. Postage 125, 150, 200, 300k.; Air 450, 700k.

Bicentenary of American Revolution. Postage 10, 15, 40, 50, 100, 125, 150, 200k.; Air 1000, 1500k.

LAS BELA

A state of Baluchistan. Now part of Pakistan.

12 pies = 1 anna; 16 annas = 1 rupee.

1

1897

1	**1**	½a. black on white	60·00	28·00
3	**1**	½a. black on grey	35·00	16·00
11	**1**	½a. black on blue	28·00	14·00
12	**1**	½a. black on green	30·00	14·00
8	-	1a. black on orange	60·00	65·00

The 1a. has the English inscription in a circle with the native inscription across the centre.

LATAKIA

The former state of the Alaouites which changed its name to Latakia. in 1930. Latakia was merged with Syria in 1936.

100 centimes = 1 piastre.

The former state of the Alaouites which changed its name to Latakia in 1930.
Latakia was merged with Syria in 1936.

1931. As 1930 stamps of Syria (T **26/27**) optd **LATTAQUIE** in French and Arabic.

65	**26**	0p.10 mauve	2·00	4·25
66	-	0p.20 blue	85	2·50
67	-	0p.20 red	1·80	6·50
68	-	0p.25 green	1·40	4·00
69	-	0p.25 violet	3·25	6·25
70	-	0p.50 violet	2·50	5·75
71	-	0p.75 red	3·50	8·00
72	-	1p. green	2·75	3·00
73	-	1p.50 brown	5·00	9·00
74	-	1p.50 green	10·00	10·00
75	-	2p. violet	4·50	3·75
76	-	3p. green	9·00	7·75
77	**27**	4p. orange	5·75	5·00
78	-	4p.50 red	7·75	13·00
79	-	6p. green	7·75	13·00
80	-	7p.50 blue	7·25	6·25
81	-	10p. brown	9·25	16·00
82	-	15p. green	12·50	26·00
83	-	25p. purple	30·00	50·00
84	-	50p. brown	32·00	50·00
85	-	100p. red	70·00	£110

1931. Air. As 1931 air stamps of Syria optd **LATTAQUIE** in French and Arabic.

86	-	0p.50 yellow	1·60	3·75
87	-	0p.50 brown	2·75	6·00
88	-	1p. brown	2·75	3·25
89	**28**	2p. blue	5·00	7·25
90	-	3p. green	6·00	7·75
91	-	5p. purple	7·75	18·00
92	-	10p. blue	10·00	14·50
93	-	15p. red	14·00	24·00
94	-	25p. orange	30·00	55·00
95	-	50p. black	44·00	55·00
96	-	100p. mauve	45·00	55·00

POSTAGE DUE STAMPS

1931. Nos. D197/D198 of Syria optd **LATTAQUIE** in French and Arabic.

D86	8p. black on blue	33·00	55·00
D87	15p. black on pink	26·00	34·00

BY APPOINTMENT TO HER MAJESTY THE QUEEN PHILATELISTS STANLEY GIBBONS LTD LONDON

STANLEY GIBBONS

LONDON 1856

STANLEY GIBBONS - THE HOME OF STAMP COLLECTING FOR OVER 160 YEARS.

Visit our store at 399 Strand for all your philatelic needs.

EVERYTHING FOR THE STAMP COLLECTOR.

- Great Britain Stamps
- Commonwealth Stamps
- Publications and Accessories
- Auctions

WHERE TO FIND US

STANLEY GIBBONS
399 STRAND
LONDON, WC2R 0LX
UNITED KINGDOM

0207 557 4436

SHOP@STANLEYGIBBONS.COM

OPENING HOURS

Mon - Fri: 9am - 5:30pm
Sat: 9:30 - 5:30pm | Sun: Closed

LATVIA

A country on the Baltic Sea. Previously part of the Russian Empire. Latvia was independent from 1918 to 1940 when it became part of the U.S.S.R.

Following the dissolution of the U.S.S.R. in 1991, Latvia once again became an independent republic.

1918. 100 kapeikas = 1 rublis.
1923. 100 santimu = 1 lats.
1991. 100 kopeks = 1 (Russian) rouble.
1992. 100 kopeks = 1 Latvian rouble.
1993. 100 santimu = 1 lats.

1

1918. Printed on back of German war maps. Imperf or perf.

15	**1**	3k. lilac	40	40
16	**1**	5k. red	40	40
17	**1**	10k. blue	40	40
18	**1**	15k. green	40	40
41	**1**	20k. orange	40	15
20	**1**	25k. grey	40	40
21	**1**	35k. brown	40	40
42	**1**	40k. purple	65	15
22	**1**	50k. violet	40	40
44	**1**	75k. green	90	15
29	**1**	3r. red and blue	1·30	1·30
30	**1**	5r. red and brown	1·30	1·30

(b) Size 28×38 mm.

33		10k. red and brown	40	50
34		35k. green and blue	40	50
35		1r. red and green	50	50

4

1919. Liberation of Riga. Imperf.

24	**4**	5k. red	40	40
25	**4**	15k. green	40	40
26	**4**	35k. brown	50	1·30

For stamps of T **1** and **4** optd with a cross, with or without Russian letters 'Z A', see under North-West Russia Nos. 21/42.

5 Rising Sun

1919. Imperf or perf.

27	**5**	10k. blue	1·30	65

6

1919. First Anniversary of Independence. (a) Size 33×45 mm.

32	**6**	10k. red and brown	1·00	3·25

7

1919. Liberation of Courland.

36	**7**	10k. red and brown	40	25
37	**7**	25k. green and blue	40	40
38	**7**	35k. blue and black	40	65
39	**7**	1r. brown and green	40	65

8

1920. Red Cross stamps. (a) On backs of blue Bolshevist notes. Perf.

46	**8**	20-30k. red and brown	2·50	4·00
47	**8**	40-55k. red and blue	2·50	4·00
48	**8**	50-70k. red and green	2·50	4·00
49	**8**	1r.-1r.30 red and grey	5·25	6·50

(b) On backs of green Western Army notes. Perf.

50		20-30k. red and brown	2·00	2·00
51		40-55k. red and blue	2·00	2·00
52		50-70k. red and green	1·60	2·50
53		1r.-1r.30 red and grey	2·30	2·50

(c) On backs of red, green and brown Bolshevist notes. Imperf.

54		20-30k. red and brown	2·00	2·00
55		40-55k. red and blue	2·00	2·00
56		50-70k. red and green	1·60	2·50
57		1r.-1r.30 red and grey	2·75	4·00

CHARITY PREMIUMS. In the above and later issues where two values are expressed, the lower value represents the franking value and the higher the price charged, the difference being the charity premium.

9

1920. Liberation of Latgale.

58	**9**	50k. pink and green	65	65
59	**9**	1r. brown and green	65	65

10

1920. First Constituent Assembly.

60A	**10**	50k. red	90	40
61A	**10**	1r. blue	90	40
62A	**10**	3r. green and brown	90	1·30
63A	**10**	5r. purple and grey	2·20	1·30

1920. Surch in white figures on black oval.

64	**6**	10r. on 1r. red and green	2·50	2·50
65	**6**	20r. on 1r. red and green	6·50	5·25
66	**6**	30r. on 1r. red and green	9·00	6·50

1920. Surch **2 DIWI RUBLI**. Perf.

67	**1**	2r. on 10k. blue	4·50	11·50
68	**4**	2r. on 35k. brown	1·30	9·00

1920. (a) Surch **WEENS** or **DIVI**, value and **RUBLI**.

69	**7**	1 (WEENS)r. on 35k. blue and black	80	65
70	**7**	2 (DIVI)r. on 10k. red and brown	1·60	1·30
71	**7**	2 (DIVI)r. on 25k. green and blue	90	65

(b) Surch **DIWI RUBLI 2**.

72	**6**	2r. on 35k. green and blue	90	65

(c) Surch **DIVI 2 RUB. 2**.

73	**10**	2r. on 50k. red	1·30	90

(d) Surch **Desmit rubli**.

74	**6**	10r. on 10r. on 1r. red and green (No. 64)	3·25	1·30

1921. Red Cross. Nos. 51/53 surch **RUB 2 RUB**.

75	**8**	2r. on 20-30k. red and brown	4·50	6·50
76	**8**	2r. on 40-55k. red and blue	4·50	6·50
77	**8**	2r. on 50-70k. red and green	4·50	6·50
78	**8**	2r. on 1r.-1r.30k. red and grey	4·50	6·50

1921. Surch in figures and words over thick bar of crossed lines.

79	**9**	10r. on 50k. pink and green	3·25	1·30
80	**9**	20r. on 50k. pink and green	9·75	6·50
81	**9**	30r. on 50k. pink and green	13·00	6·50
82	**9**	50r. on 50k. pink and green	20·00	7·75
83	**9**	100r. on 50k. pink and green	46·00	26·00

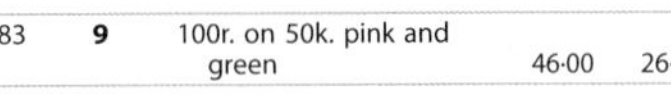

19 Bleriot XI

1921. Air. Value in RUBLU. Imperf or perf.

84	**19**	10r. green	7·75	7·25
85	**19**	20r. blue	7·75	7·25

See also Nos. 193 and 156/157.

21 Latvian Coat of Arms

22 Great Seal of Latvia

1921. Value in Kopeks or Roubles.

86	**21**	50k. violet	80	20
87b	**21**	1r. yellow	50	50
88	**21**	2r. green	25	15
89	**21**	3r. green	1·00	65
90	**21**	5r. red	2·20	50
91	**21**	6r. red	3·25	1·30
92	**21**	9r. orange	2·00	90
93	**21**	10r. blue	2·00	25
94	**21**	15r. blue	4·00	1·00
95c	**21**	20r. lilac	20·00	2·75
96	**22**	50r. brown	46·00	5·25
97	**22**	100r. blue	50·00	5·25

1923. Value in Santimi or Lats.

127	**21**	1s. mauve	25	25
129	**21**	2s. yellow	40	15
130	**21**	3s. red	25	15
100	**21**	4s. green	1·60	40
132	**21**	5s. green	1·30	25
133	**21**	6s. green and yellow	25	15
134	**21**	7s. green	1·30	25
103	**21**	10s. red	4·00	40
136d	**21**	10s. green and yellow	8·00	15
104	**21**	12s. mauve	65	65
105c	**21**	15s. purple and orange	8·50	25
107	**21**	20s. blue	4·00	25
139	**21**	20s. pink	2·50	15
108	**21**	25s. blue	1·30	25
109	**21**	30s. pink	13·00	40
140	**21**	30s. blue	4·00	25
141	**21**	35s. blue	4·00	25
110	**21**	40s. purple	5·25	40
143	**21**	50s. grey	6·25	65
144	**22**	1l. brown and bistre	21·00	50
116	**22**	2l. blue and light blue	50·00	2·50
117	**22**	5l. green and light green	£160	6·50
118	**22**	10l. red and light red	7·25	10·00

1923. Charity. War Invalids. Surch **KARA INVALIDIEM S.10S.** and cross.

112	**21**	1s.+10s. mauve	90	1·80
113	**21**	2s.+10s. yellow	90	1·80
114	**21**	4s.+10s. green	90	1·80

24 Town Hall

1925. 300th Anniversary of City of Libau.

119	-	6-12s. blue and red	6·50	9·00
120	**24**	15-25s. brown and blue	4·00	6·50
121	-	25-35s. green and violet	6·50	6·50
122	-	30-40s. lake and blue	11·50	20·00
123	-	50-60s. violet and green	17·00	26·00

Designs: Horiz—6-12s. Harbour and lighthouse; 25-35s. Spa health pavilion. Vert—30-40s. St Anna's Church; 50-60s. Arms of Libau.

1927. Surch.

124	**1**	15s. on 40k. purple	1·30	65
125	**1**	15s. on 50k. violet	4·00	2·50
126	**10**	1l. on 3r. green and brown	33·00	13·00

28 Pres. J. Cakste

1928. Death of President Cakste and Memorial Fund.

150	**28**	2-12s. orange	6·50	5·25
151	**28**	6-16s. green	6·50	5·25
152	**28**	15-25s. lake	6·50	5·25
153	**28**	25-35s. blue	6·50	5·25
154	**28**	30-40s. red	6·50	5·25

1928. Air. Value in SANTIMU or SANTIMI.

193A	**19**	10s. green	2·50	1·30
156	**19**	15s. red	5·25	2·50
157	**19**	25s. blue	9·75	4·00

29 Ruins at Rezekne

1928. Tenth Anniversary of Independence. Views.

158	**29**	6s. purple and green	2·50	65
159	-	15s. green and brown	2·50	65
160	-	20s. green and red	3·25	65
161	-	30s. brown and blue	4·00	65
162	-	50s. pink and grey	4·00	1·30
163	-	1l. sepia and brown	9·75	2·50

Designs: 15s. Jelgava (Mitau); 20s. Cesis (Wenden); 30s. Liepaja (Libau); 50s. Riga; 1l. National Theatre, Riga.

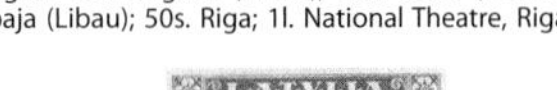

30 Venta

1928. Liberty Memorial Fund. Imperf or perf.

164B	**30**	6-16s. green	6·50	4·50
165B	-	10-20s. red	6·50	4·50
166B	-	15-25s. brown	6·50	4·50
167B	-	30-40s. blue	6·50	4·50
168B	-	50-60s. black	6·50	4·50
169B	-	1l.-1l.10s. purple	6·50	4·50

Designs: 10-20s. 'Latvia' (Woman); 15-25s. Mitau; 30-40s. National Theatre, Riga; 50-60s. Wenden; 1l.-1l.10s. Trenches, Riga Bridge.

32 Z. A. Meierovics

1929. Third Death Anniversary of Meierovics (Foreign Minister). Imperf or perf.

170B	**32**	2-4s. yellow	9·00	6·50
171B	**32**	6-12s. green	9·00	6·50
172B	**32**	15-25s. purple	9·00	6·50
173B	**32**	25-35s. blue	9·00	6·50
174B	**32**	30-40s. blue	9·00	6·50

33 J. Rainis

1930. Memorial Fund for J. Rainis (writer and politician). Imperf or perf.

175A	**33**	1-2s. purple	2·00	5·25
176A	**33**	2-4s. orange	2·00	5·25
177A	**33**	4-8s. green	2·00	5·25
178A	**33**	6-12s. brown and green	2·00	5·25
179A	**33**	10-20s. red	55·00	80·00
180A	**33**	15-30s. green and brown	55·00	80·00

34 Klemm Kl-20 over Durbe Castle

1930. Air. J. Rainis Memorial Fund. Imperf or perf.

181A	**34**	10-20s. green and red	17·00	23·00
182A	**34**	15-30s. red and green	17·00	23·00

35 **36**

1930. Anti-TB Fund.

183	-	1-2s. red and purple	1·30	65

No.	Type	Description	Mint	Used
184	-	2-4s. red and orange	1·30	65
185	**35**	4-8s. red and green	1·30	1·30
186	-	5-10s. brown and green	2·50	2·00
187	-	6-12s. yellow and green	2·50	1·30
188	-	10-20s. black and red	4·00	2·50
189	-	15-30s. green and brown	4·00	2·50
190	-	20-40s. blue and red	4·00	3·25
191	-	25-50s. lilac, blue and red	5·25	3·25
192	**36**	30-60s. lilac, green and blue	6·50	6·50

Designs: Vert As T **35**—1-2s., 2-4s. The Crusaders' Cross; 5-10s. G. Zemgalis; 6-12s. Tower; 10-20s. J. Cakste; 15-30s. Floral design; 20-40s. A. Kviesis. Horiz As T **36**—25-50s. Sanatorium.

1931. Nos. 183/192 surch.

No.	Description	Mint	Used
196	9 on 6-12s. yellow and green	2·50	3·25
197	16 on 1-2s. red and purple	33·00	39·00
198	17s. on 2-4s. red and orange	3·25	3·25
199	19 on 4-8s. red and green	9·75	14·50
200	20 on 5-10s. brown and green	6·50	14·50
201	23 on 15-30s. green and brown	2·50	2·30
202	25 on 10-20s. black and red	6·50	7·75
203	35 on 20-40s. blue and red	9·75	11·50
204	45 on 25-50s. lilac, blue and red	26·00	34·00
205	55 on 30-60s. lilac, green & bl	33·00	55·00

1931. Air. Charity. Nos. 155/157 surch **LATVIJAS AIZSARGI** and value. Imperf or perf.

No.	Type	Description	Mint	Used
206A	**19**	50 on 10s. green	22·00	25·00
207A	**19**	1l. on 15s. red	22·00	25·00
208A	**19**	1l.50 on 2s. blue	22·00	25·00

38 Foreign Invasion

1932. Militia Maintenance Fund. Imperf or perf.

No.	Type	Description	Mint	Used
209A	-	1-11s. blue and purple	5·25	5·25
210A	**38**	2-17s. orange and olive	5·25	5·25
211A	-	3-23s. red and brown	5·25	5·25
212A	-	4-34s. green	5·25	5·25
213A	-	5-45s. green	5·25	5·25

Designs: 1-11s. The Holy Oak and Kriva telling stories; 3-23s. Lacplesis, the deliverer; 4-34s. The Black Knight (enemy) slaughtered; 5-45s. Laimdota, the spirit of Latvia, freed.

39 Infantry Manoeuvres

1932. Militia Maintenance Fund. Imperf or perf.

No.	Type	Description	Mint	Used
214B	-	6-25s. purple and brown	10·50	9·00
215B	**39**	7-35s. blue and green	10·50	9·00
216B	-	10-45s. sepia and green	10·50	9·00
217B	-	12-55s. green and red	10·50	9·00
218B	-	15-75s. violet and red	10·50	9·00

Designs: Horiz—6-25s. Troops on march. Vert—10-45s. First aid to soldier; 12-55s. Army kitchen; 15-75s. General J. Balodis.

41

1932. Air. Charity. Imperf or perf.

No.	Type	Description	Mint	Used
219A	**41**	10-20s. black and green	29·00	46·00
220A	**41**	15-30s. red and grey	29·00	46·00
221A	**41**	25-50s. blue and grey	29·00	46·00

1932. Riga Exhibition of Lettish Products. Optd **Latvijas razojumu izstade Riga. 1932.g.10.-18.IX.**

No.	Type	Description	Mint	Used
222	**21**	3s. red	1·30	65
223	**21**	10s. green on yellow	1·30	65
224	**21**	20s. pink	2·50	1·30
225	**21**	35s. blue	6·50	1·30

43 Leonardo da Vinci

1932. Air. Charity. Pioneers of Aviation. Imperf or perf.

No.	Type	Description	Mint	Used
226A	-	5-25s. green and brown	33·00	33·00
227A	**43**	10-50s. green and brown	33·00	33·00
228A	-	15-75s. green and red	33·00	33·00
229A	-	20-100s. mauve and green	33·00	33·00
230A	-	25-125s. blue and brown	33·00	33·00

Designs: Vert—5s. Icarus; 15s. Jacques Charles's hydrogen balloon, 1783 (inscr 'Charliers'). Horiz—20s. Wright Type A biplane; 25s. Bleriot XI monoplane.

44 "Mourning Mother" Memorial, Riga

1933. Air. Wounded Latvian Airmen Fund. Imperf or perf.

No.	Type	Description	Mint	Used
231A	-	2-52s. brown and black	22·00	33·00
232A	**44**	3-53s. red and black	22·00	33·00
233A	-	10-60s. green and black	22·00	33·00
234A	-	20-70s. red and black	22·00	33·00

Designs: 2s. Fall of Icarus; 10s., 20s. Proposed tombs for airmen.

1933. Air. Charity. Riga–Bathurst Flight. Nos. 155/157 optd **LATVIJA-AFRIKA 1933** or surch also.

No.	Description	Mint	Used
235	10s. green	£100	£130
236	15s. red	£100	£130
237	25s. blue	£100	£130
238	50s. on 15s. red	£450	£850
239	100s. on 25s. blue	£450	£850

In the event the aircraft crashed at Neustettin, Germany, and the mail was forwarded by ordinary post.

46 Biplane under Fire at Riga

1933. Air. Charity. Wounded Latvian Airmen Fund. Imperf or perf.

No.	Type	Description	Mint	Used
240A	-	3-53s. blue and orange	60·00	65·00
241A	**46**	7-57s. brown and blue	60·00	65·00
242A	-	35-135s. black and blue	60·00	65·00

Designs: 3s. Monoplane taking off; 35s. Map and aircraft.

47 Glanville Brothers' Gee Bee Super Sportster

1933. Air. Charity. Wounded Latvian Airmen Fund. Imperf or perf.

No.	Type	Description	Mint	Used
243A	**47**	8-68s. grey and brown	80·00	£120
244A	-	12-112s. green and purple	80·00	£120
245A	-	30-130s. grey and blue	60·00	£120
246A	-	40-190s. blue and purple	80·00	£120

Designs: 12s. Supermarine S6B seaplane; 30s. Airship *Graf Zeppelin* over Riga; 40s. Dornier Do-X flying boat.

48 President's Palace

1934. 15th Anniversary of New Constitution.

No.	Type	Description	Mint	Used
247	**48**	3s. red	40	40
248	-	5s. green	40	25
249	-	10s. green	2·50	15
250	-	20s. red	2·50	15
251	-	35s. blue	90	40
252	**48**	40s. brown	90	40

Designs: 5, 10s. Arms and shield; 20s. Allegory of Latvia; 35s. Government Building.

50 A. Kronvalds

1936. Lettish Intellectuals.

No.	Type	Description	Mint	Used
253	**50**	3s. red	4·00	7·75
254	-	10s. green	4·00	7·75
255	-	20s. mauve	4·00	9·00
256	-	35s. blue	4·00	9·00

Portraits: 10s. A. Pumpurs; 20s. J. Maters; 35s. Auseklis.

51

1936. White Cross Fund. Designs incorporating Cross and Stars device as in T **51**.

No.	Type	Description	Mint	Used
257	**51**	3s. red	4·00	6·50
258	-	10s. green	4·00	6·50
259	-	20s. mauve	4·00	7·75
260	-	35s. blue	4·00	7·75

Designs: 10s. Oak leaves; 20s. Doctors and patient; 35s. Woman holding shield.

53 Independence Monument, Rauna (Ronneburg)

1937. Monuments.

No.	Type	Description	Mint	Used
261	**53**	3s. red	65	1·30
262	-	5s. green	65	1·30
263	-	10s. green	65	65
264	-	20s. red	2·00	1·30
265	-	30s. blue	2·50	2·50
266	-	35s. blue	2·50	2·50
267	-	40s. brown	4·50	4·00

Designs: Vert—10s. Independence Monument, Jelgava (Mitau); 20s. War Memorial, Valka (Walk); 30s. Independence Monument, Iecava (Eckau); 35s. Independence Monument, Riga; 40s. Colonel Kalpak's Grave, Visagalas Cemetery. Horiz—5s. Cemetery Gate, Riga.

54 President Ulmanis

1937. President Ulmanis's 60th Birthday.

No.	Type	Description	Mint	Used
268	**54**	3s. red and orange	25	15
269	**54**	5s. light green and green	25	25
270	**54**	10s. deep green and green	65	80
271	**54**	20s. purple and red	1·30	80
272	**54**	25s. grey and blue	2·20	1·30
273	**54**	30s. deep blue and blue	2·20	1·30
274	**54**	35s. indigo and blue	2·00	1·00
275	**54**	40s. light brown and brown	2·00	1·30
276	**54**	50s. green and black	2·20	1·60

55 Palace of Justice

1938. National Building Fund. Sheet 140×100 mm comprising 35 (s.) blue (T **55**) and 40 (s.) brown (Power Station, Kegums).

No.	Description	Mint	Used
MS277	Sold at 2l.	29·00	£110

56 Gaizinkalns, Livonia

57 General J. Balodis

1938. 20th Anniversary of Independence.

No.	Type	Description	Mint	Used
278	**56**	3s. red	25	15
279	-	5s. green	25	15
280	**57**	10s. green	40	20
281	-	20s. mauve	25	15
282	-	30s. blue	1·60	25
283	-	35s. slate	1·60	25
284	-	40s. mauve	1·30	40

Designs: As T **56**—5s. Latgale landscape; 30s. City of Riga; 35s. Rumba waterfall, Courland; 40s. Zemgale landscape. As T **57**—20s. President Ulmanis.

58 Elementary School, Riga

1939. Fifth Anniversary of Authoritarian Government.

No.	Type	Description	Mint	Used
285	**58**	3s. brown	65	1·30
286	-	5s. green	1·30	1·30
287	-	10s. green	2·00	1·30
288	-	20s. red	4·00	2·50
289	-	30s. blue	2·50	1·30
290	-	35s. blue	4·00	2·50
291	-	40s. purple	5·25	1·30
292	-	50s. black	6·50	1·30

Designs: 5s. Jelgava Castle; 10s. Riga Castle; 20s. Independence Memorial; 30s. Eagle and National Flag; 35s. Town Hall, Daugavpils; 40s. War Museum and Powder magazine, Riga; 50s. President Ulmanis.

1939. Fifth Year of Office of President Ulmanis. Sheet as **MS**277 optd **1934 1939 14/V.**

No.	Description	Mint	Used
MS293	Sold at 2l.	46·00	£160

59 Reaping

1939. Harvest Festival. Dated 8 X 1939.

No.	Type	Description	Mint	Used
294	**59**	10s. green	1·30	1·30
295	-	20s. red (Apples)	1·30	1·30

60 Arms of Courland, Livonia and Latgale

1940

No.	Type	Description	Mint	Used
296	**60**	1s. violet	65	65
297	**60**	2s. yellow	90	65
298	**60**	3s. red	15	25
299	**60**	5s. brown	15	25
300	**60**	7s. green	65	65
301	**60**	10s. green	2·00	40
302	**60**	20s. red	2·00	40
303	**60**	30s. brown	2·50	65
304	**60**	35s. blue	15	1·30
305	**60**	50s. green	4·00	1·30
306	**60**	1l. olive	7·75	4·00

61 Arms of Latvian Soviet Socialist Republic

1940. Incorporation of Latvia in USSR.

No.	Type	Description	Mint	Used
307	**61**	1s. violet	25	25
308	**61**	2s. yellow	25	25
309	**61**	3s. red	25	25
310	**61**	5s. olive	25	25
311	**61**	7s. green	25	1·30
312	**61**	10s. green	3·25	65
313	**61**	20s. red	2·00	25
314	**61**	30s. blue	4·00	65
315	**61**	35s. blue	25	65
316	**61**	40s. brown	3·25	2·00
317	**61**	50s. grey	4·00	2·00
318	**61**	1l. brown	5·25	2·50
319	**61**	5l. green	39·00	22·00

64 Latvian Arms

65 Latvian Arms

1991

No.	Type	Description	Mint	Used
320	**64**	5k. silver, brown & lt brn	7·25	7·00
321	**64**	10k. silver, brown & drab	40	40
322	**64**	15k. silver, sepia & brown	50	50
323	**64**	20k. silver, blue & lt blue	80	75
324	**64**	40k. silver, green and light green	1·60	1·50
325	**64**	50k. silver, brown and lilac	2·30	2·30
326	**65**	100k. multicoloured	4·00	3·75
327	**65**	200k. multicoloured	7·25	7·00

1991. Nos. 6073 and 6077a of Russia surch **LATVIJA** and new value.

No.	Description	Mint	Used
332	100k. on 7k. blue	1·30	1·30
333	300k. on 2k. brown	2·00	1·90
334	500k. on 2k. brown	3·25	3·25

335		1000k. on 2k. brown	6·50	6·25

67 Main Statue, Liberty Monument, Riga

1991

336	**67**	10k. multicoloured	25	25
337	**67**	15k. multicoloured	1·30	1·30
338	**67**	20k. multicoloured	90	90
339	**67**	30k. multicoloured	90	90
340	**67**	50k. multicoloured	90	90
341	**67**	100k. multicoloured	90	90

68 Olympic Committee Symbol

1992. Recognition of Latvian Olympic Committee.

342	**68**	50k.+25k. red, silver and drab	1·40	1·30
343	-	50k.+25k. red, silver and grey	2·75	2·50
344	**68**	100k.+50k. red, gold and bistre	2·00	1·90

Design: No. 343, as T **68** but symbols smaller and inscribed 'BERLIN 18.09.91.' at left.

69 Vaidelotis

1992. Statues from the base of the Liberty Monument, Riga.

345	-	10k. black and brown	15	15
346	**69**	20k. brown and grey	25	25
347	-	30k. deep lilac and lilac	55	50
348	**69**	30k. deep brown and brown	55	50
349	-	40k. blue and grey	70	65
350	**69**	50k. green and grey	70	65
351	-	50k. black and grey	70	65
352	-	100k. purple and mauve	1·40	1·30
353	-	200k. deep blue and blue	2·75	2·50

Designs: Nos. 345, 347, 353, Kurzeme (warrior with shield); 349, 351/352, Lachplesis (two figures).

1992. Nos. 4672, 6073 and 6077a of Russia surch **LATVIJA** and new value.

354a	1r. on 7k. blue	1·10	1·00
355	3r. on 2k. brown	70	65
356	5r. on 2k. brown	1·40	1·30
357	10r. on 2k. brown	2·00	1·90
358	25r. on 4k. red	4·75	4·50

1992. Birds of the Baltic. As Nos. 506/509 of Lithuania.

359	5r. black and red	1·10	1·00
360	5r. brown, black and red	1·10	1·00
361	5r. sepia, brown and red	1·10	1·00
362	5r. brown, black and red	1·10	1·00

Designs: Nos 359, Osprey (*Pandion haliaetus*); No. 360, Black-tailed godwit (*Limosa limosa*); No. 361, Goosander (*Mergus merganser*); No. 362, Common shelducks (*Tadorna tadorna*).

72 Children in Fancy Dress around Christmas Tree

1992. Christmas. Multicoloured.

363	2r. Type **72**	1·40	1·30
364	3r. Angel choir	70	65
365	10r. Type **72**	2·00	1·90
366	15r. Adoration of the Kings	2·75	2·50

1993. Nos. 4855, 5296 and 5295 of Russia surch **LATVIJA** and new value.

367	50r. on 6k. multicoloured	1·10	1·00
368	100r. on 6k. multicoloured	2·40	2·10
369	300r. on 6k. multicoloured	5·50	5·00

74 Kuldiga Couple

1993. Traditional Costumes. Multicoloured.

370	5s. Type **74**	25	15
371	10s. Alsunga	55	50
372	20s. Lielvarde	70	65
373	50s. Rucava	2·00	1·90
374	100s. Zemgale	4·00	3·75
375	500s. Ziemellatgale	20·00	19·00
MS376	103×88 mm. Nos. 370/375	43·00	41·00

See also Nos. 428/**MS**429, 442/**MS**443, 467/**MS**468 and 491/**MS**492.

75 Emblem

1993. National Song Festival.

377	**75**	3s. black, gold and brown	25	25
378	**75**	5s. black, gold and lilac	40	40
379	-	15s. multicoloured	70	65

Design: 15s. Abstract.

76 Pope John Paul II

1993. Papal Visit.

380	**76**	15s. multicoloured	1·40	1·30

77 Flags

1993. 75th Anniversary of First Republic.

381	**77**	5s. multicoloured	40	40
382	**77**	15s. multicoloured	95	90

78 Valters

1994. 100th Birthday of Evalds Valters (actor).

383	**78**	15s. brown, light brown and gold	95	90

79 Biathlon

1994. Winter Olympic Games, Lillehammer, Norway. Multicoloured.

384	5s. Type **79**	40	40
385	10s. Two-man bobsleigh	70	65
386	15s. One-man luge	95	90
387	100s. Figure skating	4·75	4·50
MS388	55×80 mm. 200s. As No. 385	11·00	10·50

80 Reed Hut

1994. 70th Anniversary of Latvian Ethnological Open-air Museum, Bergi.

389	**80**	5s. multicoloured	40	40

81 Streetball

1994. Basketball Festival, Riga.

390	**81**	15s. black, grey and orange	80	75

82 Kurzeme

1994. Arms (1st series). (a) Size 18×21 mm.

391	**82**	1s. red, black and silver	15	15
392	-	2s. multicoloured (Auce) (12.4.96)	25	25
393	-	3s. silver, black and blue (Zemgale)	40	40
394	-	5s. silver, black and red (Vidzeme)	55	50
395	-	8s. silver, black and blue (Livani) (1.6.95)	60	55
396	-	10s. silver, black and blue (Latgale)	70	65
396a	-	10s. multicoloured (Valmiera) (6.9.97)	70	65
397	-	13s. black, gold and silver (Preili) (12.4.96)	80	75
397a	-	15s. red, gold and black (Bauska) (26.9.98)	1·10	1·00
397b	-	16s. multicoloured (Ainazi) (1.6.95)	1·10	1·00
398	-	20s. silver, black and grey (Grobina) (1.6.95)	1·40	1·30
398a	-	20s. multicoloured (Rezekne) (6.9.97)	1·40	1·30
399	-	24s. green, black and silver (Tukums) (1.6.95)	1·50	1·40
399a	-	28s. multicoloured (Madona) (5.11.96)	1·20	1·10
400	-	30s. multicoloured (Liepaja) (26.9.98)	2·00	1·90
401	-	36s. silver, black and red (Priekule) (5.11.96)	1·80	1·60
402	-	50s. multicoloured	3·50	3·25

(b) Size 29×23½ mm.

403	100s. multicoloured	6·75	6·25
404	200s. multicoloured	15·00	14·00

Designs: 2s. Auce; 3s. Zemgale; 5s. Vidzeme; 8s. Livani; 10s. (No. 396) Latgale; 10s. (No. 396a) Valmiera; 13s. Preila; 16s. Ainazi; 20s. (No. 398) Grobina; 20s. (No. 398a) Rezekne; 24s. Tukums; 28s. Madona; 30, 100s. Riga; 36s. Priekule; 50, 200s. State Arms.

See also Nos.496a/509a.

83 Emblem

1994. 75th Anniversary of Latvia University.

405	**83**	5s. gold, blue and green	40	40

84 Coins in Scales

1994. Europa. Multicoloured.

406	10s. Type **84**	1·40	1·30
407	50s. Money chest and notes in scales	3·50	3·25

85 Eating Cherries

1994. The Fat Dormouse. Multicoloured.

408	5s. Type **85**	40	40
409	10s. Eating strawberries	80	75
410	10s. On leafy branch	80	75
411	15s. On branch of apple tree	1·40	1·30

86 Angel

1994. Christmas. Multicoloured.

412	3s. Type **86**	25	25
413	8s. Angels playing violin and flute	55	50
414	13s. Angels singing	70	65
415	100s. Wreath of candles	5·25	4·75

87 Gnome with Candle

1994. 80th Birthday of Margarita Staraste (children's writer and illustrator). Multicoloured.

416	5s. Type **87**	40	40
417	10s. Bear	55	50
418	10s. Child on sledge	55	50

88 Emblem

1994. Road Safety Year.

419	**88**	10s. multicoloured	70	65

89 Emblem

1995. 50th Anniversary of UNO.

420	**89**	15s. blue, red and silver	80	75

90 Bauska Castle (Latvia)

1995. Via Baltica Motorway Project. Multicoloured.

421	8s. Type **90**	70	65
MS422	100×110 mm. 18s. Beach Hotel, Parnu (Estonia); 18s. Type **90**; 18s. Kaunas (Lithuania)	3·50	3·25

91 White-backed Woodpecker

1995. European Nature Conservation Year. Birds. Multicoloured.

423	8s. Type **91**	1·40	1·30
424	20s. Corncrake	1·90	1·80
425	24s. White-winged black tern	2·00	1·90

92 Vaivods

1995. Birth Centenary of Cardinal Julijans Vaivods.

426	**92**	8s. multicoloured	70	65

93 Sun and Open Book

1995. 60th Anniversary of Karlis Ulmaris Schools Appeal.

427	**93**	8s. multicoloured	70	65

1995. Traditional Costumes. As T **74**. Multicoloured.

428	8s. Nica	70	65
MS429	100s. As No. 428	5·50	5·25

94 National Opera House

1995. 800th Anniversary of Riga (1st issue). Multicoloured.

430	8s. Type **94**	55	50
431	16s. National Theatre	80	75
432	24s. Art School (44×26 mm)	1·10	1·00
433	36s. Art Museum (44×26 mm)	1·60	1·50

See also Nos. 456/459, 479/482, 493/496, 522/525, 540/543 and 560/563.

95 Lacplesis, the Bear Slayer

1995. European Peace and Freedom. Multicoloured.

434	16s. Type **95**	1·40	1·30
435	50s. Spidola	3·50	3·25

96 Christmas Tree at Night

1995. Christmas. Multicoloured.

436	6s. Type **96**	40	40
437	6s. Elf flying with candle	55	50
438	15s. Cottage at night	80	75
439	24s. Elf with dog and cat	1·60	1·50

97 Stradins

1996. Birth Centenary of Pauls Stradins (surgeon).

440	**97**	8s. multicoloured	40	40

98 Zenta Maurina (writer)

1996. Europa. Famous Women.

441	**98**	36s. multicoloured	3·50	3·25

1996. Traditional Costumes. As T **74**. Multicoloured.

442	8s. Barta	70	65
MS443	100×70 mm. 100s. As No. 422	5·50	5·25

99 Children with Toys

1996. Sheet 96×97 mm.

MS444	**99** 48s. multicoloured	3·50	3·25

100 Cycling

1996. Olympic Games, Atlanta. Multicoloured.

445	8s. Type **100**	40	40
446	16s. Basketball	80	75
447	24s. Walking	1·10	1·00
448	36s. Canoeing (horiz)	1·80	1·60
MS449	85×60 mm. 100s. Throwing the javelin (horiz)	5·50	5·25

101 Swallowtail

1996. Butterflies. Multicoloured.

450	8s. Type **101**	55	50
451	24s. *Clifden's nonpareil*	1·40	1·30
452	80s. Large tiger moth	4·25	4·00

102 1912 Russo-Balt Fire Engine

1996. Latvian Car Production. Multicoloured.

453	8s. Type **102**	40	40
454	24s. 1899 Leutner-Russia carriage	1·40	1·30
455	36s. 1939 Ford-Vairogs motor car	1·60	1·50

103 Apartment Block (E. Laube)

1996. 800th Anniversary of Riga (2nd issue). Multicoloured.

456	8s. Type **103**	55	50
457	16s. Stained glass window (F. Sefels) (30×26 mm)	95	90
458	24s. Turreted buildings (E. Laube) (38×26 mm)	1·40	1·30
459	30s. Couple welcoming charioteer (mural, J. Rozentals) (38×26 mm)	1·90	1·80

104 Elves and Presents

1996. Christmas. Multicoloured.

460	6s. Type **104**	25	15
461	14s. Children with dog and Father Christmas on skis	95	90
462	20s. Child at tree and Father Christmas in armchair	1·10	1·00

105 European Nightjar

1997. 75th Anniversary of Birdlife International (conservation organisation). Multicoloured.

463	10s. Type **105**	70	65
464	20s. Greater spotted eagle	1·40	1·30
465	30s. Aquatic warbler	2·00	1·90

106 Symbols of Independence

1997. Sixth Anniversary of Independence.

466	**106**	10s. multicoloured	70	65

1997. Traditional Costumes. As T **74**. Multicoloured.

467	10s. Rietumvidzeme	95	90
MS468	100×70 mm. 100s. As No. 467	5·50	5·25

107 Turaidas Roze

1997. Europa. Tales and Legends.

469	**107**	32s. multicoloured	2·75	2·50

108 *Wappen der Herzogin von Kurland* (galleon)

1997. Baltic Sailing Ships. Multicoloured.

470	10s. Type **108**	95	90
MS471	110×70 mm. 20s. As No. 470 but with different frame; 20s. Kurshes ship (Lithuania); 20s. Maasilinn ship (Estonia)	4·00	3·75

109 Hermes and Neptune

1997. Centenary of Ventspils International Commercial Port.

472	**109**	20s. blue, silver and yellow	1·10	1·00

110 Stamp Collecting

1997. Children's Leisure Pursuits. Multicoloured.

473	10s. Type **110**	55	50
474	12s. Motorcycle trials (vert)	70	65
475	20s. Ice hockey and skiing (vert)	1·10	1·00
476	30s. Tennis, football and basketball	1·80	1·60

111 Moricsala

1997. Nature Reserves. Multicoloured.

477	10s. Type **111**	70	65
478	30s. Slitere	2·00	1·90

112 Woman, Wooden Building and Jewellery (12th-century)

1997. 800th Anniversary of Riga (3rd issue). 12th/16th-centuries. Multicoloured.

479	10s. Type **112**	55	50
480	20s. 13th-century Cathedral cloister, statue (K. Bernevics) and Seal of Bishop Albert, rosary beads and writing implement	1·10	1·00
481	30s. Livonian Order's castle, statue of V. von Plettenberg (Order Master) and weapons	1·50	1·40
482	32s. *Three Brothers* terrace, statue of St John and Seal (27×27 mm)	1·60	1·50

113 Man and Bear

1997. Christmas. Mummers. Multicoloured.

483	8s. Type **113**	55	50
484	18s. Witches	1·10	1·00
485	28s. Horse	1·60	1·50

114 Flames

1998. Winter Olympic Games, Nagano, Japan.

486	**114**	20s. multicoloured	1·10	1·00

115 Sculpture of Character

1998. Spridisi Memorial (to Anna Brigadere (writer)) Museum, Tervete.

487	**115**	10s. multicoloured	70	65

116 Song Festival

1998. Europa. National Festivals.

488	**116**	30s. multicoloured	2·00	1·90

117 Grini

1998. Nature Reserves. Multicoloured.

489	10s. Type **117**	55	50
490	30s. Teici	1·50	1·40

1998. Traditional Costumes. As T **74**. Multicoloured.

491	10s. Krustpils	95	90
MS492	100×69 mm. 100s. As No. 491 but man with Midsummer Festival headdress	55	50

118 Dannenstern House, Wooden Sculpture and Polish and Swedish Coins

1998. 800th Anniversary of Riga (4th issue). 16th/20th-centuries. Multicoloured.

493	10s. Type **118**	95	90
494	20s. Library, medallion and monument to G. Herder (poet and philosopher)	1·40	1·30
495	30s. Arsenal, Victory column, octant and compass	1·90	1·80
496	40s. Entrance gate to Warrior's Cemetery, *Mother Latvia* (statue) and 5l. coin	1·90	1·80

1998. Arms (2nd series)

496a	1s. multicoloured	15	15
496b	2s. multicoloured	15	15
496c	3s. multicoloured	15	15
497	5s. multicoloured	40	40
497a	5s. multicoloured	40	40
497b	5s. multicoloured	40	40
497c	5s. multicoloured	40	40
498d	7s. multicoloured (11.1.06)	40	40
499	10s. multicoloured	70	65
499a	10s. multicoloured	70	65
499b	10s. black, red and silver	70	65
499c	10s. multicoloured	40	40
500	15s. multicoloured	55	50
501	15s. black, blue and silver	80	75
502	15s. multicoloured	95	90
503	15s. multicoloured	95	90
504	15s. black, silver and red	95	90
504a	15s. multicoloured	95	90
504b	15s. silver and black	80	75
504c	15s. multicoloured	80	75
504d	15s. multicoloured	80	75
504e	15s. multicoloured	80	75
505	20s. multicoloured	1·10	1·00
505a	20s. blue, silver and black	1·10	1·00
505b	22s. multicoloured	1·40	1·40
505c	22s. multicoloured (11.1.06)	1·40	1·40
506	30s. multicoloured	1·40	1·30
506	31s. multicoloured (11.1.06)	1·40	1·30
506b	33s. scarlet, bronze and black	1·40	1·30
506c	35s. emerald, bronze and black	1·40	1·30
508	40s. multicoloured	2·00	1·90
509	40s. multicoloured	2·00	1·90
509a	60s. bronxe, emerald and black	2·40	2·30

Designs: No. 496a, Kurzeme; No. 496b, Auce; No. 496c, Zemgale; No. 497, Smiltene; No. 497a, Ludza; No. 497b, Valka; No. 497c, Staicele; No. 498 Aizkraukle; No. 499, Valmiera; No. 499a, Dobeje; No. 499b, Balvi; No. 499c, Sabile; No. 500, Bauska; No. 501, Ogre; No. 502, Daugavpils; No. 503, Jurmala; No. 504, Kuldiga; No. 504a, Sigulda; No. 504b, Gulbene; No. 504c, Ventspils; 504d, Cesis; No. 504e, Talis; No. 505, Aluksne; No. 505a, Dagda; No. 505b, Vecummeki; No. 505c., No. 506, Liepaja; No. 506a, Kraslava; No. 506b, Saldus; No. 506c Balozi; No. 508, Jelgava; No. 509, Jekabpils; No. 509a Limbazi; No. 509b, Stende.

119 1918 5k. Stamp

1998. 70th Anniversary of First Latvian Stamp.

510	**119**	30s. red, cream and grey	1·70	1·60

120 Dome Church, Riga

1998. Churches.

511	**120**	10s. multicoloured	75	70

121 Janis Cakste (1922–1927)

1998. Presidents.

512	**121**	10s. multicoloured	75	70

122 State Flag

1998. 80th Anniversary of Declaration of Independence. Multicoloured.

513	10s. Type **122**	45	40
514	30s. State Arms and flags	1·50	1·40

123 Elves building Snowman

1998. Christmas. Multicoloured.

515	10s. Type **123**	60	55
516	20s. Elves decorating tree	1·00	95
517	30s. Elves sledging	1·50	1·40

124 Krustkalnu Nature Reserve

1999. Europa. Parks and Gardens.

518	30s. Type **124**	2·20	2·00
519	60s. Gauja National Nature Park	4·25	4·00

125 Playing Cards and Edgars (from novel *Purva Bridejs*)

1999. Latvian Literature. Rudolfs Blaumanis.

520	**125**	110s. multicoloured	5·25	4·75

126 Council Emblem

1999. 50th Anniversary of Council of Europe.

521	**126**	30s. multicoloured	2·20	2·00

127 *Widwud* (schooner)

1999. 800th Anniversary of Riga (5th issue). Transport. Multicoloured.

522	10s. Electric tramcar No. 258 (30×26½ mm)	45	40
523	30s. Type **127**	1·50	1·40
524	40s. Biplane	1·90	1·80
525	70s. Steam locomotive No. Tk-236	3·50	3·25

128 Aglona Basilica

1999. Churches.

526	**128**	15s. multicoloured	95	85

129 Family and State Flag

1999. Tenth Anniversary of Baltic Chain (human chain uniting capitals of Latvia, Lithuania and Estonia).

527	**129**	15s. multicoloured	1·10	1·00
MS528		110×72 mm. 30s. Type **129**; 30s. Family and Lithuanian flag; 30s. Family and Estonian flag	5·50	5·25

130 Rundale Palace

1999. Palaces.

529	**130**	20s. multicoloured	1·20	1·20

131 *Perse*

1999. 90th Death Anniversary of Julijs Feders (painter).

530	**131**	15s. multicoloured	1·10	1·00

132 Gustavs Zemgals (1927–1930)

1999. Presidents.

531	**132**	15s. multicoloured	1·10	1·00

133 Harbour, Letters and Emblem

1999. 125th Anniversary of Universal Postal Union.

532	**133**	40s. multicoloured	3·00	3·00

134 Father Christmas and Candle

1999. Christmas. Multicoloured.

533	12s. Type **134**	1·10	1·00
534	15s. Children watching television	1·20	1·20
535	40s. Father Christmas placing toys under tree	3·00	3·00

135 *Artist's Model* (J. Rosentals)

2000

536	**135**	40s. multicoloured	3·00	3·00

136 Scene from *The Wagon Driver* (poem)

2000. 50th Death Anniversary of Aleksandrs Caks (poet).

537	**136**	40s. multicoloured	2·75	2·50

137 Building Europe

2000. Europa.

538	**137**	60s. multicoloured	5·50	5·00

138 Ice Hockey Players

2000. Ice Hockey.

539	**138**	70s. multicoloured	4·75	4·25

140 Central Market

2000. 800th Anniversary of Riga (6th issue). Tourist Sights. Multicoloured.

540	20s. Type **140**	1·60	1·50
541	40s. Dome Church organ (25×30 mm)	2·75	2·50
542	40s. Zoo (44×26 mm)	2·75	2·50
543	70s. The Powder Tower (25×30 mm)	4·75	4·25

141 Jelgava Palace

2000. Palaces.

544	**141**	40s. multicoloured	3·00	3·00

142 Globe and Olympic Rings

2000. Olympic Games, Sydney.

545	**142**	40s. multicoloured	4·00	3·75
546	**142**	70s. multicoloured	4·75	4·25

143 Main Statue, Liberty Monument, Riga (Karlis Zale)

2000. New Millennium. Multicoloured.

547	15s. Type **143**	1·20	1·20
548	50s. Brotherhood of Blackheads meeting house, Riga	4·00	3·75

144 Alberts Kviesis (1930–1936)

2000. Presidents.

549	**144**	15s. multicoloured	1·20	1·20

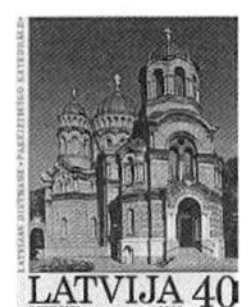
145 Orthodox Church, Riga

2000. Churches.

550	**145**	40s. multicoloured	3·00	3·00

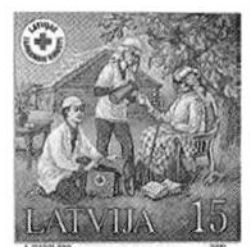
146 Nurses tending to Elderly Lady

2000. Latvian Red Cross.

551	**146**	15s. multicoloured	1·20	1·20

147 Elf and Sleigh

2000. Christmas. Multicoloured.

552	12s. Type **147**	95	85
553	15s. Cherubs	1·10	1·00
554	15s. Mary and baby Jesus	1·10	1·00

148 People around Bonfire

2001. Sovereignty.

555	**148**	40s. multicoloured	3·25	3·00

149 *When Silava's Forest Wakes* (V. Purvitis)

2001

556 **149** 40s. multicoloured 3·50 3·25

150 Karlis Ulmanis (1936–1940)

2001. Presidents.

557 **150** 15s. multicoloured 1·20 1·10

151 ML Series Steam Locomotive

2001. Narrow gauge Railway.

558 **151** 40s. multicoloured 3·50 3·25

152 Ventas Rumba (waterfall), Kuldiga

2001. Europa. Water Resources.

559 **152** 60s. multicoloured 5·25 4·75

153 Modern View of Riga

2001. 800th Anniversary of Riga (7th issue). Multicoloured.

560	15s. Type **153**	1·40	1·30
561	15s. Modern View of Riga with three spires	1·40	1·30
562	60s. 16th-century view of Riga	6·25	5·50
563	70s. 17th-century view of Riga	7·00	6·50

Nos. 560/561 are 29×32 mm and 562/563 are 52×29 mm.

Nos. 560/561 were issued together, *se-tenant*, forming a composite design.

154 Cat with Pipe (*Pussy's Water Mill* (fairytale))

2001. Literature. Karlis Skalbe (writer) Commemoration.

564 **154** 40s. multicoloured 3·50 3·25

155 Tal

2001. Tenth Death Anniversary of Mikhail Nekhemevich Tal (World Chess Champion, 1960–1961). Sheet 98×68 mm.

MS565 **155** 100s. multicoloured 8·75 8·50

156 Beach, Vidzeme, Latvia

2001. Baltic Sea Coast. Multicoloured.

566 15s. Type **156** 1·40 1·30

MS567 125×60 mm. 30s. As Type **156**; 30s. Sand dunes, Palanga, Lithuania; 30s. Rocky coastline, Lahemaa, Estonia 8·00 7·75

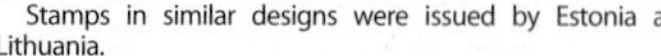

Stamps in similar designs were issued by Estonia and Lithuania.

157 Cesvaines Palace

2001. Palaces.

568 **157** 40s. multicoloured 3·50 3·25

158 Synagogue, Riga

2001

569 **158** 70s. multicoloured 6·25 5·50

159 Krisjanis Valdemars (image scaled to 56% of original size)

2001. Ship Building, Trade and Discovery. Multicoloured.

570	15s. Type **159** (founder of Naval College and ship builder)	1·40	1·30
571	70s. Hercogs Jekabs, Duke of Courland (ship builder)	5·50	5·00

160 White Rabbits

2001. Christmas. Multicoloured.

572	12s. Type **160**	1·10	95
573	15s. Dog and rabbit	1·20	1·10
574	15s. Sheep	1·20	1·10

161 Cross-country Skiers

2002. Winter Olympic Games, Salt Lake City.

575 **161** 40s. multicoloured 3·00 2·75

162 Downhill Skier

2002. Winter Paralympic Games, Salt Lake City.

576 **162** 15s. multicoloured 1·20 1·10

163 *Refugees* (Jekabs Kazaks)

2002. Art.

577 **163** 40s. multicoloured 3·25 3·00

164 Clowns

2002. Europa. Circus.

578 **164** 60s. multicoloured 5·25 4·75

165 Lady's Slipper Orchid (*Cypripedium calceolus*)

2002. Plants. Multicoloured.

579	15s. Type **165**	1·10	95
580	40s. Water chestnut (*Trapa natans*)	2·75	2·50

166 Soldier and Flag

2002. Armed Forces.

581 **166** 40s. multicoloured 2·75 2·50

167 Jancis standing in Brook (*The White Book*)

2002. Literature. 40th Death Anniversary of Janis Jaunsudrabins (writer).

582 **167** 40s. multicoloured 2·75 2·50

168 Kristians Johan Dals

2002. Kristians Johan Dals (sailor and founder of maritime school) Commemoration.

584 **168** 70s. multicoloured 5·00 4·50

169 Atlantic Cod (*Gadus morhua*)

2002. Fish. Multicoloured.

585	15s. Type **169**	1·10	95
586	40s. Wels (*Silurus glanis*)	2·75	2·50

170 Bridge over River Venta

2002. Sheet 100×70 mm.

MS587 **170** 100s. multicoloured 7·00 6·75

171 Jaunmoku Palace

2002. Palaces.

588 **171** 40s. multicoloured 2·75 2·50

172 Grebenschikov Old Believers Praying House, Riga

2002. Churches.

589 **172** 70s. multicoloured 5·00 4·50

173 Mittens and Couple wearing Traditional Winter Clothes

2002. Mittens (1st series).

590 **173** 15s. multicoloured 1·20 1·10

See also Nos. 606, 628 and 650.

174 Christmas Tree and Elf Musician

2002. Christmas. Multicoloured.

591	12s. Type **174**	90	80
592	15s. Elf musicians on present	1·10	95
593	15s. Angel	1·10	95

175 *Man enters Room* (Niklavs Srtunke)

2003. Art.

594 **175** 40s. multicoloured 2·75 2·40

176 Fly Orphide (*Ophrys insectifera*)

2003. Plants. Multicoloured.

595	15s. Type **176**	1·20	1·10
596	40s. Yew (*Taxus baccata*)	2·30	2·10

177 Scene from *Straumei* (poem)

2003. Literature. 40th Death Anniversary of Edvarts Virza (writer).

597 **177** 40s. multicoloured 3·25 3·00

178 *Riga's Towers* (Valda Batraks)

2003. Europa. Poster Art.

598 **178** 60s. multicoloured 5·25 4·75

179 Kolka Lighthouse

2003

599 **179** 60s. multicoloured 4·25 3·75

180 Baptist Church, Riga

2003. Churches.

600 **180** 70s. multicoloured 5·00 4·50

181 Bridge over River Gauja, Sigulda.

2003. Sheet 100×70 mm.

MS601 **181** 100s. multicoloured 6·25 6·00

182 *Thymallus thymallus*

2003. Fish. Multicoloured.

602	15s. Type **182**	1·20	1·10
603	30s. *Salmo salar*	2·30	2·10

183 Pied Wagtail (*Motacilla alba*)

2003

604 **183** 15s. multicoloured 1·20 1·10

184 Birinu Palace

2003. Palaces.

605 **184** 40s. multicoloured 3·25 3·00

185 Mittens and Couple, Liv

2003. Mittens (2nd series).

606 **185** 15s. multicoloured 1·20 1·10

186 Motorcycle and Sidecar

2003. Motor Sports.

607 **186** 70s. multicoloured 5·25 4·75

187 Mary and Jesus visited by Angels

2003. Christmas. Multicoloured.

608	12s. Type **187**	1·10	95
609	15s. Holy Family	1·20	1·10
610	15s. Annunciation of Mary	1·20	1·10

188 *Still Life with Triangular Ruler* (Romans Suta)

2004. Art.

611 **188** 40s. multicoloured 3·50 3·25

189 Scene from *Times of Land Surveyors*

2004. Literature. Reinis and Matiss Kaudzites (writers) Commemoration.

612 **189** 40s. multicoloured 3·00 2·75

190 Gentian (*Gentiana cruciata*)

2004. Plants. Multicoloured.

613	15s. Type **190**	1·10	95
614	30s. *Onobrychis arenaria*	2·10	1·90

191 Crowd of Fans

2004. International Ice Hockey Federation Championship, Riga (2006).

615 **191** 30s. multicoloured 2·10 1·90

192 Stars

2004. Enlargement of European Union. Multicoloured.

616	30s. Type **192**	2·10	1·90
617	30s. Flags of new members	2·10	1·90

193 Family in Rowing Boat

2004. Europa. Holidays.

618 **193** 60s. multicoloured 4·25 3·75

194 Footballers

2004. Euro 2004 Football Championship, Portugal.

619 **194** 30s. multicoloured 2·10 1·90

195 *Oncrhynchus mykiss*

2004. Fish. Multicoloured.

620	15s. Type **195**	1·50	1·30
621	30s. *Psetta maxima*	2·75	2·50

196 Statues of Liberty, New York and Riga

2004. Tenth Anniversary of Visit of Bill Clinton (president of USA, 1993–2001).

622 **196** 40s. multicoloured 3·75 3·50

197 Bridge over River Daugava, Riga.

2004. Sheet 100×70 mm.

MS623 100s. multicoloured 7·25 7·00

198 Wrestlers

2004. Olympic Games, Athens.

624 **198** 30s. multicoloured 3·00 2·75

199 St Jacob's Cathedral, Riga

2004. Churches.

625 **199** 40s. multicoloured 4·00 3·50

200 Mikelbaka Lighthouse

2004

626 **200** 60s. multicoloured 5·75 5·25

201 Jaunpils Palace

2004. Palaces.

627 **201** 40s. multicoloured 4·00 3·50

202 Mittens and Couple, Piebalga

2004. Mittens (3rd series).

628 **202** 15s. multicoloured 1·40 1·30

203 Heart, Rabbit, Bluebird and Children

2004. Christmas.

629	12s. Type **203**	1·20	1·10
630	15s. Snowman	1·40	1·30
631	15s. Angel	1·40	1·30

204 Revolution Monument, Riga

2005. Centenary of Russian Revolution.

632 **204** 12s. multicoloured 1·50 1·40

205 Gentian (*Pulsatilla patens*)

2005. Plants. Multicoloured.

633	15s. Type **205**	2·00	1·80
634	30s. *Allium ursinum*	3·00	2·75

206 Krimuldas Church

2005. Churches.

635 **206** 40s. multicoloured 3·50 3·25

207 Baron Minhauzen

2005. Adventures of Baron Minhauzen (Munchausen).

636 **207** 30s. multicoloured 3·00 2·75

208 Pig's Head, Sausages and Beer

2005. Europa. Gastronomy.

637 **208** 60s. multicoloured 6·00 5·50

209 *Mother and Child* (Janis Rozentals)

2005

638 **209** 40s. multicoloured 4·00 3·75

210 Baumanu Karlis and Music Score

2005. 170th Birth Anniversary of Karlis Baumanis (Baumanu Karlis) (composer of National Anthem).

639 **210** 20s. multicoloured 2·00 1·80

211 Kaive Oak

2005. Nature Protection. Oldest Oak Tree in Latvia. Self-adhesive.

640 **211** 15s. multicoloured 1·50 1·40

212 *Lampetra fluviatilis*

2005. Fish. Multicoloured.

641	15s. Type **212**	1·50	1·40
642	40s. *Clupea harengus*	4·00	3·75

213 Pope John Paul II

2005. Pope John Paul II Commemoration.

643	**213**	15s. multicoloured	1·50	1·40

214 Library Building

2005. National Library (Castle of Light) designed by Gunnar Birkerts. Sheet 100×70 mm.

MS644 **214**	100s. multicoloured	9·50	9·25

215 *Uguns un Nakts*

2005. Literature. Janis Rainis (writer) Commemoration.

645	**215**	40s. multicoloured	3·75	3·50

216 Viaduct, Riga.

2005. Bridges. Sheet 100×70 mm.

MS646 **216**	100s. multicoloured	9·50	9·25

217 Daugavgrivas Lighthouse

2005

647	**217**	40s. multicoloured	3·75	3·50

218 Monument and Gunars Astra

2005. Gunars Astra (human rights activist) Commemoration.

648	**218**	15s. multicoloured	1·50	1·40

219 Durbe Palace

2005. Palaces.

649	**219**	40s. multicoloured	3·50	3·25

220 Mittens and Couple, Southern Latgale

2005. Mittens (4th series).

650	**220**	15s. multicoloured	1·80	1·60

221 Goat riding Wolf

2005. Christmas. Multicoloured. Self-adhesive.

651	12s. Type **221**	1·30	1·20
652	15s. Woman, tree and dog (vert)	1·50	1·40
653	15s. Cat and woman carrying cockerel in basket (vert)	1·50	1·40

222 1996 36s. Stamp (T **98**)

2006. 50th Anniversary of Europa Stamps. Multicoloured.

654	10s. Type **222**	1·00	90
655	15s. 1997 32s. stamp (Type **107**)	1·50	1·40
656	15s. 1998 30s. stamp (Type **116**)	1·50	1·40
657	20s. 1999 30s. and 60s. stamps (As Nos. 518/519)	2·00	1·80
MS658	110×75 mm. Nos. 654/657	6·00	5·75

223 Snowboarder

2006. Winter Olympic Games, Turin.

659	**223**	45s. multicoloured	4·00	3·75

224 Stamerienas Palace

2006. Palaces.

660	**224**	95s. multicoloured	8·00	7·50

225 Zvartes Rock

2006. Nature Protection. Self-adhesive.

661	**225**	22s. multicoloured	1·90	1·80

226 Railway Bridge, Ruanu

2006. Bridges. Sheet 100×70 mm.

MS662 **226**	100s. multicoloured	8·00	7·75

227 Player

2006. World Ice Hockey Championships, Riga.

663	**227**	55s. multicoloured	4·25	4·00

228 Victory Monument

2006. 800th Anniversary of Cesis. Multicoloured.

664	22s. Type **228**	1·90	1·80
665	31s. St John's Church	2·75	2·50
666	45s. Castle Manor (horiz)	3·75	3·50
667	55s. New Castle (horiz)	4·25	4·00

229 Brooch

2006. Jewellery. Multicoloured.

668	22s. Type **229**	1·90	1·80
669	22s. Cuff	1·90	1·80

Stamps of a similar design were issued by Kazakhstan.

230 Figures, Trees and Horses

2006. Europa. Integration.

670	**230**	85s. multicoloured	7·00	6·50

231 *The Young Gypsy* (Karlis Huns)

2006. Art.

671	**231**	40s. multicoloured	3·25	3·00

232 Painting inscribed 'Jekabs Beckers'

2006. Personal Stamps. Multicoloured.

672	31s. Type **232**	2·75	2·50
673	31s. Postal emblem (horiz)	2·75	2·50

233 Lielais Kristaps (statue)

2006. Lielais Kristaps (Big Christopher) (protector of Riga).

674	**233**	36s. multicoloured	3·25	3·00

234 *Hills, Sheep and House* (Paula Anna Koskina)

2006. Winning Design in Children's Painting Competition. Self-adesive.

675	**234**	22s. multicoloured	1·90	1·80

235 Uniformed Volunteers

2006. Emergency Volunteer Corps.

676	**235**	22s. multicoloured	1·90	1·80

236 Cliffs, Staburags

2006. Natural Heritage.

677	**236**	58s. multicoloured	5·25	4·75

237 *Lynx lynx*

2006. Fauna. Multicoloured.

678	45s. Type **237**	3·75	3·50
679	55s. *Cervus elaphus*	4·25	4·00
680	45s. As Type **237** (30×48 mm) (white border at top)	4·00	3·75
681	45s. As Type **237** (30×48 mm) (white border at bottom)	4·00	3·75

238 *Pansija Pili*

2006. Literature. A. Eglitis (writer) Commemoration.

682	**238**	67s. multicoloured	6·00	5·50

239 Mersraga Lighthouse

2006

683	**239**	40s. multicoloured	3·75	3·50
684	**239**	45s. As Type **239** (30×47 mm) (white border at top)	5·50	5·00
685	**239**	45s. As Type **239** (30×47 mm) (white border at bottom)	5·50	5·00

240 City Skyline

2006. NATO Summit, Riga.

686	**240**	55s. multicoloured	4·75	4·50

241 Tree-shaped Cookie

2006. Christmas. Cookies. Multicoloured. Self-adhesive.

687	18s. Type **241**	1·60	1·50
688	22s. Star and trail	1·90	1·80
689	31s. Bell	2·75	2·50
690	45s. Moon	4·00	3·75

242 Oskar Kalpaks

2007. 125th Birth Anniversary of Oskar Kalpaks (first commander in chief national armed forces).

691	**242**	22s. multicoloured	1·90	1·80

243 Air Balloon

2007. 15th Anniversary of Mobile Telephony.

692	**243**	22s. multicoloured	1·90	1·80

244 *Tornkalna Bridge* (Ludolfs Libert)

2007. Art.
693 **244** 58s. multicoloured 5·25 4·75

245 Museum Artefacts

2007. 50th Anniversary of Pauls Stradins History of Medicine Museum.
694 **245** 22s. multicoloured 1·90 1·80

246 Baltic Coast

2007. Natural Heritage. Self-adhesive.
695 **246** 22s. multicoloured 1·90 1·80

247 Papes Lighthouse

2007
696 **247** 67s. multicoloured 5·75 5·25

248 Emblem, Compass and Scouts

2007. Europa. Centenary of Scouting.
697 **248** 85s. multicoloured 7·25 6·75

249 Krutspils Castle

2007
698 **249** 22s. multicoloured 1·90 1·80

250 House of Blackheads, Riga

2007. World Heritage Sites, Riga and Vismar. Multicoloured.
699 36s. Type **250** 3·25 3·00
700 45s. City Hall, Schtralsund and St George's Church, Vismar 4·00 3·75

Stamps of a similar design were issued by Germany.

251 Sigulda Castle

2007. 800th Anniversary of Sigulda. Multicoloured. Self-adhesive.
701 22s. Type **251** 1·30 1·30
702 31s. Bobsleigh track 2·00 2·00
703 40s. New castle ruins 2·75 2·75

252 *Vaccinium vitis*

2007. Berries and Fungi. Multicoloured.
704 22s. Type **252** 1·90 1·80
705 58s. *Cantharellus cibarius* 5·25 4·75

253 Ball containing Player

2007. Centenary of National Football.
706 **253** 45s. multicoloured 3·75 3·50

254 Railway Bridge

2007. Bridges. Sheet 100×70 mm.
MS707 **254** 100s. multicoloured 8·00 7·75

255 Early Postal Delivery

2007. 375th Anniversary of Latvian Post. Multicoloured. Self-adhesive.
708 22s. Type **255** 1·90 1·80
709 31s. Modern postal delivery 2·75 2·50

256 Decorated Metal Work

2007. Archaeology.
710 **256** 60s. multicoloured 4·75 4·50

257 *Vulpes vulpes* (fox)

2007. Fauna. Multicoloured.
711 45s. Type **257** 3·75 3·50
711a 55s. *Alces alces* (elk) 4·25 4·00

258 Child Musicians

2007. Christmas. Designs showing children. Multicoloured. Self-adhesive.
712 22s. Type **258** 1·90 1·80
713 31s. Baking 2·75 2·50
714 45s. Sledding 3·75 3·50

259 Salaspils

2008. Arms. Multicoloured.
715 22s. Type **259** 1·90 1·80
716 28s. Plavinas 2·40 2·30

717 45s. Saulkrasti 3·75 3·50

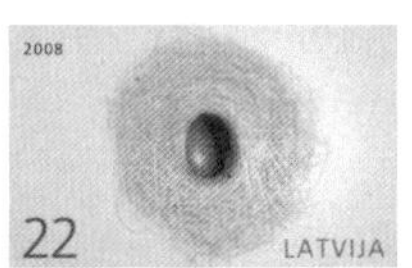

260 Egg in Nest

2008. Easter.
718 **260** 22s. multicoloured 1·90 1·80

261 *Still Life* (Leo Svemps)

2008. Art.
719 **261** 63s. multicoloured 5·50 5·00

262 Order of Three Stars (Latvia)

2008. Baltic State's Orders. Multicoloured.
720 31s. Type **262** 2·75 2·50
MS721 116×51 mm. 31s.×3, As Type **262**; Order of Vytautas the Great with Golden Chain (Lithuania); Order of National Coat of Arms (Estonia) 8·00 7·75

Stamps of similar design were issued by Estonia and Lithuania.

263 *Barbastella barbastellus*

2008. Bats. Multicoloured.
722 22s. Type **263** 1·90 1·80
723 31s. *Myotis dasycneme* 2·75 2·50
724 45s. *Barbastella barbastellus* (vert) 3·75 3·50
725 55s. *Myotis dasycneme* (vert) 4·50 4·25

264 Envelopes

2008. Europa. The Letter. Multicoloured.
726 45s. Type **264** 3·75 3·50
727 85s. Writing letter 7·25 6·75

265 Akmenraga Baka

2008. Lighthouses.
728 **265** 63s. multicoloured 5·50 5·00

266 Athlete and Controls

2008. European Orienteering Championship.
729 **266** 45s. multicoloured 3·75 3·50

267 Rock

2008. Natural Heritage. Self-adhesive.
730 **267** 22s. multicoloured 1·90 1·80

268 Exhibits

2008. Museum Foundations.
731 **268** 22s. multicoloured 1·90 1·80

269 Basketball

2008. Olympic Games, Beijing.
732 **269** 63s. multicoloured 5·50 5·00

270 Horse Dancer

2008. Fairytales.
733 **270** 22s. multicoloured 1·90 1·80

271 *Vaccinium myrtillus* (bilberry)

2008. Berry and Fungi. Multicoloured.
734 22s. Type **271** 1·90 1·80
735 58s. *Leccinum aurantiacum* (orange cap boletus) 5·25 4·75

272 Bridge over Abava River, Kandavas

2008. Bridges. Sheet 100×70 mm.
MS736 **272** 100s. multicoloured 9·50 9·25

273 Masthead

2008. 20th Anniversary of Latvijas Tautas Frontei (Latvian People's Front) and *Atmoda* (Awakening) (first independent opposition newspaper).
737 **273** 22s. multicoloured 1·90 1·80

274 *Martes martes* (European pine marten)

2008. Fauna. Multicoloured.

738	45s. Type **274**	3·75	3·50
739	55s. *Castor fiber* (beaver)	4·25	4·00

275 Maris Strombergs

2008. Maris Strombergs. BMX Olympic Gold Medallist.

740	**275**	22s. multicoloured	1·90	1·80

276 Brooches and Woollen Shawl

2008. Cultural Heritage. Decoration.

741	**276**	28s. multicoloured	2·20	2·00

277 Map as Flag and Arms

2008. 90th Anniversary of Republic.

742	**277**	31s. multicoloured	2·40	2·30

278 Mezotnes Palace, Bauska

2008. Palaces.

743	**278**	63s. multicoloured	4·75	4·50

279 Decorated Trees

2008. Christmas.

744	**279**	25s. multicoloured	2·20	2·00

280 Metalwork

2009. Cultural Heritage. Decoration.

745	**280**	98s. multicoloured	7·50	7·00

281 Dancing Boy and Animals

2009. Fairy Tales.

746	**281**	40s. multicoloured	3·50	3·25

282 Polar Bear

2009. Preserve Polar Regions and Glaciers. Sheet 120×75 mm containing T **282** and similar vert design. Multicoloured.

MS747	35s. Type **282**; 55s. Penguin and chick	7·25	7·00

283 Janis Ikaunieks and Schmidt Telescope, Baldone Observatory

2009. Europa. Astronomy. Multicoloured.

748	50s. Type **283**	4·25	4·00
749	55s. Astronomers and images of space	4·50	4·25

284 Museum Building and Exhibits

2009. National History Museum of Latvia.

750	**284**	35s. multicoloured	2·75	2·50

285 Latvija Player (European Champions, 1935)

2009. Basketball–National Sport. Multicoloured.

751	35s. Type **285**	2·75	2·50
752	40s. TTT Riga player (women's club)	3·00	2·75
753	60s. ASK Riga player (men's club)	4·50	4·25
MS754	100×70 mm. 120s. Young players	9·50	9·25

286 Bauska Castle

2009. 400th Anniversary of Bauska.

755	**286**	38s. multicoloured	3·00	2·75

287 Steam Locomotive

2009. Latvian Railways.

756	**287**	35s. multicoloured	2·75	2·50

288 Dienvidu Bridge, Riga

2009. Bridges. Sheet 100×70 mm.

MS757	**288**	100s. multicoloured	9·00	8·75

289 *Fragaria vesca* (strawberry)

2009. Berry and Fungi. Multicoloured.

758	55s. Type **289**	4·50	4·25
759	60s. *Russula paludosa*	4·75	4·50

290 *Canes lupus* (wolf)

2009. Fauna. Multicoloured.

760	35s. Type **290**	2·75	2·50
761	98s. *Lepus europaeus* (hare)	7·50	7·00

2009. Lighthouses. As T **265**. Liepaja. Multicoloured.

762	63s. Liepaja	5·50	5·00

292 National Council

2009. Centenary of Latvia Republic. Multicoloured.

763	35s. Type **292**	2·75	2·50
764	40s. Proclamation	3·25	3·00
765	100s. Constituent Assembly	7·50	7·00

293 Rocking Horse

2009. Christmas. Multicoloured.

766	35s. Type **293**	2·75	2·50
767	55s. Fish	4·00	3·75
768	60s. Snowflake	4·50	4·25

2010. Coats of Arms. As T **259**. Multicoloured.

769	35s. Viesite	2·75	2·50
770	40s. Ligatne	3·00	2·75
771	55s. Iecava	4·25	4·00

295 Hockey

2010. Olympic Winter Games, Vancouver.

772	**295**	55s. multicoloured	4·25	4·00

2010. Coats of Arms. As T **259**. Multicoloured.

773	13s. Preili	1·10	1·00

297 Peony

2010. Flowers. Peony.

774	**297**	35s. multicoloured	2·75	2·50

298 Girl carrying Books and Characters from Stories

2010. Europa. Children Books. Multicoloured.

775	55s. Type **298**	4·25	4·00
776	120s. Boy reading	9·50	8·75

299 Falling Figure

2010. EXPO 2010, Shanghai.

777	**299**	150s. multicoloured	12·00	11·00

300 Flag

2010. 20th Anniversary of Declaration of May 4th.

778	**300**	35s. multicoloured	2·75	2·50

301 Early Fire Appliance

2010. Latvian Firefighting Museum.

779	**301**	98s. multicoloured	7·50	7·00

302 *Coracias garrulus* (European Roller)

2010. Birds. Multicoloured.

780	35s. Type **302**	2·75	2·50
781	98s. *Bubo bubo* (Eagle Owl) (vert)	7·50	7·00

303 Sports Hall, Talsi

2010. Modern Architecture.

782	**303**	150s. multicoloured	11·50	10·50

304 RP Series Steam Locomotive

2010. History of Latvian Railways.

783	**304**	40s. multicoloured	3·25	3·00

2010. Berries and Fungi. As T **289**. Multicoloured.

784	55s. *Rubus ideus* (Wild Raspberry)	4·25	4·00
785	120s. *Leccinum scabrum* (birch bolete)	9·50	8·75

2010. Lighthouses. Uzavas. As T **265**. Multicoloured.

786	98s. Uzavas	7·50	7·00

307 National Flag

2010. Centenary of Latvia Republic. Multicoloured.

787	35s. Type **307**	2·75	2·50
787a	38s. Arms	3·25	3·00
787b	98s. Anthem	7·50	7·00

308 Girl decorating Tree

2010. Christmas. Multicoloured.

788	35s. Type **308**	2·75	2·50
789	60s. Boy carrying present and blue tit	4·75	4·50

309 Rabbit and Cabbage

2011. Chinese New Year. Year of the Rabbit.

790	**309**	35s. multicoloured	2·75	2·50

2011. Arms. As T **259**. Multicoloured.

791	35s. Ikskiles Novads	2·75	2·50

792 98s. Carnikavas Novads 7·50 7·00

311 Rose

2011. Flowers. Rose.
793 **311** 35s. multicoloured 2·75 2·50

312 Deer in Birch Forest

2011. Europa. Forests. Multicoloured.
794 55s. Type **312** 4·00 3·75
795 120s. Wolf in coniferous forest 7·75 7·25

313 Maps and Friedrich von Struve

2011. Struve Geodetic Arc. UNESCO World Heritage Site. Sheet 118×74 mm containing two stamps, showing Map of Arc and F. G. W. von Struve. Multicoloured.
MS796 35s.×2, Type **313** 6·75 6·50

314 Early Coins

2011. 800th Anniversary of First Coin of Riga.
797 **314** 98s. multicoloured 7·50 7·00

2011. Coats of Arms. As T **259**. Multicoloured.
798 1s. Kurzeme 25 25
799 2s. Auce 40 40
800 3s. Zemgale 55 50
801 5s. Smiltene 70 65

316 Johanna and Zanis Lipkes

2011. Johanna and Zanis Lipkes (Righteous Among the Nations (rescuers of Jews during WWII)).
802 **316** 60s. multicoloured 4·00 3·75

317 Fenikiss Railway Carriage

2011. History of Latvian Railways.
803 **317** 33s. multicoloured 2·75 2·50

318 Frieze (fragment)

2011. Personal Stamps. Multicoloured.
804 35s. Type **318** 2·75 2·50
805 55s. Borse, Riga (horiz) 4·00 3·75
806 60s. Archer (painting by Vaino Alfred Blomstedt) (horiz) 4·50 4·25

319 Cyclist

2011. 125th Anniversary of Latvian Cycling.
807 **319** 35s. multicoloured 2·75 2·50

320 Symbols of Riga Port

2011. Latvian Ports. Freeport of Riga.
808 **320** 60s. multicoloured 4·50 4·25

2011. Birds. Multicoloured.
809 35s. *Hippolais icterina* (Icterine Warbler) 2·75 2·50
810 98s. *Circaetus gallicus* (Short-toed Eagle) (vert) 7·25 6·75

T **321** is unavailable.

322 Library, Ventspili

2011. Modern Architecture
811 **322** 100s. multicoloured 7·25 6·75

323 Ships and Sailors through the Ages

2011. Centenary of Latvia Republic. Navy. Multicoloured.
812 35s. Type **323** 2·75 2·50
813 60s. Navigation 4·25 4·00
814 100s. Admiral and sailors 7·25 6·75

324 Santa and Reindeer

2011. Christmas. Multicoloured.
815 35s. Type **324** 2·75 2·50
816 60s. Santa and reindeer climbing dragon's back 4·25 4·00

2012. Arms. As T **259**. Multicoloured.
817 33s. Piltene 2·40 2·30
818 35s. Riga 2·75 2·50
819 38s. Liervardes Novads 3·00 2·75

326 Resturant and Park

2012. Library No 1. Restaurant.
820 **326** 35s. ochre and brownish black 2·75 2·50

327 Lily

2012. Flowers. Lily.
821 **327** 35s. multicoloured 2·75 2·50

2012. Coats of Arms. As T **259**. Multicoloured.
822 1s. Kurzeme 25 25
823 2s. Auce 40 40
824 3s. Zemgale 55 50
825 5s. Smiltene 70 65
826 10s. Dobele 1·40 1·30

328 Ballet Dancers

2012. Europa. Visit Latvia. Multicoloured.
827 55s. Type **328** 4·00 3·75
828 120s. National Opera Theatre 8·75 8·00

329 Lion

2012. Centenary of the Riga Zoo. Multicoloured.
829 35s. Type **329** 2·40 2·30
830 55s. Przwalski's horse 4·00 3·75
831 60s. Tree frog 4·25 4·00

330 Janis Misins

2012. 150th Birth Anniversary of Janis Misins.
832 **330** 98s. multicoloured 6·75 6·25

331 Ventspils

2012. Latvian Ports. Ventspils.
833 **331** 35s. multicoloured 2·40 2·30

332 *Hirundo rustica* (Swallow)

2012. Birds. Multicoloured.
834 35s. Type **332** 2·40 2·30
835 98s. *Carduelis carduelis* (Goldfinch) 6·75 6·25

333 Javelin Thrower

2012. Olympic Games, London.
836 **333** 60s. multicoloured 4·25 4·00

334 Manor House

2012. Ungurmuiza Estate.
837 **334** 98s. multicoloured 6·75 6·25

336 Fridrikh Tsander

2012. 125th Birth Anniversary of Fridrih Tsander (Friedrich Zander) (rocket and spaceflight pioneer).
838 **336** 60s. multicoloured 4·25 4·00

337 Jēkabs Ketlers

2012. 450th Anniversary of Kurzemes Duchy. Dukes of Duchy of Courland and Semigallia. Multicoloured.
MS839 35s. Ernsts Johans Birons; 55s. Type **337** 6·75 6·50

338 Cap

2012. 150th Anniversary of Riga Technical University.
840 **338** 98s. multicoloured 7·50 7·00

339 Carnikava Bridge, Latvia

2012. Railway Bridges of the Baltic States. Multicoloured.
841 35s. Type **339** 2·75 2·50
MS842 125×60 mm. 55s.×3, As Type **339**; Lyduvėnai Bridge, Lithuania; Narva Railway Bridge, Estonia 12·00 11·50

340 Emils Dārziņš

2012. Centenary of Latvia Republic. Composers. Multicoloured.
843 35s. Type **340** 2·75 2·50
844 60s. Jāzeps Vītols 4·50 4·25
845 100s. Tālivaldis Ķeniņš 7·25 6·75

341 Mārtiņš Pļaviņš and Jānis Šmēdiņš (Beach Volleyball bronze medalists)

2012. Olympic Medal Winners, London 2012. Multicoloured.
846 35s. Type **341** 2·75 2·50
847 35s. Māris Štrombergs (BMX gold medallist) 2·75 2·50

342 Girl with Presents

2012. Christmas. Multicoloured.
848 35s. Type **342** 2·75 2·50
849 60s. Snow covered house 4·50 4·25

343 Varakļāni

2013. Arms. Multicoloured.
850 35s. Type **343** 2·75 2·50
851 60s. Strenču Novads 4·50 4·25
852 98s. Vārkavas Novads 7·50 7·00

344 BMX Cyclist

2013. Latvian Sportsmen. Cyclists.
853 **344** 35s. multicoloured 2·75 2·50

345 Dailes Teātris (Dailes Theatre) Riga

2013. Architecture.

854	**345**	100s. multicoloured	7·25	6·75

346 Auce

2013. Arms. Multicoloured.

855	2s. Type **346**	15	10
856	3s. Zemgale	20	15
857	5s. Smiltene	40	35
858	10s. Dobele	1·00	90

347 Iris

2013. Flowers. Iris.

859	**347**	35s. multicoloured	2·75	2·50

348 Early Postal Transport

2013. Europa. Postal Transport. Multicoloured.

860	55s. Type **348**	4·00	3·75
861	120s. Modern post vehicles	8·75	8·00

349 Paul Walden

2013. 150th Birth Anniversary of Paul Walden (chemist). Sheet 85×65 mm.

MS862	**349** 100s. multicoloured	7·25	7·00

350 *Clangula hyemalis* (Long-tailed Duck)

2013. Birds. Multicoloured.

863	35s. Type **350**	2·75	2·50
864	98s. *Merops apiaster* (European Bee-eater) (vert)	7·50	7·00

351 Singers

2013. National Song Festival. Multicoloured.

MS865	35s.×2, Type **351**; Dancers	5·50	5·00

352 Postman, Envelope and Castle

2013. 150th Anniversary of First Stamp.

866	**352**	100s. multicoloured	7·25	7·00

353 Basket of Kittens

2013. Cats. Multicoloured.

867	35s. Type **353**	2·75	2·50
868	98s. Cats in doorway (vert)	7·50	7·00

354 Liepaja

2013. Latvian Ports. Liepaja.

869	**354**	98s. multicoloured	7·50	7·00

355 University Building

2013. 150th Anniversary of Latvian University of Agriculture.

870	**355**	40s. multicoloured	3·00	2·75

356 Mark Rothko

2013. 110th Birth Anniversary of Mark Rothko (artist).

871	**356**	60s. multicoloured	5·00	4·75

357 Emblem

2013. 25th Anniversary of Latvian Popular Front.

872	**357**	35s. multicoloured	2·90	2·70

358 Books and Early Printing Press

2013. 425th Anniversary of Printing in Latvia.

873	**358**	60s. multicoloured	5·00	4·75

359 Apple Blossom

2013. Breast Cancer Awareness Month.

874	**359**	4s. multicoloured	75	75

360 Rainis (Jānis Pliekšāns)

2013. Centenary of Latvia Republic. Writers. Multicoloured.

875	35s. Type **360**	2·90	2·70
876	60s. Rūdolfs Blaumanis	5·00	4·75
877	98s. Zenta Mauriņa	6·00	6·00

361 Dwarf Girl bringing Gifts on Rocking Horse

2013. Christmas. Multicoloured.

878	35s. Type **361**	2·90	2·70
879	60s. Dwarf girl carrying cat on snow-covered roof	5·00	4·75

362 Narcissuses

2014. Flowers. Multicoloured.

880	3c. Type **362**	50	50
881	47c. Croci	1·00	75
882	57c. Pansies	1·25	1·00
883	78c. Cornflowers	1·75	1·50
884	85c. Poppies	2·00	1·75
885	€1.39 Asters	2·80	2·50
MS886	84×71 mm. Nos. 880/885	10·00	10·00

363 *Imants Ziedonis Will Bloom Eternally*

2014. Imant Ziedonis (writer) Commemoration. Winner of Design-a-Stamp Competition.

887	**363**	50c. multicoloured	1·00	75

2014. European Capitals of Culture, 2014. Riga, Latvia and Umeå, Sweden.

887a	50c. Umeå Museum	4·25	4·00
887b	78c. National Library, Riga (horiz)	4·25	4·00

364 Men's Skeleton

2014. Winter Olympic Games, Sochi.

888	**364**	85c. multicoloured	6·75	6·50

365 Baltic Aircraft over City

2014. Personal Stamps. Aircraft (889, 891, 893) or Museums (890, 892, 894). Multicoloured.

889	50c. Type **365**	4·25	4·00
890	50c. Museum of Medicine (horiz)	4·25	4·00
891	78c. Aircraft over sea (horiz)	6·25	6·00
892	78c. Museum of Anatomy	6·25	6·00
893	85c. Aircraft in flight (horiz)	6·75	6·50
894	85c. Museum of Pharmaceutics	6·75	6·50

366 Tulips

2014. Flowers. Tulips.

895	**366**	50c. multicoloured	4·25	4·00

367 Bellis

2014. Flowers. Multicoloured.

896	1c. Type **367**	20	10
897	4c. *Anemone hepatica*	35	20
898	7c. Tagetes	60	50
899	50c. Lily of the Valley	4·25	4·00

368 Emblem

2014. 20th Anniversary of Latvia–Georgia Diplomatic Relations.

900	**368**	85c. multicoloured	6·75	6·50

369 Kokle

2014. Europa. Musical Instruments. Multicoloured.

901	78c. Type **369**	6·25	6·00
902	€1.71 Dūdas	12·50	12·00

370 Emblem

2014. 'TE' Television Programme.

903	**370**	50c. slate-lilac	4·25	4·00

371 *Lymnocryptes minimus* (Jack Snipe)

2014. Birds. Multicoloured.

904	50c. Type **371**	4·25	4·00
905	€1.39 *Upupa epops* (Hoopoe) (vert)	11·00	10·50

372 Martins Dukurs

2014. Winter Olympic Games, Sochi. Medal Winners. Multicoloured.

906	50c. Type **372** (Skeleton silver medalist)	4·25	4·25
907	50c. Daumants Dreiskens, Oskars Melbardis, Janis Strenga and Arvis Vilkaste (Bobsleigh team silver medalists)	4·25	4·25
908	50c. Juris Sics and Andris Sics (Luge Doubles bronze medalists)	4·25	4·25
909	50c. Juris Sics, Andris Sics, Martins Rubenis and Eliza Tiruma (Luge Relay bronze medalists)	4·25	4·25

373 Janis Cimze

2014. Birth Bicentenary of Janis Cimze (composer).

910	**373**	57c. multicoloured	4·50	4·25

374 Turaida Castle

2014. 800th Anniversary of Turaida Castle.

911	**374**	50c. multicoloured	4·25	4·00

2014. 25th Anniversary of Baltic Chain (human chain from Tallinn to Vilnius). Each black and deep blue.

912	50c. Three demonstrators	4·25	4·25
MS913	78c.×3, Five demonstrators; Three demonstrators; Child and man	24·00	24·00

376 G. F. Stender

2014. 300th Birth Anniversary of Gothards Fridrihs Stender (grammarian and lexicographer, founder of Latvian secular literature).

914	**376**	€1.39 multicoloured	11·00	10·50

377 Ainažu Lighthouse

2014. Lighthouses. Liepaja

915	**377**	71c. multicoloured	6·00	5·80

378 Latvian Academy of Arts

2014. Latvian Architecture. Latvijas Academy of Arts.

916	**378**	€1.42 multicoloured	11·25	11·00

379 Vilhelms Purvītis 1872–1945

2014. Centenary of Latvia Republic. Artists. Multicoloured.

917	57c. Type **379** (painter)	4·50	4·25
918	64c. Pēteris Upītis 1899–1989 (graphic artist)	5·00	4·75
919	78c. Kārlis Zāle 1888–1942 (sculptor)	6·25	6·00

380 Snow-covered Landscape

2014. Christmas. Multicoloured.

920	50c. Type **380**	4·25	4·00
921	85c. Riga under snow (horiz)	6·75	6·50

381 Singing Trees

2014. Singing Trees. Winning Design in Latvia's Pride Stamp Design Competition.

922	**381**	50c. multicoloured	4·25	4·00

382 Emblem

2015. Latvian Presidency of Council of European Union.

923	**382**	64c. deep grey and bright red-brown	5·00	4·75

383 Snowdrops

2015. Flowers. Multicoloured.

924	10c. Type **383**	1·00	90
925	25c. Dahlias	2·50	2·00
926	70c. Lilies	5·50	5·00
927	78c. Marigolds	6·25	6·00
928	€2.13 Sweet Peas	13·10	13·00

384 Latvian Blue Cow

2015. International Green Week Exhibition, Berlin.

929	**384**	50c. multicoloured	4·25	4·00

385 Riga Coat of Arms

2015. Arms - Heraldic Arms. Multicoloured.

930	€1 Type **385**	10·50	10·00
931	€2 Latvia	13·00	12·75
932	€5 As No. 931	16·00	15·75

386 Cityscape

2015. 750th Anniversary of Jelgavai City.

933	**386**	€1.71 multicoloured	12·50	12·00

387 Placoderm Fish Fossils

2015. Unique Exhibits of Latvian Museum of Natural History. 170th Anniversary of Museum of Natural History.

934	**387**	71c. multicoloured	6·00	5·75

388 Sunflower

2015. Flowers. Sunflower

935	**388**	50c. multicoloured	4·25	4·00

389 Dolls

2015. Europa. Old Toys. Multicoloured.

936	78c. Type **389**	6·25	6·00
937	€1.71 Teddy bears	12·50	12·00

390 Members and Building

2015. Bicentenary of Kurzemes Literary Society.

938	**390**	85c. multicoloured	6·75	6·50

391 Parliament and Statue

2015. 25th Anniversary of Independence.

939	**391**	50c. multicoloured	4·25	4·00

392 Pen as Dove

2015. UNESCO World Press Freedom Day.

940	**392**	57c. multicoloured	4·50	4·25

393 Fireman and Appliances

2015. 150th Anniversary of Latvian Fire and Rescue.

941	**393**	€1.42 multicoloured	11·25	11·00

394 *Oriolus oriolus* (Eurasian Golden Oriole)

2015. Birds. Multicoloured.

942	71c. Type **394**	4·25	4·00
943	€1.42 *Pluvialis apricaria* (European Golden Plover) (vert)	11·00	10·50

395 Aries

2015. The Zodiac. Multicoloured.

944	50c. Type **395**	4·25	4·00
945	50c. Cancer	4·25	4·00
946	50c. Libra	4·25	4·00
947	50c. Capricorn	4·25	4·00
948	50c. Taurus	4·25	4·00
949	50c. Leo	4·25	4·00
950	50c. Scorpio	4·25	4·00
951	50c. Aquarius	4·25	4·00
952	50c. Gemini	4·25	4·00
953	50c. Virgo	4·25	4·00
954	50c. Sagittarius	4·25	4·00
955	50c. Pisces	4·25	4·00

395a Rundāle Palace

2015. Latvian Architecture. Rundāle Palace.

955a	**395a**	€1.57 multicoloured	11·75	11·50

396 Salacgrivas Lighthouse

2015. Lighthouses. Salacgrivas.

956	**396**	78c. multicoloured	6·25	

397 Rainis

2015. Birth Centenaries of Elza (poet and playwright) and Jānis (poet, playwright, editor and translator) Pliekšāns (Aspazija and Rainis). Multicoloured.

MS957	50c.×2, Type **397**; Aspazija	10·00	10·00

398 Riflemen Wearing Flowers in Buttonholes

2015. Centenary of Latvian Riflemen.

958	**398**	€1.71 multicoloured	12·50	12·00

399 Janis Fridrihs Baumanis

2015. Centenary of Latvia Republic. Architects. Multicoloured.

959	50c. Type **399**	4·25	4·00
960	64c. Eižens Laube 1880–1967; Konstantins Pekšens 1859–1928; Jānis Alksnis 1869–1939	5·00	4·75
961	€1.39 Marta Stana 1913–1972	11·00	10·50

400 Parcel

2015. Christmas.

962	50c. Type **400**	4·25	4·00
963	85c. Baubles	6·75	6·50

401 Defenders and Flag

2016. 25th Anniversary of January Barricades.

964	**401**	54c. multicoloured	4·40	4·10

402 Alsungas

2016. Coats of Arms. Multicoloured.

965	50c. Type **402**	4·25	10·00
966	57c. Beverinas	4·50	4·25
967	€1.39 Smiltenes	11·00	10·00

403 Bellis

2016. Flowers. Multicoloured.

968	1c. Type **403**	20	10
969	3c. Narcissi	30	25
970	50c. Lily of the Valley	4·25	4·00

404 *Tetrao tetrix*

2016. Latvian Natural History Museum Exhibits. Birds.

971	**404**	€1.71 multicoloured	12·50	12·00

405 Waterlily

2016. Flowers.

972	**405**	50c. multicoloured	4·25	4·00

406 *Temptation* (Kārdināšana)

2016. 150th Birth Anniversary of Janis Rozentāls (artist). Multicoloured.

MS973 50c.×2, Type **406**; Janis Rozentāls		7·50	7·00

407 Emblem

2016. Latvian Floorball World Championship 2016.

974	**407**	64c. multicoloured	5·00	4·75

408 Woodland Creatures and Recycling Symbols

2016. Europa. Think Green. Multicoloured.

975	78c. Type **408**	6·25	6·00
976	78c. Roller painting contaminated landscape green	6·25	6·00

409 *Glaucidium passerinum* (Eurasian Pygmy Owl)

2016. Birds. Multicoloured.

977	71c. Type **409**	6·00	5·75
978	€1.71 *Dendrocopos major* (Great Spotted Woodpecker)	12·50	12·00

410 Victims and '14.06.1941'

2016. 75th Anniversary of Mass Deportations of June 14 1941. Multicoloured.

MS979 50c.×2, Type **410**; Soldiers (Litene massacre)		7·50	7·00

411 Anemones

2016. Flowers.

980	**411**	4c. multicoloured	35	20

412 Building Façade

2016. Latvian Architecture. Vidzeme Concert Hall, Cēsis.

981	**412**	€1.57 multicoloured	11·75	11·50

413 Bicycle Wheel

2016. 125th Birth Anniversary of Gustavs Ērenpreiss (bicycle manufacturer).

982	**413**	50c. multicoloured	4·25	4·00

414 Symbols of Change

2016. 25th Anniversary of Constitution of Latvia.

983	**414**	50c. multicoloured	4·25	4·00

415 Track and Race Cars

2016. 50th Anniversary of Biķernieki Race Track.

984	**415**	57c. multicoloured	4·50	4·25

416 Platform

2016. Latvian Railway History. Krustpils Railway Station.

985	**416**	€1.49 multicoloured	11·50	11·00

417 Flags and UN Building

2016. 25th Anniversary of Latvian Membership of United Nations.

986	**417**	54c. multicoloured	4·25	4·00

418 Andrejs Pumpurs

2016. 175th Birth Anniversary of Andrejs Pumpurs (writer and member of Young Latvia movement).

987	**418**	€1.41 multicoloured	11·25	11·00

419 Ovišu Bāka Lighthouse

2016. Lighthouses. Ovišu Bāka.

988	**419**	90c. multicoloured	6·50	6·25

420 Jānis Pommers

2016. 140th Birth Anniversary of Jānis Pommers (first Latvian Archbishop of the Latvian Orthodox Church).

989	**420**	50c. multicoloured	3·50	3·50

421 *Andreas Weide* (four-masted barquentine)

2016. Historic Ships of the 19th-century.

990	**421**	61c. multicoloured	4·50	4·25

422 Emblem

2016. 25th Baltic Assembly.

991	**422** 50c. multicoloured	3·50	3·50
MS992	80×65 mm. €1.39 As Type **422**	10·50	10·00

423 Diana Dadzite

2016. Latvian Paralympic Gold Medallists. Multicoloured.

MS993 50c.×3, Type **423**; Aigars Apinis; Edgars Bergs		11·50	11·00

424 Janis Lusis, Dianis Kula and Inese Juanzeme (javelin)

2016. Centenary of Latvia Republic. Sports Personalities. Multicoloured.

994	50c. Type **424**	3·50	3·50
995	57c. Uljana Semjonova and Jānis Krūmiņš (basketball)	4·00	4·00
996	€1.42 Sandis Ozoliņš, Sergejs Žoltoks, Helmuts Balderis, Kārlis Skrastiņš and Artūrs Irbe (ice hockey)	10·00	10·00

425 Elf flying Aircraft full of Presents

2016. Christmas. Multicoloured.

997	50c. Type **425**	3·50	3·50
998	78c. Postman holding parcel and rooster	5·50	5·50

426 Bellis

2017. Flowers. Multicoloured.

999	1c. Type **426**	15	10
1000	4c. *Anemone hepatica*	30	25
1001	7c. Tagetes	50	45
1002	10c. Snowdrops	70	65

427 Olaines

2017. Coats of Arms. Multicoloured.

1003	50c. Type **427**	3·50	3·50
1004	57c. Rojas	4·00	4·00
1005	€1.39 Màpils	10·00	9·75

428 *Rosa canina* (19th-century herbarium)

2017. Latvian Museum of Natural History.

1006	**428**	€1.42 multicoloured	10·00	10·00

429 Freesias

2017. Flowers. Freesia.

1007	**429**	64c. multicoloured	4·75	4·50

2017. Europa. Castles. Multicoloured.

1008	78c.	5·50	5·50
1009	€1.71 Bauska Castle	12·50	12·00

431 *Abraham*

2017. Historic Ships of the 19th-century.

1010	**431**	61c. multicoloured	4·50	4·25

432 Family

2017. My Family are Super Heroes.

1011	**432**	50c. multicoloured	3·50	3·50

LEBANON

A territory north of the Holy Land, formerly part of the Turkish Empire, Greater Lebanon was given a separate status under French Mandate in 1920. Until September 1923, the French occupation stamps of Syria were used and these were followed by the joint issue of 1923, Nos. 97 etc., of Syria. Independence was proclaimed in 1941, but the country was not evacuated by French troops until 1946.

100 centimes = 1 piastre; 100 piastres = 1 Lebanese pound.

1924. Stamps of France surch **GRAND LIBAN** and value

		(a) Definitive Stamps		
1	**11**	10c. on 2c. purple	1·90	2·50
2	**18**	25c. on 5c. orange	2·10	2·40
3	**18**	50c. on 10c. green	2·30	2·40
4	**15**	75c. on 15c. green	3·75	5·75
5	**18**	1p. on 20c. brown	3·00	2·10
6	**18**	1.25p. on 25c. blue	7·00	4·50
7	**18**	1.50p. on 30c. orange	4·50	8·25
8	**18**	1.50p. on 30c. red	3·75	8·50
10	**13**	2p. on 40c. red and blue	5·00	3·75
9	**15**	2.50p. on 50c. blue	3·25	3·00
11	**13**	3p. on 60c. violet and blue	11·00	13·50
12	**13**	5p. on 1f. red and yellow	12·00	12·00
13	**13**	10p. on 2f. orange and green	20·00	20·00
14	**13**	25p. on 5f. blue and buff	36·00	60·00
		(b) Pasteur issue.		
15	**30**	50c. on 10c. green	3·25	4·00
16	**30**	1,50p. on 30c. red	4·25	9·50
17	**30**	2,50p. on 50c. blue	2·75	4·25
		(c) Olympic Games issue.		
18	**31**	50c. on 10c. green and light green	41·00	70·00
19	-	1,25p. on 25c. deep red and red	41·00	70·00
20	-	1,50p. on 30c. red and black	41·00	70·00
21	-	2,50p. on 50c. blue	41·00	70·00

1924. Air. Stamps of France surch **Poste par Avion GRAND LIBAN** and value.

22 **13** 2p. on 40c. red and blue 16·00 38·00
23 **13** 3p. on 60c. violet and blue 16·00 38·00
24 **13** 5p. on 1f. red and yellow 16·00 23·00
25 **13** 10p. on 2f. orange and green 18·00 35·00

1924. Stamps of France surch **Grand Liban** (T **13**) or **Gd Liban** (others) and value in French and Arabic. (a) Definitive stamps.

26 **11** 0p.10 on 2c. purple 1·30 1·50
27 **18** 0p.25 on 5c. orange 1·60 1·50
28 **18** 0p.50 on 10c. green 3·25 3·50
29 **15** 0p.75 on 15c. green 2·00 4·25
30 **18** 1p. on 20c. brown 1·90 1·40
31 **18** 1p.25 on 25c. blue 3·50 5·00
32 **18** 1p.50 on 30c. red 2·75 2·75
33 **18** 1p.50 on 30c. orange 85·00 85·00
34 **18** 2p. on 35c. violet 3·00 8·50
35 **13** 2p. on 40c. red and blue 4·25 2·40
36 **13** 2p. on 45c. green and blue 29·00 40·00
37 **13** 3p. on 60c. violet and blue 3·50 3·75
38 **15** 3p. on 60c. violet 3·75 10·00
39 **15** 4p. on 85c. red 3·25 4·00
40 **13** 5p. on 1f. red and yellow 5·25 5·00
41 **13** 10p. on 2f. orange and green 11·50 18·00
42 **13** 25p. on 5f. blue and buff 19·00 34·00

(b) Pasteur issue.

43 **30** 0p.50 on 10c. green 1·40 1·30
44 **30** 0p.75 on 15c. green 3·25 8·75
45 **30** 1p.50 on 30c. red 3·00 1·50
46 **30** 2p. on 45c. red 6·25 8·75
47 **30** 2p.50 on 50c. blue 2·50 1·40
48 **30** 4p. on 75c. blue 4·00 4·75

(c) Olympic Games issue.

49 **31** 0p.50 on 10c. green and light green 41·00 65·00
50 - 1p.25 on 25c. deep red and red 41·00 65·00
51 - 1p.50 on 30c. red and black 41·00 65·00
52 - 2p.50 on 50c. ultramarine and blue 41·00 65·00

(d) Ronsard issue.

53 **35** 4p. on 75c. blue on bluish 3·75 10·50

1924. Air. Stamps of France surch **Gd Liban Avion** and value in French and Arabic.

54 **13** 2p. on 40c. red and blue 12·00 35·00
55 **13** 3p. on 60c. violet and blue 12·00 35·00
56 **13** 5p. on 1f. red and yellow 12·00 35·00
57 **13** 10p. on 2f. orange and green 15·00 38·00

5 Cedar of Lebanon **6** Beirut

1925. Views.

58 **5** 0p.10c. violet 90 1·60
59 **6** 0p.25c. black 1·20 2·30
60 - 0p.50c. green (Tripoli) 1·60 1·40
61 - 0p.75c. red (Beit ed-Din) 2·00 4·00
62 - 1p. purple (Baalbek ruins) 2·75 1·20
63 - 1p.25 green (Mouktara) 3·75 4·00
64 - 1p.50 pink (Tyre) 2·50 70
65 - 2p. brown (Zahle) 3·25 1·30
66 - 2p.50 blue (Baalbek) 2·75 1·70
67 - 3p. brown (Deir el-Kamar) 3·50 1·70
68 - 5p. violet (Sidon) 7·00 7·25
69 **7** 10p. purple 9·25 6·50
70 - 25p. blue (Beirut) 16·00 28·00

7 Tripoli

1925. Air. Nos. 65 and 67/69 optd **AVION** in French and Arabic.

71 - 2p. brown 5·75 11·50
72 - 3p. brown 5·75 11·50
73 - 5p. violet 5·75 11·50
74 **7** 10p. purple 5·75 11·50

1926. Air. Nos. 65 and 67/69 optd with Bleriot XI aircraft.

75 - 2p. brown 5·75 14·50
76 - 3p. brown 5·75 14·50
77 - 5p. violet 5·75 14·50
78 **7** 10p. purple 5·75 14·50

1926. War Refugee Charity. Various stamps surch **Secours aux Refugies Afft** and premium in French and Arabic. (a) Postage. Stamps of 1925.

79 **6** 0p.25+0p.25 black 3·25 7·00
80 - 0p.50+0p.25 green 3·75 14·00
81 - 0p.75+0p.25 red 3·00 11·00
82 - 1p.+0p.50 purple 4·25 13·50
83 - 1p.25+0p.50 green 4·50 17·00
84 - 1p.50+0p.50 pink 5·75 14·00
85 - 2p.+0p.75 brown 5·50 13·00
86 - 2p.50+0p.75 blue 4·75 20·00
87 - 3p.+1p. brown 5·25 19·00
88 - 5p.+1p. violet 7·50 22·00
89 **7** 10p.+2p. purple 7·50 28·00
90 - 25p.+5p. blue 7·25 34·00

(b) Air. Nos. 75/78 surch.

91 2p.+1p. brown 10·00 17·00
92 3p.+2p. brown 10·00 17·00
93 5p.+3p. violet 10·00 17·00
94 **7** 10p.+5p. purple 10·00 17·00

1926. Stamps of 1925 surch in English and Arabic.

95 - 3p.50 on 0p.75 red 3·25 3·75
97b **6** 4p. on 0p.25 black 50·00 50·00
98 - 4p.50 on 0p.75 red 4·50 3·75
99 - 6p. on 2p.50 blue 4·00 4·00
100 - 7p.50 on 2p.50 blue 3·75 4·00
101 - 12p. on 1p.25 green 3·00 4·25
102 - 15p. on 25p. blue 5·00 4·50
103 - 20p. on 1p.25 green 10·00 19·00

1927. Stamps of 1925 and provisional stamps of Lebanon optd **Republique Libanaise**.

104 **5** 0p.10 violet 70 1·80
105 - 0p.50 green 1·20 65
106 - 1p. purple 65 45
107 - 1p.50 pink 2·00 1·70
108 - 2p. brown 3·75 2·00
109 - 3p. brown 1·80 65
110 **6** 4p. on 0p.25 black (No. 97b) 1·90 65
111 - 4p.50 on 0p.75 red (No. 98) 1·60 90
112 - 5p. violet 3·75 4·25
113 - 7p.50 on 2p.50 bl (No. 100) 2·30 80
114 **7** 10p. purple 4·50 4·50
115 - 15p. on 25p. blue (No. 102) 11·00 7·50
117 - 25p. blue 14·00 42·00

1927. Air. Nos. 75/78 optd **Republique Libanaise**.

118 - 2p. brown 7·00 14·50
119 - 3p. brown 7·00 14·50
120 - 5p. violet 7·00 14·50
121 **7** 10p. purple 7·00 14·50

1928. Nos. 104/117 optd with T **10** or surch also.

145 **5** 05 on 0p.10 violet 50 1·20
124 **5** 0p.10 violet 80 90
125 - 0p.50 green 2·75 2·30
146 - 0p.50 on 0p.75 red 1·90 1·70
126 - 1p. purple 1·60 1·10
127 - 1p.50 pink 3·50 3·50
128 - 2p. brown 5·75 13·00
147 - 2p. on 1p.25 green 2·00 1·50
129 - 3p. brown 3·25 1·80
148 **6** 4p. on 0p.25 black 3·50 1·10
131 - 4p.50 on 0p.75 red 3·00 3·00
132a - 5p. violet 3·50 9·00
149 - 7p.50 on 2p.50 blue 3·00 1·80
134 **7** 10p. purple 11·00 10·50
123 - 15p. on 25p. blue 14·00 38·00
136 - 25p. blue 14·50 19·00

1928. Air. Optd or surch with aircraft, **Republique Libanaise** and line of Arabic as T **10**.

151 - 0p.50 green 1·30 5·00
152 - 0p.50 on 0p.75 red (No. 146) 1·70 2·75
153 - 1p. purple 2·50 3·75
141 - 2p. brown 5·25 8·00
154 - 2p. on 1p.25 grn (No. 147) 2·50 3·25
142 - 3p. brown 3·50 4·50
143 - 5p. violet 5·25 6·50
144 **7** 10p. purple 5·25 6·25
155 - 15p. on 25p. blue (No. 123) £275 £275
156 - 25p. blue £225 £225

14 Silkworm Larva, Cocoon and Moth

1930. Silk Congress.

157 **14** 4p. sepia 19·00 23·00
158 **14** 4½p. red 19·00 23·00
159 **14** 7½p. blue 19·00 23·00
160 **14** 10p. violet 19·00 23·00
161 **14** 15p. green 19·00 23·00
162 **14** 25p. purple 19·00 23·00

15 Cedars of Lebanon

16a Baalbek

1930. Views.

163b - 0p.10 orange (Beirut) 2·30 1·70
164 **15** 0p.20 brown 1·20 2·30
165 - 0p.25 blue (Baalbek) 75 2·10
166 - 0p.50 brown (Bickfaya) 2·50 1·50
166b - 0p.75 brown (Baalbek) 3·75 3·00
167 - 1p. green (Saida) 5·50 1·10
167a - 1p. purple (Saida) 8·25 70
168 - 1p.50 purple (Beit ed-Din) 4·50 2·40
168a - 1p.50 green (Beit ed-Din) 10·50 1·10
169 - 2p. blue (Tripoli) 6·50 1·70
170 - 3p. sepia (Baalbek) 7·75 1·70
171 - 4p. brown (Nahr-el-Kalb) 7·75 1·70
172 - 4p.50 red (Beaufort) 6·50 1·70
173 - 5p. green (Beit ed-Din) 3·50 1·50
251 - 5p. blue (Nahr el-Kalb) 3·50 1·00
174 - 6p. purple (Tyre) 9·25 2·75
175 **16a** 7p.50 blue 6·75 1·70
176 - 10p. green (Hasbaya) 11·00 1·90
177 - 15p. purple (Afka Falls) 13·00 3·75
178 - 25p. green (Beirut) 16·00 6·00
179 - 50p. green (Deir el-Kamar) 60·00 20·00
180 - 100p. black (Baalbek) 60·00 26·00

17 Jebeil (Byblos)

1930. Air. Potez 29-4 biplane and views as T **17**.

181 0p.50 purple (Rachaya) 1·80 2·00
182 1p. green (Broumana) 1·10 1·60
183 2p. orange (Baalbek) 2·50 2·50
184 3p. red (Hasroun) 2·50 2·75
185 5p. green (Byblos) 2·50 2·75
186 10p. red (Kadisha) 3·75 3·25
187 15p. brown (Beirut) 3·75 3·25
188 25p. violet (Tripoli) 5·75 5·25
189 50p. lake (Kabelais) 10·00 8·25
190 100p. brown (Zahle) 15·00 15·00

18 Skiing

1936. Air. Tourist Propaganda.

191 **18** 0p.50 green 3·50 3·75
192 - 1p. orange 4·50 5·25
193 **18** 2p. violet 4·50 5·25
194 - 3p. green 4·50 5·25
195 **18** 5p. red 6·00 5·75
196 - 10p. brown 6·50 7·25
197 - 15p. red 55·00 55·00
198 **18** 25p. green £160 £160

Design: 1, 3, 10, 15p. Jounieh Bay.

20 Cedar of Lebanon

21 President Edde

22 Lebanese Landscape

1937

199 **20** 0p.10 red 55 35
200 **20** 0p.20 blue 1·00 5·50
201 **20** 0p.25 lilac 75 5·25
202 **20** 0p.50 mauve 65 35
203 **20** 0p.75 brown 80 1·70
204 **21** 3p. violet 5·00 1·90
205 **21** 4p. brown 3·00 60
206 **21** 4p.50 red 2·75 85
207 **22** 10p. red 3·75 95
208 **22** 12½p. blue 2·10 55
209 **22** 15p. green 5·00 1·10
210 **22** 20p. brown 2·50 95
211 **22** 25p. red 7·50 90
212 **22** 50p. violet 12·50 3·25
213 **22** 100p. sepia 17·00 5·50

23 Exhibition Pavilion, Paris

1937. Air. Paris International Exhibition.

218 **23** 0p.50 black 2·20 3·25
219 **23** 1p. green 2·20 3·25
220 **23** 2p. brown 2·20 3·25
221 **23** 3p. green 2·20 3·25
222 **23** 5p. green 2·20 3·25
223 **23** 10p. red 11·50 23·00
224 **23** 15p. purple 10·50 27·00
225 **23** 25p. brown 18·00 42·00

25 Ruins of Baalbek

1937. Air.

226 - 0p.50 blue 40 40
227 - 1p. red 2·00 2·30
228 - 2p. sepia 2·40 2·75
229 - 3p. red 6·00 5·00
230 - 5p. green 2·75 2·30
231 **25** 10p. violet 2·30 85
232 - 15p. blue 2·75 3·50
233 - 25p. violet 7·25 6·50
234 - 50p. green 14·00 7·25
235 - 100p. brown 7·50 7·25

Design: 0p.50 to 5p. Beit ed-Din.

1938. Nos. 207/208 surch in English and Arabic figures.

236 **21** 2p. on 3p. violet 2·00 1·10
237 **21** 2½p. on 4p. brown 3·00 75

27 Medical College, Beirut

1938. Air. Medical Congress.

238 **27** 2p. green 3·75 7·75
239 **27** 3p. orange 4·25 5·00
240 **27** 5p. violet 6·50 11·00
241 **27** 10p. red 13·00 23·00

28 Maurice Nogues and Liore et Olivier LeO H.24-3 Flying Boat over Beirut

1938. Air. Tenth Anniversary of First Air Service between France and Lebanon.

242 **28** 10p. purple 7·50 14·50
MS242a 161×120 mm. No. 242 in block of four 70·00 75·00

16a Baalbek

1938. Surch.

243 **16a** 6p. on 7p.50 blue 3·75 3·00
244 - 7p.50 on 50p. grn (No. 179) 3·75 4·00
245 - 7p.50 on 100p. blk (No. 180) 3·25 3·75
246 **22** 12p.50 on 7p.50 blue 6·50 4·50
247 **22** 12½p. on 7p.50 blue 3·25 1·10

1939. As T **16a**, but with differing figures and Arabic inscriptions in side panels, and imprint at foot 'IMP. CATHOLIQUE-BEYROUTH-LIBAN' instead of 'HELIO VAUGIRARD'.

248 1p. green 1·80 85
249 1p.50 purple 2·40 1·50
250 7p.50 red 2·75 1·60

Design: 1p. to 7p.50, Beit ed-Din.

32 Emir Bechir Chehab

1942. First Anniversary of Proclamation of Independence.

252	**32**	0p.50 green (postage)	4·25	3·75
253	**32**	1p.50 purple	4·25	3·75
254	**32**	6p. red	4·25	3·75
255	**32**	15p. blue	4·25	3·75
256	-	10p. purple (air)	7·25	6·50
257	-	50p. green	7·75	7·25

Design: 10, 50p. Aircraft over mountains.

1943. Surch in English and Arabic and with old values cancelled with ornaments.

258	**21**	2p. on 4p. brown	8·50	7·75
259	-	6p. on 7p.50 red (No. 250)	3·00	1·70
260	**22**	10p. on 12½p. blue	2·75	1·30
261	-	2p. on 5p. blue (No. 251)	1·70	95
262	-	3p. on 5p. blue (No. 251)	1·70	95
263	**22**	6p. on 12½p. blue	2·50	1·70
264	**22**	7½p. on 12½p. blue	2·75	2·30

37 Parliament House

38 Bechamoun

1944. Second Anniversary of Proclamation of Independence.

265	**37**	25p. red (postage)	13·00	12·00
266	-	50p. blue	13·00	12·00
267	**37**	150p. blue	13·00	12·00
268	-	200p. purple	13·00	12·00

Design: 50p., 200p. Government House.

269	**38**	25p. green (air)	5·25	3·00
270	**38**	50p. orange	5·25	3·00
271	-	100p. brown	5·25	4·25
272	-	200p. violet	6·50	4·25
273	-	300p. green	22·00	20·00
274	-	500p. brown	60·00	38·00

Designs: 100p., 200p. Rachaya Citadel; 300p., 500p. Beirut.

38a Beirut Isolation Hospital **(39)**

1944. Sixth Medical Congress. Optd with T **39**.

275	**38a**	10p. red (postage)	8·50	7·75
276	**38a**	20p. blue	9·75	9·00
277	-	20p. orange (air)	4·25	3·75
278	-	50p. blue	5·50	5·00
279	-	100p. purple	7·25	6·50

Design: Nos. 277/279, Bhannes Sanatorium.

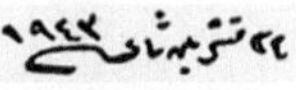

40 Trans Nov. 23, 1943

1944. First Anniversary of President's Return to Office. Nos. 265/274 optd with T **40**.

280	**37**	25p. red (postage)	22·00	20·00
281	-	50p. blue	22·00	20·00
282	**37**	150p. blue	22·00	20·00
283	-	200p. purple	22·00	20·00
284	**38**	25p. green (air)	11·00	10·00
285	-	50p. orange	18·00	17·00
286	-	100p. brown	23·00	22·00
287	-	200p. violet	36·00	34·00
288	-	300p. green	49·00	46·00
289	-	500p. brown	85·00	80·00

41 Crusader Castle, Byblos

42 Falls of R. Litani

1945

397	**41**	7p.50 red (postage)	4·50	25
398	**41**	10p. purple	6·50	40
399	**41**	12p.50 blue	16·00	40
290	**41**	15p. brown	6·50	5·75
291	**41**	20p. green	7·75	5·75
292	-	25p. blue	7·75	5·75
400	**41**	25p. violet	30·00	90
293	-	50p. red	9·00	5·75
401	**41**	50p. green	65·00	7·25
294	**42**	25p. brown (air)	4·25	2·75
295	**42**	50p. purple	7·25	4·50
296	-	200p. violet	21·00	7·25
297	-	300p. black	36·00	14·50

Designs: Horiz—Nos. 292/293, Crusader Castle, Tripoli; 296/297, Cedar of Lebanon and skier.

43 V(ictory) and National Flag

1946. Victory. 'V' in design. (a) Postage.

298	**43**	7p.50 brown, red and pink	1·00	10
299	**43**	10p. purple, pink and red	1·60	10
300	**43**	12p.50 purple, blue and red	2·30	20
301	**43**	15p. green, emerald and red	4·00	25
302	**43**	20p. myrtle, green and red	3·50	25
303	**43**	25p. blue, light blue and red	5·25	50
304	**43**	50p. blue, violet and red	8·50	2·75
305	**43**	100p. black, blue and red	14·50	5·00

44 V(ictory) and Lebanese Soldiers at Bir-Hakeim

(b) Air.

306	**44**	15p. blue, yellow and red	90	25
307	**44**	20p. red and blue	1·00	60
308	**44**	25p. blue, yellow and red	1·30	60
309	**44**	50p. black, violet and red	2·50	60
310	**44**	100p. violet and red	6·50	1·80
311	**44**	150p. brown and red	7·75	3·00
MS311a		142×230 mm. Nos. 298/311. Colours changed. Text in brown (with gum) or blue (without gum)	£160	£140

1946. As T **43** but without 'V' sign.

312		7p.50 lake, red and mauve	2·50	25
313		10p. violet, mauve and red	4·00	25
314		12p.50 brown, green and red	5·25	30
315		15p. brown, pink and red	6·50	35
316		20p. blue, orange and red	7·75	35
317		25p. myrtle, green and red	10·50	50
318		50p. blue, light blue and red	16·00	2·20
319		100p. black, blue and red	26·00	5·25

45 Grey Herons

1946

320	**45**	12p.50 red (postage)	46·00	4·75
321	**45**	10p. orange (air)	10·50	1·40
322	**45**	25p. blue	13·00	70
323	**45**	50p. green	29·00	2·00
324	**45**	100p. purple	50·00	9·00

46 Cedar of Lebanon

1946

325	**46**	0p.50 brown	90	25
326	**46**	1p. purple	1·70	25
327	**46**	2p.50 violet	5·25	25
328	**46**	5p. red	5·75	25
329	**46**	6p. grey	5·75	25

47

1946. Air. Arab Postal Congress.

330	**47**	25p. blue	2·00	85
331	**47**	50p. green	2·50	1·30
332	**47**	75p. red	4·50	2·20
333	**47**	150p. violet	9·00	3·75

48 Cedar of Lebanon

1947

333a	**48**	0p.50 brown	2·10	25
333b	**48**	2p.50 green	2·75	25
333c	**48**	5p. red	5·25	50

49 President, Bridge and Tablet

1947. Air. Evacuation of Foreign Troops from Lebanon.

334	**49**	25p. blue	2·50	1·20
335	**49**	50p. red	4·50	1·80
336	**49**	75p. black	7·75	3·50
337	**49**	150p. green	13·00	6·00

50 Crusader Castle, Tripoli

51 Jounieh Bay

1947

338	**50**	12p.50 red (postage)	13·00	65
339	**50**	25p. blue	16·00	65
340	**50**	50p. green	50·00	1·40
341	**50**	100p. violet	65·00	10·50
342	**51**	5p. green (air)	80	25
343	**51**	10p. mauve	90	25
344	**51**	15p. red	1·60	25
403	**51**	15p. green	14·50	2·00
345	**51**	20p. orange	2·50	25
345a	**51**	20p. red	2·75	50
346	**51**	25p. blue	3·25	25
347	**51**	50p. red	7·25	65
348	**51**	100p. purple	16·00	1·00
349	-	150p. purple	30·00	2·20
350	-	200p. slate	31·00	10·50
351	-	300p. black	60·00	23·00

Design: 150p. to 300p. Grand Serail Palace.

54 Phoenician Galley

1947. Air. 12th Congress of UPU, Paris.

352	-	10p. blue	2·00	90
353	-	15p. red	2·50	1·60
354	-	25p. blue	4·25	1·80
355	**54**	50p. green	9·00	2·50
356	-	75p. violet	9·75	4·00
357	-	100p. brown	13·00	6·75

Design: Vert—10p. to 25p. Posthorn.

55 Faraya Bridge and Statue

1947. Air. Red Cross Fund. Cross in red.

358	**55**	12p.50+25p. green	12·50	9·00
359	**55**	25p.+50p. blue	16·00	10·50
360	-	50p.+100p. brown	21·00	13·00
361	-	75p.+150p. violet	43·00	26·00
362	-	100p.+200p. grey	80·00	46·00

Design: 50p. to 100p. Djounie Bay and statue.

56 Cedar of Lebanon

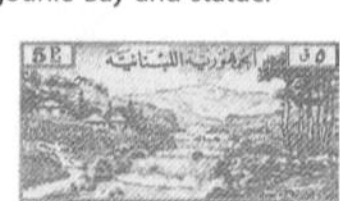

58 Lebanese Landscape

1948

363	**56**	0p.50 blue (postage)	40	15
364	**56**	1p. brown	90	20
395	**56**	1p. orange	2·00	15
365	**56**	2p.50 mauve	1·30	20
366	**56**	3p. green	3·00	25
367	**56**	5p. red	4·00	25
368	-	7p.50 red	9·75	40
369	-	10p. purple	7·00	50
370	-	12p.50 blue	16·00	50
371	-	25p. blue	23·00	1·30
372	-	50p. green	49·00	9·00
373	**58**	5p. red (air)	1·30	25
374	**58**	10p. mauve	2·00	25
375	**58**	15p. brown	5·00	25
376	**58**	20p. slate	7·50	35
377	**58**	25p. blue	13·00	1·80
378	**58**	50p. black	26·00	2·50

Design: As T **58**—Nos. 368/372, Zebaide Aqueduct.

59 Europa on Bull

1948. Third Meeting of UNESCO, Beirut.

379	**59**	10p. orange and red (postage)	4·00	2·30
380	**59**	12p.50 mauve and violet	5·25	3·50
381	**59**	25p. green and light green	5·75	3·50
382	-	30p. buff and brown	7·75	4·25
383	-	40p. green and turquoise	11·50	4·25

Design: Vert—30, 40p. Avicenna (philosopher and scientist).

61 Apollo on Sun Chariot

384	**61**	7p.50 blue & lt blue (air)	3·25	2·30
385	**61**	15p. black and grey	4·00	2·30
386	**61**	20p. brown and pink	6·50	3·50
387	-	35p. red	11·00	4·50
388	-	75p. green	23·00	10·50
MS388a		142×205 mm. Nos. 379/388. Imperf. No gum	£425	£425

Design: Horiz—35, 75p. Symbolic figure.

63 Camel

64 Sikorsky S-51 Helicopter

1949. 75th Anniversary of UPU.

389	**63**	5p. violet (postage)	2·20	1·40
390	**63**	7p.50 red	3·00	2·50
391	**63**	12p.50 blue	5·25	3·00
392	**64**	25p. blue (air)	11·00	5·00
393	**64**	50p. green	17·00	7·75
MS393a		135×190 mm. Nos. 389/393. Imperf (sold at 150p.)	£110	£110

65 Cedar of Lebanon

66 Nahr el-Kalb Bridge

1950

407	**65**	0p.50 red	65	25
408	**65**	1p. red	1·60	25
409	**65**	2p.50 violet	2·20	25
410	**65**	5p. purple	4·25	25
411	**66**	7p.50 red	5·25	25
412	**66**	10p. lilac	6·50	25
413	**66**	12p.50 blue	9·75	40
414	**66**	25p. blue	18·00	1·70
415	**66**	50p. green	49·00	9·00

67 Congressional Flags

1950. Lebanese Emigrants' Congress. Inscr 'MOIS DES EMIGRES–ETE 1950'.

416	**67**	7p.50 green (postage)	1·60	40
417	**67**	12p. mauve	2·00	40
418	-	5p. blue (air)	4·25	90
419	-	15p. violet	5·50	1·30
420	-	25p. brown	3·25	1·30
421	-	35p. green	5·50	2·30
MS421a		134×184 mm. Nos. 416/21. Imperf. No gum	£130	£130

Designs: 5, 15p. House martins; 25, 35p. President Bishara al-Khoury and building.

70 Crusader Castle, Sidon

1950. Air.

422	**70**	10p. brown	1·30	25
423	**70**	15p. green	2·00	25
424	**70**	20p. red	5·25	65
425	**70**	25p. blue	9·00	1·60
426	**70**	50p. grey	16·00	4·00

1950. Surch with figures and bars.

427	**56**	1p. on 3p. green	90	40
428	**46**	2p.50 on 6p. grey	1·30	40

73 Cedar of Lebanon **74** Nahr el-Kalb Bridge

75 Crusader Castle, Sidon

1951

429	**73**	0p.50 red (postage)	65	15
430	**73**	1p. brown	1·20	15
431	**73**	2p.50 grey	5·25	15
432	**73**	5p. purple	5·75	15
433	**74**	7p.50 red	6·75	50
434	**74**	10p. purple	9·00	40
435	**74**	12p.50 turquoise	16·00	65
436	**74**	25p. blue	23·00	2·30
437	**74**	50p. green	49·00	12·50
438	**75**	10p. turquoise (air)	1·80	25
439	**75**	15p. brown	4·00	25
440	**75**	20p. red	4·00	40
441	**75**	25p. blue	4·25	40
442	**75**	35p. mauve	9·75	4·50
443	**75**	50p. blue	18·00	3·50

T **74** is similar to T **66** but left value tablets differ.
For design as T **74** but inscr 'LIBAN', see Nos. 561/563.

76 Cedar of Lebanon **77** Baalbek

1952

444	**76**	0p.50 green (postage)	1·30	15
445	**76**	1p. brown	1·30	15
446	**76**	2p.50 blue	2·00	40
447	**76**	5p. red	3·25	40
448	**77**	7p.50 red	4·50	80
449	**77**	10p. violet	9·00	90
450	**77**	12p.50 blue	9·00	90
451	**77**	25p. blue	11·00	2·30
452	-	50p. green	33·00	4·25
453	-	100p. brown	70·00	13·00
454	-	5p. red (air)	50	15
455	-	10p. grey	80	25
456	-	15p. mauve	1·40	25
457	-	20p. orange	2·30	50
458	-	25p. blue	2·30	65
459	-	35p. blue	4·00	80
460	-	50p. green	13·00	90
461	-	100p. blue	90·00	4·00
462	-	200p. green	50·00	7·25
463	-	300p. sepia	70·00	16·00

Designs: As T **77**—Nos. 452/453, Beaufort Castle; 454/459, Beirut Airport; 460/463, Amphitheatre, Byblos.

78 Cedar of Lebanon **79** General Post Office **80** Douglas DC-4

1953

559	**78**	0p.50 blue (postage)	50	20
465	**78**	1p. red	1·70	15
466	**78**	2p.50 violet	2·10	40
560	**78**	2p.50 purple	1·20	20
467	**78**	5p. green	3·25	40
468	**79**	7p.50 red	5·25	65
469	**79**	10p. green	6·00	90
470	**79**	12p.50 turquoise	8·50	1·00
471	**79**	25p. blue	12·50	2·10
472	**79**	50p. brown	22·00	4·75
473	**80**	5p. green (air)	65	15
474	**80**	10p. red	1·30	15
475	**80**	15p. red	1·80	15
476	**80**	20p. turquoise	2·50	15
477	**80**	25p. blue	6·50	25
478	**80**	35p. brown	9·50	40
479	**80**	50p. blue	12·50	80
480	**80**	100p. sepia	23·00	7·75

For 20p. green as T **79** see No. 636.

81 Cedar of Lebanon **82** Beit ed-Din Palace **83** Baalbek

1954

481	**81**	0p.50 blue (postage)	40	25
482	**81**	1p. orange	65	25
483	**81**	2p.50 violet	1·00	40
484	**81**	5p. green	2·10	40
485	**82**	7p.50 red	3·50	80
486	**82**	10p. green	5·25	80
487	**82**	12p.50 blue	8·50	1·00
488	**82**	25p. deep blue	11·50	4·25
489	**82**	50p. turquoise	21·00	7·25
490	**82**	100p. sepia	50·00	14·50
491	**83**	5p. green (air)	65	15
492	**83**	10p. lilac	1·30	15
493	**83**	15p. red	1·40	15
494	**83**	20p. brown	2·10	15
495	**83**	25p. blue	2·30	40
496	**83**	35p. sepia	3·25	40
497	-	50p. green	10·50	65
498	-	100p. red	17·00	1·00
499	-	200p. sepia	34·00	3·50
500	-	300p. blue	60·00	7·25

Design: As T **83**—50p. to 300p. Litani Irrigation Canal.
For other values as Nos. 497/500, see Nos. 564/567.

84 Khalde Airport, Beirut

1954. Air. Opening of Beirut International Airport.

501	**84**	10p. red and pink	1·30	40
502	**84**	25p. blue and ultramarine	2·50	65
503	**84**	35p. brown and sepia	4·00	1·20
504	**84**	65p. green and turquoise	9·00	4·50

84a

1955. Arab Postal Union.

505	**84a**	12p.50 green (postage)	1·30	65
506	**84a**	25p. violet	2·00	65
507	**84a**	2p.50 brown (air)	1·30	50

85 Rotary Emblem

1955. Air. 50th Anniversary of Rotary International.

508	**85**	35p. green	2·00	1·30
509	**85**	65p. blue	3·25	2·00

86 Cedar of Lebanon **87** Jeita Grotto **88** Skiers

1955

510	**86**	0p.50 blue (postage)	50	25
511	**86**	1p. red	65	25
512	**86**	2p.50 violet	1·00	25
552	**86**	2p.50 blue	11·00	25
513	**86**	5p. green	1·70	25
514	**87**	7p.50 orange	2·30	25
515	**87**	10p. green	3·25	25
516	**87**	12p.50 blue	3·75	25
517	**87**	25p. blue	8·50	50
518	**87**	50p. green	13·00	1·30
519	**88**	5p. turquoise (air)	90	65
520	**88**	15p. red	1·60	40
521	**88**	20p. violet	2·50	40
522	**88**	25p. blue	5·25	50
523	**88**	35p. brown	7·75	90
524	**88**	50p. brown	14·50	1·30
525	**88**	65p. blue	26·00	4·25

The face value on No. 510 reads 0.50 PIASTRE; on No. 512 the '2' and '50' are different sizes and the 1 and 5p. have no dash under 'P'.
For other colours and new values as T **88** see Nos. 568/570 and for redrawn T **86** see Nos. 582/585, 686 and 695/697.

89 Visitor from Abroad

1955. Air. Tourist Propaganda.

526	**89**	2p.50 slate and purple	25	15
527	**89**	12p.50 blue & ultramarine	65	40
528	**89**	25p. blue and indigo	1·60	65
529	**89**	35p. blue and green	2·10	90
MS529a 159×110 mm. Nos. 526/529. Imperf			36·00	34·00

90 Cedar of Lebanon **91** Globe and Columns

92 Oranges

1955

530	**90**	0.50p. blue (postage)	25	15
531	**90**	1p. orange	50	15
532	**90**	2p.50 violet	90	15
533	**90**	5p. green	1·30	15
534	**91**	7p.50 red and orange	2·00	15
535	**91**	10p. green and brown	2·20	20
536	**91**	12p.50 blue and green	2·50	20
537	**91**	25p. blue and mauve	4·00	35
538	**91**	50p. green and blue	5·75	65
539	**91**	100p. brown and orange	8·50	1·60
540	**92**	5p. yellow and green (air)	65	20
541	**92**	10p. orange and green	1·30	20
542	**92**	15p. orange and green	1·60	20
543	**92**	20p. orange and brown	2·00	20
544	-	25p. violet and blue	2·75	25
545	-	35p. purple and green	4·75	40
546	-	50p. yellow and black	5·25	45
547	-	65p. yellow and green	9·75	50
548	-	100p. orange and green	13·00	1·40
549	-	200p. red and green	26·00	7·25

Designs: Vert—25p. to 50p. Grapes. Horiz—4p. to 200p. Quinces.

93 UN Emblem

1956. Air. Tenth Anniversary of UN.

550	**93**	35p. blue	7·25	5·75
551	**93**	65p. green	9·75	7·25
MS551a 90×70 mm. Nos. 550/551. Imperf			£130	£130

94 Masks, Columns and Gargoyle

1956. Air. Baalbek International Drama Festival. Inscr 'FESTIVAL INTERNATIONAL DE BAALBECK'.

553	**94**	2p.50 sepia	65	25
554	**94**	10p. green	90	40
555	-	12p.50 blue	1·00	65
556	-	25p. violet	1·60	80
557	-	35p. purple	3·50	1·30
558	-	65p. slate	5·50	2·75

Designs: Horiz—12p.50, 25p. Temple ruins at Baalbek. Vert—35p., 65p. Double bass, masks and columns.

1957. As earlier designs but redrawn. (a) Postage. As T **74** but inscr 'LIBAN'.

561		7p.50 red	2·20	20
562		10p. brown	3·00	20
563		12p.50 blue	3·75	20

(b) Air. Arabic inscription changed. New values and colours.

564	-	10p. violet	65	20
565	-	15p. orange	90	20
566	-	20p. green	1·30	25
567	-	25p. blue	1·70	25
568	**88**	35p. green	4·00	40
569	**88**	65p. purple	7·25	1·00
570	**88**	100p. brown	11·00	2·20

Design: 10p. to 25p. As Nos. 497/500.

95 President Chamoun and King Faisal II of Iraq

1957. Air. Arab Leaders' Conference, Beirut.

571	**95**	15p. orange	1·30	65
572	-	15p. blue	1·30	65
573	-	15p. maroon	1·30	65
574	-	15p. purple	1·30	65
575	-	15p. green	1·30	65
576	-	25p. turquoise	2·00	70
577	-	100p. brown	9·00	4·25
MS577a 106×151 mm. Nos. 571/6. Imperf			£120	£100

Designs: As T **95**—15p. values show President Chamoun and: King Hussein of Jordan (No. 572), Abdallah Khalil of Sudan (No. 573), President Shukri Bey al-Quwatli of Syria (No. 574) and King Saud of Saudi Arabia (No. 575); 25p. Map and President Chamoun. 44×44 mm (Diamond shape)—100p. The six Arab Leaders.

97 Runners

1957. Second Pan-Arabian Games, Beirut.

578	**97**	2p.50 sepia (postage)	1·20	65
579	-	12p.50 blue	1·70	90
580	-	35p. purple (air)	4·50	1·80
581	-	50p. green	5·50	2·50
MS581a 132×185 mm. Nos. 576/581. Imperf. No gum			£170	£160

Designs: Vert—12p.50, Footballers. Horiz—35p. Fencers; 50p. Stadium.

98 Miners

1957

582	**86**	0p.50 blue (16½×20½ mm) (postage)	50	20
582a	**86**	0p.50 violet (17×21½ mm)	40	20
583	**86**	1p. brown (16½×20½ mm)	65	20
583a	**86**	1p. purple (17×21½ mm)	50	20
584	**86**	2p.50 violet (16½×20½ mm)	90	20
584a	**86**	2p.50 blue (17×21¼ mm)	80	20
585	**86**	5p. green (16½×20½ mm)	1·30	20

586	**98**	7½p. pink	1·60	20
587	**98**	10p. brown	2·10	25
588	**98**	12½p. blue	2·75	25
589	-	25p. blue	3·25	35
590	-	50p. green	5·25	50
591	-	100p. brown	9·00	1·60
592	-	5p. green (air)	40	15
593	-	10p. orange	45	15
594	-	15p. brown	60	15
595	-	20p. purple	90	20
596	-	25p. blue	1·20	25
597	-	35p. purple	1·80	50
598	-	50p. green	3·00	80
599	-	65p. brown	5·00	85
600	-	100p. grey	6·50	2·20

Designs: Postage As T **86**—50c. inscr '0 P.50', 2p.50, Figures in uniform size; 1p., 5p. Short dash under 'P'. As T **98** Vert—25p. to 100p. Potter. Air As T **98** Horiz—5p. to 25p. Cedar of Lebanon with signs of the Zodiac, bird and ship; 35 to 100p. Chamoun Electric Power Station.

99 Cedar of Lebanon

100 Soldier and Flag

101 Douglas DC-6B at Khalde Airport

1959

601	**99**	0p.50 blue (postage)	40	20
602	**99**	1p. orange	65	20
603	**99**	2p.50 violet	90	20
604	**99**	5p. green	1·20	20
605	**100**	12p.50 blue	2·10	25
606	**100**	25p. blue	2·30	25
607	**100**	50p. brown	4·00	40
608	**100**	100p. sepia	7·25	80
609	**101**	5p. green (air)	1·30	15
610	**101**	10p. purple	1·60	15
611	**101**	15p. violet	1·80	20
612	**101**	20p. red	2·30	25
613	**101**	25p. violet	2·75	40
614	-	35p. myrtle	2·30	40
615	-	50p. turquoise	3·00	45
616	-	65p. sepia	5·75	80
617	-	100p. blue	6·50	1·30

Design: Horiz—Nos. 614/617, Factory, cogwheel and telegraph pylons.

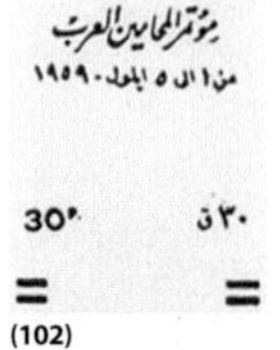
(102)

1959. Lawyers' Conference. Nos. 538 and 546 surch as T **102**.

618	30p. on 50p. myrtle and blue (postage)	2·20	1·00
619	40p. on 50p. yellow & blk (air)	2·50	1·20

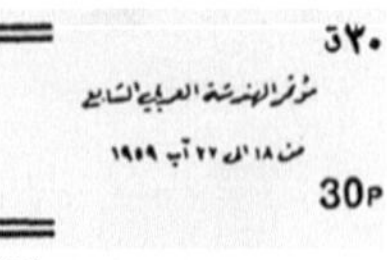
(103)

1959. Air. Engineers' Conference. Nos. 614 and 616 surch as T **103**.

620	30p. on 35p. myrtle	1·30	90
621	40p. on 65p. sepia	2·20	1·30

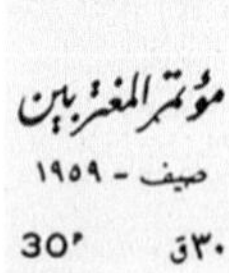
(104)

1959. Emigrants' Conference. No. 590 surch as T **104**.

622	30p. on 50p. green	1·80	40
623	40p. on 50p. green	2·50	90

105 Discus Thrower

1959. Air. Third Mediterranean Games, Beirut.

624	**105**	15p. green	90	40
625	-	30p. brown	1·30	65
626	-	40p. blue	3·00	1·20

MS626a 106×130 mm. Nos. 624/626. Imperf (sold at 100p.) £325 £325

MS626b As last but with sheet values in margins £100 £100

Designs: Vert—30p. Weightlifting. Horiz—40p. Games emblem.

106 Soldiers with Standard

1959. Air. 16th Anniversary of Independence.

627	**106**	40p. red and black	1·70	85
628	**106**	60p. red and green	2·20	1·10

1959. Surch.

629	**100**	7p.50 on 12p.50 blue	1·00	15
630	**100**	10p. on 12p.50 blue	1·20	15
631	**100**	15p. on 25p. blue	1·40	20
632	-	40p. on 50p. green (No. 590)	4·00	65
633	**88**	40p. on 65p. purple (No. 569) (air)	4·75	80

108 Planting Tree

1960. Air. 25th Anniversary of Friends of the Tree Society.

634	**108**	20p. purple and green	1·30	90
635	**108**	40p. sepia and green	2·10	1·30

1960. Air. As T **79** but colours of name and value tablets reversed.

636	20p. green	1·30	80

109 President Chehab

1960. Air.

637	**109**	5p. green	20	15
638	**109**	10p. blue	20	15
639	**109**	15p. brown	25	20
640	**109**	20p. sepia	25	20
641	**109**	30p. olive	50	25
642	**109**	40p. red	60	40
643	**109**	50p. blue	1·00	45
644	**109**	70p. purple	2·00	50
645	**109**	100p. green	4·25	1·00

110 Arab League Centre

1960. Inauguration of Arab League Centre, Cairo.

646	**110**	15p. turquoise	1·00	65

111 'Uprooted Tree'

1960. Air. World Refugee Year. (a) Size 20½×36½ mm.

647	**111**	25p. brown	1·30	90
648	**111**	40p. green	2·10	1·30

MS648a 90×110 mm. Nos. 647/648. Imperf (sold at 150p.) 65·00 65·00

(b) Size 19½×35½ mm.

648b	**111**	25p. brown	1·80	1·80
648c	**111**	40p. green	2·20	2·20

112 Martyrs' Monument

1960. Air. Martyrs' Commemoration.

649	**112**	20p. purple and green	90	50
650	**112**	40p. blue and green	1·30	90
651	-	70p. olive and black	3·00	1·30

Design: Vert—70p. Detail of statues on monument.

113 President Chehab and King Mohammed V

1960. Air. Visit of King Mohammed V of Morocco.

652	**113**	30p. chocolate and brown	1·40	65
653	**113**	70p. brown and black	2·75	1·00

114 President Chehab

1960

654	**114**	50c. green	25	20
655	**114**	2p.50 olive	35	20
656	**114**	5p. green	50	20
657	**114**	7p.50 red	80	25
658	**114**	15p. blue	1·20	40
659	**114**	50p. purple	2·50	50
660	**114**	100p. brown	5·00	90

115 Child

1960. Air. Mother and Child Days.

661	**115**	20p. red and yellow	90	25
662	**115**	20p.+10p. red and yellow	1·00	40
663	-	60p. blue and light blue	2·50	1·60
664	-	60p.+15p. blue & lt bl	3·75	1·70

Design: Nos. 663/664, Mother and child.

116 Dove, Map and Flags

1960. Air. World Lebanese Union Meeting, Beirut. Multicoloured.

665	20p. Type **116**	40	40
666	40p. Cedar of Lebanon and homing pigeons	1·30	65
667	70p. Globes and Cedar of Lebanon (horiz)	1·60	90

MS667a 110×139 mm. Nos. 665/667. Imperf (sold at 150p.) 36·00 33·00

(117)

1960. Arabian Oil Congress, Beirut. Optd with T **117**.

668	**86**	5p. green (No. 585)	90	15
669	**110**	15p. turquoise	1·80	65

1960. Air. World Refugee Year. Nos. 648b/648c surch in English and Arabic.

669a	**111**	20p.+10p. on 40p. grn	13·00	13·00
669b	**111**	30p.+15p. on 25p. brn	18·00	18·00

119 Boxing

1961. Olympic Games.

670	**119**	2p.50+2p.50 brown and blue (postage)	25	25
671	-	5p.+5p. brown & orge	50	40
672	-	7p.50+7p.50 brn & vio	80	65
673	-	15p.+15p. brown & red (air)	4·25	4·00
674	-	25p.+25p. brown & grn	4·25	4·00
675	-	35p.+35p. brown & bl	4·50	4·00

MS675a 137×118 mm. Nos. 673/5. Imperf (sold at 150p.) 47·00 47·00

Designs: 5p. Wrestling; 7p.50, Putting the shot; 15p. Fencing; 25p. Cycling; 35p. Swimming.

120 Presidnt Chehab

121 President Chehab and Map of Lebanon

1961

676	**120**	2p.50 ultramarine and blue (postage)	40	20
677	**120**	7p.50 violet and mauve	80	20
678	**120**	10p. brown and yellow	1·30	20
679	**121**	5p. green & lt green (air)	25	25
680	**121**	10p. brown and ochre	65	25
681	**121**	70p. violet and mauve	3·25	80
682	-	200p. blue and bistre	7·75	3·25

Design: Horiz—200p. Casino, Maameltein.

122 UN Emblem and Map

1961. Air. 15th Anniversary of UNO.

683	**122**	20p. purple and blue	80	40
684	-	30p. green and brown	1·30	65
685	-	50p. blue and ultramarine	2·20	1·00

MS685a 100×132 mm. Nos. 683/5. Imperf (sold at 125p.) 13·00 13·00

Designs: Vert—30p. UN emblem and Baalbek ruins. Horiz—50p. View of UN Headquarters and Manhattan.

123 Cedar of Lebanon

1961. Redrawn version of T **86** (different arrangement at foot). Shaded background.

686	**123**	2p.50 myrtle	80	15

See also Nos. 695/697.

124 Bay of Maameltein

1961. Air.

687	**124**	15p. lake	80	25
688	**124**	30p. blue	1·20	50
689	**124**	40p. sepia	2·00	80

125 Weaving

1961. Air. Labour Day.

690	-	30p. red	2·20	1·00
691	**125**	70p. blue	4·25	2·20

Design: 30p. Pottery.

126 Water-skiers

1961. Air. Tourist Month.

692	-	15p. violet and blue	1·00	50
693	**126**	40p. blue and flesh	2·20	80
694	-	70p. olive and flesh	3·25	1·70

Designs: Vert—15p. Firework display. Horiz—70p. Tourists in punt.

1961. As T **123** but plain background.

695	2p.50 yellow	1·00	20
696	5p. lake	1·30	20
697	10p. black	1·60	25

127 GPO, Beirut

1961

698	**127**	2p.50 mauve (postage)	1·00	25
699	**127**	5p. green	1·30	35
700	**127**	15p. blue	1·80	50
701	-	35p. green (air)	1·00	50
702	-	50p. brown	1·80	65
703	-	100p. black	2·50	1·00

Design: 35p. to 100p. Motor highway, Dora.

128 Cedars of Lebanon

129 Tyre Waterfront

1961

704	**128**	0p.50 green (postage)	20	20
705	**128**	1p. brown	25	20
706	**128**	2p.50 blue	40	25
707	**128**	5p. red	65	25
708	**128**	7p.50 violet	90	35
709	-	10p. purple	2·00	35
710	-	15p. blue	2·50	50
711	-	50p. green	3·00	1·70
712	-	100p. black	7·25	2·50
713	**129**	5p. red (air)	50	20
714	**129**	10p. violet	65	20
715	**129**	15p. blue	1·00	20
716	**129**	20p. orange	1·20	25
717	**129**	30p. green	1·30	35
718	-	40p. purple	1·60	50
719	-	50p. blue	2·10	80
720	-	70p. green	2·50	1·30
721	-	100p. sepia	4·75	2·10

Designs: Horiz—Nos. 709/712, Zahle. Vert—Nos. 718/721, Afka Falls.

See also Nos. 729/734.

130 UNESCO Building, Beirut

1961. Air. 15th Anniversary of UNESCO. Multicoloured.

722	20p. Type **130**	80	35
723	30p. UNESCO emblem and cedar (vert)	1·00	65
724	50p. UNESCO Building, Paris	2·10	1·00

131 Tomb of Unknown Soldier

1961. Independence and Evacuation of Foreign Troops Commemoration. Multicoloured.

725	10p. Type **131** (postage)	1·00	20
726	15p. Soldier and flag	1·40	40
727	25p. Cedar emblem (horiz) (air)	1·00	80
728	50p. Emirs Bashir and Fakhreddine (horiz)	1·40	1·00

1962. As Nos. 704/721 but with larger figures of value.

729	**128**	50c. green (postage)	50	25
730	**128**	1p. brown	65	35
731	**128**	2p.50 blue	80	40
732	-	15p. blue	5·25	65
733	**129**	5p. red (air)	50	20
734	-	40p. purple	11·00	1·30

132 Scout Bugler

1962. Lebanese Scout Movement Commemorative.

735	½p. black, yell & grn (postage)	20	15
736	1p. multicoloured	25	15
737	2½p. green, black and red	45	15
738	6p. multicoloured	1·00	15
739	10p. yellow, black and blue	1·40	20
740	15p. multicoloured (air)	1·80	25
741	20p. yellow, black and violet	2·20	40
742	25p. multicoloured	2·75	1·30

Designs: Vert—½p. T **132**; 6p. Lord Baden-Powell; 20p. Saluting hand. Horiz—1p. Scout with flag, cedar and badge; 2½p. Stretcher party, badge and laurel; 10p. Scouts at campfire; 15p. Cedar and Guide badge; 25p. Cedar and Scout badge.

133 Arab League Centre, Cairo, and Emblem

1962. Air. Arab League Week.

743	**133**	20p. ultramarine and blue	80	40
744	**133**	30p. lake and pink	1·00	65
745	**133**	50p. green and turquoise	1·80	1·00

See also Nos. 792/795.

134 Blacksmith

1962. Air. Labour Day.

746	**134**	5p. green and blue	35	15
747	**134**	10p. blue and pink	50	20
748	-	25p. violet and pink	90	40
749	-	35p. mauve and blue	1·80	65

Design: Horiz—25, 35p. Tractor.

1962. European Shooting Championships. Nos. 670/675 optd **CHAMPIONNAT D'EUROPE DE TIR 2 JUIN 1962** in French and Arabic.

750	**119**	2p.50+2p.50 (postage)	40	40
751	-	5p.+5p.	90	90
752	-	7p.50+7p.50	1·00	1·00
753	-	15p.+15p. (air)	1·60	1·60
754	-	25p.+25p.	3·50	3·50
755	-	35p.+35p.	4·25	4·25

136 Hand grasping Emblem

1962. Air. Malaria Eradication.

756	**136**	30p. brown & light brown	1·60	80
757	-	70p. violet and lilac	2·30	1·40

Design: 70p. Campaign emblem.

137 Rock Temples of Abu Simbel

1962. Nubian Monuments.

758	**137**	5p. bl & ultram (postage)	90	25
759	**137**	15p. lake and brown	1·30	40
760	-	30p. yellow and green (air)	3·00	90
761	-	50p. olive and grey	5·25	2·00

Designs: 30, 50p. Bas-relief.

138 Playing-card Symbols

1962. Air. European Bridge Championships.

762	**138**	25p. multicoloured	5·75	3·75
763	**138**	40p. multicoloured	6·00	3·75

139 Schoolboy

1962. Schoolchildren's Day.

764	**139**	30p. mult (postage)	1·00	40
765	-	45p. multicoloured (air)	1·60	90

Design: 45p. Teacher.

140

1962. Air. 19th Anniversary of Independence.

766	**140**	25p. green, red & turq	1·40	80
767	**140**	25p. violet, red & turq	1·40	80
768	**140**	25p. blue, red & turquoise	1·40	80

141 Cherries

1962. Fruits. Multicoloured.

769	0p.50 Type **141** (postage)	40	15
770	1p. Figs	65	15
771	2p.50 Type **141**	80	15
772	5p. Figs	90	15
773	7p.50 Type **141**	40	15
774	10p. Grapes	65	20
775	17p.50 Grapes	1·30	25
776	30p. Grapes	2·30	40
777	50p. Oranges	4·25	90
778	100p. Pomegranates	8·50	2·30
779	5p. Apricots (air)	25	15
780	10p. Plums	50	20
781	20p. Apples	90	25
782	30p. Plums	1·30	50
783	40p. Apples	1·40	60
784	50p. Pears	1·70	65
785	70p. Medlars	2·50	80
786	100p. Lemons	4·75	1·60

142 Reaping

1963. Air. Freedom from Hunger.

787	**142**	2p.50 yellow and blue	20	15
788	**142**	5p. yellow and green	25	15
789	**142**	7p.50 yellow and purple	50	20
790	-	15p. green and red	90	25
791	-	20p. green and red	1·60	65

Design: Horiz—15, 20p. Three ears of wheat within hand.

1963. Air. Arab League Week. As T **133** but inscr '1963'.

792	5p. violet and blue	20	15
793	10p. green and blue	50	40
794	15p. brown and blue	80	50
795	20p. grey and blue	1·20	90

143 Nurse tending Baby

1963. Air. Red Cross Centenary.

796	-	5p. green and red	20	15
797	-	20p. blue and red	50	25
798	**143**	35p. red and black	90	50
799	**143**	40p. violet and red	1·60	80

Design: Horiz—5, 20p. Blood transfusion.

144 Allegory of Music

1963. Air. Baalbek Festival.

800	**144**	35p. orange and blue	1·80	80

145 Flag and rising Sun

1963. Air. 20th Anniversary of Independence. Flag and sun in red and yellow.

801	**145**	5p. turquoise	40	25
802	**145**	10p. green	80	65
803	**145**	25p. blue	1·00	90
804	**145**	40p. drab	1·70	1·40

146 Cycling

1964. Fourth Mediterranean Games, Naples (1963).

805	**146**	2p.50 brown and purple (postage)	40	15
806	-	5p. orange and blue	50	15
807	-	10p. brown and violet	85	25
808	-	15p. orange and green (air)	1·00	40
809	-	17p.50 brown and blue	1·30	50
810	-	30p. brown and turquoise	2·00	80

MS810a 152×112 mm. Nos. 808/810. Imperf (sold at 100p.)			20·00	20·00

Designs: Vert—5p. Basketball; 10p. Running; 15p. Tennis. Horiz—17p.50, Swimming; 30p. Skiing.

147 Hyacinth

1964. Flowers. Multicoloured.

811		0p.50 Type **147** (postage)	25	15
812		1p. Type **147**	35	15
813		2p.50 Type **147**	40	15
814		5p. Cyclamen	45	15
815		7p.50 Cyclamen	65	15
816		10p. Poinsettia (vert)	90	20
817		17p.50 Anemone (vert)	1·70	35
818		30p. Iris (vert)	3·00	80
819		50p. Poppy (vert)	6·50	1·30
820		5p. Lily (vert) (air)	50	40
821		10p. Ranunculus (vert)	90	40
822		20p. Anemone (vert)	1·20	45
823		40p. Tuberose (vert)	2·10	80
824		45p. Rhododendron (vert)	2·20	80
825		50p. Jasmine (vert)	2·50	90
826		70p. Yellow broom (vert)	4·00	1·30

Nos. 816/826 are size 26½×37 mm.

148 Cedar of Lebanon

149 Cedar of Lebanon

1964

827	**148**	0p.50 green	65	25
828	**149**	0p.50 green	65	25
829	**149**	2p.50 blue	65	25
830	**149**	5p. mauve	80	25
831	**149**	7p.50 orange	1·60	25
832	**149**	17p.50 purple	2·50	35

150 Child on Rocking-horse

1964. Air. Children's Day.

833	-	5p. red, orange and green	25	15
834	-	10p. red, orange and brown	40	25
835	**150**	20p. orange, blue and ultramarine	80	65
836	**150**	40p. yellow, blue and purple	1·60	1·00

Design: Horiz—5, 10p. Girls skipping.

151 League Session

1964. Air. Arab League Meeting.

837	**151**	5p. buff, brown and black	80	40
838	**151**	10p. black	1·20	45
839	**151**	15p. turquoise	1·70	50
840	**151**	20p. mauve, brn & sepia	2·30	80

152 "Flame of Freedom"

1964. Air. 15th Anniversary of Declaration of Human Rights.

841	**152**	20p. red, pink and brown	40	25
842	-	40p. orange, blue and light blue	90	40

Design: 40p. Flame on pedestal bearing UN emblem.

153 Sick Child

1964. Air. 'Bal des Petits Lits Blancs' (Ball for children's charity).

843	**153**	2p.50 multicoloured	20	15
844	**153**	5p. multicoloured	25	15
845	**153**	15p. multicoloured	45	25
846	-	17p.50 multicoloured	1·00	40
847	-	20p. multicoloured	1·30	45
848	-	40p. multicoloured	2·00	50

Design: 55×25½ mm—17p.50 to 40p. Children in front of palace (venue of ball).

154 Clasped Wrists

1964. Air. World Lebanese Union Congress, Beirut.

849	**154**	20p. black, yellow & green	1·00	40
850	**154**	40p. black, yellow & pur	1·80	90

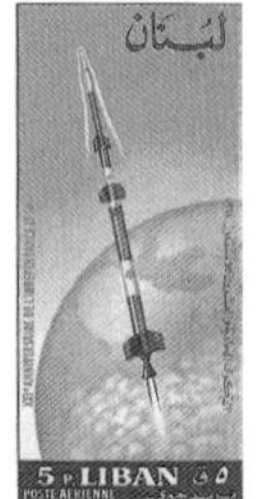
155 Rocket in Flight

1964. Air. 21st Anniversary of Independence.

851	**155**	5p. multicoloured	40	25
852	**155**	10p. multicoloured	40	25
853	-	40p. blue and black	1·40	90
854	-	70p. purple and black	2·50	2·00

Designs: Horiz—40p. to 70p. 'Struggle for Independence' (battle scene).

156 Temple Columns

1965. Baalbek Festival.

855	**156**	2p.50 black and orange (postage)	50	25
856	-	7p.50 black and blue	1·00	40
857	-	10p. multicoloured (air)	50	15
858	-	15p. multicoloured	1·00	20
859	-	25p. multicoloured	1·60	65
860	-	40p. multicoloured	2·30	80

Designs: 28×55 mm—10, 15p. Man in costume; 25, 40p. Woman in costume.

157 Swimming

1965. Olympic Games, Tokyo.

861	**157**	2p.50 black, blue and mauve (postage)	40	15
862	-	7p.50 purple, green & brn	1·60	90
863	-	10p. grey, brown & green	2·10	1·00
864	-	15p. black and green (air)	1·30	40
865	-	25p. green and purple	2·00	65
866	-	40p. brown and blue	2·30	1·00
MS866a 140×100 mm. Nos. 864/866. Imperf (sold at 100p.)			26·00	26·00

Designs: Horiz—7p.50, Fencing; 15p. Horse-jumping; 40p. Gymnastics. Vert—10p. Basketball; 25p. Rifle-shooting.

1965. (a) Postage. Birds.

867	-	5p. multicoloured	2·30	25
868	-	10p. multicoloured	2·00	35
869	-	15p. chocolate, orange & brn	5·75	50
870	-	17p.50 purple, red and blue	9·00	65
871	-	20p. black, yellow and green	11·50	80
872	-	32p.50 yellow, brown & grn	25·00	2·00

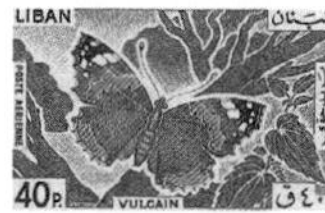
158 Red Admiral

(b) Air. Butterflies.

873	-	30p. yellow, brown and red	2·20	25
874	-	35p. blue, red and bistre	3·50	50
875	**158**	40p. brown, red and green	4·25	65
876	-	45p. brown, yellow & blue	5·25	80
877	-	70p. multicoloured	7·75	1·20
878	-	85p. black, orange & green	9·00	1·40
879	-	100p. blue and plum	13·00	1·60
880	-	200p. brown, blue & pur	23·00	1·80
881	-	300p. sepia, yellow & green	34·00	5·50
882	-	500p. brown, blue and light blue	65·00	11·00

Designs: Birds—5p. Northern bullfinch; 10p. Eurasian goldfinch; 15p. Hoopoe; 17p.50, Red-legged partridge; 20p. Golden oriole; 32p.50, European bee-eater. Butterflies—30p. Large tiger moth; 35p. Small postman; 45p. Common grayling; 70p. Swallowtail; 85p. Orange-tip; 100p. Blue morpho; 200p. *Erasmia sanguiflua*; 300p. *Papilio crassus*. 35½×25 mm—500p. Amelia's charakes.

159 Pope Paul and Pres. Helou

1965. Air. Pope Paul's Visit to Lebanon.

883	**159**	45p. violet and gold	7·75	3·50
MS883a 100×81 mm. No. 883. Imperf (sold at 100p.)			80·00	80·00

160 Sheep

1965

884	-	50c. multicoloured	2·50	25
885	-	1p. grey, black and mauve	2·50	25
886	**160**	2p.50 yellow, sepia & grn	2·75	25

Designs: 50c. Cow and calf; 1p. Rabbit.

161 Cedars of Friendship

1965. Air.

887	**161**	40p. multicoloured	2·20	40

162 Silk Manufacture

1965. Air. World Silk Congress, Beirut. Multicoloured.

888		2p.50 Type **162**	90	25
889		5p. Type **162**	1·00	25
890		7p.50 Type **162**	1·20	25
891		15p. Weaver and loom	1·30	35
892		30p. As 15p.	3·50	50
893		40p. As 15p.	5·00	80
894		50p. As 15p.	6·50	1·20

163 Parliament Building

1965. Air. Centenary of Lebanese Parliament.

895	**163**	35p. brown, ochre and red	90	50
896	**163**	40p. brown, ochre & green	1·30	80

164 UN Emblem and Headquarters

1965. Air. 20th Anniversary of UNO.

897	**164**	2p.50 blue	20	15
898	**164**	10p. red	35	15
899	**164**	17p.50 violet	50	20
900	**164**	30p. green	1·00	40
901	**164**	40p. brown	1·30	80
MS901a 101×80 mm. No. 901 in violet. Imperf (sold at 50p.)			22·00	22·00

165 Playing-card 'King'

1965. Air. World Bridge Championships, Beirut.

902	**165**	2p.50 multicoloured	25	20
903	**165**	15p. multicoloured	1·20	25
904	**165**	17p.50 multicoloured	1·80	40
905	**165**	40p. multicoloured	3·75	1·60
MS905a 105×85 mm. Nos. 903 and 905. Imperf or perf (sold at 75p.)			34·00	34·00

166 Dagger on Deir Yassin, Palestine

1965. Air. Deir Yassin Massacre.

906	**166**	50p. multicoloured	6·50	1·70

167 ITU Emblem and Symbols

1966. Air. Centenary (1965) of ITU.

907	**167**	2p.50 multicoloured	15	15
908	**167**	15p. multicoloured	50	20
909	**167**	17p.50 multicoloured	80	25
910	**167**	25p. multicoloured	1·70	40
911	**167**	40p. multicoloured	2·30	65

168 Stage Performance

1966. Air. Baalbek Festival. Multicoloured.

912		2p.50 Type **168**	40	20
913		5p. Type **168**	50	20
914		7p.50 Ballet performance (vert)	65	20
915		15p. Ballet performance (vert)	90	25
916		30p. Concert	1·30	50
917		40p. Concert	1·70	65

169 Tabarja

1966. Tourism. Multicoloured.

918		50c. Hippodrome, Beirut (postage)	40	15
919		1p. Pigeon Grotto, Beirut	50	15
920		2p.50 Type **169**	80	15
921		5p. Ruins, Beit-Mery	1·00	15
922		7p.50 Ruins, Anjar	1·30	15
923		10p. Djezzine Falls (air)	35	15
924		15p. Sidon Castle	40	15

925		20p. Amphitheatre, Byblos	50	15
926		30p. Sun Temple, Baalbek	90	20
927		50p. Palace, Beit ed-Din	1·80	25
928		60p. Nahr-el Kalb	2·30	45
929		70p. Tripoli	3·25	65

170 WHO Building

1966. Air. Inauguration of WHO Headquarters, Geneva.

930	**170**	7p.50 green	50	20
931	**170**	17p.50 red	65	45
932	**170**	25p. blue	1·30	65

171 Skiing

1966. Air. International Cedars Festival.

933	**171**	2p.50 brown, red and green	25	20
934	-	5p. multicoloured	40	20
935	-	17p.50 multicoloured	65	40
936	-	25p. red, brown and green	1·80	65

Designs: 5p. Tobogganing; 17p.50, Cedar in snow; 25p. Ski-lift.

172 Inscribed Sarcophagus

1966. Air. Phoenician Invention of the Alphabet.

937	**172**	10p. brown, black and green	20	15
938	-	15p. brown, ochre and mauve	65	25
939	-	20p. sepia, blue and ochre	1·00	40
940	-	30p. brown, orange and yellow	1·70	65

Designs: 15p. Phoenician sailing ship; 20p. Mediterranean route map showing spread of Phoenician alphabet; 30p. Kadmus with alphabet tablet.

173 Child in Bath

1966. Air. International Children's Day. Multicoloured.

941		2p. Type **173**	20	15
942		5p. Boy and doll in rowing boat	25	15
943		7p.50 Girl skiing	50	20
944		15p. Girl giving food to bird	1·20	25
945		20p. Boy doing homework	1·70	65
MS946		100×69½ mm. 50p. Children of various races (horiz). Imperf	11·00	11·00

174 Decade Emblem

1966. Air. International Hydrological Decade.

947	**174**	5p. ultramarine, bl & orge	20	15
948	**174**	10p. red, blue and orange	40	20
949	-	15p. sepia, green & orange	60	25
950	-	20p. blue, green & orange	1·20	40

Design: 15p., 20p. Similar 'wave' pattern.

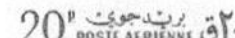

175 Rev. Daniel Bliss (founder)

1966. Air. Centenary of American University, Beirut.

951	**175**	20p. brown, yellow & grn	65	35
952	-	30p. green, brown and blue	80	45
MS953		125×85 mm. 50p. brown, orange and green. Imperf	4·00	3·25

Designs: Vert—30p. University Chapel. Horiz (59×37 mm)—50p. Rev. Daniel Bliss, University and emblem.

176 ITY Emblem

1967. International Tourist Year (1st issue). (a) Postage.

954	**176**	50c. multicoloured	20	15
955	**176**	1p. multicoloured	25	20
956	**176**	2p.50 multicoloured	40	25
957	**176**	5p. multicoloured	80	40
958	**176**	7p.50 multicoloured	1·00	50

177 Beit ed-Din Palace

(b) Air. Multicoloured.

959		10p. Tabarja	1·30	50
960		15p. Pigeon Rock, Beirut	1·70	65
961		17p.50 Type **177**	2·00	65
962		20p. Sidon	2·10	65
963		25p. Tripoli	2·30	65
964		30p. Byblos	2·50	65
965		35p. Ruins, Tyre	3·00	65
966		40p. Temple, Baalbek	3·50	65

See also Nos. 977/**MS**980a.

178 Signing Pact, and Flags

1967. Air. 22nd Anniversary of Arab League Pact.

967	**178**	5p. multicoloured	20	15
968	**178**	10p. multicoloured	35	20
969	**178**	15p. multicoloured	65	40
970	**178**	20p. multicoloured	1·20	50

179 Veterans War Memorial Building, San Francisco

1967. Air. San Francisco Pact of 1945. Multicoloured.

971		2p.50 Type **179**	1·20	50
972		5p. Type **179**	1·20	50
973		7p.50 Type **179**	1·20	50
974		10p. Scroll and flags of UN and Lebanon	1·20	50
975		20p. As 10p.	1·20	50
976		30p. As 10p.	1·20	50

180 Temple Ruins, Baalbek

1967. Air. International Tourist Year (2nd issue). Multicoloured.

977		5p. Type **180**	25	15
978		10p. Ruins, Anjar	40	15
979		15p. Ancient bridge, Nahr-Ibrahim	80	20
980		20p. Grotto, Jeita	1·00	25
MS980a		112×90 mm. 50p. Beirut (plus flag and map of Lebanon). Imperf	33·00	33·00

181

1967. Air. India Day.

981	**181**	2p.50 red	25	20
982	**181**	5p. purple	25	20
983	**181**	7p.50 brown	40	20
984	**181**	10p. blue	50	20
985	**181**	15p. green	1·00	25

182

1967. Air. 22nd Anniversary of Lebanon's Admission to UNO.

986	**182**	2p.50 red	15	15
987	**182**	5p. blue	20	15
988	**182**	7p.50 green	25	20
989	-	10p. red	40	25
990	-	20p. blue	65	35
991	-	30p. green	1·00	40
MS991a		109×85 mm. 100p. red (T **182**). Imperf	9·00	9·00

Design: 10, 20, 30p. UN Emblem.

183 Goat and Kid

1967. Animals and Fish. Multicoloured.

992		50c. Type **183** (postage)	65	20
993		1p. Cattle	65	20
994		2p.50 Sheep	65	20
995		5p. Dromedaries	65	20
996		10p. Donkey	1·30	25
997		15p. Horses	2·50	25
998		20p. Basking shark (air)	2·50	25
999		30p. Garfish	3·00	25
1000		40p. Pollack	4·50	35
1001		50p. Cuckoo wrasse	5·00	40
1002		70p. Striped red mullet	12·50	50
1003		100p. Rainbow trout	16·00	65

184 Ski Jumping

1968. Air. International Ski Congress, Beirut.

1004	**184**	2p.50 multicoloured	25	15
1005	-	5p. multicoloured	45	15
1006	-	7p.50 multicoloured	65	20
1007	-	10p. multicoloured	80	25
1008	-	25p. multicoloured	1·30	40
MS1008a		121×91 mm. 50p. multicoloured. Imperf	10·50	10·50

Designs: 5p. to 10p. Skiing (all different); 25p. Congress emblem of Cedar and skis.

185 Princess Khaskiah

1968. Air. Emir Fakhreddine II Commemoration. Multicoloured.

1009		2p.50 Type **185**	25	20
1010		5p. Emir Fakhreddine II	40	20
1011		10p. Sidon Citadel (horiz)	50	20
1012		15p. Chekif Citadel (horiz)	80	25
1013		17p.50 Beirut Citadel (horiz)	1·30	35
MS1013a		120×86 mm. 50p. Battle of Anjar. Imperf	17·00	17·00

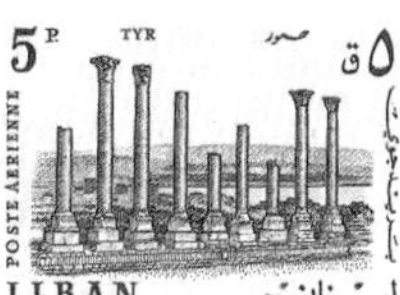

186 Colonnade

1968. Air. Tyre Antiquities.

1014	-	2p.50 brn, cream & pink	25	15
1015	**186**	5p. brown, blue & yellow	40	15
1016	-	7p.50 brown, buff & grn	65	20
1017	-	10p. brown, blue & orange	1·00	40
MS1018		120×80 mm. 10p. brown and blue. Perf or imperf (sold at 50p.)	33·00	33·00

Designs: Vert—2p.50, Roman bust; 10p. Bas-relief. Horiz—7p.50, Arch.

187 Justinian and Mediterranean Map

1968. Air. First Anniversary of Faculty of Law, Beirut.

1019		5p. Justinian (vert)	25	15
1020		10p. Justinian (vert)	40	15
1021		15p. Type **187**	50	15
1022		20p. Type **187**	90	25

188 Arab League Emblem

1968. Air. Arab Appeal Week.

1023	**188**	5p. multicoloured	25	15
1024	**188**	10p. multicoloured	40	15
1025	**188**	15p. multicoloured	50	15
1026	**188**	20p. multicoloured	90	25

189 Cedar on Globe

1968. Air. Third World Lebanese Union Congress, Beirut.

1027	**189**	2p.50 multicoloured	20	15
1028	**189**	5p. multicoloured	25	15
1029	**189**	7p.50 multicoloured	40	15
1030	**189**	10p. multicoloured	65	35

190 Jupiter's Temple Ruins, Baalbek

1968. Air. Baalbek Festival. Multicoloured.

1031		5p. Type **190**	25	15
1032		10p. Bacchus's Temple	40	20
1033		15p. Corniche, Jupiter's Temple	65	25
1034		20p. Portal, Bacchus's Temple	1·00	40
1035		25p. Columns, Bacchus's Temple	1·30	65

191 Long Jumping and Atlantes

1968. Air. Olympic Games, Mexico.

1036	**191**	5p. black, yellow and blue	25	15
1037	-	10p. black, blue & purple	40	20
1038	-	15p. multicoloured	65	25
1039	-	20p. multicoloured	1·00	40
1040	-	25p. brown	1·30	65

Designs: (each incorporating Aztec relic). 10p. High jumping; 15p. Fencing; 20p. Weightlifting; 25p. 'Sailing boat' with oars.

192 Lebanese driving Tractor (Work protection)

1968. Air. Human Rights Year. Multicoloured.

1041	10p. Type **192**	25	15
1042	15p. Citizens (Social Security)	60	20
1043	25p. Young men of three races (Unity)	1·00	35

193 Minshiya Stairs

1968. Air. Centenary of First Municipal Council (Deir el-Kamar). Multicoloured.

1044	10p. Type **193**	25	15
1045	15p. Serai kiosk	60	20
1046	25p. Ancient highway	1·00	45

194 Nurse and Child

1969. Air. UNICEF. Multicoloured.

1047	**194**	5p. black, brown and blue	20	15
1048	-	10p. black, green & yell	35	15
1049	-	15p. black, red and purple	50	15
1050	-	20p. black, blue & yellow	70	20
1051	-	25p. black, ochre & mve	1·00	25

Designs: 10p. Produce; 15p. Mother and child; 20p. Child with book; 25p. Children with flowers.

195 Ancient Coin

1969. Air. 20th Anniversary of International Museums Council (ICOM). Exhibits in National Museum, Beirut. Multicoloured.

1052	2p.50 Type **195**	25	15
1053	5p. Gold dagger, Byblos	40	15
1054	7p.50 Detail of Ahiram's Sarcophagus	65	20
1055	30p. Jewelled pectoral	1·00	40
1056	40p. Khalde 'bird' vase	1·70	1·00

196 Water-skiing

1969. Air. Water Sports. Multicoloured.

1057	2p.50 Type **196**	25	15
1058	5p. Water-skiing (group)	35	15
1059	7p.50 Paraskiing (vert)	45	20
1060	30p. Racing dinghies (vert)	1·20	50
1061	40p. Racing dinghies	1·60	1·00

197 Frontier Guard

1969. Air. 25th Anniversary of Independence. The Lebanese Army.

1062	2p. Type **197**	15	15
1063	5p. Unknown Soldier's Tomb	25	15
1064	7p.50 Army Foresters	40	15
1065	15p. Road-making	50	20
1066	30p. Military ambulance and Sud Aviation Alouette III helicopter	1·00	50
1067	40p. Skiing patrol	1·60	65

198 Concentric Red Crosses

1971. Air. 25th Anniversary of Lebanese Red Cross.

1068	**198**	15p. red and black	65	25
1069	-	85p. red and black	2·50	1·60

Design: 85p. Red Cross in shape of cedar of Lebanon.

199 Foil and Flags of Arab States

1971. Air. Tenth International Fencing Championships. Multicoloured.

1070	10p. Type **199**	15	15
1071	15p. Foil and flags of foreign nations	25	20
1072	35p. Contest with foils	90	65
1073	40p. Epee contest	1·00	80
1074	50p. Contest with sabres	1·60	90

200 *Farmers at Work* (12th-century Arab painting)

1971. Air. 50th Anniversary (1969) of ILO.

1075	**200**	10p. multicoloured	65	25
1076	**200**	40p. multicoloured	1·60	90

201 UPU Monument and New HQ Building, Berne

1971. Air. New UPU Headquarters Building, Berne.

1077	**201**	15p. red, black and yellow	50	25
1078	**201**	35p. yellow, black and orange	1·60	90

202 *Ravens setting fire to Owls* (14th-century painting)

1971. Air. Children's Day. Multicoloured.

1079	15p. Type **202**	80	25
1080	85p. *The Lion and the Jackal* (13th-century painting) (39×29 mm)	3·75	1·60

203 Arab League Flag and Map

1971. Air. 25th Anniversary of Arab League.

1081	**203**	30p. multicoloured	80	40
1082	**203**	70p. multicoloured	1·80	1·20

204 Jamhour Electricity Sub-station

1971. Air. Multicoloured.

1083	5p. Type **204**	40	20
1084	10p. Maameltein Bridge	50	20
1085	15p. Hoteliers' School	65	25
1086	20p. Litani Dam	80	35
1087	25p. Interior of TV set	90	40
1088	35p. Bziza Temple	1·20	45
1089	40p. Jounieh Harbour	1·60	50
1090	45p. Radar scanner, Beirut Airport	1·80	60
1091	50p. Hibiscus	2·30	65
1092	70p. School of Sciences Building	3·50	90
1093	85p. Oranges	4·00	1·00
1094	100p. Satellite Communications Station, Arbanieh	5·25	2·00

205 Insignia of Imam al Ouzai (theologian)

1971. Air. Lebanese Celebrities.

1095	**205**	25p. brown, gold & green	50	35
1096	-	25p. brown, gold & yell	50	35
1097	-	25p. brown, gold & yell	50	35
1098	-	25p. brown, gold & green	50	35

Portraits: No. 1096, Bechara el Khoury (poet and writer); No. 1097, Hassan Kamel el Sabbah (scientist); No. 1098, Gibran Khalil Gibran (writer).

206 IEY Emblem and Computer Card

1971. Air. International Education Year.

1099	**206**	10p. black, blue and violet	25	20
1100	**206**	40p. black, yellow and red	1·20	65

207 Dahr-el-Basheq Sanatorium

1971. Air. Tuberculosis Relief Campaign.

1101	**207**	50p. multicoloured	1·80	80
1102	-	100p. multicoloured	2·50	1·30

Design: 100p. Different view of Sanatorium.

208 'Solar Wheel' Emblem

1971. Air. 16th Baalbek Festival.

1103	**208**	15p. orange and blue	25	20
1104	-	85p. black, blue and orange	1·80	1·20

Design: 85p. Corinthian capital.

209 Field-gun

1971. Air. Army Day. Multicoloured.

1105	15p. Type **209**	2·50	1·00
1106	25p. Dassault Mirage IIICJ jet fighters	4·00	2·00
1107	40p. Army Command HQ	6·50	3·25
1108	70p. *Tarablous* (naval patrol boat)	13·00	5·25

210 Interior Decoration

1971. Air. Second Anniversary of Burning of Al-Aqsa Mosque, Jerusalem.

1109	**210**	15p. brown and deep brown	90	25
1110	**210**	35p. brown and deep brown	2·10	90

211 Lenin

1971. Air. Birth Centenary of Lenin. Multicoloured.

1111	30p. Type **211**	90	50
1112	70p. Lenin in profile	2·10	1·30

212 UN Emblem

1971. Air. 25th Anniversary of United Nations.

1113	**212**	15p. multicoloured	25	20
1114	**212**	85p. multicoloured	2·10	1·20

213 *Europa* Mosaic, Byblos

1971. Air. World Lebanese Union.

1115	**213**	10p. multicoloured	40	25
1116	**213**	40p. multicoloured	2·30	65

1972. Various stamps surch.

1117	5p. on 7p.50 (No. 922) (postage)	4·00	1·30
1118	5p. on 7p.50 (No. 958)	4·00	1·30
1119	25p. on 32p.50 (No. 872)	10·50	4·00
1120	5p. on 7p.50 (No. 1016) (air)	4·00	1·30
1121	100p. on 300p. (No. 881)	13·00	5·75
1122	100p. on 500p. (No. 882)	13·00	5·75
1123	200p. on 300p. (No. 881)	23·00	13·00

217 Morning Glory

1973. Air. Multicoloured.

1124	2p.50 Type **217**	25	20
1125	5p. Roses	40	25
1126	15p. Tulips	65	40
1127	25p. Lilies	90	45
1128	40p. Carnations	1·30	50
1129	50p. Iris	2·00	50
1130	70p. Apples	3·00	60
1131	75p. Grapes	3·25	65

1132	100p. Peaches	4·75	1·60
1133	200p. Pears	7·75	1·30
1134	300p. Cherries	10·50	2·30
1135	500p. Oranges	16·00	4·00

218 Ornate Arches

1973. Air. Lebanese Domestic Architecture.

1136	-	35p. multicoloured	1·70	65
1137	**218**	50p. multicoloured	2·50	1·30
1138	-	85p. multicoloured	4·25	2·00
1139	-	100p. multicoloured	5·00	2·75

Designs: Nos. 1136 and 1138/1139, Various Lebanese dwellings.

219 Girl with Lute

1973. Air. Ancient Costumes. Multicoloured.

1140	5p. Woman with rose	1·30	65
1141	10p. Shepherd	2·00	1·00
1142	20p. Horseman	4·00	1·70
1143	25p. Type **219**	5·75	2·50

220 Swimming

1973. Air. Fifth Pan-Arab Schools' Games, Beirut. Multicoloured.

1144	5p. Type **220**	45	15
1145	10p. Running	70	15
1146	15p. Gymnastics	90	15
1147	20p. Volleyball	1·20	20
1148	25p. Basketball	1·40	25
1149	50p. Table-tennis	3·00	50
1150	75p. Handball	3·50	65
1151	100p. Football	4·00	2·00
MS1152	121×71 mm. No. 1151. Imperf	6·25	5·75

221 Brasilia

1973. Air. 150th Anniversary of Brazil's Independence. Multicoloured.

1153	5p. Type **221**	60	25
1154	20p. Salvador (Bahia) in 1823	1·20	65
1155	25p. Map and Phoenician galley	1·70	90
1156	50p. Emperor Pedro I and Emir Fakhreddine II	2·75	2·00

222 Marquetry

1973. Air. Lebanese Handicrafts. Multicoloured.

1157	10p. Type **222**	60	20
1158	20p. Weaving	1·20	35
1159	35p. Glass-blowing	1·70	40
1160	40p. Pottery	2·30	50
1161	50p. Metal-working	3·00	65
1162	70p. Cutlery-making	4·50	90
1163	85p. Lace-making	6·00	1·30
1164	100p. Handicrafts Museum	7·00	2·20

223 Cedar of Lebanon

1974

1165	**223**	50c. green, brown and orange	60	40

224 Camp Site and Emblems

1974. Air. 11th Arab Scout Jamboree, Smar-Jubeil, Lebanon. Multicoloured.

1166	2p.50 Type **224**	40	20
1167	5p. Scout badge and map	50	20
1168	7p.50 Map of Arab countries	70	25
1169	10p. Lord Baden-Powell and Baalbek	85	25
1170	15p. Guide and camp	1·20	25
1171	20p. Lebanese Guide and Scout badge	1·40	25
1172	25p. Scouts around campfire	1·70	35
1173	30p. Globe and Scout badge	2·30	50
1174	35p. Flags of participating countries	3·50	60
1175	50p. Scout chopping wood for old man	5·25	90

225 Mail Train

1974. Centenary of UPU. Multicoloured.

1176	5p.50 Type **225**	3·50	1·00
1177	20p. Container ship	2·30	80
1178	25p. Congress building, Lausanne, and UPU HQ, Berne	2·30	90
1179	50p. Mail plane	3·50	1·30

226 Congress Building, Sofar

1974. Air. 25th Anniversary of Arab Postal Union. Multicoloured.

1180	5p. Type **226**	60	25
1181	20p. View of Sofar	1·20	65
1182	25p. APU HQ, Cairo	1·70	65
1183	50p. Ministry of Posts, Beirut	3·50	2·00

227 *Mountain Road* (O. Onsi)

1974. Air. Lebanese Paintings. Multicoloured.

1184	50p. Type **227**	2·00	90
1185	50p. *Clouds* (M. Farroukh)	2·00	90
1186	50p. *Woman* (G. K. Gebran)	2·00	90
1187	50p. *Embrace* (C. Gemayel)	2·00	90
1188	50p. *Self-portrait* (H. Serour)	2·00	90
1189	50p. *Portrait* (D. Corm)	2·00	90

228 Hunter killing Lion

1974. Air. Hermel Excavations. Multicoloured.

1190	5p. Type **228**	40	20
1191	10p. Astarte	65	25
1192	25p. Dogs hunting boar	2·50	80
1193	35p. Greco-Roman tomb	5·75	2·75

229 Book Year Emblem

1974. Air. International Book Year (1972).

1194	**229**	5p. multicoloured	25	20
1195	**229**	10p. multicoloured	65	25
1196	**229**	25p. multicoloured	2·50	80
1197	**229**	35p. multicoloured	3·75	2·75

230 Magnifying Glass

1974. Air. Stamp Day. Multicoloured.

1198	5p. Type **230**	40	20
1199	10p. Linked posthorns	50	20
1200	15p. Stamp-printing	80	25
1201	20p. Stamp in mount	1·20	50

231 Georgina Rizk in Lebanese Costume

1974. Air. Miss Universe 1971 (Georgina Rizk). Multicoloured.

1202	5p. Type **231**	25	15
1203	20p. Head-and-shoulders portrait	1·00	40
1204	25p. Type **231**	1·30	50
1205	50p. As 20p.	2·50	1·70
MS1206	156×112 mm. Nos. 1202/1205. Imperf	12·00	11·50

232 Winds

1974. Air. UN Conference on Human Environment, Stockholm, 1972. Multicoloured.

1207	5p. Type **232**	15	15
1208	25p. Mountains and plain	85	20
1209	30p. Trees and flowers	90	40
1210	40p. Sea	1·20	90
MS1211	153×113 mm. Nos. 1207/1210. Imperf	10·50	10·50

233 UNICEF Emblem and Sikorsky S-55 Helicopter

1974. Air. 25th Anniversary of UNICEF. Multicoloured.

1212	20p. Type **233**	1·00	25
1213	25p. Emblem and child welfare clinic	50	20
1214	35p. Emblem and kindergarten class	1·00	40
1215	70p. Emblem and schoolgirls in laboratory	2·00	50
MS1216	158×112 mm. Nos. 1212/1215. Imperf	8·75	8·50

234 Discus-throwing

1974. Air. Olympic Games, Munich (1972). Multicoloured.

1217	5p. Type **234**	40	25
1218	10p. Putting the shot	50	40
1219	15p. Weight-lifting	65	50
1220	35p. Running	1·30	80
1221	50p. Wrestling	2·00	1·00
1222	85p. Javelin-throwing	3·75	1·60
MS1223	175×130 mm. Nos. 1217/1222. Imperf	13·00	11·50

235 Symbols of Archaeology

1975. Air. Beirut. University City. Multicoloured.

1224	20p. Type **235**	1·30	25
1225	25p. Science and medicine	2·00	40
1226	35p. Justice and commerce	2·50	1·00
1227	70p. Industry and commerce	4·00	1·60

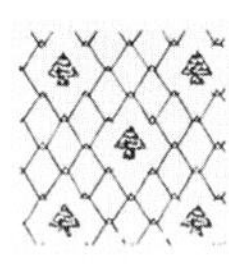
(236)

1978. Air. Various stamps optd with different patterns as T **236**. (a) Tourist Views. Nos. 1090, 1092/1093.

1228	45p. Radar scanner, Beirut Airport	2·50	90
1229	70p. School of Sciences Building	5·25	1·20
1230	85p. Oranges	5·50	1·80

(b) Flowers and Fruits. Nos. 1124/1135.

1231	2p.50 Type **217**	65	65
1232	5p. Roses	65	65
1233	15p. Tulips	1·30	65
1234	25p. Lilies	2·50	65
1235	40p. Carnations	2·50	90
1236	50p. Iris	3·75	90
1237	70p. Apples	5·25	1·20
1238	75p. Grapes	6·25	1·20
1239	100p. Peaches	6·50	2·30
1240	200p. Pears	14·50	7·25
1241	300p. Cherries	21·00	11·50
1242	500p. Oranges	31·00	18·00

(c) Lebanese Domestic Architecture. Nos. 1136/1139.

1243	-	35p. multicoloured	2·75	65
1244	**218**	50p. multicoloured	3·75	90
1245	-	85p. multicoloured	5·50	1·80
1246	-	100p. multicoloured	6·50	2·30

(d) Ancient Costumes. Nos. 1140/1143.

1247	5p. Woman with rose	65	65
1248	10p. Shepherd	80	65
1249	20p. Horseman	1·40	65
1250	25p. Type **219**	2·50	65

(e) Lebanese Handicrafts. Nos. 1157/1158, 1160/1164.

1251	10p. Type **222**	80	65
1252	20p. Weaving	1·40	65
1253	40p. Pottery	2·50	90
1254	50p. Metal-working	4·25	90
1255	70p. Cutlery-making	5·25	1·20
1256	85p. Lace-making	5·50	1·80
1257	100p. Handicraft Museum	6·50	2·30

237 Mikhail Naimy (poet) and View of al-Chakroub Baskinta

1978. Air. Mikhail Naimy Festival Week. Multicoloured.

1258	25p. Mikhail Naimy and Sannine mountains	80	15
1259	50p. Type **237**	1·80	50
1260	75p. Mikhail Naimy (vert)	3·25	90

238 Heart and Arrow

1978. Air. World Health Day. 'Down with Blood Pressure'.

1261	**238**	50p. blue, red and black	1·60	80

239 Army Badge

1980. Army Day. Multicoloured.

1262	25p. Type **239** (postage)	1·00	65
1263	50p. Statue of Emir Fakhr el Dine on horseback (air)	2·00	90
1264	75p. Soldiers with flag (horiz)	2·75	1·20

240 13th-century European King

1980. Air. 50th Anniversary (1974) of International Chess Federation. Multicoloured.

1265	50p. Rook, knight and Jubilee emblem (horiz)	2·00	1·30
1266	75p. Type **240**	3·25	2·50
1267	100p. Rook and Lebanon Chess Federation emblem	5·25	4·00
1268	150p. 18th-century French rook, king and knight	7·25	5·25
1269	200p. Painted faience rook, queen and bishop	9·00	6·50

241 Congress, UPU and Lebanon Post Emblems

1981. Air. 18th UPU Congress, Rio de Janeiro (1979).

1270	**241**	25p. blue, brown and black	2·00	90
1271	**241**	50p. pink, brown & black	3·25	1·70
1272	**241**	75p. green, brown and black	5·25	2·50

242 Children on Raft

1981. Air. International Year of the Child (1979).

1273	**242**	100p. multicoloured	6·50	4·00

243 President Sarkis

1981. Fifth Anniversary of Election of President Sarkis.

1274	**243**	125p. multicoloured	2·00	1·00
1275	**243**	300p. multicoloured	5·75	2·30
1276	**243**	500p. multicoloured	9·75	3·25

244 Society Emblem and Children

1981. Air. Centenary (1978) of Al-Makassed Islamic Welfare Society. Multicoloured.

1277	50p. Type **244**	1·00	25
1278	75p. Institute building	1·60	40
1279	100p. Al-Makassed (founder)	2·00	65

245 Stork carrying Food

1982. World Food Day (1981). Multicoloured.

1280	50p. Type **245**	1·60	50
1281	75p. Ear of wheat and globe	2·30	65
1282	100p. Fruit, fish and grain	3·25	1·20

246 WCY Emblem

1983. World Communications Year.

1283	**246**	300p. multicoloured	7·75	3·75

247 Phoenician Galley flying Scout Flag

1983. 75th Anniversary of Boy Scout Movement. Multicoloured.

1284	200p. Type **247**	4·00	2·00
1285	300p. Scouts lowering flag and signalling by semaphore	5·25	2·50
1286	500p. Camp	9·75	4·00

248 *The Soul is Back*

1983. Birth Centenary of Gibran (poet and painter). Multicoloured.

1287	200p. Type **248**	4·00	2·00
1288	300p. *The Family*	5·25	2·50
1289	500p. *Gibran*	9·75	4·00
1290	1000p. *The Prophet*	18·00	9·75
MS1291	130×151 mm. Nos. 1287/1290. Imperf (sold at L£25)	55·00	50·00

249 Cedar of Lebanon

1984

1292	**249**	5p. multicoloured	1·30	40

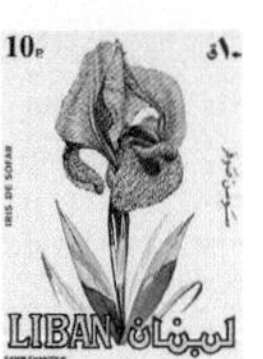

250 Iris

1984. Flowers. Multicoloured.

1293	10p. Type **250**	90	40
1294	25p. Periwinkle	1·60	80
1295	50p. Barberry	2·50	1·30

251 Dove with Laurel over Buildings

1984. Lebanese Army. Multicoloured.

1296	75p. Type **251**	2·30	90
1297	150p. Cedar and soldier holding rifle	4·50	2·10
1298	300p. Broken chain, hand holding laurel wreath and cedar	11·00	4·50

252 Temple Ruins, Fakra

1984. Multicoloured.

1299	100p. Type **252**	2·00	80
1300	200p. Temple ruins, Bziza	4·00	1·80
1301	500p. Roman arches and relief, Tyre	9·75	4·00

253 President taking Oath

1988. Installation of President Amin Gemayel.

1302	**253**	L£25 multicoloured	2·50	1·30

254 Map of South America and Cedar of Lebanon

1988. First World Festival of Lebanese Youth in Uruguay.

1303	**254**	L£5 multicoloured	1·60	65

255 Satellite, Flags and Earth

1988. *Arabsat* Telecommunications Satellite.

1304	**255**	L£10 multicoloured	1·30	65

256 Children

1988. UNICEF Child Survival Campaign.

1305	**256**	L£15 multicoloured	2·00	1·00

257 Arabic "75" and Scout Emblems

1988. 75th Anniversary (1987) of Arab Scouts Movement.

1306	**257**	L£20 multicoloured	3·25	1·30

258 President, Map and Dove

1988. International Peace Year (1986).

1307	**258**	L£50 multicoloured	5·25	2·00

259 Red Cross and Figures

1988. Red Cross.

1308	**259**	L£10+L£1 red, silver and black	2·00	1·00
1309	-	L£20+L£2 multicoloured	2·50	1·60
1310	-	L£30+L£3 silver, green and red	4·00	2·50

Designs: L£20, Helmeted heads; L£30, Globe, flame, and dove holding map of Lebanon.

260 Cedar of Lebanon

1989

1311	**260**	L£50 green and mauve	1·30	25
1312	**260**	L£70 green and brown	2·00	50
1313	**260**	L£100 green and yellow	2·30	80
1314	**260**	L£200 green and blue	4·25	1·60
1315	**260**	L£500 deep green and green	10·50	4·00

261 Dining in the Open at Zahle, 1883

1993. 50th Anniversary of Independence. Multicoloured.

1316	L£200 Type **261**	50·00	1·20
1317	L£300 Castle ruins, Saida (vert)	3·00	2·10
1318	L£500 Presidential Palace, Baabda	4·50	3·00
1319	L£1000 Sword ceremony (vert)	7·50	4·50
1320	L£3000 Model for the rebuilding of central Beirut	15·00	9·00
1321	L£5000 President Elias Hrawi and state flag (vert)	30·00	18·00
MS1322	130×149 mm. L£10000 As Nos. 1319/1324 but smaller and without face values. Imperf	£100	90·00

262 Protection of Plants

1994. Environmental Protection. Multicoloured.

1323	L£100 Type **262**	1·10	45
1324	L£200 Protection against forest fires	1·50	75
1325	L£500 Reforesting with cedars	3·50	1·80
1326	L£1000 Creation of urban green zones	6·50	3·75
1327	L£2000 Trees	11·50	6·00
1328	L£5000 Green tree in town	36·00	18·00

263 Martyrs' Monument, Beirut

1995. Martyrs' Day.

1329	**263**	L£1500 multicoloured	9·00	8·75

264 Arabic Script under Magnifying Glass and Headquarters

1996. Anniversaries and Events. Multicoloured.

1330	L£100 Type **264** (inauguration of Postal Museum, Arab League Headquarters, Cairo)	1·50	75
1331	L£500 Anniversary emblem (50th anniversary of UNICEF) (horiz)	6·00	3·75
1332	L£500 Ears of wheat and anniversary emblem (50th anniversary (1995) of FAO)	6·00	3·75
1333	L£1000 UN Building (New York) and anniversary emblem (50th anniversary (1995) of UNO)	12·00	7·50
1334	L£1000 Emblem (International Year of the Family (1994)) (horiz)	12·00	7·50

1335	L£2000 Anniversary emblem (75th anniversary (1994) of ILO) (horiz)	23·00	15·00
1336	L£2000 Emblem (50th anniversary of Arab League)	23·00	15·00
1337	L£3000 Emblem (75th anniversary (1994) of Lebanese Law Society)	30·00	23·00
1338	L£3000 Rene Moawad (former President, 70th birth anniversary (1995))	30·00	23·00

265 Commemorative Medallion

1997. First Anniversary of Shelling of Cana Refugee Camp.

1339	**265**	L£1100 multicoloured	15·00	15·00

266 Pope John Paul II and President Hrawi

1998. Papal Visit.

1340	**266**	L£10000 multicoloured	£225	£170

1999. Various stamps optd with a Fleuon values unchanged. Original numbers given.

1341	L£100 multicoloured (No. 1330)	4·00	3·75
1342	L£200 multicoloured (No. 1316)	9·50	9·00
1343	L£500 multicoloured (No. 1318)	24·00	23·00
1344	L£500 multicoloured (No. 1325)	24·00	23·00
1345	L£500 multicoloured (No. 1331)	24·00	23·00
1346	L£500 multicoloured (No. 1332)	24·00	23·00
1347	L£1000 multicoloured (No. 1319)	48·00	45·00
1348	L£1000 multicoloured (No. 1326)	48·00	45·00
1349	L£1000 multicoloured (No. 1333)	48·00	45·00
1350	L£1100 multicoloured (No. 1339)	£800	£750
1351	L£1500 multicoloured (No. 1329)	70·00	70·00
1352	L£2000 multicoloured (No. 1335)	80·00	75·00
1353	L£3000 multicoloured (No. 1337)	£140	£140
1354	L£5000 multicoloured (No. 1328)	£250	£225
1355	L£10000 multicoloured (No. 1340)	£475	£450

268 Cedar of Lebanon

1999

1356	**268**	L£100 red	95	45
1357	**268**	L£500 grey	1·60	1·20
1358	**268**	L£1000 blue	4·75	3·75
1359	**268**	L£300 turquoise	2·40	2·00
1360	**268**	L£1100 brown	6·50	4·25
1361	**268**	L£1500 violet	8·00	5·75

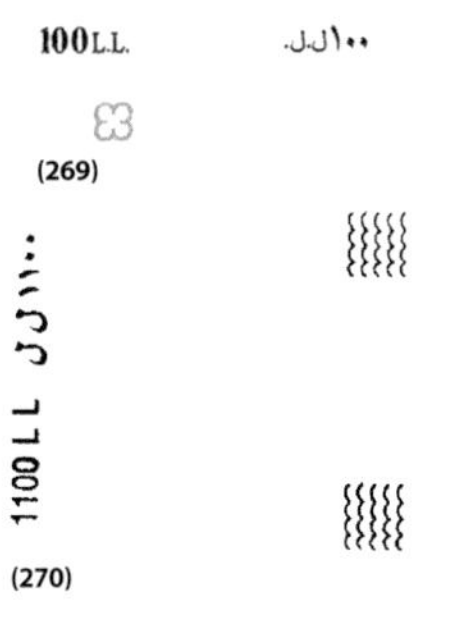

(269)

(270)

1999. Nos. 1295/1296 surch as T **269**. No. 1092 surch as T **270**.

1368	L£100 on L£50 multicoloured	1·60	90
1369	L£300 on L£75 multicoloured	3·25	2·10
1370	L£1100 on L£70 multicoloured	11·00	7·50

271 Emir Chehab's Palace, Hasbaya

1999. Buildings. Multicoloured.

1371	L£100 Type **271**	1·60	75
1372	L£300 UN Economic and Social Commission for Western Asia, Beirut	3·25	1·50
1373	L£500 Emir Fakhreddine's Palace, Deir-el-Kamar (horiz)	4·75	3·00
1374	L£1100 Grand Serail, Beirut (horiz)	8·00	6·75

1999. Nos. 1335 and 1338 optd with a Fleuron, values unchanged.

1375	L£2000 multicoloured	24·00	18·00
1376	L£3000 multicoloured	32·00	26·00

272 Flag and Soldiers

2001. Return of South Lebanon (1st series).

1377	**272**	L£1100 multicoloured	5·75	5·00

See also No. **MS**1391.

273 Ibrahim Abd el Al

2001. 93rd Birth Anniversary of Ibrahim Abd el Al (engineer).

1378	**273**	L£1000 multicoloured	5·00	5·50

274 Hand and Bars

2001. Prisoners.

1379	**274**	L£500 multicoloured	3·25	2·30

275 Emblem

2001. SOS Children's Villages.

1380	**275**	L£300 multicoloured	1·80	1·40

276 Hand holding '50'

2001. 50th Anniversaries.

1381	**276**	L£500 olive (Geneva Convention)	3·25	2·30
1382	-	L£1100 lilac (Geneva Convention)	4·75	4·50
1383	-	L£1500 multicoloured (Red Cross and Red Crescent)	6·50	6·50

Designs: L£500 T **276**; L£1100 Fist around bars and '50'; L£1500 Hand holding stylised people.

277 Ahas Abu Chabke

2001. 97th Birth Anniversary of Ahas Abu Chabke (writer).

1384	**277**	L£1500 multicoloured	7·25	6·25

278 Father Monnot and Emblem

2001. 125th Anniversary of Saint Joseph University, Beirut.

1385	**278**	L£5000 multicoloured	22·00	21·00

279 Abdallah Zakher

2001. 319th Birth Anniversary of Abdallah Zakher (first Arab printer).

1386	**279**	L£1000 multicoloured	4·75	4·50

280 UN Emblem

2001. 25th. Anniversary of UN Economic and Social Commission for Western Asia.

1387	**280**	L£10000 ultramarine, blue and mauve	48·00	44·00

281 Arabic Script

2002. Day of the Arab Woman.

1388	**281**	L£1000 multicoloured	5·00	4·50

282 Emblem

2002. Arab Summit Conference, Beirut. Multicoloured.

1389	L£2000 Type **282**	9·25	8·75
1390	L£3000 Cedar tree and President Emile Lahoud	13·50	13·00

283 President Emile Lahoud

2002. Return of Southern Lebanon (2nd series). Sheet 160×108 mm containing T **283** and similar vert designs. Multicoloured.

MS1391	L£1100×4 Type **283**; President Lahoud with raised arm; President Lahoud and map; Sword ceremony	22·00	21·00

284 Judges, Scales and Cedar Tree

2002. Martyrs. Sheet 120×90 mm.

MS1392	**284**	L£3000 multicoloured	13·50	13·00

285 UPU Emblem and Cedar Tree

2002. 125th Anniversary of Universal Postal Union.

1393	**285**	L£2000 multicoloured	8·00	7·00

286 Men seated at Table, Zouk Mikael

2002. Souks. Multicoloured.

1394	L£100 Type **286**	35	35
1395	L£300 Vendor with wheeled stall, Saida Souk	1·20	1·20
1396	L£500 Byblos (UNESCO world heritage site)	2·10	2·10
1397	L£1000 Carpet mender, Tripoli	4·25	4·25

287 Emblem and National Colours

2002. Ninth Francophile States Summit, Beirut.

1398	L£1500 Type **287**	6·50	5·25
1399	L£1500 President Lahoud	6·50	5·25

288 Emblem

2002. Beirut, Arab Culture Capital, 2002.

1400	**288**	L£2000 multicoloured	7·25	7·00

289 Roman Temple, Bziza

2002. Ruins. Multicoloured.

1401	L£1100 Type **289**	4·25	4·25
1402	L£1500 Arqa	6·00	6·00
1403	L£2000 Niha	8·50	8·50
1404	L£3000 Castle, Mousailaha	15·00	15·00

290 Lebanese Amber

2002. Fossils. Multicoloured.

1405	L£5000 Type **290**	25·00	25·00
1406	L£10000 Nematonotus longispinus	49·00	49·00

291 Tree, Signatures, Lebanese and French Leaders

2003. 60th Anniversary of Independence. Multicoloured.

1407	L£1250 Type **291**	4·75	3·25
1408	L£1250 Tree, signatures and parade	4·75	3·25
1409	L£1750 Tree, signatures and dignitaries	6·50	4·75
1410	L£1750 Tree and signatures	6·50	4·75
MS1411	160×110 mm. L£6000 Nos. 1407/1410. Imperf	21·00	17·00

292 Postal Building before Restoration, Riad El Solh–Beirut

2004. Restoration of Posts and Telecommunications Buildings. Multicoloured.

1412	L£100 Type **292**	65	30
1413	L£300 Restored building	95	50

293 Snow Scene, Faqra

2004. Tourism.

1414	**293** L£500 multicoloured	1·60	95

294 Musical Score and Emblem

2004. Al Bustan Music Festival, Riad El Solh–Beirut.

1415	**294** L£1000 multicoloured	3·25	1·90

295 Kamouaa

2004. Tourism. Ski Resorts. Multicoloured.

1416	L£100 Type **295**	50	30
1417	L£100 Aayoun Siman	50	30
1418	L£250 Laklouk (vert)	95	65
1419	L£300 Zaarour	1·30	70
1420	L£300 Kanat Bakish	1·30	70
1421	L£1000 Cedres	2·40	1·60

296 Anniversary Emblem and Hospital (1/2-size illustration)

2004. 125th Anniversary of St Georges Hospital, Beirut.

1422	**296** L£3000 multicoloured	8·00	6·50

297 Baalbeck International Festival

2004. Festivals. Multicoloured.

1423	L£500 Type **297**	1·60	1·10
1424	L£1250 Tyre (vert)	4·00	2·75
1425	L£1400 Beiteddine (vert)	4·75	3·25
1426	L£1750 Byblos (vert)	6·50	4·75

298 Rafic Hariri International Airport

2005. Buildings. Multicoloured.

1427	L£100 Type **298**	30	30
1428	L£250 Parliament	80	80
1429	L£300 Camille Chamoun Sports Centre	95	95
1430	L£500 National Museum	1·60	1·60
1431	L£1000 Government Palace	3·25	3·25
1432	L£1250 National Bank	4·00	4·00
1433	L£1400 St Paul Cathedral	4·50	4·50
1434	L£1750 Bahaeddine Hariri Mosque	5·50	5·50
1435	L£2000 Presidential Palace	6·50	6·50

299 Centenary Emblem

2005. Centenary of Rotary International.

1436	**299** L£3000 multicoloured	8·00	6·50

300 Rafic Hariri, Towers and Statue

2006. Rafic Hariri (prime minister 1992–1998 and 2000–2004) Commemoration. Multicoloured.

1437	L£1250 Type **300**	5·50	4·50
1438	L£1250 Rafic Hariri and flag	5·50	4·50
1439	L£1750 Mosque	7·50	6·25
1440	L£1750 Child kissing portrait	7·50	6·25
MS1441	160×110 mm. Nos. 1437/1440. Imperf	26·00	21·00

301 Pile of Books

2007. 50th Anniversary of Book Fair.

1442	**301** L£1000 multicoloured	3·75	3·50

302 Basil Fuleihan

2007. Basil Fuleihan (Minister of Economy and Finance 2000–2003 (assassinated in 2005)) Commemoration. Multicoloured.

1443	L£500 Type **302**	1·90	1·80
1444	L£1500 Seated at desk, signing agreement and National and EU flags	5·50	5·25
1445	L£2000 Head in hand and National Flag	7·50	7·00

303 President Chehab

2007. President Fouad Chehab Commemoration.

1446	**303** L£1400 multicoloured	4·50	4·25

304 Globe and Emblem

2007. World Information Society Summit, Tunis.

1447	**304** L£100 multicoloured	55	55

305 '125' (Arabic) enclosing Emblem

2007. 125th Anniversary of Makassed Islamic Welfare Organisation in Beirut (2003) (1448/1450 and 1453) and Saida (2004) (1451/1452). Multicoloured.

1448	L£250 Type **305**	95	90
1449	L£500 Saeb Salam (prime minister 1952, 1953, 1960–1961, 1970–1973) (Makassed chairman 1957–1982)	1·70	1·60
1450	L£1400 Rafic Hariri (prime minister 1992–1998, 2000–2004 (assassinated 2005))	5·00	4·75
1451	L£1400 Rafic Hariri (different)	5·00	4·75
1452	L£1750 Riad El Solh (first prime minister)	6·00	5·75
1453	L£1750 Omar El Daouk	6·00	5·75

306 Leopold Senghor

2007. Birth Centenary of Leopold Sedar Senghor (poet and president of Senegal 1960–1980). La Francophonie (organisation of French speaking countries).

1454	**306** L£300 multicoloured	1·30	1·20

307 Athlete (sculpture)

2007. International Year of Sports and Sports Education (2005).

1455	**307** L£500 multicoloured	2·20	2·10

308 Names of Artistes

2007. 50th Anniversary of Baalbek International Festival. Multicoloured.

1456	L£1000 Type **308**	3·25	3·25
1457	L£5000 Female artistes	11·00	10·50

309 '30'

2007. 30th Anniversary of OPEC Development Fund.

1458	**309** L£1400 multicoloured	4·50	4·25

310 Maxime Chaya and Flag on Summit

2007. Maxime Chaya (1st Lebanese climber to reach top of Mount Everest). Sheet 160×110 mm.

MS1459	**310** £3000 multicoloured	8·25	8·00

311 *Hills* (detail) (painting by Nizar Daher)

2007. Sheet 160×110 mm.

MS1460	**311** L£5000 multicoloured	13·00	12·50

312 Dove and Broken Bars (image scaled to 30% of original size)

2007. Return of Prisoners. Sheet 160×110 mm. Imperf.

MS1461	**312** L£5000 multicoloured	13·00	12·50

313 Mother and Child

2008. 125th Birth Anniversary of Gibran Khalil Gibran (writer and artist). Multicoloured.

1462	L£100 Type **313**	35	35
1463	L£500 Sultana	1·90	1·80
1464	L£1400 Gibran Museum	5·25	5·00
1465	L£2000 Khalil Gibran	7·50	7·00
MS1466	160×110 mm. L£4000 As Nos. 1462/5. Imperf	15·00	14·50

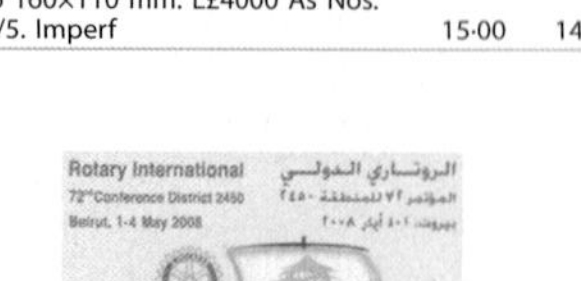

314 Flags as Rowers

2008. Rotary International Conference, Beirut.

1467	**314** L£2000 multicoloured	7·50	7·00

315 Pigeon

2008. Arab Post Day. Sheet 170×60 mm containing T **315** and similar horiz design. Multicoloured.

MS1468	L£5000 Type **315**; L£5000 Camels	19·00	18·00

316 Soldier, Flag and Moon

2008. Army Day. Multicoloured.

1469	L£500 Type **316**	1·90	1·80
1470	L£1000 Script and tree	3·75	3·50
1471	L£1250 Hand holding grain	4·75	4·50
1472	L£1750 Eye enclosing emblem	6·50	6·25
MS1473	160×110 mm. L£4500 As Nos. 1469/1472. Imperf	17·00	16·00

317 Aircraft and Envelope

2008. Tenth Anniversary of LIBANPOST. Multicoloured.
1474 L£1250 Type **317** 4·75 4·50
1475 L£1750 10th ANNIVERSARY 6·50 6·25
MS1476 160× 110 mm. L£3000 As Nos. 1474/1475. Imperf 11·50 11·00

318 Oak, Map of Mediterranean and Cedar Tree

2008. Lebanon–France Relations.
1477 **318** L£1750 multicoloured 6·50 6·25
A stamp of a similar design was issued by France.

319 Francois El Hajj

2008. First Death Anniversary of General Francois El Hajj.
1478 **319** L£1750 multicoloured 6·50 6·25

320 Charles Malik (member of Commission)

2008. 60th Anniversary of Universal Declaration of Human Rights.
1479 **320** L£2000 multicoloured 7·50 7·00

321 Emblem

2009. al-Quds 2009. Capital of Arab Culture.
1480 **321** L£1000 multicoloured 4·00 3·75

322 Pierre Deschamps (founder)

2009. Centenary of Mission Laique Francaise (network of French schools abroad).
1481 **322** L£500 multicoloured 2·00 1·90

323 Emblem

2009. Beirut. Book Capital of the World.
1482 **323** L£750 multicoloured 3·00 2·75

324 Emblem

2009. Sixth Francophone Games.
1483 **324** L£1000 multicoloured 4·00 3·75

325 Civil Defence Workers

2010. Civil Defence. Multicoloured.
1484 L£100 Type **325** 40 40
1485 L£250 Firefighters 1·00 95

326 Plants

2010. Lebanon Nature Reserves.
1486 **326** L£300 multicoloured 1·20 1·10

327 Building with Colonnade

2010. Traditional Buildings. Multicoloured.
1487 L£500 Type **327** 2·00 1·90
1488 L£1000 Two storied building with white glazed door and blue shutters 4·00 3·75
1489 L£1250 Two storied building with blue door and shutters 5·00 4·75

328 Soaps

2010. Traditional Industries. Soap.
1490 **328** L£1400 multicoloured 5·50 5·25

329 Soldier carrying Map of Lebanon as Bag

2010. Lebanese Army.
1491 **329** L£1750 multicoloured 7·00 6·75

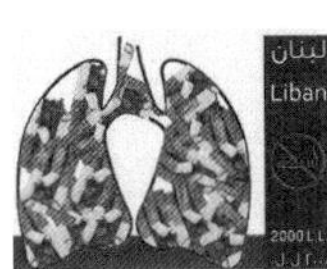

330 Lungs full of Cigarette Butts

2010. Anti Drugs and Tobacco Awareness Campaign.
1492 L£2000 multicoloured 8·00 7·50
1493 L£5000 black and scarlet-vermilion (*vert*) 20·00 19·00
Designs: L£2000 T **330**; L£5000 Needle and emblem.

331 Al Imam Al Ouzai (inscr 'Al Imam Al Ouzaai')

2010. Personalities. Al Imam Al Ouzai Commemoration.
1494 **331** L£1000 multicoloured 4·00 3·75

332 President-Elect Bachir Gemayel

2010. Martyrs. Multicoloured.
1495 L£1400 Type **332** 5·50 5·25
1496 L£1400 Kamal Jumblatt (politician) (inscr 'Kamal Joumblat') (*vert*) 5·50 5·25
1497 L£1400 Prime Minister Rashid Karame (*vert*) 5·50 5·25
1498 L£1400 Mufti Hassan Khaled 5·50 5·25
1499 L£1400 President Rene Mouawad (*vert*) 5·50 5·25
1500 L£1400 Mūsá aṣ-Ṣadr (*vert*) 5·50 5·25

333 Woman and Globe

2010. World Tourism Day. 'An Open Door for Women'.
1501 **333** L£2000 multicoloured 8·00 7·50

334 Dove and Flowers

2010. Peace.
1502 **334** L£3000 multicoloured 12·00 11·50

335 Early Writing

2011. Cradle of the Alphabet.
1503 **335** L£250 multicoloured 1·00 95

336 Hand holding Quill and Flag

2011. Arab Permanent Postal Commission.
1504 **336** L£500 multicoloured 2·00 1·90

337 Sabah

2011. Personalities. Sabah (Jeanette Gergi Feghali) (singer and actress).
1505 **337** L£1750 multicoloured 7·00 6·75

338 Nabih Abou El-Hossn

2011. Personalities. Nabih Abou El-Hassan (El0Hossn) (actor) Commemoration.
1506 **338** L£2250 multicoloured 9·00 8·50

339 Hassan Alaa Eddine

2011. Personalities. Hassan Alaa Eddine ('Chouchou') (comedian) Commemoration.
1507 **339** L£2750 multicoloured 11·00 10·50

340 Caracalla

2011. Caracalla (dance troup).
1508 **340** L£3000 multicoloured 12·00 11·50

341 Michel, Alfred, and Youssef Basbous

2011. Personalities. Basbous Brothers (sculptors).
1509 **341** L£5000 multicoloured 20·00 19·00

342 Said Akl

2011. Personalities. Said Akl (poet) Commemoration.
1510 **342** L£10000 multicoloured 40·00 38·00

343 Ehden Reserve

2011. Ehden Reserve.
1511 **343** L£750 multicoloured 3·00 2·75

344 President Frangiè

2011. President Sleiman Frangiè (Suleiman Kabalan Frangieh) Commemoration.
1512 **344** L£1000 multicoloured 4·00 3·75

345 Fayrouz (Fairuz)

2011. Personalities. Fayrouz (Nouhad Wadi Haddad) (singer).
1513 **345** L£1500 multicoloured 6·00 5·75

346 Wadih El Safi

2011. Personalities. Wadih El Safi (Wadi' Francis) (singer, songwriter and actor) Commemoration.
1514 **346** L£2000 multicoloured 8·00 7·50

347 President Sulaiman

2011. President Michel Sulaiman. Multicoloured.
1515 L£750 Type **347** 3·00 2·75

1516 L£1750 Children in background 7·00 6·75
1517 L£2500 Dove with flags as wings 10·00 9·50
1518 L£2750 United Nations emblem 11·00 10·50

348 Mother and Children

2012. Mothers' Day.
1519 **348** L£2000 multicoloured £140 £130

349 Cedar of Lebanon and Emblem

2012. 60th Anniversary of Lions International.
1520 **349** L£750 violet 3·00 2·75

350 Pope Benedict XVI and Pres. Sulaiman

2012. Pope Benedict XVI's visit to Lebanon.
1521 **350** L£1250 multicoloured 5·00 4·75

351 Emblem

2012. Tenth Anniversary of Beirut Marathon.
1522 **351** L£750 multicoloured 3·00 2·75

352 Father Christmas

2012. Christmas.
1523 **352** L£2000 multicoloured 8·00 7·50

353 *The Lebanese Emigrant*

2012. *The Lebanese Emigrant* Statue, Beirut.
1524 **353** L£500 multicoloured 2·00 1·90

354 Adel Osseiran

2012. Personalities. Adel Osseiran (politician) Commemoration.
1525 **354** L£1000 multicoloured 4·00 3·75

355 Areas of Research and Relief Map

2012. 50th Anniversary of Lebanese National Council for Scientific Research.
1526 **355** L£250 multicoloured 1·00 95

356 President Sulaiman and Symbols of Civilisations

2012. International Centre for Dialogue between Civilisations.
1527 **356** L£250 multicoloured 1·00 95

357 Ghassan Tueni

2012. Personalities. Ghassan Tueni (poitician) Commemoration.
1528 **357** L£750 multicoloured 3·00 2·75

358 Said Akl

2012. Personalities. Birth Centenary of Said Akl (writer).
1529 **358** L£500 multicoloured 2·00 1·90

359 Birds

2013. Mothers' Day.
1530 **359** L£2000 multicoloured 8·00 7·50

360 Anniversary Emblem

2013. 15th Anniversary of Libanpost.
1531 **360** L£3000 multicoloured 12·00 11·50

361 Amin Maalouf

2013. Personalities. Amin Maalouf. Member of the French Academy.
1532 **361** L£100 multicoloured 40 40

362 Flag

2013. 70th Anniversary of Independence.
1533 **362** L£1000 multicoloured 4·00 3·75

363 Father Christmas and Snowmen

2013. Christmas.
1534 **363** L£2000 multicoloured 8·00 7·50

364 Statue

2014. Armenian Genocide Memorial, Bikfaya, Lebanon.
1535 **364** L£2000 multicoloured 8·00 7·50

365 Building Façade

2014. 300th Anniversary of St Joseph University.
1536 **365** L£500 multicoloured 2·00 1·90

366 Laure Moughaizel (Attorney and Women's Rights Advocate)

2014. Personalities. Prominent Women. Multicoloured.
1537 L£2000 Type **366** 8·00 7·50
1538 L£2000 Alexandra Issa el Khoury (President of Lebanese Red Cross) 8·00 7·50
1539 L£2000 Mounira el Solh (one of first women in Lebanon and Middle East to run for parliament) 8·00 7·50
1540 L£2000 Anissa Najjar (founder of WILPF Lebanon) 8·00 7·50

367 Banknotes

2014. 50th Anniversary of Bank of Lebanon.
1541 **367** L£1750 multicoloured 7·00 6·75

368 Father and Children

2014. Fathers' Day.
1542 **368** L£1750 multicoloured 7·00 6·75

369 The Mediterranean

2014. EUROMED. Euromed 2014 Postal Conference.
1543 **369** L£1000 multicoloured 4·00 3·75

370 Fuleco (mascot)

2014. World Cup Football Championships. Brazil. Multicoloured.
1544 L£1750 Type **370** 7·00 6·75
1545 L£2000 Trophy 8·00 7·50

371 Germanos Mouakkad

2014. Personalities. Germanos Mouakkad (founder of Missionary Society of St Paul, Harissa, Lebanon) Commemoration.
1546 **371** L£250 multicoloured 1·00 95

372 Ounsi El-Hage

2014. Personalities. Poets and Philosophers. Multicoloured.
1547 L£1750 Type **372** 7·00 6·75
1548 L£1750 Kamal Youssef El-Hage 7·00 6·75
1549 L£1750 Joseph Harb 7·00 6·75

373 Youssef Bey Karam

2014. Personalities. Youssef Bey Karam (Maronite notable who fought in civil war and led a rebellion against Ottoman Empire) Commemoration.
1550 **373** L£1750 multicoloured 7·00 6·75

374 Flag as Map

2014. Independence of Lebanon.
1551 **374** L£2750 multicoloured 11·00 10·50

375 '2015'

2014. Season's Greetings.
1552 **375** L£5000 multicoloured 20·00 19·00

376 Saints Cyprien et Justine Convent, Kfifane

2015. Convents. Multicoloured.
1553 L£250 Type **376** 1·00 95
1554 L£250 Saint Jean Al Kalaa Convent, Beit Mery (*vert*) 1·00 95

1555 L£250 Saint Sauveur Convent, Beit Mery 1·00 95

377 Said Freiha

2015. Personalities. Said Freiha (journalist and founder of Dar Assayad) Commemoration.
1556 **377** L£1750 multicoloured 7·00 6·75

378 Internal Security Forces Emblem

2015. National Security Forces. Multicoloured.
1557 L£1750 Type **378** 7·00 6·75
1558 L£1750 General Security Forces emblem 7·00 6·75

379 Mother and Daughter

2015. Mothers' Day.
1559 **379** L£2000 multicoloured 8·00 7·50

380 Pierre Sadek

2015. Personalities. Second Death Anniversary of Pierre Sadek (caricaturist).
1560 **380** L£2250 multicoloured 9·00 8·50

381 Leila Osserian

2015. Personalities. Leila Osseiran and Amine El Hafez Commemoration. Multicoloured.
1561 L£1750 Type **381** 7·00 6·75
1562 L£1750 Amine El Hafez 7·00 6·75

382 Boats

2015. EUROMED. Boats of the Mediterranean.
1563 **382** L£5000 multicoloured 20·00 19·00

383 Bechara El Khoury

2015. Personalities. Politicians. Multicoloured.
1564 L£1750 Type **383** (first president) 7·00 6·75
1565 L£1750 Riad El Solh (first prime minister) 7·00 6·75

384 *The Red Sunset* (Saliba Doughy)

2015. Paintings.
1566 **384** L£2000 multicoloured 8·00 7·50

385 Flag

2015. National Flag Day.
1567 **385** £L2000 multicoloured 8·00 7·50

386 '2016'

2015. Season's Greetings.
1568 **386** L£2000 multicoloured 8·00 7·50

387 Jawad Boulos

2016. Personalities. Multicoloured.
1569 L£2000 Type **387** (politician) 8·00 7·50
1570 L£2000 Hani Fahs (Fahes) (founding member of Arab Committee for Islamic–Christian Dialogue) 8·00 7·50

388 Flags and Church of Saidet et Talleh

2016. Deir al-Qamar.
1571 **388** L£250 multicoloured 1·00 95

389 Workers

2016. International Labour Day.
1572 **389** L£2000 multicoloured 8·00 7·50

390 Monument

2016. Centenary of the Martyrs of 6 May.
1573 **390** L£2000 multicoloured 8·00 7·50

391 Fish

2015. EUROMED. Fish of the Mediterranean.
1574 **391** L£2250 multicoloured 9·00 8·50

392 Anniversary Emblem

2016. 60th Anniversary of Baalbeck Festival.
1575 **392** L£2000 multicoloured 8·00 7·50

393 Emblem as Medal

2016. Lebanese Olympic Committee.
1576 **393** L£250 multicoloured 1·00 95

394 Elie Snaifer

2016. Personalities. Elie Snaifer (comedian, actor and playwright) Commemoration.
1577 **394** L£250 multicoloured 1·00 95

395 Emblem

2016. 70th Anniversary of UPU Membership.
1578 **395** L£2000 multicoloured 8·00 7·50

396 Building Façade

2016. 140th Anniversary of La Sagesse Academic Institute.
1579 **396** L£2000 multicoloured 8·00 7·50

397 Emblem, Globe and Envelopes

2016. Arab Post Day. Multicoloured.
1580 L£10000 Type **397** 40·00 38·00
1581 L£10000 As Type **397** but with design reversed 40·00 38·00

398 Abdul Hamid Karami

2016. Personalities in the Fight for Independence. Multicoloured.
1582 L£250 Type **398** 1·00 95
1583 L£250 Adnan Al Hakim 1·00 95
1584 L£250 Camile Chamoun 1·00 95
1585 L£250 Habib Abou Chahla 1·00 95
1586 L£250 Hamid Frangieh 1·00 95
1587 L£250 Henri Pharaon 1·00 95
1588 L£250 Majid Arslan 1·00 95
1589 L£250 Maroun Kanaan 1·00 95
1590 L£250 Mohamad El Fadl 1·00 95
1591 L£250 Pierre Gemayel 1·00 95
1592 L£250 Rashid Baydoun 1·00 95
1593 L£250 Saadi Al Mounla 1·00 95
1594 L£250 Sabri Hamadeh 1·00 95
1595 L£250 Saeb Salam 1·00 95
1596 L£250 Selim Takla 1·00 95

399 Building and Emblem

2016. 150th Anniversary of American University of Beirut.
1597 **399** L£2000 multicoloured 8·00 7·50

400 Zaki Nassif

2016. Personalities. Zaki Nassif (songwriter) Commemoration.
1598 **400** L£2000 multicoloured 8·00 7·50

401 '2017'

2016. New Year.
1599 **401** L£5000 multicoloured 20·00 19·00

402 Child receiving Immunisation Drops

2017. 30th Anniversary of Anti-Polio Programme.
1600 **402** L£2000 multicoloured 8·00 7·50

403 Woman's Face

2017. International Women's Day. Women in Power.
1601 **403** L£10000 multicoloured 40·00 38·00

404 Sursock Museum

2017. Museums. Multicoloured.

1602	L£2000 Type **404**	8·00	7·50
1603	L£2000 Aquamarine (Mineral Museum, Beirut)	8·00	7·50
1604	L£2000 Phoenician sarcophagi (National Museum, Beirut (75th anniversary))	8·00	7·50

405 Building

2017. Centenary of the Islamic Orphanage.

1605	**405**	L£2000 multicoloured	8·00	7·50

406 Instruments

2017. World Music Day.

1606	**406**	L£250 multicoloured	1·00	95

407 Cedar of Lebanon

2015. EUROMED. Trees of the Mediterranean.

1607	**407**	L£2250 multicoloured	9·00	8·50

408 Mikhail Naimy

2017. Personalities. Mikhail Naimy (writer) Commemoration.

1608	**408**	L£250 multicoloured	1·00	95

409 Shaking Hands

2017. Lebanese Army Day.

1609	**409**	L£2000 multicoloured	8·00	7·50

410 Carlos Ghosn

2017. Personalities. Carlos Ghosn (business leader).

1610	**410**	L£2000 multicoloured	8·00	7·50

411 Zalfa Chamoun

2017. Personalities. Zalfa Tabet Chamoun (wife of President Camille Chamoun) Commemoration.

1611	**411**	L£2000 multicoloured	8·00	7·50

412 Nasri Chamessedine

2017. Personalities. 90th Birth Anniversary of Nasri Chamessedine (singer and actor).

1612	**412**	L£250 multicoloured	1·00	95

413 A Helping Hand

2017. Caritas Lebanon.

1613	**413**	L£2000 multicoloured	8·00	7·50

414 Mohamed Baalbaki

2017. Personalities. Mohamed Baalbaki (Press Federation President) Commemoration.

1614	**414**	L£2000 multicoloured	8·00	7·50

415 President Aoun

2017. President Michel Aoun. Multicoloured.

1615	L£5000 Type **415**	20·00	19·00
1616	L£5000 Return of National Flag to the House of the People (horiz)	20·00	19·00
1617	L£5000 President Aoun and demonstrators (horiz)	20·00	19·00

POSTAGE DUE STAMPS

1924. Postage Due stamps of France surch **GRAND LIBAN** and value in CENTIEMES or PIASTRES.

D26	**D11**	50c. on 10c. brown	6·25	8·75
D27	**D11**	1p. on 20c. green	6·25	11·00
D28	**D11**	2p. on 30c. red	6·25	8·75
D29	**D11**	3p. on 50c. purple	6·25	8·75
D30	**D11**	5p. on 1f. purple on yellow	6·25	8·75

1924. Postage Due stamps of France surch **Gd Liban** and value in French and Arabic.

D58	**D11**	0p.50 on 10c. brown	7·25	8·00
D59	**D11**	1p. on 20c. green	7·25	8·00
D60	**D11**	2p. on 30c. red	7·25	8·00
D61	**D11**	3p. on 50c. purple	7·25	9·75
D62	**D11**	5p. on 1f. purple on yell	7·25	9·75

D7 Nahr el-Kalb

1925

D75	**D7**	0p.50 brown on yellow	1·30	3·50
D76	-	1p. red on pink	1·40	5·50
D77	-	2p. black on blue	2·40	4·00
D78	-	3p. brown on orange	3·75	11·50
D79	-	5p. black on green	4·25	10·50

Designs: Horiz—1p. Pine Forest, Beirut; 2p. Pigeon Grotto, Beirut; 3p. Beaufort Castle; 5p. Baalbeck.

1927. Optd **Republique Libanaise**.

D122	**D7**	0p.50 brown on yellow	1·50	4·25
D123	-	1p. red on pink	1·80	7·25
D124	-	2p. black on blue	3·50	9·00
D125	-	3p. brown on orange	5·25	6·50
D126	-	5p. black on green	7·00	16·00

1928. Nos. D122/D126 optd with T **10**.

D145	**D7**	0p.50 brown on yellow	2·75	7·00
D146	-	1p. red on pink	2·75	8·25
D147	-	2p. black on blue	3·75	8·25
D148	-	3p. brown on orange	7·50	14·00
D149	-	5p. black on green	8·50	21·00

D18 **D19** Bas-relief from Sarcophagus of King Ahiram at Byblos

D32

1931

D191	**D18**	0p.50 black on pink	1·30	2·50
D192	-	1p. black on blue	2·30	2·75
D193	-	2p. black on yellow	2·50	2·50
D194	-	3p. black on green	3·75	3·00
D195	**D32**	5p. black on orange	12·00	13·00
D196	**D19**	8p. black on pink	7·00	11·50
D252	**D32**	10p. green	14·50	18·00
D197	-	15p. black	7·75	7·00

Designs: 1p. Bas-relief of Phoenician galley; 2p. Arabesque; 3p. Garland; 15p. Statuettes.

D43 National Museum

1945

D298	**D43**	2p. black on lemon	6·25	5·75
D299	**D43**	5p. blue on pink	7·75	7·25
D300	**D43**	25p. blue on green	10·50	9·50
D301	**D43**	50p. purple on blue	11·50	11·00

D53

1947

D352	**D53**	5p. black on green	8·50	2·20
D353	**D53**	25p. black on yellow	85·00	5·75
D354	**D53**	50p. black on blue	44·00	14·50

D59 Monument at Hermel

1948

D379	**D59**	2p. black on yellow	5·50	1·40
D380	**D59**	3p. black on pink	11·50	5·25
D381	**D59**	10p. black on blue	31·00	9·75

D67

1950

D416	**D67**	1p. red	1·30	25
D417	**D67**	5p. blue	6·50	1·30
D418	**D67**	10p. green	9·00	2·50

D78

1952

D464	**D78**	1p. mauve	40	15
D465	**D78**	2p. violet	65	40
D466	**D78**	3p. green	80	40
D467	**D78**	5p. blue	1·20	50
D468	**D78**	10p. brown	2·20	90
D469	**D78**	25p. black	17·00	2·20

D81

1953

D481	**D81**	1p. red	25	15
D482	**D81**	2p. green	40	25
D483	**D81**	3p. orange	50	25
D484	**D81**	5p. purple	65	40
D485	**D81**	10p. brown	1·30	50
D486	**D81**	15p. blue	2·50	1·20

D93

1955

D550	**D93**	1p. brown	25	25
D551	**D93**	2p. green	40	25
D552	**D93**	3p. turquoise	50	25
D553	**D93**	5p. purple	65	25
D554	**D93**	10p. green	90	40
D555	**D93**	15p. blue	1·00	45
D556	**D93**	25p. purple	2·20	1·30

D178

1967

D967	**D178**	1p. green	50	25
D968	**D178**	5p. mauve	65	40
D969	**D178**	15p. blue	1·00	90

D184 Emir Fakhreddine II

1968

D1004	**D184**	1p. slate and grey	20	15
D1005	**D184**	2p. turquoise & green	25	15
D1006	**D184**	3p. orange & yellow	35	20
D1007	**D184**	5p. purple and red	40	25
D1008	**D184**	10p. olive and yellow	65	35
D1009	**D184**	15p. blue and violet	90	65
D1010	**D184**	25p. blue & lt blue	1·30	1·00

POSTAL TAX STAMPS

These were issued between 1945 and 1962 for compulsory use on inland mail (and sometimes on mail to Arab countries) to provide funds for various purposes.

T41

(T42)

1945. Lebanese Army. Fiscal stamp as Type **T41** surch with Type **T42**.

T289	**T41**	5p. on 30c. brown	£800	4·25

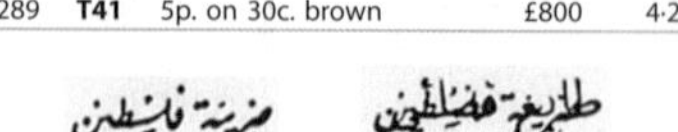

(T50) **(T51)**

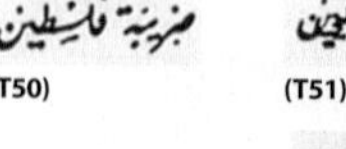

(T52)

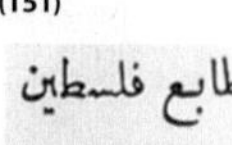

T56 Palestine stamp

1947. Aid to War in Palestine. Surch as Type **T42**. (a) With top line Type **T50**.

T338	5p. on 25c. green	36·00	3·00

T339	5p. on 30c. brown	47·00	6·00
T340	5p. on 60c. blue	80·00	4·25
T341	5p. on 3p. pink	36·00	5·50
T342	5p. on 15p. blue	36·00	2·20

(b) With top line Type **T51**.

T343	5p. on 10p. red	£160	9·50

(c) With top line Type **T52**.

T344	5p. on 3p. pink	33·00	3·00

(d) As No. T344 but with figure '5' at left instead of '0' and without inscr between figures.

T345	5p. on 3p. pink	£600	38·00

1948. Palestine Aid. No. T289 optd with Type **T56**.

T363	5p. on 30c. brown	33·00	4·25

T95 Family and Ruined House

1956. Earthquake Victims.

T559	**T95**	2p.50 brown	5·75	40

T99 Rebuilding

T100 Rebuilding

1957. Earthquake Victims.

T601	**T99**	2p.50 brown	5·75	40
T602	**T99**	2p.50 green	3·25	40
T603	**T100**	2p.50 brown	4·00	25

T132 Rebuilding

T133 Rebuilding

1961. Earthquake Victims.

T729	**T132**	2p.50 brown	3·50	25
T730	**T133**	2p.50 blue	3·50	25

LEEWARD ISLANDS

A group of islands in the Br. W. Indies, including Antigua, Barbuda, British Virgin Islands, Dominica (till end of 1939), Montserrat, Nevis and St. Christopher (St. Kitts). Stamps of Leeward Islands were used concurrent with the issues for the respective islands until they were withdrawn on the 1 July 1956.

1890. 12 pence = 1 shilling; 20 shillings = 1 pound.
1951. 100 cents = 1 West Indian dollar.

1

1890

1	1	½d. mauve and green	3·50	1·25
2	1	1d. mauve and red	8·50	20
3	1	2½d. mauve and blue	9·50	30
4	1	4d. mauve and orange	11·00	9·50
5	1	6d. mauve and brown	13·00	17·00
6	1	7d. mauve and grey	11·00	22·00
7	1	1s. green and red	23·00	60·00
8	1	5s. green and blue	£140	£325

(3)

1897. Diamond Jubilee. Optd with T **3**.

9	1	½d. mauve and green	8·00	26·00
10	1	1d. mauve and red	9·00	26·00
11	1	2½d. mauve and blue	9·50	26·00
12	1	4d. mauve and orange	55·00	80·00
13	1	6d. mauve and brown	60·00	£130
14	1	7d. mauve and grey	60·00	£130
15	1	1s. green and red	£130	£275
16	1	5s. green and blue	£450	£800

1902. Surch **One Penny**.

17	1	1d. on 4d. mauve and orange	6·50	12·00
18	1	1d. on 6d. mauve and brown	8·00	19·00
19	1	1d. on 7d. mauve and grey	6·50	16·00

1902. As T **1**, but portrait of King Edward VII.

29	½d. purple and green	5·50	2·50
21	1d. purple and red	11·00	20
22	2d. purple and brown	3·50	4·25
23	2½d. purple and blue	7·00	2·25
24	3d. purple and black	12·00	7·50
25	6d. purple and brown	2·50	8·00
26	1s. green and red	11·00	30·00
27	2s.6d. green and black	30·00	80·00
28	5s. green and blue	65·00	95·00

1907. As last, but colours changed.

36	¼d. brown	2·75	1·75
37	½d. green	6·50	2·00
38	1d. red	16·00	80
39	2d. grey	6·00	15·00
40	2½d. blue	9·50	4·25
41	3d. purple and yellow	3·50	7·50
42	6d. purple	10·00	12·00
43	1s. black on green	9·50	21·00
44	2s.6d. black and red on blue	42·00	55·00
45	5s. green and red on yellow	48·00	65·00

10 King George V

1912

46	**10**	¼d. brown	1·75	1·00
59	**10**	½d. green	1·25	75
60	**10**	1d. red	2·25	55
61	**10**	1d. violet	2·25	1·00
63	**10**	1½d. red	9·50	1·50
64	**10**	1½d. brown	2·50	10
65	**10**	2d. grey	3·00	1·00
66	**10**	2½d. yellow	14·00	70·00
67	**10**	2½d. blue	3·50	1·25
68	**10**	3d. blue	18·00	42·00
69	**10**	3d. purple on yellow	9·00	6·50
70	**10**	4d. black and red on yellow	4·25	21·00
71	**10**	5d. purple and green	2·50	4·25
53	**10**	6d. purple	4·50	9·50
54	**10**	1s. black on green	4·00	8·00
74*a*	**10**	2s. purple and blue on blue	14·00	48·00
75	**10**	2s.6d. black and red on blue	14·00	28·00
76	**10**	3s. green and violet	12·00	48·00
77	**10**	4s. black and red	21·00	42·00
57*b*	**10**	5s. green and red on yellow	50·00	85·00

10 King George V

1912. Larger type, as T **15** of Malta

79	10s. green and red on green	80·00	£140
80	£1 purple and black on red	£225	£350

1935. Silver Jubilee. As T **14a** of Kenya, Uganda and Tanganyika.

88	1d. blue and red	1·90	3·50
89	1½d. blue and grey	2·75	1·25
90	2½d. brown and blue	5·00	4·75
91	1s. grey and purple	28·00	48·00

1937. Coronation. As T **14b** of Kenya, Uganda and Tanganyika.

92	1d. red	80	1·00
93	1½d. brown	80	1·50
94	2½d. blue	90	1·50

14 King George VI

1938

95a	**14**	¼d. brown	30	2·00
96	**14**	½d. green	2·00	70
97	**14**	½d. grey	2·00	1·50
99	**14**	1d. red	2·25	1·75
100	**14**	1d. green	55	15
101	**14**	1½d. brown	1·00	50
102	**14**	1½d. orange and black	1·75	40
103	**14**	2d. grey	3·50	2·25
104	**14**	2d. red	1·40	1·25
105*a*	**14**	2½d. blue	80	1·25
106	**14**	2½d. black and purple	1·00	15
107a	**14**	3d. orange	50	85
108	**14**	3d. blue	1·00	15
109a	**14**	6d. purple	12·00	3·50
110b	**14**	1s. black on green	5·50	1·00
111a	**14**	2s. purple and blue on blue	16·00	2·00
112b	**14**	5s. green and red on yellow	35·00	16·00
113c	**14**	10s. green and red on green	£120	£100
114*b*	**14**	£1 purple and black on red	45·00	32·00

The 10s. and £1 are as T **15** of Bermuda but with portrait of King George VI.

1946. Victory. As T **59a** of Jamaica.

115	1½d. brown	15	75
116	3d. orange	15	75

1949. Silver Wedding. As T **59b/59c** of Jamaica.

117	2½d. blue	10	10
118	5s. green	7·00	11·00

1949. UPU. As T **59d/59g** of Jamaica.

119	2½d. black	15	3·00
120	3d. blue	2·00	3·00
121	6d. mauve	15	3·00
122	1s. turquoise	15	3·00

15a Arms of University

15b Princess Alice

1951. Inauguration of BWI University College.

123	**15a**	3c. orange and black	30	2·00
124	**15b**	12c. red and violet	1·00	2·00

1953. Coronation. As T **61a** of Jamaica.

125	3c. black and green	1·00	2·25

1954. As T **14** but portrait of Queen Elizabeth II facing left.

126	½c. brown	10	60
127	1c. grey	1·25	1·25
128	2c. green	1·75	10
129	3c. yellow and black	2·50	1·00
130	4c. red	1·75	10
131	5c. black and purple	2·25	1·00
132	6c. yellow	2·25	60
133	8c. blue	2·50	10
134	12c. purple	2·00	10
135	24c. black and green	2·00	20
136	48c. purple and blue	8·00	2·75
137	60c. brown and green	6·00	2·25
138	$1.20 green and red	7·00	4·25

Larger type as T **15** of Malta, but portrait of Queen Elizabeth II facing left.

139	$2.40 green and red	15·00	8·50
140	$4.80 purple and black	19·00	12·00

LESOTHO

Formerly Basutoland, attained independence on 4 October 1966 and changed its name to Lesotho.

1966. 100 cents = 1 rand.
1979. 100 lisente = 1 (ma)loti.

33 Moshoeshoe I and Moshoeshoe II

1966. Independence.

106	**33**	2½c. brown, black and red	10	10
107	**33**	5c. brown, black and blue	15	10
108	**33**	10c. brown, black and green	20	10
109	**33**	20c. brown, black and purple	25	30

1966. Nos. 69 etc. of Basutoland optd **LESOTHO**.

110A	**8**	½c. black and sepia	10	10
111A	-	1c. black and green	10	10
112A	-	2c. blue and orange	60	10
113B	**26**	2½c. sage and red	50	10
114A	-	3½c. indigo and blue	30	10
115A	-	5c. brown and green	10	10
116A	-	10c. bronze and purple	10	10
117B	-	12½c. brown and turquoise	30	20
118A	-	25c. blue and red	30	20
119B	-	50c. black and red	70	50
120B	**18**	1r. black and purple	65	1·25

35 Education, Culture and Science

1966. 20th Anniversary of UNESCO.

121	**35**	2½c. yellow and green	10	10
122	**35**	5c. green and olive	15	10
123	**35**	12½c. blue and red	35	15
124	**35**	25c. orange and blue	60	85

36 Maize

1967

125	**36**	½c. green and violet	10	10
126	-	1c. sepia and red	10	10
149	-	2c. yellow and green	10	10
128	-	2½c. black and ochre	10	10
151	-	3c. chocolate, green and brown	15	15
152	-	3½c. blue and yellow	15	40
130	-	5c. bistre and blue	20	10
131	-	10c. brown and grey	10	10
132	-	12½c. black and orange	20	10
133	-	25c. black and blue	55	20
134	-	50c. black, blue & turquoise	4·50	2·25
135	-	1r. multicoloured	65	75
136	-	2r. black, gold and purple	1·00	1·75

Designs: Horiz—½c. T **36;** 1c. Cattle; 2c. Aloes; 2½c. Basotho hat; 3c. Sorghum; 3½c. Merino sheep ('Wool'); 5c. Basotho pony; 10c. Wheat; 12½c. Angora goat ('Mohair'); 25c. Maletsunyane Falls; 50c. Diamonds; 1r. Arms of Lesotho. Vert—2r. Moshoeshoe II.

See also Nos. 191/202 and 401.

46 Students and University

1967. First Conferment of University Degrees.

137	**46**	1c. sepia, blue and orange	10	10
138	**46**	2½c. sepia, ultramarine & bl	10	10
139	**46**	12½c. sepia, blue and red	10	10
140	**46**	25c. sepia, blue and violet	15	15

47 Statue of Moshoeshoe I

1967. First Anniversary of Independence.

141	**47**	2½c. black and green	10	10
142	-	12½c. multicoloured	25	15
143	-	25c. black, green and ochre	35	25

Designs: 2½c. T **47**; 12½c. National Flag; 25c. Crocodile (National Emblem).

50 Lord Baden-Powell and Scout Saluting

1967. 60th Anniversary of Scout Movement.

144	**50**	15c. multicoloured	20	10

51 WHO Emblem and World Map

1968. 20th Anniversary of World Health Organisation.

145	**51**	2½c. blue, gold and red	15	10
146	-	25c. multicoloured	45	60

Design: 25c. Nurse and child.

55 Running Hunters

1968. Rock Paintings.

160	**55**	3c. brown, turquoise and green	20	10
161	-	3½c. yellow, olive and sepia	25	10
162	-	5c. red, ochre and brown	25	10
163	-	10c. yellow, red and purple	35	10
164	-	15c. buff, yellow and brown	50	30
165	-	20c. green, yellow and brown	60	55
166	-	25c. yellow, brown and black	65	75

Designs: Horiz—3½c. Baboons; 10c. Archers; 20c. Eland; 25c. Hunting scene. Vert—5c. Javelin thrower; 15c. Blue cranes.

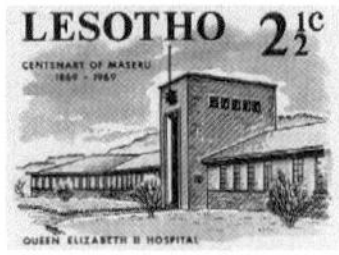

62 Queen Elizabeth II Hospital

1969. Centenary of Maseru (capital). Multicoloured.

167	2½c. Type **62**	10	10
168	10c. Lesotho Radio Station	10	10
169	12½c. Leabua Jonathan Airport	35	10
170	25c. Royal Palace	25	15

66 Rally Car passing Basuto Tribesman

1969. Roof of Africa Car Rally.

171	**66**	2½c. yellow, mauve and plum	15	10
172	-	12½c. blue, yellow and grey	20	10
173	-	15c. blue, black and mauve	20	10
174	-	20c. black, red and yellow	20	10

Designs: 12½c. Rally car on mountain road; 15c. Chequered flags and Roof of Africa Plateau; 20c. Map of rally route and Independence Trophy.

71 Gryponyx and Footprints

1970. Prehistoric Footprints (1st series).

175	-	3c. brown and sepia	90	70
176	**71**	5c. purple, pink and sepia	1·10	30
177	-	10c. yellow, black and sepia	1·25	35
178	-	15c. yellow, black and sepia	1·50	2·25
179	-	25c. blue and black	2·25	2·25

Designs: 3c. Dinosaur footprints at Moyeni; 10c. Plateosauravus and footprints; 15c. Tritylodon and footprints; 25c. Massospondylus and footprints.

No. 175 is larger, 60×23 mm.

See also Nos. 596/598.

75 Moshoeshoe I as a Young Man

1970. Death Centenary of Chief Moshoeshoe I.

180	**75**	2½c. green and mauve	10	10
181	-	25c. blue and brown	20	20

Design: 25c. Moshoeshoe I as an old man.

77 UN Emblem and '25'

1970. 25th Anniversary of United Nations.

182	**77**	2½c. pink, blue and purple	10	10
183	-	10c. multicoloured	10	10
184	-	12½c. red, blue and drab	10	25
185	-	25c. multicoloured	15	65

Designs: 10c. UN Building; 12½c. People of the World; 25c. Symbolic dove.

78 Gift Shop, Maseru

1970. Tourism. Multicoloured.

186	2½c. Type **78**	10	10
187	5c. Trout fishing	20	10
188	10c. Pony trekking	25	10
189	12½c. Skiing, Maluti Mountains	50	10
190	20c. Holiday Inn, Maseru	40	50

79 Maize

1971. As Nos. 147/158 but in new format omitting portrait, as in T **79**. New designs for 4c., 2r.

191	**79**	½c. green and violet	10	10
192	-	1c. brown and red	10	10
193	-	2c. yellow and green	10	10
194	-	2½c. black, green and yellow	10	10
195	-	3c. brown, green and yellow	10	10
196	-	3½c. blue and yellow	10	10
196a	-	4c. multicoloured	20	10
197	-	5c. brown and blue	15	10
198	-	10c. brown and grey	15	10
199	-	12½c. brown and orange	25	30
200	-	25c. slate and blue	60	40
201	-	50c. black, blue and green	6·00	4·50
202	-	1r. multicoloured	1·25	1·75
401	-	2r. brown and blue	70	2·25

Designs: Horiz—4c. National Flag. Vert—2r. Statue of Moshoeshoe I.

80 Lammergeier

1971. Birds. Multicoloured.

204	2½c. Type **80**	2·50	20
205	5c. Bald ibis	3·50	2·50
206	10c. Orange-breasted rockjumper	3·50	2·00
207	12½c. Blue bustard ('Blue korhaan')	3·75	3·50
208	15c. Painted-snipe	4·25	4·50
209	20c. Golden-breasted bunting	4·25	4·50
210	25c. Ground woodpecker	4·75	4·50

81 Lionel Collett Dam

1971. Soil Conservation. Multicoloured.

211	4c. Type **81**	10	10
212	10c. Contour ridges	10	10
213	15c. Earth dams	25	10
214	25c. Beaver dams	35	35

82 Diamond Mining

1971. Development. Multicoloured.

215	4c. Type **82**	75	40
216	10c. Pottery	30	10
217	15c. Weaving	45	60
218	20c. Construction	55	1·50

83 Mail Cart

1972. Centenary of Post Office.

219	**83**	5c. brown and pink	15	20
220	-	10c. multicoloured	15	10
221	-	15c. blue, black and brown	20	15
222	-	20c. multicoloured	30	90

Designs: Horiz—10c. Postal bus; 20c. Maseru Post Office. Vert—15c. 4d. Cape of Good Hope stamp of 1876.

84 Sprinting

1972. Olympic Games, Munich. Multicoloured.

223	4c. Type **84**	15	10
224	10c. Shot putting	20	10
225	15c. Hurdling	30	10
226	25c. Long-jumping	35	55

85 *Adoration of the Shepherds* (Matthias Stomer)

1972. Christmas.

227	**85**	4c. multicoloured	10	10
228	**85**	10c. multicoloured	10	10
229	**85**	25c. multicoloured	15	20

86 WHO Emblem

1973. 25th Anniversary of WHO.

230	**86**	20c. yellow and blue	30	30

1973. OAU. Tenth Anniversary. Nos. 194 and 196a/198 optd **O.A.U. 10th Anniversary Freedom in Unity**.

231	2½c. black, green and brown	10	10
232	4c. multicoloured	10	10
233	5c. brown and blue	10	10
234	10c. brown and blue	15	15

88 Basotho Hat and WFP Emblem

1973. Tenth Anniversary of World Food Programme. Multicoloured.

235	4c. Type **88**	10	10
236	15c. School feeding	20	15
237	20c. Infant feeding	20	20
238	25c. Food for work	25	25

89 *Aeropetes tulbaghia*

1973. Butterflies. Multicoloured.

239	4c. Type **89**	85	10
240	5c. *Papilio demodocus*	95	50
241	10c. *Cynthia cardui*	1·50	50
242	15c. *Precis hierta*	2·75	1·75
243	20c. *Precis oenone*	2·75	1·75
244	25c. *Danaus chrysippus*	3·00	2·75
245	30c. *Colotis evenina*	3·00	3·75

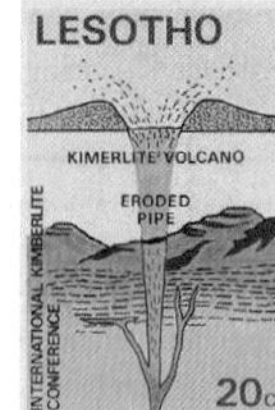

90 Kimberlite Volcano

1973. International Kimberlite Conference. Multicoloured.

246	10c. Map of diamond mines (horiz)	2·00	50
247	15c. Kimberlite-diamond rock (horiz)	2·25	2·25
248	20c. Type **90**	2·25	2·50
249	30c. Diamond prospecting	3·75	7·00

91 'Health'

1974. Youth and Development. Multicoloured.

250	4c. Type **91**	10	10
251	10c. 'Education'	15	10
252	20c. 'Agriculture'	20	10
253	25c. 'Industry'	30	20
254	30c. 'Service'	30	25

92 Open Book and Wreath

1974. Tenth Anniversary of UBLS. Multicoloured.

255	10c. Type **92**	15	10
256	15c. Flags, mortar-board and scroll	20	20
257	20c. Map of Africa	25	25
258	25c. King Moshoeshoe II capping a graduate	25	65

93 Senqunyane River Bridge, Marakabei

1974. Rivers and Bridges. Multicoloured.

259	4c. Type **93**	10	10
260	5c. Tsoelike River and bridge	10	10
261	10c. Makhaleng River Bridge	20	10
262	15c. Seaka Bridge, Orange/Senqu River	35	35
263	20c. Masianokeng Bridge, Phuthiatsana River	40	40
264	25c. Mahobong Bridge, Hlotse River	45	45

94 UPU Emblem

1974. Centenary of UPU.

265	**94**	4c. green and black	10	10
266	-	10c. orange, yellow & black	15	10
267	-	15c. multicoloured	20	60
268	-	20c. multicoloured	45	85

Designs: 10c. Map of airmail routes; 15c. Post Office HQ, Maseru; 20c. Horseman taking rural mail.

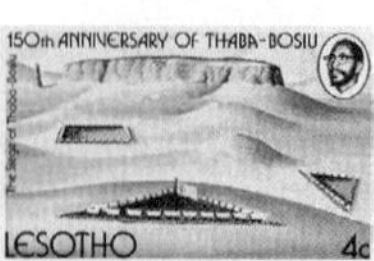

95 Siege of Thaba-Bosiu

1974. 150th Anniversary of Siege of Thaba-Bosiu. Multicoloured.

269	4c. Type **95**	10	10
270	5c. The wreath-laying	10	10
271	10c. Moshoeshoe I (vert)	25	10

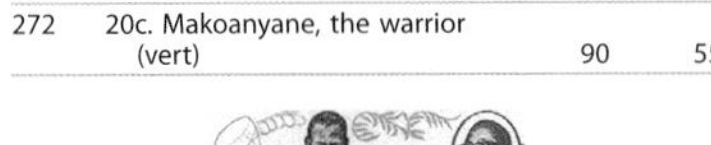

272	20c. Makoanyane, the warrior (vert)	90	55

96 Mamokhorong

1974. Basotho Musical Instruments. Multicoloured.

273	4c. Type **96**	10	10
274	10c. Lesiba	10	10
275	15c. Setolotolo	15	20
276	20c. Meropa	15	20
MS277	108×92 mm. Nos. 273/276	1·00	2·00

97 Horseman in Rock Archway

1975. Sehlabathebe National Park. Multicoloured.

278	4c. Type **97**	30	10
279	5c. Mountain view through arch	30	10
280	15c. Antelope by stream	50	45
281	20c. Mountains and lake	50	50
282	25c. Tourists by frozen waterfall	65	75

98 Morena Moshoeshoe I

1975. Leaders of Lesotho.

283	**98**	3c. black and blue	10	10
284	-	4c. black and mauve	10	10
285	-	5c. black and pink	10	10
286	-	6c. black and brown	10	10
287	-	10c. black and red	10	10
288	-	15c. black and red	20	20
289	-	20c. black and green	25	30
290	-	25c. black and blue	25	40

Designs: 4c. King Moshoeshoe II; 5c. Morena Letsie I; 6c. Morena Lerotholi; 10c. Morena Letsie II; 15c. Morena Griffith; 20c. Morena Seeiso Griffith Lerotholi; 25c. Mofumahali Mantsebo Seeiso, OBE.

The 25c. also commemorates International Women's Year.

99 Mokhibo Dance

1975. Traditional Dances. Multicoloured.

291	4c. Type **99**	15	10
292	10c. Ndlamo	20	10
293	15c. Baleseli	35	75
294	20c. Mohobelo	40	1·25
MS295	111×100 mm. Nos. 291/294	3·75	3·50

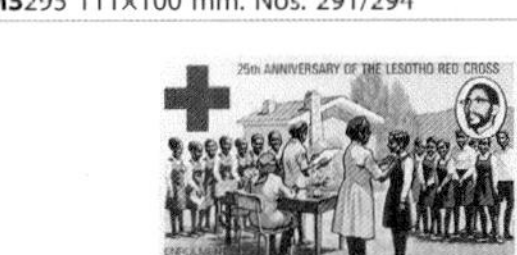

100 Enrolment

1976. 25th Anniversary of Lesotho Red Cross. Multicoloured.

296	4c. Type **100**	50	10
297	10c. Medical aid	70	10
298	15c. Rural service	1·00	1·25
299	25c. Relief supplies	1·40	2·50

101 Tapestry

1976. Multicoloured

300	2c. Type **101**	10	35
301	3c. Mosotho horseman	20	30
302	4c. Map of Lesotho	1·50	10
303	5c. Lesotho Brown diamond	75	1·00
304	10c. Lesotho Bank	30	10
305	15c. Lesotho and OAU flags	2·00	1·00
306	25c. Sehlabathebe National Park	60	35
307	40c. Pottery	60	1·00
308	50c. Prehistoric rock art	2·75	2·00
309	1r. King Moshoeshoe II (vert)	60	1·75

102 Football

1976. Olympic Games, Montreal. Multicoloured.

310	4c. Type **102**	15	10
311	10c. Weightlifting	15	10
312	15c. Boxing	35	35
313	25c. Throwing the discus	50	80

103 'Rising Sun'

1976. Tenth Anniversary of Independence. Multicoloured.

314	4c. Type **103**	10	10
315	10c. Open gates	10	10
316	15c. Broken chains	40	20
317	25c. Britten Norman Islander aircraft over hotel	50	35

104 Telephones, 1876 and 1976

1976. Centenary of Telephone. Multicoloured.

318	4c. Type **104**	10	10
319	10c. Early handset and telephone-user, 1976	15	10
320	15c. Wall telephone and telephone exchange	25	20
321	25c. Stick telephone and Alexander Graham Bell	45	50

105 *Aloe striatula*

1977. Aloes and Succulents. Multicoloured.

322	3c. Type **105**	25	10
323	4c. *Aloe aristata*	25	10
324	5c. *Kniphofia caulescens*	25	10
325	10c. *Euphorbia pulvinata*	35	10
326	15c. *Aloe saponaria*	75	30
327	20c. *Caralluma lutea*	75	50
328	25c. *Aloe polyphylla*	85	70

See also Nos. 347/354.

106 Large-toothed Rock Hyrax

1977. Animals. Multicoloured.

329	4c. Type **106**	3·00	30
330	5c. Cape porcupine	3·00	75
331	10c. Zorilla (polecat)	3·00	30
332	15c. Klipspringer	9·00	2·50
333	25c. Chacma baboon	10·00	3·75

107 'Rheumatic Man'

1977. World Rheumatism Year.

334	**107**	4c. yellow and red	10	10
335	-	10c. blue and deep blue	15	10
336	-	15c. yellow and blue	30	10
337	-	25c. red and black	40	45

Designs: Each show the 'Rheumatic Man' as T **107**—10c. Surrounded by 'pain'; 15c. Surrounded by 'chain'; 25c. Supporting globe.

108 Small-mouthed Yellowfish

1977. Fish. Multicoloured.

338	4c. Type **108**	25	10
339	10c. Mudfish	35	10
340	15c. Rainbow trout	50	35
341	25c. Barnard's mudfish	60	60

1977. No. 198 surch **3**.

342	3c. on 10c. brown and blue	1·00	1·00

110 Black and White Heads

1977. Decade for Action to Combat Racism.

343	**110**	4c. black and mauve	10	10
344	-	10c. black and blue	10	10
345	-	15c. black and orange	15	15
346	-	25c. black and green	25	25

Designs: 10c. Jigsaw pieces; 15c. Cogwheels; 25c. Handshake.

1978. Flowers. As T **105**. Multicoloured.

347	2c. *Papaver aculeatum*	10	50
348	3c. *Diascia integerrima*	10	50
349	4c. *Helichrysum trilineatum*	10	10
350	5c. *Zaluzianskya maritima*	10	10
351	10c. *Gladiolus natalensis*	15	10
352	15c. *Chironia krebsii*	20	40
353	25c. *Wahlenbergia undulata*	35	1·00
354	40c. *Brunsvigia radulosa*	65	2·00

111 Edward Jenner vaccinating Child

1978. Global Eradication of Smallpox. Multicoloured.

355	5c. Type **111**	25	35
356	25c. Head of child and WHO emblem	75	90

112 Tsoloane Falls

1978. Waterfalls. Multicoloured.

357	4c. Type **112**	15	10
358	10c. Qiloane Falls	25	10
359	15c. Tsoelikana Falls	35	60
360	25c. Maletsunyane Falls	55	1·75

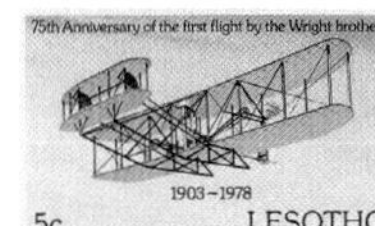

113 *Wright Flyer III*, 1903

1978. 75th Anniversary of First Powered Flight. Multicoloured.

361	5c. Type **113**	15	30
362	25c. Wilbur and Orville Wright	40	60

114 *Orthetrum farinosum*

1978. Insects. Multicoloured.

363	4c. Type **114**	10	10
364	10c. *Phymateus viridipes*	20	10
365	15c. *Belonogaster lateritis*	30	55
366	25c. *Sphodromantis gastrica*	50	90

115 Oudehout Branch in Flower

1979. Trees. Multicoloured.

367	4c. Type **115**	10	10
368	10c. Wild olive	15	10
369	15c. Blinkblaar	30	80
370	25c. Cape holly	55	1·50

116 Mampharoane

1979. Reptiles. Multicoloured.

371A	4s. Type **116**	10	10
372A	10s. Qoaane	20	10
373A	15s. Leupa	30	80
374A	25s. Masumu	60	1·50

117 Basutoland 1933 1d. Stamp

1979. Death Centenary of Sir Rowland Hill.

375	**117**	4s. multicoloured	10	10
376	-	15s. multicoloured	30	20
377	-	25s. black, orange & bistre	40	30
MS378		118×95 mm. 50s. multicoloured	60	80

Designs: 15s. Basutoland 1962 ½c. new currency definitive; 25s. Penny Black; 50s. 1972 15c. Post Office Centenary commemorative.

118 Detail of painting *Children's Games* by Brueghel

1979. International Year of the Child.

379	**118**	4s. multicoloured	10	10
380	-	10s. multicoloured	10	10
381	-	15s. multicoloured	15	15
MS382		113×88 mm. 25s. multicoloured (horiz)	55	45

Designs: 10, 15s, 25s. Different details taken from Brueghel's *Children's Games*.

119 Beer Strainer, Broom and Mat

1980. Grasswork. Multicoloured.

383	4s. Type **119**	10	10
384	10s. Winnowing basket	10	10
385	15s. Basotho hat	20	40
386	25s. Grain storage	35	65

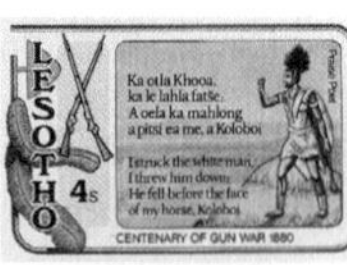

120 Praise Poet

1980. Centenary of Gun War. Multicoloured.

387	4s. Type **120**	15	10
388	5s. Lerotholi, Commander of Basotho Army	15	10
389	10s. Ambush at Qalabane	20	10
390	15s. Snider and Martini-Henry rifles	60	55
391	25s. Map showing main areas of action	70	1·25

121 Olympic Flame, Flags and Kremlin

1980. Olympic Games, Moscow. Multicoloured.

392	25s. Type **121**	25	25
393	25s. Doves, flame and flags	25	25
394	25s. Football	25	25
395	25s. Running	25	25
396	25s. Opening ceremony	25	25
MS397	110×85 mm. 1m.40 Ancient and modern athletes carrying Olympic torch	1·10	1·25

1980. Nos. 203 and 300/309 surch s or new value.

402A	2s. on 2c. Type **101**	10	30
403A	3s. on 3c. Mosotho horseman	20	30
404B	6s. on 4c. Map of Lesotho	1·00	30
406A	40s. on 40c. Pottery	45	50
409A	1m. on 1r. King Moshoeshoe II	80	1·25
410A	5s. on 5c. Lesotho Brown diamond	3·50	10
411B	10s. on 10c. Lesotho Bank	10	10
412A	25s. on 25c. Sehlabathebe National Park	1·50	30
414A	50s. on 50c. Prehistoric rock art	3·00	55
415B	75s. on 15c. Lesotho and OAU flags	1·50	1·25
417A	2m. on 2r. Statue of King Moshoeshoe I	80	1·60

123 Beer Mug

1980. Pottery. Multicoloured.

418	4s. Type **123**	10	10
419	10s. Beer brewing pot	10	10
420	15s. Water pot	15	15
421	25s. Pot shapes	25	30
MS422	150×110 mm. 40s.×4 Wedgwood plaques of Prince Philip; Queen Elizabeth II; Prince Charles; Princess Anne (each 22×35 mm).	50	90

No. **MS**422 was issued to commemorate the 250th birth anniversary of Josiah Wedgwood.

124 Queen Elizabeth the Queen Mother with Prince Charles

1980. 80th Birthday of The Queen Mother. Multicoloured.

423	5s. Type **124**	25	25
424	10s. The Queen Mother	25	25
425	1m. 1947 Basutoland Royal Visit 2d. stamp (54×43 mm)	90	90

125 Lesotho Evangelical Church, Morija

1980. Christmas. Multicoloured.

426	4s. Type **125**	10	10
427	15s. St Agnes' Anglican Church, Teyateyaneng	10	10
428	25s. Cathedral of Our Lady of Victories, Maseru	15	10
429	75s. University Chapel, Roma	45	50
MS430	110×85 mm. 1m.50 Nativity scene (43×29 mm)	50	80

126 Voyager Satellite and Jupiter

1981. Space Exploration. Multicoloured.

431	25c. Type **126**	30	25
432	25c. Voyager and Saturn	30	25
433	25c. Voyager passing Saturn	30	25
434	25c. Space Shuttle releasing satellite	30	25
435	25c. Space Shuttle launching into space	30	25
MS436	111×85 mm. 1m.40 Saturn	1·40	1·00

127 Greater Kestrel

1981. Birds. Multicoloured.

437	1s. Type **127**	15	40
438	2s. Speckled pigeon ('Rock Pigeon') (horiz)	15	40
439	3s. South African crowned crane ('Crowned Crane')	20	40
440	5s. Bokmakierie shirike ('Bokmakierie')	20	40
448	1m. Red bishop (horiz)	1·50	75
449	2m. Egyptian goose (horiz)	1·00	1·50
450	5m. Lilac-breasted roller (horiz)	1·25	4·00
504	6s. Cape robin chat ('Cape Robin')	30	10
505	7s. Yellow canary	30	10
506	10s. Red-billed pintail ('Red-billed Teal') (horiz)	30	10
507	25s. Malachite kingfisher	80	30
508	40s. Yellow-tufted malachite sunbird ('Malachite Sunbird') (horiz)	1·00	45
509	60s. Cape longclaw ('Orange-throated Longclaw') (horiz)	1·25	90
510	75s. Hoopoe ('African Hoppoe') (horiz)	1·50	90

128 Wedding Bouquet from Lesotho

1981. Royal Wedding (1st issue). Multicoloured.

451	25s. Type **128**	10	10
452	50s. Prince Charles riding	20	25
453	75s. Prince Charles and Lady Diana Spencer	30	50

129 Prince Charles and Lady Diana Spencer (image scaled to 57% of original size)

1981. Royal Wedding (2nd issue). Sheet 115×90 mm.

MS454	**129** 1m.50 multicoloured	1·00	1·25

130 *Santa planning his Annual Visit*

1981. Christmas. Paintings by Norman Rockwell. Multicoloured.

455	6s. Type **130**	15	10
456	10s. *Santa reading his Mail*	20	10
457	15s. *The Little Spooners*	25	20
458	20s. *Raleigh Rockwell Travels*	25	25
459	25s. *Ride 'em Cowboy*	25	30
460	60s. *The Discovery*	30	1·00
MS461	111×85 mm. 1m.25 *Mystic Nativity* (48×31 mm)	1·10	1·10

131 Duke of Edinburgh, Award Scheme Emblem and Flags

1981. 25th Anniversary of Duke of Edinburgh Award Scheme. Multicoloured.

462	6s. Type **131**	10	10
463	7s. Tree planting	10	10
464	25s. Gardening	25	20
465	40s. Mountain climbing	40	40
466	75s. Award Scheme emblem	70	75
MS467	111×85 mm. 1m.40 Duke of Edinburgh (45×30 mm)	1·25	1·25

132 Wild Cat

1981. Wildlife. Multicoloured.

468	6s. Type **132**	1·25	30
469	20s. Chacma baboon (44×31 mm)	2·00	70
470	25s. Cape eland	2·50	75
471	40s. Porcupine	3·25	1·75
472	50s. Oribi (44×31 mm)	3·25	1·75
MS473	111×85 mm. 1m.50 Black-backed Jackal (47×31 mm)	2·75	1·90

133 Scout Bugler

1982. 75th Anniversary of Boy Scout Movement. Multicoloured.

474	6s. Type **133**	30	25
475	30s. Scouts hiking	35	50
476	40s. Scout sketching	40	60
477	50s. Scout with flag	40	65
478	75s. Scouts saluting	45	80
MS479	117×92 mm. 1m.50 Lord Baden-Powell	1·00	2·00

134 Jules Rimet Trophy with Footballers and Flags of 1930 Finalists (Argentina and Uruguay)

1982. World Cup Football Championship, Spain. Each showing Trophy with Players and Flags from Past Finals. Multicoloured.

480	15s. Type **134**	25	25
481	15s. Czechoslovakia and Italy, 1934	25	25
482	15s. Hungary and Italy, 1938	25	25
483	15s. Brazil and Uruguay, 1950	25	25
484	15s. Hungary and W. Germany, 1954	25	25
485	15s. Sweden and Brazil, 1958	25	25
486	15s. Czechoslovakia and Brazil, 1962	25	25
487	15s. W. Germany and England, 1966	25	25
488	15s. Italy and Brazil, 1970	25	25
489	15s. Holland and W. Germany, 1974	25	25
490	15s. Holland and Argentina, 1978	25	25
491	15s. Map of World on footballs	25	25
MS492	118×93 mm. 1m.25 Bernabeu Stadium, Madrid (47×35 mm)	1·10	1·25

Nos. 480/488 show the Jules Rimet Trophy and Nos. 489/491 the World Cup Trophy.

135 Portrait of George Washington

1982. 250th Birth Anniversary of George Washington. Multicoloured.

493	6s. Type **135**	10	10
494	7s. Washington with step-children and dog	10	10
495	10s. Washington with Indian chief	15	10
496	25s. Washington with troops	25	30
497	40s. Washington arriving in New York	30	40
498	1m. Washington on parade	75	1·10
MS499	117×92 mm. 1m.25 Washington crossing the Delaware	1·00	1·00

136 Lady Diana Spencer in Tetbury, May 1981

1982. 21st Birthday of Princess of Wales. Multicoloured.

514a	30s. Lesotho coat of arms	40	50
515	50s. Type **136**	50	50
516	75s. Wedding picture at Buckingham Palace	60	80
517	1m. Formal portrait	80	1·25

137 Mosotho reading *Sesotho Bible*

1982. Centenary of *Sesotho Bible*. Multicoloured.

518	6s. Type **137**	15	20
519	15s. *Sesotho bible* and Virgin Mary holding infant Jesus	20	25
520	1m. *Sesotho bible* and Cathedral (62×42 mm)	50	75

138 Birthday Greetings

1982. Birth of Prince William of Wales. Multicoloured.

521	6s. Type **138**	3·00	4·00
522	60s. Princess Diana and Prince William	60	1·00

139 'A Partridge in a Pear Tree'

1982. Christmas. *The Twelve Days of Christmas.* Walt Disney cartoon characters. Multicoloured.

523	2s. Type **139**	10	10
524	2s. 'Two turtle doves'	10	10
525	3s. 'Three French hens'	10	10
526	3s. 'Four calling birds'	10	10
527	4s. 'Five golden rings'	10	10
528	4s. 'Six geese a-laying'	10	10
529	75s. 'Seven swans a-swimming'	1·40	1·75
530	75s. 'Eight maids a-milking'	1·40	1·75
MS531	126×101 mm. 1m.50, 'Nine ladies dancing, ten lords a-leaping, eleven pipers piping, twelve drummers drumming'	2·40	2·75

140 *Lepista caffrorum*

1983. Fungi. Multicoloured.

532	10s. Type **140**	15	10
533	30s. *Broomeia congregata*	30	40
534	50s. *Afroboletus luteolus*	60	90
535	75s. *Lentinus tuber-regium*	90	1·40

141 Ba-Leseli Dance

1983. Commonwealth Day. Multicoloured.

536	5s. Type **141**	10	10
537	30s. Tapestry weaving	15	30
538	60s. Queen Elizabeth II (vert)	25	65
539	75s. King Moshoeshoe II (vert)	30	80

142 *Dancers in a Trance* (rock painting from Ntloana Tsoana)

1983. Rock Paintings. Multicoloured.

540	6s. Type **142**	20	10
541	25s. *Baboons*, Sehonghong	45	35
542	60s. *Hunters attacking Mountain Reedbuck*, Makhetha	50	1·10
543	75s. *Eland*, Lehaha la Likhomo	50	1·60
MS544	166×84 mm. Nos. 540/3 and 10s. *Cattle herding*, Sehonghong (52×52 mm)	1·25	3·50

143 Montgolfier Balloon, 1783

1983. Bicentenary of Manned Flight. Multicoloured.

545	7s. Type **143**	15	10
546	30s. Wright brothers and *Flyer I*	30	40
547	60s. First airmail flight	50	1·25
548	1m. Concorde	2·25	2·50
MS549	180×92 mm. Nos. 545/8 and 6s. Dornier Do-28D Skyservant of Lesotho Airways (60×60 mm)	2·75	2·75

144 Rev. Eugene Casalis

1983. 150th Anniversary of Arrival of the French Missionaries. Multicoloured.

550	6s. Type **144**	10	10
551	25s. The founding of Morija	10	10
552	40s. Baptism of Libe	10	15
553	75s. Map of Lesotho	20	25

145 Mickey Mouse and Pluto greeted by Friends

1983. Christmas. Walt Disney Characters in scenes from *Old Christmas* (Washington Irving's sketchbook). Multicoloured.

554	1s. Type **145**	10	10
555	2s. Donald Duck and Pluto	10	10
556	3s. Donald Duck with Huey, Dewey and Louie	10	10
557	4s. Goofy, Donald Duck and Mickey Mouse	10	10
558	5s. Goofy holding turkey, Donald Duck and Mickey Mouse	10	10
559	6s. Goofy and Mickey Mouse	10	10
560	75s. Donald and Daisy Duck	2·00	2·40
561	1m. Goofy and Clarabell	2·50	2·75
MS562	132×113 mm. 1m.75 Scrooge McDuck, Pluto and Donald Duck	3·25	4·50

146 Danaus chrysippus

1984. Butterflies. Multicoloured.

563	1s. Type **146**	30	60
564	2s. *Aeropetes tulbaghia*	30	60
565	3s. *Colotis evenina*	35	60
566	4s. *Precis oenone*	35	60
567	5s. *Precis hierta*	35	60
568	6s. *Catopsilia florella*	35	10
569	7s. *Phalanta phalantha*	35	10
570	10s. *Acraea stenobea*	40	10
571	15s. *Cynthia cardui*	75	10
572	20s. *Colotis subfasciatus*	75	10
573	30s. *Charaxes jasius*	75	30
574	50s. *Terias brigitta*	75	40
575	60s. *Pontia helice*	75	50
576	75s. *Colotis regina*	75	50
577	1m. *Hypolimnas misippus*	75	1·50
578	5m. *Papilio demodocus*	1·50	7·50

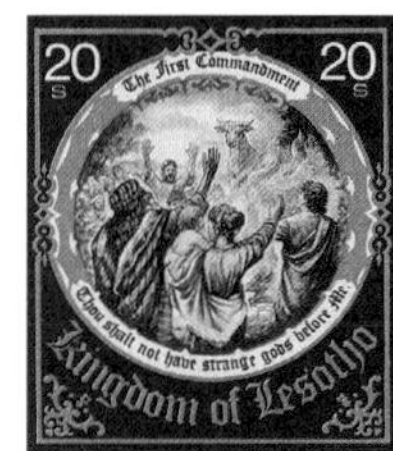

147 "Thou shalt not have Strange Gods before Me"

1984. Easter. The Ten Commandments. Multicoloured.

579	20s. Type **147**	25	30
580	20s. "Thou shalt not take the name of the Lord thy God in vain"	25	30
581	20s. "Remember thou keep holy the Lord's Day"	25	30
582	20s. "Honour thy father and mother"	25	30
583	20s. "Thou shalt not kill"	25	30
584	20s. "Thou shalt not commit adultery"	25	30
585	20s. "Thou shalt not steal"	25	30
586	20s. "Thou shalt not bear false witness against thy neighbour"	25	30
587	20s. "Thou shalt not covet thy neighbour's wife"	25	30
588	20s. "Thou shalt not covet thy neighbour's goods"	25	30
MS589	102×73 mm. 1m.50 Moses with Tablets (45×28 mm)	1·00	2·50

148 Torch Bearer

1984. Olympic Games, Los Angeles. Multicoloured.

590	10s. Type **148**	10	10
591	30s. Horse-riding	10	10
592	50s. Swimming	15	20
593	75s. Basketball	20	25
594	1m. Running	25	30
MS595	101×72 mm. 1m.50 Olympic Flame and flags	1·25	2·75

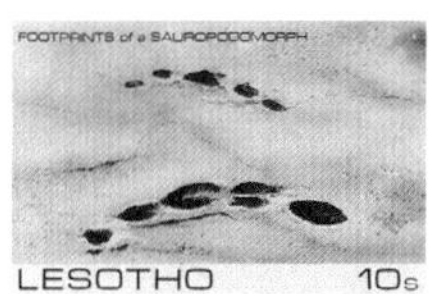

149 Sauropodomorph Footprints

1984. Prehistoric Footprints (2nd series). Multicoloured.

596	10s. Type **149**	30	30
597	30s. Lesothosaurus footprints	40	1·00
598	50s. Footprint of carnivorous dinosaur	50	1·50

150 Wells Fargo Coach, 1852

1984. Ausipex International Stamp Exhibition, Melbourne. Bicentenary of First Mail Coach Run. Multicoloured.

599	6s. Type **150**	10	10
600	7s. Basotho mail cart, *circa* 1900	10	10
601	10s. Bath mail coach, 1784	10	10
602	30s. Cobb coach, 1853	15	15
603	50s. Exhibition logo and Royal Exhibition Buildings, Melbourne (82×25 mm)	50	80
MS604	147×98 mm. 1m.75 GB Penny Black, Basutoland 1934 'OFFICIAL' optd 6d. and Western Australia 1854 4d. with frame inverted (82×25 mm)	2·25	3·75

151 *The Orient Express* (1900)

1984. Railways of the World. Multicoloured.

605	6s. Type **151**	25	15
606	15s. Class 05 streamlined steam locomotive No. 001, Germany (1935)	25	30
607	30s. Caledonian Railway steam locomotive *Cardean* (1906)	25	40
608	60s. Atchison, Topeka & Santa Fe *Super Chief* express (1940)	30	1·50
609	1m. LNER *Flying Scotsman* (1934)	30	2·00
MS610	108×82 mm. 2m. South African Railways *The Blue Train* (1972)	1·00	2·50

152 Eland Calf

1984. Baby Animals. Multicoloured.

611	15s. Type **152**	25	20
612	20s. Young chacma baboons	25	25
613	30s. Oribi calf	25	40
614	75s. Young Natal red hares	40	1·60
615	1m. Black-backed jackal pups (46×27 mm)	40	2·00

153 Crown of Lesotho

1985. Silver Jubilee of King Moshoeshoe II. Multicoloured.

616	6s. Type **153**	10	10
617	30s. King Moshoeshoe in 1960	20	30
618	75s. King Moshoeshoe in traditional dress, 1985	50	85
619	1m. King Moshoeshoe in uniform, 1985	70	1·25

154 Christ condemned to Death

1985. Easter. The Stations of the Cross. Multicoloured.

620	20s. Type **154**	25	35
621	20s. Christ carrying the Cross	25	35
622	20s. Falling for the first time	25	35
623	20s. Christ meets Mary	25	35
624	20s. Simon of Cyrene helping to carry the Cross	25	35
625	20s. Veronica wiping the face of Christ	25	35
626	20s. Christ falling a second time	25	35
627	20s. Consoling the women of Jerusalem	25	35
628	20s. Falling for the third time	25	35
629	20s. Christ being stripped	25	35
630	20s. Christ nailed to the Cross	25	35
631	20s. Dying on the Cross	25	35
632	20s. Christ taken down from the Cross	25	35
633	20s. Christ being laid in the sepulchre	25	35
MS634	138×98 mm. 2m. *The Crucifixion* (Mathias Grunewald)	1·50	3·50

155 Duchess of York with Princess Elizabeth, 1931

1985. Life and Times of Queen Elizabeth the Queen Mother. Multicoloured.

635	10s. Type **155**	25	10
636	30s. The Queen Mother in 1975	70	50
637	60s. Queen Mother with Queen Elizabeth and Princess Margaret, 1980	80	90
638	2m. Four generations of Royal Family at Prince Harry's christening, 1984	1·25	2·50
MS639	139×98 mm. 2m. Queen Elizabeth with the Princess of Wales and her children at Prince Harry's christening (37×50 mm)	2·25	2·75

156 BMW 732i

1985. Century of Motoring. Multicoloured.

640	6s. Type **156**	25	15
641	10s. Ford Crown Victoria	35	15
642	30s. Mercedes-Benz 500SE	60	50
643	90s. Cadillac Eldorado Biarritz	1·25	2·50
644	2m. Rolls-Royce Silver Spirit	1·75	4·00
MS645	139×98 mm. 2m. Rolls-Royce Silver Ghost Tourer, 1907 (37×50 mm)	4·00	6·00

157 American Cliff Swallow

1985. Birth Bicentenary of John J. Audubon (ornithologist). Designs showing original paintings. Multicoloured.

646	5s. Type **157**	40	30
647	6s. Great crested grebe (horiz)	40	30
648	10s. Vesper sparrow ('Vester Sparrow') (horiz)	55	30
649	30s. Common greenshank ('Greenshank') (horiz)	1·00	75
650	60s. Stilt sandpiper (horiz)	1·50	2·75
651	2m. Glossy ibis (horiz)	2·00	6·00

158 Two Youths Rock-climbing

1985. International Youth Year and 75th Anniversary of Girl Guide Movement. Multicoloured.

652	10s. Type **158**	20	10
653	30s. Young technician in hospital laboratory	50	40
654	75s. Three guides on parade	1·00	1·25
655	2m. Guide saluting	1·75	3·00
MS656 138×98 mm. 2m. *Olave, Lady Baden-Powell* (Grace Wheatley) (37×50 mm)		2·40	2·75

159 UN (New York) 1951 1c. Definitive and UN Flag

1985. 40th Anniversary of UNO.

657	**159** 10s. multicoloured	25	10
658	- 30s. multicoloured	60	35
659	- 50s. multicoloured	95	85
660	- 2m. black and green	5·00	6·50

Designs: Vert—30s. Ha Sofonia Earth Satellite Station; 2m. Maimonides (physician, philosopher and scholar). Horiz—50s. Lesotho Airways Fokker F.27 Friendship at Maseru Airport.

160 Cosmos

1985. Wild Flowers. Multicoloured.

661	6s. Type **160**	40	15
662	10s. Small agapanthus	55	15
663	30s. Pink witchweed	1·10	70
664	60s. Small iris	1·50	2·00
665	90s. Wild geranium or cranesbill	1·75	3·00
666	1m. Large spotted orchid	3·00	5·00

160a Mrs Jumbo and Baby Dumbo

1985. 150th Birth Anniversary of Mark Twain. Walt Disney cartoon characters illustrating various Mark Twain quotations. Multicoloured.

667	6s. Type **160a**	50	15
668	50s. Uncle Scrooge and Goofy reading newspaper	1·50	1·00
669	90s. Winnie the Pooh, Tigger, Piglet and Owl	2·00	2·00
670	1m.50 Goofy at ship's wheel	3·00	3·00
MS671 127×102 mm. 1m.25 Mickey Mouse as astronaut		4·75	3·75

160b Donald Duck as the Tailor

1985. Birth Bicentenaries of Grimm Brothers (folklorists). Walt Disney cartoon characters in scenes from *The Wishing Table*. Multicoloured.

672	10s. Type **160b**	50	20
673	60s. The second son (Dewey) with magic donkey and gold coins	1·50	1·50
674	75s. The eldest son (Huey) with wishing table laden with food	1·75	1·75
675	1m. The innkeeper stealing the third son's (Louie) magic cudgel	2·00	2·75
MS676 127×102 mm. 1m.50 The tailor and eldest son with wishing table		4·75	5·50

161 Male Lammergeier on Watch

1986. Flora and Fauna of Lesotho. Multicoloured.

677	7s. Type **161**	1·75	65
678	9s. Prickly pear	70	20
679	12s. Stapelia	70	20
680	15s. Pair of lammergeiers	2·50	60
681	35s. Pig's ears	1·10	60
682	50s. Male lammergeier in flight	3·75	2·75
683	1m. Adult and juvenile lammergeiers	3·75	4·75
684	2m. Columnar cereus	3·75	6·50
MS685 125×106 mm. 2m. Verreaux's eagle ('Black Eagle')		8·50	12·00

162 Two Players chasing Ball

1986. World Cup Football Championship, Mexico. Multicoloured.

686	35s. Type **162**	1·00	50
687	50s. Goalkeeper saving goal	1·50	1·25
688	1m. Three players chasing ball	2·50	2·75
689	2m. Two players competing for ball	4·00	5·00
MS690 104×74 mm. 3m. Player heading ball		7·00	8·50

162a Galileo and 200 inch Hale Telescope at Mount Palomar Observatory, California

1986. Appearance of Halley's Comet. Multicoloured.

691	9s. Type **162a**	75	15
692	15s. Halley's Comet and *Pioneer Venus 2* spacecraft	90	20
693	70s. Halley's Comet of 684 AD (from *Nuremberg Chronicle*, 1493)	1·60	1·40
694	3m. Comet and landing of William the Conqueror, 1066	4·25	5·50
MS695 101×70 mm. 4m. Halley's Comet over Lesotho		6·50	7·00

163 International Year of the Child Gold Coin (image scaled to 52% of original size)

1986. First Anniversary of New Currency (1980). Multicoloured.

696	30s. Type **163**	4·00	6·50
697	30s. Five maloti banknote	4·00	6·50
698	30s. Fifty lisente coin	4·00	6·50
699	30s. Ten maloti banknote	4·00	6·50
700	30s. One sente coin	4·00	6·50

These stamps were prepared in 1980, but were not issued at that time.

163a Princess Elizabeth in Pantomime

1986. 60th Birthday of Queen Elizabeth II.

701	**163a** 90s. black and yellow	50	60
702	- 1m. multicoloured	55	65
703	- 2m. multicoloured	90	1·40
MS704 119×85 mm. 4m. black and grey-brown		1·75	3·25

Designs: 1m. Queen at Windsor Horse Show, 1971; 2m. At Royal Festival Hall, 1971; 4m. Princess Elizabeth in 1934.

163b Statue of Liberty and Bela Bartok (composer)

1986. Centenary of Statue of Liberty. Immigrants to the USA. Multicoloured.

705	15s. Type **163b**	85	30
706	35s. Felix Adler (philosopher)	85	30
707	1m. Victor Herbert (composer)	3·50	2·00
708	3m. David Niven (actor)	4·50	4·25
MS709 103×74 mm. 3m. Statue of Liberty (vert)		3·50	5·00

163c Mickey Mouse and Goofy as Japanese Mail Runners

1986. Ameripex International Stamp Exhibition, Chicago. Walt Disney cartoon characters delivering mail. Multicoloured.

710	15s. Type **163c**	80	20
711	35s. Mickey Mouse and Pluto with mail sledge	1·00	30
712	1m. Goofy as postman riding Harley-Davidson motorcycle	2·00	2·75
713	2m. Donald Duck operating railway mailbag apparatus	2·25	4·00
MS714 127×101 mm. 4m. Goofy driving mail to aircraft		6·50	7·00

1986. Various stamps surch. (a) On Nos. 437 etc. (Birds).

729	9s. on 5s. Bokmakierie shrike	75	20
715	9s. on 10s. Red-billed pintail (horiz)	4·00	1·25
716	15s. on 1s. Type **127**	8·00	3·00
717	15s. on 2s. Speckled pigeon (horiz)	4·00	4·50
718	15s. on 5s. Bokmakierie shrike	3·00	35
719	15s. on 60s. Cape longclaw (horiz)	20	10
730	16s. on 25s. Malachite kingfisher	4·00	1·00
731	35s. on 25s. Malachite kingfisher	2·25	60
721	35s. on 75s. Hoopoe	22·00	16·00

(b) On Nos. 563 etc (Butterflies).

722	9s. on 30s. *Charaxes jasius*	15	10
723	9s. on 60s. *Pontia helice*	3·25	4·00
724	15s. on 1s. Type **146**	2·00	2·25
725	15s. on 2s. *Aeropetes tulbaghia*	20	20
726	15s. on 3s. *Colotis evenina*	20	20
727	15s. on 5s. *Precis hierta*	20	20
732	20s. on 4s. *Precis oenone*	20	10
728	35s. on 75s. *Colotis regina*	35	35
733	40s. on 7s. *Phalanta phalantha*	20	20

(c) No. 722 further surch.

734	3s. on 9s. on 30s. *Charaxes jasius*	1·75	1·50
735	7s. on 9s. on 30s. *Charaxes jasius*	1·75	1·50

170a Prince Andrew and Miss Sarah Ferguson

1986. Royal Wedding. Multicoloured.

736	50s. Type **170a**	40	40
737	1m. Prince Andrew	70	80
738	3m. Prince Andrew piloting helicopter	2·75	2·25
MS739 88×88 mm. 4m. Prince Andrew and Miss Sarah Ferguson (different)		3·50	4·50

171 Basotho Pony and Rider

1986. 20th Anniversary of Independence. Multicoloured.

740	9s. Type **171**	40	10
741	15s. Basotho woman spinning mohair	40	15
742	35s. Crossing river by rowing boat	50	30
743	3m. Thaba Tseka Post Office	1·00	3·00
MS744 109×78 mm. 4m. King Moshoeshoe I		4·75	8·00

171a Chip 'n' Dale pulling Christmas Cracker

1986. Christmas. Walt Disney cartoon characters. Multicoloured.

745	15s. Type **171a**	70	20
746	35s. Mickey and Minnie Mouse	90	30
747	1m. Pluto pulling Christmas taffy	1·50	2·75
748	2m. Aunt Matilda baking	1·75	4·00
MS749 126×102 mm. 5m. Huey and Dewey with gingerbread house		5·50	7·00

172 Rally Car

1987. Roof of Africa Motor Rally. Multicoloured.

750	9s. Type **172**	30	10
751	15s. Motorcyclist	35	15
752	35s. Motorcyclist (different)	55	35
753	4m. Rally car (different)	3·00	5·00

173 Lawn Tennis

1987. Olympic Games, Seoul (1988) (1st issue). Multicoloured.

754	9s. Type **173**	60	10
755	15s. Judo	60	15
756	20s. Athletics	65	20
757	35s. Boxing	75	30
758	1m. Diving	1·00	1·75
759	3m. Ten-pin bowling	2·50	5·50
MS760 Two sheets, each 75×105 mm. (a) 2m. Lawn tennis (different). (b) 4m. Football. Set of 2 sheets		6·00	5·00

See also Nos. 838/**MS**842.

174 Isaac Newton and Reflecting Telescope

1987. Great Scientific Discoveries. Multicoloured.

761	5s. Type **174**	30	10
762	9s. Alexander Graham Bell and first telephone	30	15
763	75s. Robert Goddard and liquid fuel rocket	80	75
764	4m. Chuck Yeager and Bell XS-1 rocket plane	2·75	4·50
MS765	98×68 mm. 4m. *Mariner 10* spacecraft	2·75	3·00

175 Grey Rhebuck

1987. Flora and Fauna. Multicoloured.

766	5s. Type **175**	40	15
767	9s. Cape clawless otter	40	15
768	15s. Cape grey mongoose	50	20
769	20s. Free State daisy (vert)	55	20
770	35s. River bells (vert)	65	30
771	1m. Turkey flower (vert)	1·50	2·50
772	2m. Sweet briar (vert)	1·75	3·75
773	3m. Mountain reedbuck	2·25	5·00
MS774	Two sheets, each 114×98 mm. (a) 2m. Pig-Lily (vert). (b) 4m. Cape Wildebeest	6·50	11·00

176 Scouts hiking

1987. World Scout Jamboree, Australia. Multicoloured.

775	9s. Type **176**	60	20
776	15s. Scouts playing football	65	20
777	35s. Kangaroos	80	50
778	75s. Scout saluting	1·50	1·25
779	4m. Australian scout windsurfing	3·00	6·50
MS780	96×66 mm. 4m. Outline map and flag of Australia	3·25	4·00

177 Spotted Trunkfish and Columbus's Fleet

1987. 500th Anniversary (1992) of Discovery of America by Columbus. Multicoloured.

781	9s. Type **177**	65	20
782	15s. Green turtle and ships	80	20
783	35s. Columbus watching common dolphins from ship	1·00	40
784	5m. White-tailed tropic bird and fleet at sea	6·50	8·00
MS785	105×76 mm. 4m. *Santa Maria* and Cuban Amazon in flight	6·00	4·00

No. 782 is inscribed 'Carribbean' in error.

178 *Madonna and Child* (detail)

1987. Christmas. Paintings by Raphael. Multicoloured.

786	9s. Type **178**	30	10
787	15s. *Marriage of the Virgin*	45	15
788	35s. *Coronation of the Virgin* (detail)	90	40
789	90s. *Madonna of the Chair*	2·00	3·50
MS790	75×100 mm. 3m. *Madonna and Child enthroned with Five Saints* (detail)	3·00	3·00

179 Lesser Pied Kingfisher

1988. Birds. Multicoloured.

791	2s. Type **179**	20	30
792	3s. Three-banded plover	20	30
793	5s. Spur-winged goose	20	30
794	10s. Clapper lark	20	20
795	12s. Red-eyed bulbul	30	10
796	16s. Cape weaver	30	10
797	20s. Paradise sparrow ('Red-headed Finch')	30	10
798	30s. Mountain wheater ('Mountain Chat')	35	20
799	40s. Common stonechat ('Stone Chate')	40	20
800	55s. Pied barbet	50	25
801	60s. Red-shouldered glossy starling	55	50
802	75s. Cape sparrow	60	60
803	1m. Cattle egret	60	80
804	3m. Giant kingfisher	90	2·50
805	10m. Helmeted guineafowl	1·90	7·00

1988. Royal Ruby Wedding. Nos. 701/703 optd **40TH WEDDING ANNIVERSARY H.M. QUEEN ELIZABETH II H.R.H. THE DUKE OF EDINBURGH**.

806	90s. black and yellow	90	65
807	1m. multicoloured	1·00	80
808	2m. multicoloured	1·75	1·40
MS809	119×85 mm. 4m. black and grey-brown	3·25	2·75

181 Mickey Mouse and Goofy outside Presidential Palace, Helsinki

1988. Finlandia '88 International Stamp Exhibition, Helsinki. Designs showing Walt Disney cartoon characters in Finland. Multicoloured.

810	1s. Type **181**	10	10
811	2s. Goofy and Mickey Mouse in sauna	10	10
812	3s. Goofy and Mickey Mouse fishing in lake	10	10
813	4s. Mickey and Minnie Mouse and Finlandia Hall, Helsinki	10	10
814	5s. Mickey Mouse photographing Goofy at Sibelius Monument, Helsinki	10	10
815	10s. Mickey Mouse and Goofy pony trekking	10	10
816	3m. Goofy, Mickey and Minnie Mouse at Helsinki Olympic Stadium	3·50	3·00
817	5m. Mickey Mouse and Goofy meeting Santa at Arctic Circle	4·50	4·00
MS818	Two sheets, each 127×102 mm. (a) 4m. Mickey Mouse and nephew as Lapps. (b) 4m. Daisy Duck, Goofy, Mickey and Minnie Mouse by fountain, Helsinki. Set of 2 sheets	5·50	7·00

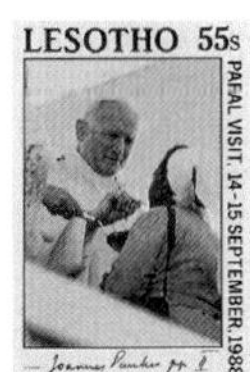

182 Pope John Paul II giving Communion

1988. Visit of Pope John Paul II. Multicoloured.

819	55s. Type **182**	40	25
820	2m. Pope leading procession	1·25	1·50
821	3m. Pope at airport	1·75	2·00
822	4m. Pope John Paul II	2·25	2·75
MS823	98×79 mm. 5m. Archbishop Morapeli (horiz)	5·00	4·50

183 Large-toothed Rock Hyrax

1988. Small Mammals of Lesotho. Multicoloured.

824	16s. Type **183**	55	15
825	40s. Ratel and black-throated honey guide (bird)	2·00	55
826	75s. Small-spotted genet	1·50	85
827	3m. Yellow mongoose	3·25	5·50
MS828	110×78 mm. 4m. Meerkat	4·00	4·00

184 *Birth of Venus* (detail) (Botticelli)

1988. Famous Paintings. Multicoloured.

829	15s. Type **184**	30	15
830	25s. *View of Toledo* (El Greco)	35	20
831	40s. *Maids of Honour* (detail) (Velasquez)	45	25
832	50s. *The Fifer* (Manet)	55	30
833	55s. *Starry Night* (detail) (Van Gogh)	55	30
834	75s. *Prima Ballerina* (Degas)	70	70
835	2m. *Bridge over Water Lilies* (Monet)	1·75	2·25
836	3m. *Guernica* (detail) (Picasso)	1·75	2·75
MS837	Two sheets, each 110×95 mm. (a) 4m. *The Presentation of the Virgin in the Temple* (Titian). (b) 4m. *The Miracle of the Newborn Infant* (Titian)	4·00	4·50

185 Wrestling

1988. Olympic Games, Seoul (2nd series). Multicoloured.

838	12s. Type **185**	10	10
839	16s. Show jumping (vert)	10	10
840	55s. Shooting	20	30
841	3m.50 As 16s. (vert)	1·40	2·00
MS842	108×77 mm. 4m. Olympic flame (vert)	2·75	3·50

186 Yannick Noah and Eiffel Tower, Paris

1988. 75th Anniversary of International Tennis Federation. Multicoloured.

843	12s. Type **186**	60	25
844	20s. Rod Laver and Sydney Harbour Bridge and Opera House	1·75	30
845	30s. Ivan Lendl and Prague	65	25
846	65s. Jimmy Connors and Tokyo (vert)	80	40
847	1m. Arthur Ashe and Barcelona (vert)	1·25	60
848	1m.55 Althea Gibson and New York (vert)	1·25	90
849	2m. Chris Evert and Vienna (vert)	1·50	1·25
850	2m.40 Boris Becker and Houses of Parliament, London (vert)	1·75	1·75
851	3m. Martina Navratilova and Golden Gate Bridge, San Francisco	2·00	2·00
MS852	98×72 mm. 4m. Steffi Graf and Berlin	3·00	3·75

No. 844 is inscribed 'SIDNEY' in error.

186a *The Averoldi Polyptych* (detail)

1988. Christmas. 500th Birth Anniversary of Titian (artist). Multicoloured.

853	12s. Type **186a**	20	10
854	20s. *Christ and the Adulteress* (detail)	20	10
855	35s. *Christ and the Adulteress* (different detail)	30	20
856	45s. *Angel of the Annunciation*	40	30
857	65s. *Saint Dominic*	55	50
858	1m. *The Vendramin Family* (detail)	75	80
859	2m. *Mary Magdalen*	1·25	1·75
860	3m. *The Tribute Money*	1·75	2·50
MS861	(a) 94×110 mm. 5m. *Mater Dolorosa*. (b) 110×94 mm. 5m. *Christ and the Woman taken in Adultery* (horiz)	6·00	8·00

187 Pilatus PC-6 Turbo Porter

1989. 125th Anniversary of International Red Cross. Aircraft. Multicoloured.

862	12s. Type **187**	90	20
863	20s. Unloading medical supplies from Cessna Caravan I	1·40	25
864	55s. de Havilland D.H.C.6 Twin Otter 200/300	1·50	75
865	3m. Douglas DC-3	3·50	4·00
MS866	109×80 mm. 4m. Red Cross logo and Douglas DC-3 (vert)	7·50	4·00

187a *Dawn Mist at Mishima*

1989. Japanese Art. Paintings by Hiroshige. Multicoloured.

867	12s. Type **187a**	30	10
868	16s. *Night Snow at Kambara*	35	10
869	20s. *Wayside Inn at Mariko Station*	35	10
870	35s. *Shower at Shono*	55	10
871	55s. *Snowfall on the Kisokaido near Oi*	65	40
872	1m. *Autumn Moon at Seba*	85	85
873	3m.20 *Evening Moon at Ryogoku Bridge*	2·00	3·00
874	5m. *Cherry Blossoms at Arashiyama*	2·25	3·75
MS875	Two sheets, each 102×76 mm. (a) 4m. *Listening to the Singing Insects at Dokanyama*. (b) 4m. *Moonlight, Nagakubo*	6·00	7·50

188 Mickey Mouse as General

1989. Philexfrance 89 International Stamp Exhibition, Paris. Designs showing Walt Disney cartoon characters in French military uniforms of the Revolutionary period. Multicoloured.

876	1s. Type **188**	10	10
877	2s. Ludwig von Drake as infantryman	10	10
878	3s. Goofy as grenadier	10	10
879	4s. Horace Horsecollar as cavalryman	10	10
880	5s. Pete as hussar	10	10
881	10s. Donald Duck as marine	10	10
882	3m. Gyro Gearloose as National Guard	3·25	3·25
883	5m. Scrooge McDuck as admiral	4·00	4·25
MS884	Two sheets, each 127×102 mm. (a) 4m. Mickey and Minnie Mouse as King Louis XVI and Marie Antoinette with Goofy as a National Guard (horiz). (b) 4m. Mickey Mouse as drummer. Set of 2 sheets	7·50	9·00

No. 879 is inscribed 'CALVARYMAN' in error.

189 *Paxillus involutus*

1989. Fungi. Multicoloured.

900	12s. Type **189**	20	10
901	16s. *Ganoderma applanatum*	20	15
902	55s. *Suillus granulatus*	45	35
903	5m. *Stereum hirsutum*	3·25	4·50
MS904	96×69 mm. 4m. *Scleroderma cepa* ('flavidum')	5·00	5·50

190 Sesotho Huts

1989. Maloti Mountains. Multicoloured.

905	1m. Type **190**	70	1·00
906	1m. American aloe and mountains	70	1·00
907	1m. River valley with waterfall	70	1·00
908	1m. Sesotho tribesman on ledge	70	1·00
MS909	86×117 mm. 4m. Spiral Aloe	3·00	4·00

Nos. 905/908 were printed together, *se-tenant*, forming a composite design.

191 Marsh Sandpiper

1989. Migrant Birds. Multicoloured.

910	12s. Type **191**	80	30
911	65s. Little stint	1·50	70
912	1m. Ringed plover	2·00	1·50
913	4m. Curlew sandpiper	3·50	5·50
MS914	97×69 mm. 5m. Ruff (vert)	9·50	10·00

192 Launch of *Apollo 11*

1989. 20th Anniversary of First Manned Landing on Moon. Multicoloured.

915	12s. Type **192**	25	10
916	16s. Lunar module *Eagle* landing on Moon (horiz)	25	15
917	40s. Neil Armstrong leaving *Eagle*	45	25
918	55s. Edwin Aldrin on Moon (horiz)	50	30
919	1m. Aldrin performing scientific experiment (horiz)	85	85
920	2m. *Eagle* leaving Moon (horiz)	1·50	1·75
921	3m. Command module *Columbia* in Moon orbit (horiz)	2·00	2·25
922	4m. Command module on parachutes	2·50	2·75
MS923	81×111 mm. 5m. Astronaut on Moon	5·50	6·00

193 English Penny Post Paid Mark, 1680

1989. World Stamp Expo '89 International Stamp Exhibition, Washington (1st issue). Stamps and Postmarks.

924	**193**	75s. red, black and stone	80	80
925	-	75s. black, grey and red	80	80
926	-	75s. violet, black & brown	80	80
927	-	75s. brown, black and light brown	80	80
928	-	75s. black and yellow	80	80
929	-	75s. multicoloured	80	80
930	-	75s. black and lilac	80	80
931	-	75s. black, red and brown	80	80
932	-	75s. red, black and yellow	80	80

Designs: No. 925, German postal seal and feather, 1807; No. 926, British Post Office in Crete 1898 20pa. stamp; No. 927, Bermuda 1848 Perot 1d. provisional; No. 928, USA Pony Express cancellation, 1860; No. 929, Finland 1856 5k. stamp; No. 930, Fiji 1870 *Fiji Times* 1d. stamp, 1870; No. 931, Sweden newspaper wrapper handstamp, 1823; No. 932, Bhor 1879 ½a. stamp.

193a Cathedral Church of St Peter and St Paul, Washington

1989. World Stamp Expo '89 International Stamp Exhibition, Washington (2nd issue). Sheet 78×61 mm.

MS933	**193a** 4m. multicoloured	2·50	3·00

193b *The Immaculate Conception*

1989. Christmas. Paintings by Velazquez. Multicoloured.

934	12s. Type **193b**	10	10
935	20s. *St Anthony Abbot and St Paul the Hermit*	15	10
936	35s. *St Thomas the Apostle*	25	25
937	55s. *Christ in the House of Martha and Mary*	35	35
938	1m. *St John writing The Apocalypse on Patmos*	60	75
939	3m. *The Virgin presenting the Chasuble to St Ildephonsus*	1·60	2·25
940	4m. *The Adoration of the Magi*	2·00	2·75
MS941	71×96 mm. 5m. *The Coronation of the Virgin*	7·00	8·00

194 Scene from 1966 World Cup Final, England

1989. World Cup Football Championship, Italy. Scenes from past finals. Multicoloured.

942	12s. Type **194**	50	10
943	16s. 1970 final, Mexico	50	15
944	55s. 1974 final, West Germany	1·00	40
945	5m. 1982 final, Spain	3·75	5·50
MS946	106×85 mm. 4m. Player's legs and symbolic football	5·00	7·00

1990. No. 889 and 798/799 surch **16 s**.

948	16s. on 12s. Red-eyed bulbul	2·25	20
948e	16s. on 30s. Mountail wheater	75	15
948f	16s. on 40s. Common stonechat	1·00	15

197 *Byblia anvatara*

1990. Butterflies. Multicoloured.

949	12s. Type **197**	80	15
950	16s. *Cynthia cardui*	90	15
951	55s. *Precis oenone*	1·40	40
952	65s. *Pseudacraea boisduvali*	1·40	65
953	1m. *Precis orithya*	2·25	1·25
954	2m. *Precis sophia*	3·25	2·50
955	3m. *Danaus chrysippus*	4·25	4·25
956	4m. *Druryia antimachus*	5·00	6·50
MS957	105×70 mm. 5m. *Papilio demodocus*	8·50	10·00

198 *Satyrium princeps*

1990. EXPO 90 International Garden and Greenery Exhibition, Osaka. Local Orchids. Multicoloured.

958	12s. Type **198**	55	15
959	16s. *Huttonaea pulchra*	60	15
960	55s. *Herschelia graminifolia*	1·25	30
961	1m. *Ansellia gigantea*	1·75	75
962	1m.55 *Polystachya pubescens*	2·00	1·75
963	2m.40 *Penthea filicornis*	2·00	2·25
964	3m. *Disperis capensis*	2·25	3·25
965	4m. *Disa uniflora*	3·00	4·00
MS966	95×68 mm. 5m. *Stenoglottis longifolia*	7·50	9·00

198a Lady Elizabeth Bowes-Lyon and Brother in Fancy Dress

1990. 90th Birthday of Queen Elizabeth the Queen Mother.

967	**198a**	1m.50 black and mauve	1·25	1·25
968	-	1m.50 black and mauve	1·25	1·25
969	-	1m.50 black and mauve	1·25	1·25
MS970		90×75 mm. 5m. brown, black and mauve	4·25	4·25

Designs: No. 968, Lady Elizabeth Bowes-Lyon in evening dress; No. 969, Lady Elizabeth Bowes-Lyon wearing hat; No. **MS**970, Lady Elizabeth Bowes-Lyon as a child.

199 King Moshoeshoe II and Prince Mohato wearing Seana-Marena Blankets

1990. Traditional Blankets. Multicoloured.

971	12s. Type **199**	10	10
972	16s. Prince Mohato wearing Seana-Marena blanket	10	10
973	1m. Pope John Paul II wearing Seana-Marena blanket	1·75	1·10
974	3m. Basotho horsemen wearing Matlama blankets	2·00	3·00
MS975	85×104 mm. 5m. Pope John Paul II wearing hat and Seana-Marena blanket (horiz)	5·50	5·50

200 Filling Truck at No. 1 Quarry

1990. Lesotho Highlands Water Project. Multicoloured.

976	16s. Type **200**	1·00	10
977	20s. Tanker lorry on Pitseng–Malibamatso road	1·00	20
978	55s. Piers for Malibamatso Bridge	1·00	30
979	2m. Excavating Mphosong section of Pitseng–Malibamatso road	3·00	3·75
MS980	104×85 mm. 5m. Sinking blasting borcholes on Pitseng–Malibamatso road	7·00	8·00

201 Mother breastfeeding Baby

1990. UNICEF Child Survival Campaign. Multicoloured.

981	12s. Type **201**	75	10
982	55s. Baby receiving oral rehydration therapy	1·25	45
983	1m. Weight monitoring	1·75	3·25

202 Men's Triple Jump

1990. Olympic Games, Barcelona (1992). Multicoloured.

984	16s. Type **202**	70	10
985	55s. Men's 200 m race	95	25
986	1m. Men's 5000 m race	1·60	1·25
987	4m. Show jumping	4·25	6·00
MS988	100×70 mm. 5m. Olympic flame (horiz)	7·00	8·00

203 *Virgin and Child* (detail, Rubens)

1990. Christmas. Paintings by Rubens. Multicoloured.

989	12s. Type **203**	20	10
990	16s. *Adoration of the Magi* (detail)	20	10
991	55s. *Head of One of the Three Kings*	45	25
992	80s. *Adoration of the Magi* (different detail)	60	60
993	1m. *Virgin and Child* (different detail)	70	70
994	2m. *Adoration of the Magi* (different detail)	1·25	1·75
995	3m. *Virgin and Child* (different detail)	2·00	2·50
996	4m. *Adoration of the Magi* (different detail)	2·25	3·25
MS997	71×100 mm. 5m. *Assumption of the Virgin* (detail)	4·25	6·00

204 Mickey Mouse at Nagasaki Peace Park

1991. Phila Nippon '91 International Stamp Exhibition, Tokyo. Walt Disney cartoon characters in Japan. Multicoloured.

998	20s. Type **204**	80	15
999	30s. Mickey Mouse on Kamakura Beach	85	20
1000	40s. Mickey and Donald Duck with Bunraku puppet	95	25
1001	50s. Mickey and Donald eating soba	1·00	35
1002	75s. Mickey and Minnie Mouse at tea house	1·40	70
1003	1m. Mickey running after Hikari express train	1·40	1·00
1004	3m. Mickey Mouse with deer at Todaiji Temple, Nara	3·25	3·50
1005	4m. Mickey and Minnie outside Imperial Palace	3·25	4·00
MS1006	Two sheets, each 127×112 mm. (a) 5m. Mickey Mouse skiing. (b) 5m. Mickey and Minnie having a picnic. Set of 2 sheets	8·00	8·50

205 Stewart Granger (*King Solomon's Mines*)

1991. Famous Films with African Themes. Multicoloured.

1007 12s. Type **205** 45 20
1008 16s. Johnny Weissmuller (*Tarzan the Ape Man*) 45 20
1009 30s. Clark Gable and Grace Kelly (*Mogambo*) 60 35
1010 55s. Sigourney Weaver and gorilla (*Gorillas in the Mist*) 1·00 55
1011 70s. Humphrey Bogart and Katharine Hepburn (*The African Queen*) 1·10 80
1012 1m. John Wayne and capture of rhinoceros (*Hatari!*) 1·75 1·00
1013 2m. Meryl Streep and de Havilland Gipsy Moth light aircraft (*Out of Africa*) 2·25 2·25
1014 4m. Arsenio Hall and Eddie Murphy (*Coming to America*) 2·75 3·50
MS1015 108×77 mm. 5m. Elsa the Lioness (*Born Free*) 3·75 4·50

206 *Satyrus aello*

1991. Butterflies. Multicoloured.

1016B 2s. Type **206** 50 1·00
1017B 3s. *Erebia medusa* 50 1·00
1018A 5s. *Melanargia galathea* 30 75
1019B 10s. *Erebia aethiops* 50 1·00
1020A 20s. *Coenonympha pamphilus* 5·00 30
1021B 25s. *Pyrameis atalanta* 65 20
1022B 30s. *Charaxes jasius* 70 10
1023B 40s. *Colias palaeno* 75 10
1024B 50s. *Colias cliopatra* 75 10
1025B 60s. *Colias philodice* 80 30
1026B 70s. *Rhumni gonepterix* 85 10
1027B 1m. *Colias caesonia* 1·50 65
1028B 2m. *Pyrameis cardui* 2·50 1·50
1029cA 3m. *Danaus chrysippus* 1·40 2·00
1030B 10m. *Apatura iris* 7·00 8·50

207 Victim of Drug Abuse

1991. Say No To Drugs Campaign.

1031 **207** 16s. multicoloured 2·00 60

208 Wattled Cranes

1991. Southern Africa Development Co-ordination Conference Tourism Promotion. Multicoloured.

1032 12s. Type **208** 2·00 1·00
1033 16s. Butterfly on flowers 2·00 1·00
1034 25s. Zebra and tourist bus at Mukorob (rock formation), Namibia 2·50 1·50
MS1035 75×117 mm. 3m. Basotho women in ceremonial dress 4·25 5·50

209 De Gaulle in 1939

1991. Birth Centenary of Charles de Gaulle (French statesman).

1036 **209** 20s. black and brown 80 15
1037 - 40s. black and purple 1·00 1·25
1038 - 50s. black and green 1·00 40
1039 - 60s. black and blue 1·00 70
1040 - 4m. black and red 3·50 4·50

Designs: 40s. General De Gaulle as Free French leader; 50s. De Gaulle as provisional President of France, 1944–1946; 60s. Charles de Gaulle in 1958; 4m. President De Gaulle.

210 Prince and Princess of Wales

1991. Tenth Wedding Anniversary of Prince and Princess of Wales. Multicoloured.

1041 50s. Type **210** 1·25 25
1042 70s. Prince Charles at polo and Princess Diana holding Prince Harry 1·25 45
1043 1m. Prince Charles with Prince Harry and Princess Diana in evening dress 1·40 70
1044 3m. Prince William and Prince Harry in school uniform 1·75 3·00
MS1045 68×91 mm. 4m. Portraits of Prince with Princess and sons 4·50 4·25

211 *St Anne with Mary and the Child Jesus*

1991. Christmas. Drawings by Albrecht Durer.

1046 **211** 20s. black and mauve 60 10
1047 - 30s. black and blue 75 20
1048 - 50s. black and green 90 25
1049 - 60s. black and red 95 30
1050 - 70s. black and yellow 1·00 60
1051 - 1m. black and orange 1·25 1·10
1052 - 2m. black and purple 2·50 2·75
1053 - 4m. black and blue 3·50 6·00
MS1054 Two sheets, each 102×127 mm. (a) 5m. black and red. (b) 5m. black and blue 6·00 7·50

Designs: 30s. *Mary on Grass Bench*; 50s. *Mary with Crown of Stars*; 60s. *Mary with Child beside Tree*; 70s. *Mary with Child beside Wall*; 1m. *Mary in Halo on Crescent Moon*; 2m. *Mary breastfeeding Child*; 4m. *Mary with Infant in Swaddling Clothes*

212 Mickey Mouse and Pluto pinning the Tail on the Donkey

1991. Children's Games. Walt Disney cartoon characters. Multicoloured.

1055 20s. Type **212** 65 15
1056 30s. Mickey playing mancala 70 20
1057 40s. Mickey rolling hoop 80 20
1058 50s. Minnie Mouse hula-hooping 90 25
1059 70s. Mickey and Pluto throwing a frisbee 1·25 75
1060 1m. Donald Duck with a diabolo 1·60 1·40
1061 2m. Donald's nephews playing marbles 2·50 3·00
1062 3m. Donald with Rubik's cube 3·00 4·00
MS1063 Two sheets, each 127×112 mm. (a) 5m. Donald's and Mickey's nephews playing tug-of-war. (b) 5m. Mickey and Donald mock fighting. Set of 2 sheets 8·50 9·00

213 Lanner Falcon

1992. Birds. Multicoloured.

1064 30s. Type **213** 80 60
1065 30s. Bateleur 80 60
1066 30s. Paradise sparrow (inscr 'Red-headed Finch') 80 60
1067 30s. Lesser striped swallow 80 60
1068 30s. Alpine swift 80 60
1069 30s. Didric cuckoo ('Diederik Cuckoo') 80 60
1070 30s. Yellow-tufted malachite sunbird ('Malachite Sunbird') 80 60
1071 30s. Burchell's gonolek ('Crimson-breasted Shrike') 80 60
1072 30s. Pin-tailed whydah 80 60
1073 30s. Lilac-breasted roller 80 60
1074 30s. Black bustard ('Korhaan') 80 60
1075 30s. Black-collared barbet 80 60
1076 30s. Secretary bird 80 60
1077 30s. Red-billed quelea 80 60
1078 30s. Red bishop 80 60
1079 30s. Ring-necked dove 80 60
1080 30s. Yellow canary 80 60
1081 30s. Cape longclaw ('Orange-throated Longclaw') 80 60
1082 30s. Cordon-bleu (inscr 'Blue Waxbill') 80 60
1083 30s. Golden bishop 80 60

Nos. 1064/1083 were printed together, *se-tenant*, forming a composite design.

214 Queen Elizabeth and Cooking at a Mountain Homestead

1992. 40th Anniversary of Queen Elizabeth II's Accession. Multicoloured.

1084 20s. Type **214** 40 15
1085 30s. View from mountains 40 20
1086 1m. Cacti and mountain 1·25 65
1087 4m. Thaba-Bosiu 3·00 3·50
MS1088 75×97 mm. 5m. Mountains at sunset 4·50 4·50

215 Minnie Mouse as Spanish Lady, 1540–1660

1992. International Stamp Exhibitions. Walt Disney cartoon characters. Multicoloured. (a) Granada '92, Spain. Traditional Spanish Costumes.

1089 20s. Type **215** 1·00 20
1090 50s. Mickey Mouse as Don Juan at Lepanto, 1571 1·25 40
1091 70s. Donald in Galician costume, 1880 1·50 70
1092 2m. Daisy Duck in Aragonese costume, 1880 3·00 3·75
MS1093 127×112 mm. 5m. Goofy the bullfighter 4·50 5·50

(b) World Columbian Stamp Expo '92. Native American Life.

1094 30s. Donald Duck making arrowheads 90 30
1095 40s. Goofy playing lacrosse 95 40
1096 1m. Mickey Mouse and Donald Duck planting corn 1·50 1·10
1097 3m. Minnie Mouse doing bead work 3·00 3·50
MS1098 127×112 mm. 5m. Mickey paddling canoe 4·50 5·50

216 Stegosaurus

1992. Prehistoric Animals. Multicoloured.

1099 20s. Type **216** 1·00 30
1100 30s. Ceratosaurus 1·10 35
1101 40s. Procompsognathus 1·40 45
1102 50s. Lesothosaurus 1·60 55
1103 70s. Plateosaurus 1·60 70
1104 1m. Gasosaurus 2·00 1·25
1105 2m. Massospondylus 2·50 3·25
1106 3m. Archaeopteryx 2·50 4·00
MS1107 Two sheets, each 105×77 mm. (a) 5m. As 50s. (b) 5m. As 3m. Set of 2 sheets 11·00 10·00

217 Men's Discus

1992. Olympic Games, Albertville and Barcelona. Multicoloured.

1108 20s. Type **217** 20 15
1109 30s. Men's long jump 25 15
1110 40s. Women's 4×100m relay 30 25
1111 70s. Women's 100m 50 50
1112 1m. Men's parallel bars 70 70
1113 2m. Men's double luge (horiz) 1·40 1·75
1114 3m. Women's 30k cross-country skiing (horiz) 1·75 2·50
1115 4m. Men's biathlon 2·00 2·75
MS1116 Two sheets, each 100×70 mm. (a) 5m. Women's figure skating. (b) 5m. Ice hockey (horiz). Set of 2 sheets 7·50 8·00

218 *Virgin and Child* (Sassetta)

1992. Christmas. Religious Paintings. Multicoloured.

1117 20s. Type **218** 55 15
1118 30s. *Coronation of the Virgin* (Master of Bonastre) 65 20
1119 40s. *Virgin and Child* (Master of SS. Cosmas and Damian) 75 25
1120 70s. *The Virgin of Great Panagia* (detail) (12th-century Russian school) 1·25 55
1121 1m. *Madonna and Child* (Vincenzo Foppa) 1·75 1·10
1122 2m. *Madonna and Child* (School of Lippo Memmi) 2·50 2·75
1123 3m. *Virgin and Child* (Barnaba da Modena) 3·00 3·75
1124 4m. *Virgin and Child with Saints* (triptych) (Simone dei Crocifissi) 3·25 4·00
MS1125 Two sheets, each 76×102 mm. (a) 5m. *Virgin and Child with Saints* (different detail) (Simone dei Crocifissi). (b) 5m. *Virgin and Child enthroned and surrounded by Angels* (Cimabue) 11·00 13·00

219 World Trade Centre, New York

1992. Postage Stamp Mega Event, New York. Sheet 100×70 mm.

MS1126 5m. **219** multicoloured 6·50 7·50

220 Baby Harp Seal (Earth Summit '92, Rio)

1993. Anniversaries and Events. Multicoloured.

1127 20s. Type **220** 1·25 50
1128 30s. Giant panda (Earth Summit '92, Rio) 1·75 50
1129 40s. Airship *Graf Zeppelin* over globe (75th death anniversary of Count Ferdinand von Zeppelin) 1·60 50
1130 70s. Woman grinding maize (International Conference on Nutrition, Rome) 60 55
1131 4m. Lt. Robinson's Royal Aircraft Factory B.E.2C shooting down Schutte Lanz SL-11 airship (75th death anniversary of Count Ferdinand von Zeppelin) 3·75 4·75

1132 5m. Valentina Tereshkova and *Vostok 6* (30th anniversary of first woman in space) 3·75 4·75

MS1133 Two sheets, each 100×70 mm. (a) 5m. Dr. Ronald McNair (*Challenger* astronaut) (International Space Year). (b) 5m. South African crowned crane (Earth Summit '92, Rio) 12·00 11·00

221 *Orpheus and Eurydice* (detail)

1993. Bicentenary of the Louvre, Paris. Paintings by Poussin. Multicoloured.

1134 70s. Type **221** 80 80
1135 70s. *Rape of the Sabine Women* (left detail) 80 80
1136 70s. *Rape of the Sabine Women* (right detail) 80 80
1137 70s. *The Death of Sapphira* (left detail) 80 80
1138 70s. *The Death of Sapphira* (right detail) 80 80
1139 70s. *Echo and Narcissus* (left detail) 80 80
1140 70s. *Echo and Narcissus* (right detail) 80 80
1141 70s. *Self-portrait* 80 80
MS1142 70×100 mm. 5m. *The Money Lender and his Wife* (57×89 mm) (Metsys) 4·75 5·00

222 Aloe

1993. Flowers. Multicoloured.

1143 20s. Type **222** 40 10
1144 30s. Calla lily 45 15
1145 40s. Bird of paradise plant 45 15
1146 70s. Amaryllis 75 40
1147 1m. Agapanthus 90 60
1148 2m. Crinum 3·75 2·25
1149 4m. Watsonia 2·50 3·25
1150 5m. Gazania 2·50 3·50
MS1151 Two sheets, each 98×67 mm. (a) 7m. Plumbago. (b) 7m. Desert Rose 8·50 9·00

223 *Precis westermanni*

1993. Butterflies. Multicoloured.

1152 20s. Type **223** 40 15
1153 40s. *Precis sophia* 50 20
1154 70s. *Precis terea* 65 45
1155 1m. *Byblia acheloia* 75 75
1156 2m. *Papilio antimachus* 1·25 1·50
1157 5m. *Pseudacraea boisduvali* 1·75 3·00
MS1158 Two sheets, each 96×62 mm. (a) 7m. *Precis oenone*. (b) 7m. *Precis octavia* 7·00 7·00

No. 1157 is inscribed 'Pesudacraea boisduvali' in error.

224 Queen Elizabeth II at Coronation (photograph by Cecil Beaton)

1993. 40th Anniversary of Coronation.

1159 **224** 20s. multicoloured 90 90
1160 - 40s. multicoloured 1·00 1·00
1161 - 1m. black and green 1·25 1·25
1162 - 5m. multicoloured 2·75 2·75
MS1163 70×100 mm. 7m. multicoloured ($42\frac{1}{2}$×$28\frac{1}{2}$ mm) 5·50 5·50

Designs: Vert—40s. St Edward's Crown and Sceptre; 1m. Queen Elizabeth the Queen Mother; 5m. Queen Elizabeth II and family. Horiz—7m. *Conversation Piece at Royal Lodge, Windsor* (detail) (Sir James Gunn).

225 East African Railways Vulcan Steam Locomotive, 1929

1993. African Railways. Multicoloured.

1164 20s. Type **225** 85 25
1165 30s. Beyer-Garratt Class 15A steam locomotive, Zimbabwe Railways, 1952 95 30
1166 40s. Class 25 steam locomotive, South African Railways, 1953 1·00 30
1167 70s. Class A 58 steam locomotive, East African Railways 1·50 60
1168 1m. Class 9E electric locomotives, South African Railways 1·60 85
1169 2m. Class 87 diesel-electric locomotive, East African Railways, 1971 2·00 1·75
1170 3m. Class 92 diesel locomotive, East African Railways, 1971 2·25 2·50
1171 5m. Class 26 steam locomotive No. 3450, South African Railways, 1982 2·75 3·75
MS1172 Two sheets, each 104×82 mm. (a) 7m. Class 6E electric locomotive, South African Railways, 1969. (b) 7m. Class 231-132BT steam locomotive, Algerian Railways, 1937 11·00 11·00

226 Court-house

1993. Traditional Houses. Multicoloured.

1173 20s. Type **226** 50 10
1174 30s. House with reed fence 55 15
1175 70s. Unmarried girls' house 1·00 40
1176 4m. Hut made from branches 3·50 5·00
MS1177 81×69 mm. 4m. Decorated houses 4·25 4·75

227 Black and White Shorthair

1993. Domestic Cats. Multicoloured.

1178 20s. Type **227** 75 25
1179 30s. Shorthair tabby lying down 75 25
1180 70s. Head of shorthair tabby 1·00 40
1181 5m. Black and white shorthair with shorthair tabby 3·00 4·00
MS1182 113×89 mm. 5m. Shorthair Tabby with rat (vert) 4·50 4·50

228 Pluto in Chung Cheng Park, Keelung

1993. Taipei '93 Asian International Stamp Exhibition, Taiwan. Walt Disney cartoon characters in Taiwan. Multicoloured.

1183 20s. Type **228** 65 10
1184 30s. Donald Duck at Chiao-Tienkung Temple Festival 75 15
1185 40s. Goofy with lantern figures 85 20
1186 70s. Minnie Mouse shopping at temple festival 1·25 40
1187 1m. Daisy Duck at Queen's Head Rock, Yehliu (vert) 1·50 70
1188 1m.20 Mickey and Minnie at National Concert Hall (vert) 1·60 1·60
1189 2m. Donald at Chiang Kai-shek Memorial Hall (vert) 1·75 2·00
1190 2m.50 Donald and Daisy at the Grand Hotel, Taipei 2·00 2·75
MS1191 Two sheets, each 128×102 mm. (a) 5m. Goofy over National Palace Museum, Taipei. (b) 6m. Mickey and Minnie at Presidential Palace Museum, Taipei (vert) 8·50 8·50

229 Tseliso 'Frisco' Khomari (Lesotho)

1994. World Cup Football Championship, USA. Multicoloured.

1192 20s. Type **229** 50 10
1193 30s. Thato 'American Spoon' Mohale (Lesotho) 55 15
1194 40s. Jozic Davor (Yugoslavia) and Freddy Rincorn (Colombia) 60 20
1195 50s. Lefika 'Mzee' Lekhotla (Lesotho) 60 25
1196 70s. Litsiso 'House-on-fire' Khali (Lesotho) 70 55
1197 1m. Roger Milla (Cameroun) 85 85
1198 1m.20 David Platt (England) 1·00 2·00
1199 2m. Karl Heinz Rummenigge (Germany) and Soren Lerby (Denmark) 1·40 2·50
MS1200 Two sheets, each 100×70 mm. (a) 6m. Klaus Lindenberger (Czechoslovakia). (b) 6m. Franco Baresi (Italy) and Ivan Hasek (Czechoslovakia) (horiz) 6·50 8·00

230 King Letsie III signing Oath of Office

1994. First Anniversary of Restoration of Democracy. Multicoloured.

1201 20s. Type **230** 20 20
1202 30s. Parliament building (horiz) 25 20
1203 50s. Swearing-in of Dr. Ntsu Mokhehle as Prime Minister (horiz) 40 25
1204 70s. Maj-Gen P. Ramaema handing Instruments of Government to Dr. Ntsu Mokhehle (horiz) 70 45

231 Aquatic River Frog

1994. Philakorea '94 International Stamp Exhibition, Seoul. Frogs and Toads. Multicoloured.

1205 35s. Type **231** 25 10
1206 50s. Bubbling kassina 35 15
1207 1m. Guttural toad 60 60
1208 1m.50 Common river frog 80 1·25
MS1209 Two sheets, each 102×72 mm. (a) 5m. Jade frog (sculpture). (b) 5m. Black Spotted frog and oriental white-eye (bird) (vert) 7·00 8·00

232 de Havilland D.H.C.6 Twin Otter and Emblem

1994. 50th Anniversary of ICAO. Multicoloured.

1210 35s. Type **232** 70 15
1211 50s. Fokker F.27 Friendship on runway 85 20
1212 1m. Fokker F.27 Friendship over Moshoeshoe I International Airport 1·40 90
1213 1m.50 Cessna light aircraft over mountains 1·75 2·25

1995. No. 1022 surch **20s**.

1214a 20s. on 30s. *Charaxes jasius* 1·50 65

234 *Tagetes minuta*

1995. Medicinal Plants. Multicoloured.

1215 35s. Type **234** 35 10
1216 50s. *Plantago lanceolata* 40 15
1217 1m. *Amaranthus spinosus* 65 60
1218 1m.50 *Taraxacum officinale* 1·10 2·00
MS1219 120×91 mm. 5m. *Dativa stramonium* 3·00 3·50

235 Pius XII College, 1962

1995. 50th Anniversary of University Studies in Lesotho. Multicoloured.

1220 35s. Type **235** 20 10
1221 50s. Campus, University of Basutoland, Bechuanaland and Swaziland, 1966 25 15
1222 70s. Campus, University of Botswana, Lesotho and Swaziland, 1970 35 15
1223 1m. Administration Block, University of Botswana, Lesotho and Swaziland, 1975 55 40
1224 1m.50 Administration Block, National University of Lesotho, 1988 75 1·10
1225 2m. Procession of Vice-Chancellors, National University of Lesotho, 1995 1·00 1·75

236 Qiloane Pinnacle, Thaba-Bosiu

1995. 20th Anniversary of World Tourism Organisation. Multicoloured.

1226 35s. Type **236** 25 10
1227 50s. Ha Mohalenyane rock formation 30 15
1228 1m. Botsoela Falls (vert) 55 45
1229 1m.50 Backpackers in Makhaleng River Gorge 80 1·50
MS1230 143×88 mm. 4m. Red Hot Pokers (38×57 mm) 2·50 3·50

No. **MS**1230 is inscribed 'RED HOT PORKERS' in error.

237 'Peace'

1995. 50th Anniversary of United Nations. Multicoloured.

1231 35s. Type **237** 45 10
1232 50s. 'Justice' (scales) 55 20
1233 1m.50 'Reconciliation' (clasped hands) (horiz) 1·00 1·90

238 'Sutter's Gold Rose'

1995. Christmas. Roses. Multicoloured.

1234 5s. Type **238** 30 10
1235 50s. 'Michele Meilland' 35 10
1236 1m. 'J. Otto Thilow' 60 50
1237 2m. 'Papa Meilland' 95 1·60

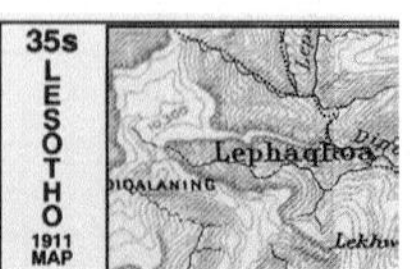

239 Part of 1911 Map showing Lephaqhoa

1996. Completion of New Standard Map of Lesotho (1994). Map Sections of Malibamatso Valley. Multicoloured. (a) 1911 Map.

1238 35s. Type **239** 45 45
1239 35s. Boritsa Tsuene 45 45
1240 35s. Molapo 45 45
1241 35s. Nkeu 45 45
1242 35s. Three rivers flowing east 45 45

1243	35s. Tibedi and Rafanyane	45	45
1244	35s. Two rivers flowing east	45	45
1245	35s. Madibatmatso River	45	45
1246	35s. Bokung River	45	45
1247	35s. Semena River	45	45

(b) 1978 Map.

1248	35s. Mountains and river valley	45	45
1249	35s. Pelaneng and Lepaqoa	45	45
1250	35s. Mamohau	45	45
1251	35s. Ha Lejone	45	45
1252	35s. Ha Thoora	45	45
1253	35s. Ha Mikia	45	45
1254	35s. Ha Kosetabole	45	45
1255	35s. Ha Seshote	45	45
1256	35s. Ha Rapooane	45	45
1257	35s. Bokong Ha Kennan	45	45

(c) 1994 Map.

1258	35s. Mafika-Lisiu Pass	45	45
1259	35s. Ha Lesaoana	45	45
1260	35s. Ha Masaballa	45	45
1261	35s. Ha Nkisi	45	45
1262	35s. Ha Rafanyane	45	45
1263	35s. Laitsoka Pass	45	45
1264	35s. "Katse Reservoir"	45	45
1265	35s. Seshote	45	45
1266	35s. Sephareng	45	45
1267	35s. Katse Dam	45	45

Nos. 1238/1247, 1248/1257 and 1258/1267 respectively were printed together, *se-tenant*, forming composite designs.

240 Adding Iodised Salt to Cooking Pot

1996. 50th Anniversary of UNICEF. Multicoloured.

1268	35s. Type **240**	25	10
1269	50s. Herdboys with livestock (horiz)	35	20
1270	70s. Children in class (horiz)	45	20
1271	1m.50 Boys performing traditional dance (horiz)	90	1·50

241 USA Basketball Team, 1936

1996. Olympic Games, Atlanta. Previous Gold Medal Winners. Multicoloured.

1272	1m. Type **241**	50	20
1273	1m.50 Brandenburg Gate and stadium, Berlin, 1936	50	30
1274	1m.50 Glen Morris (USA) (decathlon, 1936) (vert)	50	50
1275	1m.50 Saidi Aouita (Morocco) (5000 m running, 1984) (vert)	50	50
1276	1m.50 Arnie Robinson (USA) (long jump, 1976) (vert)	50	50
1277	1m.50 Hans Woellke (Germany) (shot put, 1936) (vert)	50	50
1278	1m.50 Renate Stecher (Germany) (100 m running, 1972) (vert)	50	50
1279	1m.50 Evelyn Ashford (USA) (100 m running, 1984) (vert)	50	50
1280	1m.50 Willie Davenport (USA) (110 m hurdles, 1968) (vert)	50	50
1281	1m.50 Bob Beamon (USA) (long jump, 1968) (vert)	50	50
1282	1m.50 Heidi Rosendhal (Germany) (long jump, 1972) (vert)	50	50
1283	2m. Jesse Owens (USA) (track and field, 1936) (vert)	65	70
1284	3m. Speed boat racing	85	1·00
MS1285	Two sheets, each 110×80 mm. (a) 8m. Michael Gross (Germany) (swimming, 1984) (vert). (b) 8m. Kornelia Ender (Germany) (swimming, 1976) (vert)	7·50	7·50

No. 1273 is inscribed 'BRANDEBOURG GATE' in error. No. 1274 incorrectly identifies Glen Morris as the gold medal winner in the 1936 long jump.

Nos. 1274/1282 were printed together, *se-tenant*, with the backgrounds forming a composite design.

242 Class WP Steam Locomotive (India)

1996. Trains of the World. Multicoloured.

1286	1m.50 Type **242**	85	85
1287	1m.50 Canadian Pacific steam locomotive No. 2471 (Canada)	85	85
1288	1m.50 The *Caledonian* (Great Britain)	85	85
1289	1m.50 Steam locomotive *William Mason* (USA)	85	85
1290	1m.50 *Trans-Siberian Express* (Russia)	85	85
1291	1m.50 Steam train (Switzerland)	85	85
1292	1m.50 ETR 450 high speed train (Italy)	85	85
1293	1m.50 TGV express train (France)	85	85
1294	1m.50 XPT high speed train (Australia)	85	85
1295	1m.50 *The Blue Train* (South Africa)	85	85
1296	1m.50 Intercity 225 express train (Great Britain)	85	85
1297	1m.50 *Hikari* express train (Japan)	85	85
MS1298	Two sheets, each 98×68 mm. (a) 8m. Class 52 steam locomotive (Germany) (57×43 mm). (b) 8m. ICE high speed train (Germany) (57×43 mm)	7·50	8·50

243 Mothers' Union Member, Methodist Church

1996. Christmas. Mothers' Unions. Multicoloured.

1299	35s. Type **243**	30	10
1300	50s. Roman Catholic Church	35	10
1301	1m. Lesotho Evangelical Church	65	40
1302	1m.50 Anglican Church	1·00	1·50

No. 1302 is inscribed 'Anglian' in error.

244 Hand Clasp (Co-operation for Development)

1997. Tenth Anniversary of Lesotho Highland Water Project (1996). Multicoloured.

1303	35s. Type **244**	25	10
1304	50s. Lammergeier and rock painting (Nature and Heritage)	1·75	45
1305	1m. Malibamatso Bridge (Engineering)	70	55
1306	1m.50 Katse Valley in 1986 and 1996 (75×28 mm)	1·00	1·75

No. 1305 is inscribed 'Developement' in error.

245 Land Reclamation

1997. Environment Protection. Multicoloured.

1307	35s. Type **245**	30	10
1308	50s. Throwing rubbish into bin	35	15
1309	1m. Hands holding globe and tree	65	40
1310	1m.20 Recycling symbol and rubbish	75	1·00
1311	1m.50 Collecting rain water	85	1·10

246 Schmeichel, Denmark

1997. World Cup Football Championship, France (1998). Multicoloured.

1312	1m. Type **246**	40	20
1313	1m.50 Bergkamp, Netherlands	55	55
1314	1m.50 Argentine players celebrating	55	55
1315	1m.50 Argentine and Dutch players competing for ball	55	55
1316	1m.50 Players heading ball	55	55
1317	1m.50 Goalkeeper deflecting ball	55	55
1318	1m.50 Goal-mouth melee	55	55
1319	1m.50 Argentine player kicking ball	55	55
1320	2m. Southgate, England	70	70
1321	2m.50 Asprilla, Colombia	80	85
1322	3m. Gascoigne, England	90	95
1323	4m. Giggs, Wales	1·10	1·25
MS1324	Two sheets, each 127×102 mm. (a) 8m. Littbarski, West Germany (horiz). (b) 8m. Shearer, England	5·50	7·00

247 *Spialia spio*

1997. Butterflies. Multicoloured.

1325	1m.50 Type **247**	60	60
1326	1m.50 *Leptotes pirithous*	60	60
1327	1m.50 *Acratea satis*	60	60
1328	1m.50 *Belenois aurota aurota*	60	60
1329	1m.50 *Spindasis natalensis*	60	60
1330	1m.50 *Torynesis orangica*	60	60
1331	1m.50 *Lepidochysops variabilis*	60	60
1332	1m.50 *Pinacopteryx eriphia*	60	60
1333	1m.50 *Anthene butleri livida*	60	60
MS1334	Two sheets, each 106×76 mm. (a) 8m. *Bematistes aganice*. (b) 8m. *Papilio demodocus*	8·50	8·50

Nos. 1325/1333 were printed together, *se-tenant*, with the backgrounds forming a composite design.

No. 1326 is inscribed 'Cyclyrius pirithous', No. 1332 'Pinacopteryx eriphea' and No. **MS**1334(b) 'Papalio demodocus', all in error.

248 Rock Paintings and Boy

1998. 40th Anniversary of Morija Museum and Archives. Multicoloured.

1335	35s. Type **248**	30	10
1336	45s. Hippopotamus and lower jaw bone (horiz)	55	20
1337	50s. Woman and cowhide skirt	35	20
1338	1m. Drum and thomo (musical bow)	45	40
1339	1m.50 Warrior with khau (gorget awarded for valour)	65	1·00
1340	2m. Herders with ox (horiz)	80	1·25

249 Diana, Princess of Wales

1998. Diana, Princess of Wales Commemoration. Multicoloured.

1341	3m. Type **249**	1·10	1·25
1342	3m. Wearing grey jacket	1·10	1·25
1343	3m. Wearing white polo-necked jumper	1·10	1·25
1344	3m. Wearing pearl necklace	1·10	1·25
1345	3m. Wearing white evening dress	1·10	1·25
1346	3m. Wearing pale blue jacket	1·10	1·25
MS1347	70×100 mm. 9m. Accepting bouquet	6·50	6·50

250 Atitlan Grebe

1998. Fauna of the World. Multicoloured. (a) Vert designs as T **250**.

1348	1m. Type **250**	45	40
1349	1m. Cabot's tragopan	45	40
1350	1m. Spider monkey	45	40
1351	1m. Dibatag	45	40
1352	1m. Right whale	45	40
1353	1m. Imperial amazon ('Imperial Parrot')	45	40
1354	1m. Cheetah	45	40
1355	1m. Brown-eared pheasant	45	40
1356	1m. Leatherback turtle	45	40
1357	1m. Imperial woodpecker	45	40
1358	1m. Andean condor	45	40
1359	1m. Barbary deer	45	40
1360	1m. Grey gentle lemur	45	40
1361	1m. Cuban amazon ('Cuban Parrot')	45	40
1362	1m. Numbat	45	40
1363	1m. Short-tailed albatross	45	40
1364	1m. Green turtle	45	40
1365	1m. White rhinoceros	45	40
1366	1m. Diademed sifaka	45	40
1367	1m. Galapagos penguin	45	40

(b) Horiz designs, each 48×31 mm.

1368	1m.50 Impala	60	55
1369	1m.50 Black bear	60	55
1370	1m.50 American buffalo	60	55
1371	1m.50 African elephant	60	55
1372	1m.50 Kangaroo	60	55
1373	1m.50 Lion	60	55
1374	1m.50 Giant panda	60	55
1375	1m.50 Tiger	60	55
1376	1m.50 Zebra	60	55
MS1377	Four sheets, each 98×68 mm. (a) 8m. White-bellied sunbird. (b) 8m. Golden-shouldered parrot. (c) 8m. Snail darter. (d) 8m. Monkey (47×31 mm)	11·00	11·00

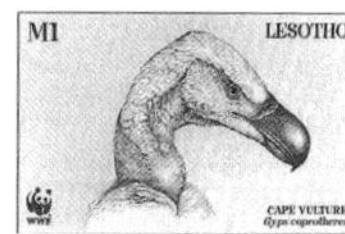

251 Cape Vulture

1998. Endangered Species. Cape Vulture. Multicoloured.

1378	1m. Type **251**	60	70
1379	1m. Looking towards ground	60	70
1380	1m. Looking over shoulder	60	70
1381	1m. Facing right	60	70

252 Siamese

1998. Cats of the World. Multicoloured.

1382	70s. Type **252**	30	20
1383	1m. Chartreux	40	25
1384	2m. Korat	65	65
1385	2m. Japanese bobtail	65	65
1386	2m. British white	65	65
1387	2m. Bengal	65	65
1388	2m. Abyssinian	65	65
1389	2m. Snowshoe	65	65
1390	2m. Scottish fold	65	65
1391	2m. Maine coon	65	65
1392	2m. Balinese	65	65
1393	2m. Persian	65	65
1394	2m. Javanese	65	65
1395	2m. Turkish angora	65	65
1396	2m. Tiffany	65	65
1397	3m. Egyptian mau	85	85
1398	4m. Bombay	95	1·10
1399	5m. Burmese	1·10	1·25
MS1400	Two sheets, each 98×69 mm. (a) 8m. Tonkinese. (b) 8m. Singapura	7·00	7·00

Nos. 1385/1390 and 1391/1396 respectively were printed together, *se-tenant*, with the backgrounds forming composite designs.

253 *Laccaria laccata*

1998. Fungi of the World. Multicoloured.

1401	70s. Type **253**	30	20
1402	1m. *Mutinus caninus*	40	40
1403	1m. *Hygrophorus psittacinus*	40	40
1404	1m. *Cortinarius obtusus*	40	40
1405	1m. *Volvariella bombycina*	40	40
1406	1m. *Cortinarius caerylescens*	40	40
1407	1m. *Laccaria amethystina*	40	40
1408	1m. *Tricholoma aurantium*	40	40
1409	1m. *Amanita excelsa* (spissa)	40	40
1410	1m. *Clavaria helvola*	40	40

1411	1m. Unidentified species (inscr 'Cortinarius caerylescens')	40	40
1412	1m. *Russula queletii*	40	40
1413	1m. *Amanita phalloides*	40	40
1414	1m. *Lactarius deliciosus*	40	40
1415	1m.50 *Tricholoma lascivum*	55	55
1416	2m. *Clitocybe geotropa*	65	65
1417	3m. *Amanita excelsa*	85	90
1418	4m. Red-capped bolete	95	1·10
MS1419	Two sheets, each 98×68 mm. (a) 8m. *Amanita pantherina*. (b) 8m. *Boletus satanas*	5·50	6·50

Nos. 1406, 1407, 1414, 1416 and **MS**1419b are inscribed 'Continarius caerylescens', 'Laccaria amethystea', 'Lactarius delicious', 'Clitocybe geotrapa' and 'Boletys satanus', all in error.

254 'Simba'

1998. World Cinema. Multicoloured. (a) Films about Africa.

1420	2m. Type **254**	60	60
1421	2m. *Call to Freedom*	60	60
1422	2m. *Cry the Beloved Country*	60	60
1423	2m. *King Solomon's Mines*	60	60
1424	2m. *Flame and the Fire*	60	60
1425	2m. *Cry Freedom*	60	60
1426	2m. *Bopha!*	60	60
1427	2m. *Zulu*	60	60

(b) Japanese Film Stars.

1428	2m. Takamine Hideko	60	60
1429	2m. James Shigeta	60	60
1430	2m. Miyoshi Umeki	60	60
1431	2m. May Ishimara	60	60
1432	2m. Sessue Hayakawa	60	60
1433	2m. Miiko Taka	60	60
1434	2m. Mori Masayuki	60	60
1435	2m. Hara Setsuko	60	60
1436	2m. Kyo Machiko	60	60
MS1437	Two sheets. (a) 68×98 mm. 10m. Lion cubs from *Born Free* (horiz). (b) 70×100 mm. 10m. Toshiro Mifune	6·50	7·00

Nos. 1420/1427 and 1428/1436 respectively were printed together, *se-tenant*, with the backgrounds forming composite designs.

No. 1423 is inscribed "KING SOLOMAN'S MINES" in error.

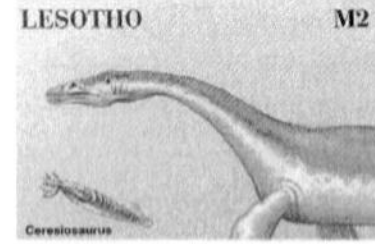

255 Ceresiosaurus

1998. Prehistoric Animals. Multicoloured.

1438	2m. Type **255**	60	60
1439	2m. Rhomaleosaurus	60	60
1440	2m. Anomalocaris	60	60
1441	2m. Mixosaurus	60	60
1442	2m. Stethacanthus	60	60
1443	2m. Dunklosteus	60	60
1444	2m. Tommotia	60	60
1445	2m. Sanctacaris	60	60
1446	2m. Ammonites	60	60
1447	2m. Rhamphorhynchus	60	60
1448	2m. Brachiosaurus	60	60
1449	2m. Mamenchisaurus hochuanensis	60	60
1450	2m. Ceratosaurus nasicornis	60	60
1451	2m. Archaeopteryx	60	60
1452	2m. Leaellynasaura amicagraphica	60	60
1453	2m. Chasmosaurus belli	60	60
1454	2m. Deinonychus and Pachyrhinosaurus	60	60
1455	2m. Deinonychus	60	60
1456	2m. Nyctosaurus	60	60
1457	2m. Volcanoes	60	60
1458	2m. Eudimorphodon	60	60
1459	2m. Apatosaurus	60	60
1460	2m. Peteinosaurus	60	60
1461	2m. Tropeognathus	60	60
1462	2m. Pteranodon ingens	60	60
1463	2m. Ornithodesmus	60	60
1464	2m. Wuerhosaurus	60	60
MS1465	Three sheets, each 100×70 mm. (a) 10m. Coelophysis (vert). (b) 10m. Tyrannosaurus (vert). (c) 10m. Woolly Rhinoceros	8·50	10·00

Nos. 1438/1446, 1447/1455 and 1456/1464 respectively were printed together, *se-tenant*, with the back-grounds forming composite designs.

256 Treefish

1998. Year of the Ocean. Fish. Multicoloured.

1466	1m. Type **256**	30	30
1467	1m. Tigerbarb	30	30
1468	1m. Bandtail puffer	30	30
1469	1m. Cod	30	30
1470	1m.50 Clown loach	45	45
1471	1m.50 Christy's lyretail	45	45
1472	1m.50 Filefish	45	45
1473	1m.50 Sicklefin killie	45	45
1474	2m. Brook trout	55	55
1475	2m. Emerald betta	55	55
1476	2m. Pacific electric ray	55	55
1477	2m. Bighead searobin	55	55
1478	2m. Weakfish	55	55
1479	2m. Red drum	55	55
1480	2m. Blue marlin	55	55
1481	2m. Yellowfin tuna	55	55
1482	2m. Barracuda	55	55
1483	2m. Striped bass	55	55
1484	2m. White shark	55	55
1485	2m. Permit	55	55
1486	2m. Purple firefish	55	55
1487	2m. Harlequin sweetlips	55	55
1488	2m. Clown wrasse	55	55
1489	2m. Bicolour angelfish	55	55
1490	2m. False cleanerfish	55	55
1491	2m. Mandarinfish	55	55
1492	2m. Regal tang	55	55
1493	2m. Clownfish	55	55
1494	2m. Bluegill	55	55
1495	2m. Grayling	55	55
1496	2m. Walleye	55	55
1497	2m. Brown trout	55	55
1498	2m. Atlantic salmon	55	55
1499	2m. Northern pike	55	55
1500	2m. Large-mouth bass	55	55
1501	2m. Rainbow trout	55	55
1502	2m. Platy variatus	55	55
1503	2m. Archerfish	55	55
1504	2m. Clown knifefish	55	55
1505	2m. Angelicus	55	55
1506	2m. Black arowana	55	55
1507	2m. Spotted scat	55	55
1508	2m. Kribensis	55	55
1509	2m. Golden pheasant	55	55
1510	3m. Harlequin tuskfish	80	80
1511	4m. Half-moon angelfish	90	90
1512	5m. Spotted trunkfish	1·10	1·10
1513	6m. Wolf eel	1·40	1·50
1514	7m. Cherubfish	1·50	1·60
MS1515	Four sheets, each 98×73 mm. (a) 12m. Common Carp. (b) 12m. Sockeye Salmon. (c) 12m. Winter Flounder. (d) 12m. Horn Shark	11·00	12·00

Nos. 1470/1473 show the face value as 'M1.5'.

257 Crowning of King Letsie III

1998. First Anniversary of Coronation of King Letsie III. Multicoloured.

1516	1m. Type **257**	65	65
1517	1m. King saluting Basotho nation	65	65
1518	1m. King Letsie in profile	65	65

258 *Pelargonium sidoides*

1998. Flowers. Multicoloured.

1519	10s. Type **258**	10	65
1520	15s. *Aponogeton ranunculiflorus*	10	65
1521	20s. *Sebaea leiostyla*	10	65
1522	40s. *Sebaea grandis*	15	45
1523	50s. *Satyrium neglectum*	15	20
1524	60s. *Massonia jasminiflora*	20	20
1525	70s. *Ajuga ophrydis*	25	20
1526	80s. *Nemesia fruticans*	25	20
1527	1m. *Aloe broomii*	35	20
1528	2m. *Wahlenbergia androsacea*	55	30
1529	2m.50 *Phygelius capensis*	65	55
1530	3m. *Dianthus basuticus*	75	70
1531	4m.50 *Rhodohypoxis baurii*	1·25	1·40
1532	5m. *Turbina oblongata*	1·25	1·40
1533	6m. *Hibiscus microcarpus*	1·40	1·75
1534	10m. *Lobelia erinus* ('Moraea stricta')	2·25	3·00

259 Japanese Akita

1999. Dogs. Multicoloured.

1535	70s. Type **259**	50	20
1536	1m. Canaan dog	55	20
1537	2m. Husky ('ESKIMO DOG')	70	60
1538	2m. Cirneco dell'Etna	70	60
1539	2m. Afghan hound	70	60
1540	2m. Finnish spitz	70	60
1541	2m. Dalmatian	70	60
1542	2m. Basset hound	70	60
1543	2m. Shar-pei	70	60
1544	2m. Boxer	70	60
1545	2m. Catalan sheepdog	70	60
1546	2m. English toy spaniel	70	60
1547	2m. Greyhound	70	60
1548	2m. Keeshond	70	60
1549	2m. Bearded collie	70	60
1550	4m.50 Norwegian elkhound	1·50	1·60
MS1551	Two sheets, each 98×69 mm. (a) 8m. Rough Collie. (b) 8m. Borzoi	7·00	7·00

Nos. 1538/1543 and 1544/1549 were printed together, *se-tenant*, with the backgrounds forming composite designs.

260 Belted Kingfisher

1999. Birds. Multicoloured.

1552	70s. Type **260**	70	20
1553	1m.50 Palm cockatoo (vert)	95	45
1554	2m. Red-tailed hawk	95	70
1555	2m. Evening grosbeak	95	85
1556	2m. Blue-winged pitta ('Lesser Blue-winged Pitta')	95	85
1557	2m. Lichtenstein's oriole ('Atlamira Oriole')	95	85
1558	2m. Rose-breasted grosbeak	95	85
1559	2m. Yellow warbler	95	85
1560	2m. Akiapolaau	95	85
1561	2m. American goldfinch	95	85
1562	2m. Common flicker ('Northern Flicker')	95	85
1563	2m. Western tanager	95	85
1564	2m. Blue jay (vert)	95	85
1565	2m. Common cardinal ('Northern Cardinal') (vert)	95	85
1566	2m. Yellow-headed blackbird (vert)	95	85
1567	2m. Red crossbill (vert)	95	85
1568	2m. Cedar waxwing (vert)	95	85
1569	2m. Vermilion flycatcher (vert)	95	85
1570	2m. Pileated woodpecker (vert)	95	85
1571	2m. Western meadowlark (vert)	95	85
1572	2m. Belted kingfisher ('Kingfisher') (vert)	95	85
1573	3m. Tufted puffin	1·25	1·25
1574	4m. Reddish egret	1·40	1·50
1575	5m. Hoatzin (vert)	1·40	1·75
MS1576	Two sheets. (a) 76×106 mm. 8m. Great egret. (b) 106×76 mm. 8m. Chestnut-flanked white-eye *Zosterops erythropleura*	7·50	8·00

No. 1553 shows the face value as 'M1.5'.

Nos. 1555/1563 and 1564/1572 were printed together, *se-tenant*, with the backgrounds forming composite designs.

261 *Cattleya dowiana*

1999. Orchids of the World. Multicoloured.

1577	1m.50 Type **261**	75	30
1578	2m. *Cochleanthes discolor*	75	75
1579	2m. *Cischweinfia dasyandra*	75	75
1580	2m. *Ceratostylis retisquama*	75	75
1581	2m. *Comparettia speciosa*	75	75
1582	2m. *Cryptostylis subulata*	75	75
1583	2m. *Cycnoches ventricosum*	75	75
1584	2m. *Dactylorhiza maculata*	75	75
1585	2m. *Cypripedium calceolus*	75	75
1586	2m. *Cymbidium finlaysonianum*	75	75
1587	2m. *Apasia epidendroides*	75	75
1588	2m. *Barkaria lindleyana*	75	75
1589	2m. *Bifrenaria tetragona*	75	75
1590	2m. *Bulbophyllum graveolens*	75	75
1591	2m. *Brassavola flagellaris*	75	75
1592	2m. *Bollea lawrenceana*	75	75
1593	2m. *Caladenia carnea*	75	75
1594	2m. *Catasetum macrocarpum*	75	75
1595	2m. *Cattleya aurantiaca*	75	75
1596	2m. *Dendrobium bellatulum*	75	75
1597	2m. *Dendrobium trigonopus*	75	75
1598	2m. *Dimerandra emarginata*	75	75
1599	2m. *Dressleria eburnea*	75	75
1600	2m. *Dracula tubeana*	75	75
1601	2m. *Disa kirstenbosch*	75	75
1602	2m. *Encyclia alata*	75	75
1603	2m. *Epidendrum pseudepidendrum*	75	75
1604	2m. *Eriopsis biloba*	75	75
1605	3m. *Diurus behrii*	1·00	1·00
1606	4m. *Ancistrochilus rothchildianus*	1·25	1·25
1607	5m. *Aerangis curnowiana*	1·40	1·40
1608	7m. *Arachnis flos-aeris*	1·75	2·00
1609	8m. *Aspasia principissa*	1·75	2·25
MS1610	Four sheets, each 110×82 mm. (a) 10m. *Paphiopedilum tonsum*. (b) 10m. *Ansellia africana*. (c) 10m. *Laelia rubescens*. (d) 10m. *Ophrys apifera*	14·00	15·00

No. 1583 was inscribed 'Cycnoches ventricsum' in error.

262 Austerity Type Series 52 Steam Locomotive, Frankfurt, 1939

1999. iBRA '99 International Stamp Exhibition, Nuremburg. Railway Locomotives. Multicoloured.

1611	7m. Type **262**	2·00	2·00
1612	8m. *Adler* and Brandenburg Gate, Berlin, 1835	2·00	2·00

263 *View of Sumida River in Snow*

1999. 150th Death Anniversary of Katsushika Hokusai (Japanese artist). Multicoloured.

1613	3m. Type **263**	75	75
1614	3m. *Two Carp*	75	75
1615	3m. *The Blind* (woman with eyes closed)	75	75
1616	3m. *The Blind* (woman with one eye open)	75	75
1617	3m. *Fishing by Torchlight*	75	75
1618	3m. *Whaling off the Goto Islands*	75	75
1619	3m. *Makamaro watching the Moon from a Hill*	75	75
1620	3m. *Peonies and Butterfly*	75	75
1621	3m. *The Blind* (old man with open eyes)	75	75
1622	3m. *The Blind* (old man with one eye open)	75	75
1623	3m. *People crossing an Arched Bridge* (four people on bridge)	75	75
1624	3m. *People crossing an Arched Bridge* (two people on bridge)	75	75
MS1625	Two sheets, each 102×72 mm. (a) 10m. *Bell-flower and Dragonfly* (vert). (b) 10m. *Moon above Yodo River and Osaka Castle* (vert). Set of 2 sheets	5·50	6·00

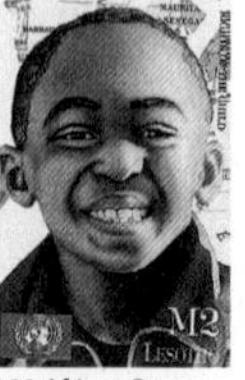

264 African Boy

1999. 10th Anniversary of United Nations Rights of the Child Convention. Multicoloured.

1626	2m. Type **264**	85	90
1627	2m. Asian girl	85	90
1628	2m. European boy	85	90

Nos. 1626/1628 were printed together, *se-tenant*, the backgrounds forming a composite design.

265 Mephistopheles appearing as Dog in Faust's Study

1999. 250th Birth Anniversary of Johann von Goethe (German writer).

1629	**265**	6m. multicoloured	1·40	1·75
1630	-	6m. blue, lilac and black	1·40	1·75
1631	-	6m. multicoloured	1·40	1·75
MS1632		76×106 mm. 12m. red, violet and black	2·75	3·25

Designs: Horiz—No. 1630, Goethe and Schiller; No. 1631, Mephistopheles disguised as a dog scorching the Earth. Vert—No. **MS**1632, Mephistopheles.

No. 1629, in addition to the normal country name, shows 'GUYANA' twice in violet across the centre of the design.

266 *Water Lily at Night* (Pan Tianshou)

1999. China '99 International Stamp Exhibition, Beijing. Paintings of Pan Tianshou (Chinese artist). Multicoloured.

1633	1m.50 Type **266**	40	50
1634	1m.50 *Hen and Chicks*	40	50
1635	1m.50 *Plum Blossom and Orchid*	40	50
1636	1m.50 *Plum Blossom and Banana Tree*	40	50
1637	1m.50 *Crane and Pine*	40	50
1638	1m.50 *Swallows*	40	50
1639	1m.50 *Eagle on the Pine* (bird looking up)	40	50
1640	1m.50 *Palm Tree*	40	50
1641	1m.50 *Eagle on the Pine* (bird looking down)	40	50
1642	1m.50 *Orchids*	40	50
MS1643	138×105 mm. 6m. *Sponge Gourd* (51×39 mm); 6m. *Dragonfly* (51×39 mm)	4·25	4·75

267 Queen Elizabeth, 1938

1999. Queen Elizabeth the Queen Mother's Century.

1644	**267**	5m. black and gold	1·50	1·50
1645	-	5m. multicoloured	1·50	1·50
1646	-	5m. black and gold	1·50	1·50
1647	-	5m. multicoloured	1·50	1·50
MS1648		153×152 mm. 15m. multicoloured	3·75	4·00

Designs: No. 1645, King George VI and Queen Elizabeth, No. 1948; 1646, Queen Mother wearing tiara, 1963; No. 1647, Queen Mother wearing blue hat, Canada, 1989. 37×50 mm—No. **MS**1648, Queen Mother outside Clarence House.

No. **MS**1648 also shows the Royal Arms embossed in gold.

268 Chinese Soldier firing Rocket, 1150

1999. New Millennium. People and Events of 12th-century (1150–1199). Multicoloured.

1649	1m.50 Type **268**	65	60
1650	1m.50 Burmese temple guardian, 1150	65	60
1651	1m.50 Troubadour serenading Lady, 1150	65	60
1652	1m.50 Abbot Suger (advisor to French Kings), 1150	65	60
1653	1m.50 Pope Adrian IV, 1154	65	60
1654	1m.50 Henry II of England, 1154	65	60
1655	1m.50 Bust of Frederick Barbarossa, King of Germany, and Holy Roman Emperor, 1155	65	60
1656	1m.50 Shogun Yoritomo of Japan, 1156	65	60
1657	1m.50 Count and Countess of Vaudemont (Crusader monument), 1165	65	60
1658	1m.50 Ibn Rushd (Arab translator), 1169	65	60
1659	1m.50 Archbishop Thomas a Becket, 1170	65	60
1660	1m.50 Leaning Tower of Pisa, 1174	65	60
1661	1m.50 Pivot windmill, 1180	65	60
1662	1m.50 Saladin (Saracen general), 1187	65	60
1663	1m.50 King Richard the Lionheart of England, 1189	65	60
1664	1m.50 Moai (statues), Easter Island, 1150 (59×39 mm)	65	60
1665	1m.50 Crusader, 1189	65	60

269 USS *New Jersey* (battleship)

1999. Maritime Developments 1700–2000. Multicoloured.

1666	4m. Type **269**	1·00	1·00
1667	4m. *Aquila* (Italian aircraft carrier)	1·00	1·00
1668	4m. *De Zeven Provincien* (Dutch cruiser)	1·00	1·00
1669	4m. HMS *Formidable* (aircraft carrier)	1·00	1·00
1670	4m. *Vittorio Veneto* (Italian cruiser)	1·00	1·00
1671	4m. HMS *Hampshire* (destroyer)	1·00	1·00
1672	4m. *France* (French liner)	1·00	1·00
1673	4m. *Queen Elizabeth 2* (liner)	1·00	1·00
1674	4m. *United States* (American liner)	1·00	1·00
1675	4m. *Queen Elizabeth* (liner)	1·00	1·00
1676	4m. *Michelangelo* (Italian liner)	1·00	1·00
1677	4m. *Mauretania* (British liner)	1·00	1·00
1678	4m. *Shearwater* (British hydrofoil ferry)	1·00	1·00
1679	4m. British Class M submarine	1·00	1·00
1680	4m. SRN 130 hovercraft	1·00	1·00
1681	4m. Italian Second World War submarine	1·00	1·00
1682	4m. SRN 3 hovercraft	1·00	1·00
1683	4m. *Soucoupe Plongeante* (oceanographic submersible)	1·00	1·00
1684	4m. *James Watt* (early steamship)	1·00	1·00
1685	4m. *Savannah* (steam/sail ship), 1819	1·00	1·00
1686	4m. *Amistad* (slave schooner)	1·00	1·00
1687	4m. American Navy brig	1·00	1·00
1688	4m. *Great Britain* (liner)	1·00	1·00
1689	4m. *Sirius* (paddle-steamer)	1·00	1·00
MS1690	Four sheets, each 106×76 mm. (a) 15m. USS *Enterprise* (aircraft carrier) (vert). (b) 15m. *Titanic* (liner). (c) 15m. German U-boat. (d) 15m. *E. W. Morrison* (Great Lakes schooner) (vert). Set of 4 sheets	15·00	16·00

Nos. 1686 and 1687 both have their names wrongly inscribed as 'ARMISTAD' and 'BRICK' on the sheet margin.

270 King Letsie III and Miss Karabo Anne Motsoeneng

2000. Wedding of King Letsie III. Multicoloured.

1691	1m. Type **270**	85	85
1692	1m. Miss Karabo Anne Motsoeneng	85	85
1693	1m. King Letsie III	85	85
1694	1m. King Letsie III and Miss Karabo Motsoeneng in traditional dress	85	85

271 *Apollo 18* and *Soyuz 19* docked in Orbit

2000. 25th Anniversary of Apollo-Soyuz Joint Project. Multicoloured.

1695	8m. Type **271**	2·00	2·00
1696	8m. *Apollo 18* and docking module	2·00	2·00
1697	8m. *Soyuz 19*	2·00	2·00
MS1698	106×76 mm. 15m. Docking module and *Soyuz 19*	4·00	4·50

272 Gena Rowlands (actress), 1978

2000. 50th Anniversary of Berlin Film Festival. Showing actors, directors and film scenes with awards. Multicoloured.

1699	6m. Type **272**	1·25	1·40
1700	6m. Vlastimil Brodsky (actor), 1975	1·25	1·40
1701	6m. Carlos Saura (director), 1966	1·25	1·40
1702	6m. Scene from *La Collectionneuse*, 1967	1·25	1·40
1703	6m. Scene from *Le Depart*, 1967	1·25	1·40
1704	6m. Scene from *Le Diable Probablement*, 1977	1·25	1·40
MS1705	97×103 mm. 15m. Scene from *Stammeheim*, 1986	4·25	4·75

No. 1704 is inscribed 'LE DIIABLE PROBABLEMENT' in error.

273 George Stephenson

2000. 175th Anniversary of Stockton and Darlington Line (first public railway). Multicoloured.

1706	8m. Type **273**	2·50	2·50
1707	8m. Stephenson's Patent locomotive	2·50	2·50
1708	8m. Robert Stephenson's Britannia Tubular Bridge, Menai Straits	2·50	2·50

274 Johann Sebastian Bach

2000. 250th Death Anniversary of Johann Sebastian Bach (German composer). Sheet 105×101 mm.

MS1709	**274**	15m. multicoloured	5·00	5·00

275 Albert Einstein

2000. Election of Albert Einstein (mathematical physicist) as *Time Magazine* Man of the Century. Sheet 117×91 mm.

MS1710	**275**	15m. multicoloured	5·50	5·50

276 Ferdinand Zeppelin and LZ-127 *Graf Zeppelin*, 1928

2000. Centenary of First Zeppelin Flight. Multicoloured.

1711	8m. Type **276**	2·25	2·25
1712	8m. LZ-130 *Graf Zeppelin II*, 1938	2·25	2·25
1713	8m. LZ-10 *Schwaben*, 1911	2·25	2·25
MS1714	83×119 mm. 15m. LZ-130 *Graf Zeppelin II*, 1938 (50×37 mm)	4·25	4·75

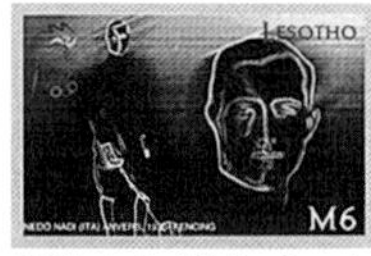

277 Nedo Nadi (Italian fencer), 1920

2000. Olympic Games, Sydney. Multicoloured.

1715	6m. Type **277**	1·75	2·00
1716	6m. Swimming (butterfly stroke)	1·75	2·00
1717	6m. Aztec Stadium, Mexico City, 1968	1·75	2·00
1718	6m. Ancient Greek boxing	1·75	2·00

278 Prince William in Evening Dress

2000. 18th Birthday of Prince William. Multicoloured.

1719	4m. Type **278**	1·40	1·40
1720	4m. Wearing coat and scarf	1·40	1·40
1721	4m. Wearing striped shirt and tie	1·40	1·40
1722	4m. Getting out of car	1·40	1·40
MS1723	100×80 mm. 15m. Prince William (37×50 mm)	4·50	4·50

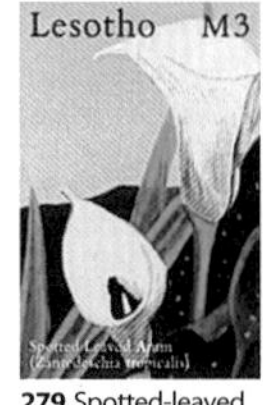

279 Spotted-leaved Arum

2000. African Flowers. Multicoloured.

1724	3m. Type **279**	85	85
1725	3m. Christmas bells	85	85
1726	3m. Lady Monson	85	85
1727	3m. Wild pomegranate	85	85
1728	3m. Blushing bride	85	85
1729	3m. Bot River protea	85	85
1730	3m. Drooping agapanthus	85	85
1731	3m. Yellow marsh Afrikander	85	85
1732	3m. Weak-stemmed painted lady	85	85
1733	3m. Impala lily	85	85
1734	3m. Beatrice Watsonia	85	85
1735	3m. Pink arum	85	85
1736	3m. Starry gardenia	85	85
1737	3m. Pink hibiscus	85	85
1738	3m. Dwarf poker	85	85
1739	3m. Coast kaffirboom	85	85
1740	3m. Rose cockade	85	85
1741	3m. Pride of Table Mountain	85	85
1742	4m. Moore's crinum	1·50	1·50
1743	5m. Flame lily	1·50	1·50
1744	6m. Cape clivia	1·60	1·60
1745	8m. True sugarbush	1·75	2·00
MS1746	Two sheets, each 107×77 mm. (a) 15m. Red Hairy Erika (horiz). (b) 15m. Green Arum. Set of 2 sheets	10·00	12·00

Nos. 1724/1729, 1730/1735 and 1736/1741 were each printed together, *se-tenant*, with the backgrounds forming composite designs.

No. 1733 is inscribed 'Llly', No. 1736 'Gardenia thunbengii' and No. 1741 'Disa unoflora,' all in error.

280 Black Rhinoceros

2000. The Stamp Show 2000, International Stamp Exhibition, London. Endangered Wildlife. Multicoloured.

1747	4m. Type **280**	1·25	1·25
1748	4m. Leopard	1·25	1·25
1749	4m. Roseate tern	1·25	1·25

1750 4m. Mountain gorilla 1·25 1·25
1751 4m. Mountain zebra 1·25 1·25
1752 4m. Zanzibar red colobus monkey 1·25 1·25
1753 4m. Cholo alethe 1·25 1·25
1754 4m. Temminck's pangolin 1·25 1·25
1755 4m. Cheetah 1·25 1·25
1756 4m. African elephant 1·25 1·25
1757 4m. Chimpanzee 1·25 1·25
1758 4m. Northern white rhinoceros 1·25 1·25
1759 5m. Blue wildebeest 1·40 1·40
1760 5m. Tree hyrax 1·40 1·40
1761 5m. Red lechwe 1·40 1·40
1762 5m. Eland 1·40 1·40
MS1763 Two sheets, each 65×118 mm. (a) 15m. Dugong (vert). (b) 15m. West African Manatee (vert). Set of 2 sheets 10·00 12·00

Nos. 1747/1752, 1753/1758 and 1759/1762 were each printed together, *se-tenant*, with the backgrounds forming composite designs.

281 Cadillac Eldorado Seville (1960)

2000. Classic Cars. Multicoloured.
1764 3m. Type **281** 90 90
1765 3m. Citroen DS (1955–1975) 90 90
1766 3m. Ford Zephyr Zodiac MK II (1961) 90 90
1767 3m. MG TF (1945–1955) 90 90
1768 3m. Porsche 356 (1949–1965) 90 90
1769 3m. Ford Thunderbird (1955) 90 90
1770 3m. Cisitalia 202 Coupe (1948–1952) 90 90
1771 3m. Dodge Viper (1990s) 90 90
1772 3m. TVR Vixen SI (1968–1969) 90 90
1773 3m. Lotus 7 (1957–1970) 90 90
1774 3m. Ferrari 275 GTB/4 (1964–1968) 90 90
1775 3m. Pegasus Touring Spider (1951–1958) 90 90
1776 4m. Fiat Type O (1913) 90 90
1777 4m. Stutz Bearcat (1914) 90 90
1778 4m. French Leyat (1924) 90 90
1779 4m. Benz gasoline-driven Motorwagon (1886) 90 90
1780 4m. Isotta Fraschini Type 8A (1925) 90 90
1781 4m. Markus Motor Carriage (1887) 90 90
1782 4m. Morris Minor (1951) 90 90
1783 4m. Hispano-Suiza Type 68 (1935) 90 90
1784 4m. MG TC (1949) 90 90
1785 4m. Morgan 4/4 (1955) 90 90
1786 4m. Jaguar XK120 (1950) 90 90
1787 4m. Triumph 1800/2000 Roadster (1946–1949) 90 90
MS1788 Four sheets. (a) 110×85 mm. 15m. AC ACE (1953–1963). (b) 110×85 mm. 15m. Morris Minor 1000 (1948–1971). (c) 85×110 mm. 15m. Ferrari F 40 (vert). (d) 110×85 mm. 15m. Bersey Electric Cab (1896). Set of 4 sheets 15·00 16·00

282 Basotho Warrior fighting 'AIDS'

2001. Fight Against Aids. Multicoloured.
1789 70c. Type **282** 65 20
1790 1m. 'Speed Kills So Does Aids' 90 30
1791 1m.50 'People with Aids need friends not rejection' 1·40 1·40
1792 2m.10 'Even when you're off duty protect the nation' 1·75 2·00

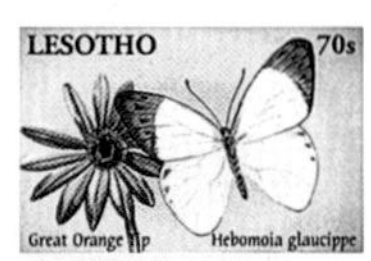

283 Great Orange Tip

2001. Butterflies. Multicoloured.
1793 70s. Type **283** 70 20
1794 1m. Red-banded pereute 80 20
1795 1m.50 Sword grass brown 85 45
1796 2m. Striped blue crow 85 65
1797 2m. Orange-banded sulphur 85 85
1798 2m. Large wood nymph 85 85
1799 2m. The postman 85 85
1800 2m. Palmfly 85 85
1801 2m. Gulf fritillary 85 85
1802 2m. Cairns birdwing 85 85
1803 2m. Common morpho 85 85
1804 2m. Common dotted border 85 85
1805 2m. African migrant 85 85
1806 2m. Large oak blue 85 85
1807 2m. The wanderer 85 85
1808 2m. Tiger swallowtail 85 85
1809 2m. Union jack 85 85
1810 2m. Saturn 85 85
1811 2m. Broad-bordered grass yellow 85 85
1812 2m. Hewitson's uraneis 85 85
1813 3m. Bertoni's antwren bird 95 95
1814 3m. Clorinde 95 95
1815 3m. Iolas blue 95 95
1816 3m. Mocker swallowtail 95 95
1817 3m. Common Indian crow 95 95
1818 3m. Grecian shoemaker 95 95
1819 3m. Small flambeau 95 95
1820 3m. Orchid swallowtail 95 95
1821 3m. Alfalfa butterfly 95 95
1822 4m. Doris butterfly 1·25 1·25
MS1823 Two sheets, each 70×100 mm. (a) 15m. Forest Queen. (b) 15m. Crimson Tip. Set of 2 sheets 15·00 16·00

Nos. 1797/1804, 1805/1812 and 1813/1820 were each printed together, *se-tenant*, with the backgrounds forming composite designs.

LESOTHO M1.50
284 Roman General and Soldiers from *Battle of Lepanto and Map of the World* (anon)

2001. Philanippon 01 International Stamp Exhibition, Tokyo. Paintings from Momoyama Era. Multicoloured.
1824 1m.50 Type **284** 60 30
1825 2m. Pikemen and musketeers from *Battle of Lepanto and Map of the World* 90 40
1826 3m. Manchurian crane from *Birds and Flowers of the Four Seasons* (Kano Eitoku) 1·00 65
1827 4m. Travellers in the mountains from *Birds and Flowers of the Four Seasons* 1·00 1·00
1828 5m. *Portrait of a Lady* (24½×81½ mm) 1·00 1·00
1829 5m. *Honda Tadakatsu* (24½×81½ mm) 1·00 1·00
1830 5m. *Wife of Goto Tokujo* (24½×81½ mm) 1·00 1·00
1831 5m. *Emperor Go-Yozei* (Kano Takanobu) (24½×81½ mm) 1·00 1·00
1832 5m. *Tenzuiin Hideyoshi's Mother, Hoshuku Sochin* (24½×81½ mm) 1·00 1·00
1833 6m. *Hosokawa Yusai* (Ishin Suden) (24½×81½ mm) 1·25 1·25
1834 6m. *Sen No Rikyu* (attr Hasegawa Tohaku) (24½×81½ mm) 1·25 1·25
1835 6m. *Oichi No Kata* (24½×81½ mm) 1·25 1·25
1836 6m. *Inaba Ittetsu* (attr Hasegawa Tohaku) (24½×81½ mm) 1·25 1·25
1837 6m. *Oda Nobunaga* (Kokei Sochin) (24½×81½ mm) 1·25 1·25
1838 7m. *Viewing the Maples at Mount Takao* 1·50 2·00
1839 8m. *The Four Accomplishments* (Kaiho Yusho) 1·50 2·25
MS1840 Two sheets. (a) 98×131 mm. 15m. *Tokugawa Ieyasu*. (b) 114×134 mm. 15m. *Toyotomi Hideyoshi*. Set of 2 sheets 9·50 11·00

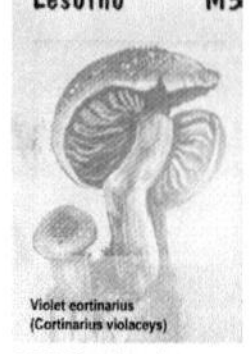

285 *Cortinarius violaceus*

2001. Belgica 2001 International Stamp Exhibition, Brussels. African Fungi. Multicoloured.
1841 3m. Type **285** 1·10 1·10
1842 3m. *Pleurocybella porrigens* 1·10 1·10
1843 3m. *Collybia velutibes* 1·10 1·10
1844 3m. *Lentinellus cochleatus* 1·10 1·10
1845 3m. *Anthurua aseroiformis* 1·10 1·10
1846 3m. Caesar's mushroom 1·10 1·10
1847 4m. *Cortinarius traganus* 1·10 1·10
1848 4m. *Peziza sarcosphaera* 1·10 1·10
1849 4m. *Russula emetica* 1·10 1·10
1850 4m. *Stropharia ambigua* 1·10 1·10
1851 4m. *Phlogiotis helvelloides* 1·10 1·10
1852 4m. *Clitocybe odora* 1·10 1·10
1853 5m. Golden false pholiota 1·25 1·25
1854 5m. *Coprinus micaceus* 1·25 1·25
1855 5m. *Hygrophorus camarophyllus* 1·25 1·25
1856 5m. *Panaeolus campanulatus* 1·25 1·25
MS1857 Two sheets, each 75×55 mm. (a) 15m. *Boletus parasiticus* (horiz). (b) 15m. *Hygrophorus hygrocybe conicus* (horiz). Set of 2 sheets 14·00 14·00

No. 1841 is inscribed 'violaceys', No. 1842 'Pleyrocybella', No. 1844 'Cochleathus', No. 1852 'Clitoeybe' and No. 1856 'Panaelus companulatus', all in error.

286 *Woman with Baby in Sunset* (Leila Hall)

2001. Winners of United Nations Children's Art Competition. Multicoloured.
1858 70s. Type **286** 65 15
1859 1m. *Herdboy with Lamb* (Chambeli Ramathe) 80 30
1860 1m.50 *Girl with AIDS Ribbon* (Chambeli Ramathe) (vert) 1·25 1·25
1861 2m.10 *Satellite Dish and Map seen through Keyhole* (Mika Sejake) (vert) 1·50 2·00

287 Black Kite

2001. Birds of Prey. Multicoloured.
1862 70s. Type **287** 80 40
1863 1m. Martial eagle 1·25 65
1864 1m.50 Bateleur 1·50 1·10
1865 2m.10 African goshawk 1·75 1·75
1866 2m.50 Lammergeier ('Bearded Vulture') 1·75 2·00
1867 3m. Jackal buzzard 2·00 2·25

No. 1865 is inscribed 'GASHAWK' in error.

288 Grass Owl

2001. Wildlife of Southern Africa. Multicoloured.
1868 1m. Type **288** 1·50 60
1869 2m.10 Klipspringer 1·50 70
1870 3m. Saddle-backed jackal 1·75 80
1871 4m. Aardvark 1·75 1·75
1872 4m. Common kestrel ('Rock Kestrel') 1·75 1·75
1873 4m. Black-footed cat 1·75 1·75
1874 4m. Springhare 1·75 1·75
1875 4m. Aardwolf 1·75 1·75
1876 4m. Rock hyrax 1·75 1·75
1877 4m. Damara zebra 1·75 1·75
1878 4m. Bontebok 1·75 1·75
1879 4m. Eland 1·75 1·75
1880 4m. Lion 1·75 1·75
1881 4m. Saddle-backed jackal 1·75 1·75
1882 4m. Black kite ('Yellow-billed Kite') 1·75 1·75
1883 5m. Black wildebeest 1·75 1·75
MS1884 Two sheets, each 90×64 mm. (a) 15m. Black-shouldered kite. (b) 15m. Caracal (vert). Set of 2 sheets 13·00 13·00

Nos. 1871/1876 and 1877/1882 were each printed together, *se-tenant*, with the backgrounds forming composite designs.

289 Queen Elizabeth wearing Purple Coat

2002. Golden Jubilee. Multicoloured.
1885 8m. Type **289** 2·75 2·50
1886 8m. Queen Elizabeth with Duke of Edinburgh on launch 2·75 2·50
1887 8m. Queen Elizabeth with mayor 2·75 2·50
1888 8m. Duke of Edinburgh wearing sunglasses 2·75 2·50
MS1889 76×108 mm. 20m. Queen Elizabeth inspecting RAF guard of honour 8·00 8·00

290 Homer Wood (Rotary pioneer)

2002. 25th Anniversary of Rotary International in Lesotho. Multicoloured.
1890 8m. Type **290** 2·25 2·25
1891 10m. Paul Harris (founder of Rotary International) 2·50 2·50
MS1892 Two sheets. (a) 60×75 mm. 25m. Coloured globe and Rotary logo. (b) 75×60 mm. 25m. Golden Gate Bridge, San Francisco, and Rotary logo (horiz) 13·00 15·00

No. 1890 is inscribed 'HORNER' in error.

291 Machache

2002. International Year of Mountains. Showing Lesotho mountains (except No. **MS**1897). Multicoloured.
1893 8m. Type **291** 2·25 2·25
1894 8m. Thabana-li-Mele 2·25 2·25
1895 8m. Qiloane 2·25 2·25
1896 8m. Thaba-Bosiu 2·25 2·25
MS1897 64×83 mm. 25m. The Matterhorn, Switzerland (vert) 8·50 9·50

No. **MS**1897 is inscribed 'Mount Rainer' in error.

292 Boys with Calf, Lithabaneng

2002. SOS Children's Villages (Kinderdorf International).
1898 **292** 10m. multicoloured 2·75 3·00

293 Spiral Aloe

2002. UN Year of Eco Tourism. Multicoloured.
1899 6m. Type **293** 1·75 2·00
1900 6m. *Athrixia gerradii* (flower) 1·75 2·00
1901 6m. Horseman and packhorse 1·75 2·00
1902 6m. Lion 1·75 2·00
1903 6m. Frog 1·75 2·00
1904 6m. Thatched building 1·75 2·00
MS1905 77×83 mm. 20m. European bee-eater (vert) 8·00 8·50

294 US Flag as Statue of Liberty with Lesotho Flag

2002. United We Stand. Support for Victims of 11 September 2001 Terrorist Attacks.
1906 **294** 7m. multicoloured 2·25 2·50

295 Sheet Bend Knot

2002. 20th World Scout Jamboree, Thailand. Multicoloured.

1907 9m. Type **295** 2·25 2·50

1908 9m. Pup and forester tents 2·25 2·50

1909 9m. Scouts in canoe 2·25 2·50

1910 9m. Life-saving 2·25 2·50

MS1911 75×59 mm. 25m. Scouts asleep in tent 7·50 9·00

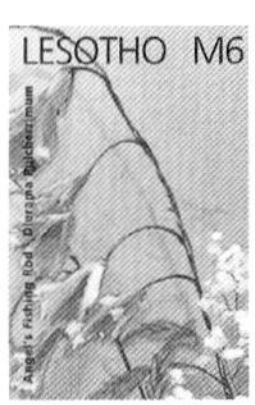

296 Angel's Fishing Rod (*Dierama pulcherrimum*)

2002. Flowers, Orchids and Insects. Multicoloured.

MS1912 100×180 mm. 6m. Type **296**; 6m. Marigold (*Calendula officinalis*); 6m. Dianthus 'Joan's Blood'; 6m. Mule pink (*Dianthus plumarius*); 6m. Tiger lily (*Lilium lancifolium*); 6m. Clematis viticella 'Comtesse de Bouchaud' 9·50 10·00

MS1913 180×100 mm. 6m. Leaf grasshopper (*Brochopeplu exalatus*); 6m. Golden-ringed dragonfly (*Cordulegaster boltoni*); 6m. Weevil-hunting wasp (*Cerceris arenaria*); 6m. European grasshopper (*Oedipoda miniata*); 6m. Thread-waisted Wasp (Ammophilia alberti); 6m. Mantid (*Mantis acontista*) (all horiz) 9·50 10·00

MS1914 95×103 mm. 6m. *Phragmipedium besseae*; 6m. *Cypripedium calceolus*; 6m. Cattleya 'Louise Georgiana'; 6m. *Brassocattleya binosa*; 6m. *Laelia gouldiana*; 6m. *Paphiopedilum maudiae* 'Alba' 9·50 10·00

MS1915 Three sheets. (a) 63×75 mm. 20m. Bleeding heart (*Dicentra spectabilis*. (b) 75×63 mm. 20m. Orb web spider (*Argiope bruennichi*). (c) 75×63 mm. 20m. *Brassavola tuberculata* Set of 3 20·00 22·00

297 Bleriot's Canard at Bagatelle, 1906

2004. Centenary of Powered Flight. Multicoloured.

MS1916 177×97 mm. 6m. Type **297**; 6m. Bleriot's Double-winged Libellule, 1907; 6m. Bleriot's No. VIII in Toury–Artenay cross-country flight, 1908; 6m. Bleriot's X12 Test Flight, 1909 6·00 7·00

MS1917 66×97 mm. 15m. Louis Bleriot's No. XI 4·50 4·75

298 Prince William

2004. 21st Birthday of Prince William. Multicoloured.

MS1918 77×148 mm. 8m. Type **298**; 8m. Wearing grey suit and tie; 8m. Wearing yellow polo shirt 6·50 7·00

MS1919 98×68 mm. 15m. Young Prince William 4·25 4·50

299 Queen Elizabeth II

2004. 50th Anniversary (2003) of Coronation. Multicoloured.

MS1920 148×85 mm. 8m. Type **299**; 8m. Wearing ivory suit and hat; 8m. Wearing royal uniform 7·50 8·00

MS1921 68×97 mm. 15m. Queen Elizabeth II 7·00 7·50

300 *Bematistes aganice*

2004. Butterflies. Multicoloured.

1922 1m.50 *Acraea rabbaiae* 1·00 50

1923 2m.10 *Alaena margaritacea* 1·40 75

1924 4m Type **300** 2·50 2·25

1925 6m. *Acraea quirina* 3·50 4·00

MS1926 117×116 mm. 6m. *Bematistes excise* (male); 6m. *Bematistes excise* (female); 6m. *Bematistes epiprotea*; 6m. *Bematistes poggei* 9·00 10·00

MS1927 67×98 mm. 15m. *Acraea satis* 6·00 7·00

301 Secretary Bird

2004. Birds. Multicoloured.

1928 1m.50 Type **301** 1·10 70

1929 2m.10 South African crowned crane ('Gray-crowned Crane') 1·50 90

1930 3m. Pied avocet 2·25 2·00

1931 5m. Common kestrel 3·75 5·00

MS1932 108×136 mm. 6m. European roller; 6m. European cuckoo ('Common Cuckoo'); 6m. Great spotted cuckoo; 6m. Pel's fishing owl 12·00 13·00

MS1933 68×97 mm. 15m. Kori bustard 7·00 7·50

302 Bald Ibis

2004. Endangered Species. Bald Ibis. Multicoloured.

1934 3m. Type **302** 2·00 2·00

1935 3m. Bald Ibis at rest 2·00 2·00

1936 3m. Bald Ibis on nest 2·00 2·00

1937 3m. Bald Ibis in flight (facing right) 2·00 2·00

MS1938 207×132 mm. Designs as Nos. 1934/1936 and 1937 (Bald Ibis facing left), each×2 13·00 14·00

303 Cape Porcupine

2004. Animals. Multicoloured.

1939 1m. Type **303** 75 30

1940 1m.50 Brown rat 1·40 55

1941 2m.10 Springhare (vert) 1·75 1·25

1942 5m. South African galago (vert) 3·75 5·00

MS1943 117×136 mm. 5m. Striped grass mouse; 5m. Greater galago; 5m. Ground pangolin; 5m. Banded mongoose 9·00 10·00

MS1944 68×98 mm. 15m. Egyption rousette (vert) 7·00 7·50

304 *Sparaxis grandiflora*

2004. Flowers. Multicoloured.

1945 1m.50 Type **304** 1·10 40

1946 2m.10 *Agapanthus africanus* 1·50 85

1947 3m. *Protea linearis* 1·75 1·75

1948 5m *Nerine cultivars* 3·00 4·50

MS1949 104×117 mm. 5m. *Kniphofia uvaria*; 5m. *Amaryllis belladonna*; 5m. *Gazania splendens*; 5m. *Erica coronata* 9·00 10·00

MS1950 68×98 mm. 15m. *Saintpaulia cultivars* 7·00 7·50

305 Qiloane Falls

2004. International Year of Freshwater. T **305** and similar horiz designs. Multicoloured.

MS1951 85×167 mm. 8m. Type **305**; 8m. Halfway down Qiloane Falls; 8m. Base of Qiloane Falls 9·50 10·00

MS1952 118×84 mm. 15m. Orange River 7·00 7·50

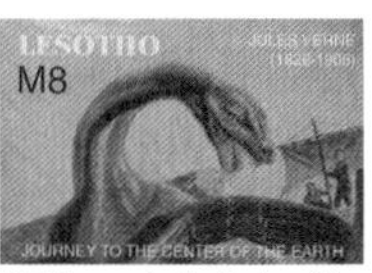

306 Mokhoro (Round House and Cooking Hut)

2005. Basotho Houses. Multicoloured.

1953 70s. Type **306** 50 15

1954 1m. Heisi (Rectangular house) Type **306** 75 45

1955 1m.50 Typical homestead 1·40 90

1956 2m.10 Mathule (Round house with porch) 1·60 1·75

No. 1953 is inscribed '70L' and No. 1956 'Mohlongoa-fat'se', both in error.

307 *Journey to the Centre of the Earth*

2005. Death Centenary of Jules Verne (writer). Multicoloured.

1957 8m. Type **307** 2·75 2·75

1958 8m. Jules Verne and *100 YEARS* 2·75 2·75

1959 8m. *20,000 Leagues under the Sea* 2·75 2·75

MS1960 107×83 mm. 15m. Jules Verne (vert) 5·00 5·50

308 USS *Arizona* (battleship)

2005. 60th Anniversary of Victory in Japan. Multicoloured.

1961 4m. Type **308** 2·25 2·25

1962 4m. Bunker at Chula Beach, Tinian Island 2·25 2·25

1963 4m. Flight crew of Bockscar (B-29 aircraft) 2·25 2·25

1964 4m. Men showing newspaper headline 2·25 2·25

1965 4m. Marker of second atomic bomb loading pit, Tinian Island 2·25 2·25

309 US Troops land on Omaha Beach

2005. 60th Anniversary of Victory in Europe. Multicoloured.

1966 4m. Type **309** 2·25 2·25

1967 4m. General George C. Marshall 2·25 2·25

1968 4m. Field Marshall Wilhelm Keitel 2·25 2·25

1969 4m. General Dwight D. Eisenhower and Lt. General George S. Patton 2·25 2·25

1970 4m. Soldiers searching through rubble 2·25 2·25

310 Pope John Paul II

2005. Pope John Paul II Commemoration.

1971 **310** 10m. multicoloured 5·50 5·50

311 Albert Einstein

2005. 50th Death Anniversary of Albert Einstein (physicist). Multicoloured.

1972 8m. Wearing glasses 3·00 3·00

1973 8m. With Nikola Tesla (inscr 'Testa') and Charles Steinmetz 3·00 3·00

1974 8m. Type **311** 3·00 3·00

MS1975 100×70 mm. 15m. On the cover of *Time* magazine (vert) 6·00 6·00

312 Uruguay Football Team, 1930

2005. 75th Anniversary of First World Cup Football Championship, Uruguay. Multicoloured.

1976 8m. Type **312** 2·50 2·50

1977 8m. Opposing players and referee 2·50 2·50

1978 8m. German team 2·50 2·50

MS1979 105×70 mm. 15m. Bodo Illgner (Germany) (vert) 4·50 5·00

313 Child eating

2005. Centenary of Rotary International. Multicoloured.

1980 8m. Type **313** 2·25 2·25

1981 8m. Classroom scene 2·25 2·25

1982 8m. Children 2·25 2·25

314 Hans Christian Andersen (statue)

2005. Birth Bicentenary of Hans Christian Andersen (writer). Multicoloured.

1983 8m. Type **314** 2·25 2·25

1984 8m. Former home of Hans Christian Andersen, Odense 2·25 2·25

1985 8m. *The Steadfast Tin Soldier* 2·25 2·25

MS1986 75×82 mm. 15m. *The Little Mermaid* 4·00 4·50

315 HMS *Victory*

2005. Bicentenary of the Battle of Trafalgar. Multicoloured.

1987 8m. Type **315** 4·25 3·50

1988 8m. Admiral Lord Horatio Nelson 4·25 3·50

1989 8m. Admiral Nelson fatally wounded 4·25 3·50

1990 8m. Ships engaged in battle 4·25 3·50

MS1991	70×100 mm. 25m. Admiral Lord Horatio Nelson and crew (50×38 mm)	16·00	15·00

316 Brownies

2005. 80th Anniversary of Lesotho Girl Guides Association. Multicoloured.

1992	70l. Type **316**	55	15
1993	1m. Procession of rangers and guides	75	35
1994	1m.50 Rangers recycling tin cans (vert)	1·25	90
1995	2m.10 Ranger and guides at Lesotho Girl Guides Headquarters	1·50	1·75
MS1996	66×98 mm. 10m. Queen 'Mamohato Seeiso (patron 1966–2003)	4·25	4·50

317 Herdboy riding Calf

2006. Herdboys. Multicoloured.

1997	70l. Type **317**	40	15
1998	1m. Feeding cattle	60	35
1999	1m.50 Three herdboys playing morabaraba and grazing cattle	90	85
2000	2m. Carrying newborn lamb on shoulders	1·10	1·50
MS2001	95×65 mm. 10m. Herdboys dancing ndlamo and practicing stick fighting	4·25	4·50

318 Woman carrying Thatch Grass

2006. Head Carrying by Mosotho Women. Multicoloured.

2002	70l. Type **318**	40	15
2003	1m. Carrying iron cooking pot on head	60	35
2004	1m.50 Carrying clay water pot on head	90	85
2005	2m.10 Carrying basket of pumpkins and maize on head and baby on back	1·10	1·50
MS2006	96×67 mm. 10m. Girl carrying basket of maize flour on head	4·25	4·50

319 Woven Grass Baskets and Broom

2006. Handicrafts. Multicoloured.

2007	70l. Type **319**	40	15
2008	1m. Artist and tapestry (vert)	60	35
2009	1m.50 Calabash, clay pots and pipe	90	85
2010	2m.10 Horn, carved fish and bird	1·10	1·50
MS2011	96×65 mm. 10m. Young girl wearing traditional headband and necklace of clay beads (vert)	4·25	4·50

320 *Spiranthes laciniata*

2007. Orchids of the World. Multicoloured.

2012	1m.50 Type **320**	1·00	50
2013	2m.10 *Triphora craigheadii*	1·25	70
2014	3m. *Arethusa bulbosa*	1·75	1·25
2015	6m. *Encyclia tampensis*	2·75	2·75
2016	6m. *Prosthechea cochleata*	2·75	2·75
2017	6m. *Vanilla pompona*	2·75	2·75
2018	6m. *Cypripedium acaule*	2·75	2·75
2019	10m. *Calypso bulbosa*	3·75	4·50
MS2020	Two sheets, each 98×68 mm. (a) 15m. *Epidendrum radicans* (horiz). (b) 15m. *Vanilla barbellata*	15·00	16·00

321 Crested Caracara

2007. Birds of the World. Multicoloured.

2021	1m. Type **321**	80	40
2022	1m.50 Wood stork	1·10	75
2023	2m.10 Tawny-shouldered blackbird	1·40	1·00
2024	6m. Great blue heron	3·00	3·00
2025	6m. Anna's hummingbird	3·00	3·00
2026	6m. Grey Silky-flycatcher	3·00	3·00
2027	6m. Limpkin	3·00	3·00
2028	15m. Jabiru	6·50	7·50
MS2029	Two sheets, each 68×97 mm. (a) 15m. Monk parakeet. (b) 15m. Western reef-heron	15·00	16·00

322 *Mylothris erlangeri*

2007. Butterflies of Africa. Multicoloured.

2030	1m. Type **322**	75	40
2031	1m.50 *Papilio nireus*	1·00	70
2032	2m.10 *Acraea terpiscore*	1·40	90
2033	10m. *Salamis temora*	6·00	7·00
MS2034	133×110 mm. 6m.×4 *Danaus chrysippus; Myrina silenus; Chrysiridia madagascariensis; Hypolimnas dexithea*	11·00	12·00
MS2035	Two sheets, each 103×72 mm. (a) 15m. *Amphicallia tigris*. (b) 15m. *Papilio demodocus*	13·00	14·00

The stamps and margins of No. **MS**2034 form a composite background design showing flowers.

323 *Amanita pantherina*

2007. African Mushrooms. Multicoloured.

2036	1m. Type **323**	75	40
2037	1m.50 *Agaricus xanthodermus*	1·00	70
2038	2m.10 *Amanita rubescens*	1·40	90
2039	6m. *Amanita phalloides*	3·00	3·00
2040	6m. *Amanita pantherina*	3·00	3·00
2041	6m. *Panaeolus papilionaceus*	3·00	3·00
2042	6m. *Amanita rubescens* (different)	3·00	3·00
2043	15m. *Amanita phalloides* (different)	6·50	7·50
MS2044	Two sheets, each 103×73 mm. (a) 15m. *Amanita panther*. (b) 15m. *Podaxis pistillaris*	13·00	14·00

324 Rowing

2008. Olympic Games, Beijing. Multicoloured.

2045	3m.50 Type **324**	1·40	1·50
2046	3m.50 Softball	1·40	1·50
2047	3m.50 Wrestling	1·40	1·50
2048	3m.50 Volleyball	1·40	1·50

2010. Third Joint Issue of Southern Africa Postal Operators Association Members. World Cup Football Championship, South Africa. Multicoloured.

MS2049	5m.×9 Namibia; South Africa; Zimbabwe; Malawi; Swaziland; Botswana; Mauritius; Lesotho; Zambia	11·00	12·00

Similar designs were issued by Botswana, Malawi, Mauritius, Namibia, South Africa, Swaziland, Zambia and Zimbabwe.

POSTAGE DUE STAMPS

1966. Nos. D9/D10 of Basutoland optd **LESOTHO**.

D11	**D2**	1c. red	30	75
D12	**D2**	5c. violet	30	90

D3

1967

D13	**D3**	1c. blue	15	3·00
D14	**D3**	2c. red	15	3·50
D15	**D3**	5c. green	20	3·50

D4

1986

D19	**D4**	2s. green	20	1·25
D20	**D4**	5s. blue	20	1·25
D21	**D4**	25s. violet	70	1·50

APPENDIX

The following stamps have either been issued in excess of postal needs, or have not been available to the public in reasonable quantities at face value.

1981

15th Anniversary of Independence. Classic Stamps of the World. 10m.×40, each embossed on gold foil.

LIBERIA

A republic on the W. coast of Africa, founded as a home for freed slaves.

100 cents = 1 dollar.

1

1860

7	**1**	6c. red	23·00	32·00
8	**1**	12c. blue	20·00	32·00
9	**1**	24c. green	23·00	32·00

1880

13	**1**	1c. blue	3·25	4·75
14	**1**	2c. red	2·25	3·25
15	**1**	6c. mauve	4·25	5·50
16	**1**	12c. yellow	4·25	6·00
17	**1**	24c. red	5·00	6·75

2

1881

18	**2**	3c. black	4·25	4·00

3

1882

47	**3**	8c. blue	3·25	3·25
20	**3**	16c. red	4·25	3·25

4

5 *Alligator* (first settlers' ship)

1886

49	**3**	1c. red	95	95
50	**3**	2c. green	95	1·00
23	**3**	3c. mauve	1·00	1·00
52	**3**	4c. brown	1·10	1·00
27	**3**	6c. grey	1·50	1·50
54	**4**	8c. grey	2·75	2·75
55	**4**	16c. yellow	4·25	4·25
29	**5**	32c. blue	17·00	17·00

7 Liberian Star

8 African Elephant

9 Oil Palm

10 President H. R. W. Johnson

11 Vai Woman

12 Seal

13 Star

15 Hippopotamus

17 President Johnson

1892

75	**7**	1c. red	30	30
76	**7**	2c. blue	30	30
77	**8**	4c. black and green	2·10	1·60
78	**9**	6c. green	85	75
79	**10**	8c. black and brown	60	75
80	**11**	12c. red	60	85
81	**12**	16c. lilac	2·10	1·60
82	**13**	24c. green on yellow	1·50	1·25
83	**12**	32c. blue	3·00	2·50
84	**15**	$1 black and blue	10·00	5·75
85	**13**	$2 brown on buff	4·25	3·75
86	**17**	$5 black and red	5·50	5·50

1893. Surch **5 5 Five Cents**.

103	**9**	5c. on 6c. green	1·50	1·50

24

1894. Imperf or roul.

117	**24**	5c. black and red	6·25	6·25

35

1897

144	**9**	1c. purple	70	35
145	**9**	1c. green	85	50
146	**15**	2c. black and bistre	1·50	1·10
147	**15**	2c. black and red	1·60	1·40
148	**8**	5c. black and lake	1·60	1·10
149	**8**	5c. black and blue	3·00	2·00
150	**10**	10c. blue and yellow	60	50
151	**11**	15c. black	60	65
152	**12**	20c. red	1·90	1·25
153	**13**	25c. green	1·25	85
154	**12**	30c. blue	4·25	3·00
155	**35**	50c. black and brown	2·10	2·75

36

1897

156	**36**	3c. red and green	25	40

1901. Official stamps of 1892–1898 optd **ORDINARY**.

175	**9**	1c. purple (No. O157)	50·00	35·00
176	**9**	1c. green (No. O158)	28·00	32·00
177	**7**	2c. blue (No. O120)	75·00	80·00
178	**15**	2c. black and brown (No. O159)	£100	45·00
179	**15**	2c. black and red (No. O160)	28·00	32·00
180	**24**	5c. green and lilac (No. O130)	£225	£225
181	**8**	5c. black and red (No. O161)	£150	£150
182	**8**	5c. black and blue (No. O162)	22·00	28·00
183	**10**	8c. black and brown (No. O122)	75·00	
184	**10**	10c. blue and yellow (No. O163)	28·00	32·00
169	**11**	12c. red (No. O92)	£100	£100
185	**11**	15c. black (No. O164)	28·00	32·00
170	**12**	16c. lilac (No. O93)		
186	**12**	16c. lilac (No. O124)	£325	£325
187	**12**	20c. red (No. O165)	32·00	38·00
171	**13**	24c. green and yellow (No. O94)	£300	£300
188	**13**	24c. green on yellow (No. O125)	32·00	38·00
189	**13**	25c. green (No. O166)	32·00	38·00
190	**12**	30c. blue (No. O167)	28·00	32·00
191	**13**	32c. blue (No. O126)	£150	£150
192	**35**	50c. black & brown (No. O168)	38·00	42·00
172	**15**	$1 black and blue (No. O96)	£1300	£1300
193	**15**	$1 black and blue (No. O127)	£225	£250
194	**13**	$2 brown on buff (No. O128)	£1300	£1300
174	**17**	$5 black and red (No. O98)	£3000	£3000
196	**17**	$5 black and red (No. O129)	£1400	£1400

1902. Surch **75c.** and bar.

206	**15**	75c. on $1 black and blue	8·25	7·75

40 Liberty

1903

209	**40**	3c. black	25	15

1903. Surch in words.

216	**12**	10c. on 16c. lilac	2·50	4·50
217	**13**	15c. on 24c. green on yell	3·00	5·00
218	**12**	20c. on 32c. blue	4·25	5·25

1904. Surch.

219	**9**	1c. on 5c. on 6c. green (No. 103)	60	80
220	**8**	2c. on 4c. black and green (No. O89)	2·50	3·25
221	**12**	2c. on 30c. blue (No. 154)	6·25	9·25

50 African Elephant **51** Head of Mercury **52** Mandingo Tribesmen

53 President Barclay and Executive Mansion

1906

224	**50**	1c. black and green	1·00	50
225	**51**	2c. black and red	15	15
226	-	5c. black and blue	2·00	75
227	-	10c. black and red	3·00	90
228	-	15c. green and violet	7·00	2·75
229	-	20c. black and orange	7·25	2·50
230	-	25c. grey and blue	75	20
231	-	30c. violet	70	15
232	-	50c. black and green	75	20
233	-	75c. black and brown	7·00	2·10
234	-	$1 black and pink	1·90	25
235	**52**	$2 black and green	3·00	35
236	**53**	$5 grey and red	5·75	50

Designs: As T **50**—5c. Chimpanzee; 15c. Agama lizard; 75c. Pygmy hippopotamus. As T **51**—10c. Great blue turaco; 20c. Great egret; 25c. Head of Liberty on coin; 30c. Figures '30'; 50c. Liberian flag. As T **53**—$1 Head of Liberty.

55 Coffee Plantation **56** Gunboat *Lark*

57 Commerce

1909. The 10c. is perf or roul.

250	**55**	1c. black and green	25	15
251	-	2c. black and red	25	15
252	**56**	5c. black and blue	1·75	35
254	**57**	10c. black and purple	25	20
255	-	15c. black and blue	1·25	35
256	-	20c. green and red	2·50	50
257	-	25c. black and brown	1·75	35
258	-	30c. brown	1·75	35
259	-	50c. black and green	2·75	60
260	-	75c. black and brown	2·25	45

Designs—As Type **55**: 2c. Pres. Barclay; 15c. Vai woman spinning cotton; 20c. Pepper plant; 25c. Village hut; 30c. Pres. Barclay (in picture frame). As Type **56**: 50c. Canoeing; 75c. Village (design shaped like a book).

1909. No. 227 surch Inland **3 Cents**.

261	3c. on 10c. black and red	4·75	5·25

1910. Surcharged **3 CENTS INLAND POSTAGE**. Perf or rouletted.

274	**57**	3c. on 10c. black and purple	35	25

1913. Various types surch with new value and bars or ornaments.

322	-	1c. on 2c. black and red (No. 251)	2·25	3·00
290	**57**	+ 2c. on 3c. on 10c. black and purple	60	2·00
323	**56**	2c. on 5c. black and blue	2·25	3·00
292	-	2c. on 15c. black and blue (No. 255)	1·25	1·25
279	-	2c. on 25c. grey & blue (A) (No. 230)	7·50	3·75
281	-	2c. on 25c. black and brown (A) (No. 257)	7·50	3·75
295	-	2c. on 25c. black and brown (B) (No. 257)	6·25	6·25
296	-	5c. on 20c. green and red (No. 256)	85	4·50
280	-	5c. on 30c. violet (C) (No. 231)	7·50	3·75
282	-	5c. on 30c. brown (C) (No. 258)	7·50	3·75
297	-	5c. on 30c. brown (D) (No. 258)	3·75	3·75
278	**36**	8c. on 3c. red and green	60	30
283	-	10c. on 50c. black and green (E) (No. 259)	9·25	5·75
299	-	10c. on 50c. black and green (F) (No. 259)	6·75	6·75
303	-	20c. on 75c. black and brown (No. 260)	3·25	6·25
304	**53**	25c. on $1 black and pink	32·00	32·00
305	-	50c. on $2 black and green (No. 235)	9·25	9·25
308	-	$1 on $5 grey and red (No. 236)	42·00	42·00

Descriptions of surcharges. (A) **1914 2 CENTS**. (B) **2** over ornaments. (C) **1914 5 CENTS**. (D) **5** over ornaments. (E) **1914 10 CENTS**. (F) **10** and ornaments.

64 House on Providence Is

65 Monrovia Harbour, Providence Is

1915

288	**64**	2c. red	20	10
289	**65**	3c. violet	20	10

1916. Liberian Frontier Force. Surch **LFF 1 C**.

332	**9**	1c. on 1c. green	£120	£120
333	**50**	1c. on 1c. black and green	£375	£375
334	**55**	1c. on 1c. black and green	2·75	4·25
335	-	1c. on 2c. black and red (No. 251)	2·75	4·25

1916. Surch **1916** over new value.

339	**1**	3c. on 6c. mauve	32·00	32·00
340	**1**	5c. on 12c. yellow	4·00	4·00
341	**1**	10c. on 24c. red	3·25	3·75

1917. Surch **1917** and value in words.

342	**13**	4c. on 25c. green	8·25	9·25
343		5c. on 30c. violet (No. 231)	60·00	65·00

1918. Surch **3 CENTS**.

345	**57**	3c. on 10c. black & purple	2·40	3·75

91 Bongo

92 African Palm Civet

93

94 Traveller's Tree

1918

349	**91**	1c. black and green	65	25
350	**92**	2c. black and red	65	25
351	-	5c. black and blue	15	10
352	**93**	10c. green	20	10
353	-	15c. green and black	2·50	20
354	-	20c. black and red	50	15
355	**94**	25c. green	3·25	25
356	-	30c. black and mauve	11·00	95
357	-	50c. black and blue	13·00	1·10
358	-	75c. black and olive	1·00	25
359	-	$1 blue and brown	4·25	25
360	-	$2 black and violet	6·00	30
361	-	$5 brown	6·00	40

Designs: As T **91**—5c. Coat of Arms; 15c. Oil palm; 20c. Statue of Mercury; 75c. Heads of Mandingos; $5 'Liberia' seated. As T **92**—50c. West African mudskipper; $1 Coast view; $2 Liberia College. As T **93**—30c. Palm-nut Vulture.

1918. Geneva Red Cross Fund. Surch **TWO CENTS** and red cross.

375	**91**	1c.+2c. black and green	75	75
376	**92**	2c.+2c. black and red	75	75
377	-	5c.+2c. black and blue	25	1·00
378	**93**	10c.+2c. green	50	1·00
379	-	15c.+2c. green and black	2·40	1·75
380	-	20c.+2c. black and red	1·50	3·00
381	**94**	25c.+2c. green	3·25	3·25
382	-	30c.+2c. black and mauve	10·50	5·75
383	-	50c.+2c. black and blue	7·00	5·75
384	-	75c.+2c. black and olive	2·10	5·25
385	-	$1+2c. blue and brown	4·25	7·00
386	-	$2+2c. black and violet	5·75	11·50
387	-	$5+2c. brown	14·00	23·00

1920. Surch **1920** and value and two bars.

393	**91**	3c. on 1c. black & green	1·50	2·75
394	**92**	4c. on 2c. black and red	1·50	3·00
395	**R42**	5c. on 10c. black & blue	3·75	4·25
396	**R42**	5c. on 10c. black and red	3·75	4·25
397	**R42**	5c. on 10c. black & grn	3·75	4·25
398	**R42**	5c. on 10c. black & vio	3·75	4·25
399	**R42**	5c. on 10c. black and red	3·75	4·25

100 Cape Mesurado

101 President D. E. Howard

1921

402	**100**	1c. green	20	10
403	**101**	5c. black and blue	25	10
404	-	10c. blue and red	80	10
405	-	15c. green and purple	3·00	50
406	-	20c. green and red	1·50	25
407	-	25c. black and yellow	2·75	50
408	-	30c. purple and green	1·00	15
409	-	50c. blue and yellow	1·00	25
410	-	75c. sepia and red	1·00	40
411	-	$1 black and red	17·00	1·00
412	-	$2 violet and yellow	24·00	1·40
413	-	$5 red and purple	22·00	1·50

Designs: Vert—10c. Arms. Horiz—15c. Crocodile; 20c. Pepper plant; 25c. Leopard; 30c. Village; 50c. 'Kru' boatman; 75c. St Paul's River; $1 Bongo (antelope); $2 Great Indian hornbill; $5 African elephant.

1921. Optd **1921**.

414	**100**	1c. green	9·25	50
415	**64**	2c. red	9·25	50
416	**65**	3c. violet	12·50	50
417	**101**	5c. black and blue	2·75	50
418	-	10c. blue and red	20·00	50
419	-	15c. green and purple	11·50	1·00
420	-	20c. green and red	5·25	60
421	-	25c. black and yellow	11·50	1·00
422	-	30c. purple and green	3·00	50
423	-	50c. blue and yellow	3·00	70
424	-	75c. sepia and red	3·75	50
425	-	$1 black and red	30·00	1·50
426	-	$2 violet and yellow	28·00	1·60
427	-	$5 red and purple	32·00	5·25

107 Arrival of First Settlers in *Alligator*

1923. Centennial issue.

466	**107**	1c. black and blue	14·00	70
467	**107**	2c. brown and red	17·00	70
468	**107**	5c. blue and olive	17·00	70
469	**107**	10c. mauve and green	4·75	70
470	**107**	$1 brown and red	7·00	70

108 J. J. Roberts Memorial

109 House of Representatives, Monrovia

110 Rubber Plantation

1923

471	**108**	1c. green	3·75	10
472	**109**	2c. brown and red	3·75	10
473	-	3c. black and lilac	25	10
474	-	5c. black and blue	42·00	15
475	-	10c. brown and grey	25	10
476	-	15c. blue and bistre	18·00	50
477	-	20c. mauve and green	2·00	50
478	-	25c. brown and red	65·00	50
479	-	30c. mauve and brown	50	20
480	-	50c. orange and purple	1·00	40
481	-	75c. blue and grey	1·50	65
482	**110**	$1 violet and red	3·75	1·00
483	-	$2 blue and orange	4·00	65
484	-	$5 brown and green	10·00	65

Designs: As T **108**—3c. Star; 5, 10c. President King; 50c. Pineapple. As T **109**—15c. Hippopotamus; 20c. Kob (antelope); 25c. African buffalo; 30c. Natives making palm oil; 75c. Carrying elephant tusk. As T **110**—$2 Stockton lagoon; $5 Styles of huts.

1926. Surch **Two Cents** and thick bar or wavy lines or ornamental scroll.

504	**91**	2c. on 1c. black and green	3·00	3·25

116 Palm Trees

117 Map of Africa

118 President King

1928

511	**116**	1c. green	40	15
512	**116**	2c. violet	20	20
513	**116**	3c. brown	35	20
514	**117**	5c. blue	55	35
515	**118**	10c. grey	70	35
516	**117**	15c. purple	3·75	1·40
517	**117**	$1 brown	42·00	15·00

1936. Nos. O518 and 512/513 surch **AIR MAIL SIX CENTS**.

525	**116**	6c. on 1c. green	£170	90·00
526	**116**	6c. on 2c. violet	£170	90·00
527	**116**	6c. on 3c. brown	£170	90·00

122 Ford Tin Goose

1936. Air. Firstt Air Mail Service of 28th February.

530	**122**	1c. black and green	25	10
531	**122**	2c. black and red	25	10
532	**122**	3c. black and violet	40	10
533	**122**	4c. black and orange	40	15
534	**122**	5c. black and blue	45	15
535	**122**	6c. black and green	45	20

1936. Nos. 350/361 surch **1936** and new values in figures.

536	**92**	1c. on 2c. black and red	30	50
537	-	3c. on 5c. black and blue	30	45
538	**93**	4c. on 10c. green	25	40
539	-	6c. on 15c. green and black	30	55
540	-	8c. on 20c. black and red	20	60
541	-	12c. on 30c. black and mauve	1·25	1·40
542	-	14c. on 50c. black and blue	1·50	1·75
543	-	16c. on 75c. black and olive	50	60
544	-	18c. on $1 blue and brown	60	80
545	-	22c. on $2 black and violet	60	95
546	-	24c. on $5 brown	75	1·25

1936. Nos. O363/O374 optd with star and **1936** or surch also in figures and words.

547	**92**	1c. on 2c. black and red	30	50
548	-	3c. on 5c. black and blue	25	50
549	**93**	4c. on 10c. green	20	45
550	-	6c. on 15c. green and brown	25	60
551	-	8c. on 20c. black and lilac	30	60
552	-	12c. on 30c. black and violet	95	1·25
553	-	14c. on 50c. black and brown	1·00	1·50
554	-	16c. on 75c. black and brown	45	60
555	-	18c. on $1 blue and olive	50	65
556	-	22c. on $2 black and olive	60	90
557	-	24c. on $5 green	75	95
558	**94**	25c. green and brown	75	1·25

126 Hippopotamus

1937

559	-	1c. black and green	1·25	60
560	-	2c. black and red	1·00	30
561	-	3c. black and purple	1·00	35
562	**126**	4c. black and orange	1·50	60
563	-	5c. black and blue	1·75	85
564	-	6c. black and green	45	20

Designs: 1c. Black and white casqued hornbill; 2c. Bushbuck; 3c. African buffalo; 5c. Western reef heron; 6c. President Barclay.

127 Tawny Eagle in Flight

128 Three-engine Flying Boat

129 Little Egrets

1938. Air.

565	**127**	1c. green	25	20
566	**128**	2c. red	15	10
567	-	3c. olive	35	20
568	**129**	4c. orange	50	10
569	**129**	5c. green	65	20
570	**128**	10c. violet	25	10
571	-	20c. mauve	30	15
572	-	30c. grey	1·25	20
573	**127**	50c. brown	1·75	20
574	-	$1 blue	1·40	25

Designs: Vert—20c., $1 Sikorsky S-43 amphibian. Horiz—3, 30c. Lesser black-backed gull in flight.

130 Immigrant Ships nearing Liberian Coast

1940. Centenary of Founding of Liberian Commonwealth.

575	**130**	3c. blue	50	15
576	-	5c. brown	20	10
577	-	10c. green	25	15

Designs: 5c. Seal of Liberia and Flags of original Settlements; 10c. Thos. Buchanan's house and portrait.

1941. Centenary of First Postage Stamps. Nos. 575/577 optd **POSTAGE STAMP CENTENNIAL 1840–1940** and portrait of Rowland Hill.

578	**130**	3c. blue (postage)	1·75	1·75
579	-	5c. brown	1·75	1·75
580	-	10c. green	1·75	1·75
581	**130**	3c. blue (air)	1·40	1·40
582	-	5c. brown	1·40	1·40
583	-	10c. green	1·40	1·40

Nos. 581/583 are additionally optd with aeroplane and **AIR MAIL**.

1941. Red Cross Fund. Nos. 575/577 surch **RED CROSS** plus Red Cross and **TWO CENTS**.

584	**130**	+ 2c. on 3c. bl (postage)	1·40	1·40
585	-	+ 2c. on 5c. brown	1·40	1·40
586	-	+ 2c. on 10c. green	1·40	1·40
587	**130**	+ 2c. on 3c. blue (air)	1·40	1·40
588	-	+ 2c. on 5c. brown	1·40	1·40
589	-	+ 2c. on 10c. green	1·40	1·40

Nos. 587/589 are additionally optd with aeroplane and **AIR MAIL**.

1941. Air. First Flight to USA Nos. 565/574 surch **First Flight LIBERIA - U.S. 1941 50c** and bar.

594	**127**	50c. on 1c.	£2500	£225
595	**128**	50c. on 2c.	£150	75·00
596	-	50c. on 3c.	£180	90·00
597	**129**	50c. on 4c.	60·00	38·00
598	**129**	50c. on 5c.	60·00	38·00
599	**128**	50c. on 10c.	45·00	38·00
600	-	50c. on 20c.	£1500	£150
601	-	50c. on 30c.	60·00	24·00
602	**127**	50c. brown	60·00	24·00
603	-	$1 blue	45·00	30·00

The first flight was cancelled and covers were sent by ordinary mail. The flight took place in 1942 and the stamps were reissued but with the date obliterated.

1942. As Nos. 594/601 but with date 1941 obliterated by two bars.

604	**127**	50c. on 1c. green	7·00	7·00
605	**128**	50c. on 2c. red	6·00	6·75
606	-	50c. on 3c. green	5·50	4·75
607	**129**	50c. on 4c. orange	4·00	6·25
608	**129**	50c. on 5c. green	2·40	2·40
609	**128**	50c. on 10c. violet	5·25	6·25
610	-	50c. on 20c. mauve	5·25	6·25
611	-	50c. on 30c. grey	4·00	4·00
612	**127**	50c. brown	4·00	4·00
613	-	$1 blue	6·25	7·50

138 Miami–Monrovia Air Route

1942. Air.

614	**138**	10c. red	20	10
615	-	12c. blue	30	10
616	-	24c. green	35	10
617	**138**	30c. green	35	10
618	**138**	35c. lilac	40	15
619	**138**	50c. purple	50	15
620	**138**	70c. olive	55	30
621	**138**	$1.40 red	75	50

Design: 12, 24c. Boeing 247 airliner over Liberian Agricultural and Industrial Fair.

139 Bushbuck

1942

622	-	1c. brown and violet	80	20
623	-	2c. brown and blue	80	20
624	-	3c. brown and green	1·25	45
625	**139**	4c. red and black	2·00	70
626	-	5c. brown and olive	1·75	70
627	-	10c. black and red	3·75	1·10

Designs: Horiz—1c. Royal antelope; 2c. Water chevrotain; 3c. Jentink's duiker; 5c. Banded duiker. Vert—10c. Diana monkey.

1944. Stamps of 1928 and 1937 surch.

628	**116**	1c. on 2c. violet	7·50	7·50
634	**126**	1c. on 4c. black & orange	48·00	40·00
629	**118**	1c. on 10c. grey	10·00	6·25
635	-	2c. on 3c. black and purple (No. 561)	50·00	40·00
630	**117**	2c. on 5c. blue	3·25	3·25
632	**116**	3c. on 2c. violet	27·00	30·00
636	-	4c. on 5c. black and blue (No. 563)	18·00	18·00
633	**118**	4c. on 10c. grey	3·25	3·25
637	-	5c. on 1c. black and green (No. 559)	85·00	45·00
638	-	6c. on 2c. black and red (No. 560)	12·50	12·50
639	-	10c. on 6c. black and green (No. 564)	14·00	12·50

1944. Air stamps of 1936 and 1938 surch.

643	**128**	10c. on 2c. red	27·00	30·00
644	**129**	10c. on 5c. green	9·50	9·50
640	**122**	30c. on 1c. black & green	80·00	50·00
645	**122**	30c. on 3c. olive (No. 567)	£120	55·00
646	**129**	30c. on 4c. orange	9·50	9·50
641	**122**	50c. on 3c. black & violet	20·00	23·00
642	**122**	70c. on 2c. black and red	50·00	50·00
647	-	$1 on 3c. olive (No. 567)	25·00	25·00
648	**127**	$1 on 50c. brown	35·00	25·00

150 President Roosevelt reviewing Troops

1945. President Roosevelt Memorial.

650	**150**	3c. black & pur (postage)	15	15
651	**150**	5c. black and blue	30	25
652	**150**	70c. black and brown (air)	1·00	1·00

151 Opening Monrovia Harbour Project

1946. Opening of Monrovia Harbour Project by President Tubman.

653	**151**	5c. blue (postage)	25	15
654	**151**	24c. green (air)	1·90	2·10

1947. As T **151**, but without inscr at top.

655	**151**	5c. violet (postage)	15	15
656	**151**	25c. red (air)	1·00	1·10

152 First Postage Stamps of United States and Liberia

1947. US Postage Stamps Centenary and 87th Anniversary of Liberian Postal Issues.

657	**152**	5c. red (postage)	30	15
658	**152**	12c. green (air)	40	15
659	**152**	22c. violet	50	20
660	**152**	50c. blue	60	25
MS661		89×193 mm. Nos. 657/660. Imperf	2·00	2·00

153 Matilda Newport Firing Canon

1947. 125th Anniversary of Defence of Monrovia.

662	**153**	1c. black & green (postage)	15	10
663	**153**	3c. black and violet	20	10
664	**153**	5c. black and blue	20	15
665	**153**	10c. black and yellow	1·50	45
666	**153**	25c. black and red (air)	1·40	35

154 Liberty

1947. Centenary of National Independence.

667	-	1c. green (postage)	20	10
668	**154**	2c. purple	20	10
669	-	3c. purple	30	15
670	-	5c. blue	40	15
671	-	12c. orange (air)	60	20
672	-	25c. red	75	35
673	-	50c. brown	90	70

Designs: Vert—1c. Liberian star; 3c. Arms of Liberia; 4c. Map of Liberia; 12c. J. J. Roberts Monument; 25c. Liberian Flag. 50c. ($26\frac{1}{2}$×33 mm)—Centenary Monument.

156 Douglas DC-3

1948. Air. First Liberian International Airways Flight (Monrovia–Dakar).

674	**156**	25c. red	1·50	1·00
675	**156**	50c. blue	2·40	1·50

157 Joseph J. Roberts

1949. Liberian Presidents. Portrait and name in black. (a) Postage.

676	-	1c. green (Roberts)	1·60	3·25
677	**157**	1c. green	15	10
678	-	1c. pink (Roberts)	25	15
679	-	2c. pink (Benson)	35	35
680	-	2c. yellow (Benson)	35	15
681	-	3c. mauve (Warner)	35	35
682	-	4c. olive (Payne)	35	55
683	-	5c. blue (Mansion)	45	55
684	-	6c. orange (Roye)	55	95
685	-	7c. green (Gardner and Russell)	70	1·25
686	-	8c. red (Johnson)	70	1·40
687	-	9c. purple (Cheeseman)	1·10	1·10
688	-	10c. yellow (Coleman)	75	35
689	-	10c. grey (Coleman)	40	20
690	-	15c. orange (Gibson)	85	40
691	-	15c. blue (Gibson)	25	15
692	-	20c. grey (A. Barclay)	1·25	70
693	-	20c. red (A. Barclay)	50	45
694	-	25c. red (Howard)	1·60	1·10
695	-	25c. blue (Howard)	50	45
696	-	50c. turquoise (King)	3·25	95
697	-	50c. purple (King)	70	60
698	-	$1 mauve (E. Barclay)	5·75	70
699	-	$1 brown (E. Barclay)	4·00	55

(b) Air.

700		25c. blue (Tubman)	1·00	55
701		25c. green (Tubman)	75	35

Nos. 676 and 678 have a different portrait of Roberts wearing a moustache.

158 Colonists and Map

1949. Multicoloured.

702		1c. Settlers approaching village (postage)	50	75
703		2c. Rubber tapping and planting	50	75

704		3c. Landing of first colonists in 1822	1·00	1·50
705		5c. Jehudi Ashmun and Matilda Newport defending stockade	50	75
706		25c. Type **158** (air)	1·25	1·50
707		50c. Africans and Coat of Arms	2·75	3·25

159 Hand holding Book

1950. National Literacy Campaign.

708	**159**	5c. blue (postage)	20	15
709	-	25c. red (air)	70	70
MS710 140×82 mm. Nos. 708/709. Imperf			1·10	1·10

Design: Vert—25c. Open book and rising sun.

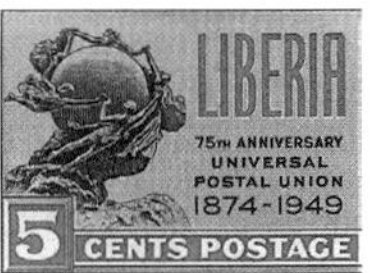

160 UPU Monument, Berne

1950. 75th Anniv of UPU.

711	**160**	5c. black and green (post)	20	15
712	-	10c. black and mauve	30	30
713	-	25c. purple & orange (air)	3·25	3·25
MS714 215×251 mm. Nos. 711/713. Imperf			3·75	3·75

Designs: Horiz—10c. Standehaus, Berne. Vert—25c. UPU Monument, Berne.

161 Carey, Ashmun and Careysburg

1952. Designs all show portrait of Ashmun.

715	-	1c. green (postage)	10	10
716	**161**	2c. blue and red	10	10
717	-	3c. green and purple	10	10
718	-	4c. green and brown	15	10
719	-	5c. red and blue	20	15
720	-	10c. blue and red	25	20
721	-	25c. black and purple (air)	35	35
722	-	50c. red and blue	1·00	45
MS723 215×252 mm. Nos. 715/722. Imperf			2·40	2·40

Designs: Vert—1c. Seal of Liberia; 3c. Harper and Harper City; 5c. Buchanan and Upper Buchanan. Horiz—4c. Marshall and Marshall City; 10c. Roberts and Robertsport; 25c. Monroe and Monrovia; 50c. Tubman and map.

162 UN Headquarters

163 Flags and UN Emblem

1952. UN Commemoration.

724	**162**	1c. blue (postage)	10	10
725	-	4c. blue and pink	15	10
726	-	10c. brown and yellow	25	20
727	**163**	25c. red and blue (air)	55	45

Designs: Horiz—4c. Liberian and UN flags and scroll; 10c. Liberian and UN emblems.

1952. World Health Conference, Monrovia. Two sheets each 153×85 mm. Nos. 724/727. Perf or imperf.

MS728 Two sheets		2·25	2·25

164 Modern Road-building

1953. Air. Transport.

729	**164**	12c. brown	15	15
730	-	25c. purple	75	30
731	-	35c. violet	1·60	30
732	-	50c. orange	65	25
733	-	70c. green	1·25	40
734	-	$1 blue	1·40	55

Designs: 25c. *African Glen* (freighter) in Monrovia Harbour; 35c. Diesel locomotive; 50c. Free Port of Monrovia; 70c. Roberts Field Airport; $1 Tubman Bridge.

165 Garden Bulbul ('Pepper Bird')

166 Blue-throated Roller ('Roller')

1953. Imperf or perf.

735	**165**	1c. red and blue	1·00	20
736	**166**	3c. blue and salmon	1·00	25
737	-	4c. brown and yellow	1·50	30
738	-	5c. turquoise and mauve	1·75	35
739	-	10c. mauve and green	1·75	35
740	-	12c. orange and brown	2·75	50

Birds: As T **165**—4c. Yellow-casqued hornbill ('Hornbill'); 5c. Giant kingfisher ('Kingfisher'). As T **166**—10c. African jacana ('Jacana'); 12c. Broad-tailed paradise whydah ('Weaver').

167 Hospital

1954. Liberian Government. Hospital Fund.

741		5c.+5c. black and purple (postage)	20	15
742		10c.+5c. black and red (air)	15	20
743	**167**	20c.+5c. black & green	25	25
744	-	25c.+5c. black, red and blue	30	20

Designs: As T **167**—5c. Medical research workers; 10c. Nurses. 46×35 mm—25c. Doctor examining patient.

168 Children of the World

1954. Air. UNICEF.

745	**168**	$5 ultramarine, red and blue	27·00	23·00

169 UN Organisations

1954. Air. UN Technical Assistance.

746	**169**	12c. black and blue	25	15
747	-	15c. brown and yellow	25	15
748	-	20c. black and green	30	20
749	-	25c. blue and red	35	25

Designs: 15c. Printers; 20c. Mechanic; 25c. Teacher and students.

1954. Air. Visit of President Tubman to USA. As Nos. 729/734 but colours changed and inscr 'COMMEMORATING PRESIDENTIAL VISIT U.S.A.—1954'.

750	**164**	12c. orange	20	20
751	-	25c. blue	80	25
752	-	35c. red	4·00	1·50
753	-	50c. mauve	80	30
754	-	70c. brown	1·10	50
755	-	$1 green	1·60	3·25

170 Football

1955. Sports.

756	-	3c. red and green (postage)	15	10
757	**170**	5c. black and orange	15	10
758	-	25c. violet and yellow	25	20
759	-	10c. blue and mauve (air)	20	15
760	-	12c. brown and blue	15	15
761	-	25c. red and green	20	20
MS762 90×140 mm. Nos. 758 and 761 Perf or imperf			90	90

Designs: Vert—3c. Tennis; 25c. Boxing (No. 758). Horiz—10c. Baseball; 12c. Swimming; 25c. Running (No. 761).

171 *Callichilia stenosepala*

1955. Flowers.

763	**171**	6c. yellow, salmon and green (postage)	15	10
764	-	7c. red, yellow and green	15	10
765	-	8c. buff, blue and green	20	10
766	-	9c. green and orange	25	15
767	-	20c. yellow, green and violet (air)	15	15
768	-	25c. yellow, green and red	20	20

Flowers: Vert—7c. *Gomphia subcordata*; 8c. *Listrostachys chudata*; 9c. *Mussaenda isertiana*. Horiz—20s. 'Costus'; 25c. *Barteria nigritiana*.

172 UN General Assembly

1955. Air. Tenth Anniversary of UN.

769		10c. blue and red	20	10
770	**172**	15c. black and violet	25	15
771	-	25c. brown and green	35	15
772	-	50c. green and red	1·00	20

Designs: Vert—10c. UN emblem; 25c. Liberian Secretary of State signing UN Charter. Horiz—50c. Page from UN Charter.

173 Tapping Rubber and Rotary Emblem

1955. 50th Anniversary of Rotary International.

773	**173**	5c. green & yell (postage)	25	15
774	-	10c. blue and red (air)	15	50
775	-	15c. brown, yellow and red	20	65
MS776 128×77 mm. 50c. blue and scarlet (as 10c. but without leaves)			80	80

Designs: 10c. Rotary International HQ, Evanston; 15c. View of Monrovia.

174 Coliseum, New York

1956. Fifth International Philatelic Exhibition, New York.

777		3c. brown and green (postage)	15	10
778	**174**	4c. brown and green	10	25
779	-	6c. purple and black	20	10
780	**174**	10c. blue and red (air)	25	15
781	-	12c. violet and orange	20	15
782	-	15c. purple and turquoise	25	20
MS783 78×129 mm. 50c. brown and emerald (as No. 782)			85	85

Designs: Vert—3c., 15c. Statue of Liberty. Horiz—6c., 12c. The Globe.

175 Chariot Race

1956. Olympic Games.

784	-	4c. brown & olive (postage)	10	10
785	-	6c. black and green	15	10
786	-	8c. brown and blue	20	10
787	**175**	10c. black and red	25	10
788	-	12c. purple and green (air)	20	15
789	-	20c. multicoloured	30	20
MS790 128×76 mm. 40c. multicoloured (as No. 789)			70	70

Designs: Horiz—4c. Olympic rings, eastern grey kangaroo and emu; 8c. Goddess of Victory; 12c., 20c. Olympic torch superimposed on map of Austrialia. Vert—6c. Discus thrower.

176 Douglas DC-6B *John Alden* at Idlewild Airport

1957. First Anniversary of Inauguration of Liberia–US.Direct Air Service.

791	**176**	3c. blue & orange (postage)	15	15
792	-	5c. black and mauve	20	20
793	**176**	12c. blue and green (air)	30	25
794	-	15c. black and brown	30	25
795	**176**	25c. blue and red	45	25
796	-	50c. black and blue	85	30

Design: 5, 15, 50c. President Tubman and *John Alden* at Roberts Field, Liberia.

177 Children's Playground

1957. Inauguration of Antoinette Tubman Child Welfare Foundation. Inscr as in T **177**.

797	**177**	4c. green and red (postage)	10	10
798	-	5c. brown and turquoise	15	10
799	-	6c. violet and bistre	15	10
800	-	10c. blue and red	20	15
801	-	15c. brown and blue (air)	20	15
802	-	35c. purple and grey	35	25
MS803 127×77 mm. 70c. lilac, red and blue (as No. 800)			85	85

Designs: 5c. Teacher with pupil; 6c. National Anthem with choristers; 10c. Children viewing welfare home; 15c. Nurse inoculating youth; 35c. Kamara triplets.

178 German Flag and Brandenburg Gate

1958. President Tubman's European Tour. Flags in national colours.

804	**178**	5c. blue (postage)	15	10
805	-	5c. brown	15	10
806	-	5c. red	15	10
807	-	10c. black (air)	25	15
808	-	15c. green	25	20
809	-	15c. blue	25	20
810	-	15c. violet	25	20

Designs: Flags of—Netherlands and windmill (No. 805); Sweden and Royal Palace, Stockholm (No. 806); Italy and Colosseum (No. 807); France and Arc de Triomphe (No. 808); Switzerland and Alpine chalet (No. 809); Vatican City and St Peter's Basilica (No. 810).

179 Map of the World

1958. Tenth Anniversary of Declaration of Human Rights.

811	**179**	3c. blue and black	25	15
812	-	5c. brown and blue	20	20
813	-	10c. orange and black	30	75
814	-	12c. black and red	40	35

Designs: 5c. UN Emblem and HQ building; 10c. UN Emblem; 12c. UN Emblem and initials of UN agencies.

180 Africans and Map

1959. Africa Freedom Day.

816	**180**	20c. orge & brn (postage)	30	30
817	-	25c. brown and blue (air)	35	20

Design: 25c. Two Africans looking at President Tubman's declaration of Africa Freedom Day.

181

1959. Inauguration of UNESCO Building, Paris.

818	**181**	25c. purple & grn (postage)	35	40
819	-	25c. red and blue (air)	35	30

Design: Horiz—No. 819 UNESCO Headquarters, Paris.

182 Abraham Lincoln

1959. 150th Birth Anniversary of Abraham Lincoln.

821	**182**	10c. black & blue (postage)	25	30
822	**182**	15c. black and orange	30	30
823	**182**	25c. black and green (air)	55	50
MS824		140×85 mm. Nos. 821/823. Imperf	1·10	1·10

183 Presidents Toure, Tubman and Nkrumah at Conference Table

1960. Big Three Conference, Saniquellie, Liberia.

825	**183**	25c. black & red (postage)	35	25
826	-	25c. black, bl & buff (air)	35	25

Design: No. 826, Medallion portraits of Presidents Toure (Guinea), Tubman (Liberia) and Nkrumah (Ghana).

184 Care of Refugees

1960. World Refugee Year.

827	**184**	25c. green & blk (postage)	35	30
828	**184**	25c. blue and black (air)	55	40
MS829		134×83 mm. Nos. 827/828	1·00	1·00

185

1960. Tenth Anniversary of African Technical Co-operation Commission (CCTA).

830	**185**	25c. green & blk (postage)	35	50
831	-	25c. brown and blue (air)	45	35

Design: No. 831, Map of Africa with symbols showing fields of assistance.

186 Weightlifting

1960. Olympic Games, Rome.

832	**186**	5c. brown & grn (postage)	20	15
833	-	10c. brown and purple	40	75
834	-	15c. brown and orange	35	30
835	-	25c. brown and blue (air)	70	80
MS836		130×80 mm. 50c. brown and violet (Athlete and Olympic Stadium). Imperf	1·50	1·50

Designs: Horiz—10c. Rowing; 25c. Javelin-throwing. Vert—15c. Walking.

187 Stamps of 1860 and Map

1960. Liberian Stamp Centenary. Stamps, etc., in green, red and blue. Colours of map and inscriptions given.

837	**187**	5c. black (postage)	25	15
838	**187**	20c. brown	40	40
839	**187**	25c. blue (air)	50	40
MS840		130×79 mm. 50c. multicoloured	1·10	1·10

188 'Guardians of Peace'

1961. Membership of UN Security Council.

841	**188**	25c. blue and red (postage)	45	35
842	-	25c. blue and red (air)	45	25
MS843		128×77 mm. 50c. green and brown (Globe and Dove). Imperf	1·10	1·10
MS844		134×88 mm. Nos. 841/842 and 50c. (as in No. **MS**843). Imperf	2·75	2·75

Design: Horiz—No. 842, Dove of Peace, Globe and UN Emblem.

189 Anatomy Class, University of Liberia

1961. 15th Anniversary of UNESCO.

845	**189**	25c. brown & grn (postage)	35	35
846	-	25c. brown and violet (air)	35	25
MS847		127×76 mm. 50c. brown and blue	85	85

Designs: Nos. 846 and **MS**847, Science class (different), University of Liberia.

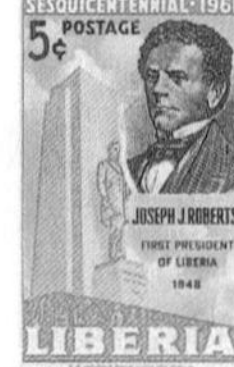

190 President Roberts

1961. 150th Birth Anniversary of Joseph J. Roberts (first President of Liberia).

848	**190**	5c. sepia & orge (postage)	20	15
849	-	10c. sepia and blue	35	15
850	-	25c. sepia and green (air)	45	35
MS851		140×83 mm. Nos. 848/850. Imperf	1·10	1·10

Designs: Horiz—10c. President Roberts and old and new presidential mansions; 25c. President Roberts and Providence Island.

191 Scout and Sports

1961. Liberian Boy Scout Movement.

852	**191**	5c. sepia & violet (postage)	25	20
853	-	10c. ochre and blue	30	20
854	-	25c. sepia and green (air)	40	30
MS855		126×76 mm. 35c. brown and blue (as No. 852)	75	75

Designs: Horiz—10c. Scout badge and scouts in camp. Vert—25c. Scout and badge.

192 Hammarskjold and UN Emblem

1962. Dag Hammarskjold Commem.

856	**192**	20c. black & blue (postage)	30	20
857	**192**	25c. black and purple (air)	35	25
MS858		127×76 mm. 50c. black and blue. Imperf	85	85

193 Campaign Emblem

1962. Malaria Eradication.

859	**193**	25c. green & red (postage)	35	25
860	-	25c. orange and violet (air)	35	25
MS861		127×71 mm. 50c. red and blue (as No. 860). Imperf	85	85

Design: -Horiz—No. 860, Campaign emblem and slogan.

194 President Tubman and New York Skyline

1962. Air. President's Visit to USA.

862	**194**	12c. multicoloured	25	15
863	**194**	25c. multicoloured	35	30
864	**194**	50c. multicoloured	70	55

195 UN Emblem

1962. UN Day.

865	**195**	20c. bistre & grn (postage)	35	30
866	-	25c. blue & deep blue (air)	45	30
MS867		127×71 mm. 50c. black and green (UN Emblem). Imperf	1·00	1·00

Design: 25c. UN emblem and flags.

196 Treasury Building

1962. Liberian Government Buildings.

868		1c. orange & blue (postage)	10	15
869	**196**	5c. violet and blue	15	10
870	-	10c. brown and buff	20	15
871	-	15c. blue and salmon	25	20
872	-	80c. yellow and brown	1·60	1·00
873	-	12c. red and green (air)	25	15
874	-	50c. blue and orange	1·00	90
875	-	70c. blue and mauve	1·40	1·00
876	**196**	$1 black and orange	2·00	1·10

Buildings: 1, 80c. Executive; 10, 50c. Information; 12, 15, 70c. Capitol.

197 FAO Emblem, Bowl and Spoon

1963. Freedom from Hunger.

877	**197**	5c. purple & turq (postage)	15	10
878	-	25c. yellow and green (air)	35	20
MS879		128×77 mm. 50c. blue and green (as 5c.)	80	80

Design: 25c. FAO emblem and globe.

198 Rocket

1963. Space Exploration.

880	**198**	10c. yellow & bl (postage)	20	15
881	-	15c. brown and blue	35	40
882	-	25c. green and orange (air)	45	30
MS883		127×76 mm. 50c. yellow and blue	1·00	1·00

Designs: Horiz—15c. Space capsule. Vert—25c. *Telstar* TV satellite; 50c. *Telstar* and rocket.

199 Red Cross

1963. Red Cross Centenary.

884	**199**	5c. green and red (postage)	15	15
885	-	10c. grey and red	20	20
886	-	25c. violet and red (air)	35	30
887	-	50c. blue and red	1·00	85

Designs: Vert—10c. Emblem and torch. Horiz—25c. Red Cross and Globe; 50c. Emblem and Globe.

200 Unity Scroll

1963. Conference of African Heads of State, Addis Ababa.

888	**200**	20c. brn & grn (postage)	40	35
889	-	25c. red and green (air)	45	30

Design: 25c. Map of Africa (inscr 'AFRICAN SUMMIT CONFERENCE').

201 Ski-jumping

1963. Winter Olympic Games, Innsbruck. (1964).

890	**201**	5c. blue and red (postage)	20	20
891	-	10c. red and blue (air)	25	25
892	-	25c. orange and green	35	35
MS893		128×77 mm. 50c. red and black	85	85

Designs: Vert—10c. Olympic flame. Horiz—25c. Olympic rings; 50c. Torch and mountains. All have mountain scenery as backgrounds.

202 President Kennedy

1964. President Kennedy Memorial Issue.

894	**202**	20c. black & blue (postage)	35	20
895	-	25c. black and purple (air)	45	25
MS896		127×78 mm. 50c. black and purple (as 20c.)	1·10	1·10

Design: Vert—25c. President Kenny, full face portrait.

203 *Relay I* Satellite

1964. Space Communications.

897		10c. orange and green	20	15
898	**203**	15c. blue and mauve	25	20
899	-	25c. yellow, black and blue	45	25
MS900 127×77 mm. 50c. red and blue			1·10	1·10

Satellites: 10c. *Syncom*; 25c. *Mariner II* 50c. Rocket in space.

204 Mt. Fuji

1964. Olympic Games, Tokyo.

901	**204**	10c. green and yellow	15	10
902	-	15c. purple and red	20	15
903	-	25c. red and buff	45	20
MS904 128×77 mm. 50c. blue and red			1·10	1·10

Designs: 15c. Japanese arch and Olympic flame; 25c. Cherry blossom and stadium; 50c. Runner and Olympic rings.

205 Scout Bugle

1965. Liberian Boy Scouts.

905		5c. brown and blue (postage)	25	15
906	**205**	10c. ochre and green	40	25
907	-	25c. blue and red (air)	50	35
MS908 128×77 mm. 50c. lemon and purple (Scout badge and Globe)			1·10	1·10

Designs: Vert—5c. Scout badge and saluting hand; 25c. Liberian flag within scout badge.

206 *The Great Emancipator* (statue)

1965. Death Centenary of Abraham Lincoln.

909	**206**	5c. brown and sepia	20	25
910	-	20c. green and light brown	35	30
911	-	25c. blue and purple	40	40
MS912 128×77 mm. 50c. purple and drab (as 20c.)			85	85

Designs: Horiz—20c. Bust of Lincoln, and President Kennedy. Vert—25c. Lincoln statue, Chicago (after St Gaudens).

207 ICY Emblem

1965. International Co-operation Year.

913	**207**	12c. brown and orange	70	25
914	**207**	25c. brown and blue	40	25
915	**207**	50c. brown and green	80	70
MS916 128 ×77 mm. **207** 50c. brown and rosine			85	85

208 ITU Emblem and Symbols

1965. Centenary of ITU.

917	**208**	25c. brn & grn (postage)	40	50
918	**208**	35c. mauve and black	60	50
919	**208**	50c. blue and red (air)	80	45
MS920 128×77 mm. Nos. 917/919. Imperf			1·75	1·75

209 President Tubman and Flag

1965. President Tubman's 70th Birthday. Multicoloured.

921	25c. Type **209** (postage)	35	30
922	25c. President and Liberian arms (air)	35	25
MS923 128×77 mm. Nos. 921/922. Imperf		75	75

210 Sir Winston Churchill

1966. Churchill Commemoration.

924	**210**	15c. black & orge (postage)	30	30
925	-	20c. black and green	35	25
926	-	25c. black and blue (air)	40	30
MS927 126×77 mm. 50c. black and purple			85	85

Designs: Horiz—20c. Churchill in uniform of Trinity House Elder Brother; 25c. Churchill and Houses of Parliament; 50c. Portrait after Karsh.

211 President Roberts

1966. Liberian Presidents.

928	**211**	1c. black and pink (postage)	10	10
929	-	2c. black and yellow	10	10
930	-	3c. black and violet	10	10
931	-	4c. black and yellow	75	50
932	-	5c. black and orange	10	10
933	-	10c. black and green	15	10
934	-	25c. black and blue	35	20
935	-	50c. black and mauve	70	65
936	-	80c. black and red	1·25	95
937	-	$1 black and brown	1·40	15
938	-	$2 black and purple	3·25	2·75
939	-	25c. black and green (air)	35	25

Presidents: 2c. Benson; 3c. Warner; 4c. Payne; 5c. Roye; 10c. Coleman; 25c. (postage) Howard; 25c. (air) Tubman; 50c. King; 80c. Johnson; $1 Barclay; $2 Cheesman.

212 Footballers and Hemispheres

1966. World Cup Football Championships.

940	**212**	10c. brown and turquoise (postage)	15	15
941	-	25c. brown and mauve	35	30
942	-	35c. brown and orange	50	45
MS943 127×77 mm. 50c. brown and blue (air)			1·50	1·10

Designs: Vert—25c. Presentation cup, football and boots; 35c. Footballer. Horiz—50c. World Cup match.

213 President Kennedy taking Oath

1966. Third Death Anniversary of President Kennedy.

944	**213**	15c. black & red (postage)	25	15
945	-	20c. purple and blue	35	20
946	-	25c. blue, black and ochre (air)	45	30
947	-	35c. blue and pink	85	45
MS948 77×127 mm. 40c. multicoloured			1·00	1·00

Designs: 20c. Kennedy stamps of 1964; 35c. President Kennedy and rocket on launch pad. Cape Kennedy; 40c. Flame of Remembrance.

214 Children on See-saw

1966. 20th Anniversary of UNICEF.

949	**214**	5c. blue and red	20	20
950	-	80c. brown and green	1·50	1·50

Design: 80c. Child playing 'Doctors'.

215 Giraffe

1966. Wild Animals. Multicoloured.

951	2c. Type **215**	10	10
952	3c. Lion	20	15
953	5c. Crocodile (horiz)	15	10
954	10c. Chimpanzees	40	20
955	15c. Leopard (horiz)	50	25
956	20c. Black rhinoceros (horiz)	60	40
957	25c. African elephant	70	50

216 Scout Emblem and Various Sports

1967. World Scout Jamboree, Idaho.

958	-	10c. purple and green (postage)	20	15
959	**216**	25c. red and blue	35	50
960	-	40c. brown and green	85	60
MS961 127×77 mm. 50c. violet and red (air)			75	75

Designs: Vert—Jamboree emblem. Horiz—40, 50c. Scout by campfire and Moon landing.

217 Pre-Hispanic Sculpture

1967. Publicity for Olympic Games, Mexico (1968).

962	**217**	10c. violet and orange	75	85
963	-	25c. orange, black and blue	35	40
964	-	40c. red and green	60	65

Designs: Vert—25c. Aztec calendar. Horiz—40c. Mexican sombrero, guitar and ceramics.

218 WHO Building, Brazzaville

1967. Inauguration of WHO's Regional Office, Brazzaville.

966	**218**	5c. yellow and blue	20	20
967	-	80c. green and yellow	1·25	1·25

Design: Vert—80c. As T **218** but in vertical format.

219 Boy with Rattle

1967. Musicians and Instruments. Multicoloured.

968	2c. Type **219**	15	15
969	3c. Tomtom and soko violin (horiz)	20	20
970	5c. Mang harp (horiz)	25	25
971	10c. Alimilim	30	30
972	15c. Xylophone drums	35	35
973	25c. Tomtoms	50	40
974	35c. Oral harp	75	60

220 Ice-hockey

1967. Publicity for Winter Olympic Games, Grenoble (1968).

975	**220**	10c. blue and green (postage)	15	20
976	-	25c. violet and blue	35	30
977	-	40c. brown and orange	85	50
MS978 127×76½ mm. 50c. black and vermillion (air)			1·00	1·00

Designs: 25c. Ski-jumping, 40c. Tobogganing; 50c. Ice skating.

221 President Tubman

1967. Re-election of Presideent Tubman for sixth Term.

979	**221**	25c. brown and blue	35	25
MS980 78×78 mm. **221** 50c. brown and blue. Imperf			75	75

222 Human Rights Emblem

1968. Human Rights Year.

981	**222**	3c. blue and red (postage)	10	10
982	**222**	80c. green and brown	1·60	1·60
MS983 128×78 mm. **222** 80c. vermillion and blue (air)			1·60	1·60

223 Dr. King and Hearse

1968. Martin Luther King Commemoration.

984	**223**	15c. brown and blue (postage)	25	20
985	-	25c. brown and blue	40	30
986	-	35c. black and olive	60	65
MS987 127×76 mm. 55c. black and brown (air)			1·00	1·00

Designs: Vert—25c. Dr. Martin Luther King. Horiz—35c. Dr. King and Lincoln Monument; 55c. President Kennedy congratulating Dr. King upon award of Nobel Peace Prize.

224 Throwing the Javelin and Statue of Diana

1968. Olympic Games, Mexico.

988	**224**	15c. violet and brown (postage)	25	15
989	-	25c. blue and red	35	15
990	-	35c. brown and green	50	30
MS991 128×77 mm. 50c. brown and blue (air)			75	75

Designs: Throwing the discus and Quetzalcoatl and sculpture; 35c. High-diving and Xochilcalco bas-relief; 50c. Horse-jumping and Aztec god.

225 President Tubman

1968. 25th Anniversary of President Tubman's Administration.

992	**225**	25c. black, brown & silver	1·10	50
MS993 78×78 mm. 80c. red, blue and silver. Imperf			2·50	2·50

Design: 80c. Unification Monument, Voinjama.

226 ILO Symbol

1969. 50th Anniversary of ILO.

994	**226**	25c. blue & gold (postage)	35	35
995	-	80c. green and gold (air)	1·50	1·40

Design: 80c. As T **226** but vert.

227 *Prince Balthasar Carlos* (Velasquez)

1969. Paintings (1st series). Multicoloured.

996	3c. Type **227**	10	10
997	5c. *Red Roofs* (Pissarro) (horiz)	20	10
998	10c. *David and Goliath* (Caravaggio) (horiz)	30	15
999	12c. *Still Life* (Chardin) (horiz)	30	15
1000	15c. *The Last Supper* (Leonardo da Vinci) (horiz)	35	15
1001	20c. *Regatta at Argenteuil* (Monet) (horiz)	50	20
1002	25c. *Judgement of Solomon* (Giorgione)	45	25
1003	35c. *The Sistine Madonna* (Raphael)	85	30

See also Nos. 1010/1017.

228 Bank Emblem on 'Tree'

1969. Fifth Anniversary of African Development Bank.

1004	**228**	25c. brown and blue	45	40
1005	**228**	80c. red and green	1·50	1·10

229 Memorial Plaque

1969. First Man on the Moon.

1006	**229**	15c. blue and ochre (postage)	25	15
1007	-	25c. blue and orange	70	20
1008	-	35c. red and slate	1·00	25
MS1009 127×76 mm. 65c. blue and vermilion (air)			95	95

Designs: Vert—25c. Moon landing and Liberian 'Kennedy' 35c. stamp of 1966; 35c. Module lifting off from Moon. Horiz—65c. *Apollo 1* astronauts.

1969. Paintings (2nd series). As T **227**. Multicoloured.

1010	3c. *The Gleaners* (Millet) (horiz)	15	10
1011	5c. *View of Toledo* (El Greco)	20	15
1012	10c. *Heads of Negroes* (Rubens) (horiz)	30	15
1013	12c. *The Last Supper* (El Greco) (horiz)	30	20
1014	15c. *Peasants Dancing* (Brueghel) (horiz)	35	20
1015	20c. *Hunters in the Snow* (Brueghel) (horiz)	40	25
1016	25c. *Descent from the Cross* (detail, Weyden)	45	30
1017	35c. *The Conception* (Murillo)	60	40

230 Peace Dove and Emblems

1970. 25th Anniversary of United Nations.

1018	**230**	5c. green & sil (postage)	15	25
1019	-	$1 blue and silver (air)	1·25	1·00

Design: $1, UN emblem and olive branch.

231 World Cup 'Football' Emblem

1970. World Cup Football Championship, Mexico.

1020	**231**	5c. brown and blue	20	15
1021	-	10c. brown and green	25	20
1022	-	25c. gold and purple	45	30
1023	-	35c. red and blue	60	45
MS1024 127×76 mm. 55c. blue, yellow and green			90	90

Designs: Vert—10c. Tlaloc Mexican Rain God; 25c. Jules Rimet Cup. Horiz—35c. Football in sombrero; 55c. Players in Aztec Stadium.

232 Japanese Singer and Festival Plaza

1970. Expo 70. Multicoloured.

1025	2c. Type **232**	10	10
1026	3c. Japanese singer and Expo hall	15	10
1027	5c. Aerial view of EXPO 70	30	10
1028	7c. Tanabata Festival	30	10
1029	8c. Awa Dance Festival	30	15
1030	25c. Sado-Okesa Dance Festival	1·10	25
MS1031 80×115 mm. Ricoh Pavilion (vert)		2·00	2·00

233 New HQ Building

1970. Inauguration of New UPU Headquarters Building, Berne.

1032	**233**	25c. brown and blue	35	35
1033	-	80c. brown and chestnut	1·50	1·50

Design: Vert—80c. Similar to T **233** but with larger UPU monument.

234 *The First Consul* (Vien)

1970. Birth Bicentenary of Napoleon Bonaparte. Multicoloured.

1034	3c. Type **234**	20	10
1035	5c. *Napoleon visiting school* (unknown artist)	30	15
1036	10c. *Napoleon Bonaparte* (detail, Isabey)	35	15
1037	12c. *The French Campaign* (Meissonier)	40	20
1038	20c. *The Abdication* (Bouchot)	80	30
1039	25c. *Meeting of Napoleon and Pope Pius VII* (Demarne)	1·50	35
MS1040 77×102 mm. 50c. *The Coronation* (David). Imperf		2·75	2·75

Design of 10c. is incorrectly attributed to Gerard on the stamp.

235 President Tubman

1970. President Tubman's 75th Birthday.

1041	**235**	25c. multicoloured	75	25
MS1042 86×112 mm. **235** 50c. multicoloured			1·40	1·40

236 *Adoration of the Magi* (Van der Weyden)

1970. Christmas. *The Adoration of the Magi* by artists as below. Multicoloured.

1043	3c. Type **236**	10	10
1044	5c. H. Memling	15	10
1045	10c. S. Lochner	25	15
1046	12c. A. Altdorfer (vert)	30	15
1047	20c. H. van der Goes	35	15
1048	25c. H. Bosch (vert)	40	30
MS1049 99×70 mm. 50c. Triptych by Andrea Mantegna. Imperf		85	85

The design in **MS**1049 is larger 58×40 mm.

237 Bapende Mask

1971. African Ceremonial Masks. Masks from different tribes. Multicoloured.

1050	2c. Type **237**	10	10
1051	3c. Dogon	15	10
1052	5c. Baoule	15	15
1053	6c. Dedougou	20	15
1054	9c. Dan	25	15
1055	15c. Bamileke	30	20
1056	20c. Bapende (different)	40	30
1057	25c. Bamileke costume	60	30

238 Astronauts on Moon

1971. *Apollo 14* Moon Mission. Multicoloured.

1058	3c. Type **238**	15	10
1059	5c. Astronaut and Moon vehicle	15	10
1060	10c. Erecting US flag on Moon	20	10
1061	12c. Splashdown	40	15
1062	20c. Astronauts leaving capsule	45	15
1063	25c. *Apollo 14* crew	60	20
MS1064 127×85 mm. 50c. Earth, Moon and 'star'		1·25	1·25

239 President Tubman and Women at Ballot Box

1971. 25th Anniversary of Liberian Women's Suffrage.

1065	**239**	3c. blue and brown	15	30
1066	-	80c. brown and green	1·50	1·50

Design: Horiz—80c. President Tubman, women and map.

240 Hall of Honour, Munich

1971. Olympic Games, Munich (1972) (1st issue). Views of Munich. Multicoloured.

1067	3c. Type **240**	15	10
1068	5c. View of central Munich	15	10
1069	10c. National Museum	20	10
1070	12c. Max Joseph's Square	25	10
1071	20c. Propylaen, King's Square	40	15
1072	25c. Liesel-Karistadt Fountain	60	20
MS1073 115×84 mm. 25c. Olympic Village, Kiel; 30c. Yachts at Kiel		1·25	1·25

See also Nos. 1106/**MS**1112.

241 American Scout

1971. World Scout Jamboree, Asagiri, Japan. Scouts in national uniforms. Multicoloured.

1074	3c. Type **241**(postage)	15	10
1075	5c. West Germany	15	10
1076	10c. Australia	20	15
1077	12c. Great Britain	25	15
1078	20c. Japan	40	20
1079	25c. Liberia	60	30
MS1080 102×76 mm. 50c. Scouts around camp fire (horiz) (air)		1·25	1·25

242 President William Tubman

1971. President Tubman Memorial Issue.

1081	**242**	3c. brown, blue and black	10	10
1082	**242**	25c. brown, purple & blk	35	35

243 Common Zebra and Foal

1971. 25th Anniversary of UNICEF. Animals with young. Multicoloured.

1083	5c. Type **243**	20	10
1084	7c. Koalas	30	15
1085	8c. Guanaco	35	15
1086	10c. Red fox and cubs	45	15
1087	20c. Savanna monkeys	65	25
1088	25c. Brown bears	90	35
MS1089 102×77 mm. 50c. Bengal tiger		1·75	1·75

244 Cross-country Skiing and Sika Deer

1971. Winter Olympic Games, Sapporo, Japan. Sports and Hokkaido Animals. Multicoloured.

No.	Description		
1090	2c. Type **244** (postage)	10	10
1091	3c. Tobogganing and black woodpecker	70	20
1092	5c. Ski-jumping and brown bear	15	10
1093	10c. Bobsleighing and common guillemots	1·00	20
1094	15c. Figure-skating and northern pika	30	20
1095	25c. Slalom skiing and Manchurian cranes	2·00	50
MS1096	102×77 mm. 50c. Japanese Imperial Family (air)	3·75	3·75

245 APU Emblem, Dove and Letter

1971. Tenth Anniversary of African Postal Union.

No.	Type	Description		
1097	**245**	25c. orange and blue	35	50
1098	**245**	80c. brown and grey	1·10	1·00

246 *Elizabeth* (emigrant ship) at Providence Island

1972. 150th Anniversary of Liberia.

No.	Type	Description		
1099	**246**	3c. green and blue (postage)	70	50
1100	-	20c. blue and orange	35	20
1101	**246**	25c. purple and orange	2·00	55
1102	-	35c. purple and green	1·10	75
MS1103		127×78 mm. 50c. red and blue (air)	3·75	3·75

Designs: Vert—Arms and Founding Fathers Monument, Monrovia. Horiz—50c. *Elizabeth* crossing the Atlantic.

247 President Tolbert and Map

1972. Inauguration of President Wm. R. Tolbert Jnr.

No.	Type	Description		
1104	**247**	25c. brown and green	35	25
1105	-	80c. brown and blue	1·60	80

Design: Vert—80c. President Tolbert standing by desk.

248 Football

1972. Olympic Games, Munich (2nd issue). Multicoloured.

No.	Description		
1106	3c. Type **248** (postage)	10	10
1107	5c. Swimming	15	10
1108	10c. Show-jumping	25	10
1109	12c. Cycling	30	15
1110	20c. Long-jumping	45	20
1111	25c. Running	60	25
MS1112	102×70 mm. 55c. Olympic Stadium (air)	1·25	1·25

249 Globe and Emblem

1972. 50th Anniversary of International Y's Men's Clubs.

No.	Type	Description		
1113	**249**	15c. violet and gold	40	15
1114	-	90c. green and blue	1·75	1·75

Design: 90c. Club emblem on World Map.

250 Astronaut and Moon Rover

1972. Moon Mission of *Apollo 16*. Multicoloured.

No.	Description		
1115	3c. Type **250** (postage)	10	10
1116	5c. Reflection on visor	10	10
1117	10c. Astronauts with cameras	15	10
1118	12c. Setting up equipment	50	15
1119	20c. *Apollo 16* emblem	65	20
1120	25c. Astronauts in Moon Rover	90	50
MS1121	97×71 mm. 55c. *Apollo 16* crew (air)	1·75	1·75

251 Emperor Haile Selassie

1972. Emperor Haile Selassie of Ethiopia's 80th Birthday.

No.	Type	Description		
1122	**251**	20c. green and yellow	40	30
1123	**251**	25c. purple and yellow	45	40
1124	**251**	35c. brown and yellow	85	85

252 HMS *Ajax* (ship of the line), 1809

1972. Famous Ships of the British Royal Navy. Multicoloured.

No.	Description		
1125	3c. Type **252** (postage)	35	25
1126	5c. HMS *Hogue* (screw ship of the line), 1848	65	25
1127	7c. HMS *Ariadne* (frigate), 1816	85	30
1128	15c. HMS *Royal Adelaide* (ship of the line), 1828	1·00	55
1129	20c. HMS *Rinaldo* (screw sloop), 1860	1·40	70
1130	25c. HMS *Nymphe* (screw sloop), 1888	1·90	1·00
MS1131	102×76 mm. 50c. HMS *Victory* (battleship), 1765 (air)	3·50	3·50

253 President Tolbert taking Oath

1972. First Year of President Tolbert Presidency.

No.	Type	Description		
1132	**253**	15c. multicoloured (postage)	65	55
1133	**253**	25c. multicoloured	95	95
MS1134		96×72 mm. **253** 55c. multicoloured (air)	1·90	1·90

254 Klaus Dibiasi and Italian Flag

1973. Olympic Games, Munich. Gold-medal Winners. Multicoloured.

No.	Description		
1135	5c. Type **254**	10	10
1136	8c. Borzov and Soviet flag	15	10
1137	10c. Yanagida and Japanese flag	15	10
1138	12c. Spitz and US flag	20	15
1139	15c. Keino and Kenyan flag	25	15
1140	25c. Meade and Union Jack	35	25
MS1141	95×70 mm. 55c. Hans Winkler and West German flag	85	85

255 Astronaut on Moon

1973. Moon Flight of *Apollo 17*. Multicoloured.

No.	Description		
1142	2c. Type **255** (postage)	10	10
1143	3c. Testing lunar rover at Cape Kennedy	10	10
1144	10c. Collecting Moon rocks	15	10
1145	15c. Lunar rover on Moon	20	15
1146	20c. *Apollo 17* crew at Cape Kennedy	30	20
1147	25c. Astronauts on Moon	35	25
MS1148	102×77 mm. 55c. *Apollo 17* emblem (air)	85	85

256 Steam Locomotive, Great Britain

1973. Historical Railways. Steam locomotives of 1895–1905. Multicoloured.

No.	Description		
1149	2c. Type **256** (postage)	25	10
1150	3c. Netherlands	35	10
1151	10c. France	65	15
1152	15c. No. 1800, USA	95	20
1153	20c. Class 150 No. 1, Japan	2·00	25
1154	25c. Germany	3·00	30
MS1155	102×77 mm. 55c. Switzerland (air)	4·50	4·50

257 OAU Emblem

1973. Tenth Anniversary of Organisation of African Unity.

No.	Type	Description		
1156	**257**	3c. multicoloured	10	10
1157	**257**	5c. multicoloured	10	10
1158	**257**	10c. multicoloured	15	10
1159	**257**	15c. multicoloured	20	15
1160	**257**	25c. multicoloured	35	25
1161	**257**	50c. multicoloured	1·00	1·00

258 Edward Jenner and Roses

1973. 25th Anniversary of WHO. Multicoloured.

No.	Description		
1162	1c. Type **258** (postage)	15	10
1163	4c. Sigmund Freud and violets	15	10
1164	10c. Jonas Salk and chrysanthemums	25	10
1165	15c. Louis Pasteur and scabious	40	15
1166	20c. Emil von Behring and mallow	45	20
1167	25c. Sir Alexander Fleming and rhododendrons	85	25
MS1168	102×77 mm. 55c. Paul Ehrlich and anemones (air)	1·50	1·50

259 Stanley Steamer, 1910

1973. Vintage Cars. Multicoloured.

No.	Description		
1169	2c. Type **259** (postage)	10	10
1170	3c. Cadillac Model A, 1903	10	10
1171	10c. Clement-Baynard, 1904	15	10
1172	15c. Rolls-Royce Silver Ghost tourer, 1907	25	15
1173	20c. Maxwell gentleman's speedster, 1905	35	20
1174	25c. Chadwick, 1907	50	25
MS1175	103×77 mm. 55c. Franklin 10 hp Crossed-engine, 1904 and 1905 (air)	1·00	1·00

260 Copernicus, Armillary Sphere and Satellite Communications System

1973. 500th Birth Anniversary of Copernicus. Multicoloured.

No.	Description		
1176	1c. Type **260** (postage)	10	10
1177	4c. Eudoxus solar system	10	10
1178	10c. Aristotle, Ptolemy and Copernicus	15	10
1179	15c. Saturn and Apollo spacecraft	25	15
1180	20c. Astronomical observatory satellite	35	20
1181	25c. Satellite tracking-station	50	25
MS1182	114×77 mm. 55c. Satellite in Mars orbit (air)	1·00	1·00

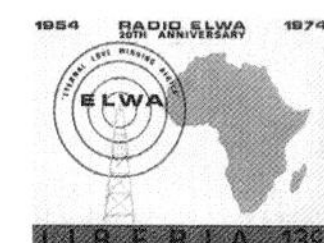

261 Radio Mast and Map of Africa

1974. 20th Anniversary of Eternal Love Winning Africa. Radio Station. Multicoloured.

No.	Description		
1183	13c. Type **261**	25	25
1184	15c. Radio mast and map of Liberia	35	25
1185	17c. Type **261**	35	50
1186	25c. As 15c.	50	40

262 *Thomas Coutts* (full-rigged sailing ship) and *Aureol* (liner)

1974. Centenary of UPU. Multicoloured.

No.	Description		
1187	2c. Type **262** (postage)	20	10
1188	3c. Boeing 707 airliner and *Brasil* (liner), satellite and Monrovia Post Office	30	10
1189	10c. US and Soviet Telecommunications satellites	15	10
1190	15c. Postal runner and Boeing 707 airliner	25	20
1191	20c. British Advanced Passenger Train (APT) and Liberian mail-van	1·50	25
1192	25c. American Pony Express rider	50	35
MS1193	115×77 mm. 55c. English mailcoach, 1784 (air)	1·00	1·00

263 Fox Terrier

1974. Dogs. Multicoloured.

No.	Description		
1194	5c. Type **263**	15	10
1195	10c. Boxer	20	10
1196	16c. Chihuahua	30	15
1197	19c. Beagle	35	20
1198	25c. Golden retriever	40	25
1199	50c. Collie	1·10	50
MS1200	115×77 mm. 75c. Kuvasz (Hungarian sheepdog)	1·60	1·60

264 West Germany v. Chile Match

1974. World Cup Football Championship, West Germany. Scenes from semi-final matches. Multicoloured.

No.	Description		
1201	1c. Type **264** (postage)	10	10
1202	2c. Australia v. East Germany	10	10
1203	5c. Brazil v. Yugoslavia	15	10
1204	10c. Zaire v. Scotland	20	10
1205	12c. Netherlands v. Uruguay	25	15
1206	15c. Sweden v. Bulgaria	30	15
1207	20c. Italy v. Haiti	40	20
1208	25c. Poland v. Argentina	60	25
MS1209	102×77 mm. 60c. World Cup and Stadium (air)	1·60	1·60

265 *Chrysiridia madagascariensis*

1974. Tropical Butterflies. Multicoloured.

1210	1c. Type **265** (postage)	10	10
1211	2c. *Catagramma sorana*	10	10
1212	5c. *Erasmia pulchella*	20	10
1213	17c. *Morpho cypris*	50	25
1214	25c. *Agrias amydon*	70	35
1215	40c. *Vanessa cardui*	1·40	45
MS1216	114×77 mm. 60c. *Pierella merels* (air)	2·00	2·00

266 President Tolbert and Gold Medallion

1974. Family of Man Award to President Tolbert. Multicoloured.

1217	3c. Type **266**	10	25
1218	$1 President Tolbert, medallion and flag	1·40	1·40

267 Churchill with Troops

1975. Birth Centenary of Sir Winston Churchill. Multicoloured.

1219	3c. Type **267** (postage)	10	10
1220	10c. Churchill and aerial combat	30	10
1221	15c. Churchill aboard Liberty ship in Channel	55	15
1222	17c. Churchill reviewing troops in desert	30	15
1223	20c. Churchill crossing Rhine	40	20
1224	25c. Churchill with Roosevelt	50	25
MS1225	113×77 mm. 60c. Churchill painting (air)	1·60	1·60

268 Marie Curie

1975. International Women's Year. Multicoloured.

1226	2c. Type **268** (postage)	10	10
1227	3c. Mahalia Jackson	10	10
1228	5c. Joan of Arc	10	10
1229	10c. Eleanor Roosevelt	15	10
1230	25c. Matilda Newport	50	25
1231	50c. Valentina Tereshkova	70	55
MS1232	106×80 mm. 75c. Vijaya Lakshmi Pandit (air)	1·25	1·25

269 Old State House, Boston, and US 2c. 'Liberty Bell' Stamp of 1926

1975. Bicentenary of American Independence.

1233	5c. Type **269**	15	10
1234	10c. George Washington and 1928 'Valley Forge' stamp	30	10
1235	15c. Philadelphia and 1937 'Constitution' stamp	45	15
1236	20c. Benjamin Franklin and 1938 'Ratification' stamp	50	15
1237	25c. Paul Revere's Ride and 1925 'Lexington–Concord' stamp	70	20
1238	50c. *Santa Maria* and 1893 'Columbus' Landing' stamp	2·25	55
MS1239	78×100 mm. 75c. *Mayflower* and US Pilgrim Fathers stamp of 1920	2·75	2·75

See also Nos. 1297/**MS**1299.

270 Dr. Schweitzer, Yellow Baboon and Lambarene Hospital

1975. Birth Centenary of Dr Albert Schweitzer. Multicoloured.

1240	1c. Type **270** (postage)	10	10
1241	3c. Schweitzer, African elephant and canoe	15	10
1242	5c. Schweitzer, African buffalo and canoe	25	20
1243	6c. Schweitzer, kob and dancer	30	10
1244	25c. Schweitzer, lioness and village woman	75	25
1245	50c. Schweitzer, common zebras and clinic scene	1·40	65
MS1246	76×97 mm. 60c. Schweitzer and staff in operating theatre (air)	2·10	2·10

271 Apollo Spacecraft

1975. Apollo–Soyuz Space Link. Multicoloured.

1247	5c. Type **271**	10	10
1248	10c. Soyuz spacecraft	15	10
1249	15c. American–Russian handclasp	20	15
1250	20c. Flags and maps of America and Russia	25	15
1251	25c. Leonov and Kubasov	35	20
1252	50c. Slayton, Brand and Stafford	95	50
MS1253	155×78 mm. 75c. Apollo and Soyuz spacecraft docked together	1·25	1·25

272 Presidents Tolbert and Stevens, and Signing Ceremony

1975. Liberia–Sierra Leone Mano River Union Agreement.

1254	**272**	2c. multicoloured	10	10
1255	**272**	3c. multicoloured	10	10
1256	**272**	5c. multicoloured	10	10
1257	**272**	10c. multicoloured	15	10
1258	**272**	25c. multicoloured	35	25
1259	**272**	50c. multicoloured	70	70

273 Figure Skating

1976. Winter Olympic Games, Innsbruck. Multicoloured.

1260	1c. Type **273** (postage)	10	10
1261	4c. Ski jumping	20	20
1262	10c. Skiing (slalom)	30	20
1263	25c. Ice hockey	60	30
1264	35c. Speed skating	90	40
1265	50c. Two-man bobsledding	1·25	65
MS1266	117×78 mm. 75c. Downhill skiing (air)	1·75	1·75

274 President Tolbert taking Oath

1976. Inauguration of President William R. Tolbert, Jr. Multicoloured.

1267	3c. Type **274**	10	10
1268	25c. President Tolbert in Presidential Chair (vert)	35	25
1269	$1 Liberian crest, flag and commemorative gold coin	1·90	1·40

275 Weightlifting

1976. Olympic Games, Montreal. Multicoloured.

1270	2c. Type **275** (postage)	10	10
1271	3c. Pole-vaulting	10	10
1272	10c. Hammer and shot-put	30	15
1273	25c. Tempest dinghies	65	35
1274	35c. Gymnastics	90	60
1275	50c. Hurdling	1·25	65
MS1276	115×77 mm. 75c. Dressage and show jumping (air)	1·75	1·75

276 Bell's Telephone and Receiver

1976. Telephone Centenary. Multicoloured.

1277	1c. Type **276** (postage)	10	10
1278	4c. Mail-coach	10	10
1279	5c. *Intelsat 4* satellite	15	10
1280	25c. Cable-ship *Dominia*, 1926	1·25	30
1281	40c. British Advanced Passenger Train (APT)	1·60	50
1282	50c. *Wright Flyer I*, airship *Graf Zeppelin* and Concorde	1·75	60
MS1283	116×78 mm. 75c. Bell making telephone call (air)	3·00	3·00

277 Gold Nugget Pendant

1976. Liberian Products (1st series). Multicoloured.

1284	1c. Mano River Bridge	10	10
1285	3c. Type **277**	10	10
1286	5c. 'V' ring	10	10
1286a	7c. As No. 1286	15	25
1287	10c. Rubber tree and tyre	15	10
1287a	15c. Combine-harvester	20	10
1287b	17c. As No. 1289	45	10
1287c	20c. Hydro-electric plant	60	45
1288	25c. Mesurado shrimp	75	25
1288a	27c. Dress and woman tie-dying cloth	80	60
1289	55c. Great barracuda	1·40	35
1289a	$1 Train carrying iron ore	4·50	60

For designs as T **277** but in a smaller size, see Nos. 1505/1508.

See also Nos. 1504a/1510.

278 Black Rhinoceros

1976. Animals. Multicoloured.

1290	2c. Type **278** (postage)	10	10
1291	3c. Bongo	10	10
1292	5c. Chimpanzee (vert)	15	10
1293	15c. Pygmy hippopotamus	40	15
1294	25c. Leopard	80	40
1295	$1 Gorilla	3·00	90
MS1296	103×78 mm. 50c. Elephant (air)	1·60	1·60

279 Statue of Liberty and Unification Monument on Maps of USA and Liberia

1976. Bicentenary of American Revolution. Multicoloured.

1297	25c. Type **279** (postage)	35	25
1298	$1 Presidents Washington and Ford (USA), Roberts and Tolbert (Liberia)	1·75	65
MS1299	78×104m. 75c. As $1 (air)	1·75	1·75

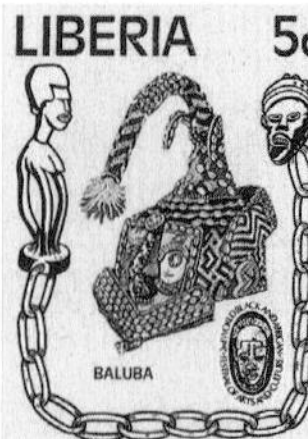

280 Baluba Masks

1977. Second World Black and African Festival of Arts and Culture, Lagos (Nigeria). Tribal Masks. Multicoloured.

1300	5c. Type **280** (postage)	10	10
1301	10c. Bateke	15	10
1302	15c. Basshilele	20	15
1303	20c. Igungun	30	15
1304	25c. Maisi	60	20
1305	50c. Kifwebe	1·10	45
MS1306	102×77 mm. 75c. Lbo mask	11·60	1·60

281 Latham's Francolin

1977. Liberian Wild Birds. Multicoloured.

1307	5c. Type **281**	50	10
1308	10c. Narina's trogon ('Narina Trogon')	80	15
1309	15c. Rufous-crowned roller	80	20
1310	20c. Brown-cheeked hornbill	85	25
1311	25c. Garden bulbul ('Pepper Bird')	1·00	35
1312	50c. African fish eagle ('Fish Eagle')	1·10	85
MS1313	104×77 mm. 80c. Gold Coast touraco	2·00	2·00

282 Alwin Schockemohle (individual jumping)

1977. Olympic Games, Montreal. Equestrian Gold-medal Winners. Multicoloured.

1314	5c. Edmund Coffin (military dressage) (postage)	15	10
1315	15c. Type **282**	40	20
1316	20c. Christine Stuckelberger (dressage)	50	30
1317	25c. Nations Prize (French team)	70	35
1318	55c. Military dressage (USA team) (air)	1·25	70
MS1319	78×104 mm. 80c. West German team (tean dressagr)	1·75	1·75

283 Queen Elizabeth II

1977. Silver Jubilee of Queen Elizabeth II. Multicoloured.

1320	15c. Type **283** (postage)	35	15
1321	25c. Queen Elizabeth and Prince Philip with President and Mrs. Tubman of Liberia	55	25
1322	80c. Queen Elizabeth, Prince Philip and Royal Arms	2·40	70
MS1323	116×78 mm. 75c. Full-faced portrait of Queen Elizabeth (air)	2·25	2·25

284 Blessing the Children

1977. Christmas. Multicoloured.

1324	20c. Type **284**	50	25
1325	25c. The Good Shepherd	70	35
1326	$1 Jesus and the Woman of Samaria at the Well	2·00	1·00

285 Dornier Do-X Flying Boat

1978. Progress in Aviation. Multicoloured.

1327	2c. Type **285**	10	10
1328	3c. Space shuttle *Enterprise* on Boeing 747	10	10
1329	5c. Edward Rickenbacker and Douglas DC-3	10	10
1330	25c. Charles Lindbergh and *Spirit of St. Louis*	45	20
1331	35c. Louis Bleriot and Bleriot XI monoplane	65	35
1332	50c. Wright Brothers and *Flyer I*	90	55
MS1333	119×80 mm. 80c. Concorde	1·40	1·40

286 Santos-Dumont's Airship *Ballon No. 9 La Badaleuse*, 1903

1978. 75th Anniversary of First Zeppelin Flight. Multicoloured.

1334	2c. Type **286** (postage)	10	10
1335	3c. Thomas Baldwin's airship *US Military No. 1*, 1908	10	10
1336	5c. Tissandier brothers' airship, 1883	10	10
1337	25c. Parseval airship PL-VII, 1912	40	20
1338	40c. Airship *Nulli Secundus II*, 1908	75	35
1339	50c. Beardmore airship R-34, 1919	85	55
MS1340	108×81 mm. 75c. Goodyear airship (air)	1·40	1·40

287 Tackling

1978. World Cup Football Championship, Argentina.

1341	**287**	2c. multicoloured (postage)	10	10
1342	-	3c. multicoloured (horiz)	10	10
1343	-	10c. multicoloured (horiz)	15	10
1344	-	25c. multicoloured (horiz)	60	20
1345	-	35c. multicoloured	80	25
1346	-	50c. multicoloured (horiz)	1·25	50
MS1347		102×78 mm. 75c. multicoloured (air)	1·60	1·60

Designs: 1341/**MS**1347 Different match scenes.

288 Coronation Chair

1978. 25th Anniversary of Coronation. Multicoloured.

1348	5c. Type **288** (postage)	10	25
1349	25c. Imperial State Crown	35	25
1350	$1 Buckingham Palace (horiz)	1·75	1·00
MS1351	103×78 mm. 75c. Coronation coach (horiz) (air)	1·10	1·10

289 Mohammed Ali Jinnah and Flags

1978. Birth Centenary of Mohammed Ali Jinnah (first Governor-General of Pakistan).

1352	**289**	30c. multicoloured	1·50	1·50

290 Carter and Tolbert Families

1978. Visit of President Carter of USA. Multicoloured.

1353	5c. Type **290**	10	10
1354	25c. Presidents Carter and Tolbert with Mrs. Carter at microphones	50	45
1355	$1 Presidents Carter and Tolbert in open car	2·00	2·00

291 Italy v. France

1978. Argentina's Victory in World Cup Football Championship. Multicoloured.

1356	1c. Brazil v. Spain (horiz) (postage)	10	10
1357	2c. Type **291**	10	10
1358	10c. Poland v. West Germany (horiz)	15	10
1359	27c. Peru v. Scotland	65	25
1360	35c. Austria v. West Germany	80	55
1361	50c. Argentinian players with Cup	1·25	80
MS1362	128×103 mm. 75c. Argentinian team (horiz) (air)	1·60	1·60

292 Timber Truck

1978. Eighth World Forestry Congress, Djakarta. Multicoloured.

1363	5c. Chopping up log (horiz)	10	10
1364	10c. Type **292**	15	10
1365	25c. Felling trees (horiz)	60	20
1366	50c. Loggers (horiz)	1·10	70

293 Presidents Gardner and Tolbert with Monrovia Post Office

1979. Centenary of UPU Membership. Multicoloured.

1367	5c. Type **293**	10	10
1368	35c. Presidents Gardner and Tolbert with UPU emblem	90	90

294 '25' and Radio Waves

1979. 25th Anniversary of Radio ELWA. Multicoloured.

1369	35c. Type **294**	75	75
1370	$1 Radio tower	2·10	2·10

295 IYC, Decade of the African Child and SOS Villages Emblems

1979. International Year of the Child. Multicoloured.

1371	5c. Type **295**	10	10
1372	25c. As Type **295** but with UNICEF instead of SOS Villages emblem	25	20
1373	35c. Type **295**	50	25
1374	$1 As No. 1372	1·40	1·40

296 Clasped Arms and Torches

1979. Organisation for African Unity Summit Conference, Monrovia. Multicoloured.

1375	5c. Type **296**	10	10
1376	27c. Masks	40	25
1377	35c. African animals	50	50
1378	50c. Thatched huts and garden bulbuls	1·50	65

297 Sir Rowland Hill and Liberian 15c. Stamp, 1974

1979. Death Centenary of Sir Rowland Hill. Multicoloured.

1379	3c. Type **297**	10	10
1380	10c. Pony Express rider	15	10
1381	15c. British mail coach	20	35
1382	25c. *John Penn* (paddle-steamer)	75	55
1383	27c. Coronation Class streamlined steam locomotive No. 6235, Great Britain	1·10	25
1384	50c. Concorde	1·50	90
MS1385	102×77 mm. $1 Curtiss Jenny, 1916	3·00	3·00

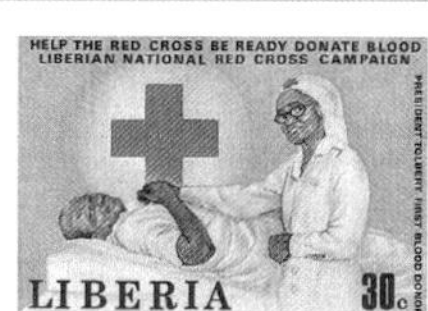

298 President Tolbert giving Blood

1979. National Red Cross Blood Donation Campaign. Multicoloured.

1386	30c. Type **298**	45	25
1387	50c. President Tolbert and Red Cross	1·00	1·00

299 *World Peace* (tanker)

1979. Second World Maritime Day and 30th Anniversary of Liberia Maritime Programme. Multicoloured.

1388	5c. Type **299**	30	15
1389	$1 *World Peace* (different)	2·25	2·00

300 *A Good Turn*

1979. Scout Paintings by Norman Rockwell. Multicoloured.

1390	5c. Scout giving first aid to pup (*A Good Scout*)	20	15
1391	5c. Type **300**	20	15
1392	5c. *Good Friends*	20	15
1393	5c. *Spirit of America*	20	15
1394	5c. *Scout Memories*	20	15
1395	5c. *The Adventure Trail*	20	15
1396	5c. *On My Honour*	20	15
1397	5c. *A Scout is Reverent*	20	15
1398	5c. *The Right Way*	20	15
1399	5c. *The Scoutmaster*	20	15
1400	10c. *A Scout is Loyal*	40	25
1401	10c. *An Army of Friendship*	35	20
1402	10c. *Carry on*	35	20
1403	10c. *A Good Scout*	35	20
1404	10c. *The Campfire Story*	35	20
1405	10c. *High Adventure*	35	20
1406	10c. *Mighty Proud*	35	20
1407	10c. *Tomorrow's Leader*	35	20
1408	10c. *Ever Onward*	35	20
1409	10c. *Homecoming*	35	20
1410	15c. *Scouts of Many Trails*	40	25
1411	15c. *America builds for Tomorrow*	40	25
1412	15c. *The Scouting Trail*	40	25
1413	15c. *A Scout is Reverent*	40	25
1414	15c. *A Scout is Helpful*	40	25
1415	15c. *Pointing the Way*	40	25
1416	15c. *A Good Sign All Over the World*	40	25
1417	15c. *To Keep Myself Physically Strong*	40	25
1418	15c. *A Great Moment*	40	25
1419	15c. *Growth of a Leader*	40	25
1420	25c. *A Scout is Loyal*	60	35
1421	25c. *A Scout is Friendly*	60	35
1422	25c. *We Too, Have a Job to Do*	60	35
1423	25c. *I Will do my Best*	60	35
1424	25c. *A Guiding Hand*	60	35
1425	25c. *Breakthrough for Freedom*	1·25	40
1426	25c. *Scouting is Outing*	60	35
1427	25c. *Beyond the Easel*	60	35
1428	25c. *Come and Get It*	60	35
1429	25c. *America's Manpower begins with Boypower*	60	35
1430	35c. *All Together*	80	45
1431	35c. *Men of Tomorrow*	80	45
1432	35c. *Friend in Need*	80	45
1433	35c. *Our Heritage*	80	45
1434	35c. *Forward America*	80	45
1435	35c. *Can't Wait*	80	45
1436	35c. *From Concord to Tranquility*	80	45
1437	35c. *We Thank Thee*	80	45
1438	35c. *So Much Concern*	80	45
1439	35c. *Spirit of '76*	80	45

301 Mrs. Tolbert and Children

1979. SOS Children's Village, Monrovia. Multicoloured.

1440	25c. Mrs. Tolbert and children (different) (horiz)	35	50
1441	40c. Type **301**	90	90

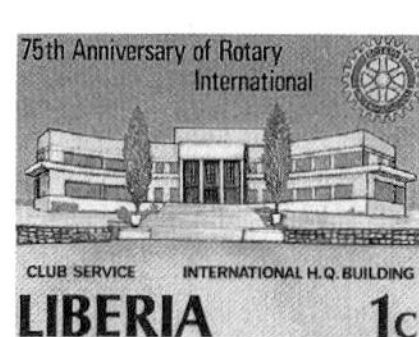

302 International Headquarters, Evanston, Illinois

1979. 75th Anniversary of Rotary International. Multicoloured.

1442	1c. Type **302**	10	10
1443	5c. Vocational services	10	10
1444	17c. Wheelchair patient and nurse (community service) (vert)	20	35
1445	27c. Flags (international service)	40	50
1446	35c. Different races holding hands around globe (health, hunger and humanity)	50	50
1447	50c. President Tolbert and map of Africa (17th anniversary of Monrovia Rotary Club) (vert)	1·00	1·00
MS1448	102×84 mm. $1 Heart (gift of life)	2·00	2·00

303 Ski Jumping

1980. Winter Olympic Games, Lake Placid. Multicoloured.

1449	1c. Type **303**	10	10
1450	5c. Pairs figure skating	10	10
1451	17c. Bobsleigh	20	35
1452	27c. Cross-country skiing	75	75
1453	35c. Speed skating	75	75
1454	50c. Ice hockey	1·00	1·00
MS1455	105×80 mm. $1 Downhill skiing	2·00	2·00

304 Presidents Tolbert of Liberia and Stevens of Sierra Leone and View of Mano River

1980. Fifth Anniversary of Mano River Union and First Anniversary (1979) of Postal Union.

1456	**304**	8c. multicoloured	15	10
1457	**304**	27c. multicoloured	45	50
1458	**304**	35c. multicoloured	80	75
1459	**304**	80c. multicoloured	1·75	1·75

305 Redemption Horn

1981. People's Redemption Council (1st series). Multicoloured.

1460	1c. Type **305**	10	10
1461	10c. M/Sgt. Doe and allegory of redemption (horiz)	10	10
1462	14c. Map, soldier and citizens (horiz)	15	15
1463	$2 M/Sgt. Samuel Doe (chairman of Council)	3·75	3·75

See also Nos. 1475/1478.

306 Players and Flags of Argentine, Uruguay, Italy and Czechoslovakia

1981. World Cup Football Championship, Spain (1982). Multicoloured.

1464	3c. Type **306**	10	10
1465	5c. Players and flags of Hungary, Italy, Germany, Brazil and Sweden	10	10
1466	20c. Players and flags of Italy, Germany, Brazil and Sweden	20	20
1467	27c. Players and flags of Czechoslovakia, Brazil, Great Britain and Germany	25	25
1468	40c. Players and flags of Italy, Brazil, Germany and Netherlands	60	60
1469	55c. Players and flags of Netherlands and Uruguay	1·10	1·10
MS1470	192×78 mm. $1 Spanish team	1·75	1·75

307 M/Sgt. Doe and Crowd

1981. First Anniversary of People's Redemption Council. Multicoloured.

1471	22c. Type **307**	20	20
1472	27c. M/Sgt. Doe and National Flag	25	25
1473	30c. Hands clasping arms, sunrise and map	45	45
1474	$1 M/Sgt. Doe, 'Justice' and soldiers	1·75	1·75

1981. People's Redemption Council (2nd series).

1475	6c. Type **305**	10	10
1476	23c. As No. 1461	20	20
1477	31c. As No. 1462	45	45
1478	41c. As No. 1463	60	60

308 John Adams

1981. Presidents of the United States (1st series). Multicoloured.

1479	4c. Type **308**	10	10
1480	5c. William Henry Harrison	10	10
1481	10c. Martin Van Buren	15	15
1482	17c. James Monroe	20	20
1483	20c. John Quincy Adams	25	25
1484	22c. James Madison	25	25
1485	27c. Thomas Jefferson	35	30
1486	30c. Andrew Jackson	55	50
1487	40c. John Tyler	80	70
1488	80c. George Washington	1·50	1·50
MS1489	102×83 mm. $1 Washington crossing the Delaware	1·75	1·75

See also Nos. 1494/**MS**1504, 1519/**MS**1528, 1533/**MS**1543 and 1715.

309 Prince Charles and Lady Diana Spencer

1981. British Royal Wedding. Multicoloured.

1490	31c. Type **309**	30	30
1491	41c. Intertwined initials	40	40
1492	62c. St Paul's Cathedral	1·10	1·10
MS1493	106×80 mm. $1 Prince Charles and Lady Dianna Spencer (horiz 58×44 mm)	1·40	1·40

1981. Presidents of the United States (2nd series). As T **308**. Multicoloured.

1494	6c. Rutherford B. Hayes	10	10
1495	12c. Ulysses S. Grant	15	15
1496	14c. Millard Fillmore	20	15
1497	15c. Zachary Taylor	20	15
1498	20c. Abraham Lincoln	25	20
1499	27c. Andrew Johnson	30	25
1500	31c. James Buchanan	50	45
1501	41c. James A. Garfield	70	60
1502	50c. James K. Polk	80	70
1503	55c. Franklin Pierce	1·00	85
MS1504	101×82 mm. $1 Washington crossing the Delaware (horiz)	1·75	1·75

1981. Liberian Products (2nd series). As T **277**, but smaller, 33×20 mm. Multicoloured.

1504a	1c. Mano River Bridge	10	10
1505	3c. Type **277**	10	10
1506	6c. Rubber tree and tyre	10	10
1506a	15c. Combine-harvester	20	15
1507	25c. Mesurado shrimp	35	35
1508	31c. Hydro-electric plant	70	70
1509	41c. Dress and woman tie-dying cloth	60	55
1509a	80c. Great barracuda	2·50	1·50
1510	$1 Diesel train carrying iron ore	5·75	1·60

310 Disabled Children

1982. International Year of Disabled People (1981). Multicoloured.

1515	23c. Type **310**	35	35
1516	62c. Child leading blind woman	1·25	95

311 Examination Room

1982. 30th Anniversary of West African Examination Council.

1517	**311**	6c. multicoloured	10	10
1518	**311**	31c. multicoloured	45	45

1982. Presidents of the United States (3rd series). As T **308**. Multicoloured.

1519	4c. William Taft	10	25
1520	5c. Calvin Coolidge	10	10
1521	6c. Benjamin Harrison	15	15
1522	10c. Warren Harding	20	25
1523	22c. Grover Cleveland	45	45
1524	27c. Chester Arthur	50	70
1525	31c. Woodrow Wilson	60	60
1526	41c. William McKinley	70	80
1527	80c. Theodore Roosevelt	1·50	1·60
MS1528	101×83 mm. $1 Signing the Constitution (horiz)	1·75	1·75

312 Lady Diana Spencer

1982. Princess of Wales. 21st Birthday. Multicoloured.

1529	31c. Type **312**	70	70
1530	41c. Lady Diana Spencer (different)	85	85
1531	62c. Lady Diana accepting flower	1·25	1·25
MS1532	103×78 mm. $1 Prince and Princess of Wales (wedding photograph)	1·75	1·75

1982. Presidents of the United States (4th series). As T **308**. Multicoloured.

1533	4c. Jimmy Carter	10	10
1534	6c. Gerald Ford	15	15
1535	14c. Harry Truman	25	25
1536	17c. Franklin D. Roosevelt	30	30
1537	23c. Lyndon B. Johnson	40	40
1538	27c. Richard Nixon	45	50
1539	31c. John F. Kennedy	50	60
1540	35c. Ronald Reagan	60	80
1541	50c. Herbert Hoover	80	90
1542	55c. Dwight D. Eisenhower	1·00	1·00
MS1543	102×83 mm. $1 *Battle of Yorktown* (horiz)	1·75	1·75

1982. Birth of Prince William of Wales. Nos. 1529/**MS**1532 optd **ROYAL BABY 21-6-82 PRINCE WILLIAM.**

1544	31c. Type **312**	45	45
1545	41c. Lady Diana Spencer (different)	60	60
1546	62c. Lady Diana accepting flower	95	95
MS1547	103×78 mm. $1 Prince and Princess of Wales (wedding photograph)	1·60	1·60

314 Lt. Col. Fallah nGaida Varney

1983. Third Anniversary of National Redemption Day. Multicoloured.

1548	3c. Type **314**	10	10
1549	6c. Commander-in-Chief Samuel Doe	10	10
1550	10c. Major-General Jlatoh Nicholas Podier	15	15
1551	15c. Brigadier-General Jeffery Sei Gbatu	20	15
1552	31c. Brigadier-General Thomas Gunkama Quiwonkpa	50	45
1553	41c. Colonel Abraham Doward Kollie	60	80
MS1554	103×78 mm. $1 As No. 1549	1·50	1·50

315 National Archives Centre

1983. Opening of National Archives Centre. Multicoloured.

1555	6c. Type **315**	10	10
1556	31c. National Archives Centre	50	45

316 *Circumcision of Christ*

1983. Christmas. 500th Birth Anniversary of Raphael. Multicoloured.

1557	6c. Type **316**	10	10
1558	15c. *Adoration of the Magi* (detail)	20	15
1559	25c. *The Annunciation* (detail)	40	35
1560	31c. *Madonna of the Baldachino*	50	45
1561	41c. *Holy Family* (detail)	60	55
1562	62c. *Madonna and Child with Five Saints* (detail)	90	85
MS1563	102×77 mm. $1.25 *Foligno Madonna* (horiz)	1·90	1·90

317 Graduates of MUR Training Programmes

1984. Tenth Anniversary (1983) of Mano River Union.

1564	6c. Type **317**	10	10
1565	25c. Map of Africa	40	35
1566	31c. Presidents and map of member states	50	45
1567	41c. President of Guinea signing Accession Agreement	70	85
MS1568	102×77 mm. 75c. Guinea's accession	1·25	1·25

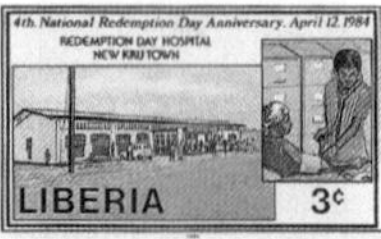

318 Redemption Day Hospital, New Kru Town

1984. Fourth Anniversary of National Redemption Day. Multicoloured.

1569	3c. Type **318**	10	10
1570	10c. Ganta–Harpa Highway project	15	15
1571	20c. Opening of Constitution Assembly	35	30
1572	31c. Commander-in-Chief Doe launching Ganta–Harper Highway project	50	45
1573	41c. Presentation of Draft Constitution	70	85

319 *Adoration of the Magi*

1984. Rubens Paintings (1st series). Multicoloured.

1574	6c. Type **319**	10	10
1575	15c. *Coronation of Catherine*	25	20
1576	25c. *Adoration of the Magi*	70	70
1577	31c. *Madonna and Child with Halo*	85	85
1578	41c. *Adoration of the Shepherds*	1·10	1·10
1579	62c. *Madonna and Child with Saints*	1·75	1·75

MS1580	102×77 mm. $1.25 *Adoration of the Saints*	3·25	3·25

See also Nos. 1612/**MS**1618.

320 Jesse Owens

1984. Olympic Games, Los Angeles. Multicoloured.

1581	3c. Type **320**	10	10
1582	4c. Rafer Johnson	10	10
1583	25c. Miruts Yifter	65	65
1584	41c. Kipchoge Keino	1·10	1·10
1585	62c. Muhammad Ali	1·75	1·75
MS1586	103×77 mm. $1.25 Wilma Rudolph (horiz)	3·25	3·25

321 Liberian Ducks and Water Birds

1984. Louisiana World Exposition. Multicoloured.

1587	6c. Type **321**	20	20
1588	31c. Bulk carrier loading ore at Buchanan Harbour	1·60	75
1589	41c. Peters' mormyrid, electric catfish, Nile perch, krib and jewel cichlid	1·50	1·10
1590	62c. Diesel train carrying iron ore	1·75	90

322 Mother and Calf

1984. Pygmy Hippopotami. Multicoloured.

1591	6c. Type **322**	20	10
1592	10c. Pair of hippopotami	80	80
1593	20c. Close-up of hippopotamus	1·40	1·40
1594	31c. Hippopotamus and map	2·10	2·10

323 Mrs. Doe and Children

1984. Indigent Children's Home, Bensonville. Multicoloured.

1595	6c. Type **323**	10	10
1596	31c. Mrs. Doe and children (different)	50	50

324 New Soldiers' Barracks

1985. Fifth Anniversary of National Redemption Day. Multicoloured.

1597	6c. Type **324**	10	10
1598	31c. Pan-African Plaza	50	50

325 Bohemian Waxwing

1985. Birth Bicentenary of John J. Audubon (ornithologist). Multicoloured.

1599	1c. Type **325**	15	10
1600	3c. Bay-breasted warbler	30	10
1601	6c. White-winged crossbill	35	15
1602	31c. Grey phalarope ('Red Phalarope')	2·00	1·00
1603	41c. Eastern bluebird	2·50	1·50
1604	62c. Common cardinal ('Northern Cardinal')	3·50	2·40

326 Germany v. Morocco, 1970

1985. World Cup Football Championship, Mexico (1986). Multicoloured.

1605	6c. Type **326**	10	10
1606	15c. Zaire v. Brazil, 1974	20	15
1607	25c. Tunisia v. Germany, 1978	60	60
1608	31c. Cameroun v. Peru, 1982 (vert)	75	75
1609	41c. Algeria v. Germany, 1982	95	95
1610	62c. Senegal team	1·40	1·40
MS1611	102×77 mm. $1.25 Liberia v Nigeria	2·75	2·75

327 *Mirror of Venus* (detail)

1985. Rubens Paintings (2nd series). Multicoloured.

1612	6c. Type **327**	10	10
1613	15c. *Adam and Eve in Paradise* (detail)	20	15
1614	25c. *Andromeda* (detail)	60	60
1615	31c. *The Three Graces* (detail)	75	75
1616	41c. *Venus and Adonis* (detail)	95	95
1617	62c. *The Daughters of Leucippus* (detail)	1·40	1·40
MS1618	102×77 mm. $1.25 *The Judgement of Paris* (horiz)	2·75	2·75

328 Women transplanting Rice

1985. World Food Day.

1619	**328**	25c. multicoloured	1·25	85
1620	**328**	31c. multicoloured	1·50	1·10

329 Queen Mother in Garter Robes

1985. 85th Birthday of Queen Elizabeth the Queen Mother. Multicoloured.

1621	31c. Type **329**	35	30
1622	41c. At the races	80	75
1623	62c. Waving to the crowds	1·10	1·10
MS1624	79×104 mm. $1.25 Wearing tiara	2·00	2·00

330 Alamo, San Antonio, Texas

1986. Ameripex '86 International Stamp Exhibition, Chicago. Multicoloured.

1625	25c. Type **330**	60	60
1626	31c. Liberty Bell, Philadelphia	75	75
1627	80c. Magnifying glass, emblem and Liberian stamps	3·00	2·25

331 Unveiling Ceremony, 1886 (after E. Moran)

1986. Centenary of Statue of Liberty. Multicoloured.

1628	20c. Type **331**	30	50
1629	31c. Frederic-Auguste Bartholdi (sculptor) and statue	75	75
1630	$1 Head of statue	2·40	2·40

332 Max Julen (Men's Giant Slalom)

1987. Winter Olympic Games, Calgary (1988). 1984 Games Gold Medallists. Multicoloured.

1631	3c. Type **332**	10	10
1632	6c. Debbi Armstrong (women's giant slalom)	10	10
1633	31c. Peter Angerer (biathlon)	35	55
1634	60c. Bill Johnson (men's downhill)	1·10	1·10
1635	80c. East German team (four-man bobsleigh)	1·40	1·40
MS1636	104×77 mm. $1.25 H. Strangassinger and F. Wembacher (double luge)	2·00	2·00

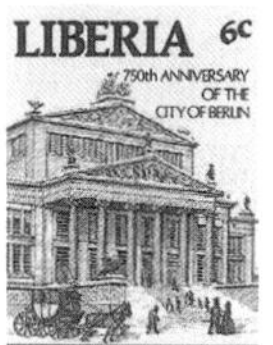

333 Royal Theatre. Gendarmenmarkt

1987. Liberian–German Friendship. 750th Anniversary of Berlin.

1637	6c. multicoloured	10	10
1638	31c. multicoloured	35	35
1639	60c. multicoloured	1·10	1·10
1640	80c. multicoloured	1·40	1·40
MS1641	100×100 mm. $1.50 buff and brown	2·50	2·50

Designs: 31c. Kaiser Frederik Museum, River spree; 60c. Charlottenburg Palace; 80c. Kaiser Wilhelm Memorial Church; $1.50 Mirak rocket and scientists, Spaceship Society airfield, Reinckendorf.

No. **MS**1641 has a diagram on the reverse identifying the people portrayed.

334 Othello and Desdemona (*Othello*)

1987. William Shakespeare. Multicoloured.

1642	3c. Type **334**	10	10
1643	6c. Romeo and Juliet (*Romeo and Juliet*)	10	10
1644	10c. Falstaff (*The Merry Wives of Windsor*)	15	10
1645	15c. Falstaff, Doll Tearsheet and Prince Hal (*Henry IV*, Part 2)	20	15
1646	31c. Hamlet holding Yorick's skull (*Hamlet*)	60	50
1647	60c. Macbeth and the three witches (*Macbeth*)	1·25	1·25
1648	80c. Lear and companions in the storm (*King Lear*)	1·75	1·75
1649	$2 William Shakespeare and Globe Theatre, Southwark	4·00	4·00

335 Emblem

1987. Amateur Radio Week. 25th Anniversary of Liberia Radio Amateur Association. Multicoloured.

1650	10c. Type **335**	15	10
1651	10c. Amateur radio enthusiasts	15	10
1652	35c. Certificate awarded to participants in anniversary 'On the Air' activity	80	70
1653	35c. Globe, flags and banner	80	70

336 Illuminated Torch Flame

1987. Centenary of Statue of Liberty. Multicoloured.

1654	6c. Type **336**	10	10
1655	6c. Scaffolding around statue's head	10	10
1656	6c. Men working on head	10	10
1657	6c. Men working on crown	10	10
1658	6c. Statue's toes	10	10
1659	15c. Statue behind *Sir Winston Churchill* (cadet schooner)	45	20
1660	15c. *Bay Queen* (harbour ferry)	45	20
1661	15c. Posters on buildings and crowd	20	15
1662	15c. Tug and schooner in bay	45	20
1663	15c. Decorated statues around building	20	15
1664	31c. Fireworks display around statue	60	50
1665	31c. Statue floodlit	60	50
1666	31c. Statue's head	60	50
1667	31c. Fireworks display around statue (different)	60	50
1668	31c. Statue (half-length)	60	50
1669	60c. Wall poster on building (vert)	1·10	1·00
1670	60c. Yachts and cabin cruisers on river (vert)	1·50	1·00
1671	60c. Measuring statue's nose (vert)	1·10	1·00
1672	60c. Plastering nose (vert)	1·10	1·00
1673	60c. Finishing off repaired nose (vert)	1·10	1·00

337 Dr. Doe (President), Dr. Moniba (Vice-President), Flags and Hands

1988. Second Anniversary of Second Republic.

1674	**337**	10c. multicoloured	15	10
1675	**337**	35c. multicoloured	65	55

338 Breast-feeding

1988. UNICEF Child Survival and Development Campaign. Multicoloured.

1676	3c. Type **338**	10	10
1677	6c. Oral rehydration therapy (vert)	10	10
1678	31c. Immunisation	60	50
1679	$1 Growth monitoring (vert)	2·00	2·00

339 Chief Justice Emmanuel N. Gbalazeh swearing-in Dr. Samuel Kanyon Doe

1988. Inauguration of Second Republic.

1680	**339**	6c. multicoloured	10	10

340 Footballer and Stadium

1988. Second Anniversary of Opening of Samuel Kanyon Doe Sports Complex.

1681	**340**	31c. multicoloured	60	50

341 Child and Volunteer reading

1988. 25th Anniversary of US Peace Corps in Liberia.

1682	**341**	10c. multicoloured	10	10
1683	**341**	35c. multicoloured	70	60

342 Pres. Doe, Farm Workers and Produce

1988. Green Revolution.

1684	**342**	10c. multicoloured	25	10
1685	**342**	35c. multicoloured	85	35

343 Olympic Rings

1988. Olympic Games, Seoul and Stamp Exhibition.
MS1686 **343** $3 multicoloured 5·50 5·50

344 Emblem

1988. 25th Anniversary of Organisation of African Unity.

1687	**344**	10c. multicoloured	10	10
1688	**344**	35c. multicoloured	70	60
1689	**344**	$1 multicoloured	2·00	2·00

345 Type GP10 Diesel Locomotive, Nimba

1988. Locomotives. Multicoloured.

1690	10c. Type **345**	25	15
1691	35c. Triple-headed diesel iron ore train	85	50

MS1692 Four sheets, each 110×80m. (a) $2 *Ince Castle* pulling the *Bristolian*. (b) $2 75 XX class locomotive No. 3697. (c) $2 *King Edward II*. (d) $2 Locomotive No. 1408 on Lostwithel–Fowey line Set of 4 sheets 14·00 14·00

346 Helping Boy to Walk

1988. 25th Anniversary of St Joseph's Catholic Hospital. Multicoloured.

1693	10c. Type **346**	10	10
1694	10c. Medical staff and hospital	10	10
1695	35c. Monk, child, candle and hospital	65	65
1696	$1 Map behind doctor with nurse holding baby	1·90	1·90

347 Baseball

1988. Olympic Games, Seoul. Multicoloured.

1697	10c. Type **347**	10	10
1698	35c. Hurdling	65	65
1699	45c. Fencing	80	80
1700	80c. Synchronised swimming	1·40	1·40
1701	$1 Yachting	1·75	1·75

MS1702 107×89 mm. $1.50 Lawn tennis 2·40 2·40

348 Monkey Bridge

1988. Multicoloured.

1703	10c. Type **348**	10	10
1704	35c. Sasa players (horiz)	40	60
1705	45c. Snake dancers	70	75

349 Tending Crops

1988. Tenth Anniversary of International Fund for Agricultural Development. Multicoloured.

1706	10c. Type **349**	10	10
1707	35c. Farmers tending livestock and spraying crops	70	60

350 Destruction of Royal Exchange, 1838

1988. 300th Anniversary of Lloyd's of London. Multicoloured.

1708	10c. Type **350**	10	10
1709	35c. Britten Norman Islander aeroplane (horiz)	60	60
1710	45c. *Chevron Antwerp* (tanker) (horiz)	70	75
1711	$1 *Lakonia* (liner) ablaze, 1963	2·00	2·00

351 Honouring Head of Operational Smile Team

1989. Third Anniversary of Second Republic.

1712	**351**	10c. black and blue	10	10
1713	**351**	35c. black and red	80	85
1714	-	50c. black and mauve	1·25	1·25

Design: 50c. President Samuel Doe at John F. Kennedy Memorial Hospital.

1989. Presidents of United States (5th series). As T **308**. Multicoloured.

1715	$1 George Bush	2·50	2·50

352 'Harmony'

1989. Liberia–Japan Friendship. 50th Anniversary of Rissho Kosei-Kai (lay Buddhist association). Multicoloured.

1716	10c. Type **352**	10	10
1717	10c. Nikkyo Niwano (founder and president of association)	10	10
1718	10c. Rissho Kosei-Kai headquarters, Tokyo	10	10
1719	50c. Eternal Buddha, Great Sacred Hall	1·40	1·40

MS1720 109×75 mm. 75c. Liberian silver $10 Hirohito coin; 75c. Liberian gold $250 Hirohito coin (each 40×22 mm) 3·35 3·25

No. **MS**1720 commemorates the death of Emperor Hirohito of Japan.

353 Union Glass Factory, Gardersville, Monrovia

1989. 15th Anniversary of Mano River Union. Multicoloured.

1721	10c. Type **353**	15	10
1722	35c. Presidents of Guinea, Sierra Leone and Liberia	70	60
1723	45c. Monrovia–Freetown highway	85	80
1724	50c. Flags, map and mail van	85	85
1725	$1 Presidents at 1988 Summit	2·00	1·90

354 Symbols of International Co-operation

1989. World Telecommunications Day.

1726	**354**	50c. multicoloured	85	85

355 *March of the Women on Versailles* (detail)

1989. Bicentenary of French Revolution and Philexfrance 89 International Stamp Exhibition, Paris. Sheet 115×100 mm.
MS1727 **355** $1.50 grey, black and red 2·40 2·40

357 Helicopter Carrier USS *Okinawa*

1989. 20th Anniversary of First Manned Landing on Moon. Multicoloured.

1728	10c. Type **357**	60	15
1729	35c. Edwin Aldrin, Neil Armstrong and Michael Collins (crew) (28×28 mm)	70	60
1730	45c. *Apollo 11* flight emblem (28×28 mm)	1·00	1·00
1731	$1 Aldrin descending to Moon's surface	2·00	2·00

MS1732 100×83 mm. $2 Astronaut and capsule on Moon's surface 3·75 3·75

358 Renovation of Statue of Liberty

1989. Philexfrance '89 International Stamp Exhibition, Paris, and World Stamp Expo '89 International Stamp Exhibition, Washington DC (1st issue). Multicoloured.

1733	25c. Type **358**	55	45
1734	25c. French contingent at statue centenary celebrations	55	45
1735	25c. Statue, officials and commemorative plaque	55	45

359 Exhibition Emblem

1989. World Stamp Expo 89 International Stamp Exhibition, Washington DC (2nd issue). Sheet 110×130 mm.
MS1736 **359** $2 black 3·75 3·75

360 Nehru and Flag

1989. Birth Centenary of Jawaharlal Nehru (Indian statesman). Multicoloured.

1737	45c. Type **360**	85	70
1738	50c. Nehru	95	80

361 Close View of Station

1990. New Standard A Earth Satellite Station. Multicoloured.

1739	10c. Type **361**	15	10
1740	35c. Distant view of station	85	85

362 Emblem

1990. 25th Anniversary of United States Educational and Cultural Foundation in Liberia. Multicoloured.

1741	10c. Type **362**	15	10
1742	45c. Similar to Type **362** but differently arranged	85	70

363 Flags, Arms, Map and Union Emblem

1990. Tenth Anniversary of Pan-African Postal Union.

1743	**363**	35c. multicoloured	70	55

364 Bomi County

1990. County Flags. Multicoloured.

1744	10c. Type **364**	10	10
1745	10c. Bong	10	10
1746	10c. Grand Bassa	10	10
1747	10c. Grand Cape Mount	10	10
1748	10c. Grand Gedeh	10	10
1749	10c. Grand Kru	10	10
1750	10c. Lofa	10	10
1751	10c. Margibi	10	10
1752	10c. Maryland	10	10
1753	10c. Montserrado	10	10
1754	10c. Nimba	10	10
1755	10c. Rivercress	10	10
1756	10c. Sinoe	10	10
1757	35c. Type **364**	65	55
1758	35c. Bong	65	55
1759	35c. Grand Bassa	65	55
1760	35c. Grand Cape Mount	65	55
1761	35c. Grand Gedeh	65	55
1762	35c. Grand Kru	65	55
1763	35c. Lofa	65	55
1764	35c. Margibi	65	55
1765	35c. Maryland	65	55
1766	35c. Montserrado	65	55

1767	35c. Nimba	65	55
1768	35c. Rivercress	65	55
1769	35c. Sinoe	65	55
1770	45c. Type **364**	85	70
1771	45c. Bong	85	70
1772	45c. Grand Bassa	85	70
1773	45c. Grand Cape Mount	85	70
1774	45c. Grand Gedeh	85	70
1775	45c. Grand Kru	85	70
1776	45c. Lofa	85	70
1777	45c. Margibi	85	70
1778	45c. Maryland	85	70
1779	45c. Montserrado	85	70
1780	45c. Nimba	85	70
1781	45c. Rivercress	85	70
1782	45c. Sinoe	85	70
1783	50c. Type **364**	1·10	1·10
1784	50c. Bong	1·10	1·10
1785	50c. Grand Bassa	1·10	1·10
1786	50c. Grand Cape Mount	1·10	1·10
1787	50c. Grand Gedeh	1·10	1·10
1788	50c. Grand Kru	1·10	1·10
1789	50c. Lofa	1·10	1·10
1790	50c. Margibi	1·10	1·10
1791	50c. Maryland	1·10	1·10
1792	50c. Montserrado	1·10	1·10
1793	50c. Nimba	1·10	1·10
1794	50c. Rivercress	1·10	1·10
1795	50c. Sinoe	1·10	1·10
1796	$1 Type **364**	2·00	2·00
1797	$1 Bong	2·00	2·00
1798	$1 Grand Bassa	2·00	2·00
1799	$1 Grand Cape Mount	2·00	2·00
1800	$1 Grand Gedeh	2·00	2·00
1801	$1 Grand Kru	2·00	2·00
1802	$1 Lofa	2·00	2·00
1803	$1 Margibi	2·00	2·00
1804	$1 Maryland	2·00	2·00
1805	$1 Montserrado	2·00	2·00
1806	$1 Nimba	2·00	2·00
1807	$1 Rivercress	2·00	2·00
1808	$1 Sinoe	2·00	2·00

365 Lady Elizabeth Bowes-Lyon as Girl

1991. 90th Birthday (1990) of Queen Elizabeth the Queen Mother. Multicoloured.

1809	10c. Type **365**	15	10
1810	$2 As Duchess of York (29×36½ mm)	4·00	4·00

367 Clasped Hands and Map

1991. National Unity. Multicoloured.

1812	35c. Type **367**	65	50
1813	45c. National Flag and map of Africa (ECOMOG (West African States Economic Community peace-keeping forces))	85	65
1814	50c. Brewer, Konneh and Michael Francis (co-chairmen) and National Flag (All-Liberia Conference)	95	75

368 Boxing

1992. Olympic Games, Barcelona. Multicoloured.

1815	45c. Type **368**	85	65
1816	50c. Football	95	75
1817	$1 Weightlifting	1·90	1·75
1818	$2 Water polo	3·75	3·50
MS1819	120×75 mm. $1.50 Running	2·75	2·75

369 Disarm Today

1993. Peace and Redevelopment. Multicoloured.

1820	50c. Type **369**	95	70
1821	$1 'Join your Parents and build Liberia'	1·90	1·40
1822	$2 "Peace must prevail in Liberia"	3·75	2·75

OFFICIAL STAMPS

1892. Stamps of 1892 optd **OFFICIAL**.

O87	**7**	1c. red	30	40
O88	**7**	2c. blue	30	50
O89	**8**	4c. black and green	50	50
O104	**9**	5c. on 6c. green (No. 89)	80	80
O90	**9**	6c. green	60	50
O91	**10**	8c. black and brown	45	45
O92	**11**	12c. red	1·10	1·10
O93	**12**	16c. lilac	1·10	1·10
O94	**13**	24c. green on yellow	1·10	1·10
O95	**12**	32c. blue	1·10	1·10
O96	**15**	$1 black and blue	22·00	8·75
O97	**13**	$2 brown on buff	9·00	6·25
O98	**17**	$5 black and red	13·50	5·75

1894. Stamps of 1892 optd **O S**.

O119	**7**	1c. red	30	20
O120	**7**	2c. blue	60	25
O121	**8**	4c. black and green	95	35
O122	**10**	8c. black and brown	80	35
O123	**11**	12c. red	1·10	40
O124	**12**	16c. lilac	1·10	40
O125	**13**	24c. green on yellow	1·10	45
O126	**12**	32c. blue	1·60	55
O127	**15**	$1 black and blue	13·50	13·50
O128	**13**	$2 brown on buff	13·50	13·50
O129	**12**	$5 black and red	80·00	55·00

1894. Stamp of 1894 in different colours optd **O S**. Imperf or roul.

O130	**24**	5c. green and lilac	1·75	2·00

1898. Stamps of 1897 optd **O S**.

O157	**9**	1c. purple	35	35
O158	**9**	1c. green	35	35
O159	**15**	2c. black and bistre	1·00	30
O160	**15**	2c. black and red	1·50	70
O161	**8**	5c. black and lake	1·50	70
O162	**8**	5c. black and blue	1·90	70
O163	**10**	10c. blue and yellow	85	80
O164	**11**	15c. black	85	80
O165	**12**	20c. red	1·40	95
O166	**13**	25c. green	85	80
O167	**12**	30c. blue	2·40	1·40
O168	**35**	50c. black and brown	2·10	1·40

1903. Stamp of 1903, but different colour, optd **O S**.

O210	**40**	3c. green	20	15

1904. Nos. O104 and O167 surch ONE **O.S.** and bars or **OS 2** and bars.

O222	**9**	1c. on 5c. on 6c. green	1·10	1·10
O223	**12**	2c. on 30c. blue	7·75	7·50

1906. Stamps of 1906, but different colours, optd **OS**.

O237	**50**	1c. black and green	50	50
O238	**51**	2c. black and red	15	15
O239	-	5c. black and blue	55	35
O240	-	10c. black and violet	2·50	60
O241	-	15c. black and brown	2·00	40
O242	-	20c. black and green	2·50	50
O243	-	25c. grey and purple	30	15
O244	-	30c. brown	50	15
O245	-	50c. green and brown	50	20
O246	-	75c. black and blue	1·10	75
O247	-	$1 black and green	55	25
O248	**52**	$2 black and purple	1·50	25
O249	**53**	$5 black and orange	3·75	30

1909. Stamps of 1909, but different colours, optd **OS. 10c.** perf or roul.

O262	**55**	1c. black and green	15	10
O263	-	2c. brown and red	15	10
O264	**56**	5c. black and blue	1·00	15
O266	**57**	10c. blue and black	50	25
O267	-	15c. black and purple	50	25
O268	-	20c. green and bistre	75	45
O269	-	25c. green and blue	70	50
O270	-	30c. blue	60	40
O271	-	50c. green and brown	2·25	40
O272	-	75c. black and violet	1·10	40

1910. No. O266 surch **3 CENTS INLAND POSTAGE**. Perf or roul.

O276	**57**	3c. on 10c. blue and black	55	45

1914. Official stamps surch: (A) **1914 2 CENTS**. (B) **+2c.** (C) **5**. (D) **CENTS 20 OFFICIAL**.

O291	**57**	+2c. on 3c. on 10c. blue and black (B) (No. O275)	60	1·60
O284	-	2c. on 25c. grey and purple (A) (No. O243)	15·00	6·25
O285	-	5c. on 30c. blue (C) (No. O270)	5·25	3·00
O286	-	20c. on 75c. black and violet (D) (No. O272)	7·00	3·00

1914. No. 233 surch **CENTS 20 OFFICIAL**.

O287	20c. on 75c. black and brown	5·25	3·00

1915. Official stamps of 1906 and 1909 surch in different ways.

O325	-	1c. on 2c. brown and red (No. O263)	2·25	2·50
O326	**56**	2c. on 5c. black and blue (No. O264)	2·50	3·00
O310	-	2c. on 15c. black and purple (No. O267)	65	45
O311	-	2c. on 25c. green and blue (No. O269)	3·75	3·75
O312	-	5c. on 20c. green and bistre (No. O268)	65	50
O313	-	5c. on 30c. green and brown (No. O270)	5·75	5·75
O314	-	10c. on 50c. green and brown (No. O271)	6·50	7·50
O316	-	20c. on 75c. black and violet (No. O272)	2·00	2·00
O317	-	25c. on $1 black and green (No. O247)	13·50	13·50
O318	**52**	50c. on $2 black and purple (No. O248)	15·00	15·00
O320	**53**	$1 on $5 black and orange (No. O249)	15·00	15·00

1915. No. O168 surch **10 10** and ornaments and bars.

O321	**35**	10c. on 50c. black & brn	9·75	9·75

1915. Military Field Post. Official stamps surch **L E F 1 c**.

O336	**50**	1c. on 1c. black and green (No. O237)	£325	£325
O337	**55**	1c. on 1c. black and green (No. O262)	3·00	3·50
O338	-	1c. on 2c. brown and red (No. O263)	2·40	2·50

1917. No. O244 surch **FIVE CENTS 1917** and bars.

O344	5c. on 30c. brown	15·00	15·00

1918. No. O266 surch **3 CENTS**.

O348	**57**	3c. on 10c. blue and black	1·40	1·50

1918. Stamps of 1918, but in different colours, optd **O S**.

O362	**91**	1c. brown and green	50	15
O363	**92**	2c. black and red	50	15
O364	-	5c. black and blue	75	10
O365	**93**	10c. blue	35	10
O366	-	15c. green and brown	1·75	40
O367	-	20c. black and lilac	55	10
O368	**94**	25c. green and brown	3·25	45
O369	-	30c. black and violet	4·75	50
O370	-	50c. black and brown	5·00	50
O371	-	75c. black and brown	2·00	15
O372	-	$1 blue and olive	3·75	30
O373	-	$2 black and olive	6·25	20
O374	-	$5 green	8·25	20

1920. Nos. O362/O363 surch **1920** and value and two bars.

O400	**91**	3c. on 1c. brown & green	95	50
O401	**92**	4c. on 2c. black and red	60	50

1921. Stamps of 1915 and 1921, in different colours, optd **O S** or **OFFICIAL**.

O428	**100**	1c. green	70	10
O429	**64**	2c. red	4·50	10
O430	**65**	3c. brown	70	10
O431	**101**	5c. brown and blue	70	10
O432	-	10c. black and purple	35	15
O433	-	15c. green and black	2·75	50
O434	-	20c. blue and brown	1·10	25
O435	-	25c. green and orange	3·75	50
O436	-	30c. red and brown	75	15
O437	-	50c. green and black	75	25
O438	-	75c. purple and blue	1·90	25
O439	-	$1 black and blue	12·50	55
O440	-	$2 green and orange	16·00	1·00
O441	-	$5 blue and green	17·00	1·75

1921. Nos. O400/O441 optd **1921**.

O442	**100**	1c. green	4·00	20
O443	**64**	2c. red	4·00	20
O444	**65**	3c. brown	4·00	25
O445	**101**	5c. brown and blue	2·40	25
O446	-	10c. black and purple	4·00	25
O447	-	15c. green and black	4·25	15
O448	-	20c. blue and brown	4·25	35
O449	-	25c. green and orange	5·00	40
O450	-	30c. red and brown	4·00	30
O451	-	50c. green and black	4·75	15
O452	-	75c. purple and blue	2·75	15
O453	-	$1 black and blue	8·75	1·10
O454	-	$2 green and orange	15·00	1·75
O455	-	$5 blue and green	16·00	3·00

1923. Stamps of 1923, but different colours, optd **O S**.

O485	**108**	1c. black and green	5·25	10
O486	**109**	2c. brown and red	5·25	10
O487	-	3c. black and blue	5·25	10
O488	-	5c. green and orange	5·25	10
O489	-	10c. purple and olive	5·25	10
O490	-	15c. blue and green	75	40
O491	-	20c. blue and lilac	75	40
O492	-	25c. brown	16·00	40
O493	-	30c. brown and blue	70	20
O494	-	50c. brown and bistre	70	30
O495	-	75c. green and grey	70	25
O496	**110**	$1 green and red	1·50	40
O497	-	$2 red and purple	2·00	50
O498	-	$5 brown and blue	3·75	50

1926. No. O362 surch **Two Cents** and either thick bar, wavy lines, ornamental scroll or two bars.

O506	**91**	2c. on 1c. brown & green	90	80

1928. Stamps of 1928 optd **OFFICIAL SERVICE**.

O518	**116**	1c. green	70	35
O519	**116**	2c. violet	1·40	50
O520	**116**	3c. brown	1·40	15
O521	**117**	5c. blue	80	15
O522	**118**	10c. grey	2·40	1·00
O523	**117**	15c. lilac	1·40	60
O524	**117**	$1 brown	40·00	16·00

1944. No. O522 surch.

O649	**118**	4c. on 10c. grey	8·00	8·00

POSTAGE DUE STAMPS

1892. Stamps of 1886 surch **POSTAGE DUE** and value in frame.

D99	**4**	3c. on 3c. mauve	1·25	1·25
D100	**4**	6c. on 6c. grey	6·25	6·25

D23

1894

D110	**D23**	2c. black and orange on yellow	95	55
D111	**D23**	4c. black & red on rose	95	55
D112	**D23**	6c. black & brn on buff	95	75
D113	**D23**	8c. black & blue on bl	1·00	75
D114	**D23**	10c. black and green on mauve	1·25	95
D115	**D23**	20c. black and violet on grey	1·25	95
D116	**D23**	40c. black and brown on green	2·50	1·75

REGISTRATION STAMPS

R22

1893

R105	**R22**	(10c.) black (Buchanan)	£275	£350
R106	**R22**	(10c.) blk (Grenville)	£1000	£1250
R107	**R22**	(10c.) black (Harper)	£1000	£1250
R108	**R22**	(10c.) black (Monrovia)	40·00	£175
R109	**R22**	(10c.) blk (Robertsport)	£500	£575

1894. Surch **10 CENTS 10** twice.

R140	**R22**	10c. blue on pink (Buchanan)	3·75	3·75
R141	**R22**	10c. green on buff (Harper)	3·75	3·75
R142	**R22**	10c. red on yellow (Monrovia)	3·75	3·75
R143	**R22**	10c. red on blue (Robertsport)	3·75	3·75

R42 President Gibson

1904

R211	**R42**	10c. black and blue (Buchanan)	1·50	25
R212	**R42**	10c. black and red ("Grenville")	1·50	25
R213	**R42**	10c. black and green (Harper)	1·50	25
R214	**R42**	10c. black and violet (Monrovia)	1·50	25

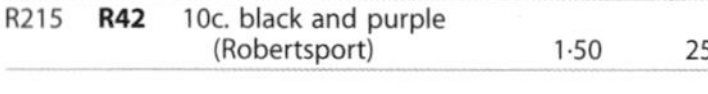

R215	**R42**	10c. black and purple (Robertsport)	1·50	25

R96 Patrol Boat *Quail*

1919. Roul or perf.

R388	**R96**	10c. blue and black (Buchanan)	90	5·75
R389	**R96**	10c. black and brown (Grenville)	90	7·50
R390	**R96**	10c. black and green (Harper)	90	5·25
R391	**R96**	10c. blue and violet (Monrovia)	90	5·75
R392	**R96**	10c. black and red (Robertsport)	90	7·50

R106 Gabon Viper

1921

R456	**R106**	10c. black and red (Buchanan)	23·00	2·50
R457	**R106**	10c. black and red (Greenville)	14·00	2·50
R458	**R106**	10c. black and blue (Harper)	18·00	2·50
R459	**R106**	10c. black and orange (Monrovia)	14·00	2·50
R460	**R106**	10c. black and green (Robertsport)	14·00	2·50

1921. Optd **1921.**

R461	**R106**	10c. black and lake	20·00	4·25
R462	**R106**	10c. black and red	20·00	4·25
R463	**R106**	10c. black and blue	20·00	4·25
R464	**R106**	10c. black and orange	20·00	4·25
R465	**R106**	10c. black and green	20·00	4·25

R111 Sailing Skiff (Buchanan)

1923. Various sea views.

R499	**R111**	10c. red and black	8·50	55
R500	-	10c. green and black	8·50	55
R501	-	10c. orange and black	8·50	55
R502	-	10c. blue and black	8·50	55
R503	-	10c. violet and black	8·50	55

Designs: No. R500, Lighter (Greenville); No. R501, Full-rigged sailing ship (Harper); No. R502, *George Washington* (liner) (Monrovia); No. R503, Canoe (Robertsport).

1941. No. 576 surch **REGISTERED 10 CENTS 10.**

R592	10c. on 5c. brown (postage)	1·40	1·40
R593	10c. on 5c. brown (air)	1·40	1·40

No. R593 is additionally optd with aeroplane and **AIR MAIL.**

SPECIAL DELIVERY STAMPS

1941. No. 576 surch with postman and **SPECIAL DELIVERY 10 CENTS 10.**

S590	10c. on 5c. brown (postage)	1·40	1·40
S591	10c. on 5c. brown (air)	1·40	1·40

No. S591 is additionally optd with aeroplane and **AIR MAIL.**

APPENDIX

The following stamps have either been issued in excess of postal needs, or have not been available to the public in reasonable quantities at face value.

1993

Flora. 70c.×6; 70c.×6.
Wildlife. 90c.×6; 90c.×6.

1994

African Children. 20c.+10c.; 70c.+20c.; 75c.+15c.; 80c.+20c.
Birds. $1×6; $1×6.
HONG KONG '94. Queen Elizabeth, the Queen Mother. 10c.; $2.
50th Anniversary of Roberts Airfield, Monrovia. 35c.×8.
National Red Cross Society. 70c.; $1×2; $2.

1995

SOS Children's Village. Tenth Anniversary of National Association for the Blind. 25c.+10c.; 80c.+20c.×2; $1.50+50c.×2.
African Animals. 70c.×2; 90c.; $1; $2.
SINGAPORE '95. Orchids. 70c.×8.
George Weah. Golden Ball Winner, 1989 and 1994. 50c.+20c.; 75c.+25c.; 80c.+20c.;$1.50+50c.
50th Anniversary of United Nations Organisation. 25; 50c.; $1; $2.
20th Anniversary of ECOWAS. 25; 50c.; $1.

1996

Centenary of Modern Olympics. 20; 35; 50c.; $1.
Butterflies. 70c.×9.
Fish. 90c.×12.
Birds. 25c.×18; 35c.; 90c.; $1.
Butterflies. 20c.×12; 25c.×12.
Olympic Games, Atlanta. 20c.×2; 35c.×2; 35c.×18; 50c.×2; $1×2.
70th Birth Anniversary of Marilyn Munroe. 20c.
Rock Performers. 35c.×8.
50th Anniversary of UNICEF. 30; 70c.; $1.
Birds. 75c.×5.
20th Death Anniversary of Mao Zedong. $1×2.
Freedom Camp. $1; $2×2.

1997

Animals. 50c.×12.
Return of Hong Kong to China. Deng Xiaoping Commemoration. 50c.; 70c.×2; $1; $1.20.
50th Wedding Anniversary of Queen Elizabeth II. 50c.×6.
World Heritage Sites. 50c.×16; 70c.×4.
Tenth Anniversary of Chernobyl Tragedy. $1.
Rapunzel story by Grimm Brothers. $1×4.
Winter Olympic, Nagano. 50c.; 70c.; 41; $2.
African Fauna. 50c.×8.
Flowers. 50c.×10.
Owls. 50c.×6.
Birds. 1; 2; 3; 4; 5; 10; 15; 20; 25; 50; 70; 75; 90c.; $1; $2; $3.
First Death Anniversary of Marcello Mastroianni. 75c.×4.
World Cup Football Championship, France. 50c.; 50c.×8; 70c.; $1; $1.50; $2×2.

1998

Noah's Ark. 15c.×25.
Endangered Species. Liberian Mongoose. 32c.×4.
Fungi. 10; 15; 20; 30; 40c.×18; 50; 75c.
Monarchs. 50c.×6; 50c.×6; 50c.×6.
Birds. 32c.×8; 30c.×12.
Mahatma Gandhi Commemoration 50c.
Pablo Picasso Commemoration. 50; 70c.; $1.
80th Anniversary of Royal Air Force. 70c.×4.
World Scout Jamboree, Chile. $1×3.
Birth Centenary of Enzo Ferrari. $1×3.
Birth Centenary of Chou Enlai. 50c.×6.
American Presidents. 75c.×4; 75c.×4; 75c.×4; 75c.×4.
Classic Cars. 32c.×4; 59c.×12.

1999

Raptors. 50c.; 50c.×12; 70c.; $1; $1.50.
Birds. 50c.×2; 50c.×12; 70c.×2; $1; $1.50.
New Year. Year of the Rabbit. Paintings by Liu Jiyou. 50c.×2
Pre-historic Animals (1st issue). 40c.×16; 50c.×2; 70c.×2; $1; $2.
Flora and Fauna. 20c.×12.
Flora. 50c.; 50c.×12; 70c.; $1; $2.
Orchids. 30c.×8; 50c.×2; 70c.×2; $1; $1.50.
Queen Elizabeth, the Queen Mother. $1×4.
CHINA '99, Macao. $20; $25×2.
Trains. 32c.; 40c.; 40c.×18; 50c.; 70c.
Dogs (1st issue). 50c.; 50c.×6; 70c.
Cats. 50c.×6; $1; $1.50.
Three Stooges. 40c.×9.
Christmas. Fauna. $5; $10; $20; $25; $30.
Cats. $5; $10; $25×6.
20th-century Ships and Aircraft. $5; $10; $15; $20; $25; $25×18; $30.
Pre-historic Animals (2nd issue). $10×48.
History of Aviation. $15×18.
Horses. $25×6.
Wild Dogs. $20×12.
Wild Cats. $20×12.
Dogs (2nd issue). $25; $25×6; $30.
30th Anniversary of First Moon Landing. 50c.×6.
Marine Life. $10; $15×10; $20; $25; $30.

2007

Diamond Wedding of Queen Elizabeth II. $35×6; $45×4.
Orchids. $20, $30, $40, $50.
Butterflies. $20, $30, $40, $50.
Birds. $20, $30, $40, $50.
Christmas 2007. $30, $40, $45, $50.

2008

Counties. $10, $10, $25, $25, $30, $30, $40, $40, $50, $50, $100, $100, $100, $100, $100.

2010

Chief Flomo Doghba Barwulor. $50.
Madam Saucoco 1816-1927. $50.
Christmas 2009. $25, $40, $50, $100.

Gibbons Stamp Monthly

FIRST CHOICE FOR STAMP COLLECTORS SINCE 1890

SUBSCRIBE AND GET £££S OFF THE COVER PRICE

SUBSCRIBE TODAY
Visit **stanleygibbons.com/gsm**
or call **01425 472 363**
overseas **+44 1425 472 363**

399 Strand, WC2R 0LX, London
Phone: **+44 1425 472 363** | Email: gsm@stanleygibbons.com
www.stanleygibbons.com

*T&Cs apply. *Saving based on a 12-month UK print subscription.*

LIBYA

A former Italian colony in N. Africa, comprising the governorates of Cyrenaica and Tripolitania. From the end of 1951 an independent kingdom including the Fezzan also. Following a revolution in 1969 the country became the Libyan Arab Republic.

1912. 100 centesimi = 1 lira.
1952. 1000 milliemes = 1 Libyan pound.
1972. 1000 dirhams = 1 dinar.

A. ITALIAN COLONY

1912. Stamps of Italy optd **LIBIA** (No. 5) or **Libia** (others).

1	**30**	1c. brown	2·50	2·10
2	**31**	2c. brown	2·50	2·30
3	**37**	5c. green	2·50	2·10
4	**37**	10c. red	8·00	1·40
5	**41**	15c. grey	£300	4·00
6	**37**	15c. grey	7·00	9·25
7	**33**	20c. orange	7·00	1·40
8	**41**	20c. orange	5·75	8·00
9	**39**	25c. blue	7·00	1·40
10	**39**	40c. brown	17·00	2·30
11	**33**	45c. green	46·00	40·00
12	**39**	50c. violet	44·00	3·50
13	**39**	60c. red	21·00	29·00
14	**34**	1l. brown and green	£120	4·00
15	**34**	5l. blue and red	£650	£450
16	**34**	10l. green and pink	60·00	£225

1915. Red Cross stamps of Italy optd **LIBIA**.

17	**53**	10c.+5c. red	5·75	17·00
18	**54**	15c.+5c. grey	23·00	35·00
19	**54**	20c. on 15c.+5c. grey	23·00	40·00
20	**54**	20c.+5c. orange	5·75	40·00

1916. No. 100 of Italy optd **LIBIA**.

21	**41**	20c. on 15c. grey	50·00	17·00

4 Roman Legionary

5 Goddess of Plenty

6 Roman Galley leaving Tripoli

7 Victory

1921

22A	**4**	1c. brown and black	3·00	8·00
23A	**4**	2c. brown and black	3·00	8·00
24A	**4**	5c. green and black	4·00	1·20
50	**4**	7½c. brown and black	1·20	9·25
51	**5**	10c. pink and black	3·50	80
52	**5**	15c. orange and brown	11·50	4·25
27A	**5**	25c. blue and deep blue	4·00	65
54	**6**	30c. brown and black	3·50	1·20
55	**6**	50c. green and black	3·50	80
30A	**6**	55c. violet and black	17·00	31·00
57	**7**	75c. red and purple	5·75	60
58	**7**	1l. brown	14·50	80
59	**6**	1l.25 blue and indigo	60	60
32A	**7**	5l. blue and black	35·00	37·00
33A	**7**	10l. green and blue	£350	£200

1922. Victory stamps of Italy optd **LIBIA**.

34	**62**	5c. green	2·30	9·25
35	**62**	10c. red	2·30	9·25
36	**62**	15c. grey	2·30	14·00
37	**62**	25c. blue	2·30	14·00

1922. Nos. 9 and 12 of Libya surch.

38	**39**	40c. on 50c. mauve	5·25	4·50
39	**39**	80c. on 25c. blue	5·25	11·50

9 *Libyan Sibyl* by Michelangelo

1924

41	**9**	20c. green	1·70	60
42	**9**	40c. brown	3·50	1·70
43	**9**	60c. blue	1·70	60
44	**9**	1l.75 orange	60	30
45	**9**	2l. red	5·75	3·00
46	**9**	2l.55 violet	9·25	17·00

1928. Air. Air stamps of Italy optd **Libia**.

63	**88**	50c. pink	17·00	17·00
64	**88**	80c. brown and purple	46·00	75·00

1928. Types of Italy optd **LIBIA** (No. 67) or **Libia** (others).

65	**92**	7½c. brown	14·50	55·00
66	**34**	1l.25 blue	80·00	29·00
67	**91**	1l.75 brown	£100	4·50

10 Bedouin Woman

1936. Tenth Tripoli Trade Fair.

68	**10**	50c. violet	3·50	4·50
69	**10**	1l.25 blue	3·50	14·00

1936. Air. Nos. 96 and 99 of Cyrenaica optd **LIBIA**.

70	-	50c. violet	5·75	65
71	**17**	1l. black	11·50	46·00

1937. Air. Stamps of Tripolitania optd **LIBIA**.

72	**18**	50c. red	1·20	65
73	**18**	60c. red	1·70	
74	**18**	75c. blue	1·70	40·00
75	**18**	80c. purple	2·30	65·00
76	**19**	1l. blue	3·25	1·40
77	**19**	1l.20 brown	2·75	90·00
78	**19**	1l.50 orange	2·75	£120
79	**19**	5l. green	2·75	£110

11 Triumphal Arch

12 Roman Theatre, Sabrata

1937. Inauguration of Coastal Highway.

80	**11**	50c. red (postage)	4·50	9·25
81	**11**	1l.25 blue	4·50	16·00
82	**12**	50c. purple (air)	4·50	9·25
83	**12**	1l. black	4·50	16·00

1937. 11th Tripoli Trade Fair. Optd **XI FIERA DI TRIPOLI**.

84	**11**	50c. red (postage)	26·00	50·00
85	**11**	1l.25 blue	26·00	50·00
86	**12**	50c. purple (air)	26·00	50·00
87	**12**	1l. black	26·00	50·00

14 Benghazi Waterfront

1938. 12th Tripoli Trade Fair.

88	**14**	5c. brown (postage)	35	1·80
89	-	10c. brown	35	1·50
90	**14**	25c. green	60	2·30
91	-	50c. violet	60	1·30
92	**14**	75c. red	1·70	3·50
93	-	1l.25 blue	2·30	7·00

Design: 10c., 50c., 1l.25, Fair Buildings.

94		50c. brown (air)	2·30	4·50
95		1l. blue	2·30	7·00

Design: Vert—50c., 1l. View of Tripoli.

16 Statue of Augustus

17 Eagle and Serpent

1938. Birth Bimillenary of Augustus the Great.

96	**16**	5c. green (postage)	60	2·30
97	-	10c. red	60	2·30
98	**16**	25c. green	1·20	1·20
99	-	50c. mauve	1·20	1·20
100	**16**	75c. red	3·00	3·50
101	-	1l.25 blue	3·00	5·75
102	**17**	50c. brown (air)	60	3·50
103	**17**	1l. mauve	3·00	5·75

Design: 10, 50c., 1l.25, Statue of Goddess of Plenty.

18 Agricultural Landscape

1939. 13th Tripoli Trade Fair. Inscr 'XIII FIERA CAMPIONARIA DE TRIPOLI' etc.

104	**18**	5c. green (postage)	1·20	1·70
105	-	20c. red	1·20	1·70
106	**18**	50c. mauve	1·20	2·30
107	-	75c. red	1·20	3·50
108	**18**	1l.25 blue	1·20	4·50

Design: 20, 75c. View of Ghadames.

109	25c. green (air)	60	3·50
110	50c. green	85	3·50
111	1l. mauve	85	4·50

Designs: Fiat G18V aeroplane over—25c., 1l. Arab and camel in desert; 50c. Fair entrance.

19 Buildings

1940. Naples Exhibition.

112	**19**	5c. brown (postage)	60	1·20
113	-	10c. orange	60	1·20
114	-	25c. green	1·20	1·80
115	**19**	50c. violet	1·50	1·80
116	-	75c. red	1·50	4·50
117	-	1l.25 blue	2·30	8·00
118	-	2l.+75c. red	2·30	25·00

Designs: Horiz—10, 75c., 2l. Oxen and plough. Vert—25c., 1l.25, Mosque.

119	50c. black (air)	1·20	3·00
120	1l. brown	1·20	3·00
121	2l.+75c. blue	1·70	10·50
122	5l.+2l.50 brown	1·70	14·00

Designs: Horiz—50c., 2l. Savoia Marchetti S.M.75 aeroplane over city; 1, 5l. Savoia Marchetti S-73 aeroplane over oasis.

19a Hitler and Mussolini

1941. Rome–Berlin Axis Commemoration.

123	**19a**	5c. orange (postage)	2·30	7·00
124	**19a**	10c. brown	2·30	7·00
125	**19a**	20c. purple	3·00	7·00
126	**19a**	25c. green	3·00	7·00
127	**19a**	50c. violet	3·00	7·00
128	**19a**	75c. red	3·00	23·00
129	**19a**	1l.25 blue	3·00	23·00
130	**19a**	50c. green (air)	5·75	40·00

B. INDEPENDENT

LIBYA
(20)

1951. Stamps of Cyrenaica optd. (a) For use in Cyrenaica, optd as T **20**.

131	**24**	1m. brown	15	15
132	**24**	2m. red	20	20
133	**24**	3m. yellow	25	25
134	**24**	4m. green	28·00	19·00
135	**24**	5m. brown	35	35
136	**24**	8m. orange	40	40
137	**24**	10m. violet	60	60
138	**24**	12m. red	1·10	1·10
139	**24**	20m. blue	1·50	1·50
140	**25**	50m. blue and brown	8·75	8·75
141	**25**	100m. red and black	14·50	14·50
142	**25**	200m. violet and blue	45·00	40·00
143	**25**	500m. yellow and green	£150	£130

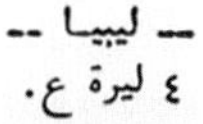

4 MAL.
LIBYA
(21)

(b) For use in Tripolitania. Surch as T **21** in Military Authority lire.

151	**24**	1mal. on 2m. red	25	25
152	**24**	2mal. on 4m. green	25	25
153	**24**	4mal. on 8m. orange	25	25
154	**24**	5mal. on 10m. violet	35	35
155	**24**	6mal. on 12m. red	35	35
156	**24**	10mal. on 20m. blue	65	65
157	**25**	24 mal. on 50m. blue and brown	3·00	3·00
158	**25**	48mal. on 100m. red	11·00	11·00
159	**25**	96mal. on 200m. violet and blue	27·00	27·00
160	**25**	240mal. on 500m. yellow and green	70·00	70·00

-- ليبيا --
٨ فرنك

8 FRANCS
LIBYA
(22)

(c) For use in Fezzan. Surch as T **22**.

166	**24**	2f. on 2m. red	20	20
167	**24**	4f. on 4m. green	30	30
168	**24**	8f. on 8m. orange	35	40
169	**24**	10f. on 10m. violet	50	50
170	**24**	12f. on 12m. red	75	70
171	**24**	20f. on 20m. blue	2·00	2·00
172	**25**	48f. on 50m. blue & brown	38·00	35·00
173	**25**	96f. on 100m. red and black	40·00	35·00
174	**25**	192f. on 200m. violet and blue	£110	80·00
175	**25**	480f. on 500m. yellow and green	£190	£190

23 King Idris

1952

176	**23**	2m. brown	10	10
177	**23**	4m. grey	10	10
178	**23**	5m. green	12·50	35
179	**23**	8m. red	40	25
180	**23**	10m. violet	12·50	15
181	**23**	12m. red	75	15
182	**23**	20m. blue	13·50	45
183	**23**	25m. brown	13·50	45
184	-	50m. blue and brown	1·75	65
185	-	100m. red and black	3·75	1·90
186	-	200m. violet and blue	6·00	3·50
187	-	500m. orange and green	25·00	17·00

Nos. 184/187 are larger.

1955. Arab Postal Union. As T **84a** of Lebanon but inscr 'LIBYE' at top.

200	5m. brown	1·20	60
201	10m. green	1·90	50
202	30m. violet	4·25	2·00

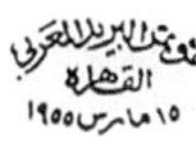

(28)

1955. Second Arab Postal Congress, Cairo. Nos. 200/202 optd with T **28**.

203	5m. brown	40	30
204	10m. green	90	50
205	30m. violet	2·25	1·25

1955. No. 177 surch.

206	**23**	5m. on 4m. grey	1·25	45

30

1955

207	**30**	1m. black on yellow	10	10
208	**30**	2m. bistre	1·40	50
209	**30**	2m. brown	10	10
210	**30**	3m. blue	10	50
211	**30**	4m. black	1·50	15
212	**30**	4m. lake	20	20
213	**30**	5m. green	40	20
214	**30**	10m. lilac	65	25
215	**30**	18m. red	15	10
216	**30**	20m. orange	25	15
217	**30**	30m. blue	50	20
218	**30**	35m. brown	65	25
219	**30**	40m. lake	1·10	40
220	**30**	50m. olive	85	25
221	-	100m. purple and slate	1·75	50
222	-	200m. lake and blue	9·25	1·40
223	-	500m. orange and green	15·00	7·25
224	-	£L1 green, brown and sepia on yellow	21·00	11·50

Nos. 221/224 are larger, 27×32 mm.
See also Nos. 242/257.

33 Immam's Tomb at Djaghboub

1956. Death Centenary of Imam Essayed Mohamed Aly el Senussi.

225	**33**	5m. green	20	20
226	**33**	10m. lilac	35	20
227	**33**	15m. red	95	75
228	**33**	30m. blue	1·60	1·25

34 Map of Libya

1956. First Anniversary of Admission to UN.

229	**34**	15m. buff and blue	30	15
230	**34**	35m. buff, purple and blue	1·00	30

35

1957. Arab Postal Congress, Tripoli.

231	**35**	15m. blue	1·75	90
232	**35**	500m. brown	12·50	6·50

36

1958. Tenth Anniversary of Declaration of Human Rights.

233	**36**	10m. violet	20	15
234	**36**	15m. green	25	20
235	**36**	30m. blue	95	15

37 FAO Emblem and Date Palms

1959. First International Dates Conference, Tripoli.

236	**37**	10m. black and violet	20	15
237	**37**	15m. black and green	50	20
238	**37**	45m. black and blue	1·00	50

1960. Inauguration of Arab League Centre, Cairo. As T **110** of Lebanon, but with Arms of Libya and inscr 'LIBYA'.

239	10m. black and green	50	20

39

1960. World Refugee Year.

240	**39**	10m. black and violet	25	15
241	**39**	45m. black and blue	1·25	75

1960. As Nos. 207 etc. On coloured paper.

242	**30**	1m. black on grey	10	10
243	**30**	2m. brown on buff	10	10
244	**30**	3m. indigo on blue	10	10
245	**30**	4m. lake on red	10	10
246	**30**	5m. green on green	10	10
247	**30**	10m. lilac on violet	10	10
248	**30**	15m. sepia on buff	10	10
249	**30**	20m. orange on orange	20	10
250	**30**	30m. red on pink	20	15
251	**30**	40m. lake on red	30	20
252	**30**	45m. blue on blue	35	20
253	**30**	50m. olive on bistre	35	20
254	-	100m. purple & slate on blue	1·25	35
255	-	200m. lake and blue on blue	3·25	1·40
256	-	500m. orange and green on green	23·00	5·50
257	-	£L1 green, brown and sepia	23·00	11·00

40 Palm Tree and Radio Mast

1960. Third Arab Telecommunications Conference, Tripoli.

258	**40**	10m. violet	15	10
259	**40**	15m. turquoise	20	10
260	**40**	45m. lake	1·40	65

41 Military Watchtower (medallion)

1961. Army Day.

261	**41**	5m. brown and green	20	10
262	**41**	15m. brown and blue	60	15

42 Zelten Field and Marsa Brega Port

1961. Inauguration of First Libyan Petrol Pipeline.

263	**42**	15m. green and buff	25	10
264	**42**	50m. brown and lavender	75	40
265	**42**	100m. blue and light blue	2·25	90

43 Broken Chain and Agricultural Scenes

1961. Tenth Anniversary of Independence.

266	**43**	15m. sepia, turquoise and green	15	10
267	-	50m. sepia, brown and buff	45	25
268	-	100m. sepia, blue & salmon	2·10	80

Designs: (embodying broken chain)—50m. Modern highway and buildings; 100m. Industrial machinery.

44 Tuareg Camel Riders

1962. International Fair, Tripoli.

269	**44**	10m. chestnut and brown	60	10
270	-	15m. green and purple	75	25
271	-	50m. blue and green	2·00	1·60
MS272		148×105 mm. Nos. 269/271. Imperf	15·00	6·00

Designs: 15m. Well; 50m. Oil derrick.

45 Campaign Emblem

1962. Malaria Eradication.

273	**45**	15m. multicoloured	25	20
274	**45**	50m. multicoloured	1·10	90
MS275		Two sheets each 68×103 mm. Nos. 273/274 (sold at 20m. and 70m. respectively)	8·50	5·00

46 Ahmed Rafik

1962. First Death Anniversary of Ahmed Rafik el Mehdawi (poet).

276	**46**	15m. green	15	10
277	**46**	20m. brown	55	20

47 Scout Badge and Handclasp

1962. Third Boy Scouts' Meeting, Tripoli.

278	**47**	5m. sepia, red and yellow	10	10
279	-	10m. sepia, yellow and blue	20	10
280	-	15m. sepia, yellow and grey	25	20
MS281		130×95 mm. 20, 30 and 50m. in colours and designs of Nos. 278/280. Imperf	2·00	1·50

Designs: 10m. Scouts and badge; 15m. Badge and camp.

48 City within Oildrop

1962. Inauguration of Essider Terminal, Sidrah Oil Pipeline.

282	**48**	15m. purple and green	45	15
283	**48**	50m. olive and brown	1·10	45

49 Red Crescent encircling Globe

1963. International Red Cross Centenary.

284	**49**	10m. multicoloured	20	15
285	**49**	15m. multicoloured	25	20
286	**49**	20m. multicoloured	90	60

50 Rainbow over Map of Tripoli

1963. International Trade Fair, Tripoli.

287	**50**	15m. multicoloured	25	20
288	**50**	30m. multicoloured	70	20
289	**50**	50m. multicoloured	1·40	60

51 Palm and Well

1963. Freedom from Hunger.

290	**51**	10m. green, brown and blue	20	10
291	-	15m. ochre, purple & green	25	20
292	-	45m. sepia, blue and salmon	1·10	75

Designs: 15m. Camel and sheep; 45m. Farmer sowing and tractor.

52 'Emancipation'

1963. 15th Anniversary of Declaration of Human Rights.

293	**52**	5m. brown and blue	10	10
294	**52**	15m. purple and blue	20	10
295	**52**	50m. green and blue	45	30

54 Map and Fair Entrance

1964. International Fair, Tripoli.

300	**54**	10m. green, brown and red	75	15
301	**54**	15m. green, brown & purple	1·00	50
302	**54**	30m. green, brown and blue	1·40	75

55 Child playing in Sun

1964. Children's Day. Sun Gold.

303	**55**	5m. violet, red and pink	10	10
304	-	15m. brown, bistre and buff	20	15
305	**55**	45m. violet, blue & lt blue	1·25	65
MS306		80×130 mm. Nos. 303/305 (sold at 100m.)	2·00	2·00

Design: 15m. Child in bird's nest.

56 Lungs and Stethoscope

1964. Anti-tuberculosis Campaign.

307	**56**	20m. violet	90	25

57 Crown and Map

1964. First Anniversary of Libyan Union.

308	**57**	5m. orange and green	15	10
309	**57**	50m. yellow and blue	1·00	50

58 Libyan Woman, Silk Moth and Cocoon

1964. Emancipation of Libyan Women.

310	**58**	10m. blue and green	15	10
311	**58**	20m. blue and yellow	55	35
312	**58**	35m. blue and pink	85	80
MS313		125×107 mm. Nos. 310/312 (sold at 100m.)	1·80	1·80

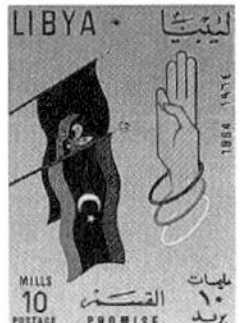
59 Flags and Scout Salute

1964. Libyan Scouts. Multicoloured.

314	10m. Type **59**	65	20
315	20m. Scout badge and saluting hands	1·25	60
MS316	120×85 mm. Nos. 314/315 (sold at 50m.)	1·80	1·80

60 Bayonet

1964. Foundation of the Senussi Army.

317	**60**	10m. brown and green	15	10
318	**60**	20m. black and orange	65	40

61 Ahmed Bahloul (poet)

1964. Ahmed Bahloul El-Sharef Commem.

319	**61**	15m. purple	20	10
320	**61**	20m. blue	65	20

62 Football

1964. Olympic Games, Tokyo. Rings in Gold.

321	5m. black and blue (Type **62**)	25	20
322	10m. black & purple (Cycling)	25	20
323	20m. black and red (Boxing)	50	20
324	30m. black and buff (Runner)	65	50
325	35m. black and olive (High-diving)	65	50
326	50m. black & green (Hurdling)	65	50
MS327	160×110 mm. Six stamps each 15m. in colours and designs of Nos. 321/326 (sold at 100m.)	9·00	9·00

Nos. 321/326 were arranged together *se-tenant* in the sheets, each block of six being superimposed with the Olympic rings symbol.

63 APU Emblem

1964. Tenth Anniversary of Arab Postal Union.

328	**63**	10m. blue and yellow	10	10
329	**63**	15m. brown and lilac	20	10
330	**63**	30m. brown and green	95	65

64 ICY Emblem

1965. International Co-operation Year.

331	**64**	5m. gold and blue (postage)	25	10
332	**64**	15m. gold and red	90	25
333	**64**	50m. gold and violet (air)	1·50	35
MS334		102×76 mm. No. 333. Imperf	3·25	3·25

65 European Bee-eater

1965. Birds. Multicoloured.

335	5m. Long-legged buzzard (vert)	1·10	30
336	10m. Type **65**	1·50	30
337	15m. Black-bellied sandgrouse	2·25	30
338	20m. Houbara bustard	2·75	55
339	30m. Spotted sandgrouse	3·50	90
340	40m. Barbary partridge (vert)	4·25	1·25

66 Fair Emblem

1965. International Trade Fair, Tripoli.

341	**66**	50m. multicoloured	75	50

67 Compass, Rocket and Balloons

1965. World Meteorological Day.

342	**67**	10m. multicoloured	10	10
343	**67**	15m. multicoloured	20	15
344	**67**	50m. multicoloured	1·00	70

68 ITU Emblem and Symbols

1965. Centenary of ITU.

345	**68**	10m. brown	10	10
346	**68**	20m. purple	15	10
347	**68**	50m. mauve	90	65

69 Lamp and Burning Library

1965. Reconstitution of Burnt Algiers Library.

348	**69**	15m. multicoloured	20	10
349	**69**	50m. multicoloured	90	25
MS350		Two sheets each 97×73 mm. Nos. 348/349 in blocks of four	4·50	4·50

70 Rose

1965. Flowers. Multicoloured.

351	1m. Type **70**	10	10
352	2m. Iris	10	10
353	3m. Cactus flower	10	10
354	4m. Sunflower	50	10

71 Sud Aviation Super Caravelle over Globe

1965. Inauguration of Kingdom of Libya Airlines.

355	**71**	5m. multicoloured	10	10
356	**71**	10m. multicoloured	20	10
357	**71**	15m. multicoloured	70	10

72 Forum, Cyrene

1965

358	**72**	50m. olive and blue	70	25
359	-	100m. brown and blue	1·25	45
360	-	200m. blue and purple	3·00	95
361	-	500m. green and red	6·50	2·75
362	-	£L1 brown and green	14·00	6·50

Designs: Vert—100m. Trajan's Arch, Leptis Magna; 200m. Apollo's Temple, Cyrene. Horiz: 500m. Antonine Temple, Sabratha; £L1 Theatre, Sabratha.

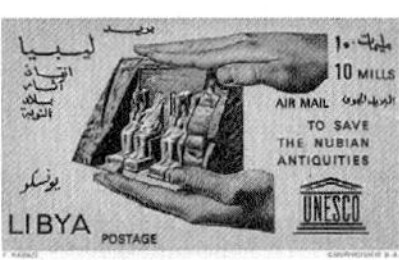
73 Helping Hands

1966. Air. Nubian Monuments Preservation.

363	**73**	10m. brown and bistre	20	10
364	**73**	15m. brown and green	25	10
365	**73**	40m. brown and chestnut	1·10	50
MS366		Three sheets each 125×87 mm. Nos. 363/365 in blocks of four	6·00	6·00

74 Germa Mausoleum

1966

367	**74**	70m. violet and brown	1·40	75

See also No. E368.

75 Globe and Satellites

1966. International Trade Fair, Tripoli.

369	**75**	15m. black, gold and green	20	10
370	**75**	45m. black, gold and blue	70	20
371	**75**	55m. black, gold and purple	95	60

76 League Centre, Cairo, and Emblem

1966. Arab League Week.

372	**76**	20m. red, green and black	10	10
373	**76**	55m. blue, red and black	65	50

77 WHO Building

1966. Air. Inauguration of WHO Headquarters, Geneva.

374	**77**	20m. black, yellow and blue (air)	20	10
375	**77**	50m. black, green and red	65	25
376	**77**	65m. black, salmon and lake	95	70
MS377		80×69 mm. 50m. black, blue and gold (air). Imperf	2·50	2·50

Design: 50m. WHO Building as T **77** on UN flag.

78 Tuareg with Camel

79 Three Tuaregs on Camels (image scaled to 30% of original size)

1966. Tuaregs.

378	**78**	10m. red	95	65
379	-	20m. blue	2·25	1·25
380	-	50m. multicoloured	4·50	3·25
MS381		160×110 mm. **79** 100m. multicoloured. Imperf	8·50	8·50

Designs: Vert—20m. As T **78** but positions of Tuareg and camel reversed. 62×39 mm: 50m. Tuareg with camel (different).

80 Leaping Deer

1966. First Arab Girl Scouts Camp (5m.) and Seventh Arab Boy Scouts Camp (25 and 65m.). Multicoloured.

382	5m. Type **80**	10	10
383	25m. Boy scouts Camp emblem (vert)	20	10
384	65m. As 25m.	1·00	50

81 Airline Emblem

1966. Air. First Anniversary of Kingdom of Libya Airlines.

385	**81**	25m. multicoloured	20	15
386	**81**	60m. multicoloured	1·00	75
387	**81**	85m. multicoloured	1·40	1·00

82 UNESCO Emblem

1967. 20th Anniversary of UNESCO.

388	**82**	15m. multicoloured	20	10
389	**82**	25m. multicoloured	90	20

83 Castle of Columns, Tolemaide

1967. Tourism.

390	**83**	25m. black, brown & violet	20	10
391	-	55m. brown, violet & black	90	50

Design: Horiz—55m. Sebba Fort.

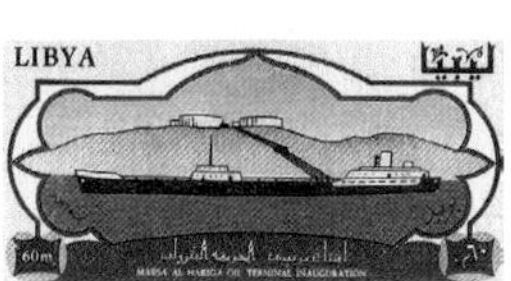
84 *British Confidence* (tanker) at Oil Terminal

1967. Inauguration of Marsa al Hariga Oil Terminal.

392	**84**	60m. multicoloured	1·75	65

85 Fair Emblem

1967. International Fair, Tripoli.

393	**85**	15m. multicoloured	50	10
394	**85**	55m. multicoloured	75	50

86 ITY Emblem

1967. International Tourist Year.

395	**86**	5m. black and blue	10	10
396	**86**	10m. blue and black	10	10
397	**86**	45m. black, blue and pink	60	15

87 Running

1967. Mediterranean Games, Tunisia. Designs showing action close-ups.

398	**87**	5m. black, orange and blue	10	10
399	-	10m. black, brown and blue	10	10
400	-	15m. black, violet and blue	10	10
401	-	45m. black, red and blue	30	25
402	-	75m. black, green and blue	75	30

Designs: 10m. Throwing the javelin; 15m. Cycling; 45m. Football; 75m. Boxing.

88 Open Book and Arab League Emblem

1967. Literacy Campaign.

403	**88**	5m. orange and violet	10	10
404	**88**	10m. green and violet	10	10
405	**88**	15m. purple and violet	15	10
406	**88**	25m. blue and violet	20	15

89 Human Rights Emblem

1968. Human Rights Year.

407	**89**	15m. red and green	15	10
408	**89**	60m. blue and orange	65	25

90 Cameleers, Fokker Friendship, Oil Rig and Map

1968. International Fair, Tripoli.

409	**90**	55m. multicoloured	95	30

91 Arab League Emblem

1968. Arab League Week.

410	**91**	10m. red and blue	10	10
411	**91**	45m. green and orange	65	50

92 Children Wrestling (statue)

1968. Children's Day. Multicoloured.

412	25m. Type **92**	45	15
413	55m. Libyan mother and children	80	55

93 WHO Emblem and Reaching Hands

1968. 20th Anniversary of WHO.

414	**93**	25m. blue and purple	25	15
415	**93**	55m. brown and blue	40	25

94 Oil Pipeline Map

1968. Inauguration of Zueitina Oil Terminal.

416	**94**	10m. multicoloured	20	10
417	**94**	60m. multicoloured	1·10	65

95 Teaching the People

1968. Eliminate Illiteracy.

418	**95**	5m. mauve	10	10
419	**95**	10m. orange	10	10
420	**95**	15m. blue	10	10
421	**95**	20m. green	20	20

96 Conference Emblem

1968. Fourth Session of Arab Labour Ministries Conference, Tripoli.

422	**96**	10m. multicoloured	10	10
423	**96**	15m. multicoloured	20	10

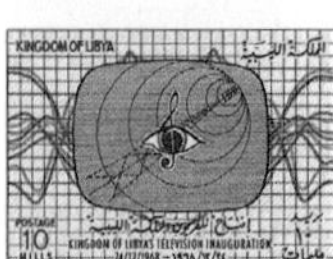
97 Treble Clef, Eye and TV Screen

1968. Inauguration of Libyan Television Service.

424	**97**	10m. multicoloured	10	10
425	**97**	30m. multicoloured	65	20

98 Bridge, Callipers and Road Sign

1968. Opening of Wadi El Kuf Bridge.

426	**98**	25m. multicoloured	15	15
427	**98**	60m. multicoloured	70	25

99 Melons

1969. Fruits. Multicoloured.

428	5m. Type **99**	10	10
429	10m. Dates	10	10
430	15m. Lemons	10	10
431	20m. Oranges	15	10
432	25m. Peaches	50	15
433	35m. Pears	90	50

See also Nos. 518/523.

100 Fair Emblem

1969. Eighth International Trade Fair, Tripoli.

434	**100**	25m. multicoloured	15	10
435	**100**	35m. multicoloured	25	15
436	**100**	40m. multicoloured	60	20

101 Hoisting Weather Balloon

1969. World Meteorological Day.

437	**101**	60m. multicoloured	1·10	65

102 Family on Staircase within Cogwheel

1969. Tenth Anniversary of Libyan Social Insurance.

438	**102**	15m. multicoloured	15	10
439	**102**	55m. multicoloured	30	25

103 ILO Emblem

1969. 50th Anniversary of ILO.

440	**103**	10m. green, black & turq	10	10
441	**103**	60m. green, black and red	70	50

104 Emblem and Desert Scene

1969. African Tourist Year.

442	**104**	15m. multicoloured	15	10
443	**104**	30m. multicoloured	65	50

105 Members of the Armed Forces and Olive Branch

1969. Revolution of 1st September.

444	**105**	5m. multicoloured	25	10
445	**105**	10m. multicoloured	35	20
446	**105**	15m. multicoloured	55	25
447	**105**	25m. multicoloured	85	40
448	**105**	45m. multicoloured	1·00	60
449	**105**	60m. multicoloured	2·10	1·00

On Nos. 444/449 the value is in white and the designer's name appears at the foot of design.

106 Dish Aerial and Flags

1970. Fifth Anniversary of Arab Satellite Communications Co-operation Agreement.

450	**106**	15m. multicoloured	50	15
451	**106**	20m. multicoloured	75	20
452	**106**	25m. multicoloured	1·00	25
453	**106**	40m. multicoloured	1·50	75

107 Arab League Flag, Arms and Map

1970. Silver Jubilee of Arab League.

454	**107**	10m. sepia, green and blue	10	10
455	**107**	15m. brown, green & orge	15	15
456	**107**	20m. purple, green & olive	50	25

1970. Revolution of 1 September. Designs as T **105**, but without imprint 'M. A. Siala' at foot, and figures of value differently inscr.

457	**105**	5m. multicoloured	25	10
458	**105**	10m. multicoloured	35	20
459	**105**	15m. multicoloured	55	25
460	**105**	25m. multicoloured	85	40
461	**105**	45m. multicoloured	1·00	60
462	**105**	60m. multicoloured	2·10	1·00

108 New Headquarters Building

1970. New UPU Headquarters Building, Berne.

463	**108**	10m. multicoloured	15	10
464	**108**	25m. multicoloured	20	20
465	**108**	60m. multicoloured	95	60

1970. Nos. 358 and 360/362 with KINGDOM OF LIBYA inscriptions obliterated.

465a	**72**	50m. olive and blue		
466	-	200m. blue and purple		
467	-	500m. green and pink		
468	-	£L1 brown and green		

These stamps were sold only for use on parcel post items. Other values may exist so overprinted, but were unauthorised.

109 Arms and Soldiers

1970. Evacuation of Foreign Military Bases in Libya.

469	**109**	15m. black and red	15	15
470	**109**	25m. yellow, blue and red	45	20
471	**109**	45m. yellow, red and green	1·25	30

110 Soldiers and Libyan Flag

1970. First Anniversary of Libyan Arab Republic.

472	**110**	20m. multicoloured	55	15
473	**110**	25m. multicoloured	70	15
474	**110**	30m. multicoloured	1·25	75

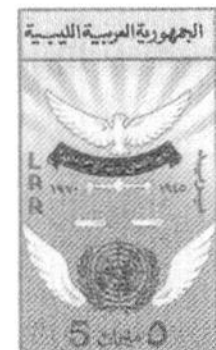
111 UN Emblem, Dove and Scales

1970. 25th Anniversary of United Nations.
475 **111** 5m. brown, red and green 25 10
476 **111** 10m. green, red & emerald 65 15
477 **111** 60m. green, red and blue 1·75 75

112 Map and Flags

1970. Signing of Tripoli Charter of Co-operation.
478 **112** 15m. green, black and red 5·00 1·50

113 Dove, UN Emblem and Globe

1971. Tenth Anniversary of UN De-colonisation Declaration.
479 **113** 15m. multicoloured 50 15
480 **113** 20m. multicoloured 75 20
481 **113** 60m. multicoloured 1·90 75

114 Education Year Emblem

1971. International Education Year.
482 **114** 5m. brown, red and black 15 10
483 **114** 10m. green, red and black 50 10
484 **114** 20m. blue, red and black 1·10 15

115 Palestinian Guerrilla

1971. Al-Fatah Movement for the Liberation of Palestine.
485 **115** 5m. multicoloured 15 10
486 **115** 10m. multicoloured 50 15
487 **115** 100m. multicoloured 1·75 1·00

116 Fair Emblem

1971. Ninth International Trade Fair, Tripoli.
488 **116** 15m. multicoloured 15 10
489 **116** 30m. multicoloured 65 20

117 OPEC Emblem

1971. Organisation of Petroleum Exporting Countries (OPEC).
490 **117** 10m. brown and yellow 15 10
491 **117** 70m. violet and pink 1·25 65

118 Global Symbol

1971. World Telecommunications Day (Nos. 494/495) and Pan-African Telecommunications Network.
492 - 5m. multicoloured 10 10
493 - 15m. multicoloured 10 10
494 **118** 25m. multicoloured 20 15
495 **118** 35m. multicoloured 50 25
Design: 5m., 15m. Telecommunications map of Africa.

119 Soldier, Torch and Flag

1971. First Anniversary of Evacuation of Foreign Troops.
496 **119** 5m. multicoloured 10 10
497 **119** 10m. multicoloured 15 10
498 **119** 15m. multicoloured 20 15

120 Ramadan Suehli

1971. Ramadan Suehli (patriot). Commem.
499 **120** 15m. multicoloured 15 10
500 **120** 55m. multicoloured 75 35
For similar portraits see Nos. 503/504, 507/508, 526/527 and 553/554.

121 Palm and Dates

1971. Second Anniversary of 1 September Revolution.
501 **121** 5m. multicoloured 20 10
502 **121** 15m. multicoloured 1·00 15

1971. 40th Death Anniversary of Omar el Mukhtar (patriot). As T **120**.
503 5m. multicoloured 10 10
504 100m. multicoloured 1·75 90

122 President Gamal Nasser

1971. First Death Anniversary of President Nasser of Egypt.
505 **122** 5m. black, green & purple 10 10
506 **122** 15m. black, purple & green 95 10

1971. 21st Death Anniversary of Ibrahim Usta Omar (poet). As T **120**.
507 25m. multicoloured 25 15
508 30m. multicoloured 80 20

123 Racial Equality Year Emblem

1971. Racial Equality Year.
509 **123** 25m. multicoloured 25 15
510 **123** 35m. multicoloured 70 15

124 APU Emblem

1971. 25th Anniversary of Founding of Arab Postal Union at Sofar Conference.
511 **124** 5m. multicoloured 10 10
512 **124** 10m. multicoloured 20 10
513 **124** 15m. multicoloured 15 10

125 Arab Postal Union Emblem and Envelopes

1971. Tenth Anniversary of African Postal Union. Multicoloured
514 10m. Type **125** 10 10
515 15m. Type **125** 15 10
516 25m. APU Emblem and dove with letter 25 15
517 55m. As 25m. 95 35

1971. Nos. 423/433 with KINGDOM OF LIBYA inscriptions obliterated.
518 15m. Type **99**
519 10m. Dates
520 15m. Lemons
521 20m. Oranges
522 25m. Peaches
523 35m. Pears

126 Book Year Emblem

1972. International Book Year.
524 **126** 15m. multicoloured 15 10
525 **126** 20m. multicoloured 25 20

1972. Ahmed Gnaba (poet) Commemoration. As T **120**.
526 20m. multicoloured 25 10
527 35m. multicoloured 65 20

127 Libyan Arms

1972. Values in Milliemes.
528 **127** 5m. multicoloured 10 10
529 **127** 10m. multicoloured 10 10
530 **127** 25m. multicoloured 15 10
531 **127** 30m. multicoloured 20 10
532 **127** 35m. multicoloured 25 10
533 **127** 40m. multicoloured 50 15
534 **127** 45m. multicoloured 60 15
535 **127** 55m. multicoloured 85 20
536 **127** 60m. multicoloured 1·00 35
537 **127** 90m. multicoloured 1·60 90
For values in dirhams and dinars see Nos. 555/562.

128 Tombs, Ghirza

1972. Libyan Antiquities. Multicoloured.
538 5m. Type **128** 10 10
539 10m. Cufic inscription, Ajdabiya 10 10
540 15m. Marcus Aurelius' Arch, Tripoli (horiz) 15 10
541 25m. Exchanging Weapons (cave painting, Wadi Zigza) 65 15

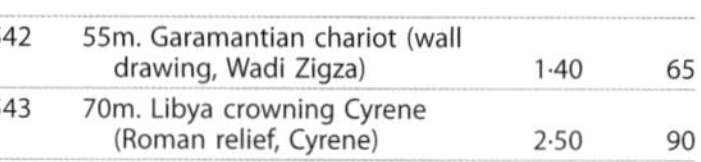
542 55m. Garamantian chariot (wall drawing, Wadi Zigza) 1·40 65
543 70m. Libya crowning Cyrene (Roman relief, Cyrene) 2·50 90

129 Fair Emblem

1972. Tenth International Trade Fair, Tripoli.
544 **129** 25m. multicoloured 20 15
545 **129** 35m. multicoloured 25 20
546 **129** 50m. multicoloured 95 25
547 **129** 70m. multicoloured 1·40 35

130 Heart and Skeletal Arm

1972. World Health Day.
548 **130** 15m. multicoloured 1·10 25
549 **130** 25m. multicoloured 2·25 75

131 Unity Symbol on Map

1972. First Anniversary of Libyan–Egyptian Federation Agreement.
550 **131** 15m. yellow, blue and black 10 10
551 **131** 20m. yellow, green & emer 20 10
552 **131** 25m. yellow, red and black 80 20

1972. Birth Centenary (1970) of Suleiman el Baruni (writer). As T **120**.
553 10m. multicoloured 95 15
554 70m. multicoloured 1·25 75

1972. New Currency (Dirhams and Dinars). As T **127**. (a) Size 19×24 mm.
555 **127** 15dh. multicoloured 10 10
556 **127** 65dh. multicoloured 75 50
557 **127** 70dh. multicoloured 90 65
558 **127** 80dh. multicoloured 1·25 65

(b) Size 27×32 mm.
559 **127** 100dh. multicoloured 1·75 2·00
560 **127** 200dh. multicoloured 3·25 1·60
561 **127** 500dh. multicoloured 7·50 5·00
562 **127** 1D. multicoloured 13·50 10·00

132

1972
563 **132** 5m. multicoloured 1·90 50
564 **132** 20m. multicoloured 7·50 1·40
565 **132** 50m. multicoloured 18·00 3·75
Nos. 563/565 were also issued with the Arabic face values expressed in the new currency.
See also Nos. 657/659.

133 Environmental Emblem

1972. UN Environmental Conservation Conference, Stockholm.
566 **133** 15dh. multicoloured 50 10
567 **133** 55dh. multicoloured 1·10 35

134 Olympic Emblems

1972. Olympic Games, Munich.
568 **134** 25dh. multicoloured 1·50 35
569 **134** 35dh. multicoloured 2·25 90

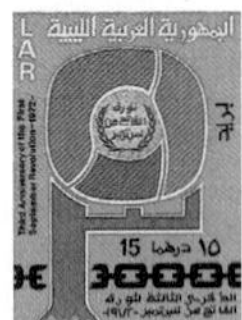
135 Symbolic Tree and 'Fruit'

1972. Third Anniversary of 1 September Revolution.

570	**135**	15dh. multicoloured	15	10
571	**135**	25dh. multicoloured	70	15

136 Dome of the Rock

1973. Dome of the Rock, Jerusalem.

572	**136**	10dh. multicoloured	10	10
573	**136**	25dh. multicoloured	50	15

137 Nicolas Copernicus

1973. 500th Birth Anniversary of Copernicus. Multicoloured.

574	15dh. Type **137**	15	10
575	25dh. *Copernicus in his Observatory* (horiz)	50	15

138 Libyan Eagle and Fair

1973. 11th International Trade Fair, Tripoli.

576	**138**	5dh. multicoloured	15	10
577	**138**	10dh. multicoloured	50	10
578	**138**	15dh. multicoloured	90	15

139 Blind Persons and Occupations

1973. Role of the Blind in Society.

579	**139**	20dh. multicoloured	5·50	1·25
580	**139**	25dh. multicoloured	10·00	2·50

140 Map and Laurel

1973. Tenth Anniversary of Organisation of African Unity.

584	**140**	15dh. multicoloured	20	10
585	**140**	25dh. multicoloured	65	45

141 Interpol HQ, Paris

1973. 50th Anniversary of International Criminal Police Organisation (Interpol).

586	**141**	10dh. multicoloured	10	10
587	**141**	15dh. multicoloured	15	10
588	**141**	25dh. multicoloured	60	20

142 Map and Emblems

1973. Census.

589	**142**	10dh. blue, black and red	3·00	65
590	**142**	25dh. green, black and blue	4·25	1·25
591	**142**	35dh. orange, black and grn	8·00	2·50

143 WMO Emblem

1973. WMO Centenary.

592	**143**	5dh. blue, black and red	10	10
593	**143**	10dh. blue, black and green	15	10

144 Footballers

1973. Second Palestine Cup Football Championship.

594	**144**	5dh. brown and green	45	20
595	**144**	25dh. brown and red	80	15

145 Revolutionary Torch

1973. Fourth Anniversary of 1 September Revolution.

596	**145**	15dh. multicoloured	20	10
597	**145**	25dh. multicoloured	85	10

146 Writing Ability

1973. Literacy Campaign.

598	**146**	25dh. multicoloured	50	15

147 Doorway of Old City Hall

1973. Centenary of Tripoli Municipality. Multicoloured.

599	10dh. Type **147**	20	10
600	25dh. Khondok fountain	50	10
601	35dh. Clock tower	75	40

148 Militiamen and Flag

1973. Libyan Militia.

602	**148**	15dh. multicoloured	15	10
603	**148**	25dh. multicoloured	55	10

149 Arabic Quotation from Speech of 15 April 1973

1973. Declaration of Cultural Revolution by Colonel Gaddafi. Multicoloured.

604	25dh. Type **149**	20	10
605	70dh. As Type **149** but text in English	60	30

150 Ploughing with Camel

1973. Tenth Anniversary of World Food Programme.

606	**150**	10dh. multicoloured	10	10
607	**150**	25dh. multicoloured	20	10
608	**150**	35dh. multicoloured	55	15

151 Human Rights Emblem

1973. 25th Anniversary of Declaration of Human Rights.

609	**151**	25dh. red, purple and blue	20	10
610	**151**	70dh. red, green and blue	1·10	30

152 Flat-headed Grey Mullet

1973. Fish. Multicoloured.

611	5dh. Type **152**	15	10
612	10dh. Zebra seabream	70	10
613	15dh. Grouper	1·00	15
614	20dh. Painted comber	1·50	20
615	25dh. Yellow-finned tunny	2·75	30

153 Lookout Post and Scout Salute

1974. 20th Anniversary of Scouting in Libya.

616	**153**	5dh. multicoloured	95	10
617	**153**	20dh. multicoloured	2·50	50
618	**153**	25dh. multicoloured	4·00	1·25

154 Emblem formed with National Flags

1974. 12th International Trade Fair, Tripoli.

619	**154**	10dh. multicoloured	50	10
620	**154**	25dh. multicoloured	75	15
621	**154**	35dh. multicoloured	1·25	35

155 Family within Protective Hands

1974. World Health Day.

622	**155**	5dh. multicoloured	15	10
623	**155**	25dh. multicoloured	50	20

156 Minaret within Star

1974. Inauguration of Benghazi University.

624	**156**	10dh. multicoloured	20	10
625	**156**	25dh. multicoloured	75	15
626	**156**	35dh. multicoloured	1·10	25

157 UPU Emblem within Star

1974. Centenary of UPU.

627	**157**	25dh. multicoloured	5·50	75
628	**157**	70dh. multicoloured	10·00	1·50

158 Traffic Lights and Signs

1974. Motoring and Touring Club of Libya.

629	**158**	5dh. multicoloured	10	10
630	**158**	10dh. multicoloured	15	10
631	**158**	25dh. multicoloured	15	10

159 Tank, Refinery and Pipeline

1974. Fifth Anniversary of 1 September Revolution.

632	**159**	5dh. multicoloured	10	10
633	**159**	20dh. multicoloured	15	10
634	**159**	25dh. multicoloured	15	10
635	**159**	35dh. multicoloured	20	15
MS636		121×81 mm. 55dh. lake, yellow and black	2·25	1·60

Design: 26×39 mm.—55dh. Figure '5' and symbols.

160 WPY Emblem and People

1974. World Population Year.

637	**160**	25dh. multicoloured	20	10
638	**160**	35dh. multicoloured	50	20

161

1975. 13th International Trade Fair, Tripoli. Libyan Costumes.

639	**161**	5dh. multicoloured	10	10
640	-	10dh. multicoloured	10	10
641	-	15dh. multicoloured	10	10
642	-	20dh. multicoloured	20	10
643	-	25dh. multicoloured	75	10
644	-	50dh. multicoloured	1·10	20

Designs: 10dh. to 50dh. Various costumes.

162 Congress Emblem

1975. Arab Workers' Congress.

645	**162**	10dh. multicoloured	10	10
646	**162**	25dh. multicoloured	15	15
647	**162**	35dh. multicoloured	50	15

163 Teacher at Blackboard

1975. Teachers' Day.

648	**163**	10dh. multicoloured	10	10
649	**163**	25dh. multicoloured	20	10

164 Human Figures, Text and Globe

1975. World Health Day.

650	**164**	20dh. multicoloured	15	10
651	**164**	25dh. multicoloured	20	10

165 Readers and Bookshelves

1975. Arab Book Exhibition.

652	**165**	10dh. multicoloured	10	10
653	**165**	25dh. multicoloured	20	10
654	**165**	35dh. multicoloured	50	15

166 Festival Emblem

1975. Second Arab Youth Festival.

655	**166**	20dh. multicoloured	15	10
656	**166**	25dh. multicoloured	20	15

1975. As Nos. 563/565 but without 'LAR'.

657	**132**	5dh. black, orange & blue	35	10
658	**132**	20dh. black, yellow & blue	75	10
659	**132**	50dh. black, green and blue	1·40	15

167 Games Emblem

1975. Seventh Mediterranean Games, Algiers.

660	**167**	10dh. multicoloured	10	10
661	**167**	25dh. multicoloured	45	10
662	**167**	50dh. multicoloured	85	20

168 Dove of Peace

1975. Sixth Anniversary of 1 September Revolution. Multicoloured.

663	25dh. Type **168**	20	10
664	70dh. Peace dove with different background	95	25
MS665	120×81 mm. 100dh. Colonel Gaddafi and desert scene. Imperf	1·25	1·25

169 Khalil Basha Mosque

1975. Mosques. Multicoloured.

666	5dh. Type **169**	10	10
667	10dh. Sidi Abdulla El Shaab	10	10
668	15dh. Sidi Ali El Fergani	10	10
669	20dh. Al Kharruba (vert)	15	10
670	25dh. Katiktha (vert)	20	10
671	30dh. Murad Agha (vert)	45	15
672	35dh. Maulai Mohamed (vert)	55	15

170 Arms and Crowds

1976. National People's Congress.

673	**170**	35dh. multicoloured	20	10
674	**170**	40dh. multicoloured	25	10

171 Dialogue Emblem

1976. Islamic–Christian Dialogue Seminar.

675	**171**	40dh. multicoloured	50	15
676	**171**	115dh. multicoloured	1·40	60

172 Woman blowing Bugle

1976. International Trade Fair, Tripoli. Multicoloured

677	10dh. Type **172**	10	10
678	20dh. Lancer	15	10
679	30dh. Drummer	65	10
680	40dh. Bagpiper	75	20
681	100dh. Woman with jug on head	1·90	35

173 Early and Modern Telephones

1976. Telephone Centenary. Multicoloured.

682	40dh. Type **173**	1·60	15
683	70dh. Alexander Graham Bell	2·75	50
MS684	Two sheets, each 120×100 mm. (a) No. 682×4; (b) No. 683×4	14·00	4·00

174 Mother and Child

1976. International Children's Day.

685	**174**	85dh. multicoloured	75	30
686	**174**	110dh. multicoloured	1·10	40

175 Hands supporting Eye

1976. World Health Day.

687	**175**	30dh. multicoloured	20	10
688	**175**	35dh. multicoloured	20	10
689	**175**	40dh. multicoloured	50	15

176 Great Grey Shrike

1976. Libyan Birds. Multicoloured.

690	5dh. Little bittern	75	25
691	10dh. Type **176**	1·40	40
692	15dh. Fulvous babbler	2·00	50
693	20dh. European bee-eater (vert)	2·75	70
694	25dh. Hoopoe	3·00	95

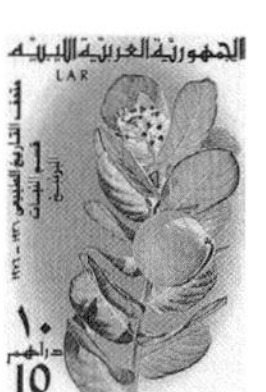
177 Barabekh Plant

1976. Natural History Museum. Multicoloured.

695	10dh. Type **177**	10	10
696	15dh. Fin whale (horiz)	15	10
697	30dh. Lizard (horiz)	20	10
698	40dh. Elephant's skull (horiz)	70	15
699	70dh. Bonnelli's eagle	4·50	55
700	115dh. Barbary sheep	2·00	40

178 Cycling

1976. Olympic Games, Montreal. Multicoloured.

701	15dh. Type **178**	10	10
702	25dh. Boxing	20	10
703	70dh. Football	95	20
MS704	120×78 mm. 150dh. Symbolic motif depicting Olympic sports	1·25	1·25

179 Global 'Tree'

1976. Non-Aligned Countries' Colombo Conference.

705	**179**	115dh. multicoloured	95	35

180 Agricultural and Industrial Symbols

1976. Seventh Anniversary of Revolution.

706	**180**	30dh. multicoloured	15	10
707	**180**	40dh. multicoloured	45	15
708	**180**	100dh. multicoloured	90	55
MS709		120×80 mm. 200dh. Musicians and oil pipeline (24×41 mm)	2·00	2·00

181 Various Sports

1976. Fifth Arab Games, Damascus.

710	**181**	15dh. multicoloured	10	10
711	**181**	30dh. multicoloured	15	10
712	**181**	100dh. multicoloured	1·00	55
MS713		120×80 mm. 145dh. Wrestlers and sporting emblems	2·10	2·10

182 Chessboard and Pieces

1976. Arab Chess Olympiad, Tripoli.

714	**182**	15dh. multicoloured	95	15
715	**182**	30dh. multicoloured	1·60	60
716	**182**	100dh. multicoloured	5·00	95

183 Ratima

1976. Libyan Flora. Multicoloured.

717	15dh. Type **183**	15	10
718	20dh. 'Sword of Crow'	15	10
719	35dh. 'Lasef'	50	10
720	40dh. 'Yadid'	80	15
721	70dh. Esparto grass	1·90	25

184 Emblem and Text

1976. International Archives Council.

722	**184**	15dh. multicoloured	10	10
723	**184**	35dh. multicoloured	15	10
724	**184**	70dh. multicoloured	55	20

186 Kaaba, Mecca

1976. Pilgrimage to Mecca.

729	**186**	15dh. multicoloured	10	10
730	**186**	30dh. multicoloured	15	10
731	**186**	70dh. multicoloured	30	20
732	**186**	100dh. multicoloured	75	30

187

1977. Coil Stamps.

733	187	5dh. multicoloured	10	10
734	187	20dh. multicoloured	10	10
735	187	50dh. multicoloured	55	40

188 Basket

1977. 15th International Trade Fair, Tripoli. Multicoloured.

736	10dh. Type 188	10	10
737	20dh. Leather bag	10	10
738	30dh. Vase	15	10
739	40dh. Slippers	45	15
740	50dh. Saddle	60	15
MS741	139×100 mm. 100dh. Horse wearing saddle and harness (49×53 mm). Imperf	65	65

189 Girl with Flowers

1977. Children's Day. Multicoloured.

742	10dh. Type 189	10	10
743	30dh. Clothes shop	15	10
744	40dh. Orchard	20	15

190 Fighters and Machine-gun

1977. Ninth Anniversary of Battle of Al-Karamah.

745	190	15dh. multicoloured	10	10
746	190	25dh. multicoloured	15	10
747	190	70dh. multicoloured	80	25

191 Protected Child

1977. World Health Day.

748	191	15dh. multicoloured	10	10
749	191	30dh. multicoloured	15	10

192 APU Emblem

1977. 25th Anniversary of Arab Postal Union.

750	192	15dh. multicoloured	10	10
751	192	30dh. multicoloured	15	10
752	192	40dh. multicoloured	20	15

193 Maps of Libya and Africa

1977. Organisation of African Unity Conference, Tripoli.

753	193	40dh. multicoloured	1·00	20
754	193	70dh. multicoloured	1·50	30

194 Heart on Map of Libya

1977. Red Crescent Commemoration.

755	194	5dh. multicoloured	10	10
756	194	10dh. multicoloured	15	10
757	194	30dh. multicoloured	65	15

195 Messenger and Jet Fighter

1977. Communications Progress. Multicoloured.

758	20dh. Type 195	15	10
759	25dh. Arab rider and Concorde	30	15
760	60dh. Satellite and aerial	55	20
761	115dh. Television relay via satellite	1·10	65
762	150dh. Camel rider and Boeing 727 airliner loading	1·75	90
763	200dh. Apollo–Soyuz link	2·25	1·10
MS764	Two sheets each 118×89 mm. (a) 300dh. Zeppelin (51×35 mm); (b) 300dh. Planetary system (51×35 mm)	4·50	4·50

196 Mosque

1977. Libyan Mosques.

765	196	40dh. multicoloured	20	15
766	-	50dh. multicoloured (vert)	50	15
767	-	70dh. multicoloured	70	20
768	-	90dh. multicoloured	85	30
769	-	100dh. multicoloured (vert)	1·00	35
770	-	115dh. multicoloured	1·25	75

Designs: 50dh. to 115dh. Various mosques.

197 Archbishop Capucci

1977. Third Anniversary of Archbishop Capucci's Imprisonment.

771	197	30dh. multicoloured	15	10
772	197	40dh. multicoloured	20	15
773	197	115dh. multicoloured	1·25	60

198 Clasped Hands and Emblems

1977. Eighth Anniversary of Revolution.

774	198	15dh. multicoloured	10	10
775	198	30dh. multicoloured	15	10
776	198	85dh. multicoloured	80	25
MS777		120×80 mm. 100dh. Star emblem	1·80	1·80

199 Swimming

1977. Arab School Sports. Multicoloured.

778	5dh. Type 199	10	10
779	10dh. Handball (horiz)	10	10
780	15dh. Football	15	10
781	25dh. Table tennis (horiz)	50	20
782	40dh. Basketball	1·10	65

200 Championship Emblem

1977. First International Turf Championships, Tripoli. Multicoloured.

783	5dh. Horse jumping fence (facing left)	10	10
784	10dh. Arab horseman	10	10
785	15dh. Type 200	15	10
786	45dh. Horse jumping fence (facing right)	55	15
787	115dh. Arab horseman racing	1·40	80
MS788	124×83 mm. 100dh. 115dh. Arab horsemen racing	75	75

201 Dome of the Rock

1977. Palestine Welfare.

789	201	5dh. multicoloured	10	10
790	201	10dh. multicoloured	10	10

202 Fort, and Hands writing Arabic Script in Book

1977. The *Green Book*. Multicoloured.

791	35dh. Type 202	15	10
792	40dh. Type 202 (text in English)	20	15
793	115dh. Dove with *Green Book* and map	1·25	70

203 Emblem

1977. World Standards Day.

794	203	5dh. multicoloured	10	10
795	203	15dh. multicoloured	10	10
796	203	30dh. multicoloured	15	10

204 Giraffe

1978. Rock Drawings from Wadi Mathendous. Multicoloured.

797	10dh. Crocodiles (horiz)	10	10
798	15dh. Elephant hunt (horiz)	10	10
799	20dh. Type 204	15	10
800	30dh. Antelope (horiz)	45	15
801	40dh. Elephant (horiz)	65	20

205 Silver Pendant

1978. 16th Tripoli International Fair.

802	205	5dh. silver, black and red	10	10
803	-	10dh. silver, black & violet	10	10
804	-	20dh. silver, black & green	10	10
805	-	25dh. silver, black and blue	15	10
806	-	115dh. silver, black & blue	1·10	70

Designs: 10dh. Silver ornamental plate; 20dh. Necklace with three pendants; 25dh. Crescent-shaped silver brooch; 115dh. Silver armband.

206 Compass and Lightning Flash

1978. Arab Cultural Education Organisation.

807	206	30dh. multicoloured	20	15
808	206	115dh. multicoloured	1·40	65

207 Dancing a Round

1978. Children's Day. Children's Paintings. Multicoloured.

809	40dh. Type 207	20	15
810	40dh. Children with placards	20	15
811	40dh. Shopping street	20	15
812	40dh. Playground	20	15
813	40dh. Wedding ceremony	20	15

208 Brickwork Clenched Fist

1978. Arab Achievements

814	208	30dh. multicoloured	20	15
815	208	115dh. multicoloured	1·10	35

209 Blood Pressure Meter

1978. World Hypertension Month.

816	209	30dh. multicoloured	15	15
817	209	115dh. multicoloured	1·25	35

210 Microwave Antenna

1978. World Telecommunications Day.

818	210	30dh. multicoloured	15	15
819	210	115dh. multicoloured	1·00	35

211 Games Emblem

1978. Third African Games, Algiers.

820	**211**	15dh. copper, violet & blk	10	10
821	**211**	30dh. silver, lilac and black	15	10
822	**211**	115dh. gold, purple & blk	1·10	35

212 Aerial View of Airport

1978. Inauguration of Tripoli International Airport. Multicoloured.

823	40dh. Type **212**	30	10
824	115dh. Terminal building	1·25	65

213 Ankara

1978. Turkish–Libyan Friendship.

825	**213**	30dh. multicoloured	15	10
826	**213**	35dh. multicoloured	15	10
827	**213**	115dh. multicoloured	1·10	35

214 Armed Forces

1978. Ninth Anniversary of 1 September Revolution. Multicoloured.

828	30dh. Type **214**	60	15
829	35dh. Tower, *Green Book* and symbols of progress	15	10
830	115dh. Industry	95	70
MS831	116×90 mm. 100dh. *Green Book* and buildings (50×40 mm)	95	70

215 Crater

1978. Second Symposium on Geology of Libya. Multicoloured.

832	30dh. Type **215**	15	10
833	40dh. Oasis	20	15
834	115dh. Crater (different)	1·10	60

216 *The Green Book* and Different Races

1978. International Anti-Apartheid Year.

835	**216**	30dh. multicoloured	15	10
836	**216**	40dh. multicoloured	20	15
837	**216**	115dh. multicoloured	85	35

217 Pilgrims, Minarets and Kaaba

1978. Pilgrimage to Mecca.

838	**217**	5dh. multicoloured	10	10
839	**217**	10dh. multicoloured	10	10
840	**217**	15dh. multicoloured	10	10
841	**217**	20dh. multicoloured	15	10

218 Clasped Hands and Globe

1978. UN Conference for Technical Co-operation between Developing Countries.

842	**218**	30dh. multicoloured	15	10
843	**218**	40dh. multicoloured	20	15
844	**218**	115dh. multicoloured	85	35

219 Workers, Rifles, Torch and Flag

1978. Arab Countries Summit Conference. Multicoloured.

845	30dh. Type **219**	15	10
846	40dh. Map of Middle East, eagle and crowd (horiz)	20	15
847	115dh. As 40dh.	85	35
848	145dh. Type **219**	1·00	45

220 Human Figure and Scales

1978. 30th Anniversary of Declaration of Human Rights.

849	**220**	15dh. multicoloured	10	10
850	**220**	30dh. multicoloured	20	15
851	**220**	115dh. multicoloured	50	35

221 Horse Racing and Fort

1978. Libyan Study Centre.

852	**221**	20dh. multicoloured	15	10
853	**221**	40dh. multicoloured	20	15
854	**221**	115dh. multicoloured	95	60

222 Lilienthal's Biplane Glider

1978. 75th Anniversary of First Powered Flight. Multicoloured

855	20dh. Type **222**	10	10
856	25dh. Lindbergh's *Spirit of St. Louis*	10	10
857	30dh. Admiral Richard Byrd's Trimotor *Floyd Bennett*	80	25
858	50dh. Bleriot 5190 Santos Dumont flying boat and airship *Graf Zeppelin*	95	35
859	115dh. Wright brothers and Wright Type A	1·10	75
MS860	Two sheets each 96×103 mm. (a) 100dh. Daedalus and Icarus: (b) 100dh. Eagle and Boeing 727	2·10	2·10

223 Libyans, Torch and Laurel Wreath

1979

861	**223**	5dh. multicoloured	10	10
862	**223**	10dh. multicoloured	10	10
863	**223**	15dh. multicoloured	10	10
864	**223**	30dh. multicoloured	20	10
865	**223**	50dh. multicoloured	20	10
866	**223**	60dh. multicoloured	25	15
867	**223**	70dh. multicoloured	30	15
868	**223**	100dh. multicoloured	75	25
869	**223**	115dh. multicoloured	85	30
870	**223**	200dh. multicoloured	1·10	45
870a	**223**	250dh. multicoloured	1·90	65
871	**223**	500dh. multicoloured	3·50	65
872	**223**	1000dh. multicoloured	6·75	3·50
872a	**223**	1500dh. multicoloured	12·50	4·25
872b	**223**	2500dh. multicoloured	23·00	7·50

Nos. 861/869 measure 18×23 mm and Nos. 870/872b 26×32 mm.

224 Mounted Dorcas Gazelle Head

1979. Coil Stamps.

873	**224**	5dh. multicoloured	15	10
874	**224**	20dh. multicoloured	25	10
875	**224**	50dh. multicoloured	80	25

225 Tortoise

1979. Libyan Animals. Multicoloured.

876	5dh. Type **225**	10	10
877	10dh. Addax (vert)	10	10
878	15dh. Algerian hedgehog	20	10
879	20dh. North African crested porcupine	20	10
880	30dh. Dromedaries	30	15
881	35dh. Wild cat (vert)	40	15
882	45dh. Dorcas gazelle (vert)	95	25
883	115dh. Cheetah	1·90	75

226 Carpet

1979. 17th Tripoli International Trade Fair.

884	**226**	10dh. multicoloured	10	10
885	-	15dh. multicoloured	10	10
886	-	30dh. multicoloured	15	10
887	-	45dh. multicoloured	15	10
888	-	115dh. multicoloured	85	35

Designs: 15dh. to 115dh. Different carpets.

227 Aircraft and People

1979. International Year of the Child. Children's Paintings (1st series). Multicoloured.

889	20dh. Type **227**	10	10
890	20dh. Shepherd with flock	10	10
891	20dh. Open air cafe	10	10
892	20dh. Boat in storm	10	10
893	20dh. Policeman on traffic duty	10	10

See also Nos. 975/979.

228 World Map, Koran and Symbols of Arab Achievements

1979. Arab Achievements

894	**228**	45dh. multicoloured	20	15
895	**228**	70dh. multicoloured	55	20

229 Radar Tower and Map

1979. World Meteorological Day.

896	**229**	15dh. multicoloured	10	10
897	**229**	30dh. multicoloured	15	10
898	**229**	50dh. multicoloured	20	15

230 Medical Care

1979. World Health Day.

899	**230**	40dh. multicoloured	20	15

231 *Carpobrotus acinaciformis*

1979. Libyan Flowers. Multicoloured.

900	10dh. Type **231**	10	10
901	15dh. *Caralluma europaea*	10	10
902	20dh. *Arum cirenaicum*	10	10
903	35dh. *Lavatera arborea*	50	15
904	40dh. *Capparis spinosa*	50	15
905	50dh. *Ranunculus asiaticus*	60	15

232 Farmer and Sheep

1979. Tenth Anniversary of Revolution. Multicoloured

906	15dh. Type **232**	10	10
907	15dh. Crowd with *The Green Book*	10	10
908	15dh. Oil field	10	10
909	15dh. Refinery	10	10
910	30dh. Dish aerial	15	10
911	30dh. Hospital	15	10
912	30dh. Doctor examining patient	15	10
913	30dh. Surgeon	15	10
914	40dh. Street, Tripoli	20	15
915	40dh. Steel mill	20	15
916	40dh. Tanks	20	15
917	40dh. Tuareg horsemen	20	15
918	70dh. Revolutionaries and *The Green Book*	70	20
919	70dh. Crowd within map of Libya	70	20
920	70dh. Mullah	70	20
921	70dh. Student	70	20
MS922	Two sheets each 97×102 mm. (a) 50dh. Revolutionary symbols (82×28 mm); (b) 50dh. Monument (83×35 mm). Imperf	1·10	1·10

233 Volleyball

1979. Universiada '79 World University Games, Mexico City. Multicoloured.

923	45dh. Type **233**	20	15
924	115dh. Football	1·10	30

234 Emblem

1979. Third World Telecommunications Exhibition, Geneva.

925	**234**	45dh. multicoloured	20	15
926	**234**	115dh. multicoloured	1·25	30

235 Seminar Emblem and Crowd

1979. International Seminar on *The Green Book.* Multicoloured.

927	10dh. Type **235**	10	10
928	35dh. Seminar in progress (horiz) (70×43 mm)	45	15
929	100dh. Colonel Gaddafi with *The Green Book*	1·00	30
MS930	89×114 mm. 100dh. Colonel Gaddafi holding *The Green Book.* Imperf	1·25	1·25

236 Horsemen in Town

1979. Evacuation of Foreign Forces. Multicoloured.

931	30dh. Type **236**	15	10
932	40dh. Tuareg horsemen	20	15
MS933	99×100 mm. 100dh. Symbols of industry, education and agriculture (86×30 mm). Imperf	55	55

237 Football Match

1979. Mediterranean Games, Split.

934	**237**	15dh. multicoloured	10	10
935	**237**	30dh. multicoloured	50	10
936	**237**	70dh. multicoloured	1·25	20

238 Cyclist and Emblem

1979. Junior Cycling Championships, Tripoli. Multicoloured.

937	15dh. Type **238**	10	10
938	30dh. Cyclists and emblem	15	10

239 Horse-jumping

1979. Pre-Olympics. Multicoloured.

939	45dh. Type **239**	20	15
940	60dh. Javelin	55	15
941	115dh. Hurdles	1·10	55
942	160dh. Football	1·40	65
MS943	Two sheets each 103×81 mm. (a) 150dh. As No. 941; (b) 150dh. As No. 942	2·60	2·60

Nos. 939/942 exist from sheets on which an overall Moscow Olympics emblem in silver was superimposed on the stamps.

240 Figure clothed in Palestinian Flag

1979. Solidarity with Palestinian People.

944	**240**	30dh. multicoloured	15	10
945	**240**	115dh. multicoloured	1·10	30

241 Ploughing

1980. World Olive Oil Year.

946	**241**	15dh. multicoloured	10	10
947	**241**	30dh. multicoloured	15	10
948	**241**	45dh. multicoloured	20	15

242 Hockey (left)

1980. National Sports. Multicoloured.

949	10dh. Type **242**	10	10
950	10dh. Hockey (right)	10	10
951	10dh. Leap-frog (left)	10	10
952	10dh. Leap-frog (right)	10	10
953	15dh. Long jump (left)	10	10
954	15dh. Long jump (right)	10	10
955	15dh. Ball catching (left)	10	10
956	15dh. Ball catching (right)	10	10
957	20dh. Wrestling (left)	10	10
958	20dh. Wrestling (right)	10	10
959	20dh. Stone throwing (left)	10	10
960	20dh. Stone throwing (right)	10	10
961	30dh. Tug-of-war (left)	15	10
962	30dh. Tug-of-war (right)	15	10
963	30dh. Jumping (left)	15	10
964	30dh. Jumping (right)	15	10
965	45dh. Horsemen (left)	45	15
966	45dh. Horsemen (right)	45	15
967	45dh. Horsemen with whips (left)	45	15
968	45dh. Horsemen with whips (right)	45	15

Nos. 949/968 were issued together, divided into *se-tenant* blocks of four within the sheet, each horizontal pair forming a composite design.

243 Pipes

1980. 18th Tripoli International Fair. Multicoloured.

969	5dh. Drum (horiz)	10	10
970	10dh. Drum (different) (horiz)	10	10
971	15dh. Type **243**	10	10
972	20dh. Bagpipes (horiz)	10	10
973	25dh. Stringed instrument and bow (horiz)	15	10
MS974	68×87 mm. 100dh. Musicians	55	55

1980. International Year of the Child (1979) (2nd issue). As T **227**. Multicoloured.

975	20dh. Horse Riding	10	10
976	20dh. Beach scene	10	10
977	20dh. Fish	10	10
978	20dh. Birthday party	10	10
979	20dh. Sheep Festival	10	10

244 Mosque and Kaaba

1980. 400th Anniversary of Hejira.

980	**244**	50dh. multicoloured	25	15
981	**244**	115dh. multicoloured	1·10	55

245 Surgical Operation and Hospital

1980. World Health Day.

982	**245**	20dh. multicoloured	10	10
983	**245**	50dh. multicoloured	50	15

246 Battle of Shoghab 'Shahat', 1913

1980. Battles (1st series). Multicoloured.

984	20dh. Gardabia, 1915	20	15
985	35dh. Gardabia	10	10
986	20dh. Type **246**	10	10
987	35dh. Shoghab 'Shahat'	20	15
988	20dh. Fundugh al-Shibani 'Garian'	10	10
989	35dh. Fundagh al-Shibani 'Garian'	20	15
990	20dh. Yefren	10	10
991	35dh. Yefren	20	15
992	20dh. Ghira 'Brak'	20	15
993	35dh. Ghira 'Brak'	20	15
994	20dh. El Hani (Shiat)	35	15
995	35dh. El Hani (Shiat)	60	25
996	20dh. Sebah	20	15
997	35dh. Sebah	20	15
998	20dh. Sirt	10	10
999	35dh. Sirt	10	10

The two values commemorating each battle were issued in *se-tenant* pairs, each pair forming a composite design.

See also Nos. 1027/1050, 1140/1163 and 1257/1280.

247 Flame

1980. Sheikh Zarruq Festival.

1000	**247**	40dh. multicoloured	20	15
1001	**247**	115dh. multicoloured	1·00	65
MS1002		93×75 mm. 100dh. multicoloured	1·40	1·40

Design: 93×75 mm. 100dh. Domes and minaret of mosque.

248 Ghadames

1980. Arabian Towns Organisation. Multicoloured.

1003	15dh. Type **248**	10	10
1004	30dh. Derna	15	10
1005	50dh. Ahmad Pasha Mosque, Tripoli	50	15

249 Guides on Hike

1980. 14th Pan-Arab Scout Jamboree. Multicoloured.

1006	15dh. Type **249**	10	10
1007	30dh. Guides cooking	15	10
1008	50dh. Cub Scouts cooking	25	15
1009	115dh. Scouts map-reading	1·10	60
MS1010	Two sheets each 67×95 mm. (a) 100dh. Type **249**; (b) 100dh. As No. 1008	1·50	1·50

250 Oil Refinery

1980. 11th Anniversary of Revolution. Multicoloured.

1011	5dh. Type **250**	10	10
1012	10dh. Recreation and youth	10	10
1013	15dh. Agriculture	10	10
1014	25dh. Boeing 727-200 airplane and liner	60	15
1015	40dh. Education	20	15
1016	115dh. Housing	95	30
MS1017	70×79 mm. 100dh. Students and workers (29×49 mm)	80	80

251 Camels, Map of Libya and Conference Emblem

1980. World Tourism Conference, Manila. Multicoloured.

1018	45dh. Type **251**	20	15
1019	115dh. Emblem, map and camel riders	95	30

252 Figures supporting OPEC Emblem

1980. 20th Anniversary of Organisation of Petroleum Exporting Countries. Multicoloured.

1020	45dh. OPEC emblem and globe	20	15
1021	115dh. Type **252**	95	30

253 Death of Omar el Mukhtar

1980. 49th Death Anniversary of Omar el Mukhtar (patriot).

1022	**253**	20dh. multicoloured	10	10
1023	**253**	35dh. multicoloured	20	15
MS1024		104×85 mm. 253 100dh. multicoloured	55	55

253a Map of Libya and Science Symbols

1980. Birth Millenary of Avicenna (philosopher) and School Scientific Exhibition. Multicoloured.

1025	45dh. Type **253a**	20	15
1026	115d. Avicenna and Exhibition Emblem	1·10	30

1981. Battles (2nd series). As T **246**. Multicoloured.

1027	20dh. Zuara	10	10
1028	35dh. Zuara	15	15
1029	20dh. Tawargha	10	10
1030	35dh. Tawargha	15	15
1031	20dh. Dernah	10	10
1032	35dh. Dernah	15	15
1033	20dh. Bir Tagreft	10	10
1034	35dh. Bir Tagreft	15	15
1035	20dh. Funduk El Jamel 'Misurata'	10	10
1036	35dh. Funduk El Jamel 'Misurata'	15	15

1037	20dh. Sidi El Khemri 'Gusbat'	10	10
1038	35dh. Sidi El Khemri 'Gusbat'	15	15
1039	20dh. El Khoms	10	10
1040	35dh. El Khoms	15	15
1041	20dh. Roghdalin 'Menshia'	10	10
1042	35dh. Roghdalin 'Menshia'	15	15
1043	20dh. Ain Zara 'Tripoli'	10	10
1044	35dh. Ain Zara 'Tripoli'	15	15
1045	20dh. Rughbat el Naga 'Benina'	10	10
1046	35dh. Rughbat el Naga 'Benina'	15	15
1047	20dh. Tobruk	10	10
1048	35dh. Tobruk	15	15
1049	20dh. Ikshadia 'Werfella'	10	10
1050	35dh. Ikshadia 'Werfella'	15	15

The two values commemorating each battle were issued in *se-tenant* pairs, each pair forming a composite design.

254 Tent, Trees and Sun

1981. Children's Day. Children's Paintings. Multicoloured.

1051	20dh. Type **254**	10	10
1052	20dh. Women	10	10
1053	20dh. Picnic	10	10
1054	20dh. Aeroplane and playing children	10	10
1055	20dh. Mosque and man with camel	10	10

255 Central Bank

1981. 25th Anniversary of Central Bank of Libya.

1056	**255**	45dh. multicoloured	15	15
1057	**255**	115dh. multicoloured	95	35
MS1058 87×61 mm. **255** 50dh. multicoloured			20	20

256 Pots

1981. Tripoli International Fair. Multicoloured.

1059	5dh. Type **256**	10	10
1060	10dh. Silver coffee pot (vert)	10	10
1061	15dh. Long-necked vase (vert)	10	10
1062	45dh. Round-bellied vase	45	15
1063	115dh. Jug	1·10	35

257 Crowd and *The Green Book* Stamp of 1977

1981. People's Authority Declaration.

1064	**257**	50dh. multicoloured	15	15
1065	**257**	115dh. multicoloured	95	35

258 Tajoura Hospital, Medical Complex, Patients receiving Treatment and WHO Emblem

1981. World Health Day.

1066	**258**	45dh. multicoloured	15	15
1067	**258**	115dh. multicoloured	95	35

259 Eye and Man on Crutches

1981. International Year of Disabled People.

1068	**259**	20dh. green, blue & black	10	10
1069	-	45dh. green, black & blue	15	15
1070	-	115dh. blue and green	1·00	35

Designs: 45dh. Globe and IYDP emblem; 115dh. Hands holding shield with IYDP emblem, eye and man on crutch.

260 Horse

1981. Libyan Mosaics. Multicoloured.

1071	10dh. Type **260**	10	10
1072	20dh. Ship	10	10
1073	30dh. Birds, fish and flowers	10	10
1074	40dh. Leopard	40	15
1075	50dh. Man playing musical instrument	50	15
1076	115dh. Fish	1·10	35

261 Racial Discrimination Emblem

1981. International Year Against Racial Discrimination.

1077	**261**	45dh. multicoloured	25	25
1078	**261**	50dh. multicoloured	55	30

262 Jet Fighters and Sud Aviation Alouette III Helicopter (left-hand stamp)

1981. 12th Anniversary of Revolution.

1079	**262**	5dh. blue and light blue	15	10
1080	-	5dh. blue and light blue	15	10
1081	-	5dh. blue and light blue	10	10
1082	-	5dh. blue and light blue	10	10
1083	-	10dh. black and blue	10	10
1084	-	10dh. black and blue	10	10
1085	-	10dh. black and blue	10	10
1086	-	10dh. black and blue	10	10
1087	-	15dh. brown & lt brown	10	10
1088	-	15dh. brown & lt brown	10	10
1089	-	15dh. brown & lt brown	10	10
1090	-	15dh. brown & lt brown	10	10
1091	-	20dh. blue and green	15	15
1092	-	20dh. blue and green	15	15
1093	-	20dh. blue and green	15	15
1094	-	20dh. blue and green	15	15
1095	-	25dh. brown and yellow	15	15
1096	-	25dh. brown and yellow	15	15
1097	-	25dh. brown and yellow	15	15
1098	-	25dh. brown and yellow	15	15
MS1099 127×102 mm. 50dh. multicoloured			30	30

Designs: Vert—No. 1080, Jet fighter (right-hand stamp); Nos. 1081/1082, Parachutists; Nos. 1083/1084, Tank parade; Nos. 1085/1086, Marching frogmen; Nos. 1087/1088, Anti-aircraft rocket trucks; Nos. 1089/1090, Missile trucks. Horiz—Nos. 1091/1092, Marching sailors; Nos. 1093/1094, Jeeps and anti-aircraft rocket trucks; Nos. 1095/1096, Armoured vehicles and landrovers; Nos. 1097/1098, Tank parade; No. **MS**1099 50dh. Marching sailors (59×34 mm).

Each pair forms a horizontal composite design, the first number being the left-hand stamp in each instance.

263 Wheat and Plough

1981. World Food Day.

1100	**263**	45dh. multicoloured	25	25
1101	**263**	200dh. multicoloured	1·75	95

264 *Pseudotergumia fidia*

1981. Butterflies. Multicoloured.

1102	5dh. Type **264**	15	10
1103	5dh. *Chazara prieuri* (sun in background)	15	10
1104	5dh. *Polygonia c-album* (trees in background)	15	10
1105	5dh. *Colias crocea* (mosque in background)	15	10
1106	10dh. *Anthocharis bellia* (face value bottom right)	15	10
1107	10dh. *Pandoriana pandora* (face value bottom left)	15	10
1108	10dh. *Melanargia ines* (face value top right)	15	10
1109	10dh. *Charaxes jasius* (face value top left)	15	10
1110	15dh. *Nymphales antiopa* (face value bottom right)	30	30
1111	15dh. *Eurodryas desfontainii* (face value bottom left)	30	30
1112	15dh. *Iphiclides podalirius* (face value top right)	30	30
1113	15dh. *Glaucopsyche melanops* (face value top left)	30	30
1114	25dh. *Spialia sertorius* (face value bottom right)	50	45
1115	25dh. *Pieris brassicae* (face value bottom left)	50	45
1116	25dh. *Lysandra albicans* (face value top right)	50	45
1117	25dh. *Celastrina argiolus* (face value top left)	50	45
MS1118 213×144 mm. Nos. 1102/1117		4·25	4·25

The four designs of each value were issued together in small sheets of four, showing composite background designs.

265 Grapes

1981. Fruit. Multicoloured.

1119	5dh. Type **265**	10	10
1120	10dh. Dates	10	10
1121	15dh. Lemons	10	10
1122	20dh. Oranges	15	15
1123	35dh. Barbary figs	20	20
1124	55dh. Pomegranate	65	30

266 IYDP Emblem and Globe

1981. International Year of Disabled Persons.

1125	**266**	45dh. multicoloured	25	25
1126	**266**	115dh. multicoloured	90	55

267 Animals (looking right)

1982. Libyan Mosaics. Multicoloured.

1127	45dh. Type **267**	50	25
1128	45dh. Orpheus	50	25
1129	45dh. Animals (looking left)	50	25
1130	45dh. Fish	50	25
1131	45dh. Fishermen	50	25
1132	45dh. Fish and ducks	50	25
1133	45dh. Farm	50	25
1134	45dh. Birds and fruit	50	25
1135	45dh. Milking	50	25

268 Koran Texts leading to Kaaba

1982. Third Koran Reading Contest. Multicoloured.

1136	10dh. Type **268**	10	10
1137	35dh. Koran and formation of the World	20	20
1138	115dh. Reading the Koran	95	55
MS1139 111×80 mm. 100dh. As No. 1138		80	80

1982. Battles (3rd series). As T **246**. Multicoloured.

1140	20dh. Hun 'Gioffra'	15	15
1141	35dh. Hun 'Gioffra'	20	20
1142	20dh. Gedabia	15	15
1143	35dh. Gedabia	20	20
1144	20dh. El Asaba 'Gianduba'	15	15
1145	35dh. El Asaba 'Gianduba'	20	20
1146	20dh. El Habela	15	15
1147	35dh. El Habela	20	20
1148	20dh. Suk El Ahad 'Tarhuna'	15	15
1149	35dh. Suk El Ahad 'Tarhuna'	20	20
1150	20dh. El Tangi	15	15
1151	35dh. El Tangi	20	20
1152	20dh. Sokna	15	15
1153	35dh. Sokna	20	20
1154	20dh. Wadi Smalus 'Jabel El Akdar'	15	15
1155	35dh. Wadi Smalus 'Jabel El Akdar'	20	20
1156	20dh. Sidi Abuagela 'Agelat'	15	15
1157	35dh. Sidi Abuagela 'Agelat'	20	20
1158	20dh. Sidi Surur 'Zeliten'	15	15
1159	35dh. Sidi Surur 'Zeliten'	20	20
1160	20dh. Kuefia	15	15
1161	35dh. Kuefia	20	20
1162	20dh. Abunjeim	15	15
1163	35dh. Abunjeim	20	20

The two values commemorating each battle were issued in *se-tenant* pairs, each pair forming a composite design.

269 Grinding Flour

1982. Tripoli International Fair. Multicoloured.

1164	5dh. Type **269**	10	10
1165	10dh. Ploughing	10	10
1166	25dh. Stacking hay	15	15
1167	35dh. Weaving	20	20
1168	45dh. Cooking	50	25
1169	100dh. Harvesting	95	50

270 'ALFATAH' forming Farm Vehicle

1982. People's Authority Declaration. Multicoloured.

1170	100dh. Type **270**	75	50
1171	200dh. Colonel Gaddafi, old man, *The Green Book* and guns	1·75	95
1172	300dh. Rejoicing crowd	2·50	1·40

271 Scout flying Model Airship

1982. 75th Anniversary of Boy Scout Movement. Multicoloured

1173		100dh. Type **271**	75	50
1174		200dh. Scouts helping injured dog	1·75	95
1175		300dh. Scout reading to old man	1·75	1·40
1176		400dh. Scout with model rocket	3·75	2·25
MS1177		Two sheets each 77×73 mm. (a) 500dh. Colonel Gaddafi and scouts (38×41 mm); (b) 500dh. *The Green Book* (38×41 mm)	4·75	4·75

272 Map of Africa and AFC Emblem

1982. African Football Cup Competition.

1178	**272**	100dh. multicoloured	95	50
1179	**272**	200dh. multicoloured	1·90	95

273 Footballer

1982. World Cup Football Championship, Spain. Multicoloured.

1180		45dh. Type **273**	25	25
1181		100dh. Footballer (different)	75	50
1182		200dh. As No. 1173	1·60	95
1183		300dh. Footballer and goalkeeper	2·25	1·40
MS1184		135×112 mm. 500dh. Type **273**	3·50	3·50

274 Palestinian Children

1982. Palestinian Children's Day. Multicoloured.

1185		20dh. Type **274**	15	15
1186		20dh. Girl with dish	15	15
1187		20dh. Child with turban	15	15
1188		20dh. Young child	15	15
1189		20dh. Young boy	15	15

275 Lanner Falcon

1982. Birds. Multicoloured.

1190		15dh. Type **275**	35	25
1191		15dh. Eurasian swift	35	25
1192		15dh. Peregrine falcon	35	25
1193		15dh. Greater flamingo	35	25
1194		25dh. Whitethroat	60	35
1195		25dh. Turtle dove	60	35
1196		25dh. Black-bellied sandgrouse	60	35
1197		25dh. Egyptian vulture	60	35
1198		45dh. Golden oriole	1·00	60
1199		45dh. European bee-eater	1·00	60
1200		45dh. River kingfisher	1·00	60
1201		45dh. European roller	1·00	60
1202		95dh. Barbary partridge	2·00	1·25
1203		95dh. Barn owl	2·00	1·25
1204		95dh. Cream-coloured courser	2·00	1·25
1205		95dh. Hoopoe	2·00	1·25
MS1206		142×214 mm. Nos. 1190/1205	14·00	14·00

The four designs of each value were printed together in *se-tenant* blocks of four, forming a composite design.

276 Nurses' Class, Operating Theatre and Doctor examining Child

1982. Teaching Hospitals.

1207	**276**	95dh. multicoloured	85	50
1208	**276**	100dh. multicoloured	85	50
1209	**276**	205dh. multicoloured	2·00	1·10

277 Map of Libya and APU Emblem

1982. 30th Anniversary of Arab Postal Union.

1210	**277**	100dh. multicoloured	95	50
1211	**277**	200dh. multicoloured	1·90	95

278 19th-century Chinese King and Diagram of Fischer v Spassky, 1972

1982. World Chess Championship, Moscow. Multicoloured

1212		100dh. Type **278**	1·25	50
1213		100dh. African king and diagram of Karpov v Korchnoi, 1978	1·25	50
1214		100dh. Modern bishop and diagram of Smyslov v Karpov, 1971	1·25	50
1215		100dh. 19th-century European rook and diagram of Tal v Vadasz, 1977	1·25	50
MS1216		87×68 mm. 500dh. Chess-piece on board	4·75	4·75

Nos. 1212/1215 were printed together, *se-tenant*, forming a composite design.

279 Hexagonal Pattern

1982. World Telecommunications Day.

1217	**279**	100dh. multicoloured	75	50
1218	**279**	200dh. multicoloured	1·50	95

280 Map of Libya and *The Green Book*

1982. 51st Anniversary of International Philatelic Federation (FIP).

1219	**280**	200dh. multicoloured	1·75	95
MS1220		70×80 mm. **280** 300dh. multicoloured	2·25	2·25

281 Family and Flag

1982. Organisation of African Unity Summit. Multicoloured.

1221		50dh. Type **281**	30	30
1222		100dh. Map, dove and symbols of industry and agriculture	75	50
1223		200dh. President Gaddafi and crowd with *The Green Book* (65×36 mm.)	1·90	95

282 President Gaddafi and Jet Aircraft

1982. 13th Anniversary of Revolution. Multicoloured.

1225		15dh. Type **282**	15	10
1226		20dh. Gaddafi, soldiers and rockets	15	10
1227		30dh. Gaddafi, sailors and naval vessels	50	25
1228		45dh. Gaddafi, soldiers and tanks	25	25
1229		70dh. Gaddafi, and armed forces	60	35
1230		100dh. Gaddafi and women soldiers	90	50
MS1231		114×100 mm. 200dh. Gaddafi, crowd and armed forces. Imperf	1·90	95

283 Palm Tree and Red Crescent

1982. 25th Anniversary of Libyan Red Crescent. Multicoloured.

1232		100dh. Type **283**	95	50
1233		200dh. '25' within crescents	1·90	95

284 Globe, Dove and Rifle

1982. Solidarity with Palestinian People.

1234	**284**	100dh. black, mauve and green	95	40
1235	**284**	200dh. black, blue and green	1·90	80

285 Gaddafi, Crowd, *The Green Book* and Emblems

1982. Al Fateh University Symposium on *The Green Book*. Multicoloured.

1236		100dh. Type **285**	95	45
1237		200dh. Gaddafi, *The Green Book*, map and emblems	1·90	95

286 Philadelphus

1983. Flowers. Multicoloured.

1238		25dh. Type **286**	15	10
1239		25dh. Hypericum	15	10
1240		25dh. Antirrhinum	15	10
1241		25dh. Lily	15	10
1242		25dh. Capparis	15	10
1243		25dh. Tropaeolum	15	10
1244		25dh. Roses	15	10
1245		25dh. Chrysanthemum	15	10
1246		25dh. *Nigella damascena*	15	10
1247		25dh. *Guilladia lanceolata*	15	10
1248		25dh. Dahlia	15	10
1249		25dh. *Dianthus caryophyllus*	15	10
1250		25dh. *Notobasis syriaca*	15	10
1251		25dh. *Nerium oleander*	15	10
1252		25dh. *Iris histroides*	15	10
1253		25dh. *Scolymus hispanicus*	15	10

287 Customs Council Building, Brussels, and Warrior on Horseback

1983. 30th Anniversary of Customs Co-operation Council. Multicoloured.

1254		25dh. Type **287**	15	10
1255		50dh. Customs building	25	20
1256		100dh. Customs building and warrior with sword	50	45

1983. Battles (4th series). As T **246**. (a) Battle of Ghaser Ahmed.

1257		50dh. multicoloured	25	20
1258		50dh. multicoloured	25	20

(b) Battle of Sidi Abuarghub.

1259		50dh. multicoloured	25	20
1260		50dh. multicoloured	25	20

(c) Battle of Ghar Yunes.

1261		50dh. multicoloured	25	20
1262		50dh. multicoloured	25	20

(d) Battle of Bir Otman.

1263		50dh. multicoloured	25	20
1264		50dh. multicoloured	25	20

(e) Battle of Sidi Sajeh.

1265		50dh. multicoloured	25	20
1266		50dh. multicoloured	25	20

(f) Battle of Ras el-Hamam.

1267		50dh. multicoloured	25	20
1268		50dh. multicoloured	25	20

(g) Battle of Zawiet Ishghefa.

1269		50dh. multicoloured	25	20
1270		50dh. multicoloured	25	20

(h) Battle of Wadi Essania.

1271		50dh. multicoloured	25	20
1272		50dh. multicoloured	25	20

(i) Battle of El-Meshiashta.

1273		50dh. multicoloured	25	20
1274		50dh. multicoloured	25	20

(j) Battle of Gharara.

1275		50dh. multicoloured	25	20
1276		50dh. multicoloured	25	20

(k) Battle of Abughelan.

1277		50dh. multicoloured	20	20
1278		50dh. multicoloured	20	20

(l) Battle of Mahruka.

1279		50dh. multicoloured	20	20
1280		50dh. multicoloured	20	20

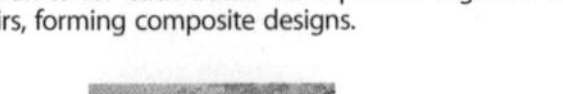

The two values for each battle were printed together in *se-tenant* pairs, forming composite designs.

288 Camel

1983. Farm Animals. Multicoloured.

1281		25dh. Type **288**	15	10
1282		25dh. Cow	15	10
1283		25dh. Horse	15	10
1284		25dh. Bull	15	10
1285		25dh. Goat	15	10
1286		25dh. Sheep dog	15	10
1287		25dh. Ewe	15	10
1288		25dh. Ram	15	10
1289		25dh. Greylag goose	35	25
1290		25dh. Helmeted guineafowl	35	25
1291		25dh. Rabbit	15	10
1292		25dh. Wood pigeon	35	25
1293		25dh. Common turkey	35	25
1294		25dh. Cockerel	15	10
1295		25dh. Hen	15	10
1296		25dh. Goose	15	10

289 Musician with Twin-horned Pipe

1983. Tripoli International Fair. Multicoloured.

1297	40dh. Type **289**	20	15
1298	45dh. Bagpipes (horiz)	25	20
1299	50dh. Horn	25	20
1300	55dh. Flute (horiz)	30	25
1301	75dh. Pipe	65	35
1302	100dh. Man and woman at well	90	45

290 Phoenician Galley

1983. 25th Anniv of International Maritime Organization. Multicoloured.

1303	100dh. Type **290**	1·25	55
1304	100dh. Ancient Greek galley	1·25	55
1305	100dh. Ancient Egyptian ship	1·25	55
1306	100dh. Roman sailing ship	1·25	55
1307	100dh. Viking longship	1·25	55
1308	100dh. Libyan xebec	1·25	55

291 Motorist

1983. Children's Day. Multicoloured.

1309	20dh. Type **291**	10	10
1310	20dh. Tractor and trailer	10	10
1311	20dh. Child with dove and globe	10	10
1312	20dh. Scout camp	10	10
1313	20dh. Dinosaur	10	10

292 President Gaddafi with Children

1983. World Health Day. Multicoloured.

1314	25dh. Type **292**	15	10
1315	50dh. Gaddafi and old man in wheelchair	25	20
1316	100dh. Gaddafi visiting sick girl (horiz)	80	45

293 Gaddafi, *The Green Book*, emblem and 'Jamahiriya'

1983. First World *The Green Book* Symposium. Multicoloured.

1317	50dh. Gaddafi, Map and *The Green Book*	25	20
1318	70dh. Syposium in session and emblem (56×37 mm)	60	30
1319	80dh. Type **293**	65	35
MS1320	148×80 mm. 100dh. Gaddafi and *The Green Books* (horiz 53×44 mm)	80	80

294 Economic Emblems on Map of Africa

1983. 25th Anniversary of African Economic Committee.

1321	**294**	50dh. multicoloured	25	20
1322	**294**	100dh. multicoloured	90	45
1323	**294**	250dh. multicoloured	1·90	1·10

295 Ali Sials

1983. Libyan Scientists. Sheet 127×101 mm containing T **295** and similar vert design. Multicoloured.

MS1324 100dh. **295**; 100dh. Ali el-Najar 1·75 1·75

296 Cuckoo Wrasse (*Labrus bimaculatus*)

1983. Fish. Multicoloured.

1325	25dh. Type **296**	30	15
1326	25dh. Streaked gurnard (*Trigoporus lastoviza*)	30	15
1327	25dh. Peacock wrasse (*Thalassoma pavo*)	30	15
1328	25dh. Mediterranean cardinalfish (*Apogon imberbis*)	30	15
1329	25dh. Atlantic mackerel (*Scomber scombrus*)	30	15
1330	25dh. Black seabream (*Spondyliosoma cantharus*)	30	15
1331	25dh. Greater weaver (*Trachinus draco*)	30	15
1332	25dh. Peacock blenny (*Blennius pavo*)	30	15
1333	25dh. Lesser red scorpionfish (*Scorpaena notata*)	30	15
1334	25dh. Painted comber (*Serranus scriba*)	30	15
1335	25dh. Angler (*Lophius piscatorius*)	30	15
1336	25dh. Stargazer (*Uranoscopus scaber*)	30	15
1337	25dh. Frigate mackerel (*Auxis thazard*)	30	15
1338	25dh. John dory (*Zeus faber*)	30	15
1339	25dh. Flying gurnard (*Dactylopterus volitans*)	30	15
1340	25dh. Corb (*Umbrina cirrosa*)	30	15

297 *Still-life* (Gauguin)

1983. Paintings. Multicoloured.

1341	50dh. Type **297**	25	20
1342	50dh. Abstract	25	20
1343	50dh. *The Conquest of Tunis by Charles V* (Rubens)	25	20
1344	50dh. *Arab Band in Horse-drawn Carriage*	25	20
1345	50dh. *Apotheosis of Gaddafi* (vert)	25	20
1346	50dh. Horses (detail of Raphael's *The Triumph of David over the Assyrians*) (vert)	25	20
1347	50dh. *Workers* (vert)	25	20
1348	50dh. *Sunflowers* (Van Gogh) (vert)	25	20

298 Basketball

1983. Olympic Games, Los Angeles. Multicoloured.

1349	10dh. Type **298**	10	10
1350	15dh. High jumping	10	10
1351	25dh. Running	15	10
1352	50dh. Gymnastics	25	20
1353	100dh. Windsurfing	80	45
1354	200dh. Shot-putting	1·50	95

299 ITU Building, Antenna and WCY Emblem

1983. World Communications Year.

1356	**299**	10dh. multicoloured	10	10
1357	**299**	50dh. multicoloured	25	20
1358	**299**	100dh. multicoloured	75	45

300 'The House is to be served by its Residents'

1983. Extracts from *The Green Book*. Multicoloured

1359	10dh. Type **300**	10	10
1360	15dh. 'Power, wealth and arms are in the hands of the people'	10	10
1361	20dh. 'Masters in their own castles' (vert)	10	10
1362	35dh. 'No democracy without popular congresses'	20	15
1363	100dh. 'The authority of the people' (vert)	50	45
1364	140dh. '*The Green Book* is the guide of humanity for final release'	1·10	70
MS1365	119×78 mm. 200dh. President Gaddafi (vert 32×47 mm)	80	80

301 Handball

1983. Second African Youth Festival. Multicoloured.

1366	100dh. Type **301**	85	45
1367	100dh. Basketball	85	45
1368	100dh. High jumping	85	45
1369	100dh. Running	85	45
1370	100dh. Football	85	45

302 Marching Soldiers

1983. 14th Anniversary of September Revolution. Multicoloured

1371	65dh. Type **302**	35	30
1372	75dh. Weapons and communications training	40	35
1373	90dh. Women with machine guns and bazookas	70	40
1374	100dh. Machine gun training	75	45
1375	150dh. Bazooka training	1·10	70
1376	250dh. Rifle training	2·00	1·10
MS1377	129×100 mm. 200dh. President Gaddafi and aides at graduation parade (58×35 mm)	1·60	1·60

303 Saluting Scouts

1983. Scout Jamborees. Multicoloured.

1378	50dh. Type **303**	25	20
1379	100dh. Scouts around camp fire	90	45
MS1380	148×92 mm. 100dh.×2 Nos. 1323/1324	1·75	1·75

Events: 50dh. Second Islamic Scout Jamboree; 100dh. 15th Pan Arab Scout Jamboree.

304 Traffic Cadets

1983. Traffic Day. Multicoloured.

1381	30dh. Type **304**	40	15
1382	70dh. Traffic policeman	70	30
1383	200dh. Police motorcyclists	1·90	1·25

305 Saadun

1983. 90th Birth Anniversary of Saadun (patriot soldier).

1384	**305**	100dh. multicoloured	90	45

306 Walter Wellman's airship *America*, 1910

1983. Bicentenary of Manned Flight. Multicoloured

1385	100dh. Type **306**	1·00	55
1386	100dh. Airship *Nulli Secundus*, 1907	1·00	55
1387	100dh. Jean-Baptiste Meusnier's balloon design, 1784	1·00	55
1388	100dh. Blanchard and Jeffries' Channel crossing, 1785 (vert)	1·00	55
1389	100dh. Pilatre de Rozier's hydrogen/hot-air balloon flight, 1784 (vert)	1·00	55
1390	100dh. First Montgolfier balloon, 1783 (vert)	1·00	55

307 Globe and Dove

1983. Solidarity with Palestinian People.

1393	**307**	200dh. green, blue & blk	1·60	95

308 Gladiators fighting

1983. Mosaics. Multicoloured.

1394	50dh. Type **308**	50	20
1395	50dh. Gladiators fighting (different)	50	20
1396	50dh. Gladiators and slave	50	20
1397	50dh. Two musicians	50	20
1398	50dh. Three musicians	50	20
1399	50dh. Two gladiators	50	20
1400	50dh. Two Romans and bound victim	50	20

1401 50dh. Leopard and man hunting deer 50 20
1402 50dh. Deer and man with boar 50 20

309 Traditional Architecture

1983. Achievements of the Revolution. Multicoloured
1403 10dh. Type **309** 10 10
1404 15dh. Camels drinking and mechanisation of farming 10 10
1405 20dh. Computer operator and industrial scene 10 10
1406 35dh. Modern architecture 15 10
1407 100dh. Surgeons and nurses treating patients and hospital 90 40
1408 140dh. Airport and aeroplane 1·25 75
MS1409 118×78 mm. 200dh. President Gaddafi (35×50 mm) 1·75 1·75

310 Flooding a River Bed

1983. Colonel Gaddafi, River Builder. Multicoloured.
1410 50dh. Type **310** 20 15
1411 50dh. Irrigation pipe and agricultural produce 20 15
1412 100dh. Colonel Gaddafi, irrigation pipe and farmland (62×44 mm) 1·00 40
1413 100dh. Colonel Gaddafi and map (68×32 mm) 1·00 40
1414 150dh. Colonel Gaddafi explaining irrigation project (35×32 mm) 1·40 65
MS1415 108×66 mm. 300dh. As No. 1413 (70×35 mm) (1984) 2·75 2·75

Nos. 1410/1412 were printed together in *se-tenant* strips of three forming a composite design.

311 Mahmud Burkis

1984. Personalities. Multicoloured.
1416 100dh. Type **311** 1·00 40
1417 100dh. Ahmed el-Bakbak 1·00 40
1418 100dh. Mohamed el-Misurati 1·00 40
1419 100dh. Mahmud Ben Musa 1·00 40
1420 100dh. Abdulhamid el-Sherif 1·00 40
1421 100dh. Mehdi el-Sherif 1·00 40
1422 100dh. Mahmud Mustafa Dreza 1·00 40
1423 100dh. Hosni Fauzi el-Amir 1·00 40
1424 100dh. Ali Haidar el-Saati 1·00 40
1425 200dh. Ahmed el-Feghi Hasan 1·50 80
1426 200dh. Bashir el-Jawab 1·50 80
1427 200dh. Ali el-Gariani 1·50 80
1428 200dh. Muktar Shakshuki 1·50 80
1429 200dh. Abdurrahman el-Busayri 1·50 80
1430 200dh. Ibbrahim Bakir 1·50 80
1431 200dh. Mahmud el-Janzuri 1·50 80

312 Windsurfing

1984. Water Sports. Multicoloured.
1432 25dh. Type **312** 30 10
1433 25dh. Dinghy sailing (orange and red sails) 30 10
1434 25dh. Dinghy sailing (mauve sails) 30 10
1435 25dh. Hang-gliding on water skis 20 10
1436 25dh. Water-skiing 20 10
1437 25dh. Angling from boat 30 10
1438 25dh. Men in speed boat 30 10
1439 25dh. Water-skiing (different) 20 10
1440 25dh. Fishing 30 10
1441 25dh. Canoeing 20 10
1442 25dh. Surfing 20 10
1443 25dh. Water-skiing (different) 20 10
1444 25dh. Scuba diving 30 10
1445 25dh. Diving 30 10
1446 25dh. Swimming in snorkel and flippers 30 10
1447 25dh. Scuba diving for fish 30 10

313 Colonel Gaddafi with Schoolchildren

1984. African Children's Day. Multicoloured.
1448 50dh. Type **313** 50 15
1449 50dh. Colonel Gaddafi and children in National Dress 50 15
1450 100dh. Colonel Gaddafi on map and children at various activities (62×43 mm) 1·90 60

314 Women in National, Casual and Military Dress

1984. Libyan Women's Emancipation. Multicoloured.
1451 55dh. Type **314** 50 20
1452 70dh. Women in traditional, casual and military dress (vert) 75 25
1453 100dh. Colonel Gaddafi and women in military dress 95 40

315 Theatre, Sabratha

1984. Roman Ruins of Cyrenaica. Multicoloured.
1454 50dh. Type **315** 20 15
1455 60dh. Temple, Cyrene 50 20
1456 70dh. Monument, Sabratha (vert) 60 25
1457 100dh. Amphitheatre, Leptis Magna 90 40
1458 150dh. Temple, Cyrene (different) 1·40 65
1459 200dh. Basilica, Leptis Magna 1·90 80

316 Silver Dirham, 115h.

1984. Arabic Islamic Coins (1st series).
1460 **316** 200dh. silver, yellow and black 1·90 85
1461 - 200dh. silver, mauve and black 1·90 85
1462 - 200dh. silver, green and black 1·90 85
1463 - 200dh. silver, orange and black 1·90 85
1464 - 200dh. silver, blue and black 1·90 85

Designs: No. 1461, Silver dirham, 93h; No. 1462, Silver dirham, 121h; No. 1463, Silver dirham, 49h; No. 1464, Silver dirham, 135h.

See also Nos. 1643/**MS**1646.

317 Men at Tea Ceremony

1984. International Trade Fair, Tripoli. Multicoloured
1465 25dh. Type **317** 15 10
1466 35dh. Woman making tea 15 15
1467 45dh. Men taking tea 20 15
1468 55dh. Family taking tea 50 20
1469 75dh. Veiled women pouring tea 70 30
1470 100dh. Robed men taking tea 1·00 40

318 Muktar Shiaker Murabet

1984. Musicians. Multicoloured.
1471 100dh. Type **318** 1·25 65
1472 100dh. El-Aref el-Jamal 1·25 65
1473 100dh. Ali Shiaalia 1·25 65
1474 100dh. Bashir Fehmi 1·25 65

319 Playing among Trees

1984. Children's Day. Designs showing children's paintings. Multicoloured.
1475 20dh. Type **319** 10 10
1476 20dh. A rainy day 10 10
1477 20dh. Weapons of war 10 10
1478 20dh. Playing on the swing 10 10
1479 20dh. Playing in the park 10 10

320 Crest and '39'

1984. 39th Anniversary of Arab League.
1480 **320** 30dh. multicoloured 15 15
1481 **320** 40dh. multicoloured 20 15
1482 **320** 50dh. multicoloured 55 20

321 Red Four-seater Car

1984. Motor Cars and Steam Locomotives. Multicoloured
1483 100dh. Type **321** 1·25 65
1484 100dh. Red three-seater car 1·25 65
1485 100dh. Yellow two-seater car with three lamps 1·25 65
1486 100dh. Covered red four-seater car 1·25 65
1487 100dh. Yellow two-seater car with two lamps 1·25 65
1488 100dh. Cream car with spare wheel at side 1·25 65
1489 100dh. Green car with spare wheel at side 1·25 65
1490 100dh. Cream four-seater car with spare wheel at back 1·25 65
1491 100dh. Locomotive pulling wagon and coach 1·40 45
1492 100dh. Purple and blue locomotive 1·40 45
1493 100dh. Cream locomotive 1·40 45
1494 100dh. Lilac and brown locomotive 1·40 45
1495 100dh. Lilac and black locomotive with red wheels 1·40 45
1496 100dh. Cream and red locomotive 1·40 45
1497 100dh. Purple and black locomotive with red wheels 1·40 45
1498 100dh. Green and orange locomotive 1·40 45

322 Stylised People and Campaign Emblem

1984. World Health Day. Anti-Polio Campaign. Multicoloured.
1499 20dh. Type **322** 10 10
1500 30dh. Stylised people and 1981 20dh. stamp 15 15
1501 40dh. Stylised people and Arabic emblem 50 15

323 Man making Slippers

1984. Handicrafts. Multicoloured.
1502 150dh. Type **323** 1·60 65
1503 150dh. Man making decorative harness 1·60 65
1504 150dh. Women forming cotton into skeins 1·60 65
1505 150dh. Woman spinning by hand 1·60 65
1506 150dh. Man weaving 1·60 65
1507 150dh. Women weaving 1·60 65

324 Telephones, Dial and Mail

1984. Postal and Telecommunications Union Congress. Multicoloured.
1508 50dh. Type **324** 50 20
1509 50dh. Woman working at computer console, dial and man working on computer 50 20
1510 100dh. Satellite, map, laurel branches and telephone handset 1·00 40

325 Armed Soldiers and Civilians

1984. Abrogation of 17 May Treaty. Multicoloured.
1511 50dh. Type **325** 65 20
1512 50dh. Map, dove and burning banner 65 20
1513 50dh. Soldiers shaking hands and crowd with banners (30×40 mm) 65 20
1514 100dh. Hands tearing treaty, Gaddafi and crowd (62×40 mm) 1·25 40
1515 100dh. Gaddafi addressing crowd 1·25 40

Nos. 1512/1514 were printed together in *se-tenant* strips of three, forming a composite design.

326 Children behind Barbed Wire

1984. Child Victims of Invasion Day. Multicoloured.
1516 70dh. Torn flags on barbed wire 70 25
1517 100dh. Type **326** 1·00 40

327 'The Party System Aborts Democracy'

1984. Quotations from *The Green Book*. Multicoloured.
1518 100dh. Type **327** 95 40
1519 100dh. Colonel Gaddafi 95 40
1520 100dh. 'Partners not wage-workers' 95 40
1521 100dh. 'No representation in lieu of the people. Representation is falsification' 95 40
1522 100dh. *The Green Book* 95 40

1523 100dh. 'Committees everywhere' 95 40
1524 100dh. 'Forming parties splits societies' 95 40
1525 100dh. Skyscraper and earthmover 95 40
1526 100dh. 'No democracy without popular congresses' 95 40

328 Man in Brown Robes

1984. Costumes. Multicoloured.
1527 100dh. Type **328** 1·25 65
1528 100dh. Woman in green dress and red shawl 1·25 65
1529 100dh. Man in ornate costume and turban 1·25 65
1530 100dh. Man in short trousers and plain shirt 1·25 65
1531 100dh. Woman in shift and trousers with white shawl 1·25 65
1532 100dh. Man in long white robe and red shawl 1·25 65

329 Footballer tackling

1984. World Cup Football Championship. Multicoloured
1533 70dh. Type **329** 70 25
1534 70dh. Footballers in magenta and green shirts 70 25
1535 70dh. Footballers in orange and lemon shirts 70 25
1536 70dh. Goalkeeper failing to save ball 70 25
1537 70dh. Footballers in yellow and brown shirts 70 25
1538 70dh. Top of Trophy and footballer in green striped shirt 70 25
1539 70dh. Top of Trophy and footballers in blue and pink shirts 70 25
1540 70dh. Footballers in black and white striped and green and red striped shirts 70 25
1541 70dh. Footballers in green and red striped shirts 70 25
1542 70dh. Foot of trophy and footballers in orange striped and blue shirts 70 25
1543 70dh. Foot of trophy and goalkeeper 70 25
1544 70dh. Goalkeeper saving headed ball 70 25
1545 70dh. Referee and footballers 70 25
1546 70dh. Footballers in white with red striped sleeves and orange shirts 70 25
1547 70dh. Footballers in white and green striped and orange shirts 70 25
1548 70dh. Footballer in pink shirt 70 25

Nos. 1533/1548 were printed in sheetlets of 16 stamps, the backgrounds to the stamps forming an overall design of a stadium.

330 Football

1984. Olympic Games, Los Angeles. Multicoloured
1549 100dh. Type **330** 1·25 65
1550 100dh. Swimming 1·25 65
1551 100dh. Throwing the discus 1·25 65
1552 100dh. Windsurfing 1·25 65
1553 100dh. Basketball 1·25 65
1554 100dh. Running 1·25 65
MS1555 Two sheets each 85×66 mm. (a) 250dh. Show jumping; (b) 250dh. Rider on rearing horse 3·25 3·25

331 Palm Trees

1984. Ninth World Forestry Congress. Multicoloured
1556 100dh. Four types of forest 1·10 40
1557 200dh. Type **331** 2·10 1·10

332 Modern Building

1984. 15th Anniversary of Revolution. Multicoloured.
1558 25dh. Type **332** 15 10
1559 25dh. Front of building 15 10
1560 25dh. Building by pool 15 10
1561 25dh. Colonel Gaddafi (three-quarter portrait) 15 10
1562 25dh. High-rise block 15 10
1563 25dh. Crane and mosque 15 10
1564 25dh. Motorway interchange 15 10
1565 25dh. House and garden 15 10
1566 25dh. Shepherd and flock 15 10
1567 25dh. Combine-harvester 15 10
1568 25dh. Tractors 15 10
1569 25dh. Scientific equipment 15 10
1570 25dh. Colonel Gaddafi (full face) 15 10
1571 25dh. Water pipeline 15 10
1572 25dh. Lighthouse 15 10
1573 25dh. Liner at quay 45 10

333 Armed Man

1984. Evacuation of Foreign Forces. Multicoloured (a) As T **333**.
1574 50dh. Type **333** 50 20
1575 50dh. Armed man (different) 50 20
1576 100dh. Men on horseback charging (62×40 mm) 1·00 40

334 Soldier flogging Civilian

(b) As T **334**.
1577 100dh. Type **334** 1·00 40
1578 100dh. Girl on horse charging soldiers 1·00 40
1579 100dh. Mounted soldiers and wounded being tended by women 1·00 40

335 Woman riding Skewbald Showjumper

1984. Equestrian Events. Multicoloured.
1580 25dh. Type **335** 15 10
1581 25dh. Man riding black showjumper (stands in background) 15 10
1582 25dh. Jockey riding chestnut horse (stands in background) 15 10
1583 25dh. Man on chestnut horse jumping in cross-country event 15 10
1584 25dh. Man riding bay horse in showjumping competition 15 10
1585 25dh. Woman on black horse in dressage competition 15 10
1586 25dh. Man on black horse in dressage competition 15 10
1587 25dh. Woman riding chestnut horse in cross-country event 15 10
1588 25dh. Jockey riding bay horse 15 10
1589 25dh. Woman on bay horse in dressage competition 15 10
1590 25dh. Man on grey horse in dressage competition 15 10
1591 25dh. Jockey riding grey steeplechaser 15 10
1592 25dh. Woman riding grey showjumper 15 10
1593 25dh. Woman riding through water in cross-country competition 15 10
1594 25dh. Woman on chestnut horse in cross-country competition 15 10
1595 25dh. Man riding dun showjumper 15 10

Nos. 1580/1595 were printed together in sheetlets of 16 stamps, the backgrounds of the stamps forming an overall design of an equestrian ring.

336 Man cleaning Corn

1984. Traditional Agriculture. Multicoloured.
1596 100dh. Type **336** 1·25 65
1597 100dh. Man using oxen to draw water from well 1·25 65
1598 100dh. Man making straw goods 1·25 65
1599 100dh. Shepherd with sheep 1·25 65
1600 100dh. Man treating animal skin 1·25 65
1601 100dh. Man climbing coconut tree 1·25 65

337 Map and Pharmaceutical Equipment

1984. Ninth Conference of Arab Pharmacists Union.
1602 **337** 100dh. multicoloured 1·25 40
1603 **337** 200dh. multicoloured 2·50 1·10

338 Crowd with Banner showing Map of North Africa

1984. Arab–African Unity. Multicoloured.
1604 100dh. Type **338** 1·25 65
1605 100dh. Crowd and men holding flags 1·25 65

339 1982 and 1983 Solidarity Stamps and Map of Palestine

1984. Solidarity with Palestinian People.
1606 **339** 100dh. multicoloured 1·25 40
1607 **339** 150dh. multicoloured 1·90 1·00

340 Boeing 747SP, 1975

1984. 40th Anniversary of International Civil Aviation Organisation. Multicoloured.
1608 70dh. Type **340** 95 30
1609 70dh. Concorde, 1969 95 30
1610 70dh. Lockheed TriStar 500, 1978 95 30
1611 70dh. Airbus Industrie A310, 1982 95 30
1612 70dh. Tupolev Tu-134A, 1962 95 30
1613 70dh. Shorts 360, 1981 95 30
1614 70dh. Boeing 727-100, 1963 95 30
1615 70dh. Sud Aviation Caravelle 10R, 1965 95 30
1616 70dh. Fokker Friendship, 1955 95 30
1617 70dh. Lockheed Constellation, 1946 95 30
1618 70dh. Martin M-130 flying boat, 1955 95 30
1619 70dh. Douglas DC-3, 1936 95 50
1620 70dh. Junkers Ju-52/3m, 1932 95 30
1621 70dh. Lindbergh's *Spirit of St. Louis*, 1927 95 30
1622 70dh. de Havilland Moth, 1925 95 30
1623 70dh. *Wright Flyer I*, 1903 95 30

Nos. 1608/1623 were printed together in sheetlets of 16 stamps, the backgrounds of the stamps forming an overall design of a runway.

341 Coin

1984. 20th Anniversary of African Development Bank. Multicoloured.
1624 50dh. Type **341** 55 20
1625 70dh. Map of Africa and '20' 1·00 25
1626 100dh. '20' and symbols of industry and agriculture 1·25 65

342 Mother and Son

1985. UNICEF Child Survival Campaign. Multicoloured.
1627 70dh. Type **342** 1·00 50
1628 70dh. Couple and children 1·00 50
1629 70dh. Colonel Gaddafi and children 1·00 50
1630 70dh. Boys in uniform 1·00 50

343 Mohamed Hamdi

1985. Musicians and Instruments. Multicoloured.
1631 100dh. Kamel el-Ghadi 1·25 65
1632 100dh. Fiddle rebab 1·25 65
1633 100dh. Ahmed el-Khogia 1·25 65
1634 100dh. Violin 1·25 65
1635 100dh. Mustafa el-Fallah 1·25 65
1636 100dh. Zither 1·25 65
1637 100dh. Type **343** 1·25 65
1638 100dh. Mask 1·25 65

344 Pipeline, River, Plants and Map

1985. Colonel Gaddafi, River Builder. Multicoloured.
1639 100dh. Type **344** 1·25 65
1640 100dh. Water droplet, river and flowers 1·25 65
1641 100dh. Dead tree with branch thriving in water droplet 1·25 65
MS1642 117×80 mm. 200dh. Map and droplet (39×39 mm) 2·25 2·25

345 Gold Dinar, 105h.

1985. Arabic Islamic Coins (2nd series). Multicoloured

1643	200dh. Type **345**	2·50	1·25
1644	200dh. Gold dinar, 91h.	2·50	1·25
1645	200dh. Gold dinar, 77h.	2·50	1·25
MS1646	110×80 mm. 300dh. Gold dinar minted in Zuela	3·50	3·50

346 Fish

1985. Fossils. Multicoloured.

1647	150dh. Type **346**	3·00	90
1648	150dh. Frog	1·90	55
1649	150dh. Mammal	1·90	55

347 Gaddafi in Robes and Hat

1985. People's Authority Declaration. Multicoloured

1650	100dh. Type **347**	1·25	65
1651	100dh. Gaddafi in black robe holding book	1·25	65
1652	100dh. Gaddafi in dress uniform without cap	1·25	65
1653	100dh. Gaddafi in black dress uniform with cap	1·25	65
1654	100dh. Gaddafi in white dress uniform	1·25	65

348 Cymbal Player

1985. International Trade Fair, Tripoli. Multicoloured

1655	100dh. Type **348**	1·25	65
1656	100dh. Piper and drummer	1·25	65
1657	100dh. Drummer and bagpipes player	1·25	65
1658	100dh. Drummer	1·25	65
1659	100dh. Tambour player	1·25	65

349 Goalkeeper catching Ball

1985. Children's Day. Multicoloured.

1660	20dh. Type **349**	10	10
1661	20dh. Child on touchline with ball	10	10
1662	20dh. Letters of alphabet as players	10	10
1663	20dh. Goalkeeper saving ball	10	10
1664	20dh. Player heading ball	10	10

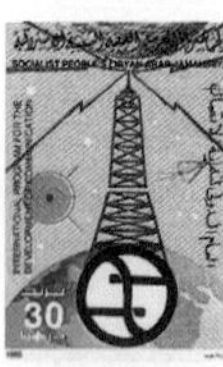

350 Emblem, Radio Transmitter and Satellite

1985. International Communications Development Programme.

1665	**350**	30dh. multicoloured	15	10
1666	**350**	70dh. multicoloured	75	25
1667	**350**	100dh. multicoloured	1·10	65

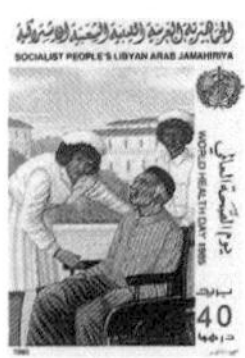

351 Nurses and Man in Wheelchair

1985. World Health Day. Multicoloured.

1668	40dh. Type **351**	50	10
1669	60dh. Nurses and doctors	75	15
1670	100dh. Nurse and child	1·25	65

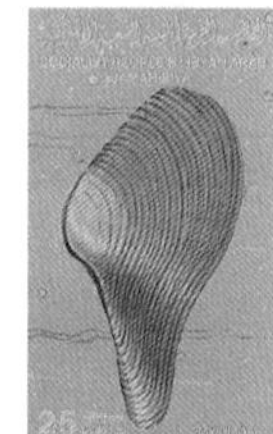

352 *Mytilidae*

1985. Sea Shells. Multicoloured.

1671	25dh. Type **352**	40	15
1672	25dh. Purple dye murex (*Muricidae*)	40	15
1673	25dh. Tuberculate cockle (*Cardiidae*)	40	15
1674	25dh. *Corallophilidae*	40	15
1675	25dh. Trunculus murex (*Muricidae*)	40	15
1676	25dh. *Muricacea*	40	15
1677	25dh. *Turridae*	40	15
1678	25dh. Nodose paper nautilus (*Argonautidae*)	40	15
1679	25dh. Giant tun (*Tonnidae*)	40	15
1680	25dh. Common pelican's-foot (*Aporrhaidae*)	40	15
1681	25dh. *Trochidae*	40	15
1682	25dh. *Cancellariidae*	40	15
1683	25dh. *Epitoniidae*	40	15
1684	25dh. *Turbinidae*	40	15
1685	25dh. Zoned mitre (*Mitridae*)	40	15
1686	25dh. Cat's-paw scallop (*Pectinidae*)	40	15

Nos. 1671/1686 were printed *se-tenant*, the backgrounds forming an overall design of the sea bed.

353 Books and Emblem

1985. International Book Fair, Tripoli.

1687	**353**	100dh. multicoloured	1·25	60
1688	**353**	200dh. multicoloured	2·25	1·25

354 Girls Skipping

1985. International Youth Year. Multicoloured.

1689	20dh. Type **354**	10	10
1690	20dh. Boys playing with stones	10	10
1691	20dh. Girls playing hopscotch	10	10
1692	20dh. Boys playing with sticks	10	10
1693	20dh. Boys playing with spinning top	10	10
MS1694	133×90 mm. 100dh. Footballer; 100dh. Basketball players	95	95

355 Abdussalam Lasmar Mosque

1985. Minarets. Multicoloured.

1695	50dh. Type **355**	50	15
1696	50dh. Zaoviat Kadria Mosque	50	15
1697	50dh. Zaoviat Amura Mosque	50	15
1698	50dh. Gurgi Mosque	50	15
1699	50dh. Mizran Mosque	50	15
1700	50dh. Salem Mosque	50	15
1701	50dh. Ghat Mosque	50	15
1702	50dh. Ahmed Karamanli Mosque	50	15
1703	50dh. Atya Mosque	50	15
1704	50dh. El Kettani Mosque	50	15
1705	50dh. Benghazi Mosque	50	15
1706	50dh. Derna Mosque	50	15
1707	50dh. El Derug Mosque	50	15
1708	50dh. Ben Moussa Mosque	50	15
1709	50dh. Ghadames Mosque	50	15
1710	50dh. Abdulwahab Mosque	50	15

356 Jamila Zemerli

1985. Teachers' Day. Multicoloured.

1711	100dh. Type **356**	1·25	65
1712	100dh. Hamida El-Anezi	1·25	65

357 *Philadelphia* exploding

1985. Battle of the *Philadelphia*. Multicoloured.

1713	50dh. Type **357**	60	20
1714	50dh. Men with swords	60	20
1715	100dh. Men fighting and ship's rigging (59×45 mm)	1·25	45

Nos. 1713/1715 were printed together, *se-tenant*, forming a composite design.

358 Gaddafi and Followers

1986. Colonel Gaddafi's Islamic Pilgrimage. Multicoloured.

1716	200dh. Gaddafi writing	2·50	1·25
1717	200dh. Gaddafi praying	2·50	1·25
1718	200dh. Gaddafi, crowds and Kaaba	2·50	1·25
1719	200dh. Gaddafi and mirror	2·50	1·25
1720	200dh. Type **358**	2·50	1·25
MS1721	116×83 mm. 300dh. Koran on stand	3·50	3·50

359 *Leucopaxillus lepistoides*

1985. Mushrooms. Multicoloured.

1722	50dh. Type **359**	1·10	25
1723	50dh. *Amanita caesarea*	1·10	25
1724	50dh. *Coriolus hirsutus*	1·10	25
1725	50dh. *Cortinarius subfulgens*	1·10	25
1726	50dh. *Dermocybe pratensis*	1·10	25
1727	50dh. *Macrolepiota excoriata*	1·10	25
1728	50dh. *Amanita curtipes*	1·10	25
1729	50dh. *Trametes ljubarskyi*	1·10	25
1730	50dh. *Pholiota aurivella*	1·10	25
1731	50dh. *Boletus edulis*	1·10	25
1732	50dh. *Geastrum sessile*	1·10	25
1733	50dh. *Russula sanguinea*	1·10	25
1734	50dh. *Cortinarius herculeus*	1·10	25
1735	50dh. *Pholiota lenta*	1·10	25
1736	50dh. *Amanita rubescens*	1·10	25
1737	50dh. *Seleroderma polyrhizum*	1·10	25

Nos. 1722/1737 were printed together, *se-tenant*, the backgrounds of the stamps forming an overall design of map of Mediterranean.

360 Woman in Purple Striped Dress

1985. Traditional Women's Costumes. Multicoloured.

1738	100dh. Type **360**	1·25	65
1739	100dh. Woman in robes covering her face	1·25	65
1740	100dh. Woman in colourful robes with heavy jewellery	1·25	65
1741	100dh. Woman in long blue striped dress	1·25	65
1742	100dh. Woman in red dress and trousers	1·25	65

361 'In Need Freedom is Latent'

1985. Quotations from *The Green Book*.

1743	**361**	100dh. lt green, grn & blk	45	35
1744	-	100dh. multicoloured	45	35
1745	-	100dh. lt green, grn & blk	45	35
1746	-	100dh. lt green, grn & blk	45	35
1747	-	100dh. multicoloured	45	35
1748	-	100dh. lt green, grn & blk	45	35
1749	-	100dh. lt green, grn & blk	45	35
1750	-	100dh. multicoloured	45	35
1751	-	100dh. lt green, grn & blk	45	35

Designs: No. 1744, Gaddafi in uniform reading; No. 1745, 'To make a party you split society'; No. 1746, 'Public sport is for all the masses'; No. 1747, *Green Books* and doves; No. 1748, 'Wage-workers are a type of slave, however improved their wages may be'; No. 1749, 'People are only harmonious with their own arts and heritages'; No. 1750, Gaddafi addressing crowd; No. 1751, 'Democracy means popular rule not popular expression'.

362 Tree and Citrus Fruits

1985. 16th Anniversary of Revolution. Multicoloured.

1752	100dh. Type **362**	1·25	65
1753	100dh. Oil pipeline and tanks	1·25	65
1754	100dh. Capital and olive branch	1·25	65
1755	100dh. Mosque and modern buildings	1·25	65
1756	100dh. Flag and mountains	1·25	65
1757	100dh. Telecommunications	1·25	65
MS1758	100×80 mm. 200dh. Gaddafi	2·40	2·40

363 Zauiet Amoura, Janzour

1985. Mosque Gateways. Multicoloured.

1759	100dh. Type **363**	1·25	65
1760	100dh. Shiaieb El-Ain, Tripoli	1·25	65
1761	100dh. Zauiet Abdussalam El-Asmar, Zliten	1·25	65
1762	100dh. Karamanli, Tripoli	1·25	65
1763	100dh. Gurgi, Tripoli	1·25	65

364 Players in Red No. 5 and Green Shirts

1985. Basketball. Multicoloured.

1764	25dh. Type **364**	15	10
1765	25dh. Players in green number 7 and red shirts	15	10
1766	25dh. Players in green number 8 and red shirts	15	10
1767	25dh. Players in red number 6 and green shirts	15	10
1768	25dh. Players in red number 4 and green number 7 shirts	15	10
1769	25dh. Players in green numbers 6 and 5 and red number 9 shirts	15	10
1770	25dh. Basket and one player in red and two in green shirts	15	10
1771	25dh. Players in red number 8 and green number 7 shirts	15	10
1772	25dh. Two players in green shirts and two in red shirts, one number 4	15	10
1773	25dh. Players in red numbers 4 and 7 and green shirts	15	10
1774	25dh. Players in red numbers 4 and 9 and green numbers 7 and 4 shirts	15	10
1775	25dh. Players in red number 6 and green shirts	15	10
1776	25dh. Players in red number 9 and green number 8 shirts	15	10
1777	25dh. Players in red number 8 and green number 5 shirts	15	10
1778	25dh. Players in red number 4 and green shirts	15	10
1779	25dh. Players in red number 5 and green number 10 shirts	15	10

Nos. 1764/1779 were printed together *se-tenant*, the backgrounds of the stamps forming an overall design of basketball court and basket.

365 People in Light Ray

1985. Evacuation of Foreign Forces. Multicoloured.

1780	100dh. Man on crutches in web and light shining on tree	1·25	65
1781	100dh. Hands pulling web away from man	1·25	65
1782	100dh. Type **365**	1·25	65

366 Stockbook, Magnifying Glass and Stamps

1985. Stamp Day. Italia '85 International Stamp Exhibition, Rome. Multicoloured.

1783	50dh. Man and desk on flying stamp above globe	65	15
1784	50dh. Type **366**	65	15
1785	50dh. Stamps escaping from wallet	65	15

367 Players

1985. World Cup Football Championship, Mexico (1st issue). Multicoloured.

1786	100dh. Type **367**	1·25	65
1787	100dh. Players in red and white number 10 and yellow shirts	1·25	65
1788	100dh. Goalkeeper and player defending goal against attack	1·25	65
1789	100dh. Goalkeeper diving to make save	1·25	65
1790	100dh. Goalkeeper jumping to make save	1·25	65
1791	100dh. Player in red and white shirt tackling player in lime shirt	1·25	65
MS1792	70×81 mm. 200dh. Players	2·25	2·25

See also Nos. 1824/**MS**1830.

368 Hands releasing Dove

1985. Solidarity with Palestinian People.

1793	**368**	100dh. multicoloured	95	35
1794	**368**	150dh. multicoloured	1·60	75

370 Headquarters and Dish Aerial

1986. First Anniversary of General Posts and Telecommunications Corporation.

1807	**370**	100dh. multicoloured	1·00	30
1808	**370**	150dh. multicoloured	1·50	75

371 Paper and Quill in Hand

1986. Peoples' Authority Declaration. Multicoloured.

1809	50dh. Type **371**	65	40
1810	50dh. Paper and globe in hand	65	40
1811	100dh. *The Green Books* and dove (53×37 mm)	1·25	65

372 Flute

1986. International Trade Fair, Tripoli. Multicoloured

1812	100dh. Type **372**	1·25	65
1813	100dh. Drums	1·25	65
1814	100dh. Double pipes	1·25	65
1815	100dh. Tambourines	1·25	65
1816	100dh. Drum hung from shoulder	1·25	65

373 Boy Scout with Fish on Hook

1986. Children's Day. Multicoloured.

1817	50dh. Type **373**	1·10	25
1818	50dh. Boy on camel	65	15
1819	50dh. Boy catching butterflies	65	15
1820	50dh. Boy playing drum	65	15
1821	50dh. Boy and giant goalkeeper on football pitch	65	15

374 Emblem, Man and Skull in Blood Droplet

1986. World Health Day. Multicoloured, background colours given.

1822	**374**	250dh. silver	2·50	1·25
1823	**374**	250dh. gold	2·50	1·25

375 Footballers

1986. World Cup Football Championship, Mexico (2nd issue). Multicoloured.

1824	50dh. Type **375**	65	15
1825	50dh. Player jumping over player on ground	65	15
1826	50dh. Referee and players	65	15
1827	50dh. Goalkeeper trying to save ball	65	15
1828	50dh. Player about to tackle	65	15
1829	50dh. Player jumping over ball	65	15
MS1830	Two sheets each 90×90 mm. (a) 200dh. Match scene; (b) 200dh. First Libyan team, 1931	2·25	2·25

376 Peas

1986. Vegetables. Multicoloured.

1831	50dh. Type **376**	45	15
1832	50dh. Marrow	45	15
1833	50dh. Beans	45	15
1834	50dh. Aubergine	45	15
1835	50dh. Corn on the cob	45	15
1836	50dh. Tomato	45	15
1837	50dh. Red pepper	45	15
1838	50dh. Zucchini	45	15
1839	50dh. Garlic	45	15
1840	50dh. Cabbage	45	15
1841	50dh. Cauliflower	45	15
1842	50dh. Celery	45	15
1843	50dh. Onions	45	15
1844	50dh. Carrots	45	15
1845	50dh. Potato	45	15
1846	50dh. Radishes	45	15

Nos. 1831/1846 were printed together in sheetlets of 16 stamps, the backgrounds of the stamps forming an overall design of a garden.

377 Health Programmes

1986. Jamahiriya Thought. Multicoloured.

1847	50dh. Type **377**	50	15
1848	50dh. Education programmes	50	15
1849	100dh. *The Green Book*, agricultural scenes and produce (agriculture programmes) (62×41 mm)	1·75	45

378 Gaddafi studying Plan

1986. Colonel Gaddafi, 'Great man-made River Builder'. Multicoloured.

1850	100dh. Type **378**	95	30
1851	100dh. Gaddafi showing planned route on map	95	30
1852	100dh. Gaddafi and old well	95	30
1853	100dh. Gaddafi in desert	95	30
1854	100dh. Gaddafi and pipe	95	30
1855	100dh. Gaddafi at pumping station	95	30
1856	100dh. Gaddafi and storage tank	95	30
1857	100dh. Workers' hut	95	30
1858	100dh. Water in cupped hands and irrigation equipment	95	30
1859	100dh. Gaddafi turning wheel at opening ceremony	95	30
1860	100dh. Laying pipes	95	30
1861	100dh. Pipe sections on lorries	95	30
1862	100dh. Gaddafi in robes holding *The Green Book*	95	30
1863	100dh. Boy giving Gaddafi bowl of fruit	95	30
1864	100dh. Boy drinking from tap	95	30
1865	100dh. Gaddafi praying	95	30

379 Gaddafi with Children

1986. Colonel Gaddafi, 'Man of Peace'. Multicoloured

1866	100dh. Type **379**	1·10	30
1867	100dh. Reading book in tent	1·10	30
1868	100dh. With his mother	1·10	30
1869	100dh. Praying in tent with his sons	1·10	30
1870	100dh. Talking to hospital patient	1·10	30
1871	100dh. Driving tractor	1·10	30

380 General Dynamics F-111 Exploding above Man with injured Child

1986. Battle of the USS *Philadelphia* and American Attack on Libya. Multicoloured. (a) As T **380**.

1872	50dh. Type **380**	40	25
1873	50dh. American aircraft carrier and escaping family	60	25
1874	100dh. *Philadelphia* exploding (59×38 mm)	1·25	50

381 Gaddafi, Ruined buildings and Stretcher-bearers

(b) As T **381**.

1875	70dh. Type **381**	80	20
1876	70dh. Burning wreckage of car and man and boy in rubble	80	20
1877	70dh. Woman and child by burning ruin	80	20
1878	70dh. Men running from bomb strike	80	20
1879	70dh. Covered body and rescue workers searching ruins	80	20
1880	70dh. Libyans and General Dynamics F-111 aeroplane tail and wing	80	25
1881	70dh. Libyans waving fists	80	20

1882	70dh. Rescue workers lifting child from rubble	80	20
1883	70dh. Weeping women and soldier carrying baby	80	20
1884	70dh. Libyans and glare of explosion	80	20
1885	70dh. Libyans and General Dynamics F-111 aeroplane wing and nose	80	25
1886	70dh. Man carrying girl	80	20
1887	70dh. Coffins held aloft by crowd	80	20
1888	70dh. Crowd carrying pictures of Gaddafi	80	20
1889	70dh. Wounded being tended	80	20
1890	70dh. Hands tending wounded baby	80	20

(c) Size 89×32 mm.

1891	100dh. General Dynamics F-111 bombers, Gaddafi and anti-aircraft rockets	1·25	35

Nos. 1872/1874 were printed together in *se-tenant* strips of three within the sheet, each strip forming a composite design.

382 'The House must be served by its own Tenant'

1986. Quotations from *The Green Book*.

1892	382	100dh. lt green, grn & blk	1·00	30
1893	-	100dh. multicoloured	1·00	30
1894	-	100dh. lt green, grn & blk	1·00	30
1895	-	100dh. lt green, grn & blk	1·00	30
1896	-	100dh. multicoloured	1·00	30
1897	-	100dh. lt green, grn & blk	1·00	30
1898	-	100dh. lt green, grn & blk	1·00	30
1899	-	100dh. multicoloured	1·00	30
1900	-	100dh. lt green, grn & blk	1·00	30

Designs: No. 1893, Gaddafi; No. 1894, 'The Child is raised by his mother'; No. 1895, 'Democracy is the Supervision of the People by the People'; No. 1896, *Green Books*; No. 1897, 'Representation is a Falsification of Democracy'; No. 1898, 'The Recognition of Profit is an Acknowledgement of Exploitation'; No. 1899, Vase of roses, iris, lilies and jasmine; No. 1900, 'Knowledge is a Natural Right of every Human Being which Nobody has the Right to deprive him of under any Pretext'.

383 Map, Chrysanthemum and Health Services

1986. 17th Anniversary of Revolution. Multicoloured.

1901	200dh. Type **383**	2·50	95
1902	200dh. Map, sunflower and agriculture programme	2·50	95
1903	200dh. *Sunflowers* (Van Gogh)	2·50	95
1904	200dh. Map, rose and defence programme	2·50	95
1905	200dh. Map, campanula and oil exploration programme	2·50	95

384 Moroccan and Libyan Women

1986. Arab–African Union. Multicoloured.

1906	250dh. Type **384**	2·50	80
1907	250dh. Libyan and Moroccan horsemen	2·50	80

385 Libyan Horseman

1986. Evacuation of Foreign Forces. Multicoloured.

1908	50dh. Type **385**	50	15
1909	100dh. Libyan horsemen trampling Italian soldiers	1·10	30
1910	150dh. Italian soldiers charging	1·50	50

386 Globe and Rose

1986. International Peace Year. Multicoloured, background colours given.

1911	**386**	200dh. green	1·90	70
1912	**386**	200dh. blue	1·90	70

387 Brick 'Fists' and Maps within Laurel Wreath

1986. Solidarity with Palestinian People. Multicoloured, background colours given.

1913	**387**	250dh. blue	2·50	80
1914	**387**	250dh. red	2·50	80

388 Drummer

1986. Folk Music. Multicoloured.

1915	70dh. Type **388**	95	20
1916	70dh. Masked stick dancer	95	20
1917	70dh. Woman dancer with pot headdress	95	20
1918	70dh. Bagpipe player	95	20
1919	70dh. Tambour player	95	20

389 Gazelles

1987. Endangered Animals. Sand Gazelle. Multicoloured.

1920	100dh. Type **389**	1·25	30
1921	100dh. Mother and calf	1·25	30
1922	100dh. Gazelle drinking	1·25	30
1923	100dh. Gazelle lying down	1·25	30

390 Oil Derricks and Crowd

1987. People's Authority Declaration. Multicoloured.

1924	500dh. Type **390**	4·00	1·75
1925	500dh. Buildings and crowd	4·00	1·75
1926	1000dh. Gaddafi addressing crowd and globe (40×38 mm)	8·00	3·25

391 Sheep and Shepherd

1987. 18th Anniversary of Revolution. Multicoloured.

1927	150dh. Type **391**	1·50	50
1928	150dh. Colonel Gaddafi in robes	1·50	50
1929	150dh. Mosque	1·50	50
1930	150dh. Water flowing from irrigation pipe	1·50	50
1931	150dh. Combine-harvester	1·50	50
1932	150dh. Colonel Gaddafi in army uniform with microphone	1·50	50
1933	150dh. Harvesting crop	1·50	50
1934	150dh. Irrigation	1·50	50
1935	150dh. Soldier with rifle	1·50	50
1936	150dh. Buildings behind Libyan with rifle	1·50	50
1937	150dh. Fountain	1·50	50
1938	150dh. Buildings and beach	1·50	50
1939	150dh. Fort and girls	1·50	50
1940	150dh. Children and hand on rifle butt	1·50	50
1941	150dh. Theatre	1·50	50
1942	150dh. Couple	1·50	50

392 Omar Abed Anabi al Mansusri

1988. Personalities. Multicoloured.

1943	100dh. Type **392**	75	30
1944	200dh. Ahmed Ali al Emrayd	1·50	70
1945	300dh. Khalifa Said Ben Asker	2·50	1·00
1946	400dh. Mohamed Ben Farhat Azawi	3·00	1·10
1947	500dh. Mohamed Souf al Lafi al Marmori	3·75	1·50

393 Gaddafi and Crowd with Raised Fists around Earthmover Bucket

1988. Freedom Festival Day.

1948	**393**	100dh. multicoloured	95	30
1949	**393**	150dh. multicoloured	1·60	75
1950	**393**	250dh. multicoloured	2·50	1·25

394 Woman and Children running

1988. Second Anniversary of American Attack on Libya. Multicoloured.

1951	150dh. Type **394**	1·40	50
1952	150dh. Gaddafi playing chess with boy	1·40	50
1953	150dh. Gaddafi and children	1·40	50
1954	150dh. Gaddafi in robes	1·40	50
1955	150dh. Gaddafi and boys praying	1·40	50
1956	150dh. Gaddafi and injured girl	1·40	50
1957	150dh. Gaddafi in robes with children (horiz)	1·40	50
1958	150dh. Gaddafi making speech (horiz)	1·40	50
1959	150dh. Gaddafi and family (horiz)	1·40	50
MS1960	Two sheets (a) 124×89 mm. 500dh. As No. 1954 (35×50 mm); (b) 89×124 mm. 500dh. As No. 1958 (50×35 mm)	7·75	7·75

395 Roses

1988. 19th Anniversary of Revolution.

1961	**395**	100dh. multicoloured	75	30
1962	**395**	250dh. multicoloured	2·00	80
1963	**395**	300dh. multicoloured	2·25	1·00
1964	**395**	500dh. multicoloured	4·25	1·50

396 Relay

1988. Olympic Games, Seoul. Multicoloured.

1965	150dh. Type **396**	1·25	50
1966	150dh. Cycling	1·25	50
1967	150dh. Football	1·25	50
1968	150dh. Tennis	1·25	50
1969	150dh. Running	1·25	50
1970	150dh. Showjumping	1·25	50
MS1971	Two sheets (a) 107×84 mm. 100dh. Arab on horse (28×40 mm); 200dh. Woman show jumper; 200dh. Male show jumper. (b) 95×75 mm. 750dh. Football (28×39 mm)	8·25	8·25

397 Dates

1988. The Palm Tree. Multicoloured.

1972	500dh. Type **397**	4·25	1·50
1973	1000dh. Tree	8·00	3·75

398 Petrol Bomb, Sling and Map

1988. Palestinian Intifada Movement. Multicoloured

1974	100dh. Type **398**	95	30
1975	200dh. Boy holding stones (45×38 mm)	1·60	70
1976	300dh. Map and flag	2·50	1·00

399 Globe, Declaration and Dove

1989. People's Authority Declaration.

1977	**399**	260dh. multicoloured	1·10	65
1978	**399**	500dh. multicoloured	2·00	1·25

400 Crowd and *The Green Books*

1989. 20th Anniversary of Revolution. Multicoloured.

1979	150dh. Type **400**	1·25	40
1980	150dh. Soldiers, Colonel Gaddafi and water pipeline	1·25	40
1981	150dh. Military hardware, Gaddafi in uniform, education, communications and medicine	1·25	40
1982	150dh. Armed horsemen	1·25	40
1983	150dh. USS *Philadelphia* exploding	1·25	55
MS1984	101×101 mm. 250dh. Gaddafi in Arab robes (35×50 mm)	1·90	1·90

401 Execution Victims, Soldiers and Colonel Gaddafi

1989. 78th Anniversary of Deportation of Libyans to Italy. Multicoloured.

1985	100dh. Type **401**	40	25
1986	100dh. Colonel Gaddafi and Libyans	40	25

1987	100dh. Soliders, deportees and Gaddafi	40	25
1988	100dh. Deportees on jetty and in boats	55	25
1989	100dh. Gaddafi and corpses	40	25
MS1990	140×92 mm. 150dh. Gaddafi and men (67×34 mm)	60	60

402 Demolition of Wall

1989. Demolition of Borders.

1991	**402**	150dh. multicoloured	1·60	1·60
1992	**402**	200dh. multicoloured	2·10	2·10

403 Emblem of Committee for supporting Intifida

1989. Palestinian Intifada Movement. Multicoloured

1993	100dh. Type **403**	1·10	1·10
1994	300dh. Crowd of youths	3·00	3·00
1995	500dh. Emblem (First anniversary of declaration of state of Palestine)	4·75	4·75

404 Circulation Diagram and Annafis

1989. Ibn Annafis (physician) Commemoration.

1996	**404**	100dh. multicoloured	1·25	1·25
1997	**404**	150dh. multicoloured	1·90	1·90

405 *The Green Books* and Fort

1990. People's Authority Declaration.

1998	**405**	300dh. multicoloured	2·75	2·75
1999	**405**	500dh. multicoloured	5·00	5·00

406 Libyan People and Soldier

1990. 20th Anniversary of American Forces Evacuation.

2000	**406**	100dh. multicoloured	1·00	1·00
2001	**406**	400dh. multicoloured	4·00	4·00

407 Eagle

1990. 21st Anniversary of Revolution.

2002	**407**	100dh. multicoloured	1·00	1·00
2003	**407**	400dh. multicoloured	4·00	4·00
2004	**407**	1000dh. multicoloured	10·50	10·50
MS2005		120×90 mm. 200dh. multicoloured (enlarged motif as T **407**). Imperf	1·90	1·90

408 Anniversary Emblem

1990. 30th Anniversary of Organisation of Petroleum Exporting Countries.

2006	**408**	100dh. multicoloured	1·00	1·00
2007	**408**	400dh. multicoloured	4·00	4·00

409 ILY Emblem and Figures

1990. International Literacy Year.

2008	**409**	100dh. multicoloured	1·10	1·10
2009	**409**	300dh. multicoloured	3·00	3·00

410 Player, Globe and Ball

1990. World Cup Football Championship, Italy.

2010	**410**	100dh. multicoloured	1·00	1·00
2011	**410**	400dh. multicoloured	4·00	4·00
2012	**410**	500dh. multicoloured	5·00	5·00
MS2013		100×80 mm. 500dh. multicoloured (Trophy, map and mascot) (38×32 mm)	5·00	5·00

411 Hand holding Ears of Wheat

1990. World Food Day. Multicoloured.

2014	500dh. Type **411**	5·00	5·00
2015	2000dh. Ploughing	20·00	20·00

412 Members' Flags

1991. Second Anniversary of Union of Arab Maghreb.

2016	**412**	100dh. multicoloured	1·10	1·10
2017	**412**	300dh. multicoloured	3·00	3·00

413 Flame, Scroll and Koran

1991. People's Authority Declaration.

2018	**413**	300dh. multicoloured	2·75	2·75
2019	**413**	400dh. multicoloured	3·75	3·75

414 Girl and International Year of the Child Emblem

1991. Children's Day. Multicoloured.

2020	100dh. Type **414**	95	95
2021	400dh. Boy and Day of the African Child emblem	3·75	3·75

415 World Health Organisation Emblem

1991. World Health Day. Multicoloured.

2022	100dh. Type **415**	95	95
2023	200dh. As Type **415** but with emblem additionally inscr 'WHO OMS'	1·90	1·90

416 Wadi el Hayat

1991. Scenes from Libya. Multicoloured.

2024	100dh. Type **416**	95	95
2025	250dh. Mourzuk (horiz)	2·50	2·50
2026	500dh. Ghadames (horiz)	5·00	5·00

417 Digging Riverbed and laying Pipes

1991. Great Man-made River. Multicoloured.

2027	50dh. Type **417**	25	15
2028	50dh. Colonel Gaddafi, agricultural projects and livestock (59×37 mm)	25	15
2029	50dh. Produce	25	15

Nos. 2027/2029 were printed together, *se-tenant*, forming a composite design.

418 '22', Roses and Broken Chain

1991. 22nd Anniversary of Revolution. Multicoloured.

2030	300dh. Type **418**	2·75	2·75
2031	400dh. '22' within wheat/cogwheel wreath and broken chain	3·75	3·75
MS2032	83×103 mm. Nos. 2030/2031	6·50	6·50

419 Emblem and Globe

1991. Telecom 91 International Telecommunications Exhibition, Geneva. Multicoloured.

2033	100dh. Type **419**	95	95
2034	500dh. Buldings and dish aerial (horiz)	4·50	4·50

420 Monument and Soldier

1991. 80th Anniversary of Deportation of Libyans to Italy. Multicoloured.

2035	100dh. Type **420**	95	95
2036	400dh. Naval transport, Libyans and soldiers	3·75	3·75
MS2037	84×103 mm. Nos. 2035/2036	4·75	4·75

421 Map

1991. Arab Unity.

2038	**421**	50dh. multicoloured	20	10
2039	**421**	100dh. multicoloured	40	20

422 Lorry

1991. Paris–Dakar Trans-Sahara Rally. Multicoloured

2040	50dh. Type **422**	20	10
2041	50dh. Blue lorry	20	10
2042	50dh. African Product lorry	20	10
2043	50dh. Tomel lorry	20	10
2044	50dh. All-terrain vehicle No. 173	20	10
2045	50dh. Mitsusuki all-terrain vehicle	20	10
2046	50dh. Michedop all-terrain vehicle	20	10
2047	50dh. All-terrain vehicle No. 401	20	10
2048	50dh. Motor cycle No. 100	20	10
2049	50dh. Rider pushing red motor cycle	20	10
2050	50dh. Rider pushing white motor cycle	20	10
2051	50dh. Motorcycle No. 98	20	10
2052	50dh. Motorcycle No. 101	20	10
2053	50dh. Motorcycle No. 80	20	10
2054	50dh. Motorcycle No. 12	20	10
2055	50dh. Motorcycle No. 45	20	10

423 Gaddafi and Camels

1992. Gaddafi, Man of Peace 1992. Multicoloured, colour of frame given.

2056	**423**	100dh. green	40	20
2057	**423**	100dh. grey	40	20
2058	**423**	100dh. red	40	20
2059	**423**	100dh. ochre	40	20
MS2060		158×121 mm. 4×150dh. As Nos. 2056/2059	1·60	1·60

424 State Arms

1992

2061	**424**	100dh. green, brn & yell	40	20
2062	**424**	150dh. green, brn & grey	60	30
2063	**424**	200dh. green, brown & bl	85	45
2064	**424**	250dh. green, brn & orge	1·10	55
2065	**424**	300dh. green, brn & vio	1·25	65
2066	**424**	400dh. green, brn & mve	1·75	90
2067	**424**	450dh. emerald, brn & grn	1·90	95

425 1991 100dh. Stamp, Tweezers, Magnifying Glass and Stamps

1992. Third Anniversary of Union of Arab Maghreb.

2068	**425**	75dh. multicoloured	30	15
2069	**425**	80dh. multicoloured	35	20

426 Horse-drawn Carriage

1992. International Trade Fair, Tripoli. Multicoloured

2070	50dh. Type **426**	20	10
2071	100dh. Horse-drawn cart	40	20

427 Emblem

1992. People's Authority Declaration.

2072	**427**	100dh. multicoloured	40	20
2073	**427**	150dh. multicoloured	60	30

428 Emblem and Camel Rider

1992. African Tourism Year.

2074	**428**	50dh. multicoloured	20	10
2075	**428**	100dh. multicoloured	40	20

429 Big-eyed Tuna

1992. Fish. Multicoloured.

2076	100dh. Type **429**	75	30
2077	100dh. Mackerel scad	75	30
2078	100dh. Little tuna (seven spines on back)	75	30
2079	100dh. Seabream (continuous dorsal fin)	75	30
2080	100dh. Spanish mackerel (four spines on back)	75	30
2081	100dh. Striped red mullet (with whiskers)	75	30

430 Horsewoman with Rifle

1992. Horse Riders. Multicoloured.

2082	100dh. Type **430**	40	20
2083	100dh. Man on rearing white horse	40	20
2084	100dh. Man on brown horse with ornate bridle	40	20
2085	100dh. Roman soldier on brown horse	40	20
2086	100dh. Man in blue coat on brown horse	40	20
2087	100dh. Arab on white horse	40	20
MS2088	110×82 mm. 250dh. Arabs on horses	1·00	1·00

431 Long Jumping

1992. Olympic Games, Barcelona. Multicoloured.

2089	50dh. Type **431**	20	10
2090	50dh. Throwing the discus	20	10
2091	50dh. Tennis	20	10
MS2092	106×82 mm. 100dh. Olympic torch and rings. Imperf	40	40

432 Palm Trees

1992. Achievements of the Revolution. Multicoloured.

2093	100dh. Type **432**	40	20
2094	150dh. Ingots and foundry	60	30
2095	250dh. Container ship	1·10	55
2096	300dh. Aeroplane	1·25	65
2097	400dh. Assembly hall	1·75	90
2098	500dh. Water pipes and Gaddafi	2·10	1·10

433 Gaddafi

1992. Multicoloured, background colours given.

2099	**433**	500dh. green	2·50	1·10
2100	**433**	1000dh. pink	5·00	2·50
2101	**433**	2000dh. blue	10·00	5·00
2102	**433**	5000dh. violet	25·00	12·50
2103	**433**	6000dh. orange	32·00	16·00

434 Laurel Wreath, Torch and '23'

1992. 23rd Anniversary of Revolution.

2104	**434**	59dh. multicoloured	20	10
2105	-	100dh. multicoloured	40	20
MS2106		110×95 mm. 250dh. emerald, gold and black	1·00	1·00

Designs: 100dh. Laurel wreath, flag. Sun and '23'. 43×35 mm—250dh. Hawk and '23'.

435 Antelope drinking

1992. Oases. Multicoloured.

2107	100dh. Type **435**	40	20
2108	200dh. Sun setting behind camel train (vert)	85	45
2109	300dh. Camel rider	1·25	65

436 Horse and Broken Chain

1992. Evacuation of Foreign Forces. Multicoloured.

2110	75dh. Type **436**	30	15
2111	80dh. Flag and broken chain	35	20

437 Monument and Dates

1992. 81st Anniversary of Deportation of Libyans to Italy.

2112	**437**	100dh. multicoloured	40	20
2113	**437**	250dh. multicoloured	1·10	55

438 Dome of the Rock and Palestinian

1992. Palestinian Intifada Movement. Multicoloured

2114	100dh. Type **438**	40	20
2115	300dh. Map, Dome of the Rock, flag and fist (vert)	1·25	65

439 Red and White Striped Costume

1992. Women's Costumes. Multicoloured.

2116	50dh. Type **439**	20	10
2117	50dh. Large red hat with silver decorations, white tunic and red wrap	20	10
2118	50dh. Brown and orange striped costume with small gold necklace and horseshoe brooch	20	10
2119	50dh. Purple and white costume	20	10
2120	50dh. Orange striped costume	20	10

440 Mohamed Ali Imsek

1993. Physicians.

2121	**440**	40dh. black, yellow and silver	15	10
2122	-	60dh. black, green and gold	20	15

Design: 60dh. Aref Adhani Arif.

441 Globe, Crops and Spoon-feeding Man

1993. International Nutrition Conference, Rome.

2123	**441**	70dh. multicoloured	35	25
2124	**441**	80dh. multicoloured	40	30

442 Gaddafi, Eagle and Oil Refinery

1993. People's Authority Declaration.

2125	**442**	60dh. multicoloured	20	15
2126	**442**	65dh. multicoloured	25	15
2127	**442**	75dh. multicoloured	25	15

443 Crowd with Tambours

1993. International Trade Fair, Tripoli. Multicoloured

2128	60dh. Type **443**	20	15
2129	60dh. Crowd with camel	20	15
2130	60dh. Dance of veiled men (horiz)	20	15
2131	60dh. Women preparing food (horiz)	20	15
MS2132	100×80 mm. 100dh. Horsemen (38×31 mm)	35	35

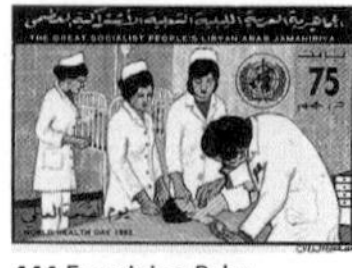

444 Examining Baby

1993. World Health Day. Multicoloured.

2133	75dh. Type **444**	25	15
2134	85dh. Medical staff attending patient	30	20

445 Girl

1993. Children's Day. Multicoloured.

2135	75dh. Type **445**	25	15
2136	75dh. Girl wearing blue and white veil and gold cuff	25	15
2137	75dh. Girl with white fluted collar and silver veil	25	15
2138	75dh. Girl with hands clasped	25	15
2139	75dh. Girl wearing blue scallop-edged veil	25	15

446 Phoenician Ship

1993. Ships. Multicoloured.

2140	50dh. Type **446**	20	15
2141	50dh. Arab galley	20	15
2142	50dh. Pharaonic ship	20	15
2143	50dh. Roman bireme	20	15
2144	50dh. Carvel	20	15
2145	50dh. Yacht (globe showing Italy)	20	15
2146	50dh. Yacht (globe showing Greece)	20	15
2147	50dh. Galeasse	20	15
2148	50dh. Nau	20	15
2149	50dh. Yacht (globe showing left half of Libya)	20	15
2150	50dh. Yacht (globe showing right half of Libya)	20	15
2151	50dh. *Santa Maria*	20	15
2152	50dh. *France* (liner)	20	15
2153	50dh. Schooner	20	15
2154	50dh. Sail/steam warship	20	15
2155	50dh. Modern liner	20	15

Nos. 2140/2155 were issued together, *se-tenant*, the centre four stamps forming a composite design.

447 Combine-harvesters

1993. 24th Anniversary of Revolution. Multicoloured.

2156	50dh. Type **447**	20	15
2157	50dh. Colonel Gaddafi	20	15

2158	50dh. Cattle behind men filling sack with grain	20	15
2159	50dh. Chickens behind shepherd with flock	20	15
2160	50dh. Oil rig	20	15
2161	50dh. Eagle and camel	20	15
2162	50dh. Industrial plant	20	15
2163	50dh. Water pipeline	20	15
2164	50dh. Man harvesting dates	20	15
2165	50dh. Man in field and boxes of produce	20	15
2166	50dh. Pile of produce	20	15
2167	50dh. Man picking courgettes	20	15
2168	50dh. Children reading	20	15
2169	50dh. Typist and laboratory worker	20	15
2170	50dh. Hand-picking crop and ploughing with tractor	20	15
2171	50dh. Tractor towing circular harrow	20	15

Nos. 2156/2171 were issued together, *se-tenant*, forming several composite designs.

448 Woman tending Youth

1993. 82nd Anniversary of Deportation of Libyans to Italy. Multicoloured.

2172	50dh. Type **448**	20	15
2173	50dh. Soldiers and Libyan family	20	15
2174	50dh. Colonel Gaddafi (in turban)	20	15
2175	50dh. Libyans in food queue	20	15
2176	50dh. Man being flogged	20	15
2177	50dh. Horseman charging between soldiers and Libyans	20	15
2178	50dh. Soldier with manacled Libyan before court	20	15
2179	50dh. Libyans gazing at hanged man	20	15
2180	50dh. Crowd of Libyans and two soldiers	20	15
2181	50dh. Soldiers guarding procession of Libyans	20	15
2182	50dh. Soldiers and manacled Libyans on quayside	20	15
2183	50dh. Deportees in boat	20	15
2184	50dh. Colonel Gaddafi (bare-headed)	20	15
2185	50dh. Two Libyan families and branch of palm tree	20	15
2186	50dh. Soldiers in disarray (ruins in background)	20	15
2187	50dh. Libyan horsemen	20	15

Nos. 2172/2187 were issued together, *se-tenant*, forming several composite designs.

449 Brooch

1994. Silver Jewellery. Multicoloured.

2188	55dh. Type **449**	20	15
2189	55dh. Armlet	20	15
2190	55dh. Pendant	20	15
2191	55dh. Pendants hanging from oblong	20	15
2192	55dh. Necklace	20	15
2193	55dh. Slippers	20	15

450 Gaddafi, Soldiers and Jet Fighters

1994. 25th Anniversary of Revolution. Multicoloured.

2194	100dh. Type **450**	35	25
2195	100dh. Libyan tribesmen and Gaddafi in uniform (59×38 mm)	35	25
2196	100dh. Peaceful pursuits and elderly couple	35	25
MS2197	110×94 mm. 1000dh. Colonel Gaddafi (39×49 mm)	1·75	1·75

Nos. 2194/2196 were issued together, *se-tenant*, forming a composite design.

451 Player and Trophy

1994. World Cup Football Championship, USA. Multicoloured.

2198	100dh. Type **451**	35	35
2199	100dh. Kicking ball with inside of foot	35	25
2200	100dh. Kicking ball in air	35	25
2201	100dh. Goalkeeper	35	25
2202	100dh. Running with ball	35	25
2203	100dh. Player taking ball on chest	35	25
MS2204	Two sheets (a) 128×86 mm. 500dh. Trophy between two players (41×50 mm); (b) 100×142 mm. 500dh. Ball, emblem, player and '1990' (50×41 mm)	3·50	3·50

452 Gaddafi

1994. 83rd Anniversary of Deportation of Libyans to Italy. Multicoloured.

2205	95dh. Type **452**	35	25
2206	95dh. Light aeroplane over rifleman	35	25
2207	95dh. Couple running from biplane	35	25
2208	95dh. Biplane flying over men and boy	35	25
2209	95dh. Man trapped beneath fallen horse	35	25
2210	95dh. Soldiers and Libyans fighting (camel's head and neck in foreground)	35	25
2211	95dh. Soldiers surrounding fallen Libyan	35	25
2212	95dh. Man carrying boy	35	25
2213	95dh. Soldier with whip raised	35	25
2214	95dh. Robed man shouting	35	25
2215	95dh. Tank and battle scene	35	25
2216	95dh. Women fleeing mounted soliers	35	25
2217	95dh. Man being flogged and woman cradling head of fallen Libyan	35	25
2218	95dh. Soldiers and Libyans fighting (camels in background)	35	25
2219	95dh. Women and soldiers on quayside	35	25
2220	95dh. Deportees in two boats	35	25

Nos. 2205/2220 were issued together, *se-tenant*, forming several composite designs.

453 Darghut

1994. Mosques. Multicoloured.

2221	70dh. Type **453**	25	15
2222	70dh. Benghazi	25	15
2223	70dh. Kabao	25	15
2224	70dh. Gouzgu	25	15
2225	70dh. Siala	25	15
2226	70dh. El Kettani	25	15

454 Armed Forces

1994. People's Authority Declaration. Multicoloured.

2227	80dh. Type **454**	30	20
2228	80dh. Truck, hand holding *The Green Book* and ears of wheat	30	20
2229	80dh. Pipes on trailers, water pipeline and family	30	20
2230	80dh. Crowd with *Green Books*	30	20
2231	80dh. Colonel Gaddafi	30	20
2232	80dh. Youths and produce	30	20

Nos. 2227/2232 were issued together, *se-tenant*, forming a composite design.

455 Sun over Cemetery, National Flag, Dove and Footprints

1994. Evacuation of Foreign Forces.

2233	**455**	65dh. multicoloured	25	15
2234	**455**	95dh. multicoloured	35	20

456 Men with Weapons and Troops in Background

1994. Gaddafi Prize for Human Rights. Multicoloured.

2235	95dh. Type **456**	35	20
2236	95dh. Men with weapons	35	20
2237	95dh. President Nelson Mandela of South Africa	35	20
2238	95dh. President Gaddafi	35	20
2239	95dh. Amerindian meditating	35	20
2240	95dh. Warriors on horseback	35	20
2241	95dh. Amerindian chief	35	20
2242	95dh. Amerindian	35	20
2243	95dh. Riflemen and aircraft	35	20
2244	95dh. Bomber, women, fire and left page of book	35	20
2245	95dh. Right page of book and surgeon operating	35	20
2246	95dh. Surgeons operating	35	20
2247	95dh. Masked revolutionaries with flag	35	20
2248	95dh. Revolutionaries raising arms with flag	35	20
2249	95dh. Young boys with stones	35	20
2250	95dh. Revolutionaries, fire and troops	35	20

Nos. 2235/2250 were issued together, *se-tenant*, forming a composite design.

457 Declaration and Flowers

1995. People's Authority Declaration. Multicoloured, colour of background given.

2251	**457**	100dh. yellow	35	20
2252	**457**	100dh. blue	35	20
2253	**457**	100dh. green	35	20

458 Emblem, Members' Flags and Map showing Member Countries

1995. 50th Anniversary of Arab League. Multicoloured, frame colour given.

2254	**458**	200f. blue	70	45
2255	**458**	200f. green	70	45
MS2256		147×120 mm. 458 1000dh.×2 as Nos. 2254/2255 but with gold decoration	6·75	6·75

459 Messaud Zentuti

1995. 60th Anniversary of National Football Team. Designs showing players. Multicoloured.

2257	100dh. Type **459**	35	20
2258	100dh. Salem Shermit	35	20
2259	100dh. Ottoman Marfua	35	20
2260	100dh. Ghaleb Siala	35	20
2261	100dh. Team, 1935	35	20
2262	100dh. Senussi Mresila	35	20

Nos. 2257/2262 were issued together, *se-tenant*, forming a composite design.

460 Dromedary

1995. Libyan Zoo. Multicoloured.

2263	100dh. Type **460**	35	20
2264	100dh. Secretary bird	35	20
2265	100dh. African wild dog	35	20
2266	100dh. Oryx	35	20
2267	100dh. Baboon	35	20
2268	100dh. Golden jackal	35	20
2269	100dh. Crowned eagle	35	20
2270	100dh. Desert eagle owl ('Eagle Owl')	35	20
2271	100dh. Desert hedgehog	35	20
2272	100dh. Sand gerbil	35	20
2273	100dh. Addax	35	20
2274	100dh. Fennec fox	35	20
2275	100dh. Lanner falcon	35	20
2276	100dh. Desert wheatear	35	20
2277	100dh. Pin-tailed sandgrouse	35	20
2278	100dh. Jerboa	35	20

Nos. 2263/2278 were issued together, *se-tenant*, the backgrounds forming a composite design.

461 Grapefruit

1995. Fruit. Multicoloured.

2279	100dh. Type **461**	35	20
2280	100dh. Wild cherry	35	20
2281	100dh. Mulberry	35	20
2282	100dh. Strawberry	35	20
2283	100dh. Plum	35	20
2284	100dh. Pear	35	20
2285	100dh. Apricot	35	20
2286	100dh. Almond	35	20
2287	100dh. Prickly pear	35	20
2288	100dh. Lemon	35	20
2289	100dh. Peach	35	20
2290	100dh. Dates	35	20
2291	100dh. Olive	35	20
2292	100dh. Orange	35	20
2293	100dh. Fig	35	20
2294	100dh. Grape	35	20

Nos. 2279/2294 were issued together, *se-tenant*, the backgrounds forming a composite design.

462 Students

1995. 26th Anniversary of Revolution. Multicoloured.

2295	100dh. Type **462**	35	20
2296	100dh. Mosque, teacher and students	35	20
2297	100dh. President Gaddafi	35	20
2298	100dh. Laboratory workers	35	20
2299	100dh. Hospital patient, doctor examining child, and nurse	35	20
2300	100dh. Surgeons operating	35	20
2301	100dh. Cobblers and keyboard operator	35	20
2302	100dh. Sound engineers and musician	35	20
2303	100dh. Crane and apartment block	35	20
2304	100dh. Silos	35	20
2305	100dh. Oil rig platform	35	20
2306	100dh. Aeroplane and ships	35	20
2307	100dh. Animals grazing and farmer	35	20
2308	100dh. Pipeline	35	20
2309	100dh. Camels at trough and crops	35	20
2310	100dh. Crops and farm vehicle	35	20

Nos. 2295/2310 were issued together, *se-tenant*, forming a composite design.

463 Scout Badge and Wildlife

1995. Scouting. Multicoloured.

2311	250dh. Type **463**	85	55
2312	250dh. Badge, butterflies and scouts with animals (59×39 mm)	85	55
2313	250dh. Badge and scouts	85	55

Nos. 2311/2313 were issued together, *se-tenant*, forming a composite design.

464 Warships and Rocket

1995. Ninth Anniversary of American Attack on Libya. Multicoloured.

2314	100dh. Type **464**	35	20
2315	100dh. Bombers, helicopters, warships and Libyans (59×49 mm)	35	20
2316	100dh. Bomber and woman holding baby	35	20

Nos. 2314/2316 were issued together, *se-tenant*, forming a composite design.

465 Gaddafi on Horseback

1995. International Trade Fair, Tripoli. Multicoloured.

2317	100dh. Type **465**	35	20
2318	100dh. Horseman	35	20
2319	100dh. Horseman (horse galloping to right)	35	20
2320	100dh. Horsemen with whips (horiz)	35	20
2321	100dh. Horseman holding rifle (horiz)	35	20
2322	100dh. Horsewoman brandishing rifle in air (horiz)	35	20
MS2323	140×100 mm. 1000dh. Close-up of horsemen (79×49 mm)	1·75	1·75

466 Dromedary and Woman with Water Jars

1995. City of Ghadames. Multicoloured.

2324	100dh. Type **466**	35	20
2325	100dh. Making cheeses	35	20
2326	100dh. Woman holding jar	35	20
2327	100dh. Feeding chickens	35	20
2328	100dh. Spinning wool	35	20
2329	100dh. Woman in traditional costume	35	20
2330	100dh. Drying grain	35	20
2331	100dh. Milking goat	35	20
2332	100dh. Making shoes	35	20
2333	100dh. Weaving	35	20
2334	100dh. Engraving brass tabletops	35	20
2335	100dh. Harvesting dates	35	20
2336	100dh. Reading scriptures	35	20
2337	100dh. Potter	35	20
2338	100dh. Washing clothes in well	35	20
2339	100dh. Picking fruit	35	20

467 Family with Torch and National Flag

1995. Evacuation of Foreign Forces.

2340	**467**	50dh. multicoloured	20	10
2341	**467**	100dh. multicoloured	35	20
2342	**467**	200dh. multicoloured	70	45

468 Honeycomb and Bees on Flowers

1995. Arab Beekeepers' Association. Multicoloured, colour of border given.

2343	**468**	100dh. mauve	35	20
2344	**468**	100dh. lilac	35	20
2345	**468**	100dh. green	35	20

469 Stubbing out Cigarette and holding Rose

1995. World Health Day. Multicoloured, colour of central band given.

2346	**469**	100dh. yellow	35	20
2347	**469**	100dh. orange	35	20

470 Dr. Mohamed Feituri

1995

2348	**470**	200dh. multicoloured	70	45

471 Gaddafi and Horsemen

1995. 84th Anniversary of Deportation of Libyans to Italy. Multicoloured.

2349	100dh. Type **471**	35	20
2350	100dh. Horsemen	35	20
2351	100dh. Battle scene	35	20
2352	100dh. Bomber over battle scene	35	20
2353	100dh. Libyans with rifles	35	20
2354	100dh. Soldiers fighting with Libyans	35	20
2355	100dh. Soldiers with weapons and man on ground	35	20
2356	100dh. Soldiers with rifles and building in background	35	20
2357	100dh. Libyans	35	20
2358	100dh. Soldiers charging men on ground	35	20
2359	100dh. Soldiers shooting at horseman	35	20
2360	100dh. Soldiers pushing Libyan to ground	35	20
2361	100dh. Horsemen charging	35	20
2362	100dh. Horses falling to ground	35	20
2363	100dh. Children	35	20
2364	100dh. Deportees in boats	35	20

Nos. 2349/2364 were issued together, *se-tenant*, forming a composite design.

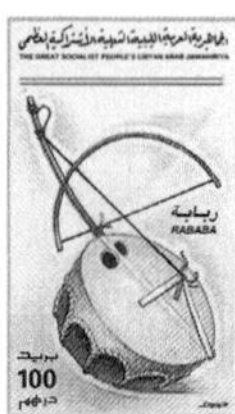

472 Rababa

1995. Musical Instruments. Multicoloured.

2365	100dh. Type **472**	35	20
2366	100dh. Nouba	35	20
2367	100dh. Clarinet	35	20
2368	100dh. Drums	35	20
2369	100dh. Magruna	35	20
2370	100dh. Zukra	35	20
2371	100dh. Zil	35	20
2372	100dh. Kaman	35	20
2373	100dh. Guitar	35	20
2374	100dh. Trumpet	35	20
2375	100dh. Tapla	35	20
2376	100dh. Gonga	35	20
2377	100dh. Saxophone	35	20
2378	100dh. Piano	35	20
2379	100dh. Ganoon	35	20
2380	100dh. Ood	35	20

473 Blue Door

1995. Doors from Mizda. Multicoloured.

2381	100dh. Type **473**	35	20
2382	100dh. Door with arch detail	35	20
2383	100dh. Door made of logs	35	20
2384	100dh. Arched door	35	20
2385	100dh. Wide door with bolts	35	20

474 Sports within Olympic Rings

1995. Centenary of International Olympic Committee. Multicoloured, colour of face value given.

2386	**474**	100dh. black	35	20
2387	**474**	100dh. red	35	20

475 Baryonyx

1995. Prehistoric Animals. Multicoloured.

2388	100dh. Type **475**	35	20
2389	100dh. Oviraptor	35	20
2390	100dh. Stenonychosaurus	35	20
2391	100dh. Tenontosaurus	35	20
2392	100dh. Yangchuanosaurus	35	20
2393	100dh. Stegotetrabelodon (facing right)	35	20
2394	100dh. Stegotetrabelodon (facing left)	35	20
2395	100dh. Psittacosaurus	35	20
2396	100dh. Heterodontosaurus	35	20
2397	100dh. Loxodonta atlantica	35	20
2398	100dh. Mammuthus africanavus	35	20
2399	100dh. Erlikosaurus	35	20
2400	100dh. Cynognathus	35	20
2401	100dh. Plateosaurus	35	20
2402	100dh. Staurikosaurus	35	20
2403	100dh. Lystrosaurus	35	20

Nos. 2388/2403 were issued together, *se-tenant*, the backgrounds forming a composite design.

476 Child and Dinosaur walking with Stick

1995. Children's Day. Multicoloured.

2405	100dh. Type **476**	35	20
2406	100dh. Child on mammoth's back	35	20
2407	100dh. Child on way to school and tortoise under mushroom	35	20
2408	100dh. Dinosaur playing football	35	20
2409	100dh. Child pointing rifle at pteranodon	35	20

477 Helicopter, Soldier and Stone-thrower

1995. Palestinian Intifada Movement. Multicoloured.

2410	100dh. Type **477**	35	20
2411	100dh. Dome of the Rock and Palestinian with flag	35	20
2412	100dh. Women with flag	35	20

Nos. 2410/2412 were issued together, *se-tenant*, forming a composite design.

478 Aeroplane, Control Tower and Tailfin

1995. 50th Anniversary of ICAO. Multicoloured, colour of face value given.

2413	**478**	100dh. blue	35	20
2414	**478**	100dh. black	35	20

479 Headquarters, New York

1995. 50th Anniversary of UNO. Multicoloured, colour of background given.

2415	**479**	100dh. pink	35	20
2416	**479**	100dh. lilac	35	20

480 *Iris germanica*

1995. Flowers. Multicoloured.

2417	200dh. Type **480**	35	20
2418	200dh. *Canna edulis*	35	20
2419	200dh. *Nerium oleander*	35	20
2420	200dh. Corn poppy (*Papaver rhoeas*)	35	20
2421	200dh. Bird of Paradise flower (*Strelitzia reginae*)	35	20
2422	200dh. *Amygdalus communis*	35	20

481 Open Hand

1996. People's Authority Declaration. Multicoloured.

2423	**481**	100dh. multicoloured	35	20
2424	**481**	150dh. multicoloured	50	30
2425	**481**	200dh. multicoloured	65	40

482 Football

1996. Olympic Games, Atlanta, USA. Multicoloured.

2426	100dh. Type **482**	35	20
2427	100dh. Long jumping	35	20
2428	100dh. Tennis	35	20
2429	100dh. Cycling	35	20
2430	100dh. Boxing	35	20
2431	100dh. Equestrian show jumping	35	20

MS2432 Two sheets each 95×78 mm. (a) 500dh. Running; (b) 500dh. Dressage 1·75 1·75

Nos. 2426/2431 were issued together, *se-tenant*, the background forming a composite design of the Games emblem.

483 Man holding Fruit

1996. 27th Anniversary of Revolution. Multicoloured.

2433	100dh. Type **483**	35	20
2434	100dh. Water flowing along chute and out of pipe	35	20
2435	100dh. Tractor, water and women with flowers	35	20
2436	100dh. Man working on pipe by water	35	20
2437	100dh. Man sewing	35	20
2438	100dh. Woman textile worker	35	20
2439	100dh. President Gaddafi in white shirt and red cape	35	20
2440	100dh. Women laboratory workers	35	20
2441	100dh. Anatomy instruction and man using microscope	35	20
2442	100dh. Child holding hand to face	35	20
2443	100dh. Woman praying before open Koran	35	20
2444	100dh. Man weaving	35	20
2445	100dh. Two aircraft	35	20
2446	100dh. Man on camel, liner and dish aerial	35	20
2447	100dh. Stern of liner and television camera	35	20
2448	100dh. Woman using microphone and woman being filmed	35	20

Nos. 2433/2448 were issued together, *se-tenant*, forming a composite design.

484 Bomb Exploding

1996. Tenth Anniversary of American Attack on Libya. Multicoloured.

2449	100dh. Type **484**	35	20
2450	100dh. Man with raised arms	35	20
2451	100dh. Woman carrying child	35	20
2452	100dh. Injured man on ground and fighter aircraft	35	20
2453	100dh. Fireman hosing down burning car	35	20
2454	100dh. Exploding aeroplane	35	20
2455	100dh. Head of President Gaddafi	35	20
2456	100dh. Aeroplane bombing tented camp	35	20
2457	100dh. Rescuers helping two women	35	20
2458	100dh. Man with bandaged head and hand	35	20
2459	100dh. Woman with hankerchief to mouth	35	20
2460	100dh. Stretcher bearers	35	20
2461	100dh. Explosion and man being carried away	35	20
2462	100dh. Explosion and man with injured hand	35	20
2463	100dh. Rescuers helping injured mother with baby	35	20
2464	100dh. Burning car and helpers tending injured boy	35	20

Nos. 2449/2464 were issued together, *se-tenant*, forming a composite design.

485 *Necora puber* (crab)

1996. Crustaceans. Multicoloured.

2465	100dh. Type **485**	35	20
2466	100dh. *Lissa chiragra* (crab)	35	20
2467	100dh. Rock lobster (*Palinurus elephas*)	35	20
2468	100dh. *Scyllarus arctus*	35	20
2469	100dh. Green crab (*Carcinus maenas*)	35	20
2470	100dh. Helmet crab (*Calappa granulata*)	35	20
2471	100dh. *Parapenaeus longirostris* (prawn)	35	20
2472	100dh. Norway lobster (*Nephrops norvegicus*)	35	20
2473	100dh. *Eriphia verrucosa* (crab)	35	20
2474	100dh. Edible crab (*Cancer pagurus*)	35	20
2475	100dh. *Penaeus kerathurus* (prawn)	35	20
2476	100dh. Mantis shrimp (*Squilla mantis*)	35	20
2477	100dh. Spider crab (*Maja squinado*)	35	20
2478	100dh. *Pilumnus hirtellus* (crab)	35	20
2479	100dh. *Pagurus alatus* (crab)	35	20
2480	100dh. *Macropodia tenuirostris*	35	20

Nos. 2465/2480 were issued together, *se-tenant*, the backgrounds forming a composite design.

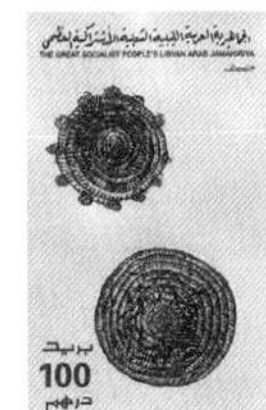

486 Mats

1996. Maghreb Handicrafts Day. Basketwork. Multicoloured.

2481	100dh. Type **486**	35	20
2482	100dh. Lidded storage vessel	35	20
2483	100dh. Bowl	35	20
2484	100dh. Mug and teapot	35	20
2485	100dh. Box with open lid	35	20
2486	100dh. Bird's-eye view of dish	35	20
2487	100dh. Pot with wide base and mouth and narrower neck	35	20
2488	100dh. Lidded pot with carrying handle	35	20
2489	100dh. Bulbous bottle-shaped carrier	35	20
2490	100dh. Large dish	35	20
2491	100dh. Oval dish with well in centre	35	20
2492	100dh. Straight-sided bottle-shaped carrier	35	20
2493	100dh. Vessel with double carrying handles and open lid	35	20
2494	100dh. Dish on stand	35	20
2495	100dh. Pot with wide base and narrow mouth	35	20
2496	100dh. Bag with lid	35	20

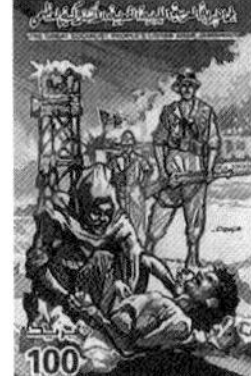

487 Woman kneeling over Boy

1996. 85th Anniversary of Deportation of Libyans to Italy. Multicoloured.

2497	100dh. Type **487**	35	20
2498	100dh. Horseman leading prisoner	35	20
2499	100dh. President Gaddafi wearing turban	35	20
2500	100dh. Old man holding stick in camp	35	20
2501	100dh. Man being flogged	35	20
2502	100dh. Horseman, soldiers and crowd wearing fezzes	35	20
2503	100dh. Prisoner, advocate and man in tricolour sash	35	20
2504	100dh. Family and soldier	35	20
2505	100dh. Soldiers guarding prisoners (boy at front)	35	20
2506	100dh. Soldiers escorting woman on camel and man on donkey	35	20
2507	100dh. Prisoners being escorted through street	35	20
2508	100dh. Prisoners in boat	35	20
2509	100dh. President Gaddafi in white embroided shirt with open hand	35	20
2510	100dh. Group of prisoners including man with raised arm	35	20
2511	100dh. Horsemen charging and soldiers	35	20
2512	100dh. Horseman with rifle	35	20

Nos. 2497/2512 were issued together, *se-tenant*, forming several composite designs.

488 Bay

1996. Horses. Multicoloured.

2513	100dh. Type **488**	35	20
2514	100dh. Light brown horse under tree (branches at right of stamp)	35	20
2515	100dh. Light brown horse by lake under tree (branch at left)	35	20
2516	100dh. Dark brown horse (edge of lake at left)	35	20
2517	100dh. Black horse with hoof raised	35	20
2518	100dh. Chestnut horse	35	20
2519	100dh. Grey horse running	35	20
2520	100dh. Piebald	35	20
2521	100dh. Head of grey and tail of black horses	35	20
2522	100dh. Head of black and tail of chestnut horses	35	20
2523	100dh. Head and rump of chestnut horses	35	20
2524	100dh. Head of chestnut horse with white mane	35	20
2525	100dh. Head of black horse and parts of three other horses	35	20
2526	100dh. Head of chestnut horse with blond mane and parts of three other horses	35	20
2527	100dh. Head of dark brown horse and parts of three other horses	35	20
2528	100dh. Head of dark brown and part of chestnut horses	35	20

Nos. 2513/2528 were issued together, *se-tenant*, forming a composite design.

489 Camel

1996. Camels. Multicoloured.

2529	200dh. Type **489**	65	40
2530	200dh. Head of camel	65	40
2531	200dh. Dark brown dromedary	65	40
2532	200dh. Long-haired Bactrian camel	65	40
2533	200dh. Light brown Bactrian camel	65	40
2534	200dh. Brown Bactrian camel with white stripe and tail	65	40

Nos. 2529/2534 were issued together, *se-tenant*, forming a composite design.

490 Photographer, Newspapers and Computer

1996. The Press and Information. Multicoloured.

2535	100dh. Type **490**	35	20
2536	200dh. Television, control desk, musicians, computer and dish aerial	65	40

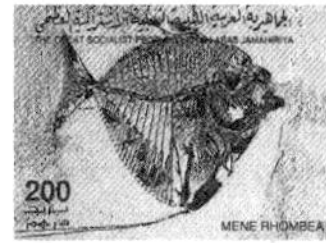

491 Mene rhombea

1996. Fossils. Multicoloured.

2537	200dh. Type **491**	65	40
2538	200dh. Mesodon macrocephalus	65	40
2539	200dh. Eyron arctiformis	65	40
2540	200dh. Stegosaurus	65	40
2541	200dh. Pteranodon	65	40
2542	200dh. Allosaurus	65	40

492 Palestinian Flag and Hands holding up Stones

1996. Palestinian Intifada Movement.

2543	**492**	100dh. multicoloured	35	20
2544	**492**	150dh. multicoloured	50	30
2545	**492**	200dh. multicoloured	65	40

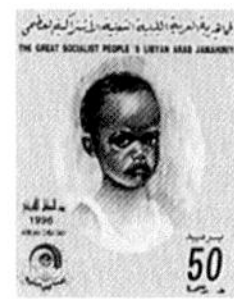

493 Child

1996. African Child Day. Multicoloured.

2546	50dh. Type **493**	10	10
2547	150dh. Type **493**	40	25
2548	200dh. Mother and child	50	35

494 Cat

1996. Children's Day. Cats. Multicoloured.

2549	100dh. Type **494**	25	15
2550	100dh. Tabby (back view with head turned)	25	15
2551	100dh. Colourpoint (black and white)	25	15
2552	100dh. Tabby adult and kitten	25	15
2553	100dh. Tortoiseshell white (sitting)	25	15

495 Family and Tower Block

1996. World Family Day. Multicoloured.

2554	150dh. Type **495**	40	25
2555	150dh. Family and car parked by palm trees	40	25
2556	200dh. Family, symbolic globe and flowers (45×26 mm)	50	35

Nos. 2554/2556 were issued together, *se-tenant*, forming a composite design.

496 Mohamed Kamel el-Hammali

1996. Libyan Teachers. Multicoloured.

2557	100dh. Type **496**	25	15
2558	100dh. Mustafa Abdalla ben-Amer	25	15
2559	100dh. Mohamed Messaud Fesheka	25	15
2560	100dh. Kairi Mustafa Serraj	25	15
2561	100dh. Muftah el-Majri	25	15
2562	100dh. Mohamed Hadi Arafa	25	15

497 Mohamed Salim

1996. Libyan Singers. Multicoloured.

2563	100dh. Type **497**	25	15
2564	100dh. Mohamed M. Sayed Bumedyen	25	15
2565	100dh. Otman Najim	25	15
2566	100dh. Mahmud Sherif	25	15
2567	100dh. Mohamed Ferjani Marghani	25	15
2568	100dh. Mohamed Kabazi	25	15

498 Snake

1996. Reptiles. Multicoloured.

2569	100dh. Type **498**	25	15
2570	100dh. Diamond-back snake beside river	25	15
2571	100dh. Turtle on water (segmented shell and large flippers)	25	15
2572	100dh. Snake wrapped around tree branch	25	15
2573	100dh. Brown lizard on tree trunk	25	15
2574	100dh. Coiled snake with head raised and mouth open	25	15
2575	100dh. Snake with head raised beside water	25	15
2576	100dh. Turtle on water (flat shell, pointed snout and small flippers)	25	15
2577	100dh. Green lizard on tree trunk	25	15
2578	100dh. Snake with wavy pattern on ground	25	15
2579	100dh. Snake with horns	25	15
2580	100dh. Chameleon	25	15
2581	100dh. Tortoise on ground (facing right)	25	15
2582	100dh. Snake on rock with head raised	25	15
2583	100dh. Tortoise on ground (facing left)	25	15
2584	100dh. Grey lizard on rock	25	15

Nos. 2569/2584 were issued together, *se-tenant*, forming a composite design.

499 Mirror and Clothes Brush

1996. International Trade Fair, Tripoli. Each silver, pink and black.

2585	100dh. Type **499**	25	15
2586	100dh. Decanter on tray	25	15
2587	100dh. Two round-bottomed flasks	25	15
2588	100dh. Two long-necked flasks	25	15
2589	100dh. Covered bowl	25	15
2590	100dh. Backs of hairbrush and mirror	25	15

500 Gaddafi and Symbolic Scenes

1997. People's Authority Declaration.

2591	**500**	100dh. multicoloured	25	15
2592	**500**	200dh. multicoloured	25	15
2593	**500**	300dh. multicoloured	25	15

501 Scouts and Stamp Album

1997. Postal Savings Bank. Multicoloured.

2594	50dh. Type **501**	10	10
2595	50dh. Two Girl Guides and albums	10	10
2596	100dh. Bank books and butterflies	25	15

Nos. 2594/2596 were issued together, *se-tenant*, forming a composite design.

502 Scientist with Test Tubes

1997. World Health Day. Multicoloured.

2597	50dh. Type **502**	10	10
2598	50dh. Scientist at microscope	10	10
2599	100dh. Doctor and nurse examining baby	25	15

Nos. 2597/2599 were issued together, *se-tenant*, forming a composite design.

503 Death enveloping Man's Head

1997. Anti-drugs Campaign.

2600	**503**	100dh. multicoloured	25	15
2601	**503**	150dh. multicoloured	40	25
2602	**503**	200dh. multicoloured	50	35

504 Library

1997. Arab National Central Library.

2603	**504**	100dh. multicoloured	25	15
2604	**504**	200dh. multicoloured	50	35
MS2605		168×118 mm. 100dh. Gaddafi, books, computer and library (105×48 mm)	30	30

505 Dancer and Local Crafts

1997. Arab Tourism Year.

2606	**505**	100dh. multicoloured	25	15
2607	**505**	200dh. multicoloured	50	25
2608	**505**	250dh. multicoloured	65	45

506 Mother and Child

1997. 28th Anniversary of Revolution. Designs showing scenes from the life of Muammar al Gaddafi. Multicoloured.

2609-2621	100dh.×13, Type **506**; Student; Speaking at microphone; Tank and crew; Wearing uniform; With raised fist; Mother, child and book; With elderly couple; Writing; With child; Fly past; Wearing uniform with gold braid; 500d. Horseman (57×85 mm)		
MS2622	125×87 mm. 500dh. Wearing brown robe (horiz)	10·50	10·50

Nos. 2609/2621 and the stamps and margin of **MS**2622, respectively, each form composite designs.

507 Silverwork

1997. International Trade Fair, Tripoli. Multicoloured

2623-2628	500dh.×6, Type **507**; Circular brooch; Necklace and square pendant; Book shaped clasp; Necklace; Band	17·00	17·00

Nos. 2623/2628 were issued together, *se-tenant*, with the background forming a composite design.

508 Ship and Crowd

1997. Evacuation of Foreign Troops.

2629	**508**	100dh. multicoloured	25	15
2630	**508**	150dh. multicoloured	40	25
2631	**508**	250dh. multicoloured	60	40

509 Slippers

1997. Maghreb Handicrafts Day. Multicoloured.

2632-2637	300dh.×6, Type **509**; Orange embroidered slippers with beads and tassels; Green and red leather slippers; Slippers with circular design on toes; Thong sandals; Red embroidered slippers with squared design	10·50	10·50

Nos. 2632/2637 were issued together, *se-tenant*, with the background forming a composite design.

510 Woman carrying Pot

1997. 86th Anniversary of Deportation of Libyans to Italy. Multicoloured.

2638-2653	200dh.×16, Type **510**; Muammar al Gaddafi; Mounted soldier; Soldier and couple; Flogging; Horseman; Leaders; Soldier and crowd; Woman with bowed head; Elderly man; Muammar al Gaddafi (different); Boats; Towers and hand; Horsemen; Horsemen (different); Horsemen and hand	16·00	16·00

Nos. 2638/2653 were issued together, *se-tenant*, with the background forming a composite design.

511 Carrying Bird

1997. Endangered Species. *Felis lybica* (Asiatic desert cat) (2654/2657) or Gazelles and Goat (**MS**2658). Multicoloured.

2654	200dh. Type **511**	1·20	90
2655	200dh. Mother and cubs	1·20	90
2656	200dh. One cat seated	1·20	90
2657	200dh. Two cats	1·25	90
MS2658	147×81 mm. Size 36×42 mm. 100dh.×3, Gazelle; Goat; Gazelle (different)	9·00	9·00

512 Explosion

1997. 11th Anniversary of American Attack on Libya. Multicoloured.

2659-2670	200dh.×16, Type **512**; *The Green Book* and aircraft; Towers and hand; Muammar al Gaddafi; Aircraft wing; Aircraft nose; Two aircraft; Aircraft tail and two men; Aircraft and missiles colliding; Gaddafi's left arm; Muammar al Gaddafi; Gaddafi's right arm; Missiles and crowd; Injured woman in bed; Gaddafi kissing girl's hand; Raised fists	22·00	22·00

Nos. 2659/2670 were issued together, *se-tenant*, forming a composite design.

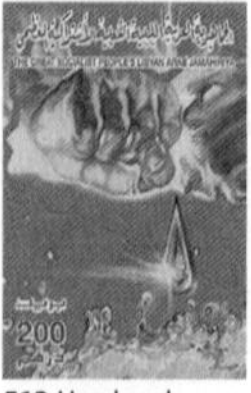

513 Hand and Droplet

1997. Man-made River (1st issue). Designs showing work on the pipeline and Muammar al Gaddafi. Multicoloured.

2671-2686	200dh.×16, Type **513**; Muammar al Gaddafi; Workmen looking at plans; Gaddafi on podium; Gaddafi facing right; Cranes; Pipes and Gaddafi; Gaddafi facing left; Looking at plans; Workman and wellhead; Pipeline and Gaddafi; Lorries carrying pipes; Turning valve; Gaddafi with clasped hands; Water falling from tap into hands; Gaddafi receiving bouquet	22·00	22·00

Nos. 2671/2686 were issued together, *se-tenant*, forming a composite design.

See also Nos. 2735/**MS**2737, 2738/2753 and 2917/2932.

514 Crowd and People's Authority Declaration

1998. People's Authority Declaration.

2687	**514**	150dh. multicoloured	1·40	90
2688	**514**	250dh. multicoloured	2·50	1·60
2689	**514**	300dh. multicoloured	2·75	1·80

515 Jar

1998. International Trade Fair, Tripoli. Multicoloured

2690-2695 400dh.×6, Type **515**; Stand; Vase; Lidded bowl on tray; Lidded bowl on pedestal; Egg-shaped container on tripod 14·00 14·00

Nos. 2690/2695 were issued together, *se-tenant* with the background forming a composite design.

516 Girl

1998. Children's Day (1st issue). Multicoloured.

2696	100dh. Type **516**	75	50
2697	100dh. Girl with arms by sides	75	50
2698	100dh. Girl with blue beaded headdress	75	50
2699	100dh. Girl facing right	75	50
2700	100dh. Girl with striped beaded headdress	75	50

See also Nos. 2754/2759.

517 Emblem

1998. World Health Day.

2701	**517**	150dh. multicoloured	1·10	70
2702	**517**	250dh. multicoloured	1·80	1·20
2703	**517**	300dh. multicoloured	2·20	1·40

518 Ship, Aircraft and Crowd

1998. 12th Anniversary of American Attack on Libya. Multicoloured.

2704-2706 100dh.×3, Type **518**; Muammar al Gaddafi (60×51 mm); Aircraft, ship, man and boy 2·20 2·20

Nos. 2704/2706 were issued together, *se-tenant*, forming a composite design.

519 Eye

1998. 35th Anniversary of National Blind Association. Multicoloured.

2707	150dh. Type **519**	1·20	80
2708	250dh. Person with white cane, guitar and books	1·90	

520 Bee and Clasped Hands

1998. Beekeeping.

2709	**520**	250dh. multicoloured	2·20	1·40
2710	**520**	300dh. multicoloured	3·00	2·00
2711	**520**	400dh. multicoloured	3·50	2·60

521 Footballer

1998. World Cup Football Championships, France. Multicoloured.

2712-2717 200dh.×6, Type **521**; Player preparing to kick ball; Player kicking with leftt leg raised; Player dribbling ball; Player kicking with left leg; Player racing towards ball 8·00 8·00

MS2718 Two sheets, each 145×104 mm. Size 42×51 mm. (a) 1000dh. Player with ball by right shoulder. (b) 1000dh. Ball passing player at head height Set of 2 sheets 8·00 8·00

522 Elderly Man and Child

1998. World Book Day. Multicoloured.

2719-2734 100dh.×16, Type **522**; Athletes; Teacher at blackboard; Harvesting crops; Machine workshop; News reader; Child and teacher holding compasses; Student using microscope; Horseman and girl student; Female teacher and student; Music lesson; Sewing machinist; Chemistry lesson; Typist; Bread making; Computer and users 11·00 11·00

523 Map of Pipeline

1998. Man-made River (2nd issue).

2735	**523**	300dh. multicoloured	2·30	1·50
2736	**523**	400dh. multicoloured	3·00	2·00

MS2737 90×115 mm. **523** 2000dh. multicoloured 14·00 14·00

524 Garlic

1998. Man-made River (3rd issue). Vegetables. Multicoloured.

2738-2753 100dh.×16, Type **524**; Broad beans; Potatoes; Maize; Leeks; Tomatoes; Carrots Beetroots; String beans; Peppers; Aubergines; Cabbages; Marrow; Squash; Onions; Cauliflowers 13·00 13·00

Nos. 2738/2753 were issued together, *se-tenant* with the background forming a composite design.

525 Girl Scout and Deer

1998. Children's Day (2nd issue). Scouts. Multicoloured.

2754-2759 400dh.×6, Type **525**; Emblem and scouts; Boy, tent, girl and flag; Palm trees, ewe and lamb; Scouts playing music; Tent and campfire 25·00 25·00

Nos. 2754/2759 were issued together, *se-tenant*, forming a composite design.

526 Muammar al Gaddafi

1998. 29th Anniversary of Revolution. Multicoloured.

2760-2775 200dh.×16, Type **526**; Horseman; Eagle; Eagle's wing and minaret; Surgeon and student; Left page of Koran; Right page; Mosque; Men with raised arms and docks; Ship; High rise building; Youth; Left of building; Pool and centre left of building; Pool and centre right of building; Right of building 21·00 21·00

MS2776 96×127 mm. 200dh. Muammar al Gaddafi (38×51 mm) 1·40 1·40

Nos. 2760/2775, and the stamps and margin of **MS**2776, respectively, each form composite designs.

527 Troops, Ship and Flag

1998. Evacuation of Foreign Troops.

2777	**527**	100dh. multicoloured	75	50
2778	**527**	150dh. multicoloured	1·10	70
2779	**527**	200dh. Multicoloured	1·40	90

528 Stamps

1998. Stamp Day.

2780	**528**	300dh. multicoloured	2·75	1·80
2781	**528**	400dh. multicoloured	3·75	2·50

529 Ship and Trucks

1998. 87th Anniversary of Deportation of Libyans to Italy. Multicoloured.

2782-2797 150dh.×16, Type **529**; Girl with bound arms; Older man; Soldiers; Aircraft attacking; Deportees; Soldier leading child; Soldiers with raised weapons and laden camel; Water being given; Soldier in boat prow; Boats; Boats (different); Man carrying woman; Horsemen; Horseman; Mother and baby 16·00 16·00

Nos. 2782/2797 were issued together, *se-tenant*, forming a composite design.

530 White Mosque

1998. Libya and Islam. Multicoloured.

2798-2807 100dh.×8, Type **530**; Mosque with pink dome; Modern mosque; Tower; Tower and mosque; Entrance to decorated mosque; Aerial view of mosque; Mosque surrounded by trees; 500dh.×2, Koran and Mecca (57×85 mm); Horseman (57×85 mm) 12·50 12·50

531 Scout and Wheelchair User

1998. Scouting and Disabilities. Multicoloured.

2808-2823 100dh.×16, Type **531**; Scouts; Scout and wheelchair user photographers; Wheelchair user and flags; Sawing wood; Campfire; Cooking; Two scouts painting; Wheelchair football; Wheelchair basketball; Amputees racing; Wheelchair table tennis; Wheelchair hockey; Wheelchair user with raised arm; Amputee cycling; Amputee throwing javelin 16·00 16·00

Nos. 2808/2823 were issued together, *se-tenant*, with background forming a composite design.

533 '30' and Gazelles

1999. 30th Anniversary of Revolution. Multicoloured.

2827-2839 100dh.×12, Type **533**; Mosque; Musician; Camel riders; Combine harvester; Ship; Ship and horse riders; Horse riders; Water pipe; Shepherd; Waterside tower; Dates; 200dh. Horseman (57×85 mm) 7·00 7·00

MS2840 130×100 mm. 200dh. Muammar al Gaddafi (38×51 mm) 1·20 1·20

Nos. 2827/2839 were issued together, *se-tenant*, forming a composite design.

535 Flags and Tower

1999. Evacuation of Foreign Troops.

2848	**535**	150dh. multicoloured	1·20	80
2849	**535**	250dh. multicoloured	1·80	1·20
2850	**535**	300dh. multicoloured	2·20	1·40

536 Muammar al Gaddafi

2000. People's Authority Declaration. Multicoloured.

2851-2853 100dh.×3, Type **536**; Family; Aircraft, high rise building and satellite dish 1·50 1·50

2854-2856 100dh.×3, Gazelle and woman weaving; Water pipeline and tap; Couple picking oranges 1·50 1·50

MS2857 Two sheets, each 110×72 mm. Size 38×51 mm. (a) 300dh. Muammar al Gaddafi. (b) 300dh. Gaddafi with raised fist 3·00 3·00

Nos. 2851/2853 and 2854/2856 were issued together, *se-tenant*, forming a composite design.

537 Camel Rider

2000. 31st Anniversary of Revolution. Multicoloured.

2858-2873 100dh.×16, Type **537**; Couple seated and camels; Muammar al Gaddafi; Demonstrators; Welder; Student; Classroom; Chemist; Mother and child; Lecture; Palm tree and boy; Scanner; Mosque interior; Earth mover and high rise building; Refinery workers; Earth mover and dates 7·75 7·75

MS2874 Two sheets, each 120×90 mm. Size 38×51 mm. (a) 300dh. Muammar al Gaddafi. (b) 300dh. Muammar al Gaddafi and boy 2·50 2·50

Nos. 2858/2873 were issued together, *se-tenant*, with the background forming a composite design.

538 Radio Operator

2000. Day of the Martyr. Multicoloured.

2875-2880 200dh.×6, Type **538**; Desert horsemen; Soldiers; Soldiers on foot and desert horsemen; Horseman with raised arm; Muammar al Gaddafi 5·50 5·50

MS2881 150×110 mm. 300dh. Reading Koran 1·50 1·50

Nos. 2875/2880 were issued together, *se-tenant*, forming a composite design.

539 A. Castellano

2000. Espana 2000 International Stamp Exhibition. Sheet 125×90 mm containing T **539** and similar vert design. Multicoloured. Imperf.

MS2882 250dh.×2, Type **539**; M. B. Karamanli 2·50 2·50

540 Muammar al Gaddafi and Symbols of Libya

2001. People's Authority Declaration.

2883	**540**	150dh. multicoloured	80	50
2884	**540**	200dh. multicoloured	1·10	70

541 Leaders

2001. Fifth Extraordinary Session of OAU Assembly of Heads of States and Governments. Multicoloured.

2885-2890 200dh.×6, Type **541**; Horsemen; Camel riders; Women dancing; Celebrations; Muammar al Gaddafi 5·50 5·50

MS2891 Two sheets, each 112×152 mm. Size 42×51 mm. (a) 500dh. Muammar al Gaddafi (b) 500dh. Set of 2 sheets 5·00 5·00

Nos. 2885/2890 were issed together, *se-tenant*, froming a composite design.

542 Saddle

2001. International Trade Fair, Tripoli. Multicoloured

2892-2897 300dh.×6, Type **542**; Saddle side view; Saddle front view; Stirrup; Saddle decorations; Oblong decorations 13·00 13·00

Nos. 2892/2897 were issued together, *se-tenant*, with the background forming a composite design.

543 Aerial Explosion

2001. 15th Anniversary of American Attack on Libya. Multicoloured.

2898-2913 100dh.×16, Type **543**; Aircraft; Pilot; Plane descending; Parachute; Pillows; Girl crying; Fire and palm trees; Missiles; Falling vase; Teddy bear; Alarm clock; Ground explosion; Survivors; Man carrying child; Family fleeing 9·50 9·50

Nos. 2898/2913 were issued together, *se-tenant*, forming a composite design.

544 Man hoeing

2001. Land Reclamation. Multicoloured.

2914-2916 250dh.×3, Type **544**; Men planting (60×39 mm); Camels 2·75 2·75

Nos. 2914/2916 were issued together, *se-tenant*, forming a composite design.

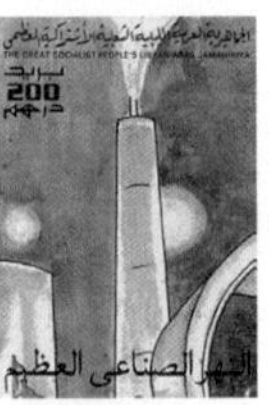

545 Chimney

2001. Man-made River (4th issue). Multicoloured.

2917-2932 200dh.×16, Type **545**; Pipe enclosing flags and crowd; Palm tree; Grapes; Rainbow enclosing man; Rainbow, bubbles and boy; Woman carrying fruit; Woman carrying jar; Woman; Woman in close up; Goose; Boy; Tabor player; Pipe player; Drummer; Tractors ploughing 19·00 19·00

Nos. 2917/2932 were issued together, *se-tenant*, forming a composite design.

546 Muammar al Gaddafi

2001. 32nd Anniversary of Revolution. Multicoloured.

2933-2936 100dh.×4, Type **546**; Buildings, pipeline and desert horsemen; Ship and camel rider; Elderly couple 1·75 1·75

2937-2940 100dh.×4, Boy and girl; Ruins and girl dancing; Camel rider; Camels and birds 1·75 1·75

2941-2944 100dh.×4, Jewellery and woman drummer; Sword fight; Desert dwellers; Woman driving tractor 1·75 1·75

2945-2948 100dh.×4, Artisans and musicians; Musicians and weaver; Workman; Gaddafi with clasped hands 1·75 1·75

MS2949 Two sheets, each 149×109 mm. Size 42×51 mm. (a) 300dh. Muammar al Gaddafi. (b) 300dh. As No. **MS**2949a but silver background 5·50 5·50

Nos. 2933/2936, 2937/2910, 2941/2944 and 2945/2948 were issued together, *se-tenant*, forming a composite design.

547 Girl

2001. International Day for Orphans.

2950	**547**	100dh. multicoloured	1·20	80
2951	**547**	200dh. multicoloured	2·00	1·30
2952	**547**	300dh. multicoloured	2·75	1·80

548 Elderly Man, Emblem and Patient

2001. Welfare Services. Protection of Elderly and Infirm.

2953	**548**	200dh. multicoloured	1·70	1·10
2954	**548**	300dh. multicoloured	2·75	1·80

549 Doorways

2002. Tourism. Multicoloured.

2955-2970 200dh.×16, Type **549**; Palm trees; Arches; Mosque; Walls; Passage and sunbeam; Rooftop; Curved wall and arch; Aerial view; Tower; Interior with tented roof; Passage and bowl; Palms and ruins; Square tower and wall; Wall of narrow bricks; Building façade 30·00 30·00

550 Emblem, Globe and '26'

2002

2971	**550**	200dh. multicoloured	1·70	1·10
2972	**550**	400dh. multicoloured	3·50	2·25

551 Muammar al Gaddafi

2002. 33rd Anniversary of Revolution. Multicoloured.

2973-2988 100dh.×16, Type **551**; Aircraft and engine; Camel rider and woman pouring tea; Craftsmen; Building and earth mover; Chemist and refinery; Ships; Hospital; Tower and control panel; Computers and operator; Water pipeline and tap; Laboratory; Television studio; Fruit and vegetables; Arab musicians; African musicians 11·00 11·00

MS2989 Two sheets, each 149×117 mm. Size 42×51 mm. (a) 300dh. Muammar al Gaddafi. (b) 300dh. As No. **MS**2989a but silver background Set of 2 sheets 5·00 5·00

Nos. 2973/2988 were issued together, *se-tenant*, forming a composite background design.

552 Emblem

2002. 50th Anniversary of Universal Declaration of Human Rights.

2990	**552**	250dh. multicoloured	2·20	1·40
2991	**552**	500dh. multicoloured	4·25	2·75

553 Emblem

2002. 125th Anniversary of Universal Postal Union.

2992	**553**	200dh. multicoloured	1·70	1·10
2993	**553**	250dh. multicoloured	2·20	1·40

554 Muammar al Gaddafi

2003. People's Authority Declaration. Multicoloured

2994-2999 200dh.×6, Type **554**; Oil platform; Water pipeline, butterflies and flowers; African musicians and dancer; Young couple; Camel riders 20·00 20·00

3000-3005 200dh.×6, As Type **554**; As No. 2995; As No. 2996; As No. 2997; As No. 2998; As No. 2999 20·00 20·00

MS3006 Two sheets, each 147×117 mm. Size 42×51 mm. (a) 300dh. Muammar al Gaddafi. (b) 300dh. As No. **MS**3006a but silver background Set of 2 sheets 5·75 5·75

555 Women using Microscope

2003. 34th Anniversary of Revolution. Women in Society. Two sheets containing T **555** and similar multicoloured designs.

MS3007 151×151 mm. 300dh.×4, Type **555**; Anatomy lesson; Doctor and child; Soldiers; 500dh.×3, Embroiderer, business woman and teacher (60×40 mm); Helicopter and service women (60×40 mm); Service women in Army vehicle (60×40 mm); 1000dh. Muammar al Gaddafi (60×40 mm) 14·00 14·00

MS3008 123×95 mm. 2000dh. Muammar al Gaddafi 16·00 16·00

556 Khairi Khaled Nuri (image scaled to 57% of original size)

2004. Khairi Khaled Nuri Commemoration.

3009	**556**	500dh. multicoloured	4·25	2·75

Nos. 3010/3016 and T **557/559** are left for the stamps of 2005, not yet received.

Nos. 3017/3018 and T **560** are left for Peoples' Authority Declaration issued on 2 March 2006, not yet received.

No. 3019 and T **561** are left for Total Eclipse issued on 29 March 2006, not yet received.

562 '37'

2006. 37th Anniversary of Revolution.

3020 **562** 1000dh. multicoloured 7·00 4·50

No. 3021 and T **563** are left for Peoples' Authority Declaration issued on 2 March 2007, not yet received.

No. 3022 and T **564** are left for African Leaders issued on 6 March 2007, not yet received.

Nos. 3023/3028 and T **565** are left for Tripoli Fair/Jewellery issued on 2 April 2007, not yet received.

No. 3029 and T **566** are left for Telecommunications and IT Fair issued on 27 May 2007, not yet received.

567 Symbols of Drug Abuse

2007. International Day Against Drug Abuse.

3030 **567** 750dh. multicoloured 6·50 4·25

No. 3031 and T **568** are left for Tripoli issued on 16 July 2007, not yet received.

No. 3032 and T **569** are left for Confederation of African Football issued on 25 August 2007, not yet received.

570 '38' and Modern Technology

2007. 38th Anniversary of Revolution.

3033 **570** 1000dh. multicoloured 7·00 4·50

MS3034 105×75 mm. As Type **570** 7·00 4·00

571 Child and Map of Africa

2007. Gaddafi Project for African Women, Children and Youth.

3035 **571** 500dh. multicoloured 4·25 2·75

Nos. 3036/3037 and T **572** are left for Koran Recital Competition issued on 24 September 2007, not yet received.

Nos. 3038/3039 and T **573** are left for 50th Anniversary of Red Crescent issued on 29 October 2007, not yet received.

574 '31' and Emblem

2008. Peoples' Authority Declaration.

3040 **574** 500dh. multicoloured 3·75 2·40

Nos. 3041/3043 and T **575** are left for Tripoli Fair issued on 2 April 2008, not yet received.

Nos. 3044/3047 and T **576** are left for Fox issued on 1 May 2008, not yet received.

No. 3048 and T **577** are left for Telecommunications and IT Fair issued on 27 May 2008, not yet received.

No. 3049 and T **578** are left for 56th Anniversary of 23 July Revolution issued on 23 July 2008, not yet received.

No. 3050 and T **579** are left for Gaddafi Project issued on 27 July 2008, not yet received.

No. 3051 and T **580** are left for Cen-Sad Session issued on 3 August 2008, not yet received.

No. 3052 and T **581** are left for Olympic Games, Beijing issued on 18 August 2008, not yet received.

Nos. 3053/3054 and T **582** are left for 39th Anniversary of Revolution issued on 1 September 2008, not yet received.

No. 3055 and T **583** are left for Mobile Phones issued on 11 September 2008, not yet received.

No. 3056 and T **584** are left for Memorising Koran Competition issued on 23 September 2008, not yet received.

No. 3057 and T **585** are left for Koran issued on 26 September 2008, not yet received.

586 Emblem

2009. Peoples' Authority Declaration.

3058 **586** 500dh. multicoloured 3·75 2·40

587 Injured Children, Raised Fist and Flag

2009. Support for Gaza.

3059 **587** 1000dh. multicoloured 7·00 4·50

588 Raised Fist

2009. Aggression.

3060 **588** 500dh. multicoloured 3·75 2·40

589 Symbols of Telecommunication and '5'

2009. Fifth Telecommunications and IT Fair.

3061 **589** 500dh. multicoloured 3·75 2·40

590 Omar Bongo Ondimba

2009. Omar Bongo Ondimba (president of Gabon) Commemoration.

3062 **590** 750dh. multicoloured 6·50 4·25

591 Emblems

2009. Mediterranean Games, Pescara. Libyan Olympic Committee.

3063 **591** 500dh. multicoloured 3·75 2·40

592 Emblem

2009. al-Quds 2009. Capital of Arab Culture.

3064 **592** 1000dh. multicoloured 7·00 4·50

593 Flags of Competing Nations and Competition Emblem

2009. Afrobasket 2009, Libya.

3065 **593** 500dh. multicoloured 3·75 2·40

594 Muammar al Gaddafi

2009. 40th Anniversary of Revolution. Sheet 90×175 mm containing T **594** and similar horiz designs. Multicoloured.

MS3066 400dh. Type **594**; 600dh. As Type **594**; 750dh. As Type **594** 13·00 13·00

595 Map of Africa and Muammar al Gaddafi

2009. Muammar al Gaddafi, Founder and Chairman of African Union.

3067 **595** 1000dh. multicoloured 7·00 4·50

MS3068 130×85 mm. 2000d. As Type **595** 13·00 13·00

596 Games Emblem

2009. Al-Fateh Futsal (indoor 5-a-side football) Continental Cup.

3069 **596** 500dh. multicoloured 3·75 2·40

597 Symbols of Post

2010. 30th Anniversary of Pan African Postal Union.

3070 **597** 500dh. multicoloured 3·75 2·40

598 Chamber

2010. 33rd Anniversary of People's Authority Declaration.

3071 **598** 500dh. multicoloured 3·75 2·40

599 Flags of Member States

2010. 22nd Session of Council of League of Arab States, Sirte.

3072 **599** 500h. multicoloured 3·75 2·40

600 Flags of Members and '50'

2010. 50th Anniversary of OPEC (Organisation of Petroleum Exporting Countries).

3073 **600** 1000dh. multicoloured 7·00 4·50

601 Airmen

2010. 40th Anniversary of Evacuation of American Airbases.

3074 **601** 1000dh. multicoloured 7·00 4·50

2010. 40th Anniversary (2009) of Al-Fateh Revolution. Multicoloured.

MS3075 400d.×40, Nationalisation of banks and insurance; Nationalisation of oil; Declaration of People's Revolution, 1973; Arab Republics' Union; Evacuation of Italian troops; Evacuation of American troops; Evacuation of British troops; Dawn of Al-Fatah, 1969; Industrial revolution; Residential projects; Agricultural revolution; Electricity network; Road network; Scietific revolution; Health and welfare; Al-Fatah, Islamic revolution; Defining line; Man-made river construction; Wajda City agreement, 1984; Producers' revolution, 1978; *The Green Book*; Jamahiriya, 1977; Students' revolution, 1976; Tunisia-Libya Agreement' African Arab Union; Community of Sahel and Saharan States; Embargo; Removal of borders; Arab Magreb Union, 1989; Green Charter for Human Rights; Demolition of jails; NATO aggression; 40th anniversary of 1st September revolution; Muammar al Gaddafi; Return of A Almagrahi; Italian apology; Muammar al Gaddafi; Telecommunications and technology; Maritime transport; Emancipation of women 30·00 30·00

603 Martin Luther King and Speech (image scaled to 47% of original size)

604 Martin Luther King and Speech (image scaled to 47% of original size)

2010. 22nd Anniversary of Green Document on Human Rights.

3076 **603** 1500d. multicoloured 8·25 7·75

3077 **604** 2000d. multicoloured 9·00 8·50

2010. 41st Anniversary of 1st September Revolution. Multicoloured.

3078 1000d. Colonel Gaddafi 7·00

MS3079 135×100 mm. 1500d. Colonel Gaddafi (as No. 3078 but gold background) 8·50

2010. Muammar al Gaddafi's Speech to the United Nations. Multicoloured.

MS3080 1000d.x6, 'Brothers in our political life....'; 'In order that colonialisation is not repeated....'; 'The solution to achieve democracy....'; 'The International Court of Justice.....'; 'Africa as of now....'; 'The International Atomic Agency....' 15·00 15·00

MS3081 1000d.x6, As **MS**3080 but inscriptions in French 15·00 15·00

MS3082 1000d.x6, As No. **MS**3080 but inscriptions in Arabic 15·00 15·00

607 Symbols of Africa and EU

2010. Third Africa–European Union Summit. Tripoli.

3083	**607**	1000d. multicoloured	7·00	5·00

608 Flag as Map

2012. 17th February Revolution.

3084	**608**	250d. multicoloured	1·75	75
3085	**608**	500d. multicoloured	3·75	2·75
3086	**5.5**	750d. multicoloured	5·50	4·50
3087	**608**	1000d. multicoloured	7·00	5·00
3088	**608**	5000d. multicoloured	14·00	14·00

609 Woman Demonstrator

2012. First Anniversary of 17th February Revolution.. Multicoloured.

3089	500d. Type **609**	3·75	2·40
3090	500d. Orchids	3·75	2·40
3091	1000d. Demonstrators	7·00	5·00

MS3092 110x80 mm. 1000d. Map and flag 7·50 7·50

610 Flag

2012. Children's Drawings. Multicoloured.

3093	100d. Type **610**	1·25	25
3094	200d. Flowers and trees	1·50	85
3095	250d. Children at zoo	1·75	75
3096	500d. House	3·75	2·75
3097	1000d. Yacht	7·00	5·00

611 61st Anniversary Emblem

2012. 61st Anniversary of Libyan Independence. Multicoloured.

3098	500d. Type **611**	3·75	2·75
3099	1000d. Stylised wheat and flag	7·00	5·00

612 Doves released from Cage

2013. Second Anniversary of 17th February Revolution. Multicoloured.

3100	250d. Type **612**	1·75	75
3101	500d. Emblem and doves	3·75	2·75
3102	1000d. Emblem, flag and dove	7·00	5·00

613 Monument

2013. Libyan Army Monument.

3103	**613**	500d. multicoloured

614 Necklace

2013. International Trade Fair, Tripoli. Jewellery. Multicoloured.

3104	500d. Type **614**	3·75	2·75
3105	500d. Emblem	3·75	2·75
3106	500d. Triangular pendant	3·75	2·75
3107	500d. Pendant with curvved top	3·75	2·75
3108	500d. Rectangular brooch	3·75	2·75
3109	500d. Earrings	3·75	2·75

615 Droplet containing Globe and Envelope

2013. International Letter Writing Competition.

3110	**615**	1000d. multicoloured	7·00	5·00

616 Flag

2013. 17th February Revolution. Multicoloured.

3111	5000d. Type **616**	7·00	5·00
3112	10000d. As Type **616**, but with sunshine behind flag	14·00	14·00

617 Hands holding Seedling, Cracked Earth and Butterfly

2013. Campaign to Combat Desertification.

3113	**617**	500d. multicoloured	3·75	2·75

618 Parliament Building

2013. 'First Parliament in the Middle East'. 50th Anniversary of Parliament.

3114	**618**	500d. multicoloured	3·75	2·75

619 Benghazi Lighthouse

2013. Benghazi Lighthouse.

3115	**619**	1000d. multicoloured	7·00	5·00

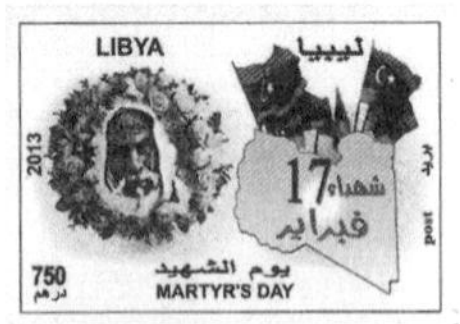

620 Omar al-Mukhtar and Emblem

2013. Martyrs' Day. Multicoloured.

3116	750d. Type **620**	5·50	4·50
3117	1000d. Flowers surrounding circular flag	7·00	5·00

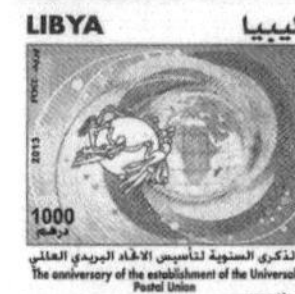

621 Emblem

2013. 139th Anniversary of Universal Postal Union.

3118	**621**	1000d. multicoloured	7·00	5·00

622 Triceratops

2013. Prehistoric Animals. Dinosaurs. Multicoloured.

MS3119 250d.x6, Type **622**; Head of Apatosaurus; Tyrannosaurus against sky; Tyrannosaurus against rocks; Apatosaurus, walking; Tyrannosaurus with head lowered 8·25 7·75

623 King Idris and '24 DECEMBER'

2013. 62nd Anniversary of Libyan Independence. Multicoloured.

3120	250d. Type **623**	1·75	75
3121	750d. Anniversary emblem	5·50	4·50
3122	1000d. King Idris and Omar al-Mukhtar	7·00	5·00

624 1951 Stamp (As Type 20)

2013. National Post Day.

3123	**624**	100d. multicoloured	1·25	50

625 Globe and Butterflies

2013. National Stamp Exhibition.

3124	**625**	100d. multicoloured	1·25	50

626 Stylised Figures

2014. Third Anniversary of 17th February Revolution. Multicoloured.

3125	500d. Type **626**	3·75	2·40
3126	750d. Demonstrators	5·50	4·50
3127	1000d. Flag as torch	7·00	5·00

627 Trophy and Emblem

2014. Football. Libya–African Nations Cup Championship Winners. Multicoloured.

3128	500d. Type **627**	3·75	2·40
3129	750d. Team members	5·50	4·50

MS3130 110x80 mm. 1000d. Team and trophy. Imperf 7·00 5·00

628 Garlic

2014. Vegetables. Multicoloured.

MS3131 500d.x6, Type **628**; Onions; Tomatoes; Peppers; Aubergines; Potatoes 10·00 9·00

629 Scouts

2014. 60th Anniversary of Libyan Scouts. Multicoloured.

3132	500d. Type **629**	3·75	2·75
3133	1000d. Ali Khalifa el-Zaidi (Chief Commissioner) (inscr 'Ali Khalefa Zaidi')	7·00	5·00

630 'Bazin with Meat'

2014. International Trade Fair, Tripoli. Food. Multicoloured.

3134	500d. Type **630**	3·75	2·75
3135	500d. Emblem	3·75	2·75
3136	500d. 'Kouskous with meat'	3·75	2·75
3137	500d. 'Bazin with fish'	3·75	2·75
3138	500d. Anniversary emblem	3·75	2·75
3139	500d. 'Kouskous with fish'	3·75	2·75

631 Sebha Castle

2014. Castles. Multicoloured.

3140	100d. Type **631**	1·25	50
3141	1000d. Murzuq Castle	7·00	5·00

632 Mosque

2014. Mosques. Multicoloured.

3142	500d. Type **632**	3·75	2·75
3143	500d. Ghadames Mosque by moonlight	3·75	2·75
3144	500d. Mosque with square tower	3·75	2·75

633 Mediterranean

2014. Euromed 2014. Postal Conference, Lemessos, Cyprus.

3145	**633**	500d. multicoloured	3·75	2·75

634 Emblem

2014. 63rd Anniversary of Libyan Army.

3146	**634**	500d. multicoloured	3·75	2·75

635 Clasped Hands

2014. Ramadan. Anniversary of Liberation of Tripoli.

3147	**635**	500d. multicoloured	3·75	2·75

636 Omar al-Mukhtar

2014. Martyrs' Day.

3148	**636**	500d. multicoloured	3·75	2·75

637 Boy Scout

2014. International Children's Day. Multicoloured.

3149	250d. Type **637**	1·75	50
3150	750d. UNICEF emblem and hands	5·50	4·50
3151	1000d. Boy scout and butterflies	7·00	5·00

638 Anniversary Emblem

2014. 50th Anniversary of Libya Insurance Company.

3152	**638**	1000d. multicoloured	7·00	5·00

639 King Idris

2014. 63rd Anniversary of Libyan Independence.

3153	**639**	1000d. multicoloured	7·00	5·00

640 Emblem

2015. Fourth Anniversary of 17th February Revolution. Multicoloured.

3154	1000d. Type **640**	7·50	5·00
3155	1000d. Demonstrators	7·50	5·00
3156	1000d. Flag	7·50	5·00

641 Three-handled Pot

2015. International Trade Fair, Tripoli. Pottery. Multicoloured.

3157	500d. Type **641**	3·75	2·75
3158	500d. Emblem	3·75	2·75
3159	500d. Jar with rope handle	3·75	2·75
3160	500d. Pestle and mortar	3·75	2·75
3161	500d. Amphora with three handles	3·75	2·75
3162	500d. Bowl hanging from rope handle	3·75	2·75

642 Boat in Harbour

2015. EUROMED. Boats of the Mediterranean.

3163	**642**	750d. multicoloured	5·50	4·50

643 Omar Al-Mukhtar

2015. Martyrs' Day. Multicoloured.

3164	500d. Type **643**	3·75	2·75
MS3165	120×80 mm. 1000d. Omar Al-Mukhtar and flag. Imperf	7·50	5·00

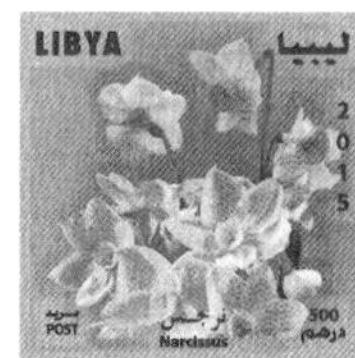

644 Narcissi

2015. Flowers. Multicoloured.

3166	500d. Type **644**	3·75	2·75
3167	500d. *Ophrys fucilfora*	3·75	2·75
3168	500d. Calla Lily	3·75	2·75
3169	500d. *Cestrum nocturnum*	3·75	2·75
3170	500d. Bird of Paradise	3·75	2·75
3171	500d. Jasmine	3·75	2·75

645 Anniversary Emblem

2015. 70th Anniversary of UNESCO.

3172	**645**	500d. multicoloured	3·75	2·75

646 Children and their Hobbies

2015. International Children's Day.

3173	**646**	500d. multicoloured	3·75	2·75

647 Ghadames Castle

2015. Castles. Multicoloured.

3174	750d. Type **647**	5·50	4·50
3175	750d. Nalout Castle ruins	5·50	4·50

648 Symbols of Libya

2015. 64th Anniversary of Libyan Independence.

3176	**648**	500d. multicoloured	3·75	2·75

649 Postman

2015. Stamp Day.

3177	**649**	500d. multicoloured	3·75	2·75

650 Dates

2015. Dates (*Phoenix dactylifera*).

3178	**650**	500d. multicoloured	3·75	2·75
3179	**650**	1000d. multicoloured	7·00	5·00
3180	**650**	2000d. multicoloured	9·00	8·00
3181	**650**	5000d. multicoloured	13·00	12·00
3182	**650**	10000d. multicoloured	14·50	13·50

651 Stamp on Stamp

2016. National Stamp Exhibition, Tripoli.

3183	**651**	1000d. multicoloured	7·00	5·00

652 Flag, Map and Laurel Wreath

2016. Fifth Anniversary of 17th February Revolution. Multicoloured.

3184	500d. Type **652**	3·75	2·75
3185	500d. Clasped hands	3·75	2·75
3186	500d. Map and script	3·75	2·75

653 Omar al-Mukhtar

2016. Martyrs' Day. Multicoloured.

3187	500d. Type **653**	3·75	2·75
MS3188	110×76 mm. 1000d. Omar al-Mukhtar on horseback. Imperf	7·50	7·50

CONCESSIONAL LETTER POST

1929. No. CL227 of Italy optd **LIBIA**.

CL68	**CL93**	10c. blue	37·00	37·00

1941. No. CL267 of Italy optd **LIBIA**.

CL123	**CL109**	10c. brown	16·00	19·00

EXPRESS LETTER STAMPS.

A. ITALIAN ISSUES

1915. Express Letter stamps of Italy optd **Libia**.

E17	**E35**	25c. pink	50·00	35·00
E18	**E41**	30c. blue and pink	10·50	50·00

E8

1921

E34	**E8**	30c. red and blue	4·00	10·50
E35	**E8**	50c. brown and red	6·00	16·00
E42	**E8**	60c. brown and red	14·50	29·00
E43	**E8**	2l. red and blue	24·00	48·00

Nos. E34 and E43 are inscribed 'EXPRES'.

1922. Nos. E17/E18 surch.

E40	**E35**	60c. on 25c. pink	20·00	23·00
E41	**E41**	1l.60 on 30c. blue and pink	26·00	50·00

1926. Nos. E42/E43 surch.

E62	**E8**	70 on 60c. brown and red	14·50	25·00
E64	**E8**	1l.25 on 60c. brown and red	8·75	5·75
E63	**E8**	2.50 on 2l. red and blue	21·00	48·00

B. INDEPENDENT ISSUES

1966. Design similar to T **74** inscr 'EXPRES'.

E368	90m. red and green	2·30	1·30

Design: Horiz—90m. Saracen Castle, Zuela.

OFFICIAL STAMPS

1952. Optd **Official** in English and Arabic.

O192	**23**	2m. brown	40	35
O193	**23**	4m. grey	65	50
O194	**23**	5m. green	4·50	1·60
O195	**23**	8m. red	2·50	75
O196	**23**	10m. violet	3·75	1·25
O197	**23**	12m. red	6·75	2·50
O198	**23**	20m. blue	13·50	5·25
O199	**23**	25m. brown	17·00	6·75

PARCEL POST STAMPS

Unused prices are for complete pairs, used prices for a half

1915. Parcel Post stamps of Italy optd **LIBIA** on each half of the stamp.

P17	**P53**	5c. brown	2·75	10·50
P18	**P53**	10c. blue	2·75	10·50
P19	**P53**	20c. black	2·75	10·50
P20	**P53**	25c. red	4·25	13·00
P21	**P53**	50c. orange	5·25	13·00
P22	**P53**	1l. violet	5·25	13·00
P23	**P53**	2l. green	6·50	16·00
P24	**P53**	3l. yellow	8·00	16·00
P25	**P53**	4l. grey	8·00	16·00
P26	**P53**	10l. purple	70·00	85·00
P27	**P53**	12l. brown	£140	£250
P28	**P53**	15l. green	£140	£250
P29	**P53**	20l. purple	£200	£375

1927. Parcel Post stamps of Italy optd **LIBIA** on each half of the stamp.

P62	**P92**	5c. brown	£17000	
P63	**P92**	10c. blue	5·25	8·50
P64	**P92**	25c. red	5·25	8·50
P65	**P92**	30c. blue	2·10	5·25
P66	**P92**	50c. orange	£120	£225
P67	**P92**	60c. red	2·10	5·25
P68	**P92**	1l. violet	44·00	£110
P69	**P92**	2l. green	55·00	£110
P70	**P92**	3l. bistre	2·75	10·50
P71	**P92**	4l. black	2·75	16·00
P72	**P92**	10l. mauve	£375	£425
P73	**P92**	20l. purple	£375	£600

POSTAGE DUE STAMPS.

A. ITALIAN ISSUES

1915. Postage Due stamps of Italy optd **Libia**.

D17	**D12**	5c. mauve and orange	3·50	11·50
D18	**D12**	10c. mauve and orange	3·50	5·75
D19	**D12**	20c. mauve and orange	4·50	9·25
D20	**D12**	30c. mauve and orange	5·75	14·00
D21	**D12**	40c. mauve and orange	7·00	16·00
D22	**D12**	50c. mauve and orange	5·75	11·50
D23	**D12**	60c. mauve and orange	7·00	18·00
D24	**D12**	60c. brown and orange	£120	£225
D25	**D12**	1l. mauve and blue	7·00	18·00
D26	**D12**	2l. mauve and blue	70·00	£130
D27	**D12**	5l. mauve and blue	90·00	£180

1934. Postage Due stamps of Italy optd **LIBIA**.

D68	**D141**	5c. brown	60	4·50
D69	**D141**	10c. blue	60	4·50
D70	**D141**	20c. red	2·30	2·30
D71	**D141**	25c. green	2·30	2·30
D72	**D141**	30c. red	2·30	8·00
D73	**D141**	40c. brown	2·30	5·75
D74	**D141**	50c. violet	3·50	70
D75	**D141**	60c. blue	3·50	22·00
D76	**D142**	1l. orange	3·50	70
D77	**D142**	2l. green	85·00	21·00
D78	**D142**	5l. violet	£140	48·00
D79	**D142**	10l. blue	23·00	70·00
D80	**D142**	20l. red	23·00	90·00

B. INDEPENDENT ISSUES

1951. Postage Due stamps of Cyrenaica optd. (a) For use in Cyrenaica. Optd as T **20**.

D144	**D26**	2m. brown	5·00	5·00
D145	**D26**	4m. green	5·00	5·00
D146	**D26**	8m. red	6·75	6·25
D147	**D26**	10m. orange	7·50	6·25
D148	**D26**	20m. yellow	11·00	10·00
D149	**D26**	40m. blue	30·00	20·00
D150	**D26**	100m. black	40·00	23·00

(b) For use in Tripolitania. Surch as T **21**.

D161	**D26**	1mal. on 2m. brown	5·50	5·00
D162	**D26**	2mal. on 4m. green	7·50	5·50
D163	**D26**	4mal. on 8m. red	12·50	10·00
D164	**D26**	10mal. on 20m. yellow	27·00	20·00
D165	**D26**	20mal. on 40m. blue	45·00	35·00

D25

1951

D188	**D25**	2m. brown	65	25
D189	**D25**	5m. green	95	50
D190	**D25**	10m. red	2·25	95
D191	**D25**	50m. blue	7·50	2·25

D53 Government Building, Tripoli 1952.

1964

D296	**D53**	2m. brown	10	10
D297	**D53**	6m. green	20	10
D298	**D53**	10m. red	70	45
D299	**D53**	50m. blue	1·25	85

D185 Men in Boat

1976. Ancient Mosaics. Multicoloured.

D725	5dh. Type **D185**	10	10
D726	10dh. Head of Medusa	10	10
D727	20dh. Peacock	10	10
D728	50dh. Fish	80	25

LIECHTENSTEIN

A small independent principality lying between Austria and Switzerland.

1912. 100 heller = 1 krone.
1921. 100 rappen = 1 franc (Swiss).

1 Prince John II

1912

4	**1**	5h. green	19·00	30·00
2	**1**	10h. red	£110	26·00
3	**1**	25h. blue	£110	85·00

2

3

1917

7	**2**	3h. violet	3·00	3·00
8	**2**	5h. green	3·00	3·00
9	**3**	10h. purple	3·00	3·00
10	**3**	15h. brown	3·00	3·00
11	**3**	20h. green	3·00	3·00
12	**3**	25h. blue	3·00	3·00

1918. 60th Anniversary of Prince John's Accession. As T **3** but dated 1858–1918 in upper corners.

13	20h. green	1·30	4·25

1920. Optd with a scroll pattern.

14	**2**	5h. green	4·50	12·00
15	**3**	10h. purple	4·50	13·00
16	**3**	25h. blue	4·50	13·00

1920. Surch.

17	**2**	40h. on 3h. violet	4·50	13·00
18	**3**	1k. on 15h. brown	4·50	13·00
19	**3**	2$\frac{1}{2}$k. on 20h. green	4·50	13·00

7

8 Castle of Vaduz

1920. Imperf.

20	**7**	5h. bistre	50	8·50
21	**7**	10h. orange	50	8·50
22	**7**	15h. blue	50	8·50
23	**7**	20h. brown	50	8·50
24	**7**	25h. green	50	8·50
25	**7**	30h. grey	50	8·50
26	**7**	40h. red	50	8·50
27	**8**	1k. blue	50	8·50

9 Prince John I

10 Arms

1920. Perf.

28	**7**	5h. bistre	50	95
29	**7**	10h. orange	50	95
30	**7**	15h. blue	50	95
31	**7**	20h. brown	50	95
32	-	25h. green	50	95
33	**7**	30h. grey	50	95
34	-	40h. purple	50	95
35	-	50h. green	50	95
36	-	60h. brown	50	95
37	-	80h. pink	50	95
38	**8**	1k. lilac	1·00	1·30
39	-	2k. blue	1·00	2·20
40	**9**	5k. black	1·00	3·00
41	-	7$\frac{1}{2}$k. grey	1·00	4·00
42	**10**	10k. brown	1·00	7·00

Designs: As T **8**—25h. St Mamertus Chapel; 40h. Gutenberg Castle; 50h. Courtyard, Vaduz Castle; 60h. Red House, Vaduz; 80h. Church Tower, Schaan; 2k. Bendern. As T **9**—7$\frac{1}{2}$k. Prince John II.

11 Madonna

1920. Prince John's 80th Birthday. Imperf or perf.

43A	**11**	50h. green	1·00	2·75
44A	**11**	80h. red	1·00	2·75
45A	**11**	2k. blue	1·00	3·75

1921. Surch **2 Rp.** and bars.

47	**7**	2r. on 10h. orange (No. 21)	1·30	38·00

14 Arms

15 St Mamertus Chapel

16 Vaduz

1921

47aB	**14**	2r. yellow	2·00	20·00
48A	**14**	2$\frac{1}{2}$r. brown	2·00	19·00
49A	**14**	3r. orange	2·00	19·00
50A	**14**	5r. green	20·00	3·00
51A	**14**	7$\frac{1}{2}$r. blue	9·75	60·00
53A	**14**	13r. brown	12·00	£130
54B	**14**	15r. violet	38·00	34·00
55	**15**	20r. black and violet	£100	3·00
56	-	25r. black and red	5·00	6·75
57	-	30r. black and green	£110	30·00
58	-	35r. black and brown	9·75	23·00
59	-	40r. black and blue	15·00	8·75
60	-	50r. black and green	24·00	12·00
61	-	80r. black and grey	45·00	£110
62	**16**	1f. black and red	80·00	80·00
65	**14**	10r. green	30·00	4·00
66	-	30r. black and blue	24·00	4·00

Designs: As T **15**—25r. Vaduz Castle; 30r. Bendern; 35r. Prince John II; 40r. Church Tower at Schaan; 50r. Gutenberg Castle; 80r. Red House, Vaduz.

1924. Surch.

63A	**14**	5 on 7$\frac{1}{2}$r. blue	2·00	5·00
64B	**14**	10 on 13r. brown	2·00	5·00

19 Vine-dresser

21 Government Bldg. and Church, Vaduz

1924

67	**19**	2$\frac{1}{2}$r. mauve and green	2·00	9·75
68	**19**	5r. blue and brown	4·00	1·50
69	**19**	7$\frac{1}{2}$r. brown and green	3·00	9·75
70	-	10r. green	16·00	1·50
71	**19**	15r. green and purple	15·00	55·00
72	-	20r. red	60·00	2·00
73	**21**	1$\frac{1}{2}$f. blue	£110	£160

Design: As T **19**—10, 20r. Castle of Vaduz.

22 Prince John II

1925. 85th Birthday of Prince John.

74	**22**	10+5r. green	70·00	34·00
75	**22**	20+5r. red	39·00	34·00
76	**22**	30+5r. blue	9·75	9·75

23

1927. 87th Birthday of Prince. Arms multicoloured.

77	**23**	10+5r. green	15·00	39·00
78	**23**	20+5r. purple	15·00	39·00
79	**23**	30+5r. blue	9·75	30·00

24 Salvage Work by Austrian soldiers

1928. Flood Relief.

80	-	5r.+5r. brown and purple	24·00	39·00
81	-	10r.+10r. brown and green	34·00	49·00
82	**24**	20r.+10r. brown and red	34·00	49·00
83	-	30r.+10r. brown and blue	30·00	49·00

Designs: 5r. Railway bridge between Buchs and Schaan; 10r. Village of Ruggell; 30r. Salvage work by Swiss soldiers.

26 Prince John II, 1858–1928

1928. 70th Anniversary of Accession of Prince John II.

84	-	10r. green and brown	9·75	9·75
85	-	20r. green and red	15·00	20·00
86	-	30r. green and blue	49·00	34·00
87	-	60r. green and mauve	£100	£150
88	**26**	1f.20 blue	80·00	£180
89	**26**	1f.50 brown	£150	£375
90	**26**	2f. red	£150	£375
91	**26**	5f. green	£150	£450

Design: Vert—10r. to 60r. Prince John II.

28 Prince Francis I

1929. Accession of Prince Francis I.

92	-	10r. green	80	5·75
93	**28**	20r. red	1·10	9·75
94	-	30r. blue	2·00	34·00
95	-	70r. brown	35·00	£200

Portraits: 10r. Prince Francis I as a boy; 30r. Princess Elsa; 70r. Prince Francis and Princess Elsa.

31 Girl Vintager

32 Prince Francis I and Princess Elsa

1930

96A	**31**	3r. red	1·50	4·00
97B	-	5r. green	5·00	4·00
98B	-	10r. lilac	5·00	4·00
99B	-	20r. red	39·00	5·00
100A	-	25r. green	12·00	65·00
101B	-	30r. blue	12·00	6·75
102C	-	35r. green	15·00	30·00
103C	-	40r. brown	15·00	12·00
104C	-	50r. black	£150	28·00
105B	-	60r. green	£150	49·00
106B	-	90r. purple	£160	£200
107B	-	1f.20 brown	£225	£400
108B	-	1f.50 blue	80·00	£100
109B	**32**	2f. brown and green	£110	£200

Designs: Vert—5r. Mt. Three Sisters-Edelweiss; 10r. Alpine cattle-alpine roses; 20r. Courtyard of Vaduz Castle; 25r. Mt. Naafkopf; 30r. Valley of Samina; 35r. Rofenberg Chapel; 40r. St Mamertus' Chapel; 50r. Kurhaus at Malbun; 60r. Gutenberg Castle; 90r. Schellenberg Monastery; 1f.20, Vaduz Castle; 1f.50, Pfaelzer club hut.

34 Monoplane over Vaduz Castle and Rhine Valley

1930. Air.

110	-	15r. brown	15·00	24·00
111	-	20r. green	34·00	34·00
112	-	25r. brown	20·00	65·00
113	-	35r. blue	30·00	60·00
114	**34**	45r. green	70·00	£120
115	**34**	1f. purple	80·00	90·00

Designs: Vert—15, 20r. Biplane over snowy mountain peak. Horiz—25, 35r. Biplane over Vaduz Castle.

35 Airship LZ-127 *Graf Zeppelin* over Alps

1931. Air.

116	**35**	1f. green	£100	£180
117	-	2f. blue	£200	£550

Design: 2f. Airship *Graf Zeppelin* (different).

37 Princess Elsa

1932. Youth Charities.

118	-	10r.+5r. green	30·00	60·00
119	**37**	20r.+5r. red	30·00	60·00
120	-	30r.+10r. blue	39·00	80·00

Designs: 22×29 mm—10r. Arms of Liechtenstein. As T **37**—30r. Prince Francis.

38 Mt. Naafkopf

1933

121	**38**	25r. orange	£375	£120
122	-	90r. green	15·00	£150
123	-	1f.20 brown	£200	£500

Designs: 90r. Gutenberg Castle; 1f.20, Vaduz Castle.

39 Prince Francis I

1933. Prince Francis's 80th Birthday.

124	**39**	10r. violet	39·00	70·00
125	**39**	20r. red	39·00	70·00
126	**39**	30r. blue	39·00	70·00

40

41 *Three Sisters*

42 Vaduz Castle

44 Prince Francis I

45 Arms of Liechtenstein

1933

127	**40**	3r. red	45	1·00
128	**41**	5r. green	7·75	3·00
129	-	10r. violet	4·00	2·00
130	-	15r. orange	45	2·00
131	-	20r. red	1·00	2·00
132	-	25r. brown	39·00	95·00
133	-	30r. blue	7·75	3·00
134	-	35r. green	12·00	24·00
135	-	40r. brown	2·40	9·75
136	**42**	50r. brown	34·00	30·00
137	-	60r. purple	3·00	13·00
138	-	90r. green	12·00	42·00
139	-	1f.20 blue	5·00	42·00
140	-	1f.50 brown	5·75	49·00
141	-	2f. brown	£110	£350
142	**44**	3f. blue	£180	£350
143	**45**	5f. purple	£550	£1800

Designs: As T **41**—10r. Schaan Church; 15r. Bendern am Rhein; 20r. Town Hall, Vaduz; 25r. Saminatal. As T **44**—2f. Princess Elsa. As T **42**—30r. Saminatal (different); 35r. Schellenberg ruins; 40r. Government Building, Vaduz; 60r. Vaduz Castle (different); 90r. Gutenberg Castle; 1f.20, Pfalzer Hut, Bettlerjoch; 1f.50, Valuna.

See also Nos. **MS**144, **MS**153, 174, 225/226 and 258.

1934. Vaduz First Liechtenstein Philatelic Exhibition. Sheet 105×125 mm.

MS144 **45**	5f. chocolate	£2750	£4000

46 Golden Eagle

1934. Air.

145a	**46**	10r. violet	9·75	34·00
146a	-	15r. orange	30·00	80·00
147a	-	20r. red	34·00	80·00
148a	-	30r. blue	34·00	80·00
149a	-	50r. green	30·00	60·00

Designs: 10r. to 20r. Golden eagles in flight; 30r. Ospreys in nest; 50r. Golden eagle on rock.

1935. Air. No. 115 surch **60 Rp.**

150	**34**	60r. on 1f. purple	60·00	£100

49 LZ-129 *Hindenburg* and Schaan Church

1936. Air.

151	**49**	1f. red	75·00	£150
152	-	2f. violet	49·00	£150

Design: 2f. LZ-127 *Graf Zeppelin* over Schaan Airport.

1936. Second Liechtenstein Philatelic Exhibition and Opening of Postal Museum, Vaduz. Sheet 165×119 mm containing two each of Nos. 131 and 133.

MS153	Sold at 2fr.	24·00	80·00

51 Masescha am Triesenberg

52 Schellenberg Castle

1937

154	-	3r. brown	45	1·00
155	**51**	5r. green and buff	45	45
156	-	10r. violet and buff	45	45
157	-	15r. black and buff	45	1·00
158	-	20r. red and buff	45	1·00
159	-	25r. brown and buff	1·00	5·00
160	-	30r. blue and buff	5·75	2·00
161	**52**	40r. green and buff	4·00	4·00
162	-	50c. brown and buff	5·00	9·75
163	-	60r. purple and buff	4·00	5·00
164	-	90r. violet and buff	30·00	60·00
165	-	1f. purple and buff	4·00	24·00
166	-	1f.20 brown and buff	15·00	45·00
167	-	1f.50 grey and buff	5·75	45·00

Designs: As T **51**—3r. Schalun ruins; 10r. Knight and Vaduz Castle; 15r. Upper Saminatal; 20r. Church and Bridge at Bendern; 25r. Steg Chapel and girl. As T **52**—30r. Farmer and orchard, Triesenberg; 50r. Knight and Gutenberg Castle; 60r. Baron von Brandis and Vaduz Castle; 90r. 'Three Sisters' mountain; 1f. Boundary-stone on Luziensteig; 1f.20, Minstrel and Gutenberg Castle; 1f.50, Lawena (Schwarzhorn).

53 Roadmakers at Triesenberg

1937. Workers' Issue.

168		10r. mauve	2·40	3·00
169	**53**	20r. red	2·40	4·00
170	-	30r. blue	2·40	5·00
171	-	50r. brown	2·40	5·75

Designs: 10r. Bridge at Malbun; 30r. Binnen Canal Junction; 50r. Francis Bridge, near Planken.

54 Josef Rheinberger

1938. Third Liechtenstein Philatelic Exhibition, Vaduz. Sheet 100×135 mm containing stamps as No. 175 in different colour in a block of four.

MS173 **54**	50r. blue	39·00	39·00

1938. Death of Prince Francis I.

174	**44**	3f. black on yellow	20·00	£160

1939. Birth Centenary of Rheinberger (composer).

175	**54**	50r. grey	1·50	8·75

55 Black-headed Gulls

1939. Air.

176	-	10r. violet (Barn swallows)	2·00	2·40
177	**55**	15r. orange	1·00	5·00
178	-	20r. red (Herring gull)	4·00	2·00
179	-	30r. blue (Common buzzard)	2·40	4·00
180	-	50r. green (Northern goshawk)	5·75	6·75
181	-	1f. red (Lammergeier)	4·00	31·00
182	-	2f. violet (Lammergeier) (different)	4·00	30·00

56 Offering Homage to First Prince

1939. Homage to Francis Joseph II.

183	**56**	20r. red	2·00	4·00
184	**56**	30r. blue	2·00	3·00
185	**56**	50r. green	2·00	4·00

57 Francis Joseph II

1939

186	-	2f. green on cream	15·00	75·00
187	-	3f. violet on cream	9·75	75·00
188	**57**	5f. brown on cream	30·00	50·00

Designs: 2f. Cantonal Arms; 3f. Arms of Principality.

58 Prince John when a Child

1940. Birth Centenary of Prince John II.

189	**58**	20r. red	1·00	4·00
190	-	30r. blue	1·00	5·75
191	-	50r. green	2·00	20·00
192	-	1f. violet	15·00	£130
193	-	1f.50 black	22·00	£110
194	-	3f. brown	6·75	39·00

Designs: As T **58**—Portraits of Prince John in early manhood (30r.), in middle age (50r.) and in later life (1f.), and Memorial tablet (1f.50). As T **44**—3f. Framed portrait of Prince John II.

60 Wine Press

1941. Agricultural Propaganda.

195		10r. brown	1·50	2·00
196	**60**	20r. purple	2·40	3·00
197	-	30r. blue	2·40	5·00
198	-	50r. green	4·00	30·00
199	-	90r. violet	4·50	34·00

Designs: 10r. Harvesting maize; 30r. Sharpening scythe; 50r. Milkmaid and cow; 90r. Girl wearing traditional headdress.

61 Madonna and Child

1941

200	**61**	10f. purple on stone	80·00	£200

62 Prince Hans Adam

1941. Princes (1st issue).

201	**62**	20r. red	1·00	3·00
202	-	30r. blue (Wenzel)	1·00	5·00
203	-	1f. grey (Anton Florian)	4·00	32·00
204	-	1f.50 green (Joseph)	4·00	34·00

See also Nos. 210/213 and 217/220.

63 St Lucius preaching

1942. 600th Anniversary of Separation from Estate of Montfort.

205	**63**	20r. red on pink	2·40	2·00
206	-	30r. blue on pink	1·50	5·00
207	-	50r. green on pink	4·50	15·00
208	-	1f. brown on pink	5·75	27·00
209	-	2f. violet on pink	6·50	27·00

Designs: 30r. Count of Montfort replanning Vaduz; 50r. Counts of Montfort-Werdenberg and Sargans signing treaty; 1f. Battle of Gutenberg; 2f. Homage to Prince of Liechtenstein.

64 Prince John Charles

1942. Princes (2nd issue).

210	**64**	20r. pink	1·00	2·00
211	-	30r. blue (Francis Joseph I)	1·00	4·00
212	-	1f. purple (Alois I)	4·00	30·00
213	-	1f.50 brown (John I)	4·00	30·00

65 Princess Georgina

1943. Marriage of Prince Francis Joseph II and Countess Georgina von Wildczek.

214		10r. purple	1·00	2·40
215	**65**	20r. red	1·00	2·40
216	-	30r. blue	1·00	2·40

Portraits: Vert—10r. Prince Francis Joseph II. Horiz (44×25 mm)—30r. Prince and Princess.

66 Alois II

1943. Princes (3rd issue).

217	**66**	20r. brown	1·00	2·00
218	-	30r. blue	2·00	3·00
219	-	1f. brown	3·00	15·00
220	-	1f.50 green	3·00	15·00

Portraits: 30r. John II; 1f. Francis I; 1f.50, Francis Joseph II.

67 Marsh Land

1943. Completion of Irrigation Canal.

221	**67**	10r. violet	45	1·00
222	-	30r. blue	75	4·00
223	-	50r. green	2·75	17·00
224	-	2f. brown	5·00	27·00

Designs: 30r. Draining the canal; 50r. Ploughing reclaimed land; 2f. Harvesting crops.

1943. Castles. As T **41**.

225		10r. grey (Vaduz)	75	1·00
226		20r. brown (Gutenberg)	1·20	2·00

69 Planken

1944. Various designs. Buff backgrounds.

227	**69**	3r. brown	45	45
228	-	5r. green (Bendern)	45	45
228a	-	5r. brown (Bendern)	55·00	2·75
229	-	10r. grey (Triesen)	45	45
230	-	15r. grey (Ruggell)	60	1·50
231	-	20r. red (Vaduz)	60	1·00
232	-	25r. brown (Triesenberg)	60	2·00
233	-	30r. blue (Schaan)	80	1·00
234	-	40r. brown (Balzers)	1·20	2·40
235	-	50r. blue (Mauren)	1·50	4·00
236	-	60r. green (Schellenberg)	8·50	12·00
237	-	90r. green (Eschen)	8·50	12·00
238	-	1f. purple (Vaduz Castle)	5·00	12·00
239	-	1f.20 brown (Valunatal)	5·00	13·50
240	-	1f.50 blue (Lawena)	5·00	13·50

70 Prince Francis Joseph II

1944

241	**70**	2f. brown and buff	12·00	34·00
242	-	3f. green and buff	7·50	24·00

Design: 3f. Princess Georgina.

See also Nos. 302/303.

72

1945. Birth of Crown Prince Johann Adam Pius (known as Prince Hans Adam).

243	**72**	20r. red, yellow and gold	2·00	1·00
244	**72**	30r. blue, yellow and gold	2·00	3·00
245	**72**	100r. grey, yellow and gold	5·75	12·00

73

1945

246	**73**	5f. blue on buff	45·00	70·00
247	**73**	5f. brown on buff	55·00	90·00

74 First Aid

1945. Red Cross. Cross in red.

248	-	10r.+10r. purple and buff	3·00	3·75
249	**74**	20r.+20r. purple and buff	3·00	5·25
250	-	1f.+1f.40 blue and buff	19·00	50·00

Designs: 10r. Mother and children; 1f. Nurse and invalid.

75 St Lucius

1946

251	**75**	10f. grey on buff	90·00	65·00

1946. Fourth Liechtenstein Philatelic Exhibition, Vaduz and 25th Anniversary of Postal Agreement with Switzerland. Sheet 84×60 mm.

MS251a 10r. (×2) Old Postal Coach (*horiz*), violet, brown and buff (sold at 3f.) 75·00 80·00

76 Red Deer Stag

1946. Wild Life.

252	**76**	20r. red	5·75	5·25
253	-	30r. blue (Arctic hare)	7·75	7·25
254	-	1f.50 green (Western capercaillie)	11·00	24·00
255	-	20r. red (Chamois)	9·75	9·00
256	-	30r. blue (Alpine marmot)	13·00	10·00
257	-	1f.50 brown (Golden eagle)	12·00	31·00
283	-	20r. red (Roebuck)	24·00	9·00
284	-	30r. green (Black grouse)	20·00	14·00
285	-	80r. brown (Eurasian badger)	80·00	95·00

1947. Death of Princess Elsa. As No. 141.

258	2f. black on yellow	9·75	28·00

79 Wilbur Wright

1948. Air. Pioneers of Flight.

259	-	10r. green	1·50	50
260	-	15r. violet	1·50	2·30
261	-	20r. brown	2·00	65
262	-	25r. red	3·00	3·75
263	-	40r. blue	3·50	3·75
264	-	50r. blue	4·00	3·75
265	-	1f. purple	6·50	7·75
266	-	2f. purple	9·75	10·00
267	**79**	5f. green	13·00	14·00
268	-	10f. black	80·00	39·00

Portraits: 10r. Leoardo da Vinci; 15r. Joseph Montgolfier; 20r. Jakob Degen; 25r. Wilhelm Kress; 40r. Etienne Robertson; 50r. William Henson; 1f. Otto Lilienthal; 2f. Salomon Andree; 10f. Icarus.

80 *Ginevra de Benci* (Da Vinci)

1949. Paintings.

269	**80**	10r. green	2·00	70
270	-	20r. red	3·00	1·60
271	-	30r. brown	5·75	1·90
272	-	40r. blue	15·00	1·90
273	-	50r. violet	12·00	14·00
274	-	60r. grey	34·00	13·00
275	-	80r. brown	5·75	8·75
276	-	90r. green	27·00	12·00
277	-	120r. mauve	5·75	11·00

Designs: 20r. *Portrait of a Young Girl* (Rubens); 30r. Self-portrait of Rembrandt in plumed hat; 40r. *Stephan Gardiner, Bishop of Winchester* (Quentin Massys); 50r. *Madonna and Child* (Hans Memling); 60r. *Franz Meister in 1456* (Jehan Fouquet); 80r. *Lute Player* (Orazio Gentileschi); 90r. *Portrait of a Man* (Bernhardin Strigel); 120r. *Portrait of a Man (Duke of Urbino)* (Raphael).

1949. No. 227 surch **5 rp.** and bars.

278	**69**	5r. on 3r. brown and buff	1·50	95

82 Posthorn and Map of World

1949. 75th Anniversary of UPU.

279	**82**	40r. blue	7·75	9·00

1949. Fifth Liechtenstein Philatelic Exhibition, Vaduz. Sheet 122×70 mm containing paintings as 1949 issue in new colours.

MS279a 10r. green (as 10r.); 20r. mauve (as 80r.); 40r. blue (as 120r.). Sold at 3f. £225 £225

83 Rossauer Castle

1949. 250th Anniversary of Acquisition of Domain of Schellenberg.

280	**83**	20r. purple	5·00	4·75
281	-	40r. blue	17·00	14·00
282	-	1f.50 red	22·00	20·00

Design: Horiz—40r. Bendern Church. Vert—1f.50, Prince Johann Adam I.

1950. Surch **100 100**.

286	**82**	100r. on 40r. blue	60·00	95·00

86 Boy cutting Loaf

1951. Agricultural scenes.

287	**86**	5r. mauve	1·00	50
288	-	10r. green	1·00	95
289	-	15r. brown	12·00	11·00
290	-	20r. brown	2·40	1·40
291	-	25r. purple	12·00	11·00
292	-	30r. green	6·75	1·10
293	-	40r. blue	22·00	14·00
294	-	50r. purple	18·00	7·00
295	-	60r. brown	18·00	6·25
296	-	80r. brown	22·00	14·50
297	-	90r. green	45·00	14·50
298	-	1f. blue	£140	14·50

Designs: 10r. Man whetting scythe; 15r. Mowing; 20r. Girl and sweet corn; 25r. Haywain; 30r. Gathering grapes; 40r. Man with scythe; 50r. Herdsman with cows; 60r. Ploughing; 80r. Girl carrying basket of fruit; 90r. Woman gleaning; 1f. Tractor hauling corn.

87 *Lock on the Canal* (Aelbert Cuyp)

88 *Willem von Heythuysen, Burgomaster of Haarlem* (Frans Hals)

1951. Paintings.

299	**87**	10r.+10r. green	19·00	14·00
300	**88**	20r.+10r. brown	19·00	28·00
301	-	40r.+10r. blue	19·00	18·00

Design: As T **87**—40r. *Landscape* (Jacob van Ruysdael).

90 Vaduz Castle

1951

302A	**70**	2f. blue	30·00	75·00
303B	-	3f. brown	£250	£400
304	**90**	5f. green	£350	£325

Design: 3f. Princess Georgina.

1952. No. 281 surch **1.20.**

308	1f.20 on 40r. blue	49·00	£110

1952. Paintings from Prince's Collection. (a) As T **80** but size 25×30 mm.

309	10r. green	5·00	1·90
305	20r. purple	90·00	5·75
307	40r. blue	30·00	12·00
312	40r. blue	75·00	95·00

Paintings: No. 309, *Portrait of a Young Man* (A. G.); No. 305, *Portrait* (Giovanni Salvoldo); No. 307, *St John* (Andrea del Sarto); No. 312, *Leonhard, Count of Hag* (Hans von Kulmbach).

(b) As T **88** (22½×24 mm).

306	30r. green	60·00	14·50
310	20r. brown	38·00	5·00
311	30r. brown	65·00	16·00

Paintings: No. 310, *St Nicholas* (Bartholomaus Zeitblom); No. 306, *Madonna and Child* (Sandro Botticelli); No. 311, *St Christopher* (Lucas Cranach the elder).

96 Lord Baden-Powell

1953. 14th International Scout Conference.

313	**96**	10r. green	5·00	1·90
314	**96**	20r. brown	31·00	4·75
315	**96**	25r. red	24·00	36·00
316	**96**	40r. blue	23·00	12·00

97 Alemannic Ornamental Disc, (*c.* AD 600)

98 Prehistoric Walled Settlement, Borscht

1953. Opening of National Museum, Vaduz.

317	**97**	10r. brown	20·00	23·00
318	**98**	20r. green	20·00	23·00
319	-	1f.20 blue	£100	65·00

Design: Vert—1f.20, Rossen jug (3000 BC).

99 Footballers

1954. Football.

320	**99**	10r. brown and red	5·50	1·90
321	-	20r. deep green and green	16·00	2·75
322	-	25r. deep brown and brown	38·00	65·00
323	-	40r. violet and grey	33·00	18·00

Designs: 20r. Footballer kicking ball; 25r. Goalkeeper; 40r. Two footballers.

For stamps in similar designs see Nos. 332/335, 340/343, 351/354 and 363/366.

1954. Nos. 299/301 surch in figures.

324	**87**	35r. on 10r.+10r. green	7·50	4·75
325	**88**	60r. on 20r.+10r. brown	38·00	21·00
326	-	65r. on 40r.+10r. blue	11·50	14·50

100 Madonna and Child

1954. Termination of Marian Year.

327	**100**	20r. brown	7·50	39·00
328	**100**	40r. black	38·00	40·00
329	**100**	1f. brown	38·00	39·00

101 Princess Georgina

1955

330	-	2f. brown	£170	95·00
331	**101**	3f. green	£170	95·00

Portrait: 2f. Prince Francis Joseph II.

1955. Mountain Sports. As T **99**.

332	10r. purple and blue	5·00	1·90
333	20r. green and bistre	12·50	1·90
334	25r. brown and blue	38·00	38·00
335	40r. green and red	38·00	14·00

Designs: 10r. Slalom racer; 20r. Mountaineer hammering in piton; 25r. Skier; 40r. Mountaineer resting on summit.

102 Crown Prince John Adam Pius

1955. Tenth Anniversary of Liechtenstein Red Cross. Cross in red.

336	**102**	10r. violet	5·50	1·40
337	-	20r. green	11·50	3·25
338	-	40r. brown	14·50	15·00
339	-	60r. red	14·50	8·25

Portraits: 20r. Prince Philip; 40r. Prince Nicholas; 60r. Princess Nora.

See also No. 350.

1956. Athletics. As T **99**.

340	10r. green and brown	4·00	1·40
341	20r. purple and green	7·50	1·40
342	40r. brown and blue	11·50	9·00

343		1f. brown and red	26·00	31·00

Designs: 10r. Throwing the javelin; 20r. Hurdling; 40r. Pole vaulting; 1f. Running.

103

1956. 150th Anniversary of Sovereignty of Liechtenstein.

344	**103**	10r. purple and gold	5·25	1·90
345	**103**	1f.20 blue and gold	25·00	9·00

104 Prince Francis Joseph II

1956. 50th Birthday of Prince Francis Joseph II.

346	**104**	10r. green	4·00	95
347	**104**	15r. blue	7·75	6·00
348	**104**	25r. purple	7·75	6·00
349	**104**	60r. brown	17·00	5·25

1956. Sixth Philatelic Exhibition, Vaduz. As T **102** but inscr '6. BRIEFMARKEN-AUSSTELLUNG'.

350		20r. green	6·25	1·40

1956. Gymnastics. As T **99**.

351		10r. green and pink	5·00	1·90
352		15r. purple and green	11·50	11·50
353		25r. green and drab	14·50	14·00
354		1f.50 brown and yellow	43·00	38·00

Designs: 10r. Somersaulting; 15r. Vaulting; 25r. Exercising with rings; 1f.50, Somersaulting on parallel bars.

105 Norway Spruce

1957. Liechtenstein Trees and Bushes.

355	**105**	10r. purple	9·50	4·75
356	-	20r. red	9·50	1·90
357	-	1f. green	14·50	16·00

Designs: 20r. Wild rose bush; 1f. Silver birch.
See also Nos. 369/371, 375/377 and 401/403.

106 Lord Baden-Powell

1957. 50th Anniversary of Boy Scout Movement and Birth Centenary of Lord Baden-Powell (founder).

358		10r. blue	2·75	2·75
359	**106**	20r. brown	2·75	2·75

Design: 10r. Torchlight procession.

107 St Mamertus Chapel

1957. Christmas.

360	**107**	10r. brown	2·75	95
361	-	40r. blue	7·50	16·00
362	-	1f.50 purple	27·00	25·00

Designs: (from St Mamertus Chapel)—40r. Altar shrine; 1f.50, *Pieta* (sculpture).
See also Nos. 372/4 and 392/4.

1958. Sports. As T **99**.

363		15r. violet and blue	2·00	2·75
364		30r. green and purple	12·50	18·00
365		40r. green and orange	19·00	18·00
366		90r. brown and green	5·00	9·00

Designs: 15r. Swimmer; 30r. Fencers; 40r. Tennis player; 90r. Racing cyclists.

108 Relief Map of Liechtenstein

1958. Brussels International Exhibition.

367	**108**	25r. violet, stone and red	2·00	1·40
368	**108**	40r. purple, blue and red	2·75	1·40

1958. Liechtenstein Trees and Bushes. As T **105**.

369		20r. brown (Sycamore)	7·25	1·90
370		50r. green (Holly)	29·00	12·00
371		90r. violet (Yew)	7·25	6·25

1958. Christmas. As T **107**.

372		20r. green	5·50	4·75
373		35r. violet	5·50	7·25
374		80r. brown	7·50	5·25

Designs: 20r. *St Maurice and St Agatha*; 35r. *St Peter*; 80r. St Peter's Chapel, Mals-Balzers.

1959. Liechtenstein Trees and Bushes. As T **105**.

375		20r. lilac (Red-berried Larch)	14·50	5·25
376		50r. red (Red-berried Elder)	11·50	7·25
377		90r. green (Linden)	7·50	7·50

109

1959. Pope Pius XII Mourning.

378	**109**	30r. purple and gold	2·30	2·00

110 Flags of Vaduz Castle and Rhine Valley

111 Harvester

1959. Views.

379	-	5r. brown	45	45
380	**110**	10r. purple	45	45
381	-	20r. mauve	60	45
382	-	30r. red	80	55
383	-	40r. green	1·10	75
384	-	50r. blue	1·10	95
385	-	60r. blue	1·40	1·10
386	**111**	75r. brown	2·20	2·50
387	-	80r. green	2·00	1·40
388	-	90r. purple	2·10	1·50
389	-	1f. brown	2·30	1·60
390	-	1f.20 red	3·25	2·50
390a	-	1f.30 green	2·50	2·30
391	-	1f.50 blue	4·00	2·75

Designs: Horiz—5r. Bendern Church; 20r. Rhine Dam; 30r. Gutenberg Castle; 40r. View from Schellenberg; 50r. Vaduz Castle; 60r. Naafkopf-Falknis Mountains (view from the Bettlerjoch); 1f.20, Harvesting apples; 1f.30, Farmer and wife; 1f.50, Saying grace at table. Vert—80r. Alpine haymaker; 90r. Girl in vineyard; 1f. Mother in kitchen.

1959. Christmas. As T **107**.

392		5r. green	1·00	45
393		60r. brown	13·00	10·00
394		1f. purple	11·50	7·00

Designs: 5r. Bendern Church belfry; 60r. Relief on bell of St Theodul's Church; 1f. Sculpture on tower of St Lucius's Church.

112 Bell 47J Ranger Helicopter

1960. Air. 30th Anniversary of First Liechtenstein Air Stamps.

395	**112**	30r. red	5·00	5·75
396	-	40r. blue	8·50	5·75
397	-	50r. purple	21·00	11·00
398	-	75r. green	4·00	5·75

Designs: 40r. Boeing 707 jetliner; 50r. Convair 990A Coronado jetliner; 75r. Douglas DC-8 jetliner.

1960. World Refugee Year. Nos. 367/368 surch **WELTFLUCHTLINGSJAHR 1960**, uprooted tree and new value.

399	**108**	30+10r. on 40r. purple, blue and red	2·50	2·50
400	**108**	50+10r. on 25r. violet, stone and red	4·25	4·25

1960. Liechtenstein Trees and Bushes. As T **105**.

401		20r. brown (Beech)	14·50	9·00
402		30r. purple (Juniper)	14·50	28·00
403		50r. turquoise (Mountain pines)	47·00	31·00

114 Europa 'Honeycomb'

1960. Europa.

404	**114**	50r. multicoloured	£140	80·00

115 Princess Gina

1960

404a	-	1f.70 violet	3·25	1·90
405	**115**	2f. blue	5·00	3·75
406	-	3f. brown	5·50	4·75

Portraits: 1f.70, Crown Prince Hans Adam; 3f. Prince Francis Joseph II.

116 Heinrich von Frauenberg

1961. Minnesingers (1st issue). Multicoloured. Reproduction from the Manessian Manuscript of Songs.

407		15r. Type **116**	65	70
408		25r. Ulrich von Liechtenstein	1·00	95
409		35r. Ulrich von Gutenberg	1·20	1·10
410		1f. Konrad von Altstatten	2·75	2·75
411		1f.50 Walther von der Vogelweide	15·00	23·00

See also Nos. 415/418 and 428/431.

117 Power Transmission

1961. Europa.

412	**117**	50r. multicoloured	70	70

117a Prince John II

1962. 50th Anniversary of First Liechtenstein Postage Stamps. Sheet 133×118 mm. T **117a** and similar horiz design.

MS412a 5r. green; 10r. red; 25r. blue. Sold at 2f.60 — 11·50 — 7·50

Designs: 10r. Prince Francis I; 25r. Prince Francis Joseph I.

118 Clasped Hands

1962. Europa.

413	**118**	50r. red and blue	1·00	95

119 Campaign Emblem

1962. Malaria Eradication.

414	**119**	50r. blue	1·00	95

1962. Minnesingers (2nd issue). As T **116**. Multicoloured.

415		20r. King Konradin	1·00	95
416		30r. Kraft von Toggenburg	2·00	1·90
417		40r. Heinrich von Veldig	2·00	1·90
418		2f. Tannhauser	2·30	2·30

120 *Pieta*

1962. Christmas.

419	**120**	30r. mauve	80	75
420	-	50r. red	1·20	1·10
421	-	1f.20 blue	2·10	2·00

Designs: 50r. Fresco with Angel; 1f.20, View of Mauren.
See also Nos. 438/440.

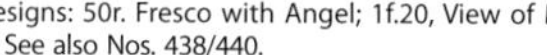

121 Prince Francis Joseph II

1963. 25th Anniversary of Reign of Prince Francis Joseph II.

422	**121**	5f. green	8·50	6·25

122 Milk and Bread

1963. Freedom from Hunger.

423	**122**	50r. brown, purple and red	1·30	95

123 Angel of Annunciation

1963. Red Cross Centenary Cross in red; background grey.

424	**123**	20r. yellow and green	50	50
425	-	80r. violet and mauve	1·20	1·10
426	-	1f. blue and ultramarine	1·70	1·60

Designs: 80r. The Epiphany; 1f. Family.

124 Europa

1963. Europa.

427	**124**	50r. multicoloured	1·90	1·30

1963. Minnesingers (3rd issue). As T **116**. Multicoloured.

428		25r. Heinrich von Sax	65	60
429		30r. Kristan von Hamle	90	80
430		75r. Werner von Teufen	1·40	1·30
431		1f.70 Hartmann von Aue	2·30	2·10

125 Olympic Rings and Flags

1964. Olympic Games, Tokyo.

432	**125**	50r. red, black and blue	95	85

126 Arms of Counts of Werdenberg, Vaduz

1964. Arms (1st issue). Multicoloured.

433		20f. Type **126**	40	35
434		30f. Barons of Brandis	50	45
435		80r. Counts of Sulz	1·00	90
436		1f.50 Counts of Hohenems	1·90	1·70

See also Nos. 443/446.

127 Roman Castle, Schaan

1964. Europa.
437 **127** 50f. multicoloured 2·00 1·20

1964. Christmas. As T **120**.
438 10r. purple 40 35
439 40r. blue 55 50
440 1f.30 purple 1·90 1·70
Designs: 10r. Masescha Chapel; 40r. *Mary Magdalene* (altar painting); 1f.30, *St Sebastian, Madonna and Child, and St Rochus* (altar painting).

128 P. Kaiser

1964. Death Centenary of Peter Kaiser (historian).
441 **128** 1f. green on cream 1·80 1·60

129 *Madonna* (wood sculpture, c. 1700)

1965
442 **129** 10f. red 15·00 9·25

1965. Arms (2nd issue). As T **126**. Multicoloured.
443 20r. Von Schellenberg 40 35
444 30r. Von Gutenberg 50 45
445 80r. Von Frauenberg 1·10 1·00
446 1f. Von Ramschwag 1·30 1·20

130 Europa 'Links' (ancient belt-buckle)

1965. Europa.
447 **130** 50r. brown, grey and blue 95 85

131 *Jesus in the Temple*

1965. Birth Centenary of Ferdinand Nigg (painter).
448 - 10r. deep green and green 40 35
449 - 30r. brown and orange 50 45
450 **131** 1f.20 green and blue 1·50 1·40
Designs: Vert—10r. *The Annunciation*; 30r. *The Magi*.

132 *Princess Gina and Prince Franz* (after painting by Pedro Leitao)

1965. Special Issue.
451 **132** 75r. multicoloured 1·00 90
See also No. 457.

133 Telecommunications Symbols

1965. Centenary of ITU.
452 **133** 25r. multicoloured 45 40

134 Tree (Wholesome Earth)

1966. Nature Protection.
453 **134** 10r. green and yellow 25 25
454 - 20r. blue and light blue 40 35
455 - 30r. blue and green 50 45
456 - 1f.50 red and yellow 1·80 1·60
Designs: 20r. Bird (Pure Air); 30r. Fish (Clean Water); 1f.50, Sun (Protection of Nature).

1966. Prince Franz Joseph II's 60th Birthday. As T **132** but with portrait of Prince Franz and inscr '1906–1966'.
457 1f. multicoloured 1·50 1·40

135 Arms of Herren von Richenstein

1966. Arms of Triesen Families. Multicoloured.
458 20r. Type **135** 40 40
459 30r. Jinker Vaistli 55 50
460 60r. Edle von Trisun 1·00 90
461 1f.20 Die von Schiel 1·50 1·40

136 Europa 'Ship'

1966. Europa.
462 **136** 50r. multicoloured 1·00 90

137 Vaduz Parish Church

1966. Restoration of Vaduz Parish Church.
463 **137** 5r. green and red 20 20
464 - 20r. purple and bistre 40 40
465 - 30r. blue and red 55 50
466 - 1f.70 brown and green 2·50 2·30
Designs: 20r. St Florin; 30r. Madonna; 1f.70, God the Father.

138 Cogwheels

1967. Europa.
467 **138** 50r. multicoloured 85 75

139 *The Man from Malanser*

1967. Liechtenstein Sagas (1st series). Multicoloured.
468 20r. Type **139** 35 35
469 30r. *The Treasure of Gutenberg* 50 45
470 1f.20 *The Giant of Guflina* 1·80 1·70
See also Nos. 492/494 and 516/518.

140 Crown Prince Hans Adam

1967. Royal Wedding. Sheet 86×95 mm comprising T **140** and similar vert design.
MS471 1f.50 indigo and blue (Type **140**); 1f.50 brown and light brown (Princess Marie) 4·75 4·50

141 Alpha and Omega

1967. Christian Symbols. Multicoloured.
472 20r. Type **141** 35 35
473 30r. 'Tropaion' (Cross as victory symbol) 50 45
474 70r. Christ's monogram 1·20 1·10

142 Father J. B. Buchel (educator, historian and poet)

1967. Buchel Commemoration.
475 **142** 1f. red and green 1·60 1·40

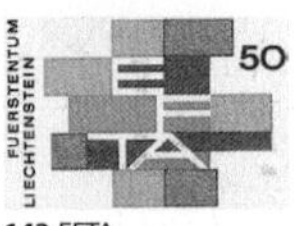

143 EFTA

1967. European Free Trade Association.
476 **143** 50r. multicoloured 85 75

144 Peter and Paul, Mauren

1967. "atrons of the Church. Multicoloured.
477 5r. St Joseph, Planken 20 15
478 10r. St Lawrence, Schaan 35 35
479 20r. Type **144** 40 40
480 30r. St Nicholas, Balzers 55 45
480a 40r. St Sebastian, Nendeln 70 55
481 50r. St George, Schellenberg 85 60
482 60r. St Martin, Eschen 95 70
483 70r. St Fridolin, Ruggell 1·10 75
484 80r. St Gallus, Triesen 1·20 90
485 1f. St Theodolus, Triesenberg 1·60 1·20
486 1f.20 St Anna, Vaduz Castle 1·80 1·40
487 1f.50 St Marie, Bendern-Camprin 2·40 1·80
488 2f. St Lucius, (patron saint of Liechtenstein) 3·50 2·40

145 Campaign Emblem

1967. Technical Assistance.
489 **145** 50r.+20r. multicoloured 1·20 1·10

146 Europa 'Key'

1968. Europa.
490 **146** 50r. multicoloured 85 75

147 Arms of Liechtenstein and Wilczek

1968. Silver Wedding Anniversary of Prince Francis Joseph II and Princess Gina.
491 **147** 75r. multicoloured 1·20 1·00

1968. Liechtenstein Sagas (2nd series). As T **139**. Multicoloured.
492 30r. *The Treasure of St Mamerten* 50 40
493 50r. *The Hobgoblin in the Bergerwald* 70 60
494 80r. *The Three Sisters* 1·30 1·00

148 Sir Rowland Hill

1968. Pioneers of Philately (1st series).
495 **148** 20r. green 40 40
496 - 30r. brown 50 45
497 - 1f. black 1·60 1·30
Portraits: 30r. Philippe de Ferrary; 1f. Maurice Burrus.
See also Nos. 504/505 and 554/556.

150 Arms of Liechtenstein

1969
498 **150** 3f.50 brown 4·75 3·25

151 Colonnade

1969. Europa.
499 **151** 50r. multicoloured 85 65

152 Biology

1969. 250th Anniversary of Liechtenstein. Multicoloured.
500 10r. Type **152** 40 40
501 30r. Physics 55 45
502 50r. Astronomy 85 65
503 80r. Art 1·30 1·20

1969. Pioneers of Philately (2nd series). As T **148**.
504 80r. brown 1·30 1·10
505 1f.20 blue 1·90 1·50
Portraits: 80r. Carl Lindenberg; 1f.20, Theodore Champion.

153 Arms of St Luzi Monastery

1969. Arms of Church Patrons. Multicoloured.
506 20r. St. Johann's Abbey 35 35
507 30r. Type **153** 50 40
508 30r. Ladies' Priory, Schanis 50 40
509 30r. Knights Hospitallers, Feldkirch 50 40
510 50r. Pfafers Abbey 85 65
511 50r. Weingarten Abbey 85 65
512 75r. St Gallen Abbey 1·20 95
513 1f.20 Ottobeuren Abbey 1·90 1·50
514 1f.50 Chur Episcopate 2·40 1·70

154 Symbolic 'T'

1969. Centenary of Liechtenstein Telegraph System.
515 **154** 30r. multicoloured 55 40

1969. Liechtenstein Sagas (3rd series). As T **139**. Multicoloured.
516 20r. *The Cheated Devil* 40 35
517 50r. *The Fiery Red Goat* 85 55
518 60r. *The Grafenberg Treasure* 95 70

155 Orange Lily

1970. Nature Conservation Year. Liechtenstein Flowers (1st series). Multicoloured.

519		20r. Type **155**	40	35
520		30r. Wild orchid	70	50
521		50r. Ranunculus	95	85
522		1f.20 Bog bean	2·00	1·80

See also Nos. 532/535 and 548/551.

156 'Flaming Sun'

1970. Europa.

523	**156**	50r. yellow, blue and green	90	65

157 Prince Wenzel

1970. 25th Anniversary of Liechtenstein Red Cross.

524	**157**	1f. multicoloured	1·70	1·30

1970. 800th Anniversary of Wolfram von Eschenbach. Sheet 73×96 mm containing vert designs similar to T **116** from the *Codex Manaesse*. Multicoloured.

MS525 30r. Wolfram von Eschenbach; 50r. Reinmar the Fiddler; 80r. Hartmann von Starkenberg; 1f.20 Friedrich von Hausen. Sold for 3f. | 5·25 | 5·00

158 Prince Francis Joseph II

1970

526	-	1f.70 green	2·75	2·00
526a	-	2f.50 blue	4·50	3·00
527	**158**	3f. black	5·25	3·50

Designs: 1f.70, Prince Hans Adam; 2f.50, Princess Gina.

159 *Mother and Child* (R. Schadler)

1970. Christmas.

528	**159**	30r. multicoloured	50	40

160 Bronze Boar (La Tene period)

1971. National Museum Inauguration.

529	**160**	25r. black, blue & ultram	45	35
530	-	30r. green and brown	50	40
531	-	75r. multicoloured	1·20	90

Designs: 30r. Ornamental peacock (Roman, 2nd-century); 75r. Engraved bowl (13th-century).

1971. Liechtenstein Flowers (2nd series). As T **155**. Multicoloured.

532		10r. Cyclamen	45	35
533		20r. Moonwort	50	40
534		50r. Superb pink	90	70
535		1f.50 Alpine columbine	2·20	1·80

161 Europa Chain

1971. Europa.

536	**161**	50r. yellow, blue & black	1·00	70

162 Part of Text

1971. 50th Anniversary of 1921 Constitution. Mulicoloured.

537		70r. Type **162**	1·30	90
538		80r. Princely crown	1·40	1·00

163 Cross-country Skiing

1971. Winter Olympic Games, Sapporo, Japan (1972). Multicoloured.

539		15r. Type **163**	50	40
540		40r. Ice hockey	70	60
541		65r. Downhill skiing	1·10	90
542		1f.50 Figure skating	2·75	2·20

164 *Madonna and Child* (sculpture, Andrea della Robbia)

1971. Christmas.

543	**164**	30r. multicoloured	70	45

165 Gymnastics

1972. Olympic Games, Munich. Multicoloured.

544		10r. Type **165**	30	25
545		20r. High jumping	55	40
546		40r. Running	70	60
547		60r. Throwing the discus	1·00	80

1972. Liechtenstein Flowers (3rd series). As T **155**. Multicoloured.

548		20r. Sulphur anemone	50	40
549		30r. Turk's-cap lily	55	50
550		60r. Alpine centaury	1·10	85
551		1f.20 Reed-mace	2·20	1·60

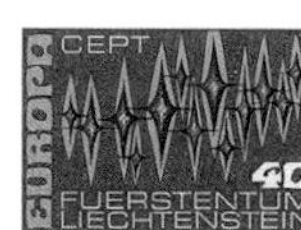

166 Communications

1972. Europa.

552	**166**	40r. multicoloured	1·00	75

167 Bendern

1972. Liba '72 Stamp Exhibition, Vaduz. Sheet 101×65 mm containing T **167** and similar horiz design.

MS553 1f. violet; 2f. red | 5·50 | 5·00

Design: 2f. Vaduz castle.

1972. Pioneers of Philately (3rd series). As T **148**.

554		30r. green	55	50
555		40r. purple	70	60
556		1f.30 blue	2·20	1·70

Portraits: 30r. Emilio Diena; 40r. Andre de Cock; 1f.30, Theodore E. Steinway.

168 *Faun*

1972. Natural Art. Motifs fashioned from roots and branches. Multicoloured.

557		20r. Type **168**	40	35
558		30r. *Dancer*	55	45
559		1f.10 *Owl*	2·00	1·50

169 *Madonna with Angels* (F. Nigg)

1972. Christmas.

560	**169**	30r. multicoloured	65	50

170 Lawena Springs

1972. Landscapes.

561	-	5r. purple and yellow	20	15
562	**170**	10r. green and light green	30	30
563	-	15r. brown and green	40	35
564	-	25r. purple and blue	50	40
565	-	30r. purple and brown	55	45
566	-	40r. purple and brown	70	50
567	-	50r. blue and lilac	1·00	65
568	-	60r. green and yellow	1·10	75
569	-	70r. blue and cobalt	1·30	90
570	-	80r. green and light green	1·40	1·00
571	-	1f. brown and green	2·10	1·30
572	-	1f.30 blue and green	2·20	1·70
573	-	1f.50 brown and blue	2·50	1·80
574	-	1f.80 brown & lt brown	3·00	2·20
575	-	2f. brown and blue	3·50	2·40

Designs: 5r. Silum; 15r. Ruggeller Reed; 25r. Steg Kirchlispitz; 30r. Feld Schellenberg; 40r. Rennhof Mauren; 50r. Tidrufe; 60r. Eschner Riet; 70r. Mittagspitz; 80r. Schaan Forest; 1f. St Peter's Chapel, Mals; 1f.30, Frommenhaus; 1f.50, Ochsenkopf; 1f.80, Hehlawangspitz; 2f. Saminaschlucht.

171 Europa Posthorn

1973. Europa.

576	**171**	30r. multicoloured	55	45
577	**171**	40r. multicoloured	70	55

172 Chambered Nautilus Goblet

1973. Treasures from Prince's Collection (1st issue). Drinking Vessels. Multicoloured.

578		30r. Type **172**	55	45
579		70r. Ivory tankard	1·10	90
580		1f.10 Silver cup	2·00	1·50

See also Nos. 589/592.

173 Arms of Liechtenstein

1973

581	**173**	5f. multicoloured	9·00	6·50

174 False Ringlet

1973. Small Fauna of Liechtenstein (1st series). Multicoloured.

582		30r. Type **174**	55	45
583		40r. Curlew	70	55
584		60r. Edible frog	1·00	85
585		80r. Grass snake	1·40	1·10

See also Nos. 596/599.

175 *Madonna* (Bartolomeo di Tommaso da Foligno)

1973. Christmas.

586	**175**	30r. multicoloured	65	50

176 *Shouting Horseman* (sculpture, Andrea Riccio)

1974. Europa. Multicoloured.

587		30r. Type **176**	55	45
588		40r. *Squatting Aphrodite* (sculpture, Antonio Susini)	70	55

1974. Treasures from Prince's Collection (2nd issue). Porcelain. As T **172**. Multicoloured.

589		30r. Vase, 19th-century	55	45
590		50r. Vase, 1740	85	65
591		60r. Vase, 1830	1·00	85
592		1f. Vase, c. 1700	1·80	1·40

177 Footballers

1974. World Cup Football Championship, West Germany.

593	**177**	80f. multicoloured	1·40	1·20

178 Posthorn and UPU Emblem

1974. Centenary of Universal Postal Union.

594	**178**	40r. black, green and gold	70	55
595	**178**	60r. black, red and gold	1·10	90

1974. Small Fauna of Liechtenstein (2nd series). As T **174**. Multicoloured.

596		15r. Mountain newt	40	35
597		25r. Adder	50	40
598		70r. Cynthia's fritillary (butterfly)	1·40	1·10
599		1f.10 Three-toed woodpecker	1·80	1·50

179 Bishop Marxer

1974. Death Centenary of Bishop Franz Marxer.

600	**179**	1f. multicoloured	1·80	1·40

180 Prince Francis Joseph II and Princess Gina

1974

601	**180**	10f. brown and gold	15·00	12·00

181 *St Florian*

1974. Christmas. Glass Paintings. Multicoloured.

602	30r. Type **181**	55	45
603	50r. *St Wendelin*	85	65
604	60r. *St Mary, Anna and Joachim*	1·00	85
605	70r. *Jesus in Manger*	1·10	90

182 Prince Constantin

1975. Liechtenstein Princes.

606	**182**	70r. green and gold	1·30	1·00
607	-	80r. purple and gold	1·50	1·20
608	-	1f.20 blue and gold	2·20	1·80

Portraits: 80r. Prince Maximilian; 1f.20, Prince Alois.

183 *Cold Sun* (M. Frommelt)

1975. Europa. Paintings. Multicoloured.

609	30r. Type **183**	55	45
610	60r. *Village* (L. Jager)	1·00	85

184 Imperial Cross

1975. Imperial Insignia (1st series). Multicoloured.

611	30r. Type **184**	55	45
612	60r. Imperial sword	1·00	85
613	1f. Imperial orb	1·70	1·30
614	1f.30 Imperial robe (50×32 *mm*)	3·75	3·25
615	2f. Imperial crown	4·00	3·50

See also Nos. 670/673.

185 Red Cross Activities

1975. 30th Anniversary of Liechtenstein Red Cross.

616	**185**	60r. multicoloured	1·10	85

186 St. Mamerten, Triesen

1975. European Architectural Heritage Year. Multicoloured.

617	40r. Type **186**	90	70
618	50r. Red House, Vaduz	1·20	95
619	70r. Prebendary buildings, Eschen	1·50	1·20
620	1f. Gutenberg Castle, Balzers	2·40	1·90

187 Speed Skating

1975. Winter Olympic Games, Innsbruck (1976). Multicoloured.

621	20r. Type **187**	55	40
622	25r. Ice hockey	60	50
623	70r. Downhill skiing	1·50	1·20
624	1f.20 Slalom	2·30	1·80

188 *Daniel in the Lions' Den*

1975. Christmas and Holy Year. Capitals in Chur Cathedral.

625	**188**	30r. violet and gold	60	50
626	-	60r. green and gold	1·20	95
627	-	90r. red and gold	1·50	1·20

Designs: 60r. *Madonna*; 90r. *St Peter*.

189 Mouflon

1976. Europa. Ceramics by Prince Hans von Liechtenstein. Multicoloured.

628	40r. Type **189**	75	60
629	80r. Ring-necked Pheasant and Brood	1·70	1·30

190 Crayfish

1976. World Wildlife Fund. Multicoloured.

630	25r. Type **190**	45	35
631	40r. Turtle	95	75
632	70r. European otter	1·40	1·10
633	80r. Northern lapwing	1·90	1·50

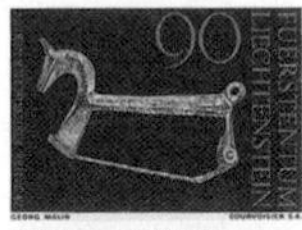

191 Roman Fibula

1976. 75th Anniversary of National Historical Society.

634	**191**	90r. multicoloured	1·90	1·50

192 Obverse of 50f. Coin depicting portrait of Prince

1976. 70th Birthday of Prince Francis Joseph II. Sheet 102×65 mm containing T **192** and similar horiz design. Multicoloured.

MS635	1f. Type **192**; 1f. Reverse of 50f. coin depicting Arms of Liechtenstein	3·75	3·50

193 Judo

1976. Olympic Games, Montreal. Multicoloured.

636	35r. Type **193**	60	50
637	50r. Volleyball	90	75
638	80r. Relay	1·40	1·20
639	1f.10 Long jumping	1·90	1·60

194 *Singing Angels*

1976. 400th Birth Anniversary (1977) of Peter Paul Rubens (painter). Multicoloured.

640	50r. Type **194**	1·00	90
641	70r. *Sons of the Artist*	1·30	1·10
642	1f. *Daughters of Cecrops* (49×39 mm)	5·75	5·50

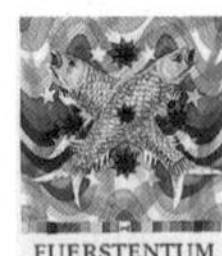

195 Pisces

1976. Signs of the Zodiac (1st series). Multicoloured.

643	20r. Type **195**	50	45
644	40r. Aries	65	55
645	80r. Taurus	1·30	1·10
646	90r. Gemini	1·50	1·30

See also Nos. 666/669 and 710/713.

196 *Child Jesus of Prague*

1976. Christmas. Monastic Wax Sculptures. Multicoloured

647	20r. Type **196**	40	35
648	50r. *The Flight into Egypt* (vert)	90	75
649	80r. *Holy Trinity* (vert)	1·40	1·20
650	1f.50 *Holy Family*	2·50	2·20

197 Sarcophagus Statue, Chur Cathedral

1976. Bishop Ortlieb von Brandis of Chur Commemoration.

651	**197**	1f.10 brown and gold	1·80	1·60

199 Map of Liechtenstein, 1721 (J. Heber)

1977. Europa. Multicoloured.

664	40r. Type **199**	75	65
665	80r. *View of Vaduz, 1815* (F. Bachmann)	1·40	1·20

1977. Signs of the Zodiac (2nd series). As T **195**. Multicoloured.

666	40r. Cancer	65	55
667	70r. Leo	1·10	1·00
668	80r. Virgo	1·40	1·20
669	1f.10 Libra	1·90	1·70

1977. Imperial Insignia (2nd series). As T **184**. Multicoloured.

670	40r. Holy Lance and Reliquary with Particle of the Cross	65	55
671	50r. St Matthew (Imperial Book of Gospels)	80	65
672	80r. St Stephen's Purse	1·30	1·10
673	90r. Tabard of Imperial Herald	1·50	1·30

200 Coin of Emperor Constantine II

1977. Coins (1st series). Multicoloured.

674	35r. Type **200**	65	55
675	70r. Lindau Brakteat	1·10	1·00
676	80r. Coin of Ortlieb von Brandis	1·40	1·20

See also Nos. 707/709.

201 Frauenthal Castle, Styria

1977. Castles.

677	**201**	20r. green and gold	45	40
678	-	50r. red and gold	95	85
679	-	80r. lilac and gold	1·50	1·30
680	-	90r. blue and gold	1·90	1·70

Designs: 50r. Gross-Ullersdorf, Moravia; 80r. Liechtenstein Castle, near Modling, Austria; 90r. Palais Liechtenstein, Alserbachstrasse, Vienna.

202 Children in Costume

1977. National Costumes. Multicoloured.

681	40r. Type **202**	65	55
682	70r. Two girls in traditional costume	1·30	1·10
683	1f. Woman in festive costume	1·90	1·70

203 Princess Tatjana

1977. Princess Tatjana.

684	**203**	1f.10 lt brn, brn & gold	2·10	1·90

204 *Angel*

1977. Christmas. Sculptures by Erasmus Kern. Multicoloured.

685	20r. Type **204**	45	40
686	50r. *St Rochus*	75	65
687	80r. *Madonna*	1·30	1·10
688	1f.50 *God the Father*	2·50	2·20

205 Palais Liechtenstein, Bankgasse, Vienna

1978. Europa.

689	**205**	40r. blue and gold	75	65
690	-	80r. red and gold	1·40	1·20

Design: 80r. Feldsberg Castle.

206 Farmhouse, Triesen

1978. Buildings. Multicoloured.

691 10r. Type **206** 25 20
692 20r. Upper village of Triesen 45 40
693 35r. Barns at Balzers 65 55
694 40r. Monastery building, Bendern 75 65
695 50r. Rectory tower, Balzers-Mals 90 75
696 70r. Rectory, Mauren 1·30 1·10
697 80r. Farmhouse, Schellenberg 1·50 1·30
698 90r. Rectory, Balzers 1·60 1·40
699 1f. Rheinberger House, Vaduz 1·80 1·50
700 1f.10 Vaduz Mitteldorf 1·90 1·70
701 1f.50 Town Hall, Triesenberg 2·50 2·20
702 2f. National Museum and Administrator's residence, Vaduz 3·25 2·75

207 Vaduz Castle

1978. 40th Anniversary of Prince Francis Joseph II's Accession. Royal Residence. Multicoloured.

703 40r. Type **207** 80 70
704 50r. Courtyard 95 85
705 70r. Hall 1·30 1·10
706 80r. High Altar, Castle Chapel 1·40 1·20

208 Coin of Prince Charles

1978. Coins (2nd series). Multicoloured.

707 40r. Type **208** 65 55
708 50r. Coin of Prince John Adam 75 65
709 80r. Coin of Prince Joseph Wenzel 1·40 1·20

1978. Signs of the Zodiac (3rd series). As T **195**. Multicoloured.

710 40r. Scorpio 65 55
711 50r. Sagittarius 90 80
712 80r. Capricorn 1·40 1·20
713 1f.50 Aquarius 2·75 2·40

209 *Portrait of a Piebald* (J. G. von Hamilton and A. Faistenberger)

1978. Paintings. Multicoloured.

714 70r. Type **209** 1·20 1·10
715 80r. *Portrait of a Blackish-brown Stallion* (J. G. von Hamilton) 1·30 1·20
716 1f.10 *Golden Carriage of Prince Joseph Wenzel* (Martin von Meytens) (48½×38 mm) 1·70 1·60

210 Adoration of the Shepherds

1978. Christmas. Church Windows, Triesenberg. Multicoloured.

717 20r. Type **210** 45 40
718 50r. Enthroned Madonna with St Joseph 80 70
719 80r. Adoration of the Magi 1·40 1·30

211 Comte AC-8 Mail Plane *St Gallen* over Schaan

1979. Europa. Multicoloured.

720 40r. Type **211** 80 70
721 80r. Airship LZ-127 *Graf Zeppelin* over Vaduz Castle 1·60 1·40

212 Child Drinking

1979. International Year of the Child. Multicoloured.

722 80r. Type **212** 1·30 1·20
723 90r. Child eating 1·60 1·40
724 1f.10 Child reading 1·80 1·70

213 Ordered Wave-field

1979. 50th Anniversary of International Radio Consultative Committee (CCIR).

725 **213** 50r. blue and black 80 70

214 Abstract Composition

1979. Liechtenstein's Entry into Council of Europe.

726 **214** 80r. multicoloured 1·30 1·20

215 Sun rising over Continents

1979. Development Aid.

727 **215** 1f. multicoloured 1·60 1·40

216 Arms of Carl Ludwig von Sulz

1979. Heraldic Windows in the Liechtenstein National Museum. Multicoloured.

728 40r. Type **216** 80 70
729 70r. Arms of Barbara von Sulz 1·20 1·10
730 1f.10 Arms of Ulrich von Ramschwag and Barbara von Hallwil 2·00 1·80

217 St Lucius and St Florian (fresco, Waltensberg-Vuorz Church)

1979. Patron Saints.

731 **217** 20f. multicoloured 26·00 24·00

218 Base of Ski Slope, Valuna

1979. Winter Olympic Games, Lake Placid (1980). Multicoloured.

732 40r. Type **218** 80 70
733 70r. Malbun and Ochsenkopf 1·10 1·00
734 1f.50 Ski-lift, Sareis 2·20 2·00

219 *The Annunciation*

1979. Christmas. Embroideries by Ferdinand Nigg. Multicoloured.

735 20r. Type **219** 45 40
736 50r. *Christmas* 90 85
737 80r. *Blessed are the Peacemakers* 1·60 1·40

220 *Maria Leopoldine von Esterhazy* (bust by Canova)

1980. Europa.

738 **220** 40r. green, turq & gold 60 55
739 - 80r. brown, red and gold 1·30 1·20

Design: 80r. Maria Theresia von Liechtenstein (after Martin von Meytens).

221 Arms of Andreas Buchel, 1690

1980. Arms of Bailiffs (1st series). Multicoloured.

740 40r. Type **221** 65 60
741 70r. Georg Marxer, 1745 1·20 1·10
742 80r. Luzius Frick, 1503 1·40 1·30
743 1f.10 Adam Oehri, 1634 2·00 1·80

See also Nos. 763/766, and 788/791.

222 3r. Stamp of 1930

1980. 50th Anniversary of Postal Museum.

744 **222** 80r. red, green and grey 1·40 1·30

223 Milking Pail

1980. Alpine Dairy Farming Implements. Multicoloured

745 20r. Type **223** 40 40
746 50r. Wooden heart dairy herd descent marker 85 75
747 80r. Butter churn 1·50 1·40

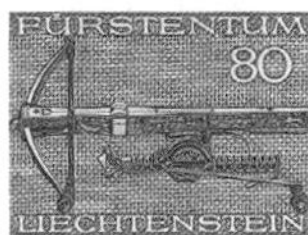
224 Crossbow

1980. Hunting Weapons.

748 **224** 80r. brown and lilac 1·40 1·30
749 - 90r. black and green 1·70 1·50
750 - 1f.10 black and stone 1·80 1·60

Designs: 90r. Spear and knife; 1f.10, Rifle and powder-horn.

225 Triesenberg Costumes

1980. Costumes. Multicoloured.

751 40r. Type **225** 70 65
752 70r. Dancers, Schellenberg 1·30 1·10
753 80r. Brass band, Mauren 1·50 1·40

226 Beech Trees, Matrula (spring)

1980. The Forest in the Four Seasons. Multicoloured.

754 40r. Type **226** 70 65
755 50r. Firs in the Valorsch (summer) 1·00 90
756 80r. Beech tree, Schaan (autumn) 1·40 1·30
757 1f.50 Edge of forest at Oberplanken (winter) 2·50 2·30

227 Angel bringing Shepherds Good Tidings

1980. Christmas. Multicoloured.

758 20r. Type **227** 40 40
759 50r. Crib 85 75
760 80r. Epiphany 1·70 1·50

228 National Day Procession

1981. Europa. Multicoloured.

761 40r. Fireworks at Vaduz Castle 70 65
762 80r. Type **228** 1·40 1·30

1981. Arms of Bailiffs (2nd series). As T **221**. Multicoloured.

763 40r. Anton Meier, 1748 70 65
764 70r. Kaspar Kindle, 1534 1·30 1·10
765 80r. Hans Adam Negele, 1600 1·50 1·40
766 1f.10 Peter Matt, 1693 2·10 1·90

229 Prince Alois and Princess Elisabeth with Francis Joseph

1981. 75th Birthday of Prince Francis Joseph II. Sheet 120×87 mm containing T **229** and similar vert designs. Multicoloured.

MS767 70r. Type **229**; 80r. Princes Alois and Francis Joseph; 150r. Prince Francis Joseph II 5·50 5·25

230 Scout Emblems

1981. 50th Anniversary of Liechtenstein Boy Scout and Girl Guide Movements.
768 **230** 20r. multicoloured 55 50

231 Symbols of Disability

1981. International Year of Disabled Persons.
769 **231** 40r. multicoloured 70 65

232 *St Theodul* (sculpture)

1981. 1600th Birth Anniversary of St Theodul.
770 **232** 80r. multicoloured 1·40 1·30

233 *Xanthoria parietina*

1981. Mosses and Lichens. Multicoloured.
771 40r. Type **233** 70 65
772 50r. *Parmelia physodes* 85 80
773 70r. *Sphagnum palustre* 1·10 1·00
774 80r. *Amblystegium serpens* 1·50 1·40

234 Gutenberg Castle

1981. Gutenberg Castle. Multicoloured.
775 20r. Type **234** 70 65
776 40r. Courtyard 1·30 1·10
777 50r. Parlour 1·40 1·30
778 1f.10 Great Hall 2·75 2·50

235 Cardinal Karl Borromaus von Mailand

1981. Famous Visitors to Liechtenstein (1st series). Multicoloured.
779 40r. Type **235** 70 65
780 70r. Johann Wolfgang von Goethe (writer) 1·10 1·00
781 89r. Alexander Dumas the younger (writer) 1·40 1·30
782 1f. Hermann Hesse (writer) 1·70 1·50
See also Nos. 804/807 and 832/835.

236 St Nicholas blessing Children

1981. Christmas. Multicoloured.
783 20r. Type **236** 40 40
784 50r. Adoration of the Kings 85 75
785 80r. Holy Family 1·50 1·40

237 Peasant Revolt, 1525

1982. Europa. Multicoloured.
786 40r. Type **237** 70 65
787 80r. King Wenceslaus with Counts (Imperial direct rule, 1396) 1·50 1·40

1982. Arms of Bailiffs (3rd series). As T **221**. Multicoloured.
788 40r. Johann Kaiser, 1664 85 75
789 70r. Joseph Anton Kaufmann, 1748 1·30 1·10
790 80r. Christoph Walser, 1690 1·40 1·30
791 1f.10 Stephan Banzer, 1658 2·10 1·90

238 Triesenberg Sports Ground

1982. World Cup Football Championship, Spain. Multicoloured.
792 15r. Type **238** 30 25
793 25r. Eschen/Mauren playing fields 50 45
794 1f.80 Rheinau playing fields, Balzers 3·00 2·75

239 Crown Prince Hans Adam

1982. Liba 82 Stamp Exhibition. Multicoloured.
795 1f. Type **239** 1·70 1·50
796 1f. Princess Marie Aglae 1·70 1·50

240 Tractor (agriculture)

1982. Rural Industries. Multicoloured.
797 30r. Type **240** 65 55
798 50r. Cutting flowers (horticulture) 85 75
799 70r. Workers with logs (forestry) 1·30 1·10
800 150r. Worker and milk (dairy farming) 2·75 2·50

241 *Neu Schellenberg*

1982. 150th Birth Anniversary of Mortiz Menzinger (artist). Multicoloured.
801 40r. Type **241** 85 75
802 50r. *Vaduz* 1·10 1·00
803 100r. *Bendern* 2·20 2·00

242 *Angelika Kauffmann* (artist, self-portrait)

1982. Famous Visitors to Liechtenstein (2nd series). Multicoloured.
804 40r. Emperor Maximilian I (after Benhard Strigel) 85 75
805 70f. Georg Jenatsch (liberator of Grisons) 1·30 1·10
806 80r. Type **242** 1·70 1·50
807 1f. St. Fidelis of Sigmaringen 2·10 1·90

243 Angel playing Lute

1982. Christmas. Details from High Altar by Jakob Russ, Chur Cathedral. Multicoloured.
808 20r. Type **243** 40 40
809 50r. Madonna and child 85 75
810 80r. Angel playing organ 1·50 1·40

244 Notker Balbulus of St Gall

1983. Europa. Multicoloured.
811 40r. Type **244** 70 65
812 80r. Hildegard of Bingen 1·50 1·40

245 Shrove Thursday

1983. Shrovetide and Lent Customs. Multicoloured.
813 40r. Type **245** 70 65
814 70r. Shrovetide carnival 1·40 1·30
815 1f.80 Lent Sunday bonfire 3·50 3·25

246 River Bank

1983. Anniversaries and Events. Multicoloured.
816 20r. Type **246** 55 50
817 40r. Montgolfier Brothers' balloon 70 65
818 50r. Airmail envelope 85 75
819 80r. Plant and hands holding spade 1·40 1·30
Events: 20r. Council of Europe river and coasts protection campaign; 40r. Bicentenary of manned flight; 50r. World Communications Year; 80r. Overseas aid.

247 *Schaan*

1983. Landscape Paintings by Anton Ender. Multicoloured.
820 40r. Type **247** 85 75
821 50r. *Gutenberg Castle* 1·00 90
822 200r. *Steg Reservoir* 4·00 3·50

248 Princess Gina

1983. Multicoloured.
823 2f.50 Type **248** 4·25 3·75
824 3f. Prince Francis Joseph II 5·50 5·00

249 Pope John Paul II

1983. Holy Year.
825 **249** 80r. multicoloured 1·40 1·30

250 Snowflakes and Stripes

1983. Winter Olympic Games, Sarajevo. Multicoloured.
826 40r. Type **250** 85 75
827 80r. Snowflake 1·40 1·30
828 1f.80 Snowflake and rays 3·25 3·00

251 Seeking Shelter

1983. Christmas. Multicoloured.
829 20r. Type **251** 40 40
830 50r. Infant Jesus 1·00 90
831 80r. Three Kings 1·40 1·30

252 Aleksandr Vassilievich Suvorov (Russian general)

1984. Famous Visitors to Liechtenstein (3rd series). Multicoloured.
832 40r. Type **252** 85 75
833 70r. Karl Rudolf von Buol-Schauenstein, Bishop of Chur 1·40 1·30
834 80r. Carl Zuckmayer (dramatist) 1·50 1·40
835 1f. Curt Goetz (actor) 2·00 1·80

253 Bridge

1984. Europa. 25th Anniversary of EPT Conference.
836 **253** 50r. blue and deep blue 85 75
837 **253** 80r. pink and brown 1·40 1·30

254 The Warning Messenger

1984. Liechtenstein Legends. The Destruction of Trisona. Each brown, grey and blue.
838 35r. Type **254** 70 65
839 50r. The buried town 1·00 90
840 80r. The spared family 1·50 1·40

255 Pole Vaulting

1984. Olympic Games, Los Angeles. Multicoloured.
841 70r. Type **255** 1·30 1·10
842 80r. Throwing the discus 1·40 1·30
843 1f. Putting the shot 1·70 1·50

256 Currency (trade and banking)

1984. Occupations. Multicoloured.
844 5r. Type **256** 20 20
845 10r. Plumber adjusting pipe (building trade) 30 25
846 20r. Operating machinery (industry: production) 40 40
847 35r. Draughtswoman (building trade: planning) 70 65
848 45r. Office worker and world map (industry: sales) 1·00 90
849 50r. Cook (tourism) 1·10 95
850 60r. Carpenter (building trade: interior decoration) 1·30 1·10
851 70r. Doctor injecting patient (medical services) 1·40 1·30
852 80r. Scientist (industrial research) 1·50 1·40
853 100r. Bricklayer (building trade) 1·70 1·50
854 120r. Flow chart (industry: administration) 2·10 1·90
855 150r. Handstamping covers (post and communications) 2·75 2·50

257 Princess Marie

1984. Multicoloured.

856	1f.70 Type **257**	2·75	1·90
857	2f. Crown Prince Hans Adam	3·50	2·50

258 Annunciation

1984. Christmas. Multicoloured.

858	35r. Type **258**	55	50
859	50r. Holy Family	1·00	90
860	80r. The Three Kings	1·50	1·50

259 Apollo and the Muses playing Music (detail from 18th-century harpsichord lid)

1985. Europa. Music Year. Multicoloured.

861	50r. Type **259**	1·00	90
862	80r. Apollo and the Muses playing music (different)	1·40	1·30

260 St Elisabeth Convent, Schaan

1985. Monasteries. Multicoloured.

863	50r. Type **260**	85	75
864	1f. Schellenberg Convent	1·70	1·50
865	1f.70 Gutenberg Mission, Balzers	3·00	2·75

261 Princess Gina and handing out of Rations

1985. 40th Anniversary of Liechtenstein Red Cross. Multicoloured.

866	20r. Type **261**	55	50
867	50r. Princess Gina and Red Cross ambulance	1·30	1·10
868	120r. Princess Gina with refugee children	2·50	2·30

262 Justice

1985. Cardinal Virtues. Multicoloured.

869	35r. Type **262**	70	65
870	50r. Temperance	85	75
871	70r. Prudence	1·10	1·00
872	1f. Fortitude	1·80	1·60

263 Papal Arms

1985. Papal Visit. Sheet 100×67 mm containing T **263** and similar vert designs. Multicoloured.

MS873	50r. Type **263**; 80r. St Maria zum Trost Chapel; 170r. *Our Lady of Liechtenstein* (statue) (29×43 mm)	5·50	5·25

264 *Portrait of a Canon* (Quentin Massys)

1985. Paintings in Metropolitan Museum, New York. Multicoloured.

874	50r. Type **264**	1·30	1·10
875	1f. *Clara Serena Rubens* (Rubens)	2·20	2·00
876	1f.20 *Duke of Urbino* (Raphael)	2·50	2·30

265 Halberd used by Charles I's Bodyguard

1985. Guards' Weapons and Armour. Multicoloured.

877	35r. Type **265**	70	65
878	50r. Morion used by Charles I's bodyguard	1·00	90
879	80r. Halberd used by Carl Eusebius's bodyguard	1·40	1·30

266 Frankincense

1985. Christmas. Multicoloured.

880	35r. Type **266**	70	65
881	50r. Gold	1·00	90
882	80r. Myrrh	1·40	1·30

267 Puppets performing Tragedy

1985. Theatre. Multicoloured.

883	50r. Type **267**	1·10	1·00
884	80r. Puppets performing comedy	1·70	1·50
885	1f.50 Opera	2·75	2·50

268 Courtyard

1986. Vaduz Castle. Multicoloured.

886	20r. Type **268**	40	40
887	25r. Keep	50	45
888	50r. Castle	85	75
889	90r. Inner gate	1·70	1·50
890	1f.10 Castle from gardens	1·80	1·60
891	1f.40 Courtyard (different)	2·50	2·30

269 Barn Swallows

1986. Europa. Birds. Multicoloured.

892	50r. Type **269**	1·00	90
893	90r. European robin	1·80	1·60

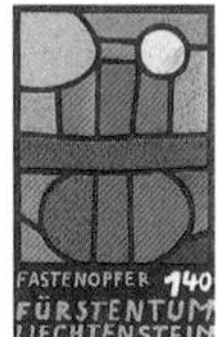

270 Offerings

1986. Lenten Fast.

894	**270** 1f.40 multicoloured	2·75	2·50

271 Palm Sunday

1986. Religious Festivals. Multicoloured.

895	35r. Type **271**	70	65
896	50r. Wedding	85	75
897	70r. Rogation Day procession	1·40	1·30

272 Karl Freiherr Haus von Hausen

1986. 125th Anniversary of Liechtenstein Land Bank.

898	**272** 50r. brown, ochre and buff	1·00	90

273 Francis Joseph II

1986. 80th Birthday of Prince Francis Joseph II.

899	**273** 3f.50 multicoloured	6·25	5·25

274 Roebuck in Ruggeller Riet

1986. Hunting. Multicoloured.

900	35r. Type **274**	70	65
901	50r. Chamois at Rappenstein	1·10	1·00
902	1f.70 Stag in Lawena	3·25	3·00

275 Cabbage and Beetroot

1986. Field Crops. Multicoloured.

903	50r. Type **275**	1·00	90
904	80r. Red cabbages	1·50	1·40
905	90r. Potatoes, onions and garlic	1·70	1·50

276 Archangel Michael

1986. Christmas. Multicoloured.

906	35r. Type **276**	70	65
907	50r. Archangel Gabriel	1·10	1·00
908	90r. Archangel Raphael	1·80	1·60

277 Silver Fir

1986. Tree Bark. Multicoloured.

909	35r. Type **277**	55	50
910	90r. Norway spruce	2·00	1·80
911	1f.40 Pedunculate oak	3·00	2·75

278 Gamprin Primary School

1987. Europa. Multicoloured.

912	50r. Type **278**	1·00	90
913	90r. Schellenberg parish church	1·80	1·60

280 Niklaus von Flue

1987. 500th Death Anniversary of Niklaus von Flue (martyr).

914	**280** 1f.10 multicoloured	2·10	1·90

281 Bullhead

1987. Fish (1st series). Multicoloured.

915	50r. Type **281**	1·10	1·00
916	90r. Brown trout	1·80	1·60
917	1f.10 European grayling	2·75	2·50

See also Nos. 959/961.

282 Prince Alois (frame as in first stamps)

1987. 75th Anniversary of First Liechtenstein Stamps.

918	**282** 2f. multicoloured	4·25	3·75

283 Staircase

1987. Liechtenstein City Palace, Vienna. Multicoloured.

919	35r. Type **283**	70	65
920	50r. Minoritenplatz doorway	1·00	90
921	90r. Staircase (different)	1·80	1·60

284 Arms

1987. 275th Anniversary of Transfer of County of Vaduz to House of Liechtenstein.

922	**284** 1f.40 multicoloured	2·75	2·50

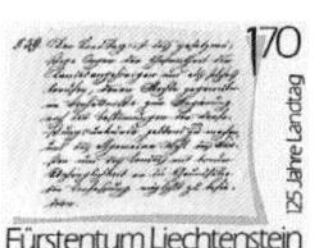

285 Constitution Charter, 1862

1987. 125th Anniversary of Liechtenstein Parliament.
923 **285** 1f.70 multicoloured 3·50 3·25

286 St Matthew

1987. Christmas. Illuminations from *Golden Book of Pfafers Abbey*. Multicoloured.
924 35r. Type **286** 85 75
925 50r. St Mark 1·10 1·00
926 60r. St Luke 1·30 1·10
927 90r. St John 2·00 1·80

287 The Toil of the Cross-country Skier

1987. Winter Olympic Games, Calgary (1988). Multicoloured.
928 25r. Type **287** 55 50
929 90r. The Courageous Pioneers of Skiing 2·00 1·80
930 1f.10 As our Grandfathers used to ride on a Bobsled 2·50 2·30

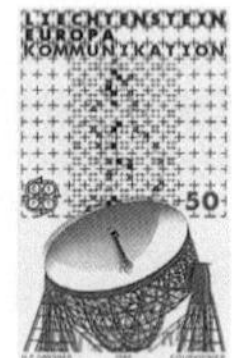

288 Dish Aerial

1988. Europa. Transport and Communications. Multicoloured
931 50r. Type **288** 1·00 90
932 90r. Maglev monorail 1·80 1·60

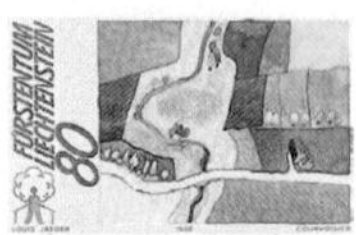

289 Agriculture

1988. European Campaign for Rural Areas. Multicoloured.
933 80r. Type **289** 1·80 1·60
934 90r. Village centre 2·10 1·90
935 1f.70 Road 2·75 2·50

290 Headphones on Books (Radio Broadcasts)

1988. Costa Rica–Liechtenstein Cultural Co-operation.
936 **290** 50r. multicoloured 1·40 1·30
937 - 1f.40 red, brown and green 4·25 3·75
Design: 1f.40, Man with pen and radio (Adult education).

291 Crown Prince Hans Adam

1988. 50th Anniversary of Accesion of Prince Francis Joseph II. Sheet 100×68 mm containing T **291** and similar vert designs. Multicoloured.
MS938 50r. Type **291**; 50r. Prince Alois; 2f. Prince Francis Joseph II 8·50 8·25

292 St Barbara's Shrine, Balzers

1988. Wayside Shrines. Multicoloured.
939 25r. Type **292** 55 50
940 35r. Shrine containing statues of Christ, St Peter and St Paul at Oberdorf, Vaduz 85 75
941 50r. St Anthony of Egypt's shrine, Fallagass, Ruggel 1·40 1·30

293 Cycling

1988. Olympic Games, Seoul. Multicoloured.
942 50r. Type **293** 1·10 1·00
943 80r. Gymnastics 2·00 1·80
944 90r. Running 2·20 2·00
945 1f.40 Equestrian event 4·00 3·50

294 Joseph and Mary

1988. Christmas. Multicoloured.
946 35r. Type **294** 70 65
947 50r. Baby Jesus 1·00 90
948 90r. Wise Men presenting gifts to Jesus 1·70 1·50

295 Letter beside Footstool (detail)

1988. *The Letter* (portrait of Marie-Theresa, Princesse de Lamballe by Anton Hickel). Multicoloured.
949 50r. Type **295** 1·30 1·10
950 90r. Desk and writing materials (detail) 2·20 2·00
951 2f. *The Letter* (complete painting) 4·25 3·75

296 Cat and Mouse

1989. Europa. Children's Games. Multicoloured.
952 50r. Type **296** 1·30 1·10
953 90r. Hide and Seek 2·10 1·90

298 Rheinberger and Score

1989. 150th Birth Anniversary of Josef Gabriel Rheinberger (composer).
954 **298** 2f.90 black, blue & purple 5·50 5·00

299 Little Ringed Plover

1989. Endangered Animals. Multicoloured.
955 25r. Type **299** 55 50
956 35r. Green tree frog 85 75
957 50r. *Libelloides coccajus* (lace-wing) 1·40 1·30
958 90r. Polecat 2·75 2·50

300 Northern Pike

1989. Fish (2nd series). Multicoloured.
959 50r. Type **300** 85 75
960 1f.10 Brown trout 2·20 2·00
961 1f.40 Stone loach 3·25 3·00

301 Return of Cattle from Alpine Pastures

1989. Autumn Customs. Multicoloured.
962 35r. Type **301** 70 65
963 50r. Peeling corn cobs 1·00 90
964 80r. Cattle market 1·80 1·60

302 Falknis

1989. Mountains. Watercolours by Josef Schadler.
965 - 5r. multicoloured 15 15
966 - 10r. multicoloured 20 20
967 - 35r. multicoloured 70 65
968 - 40r. multicoloured 85 75
969 - 45r. multicoloured 90 80
970 **302** 50r. multicoloured 1·00 90
971 - 60r. multicoloured 1·10 1·00
972 - 70r. multicoloured 1·30 1·10
973 - 75r. multicoloured 1·40 1·30
974 - 80r. violet, brown & black 1·50 1·40
975 - 1f. multicoloured 2·00 1·80
976 - 1f.20 multicoloured 2·20 2·00
977 - 1f.50 multicoloured 2·75 2·50
978 - 1f.60 multicoloured 3·75 3·25
979 - 2f. multicoloured 4·25 3·75
Designs: 5r. Augstenberg; 10r. Hahenespiel; 35r. Nospitz; 40r. Ochsenkopf; 45r. Three Sisters; 60r. Kuhgrat; 70r. Galinakopf; 75r. Plassteikopf; 80pf. Naafkopf; 1f. Schonberg; 1f.20, Bleikaturm; 1f.50, Garselliturm; 1f.60, Schwarzhorn; 2f. Scheienkopf.

303 *Melchior and Balthasar*

1989. Christmas. Details of triptych by Hugo van der Goes. Multicoloured.
981 35r. Type **303** 70 65
982 50r. *Kaspar and Holy Family* (27×34 mm) 1·00 90
983 90r. *St Stephen* 1·80 1·60

304 Mace Quartz

1989. Minerals. Multicoloured.
984 50r. Type **304** 1·10 1·00
985 1f.10 Globe pyrite 2·20 2·00
986 1f.50 Calcite 3·00 2·75

305 Nendeln Forwarding Agency, 1864

1990. Europa. Post Office Buildings. Multicoloured
987 50r. Type **305** 1·00 90
988 90r. Vaduz post office, 1976 1·80 1·60

306 Penny Black

1990. 150th Anniversary of the Penny Black.
989 **306** 1f.50 multicoloured 3·50 3·25

307 Footballers

1990. World Cup Football Championship, Italy.
990 **307** 2f. multicoloured 4·50 4·00

308 *Tureen, Oranges and Grapes*

1990. Ninth Death Anniversary of Benjamin Steck (painter). Multicoloured.
991 50r. Type **308** 1·30 1·10
992 80r. *Apples and pewter bowl* 1·80 1·60
993 1f.50 *Basket, apples, cherries and pewter jug* 3·50 3·25

309 Princess Gina

1990. Prince Francis Joseph II and Princess Gina Commemoration. Multicoloured.
994 2f. Type **309** 3·50 3·25
995 3f. Prince Francis Joseph II 5·50 5·00

310 Common Pheasant

1990. Game Birds. Multicoloured.
996 25r. Type **310** 70 65
997 50r. Black grouse 1·10 1·00
998 2f. Mallard 4·50 4·00

311 Annunciation

1990. Christmas. Paintings. Multicoloured.
999 35r. Type **311** 85 75
1000 50r. Nativity 1·00 90
1001 90r. Adoration of the Magi 1·70 1·50

312 St Nicholas

1990. Winter Customs. Multicoloured.

1002	35r. Type **312**	70	65
1003	50r. Awakening on New Year's Eve	1·00	90
1004	1f.50 Giving New Year greetings	3·25	3·00

313 Mounted Courier

1990. 500th Anniversary of Regular European Postal Services.

1005	**313**	90r. multicoloured	2·10	1·90

314 *Olympus 1* Satellite

1991. Europa. Europe in Space. Multicoloured.

1006	50r. Type **314**	1·00	90
1007	90r. *Meteosat* satellite	1·80	1·60

315 St Ignatius de Loyola (founder of Society of Jesus)

1991. Anniversaries. Multicoloured.

1008	80r. Type **315** (500th birth anniversary)	1·40	1·30
1009	90r. Wolfgang Amadeus Mozart (composer, death bicentenary)	1·70	1·50

316 UN Emblem and Dove

1991. Admission to UN Membership (1990).

1010	**316**	2f.50 multicoloured	5·00	4·50

317 Non-Commissioned Officer and Private

1991. 125th Anniversary of Last Mobilisation of Liechtenstein's Military Contingent (to the Tyrol). Multicoloured.

1011	50r. Type **317**	1·00	90
1012	70r. Tunic, chest and portrait	1·40	1·30
1013	1f. Officer and private	1·80	1·60

318 *Near Maloja* (Giovanni Giacometti)

1991. 700th Anniversary of Swiss Confederation. Paintings by Swiss artists. Multicoloured.

1014	50r. Type **318**	1·00	90
1015	80r. *Rhine Valley* (Ferdinand Gehr)	1·40	1·30
1016	90r. *Bergell* (Augusto Giacometti)	1·80	1·60
1017	1f.10 *Hoher Kasten* (Hedwig Scherrer)	2·20	2·00

319 Stampless and Modern Covers

1991. Liba 92 National Stamp Exhibition, Vaduz.

1018	**319**	90r. multicoloured	1·80	1·60

320 Princess Marie

1991. Multicoloured

1019	3f. Type **320**	5·00	4·50
1020	3f.40 Prince Hans Adam II	6·00	5·25

321 Virgin of the Annunciation (exterior of left wing)

1991. Christmas. Details of the altar from St Mamertus Chapel, Triesen. Multicoloured.

1021	50r. Type **321**	1·00	90
1022	80r. Madonna and Child (wood-carving attr. Jorg Syrlin, inner shrine)	1·40	1·30
1023	90r. Angel Gabriel (exterior of right wing)	1·80	1·60

322 Cross-country Skiers and Testing for Drug Abuse

1991. Winter Olympic Games, Albertville. Multicoloured

1024	70r. Type **322**	1·70	1·50
1025	80r. Ice hockey player tackling opponent and helping him after fall	1·80	1·60
1026	1f.60 Downhill skier and fallen skier caught in safety net	2·75	2·50

323 Relay Race, Drugs and Shattered Medal

1992. Olympic Games, Barcelona. Multicoloured.

1027	50r. Type **323**	1·00	90
1028	70r. Cycling road race	1·80	1·60
1029	2f.50 Judo	5·50	5·00

324 Aztecs

1992. Europa. 500th Anniversary of Discovery of America by Columbus. Multicoloured.

1030	80r. Type **324**	1·70	1·50
1031	90r. Statue of Liberty and New York skyline	1·80	1·60

325 Clown in Envelope ('Good Luck')

1992. Greetings Stamps. Multicoloured.

1032	50r. Type **325**	1·00	90
1033	50r. Wedding rings in envelope and harlequin violinist	1·00	90
1034	50r. Postman blowing horn (31×21 mm)	1·00	90
1035	50r. Flying postman carrying letter sealed with heart (31×21 mm)	1·00	90

326 Arms of Liechtenstein–Kinsky Alliance

1992. Liba '92 National Stamp Exhibition. Silver Wedding Anniversary of Prince Hans Adam and Princess Marie. Sheet 100×67 mm containing T **326** and similar vert design. Multicoloured.

MS1036 2f. Type **326**; 2f.50 Royal couple (photo by Anthony Buckley)	9·75	9·50

327 *Blechnum spicant*

1992. Ferns. Multicoloured.

1037	40r. Type **327**	85	75
1038	50r. Maidenhair spleenwort	1·00	90
1039	70r. Hart's-tongue	1·40	1·30
1040	2f.50 *Asplenium ruta-muraria*	5·25	4·75

328 Reading Edict

1992. 650th Anniversary of County of Vaduz.

1041	**328**	1f.60 multicoloured	4·00	3·50

329 Chapel of St Mamertus, Triesen

1992. Christmas. Multicoloured.

1042	50r. Type **329**	85	75
1043	90r. Crib, St Gallus's Church, Triesen	1·70	1·50
1044	1f.60 St Mary's Chapel, Triesen	3·00	2·75

330 Crown Prince Alois

1992

1045	**330**	2f.50 multicoloured	5·25	4·75

331 *Nafkopf and Huts, Steg*

1993. 1400th Birth Anniversary of Hans Gantner (painter). Multicoloured.

1046	50r. Type **331**	1·00	90
1047	60r. *Hunting Lodge, Sass*	1·10	1·00
1048	1f.80 *Red House, Vaduz*	3·50	3·25

332 *910805* (Bruno Kaufmann)

1993. Europa. Contemporary Art. Multicoloured.

1049	80r. Type **332**	2·00	1·80
1050	1f. *The Little Blue* (Evi Kliemand)	2·20	2·00

333 *Tale of the Ferryman* (painting)

1993. Tibetan Collection in the National Museum. Multicoloured.

1051	60r. Type **333**	1·10	1·00
1052	80r. Religious dance mask	1·70	1·50
1053	1f. *Tale of the Fish* (painting)	2·10	1·90

334 *Tree of Life*

1993. Missionary Work.

1054	**334**	1f.80 multicoloured	3·75	3·25

335 *The Black Hatter*

1993. Homage to Liechtenstein.

1055	**335**	2f.80 multicoloured	6·00	5·25

336 Crown Prince Alois and Duchess Sophie of Bavaria

1993. Royal Wedding. Sheet 100×67 mm.

MS1056 **336** 4f. multicoloured	10·00	9·50

337 Origanum

1993. Flowers. Illustrations from *Hortus Botanicus Liechtensteinsis*. Multicoloured.

1057	50r. Type **337**	1·30	1·10
1058	60r. Meadow sage	1·40	1·30
1059	1f. *Seseli annuum*	2·10	1·90
1060	2f.50 Large self-heal	5·00	4·50

338 Eurasian Badger

1993. Animals. Multicoloured.

1061	60r. Type **338**	1·30	1·10
1062	80r. Beech marten	1·80	1·60

1063	1f. Red fox	2·50	2·30

339 *Now that the Quiet Days are Coming ...* (Rainer Maria Rilke)

1993. Christmas. Multicoloured.

1064	60r. Type **339**	1·10	1·00
1065	80r. *Can You See the Light ...* (Th. Friedrich)	1·70	1·50
1066	1f. *Christmas, Christmas ...* (R. A. Schroder)	2·10	1·90

340 Ski Jump

1993. Winter Olympic Games, Lillehammer, Norway (1994). Multicoloured.

1067	60r. Type **340**	1·10	1·00
1068	80r. Slalom	1·70	1·50
1069	2f.40 Bobsleighing	5·25	4·75

341 Seal and Title Page

1994. Anniversaries. Multicoloured.

1070	60r. Type **341** (275th anniversary of Principality)	1·30	1·10
1071	1f.80 State, Prince's and Olympic flags (centenary of International Olympic Committee)	3·50	3·25

342 Andean Condor

1994. Europa. Discoveries of Alexander von Humboldt. Multicoloured.

1072	80r. Type **342**	1·80	1·60
1073	1f. *Rhexia cardinalis* (plant)	2·40	2·10

343 Football Pitch and Hopi Indians playing Kickball

1994. World Cup Football Championship, USA.

1074	**343**	2f.80 multicoloured	5·25	4·75

344 Elephant with Letter

1994. Greetings Stamps. Multicoloured.

1075	60r. Type **344**	1·40	1·30
1076	60r. Cherub with flower and hearts	1·40	1·30
1077	60r. Pig with four-leaf clover	1·40	1·30
1078	60r. Dog holding bunch of tulips	1·40	1·30

345 *Eulogy of Madness* (mobile, Jean Tinguely)

1994. Homage to Liechtenstein.

1079	**345**	4f. black, pink and violet	9·00	8·75

346 Spring

1994. Seasons of the Vine. Multicoloured.

1080	60r. Type **346**	1·40	1·30
1081	60r. Vine leaves (Summer)	1·40	1·30
1082	60r. Trunk in snowy landscape (Winter)	1·40	1·30
1083	60r. Grapes (Autumn)	1·40	1·30

Nos. 1080/1083 were issued together, *se-tenant*, forming a composite design.

347 Strontium

1994. Minerals. Multicoloured.

1084	60r. Type **347**	1·40	1·30
1085	80r. Quartz	2·10	1·90
1086	3f.50 Iron dolomite	7·00	6·25

348 *The True Light*

1994. Christmas. Multicoloured.

1087	60r. Type **348**	1·30	1·10
1088	80r. *Peace on Earth*	1·80	1·60
1089	1f. *Behold, the House of God*	2·50	2·30

349 Earth

1994. The Four Elements. Multicoloured.

1090	60r. Type **349**	1·30	1·10
1091	80r. Water	1·80	1·60
1092	1f. Fire	2·20	2·00
1093	2f.50 Air	5·25	4·75

350 'The Theme of all our Affairs must be Peace'

1995. Europa. Peace and Freedom. Quotations of Franz Josef II. Multicoloured.

1094	80r. Type **350**	1·80	1·60
1095	1f. 'Through Unity comes Strength and the Bearing of Sorrows'	2·40	2·10

351 UN Flag and Bouquet of Flowers

1995. Anniversaries and Event. Multicoloured.

1096	60r. Princess Marie with children (50th anniversary of Liechtenstein Red Cross) (horiz)	1·40	1·30
1097	1f.80 Type **351** (50th anniversary of UNO)	3·00	2·75
1098	3f.50 Alps (European Nature Conservation Year)	7·75	7·00

352 *Falknis Mountains*

1995. Birth Centenary of Anton Frommelt (painter). Multicoloured.

1099	60r. Type **352**	1·80	1·60
1100	80r. *Three Oaks*	2·50	2·30
1101	4f.10 *The Rhine*	8·50	7·50

353 'One Heart and One Soul'

1995. Greetings Stamps. Multicoloured.

1102	60r. Type **353**	1·30	1·10
1103	60r. Bandage round sunflower ('Get Well')	1·30	1·10
1104	60r. Baby arriving over rainbow ('Hurrah! Here I am')	1·30	1·10
1105	60r. Delivering letter by hot-air balloon ('Write again')	1·30	1·10

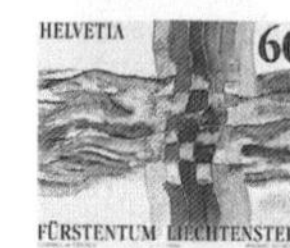

354 Coloured Ribbons woven through River

1995. Liechtenstein–Switzerland Co-operation.

1106	**354**	60r. multicoloured	1·80	1·60

No. 1106 was valid for use in both Liechtenstein and Switzerland (see No. 1308 of Switzerland).

355 Arnica

1995. Medicinal Plants. Multicoloured.

1107	60r. Type **355**	1·80	1·60
1108	80r. Giant nettle	2·20	2·00
1109	1f.80 Common valerian	4·25	3·75
1110	3f.50 Fig-wort	7·75	7·00

356 Angel (detail of painting)

1995. Christmas. Painting by Lorenzo Monaco. Multicoloured.

1111	60r. Type **356**	1·10	1·00
1112	80r. *Virgin Mary with Infant and Two Angels*	1·70	1·50
1113	1f. Angel facing left (detail of painting)	2·10	1·90

357 *Lady with Lap-dog* (Paul Wunderlich)

1995. Homage to Liechtenstein.

1114	**357**	4f. multicoloured	9·00	8·25

358 Eschen

1996. Scenes. Multicoloured.

1115	10r. Type **358**	30	25
1116	20r. Planken	50	45
1117	50r. Ruggell	1·30	1·10
1117a	60r. Balzers	1·40	1·30
1117b	70r. Schellenberg	1·50	1·40
1118	80r. Ruggell	1·70	1·50
1119	1f. Nendeln	2·10	1·90
1120	1f.10 Eschen	2·40	2·10
1121	1f.20 Triesen	2·50	2·30
1122	1f.30 Triesen	2·75	2·50
1123	1f.40 Mauren	3·00	3·25
1124	1f.70 Schaanwald	3·50	3·25
1125	1f.80 Malbun	3·75	3·50
1125a	1f.90 Schaan	4·00	3·75
1126	2f. Gamprin	4·25	3·75
1126a	2f.20 Balzers	4·50	4·00
1127	4f. Triesenberg	8·50	7·50
1128	4f.50 Bendern	9·75	8·75
1129	5f. Vaduz Castle	10·50	9·50

359 Crucible

1996. Bronze Age in Europe.

1130	**359**	90r. multicoloured	2·40	2·10

360 Kinsky and Diary Extract, 7 March 1917

1996. Europa. Famous Women. Nora, Countess Kinsky (mother of Princess Gina of Liechtenstein).

1131	**360**	90r. grey, purple and blue	2·40	2·10
1132	-	1f.10 grey, blue and purple	2·50	2·30

Design: 1f.10, Kinsky and diary extract for 28 February 1917.

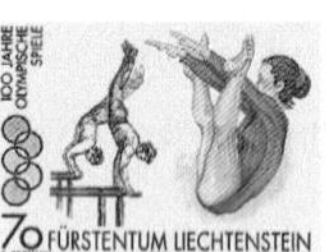

361 Gymnastics

1996. Centenary of Modern Olympic Games. Multicoloured.

1133	70r. Type **361**	1·80	1·60
1134	90r. Hurdling	2·20	2·00
1135	1f.10 Cycling	2·50	2·30

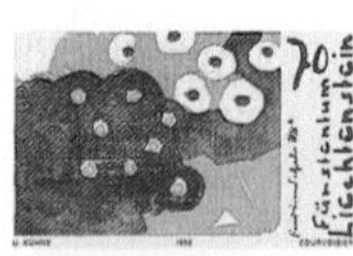

362 *Primroses*

1996. Birth Centenary of Ferdinand Gehr (painter). Multicoloured.

1136	70r. Type **362**	2·10	1·90
1137	90r. *Daisies*	2·40	2·10
1138	1f.10 *Poppy*	2·75	2·40
1139	1f.80 *Buttercups* (33×23 mm)	4·25	3·75

363 State Arms

1996

1140	**363**	10f. multicoloured	21·00	19·00

364 Veldkirch, 1550

1996. Millenary of Austria.

1141	**364**	90r. multicoloured	2·00	1·80

365 *Poltava*

1996. 43rd Death Anniversary of Eugen Zotow (painter). Multicoloured.

1142	70r. Type **365**	1·80	1·60
1143	1f.10 *Three Bathers in a Berlin Park*	2·75	2·50
1144	1f.40 *Vaduz*	3·50	3·25

366 St Matthew

1996. Christmas. Illustrations from Illuminated Manuscript *Liber Viventium Fabariensis*. Multicoloured.

1145	70r. Type **366**	1·80	1·60
1146	90r. Emblems of St Mark	2·00	1·80
1147	1f.10 Emblems of St Luke	2·20	2·00
1148	1f.80 Emblems of St John	4·50	4·25

367 Schubert

1997. Birth Bicentenary of Franz Schubert (composer).

1149	**367**	70r. multicoloured	2·00	1·80

368 The Wild Gnomes

1997. Europa. Tales and Legends. Multicoloured.

1150	90r. Type **368**	2·20	2·00
1151	1f.10 Man, pumpkin and rabbit (The Foal of Planken)	2·75	2·40

369 *Madonna and Child with St Lucius and St Florinus* (Gabriel Dreher)

1997. National Patron Saints.

1152	**369**	20f. multicoloured	55·00	50·00

370 *Phaeolepiota aurea*

1997. Fungi (1st series). Multicoloured.

1153	70r. Type **370**	1·80	1·60
1154	90r. *Helvella silvicola*	2·10	1·90
1155	1f.10 Orange peel fungus	2·75	2·50

See also Nos. 1238/1240.

371 Steam Train, Schaanwald Halt

1997. 125th Anniversary of Liechtenstein Railways. Multicoloured.

1156	70r. Type **371**	1·70	1·50
1157	90r. Diesel-electric train, Nendeln station	2·50	2·30
1158	1f.80 Electric train, Schaan-Vaduz station	4·50	4·00

372 *Girl with Flower* (Enrico Baj)

1997. Homage to Liechtenstein.

1159	**372**	70r. multicoloured	1·80	1·60

373 Basket of Roses

1997. Christmas. Glass Tree Decorations. Multicoloured.

1160	70r. Type **373**	1·80	1·60
1161	90r. Bell	2·10	1·90
1162	1f.10 Bauble	2·75	2·50

374 Cross-country skiing

1997. Winter Olympic Games, Nagano, Japan (1998). Skiing. Multicoloured.

1163	70r. Type **374**	1·80	1·60
1164	90r. Slalom	2·40	2·10
1165	1f.80 Downhill	4·25	3·75

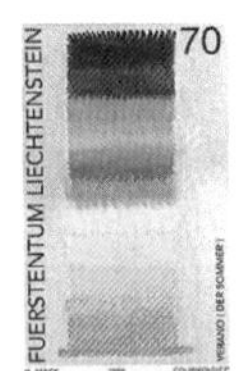

375 *Verano* (The Summer)

1998. Homage to Liechtenstein. Paintings by Heinz Mack. Multicoloured.

1166	70r. Type **375**	1·80	1·60
1167	70r. *Homage to Liechtenstein*	1·80	1·60
1168	70r. *Between Day and Dream*	1·80	1·60
1169	70r. *Salute Cirico!*	1·80	1·60

376 Prince's Festival Procession, Vaduz

1998. Europa. National Festivals. Multicoloured.

1170	90r. Type **376**	2·50	2·30
1171	1f.10 Music Societies Festival, Gutenberg Castle, Balzers	2·75	2·50

377 National Flags on Bridge

1998. 75th Anniversary of Liechtenstein–Switzerland Customs Treaty.

1172	**377**	1f.70 multicoloured	4·00	3·50

378 Goalkeeper

1998. World Cup Football Championship, France.

1173	**378**	1f.80 multicoloured	4·25	3·75

379 Clown with Queen of Hearts

1998. Greeting Stamps. Clowns. Multicoloured.

1174	70r. Type **379**	1·80	1·60
1175	70r. Clown holding four-leaf clovers	1·80	1·60
1176	70r. Clown raising hat	1·80	1·60
1177	70r. Clown holding heart	1·80	1·60

380 Wooden Milk Vat

1998. Traditional Crafts (1st series). Multicoloured.

1178	90r. Type **380**	1·80	1·60
1179	2f.20 Clog	5·00	4·50
1180	3f.50 Wheel	7·75	7·00

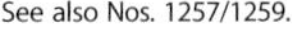
See also Nos. 1257/1259.

381 Expelling Johann Langer from Liechtenstein

1998. 150th Anniversary of 1848 Revolutions in Europe.

1181	**381**	1f.80 multicoloured	5·25	4·75

382 Virgin Mary

1998. Christmas. Multicoloured.

1182	70r. Type **382**	2·00	1·80
1183	90r. *The Nativity* (35×26 mm)	2·30	2·00
1184	1f.10 Joseph	2·75	2·40

Nos. 1182 and 1184 show details of the complete relief depicted on No. 1183.

383 Zum Lowen Guest House

1998. Preservation of Historical Environment (1st series). Hinterschellenberg. Multicoloured.

1185	90r. Type **383**	2·40	2·20
1186	1f.70 St George's Chapel (vert)	4·00	3·50
1187	1f.80 Houses	4·25	3·75

See also Nos. 1250/1252, 1274/1275, 1292/1293, 1358/1359, 1386/1387, 1428/1429, 1462/1463 and 1498.

384 Automatic and Manual Switchboards

1998. Centenary of Telephone in Liechtenstein.

1188	**384**	2f.80 multicoloured	6·75	6·00

385 Eschen

1999. 300th Anniversary of Purchase of Unterland by Prince Johann Adam. Sheet 107×68 mm containing T **385** and similar horiz design. Multicoloured.

MS1189	90r.×5 plus label, Composite design of the Unterland showing the villages of Eschen, Gamprin, Mauren, Ruggell and Schellenberg	13·50	13·00

386 Smooth Snake and Schwabbrunnen-Aescher Nature Park

1999. Europa. Parks and Gardens. Multicoloured.

1190	90r. Type **386**	2·75	2·40
1191	1f.10 Corn crake and Ruggell marsh	3·25	3·00

387 Council Anniversary Emblem and Silhouettes

1999. Anniversaries and Event. Multicoloured.

1192	70r. Type **387** (50th anniversary of Council of Europe and European Convention on Human Rights)	1·80	1·60
1193	70r. Bird with envelope in beak (125th anniversary of UPU)	1·80	1·60
1194	70r. Heart in hand (75th anniversary of Caritas Liechtenstein (welfare organisation))	1·80	1·60

388 Judo

1999. Eighth European Small States Games, Liechtenstein. Multicoloured.

1195	70r. Type **388**	2·00	1·80
1196	70r. Swimming	2·00	1·80
1197	70r. Throwing the javelin	2·00	1·80
1198	90r. Cycling	2·30	2·00
1199	90r. Shooting	2·30	2·00
1200	90r. Tennis	2·30	2·00
1201	90r. Squash	2·30	2·00
1202	90r. Table tennis	2·30	2·00
1203	90r. Volleyball	2·30	2·00

389 *Herrengasse*

1999. Paintings by Eugen Verling. Multicoloured.

1204	70r. Type **389**	2·00	1·80
1205	2f. *Old Vaduz with Castle*	5·00	4·50
1206	4f. *House in Furst-Franz-Josef Street, Vaduz*	9·75	8·75

390 Scene from *Faust*, Act I

1999. 250th Birth Anniversary of Johann Wolfgang Goethe (poet and playwright). Multicoloured.

1207	1f.40 Type **390**	3·75	3·50
1208	1f.70 Faust and the Devil sealing wager	5·25	4·75

391 *The Annunciation*

1999. Christmas. Paintings by Joseph Walser from Chapel of Our Lady of Comfort, Dux. Multicoloured.

1209	70r. Type **391**	2·00	1·80
1210	90r. *Nativity*	2·50	2·30
1211	1f.10 *Adoration*	3·00	2·75

392 Identification Mark on Door, Ubersaxen

1999. Walser Identification Marks. Multicoloured.

1212		70r. Type **392**	2·00	1·80
1213		90r. Mark on mural	2·50	2·30
1214		1f.80 Mark on axe	4·25	3·75

393 Gutenberg

1999. 600th Birth Anniversary of Johannes Gutenberg (inventor of printing press).

1215	**393**	3f.60 multicoloured	10·50	9·50

394 *The Adoration of the Shepheards* (Matthia Stomer)

2000. 2000 Years of Christianity. Sheet 108×68 mm containing T **394** and similar square design. Multicoloured.

MS1216		70r. Type **394**; 1f.10 *Three Kings* (Ferdinand Gehr)	6·75	6·50

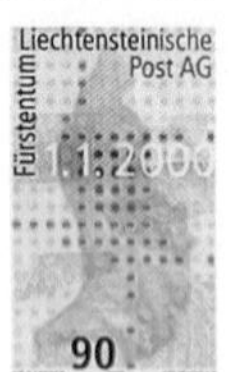

395 Emblem

2000. Provision of Postal Services by Liechtenstein Post in Partnership with Swiss Post.

1217	**395**	90r. multicoloured	2·75	2·40

396 *Mars and Rhea Silvia* (Peter Paul Rubens)

2000. Paintings. Multicoloured.

1218		70r. Type **396**	2·00	1·80
1219		1f.80 *Cupid with Soap-Bubble* (Rembrandt)	4·25	3·75

397 *Fragrance of Humus*

2000. EXPO 2000 World's Fair, Hanover, Germany. Paintings by Friedensreich Hundertwasser. Multicoloured.

1220		70r. Type **397**	2·30	2·00
1221		90r. *Do Not Wait Houses-Move*	3·00	2·75
1222		1f.10 *The Car: a Drive Towards Nature and Creation*	3·75	3·50

398 Building Europe

2000. Europa.

1223	**398**	1f.10 multicoloured	3·75	3·50

399 *Dove of Peace* (Antonio Martini)

2000. Peace 2000. Paintings by members of Association of Mouth and Foot Painting Artists. Multicoloured

1224		1f.40 Type **399**	3·75	3·50
1225		1f.70 *World Peace* (Alberto Alvarez)	4·25	3·75
1226		2f.20 *Rainbow* (Eiichi Minami)	5·50	4·75

400 Koalas on Rings (Gymnastics)

2000. Olympic Games, Sydney. Multicoloured.

1227		80r. Type **400**	2·10	1·90
1228		1f. Joey leaping over crossbar (High jump)	2·40	2·20
1229		1f.30 Emus approaching finish line (Athletics)	2·75	2·40
1230		1f.80 Duckbill platypuses in swimming race	4·75	4·25

401 *The Dreaming Bee* (Joan Miro)

2000. Inauguration of Art Museum. Multicoloured.

1231		80r. Type **401**	2·40	2·20
1232		1f.20 *Cube* (Sol LeWitt)	3·50	3·25
1233		2f. *Bouquet of Flowers* (Raelant Savery) (31×46 mm)	6·00	5·50

402 Peace Doves

2000. 25th Anniversary of Organisation for Security and Co-operation in Europe.

1234	**402**	1f.30 multicoloured	3·25	3·00

403 Root Crib

2000. Christmas. Cribs. Multicoloured.

1235		80r. Type **403**	2·00	1·80
1236		1f.30 Oriental crib	3·00	2·75
1237		1f.80 Crib with cloth figures	4·75	4·25

2000. Fungi (2nd series). As T **370**. Multicoloured.

1238		90r. *Mycena adonis*	2·40	2·20
1239		1f.10 *Chalciporus amarellus*	2·75	2·40
1240		2f. Pink waxcap	5·25	4·75

404 Postman delivering Parcel

2001. Greetings Stamps. Multicoloured.

1241		70r. Type **404**	2·00	1·80
1242		70r. Postman delivering flowers	2·00	1·80

Nos. 1241/1242 are for the stamps with the parcel (1241) and flowers (1242) intact. The parcel and flowers can be scratched away to reveal a greetings message.

405 Silver Easter Egg

2001. Decorated Easter Eggs. Multicoloured.

1243		1f.20 Type **405**	3·50	3·00
1244		1f.80 Cloissonne egg	4·50	4·00
1245		2f. Porcelain egg	5·00	4·50

406 Mountain Spring

2001. Europa. Water Resources.

1246	**406**	1f.30 multicoloured	3·00	2·75

407 Emblem

2001. Liechtenstein Presidency of Council of Europe.

1247	**407**	1f.80 multicoloured	4·00	3·50

408 Carolingian Cruciform Fibula

2001. Centenary of Historical Association. Multicoloured.

1248		70r. Type **408**	2·00	1·80
1249		70r. *Mars of Gutenberg* (statue)	2·00	1·80

409 St Theresa's Chapel, Schaanwald

2001. Preservation of Historical Environment (2nd series). Multicoloured.

1250		70r. Type **409**	2·00	1·80
1251		90r. St Johann's Torkel (wine press), Mauren	2·40	2·20
1252		1f.10 Pirsch Transformer Station, Schaanwald	2·75	2·50

410 Mary and kneeling Votant (Chapel of Our Lady, Dux, Schann)

2001. Votive Paintings. Multicoloured.

1253		70r. Type **410**	2·00	1·80
1254		1f.20 Mary and Jesus, St George among other Saints, and text of vow (St George's Chapel, Schellenberg)	3·00	2·75
1255		1f.30 Mary, St Joseph of Arimathea, St Christopher, Johann Christoph Walser (votant) and text of vow (Chapel of Our Lady, Dux, Schann)	3·50	3·00

411 Rheinberger and Scene from *Zauberwort* (song cycle)

2001. Death Centenary of Josef Gabriel Rheinberger (composer).

1256	**411**	3f.50 multicoloured	10·00	9·00

2001. Traditional Crafts (2nd series). As T **380**. Multicoloured.

1257		70r. Agricultural implements and horseshoe	2·00	1·80
1258		90r. Rake	2·50	2·30
1259		1f.20 Harness	3·00	2·75

412 Annunciation

2001. Christmas. Medallions from *The Joyful, Sorrowful and Glorious Rosary Cycle.* Multicoloured.

1260		70r. Type **412**	2·00	1·80
1261		90r. Nativity	2·50	2·30
1262		1f.30 Presentation of Jesus at the Temple	3·25	2·75

413 *Square*

2001. Paintings by Gottfried Honeggar. Multicoloured

1263		1f.80 Type **413**	5·25	4·75
1264		2f.20 *Circle*	6·50	5·75

414 Mountains and River

2002. International Year of Mountains and 50th Anniversary of the International Commission of Alpine Protection. Multicoloured.

1265		70r. Type **414**	1·80	1·60
1266		1f.20 Stylised mountains	3·00	2·75

415 *Schellenberg*

2002. 30th Death Anniversary of Friedrich Kaufmann (artist). Multicoloured.

1267		70r. Type **415**	2·00	1·80
1268		1f.30 *Schaan*	3·00	2·75
1269		1f.80 *Steg*	4·75	4·25

416 Space Shuttle and Bee

2002. Liechtenstein's participation in NASA. Space Technology and Research Students Project.

1270	**416**	90r. multicoloured	2·50	2·30

The project submitted by the Liechtenstein Gymnasium concerned the study of the effects of space on carpenter bees.

417 Man on Tightrope

2002. Europa. Circus. Multicoloured.
1271 90r. Type **417** 2·50 2·30
1272 1f.30 Juggler 3·50 3·25

418 Emblem

2002. Liba '02 National Stamp Exhibition, Vaduz (1st issue).
1273 **418** 1f.20 multicoloured 3·25 3·00
See also Nos. 1282/1283 and 1318/1320.

419 Houses, Popers

2002. Preservation of Historical Environment (3rd series). Multicoloured.
1274 70r. Type **419** 2·00 1·80
1275 1f.20 House, Weiherring 3·25 3·00

420 Footballers

2002. World Cup Football Championship, Japan and South Korea.
1276 **420** 1f.80 multicoloured 5·25 4·75

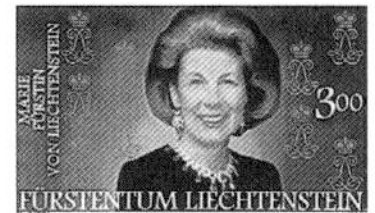

421 Princess Marie

2002. The Royal Couple. Multicoloured.
1277 3f. Type **421** 8·75 7·75
1278 3f.50 Prince Hans-Adam II 10·00 9·00

422 Ghost Orchid (*Epipogium aphyllum*)

2002. Orchids. Multicoloured.
1279 70r. Type **422** 2·00 1·80
1280 1f.20 Fly orchid (*Ophrys insectifera*) 3·00 2·75
1281 1f.30 Black vanilla orchid (*Nigritella nigra*) 3·25 3·00

423 Stamps and Emblem

2002. Liba 02 National Stamp Exhibition, Vaduz (2nd issue). 90th Anniversary of First Liechtenstein Stamps. Multicoloured.
1282 90r. Type **423** 2·50 2·30
1283 1f.30 Stamps showing royal family 3·50 3·25

424 Princess Sophie

2002. Prince Alois and Princess Sophie. Multicoloured.
1284 2f. Type **424** 5·75 5·00
1285 2f.50 Prince Alois 7·25 6·50

425 Mary and Joseph

2002. Christmas. Batik. Multicoloured.
1286 70r. Type **425** 2·00 1·80
1287 1f.20 Nativity 3·25 3·00
1288 1f.80 Flight into Egypt 4·50 4·00

426 The Eagle, Vaduz

2002. Inn Signs. Multicoloured.
1289 1f.20 Type **426** 3·00 2·75
1290 1f.80 The Angel, Balzers 4·50 4·00
1291 3f. The Eagle, Bendern 7·50 6·75

427 St Fridolin Parish Church

2003. Preservation of Historical Environment (4th series). Multicoloured.
1292 70r. Type **427** 2·00 1·80
1293 2f.50 House, Spidach (horiz) 6·25 5·75

428 Postal Emblem

2003. Europa. Poster Art.
1294 **428** 1f.20 multicoloured 3·25 3·00

429 Pruning Vines

2003. Viticulture (1st issue). Multicoloured.
1295 1f.30 Type **429** 3·75 3·50
1296 1f.80 Tying up vines 5·25 4·75
1297 2f.20 Hoeing 6·75 6·75
See also Nos. 1301/1303, 1304/1306 and 1312/1314.

430 Bridge

2003. 50th Anniversary of Liechtenstein Association for the Disabled.
1298 **430** 70r. multicoloured 2·30 2·00

431 Renovated Buildings and Ammonite

2003. Renovation of National Museum. Multicoloured.
1299 1f.20 Type **431** 3·25 3·00
1300 1f.30 Verweserhaus building and bailiff's shield 3·50 3·00

2003. Viticulture (2nd issue). As T **429**. Multicoloured.
1301 1f.20 Looping the tendrils 3·50 3·00
1302 1f.80 Removing leaves from around grapes 5·25 4·75
1303 3f.50 Reducing top growth 9·75 8·75

2003. Viticulture (3rd issue). As T **429**. Multicoloured.
1304 70r. Thinning out 2·30 2·00
1305 90r. Harvesting 3·00 2·75
1306 1f.10 Pressing the grapes 3·75 3·50

432 St George

2003. Saints (1st series). Multicoloured.
1307 1f.20 Type **432** 3·25 3·00
1308 1f.20 St Blaise 3·25 3·00
1309 1f.30 St Vitus 3·50 3·25
1310 1f.30 St Erasmus 3·50 3·25
See also Nos. 1323/1328 and 1367/1370.

433 Parents and Young on Nest

2003. Conservation of White Storks in Rhine Valley.
1311 **433** 2f.20 multicoloured 6·75 6·00

2003. Viticulture (4th issue). As T **429**. Multicoloured.
1312 70r. Tasting 2·30 2·00
1313 90r. Harvesting ice-wine grapes 3·00 2·75
1314 1f.20 Bottling 4·50 4·00

434 Archangel Gabriel appearing to Mary

2003. Christmas. Multicoloured.
1315 70r. Type **434** 2·00 1·80
1316 90r. Nativity 2·30 2·00
1317 1f.30 Three Kings 3·25 3·00

435 Cow (Laura Beck)

2003. Liba 02 National Stamp Exhibition, Vaduz (3rd issue). Children's Drawing Competition Winners. Multicoloured.
1318 70r. Type **435** 2·30 2·00
1319 1f.80 Bee (Laura Lingg) 5·25 4·75
1320 1f.80 Apple tree (Patrick Marxer) (vert) 5·25 4·75

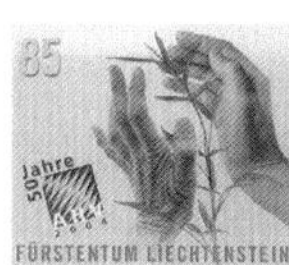

436 Hands enclosing Leaves

2004. 50th Anniversary of AHV (retirement insurance).
1321 **436** 85r. multicoloured 2·30 2·00

437 Hot Air Balloon

2004. Europa. Holidays.
1322 **437** 1f.30 multicoloured 4·50 4·00

2004. Saints (2nd series). As T **432**. Multicoloured.
1323 1f. St Achatius 2·75 2·40
1324 1f. St Margaret 2·75 2·40
1325 1f.20 St Christopher 3·00 2·75
1326 1f.20 St Pantaleon 3·00 2·75
1327 2f.50 St Cyriacus 6·00 5·50
1328 2f.50 St Aegidius 6·00 5·50

438 Bendern

2004. Tourism. Aerial views of Liechtenstein. Multicoloured.
1329 15r. Type **438** 45 40
1330 85r. Gross-Teg 2·30 2·00
1331 1f. Tuass 2·75 2·40
1332 1f.50 Oberland 3·75 3·50
1333 1f.60 Ruggeller Riet 4·00 3·75
1334 2f.50 Canal 6·00 5·50
1335 3f. Naafkopf 6·75 6·00
1336 3f.50 Rhine Valley 8·25 7·50
1337 6f. Gutenberg 14·50 13·00

439 Olympic Torch

2004. Olympic Games, Athens 2004.
1350 **439** 85r. multicoloured 3·00 2·75

440 Bee Orchid (*Ophrys apifera*)

2004. Orchids. Multicoloured.
1351 85r. Type **440** 2·30 2·00
1352 1f. *Orchis ustulata* 3·00 2·75
1353 1f.20 *Epipactis purpurata* 3·75 3·50

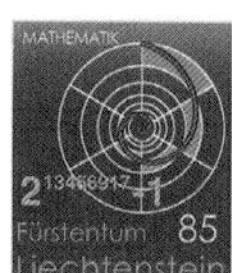

441 Mathematical Symbols

2004. Science. Multicoloured.
1354 85r. Type **441** 2·30 2·00
1355 1f. Atomic diagram (physics) 2·75 2·40
1356 1f.30 Molecular structure (chemistry) 3·00 2·75
1357 1f.80 Star map and Saturn (astronomy) 4·50 4·00

442 Two-storied House on Unterdorfstrasse (street)

2004. Preservation of Historical Environment (5th series). Multicoloured.
1358 2f.20 Type **442** 4·75 4·25
1359 2f.50 Unterdorfstrasse (street) 5·25 4·75

443 The Annunciation

2004. Christmas. Multicoloured.
1360 85r. Type **443** 3·00 2·75
1361 1f. Nativity 3·75 3·50
1362 1f.80 Adoration of the Magi 6·00 5·50

444 Ammonite

2004. Fossils. Multicoloured.

1363	1f.20 Type **444**	2·75	2·40
1364	1f.30 Sea urchin	3·00	2·75
1365	2f.20 Shark's tooth	7·50	6·75

445 Map of Europe as Manuscript (emblem of Rinascimento Virtuale)

2004. Rinascimento Virtuale (Europe-wide co-operation in digital palimpsest (old manuscripts) research).

1366	**445**	2f.50 multicoloured	6·00	5·50

2005. Saints (3rd issue). As T **432**. Multicoloured.

1367	85r. St Eustachius	2·30	2·00
1368	85r. St Dionysius	2·30	2·00
1369	1f.80 St Barbara	4·50	4·00
1370	1f.80 St Katharina	4·50	4·00

446 Female Customer, Waiters and Chef

2005. Europa. Gastronomy.

1371	**446**	1f.30 multicoloured	4·50	4·00

447 *Venus in Front of the Mirror* (Peter Paul Rubens)

2005. Liechtenstein Museum, Garden Palace, Vienna.

1372	**447**	2f.20 multicoloured	7·50	6·75

A stamp of the same design was issued by Austria.

448 Triesenberg

2005. Tourism.

1373	**448**	3f.60 multicoloured	10·50	9·50

449 *Flower Vase in a Window Niche* (Ambrosius Bosschaert)

2005. Paintings. Multicoloured.

1374	85r. Type **449**	3·75	3·50
1375	85r. *Magnolias* (Chen Hongshou)	3·75	3·50

Stamps of a similar design were issued by People's Republic of China.

450 Rossle, Schaan

2005. Inn Signs. Multicoloured.

1376	1f. Type **450**	2·40	2·20
1377	1f.40 Edelweiss, Triesenberg	3·00	2·75
1378	2f.50 Lowen, Bendern	6·00	5·50

451 Herman Sieger (founder)

2005. 75th Anniversary of Postal Museum. Multicoloured.

1379	1f.10 Type **451**	2·75	2·50
1380	1f.30 Stamps	3·00	3·00
1381	1f.80 Postcard sent by Zeppelin mail	4·75	4·25

452 Bargalla

2005. Alpine Pastures. Multicoloured.

1382	85r. Type **452**	2·30	2·10
1383	1f. Pradamee	2·75	2·50
1384	1f.30 Gritsch	3·50	3·25
1385	1f.80 Valuna	4·50	4·25

See also Nos. 1410/1412, 1448/1450 and 1470/1471.

453 Oberbendern

2005. Preservation of Historical Environment (4th series). Multicoloured.

1386	85r. Type **453**	2·30	2·10
1387	2f.50 Schwurplatz	5·75	5·25

454 *Plecotus auritus*

2005. Bats. Multicoloured.

1388	1f.80 Type **454**	5·50	5·00
1389	2f. *Myotis myotis*	6·25	5·75

455 *Virgin and Child*

2005. Christmas. Wood Carvings by Toni Gstohl. Multicoloured.

1390	85r. Type **455**	3·25	3·00
1391	1f. *Holy family*	3·50	3·25
1392	1f.30 *Three Kings*	4·50	4·25

456 Skier and Angel

2005. Winter Olympic Games, Turin. Multicoloured.

1393	1f.20 Type **456**	3·25	3·00
1394	1f.30 Cross country skier and wild boar	3·50	3·25
1395	1f.40 Slalom skier	4·25	4·00

457 *Peat Cutters*

2005. Eugen Wilhelm Schüepp (artist) Commemoration. Paintings. Multicoloured.

1396	1f. Type **457**	3·50	3·25
1397	1f.80 *Neugut, Schaan*	6·75	6·25

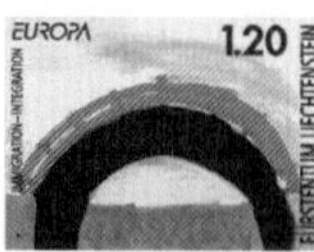

458 Bridge (Nadja Beck)

2006. Europa. Integration. Winning Entries in Children's Painting Competition. Multicoloured.

1398	1f.20 Type **458**	3·50	3·25
1399	1f.30 Face (Elisabeth Mussner)	3·75	3·50

459 *Lost in her Dreams* (Friedrich von Amerling)

2006. Liechtenstein Museum, Garden Palace, Vienna.

1400	**459**	2f.20 multicoloured	9·00	8·25

A stamp of the same design was issued by Austria.

460 Prince Johann I

2006. Bicentenary of Sovereignty. Multicoloured.

1401	85r. Type **460**	3·25	3·00
1402	1f. National Colours	3·50	3·25
1403	1f.20 Ruling house colours	4·00	3·75
1404	1f.80 State Arms	5·50	5·00

461 Woman holding Base Clef (culture)

2006. Tourism. Multicoloured.

1405	85r. Type **461**	3·25	3·00
1406	1f. Hiker (summer)	3·50	3·25
1407	1f.20 Diner (hospitality)	4·00	3·75
1408	1f.80 Skier (winter)	5·50	5·00

462 Players on Field

2006. World Cup Football Championship, Germany.

1409	**462**	3f.30 multicoloured	10·00	9·00

2006. Alpine Pastures. As T **452**. Multicoloured.

1410	85r. Lawena	2·75	2·50
1411	1f.30 Gapfahl	3·50	3·25
1412	2f.40 Gafadura	6·25	5·75

463 *The Magic Flute* (Wolfgang Amadeus Mozart)

2006. Composers and Works. Multicoloured.

1413	1f. Type **463**	3·25	3·00
1414	1f. *Radetzky March* (Johann Strauss Sr.)	3·25	3·00
1415	1f. *Rhapsody in Blue* (George Gershwin)	3·25	3·00
1416	1f. *Water Music* (George Frideric Handel)	3·25	3·00
1417	1f. *Pastoral Symphony* (Ludwig van Beethoven)	3·25	3·00
1418	1f. *Waltz of the Flowers* (Pytor Ilyich Tchaikovsky)	3·25	3·00
1419	1f. *The Swan* (Camille Saint-Saens)	3·25	3·00
1420	1f. *Midsummer Night's Dream* (Felix Mendelssohn)	3·25	3·00

464 Mozart

2006. 250th Birth Anniversary of Wolfgang Amadeus Mozart.

1421	**464**	1f.20 multicoloured	4·50	4·25

465 The Annunciation

2006. Christmas. Paintings from Chapel of St Mary, Dux. Multicoloured.

1422	85r. Type **465**	3·25	3·00
1423	1f. The Nativity	3·50	3·25
1424	1f.30 Presentation of Jesus	4·00	3·75

466 Curta Calculator

2006. Technical Innovations. Multicoloured.

1425	1f.30 Type **466**	4·50	4·25
1426	1f.40 Carrana narrow film camera	5·00	4·50
1427	2f.40 PVA sliding calliper	7·25	6·50

See also Nos. 1451/1453 and 1495/1497.

467 Governor's Residence and Liechtenstein Institute

2006. Preservation of Historical Environment (7th series). Multicoloured.

1428	1f.80 Type **467**	4·50	4·25
1429	3f.50 Buhl, Gamprin	8·75	8·00

468 Violinist (Allegro)

2007. Music. Tempo and Temperament. Multicoloured

1430	85r. Type **468**	3·00	2·75
1431	1f.80 Gramophone and flying music sheets (Capriccio)	4·50	4·25
1432	2f. Brass players (Crescendo)	6·00	5·50
1433	3f.50 Pianist and flaming piano (Con fuoco)	9·75	9·00

469 Trail Sign ('This Way')

2007. Europa. Centenary of Scouting.

1434	**469**	1f.30 multicoloured	3·75	3·50

470 *Portrait of a Lady* (Bernardino Zaganelli da Cottignola)

2007. Liechtenstein Museum, Garden Palace, Vienna.
1435 **470** 2f.40 multicoloured 6·25 6·00

A stamp of a similar design was issued by Austria.

471 Letter Post

2007. Greetings Cards. Multicoloured.
1436 85r. Type **471** 2·50 2·40
1437 1f. Boys carrying bier containing envelope (courier post) 3·25 3·00
1438 1f.30 Swallow holding envelope (airmail) 3·75 3·50

472 *Castle and Vaduz*

2007. Tourism. The Rhine. Paintings by Johann Ludwig Bleuler. Multicoloured.
1439 1f. Type **472** 2·50 2·40
1440 1f.30 *Ratikon mountains* 3·25 3·00
1441 2f.40 *Confluence of Ill and Rhine* 5·00 4·75

473 Nendeln

2007. Tourism. Liechtenstein from the Air. Multicoloured
1442 1f.10 Type **473** 3·00 3·00
1443 1f.80 Malbun 4·75 4·25
1444 2f.60 Arable land 6·25 5·75

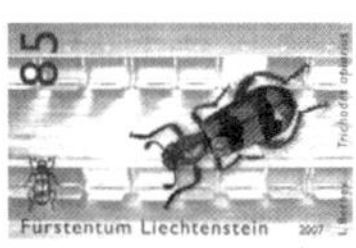

474 *Trichodes apiarius* (bee beetle)

2007. Insects. Multicoloured.
1445 85r. Type **474** 2·75 2·50
1446 1f. *Cetonia aurata* (rose chafer) 3·00 3·00
1447 1f.30 *Dytiscus marginalis* (great diving beetle) 4·75 4·25

2007. Alpine Pastures. As T **452**. Multicoloured.
1448 1f. Hintervalorsch 3·00 3·00
1449 1f.40 Sucka 4·00 3·75
1450 2f.20 Guschfiel 6·25 5·75

2007. Technical Innovations. As T **466**. Multicoloured.
1451 1f.30 Hilti hammer and drill 4·00 3·75
1452 1f.80 Kaiser walking excavator 4·75 4·25
1453 2f.40 aluFer heating surface 6·25 5·75

475 Liechtenstein from the Air

2007. SEPAC (small European mail services).
1454 **475** 1f.30 multicoloured 4·75 4·25

476 St Mary Chapel, Gamprin-Oberbuhl

2007. Christmas. Multicoloured.
1455 85r. Type **476** 2·75 2·50
1456 1f. Buel Chapel, Eschen 3·00 3·00
1457 1f.30 St Wolfgang Chapel, Triesen 4·75 4·25

477 Rainbow over Three Sisters Massif

2007. Natural Phenomena. Multicoloured.
1458 85r. Type **477** 2·75 2·50
1459 1f. Lightning over Bendern 3·00 3·00
1460 1f.80 Halo over Malbun 6·25 5·75

478 Landtagsgebaude (designed by Hansjorg Goritz)

2007. Architecture. New Parliament Building, Vaduz.
1461 **478** 1f.30 multicoloured 4·75 4·25

479 St Martin's Church

2007. Preservation of Historical Environment (8th series). Multicoloured.
1462 2f. Type **479** 6·25 5·75
1463 2f.70 Eschen Mill, St Martinsring (horiz) 7·75 7·25

480 Industrial Buildings, Spoerry-Areal, Vaduz (industry)

2008. National Identity. Liechtenstein as Brand (1st series). Multicoloured.
1464 85r. Type **480** 2·50 2·30
1465 1f. St Mamertus Chapel, Triesen (homeland) 3·00 3·00
1466 1f.30 Vaduz Castle (monarchy) 4·75 4·25

See also Nos. 1527/1529.

481 Firefighters

2008. Volunteer Civil Protection (1st issue). Volunteer Fire Service.
1467 **481** 1f. multicoloured 3·00 3·00

See also Nos. 1502, 1539/1540 and 1637/1638.

482 *Princess Marie Franziska von Liechtenstein* (Friedrich von Amerling)

2008. Liechtenstein Museum, Garden Palace, Vienna.
1468 **482** 2f.40 multicoloured 7·75 7·25

A stamp of a similar design was issued by Austria.

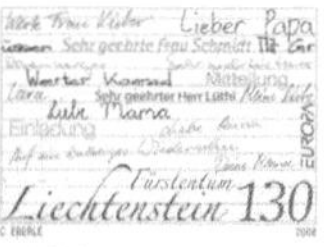

483 Script

2008. Europa. The Letter.
1469 **483** 1f.30 multicoloured 4·75 4·25

2008. Alpine Pastures. As T **452**. Multicoloured.
1470 2f.60 Schaan, Guschg 6·25 5·75
1471 3f. Balzers, Guschgle 7·75 7·25

484 Huanhuan and Jingjing (martial arts)

2008. Olympic Games, Beijing. Multicoloured.
1472 85c. Type **484** 2·30 2·20
1473 1f. Huanhuan and Yingying (football and table tennis) 3·00 3·00

485 *Osmia brevicornis*

2008. Endangered Insects. Multicoloured.
1474 85c. Type **485** 2·50 2·30
1475 1f. *Epeoloides coecutiens* 3·00 3·00
1476 1f.30 *Odynerus spinipes* 3·75 3·50

486 Marathon

2008. Paralympics, Beijing. Stylised athletes. Multicoloured.
1477 1f.30 Type **486** 4·00 3·75
1478 1f. 80 Table tennis 6·25 5·75

487 St Stephen's Cathedral (Austria)

2008. EURO 2008 Football Championships. Multicoloured.
1479 1f.30 Type **487** 4·00 3·75
1480 1f.30 Flag, dancer and musician (Liechtenstein) 4·00 3·75
1481 1f.30 Alphorn and Matterhorn (Switzerland) 4·00 3·75

488 *Mother and Queen of the Precious Blood*

2008. 150th Anniversary of Schellenberg Convent.
1482 **488** 2f.20 multicoloured 6·25 5·75

489 *Schoolmaster Lampel*

2008. Death Centenary of Heinrich Christian William Busch (writer and cartoonist). Multicoloured.
1483 1f.30 Type **489** 4·00 3·75
1484 1f.30 *Hans Huckebein* 4·00 3·75
1485 1f.30 *Max and Moritz* 4·00 3·75
1486 1f.30 *Widow Bolte* 4·00 3·75
1487 1f.30 *Pious Helen* 4·00 3·75
1488 1f.30 *Fips the Monkey* 4·00 3·75
1489 1f.30 *Tailor Bock* 4·00 3·75
1490 1f.30 *Balduin Bahlamm* 4·00 3·75

490 Karl I of Liechtenstein

2008. 400th Anniversary of Princes of Liechtenstein. Sheet 58×77 mm.
MS1491 **490** 5f. multicoloured 16·00 15·00

The stamp and margin of **MS**1491 form a composite design of painting.

491 Candle Wreath

2008. Christmas. Multicoloured.
1492 85r. Type **491** 2·50 2·30
1493 1f. Children carrying holly (horiz) 3·00 3·00
1494 1f.30 Decorated tree 4·75 4·25

2008. Technical Innovations. As T **466**. Multicoloured.
1495 1f.20 Neutrik XLR cable connector NC3MX 3·75 3·50
1496 1f.40 Ivoclar Vivadent blue phase polymerisation unit 4·75 4·50
1497 2f.20 ThyssenKrupp Presta DeltaValve control 7·50 7·25

492 Schadler Ceramics Building, Nendeln

2008. Preservation of Historical Environment (9th series).
1498 **492** 3f.80 multicoloured 13·50 12·50

493 Postworker accepting Parcel

2009. Postal Service. Multicoloured.
1499 85c. Type **493** 2·75 2·75
1500 1f. Delivering 3·50 3·25
1501 1f.30 Sorting 3·75 3·50

494 First Aid

2009. Volunteer Civil Portection (2nd series). Association of Liechtenstein Samaritan Volunteers.
1502 **494** 1f. multicoloured 3·75 3·50

495 *Unfolding* (woman and butterfly)

2009. The Printer's Art. Artistic Techniques. Linocuts by Stephan Sude
1503 1f. black and pink 2·75 2·75
1504 1f.30 black and olive 3·75 3·50
1505 2f.70 black and blue 9·50 9·00

Designs: 1f. T **495**; 1f.30 *Awareness* (man crying); 2f.70 *Fulfilment* (elderly man and mountains).

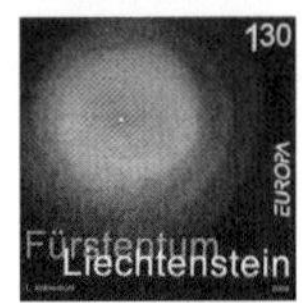

496 Super Nova (Leta Krahenbuhl)

2009. Europa. Astronomy.
1506 **496** 1f.30 multicoloured 4·75 4·50

497 Land Register

2009. Bicentenary of Land Register.
1507 **497** 3f.30 multicoloured 11·50 11·00

498 Ants and Forest

2009. Forest. Multicoloured.
1508 85c. Type **498** 3·50 3·25
1509 1f. Path through woods 3·75 3·50
1510 1f.40 Tree and rock 4·75 4·50
1511 1f.60 Mountain, lake and log pile 5·75 5·50

499 Summit Cross, Kuegrat

2009. Centenary of Alpine Association. Designs showing summit crosses. Multicoloured.
1512 1f. Type **499** 3·75 3·50
1513 1f.30 Langspitz (vert) 4·75 4·50
1514 2f.20 Rappastein (vert) 7·25 6·75
1515 2f.40 Jahn-Turm und Wolan 7·50 7·25

500 Vaduz Castle in Spring

2009. Vaduz Castle through the Seasons. Multicoloured.
1516 1f.30 Type **500** 4·75 4·50
1517 1f.80 In summer 6·75 6·25

See also Nos.1562/1563.

501 *Pieris rapae*

2009. Butterflies. Multicoloured.
1518 85c. Type **501** 2·75 2·50
1519 1f. *Parnassius apollo* 3·75 3·50
1520 1f.30 *Melanargia galathea* 4·75 4·50
1521 2f. *Vanessa atlanta* 5·75 5·50

502 Emblem

2009. 75th Anniversary of Liechtenstein Philatelic Society.
1522 **502** 1f.30 multicoloured 3·75 3·50

503 Badminton Cabinet (detail)

2009. Liechtenstein Museum, Garden Palace, Vienna. Designs showing details of Badminton Cabinet. Multicoloured.
1523 1f.30 Type **503** 3·75 3·50
1524 2f. Three birds and bouquet (detail centre) (34×49 mm) 7·50 7·25
1525 4f. Red-capped bird and lilies (detail left) 13·50 12·50

504 Chapel of St Mamerta, Trisien

2009. SEPAC (small European mail services).
1526 **504** 1f.30 multicoloured 5·75 5·50

505 Lifestyle Museum, Schellenberg

2010. National Identity. Liechtenstein as Brand (2nd series). Multicoloured.
1527 20r. Type **505** (community) 95 90
1528 50r. Former Customs House, Vaduz (finance) 1·90 1·80
1529 60r. Parish House, Bendern (dialogue) 2·75 2·50

506 Annunciation

2010. Christmas. Advent Windows created by Pupils of Primary School, Gamprin. Multicoloured.
1530 85r. Type **506** 2·75 2·50
1531 1f. Journey to Bethlehem 3·75 3·50
1532 1f.30 The Nativity 4·75 4·50
1533 1f.80 The Three Magi 5·75 5·50

507 University of Applied Sciences (Karl+Probst), Vaduz

2010. Modern Architecture (1st issue). Multicoloured.
1534 85r. Type **507** 2·75 2·50
1535 2f.60 Art Museum (Morger, Degelo and Kerez), Vaduz 7·50 7·25
1536 3f.50 Ruggell–Nofels Border Crossing between Liechtenstein and Austria (EFFEFF) 11·50 11·00

See also Nos. 1545/1546.

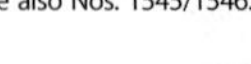

508 Alpine Skier

2010. Winter Olympic Games, Vancouver. Multicoloured.
1537 1f. Type **508** 3·75 3·50
1538 1f.80 Nordic skier 6·75 6·25

509 Mountain Rescue (Liechtenstein Mountain Rescue (founded by Liechtenstein Alpine Association))

2010. Volunteer Civil Protection (3rd series). Volunteer Rescue Services. Multicoloured.
1539 85r. Type **509** 2·75 2·50
1540 1f.30 Water rescue (founded by 'Bubbles' diving club) 4·75 4·50

510 Hillside Farming

2010. Agriculture. Multicoloured.
1541 85r. Type **510** 3·25 3·00
1542 1f. Agriculture and the environment 3·50 3·25
1543 1f.10 Technology in farming 3·75 3·50
1544 1f.30 Farm animals 4·75 4·50

511 Natural Gas Filling Station (EFFEFF), Vaduz

2010. Modern Architecture (2nd issue). Multicoloured.
1545 2f.60 Type **511** 8·50 8·00
1546 3f.60 Liechtenstein Electric Power Authority Transformer Station (Marcel Ferrier) 12·50 11·50

512 Vaduz

2010. Expo 2010, Shanghai. Multicoloured.
MS1547 1f.60 Type **512**; 1f.90 Tidal bore on Qiantang river (32×60mm) 13·50 13·00

513 Ariadne giving Theseus the Thread

2010. Liechtenstein Museum, Garden Palace, Vienna. Multicoloured.
1548 1f. Type **513** 2·75 2·50
1549 1f.40 Surrender of Golden Fleece to Jason 4·00 3·75

514 Figures supporting Roof

515 Flags of Members

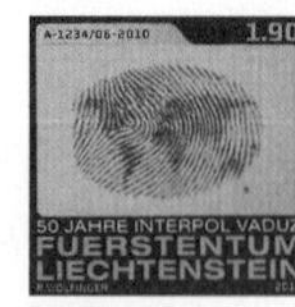

516 Finger Print

2010. 50th Anniversaries.
1550 **514** 1f. olive-bistre and black (Disability Insurance) 2·75 2·50
1551 **515** 1f.40 multicoloured (EFTA) 4·75 4·50
1552 **516** 1f.90 pale yellow-olive and slate grey (Interpol in Vaduz) 5·75 5·50

517 *Coenonympha oedippus* (false ringlet)

2010. Butterflies. Multicoloured.
1553 1f.40 Type **517** 4·75 4·50
1554 1f.60 *Gonepteryx rhamni* (brimstone) 5·75 5·50
1555 2f.60 *Papilio machaon* (Old World swallowtail) 8·50 8·00

518 Roadway and Eschnerberg

2010. Liechtenstein Panorama. Multicoloured.
1556 1f. Type **518** 2·75 2·50
1557 1f. Field and Alvier mountains 2·75 2·50

Nos. 1556/1557 were printed, *se-tenant*, forming a composite design

519 Hydropower

2010. Renewable Energy. Multicoloured.
1558 1f. Type **519** 2·75 2·50
1559 1f.40 Wood 4·00 3·75
1560 2f.80 Near-surface geothermal power 8·00 7·50

520 Children and Symbols of Magic and Fantasy

2010. Europa.
1561 **520** 1f.40 multicoloured 4·00 3·75

521 Autumn

2010. Vaduz Castle through the Seasons. Multicoloured.
1562 1f.40 Type **521** 4·00 3·75
1563 1f.90 Winter 5·50 5·25

Nos. 1564/1566 and T **522** are left for Christmas; Nos. 1567/1569 and T **523** are left for Museum of Art and Nos. 1570/1572 and T **524** are left for Brand Liechtenstein, not yet received.

525 Athletics, Volleyball and Cycling

2011. Small European States' Games 2011, Liechtenstein.
1573 85r. bronze and black 2·50 2·30
1574 1f. silver and black 2·75 2·50
1575 1f.40 gold and black 4·00 3·75

Designs: 85r. T **525**; 1f. Judo, shooting and squash; 1f.40 Table tennis, tennis and swimming

526 Quick Response Code

2011. Anniversaries.
1576 1f. multicoloured 2·75 2·50
1577 1f. black and gold (31×37 mm) 2·75 2·50

Designs: No. 1576 T **526** (150th anniversary of Landesbank); No. 1577 '50 Jahre Landesbibliothek' (50th anniversary of National Library)

527 Photovoltaic Cells

2011. Renewable Energy. Multicoloured.

1578	1f. Type **527**	2·75	2·50
1579	1f.10 Solar energy	3·25	3·00
1580	2f.90 Wind energy	8·25	8·00

528 Cloisonné Enamelled Egg from Moscow Workshop and Solemn Early Mass at Easter in St Isaac's Cathedral, St Petersburg (etching by Vasily Ivanovich Navozov)

2011. Decorated Easter Eggs, collected by Adulf Peter Goop. Multicoloured.

1581	1f. Type **528**	2·75	2·50
1582	1f.40 Faberge egg with apple blossom and Anichkov Palace on Nevsky Prospekt in St Petersburg (47×32 mm)	4·00	3·75
1583	2f.60 Egg with swan motif made by Pavel Akimovich Ovchinnikov and Red Square with St Basil's Cathedral	7·50	7·00

529 Prince Nikolaus

2011. Children of Hereditary Prince and Princess. Multicoloured.

MS1584	1f. Type **529**; 1f.80 Prince Georg; 2f. Princess Marie Caroline; 2f.60 Prince Joseph Wenzel	25·00	22·00

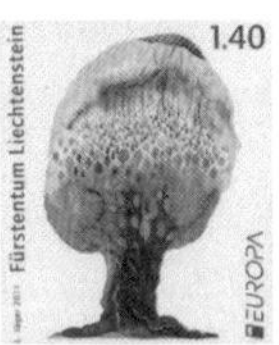

530 Tree as Ecosystem

2011. Europa. Forests.

1585	**530**	1f.40 multicoloured	4·75	4·25

531 *Inachis io* (peacock)

2011. Butterflies. Multicoloured.

1586	2f.20 Type **531**	7·25	6·75
1587	5f. *Anthocharis cardamines* (orange tip)	17·00	15·00

532 Fruit (Shirana Shahbazi)

2011. Art.

1588	**532**	1f. multicoloured	3·75	3·50

533 *Falco subbuteo* (hobby)

2011. Engangered Bird Species. 50th Anniversary of WWF. Multicoloured.

MS1589	1f.×8, Type **533**; *Glaucidium passerinum* (pygmy owl); *Jynx torquilla* (wryneck); *Oriolus oriolus* (oriole); *Luscinia megarhynchos* (nightingale); *Phoenicurus phoenicurus* (redstart); *Lanius collurio* (red-backed shrike); *Saxicola rubetra* (whinchat);	31·00	30·00

534 *Alpine Rhine*

2011. 24 Hours in Liechtenstein. Paintings by Xiao Hui Wang. Multicoloured.

1590	1f.30 Type **534**	5·25	4·75
1591	3f.70 *Water Reflections, Gutenberg Castle, Balzers*	14·00	13·00

535 Ruggell Marsh

2011. SEPAC (small European mail services).

1592	**535**	1f.40 multicoloured	5·50	5·00

536 Crib, Parish Church of St Gallus, Triesen

2011. Christmas. Cribs. Multicoloured.

1593	85r. Type **536**	3·00	2·75
1594	1f. St Florin Parish Church, Vaduz (38×32 mm)	3·75	3·25
1595	1f.40 Parish Church of the Assumption Bendern (32×38 mm)	5·00	4·50

537 Gutenberg Castle, Balzers

2011. Castles in Liectenstein. Multicoloured.

1596	1f. Type **537**	3·75	3·25
1597	1f.40 Schellenberg ruins	5·00	4·50
1598	2f. Schalun ruins	7·00	6·50
1599	2f.60 Vaduz Castle from north	9·25	8·50

538

2011. Chinese New Year. Year of the Dragon. Sheet 146×208 mm. Scarlet and gold.

MS1600	1f.90×4, Type **538**×4	27·00	26·00

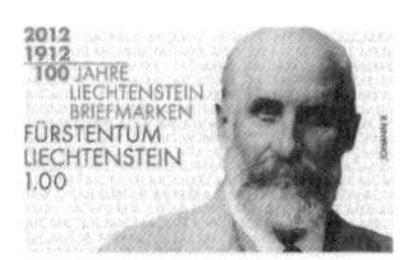

539 Franz I

2012. Centenary of Liechtenstein Stamps. Multicoloured.

1601	1f. Type **539**	3·75	3·25
1602	1f.40 Franz I	5·00	4·50
1603	2f.20 Franz Josef II	7·75	7·00
1604	2f.80 Hans-Adam II	10·00	9·00
MS1605	142×100 mm. As Nos. 1601/1604. Imperf	26·00	25·00

540 Constitutional Charter signed by Prince Johann II

2012. 150th Anniversary of Parliament and Constitution. Multicoloured.

1606	1f. Type **540**	3·75	3·25
1607	1f.40 Authorisation for Governor Karl Haus von Hausen to formally open Parliament	5·00	4·50

541 Cattle returning from Alpine Pastures

2012. Europa. Visit Liechtenstein.

1608	**541**	1f.40 multicoloured	5·00	4·50

542 Dahlia

2012. Flora. Multicoloured.

1609	85c. Type **542**	3·00	2·75
1610	1f.40 Peony	5·00	4·50
1611	5f. Zinnia	18·00	16·00

544 Swimming

2012. LOSV 2012 in London (Liechtenstein Olympic Sports Association). Multicoloured.

1614	1f. Type **544**	3·75	3·25
1615	1f.40 Tennis	5·00	4·50

545 Pfälzerhütte and Buildings

2012. Pfälzerhütte (mountain hut and inn), Liechtenstein.

1616	**545**	1f.40 multicoloured	5·00	4·50

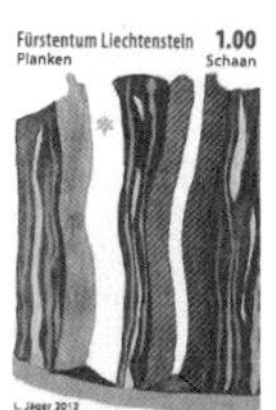

546 Planken and Schaan

2012. 300th Anniversary of Purchase of Oberland by Prince Johann Adam. Multicoloured.

MS1617	1f. Type **546**; 1f.40 Vaduz and Triesenberg; 2f.60 Triesen and Balzers	18·00	17·00

547 Guschg Herdsmen's Doll (N. Schwarz)

2012. LIBA 2012 National Stamp Exhibition. Winning Designs in Children's Drawing Competition. Multicoloured.

MS1618	1f. Type **547**; 1f.40 Giant of Guflina (R. Graf); 3f.60 The Three Sisters (G. Rodrigues-Margreiter)	22·00	21·00

548 Brasier, 1908

2012. Collections in Liechtenstein. Classic Cars. Multicoloured.

1619	85c. Type **548**	3·00	2·75
1620	1f. Stanley Steamer, 1911	3·75	3·25
1621	1f.40 Ford Model T Speedster, 1915	5·00	4·50
1622	1f.90 Hinstin, 1920	6·75	6·00

549 Till Eulenspiegel

2012. Famous Figures from Literature. Multicoloured.

MS1623	1f.×8, Type **549**; Sherlock Holmes; Don Quixote; Hamlet; Robin Hood; Robinson Crusoe; Baron Münchhausen; Quasimodo	32·00	31·00

600
(550)

2012. No. 1587 Surch as T **550.**

1624	600f. on 300f. multicoloured	12·00	11·00

551 *Christ's Descent from the Cross*

2012. Princely Treasures. Reliefs by Massimiliano Soldani-Benzi. Multicoloured.

1625	1f. Type **551**	3·75	3·25
1626	1f.40 *Christ on the Mount of Olives*	5·00	4·50

552 Geometric Shape (from *Tilings*)

2012. The Printer's Art. Art Print. Screen Printing. Multicoloured.

1627	1f. Type **552**	3·75	3·25
1628	1f.40 Geometric shape (pink)	5·00	4·50

553 Raphael

2012. Christmas. Archangels. Each gold.

1629	85c. Type **553**	3·00	2·75
1630	1f. Michael	3·75	3·25
1631	1f.40 Gabriel	5·00	4·50
1632	1f.90 Uriel	6·75	6·00

554 Snake

2012. Chinese New Year. Year of the Dragon. Sheet 208×148 mm. Scarlet and gold.

MS1633	1f.90×4, Type **554**×4	27·00	26·00

555 Fibonacci Squence

2013. Mathematics. Multicoloured.

1634	1f. Type **555**	3·75	3·25
1635	2f.60 Quotients of adjacent Fibonacci numbers	9·25	8·50
1636	4f. Golden Ratio	15·00	13·00

556 Avalanche Rescue Dogs and Handlers

2013. Volunteer Civil Protection (4th series). Multicoloured.

1637	1f. Type **556**	3·75	3·25
1638	1f.40 Civil protection	5·00	4·50

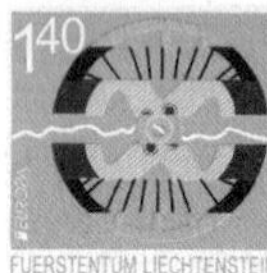

557 'Vehicle Wheels'

2013. Europa. Postal Vehicles. Winning Entry in Design-a-Stamp Competition.

1639	**557**	1f.40 multicoloured	5·00	4·50

558 Switzerland

2013. 90th Anniversary of Liechtenstein–Switzerland Customs Treaty. Multicoloured.

1640	2f. Type **558**	7·50	6·50
1641	2f. Liechtenstein	7·50	6·50

559 Old Rhine Bridge, Vaduz–Sevelan

2013. Bridges between Liechtenstein and Switzerland. Multicoloured.

1642	85c. Type **559**	3·00	2·75
1643	1f. Old Rhine Bridge side view (covered wooden bridge) (60×30 mm)	3·75	3·25
1644	1f.40 Railway bridge, Schaan - Buchs	5·00	4·50
1645	1f.90 Railway bridge, side view (60×30 mm)	6·75	6·00

See also Nos. 1672/1675.

560 Young Ibex

2013. Young Alpine Animals. Multicoloured.

1646	85c. Type **560**	3·00	2·75
1647	1f. Chamois	3·75	3·25
1648	1f.40 Marmot	5·00	4·50
1649	1f.90 Alpine Hare	6·75	6·00

561 *View of Vaduz*

2013. Painters from Liechtenstein. Hans Kliemand Commemoration

1650	1f. black and carmine	3·75	3·25
1651	1f.90 black and blue	6·75	6·00

Design: 1f. T **561**; 1f.90 *View into Rhine Valley*

562 *Gentiana rhaetica*

2013. Flora. Alpine Flowers. Multicoloured.

1652	1f. Type **562**	3·75	3·25
1653	1f.90 *Myosotis alpestris*	6·75	6·00
1654	4f. *Rhododendron hirsutum*	15·00	13·00

563 Aston Martin DB 2/4

2013. Collections in Liechtenstein. Sports and Touring Cars. Multicoloured.

1655	85c. Type **563**	3·00	2·75
1656	1f. Ferrari 250 GT PF	3·75	3·25
1657	1f.40 Jaguar XK 140	5·00	4·50
1658	1f.90 Mercedes 300 SL	6·75	6·00

564 Ballerina (dance)

2013. Performing Arts in Liechtenstein. Multicoloured.

1659	1f. Type **564**	3·00	2·75
1660	1f.40 Actors (theatre)	3·75	3·25
1661	2f. Dancers (musical theatre)	7·00	6·50
1662	4f. Magician (cabaret)	15·00	13·00

565 *Voyage of the Argonauts*

2013. Art. Ivan Masoyedov (Eugen Zotow) Commemoration. Multicoloured.

1663	1f.40 Type **565**	5·00	4·50
1664	2f.60 *Silium*	22·00	19·00

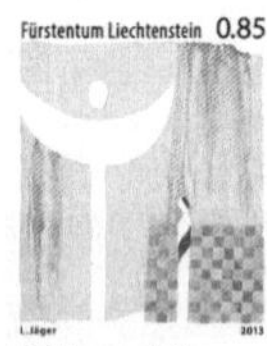

566 Annunciation

2013. Christmas. Themes from the Christmas Story. Multicoloured.

1665	85c. Type **566**	3·00	2·75
1666	1f. The Nativity	3·75	3·25
1667	1f.40 Angel appearing to shepherds	5·00	4·50
1668	1f.90 Three Kings	6·75	6·00

No. 1670 and Type **568** are left for Chinese New Year. Year of the Horse, not yet received.

567 Silk-faced Wallcovering

2012. Princely Treasures. Silk Wallcovering from Liechtenstein Museum, Vienna. Multicoloured.

MS1669	1f. Type **567**; 1f.40 Wallcovering, emblem lower; 3f.60 Wallcovering, emblem higher	24·00	23·00

569 Mountains

2013. Winter Olympic Games, Sochi.

1671	**569**	2f.60 multicoloured	9·25	8·50

570 Foot and Cycle Bridge

2014. Bridges between Liechtenstein and Switzerland (2nd issue). Multicoloured.

1672	85c. Type **570**	3·00	2·75
1673	1f. Buchs–Schaan bridge (60×30 mm)	3·50	3·25
1674	1f.40 Rhine bridge (roadway)	4·75	4·25
1675	1f.90 Bendern–Haag bridge bridge, side view (60×30 mm)	6·75	6·50

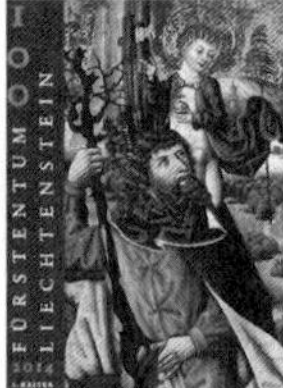

571 St Christopher carrying Christ Child

2014. Winged Altar (Gothic triptych altar donated to National Museum). Multicoloured.

MS1676	1f. Type **571**; 2f. St Sebastian; 6f. St Anne, Virgin and Child (84×44 mm)	33·00	31·00

572 J. G. Rheinberger

2014. 175th Birth Anniversary of Josef Gabriel Rheinberger (composer).

1677	**572**	1f.40 multicoloured	4·75	4·25

573 Drum

2014. Europa. Musical Instruments.

1678	**573**	1f.40 multicoloured	4·75	4·25

574 Pope John Paul II

2014. Canonisation of Pope John Paul II. Sheet 58×77 mm.

MS1679	**574** 1f.40 multicoloured	5·50	5·00

575 Denar

2014. Archaeological Finds in Liechtenstein. Coins. Multicoloured.

1680	85r. Type **575**	3·00	2·75
1681	1f. Gulden	3·50	3·25
1682	1f.40 Pfennig	4·75	4·25

576 Yellow-bellied Toad

2014. Amphibians. Multicoloured.

1683	85c. Type **576**	3·00	2·75
1684	2f.90 Crested newt	10·50	10·00
1685	3f.70 Alpine salamander	14·00	13·00

577 *Iris sibirica*

2014. Bog Flowers. Multicoloured.

1686	1f. Type **577**	3·50	3·25
1687	2f.80 *Parnassia pallustris*	10·00	9·00
1688	3f.60 *Menyanthes trifoliata*	13·75	13·00

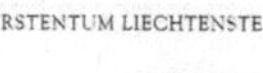

578 Rolls Royce Phantom II

2014. Collections in Liechtenstein. Saloon Cars. Multicoloured.

1689	85c. Type **578**	3·00	2·75
1690	1f. Pierce Arrow Type 133	3·50	3·25
1691	1f.40 Studebaker Big Six	4·75	4·25
1692	1f.90 Jaguar Mark IV	6·75	6·50

579 *Dust Image A*

2014. The Printer's Art. Art Print. Etching. Multicoloured.

1693	1f. Type **579**	3·50	3·25
1694	1f.40 *Dust Image B*	4·75	4·25

580 Metamorphosis Sequence 1

2014. International Year of Crystallography. Multicoloured.

1695	1f. Type **580**	3·50	3·25
1696	2f. Metamorphosis Sequence 2	7·25	6·75

581 Wheel, Boat and Donkey

2014. Lindau to Milan Courier (Lindau Messenger).

1697	**581**	1f.40 multicoloured	4·75	4·25

2014. Collections in Liechtenstein. Saloon Cars. Multicoloured.

1698	85c. As Type **578**	3·00	2·75

582 Friedenskapelle Malbun

2014. Christmas. Mountain Chapels. Multicoloured.

1699	85c. Type **582**	3·00	2·75
1700	1f. St Wendelinskapelle Steg	3·50	3·25
1701	1f.40 St Theodulskapelle Masescha	4·75	4·25

583 Famille Rose Teller

2014. Princely Treasures. Porcelain from China. Multicoloured.

1702	1f. Type **583**	3·50	3·25
1703	1f.90 Kraak-Kendi jug with siver mounts (27×43 mm)	6·75	6·50
1704	2f.80 Imari baluster vase with lid (27×43 mm)	8·25	8·00
1705	3f.60 Imari plate with lotus blossoms	13·50	13·00

584 Sheep

2014. Chinese New Year. Year of the Sheep. Sheet 146×161 mm. Scarlet and gold.

MS1706	1f.90×4, Type **584**×4	27·00	26·00

585 Geometric (Singapore)

2014. Liechtenstein and Singapore.

1707 1f.90 scarlet, grey and silver 6·75 6·50

1708 1f.90 multicoloured 6·75 6·50

Designs: 1f.90×2, Type **585;** Cityscape (Liechtenstein)

586 Prince Hans-Adam II

2014. 25th Anniversary of Accession of Prince Hans-Adam II.

1709 **586** 2f. multicoloured 7·25 6·75

2015. 70th Birth Anniversary of Prince Hans-Adam II. Multicoloured, colour of background and inscription given.

1710 1f. As Type **586** (green) 3·50 3·25

1711 2f. As Type **586** (orange-brown) 7·25 6·75

587 Hat

2015. 50th Anniversary of Liechtenstein Traditional Costume Association.

1712 **587** 85c. multicoloured 3·00 2·75

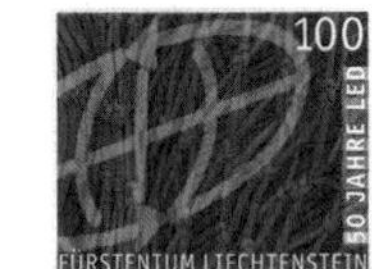

588 Net

2015. 50th Anniversary of Liechtenstein Development Service.

1713 **588** 1f. multicoloured 3·50 3·25

589 As 1912 Stamp of Liechtenstein

2015. 175th Anniversary of World's First Stamp (Penny Black).

1714 **589** 1f.40 bright blue and silver 4·75 4·25

590 Polar Bear

2015. Europa. Old Toys. Multicoloured.

1715 1f.40 Type **590** 4·75 4·25

1716 1f.40 Goat on lemon 4·75 4·25

591 Anniversary Emblem

2015. 25th Anniversary of United Nations Membership.

1717 **591** 1f.90 multicoloured 6·75 6·50

592 'Play of Light'

2015. International Year of Light.

1718 1f.90 multicoloured 6·75 6·50

593 *Succisa pratensis*

2015. Flora. Meadow Flowers. Multicoloured.

1719 85c. Type **593** 3·00 2·75

1720 1f. *Astrantia major* 3·50 3·25

1721 1f.30 *Leucanthemum vulgare* 4·50 4·25

594 Pond

2015. Nature Reserves in Liechtenstein. Multicoloured.

1722 1f. Type **594** 3·50 3·25

1723 1f. Pond (right) 3·50 3·25

1724 1f. Meadow (left) 3·50 3·25

1725 1f. Meadow (right) 3·50 3·25

595 Pelican

2015. Cathedral of St Florin Vaduz. Multicoloured.

1726 1f. Type **595** 3·50 3·25

1727 1f.40 Lamb of God 4·75 4·50

1728 1f.90 Eagle 6·75 6·50

1729 2f. Lion 7·25 6·75

596 Sand Lizard

2015. Reptiles. Multicoloured.

1730 1f.80 Type **596** 6·50 6·25

1731 2f. Smooth Snake 7·25 6·75

1732 5f. Common Lizard 18·00 17·50

597 Kaiser Auto Tractor

2015. Collections in Liechtenstein. Commercial Vehicles. Multicoloured.

1733 85c. Type **597** 3·00 2·75

1734 1f. Raimündle Tractor 3·50 3·25

1735 1f.40 Unimog 4·75 4·25

1736 1f.90 Fordson Tractor 6·75 6·50

598 Malbuntal, Liechtenstein

2015. The Alps. Multicoloured.

1737 1f.40 Type **598** 4·75 4·25

1738 1f.40 Velika Planina, Slovenia 4·75 4·25

599 Triesenberger Weinapfel

2015. Old Fruit Varieties. Apples. Multicoloured.

MS1739 1f.40×8, Type **599**; Damason Reinette; Leuser, Bohnapfel; Berlepsch; Rollapfel; Goldparmäne; Rösli Marie 20·00 20·00

600 Red Jasper Cameo

2015. Archaeological Finds in Liechtenstein. Jewellery. Multicoloured.

1740 85c. Type **600** 3·00 2·75

1741 1f. Gold ring with white chalcedony cameo 3·50 3·25

1742 1f.30 Green glass cameo 4·50 4·25

601 *Lo, How a Rose E'er Blooming*

2015. Christmas. Christmas Carols. Multicoloured.

1743 85c. Type **601** 3·00 2·75

1744 1f. *Silent Night* 3·50 3·25

1745 1f.40 *Oh, How Joyfully* 4·75 4·50

1746 1f.90 *Come, All Ye Shepherds* 6·75 6·50

602 *Adoration of the Shepherds*

2015. Princely Treasures. Paintings by Jacques Jordaens. Multicoloured.

1747 1f. Type **602** 3·50 3·25

1748 1f.40 *As the Old Ones Sing, So The Young Ones Pipe* 4·75 4·25

1749 1f.90 *Meleager and Atalante* 6·75 6·50

603 Monkey

2015. Chinese New Year. Year of the Monkey. Sheet 146×205 mm. Scarlet and gold.

MS1750 1f.90×4, Type **603**×4 27·00 26·00

604 Oak Tree

2016. Trees. Multicoloured.

1751 85c. Type **604** 3·00 2·75

1752 1f. Weeping Willow 3·50 3·25

1753 1f.50 Walnut 4·75 4·25

1754 1f.70 Aspen 6·00 5·75

1755 2f. Birch 7·25 6·75

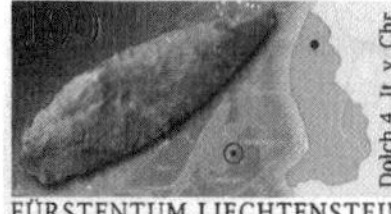

605 Knife

2016. Archaeological Finds in Liechtenstein. Utensils. Multicoloured.

1756 1f. Type **605** 3·50 3·25

1757 1f.50 Razor 4·75 4·25

1758 2f. Axe head 7·25 6·75

606 *Ruggeller Riet*

2016. Painters from Liechtenstein. Alois Ritter Commemoration. Multicoloured.

1759 1f. Type **606** 3·50 3·25

1760 2f. *Im Bofel* 7·25 6·75

607 The Four Seasons

2016. SEPAC (small European mail services).

1761 **607** 1f.50 multicoloured 4·75 4·25

608 Green and Polluted Earth

2016. Europa. Think Green. Multicoloured.

(a) Ordinary gum

1762 1f.50 Type **608** 4·75 4·00

(b) Self-adhesive

1763 1f.50 Roller painting contaminated landscape green (horiz) 4·75 4·25

609 Herbstlängler

2016. Old Fruit Varieties. Pears. Multicoloured.

MS1764 1f.×8, Type **609**; Kugeläugstler; Hermannsbirne, Rote Holzbirne; Sulser Längler; Sülibirne; Wolfsbirne; Tollbirne 20·00 20·00

610 Pond

2016. Nature Reserves in Liechtenstein. Ruggeller Riet. Multicoloured.

1765 1f. Type **610** 3·50 3·25

1766 1f. Pond (right) 3·50 3·25

1767 1f. Meadow (left) 3·50 3·25

1768 1f. Meadow (right) 3·50 3·25

611 Ship on Wheels Drinking Vessel

2016. Princely Treasures. Silversmithing. Multicoloured.

1769 1f. Type **611** 3·50 3·25

1770 1f.50 Diana riding stag 4·75 4·25

1771 2f. Nautilus cup 7·25 6·75

612 Archery

2016. Olympic Games. Rio 2016. Multicoloured.

1772	1f. Type **612**	3·50	3·25
1773	2f. Judo	7·25	6·75

613 M. Thun 490 cc. Motorcycle, 1928

2016. Collections in Liechtenstein. Motorcycles. Multicoloured.

1774	85c. Type **613**	3·00	2·75
1775	1f. Harley-Davidson 1000cc., 1920	3·50	3·25
1776	1f.50 Norton Königswellen single-cylinder 30 HP motorcycle and Type Stolz sidecar, 1948	4·75	4·50
1777	2f. Rudge, 1933	7·25	6·75

614 Maria Hilf Fraternity, Balzers

2016. Fraternities in Liechtenstein. Multicoloured.

1778	1f. Type **614**	3·50	3·25
1779	1f.50 St Anna Fraternity, Vaduz	4·50	4·25
1780	2f. St Sebastian Fraternity, Nendeln	7·25	6·75

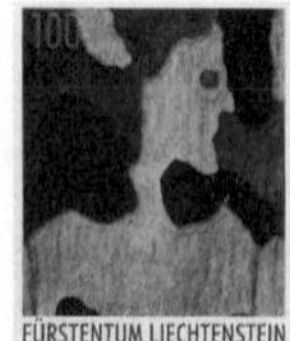

615 Woman

2016. Artistic Photography. Erich Allgäuer. Multicoloured.

1781	1f. Type **615**	3·50	3·25
1782	1f.50 Man	4·75	4·25
1783	2f. Woman wearing hat	7·25	6·75

616 *Young Woman on a Balcony* (Gerrit Dou)

2016. Art.

1784	**616**	1f.50 multicoloured	4·75	4·25

617 Lamplight

2016. Christmas. Nostalgic Christmas Cards. Multicoloured.

1785	85c. Type **617**	3·00	2·75
1786	1f. Exchanging Christmas presents (vert)	3·50	3·25
1787	1f.50 City scene (vert)	5·25	4·75
1788	2f. Winter walk	7·00	6·50

618 Badger and Mile Stone

2016. 'Liechtenstein without Us'. Multicoloured.

MS1789 2f.×3, Type **618**; Eagle; Parrots in flight — 22·00 21·00

619 Rooster

2016. Chinese New Year. Year of the Rooster. Scarlet and gold.

MS1790 2f.×4, Type **619**×4 — 29·00 28·00

620 Oats

2017. Crop Plants - Grains. Multicoloured.

1791	85c. Type **620**	3·00	2·75
1792	1f. Barley	3·50	3·25
1793	1f.50 Maize	5·25	4·75
1794	2f. Millet	7·00	6·50

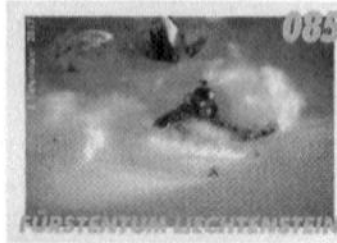

621 Snowboarding

2017. Outdoor Sports. Multicoloured.

1795	85c. Type **621**	3·00	2·75
1796	1f. Windsurfing	3·50	3·25
1797	2f. Ski-jump	7·00	6·50

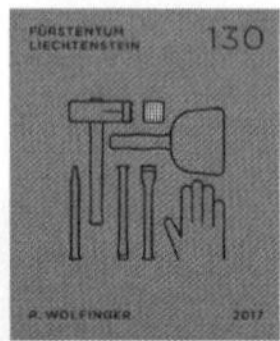

622 Stonemason

2017. Trades and Crafts

1798	1f.30 lilac, black and chrome	4·50	4·25
1799	1f.80 azure, black and cerise	6·25	5·75
1800	2f. orange-yellow and emerald	7·00	6·50

Designs: Type **622**; 1f.80 Tailor; 2f. Goldsmith

623 Vaduz Castle

2017. Europa. Castles. Multicoloured.

1801	1f.50 Type **623**	5·25	4·75
1802	1f.50 Gutenberg Castle	5·25	4·75

624 *Request for Admission*

2017. Princely Treasures. Paintings by Peter Fendi. Multicoloured.

1803	85c. Type **624**	3·00	2·75
1804	1f. *Sneaking a Peek*	3·50	3·25
1805	1f.50 *A Child's Prayer*	5·25	4·75

625 Multicoloured Handprints

2017. Diversity. 50th Anniv of HPZ Remedial Education Centre

1806	**625**	1f. multicoloured	3·50	3·25

626 Summer

2017. Nature Reserves in Liechtenstein. Gampriner Seelein. Multicoloured.

1807	1f. Type **626**	3·50	3·25
1808	1f. Summer (right)	3·50	3·25
1809	1f. Winter (left)	3·50	3·25
1810	1f. Winter (right)	3·50	3·25

627 Vaduz Castle

2017. Golden Wedding of Prince Hans-Adam II and Princess Marie of Liechtenstein. Multicoloured.

MS1811 1f.30 Type **627**; 2f.20 Royal couple; 2f.80 Twin wedding rings — 23·00 22·00

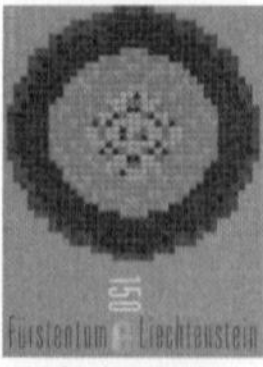

628 Apricot 'Mombacher Frühaprikose'

2017. Old Fruit Varieties. Stone Fruit. Multicoloured.

MS1812 1f.×8, Type **628**; Greengage 'Reine Claude Verte'; Plum 'Kirkespflaume'; Plum 'Hauszwetschge'; Cherry 'Schauenburger Kirsche'; Apricot 'Ungarische Beste'; Plum 'Mirabelle von Nancy'; Cherry 'Gelbe Denise' — 29·00 28·00

2017. Bicentenary of Post ('K K Briefsammelstelle Balzers'). Multicoloured.

MS1813 1f.30 Early postman and little girl; Posthorn; Early horse-drawn mail coach — 4·75 4·50

630 Settlement Area

2017. Settlement Area of Liechtenstein

1814	**630**	1f.50 multicoloured	5·25	4·75

631 *Rappastein*

2017. Mountain Paintings - Helmut Ditsch

1815	**631**	3f.80 multicoloured	13·50	12·00

OFFICIAL STAMPS

1932. Stamps of 1930 optd **REGIERUNGS DIENSTSACHE** under crown.

O118B	5r. green	15·00	22·00
O119B	10r. lilac	£100	22·00
O120B	20r. red	£110	22·00
O121B	30r. blue	24·00	30·00
O122C	35r. green	20·00	49·00
O123C	50r. black	£110	30·00
O124A	60r. green	20·00	70·00
O125B	1f.20 brown	£200	£550

1933. Nos. 121 and 123 optd **REGIERUNGS DIENSTSACHE** in circle round crown.

O126	**38**	25r. orange	60·00	80·00
O127	-	1f.20 brown	£140	£550

1934. Nos. 128 etc. optd **REGIERUNGS DIENSTSACHE** in circle round crown.

O150	**41**	5r. green	3·00	5·00
O151	-	10r. violet	5·75	5·00
O152	-	15r. orange	1·00	5·00
O153	-	20r. red	1·00	5·00
O155	-	25r. brown	5·00	30·00
O156	-	30r. blue	6·75	15·00
O157	**42**	50r. brown	2·00	6·75
O158	-	90r. green	15·00	80·00
O159	-	1f.50 brown	60·00	£400

1937. Stamps of 1937 optd **REGIERUNGS DIENSTSACHE** in circle round crown.

O174	**51**	5r. green and buff	1·00	3·00
O175	-	10r. violet and buff	2·00	4·00
O176	-	20r. red and buff	2·40	4·00
O177	-	25r. brown and buff	1·00	4·00
O178	-	30r. blue and buff	2·40	4·00
O179	-	50r. brown and buff	1·50	3·00
O180	-	1f. purple and buff	1·50	17·00
O181	-	1f.50 grey and buff	4·00	24·00

1947. Stamps of 1944 optd **DIENSTMARKE** and crown.

O255	5r. green	3·00	1·40
O256	10r. violet	3·00	1·90
O257	20r. red	4·00	1·90
O258	30r. blue	5·00	2·75
O259	50r. grey	5·00	5·25
O260	1f. red	19·00	20·00
O261	1f.50 blue	19·00	20·00

O86

1950. Buff paper.

O287	**O86**	5r. purple and grey	45	45
O288	**O86**	10r. green and mauve	45	45
O289	**O86**	20r. brown and blue	45	45
O290	**O86**	30r. purple and red	60	55
O291	**O86**	40r. blue and brown	80	75
O292	**O86**	55r. green and red	1·50	1·40
O293	**O86**	60r. grey and mauve	1·50	1·40
O294	**O86**	80r. orange and grey	1·60	1·50
O295	**O86**	90r. brown and blue	1·80	1·60
O296	**O86**	1f.20 turquoise and orange	2·40	2·30

1968. White paper.

O495	**O86**	5r. brown and orange	20	15
O496	**O86**	10r. violet and red	25	20
O497	**O86**	20r. red and green	35	35
O498	**O86**	30r. green and red	40	40
O499	**O86**	50r. blue and red	70	65
O500	**O86**	60r. orange and blue	85	75
O501	**O86**	70r. purple and green	95	90
O502	**O86**	80r. green and red	1·10	1·00
O503	**O86**	95r. green and red	1·30	1·20
O504	**O86**	1f. purple & turquoise	1·60	1·50
O505	**O86**	1f.20 brown & turq	2·20	2·20
O506	**O86**	2f. brown and orange	3·00	2·75

O198 Government Building, Vaduz

1976

O652	**O198**	10r. brown and violet	20	15
O653	**O198**	20r. red and blue	25	20
O654	**O198**	35r. blue and red	45	40
O655	**O198**	40r. violet and green	65	55
O656	**O198**	50r. green and mauve	70	60
O657	**O198**	70r. purple and green	95	85
O658	**O198**	80r. green and purple	1·10	95
O659	**O198**	90r. violet and blue	1·30	1·10

O660	**O198**	1f. grey and purple	1·40	1·20
O661	**O198**	1f.10 brown and blue	1·50	1·30
O662	**O198**	1f.50 green and red	2·00	1·80
O663	**O198**	2f. orange and blue	2·75	2·40
O664	**O198**	5f. purple and orange	18·00	16·00

POSTAGE DUE STAMPS

D11

1920

D43	**D11**	5h. red	50	60
D44	**D11**	10h. red	50	60
D45	**D11**	15h. red	50	60
D46	**D11**	20h. red	50	60
D47	**D11**	25h. red	50	70
D48	**D11**	30h. red	50	70
D49	**D11**	40h. red	50	70
D50	**D11**	50h. red	50	70
D51	**D11**	80h. red	50	70
D52	**D11**	1k. blue	65	2·40
D53	**D11**	2k. blue	65	2·40
D54	**D11**	5k. blue	65	2·75

D25

1928

D84	**D25**	5r. red and violet	2·00	5·00
D85	**D25**	10r. red and violet	2·40	5·00
D86	**D25**	15r. red and violet	4·00	22·00
D87	**D25**	20r. red and violet	4·00	5·00
D88	**D25**	25r. red and violet	4·00	15·00
D89	**D25**	30r. red and violet	13·00	23·00
D90	**D25**	40r. red and violet	13·50	24·00
D91	**D25**	50r. red and violet	16·00	30·00

D58

1940

D189	**D58**	5r. red and blue	2·40	5·75
D190	**D58**	10r. red and blue	1·00	2·00
D191	**D58**	15r. red and blue	1·50	9·75
D192	**D58**	20r. red and blue	1·50	3·00
D193	**D58**	25r. red and blue	3·00	6·50
D194	**D58**	30r. red and blue	6·50	11·00
D195	**D58**	40r. red and blue	6·50	9·75
D196	**D58**	50r. red and blue	7·50	11·00

LITHUANIA

A country on the Baltic Sea, under Russian rule until occupied by the Germans in the first World War (see German Eastern Command). It was an independent republic from 1918 to 1940, when it was incorporated into the U.S.S.R.

Lithuania declared its independence in 1990, and the U.S.S.R. formally recognized the republic in 1991.

1918. 100 skatiku = 1 auksinas.
1922. 100 centu = 1 litas.
1990. 100 kopeks = 1 rouble.
1992. Talons.
1993. 100 centu = 1 litas.

1

1918

3B	**1**	B 10s. black on buff	55·00	31·00
4B	**1**	B 15s. black on buff	55·00	31·00
5B	**1**	A 20s. black on buff	38·00	25·00
6B	**1**	A 30s. black on buff	44·00	31·00
7B	**1**	A 40s. black on buff	65·00	44·00
8B	**1**	A 50s. black on buff	50·00	31·00

Lietuvos
10
skatikų
paštas

2

1919

9	**2**	10s. black on buff	11·50	6·25
10	**2**	15s. black on buff	11·50	6·25
11	**2**	20s. black on buff	11·50	6·25
12	**2**	30s. black on buff	11·50	6·25

Lietuvos
paštas
10 sk.

3

1919

13	**3**	10s. black on buff	5·75	3·75
14	**3**	15s. black on buff	5·75	3·75
15	**3**	20s. black on buff	5·75	3·75
16	**3**	30s. black on buff	5·75	3·75
17	**3**	40s. black on buff	5·75	3·75
18	**3**	50s. black on buff	5·75	3·75
19	**3**	60s. black on buff	5·75	3·75

Lietuvos
paštas
sk. 10 sk.

4

1919

20	**4**	10s. black on buff	5·75	3·75
21	**4**	15s. black on buff	5·75	3·75
22	**4**	20s. black on buff	5·75	3·75
23	**4**	30s. black on buff	5·75	3·75
24	**4**	40s. black on buff	5·75	3·75
25	**4**	50s. black on buff	5·75	3·75
26	**4**	60s. black on buff	5·75	3·75

5 Arms

6

7

1919. 'auksinas' in lower case letters on 1 to 5a.

40	**5**	10s. pink	50	45
50	**5**	10s. orange	50	15
51	**5**	15s. violet	50	15
52	**5**	20s. blue	50	15
43	**5**	30s. orange	50	45
53	**5**	30s. bistre	50	15
54	**5**	40s. brown	3·75	2·50
55	**6**	50s. green	50	15
56	**6**	60s. red and violet	50	15
57	**6**	75s. red and yellow	50	15
37	**7**	1a. red and grey	3·75	65
38	**7**	3a. red and brown	3·75	65
39	**7**	5a. red and green	3·75	1·30

1921. As T **7**, but 'AUKSINAS' or 'AUKSINAI' in capital letters.

58	**7**	1a. red and grey	50	15
59	**7**	3a. red and brown	50	40
60	**7**	5a. red and green	50	65

11 Lithuania receiving Independence

12 Lithuania arises

1920. Second Anniversary of Independence.

65	**11**	10s. lake	4·50	3·75
66	**11**	15s. lilac	4·50	3·75
67	**11**	20s. blue	4·50	3·75
68	**12**	30s. brown	4·50	3·75
69	-	40s. green and brown	4·50	3·75
70	**12**	50s. red	4·50	3·75
71	**12**	60s. lilac	4·50	3·75
72	-	80s. red and violet	4·50	3·75
73	-	1a. red and green	4·50	3·75
74	-	3a. red and brown	4·50	3·75
75	-	5a. red and green	4·50	3·75

Designs: Vert—40s., 80s., 1a. Lithuania with chains broken. (25x25 mm)—3, 5a. Arms.

16 Arms

17 Vytautas

1920. National Assembly.

76	**16**	10s. red	1·30	65
77	**16**	15s. violet	1·30	65
78	**17**	20s. green	1·30	65
79	**16**	30s. brown	1·30	65
80	-	40s. violet and green	1·30	65
81	**17**	50s. brown and orange	3·25	2·50
82	**17**	60s. red and orange	1·30	65
83	-	80s. red, grey and black	1·30	65
84	-	1a. yellow and black	1·90	95
85	-	3a. green and black	1·90	1·50
86	-	5a. violet and black	5·00	3·75

Designs: As T **17**—40s., 80s. Gediminas. As T **16**—1a. to 5a. Sacred Oak and Altar.

20 Sower

21 Kestutis

22 Reaper

23

1921

87A	**20**	10s. red	1·30	1·30
88A	**20**	15s. mauve	65	1·90
89A	**20**	20s. blue	50	40
90A	**22**	30s. brown	3·75	3·75
91A	**21**	40s. red	40	30
92A	**22**	50s. olive	65	40
93A	**22**	60s. mauve and green	3·75	6·25
94A	**21**	80s. red and orange	65	40
95A	**21**	1a. green and brown	65	40
96A	**21**	2a. red and blue	65	40
97A	**23**	3a. blue and brown	2·50	2·50
124	**20**	4a. blue and yellow	65	1·90
98A	**23**	5a. red and grey	2·50	2·50
125	**20**	8a black and green	65	2·50
99A	**23**	10a. mauve and red	1·30	65
100A	**23**	25a. green and brown	3·25	2·50
101A	**23**	100a. grey and red	16·00	12·50

24 Flying Posthorn

25 Junkers F-13 over River Niemen

1921. Air. Inauguration of Kaunas–Konigsberg Air Service.

102	**24**	20s. blue	1·30	1·30
103	**24**	40s. orange	1·30	1·30
104	**24**	60s. green	1·30	1·30
105	**24**	80s. red	1·30	1·30
106	**25**	1a. green and red	2·50	1·30
107	-	2a. brown and blue	2·50	1·30
108	-	5a. grey and yellow	2·50	2·50

Designs: As T **25**—2a. Three Junkers F-13 monoplanes; 5a. Junkers F-13 over Gediminas Castle.

28 Allegory of Flight

1921. Air. Inauguration of Air Mail Service.

109	**28**	20s. lilac and orange	3·75	3·25
110	**28**	40s. red and blue	3·75	3·25
111	**28**	60s. olive and blue	3·75	3·25
112	**28**	80s. green and yellow	3·75	3·25
113	**28**	1a. blue and green	3·75	3·25
114	**28**	2a. red and grey	3·75	3·25
115	**28**	5a. green and purple	3·75	3·25

1922. Surch **4 AUKSINAI** with or without frame.

116	**6**	4a. on 75s. red and yellow	1·30	2·50

30 Junkers F-13

1922. Air.

118	**30**	1a. red and brown	4·50	5·00
119	**30**	3a. green and violet	4·50	5·00
120	**30**	5a. yellow and blue	4·50	5·00

31 Junkers F-13 over Gediminas Castle

1922. Air.

121	**31**	2a. red and blue	2·50	2·50
122	**31**	4a. red and brown	2·50	2·50
123	**31**	10a. blue and black	2·50	2·50

33 Pte. Luksis

1922. 'De jure' Recognition of Lithuania by League of Nations. Inscr 'LIETUVA DE JURE'.

126	**33**	20s. red and black	1·90	1·60
127	-	40s. violet and green	1·90	1·60
128	-	50s. blue and purple	1·90	1·60
129	-	60s. orange and violet	1·90	1·60
130	-	1a. blue and red	1·90	1·60
131	-	2a. brown and blue	1·90	1·60
132	-	3a. blue and brown	1·90	1·60
133	-	4a. purple and green	1·90	1·60
134	-	5a. red and brown	1·90	1·60
135	-	6a. blue	1·90	1·60
136	-	8a. yellow and blue	1·90	1·60
137	-	10a. green and violet	1·90	1·60

Designs: Vert—40s. Lt. Juozapavicius; 50s. Dr. Basanavicius; 60s. Mrs. Petkevicaite; 1a. Professor. Voldemaras; 2a. Dovidaitis; 3a. Dr. Slezevicius; 4a. Dr. Galvanauskas; 5a. Dr. Grinius; 6a. Dr. Stulginskis; 8a. President Smetona. Horiz: (39x27 mm)—10a. Stauguitis, President Smetona and Silingas.

1922. Surch.

138	**5**	1c. on 10s. orange (postage)	4·50	10·00
139	**5**	1c. on 15s. violet	6·25	10·00
143	**5**	1c. on 20s. blue	6·25	10·00
144	**5**	1c. on 30s. orange	£110	£140
145	**5**	1c. on 30s. bistre	65	1·00
146	**5**	1c. on 40s. brown	65	90
148	**22**	1c. on 50s. olive	40	25
149	**6**	2c. on 50s. green	5·00	7·50
150	**6**	2c. on 60s. red and violet	25	25
151	**6**	2c. on 75s. red and yellow	3·25	10·00
152	**20**	3c. on 10s. red	19·00	12·50
153	**20**	3c. on 15s. mauve	40	25
154	**20**	3c. on 20s. blue	65	7·50
155	**22**	3c. on 30s. brown	31·00	19·00
156	**21**	3c. on 40s. red	65	1·00
157	**7**	3c. on 1a. (No. 37)	£275	£275
158	**7**	3c. on 1a. (No. 58)	65	1·30
159	**7**	3c. on 3a. (No. 38)	£275	£275
160	**7**	3c. on 3a. (No. 59)	40	90
161	**7**	3c. on 5a. (No. 39)	£180	£180
162	**7**	3c. on 5a. (No. 60)	40	90
163	**22**	5c. on 50s. olive	25	25
164	**22**	5c. on 60s. mauve & green	31·00	31·00
165	**21**	5c. on 80s. red and orange	90	75
166	**6**	5c. on 4a. on 75s. red and yellow	2·50	20·00
168	**21**	10c. on 1a. green & brown	1·30	25
169	**21**	10c. on 2a. red and blue	40	25
170	**20**	15c. on 4a. blue and yellow	25	25
171	**23**	25c. on 3a. blue and green	31·00	50·00
172	**23**	25c. on 5a. red and grey	19·00	19·00
173	**23**	25c. on 10a. mauve and red	3·25	3·25
174	**20**	30c. on 8a. black and green	1·90	50
175	**23**	50c. on 25a. green & brown	6·25	6·25
176	**23**	1l. on 100 a grey and red	7·00	6·25
177	**24**	10c. on 20s. blue (air)	10·00	7·50
178	**24**	10c. on 40s. orange	5·00	8·75
179	**24**	10c. on 60s. green	5·00	8·75
180	**24**	10c. on 80s. red	5·00	8·75
181	**25**	20c. on 1a. green and red	31·00	25·00
182	-	20c. on 2a. (No. 107)	31·00	29·00
183	**31**	25c. on 2a. red and blue	2·50	1·90
184	**31**	30c. on 4a. red and brown	2·50	2·50
185	-	50c. on 5a. (No. 108)	5·00	2·50
186	**31**	50c. on 10a. blue and black	2·50	2·50
187	**30**	1l. on 5a. yellow and blue	44·00	50·00

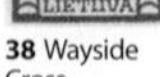

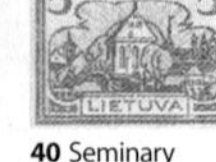

38 Wayside Cross **39** Ruins of Kaunas Castle **40** Seminary Church

1923

201	**38**	2c. brown	1·30	40
202	**38**	3c. bistre	1·90	40
203	**38**	5c. green	1·90	40
204	**38**	10c. violet	3·75	15
189	**38**	15c. red	3·75	25
190	**38**	20c. green	3·75	25
191	**38**	25c. blue	3·75	25
206	**38**	36c. brown	15·00	1·30
192	**39**	50c. green	3·75	25
193	**39**	60c. red	3·75	25
194	**40**	1l. orange and green	15·00	25
195	**40**	3l. red and grey	23·00	1·10
196	**40**	5l. brown and blue	31·00	1·50

43 Arms of Memel **44** Ruins of Trakai

1923. Union of Memel with Lithuania.

210	**43**	1c. red and green	1·30	1·30
211	-	2c. mauve	1·30	1·30
212	-	3c. yellow	1·30	1·30
213	**43**	5c. buff and blue	3·75	3·75
214	-	10c. red	2·50	2·50
215	-	15c. green	2·50	2·50
216	**44**	25c. violet	2·50	2·50
217	-	30c. red	6·25	6·25
218	-	60c. green	2·50	2·50
219	-	1l. green	2·50	2·50
220	-	2l. red	12·50	12·50
221	**44**	3l. blue	12·50	12·50
222	-	5l. blue	12·50	12·50

Designs: As T **43**—3c., 2l. Chapel of Biruta; 10c., 15c. War Memorial Kaunas. As T **44**—2, 30c. Arms of Lithuania; 60c., 5l. Memel Lighthouse; 1l. Memel Harbour.

45 Biplane

46 Biplane

1924. Air.

223	**45**	20c. yellow	2·50	1·60
224	**45**	40c. green	2·50	1·60
225	**45**	60c. red	2·50	1·60
226	**46**	1l. brown	5·00	1·60

1924. Charity. War Orphans Fund. Surch **KARO NASLAICIAMS** and premium.

227	**38**	2c.+2c. bistre (postage)	3·75	3·75
228	**38**	3c.+3c. bistre	3·75	3·75
229	**38**	5c.+5c. green	3·75	3·75
231	**38**	10c.+10c. violet	5·00	5·00
232	**38**	15c.+15c. red	6·25	6·25
233	**38**	20c.+20c. olive	7·50	7·50
235	**38**	25c.+25c. blue	19·00	19·00
236	**38**	36c.+34c. brown	19·00	19·00
237	**39**	50c.+50c. green	19·00	19·00
238	**39**	60c.+60c. red	25·00	25·00
239	**40**	1l.+1l. orange and green	25·00	25·00
240	**40**	3l.+2l. red and grey	50·00	50·00
241	**40**	5l.+3l. brown and blue	65·00	65·00
242	**45**	20c.+20c. yellow (air)	31·00	31·00
243	**45**	40c.+40c. green	31·00	31·00
244	**45**	60c.+60c. red	31·00	31·00
245	**46**	1l.+1l. brown	31·00	31·00

49 Barn Swallow carrying Letter

1926. Air.

246	**49**	20c. red	1·90	90
247	**49**	40c. orange and mauve	1·90	90
248	**49**	60c. black and blue	3·75	90

1926. Charity. War Invalids. Nos. 227/239 surch with new values and small ornaments.

249	**38**	1c.+1c. on 2c.+2c.	2·10	2·10
250	**38**	2c.+2c. on 3c.+3c.	2·10	2·10
251	**38**	2c.+2c. on 5c.+5c.	2·10	2·10
253	**38**	5c.+5c. on 10c.+10c.	4·50	4·50
254	**38**	5c.+5c. on 15c.+15c.	4·50	4·50
255	**38**	10c.+10c. on 20c.+20c.	4·50	4·50
257	**38**	10c.+10c. on 25c.+25c.	10·50	10·50
258	**38**	14c.+14c. on 36c.+34c.	12·50	12·50
259	**39**	20c.+20c. on 50c.+50c.	10·50	10·50
260	**39**	25c.+25c. on 60c.+60c.	21·00	21·00
261	**40**	30c.+30c. on 1l.+1l.	31·00	31·00

1926. Charity. War Orphans. Nos. 227/339 surch **V.P.** and new values in circular ornament.

262	**38**	1c.+1c. on 2c.+2c.	2·10	2·10
263	**38**	2c.+2c. on 3c.+3c.	2·10	2·10
264	**38**	2c.+2c. on 5c.+5c.	2·10	2·10
266	**38**	5c.+5c. on 10c.+10c.	4·50	4·50
267	**38**	10c.+10c. on 15c.+15c.	4·50	4·50
268	**38**	15c.+15c. on 20c.+20c.	4·50	4·50
270	**38**	15c.+15c. on 25c.+25c.	10·50	10·50
271	**38**	19c.+19c. on 36c.+34c.	10·50	10·50
272	**39**	25c.+25c. on 50c.+50c.	12·50	12·50
273	**39**	30c.+30c. on 60c.+60c.	21·00	21·00
274	**40**	50c.+50c. on 1l.+1l.	31·00	31·00

56

1927

275	**56**	2c. orange	2·10	15
276	**56**	3c. brown	2·10	15
277	**56**	5c. green	2·75	15
278	**56**	10c. violet	4·50	25
279	**56**	15c. red	4·50	25
280	**56**	25c. blue	4·50	25
283	**56**	30c. blue	44·00	8·75

57

1927. Dr. Basanavicius Mourning Issue.

285A	**57**	15c. red	3·25	2·50
286A	**57**	25c. blue	3·25	2·50
287A	**57**	50c. green	3·25	2·50
288A	**57**	60c. violet	6·25	5·00

58 'Vytis' of the Lithuanian Arms

1927

289	**58**	1l. green and grey	1·90	1·30
290	**58**	3l. violet and green	6·50	1·30
291	**58**	5l. brown and grey	7·50	1·90

59 President Antanas Smetona **60** Lithuania liberated

1928. Tenth Anniversary of Independence.

292	**59**	5c. green and brown	1·60	40
293	**59**	10c. black and violet	1·60	40
294	**59**	15c. brown and orange	1·60	40
295	**59**	25c. slate and blue	1·60	40
296	**60**	50c. purple and blue	1·60	40
297	**60**	60c. black and red	1·60	40
298	-	1l. brown	1·60	40

Design: Horiz—1l. Lithuania's resurrection (Angel and soldiers). Dated 1918-1928.

62 **63**

64 J. Tubelis

1930. 500th Death Anniversary of Grand Duke Vytautas.

299	**62**	2c. brown (postage)	50	15
300	**62**	3c. violet and brown	50	15
301	**62**	5c. red and green	50	15
302	**62**	10c. green and violet	50	15
303	**62**	15c. violet and red	50	15
304	**62**	30c. purple and blue	1·10	15
305	**62**	36c. olive and purple	1·60	50
306	**62**	50c. blue and green	1·10	65
307	**62**	60c. red and blue	1·10	75
308	**63**	1l. purple, grey and green	4·50	1·90
309	**63**	3l. violet, pink and mauve	6·25	3·25
310	**63**	5l. red, grey and brown	16·00	4·50
311	**63**	10l. black and blue	43·00	25·00
312	**63**	25l. green and brown	90·00	90·00
313	**64**	5c. brown, yellow and black (air)	90	50
314	**64**	10c. black, drab and blue	90	50
315	**64**	15c. blue, grey and purple	90	50
316	-	20c. red, orange and brown	1·60	1·30
317	-	40c. violet, light blue & blue	2·10	1·30
318	-	60c. black, lilac and green	2·75	1·30
319	-	1l. black, lilac and red	4·75	2·50

Designs: Horiz—20c., 40c. Vytautas and Kaunas; 60c., 1l. Vytautas and Smetona.

66 Railway Station, Kaunas

1932. Orphans' Fund. Imperf or perf.

320	**66**	5c. blue and brown	50	50
321	**66**	10c. purple and brown	50	50
322	-	15c. brown and green	1·10	95
323	-	25c. blue and green	1·60	1·40
324	-	50c. grey and olive	3·25	3·75
325	-	60c. grey and mauve	8·50	8·25
326	-	1l. blue and grey	8·50	8·25
327	-	3l. purple and green	8·50	8·25

Designs: As T **66**—15, 25c. *The Two Pines* (painting); 50c. GPO. Vert—60c., 1, 3l. Vilnius Cathedral.

68 Map of Lithuania, Memel and Vilna

1932. Air. Orphans' Fund. Imperf or perf.

328	**68**	5c. red and green	1·10	1·30
329	**68**	10c. purple and brown	1·10	1·30
330	-	15c. blue and buff	1·10	1·30
331	-	20c. black and brown	8·50	6·25
332	-	40c. purple and yellow	8·50	6·25
333	-	60c. blue and buff	10·50	11·50
334	-	1l. purple and green	10·50	11·50
335	-	2l. blue and green	10·50	11·50

Designs: 15, 20c. Aircraft over R. Niemen; 40, 60c. Town Hall, Kaunas; 1, 2l. Vytautas Church, Kaunas.

69 Vytautas escapes from Prison

71 Coronation of Mindaugas

1932. 15th Anniversary of Independence. Imperf or perf.

336	**69**	5c. purple and red (postage)	1·10	1·10
337	**69**	10c. brown and grey	1·10	1·10
338	-	15c. green and red	1·10	1·10
339	-	25c. brown and purple	3·25	3·25
340	-	50c. brown and green	3·25	3·75
341	-	60c. red and green	7·50	8·75
342	-	1l. black and blue	7·50	7·50
343	-	3l. green and purple	7·50	8·75
344	-	5c. lilac and green (air)	1·10	1·30
345	-	10c. red and green	1·10	1·30
346	**71**	15c. brown and violet	1·10	1·30
347	-	20c. black and red	5·25	3·75
348	-	40c. black and purple	7·50	6·25
349	-	60c. black and orange	10·50	12·50
350	-	1l. green and violet	10·50	11·50
351	-	2l. brown and blue	10·50	11·50

Designs: Postage. As T **69**—15, 25c. Vytautas and Jagello preaching the gospel; 50, 60c. Battle of Grunewald; 1, 3l. Proclamation of Independence. Air. As T **71**—5, 10c. Battle of Saules; 40c. Gediminas in Council; 60c. Founding of Vilnius; 1l. Russians surrendering to Gediminas; 2l. Algirdas before Moscow.

72 A. Visteliauskas

1933. 50th Anniversary of Publication of *Ausra*.

352	**72**	5c. red and green	1·10	1·30
353	**72**	10c. red and blue	1·10	1·30
354	-	15c. red and orange	1·10	1·30
355	-	25c. brown and blue	3·25	3·25
356	-	50c. blue and green	2·10	3·75
357	-	60c. deep brown & lt brown	15·00	14·00
358	-	1l. purple and red	15·00	14·00
359	-	3l. purple and blue	15·00	14·00

Portraits: 15, 25c. P. Vileisis; 50, 60c. J. Sliupas; 1, 3l. J. Basanavicius.

73 Trakai Castle

1933. Air. 550th Death Anniversary of Grand Duke Kestutis.

360	**73**	5c. blue and green	1·10	1·30
361	**73**	10c. brown and violet	1·10	1·30
362	-	15c. violet and blue	1·10	1·30
363	-	20c. purple and brown	5·00	3·75
364	-	40c. purple and blue	5·00	6·25
365	-	60c. blue and red	7·50	8·75
366	-	1l. blue and green	7·50	8·75
367	-	2l. green and violet	7·50	11·50

Designs: 15, 20c. Kestutis encounters Birute; 40, 60c. Birute; 1, 2l. Kestutis and Algirdas.

74 Mother and Child

1933. Child Welfare. (a) Postage.

373	**74**	5c. brown and green	50	50
374	**74**	10c. blue and red	50	50
375	-	15c. purple and green	50	50
376	-	25c. black and orange	2·10	2·50
377	-	50c. red and green	2·10	2·50
378	-	60c. orange and black	9·00	10·50
379	-	1l. blue and brown	9·00	10·50
380	-	3l. green and purple	9·00	10·50

Designs: Vert—15, 25c. Boy reading a book; 50, 60c. Boy with building bricks; 1, 3l. Mother and child weaving.

75 J. Tumas Vaizgantas

(b) Air. Various medallion portraits in triangular frames.

381		5c. blue and red	50	40
382		10c. green and violet	50	40
383	**75**	15c. brown and green	50	50
384	**75**	20c. blue and red	1·10	75
385	-	40c. green and lake	3·25	3·25
386	-	60c. brown and blue	2·10	7·50
387	-	1l. blue and yellow	5·25	7·50
388	-	2l. lake and green	7·50	12·50

Designs: 5, 10c. Maironis; 40, 60c. Vincas Kudirka; 1, 2l. Zemaite.

76 Captains S. Darius and S. Girenas

78 'Flight' mourning over Wreckage

1934. Air. Death of Darius and Girenas (trans-Atlantic airmen).

389	**76**	20c. red and black	15	15
390	-	40c. blue and red	15	15
391	**76**	60c. violet and black	15	15
392	**78**	1l. black and red	50	50
393	-	3l. orange and green	1·10	2·50
394	-	5l. blue and brown	4·50	5·00

Designs: Horiz—40c. Bellanca monoplane *Lituanica* over Atlantic. Vert—3l. *Lituanica* and globe; 5l. *Lituanica* and Vytis.

81 President A. Smetona

1934. President's 60th Birthday.

395	**81**	15c. red	12·50	15
396	**81**	30c. green	12·50	40
397	**81**	60c. blue	12·50	65

82

83

84 Gleaner

85

1934

398	**82**	2c. red and orange	50	25
399	**82**	5c. green	50	15
400	**83**	10c. brown	1·60	15
401	**84**	25c. brown and green	3·75	15
402	**83**	35c. red	3·75	15
403	**84**	50c. blue	7·75	15
404	**85**	1l. purple and red	55·00	25
405	**85**	3l. green	30	25
406	-	5l. purple and blue	30	25
407	-	10l. brown and yellow	2·75	6·25

Designs: Horiz as T **85**—5l., 10l. Knight.
For design as T **82** but smaller, see Nos. 411/412.

1935. Air. Honouring Atlantic Flyer Vaitkus. No. 390 optd **F. VAITKUS nugalejo Atlanta 21-22-IX-1935.**

407a		40c. blue and red	£650	£650

87 Vaitkus and Air Route

1936. Air. Felix Vaitkus's New York–Ireland Flight.

408	**87**	15c. purple	2·10	75
409	**87**	30c. green	4·50	75
410	**87**	60c. blue	5·25	2·30

1936. As T **82** but smaller (18×23 mm).

411	**82**	2c. orange	15	15
412	**82**	5c. green	20	15

88 President Smetona

1936

413	**88**	15c. red	8·50	15
414	**88**	30c. green	12·50	15
415	**88**	60c. blue	21·00	15

89

1937

416	**89**	10c. green	1·60	40
417	**89**	25c. mauve	15	15
418	**89**	35c. red	1·10	15
419	**89**	50c. brown	1·60	65
419a	**89**	1l. blue	50	1·50

90 Archer

1938. First National Olympiad Fund.

420	**90**	5c.+5c. green	8·50	12·50
421	-	15c.+5c. red	8·50	12·50
422	-	30c.+10c. blue	16·00	19·00
423	-	60c.+15c. brown	21·00	31·00

Designs: 15c. Throwing the javelin; 30c. Diving; 60c. Relay runner breasting tape.

1938. Scouts' and Guides' National Camp Fund. Nos. 420/423 optd **TAUTINE SKAUCIU** (or **SKAUTU**) **STOVYKLA** and badge.

424	**90**	5c.+5c. green	10·50	12·50
425	-	15c.+5c. red	10·50	12·50
426	-	30c.+10c. blue	10·50	19·00
427	-	60c.+15c. brown	21·00	31·00

92 President Smetona

1939. 20th Anniversary of Independence.

428	-	15c. red	50	25
429	**92**	30c. green	1·10	65
430	-	35c. mauve	1·10	65
431	**92**	60c. blue	1·60	1·30
MS431a		148×105 mm. Nos. 430/431	12·50	44·00
MS431b		Do. but imperf	95·00	£190

Design: 15, 35c. Dr. Basanvicius proclaiming Lithuanian independence.

93 Scoring a Goal

1939. Third European Basketball Championship and Physical Culture Fund.

432	-	15c.+10c. brown	8·50	60·00
433	**93**	30c.+15c. green	8·50	60·00
434	-	60c.+40c. violet	16·00	31·00

Designs: Vert—15c. Scoring a goal. Horiz (40½×36 mm)—60c. International flags and ball.

1939. Recovery of Vilnius. Nos. 428/431 optd **VILNIUS 1939-X-10** and trident.

435	-	15c. red	1·10	65
436	**92**	30c. green	1·10	65
437	-	35c. mauve	2·75	1·30
438	**92**	60c. blue	2·75	1·90

95 Vytis

1940. Liberty Issue.

439	**95**	5c. brown	15	80
440	-	10c. green	90	2·10
441	-	15c. orange	25	80
442	-	25c. brown	15	2·10
443	-	30c. green	15	1·40
444	-	35c. orange	30	2·10

Designs: 10c. Angel; 15c. Woman releasing a dove; 25c. Mother and children; 30c. Liberty Bell; 35c. Mythical animal.

96 Vilnius

1940. Recovery of Vilnius.

445	**96**	15c. brown	50	65
446	-	30c. green	1·10	1·30
447	-	60c. blue	2·10	2·50
MS447a		140×106 mm. Nos. 445/447 with gold frames	12·50	21·00

Designs—Vert: 30c. Portrait of Gediminas. Horiz: 60c. Ruins of Trakai Castle.

1940. Incorporation of Lithuania in USSR. Optd **LTSR 1940 VII 21**.

448	**82**	2c. red and orange	25	40
449	**95**	5c. brown	25	40
450	-	10c. green (No. 440)	6·00	10·00
451	-	15c. orange (No. 441)	40	65
452	-	25c. brown (No. 442)	40	1·30
453	-	30c. green (No. 443)	65	1·30
454	-	35c. orange (No. 444)	65	1·90
455	**89**	50c. brown	65	1·90

From 1940 to 1990 Lithuania used stamps of Russia.

99 Angel and Map

1990. No gum. Imperf.

456	**99**	5k. green	40	35
457	**99**	10k. lilac	55	50
458	**99**	20k. blue	80	70
459	**99**	50k. red	3·00	2·75

1990. No gum. Imperf (simulated perfs).

460	**99**	5k. green and brown	15	10
461	**99**	10k. purple and brown	55	50
462	**99**	20k. blue and brown	55	50
463	**99**	50k. red and brown	70	60

100 Vytis

101 Hill of Crosses, Siauliai

1991

464	**100**	10k. black, gold and brown	15	10
465	**100**	15k. black, gold and green	70	60
466	**100**	20k. black, gold and blue	70	60
467	**100**	30k. black, gold and red	1·10	95
468	**100**	40k. black and gold	25	25
469	**100**	50k. black, gold and violet	25	25
470	**101**	50k. brown, chestnut & blk	1·40	1·20
471	**100**	100k. black, gold & green	40	35
472	-	200k. brown, chest & blk	2·75	2·40
473	**100**	500k. black, gold and blue	3·50	3·00

Design: As T **101**—200k. Lithuanian Liberty Bell.
See also Nos. 482 and 489/490.

102 Liberty Statue, Kaunas

1991. National Day.

480	**102**	20k. mauve, silver & black	70	60

103 Angel with Trumpet

1991. First Anniversary of Declaration of Independence from USSR.

481	**103**	20k. deep green and green	70	60

1991. No gum. Imperf (simulated perfs).

482	**100**	15k. green and black	70	60

104 Wayside Crosses

1991

483	**104**	40k. green and silver	70	60
484	-	70k. brown, buff and gold	1·40	1·20
485	-	100k. brown, yellow & sil	2·00	1·80

Designs: 70k. *Madonna* (icon from Pointed Gate Chapel, Vilnius); 100k. Towers of St Anne's Church, Vilnius.

105 Candle

1991. 50th Anniversary of Resistance to Soviet and German Occupations.

486	**105**	20k. yellow, black & bistre	40	35
487	-	50k. rose, black and red	95	90
488	-	70k. multicoloured	1·40	1·30

Designs: 50k. Shield pierced by swords; 70k. Sword and wreath.

1991. No gum. Imperf.

489	**100**	25k. black and brown	55	50
490	**100**	30k. black and purple	80	70

106 World Map and Games Emblem

1991. Fourth International Lithuanians' Games.

491	**106**	20k. green, black & yellow	55	50
492	-	50k.+25k. green, black and yellow	2·20	1·90

Design: 50k. Symbolic female athlete.

107 National Flag in Ice-axe and Mt. Everest

1991. Lithuanian Expedition to Mt. Everest.

493	**107**	20k. multicoloured	40	35
494	**107**	70k. multicoloured	1·60	1·40

108 Trakai Castle

1991. 650th Death Anniversary of Grand Duke Gediminas. Each brown, ochre and green.

495		30k. Type **108**	55	50
496		50k. Gediminas	70	60
497		70k. Vilnius in 14th-century	1·40	1·20

109 Black Storks

1991. Birds in *The Red Book*. Multicoloured.

498		30k.+15k. Type **109**	1·20	1·10
499		50k. Common cranes	1·50	1·30

110 UN and National Emblems and National Flag

1992. Admission to UNO.

500	**110**	100k. multicoloured	70	60

111 National Team Emblem and Colours

1992. Winter Olympic Games, Albertville, and Summer Games, Barcelona. Multicoloured.

501	50k.+25k. Type **111**	70	60
502	130k. Winter Games emblem	1·20	1·10
503	280k. Summer Games emblem	1·70	1·50

112 Slipper Orchid

1992. Plants in *The Red Book*. Multicoloured.

504	200k. Type **112**	1·60	1·40
505	300k. Sea holly	1·80	1·60

113 Goosander (*Mergus merganser*)

1992. Birds of the Baltic. No value expressed.

506	-	B (15t.) black and green	95	85
507	-	B (15t.) brown, blk & grn	95	85
508	**113**	B (15t.) sepia, brown & grn	95	85
509	-	B (15t.) brown, blk & grn	95	85

Designs: No. 506, Osprey (*Pandion haliaetus*); No. 507, Black-tailed godwit (*Limosa limosa*); No. 509, Common shelduck (*Tadorna tadorna*).

114 Kedainiai

1992. Arms. Multicoloured.

510	2t. Type **114**	15	10
511	3t. Vilnius	40	35
512	10t. State Arms	1·40	1·20

See also Nos. 531/533, 569/571, 594/595, 628/630, 663/665, 682/684, 712/714, 742/744, 769/771 and 781/783.

115 Couple

1992. Costumes of Suvalkija.

513	**115**	2t. multicoloured	40	35
514	-	5t. multicoloured	95	85
515	-	7t. multicoloured	1·40	1·20

Designs: 5, 7t. Different costumes.

116 Zapyskis Church

1993. Churches.

516	**116**	3t. black and stone	35	30
517	-	10t. black and blue	1·10	95
518	-	15t. black and grey	1·40	1·20

Designs: 10t. Church of St Peter and St Paul, Vilnius; 15t. Church of the Resurrection, Kaunas.

1993. Nos. 467, 490 and 468 surch.

519	**100**	1t. on 30k. blk, gold & red	40	35
520	**100**	1t. on 30k. black & purple	40	35
521	**100**	3t. on 40k. black and gold	70	60

118 Jonas Basanavicius (statesman)

1993. National Day. No value expressed.

522	**118**	A (3t.) red, cinn & brn	70	60
523	-	B (15t.) grn, stone & brn	1·40	1·20

Design: No. 523, Jonas Vileisis (politician).

119 Vytautas

1993. 600th Anniversary (1987) of Accession of Grand Duke Vytautas.

524		5t. gold, red and black	40	35
525	**119**	10t. green, black and red	95	85
526	-	15t. black, yellow and red	1·40	1·20

MS527 80×120 mm. 50t. olive, black and red — 2·75 — 2·50

Designs: 5t. Seal; 15t. *Battle of Grunwald* (Jan Matejka) 50t. T **119**.

120 Simonas Daukantas (historian)

1993. Birth Anniversaries. Each brown and yellow.

528	10t. Type **120** (bicentenary)	70	60
529	20t. Vydunas (125th anniversary)	1·40	1·20
530	45t. Vincas Mykolaitis-Putinas (philosopher, centenary)	3·50	3·00

1993. Town Arms. As T **114**. Multicoloured.

531	5c. Skuodas	25	25
532	30c. Telsiai	80	70
533	50c. Klaipeda	1·60	1·40

121 *Watchtower* (M. K. Ciurlionis)

1993. World Unity Day (5c.) and Transatlantic Flight (80c.). Multicoloured.

534	5c. Type **121**	15	10
535	80c. Steponas Dariaus and Stasys Gireno	2·40	2·20

122 State Arms

1993. No value expressed.

536	**122**	A (5c.) green, brown and red	15	10
537	**122**	B (80c.) red, green and bistre	1·20	1·10

123 Pope John Paul II and View of Siluva

1993. Papal Visit. Multicoloured.

538	60c. Type **123**	1·10	95
539	60c. Pope and Hill of Crosses	1·10	95
540	80c. Pope and Kaunas	1·40	1·20
541	80c. Pope and Ausra Gates, Vilnius	1·40	1·20

124 Couple

1993. Costumes of Dzukai.

542	**124**	60c. multicoloured	1·00	90
543	-	80c. multicoloured	1·10	1·00
544	-	1l. multicoloured	1·30	1·10

Designs: 80c. to 1l. Different costumes.

125 Klaipeda Post Office

1993. 75th Anniversary of First Lithuanian Postage Stamps.

545	**125**	60c. multicoloured	70	60
546	-	60c. multicoloured	70	60
547	-	80c. multicoloured	80	70
548	-	1l. black, brown and green	1·40	1·20

Designs: No. 546, Kaunas post office; No. 547, Ministry for Post and Information, Vilnius; No. 548, First Lithuanian stamp.

126 *The Ladle Carver* (A. Gudaitis)

1993. Europa. Contemporary Art.

549	**126**	80c. multicoloured	2·00	1·80

127 European Pond Turtle

1993. Pond Life. Multicoloured.

550	80c. Type **127**	70	60
551	1l. Running toad	1·40	1·20

128 Games Emblem and Team Colours

1994. Winter Olympic Games, Lillehammer, Norway.

552	**128**	1l.10 multicoloured	1·40	1·20

129 Antanas Smetona (President 1919–1922 and 1926–1940)

1994. National Day.

553	**129**	1l. red and black	1·10	95
554	-	1l. brown and black	1·10	95

Design: No. 554, Aleksandras Stulginskis (President 1922–1926).

130 Kristijonas Donelaitis

1994. Writers. Each cream, brown and orange.

555	60c. Type **130**	70	60
556	80c. Vincas Kudirka	80	70
557	1l. Jonas Maciulis Maironis	1·20	1·10

131 State Arms

1994

558	**131**	5c. brown	15	10
559	**131**	10c. lilac	40	35
560	**131**	20c. green	55	50
612	**131**	40c. purple	40	35
613	**131**	50c. blue	45	40

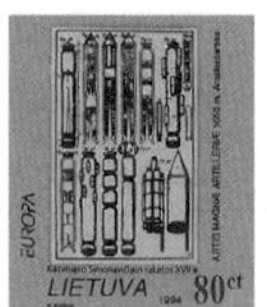

132 Rockets by Kazimieras Simonavicius (illus from *Artis Magnae Artilleriae*)

1994. Europa. Inventions and Discoveries.

561	**132**	80c. multicoloured	2·75	2·40

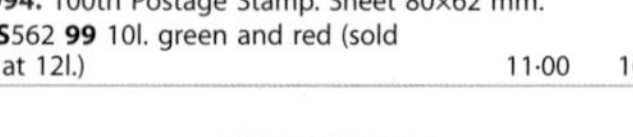

1994. 100th Postage Stamp. Sheet 80×62 mm.

MS562 **99** 10l. green and red (sold at 12l.) — 11·00 — 10·50

133 Couple

1994. 19th-century Costumes of Zemaiciai (Lowlands).

563	**133**	5c. multicoloured	15	10
564	-	80c. multicoloured	80	70
565	-	1l. multicoloured	95	85

Designs: 80c., 1l., Different costumes from Zemaiciai.

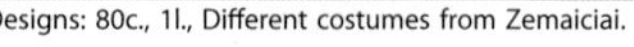

134 Music Note, Globe and Flag

1994. Lithuanians of the World Song Festival.

566	**134**	10c. multicoloured	40	35

135 State Arms

1994

567	**135**	2l. multicoloured	2·00	†
568	**135**	3l. multicoloured	2·75	2·40

See also **MS**580.

1994. Town Arms. As T **114** but size 25×32 mm. Multicoloured.

569	10c. Punia	15	10
570	60c. Alytus	70	60
571	80c. Perloja	1·10	95

136 Common Bat

1994. Mammals. Multicoloured.

572		20c. Type **136**	40	35
573		20c. Fat dormouse	40	35

137 Kaunas Town Hall

1994. Town Halls.

574	**137**	10c. black and mauve	15	10
575	-	60c. black and blue	55	50
576	-	80c. black and green	70	60

Designs: 60c. Kedainiai; 80c. Vilnius.

138 Madonna and Child

1994. Christmas.

577	**138**	20c. multicoloured	40	35

139 Steponas Kairys

1995. National Day. Signatories to 1918 Declaration of Independence.

578	**139**	20c. lilac, grey and black	25	25
579	-	20c. blue, grey and black	40	35

Design: No. 579, Pranas Dovydaitis (Head of Government, March–April 1919).

1995. Fifth Anniv of Independence. Sheet 75×105 mm.

MS580	**135**	1l.x4 multicoloured	4·00	3·75

140 Kaunas (Lithuania)

1995. Via Baltica Motorway Project. Multicoloured.

581	20c. Type **140**	40	35
MS582	100×110 mm. 1l. Beach Hotel, Parnu (Estonia); 1l. Bauska Castle (Latvia); 1l. Type **140**	4·00	3·75

141 *Lithuanian School, 1864–1904* (P. Rimsa)

1995. Europa. Peace and Freedom.

583	**141**	1l. multicoloured	2·75	2·40

142 Couple

1995. Costumes of the Highlands.

584	-	20c. multicoloured	40	35
585	-	70c. multicoloured	70	60
586	**142**	1l. multicoloured	95	85

Designs: 70c. to 1l. Different 19th-century costumes.

143 Motiejus Valancius (120th death)

1995. Anniversaries.

587	**143**	30c. cream, pur & yell	25	25
588	-	40c. cream, grn & orge	40	35
589	-	70c. cream, dp bl & pink	70	60

Designs: 40c. Zemaite (150th birth); 70c. Kipras Petrauskas (110th birth).

144 *Pieta*

1995. Day of Mourning and Hope.

590	**144**	20c. multicoloured	40	35

145 Torch-bearer

1995. Fifth World Lithuanians Games.

591	**145**	30c. multicoloured	40	35

146 *Baptria tibiale*

1995. Butterflies and Moths in *The Red Book.* Multicoloured.

592	30c. Type **146**	70	60
593	30c. Cream-spot tiger moth (*Arctia villica*)	70	60

1995. Town Arms. As T **114**. Multicoloured.

594	40c. Virbalis	70	60
595	1l. Kudirkos Naumiestis (horiz)	1·40	1·20

147 *Valerija Mesalina*

1995. 250th Birth Anniversary of Pranciskus Smuglevicius (painter).

596	**147**	40c. multicoloured	40	35

148 Trakai Island Castle

1995. Castles.

597	-	40c. multicoloured	55	50
598	**148**	70c. blue, dp blue & black	95	85
599	-	1l. multicoloured	1·20	1·10

Designs: 40c. Vilnius Upper Castle; 1l. Birzai Castle.

149 Star over Winter Scene

1995. Christmas. Multicoloured.

600	40c. Type **149**	70	60
601	1l. Churchgoers with lanterns	1·40	1·20

150 Bison

1996. The European Bison. Multicoloured.

602	30c. Type **150**	40	35
603	40c. Pair of bison	55	35
604	70c. Adult and calf	70	60
605	1l. Parents and calf	1·10	95

151 Kazys Grinius (130th)

1996. Birth Anniversaries.

606	**151**	40c. cream, brown & blue	40	35
607	-	1l. cream, bistre & yellow	80	70
608	-	1l. cream, blue and red	80	70

Designs: No. 607, Antanas Zmuidzinavicius (120th); No. 608, Balys Sruoga (centenary).

152 Vladas Mironas

1996. National Day. Signatories to 1918 Declaration of Independence.

609	**152**	40c. cream, grey and black	55	50
610	-	40c. bistre, brown and black	55	50

Design: No. 610, Jurgis Saulys.

153 Barbora Radvilaite

1996. Europa. Famous Women.

611	**153**	1l. multicoloured	2·00	1·80

154 Couple

1996. Costumes of Klaipeda. 19th-century costumes. Multicoloured.

618	40c. Type **154**	55	50
619	1l. Woman in red skirt and man in frock-coat	1·10	95
620	1l. Woman in black skirt and man in blue waistcoat	1·10	95

155 Angel

1996. Day of Mourning and Hope.

621	**155**	40c. blue, red and black	55	50
622	-	40c. green, red and black	55	50

Design: No. 622, Head of crucifix.

156 *The Discus Thrower*

1996. Olympic Games, Atlanta. Multicoloured.

623	1l. Type **156**	1·10	95

624	1l. Basketball	1·10	95

157 *Sacrifice*

1996. 85th Death Anniversary of Mikolajus Ciurlionis (artist). Multicoloured.

625	40c. Type **157**	70	60
626	40c. *Cemetery*	70	60
MS627	80×102 mm. 3l. *Sonata of the Andante* (25×36 mm); 3l. *Sonata of the Stars–Allegro* (25×36 mm)	4·75	4·50

1996. Town Arms. As T **114** but size 25×32 mm.

628	50c. multicoloured	55	50
629	90c. red, black and yellow	95	85
630	1l.20 multicoloured	1·20	1·10

Design: 50c. Seduva; 90c. Panevezys; 1l.20, Zarasai.

158 Players

1996. Lithuanian Basketball Team, Bronze Medallist, Olympic Games, Atlanta. Sheet 50×72 mm.

MS631	**158**	4l.20 multicoloured	5·50	5·25

159 Angels heralding

1996. Christmas. Multicoloured.

632	50c. Type **159**	40	35
633	1l.20 Elf riding on *Pegasus*	95	85

160 Ieva Simonaityte (writer, birth centenary)

1997. Anniversaries.

634	**160**	50c. stone, brown and green	40	35
635	-	90c. stone, grey and yellow	70	60
636	-	1l.20 stone, grn & orge	1·10	95
MS638		94×56 mm. **161** 4l.80 brown and grey (26×36 mm)	4·00	3·75

Designs: 90c. Jonas Sliupas (physician, 53rd death); 1l.20, Vladas Jurgutis (financier, 31st death).

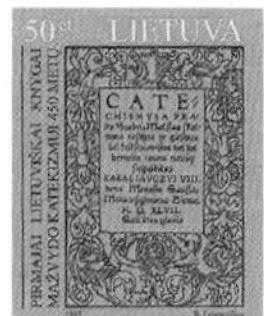

161 Title Page

1997. 450th Anniversary of Publication of *Catechism of Mazvydas* (first Lithuanian book).

637	**161**	50c. brown and grey	70	60

162 Mykolas Birziska

1997. National Day. Signatories to 1918 Declaration of Independence.

639	**162**	50c. green, lt grn & blk	70	60
640	-	50c. purple, stone and black	70	60

Design: No. 640, Kazimieras Saulys.

163 Flag on Mountain Peak

1997. Completion of Ascent of World's Highest Mountains by Vladas Vitauskas. Sheet 80×60 mm.

MS641	**163**	4l.80 multicoloured	4·00	3·75

164 *Little Witch* (Jovita Jankeviciute)

1997. Europa. Tales and Legends. Multicoloured.

642	1l.20 Type **164**	1·80	1·60
643	1l.20 *Rainbow* (Ieva Staseviciute) (horiz)	1·80	1·60

165 Lecture

1997. 600th Anniversary of First Lithuanian School.

644	**165**	50c. multicoloured	70	60

166 Kurshes Ship

1997. Baltic Sailing Ships. Multicoloured.

645	50c. Type **166**	70	60

MS646 110×70 mm. 1l.20 Kushes ship (as in Type **166** but with frame etc); 1l.20 Maasilinn ship (Estonia); 1l.20 *Wappen der Herzogin von Kurland* (galleon) (Estonia) 4·00 3·75

167 Park

1997. Centenary of Palanga Botanical Park.

647	**167**	50c. yellow, black and brown	40	35

168 Ship of Flags

1997. Second Baltic Sea Games, Lithuania.

648	**168**	90c. multicoloured	80	70

169 Elk's-horn Staff, 3000 BC

1997. Museum Exhibits. Multicoloured.

649	90c. Type **169**	80	70
650	1l.20 Silver coins of Grand Duke Kazimierz IV, 15th-century AD	1·20	1·10

170 Vytis's Cross

1997

651	**170**	5c. yellow & light yellow	15	10
652	**170**	10c. yellow and cream	20	20
653	**170**	20c. green and brown	25	25
654	**170**	35c. purple and lilac	40	35
655	**170**	50c. brown and cinnamon	70	60
656	**170**	70c. yellow and cream	70	60

171 Black Morel

1997. Fungi in *The Red Book*. Multicoloured.

660	1l.20 Type **171**	1·40	1·20
661	1l.20 Bronze boletus	1·40	1·20

172 Letter and Seal

1997. 674th Anniversary of Letters of Invitation for Migrants sent by Grand Duke Gediminas to European Cities.

662	**172**	50c. multicoloured	70	60

1997. Town Arms. As T **114** but size 25×33 mm.

663	50c. Neringa	55	50
664	90c. Vilkaviskis	80	70
665	1l.20 Pasvalys	1·40	1·20

173 Cherub holding Lantern above Town

1997. Christmas. Multicoloured.

666	50c. Type **173**	70	60
667	1l.20 Snow-covered trees	1·40	1·20

174 Figure Skaters

1998. Winter Olympic Games, Nagano, Japan.

668	**174**	1l.20 ultramarine and blue	1·40	1·20

175 Alfonsas Petrulis (priest)

1998. National Day. Signatories to 1918 Declaration of Independence.

669	**175**	50c. green, grey and black	55	50
670	-	90c. brown, lt brn & blk	80	70

Design: No. 670, Jokubas Sernas (lawyer and politician).

176 Text of Declaration and State Emblem

1998. 80th Anniversary of Declaration of Independence. Sheet 123×50 mm.

MS671	**176**	6l.60 multicoloured	5·50	5·25

177 Lyrics and Kudirka's Memorial

1998. Centenary of Tautiskai giesmei (National Anthem) by Vincas Kudirka (lyricist). Sheet 90×64 mm.

MS672	**177**	5l.20 multicoloured	4·75	4·50

178 Gustaitis and ANBO-41 (reconnaissance aeroplane)

1998. Birth Centenary of Antanas Gustaitis (pilot and aircraft constructor). Multicoloured.

673	2l. Type **178**	2·00	1·80
674	3l. ANBO-VIII (light bomber) and diagrams	2·75	2·40

179 National Song Festival

1998. Europa. National Festivals.

675	**179**	1l.20 multicoloured	2·75	2·40

180 Tadas Ivanauskas (zoologist, 27th death anniversary)

1998. Anniversaries.

676	**180**	50c. green, lt yell & yell	55	50
677	-	90c. red, yellow & orge	80	70
678	-	90c. green, yellow & orge	80	70

Designs: 45×25 mm—No. 677, Stasys Lozoraitis (diplomat, birth centenary) and Stasys Lozoraitis (diplomat, Tenth death anniversary); No. 678, Jurgis Baltrusaitis (writer and diplomat, 125th birth anniversary) and Jurgis Baltrusaitis (art historian, Fourth death anniversary).

181 Long Jumping

1998. Sixth World Lithuanian Games and Second National Games.

679	**181**	1l.35 multicoloured	1·40	1·20

182 Atlantic Salmon

1998. Fish in *The Red Book*. Multicoloured.

680	1l.40 Type **182**	1·20	1·10
681	1l.40 Whitefish (*Coregonus lavaretus*)	1·20	1·10

1998. Town Arms. As T **114** but size 25×33 mm. Multicoloured.

682	70c. Kernave	70	60
683	70c. Trakai	70	60
684	1l.35 Kaunas	1·40	1·20

183 Vilnuis–Cracow Postal Service, 1562

1998. Postal History. Multicoloured.

685	70c. Type **183**	70	60

MS686 55×86 mm. 13l. Hologram of posthorn and map of Europe, Africa and Asia (80th anniversary of first Lithuanian stamps) (39×29 mm) 11·00 10·50

184 *All Night Long* (Antanas Zmuidzinavicius)

1998. Paintings. Multicoloured.

687	70c. Type **184**	70	60
688	1l.35 *Vilnius: Bernardines' Garden* (Juozapas Marsevskis)	1·40	1·20

185 Girl holding Church

1998. Christmas. Multicoloured.

689	70c. Type **185**	70	60
690	1l.35 Couple going into tree house	1·40	1·20

186 *Mickiewicz* (statue, G. Jokounis)

1998. Birth Bicentenary of Adam Mickiewicz (poet).

691	**186**	70c. multicoloured	70	60

187 Angels holding Title Page

1999. 400th Anniversary of Publication of Translation into Lithuanian by Mikalojus Dauksa of *Postilla Catholicka* by Jacob Wujek. Sheet 60×67 mm.

MS692	**187**	5l.90 brown and silver	5·50	5·25

188 Petras Klimas (historian and diplomat)

1999. National Day. Signatories to 1918 Declaration of Independence.

693	**188**	70c. red and black	70	60
694	-	70c. blue and black	70	60

Design: No. 694, Donatas Malinauskas (diplomat).

189 Augustinas Gricius (dramatist)

1999. Birth Centenaries.

695	**189**	70c. black, cream & orge	70	60
696	-	70c. brown, cream & pink	70	60
697	-	1l.35 green, cream and orange	1·40	1·20

Designs: No. 696, Juozas Matulis (chemist); 697, Pranas Skardzius (philologian).

190 Emblem and State Flag

1999. 50th Anniversary of North Atlantic Treaty Organisation.

698	**190**	70c. multicoloured	95	85

191 Aukstaitija National Park

1999. Europa. Parks and Gardens. Multicoloured.

699	1l.35 Type **191**	1·80	1·60
700	1l.35 Curonian Spit National Park	1·80	1·60

192 Council Flag

1999. 50th Anniversary of Council of Europe.

701	**192**	70c. multicoloured	95	85

193 Boarded Clay Windmill, Melniai

1999. Windmills. Multicoloured.

702	70c. Type **193**	70	60
703	70c. Red-brick windmill, Pumpenai	70	60

194 *Dasypoda argentata*

1999. Bumble Bees. Multicoloured.

704	70c. Type **194**	70	60
705	2l. *Bombus pomorum*	2·00	1·80

195 Sculpture of UPU Emblem, Berne

1999. 125th Anniversary of Universal Postal Union.

706	**195**	70c. multicoloured	70	60

196 1918 and 1990 Stamps and Society Emblems

1999. 75th Anniversary of Lithuanian Philatelic Society.

707	**196**	1l. multicoloured	95	85

197 Cast and Producers

1999. Centenary of First Public Performance of Lithuanian Drama (*America in the Bath* by Keturakis). Sheet 99×59 mm containing T **197** and similar vert design. Multicoloured.

MS708 4l. Type **197**; 4l. Playbill	8·00	7·75

198 Family and State Flag

1999. Tenth Anniversary of the Baltic Chain (human chain uniting the capitals of Lithuania, Estonia and Latvia). Multicoloured.

709	1l. Type **198**	95	85
MS710 110×72 mm. 2l. Type **198**; 2l. Family and Estonian flag; 2l. Family and Latvian flag		6·00	5·75

199 Emblem

1999. 50th Anniversary of Establishment of Lithuanian Freedom Fight Movement.

711	**199**	70c. multicoloured	70	60

1999. Town Arms. Designs as T **114** but size 25×33 mm. Multicoloured.

712	70c. Marijampole	80	70
713	1l. Siauliai	1·10	95
714	1l.40 Rokiskis	1·50	1·30

200 Sword of General S. Zukauskas, 1927

1999. Exhibits in Vytautas Magnus War Museum. Multicoloured.

715	70c. Type **200**	1·10	95
716	3l. 17th-century Hussar's armour	2·75	2·40

201 *Horse and Bear* (fable)

1999. Birth Bicentenary of Simonas Stanevicius (writer).

717	**201**	70c. multicoloured	70	60

202 *Winter Symphony*

1999. Christmas. Multicoloured.

718	70c. Type **202**	80	70

719	1l.35 Cathedral, candles and bell (*Christmas Song*)	1·50	1·30

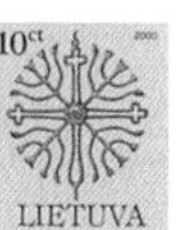

203 Top of Monument

2000. Ironwork.

720	**203**	10c. blue and brown	20	20
721	-	20c. blue and stone	40	35
722	-	1l. blue and pink	95	85
723	-	1l.30 blue and green	1·40	1·20
724	-	1l.70 blue and light blue	2·00	1·80

Designs: 20c. to 1l.70, Different examples of ornamental ironwork.

204 Jonas Vailokaitis

2000. National Day. Signatories to 1918 Declaration of Independence.

725	**204**	1l.30 orange, stone & blk	1·40	1·20
726	-	1l.70 brown, stone & blk	2·00	1·80

Design: 1l.70, Jonas Smilgevicius.

205 Declaration

2000. Tenth Anniversary of Restoration of Independence. Sheet 86×71 mm.

MS727 **205** 7l.40 multicoloured	8·00	7·75

206 Vincas Pietaris (writer, 150th anniversary)

2000. Birth Anniversaries.

728	**206**	1l. green, black and purple	1·10	95
729	-	1l.30 blue, black & brown	1·60	1·40
730	-	1l.70 brown, black & bl	2·00	1·80

Designs: 1l.30, Kanutas Ruseckas (painter, bicentenary); 1l.70, Povilas Visinskis (literary critic, 125th anniversary).

See also Nos. 753/755.

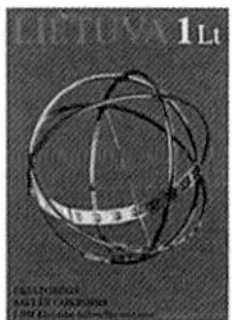

207 Equatorial Sundial

2000. Exhibits in Klaipeda Clock Museum. Multicoloured

731	1l. Type **207**	1·10	95
732	2l. Renaissance-style clock case	2·30	2·00

208 Building Europe

2000. Europa.

733	**208**	1l.70 multicoloured	2·40	2·20

209 Osprey

2000. Birds of Prey. Multicoloured.

734	1l. Type **209**	1·10	95
735	2l. Black kite	2·30	2·00

210 Grey Seal

2000. Lithuanian Marine Museum, Kopgalis. Multicoloured

736	1l. Type **210**	1·40	1·20
737	1l. Magellanic penguin (*Spheniscus magellanicus*)	1·40	1·20

211 Cycling

2000. Olympic Games, Sydney. Multicoloured.

738	1l. Type **211**	1·40	1·20
739	3l. Swimming	4·00	3·50

212 *Fairy Tale Castle* (Ciurlionis)

2000. 125th Birth Anniversary of Mikalojus Konstantinas Ciurlionis (artist and composer). Sheet 59×56 mm.

MS740 **212** 4l. multicoloured	4·75	4·50

213 Tree and Emblem

2000. Tenth Anniversary of Lithuanian Postal Service.

741	**213**	1l. multicoloured	1·40	1·20

2000. Town Arms. As T **114** but size 25×33 mm. Multicoloured.

742	1l. Raseiniai	1·20	1·10
743	1l. Taurage	1·20	1·10
744	1l.30 Utena	1·60	1·40

214 Snow-covered Village

2000. Christmas. Multicoloured.

745	1l. Type **214**	1·40	1·20
746	1l.70 Snow-covered church	2·00	1·80

215 The Nativity

2000. Holy Year (2000). Sheet 69×87 mm containing T **215** and similar vert designs. Multicoloured.

MS747 2l. Type **215**; 2l. Jesus with James and John; 2l. Crucifixion; 2l. Jesus entering Heaven	9·50	9·25

216 Neolithic Amber Artefact

2000. New Millennium.

748	**216**	1l. multicoloured	1·60	1·40

217 Medals

2000. Lithuanian Victories in Olympic Games, Sydney. Sheet 65×102 mm.

MS749	**217**	4l. multicoloured	4·75	4·50

218 Vilnius Television Tower and Flag

2001. Tenth Anniversary of Soviet Action in Vilnius.

750	**218**	1l. multicoloured	1·10	95

219 Saliamonas Banaitis

2001. National Day. Signatories to 1918 Declaration of Independence.

751	**219**	1l. brown, grey and black	1·40	1·20
752	-	2l. lilac, grey and black	2·40	2·20

Design: 2l. Justinas Staugaitis.

2001. Anniversaries. As T **206**.

753	1l. blue, red and black	1·40	1·20
754	1l. green, red and black	1·40	1·20
755	1l.70 brown, violet and black	2·00	1·80

Designs: No. 753, Juozas MikEnas (artist, birth centenary); No. 754, Pranas Vaicaitis (poet, death centenary); No. 755, Petras Vileisis (civil engineer, 150th birth anniversary).

220 Lake Galve

2001. Europa. Water Resources. Multicoloured.

756	1l.70 Type **220**	2·00	1·80
757	1l.70 River Nemunas	2·00	1·80

221 Floating Bogbean (*Nymphoides peltata*)

2001. Plants in *The Red Book*. Multicoloured.

758	2l. Type **221**	2·40	2·20
759	3l. Crossleaf heather (*Erica tetralix*)	3·75	3·25

222 Paplauja Bridge, Vilnius

2001. Bridges. Multicoloured.

760	1l. Type **222**	1·40	1·20
761	1l.30 Pakruojis, Kruoja	2·00	1·80

223 National Flag

2001. Lithunania Millenary (1st issue). Sheet 125×100 mm containing T **223** and similar horiz designs. Multicoloured.

MS762 2l. Type **223**; 2l. State Emblem; 2l. Map of Lithuania; 2l. Map of Europe 9·50 9·25

See also Nos. **MS**791, **MS**813, **MS**838, **MS**862, 886/889, **MS**914, **MS**946 and **MS**980.

224 Sand Dunes, Palanga, Lithuania

2001. Baltic Sea Coast. Multicoloured.

763	1l. Type **224**	1·40	1·20
MS764	125×60 mm. 2l. As Type **224** but with Palanga at left; 2l. Rocky coastline, Lahemaa, Estonia; 2l. Beach, Vidzeme, Latvia	7·50	7·25

225 19th-century Cottage, Kirdeikiai, Utena District

2001. 35th Anniversary of Open Air Museum, Rumsiskes. Multicoloured.

765	1l. Type **225**	1·10	95
766	2l. Farmer's house, Darlenai, Kretinga district	2·30	2·00

226 *Sadness* (sculpture)

2001. 120th Birth Anniversary of Juozas Zikaras (artist).

767	**226**	3l. multicoloured	3·50	3·00

227 Charter and King Stephan I Batory of Poland

2001. 418th Anniversary of Introduction of Postal Rates based on Weight.

768	**227**	1l. multicoloured	1·40	1·20

2001. Town Arms. As T **114** but size 25×33 mm. Multicoloured.

769	1l. Lazdijai	1·40	1·20
770	1l.30 Birzai	1·50	1·30
771	1l.70 Veliuona	1·90	1·70

228 Birds on Straw and Pine Pyramid (*Winter troubles*)

2001. Christmas and New Year. Multicoloured.

772	1l. Type **228**	1·50	1·30
773	1l.70 Birds and crib (*Jesus' cradle*)	2·20	2·00

229 Basanavicius

2001. 150th Birth Anniversary of Jonas Basanavicius (politician and signatory to 1918 Declaration of Independence). Sheet 82×60 mm.

MS774	**229**	5l. multicoloured	7·25	7·00

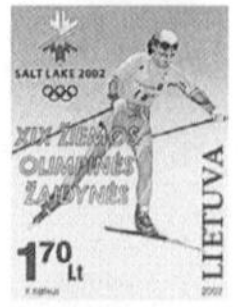

230 Skier

2002. Winter Olympic Games, Salt Lake City, USA.

775	**230**	1l.30 multicoloured	2·20	2·00

231 Kazys Bizauskas

2002. National Day. Signatories to 1918 Declaration of Independence.

776	**231**	1l. sepia, brown and black	1·20	1·00
777	-	1l. violet, brown and black	1·20	1·00

Design: No. 777 Stanislovas Narutavicius (politician).

232 Antanas Salys

2002. Birth Anniversaries. Multicoloured.

778	1l. Type **232** (linguist, centenary)	1·20	1·00
779	1l.30 Satrijos Ragana (writer, 125th anniversary)	1·50	1·30
780	1l.70 Oskaras Milasius (poet, 125th anniversary)	1·90	1·70

2002. Town Arms. As T **114** but size 25×33 mm. Multicoloured.

781	1l. Birstonas	1·20	1·00
782	1l. Anyksciai	1·20	1·00
783	1l.70 Prienai	2·20	2·00

233 Book, Archives and Seal

2002. 150th Anniversary of State Archives.

784	**233**	1l. multicoloured	1·50	1·30

234 Stoat (*Mustela erminea*)

2002. Endangered Species. Multicoloured.

785	1l. Type **234**	1·20	1·00
786	3l. Lynx (*Lynx (Felis) lynx*)	4·00	3·50

235 Strongman

2002. Europa. Circus.

787	**235**	1l.70 multicoloured	2·20	2·00

236 Ford 350 Fire Engine

2002. Bicentenary of Vilnius Fire and Rescue Service.

788	**236**	1l. multicoloured	1·20	1·00

237 Diesel Locomotive TU2

2002. Narrow-gauge Railway. Multicoloured.

789	1l.30 Type **237**	1·60	1·40
790	2l. Steam locomotive PT4	2·30	2·10

238 Flint Tool

2002. Lithuania Millenary (2nd issue) (2009). Sheet 126×100 mm containing T **238** and similar horiz designs. Multicoloured.

MS791 2l. Type **238**; 2l. Publius Cornelius Tacitus (chronicler); 2l. Viking ship; 2l. *Annals of Quedlinburg* (manuscript containing first reference to Lithuania) 9·50 9·25

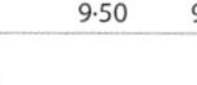

239 Rooftops

2002. 750th Anniversary of Klaipeda. Sheet 88×59 mm.

MS792	**239**	5l. multicoloured	5·75	5·50

240 Script and Exhibits

2002. Maironis Literature Museum, Kaunas. Multicoloured.

793	1l. Type **240**	1·20	1·00
794	3l. Museum buildings	4·00	3·50

241 King Zigmantas Vaza (founder of postal system)

2002. Postal History.

795	**241**	1l. multicoloured	1·50	1·30

242 Star and Clock-face

2002. Christmas and New Year. Multicoloured.

796	1l. Type **242**	1·20	1·00
797	1l.70 Christmas tree	1·90	1·70

243 *Mother and Child* (Danielius Peciulis)

2002. European Children's Day.

798	**243**	1l. multicoloured	1·50	1·30

244 Laurynas Stuoka-Gucevicius (architect)

2003. Personalities. Multicoloured.

799	1l. Type **244**	1·30	1·20
800	1l. Juozas Eretas (writer)	1·60	1·40

245 Gargzdai

2003. Town Arms. Multicoloured.

801	1l. Type **245**	1·20	1·00
802	1l. Kretinga	1·20	1·00
803	1l. Palanga	1·20	1·00
804	1l. Papile	1·20	1·00
805	1l. Rietavas	1·20	1·00

See also Nos. 827/829, 855/856, 883/885, 907/909, 956/958, 969/971, 994/996, 1036/1038 and 1057/1059.

246 Pervalka Lighthouse

2003. Lighthouses. Multicoloured.

806 1l. Type **246** 1·20 1·00
807 3l. Uostadvaris 4·00 3·50

247 Face and Pencils

2003. Europa. Poster Art.

808 **247** 1l.70 multicoloured 2·20 2·00

248 Royal Palace, Vilnius

2003. Royal Palace Restoration.

809 **248** 1l. multicoloured 1·50 1·30

249 Observatory Building

2003. 250th Anniversary of Astronomical Observatory, Vilnius University.

810 **249** 1l. multicoloured 1·50 1·30

250 *Cerambyx cerdo*

2003. Endangered Species. Beetles. Multicoloured.

811 3l. Type **250** 3·75 3·25
812 3l. Stag beetle (*Lucanus cervus*) 3·75 3·25

251 Fortifications, 1183

2003. Lithuania Millenary (3rd series). Sheet 125×100 mm containing T **251** and similar horiz designs. Multicoloured.

MS813 2l. Type **251**; 2l. The Battle of Shiauliai, 1236; 2l. The Coronation of King Mindaugas, 1253; 2l. Vilnius, 1323 8·75 8·50

252 King Mindaugas

2003. 750th Anniversary of Coronation of King Mindaugas. Sheet 87×58 mm.

MS814 **252** 5l. multicoloured 5·75 5·50

253 Hot Air Balloons

2003. 13th European Hot Air Balloon Championships, Vilnius.

815 **253** 1l.30 multicoloured 1·50 1·30

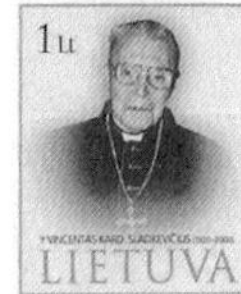

254 Cardinal Sladkevicius

2003. Third Death Anniversary of Cardinal Vincentas Sladkevicius.

816 **254** 1l. multicoloured 1·50 1·30

255 City Arms

2003. 500th Anniversary of Panevezys City.

817 **255** 1l. multicoloured 1·50 1·30

256 Post Office, Map and Postal Seal

2003. Postal History.

818 **256** 1l. multicoloured 1·50 1·30

257 Christmas Tree, Church and Houses

2003. Christmas. Multicoloured.

819 1l. Type **257** 1·50 1·30
820 1l.70 Street lamps through houses 2·20 2·00

258 Trophy and Basketball

2003. Lithuania, European Men's Basketball Champions, 2003. Sheet 62×75 mm.

MS821 **258** 5l. multicoloured 7·25 7·00

259 Plastic Glider BK-7

2003. Aviation Museum, Kaunas. Multicoloured

822 1l. Type **259** 1·20 1·00
823 1l. Training glider BRO-12 1·20 1·00

260 Jonas Aistis

2004. Anniversaries. Multicoloured.

824 1l. Type **260** (writer) (birth centenary) 1·50 1·30
825 1l. Kazimieras Buga (philologist) (80th death anniversary) 1·50 1·30
826 1l. Adolfas Jucys (scientist) (birth centenary) 1·50 1·30

2004. Town Arms. As T **245**. Multicoloured.

827 1l. Mazeikiai 1·20 1·00
828 1l.30 Radviliskis 1·50 1·30
829 1l.40 Ukmerge Palanga 1·70 1·60

261 King Steponas Batoras, Petras Skarga

2004. 425th Anniversary of Vilnius University.

830 **261** 1l. multicoloured 1·60 1·50

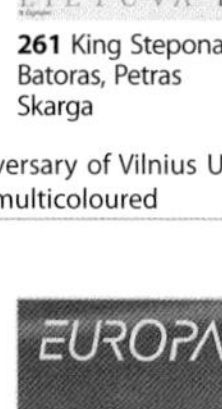

262 Parasol on Beach and University Building

2004. Europa. Holidays. Multicoloured.

831 1l.70 Type **262** 1·90 1·70
832 1l.70 Yacht at sea 1·90 1·70

263 Frontispieces

2004. Centenary of the Re-establishment of printing using Latin Characters.

833 **263** 1l.30 multicoloured 1·60 1·50

264 Lithuania Flag, Map of Europe, Stars and Shield

2004. Lithuania's Accession to the European Union. Multicoloured.

834 1l.70 Type **264** 1·90 1·70
835 1l.70 Flags of new members 1·90 1·70

265 Football

2004. Centenary of FIFA (Federation Internationale de Football Association).

836 **265** 3l. multicoloured 4·00 3·75

266 Chiune Sugihara

2004. Chiune Sugihara (Japanese Consul 1939–1940) Commemoration.

837 **266** 1l. multicoloured 1·60 1·50

267 Burning of Pilenai, 1336

2004. Lithuania Millenary (4th issue). Sheet 125×100 mm containing T **267** and similar vert designs.

MS838 2l.×4, Type **267**; Algirdas (leader of Siniye Vody battle), 1362; Jagaila establishing Lithuania as Catholic country; *Battle of Zalgiris* (detail) (painting by Janas Mateika) 10·50 10·00

268 Iguana

2004. Tadas Ivanauskas Zoology Museum. Multicoloured.

839 1l. Type **268** 1·10 1·00
840 1l. *Aquila chryaetos* 1·10 1·00

269 Show Jumping

2004. Olympic Games, Athens. Multicoloured.

841 2l. Type **269** 2·40 2·20
842 3l. Canoeing 4·00 3·75

270 Northern Eagle Owl (*Bubo bubo*)

2004. Endangered Species. Owls. Multicoloured.

843 1l.30 Type **270** 1·80 1·60
844 3l. Short-eared owl (*Asio flammeus*) 3·75 3·50

271 Aleksotas Funicular Railway

2004. Funicular Railways. Multicoloured.

845 1l. Type **271** 1·30 1·20
846 1l.30 Zaliakalnis 1·90 1·70

272 Snow-covered Tree

2004. Christmas. Multicoloured.

847 1l. Type **272** 1·60 1·50
848 1l.70 Bullfinch 2·40 2·20

273 Kazys Boruta

2005. Anniversaries. Multicoloured.

849 1l. Type **273** (writer) (birth centenary) 1·40 1·30
850 1l. Petras Kalpokas (artist) (60th death anniversary) 1·40 1·30
851 1l. Jonas Puzinas (archaeologist) (birth centenary) 1·40 1·30

274 Pink and Yellow Flowers

2005. Greetings Stamps. Multicoloured. Self-adhesive.

852 1l. Type **274** 1·60 1·50
853 1l. Orange flowers 1·60 1·50

275 Horses pulling Sulkies

2005. Centenary of Horse Races, Sartai Lake, Dusetos.

854 **275** 1l. multicoloured 1·60 1·50

2005. Town Arms. As T **245**. Multicoloured.

855 1l. Druskininkai 1·60 1·50

856 1l. Vabalninkas 1·60 1·50

276 White Cheese ('Baltas varskes suris')

2005. Europa. Gastronomy. Multicoloured.
857 1l.70 Type **276** 1·90 1·70
858 1l.70 Black bread ('Juoda duona') 1·90 1·70

277 Early Exhibition Hall, Vilnius University

2005. 150th Anniversary of National Museum. Multicoloured.
859 1l. Type **277** 1·60 1·50
860 1l. Brass jewellery 1·60 1·50

278 Train emerging from Tunnel

2005. Railway Tunnel between Vilnius and Kaunas.
861 **278** 3l. multicoloured 4·00 3·50

279 Pabaiskas Battle (1435)

2005. Lithuania Millenary (5th series). Sheet 125×100 mm containing T **279** and similar horiz designs. Multicoloured.
MS862 2l.×4, Type **279**; Valakai reform (1557); First statute (1529); Union of Lublin (1569) 12·00 11·50

The stamps and margin of **MS**862 form a composite design.

280 Ludovic Zamenhof (creator of Esperanto)

2005. 90th World Esperanto Congress, Vilnius.
863 **280** 1l. multicoloured 1·60 1·40

281 Vilnius Lutherian Evangelical Church

2005. Churches. Multicoloured.
864 1l. Type **281** 1·60 1·40
865 1l.30 St Casimir Church 1·80 1·60

282 Black-throated Diver (*Gavia arctica*)

2005. Endangered Species. Fauna and Flora. Multicoloured.
866 1l. Type **282** 1·60 1·40
867 1l. *Trapa natans* 1·60 1·40

Nos. 866/867 were issued together, *se-tenant*, forming a composite design.

283 *Allegro*

2005. 130th Birth Anniversary of Mikalojus Konstantinas Ciurlionis (artist and composer). Sheet 126×66 mm containing T **283** and similar vert designs showing painting cycle *Sonata of the Sea*. Multicoloured.
MS868 2l.×3, Type **283**; *Andante*; *Finale* 9·00 8·75

284 Mail Coach and Map

2005. Postal History.
869 **284** 1l. multicoloured 1·40 1·30

285 Snow covered Branch and Candle

2005. Christmas. Multicoloured.
870 1l. Type **285** 1·40 1·30
871 1l.70 Father Christmas 2·40 2·20

286 City Hall (1905), Jonas Basanavicius (nationalist politician) and Commemorative Medal

2005. Centenary of the Congress of Lithuanians (Great Seimas of Vilius) (beginning of independence and democracy).
872 **286** 1l. multicoloured 1·40 1·30

287 Biathlon

2006. Winter Olympic Games, Turin.
873 **287** 1l.70 multicoloured 2·40 2·20

288 Petras Rimsa (artist and sculptor)

2006. Personalities. Multicoloured.
874 1l. Type **288** 1·40 1·30
875 1l. Adolfas Sapoka (historian) 1·40 1·30
876 1l. Antanas Vaiculaitis (writer) 1·40 1·30

289 Street Scene

2006. 160th Anniversary of First Publication *The Vilnius Album* by Jonas Vilcinskis.
877 **289** 1l. multicoloured 1·40 1·30

290 Hands enclosing People

2006. 80th Anniversary of Social Insurance System.
878 **290** 1l. multicoloured 1·40 1·30

291 Cine Camera

2006. National Theatre, Music and Cinema Museum. Multicoloured.
879 1l. Type **291** 1·40 1·30
880 1l. Polyphon 1·40 1·30

292 Wheelchair Dancer and Partner

2006. Europa. Integration. Multicoloured.
881 1l.70 Type **292** 2·40 2·20
882 1l.70 Wheelchair race 2·40 2·20

2006. Town Arms. As T **245**. Multicoloured.
883 1l. Kupiskis 1·40 1·30
884 1l. Sakiai 1·40 1·30
885 1l. Silute 1·40 1·30

293 Establishment of Vilnius University, 1579

2006. Lithuania Millenary (6th series). Multicoloured.
886 2l. Type **293** 3·00 2·75
887 2l. Truce of Andrusov, 1667 3·00 2·75
888 2l. Establishment of four-years Seimas, 1788 3·00 2·75
889 2l. Uprising, 1794 3·00 2·75

294 Basilica, Vilnius Cathedral

2006. Churches. Multicoloured.
890 1l. Type **294** 1·60 1·50
891 1l.70 Basilica, Kaunas Cathedral 3·00 2·75

295 *Polysticta stelleri*

2006. Endangered Species. Multicoloured.
892 1l. Type **295** 1·60 1·50
893 1l. *Acipenser sturio* 1·60 1·50

296 Document establishing Post Board

2006. Postal History.
894 **296** 1l. multicoloured 1·60 1·50

297 Score, Performers, Mikas Petraukas (composer) and Gabrielius Landsberis-Zemkalnis (dramatist)

2006. Centenary of First Lithuania Opera. *Birute*.
895 **297** 2l. multicoloured 3·25 3·00

298 Doves

2006. Christmas. Multicoloured.
896 1l. Type **298** 1·60 1·50
897 1l 70. Star and snow-covered trees 3·00 2·75

299 Pasvalys Church Belfry

2007. Wooden Church Belfries. Designs showing 18th-century church belfries. Self-adhesive.
898 **299** 10c. blue and black 25 20
899 - 20c. yellow and black 45 40
900 - 50c. green and black 90 85
901 - 1l. cinnamon and black 1·60 1·50
902 - 1l.30 lilac and black 2·30 2·10
903 - 1l.70 bistre and black 3·00 2·75

Designs: 10c. T **299**; 20c. Rozalimas; 50c. Tryskiai; 1l. Saukenai; 1l.30 Vaiguva; 1l.70 Vajasiskis.

See also Nos. 917/921, 928/933, 964/968, 1017/1020, 1043/1045 and 1132.

300 Bernardas Brazdzionis

2007. Personalities. Multicoloured.
904 1l. Type **300** (poet) (birth centenary) 1·60 1·50
905 1l. Vytautas Kazimierasv Jonynas (sculptor) (birth centenary) 1·60 1·50
906 3l. Leonas Sapiega (politician) (450th birth anniversary) 5·00 4·50

2007. Town Arms. As T **245**. Multicoloured.
907 1l. Svencionys 1·60 1·50
908 1l.30 Kelme 2·10 1·90
909 2l. Moletai 3·25 3·00

301 Badge

2007. Europa. Centenary of Scouting. Multicoloured.
910 1l.70 Type **301** 2·75 2·50
911 1l.70 Flag 2·75 2·50

302 St Anne's and Bernardine Churches, Vilnius

2007. Churches. Multicoloured.
912 1l. Type **302** 1·60 1·50
913 1l.30 Coming of the Blessed Virgin Mary and Camaldoli Monastery, Pazaislis 2·10 1·90

303 Jonas Basanavicius (founder) and First Lithuanian Newspaper *Ausra*. 1883

2007. Lithuania Millenary (7th issue). Sheet 125×100 mm containing T **303** and similar horiz designs. Multicoloured.
MS914 3l×4. Type **303**; Knygnesys Jurgis Bielinis (clandestine nationalist book supplier) (prohibition on printing in Latin characters abolished, 1904); Legislative building (the Great Seimas Of Vilnius, 1905); Building and signatures (declaration of independence, 1918) 20·00 19·00

304 15th-century Chess Pieces

2007. Trakai History Museum. Multicoloured.

915 2l. Type **304** 3·50 3·25
916 2l. Naujieji Trakai 1600 (J. Kamarauskas) 3·50 3·25

2007. Wooden Church Belfries. As T **299**. Self-adhesive.

917 5c. green and black 25 20
918 35c. grey and black 70 65
919 1l.35 lemon and black 2·30 2·10
920 1l.55 orange and black 2·50 2·30
921 2l.15 claret and black 3·75 3·25

Designs: 5c.Vabalninkas; 35c.Varputenai; 1l.35 DeguCiai; 1l.55 GeidZiai; 2l.15 Pavandene.

305 Juozas Miltinis

2007. Birth Centenary of Juozas Miltinis (actor and theatrical producer).

922 **305** 2l.45 multicoloured 4·25 3·75

306 *Gallinago media*

2007. Cepkeliai and Kotra Nature Reserves. Multicoloured.

923 2l.90 Type **306** 4·75 4·50
924 2l.90 *Crex crex* 4·75 4·50

Nos. 923/924 were issued in horizontal *se-tenant* strips of two stamps surrounding a central stamp size label, each strip forming a composite design.

307 Document establishing Lithuania Post and First Day Covers

2007. Postal History. 15th Anniversary of Lithuania Post State Enterprise.

925 **307** 1l.35 multicoloured 2·30 2·10

308 Snowflake and Baubles

2007. Christmas. Multicoloured.

926 1l.35 Type **308** 2·30 2·10
927 2l.45 Fir twig and globe as bauble 4·25 3·75

2008. Wooden Churches. As T **299**. Each orange and black. Self-adhesive.

928 5c. Antante 25 20
929 10c. Deguciai 35 30
930 20c. Inturke 45 40
931 35c. Prienai 70 65
932 1l.35 Siaudine 2·30 2·10
933 1l.55 Uzventis 2·50 2·30

309 Martynas Jankus (publisher) (150th birth anniversary)

2008. Personalities. Multicoloured.

934 2l. Type **309** 3·50 3·25
935 2l.15 Zenonas Ivinskis (historian and philosopher) (birth centenary) 3·75 3·25
936 2l.90 Antanas Maceina (philosopher and writer) (birth centenary) 4·75 4·50

310 Jonas Basanavicius (Council chairman)

2008. 90th Anniversary of Restored State of Lithuania.

937 **310** 1l.35 multicoloured 2·30 2·10

311 Order of Vytautas the Great with Golden when Act was signed) Chain (Lithuania)

2008. Baltic States' Orders. Sheet 116×51 mm containing T **311** and similar vert designs. Multicoloured.

MS938 Size 5l.×3, As Type **311**; Order of National Coat of Arms (Estonia); Order of Three Stars (Latvia) 25·00 24·00
939 7l. As Type **294** 12·00 11·00

Stamps of similar design were issued by Estonia and Latvia.

312 Wooden Carving (Lionginas sepka)

2008. Rokiskis Regional Museum. Multicoloured.

940 1l.55 Type **312** 2·75 2·50
941 1l.55 19th-centenary women's costumes 2·75 2·50

313 Letters from Gediminas (Grand Duke of Lithuania) to Pope John XXII, 1323

2008. Europa. The Letter. Multicoloured.

942 2l.45 Type **313** 4·25 3·75
943 2l.45 Vilnius, symbols of e-mail and written letter 4·25 3·75

314 Emblem and Demonstrators

2008. 20th Anniversary of Sajudis (reform movement).

944 **314** 1l.35 multicoloured 2·30 2·10

315 Emblem

2008. Zaragoza 2008 International Water and Sustainable Development Exhibition. Self adhesive.

945 **315** 2l.45 multicoloured 4·25 3·75

316 Cabinet of Ministers, 1918

2008. Lithuania Millennary (8th issue) (2009). Sheet 125×100 mm containing T **316** and similar horiz designs. Multicoloured.

MS946 3l×6, Type **316**; Constituent Assembly, 1920; Vytautas Magnus University (University of Lithuania), Kaunas, 1922; Klaipeda incorporated into Lithuania, 1923; Opening of road to Zemaiciu (place of pilgrimage), Samogitia, 1939; Return of Vilnius, 1939 32·00 31·00

317 Steponas Darius, Stasys Girenas and Bellanca CH-300 *Lituanica*

2008. 75th Anniversary of Steponas Darius and Stasys Girenas's Transatlantic Flight.

947 **317** 2l.90 multicoloured 5·00 4·50

318 Runners

2008. Olympic Games, Beijing. Multicoloured.

948 2l.15 Type **318** 3·75 3·25
949 2l.45 Yachts 4·25 3·75

319 Virgin and Child

2008. 400th Anniversary of Apparition of Our Lady of Siluva.

950 **319** 1l.55 multicoloured 2·75 2·50

320 European Roller

2008. Endangered Species. European Roller (*Coracias garrulus*). Multicoloured.

951 1l.35 Type **320** 2·30 2·10
952 1l.35 In flight 2·30 2·10
953 1l.35 With open beak 2·30 2·10
954 1l.35 Looking over shoulder 2·30 2·10
MS955 97×81 mm. As Nos. 951/954 9·25 9·00

The stamps and margins of **MS**955 form a composite design.

2008. Town Arms. As T **245**. Multicoloured.

956 1l.35 Joniskis 2·30 2·10
957 1l.35 Jubarkas 2·30 2·10
958 3l. Sirvintos 5·00 4·50

321 Hips

2008. Christmas and New Year. Multicoloured.

959 1l.35 Type **321** 2·30 2·10
960 2l.45 Snow covered branches 4·25 3·75

322 Jonas Zemaitis (soldier)

2009. Personalities. Multicoloured.

961 1l.35 Type **322** 2·30 2·10
962 2l. Vaclovas Birziska (bibliographer) 3·50 3·25
963 2l.15 Mecislovas Reinys (priest and psychologist) 3·75 3·25

2009. Wooden Churches. As T **299**. Self-adhesive.

964 10c. yellow, sepia and black 45 40
965 20c. yellow, sepia and black 70 65
966 50c. green and black 90 85
967 1l. cinnamon and black 1·60 1·50
968 1l.35 yellow, sepia and black 3·25 3·00

Designs: 10c. As No. 929; 20c. As No. 930; 50c. As. No. 900; 1l. As No. 901; 1l.35 As No. 932.

2009. Town Arms. As T **245**. Multicoloured.

969 1l.35 Krekenava 2·30 2·10
970 1l.35 Pakruojis 2·30 2·10
971 3l. Salcininkai 5·00 4·50

323 Polar Ice

2009. Preserve Polar Regions and Glaciers. Sheet 120×80 mm containing T **323** and similar vert design. Multicoloured.

MS972 2l.90×2, Type **323**; Ice cliffs 9·75 9·50

324 Statue

2009. Vilnius. European Capital of Culture.

973 **324** 2l.15 multicoloured 3·75 3·25

325 G. M. Dallmeyer's Photoheliograph and Vilnius University

2009. Europa. Astronomy. Multicoloured.

974 2l.45 Type **325** 4·25 3·75
975 21.45 Galileo Galilei (astronomer) 4·25 3·75

326 Great Synagogue, Vilnius

2009. Great Synagogue of Vilnius.

976 **326** 1l.35 multicoloured 2·30 2·10

327 'Sun Stone' (3524 gm., one of world's largest amber pieces)

2009. Amber Museum, Palanga. Multicoloured.

977 1l.55 Type **327** 3·00 2·75
978 1l.55 Amber museum (Count Feliksas Tyskevichius's estate, built 1897) 3·00 2·75

328 Spindle Fragment

2009. Millennium Song Festival of Lithuania. Song of Centuries.

979 **328** 3l.35 multicoloured 6·75 6·00

329 Council Members (Council of Struggle for Freedom of Lithuania Movement Declaration (1949))

2009. Lithuania Millenary (9th issue). Struggle for Independence. Sheet 125×100 mm containing T **329** and similar horiz designs. Multicoloured.

MS980 3l.×6, Type **329**; Front cover (launch of *Chronicle of Catholic Church of Lithuania* (illegal) (1972)); Crowds with flags (establishment of Lithuanian Reform Movement 'Sajudis' (1988)); Document (signing of Act of Independent State Reconstruction (1990)); European flag (membership of European Union (2004)); Map (membership of Schengen Area (2007)) 35·00 34·00

The stamps and margins of **MS**980 form a common background design of the National Flag.

330 Sail Ship

2009. Tall Ships Race 2009, finishing in Klaipeda, Lithuania.

981 **330** 3l. multicoloured 5·75 5·25

No. 981 was printed, *se-tenant*, with a label showing an emblem for the occasion, the stamp and label forming a composite design.

331 Commuter Train

2009. 150th Anniversary of Lithuanian Railways.

982 **331** 2l.90 multicoloured 5·50 5·00

332 Grand Cross

2009. Grand Cross of the Order of Vytis (awarded for courage and bravery).

983 **332** 7l. multicoloured 11·50 10·50

333 *Papilio machaon*

2009. Endangered Species. Multicoloured.

984 1l.55 Type **333** 3·00 2·75

985 1l.55 *Gentiana pneumonanthe* 3·00 2·75

Nos. 984/985 were printed, *se-tenant*, each pair forming a composite design.

334 George von Struve and Triagulation Chain of Struve Arc

2009. UNESCO World Heritage List. Struve Geodetic Arc. Multicoloured.

986 2l. Type **334** 3·50 3·25

987 2l. Struve's arc point in Meskonys 3·50 3·25

335 Church and Houses in Snow

2009. Christmas and New Year. Multicoloured.

988 1l.35 Type **335** 2·30 2·10

989 2l.45 Christmas baubles and house in snow 4·25 3·75

336 Jonas Karolis Chodkevichius

2010. Personalities. Multicoloured.

990 1l.35 Type **336** (courtier, military leader and founder of Kretinga Church and Monastery) 2·30 2·10

991 1l.35 Jonas Jablonskis (linguist) 2·30 2·10

992 3l. Mykolas Krupavichius (Ecclesiastic, politician and Minister of Agriculture) 5·25 4·75

337 Skier

2010. Winter Olympic Games, Vancouver.

993 **337** 2l.45 multicoloured 4·25 4·00

2010. Town Arms. As T **245**. Multicoloured.

994 1l.35 Silale 2·30 2·10

995 2l. Jonova 3·50 3·25

996 2l.15 Varena 3·75 3·25

338 Doves

2010. 20th Anniversary of Restoration of Independence.

997 **338** 1l.35 multicoloured 2·30 2·10

339 Tree growing from Egg

2010. Easter.

998 **339** 1l.35 multicoloured 2·30 2·10

340 Balloon over Shanghai

2010. Expo 2010, Shanghai.

999 **340** 2l.90 multicoloured 5·00 4·50

341 Vladas Mikenas

2010. Birth Centenary of Vladas Mikenas (chess International Master).

1000 **341** 2l. multicoloured 3·50 3·25

342 Rabbit, Girl and Figures

2010. Europa. Children's Books. Multicoloured.

1001 2l.45 Type **342** 4·25 3·75

1002 2l.45 Letters, bird and boy 4·25 3·75

343 Oak Tree

2010. Natural Heritage. The Oak of Stelmuze. Sheet 70×70 mm.

MS1003 **343** 8l. multicoloured 14·00 13·50

344 Crown and Shield with Swords and Battle of Zalgiris (engraving by M. Bielski)

2010. 600th Anniversary of Battle of Grunvald (First Battle of Tannenberg), during the Polish–Lithuanian–Teutonic War.

1004 **344** 2l.45 multicoloured 4·25 3·75

345 St George (St Jurgis)

2010. 75th Anniversary of Kretinga Museum. Multicoloured.

1005 1l.35 Type **345** 2·30 2·10

1006 1l.35 3rd-century buckle 2·30 2·10

346 Games Emblem and Basketball Player

2010. Youth Olympic Games, Singapore 2010.

1007 **346** 2l.90 multicoloured 4·50 4·25

347 Kernavé within Landscape

2010. World Heritage Sites. Multicoloured.

1008 3l. Type **347** 4·75 4·50

1009 3l. Pathway and steps up earthwork 4·75 4·50

348 Stock Pigeon (*Columba oenas*)

2010. Endangered Species. Multicoloured.

1010 1l.35 Type **348** 2·30 2·10

1011 1l.35 Lesser Emperor dragonfly (*Anax parthenope*) 2·30 2·10

Nos. 1010/1011 were printed, *se-tenant*, forming a composite design.

349 Christ's Transfiguration Cathedral, Kaisisdorys

2010. Churches. Multicoloured.

1012 1l.35 Type **349** 2·30 2·10

1013 1l.35 St Anthony of Padua Cathedral, Telsiai 2·30 2·10

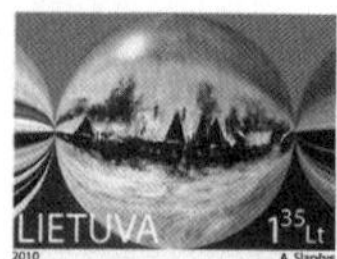

350 Snow-covered Houses

2010. Christmas and New Year. Multicoloured.

1014 1l.35 Type **350** 2·30 2·10

1015 2l.45 Winter sunset 4·25 3·75

351 Grand Cross of the Order of the Lithuanian Grand Duke Gediminas

2010. State Awards (1st series).

1016 **351** 7l. multicoloured 11·50 10·50

See also No.1050a.

2011. Wooden Churches and Belfries. As T **299**.

1017 10c. orange-yellow, olive-sepia and black 45 40

1018 50c. light blue-green and black 90 85

1019 1l. cinnamon and black 1·60 1·50

1020 1l.35 cinnamon and black 2·30 2·10

Designs: 10c. Deguchiai Church, 1757; 50c. Tryshkiai Church, 18th century; 1l. Shaukenai Church, 1l.35 Shiaudine Church, 1775.

352 Vilnius TV Tower (scene of defence)

2011. 13th January. Defenders of Freedom (unarmed resistors to military overthrow) Day.

1021 **352** 1l.35 multicoloured 2·30 2·10

353 Ball and Hoop

2011. Men's European Basketball Championship 2011, Lithuania.

1022 **353** 2l.45 multicoloured 4·25 4·00

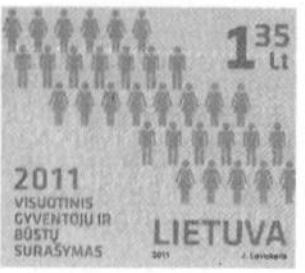

354 Figures

2011. Population and Housing Census.

1023 **354** 1l.35 multicoloured 2·30 2·10

355 Gabriele Petkevichaite-Bite (writer and philanthropist)

2011. Personalities. Multicoloured.

1024 1l.35 Type **355** 2·30 2·10

1025 2l.15 Justinas Vienozhinskis (writer) 3·75 3·25

1026 2l.90 Stasys Shalskausis (philosopher) 5·00 4·50

356 Town Hall

2011. 650th Anniversary of Kaunas. Multicoloured.
MS1027 3l.×3, Type **356**; Central Post Office; Pekunas House 16·00 15·00

357 Fields and Forest

2011. Europa. Forests. Multicoloured.
1028 2l.45 Type **357** 4·25 4·00
1029 2l.45 River and forest 4·25 4·00

358 Pope John Paul II

2011. Pilgrim Route of Pope John Paul II (following John Paul II's route during his visit in 1993).
1030 **358** 2l.15 multicoloured 3·75 3·25

359 Giraffe

2011. Lithuanian Zoo. Multicoloured.
MS1031 4l.×4, Type **359**; Pelicans; *Cichiasoma octofasciatum*; Polar bear 28·00 27·00

360 Blacksmith's Bellows and Forge

2011. Exhibits in Alytus Ethnographic Museum. Multicoloured.
1032 2l. Type **360** 3·50 3·25
1033 2l. Ceramics 3·50 3·25

361 Czesław Miłosz

2011. Birth Centenary of Czesław Miłosz (writer).
1034 **361** 3l.35 multicoloured 5·75 5·25

362 Water Measuring Station, Smalinkai (L. Meshkaityte)

2011. Bicentenary of Water Measuring (hydrometric) Station, Smalinkai.
1035 **362** 1l.35 multicoloured 2·30 2·10

2011. Town Arms. As T **245**. Multicoloured.
1036 1l.35 Plungė 2·30 2·10
1037 2l.15 Kaišiadorys 3·75 3·25
1038 2l.90 Ignalina 5·00 4·50

363 Puntukas Stone

2011. Natural Heritage. Puntukas Stone (second largest glacial erratic (rock) in Lithuania, engraved with portraits of pilots, Steponas Darius and Stasys Girėnas). Sheet 70×70 mm.
MS1039 **363** 8l. multicoloured 14·00 13·50

364 Shiauliai Cathedral

2011. Churches. Multicoloured.
1040 1l.55 Type **364** 2·75 2·50
1041 1l.55 Trakai Parish Church 2·75 2·50

365 Cavalry

2011. 775th Anniversary of Battle of Saule.
1042 **365** 2l.45 multicoloured 4·25 4·00

2011. Wooden Churches and Belfries. As T **299**. Each cinnamon and black.
1043 5c. Antazavė Church, 1794 25 20
1044 20c. Inturkė Church, 1855 45 40
1045 35c. Prienai Church, 1750 70 65

366 *Haliaeetus albicilla* (white-tailed sea eagle)

2011. Endangered Species. White-tailed Sea Eagle (*Haliaeetus albicilla*).
1046 **366** 2l.15 multicoloured 3·75 3·25

367 Gate of Dawn

2011. World Heritage Sites. Vilnius Historic Centre. Multicoloured.
1047 3l. Type **367** 5·50 5·00
1048 3l. St John's Church 5·50 5·00

368 Snowman

2011. Christmas and New Year. Multicoloured.
1049 1l.35 Type **368** 2·30 2·10
1050 2l.45 Snowflake 4·25 4·00

368a Grand Cross of the Order for Merits

2011. State Awards (2nd series).
1050a **368a** 7l. multicoloured 12·00 11·00

369 Wooden Panpipes

2012. Lithuanian Folk Music Instruments. Each dull scarlet and black.
1051 10c. Type **369** 25 20
1052 20c. Animal shaped clay pipes 45 40
1053 35c. Bladderbow bass 70 65
1054 1l. Alder bark trumpet 1·80 1·70
1055 1l.35 Kanklės (stringed instrument) from Suvalkija 2·30 2·10
1056 2l.15 Cowhorn reed-pipe 3·75 3·25

See also Nos.1094/1095 and 1110/1112.

2012. Town Arms. As T **245**. Multicoloured.
1057 1l.35 Kalvarija 2·30 2·10
1058 1l.35 Kavarskas 2·30 2·10
1059 2l.45 Naujoji Akmene 4·25 3·75

370 Mikalojus Radvila Rudasis

2012. Personalities. Multicoloured.
1060 1l.55 Type **370** 2·75 2·50
1061 2l. Domicelė Tarabildienė (artist) 3·50 3·25
1062 2l.90 Stasys Šimkus (composer and conductor) 5·00 4·50

371 *Dolomedes plantarius* (Great Raft Spider)

2012. Endangered Species. Spiders. Multicoloured.
1063 2l.90 Type **371** 5·00 4·50
1064 2l.90 *Eresus cinnaberinus* (Ladybird Spider) 5·00 4·50

372 Fresco, Saint-Pierre-la-Jeune Church, Strasbourg (detail)

2012. 625th Anniversary of Christianisation of Lithuania.
1065 **372** 1l.35 multicoloured 2·30 2·10

373 Traditional Houses

2012. Europa. Visit Lithuania. Multicoloured.
1066 2l.45 Type **373** 4·25 3·75
1067 2l.45 Woodland and lake 4·25 3·75

374 Baubliai of Dionizas Poška

2012. Year of Museums. Bicentenary of Dionizas Poška's Museum, Baubliai. Sheet 70×70 mm.
MS1068 **374** 7l. multicoloured 12·50 12·00

375 Dunes

2012. World Heritage Sites. Curonian Spit. Multicoloured.
1069 3l. Type **375** 5·50 5·00
1070 3l. Fisherman's farmstead, Kopgalis 5·50 5·00

376 Boxing

2012. Olympic Games, London. Multicoloured.
1071 3l.35 Type **376** 5·75 5·25
1072 3l.55 Single scull rower 6·25 5·75

377 Lighthouse and Harbour

2012. 760th Anniversary of Klaipėda (Memel).
1073 **377** 2l. multicoloured 3·50 3·25

378 Algirdas, Grand Duke of Lithuania and Silhouettes

2012. 650th Anniversary of Battle of Blue Waters.
1074 **378** 2l.45 multicoloured 4·25 3·75

379 Algirdas Brazauskas

2012. 80th Birth Anniversary of Algirdas Mykolas Brazauskas (politician and first freely elected president).
1075 **379** 1l.35 multicoloured 2·30 2·10

380 Banknotes

2012. 20th Anniversary of Restoration Lithuanian Monetary System.
1076 **380** 2l. multicoloured 3·50 3·25

381 Oskaras Minkovskis

2012. Oskaras Minkovskis (scientist) Commemoration.
1077 **381** 1l.35 multicoloured 2·30 2·10

382 Lyduvėnai Bridge, Lithuania

2012. Railway Bridges of the Baltic States. Multicoloured.
1078 8l. Type **382** 13·00 12·00
MS1079 125×60 mm. Size 36×30 mm. 4l.×3, As Type **382**; Narva Bridge, Estonia; Carnikava Bridge, Latvia 21·00 20·00

383 Snowy Evening

2012. Christmas and New Year. Multicoloured.
1080 1l.35 Type **383** 2·30 2·10

1081 2l.45 Snow-covered house 4·25 3·75

384 Motiejus Trakishkis (first Samogitian bishop) and *Christianisation of Lithuania* (fresco)

2013. 600th Anniversary of Samogitia Christianisation.
1082 **384** 2l.45 multicoloured 4·25 3·75

385 *Vulpes vulpes* (Fox)

2013. Zhuvintas Biosphere Reserve. Multicoloured.
MS1083 3l.×3, Type **385**; *Panurus biarmicus* (Bearded Reedling); *Dactylorhiza maculata* 17·00 16·00

386 Snake

2013. Chinese New Year. Year of the Snake.
1084 **386** 2l.90 multicoloured 5·00 4·50

387 Laser Display

2013. Laser Industry.
1085 **387** 1l.35 multicoloured 2·30 2·10

388 Antanas Strazdas (poet)

2013. Personalities. Multicoloured.
1086 1l.35 Type **388** 2·30 2·10
1087 2l. Pranas Mašiotas (writer) 3·50 3·25

389 Zignatas Sierakauskas (leader) and Rebels of 1863 (Artur Grotter)

2013. 150th Anniversary of Uprising of 1863.
1088 **389** 1l.35 multicoloured 2·30 2·10

390 *Ciconia ciconia* (White Stork)

2013. Birds.
1089 **390** 7l. multicoloured 12·00 11·00

391 Tazzari ZERO

2013. Europa. Postal Transport. Multicoloured.
1090 2l.45 Type **391** 4·25 3·75
1091 2l.45 Moskvitch 401 post car 4·25 3·75

392 *Mother* (Gryte Kučinskaitė)

2013. Mother's Day. Winning Design in Chidren's Drawing Competition.
1092 **392** 1l.35 multicoloured 2·30 2·10

393 Jean-Henri Dunant, Nurse and Flag

2013. 150th Anniversary of International Red Cross Organisation.
1093 **393** 2l.15 multicoloured 3·75 3·25

394 Alder Bark Trumpet

2013. Lithuanian Folk Music Instruments. Each dull scarlet and black.
1094 1l. Type **394** 1·80 1·70
1095 1l.35 Kanklės (stringed instrument), Suvalkija 2·30 2·10

395 *Father* (Grytė Kučinskaitė)

2013. Father's Day. Winning Design in Chidren's Drawing Competition.
1096 **395** 1l.35 multicoloured 2·30 2·10

396 Cathedral

2013. 600th Anniversary of Kaunas Cathedral Basilica.
1097 **396** 1l.35 multicoloured 2·30 2·10

397 EU Stars and Flags

2013. Lithuanian Presidency of Council of European Union.
1098 **397** 2l.45 multicoloured 4·25 3·75

398 Anchor

2013. 90th Anniversary of Transfer Of Klaipeda Port to Lithuania. Sheet 120×50 mm.
MS1099 **398** 7l. multicoloured 12·00 11·50

399 Runners

2013. 75th Anniversary of National Olympiad.
1100 **399** 1l.35 multicoloured 2·30 2·10

400 S. Darius and S. Girėnas beside *Lituanica*

2013. 80th Anniversary of Steponas Darius and Stasys Girėnas's Flight from New York to Lithuania (fatal crash).
1101 **400** 2l.90 multicoloured 5·00 4·50

401 Klaipėda Lighthouse

2013. Technical Monuments. Lighthouses. Multicoloured.
1102 2l.45 Type **401** 4·25 3·75
1103 2l.45 Ventė Cape Lighthouse 4·25 3·75

402 Land Forces Soldier Ceremonial Uniform and Junior Officer Uniform

2013. Armed Forces. Military Uniforms.
1104 **402** 1l.35 multicoloured 2·30 2·10

403 *Acrocephalus paludicola* (Aquatic Warbler)

2013. Endangered Species. Birds. Multicoloured.
1105 2l.15 Type **403** 2·30 2·10
1106 2l.90 *Anthus campestris* (Tawny Pipit) 2·30 2·10

404 Postcards

2013. Postcrossing (people from many countries sending each other traditional postcards).
1107 **404** 2l.45 multicoloured 2·30 2·10

405 Bear and Squirrel with Presents

2013. Christmas and New Year. Multicoloured.
1108 1l.35 Type **405** 1·10 1·00
1109 2l.45 Bear and squirrel watching fireworks 2·25 2·25

2013. Lithuanian Folk Music Instruments. Each dull scarlet and black.
1110 10c. As Type **369** 25 20
1111 20c. As No. 1052 (Animal shaped clay pipes) 30 25
1112 35c. As No. 1053 (Bladderbow bass) 55 50

406 Kristijonas Donelyaitis

2014. 300th Birth Anniversary of Kristijonas Donelyaitis (writer).
1113 **406** 1l.55 multicoloured 1·00 1·00

407 Bobsleigh

2014. Winter Olympic Games, Sochi. Multicoloured.
1114 2l.15 Type **407** 1·50 1·50
1115 2l.90 Ice hockey 1·75 1·75

408 Horse

2014. Chinese New Year. Year of the Horse. Sheet 69×50 mm.
MS1116 **408** 7l. multicoloured 5·00 5·00

409 Shrove Tuesday Masks

2014. Shrove Tuesday Masks.
1117 **409** 2l. multicoloured 1·50 1·50

410 Anniversary Emblem

2014. 25th Anniversary of Restoration of Vytautas Magnus University.
1118 **410** 1l.55 multicoloured 1·00 1·00

411 NATO Emblem

2014. Tenth Anniversary of Lithuania's Accession to NATO.
1119 **411** 2l.15 multicoloured 1·50 1·50

Nos. 1120/1121 are awaiting stamps, not yet received.

413 EU Flag

2014. Tenth Anniversary of European Union Membership
1122 **413** 2l.15 multicoloured 4·00 3·75

414 Ozgaris (goat horn) and Skrabala (wooden bells)

2014. Europa. Musical Instruments. Multicoloured.
1123 2l.45 Type **414** 4·00 3·75
1124 2l.45 Byrbine (reed pipe) and Kankles (zither) 4·00 3·75

415 Fish Bones and Feet

2014. Save the Baltic Sea.
1125 **415** 2l.90 multicoloured 5·25 5·00

416 Seraya Szapszal (Karaites leader)

2014. Lithuanian National Minorites. Karaites. Multicoloured.
1126 2l.15 Type **416** 4·00 3·75
1127 2l.15 Vilnius Kenesa (place of worship) 4·00 3·75

417 Choir

2014. 90th Anniversary of Lithuania Song Festival.
1128 **417** 1l.35 multicoloured 2·40 2·10

418 Hands, Globe and Lithuanian Flag

2014. Election of Lithuania to United Nations Security Council.
1129 **418** 1l.35 multicoloured 2·40 2·10

418a Five Demonstrators

2014. 25th Anniversary of Baltic Chain (human chain from Tallinn to Vilnius). Each black and deep blue.
MS1129a 7l.×3, Type **418a**; Three demonstrators; Child and man 35·00 30·00

419 Konstantin Ostrogsky and Battle Scene

2014. 800th Anniversary of Battle of Orsha.
1130 **419** 2l.60 multicoloured 4·50 4·25

420 *LituanicaSAT-1*

2014. Launch of *LituanicaSAT*-1 Satellite.
1131 **420** 2l.90 multicoloured 5·25 5·00

421 Vabalininkas Church Belfry

2014. Wooden Churches and Belfries.
1132 **421** 5c. bright yellow-green and black 10 10

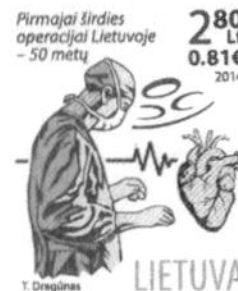

422 Surgeon and Heart

2014. 50th Anniversary of First Open Heart Surgery at Vilnius University Hospital.
1133 **422** 2l.80 multicoloured 5·00 4·75

423 Carrying Envelope

2014. Christmas and New Year. Multicoloured.
1134 1l.35 Type **423** 2·40 2·10
1135 2l.80 Santa travelling by air balloon 5·00 4·75

424 Denari (Jogaila, 1388–1390)

2015. Introduction of Euro. Lithuanian Coins showing Vytis (emblem of Lithuania state). Each olive-bistre and black.
1136 1c. Type **424** 60 50
1137 3c. Denari (Kazimiero, 1440–1492) 1·80 1·50
1138 10c. 3 grašiai coin (Žygimanto Augusto, 1562) 2·75 2·50
1139 29c. Šilingas (Jono Kazimiero, 1660) 3·50 3·00
1140 39c. Ortas (Augusto III, 1754) 3·75 3·50
1141 62c. 5 litas (1925) 4·25 4·00

425 Euro

2015. Introduction of Euro. Euro Coins.
1142 **425** 75c. multicoloured 4·75 4·50

426 *Lutra lutra*

2015. Endangered Species. Mink (*Mustela lutrola*) and Otter (*Lutra lutra*). Multicoloured.
1143 71c. Type **426** 4·50 4·00
1144 87c. *Mustela lutreola* 5·25 5·00

427 M. R. Juodasis

2015. 500th Birth Anniversary of Mikalojus Radvila Juodasis (nationalist).
1145 **427** 45c. multicoloured 4·00 3·75

428 Anniversary Emblem

2015. 25th Anniversary of Act of Independence of Lithuania.
1146 **428** 84c. multicoloured 5·25 5·00

429 Kaunas Fortress

2015. Technical Monuments. Kaunas Fortress.
1147 **429** €2.03 multicoloured 10·50 10·00

430 Wooden Puzzle

2015. Europa. Old Toys. Multicoloured.
1148 71c. Type **430** 4·50 4·25
1149 71c. Five-piece wooden puzzle 4·50 4·25

431 Jonas Juska

2015. Birth Bicentenary of Jonas Juskav (Lithuanian grammar and language pioneer).
1150 **431** 58c. multicoloured 4·20 4·10

432 Map and Pathway through Dunes

2015. Tourism. Pervalka.
1151 **432** 97c. multicoloured 6·00 5·75

433 Railway Bridge, Kretinga

2015. Bridges.
1152 **433** 87c. multicoloured 5·75 5·50

434 Mažoji Lietuva

2015. Year of Ethnographic Regions. Multicoloured.
MS1153 75c.×5, Type **434**; Žemaitija; Aukštaitija; Suvalkija; Dzūkija 12·00

435 Evening Gown

2015. Contemporary Art of Lithuania. Fashion.
1154 **435** €2.03 multicoloured 10·50 10·00

436 Symbols of Knowledge

2015. Education and Knowledge Day.
1155 **436** 45c. multicoloured 4·00 3·75

437 Mykolas Kleopas Oginskis

2015. 250th Birth Anniversary of Mykolas Kleopas Oginskis (compsoer and diplomat).
1156 **437** 81c. multicoloured 5·00 4·75

438 Code

2015. Information Technologies. World Day of IT Development.
1157 **438** 84c. multicoloured 5·25 5·00

439 Forged Products

2015. Traditional Crafts.
1158 **439** 75c. multicoloured 4·75 4·50

440 Winter Landscape

2015. Christmas and New Year. Multicoloured.
1159 39c. Type **440** 3·75 2·10
1160 81c. Tree, children and snowman 5·00 3·50

441 Vytis, 1410

2016. Lithuanian State Symbol. Vytis. Scarlet and black.
1161 1c. Type **441** 60 50
1162 3c. Vytis, 1553 1·80 1·50
1163 10c. Vytis, 1863 2·75 2·50
1164 29c. Vytis, 1929 3·50 3·00
1165 39c. Vytis, 1989 3·75 3·50
1166 62c. Vytis, 1993 4·25 4·00

442 Soldiers

2016. 25th Anniversary of Events of 13th January (Soviet Union troops attempting a coup d'etat, seized Vilnius Television Tower and Lithuanian Radio and Television Centre, and attacked Supreme Council building, killing 14 civilian protesters).
1167 **442** 45c. multicoloured 4·00 3·75

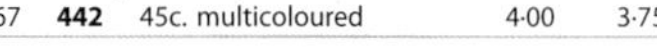

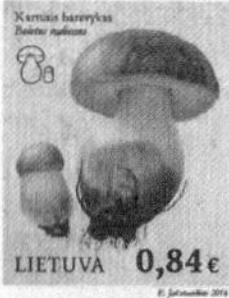

443 *Boletus radicans*

2016. Endangered Species. Fungi. Multicoloured.
1168 84c. Type **443** 5·25 5·00
1169 84c. *Gomphus clavatus* 5·25 5·00

444 Julius Juzeliūnas

2016. Birth Centenary of Julius Juzeliūnas (composer).
1170 **444** 39c. multicoloured 3·75 3·50

445 Paper Mill, Naujieji Verkiai

2016. Technical Monuments. Paper Mill, Naujieji Verkiai.
1171 **445** 58c. multicoloured 4·25 4·00

446 Oak Tree

2016. Tourism. Kaunas Oak Wood.
1172 **446** 87c. multicoloured 5·40 5·25

412 *Tyto alba* (Barn Owl)

2014. Endangered Species. Birds. Multicoloured.
1120 2l. Type **412** 3·50 3·25
1121 3l. *Glaucidium passerinum* (Eurasian Pygmy Owl) 5·25 5·00

447 Lithuanian and Japanese Parliamentary Buildings

2016. 25th Anniversary of Lithuania–Japan Diplomatic Relations.
1173 **447** €1 multicoloured 6·25 6·00

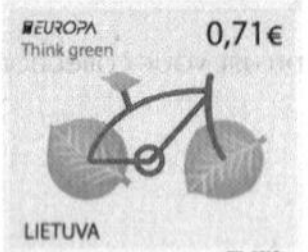

448 Bicycle with Leaves for Wheels

2016. Europa. Think Green. Multicoloured.
1174 71c. Type **448** 4·25 3·75
1175 71c. Roller painting contaminated landscape green 4·25 3·75

449 Jurgis Machiunas

2016. 115th Birth Anniversary of Jurgis (George) Machiunas (artist and founding member and central co-ordinator of Fluxus, international community of artists, architects, composers, and designers).
1176 **449** 75c. multicoloured 4·25 3·75

450 Horse

2016. Lithuanian Animals. Žemaitukas Horse (one of the oldest horse breeds in Europe). Sheet 75×50 mm.
MS1177 **450** €1.56 multicoloured 6·25 6·00

451 Cucumbers and Honey

2016. Gastronomic Heritage.
1178 **451** 39c. multicoloured 3·75 3·50

452 Swimmer

2016. Olympic Games. Rio 2016. Multicoloured.
1179 81c. Type **452** 5·00 4·75
1180 84c. Horse rider 5·25 5·00

453 UN Building and Flags

2016. 25th Anniversary of Membership of United Nations.
1181 **453** 75c. multicoloured 4·75 4·50

454 *Nude* (Petras Repšys)

2016. Contemporary Art of Lithuania. Graphics
1182 **454** 48c. black and carmine 3·75

455 Kazys Grinius

2016. 150th Birth Anniversary of Kazys Grinius (president, 1926).
1183 **455** 45c. multicoloured 2·75 2·75

456 *Auszra* (The Dawn) Newspaper

2016. Centenary of Resoration of Lithuanian Independence. Multicoloured.
MS1184 €1.16×3, Type **456**; Jonas Basanavičius (activist); *Varpas* (The Bell) newspaper 23·00 22·00

457 Emblem

2016. 25th Baltic Assembly.
1185 **457** 45c. multicoloured 2·75 2·75
MS1186 80×65 mm. 97c. As Type **457** 6·25 6·00

458 Village Christmas

2016. Christmas and New Year. Multicoloured.
1187 39c. Type **458** 2·50 2·30
1188 81c. Winter in the old town of Vilnius 5·00 4·75

459 Martin Luther and Wittenberg Church

2017. 500th Anniversary of the Reformation.
1189 **459** 39c. multicoloured 2·50 2·30

460 Stylised Star of David

2017. 25th Anniversary of Lithuania–Israel Diplomatic Relations.
1190 **460** 97c. multicoloured 6·00 5·75

461 Vytis, 14th/15th-century

2017. Lithuanian State Symbol. Vytis. Black.
1191 3c. Type **461** 20 20
1192 10c. Vytis, 15th-century 65 60
1193 39c. Vytis, 15th-century (different) 2·50 2·30
1194 42c. Vytis, 16th-century 2·75 2·50
1195 94c. Vytis, 18th-century 6·00 5·75
1196 €1 Vytis, 20th-century 6·25 6·00

462 Lithuanian Grand Duke Vytautas and Motiejus (first bishop)

2017. 600th Anniversary of Diocese of Samogitia.
1197 **462** €1 multicoloured 6·25 6·00

463 Kazys Bradūnas

2017. Birth Centenary of Kazys Bradūnas (poet).
1198 **463** 39c. multicoloured 2·50 2·30

464 Reading Newspaper (Recovery of the Lithuanian Press (7 May, 1904))

2017. Centenary of Resoration of Lithuanian Independence. Multicoloured.
MS1199 €1.16×3, Type **464**; Great Seimas of Vilnius (4–5 May, 1905); Vilnius Conference (18–22 September ,1917) 23·00 22·00

465 Algirdas Julien Greimas

2017. Birth Centenary of Algirdas Julien Greimas (scientist).
1200 **465** 39c. multicoloured 2·50 2·30

466 *Eliomys quercinus* (Garden Dormouse)

2017. Endangered Species. Rodents. Multicoloured.
1201 42c. Type **466** 2·75 2·50
1202 42c. *Sicista betulina* (Northern Birch Mouse) 2·75 2·50

467 Klaipėda Castle, 1684

2017. Europa. Castles. Sepia.
1203 81c. Type **467** 5·00 4·75
1204 81c. Biržai Castle, 1704 5·00 4·75

468 Local Cheeses

2017. Culinary Heritage. Cheese.
1205 **468** 52c. multicoloured 3·25 3·00

469 Canal Lock

2017. Technical Monuments. Old Canal Locks of King William.
1206 **469** 94c. multicoloured 6·00 5·75

470 Hillfort

2017. Tourism. Sheimynishkeliai Hillfort.
1207 **470** 39c. multicoloured 2·50 2·30

471 *Lozoriau, kelkis* (Lazarus, get up) (Stanislovas Kuzma)

2017. Contemporary Art of Lithuania. Sculpture.
1208 **471** 94c. multicoloured 6·00 5·75

472 *Lepus europaeus* (European Hare)

2017. Lithuanian Animals. Multicoloured.
MS1209 84c.×3, Type **472**; *Meles meles* (Badger); *Cervus elaphus* (Red Deer) 17·00 16·00

473 Menorah

2017. Ethnic Minorities and Communities in Lithuania. Jewish Community.

1210	**473**	94c. multicoloured	6·00	5·75

LOMBARDY AND VENETIA

Formerly known as Austrian Italy. Although these provinces used a different currency the following issues were valid throughout Austria. Lombardy was annexed by Sardinia in 1859 and Venetia by Italy in 1866.

1850. 100 centesimi = 1 lira.
1858. 100 soldi = 1 florin. 100 kreuzer = 1 gulden.

1 Arms of Austria

1850. Imperf.

1c	**1**	5c. orange	£2000	£140
2c	**1**	10c. black	£3500	£130
7	**1**	15c. red	£1600	11·50
4c	**1**	30c. brown	£3750	25·00
5e	**1**	45c. blue	£10000	80·00

1859. As T **4** and **5** of Austria (Emperor Francis Joseph I) but value in soldi. Perf.

16B	**5**	2s. yellow	£1500	£160
17A	**4**	3s. black	£3750	£400
18B	**4**	3s. green	£900	£150
19B	**5**	5s. red	£550	12·50
20A	**5**	10s. brown	£750	£130
21B	**5**	15s. blue	£3750	75·00

3 Emperor Francis Joseph I

1861

25	**3**	5s. red	£1900	8·75
26	**3**	10s. brown	£6500	65·00

4 Arms of Austria

1863

27	**4**	2s. yellow	£325	£225
33	**4**	3s. green	50·00	44·00
34	**4**	5s. red	8·75	11·50
35	**4**	10s. blue	55·00	19·00
36	**4**	15s. brown	£190	£140

JOURNAL STAMPS

J5

1858. Imperf.

J22	**J5**	1k. black	£3250	£7000
J23	**J5**	2k. red	£650	£110
J24	**J5**	4k. red	£107000	£7000

LOURENCO MARQUES

A Portuguese colony in E. Africa, now part of Mozambique, whose stamps it uses.

1895. 1000 reis = 1 milreis.
1913. 100 centavos = 1 escudo.

1895. Figures key-type inscr 'LOURENCO MARQUES'.

1	**R**	5r. yellow	60	55
2	**R**	10r. mauve	60	55
3	**R**	15r. brown	1·40	1·00
4	**R**	20r. lilac	1·40	95
10	**R**	25r. green	1·10	55
12	**R**	50r. blue	2·75	2·10
18	**R**	75r. pink	2·50	1·70
14	**R**	80r. green	7·25	4·75
7	**R**	100r. brown on yellow	3·25	1·70
16	**R**	150r. red on pink	5·75	4·75
8	**R**	200r. blue on blue	5·50	3·50
9	**R**	300r. blue on brown	5·75	3·75

1895. 700th Death Anniversary of St Anthony. Optd **L. MARQUES CENTENARIO DE S. ANTONIO MDCCCXCV** on (a) Embossed key-type inscr 'PROVINCIA DE MOCAMBIQUE'.

19	**Q**	5r. black	25·00	21·00
20	**Q**	10r. green	28·00	21·00
21	**Q**	20r. red	31·00	23·00
22	**Q**	25r. purple	38·00	23·00
23	**Q**	40r. brown	38·00	23·00
27a	**Q**	50r. blue	25·00	23·00
25	**Q**	100r. brown	£120	£110
26	**Q**	200r. violet	50·00	41·00
27	**Q**	300r. orange	80·00	70·00

(b) Figures key-type inscr 'MOCAMBIQUE'.

28	**R**	5r. orange	2·30	1·60
29	**R**	10r. mauve	2·30	1·60
30	**R**	50r. blue	2·30	1·60
35	**R**	75r. pink	55	50
32	**R**	80r. green	1·60	1·20
33	**R**	100r. brown on yellow	55	50
35a	**R**	150r. red on pink	45	35

1897. No. 9 surch **50 reis**.

36		50r. on 300r. blue on brown	£275	£250

1898. King Carlos key-type inscr 'LOURENCO MARQUES'. Name and value in black.

37	**S**	2½r. grey	50	50
38	**S**	5r. orange	50	50
39	**S**	10r. green	50	50
40	**S**	15r. brown	1·80	1·30
83	**S**	15r. green	1·20	80
41	**S**	20r. lilac	1·10	65
42	**S**	25r. green	1·10	65
84	**S**	25r. red	85	50
43	**S**	50r. blue	1·80	1·30
85	**S**	50r. brown	1·50	1·20
86	**S**	65r. blue	6·00	4·75
44	**S**	75r. pink	3·50	2·10
87	**S**	75r. purple	2·20	1·70
45	**S**	80r. mauve	3·00	2·00
46	**S**	100r. blue on blue	2·30	1·30
88	**S**	115r. brown on pink	7·00	6·25
89	**S**	130r. brown on yellow	7·00	6·25
47	**S**	150r. brown on yellow	3·50	2·10
48	**S**	200r. purple on pink	5·25	2·75
49	**S**	300r. blue on pink	3·75	2·75
90	**S**	400r. blue on yellow	7·75	6·75
50	**S**	500r. black on blue	7·50	4·00
51	**S**	700r. mauve on yellow	32·00	14·00

1899. Green and brown fiscal stamps of Mozambique, as T **9** of Macao, bisected and each half surch **Correio de Lourenco Marques** and value. Imperf.

55	5r. on half of 10r.	1·80	1·60
56	25r. on half of 10r.	2·10	1·60
57	50r. on half of 30r.	2·10	1·60
58	50r. on half of 800r.	1·80	1·30

1899. No. 44 surch **50 Reis**.

59	**S**	50r. on 75r. pink	2·30	1·60

1902. Figures and Newspaper key-types surch.

60	**V**	65r. on 2½r. brown	3·75	3·25
62	**R**	65r. on 5r. yellow	3·75	3·00
63	**R**	65r. on 15r. brown	3·75	3·00
64	**R**	65r. on 20r. lilac	3·75	3·00
66	**R**	115r. on 10r. mauve	3·75	3·00
67	**R**	115r. on 200r. blue on blue	3·75	3·00
68	**R**	115r. on 300r. blue on brn	3·75	3·00
70	**R**	130r. on 25r. green	3·50	3·25
72	**R**	130r. on 80r. green	3·75	3·25
73	**R**	130r. on 150r. red on pink	3·75	3·25
74	**R**	400r. on 50r. blue	12·50	5·50
76	**R**	400r. on 75r. pink	10·00	5·50
78	**R**	400r. on 100r. brown on yellow	7·00	4·75

1902. King Carlos key-type inscr 'LOURENCO MARQUES' optd **PROVISORIO**.

79	**S**	15r. brown	2·20	1·70
80	**S**	25r. green	2·20	1·20
81	**S**	50r. blue	3·25	1·80
82	**S**	75r. pink	4·25	2·75

1905. No. 86 surch **50 REIS**.

91	50r. on 65r. blue	4·50	3·75

1911. King Carlos key-type inscr 'LOURENCO MARQUES' optd **REPUBLICA**.

92	2½r. grey	50	35
93	5r. orange	50	35
94	10r. green	80	65
95	15r. green	80	65
96	20r. lilac	80	65
97	25r. red	1·50	90
98	50r. brown	1·30	90
99	75r. purple	2·10	90
100	100r. blue on blue	1·30	90
178	115r. brown on pink	2·10	1·80
102	130r. brown on yellow	1·50	90
103	200r. purple on pink	1·50	90
104	400r. blue on yellow	2·50	2·00
105	500r. black on blue	2·50	2·00
106	700r. mauve on yellow	3·25	2·00

1913. Surch **REPUBLICA LOURENCO MARQUES** and value on Vasco da Gama issues of (a) Portuguese Colonies.

107	¼c. on 2½r. green	2·20	1·80
108	½c. on 5r. red	2·20	1·80
109	1c. on 10r. purple	2·20	1·80
110	2½c. on 25r. green	2·20	1·80
111	5c. on 50r. blue	2·20	1·80
112	7½c. on 75r. brown	5·75	4·25
113	10c. on 100r. brown	3·25	1·80
114	15c. on 150r. brown	3·25	1·80

(b) Macao.

115	¼c. on ½a. green	1·40	1·10
116	½c. on 1a. red	1·90	1·10
117	1c. on 2a. purple	1·90	1·10
118	2½c. on 4a. green	1·90	1·40
119	5c. on 8a. blue	3·75	2·10
120	7½c. on 12a. brown	3·75	2·75
121	10c. on 16a. brown	5·00	3·50
122	15c. on 24a. brown	5·25	3·50

(c) Timor.

123	¼c. on ½a. green	5·25	3·50
124	½c. on 1a. red	7·00	5·75
125	1c. on 2a. purple	7·00	5·75
126	2½c. on 4a. green	7·00	6·50
127	5c. on 8a. blue	90	70
128	7½c. on 12a. brown	1·80	90
129	10c. on 16a. brown	1·30	1·10
130	15c. on 24a. brown	1·30	1·20

1914. Ceres key-type inscr 'LOURENCO MARQUES'.

147	**U**	¼c. green	45	35
148	**U**	½c. black	45	35
149	**U**	1c. green	45	35
150	**U**	1½c. brown	50	45
151	**U**	2c. red	50	45
152	**U**	2½c. violet	50	45
153	**U**	5c. blue	1·10	95
154	**U**	7½c. brown	1·10	95
155	**U**	8c. grey	1·10	95
140	**U**	10c. red	2·00	1·20
157	**U**	15c. purple	1·90	1·80
142	**U**	20c. green	2·20	1·80
143	**U**	30c. brown on green	2·00	1·70
144	**U**	40c. brown on pink	7·50	5·75
145	**U**	50c. orange on orange	3·50	2·75
146	**U**	1e. green on blue	3·50	2·75

1914. Provisionals of 1902 overprinted **REPUBLICA**.

166	**R**	115r. on 10r. mauve	1·20	95
167	**R**	115r. on 200r. blue on blue	1·40	95
168	**R**	115r. on 300r. blue on brn	1·40	95
161	**R**	130r. on 25r. green	2·00	1·80
164	**R**	130r. on 80r. green	2·00	1·80
169	**R**	130r. on 150r. red on pink	1·40	95
184	**R**	400r. on 50r. blue	2·20	1·70
185	**R**	400r. on 75r.	3·50	2·75

1915. Nos. 93 and 148 perf diagonally and each half surch ¼.

171	**U**	¼ on half of ½c. black	4·25	3·25
170	**S**	¼ on half of 5r. orange	4·25	3·25

Prices for Nos. 170/171 are for whole stamps.

1915. Surch **Dois centavos**.

172	**S**	2c. on 15r. (No. 83)	1·90	1·40
173	**S**	2c. on 15c. (No. 95)	1·90	1·40

1918. Red Cross Fund. Ceres key-type inscr 'LOURENCO MARQUES', optd **9-3-18** and Red Cross or surch with value in figures and bars also.

188	**U**	¼c. green	3·75	3·50
189	**U**	½c. black	3·75	3·50
190	**U**	1c. green	3·75	3·50
191	**U**	2½c. violet	3·75	3·50
192a	**U**	5c. blue	3·75	3·50
193	**U**	10c. red	4·50	4·00
194	**U**	20c. on 1½c. brown	4·50	4·00
195	**U**	30c. brown on green	5·00	4·75
196	**U**	40c. on 2c. red	5·00	4·75
197	**U**	50c. on 7½c. brown	5·00	4·75
198	**U**	70c. on 8c. grey	5·00	4·75
199	**U**	1e. on 15c. purple	5·00	4·75

1920. No. 166 surch **Um quarto de centavo**.

200	**R**	¼c. on 115r. on 10r. mauve	1·40	95

1920. No. 152 surch in figures or words.

201	**U**	1c. on 2½c. violet	1·10	65
202	**U**	1½c. on 2½c. violet	1·10	65
203	**U**	4c. on 2½c. violet	1·10	65

For other surcharges on Ceres key-type of Lourenco Marques, see Mozambique Nos. 309/310 and Nos. D44 and D46.

NEWSPAPER STAMPS

1893. Newspaper key-type inscr 'LOURENCO MARQUES'.

N1	**V**	2½r. brown	65	60

1895. 700th Death Anniversary of St Anthony. Newspaper key-type inscr 'MOCAMBIQUE' optd **L. MARQUES CENTENARIO DE S. ANTONIO MDCCCXCV.**

N36	2½r. brown	9·50	6·50

LUBECK

Formerly one of the free cities of the Hanseatic League. In 1868 joined the North German Confederation.

16 schilling = 1 mark.

1

1859. Imperf.

9	**1**	½s. lilac	70·00	£2500
10	**1**	1s. orange	£140	£2500
3	**1**	2s. brown	£180	£400
4	**1**	2½s. red	£350	£1400
6	**1**	4s. green	£140	£1000

3

1863. Rouletted.

11	**3**	½s. green	70·00	£120
13	**3**	1s. orange	£200	£300
14	**3**	2s. red	46·00	£110
16	**3**	2½s. blue	£200	£650
17	**3**	4s. bistre	90·00	£170

4

1864. Imperf.

18	**4**	1¼s. brown	50·00	£200

5

1865. Roul.

21	**5**	1½s. mauve	50·00	£140

LUXEMBOURG

An independent Grand Duchy lying between Belgium and the Saar District. Under German Occupation from 1940 to 1944.

1852. 12½ centimes = 1 silver groschen.
100 centimes = 1 franc.
1940. 100 pfennig = 1 reichsmark.
1944. 100 centimes = 1 franc (Belgian).
2002. 100 cents = 1 euro.

1 Grand Duke William III

1852. Imperf.

2	**1**	10c. black	£3500	95·00
4	**1**	1s. red	£2500	£150

3

4

1859. Imperf or roul.

21	**3**	1c. orange	65·00	12·50
23	**3**	1c. brown	65·00	12·50
17	**3**	2c. black	31·00	25·00
8	**3**	4c. yellow	£325	£275
20	**3**	4c. green	65·00	38·00
10	**4**	10c. blue	£325	31·00
24	**4**	10c. purple	£190	6·25
25	**4**	10c. lilac	£225	6·25
28	**4**	12½c. red	£275	12·50
30	**4**	20c. brown	£225	12·50
12	**4**	25c. brown	£600	£450
32	**4**	25c. blue	£1600	19·00
13	**4**	30c. purple	£500	£375
14	**4**	37½c. green	£550	£325
35	**4**	37½c. bistre	£1300	£400
39	**4**	40c. orange	65·00	£130

1872. Surch **UN FRANC**. Roul.

37	**4**	1f. on 37½c. bistre	£1400	£130

1874. Perf.

57	**3**	1c. brown	6·25	3·25
58	**3**	2c. black	8·75	3·25
42	**3**	4c. green	6·25	16·00
43	**3**	5c. yellow	£275	44·00
60	**4**	10c. lilac	31·00	3·25
61a	**4**	12½c. red	19·00	19·00
62	**4**	20c. brown	9·50	6·25
63	**4**	25c. blue	31·00	3·25
64a	**4**	30c. red	9·50	25·00
55	**4**	40c. orange	6·25	16·00

1879. Surch **Un Franc**. Perf.

56	**4**	1f. on 37½c. bistre	12·50	44·00

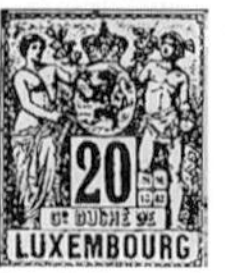

7 Agriculture and Trade

1882

81c	**7**	1c. grey	1·30	95
82c	**7**	2c. brown	40	95
83c	**7**	4c. bistre	1·30	3·25
84c	**7**	5c. green	1·50	95
85c	**7**	10c. red	19·00	95
86a	**7**	12½c. blue	3·25	47·00
87c	**7**	20c. orange	5·75	3·75
88c	**7**	25c. blue	£375	3·25
89a	**7**	30c. green	48·00	22·00
90c	**7**	50c. brown	3·25	19·00
91a	**7**	1f. lilac	3·25	44·00
92	**7**	5f. orange	65·00	£275

8 Grand Duke Adolf

1891

125c	**8**	10c. red	1·30	50
126b	**8**	12½c. green	2·50	1·30
128	**8**	20c. orange	19·00	1·30
129c	**8**	25c. blue	2·50	1·30
130b	**8**	30c. green	2·75	1·90
131b	**8**	37½c. green	5·75	5·00
132b	**8**	50c. brown	12·50	6·25
133b	**8**	1f. purple	35·00	10·00
134	**8**	2½f. black	3·25	34·00
135	**8**	5f. lake	65·00	£110

9

1895

152	**9**	1c. grey	9·50	1·30
153	**9**	2c. brown	2·50	65
154	**9**	4c. bistre	2·50	1·90
155	**9**	5c. green	19·00	65
156	**9**	10c. red	31·00	65

10

11 Grand Duke William IV

1906

157	**10**	1c. grey	40	30
158	**10**	2c. brown	40	30
159	**10**	4c. bistre	40	65
160	**10**	5c. green	65	30
231	**10**	5c. mauve	30	65
161	**10**	6c. lilac	40	95
161a	**10**	7½c. orange	40	5·00
162	**11**	10c. red	3·75	65
163	**11**	12½ slate	3·75	1·30
164	**11**	15c. brown	3·75	1·30
165	**11**	20c. orange	6·25	1·30
166	**11**	25c. blue	£190	1·30
166a	**11**	30c. olive	2·50	1·30
167	**11**	37½c. green	2·50	1·90
168	**11**	50c. brown	8·75	1·90
169	**11**	87½c. blue	5·00	25·00
170	**11**	1f. purple	11·50	3·25
171	**11**	2½f. red	£110	£130
172	**11**	5f. purple	19·00	95·00

1912. Surch **62½ cts.**

173	**11**	62½c. on 87½c. blue	7·50	3·75
173a	**11**	62½c. on 2½f. red	7·50	7·50
173b	**11**	62½c. on 5f. purple	5·00	6·25

13 Grand Duchess Adelaide

1914

174	**13**	10c. purple	25	30
175	**13**	12½c. green	25	30
176	**13**	15c. brown	25	30
176a	**13**	17½c. brown	25	95
177	**13**	25c. blue	25	30
178	**13**	30c. brown	25	1·30
179	**13**	35c. blue	25	95
180	**13**	37½c. brown	25	95
181	**13**	40c. red	30	65
182	**13**	50c. grey	50	95
183	**13**	62½c. green	65	5·00
183a	**13**	87½c. orange	65	5·00
184	**13**	1f. brown	6·25	1·90
185	**13**	2½f. red	65	5·00
186	**13**	5f. violet	15·00	75·00

1916. Surch in figures and bars.

187	**10**	2½ on 5c. green	25	65
188	**10**	3 on 2c. brown	25	65
212	**10**	5 on 1c. grey	25	65
213	**10**	5 on 4c. bistre	25	1·30
214	**10**	5 on 7½c. orange	25	65
215	**10**	6 on 2c. brown	50	65
189	**13**	7½ on 10c. red	25	65
190	**13**	17½ on 30c. brown	25	1·30
191	**13**	20 on 17½c. brown	25	65
216	**13**	25 on 37½c. sepia	25	65
217	**13**	75 on 62½c. green	25	65
218	**13**	80 on 87½c. orange	25	65
192	**13**	87½ on 1f. brown	1·30	12·50

17 Grand Duchess Charlotte

18 Vianden Castle

1921. Perf.

194	**17**	2c. brown	65	30
195	**17**	3c. green	65	30
196	**17**	6c. purple	65	30
197	**17**	10c. green	65	30
193a	**17**	15c. red*	65	50
198	**17**	15c. green	65	30
234	**17**	15c. orange	30	65
199	**17**	20c. orange	65	50
235	**17**	20c. green	30	65
200	**17**	25c. green	65	30
201	**17**	30c. red	65	30
202	**17**	40c. orange	65	30
203	**17**	50c. blue	1·30	95
236	**17**	50c. red	30	65
204	**17**	75c. red	65	1·90
237	**17**	75c. blue	30	65
205	**17**	80c. black	2·50	1·90
206a	**18**	1f. red	65	65
238	**18**	1f. blue	50	1·30
207	-	2f. blue	65	1·30
239	-	2f. brown	6·25	3·25
208	-	5f. violet	23·00	15·00

Designs: As T **18**—2f. Factories at Esch; 5f. Railway viaduct over River Alzette.

*No. 193a was originally issued on the occasion of the birth of Crown Prince Jean.

See also Nos. 219/220.

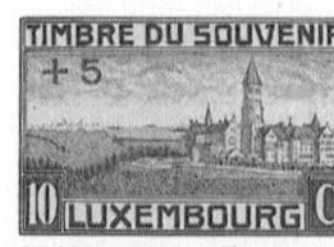

21 Monastery at Clervaux

1921. War Monument Fund.

209	**21**	10c.+5c. green	65	9·50
210	-	15c.+10c. orange	65	12·50
211	-	25c.+10c. green	65	9·50

Designs: Horiz—15c. Pfaffenthal; 25c. as T **26**.

1922. Philatelic Exhibition. Imperf.

219	**17**	25c. green	2·50	8·75
220	**17**	30c. red	2·50	8·75

26 Luxembourg

1923. Birth of Princess Elisabeth. Sheet 78×59 mm to 79×61 mm.

MS221	**26**	10f. green	£1900	£3250

1923

222a	**26**	10f. black	12·50	19·00

1923. Unveiling of War Memorial by Prince Leopold of Belgium. Nos. 209/311 surch **27 mai 1923** and additional values.

223	**21**	10+5+25c. green	2·50	25·00
224	-	15+10+25c. orange	2·50	31·00
225	-	25+10+25c. green	2·50	25·00

28 Echternach

1923

226	**28**	3f. blue	3·75	1·30

1924. Charity. Death of Grand Duchess Marie Adelaide. Surch **CARITAS** and new value.

227	**13**	12½c.+7½c. green	30	5·00
228	**13**	35c.+10c. blue	30	5·00
229	**13**	2½f.+1f. red	1·90	47·00
230	**13**	5f.+2f. violet	95	31·00

1925. Surch **5**.

240	**17**	5 on 10c. green	30	65

31

1925. Anti-TB Fund.

241	**31**	5c.+5c. violet	25	1·30
242	**31**	30c.+5c. orange	25	5·00
243	**31**	50c.+5c. brown	25	9·50
244	**31**	1f.+10c. blue	65	24·00

32 Grand Duchess Charlotte

1926

245	**32**	5c. mauve	20	30
246	**32**	10c. olive	20	30
246a	**32**	15c. black	30	65
247	**32**	20c. orange	50	65
248	**32**	25c. green	50	65
248a	**32**	25c. brown	30	65
248b	**32**	30c. green	30	65
248c	**32**	30c. violet	65	65
248d	**32**	35c. violet	6·25	65
248e	**32**	35c. green	30	65
249	**32**	40c. brown	20	30
250	**32**	50c. brown	20	30
250a	**32**	60c. green	6·25	30
251	**32**	65c. brown	30	3·25
251a	**32**	70c. violet	65	65
252	**32**	75c. red	30	1·30
252a	**32**	75c. brown	20	65
253	**32**	80c. brown	30	3·25
253a	**32**	90c. red	2·50	3·25
254	**32**	1f. black	2·50	65
254a	**32**	1f. red	95	65
255	**32**	1¼f. blue	30	1·30
255a	**32**	1¼f. yellow	19·00	2·50
255b	**32**	1¼f. green	95	65
255c	**32**	1¼f. red	19·00	3·25
255d	**32**	1½f. blue	3·25	2·50
255e	**32**	1¾f. blue	1·90	65

33 Prince Jean

1926. Child Welfare.

256	**33**	5c.+5c. black and mauve	40	1·30
257	**33**	40c.+10c. black & green	40	1·90
258	**33**	50c.+15c. black & yellow	40	1·90
259	**33**	75c.+20c. black and red	40	19·00
260	**33**	1f.50+30c. black & bl	40	22·00

34 Grand Duchess and Prince Felix

1927. International Philatelic Exhibition.

261	**34**	25c. purple	1·90	18·00
262	**34**	50c. green	2·50	28·00
263	**34**	75c. red	1·90	18·00
264	**34**	1f. black	1·90	18·00
265	**34**	1½f. blue	1·90	18·00

35 Princess Elisabeth

1927. Child Welfare.

266	**35**	10c.+5c. black and blue	40	1·30
267	**35**	50c.+10 black and brown	40	1·90
268	**35**	75c.+20c. black & orange	40	3·25
269	**35**	1f.+30c. black and red	40	19·00
270	**35**	1½f.+50c. black and blue	40	19·00

1927. Stamps of 1921 and 1926 surch.

270a	**32**	10 on 30c. green	65	65
271	**17**	15 on 20c. green	30	30
272	**32**	15 on 25c. green	30	95
273	**17**	35 on 40c. orange	30	30
274	**32**	60 on 65c. brown	30	65
275	**17**	60 on 75c. blue	30	65
276	**32**	60 on 75c. red	30	65
277	**17**	60 on 80c. black	30	95
278	**32**	60 on 80c. brown	30	95
278a	**32**	70 on 75c. brown	12·50	65
278b	**32**	75 on 90c. red	3·75	1·30
278c	**32**	1¾ on 1½f. blue	6·25	3·75

37 Clervaux

1928. Perf.

279a	**37**	2f. black	3·25	1·30

See also No. 339.

38 Princess Marie Adelaide

1928. Child Welfare.

280	**38**	10c.+5c. purple & green	65	1·90
281	**38**	60c.+10c. olive & brown	1·30	5·00
282	**38**	75c.+15c. green and red	1·90	12·50
283	**38**	1f.+25c. brown & green	3·25	38·00
284	**38**	1½f.+50c. blue & yellow	3·25	38·00

39 Princess Marie Gabrielle

1928. Child Welfare.

285	**39**	10c.+10c. green & brown	65	2·50
286	**39**	35c.+15c. brown & green	2·50	12·50
287	**39**	75c.+30c. black and red	3·25	16·00
288	**39**	1¼f.+50c. green and red	3·75	38·00
289	**39**	1¾f.+75c. black and blue	5·00	47·00

40 Prince Charles

1930. Child Welfare.

290	**40**	10c.+5c. brown & green	65	1·90
291	**40**	75c.+10c. green & brown	3·25	8·25
292	**40**	1f.+25c. violet and red	6·25	31·00
293	**40**	1¼f.+75c. black & yellow	9·50	41·00
294	**40**	1¾f.+1f.50 brown & blue	12·50	41·00

41 Arms of Luxembourg

1930

295	**41**	5c. red	1·30	65
296	**41**	10c. green	2·50	65

42 Biplane over River Alzette

1931. Air.

296a	**42**	50c. green	1·30	1·90
297	**42**	75c. brown	1·30	2·50
298	**42**	1f. red	1·30	2·50
299	**42**	1¼f. purple	1·30	2·50
300	**42**	1¾f. blue	1·30	2·50
300a	**42**	3f. black	2·50	10·00

43 Luxembourg, Lower Town

1931

301	**43**	20f. green	6·25	31·00

44 Princess Alix

1931. Child Welfare.

302	**44**	10c.+5c. grey and brown	65	1·90
303	**44**	75c.+10c. green and red	6·25	25·00
304	**44**	1f.+25c. grey and green	19·00	50·00
305	**44**	1¼f.+75c. green and violet	12·50	50·00
306	**44**	1¾f.+1f.50 grey and blue	25·00	95·00

45 Countess Ermesinde

1932. Child Welfare.

307	**45**	10c.+5c. brown	65	1·90
308	**45**	75c.+10c. violet	6·25	25·00
309	**45**	1f.+25c. red	22·00	55·00
310	**45**	1¼f.+75c. lake	22·00	65·00
311	**45**	1¾f.+1f.50 blue	22·00	65·00

46 Emperor Henry VII

1933. Child Welfare.

312	**46**	10c.+5c. brown	65	1·90
313	**46**	75c.+10c. purple	9·50	25·00
314	**46**	1f.+25c. red	19·00	65·00
315	**46**	1¼f.+75c. brown	25·00	80·00
316	**46**	1¾f.+1f.50 blue	31·00	90·00

47 Gateway of the Three Towers

1934

317	**47**	5f. green	6·25	19·00

48 Arms of John the Blind

1934. Child Welfare.

318	**48**	10c.+5c. violet	1·30	3·25
319	**48**	35c.+10c. green	6·25	19·00
320	**48**	75c.+15c. red	6·25	19·00
321	**48**	1f.+25c. red	31·00	80·00
322	**48**	1¼f.+75c. orange	31·00	80·00
323	**48**	1¾f.+1½f. blue	31·00	80·00

50 Surgeon

1935. International Relief Fund for Intellectuals.

324	-	5c. violet	1·30	1·90
325	-	10c. red	1·30	1·90
326	-	15c. olive	1·30	3·25
327	-	20c. orange	3·25	4·50
328	-	35c. green	3·25	5·75
329	-	50c. black	3·75	8·25
330	-	70c. green	6·25	9·50
331	**50**	1f. red	6·25	12·50
332	-	1f.25 turquoise	25·00	90·00
333	-	1f.75 blue	25·00	90·00
334	-	2f. brown	65·00	£190
335	-	3f. brown	75·00	£250
336	-	5f. blue	£130	£475
337	-	10f. purple	£325	£800
338	**50**	20f. green	£350	£950

Designs: Horiz—5c., 10f. Schoolteacher; 15c., 3f. Journalist; 20c., 1f.75, Engineer; 35c., 1f.25, Chemist. Vert—10c., 2f. The Arts; 50c., 5f. Barrister; 70c. University.

This set was sold at the PO at double face value.

1935. Esch Philatelic Exhibition. Imperf.

339	**37**	2f.(+50c.) black	9·50	31·00

52 Vianden

1935

340	**52**	10f. green	6·25	25·00

53 Charles I

1935. Child Welfare.

341	**53**	10c.+5c. violet	30	65
342	**53**	35c.+10c. green	95	1·30
343	**53**	70c.+20c. brown	1·90	2·50
344	**53**	1f.+25c. red	31·00	65·00
345	**53**	1f.25+75c. brown	31·00	65·00
346	**53**	1f.75+1f.50 blue	31·00	80·00

54 Town Hall

1936. 11th International Philatelic Federation Congress.

347	**54**	10c. brown	65	1·30
348	**54**	35c. green	65	1·90
349	**54**	70c. orange	95	2·50
350	**54**	1f. red	2·50	15·00
351	**54**	1f.25 violet	4·50	19·00
352	**54**	1f.75 blue	2·50	16·00

55 Wenceslas I

1936. Child Welfare.

353	**55**	10c.+5c. brown	65	65
354	**55**	35c.+10c. green	65	1·30
355	**55**	70c.+20c. slate	95	1·90
356	**55**	1f.+25c. red	5·00	28·00
357	**55**	1f.25+75c. violet	9·50	55·00
358	**55**	1f.75+1f.50 blue	9·50	34·00

1937. Dudelange Philatelic Exhibition. Sheet 125×85 mm. As No. 207 (pair) in new colour.

MS359		2f. (+3f.) brown	10·00	22·00

56 Wenceslas II

1937. Child Welfare.

360	**56**	10c.+5c. black and red	30	65
361	**56**	35c.+10c. green & purple	30	1·30
362	**56**	70c.+20c. red and blue	50	95
363	**56**	1f.+25c. red and green	3·75	28·00
364	**56**	1f.25+75c. purple & brn	5·00	28·00
365	**56**	1f.75+1f.50 blue & blk	7·50	31·00

57 St Willibrord

1938. Echternach Abbey Restoration Fund (1st issue). 1200th Death Anniversary of St Willibrord.

366	**57**	35c.+10c. green	65	95
367	-	70c.+10c. black	1·30	95
368	-	1f.25+25c. red	3·25	4·50
369	-	1f.75+50c. blue	6·25	5·00
370	-	3f.+2f. red	12·50	16·00
371	-	5f.+5f. violet	12·50	12·50

Designs: As T **57**—70c. Town Hall, Echternach; 1f.25, Pavilion, Echternach Municipal Park. 31×51 mm—1f.75, St Willibrord (from miniature). 42×38 mm: 3f. Echternach Basilica; 5f. Whitsuntide dancing procession.

See also Nos. 492/7 and 569/70.

61 Sigismond of Luxembourg

1938. Child Welfare.

372	**61**	10c.+5c. black & mauve	30	65
373	**61**	35c.+10c. black & green	30	95
374	**61**	70c.+20c. black & brown	65	95
375	**61**	1f.+25c. black and red	5·00	25·00
376	**61**	1f.25+75c. black & grey	5·00	25·00
377	**61**	1f.75+1f.50 black & bl	6·25	38·00

62 Arms of Luxembourg

63 William I

1939. Centenary of Independence.

378	**62**	35c. green	30	65
379	**63**	50c. orange	30	65
380	-	70c. green	30	65
381	-	75c. olive	95	1·90
382	-	1f. red	1·90	3·25
383	-	1f.25 violet	30	1·30
384	-	1f.75 blue	30	1·30
385	-	3f. brown	50	1·90
386	-	5f. black	50	12·50
387	-	10f. red	1·90	19·00

www.robstine-stamps.com

GOOD NEWS!

For collectors of *fine used* stamps
A fantastic array of fine used material is now available

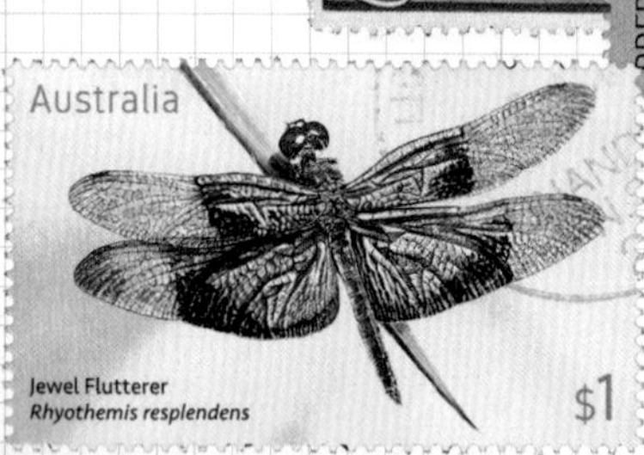

- An unrivalled selection of fine used European stamps.
- Very strong ranges of fine used Commonwealth stamps.
- Growing stocks of fine used stamps from around the world.
- All stamps listed in *www.robstine-stamps.com*
- Also visit *www.robstineextra.com* for a huge gallery of attractive items.

Contact me now for:
- comprehensive stocks
- superb quality
- easy ordering
- quick response

www.robstine-stamps.com

STANLEY GIBBONS

LONDON 1856

PERFECT ALBUMS TO STORE YOUR GB ISSUES

Stanley Gibbons Luxury Hingeless Album range offers the ultimate in quality, convenience and style.

Handsomely bound in deeply padded navy blue leatherette, this album is richly embossed with the country's national crest on the cover and spine and presented in its own slipcase.

Inside, the finest quality printed leaves have been expertly arranged with spaces for each stamp and clear protective mounts already affixed in place to enable easy insertion of your stamps. Selected illustrations and descriptions for your guidance are also included. Annual supplements are published to help keep your album up to date.

R5284	GB Lux. Vol 1 Album (1840-1970)	£170.00
R5285	GB Lux. Vol 2 Album (1970-1989)	£170.00
R5290	GB Lux. Vol 3 Album (1990-1999)	£170.00
R5295	GB Lux. Vol 4 Album (2000-2007)	£170.00
R5331	GB Lux. Vol 5 Album (2008-2011)	£170.00
R5333	GB Lux. Vol 6 Album (2012-2015)	£170.00
R5671	GB Lux. Vol 7 Album (2016-2017)	£125.00
R5284(SO)	Volume 1-7 Album Set (1840-2017)	£930.00

To order, call **01425 472 363** email **orders@stanleygibbons.com** or visit **stanleygibbons.com**

Portraits: As T **63**—70c. William II; 75c. William III; 1f. Prince Henry; 1f.25 Grand Duke Adolphe; 1f.75 William IV; 3f. Marie-Anne, wife of William IV; 5f. Grand Duchess Marie Adelaide; 10f. Grand Duchess Charlotte.

1939. Surch in figures.

388	**32**	30c. on 60c. green	30	2·50

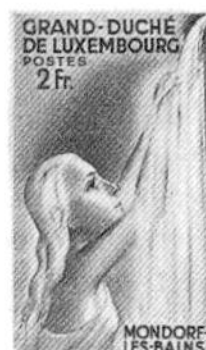

65 Allegory of Medicinal Spring

1939. Mondorf-les-Bains Propaganda.

389	**65**	2f. red	65	6·25

66 Prince Jean

1939. 20th Anniversary of Reign and of Royal Wedding.

390	**66**	10c.+5c. brn on cream	30	65
391	-	35c.+10c. green on cream	65	1·90
392	-	70c.+20c. black on cream	1·90	2·50
393	**66**	1f.+25c. red on cream	6·25	55·00
394	-	1f.25+75c. violet on cream	9·50	90·00
395	-	1f.75+1f.50 blue on cream	12·50	£110

Portraits: 35c., 1f.25, Prince Felix; 70c., 1f.75, Grand Duchess Charlotte.

1939. 20th Year of Reign of Grand Duchess Charlotte. Sheet 144×163 mm with designs as T **66** but without 'CARITAS'.

MS395a 2f. red (Type **66**); 3f. green (Prince Felix); 5f. blue (Grand Duchess Charlotte) 90·00 £190

1940. Anti-TB Fund. Surch with Cross of Lorraine and premium.

396	**65**	2f.+50c. grey	3·25	34·00

1940–44. GERMAN OCCUPATION.

1940. T **94** of Germany optd **Luxemburg**.

397	**94**	3pf. brown	45	75
398	**94**	4pf. blue	45	75
399	**94**	5pf. green	45	75
400	**94**	6pf. green	45	75
401	**94**	8pf. red	45	75
402	**94**	10pf. brown	45	75
403	**94**	12pf. red	45	75
404	**94**	15pf. purple	95	1·50
405	**94**	20pf. blue	95	1·80
406	**94**	25pf. blue	95	2·50
407	**94**	30pf. green	95	2·50
408	**94**	40pf. mauve	1·30	2·50
409	**94**	50pf. black and green	2·20	5·00
410	**94**	60pf. black and purple	2·50	5·00
411	**94**	80pf. black and blue	4·75	10·00
412	**94**	100pf. black and yellow	8·25	10·00

1940. Types of Luxembourg surch.

413	**32**	3 Rpf. on 15c. black	20	50
414	**32**	4 Rpf. on 20c. orange	20	50
415	**32**	5 Rpf. on 35c. green	20	50
416	**32**	6 Rpf. on 10c. green	20	50
417	**32**	8 Rpf. on 25c. brown	20	50
418	**32**	10 Rpf. on 40c. brown	20	50
419	**32**	12 Rpf. on 60c. green	20	50
420	**32**	15 Rpf. on 1f. red	20	50
421	**32**	20 Rpf. on 50c. brown	20	1·00
422	**32**	25 Rpf. on 5c. mauve	20	1·90
423	**32**	30 Rpf. on 70c. violet	20	1·00
424	**32**	40 Rpf. on 75c. brown	65	1·90
425	**32**	50 Rpf. on 1¼f. green	30	1·00
426	**65**	60 Rpf. on 2f. red	2·75	15·00
427	**47**	80 Rpf. on 5f. green	95	3·25
428	**52**	100 Rpf. on 10f. green	1·30	4·50

1941. Nos. 739/747 of Germany optd **Luxemburg**.

429		3pf.+2pf. brown	30	1·00
430		4pf.+3pf. blue	30	1·00
431		5pf.+3pf. green	30	1·00
432		6pf.+4pf. green	30	1·00
433		8pf.+4pf. orange	30	1·00
434		12pf.+6pf. red	30	1·00
435		15pf.+10pf. purple	45	2·50
436		25pf.+15pf. blue	65	5·75
437		40pf.+35pf. purple	2·00	9·50

1944. INDEPENDENCE REGAINED.

70 Grand Duchess Charlotte

1944

438	**70**	5c. brown	15	30
439	**70**	10c. slate	15	30
440	**70**	20c. orange	30	30
441	**70**	25c. brown	15	65
442	**70**	30c. red	65	65
443	**70**	35c. green	15	50
444	**70**	40c. blue	65	65
445	**70**	50c. violet	15	30
445a	**70**	60c. orange	4·50	30
446	**70**	70c. red	15	30
447	**70**	70c. green	1·30	1·90
448	**70**	75c. brown	65	50
449	**70**	1f. olive	15	30
450	**70**	1¼f. orange	15	80
451	**70**	1½f. orange	65	65
452	**70**	1¾f. blue	30	65
453	**70**	2f. red	6·25	65
454	**70**	2½f. mauve	9·50	8·25
455	**70**	3f. green	1·30	95
456	**70**	3½f. blue	1·30	1·30
457	**70**	5f. green	30	65
458	**70**	10f. red	30	2·50
459	**70**	20f. blue	95	31·00

71 'Britannia'

1945. Liberation.

460	-	60c.+1f.40 green	40	30
461	-	1f.20+1f.80 red	40	30
462	**71**	2f.50+3f.50 blue	40	30
463	-	4f.20+4f.80 violet	40	30

Designs: 60c. Ship symbol of Paris between Cross of Lorraine and Arms of Luxembourg; 1f.20, Man killing snake between Arms of Russia and Luxembourg; 4f.20, Eagle between Arms of USA and Luxembourg.

72 Statue of the Madonna in Procession

73 Altar and Shrine of the Madonna

1945. Our Lady of Luxembourg.

464	**72**	60c.+40c. green	40	6·25
465	-	1f.20+80c. red	40	6·25
466	-	2f.50+2f.50 blue	65	19·00
467	-	5f.50+6f.50 violet	1·90	£190
468	**73**	20f.+20f. brown	1·90	£190

MS468a 83×96 mm. 50f+50f. grey (as 1f.20) 2·50 70·00

Designs: As T **72**—1f.20, The Madonna; 2f.50, The Madonna and Luxembourg; 5f.50, Portal of Notre Dame Cathedral.

74 Lion of Luxembourg

1945

469	**74**	20c. black	40	30
470	**74**	30c. green	40	30
470a	**74**	60c. violet	65	50
471	**74**	75c. brown	40	30
472	**74**	1f.20 red	40	30
473	**74**	1f.50 violet	40	30
474	**74**	2f.50 blue	65	50

75 Members of the Maquis

1945. National War Victims Fund.

475	**75**	20c.+30c. green and buff	40	1·90
476	-	1f.50+1f. red and buff	40	1·90
477	-	3f.50+3f.50 blue & buff	90	18·00
478	-	5f.+10f. brown and buff	90	18·00

MS478a 100×110 mm. Designs and colours as Nos. 475/478 but values changed; 2f.50+2f.50, 3f.50+6f.50, 5f.+15f., 20f.+20f. 44·00 £500

Designs: 1f.50, Mother and children; 3f.50, Political prisoner; 5f. Executed civilian.

76

1946. Air.

479		1f. green and blue	65	30
480	**76**	2f. brown and yellow	65	50
481	-	3f. brown and yellow	65	50
482	-	4f. violet and grey	65	65
483	**76**	5f. purple and yellow	65	65
484	-	6f. purple and blue	65	95
485	-	10f. brown and yellow	2·50	95
486	**76**	20f. blue and grey	3·25	2·50
487	-	50f. green and light green	6·25	3·25

Designs: 1, 4, 10f. Aircraft wheel; 3, 6, 50f. Aircraft engine and castle.

76a Old Rolling Mill, Dudelange

1946. National Stamp Exhibition, Dudelange. Sheet 100×80 mm.

MS487a **76a** 50f. (+5f.) blue on buff 25·00 65·00

77 John the Blind, King of Bohemia

1946. 600th Death Anniversary of John the Blind.

488	**77**	60c.+40c. green and grey	1·30	3·75
489	**77**	1f.50+50c. red and buff	1·30	6·25
490	**77**	3f.50+3f.50 blue & grey	3·75	50·00
491	**77**	5f.+10f. brown and grey	2·50	44·00

78 Exterior Ruins of St Willibrord Basilica

79 St Willibrord

1947. Echternach Abbey Restoration (2nd issue). Inscr 'ECHTERNACH'.

492	**78**	20c.+10c. black	65	50
493	-	60c.+10c. green	95	95
494	-	75c.+25c. red	1·60	1·30
495	-	1f.50c.+50c. brown	1·90	1·30
496	-	3f.50c.+ 2f.50 blue	9·50	9·50
497	**79**	25f.+25f. purple	50·00	44·00

Designs: As T **78**—60c. Statue of Abbot Bertels; 75c. Echternach Abbey emblem; 1f.50, Ruined interior of Basilica; 3f.50, St Irmine and Pepin II carrying model of Abbey.

80 US Military Cemetery, Hamm

1947. Honouring General George S. Patton.

498	**80**	1f.50 red and buff	1·30	65
499	-	3f.50 blue and buff	6·25	5·00
500	**80**	5f. green and grey	6·25	5·00
501	-	10f. purple and grey	19·00	75·00

Portrait: 3f.50, 10f. General G. S. Patton.

82 Michel Lentz (national poet)

1947. National Welfare Fund.

502	**82**	60c.+40c. brown & buff	1·30	2·50
503	**82**	1f.50+50c. pur & buff	2·50	2·50
504	**82**	3f.50+3f.50 blue & grey	12·50	34·00
505	**82**	10f.+5f. green and grey	9·50	34·00

83 L'Oesling

1948. Tourist Propaganda.

505a	-	2f.50 brown and chocolate	3·25	95
505b	-	3f. violet	12·50	1·90
505c	-	4f. blue	9·50	1·90
506	**83**	7f. brown	31·00	1·30
507	-	10f. green	6·25	65
508	-	15f. red	6·25	1·30
509	-	20f. blue	6·25	1·30

Designs: Horiz—2f.50, Television transmitter, Dudelange; 3f. Radio Luxembourg; 4f. Victor Hugo's house, Vianden; 10f. River Moselle; 15f. Mining district. Vert—20f. Luxembourg.

85 'Dicks' (Edmund de la Fontaine)

1948. National Welfare Fund.

510	**85**	60c.+40c. brown & bistre	1·30	1·90
511	**85**	1f.50+50c. red and pink	1·30	1·90
512	**85**	3f.50+3f.50 blue & grey	18·00	34·00
513	**85**	10f.+5f. green and grey	15·00	34·00

86 Grand Duchess Charlotte

1948

513a	**86**	5c. orange	65	30
513b	**86**	10c. blue	65	30
514	**86**	15c. olive	65	30
514a	**86**	20c. purple	65	30
515	**86**	25c. grey	65	30
515a	**86**	30c. olive	65	30
515b	**86**	40c. red	65	95
515c	**86**	50c. orange	95	30
516	**86**	60c. bistre	65	30
517	**86**	80c. green	65	30
518	**86**	1f. red	1·90	30
518a	**86**	1f.20 black	1·90	50
518b	**86**	1f.25 brown	1·90	65
519	**86**	1f.50 turquoise	1·90	30
520	**86**	1f.60 grey	2·50	2·50
521	**86**	2f. purple	1·90	30
521a	**86**	2f.50 red	3·25	30
521b	**86**	3f. blue	22·00	65
521c	**86**	3f.50 red	7·50	95
522	**86**	4f. blue	7·50	95
522a	**86**	5f. violet	18·00	1·30
523	**86**	6f. purple	16·00	1·30
524	**86**	8f. green	12·50	2·50

1949. 30th Year of Reign of Grand Duchess Charlotte. Sheet 110×75 mm.

MS524a **86** 8f.+3f. blue; 12f.+5f. green; 15f.+7f. brown £225 65·00

87 Date-stamp and Map

1949. 75th Anniversary of UPU.

525	**87**	80c. green, lt green & black	1·30	1·30

526	**87**	2f.50 red, pink and black	5·00	2·50
527	**87**	4f. ultramarine, blue & black	9·50	9·50
528	**87**	8f. brown, buff and black	28·00	55·00

88 Michel Rodange

1949. National Welfare Fund.

529	**88**	60c.+40c. green and grey	1·30	1·30
530	**88**	2f.+1f. purple and claret	9·50	7·50
531	**88**	4f.+2f. blue and grey	16·00	16·00
532	**88**	10f.+5f. brown and buff	31·00	34·00

89 Young Girl

1950. War Orphans Relief Fund.

533	-	60c.+15c. turquoise	6·25	3·25
534	**89**	1f.+20c. red	12·50	3·25
535	-	2f.+30c. brown	9·50	3·25
536	**89**	4f.+75c. blue	25·00	31·00
537	-	8f.+3f. black	75·00	80·00
538	**89**	10f.+5f. purple	75·00	80·00

Design: 60c., 2f., 8f. Mother and boy.

90 J. A. Zinnen (composer)

1950. National Welfare Week.

539	**90**	60c.+10c. violet and grey	1·30	65
540	**90**	2f.+15c. red and buff	1·30	95
541	**90**	4f.+15c. blue and grey	12·50	12·50
542	**90**	8f.+5f. brown and buff	38·00	50·00

91 Ploughman and Factories

1951. To Promote United Europe.

543	**91**	80c. green and light green	31·00	19·00
544	-	1f. violet and light violet	25·00	1·30
545	-	2f. brown and grey	75·00	1·30
546	**91**	2f.50 red and orange	75·00	31·00
547	-	3f. brown and yellow	£110	47·00
548	-	4f. blue and light blue	£140	75·00

Designs: 1, 3f. Map, people and 'Rights of Man' Charter; 2, 4f. Scales balancing 'United Europe' and 'Peace'.

92 L. Menager (composer)

1951. National Welfare Fund.

549	**92**	60c.+10c. black and grey	1·30	65
550	**92**	2f.+15c. green and grey	1·30	65
551	**92**	4f.+15c. blue and grey	12·50	9·50
552	**92**	8f.+5f. purple and grey	44·00	65·00

92a T **1** and T **86**

92b T **1**

1952. National Philatelic Exhibition (CENTILUX) and Stamp Centenary.

552f	**92b**	2f. blk & grn (postage)	65·00	55·00
552g	**92b**	4f. red and green	65·00	55·00
552a	**92a**	80c. black, pur & grn (air)	1·30	95
552b	**92a**	2f.50 black, purple & red	3·25	2·50
552c	**92a**	4f. black, purple and blue	6·25	6·25
552d	**92a**	8f. black, purple and red	80·00	90·00
552e	**92a**	10f. black, purple & brn	65·00	70·00

93 Hurdling

1952. 15th Olympic Games, Helsinki.

553	**93**	1f. black and green	1·30	1·30
554	-	2f. blk & lt brn (Football)	5·00	1·30
555	-	2f.50 blk & pink (Boxing)	6·25	2·50
556	-	3f. blk & drab (Water polo)	9·50	3·25
557	-	4f. black and blue (Cycling)	41·00	12·50
558	-	8f. black and lilac (Fencing)	25·00	9·50

94 J. B. Fresez (painter)

1952. National Welfare Fund.

559	**94**	60c.+15c. green and blue	1·30	65
560	**94**	2f.+25c. brown & orange	1·30	65
561	**94**	4f.+25c. violet and grey	7·50	6·25
562	**94**	8f.+4f.75 purple & lt pur	50·00	65·00

95 Prince Jean and Princess Josephine Charlotte

1953. Royal Wedding.

563	**95**	80c. violet and deep mauve	1·30	65
564	**95**	1f.20 deep brown & brown	1·30	65
565	**95**	2f. deep green and green	3·25	65
566	**95**	3f. deep purple and purple	3·25	1·30
567	**95**	4f. deep blue and blue	16·00	2·50
568	**95**	9f. brown and red	16·00	2·50

96 Echternach Basilica

1953. Echternach Abbey Restoration (3rd issue).

569	**96**	2f. red	6·25	65
570	-	2f.50 olive	9·50	9·50

Design: 2f.50, Interior of Basilica.

97 Pierre D'Aspelt

1953. Seventh Birth Centenary of Pierre D'Aspelt.

571	**97**	4f. black	16·00	8·25

98 *Candlemas Singing*

1953. National Welfare Fund.

572	**98**	25c.+15c. carmine and red	1·30	65
573	-	80c.+20c. blue and brown	1·30	65
574	-	1f.20+30c. green & turq	2·50	1·60
575	**98**	2f.+25c. brown and red	3·25	65
576	-	4f.+50c. blue & turquoise	19·00	16·00
577	-	7f.+3f.35 lilac and violet	38·00	38·00

Designs: 80c., 4f. *The Rattles*; 1f.20, 7f. *The Easter-eggs*.

99 Foils, Mask and Gauntlet

1954. World Fencing Championships.

578	**99**	2f. deep brown and brown on cream	9·50	2·50

100 Fair Emblem

1954. Luxembourg International Fair.

579	**100**	4f. multicoloured	19·00	9·50

101 Earthenware Whistle

1954. National Welfare Fund.

580	**101**	25c.+5c. red and orange	1·30	95
581	-	80c.+20c. grey & black	1·30	95
582	-	1f.20+30c. green and cream	2·50	3·25
583	**101**	2f.+25c. brown and buff	1·30	95
584	-	4f.+50c. dp blue & blue	12·50	11·50
585	-	7f.+3f.45 violet & mve	38·00	44·00

Designs: 80c., 4f. Sheep and drum; 1f.20, 7f. Merry-go-round horses.

102 Tulips

1955. Mondorf-les-Bains Flower Show.

586	**102**	80c. red, green and brown	65	65
587	-	2f. yellow, green and red	65	65
588	-	3f. purple, green & emer	6·25	5·75
589	-	4f. orange, green and blue	8·75	8·75

Flowers: 2f. Daffodils; 3f. Hyacinths; 4f. Parrot tulips.

103

1955. First National Crafts Exhibition.

590	**103**	2f. black and grey	2·50	65

104 Charter

1955. Tenth Anniv of UN.

591	**104**	80c. blue and black	1·30	1·30
592	-	2f. brown and red	9·50	65
593	-	4f. red and blue	7·50	6·25
594	-	9f. green and brown	3·75	1·90

Symbolic Designs: 2f. Security; 4f. Justice; 9f. Assistance.

105 Christmas Day

1955. National Welfare Fund.

595		25c.+5c. red and pink	65	65
596	**105**	80c.+20c. black and grey	65	65
597	-	1f.20+30c. deep green and green	1·30	1·90
598	-	2f.+25c. deep brown and brown	1·30	65
599	**105**	4f.+50c. blue & lt blue	12·50	19·00
600	-	7f.+3f.45 purple & mve	25·00	27·00

Allegorical Designs: 25c., 2f. St Nicholas's Day; 1f.20, 7f. 12th Night.

1956. Mondorf-les-Bains Flower Show. As T **102** but inscription at top in one line. Multicoloured.

601	2f. Anemones	1·30	65
602	3f. Crocuses	5·00	4·50

1956. Roses. As T **102** but inscr at top 'LUXEMBOURG-VILLE DES ROSES'. Multicoloured.

603	2f.50 Yellow roses	8·75	8·25
604	4f. Red roses	4·50	4·50

108 Steel Plant and Girder

1956. 50th Anniversary of Esch-sur-Alzette.

605	**108**	2f. red, black & turquoise	6·25	1·30

109 Blast Furnaces and Map

1956. European Coal and Steel Community. Inscr as in T **109**.

606	**109**	2f. red	47·00	65
607	-	3f. blue	47·00	38·00
608	-	4f. green	9·50	6·50

Designs: Vert—3f. Girder supporting City of Luxembourg. Horiz—4f. Chain and miner's lamp.

110

1956. Europa.

609	**110**	2f. black and brown	£500	1·30
610	**110**	3f. red and orange	£190	£100
611	**110**	4f. deep blue and blue	12·50	9·50

111 Luxembourg Central Station

1956. Electrification of Luxembourg Railways.

612	**111**	2f. sepia and black	6·25	1·30

112 I. de la Fontaine

1956. Council of State Centenary. Inscr as in T **112**.

613	**112**	2f. sepia	2·50	65
614	-	7f. purple	4·75	1·30

Design: 7f. Grand Duchess Charlotte.

113 Arms of Echternach

1956. National Welfare Fund. Inscr 'CARITAS 1956'. Arms. Multicoloured.

615		25c.+5c. Type **113**	65	65
616		80c.+20c. Esch-sur-Alzette	65	65
617		1f.20+30c. Grevenmacher	1·30	1·90
618		2f.+25c. Type **113**	1·30	65
619		4f.+50c. Esch-sur-Alzette	9·50	9·50
620		7f.+3f.45 Grevenmacher	14·00	22·00

114 Lord Baden-Powell and Scout Emblems

1957. Birth Centenary of Lord Baden-Powell, and 50th Anniversary of Scouting Movement.

621	**114**	2f. brown and green	2·50	65
622	-	2f.50 red and violet	4·50	3·25

Design: 2f.50, as T **114** but showing Girl Guide emblems.

115 Prince Henri

1957. Prince Jean and Princess Josephine-Charlotte Foundation. Child Welfare Clinic.

623	**115**	2f. deep brown and brown	1·90	30
624	-	3f. deep green and green	6·25	6·25
625	-	4f. deep blue and blue	5·00	5·00

Designs: Horiz—3f. Children's Clinic Project. Vert—4f. Princess Marie-Astrid.

116 'Peace'

1957. Europa.

626	**116**	2f. brown	12·50	9·50
627	**116**	3f. red	£150	34·00
628	**116**	4f. purple	£130	31·00

1957. National Welfare Fund. Arms as T **113** inscr 'CARITAS 1957'. Multicoloured.

629		25c.+5c. Luxembourg	65	65
630		80c.+20c. Mersch	65	65
631		1f.20+30c. Vianden	1·30	1·30
632		2f.+25c. Luxembourg	65	65
633		4f.+50c. Mersch	8·75	10·00
634		7f.+3f.45 Vianden	10·00	14·00

117 Fair Entrance and Flags

1958. Tenth Anniversary of Luxembourg International Fair.

635	**117**	2f. multicoloured	65	50

118 Luxembourg Pavilion

1958. Brussels Exhibition.

636	**118**	2f.50 blue and red	65	50

119 St Willibrord holding Child (after Puseel)

1958. 1300th Birth Anniversary of St Willibrord.

637	-	1f. red	65	65
638	**119**	2f.50 sepia	65	30
639	-	5f. blue	1·90	1·60

Designs: 1f. St Willibrord and St Irmina holding inscribed plaque; 5f. St Willibrord and suppliant. (Miracle of the wine-cask).

119a Europa

1958. Europa.

640	**119a**	2f.50 blue and red	95	30
641	**119a**	3f.50 brown and green	1·30	65
642	**119a**	5f. red and blue	2·50	1·60

120 Open-air Theatre at Wiltz

1958. Wiltz Open-air Theatre Commemoration.

643	**120**	2f.50 sepia and grey	95	30

121 Vineyard

1958. Bimillenary of Moselle Wine Industry.

644	**121**	2f.50 brown and green	95	30

1958. National Welfare Fund. Arms as T **113** inscr 'CARITAS 1958'. Multicoloured.

645		30c.+10c. Capellen	65	65
646		1f.+25c. Diekirch	65	65
647		1f.50+25c. Redange	1·30	95
648		2f.50+50c. Capellen	65	65
649		5f.+50c. Diekirch	8·75	9·50
650		8f.50+4f.60 Redange	9·50	14·00

122 Grand Duchess Charlotte

1959. 40th Anniversary of Accession of Grand Duchess Charlotte.

651	**122**	1f.50 deep green & green	1·90	95
652	**122**	2f.50 brown & lt brown	1·90	95
653	**122**	5f. lt blue and ultramarine	3·25	2·50

123 NATO Emblem

1959. Tenth Anniversary of NATO.

654	**123**	2f.50 blue and olive	30	30
655	**123**	8f.50 blue and brown	95	75

1959. Mondorf-les-Bains Flower Show. As T **102** but inscr '1959'.

656		1f. violet, yellow and turquoise	65	65
657		2f.50 red, green and blue	95	65
658		3f. blue, green and purple	1·30	1·30

Flowers: 1f. Iris; 2f.50, Peony; 3f. Hortensia.

123a Europa

1959. Europa.

659	**123a**	2f.50 green	2·50	30
660	**123a**	5f. blue	4·50	1·90

124 Steam Locomotive and First Bars of Hymn *De Feierwon*

1959. Railways Centenary.

661	**124**	2f.50 blue and red	3·25	65

1959. National Welfare Fund. Arms as T **113** inscr 'CARITAS 1959'. Multicoloured.

662		30c.+10c. Clervaux	65	65
663		1f.+25c. Remich	65	65
664		1f.50+25c. Wiltz	1·30	1·30
665		2f.50+50c. Clervaux	65	65
666		5f.+50c. Remich	2·50	3·75
667		8f.50+4f.60 Wiltz	12·50	22·00

125 Refugees seeking Shelter

1960. World Refugee Year.

668	**125**	2f.50 blue and salmon	65	30
669	-	5f. blue and violet	65	65

Design: Horiz—5f. *The Flight into Egypt* (Biblical scene).

126 Steel Worker

1960. Tenth Anniversary of Schuman Plan.

670	**126**	2f.50 lake	65	30

127 European School, Luxembourg

1960. European School Commemoration.

671	**127**	5f. black and blue	1·90	1·60

128 Grand Duchess Charlotte

1960

672	**128**	10c. red	65	30
673	**128**	20c. red	65	30
673a	**128**	25c. orange	65	30
674	**128**	30c. drab	65	30
675	**128**	50c. green	1·30	30
676	**128**	1f. violet	1·30	30
677	**128**	1f.50 mauve	1·30	30
678	**128**	2f. turquoise	1·90	30
679	**128**	2f.50 purple	2·50	30
680	**128**	3f. dull purple	6·25	30
680a	**128**	3f.50 turquoise	9·50	3·25
681	**128**	5f. brown	5·00	30
681a	**128**	6f. turquoise	7·50	30

129 Heraldic Lion, and Tools

1960. Second National Crafts Exhibition.

682	**129**	2f.50 multicoloured	2·50	65

129a Conference Emblem

1960. Europa.

683	**129a**	2f.50 green and black	1·90	30
684	**129a**	5f. black and red	2·50	65

130 Princess Marie-Astrid

1960. National Welfare Fund. Inscr 'CARITAS 1960'. Centres and inscr in sepia.

685	**130**	30c.+10c. blue	65	65
686	-	1f.+25c. pink	65	65
687	-	1f.50+25c. turquoise	1·30	1·30
688	**130**	2f.50+50c. yellow	1·30	95
689	-	5f.+50c. lilac	1·90	6·25
690	-	8f.50+4f.60 sage	18·00	25·00

Designs: Princess Marie-Astrid standing (1, 5f.), sitting with book on lap (1f.50, 8f.50).

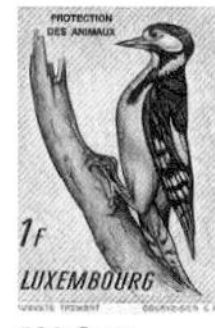

131 Great Spotted Woodpecker

1961. Animal Protection Campaign. Inscr 'PROTECTION DES ANIMAUX'.

691	**131**	1f. multicoloured	65	30
692	-	1f.50 buff, blue and black	65	65
693	-	3f. brown, buff and violet	65	65
694	-	8f.50 multicoloured	1·30	95

Designs: Vert—8f.50, Dachshund. Horiz—1f.50, Cat; 3f. Horse.

132 Patton Monument, Ettelbruck

1961. Tourist Publicity.

695	**132**	2f.50 blue and black	1·30	50
696	-	2f.50 green	1·30	50

Design: Vert—No. 696, Clervaux.

133 Doves

1961. Europa.

697	**133**	2f.50 red	65	35
698	**133**	5f. blue	1·00	40

134 Prince Henri

1961. National Welfare Fund. Inscr 'CARITAS 1961'. Centres and inscr in sepia.

699	**134**	30c.+10c. mauve	1·00	65
700	-	1f.+25c. lavender	1·00	65
701	-	1f.50+25c. salmon	1·30	1·30
702	**134**	2f.50+50c. green	1·30	65
703	-	5f.+50c. yellow	6·50	6·50
704	-	8f.50+4f.60 grey	9·75	16·00

Designs: Prince Henri when young boy (1, 5f.); youth in formal dress (1f.50, 8f.50).

135 Cyclist carrying Cycle

1962. World Cross-country Cycling Championships, Esch-sur-Alzette.

705	**135**	2f.50 multicoloured	50	35
706	-	5f. multicoloured (Emblem)	65	65

136 Europa 'Tree'

1962. Europa.

707	**136**	2f.50 multicoloured	1·00	35
708	**136**	5f. brown, green & purple	1·30	65

137 St Laurent's Church, Diekirch

1962

709	**137**	2f.50 black and brown	1·00	45

138 Prince Jean and Princess Margaretha as Babies

1962. National Welfare Fund. inscr 'CARITAS 1962'. Centres and inscr in sepia.

710	**138**	30c.+10c. buff	65	65
711	-	1f.+25c. blue	65	65
712	-	1f.50+25c. olive	1·30	65
713	-	2f.50+50c. pink	1·30	65
714	-	5f.+50c. green	3·25	5·25
715	-	8f.50+4f.60 violet	9·75	9·75

Portraits: Vert—1f., 2f.50, Prince Jean; 1f.50, 5f. Princess Margaretha, at various stages of childhood. Horiz—8f.50, The Royal Children.

139 Blackboard

1963. Tenth Anniversary of European Schools.

716	**139**	2f.50 green, red and grey	65	35

140 Benedictine Abbey, Munster

1963. Millenary of City of Luxembourg and International Philatelic Exhibition. (a) Horiz views.

717	-	1f. blue	1·00	35
718	**140**	1f.50 red	1·00	35
719	-	2f.50 green	1·00	35
720	-	3f. brown	1·00	35
721	-	5f. violet	2·00	1·20
722	-	11f. blue	4·00	3·00

Views: 1f. Bock Rock; 2f.50, Rham Towers; 3f. Grand Ducal Palace; 5f. Castle Bridge; 11f. Millenary Buildings.

(b) Vert multicoloured designs.

723		1f. *Three Towers* Gate	1·00	50
724		1f.50 Great Seal	1·00	50
725		2f.50 *The Black Virgin* (statue), St John's Church	1·00	50
726		3f. Citadel	1·30	50
727		5f. Town Hall	1·00	50

141 Colpach Castle

1963. Red Cross Centenary.

728	**141**	2f.50 red and slate	65	35

142 Human Rights

1963. Tenth Anniversary of European Human Rights Convention.

729	**142**	2f.50 blue on gold	65	35

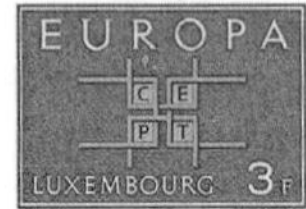

143 Co-operation

1963. Europa.

730	**143**	3f. green, orange & turq	1·00	35
731	**143**	6f. orange, red and brown	2·00	80

144 Brown trout snapping Bait

1963. World Fishing Championships, Wormeldange.

732	**144**	3f. slate	65	35

145 Telephone Dial

1963. Inauguration of Automatic Telephone System.

733	**145**	3f. green, black and blue	65	35

146 St Roch (patron saint of bakers)

1963. National Welfare Fund. Patron Saints of Crafts and Guilds. Inscr 'CARITAS 1963'. Multicoloured.

734	50c.+10c. Type **146**	65	35
735	1f.+25c. St Anne (tailors)	65	35
736	2f.+25c. St Eloi (smiths)	65	65
737	3f.+50c. St Michel (haberdashers)	65	35
738	6f.+50c. St Barthelemy (butchers)	2·00	3·25
739	10f.+5f.90 St Thibaut (seven crafts)	3·25	5·75

147 Power House

1964. Inauguration of Vianden Reservoir.

740	**147**	2f. blue, brown and red	40	40
741	-	3f. blue, turq & red	40	40
742	-	6f. brown, blue and green	50	50

Designs: Horiz—3f. Upper reservoir. Vert—6f. Lohmuhle Dam.

148 Barge entering Canal

1964. Inauguration of Moselle Canal.

743	**148**	3f. indigo and blue	65	35

149 Europa 'Flower'

1964. Europa.

744	**149**	3f. blue, brown and cream	1·00	35
745	**149**	6f. sepia, green and yellow	2·00	65

150 Students thronging New Athenaeum

1964. Opening of New Athenaeum (education centre).

746	**150**	3f. black and green	65	40

150a King Baudouin, Queen Juliana and Grand Duchess Charlotte

1964. 20th Anniversary of BENELUX.

747	**150a**	3f. brown, yellow & blue	65	35

151 Grand Duke Jean and Princess Josephine-Charlotte

1964. Accession of Grand Duke Jean.

748	**151**	3f. deep blue and light blue	50	35
749	**151**	6f. sepia and light brown	65	65

152 Three Towers

1964. National Welfare Fund. Inscr 'CARITAS 1964'. Multicoloured.

750	50c.+10c. Type **152**	35	35
751	1f.+25c. Grand Duke Adolphe Bridge	35	35
752	2f.+25c. Lower Town	35	35
753	3f.+50c. Type **152**	35	35
754	6f.+50c. Grand Duke Adolphe Bridge	2·00	3·25
755	10f.+5f.90 Lower Town	2·50	5·00

153 Rotary Emblem and Cogwheels

1965. 60th Anniversary of Rotary International.

756	**153**	3f. multicoloured	65	35

154 Grand Duke Jean

1965

757	**154**	25c. brown	65	20
758	**154**	50c. red	65	20
759	**154**	1f. blue	1·00	20
760	**154**	1f.50 purple	1·00	20
761	**154**	2f. red	1·30	20
762	**154**	2f.50 orange	1·30	50
763	**154**	3f. green	1·30	20
763b	**154**	3f.50 brown	2·00	85
764	**154**	4f. purple	2·00	25
764b	**154**	5f. green	2·00	25
765	**154**	6f. lilac	2·00	20
765b	**154**	7f. orange	1·30	65
765c	**154**	8f. blue	2·50	35
766	**154**	9f. green	2·50	35
766a	**154**	10f. black	2·50	40
767	**154**	12f. red	3·25	35
767a	**154**	14f. blue	2·50	1·00
767b	**154**	16f. green	2·50	65
767c	**154**	18f. green	2·30	1·00
767d	**154**	20f. blue	3·25	35
767e	**154**	22f. brown	2·50	2·00

155 ITU Emblem and Symbols

1965. Centenary of ITU.

768	**155**	3f. blue, lake and violet	65	35

156 Europa 'Sprig'

1965. Europa.

769	**156**	3f. turquoise, red and black	1·00	35
770	**156**	6f. brown, blue and green	2·00	65

157 *The Roman Lady of the Titelberg*

1965. National Welfare Fund. Fairy Tales. Inscr 'CARITAS 1965'. Multicoloured.

771	50c.+10c. Type **157**	25	35
772	1f.+25c. *Schappchen, the Huntsman*	25	35
773	2f.+25c. *The Witch of Koerich*	35	35
774	3f.+50c. *The Goblins of Schoendels*	35	35
775	6f.+50c. *Tollchen, Watchman of Hesperange*	65	2·50
776	10f.+5f.90 *The Old Spinster of Heispelt*	2·30	5·75

158 'Flag' and Torch

1966. 50th Anniversary of Luxembourg Workers' Union.

777	**158**	3f. red and grey	65	65

159 WHO Building

1966. Inauguration of WHO Headquarters, Geneva.

778	**159**	3f. green	65	65

160 Golden Key

1966. Tercentenary of Solemn Promise to Our Lady of Luxembourg.

779	**160**	1f.50 green	40	35
780	-	2f. red	40	35
781	-	3f. blue	40	35
782	-	6f. brown	70	50

Designs: 2f. Interior of Luxembourg Cathedral (after painting by J. Martin); 3f. Our Lady of Luxembourg (after engraving by R. Collin); 6f. Gallery pillar, Luxembourg Cathedral (after sculpture by D. Muller).

161 Europa 'Ship'

1966. Europa.

783	**161**	3f. blue and grey	1·10	35
784	**161**	6f. green and brown	2·30	65

162 Class 1800 Diesel-electric Locomotive

1966. Luxembourg Railwaymen's Philatelic Exhibition. Multicoloured.

785	1f.50 Type **162**	1·50	35
786	3f. Class 3600 electric locomotive	1·50	50

163 Grand Duchess Charlotte Bridge

1966. Tourism.

787	**163**	3f. lake	40	35

See also Nos. 807/808, 828 and 844/845.

164 Kirchberg Building and Railway Viaduct

1966. Luxembourg. uropean Centre.

788	**164**	1f.50 green	40	35
789	-	13f. blue (Robert Schuman monument)	1·10	65

165 *Mary, Veiled Matron of Wormeldange*

1966. National Welfare Fund. Luxembourg Fairy Tales. Multicoloured.

790	50c.+10c. Type **165**	30	35
791	1f.50+25c. *Jekel Warden of the Wark*	30	35
792	2f.+25c. *The Black Gentleman of Vianden*	30	65
793	3f.+50c. *The Gracious Fairy of Rosport*	40	35
794	6f.+1f. *The Friendly Shepherd of Donkolz*	1·10	2·00
795	13f.+6f.90 *The Little Sisters of Trois-Vierges*	1·50	4·50

166 *City of Luxembourg, 1850* (after engraving by N. Liez)

1967. Centenary of Treaty of London.

796	**166**	3f. brown, blue and green	75	35
797	-	6f. red, brown and blue	1·10	50

Design: Vert—6f. Plan of Luxembourg fortress *c.* 1850 (after T. de Cederstolpe).

167 Cogwheels

1967. Europa.

798	**167**	3f. purple, grey and buff	3·00	35
799	**167**	6f. sepia, purple and blue	3·75	65

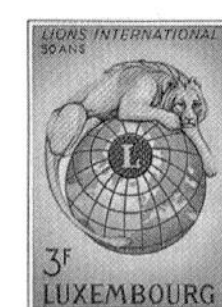

168 Lion on Globe

1967. 50th Anniversary of Lions International.

800	**168**	3f. yellow, purple & black	45	35

169 European Institutions Building, Luxembourg

1967. NATO Council Meeting, Luxembourg.

801	**169**	3f. turquoise and green	50	45
802	**169**	6f. red and pink	80	75

170 Hikers and Hostel

1967. Luxembourg Youth Hostels.

803	**170**	1f.50 multicoloured	40	40

171 Shaving-dish (after Degrotte)

1967. 200 Years of Luxembourg Pottery.

804	**171**	1f.50 multicoloured	40	40
805	-	3f. multicoloured	40	40

Design: Vert—3f. Vase, *c.* 1820.

172 Gardener

1967. Family Gardens Congress, Luxembourg.

806	**172**	1f.50 orange and green	40	40

1967. Tourism. As T **163**.

807	3f. indigo and blue	80	40
808	3f. purple, green and blue	1·20	40

Designs: Horiz—No. 807, Moselle River and quayside, Mertert. Vert—No. 808, Moselle, Church and vines, Wormeldange.

173 Prince Guillaume

1967. National Welfare Fund. Royal Children and Residence.

809	**173**	50c.+10c. brown & buff	40	40
810	-	1f.50+25c. brown & bl	40	40
811	-	2f.+25c. brown and red	40	40
812	-	3f.+50c. brown & yell	1·60	40
813	-	6f.+1f. brown & lav	1·20	2·30
814	-	13f.+6f.90 brn, grn & bl	1·60	6·75

Designs: 1f.50, Princess Margaretha; 2f. Prince Jean; 3f. Prince Henri; 6f. Princess Marie-Astrid; 13f. Berg Castle.

174 Football

1968. Olympic Games, Mexico.

815		50c. light blue and blue	80	40
816	**174**	1f.50 green and emerald	80	40
817	-	2f. yellow and green	1·20	40
818	-	3f. light orange and orange	80	40
819	-	6f. green and blue	1·20	75
820	-	13f. red and crimson	1·60	1·10

Designs: 50c. Diving; 2f. Cycling; 3f. Running; 6f. Walking; 13f. Fencing.

175 Europa 'Key'

1968. Europa.

821	**175**	3f. brown, black and green	2·40	40
822	**175**	6f. green, black and orange	3·25	75

176 Thermal Bath Pavilion, Mondorf-les-Bains

1968. Mondorf-les-Bains Thermal Baths.

823	**176**	3f. multicoloured	80	40

177 Fair Emblem

1968. 20th Anniversary of Luxembourg International Fair.

824	**177**	3f. multicoloured	80	40

178 Village Project

1968. Luxembourg SOS Children's Village.

825	**178**	3f. purple and green	80	40
826	-	6f. black, blue and purple	80	60

Design: Vert—6f. Orphan with foster-mother.

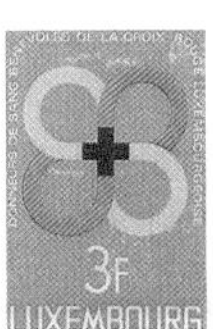

179 Blood Transfusion

1968. Blood Donors of Luxembourg Red Cross.

827	**179**	3f. red and blue	80	40

180 Fokker F.27 Friendship over Luxembourg

1968. Tourism.

828	**180**	50f. dp blue, brown & blue	8·00	40

181 Cap Institute

1968. National Welfare Fund. Luxembourg Disabled Children.

829	**181**	50c.+10c. brown and blue	40	40
830	-	1f.50+25c. brn & grn	40	40
831	-	2f.+25c. brown & yell	65	60
832	-	3f.+50c. brown and blue	65	40
833	-	6f.+1f. brown and buff	1·20	2·30
834	-	13f.+6f.90 brown and pink	3·25	6·75

Designs: 1f.50, Deaf and dumb child; 2f. Blind child; 3f. Nurse supporting disabled child; 6f. and 13f. Children (different).

182

1969. Juventus 1969 Junior International Philatelic Exhibition. Sheet 111×70 mm containing T **182** and similar vert designs. Multicoloured.

MS835	3f. Type **182**; 6f. 'Sport'; 13f. Sun, open book and ball	8·00	9·00

183 Colonnade

1969. Europa.

836	**183**	3f. multicoloured	2·40	40
837	**183**	6f. multicoloured	3·25	75

184 *The Wooden Horse* (Kutter)

1969. 75th Birth Anniversary of Joseph Kutter (painter). Multicoloured.

838	3f. Type **184**	1·20	40
839	6f. *Luxembourg* (Kutter)	1·20	90

185 ILO Emblem

1969. 50th Anniversary of International Labour Organisation.

840	**185**	3f. gold, violet and green	65	40

186 National Colours

1969. 25th Anniversary of BENELUX Customs Union.

841	**186**	3f. multicoloured	65	40

187 NATO Emblem

1969. 20th Anniversary of NATO.

842	**187**	3f. orange and brown	80	40

188 Ear of Wheat and Agrocentre, Mersch

1969. Modern Agriculture.

843	**188**	3f. grey and green	65	40

189 Echternach

1969. Tourism.

844	**189**	3f. indigo and blue	80	40
845	-	3f. blue and green	80	40

Design: No. 845, Wiltz.

190 Vianden Castle

1969. National Welfare Fund. Castles (1st series). Multicoloured.

846	50c.+10c. Type **190**	40	40
847	1f.50+25c. Lucilinburhuc	40	40
848	2f.+25c. Bourglinster	40	40
849	3f.+50c. Hollenfels	40	40
850	6f.+1f. Ansembourg	1·60	3·00
851	13f.+6f.90 Beaufort	2·40	6·75

See also Nos. 862/867.

191 Pasqueflower

1970. Nature Conservation Year. Multicoloured.

852	3f. Type **191**	80	40
853	6f. West European Hedgehogs	80	75

192 Firecrest

1970. 50 Years of Bird Protection.

854	**192**	1f.50 green, black & orge	80	40

193 'Flaming Sun'

1970. Europa.

855	**193**	3f. multicoloured	2·40	40
856	**193**	6f. multicoloured	3·25	75

194 Road Safety Assoc. Emblem and Traffic

1970. Road Safety.

857	**194**	3f. black, red and lake	50	40

195 Empress Kunegonde and Emperor Henry II (stained-glass windows, Luxembourg Cathedral)

1970. Centenary of Luxembourg Diocese.

858	**195**	3f. multicoloured	50	45

196 Population Pictograph

1970. Population Census.

859	**196**	3f. red, blue and green	50	40

197 Facade of Town Hall, Luxembourg

1970. 50th Anniversary of Union of Four Suburbs with Luxembourg City.

860	**197**	3f. brown, ochre and blue	50	40

198 UN Emblem

1970. 25th Anniversary of United Nations.

861	**198**	1f.50 violet and blue	50	40

1970. National Welfare Fund. Castles (2nd series). Designs as T **190**.

862	50c.+10c. Clervaux	40	40
863	1f.50+25c. Septfontaines	40	40
864	2f.+25c. Bourschied	40	40
865	3f.+50c. Esch-sur-Sure	40	40
866	6f.+1f. Larochette	1·20	3·00
867	13f.+6f.90 Brandenbourg	2·40	6·75

199 Monks in the Scriptorium

1971. Medieval Miniatures produced at Echternach. Multicoloured.

868	1f.50 Type **199**	80	40
869	3f. Vine-growers going to work	80	40
870	6f. Vine-growers at work and returning home	80	40
871	13f. Workers with spades and hoe	2·40	1·10

200 Europa Chain

1971

872	**200**	3f. black, brown and red	2·40	40
873	**200**	6f. black, brown and green	3·25	1·10

201 Olympic Rings and Arms of Luxembourg

1971. International Olympic Committee Meeting, Luxembourg.

874	**201**	3f. red, gold and blue	80	40

202 '50' and Emblem

1971. 50th Anniversary of Luxembourg's Christian Workers' Union (LCGB).

875	**202**	3f. purple, orange & yell	80	40

203 Artificial Lake, Upper Sure Valley

1971. Man-made Landscapes.

876	**203**	3f. blue, grey and brown	1·20	45
877	-	3f. brown, green and blue	1·20	75
878	-	15f. black, blue and brown	2·40	45

Designs: No. 877, Water-processing plant, Esch-sur-Sure; No. 878, ARBED (United Steelworks) Headquarters Building, Luxembourg.

204 Child with Coin

1971. Schoolchildren's Saving Campaign.

879	**204**	3f. multicoloured	80	40

205 Bethlehem Children

1971. National Welfare Fund. *The Nativity* wood-carvings in Beaufort Church. Multicoloured.

880	1f.+25c. Type **205**	80	40
881	1f.50+25c. Shepherds	80	40
882	3f.+50c. Virgin, Child Jesus and St Joseph	1·20	40
883	8f.+1f. Herdsmen	3·25	5·25
884	18f.+6f.50 One of the Magi	4·75	10·50

206 Coins of Belgium and Luxembourg

1972. 50th Anniversary of Belgium–Luxembourg Economic Union.

885	**206**	1f.50 silver, black & green	80	40

207 Bronze Mask (1st-century)

1972. Gallo-Roman Exhibits from Luxembourg State Museum. Multicoloured.

886	1f. Samian bowl (2nd-century) (horiz)	1·20	40
887	3f. Type **207**	1·60	40
888	8f. Limestone head (2nd/3rd-century)	3·25	1·50
889	15f. Glass 'head' flagon (4th-century)	3·25	1·10

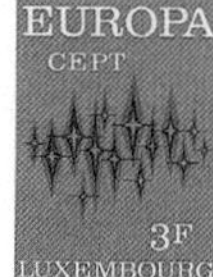

208 Communications

1972. Europa.

890	**208**	3f. multicoloured	2·40	40
891	**208**	8f. multicoloured	4·00	2·30

209 Archer

1972. Third European Archery Championships, Luxembourg.

892	**209**	3f. multicoloured	95	40

210 R. Schuman (after bronze by R. Zilli)

1972. 20th Anniversary of Establishment of European Coal and Steel Community in Luxembourg.

893	**210**	3f. green and grey	1·00	40

211 National Monument

1972. Monuments and Buildings.

894	**211**	3f. brown, green and violet	1·20	40
895	-	3f. brown, green and blue	1·20	40

Design: No. 895, European Communities' Court of Justice.

212 Renert

1972. Centenary of Publication of Michel Rodange's *Renert* (satirical poem).

896	**212**	3f. multicoloured	80	40

213 Angel

1972. National Welfare Fund. Stained Glass Windows in Luxembourg Cathedral. Multicoloured.

897	1f.+25c. Type **213**	40	40
898	1f.50+25c. St Joseph	40	40
899	3f.+50c. Holy Virgin with Child Jesus	40	40
900	8f.+1f. People of Bethlehem	2·40	5·25
901	18f.+6f.50 Angel (facing left)	6·50	13·50

214 Epona on Horseback

1973. Archaeological Relics. Multicoloured.

902	1f. Type **214**	1·20	40
903	4f. Panther attacking swan (horiz)	1·20	40
904	8f. Celtic gold coin	4·00	2·30
905	15f. Bronze boar (horiz)	3·25	1·10

215 Europa Posthorn

1973. Europa.

906 **215** 4f. orange, blue and violet 2·40 45
907 **215** 8f. green, yellow & purple 4·00 1·90

216 Bee on Honeycomb

1973. Bee-keeping.

908 **216** 4f. multicoloured 1·20 40

217 Nurse and Child

1973. Day Nurseries in Luxembourg.

909 **217** 4f. multicoloured 80 40

218 Capital, Vianden Castle

1973. Romanesque Architecture in Luxembourg.

910 **218** 4f. purple and green 80 40
911 - 8f. blue and brown 2·00 1·50

Design: 8f. Detail of altar, St Irmina's Chapel, Rosport.

219 Labour Emblem

1973. 50th Anniversary of Luxembourg Board of Labour.

912 **219** 3f. multicoloured 80 40

220 J. de Busleyden

1973. 500th Anniversary of Great Council of Malines.

913 **220** 4f. purple and brown 80 40

221 Monument, Wiltz

1973. National Strike Monument.

914 **221** 4f. green, brown and grey 1·20 40

222 Joachim and St Anne

1973. National Welfare Fund. *The Nativity*. Details from 16th-century reredos, Hachiville Hermitage. Multicoloured.

915 1f.+25c. Type **222** 40 40
916 3f.+25c. Mary meets Elizabeth 40 40
917 4f.+50c. Magus presenting gift 50 40
918 8f.+1f. Shepherds at the manger 2·40 5·25
919 15f.+7f. St Joseph with Candle 6·50 13·50

223 Princess Marie-Astrid, Association President

1974. Luxembourg Red Cross Youth Association.

920 **223** 4f. multicoloured 3·25 75

224 Flame Emblem

1974. 50th Anniversary of Luxembourg Mutual Insurance Federation.

921 **224** 4f. multicoloured 1·20 75

225 Seal of Henry VII, King of the Romans

1974. Seals in Luxembourg State Archives.

922 **225** 1f. brown, yellow & purple 80 40
923 - 3f. brown, yellow & green 80 60
924 - 4f. dk brown, yellow & brn 1·20 40
925 - 19f. brown, yellow & blue 3·25 1·50

Designs: 3f. Equestrian seal of John the Blind, King of Bohemia; 4f. Municipal seal of Diekirch; 19f. Seal of Marienthal Convent.

226 *Hind* (A. Tremont)

1974. Europa. Sculptures. Multicoloured.

926 4f. Type **226** 4·75 40
927 8f. *Abstract* (L. Wercollier) 8·00 3·50

227 Churchill Memorial, Luxembourg

1974. Birth Centenary of Sir Winston Churchill.

928 **227** 4f. multicoloured 80 45

228 Diagram of Fair

1974. New International Fair, Luxembourg-Kirchberg.

929 **228** 4f. multicoloured 80 45

229 *Theis the Blind* (artist unknown)

1974. 150th Death Anniversary of *Theis the Blind* (Mathias Schou, folk singer).

930 **229** 3f. multicoloured 80 75

230 Crowning of St Cecily and St Valerien (Hollenfels Church)

1974. Gothic Architecture.

931 **230** 4f. brown, green and violet 1·20 60
932 - 4f. black, brown and blue 1·20 60

Design: No. 932, Interior of Septfontaines Church.

231 UPU Emblem on '100'

1974. Centenary of Universal Postal Union.

933 **231** 4f. multicoloured 1·20 40
934 **231** 8f. multicoloured 2·40 1·50

232 'Benelux'

1974. 30th Anniversary of Benelux (Customs Union).

935 **232** 4f. turquoise, green & blue 2·40 45

233 Differdange

1974. Tourism.

936 **233** 4f. purple 2·40 45

234 *Annunciation*

1974. National Welfare Fund. Illustrations from *Codex Aureus Epternacensis*. Multicoloured.

937 1f.+25c. Type **234** 40 40
938 3f.+25c. *Visitation* 40 40
939 4f.+50c. *Nativity* 50 40
940 8f.+1f. *Adoration of the Magi* 2·40 6·00
941 15f.+7f. *Presentation at the Temple* 4·75 13·00

235 *Crucifixion*

1974. 50th Anniversary of Christmas Charity Stamps. Detail of cover from *Codex Aureus Epternacensis*. Sheet 80×90 mm.

MS942 **235** 20f.+10f. multicoloured 8·00 19·00

236 The Fish Market, Luxembourg

1975. European Architectural Heritage Year.

943 **236** 1f. green 1·20 40
944 - 3f. brown 3·25 75
945 - 4f. lilac 3·25 40
946 - 19f. red 3·25 1·90

Designs: Horiz—3f. Bourglinster Castle; 4f. Market Square, Echternach. Vert—19f. St Michael's Square, Mersch.

237 *Joseph Kutter* (self-portrait)

1975. Luxembourg Culture, and Europa. Paintings. Multicoloured.

947 1f. Type **237** 1·20 40
948 4f. *Remich Bridge* (N. Klopp) (horiz) 5·50 60
949 8f. *Still Life* (J. Kutter) (horiz) 8·00 3·25
950 20f. *The Dam* (D. Lang) 4·00 1·10

238 Dr. Albert Schweitzer

1975. Birth Centenary of Dr. Albert Schweitzer (medical missionary).

951 **238** 4f. blue 1·60 45

239 Robert Schuman, G. Martino and P.-H. Spaak

1975. 25th Anniversary of Robert Schuman Declaration for European Unity.

952 **239** 4f. black, gold and green 1·60 45

240 Civil Defence Emblem

1975. 15th Anniversary of Civil Defence Reorganisation.

953 **240** 4f. multicoloured 1·60 45

241 Ice Skating

1975. Sports. Multicoloured.

954 **241** 3f. purple, blue and green 1·60 75
955 - 4f. brown, green & dp brn 2·40 40
956 - 15f. blue, brown and green 4·00 1·10

Designs: Horiz—4f. Water-skiing. Vert—15f. Rock-climbing.

242 Fly Orchid

1975. National Welfare Fund. Protected Plants (1st series). Multicoloured.

957	1f.+25c. Type **242**	40	40
958	3f.+25c. Pyramid orchid	80	60
959	4f.+50c. Marsh helleborine	1·20	40
960	8f.+1f. Pasqueflower	2·40	3·75
961	15f.+7f. Bee orchid	6·50	11·50

See also Nos. 976/980 and 997/1001.

243 Grand Duchess Charlotte (80th)

1976. Royal Birthdays. Multicoloured.

962	6f. Type **243**	4·00	75
963	6f. Prince Henri (21st)	4·00	75

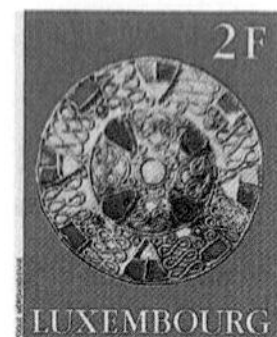

244 7th-century Disc-shaped Brooch

1976. Luxembourg Culture. Ancient Treasures from Merovingian Tombs. Multicoloured.

964	2f. Type **244**	80	40
965	5f. 5th/6th-century glass beaker (horiz)	80	75
966	6f. Ancient pot (horiz)	80	45
967	12f. 7th-century gold coin	2·40	1·90

245 Soup Tureen

1976. Europa. 19th-century Pottery. Multicoloured.

968	6f. Type **245**	4·75	40
969	12f. Bowl	8·00	3·00

246 Independence Hall, Philadelphia

1976. Bicentenary of American Revolution.

970	**246**	6f. multicoloured	1·20	60

247 Symbol representing 'Strength and Impetus'

1976. Olympic Games, Montreal.

971	**247**	6f. gold, magenta and mauve	1·20	60

248 Association Emblem and 'Sound Vibrations'

1976. 30th Anniversary of Jeunesses Musicales (Youth Music Association).

972	**248**	6f. multicoloured	1·20	60

249 Virgin and Child

1976. Renaissance Art. Multicoloured.

973	6f. Type **249**	1·20	60
974	12f. Bernard de Velbruck, Lord of Beaufort (funeral monument)	2·40	1·90

250 Alexander Graham Bell

1976. Telephone Centenary.

975	**250**	6f. green	1·20	60

1976. National Welfare Fund. Protected Plants (2nd series). As T **242**. Multicoloured.

976	2f.+25c. Gentian	40	75
977	5f.+25c. Wild daffodil	40	75
978	6f.+50c. Red helleborine (orchid)	65	75
979	12f.+1f. Late spider orchid	2·40	6·00
980	20f.+8f. Twin leaved squill	6·50	15·00

251 Johann von Goethe (poet)

1977. Luxembourg Culture. Famous Visitors to Luxembourg.

981	**251**	2f. purple	80	40
982	-	5f. violet	80	60
983	-	6f. black	1·60	45
984	-	12f. violet	1·60	1·50

Designs: 5f. Joseph Mallard William Turner (painter); 6f. Victor Hugo (writer); 12f. Franz Liszt (musician).

252 Fish Market, Luxembourg

1977. Europa. Multicoloured.

985	6f. Type **252**	4·00	75
986	12f. Grand Duke Adolphe railway bridge and European Investment Bank	6·50	3·00

253 Esch-sur-Sure

1977. Tourism.

987	**253**	5f. blue	1·20	45
988	-	6f. brown	1·20	45

Designs: 6f. Ehnen.

254 Marguerite de Busbach (founder)

1977. Anniversaries. Multicoloured.

989	6f. Type **254**	1·20	45
990	6f. Louis Braille (after Filippi)	1·20	45

Anniversaries: No. 989, 350th anniversary of foundation of Notre Dame Congregation; No. 990, 125th death anniversary.

255 10c. and 1sgr. Stamps of 1852

1977. 125th Anniversary of Luxembourg Stamps. Sheet 90×60 mm.

MS991	**255** 40f. black, chestnut and grey	11·00	10·50

256 *St Gregory the Great*

1977. Baroque Art. Sculpture from Feulen Parish Church pulpit attributed to J.-G. Scholtus.

992	**256**	6f. purple	80	75
993	-	12f. grey	1·60	1·50

Design: 12f. St Augustine.

257 Head of Medusa

1977. Roman Mosaic at Diekirch.

994	**257**	6f. multicoloured	2·40	45

258 Scene from *Orpheus and Eurydice* (Gluck)

1977. 25th Wiltz International Festival.

995	**258**	6f. multicoloured	1·60	45

259 Map of EEC and 'Europa' (R. Zilli)

1977. 20th Anniversary of Rome Treaties.

996	**259**	6f. multicoloured	1·60	45

1977. National Welfare Fund. Protected Plants (3rd series). As T **242**. Multicoloured.

997	2f.+25c. Lily of the valley	40	75
998	5f.+25c. Columbine	65	75
999	6f.+50c. Mezereon	1·20	75
1000	12f.+1f. Early spider orchid	3·25	7·50
1001	20f.+8f. Spotted orchid	5·50	15·00

260 Grand Duke Jean and Duchess Josephine-Charlotte

1978. Royal Silver Wedding. Sheet 116×67 mm.

MS1002	**260** 6f., 12f. multicoloured	4·00	3·75

261 Fountain and Youth

1978. Juphilux 78 Junior International Philatelic Exhibition. Sheet 103×72 mm containing T **261** and similar vert designs. Multicoloured.

MS1003	5f. Type **261**; 6f. Streamer; 20f. Dancing youths	7·25	9·00

MS1003 was on sale at 60f., including entrance fee of 29f., at the Exhibition, by postal application and at post offices.

262 Charles IV

1978. Europa.

1004	**262**	6f. lilac	2·40	60
1005	-	12f. red	5·50	2·75

Design: 12f. Pierre d'Aspelt (funeral monument, Mainz Cathedral).

263 Head of Our Lady of Luxembourg

1978. Anniversaries. Multicoloured.

1006	6f. Type **263** (300th anniversary of election as patron saint)	1·20	60
1007	6f. Trumpeters (135th anniversary of Grand Ducal Military Band)	1·20	60

264 Emile Mayrisch (after T. van Rysselberghe)

1978. 50th Death Anniversary of Emile Mayrisch (iron and steel magnate).

1008	**264**	6f. multicoloured	2·40	45

265 Child with Ear of Millet

1978. Solidarity 1978. Multicoloured.

1009	2f. Type **265** (Terre des Hommes)	80	60
1010	5f. Flower and lungs (70th anniversary of Luxembourg Anti-tuberculosis League)	80	60
1011	6f. Open cell (Amnesty International and 30th anniversary of Declaration of Human Rights)	1·20	60

266 Perfect Ashlar

1978. 175th Anniversary of Luxembourg Grand Lodge.

1012	**266**	6f. blue	1·60	60

267 *St Matthew*

1978. National Welfare Fund. Glass Paintings (1st series). Multicoloured.

1013	2f.+25c. Type **267**	40	40
1014	5f.+25c. *St Mark*	65	60
1015	6f.+50c. *Nativity*	80	60
1016	12f.+1f. *St Luke*	3·25	1·90
1017	20f.+8f. *St John*	4·00	9·00

See also Nos. 1035/1039 and 1055/1058.

268 Denarius of Gaius Julius Caesar

1979. Luxembourg Culture. Roman Coins in the State Museum. Multicoloured.

1018	5f. Type **268**	80	60
1019	6f. Sestertius of Faustina I	1·20	40
1020	9f. Follis of Helena	1·60	1·00
1021	26f. Solidus of Valens	3·25	2·30

See also Nos. 1040/1043 and 1060/1063.

269 Mondorf-les-Bains

1979. Tourism.

1022	**269**	5f. green, brown and blue	1·20	45
1023	-	6f. red	2·00	45

Design: 6f. Luxembourg Central Station.

270 Stage Coach

1979. Europa. Multicoloured.

1024	6f. Type **270**	9·50	75
1025	12f. Old wall telephone (vert)	9·50	3·00

271 Antoine Meyer (poet)

1979. Anniversaries.

1026	-	2f. purple	1·20	45
1027	**271**	5f. red	95	45
1028	-	6f. turquoise	95	45
1029	-	9f. grey-black	2·30	1·10

Designs: 36×36 mm—2f. Michel Pintz on trial (after L. Piedboeuf) and monument to rebels (180th anniversary of peasant uprising against French). 22×36 mm—5f. T **271** (150th anniversary of first publication in Luxembourg dialect); 6f. S. G. Thomas (centenary of purchase of Thomas patent for steel production); 9f. *Abundance crowning Work and Saving* (ceiling painting by August Vinet) (50th anniversary of Stock Exchange).

272 European Assembly

1979. First Direct Elections to European Assembly.

1030	**272**	6f. multicoloured	2·40	1·10

273 Blindfolded Cherub with Chalice

1979. Rococo Art. Details from altar of St Michael's Church by Barthelemy Namur. Multicoloured.

1031	6f. Type **273**	80	75
1032	12f. Cherub with anchor	1·60	1·50

274 Child with Traffic Symbol Balloons jumping over Traffic

1979. International Year of the Child.

1033	**274**	2f. blue, brown and red	1·20	40

275 Radio Waves, 'RTL' and Dates

1979. 50th Anniversary of Broadcasting in Luxembourg.

1034	**275**	6f. blue and red	1·60	45

1979. National Welfare Fund. Glass Paintings (2nd series). As T **267**. Multicoloured.

1035	2f.+25c. *Spring*	40	40
1036	5f.+25c. *Summer*	65	60
1037	6f.+50c. *Charity*	80	60
1038	12f.+1f. *Autumn*	1·60	3·00
1039	20f.+8f. *Winter*	3·25	10·50

1980. Luxembourg Culture. Medieval Coins in the State Museum. As T **268**. Multicoloured.

1040	2f. Grosso of Emperor Henry VII	80	40
1041	5f. Grosso of John the Blind of Bohemia	80	75
1042	6f. 'Mouton d'or' of Wenceslas I and Jeanne, Duke and Duchess of Brabant	1·60	40
1043	20f. Grosso of Wenceslas II, Duke of Luxembourg	4·00	1·50

276 State Archives Building

1980. Tourism.

1044	**276**	6f. purple, ultram & bl	2·40	45
1045	-	6f. red and brown	2·40	45

Design: Vert—No. 1045, Ettelbruck Town Hall.

277 Jean Monnet (statesman)

1980. Europa.

1046	**277**	6f. black	4·00	40
1047	-	12f. olive	5·50	1·90

Design: 12f. St Benedict of Nursia (founder of Benedictine Order) (statue in Echternach Abbey).

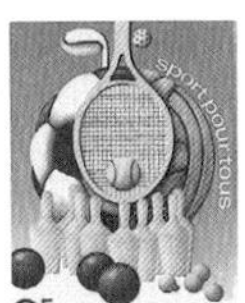

278 Sports Equipment

1980. Sports for All.

1048	**278**	6f. black, orange & green	2·40	75

279 Gloved Hand protecting Worker from Machinery

1980. Ninth World Congress on the Prevention of Accidents at Work and Occupational Diseases, Amsterdam.

1049	-	2f. multicoloured	1·20	40
1050	**279**	6f. brown, grey and red	1·20	75

Design: Vert—2f. Worker pouring molten iron.

280 *Mercury* (Jean Mich)

1980. Art Nouveau Sculpture. Statues beside entrance to State Savings Bank.

1051	**280**	8f. lilac	1·60	75
1052	-	12f. blue	1·60	1·50

Design: 12f. *Ceres* (Jean Mich).

281 Postcoded Letter

1980. Postcode Publicity.

1053	**281**	4f. brown, ochre and red	1·60	60

282 Policemen and Patrol Car

1980. 50th Anniversary of National Police Force.

1054	**282**	8f. multicoloured	1·60	60

1980. National Welfare Fund. Glass Paintings (3rd series). As T **267**. Multicoloured.

1055	4f.+50c. *St Martin*	80	40
1056	6f.+50c. *St Nicholas*	80	45
1057	8f.+1f. *Virgin and child*	1·60	1·90
1058	30f.+10f. *St George*	6·50	10·50

283 Grand Duke Jean

1981. Grand Duke Jean's 60th Birthday. Sheet 115×73 mm containing T **283** and similar vert design.

MS1059	8f. Type **283**; 12f. Grand Duke Jean's Coat of Arms; 30f. Type **283**	4·75	3·75

1981. Luxembourg Culture. Coins in the State Museum. As T **268**.

1060	4f. Patagon of Philip IV of Spain, 1635	80	40
1061	6f. 12 sols coin of Maria Theresa, 1775	1·20	60
1062	8f. 12 sols coin of Emperor Joseph II, 1789	1·20	60
1063	30f. Siege crown of Emperor Francis II, 1795	4·00	2·30

284 European Parliament Building, Luxembourg

1981. Tourism.

1064	**284**	8f. brown and blue	1·20	60
1065	-	8f. red and blue	1·20	60

Design: No. 1065, National Library.

285 Cock-shaped Whistle sold at Easter Monday Market

1981. Europa. Multicoloured.

1066	8f. Procession of beribboned sheep and town band to local fair	3·25	55
1067	12f. Type **285**	4·75	1·10

286 Staunton Knight on Chessboard

1981. Anniversaries.

1068	**286**	4f. multicoloured	1·60	60
1069	-	8f. ochre, brown & silver	1·60	60
1070	-	8f. multicoloured	1·60	60

Designs: Vert—4f. T **286** (50th anniversary of Luxembourg Chess Federation); 8f. (No. 1070), Pass-book and State Savings Bank (125th anniversary of State Savings Bank). Horiz—8f. (No. 1069), First Luxembourg banknote (125th anniversary of International Bank of Luxembourg's issuing rights).

287 Prince Henri and Princess Maria Teresa

1981. Royal Wedding.

1071	**287**	8f. multicoloured	1·20	75

288 Gliders over Useldange

1981. Aviation. Multicoloured.

1072	8f. Type **288**	1·60	60
1073	16f. Cessna 172F Skyhawk LX-AIZ and 182H Skylane sports aeroplanes	2·40	1·50
1074	35f. Boeing 747-200F over Luxembourg Findel airport terminal	4·00	1·90

289 Flame

1981. Energy Conservation.

1075	**289**	8f. multicoloured	1·20	60

290 Arms of Petange

1981. National Welfare Fund. Arms of Local Authorities (1st series). Multicoloured.

1076	4f.+50c. Type **290**	40	40
1077	6f.+50c. Larochette	50	45
1078	8f.+1f. *Adoration of the Magi* (School of Rubens)	80	60
1079	16f.+2f. Stadtbredimus	1·60	3·75
1080	35f.+12f. Weiswampach	5·50	9·75

See also Nos. 1097/1101 and 1119/1123.

291 *Apple Trees in Blossom* (Frantz Seimetz)

1982. Luxembourg Culture. Landscapes through the Four Seasons. Multicoloured.

1081	4f. Type **291**	80	60
1082	6f. *Landscape* (Pierre Blanc)	80	75
1083	8f. *The Larger Hallerbach* (Guido Oppenheim)	1·20	60
1084	16f. *Winter Evening* (Eugene Mousset)	2·40	1·50

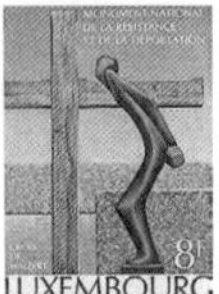
292 Cross of Hinzert and Statue *Political Prisoner* (Lucien Wercollier)

1982. National Monument of the Resistance and Deportation, Notre-Dame Cemetery.

1085	**292**	8f. multicoloured	1·20	60

293 Treaty of London, 1867, and Luxembourg Fortress

1982. Europa. Multicoloured.

1086	8f. Type **293**	4·00	75
1087	16f. Treaty of Paris, 1951, and European Coal and Steel Community Building, Luxembourg	4·75	1·50

294 St Teresa of Avila (wood statue, Carmel Monastery)

1982. Anniversaries. Multicoloured.

1088	4f. Type **294** (400th death anniversary)	80	55
1089	8f. Raoul Follereau (social worker for lepers, fifth death anniversary)	80	60

295 State Museum

1982. Tourism.

1090	**295**	8f. brown, blue and black	80	60
1091	-	8f. buff, black and blue	80	60

Design: No. 1091, Luxembourg Synagogue.

296 Bourscheid Castle

1982. Classified Monuments (1st series).

1092	**296**	6f. blue	1·60	60
1093	-	8f. red	1·60	60

Design: Horiz—8f. Vianden Castle.

See also Nos. 1142/1143 and 1165/1166.

297 Key in Lock

1982. Anniversaries. Multicoloured.

1094	4f. Type **297** (50th anniversary of International Youth Hostel Federation)	1·60	60
1095	8f. Scouts holding hands around globe (75th anniversary of Scouting Movement) (vert)	1·60	60

298 Monument to Civilian and Military Deportation

1982. Civilian and Military Deportation Monument, Hollerich Station.

1096	**298**	8f. multicoloured	1·20	60

1982. National Welfare Fund. Arms of Local Authorities (2nd series) and Stained Glass Window (8f.). As T **290**. Multicoloured.

1097	4f.+50c. Bettembourg	50	40
1098	6f.+50c. Frisange	65	45
1099	8f.+1f. *Adoration of the Shepherds* (Gustav Zanter, Hoscheid parish church)	1·20	60
1100	16f.+2f. Mamer	2·40	3·75
1101	35f.+12f. Heinerscheid	5·50	9·75

299 Modern Fire Engine

1983. Centenary of National Federation of Fire Brigades. Multicoloured.

1102	8f. Type **299**	2·40	75
1103	16f. Hand fire-pump (18th-century)	3·25	1·50

300 *Mercury* (Auguste Tremont)

1983. Anniversaries and Events.

1104	**300**	4f. multicoloured	80	60
1105	-	6f. multicoloured	80	60
1106	-	8f. brown, black and blue	80	60
1107	-	8f. deep blue and blue	80	60

Designs: No. 1104, T **300** (25th Congress of International Association of Foreign Exchange Dealers); No. 1105, NATO emblem surrounded by flags of member countries (25th anniversary of NATO); No. 1106, Echternach Cross of Justice (30th Congress of International Union of Barristers); No. 1107, Globe and customs emblem (30th anniversary of Customs Co-operation Council).

301 Robbers attacking Traveller

1983. Europa. Miniatures from *Codex Aureus Escorialensis*, illustrating *Parable of the Good Samaritan*. Multicoloured.

1108	8f. Type **301**	6·50	1·00
1109	16f. Good Samaritan helping traveller	9·50	3·00

302 Initial 'H' from *Book of Baruch*

1983. Luxembourg Culture. Echternach Abbey Giant Bible. Multicoloured.

1110	8f. Type **302**	1·20	75
1111	35f. Initial 'B' from letter of St Jerome to Pope Damasius I	3·25	2·30

303 Despatch Rider and Postcode

1983. World Communications Year. Multicoloured.

1112	8f. Type **303**	2·40	60
1113	8f. Europan Communications Satellite (horiz)	4·75	60

304 St Lawrence's Church, Diekirch

1983. Tourism.

1114	**304**	7f. orange, brown and blue	1·20	60
1115	-	10f. orange, brown & bl	1·20	60

Design: Horiz—10f. Dudelange Town Hall.

305 Basketball

1983. Anniversaries and Events. Multicoloured.

1116	7f. Type **305** (50th anniversary of Luxembourg basketball Federation)	1·60	75
1117	10f. Sheepdog (European Working Dog Championships)	1·60	75
1118	10f. City of Luxembourg (The Green Heart of Europe)	2·75	75

1983. National Welfare Fund. Arms of Local Authorities (3rd series) and Painting. As T **290**. Multicoloured.

1119	4f.+1f. Winseler	65	60
1120	7f.+1f. Beckerich	80	60
1121	10f.+1f. *Adoration of the Shepherds* (Lucas Bosch)	1·20	60
1122	16f.+2f. Feulen	2·40	3·75
1123	40f.+13f. Mertert	5·50	9·75

306 Lion and First Luxembourg Stamp

1984. Anniversaries. Each black, red and blue.

1124	10f. Type **306**	1·60	75
1125	10f. Lion and ministry buildings	1·60	75
1126	10f. Lion and postman's bag	1·60	75
1127	10f. Lion and diesel locomotive	1·60	75

Anniversaries: No. 1124, 50th anniversary of Federation of Luxembourg Philatelic Societies; No. 1125, 75th anniversary of Civil Service Trade Union Movement; No. 1126, 75th anniversary of Luxembourg Postmen's Trade Union; No. 1127, 125th anniversary of Luxembourg Railways.

307 Pedestrian Precinct

1984. Environmental Protection. Multicoloured.

1128	7f. Type **307**	1·60	75
1129	10f. City of Luxembourg sewage treatment plant	1·60	75

308 Hands supporting European Parliament Emblem

1984. Second Direct Elections to European Parliament.

1130	**308**	10f. multicoloured	1·60	75

309 Bridge

1984. Europa. 25th Anniversary of European Post and Telecommunications Conference.

1131	**309**	10f. green, dp green & blk	8·00	75
1132	**309**	16f. orange, brown & blk	12·00	3·00

310 *The Smoker* (David Teniers the Younger)

1984. Paintings. Multicoloured.

1133	4f. Type **310**	1·20	60
1134	7f. *Young Turk caressing his Horse* (Eugene Delacroix) (horiz)	1·60	75
1135	10f. *Ephiphany* (Jan Steen) (horiz)	2·40	75
1136	50f. *The Lacemaker* (Pieter van Slingelandt)	8·00	5·75

311 *The Race* (Jean Jacoby)

1984. Olympic Games, Los Angeles.

1137	**311**	10f. orange, black & blue	1·60	75

312 Pecten sp.

1984. Luxembourg Culture. Fossils in the Natural History Museum. Multicoloured.

1138	4f. Type **312**	1·20	60
1139	7f. Devil's toe-nail	1·20	75
1140	10f. Coeloceras raquinianum (ammonite)	2·00	75
1141	16f. Dapedium (fish)	2·40	1·90

1984. Classified Monuments (2nd series). As T **296**.

1142	7f. turquoise	1·20	75
1143	10f. brown	1·20	75

Designs: 7f. Hollenfels Castle; 10f. Larochette Castle.

313 *American Soldier* (statue by Michel Heitz at Clervaux)

1984. 40th Anniversary of Liberation.

1144	**313**	10f. black, red and blue	4·00	75

314 Infant astounded by Surroundings

1984. National Welfare Fund. The Child. Multicoloured

1145	4f.+1f. Type **314**	80	75
1146	7f.+1f. Child dreaming	1·20	1·10
1147	10f.+1f. Nativity (crib, Steinsel church)	2·40	1·10
1148	16f.+2f. Child sulking	5·50	6·00
1149	40f.+13f. Girl admiring flower	14·50	15·00

315 Jean Bertels (abbot of Echternach Abbey)

1985. Luxembourg Culture. Portrait Medals in State Museum (1st series). Multicoloured.

1150	4f. Type **315** (steatite medal, 1595)	80	60
1151	7f. Emperor Charles V (bronze medal, 1537)	1·20	75
1152	10f. King Philip II of Spain (silver medal, 1555)	1·60	75
1153	30f. Maurice of Orange-Nassau (silver medal, 1615)	4·75	2·30

See also Nos. 1173/1176.

316 Fencing

1985. Anniversaries. Multicoloured.

1154	10f. Type **316** (50th anniversary of Luxembourg Fencing Federation)	1·60	75
1155	10f. Benz Velo (centenary of automobile)	1·60	75
1156	10f. Telephone within concentric circles (centenary of Luxembourg telephone service)	1·60	75

317 Papal Arms

1985. Visit of Pope John Paul II.

1157	**317**	10f. multicoloured	1·60	60

318 Treble Clef within Map of National Anthem

1965. Europa. Music Year. Multicoloured.

1158	10f. Type **318** (Grand Duke Adolphe Union of choral, instrumental and folklore societies)	8·00	75
1159	16f. Neck of violin, music school and score of Beethoven's Violin Concerto *Opus 61*	13·00	3·75

319 Maquisards Badge and *Wounded Soldiers* (sculpture, Rene Weyland)

1985. 40th Anniversary of VE (Victory in Europe) Day. Sheet 120×72 mm containing T **319** and similar vert designs.

MS1160	10f. multicoloured (Type **319**); 10f. brown, black and blue (War medal); 10f. multicoloured (Union of Resistance Movements badge); 10f. black, red and blue (dove and barbed wire hands) (liberation of prison camps)	9·50	8·25

320 Little Owl

1985. Endangered Animals. Multicoloured.

1161	4f. Type **320**	2·40	75
1162	7f. European wildcat (horiz)	4·00	1·50
1163	10f. Red admiral (horiz)	6·50	1·50
1164	50f. European tree frog	12·00	6·00

1985. Classified Monuments (3rd series). As T **296**.

1165	7f. red	1·20	60
1166	10f. green	1·20	60

Designs: Horiz—7f. Echternach orangery. Vert—10f. Mohr de Waldt house.

321 Mansfeld Arms (book binding)

1985. Luxembourg Culture.

1167	**321**	10f. multicoloured	1·60	75

322 Application

1985. National Welfare Fund. Multicoloured.

1168	4f.+1f. Type **322**	80	75
1169	7f.+1f. Friendship	1·20	1·10
1170	10f.+1f. *Adoration of the Magi* (16th-century alabaster sculpture)	2·40	1·10
1171	16f.+2f. Child identifying with his favourite characters	5·50	7·50
1172	40f.+13f. Shame	16·00	14·00

1986. Luxembourg Culture. Portrait Medals in State Museum (2nd series). As T **315**.

1173	10f. multicoloured	1·60	75
1174	12f. multicoloured	1·60	60
1175	18f. black, grey and blue	1·60	1·40
1176	20f. multicoloured	2·40	1·50

Designs: 10f. Count of Monterey (silver medal, 1675); 12f. Louis XIV of France (silver medal, 1684); 18f. Pierre de Weyms (president of Provincial Council) (pewter medal, 1700); 20f. Duke of Marlborough (silver medal, 1706).

323 Bee on Flower

1986. Anniversaries. Multicoloured.

1177	12f. Type **323** (centenary of Federation of Luxembourg Beekeeper's Associations)	2·00	75
1178	12f. Table tennis player (50th anniversary of Luxembourg Table Tennis Federation)	2·00	75
1179	11f. Mosaic of woman with water jar (centenary of Mondorf State Spa)	2·00	75

324 Forest and City

1986. Europa. Multicoloured.

1180	12f. Type **324**	5·50	75
1181	20f. Mankind, industry and countryside	7·25	2·75

325 Fort Thungen

1986. Luxembourg Town Fortifications. Multicoloured

1182	15f. Type **325**	4·00	1·10
1183	18f. Invalids' Gate (vert)	4·00	1·10
1184	50f. Malakoff Tower (vert)	8·00	1·90

326 Schuman

1986. Birth Centenary of Robert Schuman (politician).

1185	**326**	2f. black and red	40	40
1186	**326**	10f. black and blue	80	60

327 Road through Red Triangle on Map

1986. European Road Safety Year.

1187	**327**	10f. multicoloured	1·20	75

328 Ascent to Chapel of the Cross, Grevenmacher

1986. Tourism.

1188	**328**	12f. multicoloured	2·40	60
1189	-	12f. brown, stone and red	2·40	60

Design: No. 1189, Relief from Town Hall facade, Esch-sur-Alzette.

329 Presentation of Letter of Freedom to Echternach (after P. H. Witkamp)

1986. 800th Birth Anniversary of Countess Ermesinde of Luxembourg.

1190	**329**	12f. brown and stone	1·60	60
1191	-	30f. buff, black and grey	3·25	1·90

Design: 30f. Seal, 1238.

330 Annunciation

1986. National Welfare Fund. Illustrations from 15th-century *Book of Hours*. Multicoloured.

1192	6f.+1f. Type **330**	2·00	75
1193	10f.+1f. Angel appearing to shepherds	1·20	75
1194	12f.+2f. Nativity	2·40	1·00
1195	18f.+2f. Adoration of the Magi	6·50	6·75
1196	20f.+8f. Flight into Egypt	10·50	13·00

331 Garden Dormouse

1987. Endangered Animals. Multicoloured.

1197	6f. Type **331**	1·60	75
1198	10f. Banded agrion (vert)	2·40	1·10
1199	12f. White-throated dipper (vert)	4·00	75
1200	25f. Salamander	5·50	3·00

332 Network Emblem

1987. 50th Anniversaries. Multicoloured.

1201	12f. Type **332** (Amateur Short Wave Network)	2·00	60
1202	12f. Anniversary Emblem (International Fair)	2·00	60

333 *St Bernard of Siena and St John the Baptist*

1987. Paintings by Giovanni Ambrogio Bevilacqua in State Museum. Multicoloured.

1203	10f. Type **333**	2·00	75
1204	18f. *St Jerome and St Francis of Assisi*	2·75	1·50

334 National Swimming Centre (Roger Taillibert)

1987. Europa. Architecture. Multicoloured.

1205	12f. Type **334**	6·50	1·00
1206	20f. European Communities' Court of Justice	9·50	3·00

335 Consecration (stained glass window by Gustav Zanter)

1987. Millenary of St Michael's Church. Multicoloured.

1207	12f. Type **335**	2·40	75
1208	20f. Baroque organ-chest	4·00	1·50

336 Charles Metz (first President) (after Jean-Baptiste Fresez)

1987. Chamber of Deputies.

1209	**336**	6f. brown	1·20	60
1210	-	12f. blue	1·60	75

Design: 12f. Chamber of Deputies building.

337 Hennesbau, Niederfeulen

1987. Rural Architecture. Each ochre, brown and blue.

1211	10f. Type **337**	2·00	90
1212	12f. 18th-century dwelling house converted to health centre, Mersch	2·00	60
1213	100f. 18th-century house converted to Post Office, Bertrange	12·00	1·90

338 Annunciation

1987. National Welfare Fund. Illustrations from 15th-century Paris *Book of Hours*. Multicoloured.

1214	6f.+1f. Type **338**	2·40	1·50
1215	10f.+1f. Visitation	2·75	2·30
1216	12f.+2f. Adoration of the Magi	4·00	2·30
1217	18f.+2f. Presentation in the Temple	8·00	6·00
1218	20f.+8f. Flight into Egypt	13·50	12·00

339 Lilies and Water-lily

1988. Luxembourg Culture. Flower Illustrations by Pierre-Joseph Redoute. Multicoloured.

1219	6f. Type **339**	1·60	75
1220	10f. Primulas and double narcissus	1·60	75
1221	12f. Tulips and chrysanthemums	4·00	1·10
1222	50f. Irises and gorterias	8·00	5·25

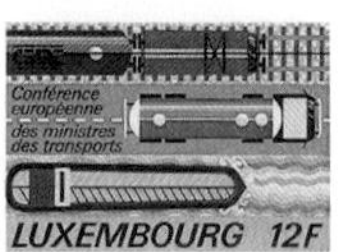

340 Rail, Road and Water Transport

1988. European Conference of Ministers of Transport, Luxembourg (No. 1223) and 25th Anniversary of Eurocontrol (air safety organisation) (No. 1224). Multicoloured.

1223	12f. Type **340**	2·40	75
1224	20f. Boeing 747 aeroplane	3·25	2·30

341 Princess Maria Teresa

1988. Juvalux 88 Ninth Youth Philately Exhibition, Luxembourg. Sheet 11×72 mm containing T **341** and similar vert designs. Multicoloured.

MS1225	12f. Type **341**; 18f. Princes Guillaume, Felix and Louis; 50f. Crown Prince Henri	13·50	13·00

342 Wiltz Town Hall and Cross of Justice

1988. Tourism. Multicoloured.

1226	10f. Type **342**	2·75	60
1227	12f. Differdange Castle (vert)	2·75	1·00

See also Nos. 1254/1255 and 1275/1276.

343 Athletes

1988. 50th Anniversary of League of Luxembourg Student Sports Associations.

1228	**343**	12f. multicoloured	2·40	1·10

344 Automated Mail Sorting

1988. Europa. Transport and Communications. Multicoloured.

1229	12f. Type **344**	12·00	75
1230	20f. Electronic communications	12·00	3·75

345 Jean Monnet (statesman, birth centenary)

1988. European Anniversaries.

1231	**345**	12f. pink, brn & lt brn	2·40	75
1232	-	12f. brown and green	2·40	75

Design: No. 1232, European Investment Bank headquarters, Kirchberg (30th anniversary).

346 Emblem and Flame

1988. Olympic Games, Seoul.

1233	**346**	12f. multicoloured	2·00	75

347 Septfontaines Castle

1988. Doorways.

1234	**347**	12f. black and brown	1·60	75
1235	-	25f. black and green	3·25	2·30
1236	-	50f. black and brown	5·50	3·00

Designs: 25f. National Library; 50f. Holy Trinity Church.

348 Annunciation to Shepherds

1988. National Welfare Fund. Illustrations from 16th-century *Book of Hours*. Multicoloured.

1237	9f.+1f. Type **348**	1·00	75
1238	12f.+2f. Adoration of the Magi	1·20	75
1239	18f.+2f. Madonna and Child	5·50	5·25
1240	20f.+8f. Pentecost	6·50	6·00

349 C. M. Spoo (promoter of Luxembourgish)

1989. Anniversaries.

1241	**349**	12f. black, red and brown	1·60	75
1242	-	18f. multicoloured	2·40	1·50
1243	-	20f. red, black and grey	3·25	2·30

Designs: 12f. T **349** (75th death anniversary); 18f. Stylised inking pad (125th anniversary of Book Workers' Federation); 20f. Henri Dunant (founder of International Red Cross) (75th anniversary of Luxembourg Red Cross).

350 Grand Ducal Family Vault Bronze (Auguste Tremont)

1989. 150th Anniversary of Independence.

1244	**350**	12f. multicoloured	2·40	75

351 *Astra* Satellite and Map on TV Screens

1989. Launch of 16-channel TV Satellite.

1245	**351**	12f. multicoloured	2·40	75

352 Cyclist

1989. Start in Luxembourg of Tour de France Cycling Race.

1246	**352**	9f. multicoloured	3·25	1·10

353 Assembly and Flag

1989. 40th Anniversary of Council of Europe.

1247	**353**	12f. multicoloured	2·00	75

354 Emblem

1989. Centenary of Interparliamentary Union.

1248	**354**	12f. yellow, blue & indigo	2·00	75

355 Hands

1989. Third Direct Elections to European Parliament.

1249	**355**	12f. multicoloured	2·40	75

356 *Three Children in a Park* (anon)

1989. Europa. Children's Games and Toys. Multicoloured.

1250	12f. Type **356**	5·50	75
1251	20f. *Child with Drum* (anon)	7·25	2·30

357 Grand Duke Jean

1989. 25th Anniversary of Accession of Grand Duke Jean.

1252	**357**	3f. black and orange	6·50	6·00
1253	**357**	9f. black and green	3·25	3·00

1989. Tourism. As T **342**. Multicoloured.

1254	12f. Clervaux Castle	2·40	75
1255	18f. 1st-century bronze wild boar, Titelberg	2·75	1·50

358 Charles IV

1989. Luxembourg History. Stained Glass Windows by Joseph Oterberger, Luxembourg Cathedral. Multicoloured.

1256	12f. Type **358**	1·60	75
1257	20f. John the Blind	2·40	1·90
1258	25f. Wenceslas II	3·25	2·30

359 St Lambert and St Blase, Fennange

1989. National Welfare Fund. Restored Chapels (1st series). Multicoloured.

1259	9f.+1f. Type **359**	1·20	60
1260	12f.+2f. St Quirinus, Luxembourg (horiz)	1·60	1·10
1261	18f.+3f. St Anthony the Hermit, Reisdorf (horiz)	3·25	4·50
1262	25f.+8f. The Hermitage, Hachiville	8·00	6·75

See also Nos. 1280/1283 and 1304/1307.

360 Funfair (650th anniversary of Schueberfouer)

1990. Anniversaries.

1263	**360**	9f. multicoloured	1·60	75
1264	-	12f. brown, pink & black	1·60	75
1265	-	18f. multicoloured	2·40	1·70

Designs: 12f. Batty Weber (writer, 50th death anniversary); 18f. Dish aerial (125th anniversary of International Telecommunications Union).

361 Troops at Fortress

1990. Luxembourg Culture. Etchings of the Fortress by Christoph Wilhelm Selig. Multicoloured.

1266	9f. Type **361**	1·60	75
1267	12f. Soldiers by weir	1·60	75
1268	20f. Distant view of fortress	4·00	2·10
1269	25f. Walls	4·75	2·30

362 Paul Eyschen (75th anniversary)

1990. Statesmen's Death Anniversaries.

1270	**362**	9f. brown and blue	1·20	75
1271	-	12f. blue and brown	1·60	75

Design: 12f. Emmanuel Servais (centenary).

363 *Psallus pseudoplatini* (male and female) on Maple

1990. Centenary of Luxembourg Naturalists' Society.

1272	**363**	12f. multicoloured	1·60	75

364 General Post Office, Luxembourg City

1990. Europa. Post Office Buildings.

1273	**364**	12f. black and brown	8·00	75
1274	-	20f. black and blue	9·50	3·00

Design: Vert—20f. Esch-sur-Alzette Post Office.

1990. Tourism. As T **342**. Multicoloured.

1275	12f. Mondercange administrative offices	3·25	60

1276	12f. Schifflange town hall and church	3·25	60

365 Hammelsmarsch Fountain (Will Lofy)

1990. Fountains. Multicoloured.

1277	12f. Type **365**	2·40	75
1278	25f. Doves Fountain	4·00	2·30
1279	50f. Maus Ketty Fountain, Mondorf-les-Bains (Will Lofy)	8·00	3·75

366 Congregation of the Blessed Virgin Mary, Vianden

1990. National Welfare Fund. Restored Chapels (2nd series). Multicoloured.

1280	9f.+1f. Type **366**	1·60	1·00
1281	12f.+2f. Notre Dame, Echternach (horiz)	2·40	1·10
1282	18f.+3f. Consoler of the Afflicted, Grentzingen (horiz)	4·00	3·75
1283	25f.+8f. St Pirmin, Kaundorf	8·00	6·75

367 Grand Duke Adolf

1990. Centenary of Nassau-Weilbourg Dynasty. Sheet 115×160 mm containing T **367** and similar vert designs. Multicoloured.

MS1284	12f. Type **367**; 12f. Grand Duchess Marie Adelaide; 18f. Grand Ducal Arms; 18f. Grand Duchess Charlotte; 20f. Grand Duke William IV; 20f. Grand Duke Jean	20·00	19·00

368 *Geastrum varians*

1991. Fungi. Illustrations by Pierre-Joseph Redoute. Multicoloured.

1285	14f. Type **368**	1·60	1·10
1286	14f. *Agaricus* (Gymnopus) *thiebautii*	1·60	1·10
1287	18f. *Agaricus* (Lepiota) *lepidocephalus*	3·00	1·50
1288	25f. *Morchella favosa*	3·25	1·90

369 *View from the Trier Road*

1991. Luxembourg Culture. 50th Death Anniversary of Sosthene Weis (painter). Multicoloured.

1289	14f. Type **369**	2·40	1·00
1290	18f. *Vauban Street and the Viaduct*	2·40	1·50
1291	25f. *St. Ulric Street* (vert)	4·00	2·30

370 Dicks (after Jean Goedert)

1991. Death Centenary of Edmond de la Fontaine (pen-name Dicks) (poet).

1292	**370**	14f. multicoloured	2·40	1·10

371 Claw grasping Piece of Metal (after Emile Kirscht)

1991. 75th Anniversary of Trade Union Movement in Luxembourg.

1293	**371**	14f. multicoloured	2·40	1·10

372 National Miners' Monument, Kayl

1991. Tourism. Multicoloured.

1294	14f. Type **372**	2·40	1·10
1295	14f. Magistrates' Court, Redange-sur-Attert (horiz)	2·40	1·10

373 Earth and Orbit of *Astra 1A* and *1B* Satellites

1991. Europa. Europe in Space. Multicoloured.

1296	14f. Type **373**	6·50	1·10
1297	18f. Betzdorf Earth Station	8·00	3·00

374 Telephone

1991. Posts and Telecommunications.

1298	**374**	4f. brown	8·00	3·75
1299	-	14f. blue	1·60	1·10

Design: 14f. Postbox.

375 1936 International Philatelic Federation Congress Stamp

1991. 50th Stamp Day.

1300	**375**	14f. multicoloured	2·40	75

The stamp illustrated on No. 1300 incorrectly shows a face value of 10f.

376 Girl's Head

1991. Mascarons (stone faces on buildings) (1st series).

1301	**376**	14f. black, buff & brown	2·00	75
1302	-	25f. black, buff and pink	2·40	1·90
1303	-	50f. black, buff and blue	4·75	3·50

Designs: 25f. Woman's head; 50f. Man's head.

See also Nos. 1320/1322.

377 Chapel of St Donatus, Arsdorf

1991. National Welfare Fund. Restored Chapels (3rd series). Multicoloured.

1304	14f.+2f. Type **377**	2·40	1·10
1305	14f.+2f. Chapel of Our Lady of Sorrows, Brandenbourg (horiz)	2·40	1·50
1306	18f.+3f. Chapel of Our Lady, Luxembourg (horiz)	4·00	3·75
1307	22f.+7f. Chapel of the Hermitage, Wolwelange	6·50	6·00

378 Jean-Pierre Pescatore Foundation

1992. Buildings. Multicoloured.

1308	14f. Type **378**	1·60	1·10
1309	14f. Higher Technology Institute, Kirchberg	1·60	1·10
1310	14f. New Fairs and Congress Centre, Kirchberg	1·60	1·10

379 Inner Courtyard, Bettembourg Castle

1992. Tourism. Multicoloured.

1311	18f. Type **379**	2·40	1·50
1312	25f. Walferdange railway station	3·25	1·90

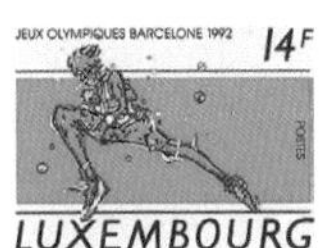

380 Athlete (detail of mural, Armand Strainchamps)

1992. Olympic Games, Barcelona.

1313	**380**	14f. multicoloured	3·25	75

381 Luxembourg Pavilion

1992. Expo '92 World's Fair, Seville.

1314	**381**	14f. multicoloured	1·60	75

382 Lions Emblem

1992. 75th Anniversary of Lions International.

1315	**382**	14f. multicoloured	2·40	75

383 Memorial Tablet (Lucien Wercollier)

1992. 50th Anniversary of General Strike.

1316	**383**	18f. brown, grey and red	2·40	1·50

384 Nicholas Gonner (editor)

1992. Europa. 500th Anniversary of Discovery of America by Columbus. Luxembourg Emigrants to America.

1317	**384**	14f. brown, black & green	6·50	1·10
1318	-	22f. blue, black & orange	6·50	3·00

Design: 22f. Nicolas Becker (writer).

385 Star and European Community Emblem

1992. Single European Market.

1319	**385**	14f. multicoloured	1·60	75

1992. Mascarons (2nd series). As T **376**.

1320	14f. black, buff and green	2·40	75
1321	22f. black, buff and blue	3·25	2·30
1322	50f. black, buff and purple	4·75	3·50

Designs: 14f. Ram's head; 22f. Lion's head; 50f. Goat's head.

386 Posthorn and Letters

1992. 150th Anniversary of Post and Telecommunications Office. Designs showing stained glass windows by Auguste Tremont. Multicoloured

1323	14f. Type **386**	1·60	1·10
1324	22f. Post rider	4·00	3·00
1325	50f. Telecommunications	4·75	4·50

387 Hazel Grouse

1992. National Welfare Fund. Birds (1st series). Multicoloured.

1326	14f.+2f. Type **387**	2·40	2·30
1327	14f.+2f. Golden oriole (vert)	2·40	2·30
1328	18f.+3f. Black stork	6·50	6·00
1329	22f.+7f. Red kite (vert)	12·00	11·50

See also Nos. 1364/1367 and 1383/1386.

388 Grand Duke Jean

1993

1330	**388**	1f. black and yellow	80	15
1331	**388**	2f. black and green	80	40
1332	**388**	5f. black and yellow	1·20	40
1333	**388**	7f. black and brown	1·20	40
1334	**388**	8f. black and green	2·00	60
1335	**388**	9f. black and mauve	1·20	60
1336	**388**	10f. black and blue	1·60	75
1337	**388**	14f. black and purple	4·00	75
1338	**388**	15f. black and green	2·40	1·10
1339	**388**	16f. black and orange	4·00	2·30
1340	**388**	18f. black and yellow	2·40	75
1341	**388**	20f. black and red	3·25	1·10
1342	**388**	22f. black and green	3·25	1·90
1343	**388**	25f. black and blue	3·25	2·30
1344	**388**	100f. black and brown	9·50	5·25

389 Old Ironworks Cultural Centre, Steinfort

1993. Tourism. Multicoloured.

1350	14f. Type **389**	2·40	75
1351	14f. Children with Grapes Fountain, Schwebsingen	2·40	75

390 Collage by Maurice Esteve

1993. New Surgical Techniques.
1352 **390** 14f. multicoloured 2·40 75

391 Hotel de Bourgogne (Prime Minister's offices)

1993. Historic Houses. Multicoloured.
1353 14f. Type **391** 2·40 75
1354 20f. Simons House (now Ministry of Agriculture) 4·00 1·50
1355 50f. Cassal House 8·00 3·75

392 *Rezlop* (Fernand Roda)

1993. Europa. Contemporary Art. Multicoloured.
1356 14f. Type **392** 2·40 1·10
1357 22f. *So Close* (Sonja Roef) 4·75 2·30

393 Monument (detail, D. Donzelli), Tetange Cemetery

1993. 75th Death Anniversary of Jean Schortgen (first worker elected to parliament).
1358 **393** 14f. multicoloured 2·40 75

394 Emblem

1993. Centenary of Artistic Circle of Luxembourg.
1359 **394** 14f. mauve and violet 2·40 75

395 European Community Ecological Label

1993. Protection of Environment.
1360 **395** 14f. blue, green & emerald 1·60 75

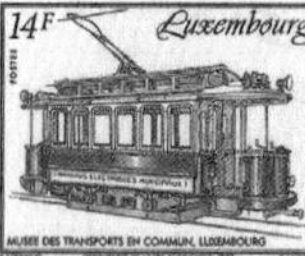

396 Tram No. 1 (Transport Museum, Luxembourg)

1993. Museum Exhibits (1st series). Multicoloured.
1361 14f. Type **396** 2·40 75
1362 22f. Iron ore tipper wagon (National Mining Museum, Rumelange) 3·25 2·30
1363 60f. Horse-drawn carriage (Arts and Ancient Crafts Museum, Wiltz) 8·00 6·00

See also Nos. 1404/1406 and 1483/1484.

1993. National Welfare Fund. Birds (2nd series). As T **387**. Multicoloured.
1364 14f.+2f. Common snipe ('Becassine') 2·40 2·30
1365 14f.+2f. River kingfisher ('Martin-Pecheur') (vert) 2·40 2·30
1366 18f.+3f. Little ringed plover ('Petit Gravelot') 4·75 4·50
1367 22f.+7f. Sand martin ('Hirondelle de Rivage') (vert) 8·00 7·50

397 *Snow-covered Landscape* (Joseph Kutter)

1994. Artists' Birth Centenaries. Multicoloured.
1368 14f. Type **397** 2·40 75
1369 14f. *The Moselle* (Nico Klopp) 2·40 75

398 Members' Flags

1994. Fourth Direct Elections to European Parliament.
1370 **398** 14f. multicoloured 1·60 1·10

399 17th-century Herald's Tabard

1994. Congresses. Multicoloured.
1371 14f. Type **399** (21st International Genealogy and Heraldry Congress) 4·00 1·10
1372 18f. International Police Association emblem on map (14th World Congress) 4·00 1·50

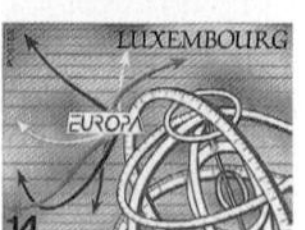

400 Arrows and Terrestrial Globe

1994. Europa. Discoveries. Multicoloured.
1373 14f. Type **400** 4·75 1·10
1374 22f. Chart, compass rose and sails 6·50 3·00

401 *Family* (Laura Lammar)

1994. International Year of the Family.
1375 **401** 25f. multicoloured 6·50 2·30

402 Crowds cheering American Soldiers

1994. 50th Anniversary of Liberation.
1376 **402** 14f. multicoloured 1·60 1·10

403 Western European Union Emblem (40th anniversary)

1994. Anniversaries and Campaign.
1377 **403** 14f. blue, lilac and ultramarine 2·40 1·10
1378 - 14f. multicoloured 2·40 1·10
1379 - 14f. multicoloured 8·00 2·30

Designs: No. 1378, Emblem (25th anniversary in Luxembourg of European Communities' Office for Official Publications); No. 1379, 10th-century BC ceramic bowl from cremation tomb, Bigelbach (European Bronze Age Campaign).

404 Munster Abbey (General Finance Inspectorate)

1994. Former Refuges now housing Government Offices. Multicoloured.
1380 15f. Type **404** 2·40 1·50
1381 25f. Holy Spirit Convent (Ministry of Finance) 3·25 2·30
1382 60f. St Maximine Abbey of Trier (Ministry of Foreign Affairs) 6·50 3·75

1994. National Welfare Fund. Birds (3rd series). As T **387**. Multicoloured.
1383 14f.+2f. Common stonechat ('Traquet Patre') (vert) 3·25 3·00
1384 14f.+2f. Grey partridge ('Perdix Grise') 3·25 3·00
1385 18f.+3f. Yellow wagtail ('Bergeronnette Printaniere') 6·50 6·00
1386 22f.+7f. Great grey shrike ('Pie-Grieche Grise') (vert) 9·50 9·00

405 *King of the Antipodes*

406/409 Panoramic View of City (image scaled to 43% of original size)

1995. Luxembourg, European City of Culture.
1387 **405** 16f. multicoloured 3·25 1·50
1388 - 16f. multicoloured 3·25 1·50
1389 - 16f. multicoloured 3·25 1·50
1390 **406** 16f. multicoloured 2·40 1·10
1391 **407** 16f. multicoloured 2·40 1·10
1392 **408** 16f. multicoloured 2·40 1·10
1393 **409** 16f. multicoloured 2·40 1·10
1394 - 16f. multicoloured 2·40 1·10

Designs: As T **405**—No. 1388, *House with Arcades and Yellow Tower*; No. 1389, *Small Path* (maze). 35×26 mm—No. 1394, Emblem.

Nos. 1390/1393 were issued together, *se-tenant*, forming the composite design illustrated.

410 Landscape and Slogan

1995. European Nature Conservation Year.
1395 **410** 16f. multicoloured 2·40 1·10

411 Colour Spectrum and Barbed Wire

1995. Europa. Peace and Freedom. 50th Anniversary of Liberation of Concentration Camps. Multicoloured.
1396 16f. Type **411** 4·00 1·50
1397 25f. Wire barbs breaking through symbolic sky and earth 4·75 3·00

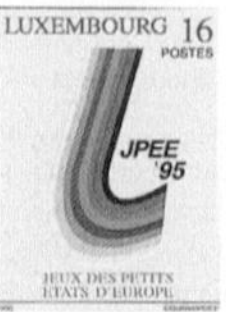

412 Emblem

1995. Anniversaries and Event. Multicoloured.
1398 16f. Type **412** (Sixth Small European States Games, Luxembourg) 2·40 1·50
1399 32f. Diagram of section through Earth (27th anniversary of underground Geodynamics Laboratory, Walferdange) (33×34 mm) 4·75 3·75
1400 80f. Anniversary emblem (50th anniversary of UNO) 9·50 7·50

413 Boeing 757

1995. 40th Anniversary of Luxembourg–Iceland Air Link.
1401 **413** 16f. multicoloured 1·60 1·30

414 Erpeldange Castle

1995. Tourism. Multicoloured.
1402 16f. Type **414** 2·40 1·30
1403 16f. Schengen Castle 2·40 1·30

1995. Museum Exhibits (2nd series). Vert designs as T **396**. Multicoloured.
1404 16f. Churn (Country Art Museum, Vianden) 2·40 1·30
1405 32f. Wine-press (Wine Museum, Ehnen) 4·75 2·50
1406 80f. Sculpture of potter (Leon Nosbusch) (Pottery Museum, Nospelt) 12·00 6·00

415 Stained Glass Window from Alzingen Church

1995. Christmas.
1407 **415** 16f.+2f. multicoloured 4·00 3·75

416 Broad-leaved Linden (*Tilia platyphyllos*)

1995. National Welfare Fund. Trees (1st series). Multicoloured.
1408 16f.+2f. Type **416** 2·40 1·70
1409 16f.+2f. Horse chestnut (*Aesculus hippocastanum*) (horiz) 2·40 1·70
1410 20f.+3f. Pedunculate oak (horiz) 4·00 3·50
1411 32f.+7f. Silver birch 6·50 6·00

See also Nos. 1432/1435 and 1458/1461.

417 Mayrisch (after Theo van Rysselberghe)

1996. 68th Death Anniversary of Emile Mayrisch (engineer).
1412 **417** A (16f.) multicoloured 2·40 1·30

418 Mounument, Place Clairefontaine (Jean Cardot)

1996. Birth Centenary of Grand Duchess Charlotte.

1413 **418** 16f. multicoloured 3·25 1·70

419 Electric Railcar

1996. 50th Anniversary of Luxembourg National Railway Company. Multicoloured.

1414 16f. Type **419** 4·00 1·30
1415 16f. Linked cars 4·00 1·30
1416 16f. Train (right-hand detail) 4·00 1·30

Nos. 1414/1416 were issued together, se-tenant, forming a composite design of a Series 2000 electric railcar set.

420 *Marie Munchen*

1996. 96th Death Anniversary of Mihaly Munkacsy (painter). Multicoloured.

1417 16f. Type **420** 2·00 1·30
1418 16f. Munkacsy (after Edouard Charlemont) (horiz) 2·00 1·30

421 Workers and Emblem

1996. Anniversaries.

1419 **421** 16f. green, orge & blk 2·40 1·30
1420 - 20f. multicoloured 2·40 1·70
1421 - 25f. multicoloured 3·25 2·50
1422 - 32f. multicoloured 4·75 3·50

Designs: Horiz—16f. T **421** (75th anniversary of Luxembourg Confederation of Christian Trade Unions); 32f. Film negative (centenary of motion pictures). Vert—20f. Transmitter and radio waves (centenary of Guglielmo Marconi's patented wireless telegraph); 25f. Olympic flame and rings (centenary of modern Olympic Games).

422 Marie de Bourgogne

1996. Europa. Famous Women. Duchesses of Luxembourg. Multicoloured.

1423 16f. Type **422** 3·25 1·30
1424 25f. Maria-Theresa of Austria 5·50 3·50

423 Handstamp

1996. Bicentenary (1995) of Registration and Property Administration.

1425 **423** 16f. multicoloured 2·40 1·30

424 *Children of different Cultures* (Michele Dockendorf)

1996. Let us Live Together. Multicoloured.

1426 16f. Type **424** 1·60 1·30
1427 16f. *L'Abbraccio* (statue, Marie-Josee Kerschen) (vert) 1·60 1·30

425 Eurasian Badger

1996. Mammals. Multicoloured.

1428 16f. Type **425** 2·40 1·30
1429 20f. Polecat 4·00 1·70
1430 80f. European otter 9·50 6·75

426 *The Birth of Christ* (icon, Eva Mathes)

1996. Christmas.

1431 **426** 16f.+2f. multicoloured 8·00 7·75

1996. National Welfare Fund. Trees (2nd series). As T **416**. Multicoloured.

1432 16f.+2f. Willow (*Salix* sp.) (horiz) 2·40 1·70
1433 16f.+2f. Ash (*Fraxinus excelsior*) 2·40 1·70
1434 20f.+3f. Mountain ash (horiz) 4·75 4·25
1435 32f.+7f. Common beech 8·00 7·75

427 John the Blind

1996. 700th Birth Anniversary of John the Blind (King of Bohemia and Count of Luxembourg).

1436 **427** 32f. multicoloured 4·00 2·50

428 Koerich Church

1997. Tourism. Multicoloured.

1437 16f. Type **428** 2·40 1·30
1438 16f. Servais House, Mersch (horiz) 2·40 1·30

429 Birthplace of Robert Schuman (politician), Luxembourg-Clausen

1997. Anniversaries. Multicoloured.

1439 16f. Type **429** (40th anniversary of Treaties of Rome establishing European Economic Community and European Atomic Energy Community) 2·40 1·30
1440 20f. National Colours forming wing of Mercury (75th anniversary of Belgium–Luxembourg Economic Union) 3·25 1·70

430 'Grand Duchess Charlotte'

1997. 11th World Federation of Rose Societies Congress, Belgium, Mondorf (Luxembourg) and the Netherlands. Roses. Multicoloured.

1441 16f. Type **430** 4·00 1·30
1442 20f. 'The Beautiful Sultana' (33×26 mm) 4·00 2·50
1443 80f. 'In Memory of Jean Soupert' (33×26 mm) 12·00 8·50

431 Badge, Luxembourg Fortress, Shako and Sword

1997. Anniversaries.

1444 **431** 16f. multicoloured 2·40 1·30
1445 - 16f. black, blue and red 2·40 1·30
1446 - 16f. brown, green and pink 2·40 1·30

Designs: As T **431**—No. 1444, T **431** (bicentenary of Grand Ducal Gendarmerie Corps); No. 1445, Cock and rabbit (75th anniversary of Luxembourg Union of Small Domestic Animals Farming Societies). 33×33 mm—No. 1446, Bather and attendant, early 1900s (150th anniversary of Mondorf spa).

432 The Beautiful Melusina

1997. Europa. Tales and Legends. Multicoloured.

1447 16f. Type **432** 4·00 1·30
1448 25f. The Hunter of Hollenfels 5·50 3·50

433 Face on Globe

1997. Juvalux 98 Youth Stamp Exhibition (1st issue). Multicoloured.

1449 16f. Type **433** 3·25 1·70
1450 80f. Postmen (painting, Michel Engels) 9·50 8·50

See also Nos. 1475/**MS**1478.

434 Emblem

1997. Sar-Lor-Lux (Saarland-Lorraine-Luxembourg) European Region.

1451 **434** 16f. multicoloured 2·40 1·30

Stamps in similar designs were issued by France and Germany.

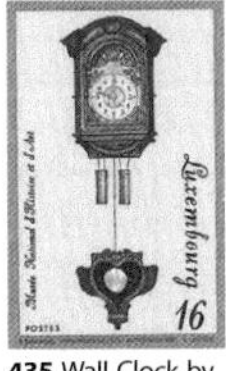

435 Wall Clock by Dominique Nauens, 1816

1997. Clocks. Multicoloured.

1452 16f. Type **435** 3·25 1·30
1453 32f. Astronomical clock by J. Lebrun, 1850 (26×44 mm) 8·00 3·50
1454 80f. Wall clock by Mathias Hebeler, 1815 12·00 6·75

436 *Kalborn Mill* (Jean-Pierre Gleis)

1997. Water Mills. Multicoloured.

1455 16f. Type **436** 3·25 1·10
1456 50f. Interior of Ramelli mill, 1588 (from book *The Water Wheel* by Wilhelm Wolfel) (vert) 6·50 4·25

437 Holy Family

1997. Christmas.

1457 **437** 16f.+2f. multicoloured 6·50 6·00

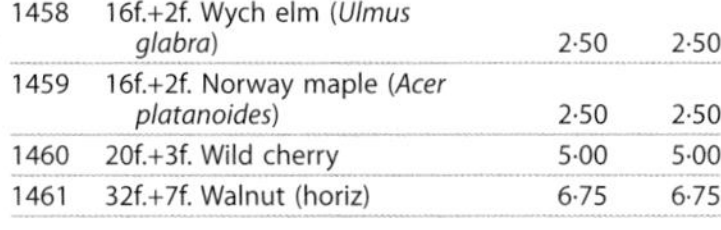

1997. National Welfare Fund. Trees (3rd series). As T **416**. Multicoloured.

1458 16f.+2f. Wych elm (*Ulmus glabra*) 2·50 2·50
1459 16f.+2f. Norway maple (*Acer platanoides*) 2·50 2·50
1460 20f.+3f. Wild cherry 5·00 5·00
1461 32f.+7f. Walnut (horiz) 6·75 6·75

438 Count Henri V

1997. 750th Anniversary of Accession of Henri V, Count of Luxembourg.

1462 **438** 32f. multicoloured 5·00 2·50

439 Rodange Church

1998. Tourism. Multicoloured.

1463 16f. Type **439** 2·50 1·30
1464 16f. Back of local authority building, Hesperange (horiz) 2·50 1·30

440 Cog and '50'

1998. Anniversaries.

1465 **440** 16f. multicoloured 3·50 1·30
1466 - 16f. multicoloured 3·50 1·30
1467 - 20f. multicoloured 3·50 1·70
1468 - 50f. black, red and stone 8·50 4·25

Designs: No. 1465, T **440** (50th anniversary of Independent Luxembourg Trade Union); No. 1466, Festival poster (Rene Wismer) (50th anniversary of Broom Festival, Wiltz); No. 1467, Memorial (death centenary of Jean Antoine Zinnen (composer of National Anthem)); No. 1468, Typewriter keys and page from first issue of *Luxemburger Wort* (150th anniversary of abolition of censorship).

441 Brown Trout

1998. Freshwater Fish. Multicoloured.

1469 16f. Type **441** 5·00 1·30
1470 25f. Bullhead 8·50 4·25
1471 50f. Riffle minnow 10·00 6·00

442 Henri VII and Flags outside Fair Venue, Kirchberg

1998. 700th Anniversary of Granting to Count Henri VII of Right to Hold a Fair. Value indicated by letter.

1472 **442** A (16f.) multicoloured 3·50 1·30

443 Fireworks over Adolphe Bridge (National Day)

1998. Europa. National Festivals. Multicoloured.

1473	16f. Type **443**	6·00	1·30
1474	25f. Stained-glass window and flame (National Remembrance Day)	6·75	3·50

444 Town Postman, 1880

1998. Juvalux '98 Youth Stamp Exhibition (2nd issue). Multicoloured.

1475	16f. Type **444**	3·50	1·30
1476	25f. Letter, 1590 (horiz)	4·25	3·50
1477	50f. Rural postman, 1880	6·00	4·25
MS1478	125×76 mm 16f., 80f. Railway viaduct and city (composite design)	21·00	20·00

445 Masonic Symbols (Paul Moutschen)

1998. 150th Anniversary of St John of Hope Freemason Lodge.

1479	**445**	16f. multicoloured	3·50	1·30

446 Echternach

1998. 1300th Anniversary of Echternach Abbey. Multicoloured.

1480	16f. Type **446**	3·50	1·30
1481	48f. Buildings in Echternach	6·50	4·75
1482	60f. Echternach Abbey	6·75	5·00

447 Spanish Morion (late 16th-century)

1998. Museum Exhibits (3rd series). City of Luxembourg History Museum. Multicoloured.

1483	16f. Type **447**	3·50	1·30
1484	80f. Wayside Cross from Hollerich (1718)	8·50	7·75

448 *Nativity* (altarpiece by Georges Saget, St Mauritius Abbey, Clervaux)

1998. Christmas.

1485	**448**	16f.+2f. multicoloured	6·75	6·50

449 *Bech*

1998. National Welfare Fund (1st series). Villages. 16th-century drawings by Jean Bertels. Multicoloured.

1486	16f.+2f. Type **449**	3·50	2·50
1487	16f.+2f. *Ermes Turf* (now Ermsdorf)	3·50	2·50
1488	20f.+3f. *Itsich* (now Itzig)	5·00	3·50
1489	32f.+7f. *Stein Hem* (now Steinheim)	6·75	8·50

See also Nos. 1510/1513 and 1550/1553.

450 Globe and Jigsaw

1998. 40th Anniversary of North Atlantic Maintenance and Supply Agency.

1490	**450**	36f. multicoloured	6·75	4·25

451 Council Building and Emblem

1999. 50th Anniversary of Council of Europe.

1491	**451**	16f. multicoloured	2·50	1·70

452 Euro Coin and Map

1999. Introduction of the Euro (European currency). Value expressed by letter.

1492	**452**	A (16f.) multicoloured	2·50	1·30

453 Tawny Owl

1999. Owls. Multicoloured.

1493	A (16f.) Type **453**	3·50	1·70
1494	32f. Eagle owl (horiz)	4·25	4·00
1495	60f. Barn owl (horiz)	8·50	8·00

454 Globe and Emblem

1999. 50th Anniversary of NATO.

1496	**454**	80f. multicoloured	8·50	6·75

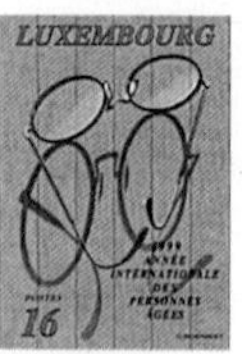
455 Spectacles

1999. International Year of the Elderly.

1497	**455**	16f. multicoloured	2·50	1·30

456 Emblem and Envelopes

1999. 125th Anniversary of Universal Postal Union.

1498	**456**	16f. multicoloured	2·50	1·30

457 Haute-Sure National Park

1999. Europa. Parks and Gardens. Multicoloured.

1499	16f. Type **457**	6·00	1·70
1500	25f. Ardennes-Eifel National Park	6·75	3·50

458 Emblem

1999. Anniversaries. Multicoloured.

1501	16f. Type **458** (75th anniversary of National Federation of Mutual Socieites)	2·50	1·30
1502	32f. Camera and roll of film (50th anniversary of Luxembourg Federation of Amateur Photographers)	4·25	3·50
1503	80f. Gymnasts (centenary of Luxembourg Gymnastics Federation)	10·00	6·75

460 Cars on Motorway

1999. 18th Birthday of Prince Guillaume.

1504	**459**	16f. multicoloured	1·70	1·30

459 Prince Guillaume

1999. Communications of the Future. Multicoloured.

1505	16f. Type **460**	2·50	1·70
1506	20f. Earth and satellite	3·50	3·00
1507	80f. Planets and spacecraft	10·00	8·50

461 A. Mayrisch de Saint-Hubert

1999. 125th Birth Anniversary of Aline Mayrisch de Saint-Hubert (President of Luxembourg Red Cross).

1508	**461**	20f. multicoloured	3·50	1·70

462 Decorated Church Tower

1999. Christmas.

1509	**462**	16f.+2f. multicoloured	5·00	4·25

1999. National Welfare Fund. Villages (2nd series). As T **449**, showing 6th-century drawings by Jean Bertels. Multicoloured.

1510	16f.+2f. *Oswiler* (now Osweiler)	4·25	2·50
1511	16f.+2f. *Bettem Burch* (now Bettembourg)	4·25	2·50
1512	20f.+3f. *Cruchte auf der Alset* (now Cruchten)	5·00	4·75
1513	32f.+7f. *Berchem*	8·50	8·00

463 *Gateway* (sketch by Goethe)

1999. 250th Birth Anniversary of Johann Wolfgang von Goethe (poet and playwright).

1514	**463**	20f. chestnut, cream & brn	3·50	1·70

464 '2000'

2000. New Millennium. Value expressed by letter. Multicoloured. Self-adhesive.

1515	A (16f.) Type **464** (blue streaks emanating from bottom right)	2·50	1·40
1516	A (16f.) Blue streaks emanating from bottom left	2·50	1·40
1517	A (16f.) Blue streaks emanating from top right	2·50	1·40
1518	A (16f.) Blue streaks emanating from top left	2·50	1·40

465 Charles V

2000. 500th Birth Anniversary of Emperor Charles V. Value expressed by letter.

1519	**465**	A (16f.) multicoloured	2·50	1·30

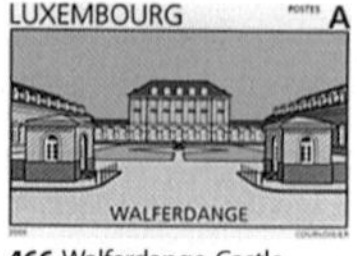
466 Walferdange Castle

2000. Tourism. Value expressed by letter. Multicoloured.

1520	A (16f.) Type **466**	1·70	1·30
1521	A (16f.) Local government offices, Wasserbillig (vert)	1·70	1·30

467 '2000' and Formulae

2000. World Mathematics Year.

1522	**467**	80f. multicoloured	13·00	8·50

468 French Horn

2000. Musical Instruments.

1523	**468**	3f. black and violet	85	45
1524	-	9f. black and green	2·50	1·30
1525	-	12f. black and yellow	1·70	1·30
1526	-	21f. black and pink	2·50	1·70
1527	-	24f. black and blue	4·25	2·10
1528	-	30f. black and pink	3·50	2·50

Designs: 9f. Electric guitar; 12f. Saxophone; 21f. Violin; 24f. Accordion; 30f. Grand piano.

469 Production and Storage Facilities, 1930s (Harry Rabinger)

2000. Centenary (1999) of Esch-sur-Alzette Gas Works.

1535	**469**	18f. multicoloured	3·50	1·30

470 Mallard

2000. Ducks. Multicoloured.

1536	18f. Type **470**	4·25	2·50
1537	24f. Common pochard (vert)	5·00	3·50
1538	30f. Tufted duck (vert)	6·75	4·25

471 Building Europe

2000. Europa.

1539	**471**	21f. multicoloured	4·25	2·10

472 Jean Monnet and Robert Schuman

2000. 50th Anniversary of Schuman Plan (proposal for European Coal and Steel Community).

1540	**472**	21f. black, blue & yellow	3·50	2·10

473 Blast Furnace

2000. 20th Anniversary of Blast Furnace 'B', Esch-Belval.

1541	**473**	A (18f.) multicoloured	4·25	1·30

474 Castle Walls and Tower (Wenzel Walk)

2000. Circular City Walks. Multicoloured.

1542	18f. Type **474**	3·50	1·70
1543	42f. Bridge and tower (Vauban walk)	6·75	5·00

475 Will Kesseler

2000. Swearing in of Prince Henri as Head of State of Grand Duchy of Luxembourg. Multicoloured.

1544	18f. Type **475**	2·50	2·40
MS1545	125×90 mm. 100f. Prince Henri in civilian clothes and Princess Maria	21·00	19·00

476 Prince Henri in Uniform and Princess Maria

2000. Modern Art (1st series). Showing paintings by artist named. Multicoloured.

1546	21f. Type **476**	3·50	1·70
1547	24f. Joseph Probst (vert)	3·50	2·50
1548	36f. Mett Hoffmann	4·25	3·50

See also Nos. 1612/1614.

477 Child before Christmas Tree

2000. Christmas.

1549	**477**	18f.+2f. multicoloured	4·25	4·00

2000. National Welfare Fund. Villages (3rd series). As T **449** showing 16th-century drawings by Jean Bertels. Multicoloured.

1550	18f.+2f. *Lorentzwiller* (now dorentzweiler)	3·50	3·00
1551	21f.+3f. *Coosturf* (now Consdorf)	4·25	3·75
1552	24f.+3f. *Elfingen* (now Elvange)	5·00	4·25
1553	36f.+7f. *Sprenckigen* (now Sprinkange)	6·75	6·50

478 Bestgensmillen Mill, Schifflange

2001. Tourism. Multicoloured.

1554	18f. Type **478**	2·50	1·70
1555	18f. Vineyard, Wormeldange (vert)	2·50	1·70

479 Nik Welter

2001. Writers' Death Anniversaries. Multicoloured.

1556	18f. Type **479** (50th)	2·50	1·70
1557	24f. Andre Gide (50th)	3·50	2·50
1558	30f. Michel Rodange (125th)	4·25	3·50

480 Signatures and Seal

2001. 50th Anniversary of Treaty of Paris.

1559	**480**	21f. multicoloured	3·50	1·70

481 Citroen 2CV Mini-Van

2001. Postal Vehicles. Multicoloured. Self-adhesive.

1560	3f. Type **481**	85	45
1561	18f. Volkswagen Beetle	2·50	1·30

482 Stream, Mullerthal

2001. Europa. Water Resources. Multicoloured. Value expressed by letter (No. 1562) or with face value (No. 1563).

1562	A (18f.) Type **482**	3·50	1·70
1563	21f. Pond and Kaltreis water tower (vert)	4·25	2·50

483 *Mother and Child* (Ger Maas)

2001. Humanitarian Projects. Multicoloured.

1564	18f. Type **483** (humanitarian aid)	3·50	1·70
1565	24f. International Organisation for Migration emblem	5·00	3·00

484 MD Helicopters MD Explorer and Rescuer

2001. Rescue Services. Multicoloured.

1566	18f. Type **484**	3·50	1·70
1567	30f. Divers and rubber dinghy	4·25	3·50
1568	45f. Fire engine and fireman wearing protective clothing	6·75	5·00

DENOMINATION. From No. 1569 Luxembourg stamps are denominated in euros only.

485 Five Cent Coin

2001. Euro Currency. Coins. Multicoloured.

1569	5c. Type **485**	75	70
1570	10c. Ten cent coin	85	75
1571	20c. Twenty cent coin	1·70	85
1572	50c. Fifty cent coin	2·50	1·70
1573	€1 One euro coin	4·25	3·50
1574	€2 Two euro coin	7·75	6·75

486 Grand Duke Henri

2001. Grand Duke Henri.

1575	**486**	1c. indigo, blue and ultramarine	30	25
1576	**486**	3c. olive, green and ultramarine	40	35
1577	**486**	7c. dp blue, blue & red	50	45
1578	**486**	22c. sepia, brown & red	95	85
1579	**486**	25c. lilac and ultramarine	95	85
1580	**486**	30c. dp green, grn & red	1·40	1·30
1581	**486**	45c. dp violet, vio & red	1·70	1·50
1582	**486**	50c. black and ultramarine	1·90	1·70
1583	**486**	52c. brown, buff and red	2·30	2·00
1584	**486**	59c. deep blue, blue and red	2·50	2·20
1585	**486**	60c. black, green and blue	2·50	2·20
1586	**486**	70c. lilac ultramarine	2·75	2·50
1587	**486**	74c. brown, stone and red	2·75	2·50
1588	**486**	80c. agate, green and blue	3·50	3·25
1589	**486**	89c. mauve, brown and red	3·75	3·50
1590	**486**	90c. brown, ochre and ultramarine	3·75	3·50
1591	**486**	€1 blue, azuree and ultramarine	4·00	3·50

Nos. 1592/5 are vacant.

487 Emblem

2001. European Year of Languages. Value expressed by letter.

1596	**487**	A (45c.) multicoloured	1·90	1·70

488 Sun, Wind-powered Generators and Houses (renewable energy)

2001. Environment and Medicine of the Future. Multicoloured.

1597	45c. Type **488**	1·90	1·70
1598	59c. Tyre, tins, bottle and carton (recycling)	2·75	2·50
1599	74c. Microscope and test-tubes (biological research)	3·75	3·50

489 St Nicholas

2001. Christmas.

1600	**489**	45c.+5c. multicoloured	2·75	2·50

490 Squirrel

2001. National Welfare Fund. Animals (1st issue). Multicoloured.

1601	45c.+5c. Type **490**	2·50	2·20
1602	52c.+8c. Wild boar	2·75	2·50
1603	59c.+11c. Hare (vert)	3·25	3·00
1604	89c.+21c. Wood pigeon (vert)	4·75	4·25

See also Nos. 1632/1635 and 1660/1663.

491 Emblem

2001. Kiwanis International (community organisation).

1605	**491**	52c. dp blue, bl & gold	2·75	2·50

492 Snowboarding

2002. Sports. Self-adhesive. Multicoloured.

1606	7c. Type **492**	40	35
1607	7c. Skateboarding	40	35
1608	7c. Inline skating	40	35
1609	45c. BMX biking	2·30	2·00
1610	45c. Beach volleyball	2·30	2·00
1611	45c. Street basketball	2·30	2·00

493 Mortiz Ney

2002. Modern Art (2nd series). Showing works by artist named. Multicoloured.

1612	22c. Type **493**	95	85
1613	45c. Dany Prum (horiz)	1·90	1·70
1614	59c. Christiane Schmit	2·75	2·50

494 Map of Europe and '1977'

2002. Anniversaries. Multicoloured.

1615	45c. Type **494** (25th anniversary of European Court of Auditors)	1·90	1·70
1616	52c. Scales of Justice and map of Europe (50th anniversary of European Communities Court of Justice)	2·75	2·50

495 Tightrope Walker

2002. Europa. The Circus. Multicoloured.

1617	45c. Type **495**	1·90	1·70
1618	52c. Clown juggling	2·75	2·50

496 Emblem

2002. 2002 Tour de France (starting in Luxembourg). Multicoloured.

1619	45c. Type **496**	1·90	1·70
1620	52c. Francois Faber (winner of 1909 Tour de France) (vert)	2·75	2·50
1621	€2.45 *The Champion* (Joseph Kutter) (vert)	10·50	9·25

497 Orchestra on Stage (50th Anniversary of Festival of Wiltz)

2002. Cultural Anniversaries. Value expressed by letter (No. 1622) or face value (No. 1623). Multicoloured.

1622	A (45c.) Type **497**	1·90	1·70
1623	€1.12 Victor Hugo and signature (birth bicentenary)	5·75	5·00

498 Grand Duke William III of Netherlands

2002. 150th Anniversary of First Luxembourg Stamp (1st issue). Sheet 121×164 mm, containing T **498** and similar horiz designs. Multicoloured.

MS1624	45c. Type **498**; 45c. Grand Duke Adolphe; 45c. Grand Duchess Charlotte; 45c. Grand Duke Henri	19·00	17·00

See also Nos. 1630/1631.

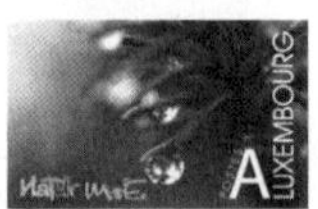

499 Water Droplet on Spruce

2002. Natural History Museum. Multicoloured. Value expressed by letter. Self-adhesive.

1625	A (45c.) Type **499**	1·90	1·70
1626	A (45c.) Mocker swallowtail	1·90	1·70
1627	A (45c.) Houseleek	1·90	1·70
1628	A (45c.) Blackthorn berries	1·90	1·70

500 Emblem

2002. 750th Anniversary of Grevenmacher City Charter.

1629	**500**	74c. multicoloured	2·75	2·50

501 Postmen in Flying Vehicles (Clare Nothumb)

2002. 150th Anniversary of First Luxembourg Stamp (2nd issue). Winning Entries in Stamp Design Competition. (a) With face value.

1630	22c. Type **501**	95	85

(b) Value expressed by letter.

1631	A (45c.) Symbols of communications and flying saucer orbiting planet (Christine Hengen) (horiz)	1·90	1·70

502 Fox

2002. National Welfare Fund. Animals (2nd series). Multicoloured.

1632	45c.+5c. Type **502**	1·90	1·70
1633	52c.+8c. Hedgehog (vert)	2·30	2·00
1634	59c.+11c. Pheasant	2·75	2·40
1635	89c.+21c. Deer (vert)	4·50	4·00

503 Place d'Armes

2002. Christmas.

1636	**503**	45c.+5c. multicoloured	1·90	1·70

No. 1636 was issued in *se-tenant* sheetlets of 12 stamps, the margins of which were impregnated with the scent of cinnamon.

504 Grand Duke Jean and Grand Duchess Josephine-Charlotte

2003. Golden Wedding Anniversary of Grand Duke Jean and Grand Duchess Josephine-Charlotte.

1637	**504**	45c. multicoloured	1·90	1·70

505 Catherine Schleimer-Kill

2003. 30th Death Anniversaries. Multicoloured.

1638	45c. Type **505** (political pioneer)	1·90	1·70
1639	45c. Lou Koster (composer)	1·90	1·70

506 Citeaux Abbey, Differdange

2003. Tourism. Multicoloured.

1640	50c. Type **506**	1·90	1·70
1641	€1 Mamer Castle	3·75	3·50
1642	€2.50 St Joseph Church, Esch-sur-Alzette (vert)	9·50	8·50

507 Pamphlets and Compact Discs

2003. 50th Anniversary of *Official Journal of European Communities* (daily publication of official reports).

1643	**507**	52c. multicoloured	2·75	2·50

508 Head and Symbols

2003. 400th Anniversary of the Athenee (secondary school), Luxembourg.

1644	**508**	45c. multicoloured	1·90	1·70

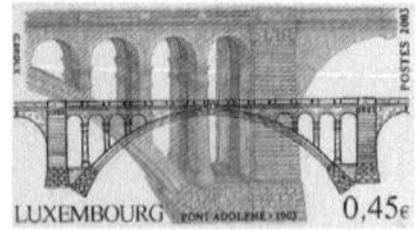

509 1952 National Lottery Poster (Roger Gerson)

2003. Europa. Poster Art. Multicoloured.

1645	45c. Type **509**	1·90	1·70
1646	52c. Tiger (1924 Commercial Fair poster) (Auguste Tremont)	2·75	2·50

510 Adolphe Bridge

2003. Bridges and Viaducts. Multicoloured.

1647	45c. Type **510** (centenary)	1·90	1·70
1648	59c. Stierchen bridge (14th-century) (38×28 mm)	2·30	2·00
1649	89c. Victor Bodson bridge (Hesperange viaduct) (38×28 mm)	3·50	3·00

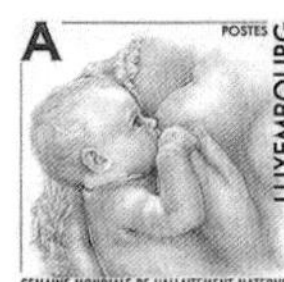

511 Woman Hoeing

2003. 75th Anniversary of Gaart an Heem (gardening association). Multicoloured.

1650	25c. Type **511**	95	85
1651	A (45c.) Woman holding rake	1·90	1·70
1652	€2 Children	7·50	6·75

512 Baby at Breast

2003. Breastfeeding Campaign.

1653	**512**	A (45c.) brown, chestnut and black	1·90	1·70

513 Light Bulb

2003. 75th Anniversary of Electricity.

1654	**513**	A (45c.) multicoloured	1·90	1·70

514 Engineering Steel Sheet Piles

2003. Made in Luxembourg. Multicoloured.

1655	60c. Type **514**	2·30	2·00
1656	70c. Medical valve	2·75	2·40
1657	80c. Technician and polyester film	3·00	2·75

515 Church and Cloud containing Buildings

2003. Christmas. Multicoloured.

1658	50c.+5c. Type **515**	2·75	2·50
1659	50c.+5c. Child, church and Christmas tree	2·75	2·50

516 Roe-deer

2003. National Welfare Fund. Animals (3rd series). Multicoloured.

1660	50c.+5c. Type **516**	2·10	1·90
1661	60c.+10c. Raccoon (horiz)	2·75	2·40
1662	70c.+10c. Weasel	3·00	2·75
1663	€1 +25c. Goshawk (horiz)	4·75	4·25

517 *Cantharellus tubaeformis*

2004. Fungi. Multicoloured. Self-adhesive.

1664	10c. Type **517**	55	50
1665	10c. *Ramaria flava*	55	50
1666	10c. *Stropharia cynea*	55	50
1667	50c. *Helvella lacunose*	2·10	1·90
1668	50c. *Anthurus archeri*	2·10	1·90
1669	50c. *Clitopilus prunulus*	2·10	1·90

518 Annual Street Market, Luxembourg-Ville

2004. Anniversaries. Multicoloured.

1670	50c. Type **518** (75th anniversary)	1·90	1·70
1671	50c. Haberdashery (centenary of Esch-sur-Alzette Commercial Union)	1·90	1·70

519 Edward Steichen

2004. Birth Anniversaries. Multicoloured.

1672	**519**	50c. lilac, brown and black	2·30	2·00
1673	-	70c. blue, buff and black	3·00	2·75

Designs: 50c. T **519** (photographer) (125th); 70c. Hugo Gernsback (science fiction writer) (120th and centenary of his emigration to USA).

520 Stylised Figures

2004. European Elections.

1674	**520**	50c. multicoloured	2·75	2·50

521 Hikers on Bridge, Mullerthal

2004. Europa. Holidays. Multicoloured.

1675	50c. Type **521**	2·30	2·00
1676	60c. Camp site, Bourscheid-Beach	2·50	2·20

522 Runners carrying Olympic Flame (A. Bilska)

2004. Sport. Winning Entries in Children's Drawing Competition. Multicoloured.

1677	50c. Type **522** (Olympic Games, Athens, 2004)	2·30	2·00
1678	60c. Basketball (L. Eyschen) (European Year of Education through Sport)	2·50	2·20

523 Building and Anniversary Emblem

2004. 50th Anniversary of European School, Luxembourg.

1679	**523**	70c. multicoloured	3·50	3·00

524 Breads and Beer

2004. Made in Luxembourg. Food. Multicoloured.

1680	35c. Type **524**	1·30	1·20
1681	60c. Meat products	2·30	2·00
1682	70c. Dairy products	2·75	2·40

525 Bull and Bear

2004. 75th Anniversary of Luxembourg Stock Exchange.

1683	**525**	50c. multicoloured	2·10	1·70

526 Museum Building (Marc Angel)

2004. National Museum of History and Art. Multicoloured.

1684	50c. Type **526**	2·10	1·70
1685	€1.10 *Young Woman with a Fan* (Luigi Rubio)	4·50	3·75
1686	€3 *Charity* (Lucas Cranach)	12·50	10·00

527 Carol Singers

2004. Christmas.

1687	**527**	50c.+5c. multicoloured	3·25	2·50

528 Skiing

2004. Sport (1st series). Multicoloured.

1688	50c.+5c. Type **528**	2·30	1·90
1689	60c.+10c. Running (vert)	3·00	2·40
1690	70c.+10c. Swimming	3·25	2·75
1691	€1+25c. Football (vert)	5·25	4·25

See also Nos. 1729/1732.

529 Tank, Soldiers and Liberation Monument, Schumannseck (Carlo Losch)

2004. Liberation of Luxembourg (1944–1945).

1692	**529**	70c. multicoloured	3·25	2·50

530 Building

2005. Luxembourg's Presidency of European Parliament. Value expressed by letter. Multicoloured. Self-adhesive.

1693	A (50c.) Type **530**	2·75	2·20
1694	A (50c.) Roman arch, Echternach Basilica	2·75	2·20
1695	A (50c.) Moselle river, Remich	2·75	2·20
1696	A (50c.) Riveted iron plate	2·75	2·20

Nos. 1693/1696 were for use on first class mail within Luxembourg.

531 *Woman* (painting) (A. Huberty)

2005. 150th Anniversary of Ettelbruck Neuro-Psychiatric Medical Centre.

1697	**531**	50c. multicoloured	2·30	1·90

532 Emblem

2005. Centenary of Rotary International.

1698	**532**	50c. multicoloured	2·10	1·70

533 Shoe Factory, Kayl-Tetange

2005. Tourism (1st series). Multicoloured.

1699	50c. Type **533**	2·10	1·70
1700	60c. Rooftops (75th anniversary of National Tourism Office)	2·50	2·00
1701	€1 St Eloi (statue), Rodange	4·25	3·50

See also Nos. 1721/1724 and 1737/1738.

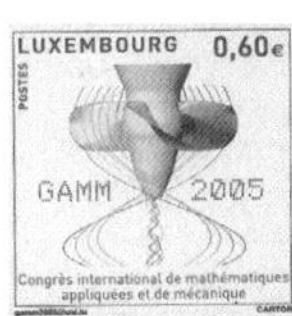

534 Turbine Air-stream Diagram

2005. GAMM 2005 International Congress of Applied Mathematics and Mechanics.

1702	**534**	60c. multicoloured	2·50	2·00

535 Parliament Building

2005. 50th Anniversary of Benelux Parliament.

1703	**535**	60c. multicoloured	2·50	2·00

536 Fingers peeling back Label

2005. Business Stamps. Multicoloured, background colour given. Self-adhesive.

1704	**536**	25c. brown	1·20	90
1705	**536**	25c. red	1·20	90
1706	**536**	25c. salmon	1·20	90
1707	**536**	25c. yellow	1·20	90
1708	**536**	50c. bronze green	2·30	1·80
1709	**536**	50c. light green	2·30	1·80
1710	**536**	50c. bright green	2·30	1·80
1711	**536**	50c. apple green	2·30	1·80

537 Facade

2005. Opening of Grand Duchess Josephine-Charlotte Concert Hall (the Philharmonie).

1712	**537**	50c. multicoloured	2·30	1·80

538 'judd mat gaardebounen' (pork and beans)

2005. Europa. Gastronomy. Multicoloured.

1713	50c. Type **538**	2·30	1·80
1714	60c. 'feierstengszalot' (diced beef and vinaigrette)	3·50	2·75

539 Rail Car CVE 357, De Jhangeli Narrow Guage Railway

2005. Railways. Multicoloured.

1715	50c. Type **539**	2·30	1·80
1716	60c. Locomotive AL-T3	2·75	2·20
1717	€2.50 Rail car PH 408	12·50	10·00

540 *Papilio machaon*

2005. Butterflies. Multicoloured.

1718	35c. Type **540**	1·60	1·30
1719	70c. *Argynnis paphia*(vert)	3·25	2·50
1720	€1.80 *Lysandra coridon*	8·25	6·50

541 Schist, Eislek

2005. Tourism (2nd issue). Minerals. Value expressed by letter. Multicoloured. Self-adhesive.

1721	A (50c.) Type **541**	2·30	1·80
1722	A (50c.) Iron ore	2·30	1·80
1723	A (50c.) Sandstone	2·30	1·80
1724	A (50c.) Conglomerate, Folschette	2·30	1·80

Nos. 1721/1724 were for use on first class mail within Luxembourg.

542 Jean Pierre Pescatore

2005. Anniversaries.

1725	**542**	50c. violet and grey	2·30	1·80
1726	-	90c. deep brown, brown and bistre brown	4·25	3·25
1727	-	€1 bistre brown and deep brown (vert)	4·50	3·50

Designs: 50c. T **542** (philanthropist) (150th death); 90c. Marcel Reuland (writer) (birth centenary); €1 Marie-Henriette Steil (writer) (75th death).

543 Shoppers

2005. Christmas.

1728	**543**	50c.+5c. multicoloured	2·50	2·00

544 Ice Skating

2005. Sport (2nd series). Multicoloured.

1729	50c.+5c. Type **544**	2·50	2·00
1730	60c.+10c. Basketball	3·75	3·00
1731	90c.+10c. Judo	4·50	3·50
1732	€1+25c. Tennis	5·75	4·50

545 Guide Dog

2005. Guide Dogs for the Blind.

1733	**545**	70c. ultramarine and yellow	3·25	2·50

No. 1733 was embossed with the value in Braille.

546 Grand Duke and Duchess

2006. 25th Wedding Anniversary of Grand Duke Henri and Grand Duchess Maria Teresa. Multicoloured.

1734	50c. Type **546**	2·30	1·80
MS1735	74×102 mm. €2.50 As No. 1734 (30×40 mm.)	11·50	11·00

547 Hands

2006. Blood Donation Campaign.

1736	**547**	50c. multicoloured	2·30	1·80

548 Pigeon Tower, Birelerhaff, Sandweiler

2006. Tourism (3rd series). Multicoloured.

1737	50c. Type **548**	2·30	1·80
1738	50c. Parc Merveilleux, Bettembourg (50th anniversary) (horiz)	2·30	1·80

549 Electric Locomotive

2006. 50th Anniversary of Electrification of Luxembourg Rail Network. Multicoloured.

1739	50c. Type **549**	2·30	1·80
1740	70c. Train on viaduct	3·25	2·50
1741	€1 Repairs to overhead cables (vert)	4·50	3·50

550 '2006'

2006. Centenary of Esch-sur-Alzette (town).

1742	**550**	50c. multicoloured	2·30	1·80

551 Hands forming Heart-shape (Anne Marie Simon)

2006. Europa. Integration. Winning entries in MMS Photograph Competition. Multicoloured.

1743	50c. Type **551**	2·30	1·80
1744	70c. Hands holding globe (Tamara da Silva)	3·50	2·75

552 Early Match (centenary of first Luxembourg football club)

2006. Football. Multicoloured.

1745	50c. Type **552**	2·30	1·80
1746	90c. Emblem and football (World Cup Football Championship, Germany)	4·25	3·25

553 'meng.post.lu'

2006. Personal Stamp.

1747	**553**	(50c.) multicoloured A	2·30	1·80

No. 1747 was for use on standard first class mail within Luxembourg.

554 Building

2006. 150th Anniversary of State Council.

1748	**554**	50c. grey, red and slate	2·30	1·80

555 Savings Bank Building

2006. 150th Anniversary of Financial Centre.

1749	555	50c. grey, ultramarine and vermilion	2·30	1·80
1750	-	50c. ultramarine and vermilion	2·30	1·80

Designs: No. 1749 T **555**; No. 1750, Dexia-BIL building.

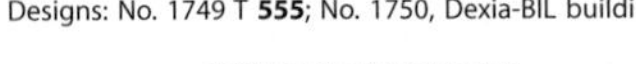

556 Figure holding Stop Drugs Sign (Victor Tesch)

2006. Drugs are not for me Campaign. Winning Designs in Children's Drawing Competition. Multicoloured.

1751	50c. Type **556**	2·30	1·80
1752	€1 Ashtray containing vegetables (Paul Hoffmann) (vert)	4·50	3·50

557 Chess Pieces

2006. 75th Anniversary of National Chess Federation.

1753	557	90c. orange, light green and green	4·25	3·25

558 Yolande Tower, Marienthal

2006. Christmas. Marienthal Cultural Heritage.

1754	558	50c.+5c. multicoloured	2·50	2·00

559 Grand Auditorium, Luxembourg Music Conservatory

2006. Pipe Organs. Designs showing pipe organs. Multicoloured.

1755	50c.+5c. Type **559**	2·50	2·00
1756	70c.+10c. Bridel	3·75	3·00
1757	90c.+10c. Mondercange Parish Church	4·50	3·50
1758	€1+25c. Luxembourg Grund	5·75	4·50

560 Flowers

2006. 75th Anniversary of Horticultural Association. Multicoloured.

1759	70c. Type **560**	3·25	2·50
1760	70c. Vegetables	3·25	2·50

Nos. 1759/1760 were issued together, *se-tenant*, forming a composite design.

561 Men with Antlered Deer Heads

2007. Luxembourg: European Capital of Culture 2007. Multicoloured. Self-adhesive.

1761	A (50c.) Type **561**	2·30	1·80
1762	A (50c.) Antlered man and deer	2·30	1·80
1763	A (50c.) Antlered men with arm raised	2·30	1·80
1764	A (50c.) Base of chair, legs and antlered man with raised arm	2·30	1·80

562 'Postes' **563** '€0,25'

2007. Self-adhesive.

1765	562	25c. multicoloured	1·20	90
1766	562	25c. multicoloured	1·20	90
1767	563	25c. multicoloured	1·20	90
1768	563	25c. multicoloured	1·20	90
1769	562	50c. multicoloured	2·30	1·80
1770	562	50c. multicoloured	2·30	1·80
1771	563	50c. multicoloured	2·30	1·80
1772	563	50c. multicoloured	2·30	1·80

564 Breakdown Truck

2007. 75th Anniversary of Automobile Club du Luxembourg (ACL).

1773	564	50c. multicoloured	2·30	1·80

565 Girl holding Bubble

2007. 75th Anniversary of Caritas Luxembourg Foundation.

1774	565	50c. multicoloured	2·30	1·80

566 Signatories

2007. 50th Anniversary of Treaty of Rome. Multicoloured.

1775	70c. Type **566**	3·25	2·50
1776	€1 List of signatories	4·50	3·50

567 Early and Modern Buildings, Ettelbreck

2007. Centenary of 'Law of 4 August 1907' conferring Town Status on Ettelbreck, Deifferdang, Diddeleng and Remeleng. Multicoloured.

1777	50c. Type **567**	2·30	1·80
1778	50c. Early buildings and gardens, Deifferdang	2·30	1·80
1779	50c. Early buildings and tower, Diddeleng	2·30	1·80
1780	50c. Early buildings, miner and modern machinery, Remeleng	2·30	1·80

568 Campsite (Jenny Spielmann)

2007. Europa. Centenary of Scouting. Winning designs in Children's Painting Competition. Multicoloured.

1781	50c. Type **568**	2·30	1·80
1782	70c. Children and globe (Jean Heuschling)	3·25	2·50

569 Musician (Rockhal)

2007. Cultural Centres. Multicoloured.

1783	50c. Type **569**	2·30	1·80
1784	70c. Grand Duke Jean Museum of Modern Art	3·25	2·50
1785	€1 Neumunster Abbey Meeting Centre	4·50	3·50

570 Letters (Stephanie Rausch)

2007. Luxembourg and Greater Regions Joint European Capital of Culture 2007. Winning Entry in Stamp Design Competition (1786).

1786	50c. Type **570**	2·30	1·80
1787	70c. Rotunda, Luxembourg Train Station	3·25	2·50

Stamps of a similar design were issued by Belgium.

571 Clio (history) and Urania (astronomy)

2007. Roman Mosaic, Vichten. Nine Muses. Sheet 111×111 mm containing T **571** and similar multicoloured designs showing muses.

MS1788	50c. Type **571**; 50c. Polyhymnia (choral singing) and Erato (lyrical poetry); 50c. Terpsichore (dance) and Melpomene (tragedy); 50c. Thalia (comedy) and Euterpe (music); €1 Calliope (epic poetry) and Homer (diamond shaped) (55×55 mm)	14·00	13·50

572 Luxembourg House, Sibiu

2007. Sibiu Joint European Capital of Culture 2007.

1789	572	70c. multicoloured	3·25	2·50

Stamps of a similar design were issued by Romania.

573 Soldier and Local Inhabitant

2007. Peace Keeping Missions of Luxembourg Army.

1790	573	70c. multicoloured	3·25	2·50

574 Robin

2007. Christmas.

1791	574	50c.+5c. multicoloured	2·50	2·00

575 Niederwilz Church

2007. Pipe Organs. Multicoloured.

1792	50c.+5c. Type **575**	2·50	2·00
1793	70c.+10c. Sandweiler (horiz)	3·75	3·00
1794	90c.+10c. St Joseph Church, Esch-sur-Alzette (horiz)	4·50	3·50
1795	€1+25c. Echternach Basilica	5·75	4·50

576 Dam and Reservoir (left)

2007. 50th Anniversary of Esch-sur-Sure Dam. Self-adhesive. Multicoloured.

1796	70c. Type **576**	3·25	2·50
1797	70c. Reservoir (right)	3·25	2·50

Nos. 1796/1797 were issued together, *se-tenant*, a composite design of the reservoir and environs.

577 St Willibrord

2008. 1350th Birth Anniversary of St Willibrord.

1798	577	50c. multicoloured	2·30	1·80

578 Orchestra

2008. 75th Anniversary of Philharmonic Orchestra. 50th Death Anniversary of Henri Pensis (composer). Multicoloured.

1799	50c. Type **578**	2·30	1·80
1800	70c. Henri Pensis	3·25	2·50

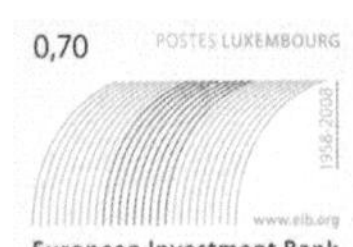

579 Emblem

2008. 50th Anniversary of European Investment Bank.

1801	579	70c. ultramarine and silver	3·25	2·50

580 Stars and 'Eurotower' (New headquarters of ECB) (designed by COOP HIMMELB(L)AU)

2008. Tenth Anniversary of Eurosysteme (unitary system of European Central Bank and EU members using the euro).

1802	580	€1 multicoloured	4·50	3·50

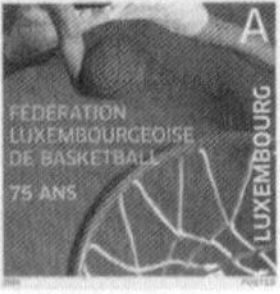

581 Ball and Basket

2008. Sport 2008. Multicoloured.

1803	A (50c.) Type **581** (75th anniversary of National Basketball Federation)	2·30	1·80
1804	A (50c.) Football and player's foot (centenary of National Football Federation)	2·30	1·80

582 10th-century Church, Rindschleiden

2008. Tourism. Multicoloured.

1805	A (50c.) Type **582**	2·30	1·80
1806	A (50c.) Leudelange (150th anniversary) (horiz)	2·30	1·80
1807	A (50c.) Diekirch (125th anniversary) (horiz)	2·30	1·80

583 Envelope containing Rainbow

2008. Europa. The Letter. Multicoloured.

1808	50c. Type **583**	2·30	1·80
1809	70c. Envelope with wings	3·25	2·50

584 Emblems

2008. Olympic Games, Beijing.

1810	**584**	70c. multicoloured	3·25	2·50

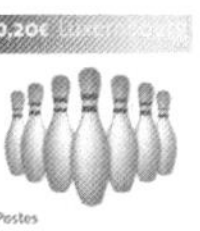
585 Skittles

2008. Happy. Multicoloured. Self-adhesive.

1811	20c. Type **585**	90	70
1811a	20c. As Type **585**	90	70
1812	20c. Parcel	90	70
1812a	20c. As No. 1812	90	70
1813	20c. Sweets	90	70
1813a	20c. As No. 1813	90	70
1814	A (50c.) Dice	2·30	1·80
1814a	A (50c.) As No. 1814	2·30	1·80
1815	A (50c.) Drum	2·30	1·80
1815a	A (50c.) As No. 1815	2·30	1·80
1816	A (50c.) Four leafed clover	2·30	1·80
1816a	A (50c.) As No. 1816	2·30	1·80

586 Symbols of Agriculture

2008. Anniversaries. Multicoloured.

1817	A (50c.) Type **586** (125th anniversary of Agricultural College, Ettelbruck)	2·30	1·80
1818	A (50c.) Stylised flower (centenary of Ligue Medico-Sociale (medical and social league))	2·30	1·80

587 Symbols of Education and Culture

2008. Centenaries. Multicoloured.

1819	A (50c.) Type **587** (Volleksbildungsbewegung (cultural and educational association))	2·30	1·80
1820	A (50c.) Dog and cat (centenary of Letzebuerger Deiereschutliga (protection of animals association))	2·30	1·80

588 Flags as '50'

2008. 50th Anniversary of NAMSA (NATO Maintenance and Supply Agency).

1821	**588**	70c. multicoloured	3·25	2·50

589 Town, River and Bridge (A. Wainer)

2008. Greetings from Luxembourg. Winning Designs in Children's Drawing Competition. Multicoloured.

1822	70c. Type **589**	3·25	2·50
1823	€1 Bridge and valley (S. Rauschenberger)	4·50	3·50

590 'ATR'

591 'A'

2008. Self-adhesive. Multicoloured.

1824	(25c.) Type **590**	1·40	1·10
1825	(25c.) ATR at top left (purple)	1·40	1·10
1826	(25c.) ATR at bottom left (green)	1·40	1·10
1827	(25c.) ATR at top right (red)	1·40	1·10
1828	A (50c.) Type **591**	2·75	2·10
1829	A (50c.) A top left	2·75	2·10
1830	A (50c.) A bottom right	2·75	2·10
1831	A (50c.) A top right	2·75	2·10

592 Buck

2008. Christmas.

1832	**592**	50c.+5c. multicoloured	3·00	2·30

593 Junglinster

2008. Pipe Organs. Multicoloured.

1833	50c.+5c. Type **593**	3·00	2·30
1834	70c.+10c. Mondorf-les-Bains (horiz)	4·25	3·25
1835	90c.+10c. Vianden	5·50	4·25
1836	€1+25c. Cathedral	6·75	5·25

594 Building

2008. Court of Justice of the European Communities.

1837	**594**	70c. multicoloured	3·75	3·00

595 Coronation

2008. 700th Death Anniversary (2009) of Henry VII.

1838	**595**	€1 multicoloured	5·50	4·25

596 Fire Appliance

2009. Firefighters. Multicoloured.

1839	20c. Type **596**	1·10	85
1840	A (50c.) Firefighter carrying child	2·75	2·10
1841	€2 Early fire appliance	11·00	8·50

597 Emblem

2009. Tenth Anniversary of the Euro.

1842	**597**	A (50c.) multicoloured	3·25	2·50

598 CGFP (General Confederation of Civil Service) Emblem

2009. Trade Union Centenaries. Multicoloured.

1843	A (50c.) Type **598**	3·25	2·50
1844	A (50c.) FNCTTFEL (National Federation of Railway Workers, Transport Workers and Employees) emblem	3·25	2·50
1845	50c. Postman (Postman's Federation)	3·25	2·50

599 Aircraft and Air Balloon

2009. Centenary of Areo-Club Luxembourgeois. Multicoloured.

1846	50c. Type **599**	3·25	2·50
1847	50c. Air balloon and aircraft (right)	3·25	2·50
1848	90c. Airport	5·75	4·75

Nos. 1846/1847 were printed together, *se-tenant*, forming a composite design.

600 Emblem

2009. European Parliamentary Elections.

1849	**600**	50c. multicoloured	3·25	2·50

601 Researcher

2009. Tenth Anniversary of National Research Fund.

1850	**601**	A (50c.) multicoloured	3·25	2·50

602 Children

2009. 125th Anniversary of Children's Houses.

1851	**602**	A (50c.) multicoloured	3·25	2·50

603 Shooting Star

2009. Europa. Astronomy. Multicoloured.

1852	50c. Type **603**	3·25	2·50
1853	70c. Galileo and satellite	4·50	3·75

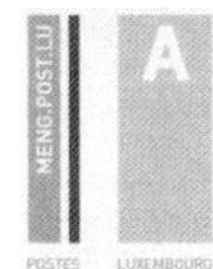
604 Red Line

2009. Personalised Stamps. New Designs for www.meng.post.lu.

1854	A (50c.) deep rose-red and grey	3·25	2·50
1855	A (70c.) bright blue and grey	4·50	3·75

Designs: (50c.) T **604**: (70c.) Blue line

No. 1854 was for use on domestic mail and No. 1855 was for use on mail within Europe.

605 Foni Tissen (artist) (birth centenary)

2009. Personalities. Multicoloured.

1856	70c. Type **605**	4·50	3·75
1857	90c. Charles Bernhoeft (photographer) (150th birth anniversary)	5·75	4·75
1858	€1 Henri Tudor (electrical engineer) (150th birth anniversary)	6·50	5·25

606 1934 5f. Stamp (As T **47**)

2009. 75th Anniversary of FSPL (federation of philatelic societies). Sheet 120×80 mm containing T **606** and similar horiz design. Multicoloured.

MS1859 50c. Type **606**; 70c. Gateway of the Three Towers	8·00	7·75

607 Modern Electric Locomotive

2009. 150th Anniversary of Railways. Multicoloured.

1860	50c. Type **607**	3·25	2·50
1861	€1 Electric goods train	6·50	5·25
1862	€3 Early steam locomotive	19·00	16·00

608 Vanden Castle

2009. SEPAC (small European mail services).

1863	**608**	70c. multicoloured	4·50	3·75

609 Louis Braille and Fingerprint

2009. Birth Bicentenary of Louis Braille (inventor of Braille writing for the blind).

1864	**609**	90c. multicoloured	5·75	4·75

No. 1864 is embossed with Braille letters.

610 Johannes Gutenberg (inventor of movable type printing)

2009. Communication. From Gutenberg to the Internet. Multicoloured.

1865	50c. Type **610**	3·25	2·50
1866	70c. @	4·50	3·75

611 Fox decorating Tree

2009. Christmas.

1867	**611**	50c.+5c. multicoloured	3·50	2·75

612 Philharmonie

2009. Pipe Organs. Designs showing pipe organs. Multicoloured.

1868	50c.+5c. Type **612**	3·50	2·75
1869	70c.+10c. Dudelange	5·00	4·25
1870	90c.+10c. Nommern	6·50	5·25
1871	€1+25c. Heiderscheid	8·00	6·50

613 Grand Duke Henri

2010. Tenth Anniversary of Accession of Grand Duke Henri. 25th Anniversary Anniv of Grand Duchess Charlotte. Multicoloured.

1872	50c. Type **613**	3·25	2·50
1873	€1 Grand Duchess Charlotte	6·50	5·25

614 Schengen Monument

2010. 25th Anniversary of Schengen Accord (setting area of free movement between countries).

1874	**614**	70c. multicoloured	4·50	3·75

615 Septfontaines Castles

2010. Tourism. Eisch Valley. Value expressed by letter. Multicoloured. Self-adhesive.

1875	(70c.) Type **615**	4·50	3·75
1876	(70c.) Hollenfels	4·50	3·75

The two stamps and margins form a composite design

616 *Arnica montana*

2010. International Year of Biodiversity. Countdown 2010 (conservation and restoration project). Multicoloured.

1877	70c. Type **616**	4·50	3·75
1878	€1 Freshwater pearl mussel (inscr 'Moule perliere')	6·50	5·25

617 Luxembourg Pavillion

2010. World Expo 2010, Shanghai, China.

1879	**617**	90c. multicoloured	5·75	4·75

618 Grand Duke Henri and Grand Duchess Maria Teresa

2010. The Grand Ducal Family. Sheet 200×138 mm.

MS1880	**681**	€3 multicoloured	22·00	21·00

619 Boy and Dragon reading

2010. Europa. Multicoloured.

1881	50c. Type **619**	3·25	2·50
1882	70c. Girl riding book lassoing horse as book	4·50	3·75

620 Old Town

2010. Philalux 2011 International Stamp Exhibition. Multicoloured.

MS1883 50c. Type **620**; 70c. Red Bridge (Grand Duchess Charlotte Bridge) and skyscrapers; €3 New buildings (60×38 mm) 35·00 34·00

621 Motorcycling

2010. Leasure and Liberty. Multicoloured.

1884	A (60c.) Type **621**	3·25	2·50
1885	A (85c.) Camping	4·50	3·75

No. l884 was for use on mail within Luxembourg and No. 1885 was for use on mail within Europe

622 Bernie

2010. Cartoons. Multicoloured.

MS1886 A (60c.)×5, Type **622**; Police Chief Harespel; Leonie Lamesch (vert); Superjhemp; Leandre Schrobiltgen 22·00 21·00

623 John of Luxembourg and Elisabeth of Bohemia

2010. 700th Anniversary of Accession of House of Luxembourg to Czech Throne.

1887	**623**	70c. multicoloured	4·50	3·75

A stamp of a similar design was issued by Czech Republic

624 Grand-Duc Adolphe de Luxembourg

2010. Roses. Multicoloured.

1888	A (60c.) Type **624**	3·75	3·00
1889	A (60c.) Bagatelle (white single)	3·75	3·00
1890	A (60c.) Bordeaux (small pink double)	3·75	3·00
1891	A (60c.) Duc de Constantine (pink, three blooms)	3·75	3·00
1892	A (60c.) Prince Jean de Luxembourg (double white)	3·75	3·00
1893	A (60c.) Clothilde Soupert (double apricot)	3·75	3·00
1894	A (60c.) Mrs E G Hill (large bright pink)	3·75	3·00
1895	A (60c.) Pierre Watine (pale pink large bloom)	3·75	3·00
1896	A (60c.) Souvenir de Maria de Zayas (rich pink)	3·75	3·00
1897	A (60c.) Yvan Misson (pale pink two blooms)	3·75	3·00

625 Symbols of Education (fight against poverty in developing countries) (Timothy Clement)

2010. European Year of Fight against Poverty and Social Exclusion. Multicoloured.

1898	A (60c.) Type **625**	3·75	3·00
1899	A (85c.) Offering tools to work (fight against poverty in industrialised countries) (Cinthya Goncalves Guerriro)	5·50	4·50

626 Anne Beffort (educationalist and writer)

2010. Personalities. Multicoloured.

1900	70c. Type **626**	4·50	3·75
1901	90c. Duc de Constantine (rose) and Jean Soupert (rose breeder)	5·75	4·75
1902	€1 Nicolas Frantz (cyclist)	6·50	5·25

627 Liner and Yacht

2010. Ships and Navigation. Multicoloured.

1903	A (60c.) Type **627**	6·50	5·25
1904	A (60c.) Yacht and container ship	6·50	5·25

Nos. 1903/1904 were printed, *se-tenant*, forming a composite design

628 Boy and Dog Sledding

2010. Christmas

1905	**628**	60c.+5c. multicoloured	4·25	3·50

629 Farrier

2010. Trades of Yesteryear. Multicoloured.

1906	60c.+5c. Type **629**	4·25	3·50
1907	85c.+10c. Basket weaver	6·00	5·00
1908	€1.10+10c. Knife grinder (horiz)	7·75	6·25
1909	€1.20+25c. Cooper (horiz)	9·25	7·50

See also Nos. 1935/1938, 1958/1961 and 1991/1994.

630 Hands grasping Arms

2011. European Year of Volunteering.

1910	**630**	A (60c.) multicoloured	3·75	3·00

631 Bowlers, Pins and Alley

2011. 50th Anniversary of Fédération luxembourgeoise des Quilleurs (nine pin bowlers).

1911	**631**	60c. multicoloured	3·75	3·00

632 Clock Tower and Perforated Edges

2011. 75th Anniversary of 'Journée du Timbre' (Stamp Day).

1912	**632**	60c. multicoloured	3·75	3·00

633 Figures with Arms raised, Pen and 'sign'

2011. 50th Anniversary of Amnesty International.

1913	**633**	60c. multicoloured	3·75	3·00

634 Prince Guillaume

2011. House of Luxembourg Dynasty. Multicoloured.

1914	85c. Type **634**	5·75	4·75
1915	€1.10 Grand Duke Jean	7·00	5·75

635 Sun draped with Grapes holding Wine Glass and Bottle

2011. Centenary of Wënzerverband (wine growers federation) (60c.) or 20th Anniversary of Appellation contrôlée Crémant de Luxembourg (85c.). Multicoloured.

1916	60c. Type **635**	3·75	3·00
1917	85c. Cork and wire	5·50	4·50

636 Girl blowing Bubbles

2011. Personalised Stamps. Multicoloured.

1918	60c. Type **636**	3·75	3·00
1919	85c. Boy dozing (vert)	5·50	4·50

637 Deciduous Forest

2011. Europa. Multicoloured.

1920	60c. Type **637**	3·75	3·00
1921	85c. Wooded valley	5·50	4·50

638 Maloo

2011. *De leschte Ritter* Cartoon created by Lucien Czuga and illustrated by Andy "ND!" Genen. Multicoloured.

MS1922 A (60c.)×4, Type **638**; Jean, The Last Knight (horiz); Pedro (horiz); Pixel the Galago 16·00 15·00

639 AIDS Ribbon as Blood Flow

2011. 30th Anniversary of Discovery of AIDS.
1923 **639** 60c. multicoloured 3·75 3·00

640 Emblem and Stars

2011. 50th Anniversary of Luxembourg Consumers Union.
1924 **640** 60c. multicoloured 3·75 3·00

641 Buildings and Walkway

2011. Cercle Cité, Luxembourg.
1925 **641** A (60c.) multicoloured 3·75 3·00

642 Franz Liszt

2011. Birth Bicentenary of Franz Liszt (composers).
1926 **642** 85c. multicoloured 5·50 4·50

643 Chemin de la Corniche

2011. SEPAC (small European mail services).
1927 **643** 85c. multicoloured 5·50 4·50

644 Globe and Chip

2011. Centenary of Comptes Chèques Postaux (CCP) (Postchèque) Service.
1928 **644** 60c. multicoloured 3·75 3·00

645 Christmas Table

2011. Christmas.
1929 **645** 60c. multicoloured 4·25 3·50

647 Scarf

2011. Cultural Heritage. UNESCO Intangible Representation of Humanity. Dancing Procession of Echternach. Multicoloured.
MS1934 60c. Type **647**; 85c. Scarf, right 9·50 9·00

2011. Trades of Yesteryear. Multicoloured.
1935 60c. +5c. Joiner 4·25 3·50
1936 85c. +10c. Potter 6·00 5·00
1937 €1.10 +10c. Stonemason (horiz) 7·75 6·25
1938 €1.20 +25c. Printer (horiz) 9·25 7·50

648 Radio Waves

2012. 75th Anniversary of Réseau Luxembourgeois des Amateurs d'Ondes Courtes (Luxembourg Amateur Radio Society).
1939 **648** 60c. multicoloured 3·75 3·00

649 Sculpture (Pit Nicolas)

2012. 50th Anniversary of Institut Grand-Ducal. Section Arts et Lettres
1940 **649** 60c. multicoloured 3·75 3·00

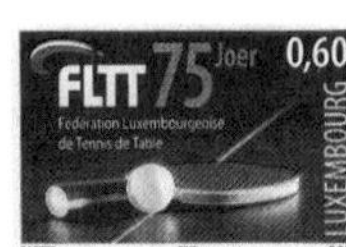

650 Paddle and Ball

2012. 75th Anniversary of 'Fédération Luxembourgeoise de Tennis de Table (FLT).
1941 **650** 60c. multicoloured 3·75 3·00

651 '10'

2012. Tenth Anniversary of the Euro.
1942 **651** 85c. multicoloured 5·50 4·50

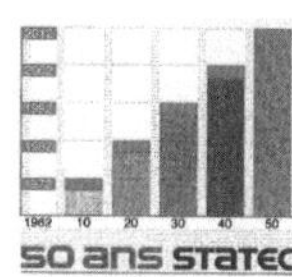

652 Graph

2012
1943 **652** 60c. multicoloured 3·75 3·00

653 Mil

654 Friends and Villains (image scaled to 33% of original size)

2012. Mil's Adventures. Multicoloured.
MS1944 **654** A (60c.)×5, Type **653** (Mil) and friends and villians 20·00 19·00

655 Monument au Souvenir (Gëlle Fra) and Traditional Buildings

2012. Europa. Visit Luxembourg. Multicoloured.
1945 60c. Type **655** 3·75 3·00
1946 85c. Mudam (Grand Duke Jean Museum of Modern Art), Philharmonie, Centre des Arts Pluriels d'Ettelbrück and Leudelange Water Tower (modern buildings) 5·50 4·50

656 COSL Emblem

2012. Olympic Games, London (No. 1948) or Centenary of Luxembourg Olympic Committee (COSL) (No. 1947). Multicoloured.
1947 60c. Type **656** 3·75 3·00
1948 €1.10 British flag and games emblem 7·00 5·75

657 Prince Guillaume and Countess Stéphanie de Lannoy

2012. Engagement of Prince Guillaume to Countess Stéphanie de Lannoy of Belgium. Multicoloured.
1949 60c. Type **657** 3·75 3·00
MS1950 120×80 mm. 60c. As Type **657**; 85c. Prince Guillaume and Countess Stéphanie de Lannoy (different) 9·25 9·00

658 Crowd and Stand Pipe (Lisa Drouet)

2012. Winning Designs in Children's Drawing Competition. Multicoloured.
1951 60c. Type **658** 3·75 3·00
1952 85c. Hill, tap and glass of water (Belinda Torres) (horiz) 5·50 4·50

659 Diving

2012. Leasure and Liberty. Multicoloured.
1953 60c. Paragliding 3·75 3·00
1954 85c. Type **659** 5·50 4·50

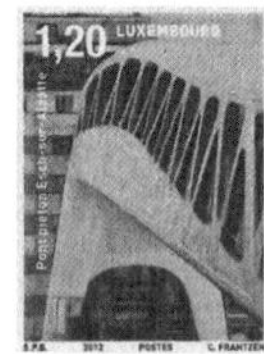

660 Gateway, Esch ('Building of the Year 2010', by Metaform Sàrl and Ney & Partners)

2012. Architecture and Mobility. Multicoloured.
1955 €1.20 Type **660** 7·75 6·25
1956 €2.20 Belval-Université station, Esch (by Atelier d'Architecture et de Design Jim Clemes) 14·00 11·50
1957 €4 Project for proposed link between the Upper Town and the Pfaffenthal district (by Steinmetz De Meyer) 26·00 21·00

660a Prince Guillaume and Countess Stéphanie de Lannoy

2012. Royal Wedding. Marriage of Prince Guillaume and Countess Stéphanie de Lannoy. Sheet 120×80 mm.
MS1957a **660a** €4 multicoloured 26·00 25·00

2012. Trades of Yesteryear. Multicoloured.
1958 60c.+5c. Washerwomen (horiz) 4·25 3·50
1959 85c.+10c. Hatter 6·00 5·00
1960 €1.10+10c. Farmer 7·75 6·25
1961 €1.20+25c. Market gardeners selling produce (horiz) 9·25 7·50

661 Mailbox

2012. Christmas. Multicoloured.
1962 60c. +5c. Type **661** 4·25 3·50
1963 85c. +10c. Envelope and tree 6·00 5·00

662 Villa Vauban

2012. 60th Anniversary of European Court of Justice.
1964 **662** 85c. multicoloured 5·50 4·50

663 Profiles

2013. European Year of Citizens.
1965 **663** 60c. multicoloured 3·75 3·00

664 Emblem

2013. 150th Anniversary of Union Grand-Duc Adolphe (UDGA).
1966 **664** 60c. multicoloured 3·75 3·00

665 Building Façade

2013. Centenary of Lycée Technique Privé Emile Metz.
1967 **665** 60c. multicoloured 3·75 3·00

666 Emblem

2013. 50th Anniversary of Round Table Luxembourg.
1968 **666** 60c. multicoloured 3·75 3·00

667 Death of Henry VII

2013. 700th Anniversary of Death of Henry VII.
1969 **667** €1.10 multicoloured 7·00 5·75

668 Nicolas Adames

2013. Personalities. Multicoloured.
1970 60c. Type **668** (theologian) 3·75 3·00
1971 60c. Putty Stein (author, composer and cabaret artist) 3·75 3·00

669 Games Mascot

2013. Games of the Small States of Europe, Luxembourg. Multicoloured.
1972 60c. Type **669** 3·75 3·00
1973 60c. Mascot (different) 3·75 3·00

670 Citroën 2 CV AZU

2013. Europa. Postal Transport. Multicoloured.
1974 60c. Type **670** 3·75 3·00
1975 85c. Renault Kangoo 5·50 4·50

671 Symbols of France and the Race

2013. Centenary of Tour de France Cycle Race. Sheet 120×80 mm.
MS1976 **671** €4 multicoloured 26·00 25·00

672 *Panthera tigris sumatrae*

2013. Fauna. Wild Cats. Small European Postal Administration Co-operation (SEPAC). Multicoloured.
1977 20c. Type **672** 1·30 1·00
1978 30c. *Lynx lynx* 1·90 1·60
1979 60c. *Felis sylvestris* (Wild Cat) 3·75 3·00

673 M11

2013. Société Électrique de l'Our (SEO)'s 11th Turbine.
1980 **673** 60c. multicoloured 3·75 3·00

674 Tentacle

2013. 'L' Series. Winning Designs in Design Friends Competition. Coil Stamps. Multicoloured.
1981 50g. (60c.) Type **674** 3·75 3·00
1982 50g. (60c.) Maze 3·75 3·00
1983 50g. (60c.) Heart 3·75 3·00
1984 50g. (60c.) Stylised chain 3·75 3·00

675 'Family of Man'

2013. The Family of Man. Photography Exhibition, Clervaux Castle (UNESCO's Memory of the World Register). Multicoloured (blue).
MS1985 60c. Type **675**; 85c. Edward Steichen (original curator) 9·50 9·00

676 Moselle

677 Moselle

2013. Tourism. Moselle Valley.
1986 **676** E 50g. (85c.) multicoloured 5·50 4·50
1987 **677** E 50g. (85c.) multicoloured 5·50 4·50

678 Pierre Werner

2013. Birth Centenary of Pierre Werner (politician).
1988 **678** 60c. multicoloured 3·75 3·00

679 Baubles

2013. Christmas. Multicoloured.
1989 60c. +5c. Type **679** 4·25 3·50
1990 85c. +10c. Single red bauble 6·00 5·00

2013. Trades of Yesteryear. Multicoloured.
1991 60c. +5c. Miller 4·25 3·50
1992 85c. +10c. Distiller (horiz) 6·00 5·00
1993 €1.10 +10c. Wheelwright 7·75 6·25
1994 €1.20 +25c. Cobbler (horiz) 9·25 7·50

680 *Aleuria aurantia* (Inscr 'Pézize orangée')

2013. Fungi. Booklet Stamps. Multicoloured.
1995 L 50g. (60c.) Type **680** 3·75 3·00
1996 L 50g. (60c.) *Boletus badius* (inscr 'Bolet bai') 3·75 3·00
1997 L 50g. (60c.) *Trametes versicolor - Polyporus versicolor* (Inscr 'Polypore versicolore') 3·75 3·00
1998 L 50g. (60c.) *Amanita muscaria* (Inscr 'Amanite tue-mouches') 3·75 3·00
1999 L 50g. (60c.) *Lycoperdon perlatum* (Inscr 'Vesse-de-loup perlée') 3·75 3·00

681 LASEP (Sports League of Primary Schools) Mascot

2014. Anniversaries. Multicoloured.
2000 60c. Type **681** (50th anniversary) 4·50 3·75
2001 60c. 'Live it Love it Scout it' (centenary of scouting in Luxembourg) 4·50 3·75
2002 60c. Ligue HMC's headquarters, Capellen and emblem (50th anniversary of Ligue HMC, (working for social, cultural and professional integration of mentally disabled people) 4·50 3·75

682 Centenary Emblem

2014. Centenary of Red Cross in Luxembourg.
2003 **682** 60c. scarlet-vermilion and black 4·50 3·75

683 Stamp Collector's Desk

2014. 80th Anniversary of 'Fédération des Sociétés philatéliques du Grand-Duché de Luxembourg'. Multicoloured.
MS2004 60c. Type **683**; 85c. Stamp on wall and Landscape on desk 11·00 10·50

684 'EUROPAWAL 25 MEE 2014'

2014. European Elections 2014.
2005 **684** 60c. multicoloured 4·50 3·75

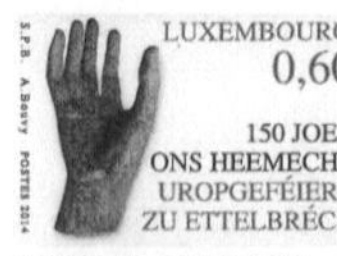

685 Hand and '150 JOER ONS HEEMECHT'

2014. 150th Anniversary of First Public Recital of *Hémecht* (poem by Michel Lentz) (National Anthem)
2006 **685** 60c. multicoloured 4·50 3·75

686 Lion

2014. 175th Anniversary of Independence of the Grand Duchy of Luxembourg.
2007 **686** 60c. multicoloured 4·50 3·75

687 Band wearing Traditional Dress

2014. Europa. Musical Instruments. Multicoloured.
2008 60c. Type **687** 4·50 3·75
2009 85c. Brass players and sheep 6·50 5·25

688 Old Quarters

2014. 20th Anniversary of Inclusion of Old Quarter and Fortifications of Luxembourg City on UNESCO World Heritage Sites List. Multicoloured.
MS2010 60c. Type **688**; 85c. Modern city 12·00 11·50

689 Flags and Inscription

2014. 50th Anniversary of Large-vessel Shipping on the Moselle.
2011 **689** 85c. multicoloured 6·50 5·25

690 Samuel Hirsch

2014. Personalities. Multicoloured.
2012 60c. Type **690** (Rabbi) 4·50 3·75
2013 60c. Marie Speyer (teacher) 4·50 3·75
2014 60c. Nikolaus Hein (writer and educationalist) 4·50 3·75

691 Cross Section of Soil (Michaela Videnova)

2014. Grand-Prix POST. Winning Designs in Children's Drawing Competition. Treasures of the Soil. Multicoloured.
2015 60c. Type **691** 4·50 3·75
2016 85c. Mole underground and watering can (Adelisa Pjanić) (vert) 6·50 5·25

692 *Tragopogon porrifolius* (Salsify)

2014. Vegetables of Yesteryear. Small European Postal Administration Co-operation (SEPAC) (No. 2017). Multicoloured.
2017 85c. Type **692** 6·50 5·25
2018 €1 *Pisum sativum* (Pea) 7·00 5·75
2019 €1.10 *Cichorium intybus* (Chicory) 7·25 6·00

693 '2 août 1914' Storming of Luxembourg City (Pierre Blanc)

2014. Centenary of Start of World War I.
2020 **693** 60c. multicoloured 4·50 3·75

694 Grand Duke Jean

2014. 50th Anniversary of Accession of HRH Grand Duke Jean.
2021 **694** L 50g. (60c.) multicoloured 4·50 3·75

695 De Dion-Bouton, 1899

2014. Cars of Yesteryear. Charity Stamps. Multicoloured.
2022 60c. +5c. Type **695** 4·50 3·75
2023 85c. +10c. Peugeot, 1904 6·50 5·25
2024 €1.10 +10c. Opel, 1909 7·00 5·75
2025 €1.20 +25c. Renault, 1910 7·25 6·00

696 Fox and Rabbit

2014. Christmas. Multicoloured.
2026 60c. +5c. Type **696** 4·50 3·75
2027 85c. +10c. Owl and mouse 6·50 5·25

697 Young Stamp Collectors

2015. 125th Anniversary of Organised Philately.
2028 **697** 60c. multicoloured 4·50 3·75

698 'XXVOAI'

2015. 25th Anniversary of Order of Architects and Consulting Engineers.
2029 **698** 60c. new blue, dull orange and black 4·50 3·75

699 Emblem

2015. 25th Anniversary of Omega 90 (palliative care and bereavement support).
2030 **699** 60c. multicoloured 4·50 3·75

700 Map

2015. Bicentenary of Grand-Duchy of Luxembourg.
2031 **700** 60c. multicoloured 4·50 3·75

701 Triumph aus Luxemburg

2015. Fruit Varieties as Cultural Asset. Multicoloured.
2032 L 50g. (60c.) Type **701** 4·50 3·75
2033 L 50g. (60c.) Gute Graue 4·50 3·75
2034 L 50g. (60c.) Luxemburger Renette 4·50 3·75
2035 L 50g. (60c.) Doppelte Philippsbirne 4·50 3·75
2036 L 50g. (60c.) Jakob Lebel 4·50 3·75
2037 L 50g. (60c.) Neue Poiteau 4·50 3·75
2038 L 50g. (60c.) Porzenapfel 4·50 3·75
2039 L 50g. (60c.) Saint Remy 4·50 3·75
2040 L 50g. (60c.) Eifeler Rambur 4·50 3·75
2041 L 50g. (60c.) Luxemburger Mostbirne 4·50 3·75

702 Grand Duke Henri

2015. Grand Duke Henri.
2042 **702** L 50g. (60c.) myrtle-green and yellowish green 4·50 3·75
2043 E 50g. (85c.) chalky blue and new blue 6·50 5·25
2044 M 50g. (€1.10) maroon and dull rose 7·25 6·00

703 Claus Cito

2015. Personalities. Multicoloured.
2045 60c. Type **703** (sculptor) 4·50 3·75
2046 60c. Robert Krieps (politician) 4·50 3·75
2047 60c. René Engelmann (writer) 4·50 3·75

704 *la shoah* (Philippe Konsbrück)

2015. 70th Anniversary of End of World War II. Luxembourg Remembers. Multicoloured.
MS2048 60c.×6, Type **704**; LTAM (emblem) (Kelly Marques); *l'enrôlement forcé* (Stéphanie Uhres) (30×30 mm); *le courage civil* (Nathalie Noé Adam) (30×30 mm); *la terreur* (Corrine Goetz); *la resistance* (Stéphane Pekala Colles) 27·00 26·00

705 Building Blocks

2015. Europa. Old Toys. Multicoloured.
2049 60c. Type **705** 4·50 3·75
2050 85c. Doll and doll's house furniture 6·50 5·25

707 Emblem of Luxembourg Presidency

2015. Luxembourg President of Council of European Union, 1 July–31 December 2015. Scarlet, black and new blue.
2051 L50g (60c.) Type **707** 4·50 5·00
2052 E50g (85c.) As Type **707**, but central design reduced 6·50 6·50

2015. Vegetables of Yesteryear. Root Crops. Multicoloured.
2053 20c. *Pastinaca sativa* (Parsnips) 1·75 1·75
2054 25c. *Apium graveolens* (Celery) 2·00 2·00
2055 35c. *Beta vulgaris* (Beetroot) 2·75 2·75

2015. 15th Anniversary of Reign of Grand Duke Henri. Multicoloured.
2056 70c. Royal couple 5·00 5·00

2015. National Museum of History and Art. Opening of the Wiltheim Wing. Multicoloured.
2057 70c. New building 5·00 5·00
2058 95c. Silver tea caddy (Johann Michael Kutzer) 6·75 6·75
2059 €1.30 *Helios* (ceramic sculpture, Villeroy and Boch) 7·50 7·50

2015. Nature Reserves in Luxembourg. Multicoloured.
2060 L50g. (60c.) Our 4·50 4·50
2061 L50g. (60c.) Obersauer 4·50 4·50
2062 L50g. (60c.) Müllerthal 4·50 4·50

2015. 175th Anniversary of Postage Stamps. Black and gold.
2063 70c. As Type **1** of Luxembourg and '175 ans du Penny Black' 5·00 5·00

713 *Leucanthemum* (Marguerite)

2015. ATR (Affranchissement à tarif réduit) (for use by not-for-profit organisations only) Stamps. Coil stamps. Flowers. Multicoloured.
2064 50g. (35c.) Type **713** 2·75 2·75
2065 50g. (35c.) *Centaurea cyanus* (Cornflower) 2·75 2·75
2066 50g. (35c.) *Carduus acanthoides* (Plumeless Thistle) 2·75 2·75
2067 50g. (35c.) *Papaver rhoeas* (Poppy) 2·75 2·75

714 Conifer in Snowy Landscape

2015. Christmas. Multicoloured.
2068 70c. +5c. Type **714** 5·25 5·25
2069 95c. +10c. Iron railings and bare trees 7·00 7·00

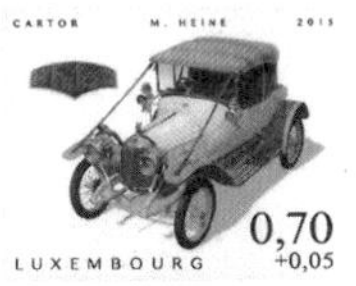

715 Philos A 4M, 1913

2015. Cars of Yesteryear. Charity Stamps. Multicoloured.
2070 70c. +5c. Type **715** 5·00 5·00
2071 95c. +10c. Morris Oxford Bullnose, 1914 6·75 6·75
2072 €1.30 +10c. Delaunay-Belleville, 1918 7·50 7·50
2073 €1.40 +25c. Berliet V8, 1919 7·75 7·75

2016. 60th Birth Anniversary of Maria-Teresa, Grand Duchess of Luxembourg. Multicoloured.
2074 70c. Grand Duchess Maria-Teresa 5·00 5·00
2075 70c. Grand Duchess Maria-Teresa, Princess Alexandra and Prince Sébastien 5·00 5·00

2016. Anniversaries. Multicoloured.
2076 70c. Emblem (tenth anniversary of CET (Centre for Equal Treatment)) 5·00 5·00
2077 70c. Symbols of port (50th anniversary of Mertert Port) 5·00 5·00
2078 70c. Stylised ships (25th anniversary of Luxembourg's maritime register) 5·00 5·00

2016. New University of Luxembourg Campus. Multicoloured.
2079 70c. Belval Campus building 5·00 5·00

719 Marcel Noppeney

2016. Personalities. Multicoloured.
2080 70c. Type **719** (writer) 5·00 5·00
2081 70c. Joseph Gaspard Hackin (archaeologist) 5·00 5·00
2082 70c. Jean Lucien Nicolas Jacoby (artist) 5·00 5·00

720 Team Lëtzebuerg Emblem

2016. Olympic Games. Rio 2016.
2083 **720** 70c. multicoloured 5·00 5·00

721 Green Star

2016. Europa. Think Green. Multicoloured.
2084 70c. Type **721** 5·00 5·00
2085 95c. Roller painting contaminated landscape green (horiz) 6·75 6·75

722 Margot

2016. Personalised Stamps. Tenth Anniversary New meng.post.lu. Pets. 60th Anniversary of First Temporary Animal Refuge. Multicoloured.
2086 70c. Type **722** 5·00 5·00
2087 95c. Goethe (dog) 6·75 6·75
2088 €1.30 Maischen (cat) (vert) 7·50 7·50

723 Mounted Postman

2016. 500th Anniversary of Thurn and Taxis Postal Route through Luxembourg. Sheet 120×80 mm.
MS2089 **723** €4 multicoloured 10·50 10·50

724 Virgin Mary

2016. 350th Anniversary of Mary, Consoler of the Afflicted, as Patroness of Luxembourg.
2090 **724** €1 multicoloured 7·00 7·00

725 Red Bridge

2016. 50th Anniversary of Rout Bréck (Red Bridge) Pont Grand-Duchesse Charlotte.
2091 **725** 70c. multicoloured 5·00 5·00

726 Christ with Crown of Thorns and Our Lady of Sorrows

2016. Albrecht Bouts Exhibition at MNHA (Luxembourg National Museum of History and Art).
2092 **726** 70c. multicoloured 5·00 5·00

727 Woodpecker (Yann Klees)

2016. Grand-Prix POST. Winning Designs in Children's Drawing Competition. Biodiversity. Multicoloured.

2093	70c. Type **727**	5·00	5·00
2094	95c. Wolf (Christine Guirsch) (horiz)	6·75	6·75

728 Spring in the Ösling. Bourscheid Castle

2016. SEPAC (small European mail services). The Four Seasons.

2095	**728** 95c. multicoloured	6·75	6·75

729 *Cucumis sativus* (Cucumber)

2016. Vegetables of Yesteryear. Multicoloured.

2096	95c. Type **729**	6·75	6·75
2097	€1.30 *Phaseolus vulgaris* (String Beans)	7·50	7·50
2098	€2 *Allium cepa proliferum* (Tree Onion)	8·50	8·50

730 'Signature'

2016. Luxembourg's Signature. Each scarlet, new blue and black.

2099	70c. Type **730**	5·00	5·00
2100	95c. Blue band	6·75	6·75
2101	€1.30 Red band	7·50	7·50

731 Minett Park

2016. Local Museums. Booklet Stamps. Multicoloured.

2102	70c. Type **731**	5·00	5·00
2103	70c. Kulturhuef	5·00	5·00
2104	70c. Rural and Artisan Museum	5·00	5·00
2105	70c. Slate Museum	5·00	5·00
2106	70c. Aviation Museum	5·00	5·00

732 St Nicholas

2016. Christmas. Multicoloured.

2107	70c. +5c. Type **732**	5·00	5·00
2108	95c. +10c. St Nicholas and children	6·75	6·75

733 Model T Ford

2016. Cars of Yesteryear. Charity Stamps. Multicoloured.

2109	70c. +5c. Type **733**	5·00	5·00
2110	95c. +10c. Donnet Zedel CI-6, 1924	6·75	6·75
2111	€1.30 +10c. Paige 6-45 Sedan, 1927	7·50	7·50
2112	€1.40 +25c. Chenard Walcker, 1928	7·75	7·75

734 Josy Barthel

2017. 25th Death Anniversary of Joseph (Josy) Barthel (Olympic Gold Medallist).

2113	**734** 70c. multicoloured	5·00	5·00

735 Jean Jules Linden

2017. Personalities. Multicoloured.

2114	70c. Type **735** (botanist)	5·00	5·00
2115	70c. Pierre Frieden (writer and politician)	5·00	5·00
2116	70c. Tony Bourg (writer and linguist)	5·00	5·00

736 Fieldgen Private School

2017. Anniversaries. Multicoloured.

2117	70c. Type **736** (125th anniversary)	5·00	5·00
2118	70c. Fifty-One International (social support agency (50th anniversary))	5·00	5·00
2119	70c. Luxembourg Alzheimer Association (30th anniversary)	5·00	5·00

737 Our Lady of Fátima

2017. Centenary of the Fatima Apparitions. Sheet 125×95 mm

MS2120	**737** 95c. multicoloured	7·00	7·00

738 Aerial View showing Lines of Fortification

2017. 150th Anniversary of Treaty of London (giving Luxembourg neutral status and enabling the removal of Prussian fortification).

2121	**738** 70c. multicoloured	5·25	4·50

739 Château de Beggen

2017. Europa. Castles. Multicoloured.

2122	70c. Type **739**	5·25	4·50
2123	95c. Château de Dommeldange	7·25	6·50

740 Musicians

2017. Military Anniversaries. Multicoloured.

2124	70c. Type **740** (175th anniversary of military band)	5·25	4·50
2125	95c. Soldiers (50th anniversary of army volunteer service)	7·25	6·50

741 Peter-Ernst von Mansfeld

2017. 500th Birth Anniversary of Peter-Ernst von Mansfeld (Governor of Luxembourg).

2126	**741** 95c. multicoloured	7·25	6·50

742 Emblem

2017. Centenary of Fédération des Sociétés Cyclistes Luxembourgeoises (FSCL).

2127	**742** 70c. new blue, rose-red and black	5·25	4·50

743 Cyclist wearing Yellow Jersey

2017. Tour de France 2017. Starting in Mondorf-les-Bains.

2128	**743** 70c. multicoloured	5·25	4·50

744 Philharmonie Luxembourg and Golden Lady Statue

2017. Multilaterale Hertogpost 2017 Stamp Exhibition. Multicoloured.

MS2129	70c. Type **744**; 95c. St John's Cathedral, Netherlands	13·00	12·50

745 Parish Church

2017. 700th Anniversary of Simmern Parish Church.

2130	**745** 70c. multicoloured	5·25	4·50

746 Post Van

2017. SEPAC (small European mail services). Handicrafts.

2132	**746** 95c. multicoloured	7·25	6·50

747 *Green Fingers* (ceramic sculpture by Ellen van der Woude)

2017. 175th Anniv of Luxembourg Post. Multicoloured.

MS2131	70c. Type **747**; 95c. Symbols of modern communication	13·00	12·50

748 Grand-Duc Adolphe de Luxembourg

2017. Roses. Coil Stamps. Multicoloured.

2132	L50g. (70c.) Type **748**	5·25	4·50
2133	L50g. (70c.) Princess Marie Adélaide	5·25	4·50
2134	L50g. (70c.) Grande-Duchesse Charlotte	5·25	4·50
2135	L50g. (70c.) Grand-Duc Jean	5·25	4·50
2136	L50g. (70c.) Grand-Duc Henri	5·25	4·50
2137	L50g. (70c.) Indépendance du Luxembourg	5·25	4·50

749 Pfaffenthal–Kirchberg Funicular

2017. Inauguration of Tramway and Pfaffenthal–Kirchberg Funicular. Multicoloured.

2138	70c. Type **749**	5·25	4·50
2139	70c. New tram linking Kirchberg to Ville-Haute (60×30 *mm*)	5·25	4·50

750 Civil and Military Order of Merit of Adolphe of Nassau

2017. National Orders of Merit. Multicoloured.

2140	70c. Type **750**	5·25	4·50
2141	70c. Order of Merit of the Grand Duchy of Luxembourg	5·25	4·50
2142	70c. Order of the Oak Crown	5·25	4·50

751 Young Couple

2017. Christmas. Multicoloured.

2143	70c. +5c. Type **751**	5·75	5·00
2144	95c. +10c. Children, snowman, tree and dog	8·00	7·25

752 Packard Standard Eight 833, 1931

2017. Cars of Yesteryear. Charity Stamps. Multicoloured.

2145	70c. +5c. Type **752**	5·75	5·00
2146	95c. +10c. Rolls-Royce 20/25, 1934	8·00	7·25

2147 €1.30 +10c. Panhard & Levassor Panoramique 6DS X71, 1936 10·50 9·50
2148 €1.40 +25c. Buick 56C, 1940 12·50 11·00

753 Symbols of Childhood

2018. 50th Anniversary of SOS Kannerduerf Lëtzebuerg.
2149 **753** 70c. multicoloured 5·25 4·50

754 Children and Parents

2018. 50th Anniversary of APEMH (Association of Parents of Mentally Disabled Children).
2150 **754** 70c. multicoloured 5·25 4·50

755 Clock Tower

2018. 125th Anniversary of Lycée de Garçons Luxembourg.
2151 **755** 70c. multicoloured 5·25 4·50

756 '60' and '50'

2018. 60th Anniversary of NATO Support and Procurement Agency (NSPA). 50th Anniversary of NSPA in Luxembourg.
2152 **756** 70c. multicoloured 5·25 4·50

757 Symbols of Cultural Heritage

2018. European Year of Cultural Heritage.
2153 **757** 70c. multicoloured 5·25 4·50

OFFICIAL STAMPS

1875. Stamps of 1859–1872 optd **OFFICIEL**. Roul.
O79 **3** 1c. brown 70·00 65·00
O80 **3** 2c. black 70·00 65·00
O81 **4** 10c. lilac £3750 £3750
O82 **4** 12½c. red £850 £950
O83 **4** 20c. brown 70·00 95·00
O84 **4** 25c. blue £450 £250
O85 **4** 30c. purple 70·00 £130
O88 **4** 40c. orange £450 £550
O87 **4** 1f. on 37½c. bistre (No. 37) £275 44·00

1875. Stamps of 1874–1879 optd **OFFICIEL**. Perf.
O89 **3** 1c. brown 16·00 47·00
O90 **3** 2c. black 19·00 55·00
O91 **3** 4c. green £160 £250
O92 **3** 5c. yellow £130 £130
O93b **4** 10c. lilac £160 £190
O111 **4** 12½c. red £130 £190
O99a **4** 25c. blue 5·00 6·25
O96 **4** 1f. on 37½c. bistre (No. 56) 65·00 95·00

1881. Stamp of 1859 optd **S. P. Roul.**
O116 **3** 40c. orange 65·00 £130

1881. Stamps of 1874–1879 optd **S. P. Perf.**
O121a **3** 1c. brown 19·00 16·00
O122a **3** 2c. black 19·00 16·00
O118 4c. green £275 £325
O123a **3** 5c. yellow £250 £325
O124a **4** 10c. lilac £250 £325
O125a **4** 12½c. red £275 £375
O126a **4** 20c. brown £110 £160
O127a **4** 25c. blue £110 £160
O128 **4** 30c. red £130 £190
O120 **4** 1f. on 37½c. bistre (No. 56) 65·00 95·00

7 Agriculture and Trade

1882. Stamps of 1882 optd **S. P.**
O141 **7** 1c. grey 65 65
O142 **7** 2c. brown 65 65
O143 **7** 4c. olive 65 80
O144 **7** 5c. green 65 95
O145 **7** 10c. red 22·00 25·00
O146 **7** 12½c. blue 2·50 8·25
O147a **7** 20c. orange 2·50 6·25
O148 **7** 25c. blue 38·00 39·00
O149a **7** 30c. olive 6·25 13·00
O150 **7** 50c. brown 1·90 4·75
O151 **7** 1f. lilac 1·90 4·75
O152 **7** 5f. orange 25·00 65·00

1891. Stamps of 1891 optd **S. P.**
O188 **8** 10c. red 30 95
O189 **8** 12½c. green 11·50 11·50
O190 **8** 20c. orange 19·00 14·50
O191a **8** 25c. blue 50 95
O192 **8** 30c. green 11·50 14·50
O193 **8** 37½c. green 11·50 14·50
O194 **8** 50c. brown 9·50 16·00
O195 **8** 1f. purple 9·50 19·00
O196 **8** 2½f. black 65·00 £120
O197 **8** 5f. lake 55·00 90·00

1898. Stamps of 1895 optd **S. P.**
O213 **9** 1c. grey 3·25 3·25
O214 **9** 2c. brown 2·50 2·75
O215 **9** 4c. bistre 2·50 2·50
O216 **9** 5c. green 12·50 9·50
O217 **9** 10c. red 44·00 55·00

1908. Stamps of 1906 optd **Officiel**.
O218 **10** 1c. grey 30 65
O219 **10** 2c. brown 30 65
O220 **10** 4c. bistre 30 65
O221 **10** 5c. green 60 65
O271 **10** 5c. mauve 20 65
O222 **10** 6c. lilac 30 65
O223 **10** 7½c. yellow 30 65
O224 **10** 10c. red 30 95
O225 **10** 12½c. slate 30 95
O226 **10** 15c. brown 50 1·30
O227 **10** 20c. orange 50 1·30
O228 **10** 25c. blue 50 1·30
O229 **10** 30c. olive 9·50 12·50
O230 **10** 37½c. green 1·30 1·30
O231 **10** 50c. brown 1·30 2·50
O232 **10** 87½c. blue 3·25 6·25
O233 **10** 1f. purple 5·00 6·25
O234 **10** 2½f. red £160 £130
O235 **10** 5f. purple 95·00 90·00

1915. Stamps of 1914 optd **Officiel**.
O236 **13** 10c. purple 30 1·30
O237 **13** 12½c. green 30 1·30
O238 **13** 15c. brown 30 1·30
O239 **13** 17½c. brown 30 1·30
O240 **13** 25c. blue 30 1·30
O241 **13** 30c. brown 2·50 9·50
O242 **13** 35c. blue 30 1·90
O243 **13** 37½c. brown 30 2·50
O244 **13** 40c. red 50 1·90
O245 **13** 50c. grey 50 1·90
O246 **13** 62½c. green 50 2·50
O247 **13** 87½c. orange 50 3·25
O248 **13** 1f. brown 50 2·50
O249 **13** 2½f. red 50 5·00
O250 **13** 5f. violet 50 6·25

1922. Stamps of 1921 optd **Officiel**.
O251 **17** 2c. brown 25 30
O252 **17** 3c. green 25 30
O253 **17** 6c. purple 25 65
O272 **17** 10c. green 20 65
O273 **17** 15c. green 20 65
O274 **17** 15c. orange 20 65
O256 **17** 20c. orange 25 65
O275 **17** 20c. green 20 65
O257 **17** 25c. green 25 65
O258 **17** 30c. red 25 65
O259 **17** 40c. orange 25 65
O260 **17** 50c. blue 40 95
O276 **17** 50c. red 30 95
O261 **17** 75c. red 40 95
O277 **17** 75c. blue 30 95
O266 **17** 80c. black 40 1·30
O263 **18** 1f. red 65 3·25
O278 **18** 1f. blue 50 2·50
O267 **-** 2f. blue 95 3·25
O279 **-** 2f. brown 2·40 8·75
O269 **-** 5f. violet 5·00 19·00

26 Luxembourg

28 Echternach

1922. Stamps of 1923 optd **Officiel**.
O268a **28** 3f. blue 65 2·50
O270 **26** 10f. black 15·00 38·00

1926. Stamps of 1926 optd **Officiel**.
O280 **32** 5c. mauve 20 30
O281 **32** 10c. green 20 30
O298 **32** 15c. black 50 1·90
O282 **32** 20c. orange 20 30
O283 **32** 25c. green 20 30
O300 **32** 25c. brown 40 1·30
O301 **32** 30c. green 75 3·25
O302 **32** 30c. violet 50 1·90
O303 **32** 35c. violet 50 1·90
O304 **32** 35c. green 50 1·90
O286 **32** 40c. brown 20 30
O287 **32** 50c. brown 20 30
O307 **32** 60c. green 50 1·30
O288 **32** 65c. brown 20 65
O308 **32** 70c. violet 4·75 10·50
O289 **32** 75c. red 20 65
O309 **32** 75c. brown 50 1·30
O291 **32** 80c. brown 20 65
O292 **32** 90c. red 30 1·30
O293 **32** 1f. black 30 95
O312 **32** 1f. red 65 3·50
O294 **32** 1¼f. blue 20 95
O313 **32** 1¼f. yellow 3·25 10·50
O314 **32** 1¼f. green 2·75 7·50
O315 **32** 1½f. blue 50 2·50
O316 **32** 1¾f. blue 65 2·50

37 Clervaux

1928. Stamp of 1928 optd **Officiel**.
O317 **37** 2f. black 65 3·25

43 Luxembourg, Lower Town

1931. Stamp of 1931 optd **Officiel**.
O318 **43** 20f. green 3·25 16·00

47 Gateway of the Three Towers

1934. Stamp of 1934 optd **Officiel**.
O319 **47** 5f. green 2·50 9·50

52 Vianden

1935. No. 340 optd **Officiel**.
O341 **52** 10f. green 2·50 12·50

POSTAGE DUE STAMPS

D12 Arms of Luxembourg

1907
D173 **D12** 5c. black and green 30 50
D174 **D12** 10c. black and green 1·90 50
D175 **D12** 12½c. black and green 65 1·60
D176 **D12** 20c. black and green 1·30 1·30
D177 **D12** 25c. black and green 25·00 1·90
D178 **D12** 50c. black and green 1·90 7·00
D179 **D12** 1f. black and green 65 6·25

1920. Surch.
D193 **D12** 15 on 12½c. blk & grn 2·50 12·50
D194 **D12** 30 on 25c. black & grn 2·50 16·00

1922
D221 **D12** 5c. red and green 30 65
D222 **D12** 10c. red and green 30 65
D223 **D12** 20c. red and green 30 65
D224 **D12** 25c. red and green 30 65
D225 **D12** 30c. red and green 65 1·30
D226 **D12** 35c. red and green 65 50
D227 **D12** 50c. red and green 65 1·30
D228 **D12** 60c. red and green 50 65
D229 **D12** 70c. red and green 65 50
D230 **D12** 75c. red and green 65 30
D231 **D12** 1f. red and green 65 3·25
D232 **D12** 2f. red and green 65 11·50
D233 **D12** 3f. red and green 2·50 22·00

D77

1946
D488 **D77** 5c. green 3·25 1·30
D489 **D77** 10c. green 3·25 95
D490 **D77** 20c. green 3·25 95
D491 **D77** 30c. green 3·25 95
D492 **D77** 50c. green 3·25 95
D493 **D77** 70c. green 3·25 1·90
D494 **D77** 75c. green 9·50 65
D495 **D77** 1f. red 3·25 65
D496 **D77** 1f.50 red 3·25 65
D497 **D77** 2f. red 3·25 65
D498 **D77** 3f. red 6·25 95
D499 **D77** 5f. red 6·25 95
D500 **D77** 10f. red 9·50 9·50
D501 **D77** 20f. red 16·00 41·00

MACAU

A former Portuguese territory in China at the mouth of the Canton River.

1884. 1000 reis = 1 milreis.
1894. 78 avos = 1 rupee.
1913. 100 avos = 1 pataca.

1884. Crown key-type inscr 'MACAU'.
10 **P** 5r. black 26·00 18·00
2 **P** 10r. orange 50·00 27·00
21 **P** 10r. green 35·00 18·00
12 **P** 20r. bistre 80·00 45·00
27 **P** 20r. red 75·00 36·00
13 **P** 25r. red 29·00 10·50
22 **P** 25r. lilac 50·00 27·00
14 **P** 40r. blue £325 £110
23 **P** 40r. buff 70·00 36·00
15 **P** 50r. green £375 £150
24 **P** 50r. blue 75·00 45·00
31 **P** 80r. grey £150 70·00
16 **P** 100r. lilac 65·00 36·00
17 **P** 200r. orange 80·00 36·00
9 **P** 300r. brown 85·00 36·00

1885. Crown key type of Macao surch **80 reis** in circle. No gum.
19 80r. on 100r. lilac £150 85·00

1885. Crown key type of Macao surch in Reis. With gum (43, 44, 45), no gum (others).
32 5r. on 25r. pink 35·00 18·00
43 5r. on 80r. grey 50·00 18·00
46 5r. on 100r. lilac £225 90·00
33 10r. on 25r. pink 65·00 36·00
38 10r. on 50r. green £600 £300
44 10r. on 80r. grey 85·00 36·00
47 10r. on 200r. orange £300 £150
35 20r. on 50r. green 65·00 27·00
45 20r. on 80r. grey £120 55·00
40 40r. on 50r. green £400 £180

Coleccione Selos de Macau 收藏 澳門郵票 Collect Macao's Stamps

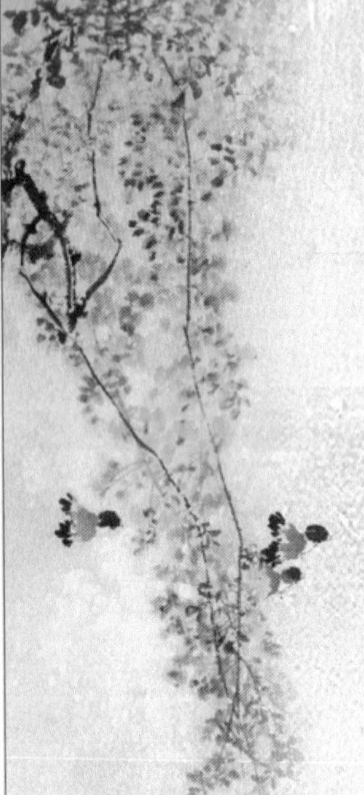

快分享到朋友圈
一起關注澳門郵票！

澳門議事亭前地 LARGO DO SENADO, MACAU
電話 Tel.: (853) 8396 8513, 2857 4491 傳真 Fax.: (853) 8396 8603, 2833 6603
電郵 E-mail: philately@ctt.gov.mo 網址 Website: http://philately.ctt.gov.mo

1885. Crown key-type of Macao surch with figure of value only and bar. No gum.

41		5 on 25r. red	50·00	36·00
42a		10 on 50r. green	50·00	36·00

9

1887. Fiscal stamps as T **9** surch **CORREIO** and new value. No gum.

50		5r. on 10r. green and brown	£130	£120
51		5r. on 20r. green and brown	£150	£120
52		5r. on 60r. green and brown	£130	£120
53		10r. on 10r. green and brown	£140	£140
54		10r. on 60r. green and brown	£170	£150
55		40r. on 20r. green and brown	£225	£170

1888. Embossed key-type inscr 'PROVINCIA DE MACAU'.

56	**Q**	5r. black	25·00	10·50
57	**Q**	10r. green	28·00	10·50
58	**Q**	20r. red	50·00	26·00
59	**Q**	25r. mauve	60·00	26·00
60	**Q**	40r. brown	60·00	36·00
61	**Q**	50r. blue	60·00	27·00
62	**Q**	80r. grey	90·00	45·00
63	**Q**	100r. brown	85·00	45·00
71	**Q**	200r. lilac	£160	55·00
72	**Q**	300r. orange	£170	60·00

1892. No. 71 surch **3030**.

73		30 on 200r. lilac	£100	48·00

1894. Embossed key-type of Macao surch **PROVISORIO**, value and Chinese characters. No gum.

75b	**Q**	1a. on 5r. black	16·00	7·50
76	**Q**	3a. on 20r. red	17·00	9·00
77	**Q**	4a. on 25r. violet	35·00	18·00
89	**Q**	5a. on 30 on 200r. lilac (No. 73)	£275	£140
78	**Q**	6a. on 40r. brown	35·00	14·50
79	**Q**	8a. on 50r. blue	65·00	36·00
80	**Q**	13a. on 80r. grey	35·00	17·00
81	**Q**	16a. on 100r. brown	65·00	36·00
82	**Q**	31a. on 200r. lilac	85·00	55·00
83	**Q**	47a. on 300r. orange	£100	55·00

1894. Figures key-type inscr 'MACAU'.

91	**R**	5r. yellow	18·00	6·75
92	**R**	10r. mauve	18·00	6·75
93	**R**	15r. brown	28·00	9·75
94	**R**	20r. lilac	36·00	10·50
95	**R**	25r. green	75·00	21·00
96	**R**	50r. blue	75·00	27·00
97	**R**	75r. pink	95·00	60·00
98	**R**	80r. green	65·00	41·00
99	**R**	100r. brown on buff	60·00	33·00
100	**R**	150r. red on pink	60·00	33·00
101	**R**	200r. blue on blue	85·00	45·00
102	**R**	300r. blue on brown	£130	60·00

1898. As Vasco da Gama types of Portugal but inscr 'MACAU'.

104	½a. green	8·75	5·25
105	1a. red	10·00	7·50
106	2a. purple	19·00	8·25
107	4a. green	25·00	11·00
108	8a. blue	41·00	24·00
109	12a. brown	55·00	38·00
110	16a. brown	60·00	38·00
111	24a. brown	70·00	45·00

Designs: ½a. Departure of fleet; 1a. Arrival at Calicut; 2a. Embarkation aat Rastello; 4a. Muse of History; 8a. Flagship *São Gabriel* and portraits of Da Gama and Camoens; 12a. Archangel Gabriel, Patron Saint of the expedition; 16a. Flagship *São Gabriel*; 24a. Vasco da Gama.

1898. King Carlos key-type inscr 'MACAU'. Name and value in black.

112	**S**	½a. grey	4·00	1·80
113	**S**	1a. yellow	4·00	1·80
114	**S**	2a. green	5·75	1·80
115	**S**	2½a. brown	11·50	5·50
116	**S**	3a. lilac	11·50	5·50
174	**S**	3a. grey	7·00	4·00
117	**S**	4a. green	16·00	12·00
175	**S**	4a. red	7·00	4·00
176	**S**	5a. brown	11·00	6·50
177	**S**	6a. brown	14·00	6·50
119	**S**	8a. blue	17·00	8·25
178	**S**	8a. brown	17·00	9·50
120	**S**	10a. blue	14·50	8·50
121	**S**	12a. pink	22·00	13·50
179	**S**	12a. purple	80·00	37·00
122	**S**	13a. mauve	25·00	13·50
180	**S**	13a. lilac	31·00	19·00
123	**S**	15a. green	£140	38·00
124	**S**	16a. blue on blue	26·00	13·50
181	**S**	18a. brown on pink	55·00	29·00
125	**S**	20a. brown on cream	60·00	20·00
126	**S**	24a. brown on yellow	32·00	16·00
127	**S**	31a. purple	44·00	21·00
182	**S**	31a. purple on pink	55·00	29·00
128	**S**	47a. blue on pink	60·00	26·00
183	**S**	47a. blue on yellow	80·00	37·00
129	**S**	78a. black on blue	95·00	36·00

1900. King Carlos key-type of Macao surch **PROVISORIO** and new value.

132	5 on 13a. mauve	20·00	6·75
133	10 on 16a. blue on blue	25·00	10·50
134	15 on 24a. brown on yellow	33·00	15·00
135	20 on 31a. purple	45·00	21·00

1902. Various types of Macao surch.

138	**Q**	6a. on 5r. black	11·00	6·75
142	**R**	6a. on 5r. yellow	10·00	5·50
136	**P**	6a. on 10r. yellow	38·00	17·00
137	**P**	6a. on 10r. green	25·00	10·50
139	**Q**	6a. on 10r. green	10·00	6·75
143	**R**	6a. on 10r. mauve	26·00	10·50
144	**R**	6a. on 15r. brown	23·00	10·50
145	**R**	6a. on 25r. green	11·50	5·50
140	**Q**	6a. on 40r. brown	11·50	6·75
146	**R**	6a. on 80r. green	11·50	5·50
148	**R**	6a. on 100r. brown on buff	19·00	8·00
149	**R**	6a. on 200r. blue on blue	13·00	5·50
151	**V**	18a. on 2½r. brown	13·00	9·00
153	**Q**	18a. on 20r. red	26·00	9·75
162	**R**	18a. on 20r. lilac	32·00	13·50
154	**Q**	18a. on 25r. mauve	£250	£100
163	**R**	18a. on 50r. blue	32·00	13·50
165	**R**	18a. on 75r. pink	32·00	13·50
155	**Q**	18a. on 80r. grey	£250	£120
156	**Q**	18a. on 100r. brown	60·00	39·00
166	**R**	18a. on 150r. red on pink	32·00	14·50
158	**Q**	18a. on 200r. lilac	£200	95·00
160	**Q**	18a. on 300r. orange	50·00	26·00
167	**R**	18a. on 300r. blue on brn	32·00	13·50

1902. King Carlos type of Macao optd **PROVISORIO**.

168	**S**	2a. green	19·00	8·25
169	**S**	4a. green	49·00	18·00
170	**S**	8a. blue	25·00	15·00
171	**S**	10a. blue	26·00	15·00
172	**S**	12a. pink	£100	36·00

1905. No. 179 surch **10 AVOS** and bar.

184	10a. on 12a. purple	47·00	24·00

1910. Due key-type of Macao, but with words 'PORTEADO' and 'RECEBER' cancelled.

185	**W**	½a. green	21·00	12·50
186	**W**	1a. green	25·00	12·50
187	**W**	2a. grey	43·00	14·50

1911. King Carlos key-type of Macao optd **REPUBLICA**.

188	**S**	½a. grey	4·75	1·80
189	**S**	1a. orange	4·00	1·30
190	**S**	2a. green	4·00	1·30
191	**S**	3a. grey	6·00	1·80
192	**S**	4a. red	9·25	2·75
193	**S**	5a. brown	9·25	4·25
194	**S**	6a. brown	9·25	4·25
195	**S**	8a. brown	9·25	4·25
196	**S**	10a. blue	9·25	4·25
197	**S**	13a. lilac	16·00	5·50
198	**S**	16a. blue on blue	16·00	7·50
199	**S**	18a. brown on pink	25·00	9·50
200	**S**	20a. brown on cream	25·00	9·50
201	**S**	31a. purple on pink	31·00	10·50
202	**S**	47a. blue on yellow	45·00	17·00
203	**S**	78a. black on blue	60·00	24·00

30

1911. Fiscal stamp surch **POSTAL 1 AVO** and bar.

204	**30**	1a. on 5r. brown, yellow and black	34·00	14·50

1911. Stamps bisected and surch.

205	**S**	2a. on half of 4a. red (No. 175)	95·00	70·00
206	**S**	5a. on half of 10a. blue (No. 120)	£4000	£1300
207	**S**	5a. on half of 10a. blue (No. 171)	£225	£160

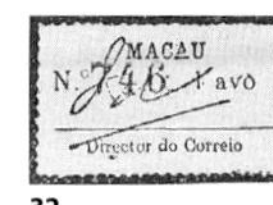

32

1911

210	**32**	1a. black	£750	£650
211	**32**	2a. black	£800	£700

1913. Provisionals of 1902 surch in addition with new value and bars over old value and optd **REPUBLICA**.

212	**R**	2a. on 18a. on 20r. lilac (No. 162)	17·00	7·25
213	**R**	2a. on 18a. on 50r. blue (No. 163)	17·00	7·25
215	**R**	2a. on 18a. on 75r. pink (No. 165)	17·00	7·25
216	**R**	2a. on 18a. on 150r. red on pink (No. 166)	17·00	7·25

1913. Provisionals of 1902 and 1905 optd **REPUBLICA**.

218	**Q**	6a. on 5r. (No. 138)	23·00	13·00
284	**R**	6a. on 5r. (No. 142)	19·00	8·00
217	**P**	6a. on 10r. (No. 137)	70·00	14·50
285	**Q**	6a. on 10r. (No. 139)	60·00	40·00
286	**R**	6a. on 10r. (No. 143)	19·00	9·50
287	**R**	6a. on 15r. (No. 144)	16·00	8·00
288	**R**	6a. on 25r. (No. 145)	17·00	9·50
220	**Q**	6a. on 40r. (No. 140)	17·00	8·75
289	**R**	6a. on 80r. (No. 146)	17·00	9·50
291	**R**	6a. on 100r. (No. 148)	17·00	9·50
292	**R**	6a. on 200r. (No. 149)	23·00	13·50
281	**S**	8a. (No. 170)	26·00	14·50
282	**S**	10a. (No. 171)	26·00	14·50
283	**S**	10a. on 12a. (No. 184)	28·00	15·00
293	**V**	18a. on 2½r. (No. 151)	26·00	13·50
229	**Q**	18a. on 20r. (No. 153)	26·00	13·00
295	**R**	18a. on 20r. (No. 162)	26·00	13·50
296	**R**	18a. on 50r. (No. 163)	28·00	15·00
298	**R**	18a. on 75r. (No. 165)	29·00	15·00
230	**Q**	18a. on 100r. (No. 156)	£140	65·00
299	**R**	18a. on 150r. (No. 166)	39·00	19·00
233	**Q**	18a. on 300r. (No. 160)	60·00	29·00
300	**R**	18a. on 300r. (No. 167)	60·00	24·00

1913. Stamps of 1911 issue surch.

252	**S**	½a. on 5a. brown	26·00	7·25
255	**S**	1a. on 13a. lilac	28·00	11·00
253	**S**	4a. on 8a. brown	55·00	12·00

1913. Vasco da Gama stamps of Macao optd **REPUBLICA**, and the 12a. surch **10 A**.

256	½a. green	7·75	3·50
257	1a. red	11·00	3·50
258	2a. purple	11·00	3·50
259	4a. green	23·00	9·50
260	8a. blue	29·00	10·50
261	10a. on 12a. brown	55·00	29·00
262	16a. brown	47·00	24·00
263	24a. brown	48·00	22·00

1913. Ceres key-type inscr 'MACAU'.

264	**U**	½a. green	3·50	1·80
310	**U**	1a. black	7·75	3·25
311	**U**	1½a. green	5·00	2·40
280	**U**	2a. green	12·50	8·00
313	**U**	3a. orange	16·00	5·00
267	**U**	4a. red	8·50	3·75
315	**U**	4a. yellow	20·00	8·00
268	**U**	5a. brown	9·25	5·50
269	**U**	6a. violet	9·25	5·50
270	**U**	8a. brown	9·25	5·50
271	**U**	10a. blue	12·50	5·50
272	**U**	12a. brown	14·00	5·50
320	**U**	14a. mauve	55·00	29·00
321	**U**	16a. grey	47·00	35·00
274	**U**	20a. red	26·00	14·50
322	**U**	24a. green	47·00	32·00
323	**U**	32a. brown	55·00	42·00
275	**U**	40a. purple	26·00	14·50
324	**U**	56a. pink	80·00	45·00
276	**U**	58a. brown on green	42·00	27·00
325	**U**	72a. brown	£100	48·00
277	**U**	76a. brown on pink	45·00	29·00
278	**U**	1p. orange on orange	80·00	37·00
326	**U**	1p. orange	£130	90·00
279	**U**	3p. green on blue	£200	£120
327	**U**	3p. turquoise	£550	£250
328	**U**	5p. red	£300	£190

1919. Surch.

301		½a. on 5a. brown (No. 268)	£130	55·00
330	**U**	1a. on 24a. grn (No. 322)	10·00	5·00
304	**S**	2a. on 6a. (No. 177)	£375	£150
302	**R**	2 on 6a. on 25r. green (No. 288)	£800	£325
303	**R**	2 on 6a. on 80r. green (No. 289)	£425	£225
331	**U**	2a. on 32a. (No. 323)	10·00	5·00
332	**U**	4a. on 12a. (No. 272)	10·00	5·50
329	**U**	5a. on 6a. violet (No. 269)	16·00	8·00
334	**U**	7a. on 8a. brn (No. 270)	14·00	8·75
335	**U**	12a. on 14a. (No. 320)	14·00	8·75
336	**U**	15a. on 16a. (No. 321)	14·00	8·75
337	**U**	20a. on 56a. pink (No. 324)	£120	65·00

50 'Portugal' and Galeasse

1934

338	**50**	½a. brown	1·70	80
339	**50**	1a. brown	1·70	80
340	**50**	2a. green	2·75	95
341	**50**	3a. mauve	2·75	95
342	**50**	4a. black	3·00	1·20
343	**50**	5a. grey	3·00	1·20
344	**50**	6a. brown	4·00	1·20
345	**50**	7a. red	4·75	1·80
346	**50**	8a. blue	4·75	1·80
347	**50**	10a. red	7·00	2·75
348	**50**	12a. blue	7·00	2·75
349	**50**	14a. green	7·00	2·75
350	**50**	15a. purple	7·00	2·75
351	**50**	20a. orange	7·75	2·75
352	**50**	30a. green	17·00	5·00
353	**50**	40a. violet	17·00	5·00
354	**50**	50a. brown	29·00	10·50
355	**50**	1p. blue	80·00	26·00
356	**50**	2p. brown	£100	34·00
357	**50**	3p. green	£275	80·00
358	**50**	5p. mauve	£350	£100

1936. Air. Stamps of 1934 optd **Aviao** and with Greek characters or surch also.

359	**40**	2a. green	6·50	2·50
360	**40**	3a. mauve	8·50	3·50
361	**40**	5a. on 6a. brown	10·00	4·25
362	**40**	7a. red	10·00	4·25
363	**40**	8a. blue	16·00	9·50
364	**40**	15a. purple	47·00	22·00

54 Vasco da Gama

56 Aeroplane over Globe

1938. Name and value in black.

365	**54**	1a. green (postage)	3·00	1·80
366	**54**	2a. brown	3·00	1·80
367	**54**	3a. violet	3·00	1·80
368	**54**	4a. green	3·00	1·80
369	-	5a. red	3·00	1·80
370	-	6a. grey	4·75	3·00
371	-	8a. purple	5·00	3·25
372	-	10a. mauve	6·25	4·00
373	-	12a. red	6·50	4·25
374	-	15a. orange	8·50	5·50
375	-	20a. blue	10·00	5·50
376	-	40a. black	25·00	12·00
377	-	50a. brown	29·00	13·50
378	-	1p. red	95·00	34·00
379	-	2p. green	£130	50·00
380	-	3p. blue	£170	65·00
381	-	5p. brown	£300	75·00
382	**56**	1a. red (air)	1·70	80
383	**56**	2a. violet	3·00	1·80
384	**56**	3a. orange	6·50	2·50
385	**56**	5a. blue	8·50	5·00
386	**56**	10a. red	10·00	6·75
387	**56**	20a. green	20·00	12·00
388	**56**	50a. brown	31·00	18·00
389	**56**	70a. red	50·00	22·00
390	**56**	1p. mauve	85·00	32·00

Designs: Nos. 369/371, Mousinho de Albuquerque; 372/374, Henry the Navigator; 375/377, Dam; 378/381, Afonso de Albuquerque.

1940. Surch.

391	**50**	1a. on 6a. brown (No. 344)	9·25	6·50
394	**50**	2a. on 6a. brown (No. 344)	5·00	4·00
395	**50**	3a. on 6a. brown (No. 344)	5·00	4·00
401	-	3a. on 6a. grey (No. 370)	£110	55·00
396	**50**	5a. on 7a. red (No. 345)	16·00	11·00
397	**50**	5a. on 8a. blue (No. 346)	20·00	13·00
398	**50**	8a. on 30a. (No. 352)	17·00	8·75
399	**50**	8a. on 40a. (No. 353)	19·00	9·25
400	**50**	8a. on 50a. (No. 354)	19·00	10·50

61 Mountain Fort

1948

No.	Type	Description	Unused	Used
410	-	1a. brown and orange	10·50	1·10
427	-	1a. violet and pink	6·25	1·80
411	**61**	2a. purple	10·50	1·10
428	**61**	2a. brown and yellow	6·25	1·80
412	-	3a. purple	15·00	3·00
429	-	3a. orange	17·00	3·00
413	-	8a. red	9·75	3·25
430	-	8a. grey	21·00	3·00
414	-	10a. purple	18·00	3·75
431	-	10a. brown and orange	29·00	7·50
415	-	20a. blue	45·00	10·50
416	-	30a. grey	75·00	15·00
432	-	30a. blue	33·00	9·00
417	-	50a. brown and buff	£120	18·00
433	-	50a. olive and green	85·00	11·50
418	-	1p. green	£250	35·00
419	-	1p. blue	£275	†
434	-	1p. brown	£250	45·00
420	-	2p. red	£275	35·00
421	-	3p. green	£300	35·00
422	-	5p. violet	£425	35·00

Designs: Horiz—1a. Macao house; 3a. Port of Macao; 8a. Praia Grande Bay; 10a. Leal Senado Sq; 20a. Sao Jerome Hill; 30a. Street scene, Macao; 50a. Relief of goddess of Ma (allegory); 5p. Forest road. Vert—1p. Cerco Gateway; 2p. Barra Pagoda, Ma-Cok-Miu; 3p. Post Office.

62 Our Lady of Fatima

1948. Honouring the Statue of Our Lady of Fatima.

No.	Type	Description	Unused	Used
423	**62**	8a. red	90·00	30·00

64 Globe and Letter

1949. 75th Anniversary of UPU.

No.	Type	Description	Unused	Used
424	**64**	32a. purple	£225	55·00

65 Bells and Dove

1950. Holy Year.

No.	Type	Description	Unused	Used
425	**65**	32a. black	55·00	15·00
426	-	50a. red	55·00	15·00

Design: 50a. Angel holding candelabra.

66 Arms and Dragon

1950

No.	Type	Description	Unused	Used
435	**66**	1a. yellow on cream	5·25	2·30
436	**66**	2a. green on green	5·25	2·30
437	**66**	10a. purple on green	21·00	5·25
438	**66**	10a. mauve on green	18·00	5·25

67 F. Mendes Pinto

1951

No.	Type	Description	Unused	Used
439	**67**	1a. indigo and blue	1·80	1·10
440	-	2a. brown and green	3·50	1·10
441	-	3a. green and light green	6·00	2·00
442	-	6a. violet and blue	7·50	2·30
443	-	10a. brown and orange	18·00	3·00
444	**67**	20a. purple and light purple	30·00	6·75
445	-	30a. brown and green	50·00	9·00
446	-	50a. red and orange	£120	23·00

Designs: 2, 10a. St. Francis Xavier; 3, 50a. J. Alvaras; 6, 30a. L. de Camoens.

68 Junk

1951

No.	Type	Description	Unused	Used
447	-	1p. ultramarine and blue	70·00	5·00
448	-	3p. black and blue	£275	38·00
449	**68**	5p. brown and orange	£375	48·00

Designs: Horiz—1p. Sampan. Vert—3p. Junk.

69 Our Lady of Fatima

1951. Termination of Holy Year.

No.	Type	Description	Unused	Used
450	**69**	60a. mauve and pink	£110	23·00

71 St Raphael Hospital

1952. First Tropical Medicine Congress, Lisbon.

No.	Type	Description	Unused	Used
451	**71**	6a. lilac and black	20·00	6·75

72 St Francis Xavier Statue

1952. 400th Death Anniversary of St Francis Xavier.

No.	Type	Description	Unused	Used
452	**72**	3a. black on cream	9·75	1·80
453	-	16a. brown on buff	30·00	6·00
454	-	40a. black on blue	44·00	9·75

Designs: 16a. Miraculous Arm of St Francis; 40a. Tomb of St Francis.

73 The Virgin

1953. Missionary Art Exhibition.

No.	Type	Description	Unused	Used
455	**73**	8a. brown and drab	10·50	2·30
456	**73**	10a. blue and brown	35·00	8·25
457	**73**	50a. green and drab	45·00	11·50

74 Honeysuckle

1953. Indigenous Flowers.

No.	Type	Description	Unused	Used
458	**74**	1a. yellow, green and red	1·50	55
459	-	3a. purple, green and yellow	1·50	55
460	-	5a. red, green and brown	1·50	55
461	-	10a. multicoloured	1·50	55
462	-	16a. yellow, green & brown	3·00	75
463	-	30a. pink, brown and green	6·75	1·50
464	-	39a. multicoloured	8·25	2·00
465	-	1p. yellow, green and purple	14·50	2·50
466	-	3p. red, brown and grey	33·00	4·50
467	-	5p. yellow, green and red	55·00	9·75

Flowers: 3a. Myosotis; 5a. Dragon claw; 10a. Nunflower; 16a. Narcissus; 30a. Peach blossom; 39a. Lotus blossom; 1p. Chrysanthemum; 3p. Plum blossom; 5p. Tangerine blossom.

75 Portuguese Stamp of 1853 and Arms of Portuguese Overseas Provinces

1954. Portuguese Stamp Centenary.

No.	Type	Description	Unused	Used
468	**75**	10a. multicoloured	23·00	5·25

76 Father M. de Nobrega and View of Sao Paulo

1954. Fourth Centenary of Sao Paulo.

No.	Type	Description	Unused	Used
469	**76**	39a. multicoloured	30·00	6·50

77 Map of Macao

1956. Map multicoloured. Values in red, inscr in brown. Colours given are of the backgrounds.

No.	Type	Description	Unused	Used
470	**77**	1a. drab	1·50	80
471	**77**	3a. slate	3·50	1·10
472	**77**	5a. brown	5·00	1·60
473	**77**	10a. buff	8·25	1·90
474	**77**	30a. blue	12·00	2·75
475	**77**	40a. green	20·00	3·25
476	**77**	90a. grey	44·00	6·00
477	**77**	1p.50 pink	55·00	8·00

78 Exhibition Emblem and Atomic Emblems

1958. Brussels International Exhibition.

No.	Type	Description	Unused	Used
478	**78**	70a. multicoloured	12·00	3·75

79 *Cinnamomum camphora*

1958. Sixth International Congress of Tropical Medicine.

No.	Type	Description	Unused	Used
479	**79**	20a. multicoloured	13·50	6·00

80 Globe girdled by Signs of the Zodiac

1960. 500th Death Anniversary of Prince Henry the Navigator.

No.	Type	Description	Unused	Used
480	**80**	2p. multicoloured	23·00	8·00

81 Boeing 707 over Ermida da Penha

1960. Air. Multicoloured.

No.	Description	Unused	Used
481	50a. Praia Grande Bay	5·25	1·20
482	76a. Type **81**	11·50	3·25
483	3p. Macao	30·00	5·00
484	5p. Mong Ha	38·00	5·00
485	10p. Shore of Praia Grande Bay	60·00	5·75

82 Hockey

1962. Sports. Multicoloured.

No.	Description	Unused	Used
486	10a. Type **82**	5·00	1·20
487	16a. Wrestling	6·25	3·25
488	20a. Table tennis	9·00	2·75
489	50a. Motorcycle racing	10·50	4·25
490	1p.20 Relay racing	38·00	7·50
491	2p.50 Badminton	75·00	14·00

83 *Anopheles hycranus sinensis*

1962. Malaria Eradication.

No.	Type	Description	Unused	Used
492	**83**	40a. multicoloured	12·00	4·25

84 Bank Building

1964. Centenary of National Overseas Bank.

No.	Type	Description	Unused	Used
493	**84**	20a. multicoloured	18·00	4·50

85 ITU Emblem and St Gabriel

1965. Centenary of ITU.

No.	Type	Description	Unused	Used
494	**85**	10a. multicoloured	9·00	3·50

86 Infante Dom Henrique Academy and Visconde de Sao Januario Hospital

1966. 40th Anniversary of Portuguese National Revolution.

No.	Type	Description	Unused	Used
495	**86**	10a. multicoloured	9·00	3·75

87 Drummer, 1548

1966. Portuguese Military Uniforms. Multicoloured.

No.	Description	Unused	Used
496	10a. Type **87**	3·75	85
497	15a. Soldier, 1548	6·75	1·70
498	20a. Arquebusier, 1649	7·50	1·70
499	40a. Infantry officer, 1783	12·00	1·80
500	50a. Infantryman, 1783	14·50	3·25
501	60a. Infantryman, 1902	33·00	4·25
502	1p. Infantryman, 1903	42·00	7·00
503	3p. Infantryman, 1904	70·00	14·00

88 O. E. Carmo and Patrol Boat *Vega*

1967. Centenary of Military Naval Association. Multicoloured.

504	10a. Type **88**	6·75	1·70
505	20a. Silva Junior and sail frigate *Don Fernando*	13·00	3·00

89 Arms of Pope Paul VI, and 'Golden Rose'

1967. 50th Anniversary of Fatima Apparitions.

506	**89**	50a. multicoloured	14·50	3·50

90 Cabral Monument, Lisbon

1968. 500th Birth Anniversary of Pedro Cabral (explorer). Multicoloured.

507	20a. Type **90**	11·00	2·50
508	70a. Cabral's statue, Belmonte	13·50	4·25

91 Adm. Gago Coutinho with Sextant

1969. Birth Centenary of Admiral Gago Coutinho.

509	**91**	20a. multicoloured	7·50	2·50

92 Church and Convent of Our Lady of the Reliquary, Vidigueira

1969. 500th Birth Anniversary of Vasco da Gama (explorer).

510	**92**	1p. multicoloured	23·00	3·50

93 L. A. Rebello da Silva

1969. Centenary of Overseas Administrative Reforms.

511	**93**	90a. multicoloured	13·00	2·00

94 Bishop D. Belchoir Carneiro

1969. 400th Anniversary of Misericordia Monastery, Macao.

512	**94**	50a. multicoloured	7·50	1·70

95 Facade of Mother Church, Golega

1969. 500th Birth Anniversary of King Manoel I.

513	**95**	30a. multicoloured	13·00	2·00

96 Marshal Carmona

1970. Birth Centenary of Marshal Carmona.

514	**96**	5a. multicoloured	4·50	1·70

97 Dragon Mask

1971. Chinese Carnival Masks. Multicoloured.

515	5a. Type **97**	2·40	85
516	10a. Lion mask	4·75	1·70

98 Portuguese Traders at the Chinese Imperial Court

1972. 400th Anniversary of Camoens' *The Lusiads* (epic poem).

517	**98**	20a. multicoloured	26·00	8·50

99 Hockey

1972. Olympic Games, Munich.

518	**99**	50a. multicoloured	7·50	1·70

100 Fairey IIID Seaplane *Santa Cruz* arriving at Rio de Janeiro

1972. 50th Anniversary of First Flight from Lisbon to Rio de Janeiro.

519	**100**	5p. multicoloured	42·00	13·00

101 Lyre Emblem and Theatre Facade

1972. Centenary of Pedro V Theatre, Macao.

520	**101**	2p. multicoloured	21·00	5·00

102 WMO Emblem

1973. Centenary of WMO.

521	**102**	20a. multicoloured	15·00	3·00

103 Visconde de Sao Januario

1974. Centenary of Visconde de Sao Januario Hospital. Multicoloured.

522	15a. Type **103**	1·70	85
523	60a. Hospital buildings of 1874 and 1974	7·50	1·70

104 Chinnery (self-portrait)

1974. Birth Bicentenary of George Chinnery (painter).

524	**104**	30a. multicoloured	7·50	3·00

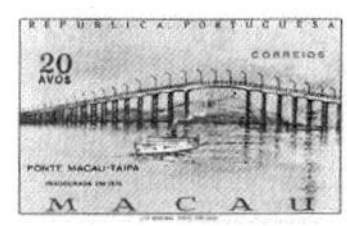

105 Macao–Taipa Bridge

1975. Inauguration of Macao–Taipa Bridge. Multicoloured.

525	20a. Type **105**	3·00	1·40
526	2p.20 View of Bridge from below	30·00	3·75

106 Man waving Banner

1975. First Anniversary of Portuguese Revolution.

527	**106**	10a. multicoloured	4·50	4·25
528	**106**	1p. multicoloured	27·00	9·00

107 Pou Chai Pagoda

1976. Pagodas. Multicoloured.

529	10p. Type **107**	29·00	9·00
530	20p. Tin Hau Pagoda	55·00	12·00

108 Symbolic Figure

1977. Legislative Assembly.

531	**108**	5a. blue, dp blue & black	15·00	8·50
532	**108**	2p. brown and black	£275	17·00
533	**108**	5p. yellow, green and black	£110	26·00

1979. Nos. 462, 464, 469, 482, 523 and 526 surch.

536	-	10a. on 16a. yellow, green and brown	13·00	6·75
537	-	30a. on 39a. multicoloured	13·50	6·75
538	**76**	30a. on 39a. multicoloured	70·00	30·00
539	-	30a. on 60a. multicoloured	13·00	7·75
540	**81**	70a. on 76a. multicoloured	60·00	12·00
541	-	2p. on 2p.20 multicoloured	15·00	10·00

111 Camoes and Macao Harbour

1981. 400th Death Anniversary (1980) of Camoes (Portuguese poet).

542	**111**	10a. multicoloured	1·80	1·70
543	**111**	30a. multicoloured	3·50	3·50
544	**111**	1p. multicoloured	8·25	5·00
545	**111**	3p. multicoloured	12·00	6·75

113 Buddha and Macao Cathedral

1981. Transcultural Psychiatry Symposium.

547	**113**	15a. multicoloured	75	60
548	**113**	40a. multicoloured	1·40	70
549	**113**	50a. multicoloured	1·50	85
550	**113**	60a. multicoloured	2·40	1·00
551	**113**	1p. multicoloured	4·75	1·40
552	**113**	2p.20 multicoloured	13·00	2·75

115 Health Services Buildings

1982. Buildings.

554	-	10a. grey, blue and yellow	60	50
555	-	20a. black, green & lt grn	75	50
556	**115**	30a. green, grey and stone	75	50
557	-	40a. yellow, lt green & grn	90	50
558	-	60a. orange, chocolate and brown	75	50
559	-	80a. pink, green & brown	1·70	60
560	-	90a. purple, blue and red	1·10	85
561	-	1p. multicoloured	2·30	85
562	-	1p.50 yellow, brn & grey	5·25	2·40
563	-	2p. purple, ultramarine and blue	3·75	1·70
564	-	2p.50 ultramarine, pink and blue	3·25	2·20
565	-	3p. yellow, green and olive	3·00	1·20
566	-	7p.50 lilac, blue and red	8·25	4·00
567	-	10p. grey, lilac and mauve	14·50	7·25
568	-	15p. yellow, brown and red	13·50	7·75

Designs: 10a. Social Welfare Institute; 20a. Holy House of Mercy; 40a. Guia lighthouse; 60a. St Lawrence's Church; 80a. St Joseph's Seminary; 90a. Pedro V Theatre; 1p. Cerco city gate; 1p.50, St Domenico's Church; 2p. Luis de Camoes Museum; 2p.50, Ruins of St Paul's Church; 3p. Palace of St Sancha (Governor's residence); 7p.50, Senate House; 10p. Schools Welfare Service building; 15p. Barracks of the Moors (headquarters of Port Captaincy and Maritime Police).

116 Heng Ho (Moon goddess)

1982. Autumn Festival. Multicoloured.

569	40a. Type **116**	3·75	2·50
570	1p. Decorated gourds	10·50	4·25
571	2p. Paper lantern	13·50	7·75
572	5p. Warrior riding Lion	27·00	12·00

117 Aerial View of Macao, Taipa and Coloane Islands

1982. Macao's Geographical Situation. Multicoloured.

573	50a. Type **117**	15·00	2·75
574	3p. Map of South China	45·00	12·00

118 Switchboard Operators (Lou Sok Man)

1983. World Communications Year. Children's Drawings. Multicoloured.

575	60a. Type **118**	3·00	1·60
576	3p. Postman and pillarbox (Lai Sok Pek)	6·50	4·75
577	6p. Globe with methods of communication (Loi Chak Keong)	12·50	6·25

119 *Asclepias curassavica*

1983. Medicinal Plants. Multicoloured.

578	20a. Type **119**	1·50	1·00
579	40a. *Acanthus ilicifolius*	3·00	1·00
580	60a. *Melastoma sanguineum*	4·25	1·30
581	70a. Indian lotus (*Nelumbo nucifera*)	6·00	1·60
582	1p.50 *Bombax malabaricum*	7·25	2·75
583	2p.50 *Hibiscus mutabilis*	13·00	6·50
MS584	143×90 mm. Nos. 578/583 (sold at 6p.50)	£225	£180

120 Galleon and Map of Macao (left)

1983. 16th-century Portuguese Discoveries. Multicoloured.

585	4p. Type **120**	10·00	6·50
586	4p. Galleon, astrolabe and map of Macao (right)	10·00	6·50

Nos. 585/586 were printed together, *se-tenant*, forming a composite design.

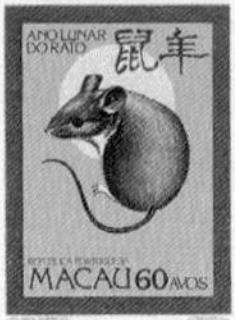

121 Rat

1984. New Year. Year of the Rat.

587	**121**	60a. multicoloured	11·00	8·00

See also No. **MS**917.

122 Detail of First Macao Stamp, 1884

1984. Centenary of Macao Stamps.

588	**122**	40a. black and red	3·00	80
589	**122**	3p. black and red	5·75	2·50
590	**122**	5p. black and brown	13·00	5·00
MS591		116×139 mm. Nos. 588/90	85·00	80·00

123 Jay

1984. Ausipex 84 International Stamp Exhibition, Melbourne. Birds. Multicoloured.

592	30a. White-throated and river kingfishers	2·20	95
593	40a. Type **123**	2·20	95
594	50a. Japanese white-eye	3·00	95
595	70a. Hoopoe	5·75	1·10
596	2p.50 Pekin robin	13·00	3·25
597	6p. Mallard	14·50	5·50

124 Hok Lou T'eng

1984. Philakorea 84 International Stamp Exhibition, Seoul. Fishing Boats. Multicoloured.

598	20a. Type **124**	1·50	80
599	60a. Tai Tong	3·00	1·60
600	2p. Tai Mei Chai	7·25	3·25
601	5p. Ch'at Pong T'o	14·50	5·50

125 Ox and Moon

1985. New Year. Year of the Ox.

602	**125**	1p. multicoloured	11·50	4·75

See also No. **MS**917.

126 Open Hand with Stylised Doves

1985. International Youth Year. Multicoloured.

603	2p.50 Type **126**	8·00	1·10
604	3p. Open hands and plants	11·00	4·00

127 President Eanes

1985. Visit of President Ramalho Eanes of Portugal.

605	**127**	1p.50 multicoloured	6·50	3·25

128 Riverside Scene

1985. 25th Anniversary of Luis de Camoes Museum. Paintings by Cheng Chi Yun. Multicoloured.

606	2p.50 Type **128**	12·50	3·25
607	2p.50 Man on seat and boy filling jar from river	12·50	3·25
608	2p.50 Playing harp in summerhouse	12·50	3·25
609	2p.50 Three men by river	12·50	3·25

129 *Euploea midamus*

1985. World Tourism Day. Butterflies. Multicoloured.

610	30a. Type **129**	3·00	80
611	50a. Great orange-tip	3·00	80
612	70a. *Lethe confusa*	4·75	95
613	2p. Purple sapphire	6·00	1·60
614	4p. *Euthalia phemius seitzi*	12·50	2·50
615	7p.50 Common birdwing	16·00	6·75
MS616	95×120 mm. Nos. 610/615	£225	£140

130 *Tou* (sailing barge)

1985. Italia '85 International Stamp Exhibition, Rome. Cargo Boats. Multicoloured.

617	50a. Type **130**	1·50	65
618	70a. *Veng Seng Lei* (motor junk)	5·00	80
619	1p. *Tong Heng Long No. 2* (motor junk)	7·25	1·60
620	6p. *Fong Vong San* (container ship)	13·00	7·25

131 Tiger and Moon

1986. New Year. Year of the Tiger.

621	**131**	1p.50 multicoloured	10·00	1·90

See also No. **MS**917.

132 View of Macao

1986. Macao, 'the Past is still Present'.

622	**132**	2p.20 multicoloured	10·00	4·00

133 Suo-na

1986. Ameripex '86 International Stamp Exhibition, Chicago. Musical Instruments. Multicoloured.

623	20a. Type **133**	5·75	2·40
624	50a. Sheng (pipes)	7·25	2·75
625	60a. Er-hu (bowed instrument)	10·00	3·25
626	70a. Ruan (string instrument)	13·00	4·00
627	5p. Cheng (harp)	35·00	5·50
628	8p. Pi-pa (lute)	41·00	9·50
MS629	119×111 mm. Nos. 623/628	£325	£180

134 *Flying Albatros* (hydrofoil)

1986. Stockholmia 86 International Stamp Exhibition. Passenger Ferries. Multicoloured.

630	10a. Type **134**	75	80
631	40a. *Tejo* (hovercraft)	6·75	1·60
632	3p. *Tercera* (jetfoil)	7·25	2·50
633	7p.50 *Cheung Kong* (high speed ferry)	15·00	5·00

135 Taipa Fortress

1986. Tenth Anniversary of Security Forces. Fortresses. Multicoloured.

634	2p. Type **135**	16·00	9·50
635	2p. St Paul on the Mount	16·00	9·50
636	2p. St Francis	16·00	9·50
637	2p. Guia	16·00	9·50

Nos. 634/637 were printed together, *se-tenant*, forming a composite design.

136 Sun Yat-sen

1986. 120th Birth Anniversary of Dr. Sun Yat-sen. Multicoloured.

638	70a. Type **136**	7·25	4·00
MS639	95×70 mm. 1p.30 Dr. Sun Yat-sen (*different*)	£100	70·00

137 Hare and Moon

1987. New Year. Year of the Hare.

640	**137**	1p.50 multicoloured	10·00	2·40

See also No. **MS**917.

138 Wa To (physician)

1987. Shek Wan Ceramics. Multicoloured.

641	2p.20 Type **138**	11·00	7·25
642	2p.20 Choi San, God of Fortune	11·00	7·25
643	2p.20 Yi, Sun God	11·00	7·25
644	2p.20 Cung Kuei, Keeper of Demons	11·00	7·25

139 Boats

1987. Dragon Boat Festival. Multicoloured.

645	50a. Type **139**	5·75	1·60
646	5p. Dragon boat prow	14·50	5·00

140 Circular Fan

1987. Fans. Multicoloured.

647	30a. Type **140**	7·25	2·50
648	70a. Folding fan with tree design	14·50	4·00
649	1p. Square-shaped fan with peacock design	41·00	5·00
650	6p. Heart-shaped fan with painting of woman and tree	44·00	13·50
MS651	113×139 mm. Nos. 647/650	£500	£250

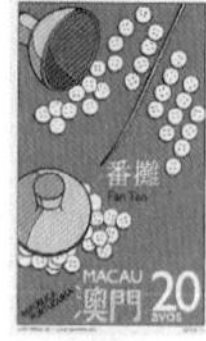

141 Fantan

1987. Casino Games. Multicoloured.

652	20a. Type **141**	11·50	6·00
653	40a. Cussec	13·00	6·75
654	4p. Baccarat	17·00	7·25
655	7p. Roulette	22·00	8·00

142 Goods Hand-cart

1987. Traditional Vehicles. Multicoloured.

656	10a. Type **142**	1·50	1·60
657	70a. Open sedan chair	4·25	2·40
658	90a. Rickshaw	7·50	3·25
659	10p. Cycle rickshaw	21·00	5·50
MS660	90×65 mm. 7p.50 Covered sedan chair	75·00	40·00

143 Dragon and Moon

1988. New Year. Year of the Dragon.

661	**143**	2p.50 multicoloured	10·00	6·50

See also No. **MS**917.

144 West European Hedgehog

1988. Protected Mammals. Multicoloured.

662	3p. Type **144**	10·00	3·25
663	3p. Eurasian badger	10·00	3·25
664	3p. European otter	10·00	3·25
665	3p. Chinese pangolin	10·00	3·25

145 Breastfeeding

1988. 40th Anniversary of WHO. Multicoloured.

666	60a. Type **145**	5·00	1·30
667	80a. Vaccinating child	6·50	1·60
668	2p.40 Donating blood	12·50	4·75

146 Bicycles

1988. Transport. Multicoloured.

669	20a. Type **146**	1·50	80
670	50a. Lambretta and Vespa	3·00	1·60
671	3p.30 Open-sided motor car	9·50	2·40
672	5p. Renault delivery truck, 1912	12·50	4·75
MS673	68×57 mm. 7p.50 Rover (1907)	95·00	48·00

147 Hurdling

1988. Olympic Games, Seoul. Multicoloured.

674	40a. Type **147**	3·00	80
675	60a. Basketball	4·25	1·00
676	1p. Football	6·50	2·40
677	8p. Table tennis	11·50	4·75
MS678	112×140 mm. Nos. 673/676; 5p. Taekwondo	95·00	80·00

148 Intelpost (electronic mail)

1988. New Postal Services. Multicoloured.

679	13p.40 Type **148**	13·00	4·00
680	40p. Express Mail Service (EMS)	16·00	12·00

149 BMW Saloon Car

1988. 35th Macao Grand Prix. Multicoloured.

681	80a. Type **149**	3·00	80
682	2p.80 Motorcycle	8·00	1·90
683	7p. Formula 3 car	17·00	5·50
MS684	115×139 mm. Nos. 681/683	£120	90·00

150 Snake and Moon

1989. New Year. Year of the Snake.

685	**150**	3p. multicoloured	14·50	4·75

See also No. **MS**917.

151 Water Carrier

1989. Traditional Occupations (1st series). Multicoloured.

686	50a. Type **151**	1·50	50
687	1p. Tan-kya (boat) woman	3·00	80
688	4p. Tin-tin man (pedlar)	5·00	3·00
689	5p. Tao-fu-fa (soya bean cheese) vendor	8·00	3·50

See also Nos. 714/717 and 743/746.

152 White Building

1989. Paintings by George Vitalievich Smirnoff in Luis Camoes Museum. Multicoloured.

690	2p. Type **152**	3·75	1·60
691	2p. Building with railings	3·75	1·60
692	2p. Street scene	3·75	1·60
693	2p. White thatched cottage	3·75	1·60

153 Common Cobra

1989. Philexfrance 89 International Stamp Exhibition, Paris. Snakes of Macao. Multicoloured.

694	2p.50 Type **153**	5·00	2·10
695	2p.50 Banded krait (*Bungarus fasciatus*)	5·00	2·10
696	2p.50 Bamboo pit viper (*Trimeresurus albolabris*)	5·00	2·10
697	2p.50 Rat snake (*Elaphe radiata*)	5·00	2·10

154 Talu

1989. Traditional Games. Multicoloured.

698	10a. Type **154**	1·90	95
699	60a. Triol (marbles)	4·25	1·20
700	3p.30 Chiquia (shuttlecock)	8·00	2·40
701	5p. Chinese chequers	9·50	4·00

155 Piaggio P-136L Flying Boat

1989. Aircraft. Multicoloured.

702	50a. Type **155**	1·20	65
703	70a. Martin M-130 flying boat	2·20	80
704	2p.80 Fairey 111D seaplane	2·50	1·60
705	4p. Hawker Osprey seaplane	5·00	2·50
MS706	105×82 mm. 7p.50 de Havilland DH.80A Puss Moth	50·00	29·00

156 Malacca

1989. World Stamp Expo '89 International Stamp Exhibition, Washington DC. Portuguese Presence in Far East. Multicoloured.

707	40a. Type **156**	85	50
708	70a. Thailand	1·60	65
709	90a. India	2·50	95
710	2p.50 Japan	4·75	1·30
711	7p.50 China	8·00	3·50
MS712	14?×130 mm. Nos. 707/711; 3p. Macao	75·00	48·00

157 Horse and Moon

1990. New Year. Year of the Horse.

713	**157**	4p. multicoloured	7·00	2·75

See also No. **MS**917.

1990. Traditional Occupations (2nd series). As T **151**. Multicoloured.

714	30a. Long-chau singer	1·90	1·10
715	70a. Cobbler	3·50	1·90
716	1p.50 Travelling penman	5·00	2·40
717	7p.50 Fisherman with wide nets	14·00	5·50

158 Penny Black and Sir Rowland Hill (postal reformer)

1990. 150th Anniversary of the Penny Black. Sheet 91×130 mm.

MS718	**158**	10p. multicoloured	44·00	29·00

159 Long-finned Grouper (*Epinephelus megachir*)

1990. Fish. Multicoloured.

719	2p.40 Type **159**	4·25	2·40
720	2p.40 Malabar snapper (*Lutianus malabaricus*)	4·25	2·40
721	2p.40 Spotted snakehead (*Ophiocepalus maculatus*)	4·25	2·40
722	2p.40 Paradise fish (*Macropodus opercularis*)	4·25	2·40

160 Porcelain

1990. New Zealand 1990 International Stamp Exhibition, Auckland. Industrial Diversification. Multicoloured.

723	3p. Type **160**	4·25	2·40
724	3p. Furniture	4·25	2·40
725	3p. Toys	4·25	2·40
726	3p. Artificial flowers	4·25	2·40
MS727	131×95 mm. Nos. 723/726	60·00	24·00

161 Cycling

1990. 11th Asian Games, Peking. Multicoloured.

728	80a. Type **161**	1·50	50

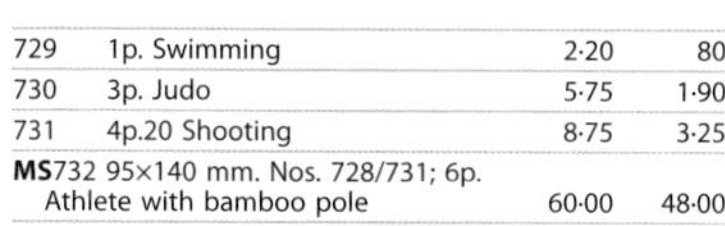

729	1p. Swimming	2·20	80
730	3p. Judo	5·75	1·90
731	4p.20 Shooting	8·75	3·25
MS732	95×140 mm. Nos. 728/731; 6p. Athlete with bamboo pole	60·00	48·00

162 Rose by Lazaro Luis

1990. Compass Roses. Designs showing roses from ancient charts by cartographer named. Multicoloured.

733	50a. Type **162**	2·20	80
734	1p. Diogo Homem	3·75	95
735	3p.50 Diogo Homem (different)	6·50	2·75
736	6p.50 Fernao Vaz Dourado	12·50	3·50
MS737	107×100 mm. 5p. Luiz Teixeira (29×39 mm)	75·00	45·00

163 Cricket Fight

1990. Betting on Animals. Multicoloured.

738	20a. Type **163**	1·90	65
739	80a. Melodious laughing thrush fight	4·25	1·30
740	1p. Greyhound racing	5·50	1·90
741	10p. Horse racing	14·50	3·50

164 Goat and Moon

1991. New Year. Year of the Goat.

742	**164**	4p.50 multicoloured	7·00	1·80

See also No. **MS**917.

1991. Traditional Occupations (3rd series). As T **151**. Multicoloured.

743	80a. Knife-grinder	1·50	80
744	1p.70 Flour-puppets vendor	3·00	95
745	3p.50 Street barber	7·00	1·90
746	4p.20 Fortune-teller	10·00	3·50

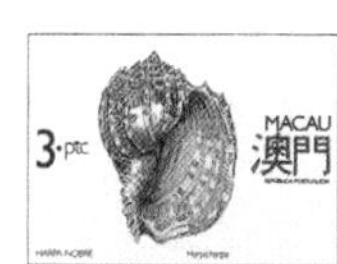

165 True Harp (*Harpa harpa*)

1991. Sea Shells. Multicoloured.

747	3p. Type **165**	5·00	2·75
748	3p. Oil-lamp tun (*Tonna zonata*)	5·00	2·75
749	3p. Bramble murex (*Murex pecten*)	5·00	2·75
750	3p. Rose-branch murex (*Chicoreus rosarius*)	5·00	2·75

The Latin names on Nos. 749/750 are incorrect.

166 Character and Backcloth

1991. Chinese Opera. Multicoloured.

751	**166**	60a. multicoloured	3·00	65
752	-	80a. multicoloured	4·25	80
753	-	1p. multicoloured	6·50	1·60
754	-	10p. multicoloured	18·00	4·75

Designs: Nos. 752/754, Different backcloths and costumes.

167 *Delonix regia* and Lou Lim Ioc Garden

1991. Flowers and Gardens (1st series). Multicoloured.

755	1p.70 Type **167**	3·00	95
756	3p. *Ipomoea cairica* and Sao Francisco Garden	4·00	1·90
757	3p.50 *Jasminum mesyi* and Sun Yat Sen Park	6·50	2·75
758	4p.20 *Bauhinia variegata* and Seac Pai Van Park	8·00	4·00
MS759	95×137 mm. Nos. 755/758	85·00	45·00

See also Nos. 815/**MS**819.

168 Portuguese Traders unloading Boats

1991. Cultural Exchange. Nambam Paintings attributed to Kano Domi. Multicoloured.

760	4p.20 Type **168**	4·25	1·90
761	4p.20 Portuguese traders displaying goods to buyers	4·25	1·90
MS762	107×74 mm. Nos. 760/761	45·00	29·00

169 Firework Display

1991. Christmas. Multicoloured.

763	1p.70 Type **169**	2·00	80
764	3p. Father Christmas	3·25	1·10
765	3p.50 Man dancing	5·00	1·80
766	4p.20 January 1st celebrations	10·00	3·50

170 Concertina Door

1992. Doors and Windows. Multicoloured.

767	1p.70 Type **170**	2·00	1·10
768	3p. Window with four shutters	4·00	2·10
769	3p.50 Window with two shutters	5·50	3·25
770	4p.20 Louvred door	8·00	4·50

171 Monkey and Moon

1992. New Year. Year of the Monkey.

771	**171**	4p.50 multicoloured	5·75	4·00

See also No. **MS**917.

172 T'it Kuai Lei

1992. Gods of Chinese Mythology (1st series). Multicoloured.

772	3p.50 (1) Type **172**	11·50	5·50
773	3p.50 (2) Chong Lei Kun	11·50	5·50
774	3p.50 (3) Cheong Kuo Lou on donkey	11·50	5·50
775	3p.50 (4) Loi Tong Pan	11·50	5·50

See also Nos. 796/799.

173 Lion Dance

1992. World Columbian Stamp Expo '92, Chicago. Chinese Dances. Multicoloured.

776	1p. Type **173**	1·70	95
777	2p.70 Lion dance (different)	3·25	1·10
778	6p. Dragon dance	6·50	2·75

174 High Jumping

1992. Olympic Games, Barcelona. Multicoloured.

779	80a. Type **174**	1·20	65
780	4p.20 Badminton	2·20	1·30
781	4p.70 Roller hockey	3·25	1·60
782	5p. Yachting	4·25	2·20
MS783	137×95 mm. Nos. 779/782	29·00	18·00

175 Na Cha Temple

1992. Temples (1st series). Multicoloured.

784	1p. Type **175**	1·70	95
785	1p.50 Kun Iam	2·50	1·10
786	1p.70 Hong Kon	3·50	2·10
787	6p.50 A Ma	7·00	4·00

See also Nos. 792/795 and 894/898.

176 Tung Sin Tong Services

1992. Centenary of Tung Sin Tong (medical and educational charity).

788	**176**	1p. multicoloured	3·25	80

177 Rooster and Dragon

1992. Portuguese–Chinese Friendship.

789	**177**	10p. multicoloured	5·75	3·25
MS790	109×74 mm. **177** 10p. multicoloured		26·00	24·00

178 Red Junglefowl

1992. New Year. Year of the Cock.

791	**178**	5p. multicoloured	5·75	1·80

See also No. **MS**917.

1993. Temples (2nd series). As T **175**. Multicoloured.

792	50a. T'am Kong	85	50
793	2p. T'in Hau	1·90	65
794	3p.50 Lin Fong	2·75	1·30
795	8p. Pau Kong	4·00	3·25

1993. Gods of Chinese Mythology (2nd series). As T **172**. Multicoloured.

796	3p.50 (1) Lam Ch'oi Wo flying on crane	4·25	3·25
797	3p.50 (2) Ho Sin Ku (goddess) on peach blossom	4·25	3·25
798	3p.50 (3) Hon Seong Chi crossing sea on basket of flowers	4·25	3·25
799	3p.50 (4) Ch'ou Kuok K'ao crossing river on plank	4·25	3·25

179 Children carrying Banners

1993. Chinese Wedding. Multicoloured.

800	3p. Type **179**	2·20	1·20
801	3p. Bride	2·20	1·20
802	3p. Bridegroom	2·20	1·20
803	3p. Wedding guests	2·20	1·20
MS804	124×106 mm. 8p. Bride and groom (50×40 mm)	22·00	19·00

Nos. 800/803 were issued together, *se-tenant*, forming a composite design.

180 Bird perched on Hand

1993. Environmental Protection.

805	**180**	1p. multicoloured	3·25	1·20

181 Eurasian Scops Owl

1993. Birds of Prey. Multicoloured.

806	3p. Type **181**	1·70	1·10
807	3p. Barn owl (*Tyto alba*)	1·70	1·10
808	3p. Peregrine falcon (*Falco peregrinus*)	1·70	1·10
809	3p. Golden eagle (*Aquila obrysaetos*)	1·70	1·10
MS810	107×128 mm. Nos. 806/809	28·00	16·00

182 Town Hall

1993. Union of Portuguese-speaking Capital Cities.

811	**182**	1p.50 green, blue and red	2·50	95

183 Portuguese Missionaries

1993. 450th Anniversary of First Portuguese Visit to Japan. Multicoloured.

812	50a. Japanese man with musket	1·50	50
813	3p. Type **183**	3·00	1·30
814	3p.50 Traders carrying goods	4·25	1·60

184 *Spathodea campanulata* and Luis de Camoes Garden

1993. Flowers and Gardens (2nd series). Multicoloured.

815	1p. Type **184**	1·00	50
816	2p. *Tithonia diversifolia* and Montanha Russa Garden	1·90	80
817	3p. *Rhodomyrtus tomentosa* and Cais Garden	2·20	1·10
818	8p. *Passiflora foetida* and Flora Garden	3·75	3·25
MS819	90×120 mm. Nos. 815/818	32·00	22·00

185 Caravel

1993. 16th-century Sailing Ships. Multicoloured.

820	1p. Type **185**	1·10	50
821	2p. Caravel (different)	1·80	80
822	3p.50 Nau	2·20	1·30
823	4p.50 Galleon	3·75	1·90
MS824	160×105 mm. Nos. 820/823	17·00	13·00

186 Saloon Car

1993. 40th Anniversary of Macao Grand Prix. Multicoloured.

825	1p.50 Type **186**	1·50	95
826	2p. Motorcycle	2·20	1·10
827	4p.50 Racing car	4·25	2·75

187 Chow-chow and Moon

1994. New Year. Year of the Dog.

828	**187**	5p. multicoloured	5·00	1·90

See also No. **MS**917.

188 Map and Prince Henry (1/2-size illustration)

1994. 600th Birth Anniversary of Prince Henry the Navigator.

829	**188**	3p. multicoloured	4·25	2·20

189 Lakeside Hut

1994. Birth Bicentenary of George Chinnery (artist). Multicoloured.

830	3p.50 Type **189**	2·50	1·60
831	3p.50 Fisherman on sea wall	2·50	1·60
832	3p.50 Harbour	2·50	1·60
833	3p.50 Sao Tiago Fortress	2·50	1·60
MS834	138×87 mm. Nos. 830/833	26·00	16·00

190 Lai Sis Exchange

1994. Spring Festival of Lunar New Year. Multicoloured.

835	1p. Type **190**	85	50
836	2p. Flower and tangerine tree decorations	1·70	80
837	3p.50 Preparing family meal	1·90	1·30
838	4p.50 Paper decorations bearing good wishes	2·75	1·90

191 'Longevity'

1994. Legends and Myths (1st series). Chinese Gods. Multicoloured.

839	3p. Type **191**	4·00	2·40
840	3p. 'Prosperity'	4·00	2·40

No.	Type	Description	Unused	Used
841		3p. 'Happiness'	4·00	2·40
MS842		138×90 mm. Nos. 839/841	26·00	19·00

See also Nos. 884/**MS**888, 930/**MS**933, 994/**MS**998 and 1035/**MS**1039.

192 Footballer

1994. World Cup Football Championship, USA. Multicoloured.

No.	Type	Description	Unused	Used
843		2p. Type **192**	1·50	65
844		3p. Tackling	2·20	1·10
845		3p.50 Heading ball	3·00	1·30
846		4p.50 Goalkeeper saving goal	4·25	2·10
MS847		138×90 mm. Nos. 843/846	21·00	16·00

193 Rice Shop

1994. Traditional Chinese Shops. Multicoloured.

No.	Type	Description	Unused	Used
848		1p. Type **193**	1·00	50
849		1p.50 Medicinal tea shop	1·20	65
850		2p. Salt-fish shop	2·20	95
851		3p.50 Pharmacy	4·25	1·30

194 Astrolabe

1994. Nautical Instruments. Multicoloured.

No.	Type	Description	Unused	Used
852		3p. Type **194**	3·00	1·60
853		3p.50 Quadrant	4·25	2·40
854		4p.50 Sextant	5·75	3·25

195 Fencing

1994. 12th Asian Games, Hiroshima, Japan. Multicoloured.

No.	Type	Description	Unused	Used
855		1p. Type **195**	1·50	65
856		2p. Gymnastics	2·20	80
857		3p. Water-polo	3·00	1·10
858		3p.50 Pole vaulting	3·75	1·90

196 Nobre de Carvalho Bridge

1994. Bridges. Multicoloured.

No.	Type	Description	Unused	Used
859		1p. Type **196**	3·75	1·60
860		8p. Friendship Bridge	7·25	4·00

197 Carp

1994. Good Luck Signs. Multicoloured.

No.	Type	Description	Unused	Used
861		3p. Type **197**	2·20	1·90
862		3p.50 Peaches	3·75	2·10
863		4p.50 Water lily	5·00	4·00

198 Angel's Head (stained glass window, Macao Cathedral)

1994. Religious Art. Multicoloured.

No.	Type	Description	Unused	Used
864		50a. Type **198**	45	40
865		1p. Holy Ghost (stained glass window, Macao Cathedral)	60	55
866		1p.50 Silver sacrarium	1·00	65
867		2p. Silver salver	1·50	80
868		3p. *Escape into Egypt* (ivory statuette)	2·30	1·10
869		3p.50 Gold and silver cup	3·00	1·30

199 Pig and Moon

1995. New Year. Year of the Pig.

No.	Type	Description	Unused	Used
870	**199**	5p.50 multicoloured	5·00	1·90

See also No. **MS**917.

200 *Lou Lim Iok Garden*

1995. Paintings of Macao by Lio Man Cheong. Multicoloured.

No.	Type	Description	Unused	Used
871		50a. Type **200**	50	50
872		1p. *Guia Fortress and Lighthouse*	65	65
873		1p.50 *Barra Temple*	85	80
874		2p. *Avenida da Praia, Taipa*	1·20	95
875		2p.50 *Kun Iam Temple*	1·90	1·60
876		3p. *St. Paul's Seminary*	2·75	1·90
877		3p.50 *Penha Hill*	3·75	2·40
878		4p. *Gates of Understanding Monument*	4·75	3·25

201 Magnifying Glass over Goods

1995. World Consumer Day.

No.	Type	Description	Unused	Used
879	**201**	1p. multicoloured	2·50	80

202 Pangolin

1995. Protection of Chinese ('Asian') Pangolin. Multicoloured.

No.	Type	Description	Unused	Used
880		1p.50 In fork of tree	2·50	95
881		1p.50 Hanging from tree by tail	2·50	95
882		1p.50 On leafy branch	2·50	95
883		1p.50 Type **202**	2·50	95

203 Kun Sai Iam

1995. Legends and Myths (2nd series). Kun Sai Iam (Buddhist god). Multicoloured.

No.	Type	Description	Unused	Used
884		3p. Type **203**	4·25	1·90
885		3p. Holding baby	4·25	1·90
886		3p. Sitting behind water lily	4·25	1·90
887		3p. With water lily and dragonfish	4·25	1·90
MS888		138×90 mm. 8p. Kun Sai Iam (*different*)	36·00	22·00

204/207 Senado Square ($^1/_3$-size illustration)

1995. Senado Square.

No.	Type	Description	Unused	Used
889	**204**	2p. multicoloured	2·20	1·10
890	**205**	2p. multicoloured	2·20	1·10
891	**206**	2p. multicoloured	2·20	1·10
892	**207**	2p. multicoloured	2·20	1·10
MS893		138×90 mm. 8p. multicoloured (Leal Senado building and Post Office Clock tower) (*horiz*)	20·00	13·00

Nos. 889/892 were issued together, *se-tenant*, forming the composite design illustrated.

1995. Temples (3rd series). As T **175**. Multicoloured.

No.	Type	Description	Unused	Used
894		50a. Kuan Tai	85	50
895		1p. Pak Tai	1·50	80
896		1p.50 Lin K'ai	1·90	95
897		3p. Se Kam Tong	3·00	1·60
898		3p.50 Fok Tak	3·75	1·90

208 Pekin Robin (*Leiothrix lutea*)

1995. Singapore '95 International Stamp Exhibition. Birds. Multicoloured.

No.	Type	Description	Unused	Used
899		2p.50 Type **208**	2·75	1·40
900		2p.50 Japanese white-eye (*Zosterops japonica*)	2·75	1·40
901		2p.50 Island canary (*Serinus canarius canarius*)	2·75	1·40
902		2p.50 Melodious laughing thrush (*Gurrulax canonus*)	2·75	1·40
MS903		137×90 mm. 10p. Magpie robin (*Copyschus saularis*)	29·00	16·00

209 Pipa

1995. International Music Festival. Musical Instruments. Multicoloured.

No.	Type	Description	Unused	Used
904		1p. Type **209**	2·50	65
905		1p. Erhu (string instrument)	2·50	65
906		1p. Gong (hand-held drum)	2·50	65
907		1p. Sheng (string instrument)	2·50	65
908		1p. Xiao (flute)	2·50	65
909		1p. Tambor (drum)	2·50	65
MS910		137×90 mm. 8p. Two players with instruments (40×29 mm)	17·00	9·50

210 Anniversary Emblem, World Map and UN Headquarters, New York

1995. 50th Anniversary of United Nations Organisation.

No.	Type	Description	Unused	Used
911	**210**	4p.50 multicoloured	3·50	2·00

211 Terminal Building

1995. Inauguration of Macao International Airport. Multicoloured.

No.	Type	Description	Unused	Used
912		1p. Type **211**	1·60	65
913		1p.50 Terminal (different)	2·30	85
914		2p. Loading aeroplane and cargo building	3·00	1·50
915		3p. Control tower	4·00	2·00
MS916		137×90 mm. 8p. Aeroplane taking off	26·00	15·00

1995. Lunar Cycle. Sheet 180×216 mm containing previous New Year designs.

No.	Type	Description	Unused	Used
MS917		12×1p.50. As Nos. 587, 602, 621, 640, 661, 685, 713, 742, 771, 791, 828 and 870	34·00	17·00

212 Rat

1996. New Year. Year of the Rat.

No.	Type	Description	Unused	Used
918	**212**	5p. multicoloured	7·00	4·25
MS919		137×90 mm. **212** 10p. multicoloured	17·00	9·75

213 Cage

1996. Traditional Chinese Cages.

No.	Type	Description	Unused	Used
920	**213**	1p. multicoloured	1·60	50
921	-	1p.50 multicoloured	2·00	65
922	-	3p. multicoloured	3·00	1·20
923	-	4p.50 multicoloured	4·25	1·70
MS924		137×90 mm. 10p. multicoloured	25·00	13·00

Designs: 1p.50 to 10p., Different cages.

214 Street

1996. Paintings of Macao by Herculano Estorninho. Multicoloured.

No.	Type	Description	Unused	Used
925		50a. Fishing boats (horiz)	1·20	40
926		1p.50 Town square	2·75	50
927		3p. Type **214**	3·00	1·00
928		5p. Townscape (horiz)	4·75	2·00
MS929		137×90 mm. 10p. Colonnaded entrance	14·00	8·25

215 Tou Tei (God of Earth)

1996. Legends and Myths (3rd series). Multicoloured.

No.	Type	Description	Unused	Used
930		3p.50 Type **215**	2·75	2·00
931		3p.50 Choi San (God of Fortune)	2·75	2·00
932		3p.50 Chou Kuan (God of the Kitchen)	2·75	2·00
MS933		137×89 mm. Nos. 930/932	25·00	13·50

216 Customers

1996. Traditional Chinese Tea Houses. Multicoloured.

No.	Type	Description	Unused	Used
934		2p. Type **216**	3·00	1·30
935		2p. Waiter with tray of steamed stuffed bread	3·00	1·30
936		2p. Newspaper vendor	3·00	1·30
937		2p. Waiter pouring tea at table	3·00	1·30
MS938		138×90 mm. 8p. Jar and food snacks	19·00	13·50

Nos. 934/947 were issued together, *se-tenant*, forming a composite design.

217 Get Well Soon

1996. Greetings stamps. Multicoloured.

No.	Type	Description	Unused	Used
939		50a. Type **217**	95	50
940		1p.50 Congratulations on new baby	2·00	70
941		3p. Happy birthday	2·50	1·20
942		4p. Wedding congratulations	3·00	1·70

218 Swimming

1996. Olympic Games, Atlanta, USA. Multicoloured.

943	2p. Type **218**	1·60	85
944	3p. Football	2·00	1·40
945	3p.50 Gymnastics	3·00	1·70
946	4p.50 Sailboarding	3·50	2·00
MS947	137×90 mm. 10p. Boxing	14·00	8·50

219 Crane (civil, 1st rank)

1996. Civil and Military Insignia of the Mandarins (1st series). Multicoloured.

948	2p.50 Type **219**	2·50	1·20
949	2p.50 Lion (military, 2nd rank)	2·50	1·20
950	2p.50 Golden pheasant (civil, 2nd rank)	2·50	1·20
951	2p.50 Leopard (military, 3rd rank)	2·50	1·20

See also Nos. 1061/**MS**1065.

220 Trawler with Multiple Nets

1996. Nautical Sciences: Fishing Nets. Multicoloured.

952	3p. Type **220**	2·75	1·40
953	3p. Modern trawler with net from stern	2·75	1·40
954	3p. Two sailing junks with common net	2·75	1·40
955	3p. Junk with two square nets at sides	2·75	1·40

Nos. 952/955 were issued together, *se-tenant*, forming a composite design.

221 National Flag and Statue (½-size illustration)

1996. 20th Anniversary of Legislative Assembly.

956	**221** 2p.80 multicoloured	3·00	1·70
MS957	138×90 mm. **221** 8p. multicoloured	19·00	8·50

222 Dragonfly

1996. Paper Kites. Multicoloured.

958	3p.50 Type **222**	3·00	1·30
959	3p.50 Butterfly	3·00	1·30
960	3p.50 Owl	3·00	1·30
961	3p.50 Swallow	3·00	1·30
MS962	138×90 mm. 8p. Chinese dragon (50×37 mm)	20·00	8·50

223 Doll

1996. Traditional Chinese Toys. Multicoloured.

963	50a. Type **223**	1·60	85
964	1p. Fish	3·00	1·70
965	3p. Painted doll	6·25	2·50
966	4p.50 Dragon	7·75	3·50

224 Ox

1997. New Year. Year of the Ox.

967	**224** 5p.50 multicoloured	5·00	5·00
MS968	137×89 mm. **224** 10p. multicoloured.	14·00	8·50

225 Colourful and Gold Twos

1997. Lucky Numbers. Multicoloured.

969	2p. Type **225**	1·60	70
970	2p.80 Eights	2·00	85
971	3p. Threes	2·20	1·00
972	3p.90 Nines	2·75	1·40
MS973	137×90 mm. 9p. Numbers around doorway of café	9·25	8·00

No. **MS**973 also commemorates Hong Kong '97 International Stamp Exhibition.

226 *Sail Boats*

1997. Paintings of Macao by Kwok Se. Multicoloured.

974	2p. Type **226**	1·60	70
975	3p. *Fortress on the Hill*	2·00	1·00
976	3p.50 *Asilum*	2·75	1·40
977	4p.50 *Portas do Cerco*	4·00	2·00
MS978	138×90 mm. 8p. *Rua de Sao Paulo* (detail) (horiz)	12·00	10·50

227 Elderly Woman

1997. Tan-Ka (boat) People. Multicoloured.

979	1p. Type **227**	1·10	50
980	1p.50 Elderly woman holding tiller	1·40	70
981	2p.50 Woman with child on back	1·90	85
982	5p.50 Man mending fishing nets	3·50	2·00

228 Entrance to Temple

1997. A-Ma Temple. Multicoloured.

983	3p.50 Type **228**	1·30	1·20
984	3p.50 Wall and terraces of Temple	1·30	1·20
985	3p.50 View of incense smoke through gateway	1·30	1·20
986	3p.50 Incense smoke emanating from pagoda	1·30	1·20
MS987	138×90 mm. Ship (representative of land reclamation in front of temple)	9·25	9·25

229 Dragon Dancers

1997. Drunken Dragon Festival. Multicoloured.

988	2p. Type **229**	1·10	70
989	3p. Dragon dancer	1·60	1·00
990	5p. Dancer holding 'tail' of dragon	2·75	2·00
MS991	138×90 mm. Dancer with dragon's head (horiz)	7·75	7·25

230 Frois with Japanese Man

1997. 400th Death Anniversary of Father Luis Frois (author of *The History of Japan*). Multicoloured.

992	2p.50 Type **230**	1·20	1·00
993	2p.50 Father Frois and church (vert)	1·20	1·00

231 Wat Lot

1997. Legends and Myths (4th series). Door Gods. Multicoloured.

994	2p.50 Type **231**	1·20	85
995	2p.50 San Su	1·20	85
996	2p.50 Chon Keng	1·20	85
997	2p.50 Wat Chi Kong	1·20	85
MS998	138×90 mm. 10p. Chon Keng and Wat Chi Kong on doors (39×39 mm)	7·75	7·25

232 Globe and First Aid and Family Health School

1997. 77th Anniversary of Macao Red Cross.

999	**232** 1p.50 multicoloured	95	85

233 Balconies

1997. Balconies.

1000	**233** 50a. multicoloured	30	35
1001	- 1p. multicoloured	45	45
1002	- 1p.50 multicoloured	60	50
1003	- 2p. multicoloured	80	70
1004	- 2p.50 multicoloured	1·20	1·20
1005	- 3p. multicoloured	1·40	1·40
MS1006	137×90 mm. 8p. multicoloured (29×39 mm)	6·25	5·00

Designs: 1p. to 8p. Various balcony styles.

234 Plant Leaf Fan

1997. Fans. Multicoloured.

1007	50a. Type **234**	45	45
1008	1p. Paper fan	60	50
1009	3p.50 Silk fan	1·40	1·40
1010	4p. Feather fan	1·90	1·70
MS1011	138×90 mm. 9p. Woman holding sandalwood fan	8·50	8·00

235 Wood

1997. Feng Shui. The Five Elements. Multicoloured.

1012	50a. Type **235**	50	35
1013	1p. Fire	70	45
1014	1p.50 Earth	85	50
1015	2p. Metal	1·00	70
1016	2p.50 Water	1·40	1·00
MS1017	138×90 mm. 10p. Centre of geomancer's chart	8·50	7·75

236 Kung Fu

1997. Martial Arts. Multicoloured.

1018	1p.50 Type **236**	85	50
1019	3p.50 Judo	1·70	1·20
1020	4p. Karate	2·50	1·70

237 Tiger

1998. New Year. Year of the Tiger.

1021	**237** 5p.50 multicoloured	3·00	2·50
MS1022	138×90 mm. **237** 10p. multicoloured	6·75	6·00

238 Soup Stall

1998. Street Traders. Multicoloured.

1023	1p. Type **238**	50	45
1024	1p.50 Snack stall	70	50
1025	2p. Clothes stall	85	70
1026	2p.50 Balloon stall	1·00	95
1027	3p. Flower stall	1·40	1·20
1028	3p.50 Fruit stall	1·70	1·50
MS1029	138×90 mm. 6p. Fruit stall (different)	4·00	3·75

239 Beco da Se

1998. Gateways. Multicoloured.

1030	50a. Type **239**	40	35
1031	1p. Patio da Ilusao	55	55
1032	3p.50 Travessa das galinhas	2·10	2·00
1033	4p. Beco das Felicidades	2·75	2·50
MS1034	138×90 mm. 9p. St Joseph's Seminary	5·75	5·50

240 Woman and Child

1998. Legends and Myths (5th series). Gods of Ma Chou. Multicoloured.

1035	4p. Type **240**	1·90	1·60
1036	4p. Woman and man's face in smoke	1·90	1·60
1037	4p. Woman with children playing instruments	1·90	1·60
1038	4p. Goddess and sailing barges	1·90	1·60
MS1039	138×90 mm. 10p. Head of goddess	9·50	9·00

241 *Sao Gabriel* (flagship)

1998. 500th Anniversary of Vasco da Gama's Voyage to India via Cape of Good Hope. Multicoloured. (a) Wrongly dated 1598 1998.

1040	1p. Type **241**	1·00	55
1041	1p.50 Vasco da Gama	1·40	75
1042	2p. *Sao Gabriel* and map of India	1·80	1·10
MS1043	138×90 mm. 8p. Compass rose	10·00	9·50

(b) Correctly dated 1498 1998.

1044	1p. Type **241**	80	40
1045	1p.50 As No. 1041	1·20	55

1046 2p. As No. 1042 1·60 95

MS1047 138×90 mm. 8p. As No. **MS**1043 5·50 5·25

242 Mermaid and Caravel

1998. International Year of the Ocean. Multicoloured.

1048 2p.50 Type **242** 1·40 1·10

1049 3p. Whale and oil-rig 1·60 1·30

MS1050 138×90 mm. Caravel and whale 6·00 5·75

243 Players

1998. World Cup Football Championship, France. Multicoloured.

1051 3p. Type **243** 1·60 1·50

1052 3p.50 Players competing for ball 2·00 1·90

1053 4p. Player kicking ball clear while being tackled 2·40 2·30

1054 4p.50 Player beating another to ball 3·00 2·75

MS1055 138×90 mm. 9p. Players and ball 8·00 7·50

244 Lio Seak Chong Mask

1998. Chinese Opera Masks. Multicoloured.

1056 1p.50 Type **244** 80 55

1057 2p. Wat Chi Kong 1·00 75

1058 3p. Kam Chin Pao 1·40 1·10

1059 5p. Lei Kwai 2·40 2·10

MS1060 138×90 mm. Opera mask 6·00 5·75

1998. Civil and Military Insignia of the Mandarins (2nd series). As T **219**. Multicoloured.

1061 50a. Lion (military, 2nd rank) 40 30

1062 1p. Bear (military, 5th rank) 80 50

1063 1p.50 Golden pheasant (civil, 2nd rank) 1·00 55

1064 2p. Silver pheasant (civil, 5th rank) 1·20 75

MS1065 138×90 mm. 9p. Crane (civil, 1st rank) 7·00 6·75

245 Smiling Buddha

1998. Kun Iam Temple. Multicoloured.

1066 3p.50 Type **245** 1·80 1·30

1067 3p.50 Pavilion and temple gardens 1·80 1·30

1068 3p.50 Temple gateway 1·80 1·30

1069 3p.50 Pagoda, stream and gardens 1·80 1·30

MS1070 138×90 mm. 10p. Temple 7·00 6·75

Nos. 1066/1069 were issued together, *se-tenant*, forming a composite design.

246 Carriage in Street

1998. Paintings of Macao by Didier Rafael Bayle. Multicoloured.

1071 2p. Type **246** 1·20 1·10

1072 3p. Street (horiz) 1·80 1·70

1073 3p.50 Building (horiz) 2·00 1·90

1074 4p.50 Kiosk in square 3·00 2·75

MS1075 138×90 mm. 8p. Balcony (horiz) 6·00 5·75

247 Dragon

1998. Tiles by Eduardo Nery (from panel at Departure Lounge of Macao Airport). Multicoloured.

1076 1p. Type **247** 60 50

1077 1p.50 Galleon 80 65

1078 2p.50 Junk 1·20 95

1079 5p.50 Phoenix 2·40 2·10

MS1080 138×90 mm. 10p. Guia Lighthouse 7·00 6·75

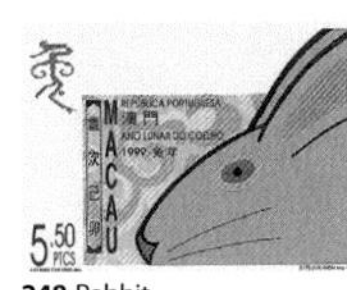

248 Rabbit

1999. New Year. Year of the Rabbit.

1081 **248** 5p.50 multicoloured 5·00 3·00

MS1082 138×90 mm. **248** 10p. multicoloured 10·00 6·75

249 Jia Bao Yu

1999. Literature. Characters from *A Dream of Red Mansions* by Cao Xue Qin. Multicoloured.

1083 2p. Type **249** 2·00 85

1084 2p. Lin Dai Yu holding pole and cherry blossom 2·00 85

1085 2p. Bao Chai holding fan 2·00 85

1086 2p. Wang Xi Feng sitting in chair 2·00 85

1087 2p. You San Jie holding sword 2·00 85

1088 2p. Qing Wen sewing "peacock" cloak 2·00 85

MS1089 138×90 mm. 8p. Jia Bao Yu and Lin Dai Yu 8·00 5·75

250 Sailing Ships

1999. Australia '99 International Stamp Exhibition, Melbourne. Oceans and Maritime Heritage. Multicoloured.

1090 1p.50 Type **250** 1·20 95

1091 2p.50 Marine life 1·80 1·30

MS1092 138×90 mm. 6p. Head of whale (vert) 3·75 3·50

251 de Havilland D.H.9 Biplane

1999. 75th Anniversary of Sarmento de Beires and Brito Pais's Portugal–Macao Flight. Multicoloured.

1093 3p. Breguet 16 Bn2 Patria 3·00 2·30

1094 3p. Type **251** 3·00 2·30

MS1095 137×104 mm. Nos. 1093/1094 5·00 4·75

252 Carrying Containers on Yoke

1999. The Water Carrier. Multicoloured.

1096 1p. Type **252** 85 40

1097 1p.50 Filling containers from pump 1·10 60

1098 2p. Lowering bucket down well 1·30 80

1099 2p.50 Filling containers from tap 1·70 1·20

MS1100 138×90 mm. 7p. Woman with containers on yoke climbing steps 4·75 4·50

253 *Sea-Me-We-3* Undersea Fibre Optic Cable

1999. Telecommunications Services. Multicoloured.

1101 50a. Type **253** 40 30

1102 1p. Dish aerial at Satellite Earth Station 65 60

1103 3p.50 Analogue mobile phone 1·90 1·60

1104 4p. Televisions 2·30 2·00

1105 4p.50 Internet and e-mail 2·75 2·40

MS1106 138×90 mm. 8p. Emblem and computer mouse (horiz) 5·50 5·25

254 Macao Cultural Centre

1999. Modern Buildings. Multicoloured.

1107 1p. Type **254** 65 50

1108 1p.50 Museum of Macao 75 60

1109 2p. Macao Maritime Museum 1·30 1·00

1110 2p.50 Ferry Terminal 1·70 1·20

1111 3p. Macao University 1·90 1·40

1112 3p.50 Public Administration building (vert) 2·10 1·60

1113 4p.50 Macao World Trade Centre (vert) 2·75 2·20

1114 5p. Coloane kart-racing track (vert) 3·00 2·40

1115 8p. Bank of China (vert) 4·50 3·75

1116 12p. National Overseas Bank (vert) 6·75 5·50

255 Health Department

1999. Classified Buildings in Tap Seac District. Multicoloured.

1117 1p.50 Type **255** 1·10 70

1118 1p.50 Central Library (face value in salmon) 1·10 70

1119 1p.50 Centre of Modern Art of the Orient Foundation (face value in yellow) 1·10 70

1120 1p.50 Portuguese Institute of the Orient (face value in light blue) 1·10 70

MS1121 138×90 mm. 10p. IPOR building 6·25 6·00

Nos. 1117/1120 were issued together, *se-tenant*, forming a composite design.

256 Teapot and Plate of Food

1999. Dim Sum. Multicoloured.

1122 2p.50 Type **256** 1·50 1·20

1123 2p.50 Plates of food, chopsticks and left half of bowls 1·50 1·20

1124 2p.50 Plates of food, glass, cups and right half of bowls 1·50 1·20

1125 2p.50 Plates of food and large teapot 1·50 1·20

MS1126 138×90 mm. 9p. Plates of food 6·00 5·50

Nos. 1122/1125 were issued together, *se-tenant*, forming a composite design.

257 *Portuguese Sailor and Chinese Woman* (Lagoa Henriques), Company of Jesus Square

1999. Contemporary Sculptures (1st series). Multicoloured.

1127 1p. Type **257** 85 60

1128 1p.50 *The Gate of Understanding* (Charters de Almeida), Praia Grande Bay (vert) 1·10 80

1129 2p.50 *Statue of the Goddess Kun Iam* (Cristina Leiria), Macao Cultural Centre (vert) 1·90 1·60

1130 3p.50 *Taipa Viewing Point* (Dorita Castel-Branco), Nobre de Carvalho Bridge, Taipa 2·30 2·00

MS1131 138×90 mm. 10p. *The Pearl* (Jose Rodrigues), Amizade rounderbout 6·25 6·00

See also Nos. 1186/**MS**1190.

258 Chinese and Portuguese Ships, Christ's Cross and Yin Yang

1999. Portuguese–Chinese Cultural Mix. Multicoloured.

1132 1p. Type **258** 65 50

1133 1p.50 Ah Mah Temple and Portuguese and Macanese architecture 85 60

1134 2p. Bridge, steps and Chinese architecture 1·30 1·00

1135 3p. Macanese architecture and Portuguese terrace 1·70 1·50

MS1136 138×90 mm. Enlargement of right-hand part of design in No. 1135 6·25 6·00

Nos. 1132/1135 were issued together, *se-tenant*, forming a composite design.

259 Globe

1999. Macao Retrospective. Multicoloured.

1137 1p. Type **259** 85 60

1138 1p.50 Roof terrace 1·30 80

1139 2p. Portuguese and Chinese people 1·70 1·20

1140 3p.50 Modern Macao 2·50 2·00

MS1141 138×90 mm. 9p. City Coat of Arms 6·00 5·75

260 Gateway

1999. Establishment of Macao as Special Administrative Region of People's Republic of China. Multicoloured.

1142 1p. Type **260** 90 65

1143 1p.50 Bridge and boat race 1·20 90

1144 2p. Wall of ruined church 1·60 1·30

1145 2p.50 Lighthouse and racing cars 1·80 1·50

1146 3p. Building facade 2·10 1·80

1147 3p.50 Stadium and orchestra 2·30 2·00

MS1148 138×90 mm. 8p. Pink flower 6·00 5·50

261 Sight-seeing Tower

2000. A New Era. Sheet 138×90 mm.

MS1149 **261** 8p. multicoloured 6·75 6·00

262 Dragon

2000. New Year. Year of the Dragon.

1150 **262** 5p.50 multicoloured 4·25 3·25

MS1151 138×90 mm. **262** 10p. multicoloured 7·00 6·25

263 Buildings

2000. Classified Buildings in Almeida Ribeiro Avenue, Macao City. Multicoloured.

1152	1p. Type **263**	70	55
1153	1p.50 Yellow and pink buildings	1·20	90
1154	2p. Yellow building	1·40	1·10
1155	3p. Purple, green and pink buildings	2·10	1·80
MS1156	138×90 mm. 9p. Beige building	6·75	6·00

SERIAL NUMBERS. In sets containing several stamps of the same denomination, the serial number is quoted in brackets to assist identification. This is the last figure in the bottom right corner of the stamp.

264 Zhong (Leong Pai Wan)

2000. Arts in Macao. Chinese Calligraphy. Showing Chinese characters by named calligraphy masters. Each black and red.

1157	3p. (1) Type **264**	2·30	1·80
1158	3p. (2) Guo (Lin Ka Sang)	2·30	1·80
1159	3p. (3) Shu (Lok Hong)	2·30	1·80
1160	3p. (4) Fa (Sou Su Fai)	2·30	1·80
MS1161	138×90 mm. 8p. Zhong, guo, shu and fa	5·50	4·25

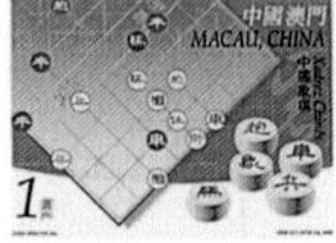
265 Chinese Chess

2000. Board Games. Multicoloured.

1162	1p. Type **265**	70	65
1163	1p.50 Chess	1·20	1·10
1164	2p. Go	1·60	1·30
1165	2p.50 Flying chess	1·10	95
MS1166	138×90 mm. 9p. Chinese checkers	7·00	6·25

266 Group of Friends

2000. Tea. Multicoloured.

1167	2p. Type **266**	1·40	1·30
1168	3p. Family drinking tea	2·10	2·00
1169	3p.50 Women drinking tea	2·50	2·40
1170	4p.50 Men drinking tea	3·25	3·00
MS1171	138×90 mm. 8p. Woman making tea	6·75	6·50

267 Tricycle Driver and Foreign Tourists

2000. Tricycle Drivers. Multicoloured.

1172	2p. (1) Type **267**	1·40	1·30
1173	2p. (2) With couple in carriage	1·40	1·30
1174	2p. (3) With empty carriage	1·40	1·30
1175	2p. (4) With feet resting on saddle	1·40	1·30
1176	2p. (5) Sitting in carriage	1·40	1·30
1177	2p. (6) Mending tyre	1·40	1·30
MS1178	138×90 mm. 8p. Standing beside tricycle (vert)	6·75	6·50

268 Monkey King standing on Tiger Skin

2000. Classical Literature. *Journey to the West* (Ming Dynasty novel). Multicoloured.

1179	1p. Type **268**	70	65
1180	1p.50 Monkey King tasting the heavenly peaches	90	90
1181	2p. Monkey King, Prince Na Zha and flaming wheels	1·40	1·30
1182	2p.50 Erlang Deity with spear	1·80	1·80
1183	3p. Heavenly Father Lao Jun	2·10	2·00
1184	3p.50 Monkey King in Buddha's hand	2·50	2·40
MS1185	138×90 mm. 9p. Monkey King holding baton (horiz)	7·25	7·00

269 *Wing of Good Winds* (Augusto Cid), Pac On Roundabout, Taipa

2000. Contemporary Sculptures (2nd series). Multicoloured.

1186	1p. Type **269**	90	90
1187	2p. *The Embrace* (Irene Vilar), Luis de Camoes Garden (vert)	1·60	1·50
1188	3p. Monument (Soares Branco), Guia's Tunnel, Outer Harbour (vert)	2·50	2·40
1189	4p. *The Arch of the Orient* (Zulmiro de Carvalho), Avienda Rodrigo Rodrigues Viaduct	3·25	3·00
MS1190	90×138 mm. 10p. *Goddess A-Ma* (Leong Man Lin). Coloane Iland	8·25	8·00

270 Decorated Pot

2000. Ceramics. Multicoloured.

1191	2p.50 (1) Type **270**	1·90	1·80
1192	2p.50 (2) Vase, dish and teapot	1·90	1·80
1193	2p.50 (3) Blue vase	1·90	1·80
1194	2p.50 (4) Cabbage-shaped pot and leaf-shaped dish	1·90	1·80
1195	2p.50 (5) Plate and fish	1·90	1·80
1196	2p.50 (6) Blue and white vase	1·90	1·80
MS1197	138×90 mm. 8p. Decorated plate (round-design)	6·75	6·50

Nos. 1191/1196 were issued together, *se-tenant*, with the backgrounds forming a composite design.

271 Phoenix crouching, Shang Dynasty

2000. Jade Ornaments. Multicoloured.

1198	1p.50 Type **271**	1·20	50
1199	2p. Archer's white jade ring, Warring States period	1·60	1·50
1200	2p.50 Dragon and phoenix, Six Dynasties	2·10	2·00
1201	3p. Pendant with dragon decoration, Western Han Dynasty	2·50	2·40
MS1202	138×90 mm. 9p. Medallion (detail) (vert)	7·50	7·00

272 Dancers with National and Special Administrative Flags

2000. First Anniversary of Macau as Special Administrative Region of People's Republic of China. Multicoloured.

1203	2p. Type **272**	1·60	1·50
1204	3p. Chinese dragons and lotus flower	2·40	2·20
MS1205	138×90 mm. 18p. Flags, statesmen and lotus flower (59×39 mm)	13·00	12·00

Nos. 1203/1204 were issued together, *se-tenant*, forming a composite design.

273 Snake

2001. New Year. Year of the Snake.

1206	**273** 5p.50 multicoloured	4·75	4·50
MS1207	138×90 mm. **273** 10p. multicoloured	7·75	7·25

274 Man holding Bottle ('Nursing Vengeance despite Hardships')

2001. Ancient Proverbs. Multicoloured.

1208	2p. (1) Type **274**	1·90	1·80
1209	2p. (2) Man waiting for a rabbit ('Trusting to Chance and Windfalls')	1·90	1·80
1210	2p. (3) Fox and tiger ('Bullying Others by Flaunting One's Powerful Connections')	1·90	1·80
1211	2p. (4) Mother with child ('Selecting a Proper Surrounding to Bring up Children')	1·90	1·80
MS1212	138×90 mm. 8p. Man stealing bell ('Burying Ones' Head in the Sand')	6·75	6·50

See also Nos. 1587/**MS**1595.

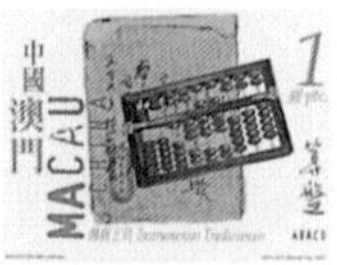
275 Abacus

2001. Traditional Tools. Multicoloured.

1213	1p. Type **275**	95	90
1214	2p. Plane	1·60	1·50
1215	3p. Iron	2·40	2·20
1216	4p. Scales	3·25	3·00
MS1217	138×90 mm. 8p. Text, scales and iron	6·75	6·50

276 Buddha

2001. Religions. Multicoloured.

1218	1p. Type **276**	70	65
1219	1p.50 Worshippers	1·20	1·10
1220	2p. Man carrying Cross and religious procession	1·60	1·50
1221	2p.50 Procession	2·10	2·00
MS1222	138×90 mm. 8p. Religious Symbols (circular design) (59×59 mm)	7·00	6·50

Nos. 1218/1219 and 1220/1221 respectively were issued together, *se-tenant*, forming a composite design.

277 Fireman and Platform Car

2001. Fire Brigade. Multicoloured.

1223	1p.50 Type **277**	1·40	1·30
1224	2p.50 Fireman wearing chemical protection suit using portable flammable gases detector and Pumping Tank vehicle	1·10	1·00
1225	3p. Foam car and fireman wearing asbestos suit using foam hose	1·25	1·10
1226	4p. Fire officers in dress uniforms and ambulance	3·25	3·00
MS1227	138×90 mm. 8p. Fireman (59×39 mm)	12·00	11·00

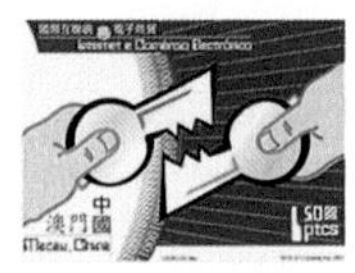
278 Electronic Keys

2001. E-Commerce. Multicoloured.

1228	1p.50 Type **278**	1·40	1·30
1229	2p. Hands passing letter (e-mail)	1·60	1·50
1230	2p.50 Mobile phone	2·40	2·20
1231	3p. Palm hand-held computer	2·75	2·75
MS1232	138×90 6p. Laptop computers (59×39 mm)	6·00	5·50

279 Emblem

2001. Choice of Beijing as 2008 Olympic Games Host City.

1233	**279** 1p. multicoloured	2·40	2·20

280 Praying

2001. Classical Literature. *Romance of the Three Kingdoms* (novel by Luo Guanzhong). Multicoloured.

1234	3p. (1) Type **280**	2·40	2·20
1235	3p. (2) Soldier and man fighting	2·40	2·20
1236	3p. (3) Men talking	2·40	2·20
1237	3p. (4) Man dreaming	2·40	2·20
MS1238	138×90 mm. 7p. Head of Soldier (horiz)	9·50	8·75

281 Baby, Doctor and Schoolchildren

2001. National Census. Multicoloured.

1239	1p. Type **281**	60	50
1240	1p.50 Street scene	1·20	60
1241	2p.50 Suspension bridge and crowd	1·90	1·80
MS1242	137×90 mm. 6p. Subjects as Nos. 1239/41 (86×37 mm)	5·25	4·75

282 Municipal Market

2001. Macau Markets. Multicoloured.

1243	1p.50 Type **282**	1·20	1·10
1244	2p.50 Building and road-side stall	1·90	1·80
1245	3p.50 Covered market	2·50	2·40
1246	4p.50 Multi-storey building	3·25	3·00
MS1247	138×90 mm. 7p. Bus station building (59×38 mm)	6·75	6·50

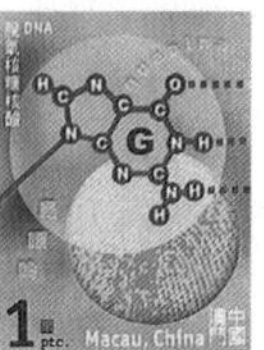
283 DNA Helix containing Guanine Base

2001. Science and Technology. Composition and Structure of DNA. Showing chemical bases of DNA. Multicoloured.

1248	1p. Type **283**	1·20	1·10
1249	2p. Helix containing cytosine base	1·90	1·80
1250	3p. Helix containing adenine base	2·50	2·40
1251	4p. Helix containing thymine base	3·50	3·25
MS1252	137×90 mm. 8p. Helix containing adenine base (different) (44×29 mm)	7·50	7·00

284 Commander Ho Yin's Garden

2001. Parks and Gardens. Multicoloured.

1253	1p.50 Type **284**	1·20	1·10
1254	2p.50 Mong Há Hill municipal park	1·90	1·80
1255	3p. City of Flowers Garden	2·40	2·20
1256	4p.50 Great Taipa Natural Park	3·25	3·00
MS1257	138×90 mm. 8p. Garden of Art	7·50	7·00

285 Trigrams and Dragons

2001. Pa Kua (martial art) (1st series). Multicoloured.

1258	2p. (1) Type **285**	1·60	1·50
1259	2p. (4) Trigrams, couple and deer	1·60	1·50
1260	2p. (7) Trigrams, fields and buffaloes	1·60	1·50
1261	2p. (3) Trigrams and volcano	1·60	1·50
1262	2p. (6) Trigrams and three men crawling	1·60	1·50
1263	2p. (2) Trigrams, man and donkey	1·60	1·50
1264	2p. (5) Trigrams, horse and carriage	1·60	1·50
1265	2p. (8) Trigrams, men with gifts and potentate	1·60	1·50
MS1266	15×90 mm. 8p. Yu Fu (Pa Kua master) (59×27 mm)	7·00	6·50

See also Nos. 1323/**MS**1331, 1367/**MS**1375, 1386/**MS**1394, 1552/**MS**1560, 1629/**MS**1637, 1739/**MS**1747 and 1847/**MS**1855.

286 Horse's Head

2002. New Year. Year of the Horse. Multicoloured.

1267	5p.50 Type **286**	5·50	5·00
MS1268	138×91 mm. 10p. As No. 1267 but design enlarged	8·50	8·00

287 Lao Lao visiting Fidalgo's House

2002. Classical Literature. *Dream of Red Mansions*. Multicoloured.

1269	2p. Type **287**	1·60	1·50
1270	2p. Jin Chuan suffering injustice	1·60	1·50
1271	2p. Proof of Dada's love for Zi Juan	1·60	1·50
1272	2p. Xiang Yun adorned with peony flowers	1·60	1·50
1273	2p. Liu Lang combing her hair	1·60	1·50
1274	2p. Miao Yu offering tea	1·60	1·50
MS1275	139×90 mm. 8p. Woman reading (The wonderful dream of love)	7·50	7·00

288 Cantao San Kong Opera Performers

2002. Festivals. Tou-Tei (God of Earth) Festival. Multicoloured.

1276	1p.50 Type **288**	1·20	1·10
1277	2p.50 Respected elders dinner	1·90	1·80
1278	3p.50 Burning of cult objects	2·75	2·75
1279	4p.50 Cooking suckling pig	3·50	3·25
MS1280	139×90 mm. 8p. Bearded man with sword (vert)	7·50	7·00

289 Facade and bas-relief of St Paul

2002. 400th Anniversary St Paul's Church, Macao. Multicoloured.

1281	1p. Type **289**	1·20	1·10
1282	3p.50 Corner of façade and ornament	3·25	3·00
MS1283	139×90 mm. 8p. Statue in alcove (30×40 mm)	7·50	7·00

290 Goalkeeper diving for Ball

2002. World Cup Football Championships, Japan and South Korea. Multicoloured.

1284	1p. Type **290**	1·60	1·50
1285	1p.50 Players tackling for ball	2·10	2·00

291 Underwater Animals and Oil Refinery

2002. Environmental Protection. Multicoloured.

1286	1p. Type **291** (marine conservation)	95	90
1287	1p.50 Boy planting tree (reforestation)	1·20	1·10
1288	2p. Emblem and bins (recycling)	1·60	1·50
1289	2p.50 Spoonbills (wetland conservation)	2·10	2·00
1290	3p. Energy plant and waste truck (energy regeneration)	1·40	1·25
1291	3p.50 Boy sweeping leaves (clean urban environment)	2·75	2·75
1292	4p. Girl blowing bubbles (air purification)	3·00	2·75
1293	4p.50 Nurse and elderly patient (health and hygiene)	3·50	3·25
1294	8p. Owl (improving city living)	6·25	6·00

292 Zheng Guanying at Home

2002. 160th Birth Anniversary of Zheng Guanying (industrialist, reformer and philanthropist). Multicoloured.

1295	1p. Type **292**	70	65
1296	2p. As young man and docks	1·40	1·30
1297	3p. As young man and alms giving	2·10	2·00
1298	3p.50 As older man and writing	2·75	2·75
MS1299	138×90 mm. 6p. Seated at table (40×60 mm)	5·75	5·25

293 Macau Tower and Skyline

2001. Honesty and Transparency. Multicoloured.

1300	1p. Type **293**	1·20	1·10
1301	3p.50 Macau skyline from Monte Fort	2·75	2·75

294 Fish Balls

2002. Street Vendor's Food. Multicoloured.

1302	1p. Type **294**	70	65
1303	1p.50 Dried beef	1·20	1·10
1304	2p. Tongue roll	1·60	1·50
1305	2p.50 Sat Kei Ma	1·90	1·80
MS1306	138×91 mm. 7p. Cookie (50×50 mm)	5·75	5·25

295 Shun ploughing

2002. *The Twenty-four Paragons of Filial Devotion* (book by Guo Jujing). Multicoloured.

1307	1p. Type **295**	1·20	1·10
1308	1p.50 Huang Xiang cooling his father's bed with fan	85	1·30
1309	2p. Meng Zong crying over bamboo shoots for mother	1·90	1·80
1310	2p.50 Wang Xiang melting ice to get fish for stepmother	2·10	2·00
1311	4p.50 Min Ziqian pleading for cruel stepmother	3·50	3·25
1312	4p.50 Jiang Shi, wife and bubbling spring	3·50	3·25
1313	4p.50 Bin Chen surrendering to be with mother	3·50	3·25
1314	4p.50 Wang Gang pleading for father's body	3·50	3·25
MS1315	95×139 mm. 7p. Tanzi bringing deer milk to his parents	6·25	6·00

296 Electroweak Unification with the help of Elephant Diagram

2002. Science and Technology. Particle Physics. Multicoloured.

1316	1p.50 Type **296**	1·60	1·50
1317	1p.50 Scales (spontaneous symmetry breaking)	1·60	1·50
1318	1p.50 Higgs boson diagram	1·60	1·50
1319	1p.50 Three families Z decay curve diagram	1·60	1·50
1320	1p.50 Quark groups (quantum cromodynamics)	1·60	1·50
1321	1p.50 Graph showing interactions and predicted interactions	1·60	1·50
MS1322	138×90 mm. 8p. DELPHI detector	7·00	6·50

2002. Pa Kua (martial art) (2nd series). As T **285**. Multicoloured.

1323	2p. (1) Trigrams, stream and Tiger	1·90	1·80
1324	2p. (4) Trigrams, man and woman	1·90	1·80
1325	2p. (7) Trigrams, couple feeding elderly person	1·90	1·80
1326	2p. (3) Trigrams, birds, men and path	1·90	1·80
1327	2p. (6) Trigrams and man sat in tree	1·90	1·80
1328	2p. (2) Trigrams and two men bowing	1·90	1·80
1329	2p. (5) Trigrams, yin/yang symbols and storks	1·90	1·80
1330	2p. (8) Trigrams and potentate	1·90	1·80
MS1331	135×90 mm. 8p. Woman with jug (59×27 mm)	7·00	6·50

297 Goat's Head

2003. Year of the Goat. Multicoloured.

1332	5p.50 Type **297**	4·75	4·50
MS1333	138×90 mm. 10p. Goat's head (detail)	7·50	7·00

298 Classmates

2003. Folk Tales. Liang Shanbo and Zhu Yingtai. Multicoloured.

1334	3p.50 (1) Type **298**	2·10	2·00
1335	3p.50 (2) Saying goodbye	2·10	2·00
1336	3p.50 (3) On terrace	2·10	2·00
1337	3p.50 (4) Yingtai's parents arranging marriage	2·10	2·00
MS1338	138×90 mm. 9p.Turning into butterflies (40×60 mm)	7·50	7·00

299 Song Jiang

2003. Classical Literature. *Outlaws of the Marsh*. Multicoloured.

1339	2p. (1) Type **299**	1·60	1·50
1340	2p. (2) Lin Chong	1·60	1·50
1341	2p. (3) Wu Song	1·60	1·50
1342	2p. (4) Lu Zhishen	1·60	1·50
1343	2p. (5) Wu Yong	1·60	1·50
1344	2p. (6) Hua Rong	1·60	1·50
MS1345	138×90 mm. 8p. Two outlaws	7·00	6·50

300 Administrative Building and Doves

2003. Tenth Anniversary of Proclamation of Basic Law of Macao. Multicoloured.

1346	1p. Type **300**	1·20	1·10
1347	4p.50 Flags, children, book and doves	3·50	3·25

301 Fungus and Chrysalis

2003. Traditional Chinese Medicine. Multicoloured.

1348	1p.50 Type **301**	1·20	1·10
1349	2p. Flowers and fruit	1·40	1·30
1350	3p. Gingko leaves and dried stems	1·90	1·80
1351	3p.50 Liquorice root and angelica	2·40	2·20
MS1352	139×90 mm. 8p. Seated man holding tea cup (horiz)	6·00	5·50

302 Two-storied Building

2003. Cultural Heritage. Architecture of Taipa and Coloane Islands. Multicoloured.

1353	1p. Type **302**	70	65
1354	1p.50 Single-storied building	1·20	1·10
1355	2p. Two buildings and dog	1·40	1·30
1356	3p.50 Dog, tree, buildings and fish	2·40	2·20
MS1357	139×90 mm. 9p. Building with bell tower (horiz)	6·25	6·00

Nos. 1353/1356 were issued together, *se-tenant*, forming a composite design.

303 Scribe

2003. Traditional Scenes from Everyday Life. Multicoloured.

1358	1p.50 Type **303**	95	90
1359	1p.50 Puppeteer	95	90
1360	1p.50 Street vendor and children	95	90
1361	1p.50 Washer woman	95	90
1362	1p.50 Lantern seller	95	90
1363	1p.50 Man carrying tray on head	95	90
1364	1p.50 Photographer	95	90
1365	1p.50 Man wearing cockerel costume	95	90
MS1366	138×90 mm. 8p. Barber	6·50	6·25

See also Nos. 1444/**MS**1452, 1512/**MS**1516 and 1573/**MS**1581.

2003. Pa Kua (martial art) (3rd series). As T **285**. Multicoloured.

1367	2p. (1) Trigrams, people and castle	1·40	1·30
1368	2p. (4) Trigrams and women with raised arms	1·40	1·30
1369	2p. (7) Trigrams and horsemen	1·40	1·30
1370	2p. (3) Trigrams and Ox	1·40	1·30
1371	2p. (6) Trigrams and water wheels	1·40	1·30
1372	2p. (2) Trigrams, masked figures and Leopard	1·40	1·30
1373	2p. (5) Trigrams and seated men and women	1·40	1·30
1374	2p. (8) Trigrams, bird and sunset	1·40	1·30
MS1375	135×90 mm. 8p. Woman and child (59×27 mm)	6·00	5·75

Nos. 1367/1374 were issued together, *se-tenant*, each showing two trigrams and a descriptive painting.

304 Astronaut

2003. First Chinese Manned Space Flight. Multicoloured.

1376	1p. Type **304**	1·40	1·30
1377	1p.50 Ship and satellite	1·90	1·80

305 Triumph TR2

2003. 50th Anniversary of Macao Grand Prix. Two sheets containing T **305** and similar multicoloured designs.

MS1378	(a) 225×156 mm. 1p. Type **305**; 1p.50 Early Brabham race car; 2p. Formula 3 race car; 3p. Grand Prix motorcyclist; 3p.50 Saloon car; 4p.50 Dallara race car. (b) 138×91 mm.12p. Anniversary emblem (38×38 mm) (circular)	28·00	27·00

306 Hua Tuo (detail, ceramic sculpture) (Pan Yushu)

2003. Macao Museum of Art. Multicoloured.

1379	1p. Type **306**	95	90
1380	1p.50 *View of Praia Grande and Penha Hill at Sunset* (George Smirnoff)	1·20	1·10
1381	2p. *Ruins of S. Paulo* (George Chinnery)	1·60	1·50
1382	2p.50 *Music in the Garden* (Su Liupeng)	1·90	1·80
MS1383	138×90 mm. 7p. *Macao, The Praia Grande* (58×55 mm)	6·00	5·50

307 Monkey's Head

2004. Year of the Monkey. Multicoloured.

1384	5p.50 Type **307**	4·00	3·75
MS1385	138×90 mm. 10p. Monkey's head (detail)	12·00	11·00

2004. Pa Kua (martial art) (4th series). As T **285**. Multicoloured.

1386	2p. (1) Trigrams, men and sack	1·40	1·30
1387	2p. (4) Trigrams and storm over hill	1·40	1·30
1388	2p. (7) Trigrams and men eating	1·40	1·30
1389	2p. (3) Trigrams and imprisoned animal	1·40	1·30
1390	2p. (6) Trigrams, waterfall and family on horseback	1·40	1·30
1391	2p. (2) Trigrams and climbers	1·40	1·30
1392	2p. (5) Trigrams and junks (boats)	1·40	1·30
1393	2p. (8) Trigrams counting	1·40	1·30
MS1394	135×90 mm. 8p. Stone carver (59×27 mm)	9·50	8·75

Nos. 1386/1393 were issued together, *se-tenant*, each showing two trigrams and a descriptive painting.

309 Li Sao and Chariot Steeds

2004. Classical Literature. *Li Sao* (poem by Qu Yuan). Showing scenes from poem. Multicoloured.

1395	1p.50 Type **309**	1·20	1·10
1396	1p.50 Cultivating orchids	1·20	1·10
1397	1p.50 With sister	1·20	1·10
1398	1p.50 With phoenix	1·20	1·10
1399	1p.50 With cart drawn by dragons	1·20	1·10
1400	1p.50 In garden	1·20	1·10
MS1401	138×90 mm. 8p. With arm outstretched (vert)	9·50	8·75

310 Guan Di

2004. Myths and Legends. Guan Di (war god). Multicoloured.

1402	1p.50 Type **310**	1·20	1·10
1403	1p.50 Wearing armour	1·60	1·50
1404	1p.50 On horseback	2·10	2·00
1405	1p.50 Wearing robes	2·50	2·40
MS1406	138×90 mm. 9p. Facing left	7·00	6·50

311 Running

2004. Olympic Games, Athens. Multicoloured.

1407	1p. Type **311**	95	90
1408	1p.50 Long jump	1·20	1·10
1409	2p. Discus	1·60	1·50
1410	3p.50 Javelin	2·40	2·20

312 *Lotus Flower in Full Bloom* (statue) and Deng Xiaoping wearing Uniform

2004. Birth Centenary of Deng Xiaoping (leader of China, 1978–1989). Multicoloured.

1411	1p. Type **312**	70	65
1412	1p.50 Deng Xiaoping and St Paul's Church	95	90
MS1413	138×90 mm. 8p. As young man and lotus flower (40×40 mm) (circular)	6·00	5·50

313 Fireworks over Waterfront

2004. International Firework Display Competition. Multicoloured.

1414	1p. Type **313**	70	65
1415	1p.50 Large burst and Macao Tower	95	90
1416	2p. Two large bursts and Macao Bridge	1·20	1·10
1417	4p.50 Large burst over Monte Hill	2·50	2·40
MS1418	138×90 mm. 9p. Trophy (vert)	6·00	5·50

314 People's Republic of China Flag

2004. 55th Anniversary of People's Republic of China. Multicoloured.

1419	1p. Type **314**	70	65
1420	1p.50 Macao flag	95	90
1421	2p. People's Republic emblem	1·20	1·10
1422	3p. Macao emblem	1·60	1·50
MS1423	138×90 mm. 7p. Imperial Palace, Beijing (59×39 mm)	6·00	5·50

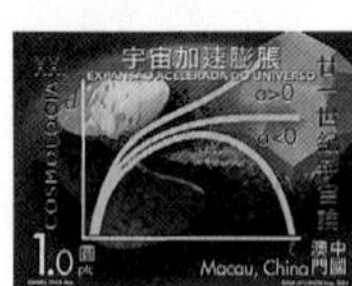
315 Graph showing Expanding Universe

2004. Science and Technology. Cosmology. Multicoloured.

1424	1p. Type **315**	70	65
1425	1p.50 Graph showing cosmic radiation	95	90
1426	2p. Galaxies (fluctuating galaxies)	1·20	1·10
1427	3p.50 Tetrahedron divided into dark matter, dark energy and the known universe	1·90	1·80
MS1428	138×90 mm. 8p. Mathematical shapes (Big Bang theory)	6·00	5·50

316 Soldier and Flag

2004. People's Republic of China Garrison, Macao. Multicoloured.

1429	1p. Type **316**	60	55
1430	1p. Tank soldier saluting	60	55
1431	1p.50 St Paul's Church and convoy	70	65
1432	1p.50 Nursing corps	70	65
1433	3p.50 Soldier at attention	1·60	1·50
1434	3p.50 Soldier charging	1·60	1·50
MS1435	138×90 mm. 8p. Soldiers carrying Flag (39×60 mm)	5·75	5·25

317 Lotus Blossom

2004. Fifth Anniversary of Macao Special Administrative Region. Multicoloured.

1436	1p.50 Type **317**	95	90
1437	2p. Blossoms and Cultural Centre	1·20	1·10
1438	2p.50 Blossoms and Monte Hill buildings	1·40	1·30
1439	3p. Blossoms, Macao Tower and Lisboa Hotel	1·60	1·50
MS1440	138×90 mm. 10p. Lotus blossom (different)	8·25	7·75

Nos. 1436/1439 were issued together, *se-tenant*, forming a composite design.

318 Airliner

2004. Tenth Anniversary of Air Macao. Sheet 138×90 mm.

MS1441	**318** 8p. multicoloured	6·00	5·50

319 Rooster

2005. New Year. Year of the Rooster.

1442	**319** 5p. multicoloured	4·00	3·75
MS1443	138×90 mm. **319** $10 multicoloured	7·00	6·50

2005. Traditional Scenes from Everyday Life. As T **303**. Multicoloured.

1444	1p.50 Cooking food on brazier	95	90
1445	1p.50 Man carrying pole of glass bowls	95	90
1446	1p.50 Craftsman working at table	95	90
1447	1p.50 Making bundles	95	90
1448	1p.50 Coconut vendor	95	90
1449	1p.50 Man cooking on griddle	95	90
1450	1p.50 Serving food under lantern	95	90
1451	1p.50 Hair braiding	95	90
MS1452	138×90 mm. 8p. Postman	5·75	5·25

320 Sai Van Bridge

2005. Opening of Sai Van Bridge linking Macao Peninsula to Taipa Island. Multicoloured.

1453	1p. Type **320**	95	90
1454	3p.50 Approach to bridge	2·10	2·00
MS1455	138×91 mm. 8p. Tower, bridge and boat (vert)	5·75	5·25

321 Central Library

2005. Libraries. Multicoloured.

1456	1p. Type **321**	70	65
1457	1p.50 Sir Robert Ho Tung library	95	90
1458	2p. Coloane library	1·20	1·10
1459	3p.50 Mong Ha library	1·90	1·80
MS1460	138×90 mm. 8p. Commercial Association Public Library (60×40 mm)	5·75	5·25

322 Mother and Child

2005. Greetings Stamps. Multicoloured.

1461	1p. Type **322**	70	65
1462	1p.50 Kangaroo with young in pocket	95	90
1463	2p. Bird and chicks in nest	1·20	1·10
1464	3p.50 Duck and ducklings	1·90	1·80

323 Chang Hung sees Ying Ying

2005. Classical Literature. *The Romance of the Western Chamber*. Multicoloured.

1465 1p.50 Type **323** 1·60 1·50
1466 1p.50 Reciting poems to each other 1·60 1·50
1467 1p.50 Chang Hung made ill 1·60 1·50
1468 1p.50 Huang Niang petitioning Madam Ts'ui 1·60 1·50
1469 1p.50 Chang Hung sleeping 1·60 1·50
1470 1p.50 Chang Hung and Ying Ying together 1·60 1·50
MS1471 139×90 mm. 8p. Ying Ying 8·25 7·75

324 Zheng He

2005. 600th Anniversary of the Voyages of Zheng He (Ma Sanbao). Multicoloured.

1472 1p. Type **324** 2·10 2·00
1473 1p.50 Giraffe 2·40 2·20
1474 1p.50 Ships and compass 2·50 2·40
MS1475 139×90 mm. 8p. Ship (50×30 mm) 8·25 7·75

Stamps of a similar design were issued by Hong Kong and People's Republic of China.

324a A Ma Temple

2005. World Heritage Sites. Multicoloured.

1476 1p. Type **324a** 95 90
1477 1p.50 St Joseph's Seminar 1·20 1·10
1478 2p. Mandarin's House 1·40 1·30
1479 3p.50 Dom Pedro V Theatre 2·10 2·00
MS1480 138×90 mm. 8p. St Paul's Church 5·75 5·25

325 Olympic Swimming Pool

2005. East Asian Games, Macao. Multicoloured.

1481 1p. Type **325** 70 65
1482 1p.50 Grand Beach 95 90
1483 2p. Tennis Academy 1·20 1·10
1484 2p.50 IPM Sports Pavilion 1·60 1·50
1485 3p.50 Macao Stadium 1·90 1·80
1486 4p.50 Tap Seac Sports Pavilion 2·40 2·20
MS1487 138×90 mm. 8p. Stadium (55×38 mm) (oval) 5·75 5·25

326 Banknote

2005. Centenary of First Macao Banknote. Multicoloured.

1488 1p. Type **326** 95 90
1489 1p.50 $5 note 1·20 1·10
1490 2p. $10 note 1·90 1·80
1491 2p.50 $50 note 2·50 2·40
MS1492 138×90 mm. 8p. $100 note 5·75 5·25

327 Weaving

2005. Chinese Inventions. Multicoloured.

1493 1p. Type **327** 95 90
1494 1p.50 Papermaking 1·20 1·10
1495 2p. Metal work 1·40 1·30
1496 4p.50 Calendar 2·50 2·40
MS1497 138×90 mm. 8p. Seismograph 5·75 5·25

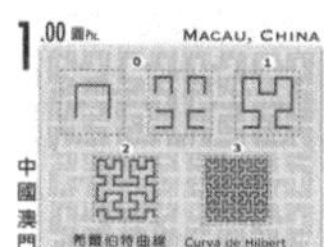

328 Hilbert's Curve

2005. Science and Technology. Chaos and Fractals. Multicoloured.

1498 1p. Type **328** 70 65
1499 1p. Tree fractal 70 65
1500 1p.50 Sierpinskis triangles 95 90
1501 1p.50 Chaos game 95 90
1502 2p. Von Koch's curve 1·40 1·30
1503 2p. Cantor set 1·40 1·30
MS1504 139×91 mm. 8p. Julia set 5·75 5·25

329 Dog's Head

2006. New Year. Year of the Dog. Multicoloured.

1505 5p.50 Type **329** 4·00 3·75
MS1506 138×90 mm. 10p. As No. 1505 7·00 6·50

330 Circular Lantern with Roosters

2006. Chinese Lanterns. Multicoloured.

1507 1p. Type **330** 95 90
1508 1p. Lantern with crowned top and small lanterns 95 90
1509 1p.50 Phoenix lantern 95 90
1510 1p.50 Fringed lantern with tassels 95 90
MS1511 138×90 mm. 8p. Circular lantern with tassels 5·75 5·25

2006. Traditional Scenes from Everyday Life. As T **303**. Multicoloured.

1512 1p.50 Cook 95 90
1513 1p.50 Tea seller and boy 95 90
1514 1p.50 Serving food 95 90
1515 1p.50 Boy and craftsman working at circular table 95 90
1515a 1p.50 Cobbler 95 90
1515b 1p.50 Potter 95 90
1515d 1p.50 Man using yoke to carry pots 95 90
1515c 1p.50 Tinsmith 95 90
MS1516 138×90 mm. 8p. Making tea 6·00 5·50

331 Hand Stamp (1845)

2006. Museum Exhibits. Communications Museum. Multicoloured.

1517 1p.50 Type **331** 95 90
1518 1p.50 Scales 95 90
1519 1p.50 Postbox (1910) 95 90
1520 1p.50 Sorting shelves 95 90
1521 1p.50 Telephone (1925) 95 90
1522 1p.50 Telephone exchange (1929) 95 90
1523 1p.50 Radio transmitter (1950) 95 90
1524 1p.50 Submarine cables (1953) 95 90
MS1525 138×90 mm. 10p. 1884 5r. stamp (first Macao stamp) (horiz) 6·00 5·50

332 Player

2006. World Cup Football Championship, Germany. Multicoloured.

1526 1p.50 Type **332** 95 90
1527 2p.50 Player running forward 1·40 1·30
1528 3p.50 Player on knees 1·90 1·80
1529 4p. Player running left 2·10 2·00

333 Peony Flowers

2006. Fans. Showing designs on fans. Multicoloured.

1530 1p.50 Type **333** 1·20 1·10
1531 1p.50 Warrior holding fan 1·20 1·10
1532 2p.50 Laughing Buddha 1·40 1·30
1533 2p.50 Snail and bamboo 1·40 1·30
1534 3p.50 Eagle 1·90 1·80
MS1535 138×90 mm. 10p. Children (detail) (40×30 mm) 12·00 11·00

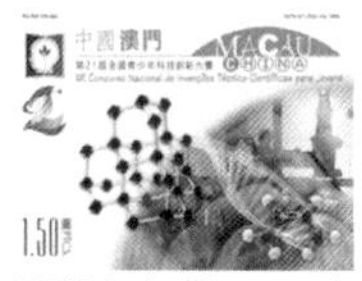

334 Molecular Diagram and DNA Strand

2006. XXI China Adolescents Science and Technology Invention Contest, Macau. Multicoloured.

1536 1p.50 Type **334** 95 90
1537 2p. Satellite dish and wind turbines 1·20 1·10
1538 2p.50 Cog and protractors 1·40 1·30
1539 3p.50 Laboratory equipment and computer mouse 1·90 1·80
MS1540 138×90 mm. 10p. Statue, building entrance and atomic symbol (40×60 mm) 6·00 5·50

335 Rua de Camilo Pessanha

2006. Streets of Macao. Multicoloured.

1541 1p.50 Type **335** 95 90
1542 1p.50 Rua de St Domingos 95 90
1543 2p.50 Calcada de St Francisco Xavier 1·40 1·30
1544 3p.50 Travessa da Paixao 1·90 1·80
MS1545 138×90 mm. 10p. Largo de Santo Agostinho 6·00 5·50

336 Script and Emblem

2006. 25th Anniversary of University of Macau. Multicoloured, background colour given.

1546 1p.50 Type **336** 1·20 1·10
1547 1p.50 Script and emblem (magenta) 1·20 1·10
1548 1p.50 Script and emblem (blue) 1·20 1·10
1549 1p.50 Script and emblem (orange) 1·20 1·10
1550 1p.50 Script and emblem (grey) 1·20 1·10
MS1551 138×90 mm. 10p. University Arms 6·00 5·50

2006. Pa Kua (martial art) (5th series). As T **285**. Multicoloured.

1552 2p. (1) Trigrams, women brushing hair 1·20 1·10
1553 2p. (4) Trigrams, elderly couple and Dragon 1·20 1·10
1554 2p. (7) Trigrams and lovers 1·20 1·10
1555 2p. (3) Trigrams three-legged pot and people 1·20 1·10
1556 2p. (6) Trigrams, carriage and well 1·20 1·10
1557 2p. (2) Trigrams and supported log 1·20 1·10
1558 2p. (5) Trigrams and women seated on carpet 1·20 1·10
1559 2p. (8) Trigrams, sage and followers 1·20 1·10
MS1560 135×90 mm. 8p. Women fishing (59×27 mm) 6·00 5·50

337 Matteo Ricci

2006. Society of Jesus. Multicoloured.

1561 1p.50 (1) Type **337** 95 90
1562 1p.50 (2) Francis Xavier 95 90
1563 3p.50 (3) Alessandro Valignano 1·90 1·80
1564 3p.50 (4) Melchior Carneiro 1·90 1·80
MS1565 138×90 mm. 10p. Inigo Loyola 6·00 5·50

338 Pig

2007. New Year. Year of the Pig.

1566 **338** 5p.50 multicoloured 3·50 3·25
MS1567 138×90 mm. **338** $10 multicoloured 10·50 10·00

339 Lao Zi

2007. Shek Wan Ceramics. Multicoloured.

1568 1p.50 (1) Type **339** 95 90
1569 1p.50 (2) Lu Yu 95 90
1570 1p.50 (3) Philosopher 95 90
1571 2p.50 (4) Luo Han 1·40 1·30
MS1572 138×90 mm. 8p. Concubine after Bathing 5·25 4·75

2007. Traditional Scenes from Everyday Life. As T **303**. Multicoloured.

1573 1p.50 Porter 95 90
1574 1p.50 Tea seller 95 90
1575 1p.50 Rickshaw 95 90
1576 1p.50 Cricket fighting 95 90
1577 1p.50 Decorating cloth 95 90
1578 1p.50 Cobbler 95 90
1579 1p.50 Parasol making 95 90
1580 1p.50 Seamstress 95 90
MS1581 138×90 mm. 10p. Dragon procession 6·00 5·50

340 Seamstress

2007. Traditional Shops. Multicoloured.

1582 1p.50 Type **340** 95 90
1583 1p.50 Herbalist 95 90
1584 2p.50 Calligrapher 1·40 1·30
1585 3p.50 Food shop 1·90 1·80
MS1586 138×90 mm.10p. Street 6·00 5·50

341 Man leaning on Shovel ('The Foolish Old Man moved Mountain')

2007. Ancient Proverbs. Multicoloured. (a) Ordinary or self-adhesive gum.

1587 1p.50 (1) Type **341** 95 90
1588 1p.50 (2) Two seated men ('A Friendship between Guan and Bao') 95 90

1589	3p.50 (3) Masked men and deer ('Calling Black White')	1·90	1·80
1590	3p.50 (4) Man holding clam and bird ('The Quarrel between Snipe and Clam')	1·90	1·80

(b) Miniature Sheet. Ordinary gum.

MS1595	138×90 mm. 8p. Horse riders	6·00	5·50

342 Tripitaka, Sandy, Pigsy and Monkey King

2007. Classical Literature. *The Journey to the West.* Multicoloured.

1596	1p.50 Type **342**	2·40	2·20
1597	1p.50 Iron Fan Princess	2·40	2·20
1598	2p. Red Boy impaled on swords	3·50	3·25
1599	2p. Subduing monkeys	3·50	3·25
1600	2p.50 Sandy, Pigsy and Monkey King	4·75	4·50
1601	2p.50 Pigsy and Seven-spider demon	4·75	4·50
MS1602	139×90 mm.10p. Monkey king	12·00	11·00

343 Robert Baden-Powell (founder) and Scout using Semaphore

2007. Centenary of Scouting. Designs showing Robert Baden Powell and scouts. Multicoloured.

1603	1p.50 Type **343**	95	90
1604	2p. Scouts saluting	1·20	1·10
1605	2p.50 Scouts and campfire	1·40	1·30
1606	3p.50 Scouts building tripod	2·10	2·00
1607	3p.50 Scouts orienteering	2·10	2·00
MS1608	138×90 mm. 10p. Monument (vert)	6·00	5·50

344 Robert Morrison as Young Man

2007. Bicentenary of Robert Morrison's Arrival in China (missionary and translator of Bible into Chinese). Multicoloured.

1609	1p.50 Type **344**	95	90
1610	3p.50 As older man	2·40	2·20

345 Mount Kangrinboqe

2007. Mainland Scenery. Sheet 138×90 mm.

MS1611	**345** 10p. multicoloured	7·00	6·50

The stamp and margins of **MS**1611 form a composite design.

346 Fibonacci Sequence

2007. Science and Technology. The Golden Ratio. Multicoloured.

1612	1p.50 Type **346**	95	90
1613	2p. Sunflower spiral	1·20	1·10
1614	2p.50 Penrose tiles	1·40	1·30
1615	3p.50 Nautilus	1·90	1·80
MS1616	138×90 mm. 10p.Greek letter phi (symbol of golden ratio)	6·00	5·50

347 Lao Zi

2007. Ethics and Moral Values. Philosophers. Multicoloured.

1617	1p.50 Type **347**	95	90
1618	2p.50 Zhuang Zi	1·40	1·30
1619	3p.50 Confucius	1·90	1·80
1620	4p. Mencius	2·40	2·20
MS1621	138×90 mm. 10p. Lao Zi, Zhuang Zi, Confucius and Mencius (circular) (41×41 mm)	6·00	5·50

348 Rat shaped Brooch (metal)

2008. New Year. The Year of the Rat. Multicoloured.

1622	1p.50 Type **348**	95	90
1623	1p.50 Carving (wood)	95	90
1624	1p.50 Rat in water (water)	95	90
1625	1p.50 Rat outlined in fireworks (fire)	95	90
1627	5p. Rat shaped teapot (earth)	2·75	2·75
MS1628	139×90 mm. 10p. As No. 1627 (49×49 mm) (diamond)	6·00	5·50

2008. Pa Kua (martial art) (6th series). As T **285**. Multicoloured.

1629	2p. (1) Trigrams and women kneeling	1·20	1·10
1630	2p. (2) Trigrams and woman on shore	1·20	1·10
1631	2p. (3) Trigrams and watermill	1·20	1·10
1632	2p. (4) Trigrams and figure with arms raised	1·20	1·10
1633	2p. (5) Trigrams and bearded man seated	1·20	1·10
1634	2p. (6) Trigrams, waterfalls and men with poles	1·20	1·10
1635	2p. (7) Trigrams and grass skirted figure holding bow	1·20	1·10
1636	2p. (8) Trigrams, banners and figure wearing armour	1·20	1·10
MS1637	135×90 mm. 10p. Fisherman (60×30 mm)	6·00	5·50

The stamp and margins of **MS**1637 form a composite design.

349 Torch

2008. Olympic Torch Relay. Multicoloured.

1638	1p.50 Type **349**	95	90
1639	3p.50 Huanhuan	1·90	1·80
MS1640	90×139 mm. 10p. Torch (40×70 mm)	6·00	5·50

350 Golden Apple

2008. Legends and Myths. Multicoloured.

1641	1p.50 Type **350**	95	90
1642	2p.50 Gordian knot	1·40	1·30
1643	3p.50 Trojan horse	1·90	1·80
1644	4p. Riddle of the sphinx	2·10	2·00
MS1645	138×90 mm. 10p. Cupid and Psyche (40×70 mm)	6·00	5·50

352 Fortaleza do Monte (Fortaleza de Nossa Senhora do Monte de Sao Paulo)

2008. World Heritage Sites. Multicoloured.

1655	1p.50 Type **352**	95	90
1656	2p. Largo do Lilau (Lilau Square)	1·20	1·10
1657	2p.50 Casa de Lou Kau (Lou Kau Mansion)	1·60	1·50
1658	3p. Largo do Senado (Senado Square)	1·90	1·80
1659	3p.50 Sam Kai Vui Kun temple	2·10	2·00
1660	4p. Igreja da Se (Cathedral Church)	2·50	2·40
1661	4p.50 Quartel dos Mouros (Moorish quarter)	2·75	2·75
1662	5p. Igreja de Santo Antonio (Church of St Anthony)	3·25	3·00

353 National Aquatic Center, Beijing

2008. Olympic Games, Beijing. Multicoloured.

1663	5p. Type **353**	3·25	3·00
MS1664	138×90 mm. 10p. National Stadium (72×55 mm)	7·00	6·50

354 Fireworks

2008. 20th International Firework Competition. Two sheets containing T **354** and similar horiz designs showing firework displays. Multicoloured.

MS1665	160×110 mm. 1p.50 Type **354**; 2p.50 Orange central burst amongst magenta; 3p.50 Shades of gold; 5p. Large multicoloured burst at right	8·00	7·50
MS1666	137×90 mm. 10p. Fireworks	7·00	6·50

355 'Celebration'

2008. World Post Day. Multicoloured.

1667	1p.50 Type **355**	95	90
1668	3p.50 UPU emblem	2·10	2·00

356 Bridge, Lijiang

2008. Mainland Scenery. Sheet 138×90 mm.

MS1669	**356** 10p. multicoloured	7·00	6·50

357 Carved Ivory Buddha

2008. Traditional Handicrafts. Multicoloured.

1670	1p.50 Type **357**	95	90
1671	2p. Ceramic jar	1·20	1·10
1672	2p.50 Basket	1·60	1·50
1673	3p50. Wooden carving	2·10	2·00
MS1674	138×90 mm. 10p. Beaded bag (60×40 mm)	7·00	6·50

358 Louis Braille

2009. Birth Bicentenary of Louis Braille (inventor of Braille writing for the blind).

1675	**358** 5p. multicoloured	3·25	3·00

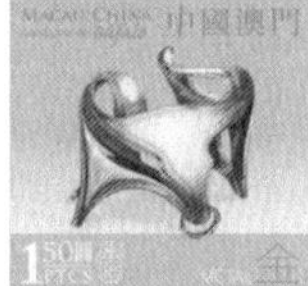
359 Metal Ox

2009. Chinese New Year. Year of the Ox. Multicoloured.

1676	1p.50 Type **359**	95	90
1677	1p.50 Ox's head (carving)	95	90
1678	1p.50 Ox's head (painting)	95	90
1679	1p.50 Fireworks	95	90
1680	5p. Ox as teapot	3·25	3·00
MS1681	138×90 mm. As No. 1680 (50×50 mm) (diamond shape)	7·00	6·50

360 People holding Incense

2009. Opening of Kun Iam Treasury. Multicoloured.

1682	1p.50 Type **360**	95	90
1683	2p.50 Woman carrying paper house, woman and gong, people holding incense	1·60	1·50
1684	3p.50 Mother with baby, people, incense and shrine	2·40	2·20
1685	4p. People, incense and stalls	2·50	2·40
MS1686	138×90 mm. 10p. Elderly woman (horiz)	7·00	6·50

Nos. 1682/1685 were printed together, *se-tenant*, forming a composite design.

361 Compactor

2009. Traditional Tools. Multicoloured.

1687	1p.50 Type **361**	95	90
1688	2p.50 Whetstone	1·60	1·50
1689	3p.50 Mill stone	2·40	2·20
1690	4p. Biscuit press	2·50	2·40
MS1691	138×90 mm. 10p. Tools (60×41 mm)	7·00	6·50

362 Vairocana Buddha, Longmen Caves, Luoyang

2009. Mainland Scenery. Sheet 138×90 mm.

MS1692	**362** 10p. multicoloured	7·00	6·50

363 Workers drilling '5.' '1.'

2009. 120th Anniversary of Labour Day (1st May). Multicoloured.

1693	1p.50 Type **363**	95	90
1694	5p. Workers digging '5.' '1.'	3·25	3·00
MS1695	138×90 mm. 10p. Workers supporting '5.' '1.'	7·00	6·50

364 Mantis stalking Cicada

2009. Ancient Proverbs. Multicoloured. Ordinary or self-adhesive gum.

1696	1p.50 Type **364**	95	90
1697	1p.50 Bird in tree ('A Fond Dream of Nanke')	95	90
1698	3p.50 Swordsman ('Songs of Chu on All Sides')	2·10	2·00
1699	3p.50 Scribe ('Give the Last Measure of Devotion')	2·10	2·00
MS1700	138×90 mm. 10p. Men on boat ('Marking the Boat to find the Sword')	6·25	6·00

365 Archway

2009. 60th Anniversary of People's Republic of China. Multicoloured.

1705	1p.50 Type **365**	95	90
1706	2p.50 Tanks	1·60	1·50
1707	3p.50 Children exercising	2·10	2·00
1708	4p. Flag and parade	2·40	2·20
MS1709	138×90 mm. 10p. As Nos. 1707/1708 (59×39 mm)	7·00	6·50

366 Bodhisattva Avalokitsvara

2009. Artwork from Cultural Mix of East and West. Paintings from Porcelain Plate. Multicoloured.

1710	1p.50 Type **366**	95	90
1711	5p. Bodhisattva Ksitigarbha	3·00	2·75

367 School Campus

2009. 120th Anniversary of Pui Ching Middle School. Multicoloured.

1712	1p.50 Type **367**	95	90
1713	2p. School buildings	1·20	1·10
1714	2p.50 School chapel	1·60	1·50
1715	3p.50 Bust and fireplace	2·10	2·00
MS1716	138×90 mm. 10p. Original building	7·00	6·50

368 Stylised Aerial View

2009. Science Centre. Multicoloured.

1717	1p.50 Type **368**	95	90
1718	2p.50 Aerial view, Exhibition Centre at left	1·60	1·50
1719	3p.50 Exhibition Centre	2·10	2·00
1720	4p. Planetarium at left	2·50	2·40
MS1721	138×90 mm. 10p. Stylised Exhibition Centre	7·00	6·50

369 Soldiers practising Martial Arts

2009. Tenth Anniversary of Chinese Army in Macau. Multicoloured.

1722	1p.50 Type **369**	95	90
1723	1p.50 Service women	95	90
1724	1p.50 Soldiers with weapons	95	90
1725	1p.50 Soldiers with children	95	90
1726	1p.50 Soldiers and children planting tree	95	90
1727	1p.50 Soldiers and tank	95	90
MS1728	105×125 mm. 10p. Soldiers on parade (40×60 mm)	7·00	6·50

370 Lotus Flower

2009. Tenth Anniversary of Macao Special Administrative Region. Multicoloured.

1729	1p.50 Type **370**	95	90
1730	1p.50 Senado Square and Macau Tower	95	90
1731	1p.50 Waterside skyline	95	90
MS1732	138×90 mm. 10p. Lotus flower and gateway (40×60 mm)	7·00	6·50

371 Tiger (Madeira (Wood))

2010. Chinese New Year. Year of the Tiger.

1733	1p.50 Type **371**	95	90
1734	1p.50 Tiger head and shoulders (Agua (water))	95	90
1735	1p.50 Stylised multicoloured tiger (Fogo (fire))	95	90
1736	1p.50 Clay tiger and cub (Terra (earth))	95	90
1737	5p. Stylised golden tiger (Metal)	3·25	3·00
MS1738	139×90 mm. 10p. Stylised golden tiger (different) (diamond shaped)	7·00	6·50

2010. Pa Kua (martial art) (7th series). As T **285**. Multicoloured.

1739	2p. (1) Trigrams, mountains and man with pack	1·20	1·10
1740	2p. (2) Trigrams and couple by lake	1·20	1·10
1741	2p. (3) Trigrams and packhorse	1·20	1·10
1742	2p. (4) Trigrams and figure crouched on rock	1·20	1·10
1743	2p. (5) Trigrams, couple and houses	1·20	1·10
1744	2p. (6) Trigrams, waterfall and figure watching from above	1·20	1·10
1745	2p. (7) Trigrams and figure looking up	1·20	1·10
1746	2p. (8) Trigrams and two men greeting	1·20	1·10
MS1747	135×90 mm. 10p. Child with rattle (60×30 mm)	7·00	6·50

Nos. 1739/1746 were issued in *se-tenant* sheetlets of eight stamps each showing two trigrams and a descriptive painting.

The stamp and margins of **MS**1747 form a composite design.

372 Women

2010. Centenary of Women's Day. Multicoloured.

1748	1p.50 (1) Type **372**	95	90
1749	2p.50 (2) Women	1·60	1·50
1750	3p.50 (3) Women	2·10	2·00
1751	4p. (4) Women	2·50	2·40
MS1752	138×90 mm. 10p. Women of different professions (40×60 mm)	7·00	6·50

Nos. 1748/1751 were printed, *se-tenant*, forming a composite design of women of the world.

373 Rabbits

2010. Expo 2010, Shanghai. Multicoloured.

1753	3p.50 Type **373**	2·10	2·00
1754	4p. Lanterns	2·50	2·40
MS1755	138×90 mm. 10p. Large pink rabbit	7·00	6·50

374 Ruins of St Paul Cathedral

2010. 60th Anniversary Bank of China, Macau Branch. Multicoloured.

1756	1p.50 Type **374**	1·20	1·10
1757	2p.50 Modern HQ	1·90	1·80
1758	3p.50 Banknote details and inverted skyline	2·50	2·40
1759	4p. Clasped hands and inverted skyline	2·75	2·75
MS1760	138×90 mm. 10p. Modern HQ and lotus flower (60×40 mm)	7·00	6·50

375 Dom Pedro V Theatre

2010. St Augustine's Square. Multicoloured.

1761	1p.50 Type **375**	1·20	1·10
1762	2p.50 Sir Robert Ho Tung Library	1·90	1·80
1763	3p.50 St Augustine Church	2·50	2·40
1764	4p. St. Joseph's Seminary and Church	2·75	2·75
MS1765	138×90 mm. St Augustine Church tower	7·00	6·50

376 St Lawrence receiving Deaconship from Pope Sixtus II (stained glass window (detail), St Lawrence Church)

2010. Church Interiors. Multicoloured.

1766	5p.50 Type **376**	3·75	3·50
MS1767	105×70 mm. 10p. Stained glass window (horiz)	7·00	6·50

Stamps of a similar design were issued by Aland Islands.

377 Buddha

2010. Woodcarving. Multicoloured.

1768	1p.50 Type **377**	1·20	1·10
1769	2p.50 Na Tcha (or Nezha)	1·90	1·80
1770	2p.50 Kun Iam (Kun Sai Iam) (Avalokitasvara Bodhisattva)	2·50	2·40
1771	4p. Mazu (Tin Hau) (goddess)	2·75	2·75
MS1772	138×90 mm. 10p. The Eight Immortals (60×30 mm)	7·00	6·50

378 Hand-cranked Bakelite and 1960's Single Unit Handsets

2010. Antique Telephones. Multicoloured.

1773	1p.50 Type **378**	1·20	1·10
1774	2p.50 Modern public telephone and early box handset	1·90	1·80
1775	3p.50 Early rotary handset and 1960's public telephone	2·50	2·40
1776	4p. Bakelite wall-mounted and metal hand-cranked box handsets	2·75	2·75
MS1777	139×90 mm. 10p. Early 1900's wall mounted telephone (60×40 mm)	7·00	6·50

379 Noodle Soup from Van Tan (Sopa de Fitas com Van-Tan)

2010. Tenth Anniversary of Macau Food Festival. Multicoloured.

1778	1p.50 Type **379**	1·20	1·10
1779	2p.50 Steamed buns (Xiaolongbao)	1·90	1·80
1780	3p.50 Sushi	2·50	2·40
1781	4p. Custard tart (Pastel de Nata)	2·75	2·75
MS1782	138×90 mm. 10p. Portuguese chicken (Galinha a portuguesa)	7·00	6·50

380 Tangzhuang (Tang suit)

2010. Traditional Costumes. Multicoloured.

1783	1p.50 Type **380**	1·20	1·10
1784	2p.50 Qipao (traditional Chinese woman's dress)	1·90	1·80
1785	3p.50 Duanyichangqun (blouse and long skirt) (traditional Han woman's costume)	2·50	2·40
1786	4p. Zhongsanzhuang (Chinese tunic suit) (Chinese 'National Costume')	2·75	2·75
MS1787	139×90 mm. 10p. Qipao and Duanyichangqun (60×40 mm)	7·00	6·50

381 Panda

2011. Pandas. Multicoloured.

1788	1p.50 Type **381**	1·20	1·10
1789	5p. Panda, facing forward	3·50	3·25
MS1790	138×90 mm. 10p. Two pandas (40×60 mm)	7·00	6·50

382 Rabbit (Madeira (wood))

2011. Chinese New Year. Year of the Rabbit. Multicoloured.

1791	1p.50 Type **382**	1·20	1·10
1792	1p.50 Rabbit (Agua (water))	1·20	1·10
1793	1p.50 Fireworks as rabbit (Fogo (fire))	1·20	1·10
1794	1p.50 Rabbit (Terra (earth))	1·20	1·10
1795	5p. Stylised rabbit (metal)	3·50	3·25
MS1796	138×90 mm. 10p. Stylised rabbit (different) (35×35 mm (diamond-shaped))	7·00	6·50

383 Ancient City of Fenghuang

2011. Mainland Scenery. Sheet 138×90 mm

MS1797	**383** 10p. multicoloured	7·00	6·50

384 Seat of Government

2011. Public Buildings and Monuments. Multicoloured.

1798	1p.50 Type **384**	1·20	1·10
1799	2p.50 Monetory Authority	1·90	1·80
1800	3p.50 Albergue da Santa Casa (old inn, now creative industries centre)	2·50	2·40
1801	4p. Macau Foundation	2·75	2·75

385 Singer with Yehu

2011. Cantonese Naamyam Singers. Multicoloured.

1802	1p.50 Type **385**	1·20	1·10
1803	2p.50 Singer on dockside with sails behind	1·90	1·80
1804	3p.50 Blind singer with stick, carrying instruments	2·50	2·40
1805	4p. Singer with guzheng on dockside with boats behind	2·75	2·75
MS1806	138×90 mm. 10p. Singer with yehu, facing left	7·00	6·50

386 Meeting when Travelling the Lake

2011. Legend of the White Snake. Multicoloured.

1807	1p.50 Type **386**	1·20	1·10
1808	1.50p. White snake exposed during Duanyang Festival	1·20	1·10
1809	2p. Lady Bai stealing herb to save Xu Xian	1·40	1·30
1810	2p. Fight between dragon and snake	1·40	1·30
1811	2p.50 Lady Bai captured in pagoda	1·40	1·30
1812	2p.50 Xu Shilin (Lady Bai's son) meets his mother at the pagoda	1·40	1·30
MS1813	138×90 mm. 10p. Flooding of Jinshan Temple (60×30 mm)	7·00	6·50

387 *Pycnonotus sinensis* (Light-vented Bulbul)

2011. 50th Anniversary of WWF. Multicoloured.

1814	1p.50 Type **387**	1·20	1·10
1815	2p.50 *Streptopelia chinensis* (Spotted turtle dove)	1·90	1·80
1816	3p.50 *Ixobrychus sinensis* (Yellow bittern)	2·50	2·40
1817	4p.50 *Centropus sinensis* (Greater coucal)	3·25	3·00
MS1818	138×90 mm. Nos. 1814/1817	9·50	8·75

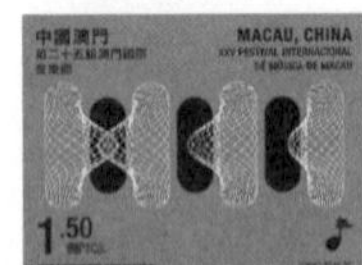
388 Piano

2011. 25th Macao International Music Festival. Each grey, black and scarlet-vermilion.

1819	1p.50 Type **388**	1·20	1·10
1820	2p.50 Trumpet	1·90	1·80
1821	3p.50 Drums	2·50	2·40
1822	4p. Strings	2·75	2·75
MS1823	138×90 mm. 10p. Sound waves	7·00	6·50

389 Lin Zexu (anti-opium campaigner)

2011. Personalities. Multicoloured.

1824	1p.50 Type **389**	1·20	1·10
1825	2p.50 Ye Ting (army commander)	1·90	1·80
1826	3p.50 Xian Xinghai (musician)	2·50	2·40
1827	4p. Ho Yin (industrialist and social activist)	2·75	2·75
MS1828	138×90 mm. 10p. Lin Zexu, Ye Ting, Xian Xinghai, Ho Yin, golden lotus flower and stars (40×60 mm)	7·00	6·50

390 Gao Jianfu (Chairman of Tongmenghui, Guangdong Branch) and 41, Nanwan Street

2011. Centenary of Xinhai Revolution (Revolution of 1911). Multicoloured.

1829	1p.50 Type **390**	1·20	1·10
1830	2p.50 Huang Xing (founder of Huaxinghui) and Monument to 72 Martyrs of Huanghuagang	1·90	1·80
1831	3p.50 Xiong Bingkun (leader Wuchung Uprising) and Wuchung Gate	2·50	2·40
1832	4p. Sun-Yat Sen (provisional president) and 292 Changjiang Road, Nanjing City	2·75	2·75
MS1833	138×90 mm. 10p. 1912 20c. stamp (As Type **41**) (60×40 mm)	7·00	6·50

391 Early Building and Stele

2011. 140th Anniversary of Kiang Wu Hospital Charitable Association

1834	1p.50 Type **391**	1·20	1·10
1835	2p.50 Sun Yat-Sen (introduces western style medicine) (statue)	1·90	1·80
1836	3p.50 Traditional wooden medicine grinder and boat-shaped vessel	2·50	2·40
1837	4p. CAT scanner	2·75	2·75
MS1838	138×90 mm. 10p. Sun Yat-Sen (statue) in close up (40×40 mm)	7·00	6·50

392 Metal Dragon

2012. Chinese New Year. Year of the Dragon. Multicoloured.

1839	1p.50 Type **392**	1·20	1·10
1840	1p.50 Dragon head and shoulders (Madeira (Wood))	1·20	1·10
1841	1p.50 Stylised multicoloured dragon (Fogo (fire))	1·20	1·10
1842	1p.50 Clay dragon teapot (Terra (earth))	1·20	1·10
1843	5p. Blue-grey dragon (Agua (water))	3·50	3·25
MS1844	139×90 mm. 12p. Blue-grey dragon (Agua (water)) (different) (diamond shaped)	8·50	8·00

393 '2012' incorporating 'No Smoking' Symbol

2012. New Era of Smoke-free Macau. Multicoloured.

1845	1p.50 Type **393**	1·20	1·10
1846	5p. No smoking symbol and aerial view of Macau	3·50	3·25

2013. Pa Kua (martial art) (8th series). As T **285**. Multicoloured.

1847	2p. (1) Trigrams, old man with stick and stunted tree	1·20	1·10
1848	2p. (2) Trigrams and men pushing Buffalo	1·20	1·10
1849	2p. (3) Trigrams and volcano and horses, two fighting	1·20	1·10
1850	2p. (4) Trigrams and two mounted soldiers in narrow pass	1·20	1·10
1851	2p. (5) Trigrams and men on mound	1·20	1·10
1852	2p. (6) Trigrams, waterfall and figure watching from below	1·20	1·10
1853	2p. (7) Trigrams and figure at foot of mountain	1·20	1·10
1854	2p. (8) Trigrams and woman carrying baby on back and yoke	1·20	1·10
MS1855	135×90 mm. 10p. Mother with child on lap (60×30 mm)	7·00	6·50

Nos. 1847/1854 were issued in *se-tenant* sheetlets of eight stamps each showing two trigrams and a descriptive painting.

The stamp and margins of **MS**1855 form a composite design.

394 'TAI FONG TAC KEI'

2012. 70th Anniversary of Tai Fung Bank. Multicoloured.

1856	1p.50 Type **394**	1·20	1·10
1857	2p.50 Central emblem	1·90	1·80
1858	3p.50 Bank emblem	2·50	2·40
1859	4p. Carved golden dragon seal	2·75	2·75
MS1860	138×90 mm. 10p. '70' over carved dragon seal (60×40 mm)	7·00	6·50

395 Boats against Harbour Wall

2012. Fishing Harbour in the Past. Multicoloured.

1861	1p.50 Type **395**	1·20	1·10
1862	2p.50 Sailing ships and houseboats	1·90	1·80
1863	3p.50 Houseboats, wooden jetties and washing on line	2·50	2·40
1864	4p. Wharf side buildings	2·75	2·75
MS1865	138×90 mm. 10p. Sailing ship and covered wharf (60×40 mm)	7·00	6·50

396 Students

2012. 80th Anniversary of Hou Kong Middle School. Multicoloured.

1866	1p.50 Type **396**	1·20	1·10
1867	2p.50 Sports	1·90	1·80
1868	3p.50 Cultural activities	2·50	2·40
1869	4p. Younger children at affiliated Primary School	2·75	2·75
MS1870	138×90 mm. 10p. Athletes parading on sports track (40×40 mm)	7·00	6·50

397 Free Nursery Services

2012. 120th Anniversary of Tung Sin Tong Charitable Society. Multicoloured.

1871	1p.50 Type **397**	1·20	1·10
1872	2p.50 Children in school (free education)	1·90	1·80
1873	3p.50 Doctor and chemist (free clinics and medications)	2·50	2·40
1874	4p. Elderly couple and mother and children (help for the needy)	2·75	2·75
MS1875	90×138 mm. 10p. Roof of society building (40×30 mm)	7·00	6·50

398 The Cowherd Treating the Ox

2012. Legend of the Cowherd and the Weaving Maid. Multicoloured.

1876	1p.50 Type **398**	1·20	1·10
1877	1.50p. Stealing the weaver's clothes whilst she is bathing	1·20	1·10
1878	2p. The cowherd farms, the weaver weaves and their children play	1·60	1·50
1879	2p. Heavenly soldiers capture the weaving maid	1·60	1·50
1880	2p.50 The couple are separated by the milky way	1·90	1·80
1881	2p.50 The gods are touched by the couple's weeping	1·90	1·80
MS1882	138×90 mm. 10p. Meeting on the Magpie Bridge once a year (40×60 mm)	7·00	6·50

399 Macau Tower, Stylised Buildings and '20'

2012. 20th Anniversary of Safeguarding Honesty and Transparency. Multicoloured.

1883	2p. Type **399**	1·60	1·50
1884	5p. Stylised harbour buildings and '20'	4·25	4·00

400 Ship painted on Rock

2012. Macau Seen by Lok Cheong. Multicoloured.

1885	1p.50 Type **400**	1·20	1·10
1886	2p.50 Autumn woodland	2·10	2·00
1887	3p.50 People walking in park	2·75	2·75
1888	4p. Large trees	3·25	3·00
MS1889	138×90 mm. 10p. City skyline (40×40 mm)	8·25	7·75

401 Henrique de Senna Fernandes

2012. Lusophone Writers. Henrique de Senna Fernandes Commemoration

1890	**401** 5p. multicoloured	4·25	4·00

402 Surgeon

2012. ORBIS (eyesight charity). 30 Years of Saving Sight. Multicoloured.

1891	1p.50 +1p. Type **402**	2·10	2·00
1892	5p. +1p. Sight test	5·00	4·50

403 Revisiting the Dream

2012. Classical Literature. *The Peony Pavilion*. Multicoloured.

1893	1p.50 Type **403**	1·20	1·10
1894	1p.50 Self portrait and last wish	1·20	1·10
1895	2p. Infernal judgement	1·40	1·30
1896	2p. Reunion and achieving the dream	1·40	1·30
1897	2p.50 Resurrection and marriage	1·60	1·50
1898	2p.50 Obtaining Imperial Court decree	1·60	1·50

MS1899	139×90 mm.10p. Dream in the garden (30×60 mm)	8·50	8·00

404 Metal Snake

2013. Chinese New Year. Year of the Snake. Multicoloured.

1900	1p.50 Type **404**	1·20	1·10
1901	1p.50 Snake head and shoulders (Madeira (Wood))	1·20	1·10
1902	1p.50 Stylised multicoloured snake (Fogo (fire))	1·20	1·10
1903	1p.50 Clay snake teapot (Terra (earth))	1·20	1·10
1904	5p. Shimmering multicoloured snake (Agua (water))	3·50	3·25
MS1905	139×90 mm. 12p. As No. 1905 (diamond shaped)	8·50	8·00

405 Shiu Ying Chau (founder)

2013. Centenary of Macau Chamber of Commerce. Multicoloured.

1906	1p.50 Type **405**	1·20	1·10
1907	2p.50 Early meeting and document	1·60	1·50
1908	3p.50 Business seal stamp and presentations	2·40	2·20
1909	4p. Ballot box and modern building	2·75	2·75
MS1910	138×90 mm. 12p. Early building (40×40 mm)	8·50	8·00

406 Kaiping Diaolou (watchtower)

2011. Mainland Scenery. Sheet 138×90 mm

MS1911	**406** 12p. multicoloured	8·50	8·00

407 Crowd

2013. 20th Anniversary of Promulgation of Basic Law of Macau. Multicoloured.

1912	1p.50 Type **407**	1·20	1·10
1913	5p. Crowd surrounding lotus flower	3·50	3·25

408 Manual Fire Appliance

2013. 130th Anniversary of Fire Brigade. Multicoloured.

1914	1p.50 Type **408**	1·20	1·10
1915	2p.50 Fire appliance with ladder, *c.* 1940	1·90	1·80
1916	3p.50 Scania aerial ladder fire appliance	2·50	2·40
1917	4p. Rosenbauer Panther airport fire appliance	2·75	2·75
MS1918	138×90 mm. 12p. Early horse-drawn appliance (40×60 mm)	8·75	8·25

409 The Nativity (carved mother-of-pearl)

2013. Museum Exhibits. Macau Museum. Multicoloured.

1919	1p.50 Type **409**	1·20	1·10
1920	2p.50 Virgin and Child (Portuguese 15th-century)	1·90	1·80
1921	3p.50 Elephant-shaped Kendi (Karak porcelain)	2·50	2·40
1922	4p. Bronze bell, St Paul's Church	2·75	2·75
MS1923	90×138 mm. 12p. Early Macau (Amacao) (copperplate engraving by Theodore de Bry, 16th-century) (60×40 mm)	8·75	8·25

410 Na Tcha born Fully Formed

2013. Beliefs and Customs. Na Tcha. Multicoloured.

1924	2p. Type **410**	1·40	1·30
1925	2p.50 Na Tcha accidently killing son of dragon king	1·90	1·80
1926	3p.50 Cutting the flesh from his bones to return it to his parents	2·50	2·40
1927	4p. Na Tcha reincarnated with Wind-Fire-Wheels, Fire-tipped Spear and Universe Ring	2·75	2·75
MS1928	138×90 mm. 12p. Na Tcha Reincarnated (different)	8·75	8·25

411 Rescue of the Young Prince

2013. Classical Literature. *Romance of the Three Kingdoms.* Multicoloured.

1929	2p. Type **410**	1·40	1·30
1930	2p.50 Control of Yi Province	1·90	1·80
1931	3p.50 Drowning of the Seven Armies	2·50	2·40
1932	4p. Zhuge Liang's Prayer to the Star	2·75	2·75
MS1933	138×90 mm. 12p. Unification under Jin Dynasty (horiz)	8·75	8·25

412 Avenida Almeida Ribeiro

2013. Streets of Macau. Multicoloured.

1934	2p. Type **412**	1·40	1·30
1935	2p.50 Calçada dos Quartéis	1·90	1·80
1936	3p.50 Claçada do Teatro	2·50	2·40
1937	4p. Breco do Lilau	2·75	2·75
MS1938	138×90 mm. 12p. Calçada da Igeja de São Lázaro (vert)	8·75	8·25

See also Nos. 2058/2065.

413 Cherub

2013. Christmas. Multicoloured.

1939	3p.50 Type **413**	2·50	2·40
1940	5p. Cherub, with head on hands	3·50	3·25
MS1941	138×90 mm. 12p. Madonna and child	8·75	8·25

414 *Yu Un* (Leong Chong Hin, Guan Wanli, Situ Qi, Chui Tak Kei and Lin Jin)

2013. Chinese Calligraphy and Painting. Famous Artists in Macau. Multicoloured.

1942	2p. Type **414**	1·40	1·30
1943	2p. *Literary Meeting in goi Meng House* (Gu Danming)	1·40	1·30
1944	2p. *Blessings of Autumn* (Huang YunYu, Guan Wanli, U Kuan Wai, Zhou Paiyun, Zhao Wenfeng, Tam Van Iao, Kam Hang, Chan Chi Vai, Chui Tak Kei and Lin Jin)	1·40	1·30
1945	2p. *Autumn* (Situ Qi, Chui Tak Kei and Huang Haoming)	1·40	1·30
1946	2p. *Announcement of Spring* (Chui Tak Kei)	1·40	1·30
1947	2p. *Heroic Kapok* (Chui Tak Kei)	1·40	1·30
MS1948	138×90 mm. 12p. Sparrows and Red Leaves (Deng Fen, Situ Qi and Lin Jin)	8·75	8·25

415 Triumph TR2 driven by Eddie Carvalho (winner of inaugural race, 1954)

2013. 60th Anniversary of Macau Grand Prix. Multicoloured.

1949	2p. Type **415**	1·40	1·30
1950	2p. Teddy Yip's (owner and director of Theodore Race Team) race car	1·40	1·30
1951	2p. Competitors in Macao Motorcycle Grand Prix	1·40	1·30
1952	2p. Emanuelle Pirro's race car (winner of Guia Touring Car Race (1991))	1·40	1·30
1953	2p. Race car No. 30	1·40	1·30
1954	2p. City of Dreams car No. 3	1·40	1·30
MS1955	138×90 mm. 12p. Race car No. 7 (55×37 mm (oval))	8·75	8·25

416 Anniversary Emblem

2013. 20th Anniversary of Macau–European Union Agreement for Trade and Co-operation. Multicoloured.

1956	1p.50 Type **416**	1·20	1·10
1957	5p. As Type **416** but emblems reversed	3·50	3·25

417 Horse

2014. Chinese New Year. Year of the Horse. Multicoloured.

1958	2p. Type **417**	1·40	1·30
1959	2p. Horse, pen and ink drawing (Agua (water))	1·40	1·30
1960	2p. Stylised multicoloured horse (Fogo (fire))	1·40	1·30
1961	2p. Clay horse teapot (Terra (earth))	1·40	1·30
1962	5p. Horse head and shoulders (Madeira (Wood))	3·50	3·25
MS1963	139×90 mm. 12p. As No. 1962 (diamond shaped)	8·75	8·25

418 Early Building

2014. 140th Anniversary of Conde de São Januário General Hospital. Multicoloured.

1964	2p. Type **418**	1·40	1·30
1965	2p.50 Modern building	1·90	1·80
1966	3p.50 Emblem	2·50	2·40
1967	4p. Anniversary emblem	2·75	2·75
MS1968	138×90 mm. 12p. Anniversary emblem and building (60×40 mm)	8·75	8·25

419 Post Office Building

2014. 130th Anniversary of Macau Post. Multicoloured.

1969	2p. Type **419**	1·40	1·30
1970	2p.50 Savings Branch	1·90	1·80
1971	3p.50 Communications Museum	2·50	2·40
1972	4p. Symbols of electronic post	2·75	2·75
MS1973	90×138 mm. 12p. Post Office building (40×41 mm)	8·75	8·25
MS1974	60×130 mm. 50p. Post Office HQ tower (30×60 mm)	35·00	33·00

420 Puppy ('Take Care')

2014. Animal Protection. Multicoloured.

1975	2p. Type **420**	1·40	1·30
1976	2p.50 White cat ('Protect')	1·90	1·80
1977	3p.50 Tabby cat ('Save')	2·50	2·40
1978	4p. Dog ('Adopt')	2·75	2·75
MS1979	138×90 mm. 12p. Hands forming heart from wire fence and dog looking through (40×60 mm)	8·75	8·25

421 Shi Jin

2014. Classical Literature. *The Outlaws of the Marsh.* Multicoloured.

1980	2p. Type **421**	1·40	1·30
1981	2p. Chai Jin	1·40	1·30
1982	2p. Yang Zhi	1·40	1·30
1983	2p. Chao Gai	1·40	1·30
1984	2p. Ruan Xiaoqi	1·40	1·30
1985	2p. Gongsun Cheng	1·40	1·30
MS1986	139×90 mm.10p. Chao Gai and Chai Jin (horiz)	7·75	7·25

422 Wu Yee Sun Library

2014. New Campus of the University of Macau. Multicoloured.

1987	2p. Type **422**	1·40	1·30
1988	2p. Administration building	1·40	1·30
1989	2p. University Mall	1·40	1·30
1990	2p. Building	1·40	1·30
MS1991	138×90 mm. 12p. Library (different)	8·75	8·25

423 Sator Square (Latin palindrome that can be read forwards, backwards, upwards or downwards)

2014. Science and Technology. Magic Squares. Multicoloured.

1992	2p. Type **423**	1·40	1·30
1993	3p. Franklin: Bent diagonals	2·10	2·00
1994	4p. Albrecht Dürer: *Melencholia 1,*	2·75	2·75
1995	5p. Su Hui-Xuan Ji Tu: Palindrome	3·50	3·25
1996	7p. Lee Sallows: Panmagic 3×3	5·00	4·50
1997	9p. Simon de la Loubère Method (using sequential diagonal numbers)	6·25	6·00
MS1998	139×90 mm.12p. Turtle showing Luo Shu's Magic Square numbers, as marks on it's shell (60×30 mm)	8·75	8·25

See also **MS**2075/**MS**2076.

424 GPO Building, Macau

2014. General Post Office Buildings. Macau–Thailand Relations. Multicoloured.
1999 5p.50 Type **424** 4·00 3·75
2000 5p.50 GPO Building, Thailand 4·00 3·75

425 Lin Zexu

2014. Museum Exhibits. Lin Zexu Memorial Museum of Macau. Multicoloured.
2001 2p. Type **425** 1·40 1·30
2002 2p. Wearing yellow cape and hat 1·40 1·30
2003 2p. Seated with western delegate 1·40 1·30
2004 2p. Greeting Portuguese leader on landing in Macau 1·40 1·30
MS2005 90×138 mm. 12p. Lin Zexu (60×40 mm) 8·75 8·25

426 Junks at Sea

2014. Macau Seen by Kam Cheong Ling. Multicoloured.
2006 2p. Type **426** 1·40 1·30
2007 2p. Street scene with fountain 1·40 1·30
2008 3p. Temple and market 1·40 1·30
2009 5p. Dom Pedro Theatre 1·40 1·30
MS2010 138×90 mm. 12p. Riverside (40×40 mm) 8·75 8·25

427 Symbols of Commerce

2014. 15th Anniversary of Macau Special Administrative Region. Multicoloured.
2011 2p. Type **427** 1·40 1·30
2012 2p. Grand Lisboa, MGM Grand and other hotels 1·40 1·30
2013 2p. Ventian Macau 1·40 1·30
2014 2p. Macau East Asian Games Dome Stadium and statue 1·40 1·30
MS2015 138×90 mm. 12p. Government Headquarters for SAR (60×40 mm) 8·75 8·25

428 Soldiers raising Flag

2014. 15th Anniversary of People's Liberation Army Garrison Stationed in Macau. Multicoloured.
2016 2p. Type **428** 1·40 1·30
2017 2p. Soldier crawling through mud 1·40 1·30
2018 2p. Discussing tactics 1·40 1·30
2019 2p. Soldier fastening helmet on child 1·40 1·30
2020 2p. Musicians 1·40 1·30
2021 2p. Soldier and instructor on firing range 1·40 1·30
MS2022 138×90 mm. 12p. Soldiers parade (60×40 mm) 8·75 8·25

2015. Chinese New Year. Year of the Goat. Multicoloured.
2023 2p. Goat (metal) 1·40 1·30
2024 2p. Goat, pen and ink drawing (Agua (water)) 1·40 1·30
2025 2p. Stylised multicoloured goat (Fogo (fire)) 1·40 1·30
2026 2p. Clay goat teapot (Terra (earth)) 1·40 1·30
2027 5p. Goats head and shoulders (Madeira (Wood)) 3·50 3·25
MS2028 139×90 mm. 12p. As No. 2027 (diamond shaped) 8·75 8·25

429 Paul Harris (founder) and Emblem

2015. 110th Anniversary of Rotary International. Multicoloured.
2029 5p.50 Type **429** 4·00 3·75
MS2030 138×90 mm. 12p. Assisting wheelchair user (40×60 mm) 8·75 8·25

430 Dunhuang

2015. Mainland Scenery. Sheet 138×90 mm.
MS2031 **430** 12p. multicoloured 8·75 8·25

431 Emblem

2015. 25th Anniversary of AICEP (Portuguese public business entity).
2032 **431** 5p.50 multicoloured 4·00 3·75

432 *Uca arcuata* (Bow Fiddler Crab)

2015. Wetlands of Macau. Multicoloured.
2033 2p. Type **432** 1·40 1·30
2034 3p. *Boleophthalmus pectinirostris* (Mudskipper) 2·10 2·00
2035 4p.50 *Microhyla ornata* (Ornate Narrow-mouthed Frog) 3·25 3·00
2036 5p.50 *Trithemis aurora* (Crimson Marsh Glider) 4·00 3·75
MS2037 138×90 mm. 12p. *Platalea minor* (Black-faced Spoonbill) 8·75 8·25

433 Birth, Macau, 1905

2015. 110th Birth Anniversary of Xian Xinghai (Sinn Sing Hoi) (composer and conductor). Multicoloured.
2038 2p. Type **433** 1·40 1·30
2039 3p. Studies in Paris, 1934 2·00 1·90
2040 4p.50 Conducting in Yanan, 1939 3·25 3·00
2041 5p.50 Treatment for TB, Moscow, 1945 4·00 3·75
MS2042 138×90 mm. 12p. Design as No. 2040, with background changed 8·75 8·25

2015. 150th Anniversary of Guia Lighthouse. World Heritage Site. Multicoloured.
2043 2p. Capela de Nossa Senhora da Guia and Guia Lighthouse 1·40 1·30
2044 5p.50 Doorway 4·00 3·75
MS2045 138×90 mm. 12p. Lighthouse through trees (*vert*) 8·75 8·25
Type **434** unavailable.

2015. Tenth Anniversary of Historic Centre of Macau as World Heritage Site. Multicoloured.
2046 2p. Senado Square and dancers 1·40 1·30
2047 3p. Kun Tai Temple and merchants 2·00 1·90
2048 4p.50 Cathedral, cleric and tourists 3·25 3·00
2049 5p.50 Holy House of Mercy, Bishop Belchior Carneiro and children 4·00 3·75
MS2050 138×90 mm. 12p. Lou Kau Mansion and tourists 8·75 8·25
Type **435** unavailable.

2015. Water and Life. Multicoloured.
2051 2p. Filling container at stand pipe, leaf and water droplets 1·40 1·30
2052 3p. Fish and scientist 2·00 1·90
2053 4p.50 Water fountain 3·25 3·00
2054 5p.50 Water in wine glass 4·00 3·75
MS2055 138×90 mm. 12p. Wallace drinking fountain (60×40 *mm*) 8·75 8·25
Type **436** unavailable.

2015. 70th Anniversary of End of World War II. '70th Anniversary of Victory of the Chinese People's War of Resistance against Japanese Aggression'. Multicoloured.
2056 2p. Machine gunner ('July 7th Incident') 1·40 1·30
2057 5p.50 Fighting at the Great Wall ('Nationwide War of Resistance') 1·40 1·30
Type **437** unavailable.

2015. Streets of Macau (2nd issue). Multicoloured.
2058 2p. Sé Street 1·40 1·30
2059 2p.50 Ervanários Street 1·90 1·80
2060 3p. Happiness Street 2·00 1·80
2061 3p.50 Fugueira Street 2·50 2·40
2062 4p. Eduardo Marques Street 2·75 2·50
2063 4p.50 Embaixador Lane 3·25 3·00
2064 5p. Erva Street 3·50 3·25
2065 5p.50 Verdades Lane 4·00 3·75
Type **438** unavailable.

439 Lion Dance

2015. Festivity. Multicoloured.
2066 2p. Type **439** 1·40 1·30
2067 4p.50 'Festividade' 3·25 3·00

440 God and the Goddess of River Xiang

2015. Literature and its Characters - Jiu Ge . Multicoloured.
2068 2p. Type **440** 1·40 1·30
2069 2p. Lords of Fate. The Greater and the Lesser 1·40 1·30
2070 2p. Lord of the East 1·40 1·30
2071 2p. Mountain Spirit 1·40 1·30
2072 2p. Hymn to the Fallen 1·40 1·30
2073 2p. Honoring the Spirits 1·40 1·30
MS2074 139×90 mm.12p. Jiu Ge (30×60 mm) 8·75 8·25

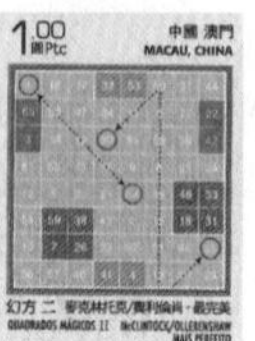
441 Inder Taneja: IXOHOXI 88

2015. Science and Technology. Magic Squares (2nd issue). Multicoloured.
MS2075 120×155 mm. 1p. Type **441**; 6p. McClintock/Ollerensha: Most Perfect; 8p. David Collison: Patchwork 8·75 8·25
MS2076 130×90 mm. 12p. Knight's Tour Method used to construct a Magic Square of Order 16 with a Closed or Re-entrant Tour (Joseph S Madachy) (60×30 mm) 8·75 8·25

442 Hand raised

2015. Tai Chi Chuan. Multicoloured.
2077 2p. Type **442** 1·40 1·30
2078 2p. right leg raised 1·40 1·30
2079 3p. Left leg raised 2·00 1·90
2080 3p. Stepping forward 2·00 1·90

443 'Origin of the Grand River'

2015. Mountains and Rivers of the Motherland. Yellow River. Multicoloured.
2081 2p. Type **443** 1·40 1·30
2082 2p. 'Winding River' 1·40 1·30
2083 2p. 'Ningxia Alluvial Plains' 1·40 1·30
2084 2p. 'Vast Territory of Hetao' 1·40 1·30
2085 2p. 'Hukou Golden Waterfall' 1·40 1·30
2086 2p. 'Shanxi Surrounded by Water Province' 1·40 1·30
2087 2p. 'Mountainous Region of Luoyang' 1·40 1·30
2088 2p. 'Picturesque Landscapes of Henan' 1·40 1·30
2089 2p. 'Clear River and Calm Sea' 1·40 1·30
MS2090 575×90 mm. 2p.×9 As Nos. 2081/2089 12·00 12·00

444 Metal Monkey

2016. Chinese New Year. Year of the Monkey. Multicoloured.
2091 2p. Type **444** 1·40 1·30
2092 2p. Wood Monkey 1·40 1·30
2093 3p. Water Monkey 2·00 1·90
2094 3p. Fire Monkey 2·00 1·90
2095 5p.50 Earth Monkey 4·00 3·75
MS2096 139×90 mm. 12p. Fire Monkey (different) (diamond shaped) 8·75 8·25

445 'Portão da Grandeza Divina'

2016. Mainland Scenery. Imperial Palace in Beijing. Multicoloured.
2097 2p. olive-grey, violet and black 1·40 1·30
2098 3p. olive-grey, orange and black 2·00 1·90
2099 4p.50 olive-grey, deep turquoise-green and black 3·25 3·00
2100 5p.50 olive-grey, myrtle green and black 4·00 3·75
MS2101 139×90 mm.12p. olive-grey, sepia and black (60×30 mm) 8·75 8·75
Designs: 2p. T **445**; 3p. 'Palacio da Paz e Longevidade'; 4p.50 'Pavilhão da Primavera e Felicidade'; 5p.50 'Pavilhão da Irradiação da Justiça'; 12p. 'Pavilhão da Harmonia Suprema'

446 Checking Identity

2016. 325th Anniversary of Public Security Police Force. Multicoloured.
2102 2p. Officers on the streets 1·40 1·30
2103 3p. Armed officers 2·00 1·90
2104 4p.50 Type **446** 3·25 3·00
2105 5p.50 Officer riding motorcycle 4·00 3·75
MS2106 138×90 mm 12p. Officer from all departments (60×40mm) 8·75 8·75

447 Mulan Decides to go to War

2016. Classical Literature. Poetry. *The Ballad of Mulan*. Multicoloured.
2107 2p. Type **447** 1·40 1·30
2108 3p. Mulan, dressed as a man, on horseback during battle 2·00 1·90
2109 4p.50 Mulan returns home 3·25 3·00
2110 5p.50 Mulan meets her fellow soldiers as woman 4·00 3·75
MS2111 138×90 mm. 12p. Mulan on horseback (30× 60 mm) 8·75 8·75

448 Pagoda

2016. Macau as Seen by Chan Chi Vai. Multicoloured.

2112	2p. Type **448**	1·40	1·30
2113	3p. Buildings reflected in the water	2·00	1·90
2114	4p.50 Tree-lined promenade	3·25	3·00
2115	5p.50 Dom Pedro Theatre	4·00	3·75
MS2116	138×90 mm. 12p. Fishing nets (60×30 mm)	8·75	8·75

449 Chu Tai Sin Shrine

2016. Museum Exhibits. Maritime Museum. Multicoloured.

2117	2p. Type **449**	1·40	1·30
2118	3p. Octant	2·00	1·90
2119	4p.50 Tai To Junk	3·25	3·00
2120	5p.50 The Black Ship	4·00	3·75
MS2121	90×138 mm. 12p. Compass (40×40 mm, circular)	8·75	8·75

CHARITY TAX STAMPS

The notes under this heading in Portugal also apply here.

43

1919. Fiscal stamp optd **TAXA DE GUERRA**.

C305	**43**	2a. green	12·50	8·00
C306	**43**	11a. green	47·00	24·00

The above was for use in Timor as well as Macao.

1925. As Marquis de Pombal issue of Portugal but inscr 'MACAU'.

C329	**C73**	2a. red	6·25	3·00
C330	-	2a. red	6·25	3·00
C331	**C75**	2a. red	7·75	3·75

C48 Our Lady of Charity (altarpiece, Macau Cathedral)

1930. No gum.

C332	**C48**	5a. brown and buff	80·00	43·00

1945. As T **C48** but values in Arabic and Chinese numerals left and right, at bottom of design. No gum.

C486	1a. olive and green	2·50	2·50
C487	2a. purple and grey	2·50	2·50
C415	5a. brown and yellow	25·00	21·00
C416	5a. blue and light blue	70·00	48·00
C417	10a. green and light green	47·00	32·00
C488	10a. blue and green	2·50	2·50
C418	15a. orange and light orange	47·00	32·00
C419	20a. red and orange	70·00	40·00
C489	20a. brown and yellow	3·00	2·75
C420	50a. lilac and buff	85·00	55·00
C472	50a. red and pink	30·00	17·00

1981. No. C487 and similar higher (fiscal) values surch **20 avos** and Chinese characters.

C546	20a. on 2a. purple on grey	3·75	3·50
C534	20a. on 1p. green & lt green	4·50	4·25
C535	20a. on 3p. black and pink	4·25	2·50
C536	20a. on 5p. brown & yellow	†	†

1981. No. C418 surch **10 avos** and Chinese characters.

C553	10a. on 15a. orange and light orange	3·75	3·50

NEWSPAPER STAMPS

1892. Embossed key-type of Macao surch **JORNAES** and value. No gum.

N73	**Q**	2½r. on 10r. green	14·50	12·00
N74	**Q**	2½r. on 40r. brown	14·00	5·25
N75	**Q**	2½r. on 80r. grey	17·00	10·50

1893. Newspaper key-type inscr 'Macau'.

N80	**V**	2½r. brown	13·00	7·50

1894. Newspaper key-type of Macao surch **½ avo PROVISORIO** and Chinese characters.

N82	½a. on 2½r. brown	8·75	5·50

POSTAGE DUE STAMPS

1904. Due key-type inscr 'MACAU'. No gum (12a. to 1p.), with or without gum (others).

D184	**W**	½a. green	2·30	1·80
D185	**W**	1a. green	3·00	1·80
D186	**W**	2a. grey	4·00	1·80
D187	**W**	4a. brown	4·75	2·20
D188	**W**	5a. orange	6·25	3·50
D189	**W**	8a. brown	7·25	4·00
D190	**W**	12a. brown	11·00	5·50
D191	**W**	20a. blue	20·00	9·50
D192	**W**	40a. red	37·00	14·50
D193	**W**	50a. orange	47·00	21·00
D194	**W**	1p. lilac	95·00	32·00

1911. Due key-types of Macao optd **REPUBLICA**.

D204	**W**	½a. green	2·00	80
D205	**W**	1a. green	3·00	1·60
D206	**W**	2a. grey	4·75	2·40
D207	**W**	4a. brown	6·25	2·40
D208	**W**	5a. orange	7·75	3·25
D209	**W**	8a. brown	9·25	4·50
D287	**W**	12a. brown	19·00	8·00
D211	**W**	20a. blue	19·00	7·25
D212	**W**	40a. red	28·00	8·75
D290	**W**	50a. orange	50·00	18·00
D291	**W**	1p. lilac	80·00	27·00

1925. Marquis de Pombal issue, as Nos. C329/C331 optd **MULTA**.

D329	**C73**	4a. red	6·25	3·75
D330	-	4a. red	6·25	3·75
D331	**C75**	4a. red	6·25	3·75

1947. As T **D1** of Portuguese Colonies, but inscr 'MACAU'.

D410	**D1**	1a. black and purple	7·25	2·75
D411	**D1**	2a. black and violet	7·75	3·25
D412	**D1**	4a. black and blue	9·25	4·75
D413	**D1**	5a. black and brown	11·00	6·50
D414	**D1**	8a. black and purple	19·00	8·00
D415	**D1**	12a. black and brown	23·00	8·00
D416	**D1**	20a. black and green	28·00	16·00
D417	**D1**	40a. black and red	36·00	16·00
D418	**D1**	50a. black and yellow	60·00	19·00
D419	**D1**	1p. black and blue	£100	23·00

50 'Portugal' and Galeasse

1949. Postage stamps of 1934 surch **PORTEADO** and new value.

D424	**50**	1a. on 4a. black	4·75	2·50
D425	**50**	2a. on 6a. brown	4·75	2·50
D426	**50**	4a. on 8a. blue	4·75	2·50
D427	**50**	5a. on 10a. red	6·00	3·00
D428	**50**	8a. on 12a. blue	9·75	4·50
D429	**50**	12a. on 30a. green	15·00	6·00
D430	**50**	20a. on 40a. violet	23·00	9·75

66 Arms and Dragon

1951. Optd **PORTEADO** or surch also.

D439	**66**	1a. yellow on cream	2·75	2·00
D440	**66**	2a. green on green	3·25	2·00
D441	**66**	7a. on 10a. mauve on green	3·75	2·30

D70

1952. Numerals in red. Name in black.

D451	**D70**	1a. blue and green	1·20	90
D452	**D70**	3a. brown and salmon	1·60	1·10
D453	**D70**	5a. slate and blue	2·30	1·10
D454	**D70**	10a. red and blue	3·00	2·10
D455	**D70**	30a. blue and brown	7·50	3·00
D456	**D70**	1p. brown and grey	15·00	6·00

MACEDONIA

Part of Austro-Hungarian Empire until 1918 when it became part of Yugoslavia. Separate stamps were issued during German Occupation in the Second World War. In 1991 Macedonia became an independent republic.

German Occupation.
100 stotinki = 1 lev.

Independent Republic.
1991. 100 paras = 1 dinar.
1992. 100 deni (de.) = 1 denar (d.).

A. GERMAN OCCUPATION

Македония

8. IX. 1944

1 лв.

(G1)

1944. Stamps of Bulgaria, 1940–1944. (a) Surch as Type **G1**.

G1	1l. on 10st. orange (No. 449)	2·75	19·00
G2	3l. on 15st. blue (No.450)	2·75	19·00

(b) Surch similar to T **G1** but larger.

G3	6l. on 10st. blue (No. 469)	4·25	32·00
G4	9l. on 15st. green (No. 470)	4·25	32·00
G5	9l. on 15st. green (No. 470)	5·25	37·00
G6	15l. on 4l. black (No.504)	21·00	75·00
G7	20l. on 7l. blue (No.505)	32·00	75·00
G8	30l. on 14l. brown (No.506)	37·00	£140

B. INDEPENDENT REPUBLIC

1 Trumpeters

1991. Obligatory Tax. Independence.

1	**1**	2d.50 black and orange	35	35

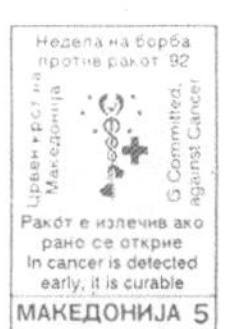

2 Emblems and Inscriptions

1992. Obligatory Tax. Anti-cancer Week. (a) T **2** showing Red Cross symbol at bottom left.

2	**2**	5d. mauve, black and blue	70	70
3	-	5d. multicoloured	70	70
4	-	5d. multicoloured	70	70
5	-	5d. multicoloured	70	70

Designs: No. 3, Flowers, columns and scanner; No. 4, Scanner and couch; No. 5, Computer cabinet.

(b) As T **2** but with right-hand inscr reading down instead of up and without Red Cross symbol.

6	5d. mauve, black & blue (as No. 2)	25	25
7	5d. multicoloured (as No. 3)	25	25
8	5d. multicoloured (as No. 4)	25	25
9	5d. multicoloured (as No. 5)	25	25

3 Red Cross Aircraft dropping Supplies

1992. Obligatory Tax. Red Cross Week. Multicoloured.

10	10d. Red Cross slogans (dated 08–15 MAJ 1992)	15	15
11	10d. Type **3**	15	15
12	10d. Treating road accident victim	15	15
13	10d. Evacuating casualties from ruined building	15	15

The three pictorial designs are taken from children's paintings.

4 'Skopje Earthquake'

1992. Obligatory Tax. Solidarity Week.

14	**4**	20d. black and mauve	15	15
15	-	20d. multicoloured	15	15
16	-	20d. multicoloured	15	15
17	-	20d. multicoloured	15	15

Designs: No. 15, Red Cross nurse with child; 16, Mothers carrying toddlers at airport; 17, Family at airport.

5 'Wood-carvers Petar and Makarie' (icon), St Joven Bigorsk Monastery, Debar

1992. First Anniversary of Independence.

18	**5**	30d. multicoloured	55	55

For 40d. in same design see No. 33.

6 Nurse with Baby

1992. Obligatory Tax. Anti-tuberculosis Week. Multicoloured.

19	20d. Anti-tuberculosis slogans (dated 14–21.IX.1992)	15	15
20	20d. Type **6**	15	15
21	20d. Nurse giving oxygen	15	15
22	20d. Baby in cot	15	15

7 *The Nativity* (fresco, Slepce Monastery)

1992. Christmas. Multicoloured.

23	100d. Type **7**	1·40	1·40
24	500d. *Madonna and Child* (fresco), Zrze Monastery	3·25	3·25

8 Mixed Bouquet

1993. Obligatory Tax. Red Cross Fund. Multicoloured.

25	20d. Red Cross slogans	15	15
26	20d. Marguerites	15	15
27	20d. Carnations	15	15
28	20d. Type **8**	15	15

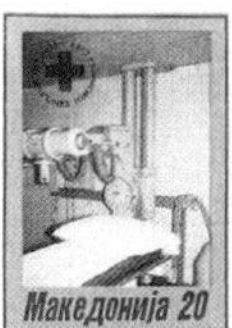

9 Radiography Equipment

1993. Obligatory Tax. Anti-cancer Week. Multicoloured.

29	20d. Anti-cancer slogans (dated 1–8 MART 1993)	15	15
30	20d. Type **9**	15	15
31	20d. Overhead treatment unit	15	15
32	20d. Scanner	15	15

1993. As No. 18 but changed value.

33	40d. multicoloured	60	60

10 Macedonian Flag

1993

34	**10**	10d. multicoloured	35	35
35	**10**	40d. multicoloured	1·40	1·40
36	**10**	50d. multicoloured	1·80	1·80

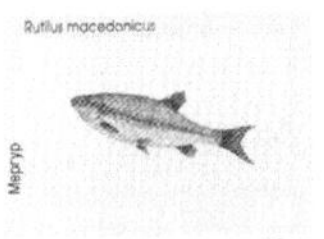

11 Macedonian Roach

1993. Fish from Lake Ohrid. Multicoloured.

37		50d. Type **11**	25	25
38		100d. Lake Ohrid salmon	35	35
39		1000d. Type **11**	3·50	3·50
40		2000d. As No. 38	4·75	4·75

12 Crucifix, St George's Monastery

1993. Easter.

41	**12**	300d. multicoloured	3·00	3·00

13 Diagram of Telecommunications Cable and Map

1993. Opening of Trans-Balkan Telecommunications Line.

42	**13**	500d. multicoloured	1·80	1·80

14 Red Cross Worker with Baby

1993. Obligatory Tax. Red Cross Week. Multicoloured.

43		50d. Red Cross inscriptions (dated 08–15 MAJ 1993)	15	15
44		50d. Type **14**	15	15
45		50d. Physiotherapist and child in wheelchair	15	15
46		50d. Stretcher party	15	15

See also No. 73.

15 Unloading UNICEF Supplies from Lorry

1993. Obligatory Tax. Solidarity Week.

47	-	50d. black, mauve and silver	15	15
48	**15**	50d. multicoloured	15	15
49	-	50d. multicoloured	15	15
50	-	50d. multicoloured	15	15

Designs: No. 47, 'Skopje Earthquake'; No. 49, Labelling parcels in warehouse; No. 50, Consignment of parcels on fork-lift truck.

See also No. 72.

16 UN Emblem and Rainbow

1993. Admission to United Nations Organisation.

51	**16**	10d. multicoloured	1·40	1·40

17 *Insurrection* (detail), (B. Lazeski)

1993. 90th Anniversary of Macedonian Insurrection.

52	**17**	10d. multicoloured	1·40	1·40
MS53		116×73 mm. 30d. multicoloured	4·25	4·25

18 Children in Meadow

1993. Obligatory Tax. Anti-tuberculosis Week. Multicoloured.

54		50d. Anti-tuberculosis slogans (dated 14–21.09.1993)	15	15
55		50d. Type **18**	15	15
56		50d. Bee on flower	15	15
57		50d. Goat behind boulder	15	15

See also No. 71.

19 Tapestry

1993. Centenary of Founding of Inner Macedonia Revolutionary Organisation.

58		4d. Type **19**	60	60
MS59		90×75 mm. 40d. Two motifs as Type **19**	4·25	4·25

20 *The Nativity* (fresco from St George's Monastery, Rajcica)

1993. Christmas. Multicoloured.

60		2d. Type **20**	50	50
61		20d. *The Three Kings* (fresco from Slepce Monastery)	3·50	3·50

21 Lily

1994. Obligatory Tax. Anti-cancer Week. Multicoloured.

62		1d. Red Cross and anti-cancer emblems	15	15
63		1d. Type **21**	15	15
64		1d. Caesar's mushroom	15	15
65		1d. Mute swans on lake	15	15

1994. Nos. 1, 18 and 34 surch.

66	**5**	2d. on 30d. multicoloured	25	25
67	**1**	8d. on 2d.50 black and orange	95	95
68	**10**	15d. on 10d. multicoloured	1·90	1·90

23 Decorated Eggs

1994. Easter.

69	**23**	2d. multicoloured	60	60

1994. Obligatory Tax. Red Cross Week. As previous designs but values, and date (No. 70), changed. Multicoloured.

70		1d. Red Cross inscriptions (dated 8–15 MAJ 1994)	15	15
71		1d. Type **18**	15	15
72		1d. As No. 50	15	15
73		1d. Type **14**	15	15

24 Kosta Racin (writer)

1994. Revolutionaries. Portraits by Dimitar Kondovski. Multicoloured.

74		8d. Type **24**	60	60
75		15d. Grigor Prlicev (writer)	1·20	1·20
76		20d. Nikola Vaptsarov (Bulgarian poet)	1·80	1·80
77		50d. Goce Delcev (founder of Internal Macedonian–Odrin Revolutionary–Organisation)	4·25	4·25

25 'Skopje Earthquake'

1994. Obligatory Tax. Solidarity Week.

78	**25**	1d. black, red and silver	35	35

26 Tree and Family

1994. Census.

79	**26**	2d. multicoloured	60	60

27 St Prohor Pcinski Monastery (venue)

1994. 50th Anniversary of Macedonian National Liberation Council. Multicoloured.

80		5d. Type **27**	60	60
MS81		108×73 mm. 50d. Aerial view of Monastery	4·25	4·25

28 Swimmer

1994. Swimming Marathon, Ohrid.

82	**28**	8d. multicoloured	85	85

29 Turkish Cancellation and 1992 30d. Stamp on Cover

1994. 150th Anniversary (1993) of Postal Service in Macedonia.

83	**29**	2d. multicoloured	60	60

30 Mastheads

1994. 50th Anniversaries of *Nova Makedonija*, *Mlad Borec* and *Makedonka* (newspapers).

84	**30**	2d. multicoloured	60	60

31 Open Book

1994. 50th Anniversary of St Clement of Ohrid Library. Multicoloured.

85		2d. Type **31**	25	25
86		10d. Page of manuscript (vert)	1·60	1·60

32 Globe

1994. Obligatory Tax. Anti-AIDS Week.

87	-	2d. red and black	15	15
88	**32**	2d. black, red and blue	15	15
89	-	2d. black, yellow and red	15	15
90	-	2d. black and red	15	15

Designs: No. 87, Inscriptions in Cyrillic (dated 01-08.12.1994); No. 89, Exclamation mark in warning triangle; No. 90, Safe sex campaign emblem.

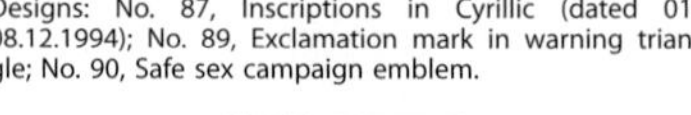

33 Wireless and Gramophone Record

1994. 50th Anniversary of Macedonian Radio.

91	**33**	2d. multicoloured	60	60

34 Macedonian Pine

1994. Flora and Fauna. Multicoloured.

92		5d. Type **34**	60	60
93		10d. Lynx	1·20	1·20

1995. Nos. 35 and 33 surch.

94	**10**	2d. on 40d. multicoloured	1·20	1·20
96	**5**	5d. on 40d. multicoloured	70	70

36 Emblems and Inscriptions

1995. Obligatory Tax. Anti-cancer Week. Multicoloured.

97		1d. Type **36**	15	15
98		1d. White lilies	15	15
99		1d. Red lilies	15	15
100		1d. Red roses	15	15

37 Fresco

1995. Easter.

101	**37**	4d. multicoloured	60	60

38 Voluntary Workers

1995. Obligatory Tax. Red Cross. Multicoloured.

102		1d. Cross and inscriptions in Cyrillic (dated 8–15 MAJ 1995)	15	15
103		1d. Type **38**	15	15
104		1d. Volunteers in T-shirts	15	15
105		1d. Globe, red cross and red crescent	15	15

39 Troops on Battlefield

1995. 50th Anniversary of End of Second World War.

106	**39**	2d. multicoloured	1·20	1·20

40 Anniversary Emblem

1995. 50th Anniversary of Macedonian Red Cross.

107	**40**	2d. multicoloured	1·20	1·20

41 Rontgen and X-Ray Lamp

1995. Centenary of Discovery of X-Rays by Wilhelm Rontgen.

108	**41**	2d. multicoloured	1·40	1·40

42 'Skopje Earthquake'

1995. Obligatory Tax. Solidarity Week.

109	**42**	1d. black, red and gold	15	15

43 Cernodrinski (dramatist)

1995. 50th Anniversary of Vojdan Cernodrinski Theatre Festival.

110	**43**	10d. multicoloured	1·20	1·20

44 Kraljevic (fresco, Markov Monastery, Skopje)

1995. 600th Death Anniversary of Marko Kraljevic (Serbian Prince).

111	**44**	20d. multicoloured	1·60	1·60

45 Puleski

1995. Death Centenary of Gorgi Puleski (linguist and revolutionary).

112	**45**	2d. multicoloured	1·20	1·20

46 Manuscript, Bridge and Emblem

1995. Writers' Festival, Struga.

113	**46**	2d. multicoloured	1·20	1·20

47 Robert Koch (discoverer of tubercule bacillus)

1995. Obligatory Tax. Anti-tuberculosis Week.

114	**47**	1d. brown, black and red	35	35

48 Child holding Parents' Hands

1995. Obligatory Tax. Childrens' Week. Self-adhesive. Imperf.

115	**48**	2d. blue	35	35

49 Maleshevija

1995. Buildings. Multicoloured.

116		2d. Type **49**	20	20
117		20d. Krakornica	1·40	1·40

50 Interior of Mosque

1995. Tetovo Mosque.

118	**50**	15d. multicoloured	1·20	1·20

51 Lumiere Brothers (inventors of cine-camera)

1995. Centenary of Motion Pictures. Multicoloured.

119	10d. Type **51**	1·20	1·20
120	10d. Milton and Janaki Manaki (Macedonian cinematographers)	1·20	1·20

Nos. 119/120 were issued together, *se-tenant*, forming a composite design.

52 Globe in Nest within Frame

1995. 50th Anniversary of UNO. Multicoloured.

121	20d. Type **52**	95	95
122	50d. Sun within frame	2·75	2·75

53 Male and Female Symbols

1995. Obligatory Tax. Anti-AIDS Week.

123	**53**	1d. multicoloured	35	35

54 Madonna and Child

1995. Christmas.

124	**54**	15d. multicoloured	1·40	1·40

55 Dalmatian Pelican

1995. Birds. Multicoloured.

125	15d. Type **55**	1·20	1·20
126	40d. Lammergeier	2·40	2·40

56 Letters of Alphabet and Jigsaw Pieces

1995. 50th Anniversary of Alphabet Reform.

127	**56**	5d. multicoloured	60	60

57 St Clement of Ohrid (detail of fresco)

1995. 700th Anniversary of Fresco, St Bogorodica's Church, Ohrid.

128	**57**	8d. multicoloured	70	70
MS129		85×67 mm. **57** 50d. multicoloured. Imperf	60·00	60·00

58 Postal Headquarters, Skopje

1995. Second Anniversary of Membership of UPU.

130	**58**	10d. multicoloured	70	70

59 Zip joining Flags

1995. Entry to Council of Europe and Organisation for Security and Co-operation in Europe.

131	**59**	20d. multicoloured	1·60	1·60

60 Hand holding out Apple

1996. Obligatory Tax. Anti-cancer Week.

132	**60**	1d. multicoloured	35	35

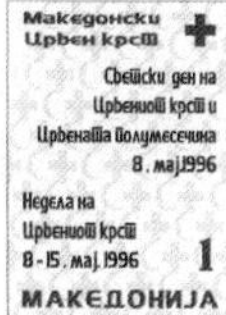
61 Inscriptions

1996. Obligatory Tax. Red Cross Week. Each red, black and yellow.

133	1d. Type **61**	15	15
134	1d. Red Cross principles in Macedonian	15	15
135	1d. Red Cross principles in English	15	15
136	1d. Red Cross principles in French	15	15
137	1d. Red Cross principles in Spanish	15	15

62 Canoeing

1996. Olympic Games, Atlanta. Designs showing statue of discus thrower and sport. Multicoloured.

138	2d. Type **62**	35	35
139	8d. Basketball (vert)	50	50
140	15d. Swimming	85	85
141	20d. Wrestling	1·30	1·30
142	40d. Boxing (vert)	2·75	2·75
143	50d. Running (vert)	3·25	3·25

63 'Skopje Earthquake'

1996. Obligatory Tax. Solidarity Week.

144	**63**	1d. gold, red and black	35	35

64 Scarecrow Drug Addict

1996. United Nations Anti-drugs Decade.

145	**64**	20d. multicoloured	1·20	1·20

65 Boy

1996. Children's Week. Children's Drawings. Multicoloured.

146	2d. Type **65**	25	25
147	8d. Girl	60	60

66 Fragment from Tomb and Tsar Samuel (after Dimitar Kondovski)

1996. Millenary of Crowning of Tsar Samuel (ruler of Bulgaria and Macedonia).

148	**66**	40d. multicoloured	2·20	2·20

67 Petrov

1996. 75th Death Anniversary of Gorce Petrov (revolutionary).

149	**67**	20d. multicoloured	1·20	1·20

68 Ohrid Seal, 1903, and State Flag

1996. Fifth Anniversary of Independence.

150	**68**	10d. multicoloured	60	60

69 Lungs on Globe

1996. Obligatory Tax. Anti-tuberculosis Week.

151	**69**	1d. red, blue and black	50	50

70 Vera Ciriviri-Trena (freedom fighter)

1996. Europa. Famous Women. Multicoloured.

152	20d. Type **70**	8·50	8·50
153	40d. Mother Teresa (Nobel Peace Prize winner and founder of Missionaries of Charity)	12·00	12·00

71 Hand holding Syringe

1996. Obligatory Tax. Anti-AIDS Week.

154	**71**	1d. black, red and yellow	35	35

72 Candle, Nuts and Fruit

1996. Christmas. Multicoloured.

155	10d. Type **72**	70	70
156	10d. Tree and carol singers	70	70

73 Daniel in the Lions' Den

1996. Early Christian Terracotta Reliefs. (a) Green backgrounds.

157	4d. Type **73**	25	25
158	8d. St Christopher and St George	50	50
159	20d. Joshua and Caleb	1·20	1·20
160	50d. Unicorn	3·00	3·00

(b) Blue backgrounds.

161	4d. Type **73**	25	25
162	8d. As No. 158	50	50
163	20d. As No. 159	1·20	1·20
164	50d. As No. 160	3·00	3·00

74 Nistrovo

1996. Traditional Houses. Multicoloured.

165	2d. Type **74**	25	25
166	8d. Brodec	70	70
167	10d. Niviste	85	85

75 *Pseudochazara cingovskii*

1996. Butterflies. Multicoloured.

168	4d. Type **75**	25	25
169	40d. Danube clouded yellow	3·00	3·00

76 UNICEF Coach

1996. 50th Anniversaries. Multicoloured.

170	20d. Type **76** (UNICEF)	1·20	1·20
171	40d. Church in Mtskheta, Georgia (UNESCO)	2·40	2·40

77 Skier

1997. 50 Years of Ski Championships at Sar Planina.

172	**77**	20d. multicoloured	1·40	1·40

78 Bell

1997. 150th Birth Anniversary of Alexander Graham Bell (telephone pioneer).

173	**78**	40d. multicoloured	2·40	2·40

79 Family and Healthy Foodstuffs

1997. Obligatory Tax. Anti-cancer Week.

174	**79**	1d. multicoloured	1·80	1·80

80 Hound

1997. Roman Mosaics from Heraklia. Multicoloured.

175	2d. Type **80**	25	25
176	8d. Steer	50	50
177	20d. Lion	1·10	1·10
178	40d. Leopard with prey	2·40	2·40
MS179	85×60 mm. 50d. Deer and plant tub. Imperf	4·75	4·75

81 Red Cross on Globe

1997. Obligatory Tax. Red Cross Week.

180	**81**	1d. mult	35	35

82 Gold Plate

1997. 1100th Anniversary of Cyrillic Alphabet. Multicoloured.

181	10d. Type **82**	70	70
182	10d. St Cyril and St Methodius	70	70

83 Schoolchildren

1997. Obligatory Tax. Solidarity Week.

183	**83**	1d. multicoloured	35	35

84 Mountain Flowers

1997. Fifth Anniversary of Ecological Association.

184	**84**	15d. multicoloured	1·20	1·20

85 Itar Pejo

1997. Europa. Tales and Legends. Multicoloured.

185	20d. Type **85**	7·25	7·25
186	40d. Stork-men	13·00	13·00

86 St Naum and St Naum's Church, Ohrid

1997. 1100th Birth Anniversary of St Naum.

187	**86**	15d. multicoloured	1·20	1·20

87 Diseased Lungs

1997. Obligatory Tax. Anti-tuberculosis Week.

188	**87**	1d. multicoloured	35	35

88 Stibnite

1997. Minerals. Multicoloured.

189	27d. Type **88**	1·80	1·80
190	40d. Lorandite	2·40	2·40

89 Dove and Sun above Child in Open Hand

1997. International Children's Day.

191	**89**	27d. multicoloured	1·70	1·70

90 Chanterelle

1997. Fungi. Multicoloured.

192	2d. Type **90**	35	35
193	15d. Bronze boletus	85	85
194	27d. Caesar's mushroom	1·60	1·60
195	50d. *Morchella conica*	2·75	2·75

91 Group of Children

1998. Obligatory Tax. Anti-AIDS Week.

196	**91**	1d. multicoloured	35	35

92 Gandhi

1998. 50th Death Anniversary of Mahatma Gandhi (Indian independence campaigner).

197	**92**	30d. multicoloured	1·40	1·40

93 Formula of Pythagoras's Theory

1998. 2500th Death Anniversary of Pythagoras (philosopher and mathematician).

198	**93**	16d. multicoloured	85	85

94 Alpine Skiing

1998. Winter Olympic Games, Nagano, Japan. Multicoloured.

199	4d. Type **94**	10	10
200	30d. Cross-country skiing	1·40	1·40

95 Novo Selo

1998. Traditional Houses. Multicoloured.

201	1d. Bogomila	10	10
202	2d. Type **95**	10	10
203	3d. Jachintse	20	20
204	4d. Jablanica	25	25
205	4d. Svekani	30	30
206	5d. Teovo	30	30
207	6d. Zdunje	35	35
208	6d. Mitrasinci	35	35
209	9d. Ratevo	50	50
210	16d. Kiselica	65	65
211	20d. Konopnica	85	85
212	30d. Ambar	1·40	1·40
213	50d. Galicnik	2·40	2·40

96 *Exodus* (Kole Manev)

1998. 50th Anniversary of Exodus of Children during Greek Civil War.

215	**96**	30d. multicoloured	1·40	1·40

97 *Proportions of Man* (Leonardo da Vinci)

1998. Obligatory Tax. Anti-cancer Week.

216	**97**	1d. multicoloured	50	50

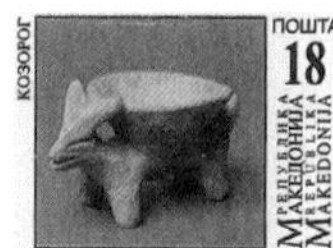

98 Bowl supported by Animal

1998. Archaeological Finds from Nedit. Multicoloured.

217	4d. Carafes	25	25
218	18d. Type **98**	70	70
219	30d. Sacred female figurine	1·40	1·40
220	60d. Stemmed cup	2·75	2·75

99 Football Pitch

1998. World Cup Football Championship, France. Multicoloured.

221	4d. Type **99**	25	25
222	30d. Globe and football pitch	1·60	1·60

100 Folk Dance

1998. Europa. National Festivals. Multicoloured.

223	30d. Type **100**	3·00	3·00
224	40d. Carnival	4·25	4·25

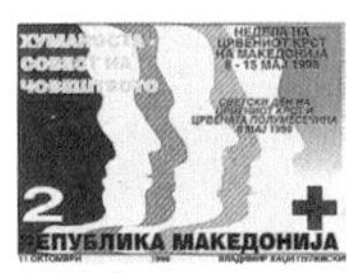

101 Profiles

1998. Obligatory Tax. Red Cross Week.

225	**101**	2d. multicoloured	50	50

102 Carnival Procession

1998. 18th Congress of Carnival Towns, Strumica.

226	**102**	30d. multicoloured	1·40	1·40

103 Hands and Red Cross

1998. Obligatory Tax. Solidarity Week.

227	**103**	2d. multicoloured	50	50

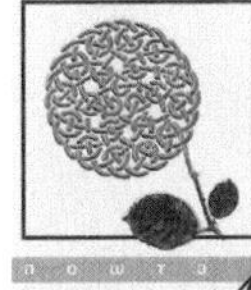

104 Flower

1998. Environmental Protection. Multicoloured.

228	4d. Type **104**	25	25
229	30d. Polluting chimney uprooting tree	1·30	1·30

105 Cupovski

1998. 120th Birth Anniversary of Dimitrija Cupovski.

230	**105**	16d. multicoloured	70	70

106 Steam Locomotive and Station

1997. 150th Anniversary of Railways in Macedonia. Multicoloured.

231	30d. Type **106**	1·80	1·80
232	60d. Steam locomotive, 1873 (horiz)	3·50	3·50

107 Doctor and Patient

1998. Obligatory Tax. Anti-tuberculosis Week.

233	**107**	2d. multicoloured	50	50

108 *Ursus spelaeus*

1998. Fossilised Skulls. Multicoloured.

234	4d. Type **108**	25	25
235	8d. *Mesopithecus pentelici*	35	35
236	18d. *Tragoceros*	95	95
237	30d. *Aceratherium incsivum*	1·40	1·40

109 Atanos Badev (composer) and Score

1998. Centenary of *Zlatoustova Liturgy*.

238	**109**	25d. multicoloured	1·20	1·20

110 Child with Kite

1998. Children's Day.

239	**110**	30d. multicoloured	1·40	1·40

111 *Cerambyx cerdo* (longhorn beetle)

1998. Insects. Multicoloured.

240	4d. Type **111**	25	25
241	8d. Alpine longhorn beetle	50	50
242	20d. European rhinoceros beetle	95	95
243	40d. Stag beetle	1·90	1·90

112 Reindeer and Snowflakes

1998. Christmas and New Year. Multicoloured.

244	4d. Type **112**	25	25
245	30d. Bread and oak leaves	1·60	1·60

113 Ribbon and Gender Symbols

1998. Obligatory Tax. Anti-AIDS Week.

246	**113**	2d. multicoloured	50	50

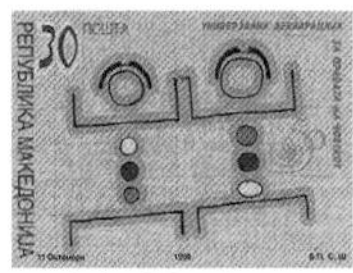

114 Stylised Couple

1998. 50th Anniversary of Universal Declaration of Human Rights.

247	**114**	30d. multicoloured	1·40	1·40

115 Sharplaninec

1999. Dogs.

248	**115**	15d. multicoloured	1·20	1·20

116 Girl's Face

1999. Obligatory Tax. Anti-cancer Week.

249	**116**	2d. multicoloured	50	50

117 *The Annunciation* (Demir Hisar, Slepce Monastery)

1999. Icons. Multicoloured.

250	4d. Type **117**	35	35
251	8d. *Saints* (St Nicholas's Church, Ohrid)	50	50
252	18d. *Madonna and Child* (Demir Hisar, Slepce Monastery)	85	85
253	30d. *Christ the Redeemer* (Zrze Monastery, Prilep)	1·30	1·30
MS254	53×74 mm. 50d. *Christ and Archangels* (Archangel Michael Church, Lesnovo Monastery, Probiotip)	3·00	3·00

118 Pandilov and *Hay Harvest*

1999. Birth Centenary of Dimitar Pandilov (painter).

255	**118**	4d. multicoloured	25	25

119 Telegraph Apparatus

1999. Centenary of the Telegraph in Macedonia.

256	**119**	4d. multicoloured	25	25

120 University and St Cyril and St Methodius

1999. 50th Anniversary of St Cyril and St Methodius University.

257	**120**	8d. multicoloured	35	35

121 Anniversary Emblem and Map of Europe

1999. 50th Anniversary of Council of Europe.

258	**121**	30d. multicoloured	1·40	1·40

122 Pelister National Park

1999. Europa. Parks and Gardens. Multicoloured.

259	30d. Type **122**	3·00	3·00
260	40d. Mavrovo National Park	4·25	4·25

123 Figures linking Raised Arms

1999. Obligatory Tax. Red Cross Week.

261	**123**	2d. multicoloured	60	60

124 People running round Globe

1999. Obligatory Tax. Solidarity Week.

262	**124**	2d. multicoloured	60	60

125 Tree

1999. Environmental Protection.

263	**125**	30d. multicoloured	1·40	1·40

126 Tsar Petur Delyan

1999. Medieval Rulers of Macedonia. Multicoloured.

264	4d. Type **126**	10	10
265	8d. Prince Gjorgji Vojteh	35	35
266	18d. Prince Dobromir Hrs	85	85
267	30d. Prince Strez	1·40	1·40

Nos. 264/267 were issued together, *se-tenant*, forming a composite design.

127 Kuzman Shaikarev (author)

1999. 125th Anniversary of First Macedonian Language Primer.

268	**127**	4d. multicoloured	25	25

128 Faces in Outline of Lungs

1999. Obligatory Tax. Anti-tuberculosis Week.

269	**128**	2d. multicoloured	60	60

129 *Crocus scardicus*

1999. Flowers. Multicoloured.

270	4d. Type **129**	25	25
271	8d. *Astragalus mayeri*	35	35
272	18d. *Campanula formanekiana*	95	95
273	30d. *Viola kosaninii*	1·40	1·40

130 Child

1999. Children's Week.

274	**130**	30d. multicoloured	1·40	1·40

131 Emblem

1999. 125th Anniversary of Universal Postal Union. Multicoloured.

275	5d. Type **131**	25	25
276	30d. Emblem (different)	1·60	1·60

132 Men on Horseback

1999. 1400th Anniversary of Slavs in Macedonia.

277	**132**	5d. multicoloured	25	25

133 Misirkov

1999. 125th Birth Anniversary (2000) of Krste Petkov Misirkov (writer).

278	**133**	5d. multicoloured	25	25

134 Pine Needles

1999. Christmas. Multicoloured.

279	5d. Type **134**	35	35
280	30d. Traditional pastry (vert)	1·40	1·40

135 Stylised Figures supporting Globe

1999. Obligatory Tax. Anti-AIDS Week.

281	**135**	2d.50 multicoloured	60	60

136 Altar Cross (19th-century), St Nikita Monastery

2000. Bimillenary of Christianity. Multicoloured.

282	5d. Type **136**	35	35
283	10d. *Akathist of the Holy Mother of God* (14th-century fresco), Marko's Monastery (horiz)	60	60
284	15d. *St Clement* (14th-century icon), Ohrid	70	70
285	30d. *Paul the Apostle* (14th-century fresco), St Andrew's Monastery	1·30	1·30
MS286	70×50 mm. 50d. Cathedral Church of St Sophia (11th-century), Ohrid (29×31 mm)	2·40	2·40

137 '2000'

2000. New Year. Multicoloured.

287	5d. Type **137**	25	25
288	30d. Religious symbols	1·20	1·20

2000. Obligatory Tax. Anti-cancer Week.

289	**138**	2d.50 multicoloured	60	60

2000. Jewellery. Multicoloured.

290	5d. Type **139**	25	25
291	10d. Bracelet, Bitola	35	35
292	20d. Earrings, Ohrid	95	95
293	30d. Butterfly brooch, Bitola	1·40	1·40

140 Magnifying Glass and Perforation Gauge

2000. 50th Anniversary of Philately in Macedonia.

294	**140**	5d. multicoloured	25	25

141 Globe and Emblem

2000. 50th Anniversary of World Meteorological Organisation.

295	**141**	30d. multicoloured	1·40	1·40

142 Men with Easter Eggs

2000. Easter.

296	**142**	5d. multicoloured	25	25

143 Stylised Figures

2000. Obligatory Tax. Red Cross Week.

297	**143**	2d.50 multicoloured	60	60

144 Building Europe

2000. Europa.

298	**144**	30d. multicoloured	3·00	3·00

145 Running

2000. Olympic Games, Sydney. Multicoloured.

299	5d. Type **145**	25	25
300	30d. Wrestling	1·60	1·60

146 Cupped Hands

2000. Obligatory Tax. Solidarity Week.

301	**146**	2d.50 multicoloured	60	60

147 Flower and Globe

2000. International Environmental Protection Day.

302	**147**	5d. multicoloured	25	25

148 Teodosija Sinaitski (printing pioneer)

2000. Printing. Multicoloured.

303	6d. Type **148**	25	25
304	30d. Johannes Gutenberg (inventor of printing press)	1·40	1·40

149 Mother Teresa

2000. Third Death Anniversary of Mother Teresa (Order of Missionaries of Charity).

305	**149**	6d. multicoloured	25	25

150 Faces and Hands

2000. Obligatory Tax. Red Cross Week.

306	**150**	3d. multicoloured	60	60

151 Little Egret

2000. Birds. Multicoloured.

307	6d. Type **151**	35	35
308	10d. Grey heron	50	50
309	20d. Purple heron	1·10	1·10
310	30d. Glossy ibis	1·70	1·70

152 Children and Tree

2000. Children's Week.

311	**152**	6d. multicoloured	25	25

153 Dimov

2000. 125th Birth Anniversary of Dimo Hadzi Dimov (revolutionary).

312	**153**	6d. multicoloured	25	25

154 Emblem

2000. 50th Anniversary of Faculty of Economics, St Cyril and St Methodius University, Skopje.

313	**154**	6d. multicoloured	25	25

155 Church and Frontispiece

2000. 250th Birth Anniversary of Joakim Krcovski (writer).

314	**155**	6d. multicoloured	1·00	1·00

156 Nativity

2000. Christmas.

315	**156**	30d. multicoloured	1·50	1·50

157 Hand holding Condom

2000. Obligatory Tax. Anti-AIDS. Week.

316	**157**	3d. multicoloured	65	65

158 Handprints and Emblem

2001. 50th Anniversary of United Nations Commissioner for Human Rights. Multicoloured.

317	6d. Type **158**	25	25

318	30d. Hands forming Globe (vert)	1·70	1·70

159 Imperial Eagle on Branch

2001. Endangered Species. The Imperial Eagle (*Aquila heliaca*). Multicoloured.

319	6d. Type **159**	25	25
320	8d. With chick	40	40
321	10d. Flying	50	50
322	30d. Head	1·40	1·40

160 Zografski

2001. 125th Death Anniversary of Partenja Zografski (historian).

323	**160**	6d. multicoloured	25	25

161 Emblem

2001. Obligatory Tax. Anti-Cancer Week.

324	**161**	3d. multicoloured	65	65

162 Woman in Costume

2001. Regional Costumes. Multicoloured.

325	6d. Type **162**	40	40
326	12d. Couple in costume	65	65
327	18d. Woman in costume	90	90
328	30d. Couple in costume	1·40	1·40
MS329	76×64 mm. 50d. Women working (30×30 mm). Imperf	2·50	2·50

163 Landscape

2001. Birth Centenary of Lazar Licenoski (artist).

330	**163**	6d. multicoloured	40	40

164 Text

2001. 50th Anniversary of State Archives.

331	**164**	6d. multicoloured	40	40

165 Jesus and Sick Man

2001. Easter.

332	**165**	6d. multicoloured	40	40

166 Children

2001. Obligatory Tax. Red Cross Week.

333	**166**	3d. multicoloured	65	65

167 Lake and Island

2001. Europa. Water Resources. Multicoloured.

334	18d. Type **167**	1·00	1·00
335	36d. Right-side of lake and island	2·20	2·20

Nos. 334/335 were issued together, *se-tenant*, forming a composite design.

168 Dimitri Berovski (nationalist leader) and Flag

2001. 125th Anniversary of Razlovci Village Uprising.

336	**168**	6d. multicoloured	40	40

169 Man carrying Red Cross Boxes

2001. Obligatory Tax. Red Cross Week.

337	**169**	3d. multicoloured	65	65

170 Championship Emblem

2001. Second Individual Chess Championship, Ohrid.

338	**170**	36d. multicoloured	1·90	1·90

171 Boats on Lake

2001. Environment Protection. Lake Dojran.

339	**171**	6d. multicoloured	40	40

172 Emblem

2001. Tenth Anniversary of Independence.

340	**172**	6d. multicoloured	40	40

173 Juniper (*Juniperus exelsa*)

2001. Trees. Multicoloured.

341	6d. Type **173**	40	40
342	12d. Macedonian oak (*Quercus macedonica*)	65	65
343	24d. Strawberry tree (*Arbutus andrachne*)	1·20	1·20
344	36d. Kermes oak (*Quercus coccifera*)	1·70	1·70

174 Man with raised Arms

2001. Obligatory Tax. Anti-Tuberculosis Week.

345	**174**	3d. multicoloured	65	65

175 Stylised Woman with Basket

2001. Children's Day.

346	**175**	6d. multicoloured	40	40

176 Children encircling Globe

2001. United Nations Year of Dialogue among Civilisations.

347	**176**	36d. multicoloured	2·20	2·20

177 Fox and Cubs

2001. 75th Anniversary of Zoological Museum.

348	**177**	6d. multicoloured	50	50

178 Icon

2001. Christmas.

349	**178**	6d. multicoloured	50	5·00

179 Faces

2001. Obligatory Tax. Anti-AIDS Week.

350	**179**	3d. multicoloured	65	65

180 Alfred Nobel

2001. Centenary of First Nobel Prize.

351	**180**	36d. multicoloured	1·90	1·90

181 Skier

2002. Winter Olympic Games, Salt Lake City, USA. Multicoloured.

352	6d. Type **181**	40	40
353	36d. Skier (different)	1·50	1·50

182 Sunrise

2002. Obligarory Tax. Anti-Cancer Week.

354	**182**	3d. multicoloured	65	65

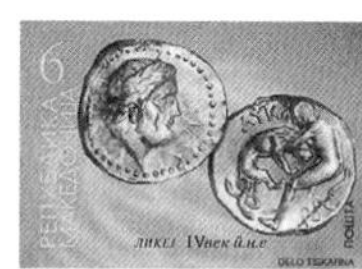

183 Likej (coin)

2002. Ancient Coins. Coins. Multicoloured.

355	6d. Type **183**	40	40
356	12d. Alexander III tetradrachm	65	65
357	24d. Lichnidos	1·20	1·20
358	36d. Philip II gold coin (stater)	1·70	1·70
MS359	85×62 mm. 50d. Coin	3·25	3·25

184 Painting and Petar Mazev

2002. Artists Birth Anniversaries. Multicoloured.

360	6d. Type **184** (75th anniversary)	50	50
361	6d. Triptych, 1978 (Dimitar Kondovski, 75th anniversary)	50	50
362	36d. *Mona Lisa (La Gioconda)* and Leonardo da Vinci (550th anniversary)	1·90	1·90

185 *The Risen Christ*

2002. Easter.

363	**185**	6d. multicoloured	50	50

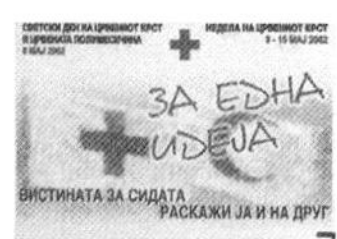

186 Red Cross and Red Crescent Flags

2002. Obligatory Tax. Red Cross Week.

364	**186**	3d. multicoloured	65	65

187 Acrobat, Bicycle, Sea Lion and Ball

2002. Europa. Circus. Multicoloured.

365	6d. Type **187**	65	65
366	36d. Circles, bicycle and ball	1·90	1·90

188 Championship Emblem, Ball and Player

2002. World Cup Football Championships, Japan and South Korea.

367	**188**	6d. multicoloured	2·30	2·30

189 Red Cross and Face

2002. Obligatory Tax. Solidarity Week.
368 **189** 3d. multicoloured 65 65

190 Tree containing Shapes

2002. Environment Protection.
369 **190** 6d. multicoloured 50 50

191 1595 Korenic Neonic Coat of Arms

2002. National Arms. Multicoloured.
370 10d. Type **191** 65 65
371 36d. 1620 Coat of Arms 1·90 1·90
See also Nos. 399/400.

192 House, Krusevo

2002. City Architecture. Multicoloured.
372 36d. Type **192** 1·30 1·30
373 50d. House, Bitola 2·50 2·50
See also Nos. 397/398.

193 Metodija Andonov-Cento

2002. Birth Centenary of Metodija Andonov-Cento (first Macedonian president).
374 **193** 6d. multicoloured 50 50

194 Nikola Karev

2002. 125th Birth Anniversary of Nikola Karev (revolutionary leader).
375 **194** 18d. multicoloured 1·00 1·00

195 Grey Partridge (*Perdix perdix*)

2002. Fauna. Multicoloured.
376 6d. Type **195** 25 25
377 12d. Wild Pig (*Sus scrofa*) 50 50
378 24d. Chamois (*Rupicapra rupicapra*) 1·00 1·00
379 36d. Rock Partridge (*Alectoris graeca*) 1·50 1·50

196 Face

2002. Obligatory Tax. Anti-Tuberculosis Week.
380 **196** 3d. multicoloured 65 65

197 House and People (child's drawing)

2002. Children's Day.
381 **197** 6d. multicoloured 50 50

198 Mary and Jesus (14th-century icon)

2002. Christmas.
382 **198** 9d. multicoloured 50 50

199 Clock, Numbers and Face

2002. Obligatory Tax. Anti-AIDS Week.
383 **199** 3d. multicoloured 65 65

200 Andreja Damjanov and Building Facade

2003. 125th Death Anniversary of Andreja Damjanov (architect).
384 **200** 36d. multicoloured 1·90 1·90

201 Gajga

2003. Traditional Musical Instruments. Multicoloured.
385 9d. Type **201** 40 40
386 10d. Tambura 40 40
387 20d. Kemene 1·30 1·30
388 50d. Tapan 2·50 2·50

202 Scouts and Campsite

2003. 50th Anniversary of Scouting in Macedonia.
389 **202** 9d. multicoloured 60 60

203 Face surrounded by Petals

2003. Obligatory Tax. Anti-Cancer Week.
390 **203** 4d. multicoloured 75 75

204 Krste Petkov Misirkov (founder)

2003. 50th Anniversary of Krste Petkov Misirkov Macedonian Language Institute.
391 **204** 9d. multicoloured 60 60

205 Red Ribbon with Red Cross and Red Crescent Emblems

2003. Obligatory Tax. Red Cross Week.
392 **205** 3d. multicoloured 75 75

206 International Graphic Art Triennial, Bitola (1994)

2003. Europa. Poster Art. Multicoloured.
393 36d. Type **206** 2·30 2·30
394 36d. *Ohrider Sommer* (1966) 2·30 2·30

207 Outstretched Hand

2003. Obligatory Tax. Solidarity Week. Litho.
395 **207** 4d. multicoloured 75 75

208 Brown Bear (*Ursus arctos*)

2003
396 **208** 9d. multicoloured 60 60

2003. City Architecture. As T **192**. Multicoloured.
397 10d. House, Skopje 60 60
398 20d. House, Resen 1·20 1·20

2003. National Arms. As T **191**. Multicoloured.
399 9d. 17th-century Arms 60 60
400 36d. 1694 Coat of Arms 2·40 2·40

209 Handball Player

2003. World Youth Handball Championships.
401 **209** 36d. multicoloured 2·30 2·30

210 Seal and Revolutionaries

2003. Centenary of Ilinden Uprising. Multicoloured.
402 9d. Type **210** 60 60
403 36d. Leaders and Mechen Kamen monument 2·40 2·40
MS404 60×75 mm. 50d. Revolutionaries (different) 3·00 3·00

211 *Self Portrait* (Nikola Martinovski)

2003. Artists' Anniversaries. Multicoloured.
405 9d. Type **211** (birth centenary) 60 60
406 36d. *Moulin de Galette* (Vincent van Gogh) (150th birth anniversary) (horiz) 2·10 2·10

212 Stylized Figure

2003. Obligatory Tax. Anti-Tuberculosis Week.
407 **212** 4d. multicoloured 75 75

213 Colchicum (*Colchicum macedonicum*)

2003. Flowers. Multicoloured.
408 9d. Type **213** 80 80
409 20d. Viola (*Viola allchariensis*) 1·60 1·60
410 36d. *Tulipa mariannae* 2·75 2·75
411 50d. *Thymus oehmianus* 4·00 4·00

214 Said Najdeni

2003. Death Centenaries. Multicoloured.
412 9d. Type **214** (Albanian writer and reformer) 70 70
413 9d. Jeronim de Rada (Italian-Albanian writer) 70 70

215 Family sheltering under Umbrella

2003. Children's Day.
414 **215** 9d. multicoloured 1·00 1·00

216 Seal and Armed Revolutionaries

2003. 125th Anniversary of Kresna Uprising.
415 **216** 9d. multicoloured 1·00 1·00

217 Dimitir Vlahov

2003. 50th Death Anniversary of Dimitir Vlahov (politician).
416 **217** 9d. multicoloured 1·00 1·00

218 Mary and Jesus (fresco)

2003. Christmas.

417	**218**	9d. multicoloured	1·00	1·00

219 Ribbon

2003. Obligatory Tax. Anti-AIDS Week.

418	**219**	4d. vermilion	1·00	1·00

220 19th-century Jug, Smojmirovo

2003. Cultural Artifacts. Multicoloured.

419	3d. Amphora	40	40
420	3d. 18th/19th-century lidded jug	40	40
421	4d. 19th-century coffee pot (horiz)	50	50
422	5d. Tassel, Vrutok	60	60
423	5d. 20th-century circular flask	60	60
424	6d. 18th/19th-century jug and ewer	70	70
425	9d. Type **220**	80	80
426	10d. Kettle, Ohrid	80	80
427	10d. 18th-century hand-bell	80	80
428	12d. Albastron (alabaster incense pot)	1·00	1·00
429	12d. 18th/19th-century pot with cover	1·40	1·40
430	20d. Chest decoration, Galicnik	2·30	2·30

221 Wilbur and Orville Wright and *Wright Flyer*

2003. Centenary of Powered Flight.

440	**221**	50d. multicoloured	3·75	3·75

222 *Street Scene* (Tomo Vladimirski)

2004. Artists' Birth Centenaries. Multicoloured.

441	9d. Type **222**	65	65
442	9d. *Ohrid Street* (Vangel Kodzoman)	65	65

223 Breast Examination

2004. Obligatory Tax. Anti-Cancer Week.

443	**223**	4d. multicoloured	1·00	1·00

224 Knives and Armour

2004. Cultural Heritage. Weapons. Multicoloured.

444	10d. Type **224**	1·00	1·00
445	20d. 19th-century sword	1·80	1·80
446	36d. 18th-century pistol	2·75	2·75
447	50d. 18th-century rifle	3·75	3·75

225 Carpet

2004. Traditional Carpets. Multicoloured.

448	36d. Type **225**	2·50	2·50
449	50d. Carpet (different)	3·75	3·75

226 Kostandin Kristoforidhi (writer)

2004. Centenary of Publication of First Albanian Dictionary in Macedonia.

450	**226**	36d. multicoloured	2·50	2·50

227 House, Kratovo

2004. City Architecture.

451	**227**	20d. multicoloured	1·50	1·50

228 Parasol and Woman Reading

2004. Europa. Holidays. Multicoloured.

452	50d. Type **228**	3·50	3·50
453	50d. Yacht and island	3·50	3·50

Nos. 452/453 were issued together, *se-tenant*, forming a composite design of a beach scene.

229 Profiles

2004. Obligatory Tax. Red Cross Week.

454	**229**	4d. multicoloured	1·00	1·00

230 Stars

2004. Application to join European Union.

455	**230**	36d. multicoloured	2·50	2·50

231 Hands enclosing Globe

2004. Obligatory Tax. Solidarity Week.

456	**231**	6d. multicoloured	1·00	1·00

232 Pelican and Lake

2004. Prespa National Park.

457	**232**	36d. multicoloured	2·50	2·50

233 Flags as Interlocking Rings

2004. Olympic Games, Athens. Multicoloured.

458	50d. Type **233**	3·50	3·50
459	50d. Rings (different)	3·50	3·50

Nos. 458/459 were issued together, *se-tenant*, forming a composite design of Olympic rings.

234 Sami Frasheri

2004. Death Centenary of Sami Frasheri (Albanian writer).

460	**234**	12d. multicoloured	1·00	1·00

235 Emblem, Feet and Ball

2004. Centenary of FIFA (Federation Internationale de Football Association).

461	**235**	100d. multicoloured	7·25	7·25

236 Marko Cepenkov

2004. Anniversaries. Multicoloured.

462	12d. Type **236** (writer) (175th birth)	1·00	1·00
463	12d. Vasil Glavinov (politician) (75th death) (vert)	1·00	1·00

237 Child blowing Bubbles

2004. Obligatory Tax. Anti-Tuberculosis Week.

464	**237**	6d. multicoloured	1·00	1·00

238 Bohemian Waxwing (*Bombycilla garrulous*)

2004. Birds. Multicoloured.

465	12d. Type **238**	1·00	1·00
466	24d. Woodchat shrike (*Lanius senato*)	2·10	2·10
467	36d. Rock thrush (*Monticola saxatilis*)	2·75	2·75
468	48d. Northern bullfinch (*Pyrrhula pyrrhula*)	4·00	4·00
MS469	86×61 mm. 60d. Wall creeper (*Tichodroma muraria*). Imperf	4·50	4·50

239 Children

2004. Children's Day.

470	**239**	12d. multicoloured	1·00	1·00

240 Binary Code

2004. World Summit on Information Technology Society (WSIS).

471	**240**	36d. multicoloured	2·50	2·50

241 Manuscript

2004. Millenary of Publication of *Asseman Gospel* (Glagolitic (early Slavonic language) liturgical gospel).

472	**241**	12d. multicoloured	1·00	1·00

242 Marco Polo

2004. 750th Birth Anniversary of Marco Polo (traveller).

473	**242**	36d. multicoloured	2·50	2·50

243 Star, Ribbons, Snowflakes and Holly

2004. Christmas.

474	**243**	12d. multicoloured	1·00	1·00

244 Hands

2004. Obligatory Tax. AIDS Week.

475	**244**	6d. multicoloured	1·00	1·00

245 Konstantin Miladinov

2005. 175th Birth Anniversary of Konstantin Miladinov (writer).

476	**245**	36d. multicoloured	2·50	2·50

246 Ash Tray

2005. Obligatory Tax. Anti-Cancer Week.

477	**246**	6d. multicoloured	1·00	1·00

247 Manuscript (16th/17th-century)

2005. Illuminated Manuscripts. Multicoloured.

478	12d. Type **247**	1·00	1·00
479	24d. Illustration (16th-century)	1·80	1·80

248 Embroidered Cloth (19th-century)

2005. Embroidery. Multicoloured.

480	36d. Type **248**	2·50	2·50
481	50d. Embroidery (20th-century)	3·75	3·75

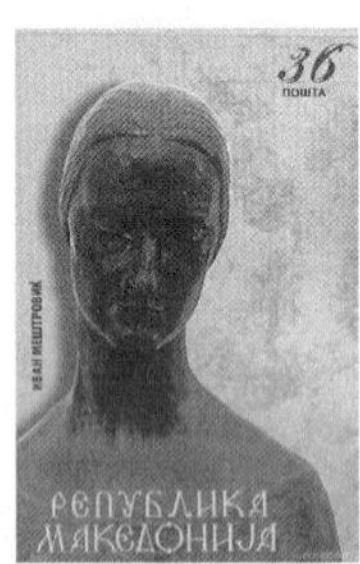

249 *Woman's Head* (sculpture) (Ivan Mestrovic)

2005. Art. Multicoloured.

482	36d. Type **249**	2·50	2·50
483	50d. *Portrait of Woman* (painting) (Paja Jovanovic) (horiz)	3·75	3·75

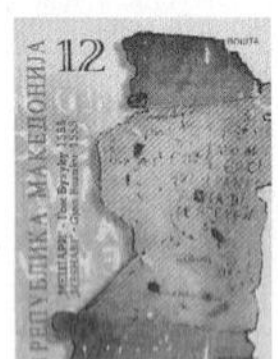

250 Fragment

2005. 450th Anniversary of *The Missal* by Gjon Buzuku (first book written and published in Albanian).

484	**250**	12d. multicoloured	1·00	1·00

251 Skanderbeg

2005. 600th Birth Anniversary of Gjergj Kastrioti (Skanderbeg) (Albanian leader).

485	**251**	36d. multicoloured	2·50	2·50

252 Henry Dunant (Red Cross founder)

2004. Obligatory Tax. Red Cross Week.

486	**252**	6d. multicoloured	1·00	1·00

253 Grain, Cake and Bread

2005. Europa. Gastronomy. Multicoloured.

487	36d. Type **253**	2·50	2·50
488	60d. Roasted meat with peppers	4·00	4·00

254 Building and Script

2005. Centenary of National Day of Vlachs (Aromanians) (imperial decree, issued by Ottoman Sultan Abdual Hamid II, which gave Vlachs their first collective rights).

489	**254**	12d. multicoloured	1·00	1·00

256 Globe as Tree

2005. Environmental Protection.

491	**256**	36d. multicoloured	2·50	2·50

257 Figure (16th-century)

2005. Carvings. Multicoloured.

492	3d. Type **257**	20	20
493	4d. Ten-sided stars shape (15th-century)	40	40
494	6d. Winged serpents (16th-century)	60	60
495	8d. Diamond shaped design (1883-1884)	80	80
496	12d. Figure, snake and animals (16th-century)	1·00	1·00

258 Ford (1905)

2005. Transport Anniversaries. Multicoloured.

497	12d. Type **258** (centenary of first car)	1·00	1·00
498	36d. Glider (50th anniversary of Macedonia aircraft)	2·50	2·50

259 Albert Einstein and Emblem

2005. International Year of Physics. Centenary of Publication of *Theory of Special Relativity*.

499	**259**	60d. multicoloured	4·50	4·50

260 Cross of Lorraine

2005. Obligatory Tax. Anti-Tuberculosis Week.

500	**260**	6d. multicoloured	1·00	1·00

261 *Malus domestica* (apples)

2005. Fruit. Multicoloured.

501	12d. Type **261**	1·00	1·00
502	24d. *Prunus persica* (peaches)	2·10	2·10
503	36d. *Prunus avium*	3·00	3·00
504	48d. *Prunus* (plums)	3·75	3·75
MS505	97×65 mm. 100d. *Pyrus* (pears) (vert)	7·25	7·25

262 Smolarski Waterfall

2005

506	**262**	24d. multicoloured	1·80	1·80

263 Hans Christian Andersen

2005. Birth Bicentenary of Hans Christian Andersen (writer).

507	**263**	12d. multicoloured	1·00	1·00

264 Kozjak Dam

2005

508	**264**	12d. multicoloured	1·00	1·00

265 '1880–8'

2005. 125th Anniversary of Brsjai Rebellion.

509	**265**	12d. multicoloured	1·00	1·00

266 Delegates

2005. Centenary of Rila Congress.

510	**266**	12d. multicoloured	1·00	1·00

267 2002 36d. Stamp (as No. 366)

2005. 50th Anniversary of Europa Stamps. Multicoloured.

511	60d. Type **267**	4·00	4·00
512	170d. 1999 30d. stamp (as Type **122**)	11·50	11·50
513	250d. 1997 20d. stamp (as Type **85**)	17·00	17·00
514	350d. 1996 40d. stamp (as No. 153)	24·00	24·00
MS515	66×132 mm. Nos. 511/514	80·00	80·00

268 Candle

2005. Christmas. Litho.

516	**268**	12d. multicoloured	1·00	1·00

269 White Water Kayaking

2005

517	**269**	36d. multicoloured	2·75	2·75

270 Hand holding Condom

2005. Obligatory Tax. Anti-AIDS Week.

518	**270**	6d. multicoloured	1·00	1·00

271 Postal Emblem

2005

519	**271**	12d. multicoloured	1·00	1·00

272 Skier

2006. Winter Olympic Games, Turin. Multicoloured.

520	36d. Type **272**	2·50	2·50
521	60d. Ice hockey player	4·00	4·00

273 Woman examining Breast

2006. Obligatory Tax. Anti-Cancer Week.

522	**273**	6d. multicoloured	1·00	1·00

274 Fresco, Monastic Church, Matejce

2006. Cultural Heritage. Multicoloured.

523	12d. Type **274**	80	80
524	24d. Isaac Celebi Mosque, Bitola	1·60	1·60

275 Leopold Senghor

2006. Birth Centenary of Leopold Sedar Senghor (Senegalese politician).

525	**275**	36d. multicoloured	2·75	2·75

276 Wooden Pattens

2006. Craftwork. Mother of Pearl Inlays. Multicoloured.
526 12d. Type **276** 1·00 1·00
527 24d. Pipes 2·10 2·10

277 Woodcarving, Church of the Holy Saviour, Skopje

2006. Birth Bicentenary of Makarie Negriev Frckovski.
528 **277** 12d. multicoloured 1·00 1·00

278 Cupola

2006. 450th Anniversary of Cupola, Church of St Peter, Rome.
529 **278** 36d. multicoloured 2·75 2·75

279 Zhivko Firfov

2006. Birth Centenary of Zhivko Firkov (composer).
530 **279** 24d. multicoloured 1·80 1·80

280 Mozart, Score and Violins

2006. 250th Birth Anniversary of Wolfgang Amadeus Mozart (composer).
531 **280** 60d. multicoloured 4·50 4·50

281 Stylised Figure

2006. Obligatory Tax. Red Cross Week.
532 **281** 6d. multicoloured 1·00 1·00

282 Coloured Balls

2006. Europa. Integration. Multicoloured.
533 36d. Type **282** 2·50 2·50
534 60d. Coloured building blocks 4·50 4·50

283 Pope John Paul II

2006. Tenth Anniversary of Europa Stamps in Macedonia. Sheet 80×70 mm containing T **283** and similar vert design. Multicoloured.
MS535 60d.×2, Type **283**; Mother Teresa 8·75 8·75

284 Greenery running to Sand through Hourglass

2006. International Year of Deserts and Desertification.
536 **284** 12d. multicoloured 1·00 1·00

285 Chequered Flag

2006. Centenary of Grand Prix Motor Race.
537 **285** 36d. multicoloured 2·75 2·75

286 Nikola Tesla

2006. 150th Birth Anniversary of Nikola Tesla (inventor).
538 **286** 24d. multicoloured 1·80 1·80

287 *Santa Maria*

2006. 500th Death Anniversary of Christopher Columbus.
539 **287** 36d. multicoloured 2·75 2·75

288 *Ancylus scalariformis*

2006. Shells. Multicoloured.
540 12d. Type **288** 1·10 1·10
541 24d. *Macedopyrgula pavlovici* 2·00 2·00
542 36d. *Gyraulus trapezoids* 3·00 3·00
543 48d. *Valvata hirsutecostata* 4·00 4·00
MS544 80×70 mm. 72d. *Ochridopyrgula macedonica* 5·75 5·75

289 Child

2006. Obligatory Tax. Anti-Tuberculosis Week.
545 **289** 6d. multicoloured 1·00 1·00

290 Girl drawing

2006. 60th Anniversary of UNICEF.
546 **290** 12d. multicoloured 1·00 1·00

291 National Park, Galicica

2006
547 **291** 24d. multicoloured 1·80 1·80

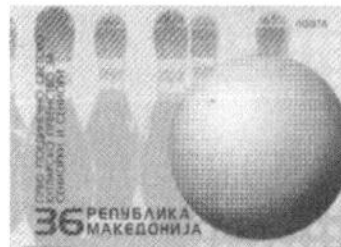
292 Ball and Pins

2006. World Ten-Pin Bowling Championship, Skopje.
548 **292** 36d. multicoloured 2·75 2·75

293 Frang Bardhi (author of the first Albanian dictionary)

2006. Personalities. Multicoloured.
549 12d. Type **293** 90 90
550 24d. Boris Trajkovski (president, 1999–2004) 90 90
551 36d. Mustafa Kemel Attaturk (founder of Turkish Republic) 2·00 2·00
552 48d. Dositheus II (Metropolitan of Macedonia) 2·00 2·00

294 Stars

2006. Christmas.
553 **294** 12d. multicoloured 1·00 1·00

295 Emblem

2006. Obligatory Tax. Anti-AIDS Week.
554 **295** 6d. multicoloured 1·00 1·00

296 Carved Stone

2007. Kokino Megalithic Observatory. Multicoloured.
555 12d. Type **296** 90 90
556 36d. Sunrise 2·75 2·75

297 Slivnik Monastery (400th anniversary)

2007. Monasteries' Anniversaries. Multicoloured.
557 12d. Type **297** 90 90
558 36d. St Nikita (700th anniversary) (vert) 2·75 2·75

298 18th/19th-century Metal Cap

2007. Crafts. Multicoloured.
559 12d. Type **298** 90 90
560 36d. 19th-century decorated box 2·75 2·75

299 *Cobitis vardarensis*

2007. Fish. Multicoloured.
561 12d. Type **299** 1·10 1·10
562 36d. *Zingel balcanicus* 2·75 2·75
563 60d. *Chondrostoma vardarense* 4·50 4·50
564 100d. *Barbus macedonicus* 7·50 7·50
MS565 60×71 mm. 100d. *Leuciscus cephalus* 7·50 7·50

299a Woman

2007. Obligatory Tax. Anti-Cancer Week.
565a **299a** 6d. multicoloured 1·00 1·00

300 *Epos of Freedom* (mosaic, detail) (Borko Lazeski)

2007. Art. Centenary of Cubism. Multicoloured.
566 36d. Type **300** 2·75 2·75
567 100d. *Head of a Woman* (Pablo Picasso) (vert) 7·50 7·50

301 Emblem and People talking

2007. International Day of Francophonie (organisation of French speaking communities).
568 **301** 12d. multicoloured 1·00 1·00

302 Cat

2007. Pets.
569 **302** 12d. multicoloured 1·00 1·00

302a Hands and Globe

2007. Obligatory Tax. Red Cross Week.
569a **302a** 6d. multicoloured 1·00 1·00

303 Camp

2007. Europa. Centenary of Scouting. Multicoloured.
570 60d. Type **303** 5·00 5·00
571 100d. Scout (vert) 7·75 7·75
MS572 60×70 mm. 160d. Emblem 32·00 32·00

303a Fresco, Basilica of San Clemente (detail)

2007. 150th Anniversary of Discovery of St Cyril's Grave.
572a **303a** 50d. multicoloured 1·00 1·00

304 Globe, Chimneys and Clock

2007. Pollution Awareness.

573	**304**	12d. multicoloured	1·00	1·00

305 Dimitri Ivanovich Mendeleev

2007. Scientific Personalities. Multicoloured.

574	36d. Type **305** (chemist and creator of first periodic tables) (death centenary)	3·00	3·00
575	36d. Carl von Linne (Linnaeus) (scientist and plant and animal classification deviser) (300th birth anniversary) (vert)	3·00	3·00

306 NATO and EPAC Emblems

2007. Euro Atlantic Security Forum, Ohrid.

576	**306**	60d. multicoloured	5·50	5·50

307 Yachts

2007. Centenary of Yacht Racing Union.

577	**307**	36d. multicoloured	3·00	3·00

308 Child and Dandelion

2007. Obligatory Tax. Anti-Tuberculosis Week.

578	**308**	6d. multicoloured	1·00	1·00

309 Maminska River Waterfall

2007. Natural Heritage.

579	**309**	12d. multicoloured	1·00	1·00

310 Dhimiter Pasko (Mitrush Kuteli)

2007. Personalities. Multicoloured.

580	12d. Type **310** (writer) (birth centenary)	1·00	1·00
581	12d. Theofan (Fan) Stilian Noli (nationalist) (125th birth anniversary)	1·00	1·00

311 Drawings and Child

2007. Children's Day.

582	**311**	12d. multicoloured	1·00	1·00

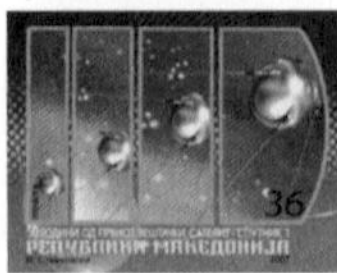

312 *Sputnik*

2007. 50th Anniversary of Space Exploration.

583	**312**	36d. multicoloured	3·00	3·00

313 Petre Prlicko

2007. Petre Prlicko (actor) Commemoration.

584	**313**	12d. multicoloured	1·00	1·00

314 Jordan Dzinot

2007. Jordan Hadzi-Konstantinov Dzinot (educator) Commemoration.

585	**314**	12d. multicoloured	1·00	1·00

315 Textile

2007

586	**315**	12d. multicoloured	1·00	1·00

316 Santa Claus

2007. Christmas.

587	**316**	12d. multicoloured	1·00	1·00

317 AIDS Ribbon

2007. Obligatory Tax. Anti-AIDS Week.

588	**317**	6d. multicoloured	1·00	1·10

318 Tose Proeski

2007. Tose Proeski (singer) Commemoration.

589	**318**	12d. multicoloured	1·00	1·00

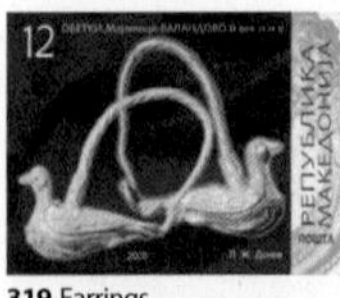

319 Earrings

2008. Cultural Heritage. Jewellery. Multicoloured.

590	12d. Type **319**	1·00	1·00

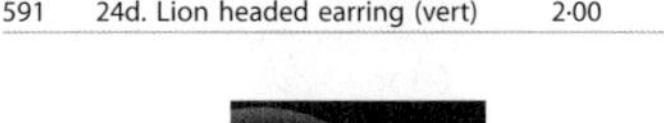

591	24d. Lion headed earring (vert)	2·00	2·00

320 Launching of Satellite *Explorer 1*

2008. 50th Anniversary of Space Exploration.

592	**320**	24d. multicoloured	2·50	2·50

321 Train

2008. Transportation.

593	**321**	100d. multicoloured	7·50	7·50

322 Child and Cigarette

2008. Obligatory Tax. Anti-Cancer Week.

594	**322**	6d. multicoloured	1·00	1·00

323 Hoopoe

2008. Hoopoe (*Upupa epops*). Multicoloured.

595	12d. Type **323**	1·00	1·00
596	24d. Head	2·00	2·00
597	48d. Facing left	3·75	3·75
598	60d. Facing right	5·00	5·00

324 Bull Dog

2008. Pets.

599	**324**	30d. multicoloured	2·30	2·30

325 Envelope and Globe

2008. Europa. The Letter. Multicoloured, background colours given.

600	50d. Type **325**	1·20	1·20
601	50d. Envelopes and globe	1·20	1·20
602	50d. As Type **325** (cobalt)	1·20	1·20
603	50d. As No. 601 (cobalt)	1·20	1·20
604	50d. As Type **325** (deep blue)	1·20	1·20
605	100d. As No. 601 (deep blue)	2·40	2·40

Nos. 600/601 602/603 and 604/605, respectively were printed together, *se-tenant*, each pair forming a composite design.

326 Stylised Figures and Globe as Jigsaw Puzzle

2008. Obligatory Tax. Red Cross Week.

606	**326**	6d. multicoloured	1·00	1·00

327 Robert Schuman (one of founders of EU)

2008. European Union. Multicoloured.

607	36d. Type **327**	3·00	3·00
608	50d. Eiffel Tower (horiz)	4·00	4·00
609	50d. Ljublijana (horiz)	4·00	4·00

328 Cupped Hands and Water

2008. Environmental Protection.

610	**328**	12d. multicoloured	3·75	3·75

329 Rudolf Diesel

2008. 150th Birth Anniversary of Rudolf Diesel (German engineer and inventor of the diesel engine).

611	**329**	30d. multicoloured	8·00	8·00

330 Sailing

2008. Olympic Games, Beijing. Designs showing stylised athletes. Multicoloured.

612	12d. Type **330**	3·75	3·75
613	18d. Gymnastics	5·75	5·75
614	20d. Tennis	6·00	6·00
615	36d. Equestrian	6·50	6·50

331 Eqrem Cabej

2008. Birth Centenary of Eqrem Cabej.

616	**331**	12d. multicoloured	3·75	3·75

332 *Helichrysum zivojinii*

2008. Flora. Multicoloured.

617	1d. Type **332**	1·00	1·00
618	12d. *Pulsatilla halleri* (horiz)	1·00	1·00
619	50d. *Stachys* (horiz)	4·00	4·00
620	72d. *Fritillaria macedonica*	5·50	5·50
MS621	59×70 mm. 72d. *Centaurea grbavacensis*	5·50	5·50

333a Figure

2008. Obligatory Tax. Anti-Tuberculosis Week.

622a	**333a**	6d. multicoloured	1·90	1·90

334 Ubava Cave

2008
623 **334** 12d. multicoloured 1·00 1·00

335 Child and Jigsaw

2008. Children's Day.
624 **335** 12d. multicoloured 1·00 1·00

336 Stylised Players

2008. European Women's Handball Championship, Macedonia.
625 **336** 30d. multicoloured 2·40 2·40

337 Annotation

2008. 700th Anniversary of Eucharistic Song by Saint John Kukuzel.
626 **337** 12d. multicoloured 1·00 1·00

338 Giacomo Puccini and Score

2008. 150th Birth Anniversary of Giacomo Puccini (composer).
627 **338** 100d. multicoloured 6·75 6·75

339 Kosta Racin

2008. Birth Centenary of Kosta Solev (Kosta Racin) (revolutionary and poet).
628 **339** 12d. multicoloured 1·00 1·00

No. 629 and T **340** are left for Centenary of Congress of Monastir (to decide on the use of Latin script for written Albanian), issued on 14 November 2008, not yet received.

341 Baubles

2008. Christmas and New Year.
630 **341** 12d. multicoloured 1·00 1·00

341a Emblem

2008. Obligatory Tax. Anti-Cancer Week.
630a **341a** 6d. multicoloured 1·00 1·00

342 Street, Ohrid

2008. Architecture.
631 **342** 12d. brown, salmon and black 1·10 1·10
632 – 12d. indigo, new blue and black 1·10 1·10
633 – 12d. indigo, greenish slate and black 1·10 1·10
634 – 12d. deep yellow-green and scarlet-vermilion 1·10 1·10
635 – 12d. black and bright green 1·10 1·10

Designs: No. 631 T **342**; No. 632 Street, Bitola; No. 633 Bridge, Skopje; No. 634 Building, Tetobo; No. 635 Building, Stip.

343 Lech Walesa

2008. Macedonia–Poland Friendship.
636 **343** 50d. multicoloured 3·75 3·75

343a St Sava

2008
636a **343a** 12d. multicoloured 1·00 1·00

344 Anvil

2009. Cultural Heritage. Multicoloured.
637 10d. Type **344** 1·00 1·00
638 20d. Hand made horse shoe 1·90 1·90

345 Yuri Gagarin

2009. 75th Birth Anniversary of Yuri Alekseyevich Gagarin (cosmonaut and first man in space).
639 **345** 50d. multicoloured 3·75 3·75

345a Figure

2009. Obligatory Tax. AIDS Awareness Week.
639a **345a** 6d. multicoloured 1·00 1·00

346 Diana, the Huntress

2009. Breast Cancer Awareness.
640 **346** 15d. multicoloured 1·70 1·70

Design: As T **2342** of USA.

347 Trajko Prokopiev and Todor Skalovski

2009. Composers Anniversaries. Multicoloured.
641 12d. Type **347** (birth centenaries) 1·10 1·10
642 60d. George Frideric Handel (150th death anniversary) and Franz Josef Haydn (death bicentenary) 4·50 4·50

348 Chestnut

2009. Horses. Multicoloured.
643 20d. Type **348** 7·00 7·00
644 50d. Bay cantering 17·00 17·00

348a Battle

2009. Obligatory Tax. 150th Anniversary of Battle of Solferino (witnessed by Henry Dunant who instigated campaign resulting in establishment of Geneva Conventions and Red Cross).
644a **348a** 6d. multicoloured 1·00 1·00

349 Macedonian Folklore Constellations (hen and chicks)

2009. Europa. Astronomy. Multicoloured.
645 50d. Type **349** 7·00 7·00
646 100d. Macedonian folklore constellations (plough) 13·00 13·00
MS647 57×77 mm 150d. Macedonian folklore constellations (rooster) (vert) 20·00 20·00

350 Prague

2009. Macedonia in Europe. Multicoloured.
648 10d. Type **350** 1·00 1·00
649 60d. Pippi Longstocking (Swedish children's book character) and European flag (vert) 4·50 4·50

351 Vrelo

2009. Caves.
650 **351** 12d. multicoloured 1·00 1·00

352 Charles Darwin (evolutionary theorist) and Anthropoid Progress

2009. Science. Birth Bicentenaries.
651 18d. multicoloured 1·10 1·10
652 18d. black, scarlet-vermilion and orange 1·10 1·10

Designs:—No. 651 T **352**; No. 652 Louis Braille (inventor of Braille writing for the blind) and Braille letters.

353 *Galeb*

2009
653 **353** 18d. multicoloured 1·10 1·10

354 Ship's Prow

2009
654 **354** 18d. multicoloured 1·10 1·10

355 Bell Tower, Prilep

2009. Cities.
655 **355** 18d. brown-purple, azure and black 1·10 1·10

See also Nos. 656, 671/676, 689a/689e, 715/721 and 773/775.

2009. Cities. As T **355**. Grey-black, dull orange and black.
656 16d. Town Hall, Strumica 1·10 1·10

356 Player, Emblem and Flag

2009. Centenary of Football in Macedonia.
657 **356** 18d. multicoloured 1·10 1·10

357 Cyclist

2009. Centenary of Giro d'Italia (cycle race). Multicoloured.
658 18d. Type **357** 1·10 1·10
659 18d. Chain wheel and pedal (horiz) 1·10 1·10

358 *Pelobates syriacus balcanicus* (Balkan spadefoot toad)

2009. Fauna. Multicoloured.
660 2d. Type **358** 1·00 1·00
661 3d. *Salmo letnica* (ohrid trout) 1·00 1·00
662 6d. *Austropotamobius torrentium macedonicus* (Macedonian stone crab) 1·00 1·00
663 8d. *Triturus macedonicus* (Macedonian crested newt) 1·00 1·00
MS664 60×70 mm. 100d. Dr. Stanko Karaman and crustaceans (vert) 2·20 2·20

358a Stethoscope and Lungs

2009. Obligatory Tax. Anti-Tuberculosis Week.
665 **358a** 6d. multicoloured 1·00 1·00

359 Paintings

2009. 150th Birth Anniversary of Dimitar Andonov Papradishki (artist).
666 **359** 16d. multicoloured 1·10 1·10

360 Charter

2009. Centenary of Elbasan High School.
667 **360** 16d. multicoloured 1·00 1·00

361 Filip Shiroka

2008. 150th Birth Anniversary of Filip Shiroka (poet).
668 **361** 16d. multicoloured 1·10 1·10

362 Krume Kepeski

2009. Birth Centenary of Krume Kepeski (linguist).
669 **362** 16d. multicoloured 1·10 1·10

363 Petre M. Andreevski

2009. 75th Birth Anniversary of Petre M. Andreevski (poet, novelist, short story writer and playwright).
670 **363** 16d. multicoloured 1·10 1·10

2009. Cities. Vert designs as T **355**

671 16d. olive-green and turquoise-blue 1·40 1·40
672 16d. orange-brown and dull ultramarine 1·40 1·40
673 16d. deep turquoise-green and bistre-brown 1·40 1·40
674 16d. dull ultramarine and bright crimson 1·40 1·40
675 16d. olive-sepia and black 1·60 1·60
676 16d. orange-brown and black 1·60 1·60

Designs: No. 671 Kicevo; No. 672 Gostivar; No. 673 Delcevo; No. 674 Struga; No. 675 Kumanovo; No. 676 Resen.

364 The Nativity

2009. Christmas.
677 **364** 16d. multicoloured 1·50 1·50

365 Profiles and Emblem

2009. Obligatory Tax. AIDS Awareness Week.
678 **365** 8d. muulticoloured 1·00 1·00

366 Helicopter

2010. Transport.
679 **366** 50d. multicoloured 3·75 3·75

367 Ski Jump and Stone Emblem

2010. Winter Olympic Games, Vancouver. Multicoloured.
680 50d. Type **367** 3·75 3·75
681 100d. Hockey and emblem 6·50 6·50

367a Profile, Hands and Emblem

2010. Obligatory Tax. AIDS Awareness Week.
681a **367a** 8d. multicoloured 1·00 1·00

368 Deep Pink Peony

2010. Centenary of International Women's Day. Multicoloured.
MS682 18d.×2, Type **368**; Pale pink peony from below 2·40 2·40

369 Frescoes

2010. 650th Anniversary of St Peter's Church, Golem Grad.
683 **369** 18d. multicoloured 1·20 1·20

370 Budgerigar

2010. Pets. Birds. Multicoloured.
684 20d. Type **370** 1·40 1·40
685 40d. Macaw (horiz) 2·75 2·75

370a Globe and Symbols of Habitation

2010. Obligatory Tax. Red Cross–Urban Life.
685a **370a** 8d. multicoloured 1·00 1·00

371 Peter Pan

2010. Europa.
686 **371** 100d. multicoloured 6·50 6·50

372 Map of Europe and Silhouettes

2010. Macedonian Chairmanship of Council of Europe.
687 **372** 18d. multicoloured 1·50 1·50

373 EU Headquarters, Brussels

2010. Macedonia in the EU. Multicoloured.
688 20d. Type **373** 1·75 1·75
689 50d. Palacio de Comunicaciones, Madrid 4·50 4·50

2010. Cities. Vert designs as T **355**. Multicoloured.
689a 16d. House, Debar 1·90 1·90
689b 16d. Terrace, Gevgelija 1·90 1·90
689c 16d. Bridge, Kratovo 1·90 1·90
689d 18d. Clock Tower, Veles 1·90 1·90
689e 18d. House, Kruševo 1·90 1·90

374 Chestnut and Tree

2010. Environmental Protection. Sweet Chestnut (*Castanea sativa*).
690 **374** 20d. multicoloured 1·75 1·75

375 Robert Schumann, Piano Keys and Musical Score

2010. Birth Bicentenary of Robert Alexander Schumann (composer).
691 **375** 50d. black, azure and orange-vermilion 4·50 4·50

376 Frédéric Chopin

2010. Birth Bicentenary of Frédéric François Chopin (composer).
692 **376** 60d. multicoloured 4·50 4·50

377 Football in Net

2010. World Cup Football Championships, South Africa
693 50d. Type **377** 4·50 4·50
694 100d. Football on centre line (vert) 8·00 8·00
MS695 70×60 mm. 150d. Championship emblem and football 12·00 12·00

378 Church St Sophia, Ohrid

2010. 50th Ohrid Summer Festival
696 **378** 18d. multicoloured 1·50 1·50

379 Mother Teresa

2010. Birth Centenary of Mother Teresa (Agnes Gonxha Bojaxhiu) (founder of Missionaries of Charity in Calcutta)
697 **379** 60d. multicoloured 4·75 4·75

380 Crescent Moon and Mosque

2010. Bayram Festival
698 **380** 50d. multicoloured 4·25 4·25

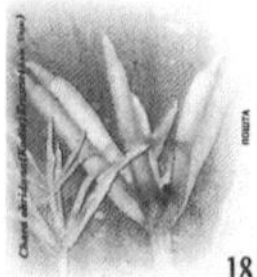

381 *Chara ohridana* (algae)

2010. Flora and Fauna of Lake Ohrid. Multicoloured.
699 18d. Type **381** 1·75 1·75
700 20d. *Gocea ohridana* (water snail) 2·00 2·00
701 44d. *Surirella spiralis* (algae) 3·25 3·25
702 100d. *Ochridaspongia Arndt* (sponge) 8·25 8·25

382 Laurel Wreath and Hand writing Poem

2010. 150th Anniversary of Award of Laurel Wreath to Grigor Prlicev (first prize for best poem in literary competition held every year in Athens) for his Poem.
703 **382** 100d. multicoloured 8·00 8·00

383 Joyful Figures

2010. Obligatory Tax. Anti-Tuberculosis Week.
704 **383** 8d. multicoloured 1·00 1·00

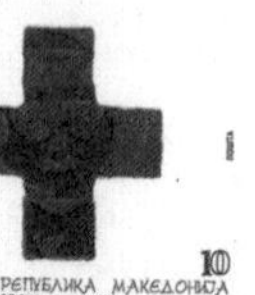

384 Henry Dunant

2010. Death Centenary of Henry Dunant (instigator of Red Cross movement).
705 **384** 10d. scarlet-vermilion and black 1·50 1·50

385 Jacques Cousteau

2010. Birth Centenary of Jacques-Yves Cousteau (marine explorer, ecologist, filmmaker, and writer).
706 **385** 20d. multicoloured 1·50 1·50

386 Robert Koch

2010. Death Centenary of Heinrich Hermann Robert Koch (isolator of anthrax, cholera and TB bacilli and winner of 1905, Nobel Prize for Medicine).
707 **386** 20d. multicoloured 1·50 1·50

387 St Naum (icon)

2010. 1100th Death Anniversary of St Naum of Ohrid (educator and one of founders of Macedonian Orthodox Church).
708 **387** 18d. multicoloured 1·50 1·50

388 Dimitar Miladinov

2010. Birth Bicentenary of Dimitar Miladinov (poet and folklorist).
709 **388** 18d. multicoloured 1·50 1·50

389 Skyline, Family and Voting Form

2010. 20th Anniversary of Multi-Party Elections.
710 **389** 16d. multicoloured 1·50 1·50

390 Marin Barleti

2010. 550th Birth Anniversary of Marin Barleti (historian and Catholic priest).
711 **390** 20d. multicoloured 1·50 1·50

391 Seated Figure

2010. Birth Centenary of Dimce Koco (artist).
712 **391** 50d. multicoloured 3·75 3·75

392 Emaciated Figures

2010. Birth Centenary of Dimo Todorovski (sculptor).
713 **392** 50d. multicoloured 3·75 3·75

393 Christmas Baskets

2010. Christmas.
714 **393** 16d. multicoloured 1·50 1·50

393a Ribbons

2010. Obligatory Tax. AIDS Awareness Week.
714a **393a** 8d. multicoloured 90 90

2010. Cities. Vert designs as T **355**. Multicoloured.

715	16d. Kavadarci	1·90	1·80
716	16d. Kriva Planka	1·90	1·80
717	16d. Negotin	1·90	1·80
718	16d. Probištip	1·90	1·80
719	18d Kosčani	1·90	1·80
720	18d Radoviš (horiz)	1·90	1·80
721	18d Sveti Nikole	1·90	1·80

394 Prince Konstantin Dragaš Coin, 1371-1395

2011. Cultural Heritage. Coins.
722 **394** 50d. multicoloured 3·50 3·50

394a Face, Flower and AIDS Ribbon

2011. Obligatory Tax. AIDS Awareness Week
722a **394a** 8d. multicoloured 90 90

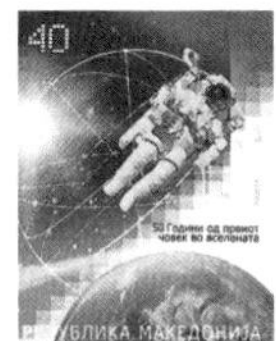
395 Space Walk

2011. 50th Anniversary of First Manned Space Flight.
723 **395** 40d. multicoloured 3·50 3·50

396 Menorah

2011. Holocaust Memorial Center for Jews of Macedonia, Skopje.
724 **396** 100d. ultramarine, chrome yellow and black 7·75 7·75

397 Karaman (Macedonian shepherd dog)

2011. Pets. Dog.
725 **397** 50d. multicoloured 3·75 3·75

398 Princess Diana

2011. 50th Birth Anniversary of Princess Diana.
726 **398** 100d. multicoloured 8·25 8·25

399 Distillation and Periodic Tables

2011. International Year of Chemistry.
727 **399** 60d. multicoloured 5·00 5·00

400 Benz Patent-Motorwagen, 1886

2011. Transport. 125th Anniversary of First Automobile (20d.) or Centenary of First Automobile in Skopje (70d.).. Multicoloured.

728	20d. Type **400**	1·75	1·75
729	70d. First car in Skopje (vert)	5·75	5·75

401 James Watt and Low-pressure Steam Engine

2011. Science. 275th Birth Anniversary of James Watt.
730 **401** 60d. multicoloured 5·00 5·00

402 Warsaw

2011. Macedonia in EU. Multicoloured.

731	40d. Type **402**	3·50	3·50
732	40d. Budapest	3·50	3·50

403 Woods in Autumn

2011. Europa. Forests. Multicoloured.

733	50d. Type **403**	2·75	2·75
734	100d. Woods in winter	5·75	5·75
MS735	70×60 mm. 100d. Woods in spring	12·00	12·00

404 Heart-shaped Labyrinth containing Red Cross

2011. Obligatory Tax. Red Cross.
736 **404** 8d. scarlet-vermilion and black 90 90

405 Front Page of *Shkupi*

2011. Centenary of *Shkupi* Newspaper.
737 **405** 60d. multicoloured 5·00 5·00

406 Book

2011. 50th Anniversary of Poetry Evenings.
738 **406** 40d. multicoloured 3·50 3·50

407 Emperor Justinian

2011. 60th Anniversary of Faculty of Law. Sheet 110×42 mm.
MS739 **407** 100d. multicoloured 8·25 8·25

408 Emblem

2011. Bayram Festival.
740 **408** 50d. multicoloured 3·50 3·50

409 Ball, Crowd and Emblem

2011. European Basketball Championship.
741 **409** 70d. multicoloured 5·75 5·75

410 Sunrise

2011. 20th Anniversary of Independence.
742 **410** 20d. multicoloured 1·75 1·75

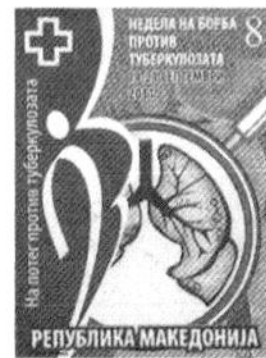
410a Lungs

2011. Obligatory Tax. Anti-Tuberculosis Week.
742a **410a** 8d. multicoloured 90 90

411 Landscape with Houses

2011. Birth Centenary of Ljubomir Belogaski (artist).
743 **411** 20d. multicoloured 1·75 1·75

412 Franz Liszt

2011. Birth Bicentenary of Franz Liszt (composer).
744 **412** 50d. black 3·75 3·75

413 Ernest Hemingway

2011. 50th Death Anniversary of Ernest Miller Hemingway (writer).
745 **413** 50d. multicoloured 3·75 3·75

414 Migjeni

2011. Birth Centenary of Millosh Gjergj Nikolla (Migjeni) (writer).
746 **414** 20d. multicoloured 1·75 1·75

415 Archbishop Angelarios

2011. Birth Centenary of Archbishop Angelarios.
747 **415** 40d. multicoloured 3·50 3·50

416 Emblem and Globe

2011. Obligatory Tax. AIDS Awareness Week.
748 **416** 8d. multicoloured 90 90

417 *Spermophilus citellus*

2011. Endangered Species. European Ground Squirrel (*Spermophilus citellus*). Multicoloured.
749 12d. Type **417** 1·10 1·10
750 24d. Adult holding food and young 2·25 2·25
751 48d. Adult facing right 3·75 3·75
752 60d. Group of adults facing right 4·50 4·50

418 *Parnassius apollo*

2011. Butterflies. Multicoloured.
753 12d. Type **418** 1·10 1·10
754 24d. *Zerynthia polyxena* 2·25 2·25
755 48d. *Parnassius mnemosyne* 3·75 3·75
756 60d. *Elphinstonia penia* 4·50 4·50

419 Oak Leaves, Acorns, Christmas Bun and Fruit

2011. Christmas.
757 **419** 18d. multicoloured 1·50 1·50

420 Gjerasim Kiriazi

2011. Gjerasim Kiriazi (preacher and educator) Commemoration.
758 **420** 20d. multicoloured 1·75 1·75

421 Woven Rug

2012. Cultural Heritage. Weaving.
759 **421** 20d. multicoloured 1·75 1·75

422 Stylised Figures

2012. Obligatory Tax. AIDS Awareness Week.
760 **422** 8d. multicoloured 90 90

423 Tortoise

2012. Pets. Tortoise.
761 **423** 100d. multicoloured 5·75 5·75

424 In Flight

2012. Transport. Aircraft. Multicoloured.
762 40d. Type **424** 3·50 3·50
763 60d. In flight, front 5·00 5·00

425 Telegraph Transmitter and Samuel Morse (inventor)

2012. 175th Anniversary of Invention of the Telegraph.
764 **425** 100d. multicoloured 8·25 8·25

426 Nicosia

2012. Macedonia in EU. Multicoloured.
765 20d. Type **426** 1·75 1·75
766 40d. Copenhagen 3·50 3·50

427 House and Aerial View of Ohrid

2012. Europa. Visit Macedonia. Multicoloured.
767 20d. Type **427** 2·75 2·75
768 100d. Alexander the Great (statue), Skopje 5·75 5·75
MS769 108×48 mm. 100d. Vardar River Bridge, Skopje 12·00 12·00

428 *Titanic*

2012. Centenary of *Titanic*.
770 **428** 100d. multicoloured 5·75 5·75

429 '20' enclosing One Dinar Coin

2012. 20th Anniversary of Monetary Independence.
771 **429** 50d. multicoloured 3·75 3·75

430 People on Earth, Red Cross and Red Crescent Symbols

2012. Obligatory Tax. Red Cross.
772 **430** 8d. multicoloured 90 90

2012. Cities. As T **355**. Multicoloured.
773 2d. Berovo 90 90
774 16d. Valandovo 1·10 1·10
775 18d. Makedonska Kamenica 1·20 1·20

431 Early Orchestra

2012. Centenary of Zani and Maleve Orchestra.
776 **431** 40d. multicoloured 3·50 3·50

432 Hurdler

2012. Olympic Games, London. Multicoloured.
777 50d. Type **432** 3·75 3·75
778 100d. Wrestling 7·50 7·50

433 Praying and Mosque

2012. Bayram Festival.
779 **433** 50d. multicoloured 3·75 3·75

434 Bacillus, Globe and Cut-out Figures

2012. Obligatory Tax. Anti-Tuberculosis Week.
780 **434** 8d. multicoloured 90 90

435 Interior of La Scala, Milan

2012. 125th Anniversary of First Performance of *Otello* (opera by Giuseppe Verdi)
781 **435** 40d. multicoloured 3·50 3·50

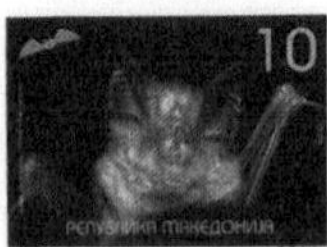
436 *Rhinolophus euryale* (Mediterranean Horseshoe Bat)

2013. Fauna. Bats. Multicoloured.
782 10d. Type **436** 90 90
783 20d. *Rhinolophus ferrumequinum* (Greater Horseshoe Bat) 1·75 1·75
784 50d. *Rhinolophus hipposideros* (Lesser Horseshoe Bat) 3·75 3·75
785 100d. *Miniopterus schreibersi* (Common Bent-wing Bat) 7·50 7·50

437 Kole Nedelkovski

2012. Birth Centenary of Kole Nedelkovski (revolutionary and poet).
786 **437** 50d. multicoloured 3·75 3·75

438 Archbishop Gavril

2012. Birth Centenary of H. H. Gavril, Archbishop of Ohrid and Macedonia (George Milosheva Gavril).
787 **438** 60d. multicoloured 5·00 5·00

439 AIDS Ribbons

2012. Obligatory Tax. AIDS Awareness Week.
788 **439** 8d. multicoloured 90 90

441 The Nativity

2012. Christmas.
790 **441** 50d. multicoloured 3·75 3·75

442 Covered Dish

2013. Cultural Heritage. Multicoloured.
791 40d. Type **442** 3·50 3·50
792 50d. Large platter 3·75 3·75

443 AIDS Ribbons as Figures

2013. Obligatory Tax. AIDS Awareness Week.

793 **443** 8d. multicoloured 90 90

444 White Rabbit

2013. Pets. Rabbit.

794 **444** 60d. multicoloured 5·00 5·00

445 Inscr 'MOTORI'

2013. Transport. Motorcycle.

795 **445** 50d. multicoloured 3·75 3·75

446 John Dunlop and Tyres

2013. Science. Anniversaries. Multicoloured.

796 40d. Type **446** (125th anniversary of patent for inflated tyres) 3·50 3·50

797 50d. Vladimir Zworykin (inventor of TV transmitting and receiving system using cathode ray tubes) (125th birth anniversary) 3·75 3·75

447 Dublin

2013. Macedonia in EU. Multicoloured.

798 40d. Type **447** 3·50 3·50

799 60d. Vilnius 5·00 5·00

448 Large Mercedes Post Van

2013. Europa. Postal Transport. Multicoloured.

800 40d. Type **448** 3·50 3·50

801 60d. Smaller VW post van 5·00 5·00

MS802 60×80 mm. 100d. Mercedes post lorry and VW Caddy post van 8·00 8·00

449 Henry Dunant

2013. Obligatory Tax. Red Cross. 150th Anniversary of Red Cross

803 **449** 8d. multicoloured 90 90

450 Ali Riza Ulqinaku

2013. Death Centenary of Ali Riza Ulqinaku (teacher)

804 **450** 16d. multicoloured 1·10 1·10

451 Rexhep Mitrovica

2013. 125th Birth Anniversary of Rexhep Mitrovica (politician and nationalist).

805 **451** 18d. multicoloured 1·20 1·20

452 St Cyril and StMethodius

2013. 1150th Anniversary of Arrival of St Cyril and StMethodius to Great Moravia.

806 **452** 40d. multicoloured 3·50 3·50

453 Damaged Building

2013. 50th Anniversary of Skopje Earthquake.

807 **453** 100d. multicoloured 7·50 7·50

454 Mosque

2013. Bayram Festival.

808 **454** 40d. multicoloured 3·50 3·50

415a Dojran

2011. Cities.

747a **415a** 18d. multicoloured 1·60 1·50

415b Demi Hisar

2011. Cities.

747b **415b** 16d. multicoloured 1·40 1·40

440 *The Elves and the Shoemaker*

2012. Bicentenary of Grimm's Fairy Tales.

789 **440** 20d. multicoloured 1·80 1·70

452a Demir Kapija

2013. Cities.

807a **452a** 16d. multicoloured 1·40 1·40

452b Makedonski Brod

2013. Cities.

807b **452b** 16d. multicoloured 1·40 1·40

455 Vasil Chekalarov

2013. Death Centenary of Vasil Chekalarov (revolutionary).

809 **455** 16d. multicoloured 1·40 1·40

456 Kokaleski

2013. 150th Death Anniversary of Gjurchin Kokaleski (nationalist leader and writer of the first known Macedonian autobiography).

810 **456** 18d. multicoloured 1·60 1·50

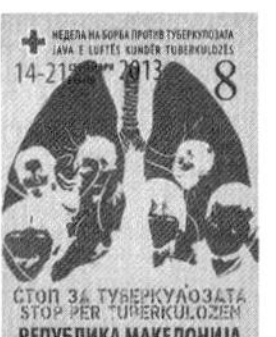

457 Lungs and Faces

2013. Obligatory Tax. Anti-Tuberculosis Week.

811 **457** 8d. multicoloured 70 70

458 Demonstrator

2013. Centenary of Ohrid-Debar Uprising.

812 **458** 60d. multicoloured 5·50 5·00

459 459 Player

2013. European Basketball Championship, Slovenia.

813 **459** 90d. multicoloured 8·00 7·75

460 St Cyril and StMethodius, National Flags and Confucius

2013. 20th Anniversary of Macedonia–China Diplomatic Relations.

814 **461** 100d. multicoloured 9·00 8·50

461 *Boletus satanas*

2013. Fungi. Multicoloured.

815 10d. Typr **461** 90 85

816 20d. *Myriostoma coliforme* 1·80 1·70

817 50d. *Caloscypha fulgens* 4·50 4·25

818 100d. *Terana caerulea* 9·00 8·50

462 Petre Bogdanov-Kocko

2013. Birth Centenary of Petre Bogdanov-Kocko (singer).

819 **462** 20d. multicoloured 1·80 1·70

463 Richard Wagner

2013. Birth Bicentenary of Richard Wagner.

820 **463** 40d. multicoloured 3·50 3·50

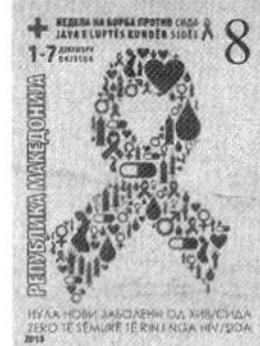

464 Symbols of AIDS as Ribbon

2013. Obligatory Tax. AIDS Awareness Week.

821 **464** 8d. multicoloured 70 70

465 The Nativity

2013. Christmas.

822 **465** 40d. multicoloured 3·50 3·50

466 Tomatoes

2013. Vegetables. Multicoloured.

823 8d. Typr **466** 70 70

824 10d. Aubergine 90 85

467 Cash Register

2014. State Lottery. Multicoloured.

825 8d. Type **467** 70 70

826 8d. Shopping trolley 70 70

468 Profiles and Ribbon

2014. Obligatory Tax. AIDS Awareness Week

827 **468** 8d. multicoloured 70 70

469 People from Many Nations

2014. Obligatory Tax. Red Cross

828	**469**	8d. multicoloured	70	70

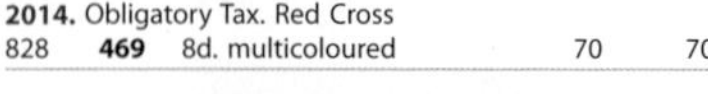

470 Filigree Belt

2014. Cultural Heritage. Filigree Jewellery

829	24d. Type **470**	2·20	2·00
830	40d. Pafta: part of belt (*vert*)	3·50	3·50

471 Ice Hockey Player

2014. Winter Olympic Games, Sochi, Russia. Multicoloured.

831	50d. Type **471**	4·50	4·25
832	100d. Ski jumper	9·00	8·50

472 Michelangelo

2014. 450th Death Anniversary of Michelangelo Buonarroti.

833	**472**	144d. multicoloured	13·00	12·00

MADAGASCAR

A large island in the Indian Ocean off the east coast of Africa. French Post Offices operated there from 1885.

In 1896 the island was declared a French colony, absorbing Diego-Suarez and Ste. Marie de Madagascar in 1898 and Nossi-Be in 1901.

Madagascar became autonomous as the Malagasy Republic in 1958; it reverted to the name of Madagascar in 1992.

100 centimes = 1 franc.
2005. 5 old francs = 1 ariary.

A. FRENCH POST OFFICES

1889. Stamps of French Colonies 'Commerce' type surch with value in figures.

1	**J**	05 on 10c. black on lilac	£900	£250
2	**J**	05 on 25c. black on red	£900	£250
4	**J**	05 on 40c. red on yellow	£275	£120
5	**J**	5 on 10c. black on lilac	£300	£140
6	**J**	5 on 25c. black on red	£300	£150
7	**J**	15 on 25c. black on red	£250	£120
3	**J**	25 on 40c. red on yellow	£750	£200

5

1891. No gum. Imperf.

9	**5**	5c. black on green	£200	39·00
10	**5**	10c. black on blue	£150	45·00
11	**5**	15c. blue on blue	£150	50·00
12	**5**	25c. brown on buff	35·00	22·00
13	**5**	1f. black on yellow	£1400	£350
14	**5**	5f. black and lilac on lilac	£2750	£1400

1895. Stamps of France optd **POSTE FRANCAISE Madagascar**.

15	**10**	5c. green	23·00	9·00
16	**10**	10c. black on lilac	60·00	55·00
17	**10**	15c. blue	85·00	22·00
18	**10**	25c. black on red	£110	25·00
19	**10**	40c. red on yellow	£100	40·00
20	**10**	50c. red	£130	55·00
21	**10**	75c. brown on orange	£140	65·00
22	**10**	1f. olive	£160	75·00
23	**10**	5f. mauve on lilac	£225	£110

1896. Stamps of France surch with value in figures in oval.

29	**10**	5c. on 1c. black on blue	£7500	£2750
30	**10**	15c. on 2c. brown on yellow	£3000	£1100
31	**10**	25c. on 3c. grey	£4000	£1200
32	**10**	25c. on 4c. red on grey	£6500	£2000
33	**10**	25c. on 40c. red on yellow	£1900	£950

B. FRENCH COLONY OF MADAGASCAR AND DEPENDENCIES

1896. Tablet key-type inscr 'MADAGASCAR ET DEPENDANCES'.

1	**D**	1c. black and red on blue	1·50	1·10
2	**D**	2c. brown and blue on buff	1·70	1·30
2a	**D**	2c. brown & blk on buff	16·00	18·00
3	**D**	4c. brown and blue on grey	2·10	1·80
17	**D**	5c. green and red	5·75	70
6	**D**	10c. black and blue on lilac	18·00	1·90
18	**D**	10c. red and blue	5·00	70
7	**D**	15c. blue and red	23·00	1·50
19	**D**	15c. grey and red	6·25	1·20
8	**D**	20c. red and blue on green	8·50	2·10
9	**D**	25c. black and red on pink	16·00	2·40
20	**D**	25c. blue and red	42·00	65·00
10	**D**	30c. brown & bl on drab	11·00	3·50
21	**D**	35c. black and red on yellow	65·00	5·25
11	**D**	40c. red and blue on yellow	11·00	2·75
12	**D**	50c. red and blue on pink	24·00	2·20
22	**D**	50c. brown and red on blue	50·00	60·00
13	**D**	75c. violet & red on orge	4·50	5·00
14	**D**	1f. green and red	24·00	3·00
15	**D**	1f. green and blue	50·00	42·00
16	**D**	5f. mauve and blue on lilac	60·00	65·00

1902. Tablet key-type stamps as above surch.

27	0.01 on 2c. brown and blue on buff	11·50	11·50
27a	0.01 on 2c. brown and black on buff	11·00	23·00
29	0.05 on 30c. brown and blue on drab	8·50	8·50
23	05 on 50c. red and blue on pink	5·25	4·00
31	0.10 on 50c. red and blue on pink	5·75	5·50
24	10 on 5f. mauve and blue on lilac	25·00	15·00
32	0.15 on 75c. violet and red on orange	4·50	4·50
33	0.15 on 1f. green and red	9·25	10·00
25	15 on 1f. green and red	6·25	4·75

1902. Nos. 59 and 61 of Diego-Suarez surch.

34	0.05 on 30c. brown and blue on drab	£180	£160
36	0.10 on 50c. red and blue on pink	£5500	£5500

4 Zebu and Lemur

1903

38	**4**	1c. purple	1·10	1·00
39	**4**	2c. brown	1·10	1·00
40	**4**	4c. brown	1·40	1·30
41	**4**	5c. green	8·75	1·60
42	**4**	10c. red	13·50	1·40
43	**4**	15c. red	20·00	1·40
44	**4**	20c. orange	4·75	2·00
45	**4**	25c. blue	46·00	3·75
46	**4**	30c. red	55·00	16·00
47	**4**	40c. lilac	60·00	5·00
48	**4**	50c. brown	75·00	31·00
49	**4**	75c. yellow	75·00	30·00
50	**4**	1f. green	75·00	60·00
51	**4**	2f. blue	95·00	40·00
52	**4**	5f. black	95·00	£120

5 Transport in Madagascar

1908

53a	**5**	1c. green and violet	35	50
54	**5**	2c. green and red	30	35
55	**5**	4c. brown and green	80	1·30
56	**5**	5c. olive and green	3·00	75
90	**5**	5c. red and black	85	1·30
57	**5**	10c. brown and pink	3·25	35
91	**5**	10c. olive and green	75	1·10
92	**5**	10c. purple and brown	45	90
58	**5**	15c. red and lilac	90	60
93	**5**	15c. green and olive	1·00	4·25
94	**5**	15c. red and blue	1·50	9·50
59	**5**	20c. brown and orange	1·70	1·50
60	**5**	25c. black and blue	9·25	1·10
95	**5**	25c. black and violet	1·80	50
61	**5**	30c. black and brown	8·50	9·50
96	**5**	30c. brown and red	1·50	2·00
97	**5**	30c. purple and green	1·00	65
98	**5**	30c. light green and green	4·25	7·50
62	**5**	35c. black and red	2·75	1·60
63	**5**	40c. black and brown	2·00	1·60
64	**5**	45c. black and green	1·90	4·00
99	**5**	45c. red and scarlet	1·00	2·75
100	**5**	45c. purple and lilac	4·50	6·50
65	**5**	50c. black and violet	1·40	1·30
101	**5**	50c. black and blue	1·10	80
102	**5**	50c. yellow and black	1·40	45
103	**5**	60c. violet on pink	1·20	2·30
104	**5**	65c. blue and black	2·50	4·50
66	**5**	75c. black and red	1·80	1·40
105	**5**	85c. red and green	2·75	8·50
67	**5**	1f. green and brown	1·20	60
106	**5**	1f. blue	1·20	1·80
107	**5**	1f. green and mauve	11·50	22·00
108	**5**	1f.10 green and brown	2·75	4·75
68	**5**	2f. green and blue	4·75	2·00
69	**5**	5f. brown and violet	17·00	20·00

1912. Tablet key-type surch.

70A	**D**	05 on 15c. grey and red	1·20	1·60
71A	**D**	05 on 20c. red and blue on green	1·50	1·80
72A	**D**	05 on 30c. brown and blue on drab	1·80	5·50
73A	**D**	10 on 75c. violet and red on orange	7·50	36·00
81	**D**	0.60 on 75c. violet and red on orange	20·00	28·00
82	**D**	1f. on 5f. mauve and blue on lilac	1·70	3·00

1912. Surch.

74	**4**	05 on 2c. brown	95	6·50
75	**4**	05 on 20c. orange	1·20	1·60
76	**4**	05 on 30c. red	1·50	4·00
77	**4**	10 on 40c. lilac	2·00	6·25
78	**4**	10 on 50c. brown	4·25	5·50
79	**4**	10 on 75c. brown	6·25	28·00
83	**4**	1f. on 5f. black	£140	£140

1915. Surch **5c** and red cross.

80	**5**	10c.+5c. brown and pink	1·70	2·75

1921. Surch **1 cent**.

84	**4**	1c. on 15c. red and lilac	75	2·75

1921. T **5** (some colours changed) surch.

109	25c. on 15c. red and lilac	1·00	7·50
85	0.25 on 35c. black and red	11·50	17·00
86	0.25 on 40c. black and brown	7·25	8·00
87	0.25 on 45c. black and green	5·00	11·50
111	25c. on 2f. green and blue	1·90	1·80
112	25c. on 5f. brown and violet	70	7·25
88	0.30 on 40c. black and brown	2·50	3·25
113	50c. on 1f. green and brown	2·00	60
89	0.60 on 75c. black and red	5·00	7·25
114	60 on 75c. violet on pink	65	70
115	65c. on 75c. black and red	2·75	7·50
116	85c. on 45c. black and green	2·50	7·75
117	90c. on 75c. pink and red	1·40	2·30
118	1f.25 on 1f. blue	1·20	4·25
119	1f.50 on 1f. lt blue & blue	2·75	70
120	3f. on 5f. violet and green	3·25	4·00
121	10f. on 5f. mauve and red	10·50	10·50
122	20f. on 5f. blue and mauve	14·50	10·00

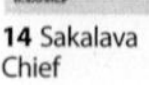

14 Sakalava Chief

15 Zebus

17 Betsileo Woman

18 General Gallieni

1930

123	**18**	1c. blue	85	80
124	**15**	1c. green and blue	30	40
125	**14**	2c. brown and red	30	1·20
177	**18**	3c. blue	35	3·00
126a	**14**	4c. mauve and brown	90	80
127	**15**	5c. red and green	50	40
128	-	10c. green and red	50	40
129	**17**	15c. red	50	40
130	**15**	20c. blue and brown	55	75
131	-	25c. brown and lilac	70	35
132	**17**	30c. green	80	1·30
133	**14**	40c. red and green	1·00	65
134	**17**	45c. lilac	2·75	3·25
178	**18**	45c. green	1·20	2·10
179	**18**	50c. brown	65	40
180	**18**	60c. mauve	60	4·00
136a	**15**	65c. mauve and brown	3·25	65
181	**18**	70c. red	2·30	5·50
137	**17**	75c. brown	2·75	65
138	**15**	90c. red	4·25	1·70
182	**18**	90c. brown	80	65
139	-	1f. blue and brown	4·00	2·75
140	-	1f. red and scarlet	1·50	1·60
140a	-	1f.25 brown and blue	4·50	2·00
183	**18**	1f.40 orange	3·00	7·25
141	**14**	1f.50 ultramarine and blue	10·00	1·40
142	**14**	1f.50 red and brown	1·80	1·60
278	**14**	1f.50 brown and red	90	2·50
184	**18**	1f.60 violet	2·75	7·00
143	**14**	1f.75 red and brown	7·50	1·30
185	**18**	2f. red	1·30	55
186a	**18**	3f. green	1·40	2·75
146	**14**	5f. brown and mauve	3·00	3·75
147	**18**	10f. orange	10·00	8·50
148	**14**	20f. blue and brown	3·75	10·00

Design: Vert—10c., 25c., 1f., 1f.25, Hova girl.

1931. Colonial Exhibition key-types inscr 'MADAGASCAR'.

149	**E**	40c. black and green	4·00	4·75
150	**F**	50c. black and mauve	4·50	5·00
151	**G**	90c. black and red	3·75	4·75
152	**H**	1f.50 black and blue	4·75	4·00

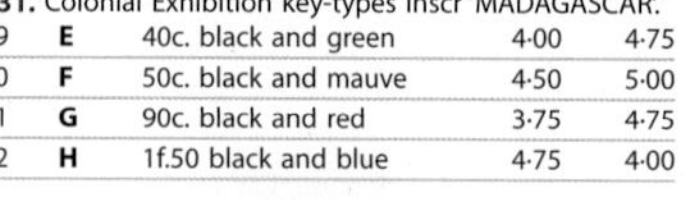

19 Bloch 120 over Madagascar

1935. Air.

153	**19**	50c. red and green	3·00	3·00
154	**19**	90c. red and green	1·10	†
155	**19**	1f.25 red and lake	3·50	5·50
156	**19**	1f.50 red and blue	2·75	3·50
157	**19**	1f.60 red and blue	1·20	6·00
158	**19**	1f.75 red and orange	14·50	6·50
159	**19**	2f. red and blue	3·25	3·50
160	**19**	3f. red and orange	1·20	2·75
161	**19**	3f.65 red and black	1·90	1·70
162	**19**	3f.90 red and green	80	4·50
163	**19**	4f. red and carmine	60·00	4·75
164	**19**	4f.50 red and black	29·00	2·75
165	**19**	5f.50 red and green	1·00	5·25
166	**19**	6f. red and mauve	1·00	3·25
167	**19**	6f.90 red and purple	85	3·50
168	**19**	8f. red and mauve	3·75	7·25
169	**19**	8f.50 red and green	4·00	5·25
170	**19**	9f. red and green	1·20	4·00
171	**19**	12f. red and brown	95	3·00
172	**19**	12f.50 red and violet	3·50	7·75
173	**19**	15f. red and orange	95	3·00
174	**19**	16f. red and green	3·75	9·25
175	**19**	20f. red and brown	6·50	8·25
176	**19**	50f. red and blue	8·25	17·00

1937. International Exhibition, Paris. As T **12a** of Ivory Coast.

187	20c. violet	2·20	4·25
188	30c. green	2·20	4·25
189	40c. red	1·80	1·90
190	50c. brown and agate	1·70	1·30
191	90c. red	2·10	2·10

192		1f.50 blue	2·10	2·10
MS192a		120×100 mm. 3f. red (as No. 139). Imperf	18·00	42·00

20 J. Laborde and Tananarivo Palace

1938. 60th Death Anniversary of Jean Laborde (explorer).

193	**20**	35c. green	1·20	1·50
194	**20**	55c. violet	1·10	1·30
195	**20**	65c. red	1·90	65
196	**20**	80c. purple	1·10	80
197	**20**	1f. red	1·40	65
198	**20**	1f.25 red	2·30	7·00
199	**20**	1f.75 blue	1·50	1·30
200	**20**	2f.15 brown	3·00	5·50
201	**20**	2f.25 blue	2·00	5·25
202	**20**	2f.50 brown	1·00	90
203	**20**	10f. green	1·50	2·30

1938. International Anti-cancer Fund. As T **16a** of Ivory Coast.

204		1f.75+50c. blue	10·50	21·00

1939. New York World's Fair. As T **16c** of Ivory Coast.

205		1f.25 red	2·00	2·00
206		2f.25 blue	2·30	3·00

1939. 150th Anniversary of French Revolution. As T **16d** of Ivory Coast.

207		45c.+25c. green and black (postage)	11·50	26·00
208		70c.+30c. brown and black	11·50	26·00
209		90c.+35c. orange and black	11·50	26·00
210		1f.25+1f. red and black	11·50	26·00
211		2f.25+2f. blue and black	11·50	26·00
212		4f.50+4f. black and orange (air)	22·00	42·00

1942. Surch **50** and bars.

213	**15**	50 on 65c. mauve and brown	5·25	70

1942. Free French Administration. Optd **FRANCE LIBRE** or surch also.

214	**14**	2c. brown and red (postage)	4·00	7·25
215	**18**	3c. blue	£170	£170
216	**15**	0.05 on 1c. green and blue	1·80	2·50
217	**20**	0.10 on 55c. violet	1·60	7·75
218	**17**	15c. red	27·00	36·00
219	**20**	0.30 on 65c. red	1·30	4·50
220	**15**	0f.50 on 0.05 on 1c. green and blue	2·30	8·00
221	**15**	50 on 65c. mauve and brown	1·40	70
222	**18**	50 on 90c. brown	1·80	1·40
223	**15**	65c. mauve and brown	4·75	8·25
224	**18**	70c. red	2·75	7·00
225	**20**	80c. purple	5·75	9·00
226	-	1.00 on 1f.25 brown and blue (No. 140a)	5·00	6·25
227	**20**	1.00 on 1f.25 red	15·00	16·00
228	**18**	1f.40 orange	4·25	6·75
229	**5**	1f.50 on 1f. blue	4·00	4·50
230	**14**	1f.50 ultramarine and blue	3·25	6·50
231	**14**	1f.50 red and brown	5·25	8·25
232	**18**	1.50 on 1f.60 violet	2·30	6·50
233	**14**	1.50 on 1f.75 red and brown	3·00	2·10
234	**20**	1.50 on 1f.75 blue	3·00	3·50
235	**18**	1f.60 violet	4·00	4·00
236	**20**	2.00 on 2f.15 brown	2·30	2·30
237	**20**	2f.25 blue	4·25	7·25
238	-	2f.25 blue (No. 206)	3·75	6·75
239	**20**	2f.50 brown	6·50	9·75
240	**5**	10f. on 5f. mauve and red	23·00	28·00
241	**20**	10f. green	8·25	7·50
242	**5**	20f. on 5f. blue and mauve	25·00	38·00
243	**14**	20f. blue and brown	£900	£1100
244	**19**	1.00 on 1f.25 red and lake (air)	14·50	16·00
245	**19**	1f.50 red and blue	19·00	22·00
246	**19**	1f.75 red and orange	£140	£140
247	**19**	3.00 on 3f.65 red and black	3·00	1·80
248	**19**	8f. red and purple	5·75	8·25
249	**19**	8.00 on 8f.50 red and green	4·75	3·25
250	**19**	12f. red and brown	7·75	7·75
251	**19**	12f.50 red and violet	6·25	4·75
252	**19**	16f. red and green	12·50	15·00
253	**19**	50f. red and blue	7·50	8·00

24 Traveller's Tree

1943. Free French Issue.

254	**24**	5c. brown	25	5·75
255	**24**	10c. mauve	25	1·00
256	**24**	25c. green	25	4·75
257	**24**	30c. orange	40	90
258	**24**	40c. blue	60	2·30
259	**24**	80c. purple	60	2·30
260	**24**	1f. blue	1·00	90
261	**24**	1f.50 red	90	70
262	**24**	2f. yellow	80	1·00
263	**24**	2f.50 blue	65	75
264	**24**	4f. blue and red	1·40	1·30
265	**24**	5f. green and black	85	1·50
266	**24**	10f. red and blue	1·20	1·00
267	**24**	20f. violet and brown	1·50	1·30

24a Fairy FC-1 Airliner

1943. Free French Administration. Air.

268	**24a**	1f. orange	40	2·00
269	**24a**	1f.50 red	40	1·80
270	**24a**	5f. purple	50	1·50
271	**24a**	10f. black	65	2·50
272	**24a**	25f. blue	1·20	4·50
273	**24a**	50f. green	1·30	1·10
274	**24a**	100f. red	1·80	1·80

24b

1944. Mutual Aid and Red Cross Funds.

275	**24b**	5f.+20f. green	95	8·00

1944. Surch **1f.50.**

276	**24**	1f.50 on 5c. brown	1·10	1·10
277	**24**	1f.50 on 10c. mauve	1·60	3·75

25a Felix Eboue

1945. Eboue.

279	**25a**	2f. black	80	70
280	**25a**	25f. green	1·40	7·00

25b 'Victory'

1946. Air. Victory.

281	**25b**	8f. red	1·20	90

1945. Surch with new value.

282	**24**	50c. on 5c. brown	65	70
283	**24**	60c. on 5c. brown	90	4·50
284	**24**	70c. on 5c. brown	90	2·75
285	**24**	1f.20 on 5c. brown	90	4·50
286	**24**	2f.40 on 25c. green	1·00	1·70
287	**24**	3f. on 25c. green	1·00	1·30
288	**24**	4f.50 on 25c. green	1·30	2·75
289	**24**	15f. on 2f.50 blue	1·20	2·50

25c Legionaries by Lake Chad

1946. Air. From Chad to the Rhine.

290	**25c**	5f. blue	2·30	7·50
291	-	10f. red	2·30	7·50
292	-	15f. green	2·30	7·50
293	-	20f. brown	2·30	7·50
294	-	25f. violet	2·30	7·50
295	-	50f. red	2·30	7·50

Designs: 10f. Battle of Koufra; 15f. Tank Battle, Mareth; 20f. Normandy Landings; 25f. Liberation of Paris; 50f. Liberation of Strasbourg.

29 General Gallieni

1946

296	-	10c. green (postage)	40	1·40
297	-	30c. orange	40	55
298	-	40c. olive	40	1·60
299	-	50c. purple	40	45
300	-	60c. blue	55	4·00
301	-	80c. green	70	4·00
302	-	1f. sepia	65	45
303	-	1f.20 green	80	4·00
304	**29**	1f.50 red	60	45
305	-	2f. black	70	45
306	-	3f. purple	85	45
307	-	3f.60 red	1·40	3·50
308	-	4f. blue	1·20	90
309	-	5f. orange	1·40	50
310	-	6f. blue	85	40
311	-	10f. lake	1·00	45
312	-	15f. brown	1·40	60
313	-	20f. blue	2·00	75
314	-	25f. brown	3·00	80
315	-	50f. blue and red (air)	2·50	2·00
316	-	100f. brown and red	3·75	1·20
317	-	200f. brown and green	7·75	4·00

Designs: As T **29**. Vert—10 to 50c. Native with spear; 6, 10f. General Duchesne; 15, 20, 25f. Lieutenant colonel Joffre. Horiz—60, 80c. Zebus; 1f., 1f.20, Sakalava man and woman; 3f.60, 4, 5f. Betsimisaraka mother and child. 49×28 mm—50f. Aerial view of Port of Tamatave. 28×51 mm—100f. Allegory of flight. 51×28 mm—Douglas DC-2 aeroplane and map of Madagascar.

36 General Gallieni and View

1946. 50th Anniversary of French Protectorate.

318	**36**	10f.+5f. purple	85	8·00

1948. Air. Discovery of Adelie Land, Antarctic. No. 316 optd **TERRE ADELIE DUMONT D'URVILLE 1840.**

319		100f. brown and red	50·00	85·00

37a People of Five Races, Bomber and Globe

1949. Air. 75th Anniversary of UPU.

320	**37a**	25f. multicoloured	4·00	4·25

37b Doctor and Patient

1950. Colonial Welfare Fund.

321	**37b**	10f.+2f. purple and green	6·75	22·00

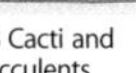

38 Cacti and Succulents

39 Long-tailed Ground Roller

40 Woman and Forest Road

1952

322	**38**	7f.50 green and blue (postage)	1·20	45
323	**39**	8f. lake	1·60	60
324	**39**	15f. blue and green	2·20	65
325	-	50f. green and blue (air)	5·00	1·30
326	-	100f. black, brown and blue	12·00	2·10
327	-	200f. brown and green	27·00	10·50
328	**40**	500f. brown, sepia and green	35·00	9·75

Designs: As T **40**—50f. Palm trees; 100f. Antsirabe Viaduct; 200f. Ring-tailed lemurs.

40a

1952. Military Medal Centenary.

329	**40a**	15f. turquoise, yellow and green	3·50	3·00

40b Normandy Landings, 1944

1954. Air. Tenth Anniversary of Liberation.

330	**40b**	15f. purple and violet	4·50	2·75

41 Marshal Lyautey

1954. Birth Centenary of Marshal Lyautey.

331	**41**	10f. indigo, blue and ultram	1·50	60
332	**41**	40f. lake, grey and black	2·00	45

42 Gallieni School

1956. Economic and Social Development Fund.

333	-	3f. brown and grey	1·80	85
334	**42**	5f. brown and chestnut	1·20	75
335	-	10f. blue and grey	1·30	80
336	-	15f. green and turquoise	1·70	50

Designs: 3f. Tamatave and tractor; 10f. Dredging canal; 15f. Irrigation.

42a Coffee

1956. Coffee.

337	**42a**	20f. sepia and brown	75	40

43 Cassava

1957. Plants.

338	**43**	2f. green, brown and blue	40	40
339	-	4f. red, brown and green	1·30	45
340	-	12f. green, brown and violet	1·40	55

Designs: 4f. Cloves; 12f. Vanilla.

Issues of 1958–1992. For issues between these dates, see under MALAGASY REPUBLIC.

362 Children with Mascot

1992. School Sports Festival (1990).

910	**362**	140f. multicoloured	35	10

363 Environmental Projects

1992. Air. World Environment Day.

911	**363**	140f. multicoloured	10	10

364 Postbox and Globe

1992. Air. World Post Day.

912	**364**	500f. multicoloured	75	25

365 Basenji

1992. Domestic Animals. Multicoloured.

913	140f. Type **365**	10	10
914	500f. Anglo-Arab horse	90	25
915	640f. Tortoiseshell cat and kitten	1·10	30
916	1025f. Siamese and colourpoint (cats)	1·60	50
917	1140f. Holstein horse	2·25	60
918	5000f. German shepherd dogs	6·50	75
MS919	104×72 mm. 1000f. Hanovarian horse, Maine coon cat and Maltese terrier (32×47 mm)	12·00	12·00

366 Foodstuffs

1992. International Nutrition Conference, Rome.

920	**366**	500f. multicoloured	1·10	25

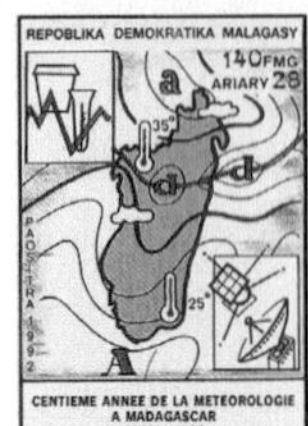

367 Weather Map

1992. Centenary of Meteorological Service.

921	**367**	140f. multicoloured	35	10

368 *Eusemia bisma*

1992. Butterflies and Moths. Multicoloured.

922	15f. Type **368**	10	10
923	35f. Tailed comet moth (vert)	10	10
924	65f. *Alcides aurora*	10	10
925	140f. *Agarista agricola*	35	10
926	600f. *Trogonoptera croesus*	1·40	30
927	850f. *Trogonodtera priamus*	1·75	45
928	1300f. *Pereute leucodrosime*	2·25	70
MS929	70×90 mm. 1500f. Sunset moth. Imperf	2·75	2·75

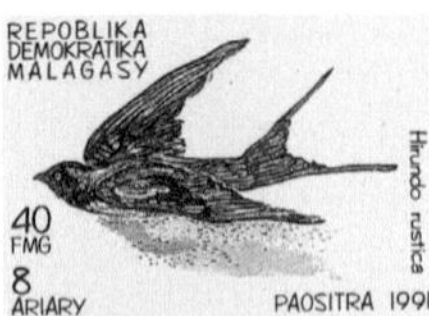

369 Barn Swallow

1992. Birds. Multicoloured.

930	40f. Type **369**	10	10
931	55f. Pied harrier (vert)	10	10
932	60f. European cuckoo (vert)	10	10
933	140f. Sacred ibis	10	10
934	210f. Purple swamphen	45	10
935	500f. Common roller	1·10	25
936	2000f. Golden oriole	4·00	1·10
MS937	69×90 mm. 1500f. Hoopoe. Imperf	3·25	3·25

370 Gymnastics

1992. Olympic Games, Barcelona. Multicoloured.

938	65f. Type **370**	10	10
939	70f. High jumping	10	10
940	120f. Archery	10	10
941	140f. Cycling	35	10
942	675f. Weightlifting	1·10	30
943	720f. Boxing	1·40	35
944	1200f. Two-man kayak	1·75	60
MS945	90×70 mm. 1600f. Olympic rings and volleyball. Imperf	2·25	2·25

371 Pusher-tug, Pangalanes Canal

1993

946	**371**	140f. multicoloured	35	10

372 BMW

1993. Motor Cars. Multicoloured.

947	20f. Type **372**	10	10
948	40f. Toyota Carina	10	10
949	60f. Cadillac	10	10
950	65f. Volvo	10	10
951	140f. Mercedes-Benz	10	10
952	640f. Ford Sierra	1·00	30
953	3000f. Honda Concerto	4·50	90
MS954	90×70 mm. 2000f. Renault 23. Imperf	3·00	3·00

373 Hyacinth Macaw

1993. Parrot Family. Multicoloured.

955	50f. Type **373**	10	10
956	60f. Cockatiel	10	10
957	140f. Budgerigar	10	10
958	500f. Jandaya conure	60	25
959	675f. Budgerigar (different)	1·10	35
960	800f. Red-fronted parakeet	1·40	45
961	1750f. Kea	2·75	65
MS962	71×91 mm. 2000f. Military macaw. Imperf	5·75	5·75

374 Broad-nosed Gentle Lemur

1993. World Post Day (1992). National Stamp Exhibition, Antananarivo. Lemurs. Sheet 90×115 mm containing T **374** and similar vert designs.

MS963	60f. Type **374**; 150f. Diadem sifaka; 250f. Indri, 350f. Ruffled lemur	1·40	1·40

375 Albert Einstein (physics, 1921) and Niels Bohr (physics, 1922)

1993. Nobel Prize Winners. Multicoloured.

964	500f. Type **375**	60	25
965	500f. Wolfgang Pauli (physics, 1945) and Max Born (physics, 1954)	60	25
966	500f. Joseph Thomson (physics, 1906) and Johannes Stark (physics, 1919)	60	25
967	500f. Otto Hahn (physics, 1944) and Hideki Yukawa (physics, 1949)	60	25
968	500f. Owen Richardson (physics, 1928) and William Shockley (physics, 1956)	60	25
969	500f. Albert Michelson (physics, 1907) and Charles Townes (physics, 1964)	60	25
970	500f. Wilhelm Wien (physics, 1911) and Lev Landau (physics, 1962)	60	25
971	500f. Carl Braun (physics, 1909) and Sir Edward Appleton (physics, 1947)	60	25
972	500f. Percy Bridgman (physics, 1946) and Nikolai Semyonov (physics, 1956)	60	25
973	500f. Sir William Ramsay (chemistry, 1904) and Glenn Seaborg (chemistry, 1951)	60	25
974	500f. Otto Wallach (chemistry, 1910) and Hermann Staudinger (chemistry, 1953)	60	25
975	500f. Richard Synge (chemistry, 1952) and Axel Theorell (chemistry, 1955)	60	25
976	500f. Thomas Morgan (medicine, 1933) and Hermann Muller (medicine, 1946)	60	25
977	500f. Allvar Gullstrand (medicine, 1911) and Willem Einthoven (medicine, 1924)	60	25
978	500f. Sir Charles Sherrington (medicine, 1932) and Otto Loewi (medicine, 1936)	60	25
979	500f. Jules Bordet (medicine, 1936) and Sir Alexander Fleming (medicine, 1945)	60	25

376 1956 Bugatti

1993. Racing Cars and Railway Locomotives. Multicoloured.

980	20f. Type **376**	10	10
981	20f. 1968 Ferrari	10	10
982	20f. 1948 Class C62 steam locomotive, 1948, Japan	10	10
983	20f. Electric train, 1975, Russia	10	10
984	140f. 1962 Lotus Mk 25	10	10
985	140f. 1970 Matra	10	10
986	140f. Diesel locomotive, 1954, Norway	10	10
987	140f. Class 26 steam locomotive, 1982, South Africa	10	10
988	1250f. 1963 Porsche	90	65
989	1250f. 1980 Ligier JS 11	90	65
990	1250f. Metroliner electric train, 1967, USA	90	65
991	1250f. Diesel train, 1982, Canada	90	65
992	3000f. 1967 Honda	2·10	1·50
993	3000f. 1992 Benetton B 192	2·10	1·50
994	3000f. Union Pacific Railroad diesel-electric locomotive, 1969, USA	2·10	2·10

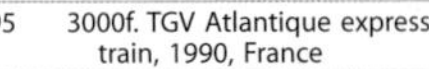

995	3000f. TGV Atlantique express train, 1990, France	2·10	2·10

377 Pharaonic Ship

1993. Ships. Multicoloured.

996	5f. Type **377**	10	10
997	5f. Mediterranean carrack	10	10
998	5f. *Great Western* (sail paddle-steamer), 1837	10	10
999	5f. *Mississippi* (paddle-steamer), 1850	10	10
1000	15f. Phoenician bireme	10	10
1001	15f. Viking ship	10	10
1002	15f. *Clermont* (first commercial paddle-steamer), 1806	10	10
1003	15f. *Pourquoi Pas?* (Charcot's ship), 1936	10	10
1004	140f. *Santa Maria* (Columbus's ship), 1492	10	10
1005	140f. HMS *Victory* (ship of the line), 1765	10	10
1006	140f. Motor yacht	10	10
1007	140f. *Bremen* (liner), 1950	10	10
1008	10000f. *Sovereign of the Seas* (galleon), 1637	9·25	80
1009	10000f. *Cutty Sark* (clipper)	9·25	80
1010	10000f. *Savannah* (nuclear-powered freighter)	9·25	80
1011	10000f. *Condor* (hydrofoil)	9·25	80

No. 999 is wrongly inscribed 'Mississipi'.

378 Johannes Gutenberg and Printing Press

1993. Inventors. Multicoloured.

1012	500f. Type **378**	60	25
1013	500f. Sir Isaac Newton and telescope	60	25
1014	500f. John Dalton and atomic theory	60	25
1015	500f. Louis Jacques Daguerre and camera	60	25
1016	500f. Michael Faraday and electric motor	60	25
1017	500f. Wright brothers and *Flyer*	60	25
1018	500f. Alexander Bell and telephone	60	25
1019	500f. Thomas Edison and telegraph	60	25
1020	500f. Karl Benz and motor vehicle	60	25
1021	500f. Sir Charles Parsons and *Turbina*	60	25
1022	500f. Rudolf Diesel and diesel locomotive	60	35
1023	500f. Guglielmo Marconi and early radio	60	25
1024	500f. Lumiere brothers and cine-camera	60	35
1025	500f. Herman Oberth and space rocket	60	25
1026	500f. John Mauchly, J. Prosper Eckert and computer	60	25
1027	500f. Arthur Shawlow, compact disc and laser	60	25

379 Leonardo da Vinci and *Virgin of the Rocks*

1993. Painters. Multicoloured.

1028	50f. Type **379**	10	10
1029	50f. Titian and *Sacred and Profane Love*	10	10
1030	50f. Rembrandt and *Jeremiah crying*	10	10
1031	50f. J. M. W. Turner and *Ulysses*	10	10
1032	640f. Michelangelo and the *Doni Tondo*	70	30
1033	640f. Peter Paul Rubens and *Self-portrait*	70	30
1034	640f. Francisco Goya and *Don Manuel Osorio de Zuniga*	70	30
1035	640f. Eugene Delacroix and *Christ on Lake Gennesaret*	70	30

1036 1000f. Claude Monet and *Poppyfield* 95 50
1037 1000f. Paul Gauguin and *Two Tahitians* 95 50
1038 1000f. Henri Marie de Toulouse-Lautrec and *Woman with a Black Boa* 95 50
1039 1000f. Salvador Dali and *St James of Compostela* 95 50
1040 2500f. Pierre Auguste Renoir and *Child carrying Flowers* 2·75 90
1041 2500f. Vincent Van Gogh and *Dr. Paul Gachet* 2·75 90
1042 2500f. Pablo Picasso and *Crying Woman* 2·75 90
1043 2500f. Andy Warhol and *Portrait of Elvis* 2·75 90

380 Sunset Moth (*Chrysiridia madagascariensis*)

1993. Butterflies, Moths and Birds. Multicoloured.
1044 45f. Type **380** 10 10
1045 45f. African monarch (*Hypolimnas misippus*) 10 10
1046 45f. Southern crested Madagascar coucal (*Coua verreauxi*) 10 10
1047 45f. African marsh owl (*Asio helvola*) 10 10
1048 60f. *Charaxes antamboulou* 10 10
1049 60f. *Papilio antenor* 10 10
1050 60f. Crested Madagascar coucal (*Coua cristata*) 10 10
1051 60f. Helmet bird (*Euryceros prevostii*) 10 10
1052 140f. *Hypolimnas dexithea* 10 10
1053 140f. *Charaxes andronodorus* 10 10
1054 140f. Giant Madagascar coucal (*Couca gigas*) 10 10
1055 140f. Madagascar red fody (*Foudia madagascarensis*) 10 10
1056 3000f. *Euxanthe madagascarensis* 3·25 45
1057 3000f. *Papilio grosesmithi* 3·25 45
1058 3000f. Sicklebill (*Falculea palliata*) 3·25 45
1059 3000f. Madagascar serpent eagle (*Eutriorchis astur*) 3·25 45

Nos. 1044/1059 were issued together, *se-tenant*, the butterfly and bird designs respectively forming composite designs.

381 Henri Dunant and Volunteers unloading Red Cross Lorry

1993. Anniversaries and Events. Multicoloured.
1060 500f. Type **381** (award of first Nobel Peace Prize, 1901) 35 25
1061 640f. Charles de Gaulle and battlefield (50th anniversary of Battle of Bir-Hakeim (1992)) 45 30
1062 1025f. Crowd at Brandenburg Gate (bicentenary (1991) and fourth anniversary of breach of Berlin Wall) 1·10 55
1063 1500f. Doctors giving health instruction to women (Rotary International and Lions International) 1·60 55
1064 3000f. Konrad Adenauer (German chancellor 1949–1963, 24th death anniversary (1991)) 3·25 60
1065 3500f. *LZ-4* (airship), 1908, and Count Ferdinand von Zeppelin (75th death anniversary (1992)) 4·00 60
MS1066 92×81 mm. 7500f. Wolfgang Mozart at piano and Salzburg (death bicentenary (1991)) 8·00 8·00

382 Guides and Anniversary Emblem

1993. Air. 50th Anniversary of Madagascan Girl Guides.
1067 **382** 140f. multicoloured 10 10

383 Player, Trophy and Ficklin Home, Macon

1993. World Cup Football Championship, United States (1992). Multicoloured.
1068 140f. Type **383** 10 10
1069 640f. Player, trophy and Herndon Home, Atlanta 65 35
1070 1025f. Player, trophy and Cultural Centre, Augusta 1·40 55
1071 5000f. Player, trophy and Old Governor's Mansion, Milledgeville 6·00 1·00
MS1072 117×80 mm. 7500f. Player on US flag 8·00 8·00

1993. Various stamps optd with emblem and inscription.
(a) Germany, World Cup Football Champion, 1990. Nos. 778/781 optd **VAINQEUR:ALLEMAGNE.**
1073 **328** 350f. multicoloured 25 15
1074 - 1000f. multicoloured 90 50
1075 - 1500f. multicoloured 1·50 80
1076 - 2500f. multicoloured 2·75 1·00

(b) Gold Medallists at Winter Olympic Games, Albertville (1992). Nos. 812/815 optd with Olympic rings, **MEDAILLE D'OR** and further inscr as below.
1077 350f. **BOB A QUATRE (AUT) INGO APPELT HARALD WINKLER GERHARD HAIDACHER THOMAS SCROLL** 25 15
1078 1000f. **1000 M. - OLAF ZINKE (GER)** 90 50
1079 1500f. **50 KM LIBRE BJOERN DAEHLIE (NOR)** 1·50 80
1080 2500f. **SUPER G MESSIEURS KJETIL-ANDRE AAMODT (NOR)** 2·75 1·25
MS1081 92×77 mm. 3000f. **GEANT MESSIEURS ALBERT TOMBA (ITA)** 3·25 3·25

(c) Anniversaries. Nos. 1060, 675 and 707 optd as listed below.
1082 500f. Red Cross and **130e ANNIVERSAIRE DE LA CREATION DE LA CROIX-ROUGE 1863–1993** 2·25 1·10
1083 550f. Lions emblem and **75eme ANNIVERSAIRE LIONS** 2·25 1·10
1084 1500f. Guitar and **THE ELVIS'S GUITAR 15TH ANNIVERSARY OF HIS DEATH 1977–1992** 1·75 80
1085 1500f. Guitar and **GUITARE ELVIS 15eme ANNIVERSAIRE DE SA MORT 1977–1992** 1·75 80

(d) 50th Death Anniversary of Robert Baden-Powell (founder of Boy Scouts). Optd **50eme ANNIVERSAIRE DE LA MORT DE BADEN POWEL** and emblem. (i) On Nos. 870/875 with scout badge in wreath.
1086 **354** 140f. multicoloured 10 10
1087 - 500f. multicoloured 35 25
1088 - 640f. multicoloured 45 30
1089 - 1025f. multicoloured 1·10 30
1090 - 1140f. multicoloured 1·10 35
1091 - 3500f. multicoloured 3·25 1·10
MS1092 119×94 mm. 4500f. multicoloured 3·75 3·75

(ii) On No. 676 with profile of Baden-Powell.
1093 1500f. multicoloured 1·75 80

(e) Bicentenary of French Republic. Nos. 761/765 optd **Republique Francaise** and emblem within oval and **BICENTENAIRE DE L'AN I DE LA REPUBLIQUE FRANCAISE.**
1094 250f. multicoloured 20 15
1095 350f. multicoloured 25 15
1096 1000f. multicoloured 1·10 50
1097 1500f. multicoloured 1·75 50
1098 2500f. multicoloured 2·75 90
MS1099 113×79 mm. 3000f. multicoloured 3·25 3·25

385 Great Green Turban

1993. Molluscs. Multicoloured.
1100 40f. Type **385** 10 10
1101 60f. Episcopal mitre 10 10
1102 65f. Common paper nautilis 10 10
1103 140f. Textile cone 10 10
1104 500f. European sea hare 90 25
1105 675f. *Harpa amouretta* 1·10 35
1106 2500f. Tiger cowrie 3·50 70
MS1107 70×91 mm. 2000f. Giant sundial. Imperf 3·00 3·00

386 Tiger Shark

1993. Sharks. Multicoloured.
1108 10f. Type **386** 10 10
1109 45f. Japanese sawshark 10 10
1110 140f. Whale shark 15 10
1111 270f. Smooth hammerhead 30 20
1112 600f. Oceanic white-tipped shark 65 35
1113 1200f. Zebra shark 1·25 80
1114 1500f. Goblin shark 1·90 1·10
MS1115 70×90 mm. 2000f. *Galeorhinus zyopterus*. Imperf 5·25 5·25

387 Map of Africa and Industry

1993. Air. African Industrialisation Day.
1116 **387** 500f. red, yellow and blue 80 50

388 Superviem Odoriko Express Train

1993. Locomotives. Multicoloured.
1117 5f. Type **388** 10 10
1118 15f. Morrison Knudsen diesel locomotive No. 801 10 10
1119 140f. ER-200 diesel train, Russia 10 10
1120 265f. General Motors GP60 diesel-electric locomotive No. EKD-5, USA 20 15
1121 300f. New Jersey Transit diesel locomotive, USA 20 15
1122 575f. ICE high speed train, Germany 40 30
1123 2500f. X2000 high speed train, Sweden 1·75 1·25
MS1124 91×71 mm. 2000f. Alsthams TGV 1·50 1·50

389 *Paphiopedilum siamense*

1993. Orchids. Multicoloured.
1125 50f. Type **389** (wrongly inscr 'Paphiopedilum') 10 10
1126 65f. *Cypripedium calceolus* 10 10
1127 70f. *Ophrys oestrifera* 10 10
1128 140f. *Cephalanthera rubra* 10 10
1129 300f. *Cypripedium macranthon* 20 15
1130 640f. *Calanthe vestita* 80 30
1131 2500f. *Cypripedium guttatum* 3·25 90
MS1132 90×70 mm. 2000f. *Oncidium tigrinum*. Imperf 2·75 2·75

390 *Necrophorus tomentosus*

1994. Beetles. Multicoloured.
1133 20f. Type **390** 10 10
1134 60f. *Dynastes tityus* 10 10
1135 140f. *Megaloxanta bicolor* 10 10
1136 605f. Searcher 40 10
1137 720f. *Chrysochroa mirabilis* 50 15
1138 1000f. *Crioceris asparagi* 70 25
1139 1500f. Rose chafer 1·10 35
MS1140 95×70 mm. 2000f. Goliath beetle. Imperf 1·40 1·40

391 Lufthansa Airliner, Germany

1994. Aircraft. Multicoloured.
1141 10f. Type **391** 10 10
1142 10f. British Aerospace/Aerospatiale Concorde supersonic jetliner of Air France 10 10
1143 10f. Air Canada airliner 10 10
1144 10f. ANA airliner, Japan 10 10
1145 60f. Boeing 747 jetliner of British Airways 10 10
1146 60f. Dornier Do-X flying boat, Germany 10 10
1147 60f. Shinmeiwa flying boat, Japan 10 10
1148 60f. Royal Jordanian airliner 10 10
1149 640f. Alitalia airliner 45 15
1150 640f. French-European Development Project Hydro 2000 flying boat 45 15
1151 640f. Boeing 314 flying boat 45 15
1152 640f. Air Madagascar airliner 45 15
1153 5000f. Emirates Airlines airliner, United Arab Emirates 3·50 1·10
1154 5000f. Scandinavian Airways airliner 3·50 1·10
1155 5000f. KLM airliner, Netherlands 3·50 1·10
1156 5000f. Air Caledonie airliner, New Caledonia 3·50 1·10

Nos. 1141/1156 were issued together, *se-tenant*, Nos. 1146/1147 and 1150/1151 forming a composite design.

392 Fork and Spoon, Sakalava

1994. Traditional Crafts. Multicoloured.
1157 30f. Silver jewellery, Mahafaly 10 10
1158 60f. Type **392** 10 10
1159 140f. Silver jewellery, Antandroy 10 10
1160 430f. Silver jewellery on table, Sakalava 30 10
1161 580f. Frames of decorated paper, Ambalavao 40 10
1162 1250f. Silver jewellery, Sakalava 90 30
1163 1500f. Marquetry table, Ambositra 1·10 35
MS1164 70×90 mm. 2000f. Carpet, Ampanihy. Imperf 1·25 1·25

393 *Chicoreus torrefactus* (shell)

1994. Marine Life. Multicoloured.
1165 15f. Type **393** 10 10
1166 15f. *Fasciolaria filamentosa* (shell) 10 10
1167 15f. Regal angelfish (*Pigopytes diacanthus*) 10 10
1168 15f. Coelacanth (*Latimeria chalumnae*) 10 10
1169 30f. *Stellaria solaris* (shell) 10 10
1170 30f. Ventral harp (*Harpa ventricosa*) 10 10
1171 30f. Blue-tailed boxfish (*Ostracion cyanurus*) 10 10
1172 30f. Clown wrasse (*Coris gaimardi*) 10 173
1173 1250f. Lobster (*Panulirus* sp.) 90 30
1174 1250f. *Stenopus hispidus* (crustacean) 90 30
1175 1250f. Undulate triggerfish (*Balistapus undulatus*) 90 30
1176 1250f. Forceps butterflyfish (*Forcipiger longirostris*) 90 30
1177 1500f. Hermit crab (*Pagure*) 1·10 35
1178 1500f. Hermit crab (*Bernard l'Hermite*) 1·10 35
1179 1500f. Diadem squirrelfish (*Adioryx diadema*) 1·10 35

1180 1500f. Lunulate lionfish (*Pterois lunulata*) 1·10 35

Nos. 1165/1180 were issued together, *se-tenant*, the backgrounds forming a composite design.

394 Arms

1994. Air. Junior Economic Chamber Zone A (Africa, Middle East and Indian Ocean) Conference, Antananarivo. Multicoloured.

1181 140f. Type **394** 10 10

1182 500f. Arms as in Type **394** but with inscriptions differently arranged (vert) 70 20

395 Troops landing on Beach

1994. 50th Anniversary of Allied Landings at Normandy. Multicoloured.

1183 1500f. Type **395** 1·10 35

1184 3000f. German troops defending ridge and allied troops (as Type **397**) 2·25 75

1185 3000f. Aeroplanes over battle scene, trooper with US flag and German officer (as Type **397**) 2·25 75

Nos. 1183/1185 were issued together, *se-tenant*, forming a composite design.

396 Emperor Angelfish

1994. Aquarium Fish. Multicoloured.

1186 10f. Type **396** 10 10

1187 30f. Siamese fighting fish 10 10

1188 45f. Pearl gourami 10 10

1189 95f. Cuckoo-wrasse 10 10

1190 140f. Blotched upsidedown catfish (*Synodontis nigreventris*) 10 10

1191 140f. Jack Dempsey (*Cichlasoma biocellatum*) 10 10

1192 3500f. Mummichog 2·50 80

MS1193 70×90 mm. 2000f. Goldfish (29×41 mm) 75 75

397 Notre Dame Cathedral, Armed Resistance Fighters and Rejoicing Crowd

1994. 50th Anniversary of Liberation of Paris by Allied Forces. Multicoloured.

1194 1500f. Crowd and Arc de Triomphe (as Type **395**) 55 15

1195 3000f. Type **397** 1·10 35

1196 3000f. Eiffel Tower and tank convoy 1·10 35

Nos. 1194/1196 were issued together, *se-tenant*, forming a composite design.

398 Emblem and '75'

1994. 75th Anniversary of ILO.

1197 **398** 140f. multicoloured 10 10

399 Biathlon

1994. Winter Olympic Games, Lillehammer, Norway. Multicoloured. (a) Without overprints.

1198 140f. Type **399** 10 10

1199 1250f. Ice hockey 45 15

1200 2000f. Figure skating 75 25

1201 2500f. Skiing (downhill) 95 30

MS1202 116×112 mm. 5000f. Skiing (slalom) 1·90 1·90

(b) Gold Medal Winners. Nos. 1198/**MS**1202 optd.

1203 140f. Optd **M. BEDARD CANADA** 10 10

1204 1250f. Optd **MEDAILLE D'OR SUEDE** 45 15

1205 2000f. Optd **O. BAYUL UKRAINE** 75 25

1206 2500f. Optd **M. WASMEIER ALLEMAGNE** 95 30

MS1207 116×112 mm. 5000f. **D. COMPAGNONI ITALIE** 1·90 1·90

401 Majestic performing Dressage Exercise and Windsor Hotel, 1892

1994. Olympic Games, Atlanta, USA. Multicoloured.. Multicoloured.

1208 640f. Type **401** 25 10

1209 1000f. Covington Courthouse, 1884, and putting the shot 35 10

1210 1500f. Table tennis and Carolton Community Activities Centre 55 15

1211 3000f. Newman Commercial Court Square, 1800, and footballer 1·10 35

MS1212 120×112 mm. 7500f. Games emblem and relay runner 2·75 2·75

402 Spider on Map of Madagascar

1994. *Archaea workmani* (spider).

1213 **402** 500f. multicoloured 20 15

403 *Oceonia oncidiflora*

1994. Flowers, Fruit, Fungi and Vegetables. Multicoloured.

1214 45f. Type **403** 10 10

1215 45f. Breadfruit (*Artocarpus altilis*) 10 10

1216 45f. *Russula annulata* 10 10

1217 45f. Sweet potato 10 10

1218 60f. *Cymbidella rhodochica* 10 10

1219 60f. *Eugenia malaceensis* 10 10

1220 60f. *Lactarius claricolor* 10 10

1221 60f. Yam 10 10

1222 140f. Vanilla orchid (*Vanilla planifolia*) 10 10

1223 140f. *Jambosa domestica* 10 10

1224 140f. *Russula tuberculosa* 10 10

1225 140f. Avocado 10 10

1226 3000f. *Phaius humblotii* 1·10 35

1227 3000f. Papaya 1·10 35

1228 3000f. *Russula fistulosa* 1·10 35

1229 3000f. Manioc 1·10 35

Nos. 1214/1229 were issued together, *se-tenant*, the backgrounds forming a composite design.

Nos. 1230/1310 and T **404**/**411** are vacant.

412 Locusts

1995. Locusts. Multicoloured.

1311 140f. Type **412** 10 10

1312 140f. Robber fly (*Asilidae*) (predator) (horiz) 10 10

1313 140f. Harvesting locusts for food (horiz) 10 10

413 Emblem

1995. Air. 20th Anniversary of Francophone.

1314 **413** 500f. multicoloured 25 25

414 Emblem

1995. 160th Anniversary of Malagasy Bible Translation.

1315 **414** 140f. multicoloured 10 10

415 'HILTON' and '25'

1995. 25th Anniversary of Hilton Hotel, Madagascar.

1316 **415** 500f. indigo, black and gold 25 25

416 Messengers

1995. World Post Day.

1317 **416** 500f. multicoloured 25 25

417 Emblem and Map

1996. 30th Anniversary of United Nations Industrial Development Organisation (ONUDI).

1318 **417** 140f. blue, brown and black 10 10

418 Symbols of Drug Abuse

1996. International Day against Drug Abuse.

1319 **418** 140f. grey, green and black 10 10

419 Tennis

1996. Olympic Games, Atlanta. Multicoloured.

1320 140f. Type **419** 10 10

1321 140f. Judo 10 10

420 Fredy Rajaofera

1997. Personalities. Multicoloured.

1322 140f. Type **420** 10 10

1323 140f. Andrianary Ratianarivo 10 10

1324 140f. Odeam Rakoto 10 10

421 '25'

1997. 25th Anniversary of Radio Nederland in Madagascar.

1325 **421** 500f. orange, black and blue 25 25

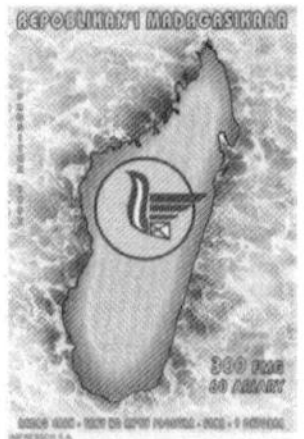

422 Map and Postal Emblem

1997. World Post Day.

1326 **422** 300f. multicoloured 20 20

423 Emblem

1997. Third Francophonie Games, Madagascar.

1327 **423** 300f. multicoloured 20 20

1328 **423** 1850f. multicoloured 55 55

424 Emblem

1999. 15th Anniversary of Indian Ocean Commission.

1329 **424** 500f. blue, black and vermilion 25 25

500 FMG
ARIARY 100

(424a)

1999. Various stamps surcharged as T **424a**.

1329a 300f. on 430f. multicoloured (No. 1160) 30 30

1329b 500f. on 170f. multicoloured (No. 468) 45 45

1329c 500f. on 555f. multicoloured (No. 896) 45 45

1329d 500f. on 580f. multicoloured (No. 1161) 45 45

1329e 500f. on 1850f. multicoloured (No. 1328) 45 45

(424b)

1999. No. 820 surcharged as T **424b**.

1329f		60f. on 350f.+20f. on 250f.+20f. multicoloured	15	15

425 Rasalama (Christian martyr)

2000. Personalities. Multicoloured.

1330		900f. Type **425**	35	35
1331		900f. Razafindrakotohasina Rahantravololona (first Malagasy woman engineer and Ministry of Economy and Commerce Water Division Chief)	35	35
1332		900f. Ralivao Ramiaramanana (first Malagasy woman doctor)	35	35
1333		900f. Cardinal Jerome-Henri Rakotomalala	35	35
1334		900f. Rakotovao Razakaboana (Minister of Finance and Planning)	35	35
1335		900f. General Gabriel Ramanantsoa (president 1972–1975)	35	35

426 'Eclipse 2001'

2001. Total Solar Eclipse.

1336	**426**	5600f. multicoloured	1·90	1·90

427 Children surrounding Globe

2001. International Year of Dialogue among Civilisations.

1337	**427**	3500f. multicoloured	1·20	1·20

428 Rice Fronds and Map

2001. Rice.

1338	**428**	450f. multicoloured	25	25
1339	**428**	900f. multicoloured	35	35

Nos. 1340/1 have been left for stamps not yet received.

429 *Chorisia ventricosa*

2002. Flora and Fauna. Multicoloured.

1342		100f. Type **429**	10	10
1343		350f. *Eichhornia crassipes* (common water hyacinth) (vert)	15	15
1344		400f. *Didieraceae*	15	15
1345		500f. Palms, Nosy Iranja beach (vert)	20	20
1346		900f. *Ravinala* (travellers' tree) (National Tree) (vert)	35	35
1347		1000f. *Propithecus verreauxi* (inscr 'Prophiteque deverreauxi') (vert)	35	35
1348		2500f. *Lemur catta* (ring-tailed lemur) (vert)	80	80
1349		3000f. *Furcifer pardalis* (chameleon)	1·10	1·10
1350		4400f. *Takhtajania perrieri*	1·30	1·30
1351		6800f. *Ravinala* (vert)	2·75	2·75

430 Albert Rakoto Ratsimamanga (scientist and diplomat)

2002. Personalities. Multicoloured.

1352		1500f. Type **430**	45	45
1353		1500f. Rakoto Frah (flautist)	45	45

431 Mahamasina Stadium

2002. 30th Anniversary of Madagascar–China Diplomatic Relations.

1354	**431**	2500f. multicoloured	85	85

432 *Xyloolaena perrieri*

2003. Indigenous Plants. Multicoloured.

1355		100f. Type **432**	10	10
1356		500f. *Megistostegium microphyllum*	20	20
1357		600f. *Tambourissa* (horiz)	20	20
1358		1000f. *Leptolaena diospyroidea*	35	35
1359		1500f. *Ochna greveanum*	40	40
1360		7500f. *Schizolaena tampoketsana*	2·75	2·75

433 Landscape, Madagascar and Japan Flags

2003. Japan International Co-operation Agency (JICA) Office in Madagascar.

1361	**433**	1500f. multicoloured	40	40

434 *Indri indri* (lemur)

2003

1362	**434**	2500f. multicoloured	65	65
1363	**434**	15000f. multicoloured	2·75	2·75

435 First Catholic Church in Madagascar, Sainte-Marie

2003. Tourism. Multicoloured.

1364		4000f. Type **435**	1·20	1·20
1365		4500f. House made of falafa, Coastal region	1·20	1·20
1366		5500f. House, High Plateau region	1·30	1·30
1367		10000f. Pirates graveyard, Sainte-Marie	2·40	2·40

436 Emblem

2003. 20th Anniversary of Indian Ocean Commission.

1368	**436**	6000f. multicoloured	1·40	1·40

437 Emblem

2004. World for Health and Road Safety.

1369	**437**	1500f. multicoloured	35	35

438 Ranavalona I

2004. Rulers. Multicoloured.

1370		100f. Type **438**	10	10
1371		400f. Ranavalona III	15	15
1372		500f. Radama I	15	15
1373		1000f. Radama II	35	35
1374		2500f. Rasoherina	80	80
1375		4000f. Andrian-ampoinimerina	1·30	1·30
1376		7500f. Ranavalona II	1·50	1·50

439 Wolf-shaped Rock, Isalo

2004. Tourism. Multicoloured.

1377		2000f. Type **439**	65	65
1378		3000f. Nosy Mitsio (vert)	70	70
1379		5000f. Beach, Fort Dauphin	1·30	1·30
1381		10000f. Traditional dancers, Ambohimanga Palace (rova)	2·40	2·40
1382		25000f. Red Tsingy (limestone peaks) Irodo	2·75	2·75

No. 1380 has been left for stamp not yet received.

Change of Currency on Stamps (values remain unchanged).
1 Ariay (a)=5 Francs (f)

440 Ostriches and Lemur

2004. Morondava Fauna.

1383	**440**	50000f. multicoloured	1·90	1·90

441 Map enclosing Canoeists and Lemur

2005. Centenary of Rotary International.

1384	**441**	2100a. multicoloured	20	20

Nos. 1385/1386 and T **442** have been left for 30th Anniversary of the Medical Co-operation between China and Madagascar, not yet received.

443 *Aerangis cryptodon*

2005. Indigenous Orchids. Multicoloured.

1387		1500a. Type **442**	15	15
1388		1500a. *Aeranthes grandiflora*	15	15
1389		1500a. *Aeranthes henrici*	15	15
1390		1500a. *Aeranthes peyrotii*	15	15
1391		1500a. *Oeceoclades spathulifera* (Inscr 'Oeccoclades spathulifera')	15	15
1392		1500a. *Angraecum sesquipedale*	15	15
1393		1500a. Inscr 'Cynorchis elata'	15	15
1394		1500a. *Angraecum viguieri*	15	15
1395		1500a. *Gastrorchis humblotii*	15	15
1396		1500a. *Gastrorchis lutea*	15	15
1397		1500a. *Gastrorchis pulcher*	15	15
1398		1500a. *Jumellea sagittata*	15	15
1399		1500a. *Microcoelia gilpinae*	15	15
1400		1500a. *Angraecum praestans*	15	15

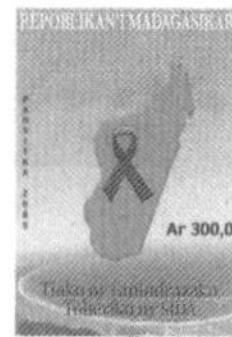

444 Map and AIDS Ribbon

2006. AIDS Awareness Campaign.

1401	**444**	300a. multicoloured	10	10

445 Pastor Rainmamonjisoa

2006. Birth Bicentenary of Mpitandrina Rainmamonjisoa.

1402	**445**	300a. pale blue and black	10	10

446 Emblem, Philatelic Tools and Stamps

2006. 20th Anniversary of Stamp Collectors Association (APM).

1403	**446**	300a. multicoloured	10	10

447 Leopold Senghor

2006. Birth Centenary of Leopold Sedar Senghor (poet and first president of Senegal (1960–1980)).

1404	**447**	2000a. multicoloured	25	25

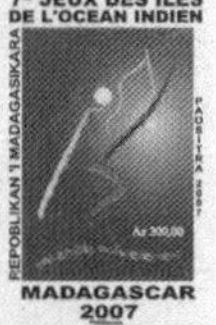

448 Emblem

2007. Seventh Indian Ocean Games, Madagascar.

1405	**448**	300a. multicoloured	10	10

449 Whale

2007. Whales Festival, Sainte Marie. Multicoloured.

1406	1100a. Type **449**	15	15
1407	3000a. Whale and two small fish (vert)	40	40

450 Regis Rajemisa-Raolison

2008. Regis Rajemisa-Raolison (writer and founder of Havatsa UPEM (Union of Writers and Poets in Malagasy)) Commemoration.

1408	**450**	300a. black and carmine-vermilion	10	10

300 ARIARY

(451)

2008. Nos. 1340 and 1371 surcharged as T **451**.

1409	300f. on 100f. multicoloured (No. 1371)	10	10
1410	300f. on 5600f. multicoloured (No. 1340)	10	10

452 Postman delivering Letter

2008. Postal Service. Part of Developement.

1411	**452**	100a. multicoloured	10	10

PARCEL POST STAMPS

1919. Receipt stamp of France surch **MADAGASCAR ET DEPENDANCES 0fr.10 COLIS POSTAUX.**

P81	0f.10 on 10c. grey	10·50	12·00

1919. Fiscal stamp of Madagascar surch **COLIS POSTAUX 0f.10.**

P82	0f.10 on 1f. pink	£150	£120

1919. Fiscal stamps surch **Madagascar et Dependances** (in capitals on No. P83) **COLIS POSTAUX 0f.10.**

P83	0f.10 pink	27·00	14·50
P84	0f.10 red and green	8·25	6·75
P85	0f.10 black and green	8·00	7·00

POSTAGE DUE STAMPS

1896. Postage Due stamps of Fr. Colonies optd **Madagascar et DEPENDANCES.**

D17	**U**	5c. blue	11·50	20·00
D18	**U**	10c. brown	9·75	10·50
D19	**U**	20c. yellow	8·25	10·00
D20	**U**	30c. red	9·25	11·00
D21	**U**	40c. mauve	75·00	70·00
D22	**U**	50c. violet	11·50	8·75
D23	**U**	1f. green	£120	80·00

D6 Governor's Palace, Tananarive

1908

D70	**D6**	2c. red	30	35
D71	**D6**	4c. violet	35	35
D72	**D6**	5c. green	35	90
D73	**D6**	10c. red	35	30
D74	**D6**	20c. olive	30	2·30
D75	**D6**	40c. brown on cream	45	5·00
D76	**D6**	50c. brown on blue	55	2·50
D77	**D6**	60c. red	80	5·00
D78	**D6**	1f. blue	1·00	3·50

1924. Surch in figures.

D123	**D6**	60c. on 1f. red	2·10	7·00
D124	**D6**	2f. on 1f. purple	1·00	4·25
D125	**D6**	3f. on 1f. blue	1·00	5·50

1942. Free French Administration. Optd **FRANCE LIBRE** or surch also.

D254	**D6**	10c. red	1·90	4·50
D255	**D6**	20c. green	1·20	4·50
D256	**D6**	0,30 on 5c. green	3·25	5·25
D257	**D6**	40c. brown on cream	2·50	4·00
D258	**D6**	50c. brown and blue	2·30	3·75
D259	**D6**	60c. red	2·75	4·00
D260	**D6**	1f. blue	1·20	3·25
D261	**D6**	1f. on 2c. purple	10·50	17·00
D262	**D6**	2f. on 4c. violet	4·75	6·25
D263	**D6**	2f. on 1f. mauve	2·50	3·75
D264	**D6**	3f. on 1f. blue	2·75	4·00

D37

1947

D319	**D37**	10c. mauve	35	6·00
D320	**D37**	30c. brown	35	6·50
D321	**D37**	50c. green	35	6·75
D322	**D37**	1f. brown	40	4·75
D323	**D37**	2f. red	1·10	4·00
D324	**D37**	3f. brown	1·30	5·00
D325	**D37**	4f. blue	1·30	6·50
D326	**D37**	5f. red	1·80	5·75
D327	**D37**	10f. green	1·40	2·75
D328	**D37**	20f. blue	2·50	9·00

APPENDIX

The following stamps have either been issued in excess of postal needs or have not been available to the public in reasonable quantities at face value.

1990

Birth Centenary of General Charles de Gaulle. 5000f.×2

1992

Olympic Games, Barcelona. 500f. (on gold foil).

1993

Bicentenary of French Republic. 1989 Philexfrance 89 issue optd. 5000f.

1994

Elvis Presley (entertainer). 10000f. (on gold foil).
World Cup Football Championship, USA 10000f. (on gold foil).
Winter Olympic Games, Lillehammer, Norway. 10000f. (on gold foil).
Olympic Games, Atlanta, USA 5000f. (on gold foil).
Centenary of Olympic Committee. 2500×2, 3500f.
Stuff of Heroes by Phillip Kaufman. 140×2, 5000f.
Sculpture and Architecture. 350f.×20
Big Cats. 10, 30, 60, 120, 140×2, 3500f.
Philakorea '94, Seoul. 100, 140, 550f.
Cathedrals. 10, 100, 120, 140, 525, 605f.
Pre-historic Animals. 35, 40, 140, 525, 640, 755, 1800f.
Sport. 5, 140, 525, 550, 640, 720, 1500f.

1995

Cinema. 100×2,140×2, 550, 1250, 5000×2, 10000f.×2
Ships. 45, 50, 60, 100, 140, 350, 3000f.

1996

25th Anniversary of Greenpeace. 1500, 3000, 3500, 5000f.
20th Anniversary of Concorde. 2000f.×4
50th Anniversary of UNICEF. 140×3, 7500f.
Personalities. 1500, 1750, 2000, 2500, 3000, 3500, 5000, 7500f.

1997

Winter Olympics, Nagano. 160, 350, 5000, 7500f.

1998

World Cup Football championship, France. 300×3, 1350×3, 3000×3, 10000f.×3
Transport. 1700×9, 2000×9, 2500×9, 3000×9, 4000×9
Pre-historic Animals. 3500×9, 3500f.×9

1999

Birds. 250×9
Chinese New Year. Year of the Rabbit. 1500f.×4
Comic Book Heroes. 1800×9, 1800×9, 3200f.×9
Betty Boop 2500f.×9
Garfield. 3200f.×9
Trains. 2000×9, 3000×9, 3000f.×9, 4000×9, 4000×9, 4000f.×9
Fauna. 300, 1700, 2050, 2400f.
Personalities. 1950f.×6
Princess Diana Commemoration. 1350f.
Fauna. 1950f.×6
25th Anniversary Anniv of Pablo Picasso. 2750, 7200, 7500f.
Scouts. 1350×4, 1500×4, 1950f.×4, 2000×4, 2500×4, 3000×4, 5000×4, 7500f.×4
30th Anniversary of Concorde. 2000f.
125th Anniversary of UPU. 1000, 1200, 1800, 3200, 3500, 5000, 5600, 7500f.
Space Exploration. 1500×8, 12500f.
Animals of the World. Elephants. 2000f.×9
Railways. 3000×9, 3500×4, 5000×4, 7500f.×4
Insects. 2000f.×9
Philex France 99. 1500f.×9
Birds. 2000×9, 2000f.×9
Flora and Fauna. 2000×4, 2000×9, 2000×9, 4000×4, 5000×4, 5000×4, 7500f.×4,
Motorcycle Racing. 2000f.×9
Art. 2000×9, 2000×9, 2500×9, 5000×9
Antonio Gaudi. 2000f.×9
Marilyn Monroe. 1750f.×9
Albert Einstein. 4000f.×4

FIRST CHOICE FOR STAMP COLLECTORS SINCE 1890

SUBSCRIBE AND GET £££S OFF THE COVER PRICE

SUBSCRIBE TODAY
Visit **stanleygibbons.com/gsm**
or call **01425 472 363**
overseas **+44 1425 472 363**

399 Strand, WC2R 0LX, London
Phone: **+44 1425 472 363** | Email: gsm@stanleygibbons.com
www.stanleygibbons.com

*T&Cs apply. *Saving based on a 12-month UK print subscription.*

MADEIRA

A Portuguese island in the Atlantic Ocean off the N.W. coast of Africa. From 1868 to 1929 and from 1980 separate issues were made.

1868. 1000 reis = 1 milreis.
1912. 100 centavos = 1 escudo.
2002. 100 cents = 1 euro.

Nos. 1/78b are stamps of Portugal optd **MADEIRA**.

1868. With curved value label. Imperf.

1	**14**	20r. bistre	£275	£200
2	**14**	50r. green	£275	£200
3	**14**	80r. orange	£300	£200
4	**14**	100r. lilac	£300	£200

1868. With curved value label. Perf.

10	**14**	5r. black	80·00	55·00
13	**14**	10r. yellow	£130	£110
14	**14**	20r. bistre	£200	£160
15	**14**	25r. red	85·00	16·00
16	**14**	50r. green	£250	£200
17	**14**	80r. orange	£250	£200
19	**14**	100r. mauve	£250	£200
20	**14**	120r. blue	£170	£110
21	**14**	240r. mauve	£700	£600

1871. With straight value label.

30	**15**	5r. black	12·00	8·50
47	**15**	10r. yellow	40·00	29·00
72a	**15**	10r. green	95·00	75·00
48	**15**	15r. brown	28·00	16·00
49	**15**	20r. bistre	44·00	29·00
34	**15**	25r. pink	16·00	6·00
51	**15**	50r. green	90·00	39·00
71	**15**	50r. blue	£170	90·00
36	**15**	80r. orange	£110	95·00
53	**15**	100r. mauve	£120	70·00
38	**15**	120r. blue	£170	£110
55	**15**	150r. blue	£250	£200
74	**15**	150r. yellow	£400	£350
39	**15**	240r. lilac	£1000	£700
67	**15**	300r. lilac	£110	95·00

1880. Stamps of 1880.

79	**16**	5r. black	37·00	28·00
77	**17**	25r. grey	40·00	28·00
78	**16**	25r. grey	40·00	15·00
78b	**16**	25r. brown	40·00	15·00

1898. Vasco da Gama. As Nos. 378/385 of Portugal.

134	**40**	2½r. green	3·75	1·90
135	-	5r. red	3·75	1·90
136	-	10r. purple	4·75	2·20
137	**43**	25r. green	4·50	2·00
138	**44**	50r. blue	13·50	5·00
139	-	75r. brown	17·00	11·50
140	-	100r. brown	18·00	11·50
141	-	150r. brown	26·00	19·00

For Nos. 134/141 with **REPUBLICA** overprint, see Nos. 455/462 of Portugal.

6 Ceres

1929. Funchal Museum Fund. Value in black.

148	**6**	3c. violet	95	80
149	**6**	4c. yellow	95	80
150	**6**	5c. blue	95	80
151	**6**	6c. brown	1·30	1·10
152	**6**	10c. red	1·30	1·10
153	**6**	15c. green	1·30	1·10
154	**6**	16c. brown	1·30	1·10
155	**6**	25c. purple	1·40	1·20
156	**6**	32c. green	1·40	1·20
157	**6**	40c. brown	1·40	1·20
158	**6**	50c. grey	1·40	1·20
159	**6**	64c. blue	1·40	1·20
160	**6**	80c. brown	1·40	1·20
161	**6**	96c. red	5·50	5·25
162	**6**	1e. black	1·10	1·10
163	**6**	1e.20 pink	1·10	1·10
164	**6**	1e.60 blue	1·10	1·10
165	**6**	2e.40 yellow	1·70	1·60
166	**6**	3e.36 green	2·40	2·10
167	**6**	4e.50 red	2·40	2·10
168	**6**	7e. blue	8·50	8·50

7 20r. Stamp, 1868

1980. 112th Anniversary of First Overprinted Madeira Stamps.

169	**7**	6e.50 black, bistre and green	45	25
170	-	19e.50 black, purple and red	1·50	1·00
MS171		140×115 mm. Nos. 169/70 (sold at 30e.)	6·75	6·75

Design: 19e.50, 100r. stamp, 1868.

8 Ox Sledge

1980. World Tourism Conference, Manila, Philippines. Multicoloured.

172		50c. Type **8**	20	15
173		1e. Wine and grapes	30	20
174		5e. Map of Madeira	75	40
175		6e.50 Basketwork	95	45
176		8e. Orchid	1·40	65
177		30e. Fishing boat	2·75	1·10

9 O Bailinho (folk dance)

1981. Europa.

178	**9**	22e. multicoloured	1·90	95
MS179		141×115 mm. No. 178×2	8·50	8·50

10 Portuguese Caravel approaching Madeira

1981. 560th Anniversary (1980) of Discovery of Madeira. Multicoloured.

180		8e.50 Type **10**	70	45
181		33e.50 Prince Henry the Navigator and map of Atlantic Ocean	2·75	1·00

11 *Dactylorhiza foliosa*

1981. Regional Flowers. Multicoloured.

182		7e. Type **11**	50	30
183		8e.50 *Geranium maderense*	55	30
184		9e. *Goodyera macrophylla*	65	20
185		10e. *Armeria maderensis*	65	25
186		12e.50 *Matthiola maderensis*	45	20
187		20e. *Isoplexis sceptrum*	1·10	70
188		27e. *Viola paradoxa*	1·90	1·20
189		30e. *Erica maderensis*	1·20	75
190		33e.50 *Scilla maderensis*	2·00	1·40
191		37e.50 *Cirsium latifolium*	1·70	1·00
192		50e. *Echium candicans*	2·75	1·50
193		100e. *Clethra arborea*	3·50	1·60

12 First Sugar Mill

1982. Europa.

199	**12**	33e.50 multicoloured	3·25	1·50
MS200		139×115 mm. No. 199×3	17·00	17·00

13 Dancer holding Dolls on Staff

1982. O Brinco Dancing Dolls. Multicoloured.

201		27e. Type **13**	2·20	1·30
202		33e.50 Dancers	3·50	1·80

14 Los Levadas Irrigation Channels

1983. Europa.

203	**14**	37e.50 multicoloured	3·25	1·30
MS204		114×140 mm. No. 203×3	21·00	21·00

15 Flag of Madeira

1983. Flag.

205	**15**	12e.50 multicoloured	1·30	45

1984. Europa. As T **398** of Portugal but additionally inscr 'MADEIRA'.

206		51e. multicoloured	4·50	2·20
MS207		113×140 mm. No. 206×3	19·00	19·00

16 Rally Car

1984. 25th Anniversary of Madeira Rally. Multicoloured.

208		16e. Type **16**	90	45
209		51e. Rally car (different)	3·25	1·60

17 Basket Sledge

1984. Transport (1st series). Multicoloured.

210		16e. Type **17**	80	45
211		35e. Hammock	1·70	1·10
212		40e. Borracheiros (wine carriers)	2·40	1·10
213		51e. Carreira local sailing boat	3·00	1·70

See also Nos. 218/221.

18 Braguinha Player

1985. Europa.

214	**18**	60e. multicoloured	4·50	1·90
MS215		140×115 mm. No. 214×3	23·00	23·00

19 Black Scabbardfish

1985. Fish (1st series). Multicoloured.

216		40e. Type **19**	2·40	1·30
217		60e. Opah	3·25	1·90

See also Nos. 222/223 and 250/253.

1985. Transport (2nd series). As T **17**. Multicoloured.

218		20e. Ox sledge	80	45
219		40e. Mountain railway	1·90	1·10
220		46e. Fishing boat and basket used by pesquitos (itinerant fish sellers)	2·50	1·80
221		60e. Coastal ferry	3·00	1·50

1986. Fish (2nd series). As T **19**. Multicoloured.

222		20e. Big-eyed tuna	1·10	45
223		75e. Alfonsino	5·25	2·10

20 Cory's Shearwater and Tanker

1986. Europa.

224	**20**	68e.50 multicoloured	5·25	2·10
MS225		140×114 mm. No. 224×3	21·00	21·00

21 Sao Lourenco Fort, Funchal

1986. Fortresses. Multicoloured.

226		22e.50 Type **21**	1·10	55
227		52e.50 Sao Joao do Pico Fort, Funchal	3·25	1·60
228		68e.50 Sao Tiago Fort, Funchal	4·25	2·10
229		100e. Nossa Senhora do Amparo Fort, Machico	5·25	1·80

22 Firecrest

1987. Birds (1st series). Multicoloured.

230		25e. Type **22**	1·10	45
231		57e. Trocaz pigeon	3·25	1·80
232		74e.50 Barn owl	4·25	2·40
233		125e. Soft-plumaged petrel	5·25	2·75

See also Nos. 240/243.

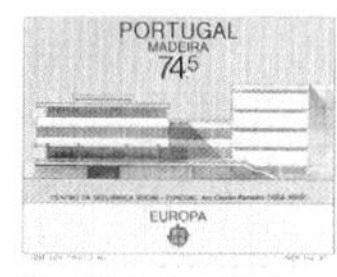

23 Social Services Centre, Funchal (Raul Chorao Ramalho)

1987. Europa. Architecture.

234	**23**	74e.50 multicoloured	4·75	2·10
MS235		140×113 mm. No. 234×4	21·00	21·00

24 Funchal Cathedral

1987. Historic Buildings. Multicoloured.

236		51e. Type **24**	3·00	1·50
237		74e.50 Old Town Hall, Santa Cruz	3·50	1·50

25 *Maria Cristina* (mail boat)

1988. Europa. Transport and Communications.

238	**25**	80e. multicoloured	5·75	2·10
MS239		139×112 mm. As No. 238×4 but with cream background	21·00	21·00

1988. Birds (2nd series). As T **22** but horiz. Multicoloured.

240		27e. European robin	1·10	30
241		60e. Streaked rock sparrow	2·75	1·70
242		80e. Chaffinch	3·75	1·80
243		100e. Northern sparrowhawk	4·25	1·80

26 Columbus and Funchal House

1988. Christopher Columbus's Houses in Madeira. Multicoloured.

244 55e. Type **26** 3·00 1·30

245 80e. Columbus and Porto Santo house (horiz) 3·25 1·70

27 Child flying Kite

1989. Europa. Children's Games and Toys. Multicoloured.

246 80e. Type **27** 5·25 2·75

MS247 139×112 mm. 80e.×2, Type **27**; 80e.×2, Child flying kite (*different*) 21·00 21·00

28 Church of St John the Evangelist

1989. Brasiliana 89 Stamp Exhibition, Rio de Janeiro. Madeiran Churches. Multicoloured.

248 29e. Type **28** 85 45

249 87e. St Clara's Church and Convent 3·75 2·10

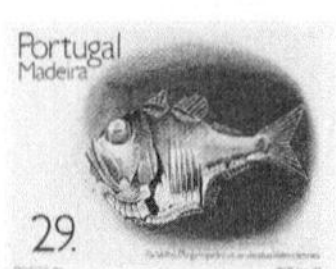

29 Spiny Hatchetfish

1989. Fish (3rd series). Multicoloured.

250 29e. Type **29** 85 20

251 60e. Dog wrasse 2·50 1·50

252 87e. Rainbow wrasse 3·75 2·00

253 100e. Madeiran scorpionfish 4·00 2·75

30 Zarco Post Office

1990. Europa. Post Office Buildings. Multicoloured.

254 80e. Type **30** 2·50 1·70

MS255 139×111 mm. 80e.×2, Type **30**; 80e.×2, Porto da Cruz Post Office 18·00 18·00

31 Bananas

1990. Sub-tropical Fruits. Multicoloured.

256 5e. Type **31** 25 15

257 10e. Thorn apple 25 15

258 32e. Avocado 90 50

259 35e. Mangoes 90 50

260 38e. Tomatoes 1·00 50

261 60e. Sugar apple 2·30 1·40

262 65e. Suriname cherries 2·20 1·30

263 70e. Brazilian guavas 2·40 1·40

264 85e. Delicious fruits 2·75 1·60

265 100e. Passion fruit 3·50 2·10

266 110e. Papayas 3·50 2·10

267 125e. Guava 3·50 2·10

32 Tunny Boat

1990. Boats. Multicoloured.

270 32e. Type **32** 70 25

271 60e. Desert Islands boat 1·70 1·00

272 70e. Maneiro 2·00 1·40

273 95e. Chavelha 3·00 2·00

33 Trocaz Pigeon

1991. The Trocaz Pigeon. Multicoloured.

274 35e. Type **33** 1·60 55

275 35e. Two pigeons 1·60 55

276 35e. Pigeon on nest 1·60 55

277 35e. Pigeon alighting on twig 1·60 55

Nos. 264/267 were issued together, *se-tenant*, forming a composite design.

34 European Remote Sensing (*ERS1*) Satellite

1991. Europa. Europe in Space. Multicoloured.

278 80e. Type **34** 3·25 2·10

MS279 140×112 mm. 80e.×2, Type **34**; 80e.×2, *Spot* satellite 18·00 18·00

35 Columbus and Funchal House

1992. Europa. 500th Anniversary of Discovery of America by Columbus.

280 **35** 85e. multicoloured 3·25 1·30

36 *Gaviao* (ferry)

1992. Inter-island Ships. Multicoloured.

281 38e. Type **36** 85 35

282 65e. *Independencia* (catamaran ferry) 1·70 1·20

283 85e. *Madeirense* (car ferry) 2·10 1·40

284 120e. *Funchalense* (freighter) 3·00 1·60

37 *Shadow thrown by Christa Maar* (Lourdes Castro)

1993. Europa. Contemporary Art. Multicoloured.

285 50e. Type **37** 3·00 1·40

MS286 140×112 mm. 90e.×2, Type **37**; 90e.×2, *Shadow thrown by Dahlia* 13·00 13·00

38 Seals Swimming

1993. Mediterranean Monk Seal. Multicoloured.

287 42e. Type **38** 1·40 70

288 42e. Seal basking 1·40 70

289 42e. Two seals on rocks 1·40 70

290 42e. Mother suckling young 1·40 70

Nos. 287/290 were issued together, *se-tenant*, forming a composite design.

39 Window of St Francis's Convent, Funchal

1993. Regional Architecture. Multicoloured.

291 42e. Type **39** 85 55

292 130e. Window of Mercy, Old Hospital, Funchal 3·00 1·90

40 Native of Cape of Good Hope and Explorer with Model Caravel

1992. Europa. Discoveries. Multicoloured.

293 90e. Type **40** 2·10 1·60

MS294 140×112 mm. 100e.×2, Type **40**; 100e.×2, Palm tree and explorer with model caravel 10·50 10·50

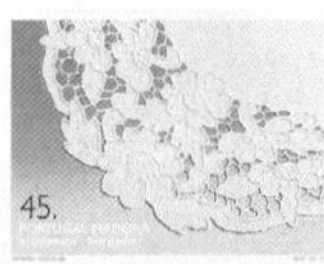

41 Embroidery

1994. Traditional Crafts (1st series). Multicoloured.

295 45e. Type **41** 75 35

296 75e. Tapestry 1·50 95

297 100e. Boots 2·00 1·30

298 140e. Wicker chair back 3·00 1·90

See also Nos. 301/304.

42 Funchal

1994. District Arms. Multicoloured.

299 45e. Type **42** 75 35

300 140e. Porto Santo 2·75 1·60

43 Bread Dough Figures

1995. Traditional Crafts (2nd series). Multicoloured.

301 45e. Type **43** 85 50

302 80e. Inlaid wooden box 1·50 85

303 95e. Bamboo cage 1·70 1·20

304 135e. Woollen bonnet 2·30 1·50

44 Guiomar Vilhena (entrepreneur)

1996. Europa. Famous Women. Multicoloured.

305 98e. Type **44** 2·10 1·10

MS306 140×112 mm. No. 305×3 6·50 6·50

45 *Adoration of the Magi*

1996. Religious Paintings by Flemish Artists. Multicoloured.

307 47e. Type **45** 80 35

308 78e. *St Mary Magdalene* 1·40 95

309 98e. *The Annunciation* (horiz) 1·70 1·20

310 140e. *St Peter, St Paul and St Andrew* (horiz) 2·10 1·50

46 *Eumichtis albostigmata* (moth)

1997. Butterflies and Moths. Multicoloured.

311 49e. Type **46** 75 35

312 80e. *Menophra maderae* (moth) 1·30 65

313 100e. Painted lady 1·50 1·20

314 140e. Large white 2·75 2·50

47 Robert Achim and Anne of Arfet (Legend of Machico)

1997. Europa. Tales and Legends. Multicoloured.

315 100e. Type **47** 2·10 1·10

MS316 140×106 mm. No. 315×3 6·50 6·50

48 New Year's Eve Fireworks Display, Funchal

1998. Europa. National Festival. Multicoloured.

317 100e. Type **48** 1·90 95

MS318 140×109 mm. No. 317×3 6·25 6·25

49 *Gonepteryx cleopatra*

1998. Butterflies and Moths. Multicoloured.

319 50e. Type **49** 75 35

320 85e. *Xanthorhoe rupicola* 1·10 75

321 100e. *Noctua teixeirai* 1·50 95

322 140e. *Xenochlorodes nubigena* 2·10 1·50

50 Madeira Island Nature Park

1999. Europa. Parks and Gardens. Multicoloured.

323 100e. Type **50** 1·50 95

MS324 153×108 mm. No. 323×3 5·25 5·25

51 Medieval Floor Tile

1999. Tiles from Frederico de Freitas Collection, Funchal. Multicoloured.

325 51e. Type **51** 75 35

326 80e. English art-nouveau tile (19th/20th-century) 1·20 85

327 95e. Persian tile (14th-century) 1·50 95

328 100e. Spanish Moor tile (13th-century) 1·60 1·10

329	140e. Dutch Delft tile (18th-century)	2·10	1·50
330	210e. Syrian tile (13th/14th-century)	3·00	2·10

52 Building Europe

2000. Europa. Multicoloured.

332	100e. Type **52**	2·75	2·10
MS333	154×108 mm. Nos. 332×3	8·50	8·50

53 Mountain Orchid

2000. Plants of Laurissilva Forest. Multicoloured.

334	52e. Type **53**	70	35
335	85e. White orchid	1·20	80
336	100e. Leafy plant	1·40	90
337	100e. Laurel	1·40	90
338	140e. Barbusano	2·10	1·50
339	350e. Visco	4·75	3·75

54 Marine Life

2001. Europa. Water Resources. Multicoloured.

341	105e. Type **54**	3·25	2·10
MS342	140×110 mm. No. 341×3	7·50	7·50

55 Musicians

2001. Traditions of Madeira. Multicoloured.

343	53e. Type **55**	70	55
344	85e. Couple carrying produce	1·20	95
345	105e. Couple selling goods	1·60	1·20
MS346	140×112 mm. 350e. Man carrying birds	5·00	5·00

56 Clown

2002. Europa. Circus.

347	**56** 54c. multicoloured	3·00	2·75
MS348	140×110 mm. No. 347×3	8·50	8·50

57 Turtle Doves (*Streptopelia turtur*)

2002. Birds. Multicoloured.

349	28c. Type **57**	1·00	65
350	28c. Perching dove	1·00	65
351	28c. Dove with raised wings	1·00	65
352	28c. Dove with chicks	1·00	65

58 1992 Theatre Festival Poster (José Brandao)

2003. Europa. Poster Art.

353	**58** 55c. multicoloured	2·50	1·80
MS354	140×113 mm. No. 353×2	4·75	4·75

59 Bird of Paradise Flower, Figure and Yachts

2004. Europa. Holidays.

355	**59** 56c. multicoloured	2·50	1·80
MS356	141×112 mm. No. 355×2	4·75	4·75

60 Selvagens White-faced Storm-Petrel (*Pelagodroma marina hypoleuca*)

2004. Selvagens Islands. Multicoloured.

357	30c. Type **60**	1·00	70
358	45c. *Monathes lowei* (plant) and beetle	1·60	1·10
359	72c. *Tarentola bischoffi*	2·75	1·80
MS360	140×112 mm. Nos. 357/359	5·75	5·75

No. **MS**360 has the stamps arranged so as to make a composite design with a description of the islands below.

61 Espetada em Pau de Louro (skewered meat)

2005. Europa. Gastronomy. Multicoloured.

361	57c. Type **61**	2·10	1·30
MS362	125×95 mm. 57c.×2, Filete de espada (fish)×2	5·50	5·50

62 Coastline

2005. Tourism. Multicoloured.

363	30c. Type **62**	85	65
364	30c. Chaffinch	85	65
365	45c. Hikers	1·30	1·00
366	45c. Windmill	1·30	1·00
367	57c. Horse riders and scuba divers	1·50	1·20
368	74c. Flowers and fireworks	2·10	1·70
MS369	125×96 mm. 30c. Girl carrying basket; €1.55 Lace and tower	5·25	5·25

Nos. 363/368 were issued together, *se-tenant*, forming a composite design.

63 *Euphorbia pulcherrima*

2006. Flowers. Multicoloured.

370	30c. Type **63**	85	65
371	45c. *Aloe arborescens*	1·30	1·00
372	57c. *Senna didymobotrya*	1·50	1·20
373	74c. *Anthurium andraeanum*	2·10	1·70
374	€1 *Strelitzia reginae*	2·75	2·20
375	€2 *Hydrangea macrophylla*	5·50	4·50

MS376	Two sheets, each 124×95 mm. (a) 45c.×4, *Rosa; Leucospermum nutans; Paphiopedilum insigne; Hippeastrum vittatum*. (b) 45c.×4, *Bougainvillea; Cymbidium; Hibiscus rosa-sinesis; Erythrina crista-galli*	10·00	10·00

64 Figures (Ana Soares)

2006. Europa. Integration. Winning Entries in ANACED (association for art and creativity by and for people with disabilities) Painting Competition. Multicoloured.

377	60c. Type **64**	1·70	1·30
MS378	125×95 mm. 60c.×2, Swimming pool (Pedro Fonseca); Blind figure with dog (Andre Gaspar)	3·25	2·75

65 Terraces

2006. Madeira Wine. Multicoloured.

379	30c. Type **65**	85	65
380	52c. Workers and baskets of grapes	1·30	1·00
381	60c. Barrels in cellar	1·70	1·30
382	75c. Barrels and glass of wine	2·10	1·70
MS383	125×95 mm. 45c. Vines; 60c. Worker amongst vines; 75c. Bottles; €1 Barrels	7·75	7·75

66 *Monachus monachus* (Mediterranean monk seal)

2007. Marine Fauna. Multicoloured.

384	30c. Type **66**	85	65
385	45c. *Caretta caretta* (loggerhead sea turtle)	85	65
386	61c. *Calonectris diomedea borealis* (Cory's shearwater)	85	65
387	75c. *Aphanopus carbo* (black scabbard fish)	85	65
MS388	126×95 mm 61c.×4, *Telmatactis cricoides* (sea anemone); *Charonia lampas; Patella aspera* (limpet); *Sparisoma cretense* (parrotfish)	7·00	7·00

67 Scarf

2007. Europa. Centenary of Scouting. Multicoloured.

389	61c. Type **67**	1·70	1·30
MS390	125×95 mm. 61c.×2, Robert Baden-Powell (founder); Hat	3·25	2·75

The stamps of **MS**390 form a composite design.

68 Water-powered Mill

2007. Sugar Cane Mills. Multicoloured.

391	30c. Type **68**	85	65
392	75c. Cattle and crushing	2·10	1·70
MS393	125×95 mm. €2.45 Ox driven mill (60×40 mm)	7·00	7·00

The stamp and margin of **MS**393 form a composite design.

69 Early City

2008. 500th Anniversary of Funchal City. Multicoloured.

394	30c. Type **69**	90	70
395	61c. Early map of city and environs	1·80	1·40
396	75c. Arms	2·20	1·70
397	€1 Ship and city from the sea	3·00	2·30
MS398	125×95 mm. (a) €2.45 King Manuel I of Portugal; (b) €2.45 Ships and harbour	13·50	13·00

The stamps and margins of **MS**398a/**MS**398b, each form a composite design.

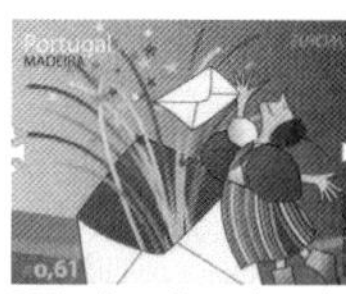
70 Envelope, Fireworks and Woman

2008. Europa. The Letter. Multicoloured.

399	61c. Type **70**	1·80	1·40
MS400	125×95 mm. 61c.×2, Houses and envelopes; As Type **70**	3·50	3·50

The stamps of **MS**400 form a composite design.

71 Ponta do Pargo

2008. Lighthouse.

401	**71** 61c. multicoloured	1·80	1·40

72 *Annona cherimola*

2009. Fruit. Multicoloured.

402	32c. Type **72**	1·10	85
403	68c. *Eugenia uniflora*	2·20	1·70
404	80c. *Persea americana*	2·50	2·00
405	€2 *Psidium guajava*	6·25	5·00
MS406	125×95 mm. €2.50 *Passiflora edulis* (80×31 mm)	7·75	7·75
MS407	125×95 mm. €2.50 *Musa* Dwarf Cavendish (80×31 mm)	7·75	7·75

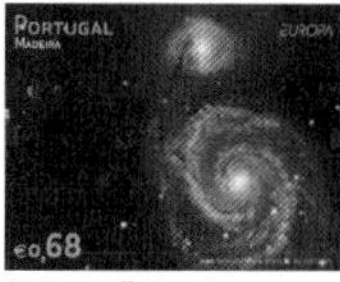
73 Constellation *Canes venatici* (spiral galaxy)

2009. Europa. Astronomy. Multicoloured.

408	68c. Type **73**	2·20	1·70
MS409	125×95 mm. 68c.×2, Telescope (built by University of Madeira student); As Type **73**	4·25	4·25

The stamps and margins of **MS**409 form a composite design.

74 Bolo do Caco (rolls)

2009. Bread. Sheet 125×95 mm.

MS410	**74** $2 multicoloured	6·25	6·25

75 *Musschia aurea*

2010. 50th Anniversary of Botanic Gardens, Rui Veira. Multicoloured.

411	32c. Type **75**	1·10	85
412	68c. *Geranium maderense*	2·20	1·70
413	80c. *Ranunculus cortusifolius*	2·50	2·00
414	€2 *Convolvulus massonii*	6·25	5·00
MS415	125×96 mm. €2 Topiary garden (80×30 mm)	6·25	5·00
MS416	125×96 mm. €2 Building, laboratory, climber and seeds (80×30 mm)	6·25	5·00

76 Girl

2010. Europa. Children's Books. Multicoloured.

417	68c. Type **76**	2·20	1·70
MS418	125×96 mm. 68c.×2, Man seated wearing hat (Father); As Type **76**	4·25	4·25

77 Walkers (Forests and Tourism)

2011. Europa. Forests. Multicoloured.

419	68c. Type **77**	2·40	2·00
MS420	125×96 mm. 68c.×2, Laurissilva Forest; As Type **77**	5·00	4·75

78 Embroidery

2011. Traditional Embroidery.

421	**478**	80c. black	2·75	2·40

79 Quinta das Cruzes

2011. Houses. Madeira Quintas. Multicoloured.

422	32c. Type **79**	1·10	95
423	68c. Jardins do Lago	2·40	2·00
424	80c. Monte Palace	2·75	2·40
425	€2 Serra Golf	7·00	6·00
MS426	125×95 mm. €1.75 Quinta do Palheiro, Casa Velha	6·25	6·00
MS427	125×95 mm. €2.30 Quinta Vigia	8·25	8·00

80 *Santa Maria*

2012. Europa. Visit Madeira. Multicoloured.

428	68c. Type **80**	2·40	2·00
MS429	125×96 mm. 68c.×2, Harbour; As Type **80**	5·00	4·75

81 Rei

2012. Levadas. Multicoloured.

430	32c. Type **81**	1·10	95
431	68c. Caldeirão Verde	2·40	2·00
432	80c. Fajã do Rodrigues	2·75	2·40
433	€2 25 Fontes	7·00	6·00
MS434	125×95 mm. €1.75 Cedros (31×80 *mm*)	6·25	6·00
MS435	125×95 mm. €2.30 Furado (31×80 *mm*)	8·25	8·00

82 Postal Quadbike

2013. Europa. Postal Vehicles. Multicoloured.

436	70c. Type **82**	2·50	2·10
MS437	125×96 mm. 68c.×2, As Type **82**; Postman delivering letters from quadbike	5·00	4·75

83 Bee

2013. Apiculture. Multicoloured.

438	36c. Type **91**	1·30	1·10
439	70c. Bee on purple flower	2·50	2·10
440	80c. Bee on white flower	2·75	2·40
441	€1.70 Bees, hives and beekeeper	6·00	5·00
MS442	125×95 mm. €1.70 Passiflora flower and bee with full pollen sacks (80×31 *mm*)	6·25	6·00
MS443	125×95 mm. €1.90 Hives and bee on leaf (80×31 *mm*)	7·00	6·75

84 As T **83** (Apiculture)

2014. Self-adhesive Stamps. Multicoloured.

444	E 20g. (72c.) Type **84**	2·50	2·20
445	E 20g. (72c.) As Type **82** (Europa. Postal Vehicles)	2·50	2·20
446	E 20g. (72c.) As No. 431 (Levadas)	2·50	2·20
447	E 20g. (72c.) As No. 412 (*Geranium maderense* (50th anniversary of Botanical Gardens)	2·50	2·20
448	E 20g. (72c.) *Eugenia uniflora* (Tropical and Sub-tropical Fruits of Madeira)	2·50	2·20

85 Brinquinho

2014. Europa. Musical Instruments. Multicoloured.

449	E 20g. (72c.) Type **85**	2·50	2·20
MS450	125×96 mm. E 20g. (72c.)×2, As Type **85**; Brinquinho, close up	5·25	5·00

86 Bolo do Caco (rolls) (As T **74**)

2015. Self-adhesive Stamps.. Multicoloured.

451	E 20g. (72c.) Type **86** (Bread)	2·50	2·20
452	E 20g. (72c.) As Type **77** (Europa. Forests)	2·50	2·20
453	E 20g. (72c.) As No. 424 (Houses)	2·50	2·20
454	E 20g. (72c.) As Type **80** (Europa. Visit Madeira)	2·50	2·20
455	E 20g. (72c.) As Type **78** (Traditional Embroidery) (*vert*)	2·50	2·20

87 'Mercado da Flor'

2015. Flower Festival. Multicoloured.

456	45c. Type **87**	1·60	1·40
457	72c. 'Decoração de Rua'	2·50	2·20
458	80c. 'Muro da Esperança'	2·75	2·40
459	€1 'Tapete de Flores'	3·50	3·00
MS460	125×95 mm. €1.80 *Anthurium andraeanum*	6·50	6·25
MS461	125×95 mm. €2 *Hliconia rostrata*	7·25	7·00

88 Potting Bench and Watering Can

2015. Europa. Old Toys. Multicoloured.

462	72c. Type **88**	2·50	2·20
MS463	125×96 mm. 72c.×2, As Type **88**; Toy taxi	5·25	5·00

89 Outdoor Nativity

2016. Christmas and New Year Festivities. Multicoloured.

464	47c. Type **89**	1·60	1·40
465	75c. Fruit and vegetable street market	2·75	2·30
466	80c. Pyramidal 'tree' of lights	2·75	2·40
467	€1 Starburst fireworks (New Year)	3·50	3·00
MS468	125×96 mm. 'New Year'. 80c. Passenger liner and fireworks; €1 As No. 467	6·50	6·25
MS469	125×96 mm. 'Christmas'. 80c. As No. 466; €1 Christ Child	6·50	6·25

90 Roller painting Contaminated Landscape Green

2016. Europa. Think Green. Multicoloured.

470	75c. Type **90**	2·75	2·30
MS471	125×96 mm. 75c.×2, Harbour; As Type **90**	5·50	5·00

2016. Self-adhesive Stamps.. Multicoloured.

472	E 20g. (72c.) As No. 413 (*Ranunculus cortusifolius* (50th anniversary of Botanical Gardens))	2·50	2·20
473	E 20g. (72c.) As No. 458 (Flower Festival)	2·50	2·20
474	E 20g. (72c.) AS Type **85** (Europa. Musical Instruments) (*vert*)	2·50	2·20
475	E 20g. (72c.) As No. 433 (Levadas)	2·50	2·20
476	E 20g. (72c.) As No. 467 (Christmas and New Year)	2·50	2·20

92 São João Baptista do Pico, Funchal

2017. Europa. Castles. Multicoloured.

477	80c. Type **92**	2·75	2·40
MS478	125×96 mm. 80c.×2, As Type **92**; São Tiago, Funchal	5·75	5·50

CHARITY TAX STAMPS

The note under this heading in Portugal also applies here.

1925. As Marquis de Pombal stamps of Portugal but inscr 'MADEIRA'.

C142	**C73**	15c. grey	2·50	2·10
C143	-	15c. grey	2·50	2·10
C144	**C 75**	15c. grey	2·50	2·10

NEWSPAPER STAMPS

1876. Newspaper stamp of Portugal optd **MADEIRA**.

N69	**N17**	2½r. green	12·00	6·00

POSTAGE DUE STAMPS

1925. Marquis de Pombal stamps as Nos. C1/C3 optd **MULTA**.

D145	**C73**	30c. grey	2·00	1·90
D146	-	30c. grey	2·00	1·90
D147	**C 75**	30c. grey	2·00	1·90

MAFEKING

A town in the Cape of Good Hope. Special stamps issued by British garrison during Boer War.

12 pence = 1 shilling; 20 shillings = 1 pound.

CHARITY TAX STAMPS

The note under this heading in Portugal also applies here.

1925. As Marquis de Pombal stamps of Portugal but inscr 'MADEIRA'.

C142	**C73**	15c. grey	2·50	2·10
C143	-	15c. grey	2·50	2·10
C144	**C 75**	15c. grey	2·50	2·10

NEWSPAPER STAMPS

1876. Newspaper stamp of Portugal optd **MADEIRA**.

N69	**N17**	2½r. green	12·00	6·00

POSTAGE DUE STAMPS

1925. Marquis de Pombal stamps as Nos. C1/C3 optd **MULTA**.

D145	**C73**	30c. grey	2·00	1·90
D146	-	30c. grey	2·00	1·90
D147	**C 75**	30c. grey	2·00	1·90

MAHRA SULTANATE OF QISHN AND SOCOTRA

The National Liberation Front took control on 1 October 1967, and full independence was granted by Great Britain on 30 November 1967. Subsequently part of South Yemen.

1000 fils = 1 dinar.

1 Mahra Flag

1967

1	**1**	5f. multicoloured	4·00	55
2	**1**	10f. multicoloured	4·00	55
3	**1**	15f. multicoloured	4·00	55
4	**1**	20f. multicoloured	4·00	55
5	**1**	25f. multicoloured	4·00	55
6	**1**	35f. multicoloured	4·00	55
7	**1**	50f. multicoloured	4·00	55
8	**1**	65f. multicoloured	4·00	55
9	**1**	100f. multicoloured	4·00	55
10	**1**	250f. multicoloured	4·00	55
11	**1**	500f. multicoloured	4·00	55

APPENDIX

The following stamps have either been issued in excess of postal needs or have not been available to the public in reasonable quantities at face value.

1967

Scout Jamboree, Idahoo. 15, 75, 100, 150f.
President Kennedy Commemoration. Postage 10, 15, 25, 50, 75, 100, 150f.; Air 250, 500f.
Olympic Games, Mexico (1968). Postage 10, 25, 50f.; Air 250, 500f.

Fot later issues see **SOUTHERN YEMEN** and **YEMEN PEOPLE'S DEMOCRATIC REPUBLIC** in Volume 6.

MALACCA

A British Settlement on the Malay Peninsula which became a state of the Federation of Malaya, incorporated in Malaysia in 1963.

100 cents = 1 dollar (Malayan).

1948. Silver Wedding. As T **59b/59c** of Jamaica.

1	10c. violet	30	1·75
2	$5 brown	35·00	50·00

1949. As T **58** of Straits Settlements.

3	1c. black	30	70
4	2c. orange	80	45
5	3c. green	30	1·75
6	4c. brown	30	10
6a	5c. purple	7·00	1·50
7	6c. grey	75	85
8	8c. red	75	7·50
8a	8c. green	9·00	8·00
9	10c. mauve	30	10
9a	12c. red	9·00	18·00
10	15c. blue	3·50	60
11	20c. black and green	1·00	8·50
11a	20c. blue	11·00	3·00
12	25c. purple and orange	1·00	70
12a	35c. red and purple	12·00	3·00
13	40c. red and purple	1·50	11·00

14	50c. black and blue	1·50	1·25
15	$1 blue and purple	21·00	35·00
16	$2 green and red	32·00	35·00
17	$5 green and brown	65·00	60·00

1949. UPU. As T **59d/59g** of Jamaica.

18	10c. purple	30	50
19	15c. blue	2·00	3·50
20	25c. orange	40	13·00
21	50c. black	60	4·75

1953. Coronation. As T **61a** of Jamaica.

22	10c. black and purple	1·75	1·50

1 Queen Elizabeth II

1954

23	**1**	1c. black	10	60
24	**1**	2c. orange	30	1·25
25	**1**	4c. brown	2·00	10
26	**1**	5c. mauve	30	2·50
27	**1**	6c. grey	10	40
28	**1**	8c. green	40	2·75
29	**1**	10c. purple	2·25	10
30	**1**	12c. red	30	3·00
31	**1**	20c. blue	30	1·25
32	**1**	25c. purple and orange	30	1·50
33	**1**	30c. red and purple	30	30
34	**1**	35c. red and purple	30	1·50
35	**1**	50c. black and blue	5·50	2·50
36	**1**	$1 blue and purple	7·00	18·00
37	**1**	$2 green and red	26·00	50·00
38	**1**	$5 green and brown	26·00	55·00

1957. As Nos. 92/102 of Kedah but inset portrait of Queen Elizabeth II.

39	-	1c. black	10	50
40	-	2c. red	10	50
41	-	4c. sepia	50	10
42	-	5c. lake	50	10
43	-	8c. green	3·00	2·50
44	-	10c. sepia	40	10
45	**15**	20c. blue	2·75	2·50
46	-	50c. black and blue	1·50	2·25
47	-	$1 blue and purple	10·00	10·00
48	-	$2 green and red	27·00	48·00
49	-	$5 brown and green	29·00	50·00

2 Copra

1960. As Nos. 39/49 but with inset picture of Melaka tree and Pelandok (mouse-deer) as in T **2**.

50	**2**	1c. black	10	30
51	-	2c. red	10	65
52	-	4c. sepia	10	10
53	-	5c. lake	10	10
54	-	8c. green	5·00	3·00
55	-	10c. purple	40	10
56	-	20c. blue	3·00	80
57	-	50c. black and blue	2·25	1·00
58	-	$1 blue and purple	7·00	3·00
59	-	$2 green and red	7·00	17·00
60	-	$5 brown and green	17·00	14·00

3 *Vanda hookeriana*

1965. As Nos. 115/121 of Kedah but with Arms of Malacca inset and inscr 'MELAKA' as in T **3**.

61	**3**	1c. multicoloured	10	2·50
62	-	2c. multicoloured	10	2·50
63	-	5c. multicoloured	1·00	40
64	-	6c. multicoloured	1·00	1·00
65	-	10c. multicoloured	30	10
66	-	15c. multicoloured	1·75	40
67	-	20c. multicoloured	2·25	1·00

The higher values used in Malacca were Nos. 20/27 of Malaysia.

4 *Papilio demoleus*

1971. Butterflies. As Nos. 124/130 of Kedah but with Arms of Malacca as in T **4**. Inscr 'melaka'.

70		1c. multicoloured	60	2·50
71		2c. multicoloured	1·00	2·50
72		5c. multicoloured	1·50	1·00
73	**4**	6c. multicoloured	1·50	3·25
74	-	10c. multicoloured	1·50	60
75	-	15c. multicoloured	2·25	20
76	-	20c. multicoloured	2·25	2·50

The higher values in use with this issue were Nos. 64/71 of Malaysia.

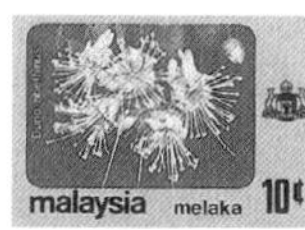

5 *Durio zibethinus*

1979. Flowers. As Nos. 135/141 of Kedah but with Arms of Malacca and inscr 'melaka' as in T **5**.

82	1c. *Rafflesia hasseltii*	10	1·25
83	2c. *Pterocarpus indicus*	10	1·25
84	5c. *Lagerstroemia speciosa*	15	1·00
85	10c. Type **5**	20	35
86	15c. *Hibiscus rosa-sinensis*	20	10
87	20c. *Rhododendron scortechinii*	25	10
88	25c. *Etlingera elatior* (inscr '*Phaeomeria speciosa*')	45	80

6 Rubber

1986. As Nos. 152/158 of Kedah but with Arms of Malacca and inscr 'MELAKA' as in T **6**.

96	1c. Coffee	10	60
97	2c. Coconuts	15	60
98	5c. Cocoa	20	20
99	10c. Black pepper	25	15
100	15c. Type **6**	40	10
101	20c. Oil palm	40	15
102	30c. Rice	40	15

7 *Nelumbium nelumbo* (sacred lotus)

2007. Garden Flowers. As Nos. 210/215 of Johore, but with Arms of Malacca as in T **7**. Multicoloured.

103	5s. Type **7**	10	10
104	10s. *Hydrangea macrophylla*	15	10
105	20s. *Hippeastrum reticulatum*	25	15
106	30s. *Bougainvillea*	40	20
107	40s. *Ipomoea indica*	50	30
108	50s. *Hibiscus rosa-sinensis*	65	35
MS109	100×85 mm. Nos. 103/108	2·25	2·25

MALAGASY REPUBLIC

The former areas covered by Madagascar and Dependencies were renamed the Malagasy Republic within the French Community on 14 October 1958. It became independent on 26 June 1960. In 1992 it reverted to the name of Madagascar.

1958. 100 centimes = 1 franc.
1976. 5 francs = 1 ariary.

1 Human Rights

1958. Tenth Anniversary of Declaration of Human Rights.

1	**1**	10f. brown and blue	1·10	75

2 Datura

1959. Tropical Flora.

2	**2**	6f. green, brown and yellow	55	40
3	-	25f. multicoloured	1·30	60

Design: Vert—25f. Poinsettia.

2a Malagasy Flag and Assembly Hall

1959. Proclamation of Malagasy Republic and French Community Commemorative (60f.).

4	**2a**	20f. red, green and purple	55	40
5	-	25f. red, green and grey	80	55
6	-	60f. multicoloured	2·20	1·00

Designs: Vert—25f. Malagasy flag on map of Madagascar; 60f. Natives holding French and Malagasy flags.

3 *Chionaema pauliani* (butterfly)

1960

7	-	30c. multicoloured (postage)	1·10	40
8	-	40c. brown, chocolate & green	1·10	40
9	-	50c. turquoise and purple	1·10	40
10	**3**	1f. red, purple and black	1·10	40
11	-	3f. black, red and olive	1·10	40
12	-	5f. green, brown and red	65	40
13	-	6f. yellow and green	80	40
14	-	8f. black, green and red	80	40
15	-	10f. green, brown & turquoise	1·40	40
16	-	15f. green and brown	1·50	40
17	-	30f. multicoloured (air)	2·50	40
18	-	40f. brown and turquoise	2·50	40
19	-	50f. multicoloured	4·50	65
20	-	100f. multicoloured	7·75	90
21	-	200f. yellow and violet	10·00	2·10
22	-	500f. brown, blue and green	20·00	3·75

Other Designs: As T **2** Horiz—5f. Sisal; 8f. Pepper; 15f. Cotton. Vert—6f. Ylang ylang (flower); 10f. Rice. 48½×27 mm—30f. Sugar cane trucks; 40f. Tobacco plantation; 500f. Mandrare Bridge.

3a Reafforestation

1960. Trees Festival.

23	**3a**	20f. brown, green and ochre	1·30	60

4

1960. Tenth Anniversary of African Technical Cooperation Commission.

24	**4**	25f. lake and green	90	55

5 President Philibert Tsiranana

1960

25	**5**	20f. brown and green	75	40

6 Young Athletes

1960. First Youth Games, Tananarive.

26	**6**	25f. brown, chestnut and blue	90	55

7 President Tsiranana

1960

27	**7**	20f. black, red and green	45	10

1960. Independence. Surch **+10 F FETES DE L'INDEPENDANCE**.

28	20f.+10f. black, red & grn	70	40

9 Ruffed Lemur

1961. Lemurs.

29	-	2f. purple & turq (postage)	20	15
30	**9**	4f. black, brown and myrtle	40	15
31	-	12f. brown and green	95	25
32	-	65f. brown, sepia and myrtle (air)	2·75	90
33	-	85f. black, sepia and green	3·00	1·30
34	-	250f. purple, black & turq	8·75	3·50

Lemurs: Vert As T **9**—2f. Grey gentle lemur; 12f. Mongoose-lemur. 48×27 mm—65f. Diadem sifaka; 85f. Indris; 250f. Verreaux's sifaka.

10 Diesel Train

1962

35	**10**	20f. myrtle	1·10	35
36	-	25f. blue	85	15

Design: 25f. President Tsiranana Bridge.

11 UN and Malagasy Flags, and Govt. Building, Tananarive

1962. Admission into UNO.

37	**11**	25f. multicoloured	50	25
38	**11**	85f. multicoloured	1·80	70

11a

1962. Malaria Eradication.

39	**11a**	25f.+5f. green	95	90

12 Ranomafana

1962. Tourist Publicity.

40	**12**	10f. purple, myrtle and blue (postage)	25	15
41	-	30f. purple, blue and myrtle	60	25
42	-	50f. blue, myrtle and purple	90	40
43	-	60f. myrtle, purple and blue	1·10	55
44	-	100f. brown, myrtle and blue (air)	1·90	1·20
MS44a		150×85 mm. For Tananarive Philatelic Exhibition. Nos. 40/44	5·75	5·50

Designs: As T **12**—30f. Tritriva Lake; 50f. Foulpointe; 60f. Fort Dauphin. 27×47½ mm—100f. Boeing 707 airliner over Nossi-Be.

13 GPO, Tamatave

1962. Stamp Day.

45	**13**	25f.+5f. brn, myrtle & bl	70	70

14 Malagasy and UNESCO. Emblems

1962. UNESCO. Conference on Higher Education in Africa, Tananarive.

46	**14**	20f. black, green and red	50	25

14a

1962. First Anniversary of Union of African and Malagasy States.

47	**14a**	30f. green	85	55

15 Hydro-electric Station

1962. Malagasy Industrialisation.

48	**15**	5f. multicoloured	10	10
49	-	8f. multicoloured	30	10
50	-	10f. multicoloured	35	25
51	-	15f. brown, black and blue	45	25
52	-	20f. multicoloured	55	25

Designs: Horiz—8f. Atomic plant; 15f. *Esso Gasikara* (tanker); 20f. Hertzian aerials at Tananarive-Fianarantsoa. Vert—10f. Oilwell.

16 Globe and Factory

1963. International Fair, Tamatave.

53	**16**	25f. orange and black	45	25

16a

1963. Freedom from Hunger.

54	**16a**	25f.+5f. lake, brown and red	95	80

17 Douglas DC-8 Airliner

1963. Air. Malagasy Commercial Aviation.

55	**17**	500f. blue, red and green	9·75	4·25

18 Central Post Office, Tananarive

1963. Stamp Day.

56	**18**	20f.+5f. brown & turq	75	70

19 Madagascar Blue Pigeon

1963. Malagasy Birds and Orchids (8f. to 12f.). Multicoloured. (a) Postage as T **19**.

57	1f. Type **19**	55	45
58	2f. Blue Madagascar coucal	55	45
59	3f. Madagascar red fody	80	45
60	6f. Madagascar pygmy kingfisher	1·00	45
61	8f. *Gastrorchis humblotii*	85	30
62	10f. *Eulophiella roempleriana*	1·30	50
63	12f. *Angraceum sesquipedale*	1·40	50

(b) Air. Horiz: 49½×28 mm.

64	40f. Helmet bird	2·30	80
65	100f. Pitta-like ground roller	4·75	1·60
66	200f. Crested wood ibis	8·75	3·00

20 Centenary Emblem and Map

1963. Red Cross Centenary.

67	**20**	30f. multicoloured	95	65

20a

1963. Air. African and Malagasy Posts and Telecommunications Union.

68	**20a**	85f. multicoloured	1·80	1·10

21 UPU Monument, Berne, and Map of Malagasy

1963. Air. Second Anniversary of Malagasy's Admission to UPU.

69	**21**	45f. blue, red and turquoise	70	25
70	**21**	85f. blue, red and violet	1·20	60

22 Arms of Fianarantsoa

1963. Town Arms (1st series). Multicoloured.

71	1f.50 Antsirabe	10	10
72	5f. Antalaha	10	10
73	10f. Tulear	30	20
74	15f. Majunga	30	15
75	20f. Type **22**	55	25
75a	20f. Manajary	30	15
76	25f. Tananarive	55	25
76a	30f. Nossi Be	55	25
77	50f. Diego-Suarez	1·60	70
77a	90f. Antsohihy	1·90	1·30

See also Nos. 174/177 and 208/209.

23 Flame, Globe and Hands

1963. 15th Anniversary of Declaration of Human Rights.

78	**23**	60f. ochre, bronze and mauve	95	55

24 Meteorological Station, Tananarive

1964. Air. World Meteorological Day.

79	**24**	90f. brown, blue and grey	1·90	1·40

25 Postal Cheques and Savings Bank Building, Tananarive

1964. Stamp Day.

80	**25**	25f.+5f. brown, bl & grn	85	80

26 Scouts beside Campfire

1964. 40th Anniversary of Malagasy Scout Movement.

81	**26**	20f. multicoloured	75	45

27 Symbolic Bird and Globe within 'Egg'

1964. Europafrique.

82	**27**	45f. brown and green	90	55

28 Statuette of Woman

1964. Malagasy Art.

83	**28**	6f. brown, blue and indigo (postage)	45	25
84	-	30f. brown, bistre & green	85	40
85	-	100f. brown, red & vio (air)	2·10	1·20

Designs: 30f. Statuette of squatting vendor. 27×48½ mm—100f. Statuary of peasant family, ox and calf.

1964. French, African and Malagasy Co-operation. As T **41a** of Ivory Coast.

86	25f. brown, chestnut and black	75	35

29 Tree on Globe

1964. University of Malagasy Republic.

87	**29**	65f. black, red and green	75	45

30 Cithern

1965. Malagasy Musical Instruments.

88	-	3f. brown, blue and mauve (postage)	45	10
89	**30**	6f. sepia, purple and green	60	10
90	-	8f. brown, black and green	75	25
91	-	25f. multicoloured	1·80	80
92	-	200f. brown, orange and green (air)	5·75	2·75

Designs: As T **30**:—f. Kabosa (lute); 8f. Hazolahy (sacred drum). Larger Vert 35½×48 mm—25f. *Valiha Player* (after E. Ralambo). 27×48 mm—200f. Bara violin.

31 Foulpointe Post Office

1965. Stamp Day.

93	**31**	20f. brown, green and orange	45	25

32 ITU Emblem

1965. ITU Centenary.

94	**32**	50f. green, blue and red	1·20	60

33 J.-J. Rabearivelo (poet)

1965. Rabearivelo Commemorative.

95	**33**	40f. brown and orange	75	40

34 Nurse weighing Baby

1965. Air. International Co-operation Year.

96	**34**	50f. black, bistre and blue	95	40
97	-	100f. purple, brown and blue	1·50	70

Design: 100f. Boy and girl.

35 President Tsiranana

1965. President Tsiranana's 55th Birthday.

98	**35**	20f. multicoloured	30	15
99	**35**	25f. multicoloured	65	25

MS100 Two sheets each 78×120 mm. (a) No. 98×4; (b) No. 99×4 — 3·50 — 3·25

36 Bearer

1965. Postal Transport.

102	-	3f. violet, blue and brown	60	40

103 - 4f. blue, brown and green 35 25
104 **36** 10f. multicoloured 45 25
105 - 12f. multicoloured 40 25
106 - 20f. multicoloured 1·20 40
107 - 25f. multicoloured 1·00 40
108 - 30f. red, brown and blue 1·80 70
109 - 65f. brown, blue and violet 1·90 85

Designs: Horiz—3f. Early car; 4f. Filanzane (litter); 12f. Pirogue; 20f. Horse-drawn mail-cart; 25f. Bullock cart; 30f. Early railway postal carriage; 65f. Hydrofoil, *Porthos*, Betsiboka.

37 Diseased Hands

1966. World Leprosy Day.
110 **37** 20f. purple, red and green 75 40

38 Planting Trees

1966. Reafforestation Campaign.
111 **38** 20f. violet, brown & turq 55 25

39 *Cicindelidae chaetodera andriana*

1966. Malagasy Insects. Multicoloured.
112 1f. Type **39** 55 20
113 6f. *Mantodea tisma freiji* 80 20
114 12f. *Cerambycini mastododera nodicollis* 1·70 40
115 45f. *Trachelophoru giraffa* 2·50 75

40 Madagascar 1c. Stamp of 1903

1966. Stamp Day.
116 **40** 25f. bistre and red 60 40

41 Betsileo Dance

1966. Folk Dances. Multicoloured.
117 2f. Bilo Sakalava dance (vert) (postage) 10 10
118 5f. Type **41** 30 10
119 30f. Antandroy dance (vert) 60 25
120 200f. Southern Malagasy dancer (air) 4·75 1·80
121 250f. Sakalava Net Dance 5·75 3·00

Nos. 120/121 are size 27×48 mm.

43 'Tree' of Emblems

1966. OCAM Conference, Tananarive.
122 **43** 25f. multicoloured 55 25

The above was issued with 'Janvier 1966' obliterated by bars, and optd **JUIN 1966**.

44 Singing Anthem

1966. National Anthem.
123 **44** 20f. brown, mauve & green 45 25

45 UNESCO. Emblem

1966. 20th Anniversary of UNESCO.
124 **45** 30f. blue, bistre and red 55 25

46 Lions Emblem

1967. 50th Anniversary of Lions International.
125 **46** 30f. multicoloured 55 40

47 Harvesting Rice

1967. International Rice Year.
126 **47** 20f. multicoloured 55 25

48 Adventist Temple, Tanambao-Tamatave

1967. Religious Buildings (1st series).
127 **48** 3f. ochre, blue and green 10 10
128 - 5f. lilac, purple and green 10 10
129 - 10f. purple, blue and green 45 20

Buildings: Vert—5f. Catholic Cathedral, Tananarive. Horiz—10f. Mosque, Tamatave.
See also Nos. 148/150.

49 Raharisoa at Piano

1967. Fourth Death Anniversary of Norbert Raharisoa (composer).
130 **49** 40f. multicoloured 95 45

50 Jean Raoult's Bleriot XI, 1911

1967. History of Malagasy Aviation.
131 **50** 5f. brown, blue and green (postage) 70 35
132 - 45f. black, blue and brown 1·40 65
133 - 500f. black, blue and ochre (air) 10·50 5·00

Designs: 45f. Bernard Bougault and flying boat, 1926. 48×27 mm—500f. Jean Dagnaux and Breguet 19A2 biplane, 1927.

51 Ministry of Communications, Tananarive

1967. Stamp Day.
134 **51** 20f. green, blue and orange 55 25

1967. Air. Fifth Anniversary of UAMPT. As T **64a** of Ivory Coast.
135 100f. mauve, bistre and red 1·80 85

52 Church, Torch and Map

1967. Centenary of Malagasy Lutheran Church.
136 **52** 20f. multicoloured 55 25

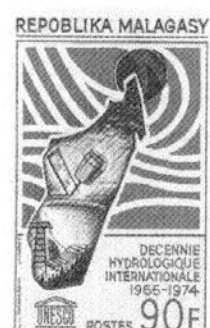

53 Map and Decade Emblem

1967. International Hydrological Decade.
137 **53** 90f. brown, red and blue 1·20 55

54 Woman's Face and Scales of Justice

1967. Women's Rights Commission.
138 **54** 50f. blue, ochre and green 75 45

55 Human Rights Emblem

1968. Human Rights Year.
139 **55** 50f. red, green and black 75 45

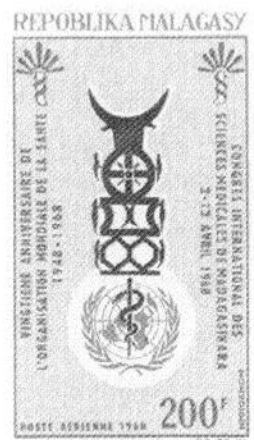

56 Congress and WHO Emblems

1968. Air. 20th Anniversary of WHO and International Medical Sciences Congress, Tananarive.
140 **56** 200f. red, blue and ochre 2·75 1·50

57 International Airport, Tananarive-Ivato

1968. Air. Stamp Day.
141 **57** 500f. blue, green and brown 8·75 4·25

1968. Nos. 33 and 38 surch.
142 **11** 20f. on 85f. (postage) 75 55
143 - 20f. on 85f. (No. 33) (air) 70 45

59 Industry and Construction

1968. Five-year Plan (1st issue).
144 **59** 10f. plum, red and green 30 10
145 - 20f. black, red and green 30 10
146 - 40f. blue, brown & ultram 75 25

Designs: Vert—20f. Agriculture. Horiz—40f. Transport.
See also Nos. 156/157.

60 Church and Open Bible

1968. 150th Anniversary of Christianity in Madagascar.
147 **60** 20f. multicoloured 55 25

61 Isotry Protestant Church, Fitiavana, Tananarive

1968. Religious Buildings (2nd series).
148 **61** 4f. brown, green and red 10 10
149 - 12f. brown, blue and violet 30 15
150 - 50f. indigo, blue and green 75 25

Designs: 12f. Catholic Cathedral, Fianarantsoa; 50f. Aga Khan Mosque, Tananarive.

62 President Tsiranana and Wife

1968. Tenth Anniversary of Republic.
151 **62** 20f. brown, red and yellow 45 10
152 **62** 30f. brown, red and blue 50 20
MS153 161×120 mm. Nos. 151/152×2 2·00 1·90

63 Cornucopia, Coins and Map

1968. 50th Anniversary of Malagasy Savings Bank.
154 **63** 20f. multicoloured 45 10

64 'Dance of the Whirlwind'

1968. Air.
155 **64** 100f. multicoloured 1·90 85

65 Malagasy Family

1968. Five-year Plan (2nd issue).
156 **65** 15f. red, yellow and blue 30 10
157 - 45f. multicoloured 65 25

Design: Vert—45f. Allegory of Achievement.

1968. Air. Philexafrique Stamp Exhibition, Abidjan (1969) (1st issue). As T **74a** of Ivory Coast.
158 100f. multicoloured 3·75 80

Design: Vert—100f. *Young Woman sealing a Lette*" (J. B. Santerre).

1969. Air. Philexafrique Stamp Exhibition, Abidjan, Ivory Coast (2nd issue). As T **74b** of Ivory Coast.
159 50f. red, green and drab 2·20 1·40

Design: 50f. Malagasy Arms, map and Madagascar stamp of 1946.

68 *Queen Adelaide receiving Malagasy Mission, London* (1836–1837)

1969

160	**68**	250f. multicoloured	5·50	4·00

69 Hand with Spanner, Cogwheels and ILO Emblem

1969. 50th Anniversary of ILO.

161	**69**	20f. multicoloured	45	25

70 Post and Telecommunications Building, Tananarive

1969. Stamp Day.

162	**70**	30f. multicoloured	75	25

71 Map, Steering Wheel and Vehicles

1969. 20th Anniversary of Malagasy Motor Club.

163	**71**	65f. multicoloured	1·00	45

72 President Tsiranana making Speech

1969. Tenth Anniversary of President Tsiranana's Assumption of Office.

164	**72**	20f. multicoloured	45	10

73 Bananas

1969. Fruits.

165	**73**	5f. green, brown and blue	45	10
166	-	15f. red, myrtle and green	95	25

Design: 15f. Lychees.

74 Start of Race and Olympic Flame

1969. Olympic Games, Mexico (1968).

167	**74**	15f. brown, red and green	50	20

75 *Malagasy Seashore, East Coast* (A. Razafinjohany)

1969. Air. Paintings by Malagasy Artists. Multicoloured.

168	100f. Type **75**	1·70	1·50
169	150f. *Sunset on the High Plateaux* (H. Ratovo)	3·75	1·90

76 Imerino House, High Plateaux

1969. Malagasy Traditional Dwellings (1st series).

170	-	20f. red, blue and green	30	15
171	-	20f. brown, red and blue	30	15
172	**76**	40f. red, blue and indigo	55	25
173	-	60f. purple, green and blue	90	35

Houses: Horiz—20f. (No. 170), Tsimihety hut, East Coast; 60f. Betsimisaraka dwellings, East Coast. Vert—20f. (No. 171), Betsileo house, High Plateaux.

See also Nos. 205/206.

77 Ambalavao Arms

1970. Town Arms (2nd series). Multicoloured.

174	10f. Type **77**	40	10
175	25f. Morondava	55	10
176	25f. Ambatondrazaka	55	10
177	80f. Tamatave	1·20	45

78 Agate

1970. Semi-precious Stones. Multicoloured.

178	5f. Type **78**	4·00	1·90
179	20f. Ammonite	13·00	3·75

1970. New UPU Headquarters Building, Berne. As T **81** of New Caledonia.

180	20f. blue, brown and mauve	50	25

80 UN Emblem and Symbols

1970. 25th Anniversary of United Nations.

181	**80**	50f. black, blue and orange	80	40

81 Astronaut and Module on Moon

1970. Air. First Anniversary of *Apollo 11* Moon-landing.

182	**81**	75f. green, slate and blue	1·50	55

82 Malagasy Fruits

1970

183	**82**	20f. multicoloured	1·20	35

83 Delessert's Lyria

1970. Sea Shells (1st series). Multicoloured.

184	5f. Type **83**	65	30
185	10f. Bramble murex	95	35
186	20f. Thorny oyster	2·00	45

See also Nos. 238/243.

84 Aye-aye

1970. International Nature Conservation Conference, Tananarive.

187	**84**	20f. multicoloured	1·50	40

85 Boeing 737 in Flight

1970. Air.

188	**85**	200f. red, green and blue	3·25	1·40

86 President Tsiranana

1970. President Tsiranana's 60th Birthday.

189	**86**	30f. brown and green	60	25

87 Calcite

1971. Minerals. Multicoloured.

190	12f. Type **87**	2·50	55
191	15f. Quartz	3·50	80

88 Soap Works, Tananarive

1971. Malagasy Industries.

192	**88**	5f. multicoloured	25	10
193	-	15f. black, brown and blue	45	10
194	-	50f. multicoloured	80	20

Designs: 15f. Chrome works, Comina-Andriamena; 50f. Textile complex, Sotema-Majunga.

89 Globe and Emblems

1971. Council Meeting of Common Market Countries with African and Malagasy Associated States, Tananarive.

195	**89**	5f. multicoloured	30	25

90 Rural Mobile Post Office

1971. Stamp Day.

196	**90**	25f. multicoloured	55	25

91 General De Gaulle

1971. Death (1970) of General Charles de Gaulle.

197	**91**	30f. black, red and blue	1·00	55

92 Palm Beach Hotel, Nossi-Be

1971. Malagasy Hotels.

198	**92**	25f. multicoloured	45	25
199	-	65f. brown, blue and green	1·00	40

Design: 65f. Hilton Hotel, Tananarive.

93 Forestry Emblem

1971. Forest Preservation Campaign.

200	**93**	3f. multicoloured	30	20

94 Jean Ralaimongo

1971. Air. Malagasy Celebrities.

201	**94**	25f. brown, red and orange	45	25
202	-	65f. brown, myrtle & green	65	25
203	-	100f. brown, ultram & bl	1·70	40

Celebrities: 65f. Albert Sylla; 100f. Joseph Ravoahangy Andrianavalona.

1971. Air. Tenth Anniversary of African and Malagasy Posts and Telecommunications Union. As T **101a** of Ivory Coast.

204	100f. UAMPT HQ, Brazzaville, and painting *Mpisikidy* (G. Rakotovao)	1·50	70

96 Vezo Dwellings, South-east Coast

1971. Malagasy Traditional Dwellings (2nd series). Multicoloured.

205	5f. Type **96**	25	10
206	10f. Antandroy hut, South coast	45	10

97 *Children and Cattle in Meadow* (G. Rasoaharijaona)

1971. 25th Anniversary of UNICEF.

207	**97**	50f. multicoloured	1·60	45

1972. Town Arms (3rd series). As T **77**. Multicoloured.

208	1f. Maintirano Arms	55	10
209	25f. Fenerive-Est	1·10	25

99 Cable-laying train

1972. Co-axial Cable Link, Tananarive–Tamatave.
210 **99** 45f. brown, green and red 1·20 55

100 Telecommunications Station

1972. Inauguration of Philibert Tsiranana Satellite Communications Station.
211 **100** 85f. multicoloured 95 55

101 President Tsiranana and Voters

1972. Presidential Elections.
212 **101** 25f. multicoloured 55 40

102 Moped Postman

1972. Stamp Day.
213 **102** 10f. multicoloured 75 25

1972. De Gaulle Memorial. No. 197 surch **MEMORIAL +20F**.
214 **91** 30f.+20f. black, red & bl 95 85

104 Exhibition Emblem and Stamps

1972. Second National Stamp Exhibition, Antanarive.
215 **104** 25f. multicoloured 45 25
216 **104** 40f. multicoloured 75 40
217 **104** 100f. multicoloured 1·70 70
MS218 151×116 mm. Nos. 215/217 4·50 4·50

105 Road and Monument

1972. Opening of Andapa–Sambava Highway.
219 **105** 50f. multicoloured 55 40

106 Petroleum Refinery, Tamatave

1972. Malagasy Economic Development.
220 **106** 2f. blue, green and yellow 45 10
221 - 100f. multicoloured 4·75 90
Design: 100f. 3600 CV diesel locomotive.

107 R. Rakotobe

1972. Air. First Death Anniversary of Rene Rakotobe (poet).
222 **107** 40f. brown, purple & orge 75 25

108 College Buildings

1972. 150th Anniversary of Razafindrahety College, Tananarive.
223 **108** 10f. purple, brown & blue 30 20

109 Volleyball

1972. African Volleyball Championships.
224 **109** 12f. black, orange & brn 45 15

110 Runners breasting Tape

1972. Air. Olympic Games, Munich. Multicoloured.
225 100f. Type **110** 1·70 90
226 200f. Judo 3·25 1·10

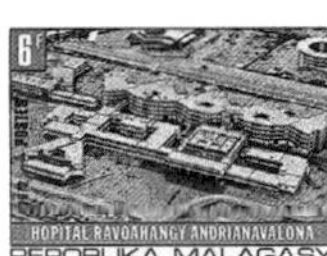

111 Hospital Complex

1972. Inauguration of Ravoahangy Andrianavalona Hospital.
227 **111** 6f. multicoloured 30 15

112 Mohair Goat

1972. Air. Malagasy Wool Production.
228 **112** 250f. multicoloured 5·25 2·75

113 Ploughing with Oxen

1972. Agricultural Expansion.
229 **113** 25f. multicoloured 1·50 45

114 *Virgin and Child* (15th-century Florentine School)

1972. Air. Christmas. Religious Paintings. Multicoloured.
230 85f. Type **114** 1·20 70
231 150f. *Adoration of the Magi* (A. Mantegna) (horiz) 2·50 1·10

115 Betsimisarka Women

1972. Traditional Costumes. Multicoloured.
232 10f. Type **115** 30 10
233 15f. Merina mother and child 45 20

116 Astronauts on Moon

1973. Air. Moon Flight of *Apollo 17*.
234 **116** 300f. purple, brown & grey 4·50 2·20

117 Natural Produce

1973. Tenth Anniversary of Malagasy Freedom from Hunger Campaign Committee.
235 **117** 25f. multicoloured 1·10 50

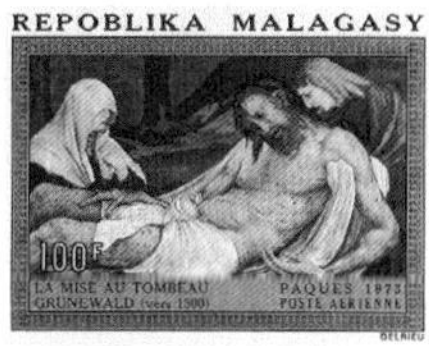

118 *The Entombment* (Grunewald)

1973. Air. Easter. Multicoloured.
236 100f. Type **118** 1·50 70
237 200f. *The Resurrection* (Grunewald) (vert) 3·00 1·40

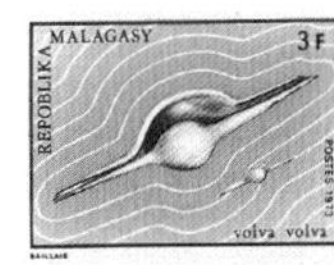

119 Shuttlecock Volva

1973. Sea Shells (2nd series). Multicoloured.
238 3f. Type **119** 20 10
239 10f. Arthritic spider conch 45 25
240 15f. Common harp 65 25
241 25f. Type **119** 95 50
242 40f. As 15f. 1·30 50
243 50f. As 10f. 2·10 65

120 Postal Courier, Tsimandoa

1973. Stamp Day.
244 **120** 50f. blue, green and brown 75 40

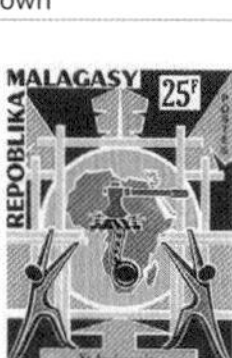

121 Africa within Scaffolding

1973. Tenth Anniversary of Organisation of African Unity.
245 **121** 25f. multicoloured 55 25

122 *Cameleon campani*

1973. Malagasy Chameleons. Multicoloured.
246 1f. Type **122** 25 10
247 5f. *Cameleon nasutus* (male) 25 10
248 10f. *Cameleon nasutus* (female) 45 20
249 40f. As 5f. 1·20 30
250 60f. Type **122** 1·70 55
251 85f. As 10f. 2·40 95

123 Excursion Carriage

1973. Air. Early Malagasy Railways. Multicoloured.
252 100f. Type **123** 2·00 1·40
253 150f. Mallet steam locomotive No. 24, 1907 3·00 1·60

124 *Cypripedium*

1973. Orchids. Multicoloured.
254 10f. Type **124** 55 10
255 25f. *Nepenthes pervillei* 80 35
256 40f. As 25f. 1·70 50
257 100f. Type **124** 3·50 1·00

1973. Pan African Drought Relief. No. 235 surch **SECHERESSE SOLIDARITE AFRICAINE** and value.
258 **117** 100f. on 25f. multicoloured 1·50 70

126 Dish Aerial and Meteorological Station

1973. Air. WMO Centenary.
259 **126** 100f. orange, blue & black 1·70 80

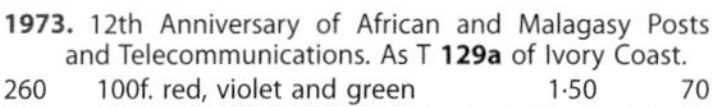
1973. 12th Anniversary of African and Malagasy Posts and Telecommunications. As T **129a** of Ivory Coast.
260 100f. red, violet and green 1·50 70

128 Greater Dwarf Lemur

1973. Malagasy Lemurs.
261 **128** 5f. brown, green and purple (postage) 95 45
262 - 25f. brown, sepia & green 2·00 90

263	-	150f. brn, grn & sepia (air)	3·75	1·50
264	**128**	200f. brown, turq & blue	5·25	2·30

Design: Vert—25f., 150f. Weasel-lemur.

129 President Kennedy

1973. Air. Tenth Death Anniversary of President John Kennedy.

265	**129**	300f. multicoloured	4·00	2·10

130 Footballers

1973. Air. World Cup Football Championship. West Germany.

266	**130**	500f. mauve, brown and light brown	7·50	3·00

CURRENCY. Issues from No. 267 to No. 389 have face values shown as 'Fmg'. This abbreviation denotes the Malagasy Franc which was introduced in 1966.

131 Copernicus, Satellite and Diagram

1974. Air. 500th Birth Anniversary of Copernicus.

267	**131**	250f. blue, brown & green	4·50	1·70

1974. No. 76a surch.

268	25f. on 30f. multicoloured	45	25

133 Agricultural Training

1974. 25th World Scouting Conference, Nairobi, Kenya.

269	**133**	4f. grey, blue and green (postage)	10	10
270	-	15f. purple, green and blue	45	25
271	-	100f. ochre, red & blue (air)	1·10	55
272	-	300f. brown, blue & black	3·75	1·50

Designs: Vert—15f. Building construction. Horiz—100f. First Aid training; 300f. Fishing.

134 Male Player, and Hummingbird on Hibiscus

1974. Air. Asia, Africa and Latin America Table-Tennis Championships, Peking.

273	**134**	50f. red, blue and brown	1·20	45
274	-	100f. red, blue and violet	2·50	95

Design: 100f. Female player and stylised bird.

135 Family and House

1974. World Population Year.

275	**135**	25f. red, orange and blue	45	10

136 Micheline Railcar

1974. Air. Malagasy Railway Locomotives.

276	**136**	50f. green, red and brown	85	50
277	-	85f. red, blue and green	1·50	70
278	-	200f. blue, lt blue & brown	3·75	1·60

Designs: 85f. Track-inspection trolley; 200f. Garratt steam locomotive, 1926.

137 UPU Emblem and Letters

1974. Air. Centenary of UPU(1st issue).

279	**137**	250f. red, blue and violet	4·25	1·70

See also No. 286.

138 Rainibetsimisaraka

1974. Rainibetsimisaraka Commemoration.

280	**138**	25f. multicoloured	55	40

1974. Air. West Germany's Victory in World Cup Football Championship. No. 266 optd **R.F.A. 2 HOLLANDE 1**.

281	**130**	500f. mauve, brown and light brown	6·50	3·50

140 Apollo and Soyuz spacecraft

1974. Air. Soviet–U.S. Space Co-operation.

282	**140**	150f. orange, green & blue	1·50	80
283	-	250f. green, blue & brown	2·75	1·20

Design: No. 283, As T **140** but different view.

141 Marble Slabs

1974. Marble Industry. Multicoloured.

284	4f. Type **141**	75	25
285	25f. Quarrying	2·20	65

1974. Air. Universal Postal Union Centenary (2nd issue). No. 279 optd **100 ANS DE COLLABORATION INTERNATIONALE**.

286	**137**	250f. red, blue and violet	2·20	1·10

143 Faces and Maps

1974. Europafrique.

287	**143**	150f. brown, red & orange	2·00	85

144 'Food in Hand'

1974. Freedom from Hunger.

288	**144**	80f. blue, brown and grey	1·00	55

145 Coton

1974. Malagasy Dogs. Multicoloured.

289	50f. Type **145**	2·40	70
290	100f. Hunting dog	3·50	1·40

146 Malagasy People

1974. Founding of Fokonolona Commune.

291	**146**	5f. multicoloured	30	10
292	**146**	10f. multicoloured	30	10
293	**146**	20f. multicoloured	35	10
294	**146**	60f. multicoloured	95	30

147 Discovering Talent

1974. National Development Council.

295	**147**	25f. multicoloured	30	10
296	**147**	35f. multicoloured	45	25

148 *Adoration of the Magi* (David)

1974. Air. Christmas. Multicoloured.

297	200f. Type **148**	3·00	1·10
298	300f. *Virgin of the Cherries and Child* (Metzys)	4·50	1·80

149 Malagasy Girl and Rose

1975. International Women's Year.

299	**149**	100f. brown, orange & grn	1·20	55

150 Colonel Richard Ratsimandrava (Head of Government)

1975

300	**150**	15f. brown, black & yellow	30	10
301	**150**	25f. brown, black and blue	35	25
302	**150**	100f. brown, black & green	1·30	45

151 Sofia Bridge

1975

303	**151**	45f. multicoloured	75	40

152 UN Emblem and Part of Globe

1975. Air. 30th Anniversary of UN Charter.

304	**152**	300f. multicoloured	3·75	1·40

153 De Grasse (after Mauzaisse) and *Randolph*

1975. Bicentenary of American Revolution (1st issue). Multicoloured.

305	40f. Type **153** (postage)	70	25
306	50f. Lafayette, *Lexington* and HMS *Edward*	95	40
307	100f. D'Estaing and *Languedoc* (air)	1·30	45
308	200f. Paul Jones, *Bonhomme Richard* and HMS *Serapis*	2·50	1·00
309	300f. Benjamin Franklin, *Millern* and *Montgomery*	4·00	1·40
MS310	127×91 mm. 500f. George Washington (after Peale) and *Hanna*. Imperf	7·50	2·30

See also Nos. 371/**MS**376.

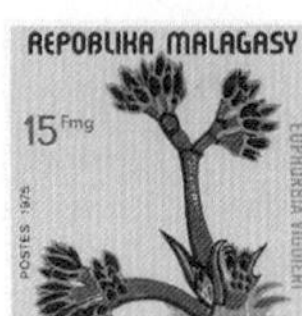

154 *Euphorbia viguieri*

1975. Malagasy Flora. Multicoloured.

311	15f. Type **154** (postage)	40	25
312	25f. *Hibiscus rosesinensis*	55	25
313	30f. *Plumeria rubra acutitolia*	80	40
314	40f. *Pachypodium rosulatum*	1·20	40
315	85f. *Turraea sericea* (air)	2·30	1·40

1975. Air. Apollo–Soyuz Space Link. Nos. 282/283 optd **JONCTION 17 JUILLET 1975**.

316	**140**	150f. orange, green & blue	1·50	70
317	-	250f. green, blue & brown	3·00	1·40

156 Temple Frieze

1975. Air. Save Borobudur Temple (in Indonesia) Campaign.

318	**156**	50f. red, orange and blue	1·50	70

157 Racial Unity

1975. Namibia Day.

319	**157**	50f. multicoloured	75	25

158 Pryer's Woodpecker

1975. International Exposition, Okinawa. Fauna. Multicoloured.

320	25f. Type **158** (postage)	65	25
321	40f. Ryukyu rabbit	1·00	25
322	50f. Toad	1·40	40
323	75f. Tortoise	2·50	70
324	125f. Sika deer (air)	2·50	80
MS325	101×82 mm. 300f. Jay	5·50	1·40

159 Lily Waterfall

1975. Lily Waterfall. Multicoloured.

326	25f. Type **159**	45	25
327	40f. Lily Waterfall (distant view)	75	25

160 Hurdling

1975. Air. Pre-Olympic Year. Olympic Games, Montreal (1976). Multicoloured.

328	75f. Type **160**	1·00	45
329	200f. Weightlifting (vert)	2·75	1·00

161 Bobsleigh Fours

1975. Winter Olympic Games, Innsbruck. Multicoloured.

330	75f. Type **161** (postage)	75	25
331	100f. Ski-jumping	1·20	45
332	140f. Speed-skating	1·80	55
333	200f. Cross-country skiing (air)	2·75	75
334	245f. Downhill skiing	3·00	1·10
MS335	116×79 mm. 450f. Pairs figure skating	4·50	2·10

162 Pirogue

1975. Malagasy Sailing-vessels. Multicoloured.

336	8f. Type **162**	95	25
337	45f. Malagasy schooner	2·30	65

163 Canoeing

1976. Olympic Games, Montreal. Multicoloured.

338	40f. Type **163** (postage)	45	25
339	50f. Sprinting and hurdling	55	25
340	100f. Putting the shot, and long-jumping (air)	1·20	25
341	200f. Gymnastics-horse and parallel bars	2·30	70
342	300f. Trampoline-jumping and high-diving	3·50	1·30
MS343	117×91 mm. 500f. Swimming	5·50	2·00

164 *Apollo 14* Lunar Module and Flight Badge

1976. Air. Fifth Anniversary of *Apollo 14* Mission.

344	**164**	150f. blue, red and green	1·80	80

1976. Air. Fifth Anniversary of *Apollo 14* Mission. No. 344 optd **5e Anniversaire de la mission APOLLO XIV**.

345	150f. blue, red and green	1·80	1·00

166 *Graf Zeppelin* over Fujiyama

1976. 75th Anniversary of Zeppelin. Multicoloured.

346	40f. Type **166** (postage)	55	25
347	50f. *Graf Zeppelin* over Rio de Janeiro	80	25
348	75f. *Graf Zeppelin* over New York	1·30	40
349	100f. *Graf Zeppelin* over Sphinx and pyramids	1·60	55
350	200f. *Graf Zeppelin* over Berlin (air)	3·25	90
351	300f. *Graf Zeppelin* over London	4·75	1·10
MS352	130×103 mm. 450f. *Graf Zeppelin* over The Vatican	5·50	2·20

167 'Prevention of Blindness'

1976. World Health Day.

353	**167**	100f. multicoloured	1·50	70

168 Aragonite

1976. Minerals and Fossils. Multicoloured.

354	25f. Type **168**	2·20	45
355	50f. Fossilised wood	3·75	90
356	150f. Celestyte	11·00	3·00

169 Alexander Graham Bell and Early Telephone

1976. Telephone Centenary. Multicoloured.

357	25f. Type **169**	30	10
358	50f. Cable maintenance, 1911	45	25
359	100f. Telephone operator and switchboard, 1895	95	25
360	200f. *Emile Baudot* cable ship	2·00	55
361	300f. Man with radio-telephone	3·00	80
MS362	133×104 mm. 500f. Telecommunications satellite	5·25	2·00

170 Children reading Book

1976. Children's Books Promotion. Multicoloured.

363	10f. Type **170**	30	10
364	25f. Children reading book (vert)	45	25

1976. Medal winners, Winter Olympic Games, Innsbruck. Nos. 330/334 optd **VAINQUEUR** and medal winner.

365	75f. Type **161** (postage)	75	45
366	100f. Ski-jumping	1·20	70
367	140f. Skating	1·80	90
368	200f. Cross-country skiing (air)	2·00	95
369	245f. Downhill skiing	2·50	1·20
MS370	116×79 mm. 450f. multicoloured	5·00	4·50

Overprints: 75f. **ALLEMAGNE FEDERALE**; 100f. **KARL SCHNABL, AUTRICHE**; 140f. **SHEILA YOUNG, ETATS-UNIS**; 200f. **IVAR FORMO, NORVEGE**; 245f. **ROSI MITTERMAIER, ALLEMAGNE DE L'OUEST**; 450f. **VIANQUEUR IRINA RODNINA ALEXANDER ZAITSEV URSS**.

The subject depicted on No. 367 is speed-skating, an event in which the gold medal was won by J. E. Storholt, Norway.

1976. Bicentenary of American Revolution (2nd issue). Nos. 305/309 optd **4 JUILLET 1776–1976** in frame.

371	**153**	40f. multicoloured (postage)	75	35
372	-	50f. multicoloured	1·10	55
373	-	100f. multicoloured (air)	1·20	90
374	-	200f. multicoloured	2·75	1·10
375	-	300f. multicoloured	4·00	1·80
MS376		127×91 mm. 500f. multicoloured	5·00	4·50

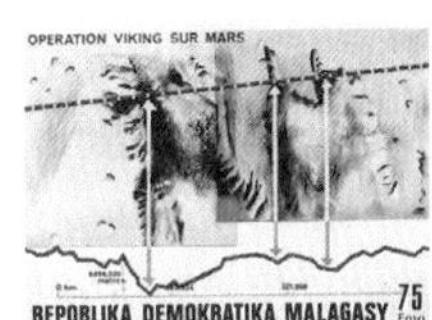

173 Descent Trajectory

1976. Viking Landing on Mars. Multicoloured.

377	75f. Type **173**	55	25
378	100f. Viking landing module separation	95	40
379	200f. Viking on Martian surface	1·80	55
380	300f. Viking orbiting Mars	2·75	85
MS381	133×90 mm. 500f. Viking spacecraft and Sun	5·25	2·10

174 Rainandriamampandry

1976. 30th Anniversary of Treaties signed by Rainandriamampandry (Foreign Minister).

382	**174**	25f. multicoloured	55	40

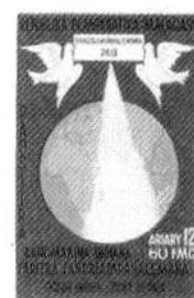
175 Doves over Globe

1976. Indian Ocean. 'Zone of Peace'. Multicoloured.

383	60f. Type **175**	55	25
384	160f. Doves flying across Indian Ocean (horiz)	40	70

1976. Olympic Games Medal Winners. Nos. 338/342 optd with names of two winners on each stamp.

385	**163**	40f. multicoloured (postage)	40	25
386	-	50f. multicoloured	55	40
387	-	100f. multicoloured (air)	1·00	55
388	-	200f. multicoloured	2·00	90
389	-	300f. multicoloured	3·00	1·50
MS390		117×91 mm. 500f.	5·25	4·75

Overprints: 40f. **V. DIBA, A. ROGOV**; 50f. **H. CRAWFORD, J. SCHALLER**; 100f. **U. BEYER, A. ROBINSON**; 200f. **N. COMANECI, N. ANDRIANOV**; 300f. **K. DIBIASI, E. VAYTSEKHOVSKAIA**; 500f. **J. MONTGOMERY and H. ANKE**.

177 Malagasy Arms

1976. First Anniversary of Malagasy Democratic Republic.

391	**177**	25f. multicoloured	45	10

178 Rabezavana (Independence Movement Leader)

1977. National Heroes. Multicoloured.

392	25f. Type **178**	30	10
393	25f. Lt. Albert Randriamaromanana	30	10
394	25f. Ny Avana Ramanantoanina (politician)	45	10
395	100f. Fasam-Pirenena National Mausoleum, Tananarive (horiz)	1·30	55

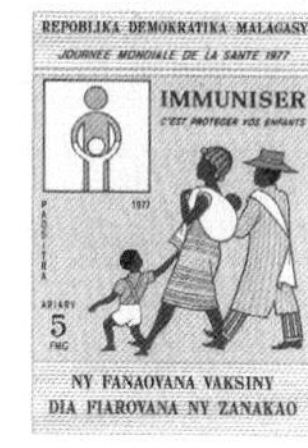

179 Family

1977. World Health Day.

396	**179**	5f. multicoloured	30	10

180 Medical School, Antananarivo

1977. 80th Anniversary of Medical School, Antananarivo.

397	**180**	250f. multicoloured	2·75	1·10

181 Rural Post Van

1977. Rural Mail.

398	**181**	35f. multicoloured	45	25

182 Morse Key and Man with Headphones

1977. 90th Anniversary of Antananarivo–Tamatave Telegraph.

399	**182**	15f. multicoloured	30	20

183 Academy Emblem

1977. 75th Anniversary of Malagasy Academy.

400	**183**	10f. multicoloured	30	10

184 Lenin and Russian Flag

1977. 60th Anniversary of Russian Revolution.
401 **184** 25f. multicoloured 2·50 45

185 Raoul Follereau

1978. 25th Anniversary of World Leprosy Day.
402 **185** 5f. multicoloured 1·50 45

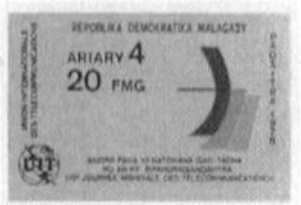

186 Microwave Antenna

1978. World Telecommunications Day.
403 **186** 20f. multicoloured 30 20

187 Co-operation

1978. Anti-Apartheid Year.
404 **187** 60f. red, black and yellow 75 30

188 Children with Instruments of Revolution

1978. Youth. Pillar of the Revolution.
405 **188** 125f. multicoloured 1·20 55

189 Tractor, Factory and Labourers

1978. Socialist Co-operatives.
406 **189** 25f. multicoloured 30 10

190 Women at Work

1979. Women. Pillar of the Revolution.
407 **190** 40f. multicoloured 45 10

191 Children with Books, Instruments and Fruit

1979. International Year of the Child.
408 **191** 10f. multicoloured 30 10

192 Ring-tailed Lemur

1979. Animals. Multicoloured.

409	25f. Type **192** (postage)	60	10
410	125f. Black lemur	2·40	25
411	1000f. Malagasy civet	11·50	2·20
412	20f. Tortoise (air)	50	35
413	95f. Black lemur (different)	1·50	55

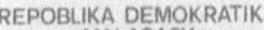

193 J. V. S. Razakandraina

1979. J. V. S. Razakandraina (poet) Commemoration.
414 **193** 25f. multicoloured 35 10

194 *Centella asiatica*

1979. Medicinal Plant.
415 **194** 25f. multicoloured 70 25

195 Map of Malagasy and Ste. Marie Telecommunications Station

1979. Telecommunications.
416 **195** 25f. multicoloured 30 10

196 Post Office, Antsirabe

1979. Stamp Day.
417 **196** 500f. multicoloured 4·50 1·40

197 Palestinians with Flag

1979. Air. Palestinian Solidarity.
418 **197** 60f. multicoloured 55 25

198 Concorde and Map of Africa

1979. 20th Anniversary of ASECNA (African Air Safety Organisation).
419 **198** 50f. multicoloured 75 25

199 Lenin addressing Meeting

1980. 110th Birth Anniversary of Lenin.
420 **199** 25f. multicoloured 75 25

200 Taxi-bus

1980. Fifth Anniversary of Socialist Revolution.
421 **200** 30f. multicoloured 45 10

201 Map illuminated by Sun

1980. 20th Anniversary of Independence.
422 **201** 75f. multicoloured 75 25

202 Military Parade

1980. 20th Anniversary of Army.
423 **202** 50f. multicoloured 55 25

203 Joseph Raseta

1980. Dr. Joseph Raseta Commemoration.
424 **203** 30f. multicoloured 45 10

204 Anatirova Temple

1980. Anatirova Temple Centenary.
425 **204** 30f. multicoloured 45 25

205 Boxing

1980. Olympic Games, Moscow. Multicoloured.

426	30f. Hurdling	75	10
427	75f. Type **205**	1·20	40
428	250f. Judo	2·50	1·10
429	500f. Swimming	4·50	2·20

206 Emblem, Map and Sun

1980. Fifth Anniversary of Malagasy Democratic Republic.
430 **206** 30f. multicoloured 45 10

207 Skier

1981. Winter Olympic Games, Lake Placid (1980).
431 **207** 175f. multicoloured 1·70 80

208 *Angraecum leonis*

1981. Flowers. Multicoloured.

432	5f. Type **208**	30	10
433	80f. *Angraecum famosum*	1·40	50
434	170f. *Angraecum sesquipedale*	2·30	1·00

209 Disabled Student

1981. International Year of Disabled People. Multicoloured.

435	25f. Type **209**	35	10
436	80f. Disabled carpenter	95	40

210 Ribbons forming Caduceus, ITU and WHO Emblems

1981. World Telecommunications Day.
437 **210** 15f. blue, black and yellow 30 10
438 **210** 45f. multicoloured 65 30

211 Valentina Tereshkova (first woman in space)

1981. Space Achievements. Multicoloured.

439	30f. Type **211**	30	10
440	80f. Astronaut on Moon	80	25
441	90f. Yuri Gagarin (first man in space)	95	50

212 Raphael-Louis Rafiringa

1981. Raphael-Louis Rafiringa Commemoration.
442 **212** 30f. multicoloured 45 10

213 Child writing Alphabet

1981. World Literacy Day.
443 **213** 30f. multicoloured 45 10

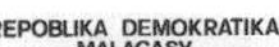

214 Ploughing and Sowing

1981. World Food Day.
444 **214** 200f. multicoloured 1·80 70

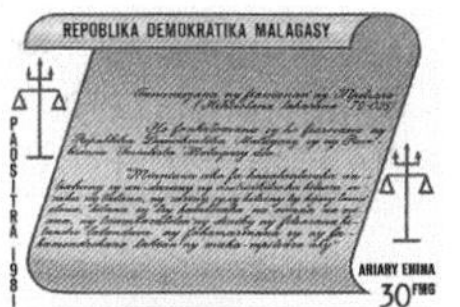

215 Magistrates' Oath

1981. Renewal of Magistrates' Oath.
445 **215** 30f. mauve and black 45 15

216 Dove

1981. Birth Centenary of Pablo Picasso.
446 **216** 80f. multicoloured 1·30 45

217 UPU Emblem and Malagasy Stamps

1981. 20th Anniversary of Admission to UPU.
447 **217** 5f. multicoloured 10 10
448 **217** 30f. multicoloured 35 10

218 Stamps forming Map of Malagasy

1981. Stamp Day.
449 **218** 90f. multicoloured 95 45

219 Hook-billed Vanga

1982. Birds. Multicoloured.
450 25f. Type **219** 90 20
451 30f. Courol 1·10 20
452 200f. Madagascar fish eagle (vert) 4·75 1·00

220 Vaccination

1982. Centenary of Discovery of Tubercule Bacillus.
453 **220** 30f. multicoloured 55 10

221 Jeannette Mpihira

1982. Jeannette Mpihira Commemoration.
454 **221** 30f. multicoloured 45 25

222 Woman's Head formed from Map of Africa

1982. Air. 20th Anniversary of Pan-African Women's Organisation.
455 **222** 80f. multicoloured 95 25

223 Pierre Louis Boiteau

1982. Pierre Louis Boiteau Commemoration.
456 **223** 30f. multicoloured 45 10

224 Andekaleka Dam

1982. Air. Andekaleka Hydro-electric Complex.
457 **224** 80f. multicoloured 95 35

225 *Sputnik 1*

1982. 25th Anniversary of First Artificial Satellite. Multicoloured.
458 10f. Type **225** 25 10
459 80f. Yuri Gagarin 75 30
460 100f. Soyuz–Salyut space station 1·00 45

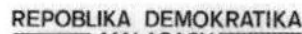

226 Heading Ball

1982. World Cup Football Championship, Spain. Multicoloured.
461 30f. Type **226** 30 10
462 40f. Running with ball 45 10
463 80f. Tackle 75 30
MS464 101×71 mm. 450f. Saving goal 4·50 2·75

227 Ploughing, Sowing and FAO Emblem

1982. World Food Day.
465 **227** 80f. multicoloured 75 45

228 Bar Scene

1982. 150th Anniversary of Edouard Manet (artist). Multicoloured.
466 5f. Type **228** 75 25
467 30f. Woman in white 1·10 45
468 170f. Man with pipe 5·00 1·10
MS469 101×81 mm. 400f. Fifer 8·50 3·00

229 Emperor Snapper

1982. Fish. Multicoloured.
470 5f. Type **229** 10 10
471 20f. Sailfish 30 10
472 30f. Lionfish 50 25
473 50f. Yellow-finned tuna 90 30
474 200f. Black-tipped grouper 3·00 85
MS475 100×80 mm. 450f. *Latimeria chalumnae* (horiz 37×26 mm) 5·00 3·25

230 Fort Mahavelona

1982. Landscapes. Multicoloured.
476 10f. Type **230** (postage) 10 10
477 30f. Ramena coast 30 10
478 400f. Jacarandas in flower (air) 4·00 1·60

231 Flags of Russia and Malagasy, Clasped Hands and Tractors

1982. 60th Anniversary of USSR. Multicoloured.
479 10f. Type **231** 10 10
480 15f. Flags, clasped hands and radio antenna 10 10
481 30f. Map of Russia, Kremlin and Lenin 35 10
482 150f. Flags, clasped hands, statue and Arms of Malagasy 1·60 70

232 Television, Drums, Envelope and Telephone

1983. World Communications Year. Multicoloured.
483 30f. Type **232** 30 10
484 80f. Stylised figures holding cogwheel 95 40

233 Axe breaking Chain on Map of Africa

1983. 20th Anniversary of Organisation of African Unity.
485 **233** 30f. multicoloured 30 10

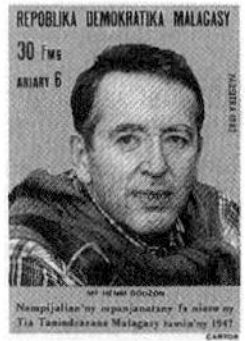
234 Henri Douzon

1983. Henri Douzon (lawyer) Commemoration.
486 **234** 30f. multicoloured 30 10

235 Montgolfier Balloon

1983. Bicentenary of Manned Flight. Sheet 110×80 mm.
MS487 **235** 500f. multicoloured 6·00 3·00

236 *Madonna and Child*

1983. 500th Birth Anniversary of Raphael. Sheet 108×80 mm.
MS488 **236** 500f. multicoloured 6·50 3·00

237 Ruffed Lemur

1984. Lemurs. Multicoloured.
489 30f. Type **237** 65 25
490 30f. Verreaux's sifaka 65 25
491 30f. Lesser mouse-lemur (horiz) 65 25
492 30f. Aye-aye (horiz) 65 25
493 200f. Indri (horiz) 4·25 1·20

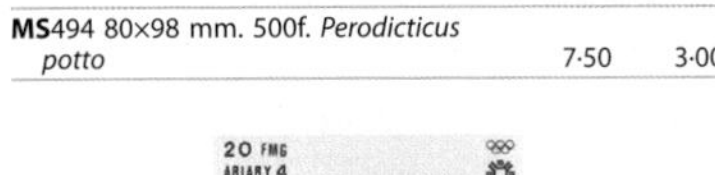

MS494 80×98 mm. 500f. *Perodicticus potto* 7·50 3·00

238 Ski Jumping

1984. Winter Olympic Games, Sarajevo. Multicoloured.

No.	Description	Mint	Used
495	20f. Type **238**	10	10
496	30f. Ice hockey	30	10
497	30f. Downhill skiing	30	10
498	30f. Speed skating	30	10
499	200f. Ice dancing	2·20	85
MS500	81×101 mm. 500f. Cross-country skiing (horiz 47×32 mm)	4·50	3·00

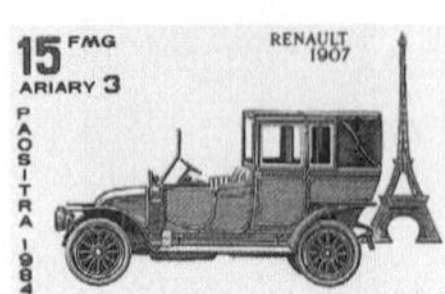

239 Renault, 1907

1984. Early Motor Cars. Multicoloured.

No.	Description	Mint	Used
501	15f. Type **239**	25	10
502	30f. Benz, 1896	45	10
503	30f. Baker, 1901	45	10
504	30f. Blake, 1901	45	10
505	200f. F.I.A.L., 1908	2·40	85
MS506	81×101 mm. 450f. Russo–Baltique, 1909	5·50	3·00

240 Pastor Ravelojaona

1984. Pastor Ravelojaona (encylopaedist) Commemoration.

No.	Description	Mint	Used
507 **240**	30f. multicoloured	30	10

241 *Noli me Tangere*

1984. 450th Death Anniversary of Correggio. Paintings by Artist.

No.	Description	Mint	Used
508 **241**	5f. multicoloured	10	10
509 -	20f. multicoloured	30	10
510 -	30f. multicoloured	45	10
511 -	80f. multicoloured	80	40
512 -	200f. multicoloured	2·20	85
MS513	81×102 mm. 400f. multicoloured	5·50	3·00

242 Paris Landmarks and Emblem

1984. 60th Anniversary of International Chess Federation. Multicoloured.

No.	Description	Mint	Used
514	5f. Type **242**	10	10
515	20f. Wilhelm Steinitz and stylised king	35	10
516	30f. Vera Menchik and stylised queen	75	30
517	30f. Anatoly Karpov and trophy	75	30
518	215f. Nona Gaprindashvili and trophy	3·50	90
MS519	101×80 mm. 400f. Children playing chess	6·00	3·00

243 Football

1984. Olympic Games, Los Angeles.

No.	Description	Mint	Used
520 **243**	100f. multicoloured	95	45

244 *Eudaphaenura splendens*

1984. Butterflies. Multicoloured.

No.	Description	Mint	Used
521	15f. Type **244**	55	10
522	50f. *Acraea hova*	1·10	25
523	50f. *Othreis boesae*	1·10	25
524	50f. *Pharmocophagus antenor*	1·10	25
525	200f. *Epicausis smithii*	3·25	1·00
MS526	101×81 mm. 400f. *Papilio delalandi* (32×47 mm)	5·50	3·00

245 Ralaimongo

1984. Birth Centenary of Jean Ralaimongo (politician).

No.	Description	Mint	Used
527 **245**	50f. multicoloured	30	10

246 Children in Brief-case

1984. 25th Anniversary of Children's Rights Legislation.

No.	Description	Mint	Used
528 **246**	50f. multicoloured	45	25

247 *Disa incarnata*

1984. Orchids. Multicoloured.

No.	Description	Mint	Used
529	20f. Type **247** (postage)	30	10
530	235f. *Eulophiella roempleriana*	2·50	1·00
531	50f. *Eulophiella roempleriana* (horiz) (air)	80	25
532	50f. *Grammangis ellisii* (horiz)	80	25
533	50f. *Grammangis spectabilis*	80	25
MS534	101×80 mm. 400f. *Gasrrorchis tuberculosa* (26×38 mm)	4·75	3·00

248 UN Emblem and Cotton Plant

1984. 20th Anniversary of United Nations Conference on Commerce and Development.

No.	Description	Mint	Used
535 **248**	100f. multicoloured	95	45

249 *Sun Princess* (Sadio Diouf)

1984. 40th Anniversary of International Civil Aviation Organisation.

No.	Description	Mint	Used
536 **249**	100f. multicoloured	95	45

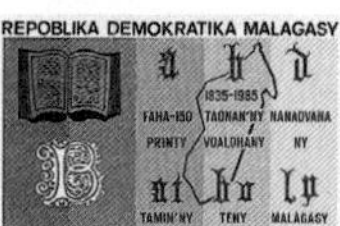

250 Bible, Map and Gothic Letters

1985. 150th Anniversary of First Bible in Malagasy Language.

No.	Description	Mint	Used
537 **250**	50f. brown, pink and black	45	20

251 Farming Scenes, Census-taker and Farmer

1985. Agricultural Census.

No.	Description	Mint	Used
538 **251**	50f. grey, black and mauve	45	20

252 Lap-dog

1985. Cats and Dogs. Multicoloured.

No.	Description	Mint	Used
539	20f. Type **252**	30	10
540	20f. Siamese cat	30	10
541	50f. Abyssinian cat (vert)	75	25
542	100f. Cocker spaniel (vert)	1·40	50
543	235f. Poodle	3·25	1·20
MS544	100×80 mm. 400f. White cat (41×27 mm)	5·50	2·75

253 Russian Soldiers in Berlin

1985. 40th Anniversary of Victory in Second World War.

No.	Description	Mint	Used
545	20f. Type **253**	30	10
546	50f. Arms of French squadron and fighter aircraft	1·10	45
547	100f. Victory parade, Red Square, Moscow	1·60	50
548	100f. French troops entering Paris (vert)	2·00	55

254 Parade in Stadium

1985. Tenth Anniversary of Malagasy Democratic Republic.

No.	Description	Mint	Used
549 **254**	50f. multicoloured	45	20

255 Medal and Independence Obelisk

1985. 25th Anniversary of Independence.

No.	Description	Mint	Used
550 **255**	50f. multicoloured	90	25

256 Peace Dove and Stylised People

1985. 12th World Youth and Students' Festival, Moscow.

No.	Description	Mint	Used
551 **256**	50f. multicoloured	45	10

257 IYY Emblem and Map of Madagascar

1985. International Youth Year.

No.	Description	Mint	Used
552 **257**	100f. multicoloured	1·00	45

258 Red Cross Centres and First Aid Post

1985. 70th Anniversary of Malagasy Red Cross.

No.	Description	Mint	Used
553 **258**	50f. multicoloured	70	20

259 *View of Sea at Saintes-Maries* (Vincent van Gogh)

1985. Impressionist Paintings. Multicoloured.

No.	Description	Mint	Used
554	20f. Type **259**	65	10
555	20f. *Rouen Cathedral in the Evening* (Claude Monet) (vert)	65	10
556	45f. *Young Girls in Black* (Pierre-Auguste Renoir) (vert)	1·10	30
557	50f. *Red Vineyard at Arles* (van Gogh)	1·50	30
558	100f. *Boulevard des Capucines, Paris* (Monet)	3·00	75
MS559	80×101 mm. 400f. *In the Garden* (Renoir) (vert)	6·75	4·50

260 Indira Gandhi

1985. Indira Gandhi (Indian Prime Minister) Commemoration.

No.	Description	Mint	Used
560 **260**	100f. multicoloured	1·10	45

261 Figures and Dove on Globe and Flag

1985. 40th Anniversary of UNO.

No.	Description	Mint	Used
561 **261**	100f. multicoloured	95	45

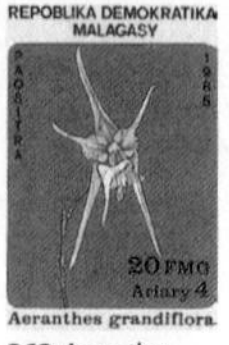

262 *Aeranthes grandiflora*

1985. Orchids. Multicoloured.

No.	Description	Mint	Used
562	20f. Type **262**	65	20
563	45f. *Angraecum magdalenae* and *Nephele oenopion* (insect) (horiz)	1·10	30
564	50f. *Aerangis stylosa*	1·30	40
565	100f. *Angraecum eburneum longicalcar* and *Hippotion batschi* (insect)	2·30	70
566	100f. *Angraecum sesquipedale* and *Xanthopan morganipredicta* (insect)	2·30	75
MS567	100×80 mm. 400f. *Angraecum eburneum superbum* and *Deilephila neri* (insect) (29×41 mm)	5·50	3·50

263 Russian and Czechoslovakian Cosmonauts

1985. Russian Interkosmos Space Programme. Multicoloured.

568	20f. Type **263**	30	10
569	20f. Russian and American flags and Apollo–Soyuz link	30	10
570	50f. Russian and Indian cosmonauts	50	25
571	100f. Russian and Cuban cosmonauts	95	45
572	200f. Russian and French cosmonauts	1·80	90
MS573	99×89 mm. 400f. Satellite (41×39 mm)	4·25	2·75

264 Emblem in '10'

1985. Tenth Anniversary of Malagasy Democratic Republic.

574	**264**	50f. multicoloured	45	20

265 Headquarters

1986. Tenth Anniversary of ARO (State insurance system).

575	**265**	50f. yellow and brown	45	25

266 *David and Uriah* (Rembrandt)

1986. Foreign Paintings in Hermitage Museum, Leningrad. Multicoloured.

576	20f. Type **266**	35	10
577	50f. *Portrait of Old Man in Red* (Rembrandt)	1·00	35
578	50f. *Danae* (Rembrandt) (horiz)	1·00	35
579	50f. *Marriage of Earth and Water* (Rubens)	1·00	35
580	50f. *Portrait of Infanta Isabella's Maid* (Rubens)	1·00	35
MS581	100×80 mm. 50f. *Holy Family* (Raphael)	5·75	3·75

267 Comet

1986. Air. Appearance of Halley's Comet.

582	**267**	150f. multicoloured	1·70	75

1986. Russian Paintings in the Tretyakov Gallery, Moscow. As T **266**. Multicoloured.

583	20f. *Fruit and Flowers* (I. Khroutsky) (horiz)	40	10
584	50f. *The Rooks have Returned* (A. Savrasov)	80	35
585	50f. *Unknown Woman* (I. Kramskoi) (horiz)	85	35
586	50f. *Aleksandr Pushkin* (O. Kiprenski)	85	35
587	100f. *March, 1895* (I. Levitan) (horiz)	1·90	70
MS588	80×101 mm. 450f. *Pavel Tretyakov* (I. Repine)	5·50	3·25

268 Sombrero, Football and Player

1986. World Cup Football Championship, Mexico.

589	**268**	150f. multicoloured	1·50	50

269 Child Care

1986. UNICEF Child Survival Campaign.

590	**269**	60f. multicoloured	55	25

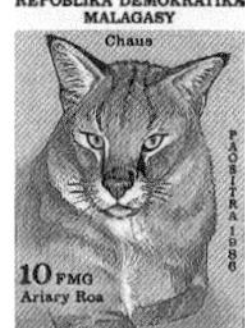

270 Jungle Cat

1986. Wild Cats. Multicoloured.

591	10f. Type **270**	35	10
592	10f. Wild cat	35	10
593	60f. Caracal	80	30
594	60f. Leopard cat	80	30
595	60f. Serval	75	30
MS596	81×100 mm. 450f. African golden cat	5·50	3·00

271 Dove above Hands holding Globe

1986. International Peace Year. Multicoloured.

597	60f. Type **271**	55	25
598	150f. Doves above emblem and map	1·40	65

272 UPU Emblem on Dove

1986. World Post Day.

599	**272**	60f. multicoloured (postage)	70	25
600	**272**	150f. blue, black and red (air)	1·50	70

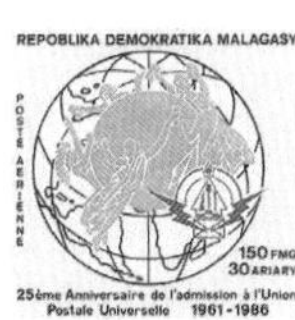

273 UPU Emblem on Globe

1986. Air. 25th Anniversary of Admission to UPU.

601	**273**	150f. multicoloured	1·50	70

274 Giant Madagascar Coucal

1986. Birds. Multicoloured.

602	60f. Type **274**	80	25
603	60f. Crested Madagascar coucal	80	25
604	60f. Rufous vangas (vert)	80	25
605	60f. Red-tailed vangas (vert)	80	25
606	60f. Sicklebill	70	25
MS607	80×100 mm. 450f. Cattle egret (41×29 mm)	5·50	3·00

275 Tortoise

1987. Endangered Animals. Multicoloured.

608	60f. Type **275**	85	30
609	60f. Crocodile	85	30
610	60f. Crested wood ibis (vert)	85	30
611	60f. Vasa parrot	85	30
MS612	80×100 mm. 450f. Black coucal (horiz)	5·50	2·50

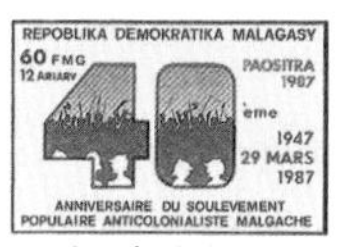

276 Crowd in '40'

1987. 40th Anniversary of Anti-colonial Uprising.

613	**276**	60f. brown, red and yellow	55	10
614	-	60f. multicoloured	55	10

Design: No. 614, Hands in broken manacles, map, rifleman and spearman.

277 Emblems, Map and Pictogram

1987. First Indian Ocean Towns Games.

615	**277**	60f. multicoloured	55	25
616	**277**	150f. multicoloured	1·40	55

278 *Sarimanok*

1987. The *Sarimanok* (replica of early dhow). Multicoloured.

617	60f. Type **278**	75	25
618	150f. *Sarimanok* (different)	1·50	55

279 Coffee Plant

1987. 25th Anniversary of African and Malagasy Coffee Producers Organisation. Multicoloured.

619	60f. Type **279**	55	25
620	150f. Map showing member countries	1·70	65

280 Rifle Shooting and Satellite

1987. Winter Olympic Games, Calgary (1988). Multicoloured.

621	60f. Type **280**	45	10
622	150f. Slalom	1·00	25
623	250f. Luge	1·70	55
624	350f. Speed skating	2·40	75
625	400f. Ice hockey	2·75	80
626	450f. Ice skating (pairs)	3·25	90
MS627	88×68 mm. 600f. Downhill (41×29 mm)	4·50	4·50

281 *Giotto* Space Probe

1987. Appearance of Halley's Comet (1986). Space Probes. Multicoloured.

628	60f. Type **281**	45	10
629	150f. *Vega 1*	1·00	25
630	250f. *Vega 2*	1·70	55
631	350f. *Planet A 1*	2·40	75
632	400f. *Planet B 1*	2·75	80
633	450f. ICE	3·25	90
MS634	88×68 mm. 600f. Sir Edmund Halley and *Giotto* (43×32 mm)	4·25	4·25

282 Piper Aztec

1987. Air. 25th Anniversary of Air Madagascar. Multicoloured.

635	60f. Type **282**	55	25
636	60f. de Havilland Twin Otter	55	25
637	150f. Boeing 747-200	1·30	55

283 Rabearivelo

1987. 50th Death Anniversary of Jean-Joseph Rabearivelo (poet).

638	**283**	60f. multicoloured	45	25

284 Communications Equipment Robot and Print-out Paper

1987. National Telecommunications Research Laboratory.

639	**284**	60f. green, black and red	45	25

285 Emblem

1987. 150th Anniversary of Execution of Rafaravavy Rasalama (Christian martyr).

640	**285**	60f. black, deep blue and blue	40	25

286 Hand using Key and Telegraphist

1987. Centenary of Antananarivo–Tamatave Telegraph.

641	**286**	60f. multicoloured	45	25

287 Bartholomeu Dias and Departure from Palos, 1492

1987. 500th Anniversary (1992) of Discovery of America by Columbus. Multicoloured.

642	60f. Type **287**	40	10
643	150f. Route around Samana Cay and Henry the Navigator	75	25

644	250f. Columbus and crew disembarking, 1492, and A. de Marchena	1·60	40
645	350f. Building Fort Navidad and Paolo del Pozzo Toscanelli	2·00	55
646	400f. Columbus in Barcelona, 1493, and Queen Isabella of Spain	2·20	70
647	450f. Columbus and *Nina*	2·40	70
MS648	91×81 mm. 600f. Columbus landing with soldiers (41×29 mm)	5·00	5·00

288 Showjumping and *Harlequin* (Picasso)

1987. Olympic Games, Barcelona (1992). Multicoloured.

649	60f. Type **288** (postage)	30	10
650	150f. Weightlifting and Barcelona Cathedral	70	25
651	250f. Hurdling and Canaletas Fountain	1·40	40
652	350f. High jumping and Parc d'Attractions	1·90	55
653	400f. Gymnast on bar and church (air)	2·20	70
654	450f. Gymnast with ribbon and Triumphal Arch	2·50	70
MS655	123×89 mm. 600f. Cross-country rider and Columbus monument	4·00	1·60

289 Anniversary Emblem, TV Tower and Interhotel *Berlin*

1987. 750th Anniversary of Berlin.

656	**289**	150f. multicoloured	50	30

290 Musician and Dancers

1987. Schools Festival.

657	**290**	60f. multicoloured	30	10

291 Madagascar Pasteur Institute and Pasteur

1987. Centenary of Pasteur Institute, Paris.

658	**291**	250f. multicoloured	1·20	50

292 *After the Shipwreck* (Eugene Delacroix)

1987. Paintings in Pushkin Museum of Fine Arts, Moscow. Multicoloured.

659	10f. Type **292**	45	10
660	60f. *Jupiter and Callisto* (Francois Boucher) (vert)	50	10
661	60f. *Still Life with Swan* (Frans Snyders)	50	10
662	60f. *Chalet in the Mountains* (Gustave Courbet)	50	10
663	150f. *At the Market* (Joachim Bueckelaer)	1·20	25
MS664	80×100 mm. 1000f. *Minerva* (Paolo Veronese) (horiz)	7·00	4·25

293 Emblem

1987. Tenth Anniversary of Pan-African Telecommunications Union.

665	**293**	250f. multicoloured	55	25

294 Family and House on Globe

1988. International Year of Shelter for the Homeless (1987). Multicoloured.

666	80f. Type **294**	15	10
667	250f. Hands forming house protecting family from rain	60	30

295 Lenin addressing Crowd

1988. 70th Anniversary of Russian Revolution. Multicoloured.

668	60f. Type **295**	55	10
669	60f. Revolutionaries	55	10
670	150f. Lenin in crowd	1·10	20

296 Broad-nosed Gentle Lemur

1988. Endangered Species. Multicoloured.

671	60f. Type **296**	40	10
672	150f. Diadem sifaka	50	25
673	250f. Indri	95	25
674	350f. Ruffed lemur	1·80	40
675	550f. Purple herons (horiz)	1·50	55
676	1500f. Nossi-be chameleon (horiz)	4·25	1·10
MS677	110×58 mm. 1500f. Long-tailed ground roller (*Uratelornis chinaera*) (horiz)	5·50	5·50

297 Ice Skating

1988. Winter Olympic Games, Calgary. Multicoloured.

678	20f. Type **297**	10	10
679	60f. Speed-skating	10	10
680	60f. Slalom	10	10
681	100f. Cross-country skiing	35	10
682	250f. Ice hockey	80	30
MS683	80×65 mm. 800f. Ski-jumping	3·00	1·50

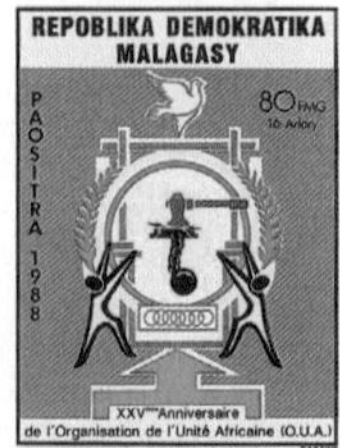
298 Dove, Axe breaking Chain and Map

1988. 25th Anniversary of Organisation of African Unity.

684	**298**	80f. multicoloured	30	10

299 Institute Building

1988. 20th Anniversary of National Posts and Telecommunications Institute.

685	**299**	80f. multicoloured	30	10

300 College

1988. Centenary of St Michael's College.

686	**300**	250f. multicoloured	45	25

301 Pierre and Marie Curie in Laboratory

1988. 90th Anniversary of Discovery of Radium.

687	**301**	150f. brown and mauve	45	15

302 Emblem

1988. Tenth Anniversary of Alma-Ata Declaration (on health and social care).

688	**302**	60f. multicoloured	30	15

303 Emblem

1988. 40th Anniversary of WHO.

689	**303**	150f. brown, blue and black	30	15

304 Ring-tailed Lemurs on Island

1988. 50th Anniversary of Tsimbazaza Botanical and Zoological Park. Multicoloured.

690	20f. Type **304**	30	15
691	80f. Ring-tailed lemur with young (25×37 mm)	40	20
692	250f. Palm tree and ring-tailed lemur within 'Zoo' (47×32 mm)	90	40
MS693	80×100 mm. 1000f. Grey gentle lemur with baby (36×51 mm)	5·00	1·80

305 Hoopoe and Blue Madagascar Coucal

1988. Scouts, Birds and Butterflies. Multicoloured.

694	80f. Type **305**	10	10
695	250f. *Chrysiridia croesus* (butterfly)	50	10
696	270f. Nelicourvi weaver and red forest fody	70	10
697	350f. *Papilio dardanus* (butterflies)	95	25
698	550f. Crested Madagascar coucal	1·50	25
699	1500f. *Argema mittrei* (butterfly)	3·75	1·10
MS700	80×114 mm. 1500f. *Anteva* (butterfly) and blue-cheeked bee-eater (35×50 mm)	4·00	1·40

306 Cattle grazing

1988. Tenth Anniversary of International Fund for Agricultural Development.

701	**306**	250f. multicoloured	45	25

307 Karl Bach and Clavier

1988. Musicians' Anniversaries. Multicoloured.

702	80f. Type **307** (death bicentenary)	15	10
703	250f. Franz Schubert and piano (160th death)	55	20
704	270f. Georges Bizet and scene from *Carmen* (150th birth)	65	25
705	350f. Claude Debussy and scene from *Pelleas et Melisande* (70th death)	90	40
706	550f. George Gershwin at piano writing score of *Rhapsody in Blue* (90th birth)	1·30	55
707	1500f. Elvis Presley (Tenth death (1987))	4·00	1·60
MS708	93×74 mm. 1500f. Nikolai Rimsky-Korsakov and *The Golden Cockerel* (80th death) (35×50 mm)	4·25	2·30

308 Books

1988. 'Ecole en Fete' Schools Festival.

709	**308**	80f. multicoloured	30	10

309 *Black Sea Fleet at Feodosiya* (Ivan Aivazovski)

1988. Paintings of Sailing Ships. Multicoloured.

710	20f. Type **309**	20	10
711	80f. *Lesnoie* (N. Semenov)	35	15
712	80f. *Seascape with Sailing Ships* (Simon de Vlieger)	35	15
713	100f. *Orel* (N. Golitsine) (horiz)	50	20
714	250f. *Naval Battle Exercises* (Adam Silo)	95	30
MS715	91×71 mm. 550f. *On the River* (Abraham Beerstraten) (36×51 mm)	3·25	1·10

310 *Tragocephala crassicornis*

1988. Endangered Beetles. Multicoloured.

716	20f. Type **310**	60	25
717	80f. *Polybothris symptuosa-gema*	1·80	45

718 250f. *Euchroea auripigmenta* 3·50 90
719 350f. *Stellognata maculata* 4·75 1·10

311 Stretcher Bearers and Anniversary Emblem

1988. 125th Anniversary of International Red Cross. Multicoloured.
720 80f. Type **311** 20 10
721 250f. Red Cross services, emblem and Henri Dunant (founder) 50 30

312 Symbols of Human Rights

1988. 40th Anniversary of Declaration of Human Rights. Multicoloured.
722 80f. Type **312** 30 10
723 250f. Hands with broken manacles holding '40' 65 30

313 Mercedes-Benz Blitzen-Benz, 1909

1989. Cars and Trains. Multicoloured.
724 80f. Type **313** 10 10
725 250f. Micheline diesel railcar *Tsikirity*, 1952, Tananarive–Moramanga line 45 10
726 270f. Bugatti coupe binder, 41 45 10
727 350f. Class 1020 electric locomotive, Germany 75 25
728 1500f. Souleze 701 diesel train, Malagasy 2·75 1·00
729 2500f. Opel racing car, 1913 4·25 1·80
MS730 98×76 mm. 2500f. Bugatti Presidential autorail and Bugatti Type 57 Atalante (39×28 mm) 6·00 2·30

314 Tyrannosaurus

1989. Prehistoric Animals. Multicoloured.
731 20f. Type **314** 10 10
732 80f. Stegosaurus 35 10
733 250f. Arsinoitherium 85 25
734 450f. Triceratops 1·30 35
MS735 91×73 mm. 600f. Sauralophus (vert) 3·75 1·40

315 *Tahitian Girls*

1989. Woman in Art. Multicoloured.
736 20f. Type **315** 10 10
737 80f. *Portrait of a Girl* (Jean-Baptiste Greuze) 30 10
738 80f. *Portrait of a Young Woman* (Titian) 30 10
739 100f. *Woman in Black* (Auguste Renoir) 40 20
740 250f. *The Lace-maker* (Vasily Tropinine) 95 55
MS741 100×80 mm. 550f. *The Annunciation* (Cima da Conegliano) 2·00 1·00

316 *Sobennikoffia robusta*

1989. Orchids. Multicoloured.
742 5f. Type **316** 10 10
743 10f. *Grammangis fallax* (horiz) 10 10
744 80f. *Angraecum sororium* 45 25
745 80f. *Cymbidiella humblotii* 45 25
746 250f. *Oenia oncidiiflora* 1·10 45
MS747 100×80 mm. 1000f. *Aerangis curnowiana* 2·75 1·50

317 Nehru

1989. Birth Centenary of Jawaharlal Nehru (Indian statesman).
748 **317** 250f. multicoloured 45 25

318 Mahamasina Sports Complex, Lake Anosy and Ampefiloha Quarter

1989. Antananarivo. Multicoloured.
749 5f. Type **318** 10 10
750 20f. Andravoahangy and Anjanahary Quarters 10 10
751 80f. Zoma market and Faravohitra Quarter 30 10
752 80f. Andohan' Analekely Quarter and 29 March Column 30 10
753 250f. Avenue de l'Independance and Jean Ralaimongo Column 55 25
754 550f. Lake Anosy, Queen's Palace and Andohalo School 1·00 45

319 Rose Quartz

1989. Ornamental Minerals. Multicoloured.
755 80f. Type **319** 40 10
756 250f. Fossilized wood 1·10 50

320 Pope and Rasoamanarivo

1989. Visit of Pope John Paul II and Beatification of Victoire Rasoamanarivo. Multicoloured.
757 80f. Type **320** 30 10
758 250f. Map and Pope 70 30

321 Map and Runner with Torch

1989. Town Games.
759 **321** 80f.+20f. multicoloured 30 10

322 Storming the Bastille

1989. Bicentenary of French Revolution (1st issue).
760 **322** 250f. multicoloured 70 25
See also Nos. 773/775.

323 Mirabeau and Gabriel Riqueti at Meeting of States General

1989. Philexfrance 89 International Stamp Exhibition, Paris. Multicoloured.
761 250f. Type **323** 50 15
762 350f. Camille Desmoulins' call to arms 85 15
763 1000f. Lafayette and crowd demanding bread 2·00 40
764 1500f. Trial of King Louis XVI 3·50 70
765 2500f. Assassination of Marat 5·75 1·10
MS766 113×79 mm. 3000f. Robespierre, Couthon, Collot d'Herbois and Prieur (59×41 mm) 14·50 5·50

324 *Mars 1*

1989. Space Probes. Multicoloured.
767 20f. Type **324** 10 10
768 80f. *Mars 3* 30 10
769 80f. *Zond 2* 30 10
770 250f. *Mariner 9* 55 25
771 270f. *Viking 2* 70 40
MS772 100×80 mm. 550f. *Phobos* (41×28 mm) 1·50 90

325 *Liberty guiding the People* (Eugene Delacroix)

1989. Bicentenary of French Revolution (2nd issue). Multicoloured.
773 5f. Type **325** (postage) 10 10
774 80f. *La Marseillaise* (Francois Rude) 50 25
775 250f. *Oath of the Tennis Court* (Jacques Louis David) (air) 85 35

326 Rene Cassin (founder)

1989. 25th Anniversary of International Human Rights Institute for French Speaking Countries.
776 **326** 250f. multicoloured 45 10

327 Mother and Young on Bamboo

1989. Golden Gentle Lemur.
777 **327** 250f. multicoloured 95 45

328 Footballer and Cavour Monument, Turin

1989. World Cup Football Championship, Italy. Multicoloured.
778 350f. Type **328** 75 25
779 1000f. Footballer and Christopher Columbus monument, Genoa 1·80 40
780 1500f. Florentine footballer, 1530, and *David* (sculpture, Michelangelo) 2·75 55
781 2500f. Footballer and *Rape of Proserpina* (sculpture, Bernini), Rome 4·75 1·30
MS782 110×77 mm. 3000f. Leonardo de Vinci monument, Milan, footballer and trophy (29×41 mm) 4·50 1·40

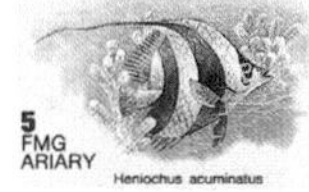

329 Pennant Coralfish

1990. Fish. Multicoloured.
783 5f. Type **329** 10 10
784 20f. Snub-nosed parasitic eel (vert) 10 10
785 80f. Manta ray (vert) 20 10
786 250f. Black-tipped grouper 75 35
787 320f. Smooth hammerhead 1·00 50
MS788 90×70 mm. 550f. Coelacanth 3·00 1·80

330 Long Jumping

1990. Olympic Games, Barcelona (1992). Multicoloured.
789 80f. Type **330** 10 10
790 250f. Pole vaulting 45 10
791 550f. Hurdling 95 25
792 1500f. Cycling 3·00 40
793 2000f. Baseball 4·00 70
794 2500f. Tennis 4·50 1·10
MS795 90×66 mm. 3000f. Football 4·50 4·50

331 *Queen of the Isalo* (rock)

1990. Natural Features. Multicoloured.
796 70f. Type **331** 20 15
797 150f. Lonjy Island (as T **332**) 35 15

332 Pipe

1990. Sakalava Craft. Multicoloured.
798 70f. Type **332** 20 15
799 150f. Combs (as T **331**) 35 15

333 Emblem and Projects

1990. 25th Anniversary of African Development Bank.

800	**333**	80f. multicoloured	40	10

334 *Voyager II* and Neptune

1990. 20th Anniversary of First Manned Landing on Moon. Multicoloured.

801	80f. Type **334**	10	10
802	250f. Hughes Hercules flying boat, Boeing 747 airliner and flying boat 'of the future'	45	10
803	550f. *NOAA* satellite tracking elephants	95	25
804	1500f. Venus and *Magellan* space probe	1·20	25
805	2000f. Halley's Comet and Concorde	2·30	40
806	2500f. *Apollo 11* landing capsule and crew	4·25	80
MS807	94×63 mm. 3000f. Astronaut, mission emblem and crew	4·50	1·40

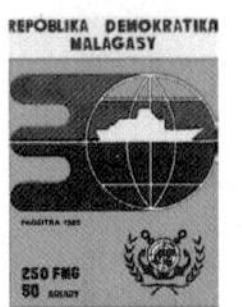
335 Liner on Globe

1990. 30th Anniversary of International Maritime Organisation.

808	**335**	250f. ultramarine, bl & blk	45	20

336 Maps showing Development between 1975 and 1990

1990. Air. 15th Anniversary of Malagasy Socialist Revolution.

809	**336**	100f. multicoloured	40	10
810	-	350f. black and grey	75	40

Design: 350f. Presidential Palaces, 1975 and 1990.

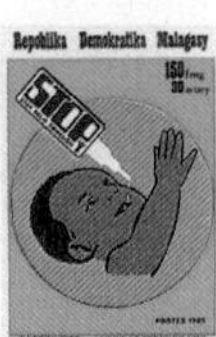
337 Oral Vaccination

1990. Anti-Polio Campaign.

811	**337**	150f. multicoloured	40	20

338 Four-man Bobsleigh

1990. Winter Olympic Games, Albertville (1992) (1st issue). Multicoloured.

812	350f. Type **338**	55	15
813	1000f. Speed skating	1·60	45
814	1500f. Cross-country skiing	2·50	55
815	2500f. Super G	4·00	1·10
MS816	92×77 mm. 3000f. Giant slalom	4·50	1·40

See also Nos. 862/**MS**869.

339 Society Emblem

1990. Air. 25th Anniversary of Malagasy Bible Society.

817	**339**	25f. multicoloured	10	10
818	-	100f. blue, black and green	35	10

Design: Vert—100f. Society emblem.

340 Mascot

1990. Third Indian Ocean Island Games, Malagasy (1st issue).

819	**340**	100f.+20f. on 80f.+20f. multicoloured	45	25
820	**340**	350f.+20f. on 250f.+20f. multicoloured	1·00	65

The games were originally to be held in 1989 and the stamps were printed for release then. The issued stamps are handstamped with the correct date and new value.

See also Nos. 822/823.

341 Symbols of Agriculture and Industry

1990. 30th Anniversary of Independence.

821	**341**	100f. multicoloured	30	10

342 Torch

1990. Third Indian Ocean Island Games, Malagasy (2nd issue).

822	**342**	100f. multicoloured	40	10
823	**342**	350f. multicoloured	80	40

343 Envelopes forming Map and Mail Transportation

1990. Air. World Post Day.

824	**343**	350f. multicoloured	1·90	35

344 Ho Chi Minh

1990. Birth Centenary of Ho Chi Minh (President of North Vietnam, 1945–1969).

825	**344**	350f. multicoloured	75	40

345 *Avahi laniger*

1990. Lemurs. Multicoloured.

826	10f. Type **345**	10	10
827	20f. *Fulvus albifrons*	25	20
828	20f. *Fulvus sanfordi*	25	20
829	100f. *Fulvus collaris*	85	25
830	100f. *Lepulemur ruficaudatus*	90	25
MS831	70×90 mm. 350f. *Fulvus fulvus*	3·00	1·50

346 Fluted Giant Clam

1990. Shells. Multicoloured.

832	40f. Type **346**	70	20
833	50f. Dimidiate and subulate augers	90	25

347 Letters in Book

1990. International Literacy Year. Multicoloured.

834	20f. Type **347**	35	20
835	100f. Open book and hand holding pen (horiz)	85	50

348 Cep

1991. Fungi. Multicoloured.

836	25f. Type **348**	10	10
837	100f. Butter mushroom	35	10
838	350f. Fly agaric	95	20
839	450f. Scarlet-stemmed boletus	1·20	30
840	680f. Flaky-stemmed witches' mushroom	1·70	45
841	800f. Brown birch bolete	2·00	60
842	900f. Orange birch bolete	2·10	80
MS843	71×90 mm. 1500f. Common puffball. Imperf	3·75	2·75

349 De Gaulle, Leclerc and Parod under Arc de Triomphe, 1944

1991. Multicoloured

844	100f. Type **349**	25	20
845	350f. *Galileo* space probe near Jupiter	75	25
846	800f. Crew of *Apollo 11* on Moon	1·40	40
847	900f. De Gaulle and Free French emblem, 1942	2·00	25
848	1250f. Concorde aircraft and German ICE high speed train	2·20	70
849	2500f. General Charles de Gaulle (French statesman)	4·75	90
MS850	144×93 mm. 3000f. Crew of *Apollo 11*. Imperf	4·50	1·40

350 Industrial and Agricultural Symbols and Arms

1991. 15th Anniversary (1990) of Republic.

851	**350**	100f. multicoloured	30	10

351 Baobab Tree

1991. Trees. Multicoloured.

852	140f. Type **351**	55	10
853	500f. *Dideria madagascariensis*	1·30	55

352 Whippet

1991. Dogs. Multicoloured.

854	30f. Type **352**	40	10
855	50f. Japanese spaniel	55	10
856	140f. Toy terrier	1·30	25
857	350f. Chow-chow	95	25
858	500f. Chihuahua	1·20	40
859	800f. Afghan hound	1·60	65
860	1140f. Papillon	2·30	90
MS861	70×91 mm. 1500f. Shih-tzu. Imperf	9·50	1·90

353 Cross-country Skiing

1991. Winter Olympic Games, Albertville (2nd issue). Multicoloured.

862	5f. Type **353**	10	10
863	15f. Biathlon	10	10
864	60f. Ice hockey	45	10
865	140f. Skiing	55	25
866	640f. Ice skating	55	25
867	1000f. Ski jumping	2·75	40
868	1140f. Speed skating	3·75	90
MS869	90×70 mm. 1500f. Ice hockey (different). Imperf	3·75	2·00

354 *Helictopleurus splendidicollis*

1992. Scouts, Insects and Fungi. Multicoloured.

870	140f. Type **354**	35	10
871	500f. *Russula radicans* (mushroom)	1·20	25
872	640f. *Cocles contemplator* (insect)	1·50	40
873	1025f. *Russula singeri* (mushroom)	2·00	55
874	1140f. *Euchroea oberthurii* (beetle)	2·50	55
875	3500f. *Lactariopsis pandani* (mushroom)	7·50	80
MS876	119×94 mm. 4500f. *Euchroea spininasuta* (beetle) and *Russula aureotacta* (mushroom)	7·25	2·10

355 Former and Present Buildings

1992. 90th Anniversary (1991) of Paul Minault College.

877	**355**	140f. multicoloured	70	25

356 Repairing Space Telescope

1992. Space. Multicoloured.

878	140f. Type **356**	25	10
879	500f. *Soho* sun probe	95	25
880	640f. *Topex-Poseidon* oceanic survey satellite	1·20	25
881	1025f. *Hipparcos* planetary survey satellite	1·60	40
882	1140f. *Voyager 2* Neptune probe	2·00	40
883	5000f. *ETS-VI* Japanese test communications satellite	8·75	1·20
MS884	85×103 mm. 7500f. *Apollo 11* crew	11·50	11·50

357 Ryuichi Sakamoto

1992. Entertainers. Multicoloured.

885	100f. Type **357**	25	10
886	350f. John Lennon	60	15
887	800f. Bruce Lee	2·00	25
888	900f. Sammy Davis jun	2·20	55
889	1250f. John Wayne	2·20	40
890	2500f. James Dean	4·00	1·20
MS891	117×79 mm. 3000f. Vivien Leigh (wrongly inscr 'Vivian Leight') and Clark Gable	4·75	4·75

358 Lychees

1992. Fruits. Multicoloured.

892	10f. Type **358**	10	10
893	50f. Oranges	10	10
894	60f. Apples	20	10
895	140f. Peaches	45	25
896	555f. Bananas (vert)	1·50	40
897	800f. Avocados (vert)	1·80	55
898	1400f. Mangoes (vert)	3·25	95
MS899	89×70 mm. 1600f. Mango, pineapple, peach, apple and grapes in dish	4·00	1·80

359 9th-century Galley

1992. Sailing Ships. Multicoloured.

900	15f. Type **359**	10	10
901	65f. Full-rigged sailing ship, 1878	30	10
902	140f. *Golden Hind* (Drake's flagship)	55	10
903	500f. 18th-century dhow	1·40	40
904	640f. *Ostrust* (galleon), 1721 (vert)	1·60	45
905	800f. Dutch caravel, 1599 (vert)	2·00	50
906	1025f. *Santa Maria* (Columbus's flagship), 1492	2·40	85
MS907	91×70 mm. 1500f. Columbus and fleet	4·50	1·60

360 Couple in Heart

1992. Anti-AIDS Campaign.

908	**360**	140f. black and mauve	45	10

361 Tending Trees

1992. Reforestation.

909	**361**	140f. dp green, black & grn	40	10

POSTAGE DUE STAMPS

D13 Independence Obelisk

1962

D45	**D13**	1f. green	10	10
D46	**D13**	2f. brown	10	10
D47	**D13**	3f. violet	10	10
D48	**D13**	4f. slate	10	10
D49	**D13**	5f. red	30	25
D50	**D13**	10f. green	30	25
D51	**D13**	20f. purple	30	25
D52	**D13**	40f. blue	75	75
D53	**D13**	50f. red	95	90
D54	**D13**	100f. black	1·80	1·60

APPENDIX

The following stamps have either been issued in excess of postal needs or have not been available to the public in reasonable quantities at face value.

1987

Winter Olympic Games, Calgary (1988). 1500f. (on gold foil).

1989

Scout and Butterfly. 5000f. (on gold foil).
Philexfrance 89 Int Stamp Exhibition, Paris. 5000f. (on gold foil).
World Cup Football Championship, Italy. 5000f. (on gold foil).

1990

Winter Olympic Games, Albertville (1992). 5000f. (on gold foil).

1991

Birth Centenary of De Gaulle. 5000f. (on gold foil).

1992

Olympic Games, Barcelona. 500f. (on gold foil).

1993

Bicentenary of French Republic. 1989 Philexfrance 89 issue optd. 5000f.

1994

Elvis Presley (entertainer). 10000f. (on gold foil).
World Cup Football Championship, USA. 10000f. (on gold foil).
Winter Olympic Games, Lillehammer, Norway. 10000f. (on gold foil).
Olympic Games, Atlanta, USA. 5000f. (on gold foil).

For further issues see under **MADAGASCAR**.

MALAWI

Formerly Nyasaland, became an independent Republic within the Commonwealth on 6 July 1966.

1964. 12 pence = 1 shilling; 20 shillings = 1 pound.
1970. 100 tambalas = 1 kwacha.

44 Dr. H. Banda (Prime Minister) and Independence Monument

1964. Independence.

211	**44**	3d. olive and sepia	10	10
212	-	6d. multicoloured	10	10
213	-	1s.3d. multicoloured	45	10
214	-	2s.6d. multicoloured	45	1·25

Designs: each with Dr. Hastings Banda—6d. Rising sun; 1s.3d. National Flag; 2s.6d. Coat of Arms.

48 Tung Tree

1964. As Nos. 199/210 of Nyasaland but inscr 'MALAWI' as in T **48**. The 9d., 1s.6d. and £2 are new values and designs.

252	½d. violet	10	10
216	1d. black and green	10	10
217	2d. brown	10	10
218	3d. brown, green and bistre	15	10
219	4d. blue and yellow	85	15
220	6d. purple, green and blue	75	10
221	9d. brown, green and yellow	30	15
258	1s. brown, blue and yellow	25	10
223	1s.3d. green and brown	50	60
259	1s.6d. brown and green	55	10
224	2s.6d. brown and blue	1·10	1·00
225	5s. multicoloured (I)	65	3·25
225a	5s. multicoloured (II)	14·00	1·00
226	10s. green, salmon and black	1·50	2·75
227	£1 brown and yellow	4·00	5·50
262	£2 multicoloured	26·00	24·00

Designs: (New)—1s.6d. Burley tobacco; £2 *Cyrestis camillus* (butterfly).

Two types of 5s. I, inscr 'LAKE NYASA'. II, inscr 'LAKE MALAWI'.

49 Christmas Star and Globe

1964. Christmas.

228	**49**	3d. green and gold	10	10
229	**49**	6d. mauve and gold	10	10
230	**49**	1s.3d. violet and gold	10	10
231	**49**	2s.6d. blue and gold	20	50
MS231a		83×126 mm. Nos. 228/231. Imperf	1·00	1·75

50 Coins

1964. Malawi's First Coinage. Coins in black and silver.

232	**50**	3d. green	10	10
233	**50**	9d. mauve	20	10
234	**50**	1s.6d. purple	25	10
235	**50**	3s. blue	35	1·10
MS235a		126×104 mm. Nos. 232/235. Imperf	1·75	1·75

1965. Nos. 223/224 surch.

236	1s.6d. on 1s.3d. green & brown	10	10
237	3s. on 2s.6d. brown and blue	20	20

52 Chilembwe leading Rebels

1965. 50th Anniversary of 1915 Rising.

238	**52**	3d. violet and green	10	10
239	**52**	9d. olive and orange	10	10
240	**52**	1s.6d. brown and blue	15	10
241	**52**	3s. turquoise and blue	20	25
MS241a		127×83 mm. Nos. 238/241	5·00	6·00

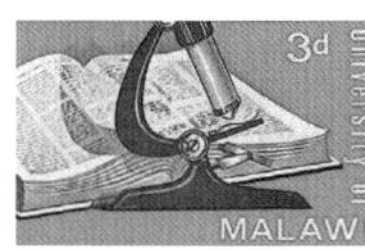

53 Learning and Scholarship

1965. Opening of Malawi University.

242	**53**	3d. black and green	10	10
243	**53**	9d. black and mauve	10	10
244	**53**	1s.6d. black and violet	10	10
245	**53**	3s. black and blue	15	40
MS246		127×84 mm. Nos. 242/245	2·50	2·50

54 *Papilio ophidicephalus*

1966. Malawi Butterflies. Multicoloured.

247	4d. Type **54**	80	10
248	9d. *Papilio desmondi* (magdae)	1·25	10
249	1s.6d. *Epamera handmani*	1·75	30
250	3s. *Amauris crawshayi*	2·75	6·00
MS251	130×100 mm. Nos. 247/250	17·00	10·00

58 British Central Africa 6d. Stamp of 1891

1966. 75th Anniversary of Postal Services.

263	**58**	4d. blue and green	10	10
264	**58**	9d. blue and red	15	10
265	**58**	1s.6d. blue and lilac	20	10
266	**58**	3s. grey and blue	30	70
MS267		83×127 mm. Nos. 263/266	5·00	3·25

59 President Banda

1966. Republic Day.

268	**59**	4d. brown, silver and green	10	10
269	**59**	9d. brown, silver and mauve	10	10
270	**59**	1s.6d. brown, silver & violet	15	10
271	**59**	3s. brown, silver and blue	25	15
MS272		83×127 mm. Nos. 268/271	2·00	3·75

60 Bethlehem

1966. Christmas.

273	**60**	4d. green and gold	10	10
274	**60**	9d. purple and gold	10	10
275	**60**	1s.6d. red and gold	15	10
276	**60**	3s. blue and gold	40	80

61 *Ilala I*

1967. Lake Malawi Steamers.

277	**61**	4d. black, yellow and green	25	10
278	-	9d. black, yellow and mauve	30	10
279	-	1s.6d. black, red and violet	40	20
280	-	3s. black, red and blue	60	1·75

Designs: 9d. *Dove*; 1s.9d. *Chauncy Maples I* (wrongly inscr 'Chauncey'); 3s. *Gwendolen*.

62 Golden Mbuna (female)

1967. Lake Malawi Cichlids. Multicoloured.

281	4d. Type **62**	30	10
282	9d. Scraped-mouthed mbuna	45	10
283	1s.6d. Zebra mbuna	60	25
284	3s. Orange mbuna	80	2·00

63 Rising Sun and Gearwheel

1967. Industrial Development.

285	**63**	4d. black and green	10	10
286	**63**	9d. black and red	10	10
287	**63**	1s.6d. black and violet	10	10
288	**63**	3s. black and blue	15	30
MS289		134×108 mm. Nos. 285/288	1·25	2·75

64 Mary and Joseph beside Crib

1967. Christmas.

290 **64** 4d. blue and green 10 10
291 **64** 9d. blue and red 10 10
292 **64** 1s.6d. blue and yellow 10 10
293 **64** 3s. deep blue and blue 15 30
MS294 114×100 mm. Nos. 290/293 1·00 3·00

65 *Calotropis procera*

1968. Wild Flowers. Multicoloured.

295 4d. Type **65** 15 10
296 9d. *Borreria dibrachiata* 15 10
297 1s.6d. *Hibiscus rhodanthus* 15 10
298 3s. *Bidens pinnatipartita* 20 95
MS299 135×91 mm. Nos. 295/298 1·75 4·00

66 Bagnall Steam Locomotive No. 1 *Thistle*

1968. Malawi Locomotives.

300 **66** 4d. green, blue and red 25 10
301 - 9d. red, blue and green 30 15
302 - 1s.6d. multicoloured 40 30
303 - 3s. multicoloured 70 3·00
MS304 120×88 mm. Nos. 300/303 1·50 6·00

Designs: 9d. Class G steam locomotive No. 49; 1s.6d. Class Zambesi diesel locomotive No. 202; 3s. Diesel railcar No. DR1.

67 *The Nativity* (Piero della Francesca)

1968. Christmas. Multicoloured.

305 4d. Type **67** 10 10
306 9d. *The Adoration of the Shepherds* (Murillo) 10 10
307 1s.6d. *The Adoration of the Shepherds* (Reni) 10 10
308 3s. *Nativity, with God the Father and Holy Ghost* (Pittoni) 15 15
MS309 115×101 mm. Nos. 305/308 35 1·60

69 Nyassa Lovebird

70 Carmine Bee-eater

1968. Birds (1st series). Multicoloured.

310 1d. Scarlet-chested sunbird (horiz) 15 50
311 2d. Violet starling (horiz) 30 20
312 3d. White-browed robin chat (horiz) 30 10
313 4d. Red-billed fire finch (horiz) 50 60
314 6d. Type **69** 2·50 15
315 9d. Yellow-rumped bishop 2·50 60
316 1s. Type **70** 1·00 15
317 1s.6d. Grey-headed bush shrike 2·50 7·00
318 2s. Paradise whydah 2·50 7·00
319 3s. African paradise flycatcher (vert) 7·00 3·25
320 5s. Bateleur (vert) 2·50 4·00
321 10s. Saddle-bill stork (vert) 2·50 7·00
322 £1 Purple heron (vert) 6·00 16·00
323 £2 Green turaco ('Livingstone's Loerie') 42·00 48·00

Sizes: 1d. to 9d. as T **69.** 1s.6d. to £2 as T **70.**

See also Nos. 473/85 and 501/4.

71 ILO Emblem

1969. 50th Anniversary of Int Labour Organisation.

324 **71** 4d. gold and green 10 10
325 **71** 9d. gold and brown 10 10
326 **71** 1s.6d. gold and brown 10 10
327 **71** 3s. gold and blue 15 15
MS328 127×89 mm. Nos. 324/327 1·00 4·75

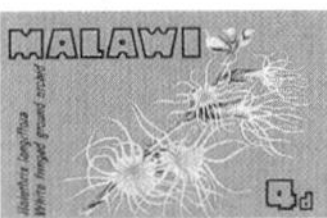

72 White-fringed Ground Orchid

1969. Orchids of Malawi. Multicoloured.

329 4d. Type **72** 15 10
330 9d. Red ground orchid 20 10
331 1s.6d. Leopard tree orchid 30 20
332 3s. Blue ground orchid 60 2·00
MS333 118×86 mm. Nos. 329/332 1·10 4·00

73 African Development Bank Emblem

1969. Fifth Anniversary of African Development Bank.

334 **73** 4d. yellow, brown and ochre 10 10
335 **73** 9d. yellow, ochre and green 10 10
336 **73** 1s.6d. yellow, ochre & brn 10 10
337 **73** 3s. yellow, ochre and blue 15 15
MS338 102×137 mm. Nos. 334/337 50 1·25

74 Dove over Bethlehem

1969. Christmas.

339 **74** 2d. black and yellow 10 10
340 **74** 4d. black and turquoise 10 10
341 **74** 9d. black and red 10 10
342 **74** 1s.6d. black and violet 10 10
343 **74** 3s. black and blue 15 15
MS344 130×71 mm. Nos. 339/343 1·00 2·25

75 *Zonocerus elegans* (grasshopper)

1970. Insects of Malawi. Multicoloured.

345 4d. Type **75** 15 10
346 9d. *Mylabris dicincta* (beetle) 15 10
347 1s.6d. *Henosepilachna elaterii* (ladybird) 20 15
348 3s. *Sphodromantis speculabunda* (mantid) 35 1·60
MS349 86×137 mm. Nos. 345/348 1·25 3·25

1970. Rand Easter Show. No. 317 optd **Rand Easter Show 1970.**

350 1s.6d. multicoloured 50 2·25

77 Runner

1970. Ninth Commonwealth Games, Edinburgh.

351 **77** 4d. blue and green 10 10
352 **77** 9d. blue and red 10 10
353 **77** 1s.6d. blue and yellow 10 10
354 **77** 3s. deep blue and blue 15 15
MS355 146×96 mm. Nos. 351/354 65 1·00

1970. Decimal Currency. Nos. 316 and 318 surch.

356 **70** 10t. on 1s. multicoloured 3·00 10

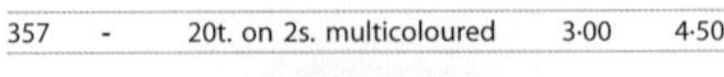

357 - 20t. on 2s. multicoloured 3·00 4·50

79 *Aegocera trimeni*

1970. Moths. Multicoloured.

358 4d. Type **79** 20 10
359 9d. *Faidherbia bauhiniae* 30 10
360 1s.6d. *Parasa karschi* 50 20
361 3s. *Teracotona euprepia* 1·25 3·50
MS362 112×92 mm. Nos. 358/361 3·75 6·50

80 Mother and Child

1970. Christmas.

363 **80** 2d. black and yellow 10 10
364 **80** 4d. black and green 10 10
365 **80** 9d. black and red 10 10
366 **80** 1s.6d. black and purple 10 10
367 **80** 3s. black and blue 15 15
MS368 166×100 mm. Nos. 363/367 1·00 3·00

1971. No. 319 surch **30t Special United Kingdom Delivery Service.**

369 30t. on 3s. multicoloured 50 2·25

No. 369 was issued for use on letters carried by an emergency airmail service from Malawi to Great Britain during the British postal strike. The fee of 30t. was to cover the charge for delivery by a private service, and ordinary stamps to pay the normal airmail postage had to be affixed as well. These stamps were in use from 8 February to 8 March.

82 Decimal Coinage and Cockerel

1971. Decimal Coinage.

370 **82** 3t. multicoloured 15 10
371 **82** 8t. multicoloured 20 10
372 **82** 15t. multicoloured 25 20
373 **82** 30t. multicoloured 35 1·50
MS374 140×101 mm. Nos. 370/373 1·00 2·50

83 Greater Kudu

1971. Decimal Currency. Antelopes. Multicoloured.

375 1t. Type **83** 10 10
376 2t. Nyala 15 15
377 3t. Mountain reedbuck 20 50
378 5t. Puku 40 1·25
379 8t. Impala 45 1·00
380 10t. Eland 60 10
381 15t. Klipspringer 1·00 20
382 20t. Suni 1·50 90
383 30t. Roan antelope 11·00 1·40
384 50t. Waterbuck 1·00 65
385 1k. Bushbuck 1·50 85
386 2k. Red forest duiker 2·75 1·50
387 4k. Common duiker 21·00 24·00

Nos. 380/387 are larger, size 25×42 mm.
No. 387 is incorrectly inscr 'Gray Duiker'.

85 Christ on the Cross

1971. Easter. Multicoloured.

388 **85** 3t. black and green 10 25
389 - 3t. black and green 10 25
390 **85** 8t. black and red 10 25
391 - 8t. black and red 10 25
392 **85** 15t. black and violet 15 30
393 - 15t. black and violet 15 30
394 **85** 30t. black and blue 20 45
395 - 30t. black and blue 20 45

MS396 Two sheets, each 95×145 mm. (a) Nos. 388, 390, 392 and 394. (b) Nos. 389, 391, 393 and 395 Set of 2 sheets 1·50 4·00

Design: Nos. 389, 391, 393, 395, The Resurrection. Both designs from *The Small Passion* (Durer).

87 *Holarrhena febrifuga*

1971. Flowering Shrubs and Trees. Multicoloured.

397 3t. Type **87** 10 10
398 8t. *Brachystegia spiciformis* 10 10
399 15t. *Securidaca longepedunculata* 15 15
400 30t. *Pterocarpus rotundifolius* 30 1·25
MS401 102×135 mm. Nos. 397/400 1·00 2·50

88 Drum Major

1971. 50th Anniversary of Malawi Police Force.

402 **88** 30t. multicoloured 65 1·50

89 *Madonna and Child* (William Dyce)

1971. Christmas. Multicoloured.

403 3t. Type **89** 10 10
404 8t. *The Holy Family* (M. Schongauer) 15 10
405 15t. *The Holy Family with St John* (Raphael) 20 20
406 30t. *The Holy Family* (Bronzino) 50 1·40
MS407 101×139 mm. Nos. 403/406 1·10 2·75

90 Vickers Viscount 700

1972. Air. Malawi Aircraft. Multicoloured.

408 3t. Type **90** 40 10
409 8t. Hawker Siddeley H.S.748 60 10
410 15t. Britten Norman Islander 85 30
411 30t. BAC One Eleven 1·40 2·75
MS412 143×94 mm. Nos. 408/411 8·00 6·00

91 Figures (Chencherere Hill)

1972. Rock Paintings.

413 **91** 3t. green and black 25 10
414 - 8t. red, grey and black 30 10
415 - 15t. multicoloured 35 30
416 - 30t. multicoloured 45 1·00
MS417 121×97 mm. Nos. 413/416 2·75 2·75

Designs: 8t. Lizard and cat (Chencherere Hill); 15t. Schematics (Diwa Hill); 30t. Sun through rain (Mikolongwe Hill).

92 Boxing

1972. Olympic Games, Munich.

No.	Type	Description	Unused	Used
418	**92**	3t. multicoloured	10	10
419	**92**	8t. multicoloured	15	10
420	**92**	15t. multicoloured	20	10
421	**92**	30t. multicoloured	35	45
MS422		110×92 mm. Nos. 418/421	1·25	1·75

93 Arms of Malawi

1972. Commonwealth Parliamentary Conference.

No.	Type	Description	Unused	Used
423	**93**	15t. multicoloured	30	35

94 *Adoration of the Kings* (Orcagna)

1972. Christmas. Multicoloured.

No.	Description	Unused	Used
424	3t. Type **94**	10	10
425	8t. *Madonna and Child Enthroned* (Florentine School)	10	10
426	15t. *Virgin and Child* (Crivelli)	20	10
427	30t. *Virgin and Child with St Anne* (Flemish School)	45	70
MS428	95×121 mm. Nos. 424/427	1·10	2·00

95 *Charaxes bohemani*

1973. Butterflies. Multicoloured.

No.	Description	Unused	Used
429	3t. Type **95**	50	10
430	8t. *Uranothauma crawshayi*	75	10
431	15t. *Charaxes acuminatus*	1·00	30
432	30t. *Amauris ansorgei* (inscr in error 'EUPHAEDRA ZADDACHI')	4·00	8·50
433	30t. *Amauris ansorgei* (inscr corrected)	5·50	8·50
MS434	145×95 mm. Nos. 429/432	7·00	12·00

96 Livingstone and Map

1973. Death Centenary of David Livingstone (1st issue).

No.	Type	Description	Unused	Used
435	**96**	3t. multicoloured	10	10
436	**96**	8t. multicoloured	15	10
437	**96**	15t. multicoloured	20	10
438	**96**	30t. multicoloured	35	60
MS439		144×95 mm. Nos. 435/438	1·00	1·75

See also No. 450/**MS**451.

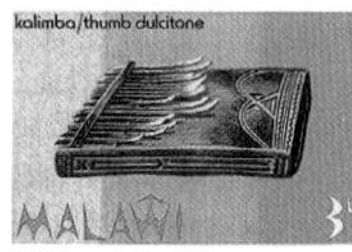

97 Thumb Dulcitone

1973. Musical Instruments. Multicoloured.

No.	Description	Unused	Used
440	3t. Type **97**	10	10
441	8t. Hand zither (vert)	15	10
442	15t. Hand drum (vert)	25	10
443	30t. One-stringed fiddle	45	60
MS444	120×103 mm. Nos. 440/443	2·50	2·00

98 The Magi

1973. Christmas.

No.	Type	Description	Unused	Used
445	**98**	3t. blue, lilac & ultramarine	10	10
446	**98**	8t. red, lilac and brown	10	10
447	**98**	15t. mauve, blue & dp mve	15	10
448	**98**	30t. yellow, lilac and brown	30	70
MS449		165×114 mm. Nos. 445/448	75	1·40

99 Stained-glass Window, Livingstonia Mission

1973. Death Centenary of David Livingstone (2nd issue).

No.	Type	Description	Unused	Used
450	**99**	50t. multicoloured	45	1·25
MS451		71×77 mm. No. 450	80	1·60

100 Large-mouthed Black Bass

1974. 35th Anniversary of Malawi Angling Society. Multicoloured.

No.	Description	Unused	Used
452	3t. Type **100**	20	10
453	8t. Rainbow trout	25	10
454	15t. Silver alestes ('Lake salmon')	40	20
455	30t. Tigerfish	70	1·90
MS456	169×93 mm. Nos. 452/455	2·50	3·00

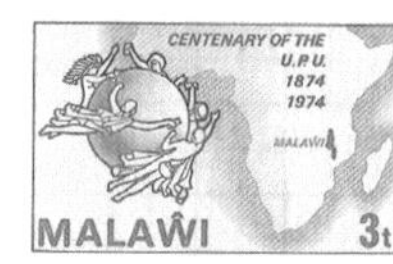

101 UPU Monument and Map of Africa

1974. Centenary of UPU.

No.	Type	Description	Unused	Used
457	**101**	3t. green and brown	10	10
458	**101**	8t. red and brown	10	10
459	**101**	15t. violet and brown	15	10
460	**101**	30t. blue and brown	30	1·10
MS461		115×146 mm. Nos. 457/460	65	2·00

102 Capital Hill, Lilongwe

1974. Tenth Anniversary of Independence.

No.	Type	Description	Unused	Used
462	**102**	3t. multicoloured	10	10
463	**102**	8t. multicoloured	10	10
464	**102**	15t. multicoloured	10	10
465	**102**	30t. multicoloured	25	35
MS466		120×86 mm. Nos. 462/465	45	1·25

103 *Madonna of the Meadow* (Bellini)

1974. Christmas. Multicoloured.

No.	Description	Unused	Used
467	3t. Type **103**	10	10
468	8t. *The Holy Family with St John and St Elizabeth* (Jordaens)	10	10
469	15t. *The Nativity* (Pieter de Grebber)	15	10
470	30t. *Adoration of the Shepherds* (Lorenzo di Credi)	30	50
MS471	163×107 mm. Nos. 467/470	75	1·50

104 Arms of Malawi

1975

No.	Type	Description	Unused	Used
472	**104**	1t. blue	20	40
472a	**104**	5t. red	65	2·25

105 African Snipe

106 Spur-winged Goose ('Spurwing Goose')

1975. Birds (2nd series). Multicoloured. (a) As T **105**.

No.	Description	Unused	Used
473	1t. Type **105**	1·50	2·50
474	2t. Double-banded sandgrouse (horiz)	1·50	2·25
475	3t. Indian blue quail ('Blue Quail') (horiz)	1·50	1·75
476	5t. Red-necked spurfowl ('Red-necked Francolin')	3·50	1·25
477	8t. Harlequin quail (horiz)	4·75	1·00

(b) As T **106**.

No.	Description	Unused	Used
480	20t. Comb duck ('Knob-billed Duck')	1·00	2·25
481	30t. Helmeted guineafowl ('Crowned Guinea Fowl')	1·25	70
482	50t. African pygmy goose ('Pigmy Goose') (horiz)	2·00	1·60
483	1k. Garganey	3·00	8·50
485	4k. African green pigeon ('Green Pigeon')	13·00	16·00
502	10t. Type **106**	2·00	1·50
503	15t. Denham's bustard ('Stanley Bustard')	2·00	2·00
504	2k. White-faced whistling duck ('White Face Tree Duck')	4·00	11·00

107 MV *Mpasa*

1975. Ships of Lake Malawi. Multicoloured.

No.	Description	Unused	Used
486	3t. Type **107**	30	10
487	8t. MV *Ilala II*	40	10
488	15t. MV *Chauncy Maples II*	75	30
489	30t. MV *Nkwazi*	1·00	3·50
MS490	105×142 mm. Nos. 486/489	2·25	4·25

See also Nos. 728/**MS**732.

108 *Habenaria splendens*

1975. Malawi Orchids. Multicoloured.

No.	Description	Unused	Used
491	3t. Type **108**	40	10
492	10t. *Eulophia cucullata*	50	10
493	20t. *Disa welwitschii*	60	25
494	40t. *Angraecum conchiferum*	1·00	2·25
MS495	127×111 mm. Nos. 491/494	7·00	8·50

109 Thick-tailed Bushbaby

1976. Malawi Animals. Multicoloured.

No.	Description	Unused	Used
496	3t. Type **109**	10	10
497	10t. Leopard	35	10
498	20t. Roan antelope	55	35
499	40t. Common zebra	1·00	3·25
MS500	88×130 mm. Nos. 496/499	2·00	3·50

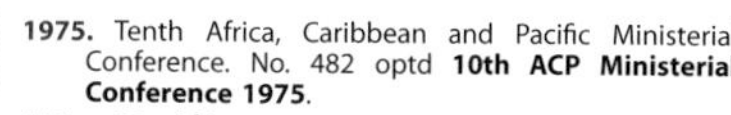
1975. Tenth Africa, Caribbean and Pacific Ministerial Conference. No. 482 optd **10th ACP Ministerial Conference 1975**.

No.	Description	Unused	Used
514	50t. African pygmy goose	1·00	2·50

111 *The Adoration of the Magi*

1975. Christmas. Religious Medallions. Multicoloured.

No.	Description	Unused	Used
515	3t. Type **111**	10	10
516	10t. *The Nativity*	15	10
517	20t. *Adoration of the Magi* (different)	20	10
518	40t. *Angel appearing to Shepherds*	50	2·50
MS519	98×168 mm. Nos. 515/518	1·50	3·75

112 Alexander Graham Bell

1976. Centenary of Telephone.

No.	Type	Description	Unused	Used
520	**112**	3t. green and black	10	10
521	**112**	10t. purple and black	10	10
522	**112**	20t. violet and black	20	10
523	**112**	40t. blue and black	50	1·40
MS524		137×114 mm. Nos. 520/523	1·10	1·75

113 President Banda

1976. Tenth Anniversary of Republic. Multicoloured.

No.	Type	Description	Unused	Used
525	**113**	3t. green	10	10
526	**113**	10t. purple	10	10
527	**113**	20t. blue	20	10
528	**113**	40t. blue	50	1·40
MS529		102×112 mm. Nos. 524/528	1·00	2·50

114 Bagnall Diesel Shunter No. 100

1976. Malawi Locomotives. Multicoloured.

No.	Description	Unused	Used
530	3t. Type **114**	40	15
531	10t. Class Shire diesel locomotive No. 503	60	15
532	20t. Nippon Sharyo diesel-hydraulic locomotive No. 301	1·10	30
533	40t. Hunslet diesel-hydraulic locomotive No. 110	1·75	6·00
MS534	130×118 mm. Nos. 530/533	3·50	7·00

1976. Centenary of Blantyre Mission. Nos. 481 and 503 optd **Blantyre Mission Centenary 1876–1976**.

No.	Description	Unused	Used
535	15t. Denham's bustard	1·50	1·50
536	30t. Helmeted guineafowl	1·75	3·75

116 Child on Bed of Straw

1976. Christmas.

No.	Type	Description	Unused	Used
537	**116**	3t. multicoloured	10	10
538	**116**	10t. multicoloured	10	10
539	**116**	20t. multicoloured	20	10
540	**116**	40t. multicoloured	40	60
MS541		135×95 mm. Nos. 537/540	1·60	2·50

117 Man and Woman

1977. Handicrafts. Wood-carvings. Multicoloured.

542	4t. Type **117**	10	10
543	10t. Elephant (horiz)	15	10
544	20t. Rhinoceros (horiz)	20	10
545	40t. Antelope	50	70
MS546	153×112 mm. Nos. 542/545	1·50	2·75

118 Chileka Airport

1977. Transport. Multicoloured.

547	4t. Type **118**	40	10
548	10t. Blantyre–Lilongwe Road	40	10
549	20t. MV *Ilala II*	75	20
550	40t. Blantyre–Nacala rail line	1·25	4·50
MS551	127×83 mm. Nos. 547/550	2·50	4·75

119 Blue-grey Mbuna

1977. Fish of Lake Malawi. Multicoloured.

552B	4t. Type **119**	30	10
553B	10t. Livingston mbuna	50	20
554A	20t. Zebra mbuna	1·25	45
555B	40t. Malawi scale-eater	1·50	1·25
MS556A	147×99 mm. Nos. 552A/555A	2·50	5·00

120 *Madonna and Child with St Catherine and the Blessed Stefano Maconi* (Borgognone)

1977. Christmas.

557	**120**	4t. multicoloured	10	10
558	-	10t. multicoloured	15	10
559	-	20t. multicoloured	25	10
560	-	40t. multicoloured	60	1·50
MS561		150×116 mm. Nos. 557/560	1·75	3·00

Designs: 10t. *Madonna and Child with the Eternal Father and Angels* (Borgognone); 20t. Bottigella altarpiece (detail, Foppa); 40t. *Madonna of the Fountain* (van Eyck).

121 *Entry of Christ into Jerusalem* (Giotto)

1978. Easter. Paintings by Giotto. Multicoloured.

562	4t. Type **121**	10	10
563	10t. *The Crucifixion*	15	10
564	20t. *Descent from the Cross*	30	10
565	40t. *Jesus appears before Mary*	50	55
MS566	150×99 mm. Nos. 562/565	1·90	2·40

122 Nyala

1978. Wildlife. Multicoloured.

567	4t. Type **122**	2·75	10
568	10t. Lion (horiz)	6·50	40
569	20t. Common zebra (horiz)	10·00	1·00
570	40t. Mountain reedbuck	11·00	7·50
MS571	173×113 mm. Nos. 567/570	38·00	12·00

123 Malamulo Seventh Day Adventist Church

1978. Christmas. Multicoloured.

572	4t. Type **123**	10	10
573	10t. Likoma Cathedral	10	10
574	20t. St Michael's and All Angels', Blantyre	20	10
575	40t. Zomba Catholic Cathedral	40	1·50
MS576	190×105 mm. Nos. 572/575	70	1·75

124 *Vanilla polylepis*

1979. Orchids. Multicoloured.

577	1t. Type **124**	50	40
578	2t. *Cirrhopetalum umbellatum*	50	40
579	5t. *Calanthe natalensis*	50	10
580	7t. *Ansellia gigantea*	50	60
581	8t. *Tridactyle bicaudata*	50	40
582	10t. *Acampe pachyglossa*	50	10
583	15t. *Eulophia quartiniana*	50	15
584	20t. *Cyrtorchis arcuata*	50	60
585	30t. *Eulophia tricristata*	1·25	30
586	50t. *Disa hamatopetala*	85	60
587	75t. *Cynorchis glandulosa*	2·00	6·50
588	1k. *Aerangis kotschyana*	1·60	1·75
589	1k.50 *Polystachya dendrobiiflora*	1·75	6·00
590	2k. *Disa ornithantha*	1·25	2·00
591	4k. *Cyrtorchis praetermissa*	1·50	5·00

125 Tsamba

1979. National Tree Planting Day. Multicoloured.

592	5t. Type **125**	20	10
593	10t. Mulanje cedar	25	10
594	20t. Mlombwa	40	20
595	40t. Mbawa	70	2·75
MS596	118×153 mm. Nos. 592/595	1·40	3·00

126 Train crossing Viaduct

1979. Opening of Salima–Lilongwe Railway Line. Multicoloured.

597	5t. Type **126**	25	15
598	10t. Diesel railcar at station	40	15
599	20t. Diesel train rounding bend	60	30
600	40t. Diesel train passing through cutting	85	2·50
MS601	153×103 mm. Nos. 597/600	2·75	4·50

127 Young Child

1979. International Year of the Child. Designs showing young children. Multicoloured; background colours given.

602	**127**	5t. green	10	10
603	-	10t. red	10	10
604	-	20t. mauve	25	10
605	-	40t. blue	45	1·60

128 1964 3d. Independence Commemorative Stamp

1979. Death Centenary of Sir Rowland Hill. Designs showing 1964 Independence Commemorative Stamps. Multicoloured.

606	5t. Type **128**	10	10
607	10t. 6d. value	10	10
608	20t. 1s.3d. value	20	10
609	40t. 2s.6d. value	35	85
MS610	163×108 mm. Nos. 606/609	75	1·40

129 River Landscape

1979. Christmas. Multicoloured.

611	5t. Type **129**	10	10
612	10t. Sunset	10	10
613	20t. Forest and hill	25	15
614	40t. Plain and mountains	50	2·25

130 Limbe Rotary Club Emblem

1980. 75th Anniversary of Rotary International.

615	**130**	5t. multicoloured	10	10
616	-	10t. multicoloured	10	10
617	-	20t. blue, gold and red	30	15
618	-	40t. gold and blue	75	2·25
MS619		105×144 mm. Nos. 615/618	1·10	2·50

Designs: 10t. Blantyre Rotary Club pennant; 20t. Lilongwe Rotary Club pennant; 40t. Rotary International emblem.

131 Mangochi District Post Office

1980. London 1980 International Stamp Exhibition.

620	**131**	5t. black and green	10	10
621	-	10t. black and red	10	10
622	-	20t. black and violet	15	10
623	-	1k. black and blue	65	1·10
MS624		114×89 mm. Nos. 620/623	1·25	2·25

Designs: 10t. New Blantyre Sorting Office; 20t. Mail transfer hut, Walala; 1k. First Nyasaland Post Office, Chiromo.

132 Agate Nodule

1980. Gemstones. Multicoloured.

625	5t. Type **132**	55	10
626	10t. Sunstone	70	10
627	20t. Smoky quartz	1·25	30
628	1k. Kyanite crystal	3·00	6·00

133 Elephants

1980. Christmas. Children's Paintings. Multicoloured.

629	5t. Type **133**	40	10
630	10t. Flowers	30	10
631	20t. Class Shire diesel train	75	20
632	1k. Malachite kingfisher	1·60	2·00

134 Suni

1981. Wildlife. Multicoloured.

633	7t. Type **134**	15	10
634	10t. Blue duiker	20	10
635	20t. African buffalo	30	15
636	1k. Lichtenstein's hartebeest	1·25	1·60

135 Kanjedza II Standard 'A' Earth Station

1981. International Communications. Multicoloured.

637	7t. Type **135**	10	10
638	10t. Blantyre International Gateway Exchange	15	10
639	20t. Kanjedza I standard 'B' earth station	25	15
640	1k. "Satellite communications"	1·50	1·90
MS641	101×151 mm. Nos. 637/640	1·75	3·25

136 Maize

1981. World Food Day. Agricultural Produce. Multicoloured.

642	7t. Type **136**	15	10
643	10t. Rice	20	10
644	20t. Finger-millet	30	20
645	1k. Wheat	1·00	1·40

137 *The Adoration of the Shepherds* (Murillo)

1981. Christmas. Paintings. Multicoloured.

646	7t. Type **137**	20	10
647	10t. *The Holy Family* (Lippi) (horiz)	25	10
648	20t. *The Adoration of the Shepherds* (Louis le Nain) (horiz)	45	15
649	1k. *The Virgin and Child, St John the Baptist and an Angel* (Paolo Morando)	1·10	2·25

138 Impala Herd

1982. National Parks. Wildlife. Multicoloured.

650	7t. Type **138**	20	10
651	10t. Lions	35	10
652	20t. Greater kudu	50	20
653	1k. Greater flamingoes	1·75	5·50

139 Kamuzu Academy

1982. Kamuzu Academy.

654	**139**	7t. multicoloured	15	10
655	-	20t. multicoloured	20	10
656	-	30t. multicoloured	30	45
657	-	1k. multicoloured	1·00	3·75

Designs: 20t. to 1k. Various views of the Academy.

140 Attacker challenging Goalkeeper

1982. World Cup Football Championship, Spain. Multicoloured.

658	7t. Type **140**	75	25
659	20t. FIFA World Cup trophy	1·60	1·25
660	30t. Football stadium	1·90	3·25
MS661	80×59 mm. 1k. Football	1·75	1·75

141 Blantyre War Memorial, St Paul's Church

1982. Remembrance Day. Multicoloured.

662	7t. Type **141**	10	10
663	20t. Zomba war memorial	15	10
664	30t. Chichiri war memorial	20	30
665	1k. Lilongwe war memorial	65	4·25

142 Kwacha International Conference Centre

1983. Commonwealth Day. Multicoloured.

666	7t. Type **142**	10	10
667	20t. Tea-picking, Mulanje	20	10
668	30t. World map showing position of Malawi	25	30
669	1k. Pres. Dr. H. Kamuzu Banda	60	1·50

143 Christ and St Peter

1983. 500th Birth Anniversary of Raphael. Details from the cartoon for *The Miraculous Draught of Fishes* Tapestry. Multicoloured.

670	7t. Type **143**	25	10
671	20t. Hauling in the Catch	55	80
672	30t. Fishing Village (horiz)	60	2·50
MS673	110×90 mm. 1k. Apostle	1·75	1·75

144 Pair by Lake

1983. African Fish Eagle. Multicoloured.

674	30t. Type **144**	1·60	2·00
675	30t. Making gull-like call	1·60	2·00
676	30t. Diving on prey	1·60	2·00
677	30t. Carrying fish	1·60	2·00
678	30t. Feeding on catch	1·60	2·00

145 Kamuzu International Airport

1983. Bicentenary of Manned Flight. Multicoloured.

679	7t. Type **145**	10	10
680	20t. Kamuzu International Airport (different)	25	15
681	30t. BAC One Eleven	40	45
682	1k. Short Empire C Class flying boat at Cape Maclear	1·10	2·75
MS683	100×121 mm. Nos. 679/682	2·00	4·00

146 *Clerodendrum myricoides*

1983. Christmas. Flowers. Multicoloured.

684	7t. Type **146**	40	10
685	20t. *Gloriosa superba*	90	15
686	30t. *Gladiolus laxiflorus*	1·00	60
687	1k. *Aframomum angustifolium*	2·25	7·00

147 Golden Mbuna

1984. Fish. Multicoloured.

688	1t. Type **147**	30	1·00
689	2t. Malawi eyebiter	30	1·00
690	5t. Blue mbuna	30	1·00
691	7t. Lombardo's mbuna	30	30
692	8t. Golden zebra mbuna	30	30
693	10t. Fairy cichlid	30	10
694	15t. Crabro mbuna	30	10
695	20t. Marbled zebra mbuna	30	10
696	30t. Sky-blue mbuna	50	20
697	40t. Venustus cichlid	60	30
698	50t. Thumbi emperor cichlid	2·50	3·25
699	75t. Purple mbuna	3·00	5·50
700	1k. Zebra mbuna	3·50	5·00
701	2k. Fairy cichlid (different)	4·00	7·00
702	4k. Mbenje emperor cichlid	5·00	11·00

Nos. 688 and 691/697 exist with different imprint dates at foot.

148 Smith's Red Hare

1984. Small Mammals. Multicoloured.

703	7t. Type **148**	20	10
704	20t. Gambian sun squirrel	35	50
705	30t. South African hedgehog	35	1·10
706	1k. Large-spotted genet	50	5·50

149 Running

1984. Olympic Games, Los Angeles. Multicoloured.

707	7t. Type **149**	15	10
708	20t. Boxing	35	20
709	30t. Cycling	75	70
710	1k. Long jumping	1·00	4·00
MS711	90×128 mm. Nos. 707/710	2·40	5·00

150 *Euphaedra neophron*

1984. Butterflies.

712	**150**	7t. multicoloured	65	20
713	-	20t. yellow, brown and red	1·50	30
714	-	30t. multicoloured	1·75	75
715	-	1k. multicoloured	2·75	8·50

Designs: 20t. *Papilio dardanus*; 30t. *Antanartia schaeneia*; 1k. *Spindasis nyassae*.

151 *Virgin and Child* (Duccio)

1984. Christmas. Religious Paintings. Multicoloured.

716	7t. Type **151**	35	10
717	20t. *Madonna and Child* (Raphael)	80	10
718	30t. *Virgin and Child* (ascr to Lippi)	1·00	40
719	1k. *The Wilton Diptych*	2·25	7·50

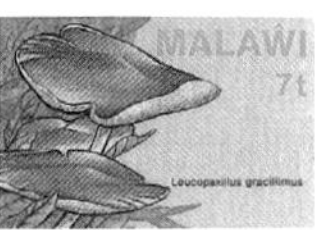

152 *Leucopaxillus gracillimus*

1985. Fungi. Multicoloured.

720	7t. Type **152**	80	30
721	20t. *Limacella guttata*	1·50	45
722	30t. *Termitomyces eurrhizus*	1·75	1·25
723	1k. *Xerulina asprata*	3·50	9·50

153 Map showing Member States and Lumberjack (Forestry)

1985. Fifth Anniversary of Southern African Development Co-ordination Conference. Designs showing map and aspects of development.

724	**153**	7t. black, green and light green	75	10
725	-	15t. black, red and pink	1·25	20
726	-	20t. black, violet and mauve	4·00	1·75
727	-	1k. black, blue and light blue	4·50	10·00

Designs: 15t. Radio mast (Communications); 20t. Diesel locomotive (Transport); 1k. Trawler and net (Fishing).

154 MV *Ufulu*

1985. Ships of Lake Malawi (2nd series). Multicoloured.

728	7t. Type **154**	90	10
729	15t. MV *Chauncy Maples II*	1·75	20
730	20t. MV *Mtendere*	2·25	65
731	1k. MV *Ilala II*	4·50	6·00
MS732	120×84 mm. Nos. 728/731	8·00	9·00

155 Stierling's Woodpecker

1985. Birth Bicentenary of John J. Audubon (ornithologist). Multicoloured.

733	7t. Type **155**	1·00	30
734	15t. Lesser seedcracker	1·75	30
735	20t. East coast akelat ('Gunning's Akalat')	1·75	65
736	1k. Boehm's bee-eater	3·25	7·00
MS737	130×90 mm. Nos. 733/736	8·00	10·00

156 *The Virgin of Humility* (Jaime Serra)

1985. Christmas. Nativity Paintings. Multicoloured.

738	7t. Type **156**	30	10
739	15t. *The Adoration of the Magi* (Stefano da Zevio)	75	15
740	20t. *Madonna and Child* (Gerard van Honthorst)	85	25
741	1k. *Virgin of Zbraslav* (Master of Vissy Brod)	2·25	5·50

157 Halley's Comet and Path of *Giotto* Spacecraft

1986. Appearance of Halley's Comet. Multicoloured.

742	8t. Type **157**	60	10
743	15t. Halley's Comet above Earth	65	15
744	20t. Comet and dish aerial, Malawi	1·00	30
745	1k. *Giotto* spacecraft	2·00	6·50

158 Two Players competing for Ball

1986. World Cup Football Championship, Mexico. Multicoloured.

746	8t. Type **158**	50	10
747	15t. Goalkeeper saving goal	75	20
748	20t. Two players competing for ball (different)	80	35
749	1k. Player kicking ball	3·00	5·50
MS750	108×77 mm. Nos. 746/749	9·00	12·00

159 President Banda

1986. 20th Anniversary of Republic. Multicoloured.

751	8t. Type **159**	1·50	2·75
752	15t. National Flag	80	15
753	20t. Malawi Coat of Arms	85	25
754	1k. Kamuzu International Airport and emblem of National Airline	3·50	6·00

160 *Virgin and Child* (Botticelli)

1986. Christmas. Multicoloured.

755	8t. Type **160**	45	10
756	15t. *Adoration of the Shepherds* (Guido Reni)	80	15
757	20t. *Madonna of the Veil* (Carlo Dolci)	1·25	35
758	1k. *Adoration of the Magi* (Jean Bourdichon)	3·75	9·00

161 Wattled Crane

1987. Wattled Crane. Multicoloured.

759	8t. Type **161**	1·50	40
760	15t. Two cranes	2·25	50
761	20t. Cranes at nest	2·25	80
762	75t. Crane in lake	4·50	12·00

162 Bagnall Steam Locomotive No. 2 *Shamrock*

1987. Steam Locomotives. Multicoloured.

767	10t. Type **162**	2·00	45

768	25t. Class D steam locomotive No. 8, 1914	2·75	70
769	30t. Bagnall steam locomotive No. 1 *Thistle*	3·00	85
770	1k. Kitson steam locomotive No. 6, 1903	6·00	13·00

163 Hippopotamus grazing

1987. Hippopotamus. Multicoloured.

771	10t. Type **163**	1·50	40
772	25t. Hippopotami in water	2·25	50
773	30t. Female and calf in water	2·25	75
774	1k. Hippopotami and cattle egret	6·00	12·00
MS775	78×101 mm. Nos. 771/774	11·00	12·50

164 *Stathmostelma spectabile*

1987. Christmas. Wild Flowers. Multicoloured.

776	10t. Type **164**	65	10
777	25t. *Pentanisia schweinfurthii*	1·50	25
778	30t. *Chironia krebsii*	1·75	55
779	1k. *Ochna macrocalyx*	3·00	9·50

165 African and Staunton Knights

1988. Chess. Local and Staunton chess pieces. Multicoloured.

780	15t. Type **165**	1·25	30
781	35t. Bishops	1·75	70
782	50t. Rooks	2·00	1·50
783	2k. Queens	6·00	12·00

166 High Jumping

1988. Olympic Games, Seoul. Multicoloured.

784	15t. Type **166**	30	10
785	35t. Javelin throwing	50	20
786	50t. Tennis	75	50
787	2k. Shot-putting	1·60	3·75
MS788	91×121 mm. Nos. 784/787	3·50	4·00

167 Evergreen Forest Warbler ('Eastern Forest Scrub Warbler')

1988. Birds. Multicoloured.

789	1t. Type **167**	50	2·00
790	2t. Yellow-throated woodland warbler ('Yellow-throated Warbler')	70	2·00
791	5t. Moustached green tinkerbird	70	1·50
792	7t. Waller's red-winged starling ('Waller's Chestnut-wing Starling')	70	2·00
793	8t. Oriole-finch	70	1·50
794	10t. White starred robin ('Starred Robin')	2·75	1·50
795	15t. Bar-tailed trogon	1·00	1·00
796	20t. Green-backed twin-spot ('Green Twinspot')	70	20
797	30t. African grey cuckoo shrike ('Grey Cuckoo Shrike')	70	20
798	40t. Black-fronted bush shrike	70	20
799	50t. White-tailed crested flycatcher	3·25	1·50
800	75t. Green barbet	70	1·25
801	1k. Lemon dove ('Cinnamon Dove')	70	1·25
802	2k. Silvery-cheeked hornbill	1·00	1·60
803	4k. Crowned eagle	1·25	2·50
804	10k. Anchieta's sunbird ('Red and Blue Sunbird')	12·00	15·00
804a	10k. As 10t.	15·00	3·75

167a Rebuilt Royal Exchange, 1844

1988. 300th Anniversary of Lloyd's of London. Multicoloured.

805	15t. Type **167a**	30	10
806	35t. Opening ceremony, Nkula Falls Hydro-electric Power Station (horiz)	70	20
807	50t. Air Malawi BAC One Eleven airliner (horiz)	3·00	75
808	2k. *Seawise University* (formerly *Queen Elizabeth*) on fire, Hong Kong, 1972	7·00	5·50

168 *Madonna in the Church* (Jan van Eyck)

1988. Christmas. Multicoloured.

809	15t. Type **168**	60	10
810	35t. *Virgin, Infant Jesus and St Anna* (da Vinci)	90	25
811	50t. *Virgin and Angels* (Cimabue)	1·25	70
812	2k. *Virgin and Child* (Baldovinetti Apenio)	3·00	6·50

169 Robust Cichlid

1989. 50th Anniversary of Malawi Angling Society. Multicoloured.

813	15t. Type **169**	60	20
814	35t. Small-scaled minnow ('Mpasa')	1·10	35
815	50t. Long-scaled yellowfish	1·50	1·40
816	2k. Tigerfish	4·00	9·50

170 Independence Arch, Blantyre

1989. 25th Anniversary of Independence. Multicoloured.

817	15t. Type **170**	80	20
818	35t. Grain silos	1·50	35
819	50t. Capital Hill, Lilongwe	2·00	1·50
820	2k. Reserve Bank Headquarters	5·00	10·00

171 Blantyre Digital Telex Exchange

1989. 25th Anniversary of African Development Bank. Multicoloured.

821	15t. Type **171**	80	20
822	40t. Dzalanyama steer	1·50	35
823	50t. Mikolongwe heifer	2·00	1·50
824	2k. Zebu bull	5·00	10·00

172 Rural House with Verandah

1989. 25th Anniversary of Malawi–United Nations Co-operation. Multicoloured.

825	15t. Type **172**	80	20
826	40t. Rural house	1·50	35
827	50t. Traditional hut and modern houses	2·00	1·50
828	2k. Tea plantation	5·00	10·00

173 St Michael and All Angels Church

1989. Christmas. Churches of Malawi. Multicoloured.

829	15t. Type **173**	80	20
830	40t. Catholic Cathedral, Limbe	1·50	35
831	50t. CCAP Church, Nkhoma	2·00	1·50
832	2k. Cathedral, Likoma Island	5·00	11·00

174 Ford Sedan, 1915

1990. Vintage Vehicles. Multicoloured.

833	15t. Type **174**	1·25	20
834	40t. Two-seater Ford, 1915	1·75	35
835	50t. Ford pick-up, 1915	2·00	1·50
836	1k. Chevrolet bus, 1930	5·00	11·00
MS837	120×85 mm. Nos. 833/836	15·00	15·00

175 Player heading Ball into Net

1990. World Cup Football Championship, Italy. Multicoloured.

838	15t. Type **175**	1·00	20
839	40t. Player tackling	1·40	35
840	50t. Player scoring goal	1·50	1·50
841	2k. World Cup	4·50	11·00
MS842	88×118 mm. Nos. 838/841	9·50	13·00

176 Anniversary Emblem on Map

1990. Tenth Anniversary of Southern Africa Development Co-ordination Conference. Multicoloured.

843	15t. Type **176**	1·00	20
844	40t. Tilapia	1·60	40
845	50t. Cedar plantation	2·00	1·50
846	2k. Male nyala (antelope)	5·00	11·00
MS847	174×116 mm. Nos. 843/846	14·00	16·00

177 *Aerangis kotschyana*

1990. Orchids. Multicoloured.

848	15t. Type **177**	1·75	25
849	40t. *Angraecum eburneum*	2·75	80
850	50t. *Aerangis luteo-alba rhodostica*	2·75	1·60
851	2k. *Cyrtorchis arcuata whytei*	6·50	12·00
MS852	85×120 mm. Nos. 848/851	15·00	15·00

178 *The Virgin and the Child Jesus* (Raphael)

1990. Christmas. Paintings by Raphael. Multicoloured.

853	15t. Type **178**	1·00	20
854	40t. *Transfiguration* (detail)	1·75	35
855	50t. *St Catherine of Alexandrie* (detail)	1·75	90
856	2k. *Transfiguration*	5·50	12·00
MS857	85×120 mm. Nos. 853/856	14·00	16·00

179 Buffalo

1991. Wildlife. Multicoloured.

858	20t. Type **179**	1·00	25
859	60t. Cheetah	2·25	1·00
860	75t. Greater kudu	2·25	1·00
861	2k. Black rhinoceros	9·00	11·00
MS862	120×85 mm. Nos. 858/861	13·00	15·00

180 Chiromo Post Office, 1891

1991. Centenary of Postal Services. Multicoloured.

863	20t. Type **180**	1·25	20
864	60t. Re-constructed mail exchange hut at Walala	2·25	85
865	75t. Mangochi post office	2·25	95
866	2k. Satellite Earth station	8·00	12·00
MS867	119×83 mm. Nos. 863/866	12·00	14·00

181 Red Locust

1991. Insects. Multicoloured.

868	20t. Type **181**	1·00	25
869	60t. Weevil	2·25	1·10
870	75t. Cotton stainer bug	2·25	1·40
871	2k. Pollen beetle	6·50	11·00

182 Child in a Manger

1991. Christmas. Multicoloured.

872	20t. Type **182**	80	20
873	60t. Adoration of the Kings and Shepherds	1·75	55
874	75t. Nativity	2·00	75
875	2k. Virgin and Child	4·75	12·00

183 Red Bishop

1992. Birds. Multicoloured.

876	75t. Type **183**	2·25	2·25
877	75t. Lesser striped swallow	2·25	2·25
878	75t. Long-crested eagle	2·25	2·25
879	75t. Lilac-breasted roller	2·25	2·25
880	75t. African paradise flycatcher	2·25	2·25
881	75t. White-fronted bee-eater	2·25	2·25
882	75t. White-winged black tern	2·25	2·25
883	75t. African fire finch ('Brown-backed Fire-finch')	2·25	2·25

884	75t. White-browed robin chat	2·25	2·25
885	75t. African fish eagle	2·25	2·25
886	75t. Malachite kingfisher	2·25	2·25
887	75t. Lesser masked weaver ('Cabani's Masked Weaver')	2·25	2·25
888	75t. Barn owl ('African Barn Owl')	2·25	2·25
889	75t. Variable sunbird ('Yellow-bellied Sunbird')	2·25	2·25
890	75t. Lesser flamingo	2·25	2·25
891	75t. South African crowned crane ('Crowned Crane')	2·25	2·25
892	75t. African pitta	2·25	2·25
893	75t. African darter	2·25	2·25
894	75t. White-faced whistling duck ('White-faced Tree-duck')	2·25	2·25
895	75t. African pied wagtail	2·25	2·25

184 Long Jumping

1992. Olympic Games, Barcelona. Multicoloured.

896	20t. Type **184**	80	20
897	60t. High jumping	1·25	60
898	75t. Javelin	1·50	90
899	2k. Running	3·50	7·00
MS900	110×100 mm. Nos. 896/899	6·50	9·00

185 The Angel Gabriel (detail, *The Annunciation*) (Philippe de Champaigne)

1992. Christmas. Religious Paintings. Multicoloured.

901	20t. Type **185**	70	20
902	75t. *Virgin and Child* (Bernandino Luini)	1·50	50
903	95t. *Virgin and Child* (Sassoferrato)	1·75	90
904	2k. Virgin Mary (detail, *The Annunciation*) (De Champaigne)	4·50	9·00

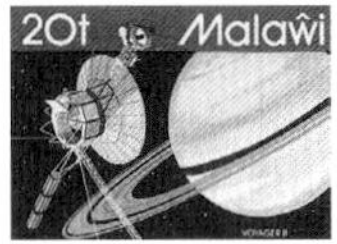

186 *Voyager 2* passing Saturn

1992. International Space Year. Multicoloured.

905	20t. Type **186**	1·00	30
906	75t. Centre of galaxy	2·00	90
907	95t. Kanjedza II Standard A Earth Station	2·00	1·00
908	2k. Communications satellite	4·50	8·00

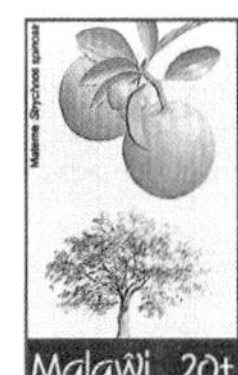

187 *Strychnos spinosa*

1993. World Forestry Day. Indigenous Fruit Trees. Multicoloured.

909	20t. Type **187**	70	20
910	75t. *Adansonia digitata*	1·50	80
911	95t. *Ximenia caffra*	1·60	1·00
912	2k. *Uapaca kirkiana*	3·25	6·50

188 *Apaturopsis cleocharis*

1993. Butterflies. Multicoloured.

913	20t. Type **188**	90	30
914	75t. *Euryphura achlys*	1·75	85
915	95t. *Cooksonia aliciae*	2·00	1·25
916	2k. *Charaxes protoclea azota*	3·00	5·50

189 The Holy Family

1993. Christmas. Multicoloured.

917	20t. Type **189**	15	10
918	75t. Shepherds and star	30	20
919	95t. Three Kings	30	30
920	2k. Adoration of the Kings	75	2·50

190 Kentrosaurus

1993. Prehistoric Animals. Multicoloured.

921	20t. Type **190**	55	30
922	75t. Stegosaurus	90	90
923	95t. Sauropod	1·00	1·00
MS924	157×97 mm. 2k. Tyrannosaurus; 2k. Dilophosaurus; 2k. Brachiosaurus; 2k. Gallimimus; 2k. Triceratops; 2k. Velociraptor	9·00	12·00

191 Socolof's Mbuna

1994. Fish. Multicoloured.

925	20t. Type **191**	25	10
926	75t. Golden mbuna	60	30
927	95t. Lombardo's mbuna	65	35
928	1k. Scraper-mouthed mbuna	65	70
929	2k. Zebra mbuna	1·40	2·25
930	4k. Elongate mbuna	2·25	4·50

192 *Ilala II* (lake vessel)

1994. Ships of Lake Malawi. Multicoloured.

931	20t. Type **192**	40	10
932	75t. *Ufulu* (tanker)	1·00	35
933	95t. *Pioneer* (steam launch)	1 10	40
934	2k. *Dove* (paddle-steamer)	1·75	3·00
MS935	85×51 mm. 5k. *Monteith* (lake vessel)	3·50	5·00

193 *Virgin and Child* (detail) (Durer)

1994. Christmas. Religious Paintings. Multicoloured.

936	20t. Type **193**	60	10
937	75t. *Wise Men present Gifts* (Franco-Flemish *Book of Hours*)	1·10	15
938	95t. *The Nativity* (detail) (Fra Filippo Lippi) (horiz)	1·25	15
939	2k. *Nativity Scene with Wise Men* (Rogier van der Weyden) (horiz)	2·25	3·50

194 President Bakili Muluzi (COMESA chairman, 1994–1995)

1995. Establishment of COMESA (Common Market for Eastern and Southern African States).

940	**194**	40t. multicoloured	15	10
941	**194**	1k.40 multicoloured	30	20
942	**194**	1k.80 multicoloured	30	55
943	**194**	2k. multicoloured	40	1·00

195 Telecommunications Training

1995. 50th Anniversary of the United Nations. Multicoloured.

944	40t. Type **195**	50	10
945	1k.40 Village women collecting water	1·00	35
946	1k.80 Mt. Mulanje	1·10	1·25
947	2k. Villagers in field	1·25	2·00
MS948	123×77 mm. Nos. 944/947	3·50	4·00

196 Teacher and Class

1995. Christmas. Multicoloured.

949	40t. Type **196**	30	10
950	1k.40 Dispensing medicine	70	25
951	1k.80 Crowd at water pump	80	1·00
952	2k. Refugees on ferries	1·00	1·60

197 *Precis tugela*

1996. Butterflies. Multicoloured.

953	60t. Type **197**	40	10
954	3k. *Papilio pelodorus*	90	45
955	4k. *Acrea acrita*	1·00	75
956	10k. *Melanitis leda*	2·25	3·50

198 Children's Party

1996. Christmas. Multicoloured.

957	10t. Type **198**	50	25
958	20t. Nativity play	75	25
959	30t. Children wearing party hats	90	25
960	60t. Mother and child	1·50	2·25

199 Map of Malawi

1997. 50th Death Anniversary of Paul Harris (founder of Rotary International). Multicoloured.

961	60t. Type **199**	50	15
962	3k. African fish eagle	1·50	80
963	4k.40 Leopard	1·00	1·25
964	5k. Rotary International emblem	1·00	1·50

200 Mother and Child

1997. 50th Anniversary of UNICEF. Multicoloured.

965	60t. Type **200**	30	10
966	3k. Children in class	65	35
967	4k.40 Boy with fish	1·25	1·50
968	5k. Nurse inoculating child	1·40	1·75

201 The Nativity

1997. Christmas. Multicoloured.

969	60t. Type **201**	30	10
970	3k. The Nativity (different)	60	30
971	4k.40 Adoration of the Magi	1·25	1·25
972	5k. The Holy Family	1·40	1·75

1998. Diana, Princess of Wales Commemoration. As T **91** of Kiribati. Multicoloured.

973	60t. Wearing red dress	20	10
974	6k. Wearing lilac jacket	40	35
975	7k. With head scarf	50	70
976	8k. Wearing blue evening dress	55	80
MS977	145×70 mm. Nos. 973/976	1·25	1·75

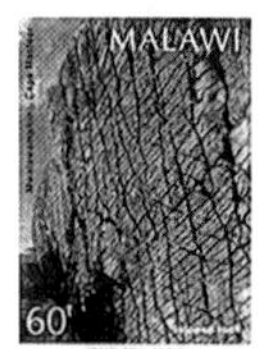

202 Tattooed Rock, Mwalawamphini, Cape Maclear

1998. Monuments. Multicoloured.

978	60t. Type **202**	20	10
979	6k. War Memorial Tower, Zomba	70	65
980	7k. Mtengatenga Postal Hut, Walala (horiz)	85	1·00
981	8k. PIM Church, Chiradzulu (horiz)	95	1·10

No. 978 is inscribed 'tatooed' and No. 979 'Memoral', both in error.

203 Woman voting

1998. 50th Anniversary of Declaration of Human Rights. Multicoloured.

982	60t. Type **203**	25	10
983	6k. Books, pens and pencils (Education)	70	65
984	7k. Man and woman on scales (Justice)	85	1·00
985	8k. Person hugging house and land (Property)	95	1·10

204 *Madonna and Child with Book*

1998. Christmas. Religious Paintings. Multicoloured.

986	60t. Type **204**	3·00	20
987	6k. *Madonna and Child*	16·00	1·75
988	7k. Angel	16·00	2·75
989	8k. *Adoration of the Magi*	16·00	3·25

205 *Madonna and Child*

1999. Christmas. Religious Paintings. Multicoloured.

990	60t. Type **205**	60	10
991	6k. *The Nativity*	1·75	55
992	7k. *Adoration of the Magi*	1·75	1·00
993	8k. *Flight into Egypt*	1·75	1·40

206 Ng'oma (hand drum)

2000. 50th Anniversary of the Commonwealth. Musical Instruments. Multicoloured.

994	60t. Type **206**	30	10
995	6k. Kaligo (single stringed fiddle)	70	55
996	7k. Kalimba (thumb dulcitone)	85	90
997	8k. Chisekese (rattle)	95	1·10

207 Map of Africa and SADC Emblem

2000. South African Development Community. Multicoloured.

998	60t. Type **207**	40	10
999	6k. Bottles of Malambe fruit juice	65	55
1000	7k. *Ndunduma* (fisheries research ship) (horiz)	1·75	1·50
1001	8k. Class Shire diesel locomotive and goods train (horiz)	2·25	2·00

208 *Madonna and Child*

2000. Christmas. Religious Paintings. Multicoloured.

1002	5k. Type **208**	45	10
1003	18k. *Adoration of the Shepherds*	1·50	1·75
1004	20k. *Madonna and Child*	1·50	1·75

209 *Euxanthe wakefieldi*

2002. Butterflies. Multicoloured.

1005	1k. Type **209**	50	1·00
1006	2k. *Pseudacraea boisdurali*	50	1·00
1007	4k. *Catacroptera cloanthe*	50	1·00
1008	5k. *Myrina silenus ficedula*	70	30
1009	10k. *Cymothoe zombana*	1·00	60
1010	20k. *Charaxes castor*	1·25	1·00
1011	50k. *Charaxes pythoduras ventersi*	2·00	2·25
1012	100k. *Iolaus lalos*	3·50	5·00

210 Puku

2003. Endangered Species. Puku (*Kobus vardonii*). Multicoloured.

1013	50k. Type **210**	1·75	2·50
1014	50k. Two males	1·75	2·50
1015	50k. Male and female	1·75	2·50
1016	50k. Herd	1·75	2·50
MS1017	204×138 mm. Nos. 1013/1016, each×2	10·00	14·00

211 Hoopoe (*Upupa epops*)

2003. Fauna and Flora of Africa. Multicoloured.

MS1018	118×137 mm. 50k. Type **211**; 50k. Grey parrot (*Psittacus erithacus*); 50k. Bateleur (*Terathopius ecaudatus*) 50k. Martial eagle (*Polemaetus bellicosus*); 50k. Masked lovebird (*Agapornis personatus*); 50k. Pel's fishing owl (*Scotopelia peli*)	9·00	10·00
MS1019	113×138 mm. 50k. *Bebearia octogramma*; 50k. *Charaxes nobilis*; 50k. *Cymothoe beckeri*; 50k. *Salamis anteva*; 50k. *Charaxes xiphares*; 50k. *Bebearia arcadius Fabricius* (all horiz)	9·00	10·00
MS1020	137×117 mm. 50k. *Pleurotus ostreatus*; 50k. *Macrolepiota procera*; 50k. *Amanita vaginata*; 50k. *Cantharellus tubaeformis*; 50k. *Hydnum repandum*; 50k. *Trametes versicolor* (all horiz)	9·00	10·00
MS1021	95×135 mm. 50k. *Angraecum eburneum*; 50k. *Ancistrochilus rothschildianus*; 50k. *Angraecum infundibulare*; 50k. *Ansellia Africana*; 50k. *Disa veitchii*; 50k. *Angraecum compactum*	9·00	10·00
MS1022	Four sheets. (a) 105×71 mm. 180k. Grey heron (*Arde cinerea*) (horiz). (b) 72×98 mm. 180k. *Carterocephalus palaemon* (horiz). (c) 68×94 mm. 180k. *Auricularia auricula*. (d) 93×66 mm. 180k. *Aerangis kotschyana* (horiz) Set of 4	16·00	18·00

212 Vickers Vimy

2004. Centenary of Powered Flight. Multicoloured.

MS1023	174×97 mm. 75k. Type **212**; 75k. D.H.9A; 75k. Messerschmitt Bf 109; 75k. Mitsubishi A6M3	4·50	5·00
MS1024	96×67 mm. 180k. Fiat CR.2	3·50	4·00

213 Corvette Convertible (1965)

2004. 50th Anniversary of the Corvette. Multicoloured.

MS1025	116×156 mm. 75k. Type **213**; 75k. Corvette Stingray (1965); 75k. Corvette (1979); 75k. Corvette (1998)	4·50	5·00
MS1026	110×83 mm. 180k. Corvette (1998)	3·50	4·00

214 Cadillac Eldorado (1959)

2004. Centenary of the Cadillac. Multicoloured.

MS1027	116×156 mm. 75k. Type **214**; 75k. Cadillac Series 62 (1962); 75k. Cadillac Sedan DeVille (1961); 75k. Cadillac V-16 (1930)	4·50	5·00
MS1028	110×85 mm. 180k. Cadillac Eldorado (1954)	3·50	4·00

215 Joop Zoetemelk (1980)

2004. Centenary of Tour de France Cycle Race. T **215** and similar vert designs showing winners. Multicoloured.

MS1029	157×96 mm. 75k. Type **215**; 75k. Bernard Hinault (1981); 75k. Bernard Hinault (1982); 75k. Laurent Fignon (1983)	5·50	6·00
MS1030	95×67 mm. 180k. Miguel Indurain (1991–1995)	4·00	4·50

216 African Fish Eagle (Namibia)

2004. First Joint Issue of Southern Africa Postal Operators Association Members. Sheet 170×95 mm containing T **216** and similar hexagonal designs showing National Birds of Association members. Multicoloured.

MS1031	15k. Type **216**; 15k. Two African fish eagles perched (Zimbabwe); 15k. Peregrine falcon (Angola); 15k. Cattle egret (Botswana); 15k. Purple-crested turaco ("Lourie") (Swaziland); 15k. Stanley ("Blue") crane (South Africa); 15k. Bar-tailed trogon (Malawi); 15k. Two African fish eagles in flight (Zambia)	6·00	7·00

The stamp depicting the bar-tailed trogon is not inscribed with the name of the country of which the bird is a National Symbol.

Miniature sheets of similar designs were also issued by Angola, Botswana, Namibia, South Africa, Swaziland, Zambia and Zimbabwe.

217 Boys in Classroom

2005. Centenary of Rotary International. Sheet 150×131 mm containing T **217** and similar horiz designs. Multicoloured.

MS1032	25k. Type **217**; 55k. Boy in wheelchair; 60k. Boys and teacher in classroom; 65k. Nurse and newborn baby in incubator	6·00	7·00

2007. Butterflies. As T **209**. Multicoloured.

1032*a*	5k. *Myrena silenus ficedula*	10	10
1032*b*	10k. *Cymothoe zombana*	20	15
1032*c*	20k. *Charaxes castor*	35	25
1032*d*	40k. *Papilio pelodorus*	60	60
1032*e*	50k. *Charaxes pythoduras ventersi*	60	60
1032*f*	65k. *Papilio pelodorus*	70	70
1032*g*	75k. *Acrea acrita*	1·00	1·00
1032*h*	100k. *Iolaus lalos*	80	80
1032*i*	105k. *Acrea acrita*	1·10	1·10
1032*j*	110k. *Euxanthe wakefieldi*	1·25	1·25
1032*k*	115k. *Pseudacraea boisdurali*	1·40	1·40

217a Nyala (pair) (Malawi)

2007. Second Joint Issue of Southern Africa Postal Operators Association Members. Multicoloured.

MS1032*l*	55k.×5 Type **217a**; Nyala (Zimbabwe); Burchell's Zebra (Botswana); Oryx (Nambia); Buffalo (Zambia)	3·25	3·25

Miniature sheets of similar designs were also issued by Botswana, Nambia, Zambia and Zimbabwe.

Botswana and Zambia also issued sheet stamps.

218 Handprint

2008. UNICEF 'STOP CHILD ABUSE'. Day of the African Child. Multicoloured.

1033	40k. Type **218**	1·00	1·00
MS1034	141×160 mm. 40k. Type **218**	1·00	1·00

219 Black Rhinoceros (*Diceros bicornis*)

2009. Endangered Animals of Malawi. Multicoloured.

MS1035	100×110 mm. 65k.×4 Type **219**; Sable antelope (*Hippotragus niger*); Zebra (*Equus zebra*); African buffalo (*Syncerus caffer*)	6·00	6·00
MS1036	100×70 mm. 325k. Roan antelope (*Hippotragus equinus*)	4·50	4·50

220 Hippopotamus

2009. Hippopotamuses of Malawi (*Hippopotamus amphibius*). Multlcoloured.

MS1037	120×100 mm. 105k.×4 Type **220**; Hippos laying in mud; Hippo standing; Two hippos in water	6·00	6·00
MS1038	100×71 mm. 325k. Hippos in water (vert)	5·50	5·50

221 Lion (*Panthera leo*)

2009. Wildlife of Malawi. Multicoloured.

MS1039	145×110 mm. 110k.×6 Type **221**; Elephant shrew (*Macroscelides proboscideus*); Black-backed jackal (*Canis mesomelas*); Reedbuck (*Redunca redunca*); African elephant (*Loxodonta africana*); Warthog (*Phacochoerus africanus*)	9·00	9·00
MS1040	70×100 mm. 325k. Leopard (*Panthera pardus*)	4·75	4·75

222 Flock of Lovebirds

2009. Endangered Species. Lilian's Lovebird (*Agapornis lilianae*). Multicoloured.

1041	115k. Type **222**	2·00	2·25
1042	115k. Six lovebirds perched on branches	2·00	2·25
1043	115k. Seven lovebirds in flight	2·00	2·25
1044	115k. Pair perched on branch and four others in flight	2·00	2·25
MS1045	112×165 mm. Nos. 1041/1044, each×2	13·00	14·00

223 Player, Football, Namibian Flag and Zakumi Mascot

2010. Third Joint Issue of Southern Africa Postal Operators Association Members. World Cup Football Championship, South Africa. Multicoloured.

1046	105k. Type **223**	1·10	1·10
1047	105k. South Africa	1·10	1·10
1048	105k. Zimbabwe	1·10	1·10
1049	105k. Malawi	1·10	1·10
1050	105k. Swaziland	1·10	1·10
1051	105k. Botswana	1·10	1·10
1052	105k. Mauritius	1·10	1·10
1053	105k. Lesotho	1·10	1·10
1054	105k. Zambia	1·10	1·10
MS1055	188×167 mm. Nos. 1046/1054	9·00	9·00

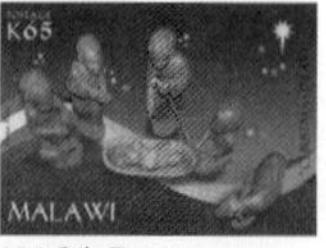

224 Crib Figures

2010. Christmas. Multicoloured: colour of lower background given.

1056	**224** 65k. orange-red	80	80

1057	65k. Indian red	80	80
1058	65k. Royal blue	80	80
1059	65k. yellowish green	80	80

225 School, Clinic and Water Pump

2011. 35th Anniversary of EU Aid Projects in Malawi. Multicoloured.

1060	65k. Type **225**	80	80
1061	65k. '35' in circle of stars and family (vert)	80	80
MS1062	86×86 mm. Nos. 1060/1061		

226 African Buffalo (*Syncerus caffer*)

2011. The Big Five. Multicoloured.

1063	80k. Type **226**	95	95
1064	100k. Leopard (*Panthera pardus*)	1·25	1·25
1065	135k. Black Rhinoceros (*Diceros birconis*)	1·50	1·50
1066	140k. African Elephant (*Loxodonta africanna*)	1·75	1·75
1067	145k. Lion (*Panthera Leos*)	1·75	1·75
MS1068	105×148 mm. Nos. 1063/1067	7·00	7·00

227 Angels proclaiming the Gospel to Shepherds

2011. Christmas. Multicoloured.

1069	80k. Type **227**	95	95
1070	100k. Shepherds lauding Jesus	1·25	1·25
1071	135k. Wise men following the Star	1·50	1·50
1072	140k. Wise men giving Jesus gifts	1·75	1·75
1073	145k. Simeon blessing baby Jesus	1·75	1·75
MS1074	110×148 mm. Nos. 1069/1073	7·00	7·00

228 Man, Tsetse Fly and Zebu

2012. Pan African Tsetse and Trypasonomiasis Eradication Campaign (PATTEC). Multicoloured.

1075	65k. Type **228**	80	80
1076	105k. PATTEC emblem	1·25	1·25
1077	110k. Tsetse flies and map of Malawi	1·40	1·40
1078	115k. Tsetse fly and map of Malawi	1·40	1·40
MS1079	91×126 mm. As Nos. 1075/1078	4·75	4·75

Nos. 1075/1078 have white borders. Stamps from **MS**1079 have coloured borders.

229 AIDS Ribbon and Map of Malawi ('Stop AIDS Keep the Promise')

2012. Campaign against AIDS. Multicoloured.

1080	80k. Type **229**	95	95
1081	100k. Couple wearing AIDS ribbons ('Male Involvement')	1·25	1·25
1082	135k. Blood test ('HTC')	1·50	1·50
1083	140k. Couple wearing AIDS ribbons ('Stop AIDS Keep the Promise')	1·75	1·75
1084	145k. Pregnant woman and nurse ('PMTCT')	1·75	1·75

A miniature sheet containing the following 5×Standard Postage stamps: 'STOP HIVAIDS'; Couple; 'Use a Condom'; 'Go for VCT'; 'Female condom empowering women' and inscribed 'NOT FOR SALE' in the sheet margin was distributed free of charge to Malawi Philatelic Bureau customers.

230 Vimbuza

2013. Traditional Dances. Multicoloured.

1085	165k. Type **230**	2·00	2·00
1086	260k. Uyeni	3·00	3·00
1087	270k. Tchopa	3·25	3·25
1088	280k. Masewe	3·25	3·25
1089	290k. Gule wa Mkulu	3·50	3·50
MS1090	180×180 mm. Nos. 1085/1089	13·50	13·50

231 MV *Mtendere* docked on the Bay

2014. Lake Malawi Scenes. Multicoloured.

1091	100k. Type **231**	1·25	1·25
1092	265k. Sunrise on Lake Malawi	3·50	3·50
1093	420k. Otter Point in Cape Maclear	5·50	5·50
1094	430k. Sunset on Lake Malawi	5·50	5·50
1095	450k. Fish Eagle poised for a kill	5·75	5·75
1096	480k. Kayaking on Lake Malawi	6·25	6·25
1097	500k. Satellite map of Lake Malawi	6·50	6·50
1098	840k. Chambo (cichlid fish) in Lake Malawi	11·00	11·00
1099	860k. Fish Eagle catching fish	11·00	11·00
1100	900k. Lizard Island on Lake Malawi	11·50	11·50
MS1101	230×80 mm. Nos. 1091/1100	70·00	70·00

232 Independence Ark

2014. 50th Anniversary of Independence. Multicoloured.

1102	330k. Type **232**	4·25	4·25
1103	520k. Hastings Kamuzu Banda (Malawi's First President)	6·75	6·75
1104	560k. Maize silos	7·25	7·25
1105	600k. Malawi Parliament	7·75	7·75
1106	670k. Zebras (Malawi Wildlife)	8·75	8·75
MS1107	123×163 mm. Nos. 1102/1106	35·00	35·00

233 Christmas Tree

2014. Christmas. Christmas Trees. Multicoloured.

1108	330k. Type **233**	1·75	1·75
1109	520k. Christmas tree with yellow lights in snow	2·50	2·50
1110	560k. Christmas tree with yellow lights and gold star in snow	2·75	2·75
1111	600k. Undecorated Christmas tree	3·00	3·00
1112	670k. Christmas tree decorated with Santa, stocking, cane, angel, berries and star	3·50	3·50
MS1113	230×100 mm. Nos. 1108/1112	12·00	12·00

234 Kampango Catfish (*Bargrus meridionalis*)

2016. Endemic Fish of Malawi. Multicoloured.

1114	100k. Type **234**	45	45
1115	200k. Assorted cichlids (yellow and blue banded species, gravelly lake bed background)	90	90
1116	200k. Assorted cichlids (yellow and mauve species, dark background)	90	90
1117	400k. Butter Fish	1·75	1·75
1118	500k. Mud Fish	2·25	2·25
1119	700k. Chambo	3·25	3·25
1120	730k. Utaka (*Copadichromis chrysonotus*)	3·25	3·25
1121	870k. Mpasa	4·00	4·00
MS1122	100×70 mm. 350k. Blue Malawi cichlid	1·60	1·60
MS1123	100×70 mm. 350k. Tilapia (*Oreochromis*)	1·60	1·60
MS1124	100×70 mm. 350k. Sanjika	1·60	1·60
MS1125	100×70 mm. 350k. Cichlid (blue); 350k. Cichlid (yellow)	3·25	3·25
MS1126	100×70 mm. 730k. *Metriaclima callainos*	3·25	3·25

235 White Dove Sparrow

2016. Indigenous Birds of Malawi

1127	200k. Type **235**	90	90
1128	400k. Emerald Cuckoo	1·75	1·75
1129	500k. Yellow-bellied Sunbird	2·25	2·25
1130	700k. Klaas's Cuckoo	3·25	3·25
1131	730k. Blue Waxbill	3·25	3·25
1132	870k. Bee-eater	4·00	4·00
MS1133	70×100 mm. 350k. White Dove Sparrow (vert)	1·60	1·60
MS1134	70×100 mm. 350k. Yellow-bellied Sunbird (vert)	1·60	1·60
MS1135	70×100 mm. 350k. Klaas's Cuckoo (vert)	1·60	1·60
MS1136	70×100 mm. 350k. Malachite Kingfisher (Inscr 'Bee Eater') (vert)	1·60	1·60
MS1137	70×100 mm. 350k. Collared Sunbird (vert)	1·60	1·60
MS1138	70×100 mm. 350k. African Yellow White-eye (vert)	1·60	1·60
MS1139	70×100 mm. 350k. Boehms Bee-eater (vert)	1·60	1·60

236 *Ximenia caffra*

2016. Wild Fruits of Malawi. Multicoloured.

1140	200k. Type **236**	90	90
1141	400k. *Strychnos spinosa*	1·75	1·75
1142	500k. *Azanza garckeana*	2·25	2·25
1143	700k. *Flacourtia indica*	3·25	3·25
1144	730k. *Ziziphus mauritiana*	3·25	3·25
1145	870k. *Vitex doniana*	4·00	4·00
MS1146	100×70 mm. 350k. *Flacourtia indica*	1·60	1·60
MS1147	100×70 mm. 350k. *Vitex doniana*	1·60	1·60
MS1148	100×70 mm. 350k. Indian Jujube	1·60	1·60
MS1149	100×70 mm. 350k. Maboque Fruta	1·60	1·60
MS1150	100×70 mm. 350k. Baobab Fruit	1·60	1·60
MS1151	100×70 mm. 730k. Masuku	3·25	3·25

237 *Syncerus caffer*

2016. Endangered Animals of Malawi. Multicoloured.

1152	100k. Type **237**	45	45
1153	200k. Two Hippopotamus on land	90	90
1154	400k. Rhinoceros and calf	1·75	1·75
1155	700k. *Panthera pardus* (close-up of leopard's face)	3·25	3·25
1156	700k. *Panthera pardus* (head of leopard)	3·25	3·25
1157	730k. *Loxodonta africana* (two elephants)	3·25	3·25
1158	870k. *Panthera leo* (lion, standing)	4·00	4·00
MS1159	70×100 mm. 350k. *Syncerus caffer* (buffalo different)	1·60	1·60
MS1160	70×100 mm. 350k. Hippopotamus, in water, mouth open	1·60	1·60
MS1161	70×100 mm. 350k. Rhinoceros	1·60	1·60
MS1162	70×100 mm. 350k. *Panthera pardus* (leopard in undergrowth)	1·60	1·60
MS1163	70×100 mm. 350k. *Loxodonta africana* (elephant drinking)	1·60	1·60
MS1164	70×100 mm. 350k. *Panthera leo* (lioness, sitting)	1·60	1·60
MS1165	70×100 mm. 350k. Zebras	1·60	1·60

K520 **(238)** K815 **(239)**

2016. Nos. 792 and 800 surch as T **238/239**

1166	520k. on 7t. Waller's Red-winged Starling	2·40	2·40
1167	815k. on 75t. Green Barbet	3·75	3·75

240 *Hibiscus sabdariffa*

2016. Herbs of Malawi. Multicoloured.

1168	100k. Type **240**	45	45
1169	200k. Neem Tree	90	90
1170	400k. Bird's Eye Chilli	1·75	1·75
1171	500k. Aloe Vera	2·25	2·25
1172	500k. *Bidens pilosa* (flower)	2·25	2·25
1173	730k. *Artemisia annua*	3·25	3·25
1174	870k. Amaranthus	4·00	4·00
MS1175	100×70 mm. 350k. Bird's Eye Chilli	1·60	1·60
MS1176	100×70 mm. 350k. *Bidens pilosa* (plant with bud, flower, and seedhead)	1·60	1·60
MS1177	100×70 mm. 350k. Silver Artemisia	1·60	1·60
MS1178	100×70 mm. 350k. Moringa	1·60	1·60
MS1179	100×70 mm. 350k. Amaranthus (different)	1·60	1·60

K600 **(241)** K900 **(242)**

2017. Nos. 797, 799 and 801/2 surch as T **241/2**

1180	600k. on 30t. African Grey Cuckoo Shrike	2·75	2·75
1181	600k. on 1k. Lemon Dove ("Cinnamon Dove")	2·75	2·75
1182	600k. on 2k. Silvery-cheeked Hornbill	2·75	2·75
1183	900k. on 50t. White-tailed Crested Flycatcher	4·00	4·00

K600 **(243)** K900 **(244)**

K1,150 **(245)** K1280 **(246)**

K2,000 **(247)**

2018. Nos. 955/6, 1005/6 and 1032d surch as T **243/7**

1184	600k. on 1k. Type **209**	2·75	2·75
1185	900k. on 65k. *Papilio pelodorus* (No. 1032d)	4·00	4·00
1186	1150k. on 4k. *Acrea acrita* (No. 955)	5·25	5·25
1187	1280k. on 2k. *Pseudacraea boisdurali* (No. 1006)	5·75	5·75
1188	2000k. on 10k. *Melanitis leda* (No. 956)	9·00	9·00

POSTAGE DUE STAMPS

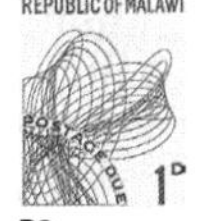

D2

1967

D6	**D2**	1d. red	15	4·50
D7	**D2**	2d. brown	20	4·50
D8	**D2**	4d. violet	35	4·75
D9	**D2**	6d. blue	25	5·00
D10	**D2**	8d. green	60	5·50
D11	**D2**	1s. black	70	6·00

1971. Values in tambalas. No accent over W of 'MALAWI'.

D12	**D2**	2t. brown	30	5·00
D13	**D2**	4t. mauve	50	3·00
D14	**D2**	6t. blue	50	3·25
D15	**D2**	8t. green	50	3·25
D16	**D2**	10t. brown	60	3·25

1975. With circumflex over W of 'MALAWI'.

D27	**D2**	2t. brown	4·00	6·50
D28	**D2**	4t. purple	4·00	6·50
D29	**D2**	6t. blue	4·00	6·50
D21	**D2**	8t. green	1·50	4·00
D31	**D2**	10t. black	4·00	6·50

MALAYA (BRITISH MILITARY ADMINISTRATION)

The following stamps were for use throughout the Malayan States and in Singapore during the period of the British Military Administration and were gradually replaced by individual issues for each state.

100 cents = 1 dollar.

1945. Straits Settlements stamps optd **B M A MALAYA**.

1b	**58**	1c. black	10	30
2a	**58**	2c. orange	20	10
4	**58**	3c. green	9·00	50
5	**58**	5c. brown	70	1·00
6a	**58**	6c. grey	30	20
7	**58**	8c. red	30	10
8a	**58**	10c. purple	50	10
10	**58**	12c. blue	1·75	22·00
12a	**58**	15c. blue	75	20
13a	**58**	25c. purple and red	1·40	30
14a	**58**	50c. black on green	1·00	10
15	**58**	$1 black and red	2·00	10
16	**58**	$2 green and red	2·75	1·00
17	**58**	$5 green and red on green	£110	£160
18	**58**	$5 purple and orange	6·50	3·00

For stamps inscribed 'MALAYA' at top and with Arabic characters at foot see under Kelantan, Negri Sembilan, Pahang, Perak, Selangor or Trengganu.

MALAYA (JAPANESE OCCUPATION)

Japanese forces invaded Malaya on 8 December 1941 and the conquest of the Malay peninsula was completed by the capture of Singapore on 15 February.

The following stamps were used in Malaya until the defeat of Japan in 1945.

100 cents = 1 dollar

(a) JOHORE

POSTAGE DUE STAMPS

(1)

1942. Nos. D1/D5 of Johore optd as T **1**.

JD1a	**D1**	1c. red	20·00	70·00
JD2a	**D1**	4c. green	65·00	80·00
JD3a	**D1**	8c. orange	80·00	95·00
JD4a	**D1**	10c. brown	16·00	50·00
JD5a	**D1**	12c. purple	48·00	55·00

大日本郵便

(2)

1943. Postage Due stamps of Johore optd with T **2**.

JD6	**D1**	1c. red	10·00	35·00
JD7	**D1**	4c. green	8·00	40·00
JD8	**D1**	8c. orange	10·00	40·00
JD9	**D1**	10c. brown	9·50	50·00
JD10	**D1**	12c. purple	11·00	65·00

(b) KEDAH

1942. Stamps of Kedah optd **DAI NIPPON 2602**.

J1	**1**	1c. black	11·00	17·00
J2	**1**	2c. green	27·00	30·00
J3	**1**	4c. violet	13·00	4·00
J4	**1**	5c. yellow	5·50	6·50
J5	**1**	6c. red	8·00	26·00
J6	**1**	8c. black	9·00	5·00
J7	**6**	10c. blue and brown	18·00	20·00
J8	**6**	12c. black and violet	42·00	60·00
J9	**6**	25c. blue and purple	16·00	29·00
J10	**6**	30c. green and red	70·00	80·00
J11	**6**	40c. black and purple	42·00	50·00
J12	**6**	50c. brown and blue	42·00	50·00
J13	**6**	$1 black and green	£140	£150
J14	**6**	$2 green and brown	£170	£170
J15	**6**	$5 black and red	80·00	£110

(c) KELANTAN

(5) Sunagawa Seal

(6) Handa Seal

1942. Stamps of Kelantan surch. (a) With T **5**. (i) New value in **CENTS**.

J16	**3**	1c. on 50c. green and orange	£550	£250
J17	**3**	2c. on 40c. orange and green	£1500	£400
J18	**3**	4c. on 30c. violet and red	£4000	£2750
J19	**3**	5c. on 12c. blue	£475	£250
J20	**3**	6c. on 25c. red and violet	£475	£250
J21	**3**	8c. on 5c. brown	£750	£170
J22	**3**	10c. on 6c. red	£100	£140
J23	**3**	12c. on 8c. green	65·00	£130
J24	**3**	25c. on 10c. purple	£2500	£2250
J25	**3**	30c. on 4c. red	£3250	£3000
J26	**3**	40c. on 2c. green	80·00	£100
J27	**3**	50c. on 1c. green and yellow	£2500	£2000
J28	**1**	$1 on 4c. black and red	50·00	95·00
J29	**1**	$2 on 5c. green & red on yell	50·00	95·00
J30	**1**	$5 on 6c. red	50·00	95·00

(ii) New Value in Cents.

J32	**3**	1c. on 50c. green and orange	£300	£130
J33	**3**	2c. on 40c. orange and green	£400	£190
J34	**3**	5c. on 12c. blue	£225	£250
J35	**3**	8c. on 5c. brown	£190	95·00
J36	**3**	10c. on 6c. red	£700	£750

(b) With T **6** and new value.

J41	**3**	1c. on 50c. green and orange	£200	£250
J42	**3**	2c. on 40c. orange and green	£275	£250
J43	**3**	8c. on 5c. brown	95·00	£170
J44	**3**	10c. on 6c. red	£150	£250
J31	**3**	12c. on 8c. green	£275	£450

(d) PENANG

(11) Okugawa Seal

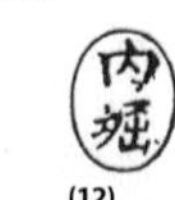

(12) Ochiburi Seal

1942. Straits Settlements stamps optd. (a) As T **11**.

(a) As T **11**

J56	**58**	1c. black	15·00	19·00
J57	**58**	2c. orange	24·00	30·00
J58	**58**	3c. green	20·00	30·00
J59	**58**	5c. brown	24·00	45·00
J60	**58**	8c. grey	40·00	50·00
J61	**58**	10c. purple	55·00	55·00
J62	**58**	12c. blue	50·00	55·00
J63	**58**	15c. blue	60·00	60·00
J64	**58**	40c. red and purple	£110	£120
J65	**58**	50c. black on green	£225	£225
J66	**58**	$1 black and red on blue	£300	£325
J67	**58**	$2 green and red	£950	£800
J68	**58**	$5 green and red on green	£3250	£1700

(b) With T **12**

J69	**58**	1c. black	£200	£170
J70	**58**	2c. orange	£200	£140
J71	**58**	3c. green	£120	£120
J72	**58**	5c. brown	£3500	£3500
J73	**58**	8c. grey	£120	£120
J74	**58**	10c. purple	£200	£225
J75	**58**	12c. blue	£140	£150
J76	**58**	15c. blue	£160	£160

1942. Stamps of Straits Settlements optd **DAI NIPPON 2602 PENANG**.

J77	**58**	1c. black	10·00	3·75
J78	**58**	2c. orange	12·00	5·00
J79	**58**	3c. green	9·50	9·00
J80	**58**	5c. brown	4·75	9·00
J81	**58**	8c. grey	3·00	1·40
J82	**58**	10c. purple	1·50	2·25
J83	**58**	12c. blue	6·50	26·00
J84	**58**	15c. blue	1·75	4·75
J85	**58**	40c. red and purple	8·50	26·00
J86	**58**	50c. black on green	3·75	40·00
J87	**58**	$1 black and red on blue	6·00	50·00
J88	**58**	$2 green and red	65·00	£110
J89	**58**	$5 green and red on green	£900	£950

(e) SELANGOR

1942. Agri-horticultural Exhibition. Stamps of Straits Settlements optd **SELANGOR EXHIBITION DAI NIPPON 2602 MALAYA**.

J90	**58**	2c. orange	12·00	24·00
J91	**58**	8c. grey	13·00	24·00

(f) SINGAPORE

(15) Malay Military Government Division Postal Services Bureau Seal

1942. Stamps of Straits Settlements optd with T **15**.

J92	**58**	1c. black	22·00	22·00
J93	**58**	2c. orange	16·00	13·00
J94	**58**	3c. green	55·00	70·00
J95	**58**	8c. grey	28·00	18·00
J96	**58**	15c. blue	21·00	15·00

(g) TRENGGANU

1942. Stamps of Trengganu optd with T **1**.

J97	**4**	1c. black	90·00	£100
J98	**4**	2c. green	£140	£140
J99	**4**	2c. on 5c. on 5c. pur & yell (No. 59)	42·00	42·00
J100	**4**	3c. brown	£100	90·00
J101	**4**	4c. red	£200	£150
J102	**4**	5c. purple on yellow	11·00	19·00
J103	**4**	6c. orange	14·00	28·00
J104	**4**	8c. grey	9·00	13·00
J105	**4**	8c. on 10c. on 10c. blue (No. 60)	13·00	50·00
J106	**4**	10c. blue	42·00	50·00
J107	**4**	12c. blue	8·00	50·00
J108	**4**	20c. purple and orange	16·00	55·00
J109	**4**	25c. green and purple	11·00	55·00
J110	**4**	30c. purple and black	18·00	50·00
J111	**4**	35c. red on yellow	40·00	65·00
J112	**4**	50c. green and red	90·00	£100
J113	**4**	$1 purple and blue on blue	£5500	£5500
J114	**4**	$3 green and red on green	80·00	£130
J115	-	$5 green and red on yellow (No. 31)	£350	£425
J116	-	$25 purple and blue (No. 40)	£2250	
J117	-	$50 green and yellow (No. 41)	£20000	
J118	-	$100 green and red (No. 42)	£2500	

1942. Stamps of Trengganu optd **DAI NIPPON 2602 MALAYA**.

J119	**4**	1c. black	17·00	13·00
J120	**4**	2c. green	£325	£275
J121	**4**	2c. on 5c. on 5c. pur on yell (No. 59)	6·50	8·00
J122	**4**	3c. brown	24·00	29·00
J123	**4**	4c. red	24·00	11·00
J124	**4**	5c. purple on yellow	6·00	13·00
J125	**4**	6c. orange	9·50	14·00
J126	**4**	8c. grey	95·00	30·00
J127	**4**	8c. on 10c. on 10c. blue (No. 60)	9·50	10·00
J128	**4**	12c. blue	11·00	50·00
J129	**4**	20c. purple and orange	21·00	20·00
J130	**4**	25c. green and purple	9·00	50·00
J131	**4**	30c. purple and black	16·00	50·00
J132	**4**	$3 green and red on green	£100	£190

1942. Stamps of Trengganu optd with T **2**.

J133	**4**	1c. black	28·00	30·00
J134	**4**	2c. green	19·00	50·00
J135	**4**	2c. on 5c. on 5c. pur on yell (No. 59)	12·00	32·00
J136	**4**	5c. purple on yellow	17·00	50·00
J137	**4**	6c. orange	18·00	50·00
J138	**4**	8c. grey	90·00	£120
J139	**4**	8c. on 10c. on 10c. blue (No. 60)	35·00	55·00
J140	**4**	10c. blue	£110	£250
J141	**4**	12c. blue	21·00	50·00
J142	**4**	20c. purple and orange	28·00	50·00
J143	**4**	25c. green and purple	29·00	55·00
J144	**4**	30c. purple and black	40·00	55·00
J145	**4**	35c. red on yellow	30·00	75·00

POSTAGE DUE STAMPS

1942. Postage Due stamps of Trengganu optd with T **2**.

JD17	**D1**	1c. red	55·00	90·00
JD18a	**D1**	4c. green	50·00	90·00
JD19	**D1**	8c. yellow	14·00	50·00
JD20	**D1**	10c. brown	14·00	50·00

(b) GENERAL ISSUES

1942. Stamps of various states optd with T **1**

(a) Straits Settlements

J146	**58**	1c. black	4·25	3·25
J147	**58**	2c. green	£4000	£3000
J148	**58**	2c. orange	4·00	2·25
J149	**58**	3c. green	4·50	2·25
J150	**58**	5c. brown	27·00	30·00
J151	**58**	8c. grey	9·00	2·25
J152	**58**	10c. purple	75·00	50·00
J153	**58**	12c. blue	£120	£160
J154	**58**	15c. blue	3·75	3·75
J155	**58**	30c. purple and orange	£4250	£4250
J156	**58**	40c. red and purple	£160	£100
J157	**58**	50c. black and green	75·00	50·00
J158	**58**	$1 black and red on blue	£100	75·00
J159	**58**	$2 green and red	£180	£225
J160	**58**	$5 green and red on green	£275	£300

There also exists a similar overprint with double-lined frame.

(b) Negri Sembilan.

J161	**6**	1c. black	19·00	13·00
J162	**6**	2c. orange	40·00	26·00
J163	**6**	3c. green	55·00	26·00
J164b	**6**	5c. brown	17·00	15·00
J165	**6**	6c. grey	£200	£150
J166	**6**	8c. red	£325	£250
J167	**6**	10c. purple	£350	£275
J168	**6**	12c. blue	£2750	£2750
J169	**6**	15c. blue	42·00	8·00
J170	**6**	25c. purple and red	28·00	38·00
J171	**6**	30c. purple and orange	£350	£300
J172a	**6**	40c. red and purple	£1700	£1300
J173	**6**	50c. black on green	£2500	£2250
J174a	**6**	$1 black and red on blue	£180	£200
J175	**6**	$5 green and red on green	£800	£1000

(c) Pahang.

J176	**15**	1c. black	55·00	50·00
J177a	**15**	3c. green	£225	£275
J178	**15**	5c. brown	20·00	13·00
J179	**15**	8c. grey	£1600	£1000
J180	**15**	8c. red	32·00	8·00
J181a	**15**	10c. purple	£375	£250
J182a	**15**	12c. blue	£1200	£1200
J183	**15**	15c. blue	£180	£120
J184	**15**	25c. purple and red	28·00	30·00
J185	**15**	30c. purple and orange	20·00	32·00
J186	**15**	40c. red and purple	30·00	38·00
J187	**15**	50c. black on green	£1900	£1900
J188	**15**	$1 black and red on blue	£170	£180
J189	**15**	$5 green and red on green	£850	£950

(d) Perak.

J190	**51**	1c. black	75·00	50·00
J191	**51**	2c. orange	38·00	20·00
J192	**51**	3c. green	35·00	32·00
J193	**51**	5c. brown	13·00	6·00
J194	**51**	8c. grey	£110	65·00
J195	**51**	8c. red	55·00	48·00
J196	**51**	10c. purple	26·00	24·00
J197	**51**	12c. blue	£300	£250
J198	**51**	15c. blue	24·00	32·00
J199	**51**	25c. purple and red	14·00	28·00
J200	**51**	30c. purple and orange	17·00	32·00
J201	**51**	40c. red and purple	£850	£400
J202	**51**	50c. black on green	55·00	60·00
J203	**51**	$1 black and red on blue	£650	£425
J204	**51**	$2 green and red	£5500	£5500
J205	**51**	$5 green and red on green	£600	

(e) Selangor.

J206	**46**	1c. black	15·00	28·00
J207	**46**	2c. green	£2750	£1500
J208	**46**	2c. orange	£100	60·00
J210c	**46**	3c. green	19·00	15·00
J211	**46**	5c. brown	7·50	5·50
J212a	**46**	6c. red	£225	£275
J213	**46**	8c. grey	35·00	17·00
J214	**46**	10c. purple	23·00	21·00
J215	**46**	12c. blue	70·00	80·00
J216	**46**	15c. blue	19·00	27·00
J217a	**46**	25c. purple and red	65·00	90·00
J218	**46**	30c. purple and orange	11·00	24·00
J219	**46**	40c. red and purple	£200	£150
J220	**46**	50c. black on green	£225	£225
J221	**48**	$1 black and red on blue	40·00	55·00
J222	**48**	$2 green and red	42·00	70·00
J223	**48**	$5 green and red on green	90·00	£120

1942. Various stamps optd **DAI NIPPON 2602 MALAYA**

(a) Stamps on Straits Settlements

J224	**58**	2c. orange	3·50	60
J225	**58**	3c. green	50·00	65·00
J226	**58**	8c. grey	12·00	4·50
J227	**58**	15c. blue	26·00	16·00

(b) Stamps of Negri Sembilan.

J228	**6**	1c. black	3·00	60
J229	**6**	2c. orange	13·00	50
J230	**6**	3c. green	9·00	50
J231	**6**	5c. brown	1·75	7·00
J232	**6**	6c. grey	7·50	7·50
J233	**6**	8c. red	9·00	1·25
J234	**6**	10c. purple	3·25	2·50
J235	**6**	15c. blue	25·00	2·50
J236	**6**	25c. purple and red	7·00	24·00
J237	**6**	30c. purple and orange	13·00	6·50
J238	**6**	$1 black and red on blue	85·00	£110

(c) Stamps of Pahang.

J239	**15**	1c. black	3·50	5·00
J240	**15**	5c. brown	1·25	70
J241	**15**	8c. red	42·00	3·50
J242	**15**	10c. purple	17·00	10·00
J243	**15**	12c. blue	4·50	25·00
J244	**15**	25c. purple and red	9·00	42·00
J245	**15**	30c. purple and orange	3·75	19·00

(d) Stamps of Perak.

J246	**51**	2c. orange	4·50	4·00
J247	**51**	3c. green	1·50	1·50
J248	**51**	8c. red	1·50	50
J249	**51**	10c. purple	22·00	9·50
J250	**51**	15c. blue	18·00	2·00
J251	**51**	50c. black on green	4·00	7·50
J252	**51**	$1 black and red on blue	£600	£650
J253	**51**	$5 green and red on green	70·00	95·00

(e) Stamps of Selangor.

J254	**46**	3c. green	2·25	6·00
J255	**46**	12c. blue	3·00	26·00
J256	**46**	15c. blue	9·00	1·50
J257	**46**	40c. red and purple	2·25	7·50
J258	**48**	$2 green and red	11·00	55·00

1942. No. 108 of Perak surch **DAI NIPPON 2602 MALAYA 2 Cents.**

J259	**51**	2c. on 5c. brown	1·75	5·50

1942. Stamps of Perak optd **DAI NIPPON YUBIN** (Japanese Postal Service) or surch also in figures and words.

J260	**51**	1c. black	7·00	11·00
J261	**51**	2c. on 5c. on 5c. brown	2·75	6·50
J262	**51**	8c. red	14·00	3·50

1943. Various stamps optd vert or horiz with T **2** or surch in figures and words

(a) Stamps of Straits Settlements

J263	**58**	8c. grey	1·40	50
J264	**58**	12c. blue	1·75	18·00
J265	**58**	40c. red and purple	4·00	7·50

(b) Stamps of Negri Sembilan.

J266	**6**	1c. black	75	5·00
J267	**6**	2c. on 5c. brown	1·00	2·75
J268	**6**	6c. on 5c. brown	40	3·50
J269	**6**	25c. purple and red	2·75	28·00

(c) Stamp of Pahang.

J270	**15**	6c. on 5c. brown	50	75

(d) Stamps of Perak.

J272	**51**	1c. black	1·25	1·75
J274	**51**	2c. on 5c. brown	60	50
J275	**51**	5c. brown	55	65
J276	**51**	8c. red	1·25	3·25
J277	**51**	10c. purple	75	1·50
J278	**51**	30c. purple and orange	5·50	9·50
J279	**51**	50c. black on green	4·50	35·00
J280	**51**	$5 green and red on green	90·00	£150

(e) Stamps of Selangor

J288	**46**	1c. black	50	60
J289	**46**	2c. on 5c. brown	2·00	50
J290	**46**	3c. on 5c. brown	30	5·00
J291	**46**	5c. brown	2·50	9·50
J293	**46**	6c. on 5c. brown	50	70
J295	**46**	$1 on 10c. purple	40	1·25
J296	**46**	$1.50 on 30c. purple and orange	40	1·25

25 Tapping Rubber

27 Japanese Shrine, Singapore

1943

J297	**25**	1c. green	1·75	55
J298	-	2c. green	1·00	20
J299	**25**	3c. grey	1·00	20
J300	-	4c. red	3·00	20
J301	-	8c. blue	50	20
J302	-	10c. purple	1·25	20
J303	**27**	15c. violet	1·75	5·00
J304	-	30c. olive	1·50	35
J305	-	50c. blue	5·00	5·00
J306	-	70c. blue	32·00	14·00

Designs: Vert—2c. Fruit; 4c. Tin dredger; 8c. War Memorial, Bukit Batok, Singapore; 10c. Fishing village; 30c. Sago palms; 50c. Straits of Johore. Horiz—70c. Malay Mosque, Kuala Lumpur.

28 Ploughman

1943. Savings Campaign.

J307	**28**	8c. violet	9·50	2·75
J308	**28**	15c. red	6·50	2·75

29 Rice-planting

1944. 'Re-birth of Malaya'.

J309	**29**	8c. red	17·00	3·25
J310	**29**	15c. mauve	4·00	3·25

大日本
マライ郵便
50 セント

(30)

1944. Stamps intended for use on Red Cross letters. Surch with T **30**

(a) On Straits Settlements

J311	**58**	50c. on 50c. black on green	10·00	24·00
J312	**58**	$1 on $1 black & red on bl	22·00	35·00
J313	**58**	$1.50 on $2 green on red	48·00	70·00

(b) On Johore.

J314	**24**	50c. on 50c. purple & red	9·52	20·00
J315	**24**	$1.50 on $2 green and red	4·25	12·00

(c) On Selangor.

J316	**48**	$1 on $1 black & red on bl	3·50	14·00
J317	**48**	$1.50 on $2 green and red	12·00	20·00

POSTAGE DUE STAMPS

1942. Postage Due stamps of Malayan Postal Union optd with T **1**.

JD21	**D1**	1c. violet	12·00	35·00
JD22	**D1**	3c. green	90·00	£100
JD23	**D1**	4c. green	£100	60·00
JD24	**D1**	8c. red	£200	£150
JD25	**D1**	10c. orange	45·00	65·00
JD26	**D1**	12c. blue	25·00	60·00
JD27	**D1**	50c. black	80·00	£120

1942. Postage Due stamps of Malayan Postal Union optd **DAI NIPPON 2602 MALAYA**.

JD28	**D1**	1c. violet	3·50	10·00
JD29	**D1**	3c. green	26·00	32·00
JD30	**D1**	4c. green	26·00	11·00
JD31	**D1**	8c. red	40·00	27·00
JD32	**D1**	10c. orange	2·00	17·00
JD33	**D1**	12c. blue	1·75	50·00

1943. Postage Due stamps of Malayan Postal Union optd with T **2**.

JD34	**D1**	1c. violet	2·25	6·00
JD35	**D1**	3c. green	2·25	4·50
JD36	**D1**	4c. green	65·00	50·00
JD37	**D1**	5c. red	1·50	5·00
JD38	**D1**	9c. orange	80	8·50
JD39	**D1**	10c. orange	2·25	9·00
JD40	**D1**	12c. blue	2·25	26·00
JD41	**D1**	15c. blue	2·25	9·00

MALAY (THAI OCCUPATION)

Stamps issued for use in the four Malay states of Kedah, Kelantan, Perlis and Trengganu ceded by Japan to Thailand on 19 October 1943 and restored to British rule on the defeat of the Japanese.

100 cents = 1 dollar.

TM1 War Memorial

1943

TM1	**TM1**	1c. yellow	30·00	32·00
TM2	**TM1**	2c. brown	12·00	20·00
TM3	**TM1**	3c. green	20·00	38·00
TM4	**TM1**	4c. purple	14·00	28·00
TM5	**TM1**	8c. red	14·00	20·00
TM6	**TM1**	15c. blue	38·00	60·00

MALAYAN FEDERATION

An independent country within the British Commonwealth, comprising all the Malay States (except Singapore) and the Settlements of Malacca and Penang. The component units retained their individual stamps. In 1963 the Federation became part of Malaysia (q.v).

100 cents (sen) = 1 Malayan dollar.

1 Tapping Rubber

1957

1	**1**	6c. blue, red and yellow	50	10
2	-	12c. multicoloured	2·25	1·00
3	-	25c. multicoloured	4·75	20
4	-	30c. red and lake	2·00	20

Designs: Horiz—12c. Federation Coat of Arms; 25c. Tin dredge. Vert—30c. Map of the Federation.

5 Prime Minister Tunku Abdul Rahman and Populace greeting Independence

1957. Independence Day.

5	**5**	10c. brown	80	10

6 United Nations Emblem

1958. UN Economic Commission for Asia and Far East Conference, Kuala Lumpur.

6	**6**	12c. red	30	80
7	-	30c. purple	40	80

Design: 30c. As T **6** but vert.

8 Merdeka Stadium, Kuala Lumpur

1958. First Anniversary of Independence.

8	**8**	10c. multicoloured	15	10
9	-	30c. multicoloured	40	70

Design: Vert—30c. Portrait of the Yang di-Pertuan Agong (Tuanku Abdul Rahman).

11 Malayan with 'Torch of Freedom'

1958. Tenth Anniversary of Declaration of Human Rights.

10		10c. multicoloured	15	10
11	**11**	30c. green	45	60

Design: Vert—10c. 'Human Rights'.

12 Mace and Malayan Peoples

1959. Inauguration of Parliament.

12	**12**	4c. red	10	10
13	**12**	10c. violet	10	10
14	**12**	25c. green	75	20

14

1960. World Refugee Year.

15	-	12c. purple	15	60
16	**14**	30c. green	15	10

Design: 12c. As T **14** but horiz.

15 Seedling Rubber Tree and Map

1960. Natural Rubber Research Conference and 15th International Rubber Study Group Meeting, Kuala Lumpur.

17	**15**	6c. multicoloured	20	1·25
18	**15**	30c. multicoloured	50	75

No. 18 is inscr 'INTERNATIONAL RUBBER STUDY GROUP 15th MEETING KUALA LUMPUR' at foot.

16 The Yang di-Pertuan Agong (Tuanku Syed Putra)

1961. Installation of Yang di-Pertuan Agong, Tuanku Syed Putra.

19	**16**	10c. black and blue	10	10

17 Colombo Plan Emblem

1961. Colombo Plan Conference, Kuala Lumpur.

20	**17**	12c. black and mauve	35	3·00
21	**17**	25c. black and green	80	2·50
22	**17**	30c. black and blue	70	1·00

18 Malaria Eradication Emblem

1962. Malaria Eradication.

23	**18**	25c. brown	20	40
24	**18**	30c. lilac	20	15
25	**18**	50c. blue	40	80

19 Palmyra Palm Leaf

1962. National Language Month.

26	**19**	10c. brown and violet	30	10
27	**19**	20c. brown and green	1·25	1·25
28	**19**	50c. brown and mauve	2·50	1·75

20 Shadows of the Future

1962. Introduction of Free Primary Education.

29	**20**	10c. purple	10	10
30	**20**	25c. ochre	60	1·25
31	**20**	30c. green	3·00	10

21 Harvester and Fisherman

1963. Freedom from Hunger.

32	**21**	25c. pink and green	3·25	3·50
33	**21**	30c. pink and lake	3·75	2·00
34	**21**	50c. pink and blue	3·50	3·00

22 Dam and Pylon

1963. Cameron Highlands Hydro-electric Scheme.

35	**22**	20c. green and violet	60	10
36	**22**	30c. turquoise and blue	1·00	1·50

MALAYAN POSTAL UNION

In 1936 postage due stamps were issued in Type **D1** for use in Negri Sembilan, Pahang, Perak, Selangor and Straits Settlements but later their use was extended to the whole of the Federation and Singapore, and from 1963 throughout Malaysia.

POSTAGE DUE STAMPS

D1

1936

D7	**D1**	1c. purple	5·00	2·00
D14	**D1**	1c. violet	70	1·60
D15	**D1**	2c. slate	1·25	2·25
D8	**D1**	3c. green	10·00	1·75
D17	**D1**	4c. sepia	70	7·00
D2	**D1**	4c. green	40·00	1·00
D9	**D1**	5c. red	6·00	1·75
D3	**D1**	8c. red	20·00	2·25
D19	**D1**	8c. orange	2·50	11·00
D11	**D1**	9c. orange	40·00	50·00
D4	**D1**	10c. orange	26·00	30
D5	**D1**	12c. blue	40·00	15·00
D20	**D1**	12c. mauve	1·25	6·00
D12	**D1**	15c. blue	£110	29·00
D21	**D1**	20c. blue	11·00	6·50
D6	**D1**	50c. black	30·00	4·50

1965. Surch **10 cents**.

D29	**D1**	10c. on 8c. on 8c. orange	60	3·00

MALAYSIA

Issues for use by the new Federation comprising the old Malayan Federation (Johore ("JOHOR"), Kedah, Kelantan, Malacca ("MELAKA"), Negri Sembilan ("NEGERI SEMBILAN"), Pahang, Penang ("PULAU PINANG"), Perak, Perlis, Selangor and Trengganu), Sabah (North Borneo), Sarawak and Singapore, until the latter became an independent state on 9 August 1965.

Stamps inscr "MALAYSIA" and state name are listed under the various states, as above.

1963. 100 cents (sen) = 1 Malaysian dollar.
1996. 100 sen = 1 ringgit.

A. NATIONAL SERIES

General issues for use throughout the Federation.

1 Federation Map

1963. Inauguration of Federation.

1	**1**	10c. yellow and violet	1·25	10
2	**1**	12c. yellow and green	1·75	60
3	**1**	50c. yellow and brown	1·75	10

2 Bouquet of Orchids

1963. Fourth World Orchid Congress, Singapore.

4	**2**	6c. multicoloured	1·25	1·25
5	**2**	25c. multicoloured	1·25	25

4 Parliament House, Kuala Lumpur

1963. Ninth Commonwealth Parliamentary Conference, Kuala Lumpur.

7	**4**	20c. mauve and gold	1·25	40
8	**4**	30c. green and gold	1·75	15

5 'Flame of Freedom' and Emblems of Goodwill, Health and Charity

1964. Eleanor Roosevelt Commemoration.

9	**5**	25c. black, red and turquoise	20	10
10	**5**	30c. black, red and lilac	20	15
11	**5**	50c. black, red and yellow	20	10

6 Microwave Tower and ITU Emblem

1965. Centenary of ITU.

12	**6**	2c. multicoloured	75	3·25
13	**6**	25c. multicoloured	2·00	60
14	**6**	50c. multicoloured	2·75	10

7 National Mosque

1965. Opening of National Mosque, Kuala Lumpur.

15	**7**	6c. red	10	10
16	**7**	15c. brown	20	10
17	**7**	20c. green	20	15

8 Air Terminal

1965. Opening of International Airport, Kuala Lumpur.

18	**8**	15c. black, green and blue	40	10
19	**8**	30c. black, green and mauve	60	20

9 Crested Wood Partridge

1965. Birds. Multicoloured.

20	25c. Type **9**	50	10
21	30c. Blue-backed fairy bluebird	60	10
22	50c. Black-naped oriole	1·25	10
23	75c. Rhinoceros hornbill	1·00	10
24	$1 Zebra dove	1·50	10
25	$2 Great argus pheasant	9·50	30
26	$5 Asiatic paradise flycatcher	20·00	3·25
27	$10 Blue-tailed pitta	45·00	13·00

For the lower values see the individual sets listed under each of the states which form Malaysia.

17 Sepak Raga (ball game) and Football

1965. Third South East Asian Peninsular Games.

28	**17**	25c. black and green	40	1·25
29	-	30c. black and purple	40	20
30	-	50c. black and blue	1·00	30

Designs: 30c. Running; 50c. Diving.

20 National Monument

1966. National Monument, Kuala Lumpur.

31	**20**	10c. multicoloured	50	10
32	**20**	20c. multicoloured	1·00	40

21 The Yang di-Pertuan Agong (Tuanku Ismail Nasiruddin Shah)

1966. Installation of Yang di-Pertuan Agong, Tuanku Ismail Nasiruddin Shah.

33	**21**	15c. black and yellow	10	10
34	**21**	50c. black and blue	20	20

22 School Building

1966. 150th Anniversary of Penang Free School.

35	**22**	20c. multicoloured	70	10
36	**22**	50c. multicoloured	90	10

23 Agriculture

1966. First Malaysia Plan. Multicoloured.

37	15c. Type **23**	20	10
38	15c. "Rural Health"	20	10
39	15c. "Communications"	3·00	15
40	15c. "Education"	20	10
41	15c. "Irrigation"	20	10

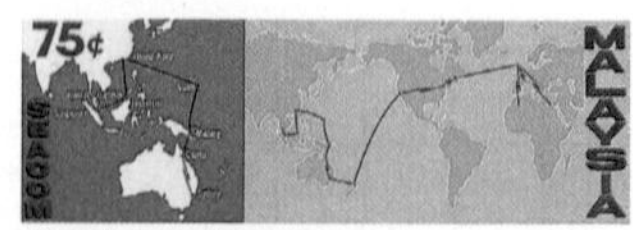

28 Cable Route Maps

1967. Completion of Malaysia–Hong Kong Link of SEACOM Telephone Cable.

42	**28**	30c. multicoloured	80	50
43	**28**	75c. multicoloured	2·50	4·25

29 Hibiscus and Paramount Rulers

1967. Tenth Anniversary of Independence.

44	**29**	15c. multicoloured	20	10
45	**29**	50c. multicoloured	1·25	80

30 Mace and Shield

1967. Centenary of Sarawak Council.

46	**30**	15c. multicoloured	10	10
47	**30**	50c. multicoloured	30	60

31 Straits Settlements 1867 8c. Stamp and Malaysian 1965 25c. Stamp

1967. Stamp Centenary.

48	**31**	25c. multicoloured	1·60	3·25
49	-	30c. multicoloured	1·60	2·75
50	-	50c. multicoloured	2·50	3·50

Designs: 30c. Straits Settlements 1867 24c. stamp and Malaysian 1965 30c. stamp; 50c. Straits Settlements 1867 32c. stamp and Malaysian 1965 50c. stamp.

34 Tapping Rubber, and Molecular Unit

1968. Natural Rubber Conference, Kuala Lumpur. Multicoloured.

51	25c. Type **34**	30	10
52	30c. Tapping rubber and export consignment	40	20
53	50c. Tapping rubber and aircraft tyres	40	10

37 Mexican Sombrero and Blanket with Olympic Rings

1968. Olympic Games, Mexico. Multicoloured.

54	30c. Type **37**	20	10
55	75c. Olympic Rings and Mexican embroidery	55	20

39 Tunku Abdul Rahman against background of Pandanus Weave

1969. Solidarity Week.

56	**39**	15c. multicoloured	15	10
57	-	20c. multicoloured	45	1·25
58	-	50c. multicoloured	50	20

Designs: Vert—20c. As T **39** (different). Horiz—50c. Tunku Abdul Rahman with pandanus pattern.

42 Peasant Girl with Sheaves of Paddy

1969. National Rice Year.

59	**42**	15c. multicoloured	15	10

60	**42**	75c. multicoloured	55	1·50

43 Satellite-tracking Aerial

1970. Satellite Earth Station.

61	**43**	15c. drab, black and blue	1·00	15
62	-	30c. multicoloured	1·00	2·75
63	-	30c. multicoloured	1·00	2·75

Design: 40×27 mm—Nos. 62/63, *Intelstat 3* in Orbit.

No. 62 has inscriptions and value in white and No. 63 has them in gold.

45 *Euploea leucostictus*

1970. Butterflies. Multicoloured.

64	25c. Type **45**	1·00	10
65	30c. *Zeuxidia amethystus*	1·50	10
66	50c. *Polyura athamas*	2·00	10
67	75c. *Papilio memnon*	2·00	10
68	$1 *Appias nero*	3·00	10
69	$2 *Trogonoptera brookiana*	3·50	10
70	$5 *Narathura centaurus*	5·00	3·75
71	$10 *Terinos terpander*	17·00	5·00

Lower values were issued for use in the individual States.

46 Emblem

1970. 50th Anniversary of International Labour Organisation.

72	**46**	30c. grey and blue	10	20
73	**46**	75c. pink and blue	20	30

47 UN Emblem encircled by Doves

1970. 25th Anniversary of United Nations.

74	**47**	25c. gold, black and brown	35	40
75	-	30c. multicoloured	35	35
76	-	50c. black and green	40	75

Designs: 30c. Line of doves and UN emblem; 50c. Doves looping UN emblem.

50 The Yang di-Pertuan Agong (Tuanku Abdul Halim Shah)

1971. Installation of Yang di-Pertuan Agong (Paramount Ruler of Malaysia).

77	**50**	10c. black, gold and yellow	20	30
78	**50**	15c. black, gold and mauve	20	30
79	**50**	50c. black, gold and blue	70	1·60

51 Bank Negara Complex

1971. Opening of Bank Negara Building.

80	**51**	25c. black and silver	2·75	3·00
81	**51**	50c. black and gold	2·00	1·50

52 Aerial View of Parliament Buildings

1971. 17th Commonwealth Parliamentary Association Conference, Kuala Lumpur. Multicoloured.

82	25c. Type **52**	1·25	50
83	75c. Ground view of Parliament Buildings (horiz, 73×23½ mm)	2·75	2·75

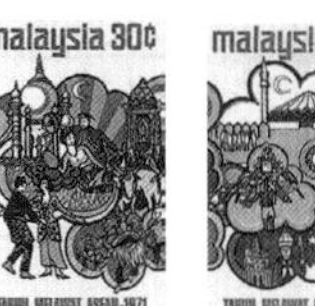

53 **54** Malaysian Carnival **55**

1971. Visit ASEAN Year.

84	**53**	30c. multicoloured	1·60	55
85	**54**	30c. multicoloured	1·60	55
86	**55**	30c. multicoloured	1·60	55

ASEAN = Association of South East Asian Nations.

Nos. 84/86 form a composite design of a Malaysian Carnival, as illustrated.

56 Trees, Elephant and Tiger

1971. 25th Anniversary of UNICEF. Multicoloured.

87	15c. Type **56**	2·50	60
88	15c. Cat and kittens	2·50	60
89	15c. Sun, flower and bird (22×29 mm)	2·50	60
90	15c. Monkey, elephant and lion in jungle	2·50	60
91	15c. Spider and butterflies	2·50	60

57 Athletics

1971. Sixth SEAP Games, Kuala Lumpur. Multicoloured.

92	25c. Type **57**	45	40
93	30c. Sepak Raga players	60	50
94	50c. Hockey	1·75	95

SEAP = South East Asian Peninsula.

58 **59** Map and Tourist Attractions **60**

1971. Pacific Area Tourist Association Conference.

95	**58**	30c. multicoloured	3·00	1·50
96	**59**	30c. multicoloured	3·00	1·50
97	**60**	30c. multicoloured	3·00	1·50

Nos. 95/97 form a composite design of a map showing tourist attractions, as illustrated.

61 Kuala Lumpur City Hall

1972. City Status for Kuala Lumpur. Multicoloured.

98	25c. Type **61**	1·25	1·50
99	50c. City Hall in floodlights	1·50	1·50

62 SOCSO Emblem

1973. Social Security Organisation.

100	**62**	10c. multicoloured	15	15
101	**62**	15c. multicoloured	15	10
102	**62**	50c. multicoloured	40	1·40

63 WHO Emblem

1973. 25th Anniv of WHO.

103	**63**	30c. multicoloured	50	25
104	-	75c. multicoloured	1·00	2·75

The 75c. is similar to T **63**, but vertical.

64 Fireworks, National Flag and Flower

1973. Tenth Anniversary of Malaysia.

105	**64**	10c. multicoloured	40	25
106	**64**	15c. multicoloured	55	15
107	**64**	50c. multicoloured	1·90	1·60

65 Emblems of Interpol and Royal Malaysian Police

1973. 50th Anniversary of Interpol. Multicoloured.

108	25c. Type **65**	1·00	50
109	75c. Emblems within '50'	2·25	2·00

66 Boeing 737 and MAS Emblem

1973. Foundation of Malaysian Airline System.

110	**66**	15c. multicoloured	35	10
111	**66**	30c. multicoloured	65	60
112	**66**	50c. multicoloured	95	1·60

67 Kuala Lumpur

1974. Establishment of Kuala Lumpur as Federal Territory.

113	**67**	25c. multicoloured	50	85
114	**67**	50c. multicoloured	1·00	1·75

68 Development Projects

1974. Seventh Annual Meeting of Asian Development Bank's Board of Governors, Kuala Lumpur.

115	**68**	30c. multicoloured	25	50
116	**68**	75c. multicoloured	80	2·00

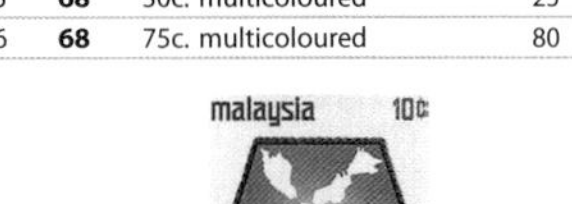

69 Scout Badge and Map

1974. Malaysian Scout Jamboree. Multicoloured.

117	10c. Type **69**	40	1·00
118	15c. Scouts saluting and flags (46×24 mm)	60	30
119	50c. Scout badge	1·25	2·50

70 Coat of Arms and Power Installations

1974. 25th Anniversary of National Electricity Board. Multicoloured.

120	30c. Type **70**	30	50
121	75c. National Electricity Board building (37×27 mm)	1·00	2·50

71 UPU and Post Office Emblems within '100'

1974. Centenary of UPU.

122	**71**	25c. green, yellow and red	20	35
123	**71**	30c. blue, yellow and red	25	35
124	**71**	75c. orange, yellow and red	65	1·75

72 Gravel Pump in Tin Mine

1974. Fourth World Tin Conference, Kuala Lumpur. Multicoloured.

125	15c. Type **72**	1·75	20
126	20c. Open-cast mine	2·00	2·50
127	50c. Dredger within ingot	3·75	5·50

73 Hockey-players, World Cup and Federation Emblem

1975. Thrid World Cup Hockey Championships.

128	**73**	30c. multicoloured	90	60
129	**73**	75c. multicoloured	2·10	2·25

74 Congress Emblem

1975. 25th Anniversary of Malaysian Trade Union Congress.

130	**74**	20c. multicoloured	20	25
131	**74**	25c. multicoloured	25	30
132	**74**	30c. multicoloured	65	60

75 Emblem of MKPW (Malayan Women's Organisation)

1975. International Women's Year.

133	**75**	10c. multicoloured	15	25
134	**75**	15c. multicoloured	30	25
135	**75**	50c. multicoloured	1·25	2·25

76 Ubudiah Mosque, Kuala Kangsar

1975. Koran Reading Competition. Multicoloured.

136	15c. Type **76**	1·75	60
137	15c. Zahir Mosque, Alor Star	1·75	60
138	15c. National Mosque, Kuala Lumpur	1·75	60
139	15c. Sultan Abu Bakar Mosque, Johore Bahru	1·75	60
140	15c. Kuching State Mosque, Sarawak	1·75	60

77 Plantation and Emblem

1975. 50th Anniversary of Malaysian Rubber Research Institute. Multicoloured.

141 10c. Type **77** 40 15
142 30c. Latex cup and emblem 1·10 70
143 75c. Natural rubber in test-tubes 2·25 2·25

77a *Hebomoia glaucippe*

1976. Multicoloured

144 10c. Type **77a** 2·75 7·00
145 15c. *Precis orithya* 2·75 7·00

78 Scrub Typhus

1976. 75th Anniversary of Institute of Medical Research. Multicoloured.

146 20c. Type **78** 40 15
147 25c. Malaria diagnosis 45 20
148 $1 Beri-beri 1·60 2·50

79 The Yang di-Pertuan Agong (Tuanku Yahya Petra)

1976. Installation of Yang di-Pertuan Agong.

149 **79** 10c. black, brown & yellow 25 10
150 **79** 15c. black, brown & mauve 40 10
151 **79** 50c. black, brown and blue 2·25 2·50

80 State Council Complex

1976. Opening of State Council Complex and Administrative Building, Sarawak.

152 **80** 15c. green and yellow 35 10
153 **80** 20c. green and mauve 45 40
154 **80** 50c. green and blue 1·00 1·40

81 EPF Building

1976. 25th Anniversary of Employees' Provident Fund. Multicoloured.

155 10c. Type **81** 15 10
156 25c. EPF emblems (27×27 mm) 35 75
157 50c. EPF Building at night 60 1·40

82 Blind People at Work

1976. 25th Anniversary of Malayan Association for the Blind. Multicoloured.

158 10c. Type **82** 15 15
159 75c. Blind man and shadow 1·25 2·75

83 Independence Celebrations, 1957

1977. First Death Anniversary of Tun Abdul Razak (Prime Minister).

160 15c. Type **83** 1·50 60
161 15c. Education 1·50 60
162 15c. Tun Razak and map (Development) 1·50 60
163 15c. 'Rukunegara' (National Philosophy) 1·50 60
164 15c. ASEAN meeting 1·50 60

84 FELDA Village Scheme

1977. 21st Anniversary of Federal Land Development Authority (FELDA). Multicoloured.

165 15c. Type **84** 30 10
166 30c. Oil palm settlement 80 2·00

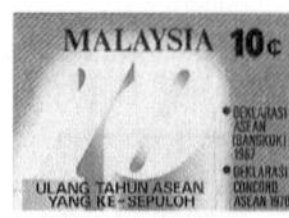

85 Figure '10'

1977. Tenth Anniversary of Association of South East Asian Nations (ASEAN). Multicoloured.

167 10c. Type **85** 10 10
168 75c. Flags of members 1·25 1·00

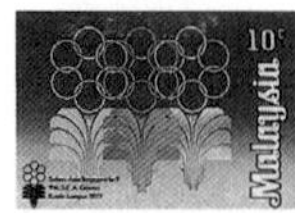

86 Games Logos

1977. Ninth South East Asia Games, Kuala Lumpur. Multicoloured.

169 10c. Type **86** 15 15
170 20c. 'Ball' 20 15
171 75c. Symbolic athletes 75 1·75

87 Islamic Development Bank Emblem

1978. Islamic Development Bank Board of Governors' Meeting, Kuala Lumpur.

172 **87** 30c. multicoloured 25 15
173 **87** 75c. multicoloured 75 85

88 Mobile Post Office

1978. Fourth Commonwealth Postal Administrations Conference, Kuala Lumpur. Multicoloured.

174 10c. Type **88** 30 10
175 25c. GPO, Kuala Lumpur 75 2·00
176 50c. Rural delivery by motorcycle 2·00 3·00

89 Boy Scout Emblem

1978. Fourth Malaysian Scout Jamboree, Sarawak. Multicoloured.

177 15c. Type **89** 50 10
178 $1 Bees and honeycomb 2·00 3·50

90 Dome of the Rock, Jerusalem

1978. Palestinian Welfare.

179 **90** 15c. multicoloured 1·00 25
180 **90** 30c. multicoloured 1·75 2·50

91 Globe and Emblems

1978. Global Eradication of Smallpox.

181 **91** 15c. black, red and blue 25 10
182 **91** 30c. black, red and green 40 30
183 **91** 50c. black, red and pink 70 95

92 'Seratus Tahun Getah Asli' and Tapping Knives Symbol

1978. Centenary of Rubber Industry.

184 **92** 10c. gold and green 10 10
185 - 20c. blue, brown and green 15 10
186 - 75c. gold and green 65 1·00

Designs: 20c. Rubber tree seedling and part of 'maxi stump'; 75c. Graphic design of rubber tree, latex cup and globe arranged to form '100'.

93 Sultan of Selangor's New Palace

1978. Inauguration of Shah Alam New Town as State Capital of Selangor. Multicoloured.

187 10c. Type **93** 15 10
188 30c. Aerial view of Shah Alam 30 15
189 75c. Shah Alam 65 2·00

94 Tiger

1979. Animals. Multicoloured.

190 30c. Type **94** 1·75 10
191 40c. Malayan flying lemur 80 10
192 50c. Lesser Malay chevrotain 1·75 10
193 75c. Leathery pangolin 1·00 10
194 $1 Malayan turtle 1·50 10
195 $2 Malayan tapir 1·50 10
196 $5 Gaur 4·50 2·00
197 $10 Orangutang (vert) 7·00 4·00

96 View of Central Bank of Malaysia

1979. 20th Anniversary of Central Bank of Malaysia. Multicoloured.

198 10c. Type **96** 10 10
199 75c. Central Bank (vert) 40 1·50

97 IYC Emblem

1979. International Year of the Child.

200 **97** 10c. gold, blue and salmon 35 20
201 - 15c. multicoloured 60 10
202 - $1 multicoloured 2·50 4·00

Designs: 15c. Children holding hands in front of globe; $1 Children playing.

98 Dam and Power Station

1979. Opening of Hydro-electric Power Station, Temengor.

203 **98** 15c. multicoloured 20 15
204 - 25c. multicoloured 35 70
205 - 50c. multicoloured 55 1·40

Designs: 25c., 50c. Different views of dam.

99 Exhibition Emblem

1979. Third World Telecommunications Exhibition, Geneva.

206 **99** 10c. orange, blue and silver 15 50
207 - 15c. multicoloured 20 10
208 - 50c. multicoloured 75 2·50

Designs: 34×24 mm—15c. Telephone receiver joining the one half of World to the other. 39×28 mm—50c. Communications equipment.

100 Tuanku Haji Ahmad Shah

1980. Installation of Tuanku Haji Ahmad Shah as Yang di-Pertuan Agong.

209 **100** 10c. black, gold and yellow 15 40
210 **100** 15c. black, gold and purple 20 10
211 **100** 50c. black, gold and blue 75 2·00

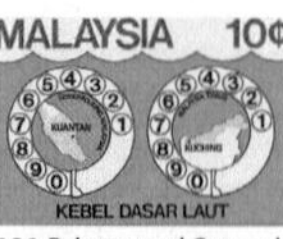

101 Pahang and Sarawak Maps within Telephone Dials

1980. Kuantan–Kuching Submarine Cable Project. Multicoloured.

212 10c. Type **101** 15 40
213 15c. Kuantan and Kuching views within telephone dials 20 10
214 50c. Pahang and Sarawak maps within telephone receiver 45 1·75

102 Bangi Campus

1980. Tenth Anniversary of National University of Malaysia. Multicoloured.

215 10c. Type **102** 15 20
216 15c. Jalan Pantai Baru campus 20 10
217 75c. Great Hall 80 3·00

103 Mecca

1980. Moslem Year 1400 AH. Commemoration.

218 **103** 15c. multicoloured 10 10
219 **103** 50c. multicoloured 30 1·50

No. 219 is inscribed in Roman lettering.

104 Disabled Child learning to Walk

1981. International Year for Disabled Persons. Multicoloured.

220 10c. Type **104** 25 30
221 15c. Girl sewing 40 10
222 75c. Disabled athlete 90 3·00

105 Industrial Scene

1981. Expo 81 Industrial Training Exposition, Kuala Lumpur and Seminar, Genting Highlands. Multicoloured.

223 10c. Type **105** 10 10
224 15c. Worker and bulldozer 15 10

225	30c. Workers at shipbuilding plant	25	35
226	75c. Agriculture and fishing produce, workers and machinery	65	2·25

106 '25'

1981. 25th Anniversary of Malaysian National Committee for World Energy Conferences. Multicoloured.

227	10c. Type **106**	20	20
228	15c. Drawings showing importance of energy sources in industry	45	10
229	75c. Symbols of various energy sources	2·50	3·75

107 Drawing showing development of Sabah from Village to Urbanized Area

1981. Centenary of Sabah. Multicoloured.

230	15c. Type **107**	50	15
231	80c. Drawing showing traditional and modern methods of agriculture	2·00	4·25

108 *Samanea saman*

1981. Trees. Multicoloured.

232	15c. Type **108**	55	10
233	50c. *Dyera costulata* (vert)	1·75	1·40
234	80c. *Dryobalanops aromatica* (vert)	2·00	4·25

109 Jamboree Emblem

1982. Fifth Malaysian and Seventh Asia–Pacific Boy Scout Jamboree. Multicoloured.

235	15c. Type **109**	35	10
236	50c. Malaysian flag and scout emblem	80	85
237	80c. Malaysian and Asia–Pacific scout emblem	1·25	4·25

110 ASEAN Building and Emblem

1982. 15th Anniversary of Ministerial Meeting of ASEAN (Association of South East Asian Nations). Multicoloured.

238	15c. Type **110**	15	10
239	$1 Flags of members	2·00	4·00

111 Dome of the Rock, Jerusalem

1982. Freedom for Palestine.

240	**111**	15c. gold, green and black	1·50	25
241	**111**	$1 silver, green and black	4·50	5·25

112 Views of Kuala Lumpur in 1957 and 1982

1982. 25th Anniversary of Independence. Multicoloured.

242	10c. Type **112**	10	10
243	15c. Malaysian industries	15	15
244	50c. Soldiers on parade	40	55
245	80c. Independence ceremony	70	3·00
MS246a	120×190 mm. Nos. 242/245	12·00	13·00

113 Shadow Play

1982. Traditional Games. Multicoloured.

247	10c. Type **113**	55	30
248	15c. Cross top	55	15
249	75c. Kite flying	2·25	4·75

114 Sabah Hats

1982. Malaysian Handicrafts. Multicoloured.

250	10c. Type **114**	25	30
251	15c. Gold-threaded cloth	25	20
252	75c. Sarawak pottery	1·25	3·75

115 Gas Exploitation Logo

1983. Export of Liquefied Natural Gas from Bintulu Field, Sarawak. Multicoloured.

253	15c. Type **115**	75	15
254	20c. *Tenaga Satu* (liquid gas tanker)	1·50	70
255	$1 Gas drilling equipment	3·50	6·50

116 Flag of Malaysia

1983. Commonwealth Day. Multicoloured.

256	15c. Type **116**	20	10
257	20c. The King of Malaysia	20	20
258	40c. Oil palm tree and refinery	25	45
259	$1 Satellite view of Earth	60	2·75

117 Nile Mouthbrooder

1983. Freshwater Fish (1st series). Multicoloured.

260	20c. Type **117**	1·00	1·75
261	20c. Common carp	1·00	1·75
262	40c. Lampan barb	1·25	2·25
263	40c. Grass carp	1·25	2·25

See also Nos. 753/762 and 1333/**MS**1337.

118 Lower Pergau River Bridge

1983. Opening of East–West Highway. Multicoloured.

264	15c. Type **118**	60	15
265	20c. Perak river reservoir bridge	80	60
266	$1 Map showing East–West highway	3·50	6·00

119 Northrop Tiger II Fighter

1983. 50th Anniversary of Malaysian Armed Forces. Multicoloured.

267	15c. Type **119**	1·25	15
268	20c. Missile boat	1·75	45
269	40c. Battle of Pasir Panjang	2·25	2·50
270	80c. Trooping the Colour	3·25	6·00

MS271	130×85 mm. Nos. 267/270	13·00	14·00

120 Helmeted Hornbill

1983. Hornbills of Malaysia. Multicoloured.

280	15c. Type **120**	1·00	15
281	20c. Wrinkled hornbill	1·25	50
282	50c. Long-crested hornbill	2·00	2·00
283	$1 Rhinoceros hornbill	3·25	5·50

121 Bank Building, Ipoh

1984. 25th Anniversary of Bank Negara. Multicoloured.

284	20c. Type **121**	40	30
285	$1 Bank building, Alor Setar	2·00	3·75

122 Sky-scraper and Mosque, Kuala Lumpur

1984. Tenth Anniversary of Federal Territory of Kuala Lumpur. Multicoloured.

286	20c. Type **122**	80	20
287	40c. Aerial view	1·60	1·40
288	80c. Gardens and clock-tower (horiz)	2·50	6·50

123 Map showing Industries

1984. Formation of Labuan Federal Territory. Multicoloured.

289	20c. Type **123**	75	25
290	$1 Flag and map of Labuan	4·25	6·50

124 Semenanjung Keris

1984. Traditional Malay Weapons. Multicoloured.

291	40c. Type **124**	1·00	1·75
292	40c. Pekakak keris	1·00	1·75
293	40c. Jawa keris	1·00	1·75
294	40c. Lada tumbuk	1·00	1·75

125 Map of World and Transmitter

1984. 20th Anniversary of Asia–Pacific Broadcasting Union. Multicoloured.

295	20c. Type **125**	40	25
296	$1 Clasped hands within '20'	2·00	5·00

126 Facsimile Service

1984. Opening of New General Post Office, Kuala Lumpur. Multicoloured.

297	15c. Type **126**	35	20
298	20c. New GPO building	45	45
299	$1 Mailbag conveyor	2·00	5·00

127 Yang di-Pertuan Agong (Tuanku Mahmood)

1984. Installation of Yang di-Pertuan Agong (Tuanku Mahmood).

300	**127**	15c. multicoloured	60	20
301	**127**	20c. multicoloured	65	20
302	-	40c. multicoloured	1·25	1·00
303	-	80c. multicoloured	2·50	5·00

Design: Horiz—40c., 80c. Yang di-Pertuan Agong and federal crest.

128 White Hibiscus

1984. Hibiscus. Multicoloured.

304	10c. Type **128**	50	30
305	20c. Red hibiscus	1·00	20
306	40c. Pink hibiscus	1·50	2·00
307	$1 Orange hibiscus	2·50	5·75

129 Parliament Building

1985. 25th Anniversary of Federal Parliament. Multicoloured.

308	20c. Type **129**	30	15
309	$1 Parliament Building (different) (horiz)	1·75	3·50

130 Banded Linsang

1985. Protected Animals of Malaysia (1st series). Multicoloured.

310	10c. Type **130**	50	10
311	40c. Slow loris (vert)	1·50	1·40
312	$1 Spotted giant flying squirrel (vert)	3·50	6·50

See also Nos. 383/386.

131 Stylised Figures

1985. International Youth Year. Multicoloured.

313	20c. Type **131**	40	15
314	$1 Young workers	3·50	5·50

132 Steam Locomotive No. 1, 1885

1985. Centenary of Malayan Railways.

315	**132**	15c. black, red and orange	1·60	50
316	-	20c. multicoloured	1·75	60
317	-	$1 multicoloured	4·25	7·00
MS318		119×59 mm. 80c. multicoloured	8·00	9·00

Designs: Horiz—20c. Class 20 diesel-electric locomotive, 1957; $1 Hitachi Class 23 diesel-electric locomotive, 1983. 48×31 mm—80c. Class 56 steam locomotive No. 564.18, *Seletar*, 1938.

133 Blue Proton Saga 1.3s Car

1985. Production of Proton Saga (Malaysian National Car). Multicoloured.

319	20c. Type **133**	80	15
320	40c. White Proton Saga 1.3s	1·40	1·00
321	$1 Red Proton Saga 1.5s	2·50	6·50

134 Penang Bridge

1985. Opening of Penang Bridge. Multicoloured.

322	20c. Type **134**	90	15
323	40c. Penang Bridge and location map	1·75	90
324	$1 Symbolic bridge linking Penang to mainland (40×24 mm)	3·50	6·00

135 Offshore Oil Rig

1985. Malaysian Petroleum Production. Multicoloured.

325	15c. Type **135**	1·25	20
326	20c. Malaysia's first oil refinery (horiz)	1·40	50
327	$1 Map of Malaysian offshore oil and gas fields (horiz)	3·75	6·00

136 Sultan Azlan Shah and Perak Royal Crest

1985. Installation of the Sultan of Perak.

328	**136**	15c. multicoloured	65	10
329	**136**	20c. multicoloured	75	25
330	**136**	$1 multicoloured	3·75	7·00

137 Crested Fireback Pheasant

1986. Protected Birds of Malaysia (1st series). Multicoloured.

331	20c. Type **137**	2·50	3·25
332	20c. Malay peacock-pheasant	2·50	3·25
333b	40c. Bulwer's Pheasant (horiz)	2·00	3·50
334b	40c. Great Argus Pheasant (horiz)	2·00	3·50

See also Nos. 394/397.

139 Two Kadazan Dancers, Sabah

1986. Pacific Area Travel Association Conference, Malaysia. Multicoloured.

335	20c. Type **139**	85	1·25
336	20c. Dyak dancer and longhouse, Sarawak	85	1·25
337	20c. Dancers and fortress, Malacca	85	1·25
338	40c. Malay dancer and Kuala Lumpur	1·25	1·50
339	40c. Chinese opera dancer and Penang Bridge	1·25	1·50
340	40c. Indian dancer and Batu Caves	1·25	1·50

140 Stylised Competitors

1986. Malaysia Games. Multicoloured.

341	20c. Type **140**	1·25	20
342	40c. Games emblems (vert)	2·25	2·00
343	$1 National and State flags (vert)	9·00	7·75

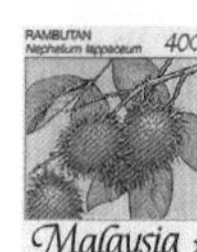

141 Rambutan

1986. Fruits of Malaysia. Multicoloured.

344	40c. Type **141**	1·50	10
345	50c. Pineapple	2·50	10
346	80c. Durian	2·00	10
347	$1 Mangosteen	3·50	10
348	$2 Star fruit	4·50	10
349	$5 Banana	4·50	50
350	$10 Mango	7·00	1·25
351	$20 Papaya	12·00	3·75

142 Skull and Slogan 'Drugs Can Kill'

1986. Tenth Anniversary of National Association for Prevention of Drug Addiction. Multicoloured.

352	20c. Type **142**	1·50	30
353	40c. Bird and slogan 'Stay Free From Drugs'	2·50	1·10
354	$1 Addict and slogan 'Drugs Can Destroy' (vert)	3·75	5·00

143 MAS Logo and Map showing Routes

1986. Inaugural Flight of Malaysian Airlines Kuala Lumpur–Los Angeles Service. Multicoloured.

355	20c. Type **143**	2·50	20
356	40c. Logo, stylised aircraft and route diagram	3·50	80
357	$1 Logo and stylised aircraft	5·00	4·50

144 Building Construction

1986. 20th Anniversary of National Productivity Council and 25th Anniversary of Asian Productivity Organisation (40c., $1). Multicoloured.

358	20c. Type **144**	85	25
359	40c. Planning and design (horiz)	1·40	1·25
360	$1 Computer-controlled car assembly line (horiz)	3·75	6·50

145 Old Seri Menanti Palace, Negri Sembilan

1986. Historic Buildings of Malaysia (1st series). Multicoloured.

361	15c. Type **145**	1·00	20
362	20c. Old Kenangan Palace, Perak	1·10	20
363	40c. Old Town Hall, Malacca	2·00	80
364	$1 Astana, Kuching, Sarawak	3·50	5·00

See also Nos. 465/468.

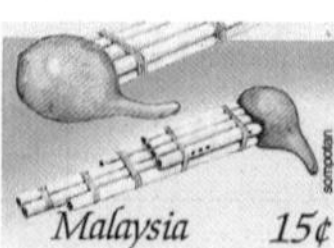

146 Sompotan (bamboo pipes)

1987. Musical Instruments of Malaysia (1st series). Multicoloured.

365	15c. Type **146**	1·40	10
366	20c. Sapih (four-stringed chordophone)	1·50	20
367	50c. Serunai (pipes) (vert)	2·50	60
368	80c. Rebab (three-stringed fiddle) (vert)	3·50	2·50

147 Modern Housing Estate

1987. International Year of Shelter for the Homeless. Multicoloured.

369	20c. Type **147**	1·25	15
370	$1 Stylised families and houses	3·50	1·75

148 Drug Addict and Family

1987. International Conference on Drug Abuse, Vienna. Multicoloured.

371	20c. Type **148**	2·00	1·50
372	20c. Hands holding drugs and damaged internal organs	2·00	1·50
373	40c. Healthy boy and broken drug capsule	2·75	1·75
374	40c. Drugs and healthy internal organs	2·75	1·75

Nos. 371/372 and 373/374 were printed together, *se-tenant*, forming composite designs.

149 Spillway and Power Station

1987. Opening of Sultan Mahmud Hydro-electric Scheme, Kenyir, Trengganu. Multicoloured.

375	20c. Type **149**	75	10
376	$1 Dam, spillway and reservoir	2·75	2·00

150 Crossed Maces and Parliament Building, Kuala Lumpur

1987. 33rd Commonwealth Parliamentary Conference. Multicoloured.

377	20c. Type **150**	25	10
378	$1 Parliament building and crossed mace emblem	1·25	1·25

151 Dish Aerial, Satellite and Globe

1987. Asia/Pacific Transport and Communications Decade. Multicoloured.

379	15c. Type **151**	65	10
380	20c. Diesel train and car	2·00	75
381	40c. Container ships and lorry	2·50	1·60
382	$1 Malaysian Airlines Boeing 747, Kuala Lumpur Airport	4·75	8·00

152 Temminck's Golden Cat

1987. Protected Animals of Malaysia (2nd series). Multicoloured.

383	15c. Type **152**	3·00	50
384	20c. Flatheaded cat	3·00	50
385	40c. Marbled cat	4·25	1·75
386	$1 Clouded leopard	7·50	7·50

153 Flags of Member Nations and '20'

1987. 20th Anniversary of Association of South East Asian Nations. Multicoloured.

387	20c. Type **153**	35	10
388	$1 Flags of member nations and globe	1·25	1·50

154 Mosque and Portico

1988. Opening of Sultan Salahuddin Abdul Aziz Shah Mosque. Multicoloured.

389	15c. Type **154**	30	10
390	20c. Dome, minarets and Sultan of Selangor	30	20
391	$1 Interior and dome (vert)	1·50	3·00

155 Aerial View

1988. Sultan Ismail Hydro-electric Power Station, Paka, Trengganu. Multicoloured.

392	20c. Type **155**	30	10
393	$1 Power station and pylons	1·40	1·50

156 Black-naped Blue Monarch

1988. Protected Birds of Malaysia (2nd series). Multicoloured.

394	20c. Type **156**	1·75	2·50
395	20c. Scarlet-backed flowerpecker	1·75	2·50
396	50c. Yellow-backed sunbird	2·50	3·25
397	50c. Black and red broadbill	2·50	3·25

157 Outline Map and Products of Sabah

1988. 25th Anniversary of Sabah and Sarawak as States of Malaysia. Multicoloured.

398	20c. Type **157**	65	80
399	20c. Outline map and products of Sarawak	65	80
400	$1 Flags of Malaysia, Sabah and Sarawak (30×40 mm)	2·00	3·50

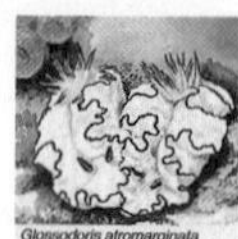

158 *Glossodoris atromarginata*

1988. Marine Life (1st series). Multicoloured.

401	20c. Type **158**	65	1·10
402	20c. Ocellate nudibranch	65	1·10
403	20c. *Chromodoris annae*	65	1·10
404	20c. *Flabellina macassarana*	65	1·10
405	20c. Ruppell's nudibranch	65	1·10
MS406	100×75 mm. $1 Blue-ringed angelfish (50×40 mm)	3·50	2·00

Nos. 401/405 were printed together, *se-tenant*, forming a composite background design.

See also Nos. 410/413, 450/453, 492/**MS**497 and 559/562.

159 Sultan's Palace, Malacca

1989. Declaration of Malacca as Historic City. Multicoloured.

407	20c. Type **159**	35	30
408	20c. Independence Memorial Building	35	30

409	$1 Porta De Santiago Fortress (vert)	1·40	2·00

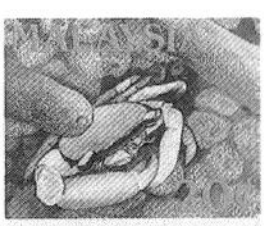

160 *Tetralia nigrolineata*

1989. Marine Life (2nd series). Crustaceans. Multicoloured.

410	20c. Type **160**	45	90
411	20c. *Neopetrolisthes maculatus* (crab)	45	90
412	40c. *Periclimenes holthuisi* (shrimp)	55	1·10
413	40c. *Synalpheus neomeris* (shrimp)	55	1·10

161 Map of Malaysia and Scout Badge

1989. Seventh National Scout Jamboree. Multicoloured.

414	10c. Type **161**	30	10
415	20c. Saluting National Flag	60	25
416	80c. Scouts around camp fire (horiz)	1·40	3·00

162 Cycling

1989. 15th South East Asian Games, Kuala Lumpur. Multicoloured.

417	10c. Type **162**	1·50	70
418	20c. Athletics	55	20
419	50c. Swimming (vert)	1·00	1·00
420	$1 Torch bearer (vert)	1·75	4·00

163 Sultan Azlan Shah

1989. Installation of Sultan Azlan Shah as Yang di-Pertuan Agong.

421	**163**	20c. multicoloured	20	15
422	**163**	40c. multicoloured	35	35
423	**163**	$1 multicoloured	1·00	3·00

164 Putra World Trade Centre and Pan-Pacific Hotel

1989. Commonwealth Heads of Government Meeting, Kuala Lumpur. Multicoloured.

424	20c. Type **164**	20	10
425	50c. Traditional dancers (vert)	60	75
426	$1 National Flag and map showing Commonwealth countries	3·00	3·00

165 Clock Tower, Kuala Lumpur City Hall and Big Ben

1989. Inaugural Malaysia Airlines '747' Non-stop Flight to London. Each showing Malaysia Airlines Boeing 747-400. Multicoloured.

427	20c. Type **165**	2·25	2·25
428	20c. Parliament Buildings, Kuala Lumpur, and Palace of Westminster	2·25	2·25
429	$1 World map showing route	5·50	5·50

166 Sloth and Map of Park

1989. 50th Anniversary of National Park. Multicoloured.

430	20c. Type **166**	1·50	30
431	$1 Pair of crested argus	4·50	5·00

167 Outline Map of South-east Asia and Logo

1990. Visit Malaysia Year. Multicoloured.

432	20c. Type **167**	1·00	25
433	50c. Traditional drums	1·25	1·25
434	$1 Scuba diving, windsurfing and yachting	2·50	3·50

168 *Dillenia suffruticosa*

1990. Wildflowers (1st series). Multicoloured.

435	15c. Type **168**	25	15
436	20c. *Mimosa pudica*	30	20
437	50c. *Ipmoea carnea*	60	90
438	$1 *Nymphaea pubescens*	80	2·75

See also Nos. 505/508.

169 Monument and Rainbow

1990. Kuala Lumpur, Garden City of Lights. Multicoloured.

439	20c. Type **169**	25	20
440	40c. Mosque and skyscrapers at night (horiz)	55	55
441	$1 Kuala Lumpur skyline (horiz)	1·40	3·75

170 Seri Negara Building

1990. First Summit Meeting of South–South Consultation and Co-operation Group, Kuala Lumpur. Multicoloured.

442	20c. Type **170**	40	15
443	80c. Summit logo	1·40	2·50

171 Alor Setar

1990. 250th Anniversary of Alor Setar. Multicoloured.

444	20c. Type **171**	40	20
445	40c. Musicians and monument (vert)	50	40
446	$1 Zahir Mosque (vert)	1·25	3·75

172 Sign Language Letters

1990. International Literacy Year. Multicoloured.

447	20c. Type **172**	70	10
448	40c. People reading	1·00	40
449	$1 Symbolic person reading (vert)	2·50	3·50

173 Leatherback Turtle

1990. Marine Life (3rd series). Sea Turtles. Multicoloured.

450	15c. Type **173**	50	10
451	20c. Common green turtle	50	15
452	40c. Olive Ridley turtle	1·00	80
453	$1 Hawksbill turtle	1·75	3·75

174 Safety Helmet, Dividers and Industrial Skyline

1991. 25th Anniversary of MARA (Council of the Indigenous People). Multicoloured.

454	20c. Type **174**	15	10
455	40c. Documents and graph	30	35
456	$1 25th Anniversary logo	75	2·25

175 *Eustenogaster calyptodoma*

1991. Insects. Wasps. Multicoloured.

457	15c. Type **175**	20	30
458	20c. *Vespa affinis indonensis*	20	20
459	50c. *Sceliphorn javanum*	50	70
460	$1 *Ampulex compressa*	75	2·50
MS461	130×85 mm. Nos. 457/460	4·25	6·00

176 Tunku Abdul Rahman Putra and Independence Rally

1991. Former Prime Ministers of Malaysia. Multicoloured.

462	$1 Type **176**	70	1·25
463	$1 Tun Abdul Razak Hussein and jungle village	70	1·25
464	$1 Tun Hussein Onn and standard-bearers	70	1·25

177 Maziah Palace, Trengganu

1991. Historic Buildings of Malaysia (2nd series). Multicoloured.

465	15c. Type **177**	40	10
466	20c. Grand Palace, Johore	40	15
467	40c. Town Palace, Kuala Langat, Selangor	70	55
468	$1 Jahar Palace, Kelantan	1·40	3·00

178 Museum Building in 1891, Brass Lamp and Fabric

1991. Centenary of Sarawak Museum. Multicoloured.

469	30c. Type **178**	30	15
470	$1 Museum building in 1991, vase and fabric	1·00	2·00

179 Rural Postman on Cycle

1992. Inauguration of Post Office Corporation. Multicoloured.

471	30c. Type **179**	90	1·00
472	30c. Urban postman on motorcycle	90	1·00
473	30c. Inner city post van	90	1·00
474	30c. Industrial post van	90	1·00
475	30c. Malaysian Airlines Boeing 747 and globe	90	1·00

180 Hill Forest and Jelutong Tree

1992. Tropical Forests. Multicoloured.

476	20c. Type **180**	35	10
477	50c. Mangrove swamp and Bakau Minyak tree	65	50
478	$1 Lowland forest and Chengal tree	1·10	2·50

181 Tuanku Ja'afar and Coat of Arms

1992. 25th Anniversary of Installation of Tuanku Ja'afar as Yang di-Pertuan Besar of Negri Sembilan. Multicoloured.

479	30c. Type **181**	30	20
480	$1 Palace, Negri Sembilan	1·00	2·25

182 Badminton Players

1992. Malaysian Victory in Thomas Cup Badminton Championship. Multicoloured.

481	$1 Type **182**	90	1·40
482	$1 Thomas Cup and Malaysian flag	90	1·40
MS483	105×80 mm. $2 Winning team (76×28 mm)	1·75	2·75

183 Women in National Costumes

1992. 25th Anniversary of ASEAN (Association of South East Asian Nations). Multicoloured.

484	30c. Type **183**	40	30
485	50c. Regional flowers	65	75
486	$1 Traditional architecture	1·25	2·25

184 Straits Settlements 1867 1½c. and Malaysian Federation 1957 10c. Stamps

1992. 125th Anniversary of Postage Stamps and Kuala Lumpur '92 International Stamp Exhibition. Multicoloured.

487	30c. Type **184**	45	90
488	30c. Straits Settlements 1867 2c. and Malaysia 1963 Federation Inauguration 12c.	45	90
489	50c. Straits Settlements 1868 4c. and Malaysia 1990 Kuala Lumpur 40c.	70	1·10
490	50c. Straits Settlements 1867 12c. and Malaysia Kuala Lumpur '92 $2	70	1·10
MS491	120×92 mm. $2 Kuala Lumpur '92 logo on Malaysian flag	1·75	2·75

185 *Acropora*

1992. Marine Life (4th series). Corals. Multicoloured.

492	30c. Type **185**	80	1·10
493	30c. *Dendronephthya*	80	1·10

494	30c. *Dendrophyllia*	80	1·10
495	30c. *Sinularia*	80	1·10
496	30c. *Melithaea*	80	1·10

MS497 100×70 mm. $2 *Subergorgia* (38×28 mm) 2·50 4·00

186 Girls smiling

1993. 16th Asian–Pacific Dental Congress. Multicoloured.

498	30c. Type **186**	50	75
499	30c. Girls smiling with koala bear	50	75
500	50c. Dentists with Japanese, Malaysian and South Korean flags	1·00	1·00
501	$1 Dentists with New Zealand, Thai, Chinese and Indonesian flags	1·25	2·00

187 View of Golf Course

1993. Centenary of Royal Selangor Golf Club. Multicoloured.

502	30c. Type **187**	60	20
503	50c. Old and new club houses	90	80
504	$1 Bunker on course (horiz)	2·00	3·50

188 *Alpinia rafflesiana*

1993. Wildflowers (2nd series). Gingers. Multicoloured.

505	20c. Type **188**	40	10
506	30c. *Achasma megalocheilos*	50	20
507	50c. *Zingiber spectabile*	90	80
508	$1 *Costus speciosus*	1·75	3·00

189 Forest under Magnifying Glass

1993. 14th Commonwealth Forestry Conference, Kuala Lumpur. Multicoloured.

509	30c. Type **189**	40	20
510	50c. Hand holding forest	65	70
511	$1 Forest in glass dome (vert)	1·40	2·75

190 White-throated Kingfisher

1993. Kingfishers. Multicoloured.

512	30c. Type **190**	1·75	2·00
513	30c. Pair of blue-eared kingfishers	1·75	2·00
514	50c. Chestnut-collared kingfisher	2·00	2·25
515	50c. Pair of three-toed kingfishers	2·00	2·25

191 SME MD3-160m Light Aircraft

1993. Langkawi International Maritime and Aerospace Exhibition '93. Multicoloured.

516	30c. Type **191**	50	20
517	50c. Eagle X-TS light aircraft	80	90
518	$1 *Kasturi* (frigate)	1·50	2·75

MS519 120×80 mm. $2 Map of Langkawi 1·90 3·00

192 Jeriau Waterfalls

1994. Visit Malaysia. Multicoloured.

520	20c. Type **192**	50	10
521	30c. Flowers	50	25
522	50c. Turtle and fish	75	65
523	$1 Orangutan and other wildlife	1·90	2·75

193 Planetarium and Planets

1994. National Planetarium, Kuala Lumpur. Multicoloured.

524	30c. Type **193**	50	25
525	50c. Static displays	65	80
526	$1 Planetarium auditorium	1·50	2·50

194 *Spathoglottis aurea*

1994. Orchids. Multicoloured.

527	20c. Type **194**	40	15
528	30c. *Paphiopedilum barbatum*	50	25
529	50c. *Bulbophyllum lobbii*	85	90
530	$1 *Aerides odorata*	1·40	2·75

MS531 120×82 mm. $2 *Grammatophyllum speciosum* (horiz) 2·50 4·00

No. **MS**531 also commemorates the Hong Kong '94 International Stamp Exhibition.

195 Decorative Bowl

1994. World Islamic Civilisation Festival '94, Kuala Lumpur. Multicoloured.

532	20c. Type **195**	20	10
533	30c. Celestial globe	30	20
534	50c. Dinar coins	50	65
535	$1 Decorative tile	95	2·00

196 Flock of Chickens and Vet examining Cat

1994. Centenary of Veterinary Services. Multicoloured.

536	30c. Type **196**	50	25
537	50c. Vet in abattoir	70	55
538	$1 Herd of cows and veterinary equipment	1·00	2·25

197 Workers laying Electric Cable

1994. Centenary of Electricity Supply. Multicoloured.

539	30c. Type **197**	40	65
540	30c. Illuminated city	40	65
541	$1 City of the future	1·00	2·00

198 Expressway from the Air

1994. Opening of North–South Expressway. Multicoloured.

542	30c. Type **198**	40	20
543	50c. Expressway junction	50	50
544	$1 Expressway bridge	1·10	2·00

199 Sultan Tuanku Ja'afar

1994. Installation of Sultan Tuanku Ja'afar as Yang di-Pertuan Agong.

545	**199**	30c. multicoloured	30	20
546	**199**	50c. multicoloured	50	50
547	**199**	$1 multicoloured	85	2·00

200 Map of Malaysia and Logo

1994. 16th Commonwealth Games, Kuala Lumpur (1998) (1st issue). Multicoloured.

548	$1 Type **200**	90	1·50
549	$1 Wira (games mascot) holding National Flag	90	1·50

See also Nos. 575/576, 627/630, 668/671, **MS**678, 693/708 and **MS**715/**MS**716.

201 Tunku Abdul Rahman Putra and National Flag

1994. Fifth Death Anniversary of Tunku Abdul Rahman Putra (former Prime Minister). Multicoloured.

550	30c. Type **201**	30	20
551	$1 The Residency, Kuala Lumpur	1·00	1·75

202 Library Building

1994. Opening of New National Library Building. Multicoloured.

552	30c. Type **202**	20	25
553	50c. Computer plan on screen	45	50
554	$1 Ancient Koran	1·00	2·00

203 *Microporus xanthopus*

1995. Fungi. Multicoloured.

555	20c. Type **203**	15	10
556	30c. *Cookeina tricholoma*	25	20
557	50c. *Phallus indusiatus* (*Dictyophora phalloidea*)	45	55
558	$1 *Ramaria* sp.	90	2·75

204 Seafans

1995. Marine Life (5th series). Corals. Multicoloured.

559	20c. Type **204**	1·00	1·50
560	20c. Feather stars	1·00	1·50
561	30c. Cup coral	1·00	1·50
562	30c. Soft coral	1·00	1·50

205 Clouded Leopard on Branch

1995. Endangered Species. Clouded Leopard. Multicoloured.

563	20c. Type **205**	70	35
564	30c. With cubs	80	40
565	50c. Crouched on branch	1·00	90
566	$1 Climbing tree	1·50	2·25

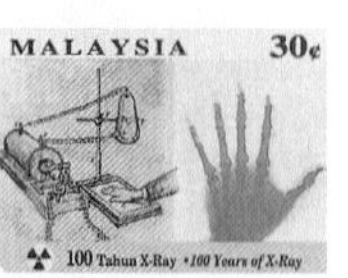

206 Early X-Ray Equipment and X-Ray of Hand

1995. Centenary of Discovery of X-Rays by Wilhelm Conrad Rontgen. Multicoloured.

567	30c. Type **206**	90	1·25
568	30c. Body scanner and brain scan	90	1·25
569	$1 Chest X-rays	1·25	2·00

207 Jembiah (curved dagger)

1995. Singapore '95 International Stamp Exhibition. Traditional Malay Weapons. Multicoloured.

570	20c. Type **207**	15	10
571	30c. Keris panjang (sword)	25	20
572	50c. Kerambit (curved dagger)	40	50
573	$1 Keris sundang (sword)	80	2·00

MS574 100×70 mm. $2 Ladig terus (dagger) 2·50 3·50

208 Badminton, Cricket, Shooting, Tennis, Hurdling, Hockey and Weightlifting

1995. 16th Commonwealth Games, Kuala Lumpur (1998) (2nd issue). Multicoloured.

575	$1 Type **208**	2·50	2·50
576	$1 Cycling, bowls, boxing, basketball, rugby, gymnastics and swimming	2·50	2·50

209 Leatherback Turtle (*Dermochelys coriacea*)

1995. Turtles. Multicoloured.

577	30c. Type **209**	1·50	1·75
578	30c. Green turtle (*Chelonia mydas*)	1·50	1·75

210 Anniversary Emblem and Symbolic People around Globe

1995. 50th Anniversary of United Nations. Multicoloured.

579	30c. Type **210**	30	20
580	$1 United Nations emblem	70	1·50

211 Boeing 747, Globe, Emblem and Malaysian Scenes

1995. 50th Anniversary of International Air Transport Association. Designs each showing Boeing 747 and Globe. Multicoloured.

581	30c. Type **211**	60	70
582	30c. Asian and Australasian scenes	60	70
583	50c. European and African scenes	90	1·00
584	50c. North and South American scenes	90	1·00

212 Proton Saga 1.5 Saloon, 1985

1995. Tenth Anniversary of Proton Cars. Multicoloured.

585	30c. Type **212**	70	90
586	30c. Iswara 1.5 aeroback, 1992	70	90
587	30c. Iswara 1.5 saloon, 1992	70	90
588	30c. Wira 1.6 saloon, 1993	70	90
589	30c. Wira 1.6 aeroback, 1993	70	90
590	30c. Proton rally car, 1994	70	90
591	30c. Satria 1.6 hatchback, 1994	70	90
592	30c. Perdana 2.0 saloon, 1995	70	90
593	30c. Wira 1.6 aeroback, 1995	70	90
594	30c. Wira 1.8 saloon, 1995	70	90

213 Ariane 4 Launch Rocket

1996. Launch of *MEASAT I* (Malaysia East Asia Satellite). Multicoloured.

595	30c. Type **213**	25	20
596	50c. Satellite over Eastern Asia	40	45
597	$1 Satellite Earth station, Langkawi	90	2·00
MS598	100×70 mm. $5 Satellite orbiting Globe (hologram) (horiz)	4·00	6·50

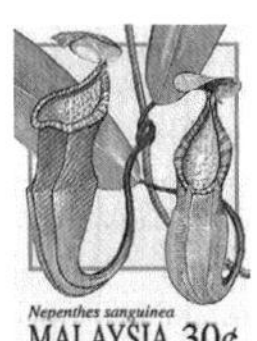

214 *Nepenthes sanguinea*

1996. Pitcher Plants. Multicoloured.

599	30c. Type **214**	25	45
600	30c. *Nepenthes macfarlanei*	25	45
601	50c. *Nepenthes rajah*	35	55
602	50c. *Nepenthes lowii*	35	55

215 Brahminy Kite

1996. Birds of Prey. Multicoloured.

603	20c. Type **215**	45	20
604	30c. Crested serpent eagle	60	25
605	50c. White-bellied sea eagle	90	75
606	$1 Crested hawk eagle	1·40	2·50
MS607	100×70 mm. $2 Blyth's Hawk Eagle (vert)	3·50	4·00

No. **MS**607 also includes the CHINA '96 ninth Asian International Stamp Exhibition logo on the sheet margin.

216 Family, Globe and Burning Drugs

1996. International Day against Drug Abuse and Illicit Trafficking. Multicoloured.

608	30c. Type **216**	65	70
609	30c. Sporting activities	65	75
610	$1 Family and rainbow	1·25	2·00

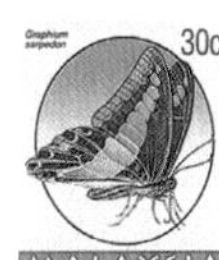

217 *Graphium sarpedon*

1996. ISTANBUL '96 International Stamp Exhibition. Butterflies. Multicoloured.

611	30c. Type **217**	1·25	1·50
612	30c. *Terinos terpander*	1·25	1·50
613	30c. *Melanocyma faunula*	1·25	1·50
614	30c. *Trogonoptera brookiana*	1·25	1·50
615	30c. *Delias hyparete*	1·25	1·50

218 Kuala Lumpur Tower

1996. Opening of Kuala Lumpur Telecommunications Tower. Multicoloured.

616	30c. Type **218**	30	20
617	50c. Diagram of top of tower	40	35
618	$1 Kuala Lumpur Tower at night	1·00	1·75
MS619	70×100 mm. $2 Top of Kuala Lumpur Tower (different) (vert)	1·75	2·75

219 CAPA Logo on Kite

1996. 14th Conference of the Confederation of Asian and Pacific Accountants. Multicoloured.

620	30c. Type **219**	25	20
621	$1 Globe and CAPA logo	75	1·40

1996. TAIPEI '96 Tenth Asian International Stamp Exhibition. As No. **MS**619, but with exhibition logo added to bottom right-hand corner of sheet.

MS622	70×100 mm. $2 Top of Kuala Lumpur Tower (vert)	1·50	2·25

220 Model of DNA Molecule

1996. Opening of National Science Centre, Kuala Lumpur. Multicoloured.

623	30c. Type **220**	25	20
624	50c. Planetary model and Science Centre	40	40
625	$1 National Science Centre	90	1·50

221 Slow Loris

1996. Stamp Week. Wuildlife. Sheet 165×75 mm, containing T **221** and similar multicoloured designs.

MS626	20s. Type **221**; 30s. Prevost's squirrel; 50s. Atlas moth; 1r. Rhinoceros hornbill (60×30 mm); 1r. White-handed gibbon (30×60 mm); 2r. Banded palm civet (60×30 mm)	3·25	4·00

222 Hurdling

1996. 16th Commonwealth Games, Kuala Lumpur (1998) (3rd issue). Multicoloured.

627	30s. Type **222**	40	55
628	30s. Running	40	55
629	50s. High jumping	50	65
630	50s. Javelin	50	65

223 Pygmy Blue Flycatcher

1997. Highland Birds. Multicoloured.

631	20s. Type **223**	45	20
632	30s. Silver-eared mesia	55	25
633	50s. Black-sided flower-pecker	70	70
634	1r. Scarlet sunbird	1·10	1·75

1997. HONG KONG '97 International Stamp Exhibition. As No. **MS**626, but with exhibition logo added to top sheet margin.

MS635	165×75 mm. 20s. Type **221**; 30s. Prevost's squirrel; 50s. Atlas moth; 1r. Rhinoceros hornbill (60×30 mm); 1r. White-handed gibbon (30×60 mm); 2r. Banded palm civet (60×30 mm)	5·50	6·50

224 Transit Train leaving Station

1997. Opening of Kuala Lumpur Light Rail Transit System. Multicoloured.

636	30s. Type **224**	1·25	1·25
637	30s. Trains in central Kuala Lumpur	1·25	1·25

225 Bowler

1997. International Cricket Council Trophy, Kuala Lumpur. Multicoloured.

638	30s. Type **225**	45	15
639	50s. Batsman	60	55
640	1r. Wicket-keeper	1·10	1·75

226 Boeing 747-400 over World Map

1997. 50th Anniversary of Aviation in Malaysia. Multicoloured.

641	30s. Type **226**	65	15
642	50s. Boeing 747-400 over Kuala Lumpur	1·10	60
643	1r. Tail fins of four airliners	1·50	2·25

227 *Schima wallichii*

1997. Highland Flowers. Multicoloured.

644	30s. Type **227**	65	80
645	30s. *Aeschynanthus longicalyx*	65	80
646	30s. *Aeschynanthus speciosa*	65	80
647	30s. *Phyllagathis tuberculata*	65	80
648	30s. *Didymocarpus quinquevulnerus*	65	80

See also Nos. 945/**MS**959

228 World Youth Football Championship Mascot

1997. Ninth World Youth Football Championship, Malaysia. Multicoloured.

649	30s. Type **228**	30	10
650	50s. Football and players	45	35
651	1r. Map of Malaysia and football	1·00	1·75

229 Members of First Conference, 1897

1997. Centenary of Rulers' Conference. Multicoloured.

652	30s. Type **229**	20	10
653	50s. State emblem	40	45
654	1r. Seal and press	80	1·75

230 ASEAN Logo and Ribbons

1997. 30th Anniversary of Association of South-east Asian Nations. Multicoloured.

655	30s. Type **230**	65	10
656	50s. '30' enclosing logo	1·00	55
657	1r. Chevrons and logo	1·50	2·00

231 *Tubastrea* sp.

1997. International Year of the Coral Reefs. Multicoloured.

658	20s. Type **231**	30	15
659	30s. *Melithaea* sp.	35	15
660	50s. *Aulostomus chinensis*	45	40
661	1r. *Symphillia* sp.	70	1·60
MS662	70×100 mm. 2r. Green Turtle (horiz)	2·00	3·00

232 Women Athletes, Scientist and Politician

1997. 20th International Pan-Pacific and South-east Asia Women's Association Conference, Kuala Lumpur. Multicoloured.

663	30s. Type **232**	40	65
664	30s. Family and house	40	65

233 1867 12c. on 4 anna with Malacca Postmark

1997. Malpex '97 Stamp Exhibition, Kuala Lumpur. 50th Anniversary of Organised Philately. Sheet 120×70 mm, containing T **233** and similar diamond-shaped designs. Multicoloured.

MS665	20s. Type **233**; 30s. 1997 Highland Birds set; 50s. 1996 Wildlife miniature sheet seen through magnifying glass; 1r. 1867 cover to Amoy	3·00	3·50

234 Group of 15 Emblem

1997. Seventh Summit Conference of the Group of 15, Kuala Lumpur. Multicoloured.

666	30s. Type **234**	15	10
667	1r. Flags of member countries	1·25	1·50

235 Hockey

1997. 16th Commonwealth Games, Kuala Lumpur (1998) (4th issue). Multicoloured.

668	30s. Type **235**	85	85
669	30s. Netball	85	85
670	50s. Cricket	1·25	1·25
671	50s. Rugby	1·25	1·25

236 False Gharial

1997. Stamp Week '97. Endangered Wildlife. Sheet 165×75 mm, containing T **236** and similar multicoloured designs.

MS672 20s. Type **236**; 30s. Western tarsier (vert); 50s. Indian sambar (vert); 2r. Crested wood partridge; 2r. Malayan bony-tongue (fish) 2·00 3·25

1997. INDEPEX '97 International Stamp Exhibition, New Delhi. As No. **MS**665, but with exhibition logo added to the sheet margin, in gold, at bottom right.

MS673 120×70 mm. 20s. Type **233**; 30s. 1997 Highlands Bird set; 50s. 1996 Wildlife miniature sheet seen through magnifying glass; 1r. 1867 cover to Amoy 1·25 2·00

237 Kundang

1998. Rare Fruits of Malaysia. Multicoloured.

674	20s. Type **237**	15	15
675	30s. Sentul	20	15
676	50s. Pulasan	30	25
677	1r. Asam gelugur	70	1·60

See also Nos. 719/726, 1324/**MS**1327 and 1981/1983.

238 Swimming Complex

1998. 16th Commonwealth Games, Kuala Lumpur (5th issue). Venues. Sheet 120×80 mm, containing T **238** and similar horiz designs. Multicoloured.

MS678 20s. Type **238**; 30s. Hockey Stadium; 50s. Indoor Stadium; 1r. Main Stadium 1·75 2·50

239 Mas (coin) from Trengganu, 1793–1808

1998. Gold coins. Multicoloured.

679	20s. Type **239**	25	15
680	30s. Kupang from Kedah, 1661–1687	25	15
681	50s. Kupang from Johore, 1597–1615	45	35
682	1r. Kupang from Kelantan, 1400–1780	70	1·50

240 Red Crescent Ambulance Boat and Emblem

1998. 50th Anniversary of Malaysian Red Crescent Society. Multicoloured.

683	30s. Type **240**	40	10
684	1r. Ambulance and casualty	1·25	1·60

241 Transit Train and Boeing 747-400 at Airport

1998. Opening of Kuala Lumpur International Airport. Designs showing control tower. Multicoloured.

685	30s. Type **241**	50	10
686	50s. Airport Terminals	85	60
687	1r. Airliner in flight	1·75	2·25

MS688 119×70 mm. 2r. Globe and control tower (22×32 mm) 2·25 2·75

242 *Solanum torvum*

1998. Medicinal Plants (1st series). Multicoloured.

689	20s. Type **242**	20	15
690	30s. *Tinospora crispa*	25	10
691	50s. *Jatropha podagrica*	45	35
692	1r. *Hibiscus rosa-sinensis*	80	1·60

See also Nos. 1234/**MS**1238 and 2055/**MS**2058.

243 Weightlifting

1998. 16th Commonwealth Games, Kuala Lumpur, Malaysia (6th issue). Sports. Multicoloured.

693	20s. Type **243**	35	40
694	20s. Badminton	35	40
695	20s. Netball	35	40
696	20s. Shooting	35	40
697	30s. Men's hockey	45	45
698	30s. Women's hockey	45	45
699	30s. Cycling	45	45
700	30s. Bowls	45	45
701	50s. Gymnastics	45	45
702	50s. Cricket	45	45
703	50s. Rugby	45	45
704	50s. Running	45	45
705	1r. Swimming	45	55
706	1r. Squash	45	55
707	1r. Boxing	45	55
708	1r. Ten-pin bowling	45	55

244 LRT Putra Type Train

1998. Modern Kuala Lumpur Rail Transport. Multicoloured.

709b	30s. Type **244**	65	15
710b	50s. LRT Star type train	55	35
711	1r. KTM commuter train	75	1·50

245 Globe and APEC Logo

1998. Asia-Pacific Econmic Co-operation Conference. Multicoloured.

712b	30s. Type **245**	30	10
713	1r. Business meeting and computer office	70	1·25

246 *Xylotrupes gideon*

1998. Stamp Week '98. Malaysian Insects. Sheet 165×75 mm, containing T **246** and similar multicoloured designs.

MS714 20s. Type **246**; 30s. *Pomponia imperatoria*; 50s. *Phyllium pulchrifolium*; 2r. *Hymenopus coronatus* (43×27 mm); 2r. *Macrolyristes corporalis* (43×27 mm) 3·00 3·75

247 Nural Hudda (Women's Air Rifle Shooting)

1998. 16th Commonwealth Games, Kuala Lumpur (7th issue). Malaysian Gold Medal Winners. Two miniature sheets, each 160×125 mm, containing multicoloured designs as T **247**.

MS715 2r. Malaysian badminton team celebrating (128×80 mm) 3·50 4·00

MS716 30s. Type **247**; 30s. Sapok Biki (48kg Boxing); 30s. G. Saravanan (50km Walk); 30s. Muhamad Hidayat Hamidon (69kg Weightlifting); 50s. Kenny Ang and Ben Heng (Tenpin Bowling Men's Doubles); 50s. Kenny Ang (Tenpin Bowling Men's Singles); 50s. Choong Tan Fook and Lee Wan Wah (Badminton Men's Doubles); 50s. Wong Choon Hann (Badminton Men's Singles); 1r. Women's Rhythmic Gymnastics team (63×26 mm) 6·00 7·50

248 Profile of Elderly Couple, World Map and Emblem

1999. International Year of the Older Person. Multicoloured.

717	1r. Type **248**	70	1·00
718	1r. Four silhouettes of elderly people, world map and emblem	70	1·00

249 *Syzygium malaccense*

1999. Rare Fruits of Malaysia. Multicoloured.

723	20s. Type **249**	20	25
724	30s. *Garcinia prainiana*	25	25
721	50s. *Mangifera caesia*	40	30
726	1r. *Salacca glabrescens*	70	90

250 Kucing Malaysia Cat

1999. Malaysian Cats. Multicoloured.

727	30s. Type **250**	40	15
728	50s. Siamese	55	35
729	1r. Abyssinian	95	1·40

MS730 Two sheets, each 81×90 mm. (a) 1r. British shorthair; 1r. Scottish fold. (B) 1r. Birman; 1r. Persian Set of 2 sheets 2·00 2·50

251 Sumatran Rhinoceros

1999. Protected Mammals of Malaysia (1st series). Multicoloured.

731	20s. Type **251**	50	15
732	30s. Panther	20	15
733	50s. Sun bear	25	25
734	1r. Indian elephant	65	1·00
739	2r. Orangutan	1·50	2·00

MS740 119×80 mm. 2r. No. 739 1·50 2·00

See also Nos. 923/**MS**932 and 1281/**MS**1285.

252 Hearts and AIDS Ribbons

1999. Fifth International Conference on AIDS in Asia and the Pacific. Each red, blue and black.

741	30s. Type **252**	35	15
742	50s. Fragmenting and stylised AIDS ribbons	55	45
743	1r. Two AIDS ribbons	90	1·50

253 P. Ramlee in Traditional Dress

1999. 70th Birth Anniversary of P. Ramlee (actor and film director) Commemoration

(a) Multicoloured

744	20s. Type **253**	55	15
745	30s. Receiving an award	65	15
746	50s. Playing part of soldier in film	85	55
747	1r. Using film camera	1·40	1·60

MS748 Two sheets, each 100×70 mm. (a) 1r. Wearing check shirt. (b) 1r. In traditional dress Set of 2 sheets 15·00 15·00

(b) Each brown, light brown and black.

749	30s. In traditional dress	1·25	1·40
750	30s. With hands raised	1·25	1·40
751	30s. Singing into microphone	1·25	1·40
752	30s. Wearing army uniform	1·25	1·40

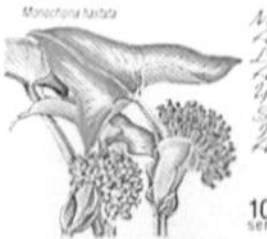
254 *Monochoria hastoria* (water plant)

1999. Freshwater Fish (2nd series). Multicoloured.

753	10s. Type **254**	20	30
754	10s. *Trichopsis vittatus*	20	30
755	15s. *Limnocharis flava* (water plant)	20	30
756	15s. *Betta imbellis*	20	30
757	25s. *Nymphaea pubescens* (water plant)	25	40
758	25s. *Trichogaster trichopterus*	25	40
759	50s. *Eichhornia crassipes* (water plant)	35	50
760	50s. *Sphaerichthys osphromenoides*	35	50
761	50s. *Ipomea aquatica* (water plant)	35	50
762	50s. *Helostoma temmincki*	35	50

No. 760 is inscribed 'Sphaerichthys osphronemodies' in error.

255 *Lagerstroemia floribunda* (tree)

1999. Trees of Malaysia. Multicoloured.

763	30s. Type **255**	40	70
764	30s. *Elateriospermum tapos*	40	70
765	30s. *Dryobalanops aromatica*	40	70
766	30s. *Alstonia angustiloba*	40	70

767	30s. *Fagraea fragrans*	40	70

256 Petronas Twin Towers, Kuala Lumpur

1999. Completion of Petronas Twin Towers Building, Kuala Lumpur. Multicoloured (except 50c.).

768	30s. Type **256**	45	15
769	50s. Construction sketches (blue, violet and black)	55	40
770	1r. Twin Towers at night	95	1·25
MS771	100×75 mm. 5r. Hologram of Twin Towers (30×50 mm)	4·00	4·50

257 Peace Hotel and Rickshaw

1999. 125th Anniversary of Taiping, Perak. Multicoloured.

772	20s. Type **257**	30	15
773	30s. Town Hall and 1930s car	30	15
774	50s. Railway Station	1·25	65
775	1r. Airport	1·50	1·75
MS776	120×69 mm. 2r. Perak Museum and horse-drawn carriage	4·50	5·00

258 Power Station at Night

1999. 50th Anniversary of Tenaga Nasional Berhad (electricity generating company). Multicoloured.

777	30s. Type **258**	35	15
778	50s. Control room and pylon	50	25
779	1r. Kuala Lumpur skyline at night	90	1·50
MS780	Two sheets, each 69×99 mm. (a) 1r. Electric cart. (b) 1r. Pylon Set of 2 sheets	2·00	2·50

259 New National Theatre and Traditional Characters

1999. Opening of New National Theatre, Kuala Lumpur. Multicoloured.

781	30s. Type **259**	30	15
782	50s. New National Theatre and horseman	55	40
783	1r. New National Theatre and traditional musician	90	1·25

260 New Yang di-Pertuan Agong and Malaysian Flag

1999. Installation of Sultan Salahuddin Abdul Aziz Shah of Selangor as Yang di-Pertuan Agong

(a) Horiz design as T **260**. Multicoloured

784	30s. Type **260**	40	15
785	50s. Yang di-Pertuan Agong and Palace	50	35
786	1r. Yang di-Pertuan Agong and Parliament Buildings	75	1·10

(b) Vert designs, 24×29 mm, showing portrait only.

787	(30s.) multicoloured (purple frame)	75	90
788	(30s.) multicoloured (yellow frame)	75	90
789	(30s.) multicoloured (blue frame)	75	90

Nos. 787/789 are inscribed 'BAYARAN POS TEMPATAN HINGGA 20GM' and were valid on local mail weighing no more than 20 g.

261 Motorway Junction outside Kuala Lumpur

1999. 21st World Road Congress, Kuala Lumpur. Multicoloured.

790	30s. Type **261**	35	15
791	50s. Damansara Puchong Bridge at night	50	30
792	1r. Aerial view of motorway junction, Selatan	90	1·25

262 Driver's Helmet and Canopy Tower, Formula 1 Circuit, Sepang

1999. Malaysian Grand Prix, Sepang. Multicoloured

(a) Designs including driver's helmet

793	20s. Type **262**	40	20
794	30s. Central Grandstand	50	20
795	50s. Formula 1 racing car	75	50
796	1r. Formula 1 racing car from Red Bull team	1·25	1·50

(b) Scenes from Sepang Formula 1 Circuit.

797	20s. Canopy Tower and Central Grandstand	40	50
798	30s. Pit building	50	50
799	50s. Wheel-change in pits	75	90
800	1r. Race in progress	1·25	1·40

263 Sultan Haji Ahmad Shah and Flowers

1999. 25th Anniversary of Installation of Sultan of Pahang. Multicoloured.

801	30s. Type **263**	55	60
802	30s. Butterfly and motorway	55	60
803	30s. Diver and beach	55	60
804	30s. Power station	55	60
805	30s. Mosque	55	60

264 World Cup

1999. World Cup Golf Championship, Mines Resort City. Multicoloured.

806	20s. Type **264**	35	15
807	30s. Emblem on golf ball	35	15
808	50s. Fairway	60	45
813	1r. First hole and club house	1·10	1·25

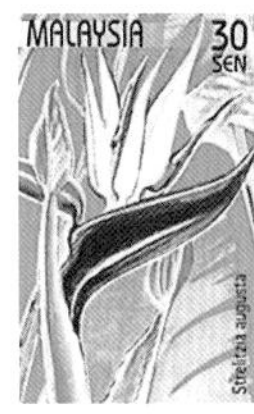

265 *Strelitzia augusta*

1999. Stamp Week '99. Heliconias. Multicoloured.

814	30s. Type **265**	55	55
815	30s. *Heliconia rostrata*	55	55
816	30s. *Heliconia psittacorum* (yellow)	55	55
817	30s. *Heliconia stricta*	55	55
818	30s. *Musa violascens*	55	55
819	30s. *Strelitzia reginae*	55	55
820	30s. *Heliconia colganta*	55	55
821	30s. *Heliconia psittacorum* (white and pink)	55	55
822	30s. *Heliconia latispatha*	55	55
823	30s. *Phaeomeria speciosa*	55	55
MS824	198×136 mm. Nos. 814/23	6·00	7·50

266 Letters and Computer Screen

1999. 125th Anniversary of Universal Postal Union. Multicoloured.

825	20s. Type **266**	20	10
826	30s. Globe and Malaysian stamps	40	10
827	50s. World map and mail plane	1·00	70
828	1r. POS Malaysia emblem	1·25	1·60

267 Fern, Pitcher Plant and Great Indian Hornbill

1999. New Millennium (1st issue). Land and History. Multicoloured (except No. MS839).

829	30s. Type **267**	50	60
830	30s. Ceramic pots and Mt. Kinabalu	50	60
831	30s. Frog and tualang (tree)	50	60
832	30s. Rolling rubber and palm trees	50	60
833	30s. Angelfish and sailing barge	50	60
834	30s. Mousedeer and traditional Malay building	50	60
835	30s. Ruler on elephant and Straits of Malacca	50	60
836	30s. Malay kris (sword) and junks	50	60
837	30s. Clock Tower, Kuala Lumpur, and A Famosa ruins	50	60
838	30s. Sailing boat and palm trees	50	60
MS839	120×80 mm. 1r. Traditional Malay sailing ship (horiz) (black and red)	2·50	3·00

See also Nos. 840/**MS**850 and **MS**866.

2000. New Millennium (2nd issue). People and Achievements. As T **267**. Multicoloured.

840	30s. Iban playing sape and traditional costumes from East Malaysia	60	60
841	30s. Hurricane lamp, shell and couple from fishing village	60	60
842	30s. Doctor with patient and toddler with mother	60	60
843	30s. Badminton player and young Malaysians	60	60
844	30s. Man with kite and traditional dancers	60	60
845	30s. Motorcycle, car and motorway	60	60
846	30s. Butterfly, Sepang motor racing circuit and airport	60	60
847	30s. High speed train and Kuala Lumpur skyline	60	60
848	30s. Computer operator and mosque	60	60
849	30s. Lorry and container port	60	60
MS850	120×80 mm. 1r. Modern airliner (horiz)	2·50	2·75

268 Pottery Vase (New Stone Age)

2000. Chinese New Year. Year of the Dragon. Artefacts and Fish. Multicoloured.

851	30s. Type **268**	60	60
852	30s. Dragon eaves tile (Western Han Dynasty)	60	60
853	30s. Bronze knocker base (Tang Dynasty)	60	60
854	30s. Jade sword pommel (Western Han Dynasty)	60	60
855	30s. Dragon statue (Tang Dynasty)	60	60
856	30s. Arawana (*Osteoglossum bicirrhosum*)	60	60
857	30s. Spotted barramundi (*Scleropages leichardti*)	60	60
858	30s. Asian bonytongue (red) (*Scleropages formosus*)	60	60
859	30s. Black arawana (*Osteoglossum ferrerirai*)	60	60
860	30s. Asian bonytongue (gold) (*Scleropages formosus*)	60	60
MS861	Two sheets, each 120×65 mm. (a) 1r. Dragon dance (square). (b) 1r. Dragon boat (square) Set of 2 sheets	2·25	3·00

269 Table Tennis Bats and Globe

2000. World Table Tennis Championships, Bukit Jalil. Multicoloured.

862	30s. Type **269**	25	10
863	50s. Mascot and logo	45	35
864	1r. Table tennis bats and ball	75	1·10
MS865	100×70 mm. 1r. Mascot and table tennis table; 1r. Bats and table tennis table	1·25	1·75

270 Malaysian Climbers on Mt. Everest

2000. New Millennium (3rd issue). Malaysian Triumphs. Two sheets, each 120×80 mm, containing T **270** and similar vert designs. Multicoloured.

MS866	(a) 50s. Type **270**; 50s. Hikers; 50s. Arctic expedition and Proton car. (b) 50s. Solo yachtsman Set of 2 sheets	3·75	4·00

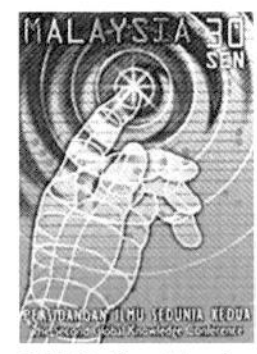

271 Outline Hand on Button

2000. Second Global Knowledge Conference, Kuala Lumpur. Multicoloured.

867	30s. Type **271**	55	60
868	30s. Outline globe	55	60
869	50s. Woman's silhouette	80	90
870	50s. Man's silhouette	80	90

272 Internal Inverted Dome

2000. Islamic Arts Museum, Kuala Lumpur. Multicoloured.

871	20s. Type **272**	40	15
872	30s. Main dome of Museum	45	15
873	50s. Ottoman panel	65	45
874	1r. Ornate Mihrab	1·25	1·75

273 Buatan Barat Prahu

2000. Traditional Malaysian Prahus (canoes). Multicoloured.

875	30s. Type **273**	35	45
876	30s. Payang prahu (red and blue hull)	35	45
877	30s. Payang prahu (red, white and green hull)	35	45
878	30s. Burung prahu	35	45

274 Unit Trust Emblem and Women with Flags

2000. Unit Trust Week. Multicoloured.

879	30s. Type **274**	50	10
880	50s. City skyline and Malaysians in traditional costume	75	50
881	1r. Map of South East Asia and Malaysians in traditional costume	1·40	2·00

275 Badminton Player and Cup Logo

2000. Thomas Cup Badminton Championships, Bukit Jalil. Multicoloured.

882	30s. Type **275**	60	60
883	30s. Thomas Cup and flags	60	60
884	30s. Championship logo and mascot	60	60
885	30s. Uber Cup and flags	60	60
886	30s. Badminton player and mascot	60	60
MS887	120×80 mm. 1r. Thomas Cup (vert)	1·75	2·25

276 Children playing Ting Ting

2000. Children's Traditional Games (1st series). Multicoloured.

888	30s. Type **276**	80	80
889	30s. Tarik Upih	80	80
890	30s. Kite flying	80	80
891	30s. Marbles	80	80
892	30s. Bicycle rim racing	80	80

277 Aspects of Computer Technology

2000. 27th Islamic Foreign Ministers' Conference, Kuala Lumpur. Multicoloured.

898	30s. Type **277**	55	60
899	30s. Traditonal Islamic scrollwork	55	60
900	30s. Conference logo	55	60
901	30s. Early coin	55	60
902	30s. Pens and satellite photograph	55	60

278 Malaysian Family on Map

2000. Population and Housing Census. Multicoloured.

903	30s. Type **278**	55	60
904	30s. Symbolic house	55	60
905	30s. People on pie-chart	55	60
906	30s. Diplomas and workers	55	60
907	30s. Male and female symbols	55	60

279 Rothchild's Peacock-pheasant

2000. Pheasants and Partridges. Multicoloured.

908	20s. Type **279**	45	20
909	30s. Crested argus (female)	55	20
910	50s. Great argus pheasant	75	50
911	1r. Crestless fireback pheasant	1·25	1·75
MS912	100×40 mm. 2r. Crested argus (male) (31×26 mm)	2·25	2·75

280 *Hopea odorata* (fruit)

2000. International Union of Forestry Research Organisations Conference, Kuala Lumpur. Multicoloured.

913	30s. Type **280**	75	75
914	30s. *Adenanthera pavonina* (seeds)	75	75
915	30s. *Shorea macrophylla* (seeds)	75	75
916	30s. *Dyera costulata* (fruits)	75	75
917	30s. *Alstonia angustiloba* (seeds)	75	75
MS918	Four sheets, each 92×71 mm. (a) Trees. 10s. *Fagraea fragrans*; 10s. *Dryobalanops aromatica*; 10s. *Terminalia catappa*; 10s. *Samanea saman*; 10s. *Dracontomelon dao*. (b) Leaves. 15s. *Heritiera javanica*; 15s. *Johannes-teijsmannia altifrons*; 15s. *Macaranga gigantea*; 15s. *Licuala grandis*; 15s. *Endospermum diadenum*. (c). Bark. 25s. *Pterocymbium javanicum*; 25s. *Dryobalanops aromatica*; 25s. *Dipterocarpus costulatus*; 25s. *Shorea leprosula*; 25s. *Ochanostachys amentacea*. (d) Forest fauna. 50s. Indian flycatcher; 50s. Slow loris; 50s. Marbled cat; 50s. Common carp; 50s. Pit viper Set of 4 sheets	6·50	7·50

No. **MS**918 contains four sheets each of five 18×22 mm designs, and a label showing the Conference logo.

281 Institute in 1901, *Brugia malayi* and Beri-Beri

2000. Centenary of Institute for Medical Research. Multicoloured.

919	30s. Type **281**	60	10
920	50s. Institute in 1953, bacteria and mosquito	85	60
921	1r. Institute in 1976, chromatogram and *Eurycoma longifolia*	1·75	2·00
MS922	120×65 mm. 2r. DNA molecule	2·75	3·00

282 Otter Civet

2000. Protected Mammals of Malaysia (2nd series). Multicoloured.

923	20s. Type **282**	60	25
924	30s. Young otter civet	60	30
925	50s. Binturong on bank	75	50
926	1r. Head of binturong	1·40	1·60
927	30s. Hose's palm civet (*Hemigalus hosei*)	60	70
928	30s. Common palm civet (*Paradoxurus hermaphroditus*)	60	70
929	30s. Masked palm civet (Paguma larvata)	60	70
930	30s. Malay civet (Viverra tangalunga)	60	70
931	30s. Three-striped palm civet (*Arctogalidia trivirgata*)	60	70
MS932	140×80 mm. 1r. Banded palm civet; 1r. Banded linsang	2·75	3·00

283 Cogwheels

2000. 50th Anniversary of RIDA-MARA (Rural and Industrial Development Authority–Council for Indigenous People). Multicoloured.

933	30s. Type **283**	40	10
934	50s. Compasses and stethoscope	55	40
935	1r. Computer disk, book and mouse	1·00	1·40

2000. Children's Traditional Games (2nd series). As T **276** but horiz. Multicoloured.

936	20s. Bailing tin	50	60
937	20s. Top-spinning	50	60
938	30s. Sepak Raga	60	70
939	30s. Letup-Letup	60	70

284 Cyclist and Pedestrians

2000. World Heart Day. Multicoloured.

940	30s. Type **284**	60	60
941	30s. Family at play	60	60
942	30s. Kite flying, football and no smoking sign	60	60
943	30s. Keep fit class	60	60
944	30s. Farmer, animals and food	60	60

Nos. 940/944 were printed together, *se-tenant*, with the backgrounds forming a composite design.

285 *Rhododendron brookeanum*

2000. Stamp Week 2000. Highland Flowers (2nd series). Multicoloured.

945	30s. Type **285**	40	50
946	30s. *Rhododendron jasminiflorum*	40	50
947	30s. *Rhododendron scortechinii*	40	50
948	30s. *Rhododendron pauciflorum*	40	50
949	30s. *Rhododendron crassifolium*	40	50
950	30s. *Rhododendron longiflorum*	40	50
951	30s. *Rhododendron javanicum*	40	50
952	30s. *Rhododendron variolosum*	40	50
953	30s. *Rhododendron acuminatum*	40	50
954	30s. *Rhododendron praetervisum*	40	50
955	30s. *Rhododendron himantodes*	40	50
956	30s. *Rhododendron maxwellii*	40	50
957	30s. *Rhododendron erocoides*	40	50
958	30s. *Rhododendron fallacinum*	40	50
MS959	55×90 mm. 1r. *Rhododendron malayanum*	1·25	1·75

No. 955 is inscribed 'Rhodadendron', No. 957 'Ericoides', both in error.

286 *Neurobasis c. chinensis*

2000. Dragonflies and Damselflies. Multicoloured.

960	30s. Type **286**	55	65
961	30s. *Aristocypha fenestrella* (blue markings on tail)	55	65
962	30s. *Vestalis gracilis*	55	65
963	30s. *Nannophya pymaea*	55	65
964	30s. *Aristocypha fenestrella* (white markings on tail)	55	65
965	30s. *Rhyothemis p. phyllis*	55	65
966	30s. *Crocothemis s. servilia*	55	65
967	30s. *Euphaea ochracea* (male)	55	65
968	30s. *Euphaea ochracea* (female)	55	65
969	30s. *Ceriagrion cerinorubellum*	55	65
970	(30s.) *Vestalis gracilis*	45	50
971	(30s.) *Crocothemis s. servilia* (male)	45	50
972	(30s.) *Trithemis aurora*	45	50
973	(30s.) *Pseudothemis jorina*	45	50
974	(30s.) *Diplacodes nebulosa*	45	50
975	(30s.) *Crocothemis s. servilia* (female)	45	50
976	(30s.) *Neurobasis c. chinensis* (male)	45	50
977	(30s.) *Burmagomphus divaricatus*	45	50
978	(30s.) *Ictinogomphus d. melaenops*	45	50
979	(30s.) *Orthetrum testaceum*	45	50
980	(30s.) *Trithemis festiva*	45	50
981	(30s.) *Brachythemis contaminata*	45	50
982	(30s.) *Neurobasis c. chinensis* (female)	45	50
983	(30s.) *Neurothemis fluctuans*	45	50
984	(30s.) *Acisoma panorpoides*	45	50
985	(30s.) *Orthetrum s. sabina*	45	50
986	(30s.) *Rhyothemis p. phyllis*	45	50
987	(30s.) *Rhyothemis obsolescens*	45	50
988	(30s.) *Neurothemis t. tulia*	45	50
989	(30s.) *Lathrecista a. asiatica*	45	50
990	(30s.) *Aethriamanta gracilis*	45	50
991	(30s.) *Diplacodes trivialis*	45	50
992	(30s.) *Neurothemis fulvia*	45	50
993	(30s.) *Rhyothemis triangularis*	45	50
994	(30s.) *Orthetrum glaucum*	40	50

Nos. 960/969 were issued together, *se-tenant*, and show the backgrounds forming a composite design.

Nos. 970/994 are inscribed 'Bayaran Pos Tempatan Hingga 20gm'. They were valid at 30s. for local mail up to 20 g.

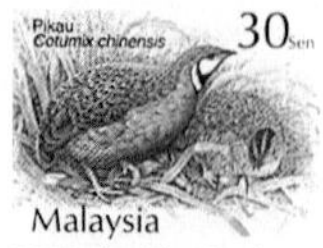

287 Indian Blue Quail

2001. Quails and Partridges. Multicoloured.

995	30s. Type **287**	60	20
996	50s. Sumatran hill partridge	1·00	75
997	1r. Bustard quail	1·75	2·40
MS998	100×170 mm. 2r. Chestnut-breasted tree partridge; 2r. Crimson-headed wood partridge	5·00	5·00

288 Federal Government Administrative Centre

2001. Formation of Putrajaya Federal Territory. Multicoloured.

999	30s. Type **288**	50	10
1000	1r. Government buildings and motorway bridge	2·00	2·50

289 Sabah and Sarawak Beadwork

2001. Sabah and Sarawak Beadwork. Multicoloured, background colours given.

1001	**289**	30s. green	50	55
1002	-	30s. blue	50	55
1003	-	30s. buff	50	55
1004	-	30s. red	50	55

Design: Nos. 1001/1004 Showing different styles of beadwork.

290 *Cananga odorata*

2001. Scented Flowers (1st series). Multicoloured.

1005	30s. Type **290**	50	10
1006	50s. *Mimusops elengi*	70	50
1007	1r. *Mesua ferrea*	1·40	2·00
MS1008	70×100 mm. 2r. *Muchelia champaca*	2·75	3·25

See also Nos.2132/**MS**2138.

291 Raja Tuanku Syed Sirajuddin

2001. Installation of Tuanku Syed Sirajuddin as Raja of Perlis.

1009	**291**	30s. multicoloured	50	15
1010	**291**	50s. multicoloured	85	60
1011	**291**	1r. multicoloured	1·40	2·00
MS1012		100×70 mm. 2r. Raja Tuanku Syed Sirajuddin and Tengku Fauziah (horiz). Multicoloured	3·00	3·25

292 Beetlenut Leaf Arrangement

2001. Traditional Malaysian Artefacts. Multicoloured.

1013	30s. Type **292**	65	80
1014	30s. Baby carrier	65	80
1015	50s. Quail trap	90	1·10
1016	50s. Ember container	90	1·10

See also Nos. 1490/1492.

293 Perodua Kancil Car, 1995

2001. Malaysia-made Motor Vehicles. Multicoloured.

1017	30s. Type **293**	45	60
1018	30s. Proton Tiara, 1995	45	60
1019	30s. Perodua Rusa, 1995	45	60
1020	30s. Proton Putra, 1997	45	60
1021	30s. Inokom Permas, 1999	45	60
1022	30s. Perodua Kembara, 1999	45	60
1023	30s. Proton GTI, 2000	45	60
1024	30s. TD 2000, 2000	45	60
1025	30s. Perodua Kenari, 2000	45	60
1026	30s. Proton Waja, 2000	45	60

294 Serama Bantam Cock

2001. Malaysian Bantams. Multicoloured.

1027	30s. Type **294**	50	15
1028	50s. Kapan bantam cock	90	60
1029	1r. Serama bantam hen	1·60	2·00
MS1030	98×70 mm. 3r. Red junglefowl hens and chicks (44×34 mm)	5·00	6·00

295 Diving

2001. 21st South East Asian Games, Kuala Lumpur. Multicoloured.

1031	20s. Type **295**	30	35
1032	30s. Rhythmic gymnastics	30	35
1033	50s. Bowling	50	70
1034	1r. Weightlifting	85	1·25
1035	2r. Cycling	2·25	2·25
MS1036	110×90 mm. 5r. Running	4·00	6·00

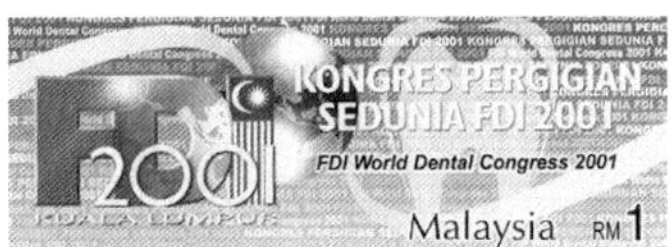

296 FDI 2001 Logo

2001. FDI 2001 World Dental Congress, Kuala Lumpur.

1037	**296**	1r. multicoloured	1·75	2·00

297 KWSP Headquarters, Kuala Lumpur

2001. 50th Anniversary of Employees' Provident Fund "Kumpulan Wang Simpanan Pekerja). Multicoloured.

1038	30s. Type **297**	30	15
1039	50s. Column chart on coins and banknotes	45	50
1040	1r. Couple with KWSP logo	90	1·40

298 Satellite and Rainforest in Shape of Malaya Peninsula

2001. Centenary of Peninsular Malaysia Forestry Department. Multicoloured.

1041	30s. Type **298**	35	15
1042	50s. Cross-section through forest and soil	75	60
1043	1r. Newly-planted forest	1·50	2·25

299 *Tridacna gigas* (clam)

2001. Stamp Week. Endangered Marine Life. Multicoloured.

1044	20s. Type **299**	40	20
1045	30s. *Hippocampus* sp. (seahorse)	50	20
1046	50s. *Oreaster occidentalis* (starfish)	70	60
1047	1r. *Cassis cornu* (shell)	1·40	2·25
MS1048	100×70 mm. 3r. Dugong	2·75	3·25

300 Hockey Player in Orange

2002. Tenth Hockey World Cup, Kuala Lumpur. Multicoloured.

1049	30s. Type **300**	55	15
1050	50s. Goalkeeper	75	65
1051	1r. Hockey player in yellow	1·50	2·00
MS1052	100×70 mm. 3r. Hockey player in blue (30×40 mm)	3·50	3·50

301 *Couroupita guianensis*

2002. Malaysia–China Joint Issue. Rare Flowers. Multicoloured.

1053	30s. Type **301**	50	10
1054	1r. *Couroupita guianensis*	1·25	1·75
1055	1r. *Camellia nitidissima*	1·25	1·75
MS1056	108×79 mm. 2r. *Schima brevifolia* buds (horiz); 2r. *Schima brevifolia* blossom	2·25	2·75

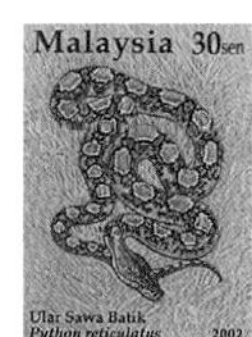

302 *Python reticulatus*

2002. Malaysian Snakes. Multicoloured.

1057	30s. Type **302**	60	30
1058	30s. *Gonyophis margaritatus*	60	30
1059	50s. *Bungarus candidus*	85	60
1060	1r. *Maticora bivirgata*	1·60	2·00
MS1061	108×78 mm. 2r. *Ophiophagus hannah* (head of adult); 2r. *Ophiophagus hannah* (juvenile)	3·50	4·00

303 Stesen Sentral Station, Kuala Lumpur

2002. Express Rail Link from Central Kuala Lumpur to International Airport. Multicoloured.

1062	30s. Type **303**	1·00	25
1063	50s. Train and Central Station	1·50	1·75
1064	50s. Train and International Airport	1·50	1·75
MS1065	Two sheets, each 106×76 mm. (a) 1r. KLIA Express and high speed train; 1r. Express and local trains. (b) 2r. KLIA Express Set of 2 sheets	5·50	6·00

304 *Paraphalaenopsis labukensis*

2002. 17th World Orchid Conference. Multicoloured.

1066	30s. Type **304**	75	80
1067	30s. *Renanthera bella*	75	80
1068	50s. *Paphiopedilum sanderianum*	1·25	50
1069	1r. *Coelogyne pandurata*	2·00	2·25
1070	1r. *Phalaenopsis amabilis*	2·00	2·25
MS1071	76×105 mm. 5r. *Cleisocentron merillianum* (45×40 mm)	5·00	6·00

305 Raja Tuanku Syed Sirajuddin of Perlis

2002. Installation of Raja Tuanku Syed Sirajuddin as Yang di-Pertuan Agong.

1072	**305**	30s. multicoloured	80	10
1073	**305**	50s. multicoloured	1·25	60
1074	**305**	1r. multicoloured	2·25	2·50

306 *Cryptocoryne purpurea*

2002. Aquatic Plants. Multicoloured.

1075	30s. Type **306**	55	10
1076	50s. *Barclaya kunstleri*	85	40
1077	1r. *Neptunia oleracea*	1·75	2·50
1078	1r. *Monochoria hastata*	1·75	2·50
MS1079	110×80 mm. 1r. *Eichhornia crassipes* (vert); 2r. *Nymphaea pubescens*	6·50	7·00

307 White-bellied Woodpecker (*Dryocopus javensis*)

2002. Malaysia–Singapore Joint Issue. Birds. Multicoloured.

1080	30s. Type **307**	90	90
1081	30s. Black-naped oriole (*Oriolus chinensis*)	90	90
1082	1r. Red-throated sunbird (*Anthreptes rhodolaema*)	2·25	2·50
1083	1r. Asian fairy bluebird (*Irena puella*)	2·25	2·50
MS1084	99×70 mm. 5r. Orange-bellied flowerpecker (*Dicaeum trigonostigma*) (60×40 mm)	6·50	7·00

Stamps with similar designs were issued by Singapore.

308 Sibu Island, Johore

2002. Tourist Beaches (1st series). Multicoloured.

1085	30s. Type **308**	70	70
1086	30s. Perhentian Islands, Trengganu	70	70
1087	50s. Manukan Island, Sabah	1·00	1·00
1088	50s. Tioman Island, Pahang	1·00	1·00
1089	1r. Singa Besar Island, Kedah	2·00	2·50
1090	1r. Pangkor Island, Perak	2·00	2·50
MS1091	110×80 mm. 1r. Ferringhi Bay, Penang; 1r. Port Dickson, Negri Sembilan	4·00	4·50

See also Nos. 1149/**MS**1153 and 2108/**MS**2112.

309 Ethnic Musicians and Dancers

2002. Malaysian Unity (1st series). Multicoloured.

1092	30s. Type **309**	70	90
1093	30s. Children playing mancala (game)	70	90
1094	50s. Children from different races (82×30 mm)	1·00	1·00
MS1095	68×99 mm. 1r. Children playing tug-of-war	2·50	3·00

See also Nos. 1893/1896.

2002. Fruits of Malaysia. As T **141** and similar vert designs but redenominated in sen and RM. Multicoloured.

1095a	40s. Type **141**	2·00	10
1095b	50s. Pineapple	2·00	10
1095g	10r. Mango	10·00	2·50
1095h	20r. Papaya	15·00	6·00

310 Zainal Abidin bin Ahmad ('Za'ba') as a Student

2002. 30th Death Anniversary of Zainal Abidin bin Ahmad ('Za'ba') (2003) (scholar). Multicoloured.

1096	30s. Type **310**	70	50
1097	50s. Za'ba with typewriter	1·00	1·40
1098	50s. Za'ba and traditional Malay building	1·00	1·40
MS1099	100×70 mm. 1r. Za'ba at desk (vert)	2·50	3·25

311 Green Kebaya, Nyonya

2002. The Kebaya Nyonya (traditional Malay women's blouse). Multicoloured.

1100	30s. Type **311**	60	50
1101	30s. Red kebaya nyonya	60	50
1102	50s. Yellow kebaya nyonya	90	1·25
1103	50s. Pink kebaya nyonya	90	1·25
MS1104	70×100 mm. 2r. Kebaya nyonya and sarong (34×69 mm)	2·50	3·50

312 Suluh Budiman Building, Sultan Idris University of Education

2002. 80th Anniversary of Sultan Idris University of Education. Multicoloured.

1105	30s. Type **312**	75	10
1106	50s. Tadahan Selatan Building	1·25	1·50
1107	50s. Chancellery Building	1·25	1·50

No. 1107 is inscribed 'Chancellory' in error.

313 Leopard Cat with Kittens

2002. Stamp Week. Wild and Domesticated Animals. Multicoloured.

1108	30s. Type **313**	75	75
1109	30s. Domestic cat and kittens	75	75
1110	1r. Lesser sulphur-crested cockatoo	2·50	2·75
1111	1r. Malay fish owl	2·50	2·75

MS1112 Two sheets, each 105×76 mm. (a) 1r. Goldfish (horiz). 1r. Porcupinefish (horiz); (b) 1r. Giant squirrel; 1r. Domestic rabbit with young Set of 2 sheets † †

314 Southern Serow

2003. Southern Serow. Multicoloured.

1113 30s. Type **314** 80 10

1114 50s. Southern serow lying down 1·00 1·50

1115 50s. Young southern serow 1·00 1·50

315 Peace Doves and Emblem

2003. 13th Conference of Heads of State or Government of the Non-Aligned Movement, Kuala Lumpur. Multicoloured.

1116 30s. Type **315** 50 65

1117 30s. Conference emblem in cupped hands 50 65

1118 50s. Emblem and outline map of Malaysia 1·00 1·25

1119 50s. '2003' with noughts containing Malaysian flag and emblem 1·00 1·25

Nos. 1116/1117 and 1118/1119 were each printed together, *se-tenant*, each pair forming a composite background design of a Malaysian flag and world map (Nos. 1116/1117) or a globe (Nos. 1118/1119).

316 Pale Pink Hybrid Tea Rose

2003. Roses in Malaysia. Multicoloured.

1120 30s. Type **316** 55 40

1121 30s. Red hybrid tea 55 40

1122 50s. Apricot hybrid tea 90 1·25

1123 50s. Pink and white striped floribunda 90 1·25

MS1124 70×100 mm. 1r. Miniature floribunda (29×40 mm); 2r. *Rosa centifolia* (29×81 mm) 3·25 4·00

See also Nos. 2005/**MS**2008.

317 Tunku Abdul Rahman

2003. Birth Centenary of Tunku Abdul Rahman (first Prime Minister of Federation of Malaya (1957–1963) and of Malaysia (1963–1970)). Multicoloured.

1125 30s. Type **317** 55 15

1126 50s. Tunku Abdul Rahman (different) 85 30

1127 1r. Tunku Abdul Rahman in ceremonial dress 1·25 1·75

1128 1r. Tunku Abdul Rahman wearing topi hat 1·25 1·75

MS1129 100×70 mm. 1r. Tunku Abdul Rahman reading Proclamation of Independence, 1957 2·00 2·25

318 Sultan Sharafuddin Idris Shah

2003. Coronation of Sultan of Selangor. Multicoloured.

1130 30s. Type **318** 80 15

1131 50s. Sultan in uniform 1·25 60

1132 1r. Sultan of Selangor (wearing crown) 2·00 2·50

319 Siamese Fighting Fish

2003. Siamese Fighting Fish (Betta splendens). Multicoloured.

1133 30s. Type **319** 75 15

1134 50s. Siamese Fighting fish (yellow) 3·00 †

1135 1r. Siamese Fighting fish (blue) 1·60 2·00

1136 1r. Siamese Fighting fish (red with fringed fins) 1·60 2·00

MS1137 99×70 mm. 50s. *Betta imbellis* (Local Fighting Fish) (33×28 mm); 50s. *Betta coccina* (Red Fighting Fish) (33×28 mm) 2·00 2·50

320 Christ Church Clock

2003. Clock Towers (1st series). Multicoloured.

1138 30s. Type **320** 55 55

1139 30s. Jubilee Clock Tower, Penang 55 55

1140 30s. Sungai Petani Clock Tower, Jalan Ibrahim 55 55

1141 30s. Teluk Intan Clock Tower 55 55

1142 30s. Sarawak State Council Monument 55 55

2003. Islands and Beaches of Malaysia (2nd series). As T **308**. Multicoloured.

1149 30s. Aerial view of Ligitan Island 55 70

1150 30s. Outline map of Ligitan Island 55 70

1151 50s. Sipadan Island 90 1·25

1152 50s. Outline map of Sipadan Island 90 1·25

MS1153 70×100 mm. 50c. Aerial view of Sipadan Island (vert); 50c. Relief map of Ligitan Island (vert) 2·25 2·75

321 Malaysian Flag and Sultan Tower, Malacca Abdul Samad Building, Kuala Lumpur

2003. 46th Independence Celebration.

1154 **321** 30s. multicoloured 75 15

1155 - 1r. multicoloured 2·00 2·00

MS1156 70×100 mm. 1r. black and grey 2·25 2·50

Designs: 59×40 mm— No. 1155, Malaysian flag; No. **MS**1156, Independence delegation in motorcade, Malacca, 1956.

322 Modenas Jaguh 175

2003. Malaysian made Motorcycles and Scooters. Multicoloured.

1157 30s. Type **322** 70 15

1158 50s. Modenas Karisma 125 90 1·25

1159 50s. Modenas Kriss 1 90 1·25

1160 50s. Modenas Kriss 2 90 1·25

1161 50s. Modenas Kriss SG 90 1·25

MS1162 Four sheets, each 100×70 mm. (a) 1r. Comel Turbulence RG125; 1r. Comel Cyclone GP150. (b) 1r. Demak Adventurer; 1r. Demak Beetle. (c) 1r. MZ 125SM; 1r. MZ Perintis 120S Classic. (d) 1r. Gagiva Momos 125R; 1r. Nitro NE150 Windstar 7·00 8·50

323 Putrajaya Convention Centre

2003. Tenth Session of Islamic Summit Conference, Putrajaya. Multicoloured.

1163 30s. Type **323** 50 65

1164 30s. Emblem 50 65

1165 50s. Putrajaya Mosque, modern Kuala Lumpur buildings and flag 90 1·25

1166 50s. Sultan Abdul Samad Building, Kuala Lumpur and Federal Government Administrative Centre, Putrajaya 90 1·25

Nos. 1165/1166 were each printed together, *se-tenant*, forming a composite design.

2003. Bangkok 2003 World Stamp Exhibition, Thailand. Nos. 1157/1161 additionally inscr with 'Bangkok' and exhibition logo.

1167 30s. Type **322** 80 25

1168 50s. Modenas Karisma 125 1·00 1·25

1169 50s. Modenas Kriss 1 1·00 1·25

1170 50s. Modenas Kriss 2 1·00 1·25

1171 50s. Modenas Kriss SG 1·00 1·25

324 Children in Circle and World Map

2003. 50th World Children's Day. Multicoloured.

1172 20s. Type **324** 75 10

1173 30s. Family outside their home 1·00 1·25

1174 30s. Girl flying kite and children with computer 1·00 1·25

1175 30s. 'Sambutan 50 tahun Hari kanak-kanak Sedunia' in child's writing 1·00 1·25

1176 30s. Open book, house, Malaysian flag, rainbow, car and flower 1·00 1·25

Nos. 1173/1174 were printed together, *se-tenant*, forming a composite design.

325 Red Leaf Monkey feeding

2003. Stamp Week. Primates of Malaysia (1st series). Multicoloured.

1177 30s. Type **325** 75 60

1178 30s. Red leaf monkey sat on branch 75 60

1179 50s. Proboscis monkey 1·25 1·50

1180 50s. Female proboscis monkey with baby 1·25 1·50

See also Nos. 2122/**MS**2126.

326 One Fathom Bank Lighthouse

2004. Lighthouses (1st series). Multicoloured.

1181 30s. Type **326** 80 80

1182 30s. Muka Head Lighthouse, Pulau Pinang 80 80

1183 30s. Pulau Undan Lighthouse, Melaka 80 80

1184 30s. Althingsburg Lighthouse, Selangor 80 80

MS1185 70×100 mm. 1r. Tanjung Tuan Lighthouse 3·50 3·50

See also Nos. 1946/**MS**1949.

327 Fauna at Seashore and in Forest

2004. Seventh Conference of Convention on Biological Diversity and First Meeting of Cartagena Protocol on Biosafety. Multicoloured.

1186 30s. Type **327** 1·10 40

1187 50s. Conference logo 1·10 1·10

1188 50s. DNA, leaf and test tube 1·10 1·10

328 Sultan of Kelantan

2004. Silver Jubilee of Sultan Ismail Petra Ibni Almarhum of Kelantan. Multicoloured.

1189 30s. Type **328** 70 20

1190 50s. Sultan and Istana Jahar, Museum of Royal Traditions and Customs 90 60

1191 1r. Sultan and Khota Bharu 1·75 2·50

329 Golf Ball, City Skyline and World Map

2004. First Commonwealth Tourism Ministers Meeting, Kuala Lumpur. Multicoloured.

1192 30s. Type **329** 65 15

1193 50s. World map and seashore 90 60

1194 1r. Logo and montage of images of Malaysia (vert) 1·40 2·00

330 Emblem

2004. National Service Programme. Multicoloured.

1195 30s. Type **330** 50 15

1196 50s. Abseiling 75 60

1197 1r. Three youths with Malaysian flag 1·50 2·00

MS1198 70×100 mm. 2r. Saluting 2·25 2·75

331 *Lanchara* (Malayan sailing ship)

2004. 30th Anniversary of Malaysia–China Diplomatic Relations. Multicoloured.

1199 30s. Type **331** 65 70

1200 30s. Chinese junk 65 70

1201 1r. Handshake and sailing ship 1·25 1·50

1202 1r. Sailing ship and flags of Malaysia and China 1·25 1·50

MS1203 100×70 mm. 2r. Niujie Mosque, Beijing and Kampung Hulu Mosque, Malacca (59×39 mm) 2·75 3·00

332 Banteng

2004. Wildlife in the Malaysian Forest. Multicoloured.

1204 30s. Type **332** 75 80

1205 30s. Gaur ('SELADANG') 75 80

1206 1r. Tiger 2·25 2·50

1207 1r. Indian elephant 2·25 2·50

MS1208 101×70 mm. 2r. Malayan tapir (vert) 2·25 2·75

333 Multimedia Super Corridor Entrance

2004. Multimedia Super Corridor. Multicoloured.
1209 30s. Type **333** 60 15
1210 50s. Globe, binary code and Petronas Towers 90 50
1211 1r. ID card, computer terminals and brain linked to Multimedia Super Corridor 1·40 2·25
MS1212 70×100 mm. 2r. Map of Multimedia Super Corridor 3·25 3·50

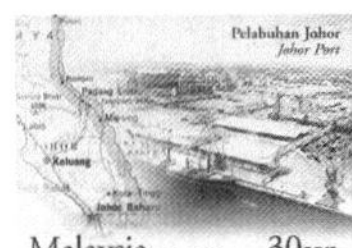

334 Johor

2004. Ports of Malaysia. Multicoloured.
1213 30s. Type **334** 1·00 1·00
1214 30s. Kota Kinabalu 1·00 1·00
1215 50s. Kuantan 1·50 1·75
1216 50s. Penang 1·50 1·75
1217 1r. Bintulu 2·00 2·00
MS1218 100×70 mm. 2r. Northpor 3·50 3·75

335 Trishaw

2004. Traditional Transportation. Multicoloured.
1219 30s. Type **335** 75 15
1220 50s. Rickshaw 1·25 50
1221 1r. Padi horse 2·00 2·50
MS1222 100×70 mm. 2r. Bullock cart (39×49 mm) 2·75 3·25

2004. World Stamp Championship, Singapore. As No. **MS**1203 but with exhibition logo and numbering added to the sheet margin.
MS1224 100×70 mm. 2r. Niujie Mosque, Beijing and Kampung Hulu Mosque, Malacca (59×39 mm) 3·00 3·50

336 Long-tailed Macaque

2004. Centenary of Matang Mangroves, Perak. Multicoloured.
1225 30s. Type **336** 90 90
1226 30s. *Sonneratia ovata* (Mangrove apple) and moth 90 90
1227 1r. Fishing boat at jetty and cockle 2·50 2·75
1228 1r. Lesser adjutant stork and Brahminy kite 2·50 2·75
MS1229 100×69 mm. 2r. Tall-stilted Mangrove 3·00 3·50

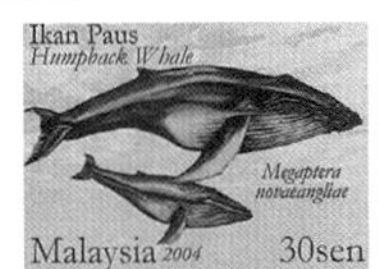

337 Humpback Whales

2004. Marine Life. Multicoloured.
1230 30s. Type **337** 1·25 35
1231 50s. Octopus 1·60 60
1232 1r. Bottlenose dolphins 2·25 2·50
MS1233 101×71 mm. 2r. Thornback ray 2·75 3·25

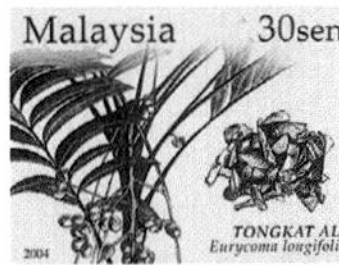

338 Tongkat Ali

2004. Medicinal Plants (2nd series). Multicoloured.
1234 30s. Type **338** 65 20
1235 50s. Kacip Fatimah 90 30
1236 1r. Kerdas 1·75 2·50
1237 1r. Buah Keras 1·75 3·25
MS1238 100×71 mm. 2r. Mas Cotek 2·75 3·25

339 *Rhododendron stenophyllum*

2005. Rare Flowers. Multicoloured.
1239 30s. Type **339** 60 55
1240 30s. *Rhododendron nervulosum* 60 55
1241 50s. *Rhododendron rugosum* 90 60
1242 1r. *Rhododendron stapfianum* 1·75 2·25
MS1243 100×70 mm. 2r. *Rhododendron lowii* (horiz) 2·50 3·00

340 Kuala Lumpur Skyline

2005. Fifth Ministers Forum in the Asia Pacific. Multicoloured.
1244 30s. Type **340** 40 15
1245 50s. Putrajaya International Convention Centre and Parliament Building 70 60
1246 1r. Kuala Lumpur International Airport 2·50 2·75

341 Crested Honey Buzzard

2005. Migratory Birds. Multicoloured.
1247 30s. Type **341** 1·50 55
1248 50s. Purple heron 2·50 1·00
1249 1r. Lesser Crested tern 4·50 4·25
MS1250 70×100 mm. 2r. Dunlin 5·00 5·50

342 Proton Gen. 2

2004. Proton Gen. 2. Multicoloured.
1251 30s. Type **342** 50 20
1252 50s. Proton Gen. 2 (blue) 75 60
1253 2r. Proton Gen. 2 (red) 1·75 2·50
MS1254 100×70 mm. 2r. Proton Gen. 2 (purple) (vert) 2·50 3·00

343 Bharata Natyam and Kathak

2005. Traditional Dances (1st series). Multicoloured.
1255 30s. Type **343** 50 15
1256 50s. Kipas and Payung 75 60
1257 1r. Zapin and Asyik 1·50 2·00
MS1258 100×70 mm. 2r. Datun julud and Sumazau 2·75 3·25
See also Nos. 2127/2131.

2005. Pacific Explorer 2005 World Stamp Expo, Sydney. No. **MS**1250 additionally inscr with 'PACIFIC EXPLORER 2005 WORLD STAMP EXPO 21-24 APRIL SYDNEY CONVENTION AND EXHIBITION CENTRE' and emblem on sheet margin.
MS1259 70×100 mm. 2r. Dunlin 3·50 4·00

344 Pucuk Rebung Gigi Yu

2005. Songket (designs on brocade textiles). Multicoloured.
1260 30s. Type **344** 35 10
1261 50s. Bunga Bertabur Pecah Lapan 55 35
1262 1r. Pucuk Rebung Gigi Yu dan Bunga Kayohan 90 1·25
1263 1r. Teluk Berantai Bunga Pecah Empat 90 1·25
MS1263a 100×70 mm. 2r. Potong Wajik Bertabur 2·00 2·50

345 Spotted-necked Dove

2005. Birds. Multicoloured.
1264 20s. Type **345** 50 10
1265 30s. Ochraceous bulbul 60 10
1266 40s. Long-tailed parakeet 1·25 20
1267 50s. White-rumped shama 1·00 25
1268 75s. Yellow-bellied ('Olive-backed') sunbird 2·00 40
1269 1r. Emerald dove ('Green-winged Pigeon') 2·75 55
1270 2r. Blue-tailed ('Banded') pitta 4·50 1·50
1271 5r. Imperial pigeon 8·00 3·50

346 Dewan Tunku Canselor University

2005. Centenary of University of Malaya. Multicoloured.
1272 30s. Type **346** 50 10
1273 50s. Perpustakaan University 75 60
1274 1r. Pusat Perubatan University 1·25 2·00
MS1275 70×100 mm. 1r. Rimba Ilmu University; 1r. Koleksi Muzium Seni Asia University 1·75 2·25

347 *Kapal Dagang* (Merchant Ship)

2005. 600th Anniversary of Trade between Malaysia and China. Multicoloured.
1276 30s. Type **347** 45 40
1277 30s. Royal Seal of the Emperor of China 45 40
1278 50s. Merchants 60 55
1279 1r. Nyonya cerami plate 1·00 1·75
MS1280 100×70 mm. 2r. Tin animal and copper coins 1·75 2·25

348 Yellow-throated Marten

2005. Protected Mammals of Malaysia (3rd series). Multicoloured.
1281 30s. Type **348** 75 50
1282 30s. Malay weasel 75 50
1283 50s. Hairy-nosed otter 1·25 60
1284 1r. Large Spotted civet 2·25 2·50
MS1285 100×70 mm. 2r. Long-tailed porcupine (vert) 5·00 5·00

349 Box Boat (Perahu Kotak)

2005. Traditional Water Transport. Multicoloured.
1286 30s. Type **349** 50 15
1287 50s. Sampan 90 60
1288 1r. Bamboo raft (Rakit buluh) 1·40 2·00
MS1289 70×100 mm. 2r. Long boat (Perahu batang) (40×50 mm) 2·50 3·00
MS1289a 70×100 mm. 2r. As No. **MS**1289 2·50 3·00

2005. Taipei 2005 International Stamp Exhibition. No. **MS**1285 additionally inscr with 'TAIPEI 2005' and emblem on sheet margin.
MS1290 100×70 mm. 2r. Long-tailed porcupine (vert) 2·50 2·75

350 Big School and Playing Field

2005. Centenary of Malay College, Kuala Kangsar. Multicoloured.
1291 30s. Type **350** 45 10
1292 50s. Prep School 75 75
1293 50s. Big Tree 75 75
MS1294 100×70 mm. 50s.×4 (22×51 mm), Sultan Idris Murshidul'Adzam Shah; Sultan Alaiddin Sulaiman Shah; Yam Tuan Tuanku Muhamad Shah; Sultan Ahmad Al-Mu'adzam Shah 2·25 2·75

351 *Varanus rudicollis*

2005. Endangered Reptiles. Multicoloured.
1295 30s. Type **351** 65 50
1296 30s. *Varanus dumerilii* 65 50
1297 50s. *Gonocephalus grandis* 1·25 60
1298 1r. *Crocodylus porosus* 2·25 2·50
MS1299 70×100 mm. 2r. *Draco quinquefasciatus* (40×50 mm) 2·25 2·75

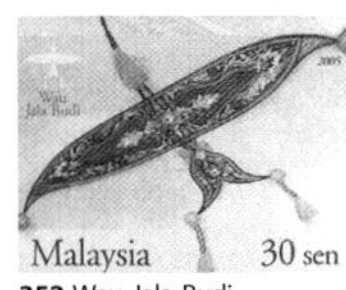

352 Wau Jala Budi

2005. Traditional Kites. Multicoloured.
1300 30s. Type **352** 35 10
1301 50s. Wau Bulan 65 50
1302 1r. Wau Kucing 1·25 1·75
MS1303 100×70 mm. 2r. Wau Merak 1·75 2·25

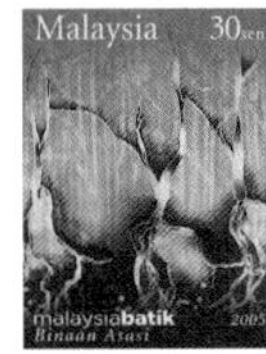

353 *Binaan Asasi* (Masrina Abdullah)

2005. Stamp Week. Malaysian Batik Designs. T **353** and similar vert designs showing motifs produced by winners of Piala Seri Endon Batik Design Competition. Multicoloured.
1304 30s. Type **353** 35 10
1305 50s. *Pesona Sutera* (Nazari Maarus) 55 40
1306 1r. *Malaysia Bersatu* (Mohd Nizamuddin Ambia) 90 1·40
MS1307 100×70 mm. 2r. *Penyatuan* (Mohd Azizi Hassan) 1·50 2·00

354 Flags of Member Countries

2005. 11th ASEAN Summit, Kuala Lumpur. Each showing summit emblem. Multicoloured.
1308 30s. Type **354** 35 10
1309 50s. 'ONE VISION IDENTITY COMMUNITY' 55 40
1310 1r. Petronas Twin Towers and city of Kuala Lumpur 1·10 1·40

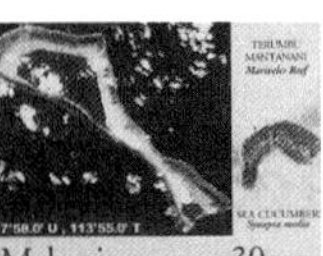

355 Mariveles Reef and *Synapta media* (sea cucumber)

2005. Malaysia's Five Islands and Reefs in the South China Sea. Multicoloured.

1311	30s. Type **355**	45	40
1312	30s. Erica Reef and *Chromodoris magnifica* (nudibranch)	45	40
1313	1r. Investigator Reef and *Chlamys rastellum* (bivalve)	1·10	1·40
1314	1r. Swallow Island and *Echinaster callosus* (sea star)	1·10	1·40
MS1315	100×70 mm. 2r. Aerial view of Malaysia's five islands and reefs, South China Sea (50×40 mm)	2·50	3·00

356 Green-winged Teal (*Anas crecca*)

2006. Wild Duck Species. Multicoloured.

1316	30s. Type **356**	70	50
1317	30s. White-winged wood duck (*Cairina scutulata*)	70	50
1318	50s. Northern pintail (*Anas acuta*)	1·00	1·00
1319	50s. Northern shoveller (*Anas clypeata*)	1·00	1·00
MS1320	100×70 mm. 2r. Great cormorant (*Phalacrocorax carbo*)	6·00	6·00

357 National Audit Academy, Negri Sembilan

2006. Centenary of National Audit Institution. Multicoloured.

1321	30s. Type **357**	40	20
1322	50s. Arms and logo of National Audit Department	65	75
1323	50s. Auditor General's reports	65	75

358 *Artocarpus sericicarpus*

2006. Rare Fruits of Malaysia (3rd series). Multicoloured.

1324	30s. Type **358**	40	20
1325	50s. *Phyllanthus acidus*	65	60
1326	1r. *Garcinia hombroniana*	1·25	1·75
MS1327	100×70 mm. 1r. *Lepisanthes alata*; 1r. *Baccaurea polyneura*	2·25	2·75

359 Mount Kinabalu, Sabah and Orchid

2006. Mountains of Malaysia. Multicoloured.

1328	30s. Type **359**	75	75
1329	30s. Mount Ledang, Johor and pitcher plant	75	75
1330	50s. Mount Jerai, Kedah and orchid	1·40	1·60
1331	50s. Mount Mulu and the Pinnacles, Sarawak	1·40	1·60
MS1332	100×70 mm. 2r. Mount Tahan, Pahang (49×39 mm)	2·25	2·75

360 *Leptobarbus hoevenii* (carp)

2006. Freshwater Fish (3rd series). Multicoloured.

1333	30s. Type **360**	75	20
1334	50s. *Hampala macrolepidota*	1·25	1·50
1335	50s. *Pangasius* sp.	1·25	1·50
1336	1r. *Probarbus jullieni*	1·75	2·00
MS1337	100×70 mm. 5r. *Clarias batrachus* and *Mystus nemurus* (silver foil hologram) (69×33 mm)	4·00	5·50

361 Mural on Facade of Balai Budaya Tun Syed Nasir

2006. 50th Anniversary of Dewan Bahasa dan Pustaka (Malay language organisation). Multicoloured.

1338	50s. Type **361**	65	65
1339	50s. Palmyra palm frond and emblem	65	65
1340	1r. Books and laptop computer	1·10	1·60

362 Oil Palm and Rubber Trees

2006. 50th Anniversary of FELDA (Federal Land Development Authority). Multicoloured.

1341	30s. Type **362**	45	15
1342	50s. Settler's houses, *c.* 1956, modern bungalow house and aerial view of oil palm estate	70	60
1343	1r. Old and new FELDA offices and new office tower, Kuala Lumpur	1·25	1·75

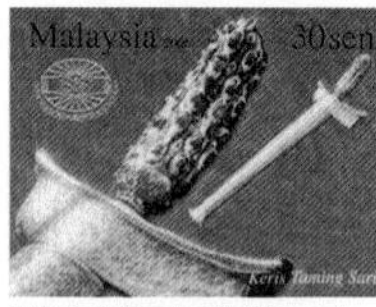

363 Keris Taming Sari (sword from Perak State Regalia)

2006. Galeri Sultan Azlan Shah. Multicoloured.

1344	30s. Type **363**	60	15
1345	50s. Galeri Sultan Azlan Shah	90	60
1346	1r. Royal aigrette	1·75	2·25

364 Hari Raya Aidil Fitri

2006. Festivals (1st series). Children's Paintings. Multicoloured.

1347	30s. Type **364**	50	15
1348	50s. Tahun Baru Cina (Chinese New Year)	75	60
1349	1r. Deepavali	1·25	1·75
MS1350	70×100 mm. 1r. Tadau Kaamatan (vert); 1r. Pesta Gawai (vert)	2·25	2·75

See also Nos. 1900/1904.

365 Malaysian Traditional Costume

2006. Traditional Costumes. Multicoloured.

1351	50s. Type **365**	80	80
1352	50s. Chinese	80	80
1353	50s. Indian	80	80
MS1354	70×100 mm. 1r. Iban; 1r. Kadazan	2·75	3·25

366 *Periophthalmodon schlosseri* (mudskipper)

2006. Stamp Week. Semi Aquatic Animals. Multicoloured.

1355	30s. Type **366**	1·00	25
1356	50s. *Pagurus bernhardus* (hermit crab)	1·25	70
1357	1r. *Cnora amboinensis* (Asian box turtle)	2·50	3·00
MS1358	119×69 mm. 1r. *Polypedates leucomystax* (four-lined tree frog); 1r. *Varanus salvator* (common monitor); 1r. *Cynogale bennettii* (otter civet); 1r. *Xenochrophistrianguligera* (triangle keelback snake) (all 29×34 mm)	3·25	3·75

367 FIGO Emblem

2006. 18th FIGO World Congress of Gynecology and Obstetrics, Kuala Lumpur. Multicoloured.

1359	30s. Type **367**	55	20
1360	50s. Congress emblem and map of the Americas	1·25	1·25
1361	50s. Silhouette of foetus, map of Asia and Congress emblem	1·25	1·25

368 Wheelchair Race

2006. Ninth Far East and South Pacific Games for the Disabled (FESPIC), Kuala Lumpur. Multicoloured.

1362	30s. Type **368**	50	15
1363	50s. Swimming	75	60
1364	1r. Wheelchair tennis	1·25	2·00
MS1365	100×70 mm. 2r. Wheelchair basketball	3·25	3·50

369 Map with Flags of China and ASEAN Countries

2006. 15th Anniversary of Dialogue between ASEAN Countries and China. Multicoloured.

1366	30s. Type **369**	1·25	35
1367	50s. Great Wall of China and motorway intersection	1·40	60
1368	1r. Red ribbons tied in knot	1·90	2·50

370 Emblem

2006. 25th General Assembly of the World Veterans Association, Kuala Lumpur. Multicoloured.

1369	30s. Type **370**	50	15
1370	50s. '25' and Kuala Lumpur Convention Centre	75	60
1371	1r. Tugu Negara Independence memorial	1·40	2·00

371 Expedition Tent and Sled in Antarctic

2006. Sharifah Mazlina Syed Abdul Kadir's South Pole Expedition (2004). Multicoloured.

1372	30s. Type **371**	1·25	40
1373	50s. Sharifah Mazlina Syed Abdul Kadir on skis with sled	2·00	90
1374	1r. Ski sailing from Hercules Inlet to South Pole	3·00	3·50

372 *Taenianotus triacanthus* (leaf scorpionfish)

2007. Marine Life. Multicoloured.

1375	50s. Type **372**	1·25	1·25
1376	50s. *Balistapus undulatus* (orange-striped triggerfish)	1·25	1·25
MS1377	100×70 mm. 1r. *Nautilus pompilius* (chambered nautilus); 1r. *Ostracionmeleagris* (spotted boxfish)	2·50	3·00

Stamps in similar designs were issued by Brunei.

373 Hornbill, Flower and Rain Forest

2007. Visit Malaysia Year. Multicoloured.

(a) Sheet stamps

1378	30s. Type **373**	70	80
1379	30s. Coral reef	70	80
1380	50s. Malaysian buildings	90	1·10
1381	50s. Malaysian crafts	90	1·10
MS1382	100×70 mm. 2r. Petronas Twin Towers (29×49 mm)	2·25	2·75

(b) Horiz designs as T **373** showing National Costumes and Dishes.

1383	30s. Malay (dancer with headdress)	50	75
1384	30s. Chinese (dancer with fans)	50	75
1385	30s. Indian (dancer in turquoise)	50	75
1386	30s. Kadazandusun of Sabah (black and gold dress)	50	75
1387	30s. Iban of Sarawak (woman wearing elaborate headdress)	50	75
1388	30s. Satay	50	75
1389	30s. Yee Sang	50	75
1390	30s. Banana leaf rice	50	75
1391	30s. Hinava (raw fish salad)	50	75
1392	30s. Manok Pansuh (chicken meat stuffed in bamboo)	50	75

374 Tuanku Mizan Zainal Abidin

2007. Installation of Tuanku Mizan Zainal Abidin, Sultan of Terengganu as Yang di-Pertuan Agong. Multicoloured.

1393	30s. Type **374**	50	20
1394	50s. Wearing white uniform	90	60
1395	1r. As Type **374** (bright mauve background)	1·75	2·50

375 *Pedostibes hosii* (brown tree toad)

2007. Frogs and Toads of Malaysia. Multicoloured.

1396	30s. Type **375**	1·00	20
1397	50s. *Megophrys nasuta* (horned toad)	1·40	1·60
1398	50s. *Nyctixalus pictus* (spotted tree frog)	1·40	1·60
MS1399	100×70 mm. 1r. *Rana laterimaculata* (lesser swamp frog) (34×33 mm)	4·00	4·00

376 Shorts SC.7 Skyvan

2007. Air Transportation in Malaysia. Multicoloured.

1400	30s. Type **376**	1·50	40
1401	50s. de Havilland Canada DHC 7-110	2·25	1·75
1402	50s. GAF N22 Nomad	2·25	1·75
MS1403	100×70 mm. 1r. Airspeed Consul; 1r. Douglas DC-3	6·00	6·00

377 J. W. W. Birch Clock Tower, Ipoh, 1917

2007. Clock Towers (2nd series). Multicoloured.

1404 30s. Type **377** 75 20
1405 50s. Atkinson Clock Tower, Kota Kinabalu, 1905 1·25 60
1406 1r. Alor Setar Clock Tower, 1912 2·25 2·50

378 Bawang Merah put to work by her Stepmother and Stepsister

2007. Traditional Children's Folk Tales. Multicoloured.

(a) Booklet stamps

1407 30s. Type **378** 65 90
1408 30s. Badang carrying rock 65 90
1409 30s. Sang Kancil crossing river on backs of crocodiles 50 55
1410 30s. Crocodile Sang Bedal seizing Sang Kerbau's leg 65 90
1411 30s. Mat Jenin daydreaming 65 90

(b) Sheetlet stamps

1412 50s. Type **378** 1·00 1·00
1413 50s. As No. 1408 1·00 1·00
1414 50s. As No. 1409 1·00 1·00
1415 50s. As No. 1410 1·00 1·00
MS1416 100×70 mm. 5r. Ship's captain Si Tanggang and his rejected mother (59×38 mm) 4·75 5·50

Nos. 1407/1408, 1409/1410, 1412/1413 and 1414/1415 each form composite background designs.

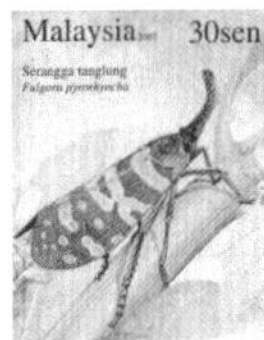

379 *Fulgora pyrorhyncha* (lantern fly)

2007. Insects. Multicoloured.

1417 30s. Type **379** 65 65
1418 30s. *Dysdercus cingulatus* (fruit bug) 65 65
1419 50s. *Valanga nigricornis* (grasshopper) 1·10 1·10
1420 50s. *Rhaphipodus hopei* (longhorn beetle) 1·10 1·10

No. **MS**1421 is left for miniature sheet not yet received.

380 Peon, Fire Brigade and Hutton Lane Police Station, Penang, 1880

2007. Bicentenary of the Establishment of the Police Force. Multicoloured.

1422 30s. Type **380** 1·00 35
1423 50s. Royal Federation of Malaya Policeman, 1958 and 'Flying Squad' anti-terrorist police in jungle, 1948 1·50 1·00
1424 50s. Modern police officers, police vehicles and Putrajaya District Police Headquarters 1·50 1·00

381 Eight Long Keris

2007. Royal Heritage of Negri Sembilan. Multicoloured.

1425 30s. Type **381** 65 20
1426 50s. Audience Hall 1·00 75
1427 1r. Raja of Negri Sembilan 1·90 3·00
MS1428 100×70 mm. 2r. Tuanku Ja'afar and Tuanku Najihah Binti Tuanku Besar Burhanudin 3·00 3·25

382 Secretariat Building, Brunei Darussalam

2007. 40th Anniversary of ASEAN (Association of South-east Asian Nations). Ancient and Modern Architecture. Multicoloured.

1429 50s. Type **382** 65 75
1430 50s. National Museum of Cambodia 65 75
1431 50s. Fatahillah Museum, Jakarta, Indonesi 65 75
1432 50s. Typical Lao house 65 75
1433 50s. Malayan Railway Headquarters Building, Kuala Lumpur, Malaysia 65 75
1434 50s. Yangon Post Office, Myanmar 65 75
1435 50s. Malacañang Palace, Philippines 65 75
1436 50s. National Museum of Singapore 65 75
1437 50s. Vimanmek Mansion, Bangkok, Thailand 65 75
1438 50s. Presidential Palace, Hanoi, Vietnam 65 75

Similar designs were issued on the same day by the ten member countries, Brunei, Cambodia, Indonesia, Laos, Myanmar, Philippines, Singapore, Thailand and Vietnam.

383 Tunku Abdul Rahman Putra Al-Haj declaring Independence, 31 August 1957

2007. 50th Anniversary of Independence. Multicoloured.

1439 30s. Type **383** 35 45
1440 30s. Petronas Twin Towers, Kuala Lumpur Tower, Government administrative building at Putrajaya, Proton car and Penang Bridge 35 45
1441 50s. Tunku Abdul Rahman Putra Al-Haj signing Declaration of Independence 65 75
1442 50s. Golden Jubilee logo 65 75
1443 30s. Dato' Onn Jafar (founder of United Malays National Organisation) 50 60
1444 30s. Tunku Abdul Rahman Putra Al-Haj (Prime Minister 1957–1970) 50 60
1445 30s. Tun Abdul Razak (Prime Minister 1970–1976) 50 60
1446 30s. Tun Tan Cheng Lock (founder of Malaysian Chinese Association) 50 60
1447 30s. Tun V. T. Sambanthan (President of Malaysian Indian Congress 1955–1973) 50 60

Designs: 1439/1447, showing Malaysian leaders and National Flag.

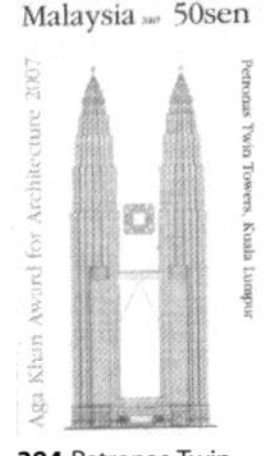

384 Petronas Twin Towers, Kuala Lumpur

2007. Aga Khan Award for Architecture.

1448 **384** 50s. grey, black and gold 4·50 1·75

385 Arms of Malaysia

2007. State Emblems. Designs showing arms. Multicoloured.

1449 50s. Type **385** 1·00 1·00
1450 50s. Kedah 1·00 1·00
1451 50s. Negeri Sembilan 1·00 1·00
1452 50s. Pahang 1·00 1·00
1453 50s. Kelantan 1·00 1·00
1454 50s. Johor 1·00 1·00
1455 50s. Perak 1·00 1·00
1456 50s. Perlis 1·00 1·00
1457 50s. Selangor 1·00 1·00
1458 50s. Terengganu 1·00 1·00
1459 50s. Sarawak 1·00 1·00
1460 50s. Pulau Pinang 1·00 1·00
1461 50s. Sabah 1·00 1·00
1462 50s. Melaka 1·00 1·00

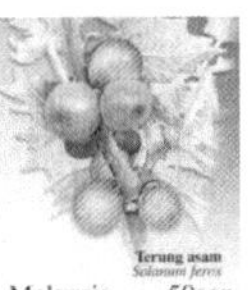

386 *Solanum ferox*

2007. Stamp Week. Rare Vegetables. Multicoloured.

1463 50s. Type **386** 70 70
1464 50s. *Momordica charantia* (bitter melon) 70 70
1465 50s. *Etlingera elatior* (torch ginger) 70 70
MS1466 120×70 mm. 1r.×4 *Luffa aegyptiaca* (smooth petola); *Psophocarpust etragonolobus* (winged bean); *Sesbania grandiflora*; *Solanum torvum* 4·50 5·00

387 Oldenburger

2007. KL Grand Prix (show-jumping), Kuala Lumpur. Designs showing horse breeds as show-jumpers. Multicoloured.

1467 30s. Type **387** 80 20
1468 50s. Hanoverian 1·25 1·25
1469 50s. Dutch warmblood 1·25 1·25

388 Merdeka Bridge, Kedah

2008. Bridges of Malaysia. Multicoloured.

1470 30s. Type **388** 45 20
1471 50s. Victoria Bridge, Perak 70 90
1472 50s. Kota Bridge, Selangor 70 90
1473 1r. Sungai Segamat Bridge, Johor 1·25 1·50

389 *Echinosorex gymnurus* (moonrat)

2008. Nocturnal Animals. Multicoloured.

1474 30s. Type **389** 70 55
1475 30s. *Mydaus javanensis* (Malay badger) 70 55
1476 50s. *Catopuma temminckii* (golden cat) 1·10 65
1477 1r. *Pteropus vampyrus* (flying fox) 2·10 2·50
MS1478 120×70 mm. 2r. *Tarsius bancanus* (tarsier) (vert); 3r. *Nycticebus coucang* (slow loris) (59×39 mm) 5·50 6·00

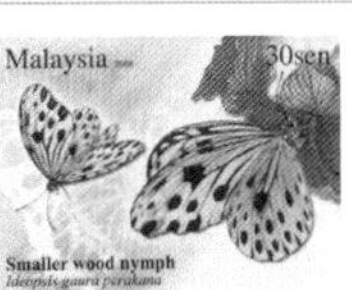

390 Smaller Wood Nymph (*Ideopsis gaura perakana*)

2008. Butterflies of Malaysia. Multicoloured.

1479 30s. Type **390** 90 90
1480 30s. Malayan lacewing (*Cethosia hypsea hypsina*) 90 90
1481 30s. Common rose (*Atrophaneura aristolochiae*) 90 90
1482 30s. Blue glassy tiger (*Ideopsis vulgaris*) 90 90
1483 30s. Green dragontail (*Lamproptera meges*) 90 90
1484 50s. Malay red harlequin (*Paralaxita damajanti damajanti*) 1·25 90
1485 1r. Glorious begum (*Agatasa calydonia calydonia*) 2·00 2·00
MS1486 114×66 mm. 5r. Five-bar swordtail (*Graphium antiphates*) (49×38 mm) 4·75 5·50

Nos. 1479/1480 were printed together, *se-tenant*, forming a composite design of butterflies on a hibiscus flower.

391 Emergency Ambulance Service

2008. Centenary of St John Ambulance in Malaysia. Multicoloured.

1487 30s. Type **391** 1·25 40
1488 50s. First aid 2·00 90
1489 1r. Cardio pulmonary resuscitation 3·50 2·75

392 Batu Giling (stone grinder for chilli or spices)

2008. Traditional Malaysian Artefacts (2nd series). Multicoloured.

1490 30s. Type **392** 55 20
1491 50s. Supu (silver tobacco container) 80 80
1492 50s. Kukur Kelapa (wooden coconut grater with metal spur) (triangular 62×31 mm) 80 80

393 Sultan of Kedah, Paddy Field, Zahir Mosque and Alor Setar in early 1950s

2008. Golden Jubilee of Sultan Abdul Halim Mu'Adzam Shah of Kedah. Multicoloured.

1493 30s. Type **393** 55 30
1494 50s. Sultan, Jalan Telok Wanjah Water Fountain and old State Secretary's office 90 70
1495 1r. Sultan, Jubilee emblem and modern Alor Setar 1·75 2·25

394 Drummer and Crew on Boat No. 6

2008. Sixth IDBF Club Crew World Championship, Penang. Designs showing dragon boats. Multicoloured.

1496 30s. Type **394** 55 20
1497 50s. Boats No. 2 and No. 5 90 60
1498 1r. Boat No. 4 and steerer in stern of other boat 1·75 2·25
MS1499 120×60 mm. 2r. Dragon boat No. 5 (79×29 mm) 2·25 2·50

395 Scouts Map reading and Lord Baden-Powell (founder of World Scouting)

2008. Centenary of the Scouts Association of Malaysia. Multicoloured.

1500 30s. Type **395** 55 20
1501 50s. Scouts crossing Monkey Bridge 90 1·00
1502 50s. Sea scouts diving, kayaking and in launch 90 1·00

396 *Semangat Ledang* (Spirit of Ledang) (Syed Ahmad Jamal) (acrylic on canvas), 2003

2008. Treasures of the Nation's Visual Arts (1st series). Artwork from the National Art Gallery of Malaysia. Multicoloured.

1503	30s. Type **396**	50	20
1504	50s. *Chuah Thean Teng* (Fruits Season) (Musim Buah) (batik), 1968 (vert)	75	65
1505	1r. *Pago-pago* (Latiff Mohidin) (oil on canvas), 1965 (35×35 mm)	1·25	1·75

See also Nos. 1822/1824.

397 Tengkoloks for Yang Di-Pertuan Agong and Sultans of the Nine Malaysian States

2008. Royal Headgear. Designs showing official tengkoloks of the Sultans of the Malaysian states. Multicoloured.

1506	50s. Type **397**	65	65
1507	50s. Black tengkolok with gold embroidery and platinum star and crescent (Yang Di-Pertuan Agong at his Coronation)	65	65
1508	50s. Black tengkolok with gold thread design and Kedah crest with diamond paddy stalks (Kedah)	65	65
1509	50s. Yellow songket destar (Negri Sembilan)	65	65
1510	50s. Purple tengkolok with embroidery (Pahang)	65	65
1511	50s. Pale blue destar with crest (Kelantan)	65	65
1512	50s. White destar with silver embroidery and crest (Perak)	65	65
1513	50s. Embroidered tengkolok with white and yellow crest (Perlis)	65	65
1514	50s. Yellow songket destar with crest (Selangor)	65	65
1515	50s. Embroidered yellow songket destar with crest (Trengganu)	65	65

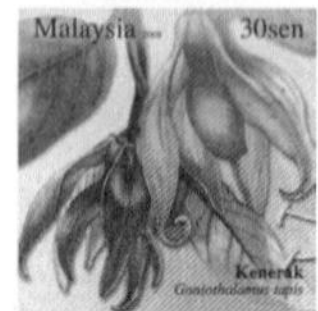

398 *Goniothalamus tapis*

2008. Unique Flowers. Multicoloured.

1516	50s. Type **398**	65	75
1517	50s. *Gloriosa superba*	65	75
1518	50s. *Quisqualis indica*	65	75
1519	50s. *Michelia figo*	65	75
MS1520	100×70 mm. 5r. *Epiphyllum oxypetalum* (38×49 mm)	5·00	5·50

399 *Soyuz TMA II* Rocket

2008. National Astronaut Programme. Multicoloured.

1521	30s. Type **399**	55	20
1522	50s. Dr. Sheikh Muszaphar Syukor Al-Masrie conducting experiments in microgravity	90	60
1523	1r. International Space Station	1·75	2·25
MS1524	100×70 mm. 1r. Launch of Dr. Al-Masrie aboard rocket, Baikonur Cosmodrome, 2007; 1r. *Soyuz TMA II* rocket in flight	2·50	3·00

400 Horned Helmet (*Cassis cornuta*)

2008. Seashells of Malaysia. Multicoloured.

1525	30s. Type **400**	60	50
1526	30s. Burnt murex (*Chicoreus brunneus*)	60	50
1527	50s. Frog shell (*Tutufa rubeta*)	90	1·00
1528	50s. Triton's trumpet (*Charonia tritonis*)	90	1·00
MS1529	90×60 mm. 2r. Venus comb murex (*Murex pecten*) (60×40 mm)	2·75	3·00

No. **MS**1529 also exists imperforate.

401 'The Kampung Boy'

2008. Malaysian Cartoons by Lat (Dato' Mohd. Nor Khalid). Nos. 1530/1538 black and red (Nos. 1530/1538) or black and silver (**MS**1539) designs.

1530	30s. Type **401**	40	45
1531	30s. Riding the pinang frond ('Permainen Anak Kampung') (58×33 mm)	40	45
1532	30s. Drawing caricature of teacher Mrs. Hew on blackboard ('Guru Sekolah Yang Garang') (58×33 mm)	40	45
1533	30s. Mat and Frankie playing at rock musicians with brush and racket ('Town Boy')	40	45
1534	30s. Lat at easel painting, spilling paint everywhere	40	45
1535	50s. As Type **401**	65	65
1536	50s. As No. 1531	65	65
1537	50s. As No. 1532	65	65
1538	50s. As No. 1533	65	65
MS1539	120×70 mm. 5r. People on pedestrian crossing ('Malaysian daily life') (60×40 mm)	4·25	4·25

402 SMK St Thomas, Kuching, Sarawak

2008. Premier Schools. Multicoloured.

1540	50s. Type **402**	75	75
1541	50s. SMK Victoria (Victoria Institution), Kuala Lumpur	75	75
1542	50s. SMK Convent Bukit Nanas, Kuala Lumpur	75	75
1543	50s. SM All Saints, Kota Kinabalu, Sabah	75	75

403 *Polyplectron malacense* (Malaysian peacock-pheasant)

2009. Unique Birds of Malaysia. Multicoloured.

1544	30s. Type **403**	75	35
1545	50s. *Mycteria cinerea* (milky stork)	1·40	1·40
1546	50s. *Myophonus robinsoni* (Malaysian whistling thrush)	1·40	1·40
MS1547	110×70 mm. 5r. *Aceros subruficollis* (wreathed hornbill)	10·00	10·00

404 Sultan of Perak and Sultan kissing Ceremonial Sword during Installation Ceremony, 1985

2009. Silver Jubilee of Sultan Azlan Muhibbuddin Shah of Perak. Multicoloured.

1548	30s. Type **404**	60	20
1549	50s. Sultan of Perak and Ubudiah Mosque	90	60
1550	1r. Sultan Azlan Muhibbuddin Shah and Raja Permaisuri Perak Tuanku Bainun	1·75	2·25

405 Malay Bride and Groom and Mosque

2009. Traditional Wedding Costumes. Multicoloured.

(a) As T **405**

1551	30s. Type **405**	60	70
1552	30s. Chinese bride and groom, and temple columns with dragons and phoenix	60	70
1553	30s. Indian bride and groom and temple	60	70
1554	30s. Orang Ulu bride and groom and traditional house	60	70
1555	30s. Bajau bride and groom and traditional house	60	70

(b) Designs as Nos. 1551/1555 but with different backgrounds.

1556	50s. Malay bride and groom and Bunga telur (wedding decoration)	80	80
1557	50s. Chinese bride and groom and red 'double happiness' symbols	80	80
1558	50s. Indian bride and groom and garland	80	80
1559	50s. Orang Ulu bride and groom and Bunga Jarau (wooden wedding ornament)	80	80
1560	50s. Bajau bride and groom and Tipo serisir (woven silk material and beadwork wedding mat)	80	80

406 Stadthuys (former Dutch governor's residence) and Old Town Square, Banda Hilir, Malacca

2009. UNESCO World Heritage Sites. Multicoloured.

1561	50s. Type **406**	80	80
1562	50s. Old City Hall (now Municipal Council building), George Town, Penang	80	80
1563	50s. Pinnacles of Gunung Api, Mulu National Park and tarsier	80	80
1564	50s. Kinabalu National Park and scarlet minivet (bird)	80	80
MS1565	70×110 mm. 50s.×4 Banda Hilir, Malacca; Lenticular cloud over mountain peak, Kinabalu National Park; Clock tower and colonial corner building, George Town, Penang; Cave, Mulu National Park (all 59×25 mm)	2·75	3·00

407 Railway, Harbour, Aircraft and Steam Locomotive ('Transportation and Port–Past')

2009. 'Engineering Excellence in Nation Building'. Multicoloured.

1566	30s. Type **407**	80	80
1567	30s. Modern buildings ('Transportation and Ports–Present')	80	80
1568	30s. Switchboard and pylon ('Telecommunication and Power–Past')	80	80
1569	30s. Satellite dish and pylons ('Telecommunication and Power–Present')	80	80
1570	50s. Bridge and dam ('Road, Bridge and Dam–Past')	1·00	1·00
1571	50s. Reservoir, roads and bridge ('Road, Bridge and Dam–Present')	1·00	1·00

Nos. 1566/1567, 1568/1569 and 1570/1571 were each printed together, *se-tenant*, each pair forming a composite design.

408 *Licuala grandis*

2009. Palm Trees. Multicoloured.

1572	50s. Type **408**	80	80
1573	50s. *Caryota mitis*	80	80
1574	50s. *Livistona saribus*	80	80
MS1575	80×80 mm. 3r. *Livistona endauensis* and *Johannesteijsmannia altifrons* (69×49 mm)	2·75	3·00

409 Whale (Clean Water)

2009. Conservation of Nature. Multicoloured.

1577	30s. Type **409**	55	55
1578	50s. Rainforest trees ('Go Green')	75	75
1579	50s. Chimneys emitting pollution ('Fresh Air')	75	75

410 Malay Traditional House, Selangor

2009. Traditional Houses. Multicoloured.

1580	50s. Type **410**	75	75
1581	50s. Dusun Lotud traditional house, Sabah	75	75
1582	50s. Kutai house, Perak	75	75
1583	50s. Twelve Pillars house, Kota Bharu, Kelantan	75	75
1584	50s. Iban long house, Sarawak	75	75
1585	50s. Semai house, Pahang	75	75
1586	50s. Limas house, Pontian, Johor	75	75
1587	50s. Long house, Kedah	75	75
1588	50s. Limas Bungkus house, Besut, Terengganu	75	75
1589	50s. Adat Minangkabau house, Negeri Sembilan	75	75
1590	50s. 'Gajah Menyusu' verandah house, Pulau Pinang	75	75
1591	50s. Long roofed house, Perlis	75	75
1592	50s. Malay house, Melaka	75	75
1593	50s. Bajau Laut, Sabah	75	75
1594	50s. Verandah house, Pahang	75	75
1595	50s. Bidayuh headhouse, Sarawak	75	75

411 *Ipomoea batatas* (sweet potato)

2009. Tuber Plants. Multicoloured.

1596	30s. Type **411**	55	55
1597	30s. *Manihot esculenta crantz* (cassava or tapioca)	55	55
1598	50s. *Pachyrrhizus erosus* (yam bean)	75	75
1599	50s. *Dioscorea alataL.* (yam)	75	75
MS1600	100×71 mm. 3r. *Colocasia esculenta* (taro) (diamond 62×63 mm)	2·75	2·75

2009. Philakorea 2009 International Stamp Exhibition, Seoul. As No. **MS**1575 additionally inscr with 'PHILAKOREA 2009 24th Asian International Stamp Exhibition' and emblem on upper right sheet margin.

MS1601	80×80 mm. 3r. *Livistona endauensis* and *Johannesteijsmannia altifrons* (69×49 mm)	2·75	2·75

412 '1 Malaysia' Logo

2009. 1 Malaysia People First Performance Now (1st series). Multicoloured.

1602 30s. Type **412** 55 55

1603 30s. National Flag in heart surrounded by Malaysians of different races 55 55

1604 30s. Malaysian citizens and light bulb 55 55

MS1605 70×100 mm. 5r. Citizens of different races surrounding Malaysia 1 logo 4·50 4·50

1606 30s. Type **413** 55 65

1607 30s. As No. 1603 55 65

1608 30s. As No. 1604 55 65

1609 30s. Citizens, laptop computer and symbols of science and technology 55 65

1610 30s. Citizens, office building and hibiscus flower 55 65

See also Nos.1741/1744.

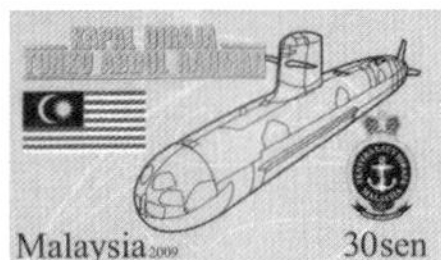

413 Plan of Submarine

2009. First Malaysian Submarine. Multicoloured.

1611 30s. Type **413** 70 60

1612 50s. New Scorpene submarine *KD Tunku Abdul Rahman* (seen from above) 1·10 1·10

1613 50s. New submarine (side view) 1·10 1·10

414 Green Energy Office at the Green Energy Centre, Bangi

2009. Energy Efficient Buildings. Multicoloured.

1614 30s. Type **414** 55 55

1615 50s. Green Technology and Water Ministry's Low Energy Office, Putrajaya 75 75

1616 1r. Energy Commission's Diamond Building, Putrajaya 90 90

415

2010. Caring Society. Multicoloured.

1616a 30s. Type **415** 55 55

1617 30s. Boy drinking (Right to Food) 55 55

1618 30s. Boy with backpack (Right to Education) 55 55

1619 30s. Girl with umbrella (Right to Protection) 55 55

1620 1r. Children and rainbow (Convention on the Rights of the Child) 1·00 1·00

No. 1620 is embossed with Braille.

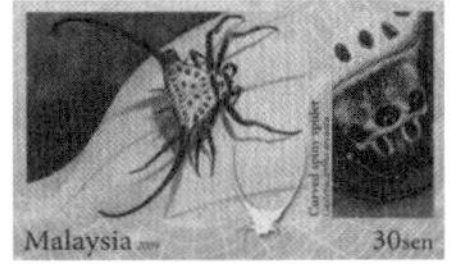

416 Curved Spiny Spider (*Gasteracantha arcuata*)

2010. Stamp Week. Multicoloured.

1621 30s. Type **416** 60 60

1622 30s. Fighting spider (*Thiania bhamoensis*) 60 60

1623 50s. St Andrew's Cross spider (*Argiope versicolor*) 75 75

1624 1r. Golden orb-web spider (*Nephila maculata*) 1·00 1·00

MS1625 100×65 mm. 5r. Black scorpion (*Heterometrus longimanus*) (hexagon 64×32 mm). Wmk sideways. P 13½ 4·50 4·50

417 Obverse of 10s. Coin showing Hibiscus Flower

2010. Malaysian Currency (1st series). Multicoloured.

1626 50s. Type **417** 65 65

1627 50s. Reverse of 10s. coin showing congkak board (for indoor games with marbles) 65 65

1628 50s. Obverse of 20s. coin showing hibiscus flower 65 65

1629 50s. Reverse of 20s. coin showing tepak sirih (box for storing betel leaves) 65 65

1630 50s. Obverse of 50s. coin showing hibiscus flower 65 65

1631 50s. Reverse of 50s. coin showing kite 65 65

MS1632 120×80 mm. 5r. New 50r. bank note (50×40 mm) 4·50 4·50

See also Nos.1885/1892.

418 Korean Tiger (*Panthera tigris altaica*)

2010. Tigers. Multicoloured.

1633 50s. Type **418** 75 75

1634 50s. Malayan tiger (*Panthera tigris jacksoni*) 75 75

Nos. 1633/1634 were printed together *se-tenant* as horizontal pairs in sheets of 20.

Nos. 1633/1634 commemorate the 50th anniversary of diplomatic relations between Malaysia and Korea.

Stamps in a similar designs were issued by South Korea.

419 *Helminthostachys zeylanica*

2010. Ferns. Multiocoloured.

1635 50s. Type **419** 60 60

1636 50s. *Stenochlaena palustris* 60 60

1637 50s. *Platycerium coronarium* 60 60

1638 50s. *Dicranopteris linearis* 60 60

1639 50s. *Diplazium esculentum* 60 60

MS1640 120x70 mm. 3r. *Asplenium nidus; Matonia pectinata* and *Dipteris conjugata* (100x45 mm). 3·50 3·50

Nos. 1635/1639 were printed together *se-tenant*, forming a composite design of ferns in a rainforest

420 Market Trader, Siti Khadijah Market, Kelantan

2010. Local Markets. Multicoloured.

1641 30s. Type **420** 50 50

1642 30s. Vegetable stalls on ground floor, Siti Khadijah Market, Kelantan 50 50

1643 50s. Food stalls, Kraf Tangan Market, Kota Kinabalu 65 65

1644 Handicraft stalls, Kraf Tangan Market, Kota Kinabalu 65 65

MS1645 110×80 mm. 1r. Handicrafts stall, Pekan Rabu Market, Kedah; Stall at Pekan Rabu Market, Kedah. 3·75 3·75

MS1646 110×80 mm. 1r. Vegetable and fish stall, Pasar Minggu Satok Market; 1r. Flower and herb stall, Pasar Minggu Satok Market. 3·75 3·75

Nos. 1641/1642 and 1643/1644 were each printed together, *se-tenant*, each pair forming a composite design of a market.

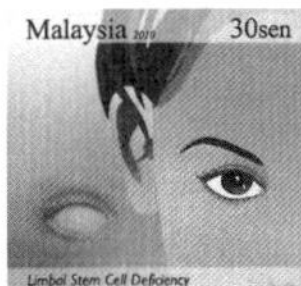

421 Limbal Stem Cell Deficiency

2010. Medical Excellence. Multicoloured.

1647 30s. Type **421** 55 55

1648 50s. Premaxilla retractor 60 60

1649 1r. Arm transplant 1·10 1·10

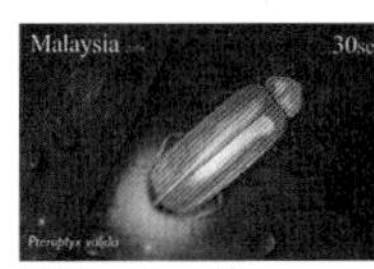

422 *Pteroptyx valida*

2010. Fireflies. Multicoloured.

1650 30s. Type **422** 40 40

1651 30s. *Pteroptx bearni* 40 40

1652 50s. *Diaphanes* sp. 55 55

1653 50s. *Lychnuris* sp. 55 55

MS1654 110×80 mm. 5r. *Pteroptx tener* (60×40 mm) 6·50 6·50

No. **MS**1654 has light reflecting ink die-stamped onto firefly's tail.

423 Komuter Locomotive

2010. 125th Anniversary of KTM (Keretapi Tanah Melayu) Railways. Multicoloured.

(a) Sheet stamps

1655 30s. Type **423** 50 50

1656 30s. ETS locomotive 50 50

1657 50s. *Blue Tiger* locomotive (70×25 mm) 75 75

1658 1r. 56 Class steam locomotive (70×25 mm) 1·00 1·00

MS1659 120×70 mm. 3r. FMSR Class T steam locomotive (in shed) (30×50 mm) 6·00 6·00

(b) Booklet stamps

1660 30s. 20 Class locomotives (70×25 mm) 50 60

1661 30s. Designs as Nos. 1655/1656 (70×25 mm) 50 60

1662 30s. As No. 1657 50 60

1663 30s. As No. 1658 50 60

1664 30s. FMSR Class T steam locomotive 50 60

424 *Nelumbium nelumbo* (Sacred Lotus)

2010. Garden Flowers. Multicoloured.

A. With imprint date '2010' at foot

1668A 30s. Type **424** 45 45

1669A 50s. *Hydrangea macrophylla* 55 55

1670A 60s. Bougainvillea 75 75

1671A 70s. *Hippeastrum reticulatum* 85 85

1672A 80s. *Hibiscus rosa-sinensis* 90 90

1673A 90s. *Ipomoea indica* 1·00 1·00

1674A 1r. *Canna orientalis* 1·40 1·40

1675A 2r. *Allamanda cathartica* 2·40 2·40

B. Without imprint date

1671B 70s. *Hippeastrum reticulatum* 85 85

1672B 80s. *Hibiscus rosa-sinensis* 90 90

1673B 90s. *Ipomoea indica* 1·10 1·10

1674B 1r. *Canna orientalis* 1·40 1·40

Nos. 1665/1667 and 1676/1678 are left for possible additions to this definitive series.

425 Tapirs and Decimated Forest

2010. Threatened Habitats. Multicoloured.

1679 60s. Type **425** 60 60

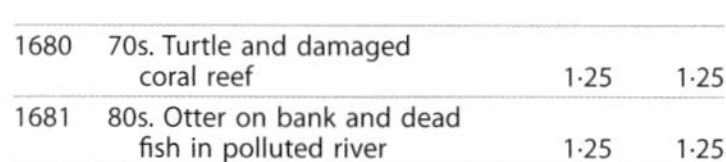

1680 70s. Turtle and damaged coral reef 1·25 1·25

1681 80s. Otter on bank and dead fish in polluted river 1·25 1·25

426 Soldiers and Tank

2010. Grand Knight of Valour Award. Multicoloured.

1682 60s. Type **426** 60 60

1683 70s. Recipients 85 85

1684 80s. Soldiers 1·25 1·25

2010. Bangkok 2010 25th Asian International Stamp Exhibition, Thailand

MS1685 120×70 mm. 3r. FMSR Class T steam locomotive (in shed) (30×50 mm) 2·75 2·75

427 Malayan Food

2010. Traditional Festive Food. Multicoloured.

(a) Booklet stamps

1691 60s. Malayan (bottom portion) 50 50

1692 60s. Chinese (bottom portion) 50 50

1693 60s. Indian (bottom portion) 50 50

1694 60s. Sabah (bottom portion) 50 50

1695 60s. Sarawak (bottom portion) 50 50

(b) Sheet stamps

1696 80s. Malayan (top portion) 70 70

1697 80s. Chinese (top portion) 70 70

1698 80s. Indian (top portion) 70 70

1699 80s. Sabah (top portion) 70 70

1700 80s. Sarawak (top portion) 70 70

1702 80s. Malayan (bottom portion) 70 70

1702 80s. Chinese (bottom portion) 70 70

1703 80s. Indian (bottom portion) 70 70

1704 80s. Sabah (bottom portion) 70 70

1705 80s. Sarawak (bottom portion) 70 70

MS1706 130×100 mm. 1r. Indian; 1r. Chinese; 1r. Malayan (all diamond shape, 48×48 mm). Wmk sideways 4·50 4·50

Nos. 1686 and 1691, 1687 and 1692, 1688 and 1693, 1689 and 1694, 1690 and 1695, 1696 and 1701, 1697 and 1702, 1698 and 1703, 1699 and 1704 and 1700 and 1705 each form composite designs showing the complete plate of food.

428 Ketuk Buluh

2010. Lifestyles of the Aboriginal People. Multicoloured.

1707 60s. Type **428** 65 65

1708 70s. Menyumpit hunter with blowpipe 90 90

1709 80s. Mengukir wood carver 1·40 1·40

429 Post Office, Jalan Kelang Lama, Kuala Lumpur

2010. Post Office Buildings. Multicoloured.

1710 60s. Type **429** 60 60

1711 60s. Layang-Layang, Johor 60 60

1712 60s. Jalan Raja, Kedah 60 60

1713 60s. Temangan, Kelantan 60 60

1714 60s. Mertimau, Malaka 60 60

1715 60s. Seremban, Negri Sembilan 60 60

1716 60s. Bukit Fraser, Pahang 60 60

1717 60s. Kuala Kangsar, Perak 60 60

1718 60s. Kaki Bukit, Perlis 60 60

1719 60s. Jalan Bagan Luar, Penang 60 60

1720	60s. Kudat, Sabah	60	60
1721	60s. Kuching, Sarawak	60	60
1722	60s. Kajang, Selangor	60	60
1723	60s. Kuala Terengganu, Trengganu	60	60
1724	60s. Kuala Lumpur and Federal Territories flag	60	60
1725	60s. Johor Bahru, and Johore flag	60	60
1726	60s. Sungai Petani and Kedah flag	60	60
1727	60s. Rantau Panjang and Kelantan flag	60	60
1728	60s. Alor Gajah and Malacca flag	60	60
1729	60s. Bandar Baru Serting and Negri Sembilan flag	60	60
1730	60s. Ringlet and Pahang flag	60	60
1731	60s. Tronoh and Perak flag	60	60
1732	60s. Kangar and Perlis flag	60	60
1733	60s. Bukit Mertajam and Penang flag	60	60
1734	60s. Kota Kinabalu and Sabah flag	60	60
1735	60s. Sarikei and Sarawak flag	60	60
1736	60s. Bukit Rotan and Selangor flag	60	60
1737	60s. Jerteh and Trengganu flag	60	60

430 Sultan Ahmad Shah, Sultanah Kalsom and Pahang Crown

2010. Heritage of Pahang. Multicoloured.

1738	60s. Type **430**	90	90
1739	80s. Sultan (in military uniform), woven cloth and handicrafts	1·10	1·10
1740	1r. Sultan Ahmad Shah and thrones	1·25	1·25

431 Satellite Image in Computer Mouse, Satellite Dish and Songket Textile Designs

2010. 1 Malaysia (2nd series). Multicoloured.

1741	30s. Type **431**	45	45
1742	30s. Traditional kite, astronaut and space shuttle	45	45
1743	50s. Petronas Twin Towers, other modern buildings and carved wood panel	65	65
1744	50s. Woven basket and biotechnology	65	65

432 Mei Mei and Devi

2010. Stamp Week. Traditional Games of the Past with Upin, Ipin and Friends (characters from TV programme). Multicoloured.

1745	60s. Type **432**	90	90
1746	60s. Grandmother Opah and Susanti	90	90
1747	60s. Upin, Ipin and Ehsan playing war game	90	90
1748	60s. Fizi and Mail playing with tin can 'telephones'	90	90
1749	60s. Upin, Jarjah and Mei Mei	90	90
1750	60s. Ipin, Jarjah and Susanti	90	90
MS1751	100×80 mm. 5r. Upin and Ipin with elder sister Ros making shadow puppets	6·50	6·50

Nos. 1745/1746, 1747/1748 and 1749/1750 were each printed together, *se-tenant*, as horizontal pairs in sheets of 20 stamps, each pair forming a composite design.

433 Boy with Rabbit

2011. Children's Pets. Multicoloured.

1752	60s. Type **433**	80	80
1753	80s. Girl with cat	1·10	1·10
1754	1r. Girl with dog	1·40	1·40
MS1755	Circular 95×95 mm. 5r. Rabbit	6·50	6·50

2011. Indipex 2011 World Philatelic Exhibition, New Delhi. No. **MS**1755 additionally inscr with INDIPEX 2011 emblem at top left of stamp.

MS1755a	Circular 95×95 mm. 5r. Rabbit	6·75	6·75

434 Funicular Railway, Bukit Pendera (Penang Hill)

2011. Highland Tourist Spots. Multicoloured.

1756	50s. Type **434**	65	65
1757	60s. Tea picking, Cameron Highlands, Pahang	90	90
1758	90s. Cable car, Gunung Mat Cincang, Langkawi, Kedah	1·10	1·10
1759	1r. Field of cabbages, Kundasang, Sabah	1·40	1·40

435 Medallion

2011. Suzuki Cup (football tournament for south-east Asian nations), Vietnam and Indonesia. Multicoloured.

1760	60s. Type **435**	90	90
1761	60s. Trophy (30×50 mm)	90	90

436 Fennel Seed

2011. Spices. Micoloured.

1762	60s. Type **436**	90	90
1763	60s. Sack of tumeric (top portion)	90	90
1764	60s. Sack of chilli (top portion)	90	90
1765	60s. Sack of coriander (top portion)	90	90
1766	60s. Sack of White pepper (top portion)	90	90
1767	60s. Sack of fennel seed (bottom portion)	90	90
1768	60s. Sack of tumeric (bottom portion)	90	90
1769	60s. Sack of chilli (bottom portiion)	90	90
1770	60s. Sack of coriander (bottom portion)	90	90
1771	60s. Sack of white pepper (bottom portion)	90	90
1772	60s. Cinnamon sticks	90	90
1773	90s. Star anise	1·10	1·10
1774	1r. Cardamom pods	1·25	1·25
MS1775	121×80 mm. 1r. White peppers, chillis, coriander and fennel seed (50×60 mm); 1r. Cinnamon sticks, star anise and tumeric (50×60 mm)	3·75	3·75

Nos. 1762 and 1767, 1763 and 1768, 1764 and 1769, 1765 and 1770 and 1766 and 1771 each form composite designs showing the complete sack of spices. Nos. 1762/1771 form a composite background design

437 18th-Century Tobacco Box

2011. Artifacts of National Heritage. Multicoloured.

1776	60s. Type **437**	90	90
1777	60s. Sultan Alau'uddin Riayat Shah gold coin	90	90
1778	60s. 15th-century bronze bell from Dong S'on, Vietnaml	90	90
1779	60s. Sultan Zainal Abidin II of Terengganu gold coin	90	90
1780	60s. Bronze statue of Avalokitesvara, 7/12th-century AD (inscr 'Statute')	90	90
1781	60s. Malay belt buckle	90	90
1782	60s. 16th-century gold coin showing deer	90	90
1783	60s. Sultan Abdul Samad of Selangor's set of sireh	90	90
1784	60s. Sultan Muzaffar Shah of Johore gold coin	90	90
1785	60s. Arch of sitting Buddha, 1000-1100 AD	90	90

438 Hibiscus Flowers and Silver Flower

2011. Personalised Stamps. Silverwork. Multicoloured (except No. 1786).

1786	35s. Type **438** (bright green, deep green and black)	80	80
1787	35s. Silver durian fruit and pink pattern	80	80
1788	65s. Pattern and screen	1·75	1·75
1789	65s. Silverwork Wau Bulan (moon kite) and blue pattern	1·75	1·75

439 'Love'

2011. Virtues. Multicoloured.

1790	60s. Type **439**	75	75
1791	60s. Bee and honeycomb ('Hardworking')	75	75
1792	60s. Smiling face ('Courteous')	75	75
1793	60s. Man bowing and taking off hat ('Mutual Respect')	75	75
1794	60s. Mountaineer on summit with flag ('Independent')	75	75
1795	60s. Green ribbon ('Awareness')	75	75
1796	60s. Outstretched hand and hand holding walking stick ('Kind Hearted')	75	75
1797	60s. 'Thank You' in seven languages ('Thankful')	†	†
1798	60s. Raised hands with smiley faces on fingertips ('Living in Harmony')	75	75
1799	60s. Raised hand ('Integrity')	75	75

440 G. P. Fuller landing Monoplane at Ampang Race Course, Kuala Lumpur, 1911

2011. Centenary of Malaysian Aviation. Multicoloured.

1800	60s. Type **440** ('The Birth of Aviation')	1·25	1·00
1801	80s. Malayan Airways aircraft on ground ('Era of Aviation Development')	1·40	1·40
1802	1r. Modern aircraft on ground ('Era of Aviation Excellence')	1·75	2·00

441 Negara Palace, Kuala Lumpur

2011. Royal Palaces. Multicoloured.

1803	1r. Type **441**	1·25	1·25
1804	1r. Seri Menanti Palace, Negri Sembilan	1·25	1·25
1805	1r. Alam Shah Palace, Klang, Selangor	1·25	1·25
1806	1r. Arau Palace, Perlis	1·25	1·25
1807	1r. Maziah Palace, Kuala Terengganu	1·25	1·25
1808	1r. Anak Bukit Palace, Kedah	1·25	1·25
1809	1r. Balai Besar Palace, Kelantan	1·25	1·25
1810	1r. Abu Bakar Palace, Pekan, Pahang	1·25	1·25
1811	1r. Besar Palace, Johore	1·25	1·25
1812	1r. Iskandariah Palace, Perak	1·25	1·25

2011. Philanippon '11 World Stamp Exhibition, Yokohama, Japan. As No. **MS**1659 additionally inscr 'PHILA NIPPON '11 2011' and emblem on upper left sheet margin.

MS1813	120×70 mm. 3r. FMSR Class T steam locomotive (in shed) (30×50 mm)	9·25	9·25

442 Malaysia's National Monument

2011. Malaysia–Indonesia Joint Issue. Multicoloured.

1814	90s. Type **442**	1·10	1·10
1815	90s. Proclamation Monument	1·10	1·10
1816	90s. Malaysia's first currency issued after Independence	1·10	1·10
1817	90s. ORI (Oeang Republik Indonesia) banknote	1·10	1·10
1818	90s. Malaya 1957 Independence Day stamp	1·10	1·10
1819	90s. Indonesia 1949 Surakarta Military Stamp	1·10	1·10
1820	90s. *Gallus gallus* (red junglefowl)	1·10	1·10
1821	90s. *Gallus varius* (green junglefowl)	1·10	1·10

443 Bajau Horseman, North Borneo (Mohammed Hoessein Enas), 1963

2011. Visual Arts (2nd series). Multicoloured.

1822	60s. Type **443**	95	95
1823	90s. *The Rooster* (Anthony Lau), 1963 (horiz)	1·25	1·25
1824	1r. *Flag* (Nik Zainal Abidin Nik Salleh), 1970 (horiz)	1·50	1·50

444 Victorian Pillar Box, Bukit Bendera, Penang

445 Victorian Pillar Box, Bukit Bendera, Penang

2011. Stamp Week. Postboxes. Multicoloured.

(a) Self-adhesive booklet stamps as T **444**

1825	60s. Type **444**	1·40	1·40
1826	60s. Wall box, Bukit Fraser, Pahang	1·40	1·40
1827	60s. Pillar box on pole, Bandaraya Bersejarah, Melaka	1·40	1·40
1828	60s. Pillar box, Seremban, Negri Sembilan	1·40	1·40
1829	60s. Wall box, Pejabat Pos Besar, Kuala Lumpur	1·40	1·40

(b) Ordinary gum. Sheet stamps as T **445**

1830	1r. Type **445**	2·25	2·25
1831	1r. Wall box, Bukit Fraser, Pahang	2·25	2·25
1832	1r. Pillar box on pole, Bandaraya Bersejarah, Melaka	2·25	2·25
1833	1r. Pillar box, Seremban, Negri Sembilan	2·25	2·25
1834	1r. Wall box, Pejabat Pos Besar, Kuala Lumpur	2·25	2·25

446 Excavating Tunnel

2011. Underground Engineering Excellence. SMART Tunnel (Stormwater Management and Road Tunnel), Kuala Lumpur. Multicoloured.

(a) Ordinary gum

1835	60s. Type **446**	80	80
1836	60s. TBM after breakthrough	80	80

1837 60s. Tunnel breakthrough 80 80

1838 60s. Construction gantry 80 80

1839 60s. Road tunnel 80 80

1840 60s. Cross section of SMART tunnel 80 80

(b) Self-adhesive

MS1841 81×90 mm. 2r. Nos. 1835 and 1837/1838; 2r. Nos. 1836 and 1839/1840 (all 35×40 mm) 6·50 6·50

447 Royal Tiara ('Gandik Diraja')

2011. Royal Institution (of the Monarchy). Multicoloured.

1842 60s. Type **447** 90 90

1843 80s. Royal Waist-Buckle ('Pending Diraja') 1·00 1·00

1844 90s. Royal Throne ('Singgahsana') 1·25 1·25

448 Cindai

2012. Legacy of the Loom (traditional textiles). Multicoloured.

1845 60s. Type **448** 90 90

1846 60s. Songket 90 90

1847 60s. Pua Kumbu 90 90

1848 60s. Ci Xiu 90 90

1849 60s. Rangkit 90 90

MS1850 115×100 mm. 3r. Ming Express robe with dragon design (normal colours) 4·50 4·50

MS1851 115×100 mm. 5r. Ming Express robe with dragon design (dragon in gold) 7·50 7·50

449 Family

2012. Yes to Life, No to Drugs. Multicoloured.

1852 60s. Type **449** 1·60 1·60

1853 60s. Children playing and boy using computer 1·60 1·60

1854 1r. People in park 2·50 2·50

450 Map of Antarctica and Malaysian Flag

2012. Malaysian Antarctic Research Programme. Multicoloured.

1855 60s. Type **450** 1·50 1·00

1856 90s. World map showing Antarctica and Malaysia 2·00 2·00

1857 90s. Researcher, Emperor penguins and bacteria (70×35 mm) 2·00 2·00

451 Red-spotted Coral Crab (*Trapezia rufopunctata*)

2012. Underwater Life. Multicoloured.

1858 60s. Type **451** 1·10 1·10

1859 60s. Mandarinfish (*Synchiropus splendidus*) 1·10 1·10

1860 60s. Blue sea star (*Linckia laevigata*) 1·10 1·10

1861 60s. Leopard moray eel (*Gymnothorax melanospilos*) 1·10 1·10

MS1862 115×70 mm. 5r. Green sea turtle (*Chelonia mydas*), robust ghostpipefish (*Solenostomus cyanopterus*) and thorny seahorse (*Hippocampus histrix*) (90×35 mm) 6·75 6·75

452 Installation of Tuanku Abdul Halim Shah

2012. Installation of Tuanku Abdul Halim Shah as 14th Yang di-Pertuan Agong. Multicoloured.

1863 60s. Type **452** 80 80

1864 80s. Tuanku Abdul Halim Shah and Tuanku Hajah Haminah (horiz) 1·00 1·00

1865 1r. Tuanku Abdul Halim Shah as head of armed forces (white uniform) 2·25 2·25

MS1866 140×75 mm. 2r. 10c. stamp issued for Installation of Tuanku Abdul Halim Shah as Fifth Yang di-Pertuan Agong, 1971; 3r. As 14th Yang di-Pertuan Agong, 2012 4·50 4·50

453 *Polygonum minus*

2012. Aromatic Plants. Multicoloured.

1867 60s. Type **453** 90 90

1868 1r. *Mentha piperita* (peppermint) 1·50 1·50

MS1869 121×80 mm. 5r. *Citrus hystrix* (Kaffir lime) (vert) 7·50 7·50

No. **MS**1869 is fragrant.

454 Gas Storage ('Securing Gas Supply')

2012. World Gas Conference, Kuala Lumpur. Multicoloured.

1870 60s. Type **454** 1·10 1·10

1871 60s. Kuala Lumpur skyline ('Enhancing Gas Demand') 1·10 1·10

1872 60s. Gas pipes and tree ('A Sustainable Future') 1·10 1·10

1873 60s. Malaysia on globe and human silhouettes holding hands ('Foundation For Growth') 1·10 1·10

2012. Indonesia 2012 World Stamp Championship and Exhibition, Jakarta. Nos. **MS**1850/**MS**1851 additionally inscr with Indonesia 2012 emblem on upper right sheet margin.

MS1874 115×100 mm. 3r. Ming Express robe with dragon design (normal colours) 4·50 4·50

MS1875 115×100 mm. 5r. Ming Express robe with dragon design (dragon in gold) 7·50 7·50

455 Penjaja Lemang

2012. Traditional Livelihoods. Multicoloured.

(a) Booklet stamps

1876 60s. Type **455** 90 90

1877 60s. Penjaja manisan 90 90

1878 60s. Tukang ubat tradisional 90 90

1879 60s. Penjaja pasembor 90 90

1880 60s. Tukang dobi 90 90

(b) Sheet stamps

1881 80s. Tukang seni kertas (paper craftsman) 1·00 1·00

1882 80s. Tukang tilik (fortune teller) 1·00 1·00

1883 1r. Penjaja satay 1·50 1·50

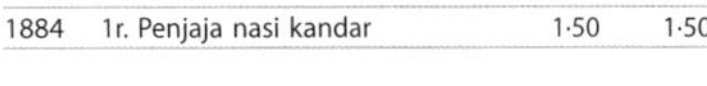

1884 1r. Penjaja nasi kandar 1·50 1·50

456 Obverse of 2011 5 sen Coin showing Hibiscus Flower

2012. Malaysian Currency (2nd series). Multicoloured.

1885 60s. Type **456** 90 90

1886 60s. Obverse of 2011 5 sen coin showing diamond pattern (mauve) 90 90

1887 60s. Obverse of 2011 10 sen coin showing hibiscus flower (pale blue) 90 90

1888 60s. Reverse of 10 sen coin showing star formed from triangles (pale blue) 90 90

1889 60s. Obverse of 20 sen coin showing hibiscus flower (pale green) 90 90

1890 60s. Reverse of 20 sen coin showing pattern with three flowers 90 90

1891 60s. Obverse of 2011 50 sen coin showing hibiscus flower 90 90

1892 60s. Reverse of 50 sen coin showing filigree pattern 90 90

457 Five Children

2012. Malaysian Unity (2nd series). Multicoloured.

1893 60s. Type **457** 90 90

1894 60s. Football, hockey stick and racket encircled by five men 90 90

1895 60s. Five dancers 90 90

1896 60s. Five people turning roundabout emblem 90 90

458 Selangor 1953 Coronation Stamp

2012. Diamond Jubilee and Visit of Duke and Duchess of Cambridge to Malaysia. Multicoloured.

1897 1r.50 Type **458** 2·50 2·50

1898 1r.50 Duke and Duchess of Cambridge 2·50 2·50

MS1899 140×70 mm. 2r.50 As Type **458**; 2r.50 Photo as No. 1898 but in oval frame 7·50 7·50

459 Hari Raya Aidiladha

2012. Malaysian Festivals (2nd series). Multicoloured.

1900 60s. Type **459** 90 90

1901 60s. Perayaan Kuih Bulan 90 90

1902 60s. Thaipusam 90 90

1903 60s. Pesta Kaul 90 90

1904 60s. Lepa Regatta 90 90

460 Tokong Cheng Hoon Teng, Melaka

2012. 750th Anniversary of Melaka (Malacca). Multicoloured.

1905 50s. Type **460** 75 75

1906 90s. Masjid Kampong Hulu, Melaka 1·25 1·25

MS1907 110×80 mm. 750s. Museum Yang DiPertua Negeri Melaka (70×35 mm) 11·00 11·00

MS1908 As **MS**1907 but with mouse deer under melaka tree emblem on upper right sheet margin 11·00 11·00

461 Postman, 1950

2012. World Post Day. Postman's Uniforms. Multicoloured.

1909 60s. Type **461** 1·25 90

1910 80s. Postman, 1970 1·40 1·25

1911 1r. Postman, 1990 1·75 1·75

MS1912 120×85 mm. 1r. Postman, 2012; 2r. Early postmen (90×35 mm) 4·50 4·50

462 Malaysian Flag and Hibiscus Flowers ('Malaysian Flag')

2012. SetemKu (Greetings Stamps). Multicoloured.

1913 60s. Type **462** 90 90

1914 60s. Balloons, fireworks and wrapped gift ('Celebration') 90 90

1915 60s. Orchids ('Yours Sincerely') 90 90

1916 60s. Pink hearts, ribbons and flowers ('Greetings') 90 90

1917 60s. Rafflesia flower, birdwing butterfly and flowers ('Flora and Fauna Malaysia') 90 90

1918 60s. Malaysian flag and hibiscus flowers ('Malaysian Flag') 90 90

1919 60s. Flower pattern ('Batik Malaysia') 90 90

1920 60s. Kuala Lumpur skyline and trees ('Malaysian Skyline') 90 90

463 BoBoiBoy kicking Football

2012. Children's Hobbies. Characters from *BoBoiBoy* (Malaysian animated series). Multicoloured.

1921 60s. Type **463** 90 90

1922 60s. Ochobot (inscr 'Memancing') (fishing) 90 90

1923 60s. Fang playing cymbals 90 90

1924 60s. Gopal Kumar taking photograph 90 90

1925 60s. Yaya Yah baking 90 90

1926 60s. Ying mounting stamps in album 90 90

MS1927 120×90 mm. 5r. Children with letters (70×45 mm) 7·50 7·50

MS1927a As No. **MS**1927 but inscr with 'Minggu Setem 2012 OMG! STAMP WEEK 2012' emblem on left sheet margin 7·50 7·50

464 1912 1c. Sheaf of Rice Stamp

2012. Postal History of Kedah. Multicoloured.

1928 90s. Type **464** 1·50 1·50

1929 90s. 1912 50c. Malay ploughing stamp 1·50 1·50

1930 90s. 1912 $5 Council Chamber, Alor Star stamp 1·50 1·50

MS1931 120×75 mm. 3r. Postcard postmarked Kedah (28×38 mm) 4·50 4·50

2013. Centenary (2012) of First Kedah Stamps and 125 Years of Postal Service in Kedah. No. **MS**1866 optd with emblem and **100 Matan Setem Kedah & 125 Tahun Perkhidmatan Pos di Kedah** in gold on sheet margin.

MS1932 140×75 mm. 2r. 10c. stamp issued for Installation of Tuanku Abdul Halim Shah as Fifth Yang di-Pertuan Agong, 1971; 3r. As 14th Yang di-Pertuan Agong, 2012 7·50 7·50

465 Banded Woodpecker (*Picus miniaceus*)

2013. Woodpeckers. Multicoloured.
1933 60s. Type **465** 1·25 90
1934 80s. Common Flameback Woodpecker (*Dinopium javanense*) 1·40 1·25
1935 1r. Lesser Yellownape Woodpecker (*Picus chlorolophus*) 1·75 1·75
MS1936 110×71 mm. 5r. White-bellied Woodpecker (*Dryocopus javensis*) (64×48 mm) 7·50 7·50

466 African Pygmy Hedgehog (*Atelerix albiventris + A. Algirus*)

2013. Exotic Pets. Multicoloured.
1937 60s. Type **466** 90 90
1938 80s. Green Iguana (*Iguana iguana*) 1·00 1·00
1939 1r. Sugar Glider (*Petaurus breviceps*) 1·50 1·50
MS1940 73×100 mm. 3m. Royal Python (*Python regius*) 4·50 4·50
MS1941 73×100 mm. 5m. As 3m. but snake is printed with transparent foil 7·50 7·50

2013. Postal History of Kedah Exhibition, Alor Setar, Kedah. No. **MS**1866 additionally inscr with emblem printed in gold in upper central sheet margin.
MS1941a 140×75 mm. 2r. 10c. stamp issued for Installation of Tuanku Abdul Halim Shah as Fifth Yang di-Pertuan Agong, 1971; 3r. As 14th Yang di-Pertuan Agong, 2012 7·50 7·50

467 Woman and Two Girls

2013. National Unity. Multicoloured.
1942 60s. Type **467** 90 90
1943 60s. Girl and boy helping blind man 90 90
1944 60s. Two students sharing laptop and girl student with book 90 90
1945 60s. Muslim woman and couple with shopping 90 90

468 Pulau Rimau, Penang

2013. Lighthouses (2nd series). Multicoloured.
1946 50s. Type **468** 1·25 75
1947 60s. Pulau Angsa, Selangor 1·50 1·50
1948 60s. Fort Cornwallis, Penang 1·50 1·50
MS1949 110×80 mm. 5r. One Fathom Bank, Selangor (vert) 7·50 7·50

2013. Australia 2013 World Stamp Expo, Melbourne. No. **MS**1949 additionally inscr with Australia 2013 kangaroo emblem and 'Centenary of Kangaroo Stamps' on left sheet margin. Multicoloured.
MS1950 110×80 mm. 5r. One Fathom Bank, Selangor (vert) 7·50 7·50

469 Asian Bearcat

2013. Wonders of Malaysian Forests. Three sheets, 130×100 mm, each containing T **469** and similar multicoloured designs.
MS1951 1r.×5 Type **469**; Berkoh Cascade; *Heteropoda davidbowie* (spider); Malayan Peacock Pheasant (50×40 mm); Bioluminescent mushroom 7·50 7·50
MS1952 1r.×5 Gould Frogmouth (bird); Helmeted Hornbill; *Rafflesia azlanii*; *Trevesia burckii*; Trilobite larvae 7·50 7·50
MS1953 1r.×5 Borneo Pygmy Elephant; Maliau Waterfall (50×40 mm); *Nepenthes veitchii* (pitcher plant); Dead Leaf Mantis; Violin Beetle 7·50 7·50

470 Sea Anemone (*Heteractis magnifica*)

2013. Living Corals. Multicoloured.
1954 60s. Type **470** 90 90
1955 60s. Soft coral (*Sarcophyton* sp) 90 90
1956 60s. Feather Stars (*Oxycomanthus bennetti*) 90 90
1957 60s. Sea Pen (*Ptilosarcus gurnevi*) 90 90
MS1958 115×71 mm. 5r. Table Coral (*Acropora* sp.) (75×26 mm) 7·50 7·50
Nos. 1954/1955 and 1956/1957 were each printed together, *se-tenant*, as horizontal pairs throughout the sheets, each pair forming a composite design.

471 *Centella asiatica* (top portion)

2013. Malaysian Salad. Multicoloured.
1959 60s. Type **471** 90 90
1960 60s. *Parkia speciosa* 90 90
1961 60s. *Annacardium occidentale* 90 90
1962 60s. *Psophocarpus tetragonolobus* 90 90
Nos. 1959/1960 and 1961/1962 were each printed together, *se-tenant*, as blocks of four stamps forming composite designs of a plate of salad.

2013. Thailand 2013 World Stamp Exhibition, Bangkok. Sheet as No. **MS**1899 but with palace background omitted and additionally inscr with pram, exhibition emblem and 'Thailand 2013 World Stamp The Magnificent Heritage' at centre of sheet.
MS1963 140×70 mm. 2r.50 As Type **458**; 2r.50 Photo as No. 1898 but in oval frame 7·50 7·50

472 Flags and Buildings of Malaysia, Singapore and Thailand (image scaled to 54% of original size)

2013. Tri-Nation Stamp Exhibition, Kuala Lumpur, Malaysia. Multicoloured.

(a) Ordinary paper
1964 90s. Type **472** 1·50 1·25
1965 2r. As Type **472** but silver background 3·00 3·00

(b) Self-adhesive
MS1966 Triangular 118×84 mm. 3r. National Flowers *Hibiscus rosasinensis* (Malaysia), *Vanda* Miss Joaquim (Singapore) and *Cassia fistula* (Thailand) (triangular 53×38 mm) 4·50 4·50

473 Museum Perak, Taiping

2013. Museums. Multicoloured.
1967 60s. Type **473** 90 90
1968 60s. Museum Negara, Kuala Lumpur (50th anniv) 90 90
1969 60s. Museum Lembah Bujang, Kedah 90 90
1970 60s. Galeria Perdana, Langkawi, Kedah 90 90
1971 60s. Museum Kota Kayang, Perlis 90 90
1972 60s. Museum Labuan 90 90
1973 60s. Museum Chimney, Labuan 90 90
1974 60s. Museum Sungai Lembing, Pahang 90 90
1975 60s. Museum Adat, Jelebu, Negri Sembilan 90 90
1976 60s. Negara Textile Museum, Kuala Lumpur 90 90

474 Tunku Abdul Rahman Putra Al-Haj, Map and Flag of Malaysia

2013. 50th Anniversary of the Federation of Malaysia
1977 **474** 60s. multicoloured 90 90

475 *Friendship World* (Lovira Jospely)

2013. Celebrating Abilities of Children with Disabilities. Colours of My World. Children's Paintings. Multicoloured.
1978 60s. Type **475** 90 90
1979 60s. *One Malaysia* (children and Malaysian flag) (Intan Syafienaz Mohamad Bakhid) 90 90
1980 60s. *Colours of My World* (Angel and globe) (Stephanie Tam Zhu Shin) 90 90
Nos. 1978/1980 are also inscr in Braille.

476 *Passiflora edulis*

2013. Rare Fruit (4th series). Multicoloured.
1981 60s. Type **476** 90 70
1982 80s. *Annona squamosa* 1·10 1·10
1983 1r.20 *Cynometra cauliflora* 1·60 1·75

(477)

2013. OMG Stamp Week. Sheet 162×84 mm containing No. 1977×4, each stamp optd with T **477** in gold.
MS1984 As No. 1977×4, each stamp optd with T **477** in gold 3·25 3·25
The lower right sheet margin of No. **MS**1984 is inscr with OMG STAMP WEEK 201' emblem in red.

478 First RHB Bank Branch, Old Market Square, Kuala Lumpur

2013. Centenary of First RHB Bank. Multicoloured.
1985 60s. Type **478** 90 90
1986 60s. First RHB Bank ATM 90 90
1987 60s. Launch of Kwong Yik Bank Headquarters 90 90
1988 60s. RHB Bank Headquarters 90 90

479 Nyonyaware

2013. Baba and Nyonya Heritage. Multicoloured.
1989 60s. Type **479** 90 90
1990 60s. Nyonya beaded slippers 90 90
1991 80s. Malacca Peranakan townhouse 1·10 1·10
1992 80s. Baba and Nyonya wedding attire 1·10 1·10
MS1993 85×100 mm. 5r. Nyonya Kebaya embroidery (50×60 mm) 7·00 7·50
No. **MS**1993 has a pattern cut out of the stamp.

480 *Panthera pardus*

2013. Endangered Big Cats of Malaysia. Multicoloured.
1994 60s. Type **480** 90 90
1995 60s. *Panthera pardus* (black) 90 90
1996 80s. *Neofelis diardi* 1·10 1·10
1997 80s. *Neofelis nebulosa* 1·10 1·10
MS1998 110×70 mm. 3r. *Panthera tigris jacksoni* (vert) 4·50 4·50
Nos. 1994/1995 were printed together, *se-tenant*, forming a composite background design showing forest with fallen tree.

481 Polo Player

2014. Chinese New Year. Year of the Horse. Multicoloured.
1999 50s. Type **481** 75 75
2000 50s. Horse and rider from DBKL (Dewan Bandaraya Kuala Lumpur) Mounted Unit 75 75
2001 80s. Horse and rider from PDRM (Polis Diraja Malaysia) Mounted Unit 1·10 1·10
2002 80s. Horse and rider from Mounted Ceremonial Squadron 1·10 1·10
MS2003 100×70 mm. 3r. Show-jumper 4·50 4·75
MS2004 100×70 mm. 5r. As 3r. but gold background 7·00 7·50

482 White Hybrid Tea Roses

2014. Roses in Malaysia (2nd series). Multicoloured.
2005 60s. Type **482** 90 75
2006 70s. Yellow Grandiflora roses 1·00 1·00
2007 1r.20 Pink English roses 1·60 1·75
MS2008 80×80 mm. 5r. Red rose and other roses (heart-shaped, 52×50 mm) 7·00 7·50
No. **MS**2008 has a rose perfume.

483 Perak Museum, Taiping, Perak and Elephant Skull

2014. Museums and Artifacts. Unveiling of the Hidden Treasures. Multicoloured.
2009 60s. Type **483** 90 90
2010 60s. Negara Museum, Kuala Lumpur (50th anniversary) and Loceng Dongson 90 90
2011 60s. Lembah Bujang Museum, Kedah and inscribed stone of Sungai Emas 90 90
2012 60s. Perdana Gallery, Langkawi, Kedah and ancient ship 90 90
2013 60s. Kota Kayang Museum, Perlis and Acuan Pitis 90 90

2014	60s. Labuan Museum, Labuan and copper teapot	90	90
2015	60s. Chimney Museum, Labuan and Menara Chimney	90	90
2016	60s. Sungai Lembing Museum, Pahang and Kiew wheel	90	90
2017	60s. Adat Museum, Jelebu, Negri Sembilan and Keris Panjang	90	90
2018	60s. Negara Textile Museum, Kuala Lumpur, Kain Sarung and Limar Songket	90	90

(484)

2014. Melaka and Jogjakarta, Cities of Museums. No. 1906 without 2012 imprint date and optd with T **484.**

2019	90s. Masjid Kampong Hulu, Melaka	1·10	1·10

485 Interior of World Scout Bureau

2014. Grand Opening of World Scout Bureau, Kuala Lumpur Office. Multicoloured.

2020	30s. Type **485**	45	45
2021	50s. Scout emblem	75	75
2022	60s. Scout Bureau, Clock Tower and Petronas Twin Towers	90	90

486 Main Terminal Building

2014. klia2 Kuala Lumpur International Airport 2 (new terminal). Multicoloured.

2023	80s. Type **486**	1·25	1·25
2024	80s. Skybridge	1·25	1·25
2025	80s. Gateway@klia2	1·25	1·25
2025	80s. Departure Hall	1·25	1·25
MS2027	100×61 mm. 5r. klia2	7·00	7·50

487 Nangka (*Artocarpus heterophyllus Lam*)

2014. Malaysian Fruits. Multicoloured.

2028	60s. Type **487**	90	60
2029	80s. Durian (*Durio zibethinus murr*)	1·10	90
2030	1r.20 Tembikai wangi (*Cucumis melo*)	1·60	1·75
2031	1r.40 Belimbing (*Averrhoa carambola*)	1·90	2·25

488 Adult's Hand holding Child's Hand and Malaysian Flag

2014. 57th Independence Celebrations.

2032	**488** 60s. multicoloured	1·00	1·00

489 Nasi Lemak

2014. Local Food. Multicoloured.

2033	1r.40 Type **489**	1·75	2·00
2034	1r.40 Satay	1·75	2·00
2035	1r.40 Egg waffle	1·75	2·00
2036	1r.40 Poon Choi	1·75	2·00
MS2037	90×170 mm. Nos. 2033/6	6·25	7·00

Similar designs were issued by Hong Kong.

490 Hang Tuah

2014. Malay Folk Stories. Multicoloured.

2038	60s. Type **490**	90	90
2039	60s. Tun Teja	90	90
2040	60s. Mahsuri	90	90
2041	60s. Merong Maha Wangsa	90	90
2042	60s. Tun Kudu	90	90
2043	60s. Tun Fatimah	90	90

491 Kuala Lumpur Convention Centre

2014. World Youth Stamp Exhibition, Kuala Lumpur (1st issue). Sheet 100×80 mm

MS2044	**491** 5r. multicoloured	7·00	7·50

492 Cancelled India 2a. and 4a. Stamps

2014. World Youth Stamp Exhibition, Kuala Lumpur (2nd issue). Multicoloured.

MS2045	100×80 mm. 1r. Type **492**; 2r. Cancelled India ½a. and 1a. stamps (40×30 mm)	4·50	4·50
MS2046	110×90 mm. 2r. *Hibiscus rosa-sinensis* (30×50 mm); 3r. *Rafflesia arnoldii* (60×50 mm)	7·00	7·50
MS2047	101×80 mm. 2r. Orangutan (*Pongo pygmaeus*) female with baby; 3r. Tigress with cub (*Panthera tigris jacksoni*) (both 50×30 mm)	7·00	7·50
MS2048	100×80 mm. 3r. Letter of 19 December 1854 with India 4a. stamps cancelled with 'Diamond of Dots' postmark (earliest known use of these stamps in Straits Settlements) (50×30 mm)	4·50	4·50
MS2049	100×80 mm. 5r. Sultan Abdul Samad Building, Kuala Lumpur (30×50 mm)	7·00	7·50
MS2050	100×80 mm. 5r. Mak Yong (traditional dance-drama) (50×60 mm)	7·00	7·50
MS2051	101×81 mm. 5r. The Princess of Gunung Ledang (folk tale) (40×60 mm)	7·00	7·50

493 Sultan Ahmad Shah of Pahang

2014. 40th Anniversary of Reign of Sultan Ahmad Shah of Pahang

2052	**493** 60s. multicoloured	1·00	1·00

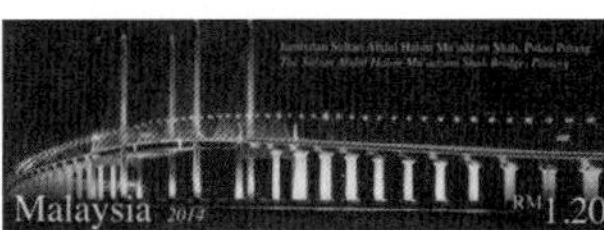

494 Sultan Abdul Halim Mu'adzam Shah Bridge, Penang

2014. Sultan Abdul Halim Mu'adzam Shah Bridge, Penang. Multicoloured.

2053	1r.20 Type **494**	1·60	1·75
2054	1r.20 Sultan Abdul Halim Mu'adzam Shah Bridge and coastline, Penang (blue background)	1·60	1·75

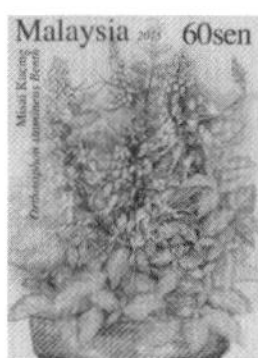

495 *Orthosiphon stamineus Benth*

2015. Medicinal Plants (3rd series). Multicoloured.

2055	60s. Type **495**	90	90
2056	70s. *Hibiscus sabdariffa L.*	1·00	1·00
2057	80s. *Andrographis paniculata*	1·10	1·10
MS2058	100×70 mm. 3r. *Clinacanthus nutans* (40×50 mm)	4·50	4·50

496 Handshake and National dress of ASEAN Countries

2015. Malaysia Chairman of ASEAN 2015. Multicoloured.

2059	60s. Type **496**	90	90
2060	80s. Hands holding up flags of ASEAN countries	1·10	1·10
2061	1r.20 Hand holding flowering plant and flags of ASEAN countries	1·60	1·60

497 Geese (*Anser cygnoides*)

2015. Farm Animals. Multicoloured.

2062	60s. Type **497**	90	75
2063	80s. Water Buffaloes (*Bubalus bubalis*)	1·10	1·10
2064	1r.20 Cock, hen and chicks (*Gallus domesticus*)	1·60	1·75
MS2065	100×80 mm. 3r. Goats (*Capra aegagrus hircus*) (48×66 mm)	4·50	4·50

498 Giant Panda, Liang Liang

2015. International Co-operative Project on Giant Panda Conservation. Multicoloured.

2066	70s. Type **498**	1·00	1·00
2067	70s. Giant Panda Xing Xing	1·00	1·00
MS2068	91×81 mm. 4r. Liang Liang; 4r. Xing Xing	11·00	11·00

No. **MS**2068 was printed on flocked paper.

499 Sultan Ibrahim Iskandar

2015. Coronation of Sultan Ibrahim Ibni Almarhum Sultan Iskandar of Johor. Multicoloured.

2069	60s. Type **499**	90	75
2070	80s. Sultan Ibrahim Iskandar (different)	1·10	1·10
2071	1r. Sultan Ibrahim Iskandar (different)	1·50	1·75
MS2072	100×85 mm. 5r. Sultan Ibrahim Ibni Almarhum Sultan Iskandar and Raja Zarith Sofiah	7·00	7·50

500 *Anoxypristis cuspidata* (Knifetooth Sawfish)

2015. Endangered Marine Life. Multicoloured.

2073	60s. Type **500**	90	70
2074	80s. *Balaenoptera musculus* (Blue Whale)	1·10	1·10
2075	1r.40 *Orcinus orca* (Killer Whale)	1·90	1·90
MS2076	100×70 mm. 5r. *Megaptera novaeangliae* (Humpback Whale) (octagon, 45×38 mm)	7·00	7·50

501 Penny Black and 2d. Blue

2015. 175th Anniversary of the Penny Black. Sheet 100×80 mm.

MS2077	**501** 3r. multicoloured	4·50	4·50

502 Sultan Nazrin Muizzuddin Shah

2015. Coronation of Sultan Nazrin Muizzuddin Shah of Perak. Multicoloured.

2078	60s. Type **502**	90	75
2079	80s. Sultan Nazrin Muizzuddin Shah and Raja Puan Besar Zara Salim Davidson	1·10	1·10
2080	1r.20 Sultan Nazrin Muizzuddin Shah wearing military uniform	1·75	1·90
MS2081	100×80 mm. 5r. Sultan Nazrin Muizzuddin Shah and Raja Puan Besar Zara Salim Davidson (different) (42×70 mm)	7·00	7·50

503 Telephones

2015. 150th Anniversary of ITU (International Telecommunications Union). Multicoloured.

2082	60s. Type **503**	90	90
2083	70s. Televisions and transmitter	1·00	1·00
2084	80s. Satellite, dish, mobile phone and world map	1·10	1·10

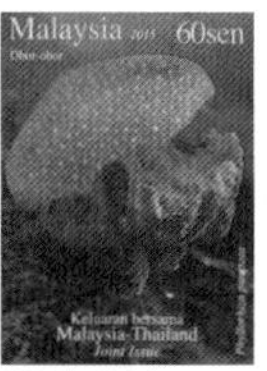

504 *Phyllorhiza punctata*

2015. Marine Creatures. Multicoloured.

2085	60s. Type **504**	90	90
2086	60s. *Hypselodoris bullockii*	90	90
2087	1r.20 *Trapezia areolata*	1·60	1·75
2088	1r.20 *Hymenocera picta*	1·60	1·75

Similar designs were issued by Thailand.

505 *Nycticorax nycticorax* (Black-crowned Night-heron)

2015. Herons and Bitterns. Multicoloured.

2089 60s. Type **505** 1·25 75
2090 70s. *Butorides striatus* (Striated Heron) 1·40 1·25
2091 80s. *Ardea cinerea* (Grey Heron) (horiz) 1·60 1·50
MS2092 110×71 mm. 5r. *Ixobrychus cinnamomeus* (Cinnamon Bittern) (50×40 mm) 7·50 7·50

No. **MS**2092 was cut around at top and left in the shape of a bittern in flight.

(484a)

2014. Four Nations Stamp Show, Bandung, Malaysia. No. **MS**1998 optd with T **484a.**

MS2019*a* 110×70 mm. 3r. *Panthera tigris jacksoni* (vert) 4·50 4·50

506 Circle South Sea Pearls and *Pinctada maxima* (pearl oyster)

2015. Pearls. Multicoloured.

2093 60s. Type **506** 90 90
2094 70s. Baroque South Sea pearls and *Pinctada maxima* (pearl oyster) 1·00 1·00
2095 80s. Drop South Sea pearls and *Pinctada maxima* (pearl oyster) 1·10 1·10
MS2096 80×80 mm. 5r. Round South Sea pearl (circular, 38 mm diameter) 7·00 7·50

507 Flags of ASEAN Member Countries

2015. ASEAN Community.

2097 **507** 50s. multicoloured 1·00 75

Similar designs were issued by other ASEAN countries.

508 Zahir Mosque, Alor Setar, Kedah

2015. Mosques. Multicoloured.

2098 70s. Type **508** 1·00 1·00
2099 80s. Kota Kinabalu City Mosque 1·10 1·10
2100 1r. National Mosque, Malaysia 1·40 1·40

509 Dancers, Drummers and Musician

2015. Malaysia Day. Multicoloured.

2101 60s. Type **509** 90 90
2102 60s. Crescent, star and outline map of Malaysia within heart (30×25 mm) 90 90
2103 70s. Stilt walker, women playing board game and others 1·00 1·00
2104 70s. Children carrying Malaysian flag (30×25 mm) 1·00 1·00
MS2105 100×70 mm. 3r. Children holding Malaysian flag (70×45 mm) 4·50 4·50

510 Paper Dove

2015. World Post Day.

2106 **510** 60s. multicoloured 1·00 1·00

511 Children with Stamp and Magnifying Glass

2015. Stamp Week. Hari OMG Stamp and Philatelic Club.

2107 **511** 60s. multicoloured 1·00 1·00

512 Tenggol Island, Terengganu

2015. Islands and Beaches of Malaysia (3rd series). Multicoloured.

2108 70s. Type **512** 1·00 1·00
2109 70s. Tinggi Island, Johor 1·00 1·00
2110 80s. Sembilang Island, Pahang 1·10 1·10
2111 80s. Satang Island, Sarawak 1·10 1·10
MS2112 100×70 mm. 3r. Mataking Island, Sabah 4·50 4·50

513 Traditional Dress of Malaysia

2015. Four Nations Stamp Exhibition, Malacca. Traditional Attire. Multicoloured.

2113 60s. Type **513** 90 90
2114 60s. Traditional dress of Indonesia 90 90
2115 60s. Traditional dress of Singapore 90 90
2116 60s. Traditional dress of Thailand 90 90
MS2117 90×80 mm. 3r. Couples in traditional dress and Exhibition emblem. Imperf 4·50 4·50

514 Hitachi Diesel Hydraulic Locomotive

2015. Malaysian Public Transport. Trains in Sabah. Multicoloured.

2118 60s. Type **514** 1·25 90
2119 70s. Railbus 1·40 1·10
2120 80s. Diesel multiple unit (DMU) 1·50 1·50
MS2121 110×70 mm. 5r. Vulcan steam locomotive (40×55 mm with rounded top to stamp) 7·50 7·50

515 Macaque (*Macaca nemestrina*)

2016. Primates of Malaysia (2nd series). Multicoloured.

2122 60s. Type **515** 90 90
2123 70s. Silvered Leaf Monkey (*Trachypithecus cristatus*) 1·00 1·00
2124 80s. White-handed Gibbon (*Hylobates lar*) 1·10 1·10
MS2125 80×80 mm. 3r. Agile Gibbon (*Hylobates agilis*) 4·50 4·50
MS2126 80×80 mm. 3r. Agile Gibbon (*Hylobates agilis*); 3r. Two Agile Gibbons including female with baby 4·50 4·50

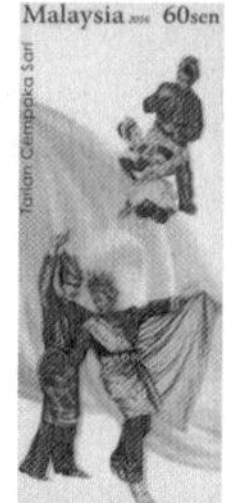

516 Cempaka Sari Dance

2016. Traditional Dances (2nd series). Multicoloured.

2127 60s. Type **516** 90 90
2128 60s. Ribbon dance 90 90
2129 60s. Odissi dance 90 90
2130 60s. Magunatip dance 90 90
2131 60s. Rejang Be'uh dance 90 90

517 Bread Flower (*Vallaris glabra*)

2016. Scented Flowers (2nd series). Multicoloured.

2132 70s. Type **517** 1·00 1·00
2133 70s. Bread Flower (*Vallaris glabra*) (three flowers facing right) 1·00 1·00
2134 80s. Yellow Saraca (*Saraca cauliflora*) 1·10 1·10
2135 80s. Yellow Saraca (*Saraca cauliflora*) and butterfly 1·10 1·10
2136 80s. Cannonball fruits (at left) and flowers (*Couroupita guianensis*) (flower spike pointing top left) 1·10 1·10
2137 80s. Cannonball Flower (*Couroupita guianensis*) (flower spike pointing bottom left) 1·10 1·10
MS2138 100×80 mm. 5r. Cape Jasmine (*Gardenia jasminoides*) (40×70 mm) 7·00 7·50

No. **MS**2138 is jasmine scented.

518 Kamaludin bin Muhammad (1922-1992)

2016. National Laureates. Multicoloured.

2139 80s. Type **518** 1·10 1·10
2140 80s. Usman bin Awang (1929-2001) 1·10 1·10
2141 80s. Muhammad bin Abdul Biang (1925-2009) 1·10 1·10

519 Longboat

2016. River Transportation in Sarawak. Multicoloured.

2142 70s. Type **519** 1·00 1·00
2143 80s. Express boat 1·10 1·10
2144 90s. Ferry boat 1·25 1·25
MS2145 100×80 mm. 3r. Raft (40×60 mm) 4·50 4·50

520 Malaysian Calligraphy

2016. Malaysian Calligraphy. Multicoloured.

2146 70s. Type **520** 1·00 1·00
2147 80s. Calligraphy (carmine background) 1·10 1·10
2148 90s. Calligraphy (green background) 1·25 1·25
MS2149 80×80 mm. 5r. Calligraphy and calligraphy tools (60×45 mm) 7·00 7·50

521 Muzium Padi, Kedah and Alor Setar Tower

2016. Tourist Destinations (1st series). Kedah and Kelantan. Multicoloured.

2150 80s. Type **521** 1·10 1·10
2151 80s. Lembah Bujang, Kedah and Candi Bendang Dalam 1·10 1·10
2152 80s. Songket and Village Handicrafts and Crafts Museum 1·10 1·10
2153 80s. Wau Bulan (moon kite) 1·10 1·10
MS2154 80×80 mm. 2r. Pulau Langkawi, Kedah; 2r. Pantai Bisikan Bayu, Kelantan (both 30×50 mm) 5·50 5·50

See also Nos. 2268/2273.

2016. Thailand 2016 32nd Asian International Stamp Exhibition, Bangkok. No. **MS**2121 optd **THAILAND 2016 32nd Asian International Stamp Exhibition 10 - 15 August 2016** in yellow on margin. Multicoloured.

MS2155 110×70 mm. 5r. Vulcan steam locomotive (40×55 mm with rounded top to stamp) 7·00 7·50

522 *Tragulus kanchil*

2016. Seven Wonders of Malaysia's Flora and Fauna. Multicoloured.

(a) Self-adhesive

MS2156 180×130 mm. 30s. Type **522**; 50s. *Meliponula ferruginea*; 50s. *Piper sarmentosum*; 60s. *Polyplectron malacense*; 60s. *Rana erythraea*; 70s. *Amyda cartilaginea*; 80s. *Tor tambroides* 5·50 6·00

(b) Ordinary gum

MS2157 100×70 mm. 2r. Panda (*Ailuropoda melanoleuca*) (vert) 3·00 3·00

No. **MS**2157 also exists imperforate.

523 Kota Malawati, Selangor

2016. Battle Sites. Multicoloured.

2158 60s. Type **523** 90 90
2159 60s. Kota Mat Salleh, Sabah 90 90
2160 80s. Kota Libau Rentap, Sarawak 1·10 1·10
2161 80s. Bukit Kepong, Johor 1·10 1·10
MS2162 100×80 mm. 3r. World War II, Kuala Pak Amat beach, Kota Bharu, Kelantan (40×50 mm) 4·50 4·50

524 Festivals

2016. International Stamps. Multicoloured.

2163 10s. Type **524** 25 30
2164 20s. Local fruits 50 30
2165 50s. Tiger, tapir, orangutan and butterfly (Wildlife) 1·25 60
2166 1r. Malaysians of different races (Unity) 1·50 1·00
2167 2r. Places of worship 2·75 2·25
2168 5r. Map and National Flag (Our Nation) 7·00 6·00
2169 10r. Flora 13·00 10·00
2170 20r. Handicrafts 22·00 20·00

525 Delivering Mail on Horseback, Kota Belud, Sabah

2016. World Post Day. Community Postmen. Multicoloured.

2171 60s. Type **525** 90 90

2172	70s. Delivering mail by longboat, Sarawak	1·00	1·00
2173	80s. Delivering mail by bicycle, east Malaysia	1·10	1·10
MS2174	100×70 mm. 3r. Community postman and local people (30×50 mm)	4·50	4·50

526 Penang Free School Buildings

2016. Bicentenary of Penang Free School, George Town, Pulau Pinang. Multicoloured.

2175	70s. Type **526**	1·00	1·00
2176	80s. Aerial view of Penang Free School	1·10	1·10
2177	90s. Penang Free School seen from playing fields	1·25	1·25
MS2178	80×80 mm. 5r. Arms (50×50 mm)	7·00	7·50

527 Kapitan Keling Mosque, George Town, Penang

2016. Places of Worship. Multicoloured.

2179	60s. Type **527**	85	85
2180	60s. St Francis Xavier Church, Melaka	85	85
2181	60s. Sri Kandaswamy Temple, Kuala Lumpur	85	85
2182	60s. Gurdwara Sahib Shapha, Kuala Lumpur	85	85
2183	60s. Tokong Tong Cave Temple, Ipoh, Perak	85	85

528 Guide, Guide Salute and Reef Knot

2016. Centenary of Girl Guides Association of Malaysia. Multicoloured.

2184	85s. Type **528**	1·25	1·25
2185	85s. Girl guides camping	1·25	1·25
2186	85s. Guide saluting, guides and badges	1·25	1·25

529 Abdul Halim Mu'adzam Shah, 14th Yang di Pertuan Agong and Palace (Head of Religion)

2016. Reign of Abdul Halim Mu'adzam Shah, 14th Yang di-Pertuan Agong

2187	85s. Type **529**	1·25	1·25
2188	95s. Abdul Halim Mu'adzam Shah inspecting soldiers (Head of Military)	1·40	1·40
2189	1r.05 Abdul Halim Mu'adzam Shah and guard of honour outside State Palace, Jalan Duta, Kuala Lumpur (Head of State)	1·50	1·50
MS2190	100×70 mm. 3r. Abdul Halim Mu'adzam Shah in vehicle, inspecting guard of honour (40×60 mm)	4·25	4·75

530 Mohamed Ridzuan Mohamed Puzi (100m – T36), Muhammed Ziyad Zolkefli (shot put – F20) and Abdul Latif Romly (long jump – T20)

2016. Malaysian Paralympic Gold Medallists, Rio de Janeiro, Brazil

2191	**530**	95s. multicoloured	1·40	1·40

531 Serama A and Serama Remaja

2017. Malaysian Serama Bantams. Multicoloured.

2192	85s. Type **531**	1·25	1·25
2193	95s. Serama B, Serama Induk and Anak Serama (chick)	1·40	1·40
2194	1r.05 Serama Muda and Serama Tanpa Lawi	1·50	1·50
MS2195	Octagonal 80×80 mm. 3r.Ayam Serama (octagonal 38×45 mm)	4·25	4·75
MS2196	Octagonal 80×80 mm. 8r.As **MS**2195 but brown sheet borders	11·00	12·00

532 Oranges and Nien Gao

2017. Festival Food (1st series). Chinese. Multicoloured.

2197	85s. Type **532**	1·25	1·25
2198	95s. Poon choi (seafood platter)	1·40	1·40
2199	1r.05 Spring rolls, lotus root soup and prawn	1·50	1·50
MS2200	Circular 80×81 mm. 5r. Candy tray (circular 38 mm diameter)	7·00	7·50

See also Nos. 2211/**MS**2214, 2225/**MS**2228 and 2260/**MS**2263.

533 Chung Ling High School Main Building

2017. Centenary of Chung Ling High School, George Town, Penang. Multicoloured.

2201	85s. Type **533**	1·25	1·25
2202	95s. Chung Ling (Private) High School Main Building	1·40	1·40
2203	1r.05 Chung Ling (Butterworth) High School Main Building	1·50	1·50
MS2204	80×80 mm. 5r. Original building design (45×60 mm)	7·00	7·50

534 *Rhynchostylis retusa*

2017. Orchids. Multicoloured.

2205	60s. Type **534**	85	85
2206	70s. *Phalaenopsis violacea*	1·00	1·00
2207	80s. *Vanda helvola*	1·10	1·10
2208	90s. *Paphiopedilum lowii*	1·25	1·25
2209	1r. *Arachnis flos-aeris*	1·40	1·40
2210	1r.10 *Papilionanthe hookeriana*	1·50	1·50

Nos. 2205/2210 have a phosphor **POS MALAYSIA** overprint.

An imperf miniature sheet containing Nos. 2205/2210 was sold for 7r., a 1r.90 premium over face value.

2017. Festival Food (2nd series). Kadazandusun and Dayak from Kaamatan (Harvest) Festival in Sabah and Gawai Festival in Sarawak. Multicoloured.

2211	60s. Tuak (rice wine–Sabah), Lihing (tapioca wine–Sarawak), Kek Lapis (layer cake), Tapai Pulut (fermented rice) and Kuih Jala (net cake)	85	85
2212	80s. Ambuyat (sticky sago–Sabah)	1·10	1·10
2213	90s. Manuk Pansuh (chicken cooked in bamboo), Hinava (Kadazandusun raw fish salad–Sabah) and Umai (raw fish salad–Melanau, Sarawak)	1·25	1·25
MS2214	Circular 80 mm diameter. 5r. Kek Lapis (layer cake) (37 mm diameter)	7·00	7·00

535 Happy Deepavali and Candle

2017. Festive Greetings. Multicoloured.

2215	80s. Type **535**	1·10	1·10
2216	80s. Happy Chinese New Year and lanterns	1·10	1·10
2217	80s. Selamat Hari Raya Aidil Fitri and lanterns	1·10	1·10
MS2218	Circular 80 mm diameter. 5r. Green, gold, red and blue diamond-shapes with greetings inscriptions, Deepavali candles, Aidil Fitri lanterns and Chinese lanterns (diamond-shape 68×68 mm)	7·00	7·00

No. **MS**2218 is a circular miniature sheet cut around in a wavy line with eight points.

536 Sultan Muhammad V

2017. Installation of Sultan Muhammad V of Kelantan as 15th Yang di-Pertuan Agong. Multicoloured.

2219	60s. Type **536**	85	85
MS2220	80×80 mm. 5r. Sultan Muhammad V speaking at Installation ceremony (40×60 mm)	7·00	7·00

537 Palm Oil Products and World Map

2017. Centenary of Oil Palm Industry. Multicoloured.

2221	60s. Type **537**	85	85
2222	80s. Harvesting oil palm fruit bunches with tractor	1·10	1·10
2223	1r. Harvesting oil palm fruit bunches with Buffalo cart	1·50	1·50
MS2224	80×80 mm. 3r. Oil palm fruit bunch and three single fruits (50×40 mm)	4·50	4·50

2017. Festival Food (3rd series). Malay. Multicoloured.

2225	60s. Raya cake, Kuih Pelita and Agar-agar (jelly)	85	85
2226	80s. Ketupat and satay	1·10	1·10
2227	90s. Lemang (bamboo sticky rice), Ketupat Palas, Rendang and Serunding	1·25	1·25
MS2228	Circular 80 mm diameter. 5r. Semperit cookies with Batang Buruk, Kuih Bangkit and Dodol (38 mm diameter)	11·00	11·00

538 Block Batik

2017. Malaysian Batik. Multicoloured.

2229	60s. Type **538**	85	85
2230	60s. Block Batik (diamond pattern)	85	85
2231	80s. Canting Batik (using batik tool)	1·10	1·10
2232	80s. Canting Batik (pattern of flowers)	1·10	1·10
2233	90s. Tie and dye batik - tie and die cloths	1·25	1·25
2234	90s. Tie and dye pattern	1·25	1·25
MS2235	100×80 mm. 3r. Metal Block; 3r. Wood Block	8·50	8·50

Nos. 2229/2230, 2231/2232 and 2233/2234 were each printed together as horizontal pairs, each pair forming a composite design.

539 MRT Feeder Bus

2017. Mass Rapid Transit. Multicoloured.

2236	60s. Type **539**	85	85
2237	60s. MRT train	85	85
2238	80s. Elevated stations	1·10	1·10
2239	90s. Passengers and MRT trains	1·25	1·25
MS2240	80×58 mm. 5r. MRT train (seen from front) (37×37 mm)	7·00	7·00

Nos. 2236/2237 were printed together in horizontal pairs, each pair forming a composite design.

540 *Hibiscus rosa-sinensis* and Butterfly

2017. 50th Anniversary of ASEAN. Multicoloured.

2241	60s. Type **540**	85	85
MS2242	50×90 mm. 3r. Hibiscus flowers and buds and butterfly (35×70 mm)	4·25	4·25

541 Games Mascot Rimau

2017. SEA (South East Asian) Games, Kuala Lumpur. Multicoloured.

2243	60s. Type **541**	85	85
2244	60s. Rimau playing badminton	85	85
2245	60s. Rimau on torch run	85	85
2246	60s. Offical games logo BANGKIT BERSAMA (rise together)	85	85

542 Two Cents on 1a., Three Cents on 1a. and Three Half Cents on ½a. Stamps

2017. 150th Anniversary of First Straits Settlements Stamps. Stamps of India surcharged for Straits Settlements. Multicoloured.

2247	60s. Type **542**	85	85
2248	80s. Four Cents on 1a., Six Cents on 2a. and Eight Cents on 2a. stamps	1·10	1·10
2249	90s. 12 Cents on 4a., 24 Cents on 8a. and 32 Cents on 2a. stamps	1·25	1·25

543 People of Different Races and Malaysian Flag

2017. Negaraku. Multicoloured.

2250	50s. Type **543**	70	70
2251	50s. Tunku Abdul Rahman Putra Al-Haj (1903-1990, Prime Minister 1957-1970), people and flag	70	70
2252	60s. Cycling past traditional shops	85	85
2253	60s. Children of different races and Malaysian flag	85	85
MS2254	70×70 mm. 3r. Map of Malaysia and flag (40×40 mm)	4·25	4·25
MS2255	70×70 mm. 6r. As No. **MS**2254	8·50	8·50

544 Girl writing Letter and Globe

2017. World Post Day. Multicoloured.

2256	50s. Type **544**	70	70
2257	50s. Man receiving letter and globe	70	70
2258	50s. Boy posting letter and globe	70	70
2259	50s. Girl receiving letter and globe	70	70

Nos. 2256/2257 and 2258/2259 were each printed together, *se-tenant*, as vertical pairs throughout the sheets, each pair forming a composite design of half of a globe.

2017. Festival Food (4th series). Indian–Deepavali. Multicoloured.

2260	60s. Vadai, Muruku, Paal Kova and Payasam	85	85
2261	80s. Thosai and Idhli	1·10	1·10
2262	90s. Nasi Daun Pisang	1·25	1·25
MS2263	80×80 mm. 5r. Bowls of sweets	7·00	7·00

545 Prince Charles

2017. 60th Anniversary of Bilateral Relations between Malaysia and Great Britain. Visit of Prince of Wales and Duchess of Cornwall to Malaysia. Multicoloured.

2264	1r. Type **545**	1·40	1·40
2265	1r. Duchess of Cornwall	1·40	1·40
MS2266	100×70 mm. 6r. Prince of Wales and Duchess of Cornwall (60×50 mm)	8·50	8·50

546 Village House, Bintulu (first meeting, 1867), Old and New Mace and Current State Legislative Assembly Building

2017. 150th Anniv of Sarawak State Legislative Assembly.

2267	**546**	60s. multicoloured	85	85

2017. Tourist Destinations (2nd series). Pahang, Perak and Terengganu. Multicoloured.

2268	60s. Abu Bakar Palace, Sungai Lembing Mines and Fraser's Hill (Pahang)	85	85
2269	60s. National Elephant Conservation Centre, Cameron Highlands Mossy Forest and Tioman Island (Pahang)	85	85
2270	60s. Leaning Tower of Teluk Intan, Ubaidah Mosque and Perak Royal Museum (Perak)	85	85
2271	60s. Taiping Zoo, Royal Belum National Park and Pangkor Island (Perak)	85	85
2272	60s. Terengganu State Museum, Masjid Kristal and Maziah Palace (Terengganu)	85	85
2273	60s. Redang Island, Rantau Abang Beach and Kenyir Lake (Terengganu)	85	85

Nos. 2268/2269, 2270/2271 and 2272/2273 were each printed together as vertical pairs, each vertical pair forming a composite background design.

POSTAGE DUE STAMPS

D1

1966

D1	**D1**	1s. red	20	7·00
D2	**D1**	2s. blue	25	2·75
D3	**D1**	4s. green	1·00	14·00
D18	**D1**	8s. green	80	6·50
D19	**D1**	10s. blue	80	3·00
D6	**D1**	12s. violet	60	4·75
D20	**D1**	20s. brown	1·00	3·50
D21	**D1**	50s. bistre	1·50	4·25

D2

1986

D22	**D2**	5s. mauve and lilac	20	1·50
D23	**D2**	10s. black and grey	30	65
D24	**D2**	20s. red and brown	45	80
D25	**D2**	50s. green and blue	1·00	1·25
D26	**D2**	1r. blue and cobalt	1·50	2·50

B. FEDERAL TERRITORY ISSUES

For use in the Federal Territories of Kuala Lumpur, Labuan (from 1984) and Putrajaya (from 2001).

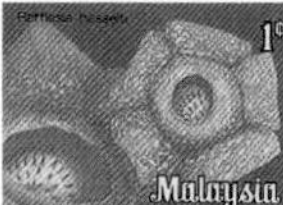

K1 *Rafflesia hasseltii*

1979. Flowers. Multicoloured.

K1	1c. Type **K1**	10	40
K2	2c. *Pterocarpus indicus*	10	40
K3	5c. *Lagerstroemia speciosa*	15	40
K4	10c. *Durio zibethinus*	15	10
K5	15c. *Hibiscus rosa-sinensis*	30	10
K6	20c. *Rhododendron scortechinii*	30	10
K7	25c. *Etlingera elatior* (inscr 'Phaeomeria speciosa')	70	10

K2 Coffee

1986. Agricultural Products of Malaysia. Multicoloured.

K15	1c. Type **K2**	10	30
K16	2c. Coconuts	10	30
K17	5c. Cocoa	15	10
K18	10c. Black pepper	20	10
K19	15c. Rubber	40	10
K20	20c. Oil palm	40	10
K21	30c. Rice	45	25
K22	50c. Coco	2·00	10

Nos. K17, K18, K20, K21 also come redominated in sen.

K3 *Nelumbium nelumbo* (sacred lotus)

2007. Garden Flowers. Multicoloured.

K26	10sc *Hydrangea macrophylla*	10	10
K27	5s. Type **K3**	15	10
K28	20s. *Hippeastrum reticulatum*	25	15
K29	3s. Bougainvillea	40	20
K30	40s. *Ipomoea indica*	50	30
K31	50s. *Hibiscus rosa-sinensis*	65	65

MALDIVE ISLANDS

A group of islands W. of Ceylon. A republic from 1 January 1953, but reverted to a sultanate in 1954. Became independent on 26 July 1965 and left the British Commonwealth, but was re-admitted as an Associate Member on 9 July 1982.

1906. 100 cents = 1 rupee.
1951. 100 larees = 1 rupee.

1906. Nos. 268, 277/279 and 283/284 of Ceylon optd **MALDIVES**.

1	**44**	2c. brown	26·00	50·00
2	**45**	3c. green	42·00	55·00
3	**45**	4c. orange and blue	55·00	90·00
4	-	5c. purple	4·25	6·50
5	**45**	15c. blue	£110	£180
6	**45**	25c. brown	£120	£225

2 Minaret, Juma Mosque, Male

1909

7a	**2**	2c. orange-brown	2·50	90
11A	**2**	2c. grey	2·75	2·00
8	**2**	3c. green	75	70
12A	**2**	3c. brown	70	2·75
9	**2**	5c. purple	75	35
15A	**2**	6c. red	1·50	5·50
10	**2**	10c. red	7·50	80
16A	**2**	10c. green	85	55
17A	**2**	15c. black	10·00	32·00
18A	**2**	25c. brown	10·00	30·00
19A	**2**	50c. purple	11·00	35·00
20B	**2**	1r. blue	16·00	6·50

5 Palm Tree and Dhow

1950

21	**5**	2l. olive	5·50	6·50
22	**5**	3l. blue	18·00	3·75
23	**5**	5l. green	18·00	3·75
24	**5**	6l. brown	1·25	2·00
25	**5**	10l. red	1·25	1·00
26	**5**	15l. orange	1·25	1·00
27	**5**	25l. purple	1·25	4·00
28	**5**	50l. violet	1·50	6·00
29	**5**	1r. brown	14·00	42·00

8 Native Products

1952

30	-	3l. blue (Fish)	2·25	60
31	**8**	5l. green	1·00	2·00

9 Male Harbour

10 Fort and Building

1956

32	**9**	2l. purple	10	10
33	**9**	3l. slate	10	10
34	**9**	5l. brown	10	10
35	**9**	6l. violet	10	10
36	**9**	10l. green	10	10
37	**9**	15l. brown	10	85
38	**9**	25l. red	10	10
39	**9**	50l. orange	10	10
40	**10**	1r. green	15	10
41	**10**	5r. blue	2·75	30
42	**10**	10r. mauve	2·75	1·25

11 Cycling

1960. Olympic Games.

43	**11**	2l. purple and green	15	1·00
44	**11**	3l. slate and purple	15	1·00
45	**11**	5l. brown and blue	15	30
46	**11**	10l. green and brown	15	30
47	**11**	15l. sepia and blue	15	30
48	-	25l. red and olive	15	30
49	-	50l. orange and violet	20	45
50	-	1r. green and purple	40	1·25

Design: Vert—25l. to 1r. Basketball.

13 Tomb of Sultan

1960

51	**13**	2l. purple	10	10
52	-	3l. green	10	10
53	-	5l. brown	3·75	4·00
54	-	6l. blue	10	10
55	-	10l. red	10	10
56	-	15l. sepia	10	10
57	-	25l. violet	10	10
58	-	50l. grey	10	10
59	-	1r. orange	15	10
60	-	5r. blue	11·00	60
61	-	10r. green	15·00	1·25

Designs: 3l. Custom House; 5l. Cowrie shells; 6l. Old Royal Palace; 10l. Road to Juma Mosque, Male; 15l. Council House; 25l. New Government Secretariat; 50l. Prime Minister's Office; 1r. Old Ruler's Tomb; 5r. Old Ruler's Tomb (distant view); 10r. Maldivian port.

Higher values were also issued, intended mainly for fiscal use.

24 'Care of Refugees'

1960. World Refugee Year.

62	**24**	2l. violet, orange and green	10	15
63	**24**	3l. brown, green and red	10	15
64	**24**	5l. green, sepia and red	10	10
65	**24**	10l. green, violet and red	10	10
66	**24**	15l. violet, green and red	10	10
67	**24**	25l. blue, brown and green	10	10
68	**24**	50l. olive, red and blue	10	10
69	**24**	1r. red, slate and violet	15	35

25 Coconuts

26 Map of Male

1961

70	**25**	2l. brown and green	10	1·25
71	**25**	3l. brown and blue	10	1·25
72	**25**	5l. brown and mauve	10	15
73	**25**	10l. brown and orange	15	15
74	**25**	15l. brown and black	20	15
75	**26**	25l. multicoloured	55	20
76	**26**	50l. multicoloured	55	40
77	**26**	1r. multicoloured	60	70

27 5c. Stamp of 1906

1961. 55th Anniversary of First Maldivian Stamp.

78	**27**	2l. purple, blue and green	10	1·25
79	**27**	3l. purple, blue and green	10	1·25
80	**27**	5l. purple, blue and green	10	15
81	**27**	6l. purple, blue and green	10	1·60
82	-	10l. green, red and purple	10	15
83	-	15l. green, red and purple	15	15
84	-	20l. green, red and purple	15	20
85	-	25l. red, green and black	20	20
86	-	50l. red, green and black	35	80
87	-	1r. red, green and black	50	2·00
MS87a		114×88 mm. No. 87 (block of four). Imperf	1·50	7·50

Designs: 10l. to 20l. Posthorn and 3c. stamp of 1906; 25l. to 1r. Olive sprig and 2c. stamp of 1906.

30 Malaria Eradication Emblem

1962. Malaria Eradication.

88	**30**	2l. brown	10	1·50
89	**30**	3l. green	10	1·50
90	**30**	5l. turquoise	10	15
91	**30**	10l. red	10	15
92	-	15l. sepia	15	15
93	-	25l. blue	20	20
94	-	50l. myrtle	25	55
95	-	1r. purple	55	80

Nos. 92/95 are as T **30**, but have English inscriptions at the side.

31 Children of Europe and America

1962. 15th Anniversary of UNICEF.

96	**31**	2l. multicoloured	10	1·50
97	**31**	6l. multicoloured	10	1·50
98	**31**	10l. multicoloured	10	15
99	**31**	15l. multicoloured	10	15
100	-	25l. multicoloured	15	15
101	-	50l. multicoloured	20	15
102	-	1r. multicoloured	25	20
103	-	5r. multicoloured	1·25	5·00

Design: Nos. 100/103, Children of Middle East and Far East.

33 Sultan Mohamed Farid Didi

1962. Ninth Anniversary of Enthronement of Sultan.

104	**33**	3l. brown and green	10	1·50
105	**33**	5l. brown and blue	15	20
106	**33**	10l. brown and blue	20	20
107	**33**	20l. brown and olive	30	25
108	**33**	50l. brown and mauve	35	45
109	**33**	1r. brown and violet	45	65

34 Royal Angelfish

1963. Tropical Fish. Multicoloured.

110	2l. Type **34**	15	1·50
111	3l. Type **34**	15	1·50
112	5l. Type **34**	20	55
113	10l. Moorish idol (fish)	35	55
114	25l. As 10l.	1·00	55
115	50l. Diadem soldierfish	1·50	70
116	1r. Powder-blue surgeonfish	1·75	75
117	5r. Racoon butterflyfish	6·25	12·00

39 Fish in Net

1963. Freedom from Hunger.

118	**39**	2l. brown and green	40	3·50
119	-	5l. brown and red	75	2·00
120	**39**	7l. brown and turquoise	95	2·00
121	-	10l. brown and blue	1·25	2·00
122	**39**	25l. brown and red	3·25	4·00
123	-	50l. brown and violet	4·75	8·00
124	**39**	1r. brown and mauve	7·00	12·00

Design: Vert—5l., 10l., 50l. Handful of grain.

41 Centenary Emblem

1963. Centenary of Red Cross.

125	**41**	2l. red and purple	30	2·00
126	**41**	15l. red and green	1·00	1·00
127	**41**	50l. red and brown	1·75	1·75
128	**41**	1r. red and blue	2·50	2·00
129	**41**	4r. red and olive	5·00	21·00

42 Maldivian Scout Badge

1964. World Scout Jamboree, Marathon (1963).

130	**42**	2l. green and violet	10	65
131	**42**	3l. green and brown	10	65
132	**42**	25l. green and blue	15	15
133	**42**	1r. green and red	55	1·50

43 Mosque, Male

1964. 'Maldives Embrace Islam'.

134	**43**	2l. purple	10	60
135	**43**	3l. green	10	60
136	**43**	10l. red	10	10
137	**43**	40l. purple	30	25
138	**43**	60l. blue	50	40
139	**43**	85l. brown	60	60

44 Putting the Shot

1964. Olympic Games, Tokyo.

140	**44**	2l. purple and blue	10	2·00
141	**44**	3l. red and brown	10	2·00
142	**44**	5l. bronze and green	15	35
143	**44**	10l. violet and purple	20	35
144	-	15l. sepia and brown	30	35
145	-	25l. indigo and blue	40	35
146	-	50l. bronze and olive	60	40
147	-	1r. purple and grey	1·00	75
MS147a 126×140 mm. Nos. 145/147. Imperf			1·75	4·50

Design: 15l. to 1r. Running.

46 Telecommunications Satellite

1965. International Quiet Sun Years.

148	**46**	5l. blue	20	75
149	**46**	10l. brown	25	75
150	**46**	25l. green	50	75
151	**46**	1r. mauve	1·00	1·25

47 Isis (wall carving, Abu Simbel)

1965. Nubian Monuments Preservation.

152	**47**	2l. green and purple	15	1·25
153	-	3l. lake and green	15	1·25
154	**47**	5l. green and purple	20	15
155	-	10l. blue and orange	35	15
156	**47**	15l. brown and violet	60	15
157	-	25l. purple and blue	90	15
158	**47**	50l. green and sepia	1·10	45
159	-	1r. ochre and green	1·50	55

Design: 3, 10, 25l., 1r. Rameses II on throne (wall carving, Abu Simbel).

48 President Kennedy and Doves

1965. Second Death Anniversary of President Kennedy.

160	**48**	2l. black and mauve	10	1·00
161	**48**	5l. brown and mauve	10	10
162	**48**	25l. blue and mauve	20	10
163	-	1r. purple, yellow and green	35	25
164	-	2r. bronze, yellow and green	50	1·10
MS164a 150×130 mm. No. 164 in block of four. Imperf			2·25	3·25

Design: 1r., 2r. President Kennedy and hands holding olive-branch.

49 'XX' and UN Flag

1965. 20th Anniversary of UN.

165	**49**	3l. blue and brown	15	70
166	**49**	10l. blue and violet	40	10
167	**49**	1r. blue and green	1·25	35

50 ICY Emblem

1965. International Co-operation Year.

168	**50**	5l. brown and bistre	40	20
169	**50**	15l. brown and lilac	60	20
170	**50**	50l. brown and olive	1·25	30
171	**50**	1r. brown and red	1·75	1·50
172	**50**	2r. brown and blue	2·00	5·00
MS173 101×126 mm. Nos. 170/172. Imperf			7·00	10·00

51 Princely Cone Shells

1966. Multicoloured.

174	2l. Type **51**	20	1·75
175	3l. Yellow flowers	20	1·75
176	5l. Reticulate distorsio and leopard shells	30	15
177	7l. Camellias	30	15
178	10l. Type **51**	1·00	15
179	15l. Crab plover and seagull	3·75	30
180	20l. As 3l.	80	30
181	30l. Type **51**	2·75	35
182	50l. As 15l.	6·00	55
183	1r. Type **51**	4·00	70
184	1r. As 7l.	3·50	70
185	1r.50 As 3l.	3·75	3·75
186	2r. As 7l.	5·00	4·25
187	5r. As 15l.	23·00	17·00
188	10r. As 5l.	23·00	25·00

The 3l., 7l., 20l., 1r. (No. 184), 1r.50 and 2r. are Diamond ($43^1/_2$×$43^1/_2$ mm).

52 Maldivian Flag

1966. First Anniversary of Independence.

189	**52**	10l. green, red and turquoise	4·00	75
190	**52**	1r. multicoloured	10·00	1·25

53 *Luna 9* on Moon

1966. Space Rendezvous and Moon Landing.

191	**53**	10l. brown, indigo and blue	40	10
192	-	25l. green and red	60	10
193	**53**	50l. brown and green	90	15
194	-	1r. turquoise and brown	1·50	35
195	-	2r. green and violet	2·00	65
196	-	5r. pink and turquoise	3·00	1·60
MS197 108×126 mm. Nos. 194/6. Imperf			3·75	7·00

Designs: 25l., 1r., 5r. *Gemini 6* and *7* rendezvous in space; 2r. Gemini spaceship as seen from the other spaceship.

54 UNESCO Emblem and Owl on Book

1966. 20th Anniversary of UNESCO. Multicoloured.

198	2l. Type **54**	40	2·50
199	3l. UNESCO emblem and globe and microscope	40	2·50
200	5l. UNESCO emblem and mask, violin and palette	80	50
201	50l. Type **54**	8·00	75
202	1r. Design as 3l.	9·00	1·00
203	5r. Design as 5l.	26·00	28·00

55 Sir Winston Churchill and Cortege

1966. Churchill Commemoration. Flag in red and blue.

204	**55**	2l. brown	40	3·50
205	-	10l. turquoise	3·25	60
206	**55**	15l. green	4·00	60
207	-	25l. violet	6·00	70
208	-	1r. brown	16·00	1·50
209	**55**	2r.50 red	26·00	23·00

Design: 10l., 25l., 1r. Churchill and catafalque.

56 Footballers and Jules Rimet Cup

1967. England's Victory in World Cup Football Championship. Multicoloured.

210	2l. Type **56**	30	2·00
211	3l. Player in red shirt kicking ball	30	2·00
212	5l. Scoring goal	30	50
213	25l. As 3l.	2·25	50
214	50l. Making a tackle	3·00	50
215	1r. Type **56**	4·75	80
216	2r. Emblem on Union Jack	7·00	7·00
MS217 100×121 mm. Nos. 214/216. Imperf		16·00	12·00

57 Ornate Butterflyfish

1967. Tropical Fish. Multicoloured.

218	2l. Type **57**	15	1·50
219	3l. Black-saddled pufferfish	20	1·50
220	5l. Blue boxfish	50	30
221	6l. Picasso triggerfish	50	40
222	50l. Semicircle angelfish	4·50	50
223	1r. As 3l.	6·50	1·00
224	2r. As 50l.	10·00	9·50

58 Hawker Siddeley H.S.748 over Hulule Airport Building

1967. Inauguration of Hulule Airport.

225	**58**	2l. violet and olive	25	75
226	-	5l. green and lavender	50	10
227	**58**	10l. violet and green	65	10
228	-	15l. green and ochre	1·00	10
229	**58**	30l. ultramarine and blue	1·75	10
230	-	50l. brown and mauve	2·50	20
231	**58**	5r. blue and orange	6·00	5·50
232	-	10r. brown and blue	8·00	9·00

Design: 5, 15, 50l., 10r. Airport building and Hawker Siddeley H.S.748.

59 'Man and Music' Pavilion

1967. World Fair, Montreal. Multicoloured.

233	2l. Type **59**	10	1·00
234	5l. 'Man and His Community' Pavilion	10	10
235	10l. Type **59**	15	10
236	50l. As 5l.	60	30
237	1r. Type **59**	1·00	50
238	2r. As 5l.	2·00	2·25
MS239 102×137 mm. Nos. 237/238. Imperf		2·50	4·75

1968. International Tourist Year (1967). Nos. 225/232 optd **International Tourist Year 1967**.

240	**58**	2l. violet and olive	20	1·25
241	-	5l. green and lavender	40	25
242	**58**	10l. violet and green	55	25
243	-	15l. green and ochre	60	25
244	**58**	30l. ultramarine and blue	80	30
245	-	50l. brown and mauve	1·00	35
246	**58**	5r. blue and orange	4·50	5·50

247	-	10r. brown and blue	5·50	8·00

61 Cub signalling and Lord Baden-Powell

1968. Maldivian Scouts and Cubs.

248	61	2l. brown, green and yellow	10	1·25
249	-	3l. red, blue and light blue	10	1·25
250	61	25l. violet, lake and red	1·50	40
251	-	1r. green, brown and light green	3·00	1·60

Design: 3l. and 1r. Scouts and Lord Baden-Powell.

62 French Satellite *A 1*

1968. Space Martyrs.

252	62	2l. mauve and blue	20	1·00
253	-	3l. violet and brown	20	1·00
254	-	7l. brown and lake	50	1·00
255	-	10l. blue, drab and black	55	20
256	-	25l. green and violet	1·25	20
257	62	50l. blue and brown	1·60	30
258	-	1r. purple and green	2·25	50
259	-	2r. brown, blue and black	2·75	2·50
260	-	5r. mauve, drab and black	3·50	4·00
MS261		110×155 mm. Nos. 258/259. Imperf	7·00	7·50

Designs: 3l., 25l. *Luna 10;* 7l., 1r. Orbiter and Mariner; 10l., 2r. Astronauts White, Grissom and Chaffee; 5r. Cosmonaut V. M. Komarov.

63 Putting the Shot

1968. Olympic Games, Mexico (1st Issue). Multicoloured.

262	2l. Type **63**	10	1·00
263	6l. Throwing the discus	25	1·00
264	10l. Type **63**	40	15
265	25l. As 6l.	55	15
266	1r. Type **63**	1·00	35
267	2r.50 As 6l.	2·25	2·75

See also Nos. 294/297.

64 *Adriatic Seascape* (Bonington)

1968. Paintings. Multicoloured.

268	50l. Type **64**	2·25	30
269	1r. *Ulysses deriding Polyphemus* (Turner)	2·75	45
270	2r. *Sailing Boat at Argenteuil* (Monet)	3·50	2·75
271	5r. *Fishing Boat at Les Saintes-Maries* (Van Gogh)	6·00	7·00

65 LZ-130 *Graf Zeppelin II* and Montgolfier's Balloon

1968. Development of Civil Aviation.

272	65	2l. brown, green and blue	20	1·25
273	-	3l. blue, violet and brown	20	1·25
274	-	5l. green, red and blue	20	20
275	-	7l. blue, purple and orange	4·00	1·75
276	65	10l. brown, blue and purple	45	20
277	-	50l. red, green and olive	1·50	30
278	-	1r. green, blue and red	3·25	60
279	-	2r. purple, bistre and blue	22·00	12·00

Designs: 3l., 1r. Boeing 707-420 and Douglas DC-3; 5l., 50l. Wright Type A and Lilienthal's glider; 7l., 2r. Projected Boeing 733 and Concorde.

66 WHO Building, Geneva

1968. 20th Anniversary of World Health Organisation.

280	66	10l. violet, turquoise & blue	1·50	30
281	66	25l. green, brown & yellow	2·00	30
282	66	1r. brown, emerald & green	4·50	1·00
283	66	2r. violet, purple and mauve	6·50	8·00

1968. First Anniversary of Scout Jamboree, Idaho. Nos. 248/251 optd **International Boy Scout Jamboree, Farragut Park, Idaho, U.S.A. August 1–9, 1967**.

284	61	2l. brown, green and yellow	10	1·00
285	-	3l. red, blue and light blue	10	1·00
286	61	25l. violet, lake and red	1·50	55
287	-	1r. green, brown and light green	4·00	2·10

68 Curlew and Common Redshank

1968. Multicoloured

288	2l. Type **68**	50	1·25
289	10l. Pacific grinning tun and Papal mitre shells	1·25	20
290	25l. Oriental angel wing and tapestry turban shells	1·75	25
291	50l. Type **68**	9·50	1·10
292	1r. As 10l.	5·50	1·10
293	2r. As 25l.	5·00	5·00

69 Throwing the Discus

1968. Olympic Games, Mexico (2nd issue). Multicoloured.

294	10l. Type **69**	10	10
295	50l. Running	20	20
296	1r. Cycling	6·00	1·25
297	2r. Basketball	8·00	4·00

70 Fishing Dhow

1968. Republic Day.

298	70	10l. brown, blue and green	1·50	50
299	-	1r. green, red and blue	11·00	2·00

Design: 1r. National Flag, Crest and map.

71 *The Thinker* (Rodin)

1969. UNESCO. 'Human Rights'. Designs showing sculptures by Rodin. Multicoloured.

300	6l. Type **71**	75	60
301	10l. *Hands*	75	20
302	1r.50 *Sister and Brother*	3·75	3·75
303	2r.50 *The Prodical Son*	4·00	4·00
MS304	112×130 mm. Nos. 302/303. Imperf	13·00	13·00

72 Module nearing Moon's Surface

1969. First Man on the Moon. Multicoloured.

305	6l. Type **72**	50	35
306	10l. Astronaut with hatchet	50	20
307	1r.50 Astronaut and module	3·25	2·25
308	2r.50 Astronaut using camera	3·50	2·75
MS309	101×130 mm. Nos. 305/308. Imperf	6·50	7·50

1969. Gold Medal Winner, Olympic Games, Mexico (1968). Nos. 295/266 optd **Gold Medal Winner Mohamed Gammoudi 5000m. run Tunisia REPUBLIC OF MALDIVES** or similar opt.

310	50l. multicoloured	60	60
311	1r. multicoloured	1·40	90

The overprint on No. 310 honours P. Trentin (cycling, France).

74 Racoon Butterflyfish

1970. Tropical Fish. Multicoloured.

312	2l. Type **74**	40	1·25
313	5l. Clown triggerfish	65	60
314	25l. Broad-barred lionfish	1·25	60
315	50l. Long-nosed butterflyfish	1·50	1·00
316	1r. Emperor angelfish	1·75	1·25
317	2r. Royal angelfish	2·25	7·50

75 Columbia Dauman Victoria, 1899

1970. 75 Years of the Automobile. Multcoloured.

318	2l. Type **75**	30	1·00
319	5l. Duryea phaeton, 1902	45	50
320	7l. Packard S-24, 1906	60	50
321	10l. Autocar Runabout, 1907	60	50
322	25l. Type **75**	1·40	50
323	50l. As 5l.	1·60	70
324	1r. As 7l.	1·75	1·00
325	2r. As 10l.	1·90	7·00
MS326	95×143 mm. Nos. 324/325	3·25	8·00

76 UN Headquarters, New York

1970. 25th Anniversary of United Nations. Multicoloured.

327	2l. Type **76**	10	1·00
328	10l. Surgical operation (WHO)	2·25	40
329	25l. Student, actress and musician (UNESCO)	3·75	50
330	50l. Children at work and play (UNICEF)	2·00	70
331	1r. Fish, corn and farm animals (FAO)	2·00	1·00
332	2r. Miner hewing coal (ILO)	7·50	7·50

77 Ship and Light Buoy

1970. Tenth Anniversary of IMCO. Multicoloured.

333	50l. Type **77**	1·25	50
334	1r. Ship and lighthouse	7·00	1·50

78 *Guitar-player and Masqueraders* (A. Watteau)

1970. Famous Paintings showing the Guitar. Multicoloured.

335	3l. Type **78**	15	80
336	7l. *Spanish Guitarist* (Manet)	25	80
337	50l. *Costumed Player* (Watteau)	1·25	40
338	1r. *Mandolin-player* (Roberti)	2·00	55
339	2r.50 *Guitar-player and Lady* (Watteau)	3·50	4·00
340	5r. *Mandolin-player* (Frans Hals)	6·50	7·50
MS341	132×80 mm. Nos. 339/340	9·50	12·00

79 Australian Pavilion

1970. EXPO 70 World Fair, Osaka, Japan. Multicoloured.

342	2l. Type **79**	15	1·00
343	3l. West German Pavilion	15	1·00
344	10l. US Pavilion	65	10
345	25l. British Pavilion	2·00	15
346	50l. Soviet Pavilion	2·50	45
347	1r. Japanese Pavilion	2·75	65

80 Learning the Alphabet

1970. International Education Year. Multicoloured.

348	5l. Type **80**	50	60
349	10l. Training teachers	60	40
350	25l. Geography lesson	2·75	60
351	50l. School inspector	2·75	80
352	1r. Education by television	3·00	1·00

1970. Philympia 1970 Stamp Exhibition, London. Nos. 306/308 optd **Philympia London 1970**.

353	10l. multicoloured	20	10
354	1r.50 multicoloured	1·25	1·00
355	2r.50 multicoloured	1·25	1·50
MS356	101×130 mm. Nos. 305/8 optd. Imperf	6·50	8·50

82 Footballers

1970. World Cup Football Championship, Mexico.

357	82	3l. multicoloured	20	1·50
358	-	6l. multicoloured	35	1·00
359	-	7l. multicoloured	35	60
360	-	25l. multicoloured	1·25	30
361	-	1r. multicoloured	2·75	1·00

Designs: 6l. to 1r. Different designs showing footballers in action.

83 Little Boy and UNICEF Flag

1971. 25th Anniversary of UNICEF. Multicoloured.

362	5l. Type **83**	10	15

363	10l. Little girl with UNICEF balloon	10	15
364	1r. Type **83**	2·00	85
365	2r. As 10l.	3·00	3·00

84 Astronauts Lovell, Haise and Swigert

1971. Safe Return of *Apollo 13*. Multicoloured.

366	5l. Type **84**	35	35
367	20l. Explosion in Space	65	25
368	1r. Splashdown	1·40	50

85 Multiracial Flower

1971. Racial Equality Year.

369	**85**	10l. multicoloured	15	15
370	**85**	25l. multicoloured	20	15

86 *Mme. Charpentier and her Children* (Renoir)

1971. Famous Paintings showing Mother and Child. Multicoloured.

371	5l. Type **86**	30	20
372	7l. *Susanna van Collen and her Daughter* (Rembrandt)	35	20
373	10l. *Madonna nursing the Child* (Titian)	45	20
374	20l. *Baroness Belleli and her Children* (Degas)	1·25	20
375	25l. *The Cradle* (Morisot)	1·25	20
376	1r. *Helena Fourment and her Children* (Reubens)	3·25	85
377	3r. *On the Terrace* (Renoir)	5·50	6·50

87 Alan Shepard

1971. Moon Flight of *Apollo 14*. Multicoloured.

378	6l. Type **87**	40	40
379	10l. Stuart Roosa	45	30
380	1r.50 Edgar Mitchell	5·50	3·50
381	5r. Mission insignia	11·00	11·00

88 *Ballerina* (Degas)

1971. Famous Paintings showing Dancers. Multicoloured.

382	5l. Type **88**	25	20
383	10l. *Dancing Couple* (Renoir)	30	20
384	2r. *Spanish Dancer* (Manet)	3·00	2·50
385	5r. *Ballerinas* (Degas)	5·50	5·00
386	10r. *La Goulue at the Moulin Rouge* (Toulouse-Lautrec)	7·50	8·00

1972. Visit of Queen Elizabeth II and Prince Philip. Nos. 382/386 optd **ROYAL VISIT 1972**.

387	**88**	5l. multicoloured	20	10
388	-	10l. multicoloured	25	10
389	-	2r. multicoloured	5·00	4·00
390	-	5r. multicoloured	9·00	8·00
391	-	10r. multicoloured	10·00	10·00

90 Book Year Emblem

1972. International Book Year.

392	**90**	25l. multicoloured	15	15
393	**90**	5r. multicoloured	1·60	2·25

91 Scottish Costume

1972. National Costumes of the World. Multicoloured.

394	10l. Type **91**	1·25	10
395	15l. Netherlands	1·50	15
396	25l. Norway	2·50	15
397	50l. Hungary	3·25	55
398	1r. Austria	3·75	80
399	2r. Spain	4·75	3·50

92 Stegosaurus

1972. Prehistoric Animals. Multicoloured.

400	2l. Type **92**	75	75
401	7l. Dimetrodon (inscr 'Edaphosaurus')	1·50	60
402	25l. Diplodocus	2·25	50
403	50l. Triceratops	2·50	75
404	2r. Pteranodon	5·50	5·00
405	5r. Tyrannosaurus	9·50	9·50

93 Cross-country Skiing

1972. Winter Olympic Games, Sapporo, Japan. Multicoloured.

406	3l. Type **93**	10	50
407	6l. Bobsleighing	10	50
408	15l. Speed skating	20	20
409	50l. Ski jumping	1·00	45
410	1r. Figure skating (pair)	1·75	70
411	2r.50 Ice hockey	5·50	3·25

94 Scout Saluting

1972. 13th Boy Scout Jamboree, Asagiri, Japan (1971). Multicoloured.

412	10l. Type **94**	75	20
413	15l. Scout signalling	95	20
414	50l. Scout blowing bugle	3·25	1·25
415	1r. Scout playing drum	4·50	2·25

95 Cycling

1972. Olympic Games, Munich. Multicoloured.

416	5l. Type **95**	1·25	30
417	10l. Running	20	20
418	25l. Wrestling	30	20
419	50l. Hurdling	50	35
420	2r. Boxing	1·50	2·00
421	5r. Volleyball	3·00	3·75
MS422	92×120 mm. 3r. As 50l.; 4r. As 10l.	5·75	8·00

96 Globe and Conference Emblem

1972. UN Environmental Conservation Conference, Stockholm.

423	**96**	2l. multicoloured	10	40
424	**96**	3l. multicoloured	10	40
425	**96**	15l. multicoloured	30	15
426	**96**	50l. multicoloured	75	45
427	**96**	2r.50 multicoloured	3·25	4·25

97 *Flowers* (Van Gogh)

1973. Floral Paintings. Multicoloured.

428	1l. Type **97**	10	60
429	2l. *Flowers in Jug* (Renoir)	10	60
430	3l. *Chrysanthemums* (Renoir)	10	60
431	50l. *Mixed Bouquet* (Bosschaert)	1·50	30
432	1r. As 3l.	2·00	40
433	5r. As 2l.	4·25	5·50
MS434	120×94 mm. 2r. As 50l.; 3r. Type **97**	7·00	8·50

1973. Gold-medal Winners, Munich Olympic Games. Nos. 420/421 optd as listed below.

435	2r. multicoloured	3·25	2·50
436	5r. multicoloured	4·25	3·75
MS437	92×120 mm. 3r. multicoloured; 4r. multicoloured	7·50	8·50

Overprints: 2r. **LEMECHEV MIDDLE-WEIGHT GOLD MEDALLIST**; 5r. **JAPAN GOLD MEDAL WINNERS**. Miniature sheet: 3r. **EHRHARDT 100 METER HURDLES GOLD MEDALLIST**; 4r. **SHORTER MARATHON GOLD MEDALLIST**.

99 Animal Care

1973. International Scouting Congress, Nairobi and Addis Ababa. Multicoloured.

438	1l. Type **99**	10	30
439	2l. Lifesaving	10	30
440	3l. Agricultural training	10	30
441	4l. Carpentry	10	30
442	5l. Playing leapfrog	10	30
443	1r. As 2l.	2·75	75
444	2r. As 4l.	4·00	4·75
445	3r. Type **99**	4·50	7·00
MS446	101×79 mm. 5r. As 3l.	8·00	14·00

100 Blue Marlin

1973. Fish. Multicoloured.

447	1l. Type **100**	10	40
448	2l. Skipjack tuna	10	40
449	3l. Blue-finned tuna	10	40
450	5l. Dolphinfish	10	40
451	60l. Humpbacked snapper	80	40
452	75l. As 60l.	1·00	40
453	1r.50 Yellow-edged lyretail	1·75	2·00
454	2r.50 As 5l.	2·00	3·00
455	3r. Spotted coral grouper	2·00	3·25
456	10r. Spanish mackerel	4·00	8·00
MS457	119×123 mm. 4r. As 2l. 5r. Type **100**	17·00	20·00

Nos. 451/452 are smaller, size 29×22 mm.

101 Golden-fronted Leafbird

1973. Fauna. Multicoloured.

458	1l. Type **101**	10	50
459	2l. Indian flying fox	10	50
460	3l. Land tortoise	10	50
461	4l. Butterfly (*Kallima inachus*)	30	50
462	50l. As 3l.	60	40
463	2r. Type **101**	5·50	4·50
464	3r. As 2l.	3·50	4·50
MS465	66×74 mm. 5r. As 4l.	16·00	20·00

102 *Lantana camara*

1973. Flowers of the Maldive Islands. Multicoloured.

466	1l. Type **102**	10	50
467	2l. *Nerium oleander*	10	50
468	3l. *Rosa polyantha*	10	50
469	4l. *Hibiscus manihot*	10	50
470	5l. *Bougainvillea glabra*	10	20
471	10l. *Plumera alba*	15	20
472	50l. *Poinsettia pulcherrima*	70	30
473	5r. *Ononis natrix*	3·75	5·50
MS474	110×100 mm. 2r. As 3l.; 3r. As 10l.	3·25	5·25

103 *Tiros* Weather Satellite

1974. Centenary of World Meteorological Organisation. Multicoloured.

475	1l. Type **103**	10	30
476	2l. *Nimbus* satellite	10	30
477	3l. *Nomad* (weather ship)	10	30
478	4l. Scanner, APT Instant Weather Picture equipment	10	30
479	5l. Richard's wind-speed recorder	10	20
480	2r. Type **103**	3·50	3·75
481	3r. As 3l.	3·75	4·00
MS482	110×79 mm. 10r. As 2l.	8·50	14·00

104 Apollo Spacecraft and President Kennedy

1974. American and Russian Space Exploration Projects. Multicoloured.

483	1l. Type **104**	10	35
484	2l. Mercury capsule and John Glenn	10	35
485	3l. *Vostok 1* and Yuri Gagarin	10	35
486	4l. *Vostok 6* and Valentina Tereshkova	10	35

487	5l. *Soyuz 11* and Salyut space-station	10	25
488	2r. *Skylab* space laboratory	3·75	3·75
489	3r. As 2l.	4·25	4·25
MS490	103×80 mm. 10r. Type **104**	13·00	15·00

105 Copernicus and *Skylab* Space Laboratory

1974. 500th Birth Anniversary of Nicholas Copernicus (astronomer). Multicoloured.

491	1l. Type **105**	10	35
492	2l. Orbital space-station of the future	10	35
493	3l. Proposed Space-shuttle craft	10	35
494	4l. *Mariner 2* Venus probe	10	35
495	5l. *Mariner 4* Mars probe	10	20
496	25l. Type **105**	1·25	20
497	1r.50 As 2l.	2·75	3·25
498	5r. As 3l.	4·50	11·00
MS499	106×80 mm. 10r. *Copernicus* orbital observatory	15·00	18·00

106 *Maternity* (Picasso)

1974. Paintings by Picasso. Multicoloured.

500	1l. Type **106**	10	40
501	2l. *Harlequin and Friend*	10	40
502	3l. *Pierrot Sitting*	10	40
503	20l. *Three Musicians*	50	20
504	75l. *L'Aficionado*	1·25	80
505	5r. *Still Life*	4·75	6·50
MS506	100×101 mm. 2r. As 20l.; 3r. As 5r.	8·50	11·00

107 UPU Emblem, Steam and Diesel Locomotives

1974. Centenary of Universal Postal Union. Multicoloured.

507	1l. Type **107**	10	30
508	2l. Paddle-steamer and modern mailboat	10	30
509	3l. Airship *Graf Zeppelin* and Boeing 747 airliner	10	30
510	1r.50 Mailcoach and motor van	1·40	1·10
511	2r.50 As 2l.	1·50	1·75
512	5r. Type **107**	2·00	3·25
MS513	126×105 mm. 4r. Type **107**	6·00	7·00

108 Footballers

1974. World Cup Football Championship, West Germany.

514	**108**	1l. multicoloured	15	20
515	-	2l. multicoloured	15	20
516	-	3l. multicoloured	15	20
517	-	4l. multicoloured	15	20
518	-	75l. multicoloured	1·00	75
519	-	4r. multicoloured	2·00	4·00
520	-	5r. multicoloured	2·00	4·00
MS521		88×95 mm. 10r. multicoloured	10·00	12·00

Designs: Nos. 515/**MS**521 show football scenes similar to Type **108**.

109 Capricorn

1974. Signs of the Zodiac. Multicoloured.

522	1l. Type **109**	25	50
523	2l. Aquarius	25	50
524	3l. Pisces	25	50
525	4l. Aries	25	50
526	5l. Taurus	25	50
527	6l. Gemini	25	50
528	7l. Cancer	25	50
529	10l. Leo	40	50
530	15l. Virgo	40	50
531	20l. Libra	40	50
532	25l. Scorpio	40	50
533	5r. Sagittarius	6·50	12·00
MS534	119×99 mm. 10r. The Sun (49×37 mm)	22·00	23·00

110 Churchill and Avro Type 683 Lancaster

1974. Birth Centenary of Sir Winston Churchill. Multicoloured.

535	1l. Type **110**	40	70
536	2l. Churchill as pilot	40	70
537	3l. Churchill as First Lord of the Admiralty	40	70
538	4l. Churchill and HMS *Eagle* (aircraft carrier)	40	70
539	5l. Churchill and de Havilland Mosquito bombers	40	45
540	60l. Churchill and anti-aircraft battery	3·75	2·00
541	75l. Churchill and tank in desert	4·00	2·00
542	5r. Churchill and Short S.25 Sunderland flying boat	15·00	15·00
MS543	113×83 mm. 10r. As 4l.	22·00	23·00

111 Bullmouth Helmet

1975. Sea Shells and Cowries. Multicoloured.

544	1l. Type **111**	10	30
545	2l. Venus comb murex	10	30
546	3l. Common or major harp	10	30
547	4l. Chiragra spider conch	10	30
548	5l. Geography cone	10	30
549	60l. Dawn cowrie (22×30 mm)	3·00	2·00
550	75l. Purplish clanculus (22×30 mm)	3·50	2·00
551	5r. Ramose murex	8·50	11·00
MS552	152×126 mm. 2r. As 3l.; 3r. As 2l.	14·00	17·00

112 Royal Throne

1975. Historical Relics and Monuments. Multicoloured.

553	1l. Type **112**	10	10
554	10l. Candlesticks	10	10
555	25l. Lamp-tree	15	10
556	60l. Royal umbrellas	30	30
557	75l. Eid-Miskith Mosque (horiz)	35	35
558	3r. Tomb of Al-Hafiz Abu-al Barakath-al Barubari (horiz)	1·60	2·75

113 Guavas

1975. Exotic Fruits. Multicoloured.

559	2l. Type **113**	10	40
560	4l. Maldive mulberry	15	40
561	5l. Mountain apples	15	40
562	10l. Bananas	20	15
563	20l. Mangoes	40	25
564	50l. Papaya	1·00	60
565	1r. Pomegranates	1·75	70
566	5r. Coconut	5·50	11·00
MS567	136×102 mm. 2r. As 10l.; 3r. As 2l.	12·00	16·00

114 *Phyllangia*

1975. Marine Life. Corals, Urchins and Sea Stars. Multicoloured.

568	1l. Type **114**	10	40
569	2l. *Madrepora oculata*	10	40
570	3l. *Acropora gravida*	10	40
571	4l. *Stylotella*	10	40
572	5l. *Acrophora cervicornis*	10	40
573	60l. *Strongylocentrotus purpuratus*	75	65
574	75l. *Pisaster ochraceus*	85	75
575	5r. *Marthasterias glacialis*	5·00	6·50
MS576	155×98 mm. 4r. As 1l. Imperf	11·00	14·00

115 Clock Tower and Customs Building within '10'

1975. Tenth Anniversary of Independence. Multicoloured.

577	4l. Type **115**	10	30
578	5l. Government offices	10	15
579	7l. Waterfront	10	20
580	15l. Mosque and minaret	10	15
581	10r. Sultan Park and museum	2·25	6·00

1975. Nordjamb 75 World Scout Jamboree, Norway. Nos. 443/**MS**446 optd **14th Boy Scout Jamboree July 29–August 7, 1975.**

582	-	1r. multicoloured	85	60
583	-	2r. multicoloured	1·25	80
584	**99**	3r. multicoloured	1·75	1·60
MS585		101×79 mm. 5r. multicoloured	7·00	8·00

117 Madura Prau

1975. Ships. Multicoloured.

586	1l. Type **117**	10	20
587	2l. Ganges patela	10	20
588	3l. Indian palla (vert)	10	20
589	4l. Odhi (dhow) (vert)	10	20
590	5l. Maldivian schooner	10	20
591	25l. *Cutty Sark* (British tea clipper)	1·50	40
592	1r. Maldivian baggala (vert)	1·75	70
593	5r. *Maldive Courage* (freighter)	3·00	6·00
MS594	99×85 mm. 10r. As 1r.	10·00	14·00

118 *Brahmophthalma wallichi* (moth)

1975. Butterflies and Moth. Multicoloured.

595	1l. Type **118**	15	30
596	2l. *Teinopalpus imperialis*	15	30
597	3l. *Cethosia biblis*	15	30
598	4l. *Idea jasonia*	15	30
599	5l. *Apatura ilia*	15	30
600	25l. *Kallima horsfieldi*	1·25	35
601	1r.50 *Hebomoia leucippe*	3·50	3·75
602	5r. *Papilio memnon*	8·00	10·00
MS603	134×97 mm. 10r. As 25l.	20·00	20·00

119 *The Dying Captive*

1975. 500th Birth Anniversary of Michelangelo. Multicoloured.

604	1l. Type **119**	10	20
605	2l. Detail of *The Last Judgement*	10	20
606	3l. *Apollo*	10	20
607	4l. Detail of Sistine Chapel ceiling	10	20
608	5l. *Bacchus*	10	20
609	1r. Detail of *The Last Judgement* (different)	1·25	30
610	2r. *David*	1·50	2·00
611	5r. *Cumaean Sibyl*	2·25	5·00
MS612	123×113 mm. 10r. As 2r.	5·00	11·00

120 Beaker and Vase

1975. Maldivian Lacquerware. Multicoloured.

613	2l. Type **120**	10	50
614	4l. Boxes	10	50
615	50l. Jar with lid	30	20
616	75l. Bowls with covers	40	30
617	1r. Craftsman at work	50	40

121 Map of Maldives

1975. Tourism. Multicoloured.

618	4l. Type **121**	40	50
619	5l. Motor launch and small craft	40	50
620	7l. Sailing-boats	40	50
621	15l. Underwater fishing	40	40
622	3r. Hulule Airport	5·00	3·00
623	10r. Motor cruisers	7·00	8·50

122 Cross-country Skiing

1976. Winter Olympic Games, Innsbruck. Multicoloured.

624	1l. Type **122**	10	20
625	2l. Speed-skating (pairs)	10	20
626	3l. Figure-skating (pairs)	10	20
627	4l. Four-man bobsleighing	10	20
628	5l. Ski-jumping	10	20
629	25l. Figure-skating (women's)	35	20
630	1r.15 Skiing (slalom)	90	1·25
631	4r. Ice-hockey	1·50	4·00
MS632	93×117 mm. 10r. Downhill Skiing	7·00	13·00

123 *General Burgoyne* (Reynolds)

1976. Bicentenary of American Revolution. Multicoloured.

633	1l. Type **123**	15	20
634	2l. *John Hancock* (Copley)	15	20
635	3l. *Death of General Montgomery* (Trumbull) (horiz)	15	20
636	4l. *Paul Revere* (Copley)	15	20
637	5l. *Battle of Bunker Hill* (Trumbull) (horiz)	15	20
638	2r. *The Crossing of the Delaware* (Sully) (horiz)	2·00	2·75
639	3r. *Samuel Adams* (Copley)	2·25	3·25
640	5r. *Surrender of Cornwallis* (Trumbull) (horiz)	2·50	3·50
MS641	147×95 mm. 10r. *Washington at Dorchester Heights* (Stuart)	17·00	20·00

124 Thomas Edison

1976. Centenary of Telephone. Multicoloured.

642	1l. Type **124**	10	40
643	2l. Alexander Graham Bell	10	40
644	3l. Telephone of 1919, 1937 and 1972	10	40
645	10l. Cable entrance into station	20	20

646	20l. Equaliser circuit assembly	30	20
647	1r. *Salernum* (cable ship)	2·25	55
648	10r. *Intelsat IV-A* and Earth Station	4·75	8·00
MS649	156×105 mm. 4r. Early telephones	7·50	9·00

1976. Interphil 76 International Stamp Exhibition, Philadelphia. Nos. 638/**MS**641 optd **MAY 29TH–JUNE 6TH "INTERPHIL" 1976**.

650	2r. multicoloured	1·50	1·75
651	3r. multicoloured	2·00	2·25
652	5r. multicoloured	2·50	2·75
MS653	147×95 mm. 10r. multicoloured	10·00	12·00

126 Wrestling

1976. Olympic Games, Montreal. Multicoloured.

654	1l. Type **126**	10	20
655	2l. Putting the shot	10	20
656	3l. Hurdling	10	20
657	4l. Hockey	10	20
658	5l. Running	10	20
659	6l. Javelin-throwing	10	20
660	1r.50 Discus-throwing	1·25	1·75
661	5r. Volleyball	2·75	5·25
MS662	135×106 mm. 10r. Throwing the hammer	8·50	12·00

127 *Dolichos lablab*

1976. Vegetables. Multicoloured.

663	2l. Type **127**	10	40
664	4l. *Moringa pterygosperma*	10	40
665	10l. *Solanum melongena*	15	15
666	20l. *Moringa pterygosperma*	3·25	2·25
667	50l. *Cucumis sativus*	50	65
668	75l. *Trichosanthes anguina*	55	75
669	1r. *Momordica charantia*	65	85
670	2r. *Trichosanthes anguina*	4·75	8·00

128 Viking approaching Mars

1977. Viking Space Mission. Multicoloured.

671	5r. Type **128**	1·90	2·75
MS672	121×89 mm. 20r. Landing module on Mars	10·00	14·00

129 Coronation Ceremony

1977. Silver Jubilee of Queen Elizabeth II. Multicoloured.

673	1l. Type **129**	10	30
674	2l. Queen and Prince Philip	10	30
675	3l. Royal couple with Princes Andrew and Edward	10	30
676	1r.15 Queen with Archbishops	65	35
677	3r. State coach in procession	1·25	75
678	4r. Royal couple with Prince Charles and Princess Anne	1·25	1·25
MS679	120×77 mm. 10r. Queen and Prince Charles	5·00	3·75

130 Beethoven and Organ

1977. 150th Death Anniversary of Ludwig van Beethoven. Multicoloured.

680	1l. Type **130**	25	30
681	2l. Queen and manuscript of *Moonlight Sonata*	25	30
682	3l. With Goethe at Teplitz	25	30
683	4l. Beethoven and string instruments	25	30
684	5l. Beethoven's home, Heiligenstadt	25	30
685	25l. Hands and gold medals	1·50	20
686	2r. Portrait and *Missa solemnis*	4·00	3·75
687	5r. Composer's hearing-aids	6·50	7·00
MS688	121×92 mm. 4r. Death mask and room where composer died	9·50	11·00

131 Printed Circuit and ITU Emblem

1977. Inauguration of Satellite Earth Station. Multicoloured.

689	10l. Type **131**	10	10
690	90l. Central Telegraph Office	45	45
691	10r. Satellite Earth Station	3·00	6·00
MS692	100×85 mm. 5r. *Intelsat IV-A* satellite over Maldives	4·50	5·50

132 *Miss Anne Ford* (Gainsborough)

1977. Artists' Birth Anniversaries. Multicoloured.

693	1l. Type **132** (250th anniversary)	10	30
694	2l. Group painting by Rubens (400th anniversary)	10	30
695	3l. *Girl with Dog* (Titian) (500th anniversary)	10	30
696	4l. *Mrs. Thomas Graham* (Gainsborough)	10	30
697	5l. *Artist with Isabella Brant* (Rubens)	10	30
698	95l. Portrait by Titian	1·25	30
699	1r. Portrait by Gainsborough	1·25	30
700	10r. *Isabella Brant* (Rubens)	4·50	7·00
MS701	152×116 mm. 5r. *Self-portrait* (Titian)	3·75	5·50

133 Lesser Frigatebirds

1977. Birds. Multicoloured.

702	1l. Type **133**	20	40
703	2l. Crab plover	20	40
704	3l. White-tailed Tropicbird	20	40
705	4l. Wedge-tailed shearwater	20	40
706	5l. Grey heron	20	40
707	20l. White tern	90	30
708	95l. Cattle egret	2·25	1·60
709	1r.25 Black-naped tern	2·50	2·50
710	5r. Pheasant coucal	6·50	8·00
MS711	124×117 mm. 10r. Green-backed heron	26·00	26·00

134 Charles Lindbergh

1977. 50th Anniversary of Lindbergh's Transatlantic Flight and 75th Anniversary of First Navigable Airships. Multicoloured.

712	1l. Type **134**	25	30
713	2l. Lindbergh and *Spirit of St. Louis*	25	30
714	3l. Lindbergh's Miles Mohawk aircraft (horiz)	25	30
715	4l. Lebaudy-Juillot airship *Morning Post* (horiz)	25	30
716	5l. Airship *Graf Zeppelin* and portrait of Zeppelin	25	30
717	1r. Airship *Los Angeles* (horiz)	1·25	30
718	3r. Lindbergh and Henry Ford	2·00	2·00
719	10r. Vickers airship R-23 rigid airship	2·75	6·00
MS720	148×114 mm. 5r. Ryan NYP Special *Spirit of St. Louis*, Statue of Liberty and Eiffel Tower; 7r.50, Airship L-31 over *Ostfriesland* (German battleship)	13·00	18·00

No. 715 is inscr 'Lebaudy I built by H. Juillot 1902'.

135 Boat Building

1977. Occupations. Multicoloured.

721	6l. Type **135**	75	45
722	15l. Fishing	1·25	20
723	20l. Cadjan weaving	1·50	20
724	90l. Mat-weaving	3·50	1·60
725	2r. Lace-making (vert)	5·50	4·75

136 Rheumatic Heart

1977. World Rheumatism Year. Multicoloured.

726	1l. Type **136**	10	30
727	50l. Rheumatic shoulder	40	20
728	2r. Rheumatic hands	75	1·25
729	3r. Rheumatic knees	85	1·40

137 Lilienthal's Biplane Glider

1978. 75th Anniversary of First Powered Aircraft. Multicoloured.

730	1l. Type **137**	25	40
731	2l. Chanute's glider	25	40
732	3l. Wright glider No. II, 1901	25	40
733	4l. A. V. Roe's Triplane I	25	40
734	5l. Wilbur Wright demonstrating Wright Type A for King Alfonso of Spain	25	40
735	10l. A. V. Roe's Avro Type D biplane	80	40
736	20l. Wright Brothers and A. G. Bell at Washington	2·25	40
737	95l. Hadley's triplane	5·50	2·25
738	5r. Royal Aircraft Factory B.E.2A biplanes at Upavon, 1914	11·50	11·00
MS739	98×82 mm. 10r. Wright Brothers' Wright Type A	14·00	16·00

No. 732 is wrongly dated 1900.

138 Newgate Prison

1978. World Eradication of Smallpox. Multicoloured.

740	15l. Foundling Hospital, London (horiz)	50	30
741	50l. Type **138**	1·25	60
742	2r. Edward Jenner (discoverer of smallpox vaccine)	2·25	4·00

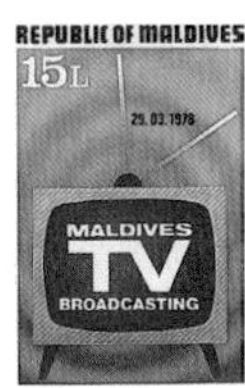

139 Television Set

1978. Inauguration of Television in Maldive Islands. Multicoloured.

743	15l. Type **139**	40	30
744	25l. Television aerials	55	30
745	1r.50 Control desk (horiz)	2·25	2·75

140 Mas Odi

1978. Ships. Multicoloured.

746	1l. Type **140**	10	35
747	2l. Battela	10	35
748	3l. Bandu odi (vert)	10	35
749	5l. *Maldive Trader* (freighter)	20	35
750	1r. *Fath-hul Baaree* (brigantine)	65	30
751	1r.25 Mas dhoni	85	1·00
752	3r. Baggala (vert)	1·10	1·75
753	4r. As 1r.25	1·10	1·75
MS754	152×138 mm. 1r. As No. 747; 4r. As No. 751	2·00	3·75

141 Ampulla

1978. 25th Anniversary of Coronation. Multicoloured.

755	1l. Type **141**	10	20
756	2l. Sceptre with Dove	10	20
757	3l. Golden Orb	10	20
758	1r.15 St Edward's Crown	30	20
759	2r. Sceptre with Cross	40	35
760	5r. Queen Elizabeth II	60	80
MS761	108×106 mm. 10r. Annointing spoon	1·75	2·25

142 Captain Cook

1978. 250th Birth Anniversary of Captain James Cook and Bicentenary of Discovery of Hawaiian Islands. Multicoloured.

762	1l. Type **142**	10	25
763	2l. Statue of Kamehameha I of Hawaii	10	25
764	3l. HMS *Endeavour*	10	25
765	25l. Route of third voyage	45	45
766	75l. HMS *Discovery*, HMS *Resolution* and map of Hawaiian Islands (horiz)	1·25	1·25
767	1r.50 Cook meeting Hawaiian islanders (horiz)	2·00	2·25
768	10r. Death of Captain Cook (horiz)	3·50	10·00
MS769	100×92 mm. 5r. HMS *Endeavour* (different)	13·00	20·00

143 *Schizophrys aspera*

1978. Crustaceans. Multicoloured.

770	1l. Type **143**	10	25
771	2l. *Atergatis floridus*	10	25
772	3l. *Perenon planissimum*	10	25
773	90l. *Portunus granulatus*	50	40
774	1r. *Carpilius maculatus*	50	40
775	2r. *Huenia proteus*	1·00	1·40
776	25r. *Etisus laevimanus*	4·50	13·00
MS777	147×146 mm. 2r. *Panulirus longipes* (vert)	2·00	2·50

144 *Four Apostles*

1978. 450th Death Anniversary of Albrecht Durer (artist).

778	**144**	10l. multicoloured	10	10
779	-	20l. multicoloured	15	10
780	-	55l. multicoloured	20	20
781	-	1r. black, brown and buff	30	30
782	-	1r.80 multicoloured	45	60

783	-	3r. multicoloured	70	1·25
MS784 141×122 mm. 10r. multicoloured			4·00	6·00

Designs: Vert—20l. *Self-portrait at 27*; 55l. *Madonna and Child with a Pear*; 1r.80, *Hare*; 3r. *Great Piece of Turf*; 10r. *Columbine*. Horiz—1r. *Rhinoceros*.

145 TV Tower and Building

1978. Tenth Anniversary of Republic. Multicoloured.

785		1l. Fishing boat (horiz)	10	60
786		5l. Montessori School (horiz)	10	40
787		10l. Type **145**	10	10
788		25l. Islet (horiz)	20	15
789		50l. Boeing 737 aircraft (horiz)	80	25
790		95l. Beach scene (horiz)	60	30
791		1r.25 Dhow at night (horiz)	75	55
792		3r. President's residence (horiz)	80	1·25
793		5r. Masjidh Afeefuddin Mosque (horiz)	1·00	3·00
MS794 119×88 mm. 3r. Fisherman casting net			2·25	4·00

146 Human Rights Emblem

1978. 30th Anniversary of Declaration of Human Rights.

795	**146**	30l. pink, lilac and green	15	15
796	**146**	90l. yellow, brown and green	40	60
797	**146**	1r.80 blue, deep blue and green	70	1·00

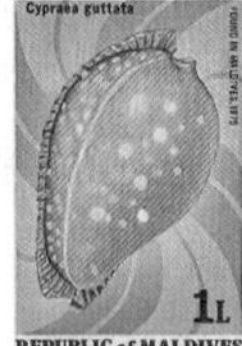

147 Great Spotted or Rare Spotted Cowrie

1979. Shells. Multicoloured.

798		1l. Type **147**	10	20
799		2l. Imperial cone	10	20
800		3l. Great green turban	10	20
801		10l. Giant spider conch	45	10
802		1r. White-toothed cowrie	2·00	40
803		1r.80 Fig cone	3·00	2·50
804		3r. Glory of the sea cone	4·50	3·75
MS805 141×110 mm. 5r. Common Pacific vase			14·00	12·00

148 Delivery by Bellman

1979. Death Centenary of Sir Rowland Hill. Multicoloured.

806		1l. Type **148**	10	20
807		2l. Mail coach, 1840 (horiz)	10	20
808		3l. First London letterbox, 1855	10	20
809		1r.55 Penny Black	40	50
810		5r. First Maldive Islands stamp	70	1·25
MS811 132×107 mm. 10r. Sir Rowland Hill			1·25	3·00

149 Girl with Teddy Bear

1979. International Year of the Child (1st issue). Multicoloured.

812		5l. Type **149**	10	10
813		1r.25 Boy with sailing boat	40	50
814		2r. Boy with toy rocket	45	55
815		3r. Boy with toy airship	60	75
MS816 108×109 mm. 5r. Boy with toy train			1·25	2·00

See also Nos. 838/**MS**847.

150 *White Feathers*

1979. 25th Death Anniversary of Henri Matisse (artist). Multicoloured.

817		20l. Type **150**	15	15
818		25l. *Joy of Life*	15	15
819		30l. *Eggplants*	15	15
820		1r.50 *Harmony in Red*	45	65
821		5r. *Still-life*	70	2·25
MS822 135×95 mm. 4r. *Water Pitcher*			4·25	4·50

151 Sari with Overdress

1979. National Costumes. Multicoloured.

823		50l. Type **151**	20	15
824		75l. Sashed apron dress	25	20
825		90l. Serape	30	25
826		95l. Ankle-length printed dress	35	30

152 *Gloriosa superba*

1979. Flowers. Multicoloured.

827		1l. Type **152**	10	10
828		3l. *Hibiscus tiliaceus*	10	10
829		50l. *Barringtonia asiatica*	20	15
830		1r. *Abutilon indicum*	40	25
831		5r. *Guettarda speciosa*	1·00	2·00
MS832 94×85 mm. 4r. *Pandanus odoratissimus*			1·75	2·75

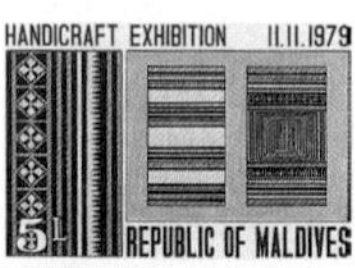

153 Weaving

1979. Handicraft Exhibition. Multicoloured.

833		5l. Type **153**	10	10
834		10l. Lacquerwork	10	10
835		1r.30 Tortoiseshell jewellery	45	55
836		2r. Carved woodwork	60	90
MS837 125×85 mm. 5r. Gold and silver jewellery			1·25	2·25

154 Mickey Mouse attacked by Bird

1979. International Year of the Child (2nd issue). Disney Characters. Multicoloured.

838		1l. Goofy delivering parcel on motor-scooter (vert)	10	10
839		2l. Type **154**	10	10
840		3l. Goofy half-covered with letters	10	10
841		4l. Pluto licking Minnie Mouse's envelopes	10	10
842		5l. Mickey Mouse delivering letters on roller skates (vert)	10	10
843		10l. Donald Duck placing letter in mailbox	10	10
844		15l. Chip 'n' Dale carrying letter	10	10
845		1r.50 Donald Duck on monocycle (vert)	75	95
846		5r. Donald Duck with ostrich in crate (vert)	2·25	3·25
MS847 127×102 mm. 4r. Pluto putting parcel in mail-box			5·00	7·00

155 Post-Ramadan Dancing

1980. National Day. Multicoloured.

848		5l. Type **155**	10	10
849		15l. Musicians and dancer, Eeduu Festival	10	10
850		95l. Sultan's ceremonial band	35	30
851		2r. Dancer and drummers Circumcision Festival	60	85
MS852 131×99 mm. 5r. Swordsmen			1·90	2·50

156 Leatherback Turtle

1980. Turtle Conservation Campaign. Multicoloured.

853		1l. Type **156**	20	30
854		2l. Flatback turtle	20	30
855		5l. Hawksbill turtle	25	30
856		10l. Loggerhead turtle	35	30
857		75l. Olive Ridley turtle	1·00	45
858		10r. Atlantic Ridley turtle	3·00	4·25
MS859 85×107 mm. 4r. Green turtle			2·00	2·75

157 Paul Harris (founder)

1980. 75th Anniversary of Rotary International Multicoloured.

860		75l. Type **157**	45	10
861		90l. Humanity	50	20
862		1r. Hunger	50	25
863		10r. Health	2·75	4·50
MS864 109×85 mm. 5r. Globe			1·75	2·50

1980. London 1980 International Stamp Exhibition. Nos. 809/**MS**811 optd **LONDON 1980**.

865		1r.55 Penny Black	2·50	1·00
866		5r. First Maldives stamp	4·00	2·75
MS867 132×107 mm. 10r. Sir Rowland Hill			7·50	8·00

159 Swimming

1980. Olympic Games, Moscow. Multicoloured.

868		10l. Type **159**	10	10
869		50l. Running	20	20
870		3r. Putting the shot	70	1·10
871		4r. High jumping	80	1·40
MS872 105×85 mm. 5r. Weightlifting			1·25	2·25

160 White-tailed Tropicbird

1980. Birds. Multicoloured.

873		75l. Type **160**	25	15
874		95l. Sooty tern	35	30
875		1r. Common noddy	35	30
876		1r.55 Curlew	50	70
877		2r. Wilson's storm petrel ('Wilson's Petrel')	60	85
878		4r. Caspian tern	1·10	1·60
MS879 124×85 mm. 5r. Red-footed booby and brown booby			8·00	9·00

161 Seal of Ibrahim II

1980. Seals of the Sultans.

880	**161**	1l. brown and black	10	10
881	-	2l. brown and black	10	10
882	-	5l. brown and black	10	10
883	-	1r. brown and black	40	30
884	-	2r. brown and black	50	70
MS885 131×95 mm. 3r. brown and black			85	1·60

Designs: 2l. Mohammed Imadudeen II; 5l. Bin Haji Ali; 1r. Kuda Mohammed Rasgefaanu; 2r. Ibrahim Iskander I; 3r. Ibrahim Iskander I (different).

162 Queen Elizabeth the Queen Mother

1980. 80th Birthday of the Queen Mother.

886	**162**	4r. multicoloured	1·00	1·25
MS887 85×110 mm. **162** 5r. multicoloured			1·60	2·00

163 Munnaru

1980. 1400th Anniversary of Hegira. Multicoloured.

888		5l. Type **163**	20	10
889		10l. Hukuru Miskiiy mosque	25	10
890		30l. Medhuziyaaraiy (shrine of saint)	30	30
891		55l. Writing tablets with verses of Koran	40	35
892		90l. Mother teaching child Koran	60	70
MS893 124×101 mm. 2r. Map of Maldives and Coat of Arms			80	1·60

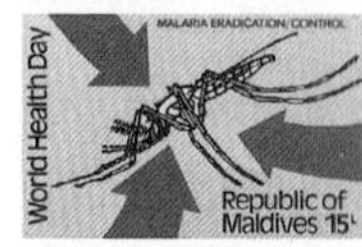

164 Malaria Eradication

1980. World Health Day.

894	**164**	15l. black, brown and red	20	10
895	-	25l. multicoloured	20	10
896	-	1r.50 brown, light brown and black	2·00	1·00
897	-	5r. multicoloured	3·25	3·00
MS898 68×85 mm. 4r. black, blue and light blue			1·25	2·50

Designs: 25l. Nutrition; 1r.50, Dental health; 4, 5r. Clinics.

165 White Rabbit

1980. Walt Disney's *Alice in Wonderland*. Multicoloured.

899		1l. Type **165**	10	10
900		2l. Alice falling into Wonderland	10	10
901		3l. Alice too big to go through door	10	10
902		4l. Alice with Tweedledum and Tweedledee	10	10
903		5l. Alice and caterpillar	10	10
904		10l. The Cheshire cat	10	10
905		15l. Alice painting the roses	10	10
906		2r.50 Alice and the Queen of Hearts	2·25	2·50
907		4r. Alice on trial	2·50	2·75
MS908 126×101 mm. 5r. Alice at the Mad Hatter's tea-party			4·50	6·50

166 Indian Ocean Ridley Turtle

1980. Marine Animals. Multicoloured.

909		90l. Type **166**	2·25	60

910 1r.25 Pennant coralfish 2·75 1·25
911 2r. Spiny lobster 3·25 1·75
MS912 140×94 mm. 4r. Oriental sweetlips and scarlet-finned squirrelfish 3·00 3·25

167 Pendant Lamp

1981. National Day. Multicoloured.
913 10l. Tomb of Ghaazee Muhammad Thakurufaan (horiz) 15 10
914 20l. Type **167** 20 10
915 30l. Chair used by Muhammad Thakurufaan 25 10
916 95l. Muhammad Thakurufaan's palace (horiz) 60 30
917 10r. Cushioned divan 2·75 4·50

168 Prince Charles and Lady Diana Spencer

1981. British Royal Wedding. Multicoloured.
918 1r. Type **168** 15 15
919 2r. Buckingham Palace 25 25
920 5r. Prince Charles, polo player 40 50
MS921 95×83 mm. 10r. State coach 75 1·10

169 First Majlis Chamber

1981. 50th Anniversary of Citizens' Majlis (grievance rights). Multicoloured.
922 95l. Type **169** 30 30
923 1r. Sultan Muhammed Shamsuddin III 35 35
MS924 137×94 mm. 4r. First written constitution (horiz) 2·25 4·00

170 *Self-portrait with a Palette*

1981. Birth Centenary of Pablo Picasso. Multicoloured.
925 5l. Type **170** 15 10
926 10l. *Woman in Blue* 20 10
927 25l. *Boy with Pipe* 30 10
928 30l. *Card Player* 30 10
929 90l. *Sailor* 50 40
930 3r. *Self-portrait* 80 1·00
931 5r. *Harlequin* 1·00 1·25
MS932 106×130 mm. 10r. *Child holding a Dove*. Imperf 2·50 3·50

171 Airmail Envelope

1981. 75th Anniversary of Postal Service.
933 **171** 25l. multicoloured 15 10
934 **171** 75l. multicoloured 25 25
935 **171** 5r. multicoloured 70 1·25

172 Boeing 737 taking off

1981. Male International Airport. Multicoloured.
936 5l. Type **172** 30 20
937 20l. Passengers leaving Boeing 737 55 20
938 1r.80 Refuelling 90 1·25
939 4r. Plan of airport 1·10 2·25
MS940 106×79 mm. 5r. Aerial view of airport 2·50 3·00

173 Homer

1981. International Year of Disabled People. Multicoloured.
941 2l. Type **173** 10 10
942 5l. Miguel Cervantes 10 10
943 1r. Beethoven 2·75 85
944 5r. Van Gogh 3·25 5·00
MS945 116×91 mm. 4r. Helen Keller and Anne Sullivan 3·25 5·50

174 Preparation of Maldive Fish

1981. Decade for Women. Multicoloured.
946 20l. Type **174** 10 10
947 90l. 16th-century Maldive women 25 25
948 1r. Farming 30 30
949 2r. Coir rope-making 55 1·10

175 Collecting Bait

1981. Fishermen's Day. Multicoloured.
950 5l. Type **175** 45 15
951 15l. Fishing boats 85 25
952 90l. Fisherman with catch 1·60 60
953 1r.30 Sorting fish 2·00 1·10
MS954 147×101 mm. 3r. Loading fish for export 1·50 2·50

176 Bread Fruit

1981. World Food Day. Multicoloured.
955 10l. Type **176** 40 10
956 25l. Hen with chicks 80 15
957 30l. Maize 80 20
958 75l. Skipjack tuna 2·50 65
959 1r. Pumpkin 3·00 70
960 2r. Coconuts 3·25 3·25
MS961 110×85 mm. 5r. Eggplant 2·50 3·50

177 Pluto and Cat

1982. 50th Anniversary of Pluto (Walt Disney Cartoon Character). Multicoloured.
962 4r. Type **177** 1·60 2·50
MS963 127×101 mm. 6r. Pluto (scene from *The Pointer*) 2·50 4·00

178 Balmoral

1982. 21st Birthday of Princess of Wales. Multicoloured.
964 95l. Type **178** 50 20
965 3r. Prince and Princess of Wales 1·25 65
966 5r. Princess on aircraft steps 1·75 95
MS967 103×75 mm. 8r. Princess of Wales 1·75 1·75

179 Scout saluting and Camp-site

1983. 75th Anniversary of Boy Scout Movement. Multicoloured.
968 1r.30 Type **179** 40 45
969 1r.80 Lighting a fire 50 60
970 4r. Life-saving 1·10 1·40
971 5r. Map-reading 1·40 1·75
MS972 128×66 mm. 10r. Scout emblem and flag of the Maldives 2·00 3·00

180 Footballer

1982. World Cup Football Championship, Spain.
973 **180** 90l. multicoloured 1·25 60
974 - 1r.50 multicoloured 1·75 1·10
975 - 3r. multicoloured 2·50 1·75
976 - 5r. multicoloured 2·75 2·50
MS977 94×63 mm. 10r. multicoloured 4·50 6·00
Designs: 1r.50 to 10r. Various footballers.

1982. Birth of Prince William of Wales. Nos. 964/**MS**967 optd **ROYAL BABY 21.6.82**.
978 95l. Type **178** 30 20
979 3r. Prince and Princess of Wales 75 65
980 5r. Princess on aircraft steps 75 95
MS981 103×75 mm. 8r. Princess of Wales 3·50 2·50

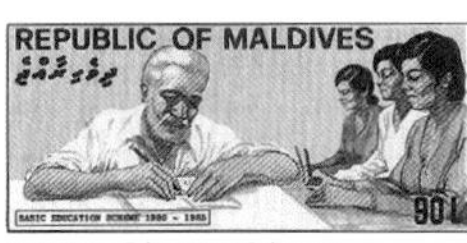

181 Basic Education Scheme

1983. National Education. Multicoloured.
982 90l. Type **181** 20 30
983 95l. Primary education 20 30
984 1r.30 Teacher training 25 30
985 2r.50 Printing educational material 45 75
MS986 100×70 mm. 6r. Thaana typewriter keyboard 1·00 2·00

182 Koch isolates the Bacillus

1983. Centenary of Robert Koch's Discovery of Tubercle Bacillus. Multicoloured.
987 5l. Type **182** 20 20
988 15l. Micro-organism and microscope 25 20
989 95l. Dr. Robert Koch in 1905 55 45
990 3r. Dr. Koch and plates from publication 95 1·75
MS991 77×61 mm. 5r. Koch in his laboratory (horiz) 1·00 2·00

183 Blohm and Voss Seaplane *Nordsee*

1983. Bicentenary of Manned Flight. Multicoloured.
992 90l. Type **183** 2·25 70
993 1r.45 Macchi Castoldi MC.72 seaplane 2·75 1·75
994 4r. Boeing F4B-3 biplane fighter 4·50 3·25
995 5r. Renard and Krebs airship *La France* 4·50 3·50
MS996 110×85 mm. 10r. Nadar's balloon *Le Geant* 3·00 4·00

184 Curved Dash Oldsmobile, 1902

1983. Classic Motor Cars. Multicoloured.
997 5l. Type **184** 20 40
998 30l. Aston Martin Tourer, 1932 60 40
999 40l. Lamborghini Muira, 1966 60 45
1000 1r. Mercedes-Benz 300SL, 1945 1·00 70
1001 1r.40 Stutz Bearcat, 1913 1·25 2·00
1002 5r. Lotus Elite, 1958 2·00 4·25
MS1003 132×103 mm. 10r. Grand Prix Sunbeam, 1924 5·50 10·00

185 Rough-toothed Dolphin

1983. Marine Mammals. Multicoloured.
1004 30l. Type **185** 1·60 60
1005 40l. Indo-Pacific hump-backed dolphin 1·60 65
1006 4r. Finless porpoise 5·00 4·00
1007 6r. Pygmy sperm whale 10·00 7·00
MS1008 82×90 mm. 5r. Striped dolphin 6·00 5·50

186 Dish Aerial

1983. World Communications Year. Multicoloured.
1009 50l. Type **186** 50 20
1010 1r. Land, sea and air communications 1·75 60
1011 2r. Ship-to-shore communications 2·50 1·75
1012 10r. Air traffic controller 4·75 7·50
MS1013 91×76 mm. 20r. Telecommunications 3·75 4·75

187 *La Donna Gravida*

1983. 500th Birth Anniversary of Raphael. Multicoloured.
1014 90l. Type **187** 25 25
1015 3r. *Giovanna d'Aragona* (detail) 75 1·40
1016 4r. *Woman with Unicorn* 75 1·90
1017 6r. *La Muta* 1·00 2·50
MS1018 121×97 mm. 10r. *The Knight's Dream* (detail) 2·50 5·50

188 Refugee Camp

1983. Solidarity with the Palestinian People. Multicoloured.
1019 4r. Type **188** 2·50 2·00
1020 5r. Refugee holding dead child 2·50 2·00
1021 6r. Child carrying food 2·75 2·50

189 Education Facilities

1983. National Development Programme. Multicoloured.

1022	7l. Type **189**	20	10
1023	10l. Health service and education	50	10
1024	5r. Growing more food	1·50	1·25
1025	6r. Fisheries development	2·25	1·50
MS1026	134×93 mm. 10r. Air transport	2·25	2·75

190 Baseball

1984. Olympic Games, Los Angeles. Multicoloured.

1027	50l. Type **190**	30	15
1028	1r.55 Backstroke swimming	65	40
1029	3r. Judo	1·40	90
1030	4r. Shot-putting	1·60	1·40
MS1031	85×105 mm. 10r. Team handball	2·40	2·75

1984. UPU Congress, Hamburg. Nos. 994/**MS**996 optd **19th UPU CONGRESS HAMBURG**.

1032	4r. Boeing F4B-3	1·75	1·40
1033	5r. *La France* airship	1·75	1·60
MS1034	110×85 mm. 10r. Nadar's balloon *Le Geant*	2·75	4·50

1984. Surch **Rf.1.45**

(a) Nos. 964/**MS**967

1035	1r.45 on 95l. Type **178**	2·00	1·50
1036	1r.45 on 3r. Prince and Princess of Wales	2·00	1·50
1037	1r.45 on 5r. Princess on aircraft steps	2·00	1·50
MS1038	103×75 mm. 1r.45 on 8r. Princess of Wales	2·00	3·75

(b) Nos. 978/**MS**981.

1039	1r.45 on 95l. Type **178**	2·00	1·50
1040	1r.45 on 3r. Prince and Princess of Wales	2·00	1·50
1041	1r.45 on 5r. Princess on aircraft steps	2·00	1·50
MS1042	103×75 mm. 1r.45 on 8r. Princess of Wales	2·00	3·75

193 Hands breaking Manacles

1984. Namibia Day. Multicoloured.

1043	6r. Type **193**	1·00	1·25
1044	8r. Namibian family	1·00	1·75
MS1045	129×104 mm. 10r. Map of Namibia	1·75	2·50

194 Island Resort and Common Terns

1984. Tourism. Multicoloured.

1046	7l. Type **194**	2·25	80
1047	15l. Dhow	1·00	15
1048	20l. Snorkelling	80	15
1049	2r. Wind-surfing	2·25	50
1050	4r. Aqualung diving	2·75	1·10
1051	6r. Night fishing	3·75	1·75
1052	8r. Game fishing	4·25	2·00
1053	10r. Turtle on beach	4·75	2·25

195 Frangipani

1984. Ausipex International Stamp Exhibition, Melbourne. Multicoloured.

1054	5r. Type **195**	2·25	1·75
1055	10r. Cooktown orchid	4·75	3·75
MS1056	105×77 mm. 15r. Sun orchid	10·00	5·50

196 Facade of Male Mosque

1984. Opening of Islamic Centre. Multicoloured.

1057	2r. Type **196**	45	50
1058	5r. Male Mosque and minaret (vert)	1·10	1·25

197 Air Maldives Boeing 737

1984. 40th Anniversary of ICAO. Multicoloured.

1059	7l. Type **197**	85	45
1060	4r. Air Lanka Lockheed L-1011 TriStar	3·25	2·00
1061	6r. Alitalia Douglas DC-10-30	4·00	3·50
1062	8r. LTU Lockheed L-1011 TriStar	4·25	4·50
MS1063	110×92 mm. 15r. Air Maldives Short S.7 Skyvan	3·75	4·00

198 Daisy Duck

1984. 50th Birthday of Donald Duck. Walt Disney Cartoon Characters. Multicoloured.

1064	3l. Type **198**	10	10
1065	4l. Huey, Dewey and Louie	10	10
1066	5l. Ludwig von Drake	10	10
1067	10l. Gyro Gearloose	10	10
1068	15l. Uncle Scrooge painting self-portrait	15	10
1069	25l. Donald Duck with camera	15	10
1070	5r. Donald Duck and Gus Goose	2·25	1·25
1071	8r. Gladstone Gander	2·50	2·00
1072	10r. Grandma Duck	3·00	2·50
MS1073	102×126 mm. 15r. Uncle Scrooge and Donald Duck in front of camera	4·75	5·00
MS1074	126×102 mm. 15r. Uncle Scrooge	4·75	5·00

199 *The Day* (detail)

1984. 450th Death Anniversary of Correggio (artist). Multicoloured.

1075	5r. Type **199**	1·00	1·50
1076	10r. *The Night* (detail)	1·50	1·75
MS1077	60×80 mm. 15r. *Portrait of a Man*	3·50	3·25

200 *Edmond Iduranty* (Degas)

1984. 150th Birth Anniversary of Edgar Degas (artist). Multicoloured.

1078	75l. Type **200**	20	20
1079	2r. *James Tissot*	50	50
1080	5r. *Achille de Gas in Uniform*	1·00	1·00
1081	10r. *Lady with Chrysanthemums*	1·75	2·00
MS1082	100×70 mm. 15r. *Self-portrait*	3·25	3·75

201 Pale-footed Shearwater ('Flest-footed Shearwater')

1985. Birth Bicentenary of John J. Audubon (ornithologist) (1st issue). Designs showing original paintings. Multicoloured.

1083	3r. Type **201**	1·75	80
1084	3r.50 Little grebe (horiz)	2·00	90
1085	4r. Great cormorant	2·00	1·00
1086	4r.50 White-faced storm petrel (horiz)	2·00	1·10
MS1087	108×80 mm. 15r. Red-necked phalarope (horiz)	4·50	4·50

See also Nos. 1192/**MS**1200.

202 Squad Drilling

1985. National Security Service. Multicoloured.

1088	15l. Type **202**	50	10
1089	20l. Combat patrol	50	10
1090	1r. Fire fighting	2·00	40
1091	2r. Coastguard cutter	2·50	1·00
1092	10r. Independence Day Parade (vert)	3·25	3·50
MS1093	128×85 mm. 10r. Cannon on saluting base and National Security Service badge	2·25	2·25

1985. Olympic Games Gold Medal Winners, Los Angeles. Nos. 1027/1031 optd.

1094	50l. Type **190** (optd **JAPAN**)	30	15
1095	1r.55 Backstroke swimming (optd **GOLD MEDALIST THERESA ANDREWS USA**)	60	55
1096	3r. Judo (optd **GOLD MEDALIST FRANK WIENEKE USA**)	1·25	1·25
1097	4r. Shot-putting (optd **GOLD MEDALIST CLAUDIA LOCH WEST GERMANY**)	1·25	1·40
MS1098	85×105 mm. 10r. Team handball (optd **U.S.A.**)	1·90	2·00

204 Queen Elizabeth the Queen Mother, 1981

1985. Life and Times of Queen Elizabeth the Queen Mother. Multicoloured.

1099	3r. Type **204**	45	60
1100	5r. Visiting the Middlesex Hospital (horiz)	65	1·00
1101	7r. The Queen Mother	85	1·25
MS1102	56×85 mm. 15r. With Prince Charles at Garter Ceremony	4·25	3·25

Stamps as Nos. 1099/1101 but with face values of 1r., 4r. and 10r. exist from additional sheetlets with changed background colours.

204a Lira da Braccio

1985. 300th Birth Anniversary of Johann Sebastian Bach (composer). Multicoloured (except No. **MS**1107).

1103	15l. Type **204a**	10	10
1104	2r. Tenor oboe	50	45
1105	4r. Serpent	90	85
1106	10r. Table organ	1·90	2·25
MS1107	104×75 mm. 15r. Johann Sebastian Bach (black and orange)	3·00	3·50

205 Mas Odi (fishing boat)

1985. Maldives Ships and Boats. Multicoloured.

1108	3l. Type **205**	15	30
1109	5l. Battela (dhow)	15	30
1110	10l. Addu odi (dhow)	15	30
1111	2r.60 Modern dhoni (fishing boat)	2·25	1·75
1112	2r.70 Mas dhoni (fishing boat)	2·25	1·75
1113	3r. Baththeli dhoni	2·50	1·75
1114	5r. *Inter I* (inter-island vessel)	3·75	3·00
1115	10r. Dhoni-style yacht	5·50	6·00

206 Windsurfing

1985. Tenth Anniversary of World Tourism Organisation. Multicoloured.

1116	6r. Type **206**	3·00	2·75
1117	8r. Scuba diving	3·25	3·00
MS1118	171×114 mm. 15r. Kuda Hithi Resort	2·75	3·00

207 United Nations Building, New York

1985. 40th Anniversary of UNO and International Peace Year. Multicoloured.

1119	15l. Type **207**	10	10
1120	2r. Hands releasing Peace Dove	40	45
1121	4r. UN Security Council meeting (horiz)	70	85
1122	10r. Lion and lamb	1·25	2·00
MS1123	76×92 mm. 15r. UN building and Peace Dove	2·25	2·75

208 Maldivian Delegate voting in UN General Assembly

1985. 20th Anniv of United Nations Membership. Multicoloured.

1124	20l. Type **208**	10	10
1125	15r. UN and Maldivian flags, and UN Building, New York	2·00	3·00

209 Youths playing Drums

1985. International Youth Year. Multicoloured.

1126	90l. Type **209**	15	20
1127	6r. Tug-of-war	80	1·10
1128	10r. Community service (vert)	1·25	2·00
MS1129	85×84 mm. 15r. Raising the flag at youth camp (vert)	2·25	3·00

210 Quotation and Flags of Member Nations

1985. First Summit Meeting of South Asian Association for Regional Co-operation, Dhaka, Bangladesh.

1130	**210** 3r. multicoloured	1·50	1·50

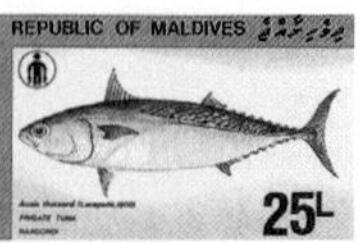

211 Mackerel Frigate

1985. Fishermen's Day. Species of Tuna. Multicoloured.

1131	25l. Type **211**	35	10

1132 75l. Kawakawa ('Little tuna') 65 15
1133 3r. Dog-toothed tuna 2·00 1·00
1134 5r. Yellow-finned tuna 2·50 1·50
MS1135 130×90 mm. 15r. Skipjack tuna 3·50 3·50

1985. 150th Birth Anniversary of Mark Twain. Designs as T **160a** of Lesotho, showing Walt Disney cartoon characters illustrating various Mark Twain quotations. Multicoloured.
1136 2l. Winnie the Pooh (vert) 10 20
1137 3l. Gepetto and Figaro the cat (vert) 10 20
1138 4l. Goofy and basket of broken eggs (vert) 10 20
1139 20l. Goofy as doctor scolding Donald Duck (vert) 25 10
1140 4r. Mowgli and King Louis (vert) 1·40 1·75
1141 13r. The wicked Queen and mirror (vert) 5·00 7·00
MS1142 126×101 mm. 15r. Mickey Mouse as Tom Sawyer on comet's tail 6·50 7·00

1985. Birth Bicentenaries of Grimm Brothers (folklorists). Designs as T **160b** of Lesotho, showing Walt Disney cartoon characters in scenes from "Dr. Knowall". Multicoloured.
1143 1l. Donald Duck as Crabb driving oxcart (horiz) 10 10
1144 5l. Donald Duck as Dr. Knowall (horiz) 10 10
1145 10l. Dr. Knowall in surgery (horiz) 10 10
1146 15l. Dr. Knowall with Uncle Scrooge as a lord (horiz) 10 10
1147 3r. Dr. and Mrs. Knowall in pony and trap (horiz) 1·10 1·50
1148 15r. Dr. Knowall and thief (horiz) 5·50 7·00
MS1149 126×101 mm. 15r. Donald and Daisy Duck as Dr. and Mrs. Knowall 6·50 7·00

211c Weapons on Road Sign

1986. World Disarmament Day. Multicoloured.
1149a 1r.50 Type **211c** 25·00 10·00
1149b 10r. Peace dove 30·00 30·00

1986. Appearance of Halley's Comet (1st issue). As T **162a** of Lesotho. Multicoloured.
1150 20l. NASA space telescope and Comet 50 25
1151 1r.50 ESA *Giotto* spacecraft and Comet 1·25 1·50
1152 2r. Japanese *Planet A* spacecraft and Comet 1·25 1·75
1153 4r. Edmond Halley and Stonehenge 2·00 3·00
1154 5r. Russian *Vega* spacecraft and Comet 2·00 3·00
MS1155 101×70 mm. 15r. Halley's Comet 8·00 10·00
See also Nos. 1206/**MS**1211.

1986. Centenary of Statue of Liberty. Multicoloured. As T **163b** of Lesotho, showing the Statue of Liberty and immigrants to the USA.
1156 50l. Walter Gropius (architect) 40 30
1157 70l. John Lennon (musician) 2·00 1·25
1158 1r. George Balanchine (choreographer) 2·00 1·25
1159 10r. Franz Werfel (writer) 4·00 7·00
MS1160 100×72 mm. 15r. Statue of Liberty (vert) 8·00 8·50

1986. Ameripex International Stamp Exhibition, Chicago. As T **163c** of Lesotho, showing Walt Disney cartoon characters and USA stamps. Multicoloured.
1161 3l. Johnny Appleseed and 1966 Johnny Appleseed stamp 10 10
1162 4l. Paul Bunyan and 1958 Forest Conservation stamp 10 10
1163 5l. Casey and 1969 Professional Baseball Centenary stamp 10 10
1164 10l. Ichabod Crane and 1974 *Legend of Sleepy Hollow* stamp 10 10
1165 15l. John Henry and 1944 75th anniversary of completion of First Transcontinental Railroad stamp 15 15
1166 20l. Windwagon Smith and 1954 Kansas Territory Centenary stamp 15 15
1167 13r. Mike Fink and 1970 Great Northwest stamp 7·00 7·00
1168 14r. Casey Jones and 1950 Railroad Engineers stamp 8·00 8·00
MS1169 Two sheets, each 127×101 mm. (a) 15r. Davy Crockett and 1967 Davy Crockett stamp. (b) 15r. Daisy Duck as Pocahontas saving Captain John Smith (Donald Duck) Set of 2 sheets 13·00 16·00

1986. 60th Birthday of Queen Elizabeth II. As T **163a** of Lesotho.
1170 1r. black and yellow 30 25
1171 2r. multicoloured 40 55
1172 12r. multicoloured 1·50 2·50
MS1173 120×85 mm. 15r. black and brown 4·00 4·25
Designs: 1r. Royal Family at Girl Guides Rally, 1938; 2r. Queen in Canada; 12r. At Sandringham, 1970; 15r. Princesses Elizabeth and Margaret at Royal Lodge, Windsor, 1940.

212 Player running with Ball

1986. World Cup Football Championship, Mexico. Multicoloured.
1174 15l. Type **212** 75 30
1175 2r. Player gaining control of ball 2·50 1·75
1176 4r. Two players competing for ball 4·00 3·50
1177 10r. Player bouncing ball on knee 7·50 8·00
MS1178 95×114 mm. 15r. Player kicking ball 5·00 6·00

1986. Royal Wedding. As T **170a** of Lesotho. Multicoloured.
1179 10l. Prince Andrew and Miss Sarah Ferguson 20 10
1180 2r. Prince Andrew 85 70
1181 12r. Prince Andrew in naval uniform 3·75 3·75
MS1182 88×88 mm. 15r. Prince Andrew and Miss Sarah Ferguson (different) 5·00 4·75

213 Moorish Idol and Sea Fan

1986. Marine Wildlife. Multicoloured.
1183 50l. Type **213** 1·50 40
1184 90l. Regal angelfish 2·00 55
1185 1r. Maldive anemonefish 2·00 55
1186 2r. Tiger cowrie and stinging coral 2·50 1·60
1187 3r. Emperor angelfish and staghorn coral 2·50 2·00
1188 4r. Black-naped tern 3·00 3·00
1189 5r. Fiddler crab and staghorn coral 2·50 3·00
1190 10r. Hawksbill turtle 3·00 5·00
MS1191 Two sheets, each 107×76 mm. (a) 15r. Long-nosed butterflyfish. (b) 15r. Oriental trumpetfish Set of 2 sheets 12·00 15·00

1986. Birth Bicentenary (1985) of John J. Audubon (ornithologist) (2nd issue). As T **201** showing original paintings. Multicoloured.
1192 3l. Little blue heron (horiz) 40 60
1193 4l. White-tailed kite 40 60
1194 5l. Greater shearwater (horiz) 40 60
1195 10l. Magnificent Frigatebird 45 40
1196 15l. Black-necked grebe ('Eared Grebe') 85 40
1197 20l. Goosander ('Common Merganser') 90 40
1198 13r. Peregrine falcon ('Great Footed Hawk') (horiz) 7·50 7·50
1199 14r. Prairie chicken ('Greater Prairie Chicken') (horiz) 7·50 7·50
MS1200 Two sheets, each 74×104 mm. (a) 15r. Fulmar ('Northern Fulmar'). (b) 15r. White-fronted goose (horiz) Set of 2 sheets 24·00 21·00

1986. World Cup Football Championship Winners, Mexico. Nos. 1174/7 optd **WINNERS Argentina 3 W. Germany 2**.
1201 15l. Type **212** 40 30
1202 2r. Player gaining control of ball 1·25 1·10
1203 4r. Two players competing for ball 2·00 2·00
1204 10r. Player bouncing ball on knee 2·75 4·25
MS1205 95×114 mm. 15r. Player kicking ball 3·00 4·25

(213b)

1986. Appearance of Halley's Comet (2nd issue). Nos. 1150/**MS**1155 optd with T **213b**.
1206 20l. NASA space telescope and Comet 65 40
1207 1r.50 ESA *Giotto* spacecraft and Comet 1·25 1·25
1208 2r. Japanese *Planet A* spacecraft and Comet 1·50 1·50
1209 4r. Edmond Halley and Stonehenge 2·00 2·50
1210 5r. Russia *Vega* spacecraft and Comet 2·00 2·50
MS1211 101×70 mm. 15r. Halley's Comet 6·00 7·00

214 Servicing Aircraft

1986. 40th Anniversary of UNESCO. Multicoloured.
1212 1r. Type **214** 80 30
1213 2r. Boat building 90 1·00
1214 3r. Children in classroom 1·00 1·40
1215 5r. Student in laboratory 1·10 2·50
MS1216 77×100 mm. 15r. Diving bell on sea bed 2·75 4·25

215 *Hypholoma fasciculare*

1986. Fungi of the Maldives. Multicoloured.
1217 15l. Type **215** 80 25
1218 50l. *Kuehneromyces mutabilis* (vert) 1·50 45
1219 1r. *Amanita muscaria* (vert) 1·75 60
1220 2r. *Agaricus campestris* 2·00 1·50
1221 3r. *Amanita pantherina* (vert) 2·00 1·75
1222 4r. *Coprinus comatus* (vert) 2·00 2·25
1223 5r. *Gymnopilus junonias* ('Pholiota spectabilis') 2·00 2·75
1224 10r. *Pluteus cervinus* 2·50 4·50
MS1225 Two sheets, each 100×70 mm. (a) 15r. *Armillaria mellea*. (b) 15r. *Stropharia aeruginosa* (vert) Set of 2 sheets 13·00 14·00

216 Ixora

1987. Flowers. Multicoloured.
1226 10l. Type **216** 10 10
1227 20l. Frangipani 10 10
1228 50l. Crinum 2·00 60
1229 2r. Pink rose 40 80
1230 4r. Flamboyant flower 60 1·50
1231 10r. Ground orchid 6·00 8·00
MS1232 Two sheets, each 100×70 mm. (a) 15r. Gardenia. (b) 15r. Oleander Set of 2 sheets 4·75 6·50

217 Guides studying Wild Flowers

1987. 75th Anniversary (1985) of Girl Guide Movement. Multicoloured.
1233 15l. Type **217** 30 20
1234 2r. Guides with pet rabbits 50 80
1235 4r. Guide observing white spoonbill 2·50 2·25
1236 12r. Lady Baden-Powell and Guide flag 2·50 6·50
MS1237 104×78 mm. 15r. Guides in sailing dinghy 2·25 3·75

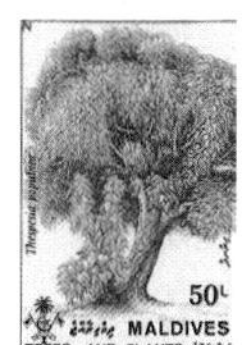
218 *Thespesia populnea*

1987. Trees and Plants. Multicoloured.
1238 50l. Type **218** 15 10
1239 1r. *Cocos nucifera* 25 20
1240 2r. *Calophyllum mophyllum* 40 40
1241 3r. *Xanthosoma indica* (horiz) 60 65
1242 5r. *Ipomoea batatas* (horiz) 1·00 1·40
1243 7r. *Artocarpus altilis* 1·25 2·25
MS1244 75×109 mm. 15r. *Cocos nucifera* (different) 2·25 3·25
No. 1241 is inscr 'Xyanthosomaindica' in error.

1987. America's Cup Yachting Championship. As T **218a** of Lesotho. Multicoloured.
1245 15l. *Intrepid*, 1970 10 10
1246 1r. *France II*, 1974 20 20
1247 2r. *Gretel*, 1962 40 60
1248 12r. *Volunteer*, 1887 2·00 3·00
MS1249 113×83 mm. 15r. Helmsman and crew on deck of *Defender*, 1895 (horiz) 2·25 3·25

219 *Precis octavia*

1987. Butterflies. Multicoloured.
1250 15l. Type **219** 45 30
1251 20l. *Atrophaneura hector* 45 30
1252 50l. *Teinopalpus imperialis* 75 40
1253 1r. *Kallima horsfieldi* 1·00 45
1254 2r. *Cethosia biblis* 1·40 1·25
1255 4r. *Idea jasonia* 2·25 2·25
1256 7r. *Papilio memnon* 2·75 4·00
1257 10r. *Aeropetes tulbaghia* 3·25 5·00
MS1258 Two sheets, each 135×102 mm. (a) 15r. *Acraea violae*. (b) 15r. *Hebomoia leucippe* Set of 2 sheets 7·50 11·00

220 Isaac Newton experimenting with Spectrum

1988. Great Scientific Discoveries. Multicoloured.
1259 1r.50 Type **220** 1·25 1·00
1260 3r. Euclid composing *Principles of Geometry* (vert) 1·60 1·75
1261 4r. Mendel formulating theory of Genetic Evolution (vert) 1·75 2·00
1262 5r. Galileo and moons of Jupiter 3·00 3·00
MS1263 102×72 mm. 15r. Apollo lunar module (vert) 4·50 5·50

221 Donald Duck and Weather Satellite

1988. Space Exploration. Walt Disney cartoon characters. Multicoloured.
1264 3l. Type **221** 10 10
1265 4l. Minnie Mouse and navigation satellite 10 10
1266 5l. Mickey Mouse's nephews talking via communication satellite 10 10
1267 10l. Goofy in lunar rover (vert) 10 10
1268 20l. Minnie Mouse delivering pizza to flying saucer (vert) 10 10
1269 13r. Mickey Mouse directing spacecraft docking (vert) 5·00 5·00
1270 14r. Mickey Mouse and *Voyager 2* 5·00 5·00
MS1271 Two sheets, each 127×102 mm. (a) 15r. Mickey Mouse at first Moon landing, 1969. (b) 15r. Mickey Mouse and nephews in space station swimming pool (vert) Set of 2 sheets 13·00 13·00

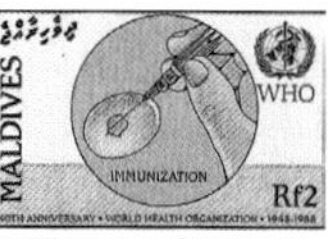
222 Syringe and Bacterium ('Immunization')

1988. 40th Anniversary of WHO. Multicoloured.
1272 2r. Type **222** 40 40
1273 4r. Tap ('Clean Water') 60 85

223 Water Droplet and Atoll

1988. World Environment Day (1987). Multicoloured.

1274	15l. Type **223**	10	10
1275	75l. Coral reef	20	40
1276	2r. Audubon's shearwaters in flight	85	1·40
MS1277	105×76 mm. 15r. Banyan tree (vert)	4·25	5·50

224 Globe, Carrier Pigeon and Letter

1988. Transport and Telecommunications Decade. Each showing central globe. Multicoloured.

1278	2r. Type **224**	75	65
1279	3r. Dish aerial and girl using telephone	1·25	1·10
1280	5r. Satellite, television, telephone and antenna tower	2·00	2·00
1281	10r. Car, ship and Lockheed TriStar airliner	11·00	6·50

1988. Royal Ruby Wedding. Nos. 1170/**MS**1173 optd **40TH WEDDING ANNIVERSARY H.M. QUEEN ELIZABETH II H.R.H. THE DUKE OF EDINBURGH**.

1282	1r. black and yellow	50	25
1283	2r. multicoloured	75	60
1284	12r. multicoloured	3·00	3·50
MS1285	120×85 mm. 15r. black and brown	4·50	4·50

226 Discus-throwing

1988. Olympic Games, Seoul. Multicoloured.

1286	15l. Type **226**	10	10
1287	2r. 100 m race	40	40
1288	4r. Gymnastics (horiz)	70	80
1289	12r. Three-day equestrian event (horiz)	2·25	3·25
MS1290	106×76 mm. 20r. Tennis (horiz)	4·00	4·75

227 Immunisation at Clinic

1988. International Year of Shelter for the Homeless. Multicoloured.

1291	50l. Type **227**	30	30
1292	3r. Prefab housing estate	1·10	1·40
MS1293	63×105 mm. 15r. Building site	1·75	2·50

228 Breadfruit

1988. Tenth Anniversary of International Fund for Agricultural Development. Multicoloured.

1294	7r. Type **228**	1·00	1·40
1295	10r. Mangoes (vert)	1·50	1·90
MS1296	103×74 mm. 15r. Coconut palm, fishing boat and yellowtail tuna	2·75	3·00

1988. World Aids Day. Nos. 1272/1273 optd **WORLD AIDS DAY** and emblem.

1297	2r. Type **222**	35	45
1298	4r. Tap ('Clean Water')	65	80

230 President Kennedy and Launch of Apollo Spacecraft

1989. 25th Death Anniversary (1988) of John F. Kennedy (American statesman). US Space Achievements. Multicoloured.

1299	5r. Type **230**	2·50	2·75
1300	5r. Lunar module and astronaut on Moon	2·50	2·75
1301	5r. Astronaut and buggy on Moon	2·50	2·75
1302	5r. President Kennedy and spacecraft	2·50	2·75
MS1303	108×77 mm. 15r. President Kennedy making speech	4·00	5·00

1989. Olympic Medal Winners, Seoul. Nos. 1286/**MS**1290 optd.

1304	15l. Type **226** (optd **J. SCHULT DDR**)	20	20
1305	2r. 100 m race (optd **C. LEWIS USA**)	65	65
1306	4r. Gymnastics (horiz) (optd **MEN'S ALL AROUND V. ARTEMOV USSR**)	1·40	1·40
1307	12r. Three-day equestrian event (horiz) (optd **TEAM SHOW JUMPING W. GERMANY**)	4·00	5·50
MS1308	106×76 mm. 20r. Tennis (horiz) (optd **OLYMPIC WINNERS MEN'S SINGLES GOLD M. MECIR CZECH SILVER T. MAYOTTE USA BRONZE B. GILBERT USA**)	6·50	7·50

On No. **MS**1308 the overprint appears on the sheet margin.

1989. 500th Birth Anniversary of Titian (artist). As T **186a** of Lesotho, showing paintings. Multicoloured.

1309	15l. *Benedetto Varchi*	10	10
1310	1r. *Portrait of a Young Man*	20	15
1311	2r. *King Francis I of France*	40	40
1312	5r. *Pietro Aretino*	1·10	1·25
1313	15r. *The Bravo*	3·50	5·50
1314	20r. *The Concert* (detail)	3·50	6·00
MS1315	Two sheets. (a) 112×96 mm. 20r. *An Allegory of Prudence* (detail). (b) 96×110 mm. 20r. *Francesco Maria della Rovere* Set of 2 sheets	8·50	11·00

1989. Tenth Anniversary of Asia-Pacific Telecommunity. Nos. 1279/1280 optd **ASIA-PACIFIC TELECOMMUNITY 10 YEARS** and emblem. Multicoloured.

1316	3r. Dish aerial and girl using telephone	1·25	1·50
1317	5r. Satellite, television, telephone and antenna tower	1·75	2·00

1989. Japanese Art. Paintings by Hokusai. As T **187a** of Lesotho. Multicoloured.

1318	15l. *Fuji from Hodogaya* (horiz)	10	10
1319	50l. *Fuji from Lake Kawaguchi* (horiz)	15	15
1320	1r. *Fuji from Owari* (horiz)	25	15
1321	2r. *Fuji from Tsukudajima in Edo* (horiz)	50	40
1322	4r. *Fuji from a Teahouse at Yoshida* (horiz)	80	90
1323	6r. *Fuji from Tagonoura* (horiz)	90	1·25
1324	10r. *Fuji from Mishima-goe* (horiz)	2·25	2·75
1325	12r. *Fuji from the Sumida River in Edo* (horiz)	2·25	2·75
MS1326	Two sheets, each 101×77 mm. (a) 18r. *Fuji from Inume Pass*. (b) 18r. *Fuji from Fukagawa in Edo* Set of 2 sheets	8·50	9·00

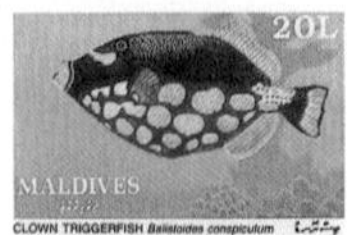
233 Clown Triggerfish

1989. Tropical Fish. Multicoloured.

1327	20l. Type **233**	25	20
1328	50l. Blue-striped snapper	35	25
1329	1r. Powder-blue surgeonfish	45	30
1330	2r. Oriental sweetlips	65	65
1331	3r. Six-barred wrasse	80	85
1332	8r. Thread-finned butterflyfish	1·50	2·50
1333	10r. Bicoloured parrotfish	1·75	2·75
1334	12r. Scarlet-finned squirrelfish	1·75	2·75
MS1335	Two sheets, each 101×73 mm. (a) 15r. Butterfly perch. (b) 15r. Semicircle angelfish Set of 2 sheets	13·00	12·00

234 Goofy, Mickey and Minnie Mouse with Takuri Type 3, 1907

1989. World Stamp Expo '89 International Stamp Exhibition, Washington (1st issue). Designs showing Walt Disney cartoon characters with Japanese cars. Multicoloured.

1336	15l. Type **234**	20	15
1337	50l. Donald and Daisy Duck in Mitsubishi Model A, 1917	40	30
1338	1r. Goofy in Datsun Roadstar, 1935	70	50
1339	2r. Donald and Daisy Duck with Mazda, 1940	1·00	75
1340	4r. Donald Duck with Nissan Bluebird 310, 1959	1·50	1·25
1341	6r. Donald and Daisy Duck with Subaru 360, 1958	1·75	1·75
1342	10r. Mickey Mouse and Pluto in Honda 5800, 1966	3·25	3·75
1343	12r. Mickey Mouse and Goofy in Daihatsu Fellow, 1966	3·75	4·25
MS1344	Two sheets, each 127×102 mm. (a) 20r. Daisy Duck with Chip 'n' Dale and Isuzu Trooper II, 1981. (b) 20r. Mickey Mouse with tortoise and Toyota Supra, 1985 Set of 2 sheets	11·00	13·00

1989. World Stamp Expo '89 International Stamp Exhibition, Washington (2nd issue). Landmarks of Washington. Sheet 62×78 mm, containing multicoloured designs as T **193a** of Lesotho, but vert.

MS1345	8r. Marine Corps Memorial, Arlington National Cemetery	2·75	3·00

235 Lunar Module *Eagle*

1989. 20th Anniversary of First Manned Landing on Moon. Multicoloured.

1346	1r. Type **235**	30	20
1347	2r. Astronaut Aldrin collecting dust samples	50	60
1348	6r. Aldrin setting up seismometer	1·25	1·75
1349	10r. President Nixon congratulating *Apollo 11* astronauts	1·90	2·50
MS1350	107×75 mm. 18r. Television picture of Armstrong about to step onto Moon (34×47 mm)	7·50	8·00

236 Jawaharlal Nehru with Mahatma Gandhi

1989. Anniversaries and Events. Multicoloured.

1351	20l. Type **236** (birth centenary)	4·25	1·50
1352	50l. Opium poppies and logo (anti-drugs campaign) (vert)	1·50	45
1353	1r. William Shakespeare (425th birth anniversary)	1·25	45
1354	2r. Storming the Bastille (bicentenary of French Revolution) (vert)	1·25	1·25
1355	3r. Concorde (20th anniversary of first flight)	5·50	4·25
1356	8r. George Washington (bicentenary of inauguration)	2·00	3·00
1357	10r. William Bligh (bicentenary of mutiny on the *Bounty*)	9·00	6·00
1358	12r. Hamburg harbour (800th anniversary) (vert)	4·50	5·50
MS1359	Two sheets. (a) 115×85 mm. 18r. Baseball players (50th anniversary of first televised game) (vert). (b) 110×80 mm. 18r. Franz von Taxis (500th anniversary of regular European postal services) (vert) Set of 2 sheets	14·00	16·00

237 Sir William van Horne (Chairman of Canadian Pacific), Locomotive and Map, 1894

1989. Railway Pioneers. Multicoloured.

1360	10l. Type **237**	25	15
1361	25l. Matthew Murray (engineer) with Blenkinsop and Murray's rack locomotive, 1810	35	20
1362	50l. Louis Favre (railway engineer) and steam locomotive entering tunnel	40	25
1363	2r. George Stephenson (engineer) and *Locomotion*, 1825	75	55
1364	6r. Richard Trevithick and *Catch-Me-Who-Can*, 1808	1·50	1·50
1365	8r. George Nagelmackers and Orient Express dining car	1·75	1·75
1366	10r. William Jessop and horse-drawn wagon, Surrey Iron Railway, 1770	2·50	2·50
1367	12r. Isambard Brunel (engineer) and GWR steam locomotive, 1833	3·00	3·00
MS1368	Two sheets, each 71×103 mm. (a) 18r. George Pullman (inventor of sleeping cars), 1864. (b) 18r. Rudolf Diesel (engineer) and first oil engine Set of 2 sheets	11·00	12·00

238 Bodu Thakurufaanu Memorial Centre, Utheemu

1990. 25th Anniversary of Independence. Multicoloured.

1369	20l. Type **238**	10	10
1370	25l. Islamic Centre, Male	10	10
1371	50l. National Flag and logos of international organisations	10	10
1372	2r. Presidential Palace, Male	30	40
1373	5r. National Security Service	85	1·25
MS1374	128×90 mm. 10r. National Emblem	5·00	5·50

239 *Louis XVI in Coronation Robes* (Duplessis)

1990. Bicentenary of French Revolution and Philexfrance '89 International Stamp Exhibition, Paris. French Paintings. Multicoloured.

1375	15l. Type **239**	20	15
1376	50l. *Monsieur Lavoisier and his Wife* (David)	45	25
1377	1r. *Madame Pastoret* (David)	65	35
1378	2r. *Oath of Lafayette, 14 July 1790* (anon)	1·00	70
1379	4r. *Madame Trudaine* (David)	1·75	1·50
1380	6r. *Chenard celebrating the Liberation of Savoy* (Boilly)	2·50	2·50
1381	10r. *An Officer swears Allegiance to the Constitution* (anon)	4·00	4·50
1382	12r. *Self Portrait* (David)	4·00	4·75
MS1383	Two sheets. (a) 104×79 mm. 20r. *The Oath of the Tennis Court, 20 June 1789* (David) (horiz). (b) 79×104 mm. 20r. *Rousseau and Symbols of the Revolution* (Jeaurat) Set of 2 sheets	13·00	14·00

239a Donald Duck, Mickey Mouse and Goofy Playing Rugby

1990. Stamp World London '90 International Stamp Exhibition. Walt Disney cartoon characters playing British sports. Multicoloured.

1384 15l. Type **239a** 30 15
1385 50l. Donald Duck and Chip 'n' Dale curling 45 25
1386 1r. Goofy playing polo 65 40
1387 2r. Mickey Mouse and nephews playing soccer 90 70
1388 4r. Mickey Mouse playing cricket 1·75 1·50
1389 6r. Minnie and Mickey Mouse at Ascot races 2·25 1·90
1390 10r. Mickey Mouse and Goofy playing tennis 3·50 3·50
1391 12r. Donald Duck and Mickey Mouse playing bowls 3·50 3·50
MS1392 Two sheets, each 126×101 mm. (a) 20r. Minnie Mouse fox-hunting. (b) 20r. Mickey Mouse playing golf Set of 2 sheets 15·00 15·00

240 Silhouettes of Queen Elizabeth II and Queen Victoria

1990. 150th Anniversary of the Penny Black.

1393 **240** 8r. black and green 3·00 3·00
1394 - 12r. black and blue 3·50 3·50
MS1395 109×84 mm. 18r. black and brown 6·00 7·00

Design: 12r. As T **240**, but with position of silhouettes reversed; 18r. Penny Black.

1990. 90th Birthday of Queen Elizabeth the Queen Mother. As T **198a** of Lesotho.

1396 6r. black, mauve and blue 1·10 1·40
1397 6r. black, mauve and blue 1·10 1·40
1398 6r. black, mauve and blue 1·10 1·40
MS1399 90×75 mm. 18r. multicoloured 3·25 3·50

Designs: No. 1396, Lady Elizabeth Bowes-Lyon; No. 1397, Lady Elizabeth Bowes-Lyon wearing headband; No. 1398, Lady Elizabeth Bowes-Lyon leaving for her wedding; No. **MS**1399, Lady Elizabeth Bowes-Lyon wearing wedding dress.

241 Sultan's Tomb

1990. Islamic Heritage Year. Each black and blue.

1400 1r. Type **241** 35 45
1401 1r. Thakurufaan's Palace 35 45
1402 1r. Male Mosque 35 45
1403 2r. Veranda of Friday Mosque 45 55
1404 2r. Interior of Friday Mosque 45 55
1405 2r. Friday Mosque and Monument 45 55

242 Defence of Wake Island, 1941

1990. 50th Anniversary of Second World War. Multicoloured.

1406 15l. Type **242** 25 20
1407 25l. Stilwell's army in Burma, 1944 30 20
1408 50l. Normandy offensive, 1944 40 25
1409 1r. Capture of Saipan, 1944 55 40
1410 2r.50 D-Day landings, 1944 90 80
1411 3r.50 Allied landings in Norway, 1940 1·10 1·10
1412 4r. Lord Mountbatten, Head of Combined Operations, 1943 1·40 1·40
1413 6r. Japanese surrender, Tokyo Bay, 1945 2·75 3·25
1414 10r. Potsdam Conference, 1945 2·75 3·00
1415 12r. Allied invasion of Sicily, 1943 3·00 3·25
MS1416 115×87 mm. 18r. Atlantic convoy 5·50 6·50

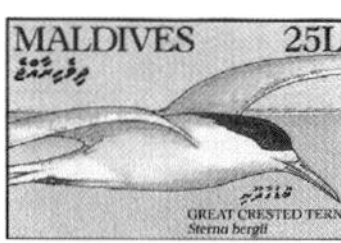

243 Crested Tern ('Great Crested Tern')

1990. Birds. Multicoloured.

1417 25l. Type **243** 15 15
1418 50l. Koel 25 25
1419 1r. White tern 35 35
1420 3r.50 Cinnamon bittern 90 1·00
1421 6r. Sooty tern 1·40 1·60
1422 8r. Audubon's shearwater 1·60 2·00
1423 12r. Common noddy ('Brown Noddy') 2·50 3·00
1424 15r. Lesser Frigatebird 2·75 3·25
MS1425 Two sheets, each 100×69 mm. (a) 18r. Grey heron. (b) 18r. White-tailed Tropicbird Set of 2 sheets 8·00 10·00

244 Emblem, Dish Aerial and Sailboards

1990. 5th South Asian Association for Regional Co-operation Summit.

1426 **244** 75l. black and orange 30 25
1427 - 3r.50 multicoloured 2·25 1·50
MS1428 112×82 mm. 20r. multicoloured 5·50 6·50

Design: 3r.50, Flags of member nations; 20r. Global warming diagram.

245 *Spathoglottis plicata*

1990. EXPO '90 International Garden and Greenery Exhibition, Osaka. Flowers. Mult.

1429 20l. Type **245** 1·25 40
1430 75l. *Hippeastrum puniceum* 1·50 50
1431 2r. *Tecoma stans* (horiz) 1·60 90
1432 3r.50 *Catharanthus roseus* (horiz) 1·60 1·60
1433 10r. *Ixora coccinea* (horiz) 3·00 3·25
1434 12r. *Clitorea ternatea* (horiz) 3·25 3·50
1435 15r. *Caesalpinia pulcherrima* 3·25 3·75
MS1436 Four sheets, each 111×79 mm. (a) 20r. *Plumeria obtusa* (horiz). (b) 20r. *Jasminum grandiflorum* (horiz). (c) 20r. *Rosa* sp (horiz). (d) 20r. *Hibiscus tiliaceous* (horiz) Set of 4 sheets 13·00 13·00

246 *The Hare and the Tortoise*

1990. International Literacy Year. Walt Disney cartoon characters illustrating fables by Aesop. Multicoloured.

1437 15l. Type **246** 35 15
1438 50l. *The Town Mouse and the Country Mouse* 60 25
1439 1r. *The Fox and the Crow* 90 35
1440 3r.50 *The Travellers and the Bear* 1·75 1·60
1441 4r. *The Fox and the Lion* 1·90 1·75
1442 6r. *The Mice Meeting* 2·50 2·50
1443 10r. *The Fox and the Goat* 3·00 3·25
1444 12r. *The Dog in the Manger* 3·00 3·50
MS1445 Two sheets, each 127×102 mm. (a) 20r. *The Miller, his Son and the Ass* (vert). (b) 20r. *The Miser's Gold* (vert) Set of 2 sheets 13·00 13·00

247 East African Railways Class 31 Steam Locomotive

1990. Railway Steam Locomotives. Multicoloured.

1446 20l. Type **247** 85 30
1447 50l. Steam locomotive, Sudan 1·10 45
1448 1r. Class GM Garratt, South Africa 1·60 60
1449 3r. 7th Class, Rhodesia 2·50 2·00
1450 5r. Central Pacific Class No. 229, USA 3·00 2·25
1451 8r. Reading Railroad No. 415, USA 3·50 3·00
1452 10r. Porter narrow gauge, Canada 3·50 3·00
1453 12r. Great Northern Railway No. 515, USA 3·50 3·50
MS1454 Two sheets, each 90×65 mm. (a) 20r. 19th-century standard American locomotive No. 315. (b) 20r. East African Railways Garratt locomotive No. 5950 Set of 2 sheets 17·00 16·00

248 Ruud Gullit of Holland

1990. World Cup Football Championship, Italy. Multicoloured.

1455 1r. Type **248** 1·50 50
1456 2r.50 Paul Gascoigne of England 2·25 1·25
1457 3r.50 Brazilian challenging Argentine player 2·25 1·60
1458 5r. Brazilian taking control of ball 2·50 2·00
1459 7r. Italian and Austrian jumping for header 3·25 3·25
1460 10r. Russian being chased by Turkish player 3·50 3·50
1461 15r. Andres Brehme of West Germany 4·00 4·50
MS1462 Four sheets, each 77×92 mm. (a) 18r. Head of an Austrian player (horiz). (b) 18r. Head of a South Korean player (horiz). (c) 20r. Diego Maradona of Argentina (horiz). (d) 20r. Schilacci of Italy (horiz) Set of 4 sheets 17·00 17·00

249 Winged Euonymus

1991. Bonsai Trees and Shrubs. Multicoloured.

1463 20l. Type **249** 50 20
1464 50l. Japanese black pine 65 35
1465 1r. Japanese five needle pine 90 55
1466 3r.50 Flowering quince 2·00 1·75
1467 5r. Chinese elm 2·50 2·50
1468 8r. Japanese persimmon 2·75 3·00
1469 10r. Japanese wisteria 2·75 3·00
1470 12r. Satsuki azalea 2·75 3·25
MS1471 Two sheets, each 89×88 mm. (a) 20r. Trident maple. (b) 20r. Sargent juniper Set of 2 sheets 12·00 14·00

250 *Summer* (Rubens)

1991. 350th Death Anniversary of Rubens. Multicoloured.

1472 20l. Type **250** 25 15
1473 50l. *Landscape with Rainbow* (detail) 40 25
1474 1r. *Wreck of Aeneas* 65 40
1475 2r.50 *Chateau de Steen* (detail) 1·25 1·00
1476 3r.50 *Landscape with Herd of Cows* 1·50 1·25
1477 7r. *Ruins on the Palantine* 2·50 2·75
1478 10r. *Landscape with Peasants and Cows* 2·75 3·00
1479 12r. *Wagon fording Stream* 3·00 3·50
MS1480 Four sheets, each 100×71 mm. (a) 20r. *Landscape at Sunset*. (b) 20r. *Peasants with Cattle by a Stream*. (c) 20r. *Shepherd with Flock*. (d) 20r. *Wagon in Stream* Set of 4 sheets 15·00 16·00

251 Greek Messenger from Marathon, 490 BC (2480th anniversary)

1991. Anniversaries and Events (1990). Multicoloured.

1481 50l. Type **251** 45 25
1482 1r. Anthony Fokker in Haarlem Spin monoplane (birth centenary) 1·00 45
1483 3r.50 *Early Bird* satellite (25th anniversary) 1·50 1·50
1484 7r. Signing Reunification of Germany agreement (horiz) 1·75 2·50
1485 8r. King John signing *Magna Carta* (775th anniversary) 2·75 2·50
1486 10r. Dwight D. Eisenhower (birth centenary) 2·25 2·75
1487 12r. Sir Winston Churchill (25th death anniversary) 5·00 4·50
1488 15r. Pres. Reagan at Berlin Wall (German reunification) (horiz) 3·00 4·50
MS1489 Two sheets. (a) 180×81 mm. 20r. German Junkers Ju88 bomber (50th anniversary of Battle of Britain) (horiz). (b) 160×73 mm. 20r. Brandenburg Gate (German reunification) (horiz) Set of 2 sheets 14·00 14·00

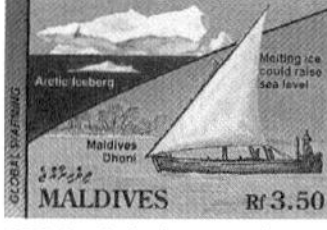

252 Arctic Iceberg and Maldives Dhoni

1991. Global Warming. Multicoloured.

1490 3r.50 Type **252** 2·00 1·25
1491 7r. Antarctic iceberg and *Maldive Trader* (freighter) 4·50 4·25

253 SAARC Emblem and Medal

1991. Year of the Girl Child.

1492 **253** 7r. multicoloured 1·75 2·00

254 Children on Beach

1991. Year of the Maldivian Child. Children's Paintings. Multicoloured.

1493 3r.50 Type **254** 2·25 1·40
1494 5r. Children in a park 2·75 2·25
1495 10r. Hungry child dreaming of food 3·75 4·25
1496 25r. Scuba diver 7·00 12·00

255 *Still Life: Japanese Vase with Roses and Anemones*

1991. Death Centenary (1990) of Vincent van Gogh (artist). Multicoloured.

1497 15l. Type **255** 60 25
1498 20l. *Still Life: Red Poppies and Daisies* 60 25
1499 2r. *Vincent's Bedroom in Arles* (horiz) 2·00 90
1500 3r.50 *The Mulberry Tree* 2·25 1·25
1501 7r. *Blossoming Chestnut Branches* (horiz) 3·25 3·25
1502 10r. *Peasant Couple going to Work* (horiz) 3·75 3·75
1503 12r. *Still Life: Pink Roses* (horiz) 4·00 4·25

1504 15r. *Child with Orange* 4·25 4·75

MS1505 Two sheets. (a) 77×101 mm. 25r. *Houses in Auvers* (70×94 mm). (b) 101×77 mm. 25r. *The Courtyard of the Hospital at Arles* (94×70 mm). Imperf Set of 2 sheets 13·00 14·00

1991. 65th Birthday of Queen Elizabeth II. As T **201** of Lesotho. Multicoloured.

1506 2r. Queen at Trooping the Colour, 1990 1·60 60
1507 5r. Queen with Queen Mother and Princess Margaret, 1973 2·75 1·75
1508 8r. Queen and Prince Philip in open carriage, 1986 3·25 3·00
1509 12r. Queen at Royal Estates Ball 3·50 3·75

MS1510 68×90 mm. 25r. Separate photographs of Queen and Prince Philip 5·75 6·50

1991. Tenth Wedding Anniversary of Prince and Princess of Wales. As T **210** of Lesotho. Multicoloured.

1511 1r. Prince and Princess skiing, 1986 1·00 20
1512 3r.50 Separate photographs of Prince, Princess and sons 2·00 1·10
1513 7r. Prince Henry in Christmas play and Prince William watching polo 2·50 2·00
1514 15r. Princess Diana at Ipswich, 1990, and Prince Charles playing polo 3·75 3·75

MS1515 68×90 mm. 25r. Prince and Princess of Wales in Hungary, and Princes William and Harry going to school 6·25 6·50

256 Boy painting

1991. Hummel Figurines. Multicoloured.

1516 10l. Type **256** 15 15
1517 25l. Boy reading at table 20 20
1518 50l. Boy with school satchel 30 30
1519 2r. Girl with basket 70 70
1520 3r.50 Boy reading 1·00 1·00
1521 8r. Girl and young child reading 2·25 2·50
1522 10r. School girls 2·25 2·50
1523 25r. School boys 4·75 6·50

MS1524 Two sheets, each 97×127 mm. (a) 5r. As No. 1519; 5r. As No. 1520; 5r. As No, 1521; 5r. As No. 1522. (b) 8r. As Type **256**; 8r. As No. 1517; 8r. As No. 1518; 8r. As No. 1523 Set of 2 sheets 9·00 11·00

257 Class C57 Steam Locomotive

1991. Phila Nippon '91 International Stamp Exhibition, Tokyo. Japanese Steam Locomotives. Mult.

1525 15l. Type **257** 50 20
1526 25l. Class 6250 locomotive, 1915 (horiz) 75 30
1527 1r. Class D51 locomotive, 1936 (horiz) 1·25 40
1528 3r.50 Class 8620 locomotive, 1914 (horiz) 2·00 1·25
1529 5r. Class 10 locomotive, 1889 (horiz) 2·25 1·75
1530 7r. Class C61 locomotive, 1947 2·50 2·75
1531 10r. Class 9600 locomotive, 1913 (horiz) 2·50 3·00
1532 12r. Class D52 locomotive, 1943 (horiz) 2·75 3·50

MS1533 Two sheets, each 118×80 mm. (a) 20r. Class C56 locomotive, 1935 (horiz). (b) 20r. Class 1080 locomotive, 1925 (horiz) Set of 2 sheets 8·00 9·00

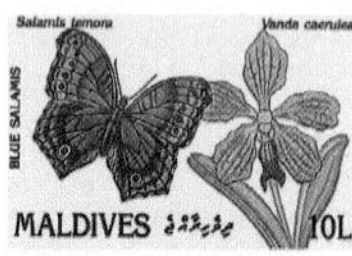

258 *Salamis temora* and *Vanda caerulea*

1991. Butterflies and Flowers. Multicoloured.

1534 10l. Type **258** 40 40
1535 25l. *Meneris tulbaghia* and *Incarvillea younghusbandii* 55 30
1536 50l. *Polyommatus icarus* and *Campsis grandiflora* 75 40
1537 2r. *Danaus plexippus* and *Thunbergia grandiflora* 1·25 90
1538 3r.50 *Colias interior* and *Medinilla magnifica* 1·75 1·75
1539 5r. *Ascalapha ordorata* and *Meconopsis horridula* 2·00 2·00
1540 8r. *Papilio memnon* and *Dillenia obovata* 2·50 3·00
1541 10r. *Precis octavia* and *Thespesia populnea* 2·50 3·00

MS1542 Two sheets, each 100×70 mm. (a) 20r. *Bombax ceiba* and *Plyciodes tharos*. (b) 20r. *Amauris niavius* and *Bombax insigne* Set of 2 sheets 10·00 12·00

259 H-II Rocket

1991. Japanese Space Programme. Multicoloured.

1543 15l. Type **259** 50 30
1544 20l. Projected H-II orbiting plane 50 30
1545 2r. Satellite *GMS-5* 1·25 75
1546 3r.50 Satellite *MOMO-1* 1·60 1·40
1547 7r. Satellite *CS-3* 2·50 2·75
1548 10r. Satellite *BS-2a, 2b* 2·75 3·00
1549 12r. H-I Rocket (vert) 3·00 3·50
1550 15r. Space Flier unit and US Space shuttle 3·00 3·50

MS1551 Two sheets, each 116×85 mm. 20r. Dish aerial, Katsura Tracking Station (vert). (b) 85×116 mm. 20r. M-3SII rocket (vert) Set of 2 sheets 13·00 13·00

260 Williams FW-07

1991. Formula 1 Racing Cars. Multicoloured.

1552 20l. Type **260** 30 20
1553 50l. Brabham/BMW BT50 turbo 45 30
1554 1r. Williams/Honda FW-11 60 45
1555 3r.50 Ferrari 312 T3 1·25 1·25
1556 5r. Lotus/Honda 99T 1·75 1·75
1557 7r. Benetton/Ford B188 2·00 2·25
1558 10r. Tyrrell P34 six-wheeler 2·25 2·50
1559 21r. Renault RE-30B turbo 4·00 5·00

MS1560 Two sheets, each 84×56 mm. (a) 25r. Brabham/BMW BT50 turbo (different). (b) 25r. Ferrari F189 Set of 2 sheets 16·00 13·00

261 Testarossa, 1957

1991. Ferrari Cars. Multicoloured.

1561 5r. Type **261** 2·00 2·00
1562 5r. 275GTB, 1966 2·00 2·00
1563 5r. Aspirarta, 1951 2·00 2·00
1564 5r. Testarossa 2·00 2·00
1565 5r. Enzo Ferrari 2·00 2·00
1566 5r. Dino 246, 1958 2·00 2·00
1567 5r. Type 375, 1952 2·00 2·00
1568 5r. Nigel Mansell's Formula 1 racing car 2·00 2·00
1569 5r. 312T, 1975 2·00 2·00

262 Franklin D. Roosevelt

1991. 50th Anniversary of Japanese Attack on Pearl Harbor. American War Leaders. Multicoloured.

1570 3r.50 Type **262** 1·75 1·50
1571 3r.50 Douglas MacArthur and map of Philippines 1·75 1·50
1572 3r.50 Chester Nimitz and Pacific island 1·75 1·50
1573 3r.50 Jonathan Wainwright and barbed wire 1·75 1·50
1574 3r.50 Ernest King and USS *Hornet* (aircraft carrier) 1·75 1·50
1575 3r.50 Claire Chennault and Curtiss Tomahawk II fighters 1·75 1·50
1576 3r.50 William Halsey and USS *Enterprise* (aircraft carrier) 1·75 1·50
1577 3r.50 Marc Mitscher and USS *Hornet* (aircraft carrier) 1·75 1·50
1578 3r.50 James Doolittle and North American B-25 Mitchell bomber 1·75 1·50
1579 3r.50 Raymond Spruance and Douglas Dauntless dive bomber 1·75 1·50

263 Brandenburg Gate and Postcard Commemorating Berlin Wall

1992. Anniversaries and Events. Multicoloured.

1580 20l. Type **263** 25 20
1581 50l. Schwarzenburg Palace 1·40 40
1582 1r. Spa at Baden 1·75 50
1583 1r.75 Berlin Wall and man holding child 50 50
1584 2r. Royal Palace, Berlin 2·50 1·00
1585 4r. Demonstrator and border guards 1·10 1·25
1586 5r. Viennese masonic seal 4·50 2·25
1587 6r. De Gaulle and Normandy landings, 1944 (vert) 2·50 2·25
1588 6r. Lilienthal's signature and *Flugzeug Nr. 16* 2·50 2·25
1589 7r. St Marx 4·25 2·75
1590 7r. Trans-Siberian Railway Class VL80T electric locomotive No. 1406 (vert) 4·00 2·75
1591 8r. Kurt Schwitters (artist) and Landesmuseum 2·50 2·75
1592 9r. Map of Switzerland and man in Uri traditional costume 3·50 3·00
1593 10r. De Gaulle in Madagascar, 1958 2·50 3·00
1594 10r. Scouts exploring coral reef 2·50 3·00
1595 11r. Scout salute and badge (vert) 2·50 3·00
1596 12r. Trans-Siberian Railway steam locomotive 4·50 3·75
1597 15r. Imperial German badges 2·50 3·75
1598 20r. Josepsplatz, Vienna 6·00 6·00

MS1599 Eight sheets. (a) 76×116 mm. 15r. General de Gaulle during Second World War (vert). (b) 101×72 mm. 18r. Ancient German helmet. (c) 101×72 mm. 18r. 19th-century shako. (d) 101×72 mm. 18r. Helmet of 1939. (e) 90×117 mm. 18r. Postcard of Lord Baden-Powell carried by rocket, 1937 (grey, black and mauve) (vert). (f) 75×104 mm. 20r. Bust of Mozart (vert). (g) 115×85 mm. 20r. Trans-Siberian Railway Class P36 steam locomotive stopped at signal (57×43 mm). (h) 117×90 mm. 20r. Czechoslovakia 1918 10h. 'Scout Post' stamp (vert) Set of 8 sheets 45·00 50·00

Anniversaries and Events: Nos. 1580, 1583, 1585, 1597, **MS**1599b/**MS**1599d, Bicentenary of Brandenburg Gate, Berlin; 1581/1582, 1584, 1586, 1589, 1598, **MS**1599f, Death bicentenary of Mozart (1991); 1587, 1593, **MS**1599a, Birth centenary of Charles de Gaulle (French statesman) (1990); 1588, Centenary of Otto Lilienthal's first gliding experiments; 1590, 1596, **MS**1599g, Centenary of Trans-Siberian Railway; 1591, 750th anniversary of Hannover; 1592, 700th anniversary of Swiss Confederation; 1594/1595, **MS**1599e, **MS**1599h, 17th World Scout Jamboree, Korea.

264 Mickey Mouse on Flying Carpet, Arabia

1992. Mickey's World Tour. Designs showing Walt Disney cartoon characters in different countries. Multicoloured.

1600 25l. Type **264** 45 20
1601 50l. Goofy and Big Ben, Great Britain 55 25
1602 1r. Mickey wearing clogs, Netherlands 75 35
1603 2r. Pluto eating pasta, Italy 1·25 75
1604 3r. Mickey and Donald doing Mexican hat dance 1·40 1·25
1605 3r.50 Mickey, Goofy and Donald as tiki, New Zealand 1·40 1·40
1606 5r. Goofy skiing in Austrian Alps 1·50 1·50
1607 7r. Mickey and city gate, Germany 1·75 2·00
1608 10r. Donald as samurai, Japan 2·00 2·25
1609 12r. Mickey as heroic statue, Russia 2·25 2·75
1610 15r. Mickey, Donald, Goofy and Pluto as German band 2·50 3·00

MS1611 Three sheets, each 83×104 mm. (a) 25r. Donald chasing leprechaun, Ireland (horiz). (b) 25r. Baby kangaroo surprising Pluto, Australia. (c) 25r. Mickey and globe Set of 3 sheets 13·00 14·00

265 Whimbrel

1992. Birds. Multicoloured.

1612 10l. Type **265** 60 1·00
1613 25l. Great egret 70 60
1614 50l. Grey heron 75 65
1615 2r. Shag 1·60 75
1616 3r.50 Roseate tern 1·75 85
1617 5r. Greater greenshank 2·25 1·10
1617a 6r.50+50l. +50l. Egyptian vulture 3·50 3·50
1618 8r. Hoopoe 2·75 2·50
1619 10r. Black-shouldered kite 2·75 2·50
1620 25r. Scarlet ibis 4·50 4·25
1620a 30r. Peregrine falcon 5·50 5·00
1620b 40r. Black kite 6·50 6·50
1621 50r. Grey plover 6·50 7·50
1621a 100r. Common shoveler 20·00 20·00

Nos. 1617a, 1620a/1620b and 1621a are larger, 23×32 mm.

1992. 40th Anniversary of Queen Elizabeth II's Accession. As T **214** of Lesotho. Multicoloured.

1622 1r. Palm trees on beach 60 25
1623 3r.50 Path leading to jetty 2·00 1·00
1624 7r. Tropical plant 2·75 2·75
1625 10r. Palm trees on beach (different) 3·00 3·25

MS1626 Two sheets, each 74×97 mm. (a) 18r. Dhow. (b) 18r. Palm trees on beach (different) Set of 2 sheets 14·00 12·00

266 Powder-blue Surgeonfish

1992. Fish. Multicoloured.

1627 7l. Type **266** 30 20
1628 20l. Catalufa 40 25
1629 50l. Yellow-finned tuna 55 30
1630 1r. Twin-spotted red snapper 75 35
1631 3r.50 Hawaiian squirrelfish 1·50 1·25
1632 5r. Picasso triggerfish 2·00 2·00
1633 8r. Bennet's butterflyfish 2·25 2·50
1634 10r. Parrotfish 2·50 2·75
1635 12r. Coral hind 2·75 3·00
1636 15r. Skipjack tuna 2·75 3·00

MS1637 Four sheets, each 116×76 mm. (a) 20r. Thread-finned butterflyfish. (b) 20r. Oriental sweetlips. (c) 20r. Two-banded anemonefish ('Clownfish'). (d) 20r. Clown triggerfish Set of 4 sheets 13·00 15·00

1992. International Stamp Exhibitions. As T **215** of Lesotho showing Walt Disney cartoon characters. Multicoloured

(a) Granada '92, Spain. The Alhambra.

1638 2r. Minnie Mouse in Court of the Lions 90 70
1639 5r. Goofy in Lions Fountain 1·75 1·75
1640 8r. Mickey Mouse at the Gate of Justice 2·25 2·75
1641 12r. Donald Duck serenading Daisy at the Vermilion Towers 2·75 3·50

MS1642 127×102 mm. 25r. Goofy pushing Mickey in wheelbarrow 5·50 6·00

(b) World Columbian Stamp Expo '92. Chicago Landmarks.

1643 1r. Mickey meeting Jean Baptiste du Sable (founder) 1·00 40
1644 3r.50 Donald Duck at Old Chicago Post Office 2·00 1·25
1645 7r. Donald at Old Fort Dearborn 3·00 2·75
1646 15r. Goofy in Museum of Science and Industry 4·00 4·50

MS1647 127×102 mm. 25r. Mickey and Minnie Mouse at Columbian Exposition, 1893 (horiz) 5·50 6·00

On No. 1646 the design is wrongly captioned as the Science and Industry Museum.

267 Coastguard Patrol Boats

1992. Centenary of National Security Service. Multicoloured.

1648 3r.50 Type **267** 2·50 1·25
1649 5r. Infantry in training 2·50 1·75
1650 10r. Aakoatey fort 2·75 3·00
1651 15r. Fire Service 11·00 10·00
MS1652 100×68 mm. 20r. Ceremonial procession, 1892 7·00 9·00

268 Flowers of the United States of America

1992. National Flowers. Multicoloured.

1653 25l. Type **268** 50 30
1654 50l. Australia 70 30
1655 2r. England 1·60 1·10
1656 3r.50 Brazil 2·00 1·50
1657 5r. Holland 2·25 2·00
1658 8r. France 2·50 3·00
1659 10r. Japan 2·75 3·00
1660 15r. Africa 3·50 4·50
MS1661 Two sheets, each 114×85 mm. (a) 25r. *Plumieria rubra, Classia fistula* and *Eugenia malaccensis* (57×43 mm). (b) 25r. *Bauhinia variegata, Catharanthus roseus* and *Plumieria alba* (57×43 mm) Set of 2 sheets 9·00 10·00

269 *Laetiporus sulphureus*

1992. Fungi. Multicoloured.

1662 10l. Type **269** 30 30
1663 25l. *Coprinus atramentarius* 40 30
1664 50l. *Ganoderma lucidum* 60 40
1665 3r.50 *Russula aurata* 1·25 1·00
1666 5r. *Grifola umbellata* ('Polyporus umbellatus') 1·75 1·75
1667 8r. *Suillus grevillei* 2·25 2·50
1668 10r. *Clavaria zollingeri* 2·50 2·50
1669 25r. *Boletus edulis* 5·00 6·00
MS1670 Two sheets, each 100×70 mm. (a) 25r. *Marasmius oreades*. (b) 25r. *Pycnoporus cinnabarinus* ('Trametes cinnabarina') Set of 2 sheets 12·00 13·00

1992. Olympic Games, Albertville and Barcelona (1st issue). As T **217** of Lesotho. Multicoloured.

1671 10l. Pole vault 20 10
1672 25l. Men's pommel horse (horiz) 25 15
1673 50l. Men's shot put 30 25
1674 1r. Men's horizontal bar (horiz) 35 30
1675 2r. Men's triple jump (horiz) 80 65
1676 3r.50 Table tennis 1·10 1·10
1677 5r. Two-man bobsled 1·40 1·40
1678 7r. Freestyle wrestling (horiz) 1·75 2·00
1679 8r. Freestyle ski-jump 1·75 2·00
1680 9r. Baseball 2·00 2·25
1681 10r. Women's cross-country Nordic skiing 2·00 2·25
1682 12r. Men's 200 m backstroke (horiz) 2·00 2·25
MS1683 Three sheets. (a) 100×70 mm. 25r. Decathalon (horiz). (b) 100×70 mm. 25r. Women's slalom skiing (horiz). (c) 70×100 mm. 25r. Men's figure skating Set of 3 sheets 12·00 13·00

See also Nos. 1684/**MS**1692.

270 Hurdling

1992. Olympic Games, Barcelona (2nd issue). Multicoloured.

1684 10l. Type **270** 10 10
1685 1r. Boxing 30 30
1686 3r.50 Women's sprinting 1·00 70
1687 5r. Discus 1·50 1·25
1688 7r. Basketball 4·50 2·75
1689 10r. Long-distance running 2·50 2·75
1690 12r. Aerobic gymnastics 2·50 3·25
1691 20r. Fencing 3·25 4·50
MS1692 Two sheets, each 70×100 mm. (a) 25r. Olympic symbol and National Flags. (b) 25r. Olympic symbol and flame Set of 2 sheets 8·50 9·00

271 Deinonychus

1992. Genova '92 International Thematic Stamp Exhibition. Prehistoric Animals. Multicoloured.

1693 5l. Type **271** 40 20
1694 10l. Styracosaurus 40 20
1695 25l. Mamenchisaurus 50 30
1696 50l. Stenonychosaurus 60 30
1697 1r. Parasaurolophus 75 40
1698 1r.25 Scelidosaurus 85 50
1699 1r.75 Tyrannosaurus 1·10 55
1700 2r. Stegosaurus 1·25 60
1701 3r.50 Iguanodon 1·50 80
1702 4r. Anatosaurus 1·50 1·00
1703 5r. Monoclonius 1·60 1·10
1704 7r. Tenontosaurus 1·90 1·90
1705 8r. Brachiosaurus 1·90 1·90
1706 10r. Euoplocephalus 2·00 2·00
1707 25r. Triceratops 3·25 4·50
1708 50r. Apatosaurus 6·00 8·00
MS1709 Four sheets, each 116×85 mm. (a) 25r. Hadrosaur hatchling. (b) 25r. Iguanodon fighting Allosaurus. (c) 25r. Tyrannosaurus attacking Triceratops. (d) 25r. Brachiosaurus and Iguanodons Set of 4 sheets 15·00 16·00

1992. Postage Stamp Mega Event, New York. Sheet 100×70 mm, containing multicoloured design as T **219** of Lesotho, but horiz.

MS1710 20r. New York Public Library 2·50 3·50

272 Destruction of LZ-129 *Hindenburg* (airship), 1937

1992. Mysteries of the Universe. T **272** and similar multicoloured designs, each in separate miniature sheet.

MS1711 Sixteen sheets, each 100×71 mm. (a) 25r. Type **272**. (b) 25r. Loch Ness Monster. (c) 25r. Crystal skull. (d) 25r. Space craft in Black Hole. (e) 25r. Ghosts (vert). (f) 25r. Flying saucer, 1947 (vert). (g) 25r. Bust of Plato (Atlantis). (h) 25r. UFO, 1973. (i) 25r. Crop circles. (j) 25r. Mil Mi-26 Russian helicopter at Chernobyl nuclear explosion. (k) 25r. Figure from Plain of Nazca. (l) 25r. Stonehenge (vert). (m) 25r. Yeti footprint (vert). (n) 25r. The Pyramid of Giza. (o) 25r. *Marie Celeste* (brigantine) (vert). (p) 25r. American Grumman TBF Avenger fighter aircraft (Bermuda Triangle) Set of 16 sheets 55·00 55·00

273 Zubin Mehta (musical director)

1992. 150th Anniversary of New York Philharmonic Orchestra. Sheet 100×70 mm.

MS1712 **273** 20r. multicoloured 6·00 6·00

274 Friedrich Schmiedl

1992. 90th Birth Anniversary of Friedrich Schmiedl (rocket mail pioneer). Sheet 104×69 mm.

MS1713 **274** 25r. multicoloured 5·50 6·50

275 Goofy in *Father's Weekend*, 1953

1992. 60th Anniversary of Goofy (Disney cartoon character). Goofy in various cartoon films. Multicoloured.

1714 10l. Type **275** 10 10
1715 50l. *Symphony Hour*, 1942 35 20
1716 75l. *Frank Duck Brings 'Em Back Alive*, 1946 45 20
1717 1r. *Crazy with the Heat*, 1947 45 20
1718 2r. *The Big Wash*, 1948 70 60
1719 3r.50 *How to Ride a Horse*, 1950 1·25 1·25
1720 5r. *Two Gun Goofy*, 1952 1·50 1·50
1721 8r. *Saludos Amigos*, 1943 (vert) 2·00 2·25
1722 10r. *How to be a Detective*, 1952 2·00 2·25
1723 12r. *For Whom the Bulls Toil*, 1953 2·25 2·50
1724 15r. *Double Dribble*, 1946 (vert) 2·25 2·50
MS1725 Three sheets, each 127×102 mm. (a) 20r. *Double Dribble*, 1946 (different) (vert). (b) 20r. *The Goofy Success Story*, 1955 (vert). (c) 20r. *Mickey and the Beanstalk*, 1947 Set of 3 sheets 10·00 10·50

276 Minnie Mouse in *Le Missioner* (Toulouse-Lautrec)

1992. Opening of Euro-Disney Resort, France. Disney cartoon characters superimposed on Impressionist paintings. Multicoloured.

1726 5r. Type **276** 1·50 1·75
1727 5r. Goofy in *The Card Players* (Cezanne) 1·50 1·75
1728 5r. Mickey and Minnie Mouse in *The Cafe Terrace, Place du Forum* (Van Gogh) 1·50 1·75
1729 5r. Mickey in *The Bridge at Langlois* (Van Gogh) 1·50 1·75
1730 5r. Goofy in *Chocolate Dancing* (Toulouse-Lautrec) 1·50 1·75
1731 5r. Mickey and Minnie in *The Seine at Asnieres* (Renoir) 1·50 1·75
1732 5r. Minnie in *Ball at the Moulin Rouge* (Toulouse-Lautrec) 1·50 1·75
1733 5r. Mickey in *Wheatfield with Cypresses* (Van Gogh) 1·50 1·75
1734 5r. Minnie in *When will you Marry?* (Gauguin) 1·50 1·75
MS1735 Four sheets. (a) 128×100 mm. 20r. Minnie as can-can dancer. (b) 128×100 mm. 20r. Goofy as cyclist. (c) 100×128 mm. 20r. Mickey as artist. (d) 100×128 mm. 20r. Donald as Frenchman (vert) Set of 4 sheets 12·00 14·00

277 Rivers

1992. South Asian Association for Regional Co-operation Year of the Environment. Natural and Polluted Environments. Multicoloured.

1736 25l. Type **277** 15 10
1737 50l. Beaches 25 10
1738 5r. Oceans 80 1·00
1739 10r. Weather 1·50 2·25

278 Jurgen Klinsmann (Germany)

1993. World Cup Football Championship, USA (1994) (1st issue). German Players and Officials. Multicoloured.

1740 10l. Type **278** 40 20
1741 25l. Pierre Littbarski 45 20
1742 50l. Lothar Matthaus 55 20
1743 1r. Rudi Voller 75 25
1744 2r. Thomas Hassler 1·25 60
1745 3r.50 Thomas Berthold 1·60 1·00
1746 4r. Jurgen Kohler 1·75 1·25
1747 5r. Berti Vogts 1·90 1·40
1748 6r. Bodo Illgner 2·25 2·25
1749 7r. Klaus Augenthaler 2·25 2·25
1750 8r. Franz Beckenbauer 2·25 2·25
1751 10r. Andreas Brehme 2·50 2·75
1752 12r. Guido Buchwald 2·50 3·25
MS1753 Two sheets, each 103×73 mm. (a) 35r. German players celebrating (horiz). (b) 35r. Rudi Voller (horiz) Set of 2 sheets 13·00 14·00

See also Nos. 1990/**MS**1998 and 2089/**MS**2101.

279 German Navy Airship L-13 bombing London, 1914–1918

1993. Anniversaries and Events. Multicoloured.

1754 1r. Type **279** 1·25 50
1755 3r.50 Radio telescope 70 1·00
1756 3r.50 Chancellor Adenauer and Pres. de Gaulle 70 1·00
1757 6r. Indian rhinoceros 6·00 2·50
1758 6r. Columbus and globe 3·25 2·00
1759 7r. Conference emblems 1·50 2·00
1760 8r. Green seaturtle 1·75 2·00
1761 10r. *America* (yacht), 1851 1·75 2·25
1762 10r. Melvin Jones (founder) and emblem 1·75 2·25
1763 12r. Columbus landing on San Salvador 3·75 3·75
1764 15r. *Voyager I* approaching Saturn 6·00 6·00
1765 15r. Adenauer, NATO flag and Lockheed Starfighter aircraft 6·00 6·00
1766 20r. *Graf Zeppelin* over New York, 1929 6·00 6·00
MS1767 Five sheets, each 111×80 mm. (a) 20r. Count Ferdinand von Zeppelin. (b) 20r. *Landsat* satellite. (c) 20r. Konrad Adenauer. (d) 20r. Scarlet macaw. (e) 20r. *Santa Maria* Set of 5 sheets 25·00 30·00

Anniversaries and Events: 1754, 1766, **MS**1767a, 75th death anniversary of Count Ferdinand von Zeppelin; 1755, 1764, **MS**1767b, International Space Year; 1756, 1765, **MS**1767c, 25th death anniversary of Konrad Adenauer; 1757, 1760, **MS**1767d, Earth Summit '92, Rio; 1758, 1763, **MS**1767e, 500th anniversary of discovery of America by Columbus; 1759, International Conference on Nutrition, Rome; 1761, Americas Cup Yachting Championship; 1762, 75th anniversary of International Association of Lions Clubs.

280 Elvis Presley

1993. 15th Death Anniversary of Elvis Presley (singer). Multicoloured.

1768 3r.50 Type **280** 90 70
1769 3r.50 Elvis with guitar 90 70
1770 3r.50 Elvis with microphone 90 70

1993. Bicentenary of the Louvre, Paris. As T **221a** of Lesotho. Multicoloured.

1771 8r. *The Study* (Fragonard) 95 1·10
1772 8r. *Denis Diderot* (Fragonard) 95 1·10
1773 8r. *Marie-Madelaine Guimard* (Fragonard) 95 1·10
1774 8r. *Inspiration* (Fragonard) 95 1·10
1775 8r. *Waterfalls, Tivoli* (Fragonard) 95 1·10
1776 8r. *The Music Lesson* (Fragonard) 95 1·10
1777 8r. *The Bolt* (Fragonard) 95 1·10
1778 8r. *Blind-man's Buff* (Fragonard) 95 1·10
1779 8r. *Self-portrait* (Corot) 95 1·10
1780 8r. *Woman in Blue* (Corot) 95 1·10
1781 8r. *Woman with a Pearl* (Corot) 95 1·10
1782 8r. *Young Girl at her Toilet* (Corot) 95 1·10
1783 8r. *Haydee* (Corot) 95 1·10
1784 8r. *Chartres Cathedral* (Corot) 95 1·10
1785 8r. *The Belfry of Douai* (Corot) 95 1·10
1786 8r. *The Bridge of Mantes* (Corot) 95 1·10
1787 8r. *Madame Seriziat* (David) 95 1·10
1788 8r. *Pierre Seriziat* (David) 95 1·10
1789 8r. *Madame De Verninac* (David) 95 1·10
1790 8r. *Madame Recamier* (David) 95 1·10
1791 8r. *Self-portrait* (David) 95 1·10
1792 8r. *General Bonaparte* (David) 95 1·10
1793 8r. *The Lictors bringing Brutus his Son's Body* (David) (left detail) 95 1·10
1794 8r. *The Lictors bringing Brutus his Son's Body* (David) (right detail) 95 1·10

MS1795	Two sheets, each 100×70 mm. (a) 20r. *Gardens of the Villa D'Este, Tivoli* (Corot) (85×52 mm). (b) 20r. *Tiger Cub playing with its Mother* (Delacroix) (85×52 mm) Set of 2 sheets	8·50	8·50

281 James Stewart and Marlene Dietrich (*Destry Rides Again*)

1993. Famous Western Films. Multicoloured.

1796	5r. Type **281**	1·50	1·10
1797	5r. Gary Cooper (*The Westerner*)	1·50	1·10
1798	5r. Henry Fonda (*My Darling Clementine*)	1·50	1·10
1799	5r. Alan Ladd (*Shane*)	1·50	1·10
1800	5r. Kirk Douglas and Burt Lancaster (*Gunfight at the O.K. Corral*)	1·50	1·10
1801	5r. Steve McQueen (*The Magnificent Seven*)	1·50	1·10
1802	5r. Robert Redford and Paul Newman (*Butch Cassidy and The Sundance Kid*)	1·50	1·10
1803	5r. Jack Nicholson and Randy Quaid (*The Missouri Breaks*)	1·50	1·10
MS1804	Two sheets, each 134×120 mm. (a) 20r. John Wayne (*The Searchers*) (French poster). (b) 20r. Clint Eastwood (*Pale Rider*) (French poster) Set of 2 sheets	9·00	7·50

1993. 40th Anniversary of Coronation. As T **224** of Lesotho.

1805	3r.50 multicoloured	1·00	1·10
1806	5r. multicoloured	1·25	1·40
1807	10r. blue and black	1·50	1·75
1808	10r. blue and black	1·50	1·75

Designs: No. 1805, Queen Elizabeth II at Coronation (photograph by Cecil Beaton); No. 1806, St Edward's Crown; No. 1807, Guests in the Abbey; No. 1808, Queen Elizabeth II and Prince Philip.

282 Blue Goatfish

1993. Fish. Multicoloured.

1809	3r.50 Type **282**	60	70
1810	3r.50 Emperor angelfish	60	70
1811	3r.50 Madagascar butterflyfish	60	70
1812	3r.50 Regal angelfish	60	70
1813	3r.50 Forceps fish ('Longnose butterflyfish')	60	70
1814	3r.50 Racoon butterflyfish	60	70
1815	3r.50 Harlequin filefish	60	70
1816	3r.50 Rectangle triggerfish	60	70
1817	3r.50 Yellow-tailed anemonefish	60	70
1818	3r.50 Clown triggerfish	60	70
1819	3r.50 Zebra lionfish	60	70
1820	3r.50 Maldive anemonefish ('Clownfish')	60	70
1821	3r.50 Black-faced butterflyfish	60	70
1822	3r.50 Bird wrasse	60	70
1823	3r.50 Checkerboard wrasse	60	70
1824	3r.50 Yellow-faced angelfish	60	70
1825	3r.50 Masked bannerfish	60	70
1826	3r.50 Thread-finned butterflyfish	60	70
1827	3r.50 Painted triggerfish	60	70
1828	3r.50 Coral hind	60	70
1829	3r.50 Pennant coralfish	60	70
1830	3r.50 Black-backed butterflyfish	60	70
1831	3r.50 Red-toothed triggerfish	60	70
1832	3r.50 Melon butterflyfish	60	70
MS1833	Two sheets. (a) 69×96 mm. 25r. Klein's butterflyfish (vert). (b) 96×69 mm. 25r. Brown anemonefish (vert) Set of 2 sheets	8·00	8·50

Nos. 1809/1820 and 1821/1832 were printed together, *se-tenant*, with the backgrounds forming composite designs.

Nos. 1810 and 1824 are both inscribed 'Angelfish' in error.

283 Gull-billed Tern

1993. Birds. Multicoloured.

1834	3r.50 Type **283**	65	70
1835	3r.50 White-tailed Tropicbird ('Long-tailed Tropicbird')	65	70
1836	3r.50 Great Frigatebird ('Frigate Bird')	65	70
1837	3r.50 Wilson's storm petrel ('Wilson's Petrel')	65	70
1838	3r.50 White tern	65	70
1839	3r.50 Brown booby	65	70
1840	3r.50 Marsh harrier	65	70
1841	3r.50 Common noddy	65	70
1842	3r.50 Green-backed heron ('Little Heron')	65	70
1843	3r.50 Ruddy turnstone ('Turnstone')	65	70
1844	3r.50 Curlew	65	70
1845	3r.50 Crab plover	65	70
1846	3r.50 Pallid harrier (vert)	65	70
1847	3r.50 Cattle egret (vert)	65	70
1848	3r.50 Koel (vert)	65	70
1849	3r.50 Tree pipit (vert)	65	70
1850	3r.50 Short-eared owl (vert)	65	70
1851	3r.50 Common kestrel ('European Kestrel') (vert)	65	70
1852	3r.50 Yellow wagtail (vert)	65	70
1853	3r.50 Grey heron ('Common Heron') (vert)	65	70
1854	3r.50 Black bittern (vert)	65	70
1855	3r.50 Common snipe (vert)	65	70
1856	3r.50 Little egret (vert)	65	70
1857	3r.50 Little stint (vert)	65	70
MS1858	Two sheets, each 105×75 mm. (a) 25r. Caspian tern. (b) 25r. Audubon's shearwater Set of 2 sheets	8·50	9·00

Nos. 1834/1845 and 1846/1857 were printed together, *se-tenant*, with the backgrounds forming composite designs.

284 Precious Wentletrap

1993. Shells. Multicoloured.

1859	7l. Type **284**	30	30
1860	15l. Common purple janthina	35	30
1861	50l. Asiatic arabian cowrie	45	30
1862	3r.50 Common or major harp	1·50	1·00
1863	4r. Amplustre or royal paper bubble	1·75	1·25
1864	5r. Sieve cowrie	1·75	1·40
1865	6r. Episcopal mitre	2·00	2·00
1866	7r. Camp pitar venus	2·00	2·25
1867	8r. Spotted or eyed auger	2·25	2·50
1868	10r. Exposed cowrie	2·50	2·50
1869	12r. Geographic map cowrie	2·75	3·50
1870	20r. Bramble murex	3·50	4·50
MS1871	Three sheets, each 104×75 mm. (a) 25r. Black-striped triton. 25r. Scorpion conch. (c) 25r. Bull-mouth helmet Set of 3 sheets	17·00	19·00

285 Sifaka Lemur

1993. Endangered Species. Multicoloured.

1872	7l. Type **285**	50	30
1873	10l. Snow leopard	50	30
1874	15l. Numbat	50	30
1875	25l. Gorilla	90	40
1876	2r. Koala	1·10	70
1877	3r.50 Cheetah	1·25	1·10
1878	5r. Yellow-footed rock wallaby	1·40	1·40
1879	7r. Orang-utan	2·25	2·25
1880	8r. Black lemur	2·25	2·25
1881	10r. Black rhinoceros	4·00	3·00
1882	15r. Humpback whale	5·00	4·00
1883	20r. Mauritius parakeet	5·50	4·50
MS1884	Three sheets, each 104×75 mm. (a) 25r. Giant panda. (b) 25r. Tiger. (c) 25r. Indian elephant Set of 3 sheets	17·00	19·00

286 Symbolic Heads and Arrows

1993. Productivity Year. Multicoloured.

1885	7r. Type **286**	1·25	1·40
1886	10r. Abstract	1·60	1·75

287 Early Astronomical Equipment

1993. Anniversaries and Events. Multicoloured.

1887	3r.50 Type **287**	1·00	1·00
1888	3r.50 *Still Life with Pitcher and Apples* (Picasso)	1·00	1·00
1889	3r.50 *Zolte Roze* (Menasze Seidenbeurel)	1·00	1·00
1890	3r.50 Prince Naruhito and engagement photographs (horiz)	1·00	1·00
1891	5r. *Bowls and Jug* (Picasso)	1·25	1·25
1892	5r. Krysztofory Palace, Cracow	1·25	1·25
1893	8r. *Jabtka i Kotara* (Waclaw Borowski)	1·75	1·90
1894	8r. Marina Kiehl (Germany) (women's downhill skiing)	1·75	1·90
1895	10r. *Bowls of Fruit and Loaves on a Table* (Picasso)	1·90	2·00
1896	10r. Masako Owada and engagement photographs (horiz)	1·90	2·00
1897	15r. American astronaut in space	2·75	3·00
1898	15r. Vegard Ulvang (Norway) (30km cross-country skiing)	2·75	3·00
MS1899	Five sheets. (a) 105×75 mm. (a) 20r. Copernicus. (b) 105×75 mm. 20r. *Green Still Life* (detail) (Picasso) (horiz). (c) 105×75 mm. 25r. *Pejzaz Morski-Port z Doplywajacym Ststkiem* (detail (Roman Sielski) (horiz). (d) 75×105 mm. 25r. Masako Owada. (e) 105×75 mm. 25r. Ice hockey goalkeeper Set of 5 sheets	21·00	23·00

Anniversaries and Events: Nos. 1887, 1897, **MS**1899a, 450th death anniversary of Copernicus (astronomer); 1888, 1891, 1895, **MS**1899b, 20th death anniversary of Picasso (artist); 1889, 1892/1893, **MS**1899c, Polska '93 International Stamp Exhibition, Poznan; 1890, 1896, **MS**1899d, Marriage of Crown Prince Naruhito of Japan; 1894, 1898, **MS**1899e, Winter Olympic Games '94, Lillehammer.

288 *Limenitis procris* and *Mussaenda*

1993. Butterflies and Flowers. Multicoloured.

1900	7l. Type **288**	40	20
1901	20l. *Danaus limniace* and *Thevetia neriifolia*	55	20
1902	25l. *Amblypodia centaurus* and *Clitoria ternatea*	55	20
1903	50l. *Papilio crino* and *Crossandra infundibuliformis*	90	20
1904	5r. *Mycalesis patnia* and *Thespesia populnia*	2·00	1·40
1905	6r.50+50l. *Idea jasonia* and *Cassia glauca*	2·25	2·50
1906	7r. *Catopsilia pomona* and *Calotropis*	2·25	2·50
1907	10r. *Precis orithyia* and *Thunbergia grandiflora*	2·75	2·75
1908	12r. *Vanessa cardui* and *Caesalpinia pulcherrima*	3·00	3·50
1909	15r. *Papilio polymnestor* and *Nerium oleander*	3·25	3·75
1910	18r. *Cirrochroa thais* and *Vinca rosea*	3·50	4·00
1911	20r. *Pachliopta hector* and *Ixora coccinea*	3·50	4·00
MS1912	Three sheets, each 105×72 mm. (a) 25r. *Cheritra freja* and *Bauhinia purpurea* (vert). (b) 25r. *Rohana parisatis* and *Plumeria acutifolia* (vert). (c) 25r. *Hebomoia glaucippe* and *Punica granatum* (vert) Set of 3 sheets	15·00	17·00

289 Airship *Graf Zeppelin* in Searchlights

1993. Aviation Anniversaries. Multicoloured.

1913	3r.50 Type **289**	2·00	65
1914	5r. Homing pigeon and message from Santa Catalina mail service, 1894	2·25	1·10
1915	10r. Eckener and airship *Graf Zeppelin*	2·75	2·50
1916	15r. Pilot's badge and loading Philadelphia–Washington mail, 1918	4·00	4·25
1917	20r. USS *Macon* (airship) and mooring mast, 1933	4·00	4·25
MS1918	Two sheets. (a) 70×100 mm. 25r. Santos Dumont's airship *Ballon No. 5* and Eiffel Tower, 1901. (b) 100×70 mm. 25r. Jean-Pierre Blanchard's balloon, 1793 (vert) Set of 2 sheets	9·00	9·00

Anniversaries: Nos. 1913, 1915, 1917, **MS**1918a, 125th birth anniversary of Hugo Eckener (airship pioneer); 1914, 1916, **MS**1918b, Bicentenary of first airmail flight.

290 Ford Model T

1993. Centenaries of Henry Ford's First Petrol Engine (Nos. 1919/1930) and Karl Benz's First Four-wheeled Car (others).

1919	**290**	3r.50 multicoloured	90	1·00
1920	-	3r.50 multicoloured	90	1·00
1921	-	3r.50 black and violet	90	1·00
1922	-	3r.50 multicoloured	90	1·00
1923	-	3r.50 multicoloured	90	1·00
1924	-	3r.50 multicoloured	90	1·00
1925	-	3r.50 multicoloured	90	1·00
1926	-	3r.50 multicoloured	90	1·00
1927	-	3r.50 multicoloured	90	1·00
1928	-	3r.50 multicoloured	90	1·00
1929	-	3r.50 multicoloured	90	1·00
1930	-	3r.50 black, brn & vio	90	1·00
1931	-	3r.50 multicoloured	90	1·00
1932	-	3r.50 multicoloured	90	1·00
1933	-	3r.50 green, blk & vio	90	1·00
1934	-	3r.50 multicoloured	90	1·00
1935	-	3r.50 multicoloured	90	1·00
1936	-	3r.50 multicoloured	90	1·00
1937	-	3r.50 multicoloured	90	1·00
1938	-	3r.50 multicoloured	90	1·00
1939	-	3r.50 multicoloured	90	1·00
1940	-	3r.50 multicoloured	90	1·00
1941	-	3r.50 multicoloured	90	1·00
1942	-	3r.50 black, brn and violet	90	1·00
MS1943		Two sheets, each 100×70 mm. (a) 25r. multicoloured. (b) 25r. multicoloured Set of 2 sheets	9·00	10·00

Designs: No. 1920, Henry Ford; 1921, Plans of first petrol engine; 1922, Ford Probe GT, 1993; 1923, Front of Ford Sportsman, 1947; 1924, Back of Ford Sportsman; 1925, Advertisement of 1915; 1926, Ford Thunderbird, 1955; 1927, Ford logo; 1928, Ford Edsel Citation, 1958; 1929, Ford half-ton pickup, 1941; 1930, Silhouette of early Ford car; 1931, Daimler-Benz Straight 8, 1937; 1932, Karl Benz; 1933, Mercedes-Benz poster; 1934, Mercedes 38-250SS, 1929; 1935, Benz Viktoria, 1893; 1936, Benz logo; 1937, Plan of Mercedes engine; 1938, Mercedes-Benz 300SL Gullwing, 1952; 1939, Mercedes-Benz SL, 1993; 1940, Front of Benz 4-cylinder car, 1906; 1941, Back of Benz 4-cylinder car and advertisement; 1942, Silhouette of early Benz car; **MS**1943a, Ford Model Y, 1933; **MS**1943b, Mercedes 300S, 1955.

Nos. 1919/1930 and 1931/1942 were printed together, se-tenant, forming a composite design.

291 Ivan, Sonia, Sasha and Peter in the Snow

1993. *Peter and the Wolf.* Scenes from Walt Disney's cartoon film. Multicoloured.

1944	7l. Type **291**	25	25
1945	15l. Grandpa and Peter	30	25
1946	20l. Peter on bridge	30	25
1947	25l. Yascha, Vladimir and Mischa	30	25

1948	50l. Sasha on lookout	45	30
1949	1r. The wolf	60	35
1950	3r.50 Peter dreaming	70	80
1951	3r.50 Peter taking gun	70	80
1952	3r.50 Peter with gun in snow	70	80
1953	3r.50 Sasha and Peter	70	80
1954	3r.50 Sonia and Peter	60	60
1955	3r.50 Peter with Ivan and Sasha	70	80
1956	3r.50 Ivan warning Peter of the wolf	70	80
1957	3r.50 Ivan, Peter and Sasha in tree	70	80
1958	3r.50 Wolf below tree	70	80
1959	3r.50 Wolf and Sonia	70	80
1960	3r.50 Sasha attacking the wolf	70	80
1961	3r.50 Sasha walking into wolf's mouth	70	80
1962	3r.50 Peter firing pop gun at wolf	70	80
1963	3r.50 Wolf chasing Sonia	70	80
1964	3r.50 Ivan tying rope to wolf's tail	70	80
1965	3r.50 Peter and Ivan hoisting wolf	70	80
1966	3r.50 Sasha and the hunters	70	80
1967	3r.50 Ivan and Peter on wolf hanging from tree	70	80
MS1968	Two sheets. (a) 102×127 mm. 25r. Sonia as an angel. (b) 127×102 mm. 25r. Ivan looking proud Set of 2 sheets	8·00	8·50

292 *Girl with a Broom* (Rembrandt)

1994. Famous Paintings by Rembrandt and Matisse. Multicoloured.

1969	50l. Type **292**	40	25
1970	2r. *Girl with Tulips* (Matisse)	90	70
1971	3r.50 *Young Girl at half-open Door* (Rembrandt)	1·25	1·10
1972	3r.50 *Portrait of Greta Moll* (Matisse)	1·25	1·10
1973	5r. *The Prophetess Hannah* (Rembrandt)	1·50	1·25
1974	6r.50 *The Idol* (Matisse)	1·75	1·75
1975	7r. *Woman with a Pink Flower* (Rembrandt)	1·75	1·75
1976	9r. *Mme Matisse in a Japanese Robe* (Matisse)	2·00	2·25
1977	10r. *Portrait of Mme Matisse* (Matisse)	2·00	2·25
1978	12r. *Lucretia* (Rembrandt)	2·25	2·50
1979	15r. *Lady with a Ostrich Feather Fan* (Rembrandt)	2·25	2·75
1980	15r. *The Woman with the Hat* (Matisse)	2·25	2·75
MS1981	Three sheets. (a) 106×132 mm. 25r. *The Music-makers* (detail) (Rembrandt). (b) 132×106 mm. 25r. *Married Couple with Three Children* (detail) (Rembrandt) (horiz). (c) 132×106 mm. 25r. *The Painter's Family* (detail) (Matisse) Set of 3 sheets	17·00	17·00

No. 1979 is inscribed 'The Lady with an Ostich Feather Fan' in error.

293 Hong Kong 1983 Space Museum Stamp and Moon-lantern Festival

1994. Hong Kong '94 International Stamp Exhibition (1st issue). Multicoloured.

1982	4r. Type **293**	65	80
1983	4r. Maldive Islands 1976 5r. Viking space mission stamp and Moon-lantern festival	65	80

Nos. 1982/1983 were printed together, *se-tenant*, forming a composite design.

294 Vase

1994. Hong Kong '94 International Stamp Exhibition (2nd issue). Qing Dynasty Cloisonne Enamelware. Multicoloured.

1984	2r. Type **294**	90	85
1985	2r. Flower holder	90	85
1986	2r. Elephant with vase on back	90	85
1987	2r. Tibetan style lama's teapot	90	85
1988	2r. Fo-Dog	90	45
1989	2r. Teapot with swing handle	90	85

295 Windischmann (USA) and Giannini (Italy)

1994. World Cup Football Championship, USA (2nd issue). Multicoloured.

1990	7l. Type **295**	30	25
1991	20l. Carnevale (Italy) and Gascoigne (England)	50	25
1992	25l. England players congratulating Platt	50	25
1993	3r.50 Koeman (Holland) and Klinsmann (Germany)	1·25	80
1994	5r. Quinn (Ireland) and Maldini (Italy)	1·40	1·00
1995	7r. Lineker (England)	2·00	1·50
1996	15r. Hassam (Egypt) and Moran (Ireland)	3·00	3·50
1997	18r. Canniggia (Argentina)	3·25	3·50
MS1998	Two sheets, each 103×73 mm. 25r. Ogris (Austria). (b) 25r. Conejo (Costa Rica) (horiz) Set of 2 sheets	13·00	12·00

296 Humpback Whale

1994. Centenary (1992) of Sierra Club (environmental protection society). Endangered Species. Multicoloured.

1999	6r.50 Type **296**	1·60	1·60
2000	6r.50 Ocelot crouched in grass	1·60	1·60
2001	6r.50 Ocelot sitting	1·60	1·60
2002	6r.50 Snow monkey	1·60	1·60
2003	6r.50 Prairie dog	1·60	1·60
2004	6r.50 Golden lion tamarin	1·60	1·60
2005	6r.50 Prairie dog eating (horiz)	1·60	1·60
2006	6r.50 Prairie dog outside burrow (horiz)	1·60	1·60
2007	6r.50 Herd of woodland caribou (horiz)	1·60	1·60
2008	6r.50 Woodland caribou facing left (horiz)	1·60	1·60
2009	6r.50 Woodland caribou facing right (horiz)	1·60	1·60
2010	6r.50 Pair of Galapagos penguins (horiz)	1·60	1·60
2011	6r.50 Galapagos penguin facing right	1·60	1·60
2012	6r.50 Galapagos penguin looking straight ahead	1·60	1·60
2013	6r.50 Bengal tiger looking straight ahead	1·60	1·60
2014	6r.50 Bengal tiger looking right	1·60	1·60
2015	6r.50 Philippine tarsier with tree trunk at left	1·60	1·60
2016	6r.50 Philippine tarsier with tree trunk at right	1·60	1·60
2017	6r.50 Head of Philippine tarsier	1·60	1·60
2018	6r.50 Sierra Club centennial emblem (black, buff and green)	1·60	1·60
2019	6r.50 Golden lion tamarin between two branches (horiz)	1·60	1·60
2020	6r.50 Golden lion tamarin on tree trunk (horiz)	1·60	1·60
2021	6r.50 Tail fin of humpback whale and coastline (horiz)	1·60	1·60
2022	6r.50 Tail fin of humpback whale at night (horiz)	1·60	1·60
2023	6r.50 Bengal tiger (horiz)	1·60	1·60
2024	6r.50 Ocelot (horiz)	1·60	1·60
2025	6r.50 Snow monkey in water climbing out of pool (horiz)	1·60	1·60
2026	6r.50 Snow monkey swimming (horiz)	1·60	1·60

297 Dome of the Rock, Jerusalem

1994. Solidarity with the Palestinians.

2027	**297**	8r. multicoloured	1·60	1·60

298 Elasmosaurus

1994. Prehistoric Animals. Multicoloured.

2028-2059	Set of 32, 2028-2059	30·00	28·00
MS2060	Two sheets, each 106×76 mm. (a) 25r. Gallimimus. (b) 25r. Plateosaurus (vert) Set of 2 sheets	8·00	8·50

Nos. 2031/2042 and 2043/2054 respectively were printed together, *se-tenant*, forming composite designs. The species depicted are, in addition to T **298**, Dilophosaurus, Avimimus, Dimorphodon, Megalosaurus, Kuehneosaurus, Dryosaurus, Kentro- saurus, Baraposaurus, Tenontosaurus, Elaphrosaurus, Maiasaura, Huayangosaurus, Rutiodon, Pianitzkysaurus, Quetzalcoatlus, Daspleto- saurus, Pleurocoelus, Baryonyx, Pentaceratops, Kritosaurus, Microvenator, Nodosaurus, Montanaceratops, Dromiceiomimus, Dryptosaurus, Parkosaurus, Chasmosaurus, Edmontonia, Anatosaurus, Velociraptor and Spinosaurus.

299 Mallet Steam Locomotive, Indonesia

1994. Railway Locomotives of Asia. Multicoloured.

2061	25l. Type **299**	20	20
2062	50l. Class C62 steam locomotive, Japan, 1948	25	20
2063	1r. Class D51 steam locomotive, Japan, 1936 (horiz)	30	20
2064	5r. Steam locomotive, India (horiz)	90	90
2065	6r.50+50l. Class W steam locomotive, India (horiz)	1·25	1·50
2066	6r.50+50l. Class C53 steam locomotive, Indonesia (horiz)	1·25	1·50
2067	6r.50+50l. Class C10 steam locomotive, Japan (horiz)	1·25	1·50
2068	6r.50+50l. Hanomag steam locomotive, India (horiz)	1·25	1·50
2069	6r.50+50l. Hikari express train, Japan (horiz)	1·25	1·50
2070	6r.50+50l. Class C55 steam locomotive, Japan, 1935 (horiz)	1·25	1·50
2071	8r. Class 485 electric locomotive, Japan (horiz)	1·50	1·75
2072	10r. Class WP steam locomotive, India (horiz)	1·75	2·00
2073	15r. Class RM steam locomotive, China (horiz)	2·00	2·25
2074	20r. Class C57 steam locomotive, Japan, 1937	2·25	2·50
MS2075	Two sheets, each 110×80 mm. (a) 25r. Steam locomotive pulling goods train, Indonesia (horiz). (b) 25r. Class 8620 steam locomotive, Japan, 1914 (horiz) Set of 2 sheets	9·00	9·50

No. 2069 is inscribed 'Hakari' in error.

300 Japanese Bobtail

1994. Cats. Multicoloured.

2076	7l. Type **300**	30	20
2077	20l. Siamese (vert)	45	20
2078	25l. Persian longhair	45	20
2079	50l. Somali (vert)	55	20
2080	3r.50 Oriental shorthair	1·25	80
2081	5r. Burmese	1·50	1·00
2082	7r. Bombay carrying kitten	1·75	1·50
2083	10r. Turkish van (vert)	1·75	1·75
2084	12r. Javanese (vert)	2·00	2·00
2085	15r. Singapura	2·25	2·75
2086	18r. Turkish angora (vert)	2·50	3·25
2087	20r. Egyptian mau (vert)	2·50	3·25
MS2088	Three sheets. (a) 70×100 mm. 25r. Birman (vert). (b) 70×100 mm. 25r. Korat (vert). (c) 100×70 mm. 25r. Abyssinian (vert) Set of 3 sheets	13·00	15·00

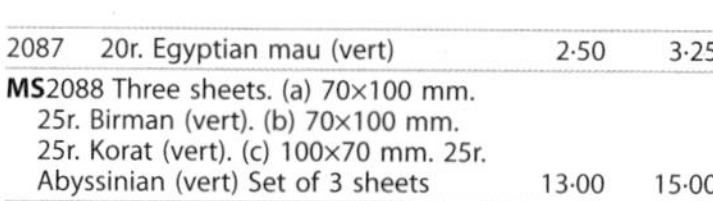

301 Franco Baresi (Italy) and Stuart McCall (Scotland)

1994. World Cup Football Championship, USA (3rd issue). Multicoloured

(a) Horiz designs.

2089	10l. Type **301**	40	40
2090	25l. Mick McCarthy (Ireland) and Gary Lineker (England)	50	50
2091	50l. J. Helt (Denmark) and R. Gordillo (Spain)	50	50
2092	5r. Martin Vasquez (Spain) and Enzo Scifo (Belgium)	1·25	1·25
2093	10r. Championship emblem	1·60	1·60
2094	12r. Tomas Brolin (Sweden) and Gordon Durie (Scotland)	1·75	1·75

(b) Vert designs.

2095	6r.50 Bebeto (Brazil)	1·25	1·25
2096	6r.50 Lothar Matthaus (Germany)	1·25	1·25
2097	6r.50 Diego Maradona (Argentina)	1·25	1·25
2098	6r.50 Stephane Chapuisat (Switzerland)	1·25	1·25
2099	6r.50 George Hagi (Rumania)	1·25	1·25
2100	6r.50 Carlos Valderama (Colombia)	1·25	1·25
MS2101	100×70 mm. 10r. Egyptian players	4·25	4·25

302 Crew of *Apollo 11*

1994. 25th Anniversary of First Manned Moon Landing. Multicoloured.

2102	5r. Type **302**	1·00	1·00
2103	5r. *Apollo 11* mission logo	1·00	1·00
2104	5r. Edwin Aldrin (astronaut) and *Eagle*	1·00	1·00
2105	5r. Crew of *Apollo 12*	1·00	1·00
2106	5r. *Apollo 12* mission logo	1·00	1·00
2107	5r. Alan Bean (astronaut) and equipment	1·00	1·00
2108	5r. Crew of *Apollo 16*	1·00	1·00
2109	5r. *Apollo 16* mission logo	1·00	1·00
2110	5r. Astronauts with US flag	1·00	1·00
2111	5r. Crew of *Apollo 17*	1·00	1·00
2112	5r. *Apollo 17* mission logo	1·00	1·00
2113	5r. Launch of *Apollo 17*	1·00	1·00
MS2114	100×76 mm. 25r. Launch of Russian rocket from Baikonur (vert)	4·00	4·75

303 Linford Christie (Great Britain) (100 m), 1992

1994. Centenary of International Olympic Committee. Gold Medal Winners. Multicoloured.

2115	7r. Type **303**	1·50	1·25
2116	12r. Koji Gushiken (Japan) (gymnastics), 1984	1·75	2·00
MS2117	106×71 mm. 25r. George Hackl (Germany) (single luge), 1994	4·50	5·00

304 US Amphibious DUKW

1994. 50th Anniversary of D-Day. Multicoloured.

2118	2r. Type **304**	75	30
2119	4r. Tank landing craft unloading at Sword Beach	1·25	60
2120	18r. Infantry landing craft at Omaha Beach	4·00	4·75
MS2121	105×76 mm. 25r. Landing craft with Canadian commandos	6·00	6·00

305 Duckpond, Suwan Folk Village

1994. Philakorea '94 International Stamp Exhibition, Seoul. Multicoloured.

No.	Description	Unused	Used
2122	50l. Type **305**	50	30
2123	3r. Pear-shaped bottle (vert)	60	70
2124	3r. Vase with dragon decoration (vert)	60	70
2125	3r. Vase with repaired lip (vert)	60	70
2126	3r. Stoneware vase with floral decoration (vert)	60	70
2127	3r. Celadon-glazed vase (vert)	60	70
2128	3r. Unglazed stone vase (vert)	60	70
2129	3r. Ritual water sprinkler (vert)	60	70
2130	3r. Long-necked celadon-glazed vase (vert)	60	70
2131	3r.50 Yongduson Park	70	75
2132	20r. Ploughing with ox, Hahoe	3·50	4·50
MS2133	70×102 mm. 25r. Hunting (detail from eight-panel painted screen) (vert)	4·50	5·50

306 US *Voyager 2* Satellite

1994. Space Exploration. Multicoloured.

No.	Description	Unused	Used
2134	5r. Type **306**	1·50	1·25
2135	5r. Russian *Sputnik* satellite	1·50	1·25
2136	5r. Apollo-Soyuz mission	1·50	1·25
2137	5r. *Apollo 10* on parachutes	1·50	1·25
2138	5r. *Apollo 11* mission flag	1·50	1·25
2139	5r. Hubble space telescope	1·50	1·25
2140	5r. Edwin 'Buzz' Aldrin (astronaut)	1·50	1·25
2141	5r. RCA lunar camera	1·50	1·25
2142	5r. Lunar Rover (space buggy)	1·50	1·25
2143	5r. Jim Irwin (astronaut)	1·50	1·25
2144	5r. *Apollo 12* lunar module	1·50	1·25
2145	5r. Astronaut holding equipment	1·50	1·25
MS2146	Two sheets. (a) 70×100 mm. 25r. David Scott (astronaut) in open hatch of *Apollo 9*. (b) 100×70 mm. 25r. Alan Shepherd Jr. (astronaut) (horiz) Set of 2 sheets	13·00	12·00

307 Mother, Child, Old Man and Town Skyline

1994. United Nations Development Programme. Multicoloured.

No.	Description	Unused	Used
2147	1r. Type **307**	25	10
2148	8r. Fisherman with son and island	1·60	2·25

308 School Band

1994. 50th Anniversary of Aminiya School. Children's Paintings. Multicoloured.

No.	Description	Unused	Used
2149	15l. Type **308**	15	10
2150	50l. Classroom	25	15
2151	1r. School emblem and hand holding book (vert)	35	15
2152	8r. School girls holding books (vert)	2·00	2·25
2153	10r. Sporting activities	2·00	2·25
2154	11r. School girls holding crown (vert)	2·00	2·75
2155	13r. Science lesson	2·25	2·75

309 Boeing 747

1994. 50th Anniversary of ICAO. Multicoloured.

No.	Description	Unused	Used
2156	50l. Type **309**	75	25
2157	1r. Hawker Siddeley ('de Havilland') Comet 4	1·00	25
2158	2r. Male International Airport	1·60	55
2159	3r. Lockheed L.1649 Super Star	1·75	85
2160	8r. European Airbus	2·50	2·75
2161	10r. Dornier Do-228	2·50	2·75
MS2162	100×70 mm. 25r. Concorde	5·00	6·00

310 Pintail ("Northern Pintail")

1995. Ducks. Multicoloured.

No.	Description	Unused	Used
2163	5r. Type **310**	1·00	1·00
2164	5r. Comb duck	1·00	1·00
2165	5r. Ruddy shelduck	1·00	1·00
2166	5r. Garganey	1·00	1·00
2167	5r. Indian whistling duck ('Lesser Whistling Duck')	1·00	1·00
2168	5r. Green-winged teal	1·00	1·00
2169	5r. Fulvous whistling duck	1·00	1·00
2170	5r. Common shoveler ('Northern Shoveler')	1·00	1·00
2171	5r. Cotton teal ('Cotton Pygmy Goose')	1·00	1·00
2172	6r.50+50l. Common pochard ('Pochard') (vert)	1·00	1·00
2173	6r.50+50l. Mallard (vert)	1·00	1·00
2174	6r.50+50l. European wigeon ('Wigeon') (vert)	1·00	1·00
2175	6r.50+50l. Common shoveler ('Northern Shoveler') (vert)	1·00	1·00
2176	6r.50+50l. Pintail ('Northern Pintail') (vert)	1·00	1·00
2177	6r.50+50l. Garganey (vert)	1·00	1·00
2178	6r.50+50l. Tufted duck (vert)	1·00	1·00
2179	6r.50+50l. Red-crested pochard ('Ferruginous Duck') (vert)	1·00	1·00
2180	6r.50+50l. Ferruginous duck ('Red-crested Pochard') (vert)	1·00	1·00
MS2181	Two sheets. (a) 100×71 mm. 25r. Spotbill duck ('Garganey'). (b) 73×100 mm. 25r. Cotton teal ('Cotton Pygmy Goose') (vert) Set of 2 sheets	7·50	8·50

Nos. 2163/2171 and 2172/2180 were printed together, *se-tenant*, forming composite designs.

311 Taj Mahal, India

1995. Famous Monuments of the World. Multicoloured.

No.	Description	Unused	Used
2182	7l. Type **311**	50	25
2183	10l. Washington Monument, USA	10	10
2184	15l. Mount Rushmore, USA	10	10
2185	25l. Arc de Triomphe, Paris (vert)	10	10
2186	50l. Sphinx, Egypt (vert)	50	20
2187	5r. El Castillo, Toltec pyramid, Yucatan	85	1·00
2188	8r. Toltec statue, Tula, Mexico (vert)	1·25	2·00
2189	12r. Victory Column, Berlin (vert)	1·60	2·50
MS2190	Two sheets, each 112×85 mm. (a) 25r. Easter Island statue (42×56 mm). (b) 25r. Stonehenge, Wiltshire (85×28 mm) Set of 2 sheets	7·50	8·50

312 Donald Duck driving Chariot

1995. History of Wheeled Transport. Scenes from Disney cartoon film *Donald and the Wheel*. Multicoloured.

No.	Description	Unused	Used
2191	3l. Type **312**	10	10
2192	4l. Donald with log	10	10
2193	5l. Donald driving Stephenson's *Rocket*	10	10
2194	10l. Donald pondering over circle (vert)	10	10
2195	20l. Donald in crashed car (vert)	10	10
2196	25l. Donald listening to early gramophone	10	10
2197	5r. Donald on mammoth	1·25	1·25
2198	20r. Donald pushing early car	3·75	4·75

313 Donald Duck playing Saxophone

1995. 60th Birthday of Donald Duck. Walt Disney cartoon characters. Multicoloured.

No.	Description	Unused	Used
2199	5r. Type **313**	90	90
2200	5r. Moby Duck playing fiddle	90	90
2201	5r. Feathry Duck with banjo and drum	90	90
2202	5r. Daisy Duck playing harp	90	90
2203	5r. Gladstone Gander with clarinet	90	90
2204	5r. Huey, Dewey and Louie with bassoon	90	90
2205	5r. Gus Goose playing flute	90	90
2206	5r. Prof. Ludwig von Drake playing trombone	90	90
2207	5r. Daisy picking flowers	90	90
2208	5r. Donald with backpack	90	90
2209	5r. Grandma Duck with kitten	90	90
2210	5r. Gus Goose and pie	90	90
2211	5r. Gyro Gearloose in space	90	90
2212	5r. Huey, Dewey and Louie photographing porcupine	90	90
2213	5r. Prof. Ludwig von Drake	90	90
2214	5r. Scrooge McDuck with money	90	90
MS2215	Four sheets. (a) 108×130 mm. 25r. Donald playing banjo. (b) 133×108 mm. 25r. Donald posing for photo. (c) 108×130 mm. 25r. Donald conducting (horiz). (d) 102×121 mm. 25r. Huey, Dewey and Louie (horiz) Set of 4 sheets	14·00	15·00

314 Islamic Centre, Male

1995. Eid Greetings. Multicoloured.

No.	Description	Unused	Used
2216	1r. Type **314**	15	15
2217	1r. Rose	15	15
2218	8r. Orchid	1·50	1·50
2219	10r. Orchid (different)	1·50	1·50

315 Killer Whale

1995. Singapore '95 International Stamp Exhibition (1st issue). Whales, Dolphins and Porpoises. Multicoloured.

No.	Description	Unused	Used
2220	1r. Type **315**	40	30
2221	2r. Bottlenose dolphins	45	35
2222	3r. Right whale	60	70
2223	3r. Pair of killer whales	60	70
2224	3r. Humpback whale	60	70
2225	3r. Pair of belugas	60	70
2226	3r. Narwhal	60	70
2227	3r. Head of blue whale	60	70
2228	3r. Bowhead whale	60	70
2229	3r. Head of fin whale	60	70
2230	3r. Pair of pilot whales	60	70
2231	3r. Grey whale	60	70
2232	3r. Sperm whale	60	70
2233	3r. Pair of goosebeaked whales	60	70
2234	3r. Hourglass dolphin	60	70
2235	3r. Bottlenose dolphin (different)	60	70
2236	3r. Dusky dolphin	60	70
2237	3r. Spectacled porpoise	60	70
2238	3r. Fraser's dolphin	60	70
2239	3r. Camerson's dolphin	60	70
2240	3r. Pair of spinner dolphins	60	70
2241	3r. Pair of Dalls dolphins	60	70
2242	3r. Spotted dolphin	60	70
2243	3r. Indus River dolphin	60	70
2244	3r. Hector's dolphin	60	70
2245	3r. Amazon River dolphin	60	70
2246	8r. Humpback whale and calf	1·25	1·50
2247	10r. Common dolphin	1·40	1·60
MS2248	Two sheets, each 100×70 mm. (a) 25r. Sperm whale (different). (b) 25r. Pair of hourglass dolphins Set of 2 sheets	9·00	9·00

See also Nos. 2302/**MS**2310.

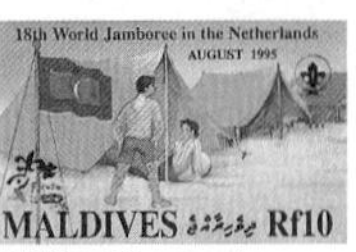

316 Scout Camp and National Flag

1995. 18th World Scout Jamboree, Netherlands. Multicoloured.

No.	Description	Unused	Used
2249	10r. Type **316**	1·75	2·00
2250	12r. Campfire cooking	1·90	2·25
2251	15r. Scouts erecting tent	2·00	2·40
MS2252	102×72 mm. 25r. Scouts around camp fire (vert)	3·50	4·00

Nos. 2249/2251 were printed together, *se-tenant*, forming a composite design.

317 Soviet Heavy Howitzer Battery

1995. 50th Anniversary of End of Second World War in Europe. Multicoloured.

No.	Description	Unused	Used
2253	5r. Type **317**	1·10	85
2254	5r. Ruins of Berchtesgaden	1·10	85
2255	5r. US Boeing B-17 Flying Fortress dropping food over the Netherlands	1·10	85
2256	5r. Soviet Ilyushin Il-1 bomber	1·10	85
2257	5r. Liberation of Belsen	1·10	85
2258	5r. Supermarine Spitfire and V-1 flying bomb	1·10	85
2259	5r. US tanks advancing through Cologne	1·10	85
2260	5r. Reichstag in ruins	1·10	85
MS2261	107×76 mm. 25r. Soviet and US troops celebrating	3·50	4·00

318 Asian Child and Dove

1995. 50th Anniversary of United Nations (1st issue). Multicoloured.

No.	Description	Unused	Used
2262	6r.50+50l. Type **318**	90	1·25
2263	8r. Globe and dove	1·00	1·40
2264	10r. African child and dove	1·10	1·50
MS2265	72×102 mm. 25r. United Nations emblem and dove	2·75	3·75

Nos. 2262/2264 were printed together, *se-tenant*, forming a composite design.

320 Asian Child eating Rice

319 United Nations Emblem

1995. 50th Anniversary of United Nations (2nd issue).

No.	Type	Description	Unused	Used
2266	319	30l. black, blue & grn	10	10
2267	-	8r. multicoloured	1·00	1·25
2268	-	11r. multicoloured	1·25	1·75
2269	-	13r. black, grey and red	1·60	2·25

Designs: 8r. Symbolic women, flag and map; 11r. UN soldier and symbolic dove; 13r. Gun barrels, atomic explosion and bomb sight.

1995. 50th Anniversary of FAO (1st issue). Multicoloured.

No.	Description	Unused	Used
2270	6r.50+50l. +50l. Type **320**	1·00	1·25
2271	8r. FAO emblem	1·00	1·25
2272	10r. African mother and child	1·00	1·25
MS2273	72×102 mm. 25r. African child and symbolic hand holding maize	5·00	6·00

See also Nos. 2311/2312.

321 Queen Elizabeth the Queen Mother

1995. 95th Birthday of Queen Elizabeth the Queen Mother.

2274 **321** 5r. brown, lt brn & blk 1·00 1·10
2275 - 5r. multicoloured 1·00 1·10
2276 - 5r. multicoloured 1·00 1·10
2277 - 5r. multicoloured 1·00 1·10
MS2278 125×100 mm. 25r. multicoloured 6·00 6·00

Designs: No. 2275, Without hat; No. 2276, At desk (oil painting); No. 2277, Queen Elizabeth the Queen Mother; No. **MS**2278, Wearing lilac hat and dress.

1995. 50th Anniversary of End of Second World War in the Pacific. As T **317**. Multicoloured.

2279 6r.50 +50l. Grumman F6F-3 Hellcat aircraft 1·50 1·50
2280 6r.50 +50l. F4-U1 fighter aircraft attacking beach 1·50 1·50
2281 6r.50 +50l. Douglas SBD Dauntless aircraft 1·50 1·50
2282 6r.50 +50l. American troops in landing craft, Guadalcanal 1·50 1·50
2283 6r.50 +50l. US marines in Alligator tanks 1·50 1·50
2284 6r.50 +50l. US landing ship 1·50 1·50
MS2285 106×74 mm. 25r. F4-U1 fighter aircraft 4·00 4·50

322 Students using Library

1995. 50th Anniversary of National Library. Multicoloured.

2286 2r. Type **322** 25 25
2287 8r. Students using library (different) 1·00 1·50
MS2288 105×75 mm. 10r. Library entrance (100×70 mm). Imperf 1·40 1·60

323 Spur-thighed Tortoise

1995. Turtles and Tortoises. Multicoloured.

2289 3r. Type **323** 70 80
2290 3r. Aldabra turtle 70 80
2291 3r. Loggerhead turtle 70 80
2292 3r. Olive Ridley turtle 70 80
2293 3r. Leatherback turtle 70 80
2294 3r. Green turtle 70 80
2295 3r. Atlantic Ridley turtle 70 80
2296 3r. Hawksbill turtle 70 80
2297 10r. Hawksbill turtle on beach 1·50 1·75
2298 10r. Pair of hawksbill turtles 1·50 1·75
2299 10r. Hawksbill turtle climbing out of water 1·50 1·75
2300 10r. Hawksbill turtle swimming 1·50 1·75
MS2301 100×70 mm. 25r. Green turtle 3·75 4·50

Nos. 2289/2296 were printed together, *se-tenant*, forming a composite design.

Nos. 2297/2300 include the WWF Panda emblem.

324 *Russula aurata* (fungi) and *Papilio demodocus* (butterfly)

1995. Singapore '95 International Stamp Exhibition (2nd issue). Butterflies and Fungi. Multicoloured.

2302 2r. Type **324** 75 75
2303 2r. *Lepista saeva* and *Kallimoides rumia* 75 75
2304 2r. *Lepista nuda* and *Hypolimnas salmacis* 75 75
2305 2r. *Xerocomus subtomentosus* (*Boletus subtomentosus* and *Precis octavia*) 75 75
2306 5r. *Gyroporus castaneus* and *Hypolimnas salmacis* 1·10 1·10
2307 8r. *Gomphidius glutinosus* and *Papilio dardanus* 1·25 1·25
2308 10r. *Russula olivacea* and *Precis octavia* 1·40 1·40
2309 12r. *Boletus edulis* and *Prepona praeneste* 1·40 1·40
MS2310 Two sheets, each 105×76 mm. (a) 25r. *Amanita muscaria* and *Kallimoides rumia* (vert). (b) 25r. *Boletus rhodoxanthus* and *Hypolimnas salmacis* (vert) Set of 2 sheets 8·00 8·00

Nos. 2302/2305 and 2306/2309 respectively were printed together, *se-tenant*, forming composite designs.

No. 2304 is inscribed 'Lapista' in error.

325 Planting Kaashi

1995. 50th Anniversary of FAO (2nd issue). Multicoloured.

2311 7r. Type **325** 90 1·10
2312 8r. Fishing boat 1·10 1·25

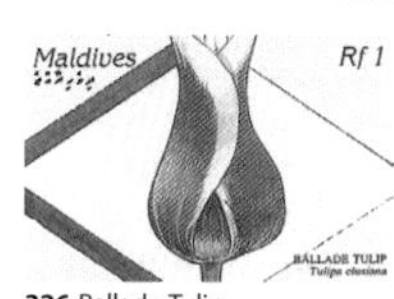

326 Ballade Tulip

1995. Flowers. Multicoloured.

2313 1r. Type **326** 25 15
2314 3r. White mallow 60 50
2315 5r. Regale trumpet lily 1·10 1·00
2316 5r. *Dendrobium* Waipahu Beauty 1·10 1·00
2317 5r. *Brassocattleya* Jean Murray 1·10 1·00
2318 5r. *Cymbidium* Fort George 1·10 1·00
2319 5r. *Paphiopedilum malipoense* 1·10 1·00
2320 5r. *Cycnoches chlorochilon* 1·10 1·00
2321 5r. *Rhyncholaelia digbgana* 1·10 1·00
2322 5r. *Lycaste deppei* 1·10 1·00
2323 5r. *Masdevallia constricta* 1·10 1·00
2324 5r. *Paphiopedilum* Clair de Lune 1·10 1·00
2325 7r. *Lilactime dahlia* 1·25 1·25
2326 8r. Blue ideal iris 1·25 1·25
2327 10r. Red crown imperial 1·40 1·40
MS2328 Two sheets, each 106×76 mm. (a) 25r. *Encyclia cochleata* (vert). (b) 25r. *Psychopsis kramerina* (vert) Set of 2 sheets 8·00 9·50

327 John Lennon with Microphone

1995. 15th Death Anniversary of John Lennon (musician). Multicoloured.

2329 5r. Type **327** 1·50 1·25
2330 5r. With glasses and moustache 1·50 1·25
2331 5r. With guitar 1·50 1·25
2332 5r. With guitar and wearing glasses 1·50 1·25
2333 5r. Wearing sun glasses and red jacket 1·50 1·25
2334 5r. Wearing headphones 1·50 1·25
MS2335 88×117 mm. 2, 3, 8, 10r. Different portraits of John Lennon 5·50 5·50
MS2336 102×72 mm. 25r. John Lennon performing 5·50 5·50

328 Elvis Presley with Microphone

1995. 60th Birth Anniversary of Elvis Presley (entertainer). Multicoloured.

2337 5r. Type **328** 90 80
2338 5r. Wearing red jacket 90 80
2339 5r. Wearing blue jacket 90 80
2340 5r. With microphone and wearing blue jacket 90 80
2341 5r. In army uniform 90 80
2342 5r. Wearing yellow bow tie 90 80
2343 5r. In yellow shirt 90 80
2344 5r. In light blue shirt 90 80
2345 5r. Wearing red and white high-collared jacket 90 80
MS2346 80×110 mm. 25r. Elvis Presley (horiz) 4·25 4·50

329 Johannes van der Waals (1919 Physics)

1995. Centenary of Nobel Prize Trust Fund. Multicoloured.

2347-2355 5r.×9 (Type **329**; Charles Guillaume (1920 Physics); Sir James Chadwick (1935 Physics); Willem Einthoven (1924 Medicine); Henrik Dam (1943 Medicine); Sir Alexander Fleming (1945 Medicine); Hermann Muller (1946 Medicine); Rodney Porter (1972 Medicine); Werner Arber (1978 Medicine)) 8·50 9·00
2356-2664 5r.×9 (Niels Bohr (1922 Physics); Ben Mottelson (1975 Physics); Patrick White (1973 Literature); Elias Canetti (1981 Literature); Theodor Kocher (1909 Medicine); August Krogh (1920 Medicine); William Murphy (1934 Medicine); John Northrop (1946 Chemistry); Luis Leloir (1970 Chemistry)) 8·50 9·00
2365-2373 5r.×9 (Dag Hammarskjold (1961 Peace); Alva Myrdal (1982 Peace); Archbishop Desmond Tutu (1984 Peace); Rudolf Eucken (1908 Literature); Aleksandr Solzhenitsyn (1970 Literature); Gabriel Marquez (1982 Literature); Chen Yang (1957 Physics); Karl Muller (1987 Physics); Melvin Schwartz (1988 Physics)) 8·50 9·00
2374-2382 5r.×9 (Robert Millikan (1923 Physics); Louis de Broglie (1929 Physics); Ernest Walton (1951 Physics); Richard Willstatter (1915 Chemistry); Lars Onsager (1968 Chemistry); Gerhard Herzberg (1971 Chemistry); William B. Yeats (1923 Literature); George Bernard Shaw (1925 Literature); Eugene O'Neill (1936 Literature)) 8·50 9·00
2383-2391 5r.×9 (Bernardo Houssay (1947 Medicine); Paul Muller (1948 Medicine); Walter Hess (1949 Medicine); Sir MacFarlane Burnet (1960 Medicine); Baruch Blumberg (1976 Medicine); Daniel Nathans (1978 Medicine); Glenn Seaborg (1951 Chemistry); Ilya Prigogine (1977 Chemistry); Kenichi Fukui (1981 Chemistry)) 8·50 9·00
2392-2400 5r.×9 (Carl Spitteler (1919 Literature); Henri Bergson (1927 Literature); Johannes Jensen (1944 Literature); Antoine-Henri Becquerel (1903 Physics); Sir William H. Bragg (1915 Physics); Sir William L. Bragg (1915 Physics); Frederik Bajer (1908 Peace); Leon Bourgeois (1920 Peace); Karl Branting (1921 Peace)) 8·50 9·00
MS2401 Six sheets. (a) 80×110 mm. 25r. Konrad bloch (1964 Medicine). (b) 80×110 mm. 25r. Samuel Beckett (1969 Literature). (c) 80×110 mm. 25r. Otto Wallach (1910 Chemistry). (d) 110×80 mm. 25r. Hideki Yukawa (1949 Physics). (e) 110×80 mm. 25r. Eisaku Sato (1974 Peace). (f) 110×80 mm. 25r. Robert Koch (1905 Medicine) Set of 6 sheets 17·00 20·00

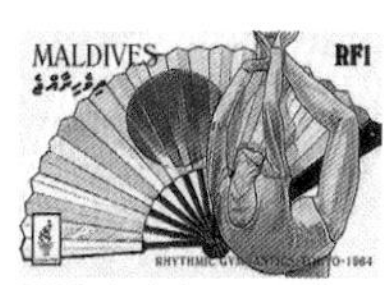

330 Rythmic Gymnast and Japanese Fan

1996. Olympic Games, Atlanta (1st issue). Multicoloured.

2402 1r. Type **330** 25 10
2403 3r. Archer and Moscow Olympics logo 50 35
2404 5r. Diver and Swedish flag 1·00 1·00
2405 5r. Canadian Maple Leaf 1·00 1·00
2406 5r. Shot putting (decathlon) 1·00 1·00
2407 5r. Moscow Olympic medal and ribbon 1·00 1·00
2408 5r. Fencer 1·00 1·00
2409 5r. Gold medal 1·00 1·00
2410 5r. Equestrian competitor 1·00 1·00
2411 5r. Sydney Opera House 1·00 1·00
2412 5r. Athlete on starting blocks 1·00 1·00
2413 5r. South Korean flag 1·00 1·00
2414 7r. High jumper and Tower Bridge, London 1·10 1·10
2415 10r. Athlete on starting blocks and Brandenburg Gate, Germany 1·40 1·60
2416 12r. Hurdler and Amsterdam Olympic logo 1·60 1·90
MS2417 Two sheets, each 113×80 mm. (a) 25r. Red Olympic Flame (vert). (b) 25r. Multicoloured Olympic Flame (vert) Set of 2 sheets 8·00 9·00

See also Nos. 2469/**MS**2488.

331 *Self Portrait* (Degas)

1996. 125th Anniversary of Metropolitan Museum of Art, New York. Multicoloured.

2418-2425 4r.×8 *Self-Portrait* (Degas); *Andromache and Astyanax* (Prud'hon); *Rene Grenier* (Toulouse-Lautrec); *The Banks of the Bievre near Bicetre* (Rousseau); *The Repast of the Lion* (Rousseau); *Portrait of Yves Gobillard-Morisot* (Degas); *Sunflowers* (Van Gogh); *The Singer in Green* (Degas) 8·00 8·50
2426-2433 4r.×8 *Still Life* (Fantin-Latour); *Portrait of a Lady in Grey* (Degas); *Apples and Grapes* (Monet); *The Englishman* (Toulouse-Lautrec); *Cypresses* (Van Gogh); *Flowers in a Chinese Vase* (Redon); *The Gardener* (Seurat); *Large Sunflowers I* (Nolde) 8·00 8·50
2434-2441 4r.×8 All by Manet: *The Spanish Singer*; *Young Man in Costume of Majo*; *Mademoiselle Victorine*; *Boating*; *Peonies*; *Woman with a Parrot*; *George Moore*; *The Monet Family in their Garden* 8·00 8·50
2442-2449 4r.×8 *Goldfish* (Matisse); *Spanish Woman: Harmony in Blue* (Matisse); *Nasturtiums and the "Dance" II* (Matisse); *The House behind Trees* (Braque); *Mada Primavesi* (Klimt); *Head of a Woman* (Picasso); *Woman in White* (Picasso); *Harlequin* (Picasso) 8·00 8·50
MS2450 Four sheets, each 95×70 mm, containing horiz designs, 81×53 mm. (a) 25r. *Northeaster* (Homer). (b) 25r. *The Fortune Teller* (De La Tour). (c) 25r. *Santo (Sanzio), Ritratto de Andrea Navagero e Agostino Beazzano* (Raphael). (d) 25r. *Portrait of a Woman* (Rubens) Set of 4 sheets 17·00 20·00

332 Mickey Mouse on Great Wall of China

1996. CHINA '96 Ninth Asian International Stamp Exhibition, Peking. Walt Disney cartoon characters in China. Multicoloured.

2451 2r. Type **332** 80 80
2452 2r. Pluto with temple guardian 80 80
2453 2r. Minnie Mouse with pandas 80 80
2454 2r. Mickey windsurfing near junks 80 80
2455 2r. Goofy cleaning grotto statue 80 80
2456 2r. Donald and Daisy Duck at Marble Boat 80 80
2457 2r. Mickey with terracotta warriors 80 80
2458 2r. Goofy with geese and masks 80 80
2459 2r. Donald and Goofy on traditional fishing boat 80 80
2460 2r. Mickey and Minnie in dragon boat 80 80
2461 2r. Donald at Peking opera 80 80

2462 2r. Mickey and Minnie in Chinese garden 80 80
2463 3r. Mickey and Minnie at the Ice Pagoda (vert) 1·00 1·00
2464 3r. Donald and Mickey flying Chinese kites (vert) 1·00 1·00
2465 3r. Goofy playing anyiwu (vert) 1·00 1·00
2466 3r. Paper cutouts of Mickey and Goofy (vert) 1·00 1·00
2467 3r. Donald and Mickey in dragon dance (vert) 1·00 1·00
MS2468 Three sheets. (a) 108×133 mm. 5r. Mickey pointing. (b) 133×108 mm. 7r. Mickey and Minnie watching Moon. (c) 133×108 mm. 8r. Donald using chopsticks Set of 3 sheets 5·50 6·00

333 Stella Walsh (Poland) (100 m sprint, 1932) on Medal

1996. Olympic Games, Atlanta (2nd issue). Previous Gold Medal Winners. Multicoloured.
2469 1r. Type **333** 25 15
2470 3r. Emile Zatopek (Czechoslovakia) (10,000 m running, 1952) and Olympic torch (vert) 50 35
2471 5r. Yanko Rousseu (Bulgaria) (lightweight, 1980) (vert) 85 85
2472 5r. Peter Baczako (Hungary) (middle heavyweight, 1980) (vert) 85 85
2473 5r. Leonid Taranenko (Russia) (heavyweight, 1980) (vert) 85 85
2474 5r. Aleksandr Kurlovich (Russia) (heavyweight, 1988) (vert) 85 85
2475 5r. Assen Zlateu (Bulgaria) (middleweight, 1980) (vert) 85 85
2476 5r. Zeng Guoqiang (China) (flyweight, 1984) (vert) 85 85
2477 5r. Yurik Vardanyan (Russia) (heavyweight, 1980) (vert) 85 85
2478 5r. Sultan Rakhmanov (Russia) (super heavyweight, 1980) (vert) 85 85
2479 5r. Vassily Alexeev (Russia) (super heavyweight, 1972) (vert) 85 85
2480 5r. Ethel Catherwood (Canada) (high jump, 1928) 85 85
2481 5r. Mildred Didrikson (USA) (javelin, 1932) 85 85
2482 5r. Francina Blankers-Koen (Netherlands) (80 m hurdles, 1948) 85 85
2483 5r. Tamara Press (Russia) (shot put, 1960) 85 85
2484 5r. Lia Manoliu (Rumania) (discus, 1968) 85 85
2485 5r. Rosa Mota (Portugal) (marathon, 1988) 85 85
2486 10r. Olga Fikotova (Czechoslovakia) (discus, 1956) on medal 1·40 1·60
2487 12r. Joan Benoit (USA) (marathon, 1984) on medal 1·60 1·90
MS2488 Two sheets. (a) 76×106 mm. 25r. Naeem Suleymanoglu (Turkey) (weightlifting, 1988) (vert). (b) 105×75 mm. 25r. Irena Szewinska (Poland) (400 m running, 1976) on medal Set of 2 sheets 8·50 9·00

No. 2469 identifies the event as 10 metres in error.

334 Queen Elizabeth II

1996. 70th Birthday of Queen Elizabeth II. Multicoloured.
2489 8r. Type **334** 1·75 1·75
2490 8r. Wearing hat 1·75 1·75
2491 8r. At desk 1·75 1·75
MS2492 125×103 mm. 25r. Queen Elizabeth and Queen Mother on Buckingham Palace balcony 6·50 6·00

335 African Child

1996. 50th Anniversary of UNICEF. Multicoloured.
2493 5r. Type **335** 75 55
2494 7r. European girl 1·00 1·25
2495 7r. Maldivian boy 1·00 1·25
2496 10r. Asian girl 1·40 1·50
MS2497 114×74 mm. 25r. Baby with toy 3·50 4·50

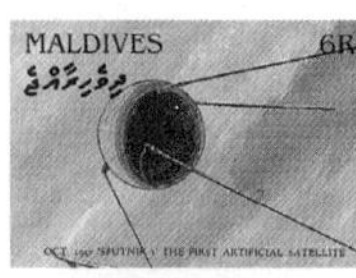

336 *Sputnik 1* Satellite

1996. Space Exploration. Multicoloured.
2498 6r. Type **336** 1·10 1·10
2499 6r. *Apollo 11* command module 1·10 1·10
2500 6r. *Skylab* 1·10 1·10
2501 6r. Astronaut Edward White walking in space 1·10 1·10
2502 6r. *Mariner 9* 1·10 1·10
2503 6r. Apollo and Soyuz docking 1·10 1·10
MS2504 104×74 mm. 25r. Launch of *Apollo 8* (vert) 4·50 5·00

337 *Epiphora albida*

1996. Butterflies. Multicoloured.
2505 7r. Type **337** 1·25 1·25
2506 7r. *Satyrus dryas* 1·25 1·25
2507 7r. *Satyrus lena* 1·25 1·25
2508 7r. *Papilio tynderaeus* 1·25 1·25
2509 7r. *Urota suraka* 1·25 1·25
2510 7r. *Satyrus nercis* 1·25 1·25
2511 7r. *Papilio troilus* (vert) 1·25 1·25
2512 7r. *Papilio cresphontes* (vert) 1·25 1·25
2513 7r. Lime swallowtail caterpillar (vert) 1·25 1·25
2514 7r. *Cynthia virginiensis* (vert) 1·25 1·25
2515 7r. Monarch caterpillar (vert) 1·25 1·25
2516 7r. *Danaus plexippus* (vert) 1·25 1·25
2517 7r. Monarch caterpillar and pupa (vert) 1·25 1·25
2518 7r. *Chlosyne harrisii* (vert) 1·25 1·25
2519 7r. *Cymothoe coccinata* (vert) 1·25 1·25
2520 7r. *Morpho rhetenor* (vert) 1·25 1·25
2521 7r. *Callicore lidwina* (vert) 1·25 1·25
2522 7r. *Heliconius erato reductimacula* (vert) 1·25 1·25
MS2523 Two sheets, each 106×76 mm. (a) 25r. *Heliconius charitonius* (vert). (b) 25r. *Heliconius cydno* (vert) Set of 2 sheets 8·50 9·00

338 Amtrak F40H Diesel-electric Locomotive, USA

1996. Trains of the World. Multicoloured.
2524 3r. Type **338** 80 80
2525 3r. Stephenson's *Experiment* 80 80
2526 3r. Indian-Pacific Intercontinental, Australia 80 80
2527 3r. Stephenson's Killingworth type steam locomotive, 1815 80 80
2528 3r. George Stephenson 80 80
2529 3r. Stephenson's *Rocket*, 1829 80 80
2530 3r. High Speed Train 125, Great Britain 80 80
2531 3r. First rail passenger coach *Experiment*, 1825 80 80
2532 3r. Union Pacific Class U25B diesel locomotive (inscr 'Tofac'), USA 80 80
2533 3r. Southern Pacific's Daylight express, 1952, USA 80 80
2534 3r. Timothy Hackworth's *Sans Pareil*, 1829 80 80
2535 3r. Chicago and North Western diesel locomotive, USA 80 80
2536 3r. Richard Trevithick's *Pen-y-Darren* locomotive, 1804 80 80
2537 3r. Isambard Kingdom Brunel 80 80
2538 3r. Great Western locomotive, 1838 80 80
2539 3r. Vistadome observation car, Canada 80 80
2540 3r. Mohawk and Hudson Railroad *Experiment*, 1832 80 80
2541 3r. ICE high speed train, Germany 80 80
2542 3r. Electric container locomotive, Germany 80 80
2543 3r. John Blenkinsop's rack locomotive, 1811 80 80
2544 3r. Diesel-electric locomotive, Western Australia 80 80
2545 3r. Timothy Hackworth's *Royal George* 1827 80 80
2546 3r. Robert Stephenson 80 80
2547 3r. Trevithick's *Newcastle* 80 80
2548 3r. Deltic diesel-electric locomotive, Great Britain 80 80
2549 3r. Stockton and Darlington Railway locomotive No. 5 *Stockton*, 1826 80 80
2550 3r. Channel Tunnel Le Shuttle train 80 80
MS2551 Three sheets, each 96×91 mm. (a) 25r. Peter Cooper's *Tom Thumb*, 1829. (b) 25r. John Jarvis's *De Witt Clinton*, 1831. (c) 25r. William Hudson's *The General*, 1855 Set of 3 sheets 13·00 13·00

No. 2524 is inscribed 'F4 OPH' in error.

339 Bongo

1996. Wildlife of the World. Multicoloured.
2552 5r. Type **339** 1·50 1·25
2553 5r. Bushbuck 1·50 1·25
2554 5r. Namaqua dove 1·50 1·25
2555 5r. Hoopoe 1·50 1·25
2556 5r. African fish eagle 1·50 1·25
2557 5r. Egyptian goose 1·50 1·25
2558 5r. Saddle-bill stork 1·50 1·25
2559 5r. Blue-breasted kingfisher 1·50 1·25
2560 5r. Yellow baboon 1·50 1·25
2561 5r. Banded duiker ('Zebra Duiker') 1·50 1·25
2562 5r. Yellow-backed duiker 1·50 1·25
2563 5r. Pygmy hippopotamus 1·50 1·25
2564 5r. Large-spotted genet 1·50 1·25
2565 5r. African spoonbill 1·50 1·25
2566 5r. White-faced whistling duck 1·50 1·25
2567 5r. Helmeted guineafowl 1·50 1·25
2568 7r. Cotton-headed tamarin (horiz) 1·75 1·50
2569 7r. European bison (horiz) 1·75 1·50
2570 7r. Tiger (horiz) 1·75 1·50
2571 7r. Western capercaillie (horiz) 1·75 1·50
2572 7r. Giant panda (horiz) 1·75 1·50
2573 7r. *Trogonoptera brookiana* (butterfly) (horiz) 1·75 1·50
2574 7r. American beaver (horiz) 1·75 1·50
2575 7r. *Leiopelma hamiltoni* (frog) (horiz) 1·75 1·50
2576 7r. Manatee (horiz) 1·75 1·50
MS2577 106×76 mm. 25r. Chimpanzee (horiz) 4·50 5·00

Nos. 2552/2559, 2560/2567 and 2568/2576 respectively were printed together, *se-tenant*, with the backgrounds forming composite designs.
No. 2553 is inscribed 'BUSHBACK' in error.

340 Giant Panda

1996. Endangered Species. Multicoloured.
2578 5r. Type **340** 1·50 1·25
2579 5r. Indian elephant 1·50 1·25
2580 5r. Arrow-poison frog 1·50 1·25
2581 5r. Mandrill 1·50 1·25
2582 5r. Snow leopard 1·50 1·25
2583 5r. California condor 1·50 1·25
2584 5r. Whale-headed stork ('Shoebill Stork') 1·50 1·25
2585 5r. Red-billed hornbill 1·50 1·25
2586 5r. Hippopotamus 1·50 1·25
2587 5r. Gorilla 1·50 1·25
2588 5r. Lion 1·50 1·25
2589 5r. South African crowned crane ('Gray Crowned Crane') 1·50 1·25
MS2590 Two sheets, each 110×80 mm. (a) 25r. Tiger (vert). (b) 25r. Leopard Set of 2 sheets 9·50 11·00

341 Mickey Mouse climbing out of Puddle

1996. Centenary of the Cinema. Cartoon Frames from *The Little Whirlwind* (Nos. 2591/2607) or *Pluto and the Flypaper"*(Nos. 2608/2624). Multicoloured.
2591 4r. Type **341** 1·25 1·25
2592 4r. Frame 2 1·25 1·25
2593 4r. Frame 3 1·25 1·25
2594 4r. Frame 4 1·25 1·25
2595 4r. Frame 5 1·25 1·25
2596 4r. Frame 6 1·25 1·25
2597 4r. Frame 7 1·25 1·25
2598 4r. Frame 8 1·25 1·25
2599 4r. Frame 9 1·25 1·25
2600 4r. Frame 10 1·25 1·25
2601 4r. Frame 11 1·25 1·25
2602 4r. Frame 12 1·25 1·25
2603 4r. Frame 13 1·25 1·25
2604 4r. Frame 14 1·25 1·25
2605 4r. Frame 15 1·25 1·25
2606 4r. Frame 16 (Mickey holding fish above head) 1·25 1·25
2607 4r. Frame 17 (Mickey throwing fish into pool) 1·25 1·25
2608 4r. Frame 1 (Pluto) 1·25 1·25
2609 4r. Frame 2 1·25 1·25
2610 4r. Frame 3 1·25 1·25
2611 4r. Frame 4 1·25 1·25
2612 4r. Frame 5 1·25 1·25
2613 4r. Frame 6 1·25 1·25
2614 4r. Frame 7 1·25 1·25
2615 4r. Frame 8 1·25 1·25
2616 4r. Frame 9 1·25 1·25
2617 4r. Frame 10 1·25 1·25
2618 4r. Frame 11 1·25 1·25
2619 4r. Frame 12 1·25 1·25
2620 4r. Frame 13 1·25 1·25
2621 4r. Frame 14 1·25 1·25
2622 4r. Frame 15 1·25 1·25
2623 4r. Frame 16 1·25 1·25
2624 4r. Frame 17 1·25 1·25
MS2625 Two sheets, 111×131 mm. (a) 25r. Frame 18 (*The Little Whirlwind*). (b) 25r. Frame 18 (*Pluto and the Flypaper*) Set of 2 sheets 12·00 15·00

342 Letter 'O' with Chinese Character

1997. HONG KONG '97 International Stamp Exhibition. Multicoloured.
2626 5r. Letter 'H' and Chinese couple 85 85
2627 5r. Type **342** 85 85
2628 5r. Letter 'N' and Chinese dragon 85 85
2629 5r. Letter 'G' and carnival dragon 85 85
2630 5r. Letter 'K' and modern office block 85 85
2631 5r. Letter 'O' and Chinese character (different) 85 85
2632 5r. Letter 'N' and Chinese fan cases 85 85
2633 5r. Letter 'G' and Chinese junk 85 85
MS2634 106×125 mm. 25r. 'HONG KONG' as on Nos. 2626/2633 (76×38 mm) 3·75 4·50

343 California Condor

1997. Birds of the World. Multicoloured.
2635 5r. Type **343** 1·00 1·00
2636 5r. Audouin's gull 1·00 1·00
2637 5r. Atlantic puffin 1·00 1·00
2638 5r. Resplendent quetzal 1·00 1·00

2639	5r. Puerto Rican amazon	1·00	1·00
2640	5r. Lesser bird of paradise	1·00	1·00
2641	5r. Japanese crested ibis	1·00	1·00
2642	5r. Mauritius kestrel	1·00	1·00
2643	5r. Kakapo	1·00	1·00
MS2644	76×106 mm. 25r. Ivory-billed woodpecker	5·50	6·00

Nos. 2635/2643 were printed together, *se-tenant*, with the backgrounds forming a composite design.

344 Ye Qiabo (China) (women's 500/1000 m speed skating, 1992)

1997. Winter Olympic Games, Nagano, Japan (1998). Multicoloured.

2645	2r. Type **344**	40	25
2646	3r. Leonhard Stock (Austria) (downhill skiing, 1980)	55	35
2647	5r. Herma von Szabo-Planck (Austria) (figure skating, 1924)	85	85
2648	5r. Katarina Witt (Germany) (figure skating, 1988)	85	85
2649	5r. Natalia Bestemianova and Andrei Bukin (Russia) (pairs ice dancing, 1988)	85	85
2650	5r. Jayne Torvill and Christopher Dean (Great Britain) (pairs ice dancing, 1984)	85	85
2651	8r. Bjorn Daehlie (Norway) (cross-country skiing, 1992)	1·25	1·25
2652	12r. Wolfgang Hoppe (Germany) (bobsleigh, 1984)	1·75	2·00
MS2653	Two sheets, each 76×106 mm. (a) 25r. Sonja Henie (Norway) (figure skating, 1924). (b) 25r. Andree Joly and Pierre Brunet (France) (pairs ice dancing, 1932) Set of 2 sheets	8·00	9·00

345 Crowned Solitary Eagle

1997. Eagles. Multicoloured.

2654	1r. Type **345**	55	25
2655	2r. African hawk eagle (horiz)	75	35
2656	3r. Lesser spotted eagle	1·00	65
2657	5r. Stellar's sea eagle	1·25	1·25
2658	5r. Bald eagle attacking	1·25	1·25
2659	5r. Bald eagle on branch	1·25	1·25
2660	5r. Bald eagle looking left	1·25	1·25
2661	5r. Bald eagle looking right	1·25	1·25
2662	5r. Bald eagle sitting on branch with leaves	1·25	1·25
2663	5r. Bald eagle soaring	1·25	1·25
2664	8r. Imperial eagle ("Spanish Imperial Eagle") (horiz)	1·75	2·00
2665	10r. Harpy eagle	1·75	2·00
2666	12r. Crested serpent eagle (horiz)	2·00	2·50
MS2667	Two sheets. (a) 73×104 mm. 25r. Bald eagle. (b) 104×73 mm. 25r. American bald eagle (horiz) Set of 2 sheets	9·00	10·00

346 Blitzer Benz, 1911

1997. Classic Cars. Multicoloured.

2668	5r. Type **346**	80	85
2669	5r. Datsun, 1917	80	85
2670	5r. Auburn 8-120, 1929	80	85
2671	5r. Mercedes-Benz C280, 1996	80	85
2672	5r. Suzuki UR-1	80	85
2673	5r. Chrysler Atlantic	80	85
2674	5r. Mercedes-Benz 190SL, 1961	80	85
2675	5r. Kwaishinha D.A.T., 1916	80	85
2676	5r. Rolls-Royce Roadster 20/25	80	85
2677	5r. Mercedes-Benz SLK, 1997	80	85
2678	5r. Toyota Camry, 1996	80	85
2679	5r. Jaguar MK 2, 1959	80	85
MS2680	Two sheets, each 100×70 mm. (a) 25r. Volkswagen, 1939. (b) 25r. Mazda RX-01 Set of 2 sheets	7·50	8·50

347 *Patris II*, Greece (1926)

1997. Passenger Ships. Multicoloured.

2681	1r. Type **347**	45	15
2682	2r. *Infanta Beatriz*, Spain (1928)	60	25
2683	3r. *Vasilefs Constantinos*, Greece (1914)	75	75
2684	3r. *Cunene*, Portugal (1911)	75	75
2685	3r. *Selandia*, Denmark (1912)	75	75
2686	3r. *President Harding*, USA (1921)	75	75
2687	3r. *Ulster Monarch*, Great Britain (1929)	75	75
2688	3r. *Matsonia*, USA (1913)	75	75
2689	3r. *France*, France (1911)	75	75
2690	3r. *Campania*, Great Britain (1893)	75	75
2691	3r. *Klipfontein*, Holland (1922)	75	75
2692	3r. *Eridan*, France (1929)	75	75
2693	3r. *Mount Clinton*, USA (1921)	75	75
2694	3r. *Infanta Isabel*, Spain (1912)	75	75
2695	3r. *Suwa Maru*, Japan (1914)	75	75
2696	3r. *Yorkshire*, Great Britain (1920)	75	75
2697	3r. *Highland Chieftain*, Great Britain (1929)	75	75
2698	3r. *Sardinia*, Norway (1920)	75	75
2699	3r. *San Guglielmo*, Italy (1911)	75	75
2700	3r. *Avila*, Great Britain (1927)	75	75
2701	8r. *Stavangerfjord*, Norway (1918)	1·50	1·75
2702	12r. *Baloeran*, Netherlands (1929)	2·00	2·25
MS2703	Four sheets. (a) 69×69 mm. 25r. *Mauritania*, Great Britain (1907). (b) 69×69 mm. 25r. *United States*, USA (1952). (c) 69×69 mm. 25r. *Queen Mary*, Great Britain (1930). (d) 91×76 mm. 25r. Royal Yacht *Britannia* and Chinese junk, Hong Kong (56×42 mm) Set of 4 sheets	18·00	18·00

No. **MS**2703d is inscribed 'BRITTANIA' in error.

348 Prayer Wheels, Lhasa

1997. 50th Anniversary of UNESCO. Multicoloured.

2704	1r. Type **348**	20	15
2705	2r. Ruins of Roman Temple of Diana, Portugal (horiz)	30	25
2706	3r. Santa Maria Cathedral, Hildesheim, Germany (horiz)	45	35
2707	5r. Vivunga National Park, Zaire	75	75
2708	5r. Valley of Mai Nature Reserve, Seychelles	75	75
2709	5r. Kandy, Sri Lanka	75	75
2710	5r. Taj Mahal, India	75	75
2711	5r. Istanbul, Turkey	75	75
2712	5r. Sana'a, Yemen	75	75
2713	5r. Bleinheim Palace, England	75	75
2714	5r. Grand Canyon National Park, USA	75	75
2715	5r. Tombs, Gondar, Ethiopia	75	75
2716	5r. Bwindi National Park, Uganda	75	75
2717	5r. Bemaraha National Reserve, Madagascar	75	75
2718	5r. Buddhist ruins at Takht-I-Bahi, Pakistan	75	75
2719	5r. Anuradhapura, Sri Lanka	75	75
2720	5r. Cairo, Egypt	75	75
2721	5r. Ruins, Petra, Jordan	75	75
2722	5r. Volcano, Ujung Kulon National Park, Indonesia	75	75
2723	5r. Terrace, Mount Taishan, China	75	75
2724	5r. Temple, Mount Taishan, China	75	75
2725	5r. Temple turret, Mount Taishan, China	75	75
2726	5r. Standing stones, Mount Taishan, China	75	75
2727	5r. Courtyard, Mount Taishan, China	75	75
2728	5r. Staircase, Mount Taishan, China	75	75
2729	5r. Terracotta Warriors, China	75	75
2730	5r. Head of Terracotta Warrior, China	75	75
2731	7r. Doorway, Abu Simbel, Egypt	90	95
2732	8r. Mandraki, Rhodes, Greece (horiz)	1·25	1·25
2733	8r. Agios Stefanos Monastery, Meteora, Greece (horiz)	1·25	1·25
2734	8r. Taj Mahal, India (horiz)	1·25	1·25
2735	8r. Cistercian Abbey of Fontenay, France (horiz)	1·25	1·25
2736	8r. Yarushima, Japan (horiz)	1·25	1·25
2737	8r. Cloisters, San Gonzalo Convent, Portugal (horiz)	1·25	1·25
2738	8r. Olympic National Park, USA (horiz)	1·25	1·25
2739	8r. Waterfall, Nahanni National Park, Canada (horiz)	1·25	1·25
2740	8r. Mountains, National Park, Argentina (horiz)	1·25	1·25
2741	8r. Bonfin Salvador Church, Brazil (horiz)	1·25	1·25
2742	8r. Convent of the Companions of Jesus, Morelia, Mexico (horiz)	1·25	1·25
2743	8r. Two-storey temple, Horyu Temple, Japan (horiz)	1·25	1·25
2744	8r. Summer house, Horyu Temple, Japan (horiz)	1·25	1·25
2745	8r. Temple and cloister, Horyu Temple, Japan (horiz)	1·25	1·25
2746	8r. Single storey temple, Horyu Temple, Japan (horiz)	1·25	1·25
2747	8r. Well, Horyu Temple, Japan (horiz)	1·25	1·25
2748	10r. Scandola Nature Reserve, France (horiz)	1·25	1·40
2749	12r. Temple on the Lake, China (horiz)	1·50	1·75
MS2750	Four sheets, each 127×102 mm. (a) 25r. Fatehpur Sikri Monument, India (horiz). (b) 25r. Temple, Chengde, China (horiz). (c) 25r. Serengeti National Park, Tanzania (horiz). (d) 25r. Buddha, Anuradhapura, Sri Lanka (horiz) Set of 4 sheets	13·00	14·00

No. 2717 is inscribed 'MADAGASGAR' and 2737 'COVENT', both in error.

349 White Doves and SAARC Logo

1997. Ninth South Asian Association for Regional Co-operation Summit, Male. Multicoloured.

2751	3r. Type **349**	40	35
2752	5r. Flags of member countries	1·00	75

350 Queen Elizabeth II

1997. Golden Wedding of Queen Elizabeth and Prince Philip. Multicoloured.

2753	5r. Type **350**	1·00	1·00
2754	5r. Royal Coat of Arms	1·00	1·00
2755	5r. Queen Elizabeth and Prince Philip at opening of Parliament	1·00	1·00
2756	5r. Queen Elizabeth and Prince Philip with Prince Charles, 1948	1·00	1·00
2757	5r. Buckingham Palace from the garden	1·00	1·00
2758	5r. Prince Philip	1·00	1·00
MS2759	100×70 mm. 25r. Queen Elizabeth II	4·00	4·50

351 Early Indian Mail Messenger

1997. Pacific '97 International Stamp Exhibition, San Francisco. Death Centenary of Heinrich von Stephan (founder of the UPU).

2760	**351**	2r. green and black	55	60
2761	-	2r. brown and black	55	60
2762	-	2r. violet	55	60

Designs: No. 2761, Von Stephan and Mercury; No. 2762, Autogyro, Washington.

352 *Dawn at Kanda Myojn Shrine*

1997. Birth Bicentenary of Hiroshige (Japanese painter). *One Hundred Famous Views of Edo*. Multicoloured.

2763	8r. Type **352**	1·25	1·25
2764	8r. *Kiyomizu Hall and Shinobazu Pond at Ueno*	1·25	1·25
2765	8r. *Ueno Yamashita*	1·25	1·25
2766	8r. *Moon Pine, Ueno*	1·25	1·25
2767	8r. *Flower Pavilion, Dango Slope, Sendagi*	1·25	1·25
2768	8r. *Shitaya Hirokoji*	1·25	1·25
MS2769	Two sheets, each 102×127 mm. (a) 25r. *Hilltop View, Yushima Tenjin Shrine*. (b) 25r *Seido and Kanda River from Shohei Bridge* Set of 2 sheets	7·50	8·50

353 Common Noddy

1997. Birds. Multicoloured.

2770	30l. Type **353**	30	45
2771	1r. Spectacled owl	75	40
2772	2r. Malay fish owl	1·25	65
2773	3r. Peregrine falcon	1·50	1·00
2774	5r. Golden eagle	1·50	1·10
2775	7r. Ruppell's parrot	1·50	1·50
2776	7r. Blue-headed parrot	1·50	1·50
2777	7r. St Vincent amazon ('St Vincent Parrot')	1·50	1·50
2778	7r. Grey parrot	1·50	1·50
2779	7r. Masked lovebird	1·50	1·50
2780	7r. Sun conure ('Sun Parakeet')	1·50	1·50
2781	8r. Bateleur	1·50	1·50
2782	10r. Whiskered tern with chicks	1·50	1·75
2783	10r. Common caracara	1·50	1·75
2784	15r. Red-footed booby	2·25	2·50
MS2785	Two sheets, each 67×98 mm. (a) 25r. American bald eagle. (b) 25r. Secretary bird Set of 2 sheets	12·00	12·00

354 *Canarina eminii*

1997. Flowers. Multicoloured.

2786	1r. Type **354**	25	15
2787	2r. *Delphinium macrocentron*	40	25
2788	3r. *Leucadendron discolor*	55	40
2789	5r. *Nymphaea caerulea*	75	60
2790	7r. *Rosa multiflora polyantha* (20×23 mm)	1·00	1·00
2791	8r. *Bulbophyllum barbigerum*	1·50	1·50
2792	8r. *Acacia seyal* (horiz)	1·50	1·50
2793	8r. *Gloriosa superba* (horiz)	1·50	1·50
2794	8r. *Gnidia subcordata* (horiz)	1·50	1·50
2795	8r. *Platycelyphium voense* (horiz)	1·50	1·50
2796	8r. *Aspilia mossambicensis* (horiz)	1·50	1·50
2797	8r. *Adenium obesum* (horiz)	1·50	1·50
2798	12r. *Hibiscus vitifolius*	2·00	2·50
MS2799	Two sheets, each 105×76 mm. (a) 25r. *Aerangis rhodosticta* (horiz). (b) 25r. *Dichrostachys cinerea* and two sailing boats (horiz) Set of 2 sheets	16·00	16·00

Nos. 2792/2797 were printed together, *se-tenant*, with the backgrounds forming a composite design.

355 Archaeopteryx

1997. Prehistoric Animals. Multicoloured

(a) Horiz designs

2800 5r. Type **355** 1·00 65
2801 7r. Diplodocus 1·10 1·10
2802 7r. Tyrannosaurus rex 1·10 1·10
2803 7r. Pteranodon 1·10 1·10
2804 7r. Montanceratops 1·10 1·10
2805 7r. Dromaeosaurus 1·10 1·10
2806 7r. Oviraptor 1·10 1·10
2807 8r. Mosasaurus 1·10 1·10
2808 12r. Deinonychus 1·10 1·10
2809 15r. Triceratops 1·10 1·10

(b) Square designs, 31×31 mm.

2810 7r. Troodon 1·10 1·10
2811 7r. Brachiosaurus 1·10 1·10
2812 7r. Saltasaurus 1·10 1·10
2813 7r. Oviraptor 1·10 1·10
2814 7r. Parasaurolophus 1·10 1·10
2815 7r. Psittacosaurus 1·10 1·10
2816 7r. Triceratops 1·10 1·10
2817 7r. Pachycephalosaurus 1·10 1·10
2818 7r. Iguanodon 1·10 1·10
2819 7r. Tyrannosaurus rex 1·10 1·10
2820 7r. Corythosaurus 1·10 1·10
2821 7r. Stegosaurus 1·10 1·10
2822 7r. Euophlocephalus 1·10 1·10
2823 7r. Compsognathus 1·10 1·10
2824 7r. Herrerasaurus 1·10 1·10
2825 7r. Styracosaurus 1·10 1·10
2826 7r. Baryonyx 1·10 1·10
2827 7r. Lesothosaurus 1·10 1·10

MS2828 Two sheets. (a) 99×79 mm. 25r. Tyrannosaurus rex (42×28 mm). (b) 73×104 mm. 25r. Archaeopteryx (31×31 mm) Set of 2 sheets 20·00 20·00

Nos. 2801/2806, 2810/2815, 2816/2821 and 2822/2827 respectively were printed together, *se-tenant*, with the backgrounds of Nos. 2801/2806 and 2810/2815 forming composite designs.

1997. World Cup Football Championship, France. As T **246** of Lesotho.

2829 1r. black 30 15
2830 2r. black 45 25
2831 3r. multicoloured 55 35
2832-9 3r.×8 black; black; multicoloured; multicoloured; black; multicoloured; black; multicoloured 3·75 4·00
2840-7 3r.×8 multicoloured; multicoloured; black; black; black; multicoloured; multicoloured; black 3·75 4·00
2848/55 3r.×8 multicoloured; multicoloured; multicoloured; black; black; multicoloured; multicoloured; multicoloured 3·75 4·00
2856 7r. black 1·10 1·10
2857 8r. black 1·40 1·40
2858 10r. multicoloured 1·50 1·60

MS2859 Three sheets. (a) 103×128 mm. 25r. multicoloured. (b) 103×128 mm. 25r. multicoloured. (c) 128×103 mm. 25r. multicoloured Set of 3 sheets 12·00 13·00

Designs: Horiz—No. 2829, Brazilian team, 1994; No. 2830, German player, 1954; No. 2831, Maradona holding World Cup, 1986; No. 2832, Brazilian team, 1958; No. 2833, Luis Bellini, Brazil, 1958; No. 2834, Brazilian team, 1962; No. 2835, Carlos Alberto, Brazil, 1970; No. 2836, Mauro, Brazil, 1962; No. 2837, Brazilian team, 1970; No. 2838, Dunga, Brazil, 1994; No. 2839, Brazilian team, 1994; No. 2840, Paulo Rossi, Italy, 1982; No. 2841, Zoff and Gentile, Italy, 1982; No. 2842, Angelo Schiavio, Italy; No. 2843, Italian team, 1934; No. 2844, Italian team with flag, 1934; No. 2845, Italian team, 1982; No. 2846, San Paolo Stadium, Italy; No. 2847, Italian team, 1938; No. 2848, English player with ball, 1966; No. 2849, Wembley Stadium, London; No. 2850, English player heading ball, 1966; No. 2851, English players celebrating, 1966; No. 2852, English and German players chasing ball, 1966; No. 2853, English player wearing No. 21 shirt, 1966; No. 2854, English team with Jules Rimet trophy, 1966; No. 2855, German player wearing No. 5 shirt, 1966; No. 2856, Argentine player holding trophy, 1978; No. 2857, English players with Jules Rimet trophy, 1966; No. 2858, Brazilian player with trophy, 1970; No. **MS**2859c, Klinsmann, Germany. Vert—No. **MS**2859a, Ronaldo, Brazil; No. **MS**2892b, Schmeichel, Denmark.

1998. Diana, Princess of Wales Commemoration. As T **249** of Lesotho. Multicoloured (except Nos. 2864, 2870, 2872, 2877 and **MS**2878b).

2860 7r. Laughing 80 85
2861 7r. With Prince William and Prince Harry 80 85
2862 7r. Carrying bouquets 80 85
2863 7r. In white evening dress 80 85
2864 7r. Wearing bow tie (brown and black) 80 85
2865 7r. Wearing black jacket 80 85
2866 7r. With Indian child on lap 80 85
2867 7r. Wearing blue evening dress 80 85
2868 7r. Wearing blue jacket and poppy 80 85
2869 7r. Wearing cream jacket 80 85
2870 7r. Wearing blouse and jacket (brown and black) 80 85
2871 7r. Wearing red jacket 80 85
2872 7r. Wearing hat (blue and black) 80 85
2873 7r. Wearing red evening dress 80 85
2874 7r. With Sir Richard Attenborough 80 85
2875 7r. Wearing jeans and white shirt 80 85
2876 7r. Wearing white jacket 80 85
2877 7r. Carrying bouquet (brown and black) 80 85

MS2878 Three sheets. (a) 100×70 mm. 25r. On ski-lift. (b) 100×70 mm. 25r. Wearing polkadot dress (brown and black). (c) 70×100 mm. 25r. Wearing garland of flowers Set of 3 sheets 12·00 13·00

356 President Nelson Mandela

1998. 80th Birthday of Nelson Mandela (President of South Africa).

2879 **356** 7r. multicoloured 1·75 1·40

357 President John F. Kennedy

1998. President John F. Kennedy Commemoration. Multicoloured, background colours given.

2880 **357** 5r. green 75 80
2881 - 5r. green 75 80
2882 - 5r. brown (inscr at right) 75 80
2883 - 5r. yellow 75 80
2884 - 5r. violet 75 80
2885 - 5r. blue 75 80
2886 - 5r. grey 75 80
2887 - 5r. brown (inscr at left) 75 80
2888 - 5r. blue (value at bottom right) 75 80

Designs: Nos. 2881/2888, Various portraits.

358 Yakovlev Yak-18 (from 1947)

1998. Aircraft in Longest Continuous Production. Multicoloured.

2889 5r. Type **358** 95 95
2890 5r. Beechcraft Bonanza (from 1947) 95 95
2891 5r. Piper Cub (1937–1982) 95 95
2892 5r. Tupolev Tu-95 (1954–1990) 95 95
2893 5r. Lockheed C-130 Hercules (from 1954) 95 95
2894 5r. Piper PA-28 Cherokee (from 1961) 95 95
2895 5r. Mikoyan Gurevich MiG-21 (from 1959) 95 95
2896 5r. Pilatus PC-6 Turbo Porter (from 1960) 95 95
2897 5r. Antonov An-2 (from 1949) 95 95

MS2898 120×90 mm. 25r. Boeing KC-135E (from 1956) (84×28 mm) 4·25 4·50

359 White American Shorthair

1998. Cats. Multicoloured.

2899 5r. Type **359** 1·25 65
2900 7r. American curl and Maine coon (horiz) 1·25 1·25
2901 7r. Maine coon (horiz) 1·25 1·25
2902 7r. Siberian (horiz) 1·25 1·25
2903 7r. Somali (horiz) 1·25 1·25
2904 7r. European Burmese (horiz) 1·25 1·25
2905 7r. Nebelung (horiz) 1·25 1·25
2906 7r. Bicolour British shorthair (horiz) 1·25 1·25
2907 7r. Manx (horiz) 1·25 1·25
2908 7r. Tabby American shorthair (horiz) 1·25 1·25
2909 7r. Silver tabby Persian (horiz) 1·25 1·25
2910 7r. Oriental white (horiz) 1·25 1·25
2911 7r. Norwegian forest cat (horiz) 1·25 1·25
2912 8r. Sphynx cat 1·10 1·10
2913 10r. Tabby American shorthair 1·25 1·25
2914 12r. Scottish fold 1·40 1·60

MS2915 Two sheets, each 98×68 mm. (a) 30r. Norwegian forest cat. (b) 30r. Snowshoe Set of 2 sheets 8·50 9·00

Nos. 2900/2905 and 2906/2911 respectively were printed together, *se-tenant*, forming composite designs.

360 Boeing 747 HS

1998. Aircraft. Multicoloured.

2916 2r. Type **360** 65 30
2917 5r. CL-215 (flying boat) 1·00 1·00
2918 5r. Orion 1·00 1·00
2919 5r. Yakolev Yak-54 1·00 1·00
2920 5r. Cessna sea plane 1·00 1·00
2921 5r. CL-215 (amphibian) 1·00 1·00
2922 5r. CL-215 SAR (amphibian) 1·00 1·00
2923 5r. Twin Otter 1·00 1·00
2924 5r. Rockwell Quail 1·00 1·00
2925 5r. F.S.W. fighter 1·00 1·00
2926 5r. V-Jet II 1·00 1·00
2927 5r. Pilatus PC-12 1·00 1·00
2928 5r. Citation Exel 1·00 1·00
2929 5r. Stutz Bearcat 1·00 1·00
2930 5r. Cessna T-37 (B) 1·00 1·00
2931 5r. Peregrine Business Jet 1·00 1·00
2932 5r. Beech 58 Baron 1·00 1·00
2933 7r. Boeing 727 1·25 1·25
2934 8r. Boeing 747-400 1·25 1·25
2935 10r. Boeing 737 1·40 1·40

MS2936 Two sheets, each 98×68 mm. (a) 25r. Beechcraft Model 18. (b) 25r. Falcon Jet Set of 2 sheets 9·00 10·00

361 Captain Edward Smith's Cap

1998. *Titanic* Commemoration. Multicoloured.

2937 7r. Type **361** 1·40 1·40
2938 7r. Deck chair 1·40 1·40
2939 7r. Fifth Officer Harold Lowe's coat button 1·40 1·40
2940 7r. Lifeboat 1·40 1·40
2941 7r. *Titanic's* wheel 1·40 1·40
2942 7r. Passenger's lifejacket 1·40 1·40

MS2943 110×85 mm. 25r. *Titanic* from newspaper picture 5·00 5·50

362 Guava Tree

1998. 20th Anniversary of International Fund of Agriculture. Multicoloured.

2944 1r. Type **362** 40 15
2945 5r. Selection of fruit 1·25 75
2946 7r. Fishing boat 1·50 1·50
2947 8r. Papaya tree 1·50 1·75
2948 10r. Vegetable produce 1·75 2·00

363 Thread-finned Butterflyfish

1998. Fish. Multicoloured.

2949 50l. Type **363** 20 30
2950 50l. Queen angelfish 20 30
2951 1r. Oriental sweetlips 30 15
2952 3r. Mandarin fish 50 50
2953 3r. Copper-banded butterflyfish 50 50
2954 3r. Harlequin tuskfish 50 50
2955 3r. Yellow-tailed demoiselle 50 50
2956 3r. Wimplefish 50 50
2957 3r. Red emperor snapper 50 50
2958 3r. Clown triggerfish 50 50
2959 3r. Common clown 50 50
2960 3r. Palette surgeonfish ('Regal Tang') 50 50
2961 5r. Emperor angelfish 80 80
2962 5r. Common squirrelfish ('Diadem Squirrelfish') 80 80
2963 5r. Lemon-peel angelfish 80 80
2964 5r. Powder-blue surgeonfish 80 80
2965 5r. Moorish idol 80 80
2966 5r. Bicolor angelfish ('Bicolor Cherub') 80 80
2967 5r. Duboulay's angelfish ('Scribbled Angelfish') 80 80
2968 5r. Two-banded anemonefish 80 80
2969 5r. Yellow tang 80 80
2970 7r. Red-tailed surgeonfish ('Achilles Tang') 1·00 1·10
2971 7r. Bandit angelfish 1·00 1·10
2972 8r. Hooded butterflyfish ('Red-headed Butterflyfish') 1·10 1·25
2973 50r. Blue-striped butterflyfish 5·50 6·50

MS2974 Two sheets, each 110×85 mm. (a) 25r. Long-nosed butterflyfish. (b) 25r. Porkfish Set of 2 sheets 7·50 8·50

364 Baden-Powell inspecting Scouts, Amesbury, 1909

1998. 19th World Scout Jamboree, Chile. Multicoloured.

2975 12r. Type **364** 1·75 2·00
2976 12r. Sir Robert and Lady Baden-Powell with children, 1927 1·75 2·00
2977 12r. Sir Robert Baden-Powell awarding merit badges, Chicago, 1926 1·75 2·00

365 Diana, Princess of Wales

1998. First Death Anniversary of Diana, Princess of Wales.

2978 **365** 10r. multicoloured 1·00 1·50

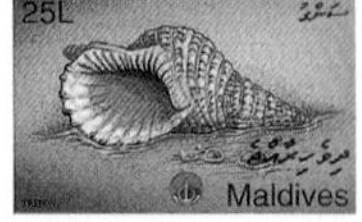

366 Triton Shell

1999. International Year of the Ocean. Marine Life. Multicoloured.

2979 25l. Type **366** 60 60
2980 50l. Napoleon wrasse 75 75
2981 1r. Whale shark 1·00 1·00
2982 3r. Grey reef shark 1·25 1·25
2983 5r. Harp seal 1·10 1·10
2984 5r. Killer whale 1·10 1·10
2985 5r. Sea otter 1·10 1·10
2986 5r. Beluga 1·10 1·10
2987 5r. Narwhal 1·10 1·10
2988 5r. Walrus 1·10 1·10
2989 5r. Sea lion 1·10 1·10
2990 5r. Humpback salmon 1·10 1·10
2991 5r. Emperor penguin 1·10 1·10
2992 7r. Blue whale 1·75 1·75
2993 7r. Skipjack tuna 1·10 1·10
2994 8r. Ocean sunfish 1·25 1·25
2995 8r. Opalescent squid 1·25 1·25
2996 8r. Electric ray 1·25 1·25
2997 8r. Corded neptune 1·25 1·25

MS2998 Three sheets, each 110×85 mm. (a) 25r. Horseshoe crab. (b) 25r. Blue whale. (c) 25r. Triton shell Set of 3 sheets 11·00 12·00

Nos. 2983/2991 were printed together, *se-tenant*, with the backgrounds forming a composite design.

367 Broderip's Cowrie

1999. Marine Life. Multicoloured.

2999 30l. Type **367** 30 35
3000 1r. White tern ('Fairy Tern') 1·25 40
3001 3r. Green-backed heron ('Darker Maldivian Green Heron') 1·75 1·10
3002 5r. Manta ray 1·25 1·10
3003 5r. Green turtle 1·25 1·10

3004	5r. Spotted dolphins	1·25	1·10
3005	5r. Moorish idols	1·25	1·10
3006	5r. Threadfin anthias	1·25	1·10
3007	5r. Goldbar wrasse	1·25	1·10
3008	5r. Palette surgeonfish	1·25	1·10
3009	5r. Three-spotted angelfish	1·25	1·10
3010	5r. Oriental sweetlips	1·25	1·10
3011	5r. Brown booby	1·25	1·10
3012	5r. Red-tailed tropicbird	1·25	1·10
3013	5r. Sooty tern	1·25	1·10
3014	5r. Striped dolphin	1·25	1·10
3015	5r. Spinner dolphin	1·25	1·10
3016	5r. Crab plover	1·25	1·10
3017	5r. Hawksbill turtle	1·25	1·10
3018	5r. Indo-Pacific sergeant	1·25	1·10
3019	5r. Yellow-finned tuna	1·25	1·10
3020	7r. Blackflag sandperch	1·25	1·25
3021	8r. Coral hind	1·40	1·40
3022	10r. Olive Ridley turtle	1·60	1·60
MS3023	Two sheets, each 110×85 mm. (a) 25r. Cinnamon bittern. (b) 25r. Blue-faced angelfish Set of 2 sheets	8·50	9·00

Nos. 3002/3010 and 3011/3019 were each printed together, *se-tenant*, with the backgrounds forming composite designs.

368 Mickey Mouse

1999. 70th Anniversary of Mickey Mouse (Disney cartoon character). Multicoloured.

3024-9	5r.×6 (Mickey Mouse: Type **368**; laughing; looking tired; frowning; smiling; winking)	5·50	5·50
3030-5	5r.×6 (Minnie Mouse: facing left and smiling; with eyes closed; with hand on head; looking surprised; smiling; looking cross)	5·50	5·50
3036-41	7r.×6 (Donald Duck: facing left and smiling; laughing; looking tired; looking cross; smiling; winking)	6·00	6·00
3042-7	7r.×6 (Daisy Duck: with half closed eyes; laughing; looking shocked; looking cross; facing forwards; with head on one side)	6·00	6·00
3048-53	7r.×6 (Goofy: facing right and smiling; with eyes closed; with half closed eyes; looking shocked; looking puzzled; looking thoughtful)	6·00	6·00
3054-9	7r.×6 (Pluto: looking shocked; with eyes closed; smiling; scowling; with tongue out (orange background); with tongue out (green background)	6·00	6·00
MS3060	Six sheets, each 127×102 mm. (a) 25r. Minnie Mouse wearing necklace. (b) 25r. Mickey with hand on head. (c) 25r. Mickey wearing baseball hat. (d) 25r. Mickey facing right (horiz). (e) 25r. Minnie looking left (includes label showing Mickey with bouquet). (f) 25r. Minnie drinking through straw Set of 6 sheets	23·00	23·00

369 Great Orange Tip

1999. Butterflies. Multicoloured.

3061	50l. Type **369**	15	25
3062	1r. Large green aporandria	25	20
3063	2r. Common mormon	40	30
3064	3r. African migrant	55	40
3065	5r. Common pierrot	85	60
3066	7r. Crimson tip (vert)	1·10	1·10
3067	7r. Tawny rajah (vert)	1·10	1·10
3068	7r. Leafwing butterfly (vert)	1·10	1·10
3069	7r. Great egg-fly (vert)	1·10	1·10
3070	7r. Blue admiral (vert)	1·10	1·10
3071	7r. African migrant (vert)	1·10	1·10
3072	7r. Common red flash (vert)	1·10	1·10
3073	7r. Burmese lascar (vert)	1·10	1·10
3074	7r. Common perriot (vert)	1·10	1·10
3075	7r. Baron (vert)	1·10	1·10
3076	7r. Leaf blue (vert)	1·10	1·10
3077	7r. Great orange tip (vert)	1·10	1·10
3078	10r. Giant red-eye	1·25	1·60
MS3079	Two sheets, each 70×100 mm. (a) 25r. Crimson tip. (b) 25r. Large oak blue Set of 2 sheets	8·50	9·50

Nos. 3066/3071 and 3072/3077 were each printed together, *se-tenant*, with the backgrounds forming composite designs.

370 Scelidosaurus

1999. Prehistoric Animals. Multicoloured.

3080	1r. Type **370**	25	15
3081	3r. Yansudaurus	45	40
3082	5r. Ornitholestes	85	70
3083	7r. Dimorphodon (vert)	1·10	1·10
3084	7r. Rhamphorhynchus (vert)	1·10	1·10
3085	7r. Allosaurus (vert)	1·10	1·10
3086	7r. Leaellynasaura (vert)	1·10	1·10
3087	7r. Troodon (vert)	1·10	1·10
3088	7r. Syntarsus (vert)	1·10	1·10
3089	7r. Anchisaurus (vert)	1·10	1·10
3090	7r. Pterenodon (vert)	1·10	1·10
3091	7r. Barosaurus (vert)	1·10	1·10
3092	7r. Iguanodon (vert)	1·10	1·10
3093	7r. Archaeopteryx (vert)	1·10	1·10
3094	7r. Ceratosaurus (vert)	1·10	1·10
3095	7r. Stegosaurus	1·10	1·10
3096	7r. Corythosaurus	1·10	1·10
3097	7r. Cetiosaurus	1·10	1·10
3098	7r. Avimimus	1·10	1·10
3099	7r. Styracosaurus	1·10	1·10
3100	7r. Massospondylus	1·10	1·10
3101	8r. Astrodon	1·10	1·25
MS3102	Two sheets, each 116×81 mm. (a) 25r. Megalosaurus (vert). (b) 25r. Brachiosaurus (vert) Set of 2 sheets	7·50	8·00

Nos. 3083/3088, 3089/3094 and 3095/3100 were each printed together, *se-tenant*, forming composite designs.

371 Express Locomotive, Egypt, 1856

1999. Trains of the World. Multicoloured.

3103	50l. Type **371**	45	35
3104	1r. Channel Tunnel Le Shuttle, France, 1994	50	20
3105	2r. Gowan and Marx locomotive, USA, 1839	70	30
3106	3r. TGV train, France, 1981	85	40
3107	5r. Ae 6/6 electric locomotive, Switzerland, 1954	1·25	70
3108	7r. Stephenson's long-boilered locomotive, Great Britain, 1846 (red livery)	1·50	1·50
3109	7r. *Cornwall*, Great Britain, 1847	1·50	1·50
3110	7r. First locomotive, Germany, 1848	1·50	1·50
3111	7r. Great Western locomotive, Great Britain, 1846	1·50	1·50
3112	7r. Standard Stephenson locomotive, France, 1837	1·50	1·50
3113	7r. *Meteor*, Great Britain, 1843	1·50	1·50
3114	7r. Class 4T diesel-electric locomotive, Great Britain, 1940–1965	1·50	1·50
3115	7r. Mainline diesel-electric locomotive No. 20101, Malaya, 1940–1965	1·50	1·50
3116	7r. Class 7000 high-speed electric locomotive, France, 1949	1·50	1·50
3117	7r. Diesel hydraulic express locomotive, Thailand, 1940–1965	1·50	1·50
3118	7r. Diesel hydraulic locomotive, Burma, 1940–1965	1·50	1·50
3119	7r. Hikari super express train, Japan, 1940–1965	1·50	1·50
3120	8r. Stephenson's long-boilered locomotive, Great Britain, 1846 (orange and green livery)	1·50	1·50
3121	10r. *Philadelphia*, Austria, 1838	1·50	1·50
3122	15r. SE and CR Class E steam locomotive, Great Britain, 1940	2·00	2·25
MS3123	Two sheets, each 110×85 mm. (a) 25r. Passenger locomotive, France, 1846. (b) 25r. Southern Railway Class *King Arthur*, steam locomotive, Great Britain, 1940 Set of 2 sheets	11·00	12·00

1999. Queen Elizabeth the Queen Mother's Century. As T **267** of Lesotho.

3124	7r. black and gold	1·25	1·25
3125	7r. black and gold	1·25	1·25
3126	7r. multicoloured	1·25	1·25
3127	7r. multicoloured	1·25	1·25
MS3128	153×157 mm. 25r. multicoloured	5·00	5·00

Designs: No. 3124, King George VI and Queen Elizabeth, 1936; No. 3125, Queen Elizabeth, 1941; No. 3126, Queen Elizabeth in evening dress, 1960; No. 3127, Queen Mother at Ascot, 1981. 37×50 mm—No. **MS**3128, Queen Mother in Garter robes.

1999. iBRA '99 International Stamp Exhibition, Nuremberg. As T **262** of Lesotho. Multicoloured.

3129	12r. *Adler* (first German railway locomotive), 1833	2·00	2·50
3130	15r. *Drache* (Henshell and Sohn's first locomotive), 1848	2·25	2·75

The captions on Nos. 3129/3130 are transposed.

1999. 150th Death Anniversary of Katsushika Hokusai (Japanese artist). As T **263** of Lesotho. Multicoloured (except No. 3133).

3131	7r. *Haunted House*	1·25	1·25
3132	7r. *Juniso Shrine at Yotsuya*	1·25	1·25
3133	7r. Drawing of bird (black, green and gold)	1·25	1·25
3134	7r. Drawing of two women	1·25	1·25
3135	7r. *Lover in the Snow*	1·25	1·25
3136	7r. *Mountain Tea House*	1·25	1·25
3137	7r. *A Coastal View*	1·25	1·25
3138	7r. *Bath House by a Lake*	1·25	1·25
3139	7r. Drawing of a horse	1·25	1·25
3140	7r. Drawing of two birds on branch	1·25	1·25
3141	7r. *Evening Cool at Ryogoku*	1·25	1·25
3142	7r. *Girls boating*	1·25	1·25
MS3143	Two sheets, each 100×70 mm. (a) 25r. *Girls gathering Spring Herbs* (vert). (b) 25r. *Scene in the Yoshiwara* (vert) Set of 2 sheets	9·00	9·50

1999. Tenth Anniversary of United Nations Rights of the Child Convention. As T **264** of Lesotho. Multicoloured.

3144	10r. Baby boy and young mother	1·60	2·00
3145	10r. Young girl laughing	1·60	2·00
3146	10r. Three children	1·60	2·00
MS3147	110×85 mm. 25r. Sir Peter Ustinov (Goodwill ambassador for UNICEF)	4·00	4·75

372 Standard Stephenson Railway Locomotive *Versailles*, 1837

1999. PhilexFrance '99 International Stamp Exhibition, Paris. Railway Locomotives. Two sheets, each 106×81 mm, containing T **372** and similar horiz design. Multicoloured.

MS3148	(a) 25r. Type **372**. (b) 25r. Stephenson long-boilered locomotive, 1841 Set of 2 sheets	8·50	9·50

373 Phobos and Demos (Martian Moons)

2000. Future Colonisation of Mars. Multicoloured.

3149	5r. Type **373**	1·25	1·10
3150	5r. Improved Hubble Telescope	1·25	1·10
3151	5r. Passenger shuttle	1·25	1·10
3152	5r. Skyscrapers on Mars	1·25	1·10
3153	5r. Martian taxi	1·25	1·10
3154	5r. Martian landing facilities	1·25	1·10
3155	5r. Vegetation in Martian biosphere	1·25	1·10
3156	5r. Walking on Mars and biosphere	1·25	1·10
3157	5r. *Mars rover*	1·25	1·10
3158	5r. Russian *Phobos 25* satellite	1·25	1·10
3159	5r. Earth and Moon	1·25	1·10
3160	5r. Space shuttle leaving Earth	1·25	1·10
3161	5r. Lighthouse on Mars	1·25	1·10
3162	5r. Mars excursion space liner	1·25	1·10
3163	5r. Mars shuttle and skyscrapers	1·25	1·10
3164	5r. *Viking Lander*	1·25	1·10
3165	5r. Mars air and water purification plant	1·25	1·10
3166	5r. Family picnic on Mars	1·25	1·10
MS3167	Two sheets, each 110×85 mm. (a) 25r. Astronaut with jet-pack. (b) 25r. Mars Set of 2 sheets	11·00	12·00

Nos. 3149/3157 and 3158/3166 were each printed together, *se-tenant*, with the backgrounds forming composite designs.

374 Coconuts

2000. Destination 2000. Maldives Campaign. Multicoloured.

3168	7r. Type **374**	2·00	2·00
3169	7r. Shoal of skipjack tuna	2·00	2·00
3170	7r. Seaplane and traditional dhow	2·00	2·00
3171	7r. *Plumeria alba*	2·00	2·00
3172	7r. Lionfish	2·00	2·00
3173	7r. Windsurfers	2·00	2·00

2000. New Millennium. People and Events of 18th-century (1750–1800). As T **268** of Lesotho. Multicoloured.

3174	3r. American bald eagle and American Declaration of Independence, 1776	1·00	90
3175	3r. Montgolfier brothers and first manned hot-air balloon flight, 1783	1·00	90
3176	3r. Napoleon and mob (French Revolution, 1789)	1·00	90
3177	3r. James Watt and drawing of steam engine, 1769	1·00	90
3178	3r. Wolfgang Amadeus Mozart (born 1756)	1·00	90
3179	3r. Front cover of *The Dream of the Red Chamber* (Chinese novel, published 1791)	1·00	90
3180	3r. Napoleon and pyramid (conquest of Egypt, 1798)	1·00	90
3181	3r. Empress Catherine the Great of Russia and St Petersburg, 1762	1·00	90
3182	3r. Joseph Priestley (discovery of oxygen, 1774)	1·00	90
3183	3r. Benjamin Franklin (publication of work on electricity, 1751)	1·00	90
3184	3r. Edward Jenner (development of smallpox vaccine, 1796)	1·00	90
3185	3r. Death of General Wolfe, 1759	1·00	90
3186	3r. *The Swing* (Jean Honore Fragonard), 1766	1·00	90
3187	3r. Ludwig von Beethoven (born 1770)	1·00	90
3188	3r. Marriage of Louis XVI of France and Marie Antoinette, 1770	1·00	90
3189	3r. Captain James Cook (exploration of Australia, 1770) (59×39 mm)	1·00	90
3190	3r. Luigi Galvani and frog (experiments into the effect of electricity on nerves and muscles, 1780)	1·00	90

The main design on No. 3184 may depict Sir William Jenner who undertook research into typhus.

On No. 3185 the uniforms are incorrectly shown as blue instead of red.

See also Nos. 3258/**MS**3264.

375 Sun and Moon over Forest

2000. Solar Eclipse Showing varying stages of eclipse as seen from Earth (Nos. 3191/3196) or Space (Nos. 3197/3202). Multicoloured.

3191	7r. Type **375**	1·50	1·50
3192	7r. 'Second Contact'	1·50	1·50
3193	7r. 'Totality'	1·50	1·50
3194	7r. 'Third Contact'	1·50	1·50
3195	7r. 'Fourth Contact'	1·50	1·50
3196	7r. Observatory	1·50	1·50
3197	7r. 'First Contact'	1·50	1·50
3198	7r. 'Second Contact'	1·50	1·50
3199	7r. 'Totality'	1·50	1·50
3200	7r. 'Third Contact'	1·50	1·50
3201	7r. 'Fourth Contact'	1·50	1·50
3202	7r. Solar and heliospheric observatory	1·50	1·50

Nos. 3191/3196 and 3197/3202 were each printed together, *se-tenant*, with the backgrounds forming composite designs.

376 Red Lacewing

2000. Butterflies of the Maldives. Multicoloured.

3203 5r. Type **376** 1·25 1·25
3204 5r. Large oak blue 1·25 1·25
3205 5r. Yellow coster 1·25 1·25
3206 5r. Great orange-tip 1·25 1·25
3207 5r. Common pierrot 1·25 1·25
3208 5r. Cruiser 1·25 1·25
3209 5r. Hedge blue 1·25 1·25
3210 5r. Common eggfly 1·25 1·25
3211 5r. Plain tiger 1·25 1·25
3212 5r. Common wall butterfly 1·25 1·25
3213 5r. Koh-i-Noor butterfly 1·25 1·25
3214 5r. Painted lady ('Indian Red Admiral') 1·25 1·25
3215 5r. Tawny rajah 1·25 1·25
3216 5r. Blue triangle 1·25 1·25
3217 5r. Orange albatross 1·25 1·25
3218 5r. Common rose swallowtail 1·25 1·25
3219 5r. Jewelled nawab 1·25 1·25
3220 5r. Striped blue crow 1·25 1·25
MS3221 Two sheets. (a) 85×110 mm. 25r. Large tree nymph. (b) 110×85 mm. 25r. Blue pansy Set of 2 sheets 11·00 12·00

Nos. 3203/3211 and 3212/3220 were each printed together, *se-tenant*, with the backgrounds forming composite designs.

No. 3219 is inscribed 'JEWELED NAWAB' in error.

377 *Martin Rijckaert*

2000. 400th Birth Anniversary of Sir Anthony Van Dyck (Flemish painter). Multicoloured.

3222 5r. Type **377** 1·60 1·60
3223 5r. *Frans Snyders* 1·60 1·60
3224 5r. *Quentin Simons* 1·60 1·60
3225 5r. *Lucas van Uffel*, 1632 1·60 1·60
3226 5r. *Nicolaes Rockox* 1·60 1·60
3227 5r. *Nicholas Lamier* 1·60 1·60
3228 5r. *Inigo Jones* 1·60 1·60
3229 5r. *Lucas van Uffel, c.* 1622–1625 1·60 1·60
3230 5r. Detail of *Margaretha de Vos, Wife of Frans Snyders* 1·60 1·60
3231 5r. *Peter Brueghel the Younger* 1·60 1·60
3232 5r. *Cornelis van der Geest* 1·60 1·60
3233 5r. *Francois Langlois as a Savoyard* 1·60 1·60
3234 5r. *Portrait of a Family* 1·60 1·60
3235 5r. *Earl and Countess of Denby and Their Daughter* 1·60 1·60
3236 5r. *Family Portrait* 1·60 1·60
3237 5r. *A Genoese Nobleman with his Children* 1·60 1·60
3238 5r. *Thomas Howard, Earl of Arundel, and His Grandson* 1·60 1·60
3239 5r. *La dama d'oro* 1·60 1·60
MS3240 Six sheets. (a) 102×127 mm. 25r. *The Painter Jan de Wael and his Wife Gertrude de Jode*. (b) 102×127 mm. 25r. *John, Count of Nassau-Siegen, and His Family*. (c) 102×127 mm. 25r. *The Lomellini Family*. (d) 102×127 mm. 25r. *Lucas and Cornelis de Wael*. (e) 127×102 mm. 25r. *Sir Kenelm and Lady Digby with their two Eldest Sons*. (f) 127×102 mm. 25r. *Sir Philip Herbert, 4th Earl of Pembroke, and His Family* (horiz) Set of 6 sheets 27·00 29·00

No. 3230 is inscribed 'Margaretha de Vos, Wife of Frans Snders' in error.

378 Japanese Railways Shinkansen, High Speed Electric Train

2000. The Stamp Show 2000 International Stamp Exhibition, London. Asian Railways. Multicoloured.

3241 5r. Type **378** 1·50 85
3242 8r. Japanese Railways Super Azusa, 12-car train 1·75 1·75
3243 10r. Tobu Railway Spacia, ten-car electric train, Japan 2·00 2·00
3244 10r. Shanghai–Nanking Railway passenger tank locomotive, China, 1909 2·00 2·00
3245 10r. Shanghai–Nanking Railway Imperial Yellow express mail locomotive, China, 1910 2·00 2·00
3246 10r. Manchurian Railway Pacific locomotive, China, 1914 2·00 2·00
3247 10r. Hankow Line mixed traffic locomotive, China, 1934 2·00 2·00
3248 10r. Chinese National Railway freight locomotive, 1949 2·00 2·00
3249 10r. Chinese National Railway mixed traffic locomotive, 1949 2·00 2·00
3250 10r. East Indian Railway passenger tank locomotive Fawn, 1856 2·00 2·00
3251 10r. East Indian Railway express locomotive, 1893 2·00 2·00
3252 10r. Bengal–Nagpur Railway Atlantic Compound locomotive, India, 1909 2·00 2·00
3253 10r. Great Peninsular Railway passenger and mail locomotive, India, 1924 2·00 2·00
3254 10r. North Western Class XS2 Pacific locomotive, India, 1932 2·00 2·00
3255 10r. Indian National Railway Class YP Pacific locomotive, India, 1949–1970 2·00 2·00
3256 15r. Japanese Railway Nozomi, high-speed electric train 2·75 3·25
MS3257 Two sheets, each 100×70 mm. (a) 25r. Indian National Railways Class WP locomotive (57×41 mm). (b) 25r. Chinese National Railway Class JS locomotive (57×41 mm) Set of 2 sheets 12·00 13·00

379 Republic Monument

2000. New Millennium (2nd issue). Multicoloured.

3258 10l. Type **379** 15 30
3259 30l. Bodu Thakurufaanu Memorial Centre 20 15
3260 1r. Modern medical facilities and new hospital 75 15
3261 7r. Male International Airport 1·60 2·00
3262 7r. Hukuru Miskiiy 1·60 2·00
3263 10r. Computer room, science lab and new school 1·75 2·00
MS3264 Three sheets, each 106×77 mm. (a) 25r. Tourist resort and fish packing factory. (b) 25r. Islamic Centre. (c) 25r. People's Majlis (assembly) Set of 3 sheets 11·00 14·00

2000. 25th Anniversary of Apollo–Soyuz Joint Project. As T **271** of Lesotho. Multicoloured.

3265 13r. *Apollo 18* and *Soyuz 19* docking (vert) 1·75 2·00
3266 13r. *Soyuz 19* (vert) 1·75 2·00
3267 13r. *Apollo 18* (vert) 1·75 2·00
MS3268 105×76 mm. 25r. *Soyuz 19* 4·00 4·50

380 George Stephenson and *Locomotion No. 1*, 1825

2000. 175th Anniversary of Stockton and Darlington Line (first public railway). Multicoloured.

3269 10r. Type **380** 2·25 2·25
3270 10r. William Hedley's *Puffing Billy* locomotive 2·25 2·25

2000. Centenary of First Zeppelin Flight. As T **276** of Lesotho. Multicoloured.

3271 13r. LZ-127 *Graf Zeppelin*, 1928 2·75 2·75
3272 13r. LZ-130 *Graf Zeppelin II*, 1938 2·75 2·75
3273 13r. LZ-9 *Ersatz*, 1911 2·75 2·75
MS3274 115×80 mm. 25r. LZ-88 (L-40), 1917 (37×50 mm) 5·50 6·00

No. 3272 is inscribed 'LZ-127' in error.

2000. Olympic Games, Sydney. As T **277** of Lesotho. Multicoloured.

3275 10r. Suzanne Lenglen, (French tennis player), 1920 2·25 2·25
3276 10r. Fencing 2·25 2·25
3277 10r. Olympic Stadium, Tokyo, 1964, and Japanese flag 2·25 2·25
3278 10r. Ancient Greek long jumping 2·25 2·25

381 White Tern

2000. Tropical Birds. Multicoloured.

3279 15l. Type **381** 35 50
3280 25l. Brown booby 40 50
3281 30l. White-collared kingfisher (vert) 40 50
3282 1r. Black-winged stilt (vert) 60 25
3283 10r. White-collared kingfisher (different) (vert) 2·00 2·00
3284 10r. Island thrush (vert) 2·00 2·00
3285 10r. Red-tailed tropicbird (vert) 2·00 2·00
3286 10r. Peregrine falcon (vert) 2·00 2·00
3287 10r. Black-crowned night heron ('Night Heron') (vert) 2·00 2·00
3288 10r. Great egret (vert) 2·00 2·00
3289 10r. Great frigatebird 2·00 2·00
3290 10r. Common noddy 2·00 2·00
3291 10r. Common tern 2·00 2·00
3292 10r. Red-footed booby ('Sula Sula') 2·00 2·00
3293 10r. Sooty tern 2·00 2·00
3294 10r. White-tailed tropicbird (*Phaethon lepturus*) 2·00 2·00
3295 13r. Ringed plover 2·00 2·00
3296 13r. Ruddy turnstone ('Turnstone') 2·00 2·00
3297 13r. Australian stone-curlew 2·00 2·00
3298 13r. Grey plover ('Black-bellied Plover') 2·00 2·00
3299 13r. Crab lover 2·00 2·00
3300 13r. Western curlew ('Curlew') 2·00 2·00
MS3301 Two sheets, each 77×103 mm. (a) 25r. Great cormorant (vert). (b) 25r. Cattle egret (vert) Set of 2 sheets 12·00 13·00

Nos. 3283/3288, 3289/3284 and 3295/3300 were each printed together, *se-tenant*, with the backgrounds forming composite designs.

No. 3294 is inscribed 'Leturus' in error.

382 *Dendrobium crepidatum*

2000. Orchids. Multicoloured.

3302 50l. Type **382** 45 50
3303 1r. *Eulophia guineensis* 55 25
3304 2r.50 *Cymbidium finlaysonianum* 85 60
3305 3r.50 *Paphiopedilum druryi* 1·00 75
3306 10r. *Angraecum germinyanum* 1·75 1·75
3307 10r. *Phalaenopsis amabilis* 1·75 1·75
3308 10r. *Thrixspermum cantipeda* 1·75 1·75
3309 10r. *Phaius tankervilleae* 1·75 1·75
3310 10r. *Rhynchostylis gigantea* 1·75 1·75
3311 10r. *Papilionanthe teres* 1·75 1·75
3312 10r. Aerides odorata 1·75 1·75
3313 10r. *Dendrobium chrysotoxum* 1·75 1·75
3314 10r. *Dendrobium anosmum* 1·75 1·75
3315 10r. *Calypso bulbosa* 1·75 1·75
3316 10r. *Paphiopedilum fairrieanum* 1·75 1·75
3317 10r. *Cynorkis fastigiata* 1·75 1·75
MS3318 Two sheets, each 96×72 mm. (a) 25r. *Cymbidium dayanum*. (b) 25r. *Spathoglottis plicata* Set of 2 sheets 8·50 9·50

Nos. 3306/3311 and 3312/3317 were each printed together, *se-tenant*, with the backgrounds forming composite designs.

383 Honda CB 750 Motorcycle, 1969

2000. A Century of Motorcycles. Multicoloured.

3319 7r. Type **383** 1·10 1·10
3320 7r. Pioneer Harley Davidson, 1913 1·10 1·10
3321 7r. Bohmerland, 1925 1·10 1·10
3322 7r. American Indian, 1910 1·10 1·10
3323 7r. Triumph Trophy 1200, 1993 1·10 1·10
3324 7r. Moto Guzzi 500S, 1928 1·10 1·10
3325 7r. Matchless, 1907 1·10 1·10
3326 7r. Manch 4 1200 TTS, 1966 1·10 1·10
3327 7r. Lambretta LD-150, 1957 1·10 1·10
3328 7r. Yamaha XJP 1200, 1990's 1·10 1·10
3329 7r. Daimler, 1885 1·10 1·10
3330 7r. John Player Norton, 1950's–1960's 1·10 1·10
MS3331 Two sheets, each 62×46 mm. (a) 25r. Harley Davidson, 1950. (b) 25r. Electra Glide, 1960 Set of 2 sheets 8·00 9·00

384 Corn Lily

2000. Flowers of the Indian Ocean. Multicoloured.

3332 5r. Type **384** 1·00 1·00
3333 5r. Clivia 1·00 1·00
3334 5r. Red hot poker 1·00 1·00
3335 5r. Crown of Thorns 1·00 1·00
3336 5r. Cape daisy 1·00 1·00
3337 5r. Geranium 1·00 1·00
3338 5r. Fringed hibiscus (horiz) 1·00 1·00
3339 5r. *Erica vestita* (horiz) 1·00 1·00
3340 5r. Bird-of-paradise flower (horiz) 1·00 1·00
3341 5r. Peacock orchid (horiz) 1·00 1·00
3342 5r. Mesembryanthemums (horiz) 1·00 1·00
3343 5r. African violets (horiz) 1·00 1·00
MS3344 Two sheets, each 112×80 mm. (a) 25r. Gladiolus. (b) 25r. Calla lily (horiz) Set of 2 sheets 8·50 9·50

Nos. 3332/3337 and 3338/3343 were each printed together, *se-tenant*, with the backgrounds forming composite designs.

385 Racoon Butterflyfish (*Chaetodon lunula*)

2000. Marine Life of the Indian Ocean. Multicoloured.

3345 5r. Type **385** 85 85
3346 5r. Wrasse (*Stethojulis albovittata*) 85 85
3347 5r. Green turtle 85 85
3348 5r. Jobfish 85 85
3349 5r. Damsel fish 85 85
3350 5r. Meyer's butterflyfish (*Chaetodon meyeri*) 85 85
3351 5r. Wrasse (*Cirrhilabrus exquisitus*) 85 85
3352 5r. Maldive anemonefish 85 85
3353 5r. Hind (*Cephalopholis* sp) 85 85
3354 5r. Regal angelfish (*Pygopolites diacanthus*) (red face value) 85 85
3355 5r. Forceps butterflyfish (*Forcipiger flavissimus*) 85 85
3356 5r. Goatfish 85 85
3357 5r. Trumpetfish 85 85
3358 5r. Butterfly perch (*Pseudanthias squamipinnis*) 85 85
3359 5r. Two-spined angelfish (*Centropyge bispinosus*) 85 85
3360 5r. Sweetlips 85 85
3361 5r. Twin-spotted wrasse (*Coris aygula*) 85 85
3362 5r. Snapper 85 85
3363 5r. Sea bass 85 85
3364 5r. Bennett's butterflyfish (*Chaetodon bennetti*) 85 85
3365 5r. Pelagic snapper 85 85
3366 5r. Cardinalfish 85 85
3367 5r. Six-barred wrasse (*Thalassoma hardwicke*) 85 85
3368 5r. Surgeonfish 85 85
3369 5r. Longnosed filefish 85 85
3370 5r. Hawaiian squirrelfish 85 85
3371 5r. Freckled hawkfish 85 85
3372 5r. McCosker's flasher wrasse 85 85
3373 5r. Regal angelfish (*Pygoplites diacanthus*) (white face value) 85 85
3374 5r. Angelfish (*Parseentzopyge venusta*) 85 85
MS3375 Four sheets, each 108×80 mm. (a) 25r. Moray eel. (b) 25r. Yellow-bellied hamlet (*Hypoplectrus aberrans*). (c) 25r. Yellow-banded angelfish (*Pomacanthus maculosus*). (d) 25r. Spiny butterflyfish (*Pygoplites diacanthus*) Set of 4 sheets 15·00 17·00

Nos. 3345/3352, 3353/3360, 3361/3368 and 3369/3374 were each printed together, *se-tenant*, with the backgrounds forming composite designs.

385a *Nobleman with Golden Chain* (Tintoretto)

2000. Espana 2000 International Stamp Exhibition, Madrid. Paintings from the Prado Museum. Multicoloured.

3376 7r. Type **385a** 1·25 1·25
3377 7r. *Triumphal Arch* (Domenichino) 1·25 1·25
3378 7r. *Don Garzia de'Medici* (Bronzino) 1·25 1·25
3379 7r. Man from *Micer Marsilio and his Wife* (Lorenzo Lotto) 1·25 1·25
3380 7r. *The Infanta Maria Antonieta Fernanda* (Jacopo Amigoni) 1·25 1·25
3381 7r. Woman from *Micer Marsilio and his Wife* 1·25 1·25
3382 7r. *Self-portrait* (Albrecht Durer) 1·25 1·25
3383 7r. *Woman and her Daughter* (Adriaen van Cronenburch) 1·25 1·25
3384 7r. *Portrait of a Man* (Albrecht Durer) 1·25 1·25
3385 7r. Wife and daughters from *The Artist and his Family* (Jacob Jordaens) 1·25 1·25
3386 7r. *Artemisia* (Rembrandt) 1·25 1·25
3387 7r. Man from *The Artist and his Family* 1·25 1·25
3388 7r. *The Painter Andrea Sacchi* (Carlo Maratta) 1·25 1·25
3389 7r. Two Turks from *The Turkish Embassy to the Court of Naples* (Giuseppe Bonito) 1·25 1·25
3390 7r. *Charles Cecil Roberts* (Pompeo Girolamo Batoni) 1·25 1·25
3391 7r. *Francesco Albani* (Andrea Sacchi) 1·25 1·25
3392 7r. Three Turks from *The Turkish Embassy to the Court of Naples* 1·25 1·25
3393 7r. *Sir William Hamilton* (Pompeo Girolamo Batoni) 1·25 1·25
3394 7r. Women from *Achilles amongst the Daughters of Lycomedes* (Rubens and Van Dyck) 1·25 1·25
3395 7r. Woman in red dress from *Achilles amongst the Daughters of Lycomedes* 1·25 1·25
3396 7r. Men from *Achilles amongst the Daughters of Lycomedes* 1·25 1·25
3397 7r. *The Duke of Lerma on Horseback* (Rubens) 1·25 1·25
3398 7r. *The Death of Seneca* (workshop of Rubens) 1·25 1·25
3399 7r. *Marie de' Medici* (Rubens) 1·25 1·25
3400 7r. *The Marquesa of Villafranca* (Goya) 1·25 1·25
3401 7r. *Maria Ruthven* (Van Dyck) 1·25 1·25
3402 7r. *Cardinal-Infante Ferdinand* (Van Dyck) 1·25 1·25
3403 7r. *Prince Frederick Hendrick of Orange-Nassau* (Van Dyck) 1·25 1·25
3404 7r. Endymion Porter from *Self-portrait with Endymion Porter* (Van Dyck) 1·25 1·25
3405 7r. Van Dyck from *Self-portrait with Endymion Porter* 1·25 1·25
3406 7r. *King Philip V of Spain* (Hyacinthe Rigaud) 1·25 1·25
3407 7r. *King Louis XIV of France* (Hyacinthe Rigaud) 1·25 1·25
3408 7r. *Don Luis, Prince of Asturias* (Michel-Ange Houasse) 1·25 1·25
3409 7r. *Duke Carlo Emanuele II of Savoy with his Wife and Son* (Charles Dauphin) 1·25 1·25
3410 7r. *Kitchen Maid* (Charles-Francois Hutin) 1·25 1·25
3411 7r. *Hurdy-gurdy Player* (Georges de la Tour) 1·25 1·25
MS3412 Six sheets. (a) 110×90 mm. 25r. *The Devotion of Rudolf I* (Peter Paul Rubens and Jan Wildens) (horiz). (b) 110×90 mm. 25r. *The Artist and his Family* (Jacob Jordaens) (horiz). (c) 90×110 mm. 25r. *The Turkish Embassy to the Court of Naples* (Guiseppe Bonito). (d) 90×110 mm. 25r. *Camilla Gonzaga, Countess of San Segundo, with her Three Children* (Parmigianino). (e) 90×110 mm. 25r. *Elizabeth of Valois* (Sofonisba Anguisciola). (f) 110×90 mm. 25r. *Duke Carlo Emanuele II of Savoy with his Wife and Son* (Charles Dauphin) Set of 6 sheets 26·00 28·00

386 Steam Locomotive *Hiawatha*, 1935

2000. Milestones in 20th-century Transport. Multicoloured.

3413 2r. 50 Steam locomotive *Papyrus*, 1934 (vert) 75 50
3414 3r. Type **386** 75 50
3415 5r. Thrust SSC rocket car, 1997 1·00 1·00
3416 5r. Curtiss R3C-2 seaplane, 1925 1·00 1·00
3417 5r. Steam locomotive *Rocket*, 1829 1·00 1·00
3418 5r. BB-9004 electric train, 1955 1·00 1·00
3419 5r. Steam locomotive *Mallard*, 1938 1·00 1·00
3420 5r. TGV electric train, 1980 1·00 1·00
3421 5r. Lockheed XP-80 aircraft, 1947 1·00 1·00
3422 5r. Mikoyan Mig 23 Foxbat aircraft, 1965 1·00 1·00
3423 5r. Hawker Tempest aircraft, 1943 1·00 1·00
3424 5r. *Bluebird* car, 1964 1·00 1·00
3425 5r. *Blue Flame* car, 1970 1·00 1·00
3426 5r. *Thrust 2* car, 1983 1·00 1·00
3427 12r. Supermarine SBG seaplane, 1931 2·00 2·25
3428 13r. MLX01 train, 1998 2·00 2·25
MS3429 Two sheets. (a) 100×75 mm. 25r. Lockheed SR-71 Blackbird aeroplane, 1976 (vert). (b) 75×100 mm. 25r. Bell X-1 aircraft, 1947 Set of 2 sheets 10·00 11·00

Nos. 3415/3420 and 3421/3426 were each printed together, *se-tenant*, with the backgrounds forming composite designs.

387 Porsche 911S, 1966

2000. The World of Porsche. Multicoloured.

3430 12r. Type **387** 1·75 2·00
3431 12r. Model 959, 1988 1·75 2·00
3432 12r. Model 993 Carrera, 1995 1·75 2·00
3433 12r. Model 356 SC, 1963 1·75 2·00
3434 12r. Model 911 Turbo, 1975 1·75 2·00
3435 12r. Contemporary model 1·75 2·00
MS3436 110×85 mm. 25r. Model Boxster, 2000 (56×42 mm) 4·00 4·50

388 Limited Edition Trans-Am, 1976

2000. The World of the Pontiac. Multicolourd.

3437 12r. Type **388** 1·75 2·00
3438 12r. Trans-Am, 1988 1·75 2·00
3439 12r. Trans-Am Coupe, 1988 1·75 2·00
3440 12r. Yellow Trans-Am, 1970–1972 1·75 2·00
3441 12r. 25th Anniversary Trans-Am, 1989 1·75 2·00
3442 12r. Trans-Am GT convertible, 1994 1·75 2·00
MS3443 110×85 mm. 25r. Trans-Am model, 1999 (56×42 mm) 4·00 4·50

389 Pierce-Arrow (1930)

2000. 20th-century Classic Cars. Multicoloured.

3444 1r. Type **389** 40 15
3445 2r. Mercedes-Benz 540K (1938) 60 30
3446 7r. Auburn Convertible Sedan (1931) 1·40 1·40
3447 7r. Mercedes SSKL (1931) 1·40 1·40
3448 7r. Packard Roadster (1929) 1·40 1·40
3449 7r. Chevrolet (1940) 1·40 1·40
3450 7r. Mercer (1915) 1·40 1·40
3451 7r. Packard Sedan (1941) 1·40 1·40
3452 7r. Chevrolet Roadster (1932) 1·40 1·40
3453 7r. Cadillac Fleetwood Roadster (1929) 1·40 1·40
3454 7r. Bentley Speed Six (1928) 1·40 1·40
3455 7r. Cadillac Fleetwood (1930) 1·40 1·40
3456 7r. Ford Convertible (1936) 1·40 1·40
3457 7r. Hudson Phaeton (1929) 1·40 1·40
3458 8r. Duesenberg J (1934) 1·40 1·40
3459 10r. Bugatti Royale (1931) 1·50 1·75
MS3460 Two sheets, each 106×81 mm. (a) 25r. Rolls Royce P-1 (1931). (b) 25r. Cord Brougham (1930) Set of 2 sheets 8·50 9·50

No. 3457 is inscribed 'HUDSIN' in error.

390 *Cortinarius collinitus*

2001. Fungi. Multicoloured.

3461 30l. Type **390** 25 35
3462 50l. *Russula ochroleuca* 25 35
3463 2r. *Lepiota acutesquamosa* 60 30
3464 3r. *Hebeloma radicosum* 70 35
3465 7r. *Tricholoma aurantium* 1·10 1·10
3466 7r. *Pholiota spectabilis* 1·10 1·10
3467 7r. *Russula caerulea* 1·10 1·10
3468 7r. *Amanita phalloides* 1·10 1·10
3469 7r. *Mycena strobilinoides* 1·10 1·10
3470 7r. *Boletus satanas* 1·10 1·10
3471 7r. *Amanita muscaria* 1·10 1·10
3472 7r. *Mycena lilacifolia* 1·10 1·10
3473 7r. *Coprinus comatus* 1·10 1·10
3474 7r. *Morchella crassipes* 1·10 1·10
3475 7r. *Russula nigricans* 1·10 1·10
3476 7r. *Lepiota procera* 1·10 1·10
3477 13r. *Amanita echinocephala* 1·75 1·75
3478 15r. *Collybia iocephala* 1·90 1·90
MS3479 Two sheets, each 112×82 mm. (a) 25r. *Tricholoma aurantium*. (b) 25r. *Lepiota procera* Set of 2 sheets 8·00 9·00

390a German Commanders looking across English Channel

2001. 60th Anniversary of Battle of Britain. Multicoloured.

3480 5r. Type **390a** 1·60 1·40
3481 5r. Armourers with German bomber 1·60 1·40
3482 5r. German Stuka dive-bombers 1·60 1·40
3483 5r. Bombing the British coast 1·60 1·40
3484 5r. German bomber over Greenwich 1·60 1·40
3485 5r. St Paul's Cathedral surrounded by fire 1·60 1·40
3486 5r. British fighter from German bomber 1·60 1·40
3487 5r. Spitfire on fire 1·60 1·40
3488 5r. Prime Minister Winston Churchill 1·60 1·40
3489 5r. British fighter pilots running to planes 1·60 1·40
3490 5r. RAF planes taking off 1·60 1·40
3491 5r. British fighters in formation 1·60 1·40
3492 5r. German bomber crashing 1·60 1·40
3493 5r. British fighters attacking 1·60 1·40
3494 5r. German bomber in sea 1·60 1·40
3495 5r. Remains of German bomber in flames 1·60 1·40
MS3496 Two sheets, each 103×66 mm. (a) 25r. Hawker Hurricane. (b) 25r. Messerschmitt ME 109 Set of 2 sheets 15·00 15·00

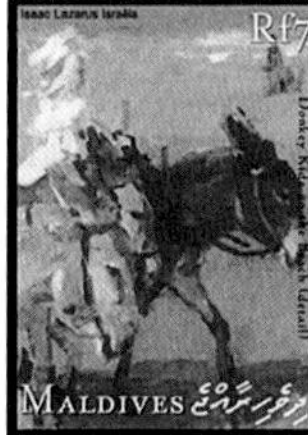

390b Donkeys from *Donkey Ride on the Beach* (Isaac Lazarus Israels)

2001. Bicentenary of Rijksmuseum, Amsterdam. Dutch Paintings. Multicoloured.

3497 7r. Type **390b** 1·25 1·25
3498 7r. *The Paternal Admonition* (Gerard ter Borch) 1·25 1·25
3499 7r. *The Sick Woman* (Jan Havicksz Steen) 1·25 1·25
3500 7r. Girls from *Donkey Ride on the Beach* 1·25 1·25
3501 7r. *Pompejus Occo* (Dick Jacobsz) 1·25 1·25
3502 7r. *The Pantry* (Pieter de Hooch) 1·25 1·25
3503 7r. Woman in doorway from *The Little Street* (Johannes Vermeer) 1·25 1·25
3504 7r. Woman with maid from *The Love Letter* (Johannes Vermeer) 1·25 1·25
3505 7r. *Woman in Blue Reading a Letter* (Johannes Vermeer) 1·25 1·25
3506 7r. Woman from *The Love Letter* 1·25 1·25
3507 7r. *The Milkmaid* (Johannes Vermeer) 1·25 1·25
3508 7r. Woman in alley from *The Little Street* 1·25 1·25
3509 7r. *Rembrandt's Mother* (Gerard Dou) 1·25 1·25
3510 7r. *Girl dressed in Blue* (Johannes Verspronck) 1·25 1·25
3511 7r. *Old Woman at Prayer* (Nicolaes Maes) 1·25 1·25
3512 7r. *Feeding the Hungry* (De Meester van Alkmaar) 1·25 1·25
3513 7r. *The Threatened Swan* (Jan Asselyn) 1·25 1·25
3514 7r. *The Daydreamer* (Nicolaes Maes) 1·25 1·25
3515 7r. *The Holy Kinship* (Geertgen Tot Sint Jans) 1·25 1·25
3516 7r. *Sir Thomas Gresham* (Anthonis Mor Vas Dashorst) 1·25 1·25
3517 7r. *Self portrait as St Paul* (Rembrandt) 1·25 1·25
3518 7r. *Cleopatra's Banquet* (Gerard Lairesse) 1·25 1·25
3519 7r. *Flowers in a Glass* (Jan Brueghel the elder) 1·25 1·25
3520 7r. *Nicolaes Hasselaer* (Frans Hals) 1·25 1·25
MS3521 Four sheets. (a) 118×78 mm. 25r. *The Syndics* (Rembrandt). (b) 88×118 mm. 25r. *Johannes Wtenbogaert* (Rembrandt). (c) 118×88 mm. 25r. *The Night Watch* (Rembrandt). (d) 118×88 mm. 25r. *Shipwreck on a Rocky Coast* (Wijnandus Johannes Nuyen) (horiz) Set of 4 sheets 18·00 21·00

391 *Windfall* (schooner), 1962

2001. Maritime Disasters. Multicoloured.

3522 5r. Type **391** 1·25 1·25
3523 5r. *Kobenhavn* (barque), 1928 1·25 1·25
3524 5r. *Pearl* (schooner), 1874 1·25 1·25
3525 5r. HMS *Bulwark* (battleship), 1914 1·25 1·25
3526 5r. *Patriot* (brig), 1812 1·25 1·25
3527 5r. *Lusitania* (liner), 1915 1·25 1·25
3528 5r. *Milton Iatrides* (coaster), 1970 1·25 1·25
3529 5r. *Cyclops* (freighter), 1918 1·25 1·25
3530 5r. *Marine Sulphur Queen* (tanker), 1963 1·25 1·25
3531 5r. *Rosalie* (full-rigged ship), 1840 1·25 1·25
3532 5r. *Mary Celeste* (sail merchantman), 1872 1·25 1·25
3533 5r. *Atlanta* (brig), 1880 1·25 1·25
MS3534 Two sheets, each 110×85 mm. (a) 25r. *L'Astrolabe* and *La Boussole* (La Perouse, 1789). (b) 25r. *Titanic* (liner), 1912 Set of 2 sheets 14·00 14·00

Nos. 3522/3527 and 3528/3533 were printed together, *se-tenant*, with the backgrounds forming composite designs.

No. 3530 is inscribed 'SULPHER' and **MS**3517a 'LA BAUSSOLE', both in error.

392 Roses

2001

3535 **392** 10r. multicoloured 1·25 1·25

393 Interior of Dharumavantha Rasgefaanu Mosque

2001. 848th Anniversary of Introduction of Islam to the Maldives. Multicoloured (except Nos. 3537/3538).

3536 10r. Type **393** 1·40 1·60
3537 10r. Plaque of Hukurumiskiiy (black and green) 1·40 1·60

3538	10r. Family studying the Holy Koran (black)	1·40	1·60
3539	10r. Class at Institute of Islamic Studies	1·40	1·60
3540	10r. Centre for the Holy Koran	1·40	1·60
3541	10r. Islamic Centre, Male	1·40	1·60
MS3542	116×90 mm. 25r. Tomb of Sultan Abdul Barakaat	3·75	4·50

394 Emperor Angelfish

2001. Fish. Multicoloured.

3543	10r. Type **394**	2·25	2·25
3544	10r. Indian Ocean lionfish (*Pterois miles*)	2·25	2·25

395 *Young Women in Mist*

2001. Philanippon '01 International Stamp Exhibition, Tokyo. Japanese Art. Multicoloured.

3545	7r. Type **395**	1·00	1·10
3546	7r. *Woman with Parasol*	1·00	1·10
3547	7r. *Courtesan*	1·00	1·10
3548	7r. *Comparison of Beauties*	1·00	1·10
3549	7r. *Barber*	1·00	1·10
3550	7r. Ichikawa Danjuro V in black robes (20×81 mm)	1·00	1·10
3551	7r. Ichikawa Danjuro V in brown robes with sword (20×81 mm)	1·00	1·10
3552	7r. Ichikawa Danjuro V with arms folded (20×81 mm)	1·00	1·10
3553	7r. Ichikawa Danjuro V seated in brown robes (20×81 mm)	1·00	1·10
3554	7r. Otani Tomoeman I and Bando Mitsugaro I (53×81 mm)	1·00	1·10
MS3555	Two sheets, each 88×124 mm. (a) 25r. *Courtesan Hinazuru* (Kitagawa Utamaro). (b) 25r. *Tsutsui Jōmyō and the Priest Ichirai* (Torii Kiyomasu I) Set of 2 sheets	8·00	9·00

Nos. 3545/3549 show paintings of women by Kitagawa Utamaro, and Nos. 3550/3554 show famous actors by Katsukawa Shunsho.

395a Victoria as a Young Girl (face value bottom left)

2001. Death Centenary of Queen Victoria. Multicoloured.

3556	10r. Type **395a**	1·40	1·60
3557	10r. Victoria in old age	1·40	1·60
3558	10r. Victoria as a young girl (face value top right)	1·40	1·60
3559	10r. Queen Victoria in mourning	1·40	1·60
MS3560	125×87 mm. 25r. Young Queen Victoria in evening dress	3·75	4·25

395b Mao as a teenager (brown background)

2001. 25th Death Anniversary of Mao Tse-tung (Chinese leader). Multicoloured.

3561	15r. Type **395b**	1·50	1·75
3562	15r. Mao as leader of Communist Party in 1930s (violet background)	1·50	1·75
3563	15r. Mao in 1940s (grey background)	1·50	1·75
MS3564	139×132 mm. 25r. Mao as leader of China in 1960s	3·50	4·00

395c Portrait in Garter robes

2001. 75th Birthday of Queen Elizabeth II. Multicoloured.

3565	7r. Type **395c**	1·75	1·75
3566	7r. Queen at Coronation	1·75	1·75
3567	7r. In evening gown and tiara	1·75	1·75
3568	7r. In uniform for Trooping the Colour	1·75	1·75
3569	7r. In Garter robes and hat	1·75	1·75
3570	7r. Queen wearing cloak of kiwi feathers	1·75	1·75
MS3571	112×138 mm. 25r. Young Queen Elizabeth	5·00	6·00

395d Alfred Piccaver (opera singer) after Annigoni as Duke of Mantua

2001. Death Centenary of Giuseppe Verdi (Italian composer). Multicoloured.

3572	10r. Type **395d**	2·50	2·25
3573	10r. Heinrich's costume from *Rigoletto* (opera)	2·50	2·25
3574	10r. Cologne's costume from *Rigoletto*	2·50	2·25
3575	10r. Cornell MacNeil (opera singer) as Rigoletto	2·50	2·25
MS3576	79×119 mm. 25r. Matteo Manvgerri (opera singer) as Rigoletto	7·00	7·00

396 Adolfo Perez Esquivel (Peace Prize, 1980)

2001. Centenary of Nobel Prizes. Prize Winners. Multicoloured.

3577	7r. Type **396**	85	90
3578	7r. Mikhail Gorbachev (Peace, 1990)	85	90
3579	7r. Betty Williams (Peace, 1976)	85	90
3580	7r. Alfonso Garcia Robles (Peace, 1982)	85	90
3581	7r. Paul d'Estournelles de Constant (Peace, 1909)	85	90
3582	7r. Louis Renault (Peace, 1907)	85	90
3583	7r. Ernesto Moneta (Peace, 1907)	85	90
3584	7r. Albert Luthuli (Peace, 1960)	85	90
3585	7r. Henri Dunant (Peace, 1901)	85	90
3586	7r. Albert Gobat (Peace, 1902)	85	90
3587	7r. Sean MacBride (Peace, 1974)	85	90
3588	7r. Elie Ducommun (Peace, 1902)	85	90
3589	7r. Simon Kuznets (Economics, 1971)	85	90
3590	7r. Wassily Leontief (Economics, 1973)	85	90
3591	7r. Lawrence Klein (Economics, 1980)	85	90
3592	7r. Friedrich von Hayek (Economics, 1974)	85	90
3593	7r. Leonid Kantorovich (Economics, 1975)	85	90
MS3594	Three sheets, each 108×127 mm. (a) 25r. Trygve Haavelmo (Economics, 1989). (b) 25r. Octavio Paz (Literature, 1990). (c) 25r. Vicente Aleixandre (Literature, 1977) Set of 3 sheets	11·00	14·00

397 Mercedes-Benz W165 Racing Car, 1939

2001. Centenary of Mercedes-Benz Cars. Multicoloured.

3595	2r.50 Type **397**	45	35
3596	5r. 460 Nurburg Sport-roadster, 1928	85	65
3597	7r. 680S racing car, 1927	1·00	1·10
3598	7r. 150, 1934	1·00	1·10
3599	7r. 540K Roadster, 1936	1·00	1·10
3600	7r. 770 Grosser Mercedes, 1932	1·00	1·10
3601	7r. 220SE, 1958	1·00	1·10
3602	7r. 500SL, 1990	1·00	1·10
3603	7r. 290, 1933	1·00	1·10
3604	7r. Model 680S, 1927	1·00	1·10
3605	7r. 300SL Coupe, 1953	1·00	1·10
3606	7r. Benz Victoria, 1911	1·00	1·10
3607	7r. 280SL, 1968	1·00	1·10
3608	7r. W125 racing car, 1937	1·00	1·10
3609	8r. Boattail Speedster, 1938	1·10	1·25
3610	15r. Blitzen Benz, 1909	1·60	1·75
MS3611	Two sheets, each 109×96 mm. (a) 25r. 370S, 1931. (b) 25r. 300SLR racing car, 1955 Set of 2 sheets	8·50	9·50

Nos. 3600 and 3606 are inscribed 'GROBERMERCEDES' or 'BENA', both in error.

398 Eusebio and Portuguese Flag

2001. World Cup Football Championship, Japan and Korea (2002). Multicoloured.

3612	1r. Type **398**	20	15
3613	3r. Johan Cruyff and Dutch flag	45	35
3614	7r. Footballer and French flag	1·00	90
3615	10r. Footballer and Japanese flag	1·25	1·25
3616	12r. World Cup Stadium, Seoul, Korea (horiz)	1·50	1·75
3617	15r. Poster for first World Cup Championship, Uruguay, 1930	1·75	2·25
MS3618	70×100 mm. 25r. Gerd Muller, 1974 World Cup Final (43×57 mm)	3·75	4·25

399 *Cymothoe lucasi*

2001. Moths and Butterflies. Multicoloured.

3619	7r. Type **399**	90	95
3620	7r. *Milionia grandis*	90	95
3621	7r. *Ornithoptera croesus*	90	95
3622	7r. *Hyantis hodeva*	90	95
3623	7r. *Ammobiota festiva*	90	95
3624	7r. *Salamis temora*	90	95
3625	7r. *Zygaena occitanica*	90	95
3626	7r. *Campylotes desgodinsi*	90	95
3627	7r. *Bhutanitis thaidina*	90	95
3628	7r. *Helicopsis endymion*	90	95
3629	7r. *Parnassius charitonius*	90	95
3630	7r. *Acaca ecucogiap*	90	95
3631	10r. *Papilio dardanus*	1·25	1·40
3632	10r. *Baomisa hieroglyphica*	1·25	1·40
3633	10r. *Troides prattorum*	1·25	1·40
3634	10r. *Funonia rhadama*	1·25	1·40
MS3635	Two sheets. (a) 83×108 mm. 25r. *Hypolera cassotis*. (b) 108×83 mm. 25r. *Euphydryas maturna* (vert)	9·50	10·00

Nos. 3621 and 3629 are inscribed 'eroesus' or 'charltonius', both in error.

400 John F. Kennedy in American Football Kit, 1927

2001. John F. Kennedy (American President) Commemoration. Multicoloured.

3636	5r. Type **400**	75	85
3637	5r. John Kennedy at Harvard, 1935	75	85
3638	5r. As US Navy officer, Solomon Islands, 1943	75	85
3639	5r. On wedding day, 1953	75	85
3640	5r. With brother, Robert, 1956	75	85
3641	5r. Presidential Inauguration, 1961	75	85
3642	5r. With First Secretary Nikita Khrushchev of USSR, 1961	75	85
3643	5r. With Prime Minister Harold MacMillan of Great Britain	75	85
3644	5r. With President Charles de Gaulle of France, 1961	75	85
3645	5r. With Prime Minister Jawaharlal Nehru of India, 1962	75	85
3646	5r. With Chancellor Konrad Adenauer of West Germany, 1963	75	85
3647	5r. With Martin Luther King (Civil Rights campaigner) 1963	75	85
MS3648	Two sheets, each 82×112 mm. (a) 25r. John Kennedy. (b) 25r. With wife, Paris, 1961	8·00	9·00

No. 3642 is inscribed 'PRIMIER' in error.

401 Princess Diana wearing Pink Jacket

2001. 40th Birth Anniversary of Diana, Princess of Wales. Multicoloured.

3649	10r. Type **401**	1·25	1·75
3650	10r. In evening dress with tiara	1·25	1·75
3651	10r. Wearing matching yellow hat and coat	1·25	1·75
3652	10r. In beige dress	1·25	1·75
MS3653	73×109 mm. 25r. Princess Diana wearing pearls	3·75	4·25

402 Running Horse (Xu Beihong)

2001. Chinese New Year. Year of the Horse. Paintings by Xu Beihong. Multicoloured.

3654	5r. Type **402**	1·50	1·50
3655	5r. Standing Horse (from back, with head up)	1·50	1·50
3656	5r. Running Horse (different)	1·50	1·50
3657	5r. Standing Horse (with head down)	1·50	1·50
3658	5r. Horse (with head up, from front)	1·50	1·50
MS3659	110×70 mm. 15r. Six Horses running (57×37 mm)	2·50	2·75

403 Swinhoe's Snipe

2002. Birds. Multicoloured.

3660	1r. Type **403**	50	25
3661	2r. Oriental honey buzzard	75	40
3662	3r. Asian koel	80	55
3663	5r. Red-throated pipet	1·00	80
3664	5r. Cattle egret	1·00	1·00
3665	5r. Barn swallow	1·00	1·00
3666	5r. Osprey	1·00	1·00
3667	5r. Green-backed heron ('Little Heron')	1·00	1·00
3668	5r. Ruddy turnstone	1·00	1·00
3669	5r. Sooty tern	1·00	1·00
3670	5r. Lesser noddy	1·00	1·00
3671	5r. Roseate tern	1·00	1·00
3672	5r. Great frigatebird ('Frigate Minor')	1·00	1·00
3673	5r. Black-shafted tern ('Saunder's Tern')	1·00	1·00
3674	5r. White-bellied storm petrel	1·00	1·00
3675	5r. Red-footed booby	1·00	1·00
3676	7r. Rose-ringed parakeet	1·40	1·40
3677	7r. Common swift	1·40	1·40
3678	7r. Lesser kestrel	1·40	1·40
3679	7r. Golden oriole	1·40	1·40
3680	7r. Asian paradise flycatcher	1·40	1·40
3681	7r. Indian roller	1·40	1·40
3682	7r. Pallid harrier	1·40	1·40

3683	7r. Grey heron	1·40	1·40
3684	7r. Blue-tailed bee-eater	1·40	1·40
3685	7r. White-breasted water hen	1·40	1·40
3686	7r. Cotton teal ('Cotton Pygmy Goose')	1·40	1·40
3687	7r. Maldivian pond heron	1·40	1·40
3688	7r. Short-eared owl	1·40	1·40
3689	10r. White spoonbill ('Eurasian Spoonbill')	1·50	1·50
3690	12r. Pied wheatear	1·75	2·00
3691	15r. Oriental pratincole	2·25	2·75
MS3692	Four sheets, each 114×57 mm. (a) 25r. White tern. (b) 25r. Greater flamingo. (c) 25r. Cinnamon bittern. (d) 25r. White-tailed tropicbird	32·00	30·00

Nos. 3664/3669, 3670/3675, 3676/3681 and 3682/3687 were each printed together, *se-tenant*, with the backgrounds forming composite designs.

404 Havana Brown

2002. Cats. Multicoloured.

3693	3r. Type **404**	70	35
3694	5r. American wirehair	1·00	60
3695	7r. Persian (horiz)	1·10	1·10
3696	7r. Exotic shorthair (horiz)	1·10	1·10
3697	7r. Ragdoll (horiz)	1·10	1·10
3698	7r. Manx (horiz)	1·10	1·10
3699	7r. Tonkinese (horiz)	1·10	1·10
3700	7r. Scottish fold (horiz)	1·10	1·10
3701	7r. British blue	1·10	1·10
3702	7r. Red mackerel manx	1·10	1·10
3703	7r. Scottish fold	1·10	1·10
3704	7r. Somali	1·10	1·10
3705	7r. Balinese	1·10	1·10
3706	7r. Exotic shorthair	1·10	1·10
3707	8r. Norwegian forest cat	1·10	1·25
3708	10r. Seal point siamese	1·25	1·60
MS3709	110×85 mm. 25r. Blue mackerel tabby cornish rex	4·00	4·50

405 Queen Elizabeth with Princess Margaret

2002. Golden Jubilee. Multicoloured.

3710	10r. Type **405**	2·50	2·50
3711	10r. Princess Elizabeth wearing white hat and coat	2·50	2·50
3712	10r. Queen Elizabeth in evening dress	2·50	2·50
3713	10r. Queen Elizabeth on visit to Canada	2·50	2·50
MS3714	76×108 mm. 25r. Paying homage, at Coronation, 1953	4·50	4·75

406 Sivatherium

2002. Prehistoric Animals. Multicoloured.

3715	7r. Type **406**	1·50	1·50
3716	7r. Flat-headed peccary	1·50	1·50
3717	7r. Shasta ground sloth	1·50	1·50
3718	7r. Harlan's ground sloth	1·50	1·50
3719	7r. European woolly rhinoceros	1·50	1·50
3720	7r. Dwarf pronghorn	1·50	1·50
3721	7r. Macrauchenia	1·50	1·50
3722	7r. Glyptodon	1·50	1·50
3723	7r. Nesodon	1·50	1·50
3724	7r. Imperial tapir and calf	1·50	1·50
3725	7r. Short-faced bear	1·50	1·50
3726	7r. Mastodon	1·50	1·50
MS3727	Two sheets, each 94×67 mm. (a) 25r. Sabre-toothed cat. (b) 25r. Mammoth	9·50	10·00

Nos. 3715/3720 and 3721/3726 were each printed together, *se-tenant*, with the backgrounds forming composite designs.

Nos. 3722 and 3726 are inscribed 'GIYPTODON' and 'MAMMOTH', both in error.

2002. International Year of Mountains. As T **219** of Lesotho, but vert. Multicoloured.

3728	15r. Ama Dablam, Nepal	1·75	2·25
3729	15r. Mount Clements, USA	1·75	2·25
3730	15r. Mount Artesonraju, Peru	1·75	2·25
3731	15r. Mount Cholatse, Nepal	1·75	2·25
MS3732	96×65 mm. 25r. Mount Jefferson, USA, and balloon	3·75	4·25

407 Downhill Skiing

2002. Winter Olympic Games, Salt Lake City. Multicoloured.

3733	12r. Type **407**	1·75	2·00
3734	12r. Ski jumping	1·75	2·00
MS3735	82×103 mm. Nos. 3733/3734	3·75	4·25

2002. 20th World Scout Jamboree, Thailand. As T **295** of Lesotho. Multicoloured.

3736	15r. Buddhist pagoda, Thailand (vert)	2·00	2·50
3737	15r. Thai scout (vert)	2·00	2·50
3738	15r. Scout badges on Thai flag (vert)	2·00	2·50
MS3739	106×78 mm. 25r. Mountain-climbing badge and knot diagrams	3·75	4·00

408 Ship, Aircraft and WCO Logo

2002. 50th Anniversary of World Customs Organisation. Sheet 135×155 mm.

MS3740	**408** 50r. multicoloured	7·50	9·00

409 Elvis Presley

2002. 25th Death Anniversary of Elvis Presley (American entertainer).

3741	**409** 5r. multicoloured	1·00	1·00

410 *Morpho menelaus*

2002. Flora and Fauna. Multicoloured.

3742	7r. Type **410**	1·50	1·50
3743	7r. *Heliconius erato*	1·50	1·50
3744	7r. *Thecla coronata*	1·50	1·50
3745	7r. *Battus philenor*	1·50	1·50
3746	7r. *Ornithoptera priamus*	1·50	1·50
3747	7r. *Danaus gilippus berenice*	1·50	1·50
3748	7r. *Ipomoea tricolor* Morning Glory	1·50	1·50
3749	7r. *Anemone coronaria* Wedding Bell	1·50	1·50
3750	7r. *Narcissus* Barrett Browning	1·50	1·50
3751	7r. *Nigella* Persian Jewel	1·50	1·50
3752	7r. *Osteospermum* Whirligig Pink	1·50	1·50
3753	7r. *Iris* Brown Lasso	1·50	1·50
3754	7r. *Laelia gouldiana*	1·50	1·50
3755	7r. *Cattleya* Louise Georgiana	1·50	1·50
3756	7r. *Laeliocattleya* Christopher Gubler	1·50	1·50
3757	7r. *Miltoniopsis* Bert Field Crimson Glow	1·50	1·50
3758	7r. *Lemboglossum bictoniense*	1·50	1·50
3759	7r. *Derosara* Divine Victor	1·50	1·50
MS3760	Three sheets. (a) 72×50 mm. 25r. *Cymothoe lurida* (butterfly). (b) 66×45 mm. 25r. Perennial Aster Little Pink Beauty. (c) 50×72 mm. 25r. *Angraecum veitchii* (vert)	10·00	11·00

Nos. 3742/3747 (butterflies), 3748/3753 (flowers) and 3754/3759 (orchids) were each printed together, *se-tenant*, with the backgrounds forming composite designs.

Nos. 3742 and 3748 are inscribed 'Menelus' or 'Impomoea', both in error.

411 Torsten Frings (Germany)

2002. World Cup Football Championship, Japan and Korea. Multicoloured.

3761	7r. Type **411**	1·00	1·00
3762	7r. Roberto Carlos (Brazil)	1·00	1·00
3763	7r. Torsten Frings (Germany) (different)	1·00	1·00
3764	7r. Ronaldo (Brazil), with one finger raised	1·00	1·00
3765	7r. Oliver Neuville (Germany)	1·00	1·00
3766	7r. Ronaldo (Brazil), heading ball	1·00	1·00
3767	7r. Eul Yong Lee (South Korea) and Alpay Ozalan (Turkey)	1·00	1·00
3768	7r. Myung Bo Hong (South Korea) and Hakan Sukur (Turkey)	1·00	1·00
3769	7r. Chong Gug Song (South Korea) and Emre Belozoglu (Turkey)	1·00	1·00
3770	7r. Chong Gug Song (South Korea) and Ergun Penbe (Turkey)	1·00	1·00
3771	7r. Ki Hyeon Seol (South Korea) and Ergun Penbe (Turkey)	1·00	1·00
3772	7r. Chong Gug Song (South Korea) and Hakan Unsal (Turkey)	1·00	1·00
MS3773	Four sheets, each 82×82 mm. (a) 15r. Cafu (Brazil) and Oliver Neuville (Germany); 15r. World Cup Trophy. (b) 15r. Dietmar Hamann (Germany); 15r. Cafu (Brazil), holding Trophy. (c) 15r. Hakan Sukur (Turkey); 15r. Sang Chul Yoo (South Korea). (d) 15r. Ilhan Mansiz (Turkey); 15r. Young Pyo Lee (South Korea)	14·00	15·00

412 Hairdresser Bear

2002. Centenary of the Teddy Bear. Multicoloured.

3774	8r. Type **412**	1·00	1·10
3775	8r. Construction worker bear	1·00	1·10
3776	8r. Gardener bear	1·00	1·10
3777	8r. Chef bear	1·00	1·10
3778	12r. Nurse bear	1·40	1·50
3779	12r. Doctor bear	1·40	1·50
3780	12r. Dentist bear	1·40	1·50
3781	12r. Bride ('MOTHER') bear	1·40	1·50
3782	12r. Brother and sister bears	1·40	1·50
3783	12r. Groom ('FATHER') bear	1·40	1·50
MS3784	Three sheets, each 110×105 mm. (a) 30r. Golfer bear. (b) 30r. Footballer bear. (c) 30r. Skier bear ('SNOW BOARDER')	11·00	12·00

413 Charles Lindbergh and *Spirit of St. Louis*

2002. 75th Anniversary of First Solo Transatlantic Flight. Multicoloured.

3785	12r. Type **413**	2·50	2·50
3786	12r. Lindbergh in flying helmet and *Spirit of St. Louis*	2·50	2·50
3787	12r. Lindbergh holding propeller	2·50	2·50
3788	12r. Lindbergh in overalls and *Spirit of St. Louis*	2·50	2·50
3789	12r. Donald Hall (designer)	2·50	2·50
3790	12r. Charles Lindbergh (pilot)	2·50	2·50
3791	12r. Lindbergh under wing of *Spirit of St. Louis*	2·50	2·50
3792	12r. Lindbergh, Mahoney and Hall at Ryan Airlines	2·50	2·50

414 Princess Diana

2002. Fifth Death Anniversary of Diana, Princess of Wales. Multicoloured.

3793	12r. Type **414**	1·75	2·00
3794	12r. In evening dress and tiara	1·75	2·00

415 Joseph Kennedy with Sons Joseph Jr. and John, 1919

2002. Presidents John F. Kennedy and Ronald Reagan Commemoration. Multicoloured.

3795	7r. Type **415**	1·00	1·25
3796	7r. John F. Kennedy aged 11	1·00	1·25
3797	7r. Kennedy inspecting Boston waterfront, 1951	1·00	1·25
3798	7r. Kennedy in naval ensign uniform, 1941	1·00	1·25
3799	7r. With sister Kathleen in London, 1939	1·00	1·25
3800	7r. Talking to Eleanor Roosevelt, 1951	1·00	1·25
3801	12r. Ronald Reagan facing right	1·50	2·00
3802	12r. Ronald Reagan (full-face portrait)	1·50	2·00

416 Wedding of Princess Juliana and Prince Bernhard, 1937

2002. Amphilex '02 International Stamp Exhibition, Amsterdam. Dutch Royal Family.

3803	**416**	7r. blue and black	1·00	1·00
3804	-	7r. brown and black	1·00	1·00
3805	-	7r. red and black	1·00	1·00
3806	-	7r. brown and black	1·00	1·00
3807	-	7r. violet and black	1·00	1·00
3808	-	7r. green and black	1·00	1·00
3809	-	7r. multicoloured	1·00	1·00
3810	-	7r. brown and black	1·00	1·00
3811	-	7r. multicoloured	1·00	1·00
3812	-	7r. multicoloured	1·00	1·00
3813	-	7r. multicoloured	1·00	1·00
3814	-	7r. multicoloured	1·00	1·00

Designs: No. 3804, Princess Juliana and Prince Bernhard with baby Princess Beatrix, 1938; No. 3805, Princess Juliana with her daughters in Canada, 1940–1945; No. 3806, Inauguration of Queen Juliana, 1948; No. 3807, Royal Family inspecting Zeeland floods, 1953; No. 3808, Queen Juliana and Prince Bernhard; No. 3809, *Princess Beatrix as a Baby* (Pauline Hille); No. 3810, *Princess Beatrix in Flying Helmet* (John Klinkenberg); No. 3811, *Princess Beatrix* (Beatrice Filius); No. 3812, *Princess Beatrix and Prince Claus* (Will Kellermann); No. 3813, *Queen Beatrix in Royal Robes* (Graswinkel); No. 3814, *Queen Beatrix* (Marjolijn Spreeuwenberg).

417 Flame Basslet

2002. Marine Life. Multicoloured.

3815	10l. Type **417**	15	60
3816	15l. Teardrop butterflyfish	20	60
3817	20l. White-tailed damselfish ('Hambug Damselfish')	20	60
3818	25l. Bridled tern (23×27 mm)	75	60
3819	50l. Clown surgeonfish ('Blue-lined Surgeonfish')	35	30
3820	1r. Common tern (23×27 mm)	1·25	30
3821	2r. Common noddy (23×27 mm)	1·75	70
3822	2r.50 Yellow-breasted wrasse	80	1·00
3823	2r.50 Blue shark (23×27 mm)	80	1·00
3824	4r. Harlequin filefish	1·00	1·00

3825	5r. Masked unicornfish ('Orangespine Unicornfish')	1·00	1·00
3826	10r. Emperor angelfish	1·75	1·75
3827	12r. Catalufa ('Bullseye')	2·00	2·25
3828	20r. Scalloped hammerhead shark (23×27 mm)	3·50	4·25

No. 3822 is inscribed 'wrass' in error.

418 Atolls from the Air

2002. 30 Years of Maldives' Tourism Promotion. Multicoloured.

3829	12r. Type **418**	2·75	2·75
3830	12r. Island beach	2·75	2·75
3831	12r. Surfing	2·75	2·75
3832	12r. Scuba diving	2·75	2·75

419 Decorated Drum

2003. 50th Anniversary of National Museum. Multicoloured.

3835	3r. Type **419**	50	40
3836	3r.50 Carved covered bowl	55	50
3837	6r.50 Ceremonial sunshade	1·00	85
3838	22r. Ceremonial headdress	3·50	5·00

420 Popeye diving

2003. Popeye (cartoon character). Multicoloured. Summer sports.

3839	7r. Type **420**	85	95
3840	7r. Surfing	85	95
3841	7r. Sailboarding	85	95
3842	7r. Baseball	85	95
3843	7r. Hurdling	85	95
3844	7r. Tennis	85	95
MS3845	120×90 mm. 25r. Volleyball (horiz)	3·25	3·75

Nos. 3839/3845 were printed together, *se-tenant*, with the backgrounds forming a composite design.

421 Father with Baby

2003. UNICEF. First Steps Campaign. Multicoloured.

3846	2r.50 Type **420**	60	35
3847	5r. Mother and baby	1·00	75
3848	20r. Campaign emblem	3·75	5·00

422 *Cypraea caputserpentis* (Cowrie)

2003. Sea Shells. Multicoloured.

3849	10r. Type **422**	2·00	2·25
3850	10r. *Trachycardium orbita* (Cardita clam)	2·00	2·25
3851	10r. *Architectonica perspective* (Sundial shell)	2·00	2·25
3852	10r. *Conus capitaneus* (Corn shell)	2·00	2·25

423 David Brown

2003. Columbia Space Shuttle Commemoration. Sheet 184×145 mm, containing T **423** and similar vert designs showing crew members. Multicoloured.

MS3853	7r. Type **423**; 7r. Commander Rick Husband; 7r. Laurel Clark; 7r. Kalpana Chawla; 7r. Michael Anderson; 7r. William McCool; 7r. Ilan Ramon	7·00	8·00

424 Queen wearing Polka Dot Jacket

2003. 50th Anniversary of Coronation.

MS3854	147×85 mm.15r. Type **424**; 15r. Queen after Coronation wearing Imperial State Crown; 15r. Queen wearing tiara (all black, deep brown and brown)	7·50	8·50
MS3855	68×98 mm. 25r. Queen wearing tiara and blue sash (multicoloured)	4·50	5·00

425 Prince William as Toddler

2003. 21st Birthday of Prince William. Multicoloured.

MS3856	148×78 mm. 15r. Type **425**; 15r. As teenager (looking forward); 15r. As teenager (looking right)	7·50	8·00
MS3857	68×98 mm. 25r. As young boy, wearing school cap	4·50	5·00

426 *Painting*

2003. 20th Death Anniversary of Joan Miro (artist). Multicoloured.

3858	3r. Type **426**	55	35
3859	5r. *Hirondelle Amour*	90	60
3860	10r. *Two Women*	1·50	1·60
3861	15r. *Women listening to Music*	2·00	2·50
MS3862	176×134 mm. 12r. *Woman and Birds*; 12r. *Nocturne*; 12r. *Morning Star*; 12r. *The Escape Ladder*	6·50	7·50
MS3863	Two sheets, each 83×104 mm. (a) 25r. *Women encircled by the Flight of a Bird*. (b) 25r. *Rhythmic Personages*. Both imperf Set of 2 sheets	7·00	8·00

427 Jabach Altarpiece (detail of drummer and piper)

2003. 475th Death Anniversary of Albrecht Dürer (artist). Multicoloured.

3864	3r. Type **427**	55	45
3865	5r. *Portrait of a Young Man*	90	65
3866	7r. *Wire-drawing Mill* (horiz)	1·25	1·40
3867	10r. *Innsbruck from the North* (horiz)	1·50	1·75
MS3868	174×157 mm. 12r. *Portrait of Jacob Muffel*; 12r. *Portrait of Hieronymus Holzschuher*; 12r. *Portrait of Johannes Kleburger*; 12r. *Self-portrait*	6·50	7·50
MS3869	145×105 mm. 25r. *The Weiden Mill*	3·50	3·75

428 *The Actor Nakamura Sojuro as Mitsukuni* (detail) (Utagawa Yoshitaki)

2003. Japanese Art. Ghosts and Demons. Multicoloured.

3870	2r. Type **428**	45	20
3871	5r. *The Actor Nakamura Sojuro as Mitsukuni* (detail of ghosts) (Utagawa Yoshitaki)	90	65
3872	7r. *The Ghost of Kohada Koheiji* (Shunkoosai Hokuei)	1·10	1·00
3873	15r. *Ariwara no Narihira as Seigen* (Utagawa Kunisada)	1·90	2·50
MS3874	149×145 mm. 10r. *The Ghost of Shikibunojo Mitsumune* (Utagawa Kunisada); 10r. *Fuwa Bansakui* (Tsukioka Yoshitoshi); 10r. *The Lantern Ghost of Oiwa* (Shunkosai Hokuei); 10r. *The Greedy Hag* (Tsukioka Yoshitoshi)	5·50	6·50
MS3875	116×86 mm. 25r. *The Spirit of Sakura Sogoro haunting Hotta Kozuke* (Utagawa Kuniyoshi)	3·25	3·50

429 Maurice Garin (1903)

2003. Centenary of Tour de France Cycle Race. Past winners. Multicoloured.

MS3876	160×100 mm. 10r. Type **429**; 10r. Henri Cornet (1904); 10r. Louis Trousselier (1905); 10r. Rene Pottier (1906)	6·50	7·00
MS3877	160×100 mm. 10r. Lucien Petit-Breton on cycle (1907); 10r. Close up of Lucien Petit-Breton (1907); 10r. Francois Faber (1909); 10r. Octave Lapize (1910)	6·50	7·00
MS3878	160×100 mm. 10r. Eddy Merckx (1974); 10r. Bernard Thevenet (1975); 10r. Lucien van Impe (1976); 10r. Bernard Thevenet (1977)	6·50	7·00
MS3879	Three sheets, each 100×70 mm. (a) 25r. Start of first Tour De France at Le Reveil Matin cafe, Montgeron. (b) 25r. Henri Desgranges (editor of *L'Auto*). (c) 25r. Bernard Hinault (1979) Set of 3 sheets	6·50	7·00

430 Santos-Dumont Monoplane No. 20 Demoiselle on Ground, 1909

2003. Centenary of Powered Flight. Multicoloured.

MS3880	176×97 mm. 10r. Type **430**; 10r. Santos-Dumont monoplane No. 20 Demoiselle taking off, 1909; 10r. Voisin-Farman No. 1 biplane, 1908; 10r. Glenn Curtiss' *Gold Bug*, 1909	7·50	8·00
MS3881	176×97 mm. 10r. Santos-Dumont's *Airship No. 1*; 10r. Santos-Dumont's *Airship No. 4*; 10r. Santos Dumont's *Ballon No. 14* and *14 bis* biplane, 1906; 10r. Santos-Dumont's *Airship No. 16*	7·50	8·00
MS3882	Two sheets, each 105×75 mm. (a) 25r. Santos-Dumont's *Ballon No. 6* circling Eiffel Tower, Paris, 1901. (b) 25r. Santos-Dumont's *14 bis* biplane,1906 Set of 2 sheets	8·00	8·50

431 *Near Taormina, Scirocco* (1924)

2003. Paul Klee (artist) Commemoration. Multicoloured.

MS3883	162×135 mm. 10r. Type **431**; 10r. *Small Town Among the Rocks* (1932);10r. *Still Life with Props* (1924); 10r. *North Room*, (1932)	4·50	5·50
MS3884	70×103 mm. 25r. *Dame Demon* (1935) (vert)	3·25	3·50

432 Man Ice-skating

2003. 25th Death Anniversary of Norman Rockwell (artist). Multicoloured.

MS3885	10r. Type **432**; 10r. Man lying on back and boy with dog; 10r. Man and boy going fishing; 10r. Man and boy sweeping leaves	4·50	5·50
MS3886	45×81 mm. 25r. Illustration for Hallmark Cards (1957). Imperf	3·50	3·75

433 *Portrait of Jaime Sabartes* (1901)

2003. 30th Death Anniversary of Pablo Picasso (artist). Multicoloured.

MS3887	133×167 mm. 10r. Type **433**; 10r. Portrait of the Artist's Wife (Olga) (1923); 10r. Portrait of Olga (1923); 10r. *Portrait of Jaime Sabartes* (1904)	8·00	8·00
MS3888	67×100 mm. 30r. *The Tragedy* (1903). Imperf	7·50	7·50

434 Ari Atoll

2003. International Year of Freshwater. Multicoloured.

MS3889	147×85 mm. 15r. Type **434**; 15r. Running tap; 15r. Desalination plant, Male	7·00	8·00
MS3890	96×66 mm. 25r. Community rain water tank	4·00	4·50

435 Goldtail Demoiselle

2003. Marine Life. Sheet 147×105 mm containing T **435** and similar horiz designs. Multicoloured.

MS3891	4r. Type **435**; 4r. Queen coris; 4r. Eight-banded butterflyfish; 4r. Meyer's butterflyfish; 4r. Exquisite butterflyfish; 4r. Yellowstripe snapper; 4r. Yellowback anthias; 4r. Black-spotted moray; 4r. Clown anemonefish	6·00	6·50

The stamps in No. **MS**3891 were printed together, *se-tenant*, with the backgrounds forming a composite design.

436 Clown Triggerfish

2003. Tropical Fish. Multicoloured.

3892	1r. Type **436**	35	15
3893	7r. Sixspot grouper	1·25	1·00
3894	10r. Long-nosed butterflyfish	1·75	1·75
3895	15r. Longfin bannerfish	2·50	3·00
MS3896	116×134 mm. 7r. Bluestreak cleaner wrasse; 7r. Threeband demoiselle; 7r. Palette surgeonfish; 7r. Emperor snapper; 7r. Bicolor angelfish; 7r. Picasso triggerfish	6·50	7·50
MS3897	72×102 mm. 25r. Chevron butterflyfish	4·50	5·00

2003. Tropical Butterflies. As T **436**. Multicoloured.

3898	3r. Yamfly (vert)	65	35
3899	5r. Striped blue crow (vert)	1·00	65
3900	8r. Indian red admiral (vert)	1·60	1·60
3901	15r. Great eggfly (vert)	2·75	3·50
MS3902	116×134 mm. 7r. Blue triangle; 7r. Monarch; 7r. Broad-bordered grass yellow; 7r. Red lacewing; 7r. African migrant; 7r. Plain tiger	6·50	7·50
MS3903	102×72 mm. 25r. Beak butterfly (vert)	4·50	5·00

2003. Birds. As T **436**. Multicoloured.

3904	15l. Great frigate bird	70	60
3905	20l. Ruddy turnstone	70	60
3906	25l. Hoopoe	90	70
3907	1r. Cattle egret	1·50	75
MS3908	116×134 mm. 7r. Red-billed tropicbird; 7r. Red-footed booby; 7r. Common tern; 7r. Caspian tern; 7r. Western ('Common') curlew; 7r. Grey ('Black-bellied') plover	8·00	8·50
MS3909	72×102 mm. 25r. Grey heron	5·50	6·00

2003. Flowers. As T **436**. Multicoloured.

3910	30l. *Coelogyne asperata* (vert)	30	25
3911	75l. *Calanthe rosea* (vert)	55	30
3912	2r. *Eria javanica* (vert)	1·25	70
3913	10r. *Spathoglottis affinis* (vert)	2·25	2·75
MS3914	116×134 mm. 7r. *Strelitzia reginae*; 7r. *Anthurium andreanum*; 7r. *Alpinia Purpurata*; 7r. *Dendrobium phalaenopsis*; 7r. *Vanda tricolo*; 7r. *Hibiscus rosa-Sinensis*	7·50	8·50
MS3915	72×102 mm. 25r. *Ipomoea crassicaulis* (vert)	5·00	5·50

437 *Fox*

2004. Hong Kong 2004 International Stamp Exhibition. 125th Birth Anniversary of Gao Jian-fu (artist). T **437** and similar vert designs. Multicoloured.

MS3916	170×149 mm. 7r. *Landscape*; 7r. *Moon Night*; 7r. Type **437**; 7r. Chinese ink and colour on paper (spider and web); 7r. Chinese ink and colour on paper (girl); 7r. Chinese ink and colour on paper (man)	6·50	7·50
MS3917	108×129 mm. 12r. *Eagle*; 12r. *Sunset*	4·00	4·50

438 German Team (1974)

2004. Centenary of FIFA (Federation Internationale de Football Association). T **438** and similar horiz designs showing winning football teams. Multicoloured.

3918	5r. Type **438**	85	85
3919	5r. Argentina (1978)	85	85
3920	5r. Italy (1982)	85	85
3921	5r. Argentina (1986)	85	85
3922	5r. Germany (1990)	85	85
3923	5r. Brazil (1994)	85	85
3924	5r. France (1998)	85	85
3925	5r. Brazil (2002)	85	85

439 F-BVFD over Rio de Janeiro

2004. Last Flight of Concorde (2003). Multicoloured.

MS3926	147×150 mm. 1r. Type **439**; 1r. F-BVFC over New York; 1r. F-BTSD over Honolulu; 1r. F-BTSD over Lisbon; 1r. F-BVFA over Washington; 1r. F-BVFD over Dakar; 1r. G-BOAC over Singapore; 1r. G-BOAA over Sydney; 1r. G-BOAD over Hong Kong; 1r. G-BOAD over Amsterdam; 1r. G-BOAE over Tokyo; 1r. G-BOAF over Madrid	4·00	4·00
MS3927	Three sheets, each 70×100 mm. (a) 25r. G-BOAC against Union Jack. (b) 25r. G-BOAG over London. (c) 25r. G-BOAG against museum exhibits Set of 3 sheets	17·00	17·00

440 *Self Portrait* (Anthony van Dyck)

2004. 300th Anniversary of St Petersburg. Treasures of the Hermitage. Multicoloured.

3928	1r. Type **440**	25	15
3929	3r. *Self Portrait* (Michael Sweets)	55	40
3930	7r. *Anna Dalkeith, Countess of Morton* (Anthony van Dyck)	1·25	1·00
3931	12r. *Lady Anna Kirk* (Anthony van Dyck)	2·00	2·75
MS3932	116×180 mm. 10r. *Portrait of Prince Alexander Kurakin* (Louis-Elisabeth Vigee-Lebrun); 10r. *Portrait of a Lady in Waiting to the Infanta Isabella* (Peter Paul Rubens); 10r. *Portrait of a Lady in Blue* (Thomas Gainsborough); 10r. *The Actor Pierre Jeliolte in the Role of Apollo* (Louis Tocque)	6·50	7·00
MS3933	Two sheets, each 102×72 mm. (a) 25r. *A Scene from Corneille's Tragedy Le Comte d'Essex* (Nicolas Lancret) (horiz). (b) 25r. *The Stolen Kiss* (Jean-Honore Fragonard) (horiz) Set of 2 sheets	7·50	8·50

441 Major General Clarence Huebner

2004. 60th Anniversary of D-Day Landings. Ten sheets containing T **441** and similar multicoloured designs.

MS3934	Five sheets. (a) 137×117 mm. 6r. Type **441**; 6r. Brig. General Anthony McAuliffe; 6r. Major General Leonard Gerow; 6r. General Adolf Galland; 6r. Brig. General W. M. Hoge; 6r. Major General Sir Percy Hobart. (b) 127×127 mm. 6r. Rear Admiral Kirk; 6r. General Field Marshal Erwin Rommel; 6r. General George Marshal; 6r. General Jan Smuts; 6r. General Lieutenant Gunther Blumentritt; 6r. Major General J. Lawton Collins. (c) 138×137 mm. 6r. Winston Churchill; 6r. Admiral Sir Bertram Ramsey; 6r. General Lieutenant Dietrich Kraiss; 6r. Major General Richard Gale; 6r. General George Patton; 6r. Major General Maxwell Taylor. (d) 138×137 mm. 6r. General Dwight Eisenhower; 6r. Field Marshal Guenther von Kluge; 6r. Air Marshal Sir Trafford Leigh-Mallory; 6r. Field Marshal Walter Model; 6r. Field Marshal Gerd von Rundstedt; 6r. Sir Arthur Tedder. (e) 137×127 mm. 6r. Lieutenant General Omar Bradley (horiz); 6r. Rear Admiral Hall (horiz); 6r. Major General Huebner (horiz); 6r. Grossadmiral Karl Donitz (horiz); 6r. Rear Admiral Wilkes (horiz); 6r. Capt. Chauncey Camp (horiz) Set of 10 sheets	40·00	40·00
MS3935	Five sheets. (a) 68×98 mm. 30r. Rear Admiral Donald Moon. (b) 68×98 mm. 30r. Lieutenant General Sir Frederick Morgan. (c) 68×98 mm. 30r. General Henry Arnold. (d) 69×99 mm. 30r. General Sir Bernard Montgomery. (e) 98×68 mm. 30r. Rear Admiral Carlton Bryant (horiz) Set of 5 sheets	32·00	32·00

442 George Herman Ruth Jr

2004. Centenary of Baseball World Series. George Herman Ruth Jr. ('Babe Ruth'). Multicoloured.

3936	3r. Type **442**	30	40
3937-3940	10r.×4, Swinging bat; Looking sombre; Carrying two bats; Looking left	3·75	4·25

443 Firefly Class 2-2-2 GR1840

2004. Bicentenary of Steam Trains. Multicoloured.

MS3941	Six sheets. (a) 105×150 mm. 12r.×4, Type **443**; French 'Single' (1854); Medoc Class 2-4-0 Swiss (1857); German 4-4-0 (1893). (b) 105×150 mm.12r.×4, Planet Class 2-2-0 (1830); American 4-4-0 (1855); *Newmar* (1846); Class 500 4-6-0 (1900). (c) 105×150 mm. 12r.×4, *Adler* 2-2-2 (1835); *Beuth* 2-2-2 (1843); *Northumbrian* 0-2-2 (1830); Class 4-6-2 (1901). (d) 150×105 mm.12r.×4, *The Evening Star*; *The Britannia*; *The George Stephenson*; Sudan Railways 310 2-8-2. (e) 150×105 mm. 12r.×4, East African Railways Garratt; Rhodesian Railways 12th Class; Class 2-6-2; Class 19d 4-8-2. (f) 150×105 mm. 12r.×4, Woodburning Beyer Garratt; Double-headed train over Kaaiman River; Garratt 4-8-2+2-8-2; Class 15 Garratt	48·00	48·00
MS3942	Six sheets. (a) 100×70 mm. 30r. *Lord Nelson*. (b) 100×70 mm. 30r. *The American*. (c) 100×70 mm. 30r. *Flying Scotsman*. (d) 100×70 mm. 30r. *Vauxhall* 2-2-0 (1834). (e) 70×102 mm.30r. *Claud Hamilton* Class 4-4-0. (f) 70×102 mm. 30r. Class P8 4-6-0 (1906)	40·00	40·00

444 *Negre Attaque par un Jaguar*

2004. 160th Birth Anniversary of Henri Rousseau (French artist). Multicoloured.

MS3943	127×127 mm. 10r.×4, Type **444**; *Paysage Exotique*; *La Cascade*; *Le Repas du Lion*	5·50	6·00
MS3944	75×92 mm. 25r. *Le Rêve* (detail). Imperf	4·00	4·50

445 *Conversation* (1909)

2004. 50th Death Anniversary of Henri Matisse (French artist). Multicoloured.

MS3945	126×128 mm. 10r.×4, Type **445**; *Still Life with a Blue Tablecloth* (1909); *Seville Still Life II* (1910–1911); *Woman before an Aquarium* (1921–1923)	5·50	6·00
MS3946	62×93 mm. 25r. *Interior at Nice* (1921). Imperf	4·00	4·50

446 *The Endless Enigma* (1938)

2004. Birth Centenary of Salvador Dali (Spanish artist). Multicoloured.

MS3947	126×127 mm. 10r.×4, Type **446**; *The Persistence of Memory* (1931); *Soft Construction with Boiled Beans – Premonition of Civil War* (1936); *Still Life moving Fast* (1956)	5·50	6·00
MS3948	100×65 mm. 25r. *Figure on the Rocks* (1926). Imperf	4·00	4·50

447 *Still Life with Peppermint Bottle and Blue Rug* (1893–1895)

2004. 165th Birth Anniversary of Paul Cezanne (French artist). Multicoloured.

MS3949	127×127 mm. 10r.×4, Type **447**; *House in Provence* (1880); *Le Chateau Noir* (1900–1904); *Basket of Apples* (1895)	7·00	7·50
MS3950	75×92 mm. 25r. *Boy in a Red Waistcoat leaning on his Elbow*. Imperf	5·50	6·00

448 Woman and Book

2004. 176th Birth Anniversary of Jules Verne (French writer). Designs showing scenes from novels.

MS3951	Five sheets, each 150×100 mm. (a) 12r.×4, agate; lemon and scarlet; lilac, lemon and scarlet; brown; lemon and scarlet; green, lemon and scarlet. (b) 12r.×4, blue; lemon and scarlet; blue, lemon and scarlet; black; lemon and scarlet; black, lemon and scarlet. (c) 12r.×4, lemon and scarlet; green, lemon and scarlet; blue and scarlet; green and scarlet. (d) 12r.×4, brown, ultramarine and scarlet; multicoloured; purple and scarlet; lilac and scarlet. (e) 12r.×4, green and scarlet; sepia and scarlet; green, lemon and scarlet; purple, lemon and scarlet	42·00	42·00
MS3952	Five sheets, each 98×67 mm. (a) 25r. brown and scarlet. (b) 25r. blue and scarlet. (c) 25r. blue, lemon and scarlet. (d) 25r. purple, lemon and scarlet. (e) 25r. brown, lemon and scarlet	26·00	26·00

Designs: **MS**3951 (a) *Family without a Name*, T **448**; Soldier; Battle scene on dockside; Men with rifles. (b) *The Lighthouse at the End of the World*, Crew on ship; Man on rocks and waves; Rocks on coastline; Man wearing hat and coastline. (c) *Michael Strogoff, Courier of the Czar*, Man held at gunpoint; Man and woman in tall grass; Two men and robed characters; Man and dog in flattened grass. (d) *Archipelago on Fire*; *Clovis Dardentor*; *The Golden Volcano*; *Le Superbe Orenoque*. (e) *Cesar Cascabel*, Men in snow storm; Moustached man; Man caught in gust; Crowd reading poster. **MS**3952 (a) 25r. The *Survivors of the Chancellor*. (b) 25r. *Cesar Cascabel*. (c) 25r. *The Lighthouse at the End of the World*. (d) 25r. *Family without a Name*. (e) 25r. *Keraban the Inflexible*.

449 Marilyn Monroe

2004. Marilyn Monroe (actress) Commemoration.

3953	**449**	7r. multicoloured	70	80

450 Olympic Gold Medal, St Louis (1904)

2004. Olympic Games, Athens. Multicoloured.

3954	2r. Type **450**	40	25
3955	5r. Greek art	75	60
3956	7r. Comte Jean de Beaumont	1·10	1·10
3957	12r. The pommel horse (horiz)	1·75	2·50

451 *Fromia monilis*

2004. Star Fish. Multicoloured.

3958	10r. Type **451**	2·00	2·25
3959	10r. *Nardoa novaecaledoniae*	2·00	2·25
3960	10r. *Fromia monilis* (red background)	2·00	2·25
3961	10r. *Linckia laevigata*	2·00	2·25

452 Silvertip Shark

2004. Sharks. Multicoloured.

MS3962	136×115 mm. 10r.×4, Type **452**; Silky shark; Great white shark; Gray reef shark	7·00	7·50
MS3963	96×65 mm. 25r. Starry smoothhound	4·50	5·00

453 *Cethosia cydippe*

2004. Butterflies. Multicoloured.

MS3964	180×111 mm. 10r.×4, Type **453**; *Amesia sanguiflua; Pericallia galactina; Limenitis dudu dudu*	7·50	8·00
MS6965	98×68 mm. 25r. *Papilio demoleus malayanus* (vert)	4·25	4·50

454 *Eurypegasus draconis*

2004. Endangered Species. *Eurypegasus draconis* (Little Dragonfish). Multicoloured.

3966	7r. Type **454**	1·10	1·25
3967	7r. Orange *Eurypegasus draconis*	1·10	1·25
3968	7r. White *Eurypegasus draconis*	1·10	1·25
3969	7r. *Eurypegasus draconis* on sandy sea bed	1·10	1·25

455 Eyelash Pit Viper

2004. Reptiles and Amphibians. Multicoloured.

MS3970	180×111 mm. 10r.×4, Type **455**; Basilisk lizard; Calico snake; Maki frog	6·00	6·50
MS3971	66×96 mm. 25r. *Naja melanoleuca* (vert)	4·00	4·50

456 *Hygrocybe psittacina*

2004. Mushrooms. Multicoloured.

MS3972	181×111 mm. 10r.×4, Type **456**; *Hygrocybe miniata; Aleuria aurantia; Thaxterogaster porphyreum*	6·50	7·00
MS3973	98×68 mm. 25r. *Galerina autumnalis* (vert)	4·25	4·75

457 Striped Dolphin

2004. Dolphins. Multicoloured.

MS3974	181×111 mm. 10r.×4, Type **457**; Amazon River dolphin; Bottlenose dolphin; Spinner dolphin	6·00	6·50
MS3975	97×66 mm. 25r. Long-snouted Spinner dolphin	4·00	4·50

458 Jupp Derwall

2005. European Football Championship 2004, Portugal. Commemoration of 1980 Cup Final between Germany and Belgium. Multicoloured.

MS3976	148×86 mm. 12r.×4, Type **458**; Rene Vandereycken; Horst Hrubesch; Estadio Olimpico	5·50	6·50
MS3977	97×86 mm. 25r. German team, 1980 (50×37 mm)	3·75	4·25

459 Deng Xiaoping

2005. Birth Centenary (2004) of Deng Xiaoping (Chinese Leader, 1978–1989). Sheet 96×67 mm.

MS3978	**459** 25r. multicoloured	3·25	3·75

460 Macroplata

2005. Prehistoric Animals. Multicoloured.

MS3979	Four sheets, each 148×111 mm. (a) 10r.×4, Type **460**; Ichthyosaurus; Shonisaurus; Archelon. (b) 10r.×4 (vert), Pterodactyl; Cearadactylus; Pterosaur; Sordes. (c) 10r.×4 (vert), Deinonychus; Styracosaurus (from front); Ornitholestes; Euoplocephalus. (d) 10r.×4 (vert), Albertosaurus; Iguanodon; Deinonychus; Baryonyx	27·00	28·00
MS3980	Four sheets, each 96×67 mm. (a) 25r. Muraenosaurus. (b) 25r. Archaeopteryx. (c) 25r. Styracosaurus (from side). (d) 25r. Leptoceratops	20·00	21·00

461 Albert Einstein

2005. 50th Death Anniversary of Albert Einstein (physicist). Multicoloured.

MS3981	110×135 mm. 15r.×4, Type **461**; Smiling; With pipe in mouth; With raised eyebrows	8·50	8·50
MS3982	55×85 mm. 25r. Albert Einstein (vert)	5·50	5·50

462 Oscar (Brazil)

2005. 75th Anniversary of First World Cup Football Championship, Uruguay. Multicoloured.

MS3983	175×130 mm. 15r.×3, Type **462**; Karl-Heinz Rummenigge (Germany); Oliver Kahn (Germany)	6·50	7·50
MS3984	124×105 mm. 25r. Karlheinz Forster (Germany)	3·75	4·00

463 Chicago Skyline

2005. Centenary of Rotary International. Multicoloured.

MS3985	151×68 mm. 15r.×3, Type **463**; Skyline with Sears Tower; Skyline (different)	6·50	7·50
MS3986	102×67 mm. 25r. Telecommunications tower	4·00	4·50

The stamps of No. **MS**3985 form a composite design showing a panoramic view of Chicago's skyline.

464 Hans Christian Andersen (statue)

2005. Birth Bicentenary of Hans Christian Andersen (writer). Multicoloured.

MS3987	70×151 mm. 15r.×3, Type **464**; Hans Christian Andersen; Statue facing left	6·50	7·50
MS3988	71×101 mm. 25r. *The Little Mermaid*	3·75	4·00

465 Admiral Cuthbert Collingwood

2005. Bicentenary of the Battle of Trafalgar. Multicoloured.

3989	10r. Type **465**	2·50	2·50
3990	10r. Napoleon Bonaparte	2·50	2·50
3991	10r. Admiral Lord Horatio Nelson	2·50	2·50
3992	10r. Captain Thomas Masterman Hardy	2·50	2·50
MS3993	99×70 mm. 25r. Ships engaged in battle	7·50	7·50

466 Elvis Presley, 1956

2005. 70th Birth Anniversary of Elvis Presley. Multicoloured.

3994	7r. Type **466**	1·10	1·10
3995	7r. On Frank Sinatra Show, 1960	1·10	1·10
3996	7r. In 1962	1·10	1·10
3997	7r. Performing in Las Vegas, 1969	1·10	1·10
3998	7r. Arriving in Hawaii, 1973	1·10	1·10
3999	7r. In concert, 1975	1·10	1·10
4000	7r. In *Love Me Tender*, 1956	1·10	1·10
4001	7r. In *Loving You*, 1957	1·10	1·10
4002	7r. In *King Creole*, 1958	1·10	1·10
4003	7r. Riding motorcycle in *Roustabout*, 1964	1·10	1·10
4004	7r. In *Double Trouble*, 1967	1·10	1·10
4005	7r. In *Live a Little, Love a Little*, 1968	1·10	1·10

467 *Purple Bird* (Anna Badger)

2006. 'Kids-Did-It!' Showing children's paintings. Multicoloured.

4006	10r. Type **467**	1·25	1·25
4007	10r. *Parrots* (Nick Abrams)	1·25	1·25
4008	10r. *Pretty Bird* (Jessie Abrams)	1·25	1·25
4009	10r. *Royal Parrot* (Ashley Mondfrans)	1·25	1·25
4010	10r. *Orange Sunflower* (Brett Walker)	1·25	1·25
4011	10r. *Red Flower Pot* (Jessica Shutt)	1·25	1·25
4012	10r. *Flower Pot* (Nick Abrams)	1·25	1·25
4013	10r. *Blue Flower Vase* Trevor Nielsen)	1·25	1·25
4014	10r. *Bubbles* (Raquel Bobolia)	1·25	1·25
4015	10r. *Bubble Fish* (Sarah Bowen)	1·25	1·25
4016	10r. *Lipfish* (Elsa Fleischer)	1·25	1·25
4017	10r. *Flounder* (Erica Malchowski)	1·25	1·25

468 *Himantura uamak*

2006. Rays. Multicoloured.

4018	20l. Type **468**	25	25
4019	1r. *Manta birostris*	50	25
4020	2r. *Taeniura lymma*	90	50
4021	20r. *Aetobatus narinari*	4·00	4·50

469 Emblem

2006. 20th Anniversary of SAARC (South Asian Association for Regional Co-operation). Sheet 115×125 mm.

MS4032	**469** 25r. multicoloured	4·25	5·50

470 Mozart

2006. 250th Birth Anniversary of Wolfgang Amadeus Mozart (composer). Multicoloured.

4033	12r. Type **470**	2·75	2·75
4034	12r. Portrait of Mozart (facing left)	2·75	2·75
4035	12r. Young Mozart	2·75	2·75
4036	12r. Bust of Mozart	2·75	2·75

471 Queen Elizabeth II and President John F. Kennedy

2006. 80th Birthday of Queen Elizabeth II. Multicoloured.

4037	15r. Type **471**	2·50	2·50
4038	15r. With President Reagan, riding horses	2·50	2·50
4039	15r. Dancing with President Ford	2·50	2·50
4040	15r. With President Bush	2·50	2·50
MS4041	126×126 mm. 25r. *Horse in a Field* (detail) (George Stubbs)	5·50	5·50

The stamp within No. **MS**4041 is incorrectly inscribed 'QUEEN ELIZABETH II'.

472 Norway 1951 Winter Olympics 55ore+20ore Stamp

2006. Winter Olympic Games, Turin. Multicoloured.

4042	7r. Type **472**	1·25	1·10
4043	8r. Poster for Winter Olympic Games, Oslo, 1952 (vert)	1·50	1·50
4044	10r. Poster for Winter Olympic Games, Garmisch-Partenkirchen, Germany, 1936 (vert)	1·75	1·75
4045	12r. Germany 1935 Winter Olympics 6pf.+4pf. skating stamp (vert)	2·00	2·25

473 '100'

2006. Centenary of Postal Service in the Maldives. Sheet 135×175 mm.
MS4046 **473** 12r. multicoloured 2·25 2·50

474 Elvis Presley

2006. 50th Anniversary of Purchase of Gracelands by Elvis Presley. Multicoloured, background tint given.
4047 12r. Type **474** (grey) 2·25 2·25
4048 12r. Elvis Presley singing (brownish grey) 2·25 2·25
4049 12r. As No. 4048 (lavender-grey) 2·25 2·25
4050 12r. As Type **474** (greenish grey) 2·25 2·25

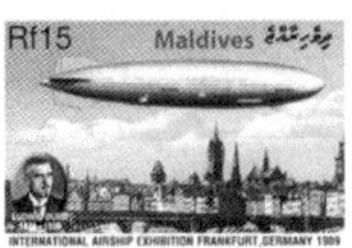

475 International Airship Exhibition, Frankfurt, Germany, 1909

2006. 50th Death Anniversary of Ludwig Durr (Zeppelin engineer). Multicoloured.
4051 15r. Type **475** 2·50 2·50
4052 15r. Hot air balloons at International Airship Exhibition, Frankfurt, 1909 2·50 2·50
4053 15r. Airship LZ-129 *Hindenburg* 2·50 2·50

476 R-7 Missile (*Sputnik 1* launcher)

2006. Space Anniversaries. Multicoloured.

(a) *Sputniks 1, 2,* and *3*
4054 8r. Type **476** 1·75 1·75
4055 8r. *Sputnik 1* 1·75 1·75
4056 8r. Inside *Sputnik 1* 1·75 1·75
4057 8r. *Sputnik 2* 1·75 1·75
4058 8r. *Sputnik 1* orbits over the Earth 1·75 1·75
4059 8r. *Sputnik 3* 1·75 1·75

(b) 20th Anniversary of *Giotto* Comet Probe.
4060 12r. Nucleus of Halley's Comet 2·25 2·25
4061 12r. Halley's Comet 2·25 2·25
4062 12r. *Giotto* Space Probe and Halley's Comet 2·25 2·25
4063 12r. Image of Halley's Comet by *Giotto* Probe 2·25 2·25
MS4064 150×100 mm. 12r.×4 *Calipso* Satellite; *CloudSat* Satellite; *Aqua* Satellite; *Aura* Satellite 8·00 9·00
MS4065 Two sheets, each 100×70 mm. (a) 25r. *Stardust* Satellite, 2004. (b) 25r. *Giotto* Comet Probe 8·00 9·00

The stamps and margins of No. **MS**4064 form a composite design showing satellites above the Earth.

477 *Pomacanthus imperator*

2007. Fish. Multicoloured.
4066 10r. Type **477** 2·25 2·25
4067 10r. *Balistoides conspicillum* 2·25 2·25
4068 10r. *Chaetodon meyeri* 2·25 2·25
4069 10r. *Dascyllus arnanus* 2·25 2·25

478 Ragged-finned Lionfish

2007. Fish of the Maldives. Multicoloured.
4070 1r. Type **478** 35 20
4071 2r. Vlaming's unicornfish 50 30
4072 10r. White-spotted grouper 2·00 2·00
4073 10r. Bicolour parrotfish 2·00 2·00
4074 10r. Blue-barred parrotfish 2·00 2·00
4075 10r. Bullethead parrotfish 2·00 2·00
4076 10r. Dusky parrotfish 2·00 2·00
4077 10r. Imperial angelfish 2·00 2·00
4078 10r. Clown triggerfish 2·00 2·00
4079 10r. Black-saddled coral trout 2·00 2·00
4080 10r. Slender grouper 2·00 2·00
4081 20r. Maldive anemonefish 3·50 4·00
MS4082 Three sheets, each 93×63 mm. (a) 30r. Picasso triggerfish. (b) 30r. Blue-faced angelfish. (c) 30r. Shadow soldierfish 12·00 13·00

479 Bar-tailed Godwit

2007. Migratory Birds of the Maldives. Multicoloured.
4083 1r. Type **479** 65 35
4084 2r. Black-headed gull 1·10 75
4085 10r. Masked booby (vert) 2·50 2·50
4086 10r. Common swifts 2·50 2·50
4087 10r. Sooty tern 2·50 2·50
4088 10r. Yellow wagtail 2·50 2·50
4089 10r. House sparrow 2·50 2·50
4090 10r. Tufted duck 2·50 2·50
4091 10r. Caspian tern 2·50 2·50
4092 10r. Southern giant petrel 2·50 2·50
4093 10r. Glossy ibis 2·50 2·50
4094 20r. Kentish plover 4·00 4·50
MS4095 Three sheets. (a) 64×94 mm. 30r. Golden-throated barbet (vert). (b) 94×64 mm. 30r. Purple herons. (c) 64×94 mm. 30r. Osprey (vert) 14·00 15·00

480 *Dendrobium formosum*

2007. Orchids of Asia. Multicoloured.
4096 1r. Type **480** 65 20
4097 2r. *Bulbophyllum* Elizabeth Ann 1·10 30
4098 10r. *Dendrobium bigibbum* 2·50 2·50
4099 10r. *Cymbidium erythrostylum* 2·50 2·50
4100 10r. *Phaius humboldtii×Phaius tuberculosis* 2·50 2·50
4101 10r. *Dendrobium farmeri* 2·50 2·50
4102 10r. *Dendrobium junceum* 2·50 2·50
4103 10r. *Bulbophyllum lasiochilum* 2·50 2·50
4104 10r. *Phaius* Microburst 2·50 2·50
4105 10r. *Coelogyne mooreana* 2·50 2·50
4106 10r. *Bulbophyllum nasseri* 2·50 2·50
4107 20r. *Spathoglottis gracilis* 4·00 4·00
MS4108 Three sheets, each 66×97 mm. (a) 30r. *Coelogyne cristata* (horiz). (b) 30r. *Dendrobium crocatum* (horiz). (c) 30r. *Bulbophyllum graveolens* (horiz) 14·00 15·00

481 *Ranunculus eschscholtzii*

2007. Flowers of the World. Multicoloured.
4109 1r. Type **481** 35 20
4110 2r. *Ratibida columnaris* 50 30
4111 10r. *Mentzelia laevicaulis* 2·00 2·00
4112 10r. *Ipomopsis aggregate* 2·00 2·00
4113 10r. *Rosa woodsii* 2·00 2·00
4114 10r. *Lewisia rediviva* 2·00 2·00
4115 10r. *Penstemon rydbergii* 2·00 2·00
4116 10r. *Machaeranthera tanacetifolia* 2·00 2·00
4117 10r. *Aquilegia coerulea* 2·00 2·00
4118 10r. *Gentiana detonsa* 2·00 2·00
4119 10r. *Linum perenne* 2·00 2·00
4120 20r. *Clintonia uniflora* 3·50 4·00
MS4121 Three sheets, each 95×67 mm. (a) 30r. *Encelia farinosa*. (b) 30r. *Epilobiumangustifolium*. (c) 30r. *Ipomoea purpurea* 12·00 13·00

482 Scout Badge

2007. Centenary of World Scouting.
4122 **482** 15r. multicoloured 2·50 2·75
MS4123 110×80 mm. **482** 25r. blue and violet 3·75 4·00

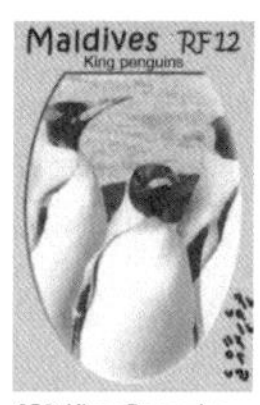

483 King Penguins

2007. International Polar Year. Penguins. Multicoloured.
4124 12r. Type **483** 2·75 2·75
4125 12r. King penguin preening 2·75 2·75
4126 12r. King penguins (green background) 2·75 2·75
4127 12r. Two king penguin chicks 2·75 2·75
4128 12r. King penguin chick with wings raised 2·75 2·75
4129 12r. King penguin chick huddled against adult 2·75 2·75
MS4130 100×70 mm. 25r. African penguin wearing party hat 6·00 6·00

484 Diana, Princess of Wales

2007. Tenth Death Anniversary of Diana, Princess of Wales. Multicoloured.
4131 8r. Type **484** 1·40 1·40
4132 8r. Wearing white hat and pearls 1·40 1·40
4133 8r. Wearing white hat and white coat with pinstripes 1·40 1·40
4134 8r. Wearing white hat and green dress with white pinstripes 1·40 1·40
4135 8r. Carrying bouquet, wearing white hat and white coat with pinstripes 1·40 1·40
4136 8r. Wearing grey jacket and grey and white hat 1·40 1·40
MS4137 100×70 mm. 25r. Wearing black jacket with white lapels and white and black hat 4·50 4·75

485 Ferrari 312 T 4

2007. 60th Anniversary of Ferrari. Multicoloured.
4138 8r. Type **485** 1·25 1·25
4139 8r. 456 GT, 1992 1·25 1·25
4140 8r. 250 GT Berlinetta, 1959 1·25 1·25
4141 8r. F1 89, 1989 1·25 1·25
4142 8r. 456M GTA, 1998 1·25 1·25
4143 8r. 735 LM, 1955 1·25 1·25
4144 8r. DINO 308 GT4, 1973 1·25 1·25
4145 8r. F 200l, 2001 1·25 1·25

486 *Chaetodon triangulum*

2007. Fish. Multicoloured.
4146 10l. Type **486** 15 25
4147 50l. *Chaetodon kleinii* 25 25
4148 12r. *Chaetodon trifasciatus* 2·25 2·25
4149 15r. *Chaetodon madagascariensis* 2·50 2·50
4150 20r. *Chaetodon lunula* 3·00 3·00

487 Elvis Presley

2008. 30th Death Anniversary of Elvis Presley (2007). Multicoloured.
4151 8r. Type **487** 1·40 1·40
4152 8r. Wearing bright blue jacket, playing guitar 1·40 1·40
4153 8r. Wearing red jacket 1·40 1·40
4154 8r. Wearing grey collarless jacket and black shirt 1·40 1·40
4155 8r. Wearing blue shirt, singing 1·40 1·40
4156 8r. Wearing red shirt, holding microphone 1·40 1·40

488 Rie Mastenbroek (Netherlands) (swimming triple gold medallist)

2008. Olympic Games, Beijing. Designs showing scenes from Olympic Games, Berlin, 1936. Multicoloured.
4157 7r. Type **488** 1·40 1·40
4158 7r. Poster for Olympic Games, Berlin, 1936 1·40 1·40
4159 7r. Jesse Owens (USA) (field and track gold medallist) 1·40 1·40
4160 7r. Jack Beresford (Great Britain) (double scull gold medallist) 1·40 1·40
MS4161 177×101 mm. Nos. 4157/4160 5·00 5·50

489 Americas Cup Yachts

2008. America's Cup Yachting Championship. Multicoloured.
4162 10r. Type **489** 1·50 1·75
4163 12r. Two yachts (green yacht in background) 1·75 2·00
4164 15r. Two yachts (*Prada* in foreground) 2·25 2·50
4165 20r. Two yachts (yellow yacht in foreground) 2·75 3·00

490 Emblem of First Scout Jamboree, Kuda Bandos, 1986

2008. 50th Anniversary of Scouting in the Maldives (5l. to 5r.) and Centenary of World Scouting (8r.). Multicoloured.
4166 5l. Type **490** 25 25
4167 10l. Second Scout Jamboree, Kuda Bandos, 1988 30 30
4168 15l. Third Scout Jamboree, Huraa, 1990 35 35
4169 20l. Fourth National Scout Jamboree, Villingili, December 1992 35 35
4170 25l. Fifth National Scout Jamboree, Villingili, September 1993 35 35
4171 30l. Jamboree '98 badge 35 35
4172 95l. Scout Jamboree 2002 50 50
4173 5r. Eighth National (Golden Jubilee) Jamboree, Hulhumale', 15–19 April, 2007 1·00 1·00

MS4174	130×172 mm. 8r. Lord Baden-Powell	1·40	1·60

Nos. 4166/4173 all show emblems.

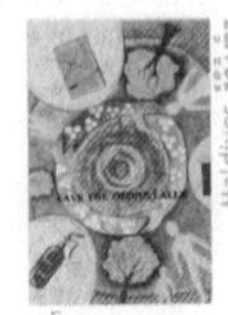

491 Rose in Ozone Layer and Pollutants

2008. International Day for the Preservation of the Ozone Layer. Sheet 177×127 mm containing T **491** and similar vert designs showing posters drawn by Maldivian students for International Ozone Day 2002. Multicoloured.

MS4175	5r. Type **491**; 12r. Two people, trees and sea with fish in ozone bubble; 15r. People standing on globe holding up ozone layer; 18r. Four people standing on island holding up ozone layer	7·00	8·00

492 Elvis Presley

2008. Elvis Presley Commemoration. Multicoloured.

4176	8r. Type **492**	1·40	1·40
4177	8r. With hand close-up in right foreground of picture	1·40	1·40
4178	8r. Wearing jumpsuit, shown in yellow with blue background	1·40	1·40
4179	8r. Holding microphone, lemon background	1·40	1·40
4180	8r. Wearing white	1·40	1·40
4181	8r. Wearing stetson, sitting on car bonnet	1·40	1·40

493 Sopwith F-1 Camel

2008. 90th Anniversary of the Royal Air Force. Multicoloured.

4182	12r. Type **493**	3·00	3·00
4183	12r. Aerospatiale Puma HC1 helicopter	3·00	3·00
4184	12r. Wessex helicopter	3·00	3·00
4185	12r. Armstrong Whitworth Atlas seaplane	3·00	3·00

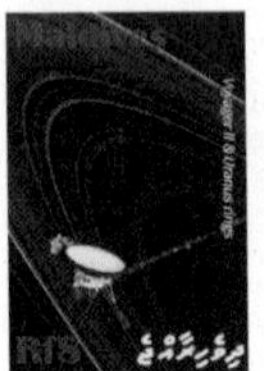

494 *Voyager II* and Uranus Rings

2008. 50 Years of Space Exploration and Satellites. Multicoloured.

4186	8r. Type **494**	1·25	1·25
4187	8r. Titan 3E Centaur rocket launches *Voyager II*, 1977	1·25	1·25
4188	8r. *Voyager II* and Neptune's Great Dark Spot	1·25	1·25
4189	8r. *Voyager II* and Jupiter's Great Red Spot	1·25	1·25
4190	8r. Technician places Voyager's Gold Record	1·25	1·25
4191	8r. *Voyager II* and Saturn's Rings	1·25	1·25
4192	12r. *Sputnik I* in space, 1957	2·00	2·00
4193	12r. Components of *Sputnik I*	2·00	2·00
4194	12r. Technician and *Sputnik I*	2·00	2·00
4195	12r. *Sputnik I* above Moon	2·00	2·00
4196	12r. *Explorer I* atop launcher *Juno I*, 1958	2·00	2·00
4197	12r. *Explorer I* and Planet Earth	2·00	2·00
4198	12r. *Explorer I* above Earth	2·00	2·00
4199	12r. Dr. James Van Allen and the Van Allen radiation belt	2·00	2·00
4200	12r. *Vanguard I* in orbit below Earth, 1953	2·00	2·00
4201	12r. Two technicians with *Vanguard I*	2·00	2·00
4202	12r. *Vanguard I* satellite and rocket	2·00	2·00
4203	12r. *Vanguard I* above Earth	2·00	2·00
4204	12r. Spitzer Space Telescope (bright star in gas cloud at right)	2·00	2·00
4205	12r. Spitzer Space Telescope (gas cloud only at foot and left of telescope)	2·00	2·00
4206	12r. Spitzer Space Telescope (bright stars in gas cloud below telescope)	2·00	2·00
4207	12r. Spitzer Space Telescope (with solar panels visible)	2·00	2·00

495 Troops in Trench

2008. 90th Anniversary of the End of World War One. Multicoloured.

MS4208	91×140 mm. 12r.×4 Type **495**; Two soldiers looking out from trench (side view); Soldiers in trench (seen from back); ANZAC soldier carrying wounded comrade	8·00	8·50
MS4209	195×178 mm. 12r.×4 Motorcycle despatch riders studying map; ANZAC troops ascending hill; Tank; Two soldiers looking out from trench (seen from back)	8·00	8·50

496 President Barack Obama

2009. Inauguration of President Barack Obama. Multicoloured.

MS4210	165×140 mm. 10r.×6 Type **496**; President Obama facing right; Michelle Obama; President Obama facing left; Michelle Obama clapping; President Obama facing camera, smiling	9·00	10·00
MS4211	85×110 mm. 30r. President Barack Obama and Michelle Obama (50×37 mm)	6·50	7·50

497 Abraham Lincoln

2009. Birth Bicentenary of Abraham Lincoln (US President 1861–1865). Sheet 136×175 mm containing T **497** and similar vert designs. Multicoloured.

MS4212	Type **497**; Seated by desk; Seated by desk, holding book; Abraham Lincoln (head turned to left)	6·00	7·00

498 Black-saddled Coralgrouper (*Plectropomus laevis*)

2009. Fish. Multicoloured.

4213	12r. Type **498**	2·25	2·25
4214	12r. Sixblotch hind (*Cephalopholis sexmaculata*)	2·25	2·25
4215	12r. Foursaddle grouper (*Epinephelus spilotoceps*)	2·25	2·25
4216	12r. Peacock hind (*Cephalopholis argus*)	2·25	2·25

499 Scotty (James Doohan)

2009. *Star Trek.* Multicoloured.

MS4217	178×127 mm. 12r.×4 Type **499**; Dr. McCoy (DeForest Kelly) (looking left); Captain Kirk (William Shatner); Mr. Spock (Leonard Nimoy) (in profile)	7·00	7·50
MS4218	127×178 mm. 12r.×4 Fleet crew; Uhura (Nichelle Nichols); Mr. Spock (speaking); Dr. McCoy (all horiz)	7·00	7·50

500 Prince Harry at Official Naming of the British Garden

2009. Visit of Prince Harry to New York. Sheet 140×100 mm.. Multicoloured.

MS4219	Type **500**; With little girl at World Trade Center site; Prince Harry speaking; Competing in Polo Classic	8·50	8·50

501 Marilyn Monroe

2009. Marilyn Monroe Commemoration.. Multicoloured.

MS4220	Type **501**; Sitting in open-top car; Wearing print blouse; Laying down (head and shoulders portrait)	7·50	8·50

502 Crimson Rose (*Atrophaneura hector*)

2009. Butterflies of Maldives. Multicoloured.

4221	10l. Type **502**	25	40
4222	16r. Common mormon (*Papilio polytes*)	3·00	3·25
4223	18r. Common jay (*Graphium dosun*)	3·25	3·50
4224	20r. Common tiger (*Danaus genutia*)	3·50	3·75
MS4225	176×75 mm. 12r.×4 Small salmon arab (*Colotis amata*); Lemon pansy (*Junonia lemonias*); Tamil yeoman (*Cirrochroa thais*); Dark blue tiger (*Tirumala septentrionis*) (all horiz)	8·00	8·50
MS4226	100×70 mm. 15r.×2 Common jezebel (*Delias eucharis*); Common gull (*Cepora nerissa*)	6·00	6·50

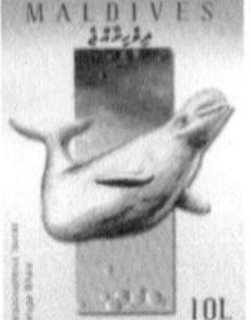

503 Beluga Whale

2009. Whales. Multicoloured.

4227	10l. Type **503**	25	40
4228	12r. Hector's beaked whale (*Mesoplodon hectori*)	2·75	2·75
4229	16r. Beaked whale (*Mesoplodon layardii*)	3·25	3·50
4230	18r. Baird's beaked whale (*Berardius bairdii*)	3·50	3·75
MS4231	150×110 mm. 12r.×6 Dwarf sperm whale (*Kogia sima*); Pygmy sperm whale (*Kogia breviceps*); Baird's beaked whale (*Berardius bairdii*); Sperm whale (*Physeter catodon*); Shepherd's beaked whale (*Tasmacetus shepherdi*); Cuvier's beaked whale (*Ziphius cavirostris*) (all horiz)	15·00	16·00

504 Y-5

2009. Centenary of Chinese Aviation and Aeropex 2009 Exhibition, Beijing. Designs showing aircraft. Multicoloured.

MS4232	145×95 mm. 9r.×4 Type **504**; Y-7; Y-8; Y-12	6·00	6·50
MS4233	120×79 mm. 25r. Xian Y7-MA60 (50×38 mm)	4·75	5·00

505 Melon-headed Whales

2009. Endangered Species. Melon-headed Whale (*Peponocephala electra*). Multicoloured.

4234	8r. Type **505**	2·00	2·00
4235	8r. Melon-headed whale	2·00	2·00
4236	8r. Four whales	2·00	2·00
4237	8r. Six whales	2·00	2·00
MS4238	112×165 mm. Nos. 4234/4237, each×2	12·00	13·00

506 *Copelandia bispora*

2009. Fungi. Multicoloured.

MS4239	180×80 mm. 8r.×4 Type **506**; *Copelandia cyanescens*; *Psilocybe semilanceata*; *Volvariella vovvacea*	7·00	7·50
MS4240	120×110 mm. 8r.×6 Dark grey fungi; Two round-headed chestnut fungi; Yellow-brown fungi with prominent gills around edge of cap; White fungi with prominent gills; Dark chestnut fungi; Two bracket fungi	8·00	8·50

507 *Apollo 11* Command Module

2009. 40th Anniversary of First Manned Landing on Moon. Multicoloured.

MS4241	130×100 mm. 12r.×4 Type **507**; *Apollo 11*; Astronaut Neil Armstrong; *Apollo 11* Lunar Module	7·00	7·50
MS4242	100×70 mm. 30r. Astronauts Michael Collins, Edwin E. Aldrin and Neil Armstrong (horiz)	5·50	6·00

508 *Nelumbo nucifera*

2009. Flowers. Multicoloured.

MS4243	150×110 mm. 10r.×6 Type **508**; *Rosa bracteata*; *Freycinetia cumingiana*; *Thespesia lampas*; *Plumeria champa*; *Plumeria cubensis*	9·00	10·00
MS4244	110×80 mm. 15r.×2 *Plumeria rubra*; *Hibiscus tiliaceus*	5·50	6·00
MS4245	110×80 mm. 15r.×2 *Lagerstroemia speciosa*; *Plumeria alba*	5·50	6·00

508a Tiger Symbol

2010. Chinese New Year. Year of the Tiger. Multicoloured.

MS4245a	25r. Type **508a**; 25r. Tiger	6·00	7·00

508b Rat

2010. Chinese Lunar Calendar. 30th Anniversary of Chinese Zodiac Stamps. Multicoloured.

MS4245b	3r.×12 Type **508b**; Ox; Tiger; Rabbit; Dragon; Snake; Horse; Ram; Monkey; Rooster; Dog; Pig	7·00	7·00

509 White-tailed Tropicbird (*Phaethon lepturus*)

2010. Birds of the Maldives. Multicoloured.

MS4246	170×106 mm. 8r.×6 Type **509**; Common tern (*Sterna hirundo*); Bar-tailed godwit (*Limosa lapponica*); Crab plover (*Dromas ardeola*); Whimbrel (*Numenius phaeopus hudsonicus*); Black-winged stilt (*Himantopus himantopus*)	9·00	9·00
MS4247	100×70 mm. 30r. Asian koel or Dhivehi kovel (*Eudynamys scolopacea*)	7·00	7·00

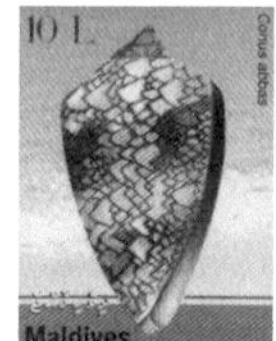

510 *Conus abbas*

2010. Seashells of Maldives. Multicoloured.

4248	10l. Type **510**	25	40
4249	12r. *Conus amadis*	1·75	1·75
4250	16r. *Conus bengalensis*	2·50	2·75
4251	18r. *Pinctada margaritifera*	3·00	3·25
MS4252	150×100 mm. 15r.×4 *Harpa costata*; *Phalium fimbria*; *Zoila friendii friendii*; *Cyprae leucodon tenuidon*	9·00	9·50

511 Olive Ridley Turtle (*Lepidochelys olivacea*)

2010. Reptiles of the Maldives. Multicoloured.

MS4253	150×100 mm. 15r.×4 Type **511**; Good sucker lizard (*Calotes versicolar*); Indian wolf snake (*Lycodon aulicus*); Green turtle (*Chelonia mydas*)	8·50	9·00
MS4254	100×70 mm. 15r. Common house gecko (*Hemidactylus frenatus*); 15r. Loggerhead turtle (*Caretta caretta gigas*)	5·50	6·00

512 Lyndon B. Johnson

2010. 50th Anniversary of Election of President John F. Kennedy. Multicoloured.

MS4255	$15r.×4 Type **512**; John F. Kennedy; Election campaign leaflets; Campaign badge	8·00	8·50
MS4256	15r.×4 President John F. Kennedy; 1955 Pulitzer Prize medal (won for book *Profiles in Courage*); Civil Rights Act, 1964; Peace Corps emblem (established by JFK, 1961)	8·00	8·50

513 Elvis Presley as Ross Carpenter

2010. Elvis Presley in Film *Girls! Girls! Girls!*, 1962. Multicoloured.

MS4257	90×125 mm. 25r. Type **513**	3·25	3·25
MS4258	125×90 mm. 25r. Wearing cap and mauve and white spotted pyjamas	3·25	3·25
MS4259	90×125 mm. 25r. Wearing white shirt, singing	3·25	3·25
MS4260	125×90 mm. 25r. Poster for *Girls! Girls! Girls!*	3·25	3·25

514 Brownies

2010. Centenary of Girlguiding. Multicoloured.

MS4261	150×100 mm. 16r.×4 Type **514**; Two guides; Guide rocking climbing; Two guides jumping for joy	8·00	8·50
MS4262	71×100 mm. 30r. Brownie saluting (vert)	4·50	4·75
MS4263	173×240 mm. 12r. 'girls worldwide say 100 YEARS of changing lives'; 12r. '58 YEARS OF GUIDING MALDIVES' (both 34×26 mm)	6·50	6·50

515 Girl standing in Corner (Aishath Shamha Nizam) (1st)

2010. Human Rights Commission of the Maldives. Prevention of Child Abuse. Winning Entries in Children's Poster Drawing Competition. Multicoloured.

MS4264	10l. Type **515**; 20l. Girl sitting on floor, silhouettes and 'Join your hands to protect us not to abuse us!!' (Shaulann Shafeeq) (3rd); 95l. Man and crying woman and boy (Sameen Moosa) (3rd); 5r. Children and 'we dont bully' in speech bubbles (Zaha Mohamed Ziyad) (2nd)	1·50	1·50
MS4265	25l. Blindfolded girl and gagged girl ('Open Your eyes! And Break our silence') (Emau Ahmed Saleem) (3rd); 50l. Three silhouettes (Rishwan Naseem) (Special Prize); 1r. Child's hand and 'THIS CHILD NEEDS HOPE' (Ahmed Nafiu) (Special Prize); 2r. Boy holding drawing and 'It Shouldn't HURT to be a CHILD' (Sam'aan Abdul Raheem) (Special Prize); 3r. Family and heart (Ummu Haanee Hussain) (1st); 4r. Wounded girl (Fathimath Shaufa Easa (2nd); 6r. Girl and 'Stop Child Abuse' (Hussain Hazim (3rd); 7r. Child fallen from bed (Fathimath Afaaf Bushree) (2nd) (all vert)	3·25	3·50

2015. Holiday Resorts. Multicoloured.

4266	15r. Kuredu Resort	1·75	1·75
4267	15r. Vilamendhoo Island Resort and Spa	1·75	1·75
4268	15r. Meeru Island Resort and Spa	1·75	1·75
4269	15r. Komandoo Island Resort and Spa	1·75	1·75
4270	15r. Veligandu Island Resort and Spa	1·75	1·75

2015. 50th Anniversary of Independence. Multicoloured.

4271	10r. Sailing boat	1·50	1·50
4272	10r. Dancing at Independence celebrations	1·50	1·50
4273	15r. Island resort	2·00	2·00
4274	15r. Anglers	2·00	2·00
4275	25r. Independence Signing Ceremony	3·00	3·00
4276	25r. Planting palm tree	3·00	3·00

APPENDIX

The following stamps have either been issued in excess of postal needs or have not been available to the public in reasonable quantities at face value.

2012

40th Anniversary of Diplomatic Relations between the Maldive Islands and People's Republic of China. 40r.x6

2013

Fauna of the Indian Ocean: Starfish of the Indian Ocean. 20r.x4; Seals of the Indian Ocean. 20r.x4; Dugongs of the Indian Ocean (*Dugong dugon*). 20r.x4; Whales of the Indian Ocean. 20r.x4; Fish of the Indian Ocean. 22r.x4; Dolphins of the Indian Ocean. 22r.x4; Birds of the Indian Ocean. 22r.x4; Seashells of the Indian Ocean. 22r.x4; Turtles of the Indian Ocean. 22r.x4; WWF. White-breasted Waterhen (*Amaurornis phoenicurus*). 22r.x4

Fauna and Flora of the Maldives: Saltwater Crocodile (*Crocodylus porosus*). 20r.x4; Lizards. 20r.x4; Water Birds. 20r.x4; Protected Marine Species. 20r.x4; Fruit Bats. 20r.x4; Birds of Prey. 22r.x4; Short-eared Owl (*Asio flammeus*). 22r.x4; Orchids. 22r.x4; Fish. 22r.x4; Tropical Butterflies. 22r.x4

70th Birth Anniversary of Bobby Fisher (chess player). 20r.x4

Brasiliana 2013 International Philatelic Exhibition, Rio de Janeiro. Confederations Cup, Brazil, 2013. Football Players. 20r.x4

Marilyn Monroe. 20r.x4

150th Birth Anniversary of Pierre de Coubertin. 20r.x4

Birth of Prince George of Cambridge. 20r.x4

95th Birthday of Nelson Mandela. 22r.x4

Elvis Presley. 22r.x4

40th Death Anniversary of Pablo Picasso. 22r.x4

85th Death Anniversary of Mahatma Gandhi. 22r.x4

50th Anniversary of the First Woman in Space Valentina Tereshkova. 22r.x4

Formula 1 Race Cars. 20r.x4

The History of the Automobile. 20r.x4

Rescue Boats. 20r.x4

Yuri Gagarin. 20r.x4

Steam Trains. 20r.x4

High-speed Trains. 22r.x4

Seaplanes. 22r.x4

Space Tourism. 22r.x4

Fire Engines. 22r.x4

Concorde. 22r.x4

2014

20th Death Anniversary of Ayrton Senna (racing driver). 20r.x4

110th Birth Anniversary of Salvador Dali. 20r.x4

Tribute to Nelson Mandela. 20r.x4

40th Death Anniversary of Charles Lindbergh (aviator). 20r.x4

90th Death Anniversary of Giacomo Puccini (composer). 20r.x4

125th Birth Anniversary of Charlie Chaplin (actor). 22r.x4

300th Birth Anniversary of Christoph Willibald Gluck (composer). 22r.x4

80th Death Anniversary of Marie Curie (chemist). 22r.x4

60th Death Anniversary of Frida Kahlo (painter). 22r.x4

25th Death Anniversary of Bette Davis (actress). 22r.x4

Masters of Impressionism (Paintings): Edouard Manet. 20r.x4; Edgar Degas. 20r.x4; Camille Pissarro. 20r.x4; Berthe Morisot. 20r.x4; Mary Cassatt. 20r.x4; 175th Birth Anniversary of Paul Cézanne. 22r.x4; Pierre-Auguste Renoir. 22r.x4; Claude Monet. 22r.x4; American Impressionists. 22r.x4; Armand Guillaumin. 22r.x4

Fauna of the Indian Ocean: Crustaceans of the Indian Ocean. 20r.x4; Frogs of the Indian Ocean. 20r.x4; Octopus of the Indian Ocean. 20r.x4; Reptiles of the Indian Ocean. 20r.x4; Sharks of the Indian Ocean. 20r.x4; Birds of Prey of the Indian Ocean. 22r.x4; Butterflies of the Indian Ocean. 22r.x4; Deep Water Creatures of the Indian Ocean. 22r.x4; Jellyfish of the Indian Ocean. 22r.x4; Owls of the Indian Ocean. 22r.x4

70th Death Anniversary of Wassily Kandinsky. 20r.x4

20th Anniversary of Channel Tunnel. 20r.x4

60th Anniversary of the Marilyn Monroe–Joe Di Maggio Marriage. 20r.x4

Centenary of the beginning of the First World War. 20r.x4

20th Anniversary of *Red List* (Endangered Species). 20r.x4

Centenary of E. Marinella, Naples. 20r.x5

60th Anniversary of Elvis Presley's First Single *That's All Right/ Blue Moon of Kentucky*. 22r.x4

60th Death Anniversary of Henri Matisse. 22r.x4

70th Death Anniversary of Louis Renault. 22r.x4

70th Anniversary of the Battle of the Bulge during the World War II. 22r.x4

China Art. Paintings of He Xiangning. 22r.x4

Greatest Flemish Painters: Pieter Brueghel the Elder and Younger. 20r.x4; Hans Memling. 22r.x4; Dieric Bouts. 20r.x4; Quentin Matsys. 20r.x4; Peter Paul Rubens. 20r.x4; Frans Hals. 22r.x4; Sir Anthony van Dyck. 22r.x4; Jan van Eyck. 22r.x4; Rogier van der Weyden. 22r.x4

World Cup Football, Brazil (1st issue). 15r.x6

Greatest Cricket Players. 20r.x4

Greatest Chess Players. 20r.x4

Greatest Judo Fighters. 20r.x4

Rally Racing. 20r.x4

Winter Olympic Games, Sochi, Russia. 20r.x4

Horse Racing. 22r.x4

Greatest Table Tennis Players. 22r.x4

Greatest Golf Players. 22r.x4

50th Anniversary of the title of World Champion Muhammad Ali. 22r.x4

250th Anniversary of the Hermitage Museum, St Petersburg, Russia. 20r.x4

450th Birth Anniversary of Galileo Galilei. 20r.x4

World Cup Football, Brazil (2nd issue). 20r.x4

50th Anniversary of Martin Luther King Jr.'s Nobel Prize. 20r.x4

Tenth Anniversary of Cassini, a space exploration mission to Saturn. 20r.x3

SIDS 2014. 3rd International Conference on Small Island Developing States, Samoa. 22r.x4

110th Birth Anniversary of Deng Xiaoping. 22r.x4

Spain's King Felipe VI. 22r.x4

85th Anniversary of round-the-world flight by the *Graf Zeppelin*. 22r.x4

17th ASEAN Games, Incheon, South Korea. 22r.x4

Mushrooms. 20r.x4

Cats. 20r.x4

Butterflies. 20r.x4

Dolphins. 20r.x4

Turtles. 20r.x4

Minerals. 22r.x4

Orchids. 22r.x4

Dogs. 22r.x4

Dinosaurs. 22r.x4

Lighthouses. 22r.x4

Birds of the Maldives: Pigeons and Fruits. 20r.x4; Water Birds and Corals. 20r.x4; Wading Birds and Insects. 20r.x4; Songbirds. 20r.x4; Pelicans. 20r.x4; Owls and Mushrooms. 22r.x4; Birds of Prey. 22r.x4; Seabirds and Shells. 22r.x4; Terns and Lighthouses. 22r.x4; Bee-eaters and Orchids. 22r.x4

2015

Transport History: Motorcycles. 20r.x4; Pioneers of Aviation. 20r.x4; Special Transport. 20r.x4; Electric Transport. 20r.x4; Sled Dogs. 20r.x4; Horse-drawn Transport. 22r.x4; Invention of Trains. 22r.x4; Maritime Timeline. 22r.x4; Spaceships. 22r.x4; Submarines. 22r.x4

World War II. 70th Anniversary of the Allied Landing in Normandy. 20r.x4

175th Birth Anniversary of Pyotr Ilyich Tchaikovsky. 20r.x4

Nobel Prize Winners 2014. 20r.x4

Chinese New Year. Year of the Goat. 20r.x4

World War II. 70th Anniversaryniv of the Liberation of Paris. 22r.x4

Indian Mars Orbiter Mission. 22r.x4

135th Birth Anniversary of Albert Einstein. 22.r.x4

75th Birth Anniversary of John Lennon. 22r.x4

80th Birthday of Sophia Loren (actress). 22r.x4

40th Birthday of Tiger Woods (golfer). 22r.x4

Fauna of Indian Subcontinent: Owls. 20r.x4; Fish. 20r.x4; Parrots. 20r.x4; Snow Leopards. 20r.x4; Dolphins. 20r.x4; Butterflies. 22r.x4; Turtles. 22r.x4; Tigers. 22r.x4; Asian Elephants. 22r.x4; Rare Monkeys. 22r.x4

Post-Impressionism 1880-1910. Paintings: Paul Gauguin. 20r.x4; Henri de Toulouse-Lautrec. 20r.x4; Henri Rousseau. 20r.x4; Robert Antoine Pinchon. 20r.x4; Paul Signac. 20r.x4; Vincent van Gogh. 22r.x4; Paul Cézanne. 22r.x4; Odilon Redon. 22r.x4; Emile Bernard. 22r.x4; Georges Lemmen. 22r.x4

70th Anniversary of the end of World War II. 20r.x4

Birth Centenary of Ingrid Bergman. 20r.x4

80th Birth Anniversary of Elvis Presley. 20r.x4

25th Anniversary of the Liberation of Nelson Mandela. 20r.x4

85th Birth Anniversary of Buzz Aldrin (astronaut). 20r.x4

The World's Strongest Chess Players. 22r.x4

Birth Centenary of Frank Sinatra. 22r.x4

Bicentenary of the Battle of Waterloo. 22r.x4

245th Birth Anniversary of Ludwig van Beethoven. 22r.x4

125th Birth Anniversary of Boris Pasternak. 22r.x4

World of Sport: Cricket. 20r.x4; Tennis. 20r.x4; Baseball. 20r.x4; Cycling. 20r.x4; Formula 1 (motor racing). 20r.x4; Table Tennis. 22r.x4; Rugby. 22r.x4; Football. 22r.x4; Water Sports. 22r.x4; Golf. 22r.x4

Rescue and Working Dogs. 20r.x4

Domestic Fauna: Cats. 20r.x4

Birds of the World: Kingfishers. 20r.x4

Beauty of Flowers: Orchids. 20r.x4

Asian Fauna. Pandas (*Ailuropoda melanoleuca*). 20r.x4

Prehistoric Fauna: Dinosaurs. 22r.x4

Killer Whales (*Orcinus orca*). 22r.x4

Birds of Prey: Eagles. 22r.x4

Birds of the World. Owls. 22r.x4

Ocean Shapes: Shells. 22r.x4

New Horizons: Mission to Pluto in 2015. 20r.x4

Heroic Age of Antarctic Exploration. Centenary of the Endurance Expedition. 20r.x4

MonacoPhil International Philatelic Exhibition, Monaco. 105th Birth Anniversary of Jacques-Yves Cousteau. 20r.x4

115th Anniversary of the Flight of the Glider by the Wright Brothers. 20r.x4

50th Anniversary of Porsche 912. 20r.x4

Vasco Da Gama. 22r.x4

Space Pioneers. 22r.x4

Rail Transport. High-speed Trains. 22r.x4

World War I. Centenary of the Invention of Gas Mask. 22r.x4

120th Death Anniversary of Louis Pasteur. 22r.x4

Conservation Projects around the Globe: Asian Elephant in Asia. *Elephas maximus maximus*. 20r.x4; Dolphins in Kenya. 20r.x4; Brown Bear in Romania. *Ursus arctos*. 20r.x4; Pandas in China. *Ailuropoda melanoleuca*. 20r.x4; Colobus Monkey in Africa. 20r.x4; Seal Protection in South Africa. *Arctocephalus pusillus*. 22r.x4; Sea Turtles. 22r.x4; Puma and Jaguar in South America. 22r.x4 Penguins in Africa. *Spheniscus demersus*. 22r.x4; Great White Shark. *Carcharodon carch–arias*. 22r.x4

Paintings: Baroque. 17th-century. 20r.x4; Dutch Golden Age. 17th-century. 20r.x4; Impressionism. 1860's-1880's. 20r.x4; Post Impressionism. 1880's–1910's. 20r.x4; Cubism. 1900's–1910's. 20r.x4; Renaissance. *c.* 1400–1600. 22r.x4; Romanticism. Mid 18th-century–mid 19th-century. 22r.x4; Realism. Mid 19th-century. 22r.x4; Symbolism. 1880's–1900's. 22r.x4; Surrealism. 1920–1960's. 22r.x4

Birth of Princess Charlotte of Cambridge. 20r.x4

330th Birth Anniversary of George Frideric Handel. 20r.x4

25th Anniversary of the Liberation of Nelson Mandela. 20r.x4

International Year of Light and Light-based Technologies. 20r.x4

Queen Elizabeth II Longest Reigning British Monarch. 20r.x4

175th Anniversary of the Penny Black. 22r.x4

155th Anniversary of the Pony Express. 22r.x4

Homage to Marilyn Monroe. 22r.x4

Scouting in Maldives 1963–2015. 22r.x4

105th Birth Anniversary of Mother Teresa. 22r.x4

Baa Atoll UNESCO Biosphere Reserve. 5, 10, 25, 50r.

Fish of the Maldives. 20r.x12

Birds of the Indian Ocean: Birds of Prey. 20r.x4

Birds of the Maldives: Ducks. 20r.x4

Fish of the Maldives. Sharks. 22r.x4

Birds of the Maldives. Terns. 22r.x4

Birds of the Indian Ocean. Wading Birds. 22r.x4

Birds of the Indian Ocean. Seabirds. 22r.x4

Fish of the Maldives. 22r.x4

175th Death Anniversary of Niccolo Paganini. 20r.x4

150th Death Anniversary of Abraham Lincoln. 20r.x4

15th Anniversary of the Tragedy of the Concorde. 20r.x4

Remembering Princess Diana. 20r.x4

Athletics World Championships, Beijing, China. 20r.x4

World War II. 70th Anniversary of the Bombing of Dresden. 22r.x4

European Football Championship, France (2016). 22r.x4

65th Birthday of Narendra Modi (Prime Minister of India). 22r.x4

Rotary in Sri Lanka and Maldives. 22r.x4

50th Anniversary of the First Spacewalks. 22r.x4

2016

WWF Green Humphead Parrotfish (*Bolbometopon muricatum*). 22r.x4
Tall Ships. 20r.x4
Seaplanes. 20r.x4
Nobel Prize Winners 2015. 20r.x4
Discovery of liquid salty water on Mars. 20r.x4
The Apollo Missions. 20r.x4
British Trains. 22r.x4
Lighthouses. 2015 International Year of Light. 22r.x4
Fire Engines. 22r.x4
Maldivian Red Crescent. 22r.x4

MALI

Federation of French Sudan and Senegal, formed in 1959 as an autonomous republic within the French Community. In August 1960 the Federation was split up and the French Sudan part became the independent Mali Republic.

100 centimes = 1 franc.

A. FEDERATION

1 Map, Flag, Mali and Torch

1959. Establishment of Mali Federation.

1	**1**	25f. multicoloured	1·60	1·20

2

1959. Air. 300th Anniversary of St Louis, Senegal.

2	**2**	85f. multicoloured	3·50	2·40

3 West African Parrotfish **4** Violet Starling

1960. (a) Postage. Fish as T **3**.

3	**3**	5f. orange, blue and bronze	60	25
4	-	10f. black, brown and turquoise	70	35
5	-	15f. brown, slate and blue	70	50
6	-	20f. black, bistre and green	1·10	60
7	-	25f. yellow, sepia and green	1·80	95
8	-	30f. red, purple and blue	2·40	1·70
9	-	85f. red, blue and green	5·50	3·50

(b) Air. Birds as T **4**.

10	**4**	100f. multicoloured	4·75	2·40
11	-	200f. multicoloured	12·00	6·00
12	-	500f. multicoloured	31·00	18·00

Designs: Horiz—10f. West African triggerfish; 15f. Guinean fingerfish; 20f. Threadfish; 25f. Shining butterflyfish; 30f. Monrovian surgeonfish; 85f. Pink dentex; 200f. Bateleur. Vert—500f. Common gonolek.

1960. Tenth Anniversary of African Technical Co-operation Commission. As T **4** of Malagasy Republic.

13		25f. purple and violet	1·90	1·20

B. REPUBLIC

1960. Nos. 6, 7, 9 and 10/12 optd **REPUBLIQUE DU MALI** and bar or bars or surch also.

14	20f. black, bistre and green (postage)	1·50	85
15	25f. red, purple and blue	2·10	85
16	85f. red, blue and green	3·75	2·10
17	100f. multicoloured (air)	5·00	2·10
18	200f. multicoloured	8·50	4·25
19	300f. on 500f. multicoloured	12·00	6·50
20	500f. multicoloured	20·00	11·00

7 President Mamadou Konate

1961

21	**7**	20f. sepia and green (postage)	40	25
22	-	25f. black and purple	55	25
23	**7**	200f. sepia and red (air)	4·00	1·20
24	-	300f. black and green	5·75	1·70

Design: 25, 300f. President Keita. Nos. 23/24 are larger, 27×38 mm.

8 UN Emblem, Flag and Map

1961. Air. Proclamation of Independence and Admission into UN.

25	**8**	100f. multicoloured	2·10	1·20
MS25a		160×100 mm. Nos. 21/22 and 25	3·00	3·00

9 Sankore Mosque, Timbuktu

1961. Air.

26	**9**	100f. brown, blue and sepia	1·90	70
27	-	200f. brown, red and green	5·25	2·30
28	-	500f. green, brown and blue	13·50	4·50

Design: 200f. View of Timbuktu; 500f. Arms and view of Bamako.

10 Africans learning Vowels

1961. First Anniversary of Independence.

29	**10**	25f. multicoloured	85	55

11 Sheep at Pool

1961

30	**11**	50c. sepia, myrtle and red	10	10
31	**A**	1f. bistre, green and blue	10	10
32	**B**	2f. red, green and blue	10	10
33	**C**	3f. brown, green and blue	10	10
34	**D**	4f. blue, green and bistre	10	10
35	**11**	5f. purple, green and blue	10	10
36	**A**	10f. brown, myrtle and blue	30	20
37	**B**	15f. brown, green and blue	30	20
38	**C**	20f. red, green and blue	45	25
39	**D**	25f. brown and blue	50	25
40	**11**	30f. brown, green and violet	75	40
41	**A**	40f. brown, green and blue	1·40	40
42	**B**	50f. lake, green and blue	70	40
43	**C**	60f. brown, green and blue	1·50	45
44	**D**	85f. brown, bistre and blue	2·30	55

Designs: A, Oxen at pool; B, House of Arts, Mali; C, Land tillage; D, Combine-harvester in rice field.

12 African Map and King Mohammed V of Morocco

1962. First Anniversary of African Conference, Casablanca.

45	**12**	25f. multicoloured	35	10
46	**12**	50f. multicoloured	70	30

13 Patrice Lumumba

1962. First Death Anniversary of Patrice Lumumba (Congo leader).

47	**13**	25f. brown and bistre	35	25
48	**13**	100f. brown and green	1·20	70

1962. Malaria Eradication. As T **11a** of Malagasy.

49		25f.+5f. blue	1·20	1·00

14 Pegasus and UPU Emblem

1962. First Anniversary of Admission into UPU.

50	**14**	85f. multicoloured	1·60	1·00

14a Posthorn on Map of Africa

1962. African Postal Union Commemoration.

51	**14a**	25f. green and brown	45	25
52	**14a**	85f. orange and green	1·20	55

15 Sansanding Dam

1962

53	**15**	25f. black, green and blue	45	25
54	-	45f. multicoloured	1·60	70

Design: Horiz—45f. Cotton plant.

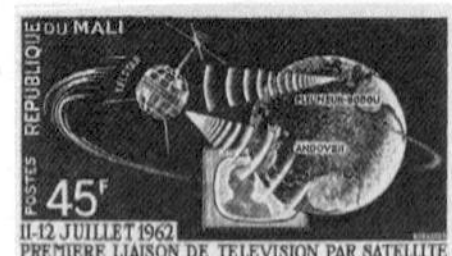

16 *Telstar* Satellite, Globe and Television Receiver

1962. First Trans-Atlantic Telecommunications Satellite Link.

55	**16**	45f. brown, violet and lake	1·10	70
56	**16**	55f. violet, olive and green	1·20	80

17 Soldier and Family

1962. Mali–Algerian Solidarity.

57	**17**	25f.+5f. multicoloured	65	55

18 Bull's Head, Laboratory Equipment and Chicks

1963. Zoological Research Centre, Sobuta.

58	**18**	25f. turq & brn (postage)	55	40
59	-	200f. turquoise, purple and bistre (air)	4·50	2·00

Design: 200f. As T **18** but horiz, 47×27 mm.

19 Tractor and Campaign Emblem

1963. Freedom from Hunger.

60	**19**	25f. purple, black and blue	60	25
61	**19**	45f. brown, green & turq	1·10	50

20 Balloon and WMO Emblem

1963. Atmospheric Research.

62	**20**	25f. multicoloured	45	25
63	**20**	45f. multicoloured	80	50
64	**20**	60f. multicoloured	1·20	65

21 Race Winners

1963. Youth Week. Multicoloured.

65	5f. Type **21**	10	10
66	10f. Type **21**	20	25
67	20f. Acrobatic dance (horiz)	65	35
68	85f. Football (horiz)	1·50	70

22 Centenary Emblem and Globe

1963. Red Cross Centenary. Inscr in black.

69	**22**	5f. multicoloured	25	15
70	**22**	10f. red, yellow and grey	40	30
71	**22**	85f. red, yellow and grey	1·90	1·00

23 Stretcher case entering Aero 145 Ambulance Aeroplane

1963. Air.

72	**23**	25f. brown, blue and green	45	25
73	-	55f. blue, ochre and brown	1·20	55
74	-	100f. blue, brown and green	2·10	95

Designs: 55f. Douglas DC-3 airliner on tarmac; 100f. Illyushin Il-18 airliner taking off.

24 South African Crowned Crane standing on Giant Tortoise

1963. Air. Fauna Protection.

75	**24**	25f. brown, red and orange	1·30	70
76	**24**	200f. multicoloured	6·25	2·75

25 UN Emblem, Doves and Banner

1963. Air. 15th Anniversary of Declaration of Human Rights.

77	**25**	50f. yellow, red and green	1·20	60

26 *Kaempferia aethiopica*

1963. Tropical Flora. Multicoloured.

78	30f. Type **26**	55	25
79	70f. *Bombax costatum*	1·70	80
80	100f. *Adenium honghel*	3·75	95

27 Pharaoh and Cleopatra, Philae

1964. Air. Nubian Monuments Preservation.

81	**27**	25f. brown and purple	85	35
82	**27**	55f. olive and purple	1·70	80

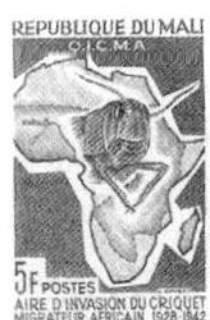

28 Locust on Map of Africa

1964. Anti-locust Campaign.

83	**28**	5f. brown, green and purple	45	20
84	-	10f. brown, green and olive	80	30
85	-	20f. brown, green and bistre	1·50	55

Designs: Vert—10f. Locust and map. Horiz—20f. Air-spraying, locust and village.

29 Football

1964. Olympic Games, Tokyo.

86	**29**	5f. purple, green and red	10	10
87	-	10f. brown, blue and sepia	35	25
88	-	15f. red and violet	55	40
89	-	85f. green, brown and violet	2·30	1·50
MS89a		190×100 mm. Nos. 86/89	5·00	5·00

Designs: Vert—10f. Boxing; 15f. Running and Olympic Flame. Horiz—85f. Hurdling. Each design has a stadium in the background.

30 Solar Flares

1964. International Quiet Sun Years.

90	**30**	45f. olive, red and blue	1·00	55

31 President Kennedy

1964. Air. First Death Anniversary of President Kennedy.

91	**31**	100f. multicoloured	2·40	1·60
MS91a		120×90 mm. No. 91 in block of four	9·00	8·50

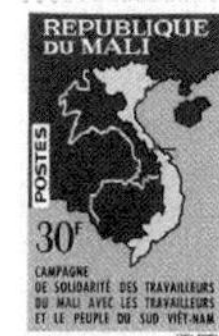

32 Map of Vietnam

1964. Mali–South Vietnam Workers' Solidarity Campaign.

92	**32**	30f. multicoloured	65	30

33 Greater Turacos ('Touraco')

1965. Air. Birds.

93	**33**	100f. green, blue and red	2·40	90
94	-	200f. black, red and blue	8·25	2·10
95	-	300f. black, ochre and green	12·00	3·25
96	-	500f. red, brown and green	21·00	6·25

Birds: Vert—200f. Abyssinian ground hornbills; 300f. Egyptian vultures. Horiz—500f. Goliath herons.

34 ICY Emblem and UN Headquarters

1965. Air. International Co-operation Year.

97	**34**	55f. ochre, purple and blue	1·10	55

35 African Buffalo

1965. Animals.

98	-	1f. brown, blue and green	10	10
99	**35**	5f. brown, orange and green	30	25
100	-	10f. brown, mauve & green	50	25
101	-	30f. brown, green and red	1·00	45
102	-	90f. brown, grey and green	2·75	1·10

Animals: Vert—1f. Waterbuck; 10f. Scimitar oryx; 90f. Giraffe. Horiz—30f. Leopard.

36 Abraham Lincoln

1965. Death Centenary of Abraham Lincoln.

103	**36**	45f. multicoloured	95	65
104	**36**	55f. multicoloured	1·30	90

37 Hughes' Telegraph

1965. Centenary of ITU.

105	-	20f. black, blue and orange	45	25
106	**37**	30f. green, brown & orange	65	50
107	-	50f. green, brown & orange	1·30	75

Designs: Vert—20f. Denis's pneumatic tube; 50f. Lescurre's heliograph.

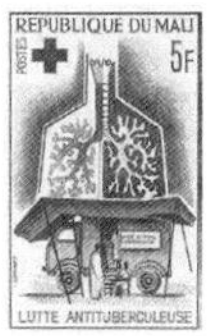

38 'Lungs' and Mobile X-Ray Unit (Anti-TB)

1965. Mali Health Service.

108	**38**	5f. violet, red and crimson	10	10
109	-	10f. green, bistre and red	45	10
110	-	25f. green and brown	65	35
111	-	45f. green and brown	1·40	75

Designs: 10f. Mother and children (Maternal and Child Care); 25f. Examining patient (Marchoux Institute); 45f. Nurse (Biological Laboratory).

39 Diving

1965. First African Games, Brazzaville, Congo.

112	**39**	5f. red, brown and blue	30	10
113	-	15f. turquoise, brown and red (Judo)	75	50

40 Pope John XXIII

1965. Air. Pope John Commemoration.

114	**40**	100f. multicoloured	2·30	1·40

41 Sir Winston Churchill

1965. Air. Churchill Commemoration.

115	**41**	100f. blue and brown	2·30	1·40

42 Dr. Schweitzer and Young African

1965. Air. Dr. Albert Schweitzer Commemoration.

116	**42**	100f. multicoloured	2·75	1·50
MS116a		160×140 mm. No. 116 in block of four	10·50	9·50

43 Leonov

1966. International Astronautic Conference, Athens (1965). Multicoloured.

117	100f. Type **43**	2·00	1·10
118	100f. White	2·00	1·10
119	300f. Cooper, Conrad, Leonov and Beliaiev (vert)	5·25	2·75

44 Vase, Quill and Cornet

1966. World Festival of Arts, Dakar, Cameroun.

120	**44**	30f. black, red and ochre	45	25
121	-	55f. red, black and green	95	50
122	-	90f. brown, orange and blue	1·80	75

Designs: 55f. Mask, brushes and palette, microphones; 90f. Dancers, mask and patterned cloth.

45 WHO Building

1966. Inauguration of WHO Headquarters, Geneva.

123	**45**	30f. green, blue and yellow	60	30
124	**45**	45f. red, blue and yellow	85	50

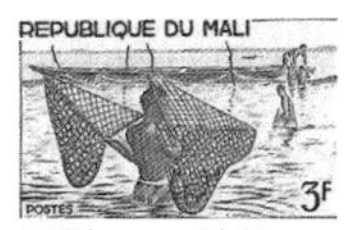

46 Fisherman with Net

1966. River Fishing.

125	**46**	3f. brown and blue	10	10
126	-	4f. purple, blue and brown	30	10
127	-	20f. purple, green and blue	50	20
128	**46**	25f. purple, blue and green	65	30
129	-	60f. purple, lake and green	1·20	50
130	-	85f. plum, green and blue	1·80	80

Designs: 4f., 60f. Collective shore fishing; 20f., 85f. Fishing pirogue.

47 Papal Arms, UN and Peace Emblems

1966. Air. Pope Paul's Visit to UN.

131	**47**	200f. blue, green & turq	3·25	1·80

48 Initiation Ceremony

1966. Mali Pioneers. Multicoloured.

132	5f. Type **48**	30	10
133	25f. Pioneers dancing	80	35

49 People and UNESCO Emblem

1966. Air. 20th Anniversary of UNESCO.

134	**49**	100f. red, green and blue	2·30	1·20

50 Footballers, Globe, Cup and Football

1966. Air. World Cup Football Championship, England.

135	**50**	100f. multicoloured	2·40	1·30

51 Cancer (The Crab)

1966. Air. Ninth International Cancer Congress, Tokyo.

136	**51**	100f. multicoloured	2·00	90

52 UNICEF Emblem and Children

1966. 20th Anniversary of UNICEF.

137	**52**	45f. blue, purple and brown	1·00	55

53 Inoculating Cattle

1967. Campaign for Preventing Cattle Plague.

138	**53**	10f. multicoloured	45	10
139	**53**	30f. multicoloured	95	40

54 Desert Vehicles in Pass

1967. Air. Crossing of the Hoggar (1924).

140	**54**	200f. green, brown & violet	6·50	3·25

55 Diamant Rocket and Francesco de Lana-Terzis's *Aerial Ship*

1967. Air. French Space Rockets and Satellites.

141	**55**	50f. blue, turquoise & pur	95	45
142	-	100f. lake, purple & turq	2·00	80
143	-	200f. purple, olive and blue	3·50	1·60

Designs: 100f. Satellite *A 1* and Jules Verne's 'rocket'; 200f. Satellite *D 1* and Da Vinci's 'bird-powered' flying machine.

56 Ancient City

1967. International Tourist Year.

144	**56**	25f. orange, blue and violet	60	30

57 Amelia Earhart and Mail Route-map

1967. Air. 30th Anniversary of Amelia Earhart's Flight, via Gao.

145	**57**	500f. multicoloured	11·00	4·75

58 *The Bird Cage*

1967. Air. Picasso Commemoration. Designs showing paintings. Multicoloured.

146	50f. Type **58**	1·30	60
147	100f. *Paul as Harlequin*	2·75	1·10
148	250f. *The Pipes of Pan*	5·50	2·50

See also Nos. 158/159 and 164/167.

59 Scout Emblems and Rope Knots

1967. Air. World Scout Jamboree, Idaho.

149	**59**	70f. red and green	1·20	40
150	-	100f. black, lake and green	1·80	55

Design: 100f. Scout with walkie-talkie radio.

60 *Chelorrhina polyphemus*

1967. Insects.

151	**60**	5f. green, brown and blue	75	30
152	-	15f. purple, brown & green	1·20	50
153	-	50f. red, brown and green	3·00	1·10

Insects: Horiz—15f. *Ugada grandicollis*; 50f. *Phymateus cinctus*.

61 School Class

1967. International Literacy Day.

154	**61**	50f. black, red and green	1·00	35

62 Europafrique

1967. Europafrique.

155	**62**	45f. multicoloured	1·10	50

63 Lions Emblem and Crocodile

1967. 50th Anniversary of Lions International.

156	**63**	90f. multicoloured	1·70	1·00

64 Water Resources

1967. International Hydrological Decade.

157	**64**	25f. black, blue and bistre	65	25

1967. Air. Toulouse-Lautrec Commemoration. Paintings as T **58**. Multicoloured.

158	100f. *Gazelle* (horse's head) (horiz)	3·00	1·60
159	300f. *Gig drawn by Cob* (vert)	7·50	3·25

65 Block of Flats, Grenoble

1968. Air. Winter Olympic Games, Grenoble.

160	**65**	50f. brown, green and blue	95	55
161	-	150f. brown, blue and ultramarine	2·30	1·10

Design: 150f. Bobsleigh course, Huez mountain.

66 WHO Emblem

1968. 20th Anniversary of WHO.

162	**66**	90f. blue, lake and green	1·30	60

67 Human Figures and Entwined Hearts

1968. World Twin Towns Day.

163	**67**	50f. red, violet and green	85	35

1968. Air. Flower Paintings. As T **58**. Multicoloured.

164	50f. *Roses and Anemones* (Van Gogh)	85	30
165	150f. *Vase of Flowers* (Manet)	2·30	75
166	300f. *Bouquet of Flowers* (Delacroix)	4·50	1·50
167	500f. *Marguerites* (Millet)	7·25	2·50

Sizes: 50f., 300f. 40×41½ mm; 150f. 36×47½ mm; 500f. 50×36 mm.

68 Dr. Martin Luther King

1968. Air. Martin Luther King Commemoration.

168	**68**	100f. black, pink and purple	1·30	65

69 Draisienne Bicycle, 1809

1968. Veteran Bicycles and Motor Cars.

169	**69**	2f. brown, mauve and green (postage)	45	15
170	-	5f. red, blue and bistre	80	40
171	-	10f. blue, brown and green	1·30	55
172	-	45f. black, green and brown	2·20	90
173	-	50f. red, green & brn (air)	1·50	45
174	-	100f. blue, mauve and bistre	3·00	90

Designs: Horiz—5f. De Dion-Bouton, 1894; 45f. Panhard-Levassor, 1914; 100f. Mercedes-Benz, 1927. Vert—10f. Michaux Bicycle, 1861; 50f. 'Bicyclette, 1918'.

70 Books, Graph and ADBA Emblem

1968. Tenth Anniversary of International African Libraries and Archives Development Association.

175	**70**	100f. red, black and brown	1·10	45

71 Football

1968. Air. Olympic Games, Mexico. Multicoloured.

176	100f. Type **71**	1·60	75
177	150f. Long-jumping (vert)	2·75	1·10

1968. Air. Philexafrique Stamp Exhibition, Abidjan, Ivory Coast, 1969 (1st issue). As T **74a** of Ivory Coast. Multicoloured.

178	200f. *The Editors* (F. M. Granet)	3·50	2·30

1969. Air. Philexafrique Stamp Exhibition, Abidjan, Ivory Coast (2nd issue). As T **74b** of Ivory Coast.

179	100f. purple, red and violet	2·20	2·10

Design: 100f. Carved animal and French Sudan stamp of 1931.

72 *Napoleon Bonaparte, First Consul* (Gros)

1969. Air. Birth Bicentenary of Napoleon Bonaparte. Multicoloured.

180	150f. Type **72**	4·00	1·60
181	200f. *The Bivouac–Battle of Austerlitz* (Lejeune) (horiz)	6·25	2·40

73 Montgolfier Balloon

1969. Air. Aviation History. Multicoloured.

No.	Type	Description	Mint	Used
182		50f. Type **73**	85	30
183		150f. Ferdinand Ferber's Glider No. 5	2·50	75
184		300f. Concorde	5·50	1·90

74 African Tourist Emblem

1969. African Tourist Year.

No.	Type	Description	Mint	Used
185	**74**	50f. red, green and blue	65	25

75 OIT and ILO Emblem

1969. 50th Anniversary of ILO.

No.	Type	Description	Mint	Used
186	**75**	50f. violet, blue and green	50	25
187	**75**	60f. slate, red and brown	75	40

76 Panhard of 1897 and Model 24-CT

1969. French Motor Industry.

No.	Type	Description	Mint	Used
188	**76**	25f. lake, black and bistre (postage)	1·00	45
189	-	30f. green and black	1·30	45
190	-	55f. red, black and purple (air)	1·40	35
191	-	90f. blue, black and red	2·10	55

Designs: 30f. Citroen of 1923 and Model DS-21; 55f. Renault of 1898 and Model 16; 90f. Peugeot of 1893 and Model 404.

77 Clarke (Australia), 10,000 m (1965)

1969. Air. World Athletics Records.

No.	Type	Description	Mint	Used
192	**77**	60f. brown and blue	45	40
193	-	90f. brown and red	75	45
194	-	120f. brown and green	1·00	65
195	-	140f. brown and slate	1·20	70
196	-	150f. black and red	1·40	75

Designs: 90f. Lusis (Russia), Javelin (1968); 120f. Miyake (Japan), Weightlifting (1967); 140f. Matson (USA), Shot-putting (1968); 150f. Keino (Kenya), 3,000 m (1965).

78 Hollow Blocks

1969. International Toy Fair, Nuremberg.

No.	Type	Description	Mint	Used
197	**78**	5f. red, yellow and grey	10	10
198	-	10f. multicoloured	30	10
199	-	15f. green, red and pink	35	20
200	-	20f. orange, blue and red	45	30

Designs: 10f. Toy donkey on wheels; 15f. 'Ducks'; 20f. Model car and race-track.

79 *Apollo 8*, Earth and Moon

1969. Air. Moon Flight of *Apollo 8*.

No.	Type	Description	Mint	Used
201	**79**	2,000f. gold	26·00	26·00

This stamp is embossed on gold foil.

1969. Air. First Man on the Moon. Nos. 182/184 optd **L'HOMME SUR LA LUNE JUILLET 1969** and **Apollo 11**.

No.	Type	Description	Mint	Used
202		50f. multicoloured	95	80
203		150f. multicoloured	3·00	1·80
204		300f. multicoloured	4·50	3·25

81 Sheep

1969. Domestic Animals.

No.	Type	Description	Mint	Used
205	**81**	1f. olive, brown and green	25	10
206	-	2f. brown, grey and red	25	10
207	-	10f. olive, brown and blue	45	20
208	-	35f. slate and red	1·50	60
209	-	90f. brown and blue	2·40	90

Animals: 2f. Goat; 10f. Donkey; 35f. Horse; 90f. Dromedary.

1969. Fifth Anniversary of African Development Bank. As T **122a** of Mauritania.

No.	Type	Description	Mint	Used
210		50f. brown, green and purple	45	25
211		90f. orange, green and brown	70	35

83 *Mona Lisa* (Leonardo da Vinci)

1969. Air. 450th Death Anniversary of Leonardo da Vinci.

No.	Type	Description	Mint	Used
212	**83**	500f. multicoloured	8·50	4·50

84 Vaccination

1969. Campaign against Smallpox and Measles.

No.	Type	Description	Mint	Used
213	**84**	50f. slate, brown and green	85	35

85 Mahatma Gandhi

1969. Air. Birth Centenary of Mahatma Gandhi.

No.	Type	Description	Mint	Used
214	**85**	150f. brown and green	2·40	90

1969. Tenth Anniversary of Aerial Navigation Security Agency for Africa and Madagascar (ASECNA). As T **94a** of Niger.

No.	Type	Description	Mint	Used
215		100f. green	1·00	50

87 West African Map and Posthorns

1970. Air. 11th Anniversary of West African Postal Union (CAPTEAO).

No.	Type	Description	Mint	Used
216	**87**	100f. multicoloured	1·00	50

1970. Air. Religious Paintings. As T **83**. Multicoloured.

No.	Type	Description	Mint	Used
217		100f. *Virgin and Child* (Van der Weydan School)	1·00	50
218		150f. *The Nativity* (The Master of Flamalle)	1·60	1·00
219		250f. *Virgin, Child and St John the Baptist* (Low Countries School)	3·75	1·90

89 Franklin D. Roosevelt

1970. Air. 25th Death Anniversary of Franklin D. Roosevelt.

No.	Type	Description	Mint	Used
220	**89**	500f. black, red and blue	5·00	3·00

90 Women of Mali and Japan

1970. EXPO 70 World Fair, Osaka, Japan.

No.	Type	Description	Mint	Used
221	**90**	100f. orange, brown & blue	95	40
222	-	150f. red, green and yellow	1·30	55

Design: 150f. Flags and maps of Mali and Japan.

91 Lenin

1970. Air. Birth Centenary of Lenin.

No.	Type	Description	Mint	Used
223	**91**	300f. black, green and flesh	4·50	1·70

92 Verne and Moon Rockets

1970. Air. Jules Verne 'Prophet of Space Travel'. Multicoloured.

No.	Type	Description	Mint	Used
224		50f. Type **92**	1·00	45
225		150f. Moon orbit	2·20	90
226		300f. Splashdown	4·00	1·90

93 ITU Emblem and Map

1970. World Telecommunications Day.

No.	Type	Description	Mint	Used
227	**93**	90f. red, brown and sepia	1·00	40

1970. New UPU Headquarters Building, Berne. As T **87a** of Ivory Coast.

No.	Type	Description	Mint	Used
228		50f. brown, green and red	45	25
229		60f. brown, blue and mauve	65	2·00

1970. Air. Space Flight of *Apollo 13*. Nos. 224/226 optd **APOLLO XIII EPOPEE SPATIALE 11-17 AVRIL 1970** in three lines.

No.	Type	Description	Mint	Used
230		50f. multicoloured	50	30
231		150f. multicoloured	1·60	85
232		300f. multicoloured	3·25	1·80

96 *Intelstat 3* Satellite

1970. Air. Space Telecommunications.

No.	Type	Description	Mint	Used
233	**96**	100f. indigo, blue & orange	95	50
234	-	200f. purple, grey and blue	1·80	70
235	-	300f. brown, orange & slate	3·25	1·60
236	-	500f. brown, blue & indigo	5·00	2·30

Designs: 200f. *Molnya I* satellite; 300f. Dish aerial, Type PB 2; 500f. *Symphony Project* satellite.

97 Auguste and Louis Lumiere, Jean Harlow and Marilyn Monroe

1970. Air. Lumiere Brothers (inventors of the cine camera) Commemoration.

No.	Type	Description	Mint	Used
237	**97**	250f. multicoloured	5·00	2·40

98 Footballers

1970. Air. World Cup Football Championship, Mexico.

No.	Type	Description	Mint	Used
238	**98**	80f. green, brown and red	85	45
239	**98**	200f. red, brown and blue	2·00	70

99 Rotary Emblem, Map and Antelope

1970. Air. Rotary International.

No.	Type	Description	Mint	Used
240	**99**	200f. multicoloured	2·75	1·30

100 'Supporting United Nations'

1970. Air. 25th Anniversary of UNO.

No.	Type	Description	Mint	Used
241	**100**	100f. blue, brown & violet	1·10	60

101 Page from 11th-century Baghdad Koran

1970. Air. Ancient Muslim Art. Multicoloured.

No.	Type	Description	Mint	Used
242		50f. Type **101**	85	25
243		200f. Tree and wild Animals (Jordanian mosaic, *c.* 730)	1·80	70
244		250f. *The Scribe* (Baghdad miniature, 1287)	2·75	1·10

1970. Air. Moon Landing of *Luna 16*. Nos. 234/235 surch **LUNA 16 PREMIERS PRELEVEMENTS AUTOMATIQUES SUR LA LUNE SEPTEMBRE 1970** and new values.

No.	Type	Description	Mint	Used
245		150f. on 200f. purple, grey and blue	1·50	75
246		250f. on 300f. brown, orange and grey	2·30	1·10

103 GPO, Bamako

1970. Public Buildings.

No.	Type	Description	Mint	Used
247	**103**	30f. olive, green and brown	45	35
248	-	40f. purple, brown & green	55	35
249	-	60f. grey, green and red	75	35
250	-	80f. brown, green and grey	1·10	40

Buildings: 40f. Chamber of Commerce, Bamako; 60f. Ministry of Public Works, Bamako; 80f. Town Hall, Segou.

104 President Nasser

1970. Air. President Gamal Nasser of Egypt. Commemoration.

No.	Type	Description	Mint	Used
251	**104**	1000f. gold	12·00	12·00

105 *The Nativity* (Antwerp School 1530)

1970. Air. Christmas. Paintings. Multicoloured.

No.	Type	Description	Mint	Used
252		100f. Type **105**	1·20	55
253		250f. *Adoration of the Shepherds* (Memling)	2·75	1·20
254		300f. *Adoration of the Magi* (17th-century Flemish school)	3·50	1·70

106 Gallet Steam Locomotive, 1882

1970. Mali Railway Locomotives from the Steam Era (1st series).

No.	Type	Description	Mint	Used
255	**106**	20f. black, red and green	1·50	60
256	-	40f. black, green & brown	2·00	75
257	-	50f. black, green & brown	3·00	95
258	-	80f. black, red and green	3·75	1·30
259	-	100f. black, green & brn	5·75	1·90

Locomotives: 40f. Felou, 1882; 50f. Bechevel, 1882; 80f. Series 1100, 1930 (inscr 'Type 23'); 100f. Class 40, 1927 (incr 'Type 141' and 'vers 1930').

See also Nos. 367/70.

107 Scouts crossing Log-bridge

1970. Scouting in Mali. Multicoloured.

No.	Type	Description	Mint	Used
260		5f. Type **107**	40	10
261		30f. Bugler and scout camp (vert)	55	25
262		100f. Scouts canoeing	1·40	45

108 Bambara de San Mask

1971. Mali Masks and Ideograms. Multicoloured.

No.	Type	Description	Mint	Used
263		20f. Type **108**	30	10
264		25f. Dogon de Bandiagara mask	40	20
265		50f. Kanaga ideogram	75	30
266		80f. Bambara ideogram	1·00	35

109 General De Gaulle

1971. Air. Charles De Gaulle Commemoration. Die-stamped on gold foil.

No.	Type	Description	Mint	Used
267	**109**	2000f. gold, red and blue	75·00	70·00

110 Alfred Nobel

1971. Air. 75th Death Anniversary of Alfred Nobel (philanthropist).

No.	Type	Description	Mint	Used
268	**110**	300f. red, brown and green	3·50	1·60

111 Tennis Player (Davis Cup)

1971. Air. World Sporting Events.

No.	Type	Description	Mint	Used
269	**111**	100f. slate, purple and blue	1·70	75
270	-	150f. olive, brown & green	2·50	1·10
271	-	200f. brown, olive and blue	3·75	1·60

Designs: Horiz—150f. Steeplechase (inscr 'Derby at Epsom' but probably represents the Grand National). Vert—200f. Yacht (Americas Cup).

112 Youth, Sun and Microscope

1971. 50th Anniversary of First BCG Vaccine Innoculation.

No.	Type	Description	Mint	Used
272	**112**	100f. brown, green and red	1·50	60

113 *The Thousand and One Nights*

1971. Air. Tales of the Arabian Nights. Multicoloured.

No.	Type	Description	Mint	Used
273		120f. Type **113**	1·70	70
274		180f. *Ali Baba and the Forty Thieves*	2·30	90
275		200f. *Aladdin's Lamp*	3·25	1·10

114 Scouts, Japanese Horseman and Mt. Fuji

1971. 13th World Scout Jamboree, Asagiri, Japan.

No.	Type	Description	Mint	Used
276	**114**	80f. plum, green and blue	85	35

115 Rose between Hands

1971. 25th Anniversary of UNICEF.

No.	Type	Description	Mint	Used
277	**115**	50f. brown, red and orange	45	25
278	-	60f. blue, green and brown	65	30

Design: Vert—60f. Nurses and children.

116 Rural Costume

1971. National Costumes. Multicoloured.

No.	Type	Description	Mint	Used
279		5f. Type **116**	10	10
280		10f. Rural costume (female)	35	25
281		15f. Tuareg	40	25
282		60f. Embroidered boubou	65	30
283		80f. Women's ceremonial costume	1·00	45

117 Olympic Rings and Events

1971. Air. Olympic Games Publicity.

No.	Type	Description	Mint	Used
284	**117**	80f. blue, purple and green	85	35

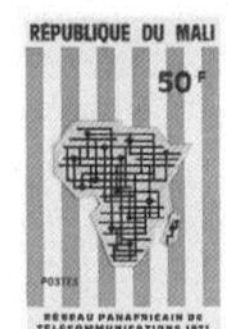

118 Telecommunications Map

1971. Pan-African Telecommunications Network Year.

No.	Type	Description	Mint	Used
285	**118**	50f. multicoloured	50	25

119 *Mariner 4* and Mars

1971. Air. Exploration of Outer Space.

No.	Type	Description	Mint	Used
286	**119**	200f. green, blue & brown	1·80	75
287	-	300f. blue, plum & purple	2·75	1·10

Design: 300f. *Venera 5* and Venus.

120 *Santa Maria* (1492)

1971. Air. Famous Ships.

No.	Type	Description	Mint	Used
288	**120**	100f. brown, violet & blue	1·20	40
289	-	150f. violet, brown & grn	1·90	80
290	-	200f. green, blue and red	2·50	90
291	-	250f. red, blue and black	3·50	1·30

Designs: 150f. *Mayflower* (1620); 200f. Battleship *Potemkin* (1905); 250f. Liner *Normandie* (1935).

121 *Hibiscus rosa-sinensis*

1971. Flowers. Multicoloured.

No.	Type	Description	Mint	Used
292		20f. Type **121**	45	20
293		50f. *Euphorbia pulcherrima*	90	25
294		60f. *Adenium obesum*	1·20	40
295		80f. *Allamanda cathartica*	1·60	55
296		100f. *Satanocrater berhautii*	2·10	65

122 Allegory of Justice

1971. 25th Anniversary of International Court of Justice, The Hague.

No.	Type	Description	Mint	Used
297	**122**	160f. chocolate, red & brn	1·30	60

123 Nat King Cole

1971. Air. Famous Musicians. Multicoloured.

No.	Type	Description	Mint	Used
298		130f. Type **123**	2·75	50
299		150f. Erroll Garner	3·25	70
300		270f. Louis Armstrong	4·50	1·00

124 Statue of Olympic Zeus (by Pheidias)

1971. Air. The Seven Wonders of the Ancient World.

No.	Type	Description	Mint	Used
301	**124**	70f. blue, brown & purple	65	25
302	-	80f. black, brown and blue	90	30
303	-	100f. blue, red and violet	1·00	35
304	-	130f. black, purple & blue	1·30	45
305	-	150f. brown, green & blue	1·60	65
306	-	270f. blue, brown & pur	2·75	90
307	-	280f. blue, purple & brn	2·75	1·10

Designs: Vert—80f. Pyramid of Cheops, Egypt; 130f. Pharos of Alexandria; 270f. Mausoleum of Halicarnassos; 280f. Colossus of Rhodes. Horiz—100f. Temple of Artemis, Ephesus; 150f. Hanging Gardens of Babylon.

125 *Family Life* (carving)

1971. 15th Anniversary of Social Security Service.

No.	Type	Description	Mint	Used
308	**125**	70f. brown, green and red	85	35

126 Slalom-skiing and Japanese Girl

1972. Air. Winter Olympic Games, Sapporo, Japan.

No.	Type	Description	Mint	Used
309	**126**	150f. brown, green & orge	1·30	65
310	-	200f. green, brown and red	1·80	85
MS311		160×100 mm. Nos. 309/10	3·75	3·50

Designs: 200f. Ice-hockey and Japanese actor.

127 *Santa Maria della Salute* (Caffi)

1972. Air. UNESCO Save Venice Campaign. Multicoloured.

No.	Type	Description	Mint	Used
312		130f. Type **127**	1·10	55
313		270f. *Rialto Bridge*	2·00	85
314		280f. *St Mark's Square* (vert)	2·40	1·00

128 Hands clasping Flagpole

1972. Air. International Scout Seminar, Cotonou, Dahomey.

315	**128**	200f. green, orange & brn	2·00	80

129 Heart and Red Cross Emblems

1972. Air. World Heart Month.

316	**129**	150f. red and blue	1·70	75

130 Football

1972. Air. Olympic Games, Munich (1st issue). Sports and Munich Buildings.

317	**130**	50f. blue, brown and green	45	25
318	-	150f. blue, brown & green	1·30	50
319	-	200f. blue, brown & green	1·60	70
320	-	300f. blue, brown & green	2·40	95
MS321		191×100 mm. Nos. 317/320	6·00	6·00

Designs: Vert—150f. Judo; 200f. Hurdling. Horiz—300f. Running.

See also Nos. 357/362.

131 *Apollo 15* and Lunar Rover

1972. Air. History of Transport Development.

322	**131**	150f. red, green and lake	1·70	75
323	-	250f. red, blue and green	4·00	1·60

Design: 250f. Montgolfier's balloon and Cugnot's steam car.

132 'UIT' on TV Screen

1972. World Telecommunications Day.

324	**132**	70f. black, blue and red	90	35

133 Clay Funerary Statue

1972. Mali Archaeology. Multicoloured.

325	30f. Type **133**	35	15
326	40f. Female Figure (wood-carving)	55	25
327	50f. Warrior (stone-painting)	75	40
328	100f. Wrought-iron ritual figures	1·40	65

134 Samuel Morse and Early Telegraph

1972. Death Centenary of Samuel Morse (inventor of telegraph).

329	**134**	80f. purple, green and red	1·40	45

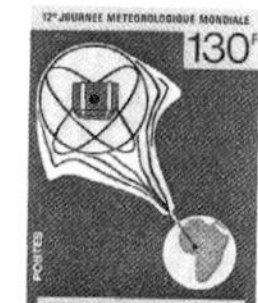

135 *Cinderella*

1972. Air. Charles Perrault's Fairy Tales.

330	**135**	70f. green, red and brown	1·40	40
331	-	80f. brown, red and green	1·50	55
332	-	150f. violet, purple & blue	2·75	80

Designs: 80f. *Puss in Boots*; 150f. *The Sleeping Beauty*.

136 Weather Balloon

1972. World Meteorological Day.

333	**136**	130f. multicoloured	1·70	75

137 Astronauts and Lunar Rover

1972. Air. Moon Flight of *Apollo 16*.

334	**137**	500f. brown, violet & grn	4·25	1·70

138 Book Year Emblem

1972. Air. International Book Year.

335	**138**	80f. gold, green and blue	1·70	70

139 Sarakole Dance, Kayes

1972. Traditional Dances. Multicoloured.

336	10f. Type **139**	45	25
337	20f. Malinke dance, Bamako	55	25
338	50f. Hunter's dance, Bougouni	75	30
339	70f. Bambara dance, Segou	95	35
340	80f. Dogon dance, Sanga	1·20	50
341	120f. Targuie dance, Timbukto	1·70	65

140 Learning the Alphabet

1972. International Literacy Day.

342	**140**	80f. black and green	85	30

141 Statue and Musical Instruments

1972. First Anthology of Mali Music.

343	**141**	100f. multicoloured	1·10	55

142 Club Banner

1972. Air. Tenth Anniversary of Bamako Rotary Club.

344	**142**	170f. purple, blue and red	1·70	75

143 Aries the Ram

1972. Signs of the Zodiac.

345	**143**	15f. brown and purple	30	25
346	-	15f. black and brown	30	25
347	-	35f. blue and red	55	25
348	-	35f. red and green	55	25
349	-	40f. brown and blue	65	30
350	-	40f. brown and purple	65	30
351	-	45f. red and blue	80	45
352	-	45f. green and red	80	45
353	-	65f. blue and violet	1·20	50
354	-	65f. brown and violet	1·20	50
355	-	90f. blue and mauve	1·70	80
356	-	90f. green and mauve	1·70	80

Designs: No. 346, Taurus the Bull; No. 347, Gemini the Twins; No. 348, Cancer the Crab; No. 349, Leo the Lion; No. 350, Virgo the Virgin; No. 351, Libra the Scales; No. 352, Scorpio the Scorpion; No. 353, Sagittarius the Archer; No. 354, Capricornus the Goat; No. 355, Aquarius the Water-carrier; No. 356, Pisces the Fish.

1972. Air. Olympic Games, Munich (2nd issue). Sports and Locations of Games since 1952. As Type **130**.

357	70f. blue, brown and red	40	25
358	90f. green, red and blue	50	25
359	140f. olive, green and brown	95	25
360	150f. brown, green and red	1·20	25
361	170f. blue, brown and purple	1·20	40
362	210f. blue, red and green	1·40	55

Designs: Vert—70f. Boxing, Helsinki Games (1952); 150f. Weightlifting, Tokyo Games (1964). Horiz—90f. Hurdling, Melbourne Games (1956); 140f. 200 metres, Rome Games (1960); 170f. Swimming, Mexico Games (1968); 210f. Throwing the javelin, Munich Games (1972).

1972. Medal Winners, Munich Olympic Games. Nos. 318/320 and 362 optd with events and names, etc.

363	150f. blue, brown and green	1·00	50
364	200f. blue, brown and green	1·50	65
365	210f. blue, red and green	1·60	70
366	300f. blue, brown and green	2·20	1·00

Overprints: 150f. **JUDO RUSKA 2 MEDAILLES D'OR**; 200f. **STEEPLE KEINO MEDAILLE D'OR**; 210f. **MEDAILLE D'OR 90m. 48**; 300f. **100m. - 200m. BORZOV 2 MEDAILLES D'OR**.

1972. Mali Locomotives (2nd series). As T **106**.

367	10f. blue, green and red	1·50	60
368	30f. blue, green and brown	3·00	1·00
369	60f. blue, brown and green	4·75	1·60
370	120f. purple, green and black	6·25	2·20

Locomotives: 10f. First Locomotive to arrive at Bamako, 1906; 30f. Steam locomotive, Thies–Bamako line, 1920; 60f. Class 40 steam locomotive, Thies–Bamako line, 1927 (inscr '141');. 120f. Alsthom series BB 100 coupled diesel, Dakar–Bamako line, 1947.

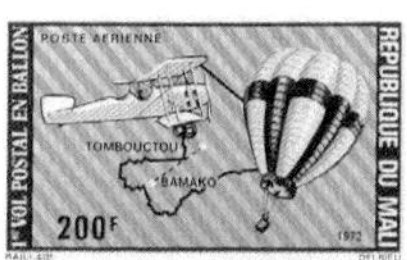

146 Emperor Haile Selassie

1972. Air. 80th Birth Anniversary of Emperor Haile Selassie.

371	**146**	70f. multicoloured	65	30

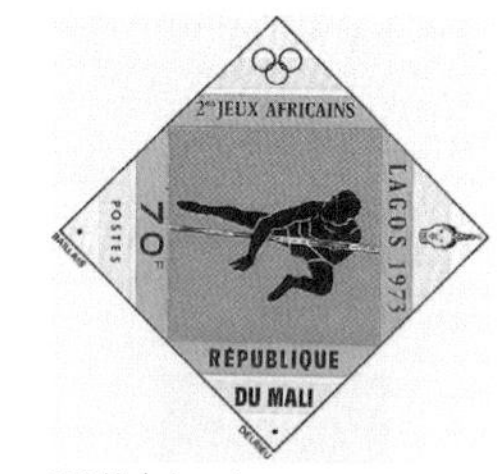

147 Balloon, Breguet 14T Biplane and Map

1972. Air. First Mali Airmail Flight by Balloon, Bamako to Timbuktu. Multicoloured.

372	200f. Type **147**	1·30	65
373	300f. Balloon, Concorde and map	2·30	95

148 High Jumping

1973. Second African Games, Lagos, Nigeria. Multicoloured.

374	70f. Type **148**	50	30
375	270f. Throwing the discus	1·60	80
376	280f. Football	2·00	1·00

149 14th-century German Bishop

1973. Air. World Chess Championship, Reykjavik, Iceland.

377	**149**	100f. lt blue, blue & brown	1·70	70
378	-	200f. red, light red & black	3·50	1·40

Design: 200f. 18th-century Indian knight (elephant).

150 Interpol Headquarters, Paris

1973. 50th Anniversary of International Criminal Police Organisation (Interpol).

379	**150**	80f. multicoloured	85	30

151 Emblem and Dove with letter

1973. Tenth Anniversary (1971) of African Postal Union.

380	**151**	70f. multicoloured	65	40

152 Fauna Protection Stamp of 1963

1973. Air. Stamp Day.

381	**152**	70f. orange, red and brown	1·70	70

153 Astronauts on Moon

1973. Moon Mission of *Apollo 17*.

382	**153**	250f. brown and blue	2·50	1·10
MS383		130×101 mm. **153** 350f. ultramarine, brown and black	2·75	2·75

154 Copernicus

1973. 500th Birth Anniversary of Copernicus.

384	**154**	300f. purple and blue	3·50	1·60

155 Disabled Africans

1973. Help the Disabled.

385	**155**	70f. orange, black and red	75	30

156 Dr. G. A. Hansen

1973. Centenary of Hansen's Identification of the Leprosy Bacillus.

386	**156**	200f. green, black and red	2·20	1·00

157 Bentley and Alfa Romeo, 1930

1973. 50th Anniversary of Le Mans 24-hour Endurance Race.

387	**157**	50f. green, orange and blue	50	1·40
388	-	100f. green, blue and red	1·00	35
389	-	200f. blue, green and red	2·50	80

Designs: 100f. Jaguar and Talbot, 1953; 200f. Matra and Porsche, 1952.

158 Scouts around Campfire

1973. International Scouting Congress, Addis Ababa and Nairobi.

390	**158**	50f. brown, red and blue	40	20
391	-	70f. brown, red and blue	55	25
392	-	80f. red, brown and green	60	30
393	-	130f. green, blue & brown	1·00	50
394	-	270f. red, violet and grey	2·00	85

Designs: Vert—70f. Scouts saluting flag; 130f. Lord Baden-Powell. Horiz—80f. Standard-bearers; 270f. Map of Africa and Scouts and Guides in ring.

159 Swimming and National Flags

1973. First Afro-American Sports Meeting, Bamako.

395	**159**	70f. green, red and blue	45	25
396	-	80f. green, red and blue	60	30
397	-	330f. blue and red	2·30	1·00

Designs: Vert—80f. Throwing the discus and javelin. Horiz—330f. Running.

1973. Pan-African Drought Relief. No. 296 surch **SECHERESSE SOLIDARITE AFRICAINE** and value.

398	200f. on 100f. multicoloured	2·00	90

161 African Mask and Old Town Hall, Brussels

1973. Air. African Fortnight, Brussels.

399	**161**	70f. violet, blue and brown	75	30

162 *Perseus* (Cellini)

1973. Air. Famous Sculptures.

400	**162**	100f. green and red	1·10	45
401	-	150f. purple and red	1·50	65
402	-	250f. green and red	2·75	95

Designs: 150f. *Pieta* (Michelangelo); 250f. *Victory of Samothrace*.

163 Stephenson's *Rocket* (1829) and French Buddicom Locomotive

1973. Air. Famous Locomotives.

403	**163**	100f. black, blue & brown	1·10	45
404	-	150f. multicoloured	1·60	75
405	-	200f. blue, slate and brown	2·40	1·00

Designs: 150f. Union Pacific steam locomotive No. 119 (1890) and Santa Fe Railroad steam locomotive *Blue Goose* (1937), USA; 200f. Mistral express (France) and Hikari express train (Japan).

164 *Apollo 11* First Landing

1973. Conquest of the Moon.

406	**164**	50f. purple, red and brown	35	25
407	-	75f. grey, blue and red	50	30
408	-	100f. slate, brown and blue	75	45
409	-	280f. blue, green and red	1·80	80
410	-	300f. blue, red and green	2·30	1·00

Designs: 75f. *Apollo 13* Recovery capsule; 100f. *Apollo 14* Lunar trolley; 280f. *Apollo 15* Lunar rover; 300f. *Apollo 17* lift off from Moon.

165 Picasso

1973. Air. Pablo Picasso (artist). Commemoration.

411	**165**	500f. multicoloured	4·75	2·30

166 President John Kennedy

1973. Air. Tenth Death Anniversary of President Kennedy.

412	**166**	500f. black, purple & gold	4·25	2·00

1973. Air. Christmas. As T **105** but dated 1973. Multicoloured.

413	100f. *The Annunciation* (V. Carpaccio) (horiz)	80	45
414	200f. *Virgin of St Simon* (F. Baroccio)	1·70	75
415	250f. *Flight into Egypt* (A. Solario)	2·10	90

167 Player and Football

1973. Air. World Football Cup Championship, West Germany.

416	**167**	150f. red, brown and green	1·20	55
417	-	250f. green, brown & violet	2·20	80

MS418	110×85 mm. 500f. multicoloured	4·50	4·50

Designs: Vert—250f. Goalkeeper and ball. Horiz—500f. Football, Arms and Church of Our Lady, Munich.

168 Cora

1973. Musical Instruments.

419	**168**	5f. brown, red and green	40	10
420	-	10f. brown and blue	45	20
421	-	15f. brown, red and yellow	55	25
422	-	20f. brown and red	65	25
423	-	25f. brown, red and yellow	75	30
424	-	30f. black and blue	95	25
425	-	35f. sepia, brown and red	95	45
426	-	40f. brown and red	1·40	50

Designs: Horiz—10f. Balafon. Vert—15f. Djembe; 20f. Guitar; 25f. N'Djarka; 30f. M'Bolon; 35f. Dozo N'Goni; 40f. N'Tamani.

169 Musicians (mosaic)

1974. Roman Frescoes and Mosaics from Pompeii.

427	**169**	150f. red, brown and grey	1·30	45
428	-	250f. brown, red & orange	1·80	65
429	-	350f. brown, orange and olive	2·50	95

Designs: Vert—250f. Alexander the Great (mosaic); 350f. Bacchante (fresco).

170 Corncob, Worker and *Kibaru* Newspaper

1974. Second Anniversary of Rural Press.

430	**170**	70f. brown and green	75	30

171 Sir Winston Churchill

1974. Air. Birth Centenary of Sir Winston Churchill.

431	**171**	500f. black	3·75	1·80

172 Chess-pieces on Board

1974. Air. 21st Chess Olympiad, Nice.

432	**172**	250f. indigo, red and blue	3·50	1·50

173 *The Crucifixion* (Alsace School *c.* 1380)

1974. Air. Easter. Multicoloured.

433	400f. Type **173**	2·50	1·30
434	500f. *The Entombment* (Titian) (horiz)	3·50	1·60

174 Lenin

1974. Air. 50th Death Anniversary of Lenin.

435	**174**	150f. purple and violet	2·30	80

175 Goalkeeper and Globe

1974. World Cup Football Championship, West Germany.

436	**175**	270f. red, green and lilac	2·00	1·10
437	-	280f. blue, brown and red	2·40	1·10

Design: 280f. World Cup emblem on football.

176 Horse-jumping Scenes

1974. Air. World Equestrian Championships, La Baule.

438	**176**	130f. brown, lilac and blue	2·00	85

177 Full-rigged Sailing Ship and Modern Liner

1974. Centenary of Universal Postal Union.

439	**177**	80f. purple, lilac & brown	45	35
440	-	90f. orange, grey and blue	70	50
441	-	270f. purple, olive & green	2·10	1·10

Designs: 90f. Breguet 14T biplane and Douglas DC-8; 270f. Steam and electric mail trains.

See also Nos. 463/464.

178 *Skylab* over Africa

1974. Air. Survey of Africa by *Skylab* Space Station.

442	**178**	200f. indigo, blue & orge	1·30	65
443	-	250f. blue, purple & orge	2·10	95

Design: 250f. Astronaut servicing cameras.

1974. Air. 11th Arab Scout Jamboree, Lebanon. Nos. 391/392 surch **130f. 11e JAMBOREE ARABE AOUT 1974 LIBAN** or **170f. CONGRES PAN-ARABE LIBAN AOUT 1974**.

444	130f. on 70f. brown, red & bl	1·40	65
445	170f. on 80f. blue, green & red	1·70	85

1974. Air. Fifth Anniversary of First Landing on Moon. Nos. 408/409 surch **130f. 1er DEBARQUEMENT SUR LA LUNE 20-VII-69** or **300f. 1er PAS SUR LA LUNE 21-VII-69.**

446	130f. on 100f. slate, brown and blue	95	55
447	300f. on 280f. blue, grn & red	2·40	1·80

1974. West Germany's Victory in World Cup Football Championship. Nos. 436/437 surch **R.F.A. 2 HOLLANDE 1** and value.

448	**175**	300f. on 270f. red, green and lilac	2·30	1·20
449	-	330f. on 280f. blue, brown and red	2·75	1·30

182 Weaver

1974. Crafts and Craftsmen. Multicoloured.

450	50f. Type **182**	45	25
451	60f. Potter	55	25
452	70f. Smith	75	30
453	80f. Wood-carver	1·00	35

183 River Niger near Gao

1974. Mali Views. Multicoloured.

454	10f. Type **183**	15	10
455	20f. *The Hand of Fatma* (rock formation, Hombori) (vert)	20	15
456	40f. Waterfall, Gouina	50	25
457	70f. Hill-dwellings, Dogon (vert)	80	35

184 Class C No. 3 (1906) and Class P (1939) Steam Locomotives, France

1974. Air. Steam Locomotives.

458	**184**	90f. indigo, red and blue	90	45
459	-	120f. brown, orange & bl	1·30	55
460	-	210f. brown, orange & bl	2·10	90
461	-	330f. black, green and blue	3·00	1·30

Designs: 120f. Baldwin (1870) and Pacific (1920) steam locomotives, USA; 210f. Class A1 (1925) and Buddicom (1847) steam locomotives; 330f. Hudson steam locomotive, 1938 (USA) and steam locomotive *Gironde*, 1839.

185 Skiing

1974. Air. 50th Anniversary of Winter Olympics.

462	**185**	300f. red, blue and green	2·30	1·10

1974. Berne Postal Convention. Centenary, Nos. 439 and 441 surch **9 OCTOBRE 1974** and value.

463	**177**	250f. on 80f. purple, lilac and brown	2·00	1·10
464	-	300f. on 270f. purple, olive and green	2·50	1·20

187 Mao Tse-tung and Great Wall of China

1974. 25th Anniversary of Chinese People's Republic.

465	**187**	100f. blue, red and green	2·20	70

188 *The Nativity* (Memling)

1974. Air. Christmas. Multicoloured.

466	290f. Type **188**	2·00	80
467	310f. *Virgin and Child* (Bourgogne School)	2·30	1·00
468	400f. *Adoration of the Magi* (Schongauer)	2·75	1·40

189 Raoul Follereau (missionary)

1974. Air. Raoul Follereau, 'Apostle of the Lepers'.

469	**189**	200f. blue	2·75	1·30
469a	**189**	200f. brown	2·75	1·30

190 Electric Train and Boeing 707

1974. Air. Europafrique.

470	**190**	100f. green, brown & blue	95	55
471	**190**	110f. blue, violet & brown	95	55

191 Dr. Schweitzer

1975. Birth Centenary of Dr Albert Schweitzer.

472	**191**	150f. turquoise, green & bl	1·60	80

192 Patients making Handicrafts and Lions International Emblem

1975. Fifth Anniversary of Samanko (Leprosy rehabilitation village). Multicoloured.

473	90f. Type **192**	85	35
474	100f. View of Samanko	1·10	40

193 *The Pilgrims at Emmaus* (Champaigne)

1975. Air. Easter. Multicoloured.

475	200f. Type **193**	1·40	55
476	300f. *The Pilgrims at Emmaus* (Veronese)	2·20	80
477	500f. *Christ in Majesty* (Limoges enamel) (vert)	4·00	1·40

194 *Journey to the Centre of the Earth*

1975. Air. 70th Death Anniversary of Jules Verne.

478	**194**	100f. green, blue & brown	75	40
479	-	170f. brown, blue & lt brn	1·10	50
480	-	190f. blue, turquoise & brn	1·30	65
481	-	220f. brown, purple & blue	1·60	75

Designs: 170f. Jules Verne and *From the Earth to the Moon*; 190f. Giant octopus from *Twenty Thousand Leagues Under the Sea*; 220f. *A Floating City*.

195 Head of *Dawn* (Tomb of the Medici)

1975. Air. 500th Birth Anniversary of Michelangelo (artist). Multicoloured.

482	400f. Type **195**	2·75	1·40
483	500f. *Moses* (marble statue, Rome)	3·50	1·60

196 Nile Pufferfish

1975. Fish (1st series).

484	**196**	60f. brown, yellow & grn	1·00	40
485	-	70f. black, brown and grey	1·30	50
486	-	80f. multicoloured	1·50	55
487	-	90f. blue, grey and green	2·00	70
488	-	110f. black and blue	3·00	80

Designs: 70f. Electric catfish; 80f. Deep-sided citharinid; 90f. Lesser tigerfish; 110f. Nile perch.

See also Nos. 544/548.

197 Astronaut

1975. Air. Soviet–US Space Co-operation.

489	**197**	290f. red, blue and black	1·20	70
490	-	300f. red, blue and black	1·50	90
491	-	370f. green, purple & black	2·00	1·10

Designs: 300f. America and Russia; 370f. New York and Moscow landmarks.

198 Einstein and Equation

1975. Air. 20th Death Anniversary of Albert Einstein.

492	**198**	90f. blue, purple & brown	1·00	50

See also Nos. 504, 507 and 519.

199 Woman with Bouquet

1975. International Women's Year.

493	**199**	150f. red and green	1·10	55

200 Morris Oxford, 1913

1975. Early Motor cars.

494	**200**	90f. violet, brown and blue	80	40
495	-	130f. red, grey and blue	1·00	40
496	-	190f. deep blue, green and blue	1·90	55
497	-	230f. brown, blue and red	1·90	70

Designs: Motor cars—130f. Franklin E, 1907; 190f. Daimler, 1900; 230f. Panhard & Levassor, 1895.

201

1975. Air. Nordjamb 75 World Scout Jamboree, Norway.

498	**201**	100f. blue, brown and lake	75	45
499	-	150f. green, brown & blue	1·00	45
500	-	290f. lake, brown and blue	2·00	95

Designs: 150f., 290f. Scouts and emblem (different).

202 Lafayette and Battle Scene

1975. Air. Bicentenary of American Revolution. Multicoloured.

501	290f. Type **202**	2·00	85
502	300f. Washington and battle scene	2·00	85
503	370f. De Grasse and Battle of the Chesapeake, 1781	2·75	1·20

1975. 20th Death Anniversary of Sir Alexander Fleming (scientist). As T **198**.
504 150f. brown, purple and blue 1·30 55

204 Olympic Rings

1975. Air. Pre-Olympic Year.
505 **204** 350f. violet and blue 2·20 95
506 - 400f. blue 2·50 1·10
Designs: 400f. Emblem of Montreal Olympics (1976).

1975. Birth Bicentenary of Andre-Marie Ampere. As T **198**.
507 90f. brown, red and violet 1·00 45

205 Tristater of Carthage

1975. Ancient Coins.
508 **205** 130f. black, blue & purple 75 35
509 - 170f. black, green & brn 1·00 55
510 - 190f. black, green and red 1·70 80
511 - 260f. black, blue & orange 2·20 1·20
Coins: 170f. Decadrachm of Syracuse; 190f. Tetradrachm of Acanthe; 260f. Didrachm of Eretrie.

1975. Air. Apollo-Soyuz Space Link. Nos. 489/91 optd ARRIMAGE 17 Juil. 1975.
512 **197** 290f. red, blue and black 2·20 80
513 - 300f. red, blue and black 2·20 80
514 - 370f. green, purple & black 2·75 1·10

207 UN Emblem and Names of Agencies forming 'ONU'

1975. 30th Anniversary of United Nations Charter.
515 **207** 200f. blue and green 1·10 60

208 *The Visitation* (Ghirlandaio)

1975. Air. Christmas. Religious Paintings.. Multicoloured.
516 290f. Type **208** 2·20 80
517 300f. *Nativity* (Fra Filippo Lippi School) 2·20 95
518 370f. *Adoration of the Magi* (Velasquez) 2·50 1·50

1975. Air. 50th Death Anniversary of Clement Ader (aviation pioneer). As T **198**.
519 100f. purple, red and blue 1·00 45

209 Concorde in Flight

1976. Air. Concorde's First Commercial Flight.
520 **209** 500f. multicoloured 4·75 2·00

210 Figure-Skating

1976. Air. Winter Olympic Games, Innsbruck. Multicoloured.
521 120f. Type **210** 75 30
522 420f. Ski-jumping 2·30 75
523 430f. Skiing (slalom) 2·50 1·00

211 Alexander Graham Bell

1976. Telephone Centenary.
524 **211** 180f. blue, brown and light brown 1·30 55

212 Chameleon

1976. Reptiles. Multicoloured.
525 20f. Type **212** 45 20
526 30f. Lizard 65 25
527 40f. Tortoise 80 35
528 90f. Python 1·90 60
529 120f. Crocodile 2·50 90

213 Nurse and Patient

1976. Air. World Health Day.
530 **213** 130f. multicoloured 85 30

214 Dr. Adenauer and Cologne Cathedral

1976. Birth Centenary Dr. Konrad Adenauer.
531 **214** 180f. purple and brown 1·30 60

215 Constructing Orbital Space Station

1976. Air. The Future in Space.
532 **215** 300f. deep blue, blue and orange 1·80 80
533 - 400f. blue, red and purple 2·75 1·10
Design: 400f. Sun and space-ship with solar batteries.

216 American Bald Eagle and Liberty Bell

1976. Air. American Revolution Bicentenary and Interphil '76 International Stamp Exhibition, Philadelphia.
534 **216** 100f. blue, purple & black 75 45
535 - 400f. brown, blue & black 2·75 90
536 - 440f. violet, green & black 2·75 1·10
Designs: Horiz—400f. Warships and American bald eagle. Vert—440f. Native Americans and American bald eagle.

217 Running

1976. Air. Olympic Games, Montreal.
537 **217** 200f. black, brown and red 1·20 45
538 - 250f. brown, green & blue 1·40 50
539 - 300f. black, blue and green 2·20 65
540 - 400f. black, blue and green 2·75 95
Designs: 250f. Swimming; 300f. Handball; 440f. Football.

218 Scouts marching

1976. Air. First All-African Scout Jamboree, Nigeria.
541 **218** 140f. brown, blue & green 95 40
542 - 180f. brown, green & grey 1·30 60
543 - 200f. violet and brown 1·50 90
Designs: Horiz—180f. Scouts tending calf. Vert—200f. Scout surveying camp at dusk.

1976. Fish (2nd series). As T **196**.
544 100f. black and blue 95 30
545 120f. yellow, brown and green 1·10 35
546 130f. turquoise, brown & black 1·30 40
547 150f. yellow, drab and green 1·40 55
548 220f. black, green and brown 2·00 70
Designs: 100f. African bonytongue; 120f. Budgett's upsidedown catfish; 130f. Double-dorsal catfish; 150f. Monod's tilapia; 220f. Big-scaled tetra.

220 Scenes from Children's Book

1976. Literature for Children.
549 **220** 130f. grey, green and red 90 45

221 'Roi de L'Air'

1976. First Issue of *L'Essor* Newspaper.
550 **221** 120f. multicoloured 1·60 55

222 Fall from Scaffolding

1976. 20th Anniversary of National Social Insurance.
551 **222** 120f. multicoloured 75 30

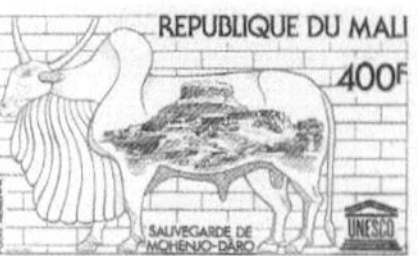

223 Moenjodaro

1976. Air. UNESCO Save Moenjodaro (Pakistan) Campaign.
552 **223** 400f. purple, blue & black 2·50 90
553 - 500f. red, yellow and blue 3·25 1·40
Design: 500f. Effigy, animals and remains.

224 Freighter, Vickers Viscount 800 and Map

1976. Air. Europafrique.
554 **224** 200f. purple and blue 1·70 80

225 Cascade of Letters

1976. 25th Anniversary of UN Postal Administration.
555 **225** 120f. orange, green & lilac 75 25

226 Moto Guzzi 254 (Italy)

1976. Motorcycling.
556 **226** 90f. red, grey and brown 75 40
557 - 120f. violet, blue and black 95 25
558 - 130f. red, grey and green 1·30 45
559 - 140f. blue, green and grey 1·30 50
Designs: 120f. BMW 900 (Germany); 130f. Honda Egli (Japan); 140f. Motobecane LT3 (France).

227 *The Nativity* (Taddeo Gaddi)

1976. Air. Christmas. Religious Paintings. Multicoloured.
560 280f. Type **227** 1·80 65
561 300f. *Adoration of the Magi* (Hans Memling) 2·00 80
562 320f. *The Nativity* (Carlo Crivelli) 2·20 95

228 Muscat Fishing Boat

1976. Ships.
563 **228** 160f. purple, green & blue 80 40
564 - 180f. green, red and blue 90 45

565 - 190f. purple, blue & green 1·00 45
566 - 200f. green, red and blue 1·20 55

Designs: 180f. Cochin Chinese junk; 190f. Dunkirk lightship *Ruytingen*; 200f. Nile felucca.

229 Rocket in Flight

1976. Air. Operation Viking.
567 **229** 500f. blue, red and lake 2·75 1·60
568 - 1000f. lake, blue and deep blue 4·50 2·50
MS569 119×90 mm. 500f. deep blue, blue and brown; 1000f. violet, mauve and black 8·75 4·75

Design: 1000f. Spacecraft on Mars.

230 President Giscard d'Estaing and Sankore Mosque, Timbuktu

1977. Air. Visit of President Giscard d'Estaing of France.
570 **230** 430f. multicoloured 4·00 1·40

231 Rocket on Launch-pad, Newton and Apple

1977. Air. 250th Death Anniversary of Isaac Newton.
571 **231** 400f. purple, red and green 3·00 1·10

232 Prince Philip and Queen Elizabeth II

1977. Air. Personalities of Decolonisation. Multicoloured.
572 180f. Type **232** 1·10 50
573 200f. General De Gaulle (vert) 1·70 65
574 250f. Queen Wilhelmina of the Netherlands (vert) 1·50 70
575 300f. King Baudouin and Queen Fabiola of Belgium 1·80 85
576 480f. Crowning of Queen Elizabeth II (vert) 3·50 1·30

233 Lindbergh and *Spirit of St Louis*

1977. Air. 50th Anniversary of Lindbergh's Transatlantic Flight.
577 **233** 420f. orange and violet 2·50 1·10
578 - 430f. blue, orange & green 3·00 1·10

Design: 430f. *Spirit of St Louis* crossing the Atlantic.

234 Village Indigobird

1977. Mali Birds. Multicoloured.
579 15f. Type **234** 55 20
580 25f. Yellow-breasted barbet 90 25
581 30f. Vitelline masked weaver 1·00 30
582 40f. Carmine bee-eater 1·30 50
583 50f. Senegal parrot 1·80 65

235 Louis Braille and Hands reading Book

1977. 125th Death Anniversary of Louis Braille (inventor of Braille system of reading and writing for the blind).
584 **235** 200f. blue, red and green 1·50 65

236 Printed Circuit

1977. World Telecommunications Day.
585 **236** 120f. red and brown 60 25

236a Chateau Sassenage, Grenoble

1977. Air. Tenth Anniversary of International French Language Council.
586 **236a** 300f. multicoloured 1·70 75

237 Airship LZ-1 over Lake Constance

1977. Air. History of the Zeppelin.
587 **237** 120f. green, brown & blue 75 40
588 - 130f. deep blue, brown and blue 85 40
589 - 350f. red, blue and deep blue 2·30 85
590 - 500f. deep blue, green and blue 3·00 95

Designs: 130f. *Graf Zeppelin* over Atlantic; 350f. Burning of *Hindenburg* at Lakehurst; 500f. Count Ferdinand von Zeppelin and *Graf Zeppelin* at mooring mast.

238 *Anaz imperator*

1977. Insects. Multicoloured.
591 5f. Type **238** 45 20
592 10f. *Sphadromantis viridis* 50 20
593 20f. *Vespa tropica* 60 25
594 35f. *Melolontha melolantha* 1·10 40
595 60f. Stag beetle 1·40 45

239 Knight and Rook

1977. Chess Pieces.
596 **239** 120f. black, green & brn 1·30 50
597 - 130f. green, red and black 1·60 60
598 - 300f. green, red and blue 3·50 1·40

Designs: Vert—130f. Pawn and Bishop. Horiz—300f. King and Queen.

240 Henri Dunant

1977. Air. Nobel Peace Prize Winners. Multicoloured.
599 600f. Type **240** (founder of Red Cross) 2·30 90
600 700f. Martin Luther King 3·25 1·10

241 Ship

1977. Europafrique.
601 **241** 400f. multicoloured 2·30 1·00

242 *Horse's Head*

1977. 525th Birth Anniversary of Leonardo da Vinci.
602 **242** 200f. brown and black 1·50 70
603 - 300f. brown 2·00 80
604 - 500f. red 3·00 1·30

Designs: 300f. *Head of Young Girl*; 500f. Self-portrait.

243 Footballers

1977. Air. Football Cup Elimination Rounds.
605 180f. brown, green & orge 65 45
606 **243** 200f. brown, green & orge 95 45
607 - 420f. grey, green and lilac 2·00 1·00

Designs: Horiz—180f. Two footballers; 420f. Tackling.

244 Friendship Hotel

1977. Inauguration of Friendship Hotel, Bamako.
608 **244** 120f. multicoloured 65 30

245 Dome of the Rock

1977. Palestinian Welfare.
609 **245** 120f. multicoloured 60 30
610 **245** 180f. multicoloured 1·00 45

246 Mao Tse-tung and Comatex Hall, Bamako

1977. Air. Mao Tse-tung Memorial.
611 **246** 300f. red 4·50 1·10

1977. Air. First Commercial Paris–New York Flight by Concorde. Optd **PARIS NEW - YORK 22.11.77.**
612 **209** 500f. multicoloured 12·00 7·25

248 *Adoration of the Magi* (Rubens)

1977. Air. Christmas. Details from *Adoration of the Magi* by Rubens.
613 **248** 400f. multicoloured 2·00 90
614 - 500f. multicoloured 2·50 1·10
615 - 600f. multicoloured (horiz) 3·00 1·50

249 *Hercules and the Nemean Lion*

1978. 400th Birth Anniversary of Peter Paul Rubens. Multicoloured.
616 200f. *Battle of the Amazons* (horiz) 1·00 45
617 300f. *Return from Labour in the Fields* (horiz) 1·60 70
618 500f. Type **249** 2·75 1·00

250 Schubert and Mute Swans

1978. Air. 150th Death Anniversary of Franz Schubert (composer). Multicoloured.
619 300f. Schubert and bars of music (vert) 1·60 70
620 420f. Type **250** 2·50 1·00

251 Cook and Shipboard Scene

1978. Air. 250th Birth Anniversary of Captain James Cook.
621 **251** 200f. blue, red and violet 1·50 50
622 - 300f. brown, blue & green 2·20 75

Design: 300f. Captain Cook meeting natives.

252 African and Chained Building

1978. World Anti-Apartheid Year.
623 **252** 120f. violet, brown & blue 60 25
624 - 130f. violet, blue & orange 70 30
625 - 180f. brown, pur & orge 1·10 50

Designs: 130f. Statue of Liberty and Africans walking to open door; 180f. African children and mule in fenced enclosure.

253 Players and Ball

1978. Air. World Cup Football Championship, Argentina.

626	**253**	150f. red, green and brown	1·00	45
627	-	250f. red, brown and green	1·60	65
628	-	300f. red, brown and blue	2·10	80

MS629 190×100 mm. 150f. emerald, chocolate and red; 250f. red, chocolate and emerald; 300f. blue, chocolate and red 5·25 4·00

Designs: Vert—250f. Player heading ball. Horiz—300f. Goalkeeper clearing ball over head of player.

254 *Head of Christ*

1978. Air. Easter. Works by Durer.

630	**254**	420f. green and brown	3·00	80
631	-	430f. blue and brown	3·00	80

Design: 430f. *The Resurrection*.

255 Red-cheeked Cordon-bleu

1978. Birds. Multicoloured.

632	20f. Type **255**	70	25
633	30f. Masked fire finch	90	25
634	50f. Red-billed fire finch	1·00	30
635	70f. African collared dove	1·50	50
636	80f. White-billed buffalo weaver	2·00	65

256 C-3 Trefle

1978. Air. Birth Centenary of Andre Citroen (automobile pioneer).

637	**256**	120f. brown, lake & green	1·20	25
638	-	130f. grey, orange and blue	1·40	45
639	-	180f. blue, green and red	2·00	45
640	-	200f. black, red and lake	2·30	65

Designs: 130f. B-2 Croisiere Noir track-laying vehicle, 1924; 180f. B-14 G Saloon, 1927; 200f. Model-11 front-wheel drive car, 1934.

1978. 20th Anniversary of Bamako Lions Club. Nos. 473/474 surch **XXe ANNIVERSAIRE DU LIONS CLUB DE BAMAKO 1958-1978** and value.

641	120f. on 90f. Type **192**	70	30
642	130f. on 100f. View of Samanko	1·00	30

258 Names of 1978 UPU members forming Map of the World

1978. Centenary of UPU Foundation Congress, Paris.

643	**258**	120f. green, orange & mve	80	30
644	-	130f. yellow, red and green	90	30

Design: 130f. Names of 1878 member states across globe.

259 Desert Scene

1978. Campaign against Desertification.

645	**259**	200f. multicoloured	1·30	55

260 Mahatma Gandhi

1978. 30th Anniversary of Gandhi's Assassination.

646	**260**	140f. brown, red and black	1·10	45

261 *Dermestes bromius*

1978. Insects. Multicoloured.

647	15f. Type **261**	45	20
648	25f. *Calosoma* sp.	55	20
649	90f. *Lopocerus variegatus*	1·00	40
650	120f. *Coccinella septempunctata*	1·10	40
651	140f. *Goliathus giganteus*	1·50	50

262 Dominoes

1978. Social Games.

652	**262**	100f. black, green and red	85	25
653	-	130f. red, black and blue	1·50	45

Design: 130f. Bridge hand.

263 Ostrich on Nest (Syrian Manuscript)

1978. Air. Europafrique. Multicoloured.

654	100f. Type **263**	1·90	60
655	110f. Common zebra (Mansur miniature)	1·90	60

1978. Air. World Cup Football Championship Finalists. Nos. 626/628 optd with results.

656	**253**	150f. red, green and brown	1·00	40
657	-	250f. red, brown and green	1·60	65
658	-	300f. red, brown and blue	2·10	75

MS659 190×100 mm. As Nos. 656/658 multicoloured 5·50 3·00

Overprints: 150f. **CHAMPION 1978 ARGENTINE**; 250f. **2e HOLLANDE**; 300f. **3e BRESIL 4e ITALIE**; **FINALE ARGENTINA 3 HOLLANDE 1**.

265 Coronation Coach

1978. Air. 25th Anniversary of Coronation of Queen Elizabeth II. Multicoloured.

660	500f. Type **265**	2·50	90
661	1000f. Queen Elizabeth II	5·00	1·70

266 Aristotle and African Animals

1978. 2300th Death Anniversary of Aristotle (Greek philosopher).

662	**266**	200f. brown, red and green	1·30	50

267 Douglas DC-3 and USA 1918 24c. stamp

1978. Air. History of Aviation.

663	**267**	80f. deep blue, red & blue	45	15
664	-	100f. multicoloured	55	25
665	-	120f. black, blue and red	75	25
666	-	130f. green, red and black	75	40
667	-	320f. violet, blue and red	1·70	70

Designs: 100f. Stampe and Renard SV-4 and Belgium Balloon stamp of 1932; 120f. Clement Ader's Avion III and France Concorde stamp of 1976; 130f. Junkers Ju-52/3m and Germany Biplane stamp of 1919; 320f. Mitsubishi A6M Zero-Sen and Japan Pagoda stamp of 1951.

268 *The Annunciation*

1978. Air. Christmas. Works by Durer.

668	**268**	420f. brown and black	2·00	70
669	-	430f. brown and green	2·00	80
670	-	500f. black and brown	2·50	90

Designs: 430f. *Virgin and Child*; 500f. *Adoration of the Magi*.

269 Launch of *Apollo 8* and Moon

1978. Air. Tenth Anniversary of First Manned Flight around the Moon.

671	**269**	200f. red, green and violet	1·40	50
672	-	300f. violet, green and red	2·20	75

Design: 300f. *Apollo 8* in orbit around the Moon.

270 UN and Human Rights Emblems

1978. 30th Anniversary of Declaration of Human Rights.

673	**270**	180f. red, blue and brown	1·10	35

271 Concorde and Clement Ader's *Eole*

1979. Air. Third Anniversary of First Commercial Concorde Flight. Multicoloured.

674	120f. Type **271**	75	40
675	130f. Concorde and *Wright Flyer I*	95	45
676	200f. Concorde and *Spirit of St Louis*	1·50	70

271a Ruff (bird) and Lubeck 1859 ½s. stamp

1979. Air. Philexafrique Stamp Exhibition, Libreville, Gabon (1st issue) and International Stamp Fair, Essen, West Germany. Multicoloured.

677	200f. Type **271a**	3·00	1·40
678	200f. Dromedary and Mali 1965 200f. stamp	3·00	1·40

See also Nos. 704/705.

1979. Air. Birth Centenary of Albert Einstein (physicist). No. 492 surch **1879-1979 130F**.

679	**198**	130f. on 90f. blue, purple and brown	1·30	65

273 *Christ carrying the Cross*

1979. Air. Easter. Works by Durer.

680	**273**	400f. black and turquoise	2·40	70
681	-	430f. black and red	2·75	80
682	-	480f. black and blue	3·25	1·10

Designs: 430f. *Christ on the Cross*; 480f. *The Great Lamentation*.

274 Basketball and St Basil's Cathedral, Moscow

1979. Air. Pre-Olympic Year. Multicoloured.

683	420f. Type **274**	2·30	95
684	430f. Footballer and Kremlin	2·30	95

275 African Manatee

1979. Endangered Animals. Multicoloured.

685	100f. Type **275**	85	20
686	120f. Chimpanzee	1·00	25
687	130f. Topi	1·10	30
688	180f. Gemsbok	1·50	45
689	200f. Giant eland	1·70	50

276 Child and IYC Emblem

1979. International Year of the Child.

690	**276**	120f. green, red and brown	65	25
691	-	200f. purple and green	1·20	50
692	-	300f. brown, mauve and deep brown	1·80	70

Designs: 200f. Girl and scout with birds; 300f. Children with calf.

277 Judo

1979. World Judo Championships, Paris.

693	**277**	200f. sepia, red and ochre	1·30	55

278 Wave Pattern and Human Figures

1979. World Telecommunications Day.

694	**278**	120f. multicoloured	65	20

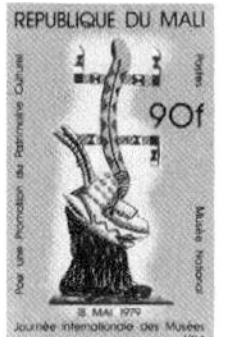

279 Goat's Head and Lizard Fetishes

1979. World Museums Day. Multicoloured.

695	90f. Type **279**	50	25
696	120f. Seated figures (wood carving)	70	30
697	130f. Two animal heads and figurine (wood carving)	90	35

280 Rowland Hill and Mali 1961 25f. stamp

1979. Death Centenary of Sir Rowland Hill.

698	**280**	120f. multicoloured	60	20
699	-	130f. red, blue and green	80	20
700	-	180f. black, green and blue	95	40
701	-	200f. black, red and purple	1·20	40
702	-	300f. blue, deep blue and red	1·90	70

Designs: 130f. Airship *Graf Zeppelin* and Saxony stamp of 1850; 180f. Concorde and France stamp of 1849; 200f. Stage coach and USA stamp of 1849; 300f. UPU emblem and Penny Black.

281 Cora Players

1979

703	**281**	200f. multicoloured	1·70	65

282 Sankore Mosque and *Adenium obesum*

1979. Philexafrique Exhibition, Libreville, Gabon (2nd issue).

704	**282**	120f. multicoloured	1·70	95
705	-	300f. red, blue and orange	3·25	1·90

Design: 300f. Horseman and satellite.

283 Map of Mali showing Conquest of Desert

1979. Operation Sahel Vert. Multicoloured.

706	200f. Type **283**	1·10	50
707	300f. Planting a tree	1·90	90

284 Lemons

1979. Fruit (1st series). Multicoloured.

708	10f. Type **284**	20	10
709	60f. Pineapple	50	15
710	100f. Papaw	75	25
711	120f. Sweet-sops	95	30
712	130f. Mangoes	1·10	35

See also Nos. 777/781.

285 Sigmund Freud

1979. 40th Death Anniversary of Sigmund Freud (psychologist).

713	**285**	300f. sepia and violet	1·70	80

286 Caillie and Camel approaching Fort

1979. 180th Birth Anniversary of Rene Caillie (explorer).

714	**286**	120f. sepia, brown & blue	85	35
715	-	130f. blue, green & brown	1·00	45

Design: 130f. Rene Caillie and map of route across Sahara.

287 *Eurema brigitta*

1979. Butterflies and Moths (1st series). Multicoloured.

716	100f. Type **287**	90	20
717	120f. *Papilio pylades*	1·10	35
718	130f. *Melanitis leda satyridae*	1·30	40
719	180f. *Gonimbrasis belina occidentalis*	1·80	60
720	200f. *Bunaea alcinoe*	1·70	65

See also Nos. 800/804.

288 Mali 1970 300f. Stamp and Modules orbiting Moon

1979. Air. Tenth Anniversary of First Moon Landing.

721	430f. Type **288**	2·20	95
722	500f. 1973 250f. stamp and rocket launch	2·50	1·20

289 Captain Cook and HMS *Resolution* off Kerguelen Islands

1979. Air. Death Bicentenary of Captain James Cook.

723	300f. Type **289**	1·70	75
724	400f. Captain Cook and HMS *Resolution* off Hawaii	2·50	1·10

290 Menaka Greyhound

1979. Dogs. Multicoloured.

725	20f. Type **290**	55	25
726	50f. Water spaniel	85	25
727	70f. Beagle	95	30
728	80f. Newfoundland	1·20	45
729	90f. Sheepdog	1·40	50

291 David Janowski

1979. Air. Chess Grand-masters.

730	**291**	100f. red and brown	80	25
731	-	140f. red, brown and blue	1·30	30
732	-	200f. blue, violet and green	1·80	50
733	-	300f. brown, ochre and red	2·75	70

Designs: 140f. Alexander Alekhine; 200f. Willi Schlage; 300f. Efim Bogoljubow.

292 *The Adoration of the Magi* 1511 (detail, Durer)

1979. Air. Christmas. Works by Durer.

734	**292**	300f. brown and orange	1·70	65
735	-	400f. brown and blue	2·30	95
736	-	500f. brown and green	3·00	1·30

Designs: 400f. *Adoration of the Magi* (1503); 500f. *Adoration of the Magi* (1511, different).

1979. Air. 20th Anniversary of ASECNA (African Air Safety Organisation). As T **198** of Malagasy but 36×27 mm.

737	120f. multicoloured	85	35

293 Globe, Rotary Emblem and Diesel-electric Train

1980. Air. 75th Anniversary of Rotary International. Multicoloured.

738	220f. Type **293**	1·40	55
739	250f. Globe, Rotary emblem and Douglas DC-10 airliner	1·60	60
740	430f. Bamako Rotary Club and emblem	2·50	10

294 African Ass

1980. Protected Animals. Multicoloured.

741	90f. Type **294**	80	25
742	120f. Addax	1·00	25
743	130f. Cheetahs	1·10	35
744	140f. Barbary sheep	1·20	45
745	180f. African buffalo	1·70	55

295 Speed Skating

1980. Air. Winter Olympic Games, Lake Placid. Multicoloured.

746	200f. Type **295**	1·00	45
747	300f. Ski jump	1·80	70
MS748	93×93 mm. As Nos. 746/747 but colours changed	3·00	2·20

296 Stephenson's *Rocket* (1829) and Mali 30f. Stamp, 1972

1980. Air. 150th Anniversary of Liverpool and Manchester Railway.

749	**296**	200f. blue, brown & green	1·20	45
750	-	300f. black, brown & turq	1·80	90

Design: 300f. *Rocket* (1829) and Mali 50f. railway stamp, 1970.

297 Horse Jumping

1980. Air. Olympic Games, Moscow.

751	**297**	200f. green, brown & blue	1·20	45
752	-	300f. blue, brown & green	1·50	70
753	-	400f. red, green & lt green	2·30	95
MS754		180×118 mm. Nos. 751/753 plus three labels	4·50	3·50

Designs: 300f. Sailing; 400f. Football.

298 Solar Pumping Station, Koni

1980. Solar Energy. Multicoloured.

755	90f. Type **298**	50	15
756	100f. Solar capture tables, Dire	60	20
757	120f. Solar energy cooker	80	25
758	130f. Solar generating station, Dire	95	30

299 Nioro Horse

1980. Horses. Multicoloured.

759	100f. Mopti	70	10
760	120f. Type **299**	85	10
761	130f. Koro	1·00	20
762	180f. Lake zone horse	1·10	45
763	200f. Banamba	1·30	70

300 *Head of Christ* (Maurice Denis)

1980. Air. Easter.

764	**300**	480f. red and brown	3·00	1·00
765	-	500f. brown and red	3·00	1·10

Design: 500f. *Christ before Pilate* (Durer).

301 Kepler and Diagram of Earth's Orbit

1980. Air. 350th Death Anniversary of J. Kepler (astronomer).

766	**301**	200f. light blue, blue & red	1·50	55
767	-	300f. mauve, violet & grn	1·80	80

Design: 300f. Kepler, Copernicus and diagram of solar system.

302 Pluto and Diagram of Orbit

1980. Air. 50th Anniversary of Discovery of Planet Pluto.

768	**302**	402f. blue, grey and mauve	2·20	90

303 *Lunokhod 1* (Tenth Anniv)

1980. Air. Space Events.

769	**303**	480f. black, red and blue	2·50	90
770	-	500f. grey, blue and red	2·50	90

Design: 500f. Apollo–Soyuz link-up.

304 Fleming and Laboratory

1980. Sir Alexander Fleming (discoverer of penicillin). Commemoration.

771	**304**	200f. green, sepia & brown	1·90	60

305 Avicenna, Medical Instruments and Herbs

1980. Birth Millenary of Avicenna (Arab physician and philosopher).

772	**305**	120f. blue, red and brown	75	30
773	-	180f. dp brn, turq & brn	1·00	50

Design: 180f. Avicenna as teacher.

306 Pilgrim at Mecca

1980. 1400th Anniversary of Hegira. Multicoloured.

774	120f. Type **306**	60	25
775	130f. Praying hands	75	25
776	180f. Pilgrims (horiz)	95	40

1980. Fruit (2nd series). As T **284**. Multicoloured.

777	90f. Guavas	60	15
778	120f. Cashews	75	15
779	130f. Oranges	90	25
780	140f. Bananas	1·00	25
781	180f. Grapefruit	1·20	40

307 Rochambeau and French Fleet at Rhode Island, 1780

1980. Air. French Support for American Independence.

782	**307**	420f. brown, turq & red	2·30	1·00
783	-	430f. black, blue and red	2·75	1·10

Design: 430f. Rochambeau, Washington and Eagle.

308 Dove and UN Emblem

1980. 60th Anniversary of League of Nations.

784	**308**	200f. blue, red and violet	95	45

309 Scene from *Around the World in 80 Days*

1980. Air. 75th Death Anniversary of Jules Verne (writer).

785	**309**	100f. red, green and brown	95	30
786	-	100f. brown, chestnut and turquoise	95	30
787	-	150f. green, brn & dp brn	1·30	45
788	-	150f. blue, violet & dp bl	1·30	45

Designs: No. 786, Concorde; No. 787, *From the Earth to the Moon*; No. 788, Astronaut on Moon.

310 Xylophone, Mask and Emblem

1980. Sixth Arts and Cultural Festival, Bamako.

789	**310**	120f. multicoloured	75	30

311 Map of Africa and Asia

1980. 25th Anniversary of Afro-Asian Bandung Conference.

790	**311**	300f. green, red and blue	1·40	60

1980. Air. Olympic Medal Winners. Nos. 751/753 optd.

791	200f. green, brown and blue	1·20	70
792	300f. blue, brown and green	1·50	90
793	400f. red, green and light green	2·30	1·10
MS794	180×118 mm. Nos. 791/793 plus three labels	5·25	5·25

Overprints: 200f. **CONCOURS COMPLET INDIVIDUEL ROMAN (It.) BLINOV (Urss) SALNIKOV (Urss)**; 300f. **FINN RECHARDT (Fin.) MAYRHOFER (Autr.) BALACHOV (Urss)**; 400f. **TCHECOSLOVAQUIE ALLEMAGNE DE L'EST URSS**.

313 Conference Emblem

1980. World Tourism Conference, Manila. Multicoloured.

795	120f. Type **313**	60	25
796	180f. Encampment outside fort and Conference emblem	1·00	45

314 Dam and Rural Scene

1980. 20th Anniversary of Independence. Multicoloured.

797	100f. Type **314**	55	25
798	120f. National Assembly Building	65	30
799	130f. Independence Monument (vert)	90	35

1980. Butterflies. (2nd series). As T **287** but dated 1980. Multicoloured.

800	50f. *Uterheisa pulchella* (postage)	75	25
801	60f. *Mylothis chloris pieridae*	85	25
802	70f. *Hypolimnas mishippus*	1·10	30
803	80f. *Papilio demodocus*	95	35
804	420f. *Denaus chrysippus* (48×36 mm) (air)	2·30	75

315 Pistol firing Cigarette and Target over Lungs

1980. Anti-smoking Campaign.

805	**315**	200f. multicoloured	1·10	60

316 Electric Train, Boeing 737 and Globe

1980. Europafrique.

806	**316**	300f. multicoloured	2·00	80

317 Map of West Africa and Agricultural Symbols

1980. Fifth Anniversary of West African Economic Council. Multicoloured.

807	100f. Type **317**	55	20
808	120f. "Transport"	60	25
809	130f. "Industry"	75	30
810	140f. "Energy"	80	35

318 General de Gaulle and Map of France

1980. Air. Tenth Death Anniversary of General Charles de Gaulle. Multicoloured.

811	420f. Type **318**	3·75	1·30
812	430f. De Gaulle and Cross of Lorraine	3·75	1·30

319 Hikari Express Train (Japan) and Mali 1972 10f. Stamp

1980. Air. Locomotives.

813	**319**	120f. blue, green and red	80	25
814	-	130f. green, blue and red	85	30
815	-	200f. orange, black & grn	1·30	50
816	-	480f. black, red and green	3·50	1·20

Designs: Horiz—130f. RTG train, USA and 20f. locomotive stamp of 1970; 200f. Rembrandt express, Germany, and 100f. locomotive stamp of 1970. Vert—480f. TGV 001 turbotrain, France, and 80f. locomotive stamp of 1970.

320 *Flight into Egypt* (Rembrandt)

1980. Air. Christmas. Multicoloured.

817	300f. *St Joseph showing the infant Jesus to St Catherine* (Lorenzo Lotto) (horiz)	1·60	70
818	400f. Type **320**	2·20	1·00
819	500f. *Christmas Night* (Gauguin) (horiz)	2·75	1·20

1980. Fifth Anniversary of African Posts and Telecommunications Union. As T **292** of Niger.

820	130f. multicoloured	85	35

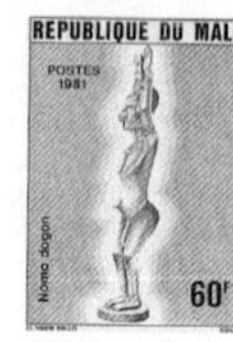

321 Nomo Dogon

1981. Statuettes. Multicoloured.

821	60f. Type **321**	35	10
822	70f. Senoufo fertility symbol	45	15
823	90f. Bamanan fertility statuette	60	20
824	100f. Senoufo captives snuff-box	65	30
825	120f. Dogon fertility statuette	90	35

322 *Self-portrait* (Blue Period)

1981. Birth Bicentenary of Pablo Picasso (artist).

826	**322**	1000f. multicoloured	6·50	2·40

323 Mambie Sidibe

1981. Mali Thinkers and Savants.

827	**323**	120f. brown, buff and red	65	30
828	-	130f. brown, buff & black	70	30

Design: 130f. Amadou Hampate Ba.

324 Mosque and Kaaba

1981. 1400th Anniversary of Hejira.

829	**324**	120f. multicoloured	60	25
830	**324**	180f. multicoloured	1·10	45

325 Tackle

1981. Air. World Cup Football Championship Eliminators. Multicoloured.

831	100f. Type **325**	75	30
832	200f. Heading the ball	1·20	50
833	300f. Running for ball	1·80	70
MS834	90×101 mm. 600f. Goalkeeper reaching for ball	3·75	2·40

326 Kaarta Zebu

1981. Cattle. Multicoloured.

835	20f. Type **326**	45	10
836	30f. Peul du Macina sebu	50	15
837	40f. Maure zebu	65	20
838	80f. Touareg zebu	1·10	35
839	100f. N'Dama cow	1·10	40

327 Crinum de Moore (*Crinum moorei*)

1981. Flowers. Multicoloured.

840	50f. Type **327**	35	10
841	100f. Double rose hibiscus (*Hibiscus rosa-sinensis*)	65	15
842	120f. Pervenche (*Catharanthus roseus*)	85	30
843	130f. Frangipani (*Plumeria rubra*)	1·00	35
844	180f. Orgueil de Chine (*Caesalpinia pulcherrima*)	1·50	55

328 Mozart and Musical Instruments

1981. Air. 225th Birth Anniversary of Mozart. Multicoloured.

845	420f. Type **328**	2·40	1·10
846	430f. Mozart and musical instruments (different)	2·40	1·10

329 *The Fall on the Way to Calvary* (Raphael)

1981. Air. Easter.

847	500f. Type **329**	2·40	1·10
848	600f. *Ecce Homo* (Rembrandt)	3·25	1·60

330 Yuri Gagarin

1981. Air. Space Anniversaries and Events.

849	**330**	200f. blue, black and red	1·00	45
850	-	200f. blue, black & lt blue	1·00	45
851	-	380f. multicoloured	1·90	70
852	-	430f. violet, black and blue	2·30	85

Designs: VertNo. 849, T **330**: first man in space (20th anniversary); No. 850, Alan Shepard, first American in space (20th anniversary); No. 851, Saturn and moons (exploration of Saturn). Horiz—No. 852, Sir William Herschel, and diagram of Uranus (discovery bicentenary).

331 Blind and Sighted Faces

1981. International Year of Disabled People.

853	**331**	100f. light brown, brown and green	55	25
854	-	120f. violet, blue and purple	75	30

Design: 120f. Mechanical hand and human hand with spanner.

332 Caduceus (Telecommunications and Health)

1981. World Telecommunications Day.

855	**332**	130f. multicoloured	90	35

333 Pierre Curie and Instruments

1981. 75th Death Anniversary of Pierre Curie (discoverer of radioactivity).

856	**333**	180f. blue, black & orange	2·10	55

334 Scouts at Well and Dorcas Gazelle

1981. Fourth African Scouting Conference, Abidjan. Multicoloured.

857	110f. Type **334**	90	35
858	160f. Scouts signalling and patas monkey	1·30	50
859	300f. Scouts saluting and cheetah (vert)	2·40	80
MS860	120×90 mm. 500f. Lord Baden-Powell (vert)	5·75	3·50

1981. Air. World Railway Speed Record. No. 816 optd **26 fevrier 1981 Record du monde de vitesse-380 km/h.**

861	480f. black, red and blue	3·25	95

336 Columbus, Fleet and US Columbus Stamp of 1892

1981. Air. 475th Death Anniversary of Christopher Columbus.

862	**336**	180f. brown, black & blue	1·20	45
863	-	200f. green, blue & brown	1·50	55
864	-	260f. black, violet and red	1·80	70
865	-	300f. lilac, red and green	2·10	90

Designs: Vert—200f. *Nina* and 1c. Columbus stamp of Spain; 260f. *Pinta* and 5c. Columbus stamp of Spain. Horiz—300f. *Santa Maria* and US 3c. Columbus stamp.

1981. 23rd World Scouting Conference, Dakar. Nos. 857/**MS**860 optd **DAKAR 8 AOUT 1981 28e CONFERENCE MONDIALE DU SCOUTISME.**

866	**334**	110f. multicoloured	90	35
867	-	160f. multicoloured	1·20	55
868	-	300f. multicoloured	2·50	90
MS869		120×90 mm. 500f. multicoloured	5·75	3·50

338 Space Shuttle after Launching

1981. Air. Space Shuttle. Multicoloured.

870	200f. Type **338**	1·00	45
871	500f. Space Shuttle in orbit	2·75	1·10
872	600f. Space Shuttle landing	3·25	1·40
MS873	86×67 mm. 700f. Space shuttle on carrier aeroplane	4·75	2·50

339 *Harlequin on a Horse*

1981. Air. Birth Centenary of Pablo Picasso. Multicoloured.

874	600f. Type **339**	4·25	1·40
875	750f. *Child with Pigeon*	5·00	1·60

340 Prince Charles, Lady Diana Spencer and St Paul's Cathedral

1981. Air. British Royal Wedding. Multicoloured.

876	500f. Type **340**	2·50	1·00
877	700f. Prince Charles, Lady Diana Spencer and coach	3·50	1·50

342 Maure Sheep

1981. Sheep. Multicoloured.

886	10f. Type **342**	20	10
887	25f. Peul sheep	35	20
888	140f. Sahael sheep	1·00	30
889	180f. Touareg sheep	1·40	45
890	200f. Djallonke ram	1·70	50

343 Heinrich von Stephan (founder of UPU), Latecoere 28 and Concorde

1981. Universal Postal Union Day.

891	**343**	400f. red and green	2·50	90

344 Woman drinking from Bowl

1981. World Food Day.

892	**344**	200f. brown, orge & mve	1·30	50

345 *The Incarnation of the Son of God* (detail, Grunewald)

1981. Air. Christmas. Multicoloured.

893	500f. Type **345**	2·75	1·00
894	700f. *The Campori Madonna* (Correggio)	3·75	1·50

1981. Air. Second Flight of Space Shuttle. **MS**873 optd **JOE ENGLE RICHARD TRULY 2eme VOL SPATIAL**.

MS895	700f. multicoloured	5·50	3·25

347 Transport and Hands holding Map of Europe and Africa

1981. Europafrique.

896	**347**	700f. blue, brown & orge	3·50	1·30

348 Guerin, Calmette, Syringe and Bacillus

1981. 60th Anniversary of First BCG Inoculation.

897	**348**	200f. brown, violet & blk	1·40	55

1982. Air. World Chess Championship, Merano. Nos. 731 and 733 optd.

898	140f. red, brown and blue	1·30	50
899	300f. brown, ochre and red	2·50	80

Overprints: 140f. **ANATOLI KARPOV VICTOR KORTCHNOI MERANO (ITALIE) Octobre-Novembre 1981**; 300f. **Octobre-Novembre 1981 ANATOLI KARPOV Champion du Monde 1981.**

350 *Nymphaea lotus*

1982. Flowers. Multicoloured.

900	170f. Type **350**	1·00	25
901	180f. *Bombax costatum*	1·00	30
902	200f. *Parkia biglobosa*	1·30	35
903	220f. *Gloriosa simplex*	1·40	50
904	270f. *Satanocrater berhautii*	1·60	60

351 Lewis Carroll and Characters from Alice Books

1982. Air. 150th Birth Anniversary of Lewis Carroll (Revd. Charles Dodgson).
905 110f. Type **351** 1·70 65
906 130f. Characters from Alice books 1·70 85
907 140f. Characters from Alice books (different) 1·90 1·10

352 *George Washington* (Gilbert Stuart)

1982. Air. 250th Birth Anniversary of George Washington.
908 **352** 700f. multicoloured 3·50 1·50

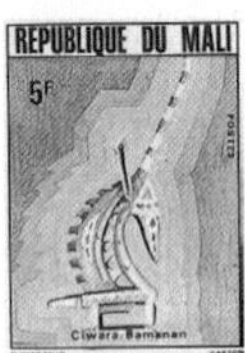

353 Ciwara Bamanan

1982. Masks. Multicoloured.
909 5f. Type **353** 15 10
910 35f. Kanga Dogon 30 10
911 180f. N Domo Bamanan 1·00 40
912 200f. Cimier (Sogoninkum Bamanan) 1·30 45
913 250f. Kpelie Senoufo 1·50 50

354 Football

1982. Air. World Cup Football Championship, Spain.
914 **354** 220f. multicoloured 1·00 45
915 - 420f. multicoloured 2·00 80
916 - 500f. multicoloured 2·40 1·00
MS917 105×85 mm. 680f. multicoloured 6·00 2·75
Designs: 420f. to 680f. Football scenes.

355 *Sputnik 1*

1982. 25th Anniversary of First Artificial Satellite.
918 **355** 270f. violet, blue and red 1·50 60

356 Lord Baden-Powell, Tent and Scout Badge

1982. Air. 125th Birth Anniversary of Lord Baden-Powell. Multicoloured.
919 300f. Type **356** 1·20 60
920 500f. Saluting scout 2·40 1·00

357 *The Transfiguration* (Fra Angelico)

1982. Air. Easter. Multicoloured.
921 680f. Type **357** 3·00 1·20
922 1000f. *Pieta* (Giovanni Bellini) 4·75 1·70

358 Doctor giving Child Oral Vaccine

1982. Anti-polio Campaign.
923 **358** 180f. multicoloured 1·00 40

359 Lions Emblem and Blind Person

1982. Lions Club Blind Day.
924 **359** 260f. orange, blue and red 1·50 35

360 'En Bon Ami' (N'Teri)

1982. Hairstyles. Multicoloured.
925 140f. Type **360** 55 25
926 150f. Tucked-in pony tail 65 25
927 160f. 'Pour l'Art' 85 40
928 180f. 'Bozo Kun' 1·30 40
929 270f. 'Fulaw Kun' 2·00 70

361 Arms Stamp of Mali and France

1982. Air. Philexfrance 82 International Stamp Exhibition, Paris. Multicoloured.
930 180f. Type **361** 1·00 30
931 200f. Dromedary caravan and 1979 Philexafrique II stamp 1·30 50

362 Fire-engine, 1850

1982. Fire-engines. Multicoloured.
932 180f. Type **362** 1·20 30
933 200f. Fire-engine, 1921 1·50 45
934 270f. Fire-engine, 1982 1·80 70

363 Gobra

1982. Zebu Cattle. Multicoloured.
935 10f. Type **363** 25 10
936 60f. Azaouak 60 15
937 110f. Maure 90 30
938 180f. Toronke 1·30 40
939 200f. Peul Sambourou 1·50 55

1982. Air. World Cup Football Championship Winners. Nos. 914/**MS**917 optd.
940 **354** 220f. multicoloured 1·20 45
941 - 420f. multicoloured 2·00 75
942 - 500f. multicoloured 2·50 1·10
MS943 105×85 mm. 680f. multicoloured 4·00 2·50
Overprints: 220f. **1 ITALIE 2 RFA 3 POLOGNE**; 420f. **POLOGNE FRANCE 3-2**; 500f. **ITALIE RFA 3-1**; 680f. **ITALIE CHAMPION 1982**.

365 *Urchin with Cherries*

1982. Air. 150th Birth Anniversary of Edouard Manet (painter).
944 **365** 680f. multicoloured 4·50 1·60

366 *Virgin and Child* (detail) (Titian)

1982. Air. Christmas. Multicoloured.
945 500f. Type **366** 2·30 1·00
946 1000f. *Virgin and Child* (Giovanni Bellini) 4·75 1·80

367 Wind-surfing

1982. Introduction of Wind-surfing as Olympic Event. Multicoloured.
947 200f. Type **367** 1·20 35
948 270f. Wind-surfer 1·50 55
949 300f. Wind-surfer (different) 1·80 70

368 Goethe

1982. Air. 150th Death Anniversary of Goethe (poet).
950 **368** 500f. brown, light brown and black 3·00 1·10

369 Valentina Tereshkova

1983. Air. 20th Anniversary of Launching of *Vostok 6*.
951 **369** 400f. multicoloured 2·00 80

370 Transatlantic Balloon *Double Eagle II*

1983. Air. Bicentenary of Manned Flight. Multicoloured.
952 500f. Type **370** 3·75 1·00
953 700f. Montgolfier balloon 4·00 1·50

371 Football

1983. Air. Olympic Games, Los Angeles. Multicoloured.
954 180f. Type **371** 95 35
955 270f. Hurdles 1·30 60
956 300f. Windsurfing 2·00 75

372 *The Transfiguration* (detail)

1983. Air. Easter. Multicoloured.
957 400f. Type **372** 2·00 90
958 600f. *The Entombment* (detail from Baglioni Retable) 3·00 1·30

373 Martin Luther King

1983. Celebrities.
959 **373** 800f. brown, blue & pur 4·00 1·40
960 - 800f. brown, red & dp red 4·00 1·40
Design: No. 960, President Kennedy.

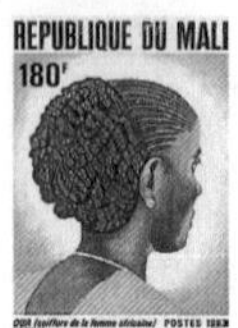

374 Oua Hairstyle

1983. Hairstyles. Multicoloured.
961 180f. Type **374** 1·10 25
962 200f. Nation (Diamani) 1·30 25
963 270f. Rond Point 1·60 40
964 300f. Naamu-Naamu 1·80 40
965 500f. Bamba-Bamba 3·25 70

375 *Family of Acrobats with Monkey*

1983. Air. Tenth Death Anniversary of Picasso.
966 **375** 680f. multicoloured 3·50 1·70

376 Lions Club Emblem and Lions

1983. Air. Lions and Rotary Clubs. Multicoloured.

967	700f. Type **376**	6·50	1·80
968	700f. Rotary Club emblem, container ship, diesel railcar and Boeing 737 airliner	6·50	1·80

377 Satellite, Antenna and Telephone

1983. World Communications Year.

969	**377**	180f. multicoloured	1·00	50

378 Lavoisier and Apparatus

1983. Bicentenary of Lavoisier's Analysis of Water.

970	**378**	300f. green, brown & blue	1·70	65

379 Banzoumana Sissoko

1983. Mali Musicians. Multicoloured.

971	200f. Type **379**	1·00	30
972	300f. Batourou Sekou Kouyate	1·60	50

380 Nicephore Niepce and Camera

1983. 150th Death Anniversary of Nicephore Niepce (pioneer of photography).

973	**380**	400f. blue, green & dp grn	2·20	70

381 Space Shuttle *Challenger*

1983. Air. Space Shuttle.

974	**381**	1000f. multicoloured	4·50	1·90

382 Young People and Map of Africa

1983. Second Pan-African Youth Festival. Multicoloured.

975	240f. Type **382**	1·30	45
976	270f. Hands reaching for map of Africa	1·40	50

383 Mercedes, 1914

1983. Air. Paris–Dakar Rally. Multicoloured.

977	240f. Type **383**	1·50	50
978	270f. Mercedes SSK, 1929	1·60	55
979	500f. Mercedes W 196, 1954	3·75	80
MS980	124×93 mm. 1000f. Modern Mercedes	8·75	80

384 Liner and UPU Emblem

1983. UPU Day.

981	**384**	240f. red, black and blue	1·30	45

385 Pawn and Bishop

1983. Air. Chess Pieces.

982	**385**	300f. grey, violet and green	2·10	50
983	-	420f. green, pink and grey	2·75	80
984	-	500f. blue, dp blue & green	3·50	1·10
MS985		119×89 mm. 700f. brown, green and black	5·50	2·40

Designs: 420f. Castle and knight; 500f. King and queen. 36×47 mm—700f. chess pieces.

386 *Canigiani Madonna*

1983. Air. Christmas. 500th Birth Anniversary of Raphael. Multicoloured.

986	700f. Type **386**	3·75	1·10
987	800f. *Madonna of the Lamb*	3·75	1·50

387 Sahara Goat

1984. Goats. Multicoloured.

988	20f. Type **387**	15	10
989	30f. Billy goat	35	10
990	50f. Billy goat (different)	50	20
991	240f. Kaarta goat	1·60	45
992	350f. Southern goat	2·30	60

388 *Leopold Zborowski* (Modigliani)

1984. Air. Birth Centenary of Modigliani (painter).

993	**388**	700f. multicoloured	5·00	1·70

389 Henri Dunant (founder of Red Cross)

1984. Air. Celebrities.

994	**389**	400f. deep blue, red & blue	2·20	65
995	-	540f. deep blue, red & blue	3·75	85

Design: 540f. Abraham Lincoln.

390 Sidney Bechet

1984. Air. Jazz Musicians. Multicoloured.

996	470f. Type **390**	4·25	1·00
997	500f. Duke Ellington	4·75	1·00

391 Microlight Aircraft

1984. Air. Microlight Aircraft. Multicoloured.

998	270f. Type **391**	1·60	55
999	350f. Lazor Gemini motorised hang-glider	1·90	80

392 Weightlifting

1984. Air. Olympic Games, Los Angeles. Multicoloured.

1000	265f. Type **392**	1·60	55
1001	440f. Show jumping	2·40	80
1002	500f. Hurdles	3·00	1·10
MS1003	130×99 mm. 700f. Sailing (vert)	5·25	2·40

393 *Crucifixion* (Rubens)

1984. Air. Easter.

1004	**393**	940f. brown & dp brown	6·00	1·70
1005	-	970f. brown and red	6·00	1·70

Design: Horiz—970f. *The Resurrection* (Mantegna).

1984. Currency revaluation. Various stamps surch. (i) UPU Day (No. 981).

1006	**384**	120f. on 240f. red, black and blue (postage)	1·40	50

(ii) Goats (Nos. 988/992).

1007	**387**	10f. on 20f. mult	20	10
1008	-	15f. on 30f. mult	20	10
1009	-	25f. on 50f. mult	35	20
1010	-	125f. on 240f. mult	1·70	50
1011	-	175f. on 350f. mult	2·20	65

(iii) Paris–Dakar Rally (No. 977).

1012	**383**	120f. on 240f. mult (air)	2·20	80

395 Mercedes Simplex

1984. Air. 150th Birth Anniversary of Gottlieb Daimler (motor car designer).

1035	**395**	350f. olive, blue and mauve	3·75	1·30
1036	-	470f. green, violet and plum	5·25	1·70
1037	-	485f. blue, violet and plum	5·25	1·80

Designs: 470f. Mercedes-Benz Type 370 S; 485f. Mercedes-Benz 500 S EC.

396 Farm Workers

1984. Progress in Countryside and Protected Essences. Multicoloured.

1038	5f. Type **396**	10	10
1039	90f. Carpentry	95	30
1040	100f. Tapestry making	95	35
1041	135f. Metal work	1·40	50
1042	515f. *Borassus flabelifer*	4·75	1·90
1043	1225f. *Vitelaria paradoxa*	11·50	2·75

397 Emblem and Child

1984. United Nations Children's Fund.

1044	**397**	120f. red, brown and green	1·30	50
1045	-	135f. red, blue and brown	1·40	60

Design: 135f. Emblem and two children.

398 UPU Emblem, Anchor and Hamburg

1984. Universal Postal Union Congress, Hamburg.

1046	**398**	135f. mauve, green and blue	1·30	50

1984. Air. Olympic Winners, Los Angeles. No. 1000/1002 optd.

1047	135f. on 265f. Optd **HALTERES 56 KGS / 1. WU (CHINE). 2. LAI (CHINE). 3. KOTAKA (JAPON)**	1·20	65
1048	220f. on 440f. Optd **DRESSAGE / PAR EQUIPES / 1. RFA 2. SUISSE / 3. SUEDE**	1·80	1·10
1049	250f. on 500f. Optd **ATHLETISME 3000 METRES STEEPLE / 1. KORIR (KENYA). / 2. MAHMOUD (FRANCE). / 3. DIEMER (E-U)**	2·50	1·60

400 Emblem

1984. Tenth Anniversary of Economic Community of West Africa.

1051	**400**	350f. multicoloured	3·25	1·50

401 Dimetrodon

1984. Prehistoric Animals. Multicoloured.

1052	10f. Type **401**	15	10
1053	25f. Iguanodon (vert)	40	15
1054	30f. Archaeopteryx (vert)	50	20
1055	120f. Type **401**	2·00	55
1056	175f. As No. 1053	2·75	80
1057	350f. As No. 1054	5·25	1·60
1058	470f. Triceratops	7·75	2·20

402 *Virgin and Child between St Joseph and St Jerome* (detail, Lorenzo Lotto)

1984. Air. Christmas.

1059	**402**	500f. multicoloured	4·75	2·50

1984. Drought Aid. No. 758 surch.

1060	470f. on 130f. mult	4·25	2·40

404 Horse Galloping

1985. Horses. Multicoloured.

1061	90f. Type **404**	1·00	40
1062	135f. Beledougou horse	1·50	55
1063	190f. Nara horse	2·10	90
1064	530f. Trait horse	6·50	2·20

405 *Clitocybe nebularis*

1985. Fungi. Multicoloured.

1065	120f. Type **405**	1·60	55
1066	200f. *Lepiota cortinarius*	2·30	85
1067	485f. *Agaricus semotus*	6·00	2·40
1068	525f. *Lepiota procera*	6·75	2·50

406 Emile Marchoux and Marchoux Institute

1985. Health. Multicoloured.

1069	120f. Type **406** (World Lepers' Day and 40th anniversary of Marchoux Institute) (postage)	1·20	50
1070	135f. Lions' emblem and Samanto Village (15th anniversary)	1·80	75
1071	470f. Laboratory technicians and polio victim (anti-polio campaign) (air)	3·75	1·60

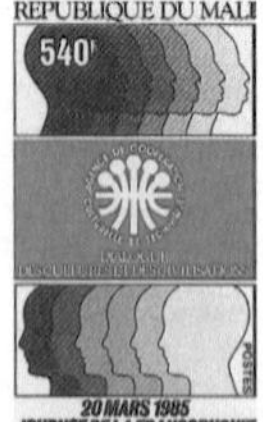

407 Profiles and Emblem

1985. 15th Anniversary of Technical and Cultural Co-operation Agency.

1072	**407**	540f. green and brown	5·50	2·30

408 River Kingfisher

1985. Air. Birth Bicentenary of John J. Audubon (ornithologist). Multicoloured.

1073	180f. Type **408**	2·20	80
1074	300f. Great bustard (vert)	3·50	1·30
1075	470f. Ostrich (vert)	6·00	2·40
1076	540f. Ruppell's griffon	6·25	2·50

409 National Pioneers Movement Emblem

1985. International Youth Year. Multicoloured.

1077	120f. Type **409**	1·20	55
1078	190f. Boy leading oxen	2·00	80
1079	500f. Sports motifs and IYY emblem	5·25	1·80

410 Sud Aviation Caravelle, Boeing 727-200 and Agency Emblem

1985. Air. 25th Anniversary of Aerial Navigation Security Agency for Africa and Madagascar (ASECNA).

1080	**410**	700f. multicoloured	6·75	3·50

411 Lion, and Scouts collecting Wood

1985. Air. Philexafrique Stamp Exhibition, Lome. Multicoloured.

1081	200f. Type **411**	2·30	1·60
1082	200f. Satellite, dish aerial and globe	2·30	1·60

412 UPU Emblem, Computer and Reservoir (Development)

1985. Philexafrique Stamp Exhibition, Lome, Togo (2nd issue). Multicoloured.

1083	250f. Type **412**	2·75	1·80
1084	250f. Satellite, girls writing and children learning from television (Youth)	2·75	1·80

413 Grey Cat

1986. Cats. Multicoloured.

1085	150f. Type **413**	1·90	70
1086	200f. White cat	2·75	1·00
1087	300f. Tabby cat	3·75	1·40

414 Hands releasing Doves and Globe

1986. Anti-apartheid Campaign. Multicoloured.

1088	100f. Type **414**	1·00	50
1089	120f. People breaking chain around world	1·30	55

415 Comet and Diagram of Orbit

1986. Air. Appearance of Halley's Comet.

1090	**415**	300f. multicoloured	3·00	1·40

416 Internal Combustion Engine

1986. Air. Centenaries of First Motor Car with Internal Combustion Engine and Statue of Liberty. Multicoloured.

1091	400f. Type **416**	4·50	1·80
1092	600f. Head of statue, and French and American flags	6·25	2·75

417 Robeson

1986. Air. Tenth Death Anniversary of Paul Robeson (singer).

1093	**417**	500f. multicoloured	6·50	2·40

418 Women tending Crop

1986. World Communications Day.

1094	**418**	200f. multicoloured	1·80	80

419 Players

1986. World Cup Football Championship, Mexico. Multicoloured.

1095	160f. Type **419**	1·70	65
1096	225f. Player capturing ball	2·30	95
MS1097	120×80 mm. 500f. Goalkeeper failing to save goal	5·25	3·00

420 Watt

1986. 250th Birth Anniversary of James Watt (inventor).

1098	**420**	110f. multicoloured	1·50	50

421 Eberth and Microscope

1986. Air. 60th Death Anniversary of Karl Eberth (discoverer of typhoid bacillus).

1099	**421**	550f. multicoloured	5·50	2·10

422 Chess Pieces on Board

1986. Air. World Chess Championship, London and Leningrad. Multicoloured.

1100	400f. Type **422**	5·00	1·80
1101	500f. Knight and board	6·50	2·40

1986. World Cup Winners. Nos. 1095/**MS**1097 optd **ARGENTINE 3 R.F.A. 2.**

1102	160f. multicoloured	2·00	1·10
1103	225f. multicoloured	2·50	1·80
MS1104	120×80 mm. 500f. multicoloured	5·50	5·50

424 Head

1986. Endangered Animals. Giant Eland. Multicoloured.

1105	5f. Type **424**	1·00	25
1106	20f. Standing by dead tree	2·30	45
1107	25f. Stepping over fallen branch	2·50	45
1108	200f. Mother and calf	15·00	3·00

425 Mermoz and *Croix du Sud*

1986. Air. 50th Anniversary of Disappearance of Jean Mermoz (aviator). Multicoloured.

1109	150f. Type **425**	1·70	70
1110	600f. CAMS 53 flying boat and monoplane	6·00	2·50
1111	625f. Map and seaplane *Comte de la Vaulx*	6·25	3·00

1986. Tenth Anniversary of Concorde's First Commercial Flight. Nos. 674/676 surch **1986–10e Anniversaire du 1er Vol Commercial Supersonique**.

1112	175f. on 120f. Type **271**	1·70	90
1113	225f. on 130f. Concorde and *Wright Flyer I*	2·00	1·10
1114	300f. on 200f. Concorde and Lindbergh's *Spirit of St Louis*	3·25	1·60

427 Hansen and Follereau

1987. Air. 75th Death Anniversary of Gerhard Hansen (discoverer of bacillus) and 10th Death Anniversary of Raoul Follereau (leprosy pioneer).

1115	**427**	500f. multicoloured	5·00	2·20

428 Model A, 1903

1987. 40th Death Anniversary of Henry Ford (motor car manufacturer). Multicoloured.

1116	150f. Type **428**	1·60	65
1117	200f. Model T, 1923	2·20	95
1118	225f. Thunderbird, 1968	2·40	1·20
1119	300f. Continental, 1963	2·75	1·60

429 Konrad Adenauer

1987. Air. 20th Death Anniversary of Konrad Adenauer (German statesman).

1120	**429**	625f. stone, brown and red	6·50	2·75

430 Runners and Buddha's Head

1987. Air. Olympic Games, Seoul (1988) (1st issue).

1121	**430**	400f. black and brown	4·00	1·80
1122	-	500f. dp green, grn & red	4·75	2·30

Design: 500f. Footballers.

See also Nos. 1133/1134.

431 Scenes from *The Jazz Singer*

1987. Air. 60th Anniversary of First Talking Picture.

1123	**431**	550f. red, brn & dp brn	7·25	3·00

432 *Apis florea*

1987. Bees. Multicoloured.

1124	100f. Type **432**	1·10	60
1125	150f. *Apis dorsata*	1·70	75
1126	175f. *Apis adonsonii*	1·90	90
1127	200f. *Apis mellifera*	2·50	1·10

433 Map, Dove and Luthuli

1987. Air. 20th Death Anniversary of Albert John Luthuli (Nobel Peace Prize winner).

1128	**433**	400f. mauve, blue & brn	3·75	1·60

434 Profiles and Lions Emblem

1987. Air. Lions International and Rotary International. Multicoloured.

1129	500f. Type **434**	4·75	2·10
1130	500f. Clasped hands and Rotary emblem	4·75	2·10

435 Anniversary Emblem and Symbols of Activities

1988. 30th Anniversary of Lions International in Mali.

1131	**435**	200f. multicoloured	1·80	95

436 Emblem and Doctor examining Boy

1988. 40th Anniversary of WHO.

1132	**436**	150f. multicoloured	1·50	70

437 Coubertin and Ancient and Modern Athletes

1988. Air. Olympic Games, Seoul (2nd issue). 125th Birth Anniversary of Pierre de Coubertin (founder of modern games). Multicoloured.

1133	240f. Type **437**	3·00	1·20
1134	400f. Stadium, Olympic rings and sports pictograms	4·00	2·40

438 *Harlequin*

1988. Air. 15th Death Anniversary of Pablo Picasso (painter).

1135	**438**	600f. multicoloured	6·75	2·50

439 Concorde and Globe

1988. Air. 15th Anniversary of First North Atlantic Crossing by Concorde.

1136	**439**	500f. multicoloured	4·75	2·30

440 President Kennedy

1988. 25th Death Anniversary of John Fitzgerald Kennedy (American President).

1137	**440**	640f. multicoloured	6·00	2·50

1988. Mali Mission Hospital, Mopti. No. 1132 surch **MISSION MALI HOPITAL de MOPTI 300F** and MEDECINS DU MONDE emblem.

1138	**436**	300f. on 150f. mult	3·00	2·10

442 Map

1988. 25th Anniversary of Organisation of African Unity.

1139	**442**	400f. multicoloured	3·75	1·80

443 Map, Leaf and Stove

1989. Air. Improved Stoves: For a Green Mali. Multicoloured.

1140	5f. Type **443**	10	10
1141	10f. Tree and stove	20	10
1142	25f. Type **443**	35	25
1143	100f. As No. 1141	1·50	50

444 Astronauts on Moon

1989. Air. 20th Anniversary of First Manned Moon Landing.

1144	**444**	300f. blue, purple & grn	1·60	60
1145	-	500f. purple, blue & brn	3·00	1·50

Design: 500f. Astronauts on Moon (different).

445 Emblem and Crossed Syringes

1989. Vaccination Programme. Multicoloured.

1146	20f. Type **445**	4·75	2·30
1147	30f. Doctor vaccinating woman	35	10
1148	50f. Emblem and syringes	55	25
1149	175f. Doctor vaccinating child	1·80	95

446 Emblem

1989. 25th Anniversary of International Law Institute of French-speaking Countries.

1150	**446**	150f. multicoloured	1·60	60
1151	**446**	200f. multicoloured	2·00	90

447 Crowd

1989. Air. Bicentenary of French Revolution and Philexfrance 89 International Stamp Exhibition, Paris.

1152	**447**	400f. red, blue and purple	4·50	1·80
1153	-	600f. violet, pur & mve	6·50	2·50

Design: 600f. Marianne and Storming of Bastille.

448 UPU Emblem and Hands holding Envelopes

1989. World Post Day.

1154	**448**	625f. multicoloured	6·25	2·75

449 Pope and Cathedral

1990. Visit of Pope John Paul II.

1155	**449**	200f. multicoloured	2·20	1·10

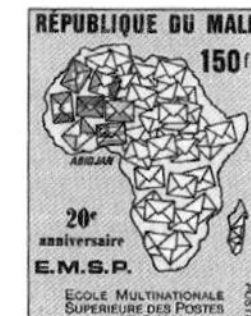

450 Envelopes on Map

1990. 20th Anniversary of Multinational Postal Training School, Abidjan.

1156	**450**	150f. multicoloured	1·70	70

451 Footballers

1990. Air. World Cup Football Championship, Italy. Multicoloured.

1157	200f. Type **451**	2·00	90
1158	225f. Footballers (different)	2·20	95
MS1159	100×75 mm. 500f. Type **451**	5·25	3·00

1990. World Cup Result. Nos. 1157/**MS**1159 optd. Multicoloured.

1160	200f. **ITALIE : 2 / ANGLETERRE : 1**	2·10	1·30
1161	225f. **R.F.A. : 1 / ARGENTINE : 0**	2·20	1·40
MS1162	100×75 mm. 500f. **1er : R.F.A. 2eme : ARGENTINE 3me : ITALIE**	5·50	5·00

453 President Moussa Traore and Bamako Bridge

1990. 30th Anniversary of Independence.

1163	**453**	400f. multicoloured	4·00	2·00

454 Man writing and Adults learning to Read

1990. International Literacy Year.

1164	**454**	150f. multicoloured	1·70	65
1165	**454**	200f. multicoloured	2·10	95

455 Woman carrying Water and Cattle at Well

1991. Lions Club (1166) and Rotary International (1167) Projects. Multicoloured.

1166	200f. Type **455** (Sixth anniversary of wells project)	2·10	1·10
1167	200f. Bamako branch emblem and hand (30th anniversary of anti-polio campaign)	2·10	1·10

456 Sonrai Dance, Takamba

1991. Dances. Multicoloured.

1168	50f. Type **456**	50	30
1169	100f. Malinke dance, Mandiani	1·00	55
1170	150f. Bamanan dance, Kono	1·50	80
1171	200f. Dogon dance, Songho	2·00	1·10

457 Bank Emblem and Map of France

1991. 50th Anniversary of Central Economic Co-operation Bank.

1172	**457**	200f. multicoloured	1·80	80

458 Women with Torch and Banner

1992. National Women's Movement for the Safeguarding of Peace and National Unity.

1173	**458**	150f. multicoloured	1·60	80

1992. Various stamps surch.

1174	-	25f. on 470f. mult (No. 1058) (postage)	30	25
1175	**420**	30f. on 110f. mult	30	25
1176	-	50f. on 300f. mult (No. 1087)	45	40
1177	-	50f. on 1225f. mult (No. 1043)	45	40
1178	-	150f. on 135f. mult (No. 1070)	1·40	70
1179	-	150f. on 190f. mult (No. 1063)	1·40	70
1180	-	150f. on 190f. mult (No. 1078)	1·40	70
1181	**400**	150f. on 350f. mult	1·40	70
1182	-	150f. on 485f. mult (No. 1067)	1·40	70
1183	-	150f. on 525f. mult (No. 1068)	1·40	70
1184	-	150f. on 530f. mult (No. 1064)	1·40	70
1185	**440**	200f. on 640f. mult	1·80	1·60
1186	-	240f. on 350f. mult (No. 1057)	2·40	1·60
1187	**448**	240f. on 625f. mult	2·50	1·60
1188	**410**	20f. on 700f. mult (air)	30	10
1189	**415**	20f. on 300f. mult	30	10
1190	-	25f. on 470f. mult (No. 1071)	30	10
1191	**408**	30f. on 180f. mult	30	10
1192	-	30f. on 500f. purple, blue and brown (No. 1145)	30	10
1193	-	100f. on 540f. mult (No. 1076)	95	55
1194	**438**	100f. on 600f. mult	95	55
1195	**444**	150f. on 300f. blue, purple and green	1·50	80
1196	**447**	150f. on 400f. red, blue and purple	1·50	80
1197	-	200f. on 300f. mult (No. 1074)	2·00	1·10
1198	-	240f. on 600f. violet, purple and mauve (No. 1153)	2·75	1·80

1992. (a) Postage. No. 1095 surch **150 f Euro 92**.

1199	**419**	150f. on 160f. mult	1·50	80

(b) Air. No. 1134 surch **150F "Barcelone 92"**.

1200	150f. on 400f. multicoloured	1·70	80

461 Map of Africa

1993. First Anniversary of Third Republic.

1201	**461**	150f. multicoloured	7·00	1·80

462 Blood, Memorial and Martyrs

1993. Second Anniversary of Martyrs' Day.

1203	**462**	150f. multicoloured	2·20	1·10
1204	**462**	160f. multicoloured	2·20	1·10

463 Polio Victims

1993. Vaccination Campaign.

1205	**463**	150f. multicoloured	7·00	1·80

464 Lecture on Problem Issues

1993. 35th Anniversary of Lions International in Mali.

1207	**464**	200f. multicoloured	1·50	80
1208	**464**	225f. multicoloured	1·50	80

465 Place de la Liberte

1993. Multicoloured, background colour of top panel given.

1209	**465**	20f. blue	10	10
1210	**465**	25f. yellow	10	10
1211	**465**	50f. pink	45	25
1212	**465**	100f. grey	95	25
1213	**465**	110f. yellow	95	40
1214	**465**	150f. green	1·20	40
1215	**465**	200f. yellow	1·90	70
1216	**465**	225f. flesh	1·90	80
1217	**465**	240f. lilac	2·40	80
1218	**465**	260f. lilac	2·50	80

466 Figure Skating

1994. Winter Olympic Games, Lillehammer. Multicoloured.

1219	150f. Type **466**	90	60
1220	200f. Giant slalom	1·20	80
1221	225f. Ski jumping	1·50	1·00
1222	750f. Speed skating	4·00	2·20
MS1223	100×69 mm. 2000f. Special slalom	6·50	6·50

467 Juan Schiaffino (Uruguay)

1994. World Cup Football Championship, USA. Players from Different Teams. Multicoloured.

1224	200f. Type **467**	90	60
1225	240f. Diego Maradona (Argentine Republic)	1·20	85
1226	260f. Paolo Rossi (Italy)	1·40	95
1227	1000f. Franz Beckenbauer (Germany)	4·75	3·25
MS1228	97×68 mm. 2000f. Just Fontaine (France)	9·75	5·50

468 Scaphonyx

1994. Prehistoric Animals. Multicoloured.

1229	5f. Type **468**	10	10
1230	10f. Cynognathus	10	10
1231	15f. Lesothosaurus	10	10
1232	20f. Scutellosaurus	10	10
1233	25f. Ceratosaurus	10	10
1234	30f. Dilophosaurus	10	10
1235	40f. Dryosaurus	10	10
1236	50f. Heterodontosaurus	10	10
1237	60f. Anatosaurus	10	10
1238	70f. Saurornithoides	30	10
1239	80f. Avimimus	30	10
1240	90f. Saltasaurus	45	10
1241	300f. Dromaeosaurus	1·60	40
1242	400f. Tsintaosaurus	2·10	55
1243	600f. Velociraptor	3·25	70
1244	700f. Ouranosaurus	3·75	80
MS1245	105×130 mm. 2000f. Daspletosaurus and Iguanodon fighting	10·50	6·50

Nos. 1229/1244 were issued together, *se-tenant*, forming a composite design.

469 *Sternuera castanea*

1994. Insects. Multicoloured.

1246	40f. Type **469**	25	20
1247	50f. *Eudicella gralli* (horiz)	45	25
1248	100f. *Homoderus mellyi*	70	50
1249	200f. *Kraussaria angulifera* (horiz)	1·30	80

470 Vaccinating Child

1994. Vaccination Campaign.

1250	**470**	150f. green and black	75	75
1251	**470**	200f. blue and black	1·30	1·30

471 Feral Rock Pigeons

1994. Birds. Multicoloured.

1252	25f. Type **471**	10	10
1253	30f. Helmeted guineafowl	10	10
1254	150f. South African crowned cranes (vert)	70	25
1255	200f. Red junglefowl (vert)	1·00	25

472 Family

1994. International Year of the Family.

1256	**472**	200f. multicoloured	45	25

473 Kirk Douglas in *Spartacus*

1994. Film Stars. Multicoloured.

1257	100f. Type **473** (postage)	50	10
1258	150f. Elizabeth Taylor in *Cleopatra*	90	25
1259	225f. Marilyn Monroe in *The River of No Return*	1·00	25
1260	500f. Arnold Swarzenegger in *Conan the Barbarian*	1·80	70
1261	1000f. Elvis Presley in *Loving You*	3·75	1·10
MS1262	149×90 mm. 1500f. Charlton Heston in *The Ten Commandments*	6·50	6·50
1263	200f. Clint Eastwood in *A Mule for Sister Sara* (inscr 'SIERRA TORRIDE') (air)	2·10	25

474 Ella Fitzgerald

1994. Jazz Singers. Multicoloured.

1264	200f. Type **474**	80	25
1265	225f. Lionel Hampton	95	25
1266	240f. Sarah Vaughan	1·20	25
1267	300f. Count Basie	1·60	55
1268	400f. Duke Ellington	1·90	70
1269	600f. Miles Davis	2·75	70
MS1270	120×81 mm. 1500f. Louis Armstrong	6·75	6·75

475 Soldiers caught in Explosion

1994. 50th Anniversary of Second World War D-Day Landings. Multicoloured. (a) Villers-Bocage.

1271	200f. Type **475**	95	25
1272	200f. Tank (29×47 mm)	95	25
1273	200f. Troops beside tank	95	25

(b) Beaumont-sur-Sarthe.

1274	300f. Bombers and troops under fire	1·40	40
1275	300f. Bombers and tanks (29×47 mm)	1·40	40
1276	300f. Tank and soldier with machine gun	1·40	40

(c) Utah Beach (wrongly inscr 'Utha').

1277	300f. Wounded troops and bow of boat	1·40	40
1278	300f. Troops in boat (29×47 mm)	1·40	40
1279	300f. Troops in boats	1·80	45

(d) Air Battle.

1280	400f. Bombers	1·80	45
1281	400f. Aircraft (29×47 mm)	1·80	45
1282	400f. Aeroplane on fire	1·80	45

(e) Sainte-Mere-Eglise.

1283	400f. Troops firing at paratrooper	1·80	45
1284	400f. Church and soldier (29×47 mm)	1·80	45
1285	400f. Paratroopers and German troops	1·80	45

Nos. 1271/1273, 1274/1276, 1277/1279, 1280/1282 and 1283/1285 respectively were issued together, *se-tenant*, forming composite designs.

476 Olympic Rings on National Flag

1994. Centenary of International Olympic Committee (1st issue).

1286	**476**	150f. multicoloured	75	35
1287	**476**	200f. multicoloured	95	55

See also Nos. 1342/**MS**1346.

477 Couple holding Condoms

1994. Anti-AIDS Campaign. Multicoloured.

1288	150f. Type **477**	75	35
1289	225f. Nurse treating patient and laboratory worker	1·20	55

478 *Venus of Brassempoury*

1994. Ancient Art. Multicoloured.

1290	15f. Type **478**	10	10
1291	25f. Cave paintings, Tanum	10	10
1292	45f. Prehistoric men painting mural	30	10
1293	50f. Cave paintings, Lascaux (horiz)	30	10
1294	55f. Painting from tomb of Amonherkhopeshef	30	10
1295	65f. God Anubis laying out Pharaoh (horiz)	30	10
1296	75f. Sphinx and pyramid, Mycerinus (horiz)	30	10
1297	85f. Bust of Nefertiti	30	10
1298	95f. Statue of Shibum	45	10
1299	100f. Cavalry of Ur (horiz)	45	10
1300	130f. Head of Mesopotamian harp	55	25
1301	135f. Mesopotamian tablet (horiz)	55	25
1302	140f. Assyrian dignitary	55	25
1303	180f. Enamel relief from Babylon (horiz)	75	25
1304	190f. Assyrians hunting	95	25
1305	200f. *Mona Lisa of Nimrod*	95	25
1306	225f. Phoenician coins (horiz)	95	25
1307	250f. Phoenician sphinx	1·20	25
1308	275f. Persian archer	1·20	25
1309	280f. Glass paste mask	1·80	25

479 *Polyptychus roseus*

1994. Multicoloured. (a) Butterflies and Moths.

1310	20f. Type **479**	10	10
1311	30f. *Elymniopsis bammakoo*	10	10
1312	40f. Silver-striped hawk moth	10	10
1313	150f. Crimson-speckled moth	75	25
1314	180f. Foxy charaxes	75	25
1315	200f. Common dotted border	80	25

(b) Plants.

1316	25f. *Disa kewensis*	10	10
1317	50f. *Angraecum eburneum*	10	10
1318	100f. *Ansellia africana*	45	10
1319	140f. Sorghum	70	10
1320	150f. Onion	75	25
1321	190f. Maize	95	25
1322	200f. Clouded agaric	95	25
1323	225f. Parasol mushroom	1·20	25
1324	500f. *Lepiota aspera*	2·10	80

(c) Insects.

1325	225f. Goliath beetle	95	35
1326	240f. Cricket	1·20	35
1327	350f. Praying mantis	1·50	40

1994. Winter Olympic Games Medal Winners, Lillehammer. Nos. 1219/**MS**1223 optd.

1328	150f. **O GRISHSHUK Y. PLATOV RUSSIE**	55	10
1329	150f. **Y. GORDEYEVA S. GRINKOV RUSSIE**	55	10
1330	200f. **M. WASMEIER ALLEMAGNE**	95	25
1331	200f. **D. COMPAGNONI ITALIE**	95	25
1332	225f. **T. WEISSFLOG ALLEMAGNE**	1·20	25
1333	225f. **E. BREDESEN NORVEGE**	1·20	25
1334	750f. **J.O. KOSS NORVEGE**	3·00	70
1335	750f. **B. BLAIR U.S.A.**	3·00	70
MS1336	Two sheets each 100×69 mm. (a) 2000f. Optd **L. KJUS NORVEGE**; (b) Optd **P. WIBERG SUEDE**	10·00	10·00

A sheetlet also exists containing Nos. 1219/1222 each optd with both of the inscriptions for that value.

1994. Results of World Cup Football Championship. Nos. 1224/**MS**1228 optd **1. BRESIL 2. ITALIE 3. SUEDE.**

1337	200f. multicoloured	95	25
1338	240f. multicoloured	95	25
1339	260f. multicoloured	1·30	25
1340	1000f. multicoloured	4·50	1·20

MS1341	87×68 mm. 2000f. multicoloured	6·50	6·50

482 Pierre de Coubertin (founder) and Torchbearer

1994. Centenary of International Olympic Committee (2nd issue). Multicoloured.

1342	225f. Type **482**	95	25
1343	240f. Coubertin designing Olympic rings	95	25
1344	300f. Athlete bearing torch and Coubertin (horiz)	1·30	25
1345	500f. Olympic rings and Coubertin at desk (horiz)	2·20	80
MS1346	117×80 mm. 600f. First Olympic ceremony and Coubertin at desk	3·00	3·00

483 Statue and Village

1994. 20th International Tourism Day. Multicoloured.

1347	150f. Type **483**	75	35
1348	200f. Sphinx, pyramids and Abu Simbel temple (horiz)	95	55

484 Reiner Klimker (dressage)

1995. Olympic Games, Atlanta (1996). Multicoloured.

1349	25f. Type **484**	10	10
1350	50f. Kristin Otto (swimming)	10	10
1351	100f. Gunther Winkler (show jumping)	45	10
1352	150f. Birgit Fischer-Schmidt (single kayak)	55	10
1353	200f. Nicole Uphoff (dressage) (vert)	95	25
1354	225f. Renate Stecher (athletics) (vert)	95	25
1355	230f. Michael Gross (swimming)	95	25
1356	240f. Karin Janz (gymnastics)	1·20	25
1357	550f. Anja Fichtel (fencing) (vert)	2·50	70
1358	700f. Heide Rosendahl-Ecker (long jump) (vert)	3·00	1·10

485 Ernst Opik, *Galileo* Probe, Shoemaker-Levy Comet and Jupiter

1995. Anniversaries and Events. Multicoloured.

1359	150f. Type **485**	55	10
1360	200f. Clyde Tombaugh (discoverer of Pluto, 1930) and *Pluto* probe	95	25
1361	500f. Henri Dunant (founder of Red Cross)	2·20	70
1362	650f. Astronauts and lunar rover (first manned moon landing, 1969)	2·75	55
1363	700f. Emblems of Lions International and Rotary International and child drinking from pump	3·00	55
1364	800f. Gary Kasparov (world chess champion, 1993)	3·50	70

486 Agriculture and Fishing (regional integration)

1995. 20th Anniversary of Economic Community of West African States. Multicoloured.

1365	150f. Type **486**	55	25
1366	200f. Emblem and handshake (co-operation) (vert)	95	25
1367	220f. Emblem and banknotes (proposed common currency)	95	40
1368	225f. Emblem and doves (peace and security)	1·00	40

487 Emblems of Alliance for Democracy in Mali and Sudanese Union-RDA

1995. Third Anniversary of New Constitution. Multicoloured.

1369	150f. Type **487** (second round of Presidential election)	55	25
1370	200f. President Alpha Oumar Konare (vert)	80	25
1371	225f. Emblems of competing parties (first round of Presidential election)	95	40
1372	240f. Map, flag and initials of parties (multi-party democracy) (vert)	1·10	40

488 Scout and Viennese Emperor Moth

1995. Scout Jamboree, Netherlands. Designs showing scouts and insects or fungi. Multicoloured.

1373	150f. Type **488**	55	10
1374	225f. Brimstone	95	25
1375	240f. Fig-tree blue	95	25
1376	500f. Clouded agaric	2·20	55
1377	650f. *Agaricus semotus*	3·00	70
1378	725f. Parasol mushroom	3·25	80
MS1379	124×85 mm. 1500f. Blue morpho	6·75	6·75

489 Paul Harris (founder) and Emblem

1995. 90th Anniversary of Rotary International. Multicoloured.

1380	1000f. Type **489**	5·00	1·40
MS1381	76×106 mm. 1500f. 1905 and present-day emblems	6·75	6·75

490 Imperial Woodpecker (*Campephilus imperialis*)

1995. Birds and Butterflies. Multicoloured.

1382	50f. Type **490**	40	20
1383	50f. Blue-crowned motmot (*Momotus momota*)	40	20
1384	50f. Keel-billed toucan (*Ramphastos sulfuratus*)	40	20
1385	50f. Blue-breasted kingfisher (*Halycon malimbica*)	40	20
1386	50f. Streamertail (*Trochilus polytmus*)	40	20
1387	50f. Common cardinal (*Cardinalis cardinalis*)	40	20
1388	50f. Resplendent quetzal (*Pharomachrus mocinno*)	40	20
1389	50f. Sun conure (*Aratinga solstitialis*)	40	20
1390	50f. Red-necked amazon (*Amazona arausiaca*)	40	20
1391	50f. Scarlet ibis (*Eudocimus ruber*)	40	20
1392	50f. Red siskin (*Carduelis cucullatus*)	40	20
1393	50f. Hyacinth macaw (*Anodorhynchus hyacinthinus*)	40	20
1394	50f. Orange-breasted bunting (*Passerina leclancherii*)	40	20
1395	50f. Red-capped manakin (*Pipra mentalis*)	40	20
1396	50f. Guianan cock of the rock (*Rupicola rupicola*)	40	20
1397	50f. Saffron finch (*Sicalis flaveola*)	40	20
1398	100f. Black-spotted barbet (*Capito niger*)	55	25
1399	100f. Amazon kingfisher (*Chloroceryle amazona*)	55	25
1400	100f. Swallow tanager (*Tersina viridis*)	55	25
1401	100f. Blue-crowned motmot (*Momotus momota*)	55	25
1402	100f. Crimson-crested woodpecker (*Campephilus melanoleucos*)	55	25
1403	100f. Red-breasted blackbird (*Leistes militaris*)	55	25
1404	100f. King vulture (*Sarcorhamphus papa*)	55	25
1405	100f. Capped heron (*Pilherodius pileatus*)	55	25
1406	100f. Black-tailed tityra (*Tityra cayana*)	55	25
1407	100f. Paradise tanager (*Tangara chilinsis*)	55	25
1408	100f. Yellow-crowned amazon (*Amazona ochrocephala*)	55	25
1409	100f. Buff-throated saltator (*Saltator maximus*)	55	25
1410	100f. Red-cowled cardinal (*Paroaria dominicana*)	55	25
1411	100f. Louisiana heron (*Egretta tricolor*)	55	25
1412	100f. Black-bellied cuckoo (*Piaya melanogaster*)	55	25
1413	100f. Barred antshrike (*Thamnophilus doliatus*)	55	25
1414	150f. Paradise whydah	75	25
1415	150f. Red-necked spurfowl ('Red-necked Francolin')	75	25
1416	150f. Whale-headed stork (inscr 'Shoebill')	75	25
1417	150f. Ruff	75	25
1418	150f. Marabou stork	75	25
1419	150f. Eastern white pelican ('White Pelican')	75	25
1420	150f. Western curlew	75	25
1421	150f. Scarlet ibis	75	25
1422	150f. Great crested grebe	75	25
1423	150f. White spoonbill	75	25
1424	150f. African jacana	75	25
1425	150f. African pygmy goose	75	25
1426	200f. Ruby-throated hummingbird	1·00	30
1427	200f. Grape shoemaker and blue morpho butterflies	1·00	30
1428	200f. Northern hobby	1·00	30
1429	200f. Black-mandibled toucan ('Cuvier Toucan')	1·00	30
1430	200f. Black-necked red cotinga and green-winged macaw	1·00	30
1431	200f. Green-winged macaws and blue and yellow macaw	1·00	30
1432	200f. Greater flamingo ('Flamingo')	1·00	30
1433	200f. Malachite kingfisher	1·00	30
1434	200f. Bushy-crested hornbill	1·00	30
1435	200f. Purple swamphen	1·00	30
1436	200f. Striped body	1·00	30
1437	200f. Painted lady	1·00	30
MS1438	Two sheets each 114×91 mm. (a) 1000f. Crimson topaz (*Topaza pella*); (b) 1000f. Lined seedeater (*Sporophila lineola*)	5·00	4·75

Stamps of the same value were issued together, in *se-tenant* sheetlets, each sheetlet forming a composite design.

491 Emblem and Scales of Justice

1995. 50th Anniversary of UNO. Multicoloured.

1439	20f. Type **491**	10	10

1440	170f. Type **491**	75	40
1441	225f. Emblem, doves and men with linked arms (horiz)	95	40
1442	240f. As No. 1441	1·10	70

492 Food Jar

1995. Cooking Utensils. Multicoloured.

1443	5f. Type **492**	10	10
1444	50f. Pestle and mortar	45	15
1445	150f. Bowl (horiz)	95	25
1446	200f. Grain sack	1·30	30
MS1447	80×110 mm. 500f. Mat	3·25	3·25

493 Lennon

1995. 15th Death Anniversary of John Lennon (musician).

1448	**493**	150f. multicoloured	95	25

494 Justus Barnes

1995. 40th Anniversary of Rock Music (1461/1466) and Centenary of Motion Pictures (others). Multicoloured. (a) Actors in Western Films.

1449	150f. Type **494**	95	55
1450	150f. William S. Hart	95	55
1451	150f. Tom Mix	95	55
1452	150f. Wallace Beery	95	55
1453	150f. Gary Cooper	95	55
1454	150f. John Wayne	95	55

(b) Leading Ladies and their Directors.

1455	200f. Marlene Dietrich and Josef von Sternberg (*The Blue Angel*)	1·30	90
1456	200f. Jean Harlow and George Cukor (*Dinner at Eight*)	1·30	90
1457	200f. Mary Astor and John Houston (*The Maltese Falcon*)	1·30	90
1458	200f. Ingrid Bergman and Alfred Hitchcock (*Spellbound*)	1·30	90
1459	200f. Claudette Colbert and Cecil B. de Mille (*Cleopatra*)	1·30	90
1460	200f. Marilyn Monroe and Billy Wilder (*Some Like it Hot*)	1·30	90

(c) Female Singers.

1461	225f. Connie Francis	1·40	90
1462	225f. The Ronettes	1·40	90
1463	225f. Janis Joplin	1·40	90
1464	225f. Debbie Harry	1·40	90
1465	225f. Cyndi Lauper	1·40	90
1466	225f. Carly Simon	1·40	90

(d) Musicals.

1467	240f. Gene Kelly in *Singin' in the Rain*	1·60	1·10
1468	240f. Cyd Charisse and Fred Astaire in *The Bandwagon*	1·60	1·10
1469	240f. Liza Minelli in *Cabaret*	1·60	1·10
1470	240f. Julie Andrews in *The Sound of Music*	1·60	1·10
1471	240f. Ginger Rogers and Fred Astaire in *Top Hat*	1·60	1·10
1472	240f. John Travolta and Karen Lynn Gorney in *Saturday Night Fever*	1·60	1·10
MS1473	Four sheets. (a) 104×74 mm. 1000f. Robert Redford; (b) 73×102 mm. 1000f. Liv Ullman and Ingmar Bergman (*Shame*); (c) 76×106 mm. 1000f. Bette Midler; (d) 76×106 mm. 1000f. Judy Garland in *The Wizard of Oz*	23·00	23·00

No. 1449 is wrongly inscribed 'George Barnes'.

495 Charles de Gaulle (French statesman, 25th death anniversary)

1995. Anniversaries. Multicoloured.

1474	150f. Type **495**	70	25
1475	200f. General de Gaulle (50th anniversary of liberation of France)	80	25
1476	240f. Enzo Ferrari (car designer, seventh death anniversary)	95	25
1477	500f. Ayrton Senna (racing driver, first death anniversary)	2·00	40
1478	650f. Paul Emile Victor (explorer, 88th birthday)	2·50	40
1479	725f. Paul Harris (founder, 90th anniversary of Rotary International)	3·25	55
1480	740f. Michael Schumacher (racing driver, 26th birth anniversary) (wrongly dated 1970)	3·25	55
1481	1000f. Jerry Garcia (popular singer, death commemoration)	4·50	70

Nos. 1482/1490 and Types **496/505** are left for possible issues not seen.

506 Djenne Mosque

1996. Mosques. Multicoloured.

1491	250f. Type **506**	2·75	1·30
1492	310f. Sankoré Mosque	3·20	1·60

507 Nanking Bridge

1996. Centenary of Chinese Postal Service.

1493	**507**	270f. multicoloured	2·50	1·30

508 Fire and Crowd

1996. Peace Bonfire, Timbuktu.

1494	**508**	180f. multicoloured	2·30	1·10
1495	**508**	250f. mullticoloured	3·00	1·50

509 Delivery

1996. Tenth Anniversary of EMS. Multicoloured

1496	30f. Type **509**	75	35
1497	40f. Eagle carrying parcel and envelope	75	40
1498	90f. Emblem and woman taking phone call (horiz)	1·00	75
1499	320f. Delivery van and emblem (horiz)	3·75	2·00

510 Kara

1996. Exhibits from National Museum. Multicoloured.

1500	5f. Type **510**	30	10
1501	10f. Hambe	30	15
1502	180f. Pinge	2·00	1·40
1503	250f. Merenkun	3·00	1·80

511 Dounouba

1996. Traditional Dances. Multicoloured.

1504	150f. Type **511**	1·30	60
1505	170f. Gomba	1·50	65
1506	225f. Sandia	2·00	85
1507	230f. Sabar	2·30	90

512 Cotton

1996. Cotton Production. Multicoloured.

1508	20f. Type **512**	25	15
1509	25f. Picking cotton (horiz)	30	20
1510	50f. Hand holding cotton	60	30
1511	310f. Emptying basket of cotton onto trailer (horiz)	3·50	2·00

513 Student

1996. Year of African Education. Multicoloured.

1512	100f. Type **513**	75	45
1513	150f. Children in classroom (horiz)	1·20	60
1514	180f. Adult literacy class (horiz)	1·40	75
1515	250f. Map enclosing uses of literacy	1·90	1·10

514 Cabral

1996. 16th Death Anniversary of Abdoul Karim (Cabral) Camara (general secretary of student union).

1516	**514**	180f. multicoloured	1·50	95
1517	**514**	250f. mutlicoloured	2·00	1·40

515 Kita Basilica

1997. Churches. Multicoloured.

1518	5f. Type **515**	20	10
1519	10f. San Cathedral	25	10
1520	150f. Bamako Cathedral	1·60	75
1521	370f. Mandiakuy Church	4·00	1·80

516 Traditional Dance Headdress

1997. Exhibits from National Museum. Multicoloured.

1522	20f. Type **516**	20	15
1523	25f. Couple (statuette)	25	20
1524	250f. Saddlebag key	2·00	1·20
1525	310f. Oil lamp	2·75	1·50

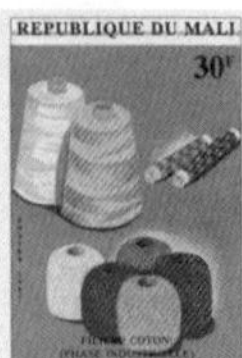
517 Yarn

1997. Cotton Industry. Multicoloured.

1526	30f. Type **517**	30	15
1527	50f. Clothes	45	25
1528	180f. Bolts of cloth	1·60	90
1529	320f. Textile printing machine	2·75	1·60

518 Addax

1998. 18th Anniversary of Pan African Postal Union.

1530	**518**	250f. multicoloured	2·50	1·30

519 Mofti Mosque

1998. Art and Culture. Multicoloured.

1531	5f. Type **519**	10	30
1532	10f. La Tanga (vert)	15	30
1533	15f. Fishermen	20	30
1534	20f. Fula woman (inscr 'La Femme Peulh') (vert)	30	30
1535	25f. Friendship Hotel (vert)	35	35
1536	30f. Hill, Sikasso (inscr 'La Mamelon de Sikasso') (vert)	40	40
1537	40f. Azalai caravan camel rider (vert)	55	55
1538	50f. Kassonike woman (vert)	70	70
1539	60f. Dogon drummer (vert)	85	1·00
1540	70f. Cattle herders (vert)	1·00	1·00
1541	80f. Doson n'goni (lute-harp) player (vert)	1·20	1·30
1542	90f. Male antelope shaped hair comb (vert)	1·30	1·40

520 Senufo Traditional House

1998. Traditional Houses. Multicoloured.

1543	25f. Type **520**	25	60
1544	180f. Sarakole (Soninke) (horiz)	1·80	1·00
1545	310f. Minianka	3·00	1·70
1546	320f. Boo	3·25	1·80

521 *Tamarindus indica* (tamarind)

1998. Trees. Multicoloured.
1547 100f. Type **521** 1·00 60
1548 150f. *Adansonia digitata* (baobab) 1·50 90
1549 180f. *Acacia* 1·80 1·10
1550 310f. *Parkia biglobosa* (néré) 3·25 1·80

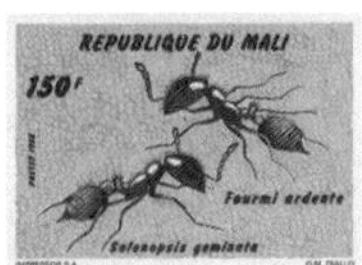

522 *Solenopsis geminata*

1998. Ants. Multicoloured.
1551 150f. Type **522** 1·50 75
1552 180f. *Camponotus pensylvanicus* (vert) 1·70 95
1553 250f. *Monorium minimum* 2·30 1·10
1554 310f. *Lasius niger* 2·75 1·60

523 Wasamba

1998. Exhibits from National Museum. Multicoloured.
1555 50f. Type **523** 40 20
1556 150f. Receptacle 1·30 55
1557 250f. Seated figure (statuette) 2·10 1·10
1558 320f. Rattle 2·75 1·60

Nos. 1559/1570 and Types **524/526** are left for possible issues not yet seen.

527 Baladji Cisse

1999. 75th Birth Anniversary of Baladji Cisse (boxer). Multicoloured.
1571 150f. Type **527** 1·50 1·50
1572 250f. Wearing suit and tie 2·50 1·50

528 Cultivating Gardens

1999. Combating Poverty Campaign. Multicoloured.
1573 150f. Type **528** 85 35
1574 180f. Building work 1·00 40
1575 750f. Nutrition (vert) 4·25 1·60
1576 1000f. Clean drinking water 5·50 2·20

529 Teacher using Blackboard

1999. Teachers' Day. Multicoloured.
1577 150f. Type **529** 90 40
1578 250f. Teacher and older students 1·50 60
1579 370f. Woman teaching adults 2·20 90
1580 390f. Classroom, girl using blackboard (horiz) 2·40 1·10

530 Aeroplane, Ship and Train

1999. 125th Anniversary of Universal Postal Union. Multicoloured.
1581 150f. Type **530** 2·00 80
1582 250f. Emblem and stylised figures holding envelopes 2·00 90
1583 310f. Emblem, eagles and antelope hair combs holding envelopes 2·50 1·00
1584 320f. Eagle holding envelope and emblem (vert) 2·75 1·10

531 Building Façade

1999. Sikasso Cathedral. Multicoloured.
1585 150f. Type **531** 1·50 80
1586 150f. Stylised cathedral 1·00 80

532 No Needle Symbol, Instructions and Doctor

2000. Combating Malaria Campaign. Multicoloured.
1587 150f. Type **532** 1·20 50
1588 150f. Two patients and no needle symbol 1·20 50
1589 150f. Child receiving interrectal infusion 1·20 50
1590 430f. Mother giving child Coprim syrup 3·25 1·80

533 Emblem and Map

2000. International Year of Volunteering
1591 **533** 250f. light green, chrome yellow and scarlet vermilion 1·50 60

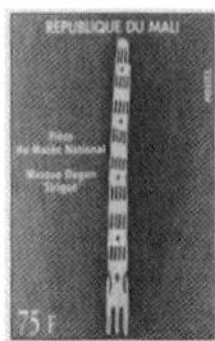

534 Sirigue (Dogon mask)

2001. Exhibits from National Museum. Multicoloured.
1596 75f. Type **534** (2004) 50 50
1597 195f. As Type **534** (2005) 1·00 1·00
1602 325f. As Type **534** 1·50 1·50

Numbers have been left for possible additions to this series.

535 Manantali Dam

2002. Regional Integration Organisation for Flow from Senegal River
1606 30f. multicoloured (2004) 1·00 1·00
1607 100f. multicoloured (2003) 1·00 1·00
1608 5000f. multicoloured 25·00 15·00

Numbers have been left for possible additions to this series.

Nos. 1613/1614 and T **536** are left for AIDS issued on 10 January 2002, not yet received.

Nos. 1615/1616 and T **537** are left for African Cup issued on 19 January 2002, not yet received.

538 Songhoi Woman

2003. African Women. Multicoloured.
1617 50f. Type **538** 50 30
1618 385f. Fula woman 3·00 2·00

539 Musicians

2003. Balafon Festival.
1619 **539** 565f. multicoloured 4·00 2·50

540 Tuareg

2005. Tourism. Multicoloured.
1620 10f. Type **540** 50 40
1621 20f. Djenne Fair 1·00 80

541 Emblem, Map and Water Droplet

2005. Water for Africa
1622 **541** 465f. multicoloured 5·00 4·00

OFFICIAL STAMPS

O9 Dogon Mask

1961
O26 **O9** 1f. violet 10 10
O27 **O9** 2f. red 10 10
O28 **O9** 3f. slate 10 10
O29 **O9** 5f. turquoise 25 25
O30 **O9** 10f. brown 30 25
O31 **O9** 25f. blue 45 25
O32 **O9** 30f. red 60 25
O33 **O9** 50f. myrtle 1·00 40
O34 **O9** 85f. purple 1·60 80
O35 **O9** 100f. green 1·90 95
O36 **O9** 200f. purple 4·00 1·90

O30 Mali Flag and Emblems

1964. Centre and flag multicoloured; frame colour given.
O90 **O30** 1f. green 10 10
O91 **O30** 2f. lavender 10 10
O92 **O30** 3f. slate 10 10
O93 **O30** 5f. purple 10 10
O94 **O30** 10f. blue 30 10
O95 **O30** 25f. ochre 30 10
O96 **O30** 30f. green 45 20
O97 **O30** 50f. orange 55 25
O98 **O30** 85f. brown 80 25
O99 **O30** 100f. red 1·00 40
O100 **O30** 200f. blue 2·10 55

O341 Arms of Gao

1981. Town Arms. Multicoloured.
O878 5f. Type **O341** 10 10
O879 15f. Tombouctou 20 10
O880 50f. Mopti 35 10
O881 180f. Segou 1·00 35
O882 200f. Sikasso 1·40 50
O883 680f. Koulikoro 3·25 1·30
O884 700f. Kayes 4·25 1·50
O885 1000f. Bamako 6·00 2·10

1984. Nos. O878/O885 surch.
O1013 15f. on 5f. Type **O341** 10 10
O1014 50f. on 15f. Tombouctou 45 20
O1015 120f. on 50f. Mopti 1·00 30
O1016 295f. on 180f. Segou 2·75 85
O1017 470f. on 200f. Sikasso 4·00 1·30
O1018 515f. on 680f. Koulikoro 5·00 1·60
O1019 845f. on 700f. Kayes 7·50 2·75
O1020 1225f. on 1000f. Bamako 11·50 3·25

POSTAGE DUE STAMPS

D9 Bambara Mask

1961
D26 **D9** 1f. black 10 10
D27 **D9** 2f. blue 10 10
D28 **D9** 5f. mauve 30 10
D29 **D9** 10f. orange 45 25
D30 **D9** 20f. turquoise 75 30
D31 **D9** 25f. purple 95 45

D28 *Polyptychus roseus*

1964. Butterflies and Moths. Multicoloured.
D83 1f. Type **D28** 10 10
D84 1f. *Deilephila nerii* 10 10
D85 2f. *Bunaea alcinoe* 30 25
D86 2f. *Gynanisa maja* 30 25
D87 3f. *Teracolus eris* 30 25
D88 3f. *Colotis antevippe* 30 25
D89 5f. *Manatha microcera* 30 25
D90 5f. *Charaxes epijasius* 30 25
D91 10f. *Hypokopelates otraeda* 55 55
D92 10f. *Lipaphnaeus leonina* 55 55
D93 20f. *Lobobunaea christyi* 1·20 1·10
D94 20f. *Gonimbrasia hecate* 1·20 1·10
D95 25f. *Hypolimnas misippus* 1·40 1·40
D96 25f. *Castopsilia florella* 1·50 1·40

1984. Nos. D83/D96 surch.
D1021 5f. on 1f. Type **D28** 10 10
D1022 5f. on 1f. *Deilephila nerii* 10 10
D1023 10f. on 2f. *Bunaea alcinoe* 10 10
D1024 10f. on 2f. *Gynanisa maja* 10 10
D1025 15f. on 3f. *Teracolus eris* 30 25
D1026 15f. on 3f. *Colotis antevippe* 30 25
D1027 25f. on 5f. *Manatha microcera* 30 25
D1028 25f. on 5f. *Charaxes epijasius* 30 25
D1029 50f. on 10f. *Hypokopelates otraeda* 50 50
D1030 50f. on 10f. *Lipaphnaeus leonina* 50 50
D1031 100f. on 20f. *Lobobunaea christyi* 1·00 1·00
D1032 100f. on 20f. *Gonimbrasia hecate* 1·00 1·00
D1033 125f. on 25f. *Hypolimnas misippus* 1·40 1·40
D1034 125f. on 25f. *Catopsilia florella* 1·50 1·50

APPENDIX

The following stamps have either been issued in excess of postal needs or have not been available to the public in reasonable quantities at face value. Such stamps may later be given full listing if there is evidence of regular postal use.

All on gold foil.

1994

World Cup Football Championship, USA. Air 3000f.
Film Stars. Air 3000f.

1996

Bridges. 100f.; 150f.; 180f.; 250f.
World Cup Football championship, France. 180f.; 250f.; 320f.; 1060f.
Winter Olympic Games, Nagano. 250f.; 310f.; 750f.; 900f.
70th Birth Anniversary of Queen Elizabeth II. 370f.×3
Symbols of China. 180f.×3
ENDA. 250f.×2

1997

Scouting. 150f.; 180f.; 250f.; 310f.; 320f.; 430f.; 460f.; 490f.; 530f.; 750f.; 900f.; 1060f.

1998

Transport. 180f.×3; 250f.×3; 320f.×3; 370f.×3; 460f.×3; 490f.×3; 530f.×3; 750f.×3
Chinese Ceramics. 500f.×2
Crested Porcupine. 250f.×4

2002

Tomb of Tutankamun. 3000f.×8

2003

Eagle. 3000f.
Yugi Gagarin Commemoration. 3000f.

2004

Personalities.300f.; 350f.; 400f.×2; 750f.×2; 1000f.×2

MALTA

An island in the Mediterranean Sea, south of Italy. After a period of self-government under various Constitutions, independence was attained on 21 September 1964. The island became a republic on 13 December 1974.

1860. 12 pence = 1 shilling; 20 shillings = 1 pound.
1972. 10 mils = 1 cent; 100 cents = M£1.
2008. 100 cents = 1 euro.

1

5

1860. Various frames.

18	**1**	½d. yellow	40·00	35·00
20	**1**	½d. green	5·50	50
22	-	1d. red	13·00	35
23	-	2d. grey	13·00	2·50
26	-	2½d. blue	50·00	1·00
27	-	4d. brown	11·00	3·00
28	-	1s. violet	50·00	12·00
30	**5**	5s. red	£110	80·00

6 Harbour of Valletta

7 Gozo Fishing Boat

8 Galley of Knights of St John

9 Emblematic Figure of Malta

10 Shipwreck of St Paul

1899

31*a*	**6**	¼d. brown	1·50	40
79	**6**	4d. black	15·00	7·00
32	**7**	4½d. brown	27·00	16·00
58	**7**	4½d. orange	4·75	4·50
59	**8**	5d. red	45·00	8·00
60	**8**	5d. green	4·75	4·00
34	**9**	2s.6d. olive	45·00	17·00
35	**10**	10s. black	£100	65·00

1902. No. 26 surch **One Penny**.

37	**10**	1d. on 2½d. blue	1·25	2·25

12

1903

47	**12**	½d. green	5·50	30
39	**12**	1d. black and red	15·00	40
49	**12**	1d. red	3·50	10
50	**12**	2d. purple and grey	18·00	3·75
51	**12**	2d. grey	6·50	7·00
52	**12**	2½d. purple and blue	40·00	60
53	**12**	2½d. blue	5·50	4·25
42	**12**	3d. grey and purple	2·00	50
54	**12**	4d. black and brown	11·00	8·50
55	**12**	4d. black and red on yellow	4·75	5·50
44	**12**	1s. grey and violet	35·00	9·00
62	**12**	1s. black on green	7·50	4·25
63	**12**	5s. green and red on yellow	65·00	75·00

13

15

17

1914

69	**13**	¼d. brown	2·00	10
71	**13**	½d. green	3·75	30
73	**13**	1d. red	1·50	10
75	**13**	2d. grey	15·00	8·50
77	**13**	2½d. blue	3·00	65
78	**13**	3d. purple on yellow	2·50	22·00
80	**13**	6d. purple	11·00	21·00
81*a*	**13**	1s. black on green	13·00	27·00
86	**15**	2s. purple and blue on blue	50·00	38·00
88	**15**	5s. green and red on yellow	£100	£110
104	**17**	10s. black	£350	£800

1918. Optd **WAR TAX**.

92	**13**	½d. green	2·25	15
93	**12**	3d. grey and purple	3·50	16·00

18

15

17

1921

100	**18**	2d. grey	12·00	1·75

1922. Optd **SELF-GOVERNMENT**.

114	**13**	¼d. brown	30	1·25
106	**13**	½d. green	2·25	4·25
116	**13**	1d. red	1·00	20
117	**18**	2d. grey	6·50	45
118	**13**	2½d. blue	1·10	2·50
108	**13**	3d. purple on yellow	5·00	27·00
109	**13**	6d. purple	7·00	42·00
110	**13**	1s. black on green	6·50	28·00
120	**15**	2s. purple and blue on blue	50·00	95·00
112	**9**	2s.6d. olive	32·00	55·00
113	**15**	5s. green and red on yellow	60·00	£100
105	**10**	10s. black	£250	£400
121	**17**	10s. black	£140	£250

1922. Surch **One Farthing**.

122	**18**	¼d. on 2d. grey	85	30

22

23

1922

123	**22**	¼d. brown	3·00	60
124	**22**	½d. green	2·50	15
125	**22**	1d. orange and purple	7·50	20
126	**22**	1d. violet	4·25	80
127	**22**	1½d. red	5·50	15
128	**22**	2d. brown and blue	3·75	1·25
129	**22**	2½d. blue	6·50	20·00
130	**22**	3d. blue	9·50	3·25
131	**22**	3d. black on yellow	5·50	26·00
132	**22**	4d. yellow and blue	3·00	6·50
133	**22**	6d. green and violet	7·50	4·75
134	**23**	1s. blue and brown	17·00	4·50
135	**23**	2s. brown and blue	14·00	25·00
136	**23**	2s.6d. purple and black	13·00	15·00
137	**23**	5s. orange and blue	21·00	50·00
138	**23**	10s. grey and brown	65·00	£160
140	**22**	£1 black and red	£110	£325

1925. Surch **Two pence halfpenny**.

142		2½d. on 3d. blue	1·75	7·50

1926. Optd **POSTAGE**.

143	**22**	¼d. brown	1·75	9·00
144	**22**	½d. green	70	15
145	**22**	1d. violet	1·00	25
146	**22**	1½d. red	1·25	60
147	**22**	2d. brown and blue	75	2·50
148	**22**	2½d. blue	1·25	2·25
149	**22**	3d. black on yellow	75	1·00
150	**22**	4d. yellow and blue	27·00	45·00
151	**22**	6d. green and violet	2·75	8·00
152	**23**	1s. blue and brown	5·50	26·00
153	**23**	2s. brown and blue	55·00	£150
154	**23**	2s.6d. purple and black	18·00	50·00
155	**23**	5s. orange and blue	10·00	50·00
156	**23**	10s. grey and brown	7·00	22·00

26

27 Valletta Harbour

28 St Publius

1926. Inscr 'POSTAGE'.

157	**26**	¼d. brown	80	15
158	**26**	½d. green	60	15
159	**26**	1d. red	3·00	2·00
160	**26**	1½d. brown	2·00	10
161	**26**	2d. grey	4·50	16·00
162	**26**	2½d. blue	4·00	3·00
162a	**26**	3d. violet	4·25	6·50
163	**26**	4d. black and red	3·75	18·00
164	**26**	4½d. violet and yellow	3·50	7·50
165	**26**	6d. violet and red	4·25	10·00
166	**27**	1s. black	7·00	13·00
167	**28**	1s.6d. black and green	8·00	23·00
168	-	2s. black and purple	8·50	28·00
169	-	2s.6d. black and red	21·00	55·00
170	-	3s. black and blue	21·00	48·00
171	-	5s. black and green	24·00	75·00
172	-	10s. black and red	65·00	£110

Designs: As T **27**—2s. Mdina (Notabile); 5s. Neolithic temple, Mnajdra. As T **28**—2s.6d. Gozo boat; 3s. Neptune; 10s. St Paul.

1928. Air. Optd **AIR MAIL**.

173	**26**	6d. violet and red	1·75	2·25

1928. As Nos. 157/172, optd **POSTAGE AND REVENUE**

174	**26**	¼d. brown	1·50	10
175	**26**	½d. green	1·50	10
176	**26**	1d. red	1·75	3·25
177	**26**	1d. brown	4·50	10
178	**26**	1½d. brown	3·00	85
179	**26**	1½d. red	4·25	10
180	**26**	2d. grey	4·25	9·00
181	**26**	2½d. blue	2·00	10
182	**26**	3d. violet	2·00	80
183	**26**	4d. black and red	2·00	1·75
184	**26**	4½d. violet and yellow	2·25	1·00
185	**26**	6d. violet and red	2·25	1·75
186	**27**	1s. black	5·50	2·50
187	**28**	1s.6d. black and green	15·00	12·00
188	-	2s. black and purple	27·00	70·00
189	-	2s.6d. black and red	17·00	21·00
190	-	3s. black and blue	23·00	24·00
191	-	5s. black and green	38·00	70·00
192	-	10s. black and red	70·00	£100

1930. As Nos. 157/172, but inscr 'POSTAGE & REVENUE'.

193		¼d. brown	60	10
194	**26**	½d. green	60	10
195	**26**	1d. brown	60	10
196	**26**	1½d. red	70	10
197	**26**	2d. grey	1·25	50
198	**26**	2½d. blue	2·00	10
199	**26**	3d. violet	1·50	20
200	**26**	4d. black and red	1·25	8·00
201	**26**	4½d. violet and yellow	3·25	1·25
202	**26**	6d. violet and red	3·00	2·75
203	**27**	1s. black	10·00	25·00
204	**28**	1s.6d. black and green	8·50	35·00
205	-	2s. black and purple	15·00	27·00
206	-	2s.6d. black and red	17·00	60·00
207	-	3s. black and blue	50·00	60·00
208	-	5s. black and green	55·00	75·00
209	-	10s. black and red	£110	£180

1935. Silver Jubilee. As T **10a** of Gambia

210	½d. black and green	50	70
211	2½d. brown and blue	2·50	4·50
212	6d. blue and olive	7·00	14·00
213	1s. grey and purple	19·00	30·00

1937. Coronation. As T **10b** of Gambia

214	½d. green	10	20
215	1½d. red	1·50	65
216	2½d. blue	1·50	80

37 Grand Harbour, Valletta

38 HMS *St Angelo*

39 Verdala Palace

1938. Various designs with medallion King George VI.

217	**37**	¼d. brown	10	10
218	**38**	½d. green	4·50	30
218a	**38**	½d. brown	55	30
219	**39**	1d. brown	7·00	40
219a	**39**	1d. green	60	10
220	-	1½d. red	3·75	30
220b	-	1½d. black	30	15
221	-	2d. black	3·75	2·00
221b	-	2d. red	40	30
222	-	2½d. blue	9·00	1·25
222a	-	2½d. violet	60	10
223	-	3d. violet	6·50	80
223a	-	3d. blue	30	20
224	-	4½d. olive and brown	50	30
225	-	6d. olive and red	3·00	30
226	-	1s. black	3·00	30
227	-	1s.6d. black and olive	8·50	4·00
228	-	2s. green and blue	5·50	7·50
229	-	2s.6d. black and red	9·00	6·00
230	-	5s. black and green	5·50	9·00
231	-	10s. black and red	19·00	19·00

Designs: As Types **38/39**. Vert—1½d. Hypogeum, Hal Saflieni; 3d. St John's Co-Cathedral; 6d. Statue of Manoel de Vilhena; 1s. Maltese girl wearing faldetta; 5s. Palace Square, Valletta; 10s. St Paul. Horiz—2d. Victoria and Citadel, Gozo; 2½d. De l'Isle Adam entering Mdina; 4½d. Ruins at Mnajdra; 1s.6d. St Publius; 2s. Mdina Cathedral; 2s.6d. Statue of Neptune.

1946. Victory. As T **11a** of Gambia

232	1d. green	15	10
233	3d. blue	75	2·00

1948. Self-government. As 1938 issue optd **SELF-GOVERNMENT 1947**.

234	**37**	¼d. brown	30	20
235	**38**	½d. brown	30	10
236	**38**	1d. green	30	10
236a	**39**	1d. grey	75	10
237	-	1½d. black	1·25	10
237b	-	1½d. green	30	10
238	-	2d. red	1·25	10
238c	-	2d. yellow	30	10
239	-	2½d. violet	80	10
239a	-	2½d. red	75	1·50
240	-	3d. blue	3·25	15
240a	-	3d. violet	50	15
241	-	4½d. olive and brown	2·75	1·00
241a	-	4½d. olive and blue	50	90
242	-	6d. olive and red	3·25	15
243	-	1s. black	3·75	40
244	-	1s.6d. black and olive	2·50	50
245	-	2s. green and blue	9·50	2·50
246	-	2s.6d. black and red	12·00	2·50
247	-	5s. black and green	30·00	3·50
248	-	10s. black and red	30·00	27·00

1949. Silver Wedding. As **11b/11c** of Gambia

249	1d. green	50	10
250	£1 blue	38·00	48·00

1949. UPU. As T **11d/11g** of Gambia

251	2½d. violet	30	10
252	3d. blue	3·00	1·00
253	6d. red	60	1·00
254	1s. black	60	2·50

53 Queen Elizabeth II when Princess

1950. Visit of Princess Elizabeth.

255	**53**	1d. green	15	15
256	**53**	3d. blue	25	20
257	**53**	1s. black	1·00	3·00

54 *Our Lady of Mount Carmel* (attrib Palladino)

1951. Seventh Centenary of the Scapular.

258	**54**	1d. green	20	30
259	**54**	3d. violet	50	10
260	**54**	1s. black	2·10	2·50

1953. Coronation. As T **11h** of Gambia

261		1½d. black and green	70	10

55 St John's Co-Cathedral

1954. Royal Visit.

262	**55**	3d. violet	45	10

56 *Immaculate Conception* (Caruana) (altar-piece, Cospicua)

1954. Centenary of Dogma of the Immaculate Conception.

263	**56**	1½d. green	15	10
264	**56**	3d. blue	15	10
265	**56**	1s. grey	35	20

57 Monument of the Great Siege, 1565

1956

266	**57**	¼d. violet	20	10
267	-	½d. orange	50	10
314	-	1d. black	50	30
269	-	1½d. green	30	10
270	-	2d. sepia	3·50	10
271	-	2½d. brown	2·25	30
272	-	3d. red	1·50	10
273	-	4½d. blue	2·50	1·00
274	-	6d. indigo	1·50	10
275	-	8d. ochre	4·50	1·00
276	-	1s. violet	1·75	10
277	-	1s.6d. turquoise	18·00	35
278	-	2s. olive	13·00	5·00
279	-	2s.6d. brown	11·00	2·50
280	-	5s. green	17·00	3·25
281	-	10s. red	38·00	16·00
282	-	£1 brown	38·00	35·00

Designs: Vert—½d. Wignacourt aqueduct horsetrough; 1d. Victory church; 1½d. Second World War memorial; 2d. Mosta Church; 3d. The King's Scroll; 4½d. Roosevelt's Scroll; 8d. Vedette (tower); 1s. Mdina Gate; 1s.6d. *Les Gavroches* (statue); 2s. Monument of Christ the King; 2s.6d. Monument of Grand Master Cottoner; 5s. Grand Master Perellos's monument; 10s. *St Paul* (statue); £1 *Baptism of Christ* (statue). Horiz—2½d. Auberge de Castile; 6d. Neolithic Temples at Tarxien.

74 Defence of Malta

1957. George Cross Commemoration. Cross in Silver.

283	**74**	1½d. green	20	10
284	-	3d. red	20	10
285	-	1s. brown	20	10

Designs: Horiz—3d. Searchlights over Malta. Vert—1s. Bombed buildings.

77 Design

1958. Technical Education in Malta. Inscr 'TECHNICAL EDUCATION'.

286	**77**	1½d. black and green	25	10
287	-	3d. black, red and grey	25	10
288	-	1s. grey, purple and black	30	10

Designs: Vert—3d. Construction. Horiz—1s. Technical School, Paola.

81 Sea Raid on Grand Harbour, Valletta

1958. George Cross Commemoration. Cross in first colour outlined in silver.

289	-	1½d. green and black	25	10
290	**81**	3d. red and black	25	10
291	-	1s. mauve and black	35	10

Designs: Horiz—1½d. Bombed-out family; 1s. Searchlight crew.

83 Air Raid Casualties

1959. George Cross Commemoration.

292	**83**	1½d. green, black and gold	30	10
293	-	3d. mauve, black and gold	30	10
294	-	1s. grey, black and gold	1·40	1·75

Designs: Horiz—3d. 'For Gallantry'. Vert—1s. Maltese under bombardment.

86 Shipwreck of St Paul (after Palombi)

87 Statue of St Paul, Rabat, Malta

1960. 19th Centenary of the Shipwreck of St Paul. Inscr as in T **86/87**.

295	**86**	1½d. blue, gold and brown	15	10
296	-	3d. purple, gold and blue	15	10
297	-	6d. red, gold and grey	25	10
298	**87**	8d. black and gold	40	60
299	-	1s. purple and gold	30	10
300	-	2s.6d. blue, green and gold	1·00	2·75

Designs: As T **88**—3d. Consecration of St Publius, First Bishop of Malta; 6d. Departure of St Paul (after Palombi). As T **87**: 1s. Angel with the *Acts of the Apostles*; 2s.6d. St Paul with the *Second Epistle to the Corinthians*.

92 Stamp of 1860

1960. Centenary of Malta Stamps. Stamp in buff and blue.

301	**92**	1½d. green	30	10
302	**92**	3d. red	35	10
303	**92**	6d. blue	1·00	1·00

93 George Cross

1961. George Cross Commemoration.

304	**93**	1½d. black, cream and bistre	30	10
305	-	3d. brown and blue	30	10
306	-	1s. green, lilac and violet	1·40	2·50

Designs: 3d. and 1s. show George Cross as T **93** over backgrounds with different patterns.

96 *Madonna Damascena*

1962. Great Siege Commemoration.

307	**96**	2d. blue	10	10
308	-	3d. red	10	10
309	-	6d. bronze	30	10
310	-	1s. purple	30	40

Designs: 3d. Great Siege Monument; 6d. Grand Master La Valette; 1s. Assault on Fort St Elmo.

1963. Freedom from Hunger. As T **41** of Gibraltar.

311		1s.6d. sepia	1·50	2·50

1963. Centenary of Red Cross. As T **42** of Gibraltar.

312		2d. red on black	25	15
313		1s.6d. red and blue	1·50	4·50

100 Bruce, Zammit and Microscope

1964. Anti-brucellosis Congress.

316	**100**	2d. brown, black and green	10	10
317	-	1s.6d. black and purple	1·25	2·00

Design: 1s.6d. Goat and laboratory equipment.

102 *Nicola Cotoner tending Sick Man* (M. Preti)

1964. First European Catholic Doctors' Congress, Valletta. Multicoloured.

318		2d. Type **102**	20	10
319		6d. St Luke and hospital	50	15
320		1s.6d. Sacra Infermeria, Valletta	1·10	1·90

106 Dove and British Crown

1964. Independence.

321	**106**	2d. olive, red and gold	30	10
322	-	3d. brown, red and gold	30	10
323	-	6d. slate, red and gold	60	15
324	**106**	1s. blue, red and gold	60	15
325	-	1s.6d. blue, red and gold	1·25	1·00
326	-	2s.6d. blue, red and gold	1·50	3·75

Designs: 3d., 1s.6d. Dove and Pope's tiara; 6d., 2s.6d. Dove and UN emblem.

109 The Nativity

1964. Christmas.

327	**109**	2d. purple and gold	10	10
328	**109**	4d. blue and gold	20	15
329	**109**	8d. green and gold	45	45

110 Neolithic Era

1965. Multicoloured.

330		½d. Type **110**	10	10
331		1d. Punic era (vert)	10	10
332		1½d. Roman era (vert)	30	10
333		2d. Proto Christian era (vert)	10	10
334		2½d. Saracenic era (vert)	1·00	10
335		3d. Siculo Norman era (vert)	10	10
336		4d. Knights of Malta (vert)	1·00	10
337		4½d. Maltese Navy (vert)	1·00	75
337b		5d. Fortifications (vert)	30	20
338		6d. French occupation (vert)	30	10
339		8d. British rule	50	10
339c		10d. Naval Arsenal	50	1·90
340		1s. Maltese Corps of the British Army	30	10
341		1s.3d. International Eucharistic Congress, 1913	2·00	1·40
342		1s.6d. Self-government, 1921	60	20
343		2s. Gozo Civic Council	70	10
344		2s.6d. State of Malta	70	50
345		3s. Independence, 1964	1·00	75
346		5s. HAFMED (Allied Forces, Mediterranean)	4·00	1·00
347		10s. The Maltese Islands (map)	2·00	5·00
348		£1 Patron Saints	2·25	5·50

Nos. 339/348 are larger, 41×29 mm from perf to perf, and include portrait of Queen Elizabeth II.

129 *Dante* (Raphael)

1965. 700th Birth Anniversary of Dante.

349	**129**	2d. blue	10	10
350	**129**	6d. green	25	10
351	**129**	2s. brown	1·10	1·50

131 Turkish Fleet

1965. 400th Anniversary of Great Siege. Multicoloured.

352		2d. Turkish camp	25	10
353		3d. Battle scene	25	10
354		6d. Type **131**	35	10
355		8d. Arrival of relief force	70	90
356		1s. Grand Master J. de La Valette's arms	35	10
357		1s.6d. "Allegory of Victory" (from mural by M. Preti)	70	30
358		2s.6d. Victory medal	1·10	3·00

Sizes: As T **131**—1s. Square: (32½×32½ mm)—others.

137 The Three Kings

1965. Christmas.

359	**137**	1d. purple and red	10	10
360	**137**	4d. purple and blue	30	30
361	**137**	1s.3d. slate and purple	30	30

138 Sir Winston Churchill

1966. Churchill Commemoration.

362	**138**	2d. black, red and gold	30	10
363	-	3d. green, olive and gold	30	10
364	**138**	1s. purple, red and gold	45	10
365	-	1s.6d. blue, ultram & gold	65	1·10

Design: 3d., 1s.6d. Sir Winston Churchill and George Cross.

140 Grand Master La Valette

1966. 400th Anniversary of Valletta. Multicoloured.

366		2d. Type **140**	10	10
367		3d. Pope Pius V	15	10
368		6d. Map of Valletta	20	10
369		1s. F. Laparelli (architect)	20	10

370 2s.6d. G. Cassar (architect) 45 60

145 President Kennedy and Memorial

1966. President Kennedy Commemoration.
371 **145** 3d. olive, gold and black 10 10
372 **145** 1s.6d. blue, gold and black 10 10

146 Trade

1966. Tenth Malta Trade Fair.
373 **146** 2d. multicoloured 10 10
374 **146** 8d. multicoloured 50 1·10
375 **146** 2s.6d. multicoloured 55 1·10

147 The Child in the Manger

1966. Christmas.
376 **147** 1d. multicoloured 10 10
377 **147** 4d. multicoloured 10 10
378 **147** 1s.3d. multicoloured 10 10

148 George Cross

1967. 25th Anniversary of George Cross Award to Malta.
379 **148** 2d. multicoloured 10 10
380 **148** 4d. multicoloured 10 10
381 **148** 3s. multicoloured 20 40

149 Crucifixion of St Peter

1967. 1900th Anniversary of Martyrdom of St Peter and St Paul.
382 **149** 2d. brown, orange & black 10 10
383 - 8d. olive, gold and black 15 10
384 - 3s. blue and black 20 20

Designs: As T **149**—3s. Beheading of St Paul. Horiz (47×25 mm)—8d. Open Bible and episcopal emblems.

152 *St Catherine of Siena*

1967. 300th Death Anniversary of Melchior Gafa (sculptor). Multicoloured.
385 2d. Type **152** 10 10
386 4d. *St Thomas of Villanova* 10 10
387 1s.6d. *Baptism of Christ* (detail) 15 10
388 2s.6d. St John the Baptist (from *Baptism of Christ*) 25 20

156 Temple Ruins, Tarxien

1967. 15th International Historical Architecture Congress, Valletta. Multicoloured.
389 2d. Type **156** 10 10
390 6d. Facade of Palazzo Falzon, Notabile 10 10
391 1s. Parish Church, Birkirkara 10 10
392 3s. Portal, Auberge de Castille 25 25

160 Angels

1967. Christmas. Multicoloured.
393 1d. Type **160** 10 10
394 8d. Crib 20 10
395 1s.4d. Angels (diferent) 20 10

163 Queen Elizabeth II and Arms of Malta

1967. Royal Visit.
396 **163** 2d. multicoloured 10 10
397 - 4d. black, purple and gold 10 10
398 - 3s. multicoloured 20 30

Designs: Vert—4d. Queen in Robes of Order of St Michael and St George. Horiz—3s. Queen and outline of Malta.

166 Human Rights Emblem and People

1968. Human Rights Year. Multicoloured.
399 2d. Type **166** 10 10
400 6d. Human Rights emblem and people (different) 10 10
401 2s. Type **166** (reversed) 10 15

169 Fair Products

1968. Malta International Trade Fair.
402 **169** 4d. multicoloured 10 10
403 **169** 8d. multicoloured 10 10
404 **169** 3s. multicoloured 20 15

170 Arms of the Order of St John and La Valette

1968. Fourth Death Centenary of Grand Master La Valette. Multicoloured.
405 1d. Type **170** 10 10
406 8d. *La Valette* (A. de Favray) (vert) 15 10
407 1s.6d. La Valette's tomb (28×23 mm) 15 10
408 2s.6d. Angels and scroll bearing date of death (vert) 20 25

174 Star of Bethlehem and Angel waking Shepherds

1968. Christmas. Multicoloured.
409 1d. Type **174** 10 10
410 8d. Mary and Joseph with shepherd watching over Cradle 15 10
411 1s.4d. Three Wise Men and Star of Bethlehem 15 20

177 Agriculture

1968. Sixth Food and Agricultural Organisation Regional Conference for Europe. Multicoloured.
412 4d. Type **177** 10 10
413 1s. FAO emblem and coin 10 10
414 2s.6d. Agriculture sowing Seeds 20 15

180 Mahatma Gandhi

1969. Birth Centenary of Mahatma Gandhi.
415 **180** 1s.6d. brown, black & gold 65 10

181 ILO Emblem

1969. 50th Anniversary of International Labour Organisation.
416 **181** 2d. blue, gold & turquoise 10 10
417 **181** 6d. sepia, gold and brown 10 10

182 Robert Samut

1969. Birth Centenary of Robert Samut (composer of Maltese National Anthem).
418 **182** 2d. multicoloured 10 10

183 Dove of Peace, UN Emblem and Sea-bed

1969. United Nations Resolution on Oceanic Resources.
419 **183** 5d. multicoloured 10 10

184 'Swallows' returning to Malta

1969. Maltese Migrants' Convention.
420 **184** 10d. black, gold and olive 10 10

185 University Arms and Grand Master de Fonseca (founder)

1969. Bicentenary of University of Malta.
421 **185** 2s. multicoloured 15 20

187 Flag of Malta and Birds

1969. Fifth Anniversary of Independence.
422 - 2d. multicoloured 10 10
423 **187** 5d. black, red and gold 10 10
424 - 10d. black, blue and gold 10 10
425 - 1s.6d. multicoloured 20 40
426 - 2s.6d. black, brown & gold 25 50

Designs: Square (31×31 mm)—2d. 1919 War Monument. Vert—10d. Tourism; 1s.6d. UN and Council of Europe emblems; 2s.6d. Trade and Industry.

191 Peasants playing Tambourine and Bagpipes

1969. Christmas. Children's Welfare Fund. Multicoloured.
427 1d.+1d. Type **191** 10 20
428 5d.+1d. Angels playing trumpet and harp 15 20
429 1s.6d.+3d. Choir boys singing 15 45

194 *The Beheading of St John* (Caravaggio)

1970. 13th Council of Europe Art Exhibition. Multicoloured.
430 1d. Type **194** 10 10
431 2d. *St John the Baptist* (M. Preti) 10 10
432 5d. Interior of St John's Co-Cathedral, Valletta 10 10
433 6d. *Allegory of the Order* (Neapolitan school) 15 10
434 8d. *St Jerome* (Caravaggio) 15 50
435 10d. Articles from the Order of St John in Malta 15 10
436 1s.6d. *The Blessed Gerard receiving Godfrey de Bouillon* (A. de Favray) 25 40
437 2s. Cape and Stolone (16th-cent) 25 55

Sizes: Horiz—1d., 8d. 56×30 mm; 2d., 6d. 45×32 mm; 10d., 2s. 63×21 mm; 1s.6d. 45×34 mm. Square—5d. 39×39 mm.

202 Artist's Impression of Fujiyama

1970. World Fair, Osaka.
438 **202** 2d. multicoloured 10 10
439 **202** 5d. multicoloured 10 10
440 **202** 3s. multicoloured 15 15

203 'Peace and Justice'

1970. 25th Anniversary of United Nations.
441 **203** 2d. multicoloured 10 10
442 **203** 5d. multicoloured 10 10
443 **203** 2s.6d. multicoloured 15 15

204 Carol-singers, Church and Star

1970. Christmas. Multicoloured.
444 1d.+½d. Type **204** 10 10
445 10d.+2d. Church, star and Angels with Infant 15 20
446 1s.6d.+3d. Church, star and nativity scene 20 40

207 Books and Quill

1971. Literary Anniversaries. Multicoloured.
447 1s.6d. Type **207** (De Soldanis (historian) death bicentenary) 10 10
448 2s. Dun Karm (poet), books, pens and lamp (birth centenary) 10 15

209 Europa 'Chain'

1971. Europa.

449	**209**	2d. orange, black and olive	10	10
450	**209**	5d. orange, black and red	10	10
451	**209**	1s.6d. orange, blk & slate	60	90

210 *St Joseph, Patron of the Universal Church* (G. Cali)

1971. Centenary of Proclamation of St Joseph as Patron Saint of Catholic Church, and 50th Anniversary of Coronation of the Statue of *Our Lady of Victories*. Multicoloured.

452	2d. Type **210**	10	10
453	5d. Statue of *Our Lady of Victories* and galley	10	10
454	10d. Type **210**	15	10
455	1s.6d. As 5d.	30	40

211 *Centaurea spathulata*

1971. National Plant and Bird of Malta. Multicoloured.

456	2d. Type **211**	10	10
457	5d. Blue rock thrush (horiz)	20	10
458	10d. As 5d.	30	15
459	1s.6d. Type **211**	30	1·25

212 Angel

1971. Christmas. Multicoloured.

460	1d.+½d. Type **212**	10	10
461	10d.+2d. Mary and the Child Jesus	15	25
462	1s.6d.+3d. Joseph lying awake	20	40
MS463	131×113 mm. Nos. 460/462	75	2·50

213 Heart and WHO Emblem

1972. World Health Day.

464	**213**	2d. multicoloured	10	10
465	**213**	10d. multicoloured	15	10
466	**213**	2s.6d. multicoloured	40	80

214 Maltese Cross

1972. Decimal Currency. Coins. Multicoloured.

467	2m. Type **214**	10	10
468	3m. Bee on honeycomb	10	10
469	5m. Earthen lampstand	10	10
470	1c. George Cross	10	10
471	2c. Classical head	10	10
472	5c. Ritual altar	10	10
473	10c. Grandmaster's galley	20	10
474	50c. Great Siege Monument	1·25	1·25

Sizes: 3m., 2c. As T **214.** 5m., 1c., 5c. 25×30 mm. 10c., 50c. 31×38 mm.

1972. Nos. 337a, 339 and 341 surch.

475	1c.3 on 5d. multicoloured	10	10
476	3c. on 8d. multicoloured	15	10
477	5c. on 1s.3d. multicoloured	15	20

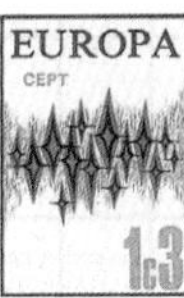

216 Communications

1972. Europa.

478	**216**	1c.3 multicoloured	10	10
479	**216**	3c. multicoloured	10	10
480	**216**	5c. multicoloured	15	35
481	**216**	7c.5 multicoloured	20	75

217 Angel

1972. Christmas.

482	**217**	8m.+2m. brown, grey and gold	10	10
483	-	3c.+1c. purple, violet and gold	15	40
484	-	7c.5+1c.5 indigo, blue and gold	20	50
MS485		137×113 mm. Nos. 482/484	1·75	3·50

Designs: No. 483, Angel with tambourine; No. 484, Singing angel.

See also Nos. 507/**MS**510.

218 Archaeology

1973. Multicoloured.

486	2m. Type **218**	10	10
487	4m. History	10	10
488	5m. Folklore	10	10
489	8m. Industry	10	10
490	1c. Fishing industry	10	10
491	1c.3 Pottery	10	10
492	2c. Agriculture	10	10
493	3c. Sport	10	10
494	4c. Yacht marina	15	10
495	5c. Fiesta	15	10
496	7c.5 Regatta	25	10
497	10c. Voluntary service	25	10
498	50c. Education	2·00	50
499	£1 Religion	2·75	2·00
500	£2 Coat of Arms (32×27 mm)	14·00	19·00
500b	£2 National Emblem (32×27 mm)	7·00	13·00

219 Europa Posthorn

1973. Europa.

501	**219**	3c. multicoloured	15	10
502	**219**	5c. multicoloured	15	35
503	**219**	7c.5 multicoloured	25	65

220 Emblem, and Woman holding Corn

1973. Anniversaries.

504	**220**	1c.3 multicoloured	10	10
505	-	7c.5 multicoloured	25	40
506	-	10c. multicoloured	30	50

Anniversaries: 1c.3, 10th anniversary of World Food Programme; 7c.5, 25th anniversary of WHO; 10c. 25th anniversary of Universal Declaration of Human Rights.

1973. Christmas. As T **217**. Multicoloured.

507	8m.+2m. Angels and organ pipes	15	10
508	3c.+1c. Madonna and Child	25	60
509	7c.5+1c.5 Buildings and Star	45	1·50
MS510	137×112 mm. Nos. 507/509	4·75	7·50

221 Girolamo Cassar (architect)

1974. Prominent Maltese.

511	**221**	1c.3 deep green, green and gold	10	10
512	-	3c. green, blue and gold	15	10
513	-	5c. brown, green and gold	20	15
514	-	7c.5 blue, lt blue & gold	20	30
515	-	10c. deep purple, purple and gold	20	40

Designs: 3c. Giuseppe Barth (ophthalmologist); 5c. Nicolo' Isouard (composer); 7c.5, John Borg (botanist); 10c. Antonio Sciortino (sculptor).

222 Air Malta Emblem

1974. Air. Multicoloured.

516	3c. Type **222**	10	10
517	4c. Boeing 720B	15	10
518	5c. Type **222**	15	10
519	7c.5 As 4c.	15	10
520	20c. Type **222**	25	40
521	25c. As 4c.	25	40
522	35c. Type **222**	35	1·00

223 Prehistoric Sculpture

1974. Europa.

523	**223**	1c.3 blue, black and gold	15	10
524	-	3c. brown, black and gold	20	15
525	-	5c. purple, black and gold	25	50
526	-	7c.5 green, black and gold	35	1·00

Designs: Vert—3c. Old Cathedral Door, Mdina; 7c.5, *Vetlina* (sculpture by A. Sciortino). Horiz—5c. Silver monstrance.

224 Heinrich von Stephan (founder) and Land Transport

1974. Centenary of UPU.

527	**224**	1c.3 green, blue & orange	30	10
528	-	5c. brown, red and green	30	10
529	-	7c.5 blue, violet and green	35	20
530	-	50c. purple, red and orange	1·00	1·25
MS531		126×91 mm. Nos. 527/30	4·75	7·50

Designs: (each containing portrait as T **224**): 5c. *Washington* (paddle-steamer) and *Royal Viking Star* (liner); 7c.5, Balloon and Boeing 747-100; 50c. UPU Buildings, 1874 and 1974.

225 Decorative Star and Nativity Scene

1974. Christmas. Multicoloured.

532	8m.+2m. Type **225**	10	10
533	3c.+1c. Shepherds	15	20
534	5c.+1c. Shepherds with gifts	20	35
535	7c.5+1c.5 The Magi	30	45

226 Swearing-in of Prime Minister

1975. Inauguration of Republic.

536	**226**	1c.3 multicoloured	10	10
537	-	5c. red and black	20	10
538	-	25c. multicoloured	60	1·00

Designs: 5c. National flag; 25c. Minister of Justice, President and Prime Minister.

227 Mother and Child (Family Life)

1975. International Women's Year.

539	**227**	1c.3 violet and gold	15	10
540	-	3c. blue and gold	15	10
541	**227**	5c. brown and gold	20	15
542	-	20c. brown and gold	60	2·50

Design: 3c., 20c. Office secretary (Public Life).

228 *Allegory of Malta* (Francesco de Mura)

1975. Europa. Multicoloured.

543	5c. Type **228**	30	10
544	15c. *Judith and Holofernes* (Valentin de Boulogne)	50	75

The 15c. is smaller, 47×23 mm.

229 Plan of Ggantija Temple

1975. European Architectural Heritage Year.

545	**229**	1c.3 black and red	10	10
546	-	3c. purple, red and brown	20	10
547	-	5c. brown and red	30	25
548	-	25c. green, red and black	1·10	3·00

Designs: 3c. Mdina skyline; 5c. View of Victoria, Gozo; 25c. Silhouette of Fort St Angelo.

230 Farm Animals

1975. Christmas. Multicoloured.

549	8m.+2m. Type **230**	25	25
550	3c.+1c. Nativity scene (50×23 mm)	40	75
551	7c.5+1c.5 Approach of the Magi	45	1·40

231 The Right to Work

1975. First Anniversary of Republic.

552	**231**	1c.3 multicoloured	10	10
553	-	5c. multicoloured	20	10
554	-	25c. red, blue and black	70	1·10

Designs: 5c. Safeguarding the Environment; 25c. National Flag.

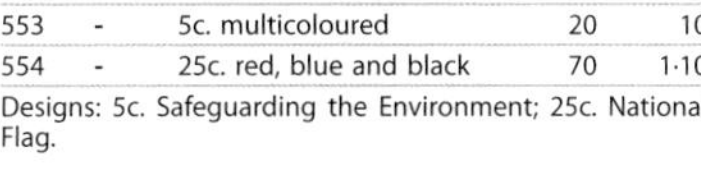

232 'Festa Tar-Rahal'

1976. Maltese Folklore. Multicoloured.

555	1c.3 Type **232**	10	10
556	5c. 'L-Imnarja' (horiz)	15	10
557	7c.5 'Il-Karnival' (horiz)	35	70
558	10c. 'Il-Gimgha L-Kbira'	55	1·40

233 Water Polo

1976. Olympic Games, Montreal. Multicoloured.

559	1c.7 Type **233**	10	10
560	5c. Sailing	25	10
561	30c. Athletics	85	1·50

234 Lace-making

1976. Europa. Multicoloured.

562	7c. Type **234**	20	35
563	15c. Stone carving	25	60

235 Nicola Cotoner

1976. 300th Anniversary of School of Anatomy and Surgery. Multicoloured.

564	2c. Type **235**	10	10
565	5c. Arm	15	10
566	7c. Giuseppe Zammit	20	10
567	11c. Sacra Infermeria	35	65

236 St. John the Baptist and St. Michael

1976. Christmas. Multicoloured.

568	1c.+5m. Type **236**	10	20
569	5c.+1c. Madonna and Child	15	60
570	7c.+1c.5 St Christopher and St Nicholas	20	80
571	10c.+2c. Complete painting (32×27 mm)	30	1·25

Nos. 568/571 show portions of *Madonna and Saints* by Domenico di Michelino.

237 Jean de la Valette's Armour

1977. Suits of Armour. Multicoloured.

572	2c. Type **237**	10	10
573	7c. Aloph de Wignacourt's armour	20	10
574	11c. Jean Jacques de Verdelin's armour	25	50

1977. No. 336 surch **1c7**.

575	1c.7 on 4d. multicoloured	25	25

239 *Annunciation*

1977. 400th Birth Anniversary of Rubens. Flemish Tapestries. Multicoloured.

576	2c. Type **239**	10	10
577	7c. *Four Evangelists*	20	10
578	11c. *Nativity*	35	45
579	20c. *Adoration of the Magi*	55	1·00

See also Nos. 592/595, 615/618 and 638/**MS**640.

240 Map and Radio Aerial

1977. World Telecommunications Day.

580	**240**	1c. black, green and red	10	10
581	**240**	6c. black, blue and red	20	10
582	-	8c. black, brown and red	30	10
583	-	17c. black, mauve and red	60	40

Design: Horiz—8, 17c. Map, aerial and aeroplane tail-fin.

241 Ta' L-Isperanza

1977. Europa. Multicoloured.

584	7c. Type **241**	30	15
585	20c. Is-Salini	35	1·00

242 Aid to Disabled Workers (detail from *Workers' Monument*)

1977. Maltese Worker Commemoration.

586	**242**	2c. orange and brown	10	10
587	-	7c. light brown and brown	15	10
588	-	20c. multicoloured	40	60

Designs: Vert—7c. Stoneworker, modern industry and ship-building (monument detail). Horiz—20c. Mother with Dead Son and Service Medal.

243 The Shepherds

1977. Christmas. Multicoloured.

589	1c.+5m. Type **243**	10	35
590	7c.+1c. The Nativity	15	55
591	11c.+1c.5 The Flight into Egypt	20	70

1978. Flemish Tapestries. (2nd series). As T **239**. Multicoloured.

592	2c. *The Entry into Jerusalem*	10	10
593	7c. *The Last Supper* (after Poussin)	20	10
594	11c. *The Raising of the Cross* (after Rubens)	25	25
595	25c. *The Resurrection* (after Rubens)	60	80

244 *Young Lady on Horseback and Trooper*

1978. 450th Death Anniversary of Albrecht Durer.

596	**244**	1c.7 black, red and blue	10	10
597	-	8c. black, red and grey	15	10
598	-	17c. black, red and grey	40	45

Designs: 8c. *The Bagpiper*; 17c. *The Virgin and Child with a Monkey*.

245 Monument to Grand Master Nicola Cotoner (Foggini)

1978. Europa. Monuments. Multicoloured.

599	7c. Type **245**	15	10
600	25c. Monument to Grand Master Ramon Perellos (Mazzuoli)	35	90

246 Goalkeeper

1978. World Cup Football Championship, Argentina. Multicoloured.

601	2c. Type **246**	10	10
602	11c. Players heading ball	15	10
603	15c. Tackling	25	35
MS604	125×90 mm. Nos. 601/3	1·50	2·50

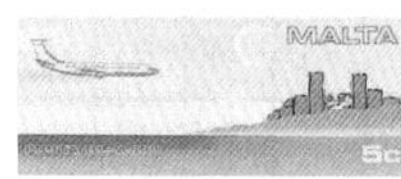

247 Boeing 707 over Megalithic Temple

1978. Air. Multicoloured.

605	5c. Type **247**	20	10
606	7c. Air Malta Boeing 720B	20	10
607	11c. Boeing 747 taking off from Luqa Airport	30	10
608	17c. Type **247**	40	30
609	20c. As 7c.	40	40
610	75c. As 11c.	75	2·40

248 Folk Musicians and Village Church

1978. Christmas. Multicoloured.

611	1c.+5m. Type **248**	10	10
612	5c.+1c. Choir of Angels	15	20
613	7c.+1c.5 Carol singers	20	35
614	11c.+3c. Folk musicians, church, Angels and carol singers (58×22 mm)	25	45

1979. Flemish Tapestries (3rd series) showing paintings by Rubens. As T **239**. Multicoloured.

615	2c. *The Triumph of the Catholic Church*	10	10
616	7c. *The Triumph of Charity*	20	10
617	11c. *The Triumph of Faith*	30	25
618	25c. *The Triumph of Truth*	95	80

249 Fishing Boat and Aircraft Carrier

1979. End of Military Facilities Agreement. Multicoloured.

619	2c. Type **249**	10	10
620	5c. Raising the flag ceremony	10	10
621	7c. Departing soldier and olive sprig	15	10
622	8c. Type **249**	30	30
623	17c. As 5c.	40	45
624	20c. As 7c.	40	45

250 Speronara (fishing boat) and Tail of Air Malta Boeing 707

1979. Europa. Communications. Multicoloured.

625	7c. Type **250**	20	10
626	25c. Coastal watch tower and radio link towers	40	75

251 Children on Globe

1979. International Year of the Child. Multicoloured.

627	2c. Type **251**	10	10
628	7c. Children flying kites (27×33 mm)	15	10
629	11c. Children in circle (27×33 mm)	20	35

252 Shells

1979. Marine Life. Multicoloured.

630	2c. Type **252**	10	10
631	5c. Loggerhead turtle	20	10
632	7c. Dolphinfish	20	10
633	25c. Noble pen shell	70	1·25

253 *The Nativity* (detail)

1979. Christmas. Paintings by Giuseppe Cali. Multicoloured.

634	1c.+5m. Type **253**	10	10
635	5c.+1c. *The Flight into Egypt* (detail)	15	15
636	7c.+1c.5 *The Nativity*	20	20
637	11c.+3c. *The Flight into Egypt*	30	50

1980. Flemish Tapestries (4th series). As T **239**. Multicoloured.

638	2c. *The Institution of Corpus Domini* (Rubens)	10	10
639	8c. *The Destruction of Idolatry* (Rubens)	20	20
MS640	114×86 mm. 50c. *Grand Master Perelles with St Jude and St Simon* (unknown Maltese artist) (vert)	80	1·60

254 Hal Saflieni Hypogeum, Paola

1980. International Restoration of Monuments Campaign. Multicoloured.

641	2c.5 Type **254**	10	15
642	6c. Vilhena Palace, Mdina	15	20
643	8c. Citadel of Victoria, Gozo (horiz)	20	40
644	12c. Fort St. Elmo, Valletta (horiz)	30	60

255 Dun Gorg Preca

1980. Birth Centenary of Dun Gorg Preca (founder of Society of Christian Doctrine).

645	**255**	2c.5 grey and black	10	10

256 Ruzar Briffa (poet)

1980. Europa.

646	**256**	8c. yellow, brown & green	15	10
647	-	30c. green, brown and lake	45	1·25

Design: 30c. Nikiol Anton Vassalli (scholar and patriot).

257 *Annunciation*

1980. Christmas. Paintings by A. Inglott. Multicoloured.

648	2c.+5m. Type **257**	10	10
649	6c.+1c. *Conception*	20	20
650	8c.+1c.5 *Nativity*	25	40
651	12c.+3c. *Annunciation, Conception* and *Nativity* (47×38 mm)	30	70

258 Rook and Pawn

1980. 24th Chess Olympiad and International Chess Federation Congress. Multicoloured.

652	2c.5 Type **258**	20	20
653	8c. Bishop and pawn	45	20
654	30c. King, queen and pawn (vert)	70	1·50

259 Barn Owl

1981. Birds. Multicoloured.

655	3c. Type **259**	30	25
656	8c. Sardinian warbler	50	25
657	12c. Woodchat shrike	60	80
658	23c. British storm petrel	1·10	1·75

260 Traditional Horse Race

1981. Europa. Folklore. Multicoloured.

659	8c. Type **260**	20	10
660	30c. Attempting to retrieve flag from end of gostra (greasy pole)	40	65

261 Stylised '25'

1981. 25th Maltese International Trade Fair.

661	**261** 4c. multicoloured	15	15
662	**261** 25c. multicoloured	50	60

262 Disabled Artist at Work

1981. International Year for Disabled Persons. Multicoloured.

663	3c. Type **262**	20	10
664	35c. Disabled child playing football	90	75

263 Wheat Ear in Conical Flask

1981. World Food Day.

665	**263** 8c. multicoloured	15	15
666	**263** 23c. multicoloured	60	50

264 Megalithic Building

1981. History of Maltese Industry. Multicoloured.

667	5m. Type **264**	10	85
668	1c. Cotton production	10	10
669	2c. Early ship-building	85	10
670	3c. Currency minting	30	10
671	5c. 'Art'	30	25
672	6c. Fishing	1·25	25
673	7c. Agriculture	30	1·50
674	8c. Stone quarrying	1·00	35
675	10c. Grape pressing	35	50
676	12c. Modern ship-building	2·00	2·25
677	15c. Energy	70	2·00
678	20c. Telecommunications	70	75
679	25c. 'Industry'	1·00	2·25
680	50c. Drilling for Water	3·00	2·75
681	£1 Sea transport	5·00	7·50
682	£3 Air transport	11·00	18·00

265 Children and Nativity Scene

1981. Christmas. Multicoloured.

683	2c. +1c. Type **265**	25	10
684	8c. +2c. Christmas Eve procession (horiz)	35	20
685	20c. +3c. Preaching midnight sermon	50	1·10

266 Shipbuilding

1982. Shipbuilding Industry.

686	**266** 3c. multicoloured	15	10
687	- 8c. multicoloured	25	15
688	- 13c. multicoloured	40	35
689	- 27c. multicoloured	1·00	1·25

Designs: 8c. to 27c. Differing shipyard scenes.

267 Elderly Man and Has-Serh (home for elderly)

1982. Care of Elderly. Multicoloured.

690	8c. Type **267**	25	20
691	30c. Elderly woman and Has-Zmien (hospital for elderly)	75	1·40

268 Redemption of Islands by Maltese, 1428

1982. Europa. Historical Events. Multicoloured.

692	8c. Type **268**	40	20
693	30c. Declaration of rights by Maltese, 1802	70	1·40

269 Stylised Footballer

1982. World Cup Football Championship, Spain.

694	**269** 3c. multicoloured	15	10
695	- 12c. multicoloured	45	55
696	- 15c. multicoloured	50	65
MS697	125×90 mm. Nos. 694/6	3·50	4·50

Designs: 12c., 15c. Various stylised footballers.

270 Angel appearing to Shepherds

1982. Christmas. Multicoloured.

698	2c.+1c. Type **270**	15	20
699	8c.+2c. Nativity and Three Wise Men bearing gifts	40	60
700	20c.+3c. Nativity scene (45×37 mm)	80	1·25

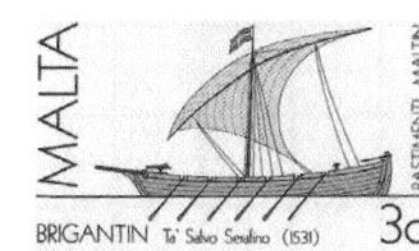

271 *Ta Salvo Serafino* (oared brigantine), 1531

1982. Maltese Ships (1st series). Multicoloured.

701	3c. Type **271**	20	10
702	8c. *La Madonna del Rosaria* (tartane), 1740	40	15
703	12c. *San Paulo* (xebec), 1743	50	40
704	20c. *Ta' Pietro Saliba* (xprunara), 1798	70	80

See also Nos. 725/728, 772/775, 792/795 and 809/812.

272 Locomotive *Manning Wardle*, 1883

1983. Centenary of Malta Railway. Multicoloured.

705	3c. Type **272**	45	15
706	13c. Locomotive *Black Hawthorn*, 1884	85	1·00
707	27c. Beyer Peacock locomotive, 1895	1·50	3·25

273 Peace Doves leaving Malta

1983. Commonwealth Day. Multicoloured.

708	8c. Type **273**	20	30
709	12c. Tourist landmarks	30	60
710	15c. Holiday beach (vert)	35	75
711	23c. Ship-building (vert)	55	1·00

274 Ggantija Megalithic Temples, Gozo

1983. Europa. Multicoloured.

712	8c. Type **274**	40	40
713	30c. Fort St Angelo	70	2·40

275 Dish Aerials (World Communications Year)

1983. Anniversaries and Events. Multicoloured.

714	3c. Type **275**	20	15
715	7c. Ships' prows and badge (25th anniversary of IMO Convention)	40	55
716	13c. Container lorries and badge (30th anniversary of Customs Co-operation Council)	75	90
717	20c. Stadium and emblem (Ninth Mediterranean Games)	65	2·25

276 Monsignor Giuseppe de Piro

1903. 50th Death Anniversary of Monsignor Giuseppe de Piro.

718	**276** 3c. multicoloured	15	15

277 Annunciation

1983. Christmas. Multicoloured.

719	2c.+1c. Type **277**	30	15
720	8c.+2c. The Nativity	70	60
721	20c.+3c. Adoration of the Magi	1·25	2·25

278 Workers at Meeting

1983. 40th Anniversary of General Workers' Union. Multicoloured.

722	3c. Type **278**	15	10
723	8c. Worker with family	35	40
724	27c. Union HQ Building	1·00	1·75

1983. Maltese Ships (2nd series). As T **271**. Multicoloured.

725	2c. *Strangier* (full-rigged ship), 1813	30	25
726	12c. *Tigre* (topsail schooner), 1839	80	1·25
727	13c. *La Speranza* (brig), 1844	80	1·25
728	20c. *Wignacourt* (barque), 1844	1·25	2·75

279 Boeing 737 9H-ABA

1984. Air. Multicoloured.

729	7c. Type **279**	50	30
730	8c. Boeing 720B	60	35
731	16c. Vickers 953 Vanguard G-APED	1·25	70
732	23c. Vickers Viscount 700	1·50	70
733	27c. Douglas DC-3 G-AGHH	1·75	80
734	38c. Armstrong Whitworth A.W.15 Atalanta G-ABTJ *Artemis*	2·25	2·75
735	75c. Marina Fiat MF.5 flying boat I-AZDL	3·25	5·00

280 Bridge

1984. Europa. 25th Anniversary of CEPT.

736	**280** 8c. green, black and yellow	35	35
737	**280** 30c. red, black and yellow	1·00	1·25

281 Early Policeman

1984. 170th Anniversary of Malta Police Force. Multicoloured.

738	3c. Type **281**	65	15
739	8c. Mounted police	1·25	65
740	11c. Motorcycle policeman	1·50	2·00
741	25c. Policeman and firemen	2·25	3·75

282 Running

1984. Olympic Games, Los Angeles. Multicoloured.

742	7c. Type **282**	25	30
743	12c. Gymnastics	50	70
744	23c. Swimming	85	1·25

283 *The Visitation* (Pietru Caruana)

1984. Christmas. Paintings from Church of Our Lady of Porto Salvo, Valletta. Multicoloured.

745	2c.+1c. Type **283**	45	65
746	8c.+2c. *The Epiphany* (Rafel Caruana) (horiz)	80	1·40
747	20c.+3c. *Jesus among the Doctors* (Rafel Caruana) (horiz)	1·75	4·00

284 Dove on Map

1984. Tenth Anniversary of Republic. Multicoloured.

748	3c. Type **284**	30	20
749	8c. Fort St Angelo	60	65
750	30c. Hands	2·10	4·75

285 1885 ½d. Green Stamp

1985. Centenary of Malta Post Office. Multicoloured.

751	3c. Type **285**	45	15
752	8c. 1885 1d. rose	65	45
753	12c. 1885 2½d. blue	90	1·40
754	20c. 1885 4d. brown	1·40	3·00
MS755	165×90 mm. Nos. 751/754	3·75	6·50

286 Boy, and Hands planting Vine

1985. International Youth Year. Multicoloured.

756	2c. Type **286**	15	15
757	13c. Young people and flowers (vert)	70	60
758	27c. Girl holding flame in hand	1·40	1·40

287 Nicolo Baldacchino (tenor)

1985. Europa. European Music Year. Multicoloured.

759	8c. Type **287**	1·25	50
760	30c. Francesco Azopardi (composer)	2·25	4·50

288 Guzeppi Bajada and Manwel Attard (victims)

1985. 66th Anniversary of 7 June 1919 Demonstrations. Multicoloured.

761	3c. Type **288**	30	15
762	7c. Karmnu Abela and Wenzu Dyer (victims)	60	40
763	35c. Model of projected Demonstration monument by Anton Agius (vert)	1·90	2·75

289 Stylised Birds

1985. 40th Anniversary of United Nations Organisation. Multicoloured.

764	4c. Type **289**	25	15
765	11c. Arrow-headed ribbons	60	1·25
766	31c. Stylised figures	1·40	3·25

290 Giorgio Mitrovich (nationalist) (death centenary)

1985. Celebrities' Anniversaries. Multicoloured.

767	8c. Type **290**	75	35
768	12c. Pietru Caxaru (poet and administrator) (400th death anniversary)	1·25	2·50

291 The Three Wise Men

1985. Christmas. Designs showing details of terracotta relief by Ganni Bonnici. Multicoloured.

769	2c.+1c. Type **291**	45	60
770	8c.+2c. Virgin and Child	1·00	1·50
771	20c.+3c. Angels	2·00	3·50

1985. Maltese Ships (3rd series). Steamships. As T **271**. Multicoloured.

772	3c. *Scotia* (paddle-steamer), 1844	85	20
773	7c. *Tagliaferro* (screw-steamer), 1822	1·00	75
774	15c. *Gleneagles* (screw-steamer), 1885	1·50	2·75
775	23c. *L'Isle Adam* (screw-steamer), 1886	2·00	3·75

292 John XXIII Peace Laboratory and Statue of St Francis of Assisi

1986. International Peace Year. Multicoloured.

776	8c. Type **292**	1·00	40
777	11c. Dove and hands holding olive branch (40×19 mm)	1·10	1·75
778	27c. Map of Africa, dove and two heads	2·75	4·75

293 Symbolic Plant and *Cynthia cardui, Vanessa atalanta* and *Polyommatus icarus*

1986. Europa. Environmental Conservation. Multicoloured.

779	8c. Type **293**	1·00	50
780	35c. Island, Neolithic frieze, sea and sun	2·00	5·00

294 Heading the Ball

1986. World Cup Football Championship, Mexico. Multicoloured.

781	3c. Type **294**	50	20
782	7c. Saving a goal	1·00	75
783	23c. Controlling the ball	3·00	5·75
MS784	125×90 mm. Nos. 781/783	7·00	8·50

295 Father Diegu

1986. Maltese Philanthropists. Multicoloured.

785	2c. Type **295**	40	30
786	3c. Adelaide Cini	50	30
787	8c. Alfonso Maria Galea	1·00	60
788	27c. Vincenzo Bugeja	2·75	6·00

296 *Nativity*

1986. Christmas. Paintings by Giuseppe D'Arena. Multicoloured.

789	2c.+1c. Type **296**	1·25	1·75
790	8c.+2c. *Nativity* (detail) (vert)	2·75	3·50
791	20c.+3c. *Epiphany*	3·75	7·00

1986. Maltese Ships (4th series). As T **271**. Multicoloured.

792	7c. *San Paul* (freighter), 1921	1·00	50
793	10c. *Knight of Malta* (mail steamer), 1930	1·25	1·75
794	12c. *Valetta City* (freighter), 1948	1·50	2·75
795	20c. *Saver* (freighter), 1959	2·25	4·50

297 European Robin

1987. 25th Anniversary of Malta Ornithological Society. Multicoloured.

796	3c. Type **297**	1·25	50
797	8c. Peregrine falcon (vert)	2·50	1·00
798	13c. Hoopoe (vert)	3·25	4·00
799	23c. Cory's shearwater	3·75	6·00

298 Aquasun Lido

1987. Europa. Modern Architecture. Multicoloured.

800	8c. Type **298**	75	60
801	35c. Church of St Joseph, Manikata	2·00	4·00

299 16th-century Pikeman

1987. Maltese Uniforms (1st series). Multicoloured.

802	3c. Type **299**	85	40
803	7c. 16th-century officer	1·60	90
804	10c. 18th-century standard bearer	1·75	2·25
805	27c. 18th-century General of the Galleys	3·75	4·75

See also Nos. 832/835, 851/854, 880/883 and 893/896.

300 Maltese Scenes, Wheat Ears and Sun

1987. Anniversaries and Events. Multicoloured.

806	5c. Type **300** (European Environment Year)	1·25	50
807	8c. Esperanto star as comet (Centenary of Esperanto)	2·00	60
808	23c. Family at house door (International Year of Shelter for the Homeless)	3·00	3·00

1987. Maltese Ships (5th series). As T **271**. Multicoloured.

809	2c. *Medina* (freighter), 1969	70	60
810	11c. *Rabat* (container ship), 1974	2·50	2·50
811	13c. *Ghawdex* (passenger ferry), 1979	2·75	2·75
812	20c. *Pinto* (car ferry), 1987	3·75	4·00

301 *The Visitation*

1987. Christmas. Illuminated illustrations, score and text from 16th-century choral manuscript. Multicoloured.

813	2c.+1c. Type **301**	50	65
814	8c.+2c. *The Nativity*	1·75	2·50
815	20c.+3c. *The Adoration of the Magi*	3·25	4·50

302 Dr. Arvid Pardo (UN representative)

1987. 20th Anniversary of United Nations Resolution on Peaceful Use of the Seabed. Multicoloured.

816	8c. Type **302**	1·00	75
817	12c. UN emblem and sea	1·75	3·00
MS818	125×90 mm. Nos. 816/817	3·00	4·50

303 Ven. Nazju Falzon (Catholic catechist)

1988. Maltese Personalities. Multicoloured.

819	2c. Type **303**	30	30
820	3c. Mgr. Sidor Formosa (philanthropist)	30	30
821	4c. Sir Luigi Preziosi (ophthalmologist)	60	30
822	10c. Fr. Anastasju Cuschieri (poet)	80	85
823	25c. Mgr. Pietru Pawl Saydon (Bible translator)	2·00	3·25

304 *St John Bosco with Youth* (statue)

1988. Religious Anniversaries. Multicoloured.

824	10c. Type **304** (death centenary)	1·00	75
825	12c. *Assumption of Our Lady* (altarpiece by Perugino, Ta' Pinu, Gozo) (Marian Year)	1·25	1·25

826	14c. *Christ the King* (statue by Sciortino) (75th anniversary of International Eucharistic Congress, Valletta)	1·50	2·00

305 Bus, Ferry and Airliner

1988. Europa. Transport and Communications. Multicoloured.

827	10c. Type **305**	1·25	75
828	35c. Control panel, dish aerial and pylons	2·00	3·75

306 Globe and Red Cross Emblems

1988. Anniversaries and Events. Multicoloured.

829	4c. Type **306** (125th anniversary of International Red Cross)	60	50
830	18c. Divided globe (Campaign for North–South Interdependence and Solidarity)	1·50	2·50
831	19c. Globe and symbol (40th anniversary of WHO)	1·50	2·50

1988. Maltese Uniforms (2nd series). As T **299**. Multicoloured.

832	3c. Private, Maltese Light Infantry, 1800	50	30
833	4c. Gunner, Malta Coast Artillery, 1802	55	35
834	10c. Field Officer, 1st Maltese Provincial Battalion, 1805	1·40	1·25
835	25c. Subaltern, Royal Malta Regiment, 1809	2·75	4·25

307 Athletics

1988. Olympic Games, Seoul. Multicoloured.

836	4c. Type **307**	30	30
837	10c. Diving	70	80
838	35c. Basketball	2·00	3·00

308 Shepherd with Flock

1988. Christmas. Multicoloured.

839	3c.+1c. Type **308**	30	30
840	10c.+2c. The Nativity	75	1·00
841	25c.+3c. Three Wise Men	1·75	2·50

309 Commonwealth Emblem

1989. 25th Anniversary of Independence. Multicoloured.

842	2c. Type **309**	25	35
843	3c. Council of Europe flag	25	35
844	4c. UN flag	30	35
845	10c. Workers, hands gripping ring and National Flag	75	95
846	12c. Scales and allegorical figure of Justice	80	1·40
847	25c. Prime Minister Borg Olivier with Independence constitution (42×28 mm)	1·60	3·25

310 New State Arms

1989

848	**310** £1 multicoloured	3·50	4·00

311 Two Boys flying Kite

1989. Europa. Children's Games. Multicoloured.

849	10c. Type **311**	75	75
850	35c. Two girls with dolls	2·00	4·00

1989. Maltese Uniforms (3rd series). As T **299**. Multicoloured.

851	3c. Officer, Maltese Veterans, 1815	45	45
852	4c. Subaltern, Royal Malta Fencibles, 1839	50	50
853	10c. Private, Malta Militia, 1856	1·50	1·50
854	25c. Colonel, Royal Malta Fencible Artillery, 1875	2·75	3·75

312 Human Figures and Buildings

1989. Anniversaries and Commemorations. Designs showing logo and stylised human figures. Multicoloured.

855	3c. Type **312** (20th anniv of UN Declaration on Social Progress and Development)	30	30
856	4c. Workers and figure in wheelchair (Malta's Ratification of European Social Charter)	35	35
857	10c. Family (40th anniversary of Council of Europe)	65	1·00
858	14c. Teacher and children (70th anniversary of Malta Union of Teachers)	80	1·50
859	25c. Symbolic knights (Knights of the Sovereign Military Order of Malta Assembly)	1·75	3·50

313 Angel and Cherub

1989. Christmas. Vault paintings by Mattia Preti from St John's Co-Cathedral, Valletta.

860	3c.+1c. Type **313**	60	60
861	10c.+2c. Two Angels	1·40	1·90
862	20c.+3c. Angel blowing trumpet	2·00	4·00

314 Presidents George H. Bush and Mikhail Gorbachev

1989. USA–USSR Summit Meeting, Malta.

863	**314** 10c. multicoloured	1·00	1·25

315 General Post Office, Auberge d'Italie, Valletta

1990. Europa. Post Office Buildings. Multicoloured.

864	10c. Type **315**	75	50
865	35c. Branch Post Office, Zebbug (horiz)	1·50	3·25

316 Open Book and Letters from Different Alphabets (International Literacy Year)

1990. Anniversaries and Events. Multicoloured.

866	3c. Type **316**	25	15
867	4c. Count Roger of Sicily and Norman soldiers (900th anniversary of Sicilian rule) (horiz)	50	25
868	19c. Communications satellite (25th anniversary of ITU) (horiz)	1·60	2·00
869	20c. Football and map of Malta (Union of European Football Association 20th Ordinary Congress, Malta)	1·60	2·00

317 Samuel Taylor Coleridge (poet) and Government House

1990. British Authors. Multicoloured.

870	4c. Type **317**	50	30
871	10c. Lord Byron (poet) and map of Valletta	90	70
872	12c. Sir Walter Scott (novelist) and Great Siege	1·00	95
873	25c. William Makepeace Thackeray (novelist) and Naval Arsenal	2·00	2·25

318 St Paul

1990. Visit of Pope John Paul II. Bronze Bas-reliefs.

874	**318** 4c. black, flesh and red	50	1·50
875	- 25c. black, flesh and red	1·50	1·75

Design: 25c. Pope John Paul II.

319 Flags and Football

1990. World Cup Football Championship, Italy. Multicoloured.

876	5c. Type **319**	35	30
877	10c. Football in net	65	1·00
878	14c. Scoreboard and football	1·00	1·75
MS879	123×90 mm. Nos. 876/878	3·00	4·25

1990. Maltese Uniforms (4th series). As T **299**. Multicoloured.

880	3c. Captain, Royal Malta Militia, 1889	1·25	55
881	4c. Field officer, Royal Malta Artillery, 1905	1·40	60
882	10c. Labourer, Malta Labour Corps, 1915	2·50	1·50
883	25c. Lieutenant, King's Own Malta Regiment of Militia, 1918	3·75	5·00

320 Innkeeper

1990. Christmas. Figures from Crib by Austin Galea, Marco Bartolo and Rosario Zammit. Multicoloured.

884	3c.+1c. Type **320**	30	50
885	10c.+2c. Nativity (41×28 mm)	70	1·25
886	25c.+3c. Shepherd with sheep	1·60	2·50

321 1919 10s. Stamp under Magnifying Glass

1991. 25th Anniversary of Philatelic Society of Malta.

887	**321** 10c. multicoloured	60	70

322 *Eurostar* Satellite and VDU Screen

1991. Europa. Europe in Space. Multicoloured.

888	10c. Type **322**	75	70
889	35c. Ariane 4 rocket and projected HOTOL aerospace-plane	1·50	2·75

323 St Ignatius Loyola (founder of Jesuits) (500th birth anniversary)

1991. Religious Commemorations. Multicoloured.

890	3c. Type **323**	30	20
891	4c. Abbess Venerable Maria Adeodata Pisani (185th birth anniversary) (vert)	35	25
892	30c. St John of the Cross (400th death anniversary)	2·00	2·75

1991. Maltese Uniforms (5th series). As T **299**. Multicoloured.

893	3c. Officer with colour, Royal Malta Fencibles, 1860	50	25
894	10c. Officer with colour, Royal Malta Regiment of Militia, 1903	1·00	60
895	19c. Officer with Queen's colour, King's Own Malta Regiment, 1968	1·90	1·75
896	25c. Officer with colour, Malta Armed Forces, 1991	2·25	2·00

324 Interlocking Arrows

1991. 25th Anniversary of Union Haddiema Maghqudin (public services union).

897	**324** 4c. multicoloured	30	30

325 Western Honey Buzzard

1991. Endangered Species. Birds. Multicoloured.

898	4c. Type **325**	2·50	2·50
899	4c. Marsh harrier	2·50	2·50
900	10c. Eleonora's falcon	2·50	2·50
901	10c. Lesser kestrel	2·50	2·50

326 Three Wise Men

1991. Christmas. Multicoloured.

902	3c.+1c. Type **326**	55	50
903	10c.+2c. Holy Family	1·00	1·40
904	25c.+3c. Two shepherds	2·00	3·25

327 Ta' Hagrat Neolithic Temple

1991. National Heritage of the Maltese Islands. Multicoloured.

905	1c. Type **327**	35	50
906	2c. Cottoner Gate	35	50
907	3c. St. Michael's Bastion, Valletta	40	50
908	4c. Spinola Palace, St. Julian's	50	15
909	5c. Birkirkara Church	60	20
910	10c. Mellieha Bay	1·25	35
911	12c. Wied iz-Zurrieq	1·40	40
912	14c. Mgarr harbour, Gozo	2·00	45
913	20c. Yacht marina	2·50	65
914	50c. Gozo Channel	3·75	1·60
915	£1 *Arab Horses* (sculpture by Antonio Sciortino)	6·00	3·25
916	£2 Independence Monument (Ganni Bonnici) (vert)	11·00	8·00

328 Aircraft Tailfins and Terminal

1992. Opening of International Air Terminal. Multicoloured.

917	4c. Type **328**	75	30
918	10c. National Flags and terminal	1·25	70

329 Ships of Columbus

1992. Europa. 500th Anniversary of Discovery of America by Columbus. Multicoloured.

919	10c. Type **329**	1·25	55
920	35c. Columbus and map of Americas	2·50	2·25

330 George Cross and Anti-aircraft Gun Crew

1992. 50th Anniversary of Award of George Cross to Malta. Multicoloured.

921	4c. Type **330**	1·00	30
922	10c. George Cross and memorial bell	1·50	1·00
923	50c. Tanker *Ohio* entering Grand Harbour	7·00	8·50

331 Running

1992. Olympic Games, Barcelona. Multicoloured.

924	3c. Type **331**	55	20
925	10c. High jumping	80	75
926	30c. Swimming	2·00	4·00

332 Church of the Flight into Egypt

1992. Rehabilitation of Historical Buildings.

927	**332**	3c. black, stone and grey	45	30
928	-	4c. black, stone and pink	45	30
929	-	19c. black, stone and lilac	2·25	3·75
930	-	25c. black, stone and green	2·50	3·75

Designs: Horiz—4c. St John's Co-Cathedral; 25c. Auberge de Provence. Vert—19c. Church of Madonna del Pillar.

333 *The Nativity* (Giuseppe Cali)

1992. Christmas. Religious Paintings by Giuseppe Cali from Mosta Church. Multicoloured.

931	3c.+1c. Type **333**	75	1·10
932	10c.+2c. *Adoration of the Magi*	1·75	2·50
933	25c.+3c. *Christ with the Elders in the Temple*	3·00	4·50

334 Malta College Building, Valletta

1992. 400th Anniversary of University of Malta. Multicoloured.

934	4c. Type **334**	75	25
935	30c. Modern University complex, Tal-Qroqq (horiz)	2·50	4·25

335 Lions Club Emblem

1993. 75th Anniversary of International Association of Lions Club. Multicoloured.

936	4c. Type **335**	50	25
937	50c. Eye (Sight First Campaign)	2·75	4·00

336 Untitled Painting by Paul Carbonaro

1993. Europa. Contemporary Art. Multicoloured.

938	10c. Type **336**	1·00	50
939	35c. Untitled painting by Alfred Chircop (horiz)	2·25	4·25

337 Mascot holding Flame

1993. Fifth Small States of Europe Games. Multicoloured.

940	3c. Type **337**	20	20
941	4c. Cycling	1·75	30
942	10c. Tennis	1·25	1·00
943	35c. Yachting	2·00	3·50
MS944	120×80 mm. Nos. 940/943	4·50	5·50

338 Learning First Aid

1993. 50th Anniversary of Award of Bronze Cross to Maltese Scouts and Guides. Multicoloured.

945	3c. Type **338**	50	20
946	4c. Bronze Cross	50	20
947	10c. Scout building camp fire	1·10	90
948	35c. Governor Lord Gort presenting Bronze Cross, 1943	2·75	4·00

339 *Papilio machaon*

1993. European Year of the Elderly. Butterflies. Multicoloured.

949	5c. Type **339**	35	20
950	35c. *Vanessa atalanta*	1·75	2·25

340 GWU Badge and Interlocking '50'

1993. 50th Anniversary of General Workers Union.

951	**340**	4c. multicoloured	35	40

341 Child Jesus and Star

1993. Christmas. Multicoloured.

952	3c.+1c. Type **341**	30	35
953	10c.+2c. Christmas tree	85	1·25
954	25c.+3c. Star in traditional window	1·60	2·75

342 Council Arms (face value top left)

1993. Inauguration of Local Community Councils. Sheet 110×93 mm, containing T **342** and similar horiz designs showing different Council Arms. Multicoloured.

MS955	5c. Type **342**; 5c. Face value top right; 5c. Face value bottom left; 5c. Face value bottom right	1·50	2·25

343 Symbolic Tooth and Probe

1994. 50th Anniversary of Maltese Dental Association. Multicoloured.

956	5c. Type **343**	35	30
957	44c. Symbolic mouth and dental mirror	2·25	2·50

344 Sir Themistocles Zammit (discoverer of Brucella microbe)

1994. Europa. Discoveries. Multicoloured.

958	14c. Type **344**	50	30
959	30c. Bilingually inscribed candelabrum of 2nd-century BC (deciphering of ancient Phoenician language)	1·90	3·25

345 Family in Silhouette (International Year of the Family)

1994. Anniversaries and Events. Multicoloured.

960	5c. Type **345**	30	20
961	9c. Stylised Red Cross (International recognition of Malta Red Cross Society)	60	50
962	14c. Animals and crops (150th anniversary of Agrarian Society)	90	80
963	20c. Worker in silhouette (75th anniversary of ILO)	1·25	1·60
964	25c. St Paul's Anglican Cathedral (155th anniversary) (vert)	1·40	1·75

346 Football and Map

1994. World Cup Football Championship, USA. Multicoloured.

965	5c. Type **346**	40	20
966	14c. Ball and goal	1·00	80
967	30c. Ball and pitch superimposed on map	2·00	4·25
MS968	123×88 mm. Nos. 965/967	3·75	4·50

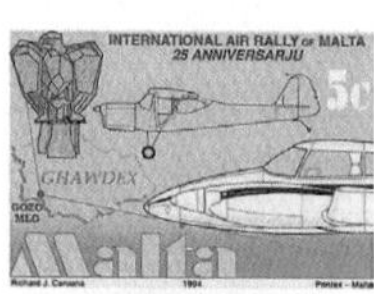

347 Falcon Trophy, Piper PA-30 Twin Commanche and Auster J-5 Autocar (25th anniversary of Malta International Rally)

1994. Aviation Anniversaries and Events. Multicoloured.

969	5c. Type **347**	50	20
970	14c. Aerospatiale (Sud) Alouette helicopter, display teams and logo (Malta International Airshow)	1·75	85
971	20c. de Havilland DH.104 Dove *City of Valetta* and Avro Type 685 York aircraft with logo (50th anniversary of ICAO)	1·90	1·75
972	25c. Airbus 320 *Nicolas Cottoner* and de Havilland DH.106 Comet aircraft with logo (50th anniversary of ICAO)	1·90	1·90

348 National Flags and Astronaut on Moon

1994. 25th Anniversary of First Manned Moon Landing.

973	**348**	14c. multicoloured	1·10	1·25

349 Virgin Mary and Child with Angels

1994. Christmas. Multicoloured.

974	5c. Type **349**	20	10
975	9c.+2c. Angel in pink (vert)	50	70
976	14c.+3c. Virgin Mary and Child (vert)	80	1·25
977	20c.+3c. Angel in green (vert)	1·25	2·50

Nos. 975/977 are larger, 28×41 mm, and depict details from T **349**.

350 Helmet-shaped Ewer

1994. Maltese Antique Silver Exhibition. Multicoloured.

978	5c. Type **350**	50	20
979	14c. Balsamina	1·10	80
980	20c. Coffee pot	1·50	2·00
981	25c. Sugar box	1·75	2·75

351 '60 plus' and Hands touching

1995. Anniversaries and Events. Multicoloured.

982	2c. Type **351** (25th anniversary of National Association of Pensioners)	15	25
983	5c. Child's drawing (Tenth anniversary of National Youth Council)	25	20
984	14c. Conference emblem (Fourth World Conference on Women, Peking, China)	50	60
985	20c. Nurse and thermometer (50th anniversary of Malta Memorial District Nursing Association)	1·25	1·40
986	25c. Louis Pasteur (biologist) (death centenary)	1·50	1·75

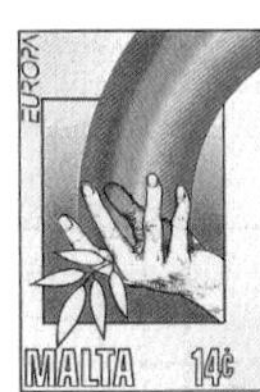

352 Hand holding Leaf and Rainbow

1995. Europa. Peace and Freedom. Multicoloured.

987	14c. Type **352**	1·00	55
988	30c. Peace Doves (horiz)	1·50	2·50

353 Junkers Ju 87B Stuka Dive Bombers over Valletta and Anti-aircraft Gun

1995. Anniversaries. Multicoloured.

989	5c. Type **353** (50th anniversary of end of Second World War)	25	25
990	14c. Silhouetted people holding hands (50th anniversary of United Nations)	55	60
991	35c. Hands holding bowl of wheat (50th Anniversary of FAO) (vert)	1·60	2·25

354 Light Bulb

1995. Maltese Electricity and Telecommunications. Multicoloured.

992	2c. Type **354**	15	25
993	5c. Symbolic owl and binary codes	25	15
994	9c. Dish aerial	35	50
995	14c. Sun and rainbow over trees	50	65
996	20c. Early telephone, satellite and Moon's surface	1·00	1·50

355 Rock Wall and Girna

1995. European Nature Conservation Year. Multicoloured.

997	5c. Type **355**	75	25
998	14c. Maltese wall lizards	2·25	80
999	44c. Aleppo pine	3·50	3·00

356 Pinto's Turret Clock

1995. Treasures of Malta. Antique Maltese Clocks. Multicoloured.

1000	1c. Type **356**	15	60
1001	5c. Michelangelo Sapiano (horologist) and clocks	50	25
1002	14c. Arlogg tal-lira clock	1·50	80
1003	25c. Sundials	2·50	3·50

357 Children's Christmas Eve Procession

1995. Christmas. Multicoloured.

1004	5c. Type **357**	25	10
1005	5c.+2c. Children with crib (vert)	30	50
1006	14c.+3c. Children with lanterns (vert)	1·00	1·25
1007	25c.+3c. Boy with lantern and balustrade (vert)	1·75	2·75

Nos. 1005/1007 are 27×32 mm and depict details from T **357**.

358 Silhouetted Children and President's Palace, San Anton

1996. Anniversaries. Multicoloured.

1008	5c. Type **358** (35th anniversary of the President's Award)	20	15
1009	14c. Nazzareno Camilleri (priest) and St Patrick's Church, Salesjani (90th birth anniversary)	50	50
1010	20c. St Mary Euphrasia and convent (birth bicentenary)	80	1·10
1011	25c. Silhouetted children and fountain (50th anniversary of UNICEF)	95	1·60

359 Carved Figures from Skorba

1996. Maltese Prehistoric Art Exhibition. Multicoloured.

1012	5c. Type **359**	25	15
1013	14c. Temple carving, Gozo	60	65
1014	20c. Carved figure of a woman, Skorba (vert)	80	1·00
1015	35c. Ghar Dalam pot (vert)	1·50	3·00

360 Mabel Strickland (politician and journalist)

1996. Europa. Famous Women. Multicoloured.

1016	14c. Type **360**	75	55
1017	30c. Inez Soler (artist, musician and writer)	2·00	2·00

361 Face and Emblem (United Nations Decade against Drug Abuse)

1996. Anniversaries and Events. Multicoloured.

1018	5c. Type **361**	20	20
1019	5c. 'Fi' and emblem (50th anniversary of Malta Federation of Industry)	20	20
1020	14c. Commemorative plaque and National Flag (75th anniversary of self-government)	60	60
1021	44c. Guglielmo Marconi and early radio equipment (centenary of radio)	1·50	2·50

362 Judo

1996. Olympic Games, Atlanta. Multicoloured.

1022	2c. Type **362**	10	20
1023	5c. Athletics	30	15
1024	14c. Diving	70	80
1025	25c. Rifle-shooting	1·10	1·60

363 *Harvest Time* (Cali)

1996. 150th Birth Anniversary of Guiseppe Cali (painter). Multicoloured.

1026	5c. Type **363**	30	25
1027	14c. *Dog* (Cali)	70	70
1028	20c. *Countrywoman in a Field* (Cali) (vert)	90	1·10
1029	25c. *Cali at his Easel* (Edward Dingli) (vert)	1·00	1·25

364 Bus No. 1990 'Diamond Star', 1920s

1996. Buses. Multicoloured.

1030	2c. Type **364**	40	10
1031	5c. No. 434 'Tom Mix', 1930s	70	25
1032	14c. No. 1764 'Verdala', 1940s	1·40	80
1033	30c. No. 3495, 1960s	2·00	2·00

365 Stained Glass Window

1996. Christmas. Multicoloured.

1034	5c. Type **365**	35	10
1035	5c.+2c. Madonna and Child (29×35 mm)	40	60
1036	14c.+3c. Angel facing right (29×35 mm)	80	1·40
1037	25c.+3c. Angel facing left (29×35 mm)	1·25	2·50

Nos. 1035/1037 show details from T **365**.

366 Hompesch Arch and Arms, Zabbar

1997. Bicentenary of Maltese Cities. Multicoloured.

1038	6c. Type **366**	30	25
1039	16c. Statue, church and Arms, Siggiewi	70	70
1040	26c. Seated statue and Arms, Zejtun	1·10	1·25
MS1041	125×90 mm. Nos. 1038/1040	5·50	4·50

367 Captain-General of the Galleys' Sedan Chair

1997. Treasures of Malta. Sedan Chairs. Multicoloured.

1042	2c. Type **367**	15	15
1043	6c. Cotoner Grandmasters' chair	30	30
1044	16c. Chair from Cathedral Museum, Mdina (vert)	70	70
1045	27c. Chevalier D'Arezzo's chair (vert)	1·10	1·10

368 Gahan carrying Door

1997. Europa. Tales and Legends. Multicoloured.

1046	16c. Type **368**	1·00	75
1047	35c. St Dimitrius appearing from painting	1·75	2·50

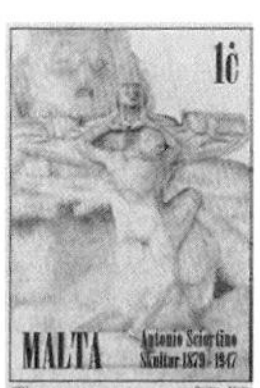

369 Modern Sculpture (Antonio Sciortino)

1997. Anniversaries. Multicoloured.

1048	1c. Type **369**	10	15
1049	6c. Joseph Calleia and film reel (horiz)	40	40
1050	6c. Gozo Cathedral (horiz)	40	40
1051	11c. City of Gozo (horiz)	60	50
1052	16c. Sculpture of head (Sciortino)	80	70
1053	22c. Joseph Calleia and film camera (horiz)	1·00	1·00

Anniversaries: 1, 16c. 50th death anniversary of Antonio Sciortino (sculptor); 6 (No. 1049), 22c. Birth centenary of Joseph Calleia (actor); 6 (No. 1050), 11c. 300th Anniversary of construction of Gozo Cathedral.

370 Dr. Albert Laferla

1997. Pioneers of Education. Multicoloured.

1054	6c. Type **370**	30	25
1055	16c. Sister Emilie de Vialar	70	70
1056	19c. Mgr. Paolo Pullicino	80	80
1057	26c. Mgr. Tommaso Gargallo	1·00	1·10

371 The Nativity

1997. Christmas. Multicoloured.

1058	6c. Type **371**	30	10
1059	6c.+2c. Mary and baby Jesus (vert)	35	50
1060	16c.+3c. Joseph with donkey (vert)	1·00	1·40
1061	26c.+3c. Shepherd with lamb (vert)	1·50	2·50

Nos. 1059/1061 show details from T **371**.

372 Plan of Fort and Soldiers in Victoria Lines

1997. Anniversaries. Multicoloured (except 6c.).

1062	2c. Type **372**	20	10
1063	6c. Sir Paul Boffa making speech (black and red)	30	25
1064	16c. Plan of fort and gun crew	90	65
1065	37c. Queue of voters	1·50	2·00

Anniversaries: 2, 16c. Centenary of Victoria Lines; 6, 37c. 50th anniversary of 1947 Self-government Constitution.

373 *Maria Amelia Grognet* (Antonine de Favray)

1998. Treasures of Malta. Costumes and Paintings.

1066	6c. Type **373**	80	50
1067	6c. Gentleman's waistcoat, *c.*1790–1810	80	50
1068	16c. Lady's dinner dress, *c.*1880	1·10	90
1069	16c. *Veneranda, Baroness Abela, and her Grandson* (De Favray)	1·10	90
MS1070	123×88 mm. 26c. City of Valletta from old print (39×47 mm)	1·60	1·60

374 Grand Master Ferdinand von Hompesch

1998. Bicentenary of Napoleon's Capture of Malta. Multicoloured.

1071	6c. Type **374**	60	80
1072	6c. French fleet	60	80
1073	16c. French landing	1·10	1·60
1074	16c. General Napoleon Bonaparte	1·10	1·60

375 Racing Two-man Luzzus

1998. Europa. Sailing Regatta, Grand Harbour. Multicoloured.

1075	16c. Type **375**	1·10	55
1076	35c. Racing four-man luzzus	1·50	2·50

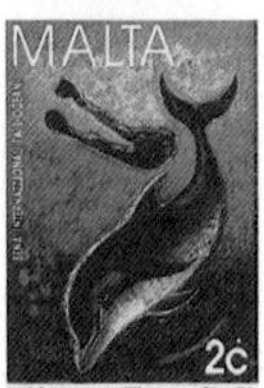

376 Dolphin and Diver

1998. International Year of the Ocean. Multicoloured.

1077	2c. Type **376**	40	25
1078	6c. Diver and sea-urchin	65	25
1079	16c. Jacques Cousteau and diver (horiz)	1·60	80
1080	27c. Two divers (horiz)	2·00	2·25

377 Goalkeeper saving Goal

1998. World Cup Football Championship, France. Players and flags. Multicoloured.

1081	6c. Type **377**	70	25
1082	16c. Two players and referee	1·40	70
1083	22c. Two footballers	1·60	2·00
MS1084	122×87 mm. Nos. 1081/1083	3·50	3·25

378 Ships' Wheels (50th anniversary of International Maritime Organisation)

1998. Anniversaries. Multicoloured.

1085	1c. Type **378**	10	30
1086	6c. Symbolic family (50th anniversary of Universal Declaration of Human Rights)	40	25
1087	11c. 'GRTU' and cogwheels (50th anniversary of General Retailers and Traders Union)	70	40
1088	19c. Mercury (50th anniversary of Chamber of Commerce)	1·10	1·40
1089	26c. Aircraft tailfins (25th anniversary of Air Malta)	2·40	2·50

379 *Rest on the Flight to Egypt*

1998. Christmas. Paintings by Mattia Preti. Multicoloured.

1090	6c. Type **379**	40	10
1091	6c.+2c. *Virgin and Child with St Anthony and St John the Baptist*	50	70
1092	16c.+3c. *Virgin and Child with St Raphael, St Nicholas and St Gregory*	1·25	1·75
1093	26c.+3c. *Virgin and Child with St John the Baptist and St Nicholas*	1·75	3·00

380 Fort St Angelo

1999. 900th Anniversary of the Sovereign Military Order of Malta. Multicoloured.

1094	2c. Type **380**	35	10
1095	6c. Grand Master De l'Isle Adam (vert)	60	25
1096	16c. Grand Master La Valette (vert)	1·25	65
1097	27c. Auberge de Castille et Leon	2·00	3·00

381 Little Ringed Plover, Ghadira Nature Reserve

1999. Europa. Parks and Gardens. Multicoloured.

1098	16c. Type **381**	2·00	55
1099	35c. River kingfisher, Simar Nature Reserve	2·50	3·00

382 Council of Europe Assembly

1999. 50th Anniversary of Council of Europe. Multicoloured.

1100	6c. Type **382**	60	25
1101	16c. Council of Europe Headquarters, Strasbourg	1·00	1·25

383 UPU Emblem and Marsamxett Harbour, Valletta

1999. 125th Anniversary of Universal Postal Union. Multicoloured.

1102	6c. Type **383**	1·25	1·50
1103	16c. Nuremberg and iBRA '99 International Stamp Exhibition emblem	1·50	1·75
1104	22c. Paris and Philexfrance '99 International Stamp Exhibition emblem	1·60	1·90
1105	27c. Peking and China '99 International Stamp Exhibition emblem	1·75	2·00
1106	37c. Melbourne and Australia '99 International Stamp Exhibition emblem	1·90	2·50

384 Couple in Luzzu

1999. Tourism. Multicoloured.

1107	6c. Type **384**	50	25
1108	16c. Tourist taking photograph	95	55
1109	22c. Man sunbathing (horiz)	1·25	1·00
1110	27c. Couple with horse-drawn carriage (horiz)	1·90	1·40
1111	37c. Caveman at Ta' Hagrat Neolithic temple (horiz)	2·50	3·25

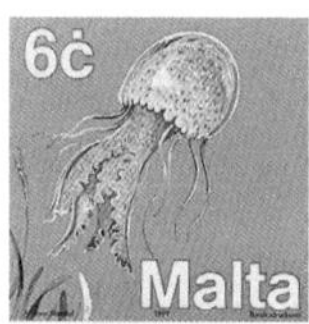

385 Common Jellyfish

1999. Marine Life of the Mediterranean. Multicoloured.

1112	6c. Type **385**	70	75
1113	6c. Peacock wrasse	70	75
1114	6c. Common cuttlefish	70	75
1115	6c. Violet sea-urchin	70	75
1116	6c. Dusky grouper	70	75
1117	6c. Common two-banded seabream	70	75
1118	6c. Star-coral	70	75
1119	6c. Spiny spider crab	70	75
1120	6c. Rainbow wrasse	70	75
1121	6c. Octopus	70	75
1122	6c. Atlantic trumpet triton	70	75
1123	6c. Mediterranean parrotfish	70	75
1124	6c. Long-snouted seahorse	70	75
1125	6c. Deep-water hermit crab	70	75
1126	6c. Mediterranean moray	70	75
1127	6c. Common starfish	70	75

Nos. 1112/1127 were printed together, *se-tenant*, forming a composite design.

386 Father Mikiel Scerri

1999. Bicentenary of Maltese Uprising against the French. Multicoloured.

1128	6c. Type **386**	75	90
1129	6c. *L-Eroj Maltin* (statue)	75	90
1130	16c. General Belgrand de Vaubois (French commander)	1·25	1·75
1131	16c. Captain Alexander Ball RN	1·25	1·75

387 Wolfgang Philip Guttenberg interceding with The Virgin (votive painting)

1999. Mellieha Sanctuary Commemoration. Multicoloured.

1132	**387** 35c. multicoloured	1·90	2·50
MS1133	123×88 mm. 6c. *Mellieha Virgin and Child* (rock painting) (vert)	1·00	1·10

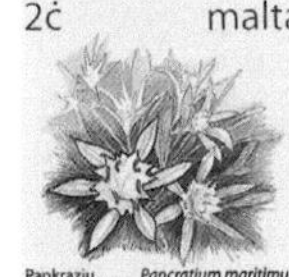

388 Sea Daffodil

1999. Maltese Flowers. Multicoloured.

1134	1c. *Helichrysum melitense*	10	20
1135	2c. Type **388**	10	30
1136	3c. *Cistus creticus*	10	50
1137	4c. Southern dwarf iris	15	35
1138	5c. *Papaver rhoeas*	1·00	60
1139	6c. French daffodil	25	25
1139a	7c. *Vitex angus-castus*	50	65
1140	10c. *Rosa sempervirens*	40	35
1141	11c. *Silene colorata*	1·25	40
1142	12c. *Cynara cardunculus*	50	45
1143	16c. Yellow-throated crocus	65	55
1144	19c. *Anthemis arvensis*	1·50	65
1145	20c. *Anacamptis pyramidalis*	1·00	70
1145a	22c. *Spartium junceum*	1·75	75
1146	25c. Large Star of Bethlehem	1·10	85
1147	27c. *Borago officinalis*	2·50	90
1147a	28c. *Crataegus azalorus*	1·75	95
1147b	37c. *Cercis siliquastrum*	2·00	1·40
1147c	45c. *Myrtus communis*	2·25	1·75
1148	46c. Wild tulip	2·25	1·75
1149	50c. *Chrysanthemum coronarium*	3·25	1·90
1149a	76c. *Pistacia lentiscus*	5·00	3·25
1150	£1 *Malva sylvestris*	5·00	4·25
1151	£2 *Adonis microcarpa*	8·00	8·50

389 Madonna and Child

1999. Christmas. Multicoloured.

1152	6c. Type **389**	60	10
1153	6c.+3c. Carol singers	65	80
1154	16c.+3c. Santa Claus	1·60	2·00
1155	26c.+3c. Christmas decorations	2·00	3·00

390 Parliament Chamber and Symbolic Luzzu

1999. 25th Anniversary of Republic. Multicoloured.

1156	6c. Type **390**	40	25
1157	11c. Parliament in session and Council of Europe emblem	60	35
1158	16c. Church and Central Bank of Malta building	80	55
1159	19c. Aerial view of Gozo and emblems	1·10	1·00
1160	26c. Computer and shipyard	1·40	1·60

391 Gift and Flowers

2000. Greetings Stamps. Multicoloured.

1161	3c. Type **391**	30	15
1162	6c. Photograph, envelope and rose	50	25
1163	16c. Flowers and silver heart	1·00	55
1164	20c. Champagne and pocket watch	1·25	1·00
1165	22c. Wedding rings and roses	1·25	1·40

392 Luzzu and Cruise Liner

2000. Malta during the 20th-century. Multicoloured.

1166	6c. Type **392**	65	25
1167	16c. Street musicians and modern street carnival	90	65
1168	22c. Family in 1900 and illuminated quayside	1·25	1·25
1169	27c. Rural occupations and Citadel, Victoria	1·75	2·50

393 Footballers and Trophy (Centenary of Malta Football Association)

2000. Sporting Events. Multicoloured.

1170	6c. Type **393**	55	25
1171	16c. Swimming and sailing (Olympic Games, Sydney)	85	55
1172	26c. Judo, shooting and running (Olympic Games, Sydney)	1·40	1·10
1173	37c. Football (European Championship)	1·75	2·50

394 Building Europe

2000. Europa.

1174	**394**	16c. multicoloured	1·25	65
1175	**394**	46c. multicoloured	2·75	3·25

395 de Havilland DH.66 Hercules, 1928

2000. Century of Air Transport, 1900–2000. Multicoloured.

1176	6c. Type **395**	85	1·10
1177	6c. LZ 127 *Graf Zeppelin*, 1933	85	1·10
1178	16c. Douglas DC-3 Dakota of Air Malta Ltd, 1949	1·60	1·90
1179	16c. Airbus Industries Airbus A320 of Air Malta	1·60	1·90
MS1180	122×87 mm. Nos. 1176/1179	4·50	5·50

Nos. 1176/1177 and 1178/1179 were each printed together, se-tenant, with the backgrounds forming composite designs.

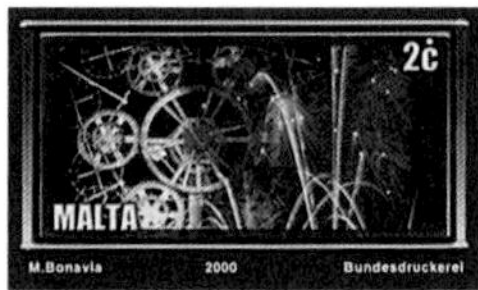

396 Catherine Wheel and Fireworks

2000. Fireworks. Multicoloured.

1181	2c. Type **396**	25	10
1182	6c. Exploding multicoloured fireworks	50	25
1183	16c. Catherine wheel	1·00	55
1184	20c. Exploding green fireworks	1·25	1·00
1185	50c. Numbered rockets in rack	2·25	5·00

397 *Boy walking Dog* (Jean Paul Zammit)

2000. Stampin' the Future (Children's stamp design competition winners). Multicoloured.

1186	6c. Type **397**	55	65
1187	6c. *Stars and Woman in Megalithic Temple* (Chiara Borg)	55	65
1188	6c. *Sunny Day* (Bettina Paris)	55	65
1189	6c. *Hands holding Heart* (Roxana Caruana)	55	65

398 Boy's Sermon, Nativity Play and Girl with Doll

2000. Christmas. Multicoloured.

1190	6c. Type **398**	65	10
1191	6c.+3c. Three Wise Men (23×27 mm)	75	85
1192	16c.+3c. Family with Father Christmas	1·75	2·25
1193	26c.+3c. Christmas tree, church and family	2·25	3·50
MS1194	174×45 mm. Nos. 1190/1193	4·75	6·50

399 Crocodile Float

2001. Maltese Carnival. Multicoloured.

1195	6c. Type **399**	40	25
1196	11c. King Karnival in procession (vert)	60	40
1197	16c. Woman and children in costumes (vert)	75	55
1198	19c. Horseman carnival float (vert)	85	1·40
1199	27c. Carnival procession	1·25	2·00
MS1200	127×92 mm. 12c. Old-fashioned clowns; 37c. Women dressed as clowns (both 32×32 mm)	2·25	3·50

400 St Elmo Lighthouse

2001. Maltese Lighthouses. Multicoloured.

1201	6c. Type **400**	65	25
1202	16c. Gurdan Lighthouse	1·25	70
1203	22c. Delimara Lighthouse	1·75	2·25

401 *The Chicken Seller* (E. Caruana Dingli)

2001. Edward Caruana Dingli (painter) Commemoration. Multicoloured.

1204	2c. Type **401**	20	30
1205	4c. *The Village Beau*	35	15
1206	6c. *The Faldetta*	50	25
1207	10c. *The Guitar Player*	80	60
1208	26c. *Wayside Orange Seller*	2·00	2·75

402 Nazju Falzon, Gorg Preca and Adeodata Pisani (candidates for Beatification)

2001. Visit of Pope John Paul II. Multicoloured.

1209	6c. Type **402**	1·00	25
1210	16c. Pope John Paul II and statue of St Paul	1·75	1·50
MS1211	123×87 mm. 75c. Pope John Paul with Nazju Falzon, Gorg Preca and Adeodata Pisani	5·00	5·50

403 Painted Frog

2001. Europa. Pond Life. Multicoloured.

1212	16c. Type **403**	1·25	65
1213	46c. Red-veined darter (dragonfly)	2·50	3·75

404 Herring Gull ('Yellow-legged Gull') (*Larus cachinnans*)

2001. Maltese Birds. Multicoloured.

1214	6c. Type **404**	85	85
1215	6c. Common kestrel (*Falco tinnunculus*)	85	85
1216	6c. Golden oriole (*Oriolus oriolus*)	85	85
1217	6c. Chaffinch (*Fringilla coelebs*) and Eurasian goldfinch (*Carduelis carduelis*)	85	85
1218	6c. Blue rock thrush (*Monticola solitarius*)	85	85
1219	6c. European bee-eater (*Merops apiaster*)	85	85
1220	6c. House martin (*Delichon urbica*) and barn swallow (*Hirundo rustica*)	85	85
1221	6c. Spanish sparrow (*Passer hispaniolensis*)	85	85
1222	6c. Spectacled warbler (*Sylvia conspicillata*)	85	85
1223	6c. Turtle dove (*Streptopelia turtur*)	85	85
1224	6c. Northern pintail (*Anas acuta*)	85	85
1225	6c. Little bittern (*Ixobrychus minutus*)	85	85
1226	6c. Eurasian woodcock (*Scolopax rusticola*)	85	85
1227	6c. Short-eared owl (*Asio flammeus*)	85	85
1228	6c. Northern lapwing (*Vanellus vanellus*)	85	85
1229	6c. Moorhen (*Gallinula chloropus*)	85	85

Nos 1214/1229 were printed together, *se-tenant*, with the backgrounds forming a composite design.

405 Whistle Flute

2001. Traditional Maltese Musical Instruments. Multicoloured.

1230	1c. Type **405**	15	50
1231	3c. Reed pipe	25	40
1232	14c. Maltese bagpipe	60	40
1233	20c. Friction drum	85	1·25
1234	25c. Frame drum	1·00	1·75

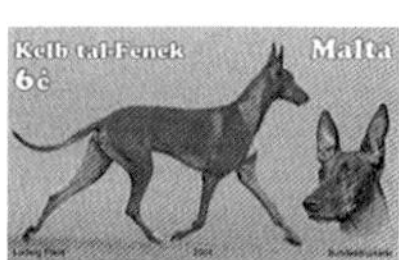

406 Kelb tal-Fenek (Pharaoh Hound)

2001. Maltese Dogs. Multicoloured.

1235	6c. Type **406**	75	25
1236	16c. Kelb tal-Kacca	1·50	55
1237	19c. Maltese	1·50	1·25
1238	35c. Kelb tal-But	2·25	3·50

407 Man with Net chasing Star

2001. Christmas. Multicoloured.

1239	6c.+2c. Type **407**	60	40
1240	15c.+2c. Father and children	1·10	1·50
1241	16c.+2c. Mother and daughter	1·10	1·50
1242	19c.+3c. Young woman with shopping bags	1·25	2·25

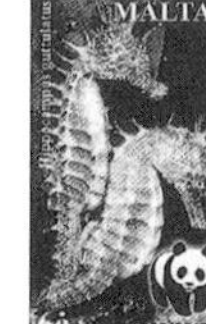

408 *Hippocampus guttulatus*

2002. Endangered Species. Mediterranean Seahorses. Multicoloured.

1243	6c. Type **408**	60	80
1244	6c. *Hippocampus hippocampus*	60	80
1245	16c. Close-up of *Hippocampus guttulatus*	90	1·75
1246	16c. *Hippocampus hippocampus* on seabed	90	1·75

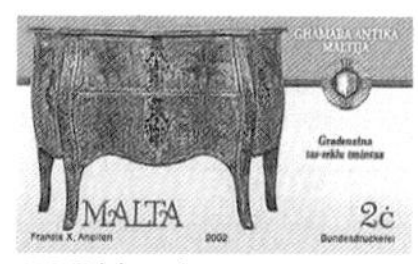

409 Sideboard

2002. Antique Furniture. Multicoloured.

1247	2c. Type **409**	25	40
1248	4c. Bureau (vert)	45	30
1249	11c. Inlaid table (vert)	70	40
1250	26c. Cabinet (vert)	1·25	85
1251	60c. Carved chest	2·50	5·00

410 Child's Face painted as Clown

2002. Europa. Circus.

1252	**410**	16c. multicoloured	1·25	1·00

411 *Hyles sammuti*

2002. Moths and Butterflies. Multicoloured.

1253	6c. Type **411**	50	55
1254	6c. *Utetheisa pulchella*	50	55
1255	6c. *Ophiusa tirhaca*	50	55
1256	6c. *Phragmatobia fulginosa melitensis*	50	55
1257	6c. *Vanessa cardui*	50	55
1258	6c. *Polyommatus icarus*	50	55
1259	6c. *Gonepteryx cleopatra*	50	55
1260	6c. *Vanessa atlanta*	50	55
1261	6c. *Eucrostes indigenata*	50	55
1262	6c. *Macroglossum stellatarum*	50	55
1263	6c. *Lasiocampa quercus*	50	55
1264	6c. *Catocala electa*	50	55
1265	6c. *Maniola jurtina hyperhispulla*	50	55
1266	6c. *Pieris brassicaei*	50	55
1267	6c. *Papilio machaon melitensis*	50	55
1268	6c. *Dainaus chrysippus*	50	55

No. 1260 is inscribed 'atalania' and 1264 'elocata', both in error.

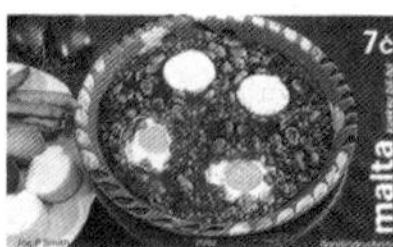

412 Kusksu Bil-ful (bean stew)

2002. Maltese Cookery. Multicoloured.

1269	7c. Type **412**	55	25
1270	12c. Qaqocc mimli (stuffed artichoke)	85	50
1271	16c. Lampuki (dorada with aubergines)	1·00	75
1272	27c. Qaghqd Tal-kavatelli (chestnut dessert)	1·75	2·75
MS1273	125×90 mm. 75c. Stuffat Tal-fenek (rabbit stew)	4·00	5·50

413 *Yavia cryptocarpa* (cactus)

2002. Cacti and Succulents. Multicoloured.

No.	Description		
1274	1c. Type **413**	15	50
1275	7c. *Aztekium hintonii* (cactus) (vert)	55	25
1276	28c. *Pseudolithos migiurtinus* (succulent)	1·25	70
1277	37c. *Pierrebraunia brauniorum* (cactus) (vert)	1·75	1·50
1278	76c. *Euphorbia turbiniformis* (succulent)	3·00	6·00

414 Chief Justice Adrian Dingli,

2002. Personalities.

No.	Type	Description		
1279	**414**	3c. green and black	25	40
1280	-	7c. green and black	70	35
1281	-	15c. brown and agate	1·25	75
1282	-	35c. brown and sepia	1·50	2·00
1283	-	50c. light blue and blue	2·50	4·25

Designs: 7c. Oreste Kirkop (opera singer); 15c. Athanasius Kircher (Jesuit scholar); 35c. Archpriest Saverio Cassar; 50c. Emmanuele Vitali (notary).

415 Mary and Joseph in Donkey Cart

2002. Christmas. Multicoloured.

No.	Description		
1284	7c. Type **415**	70	25
1285	16c. Shepherds and Kings on a bus	1·25	55
1286	22c. Holy Family and angels in luzzu (boat)	1·60	75
1287	37c. Holy Family in horse-drawn carriage	2·00	1·50
1288	75c. Nativity on Maltese fishing boat	3·75	6·00

416 Vanden Plas Princess Landaulette, 1965

2003. Vintage Cars. Multicoloured.

No.	Description		
1289	2c. Type **416**	25	60
1290	7c. Allard M type, 1948	55	25
1291	10c. Cadillac Model B, 1904	70	35
1292	26c. Fiat Cinquecento Model A Topolino, 1936	1·25	1·60
1293	35c. Ford Anglia Super, 1965	1·75	3·00

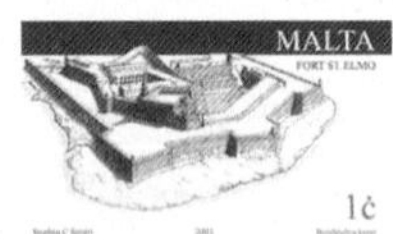

417 Fort St Elmo

2003. Maltese Military Architecture. Multicoloured.

No.	Description		
1294	1c. Type **417**	15	40
1295	4c. Rinella Battery	30	30
1296	11c. Fort St Angelo	65	40
1297	16c. Section through Reserve Post R15	1·00	60
1298	44c. Fort Tigne	2·25	4·25

418 St George on Horseback

2003. Paintings of St George.

No.	Type	Description		
1299	**418**	3c. multicoloured	25	30
1300	-	7c. multicoloured	50	30
1301	-	14c. multicoloured	75	60
1302	-	19c. multicoloured	1·10	1·40
1303	-	27c. multicoloured	1·50	2·25

Designs: 7c. to 27c. Various paintings of St George.

419 'CISKBEER'

2003. Europa. Poster Art. Multicoloured.

No.	Description		
1304	16c. Type **419**	75	55
1305	46c. 'CARNIVAL 1939'	2·25	3·50

420 Games Mascot with Javelin

2003. Games of Small European States, Malta. Multicoloured.

No.	Description		
1306	25c. Type **420**	1·25	85
1307	50c. Mascot with gun	2·25	1·75
1308	75c. Mascot with ball and net	3·75	2·75
1309	£3 Mascot with rubber ring at poolside	14·00	17·00

421 Princess Elizabeth in Malta, *c.* 1950

2003. 50th Anniversary of Coronation. Multicoloured (except No. 1312).

No.	Description		
1310	12c. black, grey and cinnamon	70	45
1311	15c. multicoloured	75	50
1312	22c. black, deep grey and grey	1·00	90
1313	60c. black, grey and deep ultramarine	2·50	3·50
MS1314	100×72 mm. £1 multicoloured	6·50	7·50

Designs: 15c. Princess Elizabeth with crowd of children, Malta, *c.* 1950; 22c. Queen Elizabeth II in evening dress with Duke of Edinburgh, Malta; 60c. Queen Elizabeth II (receiving book) and Duke of Edinburgh, Malta; £1 Queen on walkabout with crowd.

422 Valletta Bastions at Night

2003. Elton John, The Granaries, Floriana. Sheet 125×90 mm.

No.	Description		
MS1315	**422** £1.50 multicoloured	9·00	10·00

No. **MS**1315 also contains four labels showing different portraits of Elton John.

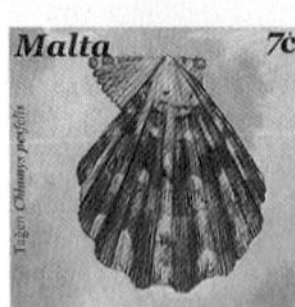

423 *Chlamys pesfelis*

2003. Sea Shells. Multicoloured.

No.	Description		
1316	7c. Type **423**	50	55
1317	7c. *Gyroscala lamellose*	50	55
1318	7c. *Phalium granulatum*	50	55
1319	7c. *Fusiturris similes*	50	55
1320	7c. *uria lurida*	50	55
1321	7c. *Bolinus brandaris*	50	55
1322	7c. *Charonia tritonis variegate*	50	55
1323	7c. *Clanculus corallinus*	50	55
1324	7c. *Fusinus syracusanus*	50	55
1325	7c. *Pinna nobilis*	50	55
1326	7c. *Acanthocardia tuberculata*	50	55
1327	7c. *Aporrhais pespelecani*	50	55
1328	7c. *Haliotis tuberculata lamellose*	50	55
1329	7c. *Tonna galea*	50	55
1330	7c. *Spondylus gaederopus*	50	55
1331	7c. *Mitra zonata*	50	55

424 Racing Yachts, Malta–Syracuse Race

2003. Yachting. Multicoloured.

No.	Description		
1332	8c. Type **424**	60	35
1333	22c. Yacht, Middle Sea Race (vert)	1·25	1·00
1334	35c. Racing yachts, Royal Malta Yacht Club (vert)	2·00	3·00

2003. As Nos. 1139a and 1143 but smaller, 23×23 mm. Self-adhesive.

No.	Description		
1335	7c. *Vitex agnus-castus*	50	40
1336	16c. *Crocus longiflorus*	1·25	1·25

425 Is-Sur ta' San Mikiel, Valletta

2003. Windmills. Each black.

No.	Description		
1337	11c. Type **425**	85	40
1338	27c. Ta' Kola, Xaghra (vert)	2·00	1·25
1339	45c. Tax-Xarolla, Zurrieq (vert)	2·75	4·50

426 The Annunciation

2003. Christmas. Multicoloured.

No.	Description		
1340	7c. Type **426**	70	30
1341	16c. Holy Family	1·00	35
1342	22c. The Shepherds following the Star (horiz)	1·40	85
1343	50c. The Three Kings with gifts (horiz)	2·75	4·50

427 Pillar Box on Seafront

2004. Letterboxes. Multicoloured.

No.	Description		
1344	1c. Type **427**	10	30
1345	16c. Pillar box on pavement	1·50	55
1346	22c. Wall pillar boxes	1·75	90
1347	37c. Pillar box inside post office	2·50	1·75
1348	76c. Square pillar box and statue	6·00	8·00

428 Tortoiseshell Cat

2004. Cats. Multicoloured.

No.	Description		
1349	7c. Type **428**	70	30
1350	27c. Tabby	1·90	1·25
1351	28c. Silver tabby	1·90	1·25
1352	50c. Ginger tabby	3·50	4·00
1353	60c. Black and white cat	3·75	4·75

429 St John Bosco

2004. Centenary of Salesians in Malta. Sheet 124×89 mm.

No.	Description		
MS1354	**429** 75c. multicoloured	3·50	5·00

430 Pipistrelle (*Pipistrellus pygmaeus*)

2004. Mammals and Reptiles. Multicoloured.

No.	Description		
1355	16c. Type **430**	85	90
1356	16c. Lesser mouse-eared bat (*Myotis blythi punicus*)	85	90
1357	16c. Weasel (*Mustela nivalis*)	85	90
1358	16c. Algerian hedgehog (*Atelerix algirus fallax*)	85	90
1359	16c. Mediterranean chameleon (*Chamaeleo chamaeleon*)	85	90
1360	16c. Sicilian shrew (*Crocidura sicula*)	85	90
1361	16c. Ocellated skink (*Chalcides ocellatus*)	85	90
1362	16c. Filfla Maltese wall lizard (*Podarcis filfolensis filfolensis*)	85	90
1363	16c. Moorish gecko (*Tarentola mauritanica*)	85	90
1364	16c. Turkish gecko (*Hemidactylus turcicus*)	85	90
1365	16c. Leopard snake (*Elaphe situla*)	85	90
1366	16c. Western whip snake (*Coluber viridiflavus*)	85	90
1367	16c. Common dolphin (*Delphinus delphis*)	85	90
1368	16c. Striped dolphin (*Stenella coeruleoalba*)	85	90
1369	16c. Mediterranean monk seal (*Monachus monachus*)	85	90
1370	16c. Green turtle (*Chelonia mydas*)	85	90

Nos. 1355/1370 were printed together, *se-tenant*, in sheetlets of 16 with the background of each horizontal pair (1355/1356, 1357/1358, 1359/1360, 1361/1362, 1363/1364, 1365/1366, 1367/1368 and 1369/1370) forming a composite design.

431 New Members Flags inside EU Stars

2004. Accession to European Union. Multicoloured.

No.	Description		
1371	16c. Type **431**	1·00	55
1372	28c. Former Prime Minister Eddie Fenech Adami and former Foreign Minister Joe Borg signing Accession Treaty	1·50	2·00

432 Children Jumping into Water

2004. Europa. Holidays. Multicoloured.

No.	Description		
1373	16c. Type **432**	1·00	55
1374	51c. Hagar Qim prehistoric temples	2·75	3·50

433 Hal Millieri Chapel, Zurrieq

2004. Chapels. Multicoloured.

No.	Description		
1375	3c. Type **433**	30	30
1376	7c. San Basilju, Mqabba	60	30
1377	39c. San Cir, Rabat	2·25	1·75
1378	48c. Santa Lucija, Mtarfa	2·50	2·75
1379	66c. Ta' Santa Marija, Kemmuna	4·25	6·00

434 Tram

2004. Trams.

No.	Type	Description		
1380	**434**	19c. green and black	1·25	65
1381	-	37c. orange and black (25×42 mm)	2·25	1·40
1382	-	50c. yellow and black (25×42 mm)	3·25	3·50
1383	-	75c. blue and black	4·50	6·00

Designs: 19c. T **434**; 37c. Tram driver; 50c. Ticket; 75c. Tram under bridge.

435 Discus Thrower

2004. Olympic Games, Athens. Multicoloured.

1384	11c. Type **435**	80	40
1385	16c. Greek column and laurel wreath	1·10	55
1386	76c. Javelin thrower	5·00	6·50

436 Children playing on Ascension Day (Luigi Brocktorff painting) (Lapsi)

2004. Festivals. Multicoloured.

1387	5c. Type **436**	45	30
1388	15c. Votive Penitentiary General Procession, Zejtun (San Girgor)	1·25	50
1389	27c. Pilgrimage in front of the Sanctuary of Our Lady of Graces, Zabbar (painting, Italo Horatio Serge) (Hadd In-Nies)	2·00	1·00
1390	51c. Children with St Martin's Bags of nuts (Michele Bellanti lithograph) (San Martin) (vert)	3·50	3·75
1391	£1 Peasants in traditional costumes singing and dancing (painting, Antoine Favray) (Mnarja) (vert)	6·50	8·50

437 Church of St Mary, Attard

2004. Art. Multicoloured.

1392	2c. Type **437**	30	35
1393	20c. Mdina Cathedral organ and music score (vert)	1·40	70
1394	57c. Statue of St Agatha (vert)	4·25	5·00
1395	62c. Il-Gifen Tork (poem) and books (vert)	4·75	6·00
MS1396	93×100 mm. 72c. Medieval painting of St Paul (vert)	4·50	6·00

438 Papier mache Bambino on rocks, Lecce

2004. Christmas. Bambino Models. Multicoloured.

1397	7c. Type **438**	55	25
1398	16c. Wax Bambino inside glass dome (vert)	1·10	55
1399	22c. Wax Bambino on back, Lija (vert)	1·50	75
1400	50c. Beeswax Bambino under tree (vert)	3·25	5·00

439 Quintinus Map

2005. Old Maps.

1401	**439**	1c. black and scarlet	15	40
1402	-	12c. multicoloured	90	50
1403	-	37c. multicoloured	2·75	2·00
1404	-	£1 multicoloured	6·50	8·25

Designs: 1c. T **439**; 12c. Copper-engraved map; 37c. Fresco map; £1 Map of Gozo.

440 Dar il-Kaptan (Respite Home)

2005. Centenary of Rotary International (humanitarian organisation). Multicoloured.

1405	27c. Type **440**	1·50	90
1406	76c. Outline of Malta and Gozo and 'ELEBRATE ROTARY'	4·75	6·00

441 Hans Christian Andersen

2005. Birth Bicentenary of Hans Christian Andersen (artist and children's writer).

1407	**441**	7c. black and silver	55	25
1408	-	22c. multicoloured	1·50	75
1409	-	60c. multicoloured	3·75	4·50
1410	-	75c. multicoloured	4·50	6·00

Designs: 7c. T **441**. 20×38 mm—22c. Scissors and paper cutting; 60c. Ugly Duckling, pen and inkwell; 75c. Moroccan travelling boots and drawing of Villa Borghese, Rome.

442 Pope John Paul II

2005. Pope John Paul II Commemoration.

1411	**442**	51c. multicoloured	4·25	4·00

443 *Coccinella septempunctata*

2005. Insects. Multicoloured.

1412	16c. Type **443**	1·10	1·25
1413	16c. *Chrysoperla carnea*	1·10	1·25
1414	16c. *Apis mellifera*	1·10	1·25
1415	16c. *Crocothemis erythraea*	1·10	1·25
1416	16c. *Anax imperator*	1·10	1·25
1417	16c. *Lampyris pallida*	1·10	1·25
1418	16c. *Henosepilachna elaterii*	1·10	1·25
1419	16c. *Forficula decipiens*	1·10	1·25
1420	16c. *Mantis religiosa*	1·10	1·25
1421	16c. *Eumenes lunulatus*	1·10	1·25
1422	16c. *Cerambyx cerdo*	1·10	1·25
1423	16c. *Gryllus bimaculatus*	1·10	1·25
1424	16c. *Xylocopa violacea*	1·10	1·25
1425	16c. *Cicada orni*	1·10	1·25
1426	16c. *Acrida ungarica*	1·10	1·25
1427	16c. *Oryctes nasicornis*	1·10	1·25

444 Cayenne Pepper, Baked, Stuffed Courgettes and Stuffed Eggplant

2005. Europa. Gastronomy. Multicoloured.

1428	16c. Type **444**	1·00	60
1429	51c. Roast rabbit	3·00	3·75

2005. Flowers. Personalised Stamps. As Nos. 1139a and 1143. Multicoloured.

1430	7c. *Vitex agnus-castus*	45	15
1431	16c. Yellow-throated crocus	80	55

446 *The Beheading of St Catherine*

2005. St Catherine in Art. Multicoloured.

1432	28c. Type **446**	1·40	1·40
1433	28c. *Martyrdom of St Catherine* (Mattia Preti) (vert)	1·40	1·40
1434	45c. *Mystic Marriage* (Francesco Zahra) (vert)	2·00	2·75
1435	45c. *St Catherine Disputing the Philosophers* (Francesco Zahra)	2·00	2·75

447 Mons. Mikiel Azzopardi (philanthropist)

2005. Personalities. Multicoloured.

1436	3c. Type **447**	30	20
1437	19c. Egidio Lapira (professor of dental surgery)	1·25	1·00
1438	20c. Letter and shield of Order of the Knights (Guzeppi Callus, doctor)	1·25	1·00
1439	46c. Hand writing musical score (Geronimo Abos, composer)	2·50	2·75
1440	76c. Gann Frangisk Abela (historian)	4·00	5·50

448 Horse-drawn Hearse

2005. Equines in Malta. Multicoloured.

1441	11c. Type **448**	1·00	40
1442	15c. Mule pulling traditional wooden plough	1·25	50
1443	62c. Mule on treadmill grinding flour	3·75	4·50
1444	66c. Horse-drawn water sprinkler cart	3·75	4·50

449 Queue outside 'Victory Kitchen' and Ruins of Royal Opera House, Valletta

2005. 60th Anniversary of End of Second World War. Battle of Malta. All showing George Cross. Multicoloured.

1445	2c. Type **449**	50	30
1446	5c. Royal Navy convoy under air attack from Savoia Marchetti S-73 Sparviero	75	25
1447	25c. Anti aircraft guns and St Publius Church, Floriana	2·00	95
1448	51c. Pilots scrambling, Hawker Hurricane, Supermarine Spitfire and Gloster Sea Gladiators	3·75	3·75
1449	£1 Tanker *Ohio* and unloading of supplies at Grand Harbour, August 1943	7·00	8·50

450 *The Nativity*

2005. Christmas. Paintings by Emvin Cremona from Sanctuary of Our Lady of Ta' Pinu, Gozo. Multicoloured.

1450	7c. Type **450**	60	25
1451	16c. *The Annunciation* (vert)	1·10	55
1452	22c. *The Adoration of the Magi*	1·50	75
1453	50c. *The Flight to Egypt* (69×30 mm)	3·50	6·00

451 Maltese, Commonwealth and CHOGM Flags

2005. Commonwealth Heads of Government Meeting (CHOGM), Valletta. Each showing Maltese and Commonwealth flags. Multicoloured.

MS1454	Four sheets, each 75×63 mm. (a) 14c. Type **451**. (b) 28c. Peace Doves. (c) 37c. Maltese Cross. (d) 75c. Silhouettes shaking hands	7·00	9·50

452 1986 8c. Butterflies Stamp

2006. 50th Anniversary of Europa Stamps. Showing Maltese Europa stamps. Multicoloured.

MS1455	120×85 mm. 5c. Type **452**; 13c. 1983 30c. Fort St Angelo stamp; 23c. 1977 20c. Is-Salini stamp; 24c. 1989 35c. Girls with dolls stamp	3·50	5·00

No. **MS**1455 has a composite background design.

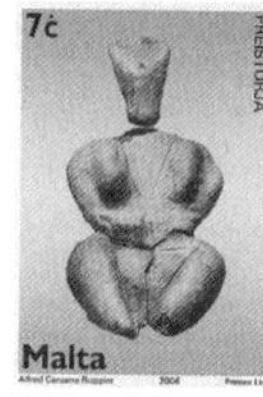

453 Female Terracotta Female Figurine, *c.* 4100 BC

2006. Ceramics in Maltese Collections. Multicoloured.

1456	7c. Type **453**	50	25
1457	16c. Roman terracotta head, *c.* 1st/3rd-century BC	1·00	55
1458	28c. Terracotta oil lamp holder, 14th/15th-century AD	1·25	1·40
1459	37c. Sicilian maiolica display plate, 18th-century	2·25	2·40
1460	60c. Modern stylised figure in Maltese costume (Ianni Bonniçi)	3·00	4·75

454 Shetland Pony

2006. Pets. Multicoloured.

1461	7c. Type **454**	85	90
1462	7c. Kelb tal-But (Maltese pocket dog)	85	90
1463	7c. Goldfish	85	90
1464	7c. Siamese cat	85	90
1465	7c. Siamese fighting fish	85	90
1466	7c. Ferret	85	90
1467	7c. Canary	85	90
1468	7c. Terrapin	85	90
1469	22c. Chinchilla	85	90
1470	22c. Budgerigar	85	90
1471	22c. Rabbit	85	90
1472	22c. Zebra finch	85	90
1473	22c. Kelb tal-Kacca (Maltese hunting dog)	85	90
1474	22c. Pigeon	85	90
1475	22c. Guinea pig	85	90
1476	22c. Cat	85	90

455 Penitents carrying Crosses

2006. Holy Week. Multicoloured.

1477	7c. Type **455**	50	15
1478	15c. Crucifixion tableau in procession	1·00	30
1479	22c. Burial of Christ tableau in procession	1·25	75

1480	27c. Statue of the Risen Christ paraded on Easter Sunday	1·50	1·10
1481	82c. Altar of Repose, Collegiate Church of St Lawrence, Vittoriosa	4·50	6·50

456 Circuit of Linked People

2006. Europa. Integration. Multicoloured.

1482	16c. Type **456**	1·00	50
1483	51c. Four rows of linked people (30×43 mm)	2·50	3·50

457 Bobby Charlton

2006. World Cup Football Championship, Germany. Multicoloured.

1484	7c. Type **457**	45	15
1485	16c. Pele	80	30
1486	27c. Franz Beckenbauer	1·25	85
1487	76c. Dino Zoff	3·50	6·00
MS1488	160×86 mm	5·50	6·50

2006. Sting Concert, Luxol Grounds. Sheet 121×86 mm containing design as No. 1188.

MS1489	£1.50 *Sunny Day* (Bettina Paris)	5·50	7·00

458 *Santa Anna* ('Gran Caracca di Rodi'), 1530

2006. Naval Vessels. Multicoloured.

1490	8c. Type **458**	80	20
1491	29c. *Guillaume Tell* (French) dismasted by HMS *Penelope*, *Lion* and *Foudroyant*, Malta, 1800 (Edwin Galea)	2·00	1·10
1492	51c. USS *Constitution*, 1837 (J. G. Evans)	3·25	3·00
1493	76c. HMS *Dreadnought* leaving Grand Harbour, November 1913	5·00	6·00
1494	£1 USS *Belknap* (frigate) and *Slava* (Soviet cruiser) providing communications support for Malta Summit, December 1989	6·00	7·50

459 Candles ('Happy Birthday')

2006. Occasions. Multicoloured.

1495	8c. Type **459**	45	15
1496	16c. Heart ('Happy Anniversary')	80	35
1497	27c. Stars holding parcel, balloon and candle ('Congratulations')	1·25	1·25
1498	37c. Balloons ('Best Wishes')	1·75	2·75

460 Wignacourt Tower

2006. Maltese Castles and Towers. Multicoloured.

1499	7c. Type **460**	65	15
1500	16c. Verdala Castle	1·25	35
1501	27c. San Lucjan Tower	1·90	1·10
1502	37c. Kemmuna Tower	2·50	1·75
1503	£1 Selmun Castle	6·00	9·00

461 Paolino Vassallo, *Inno per Natale* and Nativity

2006. Christmas Music. Showing composer and score. Multicoloured.

1504	8c. Type **461**	55	15
1505	16c. Carmelo Pace, *They Heard the Angels* and Three Magi	1·00	30
1506	22c. Paul Nani, *Maltese Christmas* and Angels	1·40	1·25
1507	27c. Carlo Diacono, *Notte di Natale*, shepherds and Angel	1·60	1·60
MS1508	120×86 mm. 50c. Wolfgang Amadeus Mozart (250th birth anniversary) and *Alma di Creatoris*	3·00	3·50

2006. Bob Geldof Concert for YMCA, Manoel Island. Sheet 121×86 mm containing design as No. 1189.

MS1509	£1.50 *Hands holding Heart* (Roxana Caruana)	7·50	8·50

462 Wrought Iron Work

2006. Crafts. Multicoloured.

1510	8c. Type **462**	55	15
1511	16c. Glass making	1·00	35
1512	22c. Filigree work	1·40	70
1513	37c. Pottery	2·00	1·75
1514	60c. Reed basketwork	3·75	5·50

463 Stone Head

2007. Prehistoric Sculptures, *c.* 3000–2500 BC. Multicoloured.

1515	15c. Type **463**	1·00	30
1516	29c. Stone bas-relief of animals (horiz)	1·75	1·10
1517	60c. Stone-carved spiral pattern (horiz)	3·75	4·25
1518	£1.50 Clay statuette of female figure	7·50	10·00

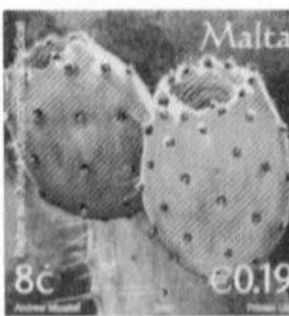

464 *Opuntia ficus-indica* (prickly pear)

2007. Maltese Fruits. Multicoloured.

1519	8c. Type **464**	50	60
1520	8c. *Vitis vinifera* (grapes)	50	60
1521	8c. *Eriobotrya japonica* (loquat)	50	60
1522	8c. *Morus nigra* (black mulberry)	50	60
1523	8c. *Ficus carica* (figs)	50	60
1524	8c. *Citrus limonum* (lemons)	50	60
1525	8c. *Pyrus communis* (pear)	50	60
1526	8c. *Prunus persica* (peaches)	50	60
1527	8c. *Punica granatum* (pomegranate)	50	60
1528	8c. *Prunus salicina* (Japanese plum)	50	60
1529	8c. *Citrullus vulgaris* (watermelon)	50	60
1530	8c. *Citrus sinensis* (orange)	50	60
1531	8c. *Olea europaea* (olives)	50	60
1532	8c. *Lycopersicon esculentum* (tomatoes)	50	60
1533	8c. *Malus domestica* (apples)	50	60
1534	8c. *Cucumis melo* (melon)	50	60

465 Wrought-iron Balcony

2007. Maltese Balconies. Multicoloured.

1535	8c. Type **465**	50	40
1536	22c. Ornate open stone balcony and recessed doorway, Gozo	1·25	1·10
1537	27c. Balustraded balcony, National Library of Malta	1·60	1·60
1538	29c. Carved stone balcony with glazed timber enclosure, Gozo	1·75	1·75
1539	46c. Two balconies on Art Deco 1930's building	2·75	4·00
MS1540	123×86 mm. 51c. Detail of balcony on Hostel de Verdelin, Valletta (horiz)	2·75	3·50

466 Lord Baden-Powell (founder) and District Commissioner Capt J. V. Abela, Malta, 1937

2007. Europa. Centenary of Scouting. Multicoloured.

1541	16c. Type **466**	1·00	60
1542	51c. Malta scouts marching, Golden Jubilee Jamboree, near Birmingham, 1957	3·00	4·00

467 St Gorg Preca

2007. Canonisation of Dun Gorg Preca. Multicoloured.

1543	8c. Type **467**	50	30
1544	£1 As Type **467** but sun rising behind Basilica	5·50	7·00

468 Rocking Horse, Tricycle and Car, all Triang (1950s)

2007. Toys from Days Gone By. Multicoloured.

1545	2c. Type **468**	10	20
1546	3c. Pedigree dolls pram (1950s), drums and skipping rope	15	20
1547	16c. Japanese tin cabin cruiser (1960s), sand pails, spade and Triang sailing boat	90	80
1548	22c. Lenci doll, Pedigree doll and 1930s Armand Marseille doll	1·25	1·10
1549	50c. Alps clockwork racing car (1950s), P.N. motorcycle (1950s) and Chad Valley delivery van (1930s)	3·25	4·50

469 *St Jerome* (Caravaggio)

2007. 400th Anniversary of the Arrival of Michelangelo Merisi (Caravaggio) in Malta. Paintings. Multicoloured.

1550	5c. Type **469**	35	35
1551	29c. *The Beheading of St.John the Baptist* (detail)	2·00	2·00
MS1552	130×86 mm. £2 *The Beheading of St John the Baptist* (vert)	15·00	18·00

470 Malta GPO Royal Enfield Motorcycle, 1954

2007. Motorcycles. Multicoloured.

1553	1c. Type **470**	15	30
1554	16c. Malta Garrison Matchless G3/L, 1941	1·25	85
1555	27c. Civilian Minerva, 1903	2·00	1·40
1556	50c. Malta Police Triumph Speed Twin, 1965	4·00	5·00

471 Heart and 'LOVE'

2007. Occasions Greetings Stamps. Multicoloured.

1557	8c. Type **471**	55	55
1558	8c. Teddy bears	55	60
1559	8c. Star decorations ('Congratulations!')	55	60
1560	8c. Pink roses ('GREETINGS')	55	60
1561	8c. Balloons	55	60
1562	8c. Champagne glasses	55	60

472 Mdina Skyline seen from Mtarfa

2007. Maltese Scenery. Designs showing watercolours by John Martin Borg. Multicoloured.

1563	11c. Type **472**	1·00	65
1564	16c. Windmill, farmhouse and church, Qrendi	1·40	85
1565	37c. Vittoriosa waterfront	2·75	2·25
1566	46c. Mgarr Harbour, Gozo	3·25	3·50
1567	76c. Xlendi Bay, Gozo	5·50	7·00

No. 1564 is inscr 'sepac'.

2007. 34U (Tree for You) Campaign. Sheet 100×66 mm containing design as No. 1531.

MS1568	75c. *Olea europaea* (olives)	4·25	5·50

473 Military Band

2007. Maltese Bands. Multicoloured.

1569	4c. Type **473**	55	40
1570	15c. Police band	2·00	1·00
1571	21c. Band playing at carnival	2·00	1·50
1572	22c. Band playing at Christmas	2·00	1·50
1573	£1 Band and conductor	8·00	10·00

474 Madonna and Baby Jesus

2007. Christmas. Showing details from painting *The Nativity* by Giuseppe Cali in St Andrew's parish church, Luqa. Multicoloured.

1574	8c. Type **474**	60	30
1575	16c. Holy Family with two countrywomen and young girl	1·25	85
1576	27c. Baby Jesus and young girl	2·00	2·50

Similar stamps were issued by the Vatican City.

475 Boys playing Football

2007. Anniversaries and Personalities. Multicoloured.

1577	4m. Type **475** (25th anniversary of Youth Football Association)	10	10
1578	9c. Children receiving religious instruction (centenary of Society of Christian Doctrine)	65	30
1579	16c. Canon Monsignor Professor Francesco Bonnici (founder of St Joseph Institute for orphan boys)	1·25	85
1580	43c. Father Manwel Magri (ethnographer, archaeologist and educator)	3·00	3·25
1581	86c. Carolina Cauchi (founder of Dominican order at Lunzjata Monastery, Gozo)	5·50	7·50
MS1582	100×70 mm. 76c. Signatories (50th anniversary of Treaty of Rome) (horiz)	4·50	6·00

476 Malta £1 Coin

2007. Coins of Malta 1972–2007. Sheet 100×66 mm.

MS1583	**476** €2.33 multicoloured	6·00	7·00

2008. Adoption of the Euro Currency (1st issue). Sheet 100×66 mm containing square design as T **476**. Multicoloured.

MS1584	€2.33 Obverse and reverse of one euro coin	3·50	4·25

477 *Aphrodite*, State of Cyprus

2008. Adoption of the Euro Currency (2nd issue). Sheet 100×62 mm containing T **477** and similar square design. Multicoloured.

MS1585	€1 Type **477**; €1 *Sleeping Lady* statuette, Malta	6·00	8·00

A similar miniature sheet was issued by Cyprus.

478 Door Knocker from Ministry of Finance, Valletta

2008. Door Knockers. Multicoloured.

1586	26c. Type **478**	1·00	65
1587	51c. Fish door knocker from Museum of Fine Arts, Valletta	1·60	1·25
1588	63c. Door knocker from Department of Industrial & Employment Relations, Valletta	1·75	2·25
1589	€1.77 Door knocker from Museum of Archaeology, Valletta	5·00	7·00

479 Shooting

2008. Olympic Games, Beijing. Multicoloured.

1590	5c. Type **479**	15	10
1591	12c. Swimming	30	20
1592	€1.57 Running	4·75	6·00

480 Postman and Mail Room (in sepia)

2008. Europa. The Letter. Multicoloured.

1593	37c. Type **480**	1·50	85
1594	€1.19 As Type **480** (in monochrome)	4·50	5·00

481 Woodcarving by Xandru Farrugia, Conversion of St Paul Church, Hal Safi

2008. Annus Paulinus 2008–2009 (2000th Birth Anniversary of St Paul). Showing statues of St Paul. Multicoloured.

1595	19c. Type **481**	80	30
1596	68c. Papier mache statue by Agostino Camilleri, St Paul's Shipwreck Church, Munxar, Gozo	2·50	2·75
1597	€1.08 Wooden statue by Giovanni Caruana, St Paul's Shipwreck Church, Rabat	4·00	5·00
MS1598	120×86 mm. €3 Wooden statue by Melchiorre Gafà, St Paul's Shipwreck Church, Valletta	9·50	11·00

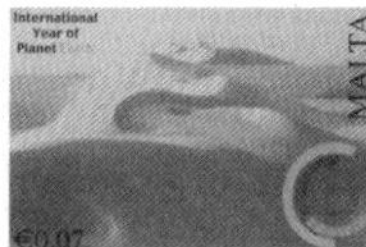

482 Sand Dunes

2008. International Year of Planet Earth. Multicoloured.

1599	7c. Type **482**	40	20
1600	86c. Single tree growing in field	3·25	3·25
1601	€1 Globe	3·75	4·00
1602	€1.77 Rocky coast	6·50	8·00

483 MSC *Musica*

2008. Cruise Liners. Multicoloured.

1603	63c. Type **483**	3·00	1·50
1604	€1.16 MS *Voyager of the Seas*	4·50	4·50
1605	€1.40 MS *Westerdam*	5·00	5·00
1606	€3 RMS *Queen Elizabeth II*	11·00	14·00

See also Nos. 1627/1630.

484 *Madonna and Child with Infant St John the Baptist* (detail) (Francesco Trevisani)

2008. Christmas. Nativity Paintings from the National Museum of Fine Arts, Valletta. Multicoloured.

1607	19c. Type **484**	60	30
1608	26c. *Nativity* (detail of Virgin and Christ Child from panel by Maestro Alberto)	90	60
1609	37c. *Virgin and Child with Infant St John the Baptist* (Carlo Maratta)	1·25	1·50

485 *Laetiorus sulphureus*

2009. Fungi. Multicoloured.

1610	5c. Type **485**	25	15
1611	12c. *Montagnea arenaria*	55	30
1612	19c. *Pleurotus eryngii*	80	40
1613	26c. *Inonotus indicus*	1·10	70
1614	€1.57 *Suillus collinitus*	5·75	7·50

486 Dornier Wal SANA Seaplane

2009. Vintage Postal Transport. Multicoloured.

1615	9c. Type **486**	75	25
1616	35c. Postmen on BSA motorcycles	2·75	1·25
1617	€2.50 Postmen with Raleigh bicycles	10·00	11·00
1618	€3 Gozo Mail Boat	10·00	11·00

487 Emblem

2009. Tenth Anniversary of the Euro.

1619	**487** €2 multicoloured	6·00	7·00

488 Galileo Galilei, his Sketch of Moon and *Apollo 11* Lunar Module *Eagle*

2009. Europa. Astronomy. Multicoloured.

1620	37c. Type **488**	1·50	1·10
1621	€1.19 William Lassell's telescope (set up in Malta 1861–1865) and Nebula M42	3·00	4·00

489 Sailing

2009. 13th Games of the Small States of Europe, Nicosia and Limassol, Cyprus. Multicoloured.

1622	10c. Type **489**	35	25
1623	19c. Judo	65	40
1624	37c. Shooting	1·40	1·10
1625	67c. Swimming	2·50	2·75
1626	€1.77 Athletics	5·00	7·00

2009. Cruise Liners (2nd series). As T **483**. Multicoloured.

1627	37c. *Seabourn Pride*	2·50	1·10
1628	68c. *Brilliance of the Seas*	3·50	2·50
1629	91c. *Costa Magica* and *Costa Atlantica*	4·50	4·50
1630	€2 MSC *Splendida*	7·50	8·50

490 Headland

2009. Scenery. Multicoloured.

1631	2c. Type **490**	15	30
1632	7c. Watchtower of Knights of the Sovereign Military Order of Malta	45	20
1633	37c. Stone salt pans, Qbajjar, Gozo	2·00	70
1634	€1.02 Segment of the Ggantija Temples, Gozo	4·00	5·50

No. 1633 is inscr 'sepac'.

491 *Mater Admirablis* (in the manner of Botticelli)

2009. Christmas. Multicoloured.

1635	19c. Type **491**	75	30
1636	37c. *Madonna and Child* (Corrado Giacquinto)	1·50	45
1637	63c. *The Madonna and Child* (follower of Simone Cantarini)	2·00	3·25

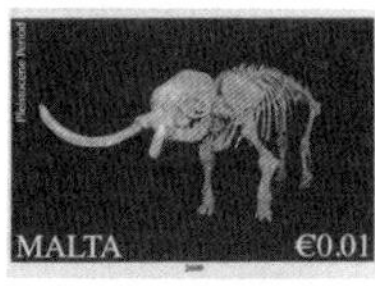

492 Skeleton of Prehistoric Animal (Pleistocene Period)

2009. History of Malta. Multicoloured.

1638	1c. Type **492**	15	30
1639	2c. Ruins of stone temple (Early Temple Period)	20	30
1640	5c. Carved stone pattern (Late Temple Period)	30	25
1641	7c. Pair of pots (Bronze Age)	35	25
1642	9c. Gold statue (Phoenician and Punic Period) (vert)	40	40
1643	10c. Mosaic (Roman Period)	40	40
1644	19c. Gold coin (Byzantine Period) (stone background) (vert)	65	30
1644a	20c. As No. 1644 (grey background) (vert) (7.3.12)	65	30
1645	26c. Fragment of carved stone (Arab Period)	90	60
1646	37c. Painting (Norman and Hohenstaufen Period) (vert)	1·25	75
1647	50c. Stone tablet carved with shield (Angevin and Aragonese) (vert)	1·75	1·75
1648	51c. Gold pattern with central Maltese Cross (Knights of St John)	1·75	1·75
1649	63c. Painting of officers and crew disembarking in rowing boats from ships (French Period)	1·75	1·75
1650	68c. George Cross (British Period) (lavender background) (vert)	2·00	2·00
1650a	69c. As No. 1650 (stone background) (vert) (7.3.12)	2·00	2·00
1651	86c. Independence (vert)	2·75	2·75
1652	€1 Republic (vert)	3·50	3·50
1653	€1.08 EU Accession (vert)	3·50	3·50
1654	€5 Arms of Malta (vert)	16·00	17·00
MS1655	170×263 mm. Nos. 1638/1654. Wmk upright	40·00	42·00

493 100 Ton Gun, Fort Rinella, Malta, 2010

2010. 100 Ton Guns. Multicoloured.

MS1656	75c.×4 Type **493**; 100 ton'gun, Fort Rinella, Malta, 1882; 100 ton gun, Napier of Magdala Battery, Gibraltar, 1880; 100 ton gun, Napier of Magdala Battery, Gibraltar, 2010	8·00	9·00

A miniature sheet containing the same designs was issued by Gibraltar.

494 Balloons

2010. Occasions Greetings Stamps. Multicoloured.

1657	19c. Type **494**	65	75
1658	19c. Aerial view of coastline and offshore rocks	65	75
1659	19c. Mortarboard and scroll	65	75
1660	19c. Woman greeting man and crowd (painting)	65	75
1661	19c. Two glasses of champagne and bottle in ice bucket (vert)	65	75
1662	19c. St John's Co-Cathedral, Valletta and fireworks (vert)	65	75

1663	19c. Hand holding trophy (vert)	65	75
1664	37c. Outline map of Malta and Gozo	1·10	1·10

495 Pope Benedict XVI

2010. Visit of Pope Benedict XVI to Malta.

MS1665	**495** €3 multicoloured	12·00	12·00

496 *Puttinu u Toninu* (Dr. Philip Farrugia Randon)

2010. Europa. Children's Books. Multicoloured.

1666	37c. Type **496**	1·50	75
1667	€1.19 *Meta l-Milied ma giex* (Clare Azzopardi)	3·25	4·50

497 Globe and National Flags

2010. World Cup Football Championship, South Africa. Multicoloured.

1668	63c. Type **497**	1·75	1·75
1669	€2.50 Zakumi the leopard mascot	6·25	7·50
MS1669a	131×80 mm. As Nos. 1668/1669	8·00	9·25

498 Maltese Wall Lizard

2010. Biodiversity. Multicoloured.

1670	19c. Type **498**	1·25	50
1671	68c. Storm petrel (vert)	3·25	2·25
1672	86c. Maltese pyramidal orchid (vert)	4·00	3·75
1673	€1.40 Freshwater crab	4·00	5·00

499 Azure Window, Gozo

2010. Natural Treasures. Multicoloured.

1674	37c. Type **499**	1·75	70
1675	51c. Blue Grotto, Zurrieq (vert)	2·50	2·00
1676	67c. Ta' Cenc, Gozo (vert)	3·00	2·75
1677	€1.16 Filfla	4·00	5·50

500 *The Adoration of the Magi* (Valerio Castello)

2010. Christmas. Multicoloured.

1678	19c. Type **500**	75	30
1679	37c. *The Flight into Egypt* (Filippo Paladini)	1·50	55
1680	63c. *Madonna di Maggio* (Pierre Guillemin) (vert)	2·25	3·25

501 Cancelled 1860 ½d. Buff Stamp

2010. 150th Anniversary of the First Malta Stamp.

MS1681	**501** €2.80 multicoloured	10·00	11·00

502 *Valletta*

2011. Treasures of Malta. Landscapes. Multicoloured.

1682	19c. Type **502**	80	30
1683	37c. *Manoel Island*	1·75	60
1684	€1.57 *Cittadella* (Gozo)	5·50	7·25

503 *Chimaera monstrosa* (Rabbitfish)

2011. 50th Anniversary of WWF (Worldwide Fund for Nature). *Chimaera monstrosa* (Rabbitfish). Multicoloured.

MS1685	51c. Type **503**; 63c. Rabbitfish (swimming towards top right; 67c. Rabbitfish (seen from front); 97c. Rabbitfish (with fins outstretched)	9·00	10·00

504 Trees, Pine Cones, Flowers and Butterfly (Nicole Sciberras)

2011. Europa. Forests. Multicoloured.

1686	37c. Type **504**	1·50	1·00
1687	€1.19 Trees, fallen tree and fungi	3·25	4·00

505 Reo Bus, Birkirkara

2011. Malta Buses. The End of an Era (1st series). Buses of the 1950s and 1960s. Make of Bus and Route given. Multicoloured.

1688	20c. Type **505**	1·50	1·50
1689	20c. Dodge T110L, Zabbar	1·50	1·50
1690	20c. Leyland Comet, Zurrieq	13·00	13·00
1691	20c. Ford V8, Zebbug-Siggiewi	1·50	1·50
1692	20c. Bedford SLD, Gudja-Ghaxaq	1·50	1·50
1693	20c. Gozo mail bus	1·50	1·50
1694	20c. Federal bus, Kalafrana	1·50	1·50
1695	20c. Dodge T110L, Siggiewi	1·50	1·50
1696	20c. Indiana bus, Rabat	1·50	1·50
1697	20c. Austin CXD, Zejtun	1·50	1·50
1698	69c. Ford V8, Sliema	3·25	3·25
1699	69c. Commer Q4, Lija	3·25	3·25
1700	69c. Fordson BB, Mosta - Naxxar	3·25	3·25
1701	69c. Thorneycroft Sturdy ZE, Mellieha	3·25	3·25
1702	69c. Bedford QL, Cospicua	3·25	3·25
1703	69c. Magirus Deutz, all routes	3·25	3·25
1704	69c. Commer Q4, Naxxar	3·25	3·25
1705	69c. Bedford SB8, Gozo	3·25	3·25
1706	69c. Thames ET7, Birkirkara - St. Julians	3·25	3·25
1707	69c. Bedford QL, private hire	3·25	3·25

See also Nos. 1842/1847.

506 MV *Ta' Pinu* (Gozo Channel Company passenger and car ferry)

2011. Maritime Malta (1st series). Multicoloured.

1708	26c. Type **506**	1·40	65
1709	37c. MV *Jean De La Valette* (Virtu Ferries catamaran)	2·25	80
1710	67c. *P23* (Maritime Squadron patrol boat)	3·25	3·50
1711	91c. MV *Spinola* (Tug Malta Bollard Pull Terminal/Escort VSP tractor tug)	4·25	5·00

See also Nos.1857/1860, 1922/1924, **MS**1951, 1994/1996 and 2012/2014.

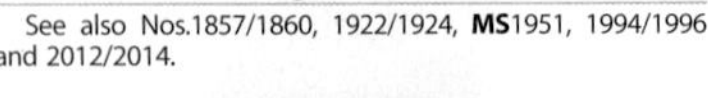

507 Mgarr, Gozo

2011. Fishing Villages. Sheet 120×81 mm.

MS1712	**507** €2.07 multicoloured	7·00	7·00

508 *The Holy Family in an Interior* (follower of Marcello Venusti, 1510-1579)

2011. Christmas. Multicoloured.

1713	20c. Type **508**	65	30
1714	37c. *The Madonna and Child with Infant St John the Baptist* (Tuscan school, *c.* 1600)	1·10	40
1715	63c. *The Rest on the Flight into Egypt* (16th-century Flemish)	1·90	2·75

509 Malta 1922 £1 Stamp

2011. 90th Anniversary of Malta Senate and Legislative Assembly. Sheet 130×85 mm.

MS1716	**509** €4.16 multicoloured	11·00	12·00

510 *Marsalforn* (H. M. Bateman)

2012. International Artists and Malta. Paintings of Maltese Landscapes by H. M. Bateman and Edward Lear. Multicoloured.

1717	20c. Type **510**	65	30
1718	26c. *Qala* (H. M. Bateman)	75	35
1719	37c. *Ghajnsielem* ((H. M. Bateman) (vert)	1·10	50
1720	67c. *Inquisitor's Palace* (Edward Lear)	1·90	2·00
1721	97c. *Gran Fontana* (Edward Lear)	3·00	3·75

511 Champagne Bottle and Glasses

2012. Occasions. Multicoloured.

1722	37c. Type **511**	1·10	1·25
1723	37c. Two gold rings (horiz)	1·10	1·25
1724	37c. Mortarboard and scroll (horiz)	1·10	1·25
1725	37c. Trophy	1·10	1·25
1726	37c. Christmas baubles and gold ribbon (horiz)	1·10	1·25
1727	37c. Fireworks behind St John's Co-Cathedral, Valletta	1·10	1·25
1728	37c. Comino coastline (horiz)	1·10	1·25
1729	37c. *Auberge de Castille* (Charles Frederick de Brocktorff) (horiz)	1·10	1·25

512 George Cross

2012. 70th Anniversary of the Award of the George Cross to Malta. Sheet 120×81 mm.

MS1730	**512** €4.16 multicoloured	11·00	12·00

513 Saluting Battery, Harbour and Fort St Angelo

2012. Europa. Visit Malta. Multicoloured.

1731	37c. Type **513**	1·25	60
1732	€1.19 Saluting Battery, harbour and Fort St Elmo	3·50	4·25

Nos. 1731/1732 were printed together, *se-tenant*, forming a composite design showing the Grand Harbour, Valletta, seen from the Upper Barakka Gardens.

514 Official London Olympic Games Logo

2012. Olympic Games, London. Multicoloured.

MS1733	37c. Type **514**; €2.11 Official mascot Wenlock	6·50	7·50

515 SS *Almeria Lykes*

2012. 70th Anniversary of Operation Pedestal (Second World War Malta supply convoy). Multicoloured.

1734	26c. Type **515**	1·25	1·25
1735	26c. HMS *Amazon*	1·25	1·25
1736	26c. HMS *Antelope*	1·25	1·25
1737	26c. HMS *Ashanti*	1·25	1·25
1738	26c. HMS *Badsworth*	1·25	1·25
1739	26c. HMS *Bicester*	1·25	1·25
1740	26c. HMS *Bramham*	1·25	1·25
1741	26c. MV *Brisbane Star*	1·25	1·25
1742	26c. RFA *Brown Ranger*	1·25	1·25
1743	26c. HMS *Cairo*	1·25	1·25
1744	26c. HMS *Charybdis*	1·25	1·25
1745	26c. MV *Clan Ferguson*	1·25	1·25
1746	26c. HMS *Coltsfoot*	1·25	1·25
1747	26c. HMS *Derwent*	1·25	1·25
1748	26c. MV *Deucalion*	1·25	1·25
1749	26c. RFA *Dingledale*	1·25	1·25
1750	26c. MV *Dorset*	1·25	1·25
1751	26c. HMS *Eagle*	1·25	1·25
1752	26c. MV *Empire Hope*	1·25	1·25
1753	26c. HMS *Eskimo*	1·25	1·25
1754	26c. HMS *Foresight*	1·25	1·25
1755	26c. HMS *Furious*	1·25	1·25
1756	26c. HMS *Fury*	1·25	1·25
1757	26c. HMS *Geranium*	1·25	1·25
1758	26c. MV *Glenorchy*	1·25	1·25
1759	26c. HMS *Hebe*	1·25	1·25
1760	26c. HMS *Hythe*	1·25	1·25
1761	26c. HMS *Icarus*	1·25	1·25
1762	26c. HMS *Indomitable*	1·25	1·25
1763	26c. HMS *Intrepid*	1·25	1·25
1764	26c. HMS *Ithuriel*	1·25	1·25

1765	26c. HMS *Jaunty*	1·25	1·25
1766	26c. HMS *Jonquil*	1·25	1·25
1767	26c. HMS *Kenya*	1·25	1·25
1768	26c. HMS *Keppel*	1·25	1·25
1769	26c. HMS *Laforey*	1·25	1·25
1770	26c. HMS *Ledbury*	1·25	1·25
1771	26c. HMS *Lightning*	1·25	1·25
1772	26c. HMS *Lookout*	1·25	1·25
1773	26c. HMS *Malcolm*	1·25	1·25
1774	26c. HMS *Manchester*	1·25	1·25
1775	26c. HMS *Matchless*	1·25	1·25
1776	26c. MV *Melbourne Star*	1·25	1·25
1777	26c. HMS *Nelson*	1·25	1·25
1778	26c. HMS *Nigeria*	1·25	1·25
1779	26c. SS *Ohio* (tanker)	1·25	1·25
1780	26c. HMS *Pathfinder*	1·25	1·25
1781	26c. HMS *Penn*	1·25	1·25
1782	26c. HMS *Phoebe*	1·25	1·25
1783	26c. MV *Port Chalmers*	1·25	1·25
1784	26c. HMS *Quentin*	1·25	1·25
1785	26c. MV *Rochester Castle*	1·25	1·25
1786	26c. HMS *Rodney*	1·25	1·25
1787	26c. HMS *Rye*	1·25	1·25
1788	26c. HMS *Salvonia*	1·25	1·25
1789	26c. SS *Santa Elisa*	1·25	1·25
1790	26c. HMS *Sirius*	1·25	1·25
1791	26c. HMS *Somali*	1·25	1·25
1792	26c. HMS *Speedy*	1·25	1·25
1793	26c. HMS *Spirea*	1·25	1·25
1794	26c. HMS *Tartar*	1·25	1·25
1795	26c. HMS *Una*	1·25	1·25
1796	26c. HMS *Utmost*	1·25	1·25
1797	26c. HMS *Vansittart*	1·25	1·25
1798	26c. HMS *Venomous*	1·25	1·25
1799	26c. HMS *Victorious*	1·25	1·25
1800	26c. HMS *Vidette*	1·25	1·25
1801	26c. SS *Waimarama*	1·25	1·25
1802	26c. MV *Wairangi*	1·25	1·25
1803	26c. HMS *Westcott*	1·25	1·25
1804	26c. HMS *Wilton*	1·25	1·25
1805	26c. HMS *Wishart*	1·25	1·25
1806	26c. HMS *Wolverine*	1·25	1·25
1807	26c. HMS *Wrestler*	1·25	1·25
1808	26c. HMS *Zetland*	1·25	1·25
1809	26c. HMS *P.34*	1·25	1·25
1810	26c. HMS *P.42*	1·25	1·25
1811	26c. HMS *P.44*	1·25	1·25
1812	26c. HMS *P.46*	1·25	1·25
1813	26c. *ML121*	1·25	1·25
1814	26c. *ML126*	1·25	1·25
1815	26c. *ML134*	1·25	1·25
1816	26c. *ML135*	1·25	1·25
1817	26c. *ML168*	1·25	1·25
1818	26c. HMS *P.211*	1·25	1·25
1819	26c. HMS *P.222*	1·25	1·25
1820	26c. *ML459*	1·25	1·25
1821	26c. *ML462*	1·25	1·25

516 Notre Dame Gate, Zabbar, 1675

2012. Treasures of Malta. Historic Gates (1st series). Multicoloured.

1822	20c. Type **516**	65	30
1823	37c. Couvre Port Gate, Vittoriosa, 1723 (vert)	1·10	40
1824	67c. Lunzjata Valley Gate, Victoria, Gozo, *c.* 1698 (vert)	1·90	2·50
1825	69c. Fort Chambray Gate, Ghajnsielem, Gozo	1·90	2·50

See also Nos. 1831/1833, 1853/1855 and 1912/1913.

517 *The Adoration of the Magi* (German follower of Rubens)

2012. Christmas. Multicoloured.

1826	20c. Type **517**	65	30
1827	37c. *The Holy Family* (circle of Denys Calvaert)	1·10	40
1828	63c. *Holy Family* (Dutch School)	1·90	2·75

518 Blessed Gerard (founder) receiving Deed of Donation from Godfrey de Bouillon (detail) (Antoine Favray)

2013. 900th Anniversary of Papal Bull by Pope Paschal II to Blessed Gerard (founder of Hospital of St John of Jerusalem, now the Sovereign Military Hospitaller Order of St John of Jerusalem of Rhodes and of Malta (Order of Malta)). Sheet 120×80 mm.

MS1829	**518** €2.47 multicoloured	8·00	8·50

519 *The Baptism of Christ*

2013. 400th Birth Anniversary of Mattia Preti (artist). Multicoloured.

MS1830	97c. Type **519**; €1.87 *Self-portrait* (31×44 mm)	9·50	10·50

520 Vilhena Fountain, Floriana, 1728

2013. Treasures of Malta. Fountains (2nd series). Multicoloured.

1831	6c. Type **520**	20	15
1832	32c. Triton Fountain, Floriana, 1959 (horiz)	1·25	35
1833	€2.62 Spinola Fountain, Valletta, late 19th-century	9·50	11·00

521 Ford Transit Mark 1 Van passing former General Post Office at Auberge d'Italie, Merchant's Street, Valletta

2013. Europa. Postal Vehicles. Multicoloured.

1834	37c. Type **521**	1·25	30
1835	€1.19 Lambretta three wheeler, Dingli Street, Sliema	3·50	4·25

522 *Riviera*

2013. European Maritime Day. Cruise Liners. Multicoloured.

1836	26c. Type **522**	1·25	65
1837	51c. *Costa Deliziosa*	2·50	2·25
1838	97c. *Ryndam*	5·00	6·00

523 Rabbit

2013. Wild and Domestic Fauna of the Maltese Islands. Multicoloured.

1839	37c. Type **523**	1·40	30
1840	€2.25 Maltese Ox	8·00	9·00

524 Grand Harbour, Malta

2013. Harbours. Sheet 121×80 mm.

MS1841	**524** €4.51 multicoloured	13·00	14·00

No. **MS**1841 was a joint issue with Curacao which issued a miniature sheet showing Schottegat Harbour.

525 Airport Bus, 1950s

2013. Malta Buses. the End of an Era (2nd series). Multicoloured.

1842	6c. Type **525**	45	25
1843	10c. Double-deck bus, Valletta. St Julian's Route, *c.* 1903	60	40
1844	37c. Victoria Hire Service bus, 1925-1934	2·00	60
1845	52c. Royal Navy Bedford SB bus, 1950s-1960s ('Royal Armed Forces Bus')	3·25	2·25
1846	€1.16 Malta Police Bus, 1970s	6·50	6·50
1847	€2.25 Magirus-Deutz 03500	9·00	10·00

526 Red Cross

2013. 150th Anniversary of the International Red Cross. Sheet 120×80 mm.

MS1848	**526** €4.57 multicoloured	13·00	14·00

527 Crib Scene

2013. Christmas. Scenes from Mechanical Nativity Crib at Jesus of Nazareth Institute, Zejtun. Multicoloured.

1849	26c. Type **527**	75	30
1850	37c. Crib scene with palm trees and Angels flying over city walls	1·10	40
1851	63c. Crib scene with flour mill	1·90	2·75
MS1852	105×68 mm. €1 Flying Angels over city walls, palm trees and flour mill; €1 Nativity (both 76×20 mm)	6·00	6·50

2014. Treasures of Malta. Fountains (3rd series). As T **520**. Multicoloured.

1853	42c. Fountain under arch, The Mall, Floriana	1·40	70
1854	59c. Fountain in front of wall, San Anton Gardens, Attard (horiz)	1·75	1·60
1855	€1.25 Fountain in wall niche, Kercem, Gozo	3·50	4·25

528 Halls of the Knights Hospitallers in Valletta, Malta and Acre, Israel

2014. The Halls of the Knights Hospitallers.

1856	**528** 51c. multicoloured	1·75	1·75

A similar stamp was issued by Israel.

529 Police Boat, Marsamxett Harbour, Valletta

2014. Maritime Malta (2nd series). Bicentenary of the Malta Police Force (26c.) and 35th Anniversary of the End of Military Facilities Agreement (€1.55). Multicoloured.

1857	26c. Type **529**	1·50	1·25
1858	26c. Police boat at Sliema Ferries	1·50	1·25
1859	€1.55 HMS *Alexander* off Fort St Angelo, 1800	7·50	7·50
1860	€1.55 HMS *London* (off Fort St Michael) leaving Malta, 1 April 1979	7·50	7·50

530 Pope John XXIII

2014. Canonisation of Pope John XXIII and Pope John Paul II. Multicoloured.

MS1861	26c. Type **530**; €1.85 Pope John Paul II	8·50	8·50

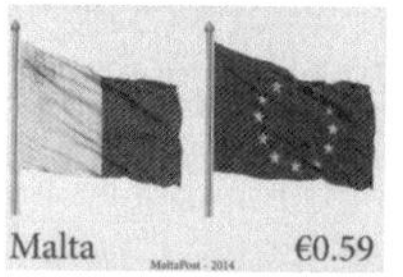

531 Flags of Malta and EU

2014. Tenth Anniversary of Malta's Accession to the European Union.

1862	**531** 59c. multicoloured	1·75	1·75

532 Musician playing Maltese Bagpipe

2014. Europa. National Musical Instruments. Details from 19th-century oil painting by Girolamo Gianni showing bagpipe and drum musicians performing at Porta Reale, Valletta. Multicoloured.

1863	59c. Type **532**	1·75	60
1864	€2.19 Drummer	6·00	7·00

533 Dove and EU Emblem

2014. Anniversaries. 50th Anniversary of Independence and 40th Anniv of the Republic of Malta. Multicoloured.

MS1865	59c. Type **533**; €3 As 1974 5c. Inauguration of Republic stamp but with '40TH ANNIVERSARY 1974-2014' inscription (44×31 mm)	11·00	12·00

534 Emblem

2014. World Cup Football Championship, Brazil. Multicoloured.

MS1866	59c. Type **534**; €1.55 Mascot Fuleco	5·50	6·00

535 *Gladiolus italicus*

2014. Maltese Flora (1st series). Multicoloured.

1867	26c. Type **535**	60	20
1868	59c. *Verbascum sinuatum*	1·50	75
1869	€1.16 *Orchis conica*	4·00	4·50

See also Nos. 1909/1911, 1932/1934 and 1960/1962.

536 Globe showing Mediterranean Sea

2014. Euromed Postal (Postal Union for the Mediterranean). The Mediterranean Sea.

1870	**536** €1.85 multicoloured	4·75	5·00

Similar designs were issued by Cyprus, Egypt, France, Greece, Jordan, Lebanon, Libya, Morocco, Palestine, Slovenia and Syria.

537 Fra' Philippe de Villiers de L'Isle-Adam (1521)

2014. Grandmasters of the Sovereign Military Order of Malta, 1530-1798. Multicoloured.

1871	26c. Type **537**	60	20
1872	26c. Fra' Pierino del Ponte (1534)	60	2·00
1873	26c. Fra' Didier de Saint-Jaille (1535)	60	20
1874	26c. Fra' Jean de Homedes (1536)	60	20
1875	26c. Fra' Claude de la Sengle (1553)	60	20
1876	26c. Fra' Jean de la Valette-Parisot (1557)	60	20
1877	26c. Fra' Pierre de Monte (1568)	60	20
1878	26c. Fra' Jean L'Evesque de la Cassière (1572)	60	20
1879	26c. Fra' Hugues Loubenx de Verdala (1582)	60	20
1880	26c. Fra' Martin Garzez (1595)	60	20
1881	26c. Fra' Alof de Wignacourt (1601)	60	20
1882	26c. Fra' Luis Mandez de Vasconcellos (1622)	60	20
1883	26c. Fra' Antoine de Paule (1623)	60	20
1884	26c. Fra' Jean-Paul de Lascaris-Castellar (1636)	60	20
1885	26c. Fra' Martin de Redin (1657)	60	20
1886	26c. Fra' Annet de Clermont-Gessant (1660)	60	20
1887	26c. Fra' Raphael Cotoner (1660)	60	20
1888	26c. Fra' Nicolas Cotoner (1663)	60	20
1889	26c. Fra' Gregorio Carafa (1680)	60	20
1890	26c. Fra' Adrien de Wignacourt (1690)	60	20
1891	26c. Fra' Ramon Perellos y Roccaful (1697)	60	20
1892	26c. Fra' Marc' Antonio Zondadari (1720)	60	20
1893	26c. Fra' Antonio Manoel de Vilhena (1722)	60	20
1894	26c. Fra' Raymond Despuig (1735)	60	20
1895	26c. Fra' Manuel Pinto de Fonseca (1741)	60	20
1896	26c. Fra' Francisco Ximenes de Texada (1773)	60	20
1897	26c. Fra' Emmanuel de Rohan-Polduc (1775)	60	20
1898	26c. Fra' Ferdinand von Hompesch zu Bolheim (1797)	60	20

538 Bighi Hospital

2014. Centenary of World War I. 'Nurse of the Mediterranean'. Military Hospitals. Multicoloured.

1899	10c. Type **538**	30	20
1900	59c. Floriana Hospital	1·75	1·75
1901	€2 HMHS *Rewa*	5·75	6·25

539

2014. Christmas. Scenes from *Bethlehem f'Għajnsielem* (re-enactment of the Nativity by people of Għajnsielem, Gozo). Multicoloured.

1902	26c. Type **539**	75	65
1903	59c. Visit of the Three Kings to the Holy Family (horiz)	1·75	1·75
1904	63c. Two shepherds by fire, Għchurch in background (horiz)	1·75	1·75
1905	€1.16 The Holy Family in the stable	3·25	3·75

540 US President Franklin D. Roosevelt and Winston Churchill, Malta Conference, 1945 ("No more let us falter")

2015. 70th Anniversary of the Yalta Conference. Multicoloured.

1906	€1 Type **540**	3·00	3·50
1907	€1 Montgomery House, Floriana (venue of Malta Conference) ("From Malta to Yalta!")	3·00	3·50
1908	€1 Winston Churchill, President Roosevelt and Stalin at Yalta Conference ("Let nobody alter!")	3·00	3·50

2015. Maltese Flora (2nd series). As T **535**. Multicoloured.

1909	26c. *Tragopogon hybridus* (Smooth Goatsbeard)	75	65
1910	59c. *Anemone coronaria* (Crown Anemone)	1·75	1·75
1911	€1.16 *Arisarum vulgare* (Friar's Cowl)	3·25	3·75

2015. Treasures of Malta (4th series). 400th Anniversary of Construction of Wignacourt Aqueduct. Multicoloured.

1912	42c. Wignacourt Arch, Fleur-de-lys (horiz)	1·25	1·00
1913	€1.55 Wignacourt Water Tower, Floriana (inscr 'Wingacourt')	4·50	5·00

541 Red Cross Nurse, Wounded Soldier and Other Soldiers

2015. ANZAC Centenary. Sheet 120×75 mm.

MS1914	**541** €3.59 multicoloured	10·00	11·00

542 Penny Black

2015. 175th Anniversary of the Penny Black. Multicoloured.

MS1915	123×80 mm. €1.21 Type **542**×3	8·25	8·75

543 Boys with Cart

2015. Europa. Old Toys. Multicoloured.

1916	59c. Type **543**	1·40	1·40
1917	€2.19 Girl running with hoop	5·00	5·50

544 Feast of St George, Victoria, Gozo ('The Festa')

2015. Culture. Multicoloured.

1918	26c. Type **544**	60	50
1919	59c. Annual Regatta, Grand Harbour	1·40	1·40
1920	€1.16 Statue of the Risen Christ carried in procession, Easter Sunday, Zebbug	2·75	3·25

No. 1919 was inscr 'sepac'.

545 Firilla

2015. Euromed Postal (Postal Union for the Mediterranean). Boats of the Mediterranean

1921	**545** €3.59 multicoloured	8·25	8·75

546 Brigantine *Concezione* in Shallow Water during Storm, 18 December 1835

2015. Maritime Malta (3rd series). Ex-Voto Paintings from the Sanctuary of Our Lady, Mellieha. Multicoloured.

1922	51c. Type **546**	1·25	1·00
1923	82c. Barque *Matutina* blown sideways onto shallow banks, 17 January 1839	2·00	2·40
1924	€1 Speronara (sailing coaster) *S. Francesco di Paula* with broken rudder, 9 December 1843	2·40	2·75

547 St John Bosco

2015. Birth Bicentenary of St. John Bosco.

1925	**547** €2 multicoloured	4·75	5·25

548 *The Allegory of the Triumph of the Order* (Mattia Preti), from St John's Co-Cathedral, Valletta

2015. 450th Anniversary of the Great Siege. Sheet 120×80 mm.

MS1926	**548** €4.25 multicoloured	10·00	11·00

549 Anniversary Emblem

2015. 70th Anniversary of the United Nations. Sheet 120×80 mm.

MS1927	**549** €3.51 multicoloured	8·25	8·75

550 *The Flight into Egypt*

2015. Christmas. Woodcuts from series *Life of the Virgin* by Albrecht Dürer. Multicoloured.

1928	26c. Type **550**	60	50
1929	59c. *The Nativity of the Lord*	1·40	1·40
1930	63c. *The Adoration of the Magi*	1·50	2·00

551 Emblem

2015. Commonwealth Heads of Government Meeting (CHOGM), Valletta. Sheet 84×84 mm.

MS1931	**551** €3 multicoloured	7·00	7·50

2016. Maltese Flora (3rd series). As T **535**. Multicoloured.

1932	26c. *Asphodelus aestivus* (branched asphodel)	60	50
1933	59c. *Anacamptis pyramidalis* (common pyramidal orchid)	1·40	1·40
1934	€1.16 *Ophrys melitensis* (Maltese spider orchid)	2·75	3·25

552 Coin of 1566

2016. 450th Anniversary of the Foundation of Valletta. Sheet 120×80 mm.

MS1935	**552** €4.25 multicoloured	10·00	11·00

553 Shearwater

2016. Endangered Species. Shearwater. Multicoloured.

MS1936	75c. Type **553**; 75c. Shearwater flying to left; 75c. Shearwater on the sea; 75c. Four shearwaters on the sea	7·00	7·50

554 Painting Contaminated Landscape Green

2016. Europa. Think Green. Multicoloured.

1937	59c. Type **554**	1·40	1·40
1938	€2.19 Human profiles containing polluted and green environments	5·00	5·50

555 *Dulber* (Yalta Historical and Literature Museum)

2016. Paintings by Nicholas Krassnoff. Multicoloured.

1939	€1 Type **555**	2·25	2·50
1940	€1 *View from Vittoriosa Gate* (Malta National Museum of Fine Arts)	2·25	2·50

Similar designs were issued by Russia.

556 Woman in Maltese Costume, Landscape with Flowers and Gozo's Cittadella (Spring)

2016. Seasons. Multicoloured.

1941	26c. Type **556**	60	50

1942	51c. Sunbathers and swimmers on sandy beach of Ghajn Tuffieha (Summer) (horiz)	1·25	1·00
1943	59c. Woman, autumn trees and Verdala Palace (Autumn)	1·40	1·40
1944	€2 Woman on shore on stormy day, Ghar-id-Dud, Sliema (Winter) (horiz)	4·50	5·00

No. 1943 was inscr 'sepac'.

558 Shooting

2016. Olympic Games, Rio de Janeiro, Brazil. Multicoloured.

1946	42c. Type **558**	95	85
1947	62c. Swimming	1·40	1·40
1948	90c. Weightlifting	2·10	2·40
1949	€1.55 Relay runner with baton	3·50	4·00

559 Dom Mintoff

2016. Birth Centenary of Dominic ('Dom') Mintoff (1916-2012, Prime Minister of Malta 1955-1958, 1971-1984).

1950	**559** €3 multicoloured	7·00	7·50

560 *HMS Hastings in Valletta Grand Harbour, 30 November 1838* (lithograph of drawing by Charles von Brocktorff)

2016. Maritime Malta (4th series). Arrival of HMS *Hastings* carrying Queen Adelaide, Valletta, 1838.

MS1951	120×80 mm. **560** €3.59 multicoloured	8·25	8·75

561 Balcony Corbel

2016. Balcony Corbels (1st series). Multicoloured.

1952	26c. Type **561**	60	50
1953	€1 Balcony corbel with carved head	2·25	2·50
1954	€1.16 Balcony corbel with carved mask	2·75	3·25

See also Nos. 1963/1965.

562 Cittadella, Ghawdex

2016. Fortifications. Multicoloured.

MS1955	120×80 mm. 59c. Type **562**; €3 First Tower, San Marino	8·25	8·75

A similar miniature sheet was issued by San Marino.

563 Mary, Joseph and Jesus

2016. Christmas. Paintings by Joseph Pulo. Multicoloured.

1956	26c. Type **563**	60	50
1957	59c. Stable with Mary, Joseph and baby Jesus in manger and Star of Bethlehem above	1·40	1·40
1958	63c. Three Wise Men giving gifts	1·40	1·40

557 Dorado (Lampuka–*Coryphaena hippurus*)

2016. Euromed Postal (Postal Union for the Mediterranean). Fish in the Mediterranean.

1945	**557** €3.59 multicoloured	8·25	8·75

564 Emblem

2017. Maltese Presidency of the Council of the European Union.

MS1959	85×85 mm. **564** €3.59 multicoloured	8·25	8·75

2017. Maltese Flora (4th series). Multicoloured.

1960	26c. *Orchis collina* (Fan-lipped Orchid)	60	50
1961	42c. *Ophrys lutea* (Yellow Bee-orchid)	95	85
1962	€1.25 *Serapias parviflora* (Small-flowered Tongue-orchid)	3·00	3·50

2017. Balcony Corbels (2nd series). Multicoloured.

1963	51c. Two balcony corbels	1·25	1·00
1964	€1.32 Square balcony with scroll corbel	3·00	3·50
1965	€1.55 Round balcony with scroll corbel	3·50	4·00

565 St Agatha Tower, Mellieha, Malta

2017. Europa. Castles. Multicoloured.

1966	59c. Type **565**	1·40	1·40
1967	€2.19 Gourgion Tower, Xewkija, Gozo	5·00	5·50

566 Peppi Pustier Mascot in Modern Uniform

2017. Postal Uniforms. Multicoloured.

1968	26c. Type **566**	60	50
1969	59c. Peppi Pustier (MaltaPost mascot) in uniform of early 2000s	1·40	1·40
1970	€1 Peppi Pustier on motorcycle wearing 1980s uniform with grey jacket	2·25	2·50
1971	€2 Peppi Pustier in early 1900s uniform	4·50	5·00

567 Boat Builder

2017. Traditional Handicrafts. Multicoloured.

1972	26c. Type **567**	60	50
1973	59c. Man making bamboo fish trap	1·40	1·40
1974	€1 Weaving	2·25	2·50
1975	€3.51 Tberfil artist decorating wheels of horse-drawn carriage	8·00	8·50

568 *Tetraclinis articulata* Tree at Mellieha

2017. Euromed Postal (Postal Union for the Mediterranean). Trees of the Mediterranean. Araar or Sandarac Tree (*Tetraclinis articulata*). Multicoloured.

1976	10c. Type **568**	25	15
1977	€3.63 *Tetraclinis articulata* tree at Qrendi	8·25	8·75

569 Siege Bell War Memorial, Valletta

2017. 75th Anniversary of Operation Pedestal.

MS1978	120×80 mm. **569** €3 multicoloured	7·00	7·50

570 Bone China Virgin Mary Statue, sculpted by Rafl Ignaz, 1874, Attard Parish Church

2017. The Feast of the Assumption of Our Lady. Multicoloured.

1979	26c. Type **570**	60	50
1980	26c. Wooden Virgin Mary statue sculpted by Mastru Anton Busuttil and Son, 1861, Dingli Parish Church	60	50
1981	26c. Wooden Virgin Mary statue, sculpted by Marjanu Gerada, 1808, Ghaxaq Parish Church	60	50
1982	26c. Virgin Mary statue sculpted by Vincenzo Dimech, 1807, Gudja Parish Church	60	50
1983	26c. Virgin Mary statue, Mgarr Parish Church	60	50
1984	26c. Virgin Mary statue, sculpted by Salvatore Dimech, 1868, Mosta Sanctuary	60	50
1985	26c. Virgin Mary statue sculpted by Xandru Farrugia, 1836, Mqabba Parish Church	60	50
1986	26c. Wooden Virgin Mary statue, sculpted by Antonio Chircop, 1837, Qrendi Parish Church	60	50
1987	26c. Virgin Mary statue, Victoria Cathedral, Gozo	60	50
1988	26c. Virgin Mary statue made by Gallard et Fils in Marseilles, 1863, Zebbug Parish Church, Gozo	60	50

571 *La Gloria Di Santa Rosa Di Lima*

2017. 350th Death Anniversary of Melchiorre Gafá (1636-1667, Maltese sculptor). Multicoloured.

1989	20c. Type **571**	45	35
1990	42c. *La Gloria Di Santa Caterina Di Siena*	95	85
1991	51c. *L'Annunciazione*	1·25	1·00
1992	€1 *L'Adorazione dei Pastori*	2·25	2·50
1993	€1.16 *La Nativita*	2·75	3·25

572 Model of Third Rate Ship-of-the-line

2017. Maritime Malta (5th series). Vessels of the Order of St John. Multicoloured.

1994	63c. Type **572**	1·40	1·40
1995	€1.85 Model of carrack *Sant Anna*	4·25	4·75
1996	€3.59 Model of third rate ship-of-the-line (different)	8·25	8·75

573 Infant Jesus Figurine, Church of the Nativity of the Virgin Mary, Naxxar

2017. Christmas. Baby Jesus Figurines. Multicoloured.

1997	26c. Type **573**	60	50
1998	51c. Baby Jesus, Church of the Immaculate Conception, Cospicua	1·25	1·00
1999	59c. Baby Jesus, Basilica of St Peter and St Paul, Nadur	1·40	1·40
2000	63c. Baby Jesus, Sanctuary of Our Lady of Grace, Zabbar	1·40	1·40

574 Tile Pattern of Green and Claret Flowers (top left portion)

2017. Traditional Floor Tile Patterns. Multicoloured.

2001	25c. Type **574**	60	50
2002	25c. Pattern of green and claret flowers (top right portion)	60	50
2003	25c. Pattern of green and claret flowers (bottom left portion)	60	50
2004	25c. Pattern of green and claret flowers (bottom right portion)	60	50
2005	29c. Pattern of four red flowers	70	60
2006	59c. Pattern with Maltese Cross	1·40	1·40
2007	75c. Pattern with green flowers and brown, red and white triangles (top left and lowe right portion)	1·75	2·00
2008	75c. Pattern with green flowers and brown, red and white triangles (top right and lower left portion)	1·75	2·00

Nos. 2001/2004 were printed together, *se-tenant*, in sheetlets of four stamps, each sheetlet forming a composite design.

Nos. 2005/2006 were each printed in separate sheetlets of four stamps.

Nos. 2007/2008 were printed together, *se-tenant*, in sheetlets of four containing two of each design, the whole sheetlet forming a composite design.

575 White Shirt, Trousers held up by Sash, Waistcoat and Cap

2018. Traditional Costumes. Multicoloured.

2009	26c. Type **575**	60	50
2010	59c. White shirt, trousers held up by sash, waistcoat and cap, with addition of horga (cloth pouch slung over shoulder)	1·40	1·40
2011	€1.16 Kabozza (hooded winter overcoat)	2·75	3·25

576 Sensile (common galley)

2018. Maritime Malta (6th series). Vessels of the Order of St John. Models from Malta Maritime Museum. Multicoloured.

2012	26c. Type **576**	60	50
2013	42c. Demi galley or half galley	95	85
2014	€1 Brigantine (ceremonial barge of Portuguese Grand Master Antonio Manoel de Vilhena)	2·25	2·50

POSTAGE DUE STAMPS

D1

1925. Imperf.

D1	**D1**	½d. black	1·25	11·00
D2	**D1**	1d. black	3·25	4·75
D3	**D1**	1½d. black	3·00	3·75
D4	**D1**	2d. black	14·00	26·00
D5	**D1**	2½d. black	2·75	2·75
D6	**D1**	3d. black on grey	9·00	15·00
D7	**D1**	4d. black on yellow	5·00	9·50
D8	**D1**	6d. black on yellow	5·00	32·00
D9	**D1**	1s. black on yellow	6·50	35·00
D10	**D1**	1s. 6d. black on yellow	20·00	75·00

D2

1925. Perf.

D11	**D2**	½d. green	1·25	60
D12	**D2**	1d. violet	1·25	45
D13	**D2**	1½d. brown	1·50	80
D14	**D2**	2d. grey	6·50	1·00
D35	**D2**	2d. brown	85	70
D36	**D2**	2½d. orange	60	70
D37	**D2**	3d. blue	60	60
D38	**D2**	4d. green	1·00	80
D39	**D2**	6d. purple	75	1·75
D40	**D2**	1s. black	90	1·50
D41	**D2**	1s.6d. red	2·75	7·50

D3 Maltese Lace

1973

D42	**D3**	2m. brown and red	10	10
D43	**D3**	3m. orange and red	10	15
D44	**D3**	5m. pink and red	15	20
D45	**D3**	1c. blue and green	30	35
D46	**D3**	2c. grey and black	40	35
D47	**D3**	3c. light brown & brown	40	35
D48	**D3**	5c. dull blue and blue	65	70
D49	**D3**	10c. lilac and plum	85	1·00

D4

1993

D50	**D4**	1c. magenta and mauve	20	30
D51	**D4**	2c. blue and light blue	25	40
D52	**D4**	5c. green and turquoise	35	45
D53	**D4**	10c. orange and yellow	55	55

MANAMA

A dependency of Ajman.

100 dirhams = 1 riyal.

1966. Nos. 10, 12, 14 and 18 of Ajman surch **Manama** in English and Arabic and new value.

1	40d. on 40n.p. multicoloured	95	95
2	70d. on 70n.p. multicoloured	95	95
3	1r.50 on 1r.50 multicoloured	2·75	2·75
4	10r. on 10r. multicoloured	11·50	11·50

1967. Nos. 140/148 of Ajman optd **MANAMA** in English and Arabic. (a) Postage.

5	15d. blue and brown	25	25
6	30d. brown and black	40	40
7	50d. black and brown	70	70
8	70d. violet and black	70	70
	(b) Air.		
9	1r. green and brown	95	95
10	2r. mauve and black	1·90	1·90
11	3r. black and brown	2·75	2·75
12	5r. brown and black	6·00	6·00
13	10r. blue and brown	11·00	11·00

APPENDIX

The following stamps have either been issued in excess of postal needs or have not been available to the public in reasonable quantities at face value. Such stamps may later be given full listing if there is evidence of regular postal use.

1966. New Currency Surcharges. Stamps of Ajman surch **Manama** in English and Arabic and new value.

(a) Nos. 19/20 and 22/24 (Kennedy). 10d. on 10n.p., 15d. on 15n.p., 1r. on 1r., 2r. on 2r., 3r. on 3r.
(b) Nos. 27, 30 and 35/36 (Olympics). 5d. on 5n.p., 25d. on 25n.p., 3r. on 3r., 5r. on 5r.
(c) Nos. 80/82 and 85 (Churchill). 50d. on 50n.p., 75d. on 75n.p., 1r. on 1r., 5r. on 5r.
(d) Nos. 95/98 (Space). Air 50d. on 50n.p., 1r. on 1r., 3r. on 3r., 5r. on 5r.

1967

World Scout Jamboree, Idaho. Postage 30, 70d., 1r.; Air 2, 3, 4r.
Olympic Games, Mexico (1968). Postage 35, 65, 75d., 1r.; Air 1r.25, 2, 3, 4r.
Winter Olympic Games, Grenoble (1968). Postage 5, 35, 60, 75d.; Air 1, 1r.25, 2, 3r.
Paintings by Renoir and Terbrugghen. Air 35, 65d., 1, 2r.×3.

1968

Paintings by Velazquez. Air 1r.×2, 2r.×2.
Costumes. Air 30d.×2, 70d.×2, 1r.×2, 2r.×2.
Olympic Games, Mexico. Postage 1r.×4; Air 2r.×4.
Satellites and Spacecraft. Air 30d.×2, 70d.×2, 1r.×2, 2r.×2, 3r.×2.
Human Rights Year. Kennedy Brothers and Martin Luther King. Air 1r.×3, 2r.×3.
Sports Champions, Famous Footballers. Postage 15, 20, 50, 75d., 1r.; Air 10r.
Heroes of Humanity. Circular designs on gold or silver foil. 60d.×12.
Olympic Games, Mexico. Circular designs on gold or silver foil. Air 3r.×8.
Mothers' Day. Paintings. Postage 1r.×6.
Kennedy Brothers Commemoration. Postage 2r.; Air 5r.
Cats (1st series). Postage 1, 2, 3d.; Air 2, 3r.
Fifth Death Anniversary of President Kennedy. Air 10r.
Space Exploration. Postage 5, 10, 15, 20, 25d.; Air 15r.
Olympic Games, Mexico. Gold Medals. Postage 2r.×4; Air 5r.×4.
Christmas. Air 5r.

1969

Sports Champions. Cyclists. Postage 1, 2, 5, 10, 15, 20d.; Air 12r.
Sports Champions. German Footballers. Postage 5, 10, 15, 20, 25d.; Air 10r.
Sports Champions. Motor-racing Drivers. Postage 1, 5, 10, 15, 25d.; Air 10r.
Motor-racing Cars. Postage 1, 5, 10, 15, 25d.; Air 10r.
Sports Champions. Boxers. Postage 5, 10, 15, 20d.; Air 10r.
Sports Champions. Baseball Players. Postage 1, 2, 5, 10, 15d.; Air 10r.
Birds. Air 1r.×11.
Roses. Postage 1r.×6.
Animals. Air 1r.×6.
Paintings by Italian Artists. 5, 10, 15, 20d., 10r.
Great Composers. Air 5, 10, 25d., 10r.
Paintings by French Artists. 1r.×4.
Nude Paintings. Air 2r.×4.
Kennedy Brothers. Air 2, 3, 10r.
Olympic Games, Mexico. Gold Medal Winners. Postage 1, 2d., 10r.; Air 10d., 5, 10r.
Paintings of the Madonna. Postage 10d.; Air 10r.
Space Flight of *Apollo 9*. Optd on 1968 Space Exploration issue. Air 15r.
Space Flight of *Apollo 10*. Optd on 1968 Space Exploration issue. Air 15r.
First Death Anniversary of Gagarin. Optd on 1968 Space Exploration issue. 5d.
Second Death Anniversary of Edward White (astronaut). Optd on 1968 Space Exploration issue. 10d.
First Death Anniversary of Robert Kennedy. Optd on 1969 Kennedy Brothers issue. Air 2r.
Olympic Games, Munich (1972). Optd on 1969 Mexico Gold Medal Winners issue. Air 10d., 5, 10r.
Moon Mission of *Apollo 11*. Air 1, 2, 3r.
Christmas. Paintings by Brueghel. Postage 1, 2, 4, 5, 10d.; Air 6r.

1970

Soyuz and Apollo Space Programmes. Postage 1, 2, 4, 5, 10d.; Air 3, 5r.
Kennedy and Eisenhower Commemoration. Embossed on gold foil. Air 20r.
Lord Baden-Powell Commemoration. Embossed on gold foil. Air 20r.
World Cup Football Championship, Mexico. Postage 20, 40, 60, 80d., 1r.; Air 3r.
Brazil's Victory in World Cup Football Championship. Optd on 1970 World Cup issue. Postage 20, 40, 60, 80d., 1r.; Air 3r.
Paintings by Michelangelo. Postage 1, 2, 4, 5, 10d.; Air 6r.
World Fair Expo 70, Osaka, Japan. Air 25, 50, 75d., 1, 2, 3, 12r.
Paintings by Renoir. Postage 1, 2, 5, 6, 10d.; Air 5, 12r.
Olympic Games, Rome, Tokyo, Mexico and Munich. Postage 15, 30, 50, 70d.; Air 2, 5r.
Winter Olympic Games, Sapporo (1972) (1st issue). Postage 2, 3, 4, 10d.; Air 2, 5r.
Christmas. Flower Paintings by Brueghel. Postage 5, 20, 25, 30, 50d.; Air 60d., 1, 2r.

1971

Winter Olympic Games, Sapporo (2nd issue). Postage 1, 2, 3, 4, 5, 6, 8, 10, 12, 15, 20, 25, 30, 35, 40, 50d.; Air 75d, 1, 2, 2r.50.
Roses. Postage 5, 20, 25, 30, 50d.; Air 60d., 1, 2r.
Birds. Postage 5, 20, 25, 30, 50d.; Air 60d., 1, 2r.
Paintings by Modigliani. Air 25, 50, 60, 75d., 1r.50, 3r.
Paintings by Rubens. Postage 1, 2, 3, 4, 5, 10d.; Air 2, 3r.
Philatokyo '71 Stamp Exhibition, Paintings by Hokusai and Hiroshige. Postage 10, 15, 20, 25, 50, 75d.; Air 1, 2r.
25th Anniversary of United Nations. Optd on 1970 Christmas issue. Postage 5, 20, 25, 30, 50d.; Air 60d., 1, 2r.
British Military Uniforms. Postage 5, 20, 25, 30, 50d.; Air 60d., 1, 2r.
Space Flight of *Apollo 14*. Postage 15, 25, 50, 60, 70d.; Air 5r.
Space Flight of *Apollo 15*. Postage 25, 40, 50, 60d.; Air 1, 6r.
13th World Scout Jamboree, Asagiri, Japan (1st issue). Postage 1, 2, 3, 5, 7, 10, 12, 15, 20, 25, 30, 35, 40, 50, 65, 80d.; Air 1r., 1r.25, 1r.50, 2r.
World Wild Life Conservation. Postage 1, 2, 3, 5, 7, 10, 12, 15, 20, 25, 30, 35, 40, 50, 65, 80d.; Air 1r., 1r.25, 1r.50, 2r.
13th World Scout Jamboree, Asagiri, Japan (2nd issue). Stamps. Postage 10, 15, 20, 25, 50, 75d.; Air 1, 2r.
Winter Olympic Games, Sapporo (3rd issue). Postage 1, 2, 3, 4, 5, 10d.; Air 2, 3r.
Cats (2nd series). Postage 15, 25, 40, 60d.; Air 3, 10r.
Lions International Clubs. Optd on 1971 Uniforms issue. Postage 5, 20, 25, 30, 50d.; Air 60d., 1, 2r.
Paintings of Ships. Postage 15, 20, 25, 30, 50d.; Air 60d., 1, 2r.
Great Olympic Champions. Postage 25, 50, 75d., 1r.; Air 5r.
Prehistoric Animals. Postage 15, 20, 25, 30, 50, 60d.; Air 1, 2r.
Footballers. Postage 5, 10, 15, 20, 40d.; Air 5r.
Royal Visit of Queen Elizabeth II to Japan. Postage 10, 20, 30, 40, 50d.; Air 2, 3r.
Fairy Tales. Stories by Hans Andersen. Postage 1, 2, 4, 5, 10d.; Air 3r.
World Fair, Philadelphia (1976). American Paintings. Postage 20, 25, 50, 60, 75d.; Air 3r.
Fairy Tales. Well-known stories. Postage 1, 2, 4, 5, 10d.; Air 3r.
Space Flight of *Apollo 16*. Postage 20, 30, 40, 50, 60d.; Air 3, 4r.
Tropical Fish. Postage 1, 2, 3, 4, 5, 10d.; Air 2, 3r.
European Tour of Emperor Hirohito of Japan. Postage 1, 2, 4, 5, 10d.; Air 6r.
Meeting of President Nixon and Emperor Hirohito of Japan in Alaska. Optd on 1971 Emperor's Tour issue. Air 6r.
2500th Anniversary of Persian Empire. Postage 10, 20, 30, 40, 50d.; Air 3r.
Space Flight of *Apollo 15* and Future Developments in Space. Postage 10, 15, 20, 25, 50d.; Air 1, 2r.

1972

150th Death Anniversary (1971) of Napoleon. Postage 10, 20, 30, 40d.; Air 1, 2, 3, 4r.
First Death Anniversary of General de Gaulle. Postage 10, 20, 30, 40d.; Air 1, 2, 3, 4r.
Paintings from the Alte Pinakothek, Munich. Postage 5, 10, 15, 20, 25d.; Air 5r.
Tour de France Cycle Race. Postage 5, 10, 15, 20, 25, 30, 35, 40, 45, 50, 55, 60d.; Air 65, 70, 75, 80, 85, 90, 95d., 1r.
Cats and Dogs. Postage 10, 20, 30, 40, 50d.; Air 1r.
25th Anniversary of UNICEF Optd on 1971 World Scout Jamboree, Asagiri (2nd issue). Postage 10, 15, 20, 25, 50, 75d.; Air 1, 2r.
Past and Present Motor cars. Postage 10, 20, 30, 40, 50d.; Air 1r.
Military Uniforms. 1r.×11.

The United Arab Emirates Ministry of Communications took over the Manama postal service on 1 August 1972. Further stamps inscribed "Manama" issued after that date were released without authority and had no validity.

MANCHUKUO

Issues for the Japanese puppet Government set up in 1932 under President (later Emperor) Pu Yi.

100 fen = 1 yuan.

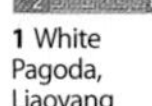

1 White Pagoda, Liaoyang

2 Pu Yi, later Emperor Kang-teh

1932. (a) With five characters in top panel as T **1** and **2**.

1	**1**	½f. brown	3·25	90
2	**1**	1f. red	4·00	40
24	**1**	1f. brown	5·50	1·10
25	**1**	1½f. violet	8·00	4·00
4	**1**	2f. grey	9·50	1·00
26	**1**	2f. blue	12·00	4·25
27	**1**	3f. brown	8·00	1·10
6	**1**	4f. green	6·50	45
28	**1**	4f. brown	£110	6·00
7	**1**	5f. green	8·50	1·40
8	**1**	6f. red	22·00	4·00
9	**1**	7f. grey	7·00	1·75
10	**1**	8f. brown	32·00	35·00
11	**1**	10f. orange	12·00	75
12	**2**	13f. brown	26·00	13·00
13	**2**	15f. red	40·00	4·00
14	**2**	16f. blue	50·00	13·00
15	**2**	20f. brown	24·00	1·90
16	**2**	30f. orange	35·00	4·00
17	**2**	50f. green	65·00	5·50
31	**2**	1y. violet	80·00	27·00
		(b) With six characters in top panel.		
40	**1**	½f. brown	1·25	70
41	**1**	1f. brown	1·40	45
42	**1**	1½f. violet	1·75	1·10
43	**1**	3f. brown	2·00	45
44	**1**	5f. blue	40·00	2·00
45	**1**	5f. slate	15·00	3·25
46	**1**	6f. red	5·50	1·60
47	**1**	7f. grey	5·25	2·50
48	**1**	9f. orange	6·00	1·25
55	**1**	10f. blue	35·00	1·40
56	**2**	13f. brown	32·00	35·00
49	**2**	15f. red	8·50	1·50
50	**2**	18f. green	75·00	10·00
51	**2**	20f. brown	8·50	2·25
52	**2**	30f. brown	8·50	1·60
53	**2**	50f. green	15·00	2·75
54	**2**	1y. violet	45·00	17·00

3 Map and Flags

1933. First Anniversary of Republic.

19	**3**	1f. orange	10·00	4·00
20	-	2f. green	50·00	45·00
21	**3**	4f. red	10·00	3·75
22	-	10f. blue	75·00	75·00

Design: 2, 10f. Council Hall, Hsinking.

6 Emperor's Palace

1934. Enthronement of Emperor.

32	**6**	1½f. brown	9·00	6·00
33	-	3f. red	8·00	4·00
34	**6**	6f. green	27·00	20·00
35	-	10f. blue	35·00	30·00

Design: 3f., 10f. Phoenixes.

1934. Stamps of 1932 surch with four Japanese characters.

36	**1**	1f. on 4f. green (No. 6)	25·00	12·00
37	**1**	3f. on 4f. green (No. 6)	£225	£170
38	**1**	3f. on 4f. brown (No. 28)	32·00	15·00
39	**2**	3f. on 16f. blue (No. 14)	50·00	50·00

In No. 38 the left hand upper character of the surcharge consists of three horizontal lines.

12 Orchid Crest of Manchukuo

13 Changpai Mountain and Sacred Lake

1935. China Mail.

64	**12**	2f. green	3·00	90
65	**12**	2½f. violet	1·25	1·00
66	**13**	4f. green	9·00	1·10
67	**13**	5f. blue	65	1·00
68	**12**	8f. yellow	12·00	2·00
60	**13**	12f. red	45·00	22·00
70	**13**	13f. brown	2·50	2·50

15 Mt. Fuji

16 Phoenixes

1935. Visit of Emperor Kang-teh to Japan.

71	**15**	1½f. green	6·50	5·25

72	16	3f. orange	6·50	6·00
73	15	6f. red	12·00	12·00
74	16	10f. blue	20·00	18·00

17 Symbolic of Accord

1936. Japan–Manchukuo Postal Agreement.

75	17	1½f. brown	10·00	10·00
76	-	3f. purple	2·00	5·25
77	17	6f. red	26·00	20·00
78	-	10f. blue	38·00	30·00

Design: Horiz—3f., 10f. Department of Communications.

19 State Council Building, Hsinking

20 Chengte Palace, Jehol

1936

79	19	½f. brown	90	60
80	19	1f. red	65	20
81	19	1½f. lilac	9·00	8·00
82	A	2f. green	85	20
83	19	3f. brown	2·00	75
84	B	4f. green	1·10	20
149	19	5f. black	80	4·00
86	A	6f. red	1·50	60
87	B	7f. black	2·75	90
88	B	9f. red	2·75	90
89	20	10f. blue	3·25	40
90	B	12f. orange	2·50	35
91	B	13f. brown	£110	£120
92	B	15f. red	9·00	1·10
93	C	18f. green	48·00	48·00
94	C	19f. green	12·00	5·50
95	A	20f. brown	3·75	80
96	20	30f. brown	3·75	80
97	D	38f. blue	45·00	45·00
98	D	39f. blue	4·00	4·25
99	A	50f. green	5·00	1·00
154	20	1y. purple	3·50	5·00

Designs: A, Carting soya-beans; B. Peiling Mausoleum; C, Aircraft and grazing sheep (domestic and China air mail); D, Nakajima-built Fokker F.VIIb/3m aeroplane over Sungari River railway bridge (air mail to Japan).

21 Sun rising over Fields

22 Shadowgraph of old and new Hsinking

1937. Fifth Anniversary of Founding of State.

101	21	1½f. red	32·00	32·00
102	22	3f. green	8·00	8·00

1937. China Mail. Surch in Chinese characters.

108	12	2½f. on 2f. green	7·00	6·00
110	13	5f. on 4f. green	22·00	18·00
111	13	13f. on 12f. brown	45·00	38·00

27 Pouter Pigeon and Hsinking

1937. Completion of Five Year Reconstruction Plan for Hsinking.

112	27	2f. purple	10·00	7·50
113	-	4f. red	13·00	4·00
114	27	10f. green	25·00	14·00
115	-	20f. blue	35·00	24·00

Design: 4, 20f. Flag over Imperial Palace.

29 Manchukuo

30 Japanese Residents Assn. Building

1937. Japan's Relinquishment of Extra-territorial Rights.

116	29	2f. red	2·75	1·75
117	30	4f. green	8·00	3·25
118	30	8f. orange	15·00	11·00
119	-	10f. blue	16·00	12·00
120	-	12f. violet	22·00	15·00
121	-	20f. brown	32·00	20·00

Designs: As T **30**—10, 20f. Department. of Communications Building. Horiz—12f. Ministry of Justice.

32 'Twofold Happiness'

1937. New Year's Greetings.

122	32	2f. red and blue	8·00	1·50

33 Red Cross on Map and Globe

1938. Inauguration of Manchukuo Red Cross Society.

123	33	2f. red	3·00	3·00
124	33	4f. green	3·00	3·00

34 Map of Railway Lines

35 Asia Express

1939. Completion of 10,000 Kilometres of Manchurian Railways.

125	34	2f. blue and orange	4·50	5·00
126	35	4f. deep blue and blue	4·50	5·00

36 Manchurian Cranes over Shipmast

1940. Second Visit of Emperor Kang-teh to Japan.

127	36	2f. purple	2·00	4·00
128	36	4f. green	2·00	4·00

37 Census Official and Manchukuo

38 Census Slogans in Chinese and Mongolian

1940. National Census.

129	37	2f. brown and yellow	1·25	3·00
130	38	4f. deep green and green	1·25	3·00

39 Message of Congratulation

40 Dragon Dance

1940. 2600th Anniversary of Founding of Japanese Empire.

131	39	2f. red	1·00	3·00
132	40	4f. blue	1·00	3·00

41 Recruit

紀念新嘉坡
復歸我東亞
康德九年

(42)

1941. Enactment of Conscription Law.

133	41	2f. red	1·25	3·00
134	41	4f. blue	1·25	3·00

1942. Fall of Singapore. Stamps of 1936 optd with T **42**.

135	A	2f. green	1·40	4·00
136	B	4f. green	1·40	4·00

43 Kenkoku Shrine

44 Achievement of Fine Crops

45 Women of Five Races Dancing

46 Map of Manchukuo

1942. Tenth Anniversary of Founding of State.

137	43	2f. red	80	3·00
138	44	3f. orange	2·75	4·50
139	43	4f. lilac	90	3·00
140	45	6f. green	1·60	4·00
141	46	10f. red on yellow	2·25	4·00
142	-	20f. blue on yellow	5·00	6·50

Design: Horiz—20f. Flag of Manchukuo.

1942. First Anniversary of Greater East Asia War. Stamps of 1936 optd with native characters above date 8.12.8.

143	19	3f. brown	1·00	3·00
144	A	6f. red	1·00	3·00

1943. Labour Service Law Proclamation. Stamps of 1936 optd with native characters above heads of pick and shovel.

145	19	3f. brown	1·00	3·25
146	A	6f. red	1·00	3·25

49 Nurse and Stretcher

1943. Fifth Anniversary of Manchukuo Red Cross Society.

147	49	6f. green	1·25	3·25

50 Furnace at Anshan Plant

1943. Second Anniversary of Greater East Asia War.

148	50	6f. red	1·50	4·00

51 Chinese characters

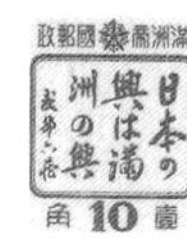
52 Japanese characters

1944. Friendship with Japan. (a) Chinese characters.

155	51	10f. red	1·00	2·00
156	51	40f. green	3·75	4·50

(b) Japanese characters.

157	52	10f. red	1·00	2·00
158	52	40f. green	3·75	4·50

53 'One Heart One Soul'

1945. Tenth Anniversary of Emperor's Edict.

159	53	10f. red	1·40	10·00

MARIANA ISLANDS

A group of Spanish islands in the Pacific Ocean of which Guam was ceded to the U.S.A. and the others to Germany. The latter are now under U.S. Trusteeship.

100 pfennig = 1 mark.

1899. German stamps optd **Marianen**.

7	8	3pf. brown	18·00	43·00
8	8	5pf. green	24·00	46·00
9	9	10pf. red	30·00	65·00
10	9	20pf. blue	36·00	£180
11	9	25pf. orange	90·00	£225
12	9	50pf. brown	90·00	£300

1901. Yacht key-type inscr 'MARIANEN'.

13	N	3pf. brown	1·60	2·40
14	N	5pf. green	1·60	2·75
15	N	10pf. red	1·60	6·00
16	N	20pf. blue	1·80	10·00
17	N	25pf. black & red on yellow	2·40	18·00
18	N	30pf. black & orge on buff	2·40	19·00
19	N	40pf. black and red	2·40	19·00
20	N	50pf. black & pur on buff	3·00	22·00
21	N	80pf. black and red on rose	3·50	36·00
22	O	1m. red	6·50	£100
23	O	2m. blue	9·00	£130
24	O	3m. black	12·00	£190
25	O	5m. red and black	£225	£700

MARIENWERDER

A district of E. Prussia where a plebiscite was held in 1920. As a result the district remained part of Germany. After the War of 1939–45 it was returned to Poland and reverted to its original name of Kwidzyn.

100 pfennig = 1 mark.

1

1920

1	1	5pf. green	1·00	4·00
2	1	10pf. red	1·00	3·25
3	1	15pf. grey	1·00	4·50
4	1	20pf. brown	1·00	3·25
5	1	25pf. blue	1·00	4·50
6	1	30pf. orange	1·40	4·50
7	1	40pf. brown	1·00	5·25
8	1	50pf. violet	1·00	4·00
9	1	60pf. brown	6·50	6·50
10	1	75pf. brown	1·40	4·00
11	1	1m. brown and green	1·00	3·25
12	1	2m. purple	3·25	7·50
13	1	3m. red	7·75	11·50
14	1	5m. blue and red	46·00	33·00

1920. Stamps of Germany inscr 'DEUTSCHES REICH' optd or surch **Commission Interalliee Marienwerder**.

15	10	5pf. green	23·00	46·00
16	10	20pf. blue	11·50	46·00
17	10	50pf. black & purple on buff	£600	£1300
18	10	75pf. black and green	7·75	15·00
19	10	80pf. black and red on rose	£120	£200
25	12	1m. red	4·00	11·50
21	24	1m. on 2pf. grey	46·00	80·00
26	12	1m.25 green	5·25	13·50
27	12	1m.50 brown	6·50	16·00
22	24	2m. on 2½pf. grey	23·00	33·00
28	13	2m.50 purple	4·00	13·50
23	10	3m. on 3pf. brown	23·00	33·00
24	24	5m. on 7½pf. orange	23·00	33·00

1920. As T **1**, with inscription at top changed to 'PLEBISCITE'.

29	24	5pf. green	5·75	3·25
30	24	10pf. red	5·75	3·25
31	24	15pf. grey	21·00	22·00
32	24	20pf. brown	4·00	3·25
33	24	25pf. blue	22·00	29·00
34	24	30pf. orange	4·00	2·50
35	24	40pf. brown	4·00	2·50
36	24	50pf. violet	3·25	3·25
37	24	60pf. brown	10·50	9·00
38	24	75pf. brown	10·50	9·00
39	24	1m. brown and green	4·00	2·50
40	24	2m. purple	4·00	2·50
41	24	3m. red	4·00	3·25
42	24	5m. blue and red	6·50	4·50

MARSHALL ISLANDS

A group of islands in the Pacific Ocean, a German protectorate from 1885. From 1920 to 1947 it was a Japanese mandated territory and from 1947 part of the United States Trust Territory of the Pacific Islands, using United States stamps. In 1984 it assumed control of its postal services, and became independent in 1991.

A. German Protectorate.
100 pfennig = 1 mark.

B. Republic.
100 cents = 1 dollar.

A. GERMAN PROTECTORATE

1897. Stamps of Germany (a) optd **Marschall-Inseln**.

No.	Type	Description	Mint	Used
G1	**8**	3pf. brown	£5500	£3000
G2	**8**	5pf. green	£800	£650
G3	**9**	10pf. red	90·00	£130
G4	**9**	20pf. blue	90·00	£140

(b) optd **Marshall-Inseln**.

No.	Type	Description	Mint	Used
G5	**8**	3pf. brown	6·50	7·75
G6	**8**	5pf. green	13·00	18·00
G7	**9**	10pf. red	18·00	23·00
G8	**9**	20pf. blue	23·00	36·00
G9	**9**	25pf. orange	26·00	60·00
G10	**9**	50pf. brown	42·00	65·00

1901. Yacht key-type inscr 'MARSHALL INSELN'.

No.	Type	Description	Mint	Used
G11	**N**	3pf. brown	95	2·40
G12	**N**	5pf. green	95	2·40
G13	**N**	10pf. red	95	6·50
G14	**N**	20pf. blue	1·30	13·00
G15	**N**	25pf. black & red on yell	1·40	23·00
G16	**N**	30pf. black & orge on buff	1·40	23·00
G17	**N**	40pf. black and red	1·40	23·00
G18	**N**	50pf. black & pur on buff	2·20	34·00
G19	**N**	80pf. black & red on rose	4·25	50·00
G20	**O**	1m. red	6·00	£120
G21	**O**	2m. blue	8·50	£170
G22	**O**	3m. black	12·50	£300
G23	**O**	5m. red and black	£225	£700

B. REPUBLIC

1 Canoe

1984. Inauguration of Postal Independence. Multicoloured.

No.	Description	Mint	Used
1	20c. Type **1**	75	70
2	20c. Fish and net	75	70
3	20c. Navigational stick-chart	75	70
4	20c. Islet with coconut palms	75	70

2 Mili Atoll

1984. Maps. Multicoloured.

No.	Description	Mint	Used
5	1c. Type **2**	15	10
6	3c. Likiep Atoll	15	10
7	5c. Ebon Atoll	20	10
8	10c. Jaluit Atoll	30	20
9	13c. Ailinginae Atoll	35	30
10	14c. Wotho Atoll	35	35
11	20c. Kwajalein and Ebeye Atolls	55	50
12	22c. Enewetak Atoll	65	60
13	28c. Ailinglaplap Atoll	75	70
14	30c. Majuro Atoll	85	75
15	33c. Namu Atoll	90	85
16	37c. Rongelap Atoll	1·00	95
16a	39c. Taka and Utirik Atolls	1·10	1·00
16b	44c. Ujelang Atoll	1·20	1·10
16c	50c. Aur and Maloclap Atolls	1·40	1·30
17	$1 Arno Atoll	2·75	2·50
18	$2 Wotje and Erikub Atolls	6·00	5·50
19	$5 Bikini Atoll	13·00	12·00
20	$10 Mashallese stick chart (31×31 mm)	26·00	24·00

3 German Marshall Islands 1900 3pf. Optd Stamp

1984. 19th Universal Postal Union Congress Philatelic Salon, Hamburg.

No.	Type	Description	Mint	Used
21	**3**	40c. brown, black and yellow	1·00	90
22	-	40c. brown, black and yellow	1·00	90
23	-	40c. blue, black and yellow	1·00	90
24	-	40c. multicoloured	1·00	90

Designs: No. 22, German Marshall Islands 1901 3pf. 'Yacht' stamp; No. 23, German Marshall Islands 1897 20pf. stamp; No. 24, German Marshall Islands 1901 5m. 'Yacht' stamp.

4 Common Dolphin

1984. Ausipex 84 International Stamp Exhibition, Melbourne. Dolphins. Multicoloured.

No.	Description	Mint	Used
25	20c. Type **4**	75	70
26	20c. Risso's dolphin	75	70
27	20c. Spotter dolphins	75	70
28	20c. Bottle-nosed dolphin	75	70

5 Star over Bethlehem and Text

1984. Christmas. Multicoloured.

No.	Description	Mint	Used
29	20c. Type **5**	65	60
30	20c. Desert landscape	65	60
31	20c. Two kings on camels	65	60
32	20c. Third king on camel	65	60

6 Traditional Chief and German and Marshallese Flags

1984. Fifth Anniversary of Constitution. Multicoloured.

No.	Description	Mint	Used
33	20c. Type **6**	55	50
34	20c. President Amata Kabua and American and Marshallese flags	55	50
35	20c. Admiral Chester W. Nimitz and Japanese and Marshallese flags	55	50
36	20c. Trygve H. Lie (first Secretary-General of United Nations) and UN and Marshallese flags	55	50

7 Leach's Storm Petrel ('Forked-tailed Petrel')

1985. Birth Bicentenary of John J. Audubon (ornithologist). Multicoloured.

No.	Description	Mint	Used
37	22c. Type **7** (postage)	90	80
38	22c. Pectoral sandpiper	90	80
39	44c. Brown booby ('Booby Gannet') (air)	1·50	1·40
40	44c. Whimbrel ('Great Esquimaux Curlew')	1·50	1·40

8 Black-spotted Triton

1985. Sea Shells (1st series). Multicoloured.

No.	Description	Mint	Used
41	22c. Type **8**	70	65
42	22c. Monodon murex	70	65
43	22c. Diana conch	70	65
44	22c. Great green turban	70	65
45	22c. Rose-branch murex	70	65

See also Nos. 85/89, 131/135 and 220/224.

9 Woman as Encourager and Drum

1985. International Decade for Women. Multicoloured.

No.	Description	Mint	Used
46	22c. Type **9**	65	60
47	22c. Woman as Peacemaker and palm branches	65	60
48	22c. Woman as Nurturer and pounding stone	65	60
49	22c. Woman as Benefactress and lesser frigate bird	65	60

Nos. 46/49 were printed together in *se-tenant* blocks of four within the sheet, each block forming a composite design.

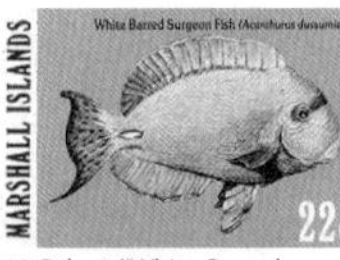

10 Palani ('White Barred Surgeon Fish')

1985. Lagoon Fish. Multicoloured.

No.	Description	Mint	Used
50	22c. Type **10**	1·10	1·00
51	22c. Silver-spotted squirrelfish ('White Blotched Squirrel Fish')	1·10	1·00
52	22c. Spotted boxfish	1·10	1·00
53	22c. Saddle butterflyfish	1·10	1·00

11 Basketball

1985. International Youth Year. Multicoloured.

No.	Description	Mint	Used
54	22c. Type **11**	65	60
55	22c. Elderly woman recording for oral history project	65	60
56	22c. Islander explaining navigational stick charts	65	60
57	22c. Dancers at inter-atoll music and dance competition	65	60

12 American Board of Commissions for Foreign Missions Stock Certificate

1985. Christmas. *Morning Star 1* (first Christian missionary ship to visit Marshall Islands). Multicoloured.

No.	Description	Mint	Used
58	14c. Type **12**	35	35
59	22c. Launching of *Morning Star 1*, 1856	70	65
60	33c. Departure from Honolulu, 1857	95	90
61	44c. Entering Ebon Lagoon, 1857	1·30	1·20

13 *Giotto* and Section of Comet Tail

1985. Appearance of Halley's Comet. Designs showing comet over Roi-Namur Island. Multicoloured.

No.	Description	Mint	Used
62	22c. Space shuttle and comet	1·60	1·50
63	22c. *Planet A* space probe and dish aerial	1·60	1·50
64	22c. Type **13**	1·60	1·50
65	22c. *Vega* satellite and buildings on island	1·60	1·50
66	22c. Sir Edmund Halley, satellite communications ship and aircraft	1·60	1·50

Nos. 62/66 were printed together, *se-tenant*, forming a composite design.

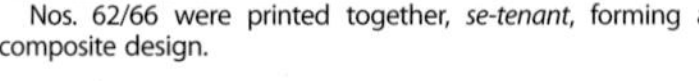

14 Mallow

1985. Medicinal Plants. Multicoloured.

No.	Description	Mint	Used
67	22c. Type **14**	70	65
68	22c. Half-flower	70	65
69	22c. *Guettarda speciosa*	70	65
70	22c. Love-vine	70	65

15 Trumpet Triton

1986. World Wildlife Fund. Marine Life. Multicoloured.

No.	Description	Mint	Used
71	14c. Type **15**	2·20	2·00
72	14c. Giant clam	2·20	2·00
73	14c. Small giant clam	2·20	2·00
74	14c. Coconut crab	2·20	2·00

16 Consolidated PBY-5A Catalina Amphibian

1986. Air. Ameripex 86 International Stamp Exhibition, Chicago. Mail Planes. Multicoloured.

No.	Description	Mint	Used
75	44c. Type **16**	1·40	1·30
76	44c. Grumman SA-16 Albatross	1·40	1·30
77	44c. Douglas DC-6B	1·40	1·30
78	44c. Boeing 727-100	1·40	1·30
MS79	89×63 mm. $1 Douglas C-54 Globester	5·50	5·00

17 Islanders in Outrigger Canoe

1986. 40th Anniversary of Operation Crossroads (atomic bomb tests on Bikini Atoll). Multicoloured.

No.	Description	Mint	Used
80	22c. Type **17** (postage)	85	80
81	22c. Advance landing of amphibious DUKW from USS *Sumner*	85	80
82	22c. Loading *LST 1108* (tank landing ship) for islanders' departure	85	80
83	22c. Man planting coconuts as part of reclamation programme	85	80
MS84	101×77 mm. 44c. USS *Saratoga* (bomb target) (air)	6·50	6·00

1986. Sea Shells (2nd series). As T **8**. Multicoloured.

No.	Description	Mint	Used
85	22c. Ramose ('Rose') murex	85	80
86	22c. Orange spider conch	85	80
87	22c. Red-mouth frog shell	85	80
88	22c. Laciniate conch	85	80
89	22c. Giant frog shell	85	80

18 Blue Marlin

1986. Game Fish. Multicoloured.

No.	Description	Mint	Used
90	22c. Type **18**	1·10	1·00
91	22c. Wahoo	1·10	1·00
92	22c. Dolphinfish	1·10	1·00
93	22c. Yellow-finned tuna	1·10	1·00

19 Flowers (top left)

1986. International Peace Year. Multicoloured.

No.	Description	Mint	Used
94	22c. Type **19** (Christmas) (postage)	95	90
95	22c. Flowers (top right)	95	90
96	22c. Flowers (bottom left)	95	90
97	22c. Flowers (bottom right)	95	90
98	44c. Head of Statue crowned with flowers (24×39 mm) (centenary of Statue of Liberty) (air)	1·60	1·40

Nos. 94/97 were issued together, *se-tenant*, in blocks of four within the sheet, each block forming a composite design of mixed flower arrangement.

20 Girl Scout giving Plant to Patient

1986. Air. 20th Anniversary of Marshall Island Girl Scouts and 75th Anniversary (1987) of United States Girl Scout Movement. Multicoloured.

99	44c. Type **20**	1·40	1·30
100	44c. Giving salute	1·40	1·30
101	44c. Girl scouts holding hands in circle	1·40	1·30
102	44c. Weaving pandana and palm branch mats	1·40	1·30

21 Wedge-tailed Shearwater

1987. Air. Sea Birds. Multicoloured.

103	44c. Type **21**	1·70	1·50
104	44c. Red-footed booby	1·70	1·50
105	44c. Red-tailed tropicbird	1·70	1·50
106	44c. Lesser frigatebird ('Great Frigatebird')	1·70	1·50

22 *James T. Arnold*, 1854

1987. Whaling Ships. Multicoloured.

107	22c. Type **22**	1·00	95
108	22c. *General Scott*, 1859	1·00	95
109	22c. *Charles W. Morgan*, 1865	1·00	95
110	22c. *Lucretia*, 1884	1·00	95

23 Lindbergh's *Spirit of St Louis* and Congressional Medal of Honour, 1927

1987. Aviators. Multicoloured.

111	33c. Type **23**	1·10	1·00
112	33c. Charles Lindbergh and Chance Vought F4U Corsair fighter, Marshall Islands, 1944	1·10	1·00
113	39c. William Bridgeman and Consolidated B-24 Liberator bomber, Kwajalein, 1944	1·20	1·10
114	39c. Bridgeman and Douglas Skyrocket, 1951	1·20	1·10
115	44c. John Glenn and Chance Vought F4U Corsair fighters, Marshall Islands, 1944	1·40	1·30
116	44c. Glenn and *Friendship 7* space capsule	1·40	1·30

24 Earhart's Lockheed 10E Electra taking off from Lae, New Guinea

1987. Air. Capex '87 International Stamp Exhibition, Toronto. 50th Anniversary of Amelia Earhart's Round the World Flight Attempt. Multicoloured.

117	44c. Type **24**	1·40	1·30
118	44c. US Coastguard cutter *Itasca* waiting off Howland Island for Electra	1·40	1·30
119	44c. Islanders and crashed Electra on Mili Atoll	1·40	1·30
120	44c. Japanese patrol boat *Koshu* recovering Electra	1·40	1·30
MS121	88×62 mm. $1 Earhat's flight route (41×8 mm)	4·25	4·00

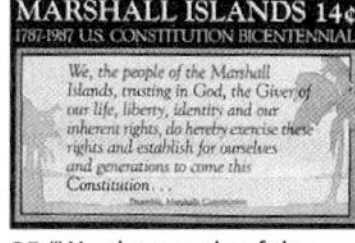

25 "We, the people of the Marshall Islands ..."

1987. Bicentenary of United States of America Constitution. Multicoloured.

122	14c. Type **25**	40	35
123	14c. Marshall Is. and USA Emblems	40	35
124	14c. "We the people of the United States ..."	40	35
125	22c. "All we have and are today as a people ..."	70	65
126	22c. Marshall Is. and USA flags	70	65
127	22c. "... to establish Justice ..."	70	65
128	44c. "With this Constitution ..."	1·40	1·30
129	44c. Marshall Is. stick chart and U.S. Liberty Bell	1·40	1·30
130	44c. "... to promote the general Welfare ..."	1·40	1·30

The three designs of each value were printed together, *se-tenant*, the left hand stamp of each strip bearing quotations from the preamble to the Marshall Islands Constitution and the right hand stamp, quotations from the United States Constitution preamble.

1987. Sea Shells (3rd series). As T **8**. Multicoloured.

131	22c. Magnificent cone	70	65
132	22c. Pacific partridge tun	70	65
133	22c. Scorpion spider conch	70	65
134	22c. Common hairy triton	70	65
135	22c. Arthritic ('Chiragra') spider conch	70	65

26 Planting Coconut

1987. Copra Industry. Multicoloured.

136	44c. Type **26**	1·00	90
137	44c. Making copra	1·00	90
138	44c. Bottling extracted coconut oil	1·00	90

27 "We have seen his star in the east ..."

1987. Christmas. Multicoloured.

139	14c. Type **27**	35	35
140	22c. "Glory to God in the highest; ..."	70	65
141	33c. "Sing unto the Lord a new song ..."	95	90
142	44c. "Praise him in the cymbals and dances; ..."	1·30	1·20

28 Reef Heron ('Pacific Reef Heron')

1988. Shore and Water Birds. Multicoloured.

143	44c. Type **28**	1·40	1·20
144	44c. Bar-tailed godwit	1·40	1·20
145	44c. Blue-faced booby ('Masked Booby')	1·40	1·20
146	44c. Northern shoveler	1·40	1·20

29 Maroon Anemonefish ('Damselfish')

1988. Fish. Multicoloured.

147	1c. Type **29**	15	15
148	3c. Black-faced butterflyfish	20	15
149	14c. Stocky hawkfish	35	30
150	15c. White-spotted puffer ('Balloonfish')	40	35
151	17c. Starry pufferfish ('Trunk Fish')	50	45
152	22c. Moon ('Lyretail') wrasse	55	50
153	25c. Six-banded parrotfish	65	60
154	33c. Spotted ('White-spotted') boxfish	85	75
155	36c. Yellow ("Spotted") boxfish	95	85
156	39c. Red-tailed surgeonfish	1·10	95
157	44c. Forceps ('Long-snouted') butterflyfish	1·20	1·10
158	45c. Oriental trumpetfish	1·20	1·10
159	56c. False-eyed pufferfish ('Sharp-nosed Puffer')	1·60	1·40
160	$1 Yellow seahorse	2·75	2·50
161	$2 Ghost pipefish	5·00	4·75
162	$5 Clown triggerfish ('Big-spotted Triggerfish')	11·50	10·50
163	$10 Blue-finned trevally ('Blue Jack') (50×28 mm)	25·00	23·00

30 Javelin Thrower

1988. Olympic Games, Seoul. Multicoloured.

166	15c. Type **30**	60	55
167	15c. Drawing javelin back and star	60	55
168	15c. Javelin drawn back fully (value at left)	60	55
169	15c. Commencing throw (value at right)	60	55
170	15c. Releasing javelin	60	55
171	25c. Runner and star (left half)	70	65
172	25c. Runner and star (right half)	70	65
173	25c. Runner (value at left)	70	65
174	25c. Runner (value at right)	70	65
175	25c. Finish of race	70	65

Nos. 166/170 were printed together, *se-tenant*, forming a composite design of a javelin throw with background of the Marshallese flag. Nos. 171/175 were similarly arranged forming a composite design of a runner and flag.

31 *Casco* sailing through Golden Gate of San Francisco

1988. Centenary of Robert Louis Stevenson's Pacific Voyages. Multicoloured.

176	25c. Type **31**	1·10	1·00
177	25c. *Casco* at the Needles of Ua-Pu, Marquesas	1·10	1·00
178	25c. *Equator* leaving Honolulu	1·10	1·00
179	25c. Chieftain's canoe, Majuro Lagoon	1·10	1·00
180	25c. Bronze medallion depicting Stevenson by Augustus St Gaudens, 1887	1·10	1·00
181	25c. *Janet Nicoll* (inter-island steamer), Majuro Lagoon	1·10	1·00
182	25c. Stevenson's visit to maniap of King Tembinoka of Gilbert Islands	1·10	1·00
183	25c. Stevenson in Samoan canoe, Apia Harbour	1·10	1·00
184	25c. Stevenson on horse Jack at Valima (Samoan home)	1·10	1·00

32 Spanish Ragged Cross Ensign (1516–1785) and Magellan's Ship *Vitoria*

1988. Exploration Ships and Flags. Multicoloured.

185	25c. Type **32**	90	75
186	25c. British red ensign (1707–1800), *Charlotte* and *Scarborough* (transports)	90	75
187	25c. American flag and ensign (1837–1845), USS *Flying Fish* (schooner) and USS *Peacock* (sloop)	90	75
188	25c. German flag and ensign (1867–1919) and *Planet* (auxiliary schooner)	90	75

33 Father Christmas in Sleigh

1988. Christmas. Multicoloured.

189	25c. Type **33**	85	75
190	25c. Reindeer over island with palm huts and trees	85	75
191	25c. Reindeer over island with palm trees	85	75
192	25c. Reindeer and billfish	85	75
193	25c. Reindeer over island with outrigger canoe	85	75

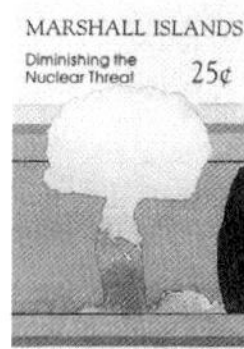

34 Nuclear Test on Bikini Atoll

1988. 25th Anniversary of Assassination of John F. Kennedy (American President). Multicoloured.

194	25c. Type **34**	95	90
195	25c. Kennedy signing Test Ban Treaty	95	90
196	25c. Kennedy	95	90
197	25c. Kennedy using hot-line between Washington and Moscow	95	90
198	25c. Peace Corps volunteers	95	90

35 SV-5D PRIME Vehicle Launch from Vandenberg Air Force Base

1988. Kwajalein Space Shuttle Tracking Station. Multicoloured.

199	25c. Type **35** (postage)	90	85
200	25c. Re-entry of SV-5D	90	85
201	25c. Recovery of SV-5D off Kwajalein	90	85
202	25c. Space shuttle *Discovery* over Kwajalein	90	85
203	45c. Shuttle and astronaut over Rongelap (air)	1·40	1·30

Nos. 199/202 were printed together, *se-tenant*, forming a composite design.

36 1918 Typhoon Monument, Majuro

1989. Links with Japan. Multicoloured.

204	45c. Type **36**	1·40	1·20
205	45c. Japanese seaplane base and railway, Djarret Islet, 1940s	1·40	1·20
206	45c. Japanese fishing boats	1·40	1·20
207	45c. Japanese skin-divers	1·40	1·20

37 *Island Woman*

1989. Links with Alaska. Oil Paintings by Claire Fejes. Multicoloured.

208	45c. Type **37**	1·30	1·20
209	45c. *Kotzebue, Alaska*	1·30	1·20
210	45c. *Marshallese Madonna*	1·30	1·20

38 Dornier Do-228

1989. Air. Aircrafts. Multicoloured.

211	12c. Type **38**	35	35
212	36c. Boeing 737	1·20	1·10
213	39c. Hawker Siddeley H.S. 748	1·40	1·30
214	45c. Boeing 727	1·70	1·50

1989. Sea Shells (4th series). As T **8**. Multicoloured.

220	25c. Pontifical mitre	1·00	95
221	25c. Tapestry turban	1·00	95
222	25c. Flame mouthed ('Bull-mouth') helmet	1·00	95
223	25c. Prickly Pacific drupe	1·00	95
224	25c. Blood-mouth conch	1·00	95

39 Illustration by Sanko Inoue of *In Praise of Sovereigns* (poem)

1989. Emperor Hirohito of Japan Commemoration. Sheet 106×88 mm.

MS225	**39** $1 multicoloured	3·00	2·75

40 Wandering Tattler

1989. Birds. Multicoloured.

226	45c. Type **40**	1·70	1·60
227	45c. Ruddy turnstone	1·70	1·60
228	45c. Pacific golden plover	1·70	1·60
229	45c. Sanderling	1·70	1·60

41 *Bussard* (German cruiser) and 1897 Ship's Post Cancellation

1989. Philexfrance 89 International Stamp Exhibition, Paris. Marshall Islands Postal History. Multicoloured.

230	25c. Type **41**	2·40	2·20
231	25c. First day cover bearing first Marshall Islands stamps and US 10c. stamp	2·40	2·20
232	25c. Consolidated PBY-5 Catalina flying boats, floating Fleet Post Office (*LST 119*), Majuro, and 1944 US Navy cancellation	2·40	2·20
233	25c. Nakajima A6M2 Rufe seaplane, mailboat off Mili Island and Japanese cancellation	2·40	2·20
234	25c. Majuro Post Office	2·40	2·20
235	25c. Consolidated PBY-5A Catalina amphibian, outrigger canoe and 1951 US civilian mail cancellation	2·40	2·20
236	45c. *Morning Star V* (missionary ship) and 1905 Jaluit cancellation	1·30	1·20
237	45c. 1906 registered cover with Jaluit cancellation	1·30	1·20
238	45c. *Prinz Eitel Freiderich* (auxiliary cruiser) and 1914 German ship's post cancellation	1·30	1·20
239	45c. *Scharnhorst* (cruiser) leading German Asiatic Squadron and 1914 ship's post cancellation	1·30	1·20
MS240	93×80 mm. $1 German 20pf. stamp with 1889 Jaluit cancellation	14·50	10·50

Nos. 230/235 were printed together, *se-tenant*, Nos. 231 and 234 forming a composite design to commemorate the Fifth anniversary of Marshall Islands Independent Postal Service.

42 Launch of *Apollo 11*

1989. 20th Anniversary of First Manned Moon Landing. Multicoloured.

241	25c. Type **42**	2·00	1·80
242	25c. Neil Armstrong	2·00	1·80
243	25c. Descent of lunar module to moon's surface	2·00	1·80
244	25c. Michael Collins	2·00	1·80
245	25c. Planting flag on Moon	2·00	1·80
246	25c. Edwin 'Buzz' Aldrin	2·00	1·80
MS247	114×87 mm. $1 Astronaut on lunar surface (70×29 mm)	9·75	7·25

43 Polish Cavalry and German Tanks

1989. History of Second World War. Multicoloured. (a) 1st issue. Invasion of Poland, 1939.

248	25c. Type **43**	1·00	90

(b) 2nd issue. Sinking of HMS *Royal Oak*, 1939.

249	45c. U-boat and burning battleship	1·60	1·40

(c) 3rd issue. Invasion of Finland, 1939.

250	45c. Troops on skis and tanks	1·60	1·40

(d) 4th issue. Battle of the River Plate, 1939.

251	45c. HMS *Exeter* (cruiser)	1·60	1·40
252	45c. HMS *Ajax* (cruiser)	1·60	1·40
253	45c. *Admiral Graf Spee* (German battleship)	1·60	1·40
254	45c. HMNZS *Achilles* (cruiser)	1·60	1·40

See also Nos. 320/344, 359/384, 409/40, 458/477, 523/548 and 575/595.

44 Angel with Horn

1989. Christmas. Multicoloured.

255	25c. Type **44**	1·20	1·10
256	25c. Angel singing	1·20	1·10
257	25c. Angel with lute	1·20	1·10
258	25c. Angel with lyre	1·20	1·10

45 Dr. Robert Goddard

1989. Milestones in Space Exploration. Multicoloured.

259	45c. Type **45** (first liquid fuel rocket launch, 1926)	1·60	1·40
260	45c. *Sputnik 1* (first man-made satellite, 1957)	1·60	1·40
261	45c. Rocket lifting off (first American satellite, 1958)	1·60	1·40
262	45c. Yuri Gagarin (first man in space, 1961)	1·60	1·40
263	45c. John Glenn (first American in Earth orbit, 1962)	1·60	1·40
264	45c. Valentina Tereshkova (first woman in space, 1963)	1·60	1·40
265	45c. Aleksei Leonov (first space walk, 1965)	1·60	1·40
266	45c. Edward White (first American space walk, 1965)	1·60	1·40
267	45c. *Gemini 6* and *7* (first rendezvous in space, 1965)	1·60	1·40
268	45c. *Luna 9* (first soft landing on the Moon, 1966)	1·60	1·40
269	45c. *Gemini 8* (first docking in space, 1966)	1·60	1·40
270	45c. *Venera 4* (first successful Venus probe, 1967)	1·60	1·40
271	45c. Moon seen from *Apollo 8* (first manned orbit of Moon, 1968)	1·60	1·40
272	45c. Neil Armstrong and US flag (first man on Moon, 1969)	1·60	1·40
273	45c. *Soyuz 11* and *Salyut 1* space station (first space station crew, 1971)	1·60	1·40
274	45c. Lunar rover of *Apollo 15* (first manned lunar vehicle, 1971)	1·60	1·40
275	45c. *Skylab 1* (first American space station, 1973)	1·60	1·40
276	45c. *Pioneer 10* and Jupiter (first flight past Jupiter, 1973)	1·60	1·40
277	45c. Apollo and Soyuz craft approaching each other (first international joint space flight, 1975)	1·60	1·40
278	45c. *Viking 1* on Mars (first landing on Mars, 1976)	1·60	1·40
279	45c. *Voyager 1* and Saturn's rings (first flight past Saturn, 1979)	1·60	1·40
280	45c. *Columbia* (first space shuttle flight, 1981)	1·60	1·40
281	45c. Satellite in outer space (first probe beyond the solar system, 1983)	1·60	1·40
282	45c. Astronaut (first untethered space walk, 1984)	1·60	1·40
283	45c. Launch of space shuttle *Discovery*, 1988	1·60	1·40

46 White-capped Noddy ('Black Noddy')

1990. Birds. Multicoloured.

284	1c. Type **46**	20	15
285	5c. Red-tailed tropicbird	25	20
286	9c. Whimbrel	25	20
287	10c. Sanderling	35	25
288	12c. Black-naped tern	40	35
289	15c. Wandering tattler	50	45
290	20c. Bristle-thighed curlew	65	60
291	22c. Greater scaup	70	65
292	23c. Common (inscr 'Northern') shoveler	70	65
293	25c. Common (inscr 'Brown') noddy	80	70
294	27c. Sooty tern	85	80
295	28c. Sharp-tailed sandpiper	85	80
296	29c. Wedge-tailed shearwater	90	85
297	30c. Pacific golden plover	90	85
298	35c. Brown booby	1·10	1·00
299	36c. Red-footed booby	1·10	1·10
300	40c. White tern	1·20	1·10
301	45c. Green-winged (inscr 'Common') teal	1·50	1·40
302	50c. Great frigatebird	1·70	1·60
303	52c. Crested tern (inscr 'Great Crested Tern')	1·80	1·60
304	65c. Lesser sand plover	2·00	1·90
305	75c. Little tern	2·40	2·20
306	$1 Reef heron (inscr 'Pacific')	3·00	2·75
307	$2 Blue-faced (inscr 'Masked') booby	6·50	6·00
MS308	92×119 mm. Nos. 285, 289, 293 and 302	4·75	4·25

47 Lodidean (coconut-palm leaf windmill)

1990. Children's Games. Multicoloured.

309	25c. Type **47**	1·30	1·20
310	25c. Lejonjon (juggling green coconuts)	1·30	1·20
311	25c. Etobobo (coconut leaf musical instrument)	1·30	1·20
312	25c. Didmakol (pandanus leaf flying-toy)	1·30	1·20

48 Penny Black

1990. 150th Anniversary of the Penny Black. Multicoloured.

313	25c. Type **48**	1·70	1·60
314	25c. Essay of James Chalmers's cancellation	1·70	1·60
315	25c. Stamp essay by Robert Sievier	1·70	1·60
316	25c. Stamp essay by Charles Whiting	1·70	1·60
317	25c. Stamp essay by George Dickinson	1·70	1·60
318	25c. 'City' medal by William Wyon (struck to commemorate Queen Victoria's first visit to City of London)	1·70	1·60
MS319	114×86 mm. $1 Charles Heath and original engraving for master die (71×29 mm)	6·50	6·00

1990. History of Second World War. As T **43**. Multicoloured. (a) 5th issue. Invasions of Denmark and Norway, 1940.

320	25c. German soldier and Stuka dive bombers in Copenhagen	1·00	95
321	25c. Norwegian soldiers, burning building and German column	1·00	95

(b) 6th issue. Katyn Forest Massacre of Polish Prisoners, 1940.

322	25c. Bound hands and grave (vert)	1·00	95

(c) 7th issue. Appointment of Winston Churchill as Prime Minister of Great Britain, 1940.

323	45c. Union Jack, Churchill and war scenes	1·80	1·60

(d) 8th issue. Invasion of Low Countries, 1940.

324	25c. Bombing of Rotterdam	1·00	95
325	25c. Invasion of Belgium	1·00	95

(e) 9th issue. Evacuation at Dunkirk, 1940.

326	45c. British bren-gunner on beach	1·80	1·60
327	45c. Soldiers queueing for boats	1·80	1·60

Nos. 326/327 were issued together, *se-tenant*, forming a composite design.

(f) 10th issue. German Occupation of Paris, 1940.

328	45c. German soldiers marching through Arc de Triomphe (vert)	1·80	1·60

(g) 11th issue. Battle of Mers-el-Kebir, 1940.

329	25c. Vice-Admiral Sir James Somerville, Vice-Admiral Marcel Gensoul and British and French battleships	1·00	95

(h) 12th issue. The Burma Road, 1940.

330	25c. Allied and Japanese forces (vert)	1·00	95

(i) 13th issue. British Bases and American Destroyers Lend-lease Agreement, 1940.

331	45c. HMS *Georgetown* (formerly USS *Maddox*)	1·80	1·60
332	45c. HMS *Banff* (formerly USCGC *Saranac*)	1·80	1·60
333	45c. HMS *Buxton* (formerly USS *Edwards*)	1·80	1·60
334	45c. HMS *Rockingham* (formerly USS *Swasey*)	1·80	1·60

(j) 14th issue. Battle of Britain, 1940.

335	45c. Supermarine Spitfire Mk 1A fighters	1·80	1·60
336	45c. Hawker Hurricane Mk 1 and Spitfire fighters	1·80	1·60
337	45c. Messerschmitt Bf 109E fighters	1·80	1·60
338	45c. Junkers Ju 87B-2 Stuka dive bomber	1·80	1·60

Nos. 335/338 were issued together, *se-tenant*, forming a composite design.

(k) 15th issue. Tripartite Pact, 1940.

339	45c. Officers' caps of Germany, Italy and Japan (vert)	1·80	1·60

(l) 16th issue. Election of Franklin D. Roosevelt for Third United States Presidential Term, 1940.

340	25c. Roosevelt (vert)	1·00	95

(m) 17th issue. Battle of Taranto, 1940.

341	25c. HMS *Illustrious* (aircraft carrier)	1·00	95
342	25c. Fairey Swordfish bomber	1·00	95
343	25c. *Andrea Doria* (Italian battleship)	1·00	95
344	25c. *Conte di Cavour* (Italian battleship)	1·00	95

Nos. 341/344 were issued together, *se-tenant*, forming a composite design.

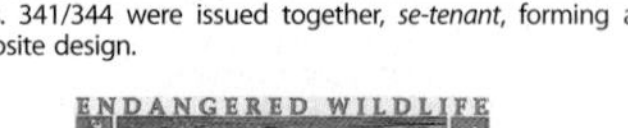

49 Pacific Green Turtles

1990. Endangered Turtles. Multicoloured.

345	25c. Type **49**	1·40	1·30
346	25c. Pacific green turtle swimming	1·40	1·30
347	25c. Hawksbill turtle hatching	1·40	1·30
348	25c. Hawksbill turtle swimming	1·40	1·30

50 Stick Chart, Outrigger Canoe and Flag

1990. Fourth Anniversary of Ratification of Compact of Free Association with United States.

349	**50**	25c. multicoloured	1·40	1·10

51 Brandenburg Gate, Berlin

1990. Re-unification of Germany.

350	**51**	45c. multicoloured	1·90	1·60

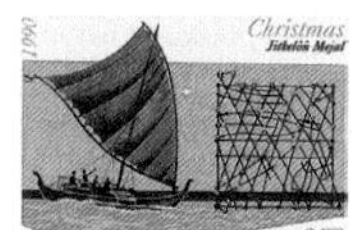

52 Outrigger Canoe and Stick Chart

1990. Christmas. Multicoloured.
351 25c. Type **52** 1·30 1·20
352 25c. Missionary preaching and *Morning Star* (missionary ship) 1·30 1·20
353 25c. British sailors dancing 1·30 1·20
354 25c. Electric guitar and couple dancing 1·30 1·20

53 Harvesting Breadfruit

1990. Breadfruit. Multicoloured.
355 25c. Type **53** 1·30 1·20
356 25c. Peeling breadfruit 1·30 1·20
357 25c. Soaking breadfruit 1·30 1·20
358 25c. Kneading dough 1·30 1·20

1991. History of Second World War. As T **43**. Multicoloured. (a) 18th issue. Four Freedoms Speech to US Congress by President Franklin Roosevelt, 1941.
359 30c. Freedom of Speech 1·00 95
360 30c. Freedom from Want 1·00 95
361 30c. Freedom of Worship 1·00 95
362 30c. Freedom from Fear 1·00 95

(b) 19th issue. Battle of Beda Fomm, 1941.
363 30c. Tank battle 1·00 95

(c) 20th issue. German Invasion of Balkans, 1941.
364 29c. German Dornier DO-17Z bombers over Acropolis, Athens (Greece) (vert) 1·00 95
365 29c. German tank and Yugoslavian Parliament building (vert) 1·00 95

(d) 21st issue. Sinking of the *Bismarck* (German battleship), 1941.
366 50c. HMS *Prince of Wales* (battleship) 1·70 1·60
367 50c. HMS *Hood* (battle cruiser) 1·70 1·60
368 50c. *Bismarck* 1·70 1·60
369 50c. Fairey Swordfish torpedo bombers 1·70 1·60

(e) 22nd issue. German Invasion of Russia, 1941.
370 30c. German tanks 1·00 95

(f) 23rd issue. Declaration of Atlantic Charter by United States and Great Britain, 1941.
371 29c. USS *Augusta* (cruiser) and Pres. Roosevelt of United States (vert) 1·00 95
372 29c. HMS *Prince of Wales* (battleship) and Winston Churchill (vert) 1·00 95
Nos. 371/372 were issued together, *se-tenant*, forming a composite design.

(g) 24th issue. Siege of Moscow, 1941.
373 29c. German tanks crossing snow-covered plain 1·00 95

(h) 25th issue. Sinking of USS *Reuben James*, 1941.
374 30c. USS *Reuben James* (destroyer) 1·00 95
375 30c. German U-boat 562 (submarine) 1·00 95
Nos. 374/375 were issued together, *se-tenant*, forming a composite design.

(i) 26th issue. Japanese Attack on Pearl Harbor, 1941.
376 50c. American aircrafts (inscr 'Peal Harbor') (vert) 1·70 1·60
376b As No. 376 but inscr "Pearl Harbor" 4·00 3·25
377 50c. Japanese dive bombers (vert) 1·70 1·60
378 50c. USS *Arizona* (battleship) (vert) 1·70 1·60
379 50c. *Akagi* (Japanese aircraft carrier) (vert) 1·70 1·60
Nos. 376/379 were issued together, *se-tenant*, forming a composite design.

(j) 27th issue. Japanese Capture of Guam, 1941.
380 29c. Japanese troops (vert) 1·00 95

(k) 28th issue. Fall of Singapore to Japan, 1941.
381 29c. Japanese soldiers with Japanese flag, Union Jack and white flag 1·00 95

(l) 29th issue. Formation of 'Flying Tigers' (American volunteer group), 1941.
382 50c. American Curtiss Tomahawk fighters 1·70 1·60
383 50c. Japanese Mitsubishi Ki-21 Sally bombers 1·70 1·60
Nos. 382/383 were issued together, *se-tenant*, forming a composite design.

(m) 30th issue. Fall of Wake Island to Japan, 1941.
384 29c. American Grumman Wildcat fighters and Japanese Mitsubishi G3M Nell bombers over Wake Island 1·00 95

54 Boeing 747 carrying *Columbia* to Launch Site

1991. Ten Years of Space Shuttle Flights. Multicoloured.
385 50c. Type **54** 1·60 1·50
386 50c. Orbital release of Long Duration Exposure Facility from *Challenger*, 1984 1·60 1·50
387 50c. Shuttle launch at Cape Canaveral 1·60 1·50
388 50c. Shuttle landing at Edwards Air Force Base 1·60 1·50
Nos. 385/388 were issued together, *se-tenant*, the backgrounds forming a composite design.

55 *Ixora carolinensis*

1991. Native Flowers. Multicoloured.
389 52c. Type **55** 1·60 1·40
390 52c. Glory-bower (*Clerodendum inerme*) 1·60 1·40
391 52c. *Messerschmidia argentea* 1·60 1·40
392 52c. *Vigna marina* 1·60 1·40
MS393 92×120 mm. Nos. 389/92 7·25 6·50
No. **MS**393 commemorates Phila Nippon'91 International Stamp Exhibition, Tokyo.

56 American Bald Eagle and Marshall Islands and US Flags

1991. United States Participation in Operation Desert Storm (campaign to liberate Kuwait).
394 **56** 29c. multicoloured 1·30 1·20

57 Red-footed Booby

1991. Birds. Multicoloured.
395 29c. Type **57** 2·00 1·80
396 29c. Great frigatebird (facing right) 2·00 1·80
397 29c. Brown booby 2·00 1·80
398 29c. White tern 2·00 1·80
399 29c. Great frigatebird (facing left) 2·00 1·80
400 29c. White-capped noddy ('Black Noddy') 2·00 1·80
MS401 113×87 mm. $1 White-tailed tropicbirds (74×32 mm) 9·00 8·50

58 Dornier Do-228

1991. Passenger Aircraft. Multicoloured.
402 12c. Type **58** 35 30
403 29c. Douglas DC-8 jetliner 1·00 95
404 50c. Hawker Siddeley H.S. 748 airliner 1·70 1·60
405 50c. Saab 2000 1·70 1·60

59 UN and State Emblems and Outrigger Canoe

1991. Admission of Marshall Islands to the United Nations.
406 **59** 29c. multicoloured 1·20 1·10

60 Dove and Glory-bower Flowers

1991. Christmas.
407 **60** 30c. multicoloured 1·30 1·20

61 State Flag and Dove

1991. 25th Anniversary of Peace Corps in Marshall Islands.
408 **61** 29c. multicoloured 1·20 1·10

1992. History of Second World War. As T **43**. Multicoloured. (a) 31st issue. Arcadia Conference, Washington DC, 1942.
409 29c. President Franklin Roosevelt of USA, Winston Churchill of Great Britain, White House and United Nations emblem 1·20 1·10

(b) 32nd issue. Fall of Manila to Japan, 1942.
410 50c. Japanese tank moving through Manila 1·60 1·50

(c) 33rd issue. Capture of Rabaul by Japan, 1942.
411 29c. Japanese flag, Admiral Yamamoto, General Douglas MacArthur and US flag 1·20 1·10

(d) 34th issue. Battle of the Java Sea, 1942.
412 29c. Sinking of the *De Ruyter* (Dutch cruiser) 1·20 1·10

(e) 35th issue. Capture of Rangoon by Japan, 1942.
413 50c. Japanese tank and soldiers in Rangoon (vert) 1·60 1·50

(f) 36th issue. Japanese Landing on New Guinea, 1942.
414 29c. Japanese soldiers coming ashore 1·20 1·10

(g) 37th issue. Evacuation of General Douglas MacArthur from Corregidor, 1942.
415 29c. MacArthur 1·20 1·10

(h) 38th issue. British Raid on Saint Nazaire, 1942.
416 29c. HMS *Campbeltown* (destroyer) and motor torpedo boat 1·20 1·10

(i) 39th issue. Surrender of Bataan, 1942.
417 29c. Prisoners on 'death' march (vert) 1·20 1·10

(j) 40th issue. Doolittle Raid on Tokyo, 1942.
418 50c. North American B-25 Mitchell bomber taking off from USS *Hornet* (aircraft carrier) (vert) 1·70 1·60

(k) 41st issue. Fall of Corregidor to Japan, 1942.
419 29c. Lt.-Gen. Jonathan Wainwright 1·20 1·10

(l) 42nd issue. Battle of the Coral Sea, 1942.
420 50c. USS *Lexington* (aircraft carrier) and Grumman F4F-3 Wildcat fighter (inscr 'U.S.S. Lexington') 1·40 1·30
420b As No. 420 but additionally inscr with aircraft name 3·00 2·75
421 50c. Japanese Aichi D3A 1 Val and Nakajima B5N2 Kate dive bombers (wrongly inscr 'Mitsubishi A6M2 Zero') 1·40 1·30
421a As No. 421 but inscr corrected 3·00 2·75
422 50c. American Douglas TBD-1 Devastator torpedo bombers (wrongly inscr 'U.S. Douglas SBD Dauntless') 1·40 1·30
422a As No. 422 but with inscr corrected 3·00 2·75
423 50c. *Shoho* (Japanese aircraft carrier) and Mitsubishi A6M2 Zero-Sen fighters (inscr 'Japanese carrier Shoho') 1·40 1·30
423a As No. 423 but additionally inscr with aircraft name 3·00 2·75

The four designs were issued together, *se-tenant*, each pair forming a composite design.

(m) 43rd issue. Battle of Midway, 1942.
424 50c. *Akagi* (Japanese aircraft carrier) 1·60 1·50
425 50c. USS *Yorktown* (aircraft carrier) 1·60 1·50
426 50c. American Douglas SBD Dauntless dive bombers 1·60 1·50
427 50c. Japanese Nakajima B5N2 Kate dive bombers 1·60 1·50
Nos. 424/427 were issued together, *se-tenant*, forming a composite design.

(n) 44th issue. Destruction of Lidice (Czechoslovakian village), 1942.
428 29c. Cross and memorial at Lidice 1·20 1·10

(o) 45th issue. German Capture of Sevastopol, 1942.
429 29c. German siege gun *Dora* (vert) 1·20 1·10

(p) 46th issue. Destruction of Convoy PQ-17, 1942.
430 29c. British merchant ship 1·20 1·10
431 29c. German U-boat 1·20 1·10

(q) 47th issue. Marine Landing on Guadalcanal, 1942.
432 29c. American marines landing on beach 1·20 1·10

(r) 48th issue. Battle of Savo Island, 1942.
433 29c. Admiral Mikawa of Japan (vert) 1·20 1·10

(s) 49th issue. Dieppe Raid, 1942.
434 29c. Soldiers landing at Dieppe 1·20 1·10

(t) 50th issue. Battle of Stalingrad, 1942.
435 50c. Heroes monument and burning buildings (vert) 1·90 1·60

(u) 51st issue. Battle of Eastern Solomon Islands, 1942.
436 29c. Aircraft over USS *Enterprise* (aircraft carrier) 1·20 1·10

(v) 52nd issue. Battle of Cape Esperance, 1942.
437 50c. American cruiser firing guns at night 1·90 1·60

(w) 53rd issue. Battle of El Alamein, 1942.
438 29c. General Bernard Montgomery of Great Britain and General Erwin Rommel of Germany 1·20 1·10

(x) 54th issue. Battle of Barents Sea, 1942.
439 29c. HMS *Sheffield* (cruiser) 1·20 1·10
440 29c. *Admiral Hipper* (German cruiser) 1·20 1·10

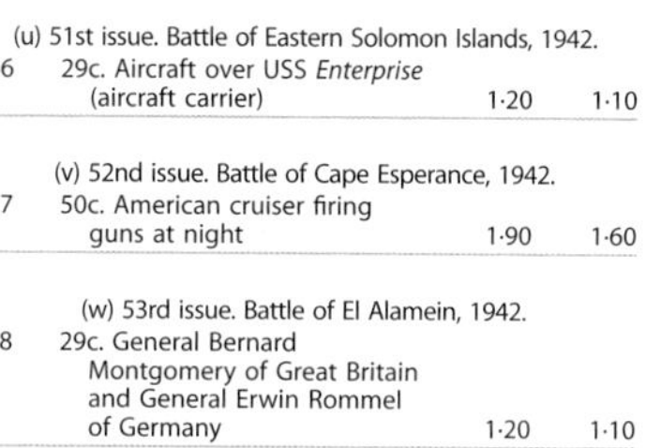

62 *Emlain* (bulk carrier)

1992. Ships flying the Marshall Islands Flag. Multicoloured.
441 29c. Type **62** 1·30 1·20
442 29c. *CSK Valiant* (tanker) 1·30 1·20
443 29c. *Ionmeto* (fisheries protection vessel) 1·30 1·20
444 29c. *Micro Pilot* (inter-island freighter) 1·30 1·20

63 Northern Pintail

1992. Nature Protection.
445 **63** 29c. multicoloured 1·40 1·30

64 Tipnol (outrigger canoe)

1992. Legends of Discovery. Multicoloured.
446 50c. Type **64** 1·60 1·40
447 50c. *Santa Maria* (reconstruction of Columbus's flagship) 1·60 1·40
448 50c. Constellation Argo Navis 1·60 1·40
449 50c. Sailor and tipnol 1·60 1·40
450 50c. Christopher Columbus and *Santa Maria* 1·60 1·40
451 50c. Astronaut and Argo Navis constellation 1·60 1·40
MS452 114×87 mm. $1 Columbus, sailor and astronaut (74×31 mm) 5·75 5·50

65 Basket Making

1992. Handicrafts. Multicoloured.

453	29c. Type **65**	1·00	95
454	29c. Boy holding model outrigger canoe	1·00	95
455	29c. Man carving boat	1·00	95
456	29c. Fan making	1·00	95

66 Christmas Offering

1992. Christmas.

457	**66** 29c. multicoloured	1·00	95

1993. History of Second World War. As T **43**. Multicoloured. (a) 55th issue. Casablanca Conference, 1943.

458	29c. President Franklin Roosevelt and Winston Churchill	1·20	1·10

(b) 56th issue. Liberation of Kharkov, 1943.

459	29c. Russian tank in Kharkov	1·20	1·10

(c) 57th issue. Battle of the Bismarck Sea, 1943.

460	50c. Japanese Mitsubishi A6M Zero-Sen fighters and *Arashio* (Japanese destroyer)	1·60	1·40
461	50c. American Lockheed P-38 Lightnings and Australian Bristol Beaufighter fighters	1·60	1·40
462	50c. *Shirayuki* (Japanese destroyer)	1·60	1·40
463	50c. American A-20 Havoc and North American B-52 Mitchell bombers	1·60	1·40

Nos 460/463 were issued together, *se-tenant*, forming a composite design.

(d) 58th issue. Interception of Yamamoto, 1943.

464	50c. Admiral Yamamoto	1·60	1·40

(e) 59th issue. Battle of Kursk, 1943.

465	29c. German Tiger 1 tank	1·30	1·20
466	29c. Soviet T-34 tank	1·30	1·20

Nos. 465/466 were issued together, *se-tenant*, forming a composite design.

(f) 60th issue. Allied Invasion of Sicily, 1943.

467	52c. General George Patton, Jr	1·60	1·50
468	52c. General Bernard Montgomery	1·60	1·50
469	52c. Americans landing at Licata	1·60	1·50
470	52c. British landing south of Syracuse	1·60	1·50

(g) 61st issue. Raids on Schweinfurt, 1943.

471	50c. American Boeing B-17F Flying Fortress bombers and German Messerschmitt Bf 109 fighter	1·60	1·40

(h) 62nd issue. Liberation of Smolensk, 1943.

472	29c. Russian soldier and burning buildings (vert)	1·20	1·10

(i) 63rd issue. Landing at Bougainville, 1943.

473	29c. American Marines on beach at Empress Augusta Bay	1·20	1·10

(j) 64th issue. US Invasion of Tarawa, 1943.

474	50c. American Marines	1·60	1·40

(k) 65th issue. Teheran Allied Conference, 1943.

475	52c. Winston Churchill of Great Britain, President Franklin Roosevelt of USA and Josef Stalin of Russia (vert)	1·60	1·50

(l) 66th issue. Battle of North Cape, 1943.

476	29c. HMS *Duke of York* (British battleship)	1·20	1·10
477	29c. *Scharnhorst* (German battleship)	1·20	1·10

67 Atoll Butterflyfish

1993. Reef Life. Multicoloured.

478	50c. Type **67**	2·20	2·00
479	50c. Brick soldierfish	2·20	2·00
480	50c. Caerulean damselfish	2·20	2·00
481	50c. Japanese inflator-filefish	2·20	2·00
482	50c. Arc-eyed hawkfish	2·20	2·00
483	50c. Powder-blue surgeonfish	2·20	2·00
MS484	114×87 mm. $1 Bridled parrotfish (74×32 mm)	8·75	7·75

68 *Britannia* (full-rigged ship)

1993. Ships. Multicoloured. (a) Size 35×20 mm.

485	10c. *San Jeronimo* (Spanish galleon)	30	25
486	14c. USCG *Cape Corwin* (fisheries patrol vessel)	55	50
487	15c. Type **68**	55	50
488	19c. *Micro Palm* (inter-island freighter)	65	55
489	20c. *Eendracht* (Dirk Hartog's ship)	65	55
490	23c. HMS *Cornwallis* (sail frigate)	75	65
491	24c. USS *Dolphin* (schooner)	80	70
492	29c. *Morning Star I* (missionary brigantine)	95	85
493	30c. *Rurik* (Otto von Kotzebue's brig) (inscr 'Rurick')	95	85
494	32c. *Vitoria* (Magellan's flagship)	1·00	90
495	35c. *Nautilus* (German gunboat)	1·20	1·10
496	40c. *Nautilus* (British brig)	1·40	1·20
497	45c. *Nagara* and *Isuzu* (Japanese cruisers)	1·50	1·30
498	46c. *Equator* (schooner)	1·60	1·40
499	50c. USS *Lexington* (aircraft carrier)	1·70	1·50
500	52c. HMS *Serpent* (brig)	1·80	1·60
501	55c. *Potomac* (whaling ship)	1·90	1·60
502	60c. USCG *Assateague* (cutter)	2·00	1·80
503	75c. *Scarborough* (transport)	2·50	2·20
504	78c. *Charles W. Morgan* (whaling ship)	2·75	2·40
505	95c. *Tanager* (inter-island steamer)	3·00	2·75
506	$1 *Tole Mour* (hospital schooner)	3·25	2·75
507	$2.90 Fishing vessels	9·25	8·00
508	$3.00 *Victoria* (whaling ship)	9·50	8·50
669	32c. As Type **68**	1·20	1·00
670	32c. USS *Dolphin* (schooner)	1·20	1·00
671	32c. *Morning Star I* (missionary brigantine)	1·20	1·00
672	32c. USS *Lexington* (aircraft carrier)	1·20	1·00
673	32c. *Micro Palm* (inter-island freighter)	1·20	1·00
674	32c. HMS *Cornwallis* (sail frigate)	1·20	1·00
675	32c. HMS *Serpent* (brig)	1·20	1·00
676	32c. *Scarborough* (transport)	1·20	1·00
677	32c. *San Jeronimo* (Spanish galleon)	1·20	1·00
678	32c. *Rurik* (Otto van Kotzebue's brig) (inscr 'Rurick')	1·20	1·00
679	32c. *Nautilus* (German gunboat)	1·20	1·00
680	32c. Fishing vessels	1·20	1·00
681	32c. Malmel outrigger canoe	1·20	1·00
682	32c. *Eendracht* (Dirk Hartog's ship)	1·20	1·00
683	32c. *Nautilus* (British brig)	1·20	1·00
684	32c. *Nagara* and *Isuzu* (Japanese cruisers)	1·20	1·00
685	32c. *Potomac* (whaling ship)	1·20	1·00
687	32c. USCG *Assateague* (cutter)	1·20	1·00
688	32c. *Charles W. Morgan* (whaling ship)	1·20	1·00
689	32c. *Victoria* (whaling ship)	1·20	1·00
690	32c. USCG *Cape Corwin* (fisheries patrol vessel)	1·20	1·00
691	32c. *Equator* (schooner)	1·20	1·00
692	32c. *Tanager* (inter-island steamer)	1·20	1·00
693	32c. *Tole Mour* (hospital schooner)	1·20	1·00

(b) Size 46×26 mm.

509	$1 Enewetak outrigger canoe	3·25	2·75
510	$2 Jaluit outrigger canoe	6·50	5·50
511	$5 Ailuk outrigger canoe	16·00	14·00
512	$10 Racing outrigger canoes	32·00	28·00

69 Capitol Complex

1993. Inauguration of New Capitol Complex, Majuro. Multicoloured.

513	29c. Type **69**	95	85
514	29c. Parliament building	95	85
515	29c. National Seal (vert)	95	85
516	29c. National Flag (vert)	95	85

70 *Eagle*

1993. Marshall Islands Registration of *Eagle* (oil tanker). Sheet 115×87 mm.

MS517	**70** 50c. multicoloured	1·60	1·40

71 Woman with Breadfruit

1993. Marshallese Life in the 1800s. Designs adapted from sketches by Louis Choris. Multicoloured.

518	29c. Type **71**	1·20	1·10
519	29c. Canoes and warrior	1·20	1·10
520	29c. Chief and islanders	1·20	1·10
521	29c. Drummer and dancers	1·20	1·10

72 Singing Silent Night

1993. Christmas.

522	**72** 29c. multicoloured	1·20	1·10

1994. History of Second World War. As T **43**. Multicoloured. (a) 67th issue. Appointment of General Dwight D. Eisenhower as Commander of Supreme Headquarters, Allied Expeditionary Force, 1944.

523	29c. Eisenhower	1·40	1·20

(b) 68th issue. Invasion of Anzio, 1944.

524	50c. Troops landing	2·00	1·80

(c) 69th issue. Lifting of Siege of Leningrad, 1944.

525	52c. St Isaac's Cathedral and soldier with Soviet flag	2·20	1·90

(d) 70th issue. US Liberation of Marshall Islands, 1944.

526	29c. Douglas SBD Dauntless dive bombers	1·40	1·20

(e) 71st issue. Japanese Defeat at Truk, 1944.

527	29c. Admirals Spruance and Marc Mitscher (vert)	1·40	1·20

(f) 72nd issue. US Bombing of Germany, 1944.

528	52c. Boeing B-17 Flying Fortress bombers	2·10	1·80

(g) 73rd issue. Allied Liberation of Rome, 1944.

529	50c. Lt.-Gen. Mark Clark and flowers in gun barrel (vert)	2·00	1·80

(h) 74th issue. Allied Landings in Normandy, 1944.

530	75c. Airspeed A.S.51 Horsa gliders (inscr 'Horsa Gliders')	2·75	2·40
530b	As No. 530 but inscr 'Horsa Gliders, Parachute Troops'	5·25	4·50
531	75c. Hawker Typhoon 1B and North American P-51B Mustang fighters (wrongly inscr 'U.S. P51B Mustangs, British Hurricanes')	2·75	2·40
531a	As No. 531 but inscr corrected	5·25	4·50
532	75c. German gun defences (inscr 'German Gun Defenses')	2·75	2·40
532a	As No. 523 but inscr 'German Gun Defenses, Pointe du Hoc'	5·25	4·50
533	75c. Allied amphibious landing	2·75	2·40

The four designs were issued together, *se-tenant*, forming a composite design.

(i) 75th issue. V-1 Bombardment of England, 1944.

534	50c. V-1 flying bomb over River Thames	2·00	1·80

(j) 76th issue. US Marines Land on Saipan, 1944.

535	29c. US and Japanese troops	1·40	1·20

(k) 77th issue. First Battle of the Philippine Sea, 1944.

536	50c. Grumman F6F-3 Hellcat fighter	2·00	1·80

(l) 78th issue. US Liberation of Guam, 1944.

537	29c. Naval bombardment	1·40	1·20

(m) 79th issue. Warsaw Uprising, 1944.

538	50c. Polish Home Army fighter	2·00	1·80

(n) 80th issue. Liberation of Paris, 1944.

539	50c. Allied troops marching along Champs Elysee	2·00	1·80

(o) 81st issue. US Marines Land on Peleliu, 1944.

540	29c. Amphibious armoured tracked vehicle	1·40	1·20

(p) 82nd issue. General Douglas MacArthur's Return to Philippines, 1944.

541	52c. McArthur and soldiers	2·20	1·90

(q) 83rd issue. Battle of Leyte Gulf, 1944.

542	52c. American motor torpedo boat and Japanese warships	2·20	1·90

(r) 84th issue. Sinking of the *Tirpitz* (German battleship), 1944.

543	50c. Avro Lancaster bombers	2·00	1·80
544	50c. *Tirpitz* burning	2·00	1·80

(s) 85th issue. Battle of the Bulge, 1944.

545	50c. Infantrymen	2·00	1·80
546	50c. Tank driver and tanks	2·00	1·80
547	50c. Pilot and aircraft	2·00	1·80
548	50c. Lt.-Col. Creighton Abrams and Brig.-Gen. Anthony McAuliffe shaking hands	2·00	1·80

1994. Hong Kong '94 International Stamp Exhibition. British Ships. Sheet 131×93 mm containing horiz designs as Nos. 487, 490, 500 and 503 but size 46×27 mm.

MS549	15c. *Britannia*; 23c. HMS *Cornwallis*; 52c. HMS *Serpent*; 75c. *Scarborough*	6·25	5·50

73 Magnifying Glass over Constitution Committee

1994. 15th Anniversary of Marshall Islands Constitution. Sheet 100×87 mm.

MS550	**73** $2.90 multicoloured	8·75	7·75

74 Traditional Messenger and Outrigger Canoe

1994. Tenth Anniversary of Independent Postal Service. Sheet 115×87 mm.

MS551	**74** 29c. multicoloured	1·40	1·30

75 Footballers

1994. World Cup Football Championship, USA. Multicoloured.

552	50c. Type **75**	2·50	2·20
553	50c. Footballers (different)	2·50	2·20

Nos. 552/553 were issued together, *se-tenant*, forming a composite design.

76 Neil Armstrong stepping onto Moon

1994. 25th Anniversary of First Manned Moon Landing. Multicoloured.

554	75c. Type **76**	2·20	2·00
555	75c. Planting US flag on Moon	2·20	2·00
556	75c. Astronauts saluting	2·20	2·00
557	75c. President John F. Kennedy and Armstrong	2·20	2·00
MS558	93×120 mm. Nos. 554/557	9·25	8·00

77 Solar System

1994. The Solar System. Multicoloured.

559	50c. Type **77**	1·70	1·50
560	50c. Sun	1·70	1·50
561	50c. Moon	1·70	1·50
562	50c. Mercury	1·70	1·50
563	50c. Venus	1·70	1·50
564	50c. Earth	1·70	1·50
565	50c. Mars	1·70	1·50
566	50c. Jupiter	1·70	1·50
567	50c. Saturn	1·70	1·50
568	50c. Uranus	1·70	1·50
569	50c. Neptune	1·70	1·50
570	50c. Pluto	1·70	1·50

78 Meadow Argus

1994. Philakorea 1994 International Stamp Exhibition, Seoul. Butterflies. Sheet 160×62 mm containing T **78** and similar horiz designs. Multicoloured.
MS571 29c. Type **78**; 52c. Brown awl; $1 Common (inscr 'Great') eggfly 8·50 7·50

1994. 50th Anniversary of General Douglas MacArthur's Return to Philippines. Sheet 150×62 mm containing previous designs.
MS572 50c. As No. 415; 50c. As No. 541 but with inscription at right-hand sideways 3·50 3·25

79 Church and Christmas Tree (Ringo Baso)

1994. Christmas.

573	**79**	29c. multicoloured	1·40	1·30

80 Pig

1995. New Year. Year of the Pig. Sheet 115×87 mm.
MS574 **80** 50c. multicoloured 2·00 1·80

1995. History of Second World War. As T **43**. Multicoloured. (a) 86th issue. Yalta Conference, 1945.

575	32c. Josef Stalin of USSR, Winston Churchill of Great Britain and Franklin Roosevelt of USA (vert)	1·20	1·10

(b) 87th issue. Allied Bombing of Dresden, 1945.

576	55c. *Europe* (Meissen porcelain statuette), flames and bombers (vert)	2·10	1·80

(c) 88th issue. US Marine Invasion of Iwo Jima, 1945.

577	$1 Marines planting flag on Mt. Suribachi (vert)	3·50	3·25

(d) 89th issue. US Capture of Remagen Bridge, Germany, 1945.

578	32c. Troops and tanks crossing bridge (vert)	1·20	1·10

(e) 90th issue. US Invasion of Okinawa, 1945.

579	55c. Soldiers throwing grenades (vert)	2·10	1·80

(f) 91st issue. Death of Franklin D. Roosevelt, 1945.

580	50c. Funeral cortege	1·90	1·70

(g) 92nd issue. US and USSR Troops meet at Elbe, 1945.

581	32c. American and Soviet troops	1·20	1·10

(h) 93rd issue. Capture of Berlin by Soviet Troops, 1945.

582	60c. Soviet Marshal Georgi Zhukov and Berlin landmarks	2·30	2·00

(i) 94th issue. Allied Liberation of Concentration Camps, 1945.

583	55c. Inmates and soldier cutting barbed-wire fence	2·10	1·80

(j) 95th issue. V-E (Victory in Europe) Day, 1945.

584	75c. Signing of German surrender, Rheims	2·50	2·20
585	75c. Soldier kissing girl, Times Square, New York	2·50	2·20
586	75c. Victory Parade, Red Square, Moscow	2·50	2·20
587	75c. Royal Family and Churchill on balcony of Buckingham Palace, London	2·50	2·20

(k) 96th issue. Signing of United Nations Charter, 1945.

588	32c. US President Harry S. Truman and Veterans' Memorial Hall, San Francisco	1·20	1·10

(l) 97th issue. Potsdam Conference, 1945.

589	55c. President Harry S. Truman of USA, Winston Churchill and Clement Attlee of Great Britain and Josef Stalin of USSR	2·10	1·80

(m) 98th issue. Resignation of Winston Churchill, 1945.

590	60c. Churchill leaving 10 Downing Street (vert)	2·20	1·90

(n) 99th issue. Dropping of Atomic Bomb on Hiroshima, 1945.

591	$1 Boeing B-29 Superfortress bomber *Enola Gay* and mushroom cloud	3·75	3·25

(o) 100th issue. V-J (Victory in Japan) Day, 1945.

592	75c. Mount Fuji and warships in Tokyo Bay	2·75	2·50
593	75c. USS *Missouri* (battleship)	2·75	2·50
594	75c. Admiral Chester Nimitz signing Japanese surrender watched by General Douglas MacArthur and Admirals William Halsey and Forest Sherman	2·75	2·50
595	75c. Japanese Foreign Minister Shigemitsu, General Umezu and delegation	2·75	2·50

Nos. 592/595 were issued together, *se-tenant*, each pair forming a composite design.

81 Scuba Diver, Meyer's Butterflyfish and Red-tailed Surgeonfish ('Achilles Tang')

1995. Undersea World (1st series). Multicoloured.

596	55c. Type **81**	1·90	1·60
597	55c. Moorish idols and scuba diver	1·90	1·60
598	55c. Pacific green turtle and anthias ('Fairy Basslet')	1·90	1·60
599	55c. Anthias ("Fairy Basslet"), emperor angelfish and orange-finned anemonefish	1·90	1·60

Nos. 596/599 were issued together, *se-tenant*, forming a composite design.
See also Nos. 865/868.

82 USS *PT 109* (motor torpedo boat)

1995. 35th Anniversary of Election of John F. Kennedy as US President. Multicoloured.

600	55c. Type **82** (Second World War command)	1·70	1·50
601	55c. Presidential inauguration	1·70	1·50
602	55c. Peace corps on agricultural project in Marshall Islands	1·70	1·50
603	55c. US Boeing B-29 Superfortress and warships superintending removal of Soviet missiles from Cuba	1·70	1·50
604	55c. Kennedy signing Nuclear Test Ban Treaty, 1963	1·70	1·50
605	55c. Eternal flame on Kennedy's grave, Arlington National Cemetery, Washington DC	1·70	1·50

83 Marilyn Monroe

1995. 69th Birth Anniversary of Marilyn Monroe (actress). Multicoloured.

606	75c. Type **83**	2·40	2·10
607	75c. Monroe (face value top right)	2·40	2·10
608	75c. Monroe (face value bottom left)	2·40	2·10
609	75c. Monroe (face value bottom right)	2·40	2·10

84 President Harry Truman and Veteran's Memorial Hall, San Francisco

1995. 50th Anniversary of United Nations Organisation. Sheet 111×86 mm.
MS610 **84** $1 multicoloured 3·50 3·25

85 *Mir* (Soviet space station)

1995. Docking of *Atlantis* with *Mir* Space Station (611/612) and 20th Anniversary of Apollo–Soyuz Space Link (613/614). Multicoloured.

611	75c. Type **85**	2·20	2·00
612	75c. *Atlantis* (US space shuttle)	2·20	2·00
613	75c. Apollo (U.S. spacecraft)	2·20	2·00
614	75c. Soyuz (Soviet spacecraft)	2·20	2·00

Nos. 611/614 were issued together, *se-tenant*, forming a composite design.

86 Siamese and Exotic Shorthair

1995. Cats. Multicoloured.

615	32c. Type **86**	1·70	1·50
616	32c. American shorthair tabby and red Persian	1·70	1·50
617	32c. Maine coon and Burmese	1·70	1·50
618	32c. Himalayan and Abyssinian	1·70	1·50

87 Sailfish and Tuna

1995. Pacific Game Fish. Multicoloured.

619	60c. Type **87**	2·20	2·00
620	60c. Albacores	2·20	2·00
621	60c. Wahoo	2·20	2·00
622	60c. Blue marlin	2·20	2·00
623	60c. Yellow-finned tunas	2·20	2·00
624	60c. Giant trevally	2·20	2·00
625	60c. Dolphin (fish)	2·20	2·00
626	60c. Short-finned mako	2·20	2·00

Nos. 619/626 were issued together, *se-tenant*, forming a composite design.

88 Inedel's Magic Kite

1995. Folk Legends (1st series). Multicoloured.

627	32c. Type **88**	1·20	1·00
628	32c. Lijebake rescues her granddaughter	1·20	1·00
629	32c. Jebro's mother invents the sail	1·20	1·00
630	32c. Limajnon escapes to the moon	1·20	1·00

See also Nos. 727/730 and 861/864.

89 *Paphiopedilum armenaicum*

1995. Singapore '95 International Stamp Exhibition. Orchids. Sheet 93×120 mm containing T **89** and similar vert designs. Multicoloured.
MS631 32c. Type **89**; 32c. *Masdevallia veitchiana*; 32c. *Cattleya francis*; 32c. *Cattleya x guatemalensis* 4·00 3·50

90 Suzhou Gardens

1995. International Stamp and Coin Exhibition, Peking. Sheet 110×87 mm.
MS632 **90** 50c. multicoloured 1·60 1·40

91 Shepherds gazing at Sky

1995. Christmas.

633	**91**	32c. multicoloured	1·00	90

92 Messerschmit Me 262-la Schwalbe

1995. Jet Fighters. Multicoloured.

634	32c. Type **92**	1·10	95
635	32c. Gloster Meteor F Mk 8	1·10	95
636	32c. Lockheed F-80 Shooting Star	1·10	95
637	32c. North American F-86 Sabre	1·10	95
638	32c. F9F-2 Panther	1·10	95
639	32c. Mikoyan Gurevich MiG-15	1·10	95
640	32c. North American F-100 Super Sabre	1·10	95
641	32c. Convair TF-102A Delta Dagger	1·10	95
642	32c. Lockheed F-104 Starfighter	1·10	95
643	32c. Mikoyan Gurevich MiG-21 MT	1·10	95
644	32c. F8U Crusader	1·10	95
645	32c. Republic F-105 Thunderchief	1·10	95
646	32c. Saab J35 Draken	1·10	95
647	32c. Fiat G-91Y	1·10	95
648	32c. McDonnell Douglas F-4 Phantom II	1·10	95
649	32c. Saab JA 37 Viggen	1·10	95
650	32c. Dassault Mirage F1C	1·10	95
651	32c. Grumman F-14 Tomcat	1·10	95
652	32c. F-15 Eagle	1·10	95
653	32c. General Dynamics F-16 Fighting Falcon	1·10	95
654	32c. Panavia Tornado F Mk 3	1·10	95
655	32c. Sukhoi Su-27UB	1·10	95

656	32c. Dassault Mirage 2000C	1·10	95
657	32c. Hawker Siddeley Sea Harrier FRS.MK1	1·10	95
658	32c. F-117 Nighthawk	1·10	95

93 Rabin

1995. Yitzhak Rabin (Israeli Prime Minister) Commemoration.

659	**93**	32c. multicoloured	1·20	1·00

94 Rat

1996. New Year. Year of the Rat. Sheet 110×84 mm.

MS660	**94** 50c. multicoloured	2·00	1·80

95 Blue-grey Noddy

1996. Birds. Multicoloured.

661	32c. Type **95**	1·80	1·60
662	32c. Spectacled tern ('Gray-backed Tern')	1·80	1·60
663	32c. Blue-faced booby ('Masked Booby')	1·80	1·60
664	32c. Black-footed albatross	1·80	1·60

96 Cheetah

1996. Big Cats. Multicoloured.

665	55c. Type **96**	2·00	1·70
666	55c. Tiger	2·00	1·70
667	55c. Lion	2·00	1·70
668	55c. Jaguar	2·00	1·70

97 5l. Stamp

1996. Centenary of Modern Olympic Games. Designs reproducing 1896 Greek Olympic stamps. Multicoloured.

694	60c. Type **97**	1·60	1·40
695	60c. 60l. stamp	1·60	1·40
696	60c. 40l. stamp	1·60	1·40
697	60c. 1d. stamp	1·60	1·40

98 Undersea Eruptions form Islands

1996. History of Marshall Islands. Multicoloured.

698	55c. Type **98**	1·50	1·30
699	55c. Coral reefs grow around islands	1·50	1·30
700	55c. Storm-driven birds carry seeds to atolls	1·50	1·30
701	55c. First human inhabitants arrive, 1500 BC	1·50	1·30
702	55c. Spanish explorers discover islands, 1527	1·50	1·30
703	55c. John Marshall charts islands, 1788	1·50	1·30
704	55c. German Protectorate, 1885	1·50	1·30
705	55c. Japanese soldier on beach, 1914	1·50	1·30
706	55c. American soldiers liberate islands, 1944	1·50	1·30
707	55c. Evacuation of Bikini Atoll for nuclear testing, 1946	1·50	1·30
708	55c. Marshall Islands becomes United Nations Trust Territory, 1947	1·50	1·30
709	55c. People and National Flag (independence, 1986)	1·50	1·30

99 Presley

1996. 40th Anniversary of Elvis Presley's First Number One Hit Record *Heartbreak Hotel*.

710	**99**	32c. multicoloured	1·20	1·10

100 Palace Museum, Shenyang

1996. China 96 International Stamp Exhibition, Peking. Sheet 110×88 mm.

MS711	**100** 50c. multicoloured	1·70	1·50

101 Dean

1996. 65th Birth Anniversary of James Dean (actor).

712	**101**	32c. multicoloured	1·20	1·10

102 1896 Quadricycle

1996. Centenary of Ford Motor Vehicle Production. Multicoloured.

713	60c. Type **102**	1·30	1·20
714	60c. 1903 Model A Roadster	1·30	1·20
715	60c. 1909 Model T touring car	1·30	1·20
716	60c. 1929 Model A station wagon	1·30	1·20
717	60c. 1955 Thunderbird	1·30	1·20
718	60c. 1964 Mustang convertible	1·30	1·20
719	60c. 1995 Explorer	1·30	1·20
720	60c. 1996 Taurus	1·30	1·20

103 Evacuees boarding *LST 1108* (tank landing ship)

1996. 50th Anniversary of Operation Crossroads (nuclear testing) at Bikini Atoll. Multicoloured.

721	32c.+8c. Type **103**	1·40	1·20
722	32c.+8c. US Navy preparation of site	1·40	1·20
723	32c.+8c. Explosion of *Able* (first test)	1·40	1·20
724	32c.+8c. Explosion of *Baker* (first underwater test)	1·40	1·20
725	32c.+8c. Ghost fleet (targets)	1·40	1·20
726	32c.+8c. Bikinian family	1·40	1·20

1996. Folk Legends (2nd series). As T **88**. Multicoloured.

727	32c. Letao gives gift of fire	1·00	90
728	32c. Mennin Jobwodda flying on giant bird	1·00	90
729	32c. Koko chasing Letao in canoe	1·00	90
730	32c. Mother and girl catching Kouj (octopus) to cook	1·00	90

104 Pennsylvania Railroad Class K4, USA

1996. Steam Railway Locomotives. Multicoloured.

731	55c. Type **104**	1·40	1·30
732	55c. *Big Boy*, USA	1·40	1·30
733	55c. Class A4 *Mallard*, Great Britain	1·40	1·30
734	55c. Class 242, Spain	1·40	1·30
735	55c. Class 01 No. 052, Germany	1·40	1·30
736	55c. Class 691 No. 031, Italy	1·40	1·30
737	55c. *Royal Hudson*, Canada	1·40	1·30
738	55c. *Evening Star*, Great Britain	1·40	1·30
739	55c. Class 520, South Australia	1·40	1·30
740	55c. Class 232.U.2, France	1·40	1·30
741	55c. Class QJ *Advance Forward*, China	1·40	1·30
742	55c. Class C62 *Swallow*, Japan	1·40	1·30

1996. Tenth Asian International Stamp Exhibition, Taipeh. Sheet 120×92 mm containing designs as Nos. 596/599 but values changed, inscriptions rearranged and with additional inscr in Chinese or English.

MS743	32c. Scuba diver, Meyer's butterflyfish and red-tailed surgeonfish ('Achilles tang'); 32c. Moorish idols and scuba diver; 32c. Pacific green turtle and anthias ('Fairy Basslet'); 32c. Anthias ('Fairy Basslet'), emperor angelfish and orange-finned anemonefish	5·00	4·50

105 Stick Chart, Outrigger Canoe and Flag

1996. Tenth Anniversary of Ratification of Compact of Free Association with USA.

744	**105**	$3 multicoloured	10·00	8·75

106 *Madonna and Child with Four Saints* (detail, Rosso Fiorentino)

1996. Christmas.

745	**106**	32c. multicoloured	1·00	90

107 Curtiss JN-4 Jenny

1996. Biplanes. Multicoloured.

746	32c. Type **107**	1·20	1·00
747	32c. SPAD XIII	1·20	1·00
748	32c. Albatros	1·20	1·00
749	32c. de Havilland D.H.4 Liberty	1·20	1·00
750	32c. Fokker Dr-1	1·20	1·00
751	32c. Sopwith Camel	1·20	1·00
752	32c. Martin MB-2	1·20	1·00
753	32c. Martin MB-3A Tommy	1·20	1·00
754	32c. Curtiss TS-1	1·20	1·00
755	32c. P-1 Hawk	1·20	1·00
756	32c. Boeing PW-9	1·20	1·00
757	32c. Douglas O-2-H	1·20	1·00
758	32c. LB-5 Pirate	1·20	1·00
759	32c. O2U-1 Corsair	1·20	1·00
760	32c. Curtiss F8C Helldiver	1·20	1·00
761	32c. Boeing F4B-4	1·20	1·00
762	32c. J6B Gerfalcon	1·20	1·00
763	32c. Martin BM	1·20	1·00
764	32c. FF-1 Fifi	1·20	1·00
765	32c. C.R.32 Cricket	1·20	1·00
766	32c. Polikarpov I-15 Gull	1·20	1·00
767	32c. Fairey Swordfish	1·20	1·00
768	32c. Aichi D1A2	1·20	1·00
769	32c. Grumman F3F	1·20	1·00
770	32c. SOC-3 Seagull	1·20	1·00

108 Fan-making

1996. Traditional Crafts. Multicoloured. Self-adhesive gum (780, 782); ordinary or self-adhesive gum (others).

771	32c. Type **108**	75	65
772	32c. Boys sailing model outrigger canoes (country name at right)	75	65
773	32c. Carving canoes	75	65
774	32c. Weaving baskets (country name at right)	75	65
780	32c. As No. 772 but with country name at left	1·10	95
782	32c. As No. 774 but with country name at left	1·10	95

109 Chinese Character and Ox

1997. New Year. Year of the Ox. Sheet 110×87 mm.

MS783	**109** 60c. multicoloured	2·40	2·10

110 'Rocking '50s'

1997. 20th Death Anniversary of Elvis Presley (entertainer). Different portraits. Multicoloured.

784	32c. Type **110**	1·10	95
785	32c. 'Soaring '60s'	1·10	95
786	32c. 'Sensational '70s'	1·10	95

111 Kabua

1997. President Amata Kabua Commemoration. Multicoloured.

787	32c. Type **111**	1·20	1·00
788	60c. As Type **111** but inscr in English at left and right and in Marshallese at foot	2·00	1·80

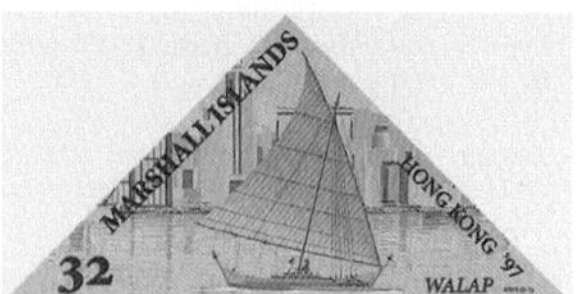

112 Hong Kong by Day and Outrigger Canoe

1997. Hong Kong '97 International Stamp Exhibition. Two sheets, each 168×66 mm containing triangular designs as T **112**. Multicoloured.

MS789	Two sheets. (a) 32c. Type **112**; 32c. Hong Kong by day and junk. (b) 32c. Hong Kong at night and outrigger canoe; 32c. Hong Kong at night and junk	4·50	4·00

113 St Andrew

1997. Easter. 140th Anniversary of Introduction of Christianity to the Marshall Islands. The 12 Disciples. Multicoloured.

790	60c. Type **113**	1·90	1·70
791	60c. St Matthew	1·90	1·70
792	60c. St Philip	1·90	1·70

793	60c. St Simon	1·90	1·70
794	60c. St Thaddeus	1·90	1·70
795	60c. St Thomas	1·90	1·70
796	60c. St Bartholomew	1·90	1·70
797	60c. St John	1·90	1·70
798	60c. St James the Lesser	1·90	1·70
799	60c. St James the Greater	1·90	1·70
800	60c. St Paul	1·90	1·70
801	60c. St Peter	1·90	1·70
MS802	110×87 mm. $3 *The Last Supper* (Peter Paul Rubens) (78×48 mm)	10·50	9·00

114 Immigrants arriving at Ellis Island, New York, 1900

1997. The 20th-century (1st series). Decade of New Possibilities, 1900–1909. Multicoloured.

803	60c. Type **114**	1·90	1·70
804	60c. Chinese and Dowager Empress Ci Xi, 1900 (Boxer Rebellion)	1·90	1·70
805	60c. George Eastman (inventor of box camera) photographing family, 1900	1·90	1·70
806	60c. Walter Reed (discoverer of yellow fever transmission by mosquito), 1900	1·90	1·70
807	60c. Sigmund Freud (pioneer of psychoanalysis) (publication of *Interpretation of Dreams*, 1900)	1·90	1·70
808	60c. Guglielmo Marconi sending first transatlantic wireless message, 1901	1·90	1·70
809	60c. Enrico Caruso (opera singer) (first award of Gold Disc for one million record sales, 1903)	1·90	1·70
810	60c. Wright Brothers' *Flyer I* (first powered flight, Kitty Hawk, 1903)	1·90	1·70
811	60c. Albert Einstein and formula (development of *Theory of Relativity*, 1905)	1·90	1·70
812	60c. White ensign and HMS *Dreadnought* (battleship), 1906	1·90	1·70
813	60c. San Francisco earthquake, 1906	1·90	1·70
814	60c. Mohandas Gandhi and protestors, Johannesburg, South Africa, 1906	1·90	1·70
815	60c. Pablo Picasso and *Les Demoiselles d'Avignon*, 1907	1·90	1·70
816	60c. First Paris–Peking motor car race, 1907	1·90	1·70
817	60c. Masjik-i-Salaman oil field, Persia, 1908	1·90	1·70

See also Nos. 872/886, 948/962, 975/989, 1067/1081, 1165/1179, 1218/1232, 1239/1253, 1256/1270 and 1303/1317.

115 Deng Xiaoping

1997. Deng Xiaoping (Chinese statesman) Commemoration.

818	**115** 60c. multicoloured	2·10	1·90

116 German Marshall Islands 1899 3pf. Stamp

1997. Pacific 97 International Stamp Exhibition, San Francisco. Centenary of Marshall Islands Postage Stamps. Multicoloured.

819	50c. Type **116**	1·60	1·40
820	50c. German Marshall Islands 1899 5pf. stamp	1·60	1·40
821	50c. German Marshall Islands 1897 10pf. stamp	1·60	1·40
822	50c. German Marshall Islands 1897 20pf. stamp	1·60	1·40
823	50c. Unissued German Marshall Islands 25pf. stamp	1·60	1·40
824	50c. Unissued German Marshall Islands 50pf. stamp	1·60	1·40

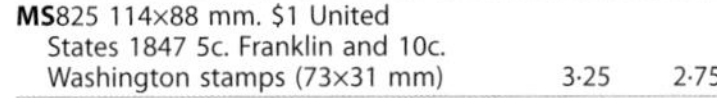

MS825	114×88 mm. $1 United States 1847 5c. Franklin and 10c. Washington stamps (73×31 mm)	3·25	2·75

117 Curlew on Seashore

1997. The Bristle-thighed Curlew. Multicoloured.

826	16c. Type **117**	95	85
827	16c. Flying	95	85
828	16c. Running	95	85
829	16c. Standing on branch	95	85

118 Bank of China, Hong Kong

1997. Return of Hong Kong to China. Sheet 87×110 mm.

MS830	**118** 50c. multicoloured	2·00	1·80

119 Pacific Arts Festival Canoe, Enewetak

1997. Traditional Outrigger Canoes. Multicoloured.

831	32c. Type **119**	1·20	1·00
832	32c. Kor Kor racing canoes	1·20	1·00
833	32c. Large voyaging canoe, Jaluit	1·20	1·00
834	32c. Sailing canoe, Ailuk	1·20	1·00

120 Douglas C-54 Skymaster Transport

1997. Aircraft of United States Air Force (1st series). Multicoloured.

835	32c. Type **120**	1·20	1·00
836	32c. Boeing B-36 Peacemaker	1·20	1·00
837	32c. North American F-86 Sabre jet fighter	1·20	1·00
838	32c. Boeing B-47 Stratojet jet bomber	1·20	1·00
839	32c. Douglas C-124 Globemaster II transport	1·20	1·00
840	32c. Lockheed C-121 Constellation	1·20	1·00
841	32c. Boeing B-52 Stratofortress jet bomber	1·20	1·00
842	32c. North American F-100 Super Sabre jet fighter	1·20	1·00
843	32c. Lockheed F-104 Starfighter jet fighter	1·20	1·00
844	32c. Lockheed C-130 Hercules transport	1·20	1·00
845	32c. Republic F-105 Thunderchief jet fighter	1·20	1·00
846	32c. KC-135 Stratotanker	1·20	1·00
847	32c. Convair B-58 Hustler jet bomber	1·20	1·00
848	32c. McDonnell Douglas F-4 Phantom II jet fighter	1·20	1·00
849	32c. Northrop T-38 Talon trainer	1·20	1·00
850	32c. Lockheed C-141 StarLifter jet transport	1·20	1·00
851	32c. General Dynamics F-111 Aardvark jet fighter	1·20	1·00
852	32c. SR-71 Blackbird	1·20	1·00
853	32c. Lockheed C-5 Galaxy jet transport	1·20	1·00
854	32c. A-10 Thunderbolt II bomber	1·20	1·00
855	32c. F-15 Eagle fighter	1·20	1·00
856	32c. General Dynamics F-16 Fighting Falcon jet fighter	1·20	1·00
857	32c. Lockheed F-117 Nighthawk Stealth bomber	1·20	1·00
858	32c. B-2 Spirit	1·20	1·00
859	32c. C-17 Globemaster III transport	1·20	1·00

See also Nos. 1272/1296.

121 USS *Constitution*

1997. Bicentenary of Launch of USS *Constitution* (frigate).

860	**121** 32c. multicoloured	1·20	1·00

1997. Folk Legends (3rd series). As T **88**. Multicoloured.

861	32c. The Large Pool of Mejit	1·20	1·00
862	32c. The Beautiful Woman of Kwajalein	1·20	1·00
863	32c. Sharks and Lowakalle Reef	1·20	1·00
864	32c. The Demon of Adrie	1·20	1·00

1997. Undersea World (2nd series). As T **81**. Multicoloured.

865	60c. Watanabe's angelfish, blue-finned trevallys ('Bluefin Jack'), grey reef shark and scuba diver	2·00	1·80
866	60c. Scuba diver, anchor and racoon butterflyfish	2·00	1·80
867	60c. Lionfish and flame angelfish	2·00	1·80
868	60c. Square-spotted anthias ('Fairy Basslet'), anchor, scuba diver with torch and orange-finned anemonefish	2·00	1·80

Nos. 865/868 were issued together, *se-tenant*, forming a composite design.

122 Diana, Princess of Wales, aged 20

1997. Diana, Princess of Wales Commemoration. Multicoloured.

869	60c. Type **122**	2·00	1·80
870	60c. Wearing pearl drop earrings (aged 27)	2·00	1·80
871	60c. Wearing pearl choker (aged 36)	2·00	1·80

123 Flags and Suffragettes

1997. The 20th-century (2nd series). Decade of Revolution and Great War, 1910–1919. Multicoloured.

872	60c. Type **123**	2·10	1·60
873	60c. Nobel Prize medal, Ernest Rutherford and diagram of atom, 1911	2·10	1·60
874	60c. Sun Yat-Sen (Chinese Revolution, 1911–1912)	2·10	1·60
875	60c. Sinking of the *Titanic* (liner), 1912	2·10	1·60
876	60c. Igor Stravinsky (composer) and score of *The Rite of Spring*, 1913	2·10	1·60
877	60c. Building motor car (introduction of assembly line construction of motor vehicles by Ford Motor Company), 1913	2·10	1·60
878	60c. Countess Sophie Chotek and Archduke Franz Ferdinand of Austria, 1914 (assassination in Sarajevo leads to First World War)	2·10	1·60
879	60c. Torpedo striking *Lusitania* (liner), 1915	2·10	1·60
880	60c. Battle of Verdun, 1916	2·10	1·60
881	60c. Patrick Pearse and proclamation of Irish Republic (Easter Rebellion, 1916)	2·10	1·60
882	60c. Western wall, Jerusalem (Balfour Declaration of Jewish Homeland, 1917)	2·10	1·60
883	60c. *Aurora* (cruiser) signals start of Russian Revolution, 1917	2·10	1·60
884	60c. Fokker Dr.1 Biplanes and 'Red' Baron Manfred von Richthofen (fighter pilot), 1918	2·10	1·60
885	60c. Armed revolutionaries, Berlin, 1918	2·10	1·60
886	60c. Meeting of heads of state (Treaty of Versailles, 1919)	2·10	1·60

124 Cherub

1997. Christmas. Details of *Sistine Madonna* by Raphael. Multicoloured.

887	32c. Type **124**	1·00	90
888	32c. Cherub resting head on folded arms	1·00	90

125 USS *Alabama* (battleship), 1942

1997. Ships named after US States. Multicoloured.

889	20c. Type **125**	70	65
890	20c. USS *Alaska* (cruiser), 1869, and junk	70	65
891	20c. USS *Arizona* (battleship), 1916	70	65
892	20c. USS *Arkansas* (battleship), 1912	70	65
893	20c. USS *California* (cruiser), 1974	70	65
894	20c. USS *Colorado* (battleship), 1921, and landing craft	70	65
895	20c. USS *Connecticut* (gunboat), 1776, with fleet	70	65
896	20c. USS *Delaware* (ship of the line), 1828	70	65
897	20c. USS *Florida* (cruiser), 1967	70	65
898	20c. USS *Georgia* (battleship), 1906	70	65
899	20c. USS *Honolulu* (cruiser), 1938	70	65
900	20c. USS *Idaho* (battleship), 1919	70	65
901	20c. USS *Illinois* (battleship), 1901	70	65
902	20c. USS *Indiana* (battleship), 1895	70	65
903	20c. USS *Iowa* (battleship), 1943	70	65
904	20c. USS *Kansas* (battleship), 1907	70	65
905	20c. USS *Kentucky* (battleship), 1900	70	65
906	20c. USS *Louisiana* (frigate), 1812	70	65
907	20c. USS *Maine* (battleship), 1895	70	65
908	20c. USS *Maryland* (frigate), 1799	70	65
909	20c. USS *Massachusetts* (battleship), 1942	70	65
910	20c. USS *Michigan* (paddle-gunboat), 1843	70	65
911	20c. USS *Minnesota* (corvette), 1857	70	65
912	20c. USS *Mississippi* (paddle-gunboat), 1841, and junk	70	65
913	20c. USS *Missouri* (battleship), 1944, in Tokyo Bay	70	65
914	20c. USS *Montana* (battleship), 1908	70	65
915	20c. USS *Nebraska* (battleship), 1907	70	65
916	20c. USS *Nevada* (battleship), 1916, at Pearl Harbor	70	65
917	20c. USS *New Hampshire* (battleship), 1908, and Statue of Liberty	70	65
918	20c. USS *New Jersey* (battleship), 1943	70	65
919	20c. USS *New Mexico* (battleship), 1918, in Tokyo Bay	70	65
920	20c. USS *New York* (frigate), 1800, and felucca	70	65
921	20c. USS *North Carolina* (battleship), 1941	70	65
922	20c. USS *North Dakota* (battleship), 1910	70	65
923	20c. USS *Ohio* (ship of the line), 1838	70	65
924	20c. USS *Oklahoma* (battleship), 1916	70	65
925	20c. USS *Oregon* (battleship), 1896	70	65
926	20c. USS *Pennsylvania* (battleship), 1905	70	65
927	20c. USS *Rhode Island* (paddle-gunboat), 1861	70	65

928 20c. USS *South Carolina* (frigate), 1783 70 65
929 20c. USS *South Dakota* (battleship), 1942 70 65
930 20c. USS *Tennessee* (battleship), 1906 70 65
931 20c. USS *Texas* (battleship), 1914 70 65
932 20c. USS *Utah* (battleship), 1911 70 65
933 20c. USS *Vermont* (battleship), 1907 70 65
934 20c. USS *Virginia* (schooner), 1798 70 65
935 20c. USS *Washington* (battleship), 1941 70 65
936 20c. USS *West Virginia* (battleship), 1923 70 65
937 20c. USS *Wisconsin* (battleship), 1944 70 65
938 20c. USS *Wyoming* (monitor), 1902 70 65

Dates given are those of either launch or commission.

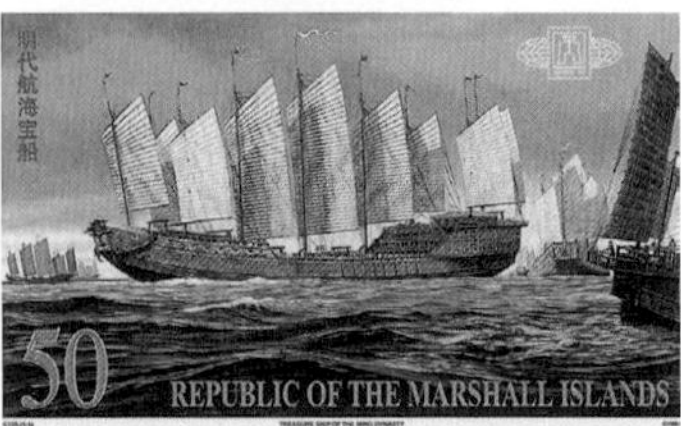

126 Treasure Junks, Ming Dynasty

1997. Shanghai 1997 International Stamp and Coin Exhibition. Sheet 110×87 mm.
MS939 **126** 50c. multicoloured 2·00 1·80

127 Chinese Character and Tiger

1998. New Year. Year of the Tiger. Sheet 110×87 mm.
MS940 **127** 60c. multicoloured 2·40 2·10

128 Presley

1998. 30th Anniversary of First Television Special by Elvis Presley (entertainer). Multicoloured.
941 32c. Type **128** 95 85
942 32c. Presley in black leather jacket 95 85
943 32c. Presley in white suit in front of ELVIS in lights 95 85

129 Chiragra Spider Conch (*Lambis chiragra*)

1998. Sea Shells. Multicoloured.
944 32c. Type **129** 1·10 95
945 32c. Fluted giant clam (*Tridacna squamosa*) 1·10 95
946 32c. Adusta murex (*Chicoreus brunneus*) 1·10 95
947 32c. Golden cowrie (*Cypraea aurantium*) 1·10 95

130 Family listening to Radio

1998. The 20th-century (3rd series). Decade of Optimism and Disillusionment, 1920–1929. Multicoloured.
948 60c. Type **130** 2·00 1·80
949 60c. Leaders from Japan, United States, France, Great Britain and Italy (Washington Conference, 1920) 2·00 1·80
950 60c. Ludwig Mies van der Rohe (architect), 1922 2·00 1·80
951 60c. Mummiform coffin of Tutankhamun (discovery of tomb, 1922) 2·00 1·80
952 60c. Workers from USSR, 1923 (emergence of USSR as communist state) 2·00 1·80
953 60c. Kemal Ataturk (first president of modern Turkey, 1923) (break-up of Turkish Empire) 2·00 1·80
954 60c. Bix Beiderbecke (trumpeter) and flappers (dancers), 1924 (Jazz Age) 2·00 1·80
955 60c. Robert Goddard demonstrates first liquid-propelled rocket, 1926 2·00 1·80
956 60c. Poster for *The Jazz Singer* (second talking picture, 1926) 2·00 1·80
957 60c. Benito Mussolini assumes total power in Italy, 1926 2·00 1·80
958 60c. Explosive glare and Leonardo da Vinci's *Proportion of Man* (Big Bang Theory of beginning of Universe, 1927) 2·00 1·80
959 60c. Sir Alexander Fleming discovers penicillin, 1928 2·00 1·80
960 60c. John Logie Baird invents television, 1926 2·00 1·80
961 60c. Airship *Graf Zeppelin* above Mt. Fuji, Japan (first round the world flight, 1929) 2·00 1·80
962 60c. US stock market crash, 1929 (economic depression) 2·00 1·80

131 Pahi Sailing Canoe, Tuamotu Archipelago

1998. Canoes of the Pacific. Multicoloured.
963 32c. Type **131** 1·10 95
964 32c. Maori war canoe, New Zealand 1·10 95
965 32c. Wa'a Kaukahi fishing canoe, Hawaii 1·10 95
966 32c. Amatasi sailing canoe, Samoa 1·10 95
967 32c. Ndrua sailing canoe, Fiji Islands 1·10 95
968 32c. Tongiaki voyaging canoe, Tonga 1·10 95
969 32c. Tipairua travelling canoe, Tahiti 1·10 95
970 32c. Walap sailing canoe, Marshall Islands 1·10 95

132 Douglas C-54 Skymaster Transport

1998. 50th Anniversary of Berlin Airlift (relief of Berlin during Soviet blockade). Multicoloured.
971 60c. Type **132** 2·20 1·90
972 60c. Avro Type 685 York transport 2·20 1·90
973 60c. Crowd and building 2·20 1·90
974 60c. Crowd 2·20 1·90

Nos. 971/974 were issued together, *se-tenant*, forming a composite design.

133 Soup Kitchens, 1930 (depression)

1998. The 20th-century (4th series). Decade of the Great Depression, 1930–1939. Multicoloured.
975 60c. Type **133** 2·10 1·80
976 60c. Ernest Lawrence and first cyclotron, 1931 (splitting of atom) 2·10 1·80
977 60c. Forced collectivisation of farms in Soviet Union, 1932 (Stalin era) 2·10 1·80
978 60c. Torchlight Parade celebrates rise of Hitler to power, 1933 (fascism) 2·10 1·80
979 60c. Dneproges Dam on Dnepr River, 1933 (harnessing of nature) 2·10 1·80
980 60c. Streamlined locomotive *Zephyr* (record-breaking run, Denver to Chicago, 1934) 2·10 1·80
981 60c. Douglas DC-3 airliner (first all-metal airliner, 1936) 2·10 1·80
982 60c. Pablo Picasso (artist) and *Guernica* (German bombing during Spanish Civil War, 1937) 2·10 1·80
983 60c. *Hindenburg* (airship disaster), 1937 (media reporting) 2·10 1·80
984 60c. Families fleeing ruins (Japanese assault on Nanjing, 1937) 2·10 1·80
985 60c. Neville Chamberlain declares 'Peace in our Time', 1938 (appeasement) 2·10 1·80
986 60c. Chester Carlson (invention of xerography, 1938) 2·10 1·80
987 60c. Jew and Star of David (Kristallnacht (Nazi violence against Jews), 1938) 2·10 1·80
988 60c. Junkers Stuka bombers over Poland, 1939 (start of Second World War) 2·10 1·80
989 60c. Audience (premiere of *Gone with the Wind*, 1939) (movies) 2·10 1·80

134 Coronation of Tsar Nicholas II, 1896

1998. 80th Death Anniversary of Tsar Nicholas II and his Family. Multicoloured.
990 60c. Type **134** 2·00 1·80
991 60c. *Varyag* (cruiser) and Tsar (Russo–Japanese war, 1904–1905) 2·00 1·80
992 60c. Troops firing on crowd, Tsar and October manifesto, 1905 2·00 1·80
993 60c. Peasant sowing, Tsar and Rasputin, 1905 2·00 1·80
994 60c. Mounted troops, Tsar and Nicholas II at strategy meeting, 1915 2·00 1·80
995 60c. Abdication, Tsar and Ipateva House, Ekaterinburg, 1917 2·00 1·80
MS996 87×61 mm. $3 Royal Family. Imperf 10·00 8·75

135 Babe Ruth

1998. 50th Death Anniversary of Babe Ruth (baseball player).
997 **135** 32c. multicoloured 1·20 1·00

136 NC-4

1998. Aircraft of United States Navy. Multicoloured.
998 32c. Type **136** 1·20 1·00
999 32c. Consolidated PBY-5 Catalina flying boat 1·20 1·00
1000 32c. TBD Devastator 1·20 1·00
1001 32c. SB2U Vindicator 1·20 1·00
1002 32c. Grumman F4F Wildcat fighter 1·20 1·00
1003 32c. Vought-Sikorsky OS2U Kingfisher seaplane 1·20 1·00
1004 32c. Douglas SBD Dauntless bomber 1·20 1·00
1005 32c. Chance Vought F4U Corsair fighter 1·20 1·00
1006 32c. Curtiss SB2C Helldiver bomber 1·20 1·00
1007 32c. Lockheed PV-1 Ventura bomber 1·20 1·00
1008 32c. Grumman TBM Avenger bomber 1·20 1·00
1009 32c. Grumman F6F Hellcat fighter 1·20 1·00
1010 32c. PB4Y-2 Privateer 1·20 1·00
1011 32c. A-1J Skyraider 1·20 1·00
1012 32c. McDonnell F2H-2P Banshee 1·20 1·00
1013 32c. F9F-2B Panther 1·20 1·00
1014 32c. P5M Marlin 1·20 1·00
1015 32c. F-8 Crusader 1·20 1·00
1016 32c. McDonnell Douglas F-4 Phantom II fighter 1·20 1·00
1017 32c. A-6 Intruder 1·20 1·00
1018 32c. Lockheed P-3 Orion reconnaissance 1·20 1·00
1019 32c. Vought A-70 Corsair II 1·20 1·00
1020 32c. Douglas A-4 Skyhawk bomber 1·20 1·00
1021 32c. S-3 Viking 1·20 1·00
1022 32c. F/A-18 Hornet 1·20 1·00

137 Classic Six, 1912

1998. Chevrolet Vehicles. Multicoloured.
1023 60c. Type **137** 2·00 1·80
1024 60c. Sport Roadster, 1931 2·00 1·80
1025 60c. Special Deluxe, 1941 2·00 1·80
1026 60c. Cameo Carrier Fleetside, 1955 2·00 1·80
1027 60c. Corvette, 1957 2·00 1·80
1028 60c. Bel Air, 1957 2·00 1·80
1029 60c. Camaro, 1967 2·00 1·80
1030 60c. Chevelle SS 454, 1970 2·00 1·80

138 Letter 'A' and President Amata Kabua

1998. Marshallese Alphabet and Language. Multicoloured.
1031 33c. Type **138** 1·20 1·00
1032 33c. Letter 'A' and woman weaving 1·20 1·00
1033 33c. Letter 'B' and butterfly 1·20 1·00
1034 33c. Letter 'D' and woman wearing garland of flowers 1·20 1·00
1035 33c. Letter 'E' and fish 1·20 1·00
1036 33c. Letter 'I' and couple in front of rainbow 1·20 1·00
1037 33c. Letter 'J' and woven mat 1·20 1·00
1038 33c. Letter 'K' and Government House 1·20 1·00
1039 33c. Letter 'L' and night sky 1·20 1·00
1040 33c. Letter 'L' and red-tailed tropicbird 1·20 1·00
1041 33c. Letter 'M' and breadfruit 1·20 1·00
1042 33c. Letter 'M' and arrowroot plant 1·20 1·00
1043 33c. Letter 'N' and coconut tree 1·20 1·00
1044 33c. Letter 'N' and wave 1·20 1·00
1045 33c. Letter 'N' and shark 1·20 1·00
1046 33c. Letter 'O' and fisherman 1·20 1·00
1047 33c. Letter 'O' and tattooed woman 1·20 1·00
1048 33c. Letter 'O' and lionfish 1·20 1·00
1049 33c. Letter 'P' and visitor's hut 1·20 1·00
1050 33c. Letter 'R' and whale 1·20 1·00
1051 33c. Letter 'T' and outrigger sailing canoe 1·20 1·00
1052 33c. Letter 'U' and fire 1·20 1·00
1053 33c. Letter 'U' and whale's fin 1·20 1·00
1054 33c. Letter 'W' and woven leaf sail 1·20 1·00

139 Trust Company of the Marshall Islands Offices, 1998

1998. New Buildings. Multicoloured.
1055 33c. Type **139** 1·00 90
1056 33c. Embassy of the People's Republic of China, 1996 1·00 90
1057 33c. Outrigger Marshall Islands Resort, 1996 1·00 90

140 Midnight Angel

1998. Christmas.
1058 **140** 33c. multicoloured 1·10 95

141 Launch of *Friendship 7*, 1962

1998. John Glenn's (astronaut) Return to Space. Multicoloured.

No.	Description		
1059	60c. Type **141**	2·00	1·80
1060	60c. John Glenn, 1962, and Earth	2·00	1·80
1061	60c. *Friendship 7* orbiting Earth	2·00	1·80
1062	60c. Launch of space shuttle *Discovery*, 1998	2·00	1·80
1063	60c. John Glenn, 1998, and flag	2·00	1·80
1064	60c. *Discovery* orbiting Earth, 1998	2·00	1·80
MS1065	115×87 mm. $3 US 4c. Project Mercury stamp, 1962 (74×32 mm)	9·50	8·50

143 British and German Planes over St Paul's Cathedral (Battle of Britain, 1940)

1998. The 20th-century (5th series). Decade of War and Peace, 1940–1949. Multicoloured.

No.	Description		
1067	60c. Type **143**	1·90	1·70
1068	60c. Japanese aircraft attack American battleship (Pearl Harbor, 1941) (global warfare)	1·90	1·70
1069	60c. Wernher von Braun and missiles (first surface to surface guided missile, 1942)	1·90	1·70
1070	60c. The Dorsey Brothers (Big Bands, 1942)	1·90	1·70
1071	60c. Soviet worker building weaponry (fight for survival against Germans, 1943)	1·90	1·70
1072	60c. Concentration camp prisoners (the Holocaust, 1945)	1·90	1·70
1073	60c. Mushroom cloud and skull (first atomic bomb tested, Alamogordo, New Mexico, 1945)	1·90	1·70
1074	60c. Families reunited (end of war, 1945)	1·90	1·70
1075	60c. Eniac computer and worker (first electronic digital computer goes into operation, 1946)	1·90	1·70
1076	60c. American delegate (United Nations, 1946)	1·90	1·70
1077	60c. Nuremberg Tribunal (trials of Germans for war crimes 1946)	1·90	1·70
1078	60c. George Marshall (US Secretary of State) and Europeans (Marshall Plan, 1947)	1·90	1·70
1079	60c. William Shockley, John Bardeen and Walter Brattain (development of transistor, 1948)	1·90	1·70
1080	60c. Berlin Airlift, 1948–1949 (Cold War)	1·90	1·70
1081	60c. Mao Tse-tung proclaiming People's Republic of China, 1949	1·90	1·70

144 Trireme

1998. Warships. Multicoloured.

No.	Description		
1082	33c. Type **144**	1·20	1·00
1083	33c. Roman galley ('Trireme Romano')	1·20	1·00
1084	33c. Viking longship	1·20	1·00
1085	33c. Ming treasure ship	1·20	1·00
1086	33c. *Mary Rose* (English galleon)	1·20	1·00
1087	33c. *Nuestra Senora del Rosario* (Spanish galleon)	1·20	1·00
1088	33c. Korean 'turtle' ship	1·20	1·00
1089	33c. *Brederode* (Dutch ship of the line)	1·20	1·00
1090	33c. Venetian galley	1·20	1·00
1091	33c. *Santissima Trinidad* (Spanish ship of the line)	1·20	1·00
1092	33c. *Ville de Paris* (French ship of the line)	1·20	1·00
1093	33c. HMS *Victory* (ship of the line)	1·20	1·00
1094	33c. *Bonhomme Richard* (American sail frigate)	1·20	1·00
1095	33c. USS *Constellation* (sail frigate)	1·20	1·00
1096	33c. USS *Hartford* (steam frigate)	1·20	1·00
1097	33c. Fijian Ndrua canoe	1·20	1·00
1098	33c. HMS *Dreadnought* (battleship)	1·20	1·00
1099	33c. HMAS *Australia* (battle cruiser)	1·20	1·00
1100	33c. HMS *Dorsetshire* (cruiser)	1·20	1·00
1101	33c. *Admiral Graf Spee* (German battleship)	1·20	1·00
1102	33c. *Yamato* (Japanese battleship)	1·20	1·00
1103	33c. USS *Tautog* (submarine)	1·20	1·00
1104	33c. *Bismarck* (German battleship)	1·20	1·00
1105	33c. USS *Hornet* (aircraft carrier)	1·20	1·00
1106	33c. USS *Missouri* (battleship)	1·20	1·00

145 Chinese Character and Rabbit

1999. New Year. Year of the Rabbit. Sheet 110×87 mm.

No.	Description		
MS1107	**145** 60c. multicoloured	2·40	2·10

146 Pacific Golden Plover ('Lesser Golden Plover')

1999. Birds. Multicoloured.

No.	Description		
1108	1c. Type **146**	15	15
1109	3c. Grey-rumped sandpiper ('Siberian (gray-tailed) Tattler')	20	20
1110	5c. Black-tailed godwit	25	20
1113	20c. Common noddy ('Brown Noddy')	1·00	90
1114	22c. White tern ('Common Fairy Tern')	1·30	1·10
1116	33c. Micronesian pigeon	1·80	1·50
1117	40c. Franklin's gull	2·50	2·20
1118	45c. Rufous-necked sandpiper ('Rufous-necked Stint')	3·25	2·75
1119	55c. Long-tailed koel ('Long-tailed Cuckoo')	4·00	3·50
1121	75c. Kermadec petrel	11·00	9·50
1122	$1 Christmas Island shearwater ('Christmas Shearwater')	18·00	15·00
1123	$1.20 Purple-capped fruit dove	28·00	25·00
1124	$2 Lesser sand plover ('Mongolian Plover')	5·00	4·75
1125	$3.20 Cattle egret	8·25	7·50
1127	$5 Dunlin	12·50	11·50
1129	$10 Eurasian tree sparrow	19·00	17·00

1999. Canoes of the Pacific. Multicoloured. (a) Size 49×30 mm.

No.	Description		
1130	33c. Type **131**	1·10	95
1131	33c. As No. 964	1·10	95
1132	33c. As No. 965	1·10	95
1133	33c. As No. 966 but inscr changed to 'Tongiaki voyaging canoe, Tonga'	1·10	95
1134	33c. As No. 967	1·10	95
1135	33c. As No. 968 but inscr changed to 'Amatasi sailing canoe, Samoa'	1·10	95
1136	33c. As No. 969	1·10	95
1137	33c. As No. 970	1·10	95

(b) Size 39×24 mm.

No.	Description		
1138	33c. Type **131**	1·20	1·10
1139	33c. As No. 1131	1·20	1·10
1140	33c. As No. 1132	1·20	1·10
1141	33c. As No. 1133	1·20	1·10
1142	33c. As No. 1134	1·20	1·10
1143	33c. As No. 1135	1·20	1·10
1144	33c. As No. 1136	1·20	1·10
1145	33c. As No. 1137	1·20	1·10

Nos. 1138/1145 were self-adhesive.

147 Tecumseh

1999. Great American Indian Chiefs. Multicoloured.

No.	Description		
1146	60c. Type **147**	1·90	1·70
1147	60c. Powhatan	1·90	1·70
1148	60c. Hiawatha	1·90	1·70
1149	60c. Dull Knife	1·90	1·70
1150	60c. Sequoyah	1·90	1·70
1151	60c. Sitting Bull	1·90	1·70
1152	60c. Cochise	1·90	1·70
1153	60c. Red Cloud	1·90	1·70
1154	60c. Geronimo	1·90	1·70
1155	60c. Chief Joseph	1·90	1·70
1156	60c. Pontiac	1·90	1·70
1157	60c. Crazy Horse	1·90	1·70

148 State Flag

1999

No.	Description		
1158	**148** 33c. multicoloured	1·10	95

149 Plumeria

1999. Flowers of the Pacific. Multicoloured.

No.	Description		
1159	33c. Type **149**	1·10	95
1160	33c. Vanda	1·10	95
1161	33c. Ilima	1·10	95
1162	33c. Tiare	1·10	95
1163	33c. White ginger	1·10	95
1164	33c. Hibiscus	1·10	95

150 Family watching Television

1999. The 20th-century (6th series). Decade of Peril and Progress, 1950–1959. Multicoloured.

No.	Description		
1165	60c. Type **150**	1·90	1·70
1166	60c. UN landing at Inchon, Korea, 1950 (Cold War)	1·90	1·70
1167	60c. Vaccination against polio, 1952	1·90	1·70
1168	60c. American hydrogen bomb test, Enewetak Atoll, 1952 (Arms race)	1·90	1·70
1169	60c. James Watson and Francis Crick (scientists) and DNA double helix, 1953 (unravelling of genetic code)	1·90	1·70
1170	60c. Sir Edmund Hillary, Tenzing Norgay and Mt. Everest, 1953	1·90	1·70
1171	60c. Coronation of Queen Elizabeth II, Westminster Abbey, 1953	1·90	1·70
1172	60c. Singer and dancers, 1954 (rock 'n' roll music)	1·90	1·70
1173	60c. Ho Chi Minh and Vietnamese troops celebrating victory over French garrison at Dien Bien Phu, 1954 (end of colonial empires)	1·90	1·70
1174	60c. People of different races on bus, 1955 (condemnation of racial discrimination)	1·90	1·70
1175	60c. Hungarians firing on Russian tanks, Budapest, 1956 (challenge to Communism)	1·90	1·70
1176	60c. Signing of Treaty of Rome, 1957 (European union)	1·90	1·70
1177	60c. Launch of Russian *Sputnik*, 1957 (space race)	1·90	1·70
1178	60c. de Havilland DH.106 Comet (first commercial jet airline service, 1958)	1·90	1·70
1179	60c. Jack Kilby (inventor) and first microchip, 1959	1·90	1·70

151 HMAS *Australia* (battle Cruiser)

1999. Australia 99 International Stamp Exhibition, Melbourne. Sheet 190×116 mm.

No.	Description		
MS1180	**151** $1.20 multicoloured	4·50	3·75

152 Presley

1999. Elvis Presley, 'Artist of the Century'.

No.	Description		
1181	**152** 33c. multicoloured	1·20	1·00

153 5m. Stamp

1999. iBRA '99 International Stamp Exhibition, Nuremberg, Germany. Multicoloured.

No.	Description		
1182	60c. Type **153**	1·90	1·70
1183	60c. 3m. stamp	1·90	1·70
1184	60c. 2m. stamp	1·90	1·70
1185	60c. 1m. stamp	1·90	1·70

154 Magnifying Glass over Committee Members

1999. 20th Anniversary of Marshall Islands Constitution.

No.	Description		
1186	**154** 33c. multicoloured	1·10	95

155 Marshall Island Stamps

1999. 15th Anniversary of Marshall Islands Postal Service. Multicoloured.

No.	Description		
1187	33c. Type **155**	1·10	95
1188	33c. Butterfly, fish, canoe and flower stamps	1·10	95
1189	33c. President Amata Kabua, flower and legend stamps	1·10	95
1190	33c. Stamps and magnifying glass	1·10	95

Nos. 1187/1190 were issued together, *se-tenant*, forming a composite design.

156 Martin B-10B

1999. Legendary Aircraft. Multicoloured.

No.	Description		
1191	33c. Type **156**	1·10	95
1192	33c. A-17A Nomad	1·10	95
1193	33c. Douglas B-18 Bolo bomber	1·10	95
1194	33c. Boeing B-17F Flying Fortress bomber	1·10	95
1195	33c. A-20 Havoc	1·10	95
1196	33c. North American B-25B Mitchell bomber	1·10	95
1197	33c. Consolidated B-24D Liberator bomber	1·10	95
1198	33c. North American P-51B Mustang fighter	1·10	95
1199	33c. Martin B-26 Marauder bomber	1·10	95
1200	33c. A-26B Invader	1·10	95
1201	33c. P-59 Airacomet	1·10	95
1202	33c. KC-97 Stratofreighter	1·10	95
1203	33c. A-1J Skyraider	1·10	95
1204	33c. P2V-7 Neptune	1·10	95
1205	33c. B-45 Tornado	1·10	95

1206	33c. Boeing B-50 Superfortress	1·10	95
1207	33c. AJ-2 Savage	1·10	95
1208	33c. F9F Cougar	1·10	95
1209	33c. Douglas A-3 Skywarrior jet bomber	1·10	95
1210	33c. English Electric B-57E Canberra jet bomber	1·10	95
1211	33c. EB-66 Destroyer	1·10	95
1212	33c. E-2A Hawkeye	1·10	95
1213	33c. Northrop F-5E Tiger II jet fighter	1·10	95
1214	33c. AV-8B Harrier II	1·10	95
1215	33c. B-1B Lancer	1·10	95

157 Astronaut on Moon

1999. Philexfrance 99 International Stamp Exhibition, Paris. Sheet 131×70 mm.

MS1216	**157** $1 multicoloured	3·25	3·00

158 *Alrehab* (gas tanker)

1999. Marshall Islands Maritime Administration. Sheet 110×87 mm.

MS1217	**158** 60c. multicoloured	2·40	2·10

159 T. H. Maiman and Ruby Crystal Laser, 1960

1999. The 20th-Century (7th series). Decade of Upheaval and Exploration 1960–1969. Multicoloured.

1218	60c. Type **159**	2·00	1·80
1219	60c. Young couple (birth control pill, 1960)	2·00	1·80
1220	60c. Yuri Gagarin (first man in space, 1961)	2·00	1·80
1221	60c. John F. Kennedy (President of USA, 1960–1963) making speech in Berlin, 1961 (failures of Communism)	2·00	1·80
1222	60c. Rachel Carson and endangered species (publication of *Silent Spring*, 1962)	2·00	1·80
1223	60c. John F. Kennedy and Russian President Nikita Khrushchev (Cuban missile crisis, 1962)	2·00	1·80
1224	60c. Pope John XXIII and crowds (Spirit of Ecumenism)	2·00	1·80
1225	60c. Hikari express train, Japan (new railway record speeds, 1964)	2·00	1·80
1226	60c. Chinese workers waving banners (Chinese cultural revolution, 1965)	2·00	1·80
1227	60c. Soldier with gun (Arab–Israeli six-day war, 1967)	2·00	1·80
1228	60c. Surgeons (first human heart transplants, 1967)	2·00	1·80
1229	60c. American soldiers in jungle (Vietnam war)	2·00	1·80
1230	60c. Robert F. Kennedy (US presidential candidate) and statue of Abraham Lincoln (political assassinations)	2·00	1·80
1231	60c. British Aerospace/ Aerospatiale Concorde supersonic jetliner (maiden flight, 1969)	2·00	1·80
1232	60c. Neil Armstrong and Buzz Aldrin planting American flag (first men on Moon, 1969)	2·00	1·80

160 Astronaut Saluting

1999. 30th Anniversary of First Manned Moon Landing. Sheet 110×97 mm containing T **160** and similar vert designs. Multicoloured.

MS1233	33c. Type **160**; 33c. American flag and Lunar Rover; 33c. Astronaut (different)	3·25	3·00

161 *Los Reyes* (Alvarao de Menana de Neyra's galleon, 1568)

1999. European Exploration of Marshall Islands. Multicoloured.

1234	33c. Type **161**	1·20	1·10
1235	33c. HMS *Dolphin* (Samuel Wallis's frigate, 1767)	1·20	1·10
1236	33c. *Scarborough* (John Marshall's transport, 1788)	1·20	1·10
1237	33c. *Rurik* (Otto van Kotzebue's brig, 1817)	1·20	1·10

No. 1236 is wrongly inscribed 'Scarsborough' and No. 1237 'Rurick'.

162 Nativity

1999. Christmas.

1238	**162**	33c. multicoloured	1·10	95

163 First Scheduled Transatlantic Flight of Boeing 747 Jetliner, 1970

1999. The 20th-century (8th series). Decade of Detente and Discovery 1970–1979. Multicoloured.

1239	60c. Type **163**	2·00	1·80
1240	60c. Mao Tse Tung and US President Richard Nixon (visit to China, 1972)	2·00	1·80
1241	60c. Terrorist with gun (murder of Israeli athletes at Munich Olympics, 1972)	2·00	1·80
1242	60c. US *Skylab* and USSR Salyut space stations orbiting Earth	2·00	1·80
1243	60c. Cars queueing for petrol (oil crisis, 1973)	2·00	1·80
1244	60c. Terracotta warriors (discovery of Qin Shi Huang's tomb at Xian, China, 1974)	2·00	1·80
1245	60c. Skulls and Cambodians in paddy fields	2·00	1·80
1246	60c. Apollo–Soyuz link-up, 1975 (era of detente)	2·00	1·80
1247	60c. *Eagle* (cadet ship) in New York Harbour (bicentenary of US Independence, 1976)	2·00	1·80
1248	60c. Computer and family (personal computers reach markets, 1977)	2·00	1·80
1249	60c. Scanner and scanned images (diagnostic tools revolutionise medicine, 1977)	2·00	1·80
1250	60c. Volkswagen Beetle motor car, 1978	2·00	1·80
1251	60c. President Anwar Sadat of Egypt, US President Jimmy Carter and Israeli Prime Minister Menachim Begin, 1978 (peace in Middle East)	2·00	1·80
1252	60c. Compact disc, 1979	2·00	1·80
1253	60c. Ayatollah Khomeini becomes Iran's leader, 1979	2·00	1·80

164 Earth in Darkness, December 31, 1999

1999. Year 2000. Multicoloured.

1254	33c. Type **164**	1·20	1·00
1255	33c. Earth in sunlight, 1 January 2000	1·20	1·00

Nos. 1254/1255 were issued together, *se-tenant*, forming a composite design.

165 Lech Walesa and Protestors at Gdansk Shipyard, Poland, 1980

2000. The 20th-century (9th series). Decade of People and Democracy, 1980–1989. Multicoloured.

1256	60c. Type **165**	1·90	1·70
1257	60c. Doctor treating AIDS patient, 1981	1·90	1·70
1258	60c. Prince and Princess of Wales (Royal wedding, 1981)	1·90	1·70
1259	60c. Man and computer (IBM personal computers introduced 1981)	1·90	1·70
1260	60c. British Aerospace Sea Harrier and warships (Falkland Islands war, 1982)	1·90	1·70
1261	60c. Man using mobile phone (first commercial wireless cellular system, Chicago, 1983)	1·90	1·70
1262	60c. Girl playing football (camcorders, 1983)	1·90	1·70
1263	60c. Astronauts (space shuttle *Challenger* explodes, 1986)	1·90	1·70
1264	60c. Power station and man wearing protective clothing (Chernobyl Nuclear Power Station disaster, 1986)	1·90	1·70
1265	60c. Mikhail Gorbachev and workers (era of Glasnost (openness) and Perestroika (restructuring) in USSR, 1987)	1·90	1·70
1266	60c. Northrop B-24 Spirit, 1988	1·90	1·70
1267	60c. Boeing 747 wreckage (bombing of Pan-American flight 103 over Lockerbie, Scotland, 1988)	1·90	1·70
1268	60c. *Exxon Valdez* (oil-tanker) and whales (oil spill off Alaskan Coast, 1989)	1·90	1·70
1269	60c. Student demonstrators and police in Tiananmen Square, China, 1989	1·90	1·70
1270	60c. German breaking down wall (dismantling of Berlin Wall, 1989)	1·90	1·70

166 Chinese Dragon

2000. New Year. Year of the Dragon. Sheet 110×87 mm.

MS1271	**166** 60c. multicoloured	2·40	2·10

167 Boeing P-26A Peashooter fighter

2000. Legendary Aircraft (2nd series). Multicoloured.

1272	33c. Type **167**	1·10	95
1273	33c. Stearman N2S-1 Kaydett biplane	1·10	95
1274	33c. Seversky P-35A	1·10	95
1275	33c. Curtiss P-36A Hawk	1·10	95
1276	33c. Curtiss P-40B Warhawk fighter	1·10	95
1277	33c. Lockheed P-38 Lightning fighter	1·10	95
1278	33c. Bell P-39D Airacobra fighter	1·10	95
1279	33c. Curtiss C-46 Commando airliner	1·10	95
1280	33c. Republic P-47D Thunderbolt fighter	1·10	95
1281	33c. Northrop P-61A Black Widow	1·10	95
1282	33c. Boeing B-29 Superfortress bomber	1·10	95
1283	33c. Grumman F7F-3N Tigercat	1·10	95
1284	33c. Grumman F8F-2 Bearcat	1·10	95
1285	33c. North American F-82 Twin Mustang	1·10	95
1286	33c. Republic F-84G Thunderjet jet fighter	1·10	95
1287	33c. North American FJ-1 Fury	1·10	95
1288	33c. Fairchild C-119C Flying Boxcar	1·10	95
1289	33c. Douglas F3D-2 Skynight	1·10	95
1290	33c. Northrop F-89D Scorpion	1·10	95
1291	33c. Lockheed F-94B Starfire	1·10	95
1292	33c. Douglas F4D Skyray	1·10	95
1293	33c. McDonnell F3H-2 Demon	1·10	95
1294	33c. McDonnell RF-101A/C Voodoo	1·10	95
1295	33c. Lockheed U-2F Dragon Lady	1·10	95
1296	33c. Rockwell OV-10 Bronco	1·10	95

168 'Masquerade'

2000. Garden Roses. Multicoloured.

1297	33c. Type **168**	1·10	95
1298	33c. 'Tuscany Superb'	1·10	95
1299	33c. 'Frau Dagmar Hastrup'	1·10	95
1300	33c. 'Ivory Fashion'	1·10	95
1301	33c. 'Charles de Mills'	1·10	95
1302	33c. 'Peace'	1·10	95

169 Container Ships (political reform in Poland, 1990)

2000. The 20th-century (10th series). Decade of Globalisation and Hope, 1990–1999. Multicoloured.

1303	60c. Type **169**	1·90	1·70
1304	60c. Fighter planes over burning oil wells, 1991	1·90	1·70
1305	60c. Nelson Mandela and F. W. de Klerk (abolition of apartheid, 1991)	1·90	1·70
1306	60c. Tim Berners-Lee and computer (creator of World Wide Web, 1991)	1·90	1·70
1307	60c. Boris Yeltsin (President of Russian Federation, 1991)	1·90	1·70
1308	60c. Yitzhak Rabin, Bill Clinton and Yasir Arafat (signing of Middle East Peace Accord, Washington DC, 1993)	1·90	1·70
1309	60c. High-speed train (inauguration of the Channel Tunnel between United Kingdom and France, 1994)	1·90	1·70
1310	60c. Family (Bosnian civil war, 1995)	1·90	1·70
1311	60c. Athletes (Atlanta Olympic Games, 1996)	1·90	1·70
1312	60c. Sheep (researchers clone Dolly, 1997)	1·90	1·70
1313	60c. Hong Kong and Chinese flag (return of Hong Kong to Chinese rule, 1997)	1·90	1·70
1314	60c. *Sojourner* (roving vehicle) (Mars Pathfinder mission, 1997)	1·90	1·70
1315	60c. Deaths of Diana, Princess of Wales and Mother Teresa, 1997	1·90	1·70
1316	60c. Rebuilding of German Reichstag, 1999	1·90	1·70
1317	60c. People of different races (birth of World's sixth billionth inhabitant, 1999)	1·90	1·70

170 Panda

2000. Giant Pandas. Multicoloured.

1318	33c. Type **170**	1·20	1·00
1319	33c. Adult facing cub	1·20	1·00
1320	33c. Adult holding cub	1·20	1·00
1321	33c. Two adults	1·20	1·00
1322	33c. Moving rock	1·20	1·00
1323	33c. Cub beside adult eating bamboo	1·20	1·00

171 George Washington

2000. American Presidents. Multicoloured.

1324	1c. Type **171**	20	15
1325	2c. John Adams	20	15
1326	3c. Thomas Jefferson	20	15
1327	4c. James Madison	20	15
1328	5c. James Monroe	20	15
1329	6c. John Quincy Adams	20	15
1330	7c. Andrew Jackson	35	30
1331	8c. Martin van Buren	35	30
1332	9c. William Henry Harrison	35	30
1333	10c. John Tyler	35	30
1334	11c. James K. Polk	35	30
1335	12c. Zachary Taylor	35	30
1336	13c. Millard Filmore	45	40
1337	14c. Franklin Pierce	45	40
1338	15c. James Buchanan	45	40
1339	16c. Abraham Lincoln	45	40
1340	17c. Andrew Johnson	45	40
1341	18c. Ulysses S. Grant	45	40
1342	19c. Rutherford B. Hayes	65	55
1343	20c. James A. Garfield	65	55
1344	21c. Chester A. Arthur	65	55
1345	22c. Grover Cleveland	65	55
1346	23c. Benjamin Harrison	65	55
1347	24c. The White House	65	55
1348	25c. William McKinley	80	70
1349	26c. Theodore Roosevelt	80	70
1350	27c. William H. Taft	80	70
1351	28c. Woodrow Wilson	80	70
1352	29c. Warren G. Harding	80	70
1353	30c. Calvin Coolidge	80	70
1354	31c. Herbert C. Hoover	95	85
1355	32c. Franklin D. Roosevelt	95	85
1356	33c. Harry S. Truman	95	85
1357	34c. Dwight D. Eisenhower	95	85
1358	35c. John F. Kennedy	95	85
1359	36c. Lyndon B. Johnson	95	85
1360	37c. Richard M. Nixon	1·10	1·00
1361	38c. Gerald R. Ford	1·10	1·00
1362	39c. James E. Carter	1·10	1·00
1363	40c. Ronald W. Reagan	1·10	1·00
1364	41c. George H. Bush	1·10	1·00
1365	42c. William J. Clinton	1·10	1·00

172 LZ-1 (first Zeppelin airship), 1900

2000. Centenary of Zeppelin Airships. Multicoloured.

1366	33c. Type **172**	1·30	1·10
1367	33c. *Graf Zeppelin I*, 1928	1·30	1·10
1368	33c. *Hindenburg*, 1936	1·30	1·10
1369	33c. *Graf Zeppelin II*, 1937	1·30	1·10

173 Churchill in South Africa as War Correspondent, 1899–1900

2000. 35th Death Anniversary of Winston Churchill (British Prime Minister, 1940–1945 and 1951–1955). Multicoloured.

1370	60c. Type **173**	2·00	1·80
1371	60c. Churchill and Clementine Hozier on wedding day, 1908	2·00	1·80
1372	60c. Kaiser Wilhelm II, Churchill and clock tower, Houses of Parliament	2·00	1·80
1373	60c. Various portraits of Churchill between 1898 and 1960	2·00	1·80
1374	60c. Wearing naval cap (First Lord of the Admiralty, 1939–1940)	2·00	1·80
1375	60c. Churchill giving 'Victory' sign and St Paul's Cathedral (Prime Minister, 1940–1945)	2·00	1·80
MS1376	87×61 mm. $1 Winston Churchill receiving knighthood, 1946. Imperf	3·25	3·00

The top edge of **MS**1376 is perforated.

174 Cannon, Flag and Soldier preparing to Fire (Army)

2000. 225th Anniversary of United States Military Forces. Multicoloured.

1377	33c. Type **174**	1·10	95
1378	33c. Ship, flag and officer looking through telescope (Navy)	1·10	95
1379	33c. Ship, cannon and mariner drawing sword (Marines)	1·10	95

175 Nitijela (elected lower house) Complex

2000. Multicoloured.

1380	33c. Type **175**	1·10	95
1381	33c. Capitol building	1·10	95
1382	33c. National Seal and Nitijela Complex (vert)	1·10	95
1383	33c. National Flag and Nitijela Complex (vert)	1·10	95

176 *Half Moon* (Hudson)

2000. Sailing Ships. Multicoloured.

1384	60c. Type **176**	2·00	1·80
1385	60c. *Grande Hermine* (Cartier)	2·00	1·80
1386	60c. *Golden Hind* (Drake)	2·00	1·80
1387	60c. *Matthew* (Cabot) (wrongly inscr 'Mathew')	2·00	1·80
1388	60c. *Vitoria* (Magellan) (inscr 'Victoria')	2·00	1·80
1389	60c. *Sao Gabriel* (Vasco da Gama)	2·00	1·80

177 As a Young Girl, 1904

2000. Queen Elizabeth the Queen Mother's Century. Multicoloured.

1390	60c. Type **177**	2·00	1·80
1391	60c. Wearing a turquoise hat, 1923	2·00	1·80
1392	60c. Wearing pearl necklace, 1940	2·00	1·80
1393	60c. Wearing purple hat, 1990	2·00	1·80

178 Green Sea Turtle

2000. Marine Life. Multicoloured.

1394	33c. Type **178**	1·20	1·00
1395	33c. Blue-girdled angelfish	1·20	1·00
1396	33c. Clown triggerfish	1·20	1·00
1397	33c. Harlequin tuskfish	1·20	1·00
1398	33c. Lined butterflyfish	1·20	1·00
1399	33c. Whitebonnet anemonefish	1·20	1·00
1400	33c. Long-nose filefish	1·20	1·00
1401	33c. Emperor angelfish	1·20	1·00

Nos. 1394/1401 were issued together, *se-tenant*, forming the composite design of the reef.

179 Holly Blue Butterfly

2000. Butterflies. Multicoloured.

1402	60c. Type **179**	2·20	1·90
1403	60c. Swallowtail butterfly	2·20	1·90
1404	60c. Clouded yellow butterfly	2·20	1·90
1405	60c. Small tortoiseshell butterfly	2·20	1·90
1406	60c. Nettle-tree butterfly	2·20	1·90
1407	60c. Long tailed blue butterfly	2·20	1·90
1408	60c. Cranberry blue butterfly	2·20	1·90
1409	60c. Small heath butterfly	2·20	1·90
1410	60c. Pontic blue butterfly	2·20	1·90
1411	60c. Lapland fritillary butterfly	2·20	1·90
1412	60c. Large blue butterfly	2·20	1·90
1413	60c. Monarch butterfly	2·20	1·90

180 Brandenburg Gate, Berlin and Flag

2000. Tenth Anniversary of Reunification of Germany.

1414	**180** 33c. multicoloured	1·20	1·00

181 USS *S-44* Submarine, 1925

2000. Centenary of United States Submarine Fleet. Multicoloured.

1415	33c. Type **181**	1·20	1·00
1416	33c. USS *Gato*, 1941	1·20	1·00
1417	33c. USS *Wyoming*, 1996	1·20	1·00
1418	33c. USS *Cheyenne*, 1997	1·20	1·00

182 Decorated Trees

2000. Christmas.

1419	**182** 33c. multicoloured	1·20	1·00

183 Sun Yat-sen as Young Boy, 1866

2000. 75th Death Anniversary of Dr. Sun Yat-sen (President of Republic of China, 1912–1925). Multicoloured.

1420	60c. Type **183**	2·20	1·90
1421	60c. With family in Honolulu, 1879 and amongst other students in Hong Kong	2·20	1·90
1422	60c. As President of Tong Meng Hui, 1905	2·20	1·90
1423	60c. Empress Dowager (Revolution, 1911)	2·20	1·90
1424	60c. As President of Republic of China, 1912	2·20	1·90
1425	60c. Flag and various portraits of Sun Yat-sen	2·20	1·90
MS1426	87×61 mm. $1 Memorial, Nanjing, Sun Yat-sen and Great Wall of China. Imperf	3·75	3·25

The top edge of **MS**1426 is perforated.

184 Snake

2001. New Year. Year of the Snake. Sheet 111×88 mm.

MS1427	**184** 80c. multicoloured	3·25	3·00

185 Carnations

2001. Flowers. Multicoloured.

1428	34c. Type **185**	1·20	1·10
1429	34c. Violet	1·20	1·10
1430	34c. Jonquil	1·20	1·10
1431	34c. Sweet pea	1·20	1·10
1432	34c. Lily of the valley	1·20	1·10
1433	34c. Rose	1·20	1·10
1434	34c. Larkspur	1·20	1·10
1435	34c. Poppy	1·20	1·10
1436	34c. Aster	1·20	1·10
1437	34c. Marigold	1·20	1·10
1438	34c. Chrysanthemum	1·20	1·10
1439	34c. Poinsettia	1·20	1·10

186 Walap (canoe), Jaluitt

2001. Sailing Canoes.

1440	**186** $5 green	18·00	15·00
1441	- $10 blue	35·00	31·00

Design: $10 Walap, Enewetak.

187 Amata Kabua (first President)

2001. Personalities. Multicoloured.

1442	34c. Type **187**	1·20	1·00
1443	37c. Oscar Debrum (statesman)	1·20	1·00
1444	55c. Robert Reimers (entrepreneur)	1·90	1·70
1445	57c. Atlan Anien (legislator)	2·10	1·80
1446	80c. Father Leonard Hacker (humanitarian)	2·75	2·50
1447	$1 Dwight Heine (educator)	3·50	3·25
1448	$3.85 Tipne Philippo (senator)	12·50	11·00
1449	$13.65 Henchi Balos (senator)	42·00	37·00

188 Red Admiral

2001. Butterflies (1st series). Multicoloured.

1450	80c. Type **188**	3·00	2·50
1451	80c. Moroccan orange tip	3·00	2·50
1452	80c. Silver-studded blue	3·00	2·50
1453	80c. Marbled white	3·00	2·50
1454	80c. False Apollo	3·00	2·50
1455	80c. Ringlet	3·00	2·50
1456	80c. Map	3·00	2·50
1457	80c. Fenton's wood white	3·00	2·50
1458	80c. Grecian copper	3·00	2·50
1459	80c. Pale Arctic clouded yellow	3·00	2·50
1460	80c. Great banded greyling	3·00	2·50
1461	80c. Cardinal	3·00	2·50

See also Nos. 1565/1576, 1697/1708 and 1947/1958.

189 *Tom Thumb*

2001. Fairytales. Multicoloured.

1462	34c. Type **189**	1·20	1·10
1463	34c. *Three Little Pigs*	1·20	1·10
1464	34c. *Gulliver's Travels*	1·20	1·10
1465	34c. *Cinderella*	1·20	1·10
1466	34c. *Gallant John*	1·20	1·10
1467	34c. *The Ugly Duckling*	1·20	1·10
1468	34c. *Fisher and the Goldfish*	1·20	1·10

190 Pirogues

2001. Racing Watercraft. Multicoloured.

1469	34c. Type **190**	1·40	1·20
1470	34c. Windsurfers	1·40	1·20
1471	34c. Yachts	1·40	1·20
1472	34c. Sailing dinghies	1·40	1·20

191 Yuri Alekseyevich Gagarin

2001. 40th Anniversary of First Manned Space Flight. Multicoloured.

1473	80c. Type **191**	3·00	2·50
1474	80c. Alan Bartlett Shepard	3·00	2·50
1475	80c. Virgil Ivan (Gus) Grissom	3·00	2·50
1476	80c. Gherman Stepanovich Titov	3·00	2·50

192 2000–2001 Marshall Island Stamps

2001. Stamp Day.

1477	**192**	34c. multicoloured	1·40	1·20

193 *Friendship 7* Spacecraft and John Glenn (first USA manned orbit of Earth, 1962)

2001. Space Exploration. Multicoloured.

1478	80c. Type **193**	3·00	2·50
1479	80c. First space walk, 1965	3·00	2·50
1480	80c. First man on moon, 1969	3·00	2·50
1481	80c. First space shuttle voyage, 1977	3·00	2·50

194 Longnose Butterflyfish, Star Puffer and Star Fish

2001. Coral Reef Fauna. Multicoloured.

1482	34c. Type **194**	1·30	1·10
1483	34c. Nautilus	1·30	1·10
1484	34c. Raccoon butterflyfish	1·30	1·10
1485	34c. Porkfish and grouper	1·30	1·10

195 Basketball

2001. Sport. Multicoloured.

1486	34c. Type **195**	1·30	1·10
1487	34c. Bowling	1·30	1·10
1488	34c. Table tennis	1·30	1·10
1489	34c. Kayaking	1·30	1·10

196 Aries

2001. Signs of the Zodiac. Multicoloured.

1490	34c. Type **196**	1·30	1·10
1491	34c. Taurus	1·30	1·10
1492	34c. Gemini	1·30	1·10
1493	34c. Cancer	1·30	1·10
1494	34c. Leo	1·30	1·10
1495	34c. Virgo	1·30	1·10
1496	34c. Libra	1·30	1·10
1497	34c. Scorpio	1·30	1·10
1498	34c. Sagittarius	1·30	1·10
1499	34c. Capricorn	1·30	1·10
1500	34c. Aquarius	1·30	1·10
1501	34c. Pisces	1·30	1·10

197 Black Cat (Tan Axi)

2001. Philanippon 2001 International Stamp Exhibition. Children's Paintings. Multicoloured.

1502	34c. Type **197**	3·00	2·50
1503	34c. Brown cat (Tan Axi)	3·00	2·50
1504	34c. Cliffs (Wang Xihai)	3·00	2·50
1505	34c. Boat and bridge (Li Yan)	3·00	2·50
1506	34c. Rooster (Wang Xinlan)	3·00	2·50
1507	34c. Great Wall of China (Lui Zhong)	3·00	2·50
1508	34c. Crane (Wang Lynn)	3·00	2·50
1509	34c. Baboon with basket (Wang Yani)	3·00	2·50
1510	34c. Baboon in tree (Wang Yani)	3·00	2·50
1511	34c. Umbrella (Sun Yuan)	3·00	2·50
1512	34c. Baboon with fruit (Wang Yani)	3·00	2·50
1513	34c. Baboon riding ox (Wang Yani)	3·00	2·50

198 Raymond Spruance (head of Cruiser Division 5)

2001. Naval Heroes of World War II in the Pacific. Sheet 117×144 mm containing T **198** and similar vert designs. Multicoloured.

MS1514 80c.×9, Type **198**; Arleigh Burke (destroyer fleet commander); Ernest King (Commander in Chief of the USA Fleet); Richmond Turner (Amphibious Forces commander); Marc Mitscher (Fleet Air commander, Solomon Islands); Chester Nimitz (Pacific Fleet commander); Edward O'Hare (naval pilot); William Halsey Jr. (Guadalcanal campaign commander); Albert, Francis, George, Joseph and Madison Sullivan (brothers) 26·00 23·00

199 Stutz Bearcat (1916)

2001. Vintage Cars (1st series). Multicoloured.

1515	34c. Type **199**	1·20	1·10
1516	34c. Stanley Steamer (1909)	1·20	1·10
1517	34c. Citroen 7CV (1934)	1·20	1·10
1518	34c. Rolls-Royce Silver Ghost (1910)	1·20	1·10
1519	34c. Daimler (1927)	1·20	1·10
1520	34c. Hispano Suiza (1935)	1·20	1·10
1521	34c. Lancia Lambda V4 (1928)	1·20	1·10
1522	34c. Volvo OV4 (1927)	1·20	1·10

See also Nos. 1553/1560, 1660/1667, 1719/1726, 1743/1750 and 1883/1890.

200 USA Flag and 'Blessed are those who mourn for they shall be comforted'

2001. Support for Victims of Attack on World Trade Centre, New York (1st issue). Multicoloured.

1523	34c. Type **200**	1·20	1·10
1524	34c. Statue of Liberty, New York and script	1·20	1·10
1525	34c. 'An attack on freedom anywhere is an attack on freedom everywhere'	1·20	1·10
1526	34c. 'In the great struggle of good versus evil good will prevail'	1·20	1·10
1527	34c. Statue of Freedom, Washington and script	1·20	1·10
1528	34c. 'In the face of terrorism we remain one nation under God indivisible'	1·20	1·10
MS1529	$1 Rescue workers, service personnel and New York citizens (75×34 mm)	3·75	3·25

See also No. 1552.

201 Adoration of the Shepherds

2001. Christmas. Multicoloured.

1530	34c. Type **201**	1·30	1·10
1531	34c. Angel on high	1·30	1·10
1532	34c. Adoration of the Magi	1·30	1·10
1533	34c. Nativity	1·30	1·10

202 Supermarine Sea Eagle

2001. Classic Aircraft. Multicoloured.

1534	80c. Type **202**	3·00	2·50
1535	80c. Gloster Sea Gladiator	3·00	2·50
1536	80c. de Havilland DHC-6 Twin Otter	3·00	2·50
1537	80c. Shorts 350 airliner	3·00	2·50
1538	80c. Sandringham Flying Boat	3·00	2·50
1539	80c. de Havilland DHC-7	3·00	2·50
1540	80c. Beech Duke B60	3·00	2·50
1541	80c. Fokker/Fairchild Friendship F27	3·00	2·50
1542	80c. Consolidated B-24J Liberator	3·00	2·50
1543	80c. Vickers 953C Merchantman	3·00	2·50

203 Decorated Horse

2002. New Year. Year of the Horse. Sheet 110×86 mm.

MS1544	**203**	80c. multicoloured	3·25	3·00

204 Frilled Dog Winkle (*Nucella lamellose*)

2002. Sea Shells. Multicoloured.

1545	34c. Type **204**	1·30	1·10
1546	34c. Reticulated cowrie-helmet (*Cypraecassis testiculus*)	1·30	1·10
1547	34c. New England neptune (*Neptunea decemcostata*)	1·30	1·10
1548	34c. Calico scallop (*Argopecten gibbus*)	1·30	1·10
1549	34c. Lightning whelk (*Busycon contrarium*)	1·30	1·10
1550	34c. Hawk-wing conch (*Strombus raninus*) (inscr 'ranius')	1·30	1·10

205 Queen Elizabeth II

2002. Golden Jubilee. 50th Anniversary of Queen Elizabeth II's Accession to the Throne. Sheet 110×87 mm.

MS1551	**205**	80c. multicoloured	3·00	2·75

206 Rescue Workers, Service Personnel and New York Citizens

2002. Support for Victims of Attack on World Trade Centre, New York (2nd issue).

1552	**206**	34c. multicoloured	1·30	1·10

2002. Vintage Cars (2nd series). As T **199**. Multicoloured.

1553	34c. Le Zebre (1909)	1·30	1·10
1554	34c. Hammel (1886)	1·30	1·10
1555	34c. Wolseley (1902)	1·30	1·10
1556	34c. Eysink (1899)	1·30	1·10
1557	34c. Dansk (1903)	1·30	1·10
1558	34c. Spyker (1907)	1·30	1·10
1559	34c. Fiat Zero (1913)	1·30	1·10
1560	34c. Weber (1902)	1·30	1·10

207 Mixed Coral

2002. Marine Life (1st series). Showing corals and fish. Multicoloured.

1561	34c. Type **207**	1·30	1·10
1562	34c. Chalice coral	1·30	1·10
1563	34c. Elkhorn coral	1·30	1·10
1564	34c. Finger coral	1·30	1·10

See also Nos. 1762/1763.

2002. Butterflies (2nd series). As T **88**. Multicoloured.

1565	80c. Grayling	3·00	2·50
1566	80c. Eastern festoon	3·00	2·50
1567	80c. Speckled wood	3·00	2·50
1568	80c. Cranberry fritillary	3·00	2·50
1569	80c. Bath white	3·00	2·50
1570	80c. Meadow brown	3·00	2·50
1571	80c. Two-tailed pasha	3·00	2·50
1572	80c. Scarce swallowtail	3·00	2·50
1573	80c. Dusky grizzled skipper	3·00	2·50
1574	80c. Provencal short-tailed blue	3·00	2·50
1575	80c. The dryal	3·00	2·50
1576	80c. Comma	3·00	2·50

208 *Horses* (Giorgio de Chiroco)

2002. Horse Paintings. Multicoloured.

1577 34c. Type **208** 1·20 1·10
1578 34c. *Tartar Envoys giving Horse to Qianlong* (Guiseppe Castiglione) 1·20 1·10
1579 34c. *Gathering Seaweed* (Anton Mauve) 1·20 1·10
1580 34c. *Mares and Foals* (George Stubbs) 1·20 1·10
1581 34c. *Mare and Foal in spring Meadow* (Wilson Hepple) 1·20 1·10
1582 34c. *Horse with Child and Dog* (Natale Attanasio) 1·20 1·10
1583 34c. *The Horse* (Waterhouse Hawkins) 1·20 1·10
1584 34c. *Attendants and Horse* (Edgar Degas) 1·20 1·10
1585 34c. *Mares and Foals in Landscape* (George Stubbs) 1·20 1·10
1586 34c. *The Horse* (Guliemo Clardi) 1·20 1·10
1587 34c. *Little Blue Hors* (Franz Marc) 1·20 1·10
1588 34c. Sketch for *Firebird* (ballet) (Pavel Kuznetsov) 1·20 1·10
MS1589 110×87 mm. 80c. *Emperor Qianlong leaving for his Summer Residence* (Guiseppe Castiglione) (inscr 'Casiglione') 3·50 3·25

209 Ivan and his Brothers shoot Arrows

2002. The Frog Princess (fairytale). Multicoloured.

1590 37c. Type **209** 1·30 1·20
1591 37c. First brother finds a wife 1·30 1·20
1592 37c. Second brother finds a wife 1·30 1·20
1593 37c. Ivan and the frog princess 1·30 1·20
1594 37c. Ivan presents shirt to king 1·30 1·20
1595 37c. Ivan presents bread to king 1·30 1·20
1596 37c. Princess arrives at ball 1·30 1·20
1597 37c. Princess dances for king 1·30 1·20
1598 37c. Princess says goodbye to Ivan 1·30 1·20
1599 37c. Ivan and little hut 1·30 1·20
1600 37c. Ivan and princess re-united 1·30 1·20
1601 37c. Ivan and princess on magic carpet 1·30 1·20

210 Armoured Horse and Rabbit

2002. Carousel Animals. Multicoloured.

1602 80c. Type **210** 3·00 2·50
1603 80c. Zebra and camel 3·00 2·50
1604 80c. Horse, Angel and reindeer 3·00 2·50
1605 80c. Horse, frog and tiger 3·00 2·50

211 Lesser Golden Plover

2002. Birds. Multicoloured.

1606 37c. Type **211** 1·30 1·20
1607 37c. Siberian tattler 1·30 1·20
1608 37c. Brown noddy 1·30 1·20
1609 37c. Fairy tern 1·30 1·20
1610 37c. Micronesian pigeon 1·30 1·20
1611 37c. Long-tailed cuckoo 1·30 1·20
1612 37c. Christmas shearwater 1·30 1·20
1613 37c. Eurasian tree sparrow 1·30 1·20
1614 37c. Black-tailed godwit 1·30 1·20
1615 37c. Franklin's gull 1·30 1·20
1616 37c. Rufous-necked stint 1·30 1·20
1617 37c. Kermadec petrel 1·30 1·20
1618 37c. Purple-capped fruit dove 1·30 1·20
1619 37c. Mongolian plover 1·30 1·20
1620 37c. Cattle egret 1·30 1·20
1621 37c. Dunlin 1·30 1·20

212 Benjamin Franklin, Inventor (Gherman Komlev)

2002. Benjamin Franklin, Commemoration. Multicoloured.

1622 80c. Type **212** 3·00 2·50
1623 80c. Benjamin Franklin, scholar (David Martin) 3·00 2·50

213 Loggerhead Turtle

2002. Sea Turtles. Multicoloured.

1624 37c. Type **213** 1·40 1·20
1625 37c. Leatherback 1·40 1·20
1626 37c. Hawksbill 1·40 1·20
1627 37c. Green 1·40 1·20

214 *The Stamp Collector*

2002. 50th Anniversary of International Federation of Stamp Dealers' Association (IFSDA). Paintings by Lyle Tayson. Multicoloured.

1628 80c. Type **214** 2·75 2·50
1629 80c. *The First Day of Issue* 2·75 2·50
1630 80c. *Father and Daughter Collectors* 2·75 2·50
1631 80c. *The Young Collector* 2·75 2·50
1632 80c. *Sharing Dad's Stamp Collection* 2·75 2·50
1633 80c. *The New Generation* 2·75 2·50

215 *Hartford*

2002. USA Naval Sail Ships. Multicoloured.

1634 37c. Type **215** 1·30 1·20
1635 37c. *Bon Homme Richard* 1·30 1·20
1636 37c. *Prince de Neufchatel* 1·30 1·20
1637 37c. *Ohio* 1·30 1·20
1638 37c. *Onkahye* 1·30 1·20
1639 37c. *Oneida* 1·30 1·20

216 Black Widow Spider

2002. Insects. Multicoloured.

1640 23c. Type **216** 85 75
1641 23c. Elderberry longhorn 85 75
1642 23c. Lady beetle 85 75
1643 23c. Yellow garden spider 85 75
1644 23c. Dogbane beetle 85 75
1645 23c. Flower fly 85 75
1646 23c. Assassin bug 85 75
1647 23c. Ebony jewel wing 85 75
1648 23c. Velvet ant 85 75
1649 23c. Monarch caterpillar 85 75
1650 23c. Monarch butterfly 85 75
1651 23c. Eastern Hercules beetle 85 75
1652 23c. Bombardier beetle 85 75
1653 23c. Dung beetle 85 75
1654 23c. Spotted water beetle 85 75
1655 23c. True katydid 85 75
1656 23c. Spiny-backed spider 85 75
1657 23c. Periodical cicada 85 75
1658 23c. Scorpion fly 85 75
1659 23c. Jumping spider 85 75

2002. Vintage Cars (3rd series). As T **199**. Multicoloured.

1660 34c. Hotchkiss (1934) 2·75 2·50
1661 34c. De Dion Bouton (1909) 2·75 2·50
1662 34c. Renault (1922) 2·75 2·50
1663 34c. Amilcar Surbaisse (1927) 2·75 2·50
1664 34c. Austin (1943) 2·75 2·50
1665 34c. Peugeot Bebe (1927) 2·75 2·50
1666 34c. O.M. Superba (1913) 2·75 2·50
1667 34c. Elizade-Tipo (1922) 2·75 2·50

218 Elizabeth Bowes-Lyon (1904)

2002. Queen Elizabeth the Queen Mother Commemoration. Multicoloured.

1668 80c. Type **218** 2·75 2·50
1669 80c. Duchess of York (1923) 2·75 2·50
1670 80c. Queen Elizabeth wearing pearl necklace (1940) 2·75 2·50
1671 80c. Queen Elizabeth the Queen Mother wearing blue outfit (1990) 2·75 2·50

219 *Regal Princess* (cruise liner), Majuro Lagoon, Marshall Islands

2002. World War II Veterans Visit Sites in the South Pacific. Sheet 110×88 mm.

MS1672 **219** 80c. multicoloured 3·00 2·75

220 William Sims (commander USA Navy in Europe)

2002. World War I Military Heroes. Multicoloured.

1673 80c. Type **220** 2·75 2·50
1674 80c. William Mitchell (senior aviation officer) and de Havilland D.H.4 2·75 2·50
1675 80c. Freddie Stowers (posthumous Medal of Honor) 2·75 2·50
1676 80c. Smedley Butler (United States Marine Corps) 2·75 2·50
1677 80c. Edward Rickenbacker (USA flying ace) and SPAD S.X.III 2·75 2·50
1678 80c. Alvin York (French Medaille Militaire, Croix de Guerre, Italian Groce de Guerra and Medal of Honor) 2·75 2·50
1679 80c. John Lejeune (division commander) 2·75 2·50
1680 80c. John Pershing (Commander-in-Chief American expeditionary force in Europe) 2·75 2·50

221 Snowman Cookie

2002. Christmas. Multicoloured.

1681 37c. Type **221** 1·30 1·20
1682 37c. Snowman cookie wearing hat 1·30 1·20

222 Decorated Ram

2003. New Year. Year of the Ram.

MS1683 **222** 80c. multicoloured 3·00 2·75

223 Indel's Magic Kite

2003. Folktales. Multicoloured.

1684 50c. Type **223** 1·70 1·50
1685 50c. Lijebake rescues her Granddaughter 1·70 1·50
1686 50c. Jebro's Mother invents the Sail 1·70 1·50
1687 50c. Limajnon escapes to the Moon 1·70 1·50

224 UN Emblem, Outrigger Canoe and Marshall Islands Emblem

2003. 12th Anniversary of Marshall Islands' Membership of United Nations.

1688 **224** 60c. multicoloured 2·20 1·90

225 Lagajimi (Franz Hernsheim)

2003. Cultural Heritage (1st issue). Multicoloured.

1689 37c. Type **225** 1·20 1·10
1690 37c. Traditional house (50×42 mm) 1·20 1·10
1691 37c. Lake, Jabwor, Jaluit Atoll (50×42 mm) 1·20 1·10
1692 37c. Kabua (Franz Hernsheim) 1·20 1·10
1693 37c. Children wearing traditional dress 1·20 1·10
1694 37c. Jaluit Pass (Franz Hernsheim) (50×42 mm) 1·20 1·10
1695 37c. Traditional Canoe (Franz Hernsheim) (50×42 mm) 1·20 1·10
1696 37c. Fisherman 1·20 1·10

See also Nos. 1727/1734, 1931/1935, 1978/1982, 2053/2057, 2242/2246, 2378/2382, 2538/2542 and 2684/2688.

2003. Butterflies (3rd series). As T **188**. Multicoloured.

1697 80c. False grayling 2·75 2·40
1698 80c. Green hairstreak 2·75 2·40
1699 80c. Purple-shot copper 2·75 2·40
1700 80c. Black-veined white 2·75 2·40
1701 80c. Arctic grayling 2·75 2·40
1702 80c. Greek clouded yellow 2·75 2·40
1703 80c. American painted lady 2·75 2·40
1704 80c. Wall brown 2·75 2·40
1705 80c. Polar fritillary 2·75 2·40
1706 80c. Mountain clouded yellow 2·75 2·40
1707 80c. Camberwell beauty 2·75 2·40
1708 80c. Large white 2·75 2·40

226 *Wright Flyer I*

2003. Centenary of Powered Flight. Multicoloured.

1709	37c. Type **226**	1·20	1·10
1710	37c. Curtiss JN-3	1·20	1·10
1711	37c. Douglas World Cruiser	1·20	1·10
1712	37c. Ryan NYP *Spirit of St Louis*	1·20	1·10
1713	37c. Lockheed Vega 5	1·20	1·10
1714	37c. Boeing 314 Clipper	1·20	1·10
1715	37c. Douglas C-47 Skytrain	1·20	1·10
1716	37c. Boeing B-50 Superfortress	1·20	1·10
1717	37c. Antonov An-225 Mriya	1·20	1·10
1718	37c. B-2 Spirit	1·20	1·10

2003. Vintage Cars (4th series). As T **199**. Multicoloured.

1719	37c. Alfa Romeo (1927)	1·20	1·10
1720	37c. Austro-Daimler Prince Henry (1912)	1·20	1·10
1721	37c. Mors 14/20 Tourer (1923)	1·20	1·10
1722	37c. AC Tourer (1926)	1·20	1·10
1723	37c. Scania (1903) and Vabis (1897)	1·20	1·10
1724	37c. Graf und Stift (1914)	1·20	1·10
1725	37c. Pic-Pic (1919)	1·20	1·10
1726	37c. Hispano Suiza-Alfonso XIII (1911)	1·20	1·10

2003. Cultural Heritage (2nd issue) As T **225**. Multicoloured.

1727	37c. Kabua's daughter	1·20	1·10
1728	37c. Walap (50×42 mm)	1·20	1·10
1729	37c. Jabwor, Jaluit Atoll (50×42 mm)	1·20	1·10
1730	37c. Traditional and modern dress	1·20	1·10
1731	37c. Nemedj	1·20	1·10
1732	37c. Typhoon damage, 1905 (50×42 mm)	1·20	1·10
1733	37c. Marshallese kor kor (50×42 mm)	1·20	1·10
1734	37c. Grandfather	1·20	1·10

227 Bauble containing Snow Scene

2003. Christmas. Multicoloured.

1735	37c. Type **227**	1·20	1·10
1736	37c. Jack-in-the-box	1·20	1·10
1737	37c. Toy soldier	1·20	1·10
1738	37c. Reindeer	1·20	1·10

228 Decorated Monkey

2004. New Year. Year of the Monkey.

MS1739	**228** 80c. multicoloured	3·25	3·00

229 *Bonhomme Richard*

2004. 225th Anniversaries. Multicoloured.

1740	37c. Type **229** (American revolution sea battle)	1·20	1·10
1741	37c. HMS *Resolution* (Captain Cook's final voyages)	1·20	1·10
1742	37c. HMS *Resolution* (different) (Captain Cook's final voyages)	1·20	1·10

2004. Vintage Cars (5th series). As T **199**. Multicoloured.

1743	37c. Wolseley-Siddeley (1906)	1·20	1·10
1744	37c. Mors (1901)	1·20	1·10
1745	37c. Hutton (1908)	1·20	1·10
1746	37c. Metallurgique (1907)	1·20	1·10
1747	37c. Benz (1902)	1·20	1·10
1748	37c. Cudell (1900)	1·20	1·10
1749	37c. Peugeot (1906)	1·20	1·10
1750	37c. Inscr 'The 60 Mercedes'	1·20	1·10

230 "THANK YOU"

2004. Greetings Stamps. Sheet 148×104 mm containing T **230** and similar vert designs. Multicoloured.

MS1751	37c.×8, Type **230**; 'CONGRATULATIONS'; 'HAPPY BIRTHDAY'; 'Best Wishes'; 'Get Well Soon'; 'LOVE YOU DAD'; 'Love you Mom'; Bouquet of greetings	10·00	8·75

231 Runner and Outrigger Canoe

2004. 20th Anniversary of Marshall Islands Postal Service.

1752	**231** 37c. multicoloured	1·40	1·20
1753	**231** 60c. multicoloured	2·20	1·90
1754	**231** $2.30 multicoloured	8·00	7·00

No. 1752 was for use on first class mail, No. 1753 was for use on international mail and No. 1754 was for use on certified mail.

232 Expeditionary Corps aboard Boat

2004. Bicentenary of Meriwether Lewis and William Clark's Expedition to Explore the West Coast of America (1st issue). Multicoloured.

1755	37c. Type **232**	1·20	1·10
1756	37c. Clark and Sacagawea (Shoshone guide)	1·20	1·10
1757	37c. Lewis and Clark and bison herd	1·20	1·10

See also Nos. 1831/1833, 1838/1840, 1856/1858, 1895/1897, 1928/1930 and 1976/1977.

233 Horsa Gliders and Parachute Troops

2004. 60th Anniversary of D-Day (invasion of German occupied French coast). Multicoloured.

1758	37c. Type **233**	1·20	1·10
1759	37c. Typhoon-1B and P518 Mustangs	1·20	1·10
1760	37c. Gun emplacements	1·20	1·10
1761	37c. Allied craft and soldiers landing	1·20	1·10

Nos. 1758/1761 were issued together, *se-tenant*, forming a composite design.

234 Chambered Nautilus, Map Cowrie and Trumpet Triton

2004. Marine Life (2nd series). Multicoloured.

1762	37c. Type **234**	1·20	1·10
1763	37c. Marlin spike, turban shell and Toulerei's cowrie	1·20	1·10

235 Ronald Reagan

2004. Ronald Reagan (president of USA, 1980–1988) Commemoration.

1764	**235** 60c. multicoloured	1·20	1·10

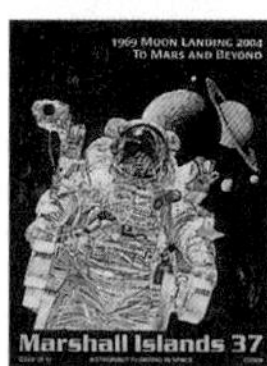

236 Astronaut in Space

2004. 35th Anniversary of First Moon Walk. Multicoloured.

1765	37c. Type **236**	1·20	1·10
1766	37c. Astronaut and Saturn	1·20	1·10
1767	37c. Astronaut and Space Shuttle	1·20	1·10
1768	37c. Two astronauts	1·20	1·10

237 Making Fans

2004. Festival of Pacific Arts, Koror, Palau. Multicoloured.

1769	37c. Type **237**	1·20	1·10
1770	37c. Basket makers	1·20	1·10
1771	37c. Carving canoes	1·20	1·10
1772	37c. Boys and toy outrigger canoes	1·20	1·10
1773	37c. Older woman and white ginger flowers	1·20	1·10
1774	37c. Boy and vandal flower	1·20	1·10
1775	37c. Man and tiare flower	1·20	1·10
1776	37c. Young woman and hibiscus flower	1·20	1·10
1777	37c. Woman carrying breadfruit	1·20	1·10
1778	37c. Canoes and tattooed man	1·20	1·10
1779	37c. Men in traditional dress	1·20	1·10
1780	37c. Drummer and dancers	1·20	1·10

238 *Wright Flyer I*

2004. Aircraft. Multicoloured.

1781	23c. Type **238**	75	65
1782	23c. Bleriot XI	75	65
1783	23c. Curtiss *Golden Flyer*	75	65
1784	23c. Curtiss Flying Boat	75	65
1785	23c. Deperdussin Racer	75	65
1786	23c. Sikorsky Ilya Muromets	75	65
1787	23c. Fokker EI	75	65
1788	23c. Junkers JI	75	65
1789	23c. S.E.5a	75	65
1790	23c. Handley Page O/400	75	65
1791	23c. Fokker D.VII	75	65
1792	23c. Junkers F.13	75	65
1793	23c. Lockheed Vega	75	65
1794	23c. M-130 Pan Am Clipper	75	65
1795	23c. Messerschmitt Bf.109	75	65
1796	23c. Spitfire	75	65
1797	23c. Junkers Ju88	75	65
1798	23c. A6M Zero	75	65
1799	23c. Ilyushin Il-2	75	65
1800	23c. Heinkel He-178	75	65
1801	23c. C-47 Skytrain	75	65
1802	23c. Piper Cub	75	65
1803	23c. Avro Lancaster	75	65
1804	23c. B-17F Flying Fortress	75	65
1805	23c. Messrschmitt Me-262	75	65
1806	23c. B-29 Superfortress	75	65
1807	23c. P-51 Mustang	75	65
1808	23c. Yak 9	75	65
1809	23c. Bell Model 47	75	65
1810	23c. Bell X-1	75	65
1811	23c. Beechcraft Bonanza	75	65
1812	23c. AN-225 Mriya	75	65
1813	23c. B-47 Stratojet	75	65
1814	23c. MIG-15	75	65
1815	23c. Saab J35 Draken	75	65
1816	23c. B-52 Stratofortress	75	65
1817	23c. Boeing 367-80	75	65
1818	23c. U-2	75	65
1819	23c. C-130 Hercules	75	65
1820	23c. F-4 Phantom II	75	65
1821	23c. North American X-15	75	65
1822	23c. Sikorsky S-61 helicopter	75	65
1823	23c. Learjet 23	75	65
1824	23c. SR-71 Blackbird	75	65
1825	23c. Boeing 747	75	65
1826	23c. Concorde	75	65
1827	23c. Airbus A300	75	65
1828	23c. MIG-29	75	65
1829	23c. F-117A Nighthawk	75	65
1830	23c. F/A-22 Raptor	75	65

2004. Bicentenary of Meriwether Lewis and William Clark's Expedition to Explore the West Coast of America (2nd issue). As T **232**. Multicoloured.

1831	37c. Celebrating July 4th	1·20	1·10
1832	37c. Corps surrounding flag (burial of Charles Floyd)	1·20	1·10
1833	37c. Smoking peace pipe	1·20	1·10

239 John Wayne

2004. 25th Anniversary Anniv of John Wayne (actor).

1834	**239** 37c. multicoloured	1·20	1·10

240 Penny Black Stamp

2004. 23rd Universal Postal Union Congress, Bucharest. Sheet 100×92 mm containing T **240** and similar horiz designs. Multicoloured.

MS1835	$1×4, Type **240** (first postage stamp); First Romanian stamp (1858); First Marshall Islands' stamp (1897); First Republic of Marshall Islands' stamp (1984)	13·50	12·00

241 Emperor Angelfish

2004. Pacific Coral Reef. Sheet 179×104 mm containing T **241** and similar vert designs. Multicoloured.

MS1836	37c.×10, Type **241**; Pink anemone fish; Humphead wrasse and moorish idol; Black-spotted puffer; Snowflake moray eel; Lionfish; Bumphead parrotfish and threadfin butterflyfish; Hawksbill turtle; Triton's trumpet; Oriental sweetlips.	12·50	11·00

242 Angel

2004. Christmas. Sheet 144×118 mm containing T **242** and similar horiz designs. Multicoloured.

MS1837	37c.×9, Type **242**; God crowned; Adoration of the kings; Three wise men; Procession of poor people; Shepherds; Flight into Egypt; Nativity; Jesus and animals	11·00	9·75

2004. Bicentenary of Meriwether Lewis and William Clark's Expedition to Explore the West Coast of America (3rd issue). As T **232**. Multicoloured.

1838	37c. Interpreters	1·20	1·10
1839	37c. Hunting bison	1·20	1·10
1840	37c. Attack by Sioux	1·20	1·10

243 Infantryman

2004. 60th Anniversary of Battle of the Bulge. Multicoloured.

1841	37c. Type **243**	1·20	1·10
1842	37c. Tank division soldier	1·20	1·10
1843	37c. Aviator	1·20	1·10
1844	37c. Lt. Colonel Creighton Abrams and General Anthony McAuliffe (inscr 'Anathony')	1·20	1·10

244 George Washington

2005. Presidents of USA. Sheet 214×150 mm containing T **244** and similar vert designs. Colours given.

MS1845 1c. green (Type **244**); 2c. rose (John Adams); 3c. violet (Thomas Jefferson); 4c. purple (James Madison); 5c. blue (James Monroe); 6c. red (John Quincy Adams); 7c. brown (Andrew Jackson); 8c. green (Martin van Buren); 9c. claret (William Henry Harrison); 10c. brown (John Tyler); 11c. blue (James K. Polk); 12c. mauve (Zachary Taylor); 13c. green (Millard Fillmore); 14c. blue (Franklin Pierce); 15c. blue (James Buchanan); 16c. green (Abraham Lincoln); 17c. vermilion (Andrew Johnson); 18c. chestnut (Ulysses S. Grant); 19c. green (Rutherford B. Hayes); 20c. rose (James A. Garfield); 21c. violet (Chester A. Arthur); 22c. purple (Grover Cleveland); 23c. turquoise blue (Benjamin Harrison); 24c. red (Grover Cleveland (2nd term)); 25c. brown (William McKinley); 26c. green (Theodore Roosevelt); 27c. claret (William Howard Taft); 28c. brown (Woodrow Wilson); 29c. blue (Warren G. Harding); 30c. mauve (Calvin Coolidge); 31c. green (Herbert Hoover); 32c. blue (Franklin D. Roosevelt); 33c. blue (Harry S. Truma); 34c. green (Dwight D. Eisenhower); 35c. vermilion (John F. Kennedy); 36c. chestnut (Lyndon B. Johnson); 37c. green (Richard M. Nixon); 38c. rose (Gerald R. Ford); 39c. violet (Jimmy Carter); 40c. purple (Ronald W. Reagan); 41c. blue (George H. W. Bush); 42c. red (William J. Clinton); 43c. brown (George W. Bush); 60c. green (The White House); $1 claret (The White House) 46·00 41·00

245 Rooster

2005. New Year. Year of the Rooster. Sheet 111×87 mm.

MS1846 **245** $1 multicoloured 3·25 3·00

246 Children, Red Cross and Globe

2005. Centenary of Rotary International.

1847	**246** 37c. multicoloured	1·20	1·10

247 Hibiscus 'Burgundy Blush'

2005. Hibiscus (1st issue). Designs showing cultivated varieties of Hibiscus. Multicoloured.

1848	37c. Type **247**	1·20	1·10
1849	60c. 'Fiesta'	2·00	1·70
1850	80c. 'June's Joy'	2·50	2·20
1851	$1 'Norman Lee'	3·25	2·75

See also Nos. 1874/1877 and 1960/1963.

248 *The Princess and the Pea*

2005. Birth Bicentenary of Hans Christian Andersen (writer). Multicoloured.

1852	37c. Type **248**	1·20	1·10
1853	37c. *Thumbelina*	1·20	1·10
1854	37c. *The Little Mermaid*	1·20	1·10
1855	37c. *The Emperor's New Suit*	1·20	1·10

2005. Bicentenary of Meriwether Lewis and William Clark's Expedition to Explore the West Coast of America (4th issue). As T **232**. Multicoloured.

1856	37c. Grizzly bear	1·20	1·10
1857	37c. Lewis reaches the Great Falls	1·20	1·10
1858	37c. Sacagawea reunited with her brother	1·20	1·10

249 Modern Cover

2005. Stamp Day. 50th Anniversary of American First Day Cover Society (AFDCS). Multicoloured.

1859	37c. Type **249**	1·20	1·10
1860	37c. First Marshall Islands' Postal Service issue	1·20	1·10
1861	37c. US First Man on the Moon cancellation	1·20	1·10
1862	37c. Marshall Island Stamp Day 2005 issue	1·20	1·10

250 German Surrender, Rheims

2005. 60th Anniversary of Victory in Europe. Multicoloured.

1863	37c. Type **250**	1·20	1·10
1864	37c. Celebrating, Times Square, New York	1·20	1·10
1865	37c. Victory Parade, Moscow	1·20	1·10
1866	37c. Royal family and Winston Churchill, Buckingham Palace	1·20	1·10

251 Pope John Paul II

2005. Pope John Paul II Commemoration. Multicoloured.

1867	37c. Type **251**	1·20	1·10
1868	37c. Wearing mitre, red cape and holding staff	1·20	1·10
1869	37c. Facing right	1·20	1·10
1870	37c. Facing left with raised hand	1·20	1·10
1871	37c. Wearing mitre and green cape with raised hand	1·20	1·10

252 People of Many Nations

2005. 60th Anniversary of United Nations. Multicoloured.

1872	37c. Type **252**	1·20	1·10
1873	80c. People of many nations (different)	2·50	2·20

Nos. 1872/1873 were issued together, *se-tenant*, forming a composite design.

2005. Hibiscus (2nd issue). Multicoloured.

1874	1c. 'Margaret Okano'	30	30
1875	24c. 'Cameo Queen'	90	75
1876	39c. 'Madonna'	1·30	1·10
1877	$4 'Estrella Red'	12·50	11·00

253 *Columbia* Space Shuttle

2005. Re-start of Space Shuttle Flights 26 July 2005. Multicoloured.

1878	37c. Type **253**	1·20	1·10
1879	37c. *Discovery*	1·20	1·10
1880	37c. *Endeavour*	1·20	1·10
1881	37c. *Challenger*	1·20	1·10
1882	37c. *Atlantis*	1·20	1·10

2005. Vintage Cars (6th series). As T **199**. Multicoloured.

1883	37c. Excelsior (1925)	1·20	1·10
1884	37c. Adler K (1912)	1·20	1·10
1885	37c. Thulin (1920)	1·20	1·10
1886	37c. Palladium (1913)	1·20	1·10
1887	37c. Minerva (1926)	1·20	1·10
1888	37c. Elizalde (1922)	1·20	1·10
1889	37c. Rolls Royce Silver Ghost (1911)	1·20	1·10
1890	37c. Invicta (1931)	1·20	1·10

254 *Fujiyama* and Tokyo Bay

2005. 60th Anniversary of Victory in Japan. Multicoloured.

1891	37c. Type **254**	1·20	1·10
1892	37c. *Missouri*	1·20	1·10
1893	37c. USA signing treaty	1·20	1·10
1894	37c. Japanese delegation	1·20	1·10

Nos. 1891/1892 and 1893/1894, respectively were issued together, in *se-tenant* pairs, forming composite design.

2005. Bicentenary of Meriwether Lewis and William Clark's Expedition to Explore the West Coast of America (5th issue). As T **232**. Multicoloured.

1895	37c. Crossing the Bitterroots	1·20	1·10
1896	37c. Peace agreement	1·20	1·10
1897	37c. Reaching the ocean	1·20	1·10

255 Trireme Galley

2005. Bicentenary of Battle of Trafalgar. Multicoloured.

1898	37c. Type **255**	1·20	1·10
1899	37c. Trireme Romano	1·20	1·10
1900	37c. Viking longship	1·20	1·10
1901	37c. Ming Dynasty treasure ship	1·20	1·10
1902	37c. *Mary Rose*	1·20	1·10
1903	37c. *Nuestra Senora del Rosario*	1·20	1·10
1904	37c. Korean turtle ship	1·20	1·10
1905	37c. *Brederode*	1·20	1·10
1906	37c. *Galera Veneziana*	1·20	1·10
1907	37c. *Santisima Trinidad*	1·20	1·10
1908	37c. *Ville de Paris*	1·20	1·10
1909	37c. HMS *Victory*	1·20	1·10
1910	37c. *Bonhomme Richard*	1·20	1·10
1911	37c. USS *Constellation*	1·20	1·10
1912	37c. USS *Hartford*	1·20	1·10
1913	37c. *Fijian Ndrua*	1·20	1·10
1914	37c. HMS *Dreadnought*	1·20	1·10
1915	37c. HMAS *Australia*	1·20	1·10
1916	37c. HMS *Dorsetshire*	1·20	1·10
1917	37c. Admiral *Graf Spee*	1·20	1·10
1918	37c. *Yamato*	1·20	1·10
1919	37c. USS *Tautog*	1·20	1·10
1920	37c. *Bismarck*	1·20	1·10
1921	37c. USS *Hornet*	1·20	1·10
1922	37c. USS *Missouri*	1·20	1·10
MS1923	110×87 mm. $2 HMS *Victory*. Imperf	6·75	6·00

256 Angel

2005. Christmas. Multicoloured.

1924	37c. Type **256**	1·20	1·10
1925	37c. Three Angels	1·20	1·10
1926	37c. Angel blowing horn	1·20	1·10
1927	37c. Angel playing harp	1·20	1·10

2005. Bicentenary of Meriwether Lewis and William Clark's Expedition to Explore the West Coast of America (6th issue). As T **232**. Multicoloured.

1928	37c. First universal voter	1·20	1·10
1929	37c. Leaving Fort Clatsop	1·20	1·10
1930	37c. At Pompey's Pillar	1·20	1·10

2005. Cultural Heritage (3rd issue). As T **225**. Multicoloured.

1931	37c. First Catholic Church, Jabwor, Jaluit Atoll	1·20	1·10
1932	37c. Women, Jaluit Atoll	1·20	1·10
1933	37c. Canoes, Jaluit harbour	1·20	1·10
1934	37c. Nelu and his wife Ledagoba	1·20	1·10
1935	37c. Old man, Ebon Atoll	1·20	1·10

257 *Benjamin Franklin* (J. S. Duplessis)

2006. 300th Birth Anniversary of Benjamin Franklin (scientist and statesman). Portraits of Benjamin Franklin, Artist given. Multicoloured.

1936	48c. Type **257**	1·60	1·40
1937	48c. David K. Stone	1·60	1·40
1938	48c. Mason Chamberlain	1·60	1·40
1939	48c. John Trumbull	1·60	1·40
1940	48c. Bust (James Earle Fraser)	1·60	1·40
1941	48c. David Martin	1·60	1·40
1942	48c. Benjamin West	1·60	1·40
1943	48c. J. B. Greuze	1·60	1·40
1944	48c. After C. N. Cochin	1·60	1·40

258 Dog

2006. New Year. Year of the Dog. Sheet 110×87 mm.

MS1945 **258** $1 multicoloured 3·25 3·00

259 Heart

2006. St. Valentine's Day.

1946	**259** 39c. multicoloured	1·30	1·10

2006. Butterflies (4th series). As T **188**. Multicoloured.

1947	84c. Peacock	2·75	2·40
1948	84c. Southern comma	2·75	2·40
1949	84c. Pale clouded yellow	2·75	2·40
1950	84c. Common blue	2·75	2·40
1951	84c. Wood white	2·75	2·40
1952	84c. Baltic grayling	2·75	2·40
1953	84c. Purple emperor	2·75	2·40
1954	84c. Silky ringlet	2·75	2·40
1955	84c. Peak white	2·75	2·40
1956	84c. Idas blue	2·75	2·40
1957	84c. Camberwell beauty	2·75	2·40
1958	84c. Chequered skipper	2·75	2·40

260 Yuri Gagarin, *Vostok I* and Earth

2006. 45th Anniversary of First Manned Space Flight.

1959	**260** 39c. multicoloured	1·30	1·10

2006. Hibiscus (3rd issue). As T **247** showing cultivated varieties of Hibiscus. Multicoloured.

1960	10c. 'Butterscotch Sundae'	30	30
1961	63c. 'Magic Moments'	2·00	1·80
1962	84c. 'Joanne Boulin'	2·75	2·50
1963	$4.05 'Capsicum Red'	13·00	11·00

261 Nathan Hale (1925)

2006. Historical Stamps, 1922–1925. Sheet 114×155 mm containing T **261** and similar designs showing stamps of America inscr 'Marshall Island Postage'. Colours given.

MS1964	½c. sepia (Type **261**); 1c. green (Benjamin Franklin) (1923); 1½c. brown (Warren G. Harding) (1925); 2c. carmine (George Washington) (1923); 3c. violet (Abraham Lincoln) (1923); 4c. brown (Martha Washington) (1923); 5c. blue (Theodore Roosevelt) (1922); 6c. red (James Garfield) (1922); 7c. black (William McKinley) (1922); 8c. green (Ulysses S. Grant) (1923); 9c. rose (Thomas Jefferson) (1923); 10c. orange (James Monroe) (1923); 11c. blue (Rutherford B. Hayes) (1922); 12c. plum (Grover Cleveland) (1923); 14c. indigo (Indian Chief) (1923); 15c. grey (Statue of Liberty); 20c. carmine (Golden Gate) (1923) (horiz); 25c. green (Niagara Falls) (1922) (horiz); 30c. brown (American bison) (1923) (horiz); 50c. green (Arlington Amphitheatre and Unknown Soldier's Tomb) (1922) (horiz)	7·50	6·75

262 American 1923 14c. Stamp inscr 'Marshall Island Postage'

2006. WASHINGTON 2006 International Stamp Exhibition. Sheet 115×90 mm containing T **262** and similar design showing stamps of America inscr 'Marshall Island Postage'. Imperf.

MS1965	14c. indigo; 30c. brown	2·20	2·00

Designs: T **262**; 30c. 1923 30c. stamp (bison).

263 Grey Reef Shark

2006. Sharks. Multicoloured.

1966	39c. Type **263**	1·30	1·10
1967	39c. Silvertip	1·30	1·10
1968	39c. Blacktip	1·30	1·10
1969	39c. Whitetip	1·30	1·10

264 Evacuation (As Type **103**)

2006. 60th Anniversary of Operation Crossroads (nuclear testing on Bikini Atoll). Multicoloured.

1970	39c. Type **264**	1·30	1·10
1971	39c. As No. 722	1·30	1·10
1972	39c. As No. 723	1·30	1·10
1973	39c. As No. 724	1·30	1·10
1974	39c. As No. 725	1·30	1·10
1975	39c. As No. 726	1·30	1·10

2006. Bicentenary of Meriwether Lewis and William Clark's Expedition to Explore the West Coast of America (7th issue). As T **232**. Multicoloured.

1976	37c. Leaving Sacagawea and Charbonneau	1·30	1·10
1977	37c. Returning to St. Louis	1·30	1·10

2006. Cultural Heritage (4th issue). As T **225**. Multicoloured.

1978	39c. Harbour, Jabwor, Jaluit Atol	1·30	1·10
1979	39c. Irooj and family, Jabwor, Jaluit Atoll	1·30	1·10
1980	39c. Traditional voyaging canoe, Jaluit Atoll	1·30	1·10
1981	39c. Mission sisters and girls washing clothes, Jaluit	1·30	1·10
1982	39c. Traditional homes on Mile Atoll	1·30	1·10

265 *Cape Norviega*

2006. Maritime and Corporate Registry. Multicoloured.

1983	39c. Type **265**	1·30	1·10
1984	39c. *Front Century*	1·30	1·10
1985	39c. *Ashley*	1·30	1·10
1986	39c. *TI Africa*	1·30	1·10
1987	39c. *Discoverer Enterprise*	1·30	1·10
1988	39c. *Genmar Spyridon*	1·30	1·10
1989	39c. *Rickmers New Orleans*	1·30	1·10
1990	39c. *LNG Aquarius*	1·30	1·10
1991	39c. *Centurion*	1·30	1·10
1992	39c. *Barkald*	1·30	1·10

266 Dove, Baubles and Shell

2006. Christmas.

1993	**266** 39c. multicoloured	1·30	1·10

267 'Happy Birthday'

2007. Greetings Stamps. Multicoloured.

1994	39c. Type **267**	1·30	1·10
1995	39c. 'CONGRATULATIONS'	1·30	1·10
1996	39c. 'THANK YOU'	1·30	1·10
1997	39c. 'Best Wishes'	1·30	1·10

268 Pig

2007. New Year.Year of the Pig. Sheet 110×87 mm.

MS1998	**268** $1 multicoloured	3·25	2·75

269 Inscr 'Art Deco Train'

2007. Trains. Multicoloured.

1999	39c. Type **269**	1·30	1·10
2000	39c. Pennsylvania electric locomotive GG1 4800	1·30	1·10
2001	39c. General Motors EMD E1 (Atchison, Topeka and Santa Fe Railway' No2A) pulling *Super Chief* streamliner (Inscr 'Santa Fe 'Chief')	1·30	1·10
2002	39c. Streamlined 4-4-2 class A steam locomotive pulling *Hiawatha* (Inscr 'Hiawatha')	1·30	1·10
2003	39c. 20th-century Limited	1·30	1·10
2004	39c. Southern Pacific GS-4 4-8-4 steam locomotive *Daylight*	1·30	1·10

270 Spotted Dolphin (Inscr 'Spotter Dolphin')

2007. Dolphins. Multicoloured.

2005	39c. Type **270**	1·30	1·10
2006	39c. Bottlenose dolphin	1·30	1·10
2007	39c. Risso's dolphin	1·30	1·10
2008	39c. Common dolphin	1·30	1·10

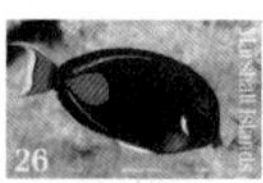

271 Achilles Tang

2007. Fish. Multicoloured.

2009	26c. Type **271**	90	75
2010	41c. Regal angelfish	1·40	1·20
2011	52c. Saddled butterflyfish	1·80	1·50
2012	61c. Tinker's butterflyfish	2·00	1·80

272 Yuri Gagarin (First man in space)

2007. 50th Anniversary of Space Exploration. Multicoloured.

2013	41c. Type **272**	1·30	1·10
2014	41c. *Sputnik* (First man made satellite)	1·30	1·10
2015	41c. Neil Armstrong and Buzz Aldrin (First men on the moon)	1·30	1·10
2016	41c. Apollo-Soyuz docking (First joint USA–Soviet Union space programme)	1·30	1·10
2017	41c. Valentina Tereshkova (First woman in space)	1·30	1·10
2018	41c. Lunar roving vehicle	1·30	1·10
2019	41c. Alexey Leonov (First space walk)	1·30	1·10
2020	41c. *Viking 1* (First landing on Mars)	1·30	1·10
2021	41c. *Venera 4* (First probe on Venus)	1·30	1·10
2022	41c. John Glenn aboard *Friendship 7* (First American in orbit)	1·30	1·10

273 'Helping Others'

2007. Centenary of Scouting. Multicoloured.

2023	41c. Type **273**	1·30	1·10
2024	41c. 'Physically Strong'	1·30	1·10
2025	41c. 'Mentally Awake'	1·30	1·10
2026	41c. 'Fun and Adventure'	1·30	1·10

274 Purple Heart

2007. 225th Anniversary of Purple Heart.

2027	**274** 41c. multicoloured	1·30	1·10

275 C-54 Skymaster

2007. 60th Anniversary of USA Airforce. Multicoloured.

2028	41c. Type **275**	1·30	1·10
2029	41c. B-36 Peacemaker	1·30	1·10
2030	41c. F-86 Sabre	1·30	1·10
2031	41c. B-47 Stratojet	1·30	1·10
2032	41c. C-124 Globemaster	1·30	1·10
2033	41c. C-121 Constellation	1·30	1·10
2034	41c. B-52 Stratofortress	1·30	1·10
2035	41c. F-100 Super Sabre	1·30	1·10
2036	41c. F-104 Starfighter	1·30	1·10
2037	41c. C-130 Hercules	1·30	1·10
2038	41c. F-105 Thunderchief	1·30	1·10
2039	41c. KC-135 Stratotanker	1·30	1·10
2040	41c. B-58 Hustler	1·30	1·10
2041	41c. F-4 Phantom II	1·30	1·10
2042	41c. T-38 Talon	1·30	1·10
2043	41c. C-141 Starlifter	1·30	1·10
2044	41c. F-111 Aardvark	1·30	1·10
2045	41c. SR-71 *Blackbird*	1·30	1·10
2046	41c. C-5 Galaxy	1·30	1·10
2047	41c. A-10 Thunderbolt II	1·30	1·10
2048	41c. F-15 Eagle	1·30	1·10
2049	41c. F-16 Fighting Falcon	1·30	1·10
2050	41c. F-117 Nighthawk	1·30	1·10
2051	41c. B-2 Spirit	1·30	1·10
2052	41c. C-17 Globemaster III	1·30	1·10

2007. Cultural Heritage (5th issue). As T **225**. Multicoloured.

2053	41c. Lonkwon getting fish from his fish trap	1·30	1·10
2054	41c. Alele style fishing, Bilarek	1·30	1·10
2055	41c. Lanju and family	1·30	1·10
2056	41c. Outrigger with sail	1·30	1·10
2057	41c. Lien and Litublan collecting shells	1·30	1·10

276 *Domani*, Bikini

2007. Marshall Island Maritime Registry. Yachts. Multicoloured.

2058	41c. Type **276**	1·30	1·10
2059	41c. *Excellence III*, Jaluit	1·30	1·10
2060	41c. *Aquasition*, Bikini	1·30	1·10
2061	41c. *Perfect Symmetry* 5, Jaluit	1·30	1·10
2062	41c. *Happy Days*, Bikini	1·30	1·10
2063	41c. *Mystique*, Jaluit	1·30	1·10
2064	41c. *Halcyon Days*, Jaluit	1·30	1·10
2065	41c. *Man of Steel*, Jaluit	1·30	1·10
2066	41c. *Marathon*, Bikini	1·30	1·10
2067	41c. *Sinbad*, Jaluit	1·30	1·10

277 Santa Claus

2007. Christmas. Showing Santa Claus. Multicoloured.

2068	41c. Type **277**	1·30	1·10
2069	41c. Waving by fireplace	1·30	1·10
2070	41c. Holding present	1·30	1·10
2071	41c. Waving from sleigh	1·30	1·10

278 Scotland

2008. Greetings Stamps. Designs showing bouquets and country names. Multicoloured.

2072	41c. Type **278**	1·30	1·10
2073	41c. Jersey	1·30	1·10
2074	41c. Gibraltar	1·30	1·10
2075	41c. Dominica	1·30	1·10
2076	41c. Canada	1·30	1·10
2077	41c. Cyprus	1·30	1·10
2078	41c. Turks and Cacos Islands	1·30	1·10
2079	41c. Bahamas	1·30	1·10
2080	41c. Montserrat	1·30	1·10
2081	41c. Cayman Islands	1·30	1·10
2082	41c. Bangladesh	1·30	1·10
2083	41c. Falkland Islands	1·30	1·10
2084	41c. Grenada	1·30	1·10
2085	41c. Nevis	1·30	1·10
2086	41c. Jamaica	1·30	1·10
2087	41c. Australia	1·30	1·10
2088	41c. Fiji	1·30	1·10
2089	41c. New Hebrides	1·30	1·10
2090	41c. Pitcairn Islands	1·30	1·10
2091	41c. Cook Islands	1·30	1·10
2092	41c. Tonga	1·30	1·10
2093	41c. Seychelles	1·30	1·10
2094	41c. Zimbabwe	1·30	1·10
2095	41c. Christmas Island	1·30	1·10
2096	41c. Antigua	1·30	1·10

279 Year of the Pig

2008. Chinese New Year. Designs showing animals. Multicoloured.

2097	26c. Type **279**	80	70

2098	26c. Ram	80	70
2099	26c. Horse	80	70
2100	26c. Tiger	80	70
2101	26c. Dog	80	70
2102	26c. Rabbit	80	70
2103	26c. Dragon	80	70
2104	26c. Ox	80	70
2105	26c. Rooster	80	70
2106	26c. Monkey	80	70
2107	26c. Snake	80	70
2108	26c. Rat	80	70

280 St Augustine

2008. Lighthouses. Multicoloured.

2109	41c. Type **280**	1·30	1·10
2110	41c. Old Cape Henry	1·30	1·10
2111	41c. Cape Lookout	1·30	1·10
2112	41c. Tybee Island	1·30	1·10
2113	41c. Morris Island	1·30	1·10
2114	41c. Hillsboro Inlet	1·30	1·10

281 Lions

2008. Big Cats. Multicoloured.

2115	41c. Type **281**	1·30	1·10
2116	41c. Ocelots	1·30	1·10
2117	41c. White Siberian tigers	1·30	1·10
2118	41c. Tigers	1·30	1·10
2119	41c. Servals	1·30	1·10
2120	41c. Cougars	1·30	1·10
2121	41c. Lynx	1·30	1·10
2122	41c. Jaguars	1·30	1·10
2123	41c. Panthers	1·30	1·10
2124	41c. Clouded leopards	1·30	1·10
2125	41c. Cheetahs	1·30	1·10
2126	41c. Snow leopards	1·30	1·10

282 HMS *Victory*

2008. Sailing Ships. Multicoloured.

2127	41c. Type **282**	1·30	1·10
2128	41c. *La Grande Hermine*	1·30	1·10
2129	41c. *Constitution*	1·30	1·10
2130	41c. *Fram*	1·30	1·10
2131	41c. *Tovarisch I*	1·30	1·10
2132	41c. *Ark* and *Dove*	1·30	1·10
2133	41c. *Rainbow*	1·30	1·10
2134	41c. *Great Republic*	1·30	1·10
2135	41c. HMS *Resolution*	1·30	1·10
2136	41c. *La Dauphine*	1·30	1·10
2137	41c. *Kruzenshtern*	1·30	1·10
2138	41c. *Golden Hind*	1·30	1·10

283 Cassiopeia

2008. Constellations. Multicoloured.

2139	41c. Type **283**	1·30	1·10
2140	41c. Ursa Major	1·30	1·10
2141	41c. Corvus	1·30	1·10
2142	41c. Camelopardalis	1·30	1·10
2143	41c. Cygnus	1·30	1·10
2144	41c. Andromeda	1·30	1·10
2145	41c. Capricornus	1·30	1·10
2146	41c. Canis Major	1·30	1·10
2147	41c. Dorado	1·30	1·10
2148	41c. Libra	1·30	1·10
2149	41c. Lynx	1·30	1·10
2150	41c. Serpentarius	1·30	1·10
2151	41c. Eridanus	1·30	1·10
2152	41c. Pavo	1·30	1·10
2153	41c. Orion	1·30	1·10
2154	41c. Leo Minor	1·30	1·10
2155	41c. Pegasus	1·30	1·10
2156	41c. Corona Borealis	1·30	1·10
2157	41c. Phoenix	1·30	1·10
2158	41c. Aquarius	1·30	1·10

284 Aircraft ('USA liberates Marshall Islands')

2008. Marine Corps Heroes. Multicoloured.

2159	42c. Type **284**	1·30	1·10
2160	42c. John Lejune	1·30	1·10
2161	42c. Holland Smith	1·30	1·10
2162	42c. Smedley D. Butler	1·30	1·10
2163	42c. Daniel J. Daly	1·30	1·10
2164	42c. Lewis 'Chesty' Puller	1·30	1·10
2165	42c. John Basilone	1·30	1·10
2166	42c. Alexander Vandergrift	1·30	1·10
2167	42c. Gregory 'Pappy' Boyington	1·30	1·10
2168	42c. Marines raising flag on Iwo Jima	1·30	1·10

285 Longnose Butterflyfish

2008. Tropical Fish. Multicoloured.

2169	94c. Type **285**	3·00	2·75
2170	$4.80 Longfin bannerfish	16·00	13·50
2171	$16.50 Emperor butterflyfish	48·00	42·00

286 Blue-grey Tanager

2008. Birds. Multicoloured.

2172	42c. Type **286**	1·30	1·10
2173	42c. St Vincent parrot	1·30	1·10
2174	42c. Green-throated carib	1·30	1·10
2175	42c. Yellow oriole	1·30	1·10
2176	42c. Blue-hooded euphonia	1·30	1·10
2177	42c. Crested honeycreeper	1·30	1·10
2178	42c. Purple-capped fruit dove	1·30	1·10
2179	42c. Green magpie	1·30	1·10
2180	42c. Bay-headed tanager	1·30	1·10
2181	42c. Bananaquit	1·30	1·10
2182	42c. Cardinal honeyeater	1·30	1·10
2183	42c. Toucan	1·30	1·10
2184	42c. Cattle egret	1·30	1·10
2185	42c. Ringed kingfisher	1·30	1·10
2186	42c. Red-necked parrot	1·30	1·10
2187	42c. Purple gallinule	1·30	1·10
2188	42c. Copper-rumped hummingbird	1·30	1·10
2189	42c. Micronesian pigeon	1·30	1·10
2190	42c. Painted bunting	1·30	1·10
2191	42c. Black-naped oriole	1·30	1·10
2192	42c. Channel-billed toucan	1·30	1·10
2193	42c. Saddle-billed stork	1·30	1·10
2194	42c. Blood pheasant	1·30	1·10
2195	42c. Grey crowned crane	1·30	1·10
2196	42c. Little blue heron	1·30	1·10

287 Camasaurus

2008. Dinosaurs. Multicoloured.

2197	42c. Type **287**	1·30	1·10
2198	42c. Allosaurus	1·30	1·10
2199	42c. Parasaurolophus	1·30	1·10
2200	42c. Ornithomimus	1·30	1·10
2201	42c. Goniopholis	1·30	1·10
2202	42c. Camptosaurus	1·30	1·10
2203	42c. Edmontia	1·30	1·10
2204	42c. Ceratosaurus	1·30	1·10
2205	42c. Stegosaurus	1·30	1·10
2206	42c. Einiosaurus	1·30	1·10
2207	42c. Brachiosaurus	1·30	1·10
2208	42c. Corythosaurus	1·30	1·10

2008. Tropical Fish. As T **285**. Multicoloured.

2209	27c. Copperband butterflyfish	90	75
2210	42c. Threadfin butterflyfish	1·30	1·10

288 Lefty's Deceiver

2008. Fishing Flies. Sheet 70×134 mm containing T **288** and similar multicoloured designs.

MS2211 42c.×5, Type **288**; Apte Tarpon; Royal Wulff (50×47 mm); Muddler Minnow; Jock Scott — 6·75 — 6·00

289 Wild Bill Hickok (gunfighter and scout)

2008. Wild West Characters. Multicoloured.

2212	42c. Type **289**	1·30	1·10
2213	42c. Jim Bridger (frontiersman)	1·30	1·10
2214	42c. Geronimo (leader of the Chiricahua Apache)	1·30	1·10
2215	42c. Charles Goodnight (cattle rancher)	1·30	1·10
2216	42c. Chief Joseph (humanitarian and peacemaker)	1·30	1·10
2217	42c. Kit Carson (frontiersman)	1·30	1·10
2218	42c. Jim Beckwourth (writer of *The Life and Adventures of James P. Beckwourth*)	1·30	1·10
2219	42c. Wyatt Earp (law officer known for his participation in the Gunfight at the O.K. Corral)	1·30	1·10
2220	42c. Bat Masterson (buffalo hunter, US Marshal and columnist for New York Morning Telegraph)	1·30	1·10
2221	42c. Bill Pickett (cowboy and rodeo performer)	1·30	1·10
2222	42c. Bill Tilghman (lawman and gunslinger)	1·30	1·10
2223	42c. Annie Oakley (Phoebe Ann Mosey) (sharpshooter and exhibition shooter)	1·30	1·10
2224	42c. Buffalo Bill (William Frederick Cody) (soldier, bison hunter and showman)	1·30	1·10
2225	42c. Nellie Cashman (Angel of Tombstone) (philanthropist)	1·30	1·10
2226	42c. Sacagawea (Shoshone woman who accompanied the Lewis and Clark expedition to explore Western United States)	1·30	1·10
2227	42c. John Fremont (military officer, explorer, the first candidate of the Republican Party for the office of President)	1·30	1·10

290 Blue Whale

2008. Endangered Species. Multicoloured.

2228	42c. Type **290**	1·30	1·10
2229	42c. Amazonian manatee	1·30	1·10
2230	42c. Hawaiian monk seal	1·30	1·10
2231	42c. Green turtle	1·30	1·10
2232	42c. Giant clam	1·30	1·10
2233	42c. Killer whale	1·30	1·10

2008. Tropical Fish. As T **285**. Multicoloured.

2234	1c. Banded butterflyfish	15	15
2235	3c. Damsel	25	20
2236	5c. Pink skunk clownfish	30	25
2237	60c. Beau gregory damsel	2·00	1·80
2238	61c. Porkfish	2·00	1·80
2239	63c. Goatfish	2·00	1·80
2240	$1 Royal gramma	3·25	2·75
2241	$4.05 Blue striped blenny	16·00	14·00

2008. Cultural Heritage (6th issue). As T **225**. Multicoloured.

2242	42c. Lokeinlik wearing traditional mat for men	1·30	1·10
2243	42c. Limekto weaving hat from kimej	1·30	1·10
2244	42c. Unfinished outrigger	1·30	1·10
2245	42c. Boys in Mejit	1·30	1·10
2246	42c. Lonkoon with fish trap	1·30	1·10

291 *Mariner 10* and Mercury

2008. Space Exploration. 50th Anniversary of NASA. Multicoloured.

2247	42c. Type **291**	1·30	1·10
2248	42c. *Voyager 2* and Uranus	1·30	1·10
2249	42c. *Mariner 2* and Venus	1·30	1·10
2250	42c. *Voyager 2* and Pluto	1·30	1·10
2251	42c. *Pioneer 11* and Jupiter	1·30	1·10
2252	42c. *Landsat* and Earth	1·30	1·10
2253	42c. *Lunar Orbiter* and Moon	1·30	1·10
2254	42c. *Voyager 2* and Saturn	1·30	1·10
2255	42c. *Viking Orbiter* and Mars	1·30	1·10
2256	42c. *Voyager 2* and Neptune	1·30	1·10

292 *Silent Night*

2008. Christmas Ornaments. Designs showing illustrations of Christmas carols and songs. Multicoloured.

2257	42c. Type **292**	1·30	1·10
2258	42c. *We Three Kings*	1·30	1·10
2259	42c. *Deck the Halls*	1·30	1·10
2260	42c. *Hark the Herald Angels Sing*	1·30	1·10
2261	42c. *O Little Town of Bethlehem*	1·30	1·10
2262	42c. *Joy to the World*	1·30	1·10
2263	42c. *Jingle Bells*	1·30	1·10
2264	42c. *O Come All Ye Faithful*	1·30	1·10

293 Barn Owl

2008. Owls. Multicoloured.

2265	42c. Type **293**	1·30	1·10
2266	42c. Barred owl	1·30	1·10
2267	42c. Burrowing owl	1·30	1·10
2268	42c. Snowy owl	1·30	1·10
2269	42c. Great horned owl	1·30	1·10
2270	42c. Spotted owl	1·30	1·10

294 USA 1918 6c. Airmail Stamp (As T **139**)

2008. 90th Anniversary of First USA Airmail Stamp. Sheet 110×87 mm.

MS2271 **294** $1 multicoloured — 3·25 — 2·75

295 Isle of Man

2009. Greetings Stamps. Designs showing bouquets and country names. Multicoloured.

2272	42c. Type **295**	1·30	1·10
2273	42c. St Lucia	1·30	1·10
2274	42c. Grenada	1·30	1·10
2275	42c. Bermuda	1·30	1·10
2276	42c. Anguilla	1·30	1·10
2277	42c. Barbados	1·30	1·10
2278	42c. Belize	1·30	1·10
2279	42c. St Kitts	1·30	1·10
2280	42c. Hong Kong	1·30	1·10
2281	42c. British Virgin Islands	1·30	1·10
2282	42c. St Vincent	1·30	1·10
2283	42c. Tristan da Cunha	1·30	1·10
2284	42c. St Helena	1·30	1·10
2285	42c. British Antarctic Territory	1·30	1·10
2286	42c. St Vincent and the Grenadines	1·30	1·10
2287	42c. New Zealand	1·30	1·10
2288	42c. Papua New Guinea	1·30	1·10
2289	42c. Western Samoa	1·30	1·10
2290	42c. Solomon Islands	1·30	1·10
2291	42c. Brunei	1·30	1·10
2292	42c. Swaziland	1·30	1·10
2293	42c. Botswana	1·30	1·10
2294	42c. Maldives	1·30	1·10
2295	42c. Ghana	1·30	1·10
2296	42c. Sierra Leone	1·30	1·10

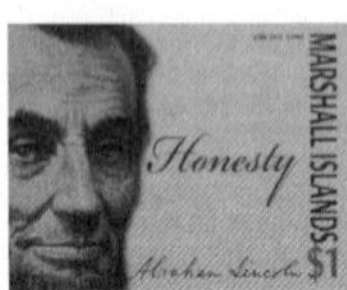

296 Abraham Lincoln (Honesty)

2009. Birth Bicentenary of Abraham Lincoln (USA president 1861–1865). Multicoloured.

2297	$1 Type **296**	3·25	2·75
2298	$1 As Type **296** (Equality)	3·25	2·75
2299	$1 As Type **296** (Unity)	3·25	2·75
2300	$1 As Type **296** (Liberty)	3·25	2·75

297 Elisha Kent Kane

2009. Centenary of Robert Peary's Expedition to North Pole. Multicoloured.

2301	42c. Type **297**	1·30	1·10
2302	42c. Robert Peary and Matthew Henson	1·30	1·10
2303	42c. Vilhjalmur Stefansson	1·30	1·10
2304	42c. Adolphus Washington Greely	1·30	1·10

298 Black Hawk

2009. Native Americans. Multicoloured.

2305	44c. Type **298**	1·40	1·20
2306	44c. Colorow	1·40	1·20
2307	44c. Looking Glass	1·40	1·20
2308	44c. Dull Knife	1·40	1·20
2309	44c. Mangas Coloradas	1·40	1·20
2310	44c. Red Cloud	1·40	1·20
2311	44c. Little Raven	1·40	1·20
2312	44c. Black Kettle	1·40	1·20
2313	44c. Standing Bear	1·40	1·20
2314	44c. Little Crow	1·40	1·20
2315	44c. Seattle	1·40	1·20
2316	44c. Washakie	1·40	1·20

299 Richard I. Bong

2009. Military Heroes of the Air. Multicoloured.

2317	44c. Type **299**	1·40	1·20
2318	44c. Charles 'Chuck' Yeager	1·40	1·20
2319	44c. Lauris Norstad	1·40	1·20
2320	44c. William 'Billy' Mitchell	1·40	1·20
2321	44c. Curtis E. LeMay	1·40	1·20
2322	44c. Edward Henry O'Hare	1·40	1·20
2323	44c. Claire L. Chennault	1·40	1·20
2324	44c. George C. Kenney	1·40	1·20
2325	44c. James 'Jimmy' Doolittle	1·40	1·20
2326	44c. Paul W. Tibbets Jr.	1·40	1·20
2327	44c. Benjamin O. Davis Jr.	1·40	1·20
2328	44c. Carl 'Tooey' Spaatz	1·40	1·20
2329	44c. Ira C. Eaker	1·40	1·20
2330	44c. Edward 'Eddie' Rickenbacker	1·40	1·20
2331	44c. Henry 'Hap' Arnold	1·40	1·20
2332	44c. Outrigger canoe and Marshall Islands	1·40	1·20

300 Outrigger Canoe and Islands

2009. 25th Anniversary of Marshall Islands Postal Service. Sheet 110×87 mm.

MS2333	**300** 44c. multicoloured	1·90	1·70

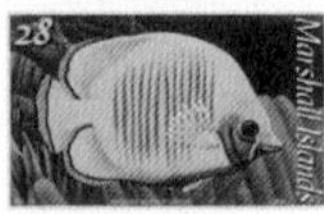

301 Masked Butterflyfish

2009. Marine Fauna. Multicoloured.

2334	28c. Type **301**	90	75
2335	44c. Queen angelfish	1·40	1·20
2336	88c. Clownfish	2·75	2·40
2337	98c. Starfish	3·25	2·75
2338	$1.22 Orca whales	3·75	3·25

2009. Constellations. As T **283**. Multicoloured.

2339	44c. Antinous	1·40	1·20
2340	44c. Aquilla	1·40	1·20
2341	44c. Cancer	1·40	1·20
2342	44c. Canis minor	1·40	1·20
2343	44c. Leo	1·40	1·20
2344	44c. Ara	1·40	1·20
2345	44c. Sextans uraniae	1·40	1·20
2346	44c. Cephus	1·40	1·20
2347	44c. Apus	1·40	1·20
2348	44c. Indus	1·40	1·20
2349	44c. Ursa minor	1·40	1·20
2350	44c. Grus	1·40	1·20
2351	44c. Centaurus	1·40	1·20
2352	44c. Cetus	1·40	1·20
2353	44c. Pisces volans	1·40	1·20
2354	44c. Lupus	1·40	1·20
2355	44c. Equuleus	1·40	1·20
2356	44c. Draco	1·40	1·20
2357	44c. Bootes	1·40	1·20
2358	44c. Scorpius	1·40	1·20

302 Summertime

2008. Roses. Multicoloured.

2359	44c. Type **302**	1·40	1·20
2360	44c. Champagne Moment	1·40	1·20
2361	44c. Tickled Pink	1·40	1·20
2362	44c. Sweet Haze	1·40	1·20
2363	44c. Lucky!	1·40	1·20

303 Montgolfier Hot Air Balloon

2009. Hot Air Balloons. Multicoloured.

2364	44c. Type **303**	1·40	1·20
2365	44c. *Intrepid*	1·40	1·20
2366	44c. *ExplorerII*	1·40	1·20
2367	44c. *Double Eagle*	1·40	1·20
2368	44c. Contemporary hot air balloons	1·40	1·20

304 Early Phase

2009. Solar Eclipse 2009, Marshall Islands. Multicoloured.

2369	44c. Type **304**	1·40	1·20
2370	44c. Eclipse	1·40	1·20
2371	44c. Final phase	1·40	1·20

305 *Samson*

2009. Steam Locomotives. Multicoloured.

2372	44c. Type **305**	1·40	1·20
2373	44c. *Best Friend of Charleston*	1·40	1·20
2374	44c. *John Bull*	1·40	1·20
2375	44c. *Gowan & Marx*	1·40	1·20
2376	44c. *Stourbridge Lion*	1·40	1·20
2377	44c. *Brother Jonathan*	1·40	1·20

2009. Cultural Heritage (7th issue). As T **225**. Multicoloured.

2378	44c. Making arrowroot	1·40	1·20
2379	44c. Boats and lagoon	1·40	1·20
2380	44c. Family in front of house with pandanus roof	1·40	1·20
2381	44c. Man carrying fish trap	1·40	1·20
2382	44c. Weaving baskets	1·40	1·20

306 Philippine Eagle

2008. Eagles. Multicoloured.

2383	44c. Type **306**	1·40	1·20
2384	44c. Tawny eagle	1·40	1·20
2385	44c. Martial eagle	1·40	1·20
2386	44c. Bald eagle	1·40	1·20
2387	44c. African fish eagle	1·40	1·20
2388	44c. Bateleur eagle	1·40	1·20
2389	44c. Golden eagle	1·40	1·20
2390	44c. Harpy eagle	1·40	1·20

307 Beagle and Boston Terrier

2009. Dogs. Multicoloured.

2391	44c. Type **307**	1·40	1·20
2392	44c. Chesapeake Bay retriever and cocker spaniel	1·40	1·20
2393	44c. Alaskan malamute and collie	1·40	1·20
2394	44c. Water spaniel and basset hound	1·40	1·20
2395	44c. Coonhound and foxhound	1·40	1·20
MS2396	140×102 mm. All horiz. 98c.×4, Old English sheepdog; Irish setter; Welsh springer spaniel; West Highland terrier	8·75	7·75

308 Christmas Wreath

2009. Christmas Wreaths. Designs showing wreaths. Multicoloured.

2397	44c. Type **308**	1·40	1·20
2398	44c. Traditional	1·40	1·20
2399	44c. Tropical	1·40	1·20
2400	44c. Colonial	1·40	1·20
2401	44c. Chilli	1·40	1·20

309 Giant Anteater

2009. Endangered Species. Multicoloured.

2402	44c. Type **309**	1·40	1·20
2403	44c. Caracal	1·40	1·20
2404	44c. Yak	1·40	1·20
2405	44c. Giant panda	1·40	1·20
2406	44c. Black-footed ferret	1·40	1·20
2407	44c. Black rhinoceros	1·40	1·20
2408	44c. Golden lion tamarin	1·40	1·20
2409	44c. African elephant	1·40	1·20
2410	44c. Persian fallow deer	1·40	1·20
2411	44c. Polar bear	1·40	1·20
2412	44c. Ocelot	1·40	1·20
2413	44c. Gorilla	1·40	1·20

310 Mastodon in Grasslands

2009. Prehistoric Animals. Multicoloured.

2414	44c. Type **310**	1·40	1·20
2415	44c. Eohippus	1·40	1·20
2416	44c. Woolly mammoth	1·40	1·20
2417	44c. Sabre-toothed cat	1·40	1·20
2418	44c. Mastodon mother and calf drinking	1·40	1·20

311 Giant Tun

2009. Seashells. Multicoloured.

2419	44c. Type **311**	1·40	1·20
2420	44c. Pilgrims scallop	1·40	1·20
2421	44c. Gibbula magus	1·40	1·20
2422	44c. Paper nautilus	1·40	1·20

312 Aquarius

2010. Signs of the Zodiac. Multicoloured.

2423	44c. Type **312**	1·40	1·20

2424	44c. Pisces	1·40	1·20
2425	44c. Aries	1·40	1·20
2426	44c. Taurus	1·40	1·20
2427	44c. Gemini	1·40	1·20
2428	44c. Cancer	1·40	1·20
2429	44c. Leo	1·40	1·20
2430	44c. Virgo	1·40	1·20
2431	44c. Libra	1·40	1·20
2432	44c. Scorpio	1·40	1·20
2433	44c. Sagittarius	1·40	1·20
2434	44c. Capricorn	1·40	1·20

313 European Widgeon

2010. Waterfowl. Multicoloured.

2435	44c. Type **313**	1·40	1·20
2436	44c. Tufted duck	1·40	1·20
2437	44c. Mallard	1·40	1·20
2438	44c. Gadwall	1·40	1·20
2439	44c. Snow goose	1·40	1·20
2440	44c. Pintail	1·40	1·20
2441	44c. Northern shoveler	1·40	1·20
2442	44c. Canvasback	1·40	1·20

314 Osceola

2010. Native American Personalities. Multicoloured.

2443	44c. Type **314**	1·40	1·20
2444	44c. Lone Wolf	1·40	1·20
2445	44c. Menawa	1·40	1·20
2446	44c. Wabasha	1·40	1·20
2447	44c. Captain Jack	1·40	1·20
2448	44c. Quanah Parker	1·40	1·20
2449	44c. Ouray	1·40	1·20
2450	44c. Manuelito	1·40	1·20
2451	44c. Cochise	1·40	1·20
2452	44c Satanta	1·40	1·20
2453	44c. Massasoit	1·40	1·20
2454	44c. Red Eagle	1·40	1·20

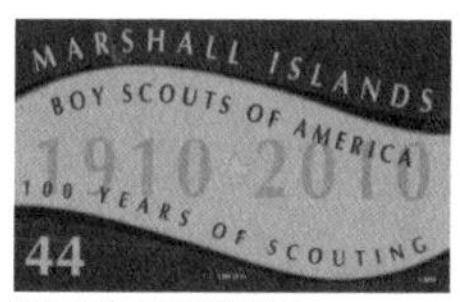

315 Anniversary Emblem

2010. Centenary of American Boy Scout Movement.

2455	**315**	44c. multicoloured	1·40	1·20
2456		44c. multicoloured	1·40	1·20
2457		44c. multicoloured	1·40	1·20
2458		44c. multicoloured	1·40	1·20

316 Gibbula Magus

2010. Sea Shells. Multicoloured.

2459	98c. Type **316**	3·25	2·75
2460	98c. Paper Nautilus	3·25	2·75
2460	98c. Giant Tun	3·25	2·75
2462	98c. Pilgrims Scallop	3·25	2·75

317 Nicolaus Copernicus

2010. Early Astronomers. Multicoloured.

2463	44c. Type **317**	1·40	1·20
2464	44c. Johannes Kepler	1·40	1·20
2465	44c. Galileo Galilei	1·40	1·20
2466	44c. Isaac Newton	1·40	1·20
2467	44c. Wilhelm Hirschel	1·40	1·20

318 Mandarin Goby

2010. Fish.

2468	**318**	28c. multicoloured	95	85

319 Columba

2010. Constellations. Multicoloured.

2469	44c. Type **319**	1·40	1·20
2470	44c. Virgo	1·40	1·20
2471	44c. Argo Navis	1·40	1·20
2472	44c. Toucan	1·40	1·20
2473	44c. Aries	1·40	1·20
2474	44c. Coma Bernices	1·40	1·20
2475	44c. Delphinus	1·40	1·20
2476	44c. Perseus	1·40	1·20
2477	44c. Taurus	1·40	1·20
2478	44c. Monoceros	1·40	1·20
2479	44c. Gemini	1·40	1·20
2480	44c. Vulpecula	1·40	1·20
2481	44c. Lepus	1·40	1·20
2482	44c. Auriga	1·40	1·20
2483	44c. Pisces	1·40	1·20
2484	44c. Sagittarius	1·40	1·20
2485	44c. Crater	1·40	1·20
2486	44c. Lyra	1·40	1·20
2487	44c. Hercules	1·40	1·20
2488	44c. Canes Venatici	1·40	1·20

320 Aa Amata (first name of First President)

2010. Marshallese Alphabet. Multicoloured.

2489	44c. Type **320**	1·40	1·20
2490	44c. Āā Āj ('to weave')	1·40	1·20
2491	44c. Bb Babbub (butterfly)	1·40	1·20
2492	44c. Dd Deo ('beautiful young lady')	1·40	1·20
2493	44c. Ee Ek (fish)	1·40	1·20
2494	44c. Ii Iokwe ('you are a rainbow')	1·40	1·20
2495	44c. Jj Jaki (mat)	1·40	1·20
2496	44c. Kk Imon Kien (House of Government)	1·40	1·20
2497	44c. Ll Lokantur ('Capella, mother of all great stars')	1·40	1·20
2498	44c. Ll Lokwajek (red-tailed tropicbird)	1·40	1·20
2499	44c. Mm Ma (breadfruit)	1·40	1·20
2500	44c. Mm Makmok (arrowroot)	1·40	1·20
2501	44c. Nn Ni (coconut tree)	1·40	1·20
2502	44c. Nn No (ocean wave)	1·40	1·20
2503	44c. Nn Niin-pako (shark tooth)	1·40	1·20
2504	44c. Oo Ok (fish net)	1·40	1·20
2505	44c. Oo Eo (tattoo)	1·40	1·20
2506	44c. Ōō Ōō (lionfish)	1·40	1·20
2507	44c. Pp Pelak (visitor's hut)	1·40	1·20
2508	44c. Rr Raj (whale)	1·40	1·20
2509	44c. Tt Tipnōl (outrigger sailing canoe)	1·40	1·20
2510	44c. Uu Urur (fire)	1·40	1·20
2511	44c. Ūū Ūlin-raj (dorsal fin of whale)	1·40	1·20
2512	44c. Ww Wōjlā (woven pandanus leaf sail)	1·40	1·20

321 Statue of Liberty

2010. 125th Anniversary of Statue of Liberty (designed by Frédéric-Auguste Bartholdi). Multicoloured.

MS2513	44c.×9, Type **321**; At night; With storm clouds behind; Head and arm with lights lit and flag behind; Head and arm, with close up of head and Frédéric-Auguste Bartholdi behind; Head, arm and book; Head only; Torch only; Head with lights lit	13·00	11·50

322 Duesenberg (1935)

2010. Classic Cars. Multicoloured.

MS2514	44c.×5, Type **322**; Packard (1932); Locomobile (1928); Cord (1931); Pierce Arrow (1929)	7·25	6·25

323 Carousel Horse's Head

2010. Carousel Horses. Multicoloured.

2515	44c. Type **323**	1·40	1·20
2516	44c. Dun, with black mane and red bridle	1·40	1·20
2517	44c. Palamino, with armoured head and neck covering	1·40	1·20
2518	44c. Palamino, with pale mane and blue acoutrements	1·40	1·20
2519	44c. Black, with red and yellow bridle	1·40	1·20
2520	44c. Grey, with yellow and red bridle	1·40	1·20

324 *Nevada*

2010. World War II Warships of the South Pacific. Multicoloured.

2521	44c. Type **324**	1·40	1·20
2522	44c. *Missouri*	1·40	1·20
2523	44c. *Wisconsin*	1·40	1·20
2524	44c. *Oregon*	1·40	1·20
2525	44c. *Massachusetts*	1·40	1·20
2526	44c. *North Carolina*	1·40	1·20
2527	44c. *Texas*	1·40	1·20
2528	44c. *Idaho*	1·40	1·20
2529	44c. *New Jersey*	1·40	1·20
2530	44c. *Colorado*	1·40	1·20
2531	44c. *South Dakota*	1·40	1·20
2532	44c. *New Mexico*	1·40	1·20
2533	44c. *Washington*	1·40	1·20
2534	44c. *Iowa*	1·40	1·20
2535	44c. *Iowa*	1·40	1·20

2010. Sea Shells. As T **316**. Multicoloured.

2536	28c. Pilgrim's scallop	95	85
2537	98c. *Gibbula magus*	3·25	2·75

2010. Cultural Heritage. As T **225** (8th issue). Multicoloured.

2538	44c. Church buildings, Likiep, *c*.1912	1·40	1·20
2539	44c. Ijuran ready to launch, *c*.1921	1·40	1·20
2540	44c. Islanders, *c*.1904	1·40	1·20
2541	44c. Lejek with fish trap on Korkor, Likiep Lagoon, *c*.1920	1·40	1·20
2542	44c. Landscape with outrigger and sailboat, *c*.1904	1·40	1·20

325 Santa Claus

2010. Christmas. Multicoloured.

2543	44c. Type **325**	1·40	1·20
2544	44c. Reading list	1·40	1·20
2545	44c. Facing left, head tilted to right	1·40	1·20
2546	44c. Facing left, laughing	1·40	1·20

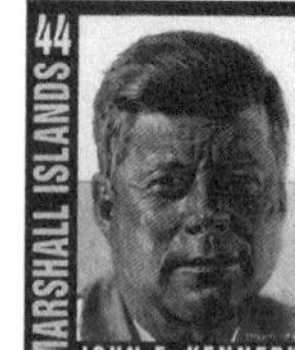

326 John F. Kennedy (Mark Sculer)

2010. 50th Anniversary of John F. Kennedy's Election. Multicoloured.

2547	44c. Type **326**	1·40	1·20
2548	44c. Facing left (Mort Kunstler)	1·40	1·20
2549	44c. With eyes downcast (Ed Vebell)	1·40	1·20
2550	44c. Facing right (Paul and Chris Calle)	1·40	1·20
2551	44c. Facing front (Dean Ellis)	1·40	1·20
2552	44c. In profile (Paul Calle)	1·40	1·20

327 *Psygmorchis pusilla*

2010. Endangered Species. Multicoloured.

2553	44c. Type **327**	1·40	1·20
2554	44c. *Cycnoches*	1·40	1·20
2555	44c. *Aerangis modesta*	1·40	1·20
2556	44c. *Ansellia africana*	1·40	1·20
2557	44c. *Vanda coerulea*	1·40	1·20
2558	44c. *Dendrobium cruentum*	1·40	1·20
2559	44c. *Phragmipedium kovachii*	1·40	1·20
2560	44c. *Cymbidium ensifolium*	1·40	1·20
2561	44c. *Laelia milleri*	1·40	1·20

328 Monarch

2010. Butterflies. Multicoloured.

2562	44c. Type **328**	1·40	1·20
2563	44c. Brimstone	1·40	1·20
2564	44c. Blue-spotted hairstreak	1·40	1·20
2565	44c. Small tortoiseshell	1·40	1·20
2566	44c. Small skipper	1·40	1·20
2567	44c. Large blue	1·40	1·20
2568	44c. Large copper	1·40	1·20
2569	44c. Eastern orange tip	1·40	1·20
2570	44c. Red admiral	1·40	1·20
2571	44c. American painted lady	1·40	1·20
2572	44c. Great eggfly	1·40	1·20
2573	44c. Dark green fritillary	1·40	1·20

329 Tulips

2011. Tulips. Multicoloured.

2574	44c. Type **329**	1·40	1·20
2575	44c. Bowl of tulips	1·40	1·20
2576	44c. Mauve and purple tulips	1·40	1·20
2577	44c. Orange tulip	1·40	1·20
2578	44c. Orange and yellow tuips	1·40	1·20
2579	44c. Large orange and two smaller tulips	1·40	1·20

330 Rabbit

2011. Chinese New Year. Year of the Rabbit. Multicoloured, background colour given.

2580	98c. Type **330**	3·25	2·75
2581	98c. As Type **330** (carmine)	3·25	2·75
2582	98c. As Type **330** (orange-brown)	3·25	2·75
2583	98c. AsType **330** (bottle-green)	3·25	2·75

331 Ronald Reagan

2011. Birth Centenary of Ronald Reagan. Multicoloured.

2584	44c. Type **331**	1·40	1·20
2585	44c. As young man with radio microphone	1·40	1·20
2586	44c. As an cinema actor	1·40	1·20
2587	44c. As Governor of California	1·40	1·20
2588	44c. As President of USA	1·40	1·20

332 Centenary of First Airmail Flight

2011. Firsts in Flight (1st series). The Mail Takes Flight. Multicoloured.

2590	44c. Type **332**	1·40	1·20
2591	44c. First Airmail Service in America	1·40	1·20
2592	44c. First US Coast-to-Coast Airmail Service	1·40	1·20
2593	44c. First Permanent US Transcontinental Airmail Service	1·40	1·20
2594	44c. First International Airmail Service	1·40	1·20

See also Nos. 2619/2623, 2672/2676, 2701/2705 and 2715/2709.

333 Green Turtle

2011. Sea Turtles. Multicoloured.

2595	1c. Type **333**	15	15
2596	2c. Loggerhead Turtle	20	15
2597	5c. Leatherhead Turtle	25	20
2598	$10 Hawksbill Turtle	32·00	28·00

334 Flora and Fauna of the Seabed

2011. Corals. Multicoloured.

2599	29c. Type **334**	95	85
2600	29c. Chalis coral	95	85
2601	29c. Elkhorn coral	95	85
2602	29c. Brain coral	95	85
2603	29c. Finger coral	95	85

335 Pontiac

2011. Native American Personalities. Multicoloured.

2604	44c. Type **335**	1·40	1·20
2605	44c. Barboncito	1·40	1·20
2606	44c. Geronimo	1·40	1·20
2607	44c. Victorio	1·40	1·20
2608	44c. Sitting Bull	1·40	1·20
2609	44c. Cornplanter	1·40	1·20
2610	44c. Uncas	1·40	1·20
2611	44c. Little Wolf	1·40	1·20
2612	44c. Crazy Horse	1·40	1·20
2613	44c. Gall	1·40	1·20
2614	44c. Joseph	1·40	1·20
2615	44c. Tecumseh	1·40	1·20

336 Liftoff and Commemorative Medal

2011. 50th Anniversary of First Manned Space Flight. Multicoloured.

2616	$1 Type **336**	3·25	2·75
2617	$1 Yuri Gagarin and orbit of globe	3·25	2·75
2618	$1 *Yuri Gagarin* (statue), Moscow and medal	3·25	2·75

337 First Manned Flight

2011. Firsts in Flight (2nd series). Learning to Fly. Multicoloured.

2619	44c. Type **337**	1·40	1·20
2620	44c. First Manned Flight of Semi-Controlled Airship	1·40	1·20
2621	44c. First Powered Aircraft Leaves the Ground	1·40	1·20
2622	44c. First Manned Flight of Powered, Controlled Airship	1·40	1·20
2623	44c. First Controlled, Powered Flight	1·40	1·20

338 Flowers

2011. Royal Wedding of Prince William and Catherine Middleton. Multicoloured.

2624	44c. Type **338**	1·40	1·20
2625	44c. Yellow flowers	1·40	1·20
2626	44c. Blue harebells	1·40	1·20
2627	44c. White convolvulus with dark centres	1·40	1·20
2628	44c. Reddish brown flowers	1·40	1·20
2629	44c. White hibiscus	1·40	1·20
2630	44c. Purple and white orchids	1·40	1·20
2631	44c. Datura flowers	1·40	1·20
2632	44c. Pink nerines	1·40	1·20
2633	44c. Bouquet of white flowers	1·40	1·20
2634	44c. Yellow and brown flowers	1·40	1·20
2635	44c. Pink pom-pom shaped flowers	1·40	1·20
2636	44c. White flowers and green and white sprays	1·40	1·20
2637	44c. Yellow trumpet shaped flowers	1·40	1·20
2638	44c. White datura flowers with pink edges	1·40	1·20

339 Andrew

2011. 400th Anniversary of *King James Bible.* Multicoloured.

2639	44c. Type **339**	1·40	1·20
2640	44c. Philip	1·40	1·20
2641	44c. Simon	1·40	1·20
2642	44c. James (inscr 'the lesser')	1·40	1·20
2643	44c. Paul	1·40	1·20
2644	44c. Matthew	1·40	1·20
2645	44c. James (inscr 'the greater')	1·40	1·20
2646	44c. Jude (inscr 'Thaddeus')	1·40	1·20
2647	44c. Peter	1·40	1·20
2648	44c. John	1·40	1·20
2649	44c. Bartholomew	1·40	1·20
2650	44c. Thomas	1·40	1·20

340 Great Eggfly

2011. Garden Fauna and Flora. Multicoloured.

2651	44c. Type **340**	1·40	1·20
2652	44c. Passion flower	1·40	1·20
2653	44c. Ladybird (inscr 'Ladybug')	1·40	1·20
2654	44c. Emperor dragonfly	1·40	1·20
2655	44c. Sweet white violet	1·40	1·20
2656	44c. Magpie moth	1·40	1·20
2657	44c. Bluets	1·40	1·20
2658	44c. Katydid	1·40	1·20
2659	44c. Painted Lady	1·40	1·20
2660	44c. Bumble bee	1·40	1·20
2661	44c. Stag beetle	1·40	1·20
2662	44c. Large tortoisehell	1·40	1·20

341 King Penguin enclosing Research Ship

2011. 50th Anniversary of Antarctic Treaty. Multicoloured.

2663	98c. Type **341** (6-1)	3·25	2·75
2664	98c. Emperor penguin looking down at chick (6-2)	3·25	2·75
2665	98c. As Type **341** (light bluish violet) (6-3)	3·25	2·75
2666	98c. Two King penguins (6-4)	3·25	2·75
2667	98c. Emperor penguin and chick, facing left (6-5)	3·25	2·75
2668	98c. Two King penguins with chicks at feet (6-6)	3·25	2·75
2669	98c. As Type **341** (bluish violet) (6-7)	3·25	2·75
2670	98c. Two King penguins with chick between (6-8)	3·25	2·75
2671	98c. As Type **341** (deep reddish violet) (6-9)	3·25	2·75

342 First Flight to Land on a Ship

2011. Firsts in Flight (3rd series). Multicoloured.

2672	44c. Type **342**	1·40	1·20
2673	44c. First Non-stop N. American Coast-to-Coast Flight	1·40	1·20
2674	44c. First Non-stop Transatlantic Flight	1·40	1·20
2675	44c. First Round the World Flight	1·40	1·20
2676	44c. First Flight Over the North Pole	1·40	1·20

343 Pirogues and 'PRIORITY FLAT RATE'

2011. Special Rate Stamps. Multicoloured.

2677	$4.95 Type **343**	16·00	14·00
2678	$10.95 Frangipani and 'MEDIUM FLAT RATE'	35·00	31·00
2679	$13.95 Flag and *'INTERNATIONAL FLAT RATE'*	45·00	39·00
2680	$14.95 Coconut palms and 'LARGE FLAT RATE'	48·00	42·00
2681	$18.30 Micronesian Imperial pigeons and *'EXPRESS FLAT RATE'*	60·00	50·00
2682	$29.95 Triton shell and 'INTERNATIONAL FLAT RATE'	95·00	85·00

343a Space Shuttle

2011. Farewell to Space Shuttle. 30th Anniversary of Space Shuttle First Flight. Multicoloured.

MS2683	44c.×7, Type **343a**; Take off; Eagle and shuttle; In orbit; Returning to earth; Breaking away from launch vehicle; Shuttle and planets	9·75	8·50

344 Celebration of Alfonso Capelle's Kemen (*c.*1910)

2011. Cultural Heritage (9th issue). Multicoloured.

2684	44c. Type **344**	1·40	1·20
2685	44c. Three women making pandanus thatch (c.1918)	1·40	1·20
2686	44c. Men spearfishing on reef oceanside Likiep (*c.*1914)	1·40	1·20
2687	44c. Men in boat house grinding arrowroot (c.1909)	1·40	1·20
2688	44c. Boat *Vilma* being launched at Likiep (*c.*1904)	1·40	1·20

345 Blue-banded Surgeonfish

2011. Fish of the Pacific. Multicoloured.

2689	44c. Type **345**	1·40	1·20
2690	44c. Achilles Tang	1·40	1·20
2691	44c. Regal Angelfish	1·40	1·20
2692	44c. Coral Grouper	1·40	1·20
2693	44c. Peacock Grouper	1·40	1·20
2694	44c. Bennett's Butterflyfish	1·40	1·20
2695	44c. Blue-faced Angelfish (inscr 'Bleeker's Angelfish')	1·40	1·20
2696	44c. Orangespin Unicornfish	1·40	1·20
2697	44c. Flame Angelfish	1·40	1·20
2698	44c. Palette Surgeonfish	1·40	1·20
2699	44c. Picasso Triggerfish (inscr 'Picassofish')	1·40	1·20
2700	44c. Oriental Sweetlips	1·40	1·20

346 First Turbojet Flight

2011. Firsts in Flight (4th series). Multicoloured.

2701	44c. Type **346**	1·40	1·20
2702	44c. First Jet Fighter Flight	1·40	1·20
2703	44c. First Jet Passenger Service	1·40	1·20
2704	44c. First Transatlantic Jet Passenger Service	1·40	1·20
2705	44c. First Supersonic Commercial Aircraft	1·40	1·20

347 Capitol Building

2011. National Icons.

2706	64c. Type **347**	2·10	1·80
2707	64c. Nitijela (Parliament)	2·10	1·80
2708	64c. National Seal (vert)	2·10	1·80
2709	64c. National Flag (vert)	2·10	1·80

348 29c. Stamp of 1991 (As T **59**)

2011. 20th Anniversary of Admission to United Nations. Sheet 83×82 mm.

MS2710	**348** $4.95 multicoloured	16·00	14·00

349 Christmas Shopping

2011. Christmas. Multicoloured.

MS2711	10c. Type **349**; 20c. Bringing tree into kitchen; 30c. Putting wreath on door; 40c. Choir in church; 50c. Bringing home the tree; 60c. Winter sleigh ride; 70c. Sleigh arrivng at church; 80c. People mounting large sleigh; 90c. Carollers outside church; $1 Sleigh approaching stream with ducks; $1.10 Cowboy father bringing home presents, tree and wreath on horseback; $1.20 Carollers outside house	26·00	22·00

350 National Seal

2011. 25th Anniversary of Compact of Free Association with the United States. Multicoloured.

2712	98c. Type **350**	3·25	2·75
2713	98c. Walap (traditional ocean-going sailboat)	3·25	2·75
2714	98c. National Flag	3·25	2·75

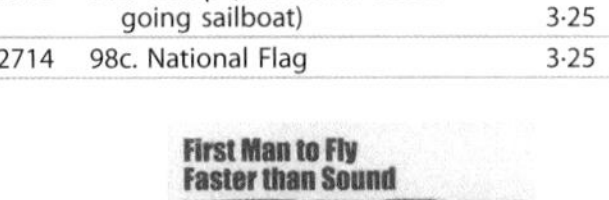

351 First Man to Fly Faster Than Sound

2011. Firsts in Flight (5th series). Multicoloured.

2715	44c. Type **351**	1·40	1·20
2716	44c. First Man in Space	1·40	1·20
2717	44c. First Astronaut in Space	1·40	1·20
2718	44c. First Man to Walk in Space	1·40	1·20
2719	44c. First Man on the Moon	1·40	1·20

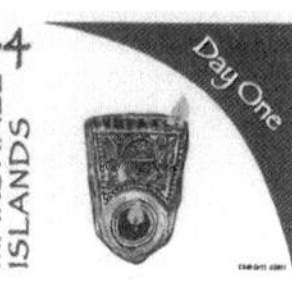

352 Lamp (First Day of Hanukkah)

2011. Eight Days of Hanukkah. Multicoloured.

2720	44c. Type **352**	1·40	1·20
2721	44c. Day Two	1·40	1·20
2722	44c. Day Three	1·40	1·20
2723	44c. Day Four	1·40	1·20
2724	44c. Day Five	1·40	1·20
2725	44c. Day Six	1·40	1·20
2726	44c. Day Seven	1·40	1·20
2727	44c. Day Eight	1·40	1·20

353 Burma Road

2011. World War II. 70th Anniversary of Events of 1941. Multicoloured.

2728	44c. Type **353**	1·40	1·20
2729	44c. Peacetime draft	1·40	1·20
2730	44c. USA as 'Great Arsenal'	1·40	1·20
2731	44c. Lend-lease Act	1·40	1·20
2732	44c. Franklin D. Roosevelt and Winston Churchill draft Atlantic charter	1·40	1·20
2733	44c. *Rueben* sunk by German U-boat	1·40	1·20
2734	44c. USA mobilises Civil Defence	1·40	1·20
2735	44c. Henry J. Kaiser supplies 'Liberty' ships	1·40	1·20
2736	44c. Japanese attack at Pearl Harbor	1·40	1·20
2737	44c. USA Congress declares war on Japan	1·40	1·20

354 Stained Glass Window, Santa Maria del Fiore Cathedral

2011. Stained Glass Windows. Multicoloured.

2738	44c. Type **354**	1·40	1·20
2739	44c. Window showing horseman, Nidaros Cathedral	1·40	1·20
2740	44c. Quartered circular window, Canterbury Cathedral	1·40	1·20
2741	44c. Quartered square window showing crowd and dogs, Notre Dame Cathedral, Tournai	1·40	1·20
2742	44c. Bisected square window, Cathedral of Monaco	1·40	1·20
2743	44c. Quartered square window showing two crowned men, Saint John's Church, Gouda	1·40	1·20
2744	44c. Two arched windows with circular upper extensions	1·40	1·20
2745	44c. Large arched window, Cathedral of Saint Mary the Crowned	1·40	1·20
2746	44c. Two arched windows with curving upper extensions, Church of Saint Saviour, Paris	1·40	1·20

355 Rhododendron Bloom

2012. Rhododendrons. Multicoloured.

2747	45c. Type **355**	1·50	1·30
2748	45c. Two pale pink blooms	1·50	1·30
2749	45c. One deep pink bloom	1·50	1·30
2750	45c. Two deep orange-red blooms	1·50	1·30
2751	45c. Several single flower sprays	1·50	1·30
2752	45c. Yellow bloom and buds	1·50	1·30
2753	45c. Two yellow-orange single flower sprays and buds	1·50	1·30
2754	45c. Two deep pink blooms	1·50	1·30
2755	45c. One white bloom above several leaves	1·50	1·30

356 Fauna of the Ocean

2012. Ocean Life.

2756	**356** 45c. multicoloured	1·50	1·30

357 Dragon

2012. Chinese New Year. Year of the Dragon. Multicoloured, background colour given.

2757	$1.05 Type **357**	3·50	3·00
2758	$1.05 As Type **357** (flesh)	3·50	3·00
2759	$1.05 As Type **357** (yellow-brown)	3·50	3·00
2760	$1.05 As Type **357** (sage-green)	3·50	3·00

358 10p. Dull Orange British Machin Stamp

2012. Queen Elizabeth II's Diamond Jubilee.

2761	$1.05 Type **358**	3·50	3·00
2762	$1.05 20p. bright green	3·50	3·00
2763	$1.05 30p. olive green	3·50	3·00
2764	$1.05 40p. azure blue	3·50	3·00
2765	$1.05 50p. grey	3·50	3·00
2766	$1.05 60p. emerald green	3·50	3·00

359 Right Whales

2012. Whales. Multicoloured.

2767	32c. Type **359**	1·10	95
2768	32c. Killer Whales	1·10	95
2769	32c. Gervais's Whales	1·10	95
2770	32c. Blue Whales	1·10	95

360 Traditional Chuuk War Canoe

2012. Special Rate Stamps. Multicoloured.

2771	$5.15 Type **360**	17·00	14·50
2772	$11.35 *Cymbidium* orchid and 'MEDIUM FLAT RATE'	37·00	33·00
2773	$15.45 Early inhabitants arrive and '*INTERNATIONAL FLAT RATE*'	50·00	45·00
2774	$16.95 Mandarinfish and 'LARGE FLAT RATE'	55·00	49·00
2775	$18.95 *Hibiscus rosa-sinensis* and '*EXPRESS FLAT RATE*' (inscr 'Hhibiscus')	60·00	55·00
2776	$38 Seahorse and 'INTERNATIONAL FLAT RATE'	£120	£110

361 Black-footed Albatross

2012. Sea Birds. Multicoloured.

2777	85c. Type **361**	3·00	2·50
2778	$1.05 Red-tailed Tropicbird	3·50	3·00

362 Terracotta Soldier

2012. Terracotta Warriors from the Tomb of Qin Shi Huang. Multicoloured.

2779	45c. Type **362**	1·50	1·30
2780	45c. Soldier kneeling	1·50	1·30
2781	45c. Head and shoulders of several soldiers	1·50	1·30
2782	45c. Head of soldier with hair tied in tall bun	1·50	1·30
2783	45c. Soldier facing front	1·50	1·30
2784	45c. Group of soldiers facing left	1·50	1·30

363 Inuit Couple

2012. Inuit People. Multicoloured.

2785	45c. Type **363**	1·50	1·30
2786	45c. Craft making	1·50	1·30
2787	45c. Drummers and dancers	1·50	1·30
2788	45c. Fishing	1·50	1·30
2789	45c. Family	1·50	1·30
2790	45c. Hunters	1·50	1·30

364 Husking Nuts

2012. Tobolar Coconut Tree Ropes and Twine. Multicoloured.

2791	45c. Type **364**	1·50	1·30
2792	45c. Soaking husks	1·50	1·30
2793	45c. Pounding husks	1·50	1·30
2794	45c. Twisting fibres to make rope and twine	1·50	1·30

365 Charles Darwin

2012. Scientists. Multicoloured.

2795	45c. Type **365**	1·50	1·30
2796	45c. William Harvey	1·50	1·30
2797	45c. Robert Boyle	1·50	1·30
2798	45c. Johannes Kepler	1·50	1·30
2799	45c. Thomas Edison	1·50	1·30
2800	45c. Andre-Marie Ampere	1·50	1·30
2801	45c. Michael Faraday	1·50	1·30
2802	45c. Jons Jacob Berzelius	1·50	1·30
2803	45c. James Watt	1·50	1·30
2804	45c. Galileo Galilei	1·50	1·30
2805	45c. Andreas Vesalius	1·50	1·30
2806	45c. Antoine Lavoisier	1·50	1·30
2807	45c. Dmitry Medeleyev	1·50	1·30
2808	45c. Carl Gauss	1·50	1·30
2809	45c. Isaac Newton	1·50	1·30
2810	45c. Gregor Mendel	1·50	1·30
2811	45c. John Dalton	1·50	1·30
2812	45c. Carl Linnaeus	1·50	1·30
2813	45c. Robert Fulton	1·50	1·30
2814	45c. William Thomson, Baron Kelvin	1·50	1·30

366 Altocumulus undulates

2012. Clouds. Multicoloured.

2815	45c. Type **366**	1·50	1·30
2816	45c. Altostratus translucidus	1·50	1·30
2817	45c. Cirrostratus fibratus	1·50	1·30
2818	45c. Cumulus congestus	1·50	1·30
2819	45c. Cumulonimbus incus	1·50	1·30
2820	45c. Cirrus radiatus	1·50	1·30
2821	45c. Cirrocumulus undulatus	1·50	1·30
2822	45c. Cumulonimbus humilus	1·50	1·30
2823	45c. Cumulus humilus	1·50	1·30
2824	45c. Cumulonimbus mammatus	1·50	1·30
2825	45c. Stratus opacus	1·50	1·30
2826	45c. Altocumulus castellanus	1·50	1·30
2827	45c. Altocumulus stratiformus	1·50	1·30
2828	45c. Altocumulus lenticularis	1·50	1·30
2829	45c. Stratocumulus undulatus	1·50	1·30

367 Masked Woodswallow

2012. Birds of the Pacific. Multicoloured.

2830	45c. Type **367**	1·50	1·30
2831	45c. Golden-shouldered parrot	1·50	1·30
2832	45c. Regent Bowerbird	1·50	1·30
2833	45c. King Parrot	1·50	1·30
2834	45c. Rainbow Pitta	1·50	1·30
2835	45c. Rainbow Bee-eater	1·50	1·30
2836	45c. White-tailed Kingfisher	1·50	1·30
2837	45c. Spotted Catbird	1·50	1·30
2838	45c. Rainbow Bee-eater in flight	1·50	1·30
2839	45c. Western Magpie	1·50	1·30

368 Lt. Col. James Doolittle organises Bombing Raids on Tokyo

2012. World War II. 70th Anniversary of Events of 1942. Multicoloured.

No.	Description	Unused	Used
2840	44c. Type **368**	1·50	1·30
2841	44c. War rationing	1·50	1·30
2842	44c. Battle of Coral Sea	1·50	1·30
2843	44c. Corregidor falls to Japanese	1·50	1·30
2844	44c. Japanese land on Aleutian Islands	1·50	1·30
2845	44c. Allies decipher enemy code	1·50	1·30
2846	44c. Battle of Midway	1·50	1·30
2847	44c. Women in war ('Rosie the Riveter' poster)	1·50	1·30
2848	44c. Marines land on Solomon Islands	1·50	1·30
2849	44c. Allies land in North Africa	1·50	1·30

369 Austrian Euro Coin

2012. Tenth Anniversary of the Euro. Multicoloured.

No.	Description	Unused	Used
2850	45c. Type **369**	1·50	1·30
2851	45c. Belgium	1·50	1·30
2852	45c. Finland	1·50	1·30
2853	45c. France	1·50	1·30
2854	45c. Germany	1·50	1·30
2855	45c. Greece	1·50	1·30
2856	45c. Ireland	1·50	1·30
2857	45c. Italy	1·50	1·30
2858	45c. Luxembourg	1·50	1·30
2859	45c. Netherlands	1·50	1·30
2860	45c. Portugal	1·50	1·30
2861	45c. Spain	1·50	1·30

370 USA 1961 4c. Stamp (As T **622**)

2012. 150th Anniversary of American Civil War. Multicoloured.

No.	Description	Unused	Used
MS2862	45c.×5, Type **370**; USA 1965 5c. Stamp (As Type **626**) (50×47mm); USA 1963 5c. Stamp (As Type **624**); USA 1962 4c. Stamp (As Type **623**); USA 1964 5c. Stamp (As Type **625**)	7·75	7·00

371 Traditional Dance

2012. Native American Dances. Multicoloured.

No.	Description	Unused	Used
2863	45c. Type **371**	1·50	1·30
2864	45c. Raven dance	1·50	1·30
2865	45c. Fancy dance	1·50	1·30
2866	45c. Hoop dance	1·50	1·30
2867	45c. Grass dance	1·50	1·30
2868	45c. Butterfly dance	1·50	1·30

372 USS *Constitution* and HMS *Guerrière*

2012. Bicentenary of the War of 1812. Sheet 133×70mm.

No.	Description	Unused	Used
MS2869	**372** $4.95 multicoloured	17·00	14·50

373 A Partridge in a Pear Tree

2012. 12 Days of Christmas. Multicoloured.

No.	Description	Unused	Used
2870	45c. Type **373**	1·50	1·30
2871	45c. Two Turtle Doves	1·50	1·30
2872	45c. Three French Hens	1·50	1·30
2873	45c. Four Calling Birds	1·50	1·30
2874	45c. Five Gold Rings	1·50	1·30
2875	45c. Six Geese a-Laying	1·50	1·30
2876	45c. Seven Swans a-Swimming	1·50	1·30
2877	45c. Eight Maids a-Milking	1·50	1·30
2878	45c. Nine Drummers Drumming	1·50	1·30
2879	45c. Ten Pipers Piping	1·50	1·30
2880	45c. Eleven Ladies Dancing	1·50	1·30
2881	45c. Twelve Lords a-Leaping	1·50	1·30

374 Alabama

2012. Locomotives of the 50 States of USA. Multicoloured.

No.	Description	Unused	Used
2882	45c. Type **374**	1·50	1·30
2883	45c. Alaska	1·50	1·30
2884	45c. Arizona	1·50	1·30
2885	45c. Arkansas	1·50	1·30
2886	45c. California	1·50	1·30
2887	45c. Colorado	1·50	1·30
2888	45c. Connecticut	1·50	1·30
2889	45c. Delaware	1·50	1·30
2890	45c. Florida	1·50	1·30
2891	45c. Georgia	1·50	1·30
2892	45c. Hawaii	1·50	1·30
2893	45c. Idaho	1·50	1·30
2894	45c. Illinois	1·50	1·30
2895	45c. Indiana	1·50	1·30
2896	45c. Iowa	1·50	1·30
2897	45c. Kansas	1·50	1·30
2898	45c. Kentucky	1·50	1·30
2899	45c. Louisiana	1·50	1·30
2900	45c. Maine	1·50	1·30
2901	45c. Maryland	1·50	1·30
2902	45c. Massachusetts	1·50	1·30
2903	45c. Michigan	1·50	1·30
2904	45c. Minnesota	1·50	1·30
2905	45c. Mississippi	1·50	1·30
2906	45c. Missouri	1·50	1·30
2907	45c. Montana	1·50	1·30
2908	45c. Nebraska	1·50	1·30
2909	45c. Nevada	1·50	1·30
2910	45c. New Hampshire	1·50	1·30
2911	45c. New Jersey	1·50	1·30
2912	45c. New Mexico	1·50	1·30
2913	45c. New York	1·50	1·30
2914	45c. North Carolina	1·50	1·30
2915	45c. North Dakota	1·50	1·30
2916	45c. Ohio	1·50	1·30
2917	45c. Oklahoma	1·50	1·30
2918	45c. Oregon	1·50	1·30
2919	45c. Pennsylvania	1·50	1·30
2920	45c. Rhode Island	1·50	1·30
2921	45c. South Carolina	1·50	1·30
2922	45c. Gregor Mendel	1·50	1·30
2923	45c. South Dakota	1·50	1·30
2924	45c. Tennesse	1·50	1·30
2925	45c. Texas	1·50	1·30
2926	45c. Utah	1·50	1·30
2927	45c. Vermont	1·50	1·30
2928	45c. Virginia	1·50	1·30
2930	45c. Washington	1·50	1·30
2931	45c. West Virginia	1·50	1·30
2932	45c. Wisconsin	1·50	1·30
2933	45c. Wyoming	1·50	1·30

375 Traditional Chuuk War Canoe

2012. Priority Flat Rate Stamp.

No.	Description	Unused	Used
2934	**375** $5.15 multicoloured	17·00	14·50

376 Great Hornbill

2013. Birds of the World (1st issue). Multicoloured.

No.	Description	Unused	Used
2935	45c. Type **376**	1·50	1·30
2936	45c. Peregrine Falcon	1·50	1·30
2937	45c. Bald Eagle	1·50	1·30
2938	45c. Channel-billed Toucan	1·50	1·30
2939	45c. Secretary Bird	1·50	1·30
2940	45c. Black-bellied Bustard	1·50	1·30
2941	45c. Toco Toucan	1·50	1·30
2942	45c. Hyacinth Macaw	1·50	1·30
2943	45c. Burrowing Owls	1·50	1·30
2944	45c. Bald Ibis and chick	1·50	1·30

See also Nos. 2976/2985, 3037/3046 and 3093/3102.

377 Early Settler

2013. 225th Anniversary of Australia. Multicoloured.

No.	Description	Unused	Used
2945	46c. Type **377**	1·50	1·30
2946	46c. Tennis racquet, star and coin (inscr 'AUSTALIAN CRICKET')	1·50	1·30
2947	46c. Sydney Opera House	1·50	1·30
2948	46c. Batsman and score	1·50	1·30
2949	46c. Yacht (inscr 'SOUTHERN CROSS AND SHIP')	1·50	1·30
2950	46c. Federation Star, English clipper and sextant	1·50	1·30
2951	46c. Australian Parliament House	1·50	1·30
2952	46c. William Shakespeare and Federation Stars	1·50	1·30
2953	46c. English Parliament building	1·50	1·30
2954	46c. Queen Elizabeth II	1·50	1·30

378 Racoon Butterflyfish

2013. Marine Animals. Multicoloured.

No.	Description	Unused	Used
2955	33c. Type **378**	1·10	95
2956	46c. Dolphin	1·50	1·30
2957	$1.10 Long-nosed Butterflyfish (horiz)	3·50	3·00
2958	$5.60 Tiger Shark (horiz)	18·00	16·00
2959	$12.35 Star Puffer (horiz)	41·00	36·00
2960	$16.85 Nassau Grouper (horiz)	55·00	49·00
2961	$23.95 Pork Fish (horiz)	80·00	70·00

379 Snake

2013. Chinese New Year. Year of the Snake. Multicoloured, background colour given.

No.	Description	Unused	Used
2962	$1.10 Type **379**	3·50	3·00
2963	$1.10 As Type **379** (flesh)	3·50	3·00
2964	$1.10 As Type **379** (yellow-brown)	3·50	3·00
2965	$1.10 As Type **379** (sage-green)	3·50	3·00

380 White Camellias

2013. Camellias of Yunan. Multicoloured.

No.	Description	Unused	Used
2966	46c. Type **380**	1·50	1·30
2967	46c. Two veriegated red	1·50	1·30
2968	46c. Three purplish pink	1·50	1·30
2969	46c. One variegated pink with two buds	1·50	1·30
2970	46c. Two medium pink with bud	1·50	1·30
2971	46c. Two pale pink	1·50	1·30
2972	46c. One red	1·50	1·30
2973	46c. Three palest pink	1·50	1·30

381 Starfish

2013. Special Rate Stamps. Express Mail Rate Change. Marine Life. Multicoloured.

No.	Description	Unused	Used
2974	$19.95 Type **381**	65·00	60·00
2975	$44.95 Grouper	£150	£130

382 Hadada Ibis

2013. Birds of the World (2nd issue). Multicoloured.

No.	Description	Unused	Used
2976	46c. Type **382**	1·50	1·30
2977	46c. White-faced Whistling Duck	1·50	1·30
2978	46c. Scarlet Ibis	1·50	1·30
2979	46c. Fulvous Tree Ducks	1·50	1·30
2980	46c. Knob-billed Goose	1·50	1·30
2981	46c. Egyptian Goose	1·50	1·30
2982	46c. Baikal Teal	1·50	1·30
2983	46c. Humboldt's Penguins	1·50	1·30
2984	46c. Whooping Cranes	1·50	1·30
2985	46c. Red Breasted Goose	1·50	1·30

383 White Cats with Pink Flowers

2013. Cats. Multicoloured.

No.	Description	Unused	Used
2986	33c. Type **383**	1·10	95
2987	33c. Cats with basket and grasshopper	1·10	95
2988	33c. Cats with orange and yellow flowers	1·10	95
2989	33c. Incrs 'Cats with hummingbirds'	1·10	95
2990	33c. Cats with pink flowers	1·10	95
2991	33c. Cats with blue flowers and butterflies	1·10	95

384 George Washington

2013. Presidents of USA. Multicoloured.

No.	Description	Unused	Used
2992	46c. Type **384**	1·50	1·30
2993	46c. John Adams	1·50	1·30
2994	46c. Thomas Jefferson	1·50	1·30
2995	46c. James Madison	1·50	1·30
2996	46c. James Monroe	1·50	1·30
2997	46c. John Quincy Adams	1·50	1·30
2998	46c. Andrew Jackson	1·50	1·30
2999	46c. Martin Van Buren	1·50	1·30
3000	46c. William Henry Harrison	1·50	1·30
3001	46c. John Tyler	1·50	1·30
3002	46c. James K. Polk	1·50	1·30
3003	46c. Zachary Taylor	1·50	1·30
3004	46c. Millard Fillmore	1·50	1·30
3005	46c. Franklin Pierce	1·50	1·30
3006	46c. James Buchanan	1·50	1·30
3007	46c. Abraham Lincoln	1·50	1·30
3008	46c. Andrew Johnson	1·50	1·30
3009	46c. Ulysses S. Grant	1·50	1·30
3010	46c. Rutherford B. Hayes	1·50	1·30
3011	46c. James Garfield	1·50	1·30
3012	46c. Chester A. Arthur	1·50	1·30
3013	46c. Grover Cleveland	1·50	1·30
3014	46c. Benjamin Harrison	1·50	1·30
3015	46c. Peace Medal	1·50	1·30

3016 46c. William McKinley 1·50 1·30
3017 46c. Theodore Roosevelt 1·50 1·30
3018 46c. William H. Taft 1·50 1·30
3019 46c. Woodrow Wilson 1·50 1·30
3020 46c. Warren G. Harding 1·50 1·30
3021 46c. Calvin Coolidge 1·50 1·30
3022 46c. Herbert Hoover 1·50 1·30
3023 46c. Franklin D. Roosevelt 1·50 1·30
3024 46c. Harry S. Truman 1·50 1·30
3025 46c. Dwight D. Eisenhower 1·50 1·30
3026 46c. John F. Kennedy 1·50 1·30
3027 46c. Lyndon B. Johnson 1·50 1·30
3028 46c. Richard M. Nixon 1·50 1·30
3029 46c. Gerald R. Ford 1·50 1·30
3030 46c. James Carter 1·50 1·30
3031 46c. Ronald Reagan 1·50 1·30
3032 46c. George H. W. Bush 1·50 1·30
3033 46c. William Jefferson Clinton 1·50 1·30
3034 46c. George W. Bush 1·50 1·30
3035 46c. Presidential Seal 1·50 1·30
3036 46c. The White House 1·50 1·30

385 Caribbean Flamingo

2013. Birds of the World (3rd issue). Multicoloured.
3037 46c. Type **385** 1·50 1·30
3038 46c. Dalmation Pelican 1·50 1·30
3039 46c. Piping Plover 1·50 1·30
3040 46c. Coscoroba Swan 1·50 1·30
3041 46c. Hawaiian Goose 1·50 1·30
3042 46c. Brown Pelican 1·50 1·30
3043 46c. Jabiru 1·50 1·30
3044 46c. King Penguins 1·50 1·30
3045 46c. White Spoonbill 1·50 1·30
3046 46c. Blue Cranes 1·50 1·30

386 John F. Kennedy

2013. 50th Anniversary of John F. Kennedy's 'Ich Bin Ein Berliner' Speech. Sheet 110×87 mm.
MS3047 **386** $2 multicoloured 6·50 5·75

387 No.42 Calugareni Locomotive

2013. Legendary Steam Locomotives. Multicoloured.
3048 46c. Type **387** 1·50 1·30
3049 46c. Beyer Peacock 2-6-4T 1·50 1·30
3050 46c. Adam Brown 1·50 1·30
3051 46c. Baldwin 4-6-0 1·50 1·30
3052 46c. 15A Class Garret 1·50 1·30
3053 46c. Enterprise 1845 1·50 1·30
3054 46c. Grahamstown 1·50 1·30
3055 46c. Flying Scotsman 1·50 1·30
3056 46c. Black Hawthorne 1·50 1·30
3057 46c. British LNER *Mallard* 4-6-2 1·50 1·30

388 Cheyenne Headdress

2013. Native American Headdresses. Multicoloured.
3058 46c. Type **388** 1·50 1·30
3059 46c. Flathead 1·50 1·30
3060 46c. Inscr 'American Indian Headress' 1·50 1·30
3061 46c. Shoshone 1·50 1·30
3062 46c. Assiniboinne 1·50 1·30

389 'Executive Order 9981'

2013. Civil Rights Movement in America. 50th Anniversary of Martin Luther King's 'I Have a Dream' Speech. Multicoloured.
3063 46c. Type **389** 1·50 1·30
3064 46c. 'Brown v. Board of Education' 1·50 1·30
3065 46c. 'Montgomery Bus Boycott' 1·50 1·30
3066 46c. 'Little Rock Nine' 1·50 1·30
3067 46c. 'Lunch Counter Sit-ins' 1·50 1·30
3068 46c. 'Freedom Riders' 1·50 1·30
3069 46c. Martin Luther King 1·50 1·30
3070 46c. 'Civil Rights Act' 1·50 1·30
3071 46c. 'Selma March' 1·50 1·30
3072 46c. 'Voting Rights Act' 1·50 1·30

390 Overcoming the U-Boat Menace

2013. World War II. 70th Anniversary of Events of 1943. Multicoloured.
3073 46c. Type **390** 1·50 1·30
3074 46c. Medics Saving Lives 1·50 1·30
3075 46c. Allies Invade Sicily 1·50 1·30
3076 46c. B-24 Liberators Bomb Ploesti Refineries 1·50 1·30
3077 46c. Soldier Writing Letter 1·50 1·30
3078 46c. Allied Forces Land at Salerno 1·50 1·30
3079 46c. Bonds and Stamps Help War Effort 1·50 1·30
3080 46c. Willie and Joe 1·50 1·30
3081 46c. Gold Star with Flag 1·50 1·30
3082 46c. Marines Land on Tarawa Atoll 1·50 1·30

391 Didmakol

2013. Children's Games. Multicoloured.
3083 46c. Type **391** 1·50 1·30
3084 46c. Etobobo 1·50 1·30
3085 46c. Lejonjon 1·50 1·30
3086 46c. Lodidean 1·50 1·30

392 *Discovery*

2013. 25th Anniversary of Re-Launch of *Discovery* and Shuttle Programme. Multicoloured.
3087 46c. Type **392** 1·50 1·30
3088 46c. *Discovery* launch 1·50 1·30
3089 46c. *Discovery* launch (different) 1·50 1·30
3090 46c. *Discovery* in orbit 1·50 1·30
3091 46c. *Discovery*, Space Station and space walk 1·50 1·30
3092 46c. *Discovery* and John Glenn (oldest person's space flight, 1998) 1·50 1·30

393 Golden Conure

2013. Birds of the World (4th issue). Multicoloured.
3093 46c. Type **393** 1·50 1·30
3094 46c. Major Mitchell's Cockatoos 1·50 1·30
3095 46c. Eastern Bluebirds 1·50 1·30
3096 46c. Giant Scops Owl 1·50 1·30
3097 46c. Thick-Billed Parrot 1·50 1·30
3098 46c. Blue-Crowned Pigeon 1·50 1·30
3099 46c. American Kestrels 1·50 1·30
3100 46c. White-breasted Silver-eyes 1·50 1·30
3101 46c. St Lucia Amazon 1·50 1·30
3102 46c. California Condor 1·50 1·30

394 Chance Vought F4U Corsair

2013. Legendary Aircraft of World War II. 75th Anniversary of First Flight of Curtiss P-40 Warhawk. Multicoloured.
3103 46c. Type **394** 1·50 1·30
3104 46c. Curtiss C-46 Commando 1·50 1·30
3105 46c. Mitsubishi A6M Zero 1·50 1·30
3106 46c. Boeing B-29 Superfortress 1·50 1·30
3107 46c. Messerschmitt Bf 109 1·50 1·30
3108 46c. Junkers Ju 88 1·50 1·30
3109 46c. Lockheed P-38 Lightning 1·50 1·30
3110 46c. Douglas A-26 Invader 1·50 1·30
3111 46c. Boeing B-17 Flying Fortress 1·50 1·30
3112 46c. North American P-51 Mustang 1·50 1·30
3113 46c. Ilyushin Il-2 1·50 1·30
3114 46c. Curtiss P-40 Warhawk 1·50 1·30
3115 46c. Douglas C-47 Skytrain 1·50 1·30
3116 46c. Consolidated B-24 Liberator 1·50 1·30
3117 46c. Supermarine Spitfire 1·50 1·30
3118 46c. North American B-25 Mitchell 1·50 1·30
3119 46c. Consolidated PBY Catalina 1·50 1·30
3120 46c. Martin B-26 Marauder 1·50 1·30
3121 46c. Grumman TBM-1C Avenger 1·50 1·30
3122 46c. Avro Lancaster 1·50 1·30
3123 46c. Yakovlev Yak-9 1·50 1·30
3124 46c. Grumman F6F Hellcat 1·50 1·30
3125 46c. Douglas C-54 Skymaster 1·50 1·30
3126 46c. Consolidated PB4Y-2 Privateer 1·50 1·30
3127 46c. Republic P-47 Thunderbolt 1·50 1·30

395 The Annunciation

2013. The Story of Christmas. Multicoloured.
3128 46c. Type **395** 1·50 1·30
3129 46c. Journey to Bethlehem 1·50 1·30
3130 46c. The Holy Family 1·50 1·30
3131 46c. Angel speaks to the shepherds 1·50 1·30
3132 46c. The Three Magi 1·50 1·30
3133 46c. The Nativity 1·50 1·30

396 Abraham Lincoln

2013. 150th Anniversary of Gettysburg Address. Multicoloured.
3134 46c. Type **396** 1·50 1·30
3135 46c. Battle of Gettysburg (50×47 mm) 1·50 1·30
3136 46c. Ulysses S. Grant 1·50 1·30
3137 46c. Jefferson Davis 1·50 1·30
3138 46c. Robert E. Lee 1·50 1·30

397 Produce and Stained Glass Window

2013. 150th Anniversary of Celebration of Thanksgiving. Sheet 110×87 mm.
MS3139 **397** $2 multicoloured 6·50 5·75

398 Consolidated B-24D Liberator

2014. Military Aircraft Diagrams (1st series). Multicoloured.
3140 46c. Type **398** 1·50 1·30
3141 46c. Lockheed F-104 Starfighter 1·50 1·30
3142 46c. Boeing KC-135 Stratotanker 1·50 1·30
3143 46c. McDonnell Douglas AV-8B Harrier II 1·50 1·30
3144 46c. Curtiss P-40 Warhawk 1·50 1·30
3145 46c. McDonnell Douglas F/A-18 Hornet 1·50 1·30
3146 46c. Lockheed P-38 Lightning 1·50 1·30
3147 46c. North American F-100 Super Sabre 1·50 1·30
3148 46c. Boeing P-26 Peashooter 1·50 1·30
3149 46c. General Dynamics F-16 Fighting Falcon 1·50 1·30
3150 46c. Douglas TBD Devastator 1·50 1·30
3151 46c. McDonnell Douglas F-15 Eagle 1·50 1·30
3152 46c. Lockheed C-130 Hercules 1·50 1·30
3153 46c. Republic F-105 Thunderchief 1·50 1·30
3154 46c. Boeing B-17 Flying Fortress 1·50 1·30

See also Nos. 3208/3222 and 3280/3294.

399 Two Catamarans

2014. 30th Anniversary of Marshall Islands Postal Service. Sheet 110×87 mm.
MS3155 **399** $5.60 multicoloured 19·00 18·00

400 Reticulated Helmet Seashell

2014. Sea Shells. Change of Postage Rate. Multicoloured.
3156 34c. Type **400** 1·20 1·00
3157 49c. Neptune Seashell 1·70 1·50
3158 $1.15 Calico Scallop Seashell 4·00 3·50

401 Garden Insects

2014. Garden Insects. Multicoloured.
3159 49c. Type **401** 1·70 1·50
3160 49c. Checkered Beetle 1·70 1·50
3161 49c. Lacewing 1·70 1·50
3162 49c. Inscr 'Red Admiral Butterfly' 1·70 1·50
3163 49c. Honey Bee 1·70 1·50
3164 49c. Inscr 'Leaf Skeletoniser' 1·70 1·50
3165 49c. Drone Fly 1·70 1·50
3166 49c. Bumblebee 1·70 1·50
3167 49c. Inscr 'Lamellicorn Beetle' 1·70 1·50
3168 49c. Garden insects (different) 1·70 1·50

402 Carrickfergus Castle

2014. Castles of Great Britain. Multicoloured.
3169 $1.15 Type **402** 4·00 3·50
3170 $1.15 Windsor Castle 4·00 3·50
3171 $1.15 Caernarfon Castle 4·00 3·50
3172 $1.15 Edinburgh Castle 4·00 3·50

403 Continental Colours

2014. Stars and Stripes. Multicoloured.

3173	49c. Type **403**	1·70	1·50
3174	49c. Bennington flag	1·70	1·50
3175	49c. Forster flag (carried by Minutemen at the Battles of Lexington and Concord)	1·70	1·50
3176	49c. Sons of Liberty flag (13 American Colonies Society)	1·70	1·50
3177	49c. Brandywine flag (7th Pennsylvania Regiment flag carried at the Battle of Brandywine)	1·70	1·50
3178	49c. Pierre L'Enfant designed flag	1·70	1·50
3179	49c. Indian Peace flag (showing USA eagle and presented to friendly Native American nations)	1·70	1·50
3180	49c. Star-spangled banner	1·70	1·50
3181	49c. 'Great Star' flag	1·70	1·50
3182	49c. Fort Sumter Flag	1·70	1·50
3183	49c. 'Centennial' flag	1·70	1·50
3184	49c. 29-star flag flying over battlefield	1·70	1·50
3185	49c. 38-star flag	1·70	1·50
3186	49c. Suffragettes with 48-star flag	1·70	1·50
3187	49c. 50-star flag on the moon	1·70	1·50

404 Switzerland

2014. European Costume. Multicoloured.

3188	49c. Type **404**	1·70	1·50
3189	49c. Monaco	1·70	1·50
3190	49c. Luxembourg	1·70	1·50
3191	49c. Spain	1·70	1·50
3192	49c. Belgium	1·70	1·50
3193	49c. Denmark	1·70	1·50
3194	49c. Italy	1·70	1·50
3195	49c. Ireland	1·70	1·50
3196	49c. Norway	1·70	1·50
3197	49c. Great Britain	1·70	1·50
3198	49c. Portugal	1·70	1·50
3199	49c. Turkey	1·70	1·50
3200	49c. France	1·70	1·50
3201	49c. Sweden	1·70	1·50
3202	49c. Iceland	1·70	1·50
3203	49c. Germany	1·70	1·50
3204	49c. Netherlands	1·70	1·50
3205	49c. Greece	1·70	1·50
3206	49c. Liechtenstein	1·70	1·50
3207	49c. Finland	1·70	1·50

405 Lockheed F-80 Shooting Star

2014. Military Aircraft Diagrams (2nd series). Multicoloured.

3208	49c. Type **405**	1·70	1·50
3209	49c. Lockheed SR-71 Blackbird	1·70	1·50
3210	49c. Lockheed U-2	1·70	1·50
3211	49c. North American F-86 Sabre	1·70	1·50
3212	49c. Grumman F-14 Tomcat	1·70	1·50
3213	49c. Grumman F6F Hellcat	1·70	1·50
3214	49c. Republic P-47 Thunderbolt	1·70	1·50
3215	49c. Lockheed F-117 Nighthawk	1·70	1·50
3216	49c. Lockhedd C-5 Galaxy	1·70	1·50
3217	49c. Boeing B-52 Stratofortress	1·70	1·50
3218	49c. McDonnell Douglas F-4 Phantom II	1·70	1·50
3219	49c. North American Aviation P-51 Mustang	1·70	1·50
3220	49c. Douglas SBD Dauntless	1·70	1·50
3221	49c. Rockwell (Boeing) B-1 Lancer	1·70	1·50
3222	49c. Consolidated PBY-5 Catalina	1·70	1·50

2014. Sea Shells. As T **400**. Multicoloured.

3223	4c. Hawk-winged Conch	50	45
3224	$19.99 Frilled Dogwinkle	65·00	55·00

406 White Willow

2014. Trees. Multicoloured.

3225	49c. Type **406**	1·70	1·50
3226	49c. Poplars	1·70	1·50
3227	49c. Oak	1·70	1·50
3228	49c. Birch	1·70	1·50
3229	49c. Maple	1·70	1·50
3230	49c. Larch	1·70	1·50

407 Tug towing Ship through Canal

2014. Centenary of Panama Canal. Sheet 110×87 mm.

MS3231	**407** $5.60 multicoloured	18·00	16·00

408 Golden Manella

2014. Endangered Species. Amphibians and Reptiles. Multicoloured.

3232	49c. Type **408**	1·70	1·50
3233	49c. Carpet Chameleon	1·70	1·50
3234	49c. Emerald Tree Boa	1·70	1·50
3235	49c. Dyeing Poison Frog	1·70	1·50
3236	49c. Golfodulcean Poison Frog	1·70	1·50
3237	49c. Peruvian Rainbow Boa	1·70	1·50
3238	49c. Panther Chameleon	1·70	1·50
3239	49c. Tomato Frog	1·70	1·50
3240	49c. Red and Blue Poison Frog	1·70	1·50
3241	49c. Flap-necked Chameleon	1·70	1·50
3242	49c. Amazon Tree Boa	1·70	1·50
3243	49c. Yellow-banded Poison Frog	1·70	1·50

409 Battle Scene

2014. Bicentenary of Star-Spangled Banner. Sheet 110×87 mm.

MS3244	**409** $5.60 multicoloured	18·00	16·00

410 Allied Forces retake New Guinea

2014. World War II. 70th Anniversary of Events of 1944. Multicoloured.

3245	49c. Type **410**	1·70	1·50
3246	49c. US Planes attack Berlin and aircraft plants near city	1·70	1·50
3247	49c. 'Invasions Is On!'	1·70	1·50
3248	49c. Airborn units spearhead ground attacks	1·70	1·50
3249	49c. Submarine warfare cripples Japan's shipping routes	1·70	1·50
3250	49c. Paris and Rome are liberated by Allies	1·70	1·50
3251	49c. Operation Forager, US Forces invade Saipan	1·70	1·50
3252	49c. Red Ball Express speeds vital supplies to Allies	1·70	1·50
3253	49c. Battle for Leyte Gulf	1·70	1·50
3254	49c. Battle of the Bulge	1·70	1·50

2014. Sea Shells. As T **400**. Priority Rate. Multicoloured.

3255	$5.75 Three shells, Cone central	19·00	17·00
3256	$5.95 Five shells, Scallop central	20·00	17·00
3257	$6.10 Three shells, Cowrie central	21·00	18·00
3258	$12.65 Three shells, Cowrie central, Scallop at left	43·00	38·00
3259	$17.90 Three shells, Scallop central	60·00	50·00

411 Count Dracula

2014. Movie Monsters. Multicoloured.

3260	49c. Type **411**	1·70	1·50
3261	49c. Frankenstein's Monster	1·70	1·50
3262	49c. Phantom of the Opera	1·70	1·50
3263	49c. The Mummy	1·70	1·50
3264	49c. The Wolf Man	1·70	1·50
3265	49c. Count Dracula (different)	1·70	1·50
3266	49c. Frankenstein's Monster (different)	1·70	1·50
3267	49c. Phantom of the Opera (different)	1·70	1·50
3268	49c. The Mummy (different)	1·70	1·50
3269	49c. The Wolf Man (different)l	1·70	1·50

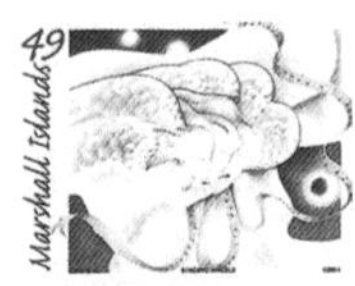

412 'Singing Angels'

2014. Christmas. The Journey to Bethlehem. Multicoloured.

3270	49c. Type **412**	1·70	1·50
3271	49c. 'Shepherd with Flock'	1·70	1·50
3272	49c. 'Three Kings Following Star'	1·70	1·50
3273	49c. 'Three Kings at Manger'	1·70	1·50
3274	49c. 'Mary and Baby Jesus'	1·70	1·50
3275	49c. 'White Doves'	1·70	1·50

413 Golden Seahorse

2014. Seahorses. Multicoloured.

3276	49c. Type **413** ('Lined Seahorse')	1·70	1·50
3277	49c. Red and green ('Horned Seahorse')	1·70	1·50
3278	49c. Brown and white ('Lined Seahorse')	1·70	1·50
3279	49c. Golden (different) ('Lined Seahorse')	1·70	1·50

414 Fokker D VII

2014. Military Aircraft Diagrams (3rd series). Multicoloured.

3280	49c. Type **414**	1·70	1·50
3281	49c. Saab J35 Draaken	1·70	1·50
3282	49c. Messerschmit Bf 109	1·70	1·50
3283	49c. Yakovlev Yak-9	1·70	1·50
3284	49c. Mikoyan MiG-29	1·70	1·50
3285	49c. Fairchild Republic A-10 Thunderbolt II	1·70	1·50
3286	49c. Messerschmitt Me 262	1·70	1·50
3287	49c. Northrop B-2 Spirit	1·70	1·50
3288	49c. Supermarine Spitfire	1·70	1·50
3289	49c. Boeing B-29 Superfortress	1·70	1·50
3290	49c. North American X-15	1·70	1·50
3291	49c. Avro Lancaster	1·70	1·50
3292	49c. Mitsubishi A6M Zero	1·70	1·50
3293	49c. Lockheed Martin F-22 Raptor	1·70	1·50
3294	49c. Junkers J1 Monoplane	1·70	1·50

415 Rocketman

2014. Kids' Space Adventures. Multicoloured.

3295	49c. Type **415**	1·70	1·50
3296	49c. Rocket	1·70	1·50
3297	49c. Astronaut	1·70	1·50
3298	49c. Space walk	1·70	1·50

416 Flowers

2014. Manuscript Illumination. Flowers. Multicoloured.

3299	49c. Type **416**	1·70	1·50
3300	49c. Lily	1·70	1·50
3301	49c. Iris	1·70	1·50
3302	49c. Thistles	1·70	1·50
3303	49c. Rose	1·70	1·50
3304	49c. Pansy	1·70	1·50
3305	49c. Wild Strawberry	1·70	1·50
3306	49c. Tulip	1·70	1·50
3307	49c. Three Pansies	1·70	1·50
3308	49c. Flowers and wild Strawberry	1·70	1·50

417 'HAPPY BIRTHDAY'

2015. Greetings Stamps. Multicoloured.

3309	49c. Type **417**	1·70	1·50
3310	49c. 'Thinking of You'	1·70	1·50
3311	49c. 'Love'	1·70	1·50
3312	49c. 'Thank You'	1·70	1·50
3313	49c. 'BEST WISHES'	1·70	1·50
3314	49c. 'CONGRATULATIONS'	1·70	1·50

418 Triceratops

2015. Dinosaur Bones. Multicoloured.

3315	34c. Type **418**	1·20	1·00
3316	34c. Stegosaurus	1·20	1·00
3317	34c. Protoceratops	1·20	1·00
3318	34c. Tyrannosaurus	1·20	1·00

419 Butterflyfish

2015. Best of Marshall Islands. Reef Life (As Nos. 478/484). Multicoloured.

MS3319	$1×6, Type **419** (As No. 478); Brick Soldierfish (As No. 479); Caerulean Damselfish (As No. 480); Japanese Inflator-Filefish (As No. 481); Arc-eyed Hawkfish (As No. 482); Powder-Blue Surgeonfish (As No. 483); $2.50 Bridled Parrotfish (As **MS**484) (74×32 mm)	18·00	18·00

420 Blueberries

2015. Sweet Berries. Multicoloured.

3320	49c. Type **420**	1·70	1·50
3321	49c. Raspberries	1·70	1·50
3322	49c. Berries	1·70	1·50
3323	49c. Strawberries	1·70	1·50
3324	49c. Blackberries	1·70	1·50

421 Ram

2015. Chinese New Year. Year of the Ram. Multicoloured, background colour given.

3325	$1.15 Type **421**	3·50	3·00
3326	$1.15 As Type **421** (flesh)	3·50	3·00
3327	$1.15 As Type **421** (yellow-brown)	3·50	3·00
3328	$1.15 As Type **421** (sage-green)	3·50	3·00

422 *Chicoreus bruneus*

2015. Best of Marshall Islands. Marshall Islands Seashells. Multicoloured.

3329	49c. Type **422**	1·70	1·50
3330	49c. *Cypraea auratium*	1·70	1·50
3331	49c. *Lambus chiragra*	1·70	1·50
3332	49c. *Tridacna squamosa*	1·70	1·50

423 Pacific Arts Festival Canoe *Walap of Enewetak*

2015. Best of Marshall Islands. Marshall Islands Canoes. Multicoloured.

3333	49c. Type **423**	1·70	1·50
3334	49c. Large Voyaging Canoe *Walap of Jaluit*	1·70	1·50
3335	49c. Racing Canoe *Kor Kor*	1·70	1·50
3336	49c. Sailing Canoe *Tipnol of Aluk*	1·70	1·50

424 *Los Reyes* Galleon, Spain, 1568

2015. Best of Marshall Islands. Ships of Early European Navigators. Multicoloured.

3337	49c. Type **423** (As No. 1234)	1·70	1·50
3338	49c. *Dolphin* Frigate, Great Britain, 1767 (As No. 1235)	1·70	1·50
3339	49c. *Scarborough* Barque, Great Britain, 1788 (As No. 1236)	1·70	1·50
3340	49c. *Rurick* Brig, Russia 1817 (As No. 1237)	1·70	1·50

425 Blue Tang

2015. Sea Wonders. Multicoloured.

3341	49c. Type **425**	1·70	1·50
3342	49c. Loggerhead Turtle	1·70	1·50
3343	49c. Hammerhead Shark	1·70	1·50
3344	49c. Commerson's Dolphin	1·70	1·50
3345	49c. Humpback Whale	1·70	1·50
3346	49c. Seahorse	1·70	1·50
3347	49c. Peal's Porpoise	1·70	1·50
3348	49c. Sea Anemone	1·70	1·50
3349	49c. Bowhead Whale	1·70	1·50
3350	49c. Flying Gurnard Fish	1·70	1·50
3351	49c. Spotted Trunk Fish	1·70	1·50
3352	49c. Four-eyed Butterflyfish	1·70	1·50
3353	49c. Bottlenose Dolphin	1·70	1·50
3354	49c. Blue Whale	1·70	1·50
3355	49c. Blue Shark	1·70	1·50

426 Yellow Spotted Eagle Ray

2015. Rays. Multicoloured.

3356	7c. Manta Ray	35	30
3357	22c. Type **426**	1·00	75
3358	35c. Brown Spotted Eagle Ray	1·20	1·00
3359	$1.20 Southern Stingray	4·25	4·00

427 Penny Black

2015. 175th Anniversary of Penny Black Stamp. Sheet 110×87 mm.

MS3360	**427** $5.60 black	19·00	19·00

428 Confederate and Union Soldiers and Flags

2015. 150th Anniversary of End of American Civil War. Sheet 110×87 mm.

MS3361	**428** $5.60 multicoloured	19·00	19·00

429 Postbox, Mail Coach and Postman, Sweden

2015. Postal Relics. Multicoloured.

3362	49c. Type **429**	1·70	1·50
3363	49c. Germany	1·70	1·50
3364	49c. Australia	1·70	1·50
3365	49c. Canada	1·70	1·50
3366	49c. Great Britain	1·70	1·50
3367	49c. Switzerland	1·70	1·50
3368	49c. France	1·70	1·50
3369	49c. United States	1·70	1·50
3370	49c. Austria	1·70	1·50
3371	49c. Japan	1·70	1·50
3372	49c. Brazil	1·70	1·50
3373	49c. China	1·70	1·50

430 Red-billed Hornbill

2015. Winged Wonders. Multicoloured.

3374	49c. Type **430**	1·70	1·50
3375	49c. Great Black-Backed Gull	1·70	1·50
3376	49c. Barn Owl	1·70	1·50
3377	49c. Eastern White Pelican	1·70	1·50
3378	49c. Sea Eagle	1·70	1·50
3379	49c. Tibetan Eared Pheasant	1·70	1·50
3380	49c. Hermit Ibis	1·70	1·50
3381	49c. Common Heron	1·70	1·50
3382	49c. Bearded Vulture	1·70	1·50
3383	49c. Kingfisher	1·70	1·50
3384	49c. White-Breasted Cormorant	1·70	1·50
3385	49c. White Egret	1·70	1·50
3386	49c. Broad-Winged Hawk	1·70	1·50
3387	49c. Greater Flamingo	1·70	1·50
3388	49c. Peregrin Falcon	1·70	1·50

431 Apollo and Soyuz

2015. 40th Anniversary of Apollo-Soyuz Joint Mission. Sheet 110×87 mm.

MS3389	**431** $3 multicoloured	8·00	8·00

432 Capitol Building

2015. National Icons. Multicoloured.

3390	$1.20 T **432** (As Type **347**)	4·25	4·00
3391	$1.20 Nitijela (Parliament) (As No. 2707)	4·25	4·00
3392	$1.20 National Seal (As No. 2708) (vert)	4·25	4·00
3393	$1.20 National Flag (As No. 2709) (vert)	4·25	4·00

433 US Marines Storm Ashore: Take Suribachi

2015. World War II. 70th Anniversary of Events of 1945. Multicoloured.

3394	49c. Type **410**	1·70	1·50
3395	49c. MacArthur Back in Luzon	1·70	1·50
3396	49c. Marines Land on Okinawa: Push Forward from Beachhead	1·70	1·50
3397	49c. US and Russian Soldiers Link-up at Elbe River	1·70	1·50
3398	49c. Allied Forces Liberate Concentration Camps	1·70	1·50
3399	49c. War in Europe is Ended	1·70	1·50
3400	49c. War Uproots Millions: Europe Filled with Refuges	1·70	1·50
3401	49c. First Atomic Bomb Dropped on Japan	1·70	1·50
3402	49c. War Over: Japan Surrenders	1·70	1·50
3403	49c. War Ends: Troops Return Home	1·70	1·50

434 Tipnol

2015. Best of Marshall Islands. Legends of Discovery. Multicoloured.

3404	$1 Type **434** (As Type **64**)	3·50	3·00
3405	$1 *Santa Maria* (reconstruction of Columbus's flagship) (As No. 447)	3·50	3·00
3406	$1 Constellation Argo Navis (As No. 448)	3·50	3·00
3407	$1 Sailor and tipnol (As No. 449)	3·50	3·00
3408	$1 Christopher Columbus and *Santa Maria* (As No. 450)	3·50	3·00
3409	$1 Astronaut and Argo Navis constellation (As No. 451)	3·50	3·00
MS3410	114×87 mm. $2.50 Columbus, sailor and astronaut (74×31 mm) (As No. **MS**452)	8·00	8·00

435 Brandenburg Gate

2015. 25th Anniversary of German Re-unification. Sheet 110×87 mm.

MS3411	**435** $5.60 multicoloured	19·00	19·00

436 Snow Leopard

2015. Land Wonders. Multicoloured.

3412	49c. Type **436**	1·70	1·50
3413	49c. Pampas Deer	1·70	1·50
3414	49c. Musk Ox	1·70	1·50
3415	49c. Maned Wolf	1·70	1·50
3416	49c. Okapi	1·70	1·50
3417	49c. Chinese Yellow Bull	1·70	1·50
3418	49c. Chinese Porcupine	1·70	1·50
3419	49c. Arabian Oryx	1·70	1·50
3420	49c. Clawless Otter	1·70	1·50
3421	49c. Siberian Tiger	1·70	1·50
3422	49c. Bridled Nail-tailed Wallaby	1·70	1·50
3423	49c. Jaguar	1·70	1·50
3424	49c. Hairy Nosed Wambat	1·70	1·50
3425	49c. Chimpanzee	1·70	1·50
3426	49c. Polar Bear	1·70	1·50

437 Snowflakes (image scaled to NaN% of original size)

438 Snowflakes (image scaled to 25% of original size)

439 Snowflakes (image scaled to 43% of original size)

2015. Christmas. Snowflakes. Multicoloured.

MS3427	194×110mm. Vert. 49c.×10, Type **437**; Snowflakes as T **438**	26·00	22·00
MS3428	110×92 mm. Horiz. $1.20×4, Snowflakes as T **439**	26·00	22·00

440 Kijeek An Letao

2015. Marshall Islands Legends. Multicoloured.

No.	Description	Mint	Used
3429	49c. Type **440**	1·70	1·50
3430	49c. Mennin Jobwodda	1·70	1·50
3431	49c. Wa Kone, Waan Letao	1·70	1·50
3432	49c. Kouj	1·70	1·50
3433	49c. The Large Pool of Mejit	1·70	1·50
3434	49c. The Beautiful Woman of Kwajalein	1·70	1·50
3435	49c. Sharks and Lowakalle Reef	1·70	1·50
3436	49c. The Demon of Adrie	1·70	1·50

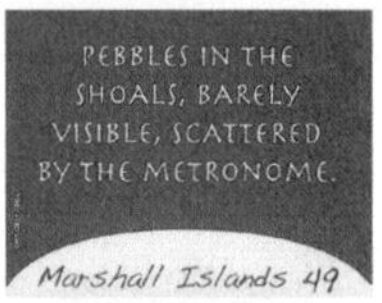

441 'Pebble in the Shoals.'

2016. The Art of Haiku. Haiku by John Clark Helzer. Blue-grey.

No.	Description	Mint	Used
3437	49c. Type **441**	1·70	1·50
3438	49c. 'Unnoticed by the Sun.'	1·70	1·50
3439	49c. 'The Harmony of the Waterfall.'	1·70	1·50
3440	49c. 'Murmuring Dunes hide the Land from the Sea.'	1·70	1·50
3441	49c. 'Waving Columns of Sandpipers Parade.'	1·70	1·50
3442	49c. 'Sometimes even the Sailor.'	1·70	1·50
3443	49c. Left Ashore by the Tide	1·70	1·50
3444	49c. 'Then, a Tiny Cloud begins to Dance.'	1·70	1·50
3445	49c. 'As Noon Sang.'	1·70	1·50
3446	49c. 'Under Jagged Waves.'	1·70	1·50
3447	49c. 'Twice the Butterfly Knocks.'	1·70	1·50
3448	49c. 'To Truly Reshape the Landscape.'	1·70	1·50
3449	49c. 'Always Changing Clouds Float By.'	1·70	1·50
3450	49c. 'Above the Sunburned Beaches.'	1·70	1·50
3451	49c. 'The Fluttering Sail.'	1·70	1·50
3452	49c. 'The Stone Path Leading Down to the Shore.'	1·70	1·50
3453	49c. 'The Day Passed Without a Remark.'	1·70	1·50
3454	49c. 'The Canoe Holds a Bed of Pandanus Leave.'	1·70	1·50
3455	49c. 'Past Shimmering Reefs.'	1·70	1·50
3456	49c. 'What the Night Really Wants at the End of the Day.'	1·70	1·50

442 442 *Concorde*

2016. 40th Anniversary of *Concorde*'s First Commercial Flight. Sheet 110×87 mm.

No.	Description	Mint	Used
MS3457	**442** $4 multicoloured	15·00	15·00

443 Monkey

2016. Chinese New Year. Year of the Monkey. Multicoloured, background colour given.

No.	Description	Mint	Used
3458	$1.20 Type **443**	3·50	3·00
3459	$1.20 As Type **443** (flesh)	3·50	3·00
3460	$1.20 As Type **443** (yellow-brown)	3·50	3·00
3461	$1.20 As Type **443** (sage-green)	3·50	3·00

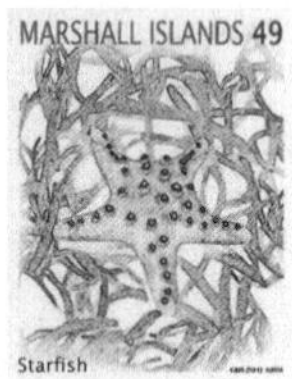

444 Starfish

2016. Wildlife. Multicoloured.

No.	Description	Mint	Used
3462	49c. Type **444**	1·70	1·50
3463	49c. Common Dolphin	1·70	1·50
3464	49c. Blue Whale	1·70	1·50
3465	49c. Megapode	1·70	1·50
3466	49c. Leatherback Turtle	1·70	1·50
3467	49c. Dove	1·70	1·50
3468	49c. Hawksbill Turtle	1·70	1·50
3469	49c. Grouper	1·70	1·50
3470	49c. Manta Ray	1·70	1·50
3471	49c. Tuna	1·70	1·50

SPECIAL DELIVERY STAMP

E142 Antonov An-124 delivering Supplies

1998. Drought Relief. Sheet 110×87 mm.

No.	Description	Mint	Used
MSE1066	**E142** $3.20 multicoloured	11·00	9·50

Gibbons Stamp Monthly

FIRST CHOICE FOR STAMP COLLECTORS SINCE 1890

SUBSCRIBE AND GET £££S OFF THE COVER PRICE

SUBSCRIBE TODAY

Visit **stanleygibbons.com/gsm**
or call **01425 472 363**
overseas **+44 1425 472 363**

399 Strand, WC2R 0LX, London
Phone: **+44 1425 472 363** | Email: gsm@stanleygibbons.com
www.stanleygibbons.com

*T&Cs apply. *Saving based on a 12-month UK print subscription.*

STANLEY GIBBONS
LONDON 1856

STOCKBOOKS

Deluxe - available in a range of four colours.

A deluxe A4 stock book with padded leather cover.
Black pages with 9 clear strips and clear interleaving.

Luxury Leather 64 Page - £49.95

● R2672BLK ● R2672BLU ● R2672GRN ● R2672MAR

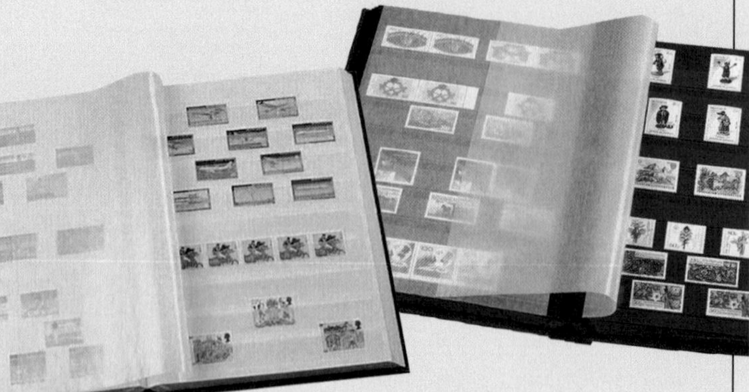

Standard (A4 size)

16 Page (black) with 9 glassine strips and double glassine interleaving

● R2680BLK ● R2680BLU ● R2680GRN

To order, call **01425 472 363**
email **orders@stanleygibbons.com**
or visit **stanleygibbons.com**

MARTINIQUE

An island in the West Indies, now an overseas department using the stamps of France.

100 centimes = 1 franc.

1886. Stamp of French Colonies, 'Commerce'' type. (a) Surch **MARTINIQUE** and new value.

3	**J**	01 on 20c. red on green	16·00	25·00
1	**J**	5 on 20c. red on green	70·00	75·00
2	**J**	5c. on 20c. red on green	£16000	£16000
4	**J**	05 on 20c. red on green	12·00	9·00
5	**J**	15 on 20c. red on green	£200	£180
6	**J**	015 on 20c. red on green	75·00	80·00

(b) Surch **MQE 15 c.**

7	15c. on 20c. red on green	£100	£120

1888. Stamps of French Colonies, 'Commerce' type, surch **MARTINIQUE** and value, thus **01 c.**

10	**J**	01c. on 4c. brown on grey	11·50	4·50
11	**J**	05c. on 4c. brown on grey	£1500	£1400
12	**J**	05c. on 10c. black and lilac	£100	75·00
13	**J**	05c. on 20c. red on green	24·00	21·00
14	**J**	05c. on 30c. brown on drab	25·00	40·00
15	**J**	05c. on 35c. black on yellow	40·00	23·00
16	**J**	05c. on 40c. red on yellow	60·00	48·00
17	**J**	15c. on 4c. brown on grey	£12000	£11000
18	**J**	15c. on 20c. red on green	£150	£120
19	**J**	15c. on 25c. black on pink	22·00	13·50
20	**J**	15c. on 75c. red on pink	£190	£160

1891. Postage Due stamps of French Colonies surch **TIMBRE-POSTE MARTINIQUE** and value in figures.

21	**U**	05c. on 5c. black	15·00	21·00
25	**U**	05c. on 10c. black	10·50	7·75
22	**U**	05c. on 15c. black	11·50	9·00
23	**U**	15c. on 20c. black	21·00	15·00
24	**U**	15c. on 30c. black	29·00	15·00

1891. Stamp of French Colonies, 'Commerce' type, surch **TIMBRE-POSTE 01c. MARTINIQUE.**

9	**J**	01c. on 2c. brown on buff	2·75	2·50

1892. Stamp of French Colonies, 'Commerce' type, surch **1892 MARTINIQUE** and new value.

31	**J**	15c. on 25c. black on pink	38·00	48·00

1892. Tablet key-type inscr 'MARTINIQUE', in red (1, 5, 15, 25, 75c., 1f.) or blue (others).

33	**D**	1c. black on blue	1·80	1·20
34	**D**	2c. brown on buff	1·80	1·60
35	**D**	4c. brown on grey	2·30	2·75
36	**D**	5c. green on green	4·50	1·50
37	**D**	10c. black on lilac	10·00	1·50
47	**D**	10c. red	7·25	1·20
38	**D**	15c. blue	55·00	4·75
48	**D**	15c. grey	18·00	1·90
39	**D**	20c. red on green	32·00	9·75
40	**D**	25c. black on pink	26·00	2·40
49	**D**	25c. blue	22·00	46·00
41	**D**	30c. brown on drab	22·00	22·00
50	**D**	35c. black on yellow	16·00	6·25
42	**D**	40c. red on yellow	48·00	26·00
43	**D**	50c. red on pink	27·00	13·50
51	**D**	50c. brown on blue	37·00	48·00
44	**D**	75c. brown on orange	35·00	23·00
45	**D**	1f. green	34·00	27·00
52	**D**	2f. violet on pink	85·00	85·00
53	**D**	5f. mauve on lilac	£110	£120

1903. Postage Due stamp of French Colonies surch **TIMBRE POSTE 5 F. MARTINIQUE COLIS POSTAUX.**

53a	**U**	5f. on 60c. brown on buff	£600	£700

Despite the surcharge No. 53a was for use on letters as well as parcels.

1904. Nos. 41 and 43 surch **10 c.**

54	**D**	10c. on 30c. brown and drab	12·00	22·00
55	**D**	10c. on 5f. mauve on lilac	12·50	38·00

1904. Surch **1904 0f10.**

56	**D**	0f.10 on 30c. brown on drab	19·00	44·00
57	**D**	0f.10 on 40c. red on yellow	24·00	26·00
58	**D**	0f.10 on 50c. red on pink	20·00	44·00
59	**D**	0f.10 on 75c. brown on orange	16·00	42·00
60	**D**	0f.10 on 1f. green	32·00	46·00
61	**D**	0f.10 on 5f. mauve on lilac	£200	£200

13 Martinique Woman

14 Fort-de-France

15 Woman and Sugar Cane

1908

62	**13**	1c. chocolate and brown	25	25
63	**13**	2c. brown and green	30	35
64	**13**	4c. brown and purple	90	55
65	**13**	5c. brown and green	1·80	40
87	**13**	5c. brown and orange	60	40
66	**13**	10c. brown and red	5·75	50
88	**13**	10c. olive and green	2·50	1·80
89	**13**	10c. red and purple	1·80	1·10
67	**13**	15c. red and purple	2·30	1·10
90	**13**	15c. olive and green	1·00	40
91	**13**	15c. red and blue	3·00	1·80
68	**13**	20c. brown and lilac	2·50	2·00
69	**14**	25c. brown and blue	4·50	1·30
92	**14**	25c. brown and orange	1·90	50
93	**14**	30c. brown and red	3·50	6·00
94	**14**	30c. brown and carmine	1·30	6·50
95	**14**	30c. brown and light brown	1·50	1·80
96	**14**	30c. green and blue	3·25	1·50
71	**14**	35c. brown and lilac	1·70	1·60
72	**14**	40c. brown and green	1·60	65
73	**14**	45c. chocolate and brown	3·00	3·25
74	**14**	50c. brown and red	3·75	3·25
97	**14**	50c. brown and blue	3·00	4·25
98	**14**	50c. green and red	3·00	35
99	**14**	60c. pink and blue	2·50	6·75
100	**14**	65c. brown and violet	4·75	8·50
75	**14**	75c. brown and black	1·60	3·75
101	**14**	75c. blue and deep blue	3·75	2·75
102	**14**	75c. blue and brown	6·25	6·25
103	**14**	90c. carmine and red	11·00	19·00
76	**15**	1f. brown and red	3·75	3·25
104	**15**	1f. blue	3·75	3·25
105	**15**	1f. green and red	4·75	4·00
106	**15**	1f.10 brown and violet	6·75	12·50
107	**15**	1f.50 light blue and blue	12·00	13·00
77	**15**	2f. brown and grey	5·50	3·25
108	**15**	3f. mauve on pink	23·00	32·00
78	**15**	5f. brown and red	13·00	34·00

1912. Stamps of 1892 surch.

79A	**D**	05 on 15c. grey	85	65
80A	**D**	05 on 25c. black on pink	1·30	3·00
81A	**D**	10 on 40c. red on yellow	3·75	7·50
82A	**D**	10 on 5f. mauve on lilac	3·25	9·25

1915. Surch **5c** and red cross.

83	**13**	10c.+5c. brown and red	2·75	3·75

1920. Surch in figures.

115	**13**	0.01 on 2c. brown and green	3·50	10·50
109	**13**	0.01 on 15c. red and purple	80	6·50
110	**13**	0.02 on 15c. red and purple	1·10	6·50
84	**13**	05 on 1c. chocolate & brn	4·75	5·00
111	**13**	0.05 on 15c. red and purple	70	7·25
116	**13**	0.05 on 20c. brown and lilac	4·50	10·50
85	**13**	10 on 2c. brown and green	1·70	1·60
117	**14**	0.15 on 30c. brown and red	19·00	44·00
86	**13**	25 on 15c. red and purple	2·50	4·50
121	**13**	25c. on 15c. red and purple	75	5·50
119	**14**	0.25 on 50c. brown and red	£325	£350
120	**14**	0.25 on 50c. brown and blue	8·25	13·00
122	**15**	25c. on 2f. brown and grey	1·00	6·25
123	**15**	25c. on 5f. brown and red	2·50	6·50
112	**14**	60 on 75c. pink and blue	1·30	65
113	**14**	65 on 45c. brown and light brown	2·75	6·50
114	**14**	85 on 75c. brown and black	2·50	8·75
124	**14**	90c. on 75c. carmine and red	4·50	4·75
125	**15**	1f.25 on 1f. blue	1·20	3·00
126	**15**	1f.50 on 1f. ultram & bl	2·75	2·00
127	**15**	3f. on 5f. green and red	3·75	5·25
128	**15**	10f. on 5f. red and green	15·00	38·00
129	**15**	20f. on 5f. violet and brown	23·00	55·00

1931. Colonial Exhibition key-types inscr 'MARTINIQUE'.

130	**E**	40c. black and green	7·75	11·50
131	**F**	50c. black and mauve	7·75	7·75
132	**G**	90c. black and red	7·75	12·00
133	**H**	1f.50 black and blue	7·75	9·50

26 Basse Pointe Village

27 Government House, Fort-de-France

28 Martinique Woman

1933

134	**26**	1c. red on pink	65	2·30
135	**27**	2c. blue	30	4·00
136	**27**	3c. purple	1·10	6·50
137	**26**	4c. green	40	4·50
138	**27**	5c. purple	40	45
139	**26**	10c. black on pink	35	40
140	**27**	15c. black on red	40	45
141	**28**	20c. brown	40	45
142	**26**	25c. purple	65	40
143	**27**	30c. green	1·50	55
144	**27**	30c. blue	90	6·00
145	**28**	35c. green	1·30	2·00
146	**28**	40c. brown	85	65
147	**27**	45c. brown	4·00	4·50
148	**27**	45c. green	2·30	5·50
149	**27**	50c. red	1·20	40
150	**26**	55c. red	2·50	3·75
151	**26**	60c. blue	1·20	6·75
152	**28**	65c. red on blue	1·80	2·75
153	**28**	70c. purple	2·00	5·75
154	**26**	75c. brown	3·00	2·00
155	**27**	80c. violet	1·30	2·30
156	**26**	90c. red	4·25	1·90
157	**26**	90c. purple	2·10	4·00
158	**27**	1f. black on green	3·00	1·70
159	**27**	1f. red	95	2·75
160	**28**	1f.25 violet	3·00	3·75
161	**28**	1f.25 red	2·75	6·00
162	**28**	1f.40 blue	2·50	4·50
163	**27**	1f.50 blue	1·30	90
164	**27**	1f.60 brown	2·50	3·25
165	**28**	1f.75 green	21·00	7·25
166	**28**	1f.75 blue	3·00	2·50
167	**26**	2f. blue on green	2·75	1·50
168	**28**	2f.25 blue	3·25	7·25
169	**26**	2f.50 purple	2·75	3·75
170	**28**	3f. purple	2·75	1·60
171	**28**	5f. red on pink	2·75	1·90
172	**26**	10f. blue on blue	2·30	2·00
173	**27**	20f. red on yellow	2·50	2·50

30 Belain d'Esnambuc, 1635

31 Schoelcher and Abolition of Slavery, 1848

1935. West Indies Tercentenary.

174	**30**	40c. brown	5·75	9·00
175	**30**	50c. red	6·00	9·25
176	**30**	1f.50 blue	15·00	21·00
177	**31**	1f.75 red	20·00	23·00
178	**31**	5f. brown	15·00	22·00
179	**31**	10f. green	14·00	13·50

1937. International Exhibition, Paris. As T **16** of Mauritania.

180	20c. violet	2·50	6·25
181	30c. green	2·50	5·25
182	40c. red	2·50	4·25
183	50c. brown and agate	2·50	2·40
184	90c. red	2·75	3·25
185	1f.50 blue	2·75	2·75
MS185a	120×100 mm. 3f. green (as 20c.) Imperf	14·00	34·00

1938. International Anti-cancer Fund. As T **22** of Mauritania.

186	1f.75+50c. blue	14·00	28·00

1939. New York World's Fair. As T **28** of Mauritania.

187	1f.25 red	1·70	6·75
188	2f.25 blue	1·80	6·50

1939. 150th Anniversary of French Revolution. As T **29** of Mauritania.

189	45c.+25c. green and black	12·50	23·00
190	70c.+30c. brown and black	12·50	23·00
191	90c.+35c. orange and black	12·50	23·00
192	1f.25+1f. red and black	12·50	23·00
193	2f.25+2f. blue and black	12·50	23·00

1944. Mutual Aid and Red Cross Funds. As T **19b** of Oceanic Settlements.

194	5f.+20f. violet	1·20	9·00

1945. Eboue. As T **20a** of Oceanic Settlements.

195	2f. black	50	70
196	25f. green	95	6·00

1945. Surch.

197	**27**	1f. on 2c. blue	2·50	1·20
198	**26**	2f. on 4c. olive	1·00	1·80
199	**27**	3f. on 2c. blue	2·75	1·40
200	**28**	5f. on 65c. red on blue	1·80	1·80
201	**28**	10f. (DIX f.) on 65c. red on blue	3·00	1·90
202	**27**	20f. (VINGT f.) on 3c. pur	3·00	3·00

33 Victor Schoelcher

1945

203	**33**	10c. blue and violet	45	5·25
204	**33**	30c. brown and red	1·10	5·25
205	**33**	40c. blue and light blue	80	5·25
206	**33**	50c. red and purple	1·00	3·25
207	**33**	60c. orange and yellow	1·60	4·50
208	**33**	70c. purple and brown	1·60	7·50
209	**33**	80c. green and light green	1·70	7·00
210	**33**	1f. blue and light blue	75	1·60
211	**33**	1f.20 violet and purple	85	7·50
212	**33**	1f.50 red and orange	60	1·70
213	**33**	2f. black and grey	90	1·00
214	**33**	2f.40 red and pink	1·70	7·75
215	**33**	3f. pink and light pink	1·20	75
216	**33**	4f. ultramarine and blue	1·20	2·75
217	**33**	4f.50 turquoise and green	1·30	1·50
218	**33**	5f. light brown and brown	1·30	1·40
219	**33**	10f. purple and mauve	1·40	1·30
220	**33**	15f. red and pink	1·80	1·60
221	**33**	20f. olive and green	2·00	2·40

1945. Air. As No. 299 of New Caledonia.

222	50f. green	90	3·50
223	100f. red	1·30	6·25

1946. Air. Victory. As T **20b** of Oceanic Settlements.

224	8f. blue	1·40	6·25

1946. Air. From Chad to the Rhine. As T **25a** of Madagascar.

225	5f. orange	1·60	6·75
226	10f. green	1·60	6·75
227	15f. red	1·60	7·50
228	20f. brown	1·80	6·00
229	25f. blue	1·70	7·00
230	50f. grey	2·00	5·50

34 Martinique Woman

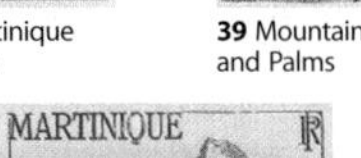

39 Mountains and Palms

35 Local Fishing Boats and Rocks

40 West Indians and Latecoere 611 (flying boat)

1947

231	**34**	10c. lake (postage)	30	5·50
232	**34**	30c. blue	45	5·75
233	**34**	50c. brown	45	7·00
234	**35**	60c. green	1·10	5·75
235	**35**	1f. lake	1·10	1·70
236	**35**	1f.50 violet	1·10	5·25
237	-	2f. green	2·00	4·25
238	-	2f.50 brown	2·00	7·50
239	-	3f. blue	2·50	3·75
240	-	4f. brown	2·50	4·75
241	-	5f. green	2·50	3·25
242	-	6f. mauve	2·30	1·50
243	-	10f. blue	2·75	3·00
244	-	15f. lake	3·00	3·00
245	-	20f. brown	3·00	3·00
246	**39**	25f. violet	3·50	3·50
247	**39**	40f. green	3·50	7·00
248	**40**	50f. purple (air)	8·50	9·75
249	-	100f. green	8·25	11·50
250	-	200f. violet	38·00	65·00

Designs: Horiz As T **35**—2f. to 3f. Gathering sugar cane; 4f. to 6f. Mount Pele; 10f. to 20f. Fruit products. As T **40** Vert—100f. Aircraft over landscape. Horiz—200f. Wandering albatross in flight.

POSTAGE DUE STAMPS

1927. Postage Due stamps of France optd **MARTINIQUE.**

D130	**D11**	5c. blue	1·70	4·50
D131	**D11**	10c. brown	1·90	4·75
D132	**D11**	20c. olive	2·00	9·25
D133	**D11**	25c. red	2·50	11·00
D134	**D11**	30c. red	3·25	11·50
D135	**D11**	45c. green	4·50	12·00
D136	**D11**	50c. purple	5·00	23·00
D137	**D11**	60c. green	5·75	20·00
D138	**D11**	1f. red on yellow	8·00	28·00
D139	**D11**	2f. mauve	11·00	46·00
D140	**D11**	3f. red	11·50	50·00

D29 Fruit

1933

D174	**D29**	5c. blue on green	90	3·75
D175	**D29**	10c. brown	1·10	6·25
D176	**D29**	20c. blue	1·70	7·75
D177	**D29**	25c. red on pink	2·00	7·50
D178	**D29**	30c. purple	1·70	7·25
D179	**D29**	45c. red on yellow	1·10	5·50
D180	**D29**	50c. brown	1·70	8·75
D181	**D29**	60c. green	1·70	8·75
D182	**D29**	1f. black on red	2·20	9·25
D183	**D29**	2f. purple	2·20	8·75
D184	**D29**	3f. blue on blue	2·20	9·25

D43 Map of Martinique

1947

D251	**D43**	10c. blue	40	7·00
D252	**D43**	30c. green	40	7·25
D253	**D43**	50c. blue	50	7·50
D254	**D43**	1f. orange	75	7·00
D255	**D43**	2f. purple	2·00	7·00
D256	**D43**	3f. purple	1·80	6·75
D257	**D43**	4f. brown	2·75	8·50
D258	**D43**	5f. red	2·00	8·50
D259	**D43**	10f. black	2·50	8·75
D260	**D43**	20f. green	2·75	10·50

MAURITANIA

A French colony extending inland to the Sahara, incorporated in French West Africa from 1945 to 1959. In 1960 Mauritania became an independent Islamic republic.

1906. 100 centimes = 1 franc.
1973. 100 cents = 1 ouguiya (um).

1906. Faidherbe, Palms and Balay key-types inscr 'MAURITANIE' in blue (10, 40c., 5f.) or red (others).

1	**I**	1c. grey	1·00	1·00
2	**I**	2c. brown	1·80	1·00
3	**I**	4c. brown on blue	3·50	3·25
4	**I**	5c. green	3·00	3·25
5	**I**	10c. pink	16·00	11·00
6	**J**	20c. black on blue	20·00	42·00
7	**J**	25c. blue	9·75	18·00
8	**J**	30c. brown on pink	£120	£100
9	**J**	35c. black on yellow	7·00	14·00
10	**J**	40c. red on blue	9·25	20·00
11	**J**	45c. brown on green	11·00	21·00
12	**J**	50c. violet	10·50	19·00
13	**J**	75c. green on orange	8·00	16·00
14	**K**	1f. black on blue	28·00	46·00
15	**K**	2f. blue on pink	65·00	£110
16	**K**	5f. red on yellow	£160	£160

6 Merchants crossing Desert

1913

18	**6**	1c. brown and lilac	30	55
19	**6**	2c. blue and black	40	1·00
20	**6**	4c. black and violet	40	1·30
21	**6**	5c. green and light green	2·50	1·80
37	**6**	5c. red and purple	65	3·25
22	**6**	10c. orange and pink	3·25	4·50
38	**6**	10c. green and light green	85	3·50
39	**6**	10c. pink on blue	50	3·75
23	**6**	15c. black and brown	80	3·50
24	**6**	20c. orange and brown	2·75	4·00
25	**6**	25c. ultramarine and blue	5·50	7·50
40	**6**	25c. red and green	2·30	1·50
26	**6**	30c. pink and green	4·25	6·50
41	**6**	30c. orange and red	2·50	6·50
42	**6**	30c. yellow and black	65	3·25
43	**6**	30c. light green and green	4·00	9·50
27	**6**	35c. violet and brown	1·70	7·25
44	**6**	35c. light green and green	1·40	7·50
28	**6**	40c. green and brown	3·50	7·25
29	**6**	45c. brown and orange	1·70	5·00
30	**6**	50c. pink and lilac	2·00	7·00
45	**6**	50c. ultramarine and blue	1·40	4·25
46	**6**	50c. blue and green	2·30	2·50
47	**6**	60c. violet on pink	2·00	7·25
48	**6**	65c. blue and brown	2·00	6·25
31	**6**	75c. brown and blue	2·30	5·75
49	**6**	85c. brown and green	1·20	7·75
50	**6**	90c. pink and red	2·75	7·25
32	**6**	1f. black and red	1·80	3·25
51	**6**	1f.10 red and mauve	10·50	38·00
52	**6**	1f.25 brown and blue	5·25	8·50
53	**6**	1f.50 blue and light blue	2·30	7·75
54	**6**	1f.75 red and green	3·50	7·00
55	**6**	1f.75 ultramarine and blue	2·50	7·25
33	**6**	2f. violet and orange	2·50	5·00
56	**6**	3f. mauve on pink	2·50	5·75
34	**6**	5f. blue and violet	4·50	10·00

1915. Surch **5c** and red cross.

35	**6**	10c.+5c. orange and pink	2·30	3·50
36	**6**	15c.+5c. black and brown	2·30	6·75

1922. Surch in figures and bars (some colours changed).

60	**6**	25c. on 2f. violet and orange	2·00	8·25
57	**6**	60 on 75c. violet on pink	1·30	4·50
58	**6**	65 on 15c. black and brown	2·75	9·75
59	**6**	85 on 75c. brown and blue	2·75	9·75
61	**6**	90c. on 75c. pink and red	3·25	10·00
62	**6**	1f.25 on 1f. ultram & blue	1·80	8·50
63	**6**	1f.50 on 1f. blue & light blue	1·90	5·50
64	**6**	3f. on 5f. mauve and brown	8·75	28·00
65	**6**	10f. on 5f. green and mauve	8·75	23·00
66	**6**	20f. on 5f. orange and blue	9·00	24·00

1931. Colonial Exhibition key-types inscr 'MAURITANIE'.

67	**E**	40c. green and black	11·00	34·00
68	**F**	50c. purple and black	6·50	13·50
69	**G**	90c. red and black	6·50	14·00
70	**H**	1f.50 blue and black	8·50	14·00

16 Commerce

1937. International Exhibition, Paris.

71	**16**	20c. violet	1·60	2·75
72	-	30c. green	1·60	3·75
73	-	40c. red	1·60	3·75
74	-	50c. brown	1·60	2·20
75	-	90c. red	1·80	2·40
76	-	1f.50 blue	1·80	2·75
MS76a		120× 100 mm. 3f. blue. Imperf	13·00	26·00

Design: As T **16**—50c. Agriculture; 3f. T **16**. Horiz—30c. sailing ships; 40c. Women of Three races; 90c. France extends Torch of Civilisation; 1f.50 Diane de Poitiers.

22 Pierre and Marie Curie

1938. International Anti-cancer Fund.

76b	**22**	1f.75+50c. blue	8·50	32·00

23 Man on Camel

24 Warriors

25 Encampment

26 Mauritanians

1938

77	**23**	2c. purple	40	3·75
78	**23**	3c. blue	35	3·50
79	**23**	4c. lilac	55	3·75
80	**23**	5c. red	35	3·00
81	**23**	10c. red	50	3·75
82	**23**	15c. violet	1·00	6·75
83	**24**	20c. red	65	1·20
84	**24**	25c. blue	70	3·50
85	**24**	30c. purple	55	4·25
86	**24**	35c. green	95	7·25
87	**24**	40c. red	1·00	5·50
88	**24**	45c. green	1·60	4·50
89	**24**	50c. violet	65	6·50
90	**25**	55c. lilac	1·40	4·25
91	**25**	60c. violet	1·70	7·00
92	**25**	65c. green	1·40	7·50
93	**25**	70c. red	1·40	6·75
94	**25**	80c. blue	1·80	9·00
95	**25**	90c. lilac	1·50	6·00
96	**25**	1f. red	2·30	5·75
97	**25**	1f. green	1·10	2·30
98	**25**	1f.25 red	2·30	5·25
99	**25**	1f.40 blue	2·50	5·25
100	**25**	1f.50 violet	1·10	4·25
100a	**25**	1f.50 red	£140	£140
101	**25**	1f.60 brown	3·25	5·25
102	**26**	1f.75 blue	1·80	2·75
103	**26**	2f. lilac	1·30	4·00
104	**26**	2f.25 blue	2·30	6·75
105	**26**	2f.50 brown	2·30	4·25
106	**26**	3f. green	95	3·75
107	**26**	5f. red	2·00	6·25
108	**26**	10f. purple	2·00	6·00
109	**26**	20f. red	2·20	4·75

27 Rene Caillie (explorer)

1939. Death Centenary of Caillie.

110	**27**	90c. orange	1·30	4·50
111	**27**	2f. violet	1·30	4·50
112	**27**	2f.25 blue	1·30	4·50

28

1939. New York World's Fair.

113	**28**	1f.25 red	1·20	4·50
114	**28**	2f.25 blue	1·20	3·00

29 Storming the Bastille

1939. 150th Anniversary of French Revolution.

115	**29**	45c.+25c. green and black	11·50	22·00
116	**29**	70c.+30c. brown and black	11·50	22·00
117	**29**	90c.+35c. orange and black	11·50	22·00
118	**29**	1f.25+1f. red and black	11·50	22·00
119	**29**	2f.25+2f. blue and black	11·50	22·00

30 Twin-engine Airliner over Jungle

1940. Air.

120	**30**	1f.90 blue	1·60	6·50
121	**30**	2f.90 red	80	7·50
122	**30**	4f.50 green	1·20	6·00
123	**30**	4f.90 olive	1·50	3·75
124	**30**	6f.90 orange	1·90	5·00

1941. National Defence Fund. Surch **SECOURS NATIONAL** and value.

124a	+1f. on 50c. (No. 89)	6·00	9·00
124b	+2f. on 80c. (No. 94)	14·50	21·00
124c	+2f. on 1f.50 (No. 100)	14·50	21·00
124d	+3f. on 2f. (No. 103)	14·50	21·00

31a Ox Caravan

1942. Marshal Petain issue.

124e	**31a**	1f. green	1·70	4·00
124f	**31a**	2f.50 blue	90	4·00

1942. Air. Colonial Child Welfare Fund. As Nos. 98g/98i of Niger.

124g	1f.50+3f.50 green	95	7·25
124h	2f.+6f. brown	95	7·25
124i	3f.+9f. red	95	7·25

1942. Air. Imperial Fortnight. As No. 98j of Niger.

124j	1f.20+1f.80 blue and red	95	8·25

32 Twin-engine Airliner over Camel Caravan

1942. Air. T **32** inscr 'MAURITANIE' at foot.

124k	**32**	50f. orange and yellow	3·00	9·25

1944. Surch.

125	**25**	3f.50 on 65c. green	1·10	60
126	**25**	4f. on 65c. green	1·40	70
127	**25**	5f. on 65c. green	1·50	1·20
128	**25**	10f. on 65c. green	1·50	1·20
129	**27**	15f. on 90c. orange	2·20	1·80

ISLAMIC REPUBLIC

35 Flag of Republic

1960. Inauguration of Islamic Republic.

130	**35**	25f. bistre, green and brown on rose	4·00	4·50

36

1960. Tenth Anniversary of African Technical Co-operation Commission.

131	**36**	25f. blue and turquoise	3·00	3·50

37 Well **38** Slender-billed Gull

1960

132	**37**	50c. purple and brown (postage)	10	10
133	-	1f. bistre, brown and green	10	10
134	-	2f. brown, green and blue	10	10
135	-	3f. red, sepia and turquoise	55	25
136	-	4f. buff and green	75	40
137	-	5f. chocolate, brown and red	30	10
138	-	10f. blue, black and brown	30	10
139	-	15f. multicoloured	45	25
140	-	20f. brown and green	45	25
141	-	25f. blue and green	70	25
142	-	30f. blue, violet and bistre	85	25
143	-	50f. brown and green	1·20	55
144	-	60f. purple, red and green	1·80	70
145	-	85f. brown, sepia and blue	5·50	2·50
146	-	100f. brn, choc & bl (air)	4·25	2·75
147	-	200f. myrtle, brown & sepia	6·75	4·75
148	**38**	500f. sepia, blue and brown	22·00	10·50

Designs: Vert As T **37**—2f. Harvesting dates; 5f. Harvesting millet; 25, 30f. Seated dance; 50f. 'Telmidi' (symbolic figure); 60f. Metalsmith; 85f. Scimitar oryx; 100f. Greater flamingo; 200f. African spoonbill. Horiz—3f. Barbary sheep; 4f. Fennec foxes; 10f. Cordwainer; 15f. Fishing-boat; 20f. Nomad school.

39 Flag and Map

1960. Proclamation of Independence.

149	**39**	25f. green, brown and chestnut	75	40

42 European, African and Boeing 707 Airliners

1962. Air. Air Afrique Airline.

150	**42**	100f. green, brown and bistre	3·00	1·60

43 Campaign Emblem

1962. Malaria Eradication.

151	**43**	25f.+5f. olive	95	90

44 UN Headquarters and View of Nouakchott

1962. Admission to UNO.

152	**44**	15f. brown, black and blue	45	40
153	**44**	25f. brown, myrtle and blue	50	50
154	**44**	85f. brown, purple and blue	1·60	1·60

45 Union Flag

1962. First Anniversary of Union of African and Malagasy States.

155	**45**	30f. blue	95	90

46 Eagle and Crescent over Nouakchott

1962. Eighth Endemic Diseases Eradication Conference, Nouakchott.

156	**46**	30f. green, brown and blue	80	65

47 Diesel Mineral Train

1962

157	**47**	50f. multicoloured	3·00	1·40

1962. Air. First Anniversary of Admission to UNO. As T **44** but views from different angles and inscr '1 er ANNIVERSAIRE 27 OCTOBRE 1962'.

158		100f. blue, brown & turquoise	1·70	1·30

49 Map and Agriculture

1962. Second Anniversary of Independence.

159	**49**	30f. green and purple	95	55

50 Congress Representatives

1962. First Anniversary of Unity Congress.

160	**50**	25f. brown, myrtle and blue	55	35

51 Globe and Emblem

1962. Freedom from Hunger.

161	**51**	25f.+5f. blue, brown and purple	95	90

52 Douglas DC-3 Airliner over Nouakchott Airport

1963. Air. Creation of National Airline.

162	**52**	500f. myrtle, brown and blue	13·50	5·75

53 Open-cast Mining, Zouerate

1963. Air. Mining Development. Multicoloured.

163	100f. Type **53**	2·00	70
164	200f. Port-Etienne	5·00	1·40

54 Striped Hyena

1963. Animals.

165	**54**	50c. black, brown and myrtle	10	10
166	-	1f. black, blue and buff	10	10
167	-	1f.50 brown, olive & pur	20	10
168	-	2f. purple, green and red	30	10
169	-	5f. bistre, blue and ochre	30	25
170	-	10f. black and ochre	55	25
171	-	15f. purple and blue	55	25
172	-	20f. bistre, purple and blue	75	40
173	-	25f. ochre, brown & turq	1·20	40
174	-	30f. bistre, brown and blue	1·70	40
175	-	50f. bistre, brown and green	2·40	85
176	-	60f. bistre, brown & turq	3·00	1·40

Animals: Horiz—1f. Spotted hyena; 2f. Guinea baboons; 10f. Leopard; 15f. Bongos; 20f. Aardvark; 30f. North African crested porcupine; 60f. Chameleon. Vert—1f.50, Cheetah; 5f. Dromedaries; 25f. Patas monkeys; 50f. Dorcas gazelle.

56 Posts and Telecommunications

1963. Air. African and Malagasy Posts and Telecommunications Union.

177	**56**	85f. multicoloured	1·50	85

57 *Telstar* Satellite

1963. Air. Space Telecommunications.

178	**57**	50f. brown, purple and green	80	60
179	-	100f. blue, brown and red	1·70	80
180	-	150f. turquoise and brown	3·00	1·80

Designs: 100f. *Syncom* satellite; 150f. *Relay* satellite.

58 *Tiros* Satellite

1963. Air. World Meteorological Day.

181	**58**	200f. brown, blue and green	5·00	2·20

59 Airline Emblem

1963. Air. First Anniversary of Air Afrique and DC-8 Service Inauguration.

182	**59**	25f. multicoloured	75	30

60 UN Emblem, Sun and Birds

1963. Air. 15th Anniversary of Declaration of Human Rights.

183	**60**	100f. blue, violet and purple	2·00	1·10

61 Cogwheels and Wheat

1964. Air. European–African Economic Convention.

184	**61**	50f. multicoloured	1·70	1·10

62 Lichtenstein's Sandgrouse

1964. Air. Birds.

185	**62**	100f. ochre, brown and green	3·50	1·40
186	-	200f. black, brown and blue	5·75	2·30
187	-	500f. slate, red and green	17·00	7·25

Designs: 200f. Reed cormorant; 500f. Dark chanting goshawk.

63 Temple, Philae

1964. Air. Nubian Monuments Preservation.

188	**63**	10f. brown, black and blue	75	25
189	**63**	25f. slate, brown and blue	95	65
190	**63**	60f. chocolate, brown and blue	2·00	1·00

64 WMO Emblem. Sun and Lightning

1964. World Meteorological Day.

191	**64**	85f. blue, orange and brown	1·80	1·00

65 Radar Antennae and Sun Emblem

1964. International Quiet Sun Years.

192	**65**	25f. red, green and blue	75	55

66 Bowl depicting Horse-racing

1964. Air. Olympic Games, Tokyo.

193	**66**	15f. brown and bistre	75	45
194	-	50f. brown and blue	1·30	70
195	-	85f. brown and red	2·30	1·50
196	-	100f. brown and green	2·75	1·70
MS196a 191×100 mm. Nos. 193/196			9·00	9·00

Designs: Vert—50f. Running (vase); 85f. Wrestling (vase). Horiz—100f. Chariot-racing (bowl).

67 Flat-headed Grey Mullet

1964. Marine Fauna.

197	**67**	1f. green, blue and brown	30	25
198	-	5f. purple, green and brown	30	25
199	-	10f. green, ochre and blue	45	25
200	-	60f. slate, green and brown	2·75	1·20

Designs: Vert—5f. Lobster (*Panulirus mauritanicus*); 10f. Lobster (*Panulirus regius*). Horiz—60f. Meagre.

68 'Co-operation'

1964. French, African and Malagasy Co-operation.

201	**68**	25f. brown, green and mauve	75	55

69 President Kennedy

1964. Air. First Death Anniversary of President Kennedy.

202	**69**	100f. multicoloured	2·00	1·40
MS202a 90×130 mm. No. 202 in block of four			8·25	8·25

70 *Nymphaea lotus*

1965. Mauritanian Flowers.

203	**70**	5f. green, red and blue	30	25
204	-	10f. green, ochre and purple	30	25
205	-	20f. brown, red and sepia	60	30
206	-	45f. turquoise, purple and green	1·50	80

Flowers: Vert—10f. *Acacia gommier*; 45f. *Caralluma retrospiciens*. Horiz—20f. *Adenium obesum*.

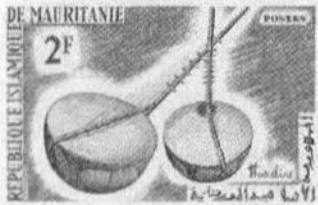

71 Hardine

1965. Musical Instruments and Musicians.

207	**71**	2f. brown, bistre and blue	30	25
208	-	8f. brown, bistre and red	45	25
209	-	25f. brown, black and green	75	25
210	-	40f. black, blue and violet	1·20	55

Designs: 8f. Tobol (drums); 25f. Tidinit (Violins); 40f. Native band.

72 Abraham Lincoln

1965. Death Centenary of Abraham Lincoln.

211	**72**	50f. multicoloured	1·00	50

73 Early Telegraph and Relay Satellite

1965. Air. Centenary of ITU.

212	**73**	250f. green, mauve and blue	6·00	4·00

74 Palms in the Adrar

1965. Tourism and Archaeology (1st series).

213	**74**	1f. green, brown and blue	10	10
214	-	4f. brown, red and blue	30	10
215	-	15f. multicoloured	45	25
216	-	60f. sepia, brown and green	1·40	70

Designs: Vert—4f. Chinguetti Mosque. Horiz—15f. Claypits; 60f. Carved doorway, Qualata.

See also Nos. 255/258.

75 'Attack on Cancer' (the Crab)

1965. Air. Campaign against Cancer.

217	**75**	100f. red, blue and ochre	1·80	85

76 Wooden Tea Service

1965. Native Handicrafts.

218	**76**	3f. brown, ochre and slate	10	10
219	-	7f. purple, orange and blue	30	25
220	-	25f. brown, black and red	55	40
221	-	50f. red, green and orange	1·20	55

Designs: Vert—7f. Snuff-box and pipe; 25f. Damasquine dagger. Horiz—50f. Mederdra chest.

77 Nouakchott Wharf

1965. Mauritanian Development.

222		5f. green and brown	30	25
223	**77**	10f. red, turquoise and blue	30	10
224	-	30f. red, brown and purple	70	25
225	-	85f. violet, lake and blue	1·50	75

Designs: Vert—5f., 30f. Choum Tunnel. Horiz—85f. Nouakchott Hospital.

78 Sir Winston Churchill

1965. Air. Churchill Commemoration.

226	**78**	200f. multicoloured	3·50	1·60

79 Rocket Diamant

1966. Air. French Satellites.

227	**79**	30f. green, red and blue	75	45
228	-	60f. purple, blue and turquoise	1·30	70
229	-	90f. lake, violet and blue	2·20	1·00

Designs: Horiz—60f. Satellite *A 1* and Globe; 90f. Rocket Scout and satellite *FR 1*.

80 Dr. Schweitzer and Hospital Scene

1966. Air. Schweitzer Commemoration.

230	**80**	50f. multicoloured	1·70	85

81 Stafford, Schirra and *Gemini 6*

1966. Air. Space Flights. Multicoloured.

231	50f. Type **81**	80	45
232	100f. Borman, Lovell and *Gemini 7*	1·80	75
233	200f. Beliaiev, Leonov and *Voskhod 2*	3·50	1·70

82 African Woman and Carved Head

1966. World Festival of Negro Arts, Dakar.

234	**82**	10f. black, brown and green	30	10
235	-	30f. purple, black and blue	45	25
236	-	60f. purple, red and orange	1·20	70

Designs: 30f. Dancers and hands playing cornet; 60f. Cine-camera and village huts.

83 'Dove' over Map of Africa

1966. Air. Organisation of African Unity (OAU).

237	**83**	100f. multicoloured	1·20	60

84 Satellite *D 1*

1966. Air. Launching of Satellite *D 1*.

238	**84**	100f. plum, brown and blue	1·70	1·10

85 Breguet 14T2 Salon

1966. Air. Early Aircraft.

239	**85**	50f. indigo, blue and bistre	1·20	30
240	-	100f. green, purple and blue	2·20	70
241	-	150f. turquoise, brown and blue	4·75	2·20
242	-	200f. indigo, blue and purple	6·75	3·25

Aircraft: 100f. Farman Goliath; 150f. Couzinet *Arc en Ciel*; 200f. Latecoere 28-3 seaplane *Comte de la Vaulx*.

86 *Acacia ehrenbergiana*

1966. Mauritanian Flowers. Multicoloured.

243	10f. Type **86**	35	10
244	15f. *Schouwia purpurea*	50	25
245	20f. *Ipomaea asarifolia*	60	25
246	25f. *Grewia bicolor*	95	30
247	30f. *Pancratium trianthum*	1·30	45
248	60f. *Blepharis linariifolia*	2·10	75

87 DC-8F and Air Afrique Emblem

1966. Air. Inauguration of Douglas DC-8F Air Services.

249	**87**	30f. grey, black and red	75	45

88 *Raft of the Medusa* (after Gericault)

1966. Air. 150th Anniversary of Shipwreck of the *Medusa*.

250	**88**	500f. multicoloured	13·00	8·75

89 *Myrina silenus*

1966. Butterflies. Multicoloured.

251	5f. Type **89**	75	35
252	30f. *Colotis danae*	2·20	70
253	45f. *Hypolimnas misippus*	3·25	95
254	60f. *Danaus chrysippus*	4·75	1·60

90 'Hunting' (petroglyph from Tenses, Adrar)

1966. Tourism and Archaeology (2nd series).
255 **90** 2f. chestnut and brown 45 10
256 - 3f. brown and blue 60 25
257 - 30f. green and red 1·20 45
258 - 50f. brown, green and purple 2·20 1·20
Designs: 3f. 'Fighting' (petroglyph from Tenses, Adrar); 30f. Copper jug (from Le Mreyer, Adrar); 50f. Camel and caravan.

91 Cogwheels and Ears of Wheat

1966. Air. Europafrique.
259 **91** 50f. multicoloured 1·20 50

92 UNESCO Emblem

1966. 20th Anniversary of UNESCO.
260 **92** 30f. multicoloured 75 40

93 Olympic Village, Grenoble

1967. Publicity for Olympic Games (1968).
261 - 20f. brown, blue and green 50 30
262 **93** 30f. brown, green and blue 75 45
263 - 40f. brown, purple and blue 1·00 60
264 - 100f. brown, green and black 2·30 1·10
Designs: Vert—20f. Old and new buildings, Mexico City; 40f. Ice rink, Grenoble and Olympic torch. Horiz—100f. Olympic stadium, Mexico City.

94 South African Crowned Crane

1967. Air. Birds. Multicoloured.
265 100f. Type **94** 3·00 1·10
266 200f. Great egret 5·25 1·70
267 500f. Ostrich 15·00 5·75

95 Globe, Rockets and Eye

1967. Air. World Fair, Montreal.
268 **95** 250f. brown, blue and black 4·50 1·90

96 Prosopis

1967. Trees.
269 **96** 10f. green, blue and brown 40 10
270 - 15f. green, blue and purple 55 20
271 - 20f. green, purple and blue 60 25
272 - 25f. brown and green 75 40
273 - 30f. brown, green and red 1·10 45
Trees: 15f. Jujube; 20f. Date palm; 25f. Peltophorum; 30f. Baobab.

97 Jamboree Emblem and Scout Kit

1967. World Scout Jamboree, Idaho.
274 **97** 60f. blue, green and brown 1·20 45
275 - 90f. blue, green and red 1·80 70
Design: Horiz—90f. Jamboree emblem and scouts.

98 Weaving

1967. Advancement of Mauritanian Women.
276 **98** 5f. red, black and violet 30 10
277 - 10f. black, violet and green 30 10
278 - 20f. black, purple and blue 55 25
279 - 30f. blue, black and brown 80 40
280 - 50f. black, violet and indigo 1·10 45
Designs: Vert—10f. Needlework; 30f. Laundering. Horiz—20f. Nursing; 50f. Sewing (with machines).

99 Atomic Symbol

1967. Air. International Atomic Energy Agency.
281 **99** 200f. blue, green and red 3·50 1·50

100 Cattle

1967. Campaign for Prevention of Cattle Plague.
282 **100** 30f. red, blue and green 95 55

101 Map of Africa, Letters and Pylons

1967. Air. Fifth Anniversary of UAMPT.
283 **101** 100f. green, brown & pur 1·50 75

102 *Francois of Rimini* (Ingres)

1967. Air. Death Centenary of Jean Ingres (painter). Multicoloured.
284 90f. Type **102** 2·00 80
285 200f. *Ingres in his Studio* (Alaux) 3·75 1·50
See also Nos. 306/308.

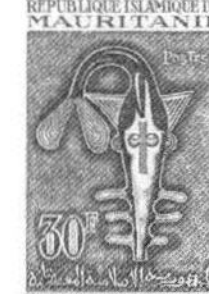

103 Currency Tokens

1967. Fifth Anniversary of West African Monetary Union.
286 **103** 30f. grey and orange 55 25

104 *Hyphaene thebaica*

1967. Mauritanian Fruits.
287 **104** 1f. brown, green and purple 20 10
288 - 2f. yellow, green and brown 25 10
289 - 3f. olive, green and violet 40 20
290 - 4f. red, green and brown 45 20
291 - 5f. orange, brown and green 55 25
Fruits: Horiz—2f. *Balanites aegyptiaca*; 4f. *Ziziphus lotus*. Vert—3f. *Adansonia digitata*; 5f. *Phoenix dactylifera*.

105 Human Rights Emblem

1968. Human Rights Year.
292 **105** 30f. yellow, green and black 75 25
293 **105** 50f. yellow, brown and black 95 55

106 Chancellor Adenauer

1968. Air. Adenauer Commemoration.
294 **106** 100f. sepia, brown and blue 2·00 85
MS295 120×170 mm. No. 294×4 8·25 8·25

107 Skiing

1968. Air. Olympic Games, Grenoble and Mexico.
296 **107** 20f. purple, indigo & blue 45 10
297 - 30f. brown, green and plum 55 25
298 - 50f. green, blue and ochre 80 40
299 - 100f. green, red and brown 1·80 65
Designs: Vert—30f. Horse-vaulting; 50f. Ski-jumping. Horiz—100f. Hurdling.

108 Mosque, Nouakchott

1968. Tourism. Multicoloured.
300 30f. Type **108** 45 25
301 45f. Amogjar Pass 60 30
302 90f. Cavaliers' Tower, Boutilimit 1·10 60

109 Man and WHO Emblem

1968. Air. 20th Anniversary of WHO.
303 **109** 150f. blue, purple and brown 2·50 1·10

110 UNESCO Emblem and 'Movement of Water'

1968. International Hydrological Decade.
304 **110** 90f. green and lake 95 50

111 UPU Building, Berne

1968. Admission of Mauritania to UPU.
305 **111** 30f. brown and red 55 25

1968. Air. Paintings by Ingres. As T **102**. Multicoloured.
306 100f. *Man's Torso* 1·90 85
307 150f. *The Iliad* 3·00 1·30
308 250f. *The Odyssey* 5·00 2·20

112 Land-yachts crossing Desert

1968. Land-yacht Racing.
309 **112** 30f. blue, yellow and orange 75 30
310 - 40f. purple, blue and orange 95 40
311 - 60f. green, yellow and orange 1·50 70
Designs: Horiz—40f. Racing on shore. Vert—60f. Crew making repairs.

113 Dr. Martin Luther King

1968. Air. 'Apostles of Peace'.
312 **113** 50f. brown, blue and olive 95 45
313 - 50f. brown and blue 1·00 45
MS314 121×161 mm. Nos. 312/313×2 alternately *se-tenant* 4·25 4·25
Design: No. 313, Mahatma Gandhi.

113a *Surprise Letter* (C. A. Coypel)

1968. Air. Philexafrique Stamp Exhibition, Abidjan, Ivory Coast (1969) (1st issue).
315 **113a** 100f. multicoloured 3·75 3·50
See also No. 322.

114 Donkey and Foal

1968. Domestic Animals. Multicoloured.

No.	Type	Description		
316		5f. Type **114**	35	10
317		10f. Ewe and lamb	55	25
318		15f. Dromedary and calf	65	30
319		30f. Mare and foal	95	40
320		50f. Cow and calf	1·40	60
321		90f. Goat and kid	2·75	80

114a Forest Scene and Stamp of 1938

1969. Air. Philexafrique Stamp Exhibition, Abidjan, Ivory Coast (2nd issue).

No.	Type	Description		
322	**114a**	50f. purple, green and brown	2·30	2·10

114b *Napoleon at Council of Five Hundred* (Bouchot)

1969. Air. Birth Bicentenary of Napoleon Bonaparte. Multicoloured.

No.	Type	Description		
323		50f. **114b**	2·20	1·10
324		90f. *Napoleon's Installation by the Council of State* (Conder)	3·00	1·70
325		250f. *The Farewell of Fontainebleau* (Vernet)	7·50	4·25

115 Map and ILO Emblem

1969. 50th Anniversary of ILO.

No.	Type	Description		
326	**115**	50f. multicoloured	75	40

116 Monitor Lizard

1969. Reptiles. Multicoloured.

No.	Type	Description		
327		5f. Type **116**	55	25
328		10f. Horned viper	80	40
329		30f. Black-collared cobra	1·90	55
330		60f. Rock python	3·00	1·60
331		85f. Nile crocodile	5·25	1·90

117 Date Palm, *Parlatoria blanchardi* and *Pharoscymus anchorage*

1969. Date-palms. Protection Campaign.

No.	Type	Description		
332	**117**	30f. blue, red and green	1·90	90

118 Camel and Emblem

1969. Air. African Tourist Year.

No.	Type	Description		
333	**118**	50f. purple, blue and orange	1·20	60

119 Dancers and Baalbek Columns

1969. Baalbek Festival, Lebanon.

No.	Type	Description		
334	**119**	100f. brown, red and blue	1·80	70

120 *Apollo 8* and Moon

1969. Air. Moon Flight of *Apollo 8*. Embossed on gold foil.

No.	Type	Description		
335	**120**	1,000f. gold	24·00	24·00

121 Wolde (marathon)

1969. Air. Gold Medal Winners, Mexico Olympic Games.

No.	Type	Description		
336	**121**	30f. red, brown and blue	45	25
337	-	70f. red, brown and green	95	50
338	-	150f. green, bistre and red	2·30	1·10

Designs: 70f. Beamon (athletics); 150f. Vera Caslavska (gymnastics).

122 London–Istanbul Route-Map

1969. Air. London–Sydney Motor Rally.

No.	Type	Description		
339	**122**	10f. brown, blue and purple	20	10
340	-	20f. brown, blue and purple	50	25
341	-	50f. brown, blue and purple	95	45
342	-	70f. brown, blue and purple	1·40	55
MS343		131×101 mm. Nos. 339/342	3·75	3·75

Route: Maps—20f. Ankara–Teheran; 50f. Kandahar–Bombay; 70f. Perth–Sydney.

122a Bank Emblem

1969. Fifth Anniversary of African Development Bank. Multicoloured.

No.	Type	Description		
344	**122a**	30f. brown, green & blue	55	25

123 Pendant

1969. Native Handicrafts.

No.	Type	Description		
345	**123**	10f. brown and purple	30	10
346	-	20f. red, black and blue	65	25

Design: Horiz—20f. Rahla headdress.

124 Sea-water Desalination Plant, Nouakchott

1969. Economic Development.

No.	Type	Description		
347	**124**	10f. blue, purple and red	35	30
348	-	15f. black, lake and blue	35	30
349	-	30f. black, purple and blue	45	25

Designs: 15f. Fishing quay, Nouadhibou; 30f. Meat-processing plant, Kaedi.

125 Lenin

1970. Birth Centenary of Lenin.

No.	Type	Description		
350	**125**	30f. black, red and blue	2·10	70

126 *Sternocera interrupta*

1970. Insects.

No.	Type	Description		
351	**126**	5f. black, buff and brown	40	35
352	-	10f. brown, yellow & lake	50	30
353	-	20f. olive, purple and brown	95	35
354	-	30f. violet, green and brown	1·70	50
355	-	40f. brown, blue and lake	3·00	95

Insects: 10f. *Anoplocnemis curvipes*; 20f. *Julodis aequinoctialis*; 30f. *Thermophilum sexmaculatum marginatum*; 40f. *Placaederus denticornis*.

127 Footballers and Hemispheres

1970. World Cup Football Championship, Mexico.

No.	Type	Description		
356	**127**	25f. multicoloured	45	25
357	-	30f. multicoloured	60	25
358	-	70f. multicoloured	1·20	60
359	-	150f. multicoloured	2·40	95

Designs: 30, 70, 150f. As T **127**, but with different players.

1970. New UPU Headquarters Building. As T **81** of New Caledonia.

No.	Type	Description		
360		30f. red, brown and green	75	40

128 Japanese Musician, Emblem and Map on Palette

1970. Air. EXPO 70 World Fair, Osaka, Japan. Multicoloured.

No.	Type	Description		
361		50f. Type **128**	75	30
362		75f. Japanese fan	1·20	50
363		150f. Stylised bird, map and boat	2·20	1·00

129 UN Emblem and Examples of Progress

1970. Air. 25th Anniversary of UNO.

No.	Type	Description		
364	**129**	100f. green, brown and blue	1·50	80

130 Vladimir Komarov

1970. Air. Lost Heroes of Space (1st series).

No.	Type	Description		
365	**130**	150f. brown, orge & slate	2·20	95
366	-	150f. brown, blue and slate	2·20	95
367	-	150f. brown, orge & slate	2·20	95
MS368		130×100 mm. Nos. 365/367	7·25	7·25

Heroes: No. 366, Elliott See; 376, Yuri Gagarin.

See also Nos. 376/**MS**379.

131 Descent of *Apollo 13*

1970. Air. Space Flight of *Apollo 13*.

No.	Type	Description		
369	**131**	500f. red, blue and gold	8·75	8·75

132 Woman in Traditional Costume

1970. Traditional Costumes. As T **132**.

No.	Type	Description		
370	**132**	10f. orange and brown	60	35
371	-	30f. blue, red and brown	1·30	45
372	-	40f. brown, purple and red	1·60	45
373	-	50f. blue and brown	1·90	50
374	-	70f. brown, choc & bl	2·20	80

133 Arms and State House

1970. Air. Tenth Anniversary of Independence.

No.	Type	Description		
375	**133**	100f. multicoloured	1·50	60

1970. Air. Lost Heroes of Space (2nd series). As T **130**.

No.	Type	Description		
376		150f. brown, blue & turquoise	2·20	90
377		150f. brown, blue & turquoise	2·20	90
378		150f. brown, blue and orange	2·20	90
MS379		130×100 mm. Nos. 376/8	7·25	6·75

Heroes: No. 376, Roger Chaffee; No. 377, Virgil Grissom; No. 378, Edward White.

134 Greek Wrestling

1971. Air. Pre-Olympics Year.

No.	Type	Description		
380	**134**	100f. brown, purple & blue	2·20	1·10

135 People of Different Races

1971. Racial Equality Year.

381	**135**	30f. plum, blue and brown	70	25
382	-	40f. black, red and blue	1·00	30

Design: Vert—40f. European and African hands.

136 President Nasser

1971. Air. President Gamal Nasser of Egypt Commemoration.

383	**136**	100f. multicoloured	1·20	55

137 General De Gaulle in Uniform

1971. De Gaulle Commemoration. Multicoloured.

384	40f. Type **137**	2·30	90
385	100f. De Gaulle as President of France	5·25	1·80

138 Scout Badge, Scout and Map

1971. Air. 13th World Scout Jamboree, Asagiri, Japan.

387	**138**	35f. multicoloured	50	25
388	**138**	40f. multicoloured	75	25
389	**138**	100f. multicoloured	1·50	55

139 Diesel Locomotive

1971. Miferma Iron-ore Mines. Multicoloured.

390	35f. Iron ore train	2·20	1·00
391	100f. Type **139**	5·50	2·30

Nos. 390/391 were issued together, *se-tenant*, forming a composite design.

139a Headquarters, Brazzaville, and Ardin Musicians

1971. Air. Tenth Anniversary of African and Malagasy Posts and Telecommunications Union.

392	**139a**	100f. multicoloured	1·50	85

140 APU Emblem and Airmail Envelope

1971. Air. Tenth Anniversary of African Postal Union.

393	**140**	35f. multicoloured	75	45

141 UNICEF Emblem and Child

1971. 25th Anniversary of UNICEF.

394	**141**	35f. black, brown and blue	70	25

142 Moslem King (*c.* 1218)

1972. Air. Moslem Miniatures. Multicoloured.

395	35f. Type **142**	60	10
396	40f. Enthroned Prince (Egypt, *c.* 1334)	95	45
397	100f. Pilgrims' Caravan (Maquamat, Baghdad, 1237)	2·20	85

1972. Air. UNESCO Save Venice Campaign. As T **135a** of Niger. Multicoloured.

398	45f. *Quay and Ducal Palace* (Carlevaris) (vert)	95	45
399	100f. *Grand Canal* (Canaletto)	2·00	90
400	250f. *Santa Maria della Salute* (Canaletto)	4·75	2·10

143 Hurdling

1972. Air. Olympic Games, Munich.

401	**143**	75f. purple, orange & grn	95	40
402	**143**	100f. purple, blue & brn	1·50	60
403	**143**	200f. purple, lake & green	2·75	1·00
MS404		191×100 mm. Nos. 401/403	6·75	6·75

144 Nurse tending Baby

1972. Mauritanian Red Crescent Fund.

405	**144**	35f.+5f. multicoloured	95	90

145 Samuel Morse and Morse Key

1972. World Telecommunications Day. Multicoloured.

406	35f. Type **145**	65	25
407	40f. *Relay* satellite and hemispheres	80	25
408	75f. Alexander Graham Bell and early telephone	1·40	55

146 Spirifer Shell

1972. Fossil Shells. Multicoloured.

409	25f. Type **146**	3·25	95
410	75f. Trilobite	5·50	2·75

147 *Luna 16* and Moon Probe

1972. Air. Russian Exploration of the Moon.

411	**147**	75f. brown, blue and green	95	35
412	-	100f. brown, grey & violet	1·30	60

Design: Horiz—100f. *Lunokhod 1*.

1972. Air. Gold Medal Winners, Munich. Nos. 401/403 optd as listed below.

413	**143**	75f. purple, orange & grn	1·00	35
414	**143**	100f. purple, blue & brn	1·50	55
415	**143**	200f. purple, lake & green	3·00	90

Overprints:—75f. **110m. HAIES MILBURN MEDAILLE D'OR**; 100f. **400m. HAIES AKII-BUA MEDAILLE D'OR**; 200f. **3,000m. STEEPLE KEINO MEDAILLE D'OR**.

149 Africans and 500f. Coin

1972. Tenth Anniversary of West African Monetary Union.

416	**149**	35f. grey, brown and green	70	30

1973. Air. Moon Flight of *Apollo 17*. No. 267 surch **Apollo XVII Decembre 1972** and value.

417	250f. on 500f. multicoloured	3·75	1·80

151 Mediterranean Monk Seal with Young

1973. Seals. Multicoloured.

418	40f. Type **151** (postage)	3·75	95
419	135f. Head of Mediterranean monk seal (air)	5·00	2·75

152 *Lion and Crocodile* (Delacroix)

1973. Air. Paintings by Delacroix. Multicoloured.

420	100f. Type **152**	2·30	1·10
421	250f. *Lion attacking Forest Hog*	5·25	2·75

153 'Horns of Plenty'

1973. Tenth Anniversary of World Food Programme.

422	**153**	35f. multicoloured	55	30

154 UPU Monument, Berne, and Globe

1973. World UPU Day.

423	**154**	100f. blue, orange & green	1·80	95

155 Nomad Encampment and Eclipse

1973. Total Eclipse of the Sun.

424	**155**	35f. purple and green	70	25
425	-	40f. purple, red and blue	70	25
426	-	140f. purple and red	2·75	1·00
MS427		173×100 mm. As Nos. 424/426 but colours changed; 35f. ultramarine and purple; 40f. ultramarine, orange and purple; 140f. ultramarine and purple	4·50	4·25

Designs: Vert—40f. Rocket and Concorde. Horiz—140f. Observation team.

1973. Drought Relief. African Solidarity. No. 320 surch **SECHERESSE SOLIDARITE AFRICAINE** and value.

428	20um. on 50f. multicoloured	95	55

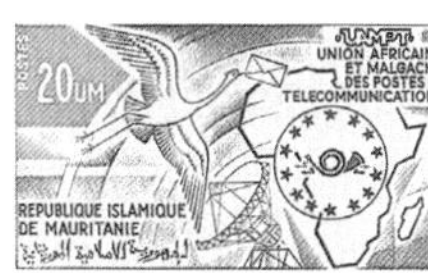
155a Crane with Letter and Union Emblem

1973. 12th Anniversary of African and Malagasy Posts and Telecommunications Union.

429	**155a**	20um. brown, lt brn & orge	1·20	55

157 Detective making Arrest and Fingerprint

1973. 50th Anniversary of International Criminal Police Organisation (Interpol).

430	**157**	15um. violet, red & brown	1·20	60

1974. Various stamps surch with values in new currency. (a) Postage. (i) Nos. 345/346.

431	**123**	27um. on 10f. brn & pur	1·70	80
432	-	28um. on 20f. red, blk & bl	2·00	1·20
		(ii) Nos. 351/355.		
433	**126**	5um. on 5f. black, buff and brown	60	25
434	-	7um. on 10f. brown, yellow and lake	75	25
435	-	8um. on 20f. olive, purple and brown	95	45
436	-	10um. on 30f. violet, purple and brown	1·50	55
437	-	20um. on 40f. brown, blue and lake	2·75	1·20
		(iii) Nos. 409/410.		
438	**146**	5um. on 25f. multicoloured	2·50	1·10
439	-	15um. on 75f. mult	4·25	2·30
		(iv) No. 418.		
440	**151**	8um. on 40f. multicoloured	1·20	55
		(b) Air. (i) Nos. 395/397.		
441	**142**	7um. on 35f. mult	45	25
442	-	8um. on 40f. mult	75	25
443	-	20um. on 100f. mult	2·00	80
		(ii) No. 419.		
444		27um. on 135f. mult	2·75	1·10
		(iii) Nos. 420/421.		
445	**152**	20um. on 100f. mult	2·00	90
446	-	50um. on 250f. mult	4·50	2·30
		(iv) Nos. 424/426.		
447	**155**	7um. on 35f. purple and green	45	25
448	-	8um. on 40f. pur, red and blue	75	25
449	-	28um. on 140f. pur & red	2·20	80

159 Footballers

1974. Air. World Cup Football Championship, West Germany.

450	**159**	7um. multicoloured	55	25
451	**159**	8um. multicoloured	75	25
452	**159**	20um. multicoloured	1·60	80
MS453		120×105 mm. 30um. multicoloured	2·75	2·75

160 Jules Verne and Scenes from Books

1974. Air. Jules Verne 'Prophet of Space Travel' and *Skylab* Flights Commemoration.

454	**160**	70um. silver	7·25	7·25
455	-	70um. silver	7·25	7·25
456	**160**	250um. gold	22·00	22·00

457 - 250um. gold 22·00 22·00

Designs: Nos. 455, 457, *Skylab* in Space.

161 Sir Winston Churchill

1974. Air. Birth Centenary of Sir Winston Churchill.

458 **161** 40um. red and purple 2·75 1·40

162 UPU Monument and Globes

1974. Centenary of UPU.

459 **162** 30um. red, green & dp grn 2·50 1·10

460 **162** 50um. red, lt blue & blue 4·50 1·70

163 5 Ouguiya Coin and Banknote

1974. First Anniversary of Introduction of Ouguiya Currency.

461 **163** 7um. black, green and blue 55 25

462 - 8um. black, mauve and green 60 25

463 - 20um. black, blue and red 1·50 65

Designs: 8um. 10 ouguiya coin and banknote; 20um. 20 ouguiya coin and banknote.

164 Lenin

1974. Air. 50th Death Anniversary of Lenin.

464 **164** 40um. green and red 4·00 1·80

1974. Treaty of Berne Centenary. Nos. 459/460 optd **9 OCTOBRE 100 ANS D'UNION POSTALE INTERNATIONALE.**

465 **162** 30um. red, green and deep green 2·50 1·40

466 **162** 50um. red, light blue and blue 4·50 1·80

1975. Nos. 287/291 surch in new currency.

467 - 1um. on 5f. orange, brown and green 10 10

468 - 2um. on 4f. red, green and brown 30 10

469 - 3um. on 2f. yellow, green and brown 30 25

470 **104** 10um. on 1f. brown, green and purple 80 30

471 - 12um. on 3f. olive, green and violet 1·20 45

166 Two Hunters

1975. Rock-carvings, Zemmour.

472 **166** 4um. red and brown 70 10

473 - 5um. purple 95 35

474 - 10um. blue and light blue 1·60 80

Designs: Vert—5um. Ostrich. Horiz—10um. Elephant.

167 Mauritanian Women

1975. Air. International Women's Year.

475 **167** 12um. purple, brown and blue 75 25

476 - 40um. purple, brown and blue 2·75 1·10

Designs: 40um. Head of Mauritanian woman.

168 Combined European and African Heads

1975. Europafrique.

477 **168** 40um. brown, red & bistre 2·75 1·10

169 Dr. Schweitzer

1975. Birth Centenary of Dr. Albert Schweitzer.

478 **169** 60um. olive, brown & green 4·00 2·30

1975. Pan-African Drought Relief. Nos. 301/302 surch **SECHERESSE SOLIDARITE AFRICAINE** and value.

479 15um. on 45f. multicoloured 1·50 70

480 25um. on 90f. multicoloured 2·30 1·10

171 Akoujt Plant and Man with Camel

1975. Mining Industry.

481 **171** 10um. brown, blue & orge 95 40

482 - 12um. blue, red and brown 1·30 60

Design: 12um. Mining operations.

172 Fair Emblem

1975. Nouakchott National Fair.

483 **172** 10um. multicoloured 75 40

173 Throwing the Javelin

1975. Air. Pre-Olympic Year. Olympic Games, Montreal (1976).

484 **173** 50um. red, green & brown 3·00 1·80

485 - 52um. blue, brown and red 3·00 1·80

Design: 52um. Running.

174 Commemorative Medal

1975. 15th Anniversary of Independence. Multicoloured.

486 10um. Type **174** 90 45

487 12um. Map of Mauritania 1·20 45

175 Soyuz Cosmonauts Leonov and Kubasov

1975. Apollo–Soyuz Space Link. Multicoloured.

488 8um. Type **175** (postage) 75 25

489 10um. Soyuz on launch-pad 95 40

490 20um. Apollo on launch-pad (air) 1·30 55

491 50um. Cosmonauts meeting astronauts 2·75 1·10

492 60um. Parachute splashdown 3·50 1·60

MS493 103×77 mm. 100um. Leonov Kubasov, Brand, Stafford and Slayton 5·50 2·50

176 Foot-soldier of Lauzun's Legion

1976. Bicentenary of American Independence. Multicoloured.

494 8um. Type **176** (postage) 85 25

495 10um. 'Green Mountain' infantryman 1·20 45

496 20um. Lauzun Hussars officer (air) 1·20 50

497 50um. Artillery officer of 3rd Continental Regiment 3·50 1·10

498 60um. Grenadier of Gatinais' Regiment 4·25 1·60

MS499 100×125 mm. 100um. Soldier of Washington Guards 6·75 2·50

1976. Tenth Anniversary of Arab Labour Charter. No. 408 surch **10e ANNIVERSAIRE DE LA CHARTE ARABE DU TRAVAIL** in French and Arabic.

500 12um. on 75f. blue, blk & grn 95 45

178 Commemorative Text on Map

1976. Reunification of Mauritania.

501 **178** 10um. green, lilac and deep green 95 45

181 Running

1976. Air. Olympic Games, Montreal.

514 **181** 10um. brown, green and violet 90 40

515 - 12um. brown, green and violet 1·10 60

516 - 52um. brown, green and violet 3·50 2·10

Designs: 12um. Vaulting (gymnastics); 52um. Fencing.

182 LZ-4 at Friedrichshafen

1976. 75th Anniversary of Zeppelin Airship. Multicoloured.

517 5um. Type **182** (postage) 30 10

518 10um. *Schwaben* over German Landscape 55 25

519 12um. *Hansa* over Heligoland 75 40

520 20um. *Bodensee* and Doctor H. Durr 1·40 55

521 50um. *Graf Zeppelin* over Capitol, Washington (air) 3·25 1·30

522 60um. *Graf Zeppelin II* crossing Swiss Alps 4·25 1·60

MS523 130×104 mm. 100um. *Hindenberg* over Olympic Stadium, Berlin 7·50 2·30

183 Temple and Bas-relief

1976. UNESCO Save Moenjodaro (Pakistan) Campaign.

524 **183** 15um. multicoloured 1·20 55

184 Sacred Ibis and Yellow-billed Stork

1976. Air. Mauritanian Birds. Multicoloured.

525 50um. Type **184** 3·00 1·40

526 100um. Marabou storks (horiz) 6·00 2·30

527 200um. Long-crested and Martial eagles 13·00 5·50

185 Alexander Graham Bell, Early Telephone and Satellite

1976. Telephone Centenary.

528 **185** 10um. blue, lake and red 95 35

186 Mohammed Ali Jinnah

1976. Birth Centenary of Mohammed Ali Jinnah (first Governor-General of Pakistan).

529 **186** 10um. multicoloured 55 40

187 Capsule Assembly

1977. Viking Space Mission. Multicoloured.

530 10um. Misson Control (horiz) (postage) 60 25

531 12um. Type **187** 95 25

532 20um. Viking in flight (horiz) (air) 1·00 25

533	50um. Viking over Mars (horiz)	2·75	65
534	60um. Parachute descent	3·00	90
MS535	103×79 mm. 100um. Viking on Mars	5·50	1·80

188 Bush Hare

1977. Mauritanian Animals. Multicoloured.

536	5um. Type **188**	45	20
537	10um. Golden jackals	1·00	45
538	12um. Warthogs	1·40	60
539	14um. Lion and lioness	1·70	75
540	15um. African elephants	2·75	1·10

189 Frederic and Irene Joliot-Curie (Chemistry, 1935)

1977. Nobel Prize-winners. Multicoloured.

541	12um. Type **189** (postage)	1·40	25
542	15um. Emil von Behring and nurse inoculating patient (1901)	95	25
543	14um. George Bernard Shaw and scene from *Androcles and the Lion* (1925) (air)	95	25
544	55um. Thomas Mann and scene from *Joseph and his Brethren* (1929)	3·00	75
545	60um. International Red Cross and scene on Western Front (Peace Prize) (1917)	3·50	90
MS546	117×80 mm. 100um. General George C. Marshall (Peace, 1953)	8·00	2·20

190 APU Emblem

1977. 25th Anniversary of Arab Postal Union.

547	**190**	12um. multicoloured	75	45

191 Oil Lamp

1977. Pottery from Tegdaoust.

548	**191**	1um. olive, brown and blue	10	10
549	-	2um. mauve, brown and blue	30	10
550	-	5um. orange, brown and blue	45	25
551	-	12um. brown, green and red	1·00	40

Designs: 2um. Four-handled tureen; 5um. Large jar—12um. Narrow-necked jug.

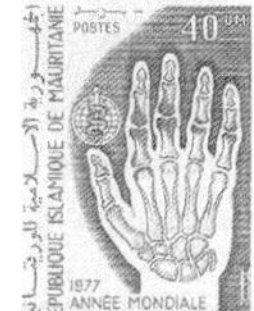

192 Skeleton of Hand

1977. World Rheumatism Year.

552	**192**	40um. orange, brown and green	3·00	1·60

193 Holy Kaaba, Mecca

1977. Air. Pilgrimage to Mecca.

553	**193**	12um. multicoloured	1·20	65

194 Charles Lindbergh and *Spirit of St Louis*

1977. History of Aviation. Multicoloured.

554	12um. Type **194**	75	25
555	14um. Clement Ader and *Eole*	95	25
556	15um. Louis Bleriot and Bleriot XI	1·10	40
557	55um. General Italo Balbo and Savoia Marchetti S-55X flying boats	3·50	90
558	60um. Concorde	3·75	1·10
MS559	116×91 mm. 100um. Lindbergh standing beside *Spirit of St Louis*	7·25	2·10

195 Dome of the Rock

1977. Palestinian Welfare.

560	**195**	12um. multicoloured	75	40
561	**195**	14um. multicoloured	95	55

196 Two Players

1977. World Cup Football Championship. Elimination Rounds. Multicoloured.

562	12um. Type **196** (postage)	60	10
563	14um. Sir Alf Ramsey and Wembley Stadium	75	25
564	15um. A throw-in	95	25
565	50um. Football and emblems (air)	2·75	85
566	60um. Eusebio Ferreira	3·25	1·30
MS567	119×81 mm. 100um. Players exchanging pennants	6·00	1·70

197 *Helene Fourment and Her Children* (Rubens)

1977. 400th Birth Anniversary of Rubens. Paintings. Multicoloured.

568	12um. Type **197**	75	25
569	14um. *The Marquis of Spinola*	95	45
570	67um. *The Four Philosophers*	4·25	90
571	69um. *Steen Castle and Park* (horiz)	5·00	1·10
MS572	90×116 mm. 100um. *Rubens and Helene Fourment in the Garden*	6·75	2·10

198 Addra Gazelles

1978. Endangered Animals. Multicoloured.

573	5um. Scimitar oryx (horiz)	55	25
574	12um. Type **198**	1·40	25
575	14um. African manatee (horiz)	1·90	25
576	55um. Barbary sheep	5·00	90
577	60um. African elephant (horiz)	5·50	90
578	100um. Ostrich	7·50	1·50

199 Clasped Hands and President Giscard d'Estaing of France

1978. Air. Franco-African Co-operation. Embossed on foil.

579	**199**	250um. silver	13·00	13·00
580	**199**	500um. gold	28·00	28·00

199a Earth-mover and Route Map

1978. Nouakchott–Nema Highway. Multicoloured.

580a	12um. Type **199a**	10·00	7·00
580b	14um. Bulldozer and route map	12·00	8·00

200 Footballers

1978. World Cup Football Championship, Argentina. Multicoloured.

581	12um. Type **200**	70	30
582	14um. World Cup	80	45
583	20um. FIFA flag and football	1·40	50
MS584	82×70 mm. 50um. World Cup and football (horiz)	3·00	1·40

201 Raoul Follereau and St George fighting Dragon

1978. 25th Anniversary of Raoul Follereau Foundation.

585	**201**	12um. brown and green	1·90	90

202 Emblem and People holding Hands

1978. International Anti-Apartheid Year.

586	-	25um. brown, blue and red	1·30	80
587	**202**	30um. brown, blue & green	2·20	1·10

Design: Horiz—25um. Emblem and people behind fence.

203 Charles de Gaulle

1978. Personalities. Multicoloured.

588	12um. Type **203**	1·50	45
589	14um. King Baudouin of Belgium	1·30	45
590	55um. Queen Elizabeth II (25th anniversary of Coronation)	3·25	1·30

1978. Air. Philexafrique Stamp Exhibition, Libreville (Gabon) (1st issue), and Second International Stamp Fair, Essen (West Germany). As T **262** of Niger. Multicoloured.

591	20um. Water rail and Hamburg 1859 ½s. stamp	2·50	1·60
592	20um. Spotted hyena and Mauritania 1967 100f. South African crowned crane stamp	2·50	1·60

See also Nos. 619/620.

1978. Argentina's Victory in World Cup Football Championship. Nos. 562/**MS**567 optd **ARGENTINE–PAYS BAS 3-1** in English and Arabic.

593	**196**	12um. mult (postage)	75	25
594	-	14um. multicoloured	95	40
595	-	15um. multicoloured	1·20	70
596	-	50um. multicoloured (air)	2·75	1·70
597	-	60um. multicoloured	3·25	2·10
MS598		119×81 mm. 100um. multicoloured	6·00	5·75

205 View of Nouakchott

1978. 20th Anniversary of Nouakchott.

599	**205**	12um. multicoloured	75	50

206 Human Rights Emblem

1978. 30th Anniversary of Declaration of Human Rights.

600	**206**	55um. red and blue	3·00	1·60

207 *Wright Flyer I* and Clement Ader's *Avion III*

1979. Air. 75th Anniversary of First Powered Flight.

601	**207**	15um. grey, red and blue	95	55
602	-	40um. violet, blue & brn	2·75	1·50

Design: 40um. Concorde and *Wright Flyer I*.

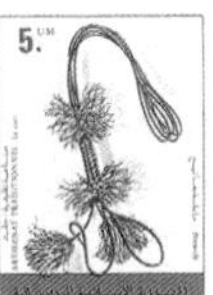
208 Key Chain

1979. Handicrafts. Multicoloured.

603	5um. Type **208**	45	25
604	7um. Tooth-brush case	55	30
605	10um. Knife sheath	75	40

209 *Market Peasant and Wife*

1979. 450th Birth Anniversary of Albrecht Durer (artist). Each black and red.

606	12um. Type **209**	75	40
607	14um. *Young Peasant and his Wife*	1·30	75
608	55um. *Mercenary with Banner*	3·00	1·10
609	60um. *St. George and the Dragon*	3·75	1·30
MS610	114×107 mm. 100um. *Group of Mercenaries* (horiz)	6·50	4·00

210 Seated Buddha, Temple of Borobudur

1979. UNESCO Campaign for Preservation of Historic Monuments. Multicoloured.

611	12um. Type **210**	75	45
612	14um. Carthaginian warrior and hunting dog	95	45
613	55um. Erechtheum Caryatid, Acropolis	3·00	1·70

211 Rowland Hill and Paddle-steamer *Sirius*

1979. Death Centenary of Sir Rowland Hill. Multicoloured.

614	12um. Type **211**	60	10
615	14um. Hill and *Great Republic* (paddle-steamer)	95	25
616	55um. Hill and *Mauretania I* (liner)	2·75	80
617	60um. Hill and *Stirling Castle* (liner)	3·50	95
MS618	113×89 mm. 100um. Rowland Hill and Mauritanian 1906 25c. stamp	6·00	1·70

212 Satellite over Earth

1979. Philexafrique Exhibition, Libreville (2nd issue).

619	-	12um. multicoloured	1·30	70
620	**212**	30um. red, blue and lilac	3·25	1·90

Design: Horiz—12um. Embossed leather cushion cover.

213 Mother and Children

1979. International Year of the Child. Multicoloured.

621	12um. Type **213**	60	30
622	14um. Mother with sleeping baby	95	55
623	40um. Children playing with ball	2·40	1·30

1979. Tenth Anniversary of *Apollo 11* Moon Landing. Nos. 530/**MS**535 optd **ALUNISSAGE APOLLO XI JUILLET 1969**, with Lunar module, or surch also.

624	10um. Mission Control (horiz) (postage)	75	45
625	12um. Type **187**	70	45
626	14um. on 20um. Viking in flight (horiz) (air)	75	45
627	50um. Viking over Mars (horiz)	2·75	1·50
628	60um. Parachute descent	3·00	1·80
MS629	103×79 mm. 100um. multicoloured	6·00	5·75

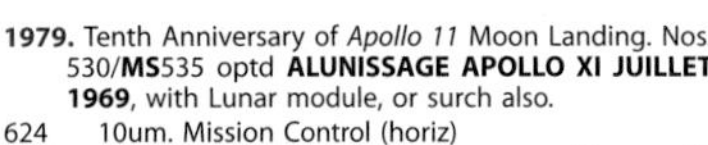

215 Sprinter on Starting-blocks

1979. Pre-Olympic Year. Multicoloured.

630	12um. Type **215**	65	25
631	14um. Female runner	95	25
632	55um. Male runner leaving start	2·75	70
633	60um. Hurdling	3·25	80
MS634	102×78 mm. 100um. Male runner	6·00	1·70

215a Skipper

1979. Fish. Multicoloured.

634a	1um. Type **215a**	40	30
634b	2um. Swordfish		
634c	5um. Tub gurnard	55	25

216 Ice Hockey

1979. Winter Olympic Games, Lake Placid (1980). Ice Hockey. Multicoloured.

635	10um. Type **216**	55	10
636	12um. Saving a goal	65	10
637	14um. Goalkeeper and player	80	25
638	55um. Two players	2·50	75
639	60um. Goalkeeper	3·00	85
640	100um. Tackle	4·50	1·50

217 Woman pouring out Tea

1980. Taking Tea.

641	**217**	1um. multicoloured	10	10
642	**217**	5um. multicoloured	45	25
643	**217**	12um. multicoloured	75	45

218 Koran, World Map and Symbols of Arab Achievements

1980. Arab Achievements.

644	**218**	12um. multicoloured	60	45
645	**218**	15um. multicoloured	95	45

1980. Winter Olympics Medal Winners. Nos. 635/640 optd.

646	10um. Optd **Medaille de bronze SUEDE**	55	25
647	12um. Optd **MEDAILLE DE BRONZE SUEDE**	60	25
648	14um. Optd **Medaille d'argent U.R.S.S.**	80	40
649	55um. Optd **MEDAILLE D'ARGENT U.R.S.S.**	2·50	1·10
650	60um. Optd **MEDAILLE D'OR ETATS-UNIS**	3·00	1·30
651	100um. Optd **Medaille d'or ETATS-UNIS**	4·50	2·20

220 Holy Kaaba, Mecca

1980. Pilgrimage to Mecca. Multicoloured.

652	10um. Type **220**	1·20	45
653	50um. Pilgrims outside Mosque	3·50	1·70

221 Mother and Child

1980. World Red Cross Societies Day.

654	**221**	20um. multicoloured	7·50	1·30

222 Crowd greeting Armed Forces

1980. Armed Forces Festival.

655	**222**	12um. multicoloured	60	25
656	**222**	14um. multicoloured	95	40

223 Horse jumping Bar

1980. Olympic Games, Moscow. Multicoloured.

657	10um. Type **223**	55	10
658	20um. Three day eventing	1·20	25
659	50um. Horse jumping brick wall (horiz)	2·75	75
660	70um. Horse jumping stone wall	4·00	95
MS661	77×104 mm. 100um. Horse's head	6·50	2·30

224 Trees on Map of Mauritania

1980. Tree Day.

662	**224**	12um. multicoloured	1·20	60

225 *Rembrandt's Mother*

1980. Paintings by Rembrandt. Multicoloured.

663	10um. *Self-portrait*	75	25
664	20um. Type **225**	1·20	40
665	50um. *Portrait of a Man in Oriental Costume*	2·75	70
666	70um. *Titus Lisant*	3·50	1·20
MS667	104×79 mm. 100um. *The Polish Cavalier* (horiz)	6·00	2·10

226 Footballers

1980. Air. World Cup Football Championship, Spain (1982). Multicoloured.

668	10um. Type **226**	55	10
669	12um. Goalkeeper and players	60	25
670	14um. Goalkeeper catching ball	80	25
671	20um. Fighting for possession	1·00	45
672	67um. Tackle	3·50	90
MS673	103×81 mm. 100um. Match scene	6·00	2·10

1980. Olympic Medal Winners. Nos. 657/**MS**661 optd.

674	10um. Optd **VAINQUEUR KOWALLZYK (POL)**	55	25
675	20um. Optd **VAINQUEUR THEURER (AUTR)**	95	40
676	50um. Optd **VAINQUEUR URSS**	2·30	90
677	70um. Optd **VAINQUEUR ROMAN (IT)**	3·50	1·80
MS678	77×104 mm. 100um. Optd **VAINQUEUR/URSS**	6·00	5·75

228 *Mastodonte del Giovi*, 1853, Italy

1980. Steam Locomotives. Multicoloured.

679	10um. Type **228**	80	25
680	12um. Diesel ore train	95	25
681	14um. Chicago, Milwaukee and St Paul Railway locomotive No. 810, USA	1·10	25
682	20um. Bury steam locomotive, 1837, Great Britain	1·50	40
683	67um. Locomotive No. 170, France	5·00	90
684	100um. Berlin–Potsdam line, Germany	7·25	1·40

229 Palm Tree, Crescent and Star, Maize and Map

1980. 20th Anniversary of Independence.

685	**229**	12um. multicoloured	60	25
686	**229**	15um. multicoloured	95	45

230 El Haram Mosque

1981. 15th Century of Hegira. Multicoloured.

687	2um. Type **230**	10	10
688	12um. Medine Mosque	60	35
689	14um. Chinguetti Mosque	95	45

231 Space Shuttle in Orbit

1981. Air. Space Shuttle. Multicoloured.

690	12um. Type **231**	60	10
691	20um. Shuttle and space station	1·00	25
692	50um. Shuttle performing experiment	2·40	75
693	70um. Shuttle landing	3·50	1·00
MS694	103×78 mm. 100um. Shuttle and carrier aeroplane	6·00	1·60

232 *The Harlequin*

1981. Air. Birth Centenary of Pablo Picasso. Multicoloured.

695	12um. Type **232**	75	15
696	20um. *Vase of Flowers*	1·20	40
697	50um. *Three Women at a Fountain* (horiz)	2·75	85
698	70um. *Dinard Landscape* (horiz)	3·75	1·20
699	100um. *Le Dejeuner sur l'Herbe* (horiz)	5·25	1·70

233 IYDP Emblem

1981. International Year of Disabled People.

700	**233**	12um. violet, gold and blue	95	55

234 Open Landau

1981. British Royal Wedding. Multicoloured.

701	14um. Type **234**	80	25
702	18um. Light carriage	1·00	25
703	77um. Closed coupe	3·50	1·30
MS704	117×78 mm. 100um. Coach	6·50	1·70

235 George Washington

1981. Bicentenary of Battles of Yorktown and Chesapeake Bay. Multicoloured.

705	14um. Type **235**	60	25
706	18um. Admiral de Grasse	95	25
707	63um. Surrender of Cornwallis at Yorktown (horiz)	3·25	1·10
708	81um. Battle of Chesapeake Bay (horiz)	4·00	1·50

236 Columbus and *Pinta*

1981. 450th Death Anniversary of Christopher Columbus. Multicoloured.

709	19um. Type **236**	1·70	55
710	55um. Columbus and *Santa Maria*	4·75	1·20

237 Wheat and FAO Emblem

1981. World Food Day.

711	**237**	19um. multicoloured	95	55

238 Kemal Ataturk

1981. Birth Centenary of Kemal Ataturk (Turkish statesman).

712	**238**	63um. multicoloured	3·00	1·60

239 Eastern White Pelicans

1981. Birds of the Arguin. Multicoloured.

713	2um. Type **239**	80	30
714	18um. Greater flamingoes	2·75	1·10

240 Hand holding Torn Flag

1981. Battle of Karameh Commemoration.

715	**240**	14um. multicoloured	95	50

241 *Dermochelys coiacer*

1981. Turtles. Multicoloured.

716	1um. Type **241**	75	35
717	3um. *Chelonia mydas*	1·00	35
718	4um. *Eretmochelys imbricata*	1·40	55

242 Sea Scouts

1982. 75th Anniversary of Boy Scout Movement. Multicoloured.

719	14um. Type **242**	95	45
720	19um. Scouts boarding rowing boat	1·20	40
721	22um. Scouts in rowing boat	1·40	55
722	92um. Scouts in yacht	4·75	1·50
MS723	105×80 mm. 100um. Lord Baden-Powell and Sea Scout	6·00	1·60

243 Deusenberg, 1921

1982. 75th Anniversary of French Grand Prix Motor Race. Multicoloured.

724	7um. Type **243**	75	25
725	12um. Alfa Romeo, 1932	95	25
726	14um. Juan Fangio	1·20	40
727	18um. Renault, 1979	1·30	55
728	19um. Niki Lauda	1·30	55
MS729	114×89 mm. 100um. French Grand Prix, 1979	6·75	2·30

244 APU Emblem

1982. 30th Anniversary of Arab Postal Union.

730	**244**	14um. orange and brown	75	45

245 Hexagonal Pattern

1982. World Telecommunications Day.

731	**245**	21um. multicoloured	95	60

246 Environmental Emblem on Map

1982. Tenth Anniversary of UN Environmental Programme.

732	**246**	14um. blue and light blue	75	45

247 Princess of Wales

1982. 21st Birthday of Princess of Wales. Multicoloured.

733	21um. Type **247**	95	45
734	77um. Princess of Wales (different)	3·75	90
MS735	112×80 mm. 100um. Princess of Wales	5·25	1·50

248 Straw Hut

1982. Traditional Houses. Multicoloured.

736	14um. Type **248**	75	40
737	18um. Thatched hut	95	55
738	19um. Tent	1·00	65

1982. Birth of Prince William of Wales. Nos. 701/**MS**704 surch **NAISSANCE ROYALE 1982.**

739	14um. Type **234**	75	40
740	18um. Light carriage	95	45
741	77um. Closed coupe	3·50	1·70
MS742	117×78 mm. 100um. Coach	5·25	1·80

1982. Air. World Cup Football Championship Results. Nos. 668/**MS**673 optd **ITALIE 3 ALLEMAGNE (R.F.A.) 1.**

743	10um. Type **226**	55	25
744	12um. Goalkeeper punching ball	60	25
745	14um. Goalkeeper catching ball	80	40
746	20um. Three players	1·00	45
747	67um. Tackle	3·50	1·40
MS748	103×81 mm. 100um. Match scene	5·25	1·60

251 Cattle at Collinaire Dam, Hodh El Gharbi

1982. Agricultural Development.

749	14um. Type **251**	3·50	1·80
750	18um. Irrigation canal, Gorgol	4·75	2·10

252 Desert Rose

1982. Desert Rose.

751	**252**	21um. multicoloured	7·25	1·90

253 Montgolfier Balloon, 1783

1982. Bicentenary of Manned Flight. Multicoloured.

752	14um. Type **253**	1·00	25
753	18um. Charles's hydrogen balloon ascent, 1783 (horiz)	1·00	25
754	19um. Goodyear Aerospace airship	1·00	45
755	55um. Nieuport 11 *Bebe* biplane (horiz)	2·75	70
756	63um. Concorde (horiz)	3·00	80
757	77um. *Apollo 11* on Moon	3·50	95

No. 754 is wrongly inscribed 'Zeppelin'.
See also Nos. 768/**MS**772

254 Ouadane

1983. Protection of Ancient Sites. Multicoloured.

758	14um. Type **254**	70	30
759	18um. Chinguetti	80	45
760	24um. Oualata	1·00	60
761	30um. Tichitt	1·50	80

255 Manuscript

1983. Ancient Manuscripts. Multicoloured.

762	2um. Type **255**	20	10
763	5um. Decorated manuscript	30	10
764	7um. Shield-shaped patterned manuscript	50	25

256 IMO Emblem

1983. 25th Anniv of IMO.

765	**256**	18um. multicoloured	95	55

257 WCY Emblem

1983. World Communications Year.

766	**257**	14um. multicoloured	75	45

258 Customs Emblems

1983. 30th Anniversary of Customs Co-operation Council.

767	**258**	14um. multicoloured	75	45

259 Pilatre de Rozier and Montgolfier Balloon

1983. Bicentenary of Manned Flight. Multicoloured.

768	10um. Type **259** (postage)	55	25
769	14um. John Wise and balloon *Atlantic*	1·10	25
770	25um. Charles Renard and Renard and Krebs' airship *La France* (horiz)	1·40	35
771	100um. Henri Juillot and Lebaudy-Juillot airship *Patrie* (horiz) (air)	6·00	1·40
MS772	101×81 mm. 100um. Joseph Montgolfier and balloon (46×37 mm)	6·00	1·70

260 Grinding Stone

1983. Prehistoric Grindstones. Multicoloured.

773	10um. Type **260**	1·00	55
774	14um. Pestle and mortar	1·50	65
775	18um. Grinding dish	2·10	1·10

261 Basketball

1983. Pre-Olympic Year. Multicoloured.

776	1um. Type **261** (postage)	20	10
777	20um. Wrestling	95	55
778	50um. Show-jumping	2·30	1·00
779	77um. Running (air)	4·25	1·30
MS780	85×85 mm. 100um. Football (41×35 mm)	5·25	1·60

262 Lord Baden-Powell (founder of Scout Movement)

1984. Celebrities. Multicoloured.

781	5um. Type **262** (postage)	30	10
782	14um. Goethe (poet)	75	35
783	25um. Rubens and detail of painting *The Virgin and Child*	1·30	45
784	100um. P. Harris (founder of Rotary International) (air)	5·50	1·40
MS785	85×75 mm. 100um. Rembrandt and painting *Arthemis* (38×47 mm)	5·50	1·60

263 Blue-finned Tuna

1984. Fishing Resources. Multicoloured.

786	1um. Type **263**	10	10
787	2um. Atlantic mackerel	10	10
788	5um. European hake	45	25
789	14um. Atlantic horse-mackerel	1·20	70
790	18um. Building a fishing boat	1·50	80

264 Durer and *Madonna and Child*

1984. Multicoloured.

791	10um. Type **264** (postage)	60	25
792	12um. *Apollo 11* and astronaut (15th anniversary of first manned Moon landing)	75	35
793	50um. Chess pieces and globe	2·40	1·50
794	77um. Prince and Princess of Wales (air)	3·75	2·20
MS795	80×80 mm. 100um. Prince and Princess of Wales (38×41 mm)	6·00	4·00

265 Start of Race

1984. Olympic Games, Los Angeles. Multicoloured.

796	14um. Type **265**	75	40
797	18um. Putting the shot (vert)	1·00	55
798	19um. Hurdling (vert)	1·10	55
799	44um. Throwing the javelin (vert)	2·50	1·30
800	77um. High jumping	5·00	1·20
MS801	103×77 mm. 100um. Steeplechase (vert)	6·50	6·50

266 Feeding Dehydrated Child from Glass

1984. Infant Survival Campaign. Multicoloured.

802	1um. Type **266**	10	10
803	4um. Breast-feeding baby	30	10
804	10um. Vaccinating baby	50	30
805	14um. Weighing baby	45	45

267 Aerial View of Complex

1984. Nouakchott Olympic Complex.

806	**267** 14um. multicoloured	95	55

268 Tents and Mosque Courtyard

1984. Pilgrimage to Mecca. Multicoloured.

807	14um. Type **268**	75	55
808	18um. Tents and courtyard (different)	1·20	80

269 Emblem

1984. Tenth Anniversary of West African Economic Community.

809	**269** 14um. multicoloured	85	55

270 S. van den Berg (windsurfing)

1984. Air. Olympic Games Sailing Gold Medallists. Multicoloured.

810	14um. Type **270**	95	50
811	18um. R. Coutts (Finn class)	1·20	60
812	19um. Spain (470 class)	1·50	70
813	44um. USA (Soling class)	3·25	1·50
MS814	110×80 mm. 100um. USA (Flying Dutchman class)	5·25	1·60

1984. Drought Relief. No. 537 surch **Aide au Sahel 84.**

815	18um. on 10um. multicoloured	1·20	70

272 Profiles and Emblem

1985. 15th Anniversary of Technical and Cultural Co-operation Agency.

816	**272** 18um. blue, deep blue and red	95	70

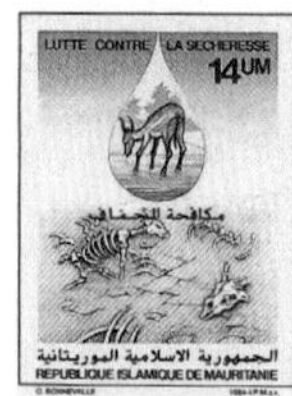

273 Animal drinking in Water Droplet and Skeletons

1985. Campaign against Drought. Multicoloured.

817	14um. Type **273**	95	55
818	18um. Lush trees by river in water droplet and dead trees	1·40	80

274 Replanting Trees

1985. Anti-desertification Campaign. Multicoloured.

819	10um. Type **274**	60	45
820	14um. Animals fleeing from forest fire	95	55
821	18um. Planting grass to hold sand dunes	1·40	80

275 Emblem

1985. 30th Anniversary (1984) of Arab League.

822	**275** 14um. green and black	75	55

276 Map, IYY Emblem and Youths

1985. Air. Philexafrique Stamp Exhibition, Lome. Multicoloured.

823	40um. Type **276** (International Youth Year)	2·30	1·70
824	40um. Nouadhibou oil refinery	2·30	1·70

See also Nos. 837/838.

277 Bonaparte's Gulls

1985. Air. Birth Bicentenary of John J. Audubon (ornithologist). Multicoloured.

825	14um. Wester tanager and scarlet tanager	95	40
826	18um. Type **277**	1·30	50
827	19um. Blue jays	1·50	65
828	44um. Black skimmer	3·25	1·50
MS829	85×110 mm. 100um. American darters	7·75	5·25

278 Locomotive *Adler*, 1835

1985. Anniversaries. Multicoloured.

830	12um. Type **278** (150th anniversary of German railways)	75	25
831	18um. Class 10 steam locomotive, 1956 (150th anniversary of German railways)	1·00	55
832	44um. Johann Sebastian Bach (composer, 300th birth anniversary European Music Year)	2·00	1·30
833	77um. Georg Frederick Handel (composer, 300th birth anniversary European Music Year)	3·50	2·20
834	90um. Statue of Liberty (centenary) (vert)	4·25	2·75
MS835	80×102 mm. 100um. Queen Elizabeth, the Queen Mother (85th birthday)	5·25	3·25

279 Globe and Emblem

1985. World Food Day.

836	**279** 18um. multicoloured	95	65

280 Tending Sheep and reading Book

1985. Air. Philexafrique Stamp Exhibition, Lome, Togo (2nd issue). Multicoloured.

837	50um. Type **280**	3·25	2·10
838	50um. Dock, iron ore mine and diesel train	3·25	2·10

281 Map showing Industries

1985. 25th Anniversary of Independence.

839	**281** 18um. multicoloured	95	60

282 Development

1986. International Youth Year. Multicoloured.

840	18um. Type **282**	80	45
841	22um. Re-afforestation (voluntary work)	1·00	60
842	25um. Hands reaching from globe to dove (peace) (vert)	1·20	75

283 Latecoere Seaplane *Comte de la Vaulx* and Map

1986. Air. 55th Anniversary (1985) of First Commercial South Atlantic Flight. Multicoloured.

843	18um. Type **283**	75	45
844	50um. Piper Twin Commanche aeroplanes crossing between maps of Africa and South America	2·20	1·40

284 Toujounine Earth Receiving Station

1986

845	**284**	25um. multicoloured	1·20	70

285 Heads of Mother and Pup

1986. World Wildlife Fund. Mediterranean Monk Seal. Multicoloured.

846	2um. Type **285**	1·20	50
847	5um. Mother and pup on land	1·80	70
848	10um. Mother and pup swimming	2·75	90
849	18um. Seal family	4·75	1·20
MS850	104×80 mm. 50um. Seal in water	8·25	2·75

286 Player and 1970 25f. Stamp

1986. Air. World Cup Football Championship, Mexico. Multicoloured.

851	8um. Type **286**	45	10
852	18um. Player and 1970 30f. stamp	80	40
853	22um. Player and 1970 70f. stamp	1·00	50
854	25um. Player and 1970 150f. stamp	1·20	70
855	40um. Player and World Cup trophy on 'stamp'	2·00	1·00
MS856	194×80 mm. 100um. Players	4·75	2·50

287 Weaving

1986

857	**287**	18um. multicoloured	95	55

288 Emblem, Boeing 737, Douglas DC-10 and Map

1986. Air. 25th Anniversary of Air Afrique.

858	**288**	26um. multicoloured	1·20	60

289 Indian, *Santa Maria* and Route Map

1986. 500th Anniversary (1992) of Discovery of America by Christopher Columbus. Multicoloured.

859	2um. Type **289** (postage)	10	10
860	22um. Indian, *Nina* and map	90	55
861	35um. Indian, *Pinta* and map	1·50	80
862	150um. Indian, map and Christopher Columbus (air)	6·75	3·00
MS863	82×65 mm. 100um. Globe, Indian and Columbus (50×41 mm)	5·00	3·00

290 J. H. Dort, Comet Picture and Space Probe *Giotto*

1986. Appearance of Halley's Comet. Multicoloured.

864	5um. Type **290** (postage)	30	10
865	18um. William Huggins (astronomer) and Ariane space rocket	75	35
866	26um. E. J. Opik and space probes *Giotto* and *Vega*	1·20	60
867	80um. F. L. Whipple and *Planet A* space probe (air)	3·75	1·60
MS868	109×67 mm. 100um. Sir Edmund Halley, *Giotto* space probe and comet (50×35 mm)	4·50	3·00

291 Astronauts

1986. *Challenger* Astronauts Commemoration. Multicoloured.

869	7um. Type **291** (postage)	30	10
870	22um. Judith Resnik and astronaut	95	45
871	32um. Ellison Onizuka and Ronald McNair	1·30	75
872	43um. Christa Corrigan McAuliffe (air)	2·00	95
MS873	69×99 mm. 100um. Astronauts (different)	4·50	2·75

292 Red Seabream

1986. Fish and Birds. Multicoloured.

874	4um. Type **292**	25	25
875	22um. White spoonbills	1·50	80
876	32um. Bridled terns	1·80	1·10
877	98um. Sea-trout	5·25	3·50

See also Nos. 896/900.

293 Arrow through Victim

1986. Fourth Anniversary of Massacre of Palestinian Refugees in Sabra and Shatila Camps, Lebanon.

878	**293**	22um. black, gold and red	95	60

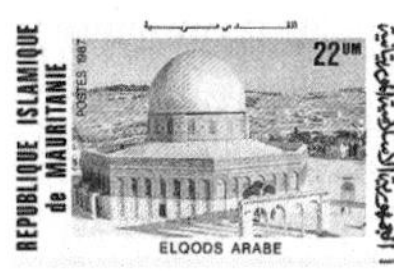

294 Fisherman

1986. World Food Day.

879	**294**	22um. multicoloured	95	55

295 Dome of the Rock

1987. Arab Jerusalem.

880	**295**	22um. multicoloured	95	55

296 Boxing

1987. Air. Olympic Games, Seoul (1988) (1st issue). Multicoloured.

881	30um. Type **296**	1·20	65
882	40um. Judo	1·80	85
883	50um. Fencing	2·30	1·00
884	75um. Wrestling	3·50	1·60
MS885	104×80 mm. 150um. Judo (different)	7·00	3·75

See also Nos. 902/**MS**906.

297 Cordoue Mosque

1987. 1200th Anniversary of Cordoue Mosque.

886	**297**	30um. multicoloured	1·40	70

298 Women's Slalom

1987. Air. Winter Olympic Games, Calgary (1988). Multicoloured.

887	30um. Type **298**	1·40	65
888	40um. Men's speed skating	1·80	85
889	50um. Ice hockey	2·30	1·00
890	75um. Women's downhill skiing	3·50	1·60
MS891	104×79 mm. 150um. Men's cross-country skiing	7·00	3·00

299 Adults at Desk

1987. Literacy Campaign. Multicoloured.

892	18um. Type **299**	85	55
893	20um. Adults and children reading	1·20	80

300 People queueing for Treatment

1987. World Health Day.

894	**300**	18um. multicoloured	95	55

301 Map within Circle

1988. National Population and Housing Census.

895	**301**	20um. multicoloured	95	55

1988. Fish and Birds. Horiz designs as T **292**. Multicoloured.

896	1um. Small-horned blenny	45	25
897	7um. Grey triggerfish	1·90	50
898	15um. Skipjack tuna	3·25	1·10
899	18um. Great cormorants	1·30	70
900	80um. Royal terns	5·50	3·25

302 People with Candles

1988. 40th Anniversary of WHO.

901	**302**	30um. multicoloured	1·40	65

303 Hammer Throwing

1988. Air. Olympic Games, Seoul (2nd issue). Multicoloured.

902	20um. Type **303**	95	35
903	24um. Discus	1·20	40
904	30um. Putting the shot	1·40	50
905	150um. Javelin throwing	6·50	2·75
MS906	107×83 mm. 170um. Javelin throwing (different)	7·50	4·00

1988. Winter Olympic Games Gold Medal Winners. Nos. 887/**MS**891 optd.

907	30um. Optd **Medaille d'or Vreni Schneider (Suisse)**	1·50	80
908	40um. Optd **Medaille d'or 1500m. Andre Hoffman (R.D.A.)**	2·00	1·20
909	50um. Optd **Medaille d'or U.R.S.S.**	2·30	1·40
910	75um. Optd **Medaille d'or Marina Kiehl (R.F.A.)**	3·75	2·20
MS911	150um. Optd **Medaille d'or 15 km Mikhail Deviatiarov (USSR)**	7·25	3·75

305 Flags and Globe

1988. 75th Anniversary of Arab Scout Movement.

912	**305**	35um. multicoloured	1·50	80

306 Men at Ballot Box

1988. First Municipal Elections. Multicoloured.

913	20um. Type **306**	95	40
914	24um. Woman at ballot box	1·30	55

307 Emblem

1988. 25th Anniversary of Organisation of African Unity.

915	**307**	40um. multicoloured	1·80	90

308 Ploughing with Oxen

1988. Tenth Anniversary of International Agricultural Development Fund.

916	**308**	35um. multicoloured	2·00	1·00

309 Port Activities

1989. First Anniversary of Nouakchott Free Port.

917	**309**	24um. multicoloured	1·50	85

310 *Heliothis armigera*

1989. Plant Pests. Multicoloured.

918	2um. Type **310**	10	10
919	6um. *Aphis gossypii*	30	10
920	10um. *Agrotis ypsilon*	55	25
921	20um. *Chilo* sp.	1·20	45
922	24um. *Plitella xylostella*	1·50	55
923	30um. *Henosepilachna elaterii*	1·70	55
924	42um. *Trichoplusia ni*	2·50	1·00

311 *Nomadacris septemfasciata*

1989. Locusts. Multicoloured.

925	5um. Type **311**	45	10
926	20um. Locusts mating	1·00	50
927	24um. Locusts emerging from chrysallis	1·30	50
928	40um. Locusts flying	2·30	1·00
929	88um. Locust (different)	5·00	2·00

312 Men of Different Races embracing

1989. Philexfrance '89 International Stamp Exhibition, Paris, and Bicentenary of French Revolution.

930	**312**	35um. multicoloured	1·80	85

313 Footballers

1989. World Cup Football Championship, Italy (1990) (1st issue).

931	**313**	20um. multicoloured	95	55

See also Nos. 937/941.

314 Attan'eem Migat, Mecca

1989. Pilgrimage to Mecca.

932	**314**	20um. multicoloured	95	45

315 Emblem

1989. 25th Anniversary of African Development Bank.

933	**315**	37um. black and mauve	1·50	70

316 Carpet

1989

934	**316**	50um. multicoloured	2·75	1·20

317 Youths

1989. Second Anniversary of Palestinian Intifada Movement.

935	**317**	35um. multicoloured	1·80	75

318 Member Countries' Leaders

1990. First Anniversary of Arab Maghreb Union.

936	**318**	50um. multicoloured	2·20	1·00

319 Players

1990. Air. World Cup Football Championship, Italy (2nd issue).

937	**319**	50um. multicoloured	2·30	95
938	-	60um. multicoloured	2·75	1·00
939	-	70um. multicoloured	3·50	1·20
940	-	90um. multicoloured	4·50	1·50
941	-	150um. multicoloured	7·00	2·40

Designs: 60 to 150um. Show footballers.

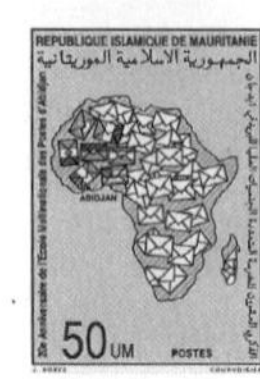
320 Envelopes on Map

1990. 20th Anniversary of Multi-national Postal Training School, Abidjan.

942	**320**	50um. multicoloured	2·20	95

321 Books and Desk

1990. International Literacy Year.

943	**321**	60um. multicoloured	2·75	1·40

322 Maps and Earth-moving Vehicles

1990. Mineral Resources.

944	**322**	60um. multicoloured	3·25	1·70

323 Dressage

1990. Olympic Games, Barcelona (1992). Multicoloured.

945	5um. Type **323** (postage)	25	25
946	50um. Archery	2·00	80
947	60um. Throwing the hammer	2·30	1·30
948	75um. Football	3·00	1·20
949	90um. Basketball	4·00	1·40
950	220um. Table tennis (air)	9·00	3·25
MS951	120×84 mm. 150um. Running	7·00	2·75

324 Emblem

1990. Second Anniversary of Declaration of State of Palestine.

952	**324**	85um. multicoloured	3·75	2·10

325 Camp

1990. Integration of Repatriates from Senegal. Multicoloured.

953	50um. Type **325**	2·50	1·40
954	75um. Women's sewing group	3·75	2·10
955	85um. Water collection	4·75	2·10

326 Map, Dove and Mandela

1990. Release from South African Prison of Nelson Mandela.

956	**326**	85um. multicoloured	4·00	2·30

327 Downhill skiing

1990. Winter Olympic Games, Albertville (1992). Multicoloured.

957	60um. Type **327** (postage)	2·40	95
958	75um. Cross-country skiing	3·25	1·20
959	90um. Ice hockey	4·00	1·50
960	220um. Figure skating (pairs) (air)	9·50	3·25
MS961	137×95 mm. 150um. Slalom	6·75	4·00

328 Blue Leg

1991. Scouts, Fungi and Butterflies. Multicoloured.

962	5um. Type **328** (postage)	40	10
963	50um. *Agaricus bitorquis edulis*	2·40	80
964	60um. *Bunea alcinoe* (butterfly)	2·75	1·00
965	90um. *Salamis cytora* (butterfly)	4·50	1·60
966	220um. *Bronze boletus*	10·00	3·50
967	75um. *Cyrestis camillus* (butterfly) (air)	3·00	1·60
MS968	85×107 mm. 150um. *Mesoacidalia aglaja* (butterfly) and *Clathrus rubber*	7·50	7·25

329 Dish Aerials and Transmitting Tower

1991. 30th Anniversary of Independence. Multicoloured.

969	50um. Type **329**	1·00	65
970	60um. Container ship in dock	2·20	1·40
971	100um. Workers in field	3·25	1·80

330 Woman carrying Bucket of Water

1991. World Meteorological Day.

972	**330**	100um. multicoloured	5·00	2·75

331 Health Centre

1991. 20th Anniversary of Medecins sans Frontieres (international medical relief organisation).

973	**331**	60um. multicoloured	3·00	1·60

332 Cats

1991. Domestic Animals. Multicoloured.

974	50um. Type **332**	2·20	1·40
975	60um. Basenji dog	3·50	2·10

333 Globe and Stylised Figures

1991. World Population Day.

976	**333**	90um. multicoloured	4·00	2·10

334 Blind Woman with Sight restored

1991. Anti-blindness Campaign.

977	**334**	50um. multicoloured	2·75	1·40

335 Nouakchott Electricity Station

1991. Second Anniversary of Nouakchott Electricity Station.

978	**335**	50um. multicoloured	2·75	1·20

336 Quarrying

1993. Mineral Exploitation, Haoudat. Multicoloured.

979	50um. Type **336**	2·50	1·40
980	60um. Dry land	3·00	1·90

337 Camel Train

1993

981	**337**	50um. multicoloured	2·50	1·50
982	**337**	60um. multicoloured	2·75	1·90

338 Palestinians

1993. Palestinian Intifada Movement. Multicoloured.

983	50um. Type **338**	2·50	1·50
984	60um. Palestinian children by fire (horiz)	3·00	1·90

339 Four-man Bobsleighing

1993. Winter Olympic Games, Lillehammer. Multicoloured.

985	10um. Type **339** (postage)	45	20
986	50um. Luge	1·80	90
987	60um. Figure skating	2·20	1·00
988	80um. Skiing	3·00	1·60
989	220um. Cross-country skiing	9·00	4·25
MS990	121×82 mm. 150um. Ski jumping (air)	6·75	3·50

340 Soldier Field, Chicago

1994. World Cup Football Championship, USA. Players and Stadiums. Multicoloured.

991	10um. Type **340**	45	20
992	50um. Foxboro Stadium, Boston	1·80	90
993	60um. Robert F. Kennedy Stadium, Washington DC	2·20	1·00
994	90um. Stanford Stadium, San Francisco	3·00	1·60
995	220um. Giant Stadium, New York	9·00	4·25
MS996	123×84 mm. 150um. Rose Bowl, Los Angeles	6·75	3·50

341 Anniversary Emblem and 1962 15f. Stamp

1995. 50th Anniversary of UNO.

997	**341**	60um. multicoloured	1·50	90

342 Stabilising Desert

1995. 50th Anniversary of FAO. Multicoloured.

998	50um. Type **342**	1·20	75
999	60um. Fishermen launching boat	1·50	95
1000	90um. Planting crops	2·00	1·40

345 Weaving

1995. Crafts. Multicoloured.

1006	50um. Type **345**		
1007	60um. Metalwork		

346 Door

1995. Tourism. Re-vitalisation of Ancient Towns. Multicoloured.

1008	10um. Type **346**		
1009	20um. Arch and rubble		
1010	40um. Town in desert		
1011	50um. Door in ornate wall		

347 Start of Race

1996. Olympic Games, Atlanta, USA. Multicoloured.

1012	20um. Type **347**		
1013	30um. Start of race (horiz)		
1014	40um. Running in lane		
1015	50um. Long-distance race (horiz)		

348 Beaded Locks and Headdress

1996. Traditional Hairstyles. Multicoloured.

1016	50um. Type **348**		
1017	60um. Woman with hair adornments		

349 Ball-in-Pot Game

1996. Traditional Games. Multicoloured.

1018	50um. Type **349**		
1019	60um. Strategy game with spherical and conical pieces (horiz)		
1020	90um. Pegs-in-board game (horiz)		

350 Family

1996. 50th Anniversary of United Nations Children's Fund. The Rights of the Child. Showing children's drawings. Multicoloured.

1021	50um. Type **350**		
1022	60um. Boy in wheelchair		

OFFICIAL STAMPS

O41 Cross of Trarza

1961

O150	**O41**	1f. purple and blue	10	10
O151	**O41**	3f. myrtle and red	10	10
O152	**O41**	5f. brown and green	30	10
O153	**O41**	10f. blue and turquoise	30	10
O154	**O41**	15f. orange and blue	40	25
O155	**O41**	20f. green and myrtle	55	25
O156	**O41**	25f. red and orange	55	40
O157	**O41**	30f. green and purple	75	55
O158	**O41**	50f. sepia and red	1·20	70
O159	**O41**	100f. blue and orange	2·00	1·10
O160	**O41**	200f. red and green	4·50	2·30

O179

1976

O502	**O179**	1um. multicoloured	10	10
O503	**O179**	2um. multicoloured	10	10
O504	**O179**	5um. multicoloured	30	10
O505	**O179**	10um. multicoloured	55	25
O506	**O179**	12um. multicoloured	80	45
O507	**O179**	40um. multicoloured	2·50	1·40
O508	**O179**	50um. multicoloured	3·00	1·60

POSTAGE DUE STAMPS

1906. Stamps of 1906 optd **T** in a triangle.

D18	**I**	5c. green and red	65·00	
D19	**I**	10c. pink and blue	65·00	
D20	**J**	20c. black and red on blue	95·00	
D21	**J**	25c. blue and red	95·00	
D22	**J**	30c. brown & red on pink	£200	
D23	**J**	40c. red on blue	£700	
D24	**J**	50c. violet and red	£200	
D25	**K**	1f. black and red on blue	£300	

1906. Natives key-type inscr 'MAURITANIE' in blue (10, 30c.) or red (others).

D25a	**L**	5c. green	2·10	1·80
D26	**L**	10c. purple	3·25	3·25
D27	**L**	15c. blue on blue	6·25	5·25
D28	**L**	20c. black on yellow	7·25	11·00
D29	**L**	30c. red on cream	9·25	13·00
D30	**L**	50c. violet	14·50	42·00
D31	**L**	60c. black on buff	11·00	23·00
D32	**L**	1f. black on pink	18·00	44·00

1914. Figure key-type inscr 'MAURITANIE'.

D35	**M**	5c. green	35	2·50
D36	**M**	10c. red	30	50
D37	**M**	15c. grey	50	4·75
D38	**M**	20c. brown	50	5·75
D39	**M**	30c. blue	65	5·75
D40	**M**	50c. black	1·10	5·00
D41	**M**	60c. orange	1·20	4·00
D42	**M**	1f. violet	1·30	5·00

1927. Surch in figures.

D67	**M**	2f. on 1f. purple	2·75	11·00
D68	**M**	3f. on 1f. brown	3·00	11·50

D40 Qualata Motif

1961

D150	**D40**	1f. yellow and purple	10	10
D151	**D40**	2f. grey and red	10	10
D152	**D40**	5f. pink and red	30	25
D153	**D40**	10f. green and myrtle	45	25
D154	**D40**	15f. brown and drab	45	25
D155	**D40**	20f. blue and red	60	25
D156	**D40**	25f. red and green	95	70

D55 Ruppell's Griffon

1963. Birds. Multicoloured.

D177	50c. Type **D55**	20	10
D178	50c. Common crane	20	10
D179	1f. Eastern white pelican	25	10
D180	1f. Garganey	25	10
D181	2f. Golden oriole	30	10
D182	2f. Variable sunbird	30	10
D183	5f. Great snipe	45	10
D184	5f. Common shoveler	45	40
D185	10f. Vulturine guineafowl	90	90
D186	10f. Black stork	90	90
D187	15f. Grey heron	1·10	1·10
D188	15f. White stork	1·10	1·10
D189	20f. Paradise whydah	1·60	1·60
D190	20f. Red-legged partridge	1·60	1·60
D191	25f. Little stint	2·10	2·10
D192	25f. Arabian bustard	2·10	2·10

D180

1976

D509	**D180**	1um. multicoloured	10	10
D510	**D180**	3um. multicoloured	30	25
D511	**D180**	10um. multicoloured	55	55
D512	**D180**	12um. multicoloured	65	65
D513	**D180**	20um. multicoloured	1·00	95

APPENDIX

The following stamps have either been issued in excess of postal needs or have not been available to the public in a reasonable quantities at face value. Such stamps may later be given full listing if there is evidence of regular postal use.

1962

World Refugee Year (1960). Optd on 1960 Definitive issue, 30, 50, 60f.

Olympic Games in Rome (1960) and Tokyo (1964). Surch on 1960 Definitive issue 75f. on 15f., 75f. on 20f.

European Steel and Coal Community and Exploration of Iron-ore in Mauritania. Optd on 1960 Definitive issue. Air 500f.
Malaria Eradication. Optd on 1960 Definitive issue. Air. 100, 200f.

MAURITIUS

An island in the Indian Ocean, east of Madagascar. Attained self-government on 1 September 1967, and became independent on 12 March 1968.

1847. 12 pence = 1 shilling; 20 shillings = 1 pound.
1878. 100 cents = 1 rupee.

1 ("POST OFFICE")

1847. Imperf.

1	**1**	1d. red	—	£1300000
2	**1**	2d. blue	—	£1500000

2 ("POST PAID")

1856

23	**2**	1d. red	£6500	£800
25	**2**	2d. blue	£800	£1200

3

1858. Surch FOUR-PENCE. Imperf.

26	**3**	4d. green	£1800	£450

1858. No value on stamps. Imperf.

27	**3**	(4d.) green	£450	£200
28	**3**	(6d.) red	65·00	£120
29	**3**	(9d.) purple	£900	£225

5

1859. Imperf.

32	**5**	6d. blue	£800	55·00
33	**5**	6d. black	45·00	65·00
34	**5**	1s. red	£3250	70·00
35	**5**	1s. green	£650	£150

6

1859

39	**6**	2d. blue	£4750	£900

8

1859. Imperf.

42	**8**	1d. red	£10000	£1400
44	**8**	2d. blue	£6000	£850

9

10

1860

56	**9**	1d. purple	80·00	17·00
57	**9**	1d. brown	£100	13·00
59	**9**	2d. blue	75·00	13·00
61a	**9**	3d. red	90·00	21·00
62	**9**	4d. red	95·00	3·75
50	**9**	6d. grey	£400	£110
63	**9**	6d. violet	£425	50·00
65	**9**	6d. green	£250	6·50
51	**9**	9d. purple	£200	42·00
66	**9**	9d. green	£190	£400
67	**10**	10d. red	£375	60·00
53	**9**	1s. green	£900	£200
69	**9**	1s. blue	£130	30·00
70	**9**	1s. yellow	£300	12·00
71	**9**	5s. mauve	£275	55·00

1862. Perf.

54	**5**	6d. black	42·00	£110
55	**5**	1s. green	£2750	£325

HALF
PENNY
(11)

1876. Surcharged with T **11**.

76	**9**	½d. on 9d. purple	27·00	25·00
77	**10**	½d. on 10d. red	5·50	30·00

HALF PENNY
(13)

1877. Surch with T **13** (No. 79) or in words (others).

79	**10**	½d. on 10d. red	13·00	50·00
80	**9**	1d. on 4d. red	28·00	30·00
81	**9**	1s. on 5s. mauve	£350	£120

1878. Surch.

83	**10**	2c. red	20·00	25·00
84	**9**	4c. on 1d. brown	28·00	13·00
85	**9**	8c. on 2d. blue	85·00	4·25
86	**9**	13c. on 3d. red	28·00	55·00
87	**9**	17c. on 4d. red	£190	4·50
88	**9**	25c. on 6d. blue	£275	8·00
89	**9**	38c. on 9d. purple	50·00	£100
90	**9**	50c. on 1s. green	90·00	6·50
91	**9**	2r.50 on 5s. mauve	24·00	29·00

18

19

1879. Various frames.

101	**18**	1c. violet	3·25	45
102	**18**	2c. red	40·00	8·50
103	**18**	2c. green	6·00	60
93	**19**	4c. orange	65·00	3·50
105	**19**	4c. red	7·00	1·00
106	-	8c. blue	6·50	1·50
95	-	13c. grey	£180	£325
107	-	15c. brown	9·50	1·25
108	-	15c. blue	14·00	1·75
109	-	16c. brown	13·00	2·75
96	-	17c. red	95·00	10·00
110	-	25c. olive	16·00	4·00
98	-	38c. purple	£200	£375
99	-	50c. green	8·00	7·00
111	-	50c. orange	45·00	23·00
100	-	2r.50 purple	55·00	80·00

1883. No. 96 surch **16 CENTS**.

112	16c. on 17c. red	£170	55·00

1883. No. 96 surch **SIXTEEN CENTS**.

115	16c. on 17c. red	£110	2·50

1885. No. 98 surch **2 CENTS** with bar.

116	2c. on 38c. purple	£160	45·00

1887. No. 95 surch **2 CENTS** without bar.

117	2c. on 13c. grey	75·00	£120

1891. Surch in words with or without bar.

123	**18**	1c. on 2c. violet	2·50	2·25
124	-	1c. on 16c. brown (No. 109)	3·75	5·50
118	**19**	2c. on 4c. red	3·00	1·00
119	-	2c. on 17c. red (No. 96)	£140	£150
120	**9**	2c. on 38c. on 9d. purple (No. 89)	17·00	8·50
121	-	2c. on 38c. purple (No. 98)	12·00	19·00

36

1895

127	**36**	1c. purple and blue	1·00	1·50
128	**36**	2c. purple and orange	8·50	50
129	**36**	3c. purple	70	50
130	**36**	4c. purple and green	6·00	50
131	**36**	6c. green and red	7·50	4·00
132	**36**	18c. green and blue	24·00	3·50

37

1898. Diamond Jubilee.

133	**37**	36c. orange and blue	14·00	29·00

1899. Surch in figures and words.

137	-	4c. on 16c. brown (No. 109)	17·00	28·00
134	**36**	6c. on 18c. (No. 132)	2·00	1·00
156	**36**	12c. on 18c. (No. 132)	4·00	13·00
163	**37**	12c. on 36c. (No. 133)	3·00	1·25
135	**37**	15c. on 36c. (No. 133)	4·25	1·75

40 Admiral Mahe de Labourdonnais, Governor of Mauritius 1735–46

1899. Birth Bicentenary of Labourdonnais.

136	**40**	15c. blue	35·00	4·75

42

1900

138	**36**	1c. grey and black	50	10
139	**36**	2c. purple	1·00	20
140	**36**	3c. green & red on yellow	4·25	1·25
141	**36**	4c. purple & red on yellow	3·50	40
142	**36**	4c. green and violet	3·50	2·00
167a	**36**	4c. black and red on blue	16·00	10
144	**36**	5c. purple on buff	12·00	£120
145	**36**	5c. purple & black on buff	2·50	2·50
146	**36**	6c. purple and red on red	5·00	80
147	**36**	8c. green & black on buff	5·50	18·00
148	**36**	12c. black and red	3·00	2·25
149	**36**	15c. green and orange	35·00	10·00
171	**36**	15c. black & blue on blue	4·00	35
151a	**36**	25c. green & red on green	6·00	30·00
174	**36**	50c. green on yellow	3·25	9·00
175	**42**	1r. grey and red	48·00	60·00
154	**42**	2r.50 green & blk on blue	40·00	£160
155	**42**	5r. purple and red on red	£110	£180

1902. Optd Postage & Revenue.

157	**36**	4c. purple and red on yellow	2·50	20
158	**36**	6c. green and red	3·50	3·25
159	**36**	15c. green and orange	9·00	1·25
160	-	25c. olive (No. 110)	9·00	3·50
161	-	50c. green (No. 99)	28·00	8·00
162	-	2r.50 purple (No. 100)	£130	£225

46

1910

205	**46**	1c. black	1·00	1·00
206	**46**	2c. brown	1·00	10
207	**46**	2c. purple on yellow	4·00	3·25
183	**46**	3c. green	3·00	10
209	**46**	4c. green and red	1·50	1·75
210	**46**	4c. green	1·00	10
211	**46**	4c. brown	6·50	4·00
186	**46**	6c. red	7·50	20
213	**46**	6c. mauve	1·25	10
187	**46**	8c. orange	3·50	2·75
215	**46**	10c. grey	2·00	3·25
216	**46**	10c. red	15·00	9·00
217	**46**	12c. red	1·50	40
218	**46**	12c. grey	1·75	7·50
219b	**46**	15c. blue	1·00	25
220	**46**	20c. blue	2·00	80
221	**46**	20c. purple	8·50	17·00

47

1910

185	**47**	5c. grey and red	4·25	3·00
188	**47**	12c. grey	4·50	2·75
190	**47**	25c. black & red on yellow	2·00	12·00
191	**47**	50c. purple and black	5·00	23·00
192	**47**	1r. black on green	22·00	17·00
193	**47**	2r.50 black and red on blue	30·00	75·00
194	**47**	5r. green and red on yellow	48·00	95·00
195	**47**	10r. green and red on green	£170	£300

48

1913

223	**48**	1c. black	2·25	3·25
224	**48**	2c. brown	1·25	10
225	**48**	3c. green	3·00	40
226	**48**	4c. green and red	3·50	30
226c	**48**	4c. green	16·00	45
227	**48**	5c. grey and red	1·00	10
228	**48**	6c. brown	5·50	60
229	**48**	8c. orange	3·75	20·00
230	**48**	10c. red	4·75	20
232	**48**	12c. red	65	3·75
198	**48**	12c. grey	9·50	1·00
233	**48**	15c. blue	4·75	20
234	**48**	20c. purple	6·00	40
235	**48**	20c. blue	10·00	2·75
236	**48**	25c. black & red on yellow	1·50	15
237	**48**	50c. purple and black	7·50	4·50
238	**48**	1r. black on green	7·50	2·00
239	**48**	2r.50 black & red on blue	20·00	18·00
240	**48**	5r. green and red on yellow	50·00	£110
204*d*	**48**	10r. green and red on green	55·00	£190

1924. As T **42** but Arms similar to T **46**.

222	50r. purple and green	£950	£2750

1925. Surch with figures, words and bar.

242	**46**	3c. on 4c. green	9·50	7·00
243	**46**	10c. on 12c. red	45	1·75
244	**46**	15c. on 20c. blue	60	1·75

50a Windsor Castle

1935. Silver Jubilee.

245	**50a**	5c. blue and grey	50	10
246	**50a**	12c. green and blue	4·50	10
247	**50a**	20c. brown and blue	5·50	20
248	**50a**	1r. grey and purple	29·00	50·00

50b King George VI and Queen Elizabeth

1937. Coronation.

249	**50b**	5c. violet	40	20
250	**50b**	12c. red	75	2·25
251	**50b**	20c. blue	1·75	1·00

51

1938

252	**51**	2c. grey	30	10
253	**51**	3c. purple and red	2·00	2·00
254*b*	**51**	4c. green	2·50	2·25
255*a*	**51**	5c. violet	3·25	20
256*b*	**51**	10c. red	2·50	20
257	**51**	12c. orange	1·00	20
258	**51**	20c. blue	1·00	10
259b	**51**	25c. purple	9·00	10
260b	**51**	1r. brown	20·00	1·75

261a	**51**	2r.50 violet	42·00	30·00
262a	**51**	5r. olive	38·00	45·00
263a	**51**	10r. purple	17·00	48·00

1946. Victory. As T **8a** of Pitcairn Islands.

264	5c. violet	10	75
265	20c. blue	20	25

52 1d. "Post Office" Mauritius and King George VI

1948. Cent of First British Colonial Stamp.

266	**52**	5c. orange and mauve	10	50
267	**52**	12c. orange and green	15	50
268	-	20c. blue	20	10
269	-	1r. blue and brown	1·25	30

Design:—20c., 1r. As Type **52**, but showing 2d. "Post Office" Mauritius.

1948. Silver Wedding. As T **8b/c** of Pitcairn Islands.

270	5c. violet	10	10
271	10r. mauve	17·00	42·00

1949. U.P.U. As T **8d/g** of Pitcairn Islands.

272	12c. red	50	4·00
273	20c. blue	2·25	2·50
274	35c. purple	60	1·50
275	1r. brown	50	20

55 Aloe Plant

60 Legend of Paul and Virginie

67 Arms of Mauritius

1950

276	-	1c. purple	10	50
277	-	2c. red	15	10
278	**55**	3c. green	60	4·50
279	-	4c. green	20	3·25
280	-	5c. blue	15	10
281	-	10c. red	30	75
282	-	12c. green	1·50	3·00
283	**60**	20c. blue	1·00	15
284	-	25c. red	2·50	40
285	-	35c. violet	40	10
286	-	50c. green	2·75	50
287	-	1r. brown	9·50	10
288	-	2r.50 orange	23·00	21·00
289	-	5r. brown	25·00	21·00
290	**67**	10r. blue	17·00	48·00

Designs:—Horiz: 1c. Labourdonnais sugar factory; 2c. Grand Port; 5c. Rempart Mountain; 10c. Transporting cane; 12c. Mauritius dodo and map; 35c. Government House, Reduit; 1r. Timor deer; 2r.50, Port Louis; 5r. Beach scene. Vert: 4c. Tamarind Falls; 25c. Labourdonnais statue; 50c. Pieter Both Mountain.

1953. Coronation. As T **8i** of Pitcairn Islands.

291	10c. black and green	1·50	15

69 Historical Museum, Mahebourg

1953. As 1950 but portrait of Queen Elizabeth II. Designs as for corresponding values except where stated.

293	-	2c. red	10	10
294	-	3c. green	30	40
295	-	4c. purple (as 1c.)	10	1·00
296	-	5c. blue	10	10
314	-	10c. green (as 4c.)	15	10
298	**69**	15c. red	10	10
299	-	20c. red (as 25c.)	15	20
300	-	25c. blue (as 20c.)	1·50	10
301	-	35c. violet	20	10
302	-	50c. green	55	85
315	-	60c. green (as 12c.)	4·00	10
303	-	1r. sepia	30	10
316	-	2r.50 orange	13·00	8·50
305	-	5r. brown	28·00	10·00
306	-	10r. blue	17·00	2·00

70 Queen Elizabeth II and King George III (after Lawrence)

1961. 150th Anniv of British Post Office in Mauritius.

307	**70**	10c. black and red	10	10
308	**70**	20c. ultramarine and blue	30	50
309	**70**	35c. black and yellow	40	50
310	**70**	1r. purple and green	60	30

1963. Freedom from Hunger. As T **21a** of Pitcairn Islands.

311	60c. violet	40	10

1963. Cent of Red Cross. As T **20b** of Pitcairn Islands.

312	10c. red and black	15	10
313	60c. red and blue	60	20

71 Bourbon White-eye

1965. Birds. Multicoloured.

317	2c. Type **71** (yellow background)	40	15
318	3c. Rodriguez fody ("Rodrigues Fody") (brown background)	1·00	15
319	4c. Mauritius olive white-eye ("Olive White-Eye")	30	15
340	5c. Mascarene paradise flycatcher ("Paradise Flycatcher")	70	15
321	10c. Mauritius fody	30	10
322	15c. Mauritius parakeet ("Parrakeet") (grey background)	2·00	40
323	20c. Mauritius greybird ("Cuckoo-Shrike") (yellow background)	2·00	10
324	25c. Mauritius kestrel ("Kestrel")	2·00	30
341	35c. Pink pigeon	30	15
326	50c. Reunion bulbul ("Mascarene Bul-Bul")	50	65
327	60c. Mauritius blue pigeon (extinct) ("Dutch Pigeon") (yellow background)	60	10
328	1r. Mauritius dodo (extinct) (olive background)	12·00	10
329	2r.50 Rodriguez solitaire (extinct) ("Rodrigues Solitaire")	5·00	10·00
330	5r. Mauritius red rail (extinct) ("Red Rail")	15·00	17·00
331	10r. Broad-billed parrot (extinct)	35·00	38·00

For some values with background colours changed see Nos. 370/5.

1965. Centenary of I.T.U. As T **24a** of Pitcairn Islands.

332	10c. orange and green	20	10
333	60c. yellow and violet	70	20

1965. I.C.Y. As T **24b** of Pitcairn Islands.

334	10c. purple and turquoise	15	10
335	60c. green and violet	30	20

1966. Churchill Commemoration. As T **24c** of Pitcairn Islands.

336	2c. blue	10	4·00
337	10c. green	40	10
338	60c. brown	1·75	20
339	1r. violet	1·75	20

1966. 20th Anniv of UNESCO. As T **25b/d** of Pitcairn Islands.

342	5c. multicoloured	25	30
343	10c. yellow, violet and green	30	10
344	60c. black, purple and orange	1·40	15

86 Red-tailed Tropic Bird

1967. Self-Government. Multicoloured.

345	2c. Type **86**	25	3·00
346	10c. Rodriguez brush warbler	80	10
347	60c. Rose-ringed parakeet (extinct) ("Rodrigues Parakeet")	85	10
348	1r. Grey-rumped swiftlet ("Mauritius Swiftlet")	90	10

1967. Self-Government. Nos. 317/31 optd **SELF GOVERNMENT 1967**.

349	**71**	2c. multicoloured	10	50
350	-	3c. multicoloured	10	50
351	-	4c. multicoloured	10	50
352	-	5c. multicoloured	10	10
353	-	10c. multicoloured	10	10
354	-	15c. multicoloured	10	30
355	-	20c. multicoloured	15	10
356	-	25c. multicoloured	15	10
357	-	35c. multicoloured	20	10
358	-	50c. multicoloured	30	15
359	-	60c. multicoloured	30	10
360	-	1r. multicoloured	1·50	10
361	-	2r.50 multicoloured	1·00	2·25
362	-	5r. multicoloured	6·00	3·25
363	-	10r. multicoloured	10·00	15·00

91 Flag of Mauritius

1968. Independence. Multicoloured.

364	2c. Type **91**	10	2·50
365	3c. Arms and Mauritius dodo emblem	20	2·50
366	15c. Type **91**	60	10
367	20c. As 3c.	60	10
368	60c. Type **91**	1·10	10
369	1r. As 3c.	1·10	10

1968. As Nos. 317/8, 322/3 and 327/8 but background colours changed as below.

370	**71**	2c. olive	20	4·50
371	-	3c. blue	1·75	9·00
372	-	15c. brown	55	20
373	-	20c. buff	3·50	4·00
374	-	60c. red	1·50	1·25
375	-	1r. purple	3·25	1·50

93 Dominique rescues Paul and Virginie

1968. Bicentenary of Bernardin de St. Pierre's Visit to Mauritius. Multicoloured.

376	2c. Type **93**	10	1·25
377	15c. Paul and Virginie crossing the river (vert)	65	10
378	50c. Visit of Labourdonnais to Madame de la Tour	1·25	10
379	60c. Meeting of Paul and Virginie in Confidence (vert)	1·25	10
380	1r. Departure of Virginie for Europe	1·25	20
381	2r.50 Bernardin de St. Pierre (vert)	1·75	3·75

99 Black-spotted Emperor

1969. Multicoloured (except 10, 15, 25, 60c.).

382	2c. Type **99**	10	2·75
383	3c. Red reef crab	10	3·50
384	4c. Episcopal mitre	2·50	4·50
385	5c. Black-saddled pufferfish ("Bourse")	30	10
386	10c. Starfish (red, black and flesh)	2·00	10
387	15c. Sea urchin (brown, black and blue)	30	10
388	20c. Fiddler crab	65	70
389	25c. Spiny shrimp (red, black and green)	30	3·75
390	30c. Single harp shells and double harp shell	1·50	1·75
483	35c. Common paper nautilus	1·75	15
484	40c. Spanish dancer	1·00	60
448	50c. Orange spider conch and violet spider conch	45	10
449b	60c. Blue marlin (black, pink and blue)	65	10
487	75c. *Conus clytospira*	1·25	1·50
396	1r. Dolphinfish	60	10
452	2r.50 Spiny lobster	2·00	4·50
453	5r. Ruby snapper ("Sacre chien rouge")	2·00	2·00
399w	10r. Yellow-edged lyretail ("Croissant queue jaune")	1·50	1·50

117 Gandhi as Law Student

1969. Birth Cent of Mahatma Gandhi. Multicoloured.

400	2c. Type **117**	30	20
401	15c. Gandhi as stretcher-bearer during Zulu Revolt	65	10
402	50c. Gandhi as Satyagrahi in South Africa	80	50
403	60c. Gandhi at No. 10 Downing Street, London	80	10
404	1r. Gandhi in Mauritius, 1901	90	10
405	2r.50 Gandhi, the "Apostle of Truth and Non-Violence"	2·00	2·00
MS406	153×153 mm. Nos. 400/5	13·00	8·00

124 Frangourinier Cane-crusher (18th-cent)

1969. 150th Anniv of Telfair's Improvements to the Sugar Industry. Multicoloured.

407	2c. Three-roller Vertical Mill	10	20
408	15c. Type **124**	10	10
409	60c. Beau Rivage Factory, 1867	10	10
410	1r. Mon Desert-Alma Factory, 1969	10	10
411	2r.50 Dr. Charles Telfair (vert)	25	1·25
MS412	159×88 mm. Nos. 407/11	1·75	2·50

1970. Expo '70. Nos. 394 and 396 optd **EXPO '70' OSAKA**.

413	60c. black, red and blue	10	10
414	1r. multicoloured	20	20

129 Morne Plage, Mountain and Boeing 707

1970. Inauguration of Lufthansa Flight, Mauritius–Frankfurt. Multicoloured.

415	25c. Type **129**	30	20
416	50c. Boeing 707 and map (vert)	30	20

131 Lenin as a Student

1970. Birth Centenary of Lenin.

417	**131**	15c. green and silver	10	10
418	-	75c. brown	20	20

Design:—75c. Lenin as founder of USSR.

133 2d. "Post Office" Mauritius and original Post Office

1970. Port Louis, Old and New. Multicoloured.

419	5c. Type **133**	20	10
420	15c. GPO Building (built 1870)	20	10
421	50c. Mail coach (c. 1870)	80	15
422	75c. Port Louis Harbour (1970)	95	25
423	2r.50 Arrival of Pierre A. de Suffren (1783)	1·00	3·00
MS424	165×95 mm. Nos. 419/23	5·25	8·50

138 UN Emblem and Symbols

1970. 25th Anniv of U.N.

425	**138**	10c. multicoloured	10	10
426	**138**	60c. multicoloured	40	10

139 Rainbow over Waterfall

1971. Tourism. Multicoloured.

427	10c. Type **139**	25	10
428	15c. Trois Mamelles Mountains	25	10
429	60c. Beach scene	35	10
430	2r.50 Marine life	50	1·50

Nos. 427/30 have inscriptions on the reverse.

140 "Crossroads" of Indian Ocean

1971. 25th Anniv of Plaisance Airport. Multicoloured.

431	15c. Type **140**	45	10
432	60c. Boeing 707 and Terminal buildings	70	10
433	1r. Air hostesses on gangway	75	10
434	2r.50 Farman F.190, Roland Garros' aeroplane, Choisy Airfield, 1937	2·25	4·50

141 Princess Margaret Orthopaedic Centre

1971. Third Commonwealth Medical Conference. Multicoloured.

435	10c. Type **141**	10	10
436	75c. Operating theatre in National Hospital	50	20

142 Queen Elizabeth II and Prince Philip

1972. Royal Visit. Multicoloured.

455	15c. Type **142**	15	10
456	2r.50 Queen Elizabeth II (vert)	2·00	2·00

143 Theatre Facade

1972. 150th Anniv of Port Louis Theatre. Multicoloured.

457	10c. Type **143**	10	10
458	1r. Theatre auditorium	40	20

144 Pirate Dhow

1972. Pirates and Privateers. Multicoloured.

459	15c. Type **144**	65	15
460	60c. Treasure chest (vert)	1·00	20
461	1r. Lemene and *L'Hirondelle* (vert)	1·25	20
462	2r.50 Robert Surcouf	4·50	8·00

145 Mauritius University

1973. Fifth Anniv of Independence. Multicoloured.

463	15c. Type **145**	10	10
464	60c. Tea development	15	15
465	1r. Bank of Mauritius	15	15

146 Map and Hands

1973. O.C.A.M. Conference. Multicoloured.

466	10c. OCAM emblem (horiz)	10	10
467	2r.50 Type **146**	40	45

OCAM = Organisation Commune Africaine Malgache et Mauricienne.

147 WHO Emblem

1973. 25th Anniv of W.H.O.

468	**147**	1r. multicoloured	10	10

148 Meteorological Station, Vacoas

1973. Centenary of I.M.O./W.M.O.

469	**148**	75c. multicoloured	30	70

149 Capture of the *Kent* 1800

1973. Birth Bicentenary of Robert Surcouf (privateer).

470	**149**	60c. multicoloured	50	85

150 P. Commerson

1974. Death Bicentenary (1973) of Philibert Commerson (naturalist).

471	**150**	2r.50 multicoloured	30	40

151 Cow being Milked

1974. Eighth F.A.O. Regional Conf for Africa, Mauritius.

472	**151**	60c. multicoloured	20	20

152 Mail Train

1974. Centenary of U.P.U. Multicoloured.

473	15c. Type **152**	40	15
474	1r. New GPO, Port Louis	40	20

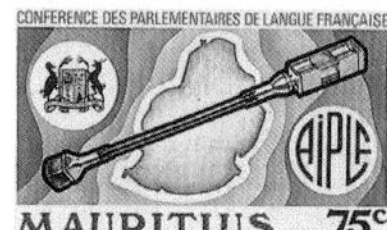

153 *Cottage Life* (F. Leroy)

1975. Aspects of Mauritian Life. Paintings. Mult.

493	15c. Type **153**	20	10
494	60c. *Milk Seller* (A. Richard) (vert)	35	10
495	1r. *Entrance of Port Louis Market* (Thuillier)	35	10
496	2r.50 *Washerwoman* (Max Boullee) (vert)	90	80

154 Mace across Map

1975. French-speaking Parliamentary Assemblies Conference, Port Louis.

497	**154**	75c. multicoloured	30	1·25

155 Woman with Lamp ("The Light of the World")

1976. International Women's Year.

498	**155**	2r.50 multicoloured	35	2·00

156 Parched Landscape

1976. Drought in Africa. Multicoloured.

499	50c. Type **156**	15	30
500	60c. Map of Africa and carcass (vert)	15	30

157 *Pierre Loti*, 1953–70

1976. Mail Carriers to Mauritius. Multicoloured.

501	10c. Type **157**	70	10
502	15c. *Secunder*, 1907	95	10
503	50c. *Hindoostan*, 1842	1·60	15
504	60c. *St. Geran*, 1740	1·75	15
505	2r.50 *Maen*, 1638	4·00	7·50
MS506	115×138 mm. Nos. 501/5	10·00	13·00

158 "The Flame of Hindi carried across the Seas"

1976. Second World Hindi Convention. Multicoloured.

507	10c. Type **158**	10	10
508	75c. Type **158**	10	30
509	1r.20 Hindi script	20	1·25

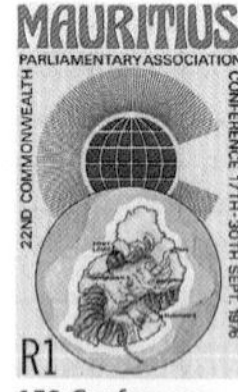

159 Conference Logo and Map of Mauritius

1976. 22nd Commonwealth Parliamentary Association Conference. Multicoloured.

510	1r. Type **159**	40	10
511	2r.50 Conference logo	60	2·00

160 King Priest and Breastplate

1976. Moenjodaro Excavations, Pakistan. Mult.

512	60c. Type **160**	50	10
513	1r. House with well and goblet	65	10
514	2r.50 Terracotta figurine and necklace	1·75	1·00

161 Sega Scene

1977. Second World Black and African Festival of Arts and Culture, Nigeria.

515	**161**	1r. multicoloured	30	15

162 The Queen with Sceptre and Rod

1977. Silver Jubilee. Multicoloured.

516	50c. The Queen at Mauritius Legislative Assembly, 1972	15	10
517	75c. Type **162**	20	10
518	5r. Presentation of Sceptre and Rod	55	75

163 *Hugonia tomentosa*

1977. Indigenous Flowers. Multicoloured.

519	20c. Type **163**	25	10
520	1r. *Ochna mauritiana* (vert)	45	10
521	1r.50 *Dombeya acutangula*	60	20
522	5r. *Trochetia blackburniana* (vert)	1·25	1·50
MS523	130×130 mm. Nos. 519/22	4·25	8·00

164 de Havilland Twin Otter 200/300

1977. Inaugural International Flight of Air Mauritius. Multicoloured.

524	25c. Type **164**	60	10
525	50c. de Havilland Twin Otter 200/300 and Air Mauritius emblem	80	10
526	75c. Piper Navajo and Boeing 747-100	95	20
527	5r. Boeing 707	3·00	3·75
MS528	110×152 mm. Nos. 524/7	9·00	9·00

165 Portuguese Map of Mauritius, 1519

1978

529B	**165**	10c. multicoloured	1·00	1·25
530A	-	15c. multicoloured	1·50	2·75
531A	-	20c. multicoloured	80	2·75
532A	-	25c. multicoloured	60	2·00
533B	-	35c. multicoloured	1·00	20
534A	-	50c. multicoloured	50	75
535A	-	60c. multicoloured	60	2·75
536A	-	70c. multicoloured	2·75	4·00
537B	-	75c. multicoloured	1·75	4·00
538A	-	90c. multicoloured	4·00	4·25
539A	-	1r. multicoloured	60	50
540A	-	1r.20 multicoloured	1·75	4·00
541B	-	1r.25 multicoloured	1·75	20
542A	-	1r.50 multicoloured	1·00	2·75
543A	-	2r. multicoloured	60	70
544A	-	3r. multicoloured	60	50
545A	-	5r. multicoloured	60	1·75
546A	-	10r. multicoloured	1·50	1·00
547A	-	15r. multicoloured	1·50	3·00
548A	-	25r. green, black & brn	2·50	3·25

Designs:—Horiz: 15c. Dutch Occupation, 1638–1710; 20c. Map by Van Keulen, *c.* 1700; 50c. Construction of Port Louis, *c.* 1736; 70c. Map by Bellin, 1763; 90c. Battle of Grand Port, 1810; 1r. Landing of the British, 1810; 1r.20, Government House, *c.* 1840; 1r.50, Indian immigration, 1835; 2r. Race Course, *c.* 1870; 3r. Place d'Armes, *c.* 1880; 5r. Royal Visit postcard, 1901; 10r. Royal College, 1914; 25r. First Mauritian Governor-General and Prime Minister. Vert: 25c. Settlement on Rodriguez, 1691; 35c. French settlers Charter, 1715; 60c. Pierre Poivre, *c.* 1767; 75c. First coinage, 1794; 1r.25 Lady Gomm's Ball, 1847; 15r. Unfurling of Mauritian flag.

166 Mauritius Dodo

1978. 25th Anniv of Coronation.

549		3r. grey, black and blue	25	45
550		3r. multicoloured	25	45
551	**166**	3r. grey, black and blue	25	45

Designs:—No. 549, Antelope of Bohun; No. 550, Queen Elizabeth II.

167 Problem of Infection, World War I

1978. 50th Anniv of Discovery of Penicillin.

552	**167**	20c. multicoloured	85	10
553	-	1r. multicoloured	1·75	75
554	-	1r.50 black, brown & grn	2·50	1·40
555	-	5r. multicoloured	3·25	6·00
MS556		150×90 mm. Nos. 552/5	10·00	12·00

Designs:—1r. First mould growth, 1928; 1r.50, *Penicillium chrysogenum* (*notatum*); 5r. Sir Alexander Fleming.

168 *Papilio manlius* (butterfly)

1978. Endangered Species. Multicoloured.

557		20c. Type **168**	2·00	50
558		1r. Geckos	1·00	10
559		1r.50 Greater Mascarene flying fox	1·25	1·00
560		5r. Mauritius kestrel	14·00	9·50
MS561		154×148 mm. Nos. 557/60	50·00	18·00

169 Ornate Table

1978. Bicentenary of Reconstruction of Chateau Le Reduit. Multicoloured.

562		15c. Type **169**	10	10
563		75c. Chateau Le Reduit	10	10
564		3r. Le Reduit gardens	40	45

170 Whitcomb Diesel Locomotive 65H.P., 1949

1979. Railway Locomotives. Multicoloured.

565		20c. Type **170**	20	10
566		1r. *Sir William*, 1922	40	10
567		1r.50 Kitson type 1930	60	45
568		2r. Garratt type, 1927	75	85
MS569		128×128 mm. Nos. 565/8	3·25	4·50

171 Father Laval and Crucifix

1979. Beatification of Father Laval (missionary). Multicoloured.

570		20c. Type **171**	15	10
571		1r.50 Father Laval	40	10
572		5r. Father Laval's tomb (horiz)	85	1·50
MS573		150×96 mm. Nos. 570/2	2·75	3·50

172 Astronaut descending from Lunar Module

1979. Tenth Anniv of Moon Landing. Multicoloured. Self-adhesive.

574		20c. Type **172**	40	60
575		3r. Astronaut performing experiment on Moon	70	1·40
576		5r. Astronaut on Moon	5·00	8·50

173 Great Britain 1855 4d. Stamp and Sir Rowland Hill

1979. Death Cent of Sir Rowland Hill. Mult.

577		25c. Type **173**	10	10
578		2r. 1954 60c. definitive	70	55
579		5r. 1847 1d. "POST OFFICE"	1·25	1·75
MS580		120×89 mm. 3r. 1847 2d. "POST OFFICE"	1·75	2·00

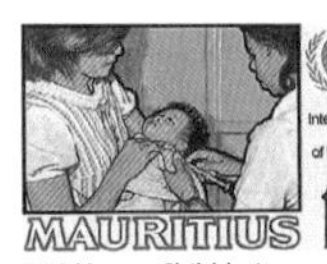

174 Young Child being Vaccinated

1979. International Year of the Child.

581	**174**	15c. multicoloured	10	10
582	-	25c. multicoloured	10	10
583	-	1r. black, blue and light blue	20	10
584	-	1r.50 multicoloured	40	35
585	-	3r. multicoloured	70	1·10

Designs:—Horiz: 25c. Children playing; 1r.50, Girls in chemistry laboratory; 3r. Boy operating lathe. Vert: 1r. IYC emblem.

175 The Lienard Obelisk

1980. Pamplemousses Botanical Gardens. Multicoloured.

586		20c. Type **175**	15	10
587		25c. Poivre Avenue	15	10
588		1r. Varieties of Vacoas	30	10
589		2r. Giant water lilies	60	60
590		5r. Mon Plaisir (mansion)	1·00	3·50
MS591		152×105 mm. Nos. 586/90	3·50	5·50

176 *Emirne* (French steam packet)

1980. London 1980 International Stamp Exhibition. Mail-carrying Ships. Multicoloured.

592		25c. Type **176**	35	10
593		1r. *Boissevain* (cargo liner)	55	10
594		2r. *La Boudeuse* (Bougainville's ship)	75	70
595		5r. *Sea Breeze* (English clipper)	1·00	2·75

177 Blind Person Basket-making

1980. Birth Centenary of Helen Keller (campaigner for the handicapped). Multicoloured.

596		25c. Type **177**	20	10
597		1r. Deaf child under instruction	45	10
598		2r.50 Helen reading braille	70	35
599		5r. Helen at graduation, 1904	1·25	1·25

178 Prime Minister Sir Seewoosagur Ramgoolam

1980. 80th Birthday and 40th Year in Parliament of Prime Minister Sir Seewoosagur Ramgoolam.

600	**178**	15r. multicoloured	1·50	2·50

179 Headquarters, Mauritius Institute

1980. Centenary of Mauritius Institute. Mult.

601		25c. Type **179**	15	10
602		2r. Rare copy of Veda	50	20
603		2r.50 Glory of India cone shell	65	25
604		5r. "Le Torrent" (painting by Harpignies)	85	1·50

180 *Hibiscus liliiflorus*

1981. Flowers. Multicoloured.

605		25c. Type **180**	20	10
606		2r. *Erythrospermum monticolum*	70	65
607		2r.50 *Chasalia boryana*	75	1·25
608		5r. *Hibiscus columnaris*	1·25	3·25

181 Beau-Bassin/ Rose Hill

1981. Coats of Arms of Mauritius Towns. Multicoloured.

609		25c. Type **181**	10	10
610		1r.50 Curepipe	30	25
611		2r. Quatre-Bornes	35	30
612		2r.50 Vacoas/Phoenix	40	50
613		5r. Port Louis	70	1·40
MS614		130×130 mm. Nos. 609/13	2·25	6·50

182 Prince Charles as Colonel-in-Chief, Royal Regiment of Wales

1981. Royal Wedding. Multicoloured.

615		25c. Wedding bouquet from Mauritius	10	10
616		2r.50 Type **182**	40	15
617		10r. Prince Charles and Lady Diana Spencer	80	90

183 Emmanuel Anquetil and Guy Rozemont

1981. Famous Politicians and Physician.

618	**183**	20c. black and red	10	10
619	-	25c. black and yellow	10	10
620	-	1r.25 black and green	30	50
621	-	1r.50 black and red	35	25
622	-	2r. black and blue	45	30
623	-	2r.50 black and brown	50	90
624	-	5r. black and blue	2·00	2·75

Designs:—25c. Remy Ollier and Sookdeo Bissoondoyal; 1r.25, Maurice Cure and Barthelemy Ohsan; 1r.50, Sir Guy Forget and Renganaden Seeneevassen; 2r. Sir Abdul Razak Mohamed and Jules Koenig; 2r.50, Abdoollatiff Mahomed Osman and Dazzi Rama (Pandit Sahadeo); 5r. Sir Thomas Lewis (physician) and electrocardiogram.

184 Drummer and Piper

1981. Religion and Culture. Multicoloured.

625		20c. Type **184**	10	10
626		2r. Swami Sivananda (vert)	1·25	1·25
627		5r. Chinese Pagoda	1·50	3·75

The 20c. value commemorates the World Tamil Culture Conference (1980).

185 "Skills"

1981. 25th Anniv of Duke of Edinburgh Award Scheme. Multicoloured.

628		25c. Type **185**	10	10
629		1r.25 "Service"	10	10
630		5r. "Expeditions"	30	30
631		10r. Duke of Edinburgh	50	70

186 Kaaba (sacred shrine, Great Mosque of Mecca)

1981. Moslem Year 1400 A.H. Commemoration. Multicoloured.

632		25c. Type **186**	30	10
633		2r. Mecca	80	80
634		5r. Mecca and Kaaba	1·40	2·75

187 Scout Emblem

1982. 75th Anniv of Boy Scout Movement and 70th Anniv of Scouting in Mauritius.

635	**187**	25c. lilac and green	10	10
636	-	2r. brown and ochre	35	30
637	-	5r. green and olive	65	80
638	-	10r. green and blue	1·00	1·75

Designs:—2r. Lord Baden-Powell and Baden-Powell House; 5r. Grand Howl; 10r. Ascent of Pieter Both.

188 Charles Darwin

1982. 150th Anniv of Charles Darwin's Voyage. Multicoloured.

639	25c. Type **188**	20	10
640	2r. Darwin's telescope	50	45
641	2r.50 Darwin's elephant ride	1·25	75
642	10r. HMS *Beagle* beached for repairs	1·50	3·00

189 Bride and Groom at Buckingham Palace

1982. 21st Birthday of Princess of Wales. Mult.

643	25c. Mauritius coat of arms	10	10
644	2r.50 Princess Diana in Chesterfield, November 1981	40	45
645	5r. Type **189**	60	90
646	10r. Formal portrait	1·75	2·50

190 Prince and Princess of Wales with Prince William

1982. Birth of Prince William of Wales.

647	**190**	2r.50 multicoloured	1·25	65

191 Bois Fandamane Plant

1982. Centenary of Robert Koch's Discovery of Tubercle Bacillus. Multicoloured.

648	25c. Type **191**	30	10
649	1r.25 Central market, Port Louis	60	40
650	2r. Bois Banane plant	70	75
651	5r. Platte de Lezard plant	80	2·50
652	10r. Dr. Robert Koch	1·25	4·00

192 Arms and Flag of Mauritius

1983. Commonwealth Day. Multicoloured.

653	25c. Type **192**	10	10
654	2r.50 Satellite view of Mauritius	20	30
655	5r. Harvesting sugar cane	30	75
656	10r. Port Louis harbour	95	1·50

193 Early Wall-mounted Telephone

1983. World Communications Year. Mult.

657	25c. Type **193**	15	10
658	1r.25 Early telegraph apparatus (horiz)	45	20
659	2r. Earth satellite station	55	50
660	10r. First hot-air balloon in Mauritius, 1784 (horiz)	95	2·75

194 Map of Namibia

1983. Namibia Day. Multicoloured.

661	25c. Type **194**	60	10
662	2r.50 Hand breaking chains	1·50	75
663	5r. Family and settlement	2·00	2·25
664	10r. Diamond mining	5·50	3·75

195 Fish Trap

1983. Fishery Resources. Multicoloured.

665	25c. Type **195**	15	10
666	1r. Fishing boat (horiz)	30	15
667	5r. Game fishing	55	2·50
668	10r. Octopus drying (horiz)	80	4·00

196 Swami Dayananda

1983. Death Centenary of Swami Dayananda. Multicoloured.

669	25c. Type **196**	15	10
670	35c. Last meeting with father	15	10
671	2r. Receiving religious instruction	60	65
672	5r. Swami demonstrating strength	90	2·75
673	10r. At a religious gathering	1·25	4·25

197 Adolf von Plevitz

1983. 125th Anniv of Arrival in Mauritius of Adolf von Plevitz (social reformer). Multicoloured.

674	25c. Type **197**	20	10
675	1r.25 La Laura, Government school	60	30
676	5r. Von Plevitz addressing Commission of Enquiry, 1872	1·40	3·00
677	10r. Von Plevitz with Indian farm workers	2·00	4·50

198 Courtship Chase

1984. The Mauritius Kestrel. Multicoloured.

678	25c. Type **198**	85	30
679	2r. Kestrel in tree (vert)	2·00	1·25
680	2r.50 Young kestrel	2·25	2·25
681	10r. Head (vert)	3·25	8·50

199 Wreck of SS *Tayeb*

1984. 250th Anniv of *Lloyd's List* (newspaper). Multicoloured.

682	25c. Type **199**	30	10
683	1r. SS *Taher*	95	15
684	5r. East Indiaman *Triton*	2·50	2·75
685	10r. MS *Astor*	3·00	6·50

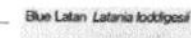

200 Blue Latan Palm

1984. Palm Trees. Multicoloured.

686	25c. Type **200**	10	10
687	50c. *Hyophorbe vaughanii*	20	20
688	2r.50 *Tectiphiala ferox*	1·50	1·75
689	5r. Round Island bottle-palm	2·25	3·50
690	10r. *Hyophorbe amaricaulis*	3·50	7·00

201 Slave Girl

1984. 150th Anniv of Abolition of Slavery and Introduction of Indian Immigrants.

691	**201**	25c. purple, lilac and brown	15	10
692	-	1r. purple, lilac and brown	70	10
693	-	2r. purple and lilac	1·50	1·00
694	-	10r. purple and lilac	7·00	11·00

Designs:—Vert: 1r. Slave market. Horiz: 2r. Indian immigrant family; 10r. Arrival of Indian immigrants.

202 75th Anniversary Production of *Faust* and Leoville L'Homme

1984. Centenary of Alliance Francaise (cultural organization). Multicoloured.

695	25c. Type **202**	20	10
696	1r.25 Prize-giving ceremony and Aunauth Beejadbur	70	50
697	5r. First headquarters and Hector Clarenc	2·00	3·00
698	10r. Lion Mountain and Labourdonnais	2·50	5·50

203 The Queen Mother on Clarence House Balcony, 1980

1985. Life and Times of Queen Elizabeth the Queen Mother. Multicoloured.

699	25c. The Queen Mother in 1926	60	10
700	2r. With Princess Margaret at Trooping the Colour	1·50	45
701	5r. Type **203**	1·60	1·75
702	10r. With Prince Henry at his christening (from photo by Lord Snowdon)	1·90	4·25

MS703 91×73 mm. 15r. Reopening the Stratford Canal, 1964 — 6·50 — 5·50

204 High Jumping

1985. Second Indian Ocean Islands Games. Multicoloured.

704	25c. Type **204**	40	10
705	50c. Javelin-throwing	70	30
706	1r.25 Cycling	5·00	2·25
707	10r. Wind surfing	8·50	15·00

205 Adult and Fledgling Pink Pigeons

1985. Pink Pigeon. Multicoloured.

708	25c. Type **205**	3·75	50
709	2r. Pink pigeon displaying at nest	9·00	2·00
710	2r.50 On nest	9·50	4·00
711	5r. Pair preening	13·00	16·00

206 Caverne Patates, Rodrigues

1985. Tenth Anniv of World Tourism Organization. Multicoloured.

712	25c. Type **206**	50	10
713	35c. Coloured soils, Chamarel	50	40
714	5r. Serpent Island	5·00	5·50
715	10r. Coin de Mire Island	7·00	11·00

207 Old Town Hall, Port Louis

1985. 250th Anniv of Port Louis. Multicoloured.

716	25c. Type **207**	20	10
717	1r. Al-Aqsa Mosque (180th anniv)	1·75	10
718	2r.50 Vase and trees (250th anniv of settlement of Tamil-speaking Indians)	1·50	2·00
719	10r. Port Louis Harbour	7·50	13·00

208 Edmond Halley and Diagram

1986. Appearance of Halley's Comet. Multicoloured.

720	25c. Type **208**	65	10
721	1r.25 Halley's Comet (1682) and Newton's Reflector	1·50	50
722	3r. Halley's Comet passing Earth	2·00	2·25
723	10r. *Giotto* spacecraft	4·00	9·00

1986. 60th Birthday of Queen Elizabeth II. As T **246a** of Papua New Guinea. Multicoloured.

724	25c. Princess Elizabeth wearing badge of Grenadier Guards, 1942	15	10
725	75c. Investiture of Prince of Wales, 1969	20	10
726	2r. With Prime Minister of Mauritius, 1972	30	25
727	3r. In Germany, 1978	45	40
728	15r. At Crown Agents Head Office, London, 1983	1·25	2·00

209 Maize (World Food Day)

1986. International Events. Multicoloured.

729	25c. Type **209**	10	10
730	1r. African Regional Industrial Property Organization emblem (Tenth anniv)	30	10
731	1r.25 International Peace Year emblem	65	50
732	10r. Footballer and Mauritius Football Association emblem (World Cup Football Championship, Mexico)	4·00	10·00

210 *Cryptopus elatus*

1986. Orchids. Multicoloured.

733	25c. Type **210**	50	10
734	2r. *Jumellea recta*	1·25	45
735	2r.50 *Angraecum mauritianum*	1·40	75
736	10r. *Bulbophyllum longiflorum*	2·25	5·50

211 Hesketh Bell Bridge

1987. Mauritius Bridges. Multicoloured.

758	25c. Type **211**	35	10
759	50c. Sir Colville Deverell Bridge	50	20
760	2r.50 Cavendish Bridge	90	75
761	5r. Tamarin Bridge	1·10	2·00
762	10r. Grand River North West Bridge	1·25	2·50

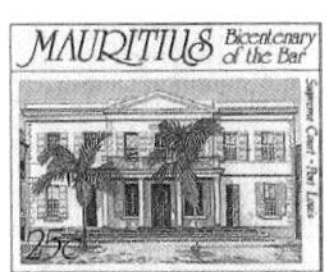

212 Supreme Court, Port Louis

1987. Bicentenary of the Mauritius Bar. Multicoloured.

763	25c. Type **212**	10	10
764	1r. District Court, Flacq	40	10
765	1r.25 Statue of Justice	50	20
766	10r. Barristers of 1787 and 1987	2·00	2·50

213 Mauritius Dodo Mascot

1987. International Festival of the Sea. Multicoloured.

767	25c. Type **213**	70	20
768	1r.50 Yacht regatta (horiz)	2·25	1·00
769	3r. Water skiing (horiz)	3·25	3·75
770	5r. *Svanen* (barquentine)	3·75	8·00

214 Toys

1987. Industrialization. Multicoloured.

771	20c. Type **214**	10	10
772	35c. Spinning factory	10	10
773	50c. Rattan furniture	10	10
774	2r.50 Spectacle factory	85	80
775	10r. Stone carving	2·50	3·00

215 Maison Ouvriere (Int Year of Shelter for the Homeless)

1987. Art and Architecture.

776	**215**	25c. multicoloured	15	10
777	-	1r. black and grey	20	10
778	-	1r.25 multicoloured	45	40
779	-	2r. multicoloured	75	70
780	-	5r. multicoloured	1·50	2·75

Designs:—1r. *Paul et Virginie* (lithograph); 1r.25, Chateau de Rosnay; 2r. *Vieille Ferme* (Boulle); 5r. *Trois Mamelles*.

216 University of Mauritius

1988. 20th Anniv of Independence. Multicoloured.

781	25c. Type **216**	10	10
782	75c. Anniversary gymnastic display	20	10
783	2r.50 Hurdlers and aerial view of Sir Maurice Rault Stadium	70	55
784	5r. Air Mauritius aircraft at Sir Seewoosagur Ramgoolam International Airport	1·40	1·60
785	10r. Governor-General Sir Veerasamy Ringadoo and Prime Minister Anerood Jugnauth	2·25	3·00

217 Breast Feeding

1988. 40th Anniv of W.H.O. Multicoloured.

786	20c. Type **217**	15	10
787	2r. Baby under vaccination umbrella and germ droplets	1·25	70
788	3r. Nutritious food	1·40	1·25
789	10r. WHO logo	2·75	3·75

218 Modern Bank Building

1988. 150th Anniv of Mauritius Commercial Bank Ltd.

790	**218**	25c. black, green and blue	10	10
791	-	1r. black and red	20	10
792	-	1r.25 multicoloured	40	30
793	-	25r. multicoloured	6·50	8·50

Designs:—Horiz: 1r. Mauritius Commercial Bank, 1897; 25r. 15 dollar bank note of 1838. Vert: 1r.25, Bank Arms.

219 Olympic Rings and Athlete

1988. Olympic Games, Seoul. Multicoloured.

794	25c. Type **219**	10	10
795	35c. Wrestling	15	15
796	1r.50 Long distance running	75	60
797	10r. Swimming	2·50	4·25

220 Nature Park

1989. Protection of the Environment. Multicoloured.

798B	15c. Underwater view	1·00	1·25
799B	20c. As 15c.	15	1·75
808A	30c. Common greenshank ("Greenshank")	1·50	1·00
801B	40c. Type **220**	20	60
810A	50c. Round Island (vert)	20	60
801cB	60c. As 50c.	20	30
811A	75c. Bassin Blanc	20	60
812A	1r. Mangrove (vert)	20	10
802A	1r.50 Whimbrel	1·00	1·25
813A	2r. Le Morne	30	20
803A	3r. Marine life	30	30
804B	4r. Fern tree (vert)	30	35
814A	5r. Riviere du Poste estuary	60	50
805A	6r. Ecological scenery (vert)	60	50
806B	10r. *Phelsuma ornata* (gecko) on plant (vert)	1·00	1·75
806aB	15r. Benares waves	1·50	3·00
817B	25r. Migratory birds and map (vert)	1·90	3·00

221 La Tour Sumeire, Port Louis

1989. Bicentenary of the French Revolution.

818	**221**	30c. black, green & yellow	15	10
819	-	1r. black, brown and light brown	35	10
820	-	8r. multicoloured	2·50	2·75
821	-	15r. multicoloured	3·25	4·50

Designs:—1r. Salle de Spectacle du Jardin; 8r. Portrait of Comte de Malartic; 15r. Bicentenary logo.

222 Cardinal Jean Margeot

1989. Visit of Pope John Paul II. Multicoloured.

822	30c. Type **222**	30	10
823	40c. Pope John Paul II and Prime Minister Jugnauth, Vatican, 1988	1·50	25
824	3r. Mere Marie Magdeleine de la Croix and Chapelle des Filles de Marie, Port Louis, 1864	1·50	1·25
825	6r. St. Francois d'Assise Church, Pamplemousses, 1756	2·25	2·75
826	10r. Pope John Paul II	8·00	9·00

223 Nehru

1989. Birth Centenary of Jawaharlal Nehru (Indian statesman). Multicoloured.

827	40c. Type **223**	1·75	25
828	1r.50 Nehru with daughter, Indira, and grandsons	3·00	1·00
829	3r. Nehru and Gandhi	6·00	3·50
830	4r. Nehru with Presidents Nasser and Tito	3·75	3·50
831	10r. Nehru with children	7·50	12·00

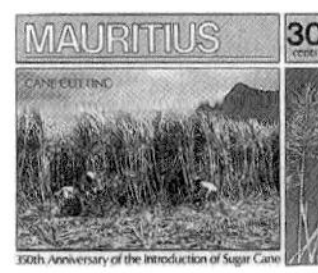

224 Cane Cutting

1990. 350th Anniv of Introduction of Sugar Cane to Mauritius. Multicoloured.

832	30c. Type **224**	15	10
833	40c. Sugar factory, 1867	20	10
834	1r. Mechanical loading of cane	40	10
835	25r. Modern sugar factory	11·00	15·00

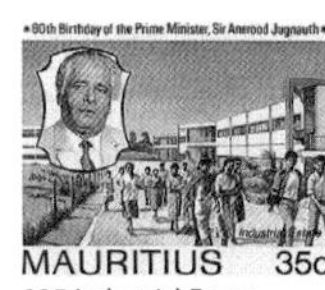

225 Industrial Estate

1990. 60th Birthday of Prime Minister Sir Anerood Jugnauth. Multicoloured.

836	35c. Type **225**	15	10
837	40c. Sir Anerood Jugnauth at desk	15	10
838	1r.50 Mauritius Stock Exchange symbol	55	30
839	4r. Jugnauth with Governor-General Sir Seewoosagur Ramgoolam	1·75	2·25
840	10r. Jugnauth greeting Pope John Paul II	16·00	16·00

226 Desjardins (naturalist) (150th death anniv)

1990. Anniversaries. Multicoloured.

841	30c. Type **226**	30	10
842	35c. Logo on TV screen (25th anniv of Mauritius Broadcasting Corporation) (horiz)	30	10
843	6r. Line Barracks (now Police Headquarters) (250th anniv)	5·00	5·00
844	8r. Town Hall, Curepipe (centenary of municipality) (horiz)	3·50	6·00

227 Letters from Alphabets

1990. International Literacy Year. Multicoloured.

845	30c. Type **227**	30	10
846	1r. Blind child reading Braille	2·50	15
847	3r. Open book and globe	3·50	2·25
848	10r. Book showing world map with quill pen	13·00	15·00

1991. 65th Birthday of Queen Elizabeth II and 70th Birthday of Prince Philip. As T **120a** of Pitcairn Islands. Multicoloured.

849	8r. Queen Elizabeth II	1·75	2·75
850	8r. Prince Philip in Grenadier Guards ceremonial uniform	1·75	2·75

228 City Hall, Port Louis (25th anniv of City status)

1991. Anniversaries and Events. Multicoloured.

851	40c. Type **228**	10	10
852	4r. Colonel Draper (race course founder) (150th death anniv) (vert)	1·75	2·00
853	6r. Joseph Barnard (engraver) and "POST PAID" 2d. stamp (175th birth anniv) (vert)	2·00	2·75
854	10r. Supermarine Spitfire *Mauritius II* (50th anniv of Second World War)	4·50	8·00

229 *Euploea euphon*

1991. Phila Nippon '91 International Stamp Exhibiion, Tokyo. Butterflies. Multicoloured.

855	40c. Type **229**	60	20
856	3r. *Hypolimnas misippus* (female)	1·90	1·00
857	8r. *Papilio manlius*	3·50	4·50
858	10r. *Hypolimnas misippus* (male)	3·50	4·75

230 Green Turtle, Tromelin

1991. Indian Ocean Islands. Multicoloured.

859	40c. Type **230**	50	20
860	1r. Glossy ibis ("Ibis"), Agalega	1·50	40
861	2r. Takamaka flowers, Chagos Archipelago	1·60	1·10
862	15r. Violet spider conch sea shell, St. Brandon	7·00	12·00

231 Pres. Veerasamy Ringadoo and President's Residence

1992. Proclamation of Republic. Multicoloured.

863 40c. Type **231** 10 10
864 4r. Prime Minister Anerood Jugnauth and Government House 1·00 1·25
865 8r. Children and rainbow 2·25 4·50
866 10r. Presidential flag 10·00 10·00

232 Ticolo (mascot)

1992. Eighth African Athletics Championships, Port Louis. Multicoloured.

867 40c. Type **232** 10 10
868 4r. Sir Anerood Jugnauth Stadium (horiz) 75 1·25
869 5r. High jumping (horiz) 90 1·40
870 6r. Championships emblem 1·25 1·90

233 Bouquet (25th anniv of Fleurir Maurice)

1992. Local Events and Anniversaries. Multicoloured.

871 40c. Type **233** 15 10
872 1r. Swami Krishnanandji Maharaj (25th anniv of arrival) 60 10
873 2r. Boy with dog (humane education) (horiz) 2·00 75
874 3r. Commission Headquarters (Tenth anniv of Indian Ocean Commission) (horiz) 1·40 1·00
875 15r. Radio telescope antenna, Bras d'Eau (project inauguration) (horiz) 4·75 9·50

234 Bank of Mauritius Headquarters

1992. 25th Anniv of Bank of Mauritius. Multicoloured.

876 40c. Type **234** 10 10
877 4r. Dodo gold coin (horiz) 2·25 1·10
878 8r. First bank note issue (horiz) 3·25 3·75
879 15r. Graph of foreign exchange reserves, 1967–92 (horiz) 5·50 9·50

235 Housing Development

1993. 25th Anniv of National Day. Multicoloured.

880 30c. Type **235** 10 10
881 40c. Gross domestic product graph on computer screen 10 10
882 3r. National Colours on map of Mauritius 40 60
883 4r. Ballot box 45 75
884 15r. Grand Commander's insignia for Order of Star and Key of the Indian Ocean 2·00 5·00

236 Bell 206 B JetRanger Helicopter

1993. 25th Anniv of Air Mauritius Ltd. Mult.

885 40c. Type **236** 1·25 30
886 3r. Boeing 747SP 1·75 1·25
887 4r. Aerospatiale/Aeritalia ATR 42 2·00 1·75
888 10r. Boeing 767-200ER 5·00 7·50
MS889 150×91 mm. Nos. 885/8 11·00 13·00

1993. No. 811 surch **40cs**.

890 40c. on 75c. Bassin Blanc 1·75 60

238 French Royal Charter, 1715, and Act of Capitulation, 1810

1993. Fifth Summit of French-speaking Nations. Multicoloured.

891 1r. Type **238** 90 10
892 5r. Road signs 3·00 2·50
893 6r. Code Napoleon 3·00 3·25
894 7r. Early Mauritius newspapers 3·00 3·50

239 *Scotia* (cable ship) and Map of Cable Route

1993. Centenary of Telecommunications. Multicoloured.

895 40c. Type **239** 1·25 30
896 3r. Morse key and code 1·75 1·00
897 4r. Signal Mountain Earth station 2·00 1·75
898 8r. Communications satellite 3·25 6·50

240 Indian Mongoose

1994. Mammals. Multicoloured.

899 40c. Type **240** 40 10
900 2r. Indian black-naped hare 1·25 40
901 8r. Pair of crab-eating macaques 3·25 4·00
902 10r. Adult and infant common tenrec 3·50 4·50

241 Dr Edouard Brown-Sequard (physiologist) (death cent)

1994. Anniversaries and Events. Multicoloured.

903 40c. Type **241** 15 10
904 4r. Family in silhouette (International Year of the Family) 45 55
905 8r. World Cup and map of USA (World Cup Football Championship, USA) 1·50 2·25
906 10r. Control tower, SSR International Airport (50th anniv of Civil Aviation Organization) 1·75 2·75

242 *St. Geran* leaving L'Orient for Isle de France, 1744

1994. 250th Anniv of Wreck of *St. Geran* (sailing packet). Multicoloured.

907 40c. Type **242** 55 10
908 5r. In rough seas off Isle de France 1·40 80
909 6r. Bell and main mast 1·40 1·50
910 10r. Artifacts from wreck 1·90 3·75
MS911 119×89 mm. 15r. *St. Geran* leaving L'Orient (vert) 5·50 6·50

243 Ring-a-ring-a-roses

1994. Children's Games and Pastimes. Children's paintings. Multicoloured.

912 30c. Type **243** 10 10
913 40c. Skipping and ball games 10 10
914 8r. Water sports 1·40 2·25
915 10r. Blind man's buff 1·40 2·25

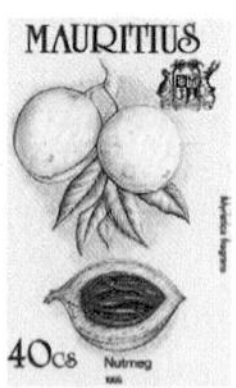

244 Nutmeg

1995. Spices. Multicoloured.

916 40c. Type **244** 15 10
917 4r. Coriander 1·00 75
918 5r. Cloves 1·10 85
919 10r. Cardamom 2·00 3·00

244a HMS *Mauritius* (cruiser)

1995. 50th Anniv of End of Second World War. Multicoloured.

920 5r. Type **244a** 2·00 2·50
921 5r. Mauritian soldiers and map of North Africa 2·00 2·50
922 5r. Consolidated PBY-5 Catalina flying boat, Tombeau Bay 2·00 2·50

245 Mare Longue Reservoir

1995. Anniversaries. Multicoloured.

923 40c. Type **245** (50th anniv of construction) 15 10
924 4r. Mahebourg to Curepipe road (bicentenary of construction) 1·25 1·40
925 10r. Buildings on fire (centenary of Great Fire of Port Louis) 2·75 4·00

246 Ile Plate Lighthouse

1995. Lighthouses. Multicoloured.

926 30c. Type **246** 1·00 30
927 40c. Pointe aux Caves 1·00 30
928 8r. Ile aux Fouquets 3·25 4·25
929 10r. Pointe aux Canonniers 3·75 4·50
MS930 130×100 mm. Nos. 926/9 11·00 11·00

247 Symbolic Children under UNICEF Umbrella

1995. 50th Anniv of United Nations. Multicoloured.

931 40c. Type **247** 20 10
932 4r. Hard hat and building construction (ILO) 65 55
933 8r. Satellite picture of cyclone (WMO) 1·40 1·75
934 10r. Bread and grain (FAO) 1·60 1·90

248 COMESA Emblem

1995. Inauguration of Common Market for Eastern and Southern Africa.

935 **248** 60c. black and pink 25 10
936 **248** 4r. black and blue 75 60
937 **248** 8r. black and yellow 1·25 1·75
938 **248** 10r. black and green 1·60 2·00

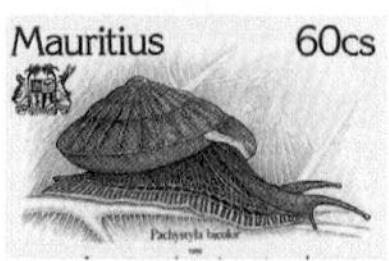

249 *Pachystyla bicolor*

1996. Snails. Multicoloured.

939 60c. Type **249** 20 10
940 4r. *Gonidomus pagodus* 75 65
941 5r. *Harmogenanina implicata* 75 75
942 10r. *"ropidophora eugeniae* 1·25 2·25

250 Boxing

1996. Centenary of Modern Olympic Games. Multicoloured.

943 60c. Type **250** 10 10
944 4r. Badminton 60 50
945 5r. Basketball 1·25 1·00
946 10r. Table tennis 1·40 2·25

251 *Zambezia* (freighter)

1996. Ships. Multicoloured.

947 60c. Type **251** 45 10
948 4r. *Sir Jules* (coastal freighter) 1·10 70
949 5r. *Mauritius* (cargo liner) 1·40 1·25
950 10r. *Mauritius Pride* (container ship) 1·90 3·00
MS951 125×91 mm. Nos. 947/50 4·25 6·00

252 Posting a Letter

1996. 150th Anniv of the Post Office Ordinance. Multicoloured.

952 60c. Type **252** 20 10
953 4r. "B53" duplex postmark 60 55
954 5r. Modern mobile post office 85 75
955 10r. Carriole (19th-century horse-drawn postal carriage) 1·75 2·50

253 Vavang

1997. Fruits. Multicoloured.

956 60c. Type **253** 15 10
957 4r. Pom zako 60 55
958 5r. Zambos 75 70
959 10r. Sapot negro 1·40 2·25

254 Governor Mahe de la Bourdonnais and Map

1997. Aspects of Mauritius History. Multicoloured.

960	60c. Type **254**	1·25	30
961	1r. La Perouse and map of Pacific	1·75	30
962	4r. Governor Sir William Gomm and Lady Gomm's Ball, 1847	1·75	1·25
963	6r. George Clark discovering skeleton of dodo, 1865	2·25	2·00
964	10r. Professor Brian Abel-Smith and Social Policies report of 1960	1·75	4·00

255 1d. "POST OFFICE" Mauritius

1997. 150th Anniv of "POST OFFICE" Stamps. Multicoloured.

965	60c. Type **255**	55	30
966	4r.2d. "POST OFFICE" Mauritius	1·25	1·25
967	5r. "POST OFFICE" 1d. and 2d. on gold background	2·00	2·25
968	10r. "POST OFFICE" 2d. and 1d. on silver background	3·25	4·75
MS969	127×90 mm. 20r. "POST OFFICE" stamps on cover to Bordeaux	5·50	6·50

256 Wheelwright

1997. Small Businesses. Multicoloured.

970	60c. Type **256**	15	10
971	4r. Laundryman	60	55
972	5r. Shipwright	1·50	90
973	15r. Quarryman	4·00	5·50

257 *Phelsuma guentheri* (gecko)

1998. Geckos. Multicoloured.

974	1r. Type **257**	35	10
975	6r. *Nactus serpensinsula durrelli*	1·00	1·00
976	7r. *Nactus coindemirensis*	1·25	1·75
977	8r. *Phelsuma edwardnewtonii*	1·25	1·75

258 Steam Train on Viaduct

1998. Inland Transport. Multicoloured.

978	40c. Type **258**	50	20
979	5r. Early lorry	1·00	70
980	6r. Bus in town street	1·25	1·10
981	10r. Sailing barge at wharf	1·75	3·00

259 President Nelson Mandela

1998. State Visit of President Nelson Mandela of South Africa.

982	**259**	25r. multicoloured	3·00	4·00

260 Count Maurice of Nassau and Dutch Landing

1998. 400th Anniv of Dutch Landing on Mauritius. Multicoloured.

983	50c. Type **260**	65	30
984	1r. Fort Frederik Hendrik and sugar cane	65	30
985	7r. Dutch map of Mauritius (1670)	2·75	2·75
986	8r. Diagram of landing	2·75	2·75

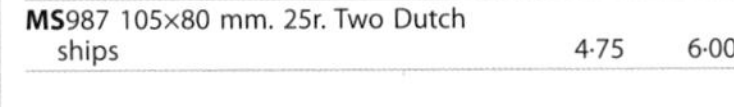

MS987	105×80 mm. 25r. Two Dutch ships	4·75	6·00

261 Cascade Balfour

1998. Waterfalls. Multicoloured.

988	1r. Type **261**	55	10
989	5r. Rochester Falls	1·40	80
990	6r. Cascade G.R.S.E. (vert)	1·60	1·25
991	10r. 500ft. Cascade (vert)	3·00	4·50

262 Plan of Le Reduit

1998. 250th Anniv of Chateau Le Reduit. Multicoloured.

992	1r. Type **262**	30	10
993	4r. *Le Chateau du Reduit, 1814* (P. Thuillier)	75	65
994	5r. "Le Reduit, 1998" (Hassen Edun)	85	80
995	15r. Commemorative monument	2·50	4·00

263 Governor Mahe de la Bourdonnais on 15c. Stamp of 1899

1999. 300th Birth Anniv of Governor Mahe de la Bourdonnais.

996	**263**	7r. blue, black and red	1·60	1·90

264 *Clerodendron laciniatum*

1999. Local Plants. Multicoloured.

997	1r. Type **264**	25	10
998	2r. *Senecio lamarckianus*	40	20
999	5r. *Cylindrocline commersonii*	80	75
1000	9r. *Psiadia pollicina*	1·25	2·50

265 *The Washerwomen* (Herve Masson)

1999. Mauritius through Local Artists' Eyes. Multicoloured.

1001	1r. Type **265**	25	10
1002	3r. *The Casino* (Gaetan de Rosnay)	65	60
1003	4r. *The Four Elements* (Andree Poilly)	75	75
1004	6r. *Going to Mass* (Xavier Le Juge de Segrais)	1·10	1·75

266 Old Chimney, Alma

1999. Old Sugar Mill Chimneys. Multicoloured.

1005	1r. Type **266**	25	10
1006	2r. Antoinette	50	20
1007	5r. Belle Mare	90	90
1008	7r. Grande Rosalie	1·25	2·00
MS1009	132×100 mm. Nos. 1005/8	2·75	3·25

267 Mosquito and Sprayer (Eradication of Malaria)

1999. 20th-century Achievements. Multicoloured.

1010	1r. Type **267**	45	10
1011	2r. Judge's robes, silhouette and airliner (emancipation of women)	1·00	30
1012	5r. Conference room (international conference centre)	1·00	1·00
1013	9r. Spoons full of sugar (development of sugar industry)	2·00	3·00

268 Crest

2000. 150th Anniv of Mauritius Chamber of Commerce and Industry. Multicoloured.

1014	1r. Type **268**	50	25
1015	2r. Unity, Vision and Service logos	75	40
1016	7r. Francis Channell (First Secretary, 1850–72)	1·75	2·25
1017	15r. Louis Lechelle (First President, 1850)	2·75	5·50

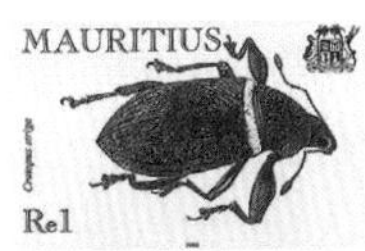

269 *Cratopus striga* (beetle)

2000. Beetles. Multicoloured.

1018	1r. Type **269**	25	10
1019	2r. *Cratopus armatus*	35	15
1020	3r. *Cratopus chrysochlorus*	55	40
1021	15r. *Cratopus nigrogranatus*	2·25	3·00
MS1022	130×100 mm. Nos. 1018/21	3·50	4·00

270 Handball

2000. Olympic Games, Sydney. Multicoloured.

1023	1r. Type **270**	25	10
1024	2r. Archery	50	15
1025	5r. Sailing	85	75
1026	15r. Judo	2·00	3·00

271 Sir Seewoosagur Ramgoolam greeting Mother Teresa, 1984

2000. Birth Centenary of Sir Seewoosagur Ramgoolam (former Prime Minister). Multicoloured.

1027	1r. Type **271**	1·25	30
1028	2r. Election as member of Legislative Council, 1948 (vert)	35	15
1029	5r. As a student, 1926 (vert)	80	70
1030	15r. As Prime Minister, 1968 (vert)	2·00	3·25

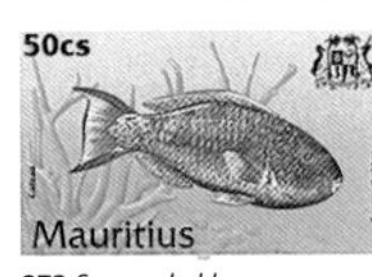

272 *Scarus ghobban*

2000. Fish. Multicoloured.

1031	50c. Type **272**	35	75
1032	1r. *Cephalopholis sonnerati*	45	10
1033	2r. *Naso brevirostris*	65	15
1034	3r. *Lethrinus nebulosus*	80	15
1035	4r. *Centropyge debelius*	1·00	20
1036	5r. *Amphiprion chrysogaster*	1·00	25
1037	6r. *Forcipiger flavissimus*	1·25	35
1038	7r. *Acanthurus leucosternon*	1·25	50
1039	8r. *Pterois volitans*	1·40	60
1040	10r. *Siderea grisea*	1·50	85
1041	15r. *Carcharhinus wheeleri*	2·00	2·50
1042	25r. *Istiophrous platypterus*	2·50	3·75
MS1043	Three sheets, each 132×102 mm. (a) Nos. 1031/3 and 1042. (b) Nos. 1035 and 1038/40. (c) Nos. 1034, 1036/7 and 1041 Set of 3 sheets	7·50	9·00

273 Affan Tank Wen

2000. Famous Mauritians. Multicoloured.

1044	1r. Type **273**	30	10
1045	5r. Alphonse Ravatoni	75	50
1046	7r. Dr. Idrice Goumany	1·10	1·25
1047	9r. Anjalay Coopen	1·40	1·75

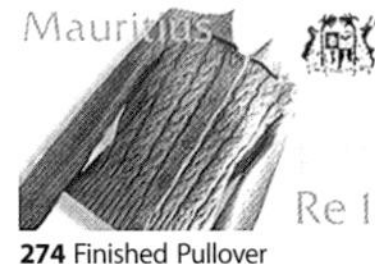

274 Finished Pullover

2001. Textile Industry. Multicoloured.

1048	1r. Type **274**	40	10
1049	3r. Computer-aided machinery	75	50
1050	6r. T-shirt folding	1·40	1·10
1051	10r. Embroidery machine	1·90	2·50

275 African Slave and Indian Indentured Labourer

2001. Anti-slavery and Indentured Labour Campaign Commemoration.

1052	**275**	7r. multicoloured	1·60	2·00

276 *Foetidia mauritiana*

2001. Trees. Multicoloured.

1053	1r. Type **276**	40	10
1054	3r. *Diospyros tessellaria*	85	30
1055	5r. *Sideroxylon puberulum*	1·25	85
1056	15r. *Gastonia mauritiana*	2·75	4·00

277 *Geographe* and *Naturaliste* (French corvettes)

2001. Bicentenary of Baudin's Expedition to New Holland (Australia). Multicoloured.

1057	1r. Type **277**	55	25
1058	4r. Capt. Nicholas Baudin and map of voyage	1·25	55
1059	6r. Mascarene martin (bird)	1·50	1·25
1060	10r. M. F. Peron and title page of book (vert)	1·75	2·75

278 Hotel School

2001. Mauritius Economic Achievements during the 20th Century. Multicoloured.

1061	2r. Type **278**	40	15
1062	3r. Steel bar milling	50	30
1063	6r. Solar energy panels, Agalega	1·00	1·00
1064	10r. Indian Ocean Rim Association for Regional Co-operation	1·75	2·75

279 Gandhi on Mauritius Stamp of 1969

2001. Centenary of Gandhi's Visit to Mauritius.

1065	**279**	15r. multicoloured	2·75	3·25

280 De-husking Coconuts

2001. Coconut Industry. Multicoloured.

1066	1r. Type **280**	35	10
1067	5r. Shelling coconuts (horiz)	90	55
1068	6r. Drying copra (horiz)	1·10	1·00
1069	10r. Extracting coconut oil	2·00	2·75

281 New Container Port

2002. Tenth Anniv of Republic. Multicoloured.

1070	1r. Type **281**	60	20
1071	4r. Symbols of Mauritius stock exchange	70	55
1072	5r. New reservoir under construction	90	90
1073	9r. Motorway junction	2·00	2·50

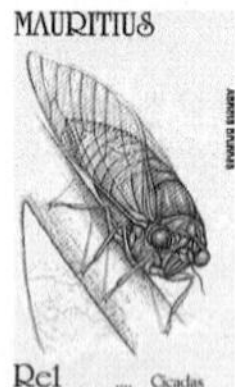

282 *Abricta*

2002. Cicadas. Multicoloured.

1074	1r. Type **282**	30	15
1075	6r. *Fractuosella darwini*	85	75
1076	7r. *Distantada thomaseti*	95	1·10
1077	8r. *Dinarobia claudeae*	1·10	1·40
MS1078	130×100 mm. Nos. 1074/7	3·25	4·00

283 Map by Alberto Cantino, 1502

2002. 16th-century Maps of the South-west Indian Ocean. Multicoloured.

1079	1r. Type **283**	60	20
1080	3r. Map by Jorge Reinel, 1520	1·25	65
1081	4r. Map by Diogo Ribeiro, 1529	1·25	1·00
1082	10r. Map by Gerard Mercator, 1569	2·50	2·75

284 Constellation of Orion

2002. Constellations. Multicoloured.

1083	1r. Type **284**	40	15
1084	7r. Sagittarius	1·00	90
1085	8r. Scorpius	1·10	1·25
1086	9r. Southern Cross	1·25	1·75

285 African Growth and Opportunity Act Logo

2003. Second United States/Sub-Saharan Africa Trade and Economic Co-operation Forum.

1087	**285**	1r. red, blue and yellow	25	10
1088	**285**	25r. red, ultramarine and blue	2·75	3·50

286 Echo Parakeet Chick

2003. Endangered Species. Echo Parakeet. Multicoloured.

1089	1r. Type **286**	65	25
1090	2r. Fledgling	1·00	50
1091	5r. Female parakeet	1·50	1·25
1092	15r. Male parakeet	2·50	3·25

287 *Trochetia boutoniana*

2003. Trochetias. Multicoloured.

1093	1r. Type **287**	30	10
1094	4r. *Trochetia uniflora*	75	40
1095	7r. *Trochetia triflora*	1·25	1·50
1096	9r. *Trochetia parviflora*	1·50	2·50

288 Dolphin Emblem (Sixth Indian Ocean Games, Mauritius)

2003. Anniversaries and Events. Multicoloured.

1097	2r. Type **288**	50	20
1098	6r. Crop in field and emblem (150th anniv of Mauritius Chamber of Agriculture)	1·00	80
1099	9r. Journal of voyage of Bonne-Esperance (250th anniv of visit of Abbe de la Caille)	1·60	2·25
1100	10r. Sugar cane and emblem (50th anniv of Mauritius Sugar Industry Research Institute)	1·60	2·25

289 Batterie de la Pointe du Diable

2003. Fortifications. Multicoloured.

1101	2r. Type **289**	40	20
1102	5r. Donjon St. Louis	80	60
1103	6r. Martello Tower	1·00	1·00
1104	12r. Fort Adelaide	1·75	2·75

290 Emblem

2004. 20th Anniv of the Indian Ocean Commission.

1105	**290**	10r. multicoloured	1·60	2·00

291 Le Pouce

2004. Mountains. Multicoloured.

1106	2r. Type **291**	30	15
1107	7r. Corps de Garde	1·00	80
1108	8r. Le Chat et La Souris	1·10	80
1109	25r. Piton du Milieu	3·00	5·50

292 Tinman

2004. Traditional Trades. Multicoloured.

1110	2r. Type **292**	30	15
1111	7r. Shoe maker	90	80
1112	9r. Blacksmith	1·40	1·40
1113	15r. Basket maker	2·00	3·25

293 Work Station, Emblem and SADC Head Quarters

2004. 24th Southern African Development Community Summit. Multicoloured.

1114	2r. Type **293**	30	30
1115	50r. As Type **293** but with "24th SADC Summit" in bright purple banner	4·50	6·00

294 Plaine Corail Airport

2004. Rodrigues Regional Assembly. Multicoloured.

1116	2r. Type **294**	50	20
1117	7r. Eco Tourism	1·25	1·75
1118	8r. Agricultural products	1·25	1·75
1119	10r. Coat-of-Arms	1·40	2·00

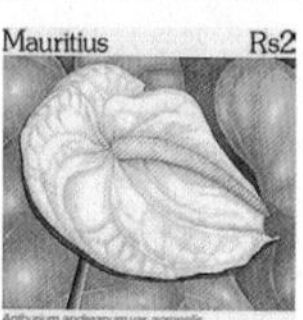

295 *Anthurium andreanum var acropolis*

2004. Anthurium Species. Multicoloured.

1120	2r. Type **295**	30	15
1121	8r. *Anthurium andreanum var tropical*	1·10	1·00
1122	10r. *Anthurium andreanum var paradisio*	1·40	1·40
1123	25r. *Anthurium andreanum var fantasia*	3·00	4·75

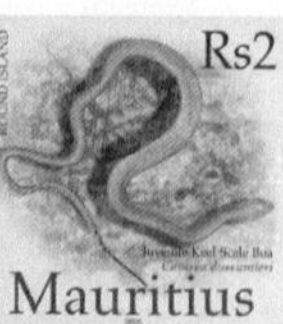

296 Juvenile Keel Scale Boa

2005. Round Island. Multicoloured.

1124	2r. Type **296**	40	15
1125	8r. Hurricane palm	1·10	1·10
1126	9r. Round Island petrel	2·00	1·75
1127	25r. Mazambron	3·25	5·50

297 Counter Services

2005. Postal Services. Multicoloured.

1128	2r. Type **297**	40	10
1129	7r. Mail sorting	1·25	1·00
1130	8r. Mail distribution	1·50	1·50
1131	10r. Mail transfer	1·75	2·25

298 Vagrant Depot

2005. Stone Buildings. Multicoloured.

1132	2r. Type **298**	25	10
1133	7r. Postal Museum, Port Louis	80	85
1134	16r. Carnegie Library, Curepipe	2·25	3·50

299 100 Gun Ship

2005. Model Ships. Multicoloured.

1135	7r. Type **299**	90	60
1136	8r. Sampan	1·00	85
1137	9r. Roman galley	1·10	1·10
1138	16r. Drakkur	2·25	3·50
MS1139	129×98 mm. 25r. Prow of drakkur with figurehead (horiz)	3·25	4·00

300 The Market

2006. Bicentenary of Mahebourg. Multicoloured.

1140	2r. Type **300**	35	10
1141	7r. Regattas	1·00	75
1142	8r. Le Lavoir	1·25	1·00
1143	16r. Pointe des Regates	2·25	3·50
MS1144	137×87 mm. 16r. Francois Mahe de la Bourdonnais (Governor 1735–46) (vert); 16r. Charles Decaen (Governor, 1803–10) (vert)	4·50	5·50

301 Prof. Basdeo Bissoondoyal

2006. Birth Centenary of Professor Basdeo Bissoondoyal (Indo-Mauritian scholar, writer and social reformer).

1145	**301**	10r. multicoloured	1·60	2·00

302 Indian Mynah (biological control of locusts), 1763

2006. Ecology. Multicoloured.

1146	2r. Type **302**	1·00	30
1147	8r. Fish and artificial reef (fish repopulation), 1980	1·25	1·00
1148	10r. Terraces (erosion control), Rodrigues, 1958	1·75	1·60
1149	25r. Giant tortoises (first captive breeding programme), 1881	4·50	5·50

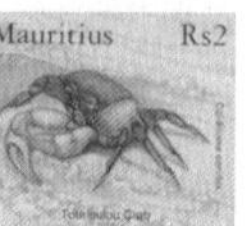

303 *Cardisoma carnifex* (tourloulou crab)

2006. Non Marine Crabs. Multicoloured.

1150	2r. Type **303**	45	15
1151	7r. *Geograpsus grayi* (land crab)	1·10	90
1152	8r. *Varuna litterata* (freshwater crab)	1·25	1·25
1153	25r. *Birgus latro* (coconut crab)	3·00	3·50

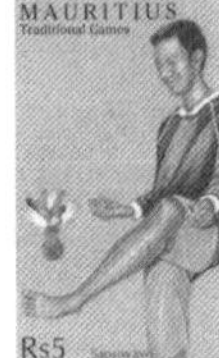

304 Sapsiwaye

2006. Traditional Children's Games. Multicoloured.

1154	5r. Type **304**	60	40
1155	10r. Marbles (horiz)	1·00	1·00
1156	15r. Hop scotch (horiz)	1·50	2·00
1157	25r. Kite flying	2·40	3·00

305 *Acropora rodriguensis*

2007. Corals. Multicoloured.

1158	3r. Type **305**	40	25
1159	5r. *Dendronephthya* sp.	50	35
1160	10r. *Ctenella chagius*	90	80
1161	15r. *Porites lobata*	1·40	1·60
1162	22r. *Acropora clathrata*	1·75	2·50
1163	25r. *Tubastrea coccinea*	1·90	2·50

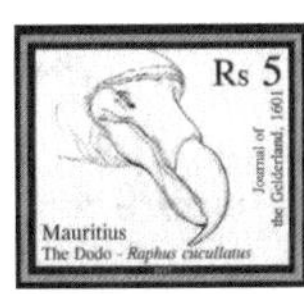

306 Drawing from Journal of the *Gelderland*, 1601

2007. Dodo (*Raphus cucullatus*). Multicoloured.

1164	5r. Type **306**	1·00	55
1165	10r. Pen drawing by Adrian Van de Venne, 1626	1·50	90
1166	15r. Painting published by Harrison, 1798	2·00	2·00
1167	25r. Chromolithograph by J. W. Frohawk, 1905	2·75	3·50
MS1168	122×90 mm. 25r. Painting by Julian Pender Hulme, 2001 (28×45 mm)	13·00	13·00

307 Computer Screen showing Globe and Postman

2007. 24th UPU Congress, Nairobi.

1169	**307**	50r. multicoloured	3·25	4·25

308 Ministers and Arms of Colony, 1957

2007. Anniversaries and Events. Multicoloured.

1170	5r. Type **308** (50th anniv of Ministerial System)	75	50
1171	10r. Statue of Manilall Doctor (centenary of arrival) (vert)	1·40	1·00
1172	15r. Scout camp and badge (centenary of scouting) (vert)	2·00	2·00
1173	25r. Port Louis Observatory (175th anniv of first meteorological observatory)	3·00	3·50

309 Bernardin de St. Pierre, 1737–1814 (*Paul et Virginie*)

2008. Mauritius in World Literature. Designs showing authors. Multicoloured.

1175	5r. Type **309**	60	30
1176	10r. Alexandre Dumas, 1802–70 (*Georges*)	1·00	70
1177	15r. Charles Baudelaire, 1821–67 (sonnet *A une Dame Creole*)	1·60	1·75
1178	22r. Mark Twain, 1835–1910 (*Following the Equator*)	2·25	2·50
1179	25r. Joseph Conrad, 1857–1924 (*A Smile of Fortune*)	2·25	2·50

310 *Myonima obovata*

2009. Indigenous Flowers of Mauritius. Multicoloured.

1180	3r. Type **310**	20	10
1181	4r. *Cylindrocline lorencei*	25	15
1182	5r. *Crinum mauritianum*	30	20
1183	6r. *Elaeocarpus bojeri*	35	20
1184	7r. *Bremeria landia*	35	20
1185	8r. *Distephanus populifolius*	45	35
1186	9r. *Gaertnera longifolia* var. *longifolia*	45	35
1187	10r. *Dombeya acutangula* var. *rosea*	65	40
1188	15r. *Aphloia theiformis*	90	60
1189	22r. *Barleria observatrix*	1·40	90
1190	25r. *Roussea simplex*	1·60	1·20
1191	50r. *Hibiscus fragilis*	3·00	2·50

311 *Cylindraspis peltastes*

2009. Extinct Mauritian Giant Tortoises. Multicoloured.

1192	5r. Type **311**	60	30
1193	10r. *Cylindraspis vosmaeri* (vert)	1·00	70
1194	15r. *Cylindraspis inepta*	1·60	1·75
1195	25r. *Cylindraspis triserrata* (vert)	2·50	3·25
MS1196	117×72 mm. 50r. *Cylindraspis peltastes* grazing. Wmk sideways	4·00	5·00

312 Brand Mauritius Logo

2009. Branding Mauritius. Multicoloured.

1197	7r. Type **312**	50	65
1198	7r. Pieter Both Mountain	50	65

Nos. 1197-1198 were printed together *se-tenant*, in vertical pairs throughout the sheets.

313 Dragons

2009. Anniversaries and Events. Multicoloured.

1199	7r. Type **313** (Centenary (2008) of Chinese Chamber of Commerce, Mauritius)	65	30
1200	14r. Dr. K. Hazareesingh (writer) (birth centenary) (vert)	1·25	1·00
1201	20r. Document and map of 1809 (bicentenary of capture of Rodrigues Island by the British)	2·00	2·50
1202	21r. T. Callychurn (birth centenary) (vert)	2·00	2·50

313a Player, Football, Mauritius Flag and Zakumi Mascot

2010. Third Joint Issue of Southern Africa Postal Operators Association Members. World Cup Football Championship, South Africa. Multicoloured.

1202a	7r. Type **313a**	4·50	4·00
MS1202b	181×160 mm. 7r.×9 Namibia; South Africa; Zimbabwe; Malawi; Swaziland; Botswana; As No. 1202a; Lesotho; Zambia	15·00	15·00

314 Al-Idrissi

2010. Al-Idrissi (geographer and cartographer) Commemoration.

1203	**314**	27r. multicoloured	2·25	2·75

315 Mauritius 1847 2d. Blue

2010. Expo 2010, Shanghai, China.

1204	**315**	30r. deep violet-blue and vermilion	2·25	2·75

316 Battle of Grand Port, 1810

2010. Bicentenary of the Battle of Grand Port. Multicoloured.

1205	14r. Type **316**	1·25	1·25
1206	21r. Map of Ile de la Passe	2·00	2·50

317 Sir Seewoosagur Ramgoolam

2010. Sir Seewoosagur Ramgoolam ('Father of the Nation') Commemoration

1207	**317**	100r. multicoloured	6·75	8·00

The centre of No. 1207 is embossed in 22 carat gold.

318 'Acte de Capitulation'

2010. Bicentenary of the British Conquest of Isle de France. Multicoloured.

1208	2r. Type **318**	50	25
1209	7r. British troops on road to Port Louis, 1810 (horiz)	1·00	1·25

319 The Steps at Aapravasi Ghat

2011. Mauritius in World Heritage. Multicoloured.

1210	7r. Type **319**	60	35
1211	14r. Le Morne (The Mountain) (horiz)	1·10	1·00
1212	15r. The Monument, Le Morne (horiz)	1·25	1·40
1213	25r. The hospital kitchen, Aapravasi Ghat	2·00	2·75
MS1214	120×100 mm. Nos. 1210/13	4·50	5·00

320 19th-century Census Form

2011. Anniversaries and Events. Multicoloured.

1215	7r. Type **320** (Population Census 2011)	60	30
1216	14r. Sir Moilin Jean Ah Chuen (industrialist) (birth centenary) (vert)	1·10	1·00
1217	21r. Dr. Maurice Curé (founder of Mauritius Labour Party) (125th birth anniv) (vert)	1·60	2·25
1218	25r. Aerial view of Médine sugar factory (centenary of the Médine sugar estates)	2·00	2·75

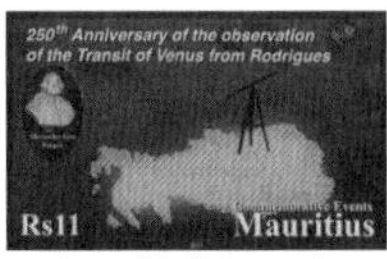

321 Map of Rodrigues and Telescope

2011. Commemorative Events. Multicoloured.

1219	11r. Type **321** (250th anniv of the observation of the transit of Venus from Rodrigues)	1·00	1·25
1220	12r. Laboratory (International Year of Chemistry)	1·00	1·25
1221	17r. Forest (International Year of Forests)	1·40	1·75

322 Emblem

2011. HIV/AIDS Awareness. 30th Anniv of Discovery of HIV/AIDS Virus

1222	**322**	7r. multicoloured	1·75	1·25

323 Post Office, La Criée

2011. 150th Anniv of Post Office in Rodrigues

1223	**323**	21r. multicoloured	2·50	2·50

324 Tea Leaves

2011. Tea Industry. Multicoloured.

1224	7r. Type **324**	60	40
1225	8r. Tea picking (horiz)	80	50
1226	15r. Leaf tea and tea bags (horiz)	1·10	1·25
1227	25r. Pouring cup of tea	1·75	2·25

325 Grand Port District Port

2012. Law Day. Multicoloured.

1228	7r. Type **325**	60	40
1229	8r. Interior of Court of Justice	80	50
1230	15r. Sir Michel Rivalland (Chief Justice 1967-70) (vert)	1·10	75
1231	20r. The Gavel	1·60	2·25

326 Racing

2012. Bicentenary of Mauritius Turf Club. Multicoloured.

1232 7r. Type **326** 60 40
1233 10r. Aerial view of racetrack Champ de Mars 1·00 70
1234 14r. Grandstand, 1917 1·10 75
1235 21r. Insignia of Mauritius Turf Club (vert) 1·60 2·25
MS1236 117×73 mm. 50r. The Paddock 3·50 4·00

327 Old and New Custom House

2012. Customs Department in Mauritius. Multicoloured.

1237 7r. Type **327** 60 40
1238 8r. Customs officers scanning packages 80 50
1239 20r. Canine Unit sniffer dog and handler checking packages (vert) 1·60 1·90
1240 25r. Marine Unit 1·75 2·25

328 Emblem

2012. Anniversaries and Events. Multicoloured.

1241 6r. Type **328** (International Year of Co-operatives) 50 35
1242 14r. Flags of Mauritius and People's Republic of China (40th anniv of Diplomatic Relations) 1·00 90
1243 21r. Emblem (centenary of scouting in Mauritius) 1·60 1·90

329 Marcel Cabon (1912-72, writer, journalist and poet)

2012. Eminent Personalities. Multicoloured.

1244 6r. Type **329** 50 35
1245 10r. Goolam Mahomed Dawjee Atchia (1890-1966, politician) 1·10 1·25

330 Foot Messenger, 1772

2012. 240th Anniv of Postal Services in Mauritius. Multicoloured.

1246 7r. Type **330** 60 65
1247 7r. Packet mail landing, 1915 60 65
1248 7r. Express letter messenger, 1930 60 65
1249 7r. Inland mail arrival, 1935 60 65
1250 7r. Delivery of mail bags by van, 2012 60 65
MS1251 140×100 mm. 25r. Mauritius 1847 1d. red stamp and copper plate; 25r. Mauritius 1847 2d. deep blue stamp and copper plate (both 42×28 mm) 3·50 3·75

331 Prison de Belle Mare

2013. Sites and Monuments. Multicoloured.

1252 5r. Type **331** 50 35
1253 9r. Château de Bel Ombre 90 75
1254 10r. IBL Building - Bowen Square 1·10 1·00

1255 18r. Le Batelage 1·40 1·75

332 Solar Energy ('Maurice Ile Durable')

2013. Anniversaries and Events. Multicoloured.

1256 2r. Type **332** 20 10
1257 3r. Red Cross emblem and Henri Dunant (founder) (150th anniv of the Red Cross) 30 20
1258 6r. Wind Energy ('Maurice Ile Durable') 50 35
1259 18r. Emblem (63rd FIFA Congress, Pailles, Mauritius) 1·40 1·90

333 Hurricane Palm (*Hyophorbe amaricaulis*)

2013. Fauna and Flora. Multicoloured.

1260 3r. Type **333** 30 20
1261 10r. Orchid (*Oeoniella polystachys*), Bras D'Eau National Park 1·10 75
1262 18r. Mascarene Swallow (*Phedina borbonica*), Bras d'Eau National Park 1·40 1·90

334 Hervé Masson (1919-90, painter)

2013. Eminent Personalities. Multicoloured.

1263 9r. Type **334** 90 70
1264 26r. Prof. Alexander de Smith (1922-74, Constitutional Commissioner for Mauritius in 1960s) 1·75 2·25

335 Dragonfly

2014. Fauna and Flora. Multicoloured.

1265 7r. Type **335** 60 50
1266 14r. Roussette de Rodrigues (Rodrigues Flying Fox) 1·25 1·00
1267 25r. Pignon d'Inde (Physic Nut) (vert) 2·10 2·75

336 Pere Laval (French Catholic priest and missionary, 150th death anniv)

2014. Anniversaries and Events. Multicoloured.

1268 8r. Type **336** 70 60
1269 14r. Children standing in cupped hands (Tenth anniv of the creation of the Ombudsperson for Children's Office) 1·25 1·25
1270 15r. Reverend Jean Joseph Lebrun (bicent of arrival in Mauritius) 1·25 1·25
1271 25r. Mobile phones (25 Years of the introduction of mobile phones to Mauritius) 2·10 2·40

337 Green Turtle

2014. Green Turtle

1272 **337** 14r. multicoloured 1·25 1·25

338 Canal Dayot

2015. Disaster Risk Reduction

1273 **338** 17r. multicoloured 1·60 1·60

339 Emblem

2015. Ninth Indian Ocean Island Games, Réunion Island

1274 **339** 17r. multicoloured 1·60 1·60

340 Corvette *Le Chasseur* (Guillaume Dufresne d'Arsel) off Mont du Rempart, Mauritius, 20 September 1715

2015. 300th Anniv of the French Landing in Mauritius

1275 **340** 17r. multicoloured 1·75 1·75

341 National Archives

2015. Bicentenary of the National Archives

1276 **341** 10r. multicoloured 1·00 1·00

342 Emblem

2016. UN Sustainable Development Goals

1277 **342** 27r. multicoloured 2·75 2·75

343 Giant Mottled Eel (*Anguilla marmorata*)

2016. Freshwater Fauna. Multicoloured.

1278 1r. Type **343** 10 10
1279 10r. Water Scorpion (*Laccotrephes annulipes*) 1·00 1·00
1280 18r. Nile Tilapia (*Oreochromis niloticus*) 1·75 1·75
1281 32r. Freshwater Shrimp (*Macrobrachium lar*) 3·25 3·25

344 New Dornier Coastguard Aircraft

2016. Maritime Air Squadron.

1282 **344** 11r. multicoloured 1·10 1·10

345 Powder Mills

2016. Nature Walks. Multicoloured.

1283 2r. Type **345** 20 20
1284 20r. Sophie 2·00 2·00

346 *Bacopa monnieri*

2016. Freshwater Flora. Multicoloured.

1285 11r. Type **346** 1·10 1·10
1286 13r. *Ludwigia octovalvis* 1·25 1·25
1287 16r. *Nelumbo nucifera* (white flower) 1·60 1·60
1288 31r. *Nelumbo nucifera* (white flower with pink edges) 3·00 3·00

347 Runner, Fruit and Vegetables ('PREVENT DIABETES ADOPT A HEALTHY LIFESTYLE')

2016. World Diabetes Day.

1289 **347** 10r. multicoloured 1·00 1·00

EXPRESS DELIVERY STAMPS

1903. No. 136 surch **EXPRESS DELIVERY (INLAND) 15c.**

E1 **40** 15c. on 15c. blue 20·00 50·00

1903. No. 136 surch **EXPRESS DELIVERY (INLAND) 15c.**

E3 **40** 15c. on 15c. blue 14·00 4·50

1904. T **42** without value in label, surch (FOREIGN) EXPRESS DELIVERY 18 CENTS.

E5 **42** 18c. green 5·00 45·00

E6 **42** 15c. green 26·00 8·50

POSTAGE DUE STAMPS

D1

1933

D1 **D1** 2c. black 1·25 50
D2 **D1** 4c. violet 50 65
D3 **D1** 6c. red 60 80
D11 **D1** 10c. green 30 2·00
D5 **D1** 20c. blue 70 3·50
D13 **D1** 50c. purple 1·00 15·00
D7 **D1** 1r. orange 70 17·00

1982. Nos. 530/1, 535, 540, 542 and 547 surch **POSTAGE DUE** and value.

D14 10c. on 15c. Dutch Occupation, 1638–1710 20 30
D15 20c. on 20c. Van Keulen's map, *c.* 1700 30 30
D16 50c. on 60c. Pierre Poivre, *c.* 1767 (vert) 30 30
D17 1r. on 1r.20 Government House, *c.* 1840 40 30

D18	1r.50 on 1r.50 Indian immigration, 1835	50	75
D19	5r. on 15r. Unfurling Mauritian flag, 1968	1·00	2·00

MAYOTTE

One of the Comoro Islands adjacent to Madagascar.

In 1974 (when the other islands became an independent state) Mayotte was made an Overseas Department of France, using French stamps. From 1997 it again had its own issues.

100 centimes = 1 franc.

1892. "Tablet" key-type inscr "MAYOTTE".

1	**D**	1c. black and red on blue	2·10	1·40
2	**D**	2c. brown and blue on buff	2·50	2·20
3	**D**	4c. brown and blue on grey	3·50	3·00
4	**D**	5c. green and red on green	6·00	4·75
5	**D**	10c. black and blue on lilac	11·50	10·50
15	**D**	10c. red and blue	95·00	80·00
6	**D**	15c. blue and red	28·00	19·00
16	**D**	15c. grey and red	£190	£180
7	**D**	20c. red and blue on green	23·00	20·00
8	**D**	25c. black and red on pink	20·00	15·00
17	**D**	25c. blue and red	20·00	22·00
9	**D**	30c. brown and blue on drab	31·00	35·00
18	**D**	35c. black and red on yellow	14·00	11·00
10	**D**	40c. red and blue on yellow	28·00	26·00
19	**D**	45c. black on green	28·00	30·00
11	**D**	50c. red and blue on pink	44·00	39·00
20	**D**	50c. brown and red on blue	38·00	46·00
12	**D**	75c. brown & red on orange	38·00	50·00
13	**D**	1f. green and red	44·00	45·00
14	**D**	5f. mauve and blue on lilac	£190	£190

1912. Surch in figures.

22A	**D**	05 on 4c. brown and blue on grey	3·00	5·50
23A	**D**	05 on 15c. blue and red	3·00	3·00
21A	**D**	05 on 20c. brown and blue on buff	4·00	8·25
24A	**D**	05 on 20c. red and blue on green	2·50	5·75
25A	**D**	05 on 25c. black and red on pink	3·00	4·25
26A	**D**	05 on 30c. brown and blue on drab	3·00	6·00
27A	**D**	10 on 40c. red and blue on yellow	2·75	5·75
28A	**D**	10 on 45c. black and red on green	2·75	3·00
29A	**D**	10 on 50c. red and blue on pink	6·25	10·50
30A	**D**	10 on 75c. brown and red on orange	4·50	8·75
31A	**D**	10 on 1f. green and red	5·00	8·75

1997. Stamps of France optd **MAYOTTE**. (a) Nos. 2907/10, 2912, 2917, 2924 and 2929/30.

40	**1118**	10c. brown	85	40
41	**1118**	20c. green	40	40
42	**1118**	50c. violet	40	40
43	**1118**	1f. orange	70	70
44	**1118**	2f. blue	1·40	1·40
45	**1118**	2f.70 green	1·90	1·60
46	**1118**	3f.80 blue	2·40	1·90
47	**1118**	5f. blue	3·50	3·00
48	**1118**	10f. violet	7·00	5·50

(b) No. 3121. No value expressed.

49	**1118**	(–) red	1·90	1·60

No. 49 was sold at 3f.

6 Ylang-ylang

1997

50	**6**	2f.70 multicoloured	1·90	1·60

7 Arms

1997

51	**7**	3f. multicoloured	2·00	1·60

8 Terminal Building and Aeroplane

1997. Air. Inauguration of New Airport.

52	**8**	20f. indigo, red and blue	12·50	11·50

9 Le Banga

1997

53	**9**	3f.80 multicoloured	2·50	1·90

10 Dzen-dze (musical instrument)

1997

54	**10**	5f.20 multicoloured	3·25	2·75

1997. Stamps of France optd **MAYOTTE**. (a) On Nos. 3415/20, 3425, 3430 and 3432.

55	**1318**	10c. brown	40	40
56	**1318**	20c. green	40	40
57	**1318**	50c. violet	55	50
58	**1318**	1f. orange	70	65
59	**1318**	2f. blue	1·30	1·10
60	**1318**	2f.70 green	1·80	1·10
61	**1318**	3f.80 blue	2·40	1·90
62	**1318**	5f. blue	3·25	2·40
63	**1318**	10f. violet	3·25	5·25

(b) On No. 3407. No value expressed. Ordinary or self-adhesive gum.

65	**1318**	(3f.) red	2·30	2·30

11 Lemur

1997

71	**11**	3f. brown and red	2·30	2·00

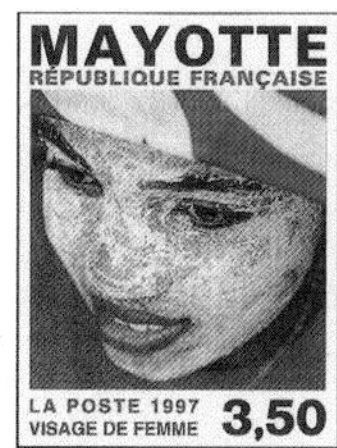

12 Woman's Face

1997

72	**12**	3f.50 multicoloured	2·20	1·90

13 Fish and Corals

1997. Marine Life.

73	**13**	3f. multicoloured	2·10	1·80

14 Reunion, Maps and Aeroplane

1997. Air. 20th Anniv of First Mayotte–Reunion Air Flight.

74	**14**	5f. black, blue and green	4·00	3·00

15 Longoni Port

1998

75	**15**	2f.70 multicoloured	1·90	1·60

16 Indian Ocean Green Turtle

1998

76	**16**	3f. multicoloured	2·30	2·00

17 Family on Island

1998. Family Planning.

77	**17**	1f. multicoloured	90	70

18 Cattle Egret on Zebu's Head

1998. Air.

78	**18**	30f. multicoloured	16·00	15·00

19 Children in Costume

1998. Children's Carnival.

79	**19**	3f. multicoloured	1·90	1·60

20 *Salama Djema II* (ferry)

1998. Mamoudzou–Dzaoudzi Ferry.

80	**20**	3f.80 multicoloured	2·50	2·20

21 Tsingoni Mosque

1998

81	**21**	3f. multicoloured	1·90	1·60

22 Mariama Salim

1998. Second Death Anniv of Mariama Salim (women's rights activist).

82	**22**	2f.70 multicoloured	1·80	1·60

23 Spreading Nets

1998. Traditional Fishing, Djarifa.

83	**23**	2f. multicoloured	1·60	1·30

24 Emperor Angelfish

1998

84	**24**	3f. multicoloured	2·10	1·90

25 Chombos and Workers

1998. The Chombo (agricultural tool).

85	**25**	3f. multicoloured	1·90	1·70

26 Map of Mayotte

1999

86	**26**	3f. multicoloured	1·90	1·70

27 Reservoir, Combani

1999

87	**27**	8f. multicoloured	4·75	4·50

28 Coral Hind

1999. Lagoon Fishes. Multicoloured.

88	2f.70 Type **28**	1·60	1·50
89	3f. Lionfish (horiz)	1·90	1·70
90	5f.20 Regal angelfish (horiz)	3·25	2·75
91	10f. Powder-blue surgeonfish (horiz)	6·00	5·25

1999. The Euro (European currency). No. 3553 of France optd **MAYOTTE**.

92	**1376**	3f. red and blue	1·90	1·40

29 Genet

1999

93 **29** 5f.40 orange, black & stone 3·25 3·00

30 Baobab Tree

1999

94 **30** 8f. multicoloured 4·75 4·00

1999. Philexfrance 99 International Stamp Exhibition, Paris. Sheet 150×120 mm.

MS95 No. 51×4, multicoloured 11·00 9·00

31 Prefecture Building

1999. Dzaoudzi Prefecture.

96 **31** 3f. multicoloured 1·90 1·50

32 Pirogues

1999. Pirogues. Sheet 163×84 mm containing T **32** and similar multicoloured designs.

MS97 5f. Type **32**; 5f. Two pirogues (vert); 5f. Three pirogues 13·00 11·50

33 Vanilla

1999

98 **33** 4f.50 multicoloured 2·50 2·00

34 "Le Deba"

1999. Air.

99 **34** 10f. multicoloured 6·50 5·25

35 Map of Mayotte, Arrow and "2000"

1999. Year 2000.

100 **35** 3f. multicoloured 1·90 1·40

36 Soulou Waterfall

1999

101 **36** 10f. multicoloured 5·50 5·25

37 Sailing Boat

2000. Indian Ocean.

102 **37** 3f. multicoloured 2·00 1·40

38 Two Whales

2000. Whales.

103 **38** 5f.20 multicoloured 3·25 2·75

39 Emblem

2000. District 920 of Inner Wheel (women's section of Rotary International).

104 **39** 5f.20 multicoloured 3·25 2·75

40 L'île au Lagon

2000

105 **40** 3f. multicoloured 1·90 1·50

41 Woman wearing Traditional Clothes

2000. Women of Mayotte. Sheet 90×70 mm containing T **41** and similar vert design. Multicoloured.

MS106 3f. Type **41**; 5f.20, Women wearing modern clothes 7·00 6·25

42 Tyre Race

2000

107 **42** 3f. multicoloured 1·90 1·50

43 Sultan Andriantsouli's Tomb

2000

108 **43** 5f.40 multicoloured 3·50 2·75

44 Horned Helmet

2000. Shells. Multicoloured.

109 3f. Type **44** 2·50 2·10

110 3f. Trumpet triton (*Charonia tritonis*) 2·50 2·10

111 3f. Bullmouth helmet (*Cypraecassis rufa*) 2·50 2·10

112 3f. Humpback cowrie (*Cyprae mauritiana*) (wrongly inscr "mauritania") and tiger cowrie (*Cyprae tigris*) 2·50 2·10

Nos. 109/12 were issued together, *se-tenant*, with the backgrounds forming a composite design of a beach.

45 M'Dere

2000. First Death Anniv of Zena M'Dere.

113 **45** 3f. multicoloured 1·80 1·40

46 Distillery

2000. Ylang-ylang Distillery.

114 **46** 2f.70 multicoloured 1·70 1·40

47 Building

2000. New Hospital.

115 **47** 10f. multicoloured 5·50 4·75

48 Map of Mayotte

2001

116 **48** 2f.70 black and green 1·80 1·30

2001. No value expressed. As T **48**.

117 (3f.) black and red 2·00 1·40

49 Mother breast-feeding

2001. Breast-feeding.

130 **49** 3f. multicoloured 1·90 1·60

50 Pilgrims

2001. Pilgrimage to Mecca.

131 **50** 2f.70 multicoloured 1·70 1·40

51 Bush Taxi

2001

132 **51** 3f. multicoloured 1·80 1·40

52 Children playing Football

2001

133 **52** 3f. multicoloured 1·80 1·40

53 Pyjama Cardinalfish

2001

134 **53** 10f. multicoloured 6·00 6·00

54 Legionnaire, Map and Market Scene

2001. 25th Anniv of Mayotte Foreign Legion Detachment.

135 **54** 5f.20 multicoloured 3·25 2·75

55 Bats in Tree

2001. The Comoro Roussette. Sheet 65×90 mm containing T **55** and similar horiz design. Multicoloured.

MS136 3f. Type **55**; 5f.20, Bat in flight 8·00 7·75

56 Aeroplanes and Club House

2001. Air. Dzaoudzi Flying Club.

137 **56** 20f. multicoloured 11·50 10·00

57 Military Personnel and Building

2001. First Anniv of Adapted Military Service Units.

138 **57** 3f. multicoloured 1·80 1·40

58 *Protea* sp.

2001. Flower and Fruit. Multicoloured.

139 3f. Type **58** 1·80 1·50

140 5f.40 Selection of fruit 3·25 2·75

59 Dziani Dzaha Lake

2001

141 **59** 5f.20 multicoloured 3·00 2·50

60 Mayotte Post Office

2001

142 **60** 10f. multicoloured 5·50 5·00

2002. Stamps of France optd **MAYOTTE**. (a) Nos. 3770/85.

143 **1318** 1c. yellow 40 45

144 **1318** 2c. brown 40 45

145 **1318** 5c. green 40 45

146 **1318** 10c. violet 55 55

147	**1318**	20c. orange	95	90
148	**1318**	41c. green	1·70	1·30
149	**1318**	50c. blue	2·00	1·60
150	**1318**	53c. green	2·20	1·80
151	**1318**	58c. blue	2·40	1·90
152	**1318**	64c. orange	2·75	2·10
153	**1318**	67c. blue	2·75	2·30
154	**1318**	69c. mauve	3·00	2·40
155	**1318**	€1 turquoise	3·75	3·25
156	**1318**	€1.02 green	3·75	3·25
157	**1318**	€2 violet	7·50	6·50

(b) No value expressed. No. 3752.

158	(46c.) red	1·90	1·50

No. 158 was sold at the rate for inland letters up to 20 grammes.

61 Arms

2002. Attainment of Department Status within France (11 July 2001).

167	**61**	46c. multicoloured	2·30	1·80

62 Runners

2002. Athletics.

168	**62**	41c. multicoloured	2·10	1·60

63 Mangroves, Kaweni Basin

2002

169	**63**	€1.52 multicoloured	6·25	5·50

64 Building Facade

2002. 25th Anniv of Mayotte Commune.

170	**64**	46c. multicoloured	2·10	1·70

65 Women processing Salt

2002. Salt Production at Bandrele.

171	**65**	79c. multicoloured	3·75	3·00

66 House and People

2002. National Census.

172	**66**	46c. multicoloured	2·20	1·80

67 Sunbird (inscr "Souimanga")

2002. Birds. Sheet 61×141 mm containing T **67** and similar horiz designs. Multicoloured.

MS173 46c. Type **67**; 46c. Drongo; 46c. Olive white eye (inscr "Oiseau-lunette"); 46c. Red-headed fody (inscr "Foudy") 10·00 8·25

68 Processing Machinery

2002. Remains of the Sugar Industry.

174	**68**	82c. multicoloured	3·50	3·00

69 Mount Choungui

2002

175	**69**	46c. multicoloured	2·30	1·90

70 Jack Fruit (inscr "Le Jaquier")

2002

176	**70**	€1.22 multicoloured	5·00	4·50

71 Museum Buildings

2003. Vanilla and Ylang Ylang Eco-museum.

177	**71**	46c. multicoloured	2·40	2·00

72 Bananas

2003

178	**72**	79c. multicoloured	3·50	3·00

73 Woman with Painted Face

2003. Festival Masks.

179	**73**	46c. multicoloured	2·30	1·90

74 Sailfish

2003

180	**74**	79c. multicoloured	4·00	3·00

75 Gecko

2003

181	**75**	50c. multicoloured	2·40	2·00

76 Mraha Board and Counters (game)

2003

182	**76**	€1.52 brown and mauve	7·00	5·75

77 Mtzamboro College

2003

183	**77**	45c. multicoloured	2·30	1·90

78 Ziyara de Pole

2003

184	**78**	82c. multicoloured	4·00	3·25

79 Players, Ball and Basket

2003. Basketball.

185	**79**	50c. multicoloured	2·75	2·10

80 Dzaoudzi Islet (1/2-size illustration)

2003

186	**80**	$1.50 multicoloured	8·00	6·00

81 Women Dancing ("Le Wadaha")

2004

187	**81**	50c. multicoloured	2·40	2·10

2004. Map. As T **48** but new currency.

188	**48**	1c. yellow and black	40	40
189	**48**	2c. grey and black	40	40
190	**48**	5c. green and black	45	40
191	**48**	10c. mauve and black	50	45
192	**48**	20c. orange and black	80	70
193	**48**	45c. blue green and black	1·80	1·60
194	**48**	50c. ultramarine and black	1·90	1·70
195	**48**	€1 green and black	3·75	3·50
196	**48**	€2 violet and black	7·50	6·75

82 Blue Argus (*Junonia* (Precis) *rhadama*)

2004. Butterflies. Sheet 100×80 mm containing T **82** and similar horiz designs. Multicoloured.

MS200 50c.×4 Type **82**; Citrus butterfly (*Papilio demodocus*); *Acraea ranavalona; Danaus chrysippus* 9·50 8·25

83 Sada Bay

2004

201	**83**	90c. multicoloured	3·75	3·50

84 Papaya Tree and Fruit

2004

202	**84**	50c. multicoloured	2·40	2·10

85 Filigree Jewellery

2004

203	**85**	€2.40 ultramarine, black and gold	10·50	9·50

86 Bridge over Kwale River

2004

204	**86**	50c. multicoloured	2·40	2·10

87 Maki (monkey) and Young

2004

205	**87**	75c. multicoloured	3·50	3·00

88 Mamas Brochettis (street vendor)

2004

206	**88**	45c. multicoloured	2·20	1·90

89 Playing Dominoes

2004

207	**89**	75c. multicoloured	3·50	3·00

90 Ylang-ylang

2005

208	**90**	50c. multicoloured	4·00	3·00

91 Two Women

2005. Women's Traditional Costume.

209	**91**	53c. multicoloured	3·00	2·30

92 Breadfruit Tree and Fruit

2005				
210	**92**	64c. multicoloured	2·75	2·50

93 Baleen Whale

2005. Sea Mammals. Sheet 100×80 mm containing T **93** and similar horiz designs. Multicoloured.

MS211 53c.×4 Type **93**; Beaked dolphins; Great sperm whale; Dugongs 10·50 9·50

The stamps and margins of **MS**211 form a composite design.

94 Emblem

2005. Centenary of Rotary International.

212	**94**	90c. multicoloured	4·00	3·50

95 Symbols of Island Life

2005. My Island.

213	**95**	48c. multicoloured	2·40	2·10

96 Mamoudzou

2005				
214	**96**	48c. multicoloured	2·20	1·90

97 Fishing from a Pirogue

2005				
215	**97**	75c. multicoloured	3·25	2·75

98 Tam Tam Boeuf (festival)

2005				
216	**98**	53c. multicoloured	2·50	2·10

98a Blacksmithing

2005				
216a	**98a**	53c. multicoloured	2·50	2·10

99 Woman grating Coconut

2006				
217	**99**	53c. multicoloured	2·50	2·10

100 Stall Holders

2006. Bush Market.

218	**100**	53c. multicoloured	2·50	2·10

101 *Les Amphidromes* (ferry)

2006				
219	**101**	€1.07 multicoloured	4·75	4·25

102 Moya Beach

2006				
220	**102**	48c. multicoloured	2·40	2·10

103 Turtle

2006. Turtle Protection. Sheet 60×110 mm containing T **103** and similar horiz designs showing turtles. Multicoloured.

MS221 53c.×3, Type **103**; Laying eggs; Hatchlings 9·25 8·25

The stamps and margins of **MS**221 form a composite design.

104 *Aloe mayottensis* (inscr 'Aloes mayottensis')

2006				
222	**104**	53c. multicoloured	2·40	2·10

105 Frangipani

2006				
223	**105**	53c. multicoloured	2·40	2·10

106 Moulidi Dance

2006				
224	**106**	75c. multicoloured	3·75	3·25

107 Tropicbird

2006				
225	**107**	54c. multicoloured	2·75	2·30

108 Stamps as Map

2007. Tenth Anniv of Mayotte Philately.

226	**108**	54c. multicoloured	2·40	2·10

109 *Phanelopsis*

2007				
227	**109**	54c. multicoloured	2·75	2·30

110 Building Facade

2007. Bicentenary of Court of Auditors.

228	**110**	54c. new blue and vermilion	2·50	2·10

111 *Phyllostachys edulis*

2007. Giant Bamboos.

229	**111**	€1.01 multicoloured	5·00	4·50

112 Seahorse

2007. 30th Anniv of General Council.

230	**112**	54c. multicoloured	3·00	2·75

113 Traditional House

2007				
231	**113**	54c. multicoloured	2·75	2·40

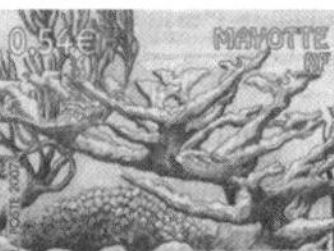
114 Elk Horn Coral

2007. Coral. Sheet 60×110 mm containing T **114** and similar horiz designs showing coral. Multicoloured.

MS232 54c.×4, Type **114**; Gorgon fan; Staghorn coral; Brain coral 12·50 11·50

The stamps and margins of **MS**232 form a composite design.

115 Mango Tree

2007				
233	**115**	54c. multicoloured	3·25	3·00

116 Chameleon

2007				
234	**116**	54c. multicoloured	3·25	3·00

117 N'Gouja Beach

2007				
235	**117**	54c. multicoloured	3·25	3·00

118 'Le voule'

2007				
236	**118**	54c. multicoloured	3·25	3·00

119 Coconut Palm

2008				
237	**119**	54c. multicoloured	3·25	3·00

120 Zebu

2008				
238	**120**	54c. multicoloured	3·25	3·00

121 Cinnamon

2008. Spices. Sheet 100×80 mm containing T **121** and similar horiz designs. Multicoloured.

MS239 55c.×4, Type **121**; Nutmeg; Circuma; Ginger 11·50 10·50

122 *Hibiscus*

2008
240 **122** 55c. multicoloured 4·50 4·50

123 'Le Grand Mariage'

2008
241 **123** 55c. multicoloured 4·50 4·50

124 Younoussa Bamana

2008. Younoussa Bamana (politician and first prefect) Commemoration.
242 **124** 55c. multicoloured 4·50 4·50

125 'Le M'Biwi' (dance)

2008
243 **125** 55c. multicoloured 4·50 4·50

126 Embroidery

2008
244 **126** 55c. multicoloured 4·50 4·25

127 Building Façade

2008. Inauguration of New Town Hall, Mamoudzou.
245 **127** 55c. multicoloured 4·50 4·25

128 'Le Cardinal' (red cardinal fody)

2009
246 **128** 55c. multicoloured. 4·50 4·25

129 Central Electricity Plant, Longini

2009
247 **129** 55c. multicoloured 4·50 4·25

130 'La pêche au pétromax' (night fishing with petromax lantern)

2009
248 **130** 56c. multicoloured 4·50 4·25

131 Tamarind Tree and Fruit

2009
249 **131** 56c. multicoloured 4·50 4·25

132 Oranges

2009. Fruit. Sheet 100×80 mm containing T **132** and similar horiz designs. Multicoloured
MS250 56c.×4, Type **132**; Grapefruit; Lemon; Combava (kaffir lime) 14·00 13·00

133 'Les Quatres Freres'

2009. Les Quatres Freres Islands. Sheet 120×110 mm containing T **133** and similar horiz design. Multicoloured.
MS251 56c.×2, Type **133**; Les Quatres Freres at sunset 7·00 6·75

134 Jasmine

2009
252 **134** 56c. multicoloured 3·50 3·25

135 Le Gaboussi

2009. Musical Instruments.
253 **135** 56c. multicoloured 3·50 3·25

136 Welcome!

2010. Karibu Maoré - Welcome
254 **136** 56c. multicoloured 3·50 3·25

137 Woman making Basket

2010. Basketry
255 **137** 56c. multicoloured 3·50 3·25

138 Governor's House

2010. Governor's Residence
256 **138** 56c. multicoloured 3·50 3·25

139 *Platycerium alcicorne*

2010. Flora
257 **139** 56c. multicoloured 3·50 3·25

140 'Epervier de Mayotte' (Sparrow Hawk)

2010. Birds. Falcon
258 **140** 56c. multicoloured 3·50 3·25

141 Bookshelf

2010. Carved Bookshelf
259 **141** 58c. multicoloured 3·50 3·25

142 Directorate Headquarters

2010. Directorate of Customs
260 **142** 58c. multicoloured 3·50 3·25

143 Dancers

2010. Chigoma Dance
261 **143** 95c. multicoloured 5·00 4·75

144 Delivery by Quad Bike

2010. Quad Bike Postal Delivery
262 **144** 58c. multicoloured 3·50 3·25

145 Woman with Braided Bun

2011. Women's Hairstyles. Multicoloured.
MS263 58c.×4, Type **145**; Long braids held by clip; Braids pulled into bun, wearing red; Braids worn up with long fringe 12·50 12·00

146 Grand Mosque de Mtsapéré

2011. Grand Mosque de Mtsapéré
264 **146** 58c. multicoloured 4·50 4·25

147 Sultan Andriansouli, Commander Passot and Ships in Harbour

2011. 170th Anniv of Annexation of Mayotte to France
265 **147** 58c. chestnut and sepia 4·50 4·25

148 'Le Guêpier' (Bee-eaters)

2011. Birds. Bee-Eater
266 **148** 58c. multicoloured 4·50 4·25

149 Woman carrying Laundry ('Le Retour du Lavoir Traditionnel')

2011. Traditional Life
267 **149** 58c. multicoloured 4·50 4·25

150 'Ilot de Sable Blanc'

2011. Tourism - White Sand Island
268 **150** 58c. multicoloured 4·50 4·25

151 'Le Martin Pêcheur' (Kingfisher)

2011. Birds. Kingfisher
269 **151** 58c. multicoloured 4·50 4·25

152 Ceremony

2011. Madjiliss Ceremony
270 **152** 58c. multicoloured 4·50 4·25

153 Mtzamboro Island Oranges and Orange Tree

2011. Trees of Mayotte. Multicoloured.

271	58c. Type **153**		4·50	4·25
272	58c. Kapok tree and kapok		4·50	4·25

154 Lake Karehani

2011. Tourism - Lake Karehani

273	**154**	60c. multicoloured	4·50	4·25

155 Divers

2011. Scuba Diving

274	**155**	60c. multicoloured	4·50	4·25

156 'Les Moucherolles' (Malagasy Paradise Flycatchers)

2011. Birds. Malagasy Paradise Flycatcher

275	**156**	60c. multicoloured	4·50	4·25

157 Marketplace

2011. Market

276	**157**	60c. multicoloured	4·50	4·25

158 Woman, 1892 2c. Stamp of Mayotte and 1997 10c. Stamp of France

2011. Indian Ocean Stamp Exhibition, Mayotte

277	**158**	60c. multicoloured	4·50	4·25

159 Map of Mayotte

2011. Overseas Collective of Mayotte's change to 101st Department of France on 31 March 2011

278	**159**	60c. multicoloured	4·50	4·25

160 Woman and Pots

2011. Pottery

279	**160**	60c. multicoloured	4·50	4·25

161 Le Padza de Dapani

2011. Tourism - Le Padza de Dapani

280	**161**	60c. multicoloured	4·50	4·25

162 Man with Net

2011. Aquaculture

281	**162**	60c. multicoloured	4·50	4·25

163 Fish Seller and Customers

2011. Fish Seller

282	**163**	60c. multicoloured	4·50	4·25

164 North Coast

2011. Tourism - North Coast

283	**164**	60c. multicoloured	4·50	4·25

165 *Marion Dufresne* in Mamoudzou Lagoon

2011. Ships

284	**165**	60c. multicoloured	4·50	4·25

STANLEY GIBBONS

LONDON 1856

DUAL WAVE UV LAMP

Without question the most versatile ultraviolet lamp on the market, the Stanley Gibbons Dual Wave UV Lamp detects all fluorescent and phosphor bands, inks and paper coatings, making it the perfect accessory for collectors of any country whose modern issues display these features.

The main deficiencies with most lamps on the market are that they require total darkness for effective use and their unshielded light source presents a potential danger to the eyes.

The Dual Wave UV Lamp has been specially developed exclusively for Stanley Gibbons to overcome both these issues, with its 'hidden' bulb and separate eye-piece allowing safe and effective use at fairs and exhibitions as well as in the home.

R2573 £119

Broad wavelength covers both short-wave & long-wave phosphors

Detects fluorescent bands, papers & other devices

Detects cleaned pen cancellations & paper repairs

Powerful bulb gives much stronger reaction than other lamps

Safe to use: Ultraviolet bulb shielded from eye

To order, call **01425 472 363**
email **orders@stanleygibbons.com**
or visit **stanleygibbons.com**

MECKLENBURG-SCHWERIN

In northern Germany. Formerly a Grand Duchy, Mecklenburg-Schwerin joined the North German Confederation in 1868.

48 schilling = 1 thaler.

1

2

1856. Imperf.

1	**1**	4/4s. red	£250	£200
1a	**1**	4/4s. red	†	£225
2	**2**	3s. yellow	£160	£100
4	**2**	5s. blue	£375	£475

See note below No. 7.

1864. Roul.

5a	**1**	1/4s. red	†	£4000
6a	**1**	1/4s. red	†	£225
5	**1**	4/4s. red	£4500	£3000
6	**1**	4/4s. red	£650	£130
11	**2**	2s. purple	£400	£400
9	**2**	3s. yellow	£250	£200
7	**2**	5s. bistre	£250	£400

Nos. 1, 1a, 5, 5a have a dotted background, Nos. 6 and 6a a plain background. Prices for Nos. 1a, 5a and 6a are for quarter stamps; prices for Nos. 1, 5 and 6 are for the complete on cover stamp (four quarters) as illustrated in Type **1**.

MECKLENBURG-STRELITZ

In northern Germany. Formerly a Grand Duchy, Mecklenburg-Strelitz joined the North German Confederation in 1868.

30 silbergroschen = 1 thaler.

1

2

1864. Roul. Various frames.

2	**1**	1/4sgr. orange	£275	£4000
3	**1**	1/3sgr. green	£140	£2250
6	**1**	1sch. mauve	£475	£5000
7	**2**	1sgr. red	£225	£300
9	**2**	2sgr. blue	80·00	£1300
11	**2**	3sgr. bistre	65·00	£2000

MEMEL

A seaport and district on the Baltic Sea, formerly part of Germany. Under Allied control after the 1914–18 war, it was captured and absorbed by Lithuania in 1923 and returned to Germany in 1939. From 1945 the area has been part of Lithuania.

1920. 100 pfennig = 1 mark.
1923. 100 centu = 1 litas.

1920. Stamps of France surch MEMEL and pfennig or mark with figure of value.

1	**18**	5pf. on 5c. green	1·30	5·75
2	**18**	10pf. on 10c. red	1·00	4·50
3	**18**	20pf. on 25c. blue	2·00	6·50
4	**18**	30pf. on 30c. orange	1·30	5·75
19	**18**	40pf. on 20c. brown	11·50	26·00
5	**18**	50pf. on 35c. violet	50	5·75
6	**13**	60pf. on 40c. red and blue	65	6·50
7	**13**	80pf. on 45c. green and blue	2·00	7·75
8	**13**	1m. on 50c. brown and lilac	90	6·50
9	**13**	1m.25 on 60c. violet & blue	2·10	16·00
10	**13**	2m. on 1f. red and green	1·00	5·75
11	**13**	3m. on 2f. orange and green	39·00	£120
12	**13**	3m. on 5f. blue and buff	36·00	£120
13	**13**	4m. on 2f. orange and green	80	6·50
14	**13**	10m. on 5f. blue and buff	5·25	26·00
15	**13**	20m. on 5f. blue and buff	70·00	£250

1920. Stamps of Germany inscr "DEUTSCHES REICH" optd Memel- gebiet or Memelgebiet.

25	**10**	5pf. green	6·25	17·00
26	**10**	10pf. red	3·25	16·00
27	**10**	10pf. orange	50	5·75
28	**24**	15pf. brown	4·50	21·00
29	**10**	20pf. blue	2·00	9·00
30	**10**	30pf. black & orange on buff	2·20	13·50
31	**10**	30pf. blue	65	5·75
32	**10**	40pf. black and red	45	5·75
33	**10**	50pf. black & purple on buff	50	5·75
34	**10**	60pf. green	2·50	10·50
35	**10**	75pf. black and green	4·50	36·00
36	**10**	80pf. blue	2·30	16·00
37	**12**	1m. red	50	5·75
38	**12**	1m.25 green	22·00	85·00
39	**12**	1m.50 brown	7·75	48·00
40	**13**	2m. blue	9·00	21·00
41	**13**	2m.50 purple	20·00	£100

1921. Nos. 2-3, 5, 8, 10, 19 and 49 further surch in large figures.

42	**18**	15 on 10pf. on 10c. red	65	3·25
43	**18**	15 on 20pf. on 25c. blue	65	5·25
44	**18**	15 on 50pf. on 35c. violet	65	5·25
45	**18**	60 on 40pf. on 20c. brown	65	3·25
46	**13**	75 on 60pf. on 40c. red and blue	1·30	6·50
47	**13**	1,25 on 1m. on 50c. brown and lilac	1·00	3·25
48	**13**	5,00 on 2m. on 1f. red and green	1·60	7·75

1921. Surch **MEMEL** and Pfennig or Mark with figure of value.

60	**18**	5pf. on 5c. orange	40	2·30
61	**18**	10pf. on 10c. red	1·30	9·00
62	**18**	10pf. on 10c. green	40	2·30
63	**18**	15pf. on 10c. green	40	2·30
64	**18**	20pf. on 20c. brown	13·00	65·00
65	**18**	20pf. on 25c. blue	13·00	65·00
66	**18**	25pf. on 5c. orange	40	2·30
67	**18**	30pf. on 30c. red	2·00	9·00
68	**18**	35pf. on 35c. violet	25	1·30
77	**13**	40pf. on 40c. red and blue	40	2·30
69	**15**	50pf. on 50c. blue	40	2·30
49	**13**	60pf. on 40c. red and blue	7·75	33·00
71	**15**	75pf. on 15c. green	25	1·30
70	**18**	75pf. on 35c. violet	50	2·30
78	**13**	80pf. on 45c. green & blue	50	2·30
72	**18**	1m. on 25c. blue	25	1·30
79	**13**	1m. on 40c. red and blue	50	4·00
73	**18**	1¼m. on 30c. red	25	1·30
80	**13**	1m.25 on 60c. violet & bl	60	3·25
81	**13**	1m.50 on 45c. green & bl	50	4·00
82	**13**	2m. on 45c. green and blue	1·30	4·50
83	**13**	2m. on 1f. red and green	50	4·00
84	**13**	2¼m. on 40c. red and blue	35	1·30
85	**13**	2½m. on 60c. violet and blue	1·30	4·50
74	**18**	3m. on 5c. orange	65	7·75
86	**13**	3m. on 60c. violet and blue	2·00	8·50
87	**13**	4m. on 45c. green and blue	25	1·30
88	**13**	5m. on 1f. red and green	50	4·50
75	**15**	6m. on 15c. green	1·30	8·50
89	**13**	6m. on 60c. violet and blue	25	1·30
90	**13**	6m. on 2f. orange & green	50	4·25
76	**18**	8m. on 30c. red	1·30	22·00
91	**13**	9m. on 1f. red and green	25	1·30
92	**13**	9m. on 5f. blue and buff	65	5·25
93	**13**	10m. on 45c. green & blue	1·30	8·50
51	**13**	10m. on 5f. blue and buff	4·00	14·50
94	**13**	12m. on 40c. red and blue	65	4·00
95	**13**	20m. on 40c. red and blue	1·30	8·50
52	**13**	20m. on 45c. green & blue	10·50	46·00
96	**13**	20m. on 2f. orange & green	65	4·00
97	**13**	30m. on 60c. violet & blue	1·30	8·50
98	**13**	30m. on 5f. blue and buff	4·50	33·00
99	**13**	40m. on 1f. red and green	1·30	11·00
100	**13**	50m. on 2f. orange & green	13·00	80·00
101	**13**	80m. on 2f. orange & green	1·30	11·00
102	**13**	100m. on 5f. blue and buff	2·00	23·00

1921. Air. Nos. 6/8, 10, 13 and 49/50 optd **FLUGPOST** in double-lined letters.

53	**13**	60pf. on 40c. red and blue	50·00	£250
54	**13**	60pf. on 40c. red and blue (No. 49)	6·50	33·00
55	**13**	80pf. on 45c. green and blue	6·50	33·00
56	**13**	1m. on 50c. brown and lilac	7·75	23·00
57	**13**	2m. on 1f. red and green	5·75	26·00
58	**13**	3m. on 60c. violet and blue (No. 50)	5·25	26·00
59	**13**	4m. on 2f. orange and green	6·50	33·00

1922. Air. Nos. 13, 50, 77/81, 83, 86, 88, 90 and 92 further optd Flugpost in script letters.

103	**13**	40pf. on 40c. red and blue (No. 77)	65	6·50
104	**13**	80pf. on 45c. green and blue (No. 78)	65	6·50
105	**13**	1m. on 40c. red and blue (No. 68)	65	6·50
106	**13**	1m.25 on 60c. violet and blue (No. 80)	1·30	10·50
107	**13**	1m.50 on 45c. green and blue (No. 81)	1·30	10·50
108	**13**	2m. on 1f. red and green (No. 83)	1·30	10·50
110	**13**	3m. on 60c. violet and blue (No. 86)	1·30	10·50
111	**13**	4m. on 2f. orange and green (No. 13)	1·30	10·50
112	**13**	5m. on 1f. red and green (No. 88)	2·00	10·50
113	**13**	6m. on 2f. orange and green (No. 90)	2·00	10·50
114	**13**	9m. on 5f. blue and buff (No. 92)	2·00	10·50

1922. Air. Surch as in 1921 and optd **FLUGPOST** in ordinary capitals.

115	**13**	40pf. on 40c. red and blue	2·20	26·00
116	**13**	1m. on 40c. red and blue	2·20	26·00
117	**13**	1m.25 on 60c. violet and blue	2·20	26·00
118	**13**	1m.50 on 45c. green and blue	2·20	26·00
119	**13**	2m. on 1f. red and green	2·20	26·00
120	**13**	3m. on 60c. violet and blue	2·20	26·00
121	**13**	4m. on 2f. orange & green	2·20	26·00
122	**13**	5m. on 1f. red and green	2·20	26·00
123	**13**	6m. on 2f. orange & green	2·20	26·00
124	**13**	9m. on 5f. blue and buff	2·20	26·00

1922. Nos. 62, 64 and 69 further surch as in 1921 but with additional surch Mark obliterating Pfennig.

125	**18**	10m. on 10pf. on 10c. green (No. 62)	1·30	13·00
126	**18**	20m. on 20pf. on 20c. brown (No. 64)	65	7·75
127	**15**	50m. on 50pf. on 50c. blue (No. 69)	4·00	29·00

1923. Nos. 77 and 80 with additional surch.

128	**13**	40m. on 40pf. on 40c. red and blue	1·30	8·50
129	**13**	80m. on 1m.25 on 60c. violet and blue	2·00	12·00

1923. Nos. 72 and 82 surch with large figures.

130	**13**	10m. on 2m. on 45c. green and blue	3·25	22·00
131	**18**	25m. on 1m. on 25c. blue	3·25	23·00

LITHUANIAN OCCUPATION

The port and district of Memel was captured by Lithuanian forces in 1923 and incorporated into Lithuania.

1

1923. (a) Surch **KLAIPEDA** (MEMEL) and value over curved line and MARKIU.

1	**1**	10m. on 5c. blue	1·30	10·50
2	**1**	25m. on 5c. blue	1·30	10·50
3	**1**	50m. on 25c. red	1·30	10·50
4	**1**	100m. on 25c. red	1·60	10·50
5	**1**	400m. on 1l. brown	2·50	18·00

(b) Surch **Klaipeda** (Memel) and value over two straight lines and Markiu.

6	**1**	10m. on 5c. blue	2·00	19·00
7	**1**	25m. on 5c. blue	2·00	19·00
8	**1**	50m. on 25c. red	2·00	19·00
9	**1**	100m. on 25c. red	2·00	19·00
10	**1**	400m. on 1l. brown	2·50	24·00
11	**1**	500m. on 1l. brown	2·50	24·00

(c) Surch **KLAIPEDA** (Memel) and value over four stars and MARKIU.

12	**1**	10m. on 5c. blue	2·50	15·00
13	**1**	20m. on 5c. blue	2·50	15·00
14	**1**	25m. on 25c. red	2·50	21·00
15	**1**	50m. on 25c. red	5·00	21·00
16	**1**	100m. on 1l. brown	5·00	29·00
17	**1**	200m. on 1l. brown	7·00	30·00

5

1923

18	**5**	10m. brown	50	10·50
19	**5**	20m. yellow	50	10·50
20	**5**	25m. orange	50	12·50
21	**5**	40m. violet	50	11·00
22	**5**	50m. green	2·00	20·00
23	**5**	100m. red	90	11·50
24	**5**	300m. green	9·75	£225
25	**5**	400m. brown	90	11·50
26	**5**	500m. purple	9·75	£225
27	**5**	1000m. blue	1·70	20·00

7 Liner, Memel Port

8 Memel Arms

9 Memel Lighthouse

1923. Uniting of Memel with Lithuania and Amalgamation of Memel Harbours.

28	**7**	40m. green	6·75	60·00
29	**7**	50m. brown	6·75	60·00
30	**7**	80m. green	6·75	60·00
31	**7**	100m. red	6·75	60·00
32	**8**	200m. blue	6·75	60·00
33	**8**	300m. brown	6·75	60·00
34	**8**	400m. purple	6·75	60·00
35	**8**	500m. orange	6·75	60·00
36	**8**	600m. green	6·75	60·00
37	**9**	800m. blue	6·75	60·00
38	**9**	1000m. purple	6·75	60·00
39	**9**	2000m. red	6·75	60·00
40	**9**	3000m. green	6·75	60·00

1923. No. 123 of Memel surch Klaipeda, value and large M between bars, sideways.

41	100m. on 80 on 1m.25 on 60c.	5·75	£110
42	400m. on 80 on 1m.25 on 60c.	7·75	£110
43	500m. on 80 on 1m.25 on 60c.	5·75	£110

1923. Surch in CENTU.

44	**5**	2c. on 300m. green	10·50	16·00
45	**5**	3c. on 300m. green	11·50	21·00
46	**5**	10c. on 25m. orange	11·50	16·00
47	**5**	15c. on 25m. orange	11·50	16·00
48	**5**	20c. on 500m. purple	16·00	33·00
49	**5**	30c. on 500m. purple	13·00	16·00
50	**5**	50c. on 500m. purple	21·00	39·00

1923. Surch (thin or thick figures) in CENT. or LITAS.

60	**5**	2c. on 10m. brown	9·75	£120
51	**5**	2c. on 20m. yellow	5·25	26·00
52	**5**	2c. on 50m. green	5·25	21·00
63	**5**	3c. on 10m. brown	26·00	£160
53	**5**	3c. on 40m. violet	7·75	23·00
54	**5**	3c. on 300m. green	5·25	11·50
55	**5**	5c. on 100m. red	10·50	11·50
56	**5**	5c. on 300m. green	6·50	20·00
57	**5**	10c. on 400m. brown	16·00	33·00
67	**5**	15c. on 25m. orange	£250	£1100
58	**5**	30c. on 500m. purple	10·50	26·00
68	**5**	50c. on 1000m. blue	10·50	20·00
69	**5**	1l. on 1000m. blue	13·00	39·00

1923. Surch in CENT. or LITAS.

70	**7**	15c. on 40m. green	8·50	49·00
71	**7**	30c. on 50m. brown	8·50	38·00
72	**7**	30c. on 80m. green	8·50	60·00
73	**7**	30c. on 100m. red	8·50	26·00
74	**8**	50c. on 200m. blue	8·50	49·00
75	**8**	50c. on 300m. brown	8·50	26·00
76	**8**	50c. on 400m. purple	8·50	46·00
77	**8**	50c. on 500m. orange	8·50	26·00
78	**8**	1l. on 600m. green	8·50	55·00
79	**9**	1l. on 800m. blue	9·75	60·00
80	**9**	1l. on 1000m. purple	9·75	60·00
81	**9**	1l. on 2000m. red	9·75	60·00
82	**9**	1l. on 3000m. green	9·75	60·00

1923. Surch in large figures and Centu and bars reading upwards.

83	**1**	10c. on 25m. on 5c. blue (No. 2)	50·00	£200
84	**1**	15c. on 100m. on 25c. red (No. 4)	65·00	£600
85	**1**	30c. on 400m. on 1l. brown (No. 5)	13·00	80·00
86	**1**	60c. on 50m. on 25c. red (No. 8)	65·00	£500

1923. Surch in large figures and CENT. and bars.

87	**7**	15c. on 50m. brown	£350	£3250
88	**7**	25c. on 100m. red	£140	£2000
89	**8**	30c. on 300m. brown	£275	£2000
90	**8**	60c. on 500m. orange	£170	£2000

1923. Surch in Centu or Centai (25c.) between bars.

91	**5**	15c. on 10m. brown	46·00	£300
92	**5**	15c. on 20m. yellow	5·25	50·00
93	**5**	15c. on 25m. orange	8·50	£100
94	**5**	15c. on 40m. violet	4·00	50·00
95	**5**	15c. on 50m. green	4·50	39·00
96	**5**	15c. on 100m. red	4·50	39·00
97	**5**	15c. on 400m. brown	4·00	33·00
98	**5**	15c. on 1000m. blue	£100	£800
99	**5**	25c. on 10m. brown	18·00	£170
100	**5**	25c. on 20m. yellow	4·50	50·00
101	**5**	25c. on 25m. orange	9·00	80·00
102	**5**	25c. on 40m. violet	7·75	80·00
103	**5**	25c. on 50m. green	4·50	39·00
104	**5**	25c. on 100m. red	4·00	39·00
105	**5**	25c. on 400m. brown	4·00	39·00
106	**5**	25c. on 1000m. blue	£100	£800
107	**5**	30c. on 10m. brown	49·00	£325
108	**5**	30c. on 20m. yellow	7·75	65·00
109	**5**	30c. on 25m. orange	9·00	£100
110	**5**	30c. on 40m. violet	6·50	39·00
111	**5**	30c. on 50m. green	5·25	39·00
112	**5**	30c. on 100m. red	5·25	39·00
113	**5**	30c. on 400m. brown	5·25	39·00
114	**5**	30c. on 1000m. blue	£100	£800

MEXICO

A republic of Central America. From 1864–67 an Empire under Maximilian of Austria.

8 reales = 100 centavos = 1 peso.

1 Miguel Hidalgo y Costilla

1856. With or without optd district name. Imperf.

1c	**1**	½r. blue	27·00	27·00
6	**1**	½r. orange	13·00	16·00
8c	**1**	½r. black on buff	25·00	37·00
9b	**1**	1r. black on green	4·25	9·25
7b	**1**	2r. green	34·00	21·00
10c	**1**	2r. black on red	2·50	10·00
4b	**1**	4r. red	85·00	£100
11b	**1**	4r. black on yellow	39·00	65·00
12a	**1**	4r. red on yellow	85·00	£110
5c	**1**	8r. lilac	£140	£140
13a	**1**	8r. black on brown	85·00	£170
14a	**1**	8r. green on brown	£110	£140

2

1864. Perf.

15a	**2**	1r. red	65
16a	**2**	2r. blue	65
17a	**2**	4r. brown	1·10
18a	**2**	1p. black	1·70

3 Arms of Mexico

1864. Imperf.

19a	**3**	½r. brown	£110	£100
31	**3**	½r. purple	49·00	43·00
31c	**3**	½r. grey	70·00	70·00
32b	**3**	1r. blue	8·75	5·50
33	**3**	2r. orange	4·00	2·50
34	**3**	4r. green	85·00	36·00
35b	**3**	8r. red	£130	80·00
30	**3**	3c. brown	£1000	£2250

4 Emperor Maximilian

1864. Imperf.

36c	**4**	7c. grey	22·00	70·00
40	**4**	7c. purple	£425	£4750
41	**4**	13c. blue	8·25	9·25
42	**4**	25c. orange	7·25	8·50
39c	**4**	50c. green	12·00	26·00

7 Hidalgo

1868. Imperf or perf.

67	**7**	6c. black on brown	28·00	19·00
68	**7**	12c. black on green	26·00	8·50
69	**7**	25c. blue on pink	15·00	6·50
70b	**7**	50c. black on yellow	£150	18·00
71	**7**	100c. black on brown	£225	75·00
76	**7**	100c. brown on brown	£160	33·00

8 Hidalgo

1872. Imperf or perf.

87	**8**	6c. green	10·50	10·50
88	**8**	12c. blue	1·70	1·40
94	**8**	25c. red	2·20	1·00
90	**8**	50c. yellow	£120	27·00
91	**8**	100c. lilac	80·00	41·00

9 Hidalgo

10 Hidalgo

1874. Various frames. Perf.

102a	**9**	4c. orange	6·50	8·50
97	**10**	5c. brown	3·00	2·00
98	**9**	10c. black	1·40	85
105	**9**	10c. orange	1·40	85
99	**10**	25c. blue	60	45
107	**9**	50c. green	8·75	8·75
108	**9**	100c. red	12·00	10·00

15 Benito Juarez

1879

115	**15**	1c. brown	2·75	2·75
116	**15**	2c. violet	2·75	3·00
117	**15**	5c. orange	1·50	1·00
118	**15**	10c. blue	2·00	1·70
127a	**15**	10c. brown	2·00	
128	**15**	12c. brown	5·00	5·50
129	**15**	18c. brown	6·00	10·00
130	**15**	24c. mauve	6·00	7·50
119	**15**	25c. red	5·50	20·00
132	**15**	25c. brown	3·75	
120	**15**	50c. green	10·00	34·00
134	**15**	50c. yellow	55·00	£225
121	**15**	85c. violet	13·50	£170
122	**15**	100c. black	17·00	50·00
137	**15**	100c. orange	65·00	£275

16

1882

138	**16**	2c. green	7·50	5·50
139	**16**	3c. red	7·50	5·50
140	**16**	6c. blue	4·00	5·75

17 Hidalgo

1884

141	**17**	1c. green	2·75	50
142	**17**	2c. green	4·50	1·40
157	**17**	2c. red	17·00	2·40
143	**17**	3c. green	8·50	1·40
158	**17**	3c. brown	13·50	4·00
144	**17**	4c. green	11·00	1·40
159	**17**	4c. red	27·00	12·00
145	**17**	5c. green	12·00	1·00
160	**17**	5c. blue	17·00	2·40
146	**17**	6c. green	10·00	1·00
161	**17**	6c. brown	20·00	4·00
147	**17**	10c. green	11·00	50
162	**17**	10c. orange	17·00	1·00
148	**17**	12c. green	20·00	2·40
163	**17**	12c. brown	37·00	6·00
149	**17**	20c. green	60·00	1·70
150	**17**	25c. green	95·00	3·50
164	**17**	25c. blue	£140	13·50
151	**17**	50c. green	40	3·50
152	**17**	1p. blue	40	7·50
153	**17**	2p. blue	40	15·00
154	**17**	5p. blue	£225	£140
155	**17**	10p. blue	£350	£150

18

1886

196	**18**	1c. green	50	25
209	**18**	2c. red	85	70
167	**18**	3c. lilac	8·00	5·00
189	**18**	3c. red	70	40
198	**18**	3c. orange	2·75	1·40
168	**18**	4c. lilac	12·00	3·50
199	**18**	4c. orange	2·75	2·00
211	**18**	4c. red	2·75	2·75
191	**18**	5c. blue	40	35
170	**18**	6c. lilac	20·00	5·00
200	**18**	6c. orange	4·00	1·40
213	**18**	6c. red	2·50	1·90
171	**18**	10c. lilac	15·00	75
185a	**18**	10c. brown	29·00	6·75
193	**18**	10c. red	35	25
201	**18**	10c. orange	19·00	1·40
172	**18**	12c. lilac	17·00	9·50
215	**18**	12c. red	12·00	12·00
173	**18**	20c. lilac	£110	70·00
194	**18**	20c. red	2·40	1·00
202	**18**	20c. orange	34·00	4·00
174	**18**	25c. lilac	47·00	12·00
203	**18**	25c. orange	11·00	3·00
217	**18**	25c. red	11·00	3·00
206	**18**	5p. red	£850	£600
207	**18**	10p. red	£1300	£850

19 Foot Postman

20 Mounted Postman and Pack Mules

21 Statue of Cuauhtemoc

22 Mailcoach

23 Steam Mail Train

1895

253	**19**	1c. green	2·00	35
219	**19**	2c. red	2·50	70
220	**19**	3c. brown	2·50	70
221	**20**	4c. orange	8·50	1·00
257	**21**	5c. blue	4·75	25
223	**22**	10c. purple	3·00	70
224	**20**	12c. olive	34·00	8·50
225	**22**	15c. blue	19·00	2·00
226	**22**	20c. red	22·00	2·00
227	**22**	50c. mauve	47·00	11·00
228	**23**	1p. brown	60·00	24·00
229	**23**	5p. red	£200	£130
230	**23**	10p. blue	£450	£225

27

28 Juanacatlan Falls

29 Popocatepetl

30 Cathedral, Mexico

1899. Various frames for T **27**.

266	**27**	1c. green	1·20	25
276	**27**	1c. purple	95	25
267	**27**	2c. red	2·75	25
277	**27**	2c. green	1·30	50
268	**27**	3c. brown	1·90	25
278	**27**	4c. red	3·00	30
269	**27**	5c. blue	3·00	25
279	**27**	5c. orange	75	25
270	**27**	10c. brown and purple	4·00	25
280	**27**	10c. orange and blue	3·00	25
271	**27**	15c. purple and lavender	5·00	25
272	**27**	20c. blue and red	5·75	25
273a	**28**	50c. black and purple	27·00	1·50
281	**28**	50c. black and red	49·00	4·00
274	**29**	1p. black and blue	50·00	2·40
275	**30**	5p. black and red	£170	8·00

32 Josefa Ortiz

40 Hidalgo at Dolores

1910. Centenary of First Independence Movement.

282	**32**	1c. purple	20	25
283	-	2c. green	25	25
284	-	3c. brown	40	25
285	-	4c. red	1·50	30
286	-	5c. orange	25	25
287	-	10c. orange and blue	95	25
288	-	15c. lake and slate	5·00	35
289	-	20c. blue and lake	3·00	25
290	**40**	50c. black and brown	7·50	1·10
291	-	1p. black and blue	9·00	1·30
292	-	5p. black and red	37·00	10·00

Designs:—As Type **32**: 2c. L. Vicario; 3c. L. Rayon; 4c. J. Aldama; 5c. M. Hidalgo; 10c. I. Allende; 15c. E. Gonzalez; 20c. M. Abasolo. As Type **40**: 1p. Mass on Mt. of Crosses; 5p. Capture of Granaditas.

REVOLUTIONARY PROVISIONALS

For full list of the provisional issues made during the Civil War from 1913 onwards, see the Stanley Gibbons Central America Catalogue.

CONSTITUTIONALIST GENERAL ISSUES

CT1

1914. "Transitorio".

CT1	**CT1**	1c. blue	30	30
CT2	**CT1**	2c. green	40	25
CT3	**CT1**	4c. blue	7·50	1·70
CT4	**CT1**	5c. green	7·50	2·00
CT9	**CT1**	5c. green	70	40
CT5	**CT1**	10c. red	30	30
CT6	**CT1**	20c. brown	40	40
CT7	**CT1**	50c. red	1·70	2·40
CT8	**CT1**	1p. violet	9·50	11·00

The words of value on No. CT4 are 2×14 mm and on No. CT9 are 2½×16 mm.

1914. Victory of Torreon. Nos. CT1/7 optd Victoria de TORREON ABRIL 2-1914.

CT10	1c. blue	£140	£120
CT11	2c. green	£150	£140
CT12	4c. blue	£170	£200
CT13	5c. green	24·00	34·00
CT14	10c. red	£100	£100
CT15	20c. brown	£1700	£1700
CT16	50c. red	£2250	£2250

CT3

1914. Handstamped with Type **CT3**. (a) Nos. D282/6.

CT17	**D32**	1c. blue	2·40	2·75
CT18	**D32**	2c. blue	2·40	2·75
CT19	**D32**	4c. blue	2·40	2·75
CT20	**D32**	5c. blue	2·40	2·75
CT21	**D32**	10c. blue	2·40	2·75

(b) Nos. 282/92.

CT22	**32**	1c. purple	1·00	40
CT23	-	2c. green	2·00	85

CT24	-	3c. brown	2·00	85
CT25	-	4c. red	3·50	1·40
CT26	-	5c. orange	70	25
CT27	-	10c. orange and blue	4·00	1·40
CT28	-	15c. lake and slate	6·75	2·00
CT29	-	20c. blue and lake	13·50	4·00
CT30	40	50c. black and brown	16·00	5·50
CT31	-	1p. black and blue	34·00	6·75
CT32	-	5p. black and red	£120	£100

CT4

1914

CT33	**CT4**	1c. pink	2·00	27·00
CT34	**CT4**	2c. green	4·25	24·00
CT35	**CT4**	3c. orange	6·00	50·00
CT36	**CT4**	5c. red	3·75	10·00
CT37	**CT4**	10c. green	6·00	47·00
CT38	**CT4**	25c. blue	12·00	

CT5

1914. "Denver" issue.

CT39	**CT5**	1c. blue	25	35
CT40	**CT5**	2c. green	35	30
CT41	**CT5**	3c. orange	35	35
CT42	**CT5**	5c. red	35	25
CT43	**CT5**	10c. red	45	55
CT44	**CT5**	15c. mauve	80	1·20
CT45	**CT5**	50c. yellow	1·40	1·70
CT46	**CT5**	1p. violet	5·75	8·00

1914. Optd **GOBIERNO CONSTITUCIONALISTA**. (a) Nos. 279 and 271/2.

CT50	5c. orange	£170	£170
CT51	15c. purple and lavender	£225	£225
CT52	20c. blue and red	£700	£350

(b) Nos. D282/6.

CT53	**D32**	1c. blue	3·25	3·50
CT54	**D32**	2c. blue	4·00	3·50
CT55	**D32**	4c. blue	17·00	18·00
CT56	**D32**	5c. blue	17·00	18·00
CT57	**D32**	10c. blue	3·75	3·50

(c) Nos. 282/92.

CT58	**32**	1c. purple	25	25
CT59	-	2c. green	25	25
CT60	-	3c. brown	25	25
CT61	-	4c. red	35	35
CT62	-	5c. orange	25	25
CT63	-	10c. orange and blue	25	25
CT64	-	15c. lake and slate	45	40
CT65	-	20c. blue and lake	50	45
CT66	**40**	50c. black and brown	1·20	1·00
CT67	-	1p. black and blue	5·00	3·50
CT68	-	5p. black and red	27·00	20·00

CONVENTIONIST ISSUES

(CV1) Villa–Zapata Monogram

1914. Optd with Type **CV1**. (a) Nos. 266/75.

CV1	**27**	1c. green	£150	
CV2	**27**	2c. red	£150	
CV3	**27**	3c. brown	£120	
CV4	**27**	5c. blue	£140	
CV5	**27**	10c. brown and purple	£140	
CV6	**27**	15c. purple and lavender	£325	
CV7	**27**	20c. blue and red	£425	
CV8	**28**	50c. black and red	£350	
CV9	**29**	1p. black and blue	£350	
CV10	**30**	5p. black and red	£425	

(b) Nos. 276/80.

CV11	**27**	1c. purple	£150	
CV12	**27**	2c. green	£300	
CV13	**27**	4c. red	£150	
CV14	**27**	5c. orange	31·00	
CV15	**27**	10c. orange and blue	£200	

(c) Nos. D282/6.

CV16	**D32**	1c. blue	5·50	6·00
CV17	**D32**	2c. blue	5·50	6·00
CV18	**D32**	4c. blue	5·50	6·00
CV19	**D32**	5c. blue	5·50	6·00
CV20	**D32**	10c. blue	5·50	6·00

(d) Nos. 282/92.

CV21	**32**	1c. purple	70	85
CV22	-	2c. green	35	65
CV23	-	3c. brown	50	60
CV24	-	4c. red	3·25	2·50
CV25	-	5c. orange	20	1·60
CV26	-	10c. orange and blue	5·75	3·75
CV27	-	15c. lake and slate	2·50	4·50
CV28	-	20c. blue and lake	4·75	4·75
CV29	**40**	50c. black and brown	10·50	8·75
CV30	-	1p. black and blue	14·50	14·00
CV31	-	5p. black and red	£100	90·00

CONSTITUTIONALIST PROVISIONAL ISSUES

CT10

1914. Nos. 282/92 handstamped with Type **CT10**.

CT69	**32**	1c. purple	4·50	4·50
CT70	-	2c. green	4·50	4·50
CT71	-	3c. brown	4·50	4·50
CT72	-	4c. red	6·50	5·50
CT73	-	5c. orange	2·00	2·00
CT74	-	10c. orange and blue	6·50	5·50
CT75	-	15c. lake and slate	6·50	5·50
CT76	-	20c. blue and lake	8·00	7·00
CT77	**40**	50c. black and brown	18·00	18·00
CT78	-	1p. black and blue	32·00	
CT79	-	5p. black and red	£130	

CT11 Carranza Monogram

1915. Optd with Type **CT11**. (a) No. 271.

CT80	**27**	15c. purple and lavender	85·00	55·00

(b) No. 279.

CT81	**27**	5c. orange	20·00	13·50

(c) Nos. D282/6.

CT82	**D32**	1c. blue	13·50	17·00
CT83	**D32**	2c. blue	13·50	17·00
CT84	**D32**	4c. blue	13·50	17·00
CT85	**D32**	5c. blue	13·50	17·00
CT86	**D32**	10c. blue	13·50	17·00

(d) Nos. 282/92.

CT87	**32**	1c. purple	50	60
CT88	-	2c. green	45	40
CT89	-	3c. brown	50	50
CT90	-	4c. red	95	95
CT91	-	5c. orange	20	20
CT92	-	10c. orange and blue	90	90
CT93	-	15c. lake and slate	90	1·00
CT94	-	20c. blue and lake	95	1·10
CT95	**40**	50c. black and brown	6·00	6·00
CT96	-	1p. black and blue	10·00	9·00
CT97	-	5p. black and red	75·00	65·00

GENERAL ISSUES

43 Coat of Arms

44 Statue of Cuauhtemoc

45 Ignacio Zaragoza

1915. Portraits as T **45**. Roul or perf.

293	**43**	1c. violet	20	15
294	**44**	2c. green	40	15
304	**45**	3c. brown	45	25
305	**45**	4c. red (Morelos)	45	30
306	**45**	5c. orange (Madero)	65	30
307	**45**	10c. blue (Juarez)	90	30

46 Map of Mexico

47 Lighthouse, Veracruz

48 Post Office, Mexico City

1915

299	**46**	40c. grey	65	35
433	**46**	40c. mauve	1·10	25
300	**47**	1p. grey and brown	85	50
411	**47**	1p. grey and blue	42·00	1·30
301	**48**	5p. blue and lake	8·50	4·25
412	**48**	5p. grey and green	1·60	10·50

(49)

1916. Silver Currency. Optd with T 49. (a) No. 271.

309	**27**	15c. purple and lavender	£400	£375

(b) No. 279.

309a	**27**	5c. orange	£110	£120

(c) Nos. 282/92.

310	**32**	1c. purple	9·00	8·50
311	-	2c. green	50	35
312	-	3c. brown	55	35
313	-	4c. red	5·50	6·75
314	-	5c. orange	25	20
315	-	10c. orange and blue	1·10	1·30
316	-	15c. lake and slate	1·60	2·50
317	-	20c. blue and lake	1·60	2·50
318	**40**	50c. black and brown	8·00	5·00
319	-	1p. black and blue	14·00	5·75
320	-	5p. black and red	£150	£150

(d) Nos. CT1/3 and CT5/8.

320b	**CT1**	1c. blue	21·00	†
320c	**CT1**	2c. green	10·50	†
320d	**CT1**	4c. blue	£275	†
320e	**CT1**	10c. red	1·80	†
320f	**CT1**	20c. brown	2·50	†
320g	**CT1**	50c. red	13·00	†
320h	**CT1**	1p. violet	21·00	†

(e) Nos. CT39/46.

321	**CT5**	1c. blue	3·50	13·50
322	**CT5**	2c. green	3·50	8·00
323	**CT5**	3c. orange	45	8·00
324	**CT5**	5c. red	45	8·00
325	**CT5**	10c. red	45	6·75
326	**CT5**	15c. mauve	45	8·00
327	**CT5**	50c. yellow	1·10	10·00
328	**CT5**	1p. violet	9·75	17·00

(f) Nos. CT58/68.

329	**32**	1c. purple	2·30	3·50
330	-	2c. green	70	50
331	-	3c. brown	65	60
332	-	4c. red	65	60
333	-	5c. orange	90	30
334	-	10c. orange and blue	70	50
335	-	15c. lake and slate	75	75
336	-	20c. blue and lake	75	75
337	**40**	50c. black and brown	7·00	5·00
338	-	1p. black and blue	14·00	13·50
339	-	5p. black and red	£140	£120

(g) Nos. CV21/8.

340	**32**	1c. purple	9·75	13·00
341	-	2c. green	1·30	95
342	-	3c. brown	2·75	4·00
343	-	4c. red	11·50	13·00
344	-	5c. orange	4·00	5·00
345	-	10c. orange and blue	10·50	12·00
346	-	15c. lake and slate	10·50	12·00
347	-	20c. blue and lake	10·50	12·00

(h) Nos. CT87/96.

348	**32**	1c. purple	4·50	4·25
349	-	2c. green	50	50
350	-	3c. brown	45	50
351	-	4c. red	6·75	7·75
352	-	5c. orange	80	20
353	-	10c. orange and blue	1·30	1·60
354	-	15c. lake and slate	1·10	50
355	-	20c. blue and red	1·10	90
356	**40**	50c. black and brown	6·75	7·75
357	-	1p. black and blue	10·00	9·75

50 V. Carranza

1916. Carranza's Triumphal Entry into Mexico City.

358	**50**	10c. brown	12·50	13·00
359	**50**	10c. blue	1·30	85

(51)

1916. Optd with T **51**. (a) Nos. D282/6.

360	**D32**	5c. on 1c. blue	2·20	2·10
361	**D32**	10c. on 2c. blue	2·20	2·10
362	**D32**	20c. on 4c. blue	2·20	2·10
363	**D32**	25c. on 5c. blue	2·20	2·10
364	**D32**	60c. on 10c. blue	1·30	1·30
365	**D32**	1p. on 1c. blue	1·30	1·30
366	**D32**	1p. on 2c. blue	1·30	1·30
367	**D32**	1p. on 4c. blue	75	70
368	**D32**	1p. on 5c. blue	2·20	2·10
369	**D32**	1p. on 10c. blue	2·20	2·10

(b) Nos. 282, 286 and 283.

370	**32**	5c. on 1c. purple	45	45
371	**32**	10c. on 1c. purple	45	45
372	-	20c. on 5c. orange	45	45
373	-	25c. on 5c. orange	45	45
374	-	60c. on 2c. green	22·00	16·00

(c) Nos. CT39/40.

375	**CT5**	60c. on 1c. blue	2·75	5·00
376	**CT5**	60c. on 2c. green	2·75	5·00

(d) Nos. CT58, CT62 and CT59.

377	**32**	5c. on 1c. purple	45	45
378	-	10c. on 1c. purple	85	80
379	-	25c. on 5c. purple	45	45
380	-	60c. on 2c. green	£250	£275

(e) No. CV25.

381	25c. on 5c. orange	20	15

(f) Nos. CT87, CT91 and CT88.

382	**32**	5c. on 1c. purple	13·00	16·00
383	-	10c. on 1c. purple	4·25	6·25
385	-	25c. on 5c. orange	90	1·30
386	-	60c. on 2c. green	£275	†

1916. Nos. D282/6 surch GPM and value.

387	**D32**	$2.50 on 1c. blue	1·10	1·00
388	**D32**	$2.50 on 2c. blue	9·25	†
389	**D32**	$2.50 on 4c. blue	9·25	†
390	**D32**	$2.50 on 5c. blue	9·25	†
391	**D32**	$2.50 on 10c. blue	9·25	†

52a Arms

1916

392	**52a**	1c. purple	25	15

53 Zaragoza

1917. Portraits. Roul or perf.

393	**53**	1c. violet	1·70	80
393a	**53**	1c. grey	4·25	65
394	-	2c. green (Vazquez)	1·30	45
395	-	3c. brown (Suarez)	1·30	80
396	-	4c. red (Carranza)	2·20	80
397	-	5c. blue (Herrera)	2·20	35
398	-	10c. blue (Madero)	3·50	45
399	-	20c. lake (Dominguez)	34·00	1·70
400	-	30c. purple (Serdan)	80·00	2·50
401	-	30c. black (Serdan)	90·00	3·25

1919. Red Cross Fund. Surch with cross and premium.

413	5c.+3c. blue (No. 397)	16·00	16·00
414	10c.+5c. blue (No. 398)	18·00	16·00

56 Meeting of Iturbide and Guerrero

1921. Centenary of Declaration of Independence.

415	**56**	10c. brown and blue	23·00	3·00
416	-	10p. black and brown	22·00	36·00

Design:—10p. Entry into Mexico City.

58 Golden Eagle

1922. Air.

454	**58**	25c. sepia and lake	45	25
455	**58**	25c. sepia and green	45	25
456	**58**	50c. red and blue	90	25

59 Morelos Monument

60 Fountain and Aqueduct

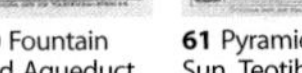
61 Pyramid of the Sun, Teotihuacan

62 Castle of Chapultepec

63 Columbus Monument

64 Juarez Colonnade

65 Monument to Dona Josefa Ortiz de Dominguez

66 Cuauhtemoc Monument

68 Ministry of Communications

69 National Theatre and Palace of Fine Arts

74 Benito Juarez

1923. Roul or perf.

436	**59**	1c. brown	45	25
437	**60**	2c. red	25	15
438	**61**	3c. brown	25	15
440	**63**	4c. green	25	15
429	**62**	4c. green	1·30	25
441	**63**	5c. orange	25	15
453	**74**	8c. orange	25	15
423	**64**	10c. brown	4·25	15
442	**66**	10c. lake	25	15
443	**65**	20c. blue	80	25
426	**66**	30c. green	49·00	1·60
432	**64**	30c. green	90	15
434	**68**	50c. brown	90	25
435	**69**	1p. blue and lake	90	85

70

72 Sr. Francisco Garcia y Santos

73 Post Office, Mexico City

1926. Second Pan-American Postal Congress. Inscr as in T **70/3**.

445	**70**	2c. red	2·20	80
446	-	4c. green	2·75	1·00
447	**70**	5c. orange	2·20	85
448	-	10c. red	3·50	1·00
449	**72**	20c. blue	3·50	1·30
450	**72**	30c. green	6·25	3·25
451	**72**	40c. mauve	11·00	3·00
452	**73**	1p. blue and brown	22·00	8·50

Design:—As Type **70**: 4c., 10c. Map of North and South America.

1929. Child Welfare. Optd **Proteccion a la Infancia**.

457	**59**	1c. brown	45	25

77

1929. Obligatory Tax. Child Welfare.

459	**77**	1c. violet	25	25
461	**77**	2c. green	55	25
462	**77**	5c. brown	55	25

79 Capt. Emilio Carranza

1929. Air. First Death Anniv of Carranza (airman).

463	**79**	5c. sepia and green	1·30	70
464	**79**	10c. red and sepia	1·40	80
465	**79**	15c. green and violet	3·25	1·30
466	**79**	20c. black and sepia	1·30	80
467	**79**	50c. black and red	6·75	2·75
468	**79**	1p. sepia and black	13·50	5·00

80

1929. Air. Perf or roul (10, 15, 20, 50c.), roul (5, 25c.), perf (others).

476a	**80**	5c. blue	25	15
477	**80**	10c. violet	25	15
478	**80**	15c. red	30	15
479	**80**	20c. brown	55	15
480	**80**	25c. purple	1·10	85
472	**80**	30c. black	20	15
473	**80**	35c. blue	35	25
481	**80**	50c. red	1·10	85
474	**80**	1p. blue and black	1·30	60
475	**80**	5p. blue and red	4·00	3·75
476	**80**	10p. brown and violet	6·25	7·25

81

1929. Air. Aviation Week.

482	**81**	20c. violet	1·30	1·00
483	**81**	40c. green	90·00	80·00

1930. Second Pan-American Postal Congress issue optd HABILITADO 1930.

484	**70**	2c. red	4·00	2·20
485	-	4c. green	4·00	2·50
486	**70**	5c. orange	4·00	1·90
487	-	10c. red	8·00	2·50
488	**72**	20c. blue	9·75	3·50
489	**72**	30c. green	9·00	4·00
490	**72**	40c. mauve	13·50	8·50
491	**73**	1p. blue and brown	11·50	7·25

1930. Air. National Tourist Congress. Optd Primer Congreso Nacional de Turismo. Mexico. Abril 20-27 de 1930.

492	**80**	10c. violet (No. 477)	2·20	1·30

1930. Obligatory Tax. Child Welfare. Surch HABILITADO $0.01.

494	**77**	1c. on 2c. green	2·75	1·30
495	**77**	1c. on 5c. brown	1·30	80

1930. Air. Optd HABILITADO 1930.

496	**79**	5c. sepia and green	6·25	5·25
497	**79**	15c. green and violet	11·00	8·50

1930. Air. Optd HABILITADO Aereo 1930-1931.

498	**79**	5c. sepia and green	6·75	6·50
499	**79**	10c. red and sepia	3·75	4·00
500	**79**	15c. green and violet	7·25	7·00
501	**79**	20c. black and sepia	7·50	5·50
502	**79**	50c. black and red	13·50	10·50
503	**79**	1p. sepia and black	4·00	3·00

1931. Obligatory Tax. Child Welfare. No. CT58 optd PRO INFANCIA.

504	**32**	1c. purple	45	50

87

1931. Fourth Centenary of Puebla.

505	**87**	10c. brown and blue	3·25	50

88

1931. Air. Aeronautic Exhibition.

506	**88**	25c. lake	4·00	4·25

1931. Nos. 446/52 optd HABILITADO 1931.

508	-	4c. green	70·00	†
509	**70**	5c. orange	13·50	†
510	-	10c. red	13·50	†
511	**72**	20c. blue	13·50	†
512	**72**	30c. green	22·00	†
513	**72**	40c. mauve	32·00	†
514	**73**	1p. blue and brown	29·00	†

1931. Air. Surch HABILITADO Quince centavos. Perf or rouletted.

516	**80**	15c. on 20c. sepia	60	80

1932. Air. Surch in words and figures. Perf. or roul.

517	**88**	20c. on 25c. lake	70	25
521	**80**	30c. on 20c. sepia	35	15
519	**58**	40c. on 25c. sepia and lake	1·00	95
520	**58**	40c. on 25c. sepia & green	38·00	37·00
522	**80**	80c. on 25c. (No. 480)	1·60	1·30

1932. Air. Fourth Death Anniv of Emilio Carranza. Optd HABILITADO AEREO-1932.

523	**79**	5c. sepia and green	5·50	3·00
524	**79**	10c. red and sepia	5·50	3·00
525	**79**	15c. green and violet	5·50	3·00
526	**79**	20c. black and sepia	5·50	3·00
527	**79**	50c. black and red	38·00	36·00

92 Fray Bartolome de las Casas

1933. Roul.

528	**92**	15c. blue	20	15

93 Mexican Geographical and Statistical Society's Arms

94 National Theatre and Palace of Fine Arts

1933. 21st International Statistical Congress and Centenary of Mexican Geographical and Statistical Society.

529	**93**	2c. green (postage)	1·60	60
530	**93**	5c. brown	1·80	50
531	**93**	10c. blue	80	15
533	**94**	20c. violet and red (air)	3·50	1·50
534	**94**	30c. violet and brown	7·25	6·50
532	**93**	1p. violet	65·00	55·00
535	**94**	1p. violet and green	70·00	75·00

95 Mother and Child

98 Nevada de Toluca

1934. National University. Inscr "PRO-UNIVERSIDAD".

543	**95**	1c. orange (postage)	25	15
544	-	5c. green	2·20	50
545	-	10c. lake	2·75	80
546	-	20c. blue	8·50	5·25
547	-	30c. black	16·00	13·00
548	-	40c. brown	26·00	17·00
549	-	50c. blue	55·00	50·00
550	-	1p. black and red	£100	47·00
551	-	5p. brown and black	£225	£225
552	-	10p. violet and brown	£1100	£950

Designs:—5c. Archer; 10c. Festive headdress; 20c. Woman decorating pot; 30c. Indian and Inca Lily; 40c. Potter; 50c. Sculptor; 1p. Gold craftsman; 5p. Girl offering fruit; 10p. Youth burning incense.

553	**98**	20c. orange (air)	4·00	3·00
554	-	30c. purple and mauve	8·00	5·75
555	-	50c. brown and green	9·00	9·50
556	-	75c. green and black	9·00	14·50
557	-	1p. blue and green	11·00	10·50
558	-	5p. blue and brown	60·00	85·00
559	-	10p. red and blue	£160	£170
560	-	20p. red and brown	£1300	£1400

Designs:—Aeroplane over: 30c. Pyramids of the Sun and Moon, Teotihuacan; 50c. Mt. Ajusco; 75c. Mts. Ixtaccihuatl and Popocatepetl; 1p. Bridge over R. Papagallo; 5p. Chapultepec Castle entrance; 10p. Orizaba Peak, Mt. Citlaltepetl; 20p. Girl and Aztec calendar stone.

101 Zapoteca Indian Woman

110 Coat of Arms

1934. Pres. Cardenas' Assumption of Office. Designs as Type 101 and 110. Imprint "OFICINA IMPRESORA DE HACIENDA-MEXICO" at foot of stamp. (a) Postage.

561	-	1c. orange	90	15
562	**101**	2c. green	90	15
563	-	4c. red	1·30	15
564	-	5c. brown	90	15
565	-	10c. blue	1·10	15
565a	-	10c. violet	1·70	15
566	-	15c. blue	5·50	35
567	-	20c. green	2·75	15
567a	-	20c. blue	2·00	15
568	-	30c. red	1·30	15
653	-	30c. blue	1·30	15
569	-	40c. brown	1·30	15
570	-	50c. black	1·30	15
571	**110**	1p. red and brown	3·50	15
572	-	5p. violet and orange	11·00	80

Designs:—1c. Yalalteca Indian; 4c. Revolution Monument; 5c. Los Remedios Tower; 10c. Cross of Palenque; 15c. Independence Monument, Mexico City; 20c. Independence Monument, Puebla; 30c. "Heroic Children" Monument, Mexico City; 40c. Sacrificial Stone; 50c. Ruins of Mitla, Oaxaca; 5p. Mexican "Charro" (Horseman).

112 Mictlantecuhtli

120 "Peasant admiration"

(b) Air.

573	**112**	5c. black	45	15
574	-	10c. brown	1·00	15
575	-	15c. green	1·30	15
576	-	20c. red	3·25	15
577	-	30c. olive	70	15
577a	-	40c. blue	1·30	15
578	-	50c. green	2·75	15
579	-	1p. red and green	3·75	15
580	**120**	5p. black and red	7·50	70

Designs:—Horiz: 10c. Temple at Quetzalcoatl; 15c. Aeroplane over Citlaltepetl; 20c. Popocatepetl; 30c. Pegasus; 50c. Uruapan pottery; 1p. "Warrior Eagle". Vert: 40c. Aztec idol.

121 Tractor

1935. Industrial Census.

581	**121**	10c. violet	4·00	50

1935. Air. Amelia Earhart Flight to Mexico. No. 576 optd AMELIA EARHART VUELO DE BUENA VOLUNTAD MEXICO 1935.

581a	20c. red	£3500	£4250

122 Arms of Chiapas

1935. Annexation of Chiapas Centenary.

582	**122**	10c. blue	55	15

123 E. Zapata

124 Francisco Madero

1935. 25th Anniv of Revolutionary Plans of Ayala and San Luis Potosi.

583	**123**	10c. violet (postage)	80	15
584	**124**	20c. red (air)	35	15

129 Nuevo Laredo Road

131 Rio Corona Bridge

1936. Opening of Nuevo Laredo Highway (Mexico City–U.S.A.).

591 - 5c. red and green (postage) 35 15
592 - 10c. grey 55 15
593 **129** 20c. green and brown 1·50 1·00

Designs:—As Type **129**: 5c. Symbolical Map of Mexico–USA road; 10c. Matalote Bridge.

594 - 10c. blue (air) 20 15
595 **131** 20c. orange and violet 35 15
596 - 40c. green and blue 55 50

Designs:—As Type **131**: 10c. Tasquillo Bridge over Rio Tula; 40c. Guayalejo Bridge.

1936. First Congress of Industrial Medicine and Hygiene. Optd PRIMER CONGRESO NAL. DE HIGIENE Y. MED. DEL TRABAJO.

597 10c. violet (No. 565a) 65 50

1937. As Nos. 561/4, 565a and 576, but smaller. Imprint at foot changed to "TALLERES DE IMP.(RESION) DE EST. (AMPILLAS) Y VALORES-MEXICO".

600 - 4c. red 1·20 15
601 - 5c. brown 1·10 15
602 - 10c. violet 1·00 15
603 - 20c. red (air) 2·20 15
708 - 1c. orange (postage) 1·30 15
709 **101** 2c. green 1·30 15

134 Blacksmith

1938. Carranza's "Plan of Guadelupe". 25th Anniv. Inscr "CONMEMORATIVO PLAN DE GUADALUPE", etc.

604 **134** 5c. brown & blk (postage) 90 15
605 - 10c. brown 35 15
606 - 20c. orange and brown 6·75 1·00
607 - 20c. blue and red (air) 55 35
608 - 40c. red and blue 80 35
609 - 1p. blue and yellow 5·50 2·50

Designs:—Vert: 10c. Peasant revolutionary; 20c. Preaching revolt. Horiz: 20c. Horseman; 40c. Biplane; 1p. Mounted horseman.

140 Arch of the Revolution

141 Cathedral and Constitution Square

1938. 16th International Town Planning and Housing Congress, Mexico City. Inscr as in T 140/1.

610 **140** 5c. brown (postage) 2·30 60
611 - 5c. olive 10·50 2·20
612 - 10c. orange 18·00 11·00
613 - 10c. brown 80 15
614 - 20c. black 23·00 16·00
615 - 20c. lake 4·50 4·25

Designs:—As Type **140**: 10c. National Theatre; 20c. Independence Column.

616 **141** 20c. red (air) 45 25
617 - 20c. violet 18·00 10·50
619 - 40c. green 9·00 5·25
620 - 1p. slate 9·00 5·25
621 - 1p. light blue 9·00 5·25

Designs:—As Type **141**: 40c. Chichen Itza Ruins (Yucatan); 1p. Acapulco Beach.

142 Mosquito and Malaria Victim

1939. Obligatory Tax. Anti-malaria Campaign.

622 **142** 1c. blue 2·00 25

143 Statue of an Indian

144 Statue of Woman Pioneer and Child

1939. Tulsa Philatelic Convention, Oklahoma.

623 **143** 10c. red (postage) 55 15
624 **144** 20c. brown (air) 1·10 45
625 **144** 40c. green 2·75 1·30
626 **144** 1p. violet 1·80 95

1939. Air. F. Sarabia non-stop Flight to New York. Optd SARABIA Vuelo MEXICO-NUEVA YORK.

626a **146** 20c. blue and red £475 £550

145 Mexican Pavilion, World's Fair

146 Morelos Statue on Mexican Pavilion

1939. New York World's Fair.

627 **145** 10c. green & blue (postage) 70 15
628 **146** 20c. green (air) 70 50
629 **146** 40c. purple 2·20 1·40
630 **146** 1p. brown and red 1·50 1·00

147 J. de Zumarraga

1939. 400th Anniv of Printing in Mexico.

631 **147** 2c. black (postage) 1·20 25
632 - 5c. green 1·20 15
633 - 10c. red 35 15
634 - 20c. blue (air) 35 15
635 - 40c. green 1·00 15
636 - 1p. red and brown 1·70 70

Designs:—5c. First printing works in Mexico; 10c. Antonio D. Mendoza; 20c. Book frontispiece; 40c. Title page of first law book printed in America; 1p. Oldest Mexican Colophon.

152 "Building"

154 "Transport"

1939. National Census. Inscr "CENSOS 1939 1940".

637 **152** 2c. red (postage) 1·30 15
638 - 5c. green 20 15
639 - 10c. brown 20 15
640 **154** 20c. blue (air) 1·10 15
641 - 40c. orange 80 25
642 - 1p. violet and blue 2·75 80

Designs:—As Type **152**: 5c. "Agriculture"; 10c. "Commerce". As Type **154**: 40c. "Industry"; 1p. "Seven Censuses".

155 "Penny Black"

1940. Centenary of First Adhesive Postage Stamps.

643 **155** 5c. yellow & black (postage) 1·00 50
644 **155** 10c. purple 25 15
645 **155** 20c. red and blue 25 15
646 **155** 1p. red and grey 7·50 4·25
647 **155** 5p. blue and black 40·00 31·00
648 **155** 5c. green and black (air) 90 60
649 **155** 10c. blue and brown 90 25
650 **155** 20c. violet and red 60 15
651 **155** 1p. brown and red 7·25 4·75
652 **155** 5p. brown and green 75·00 60·00

156 Roadside Monument

1940. Opening of Highway from Mexico City to Guadalajara.

654 **156** 6c. green 80 15

159 Original College at Patzcuaro

1940. Fourth Centenary of National College of St. Nicholas de Hidalgo.

655 - 2c. violet (postage) 1·40 50
656 - 5c. red 90 15
657 - 10c. olive 90 35
658 **159** 20c. green (air) 55 15
659 - 40c. orange 65 35
660 - 1p. violet, brown & orange 1·50 95

Designs:—Vert: 2c. V. de Quiroga; 5c. M. Ocampo; 10c. St. Nicholas College Arms; 40c. Former College at Morelia. Horiz: 1p. Present College at Morelia.

163 Pirate Galleon

1940. 400th Anniv of Campeche. Inscr as in T 163.

661 10c. red & brown (postage) 4·00 1·40
662 **163** 20c. brown and red (air) 1·50 70
663 - 40c. green and black 2·00 80
664 - 1p. black and blue 6·75 3·00

Designs:—10c. Campeche City Arms; 40c. St. Miguel Castie; 1p. Temple of San Francisco.

165 Helmsman

1940. Inauguration of Pres. Camacho.

665 **165** 2c. orange & black (postage) 3·25 60
666 **165** 5c. blue and brown 9·00 3·50
667 **165** 10c. olive and brown 3·25 85
668 **165** 20c. grey and orange (air) 2·20 1·00
669 **165** 40c. brown and green 2·30 1·60
670 **165** 1p. purple and red 3·25 2·10

166 Miguel Hidalgo y Costilla

1940. Compulsory Tax. Dolores Hidalgo Memorial Fund.

671 **166** 1c. red 65 25

168 Javelin throwing

1941. National Athletic Meeting.

675 **168** 10c. green 5·50 50

169 Dark Nebula in Orion

1942. Inauguration of Astro-physical Observatory at Tonanzintla, Puebla.

676 **169** 2c. blue & violet (postage) 4·75 2·20
677 - 5c. blue 11·50 2·75
678 - 10c. blue and orange 12·50 80
679 - 20c. blue and green (air) 15·00 3·00
680 - 40c. blue and red 12·50 4·25
681 - 1p. black and orange 16·00 4·75

Designs:—5c. Solar Eclipse; 10c. Spiral Galaxy of the "Hunting Dog"; 20c. Extra-Galactic Nebula in Virgo; 40c. Ring Nebula in Lyra; 1p. Russell Diagram.

171 Ruins of Chichen-Itza

172 Merida Nunnery

1942. 400th Anniv of Merida. Inscr as in T 171/2.

682 **171** 2c. brown (postage) 1·80 80
683 - 5c. red 2·75 60
684 - 10c. violet 2·00 25
685 **172** 20c. blue (air) 1·80 80
686 - 40c. green 2·75 2·10
687 - 1p. red 3·25 2·10

Designs:—Vert: 5c. Mayan sculpture; 10c. Arms of Merida; 40c. Montejo University Gateway. Horiz: 1p. Campanile of Merida Cathedral.

173 "Mother Earth"

1942. Second Inter-American Agricultural Conference.

688 **173** 2c. brown (postage) 2·20 45
689 - 5c. blue 4·00 1·10
690 - 10c. orange 1·60 60
691 - 20c. green (air) 2·30 70
692 - 40c. brown 2·00 80
693 - 1p. violet 3·25 2·20

Designs:—5c. Sowing wheat; 10c. Western Hemisphere carrying torch; 20c. Corn; 40c. Coffee; 1p. Bananas.

175 Hidalgo Monument

1942. 400th Anniv of Guadalajara.

694 **175** 2c. brown & blue (postage) 55 35
695 - 5c. red and black 1·80 50
696 - 10c. blue and red 1·80 45
697 - 20c. black and green (air) 2·20 80
698 - 40c. green and olive 2·75 1·00
699 - 1p. violet and brown 2·50 1·40

Designs:—Vert: 5c. Government Palace; 10c. Guadalajara. Horiz: 20c. St. Paul's Church, Zapopan; 40c. Sanctuary of Our Lady of Guadalupe; 1p. Arms of Guadalajara.

186 Saltillo Athenaeum, Coahuila

1942. 75th Anniv of Saltillo Athenaeum.

700 **186** 10c. black 2·75 80

189 Birthplace of Allende

1943. 400th Anniv of San Miguel de Allende.

701	-	2c. blue (postage)	90	45
702	-	5c. brown	1·10	35
703	-	10c. black	2·75	1·00
704	-	20c. green (air)	1·30	60
705	**189**	40c. purple	1·80	60
706	-	1p. red	3·50	2·50

Designs:—Vert: 2c. Cupola de las Monjas; 5c. Gothic Church; 10c. Gen. de Allende. Horiz: 20c. San Miguel de Allende; 1p. Church seen through cloisters.

190 "Liberty"

1944

707	**190**	12c. brown	35	15

192 Dr. de Castorena

1944. Third National Book Fair.

732	**192**	12c. brown (postage)	70	15
733	-	25c. green (air)	75	15

Design:—25c. Microphone, book and camera.

194 "Flight"

1944. Air.

734	**194**	25c. brown	50	15

195 Hands clasping Globe

1945. Inter-American Conference.

735	**195**	12c. red (postage)	60	15
736	**195**	1p. green	1·10	30
737	**195**	5p. brown	7·25	5·00
738	**195**	10p. black	14·50	8·75
739	**195**	25c. orange (air)	50	20
740	**195**	1p. green	60	35
741	**195**	5p. blue	3·00	2·30
742	**195**	10p. red	8·25	5·50
743	**195**	20p. blue	17·00	14·00

196 La Paz Theatre, San Luis Potosi

1945. Reconstruction of La Paz Theatre, San Luis Potosi.

744	**196**	12c. pur & blk (postage)	40	15
745	**196**	1p. blue and black	70	40
746	**196**	5p. red and black	6·75	5·50
747	**196**	10p. green and black	16·00	13·00
748	**196**	30c. green (air)	40	15
749	**196**	1p. purple and green	50	40
750	**196**	5p. black and green	3·75	2·75
751	**196**	10p. blue and green	7·25	4·75
752	**196**	20p. green and black	16·00	11·00

197 Fountain of Diana the Huntress

1945

753	**197**	3c. violet	55	15

198 Removing Bandage

1945. Literacy Campaign.

754	**198**	2c. blue (postage)	30	20
755	**198**	6c. orange	50	20
756	**198**	12c. blue	50	20
757	**198**	1p. olive	60	30
758	**198**	5p. red and black	3·00	2·40
759	**198**	10p. green and blue	24·00	22·00
760	**198**	30c. green (air)	20	20
761	**198**	1p. red	60	35
762	**198**	5p. blue	4·50	2·75
763	**198**	10p. red	7·25	5·50
764	**198**	20p. brown and green	35·00	26·00

199 Founder of National Post Office

1946. Foundation of Posts in Mexico in 1580.

765	**199**	8c. black	1·60	25

200 ONU, Olive Branch and Globe

201 ONU and Flags of United Nations

1946. United Nations.

766	**200**	2c. olive (postage)	30	15
767	**200**	6c. brown	30	20
768	**200**	12c. blue	20	15
769	**200**	1p. green	60	45
770	**200**	5p. red	4·75	5·50
771	**200**	10p. blue	24·00	22·00
772	**201**	3c. brown (air)	20	15
773	**201**	1p. grey	60	30
774	**201**	5p. green and brown	2·40	1·40
775	**201**	10p. brown and sepia	5·75	4·25
776	**201**	20p. red and slate	16·00	10·00

202 Zacatecas City Arms

205 Don Genaro Codina and Zacatecas

1946. 400th Anniv of Zacatecas.

777	**202**	2c. brown (postage)	60	15
778	-	12c. blue	30	15
779	-	1p. mauve	75	20
780	-	5p. red	5·75	3·25
781	-	10p. black and blue	37·00	11·00

Designs:—1p. Statue of Gen. Ortega; 5p. R. L. Velarde (poet); 10p. F. G. Salinas.

782		30c. grey (air)	20	15
783	**205**	1p. green and brown	40	35
784	-	5p. green and red	3·50	3·25
785	-	10p. brown and green	14·50	8·25

Portraits: 30c. Fr. Margil de Jesus; 5p. Gen. Enrique Estrada; 10p. D. Fernando Villalpando.

207 Learning Vowels

1946. Education Plan.

786	**207**	1c. sepia	50	20

208 Postman

1947

787	**208**	15c. blue	30	15

209 Roosevelt and First Mexican Stamp

210 10c. USA 1847 and Mexican Eagle

1947. U.S.A. Postage Stamp Centenary.

788	**209**	10c. brown (postage)	2·40	1·10
789	-	15c. green	40	15
790	-	25c. blue (air)	95	55
791	**210**	30c. black	70	25
792	-	1p. blue and red	1·40	45

Designs:—15c. as Type **209** but vert; 25c., 1p. as Type **210** but horiz.

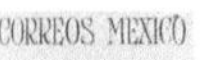

213 Justo Sierra

214 Ministry of Communications

212 Douglas DC-4

1947

793	-	10p. red and brown (air)	1·90	1·60
794	**212**	20p. red and blue	3·00	3·00
795	**213**	10p. green and brown (postage)	£140	26·00
796	**214**	20p. mauve and green	1·40	2·30

Design:—Horiz: 10p. E. Carranza.

215 Manuel Rincon

217 Vicente Suarez

1947. Battle Centenaries. Portraits of "Child Heroes" etc. Inscr "1er CENTENARIO CHAPULTEPEC ("CHURUBUSCO" or "MOLINO DEL REY") 1847 1947".

797	-	2c. black (postage)	60	15
798	-	5c. red	40	15
799	-	10c. brown	30	15
800	-	15c. green	30	15
801	**215**	30c. olive	50	15
802	-	1p. blue	60	45
803	-	5p. red and blue	2·50	2·00

Designs:—Vert: 2c. Francisco Marquez; 5c. Fernando Montes de Oca; 10c. Juan Escutin; 15c. Agustin Melgar; 1p. Lucas Balderas; 5p. Flag of San Blas Battalion.

804	**217**	25c. violet (air)	20	15
805	-	30c. blue	20	15
806	-	50c. green	40	15
807	-	1p. violet	50	15
808	-	5p. brown and blue	2·10	2·20

Designs:—Horiz: 30c. Juan de la Barrera; 50c. Military Academy; 1p. Pedro Maria Anaya; 5p. Antonio de Leon.

218 Puebla Cathedral

221 Dance of the Half Moons, Puebla

1950. (a) Postage. As T **218**.

835	-	3c. blue	80	35
874	-	5c. brown	80	35
875a	-	10c. green	3·25	35
876a	-	15c. green	1·00	40
877e	**218**	20c. blue	4·50	1·10
840	-	30c. red	1·30	35
879	-	30c. brown	65	35
880b	-	40c. orange	1·30	35
1346b	-	50c. blue	2·50	35
1327b	-	80c. green	2·50	65
843	-	1p. brown	11·00	35
1011ab	-	1p. grey	2·00	35
1346f	-	1p. green	2·50	35
1327d	-	3p. red	2·50	65
1012a	-	5p. blue and green	8·50	75
1013ab	-	10p. black and blue	14·50	5·00
846	-	20p. violet and green	11·50	14·00
1014	-	20p. violet and black	16·00	7·75
1327e	-	50p. orange and green	19·00	12·50

Designs: 3c., 3p. La Purisima Church, Monterrey; 5c. Modern building, Mexico City; 10c. Convent of the Nativity, Tepoztlan; 15c., 50p. Benito Juarez; 30c., 80c. Indian dancer, Michoacan; 40c. Sculpture, Tabasco; 50c. Carved head, Veracruz; 1p. Actopan Convent and carved head; 5p. Galleon, Campeche; 10p. Francisco Madero; 20p. Modern building, Mexico City.

(b) Air. As T **221**.

897		5c. blue	65	35
898a		10c. brown	70	35
899a		20c. red	70	35
850		25c. brown	3·00	35
851		30c. olive	1·30	35
902		35c. violet	2·40	35
1327f	-	40c. blue	1·30	50
904c		50c. green	1·40	30
1056	-	80c. red	2·20	65
906a	**221**	1p. grey	4·50	40
1327h	-	1p.60 red	4·50	65
1327i	-	1p.90 red	4·50	65
907ab	-	2p. brown	1·40	75
908	-	2p.25 purple	90	90
1327j	-	4p.30 blue	1·50	40
1017a	-	5p. orange and brown	12·00	1·30
1327k	-	5p.20 lilac	2·50	50
1327l	-	5p.60 green	5·00	65
895		10p. blue and black	12·50	1·60
859a		20p. blue and red	£700	£120

Designs:—5c., 1p.90 Bay of Acapulco; 10c., 4p.30, Dance of the Plumes, Oaxaca; 20c. Mayan frescoes, Chiapas; 25c., 2p.25, 5p.60, Masks, Michoacan; 30c. Cuauhtemoc; 35c., 2p., 5p.20, Taxco, Guerrero; 40c. Sculpture, San Luis Potosi; 50c., 1p.60, Ancient carvings, Chiapas; 80c. University City, Mexico City; 5p. Architecture, Queretaro; 10p. Hidalgo; 20p. National Music Conservatoire, Mexico City.

222 Arterial Road

1950. Opening of Mexican Section of Pan-American Highway. Inscr "CARRETERA INTER-NACIONAL 1950".

860		15c. violet (postage)	90	35
861	**222**	20c. blue	55	35
862	-	25c. pink (air)	4·25	35
863	-	35c. green	40	35

Designs:—Horiz: 15c. Bridge; 25c. Pres. M. Aleman, bridge and map; 35c. B. Juarez and map.

224 Diesel Locomotive and Map

1950. Inauguration of Mexico–Yucatan Railway.

864		15c. purple (postage)	2·10	35
865	**224**	20c. red	80	35
866	-	25c. green (air)	75	35
867	-	35c. blue	55	35

Designs:—Vert: 15c. Rail-laying. Horiz: 25c. Diesel trains crossing Isthmus of Tehuantepec; 35c. M. Aleman and railway bridge at Coatzacoalcos.

227 Hands and Globe

1950. 75th Anniv of U.P.U.

868		50c. violet (postage)	55	35
869		25c. red (air)	45	35
870	**227**	80c. blue	70	40

Designs—Horiz: 25c. Aztec runner. Vert: 50c. Letters "UPU".

228 Miguel Hidalgo **229**

1953. Birth Bicentenary of Hidalgo.

871	**228**	20c. sepia & blue (postage)	2·30	35
872	-	25c. lake and blue (air)	1·30	35
873	**229**	35c. green	1·30	40

Design:—As Type **229**: 25c. Full face portrait.

231 Aztec Athlete **232** View and Mayan Bas-relief

1954. Seventh Central American and Caribbean Games.

918	**231**	20c. blue & pink (postage)	1·40	35
919	**232**	25c. brown and green (air)	1·40	45
920	-	35c. turquoise and purple	1·10	35

Design:—35c. Stadium.

233 **234**

1954. Mexican National Anthem Centenary.

921	**233**	5c. lilac and blue (postage)	1·10	35
922	**233**	20c. brown and purple	1·30	35
923	**233**	1p. green and red	90	55
924	**234**	25c. blue and lake (air)	75	35
925	**234**	35c. purple and blue	40	35
926	**234**	80c. green and blue	45	35

235 Torchbearer and Stadium **236** Aztec God and Map

1955. Second Pan-American Games, Mexico City. Inscr "II JUEGOS DEPORTIVOS PANAMER-ICANOS".

927	**235**	20c. green & brn (postage)	1·30	35
928	**236**	25c. blue and brown (air)	95	45
929	-	35c. brown and red	95	45

Design:—As Type **236**: 35c. Stadium and map.

237 Olin Design

1956. Mexican Stamp Centenary.

930	**237**	5c. green & brn (postage)	65	35
931	-	10c. blue and grey	65	35
932	-	30c. purple and red	50	35
933	-	50c. brown and blue	55	35
934	-	1p. black and green	70	35
935	-	5p. sepia and bistre	3·00	3·25
MS936 190×150 mm. Nos. 930/5. Imperf (sold at 15p.)			85·00	90·00

Designs:—As Type **237**: 10c. Tohtli bird; 30c. Zochitl flower; 50c. Centli corn; 1p. Mazatl deer; 5p. Teheutli man's head.

238 Feathered Serpent and Mask

937	**238**	5c. black (air)	65	35
938	-	10c. blue	65	35
939	-	50c. purple	45	35
940	-	1p. violet	65	35
941	-	1p.20 mauve	65	35
942	-	5p. turquoise	2·40	1·90
MS943 190×150 mm. Nos. 937/42 (sold at 15p.)			70·00	75·00

Designs:—As Type **238**: 10c. Bell tower, coach and Viceroy Enriquez de Almanza; 50c. Morelos and cannon; 1p. Mother, child and mounted horseman; 1p.20, Sombrero and spurs; 5p. Emblems of food and education and pointing hand.

239 Stamp of 1856

1956. Centenary Int Philatelic Exn, Mexico City.

944	**239**	30c. blue and brown	1·10	35

240 F. Zarco **241** V. Gomez Farias and M. Ocampo

1956. Inscr "CONSTITUYENTE(S) DE 1857".

945	-	25c. brown (postage)	1·10	55
946	-	45c. blue	70	35
947	-	60c. purple	70	40
1346d	**240**	70c. blue	1·30	45
1327c	-	2p.30 blue	1·50	50
949	**241**	15c. blue (air)	80	35
1327g	-	60c. green	1·30	50
950	-	1p.20 violet and green	1·00	40
951	**241**	2p.75 purple	1·30	95

Portraits:—As T **240** (postage): 25, 45c., 2p.30, G. Prieto; 60c. P. Arriagan. As T **41** (air): 60c., 1p.20, L. Guzman and I. Ramirez.

242 Paricutin Volcano

1956. Air. 20th International Geological Congress.

952	**242**	50c. violet	70	35

243 Map of Central America and the Caribbean

1956. Air. Fourth Inter-American Congress of Caribbean Tourism.

953	**243**	25c. blue and grey	45	35

244 Assembly of 1857 **245** Mexican Eagle and Scales

1957. Centenary of 1857 Constitution.

958	-	30c. gold & lake (postage)	70	35
959	**244**	1p. green and sepia	45	35
960	**245**	50c. brown and green (air)	40	35
961	-	1p. lilac and blue	65	35

Designs:—Vert: 30c. Emblem of Constitution. Horiz: 1p. (Air), "Mexico" drafting the Constitution.

246 Globe, Weights and Dials

1957. Air. Centenary of Adoption of Metric System in Mexico.

962	**246**	50c. black and silver	55	35

247 Train Disaster

1957. Air. 50th Anniv of Heroic Death of Jesus Garcia (engine driver) at Nacozari.

963	**247**	50c. purple and red	45	35

248 Oil Derrick

1958. 20th Anniv of Nationalization of Oil Industry.

964	**248**	30c. black & blue (postage)	65	35
965	-	5p. red and blue	7·75	5·50
966	-	50c. green and black (air)	45	35
967	-	1p. black and red	55	35

Designs:—Horiz: 50c. Oil storage tank and "AL SERVICIO DE LA PATRIA" ("At the service of the Fatherland"); 1p. Oil refinery at night. Vert: 5p. Map of Mexico and silhouette of oil refinery.

249 Angel, Independence Monument, Mexico City

1958. Air. Tenth Anniv of Declaration of Human Rights.

968	**249**	50c. blue	40	35

250 UNESCO Headquarters, Paris

1959. Inauguration of UNESCO Headquarters Building, Paris.

969	**250**	30c. black and purple	75	35

251 UN Headquarters, New York

1959. U.N. Economic and Social Council Meeting, Mexico City.

970	**251**	30c. blue and yellow	75	35

252 President Carranza

1960. President Carranza Year (1959) and his Birth Centenary.

971	**252**	30c. pur & grn (postage)	55	35
972	-	50c. violet and salmon (air)	40	35

Design:—Horiz: 50c. Inscription "Plan de Guadalupe Constitucion de 1917" and portrait as Type **252**.

253 Alexander von Humboldt (statue)

1960. Death Centenary of Alexander von Humboldt (naturalist).

973	**253**	40c. green and brown	55	35

254 Alberto Braniff's Voisin Boxkite and Bristol Britannia

1960. Air. 50th Anniv of Mexican Aviation.

974	**254**	50c. brown and violet	75	35
975	**254**	1p. brown and green	55	35

255 Francisco I. Madero

1960. Visit to Mexico of Members of Elmhurst Philatelic Society (American Society of Mexican Specialists). Inscr "HOMENAJE AL COLEC-CIONISTA".

976	**255**	10p. sepia, green and purple (postage)	£110	£100
977	-	20p. sepia, green and purple (air)	£120	£130

Design:—As No. 859a 20p. National Music Conservatoire inscr "MEX. D.F.".

257 Dolores Bell

1960. 150th Anniv of Independence.

978	**257**	30c. red & green (postage)	3·50	35
979	-	1p. sepia and green	55	35
980	-	5p. blue and purple	7·25	7·00
981	-	50c. red and green (air)	50	35
982	-	1p.20 sepia and blue	70	35
983	-	5p. sepia and green	8·25	3·00

Designs:—Vert: No. 979, Independence Column; 980, Hidalgo, Dolores Bell and Mexican Eagle. Horiz: No. 981, Mexican Flag; 982, Eagle breaking chain and bell tolling; 983, Dolores Church.

259 Children at Desk, University and School Buildings

1960. 50th Anniv of Mexican Revolution.

984	-	10c. multicoloured (postage)	95	35
985	-	15c. brown and green	4·00	70
986	-	20c. blue and brown	1·40	35
987	-	30c. violet and sepia	55	35
988	**259**	1p. slate and purple	75	35
989	-	5p. grey and purple	8·25	4·75
990	-	50c. black and blue (air)	55	35
991	-	1p. green and red	70	35
992	-	1p.20 sepia and green	70	40
993	-	5p. lt blue, blue & mauve	7·25	2·75

Designs:—No. 984, Pastoral scene ($35\frac{1}{2}\times45\frac{1}{2}$ mm). As Type **259** Vert: No. 985, Worker and hospital buildings; No. 986, Peasant, soldier and marine; No. 987, Power lines and pylons; No. 989, Coins, banknotes and bank entrance. Horiz: No. 990, Douglas DC-8 airliner; No. 991, Riggers on oil derrick; No. 992, Main highway and map; No. 993, Barrage.

261 Count S. de Revillagigedo

1960. Air. National Census.

994	**261**	60c. black and lake	80	35

262 Railway Tunnel

1961. Opening of Chihuahua State Railway.

995 **262** 40c. black & grn (postage) 1·20 35
996 - 60c. blue and black (air) 1·20 35
997 - 70c. black and blue 1·20 35

Designs:—Horiz: 60c. Railway tracks and map of railway; 70c. Railway viaduct.

263 Mosquito Globe and Instruments

1962. Malaria Eradication.

998 **263** 40c. brown and blue 55 35

264 Pres. Goulart of Brazil

1962. Visit of President of Brazil.

999 **264** 40c. bistre 1·40 35

265 Soldier and Memorial Stone

1962. Centenary of Battle of Puebla.

1000 **265** 40c. sepia and green (postage) 45 35
1001 - 1p. olive and green (air) 80 35

Design:—Horiz: 1p. Statue of Gen. Zaragoza.

266 Draughtsman and Surveyor

1962. 25th Anniv of National Polytechnic Institute.

1002 **266** 40c. turquoise and blue (postage) 1·30 35
1003 - 1p. olive and blue (air) 80 35

Design:—Horiz: 1p. Scientist and laboratory assistant.

267 Plumb-line

1962. Mental Health.

1004 **267** 20c. blue and black 2·10 35

268 Pres. J. F. Kennedy

1962. Air. Visit of U.S. President.

1005 **268** 80c. blue and red 2·20 55

269 Tower and Cogwheels

1962. Century 21 Exhibition ("World's Fair"), Seattle.

1006 **269** 40c. black and green 45 35

270 Globe and OEA Emblem

1962. Inter-American Economic and Social Council.

1007 **270** 40c. sepia and grey (postage) 45 35
1008 - 1p.20 sepia & violet (air) 80 35

Design:—Horiz: 1p.20, Globe, Scroll and OEA emblem.

271 Pres. Alessandri of Chile

1962. Visit of President of Chile.

1009 **271** 20c. brown 1·10 35

272 Balloon over Mexico City

1962. Air. First Mexican Balloon Flight Centenary.

1010 **272** 80c. black and blue 2·30 80

273 "ALALC" Emblem

1963. Air. Second "ALALC" Session.

1023 **273** 80c. purple and orange 1·70 45

274 Pres. Betancourt of Venezuela

1963. Visit of President of Venezuela.

1024 **274** 20c. blue 1·10 35

275 Petroleum Refinery

1963. Air. 25th Anniv of Nationalization of Mexican Petroleum Industry.

1025 **275** 80c. slate and orange 80 35

276 Congress Emblem

1963. 19th International Chamber of Commerce Congress, Mexico City.

1026 **276** 40c. brown and black (postage) 80 35
1027 - 80c. black and blue (air) 1·20 45

Design:—Horiz: 80c. World map and "CIC" emblem.

277 Campaign Emblem

1963. Freedom from Hunger.

1028 **277** 40c. red and blue 90 35

278 Arms and Mountain

1963. Fourth Centenary of Durango.

1029 **278** 20c. brown and blue 90 35

279 B. Dominguez

1963. Birth Centenary of B. Dominguez (revolutionary).

1030 **279** 20c. olive and green 90 35

280 Exhibition Stamp of 1956

1963. 77th American Philatelic Society Convention, Mexico City.

1031 **280** 1p. brown & bl (postage) 1·80 1·00
1032 - 5p. red (air) 3·75 2·30

Design:—Horiz: 5p. EXMEX "stamp" and "postmark".

281 Pres. Tito

1963. Air. Visit of President of Yugoslavia.

1033 **281** 2p. green and violet 2·75 95

283 Part of UIA Building

1963. Air. International Architects' Day.

1034 **283** 80c. grey and blue 95 35

284 Red Cross on Tree

1963. Red Cross Centenary.

1035 **284** 20c. red & grn (postage) 55 35
1036 - 80c. red and green (air) 1·80 45

Design:—Horiz: 80c. Red Cross on dove.

285 Pres. Estenssoro

1963. Visit of President of Bolivia.

1037 **285** 40c. purple and brown 90 35

286 Jose Morelos

1963. 150th Anniv of First Anahuac Congress.

1038 **286** 40c. bronze and green 80 35

287 Don Quixote as Skeleton

1963. Air. 50th Death Anniv of Jose Posada (satirical artist).

1039 **287** 1p.20 black 2·30 70

288 University Arms

1963. 90th Anniv of Sinaloa University.

1040 **288** 40c. bistre and green 90 35

289 Diesel-electric Train

1963. 11th Pan-American Railways Congress, Mexico City.

1041 **289** 20c. brn & blk (postage) 1·30 70
1042 - 1p.20 blue and violet (air) 1·30 55

Design:—1p.20, Steam and diesel-electric locomotives and horse-drawn tramcar.

290 "FSTSE" Emblem

1964. 25th Anniv of Workers' Statute.

1075 **290** 20c. sepia and orange 65 35

291 Mrs. Roosevelt, Flame and UN Emblem

1964. Air. 15th Anniv of Declaration of Human Rights.
1076 **291** 80c. blue and orange 1·30 35

292 Pres. De Gaulle

1964. Air. Visit of President of France.
1077 **292** 2p. blue and brown 3·75 1·30

293 Pres. Kennedy and Pres. A. Lopez Mateos

1964. Air. Ratification of Chamizal Treaty (1963).
1078 **293** 80c. black and blue 1·30 35

294 Queen Juliana and Arms

1964. Air. Visit of Queen Juliana of the Netherlands.
1079 **294** 20c. bistre and blue 1·90 35

295 Academy Emblem

1964. Centenary of National Academy of Medicine.
1080 **295** 20c. gold and black 65 35

296 Lieut. Jose Azueto and Cadet Virgillo Uribe

1964. Air. 50th Anniv of Heroic Defence of Veracruz.
1081 **296** 40c. green and brown 75 35

297 Arms and World Map

1964. Air. International Bar Assn Conf, Mexico City.
1082 **297** 40c. blue and brown 1·00 35

298 Colonel G. Mendez

1964. Centenary of Battle of the Jahuactal Tabasco.
1083 **298** 40c. olive and brown 75 35

299 Dr. Jose Rizal

1964. 400 Years of Mexican–Philippine Friendship. Inscr "1564 AMISTAD MEXICANO-FILIPINA 1964".
1084 **299** 20c. blue & grn (postage) 90 35
1085 - 40c. blue and violet 1·00 35
1086 - 80c. blue & lt blue (air) 4·00 65
1087 - 2p.75 black and yellow 4·50 1·60

Designs:—As Type **299**: Vert: 40c. Legaspi. Horiz: 80c. *San Pedro* (16th-century Spanish galleon). LARGER (44×36 mm): 2p.75, Ancient map of Pacific Ocean.

300 Zacatecas

1964. 50th Anniv of Conquest of Zacatecas.
1088 **300** 40c. green and red 90 35

301 Morelos Theatre, Aguascalientes

1965. 50th Anniv of Aguascalientes Convention.
1089 **301** 20c. purple and grey 65 35

302 Andres Manuel del Rio

1965. Andres M. del Rio Commemoration.
1090 **302** 30c. black 65 35

303 Netzahualcoyotl Dam

1965. Air. Inauguration of Netzahualcoyotl Dam.
1091 **303** 80c. slate and purple 90 35

304 J. Morelos (statue)

1965. 150th Anniv (1964) of First Constitution.
1092 **304** 40c. brown and green 65 35

305 Microwave Tower

1965. Air. Centenary of I.T.U.
1093 **305** 80c. blue and indigo 1·00 50
1094 - 1p.20 green and black 1·00 50

Design:—1p.20, Radio-electric station.

306 Fir Trees

1965. Forest Conservation.
1095 **306** 20c. green and blue 50 35

The inscription "¡CUIDALOS!" means "CARE FOR THEM!".

307 ICY Emblem

1965. International Co-operation Year.
1096 **307** 40c. brown and green 50 35

308 Camp Fire and Tent

1965. Air. World Scout Conference, Mexico City.
1097 **308** 30c. ultramarine and blue 1·10 50

309 King Baudouin and Queen Fabiola

1965. Air. Visit of Belgian King and Queen.
1098 **309** 2p. blue and green 1·80 65

310 Mexican Antiquities and Unisphere

1965. Air. New York World's Fair.
1099 **310** 80c. green and yellow 90 35

311 Dante (after R. Sanzio)

1965. Air. Dante's 700th Birth Anniv.
1100 **311** 2p. red 2·10 1·30

312 Sling-thrower

1965. Olympic Games (1968) Propaganda (1st series). Museum pieces.
1101 **312** 20c. blue & olive (postage) 3·75 35
1102 - 40c. sepia and red 1·30 35
1103 - 80c. slate and red (air) 1·10 35
1104 - 1p.20 indigo and blue 1·40 45
1105 - 2p. brown and blue 1·00 35
MS1106 140×90 mm. Nos. 1101/4 (sold at 3p.90). Imperf. No gum 4·75 4·75
MS1107 71×90 mm. No. 1105 (sold at 3p.). Imperf. No gum 4·75 4·75

Designs:—As Type **312**: Vert: 40c. Batsman. Horiz: 2p. Ball game. Horiz (36×20 mm): 80c. Fieldsman. 1p.20, Score-board.

See also Nos.1121/**MS**1127, 1140/**MS**1150 and 1158/**MS**1169.

313 Jose M. Morelos y Pavon (leader of independence movement)

1965. 150th Anniv of Morelos's Execution.
1108 **313** 20c. black and blue 65 35

314 Agricultural Produce

1966. Centenary of Agrarian Reform Law.
1109 **314** 20c. red 65 35
1110 - 40c. black 65 35

Design:—40c. Emilio Zapata, pioneer of agrarian reform.

315 Ruben Dario

1966. Air. 50th Death Anniv of Ruben Dario (Nicaraguan poet).
1111 **315** 1p.20 sepia 1·00 65

316 Father Andres de Urdaneta and Compass Rose

1966. Air. 400th Anniv of Father Andres de Urdaneta's Return from the Philippines.
1112 **316** 2p.75 black 2·10 1·00

317 Flag and Postal Emblem

1966. Ninth Postal Union of Americas and Spain Congress (U.P.A.E.), Mexico City.
1113 **317** 40c. blk & grn (postage) 65 40
1114 - 80c. black & mauve (air) 40 40
1115 - 1p.20 black and blue 50 40

Designs:—Vert: 80c. Flag and posthorn. Horiz: 1p.20, UPAE emblem and flag.

318 Friar B. de Las Casas

1966. 400th Death Anniv of Friar Bartolome de Las Casas ("Apostle of the Indies").
1116 **318** 20c. black on buff 65 40

319 ESIME Emblem and Diagram

1966. 50th Anniv of Higher School of Mechanical and Electrical Engineering.
1117 **319** 20c. green and grey 50 35

320 U Thant and UN Emblem

1966. Air. U.N. Secretary-General U Thant's Visit to Mexico.
1118 **320** 80c. black and blue 1·30 40

321 "1966 Friendship Year"

1966. Air. "Year of Friendship" with Central American States.
1119 **321** 80c. green and red 50 35

322 FAO Emblem

1966. International Rice Year.
1120 **322** 40c. green 50 35

323 Running and Jumping

1966. Olympic Games (1968) Propaganda (2nd series).
1121 **323** 20c. black & bl (postage) 1·30 40
1122 - 40c. black and lake 1·30 40
MS1123 100×60 mm. As Nos. 1121/2. Imperf 4·50 4·00

1124 80c. black & brown (air) 75 40
1125 2p.25 black and green 1·30 65
1126 2p.75 black and violet 2·75 75
MS1127 125×70 mm. As Nos. 1124/6. Imperf (sold at 8p.70) 5·00 5·75
Designs:—40c. Wrestling. Larger (57×20 mm): 80c. Obstacle race; 2p.25, American football; 2p.75, Lighting Olympic flame.

324 UNESCO Emblem

1966. Air. 20th Anniv of UNESCO.
1128 **324** 80c. multicoloured 75 40

325 Constitution of 1917

1967. 50th Anniv of Mexican Constitution.
1129 **325** 40c. black (postage) 1·00 40
1130 - 80c. brown & ochre (air) 65 40
Design:—80c. President V. Carranza.

326 Earth and Satellite

1967. Air. World Meteorological Day.
1131 **326** 80c. blue and black 75 35

327 Oil Refinery

1967. Seventh World Petroleum Congress, Mexico City.
1132 **327** 40c. black and blue 65 40

328 Nayarit Indian

1967. 50th Anniv of Nayarit State.
1133 **328** 20c. black and green 50 35

329 Degollado Theatre

1967. Cent of Degollado Theatre, Guadalajara.
1134 **329** 40c. brown and mauve 40 35

330 Mexican Eagle and Crown

1967. Centenary of Triumph over the Empire.
1135 **330** 20c. black and ochre 50 35

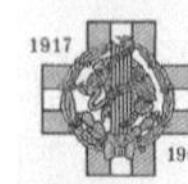

331 School Emblem

1967. Air. 50th Anniv of Military Medical School.
1136 **331** 80c. green and yellow 65 40

332 Capt. H. Ruiz Gavino

1967. Air. 50th Anniv of First Mexican Airmail Flight, Pachuca–Mexico City.
1137 **332** 80c. brown and black 40 35
1138 - 2p. brown and black 75 50
Design:—Horiz: 2p. de Havilland D.H.6A biplane.

333 Marco Polo

1967. Air. International Tourist Year.
1139 **333** 80c. red and black 50 35

334 Canoeing

1967. Olympic Games (1968) Propaganda (3rd series).
1140 **334** 20c. black & bl (postage) 75 40
1141 - 40c. black and red 65 40
1142 - 50c. black and green 65 40
1143 - 80c. black and violet 1·30 40
1144 - 2p. black and orange 2·50 50
MS1145 Two sheets each 130×90 mm. Nos. 1140/2 (sold at 1p.50) and Nos. 1143/4 (sold at 3p.50). Imperf 17·00 12·00

1146 80c. black & mauve (air) 65 40
1147 1p.20 black and green 65 40
1148 2p. black and lemon 1·90 65
1149 5p. black and yellow 2·30 1·30
MS1150 Two sheets each 130×90 mm. Nos. 1146/7 (sold at 2p.50) and Nos. 1148/9 (sold at 9p.). Imperf 15·00 10·00
Designs:—40c. Basketball; 50c. Hockey; 80c. (No. 1143), Cycling; 80c. (No. 1146), Diving; 1p.20, Running; 2p. (No. 1144), Fencing; 2p. (No. 1148), Weightlifting; 5p. Football.

335 A. del Valle-Arizpe (writer)

1967. Centenary of Fuente Athenaeum, Saltillo.
1151 **335** 20c. slate and brown 65 50

336 Hertz and Clark Maxwell

1967. Air. International Telecommunications Plan Conference, Mexico City.
1152 **336** 80c. green and black 75 40

337 P. Moreno

1967. 150th Death Anniv of Pedro Moreno (revolutionary).
1153 **337** 40c. black and blue 65 35

338 Gabino Berreda (founder of Preparatory School)

1968. Centenary of National Preparatory and Engineering Schools.
1154 **338** 40c. red and blue 75 40
1155 - 40c. blue and black 75 40
Design:—No. 1155, Staircase, Palace of Mining.

339 Exhibition Emblem

1968. Air. Efimex '68 International Stamp Exhibition, Mexico City.
1156 **339** 80c. green and black 75 40
1157 **339** 2p. red and black 75 40
The emblem reproduces the "Hidalgo" Official stamp design of 1884.

1968. Olympic Games (1968) Propaganda (4th series). Designs as T 334, but inscr "1968".
1158 20c. black and olive (postage) 65 35
1159 40c. black and purple 65 35
1160 50c. black and green 65 35
1161 80c. black and mauve 1·30 40
1162 1p. black and brown 3·75 75
1163 2p. black and grey 6·25 2·50
MS1164 Two sheets each 106×70 mm. Nos. 1158/60 (sold at 1p.50) and Nos. 1161/3 (sold at 5p.). Imperf 18·00 10·50

1165 80c. black and blue (air) 40 35
1166 1p. black and turquoise 50 35
1167 2p. black and yellow 1·00 50
1168 5p. black and brown 2·00 1·90
MS1169 Two sheets each 106×70 mm. Nos. 1165/6 (sold at 2p.50) and Nos. 1167/8 (sold at 9p.). Imperf 13·00 9·50
Designs:—20c. Wrestling; 40c. Various sports; 50c. Water-polo; 80c. (No. 1161), Gymnastics; 80c. (No. 1165), Yachting; 1p. (No. 1162), Boxing; 1p. (No. 1166), Rowing; 2p. (No. 1163), Pistol-shooting; 2p. (No. 1167), Volleyball; 5p. Horse-racing.

340 Dr. Martin Luther King

1968. Air. Martin Luther King Commemorative.
1170 **340** 80c. black and grey 65 40

341 Olympic Flame **342** Emblems of Games

1968. Olympic Games, Mexico. (i) Inaug Issue.
1171 **341** 10p. multicoloured 7·50 4·00

(ii) Games Issue. Multicoloured designs as T **341** (20, 40, 50c. postage and 80c., 1, 2p. air) or as T **342** (others).
1172 20c. Dove of Peace on map (postage) 50 40
1173 40c. Stadium 65 40
1174 50c. Telecommunications Tower, Mexico City 65 40
1175 2p. Palace of Sport, Mexico City 5·00 90
1176 5p. Cultural symbols of Games 12·50 2·00
MS1177 Two sheets each 110×70 mm. Nos. 1172/4 (sold at 1p.50) and Nos. 1175/6 (sold at 9p.). Imperf 45·00 41·00

1178 80c. Dove and Olympic rings (air) 40 40
1179 1p. "The Discus-thrower" 50 40
1180 2p. Olympic medals 1·30 90
1181 5p. Type **342** 5·75 2·40
1182 10p. Line-pattern based on "Mexico 68" and rings 4·00 2·50
MS1183 Two sheets each 110×70 mm. Nos. 1178/80 (sold at 5p.) and Nos. 1181/2 (sold at 20p.). Imperf 38·00 35·00

1968. Air. Efimex 68 International Stamp Exhibition, Mexico City. Sheet 100×70 mm. Imperf.
MS1184 **339** 5p. ultramarine and black 4·50 3·75

343 Arms of Vera Cruz

1969. 450th Anniv of Vera Cruz.
1185 **343** 40c. multicoloured 65 40

344 *Father Palou* (M. Guerrero)

1969. Air. 220th Anniv of Arrival in Mexico of Father Serra (colonizer of California).
1186 **344** 80c. multicoloured 75 35
It was intended to depict Father Serra in this design, but the wrong detail of the painting by Guerrero, which showed both priests, was used.

345 Football and Spectators

1969. Air. World Cup Football Championship (1st issue). Multicoloured.
1187 80c. Type **345** 1·30 40
1188 2p. Foot kicking ball 1·30 40
See also Nos. 1209/10.

346 Underground Train

1969. Inauguration of Mexico City Underground Railway System.

1189 **346** 40c. multicoloured 65 35

347 Mahatma Gandhi

1969. Air. Birth Centenary of Mahatma Gandhi.

1190 **347** 80c. multicoloured 50 35

348 Footprint on Moon

1969. Air. First Man on the Moon.

1191 **348** 2p. black 75 40

349 Bee and Honeycomb

1969. 50th Anniv of I.L.O.

1192 **349** 40c. brown, blue & yell 50 35

350 "Flying" Dancers and Los Nichos Pyramid, El Tajin

1969. Tourism (1st series). Multicoloured.

1193	40c. Type **350** (postage)	75	35
1193a	40c. Puerto Vallarta, Jalisco (vert)	75	35
1194	80c. Acapulco (air)	1·50	40
1195	80c. Pyramid, Teotihuacan	1·50	40
1196	80c. "El Caracol" (Maya ruin), Yucatan	1·50	40

See also Nos. 1200/2 and 1274/7.

351 Red Crosses and Sun

1969. Air. 50th Anniv of League of Red Cross Societies.

1197 **351** 80c. multicoloured 50 35

352 *General Allende* (D. Rivera)

1969. Birth Bicentenary of General Ignacio Allende ("Father of Mexican Independence").

1198 **352** 40c. multicoloured 50 35

353 Dish Aerial

1969. Air. Inauguration of Satellite Communications Station, Tulancingo.

1199 **353** 80c. multicoloured 65 35

1969. Tourism (2nd series). As T **350** but dated "1970". Multicoloured.

1200	40c. Puebla Cathedral	75	35
1201	40c. Anthropological Museum, Mexico City	75	35
1202	40c. Belaunzaran Street, Guanajuato	75	35

354 Question Marks

1970. Ninth National and Fifth Agricultural Census. Multicoloured.

1204	20c. Type **354**	50	35
1205	40c. Horse's head and agricultural symbols	40	35

355 Diagram of Human Eye

1970. 21st International Ophthalmological Congress, Mexico City.

1206 **355** 40c. multicoloured 50 35

356 Cadet Ceremonial Helmet and Kepi

1970. 50th Anniv of Military College Reorganization.

1207 **356** 40c. multicoloured 40 35

357 Jose Pino Suarez

1970. Birth Centenary (1969) of Jose Maria Pino Suarez (statesman).

1208 **357** 40c. multicoloured 40 35

358 Football and Masks

1970. Air. World Cup Football Championship (2nd issue). Multicoloured.

1209	80c. Type **358**	1·30	40
1210	2p. Football and Mexican idols	1·30	50

359 "STORTMEX" Emblem

1970. Air. SPORTMEX Philatelic Exhibition, Mexico City. Miniature sheet 60×50 mm.

MS1211 **359** 2p. carmine and grey 8·25 5·75

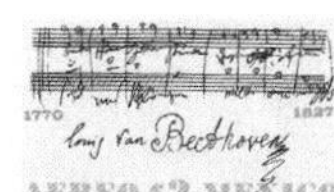

360 Composition by Beethoven

1970. Air. Birth Bicentenary of Beethoven.

1212 **360** 2p. multicoloured 1·00 40

361 Arms of Celaya

1970. 400th Anniv of Celaya.

1213 **361** 40c. multicoloured 65 35

362 "General Assembly"

1970. Air. 25th Anniv of U.N.O.

1214 **362** 80c. multicoloured 50 35

363 "Eclipse de Sol"

1970. Total Eclipse of the Sun.

1215 **363** 40c. black 50 35

364 *Galileo* (Susterman)

1971. Air. Conquest of Space. Early Astronomers. Multicoloured.

1216	2p. Type **364**	1·00	40
1217	2p. *Kepler* (unknown artist)	1·00	40
1218	2p. *Sir Isaac Newton* (Kneller)	1·00	40

365 *Sister Juana* (M. Cabrera)

1971. Air. Mexican Arts and Sciences (1st series). Paintings. Multicoloured.

1219	80c. Type **365**	75	35
1220	80c. *El Paricutin* (volcano) (G. Murillo)	75	35
1221	80c. *Men of Flames* (J. C. Orozco)	75	35
1222	80c. *Self-portrait* (J. M. Velasco)	75	35
1223	80c. *Mayan Warriors (Dresden Codex)*	75	35

See also Nos. 1243/7, 1284/8, 1323/7, 1351/5, 1390/4, 1417/21, 1540/4, 1650/4, 1688/92, 1750/4, 1834,1845, 1880 and 1904/5.

366 Stamps from Venezuela, Mexico and Colombia

1971. Air. Philately for Peace. Latin-American Stamp Exhibitions.

1224 **366** 80c. multicoloured 65 35

367 Lottery Balls

1971. Bicentenary of National Lottery.

1225 **367** 40c. black and green 50 40

368 *Francisco Clavijero* (P. Carlin)

1971. Air. Return of the Remains of Francisco Javier Clavijero (historian) to Mexico (1970).

1226 **368** 2p. brown and green 75 40

369 Vasco de Quiroga and "Utopia" (O'Gorman)

1971. 500th Birth Anniv of Vasco de Quiroga, Archbishop of Michoacan.

1227 **369** 40c. multicoloured 40 35

370 *Amado Nervo* (artist unknown)

1971. Birth Centenary of Amado Nervo (writer).

1228 **370** 80c. multicoloured 40 35

371 ITU Emblem

1971. Air. World Telecommunications Day.

1229 **371** 80c. multicoloured 40 35

372 *Mariano Matamoros* (D. Rivera)

1971. Air. Birth Bicentenary of Mariano Matamoros (patriot).

1230 **372** 2p. multicoloured 75 35

373 *General Guerrero* (O'Gorman)

1971. Air. 150th Anniv of Independence from Spain.

1231 **373** 2p. multicoloured 65 35

374 Loudspeaker and Sound Waves

1971. 50th Anniv of Radio Broadcasting in Mexico.

1232 **374** 40c. black, blue and green 50 35

375 Pres. Cardenas and Banners

1971. First Death Anniv of General Lazaro Cardenas.
1233 **375** 40c. black and lilac 50 35

376 Stamps of Venezuela, Mexico, Colombia and Peru

1971. Air. EXFILIMA 71 Stamp Exhibition Lima, Peru.
1234 **376** 80c. multicoloured 75 35

377 Abstract of Circles

1971. Air. 25th Anniv of UNESCO.
1235 **377** 80c. multicoloured 50 35

378 Piano Keyboard

1971. First Death Anniv of Agustin Lara (composer).
1236 **378** 40c. black, blue & yellow 50 35

379 "Mental Patients"

1971. Air. Fifth World Psychiatric Congress, Mexico City.
1237 **379** 2p. multicoloured 75 35

380 City Arms of Monterrey

1971. 375th Anniv of Monterrey.
1238 **380** 40c. multicoloured 50 35

381 Durer's Bookplate

1971. Air. 500th Anniv of Albrecht Durer (artist).
1239 **381** 2p. black and brown 1·10 35

382 Scientific Symbols

1972. Air. First Anniv of National Council of Science and Technology.
1240 **382** 2p. multicoloured 65 35

383 Emblem of Mexican Cardiological Institute

1972. World Health Month. Multicoloured.
1241 40c. Type **383** (postage) 65 35
1242 80c. Heart specialists (air) 65 35

1972. Air. Mexican Arts and Sciences (2nd series). Portraits. As T **365**.
1243 80c. brown and black 1·90 40
1244 80c. green and black 1·90 40
1245 80c. brown and black 1·90 40
1246 80c. blue and black 1·90 40
1247 80c. red and black 1·90 40

Portraits:—Nos. 1243, King Netzahualcoyotl of Texcoco (patron of the arts); No. 1244, J. R. de Alarcon (lawyer); No. 1245, J. J. Fernandez de Lizardi (writer); No. 1246, E. G. Martinez (poet); No. 1247, R. L. Velardo (author).

384 Rotary Emblems

1972. Air. 50th Anniv of Rotary Movement in Mexico.
1248 **384** 80c. multicoloured 50 35

385 Indian Laurel and Fruit

1972. Centenary of Chilpancingo as Capital of Guerrero State.
1249 **385** 40c. black, gold and green 50 35

386 Track of Car Tyre

1972. Air. 74th Assembly of International Tourist Alliance, Mexico City.
1250 **386** 80c. black and grey 50 35

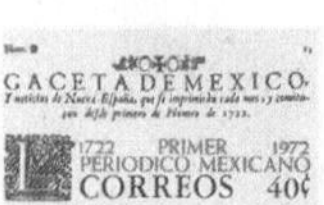

387 First issue of *Gaceta De Mexico*

1972. 250th Anniv of Publication of *Gaceta De Mexico* (First newspaper to be published in Latin America).
1251 **387** 40c. multicoloured 50 35

388 Emblem of Lions Organization

1972. Lions' Clubs Convention, Mexico City.
1252 **388** 40c. multicoloured 50 35

389 *Zaragoza* (cadet sail corvette)

1972. 75th Anniv of Naval Academy, Veracruz.
1253 **389** 40c. multicoloured 50 35

390 *Margarita Maza de Juarez* (artist unknown)

1972. Death Centenary of Pres. Benito Juarez.
1254 **390** 20c. mult (postage) 65 35
1255 - 40c. multicoloured 65 35
1256 - 80c. black and blue (air) 40 35
1257 - 1p.20 multicoloured 40 35
1258 - 2p. multicoloured 50 35

Designs:—40c. *Benito Juarez* (D. Rivera); 80c. Page of Civil Register with Juarez signature; 1p.20, *Benito Juarez* (P. Clave); 2p. *Benito Juarez* (J. C. Orozco).

391 Emperor Justinian I (mosaic)

1972. 50th Anniv of Mexican Bar Association.
1259 **391** 40c. multicoloured 1·10 35

392 Atomic Emblem

1972. Air. 16th General Conference of Int Atomic Energy Organization, Mexico City.
1260 **392** 2p. black, blue and grey 65 35

393 Caravel on "Stamp"

1972. Stamp Day of the Americas.
1261 **393** 80c. violet and brown 75 35

394 *Sobre las Olas* (sheet-music cover by O'Brandstetter)

1972. Air. 28th International Authors' and Composers' Society Congress, Mexico City.
1262 **394** 80c. brown 50 35

395 *Mother and Child* (G. Galvin)

1972. Air. 25th Anniv of UNICEF.
1263 **395** 80c. multicoloured 1·30 35

396 *Father Pedro de Gante* (Rodriguez y Arangorti)

1972. Air. 400th Death Anniv of Father Pedro de Gante (founder of first school in Mexico).
1264 **396** 2p. multicoloured 65 35

397 Olympic Emblems

1972. Olympic Games, Munich.
1265 **397** 40c. multicoloured (postage) 1·30 35
1266 - 80c. multicoloured (air) 50 35
1267 - 2p. black, green and blue 90 35

Designs:—Horiz: 80c. "Football". Vert: 2p. Similar to Type **397**.

398 Books on Shelves

1972. International Book Year.
1268 **398** 40c. multicoloured 40 35

399 Common Snook ("Pure Water")

1972. Anti-pollution Campaign.
1269 **399** 40c. black & bl (postage) 65 35
1270 - 80c. black and blue (air) 40 35

Design:—Vert: 80c. Pigeon on cornice ("Pure Air").

400 "Footprints on the Americas"

1972. Air. Tourist Year of the Americas.
1271 **400** 80c. multicoloured 65 35

401 Stamps of Mexico, Colombia, Venezuela, Peru and Brazil

1973. Air. EXFILBRA 72 Stamp Exhibition, Rio de Janeiro, Brazil.
1272 **401** 80c. multicoloured 65 35

402 *Metlac Viaduct* (J. M. Velasco)

1973. Centenary of Mexican Railways.
1273 **402** 40c. multicoloured 2·50 35

403 Ocotlan Abbey

1973. Tourism (3rd series). Multicoloured.

1274	40c. Type **403** (postage)	75	35
1275	40c. Indian hunting dance, Sonora (vert)	75	35
1276	80c. Girl in local costume (vert) (air)	75	35
1277	80c. Sport fishing, Lower California	75	35

404 "God of the Winds"

1973. Air. Centenary of W.M.O.

1278	**404**	80c. black, blue & mauve	1·00	40

405 Copernicus

1973. Air. 500th Birth Anniv of Copernicus (astronomer).

1279	**405**	80c. green	1·00	35

406 Cadet

1973. 150th Anniv of Military College.

1280	**406**	40c. multicoloured	75	35

407 *Francisco Madero* (D. Rivera)

1973. Birth Centenary of Pres. Francisco Madero.

1281	**407**	40c. multicoloured	40	35

408 Antonio Narro (founder)

1973. 50th Anniv of "Antonio Narro" Agricultural School, Saltillo.

1282	**408**	40c. grey	65	35

409 San Martin Statue

1973. Air. Argentina's Gift of San Martin Statue to Mexico City.

1283	**409**	80c. multicoloured	40	35

1973. Air. Mexican Arts and Sciences (3rd series). Astronomers. As T **365** but dated "1973".

1284	80c. green and red	40	35
1285	80c. multicoloured	40	35
1286	80c. multicoloured	40	35
1287	80c. multicoloured	40	35
1288	80c. multicoloured	40	35

Designs:—No. 1284, Aztec "Sun" stone; No. 1285, Carlos de Siguenza y Gongora; No. 1286, Francisco Diaz Covarrubias; No. 1287, Joaquin Gallo; No. 1288, Luis Enrique Erro.

410 Caryon Molecules

1973. 25th Anniv of Chemical Engineering School.

1289	**410**	40c. black, yellow and red	40	35

411 Fist with Pointing Finger

1974. Promotion of Exports.

1294	**411**	40c. black and green	40	35

412 EXMEX 73 Emblem

1974. EXMEX 73 National Stamp Exhibition, Cuernavaca.

1295	**412**	40c. black (postage)	40	35
1296	-	80c. multicoloured (air)	40	35

Design:—80c. Cortes' Palace, Cuernavaca.

413 Manuel Ponce

1974. 25th Death Anniv (1973) of Manuel M. Ponce (composer).

1297	**413**	40c. multicoloured	40	35

414 Gold Brooch, Mochica Culture

1974. Air. Exhibition of Peruvian Gold Treasures, Mexico City.

1298	**414**	80c. multicoloured	40	35

415 CEPAL Emblem and Flags

1974. Air. 25th Anniv of U.N. Economic Commission for Latin America (C.E.P.A.L.).

1299	**415**	80c. multicoloured	40	35

416 Baggage

1974. Air. 16th Confederation of Latin American Tourist Organizations (C.O.T.A.L.) Convention, Acapulco.

1300	**416**	80c. multicoloured	40	35

417 Silver Statuette

1974. First International Silver Fair, Mexico City.

1301	**417**	40c. multicoloured	40	35

418 *The Enamelled Saucepan* (Picasso)

1974. Air. First Death Anniv of Pablo Picasso (artist).

1302	**418**	80c. multicoloured	90	35

419 Dancing Dogs (Indian statuette)

1974. Sixth Season of Dog Shows.

1303	**419**	40c. multicoloured	40	35

420 Mariano Azuela

1974. Birth Cent (1973) of Mariano Azuela (writer).

1304	**420**	40c. multicoloured	40	35

421 Tepotzotlan Viaduct

1974. National Engineers' Day.

1305	**421**	40c. black and blue	90	35

422 R. Robles (surgeon)

1974. 25th Anniv of W.H.O.

1306	**422**	40c. brown and green	40	35

423 UPU Emblem

1974. Exfilmex 74 Inter-American Stamp Exhibition, Mexico City.

1307	**423**	40c. black and green on yellow (postage)	40	35
1308	**423**	80c. black and brown on yellow (air)	40	35

424 Demosthenes

1974. Second Spanish-American Reading and Writing Studies Congress, Mexico City.

1309	**424**	20c. green and brown	65	35

425 Lincoln Standard Biplane

1974. Air. 50th Anniv of "Mexicana" (Mexican Airlines). Multicoloured.

1310	80c. Type **425**	40	35
1311	2p. Boeing 727-200 jetliner	40	35

426 Map and Indian Head

1974. 150th Anniv of Union with Chiapas.

1312	**426**	20c. green and brown	40	35

427 Sonar Waves

1974. Air. First International Electrical and Electronic Communications Congress, Mexico City.

1313	**427**	2p. multicoloured	40	30

428 S. Lerdo de Tejada

1974. Centenary of Restoration of Senate.

1314	**428**	40c. black and blue	40	35

429 Manuscript of Constitution

1974. 150th Anniv of Federal Republic.

1315	**429**	40c. black and green	40	35

430 Ball in Play

1974. Air. Eighth World Volleyball Championships, Mexico City.

1316	**430**	2p. black, brown & orge	40	30

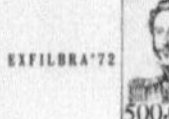

431 (image scaled to 47% of original size)

1974. Air. Exfilmex 74 Stamp Exhibition, Mexico City. Sheet 105×70 mm. Imperf.

MS1317	**431**	10p. multicoloured	5·25	2·50

432 F. C. Puerto

1974. Air. Birth Centenary of Felipe Carrillo Puerto (politician and journalist).

1318	**432**	80c. brown and green	40	40

433 Mask, Bat and Catcher's Glove

1974. Air. 50th Anniv of Mexican Baseball League.

1319	**433**	80c. brown and green	40	40

434 UPU Monument

1974. Centenary of U.P.U.

1320	**434**	40c. brown and blue (postage)	40	35
1321	-	80c. multicoloured (air)	40	35
1322	-	2p. brown and green	40	35

Designs:—80c. Man's face as letter-box, Colonial period; 2p. Heinrich von Stephan, founder of UPU.

1974. Air. Mexican Arts and Sciences (4th series). Music and Musicians. As T **365** but dated "1974". Multicoloured.

1323	80c. *Musicians – Mayan painting, Bonampak*	40	40
1324	80c. First Mexican-printed score, 1556	40	40
1325	80c. Angela Peralta (soprano and composer)	40	40
1326	80c. Miguel Lerdo de Tejada (composer)	40	40
1327	80c. *Silvestre Revueltas* (composer) (bronze by Carlos Bracho)	40	40

435 IWY Emblem

1975. Air. International Women's Year.

1328	**435**	1p.60 black and red	40	30

436 Economic Charter

1975. Air. U.N. Declaration of Nations' Economic Rights and Duties.

1329	**436**	1p.60 multicoloured	40	35

437 Jose Maria Mora

1975. 150th Anniv of Federal Republic.

1330	**437**	20c. multicoloured	40	35

438 Trans-Atlantic Balsa Raft *Acali*

1975. Air. Trans-Atlantic Voyage of "Acali", Canary Islands to Yucatan (1973).

1331	**438**	80c. multicoloured	40	35

439 Dr. M. Jimenez

1975. Air. Fifth World Gastroenterological Congress.

1332	**439**	2p. multicoloured	65	35

440 Aztec Merchants with Goods (*Codex Florentino*)

1975. Centenary (1974) of Mexican Chamber of Commerce.

1333	**440**	80c. multicoloured	40	35

441 Miguel de Cervantes Saavedra (Spanish author)

1975. Air. Third International Cervantes Festival, Guanajuato.

1334	**441**	1p.60 red and black	40	30

442 4-reales Coin of 1675

1975. Air. International Numismatics Convention "Mexico 74".

1335	**442**	1p.60 bronze and blue	65	35

443 Salvador Novo

1975. Air. First Death Anniv of Salvador Novo (poet and writer).

1336	**443**	1p.60 multicoloured	40	35

444 *Self-portrait* (Siqueiros)

1975. Air. First Death Anniv of David Alfaro Siqueiros (painter).

1337	**444**	1p.60 multicoloured	40	35

445 General Juan Aldama (detail from mural by Diego Rivera)

1975. Birth Bicentenary (1974) of General Aldama.

1338	**445**	80c. multicoloured	40	35

466 Perforation Gauge

1975. Air. International Women's Year and World Conference.

1339	**446**	1p.60 blue and pink	40	30

447 Eagle and Snake (*Codex Duran*)

1975. 650th Anniv of Tenochtitlan (now Mexico City). Multicoloured.

1340	80c. Type **447** (postage)	40	35
1341	1p.60 Arms of Mexico City (air)	40	35

448 Domingo F. Sarmiento (educator and statesman)

1975. Air. First International Congress of "Third World" Educators, Acapulco.

1342	**448**	1p.60 green and brown	40	35

449 Teachers' Monument, Mexico City

1975. Air. Mexican–Lebanese Friendship.

1343	**449**	4p.30 green and brown	65	35

450 Games' Emblem

1975. Air. Seventh Pan-American Games, Mexico City.

1344	**450**	1p.60 multicoloured	40	35

451 Julian Carrillo (composer)

1975. Birth Centenary of J. Carrillo.

1345	**451**	80c. brown and green	40	35

452 Academy Emblem

1975. Cent of Mexican Languages Academy.

1346	**452**	80c. yellow and brown	40	35

453 University Building

1975. 50th Anniv of Guadalajara University.

1347	**453**	80c. black, brown & pink	40	35

454 Dr. Atl

1975. Air. Atl (Gerardo Murillo, painter and writer). Birth Centenary.

1348	**454**	4p.30 multicoloured	65	35

455 Road Builders

1975. 50 Years of Road Construction and 15th World Road Congress, Mexico City.

1349	**455**	80c. black & grn (postage)	40	35
1350	-	1p.60 black & blue (air)	40	35

Design: —1p.60, Congress emblem.

1975. Air. Mexican Arts and Sciences (5th series). As T **365**, but dated "1975". Multicoloured.

1351	1p.60 Title page, F. Hernandez' *History of New Spain*	40	35
1352	1p.60 A. L. Herrera (naturalist)	40	35
1353	1p.60 Page from *Badiano Codex* (Aztec herbal)	40	35
1354	1p.60 A. Rosenblueth Stearns (neurophysiologist)	40	35
1355	1p.60 A. A. Duges (botanist and zoologist)	40	35

456 Car Engine Parts

1975. Mexican Exports. Multicoloured.

1356	-	5c. blue (postage)	1·30	30
1471	-	20c. black	90	35
1356b	-	40c. brown	1·30	40
1356c	**456**	50c. blue	1·40	35
1472	**456**	50c. black	1·10	30
1473	-	80c. red	1·60	40
1474	-	1p. violet and yellow	80	35
1358	-	1p. black and orange	1·30	50
1475	-	2p. blue and turquoise	1·30	35
1476	-	3p. brown	1·30	35
1359ba	-	4p. red and brown	95	30
1359ca	-	5p. brown	1·30	45

1359d	-	6p. red	80	35
1359e	-	6p. grey	65	35
1359f	-	7p. blue	65	35
1359g	-	8p. brown	1·30	40
1359h	-	9p. blue	1·30	40
1360a	-	10p. lt green & green	1·70	45
1360ac	-	10p. red	30	35
1360ad	-	15p. orange and brown	1·00	35
1480	-	20p. black	8·00	1·20
1360bc	-	20p. black and red	65	35
1360be	-	25p. chestnut	1·30	50
1360bh	-	35p. chestnut	1·30	40
1360bk	-	40p. yellow and chestnut	1·30	40
1360bl	-	40p. gold and green	1·30	40
1360bm	-	40p. black	40	40
1360c	-	50p. multicoloured	10·00	2·20
1360d	-	50p. yellow and blue	4·50	80
1360da	-	50p. red and green	90	30
1360db	-	60p. brown	95	35
1360dc	-	70p. brown	2·30	1·00
1360de	-	80p. gold and mauve	2·30	60
1360df	-	80p. blue	1·10	35
1360dg	-	90p. blue and green	1·10	40
1360e	-	100p. red, green and grey	3·25	1·10
1360ea	-	100p. brown	95	40
1360f	-	200p. yellow, green and grey	6·00	65
1360fb	-	200p. yellow and green	1·60	35
1360g	-	300p. blue, red and grey	5·75	2·50
1360gb	-	300p. blue and red	1·90	35
1360h	-	400p. bistre, chestnut and grey	3·75	1·10
1360ha	-	450p. brown and mauve	1·40	35
1360i	-	500p. green, orange and grey	5·00	95
1360ia	-	500p. grey and blue	1·20	35
1360j	-	600p. multicoloured	5·00	65
1360k	-	700p. black, red and green	10·00	65
1360ka	-	750p. black, red and green	3·75	65
1360l	-	800p. brown & dp brown	5·00	75
1360m	**456**	900p. black	5·00	65
1360n	-	950p. blue	3·75	65
1481a	-	1000p. black, red and grey	7·50	1·40
1360p	-	1000p. red and black	3·75	65
1360q	-	1100p. grey	3·00	1·00
1360r	-	1300p. red, green and grey	4·50	65
1360rb	-	1300p. red and green	3·25	65
1360rc	-	1400p. black	3·75	65
1360s	-	1500p. brown	3·75	75
1360t	-	1600p. orange	3·75	65
1360u	-	1700p. green and deep green	3·75	75
1360w	-	1900p. blue and green	6·25	7·50
1481b	-	2000p. black and grey	7·50	1·80
1360x	-	2000p. black	6·25	65
1360y	-	2100p. black, orange and grey	6·25	3·75
1360yb	-	2200p. red	3·75	1·00
1360z	-	2500p. blue and grey	6·25	1·40
1360zb	-	2800p. black	10·00	1·00
1481c	-	3000p. green, grey and orange	7·00	2·20
1360zc	**456**	3600p. black and grey	6·25	1·30
1360zd	-	3900p. grey and blue	14·00	1·60
1481d	-	4000p. yellow, grey and red	6·25	2·75
1360zf	-	4800p. red, green and grey	10·00	1·60
1481e	-	5000p. grey, green and orange	6·25	3·25
1360zh	-	6000p. green, yellow and grey	10·00	1·90
1360zi	-	7200p. multicoloured	12·50	2·30
1361	-	30c. bronze (air)	85	40
1482	-	50c. green and brown	85	35
1361a	-	80c. blue	80	35
1361b	-	1p.60 black and orange	80	35
1361c	-	1p.90 red and green	1·20	35
1361d	-	2p. gold and blue	1·30	40
1485	-	2p.50 red and green	85	35
1486	-	4p. yellow and brown	85	35
1361f	-	4p.30 mauve and green	95	40
1361g	-	5p. blue and yellow	2·20	45
1361h	-	5p.20 black and red	1·70	40
1361i	-	5p.60 green and yellow	1·20	45
1488	-	10p. green and light green	1·80	95
1361j	-	20p. black, red and green	2·20	65
1361k	-	50p. multicoloured	8·75	2·50

Designs:—Postage. 5c., 6, 1600p. Steel tubes; 20c., 40 (No. 1360bm), 1400, 2800p. Laboratory flasks; 40c., 100p. (No. 1360ea) Cup of coffee; 80c., 10 (No. 1360ac), 2200p. Steer marked with beef cuts; 1, 3000p. Electric cable; 2, 90, 1900p. Abalone shell; 3, 60p. Men's shoes; 4p. Ceramic tiles; 5, 1100p. Chemical formulae; 7, 8, 9, 80 (No. 1360df), 2500p. Textiles; 10 (No. 1360a), 1700p. Tequila; 15p. Honeycomb; 20 (No. 1480), 2000p. Wrought iron; 20 (No. 1360bc), 2100p. Bicycles; 25, 70, 1500p. Hammered copper vase; 35, 40 (No. 1360bl), 50 (No. 1360d), 80p. (No. 1360de) Books; 50 (No. 1360c), 600p. Jewellery; 50 (No. 1360da), 4800p. Tomato; 100 (No. 1360e), 1300p. Strawberries; 200, 6000p. Citrus fruit; 300p. Motor vehicles; 400, 450p. Printed circuit; 500 (No. 1360i), 5000p. Cotton boll; 500 (No. 1360ib), 3900p. Valves (petroleum) industry; 700, 750, 7200p. Film; 800p. Construction materials; 1000p. Farm machinery; 4000p. Bee and honeycomb. AIR. 30c. Hammered copper vase; 50c. Electronic components; 80c. Textiles; 1p.60, Bicycles; 1p.90, Valves (petroleum) industry; 2p. Books; 2p.50, Tomato; 4p. Bee and honeycomb; 4p.30, Strawberry; 5p. Motor vehicles; 5p.20, Farm machinery; 5p.60, Cotton boll; 10p. Citrus fruit; 20p. Film; 50p. Cotton.

457 Aguascalientes Cathedral

1975. 400th Anniv of Aguascalientes.

1362	**457**	50c. black and green	1·30	35

458 J. T. Bodet

1975. First Death Anniv of Jaime T. Bodet (author and late Director-General of UNESCO).

1363	**458**	80c. brown and blue	40	35

459 Fresco (J. C. Orozco)

1975. 150th Anniv of Mexican Supreme Court of Justice.

1364	**459**	80c. multicoloured	40	35

460 *Death of Cuautemoc* (Chavez Morado)

1975. 450th Death Anniv of Emperor Cuautemoc.

1365	**460**	80c. multicoloured	40	35

461 Allegory of Irrigation

1976. 50th Anniv of Nat Irrigation Commission.

1366	**461**	80c. deep blue and blue	40	35

462 City Gateway

1976. 400th Anniv of Leon de los Aldamas, Guanajuato.

1367	**462**	80c. yellow and purple	40	35

463 Early Telephone

1976. Air. Telephone Centenary.

1368	**463**	1p.60 black and grey	40	35

464 Gold Coin

1976. Air. Fourth International Numismatics Convention.

1369	**464**	1p.60 gold, brown & blk	40	35

465 Tlaloc (Aztec god of rain) and Calles Dam

1976. Air. 12th Int Great Dams Congress.

1370	**465**	1p.60 purple and green	40	35

466 Perforation Gauge

1976. Air. Interphil '76 International Stamp Exhibition, Philadelphia.

1371	**466**	1p.60 black, red and blue	40	35

467 Rainbow over Industrial Skyline

1976. Air. U.N. Conf on Human Settlements.

1372	**467**	1p.60 multicoloured	40	35

470 Liberty Bell

1976. Air. Bicentenary of American War of Independence.

1378	**470**	1p.60 blue and mauve	40	35

471 Forest Fire

1976. Fire Prevention Campaign.

1379	**471**	80c. multicoloured	40	35

472 Peace Texts

1976. Air. 30th International Asian and North American Science and Humanities Congress, Mexico City.

1380	**472**	1p.60 multicoloured	40	35

473 Children on TV Screen

1976. Air. First Latin-American Forum on Children's Television.

1381	**473**	1p.60 multicoloured	40	35

474 Scout's Hat

1976. 50th Anniv of Mexican Boy Scout Movement.

1382	**474**	80c. olive and brown	40	35

475 Exhibition Emblem

1976. Mexico Today and Tomorrow Exhibition.

1383	**475**	80c. black, red & turq	40	35

476 New Buildings

1976. Inaug of New Military College Buildings.

1384	**476**	50c. brown and ochre	40	35

477 Dr. R. Vertiz

1976. Centenary of Ophthalmological Hospital of Our Lady of the Light.

1385	**477**	80c. brown and black	40	35

478 Guadalupe Basilica

1976. Inauguration of Guadalupe Basilica.

1386	**478**	50c. bistre and black	40	35

479 "40" and Emblem

1976. 40th Anniv of National Polytechnic Institute.

1387	**479**	80c. black, red and green	40	35

480 Blast Furnace

1976. Inauguration of Lazaro Cardenas Steel Mill, Las Truchas.

1388	**480**	50c. multicoloured	40	35

481 Natural Elements

1976. Air. World Urbanization Day.

1389	**481**	1p.60 multicoloured	40	35

1976. Air. Mexican Arts and Sciences (6th series). As T **365** but dated "1976". Multicoloured.

1390	1p.60 black and red	50	35
1391	1p.60 multicoloured	50	35
1392	1p.60 black and yellow	50	35
1393	1p.60 multicoloured	50	35
1394	1p.60 brown and black	50	35

Designs:—No. 1390, *The Signal* (Angela Gurria); No. 1391, *The God of Today* (L. Ortiz Monasterio); No. 1392, *The God Coatlicue* (traditional Mexican sculpture); No. 1393, *Tiahuicole* (Manuel Vilar); No. 1394, *The Horseman* (Manuel Tolsa).

482 Score of *El Pesebre*

1977. Air. Birth Centenary of Pablo Casals (cellist).

1395	**482**	4p.30 blue and brown	65	35

483 "Man's Destruction"

1977. Air. Tenth Anniv of Treaty of Tlatelolco.

1396	**483**	1p.60 multicoloured	40	35

484 Saltillo Cathedral

1977. 400th Anniv of Founding of Saltillo.

1397	**484**	80c. brown and yellow	40	35

485 Light Switch, Pylon and Engineers

1977. 40 Years of Development in Mexico. Federal Electricity Commission.

1398	**485**	80c. multicoloured	40	35

486 Footballers

1977. Air. 50th Anniv of Mexican Football Federation.

1399	**486**	1p.60 multicoloured	40	35
1400	-	4p.30 yellow, blue & blk	65	35

Design:—4p.30, Football emblem.

487 Hands and Scales

1977. Air. 50th Anniv of Federal Council of Reconciliation and Arbitration.

1401	**487**	1p.60 orange, brn & blk	40	35

488 Flags of Spain and Mexico

1977. Resumption of Diplomatic Relations with Spain.

1402	**488**	50c. multicoloured (postage)	40	35
1403	**488**	80c. multicoloured	40	35
1404	-	1p.60 black and grey (air)	40	35
1405	-	1p.90 red, green & lt grn	40	35
1406	-	4p.30 grey, brown & grn	75	35

Designs:—1p.60, Arms of Mexico and Spain; 1p.90, Maps of Mexico and Spain; 4p.30, President Jose Lopez Portillo and King Juan Carlos.

489 Tlaloc (weather god)

1977. Air. Centenary of Central Meterological Observatory.

1407	**489**	1p.60 multicoloured	40	35

490 Ludwig van Beethoven

1977. Air. 150th Death Anniv of Beethoven.

1408	**490**	1p.60 green and brown	65	35
1409	**490**	4p.30 red and blue	1·00	35

491 A. Serdan

1977. Birth Centenary of Aquiles Serdan (revolutionary martyr).

1410	**491**	80c. black, turq & grn	40	35

492 Mexico City–Guernavaca Highway

1977. Air. 25th Anniv of First National Highway.

1411	**492**	1p.60 multicoloured	40	35

493 Poinsettia

1977. Christmas.

1412	**493**	50c. multicoloured	40	35

494 Arms of Campeche

1977. Air. Bicentenary of Naming of Campeche.

1413	**494**	1p.60 multicoloured	40	35

495 Tractor and Dam

1977. Air. U.N. Desertification Conference, Mexico City.

1414	**495**	1p.60 multicoloured	40	35

496 Congress Emblem

1977. Air. 20th World Education, Hygiene and Recreation Congress.

1415	**496**	1p.60 multicoloured	40	35

497 Freighter *Rio Yaqui*

1977. Air. 60th Anniv of National Merchant Marine.

1416	**497**	1p.60 multicoloured	40	35

498 Mayan Dancer

1977. Air. Mexican Arts and Sciences (7th series). Pre-colonial statuettes.

1417	**498**	1p.60 red, black and pink	50	35
1418	-	1p.60 blue, black and light blue	50	35
1419	-	1p.60 grey, black and yellow	50	35
1420	-	1p.60 green, black and turquoise	50	35
1421	-	1p.60 red, black and grey	50	40

Designs:—No. 1418, Aztec god of dance; No. 1419, Snake dance; No. 1420, Dancer, Monte Alban; No. 1421, Dancer, Totonaca.

499 Hospital Scene

1978. Air. 35th Anniv of Mexican Social Insurance Institute. Multicoloured.

1422	1p.60 Type **499**	40	35
1423	4p.30 Workers drawing benefits	75	35

500 Moorish Fountain

1978. Air. 450th Anniv of Chiapa de Corzo, Chiapas.

1424	**500**	1p.60 multicoloured	40	35

501 Telephones, 1878 and 1978

1978. Centenary of Mexican Telephone.

1425	**501**	80c. red and salmon	40	35

502 Oilwell

1978. 40th Anniv of Nationalization of Oil Resources.

1426	**502**	80c. red and salmon (postage)	40	35
1427	-	1p.60 blue and red (air)	65	35
1428	-	4p.30 black, light blue and blue	75	35

Designs:—1p.60, General I. Cardenas (President, 1938); 4p.30, Oil rig, Gulf of Mexico.

503 Arms of San Cristobal de las Casas

1978. Air. 450th Anniv of San Cristobal de las Casas, Chiapas.

1429	**503**	1p.60 purple, pink and black	40	35

504 Fairchild FC-71 Mail Plane

1978. Air. 50th Anniv of First Mexican Airmail Route.

1430	**504**	1p.60 multicoloured	40	35
1431	**504**	4p.30 multicoloured	65	35

505 Globe and Cogwheel

1978. Air. World Conference on Technical Co- operation between Underdeveloped Countries. Multicoloured.

1432	1p.60 Type **505**	40	35
1433	4p.30 Globe and cogwheel joined by flags	65	35

506 Blood Pressure Gauge and Map of Mexico

1978. Air. World Hypertension Month and World Health Day.

1434	**506**	1p.60 blue and red	40	35
1435	-	4p.30 salmon and blue	50	35

Design:—4p.30, Hand with stethoscope.

507 Kicking Ball

1978. Air. World Cup Football Championship, Argentina.

1436	**507**	1p.60 bl, lt orge & orge	65	35
1437	-	1p.90 blue, brn & orge	75	35
1438	-	4p.30 blue, grn & orge	90	35

Designs:—1p.90, Saving a goal; 4p.30, Footballer.

508 Francisco (Pancho) Villa

1978. Air. Birth Centenary of Francisco Villa (revolutionary leader).

1439	**508**	1p.60 multicoloured	65	35

509 Emilio Carranza Stamp of 1929

1978. Air. 50th Anniv of Mexico–Washington Flight by Emilio Carranza.

1440	**509**	1p.60 red and brown	40	35

510 Woman and Calendar Stone

1978. Air. Miss Universe Contest, Acapulco.

1441	**510**	1p.60 black, brn & red	50	35
1442	**510**	1p.90 black, brn & grn	50	35
1443	**510**	4p.30 black, brn & red	75	35

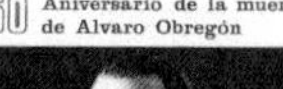

511 *Alvaro Obregon* (J. Romero)

1978. Air. 50th Death Anniv of Alvaro Obregon (statesman).

1444	**511**	1p.60 multicoloured	40	35

512 Institute Emblem

1978. 50th Anniv of Pan-American Institute for Geography and History.

1445	**512**	80c. blue and black (postage)	50	35
1446	-	1p.60 green and black (air)	65	35
1447	-	4p.30 brown and black	75	35

Designs:—1p.60, 4p.30, Designs as Type **512**, showing emblem.

513 Sun rising over Ciudad Obregon

1978. Air. 50th Anniv of Ciudad Obregon.

1448	**513**	1p.60 multicoloured	40	35

514 Mayan Statue, Rook and Pawn

1978. Air. World Youth Team Chess Championship, Mexico City.

1449	**514**	1p.60 multicoloured	50	35
1450	**514**	4p.30 multicoloured	90	35

515 Aristotle

1978. Air. 2300th Death Anniv of Aristotle.

1451	**515**	1p.60 grey, blue and yellow	40	35
1452	-	4p.30 grey, red and yellow	75	35

Design:—4p.30, Statue of Aristotle.

516 Mule Deer

1978. Air. World Youth Team Chess Championship, Mexico City.

1453		1p.60 Type **516**	1·90	35
1454		1p.60 Ocelot	1·90	35

See also Nos. 1548/9, 1591/2, 1638/9 and 1683/4.

517 Man's Head and Dove

1978. Air. International Anti-Apartheid Year.

1455	**517**	1p.60 grey, red and black	40	35
1456	-	4p.30 grey, lilac and black	65	35

Design:—4p.30, Woman's head and dove.

518 *Dahlia coccinea*. ("Dalia" on stamp)

1978. Mexican Flowers (1st series). Multicoloured.

1457		50c. Type **518**	75	35
1458		80c. *Plumeria rubra*	90	35

See also Nos. 1550/1, 1593/4, 1645/6, 1681/2, 1791/2 and 1913/14.

519 Emblem

1978. Air. 12th World Architects' Congress.

1459	**519**	1p.60 red, black and orange	40	35

520 Dr. Rafael Lucio

1978. Air. 11th International Leprosy Congress.

1460	**520**	1p.60 green	40	35

521 Franz Schubert and *Death and the Maiden*

1978. Air. 150th Death Anniv of Franz Schubert (composer).

1461	**521**	4p.30 brown, black and green	65	35

522 Decorations and Candles

1978. Christmas. Multicoloured.

1462		50c. Type **522** (postage)	40	35
1463		1p.60 Children and decoration (air)	40	35

523 Antonio Vivaldi

1978. Air. 300th Birth Anniv of Antonio Vivaldi (composer).

1464	**523**	4p.30 red, stone and brown	50	30

524 *Wright Flyer III*

1978. Air. 75th Anniv of First Powered Flight.

1465	**524**	1p.60 orange, yell & mve	50	30
1466	-	4p.30 yellow, red & flesh	75	35

Design: 4p.30, Side view of Wright Flyer I.

525 Albert Einstein and Equation

1979. Air. Birth Centenary of Albert Einstein (physicist).

1467	**525**	1p.60 multicoloured	90	35

526 Arms of Hermosillo

1979. Centenary of Hermosillo, Sonora.

1468	**526**	80c. multicoloured	40	35

527 Sir Rowland Hill

1979. Air. Death Centenary of Sir Rowland Hill.

1469	**527**	1p.60 multicoloured	40	35

528 "Children" (Adriana Blas Casas)

1979. Air. International Year of the Child.

1470	**528**	1p.60 multicoloured	40	35

529 Registered Letter from Mexico to Rome, 1880

1979. Air. Mepsipex 79, Third International Exhibition of Elmhurst Philatelic Society, Mexico City.

1499	**529**	1p.60 multicoloured	40	35

530 Football

1979. Universiada 79, Tenth World University Games, Mexico City (1st issue).

1500	**530**	50c. grey, black and blue (postage)	40	35
1501	-	80c. multicoloured	40	35
1502	-	1p. multicoloured	40	35
MS1503		105×75 mm. 5p. multicoloured. Imperf	4·00	3·75
1504		1p.60 multicoloured (air)	40	40
1505		4p.30 multicoloured	55	40
MS1506		105×75 mm. 10p. multicoloured. Imperf	3·25	3·25

Designs—Vert: 80c. Aztec ball player; 1p. Wall painting of athletes; 1p.60, Games emblem, 4p.30, Flame and dove. Horiz: 5p. Runners; 10p. Gymnasts.

See also Nos. 1514/**MS**1520.

531 Josefa Ortiz de Dominguez

1979. 150th Death Anniv of Josefa Ortiz de Dominguez (Mayor of Queretaro).

1507	**531**	80c. pink, black and bright pink	40	35

532 "Allegory of National Culture" (Alfaro Siqueiros)

1979. 50th Anniv of National University's Autonomy. Multicoloured.

1508		80c. Type **532** (postage)	50	35
1509		3p. "The Conquest of Energy" (Chavez Morado)	65	35
1510		1p.60 "The Return of Quetzalcoatl" (Chavez Morado) (air)	50	35
1511		4p.30 "Students reaching for Culture" (Alfaro Siqueiros)	75	35

533 Messenger and U.P.U. Emblem

1979. Air. Centenary of Mexico's Admission to U.P.U.

1512	**533**	1p.60 yellow, black and brown	40	35

534 Emiliano Zapata (after Diego Rivera)

1979. Birth Centenary of Emiliano Zapata (revolutionary).

1513	**534**	80c. multicoloured	40	35

535 Football

1979. Universiada '79, Tenth World University Games, Mexico City (2nd issue). Multicoloured.

1514	50c. Type **535** (postage)	40	35
1515	80c. Volleyball	40	35
1516	1p. Basketball	40	35
MS1517	105×75 mm. 5p. Fencing. Imperf	3·25	3·00
1518	1p.60 Tennis (air)	40	35
1519	5p.50 Swimming	65	35
MS1520	105×75 mm. 10p. Sports emblems (light green, black and green). Imperf	2·20	2·20

536 Tepoztlan, Morelos

1979. Tourism (1st series). Multicoloured.

1526	80c. Type **536** (postage)	40	35
1527	80c. Mexacaltitan, Nayarit	40	35
1528	1p.60 Agua Azul waterfall, Chipas (air)	40	35
1529	1p.60 King Coliman statue, Colima	40	35

See also Nos. 1631/4 and 1675/8.

537 Congress Emblem

1979. Air. 11th Congress and Assembly of International Industrial Design Council.

1530	**537**	1p.60 black, mauve and turquoise	40	35

538 Edison Lamp

1979. Air. Centenary of Electric Light.

1531	**538**	1p.60 multicoloured	40	35

539 Martin de Olivares (postmaster)

1979. 400th Anniv of Royal Proclamation of Mail Services in the New World. Multicoloured.

1532	80c. Type **539** (postage)	40	35
1533	1p.60 Martin Enriquez de Almanza (viceroy of New Spain) (air)	50	35
1534	5p.50 King Philip II of Spain	65	35
MS1535	122×92 mm. 10p. Spanish galleon (horiz). Imperf	9·00	2·10

540 Assembly Emblem

1979. Air. 8th General Assembly of Latin American Universities Union.

1536	**540**	1p.60 multicoloured	40	35

541 Shepherd

1979. Christmas. Multicoloured.

1537	50c. Type **541** (postage)	40	35
1538	1p.60 Girl and Christmas tree (air)	40	35

542 Moon Symbol from Mexican Codex

1979. Air. Tenth Anniv of First Man on Moon.

1539	**542**	2p.50 multicoloured	40	35

543 Church, Yanhuitlan

1980. Air. Mexican Arts and Sciences (8th series). Multicoloured.

1540	1p.60 Type **543**	50	35
1541	1p.60 Monastery, Yuriria	50	35
1542	1p.60 Church, Tlayacapan	50	35
1543	1p.60 Church, Actopan	50	35
1544	1p.60 Church, Acolman	50	35

544 Steps and Snake's Head

1980. National Pre-Hispanic Monuments (1st series). Multicoloured.

1545	80c. Type **544** (postage)	40	30
1546	1p.60 Doble Tlaloc (rain god) (air)	50	30
1547	5p.50 Coyolzauhqui (moon goddess)	65	35

See also Nos. 1565/7 and 1605/7.

1980. Mexican Fauna (2nd series). As T **516**. Multicoloured.

1548	80c. Common turkey (postage)	65	35
1549	1p.60 Greater flamingo (air)	1·20	40

1980. Mexican Flowers (2nd series). As T **518**. Multicoloured.

1550	80c. "Tajetes erecta" (postage)	65	35
1551	1p.60 "Vanilla planifolia" (air)	95	35

545 Jules Verne

1980. Air. 75th Death Anniv of Jules Verne (author).

1552	**545**	5p.50 brown and black	75	30

546 Skeleton smoking Cigar (after Guadalupe Posada)

1980. Air. World Health Day. Anti-smoking Campaign.

1553	**546**	1p.60 purple, blue & red	40	35

547 China Poblana, Puebla

1980. National Costumes (1st series). Multicoloured.

1554	50c. Type **547** (postage)	40	35
1555	80c. Jarocha, Veracruz	40	35
1556	1p.60 Chiapaneca, Chiapas (air)	50	35

See also Nos. 1588/90.

548 Family

1980. 10th Population and Housing Census.

1557	**548**	3p. black and silver	50	35

549 Cuauhtemoc (last Aztec Emperor)

1980. Pre-Hispanic Personalities (1st series). Multicoloured.

1558	80c. Type **549**	40	35
1559	1p.60 Nezahualcoyotl (governor of Tetzcoco)	40	35
1560	5p.50 Eight Deer Tiger's Claw (11th Mixtec king)	90	35

See also Nos. 1642/4 and 1846/8.

550 Xipe (Aztec god of medicine)

1980. 22nd World Biennial Congress of International College of Surgeons, Mexico City.

1561	**550**	1p.60 multicoloured	40	35

551 Bronze Medal

1980. Olympic Games, Moscow.

1562	**551**	1p.60 bronze, black and turquoise	40	35
1563	-	3p. silver, black and blue	65	35
1564	-	5p.50 gold, black and red	90	35

Designs:—3p. Silver medal; 5p.50, Gold medal.

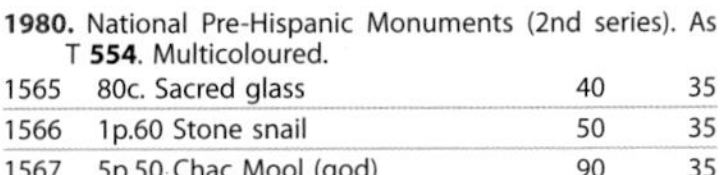

1980. National Pre-Hispanic Monuments (2nd series). As T **554**. Multicoloured.

1565	80c. Sacred glass	40	35
1566	1p.60 Stone snail	50	35
1567	5p.50 Chac Mool (god)	90	35

552 Sacromonte Sanctuary, Amecameca

1980. Colonial Architecture (1st series).

1568	**552**	2p.50 grey and black	50	35
1569	-	2p.50 grey and black	50	35
1570	-	3p. grey and black	65	35
1571	-	3p. grey and black	65	35

Designs:—Horiz: No. 1552, St. Catherine's Convent, Patzcuaro; No. 1554, Hermitage, Cuernavaca. Vert: No. 1553, Basilica, Culiapan.

See also Nos. 1617/20, 1660/3, 1695/8 and 1784/7.

553 Quetzalcoatl (god)

1980. World Tourism Conference, Manila, Philippines.

1572	**553**	2p.50 multicoloured	40	35

554 Arms of Sinaloa

1980. 150th Anniv of Sinaloa State.

1573	**554**	1p.60 multicoloured	40	35

555 Straw Angel

1980. Christmas. Multicoloured.

1574	50c. Type **555**	50	35
1575	1p.60 Poinsettia in a jug	50	35

556 Congress Emblem

1980. Fourth International Civil Justice Congress.

1576	**556**	1p.60 multicoloured	40	35

557 Glass Demijohn and Animals

1980. Mexican Crafts (1st series). Multicoloured.

1577	50c. Type **557**	40	35
1578	1p. Poncho	40	35
1579	3p. Wooden mask	75	35

See also Nos. 1624/6.

558 *Simon Bolivar* (after Paulin Guerin)

1980. 150th Death Anniv of Simon Bolivar.
1580 **558** 4p. multicoloured 90 35

559 Vicente Guerrero

1981. 150th Death Anniv of Vicente Guerrero (liberator).
1581 **559** 80c. multicoloured 45 35

560 Valentin Gomez Farias

1981. Birth Bicentenary of Valentin Gomez Farias.
1582 **560** 80c. black and green 45 35

561 Table Tennis Balls in Flight

1981. First Latin-American Table Tennis Cup.
1583 **561** 4p. multicoloured 1·10 35

562 Jesus Gonzalez Ortega

1981. Death Centenary of Jesus Gonzalez Ortega.
1584 **562** 80c. light brown & brown 45 35

563 Gabino Barreda

1981. Death Centenary of Gabino Barreda (politician).
1585 **563** 80c. pink, black and green 45 35

564 Benito Juarez

1981. 175th Birth Anniv of Benito Juarez (patriot).
1586 **564** 1p.60 green, brn & lt brn 45 35

565 Foundation Monument

1981. 450th Anniv of Puebla City.
1587 **565** 80c. multicoloured 45 35

1981. National Costumes (2nd series). Vert designs as T **547**. Multicoloured.
1588 50c. Purepecha, Michoacan 45 35
1589 80c. Charra, Jalisco 45 35
1590 1p.60 Mestiza, Yucatan 45 35

1981. Mexican Fauna (3rd series). Vert designs as T **516**. Multicoloured.
1591 80c. Northern mockingbird 1·20 35
1592 1p.60 Mexican trogon 2·30 60

1981. Mexican Flowers (3rd series). Vert designs as T **518**. Multicoloured.
1593 80c. Avocado 45 35
1594 1p.60 Cacao 45 35

566 *Martyrs of Cananea* (David A. Siqueiros)

1981. 75th Anniv of Martyrs of Cananea.
1595 **566** 1p.60 multicoloured 45 35

567 Toy Drummer with One Arm

1981. International Year of Disabled People.
1596 **567** 4p. multicoloured 90 50

568 Arms of Queretaro

1981. 450th Anniv of Queretaro City.
1597 **568** 80c. multicoloured 45 35

569 Mexican Stamp of 1856 and Postal Service Emblem

1981. 125th Anniv of First Mexican Stamp.
1598 **569** 4p. multicoloured 75 35

570 Sir Alexander Fleming

1981. Birth Centenary of Sir Alexander Fleming (discoverer of penicillin).
1599 **570** 5p. blue and orange 1·20 35

571 Union Congress Building and Emblem

1981. Opening of New Union Congress Building.
1600 **571** 1p.60 green and red 45 35

572 St. Francisco Xavier Claver

1981. 250th Birth Anniv of St. Francis Xavier Claver.
1601 **572** 80c. multicoloured 45 35

573 Desislava (detail of Bulgarian Fresco)

1981. 1300th Anniv of Bulgarian State. Mult.
1602 1p.60 Type **573** 45 35
1603 4p. Horse-headed cup from Thrace 90 35
1604 7p. Madara Horseman (relief) 1·20 35

1981. Pre-Hispanic Monuments. As T **544**. Multicoloured.
1605 80c. Seated God 60 35
1606 1p.60 Alabaster deer's head 90 35
1607 4p. Jade fish 1·20 35

574 Pablo Picasso

1981. Birth Centenary of Pablo Picasso (artist).
1608 **574** 5p. deep green and green 1·40 50

575 Shepherd

1981. Christmas. Multicoloured.
1609 50c. Type **575** 45 35
1610 1p.60 Praying girl 45 35

576 Wheatsheaf

1981. World Food Day.
1611 **576** 4p. multicoloured 60 35

577 Thomas Edison, Lightbulb and Gramophone

1981. 50th Death Anniv of Thomas Edison (inventor).
1612 **577** 4p. stone, brown & green 60 35

578 Co-operation Emblem and Wheat

1981. International Meeting on Co-operation and Development, Cancun.
1613 **578** 4p. blue, grey and black 60 35

579 Globe and Diesel Locomotive

1981. 15th Pan-American Railway Congress.
1614 **579** 1p.60 multicoloured 1·50 35

580 Film Frame

1981. 50th Anniv of Mexican Sound Movies.
1615 **580** 4p. grey, black and green 60 35

581 Postcode and Bird delivering Letter

1981. Inauguration of Postcodes.
1616 **581** 80c. multicoloured 60 35

1981. Colonial Architecture (2nd series). As T **552**. Multicoloured.
1617 4p. Mascarones House 60 35
1618 4p. La Merced Convent 60 35
1619 5p. Chapel of the Third Order, Texcoco 75 35
1620 5p. Father Tembleque Aqueduct, Otumba 75 35

582 *Martyrs of Rio Blanco* (Orozco)

1982. 75th Anniv of Martyrs of Rio Blanco.
1621 **582** 80c. multicoloured 45 35

583 Ignacio Lopez Rayon

1982. 150th Death Anniv of Ignacio Lopez Rayon.
1622 **583** 1p.60 green, red & black 45 35

584 Postal Headquarters

1982. 75th Anniv of Postal Headquarters.
1623 **584** 4p. pink and green 45 35

1982. Mexican Crafts (2nd series). As T **557**. Multicoloured.
1624 50c. *Eye of god* (Huichol art) 45 35
1625 1p. Ceramic snail 60 35
1626 3p. Tiger mask 60 35

585 Postcoded Letter and Bird

1982. Postcode Publicity.
1627 **585** 80c. multicoloured 45 35

586 Dr. Robert Koch and Cross of Lorraine

1982. Centenary of Discovery of Tubercle Bacillus.
1628 **586** 4p. multicoloured 1·10 35

587 Military Academy

1982. 50th Anniv of Military Academy.
1629 **587** 80c. yellow, black & gold 45 35

588 Arms of Oaxaca

1982. 450th Anniv of Oaxaca City.
1630 **588** 1p.60 multicoloured 45 35

1982. Tourism (2nd series). As T **563**. Multicoloured.
1631 80c. Basaseachic Falls, Chihuahua 60 35
1632 80c. Natural rock formation, Pueblo Nuevo, Durango 60 35
1633 1p.60 Mayan City of Edzna, Campeche 75 35
1634 1p.60 La Venta (Olmeca sculpture, Tabasco) 75 35

589 Footballers

1982. World Cup Football Championship, Spain. Multicoloured.
1635 1p.60 Type **589** 1·10 35
1636 4p. Dribbling 1·50 35
1637 7p. Tackling 1·80 35

590 Hawksbill Turtles

1982. Mexican Fauna. Multicoloured.
1638 1p.60 Type **590** 1·90 35
1639 4p. Grey Whales 3·75 35

591 Vicente Guerrero

1982. Birth Bicentenary of Vicente Guerrero (independence fighter).
1640 **591** 80c. multicoloured 45 35

592 Symbols of Peace and Communication

1982. Second U.N. Conference on the Exploration and Peaceful Uses of Outer Space, Vienna.
1641 **592** 4p. multicoloured 45 35

1982. Pre-Hispanic Personalities (2nd series). As T **549**. Multicoloured.
1642 80c. Tariacuri 45 35
1643 1p.60 Acamapichtli 60 35
1644 4p. Ten Deer Tiger's breastplate 75 35

593 Pawpaw (*Carica papaya*)

1982. Mexican Flora. Multicoloured.
1645 80c. Type **593** 1·20 35
1646 1p.60 Maize ("Zea mays") 1·50 35

594 Astrologer

1982. Native Mexican Codices. Florentine Codex. Multicoloured.
1647 80c. Type **594** 45 35
1648 1p.60 Arriving at School 60 35
1649 4p. Musicians 75 35

595 Manuel Gamio (anthropologist)

1982. Mexican Arts and Scientists. Multicoloured.
1650 1p.60 Type **595** 60 35
1651 1p.60 Isaac Ochoterena (biologist) 60 35
1652 1p.60 Angel Maria Garibay (philologist) 60 35
1653 1p.60 Manuel Sandoval Vallarta (nuclear physicist) 60 35
1654 1p.60 Guillermo Gonzalez Camarena (electronics engineer) 60 35

596 State Archives Building

1982. Inaug of State Archives Building.
1655 **596** 1p.60 black and green 45 35

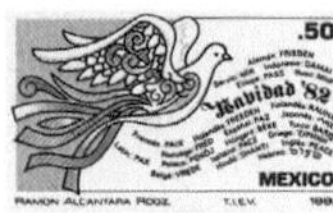

597 Dove and Peace Text

1982. Christmas. Multicoloured.
1656 50c. Type **597** 45 35
1657 1p.60 Dove and Peace text (different) 60 35

598 Hands holding Food

1982. Mexican Food System.
1658 **598** 1p.60 multicoloured 45 35

599 "Revolutionary Mexico" Stamp, 1956

1982. Inauguration of Revolution Museum, Chihuahua.
1659 **599** 1p.60 grey and green 45 35

1982. Colonial Architecture (3rd series). As T **552**. Multicoloured.
1660 1p.60 College of Sts. Peter and Paul, Mexico City 60 35
1661 8p. Convent of Jesus Maria, Mexico City 90 35
1662 10p. Open Chapel, Tlalmanalco 1·10 35
1663 14p. Convent, Actopan 1·20 35

600 Alfonso Garcia Robles and Laurel

1982. Alfonso Garcia Robles (Nobel Peace Prize Winner) Commemoration.
1664 **600** 1p.60 grey, black & gold 60 35
1665 - 14p. pink, black and gold 1·40 35

Design:—14p. Robles and medal.

601 Jose Vasconcelos

1982. Birth Centenary of Jose Vasconcelos (philosopher).
1666 **601** 1p.60 black and blue 45 35

602 WCY Emblem and Methods of Communication

1983. World Communications Year.
1667 **602** 16p. multicoloured 60 35

603 Sonora State Civil War Stamp, 1913

1983. Herfilex 83 Mexican Revolution Stamp Exhibition.
1668 **603** 6p. brown, black & green 45 35

604 *Nauticas Mexico* (container ship), World Map and IMO Emblem

1983. 25th Anniv of International Maritime Organization.
1669 **604** 16p. multicoloured 75 35

605 Doctor treating Patient

1983. Constitutional Right to Health Protection.
1670 **605** 6p. green and red 45 35

606 Valentin Gomez Farias (founder) and Arms of Society

1983. 150th Anniv of Mexican Geographical and Statistical Society.
1671 **606** 6p. multicoloured 45 35

607 Football

1983. Second World Youth Football Championship, Mexico.
1672 **607** 6p. black and green 60 35
1673 **607** 13p. black and red 90 35
1674 **607** 14p. black and blue 90 35

1983. Tourism. As T **536**. Multicoloured.
1675 6p. Federal Palace, Queretaro 60 35
1676 6p. Water tank, San Luis Potosi 60 25
1677 13p. Cable car, Zacatecas 90 25
1678 14p. Carved head of Kohunlich, Quintana Roo 90 25

608 Bolivar on Horseback

1983. Birth Bicentenary of Simon Bolivar.
1679 **608** 21p. multicoloured 90 35

609 Angela Peralta

1983. Death Centenary of Angela Peralta (opera singer).
1680 **609** 9p. light brown & brown 60 35

610 Agave

1983. Mexican Flora and Fauna (5th series). Multicoloured.
1681 9p. Type **610** 1·40 35
1682 9p. Sapodilla 1·40 35
1683 9p. Swallowtail 3·50 35
1684 9p. Boa constrictor 3·50 35

611 Two Candles

1983. Christmas. Multicoloured.
1685 9p. Type **611** 45 35
1686 20p. Three candles 75 35

612 SCT Emblem

1983. Integral Communications and Transport System.
1687 **612** 13p. blue and black 60 35

613 Carlos Chavez (musician)

1983. Mexican Arts and Sciences (10th series). Contemporary Artists. Multicoloured.
1688 **613** 9p. brown, light brown and deep brown 75 35
1689 - 9p. brown, light brown and deep brown 75 35
1690 - 9p. deep brown, light brown and brown 75 35
1691 - 9p. light brown, deep brown and brown 75 35
1692 - 9p. deep brown, stone and brown 75 35

Designs:—No. 1689, Francisco Goitia (painter); No. 1690, S. Diaz Miron (poet); No. 1691, Carlos Bracho (sculptor); No. 1692, Fanny Anitua (singer).

614 Orozco (self-portrait)

1983. Birth Centenary of Jose Clemente Orozco (artist).
1693 **614** 9p. multicoloured 60 35

615 Human Rights Emblem

1983. 35th Anniv of Human Rights Declaration.
1694 **615** 20p. deep blue, yellow and blue 60 35

1983. Colonial Architecture (4th series). As T **552**. Each grey and black.
1695 9p. Convent, Malinalco 75 35
1696 20p. Cathedral, Cuernavaca 1·10 35
1697 21p. Convent, Tepeji del Rio 1·10 35
1698 24p. Convent, Atlatlahucan 1·10 35

616 Antonio Caso and Books

1983. Birth Centenary of Antonio Caso (philospher).
1699 **616** 9p. blue, lilac and red 60 35

617 Joaquin Velazquez

1983. Bicentenary of Royal Legislation on Mining.
1700 **617** 9p. multicoloured 60 35

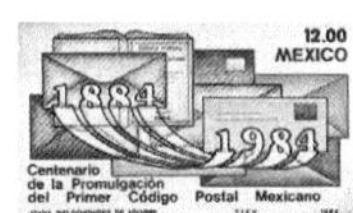

618 Book and Envelopes

1984. Centenary of First Postal Laws.
1701 **618** 12p. multicoloured 75 35

619 Children dancing around Drops of Anti-Polio Serum

1984. World Anti-polio Campaign.
1702 **619** 12p. multicoloured 75 35

620 Muscovy Duck

1984. Mexican Fauna (6th series). Multicoloured.
1703 12p. Type **620** 1·10 35
1704 20p. Red-billed whistling duck 1·20 35

621 Xoloitzcuintle Dog

1984. World Dog Show.
1705 **621** 12p. multicoloured 1·50 35

622 Bank Headquarters

1984. Centenary of National Bank.
1706 **622** 12p. multicoloured 75 35

623 Hands holding Trees

1984. Protection of Forest Resources.
1707 **623** 20p. multicoloured 90 35

624 Putting the Shot

1984. Olympic Games, Los Angeles. Multicoloured.
1708 14p. Type **624** 75 35
1709 20p. Show jumping 1·10 35
1710 23p. Gymnastics (floor exercise) 1·10 35
1711 24p. Diving 1·10 35
1712 25p. Boxing 1·10 35
1713 26p. Fencing 1·10 35
MS1714 56×61 mm. 40p. Gymnastics (rings exercise). Imperf 4·50 2·00

625 Mexican and Russian Flags

1984. 60th Anniv of Diplomatic Relations with U.S.S.R.
1715 **625** 23p. multicoloured 90 35

626 Hand holding UN emblem

1984. International Population Conference.
1716 **626** 20p. multicoloured 90 35

627 Gen. Mugica

1984. Birth Centenary of General Francisco Mugica (politician).
1717 **627** 14p. brown and black 45 35

628 Emblem and Dates

1984. 50th Anniv of Economic Culture Fund.
1718 **628** 14p. brown, black and red 60 35

629 Airline Emblem

1984. 50th Anniv of Aeromexico (state airline).
1719 - 14p. multicoloured 75 35
1720 **629** 20p. black and red 75 35

Design:—36×44 mm: 14p. *Red Cactus* (sculpture, Sebastian).

630 Palace of Fine Arts

1984. 50th Anniv of Palace of Fine Arts.
1721 **630** 14p. blue, black and brown 45 35

631 Metropolitan Cathedral (detail of facade)

1984. 275th Anniv of Chihuahua City.
1722 **631** 14p. brown and black 45 35

632 Coatzacoalcos Bridge

1984. Inaug of Coatzacoalcos Bridge.
1723 **632** 14p. multicoloured 45 35

633 Dove and Hand holding Flame

1984. World Disarmament Week.
1724 **633** 20p. multicoloured 45 35

634 Christmas Tree and Toy Train

1984. Christmas. Multicoloured.
1725 14p. Type **634** 45 35
1726 20p. Breaking the pinata (balloon filled with gifts) (vert) 45 35

635 Ignacio Manuel Altamirano

1984. 150th Birth Anniv of Ignacio Manuel Altamirano (politician and journalist).
1727 **635** 14p. red and black 45 35

636 Maps, Graph and Text

1984. 160th Anniv of State Audit Office.
1728 **636** 14p. multicoloured 45 35

637 Half a Football and Mexican Colours

1984. Mexico, Site of 1986 World Cup Football Championship. Multicoloured.
1729 20p. Type **637** 3·00 35
1730 24p. Football and Mexican colours 3·25 35

638 Romulo Gallegos

1984. Birth Centenary of Romulo Gallegos.
1731 **638** 20p. black and blue 45 35

639 State Arms and Open Register

1984. 125th Anniv of Mexican Civil Register.
1732 **639** 24p. blue 60 35

640 Mexican Flag

1985. 50th Anniv of National Flag.
1733 **640** 22p. multicoloured 90 35

641 Johann Sebastian Bach

1985. 300th Birth Anniv of Johann Sebastian Bach (composer).
1734 **641** 35p. red and black 60 35

642 IYY Emblem

1985. International Youth Year.
1735 **642** 35p. purple, gold and black 60 35

643 Children and Fruit within Book

1985. Child Survival Campaign.
1736 **643** 36p. multicoloured 60 35

644 Commemorative Medallion

1985. 450th Anniv of State Mint.
1737 **644** 35p. gold, mauve & blue 60 35

645 Victor Hugo, Text and Gateway

1985. Death Centenary of Victor Hugo (novelist).
1738 **645** 35p. grey 60 35

646 Hidalgo 8r. Stamp, 1856

1985. Mexifil 85 Stamp Exhibition.
1739 **646** 22p. grey, black and purple 45 35
1740 - 35p. grey, black and blue 75 35
1741 - 36p. multicoloured 75 35
MS1742 101×80 mm. 90p. multicoloured. Imperf 4·75 2·20
Designs:—35p. Carranza 10c. stamp, 1916; 36p. Juarez 50p. stamp, 1975; 90p. 1881 cover.

647 Rockets, Satellite, Nurse and Computer Operator

1985. Launching of First Morelos Satellite. Mult.
1743 22p. Type **647** 45 35
1744 36p. Camera, dish aerial, satellite and computers 45 35
1745 90p. Camera, dish aerial, satellite, television and couple telephoning 1·10 70
MS1746 160×95 mm. 100p. As Nos. 1743/5. Imperf 5·50 3·00
Nos. 1743/5 were printed together, *se-tenant*, forming a composite design.

648 Conifer

1985. Ninth World Forestry Congress, Mexico.
1747 **648** 22p. brown, black and green 90 35
1748 - 35p. brown, black and green 90 35
1749 - 36p. brown, black and green 90 35
Designs:—35p. Silk-cotton trees; 36p. Mahogany tree.

649 Martin Luis Guzman

1985. Mexican Arts and Sciences (11th series). Contemporary Writers.
1750 **649** 22p. grey and blue 90 35
1751 - 22p. grey and blue 90 35
1752 - 22p. grey and blue 90 35
1753 - 22p. grey and blue 90 35
1754 - 22p. grey and blue 90 35
Designs:—No. 1751, Augustin Yanez; 1752, Alfonso Reyes; 1753, Jose Ruben Romero; 1754, Artemio de Valle-Arizpe.

650 Miguel Hidalgo

1985. 175th Anniv of Independence Movement. Each green, black and red.
1755 22p. Type **650** 45 35
1756 35p. Jose Ma. Morelos 45 35
1757 35p. Ignacio Allende 45 35
1758 36p. Leona Vigario 45 35
1759 110p. Vicente Guerrero 1·20 95
MS1760 157×127 mm. 90p. emblem (48×41 mm). Imperf 4·75 3·00

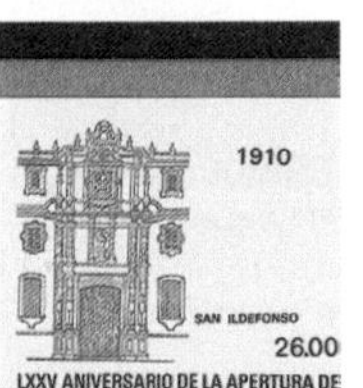

651 San Ildefonso

1985. 75th Anniv of National University. Mult.
1761 26p. Type **651** 90 35
1762 26p. Emblem 90 35
1763 40p. Modern building 1·10 35
1764 45p. 1910 crest and Justo Sierra (founder) 1·20 35
1765 90p. University crest 2·10 70

652 Rural and Industrial Landscapes

1985. 25th Anniv of Inter-American Development Bank.
1766 **652** 26p. multicoloured 45 35

653 Guns and Doves

1985. United Nations Disarmament Week.
1767 **653** 36p. multicoloured 45 35

654 Hands and Dove

1985. 40th Anniv of U.N.O.
1768 **654** 26p. multicoloured 45 35

655 Girls Skipping (Mishinoya K. Maki)

1985. Christmas. Children's Paintings. Mult.
1769 26p. Disabled and able-bodied children playing (Margarita Salazar) 45 35
1770 35p. Type **655** 45 35

656 Soldadera

1985. 75th Anniv of 1910 Revolution. Each red, black and green.
1771 26p. Type **656** 45 35
1772 35p. Pancho Villa 60 35
1773 40p. Emiliano Zapata 60 35
1774 45p. Venustiano Carranza 60 35
1775 110p. Francisco Madero 90 50
MS1776 122×88 mm. 90p. emblem (48×40 mm). Imperf 4·75 3·00

657 *Vigilante* (Federico Silva)

1985. Second "Morelos" Telecommunications Satellite Launch.
1777 - 26p. black and blue 45 35
1778 **657** 35p. grey, pink and black 45 35
1779 - 45p. multicoloured 60 35
MS1780 90×60 mm. 100p. multicoloured (46×36 mm). Imperf 6·00 2·40
Designs:—Vert: 26p. *Cosmonaut* (sculpture by Sebastian). Horiz: 45p. *Mexican Astronaut* (painting by Cauduro); 100p. Satellite transmitting to Earth.

658 "Mexico" holding Book

1985. 25th Anniv of Free Textbooks National Commission.
1781 **658** 26p. multicoloured 45 35

659 Olympic Stadium, University City

1985. World Cup Football Championship, Mexico. Each grey and black.
1782 26p. Type **659** 45 35
1783 45p. Azteca Stadium 45 35
See also Nos. 1796/**MS**1801.

1985. Colonial Architecture (5th series). Vert designs as T **552**. Each brown and black.
1784 26p. Vizcayan College, Mexico City 75 35
1785 35p. Counts of Heras y Soto Palace, Mexico City 75 35
1786 40p. Counts of Calimaya Palace, Mexico City 90 35
1787 45p. St. Carlos Academy, Mexico City 90 35

661 Luis Enrique Erro Planetarium

1986. 50th Anniv of National Polytechnic Institute. Multicoloured.
1788 40p. Type **661** 75 35
1789 65p. National School of Arts and Crafts 90 35

1790 75p. Founders, emblem and "50" 1·10 50

1986. Mexican Flowers (6th series). As T **518**. Multicoloured.
1791 40p. Calabash 1·50 35
1792 65p. *Nopalea coccinellifera* (cactus) 2·10 50

663 Doll

1986. World Health Day.
1793 **663** 65p. multicoloured 60 35

664 Halley and Comet

1986. Appearance of Halley's Comet.
1794 **664** 90p. multicoloured 1·10 35

665 Emblem

1986. Centenary of Geological Institute.
1795 **665** 40p. multicoloured 60 35

666 *Three Footballers with Berets*

1986. World Cup Football Championship, Mexico (2nd issue). Paintings by Angel Zarraga. Multicoloured.
1796 30p. Type **666** 60 35
1797 40p. *Portrait of Ramon Novaro* 60 35
1798 65p. *Sunday* 90 50
1799 70p. *Portrait of Ernest Charles Gimpel* 1·10 60
1800 90p. *Three Footballers* 1·20 85
MS1801 120×90 mm. 110p. Flags and footballing scenes. Imperf 9·75 3·50

667 Ignacio Allende

1986. 175th Death Annivs of Independence Heroes. Multicoloured.
1802 40p. Type **667** 60 35
1803 40p. Miguel Hidalgo (after J. C. Orozco) 60 35
1804 65p. Juan Aldama 75 35
1805 75p. Mariano Jimenez 75 35

668 Mexican Arms over "FTF"

1986. 50th Anniv of Fiscal Tribunal.
1806 **668** 40p. black, blue and grey 60 35

669 Nicolas Bravo

1986. Birth Bicentenary of Nicolas Bravo (independence fighter).
1807 **669** 40p. multicoloured 75 35

670 *Zapata Landscape*

1986. Paintings by Diego Rivera. Multicoloured.
1808 50p. Type **670** 75 50
1809 80p. *Nude with Arum Lilies* 90 50
1810 110p. *Vision of a Sunday Afternoon Walk on Central Avenue* (horiz) 1·20 60

671 Guadalupe Victoria

1986. Birth Bicentenary of Guadalupe Victoria (first President).
1811 **671** 50p. multicoloured 60 35

672 People depositing Produce

1986. 50th Anniv of National Depositories.
1812 **672** 40p. multicoloured 60 35

673 Pigeon above Hands holding Posthorn

1986. World Post Day.
1813 **673** 120p. multicoloured 75 35

674 Emblem

1986. Foundation of National Commission to Mark 500th Anniv (1992) of Discovery of America.
1814 **674** 50p. black and red 60 35

675 Ministry of Mines

1986. 15th Pan-American Roads Congress.
1815 **675** 80p. grey and black 60 35

676 Liszt

1986. 175th Birth Anniv of Franz Liszt (composer).
1816 **676** 100p. brown and black 75 35

677 UN and Pax Cultura Emblems

1986. International Peace Year.
1817 **677** 80p. blue, red and black 60 35

678 Jose Maria Pino Suarez (First Vice-President of Revolutionary Govt.)

1986. Famous Mexicans buried in The Rotunda of Illustrious Men (1st series).
1818 **678** 50p. multicoloured 60 35
See also Nos. 1823/4, 1838 and 1899.

679 King

1986. Christmas. Multicoloured.
1819 50p. Type **679** 60 35
1820 80p. Angel 60 35

680 *Self-portrait*

1986. Birth Centenary of Diego Rivera (artist).
1821 **680** 80p. multicoloured 60 35

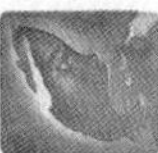

681 Baby receiving Vaccination

1987. National Days for Poliomyelitis Vaccination.
1822 **681** 50p. multicoloured 60 35

1987. Famous Mexicans buried in The Rotunda of Illustrious Men (2nd series). As T **678**. Mult.
1823 100p. Jose Maria Iglesias 90 50
1824 100p. Pedro Sainz de Baranda 90 50

682 Perez de Leon College

1987. Centenary of Higher Education.
1825 **682** 100p. multicoloured 90 50

683 Kino and Map

1987. 300th Anniv of Father Eusebio Francisco Kino's Mission to Pimeria Alta.
1826 **683** 100p. multicoloured 90 50

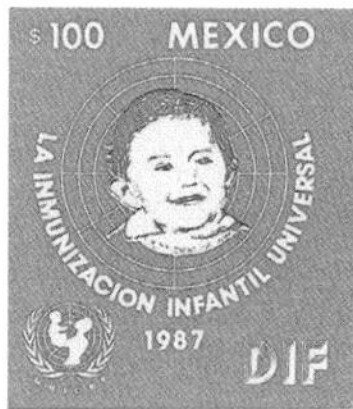

684 Baby's Head

1987. Child Immunization Campaign.
1827 **684** 100p. deep blue and blue 90 50

685 Staircase

1987. 50th Anniv of Puebla Independent University.
1828 **685** 200p. grey, pink and black 1·50 70

686 "5th of May, 1862, and the Siege of Puebla" Exhibition Poster, 1887

1987. 125th Anniv of Battle of Puebla.
1829 **686** 100p. multicoloured 75 35

687 Stylized City

1987. Metropolis 87 World Association of Large Cities Congress.
1830 **687** 310p. red, black and green 2·00 95

688 Lacquerware Tray, Uruapan, Michoacan

1987. Handicrafts. Multicoloured.
1831 100p. Type **688** 1·10 35
1832 200p. Woven blanket, Santa Ana Chiautempan, Tlaxcala 1·70 70
1833 230p. Ceramic jar with lid, Puebla, Puebla 1·80 85

689 Genaro Estrada (author and pioneer of democracy)

1987. Mexican Arts and Sciences (12th series).
1834 **689** 100p. brown, black and pink 75 35

690 *Native Traders* (mural, P. O'Higgins)

1987. 50th Anniv of National Foreign Trade Bank.
1835 **690** 100p. multicoloured 75 35

691 Diagram of Longitudinal Section through Ship's Hull

1987. 400th Anniv of Publication of First Shipbuilding Manual in America, Diego Garcia de Palacio's "Instrucion Nautica".
1836 **691** 100p. green, blue & brn 75 35

692 Man carrying Sack of Maize Flour

1987. 50th Anniv of National Food Programme.
1837 **692** 100p. multicoloured 75 35

1987. Mexicans in Rotunda of Illustrious Men (3rd series). As T **678**. Multicoloured.
1838 100p. Leandro Valle 75 35

693 *Self-portrait with Skull*

1987. Paintings by Saturnino Herran.
1839 **693** 100p. brown and black 75 35
1840 - 100p. multicoloured 75 35
1841 - 400p. multicoloured 2·75 1·70
Designs:—No. 1840, *The Offering*; 1841, *Creole with Shawl*.

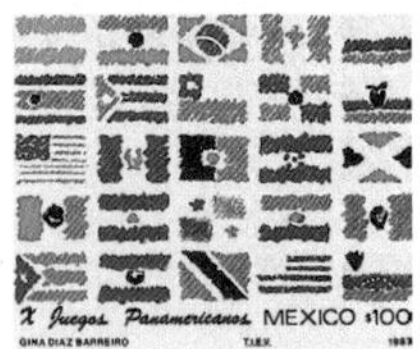

694 Flags of Competing Countries

1987. Tenth Pan-American Games, Indianapolis.
1842 **694** 100p. multicoloured 60 35
1843 - 200p. black, red and green 75 35
Design:—200p. Running.

695 Electricity Pylon

1987. 50th Anniv of Federal Electricity Commission.
1844 **695** 200p. multicoloured 90 50

1987. Mexican Arts and Sciences (13th series). As T **689**. Multicoloured.
1845 100p. J. E. Hernandez y Davalos (author) 60 35

1987. Pre-Hispanic Personalities (3rd series). As T **549**. Multicoloured.
1846 100p. Xolotl (Chichimeca commander) 60 50
1847 200p. Nezahualpilli (leader of Tezcoco tribe) 1·10 70
1848 400p. Motecuhzoma Ilhuicamina (leader of Tenochtitlan tribe) 2·30 85

696 Stylized Racing Car

1987. Mexico Formula One Grand Prix.
1849 **696** 100p. multicoloured 60 35

697 Mexican Cultural Centre, Mexico City

1987. Mexican Tourism.
1850 **697** 100p. multicoloured 60 35

698 *Santa Maria* and 1922 Mexican Festival Emblem

1987. 500th Anniv of "Meeting of Two Worlds" (discovery of America by Columbus) (1st issue).
1851 **698** 150p. multicoloured 4·50 50
See also Nos. 1902, 1941, 1979, 2038 and 2062/**MS**2067.

699 16th-century Spanish Map of Mexico City

1987. 13th International Cartography Conference.
1852 **699** 150p. multicoloured 60 35

1987. Mexican Tourism. As T **697**. Multicoloured.
1853 150p. Michoacan 45 35
1854 150p. Garcia Caves, Nuevo Leon 45 35
1855 150p. View of Mazatlan, Sinaloa 45 35

700 Pre-Hispanic Wedding Ceremony

1987. Native Codices. Mendocino Codex. Mult.
1856 150p. Type **700** 75 35
1857 150p. Moctezuma's council chamber 75 35
1858 150p. Foundation of Tenochtitlan 75 35

701 Dove with Olive Twig

1987. Christmas.
1859 **701** 150p. mauve 60 35
1860 - 150p. blue 60 35
Design:—No. 1860, As T **701** but dove facing left.

702 *Royal Ordinance for the Carriage of Maritime Mail Title Page*

1987. World Post Day.
1861 **702** 150p. green and grey 45 35
MS1862 129×102 mm. 600p. yellow and lake. Imperf 4·75 1·10
Design:—600p. Detail of register of inland mail 29 June, 1857.

703 Circle of Flags

1987. First Meeting of Eight Latin-American Presidents, Acapulco. Multicoloured.
1863 250p. Type **703** 60 35
1864 500p. Flags and doves 1·20 85

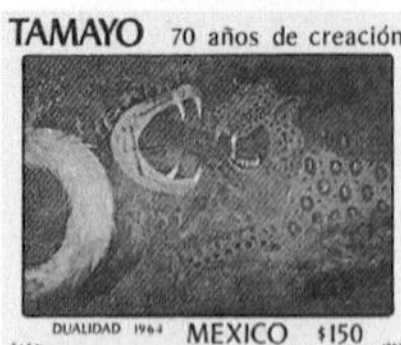

704 "Dualidad 1964"

1987. Rufino Tamayo (painter). "70 Years of Creativity".
1865 **704** 150p. multicoloured 60 35

705 Train on Metlac Viaduct

1987. 50th Anniv of Railway Nationalization.
1866 **705** 150p. multicoloured 75 35

706 *Stradivarius at Work* (detail, 19th-century engraving)

1987. 250th Death Anniv of Antonio Stradivarius (violin-maker).
1867 **706** 150p. light violet and violet 60 35

707 Statue of Manuel Crescensio Rejon (promulgator of Yucatan State Constitution)

1988. Constitutional Tribunal, Supreme Court of Justice.
1868 **707** 300p. multicoloured 90 60

708 American Manatee

1988. Animals. Multicoloured.
1869 300p. Type **708** 1·40 50
1870 300p. Mexican mole salamander 1·40 50

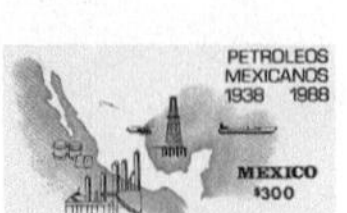

709 Map and Oil Industry Symbols

1988. 50th Anniv of Pemex (Nationalized Petroleum Industry).
1871 **709** 300p. blue and black 75 50
1872 - 300p. multicoloured 75 50
1873 - 500p. multicoloured 1·10 60
Designs:—36×43 mm: No. 1872, PEMEX emblem. 43×36 mm: No. 1873, "50" and oil exploration platform.

710 *The Vaccination*

1988. World Health Day (1874) and 40th Anniv of W.H.O. (1875). Paintings by Diego Rivera.
1874 **710** 300p. brown and green 90 50
1875 - 300p. multicoloured 90 50
Design:—43×36 mm: No. 1875, *The People demand Health*.

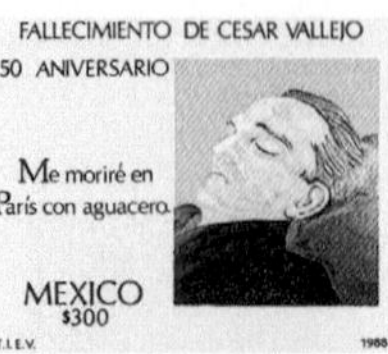

711 *Death Portrait* (Victor Delfin)

1988. 50th Death Anniv of Cesar Vallejo (painter and poet). Multicoloured.
1876 300p. Type **711** 1·40 50
1877 300p. Portrait by Arnold Belkin and "Hoy me palpo ..." 1·40 50
1878 300p. Portrait as in T **711** but larger (30×35 mm) 1·40 50
1879 300p. Portrait as in No. 1877 but larger (23×35 mm) 1·40 50

1988. Mexican Arts and Sciences (14th series). As T **689**.
1880 300p. brown, black and violet 90 50
Design:—300p. Carlos Pellicer (poet).

712 Girl and Boy holding Stamp in Tweezers

1988. Mepsirrey '88 Stamp Exhibition, Monterrey. Multicoloured.

1881	300p. Type **712**	90	50
1882	300p. Envelope with "Monterrey" handstamp	90	50
1883	500p. Exhibition emblem	1·40	85

713 Hernandos Rodriguez Racing Circuit, Mexico City

1988. Mexico Formula One Grand Prix.

1884	**713**	500p. multicoloured	1·80	70

714 Lopez Verlarde and Rose

1988. Birth Centenary of Ramon Lopez Verlarde (poet). Multicoloured.

1885	300p. Type **714**	75	35
1886	300p. Abstract	75	35

715 Emblem

1988. 50th Anniv of Military Sports.

1887	**715**	300p. multicoloured	75	35

716 Chrysanthemum, Container Ship and Flags

1988. Centenary of Mexico–Japan Friendship, Trade and Navigation Treaty.

1888	**716**	500p. multicoloured	1·20	60

717 Map

1988. Oceanographical Assembly.

1889	**717**	500p. multicoloured	1·20	60

718 Runners

1988. Olympic Games, Seoul. Multicoloured.

1890	500p. Type **718**	1·50	60

MS1891 72×55 mm. 700p. Flame, Seoul emblem and mascot and Barcelona emblem. Imperf	5·25	1·20

719 Boxer and Flags

1988. 25th Anniv of World Boxing Council.

1892	**719**	500p. multicoloured	1·20	60

720 Hospital and Emblem

1988. 125th Anniv of Red Cross.

1893	**720**	300p. grey, red and black	75	35

721 Posada

1988. 75th Death Anniv of Jose Guadalupe Posada (painter).

1894	**721**	300p. black and silver	75	35

722 *Danaus plexippus*

1988. Endangered Insects. The Monarch Butterfly. Multicoloured.

1895	300p. Type **722**	3·75	50
1896	300p. Butterflies on wall	3·75	50
1897	300p. Butterflies on leaves	3·75	50
1898	300p. Caterpillar, butterfly and chrysalis	3·75	50

1988. Mexicans in Rotunda of Illustrious Persons (4th series). As T **678**. Multicoloured.

1899	300p. Manuel Sandoval Vallarta	75	35

723 Envelopes forming Map

1988. World Post Day.

1900	**723**	500p. black and blue	1·20	60

MS1901 75×44 mm. 700p. multicoloured	4·75	1·20

Design:—700p. Envelope, doves and globe.

724 Indian and Monk writing

1988. 500th Anniv of "Meeting of Two Worlds" (2nd issue). Yanhuitian Codex.

1902	**724**	500p. multicoloured	1·40	70

725 Man watering Plant

1988. World Food Day. "Rural Youth".

1903	**725**	500p. multicoloured	1·20	60

1988. Mexican Arts and Sciences (15th series). As T **689**.

1904	300p. black and grey	75	35
1905	300p. brown, black & yellow	75	35

Designs:—No. 1904, Alfonso Caso; 1905, Vito Alessio Robles.

726 Act

1988. 175th Anniv of Promulgation of Act of Independence.

1906	**726**	300p. flesh and brown	75	35

727 *Self-portrait 1925*

1988. 25th Death Anniv of Antonio Ruiz (painter). Multicoloured.

1907	300p. Type **727**	75	35
1908	300p. *La Malinche*	75	35
1909	300p. *March Past*	75	35

728 Children and Kites

1988. Christmas. Multicoloured.

1910	300p. Type **728**	1·10	35
1911	300p. Food (horiz)	1·10	35

729 Emblem

1988. 50th Anniv of Municipal Workers Trade Union.

1912	**729**	300p. black and brown	90	50

1988. Mexican Flowers (7th series). As T **518**. Multicoloured.

1913	300p. *Mimosa tenuiflora*	1·10	35
1914	300p. *Ustilago maydis*	1·10	35

731 "50" and Emblem

1989. 50th Anniv of State Printing Works.

1915	**731**	450p. brown, grey and red	1·10	60

732 Arms and Score of National Anthem

1989. 145th Anniv of Dominican Independence.

1916	**732**	450p. multicoloured	1·10	60

733 Emblem

1989. Centenary of International Boundary and Water Commission.

1917	**733**	1100p. multicoloured	2·50	1·40

734 Emblem

1989. Tenth International Book Fair, Mineria.

1918	**734**	450p. multicoloured	1·10	60

735 Composer at Work

1989. 25th Anniv of Society of Authors and Composers.

1919	**735**	450p. multicoloured	1·10	60

736 People

1989. Anti-AIDS Campaign.

1920	**736**	450p. multicoloured	1·10	60

737 Vicario

1989. Birth Bicentenary of Leona Vicario (Independence fighter).

1921	**737**	450p. brown, deep brown and black	1·10	60

738 Statue of Reyes

1989. Birth Centenary of Alfonso Reyes (writer).

1922	**738**	450p. multicoloured	1·10	60

739 Speeding Cars

1989. Mexico Formula One Grand Prix.
1923 **739** 450p. multicoloured 1·10 60

740 Sea and Mountains

1989. 14th Travel Agents' Meeting, Acapulco.
1924 **740** 1100p. multicoloured 2·30 1·20

741 Huehuetcotl (god)

1989. 14th International Congress on Ageing.
1925 **741** 450p. pink, black and stone 1·20 60

742 Revolutionary and Battle Site

1989. 75th Anniv of Battle of Zacatecas.
1926 **742** 450p. black 1·10 60

743 Catchers

1989. Baseball Professionals' Hall of Fame. Multicoloured.
1927 550p. Type **743** 2·75 85
1928 550p. Striker 2·75 85
Nos. 1927/8 were printed together, *se-tenant*, forming a composite design.

744 Bows and Arrows

1989. World Archery Championships, Switzerland. Multicoloured.
1929 650p. Type **744** 2·75 85
1930 650p. Arrows and target 2·75 85
Nos. 1929/30 were printed together, *se-tenant*, forming a composite design.

745 Arms

1989. Centenary of Tijuana.
1931 **745** 1100p. multicoloured 2·10 1·30

746 Storming the Bastille

1989. Bicentenary of French Revolution.
1932 **746** 1300p. multicoloured 2·50 1·40

747 Mina

1989. Birth Bicentenary of Francisco Xavier Mina (independence fighter).
1933 **747** 450p. multicoloured 1·10 50

748 Cave Paintings

1989. 25th Anniv of National Anthropological Museum, Chapultepec.
1934 **748** 450p. multicoloured 1·20 60

749 Runners

1989. Seventh Mexico City Marathon.
1935 **749** 450p. multicoloured 1·10 50

750 Printed Page

1989. 450th Anniv of First American and Mexican Printed Work.
1936 **750** 450p. multicoloured 1·10 50

751 Posthorn and Cancellations

1989. World Post Day.
1937 **751** 1100p. multicoloured 1·80 1·20

752 *Aguascalientes in History* (Osvaldo Barra)

1989. 75th Anniv of Aguascalientes Revolutionary Convention.
1938 **752** 450p. multicoloured 90 50

753 Patterns

1989. America. Pre-Columbian Culture.
1939 450p. Type **753** 1·20 50
1940 450p. Traditional writing 1·20 50

754 Old and New World Symbols

1989. 500th Anniv of "Meeting of Two Worlds" (3rd issue).
1941 **754** 1300p. multicoloured 2·30 1·30

755 Cross of Lorraine

1989. 50th Anniv of Anti-tuberculosis National Committee.
1942 **755** 450p. multicoloured 90 50

756 Mask of God Murcielago

1989
1943 **756** 450p. green, black & mve 1·20 50

757 Bank

1989. 125th Anniv of Serfin Commercial Bank.
1944 **757** 450p. blue, gold and black 90 50

758 Cortines

1989. Birth Centenary of Adolfo Ruiz Cortines (President, 1952–58).
1945 **758** 450p. multicoloured 90 50

759 Man with Sparkler

1989. Christmas. Multicoloured.
1946 450p. Type **759** 1·10 50
1947 450p. People holding candles (horiz) 1·10 50

760 Emblem

1989. 50th Anniv of National Institute of Anthropology and History.
1948 **760** 450p. gold, red and black 90 50

761 Steam Locomotive, Diesel Train and Felipe Pescador

1989. 80th Anniv of Nationalization of Railways.
1949 **761** 450p. multicoloured 1·80 50

762 Bridge

1990. Opening of Tampico Bridge.
1950 **762** 600p. black, gold and red 1·20 60

763 Smiling Children

1990. Child Vaccination Campaign.
1951 **763** 700p. multicoloured 1·40 70

764 People in Houses

1990. 11th General Population and Housing Census.
1952 **764** 700p. green, yell & lt grn 1·40 70

765 Stamp under Magnifying Glass

1990. Tenth Anniv of Mexican Philatelic Association.
1953 **765** 700p. multicoloured 1·10 60

766 Archive

1990. Bicentenary of National Archive.
1954 **766** 700p. blue 1·10 60

767 Emblem and "90"

1990. First International Poster Biennale.
1955 **767** 700p. multicoloured 1·10 60

768 Messenger, 1790

1990. Stamp World London 90 International Stamp Exhibition.

1956 **768** 700p. yellow, red & black 1·40 60

769 Penny Black

1990. 150th Anniv of the Penny Black.

1957 **769** 700p. black, red and gold 1·10 60

770 National Colours and Pope John Paul II

1990. Papal Visit.

1958 **770** 700p. multicoloured 1·80 60

771 Church

1990. 15th Travel Agents' Congress.

1959 **771** 700p. multicoloured 1·40 60

772 Mother and Child

1990. Mother and Child Health Campaign.

1960 **772** 700p. multicoloured 1·10 60

773 Smoke Rings forming Birds

1990. World Anti-Smoking Day.

1961 **773** 700p. multicoloured 1·10 60

774 Globe as Tree

1990. World Environment Day.

1962 **774** 700p. multicoloured 1·10 60

775 Racing Car and Chequered Flag

1990. Mexico Formula One Grand Prix.

1963 **775** 700p. black, red and green 1·10 60

776 Aircraft Tailfin

1990. 25th Anniv of Airports and Auxiliary Services.

1964 **776** 700p. multicoloured 1·10 60

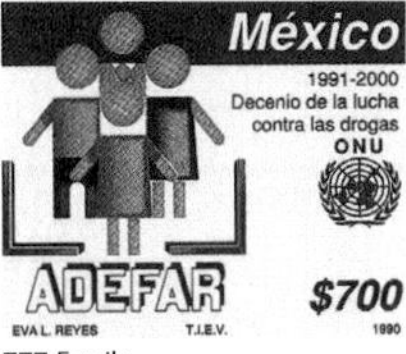

777 Family

1990. United Nations Anti-drugs Decade.

1965 **777** 700p. multicoloured 1·10 60

778 Tree Trunk

1990. Forest Conservation.

1966 **778** 700p. multicoloured 1·50 60

779 Emblem

1990. Solidarity.

1967 **779** 700p. multicoloured 1·10 60

See also No. 2047.

780 Columns and Native Decoration

1990. World Heritage Site. Oaxaca.

1968 **780** 700p. multicoloured 1·10 60

781 Elegant Tern

1990. Conservation of Rasa Island, Gulf of California.

1969 **781** 700p. grey, black and red 3·75 60

782 Institute Activities

1990. 25th Anniv of Mexican Petroleum Institute.

1970 **782** 700p. blue and black 1·10 60

783 National Colours, City Monuments and Runners

1990. 18th International Mexico City Marathon.

1971 **783** 700p. black, red & green 1·10 60

784 Facade

1990. 50th Anniv of Colima University.

1972 **784** 700p. multicoloured 1·10 60

785 Abstract

1990. Mexico City Consultative Council.

1973 **785** 700p. multicoloured 1·70 60

786 Electricity Worker

1990. 30th Anniv of Nationalization of Electricity Industry.

1974 **786** 700p. multicoloured 1·10 60

787 Violin and Bow

1990. 50th Death Anniv of Silvestre Revueltas (violinist).

1975 **787** 700p. multicoloured 1·10 60

788 Building

1990. 450th Anniv of Campeche.

1976 **788** 700p. multicoloured 1·10 60

789 Crossed Rifle and Pen

1990. 80th Anniv of San Luis Plan.

1977 **789** 700p. multicoloured 1·10 60

790 Emblem

1990. 14th World Supreme Councils Conference.

1978 **790** 1500p. multicoloured 2·50 1·40

791 Spanish Tower and Mexican Pyramid

1990. 500th Anniv of "Meeting of Two Worlds" (4th issue).

1979 **791** 700p. multicoloured 1·40 60

792 Glass of Beer, Ear of Barley and Hop

1990. Centenary of Brewing Industry.

1980 **792** 700p. multicoloured 1·10 60

793 Carving

1990. Bicentenary of Archaeology in Mexico.

1981 **793** 1500p. multicoloured 2·75 1·40

794 Ball-game Field

1990. 16th Central American and Caribbean Games. Multicoloured.

1982 750p. Type **794** 1·70 70

1983 750p. Amerindian ball-game player 1·70 70

1984 750p. Amerindian ball-game player (different) (horiz) 1·70 70

1985 750p. Yutsil and Balam (mascots) (horiz) 1·70 70

795 Globe and Poinsettia

1990. Christmas. Multicoloured.

1986 700p. Type **795** 1·20 60
1987 700p. Fireworks and candles 1·20 60

796 Dog (statuette)

1990. 50th Anniv of Mexican Canine Federation.

1988 **796** 700p. multicoloured 1·80 60

797 Microscope, Dolphin and Hand holding Map

1991. 50th Anniv of Naval Secretariat.

1989 **797** 1000p. gold, black & blue 1·50 85

798 Means of Transport

1991. Accident Prevention.

1990 **798** 700p. multicoloured 1·20 85

799 Products in Bags

1991. 15th Anniv of National Consumer Institute.

1991 **799** 1000p. multicoloured 1·80 1·10

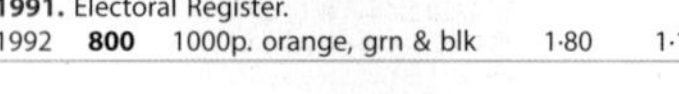

800 "In order to Decide, Register"

1991. Electoral Register.

1992 **800** 1000p. orange, grn & blk 1·80 1·10

801 Basketball Player

1991. Olympic Games, Barcelona (1992) (1st issue).

1993 **801** 1000p. black and yellow 1·80 1·10

See also Nos. 2050, 2057 and 2080/**MS**2090.

802 Flowers and Caravel

1991. America (1990). Natural World. Mult.

1994 700p. Type **802** 2·30 70
1995 700p. Right half of caravel, blue and yellow macaw and flowers 2·30 70

Nos. 1994/5 were issued together, *se-tenant*, forming a composite design.

803 Children in Droplet

1991. Children's Month. Vaccination Campaign.

1996 **803** 1000p. multicoloured 2·00 1·10

804 Map

1991. World Post Day (1990).

1997 **804** 1500p. multicoloured 2·50 1·70

805 Dove and Children

1991. Children's Days for Peace and Development.

1998 **805** 1000p. multicoloured 1·80 1·10

806 Dove

1991. Family Health and Unity.

1999 **806** 1000p. multicoloured 1·80 1·10

807 Mining

1991. 500th Anniv of Mining.

2000 **807** 1000p. multicoloured 1·80 1·10

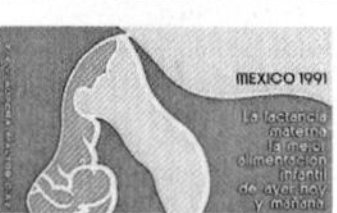

808 Mother feeding Baby

1991. Breastfeeding Campaign.

2001 **808** 1000p. buff, blue & brn 1·80 1·10

809 Emblem

1991. 16th Tourism Fair, Acapulco.

2002 **809** 1000p. green & dp green 2·00 1·30

810 Rotary Emblem and Independence Monument, Mexico City

1991. Rotary International Convention. "Let us Preserve the Planet Earth".

2003 **810** 1000p. gold and blue 2·00 1·30

811 "Communication"

1991. Centenary of Ministry of Transport and Communications (S.C.T.). Multicoloured.

2004 1000p. Type **811** 2·30 1·30
2005 1000p. Boeing 737 landing 2·30 1·30
2006 1000p. Facsimile machine 2·30 1·30
2007 1000p. Van 2·30 1·30
2008 1000p. Satellites and Earth 2·30 1·30
2009 1000p. Railway freight wagons on bridge 2·30 1·30
2010 1000p. Telephone users 2·30 1·30
2011 1000p. Road bridge over road 2·30 1·30
2012 1000p. Road bridge and cliffs 2·30 1·30
2013 1000p. Stern of container ship and dockyard 2·30 1·30
2014 1000p. Television camera and presenter 2·30 1·30
2015 1000p. Front of truck at toll gate 2·30 1·30
2016 1000p. Roadbuilding ("Solidarity") 2·30 1·30
2017 1500p. Boeing 737 and control tower 2·50 1·50
2018 1500p. Part of fax machine, transmitters and dish aerials on SCT building 2·50 1·50
2019 1500p. Satellite (horiz) 2·50 1·50
2020 1500p. Diesel and electric trains 2·50 1·50
2021 1500p. SCT building 2·50 1·50
2022 1500p. Road bridge over ravine 2·50 1·50
2023 1500p. Bow of container ship and dockyard 2·50 1·50
2024 1500p. Bus at toll gate 2·50 1·50
2025 1500p. Rear of truck and trailer at toll gate 2·50 1·50

Nos. 2005/25 were issued together, *se-tenant*, each block containing several composite designs.

812 Jaguar

1991. Lacandona Jungle Conservation.

2026 **812** 1000p. black, orge & red 2·30 1·30

813 Driver and Car

1991. Mexico Formula 1 Grand Prix.

2027 **813** 1000p. multicoloured 2·30 1·30

814 Emblem and Left-hand Sections of Sun and Earth

1991. Total Eclipse of the Sun. Multicoloured.

2028 1000p. Type **814** 2·30 1·80
2029 1000p. Emblem and right-hand sections of sun and Earth 2·30 1·80
2030 1500p. Emblem and centre of sun and Earth showing north and central America 2·30 1·80

Nos. 2028/30 were issued together, *se-tenant*, forming a composite design.

815 *Solidarity* (Rufino Tamayo)

1991. First Latin American Presidential Summit, Guadalajara.

2031 **815** 1500p. black, orge & yell 2·75 1·70

816 Bridge

1991. Solidarity between Nuevo Leon and Texas.

2032 **816** 2000p. multicoloured 3·75 2·50

817 Runners

1991. 9th Mexico City Marathon.

2033 **817** 1000p. multicoloured 1·80 1·00

818 Cogwheel

1991. 50th Anniv (1990) of National Chambers of Industry and Commerce.

2034 **818** 1500p. multicoloured 2·30 1·40

819 Emblem

1991. 55th Anniv of Federation Fiscal Tribunal.

2035 **819** 1000p. silver and blue 2·00 1·30

820 National Colours forming Emblem

1991. Solidarity—Let us Unite in order to Progress.

2036 **820** 1000p. multicoloured 1·80 1·00

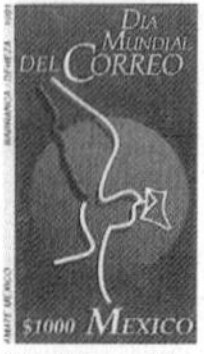

821 Dove with Letter

1991. World Post Day.

2037 **821** 1000p. multicoloured 1·80 1·00

822 World Map

1991. 500th Anniv of "Meeting of Two Worlds" (5th issue).

2038 **822** 1000p. multicoloured 3·50 1·30

823 Caravel, Sun and Trees

1991. America. Voyages of Discovery. Mult.
2039 1000p. Type **823** 2·30 1·30
2040 1000p. Storm cloud, caravel and broken snake 2·30 1·30

824 Flowers and Pots

1991. Christmas. Multicoloured.
2041 1000p. Type **824** 2·00 1·00
2042 1000p. Children with decoration 2·00 1·00

825 Abstract

1991. Carlos Merida (artist) Commemoration.
2043 **825** 1000p. multicoloured 2·40 1·30

826 Score and Portrait

1991. Death Bicentenary of Wolfgang Amadeus Mozart (composer).
2044 **826** 1000p. multicoloured 2·75 1·00

827 Kidney Beans and Maize

1991. Self-sufficiency in Kidney Beans and Maize.
2045 **827** 1000p. multicoloured 1·80 1·00

828 City Plan

1991. 450th Anniv of Morelia.
2046 **828** 1000p. brown, stone and red 2·30 1·10

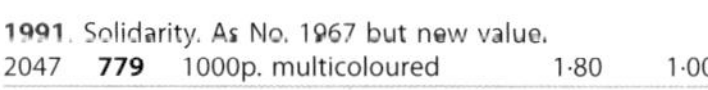
1991. Solidarity. As No. 1967 but new value.
2047 **779** 1000p. multicoloured 1·80 1·00

829 Merida

1992. 450th Anniv of Merida.
2048 **829** 1300p. multicoloured 2·50 1·40

830 Colonnade

1992. Bicentenary of Engineering Training in Mexico.
2049 **830** 1300p. blue and red 2·00 1·10

831 Horse Rider

1992. Olympic Games, Barcelona (2nd issue).
2050 **831** 2000p. multicoloured 3·00 1·80

832 City Arms

1992. 450th Anniv of Guadalajara. Multicoloured.
2051 1300p. Type **832** 2·00 1·10
2052 1300p. *Guadalajara Town Hall* (Jorge Navarro) 2·00 1·10
2053 1300p. *Guadalajara Cathedral* (Gabriel Flores) 2·00 1·10
2054 1900p. *Founding of Guadalajara* (Rafael Zamarripa) 2·75 1·70
2055 1900p. Anniversary emblem (Ignacio Vazquez) 2·75 1·70

833 Children and Height Gauge

1992. Child Health Campaign.
2056 **833** 2000p. multicoloured 3·25 1·80

834 Olympic Torch and Rings

1992. Olympic Games, Barcelona (3rd issue).
2057 **834** 2000p. multicoloured 3·25 1·80

835 Horse and Racing Car

1992. 500th Anniv of the Wheel and the Horse in America. Mexico Formula 1 Grand Prix.
2058 **835** 1300p. multicoloured 2·10 1·30

836 Satellite and Map of Americas

1992. Americas Telecom '92 Telecommunications Exhibition.
2059 **836** 1300p. multicoloured 2·10 1·30

837 Human Figure and Cardiograph

1992. World Health Day.
2060 **837** 1300p. black, red and blue 2·10 1·30

838 Emblem

1992. 60th Anniv of Military Academy.
2061 **838** 1300p. red, yellow & blk 2·10 1·30

839 *Inspiration of Christopher Columbus* (Jose Maria Obregon)

1992. 500th Anniv of "Meeting of Two Worlds" (6th issue). Granada 92 International Stamp Exhibition.
2062 1300p. Type **839** 3·75 1·30
2063 1300p. *Racial Encounter* (Jorge Gonzalez Camarena) 3·75 1·30
2064 2000p. *Origin of the Sky* (Selden Codex) 5·75 1·80
2065 2000p. *Quetzalcoatl and Tezcatlipoca* (Borhomico Codex) 5·75 1·80
2066 2000p. *From Spaniard and Indian, mestizo* 5·75 1·80
MS2067 107×84 mm. 7000p. *Human Culture* (Camarena). Imperf 30·00 7·00

840 Complex

1992. National Medical Centre.
2068 **840** 1300p. multicoloured 2·10 1·30

841 Children, Dove and Globe

1992. Children's Rights.
2069 **841** 1300p. multicoloured 2·40 1·30

842 New-born Baby

1992. Traditional Childbirth.
2070 **842** 1300p. multicoloured 2·10 1·30

1992. World Columbian Stamp Expo '92, Chicago. Nos. 2062/6 optd **WORLD COLUMBIAN STAMP EXPO '92 MAY 22-31, 1992 - CHICAGO** and emblem.
2071 1300p. mult (No. 2062) 24·00 22·00
2072 1300p. mult (No. 2063) 24·00 22·00
2073 2000p. mult (No. 2064) 24·00 22·00
2074 2000p. mult (No. 2065) 24·00 22·00
2075 2000p. mult (No. 2066) 24·00 22·00
MS2076 7000p. multicoloured £130 £120

844 Ships sailing from Old to New World

1992. 500th Anniv of Meeting of Two Worlds (7th issue). World Columbian Stamp Expo 92, Chicago (2nd issue). Sheet 72×55 mm. Imperf.
MS2077 **844** 7000p. multicoloured 13·50 7·00

845 Arms of Colleges

1992. Bicentenary of Mexico Notary College.
2078 **845** 1300p. multicoloured 2·10 1·40

846 Trees and Cacti

1992. Tree Day.
2079 **846** 1300p. multicoloured 2·10 1·40

847 Boxing

1992. Olympic Games, Barcelona (4th issue). Mult.
2080 1300p. Type **847** 2·10 1·40
2081 1300p. High jumping 2·10 1·40
2082 1300p. Fencing 2·10 1·40
2083 1300p. Shooting 2·10 1·40
2084 1300p. Gymnastics 2·10 1·40
2085 1900p. Rowing 4·00 2·00
2086 1900p. Running 4·00 2·00
2087 1900p. Football 4·00 2·00
2088 1900p. Swimming 4·00 2·00
2089 2000p. Equestrian 4·00 2·00
MS2090 80×60 mm. 7000p. Athlete carrying flame (38×23 mm) 23·00 9·75

848 Athlete

1992. Tenth Mexico City Marathon.
2091 **848** 1300p. multicoloured 2·10 1·30

849 Emblem

1992. Solidarity.
2092 **849** 1300p. multicoloured 2·10 1·30

850 Stylized Ship and Globe

1992. Genova 92 International Thematic Stamp Exhibition. Sheet 81×60 mm.
MS2093 **850** 7000p. multicoloured 18·00 7·75

851 Television, Map and Radio

1992. 50th Anniv of National Chamber of Television and Radio Industry.
2094 **851** 1300p. multicoloured 2·10 1·30

852 Letter orbiting Globe

1992. World Post Day.
2095 **852** 1300p. multicoloured 2·10 1·30

853 Satellite above South and Central America and Flags

1992. American Cadena Communications System.

2096 **853** 2000p. multicoloured 4·25 2·00

854 Gold Compass Rose

1992. America. 500th Anniv of Discovery of America by Columbus. Multicoloured.

2097 2000p. Type **854** 4·25 2·00

2098 2000p. Compass rose (different) and fish 4·25 2·00

Nos. 2097/8 were issued together, *se-tenant*, forming a composite design.

855 Scroll

1992. 400th Anniv of San Luis Potosi.

2099 **855** 1300p. black and mauve 2·10 1·30

856 Berrendos Deer

1992. Conservation.

2100 **856** 1300p. multicoloured 2·75 1·30

857 Schooner, Landing Ship, Emblem and Sailors

1992. Navy Day.

2101 **857** 1300p. multicoloured 2·10 1·30

858 Christmas Tree, Children and Crib

1992. Christmas. Children's Drawings. Mult.

2102 1300p. Type **858** 2·30 1·30

2103 2000p. Street celebration (horiz) 4·50 2·00

859 Anniversary Emblem

1993. 50th Anniv of Mexican Social Security Institute (1st issue).

2104 **859** 1p.50 green, gold & blk 2·30 1·50

See also Nos. 2110 and 2152/3.

860 Emblem

1993. Centenary of Mexican Ophthalmological Society.

2105 **860** 1p.30 multicoloured 2·00 1·40

861 Children

1993. Children's Month.

2106 **861** 1p.30 multicoloured 2·00 1·40

862 Society Arms and Founders

1993. 160th Anniv of Mexican Geographical and Statistical Society.

2107 **862** 1p.30 multicoloured 2·00 1·40

863 1824 Constitution

1993. 150th Death Anniv of Miguel Ramos Arizpe, "Father of Federalism".

2108 **863** 1p.30 multicoloured 2·00 1·40

864 Gomez, Children and Hospital

1993. 50th Anniv of Federico Gomez Children's Hospital.

2109 **864** 1p.30 multicoloured 2·00 1·40

865 Doctor with Child

1993. 50th Anniv of Mexican Social Security Institute (2nd issue). Medical Services.

2110 **865** 1p.30 multicoloured 2·00 1·40

866 Mother feeding Baby

1993. Health begins at Home.

2111 **866** 1p.30 multicoloured 2·00 1·40

867 Seal and Map

1993. Upper Gulf of California Nature Reserve.

2112 **867** 1p.30 multicoloured 2·40 1·40

868 Cantinflas

1993. Mexican Film Stars. Mario Moreno (Cantinflas).

2113 **868** 1p.30 black and blue 2·40 1·40

See also Nos. 2156/60.

869 Campeche

1993. Tourism. Value expressed as "NS". Mult.

2114	90c. Type **869**	1·90	1·00
2115	1p. Guanajuato	2·30	1·10
2263	1p.10 As No. 2115	2·75	55
2116	1p.30 Colima	2·75	1·10
2264	1p.80 As No. 2124	1·50	85
2265	1p.80 As No. 2118	2·10	85
2266	1p.80 As No. 2116	1·50	85
2267	1p.80 As Type **869**	1·50	85
2117	1p.90 Michoacan (vert)	4·50	1·50
2118	2p. Coahuila	4·25	1·50
2269	2p. As No. 2266	2·30	1·00
2119	2p.20 Queretaro	5·00	1·80
2272	2p.40 As No. 2123	2·75	1·10
2120	2p.50 Sonora	6·75	2·00
2274	2p.70 As No. 2122	4·50	1·40
2121	2p.80 Zacatecas (vert)	7·25	2·10
2276	3p. Type **869**	5·75	1·40
2278	3p.40 As No. 2122	5·75	1·50
2122	3p.70 Sinaloa	15·00	2·75
2280	3p.80 As No. 2272	4·25	1·70
2123	4p.40 Yucatan	10·00	3·25
2124	4p.80 Chiapas	11·50	3·50
2125	6p. Mexico City	15·00	4·50
2290	6p.80 As No. 2120	7·50	2·75

See also Nos. 2410/29.

870 Dr. Maximiliano Ruiz Castaneda

1993. 50th Anniv of Health Service. Multicoloured.

2126 1p.30 Type **870** 2·00 1·40

2127 1p.30 Dr. Bernardo Sepulveda Gutierrez 2·00 1·40

2128 1p.30 Dr. Ignacio Chavez Sanchez 2·00 1·40

2129 1p.30 Dr. Mario Salazar Mallen 2·00 1·40

2130 1p.30 Dr. Gustavo Baz Prada 2·00 1·40

871 Brazil 30r. "Bull's Eye" Stamp

1993. 150th Anniv of First Brazilian Stamps.

2131 **871** 2p. multicoloured 3·00 2·10

872 Runners

1993. 11th Mexico City Marathon.

2132 **872** 1p.30 multicoloured 2·00 1·40

873 Emblem

1993. Solidarity.

2133 **873** 1p.30 multicoloured 2·00 1·40

874 Open Book and Symbols

1993. 50th Anniv of Monterrey Institute of Technology and Higher Education. Multicoloured.

2134 1p.30 Type **874** 2·00 1·40

2135 2p. Buildings and mountains 3·25 2·10

Nos. 2134/5 were issued together, *se-tenant*, forming a composite design.

875 Cogwheels and Emblem

1993. 75th Anniv of Concamin.

2136 **875** 1p.30 multicoloured 2·00 1·40

876 Torreon

1993. Centenary of Torreon.

2137 **876** 1p.30 multicoloured 2·00 1·40

877 Emblem

1993. Europalia 93 Mexico Festival.

2138 **877** 2p. multicoloured 3·00 2·10

878 Globe in Envelope

1993. World Post Day.

2139 **878** 2p. multicoloured 3·00 2·10

879 Gen. Guadalupe Victoria

1993. 150th Death Anniv of General Manuel Guadalupe Victoria (first President, 1824–28).

2140 **879** 1p.30 multicoloured 2·00 1·40

880 Emblem

1993. National Civil Protection System and International Day for Reduction of Natural Disasters.

2141 **880** 1p.30 red, black & yell 2·00 1·40

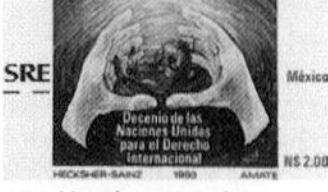

881 Hands protecting Foetus

1993. United Nations Decade of International Law.

2142 **881** 2p. multicoloured 3·00 2·10

882 Torch Carrier

1993. 20th National Wheelchair Games.

2143 **882** 1p.30 multicoloured 2·00 1·40

883 Peon y Contreras

1993. 150th Birth Anniv of Jose Peon y Contreras (poet, dramatist and founder of National Romantic Theatre).

2144 **883** 1p.30 violet and black 2·00 1·40

884 Horned Guan

1993. America. Endangered Birds. Multicoloured.

2145	2p. Type **884**	5·75	2·10
2146	2p. Resplendent quetzal on branch (horiz)	5·75	2·10

885 Presents around Trees

1993. Christmas. Multicoloured.

2147	1p.30 Type **885**	2·40	1·40
2148	1p.30 Three wise men (horiz)	2·40	1·40

886 Satellites orbiting Earth

1993. Solidarity.

2149	**886**	1p.30 multicoloured	2·00	1·40

887 School and Arms

1993. 125th Anniv of National Preparatory School.

2150	**887**	1p.30 multicoloured	2·00	1·40

888 Emblem on Map

1993. 55th Anniv of Municipal Workers Trade Union.

2151	**888**	1p.30 multicoloured	2·00	1·40

889 Hands

1993. 50th Anniv of Mexican Social Security Institute (3rd issue). Multicoloured.

2152	1p.30 Type **889** (social security)	2·00	1·40
2153	1p.30 Ball, building blocks, child's painting and dummy (day nurseries)	2·00	1·40

890 Mezcala Solidarity Bridge

1993. Tourism. Multicoloured.

2154	1p.30 Type **890**	2·00	1·40
2155	1p.30 Mexico City–Acapulco motorway	2·00	1·40

1993. Mexican Film Stars. As T **868**.

2156	1p.30 black and blue	2·00	1·40
2157	1p.30 black and orange	2·00	1·40
2158	1p.30 black and green	2·00	1·40
2159	1p.30 black and violet	2·00	1·40
2160	1p.30 black and pink	2·00	1·40

Designs:—No, 2156, Pedro Armendariz in *Juan Charrasqueado*; No. 2157, Maria Felix in *The Lover*; No. 2158, Pedro Infante in *Necesito dinero*; No. 2159, Jorge Negrete in *It is not enough to be a Peasant*; No. 2160, Dolores del Rio in *Flor Silvestre*.

891 Estefania Castaneda Nunez

1994. 72nd Anniv of Secretariat of Public Education. Educationists. Multicoloured.

2161	1p.30 Type **891**	2·10	1·40
2162	1p.30 Lauro Aguirre Espinosa	2·10	1·40
2163	1p.30 Rafael Ramirez Castaneda	2·10	1·40
2164	1p.30 Moises Saenz Garza	2·10	1·40
2165	1p.30 Gregorio Torres Quintero	2·10	1·40
2166	1p.30 Jose Vasconcelos	2·10	1·40
2167	1p.30 Rosaura Zapato Cano	2·10	1·40

892 Zapata (after H. Velarde)

1994. 75th Death Anniv of Emiliano Zapata (revolutionary).

2168	**892**	1p.30 multicoloured	2·40	1·40

893 Emblem and Worker

1994. 75th Anniv of I.L.O.

2169	**893**	2p. multicoloured	3·00	2·20

894 Map and Emblem

1994. 50th Anniv of National Schools Building Programme Committee.

2170	**894**	1p.30 multicoloured	2·10	1·40

895 *Earth and Communication* (frieze, detail)

1994. Third Death Anniv of Francisco Zuniga (sculptor).

2171	**895**	1p.30 multicoloured	2·40	1·40

896 Flower and Children

1994. Children's Organization for Peace and Development.

2172	**896**	1p.30 multicoloured	2·50	1·40

897 Greater Flamingo

1994. DUMAC Nature Protection Organization.

2173	**897**	1p.30 multicoloured	3·75	1·40

898 Children and Silhouette of Absentee

1994. Care and Control of Minors.

2174	**898**	1p.30 black and green	2·50	1·40

899 Man and Letters

1994. 34th World Advertising Congress, Cancun.

2175	**899**	2p. multicoloured	3·00	2·20

900 Route Map

1994. 50th Anniv of National Association of Importers and Exporters.

2176	**900**	1p.30 multicoloured	2·10	1·40

901 Head and Emblem

1994. International Telecommunications Day.

2177	**901**	2p. multicoloured	3·00	2·20

902 Animals

1994. Yumka Wildlife Centre, Villahermosa.

2178	**902**	1p.30 multicoloured	2·40	1·40

903 Town Centre

1994. UNESCO World Heritage Site, Zacatecas.

2179	**903**	1p.30 multicoloured	3·00	1·40

904 Mother and Baby

1994. Friendship Hospital. Mother and Child Health Month.

2180	**904**	1p.30 multicoloured	2·50	1·40

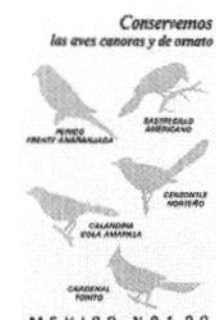

906 Song and Ornamental Birds

1994. Prevention of Mental Retardation.

2181	**905**	1p.30 multicoloured	2·10	1·40

905 Foot and Heart

1994. Nature Conservation. Multicoloured.

2182	1p.30 Type **906**	2·10	1·40
2183	1p.30 Game birds (silhouettes)	2·10	1·40
2184	1p.30 Threatened animals (silhouettes)	2·10	1·40
2185	1p.30 Animals in danger of extinction (silhouettes)	2·10	1·40
2186	1p.30 Orange-fronted conures	2·10	1·40
2187	1p.30 Yellow-tailed oriole	2·10	1·40
2188	1p.30 Pyrrhuloxias	2·10	1·40
2189	1p.30 Loggerhead shrike	2·10	1·40
2190	1p.30 Northern mockingbird	2·10	1·40
2191	1p.30 Common turkey	2·10	1·40
2192	1p.30 White-winged dove	2·10	1·40
2193	1p.30 Red-billed whistling duck	2·10	1·40
2194	1p.30 Snow goose	2·10	1·40
2195	1p.30 Gambel's quail	2·10	1·40
2196	1p.30 Peregrine falcon	2·10	1·40
2197	1p.30 Jaguar	2·10	1·40
2198	1p.30 Jaguarundi	2·10	1·40
2199	1p.30 Mantled howler monkey	2·10	1·40
2200	1p.30 Californian sealions	2·10	1·40
2201	1p.30 Pronghorn	2·10	1·40
2202	1p.30 Scarlet macaw	2·10	1·40
2203	1p.30 Mexican prairie dogs	2·10	1·40
2204	1p.30 Wolf	2·10	1·40
2205	1p.30 American manatee	2·10	1·40

907 Player

1994. World Cup Football Championship, U.S.A. Multicoloured.

2206	2p. Type **907**	3·00	2·20
2207	2p. Goalkeeper	3·00	2·20

Nos. 2206/7 were issued together, *se-tenant*, forming a composite design.

908 Fish

1994. International Fishing Festival, Veracruz.

2208	**908**	1p.30 multicoloured	2·10	1·40

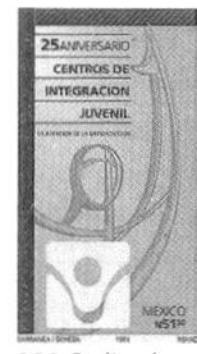

909 Stylized Figure and Emblem

1994. 25th Anniv of Juvenile Integration Centres.

2209	**909**	1p.30 multicoloured	1·80	1·30

910 *Butterflies* (Carmen Parra)

1994. 50th Anniv of Diplomatic Relations with Canada.

2210	**910**	2p. multicoloured	3·75	2·10

911 Emblems

1994. 20th Anniv of National Population Council.

2211	**911**	1p.30 multicoloured	2·10	1·30

912 Emblem and Family

1994. International Year of the Family.

2212	**912**	2p. multicoloured	3·50	1·80

913 Runner breasting Tape

1994. 12th Mexico City International Marathon.
2213 **913** 1p.30 multicoloured 2·40 1·30

914 Giant Panda

1994. Chapultepec Zoo.
2214 **914** 1p.30 multicoloured 3·75 1·40

915 Tree

1994. Tree Day.
2215 **915** 1p.30 brown and green 2·10 1·30

916 Anniversary Emblem

1994. 60th Anniv of Economic Culture Fund.
2216 **916** 1p.30 multicoloured 2·10 1·30

917 Statue and Light Rail Transit Train

1994. 25th Anniv of Mexico City Transport System.
2217 **917** 1p.30 multicoloured 2·40 1·30

918 Cathedral and Gardens

1994. 350th Anniv of Salvatierra City, Guanajuato.
2218 **918** 1p.30 purple, grey and black 2·10 1·30

919 State Flag and National Anthem

1994. National Symbols Week.
2219 **919** 1p.30 multicoloured 2·30 1·30

920 Building and Anniversary Emblem

1994. 40th Anniv of University City.
2220 **920** 1p.30 multicoloured 2·10 1·30

921 Figures with Flags

1994. Fifth Solidarity Week.
2221 **921** 1p.30 black, red and green 2·10 1·30

922 Lopez Mateos

1994. 25th Death Anniv of Adolfo Lopez Mateos (President, 1958–64).
2222 **922** 1p.30 multicoloured 2·10 1·30

923 Palace Facade

1994. 60th Anniv of Palace of Fine Arts.
2223 **923** 1p.30 black and grey 2·30 1·30

924 Rings and "100"

1994. Centenary of International Olympic Committee.
2224 **924** 2p. multicoloured 4·00 1·80

925 *Quarter Horse* (Juan Rayas)

1994. Horses. Paintings by artists named. Multicoloured.
2225 1p.30 *Aztec horse* (Heladio Velarde) 2·10 1·50
2226 1p.30 Type **925** 2·10 1·50
2227 1p.30 *Quarter horse* (Rayas) (different) 2·10 1·50
2228 1p.30 *Vaquero on horseback* (Velarde) 2·10 1·50
2229 1p.30 *Aztec horse* (Velarde) 2·10 1·50
2230 1p.30 *Rider with lance* (Velarde) 2·10 1·50

926 Emblem

1994. Inauguration of 20 November National Medical Centre.
2231 **926** 1p.30 multicoloured 2·10 1·30

927 Saint-Exupery and The Little Prince (book character)

1994. 50th Death Anniv of Antoine de Saint-Exupery (pilot and writer).
2232 **927** 2p. multicoloured 3·50 1·80

928 Man writing Letters to Woman

1994. World Post Day.
2233 **928** 2p. multicoloured 3·25 1·80

929 Urban Postman on Bicycle

1994. America. Postal Transport. Multicoloured.
2234 2p. Type **929** 2·75 1·80
2235 2p. Rural postman on rail tricycle 2·75 1·80

Nos. 2234/5 were issued together, *se-tenant*, forming a composite design.

930 *Couple* (Sofia Bassi)

1994. Ancestors' Day.
2236 **930** 1p.30 multicoloured 2·10 1·30

931 Water Drop and Hand

1994. National Clean Water Programme.
2237 **931** 1p.30 multicoloured 2·10 1·30

932 Dr. Mora

1994. Birth Bicentenary of Dr. Jose Maria Luis Mora (journalist and politician).
2238 **932** 1p.30 multicoloured 2·10 1·30

933 Theatre and Soler (actor)

1994. 15th Anniv of Fernando Soler Theatre, Saltillo, Coahuila.
2239 **933** 1p.30 multicoloured 2·10 1·30

934 Allegory of Flight

1994. 50th Anniv of I.C.A.O.
2240 **934** 2p. multicoloured 2·75 1·80

935 Museum's Central Pillar

1994. 30th Anniv of National Anthropological Museum.
2241 **935** 1p.30 multicoloured 2·10 1·30

936 Theatrical Masks

1994. 60th Anniv of National Association of Actors.
2242 **936** 1p.30 multicoloured 2·10 1·30

937 Allende

1994. 225th Birth Anniv of Ignacio Allende (independence hero).
2243 **937** 1p.30 multicoloured 2·10 1·30

938 Chapultepec Castle

1994. 50th Anniv of National History Museum.
2244 **938** 1p.30 multicoloured 2·30 1·30

939 Dome

1994. Centenary of Coahuila School.
2245 **939** 1p.30 multicoloured 2·10 1·30

940 Anniversary Emblem

1994. 40th Anniv of Pumas University Football Club.
2246 **940** 1p.30 blue and gold 2·10 1·30

941 Decorated Tree

1994. Christmas. Multicoloured.
2247 2p. Type **941** 2·75 1·80
2248 2p. Couple watching shooting star (horiz) 2·75 1·80

942 Valley

1994. Solidarity. Chalco Valley.
2249 **942** 1p.30 multicoloured 2·10 1·30

943 Ines de la Cruz (after Miguel de Cabrera)

1995. 300th Birth Anniv of Juana Ines de la Cruz (mystic poet).

2250 **943** 1p.80 multicoloured 2·40 1·10

944 X-Ray of Hand and Rontgen

1995. Centenary of Discovery of X-Rays by Wilhelm Rontgen.

2251 **944** 2p. multicoloured 2·10 1·30

945 Ignacio Altamirano

1995. Teachers' Day.

2252 **945** 1p.80 black, green & bl 2·40 1·10

946 Emblem

1995. World Telecommunications Day. "Telecommunications and the Environment".

2253 **946** 2p.70 multicoloured 2·75 1·50

947 Anniversary Emblem

1995. 40th Anniv of National Institute of Public Administration.

2254 **947** 1p.80 green, mve & lilac 2·40 1·10

948 Marti

1995. Death Centenary of Jose Marti (Cuban writer and revolutionary).

2255 **948** 2p.70 multicoloured 3·00 1·50

949 Carranza

1995. 75th Death Anniv of Venustiano Carranza (President 1914–20).

2256 **949** 1p.80 multicoloured 2·40 1·10

950 Kite

1995. 20th Anniv of National Tourist Organization.

2257 **950** 2p.70 multicoloured 2·75 1·50

951 Drugs, Skull and Unhappy Face

1995. International Day against Drug Abuse and Trafficking. Multicoloured.

2258	1p.80 Type **951**	2·40	1·10
2259	1p.80 Drug addict on swing	2·40	1·10
2260	1p.80 Faces behind bars	2·40	1·10

952 Cardenas del Rio

1995. Birth Centenary of Gen. Lazaro Cardenas del Rio (President 1934–40).

2261 **952** 1p.80 black 2·40 1·10

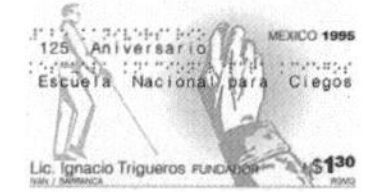

953 Man with White Stick and Hand reading Braille

1995. 125th Anniv of National Blind School. Mult.

2262 **953** 1p.30 brown and black 2·40 1·00

954 Northern Pintails

1995. Animals. Multicoloured.

2295	2p.70 Type **954**	3·00	2·20
2296	2p.70 Belted kingfisher	3·00	2·20
2297	2p.70 Orange tiger	3·00	2·20
2298	2p.70 Hoary bat	3·00	2·20

955 Runners

1995. 13th International Marathon, Mexico City.

2299 **955** 2p.70 multicoloured 2·75 1·50

956 Envelopes

1995. 16th Congress of Postal Union of the Americas, Spain and Portugal, Mexico City.

2300 **956** 2p.70 multicoloured 2·75 1·50

957 Pasteur

1995. Death Centenary of Louis Pasteur (chemist).

2301 **957** 2p.70 blue, black and green 3·00 1·50

958 Hands holding Envelopes

1995. World Post Day.

2302 **958** 2p.70 multicoloured 2·40 1·40

959 Basket of Shopping

1995. World Food Day.

2303 **959** 1p.80 multicoloured 2·40 1·40

960 Anniversary Emblem

1995. 50th Anniv of F.A.O.

2304 **960** 2p.70 multicoloured 2·40 1·40

961 Elias Calles

1995. 50th Death Anniv of General Plutarco Elias Calles (President 1924–28).

2305 **961** 1p.80 multicoloured 2·30 1·40

962 Cuauhtemoc

1995. 500th Birth Anniv of Cuauhtemoc (Aztec Emperor of Tenochtitlan).

2306 **962** 1p.80 multicoloured 2·10 1·40

963 National Flag, National Anthem and Constitution

1995. National Constitution and Patriotic Symbols Day.

2307 **963** 1p.80 multicoloured 2·10 1·40

964 Flags as Tail of Dove

1995. 50th Anniv of U.N.O.

2308 **964** 2p.70 multicoloured 2·40 1·40

965 Aeroplane, Streamlined Train and Motor Vehicle

1995. International Passenger Travel Year.

2309 **965** 2p.70 multicoloured 2·30 1·50

966 *The Holy Family* (Andres de Concha)

1995. 30th Anniv of Museum of Mexican Art in the Vice-regency Period.

2310 **966** 1p.80 multicoloured 2·30 1·00

967 Pedro Maria Anaya

1995. Generals in Mexican History. Each black, yellow and gold.

2311	1p.80 Type **967**	1·80	1·00
2312	1p.80 Felipe Berriozabal	1·80	1·00
2313	1p.80 Santos Degollado	1·80	1·00
2314	1p.80 Sostenes Rocha	1·80	1·00
2315	1p.80 Leandro Valle	1·80	1·00
2316	1p.80 Ignacio Zaragoza	1·80	1·00

968 Children playing in Garden (Pablo Osorio Gomez)

1995. Christmas. Children's Drawings. Multicoloured.

2317	1p.80 Type **968**	1·50	1·00
2318	2p.70 Adoration of the Wise Men (Oscar Enrique Carrillo)	2·30	1·50

969 Emblem

1995. Tenth Anniv of Mexican Health Foundation.

2319 **969** 1p.80 multicoloured 2·10 1·40

970 Ocelot

1995. Nature Conservation.

2320 **970** 1p.80 multicoloured 2·40 1·40

971 Louis Lumiere and Cine-camera

1995. Centenary of Motion Pictures.

2321 **971** 1p.80 black, mauve and blue 2·10 1·40

972 Library

1995. National Education Library, Mexico City.

2322 **972** 1p.80 green, blue and yellow 2·10 1·40

973 *Proportions of Man* (Leonardo da Vinci)

1995. 50th Anniv of National Science and Arts Prize.

2323 **973** 1p.80 multicoloured 2·40 1·40

974 Pedro Vargas

1995. Radio Personalities. Multicoloured.

2324	1p.80 Type **974**	2·00	1·40
2325	1p.80 Agustin Lara	2·00	1·40
2326	1p.80 Aguila Sisters	2·00	1·40
2327	1p.80 Tona "La Negra"	2·00	1·40
2328	1p.80 F. Gabilondo Soler "Cri-Cri"	2·00	1·40
2329	1p.80 Emilio Teuro	2·00	1·40
2330	1p.80 Gonzalo Curiel	2·00	1·40
2331	1p.80 Lola Beltran	2·00	1·40

975 Robot Hand holding Optic Fibres

1995. 25th Anniv of Science and Technology Council.

2332	**975**	1p.80 multicoloured	2·40	1·40

976 Grumman Gulfstream IV

1996. National Aviation Day. Multicoloured.

2333	1p.80 Boeing 727 and Standard JR biplane	2·30	1·40
2334	1p.80 Republic P-47 Thunderbolt. 201 Squadron, 1945	2·30	1·40
2335	2p.70 Ley Airport and Boeing 727	3·00	2·10
2336	2p.70 Type **976**	3·00	2·10

977 Child and Caso

1996. Birth Centenary of Dr. Alfonso Caso (anthropologist).

2337	**977**	1p.80 multicoloured	2·00	1·40

978 Silverio Perez, Carlos Arruza and Manolo Martinez

1996. 50th Anniv of Plaza Mexico (bullring). Matadors. Multicoloured.

2338	1p.80 Type **978**	2·00	1·40
2339	2p.70 Roldolfo Gaona, Fermin Espinosa and Lorenzo Garza	3·00	2·10

Nos. 2338/9 were issued together, *se-tenant*, forming a composite design of the bullring.

979 Bag of Groceries

1996. 20th Anniv of Federal Consumer Council.

2340	**979**	1p.80 multicoloured	2·00	1·40

980 Treatment of Fracture (from *Sahagun Codex*)

1996. 50th Anniv of Mexican Society of Orthopaedics.

2341	**980**	1p.80 multicoloured	2·00	1·40

981 Rulfo

1996. 10th Death Anniv of Juan Rulfo (writer).

2342	**981**	1p.80 multicoloured	2·00	1·40

982 Anniversary Emblem and Map of Mexico

1996. 60th Anniv of National Polytechnic Institute.

2343	**982**	1p.80 grey, black and red	2·00	1·30

983 Healthy Hand reaching for Sick Hand

1996. United Nations Decade against the Abuse and Illicit Trafficking of Drugs. Multicoloured.

2344	1p.80 Type **983**	2·10	1·30
2345	1p.80 Man helping addict out of dark hole	2·10	1·30
2346	2p.70 Stylized figures	3·25	1·80

984 Gymnastics

1996. Olympic Games, Atlanta, U.S.A. Multicoloured.

2347	1p.80 Type **984**	1·80	1·30
2348	1p.80 Hurdling	1·80	1·30
2349	2p.70 Football	2·75	1·80
2350	2p.70 Running	2·75	1·80
2351	2p.70 Show jumping	2·75	1·80

985 Cameraman and Film Frames of Couples

1996. Centenary of Mexican Films. Multicoloured.

2352	1p.80 Type **985**	1·20	70
2353	1p.80 Camera and film frames of individuals	1·20	70

986 Scales

1996. 60th Anniv of Fiscal Tribunal.

2354	**986**	1p.80 multicoloured	2·00	1·30

987 Runners' Feet

1996. 14th Mexico City International Marathon.

2355	**987**	2p.70 multicoloured	2·00	1·30

988 Flask, Open Books, Atomic Model and Microscope

1996. Science.

2356	**988**	1p.80 multicoloured	2·10	1·30

989 *Allegory of Foundation of Zacatecas* (anon)

1996. 450th Anniv of Zacatecas.

2357	**989**	1p.80 multicoloured	2·10	1·30

990 Rural Education

1996. 25th Anniv of National Council for the Improvement of Education.

2358	**990**	1p.80 multicoloured	2·10	1·30

991 *The Foundation of Monterrey* (Crescencio Garza)

1996. 400th Anniv of Monterrey. Sheet 100×72 mm.

MS2359	**991**	7p.40 multicoloured	8·25	7·00

992 Emblem

1996. Family Planning Month.

2360	**992**	1p.80 green, mauve and blue	2·00	1·30

993 Flag of the "Three Guarantees", 1821

1996. 175th Anniv of Declaration of Independence.

2361	**993**	1p.80 multicoloured	2·00	1·30

994 Blue Morpho, Monkey, Harpy Eagle and other Birds

1996. Nature Conservation. Multicoloured.

2362	1p.80 Type **994**	1·20	85
2363	1p.80 Turtle dove, yellow grosbeak with chicks in nest, trogon and hummingbird	1·20	85
2364	1p.80 Mountains, monarchs (butterflies) in air and American black bear with cub	1·20	85
2365	1p.80 Fishing buzzard, mule deer, lupins and monarchs (butterflies) on plant	1·20	85
2366	1p.80 Scarlet macaws, monarchs, toucan, peafowl and spider monkey hanging from tree	1·20	85
2367	1p.80 Resplendent quetzal, emerald toucanet, bromeliads and tiger-cat	1·20	85
2368	1p.80 Parrots, white-tailed deer and rabbit by river	1·20	85
2369	1p.80 Snake, wolf, puma and lizard on rock and blue-capped bird	1·20	85
2370	1p.80 Coyote, prairie dogs at burrow, quail on branch, deer, horned viper and caracara on cactus	1·20	85
2371	1p.80 Jaguar, euphonias, long-tailed bird, crested bird and bat	1·20	85
2372	1p.80 "Martucha", peacock, porcupine, butterfly and green snake	1·20	85
2373	1p.80 Blue magpie, green-headed bird, owl, woodpecker and hummingbird by river	1·20	85
2374	1p.80 Cinnamon cuckoo in tree, fox by river and green macaws in tree	1·20	85
2375	1p.80 Wild sheep by rocks, bird on ocotillo plant, bats, owl, lynx and woodpecker on cactus	1·20	85
2376	1p.80 Ant-eater climbing sloping tree, jaguarundi, bat, orchid and ocellated turkey in undergrowth	1·20	85
2377	1p.80 Ocelot, "grison", coral snake, "temazate", paca and otter by river	1·20	85
2378	1p.80 Grey squirrel in tree, salamander, beaver, bird, shrew-mole, mountain hen and racoon by river	1·20	85
2379	1p.80 Butterfly, trogon in red tree, "chachalaca", crested magpie and "tejon"	1·20	85
2380	1p.80 Bat, "tlalcoyote", "rata neotoma", "chichimoco", hare, cardinal (bird), lizard, kangaroo rat and tortoise	1·20	85
2381	1p.80 Beetle on leaf, tapir, tree frog and "tunpache"	1·20	85
2382	1p.80 Crocodile, insect, cup fungus, boa constrictor and butterfly	1·20	85
2383	1p.80 Armadillo, "tlacuache", iguana, turkey and butterfly	1·20	85
2384	1p.80 Turkey, collared peccary, zorilla, lizard, rattlesnake and mouse	1·20	85
2385	1p.80 Cacomistle, "matraca", lark, collared lizard and cacti	1·20	85

Nos. 2362/85 were issued together, *se-tenant*, forming a composite design of habitats and wildlife under threat.

995 Bird with Letter in Beak

1996. World Post Day.

2386	**995**	2p.70 multicoloured	2·30	1·10

996 Institute

1996. 50th Anniv of Salvador Zubiran National Nutrition Institute.

2387	**996**	1p.80 multicoloured	2·00	1·40

997 Constantino de Tarnava

1996. 75th Anniv of Radio Broadcasting in Mexico.

2388	**997**	1p.80 multicoloured	2·00	1·40

998 *Portrait of a Woman* (Baltasar de Echave Ibia)

1996. Virreinal Art Gallery. Multicoloured.

2389	1p.80 Type **998**	2·00	70
2390	1p.80 *Portrait of the Child Joaquin Manuel Fernandez de Santa Cruz* (Nicolas Rodriguez Xuarez)	2·00	70
2391	1p.80 *Portrait of Dona Maria Luisa Gonzaga Foncerrada y Labarrieta* (Jose Maria Vazquez)	2·00	70
2392	1p.80 *Archangel Michael* (Luis Juarez)	2·40	1·10
2393	2p.70 *Virgin of the Apocalypse* (Miguel Cabrera)	2·40	1·10

999 Isidro Fabela and Genaro Estrada

1996. Precursors of Foreign Policy.

2394	**999**	1p.80 multicoloured	2·00	1·40

1000 Maize

1996. World Food Day.

2395	**1000**	2p.70 multicoloured	2·00	1·40

1001 Underground Train around Globe

1996. International Metros Conference.
2396 **1001** 2p.70 multicoloured 2·30 1·40

1002 Star (Elias Martin del Campo)

1996. Christmas. Multicoloured.
2397 1p. Type **1002** 1·20 70
2398 1p.80 Man with star-shaped bundles on stick (Ehecatl Cabrera Franco) (vert) 2·10 1·40

1003 Henestrosa

1996. Andres Henestrosa (writer) Commemoration.
2399 **1003** 1p.80 multicoloured 2·00 1·40

1004 Old and New Institute Buildings

1996. 50th Anniv of National Cancer Institute.
2400 **1004** 1p.80 multicoloured 2·00 1·40

1005 Emblem

1996. Paisano Programme.
2401 **1005** 2p.70 multicoloured 2·00 1·40

1006 Painting

1996. Birth Centenary of David Alfaro Siqueiros (painter).
2402 **1006** 1p.80 multicoloured 2·00 1·40

1007 Dr. Jose Maria Barcelo de Villagran

1996. 32nd National Assembly of Surgeons.
2403 **1007** 1p.80 multicoloured 2·00 1·40

1008 Black Bears

1996. Nature Conservation.
2404 **1008** 1p.80 multicoloured 3·00 1·40

1009 Smiling Sun

1996. 50th Anniv of UNICEF.
2405 **1009** 1p.80 multicoloured 2·00 1·40

1010 Library

1996. 350th Anniv of Palafoxiana Library, Puebla.
2406 **1010** 1p.80 multicoloured 2·00 1·40

1011 Sphere and Atomic Symbol

1996. National Institute for Nuclear Research.
2407 **1011** 1p.80 multicoloured 2·00 1·40

1012 Sun's Rays and Earth

1996. World Day for the Preservation of the Ozone Layer.
2408 **1012** 1p.80 multicoloured 2·00 1·40

1013 Sculpture

1996. 30 Years of Work by Sebastian (sculptor).
2409 **1013** 1p.80 multicoloured 2·00 1·40

1997. Tourism. As Nos. 2263 etc but with value expressed as "$".

2409a	50c. Coahuila	95	40
2409b	70c. Yucatan	1·10	40
2410	1p. Colima	1·50	40
2411	1p.80 Chiapas	1·50	40
2412	2p. Colima	1·50	55
2413	2p. Guanajuato	1·50	40
2413a	2p. Coahiula	1·50	55
2414	2p.30 Chiapas	2·30	55
2415	2p.50 Queretaro	2·30	70
2415a	2p.50 Yucatan	1·90	55
2416	2p.60 Colima	3·00	55
2417	2p.70 Mexico City	3·00	70
2418	3p. Type **869**	3·00	85
2418a	3p. Michoacan	2·75	1·00
2419	3p.10 Coahuila	3·00	70
2420	3p.40 Sinaloa	3·00	1·10
2421	3p.50 Mexico City	3·50	1·00
2421a	3p.60 Sonora	3·75	85
2421b	3p.60 Coahuila	2·75	85
2421c	3p.70 Campeche	3·75	85
2422	4p. Michoacan (vert)	4·50	1·00
2422a	4p.20 Guanajuato	2·75	85
2422b	4p.20 Zacatecas	3·75	85
2423	4p.40 Yucatan	4·50	1·00
2423a	4p.50 Mexico City	4·50	1·00
2424	4p.90 Sonora	4·50	1·10
2425	5p. Queretaro	4·50	1·40
2426	5p. Colima	6·00	85
2426a	5p.30 Michoacan (vert)	4·75	1·10
2426b	5p.90 Queretaro	4·75	1·10
2427	6p. Zacatecas (vert)	6·00	1·30
2427a	6p. Sinaloa	4·75	1·40
2427b	6p. Coahuila	4·75	1·40
2427c	6p.50 Sinaloa	7·50	1·30
2428	7p. Sonora	9·00	1·50
2428a	8p. Zacatecas (vert)	9·50	1·70
2428b	8p. Sinaloa	7·25	1·50
2429	8p.50 Mexico City	10·50	1·70
2430	8p.50 Zacatecas	6·50	1·40
2433	10p. Campeche	20·00	7·00
2433a	10p. Chiapas	11·50	3·50

1014 Pellicer (after D. Rivera)

1997. Birth Centenary of Carlos Pellicer (lyricist).
2435 **1014** 2p.30 multicoloured 2·00 1·40

1015 Eloy Blanco (after Oswaldo)

1997. Birth Centenary (1996) of Andres Eloy Blanco (poet).
2436 **1015** 3p.40 multicoloured 2·40 1·40

1016 Book, Inkwell and Pencil

1997. Confederation of American Educationalists' International Summit Conference.
2437 **1016** 3p.40 multicoloured 2·10 1·30

1017 Tree, Globe and Atomic Cloud

1997. 30th Anniv of Tlatelolco Treaty (Latin American and Caribbean treaty banning nuclear weapons).
2438 **1017** 3p.40 multicoloured 2·40 1·30

1018 Foyer

1997. 90th Anniv of Fifth Main Post Office. Sheet 100×72 mm.
MS2439 **1018** 7p.40 multicoloured 9·75 9·00

1019 Felipe Angeles

1997. Noted Generals. Multicoloured.
2440 2p.30 Type **1019** 1·40 85
2441 2p.30 Joaquin Amaro Dominguez 1·40 85
2442 2p.30 Mariano Escobedo 1·40 85
2443 2p.30 Jacinto Trevino Glez 1·40 85
2444 2p.30 Candido Aguilar Vargas 1·40 85
2445 2p.30 Francisco Urquizo 1·40 85

1020 Woman dancing

1997. International Women's Day.
2446 **1020** 2p.30 multicoloured 2·00 85

1021 "Grammar" (Juan Correa)

1997. First International Spanish Language Congress.
2447 **1021** 3p.40 multicoloured 3·25 2·20

1022 Chavez

1997. Birth Centenary of Dr. Ignacio Chavez.
2448 **1022** 2p.30 multicoloured 1·40 85

1023 State Emblem and Venustiano Carranza (President 1915–20)

1997. 80th Anniv of 1917 Constitution.
2449 **1023** 2p.30 multicoloured 1·40 85

1024 Yanez

1997. 50th Anniv of First Edition of "At the Water's Edge" by Agustin Yanez.
2450 **1024** 2p.30 multicoloured 1·40 85

1025 Mexican Mythological Figures (Luis Nishizawa)

1997. Centenary of Japanese Immigration.
2451 **1025** 3p.40 red, gold and black 3·25 2·20

1026 Rafael Ramirez

1997. Teachers' Day.
2452 **1026** 2p.30 green and black 1·40 85

1027 University

1997. 40th Anniv of Autonomous University of Lower California.
2453 **1027** 2p.30 multicoloured 1·40 85

1028 Dove flying Free

1997. International Day against Illegal Use and Illicit Trafficking of Drugs. Multicoloured.
2454 2p.30 Type **1028** 2·10 85
2455 3p.40 Dove imprisoned behind bars 2·75 1·30
2456 3p.40 Man opening cage 2·75 1·30

Nos. 2454/6 were issued together, *se-tenant*, forming a composite design.

1029 Freud

1997. 58th Death Anniv of Sigmund Freud (pioneer of psychoanalysis).

2457 **1029** 2p.30 blue, green and violet 1·70 85

1030 School Arms

1997. Centenary of Naval School.

2458 **1030** 2p.30 multicoloured 1·70 85

1031 Emblem

1997. Introduction of New Social Security Law.

2459 **1031** 2p.30 multicoloured 1·70 85

1032 Globes and Anniversary Emblem

1997. 60th Anniv of National Bank of Foreign Commerce.

2460 **1032** 3p.40 multicoloured 2·30 1·30

1033 Common Porpoises

1997. Nature Conservation.

2461 **1033** 2p.30 multicoloured 3·75 1·70

1034 Passenger Airliners, 1947 and 1997

1997. 50th Anniv of Mexican Air Pilots' College.

2462 **1034** 2p.30 multicoloured 2·30 85

1035 Runners

1997. 15th Mexico City Marathon.

2463 **1035** 3p.40 multicoloured 2·40 1·30

1036 Hospital Entrance

1997. 150th Anniv of Juarez Hospital.

2464 **1036** 2p.30 multicoloured 1·70 85

1037 Battle of Padierna

1997. 150th Anniversaries of Battles. Multicoloured.

2465 2p.30 Type **1037** 1·70 85

2466 2p.30 Battle of Churubusco 1·70 85

2467 2p.30 Battle of Molino del Rey 1·70 85

2468 2p.30 Defence of Chapultepec Fort 1·70 85

1038 Prieto

1997. Death Centenary of Guillermo Prieto (writer).

2469 **1038** 2p.30 blue 1·70 85

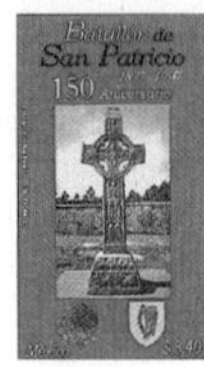

1039 Commemorative Cross

1997. 150th Anniv of Mexican St. Patrick's Battalion.

2470 **1039** 3p.40 multicoloured 3·75 2·50

1040 Emblem

1997. Adolescent Reproductive Health Month.

2471 **1040** 2p.30 multicoloured 1·70 85

1041 Bird carrying Letter

1997. World Post Day. Multicoloured.

2472 3p.40 Type **1041** 2·30 1·30

2473 3p.40 Heinrich von Stephan (founder of UPU) (horiz) 2·30 1·30

1042 Gomez Morin

1997. Birth Centenary of Manuel Gomez Morin (politician).

2474 **1042** 2p.30 multicoloured 1·70 85

1043 Hospital

1997. 50th Anniv of Dr. Manuel Gea Gonzalez General Hospital.

2475 **1043** 2p.30 multicoloured 1·70 85

1044 Emblem

1997. 75th Anniv of Mexican Bar College of Law.

2476 **1044** 2p.30 red and black 1·70 85

1045 Children celebrating Christmas (Ana Botello)

1997. Christmas. Children's Paintings. Multicoloured.

2477 2p.30 Type **1045** 2·00 85

2478 2p.30 Children playing blind-man's-buff (Adrian Laris) 2·00 85

1046 Emblem and Hospital Facade

1997. Centenary of Central University Hospital, Chihuahua.

2479 **1046** 2p.30 multicoloured 1·70 85

1047 Molina and Nobel Medal

1997. Dr. Mario Molina (winner of Nobel Prize for Chemistry, 1995).

2480 **1047** 3p.40 multicoloured 2·10 1·10

1048 Products and Storage Shelves

1997. National Chamber of Baking Industry. Multicoloured.

2481 2p.30 Type **1048** 2·00 85

2482 2p.30 Baker putting loaves in oven 2·00 85

2483 2p.30 Wedding cake, ingredients and baker 2·00 85

Nos. 2481/3 were issued together, *se-tenant*, forming a composite design.

1049 *Buildings* (Jose Chavez Morado)

1997. 25th Cervantes Festival, Guanajuato.

2484 **1049** 2p.30 multicoloured 1·70 85

1050 Galleon and Map of Loreto, California

1997. 300th Anniv of Loreto.

2485 **1050** 2p.30 multicoloured 1·70 85

1051 Sword and Rifle

1998. 50th Anniv of Military Academy, Puebla.

2486 **1051** 2p.30 multicoloured 1·70 85

1052 Hands holding Children on Heart

1998. International Women's Day.

2487 **1052** 2p.30 multicoloured 1·70 85

1053 Dancers (5th of May Festival)

1998. Festivals.

2488 **1053** 3p.50 multicoloured 2·30 1·30

1054 Eiffel Tower, Player and Flag

1998. World Cup Football Championship, France. Multicoloured.

2489 2p.30 Type **1054** 2·30 85

2490 2p.30 Mascot, Eiffel Tower and flag 2·30 85

MS2491 118×202 mm. (a) 6p.20, As No. 2490 (23×40 mm); (b) 8p.60, As No. 2489 (23×40 mm) 15·00 14·00

1055 Sierra

1998. 150th Birth Anniv of Justo Sierra (educationist).

2492 **1055** 2p.30 multicoloured 1·70 85

1056 Zubiran

1998. Birth Centenary of Salvador Zubiran (physician).

2493 **1056** 2p.30 multicoloured 1·70 85

1057 Emblem

1998. 50th Anniv of Organization of American States.

2494 **1057** 3p.40 multicoloured 2·40 1·10

1058 University Emblem

1998. 25th Anniv of People's Autonomous University of Puebla State.

2495 **1058** 2p.30 red, silver and black 1·70 85

1059 Soledad Anaya Solorzano

1998. Teachers' Day.
2496 **1059** 2p.30 bistre, black and cream 1·70 85

1060 Crops

1998. 250th Anniv of Tamaulipas (formerly New Santander) (1st issue).
2497 **1060** 2p.30 multicoloured 1·70 85

See also Nos. 2548.

1061 Macuilxochitl

1998. 20th Anniv of Sports Lottery.
2498 **1061** 2p.30 multicoloured 1·70 85

1062 Manila Galleon

1998. Centenary of Philippine Independence.
2499 **1062** 3p.40 multicoloured 2·00 1·40
MS2500 99×70 mm. 7p.40 Motif as in Type **1062** but with additional Philippine flag 8·25 7·75

1063 Garcia Lorca

1998. Birth Centenary of Federico Garcia Lorca (poet).
2501 **1063** 3p.40 multicoloured 1·70 70

1064 Emblems

1998. 50th Anniv of Universal Declaration of Human Rights.
2502 **1064** 3p.40 green and black 2·00 70

1065 Open Book and Dove

1998. International Day against the Use and Illegal Trafficking of Drugs.
2503 **1065** 2p.30 multicoloured 1·70 70

1066 Alfonso Herrera (founder) and Leopard

1998. 75th Anniv of Chapultepec Zoo.
2504 **1066** 2p.30 multicoloured 1·70 70

1067 Tree

1998. Tree Day.
2505 **1067** 2p.30 multicoloured 1·70 70

1068 St. Peter and St. Paul's Monastery, Teposcolula

1998. Inauguration of Philatelic Museum, Oaxaca. Multicoloured.
2506 2p.30 Type **1068** 3·00 1·70
2507 2p.30 Clay pot, San Bartolo Coyotepec 3·00 1·70
2508 2p.30 *The Road* (painting, Francisco Toledo) 4·50 2·50
2509 2p.30 Gold pectoral from Tomb 7, Monte Alban 4·50 2·50

1069 Juarez

1998. 126th Death Anniv of Benito Juarez (President 1859–64 and 1867–72).
2510 **1069** 2p.30 stone, black and brown 1·70 70

1070 Cultural Museum

1998. St. Dominic's Cultural Centre, Oaxaca. Multicoloured.
2511 2p.30 Type **1070** 1·70 70
2512 2p.30 Francisco de Burgoa Library 1·70 70
2513 2p.30 Historical botanic garden 1·70 70
2514 3p.40 St. Dominic's Monastery (after Teodoro Velasco) 2·50 1·10

1071 Frigate Bird, Blue-footed Booby, Whales and Cacti

1998. Marine Life. Multicoloured.
2515 2p.30 Type **1071** 2·00 1·10
2516 2p.30 Albatross, humpback whale and seagulls 2·00 1·10
2517 2p.30 Tail of whale and swordfish 2·00 1·10
2518 2p.30 Fish eagle, flamingo, herons and dolphins 2·00 1·10
2519 2p.30 Turtles, flamingoes, cormorant and palm tree 2·00 1·10
2520 2p.30 Oystercatcher, turnstone, elephant seal and sealions 2·00 1·10
2521 2p.30 Dolphin, turtle, seagulls and swallows 2·00 1·10
2522 2p.30 Killer whale, dolphins and ray 2·00 1·10
2523 2p.30 Flamingoes, pelican, kingfishers and spider 2·00 1·10
2524 2p.30 Crocodile, roseate spoonbill and tiger heron 2·00 1·10
2525 2p.30 Schools of sardines and anchovies 2·00 1·10
2526 2p.30 Turtle, squid, gold-finned tunnyfish and shark 2·00 1·10
2527 2p.30 Jellyfish, dolphins and fish 2·00 1·10
2528 2p.30 Dolphinfish, barracudas and haddock 2·00 1·10
2529 2p.30 Manatee, fish, anemone and coral 2·00 1·10
2530 2p.30 Seaweed, starfish, coral and fish 2·00 1·10
2531 2p.30 Hammerhead shark, angelfish, gudgeon, eels and coral 2·00 1·10
2532 2p.30 Shrimps, ray and other fish 2·00 1·10
2533 2p.30 Octopus, bass, crayfish and other fish 2·00 1·10
2534 2p.30 Turtle, porcupinefish, coral, angelfish and other fish 2·00 1·10
2535 2p.30 Abalone, clams, razor clam, crayfish and anemone 2·00 1·10
2536 2p.30 Seahorses, angelfish, coral and shells 2·00 1·10
2537 2p.30 Octopus, turtle, crab and moray eel 2·00 1·10
2538 2p.30 Butterflyfish and other fish 2·00 1·10
2539 2p.30 Reef shark, angelfish and corals 2·00 1·10

Nos. 2515/39 were issued together, *se-tenant*, forming a composite design.

1072 Runners

1998. 16th International Marathon, Mexico City.
2540 **1072** 3p.40 multicoloured 2·40 1·30

1073 Aztec Deity

1998. World Tourism Day.
2541 **1073** 3p.40 multicoloured 2·40 1·30

1074 Lucas Alaman (founder)

1998. 175th Anniv of National Archives.
2542 **1074** 2p.30 green, red and black 2·40 1·30

1075 Emblem

1998. 75th Anniv of Interpol.
2543 **1075** 3p.40 multicoloured 2·40 1·30

1076 Stylized Couple

1998. Healthy Pregnancy Month.
2544 **1076** 2p.30 multicoloured 2·10 70

1077 Painting by Luis Nishizawa

1998
2545 **1077** 2p.30 multicoloured 2·30 70

1078 Key and Globe

1998. World Post Day.
2546 **1078** 3p.40 multicoloured 2·40 1·30

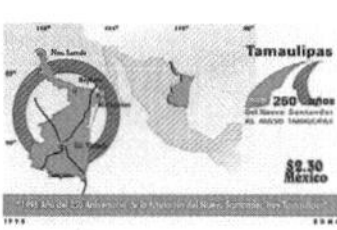

1079 College Campus

1998. 175th Anniv of Military College.
2547 **1079** 2p.30 multicoloured 2·40 70

1080 Map

1998. 250th Anniv of Tamaulipas (formerly New Santander) (2nd issue).
2548 **1080** 2p.30 multicoloured 2·30 70

1081 Golden Eagle

1998. Nature Conservation.
2549 **1081** 2p.30 multicoloured 3·50 1·70

1082 Woman and Potatoes

1998. World Food Day.
2550 **1082** 3p.40 multicoloured 2·40 1·30

1083 Mexico arrowed on Globe

1998. National Migration Week.
2551 **1083** 2p.30 multicoloured 2·40 70

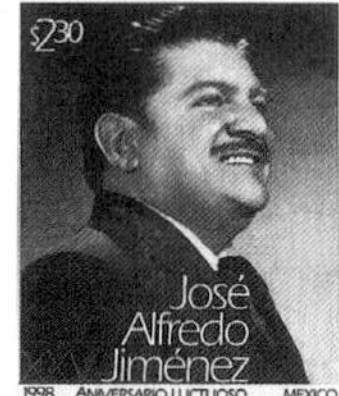

1084 Jimenez

1998. 25th Death Anniv of Jose Alfredo Jimenez (writer).
2552 **1084** 2p.30 multicoloured 2·40 70

1085 Oil Rig and Emblem

1998. 25th Anniv of Mexican Petroleum Engineers' Association.
2553 **1085** 3p.40 multicoloured 2·40 1·30

1086 Mexican Stone Carving and Eiffel Tower

1998. Mexican–French Economic and Cultural Co-operation.
2554 **1086** 3p.40 multicoloured 3·50 1·10

1087 Franciscan Monastery, Colima

1998. 475th Anniv of Colima.
2555 **1087** 2p.30 multicoloured 2·30 70

1088 Wise Men approaching Stable

1998. Christmas. Multicoloured. Self-adhesive.
2556 2p.30 Type **1088** 2·30 70
2557 3p.40 Decorations and pot (vert) 3·00 1·30

1089 Woman with Baby

1998. 50th Anniv of National Institute of Indigenous Peoples.
2558 **1089** 2p.30 multicoloured 2·40 70

1090 Eagle holding Statute

1998. 60th Anniv of Federation of Civil Servants' Trade Unions.
2559 **1090** 2p.30 multicoloured 2·40 70

1091 Aeroplane and Aztec Bird-man

1998. 25th Anniv of Latin-American Civil Aviation Commission.
2560 **1091** 3p.40 multicoloured 2·50 1·30

1092 University Arms

1998. 125th Anniv of Sinaloa Autonomous University.
2561 **1092** 2p.30 multicoloured 2·40 70

1093 Pope John Paul II, Madonna and Map of the Americas

1999. Papal Visit. Sheet 101×73 mm.
MS2562 **1093** 10p. multicoloured 9·00 8·50

1094 *Satmex 5* and Earth

1999. Launch of "Satmex 5" Satellite.
2563 **1094** 3p. multicoloured 3·00 70

1095 Maracas Player and Streamers

1999. Veracruz Carnival.
2564 **1095** 3p. multicoloured 1·70 70

1096 Couple in Hammock

1999. Bicentenary of Acapulco, Guerrero. Mult.
2565 3p. Type **1096** 2·30 70
2566 4p.20 Diving from cliff 3·00 1·00

Nos. 2565/6 were issued together, *se-tenant*, forming a composite design.

1097 Internet Website

1999. International Women's Day.
2567 **1097** 4p.20 multicoloured 2·40 1·00

1098 *Mexico* (Jorge Gonzalez Camarena)

1999. 40th Anniv of National Commission for Free Textbooks.
2568 **1098** 3p. multicoloured 2·30 70

see also Nos.2584/6.

1099 Family Members

1999. 25th Anniv of National Population Council.
2569 **1099** 3p. multicoloured 1·50 70

1100 Diaz fighting Bull

1999. Death Centenary of Ponciano Diaz (toreador). Sheet 95×240 mm.
MS2570 **1100** 10p. multicoloured 9·00 8·50

1101 Guadalupe Ceniceros de Perez

1999. Teachers' Day.
2571 **1101** 3p. multicoloured 2·50 70

1102 Pitcher

1999. 75th Anniv of Mexican Baseball League. Each black and grey.
2572 3p. Type **1102** 2·75 1·40
2573 3p. Catcher 2·75 1·40
2574 3p. Skeletal pitcher 2·75 1·40
2575 3p. Pitcher (different) 2·75 1·40

1103 10p. Banknote

1999. 115th Anniv of National Bank of Mexico. Multicoloured.
2576 3p. Type **1103** 3·00 1·40
2577 3p. Former and current headquarters 3·00 1·40

1104 German Shepherd

1999. World Dog Show. Sheet 98×110 mm containing T **1104** and similar vert designs. Multicoloured.
MS2578 3p. Type **1104**; 3p. Rottweiler; 4p.20 Chihuahua; 4p.20 Xoloitzcuintle 11·50 10·50

1105 Couple holding Hands

1999. International Day against Illegal Use and Illicit Trafficking of Drugs.
2579 **1105** 4p.20 multicoloured 4·25 1·40

1106 Skyscraper

1999. 65th Anniv of National Financial Institute.
2580 **1106** 3p. multicoloured 4·25 1·10

1107 Tree

1999. Tree Day.
2581 **1107** 3p. multicoloured 4·25 1·10

1108 Registration Documents and Fingerprint

1999. 140th Anniv of National Civil Register.
2582 **1108** 3p. multicoloured 2·10 1·10

1109 Runner's Feet

1999. 17th International Marathon, Mexico City.
2583 **1109** 4p.20 multicoloured 5·25 1·70

1110 Children, Flag and Book on Island ("Conoce nuestra Constitucion")

1999. 40th Anniv of National Commission for Free Textbooks (2nd issue). Multicoloured.
2584 3p. Type **1110** 2·10 1·10
2585 3p. Children dancing ("Tsuni tsame") 2·10 1·10
2586 3p. Bird on flower ("Ciencias naturales") 2·10 1·10

1111 *Self-portrait*

1999. Birth Centenary of Rufino Tamayo (artist).
2587 **1111** 3p. multicoloured 3·75 1·00

1112 Building

1999. Bicentenary of Toluca City.
2588 **1112** 3p. black and copper 2·10 1·00

1113 State Arms, Model Figures and Signature

1999. 175th Anniv of State of Mexico.
2589 **1113** 3p. multicoloured 2·10 1·00

1114 "50" and Map of Americas

1999. 50th Anniv of Union of Universities of Latin America.
2590 **1114** 4p.20 multicoloured 2·75 1·40

1115 Emblem

1999. 40th Anniv of Institute of Security and Social Services of State Workers (I.S.S.S.T.E.).
2591 **1115** 3p. multicoloured 2·10 1·10

1116 Map and State Emblem

1999. 25th Anniv of State of Baja California Sur.
2592 **1116** 3p. multicoloured 2·10 1·10

1117 Emblem, "25" and Map

1999. 25th Anniv of Mexican Family Planning.
2593 **1117** 3p. multicoloured 2·10 1·10

1118 Harpy Eagle

1999. Nature Conservation.
2594 **1118** 3p. multicoloured 3·50 1·10

1119 Stone Carving and Arms

1999. 25th Anniv of State of Quintana Roo.
2595 **1119** 3p. multicoloured 2·40 1·10

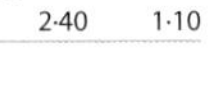

1120 UPU Messengers

1999. 125th Anniv of Universal Postal Union.
2596 **1120** 4p.20 multicoloured 4·50 1·40

1121 Globe and Stamps

1999. World Post Day.
2597 **1121** 4p.20 multicoloured 4·00 1·40

1122 Emblem and Monument

1999. 12th General Assembly of International Council on Monuments and Sites.
2598 **1122** 4p.20 silver, blue and black 2·75 1·40

1123 Chavez and Revueltas

1999. Birth Centenaries of Carlos Chavez and Silvestre Revueltas (composers).
2599 **1123** 3p. multicoloured 2·10 1·00

1124 Emblem

1999. 25th Anniv of Autonomous Metropolitan University.
2600 **1124** 3p. multicoloured 2·10 1·00

1125 Map, Cave Painting and State Arms

1999. 150th Anniv of State of Guerrero.
2601 **1125** 3p. multicoloured 2·40 1·00

1126 "Mexico 1999" in Star and Children (Alfredo Carciarreal)

1999. Christmas. Children's Drawings. Multicoloured.
2602 3p. Type **1126** 3·00 70
2603 4p.20 Christmas decorations (Rodrigo Santiago Salazar) 3·75 1·00

1127 Anniversary Emblem

1999. 20th Anniv of National Commission on Professional Education.
2604 **1127** 3p. green, ultramarine and black 1·80 1·00

1128 Humboldt (naturalist)

1999. Bicentenary of Alexander von Humboldt's Exploration of South America.
2605 **1128** 3p. multicoloured 3·25 1·70

1129 National Free University

1999. Education. Sheet 223×135 mm in shape of flag containing T **1129** and similar multicoloured designs.
MS2606 3p. Type **1129**; 3p. National Polytechnic Institute and Metropolitan Free University (79×24 mm); 3p. Justo Sierra and Jose Nasconcelos and SEP emblem; 3p. National Commission for Free Text-books and teachers (General Directorate of Schoolteachers) (79×24 mm); 4p.20 Reading campaign emblem and students working (oval-shaped, 39×49 mm) 13·50 12·50

1130 Emblem and Crowd

2000. Census.
2607 **1130** 3p. multicoloured 2·00 1·10

1131 Woman ascending Stairs

2000. International Women's Day.
2608 **1131** 4p.20 multicoloured 2·75 1·70

1132 Politicians and Constitution

2000. Democracy. Sheet 227×139 mm in shape of flag containing T **1132** and similar multicoloured designs.
MS2609 3p. Type **1132**; 3p. Politicians and newspaper headlines (38×24 mm); 3p. Horsemen; 3p. Politicians and boy carrying newspapers (38×24 mm); 4p.20 Boy posting voting paper and electoral card (oval-shaped, 39×49 mm) 13·50 12·50

1133 Children using Computers

2000. Millennium Messages. Sheet 101×74 mm.
MS2610 **1133** 10p. multicoloured 12·00 11·00

1134 Totonaca Temple, El Tajin

2000
2611 **1134** 3p. multicoloured 4·50 1·10

1135 Emblem, Books and Keyboard

2000. 50th Anniv of National Association of Universities and Institutes of Higher Education.
2612 **1135** 3p. multicoloured 2·10 1·10

1136 Emblem

2000. 25th Tourism Fair, Acapulco.
2613 **1136** 4p.20 multicoloured 2·75 1·40

1137 Men in Canoe and Sailing Ship

2000. 500th Anniv of the Discovery of Brazil.
2614 **1137** 4p.20 multicoloured 4·50 1·70

1138 Luis Alvarez Barret

2000. Teachers' Day.
2615 **1138** 3p. multicoloured 2·00 1·10

1139 Flying Cars and Boy with Dog (Alejandro Guerra Millan)

2000. Stampin the Future. Winning Entries in Children's International Painting Competition. Mult.
2616 3p. Type **1139** 2·00 1·10
2617 4p.20 Houses and space ships (Carlos Hernandez Garcia) 2·75 1·40

1140 Emblem

2000. Fourth Asian–Pacific Telecommunications and Information Industry Economic Co-operation Forum.
2618 **1140** 4p.20 multicoloured 3·00 1·40

1141 Young Children

2000. International Anti-drugs Day.
2619 **1141** 4p.20 multicoloured 3·50 1·40

1142 Pre-hispanic Sculpture

2000. Provision for Two Million Homes by the National Institute for Worker's Houses. Sheet 115×170 mm containing T **1142** and similar multicoloured designs.
MS2620 3p. Type **1142**; 3p. Sculpture of temple; 10p. Human figures sitting in circle (sculpture) (oval-shaped, 49×39 mm) 13·50 12·50

1143 Mosaica and Men in Costume

2000. Identity and Culture. Sheet 227×139 mm in shape of a flag containing T **1143** and similar multicoloured designs.
MS2621 3p. Type **1143**; 3p. Film actors (79×25 mm); 3p. Gondolas and horse riding act; 3p. Table of food (79×25 mm); 4p.20 Acrobats and children wearing national costumes (oval-shaped, 39×49 mm) 14·50 13·50

1144 Pictograms

2000. Convive (disabled persons' organization).
2622 **1144** 3p. multicoloured 2·75 1·10

1145 Globe and Member Flags

2000. 20th Anniv of Association of Latin American Integration.
2623 **1145** 4p.20 multicoloured 3·00 1·40

1146 Emblem

2000. 125th Anniv of Restoration of Senate.
2624 **1146** 3p. multicoloured 2·30 1·10

1147 Drawings and Skeleton (image scaled to 49% of original size)

2000. EXPO 2000 World's Fair, Hanover, Germany. Sheet 223×222 mm containing T **1147** and similar horiz designs. Multicoloured.
MS2625 1p. Type **1147**; 1p. Musicians, stone devil and child's face; 1p.80 Painting and eye; 1p.80 Drawing and old photographs; 2p. Computer, factory and car assembly line; 2p. Stone carvings, paintings and modern art; 3p. Chameleon, parrots and fish; 3p. Jewellery, fruit and weaving; 3p. Construction site, machinist and combine harvester; 3p.60 Globe and exhibition building, Hanover; 4p.20 Emblem (oval-shaped, 39×49 mm) 23·00 21·00

1148 Building Façade and Bank Note

2000. 75th Anniv of Bank of Mexico. Sheet 100×72 mm.
MS2626 10p. multicoloured 7·50 7·00

1149 Runners crossing Finishing Line

2000. 18th International Marathon, Mexico City.
2627 **1149** 4p.20 multicoloured 3·75 1·70

1150 Athletes and Sydney Opera House

2000. Olympic Games, Sydney.
2628 **1150** 4p.20 multicoloured 3·75 1·70

1151 Emblem and Family

2000. Paisano Programme (support for Mexicans returning home from abroad).
2629 **1151** 4p.20 multicoloured 3·00 1·70

1152 Emblem

2000. 2nd International UNESCO World Conference, Colima.
2630 **1152** 4p.20 multicoloured 3·75 1·70

1153 Profiles

2000. Women's Health Month.
2631 **1153** 3p. multicoloured 2·30 1·10

1154 Building and Emblem

2000. 250th Anniv of Ciudad Victoria, Tamaulipas.
2632 **1154** 3p. multicoloured 2·30 1·10

1155 Bird holding Letter

2000. World Post Day.
2633 **1155** 4p.20 multicoloured 3·75 1·70

1156 Emblem

2000. 50th Anniv of National Human Rights Commission.
2634 **1156** 3p. silver and blue 2·30 1·10

1157 Doctors and Ambulance

2000. New Millennium. Sheet 223×135 mm in shape of flag, containing T **1157** and similar multicoloured designs.
MS2635 3p. Type **1157**; 3p. Posters, doctors and globe (79×25 mm); 3p. Children receiving injections; 3p. Poster showing tractor and crowd demonstrating (79×25 mm); 4p.20, Modern medical technology (oval-shaped, 39×49 mm) 13·50 12·50

1158 Clouds and Emblem

2000. 50th Anniv of World Meteorological Organization.
2636 **1158** 3p. multicoloured 2·75 1·10

1159 Emblem

2000. 50th Anniv of International Diabetes Federation.
2637 **1159** 4p.20 gold and red 2·75 1·70

1160 Contemporary Art with Sculpture

2000. Art. Sheet 223×39 mm in shape of flag, containing T **1160** and similar multicoloured designs.
MS2638 3p. Type **1160**; 3p. Photographs (39×25 mm); 3p. Opera singer and movie actors; 3p. Dancers (39×25 mm); 4p.20 Ballet dancers and musicians (oval-shaped, 39×49 mm) 13·50 12·50

1161 Samuel Morse, Juan de la Granja and Telegraph Apparatus

2000. 150th Anniv of Telegraph in Mexico.
2639 **1161** 3p. multicoloured 2·30 1·10

Samuel Morse invented the telegraph and Morse code system and Juan de la Granja introduced the telegraph to Mexico.

1162 Bunuel

2000. Birth Centenary of Luis Bunuel (film director).
2640 **1162** 3p. silver, black and red 3·00 1·10

1163 Lightning

2000. 25th Anniv of Electric Investigation Institute.
2641 **1163** 3p. multicoloured 3·00 1·10

1164 Building Customs House, and Bridge

2000. Centenary of Customs.
2642 **1164** 3p. multicoloured 2·30 1·10

1165 Star and Girl (Maria Carina Lona Martinez)

2000. Christmas. Children's paintings. Multicoloured.
2643 3p. Type **1165** 2·30 1·10
2644 4p.20 Poinsettia (Daniela Escamilla Rodriguez) 3·75 1·40

1166 Television Set and Emblem

2000. 50th Anniv of Television in Mexico.
2645 **1166** 3p. multicoloured 3·00 1·10

1167 Adamo Boari (architect)

2000. Centenary of Commencement of Construction of Postal Headquarters, Mexico City. Sheet 92×100 mm, containing T **1167** and similar designs. Multicoloured.
MS2646 3p. multicoloured; 3p. black, brown and red; 3p. multicoloured; 10p. black, brown and red (71×39 mm) 13·00 12·00

Designs:—As Type **1167**—3p. Building facade; 3p. Gonzalo Garita y Frontera (engineer). 71×39 mm—10p. Completed building.

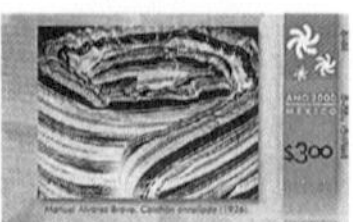

1168 Coiled Mattress (Manuel Alvarez Bravo)

2000. Photography. Sheet 223×135 mm in shape of flag, containing T **1168** and similar multicoloured designs.
MS2647 3p. Type **1168**; 3p. Various portraits (79×25 mm); 3p. Roses (Tina Modotti); 3p. Various photographs including a lift, a lake, a 1925 car, a helicopter, a ruined building, a street scene, men in costume and boot heels (79×25 mm); 4p.20 Men in gas masks (oval-shaped, 39×49 mm) 13·50 12·50

1169 Pyramid of the Niches

2000. El Tajin.
2648 **1169** 3p. multicoloured 4·50 1·10

1170 Manatee

2000. Nature Conservation.
2649 **1170** 3p. multicoloured 4·50 1·40

1171 Sarabia

2000. Birth Centenary of Francisco Sarabia (aviator).
2650 **1171** 3p. multicoloured 3·50 1·40

1172 Telephone Exchange and Fabric Shops

2000. Industry. Sheet 223×135 mm in shape of flag, containing T **1172** and similar multicoloured designs.
MS2651 3p. Type **1172**; 3p. Tractor and modern farming (39 ×25 mm); 3p. Traditional farming methods and car; 3p. Manufacturing and industrial plant (39×25 mm); 4p.20 Globe and industries (oval-shaped, 39×49 mm) 13·50 12·50

1173 Stamps and Post Collection

2000. Forms of Communication. Sheet 223×135 mm in shape of flag, containing T **1173** and similar multicoloured designs.
MS2652 3p. Type **1173**; 3p. Telephone operators and telegraph clerk (39×25 mm); 3p. Old and modern train and station; 3p. Motorway (39×25 mm); 4p.20 Globe and satellite and satellite dish (oval-shaped, 39×49 mm) 13·50 12·50

2001. Tourism. As Nos. 2410 etc but with face value changed.
2658 6p.50 Queretaro 6·00 1·10
2662 11p.50 Queretaro 12·00 2·75
2668 30p Queretaro 23·00 7·00

1174 Chiapas

2001. Tourism.
2670 **1174** 1p.50 multicoloured 2·30 2·10
2673 **1174** 8p.50 multicoloured 7·25 5·50

1175 Emblem, Book and Building

2001. 50th Anniv of National Autonomous University.
2680 **1175** 3p. multicoloured 3·00 1·40

1176 Woman

2001. International Women's Day.
2681 **1176** 4p.20 multicoloured 2·75 2·00

1177 Cement Factory

2001. 53rd Anniv of National Cement Chamber.
2682 **1177** 3p. multicoloured 2·10 1·40

1178 Vasconcelos and Ink Pen

2001. 42nd Death Anniv of Jose Vasconcelos (lawyer).
2683 **1178** 3p. multicoloured 2·10 1·40

1179 People Running and Flames

2001. 50th Anniv of United Nations High Commissioner for Refugees.
2684 **1179** 4p.20 multicoloured 2·75 2·00

1180 *Self-portrait wearing Jade Necklace*

2001. Frida Kahlo (artist) Commemoration.
2685 **1180** 4p.20 multicoloured 3·75 2·00

A stamp of similar design was issued by the United States of America.

1181 Stylized Bird

2001. Anti-drugs Campaign.
2686 **1181** 4p.20 multicoloured 3·75 2·00

1182 De la Cueva

2001. Birth Centenary of Mario de la Cueva (university director).
2687 **1182** 3p. blue and gold 2·10 1·40

1183 Emblem

2001. International Year of Volunteers.
2688 **1183** 4p.20 multicoloured 2·75 2·00

1184 Women and Flowers (painting)

2001. Rodolfo Morales (artist) Commemoration. Sheet 121×60 mm.
MS2689 **1184** 10p. multicoloured 7·50 6·25

1185 Owl

2001. 65th Anniv of Federal Justice Tribunal.
2690 **1185** 3p. multicoloured 2·10 1·40

1186 Emblems and Building

2001. 450th Anniv of University of Mexico.
2691 **1186** 3p. multicoloured 2·10 1·40

1187 Adela Formoso

2001. 20th Death Anniv of Adela Formoso de Obregon Santalla (women's rights activist).
2692 **1187** 3p. multicoloured 2·10 1·40

1188 Daniel Villegas

2001. 25th Death Anniv of Daniel Cosío Villegas (historian).
2693 **1188** 3p. multicoloured 2·10 1·40

1189 Past and Present Pharmaceutical Drugs

2001
2694 **1189** 3p. multicoloured 2·40 1·40

1190 Girl with Grandfather

2001. Grandparents Day.
2695 **1190** 3p. multicoloured 2·10 1·40

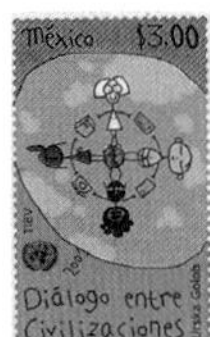

1191 Children encircling Globe

2001. United Nations Year of Dialogue among Civilizations.
2696 **1191** 3p. multicoloured 3·00 1·40

1192 Envelope as Bicycle

2001. Stamp Day.
2697 **1192** 3p. yellow, red and blue 3·00 1·40

1193 Lily

2001. Women's Health Day.
2698 **1193** 3p. multicoloured 2·10 1·40

1194 Eye and People

2001. 25th Anniv of Ophthalmic Institute.
2699 **1194** 4p.20 multicoloured 2·75 2·10

1195 Tufted Jay (*Cyanocorax dickeyi*)

2001. Endangered Species.
2700 **1195** 5p.30 multicoloured 4·50 2·40

1196 Children (Eunice Gonzalez)

2001. Christmas. Children's Paintings. Multicoloured.
2701 3p. Type **1196** 3·00 1·40
2702 4p.20 Candles (Javier Nunez) 4·50 2·00

1197 Nurse and Children

2001. Educational Scholarship Fund for Indigenous Children. Sheet 101×72 mm. P 14.
MS2703 **1197** 3p. multicoloured 2·30 2·10

1198 Technicians

2001. National Fund for Education. Sheet 101×72 mm.
MS2704 **1198** 3p. multicoloured 2·30 2·10

1199 Boy and Girl

2001. Children's Accident Prevention Campaign.
2705 **1199** 3p. multicoloured 2·30 1·40

1200 Apple

2001. World Food Day.
2706 **1200** 3p. multicoloured 2·30 1·40

1201 Wild Sheep

2002. Endangered Species.
2707 **1201** 6p. multicoloured 4·75 2·75

1202 Squash and Snail

2002. Birth Centenary of Manuel Alvarez Bravo (photographer).
2708 **1202** 6p. black 4·25 2·75

1203 Chinese Dragon and Quetzalcoatl

2002. 30th Anniv of China—Mexico Diplomatic Relations.
2709 **1203** 6p. multicoloured 4·00 2·75

1204 Mangroves

2002. Conservation. Multicoloured.

2710	50c. Type **1204**	40	35
2710a	50c. No. 2732	40	35
2734	50c. Deserts (No. 2732)	75	35
2711	1p. Rivers	40	35
2711a	1p. No. 2728	45	35
2711b	1p. Lakes and lagoons (No. 2733)	45	35
2712	1p. Forests	55	35
2735	1p. Orchids (No. 2728)	75	35
2713	1p.50 Terrestrial mammals	75	35
2714	2p. Cacti	1·10	35
2715	2p. Cloud forest	1·10	35
2716	2p.50 No. 2715	1·40	65
2717	2p.50 No. 2713	1·40	65
2717a	2p.50 No. 2720	1·40	65
2736	2p.50 No. 2720	1·50	70
2718	4p.50 Birds	2·30	70
2719	5p. Reptiles	2·75	75
2720	5p. Marine turtles	2·75	75
2720a	5p. No. 2733	2·20	70
2720b	5p. Tropical forests (No. 2724)	2·20	70
2721	6p. Birds of prey	3·00	90
2722	6p. Butterflies	3·00	90
2722a	6p.50 No. 2712	2·75	1·30
2722b	6p.50 No. 2725	2·75	1·30
2722c	6p.50 No. 2719	2·75	1·30
2722d	6p.50 No. 2718	2·75	1·30
2722e	6p.50 Rivers (No. 2711)	2·75	1·30
2738	6p.50 Marine mammals (No. 2725)	55·00	70·00
2739	6p.50 Birds (No. 2718)	3·00	1·40
2723	7p. Reefs	3·50	1·10
2723a	7p. No. 2724	2·75	1·30
2740	7p. Seas (No. 2729)	4·50	2·10
2723b	7p.50 No. 2729	3·50	1·50
2723c	7p.50 No. 2713	3·50	1·50
2723d	7p.50 No. 2727	3·50	1·50
2740a	7p.50 Wild cats (No. 2727)	4·50	2·10
2724	8p.50 Tropical forests	4·25	1·30
2741	8p.50 Marine mammals (No. 2725)	5·25	2·50
2725	10p. Marine mammals	5·25	1·50
2726	10p. No. 2713	5·25	1·50
2727	10p.50 Wild cats	5·25	1·80
2728	10p.50 Orchids	5·25	1·80
2728a	10p.50 No. 2723	5·25	1·80
2741a	10p.50 Wild cats (No. 2727)	9·75	4·50
2729	11p.50 Seas	5·75	1·80
2730	11p.50 Coastal birds	5·75	1·80
2731	12p. No. 2724	6·00	1·80
2731a	13p. No. 2711	3·75	1·80
2731b	13p. No. 2710	3·75	1·80
2731c	13p. No. 2715	3·75	1·80
2731d	14p.50 No. 2730	8·25	3·75
2731e	14p.50 Marine mammals (No. 2725)	8·25	3·75
2732	30p. Deserts	15·00	4·50
2733	30p. Lakes and lagoons	15·00	4·50
2733a	30p.50 No. 2722	11·00	5·25
2733b	30p.50 Sea turtles (No. 2720)	11·00	5·25

1205 Emblems

2002. Olympic Games, Salt Lake City, USA.
2760 **1205** 8p.50 multicoloured 6·00 2·50

1206 Stylized Ship

2002. Centenary of Modernization of Veracruz Artificial Port.
2761 **1206** 6p. multicoloured 4·25 2·10

1207 Mayan Head and Korean Symbol

2002. 40th Anniv of Korea—Mexico Diplomatic Relations.
2762 **1207** 8p.50 multicoloured 4·25 2·10

1208 Mexico City Buildings

2002. Consultative Council for the Restoration of Historic Buildings.
2763 **1208** 6p. multicoloured 4·25 2·10

1209 Emblem

2002. International Women's Day. National Women's Institute.
2764 **1209** 8p.50 blue and vermilion 5·50 2·50

1210 *La Despedida del Revolucionario*

2002. 150th Birth Anniv of Jose Guadalupe Posada (artist).
2765 **1210** 6p. black and olive 4·25 2·10

1211 Jose Sierra Mendez

2002. 90th Death Anniv of Jose Sierra Mendez (writer).
2766 **1211** 6p. multicoloured 4·25 2·10

1212 "Esteban and the Striped Cat" (Abel Quezada)

2002. United Nations Special Session for Children.
2767 **1212** 6p. multicoloured 4·25 2·10

1213 Alberto Lhuillier (discoverer), Ruins and Mayan Head

2002. 50th Anniv of Discovery of Tumba de Pakal (Mayan archaeological site).
2768 **1213** 6p. multicoloured 4·25 2·10

1214 Players at Goalmouth

2002. World Cup Football Championship, Japan and South Korea.
2769 **1214** 8p.50 multicoloured 6·00 2·50

1215 Pot with Map of Americas holding People as Tree

2002. International Day against Drug Abuse.
2770 **1215** 6p. multicoloured 4·25 2·10

1216 Stylized Map of Americas

2002. Fifth Mexico—Central American Summit.
2771 **1216** 6p. multicoloured 4·25 2·10

1217 Mountain

2002. International Year of Mountains.
2772 **1217** 6p. multicoloured 4·25 2·10

1218 Boy wearing Traditional Costume

2002. International Day of Indigenous Peoples.
2773 **1218** 6p. multicoloured 4·25 2·10

1219 High Tension Power Lines

2002. Federal Commission of Electricity.
2774 **1219** 6p. multicoloured 4·25 2·10

1220 Face enclosed in Blood Droplet

2002. National Blood Donors' Day.
2775 **1220** 6p. multicoloured 4·25 2·10

1221 Apple and Map of Mexico

2002. Administrative Secretariat for Development Control (SECODAM).
2776 **1221** 6p. multicoloured 4·25 2·10

1222 Scales and Code

2002. Code of Practise for Public Administrations.
2777 **1222** 6p. multicoloured 4·25 2·10

1223 Clasped Hands

2002. International Day of Tourism.
2778 **1223** 8p.50 purple, black and lemon 5·75 2·50

1224 Torso, Electrocardiogram Diagram and Watch

2002. National Organ Donation Week.
2779 **1224** 6p. multicoloured 4·25 2·10

1225 Birds and Envelopes

2002. Stamp Day.
2780 **1225** 8p.50 multicoloured 5·75 2·50

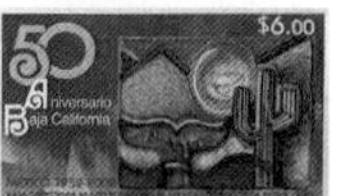
1226 Mountains, Whale Tail, Sun and Cactus

2002. 50th Anniv of Baja California Peninsula.
2781 **1226** 6p. multicoloured 4·25 2·10

1227 Stairs

2002. Birth Centenary of Luis Barragan (architect).
2782 **1227** 6p. multicoloured 4·25 2·10

1228 *Man's Conquest of the Air* (detail) (Juan O'Gorman)

2002. 50th Anniv of Mexico City Airport. Details from "Man's Conquest of the Air" by Juan O'Gorman. Multicoloured.
2783 6p. Type **1228** 4·25 2·10
2784 6p. Early aviators, parachutist and man wearing protective suit 4·25 2·10
2785 8p.50 Mexico city and aviators 5·00 2·50
Nos. 2783/5 were issued together, *se-tenant* forming a composite design.

1229 Mexican and Spanish Flags

2002. 25th Anniv of Renewal of Spain—Mexico Diplomatic Relations.
2786 **1229** 8p.50 multicoloured 5·00 2·50

1230 Globe, "e" and Binary Codes

2002. 75th Anniv of the Development of Information Technology in Mexico.
2787 **1230** 6p. violet, vermilion and black 4·00 2·10

1231 Anniversary Emblem

2002. Centenary of Pan American Health Organization.
2788 **1231** 8p.50 multicoloured 5·50 2·50

1232 Nezahualcoyotl

2002. 600th Birth Anniv of Nezahualcoyotl (King of the Texcoco).
2789 **1232** 6p. multicoloured 4·25 2·10

1233 Nativity (Sara Elisa Miranda Alcaraz)

2002. Christmas. Children's Paintings. Multicoloured.
2790 6p. Type **1233** 4·25 2·10
2791 8p.50 Nativity (Alejandro Ruiz Sampedro) 5·00 2·50

1234 Emblem

2002. Life without Violence Campaign.
2792 **1234** 8p.50 multicoloured 5·50 2·50

1235 Early Biplane

2003. Centenary of Powered Flight. Phosphorescent markings.
2793 **1235** 8p.50 multicoloured 5·00 2·50

1236 Emblem

2003. 60th Anniv of Iberoamericana University, Mexico City.
2794 **1236** 6p. multicoloured 3·50 2·10

1237 Woman

2003. International Woman's Day.
2795 **1237** 8p.50 multicoloured 4·75 2·50

1238 City Arms and Buildings

2003. Centenary of Mexicali City.
2796 **1238** 6p. multicoloured 3·50 2·10

1239 Dam and Crane

2003. 50th Anniv of Industry and Construction (cmic).
2797 **1239** 6p. multicoloured 3·75 2·10

1240 Emblem and Children

2003. 60th Anniv of Frederico Gomez Children's Hospital.
2798 **1240** 6p. multicoloured 3·75 2·10

1241 Miguel Hildago y Costilla

2003. 250th Birth Anniv of Miguel Hildago y Costilla (social reformer and independence pioneer).
2799 **1241** 6p. multicoloured 17·00 14·00

1242 Gregorio Torres Quintero

2003. Teacher's Day. Gregorio Torres Quintero (writer) Commemoration.
2800 **1242** 6p. multicoloured 17·00 14·00

1243 Telescope, Planets and Eclipse

2003. 125th Anniv of National Astronomical Observatory.
2801 **1243** 6p. multicoloured 3·75 2·10

1244 Film, Cigarette and Stop Sign

2003. International No-Smoking Day. Smoking-free Cinemas Campaign.
2802 **1244** 8p.50 multicoloured 4·75 2·50

1245 Map

2003. First Satellite Network.
2803 **1245** 6p. multicoloured 3·75 2·10

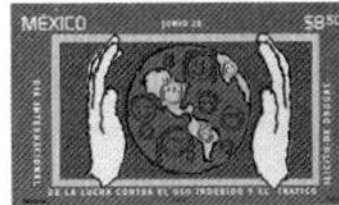
1246 Hands enclosing Globe

2003. International Day against Drug Abuse.
2804 **1246** 8p.50 multicoloured 4·75 2·50

1247 Baseball and Bat

2003. 30th Anniv of Professional Baseball Hall of Fame.
2805 **1247** 6p. multicoloured 3·75 2·10

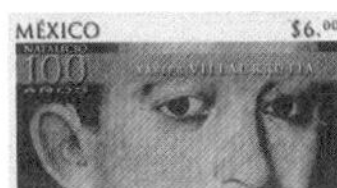
1248 Xavier Villaurrutia

2003. Birth Centenary of Xavier Villaurrutia (writer).
2806 **1248** 6p. multicoloured 3·75 2·10

1249 Early Vet and Modern Veterinary Surgery

2003. 150th Anniv of Veterinary Education in Mexico and America.
2807 **1249** 6p. multicoloured 3·75 2·10

1250 University Building

2003. 25th Anniv of National Teachers' University.
2808 **1250** 6p. multicoloured 3·75 2·10

1251 *Tlaloc* (sculpture) (Federico Silva)

2003. Museo Federico Silva (contemporary culture museum), San Luis Potosi.
2809 **1251** 6p. multicoloured 3·75 2·10

1252 Family

2003. National Seminar on Organ Donation.
2810 **1252** 6p. multicoloured 3·75 2·10

1253 Bird carrying Envelope

2003. Stamp Day.
2811 **1253** 8p.50 multicoloured 4·75 2·50

1254 Voting Slip, Ballot Box and Women

2003. 50th Anniv of Vote for Women.
2812 **1254** 6p. multicoloured 3·75 2·10

1255 Secretariat Building

2003. 60th Anniv of Health Secretariat.
2813 **1255** 6p. multicoloured 3·75 2·10

1256 Auditorium

2003. Centenary of Juarez Theatre, Guanajuato City.
2814 **1256** 6p. multicoloured 3·75 2·10

1257 Emblem

2003. 450th Anniv of First Chair of Law in America.
2815 **1257** 8p.50 multicoloured 4·75 2·50

1258 "Development and Impact of the Electricity" (German Reyes Retana)

2003. Centenary of Centralized Light and Power.
2816 **1258** 6p. multicoloured 3·75 2·10

1259 The Nativity (Valeria Baez)

2003. Christmas. Children's Paintings. Multicoloured.
2817 6p. Type **1259** 3·75 2·10
2818 8p.50 Nativity (Octavio Aleman) 4·75 2·50

1260 Laughing Child

2003. Rights of the Child.
2819 **1260** 6p. multicoloured 3·75 2·10

1261 Globe as Heart and Leaves

2003. International Day of Freshwater.
2820 **1261** 8p.50 multicoloured 4·75 2·50

1262 College Facade and Students

2003. 25th Anniv of Professional Technical College (CONALEP).
2821 **1262** 6p. multicoloured 3·75 2·10

1263 John Paul II

2004. 25th Anniv of Pope John Paul II's First Visit to Mexico.
2822 **1263** 6p. multicoloured 3·75 2·10

1264 Agustin Yanez

2004. Birth Centenary of Agustin Yanez (writer and politician).
2823 **1264** 8p.50 multicoloured 4·50 2·50

1265 Enrique Aguilar Gonzalez

2004. Teachers' Day. Enrique Aguilar Gonzalez Commemoration.
2824 **1265** 8p.50 blue 4·50 2·50

1266 Satellite, Cable and Globe

2004. 50th Anniv of Cable Television.
2825 **1266** 6p. multicoloured 3·75 2·10

1267 Quartz and Society Emblem

2004. Centenary of Geological Society.
2826 **1267** 8p.50 multicoloured 4·50 2·50

1268 Stylized Figures

2004. International Day against Drug Abuse.
2827 **1268** 8p.50 multicoloured 4·50 2·50

1269 Salvador Novo

2004. Writer's Birth Centenaries. Multicoloured.
2828 7p. Type **1269** 4·00 2·20
2829 7p. Gilberto Owen 4·00 2·20
2830 7p. Celestino Gorostiza 4·00 2·20

1270 Boys and Centenary Emblem

2004. Centenary of FIFA (Federation Internationale de Football).
2831 **1270** 11p.50 multicoloured 6·50 3·50

1271 Borola Tacuche

2004. La Familia Burron (comic created by Gabriel Vargas Bernal).
2832 **1271** 6p. multicoloured 3·50 1·90

1272 Athena, Columns and Swimmer

2004. Olympic Games, Athens.
2833 **1272** 10p.50 multicoloured 6·00 3·25

1273 Mountain and Town

2004. 450th Anniv of Fresnillo.
2834 **1273** 7p. multicoloured 4·00 2·20

1274 University Building

2004. 50th Anniv of Chihuahua University.
2835 **1274** 7p. multicoloured 4·00 2·20

1275 Building

2004. Economic and Cultural Fund (CFE).
2836 **1275** 8p.50 multicoloured 4·75 2·75

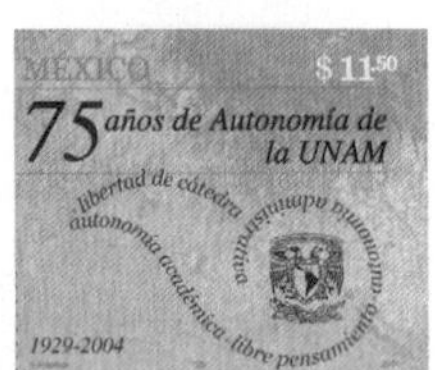

1276 Emblem

2004. 75th Anniv of National Independent University (UNAM).
2837 **1276** 11p.50 multicoloured 6·50 3·50

1277 Building Facade

2004. 70th Anniv of Palace of Arts.
2838 **1277** 7p. multicoloured 4·00 2·20

1278 Fund Workers

2004. 45th Anniv of Official Federal Social Fund (ISSSTE).
2839 **1278** 6p. multicoloured 3·50 1·90

1279 City Symbols and Plaque

2004. 300th Anniv of Completion of Campeche City Walls.
2840 **1279** 6p. multicoloured 3·50 1·90

1280 Francisco Gonzalez Bocanegra (lyricist) and Jaime Nuno (composer)

2004. 150th Anniv of National Anthem.
2841 **1280** 6p.50 multicoloured 3·75 2·10

1281 Dove holding Envelope and Post Box

2004. Stamp Day.
2842 **1281** 6p. magenta 3·50 1·90

1282 Envelope and Seal

2004. 125th Anniv of Universal Postal Union Membership.
2843 **1282** 8p.50 multicoloured 4·75 2·75

1283 Cameraman and Images

2004. 45th Anniv of Once Television Station (Channel 11).
2844 **1283** 8p.50 multicoloured 4·75 2·75

1284 "180"

2004. 180th Anniv of Control Board (ASF).
2845 **1284** 6p.50 multicoloured 3·75 2·10

1285 General Escobedo (statue)

2004. 400th Anniv of General Escobedo Municipality.
2846 **1285** 8p.50 multicoloured 4·75 2·75

1286 Seated Woman

2004. 75th Anniv of Health Secretariat.
2847 **1286** 8p.50 multicoloured 4·75 2·75

1287 Boy listening to Radio

2004. 60th Anniv of Radio Educacion (XEEP).
2848 **1287** 6p.50 multicoloured 3·75 2·10

1288 Building Facade

2004. 50th Anniv of SCT (ministry of transport) National Centre. Multicoloured.
2849 6p.50 Type **1288** 3·75 2·10
MS2850 92×100 mm. 7p.50 As No. 2849 (72×39 mm) 6·00 5·25

1289 Miguel Hidalgo, Benito Juarez and Francisco I. Madero (painting) (David Alfaro Siqueiros)

2004. 45th Anniv of National Free Books Committee.
2851 **1289** 10p.50 multicoloured 6·00 4·00

1290 Couple watching Sky (Coral Juarez Cuapio)

2004. Christmas. Children's Paintings. Mult.
2852 7p.50 Type **1290** 4·25 3·00
2853 10p.50 Pinata and presents (Malinalli Ramirez MTZ) (vert) 6·00 4·00

1291 Car, Seat Belt and Roadway

2004. Road Accident Prevention Campaign.
2854 **1291** 8p.50 multicoloured 4·75 3·25

1292 Amethyst

2004. Minerals.
2855 **1292** 8p.50 multicoloured † †

1293 Building Facade

2005. Centenary of General Hospital.
2856 **1293** 6p.50 multicoloured 3·75 2·50

1294 Faces

2005. International Women's Day.
2857 **1294** 6p.50 multicoloured 3·75 2·50

1295 Face

2005. 50th Anniv of "Pedro Paramo" (novel by Juan Rulfo).
2858 **1295** 6p.50 multicoloured 3·75 2·50

1296 Athletes

2005. Universiada 2005 (games).
2859 **1296** 7p.50 multicoloured 4·25 3·00

1297 Globe, Child and Vaccine Droplets

2005. World without Polio Campaign.
2860 **1297** 10p.50 multicoloured 6·00 4·25

1298 Eulalia Guzman

2005. Teachers' Day. Eulalia Guzman Commem.
2861 **1298** 6p.50 multicoloured 3·75 2·50

1299 Don Quixote

2005. 400th Anniv of Publication of *Don Quixote de la Mancha* (novel by Miguel de Cervantes). Sheet 120×159 mm containing T **1299** and similar horiz designs. Multicoloured.
MS2862 6p.50 Type **1299**; 10p.50 Riding Rocinante; 10p.50 Don Quixote 16·00 14·00

1300 Albert Einstein riding Bicycle

2005. International Year of Physics.
2863 **1300** 7p.50 multicoloured 4·25 3·00

1301 Flower of Hands and Emblem

2005. National Commission for Human Rights.
2864 **1301** 6p.50 multicoloured 3·75 2·50

1302 Building Facade

2005. Centenary of National Association of Architects.
2865 **1302** 6p.50 multicoloured 3·75 2·50

1303 Child and Hands

2005. International Day against Drug Abuse.

2866	**1303** 10p.50 multicoloured	6·00	4·25

1304 Eye and Emblem

2005. Transparency and Access to Information.

2867	**1304** 6p.50 multicoloured	3·75	2·50

1305 Players

2005. Baseball.

2868	**1305** 7p.50 multicoloured	4·25	3·00

1306 Memin Pinguin

2005. "Memin Pinguin" (comic character created by Yolanda Vargas). Multicoloured.

2869	6p.50 Type **1306**	3·75	2·50
2870	6p.50 Holding flower	3·75	2·50
2871	6p.50 Delivering papers	3·75	2·50
2872	6p.50 Wearing evening clothes	3·75	2·50
2873	6p.50 With mother	3·75	2·50

1307 Juan O'Gorman

2005. Birth Centenary of Juan O'Gorman (artist).

2874	**1307** 7p.50 multicoloured	4·25	3·00

1308 Silver

2005. Minerals. Multicoloured.

2875	6p.50 Type **1308**	3·75	2·50
2876	6p.50 Acanthitite	3·75	2·50
2877	6p.50 Marcasite	3·75	2·50
2878	6p.50 Meteorite	3·75	2·50
2879	6p.50 Gold	3·75	2·50
2880	6p.50 Galena	3·75	2·50
2881	6p.50 Pyrites	3·75	2·50
2882	6p.50 Inscr "Yeso" (plaster)	3·75	2·50
2883	6p.50 Mango Calcite	3·75	2·50
2884	6p.50 Baryte	3·75	2·50
2885	6p.50 Stephanite	3·75	2·50
2886	6p.50 Red Calcite	3·75	2·50
2887	6p.50 Calcite	3·75	2·50
2888	6p.50 Asbestos	3·75	2·50
2889	6p.50 Valencianite	3·75	2·50
2890	6p.50 Livingstonite	3·75	2·50
2891	6p.50 Beryl	3·75	2·50
2892	6p.50 Smithsonite	3·75	2·50
2893	6p.50 Flouride	3·75	2·50
2894	6p.50 Amethyst	3·75	2·50
2895	6p.50 Azurite	3·75	2·50
2896	6p.50 Inscr "Leminorfita"	3·75	2·50
2897	6p.50 Apatite	3·75	2·50
2898	6p.50 Pyromorphyte	3·75	2·50
2899	6p.50 Actinolite	3·75	2·50

1309 Miguel Dominguez (independence leader)

2005. Anniversaries. Multicoloured.

2900	6p.50 Type **1309** (175th anniv of National Supreme Court)	3·75	2·50
2901	6p.50 Building (Tenth anniv of Federal Justice Administration)	3·75	2·50
2902	10p.50 Jose Maria Morelos (independence leader) (190th anniv of Supreme Court)	6·00	4·25
MS2903	140×115 mm. Nos. 2900/2	13·50	12·50

1310 Ignacio Vallarta

2005. 175th Birth Anniv of Ignacio Vallarta (politician).

2904	**1310** 7p.50 multicoloured	4·25	3·00

1311 Plants and Buildings

2005. EXPO 2005, Aichi, Japan.

2905	**1311** 13p. multicoloured	7·50	5·00

1312 Building Facades and Open Book

2005. 150th Anniv of Federal District Supreme Court. Multicoloured.

2906	6p.50 Type **1312**	3·75	2·50
2907	6p.50 Ink well, trees and buildings	3·75	2·50
2908	7p.50 Court building, gavel and ink stand	4·25	3·00

1313 Globe and International Buildings

2005. Stamp Day.

2909	**1313** 10p.50 multicoloured	6·00	4·00

1314 Fundacion Jesus Alvarez del Castillo Building

2005. Centenary of Jalisco Philatelic Organization. Phosphorescent markings.

2910	**1314** 6p.50 multicoloured	3·75	2·50

1315 Statue and Cedar of Lebanon Tree

2005. 125th Anniv of Lebanese Immigration.

2911	**1315** 10p.50 multicoloured	6·00	4·00

1316 Rodolfo Usigli

2005. Birth Centenary of Rodolfo Usigli (writer).

2912	**1316** 7p.50 multicoloured	4·25	3·00

1317 Ships and Fort

2005. San Juan de Ulua, last Spanish Redoubt (battle for independence).

2913	**1317** 7p.50 multicoloured	4·25	3·00

1318 Colonnade and Horseman (statue)

2005. Centenary of Gomez Palace, Durango.

2914	**1318** 6p.50 multicoloured	3·75	2·50

1319 Flag, Dove and Emblem

2005. 60th Anniv of United Nations Membership.

2915	**1319** 10p.50 multicoloured	6·00	4·00

1320 Terracotta Pot

2005. Crafts. Multicoloured.

2916	50c. Type **1320**	50	35
2917	1p. Lacquered chest	70	45
2918	1p.50 Horn comb	1·00	70
2919	2p. Black jar	1·20	80
2920	2p.50 Paper bull	1·50	1·00
2921	5p. Silk shawl	3·00	2·00
2922	6p.50 Wooden mask	3·75	3·00
2923	6p.50 Tin cockerel	3·75	3·00
2924	6p.50 Model house and garden	3·75	3·00
2925	6p.50 Glazed and decorated bowl	3·75	3·00
2926	6p.50 Decorated vase	3·75	3·00
2926a	6p.50 Mask	1·30	1·00
2927	7p. Woman wearing traditional dress (statue)	4·00	3·25
2928	7p.50 Copper ridged vase	4·25	3·50
2929	9p. Embroidered tablecloth	5·00	4·00
2930	10p.50 Woven basket	6·00	4·75
2931	13p. Silver pear	7·25	5·75
2932	14p.50 Amber marimba	8·25	6·50
2933	30p.50 Obsidian and opal turtle	17·00	13·50

1321 Jean-Baptiste De La Salle (founder)

2005. Centenary of Christian Brothers (educational organization) in Mexico.

2961	**1321** 6p.50 multicoloured	3·75	3·00

1322 Cactus as Menorah

2005. Centenary of Jewish Community in Mexico.

2962	**1322** 7p.50 multicoloured	4·25	3·50

1323 Decorated Toys

2005. Indigenous Popular Culture.

2963	**1323** 6p.50 multicoloured	3·75	3·00

1324 Pinata and Nativity (Jose R. Angulo)

2005. Christmas. Multicoloured.

2964	6p.50 Type **1324**	3·75	3·00
2965	7p.50 Multicoloured pinata (Jose Bauza Acevedo)	4·25	3·50

1325 Man as Machine

2006. 70th Anniv of National Technical Services. Sheet 100×90 mm.

MS2966	**1325** 10p.50 multicoloured	6·25	5·75

1326 Mozart

2006. 250th Birth Anniv of Wolfgang Amadeus Mozart (composer and musician).

2967	**1326** 7p.50 multicoloured	4·25	3·50

1327 Floodlit Building

2006. 50th Anniv of UNAM Central Library.

2968	**1327** 6p.50 multicoloured	3·75	3·00

1328 Tower

2006. 50th Anniv of Latin American Tower.
2969 **1328** 6p.50 multicoloured 3·75 3·00

1329 Isidro Castillo Perez

2006. Teacher's Day. Isidro Castillo Perez Commemoration.
2970 **1329** 6p.50 multicoloured 3·75 3·00

1330 Book enclosing Building and Shelving

2006. Vasconcelos Library—Cultural Space.
2971 **1330** 6p.50 multicoloured 3·75 3·00

1331 Map and Women

2006. International Women's Day.
2972 **1331** 6p.50 multicoloured 3·75 3·00

1332 Feet and Ball

2006. World Cup Football Championship, Germany.
2973 **1332** 13p. multicoloured 7·50 6·00

1333 Benito Juarez Garcia

2006. Birth Bicentenary of Benito Juarez Garcia (politician). Sheet 100×215 mm.
MS2974 **1333** 13p. multicoloured 7·75 6·50

1334 Statues and Ship

2006. 50th Anniv of Navy School.
2975 **1334** 6p.50 multicoloured 3·75 3·00

1335 El Chavo del Ocho

2006. Television Heroes. Characters created by Roberto Gomez Bolanos (Chespirito). Multicoloured.
2976 6p.50 Type **1335** 3·75 3·00
2977 7p.50 El Chapulin Colorado 4·25 3·50
2978 10p.50 El Chavo del Ocho with leg raised 6·00 4·75
2979 13p. El Chapulin Colorado (different) 7·50 6·00
2980 14p.50 El Chavo del Ocho (different) 8·25 6·50
Nos. 2976/80 were issued together, *se-tenant*, forming a composite design.

1336 Cacti and Desert

2006. International Year of Deserts and Desertification.
2981 **1336** 6p.50 multicoloured 3·75 3·00

1337 Inscr "Muzzy"

2006. Dinosaurs. Sheet 96×131 mm containing T **1337** and similar multicoloured designs.
MS2982 6p.50 Type **1337**; 7p.50 Inscr "Sabinosaurio" (40×48 mm); 10p.50 Inscr "Monstruo de aramberri" (40×48 mm) 14·00 11·00
The stamps and background of No. **MS**2982 form a composite design.

1338 Students and Engineering Constructions

2006. 50th Anniv of Engineering Institute (UNAM).
2983 **1338** 6p.50 multicoloured 3·75 3·00

1339 Dove carrying Envelope

2006. World Post Day.
2984 **1339** 13p. multicoloured 7·50 6·00

1339a Miguel Hidalgo y Costilla (Agusascalientes)

2006. 150th Anniv of First Stamp. Sheet 195×218 mm containing T **1339a** and similar multicoloured designs showing Miguel Gregorio Antonio Ignacio Hidalgo y Costilla Gallaga Mondarte Villaseñor (Roman Catholic priest and revolutionary rebel leader) and district name.
MS2984a 6p.50×7, Type **1339a** (Agusascalientes); Colima; Edo. de Mexico; Michoacan; Nayarit; Quintana Roo; Tamaulipas; 7p.50×7, Baja California; Chiapas; Guanajuato; Morelos; Nuevo Leon; San Luis Potosi; Tlaxcala; 9p.×7, Baja California Sur; Chihuahua; Guerrero; Oxaca; Sinaloa; Veracruz; 10p.50×7, Campeche; Distrito Federal; Hidalgo; Puebla; Sonora; Yucatan; 13p.×7, Coahuila; Durango; Jalisco; Queretaro; Tabasco; Zacatecas; 50p. Miguel Hidalgo y Costilla (72×24 mm) £150 £140

1340 Chabelo (cartoon)

2006. Television Heroes. Characters created by Xavier Lopez. Multicoloured.
2985 6p.50 Type **1340** 3·75 3·00
2986 10p.50 Chabelo (Xavier Lopez) 6·00 4·75
No. 2985/6 were issued together, *se-tenant*, forming a composite design.

1341 Postman (statue) and Envelopes

2006. 75th Anniv of Postmen's Day.
2987 **1341** 6p.50 multicoloured 3·75 3·00

1342 Building Facade

2006. 50th Anniv of University.
2988 **1342** 10p.50 multicoloured 6·00 4·75

1343 Children

2006. Children—The Future.
2989 **1343** 10p.50 multicoloured 6·00 4·75

1344 Andres Henestrosa

2006. Birth Centenary of Andres Henestrosa (writer).
2990 **1344** 9p. multicoloured 5·00 4·00

1345 Edmundo O'Gorman

2006. Birth Centenary of Edmundo O'Gorman (historian).
2991 **1345** 10p.50 multicoloured 6·00 4·75

1346 Satellite

2006. Centenary of Mexico's Membership of International Telecommunications Union.
2992 **1346** 7p. multicoloured 4·00 3·25

1347 Baubles (Ricardo Salas Pineda)

2006. Children's Drawings. Christmas. Multicoloured.
2993 7p.50 Type **1347** 4·25 3·50
2994 10p.50 Holly and baubles (Maria Jose Gaytia) 6·00 4·75

1348 Newspapers

2006. 90th Anniv of Journalism in Mexico.
2995 **1348** 10p.50 multicoloured 6·00 4·75

1349 Apple and Book

2007. Teachers' Day.
2996 **1349** 7p.50 multicoloured 4·25 3·50

1350 *Autorretrato con Changuito* (self portrait with small monkey)

2007. Birth Centenary of Frida Kahlo (artist).
2997 **1350** 13p. multicoloured 7·50 6·00

1351 Dove

2007. Centenary of Scouting. Multicoloured.
2998 6p.50 Type **1351** 3·75 3·00
2999 10p.50 Emblem 6·00 4·75
No. 2998/9 were issued together, *se-tenant*, forming a composite design.

1352 Carved Ring (Gran juego de pelota) and Temple of the Jaguars

2007. Archaeology. Chichen Itza. Sheet 161×94 mm containing T **1352** and similar horiz designs. Multicoloured.
MS3000 6p.50 Type **1352**; 6p.50 Thousand columns; 10p.50 El Caracol observatory; 13p. Chac Mool (statue); 13p. Carved head of jaguar and El Castillo 28·00 22·00
The stamps, label and margins of **MS**3000 form a composite design.

1353 Cathedral, Marlin and Map

2007. 150th Anniv of Colima.
3001 **1353** 10p.50 multicoloured 6·00 4·75

1354 Boy writing (fresco)

2007. Centenary of Postal Palace. Sheet 220×196 mm containing T **1354** and similar multicoloured designs.

MS3002 5p.50 Type **1354**; 5p.50 Boy using telegraph machine; 6p.50 Two boys hand stamping; 6p.50 Two boys with hand press and ink; 6p.50 Boy with hammer and cog wheel; 6p.50 Clocks; 6p.50 Early photographs and UPU emblem (statue) (80×24 mm); 9p. Boy as Mercury; 9p. Two boys emptying mail bag; 10p.50 Two boys with letters; 13p. Boy sending carrier pigeon; 13p. Boy reading letter from carrier pigeon; 14p.50 Stairwell (40×48 mm); 14p.50 Glass roof (40×48 mm); 15p.50 Central staircases (80×48 mm); 39p.50 Postal building facade (80×48 mm) 80·00 75·00

The stamps and margins of **MS**3002 form a composite background design.

1355 Steam Locomotive and Museum

2007. Centenary of Torreon, Coahuila. Mult.

3003	5p. Type **1355**	3·00	2·30
3004	6p.50 Bridge over Nazas River and Our Lady of Guadalupe Parish Church	3·75	3·00
3005	6p.50 Isauro Martinez theatre	3·75	3·00
3006	14p.50 Cristo del Cerro de las Noas	8·25	6·50
3007	14p.50 Dunes and Tower	8·25	6·50

No. 3003/7 were issued together, *se-tenant*, forming a composite design.

1356 Dove (peace)

2007. Universal Cultural Forum, Monterey. Mult.

3008	7p. Type **1356**	4·00	3·25
3009	7p.50 Child writing and books (knowledge)	4·25	3·50
3010	7p.50 Hand holding fruit, children and wind turbine (sustainability)	4·25	3·50
3011	13p. African woman, traditional costume and calligrapher (cultural diversity)	7·25	5·75
3012	13p. Primitive statue and Thai dolls	7·25	5·75

No. 3008/12 were issued together, *se-tenant*, forming a composite design.

1357 Olympic Stadium

2007. Cultural Heritage. National Autonomous University of Mexico (Ciudad Universitaria). Multicoloured.

3013	6p.50 Type **1357**	3·75	3·00
3014	9p. Building on pillars with decorated facade	5·00	4·00
3015	13p. Tall building	7·25	5·75

No. 3013/15 were issued together, *se-tenant*, forming a composite background design.

1358 University Building Facade

2007. 50th Anniv of Universidad Autonoma de Baja California.

3016	**1358** 7p.50 multicoloured	4·25	3·50

1359 Leaves and Trees

2007. Ozone Layer Protection Campaign. Mult.

3017	7p. Type **1359**	4·00	3·25
3018	14p.50 Hands enclosing Earth	8·25	6·50

Nos. 3017/18 were issued together, *se-tenant*, forming a composite design.

1360 *St Christopher* (Nicolas Rodriguez Juarez)

2007. Sacred Art.

3019	**1360** 6p.50 multicoloured	3·75	3·00

1361 Central Plaza, School of Plastic Arts

2007. 50th Anniv of Universidad Autonoma de Coahuila.

3020	**1361** 7p.50 multicoloured	4·25	3·50

1362 Envelopes

2007. Stamp Day. Multicoloured.

3021	7p. Type **1362**	4·00	3·25
3022	10p.50 Envelopes	6·00	4·75

No. 3021/2 were issued together, *se-tenant*, forming a composite design.

1363 Stylized Figures

2007. Rights for the Disabled.

3023	**1363** 6p.50 multicoloured	3·75	3·00

1364 Caminito de la Escuela

2007. Birth Centenary of Francisco Gabiliando Soler (Cri-Cri) (composer and performer of children's songs). Sheet 141×141 mm containing T **1364** and similar vert designs. Multicoloured.

MS3024 5p. Type **1364**; 5p. Caminito de la Escuela (different); 6p.50 la Patita; [6p.50] La Muneca Fea; 6p.50 Gato de Barrio; 6p.50 Bombon I; 6p.50 Cochinitos Domilones; 6.50p. Cochinitos Domilones (different); 6p.50 Di Por Que; 6p.50 El Raton Vaquero; 6p.50 Negrito Sandia; 7p. Cri-Cri (cricket); 7p. Francisco Gabiliando Soler; 7p. Song; 7p.50 El Chorrito 43·00 38·00

1365 Building Facade

2007. 50th Anniv of Administration Degree.

3025	**1365** 7p.50 multicoloured	4·25	3·50

1366 Sail Ship

2007. Ship Sailing School, Cuahtemoc.

3026	**1366** 7p.50 multicoloured	4·25	3·50

1367 Girl writing Letter

2007. Day of the Postman. Multicoloured.

3027	6p.50 Type **1367**	3·75	3·00
3028	6p.50 Girl posting letter	3·75	3·00
3029	6p.50 Postman riding bicycle	3·75	3·00
3030	6p.50 Boy receiving letter	3·75	3·00
3031	6p.50 Early mail boat	3·75	3·00
3032	6p.50 Postman	3·75	3·00
3033	6p.50 Modern post woman	3·75	3·00
3034	6p.50 Early horse-drawn mail van	4·00	3·00
3035	6p.50 Early post men	4·00	3·00
3036	6p.50 Modern postman riding bicycle	4·00	3·00
3037	6p.50 Early postman riding bicycle	6·00	4·75
3038	6p.50 Post men	6·00	4·75
3039	6p.50 Postman riding motorcycle	6·00	4·75
3040	10p.50 Postman (painting)	6·00	4·75

1368 Popocatepetl (Mexico)

2007. Mountains. Multicoloured.

3041	6p.50 Type **1368**	3·75	3·00
3042	6p.50 Mount Gongga (China)	3·75	3·00

Stamps of a similar design were issued by China.

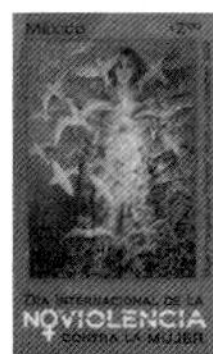
1369 Woman and Doves

2007. International 'No Violence Against Women' Day.

3043	**1369** 7p. multicoloured	4·00	3·00

1370 Mariano Otero (politician) and Supreme Court (mural by Alfredo Zake)

2007. Amparo Law, Constitutional Proceeding to Protect Citizen's Rights .

3044	**1370** 10p.50 multicoloured	6·00	4·75

1371 Scribe (statue)

2007. Archaeology. Monte Alban. Sheet containing T **1371** and similar horiz designs. Multicoloured.

MS3045 6p.50 6p.50 Type **1371**; 6p.50 Man wearing jaguar headdress (detail, statue); 10p.50 Urn and platform; 13p. Platform and ruins, Central Plaza; 13p. Obserservatory platform, Central Plaza 28·00 25·00

The stamp, margins and label of **MS**3045 form a composite design of the site.

1372 Candle

2007. Christmas. Multicoloured.

3046	6p.50 Type **1372**	3·75	3·00
3047	7p. Bells	4·00	3·00
3048	10p.50 Angel	6·00	4·75
3049	13p.50 Three Kings	7·75	6·00
3050	14p.50 The Nativity	8·25	6·50

1373 Bulldogs

2007. Dogs. Multicoloured.

3051	6p.50 Type **1373**	3·75	3·00
3052	6p.50 Rotweilers	3·75	3·00
3053	6p.50 Boxers	3·75	3·00
3054	6p.50 Beagles	3·75	3·00
3055	7p. Bulldog (head)	4·00	3·00
3056	7p. Rottweiller (head)	4·00	3·00
3057	7p. Boxer (head)	4·00	3·00
3058	7p. Beagle (head)	4·00	3·00
3059	10p.50 Bulldog	6·00	4·75
3060	10p.50 Rottweiller	6·00	4·75
3061	10p.50 Boxer	6·00	4·75
3062	10p.50 Beagle	6·00	4·75

1374 Burning Train

2007. Death Centenary of Jesus Garcia Corona (train explosion hero).

3063	**1374** 10p.50 multicoloured	6·00	4·75

1375 Stylized Towers

2007. 50th Anniv of Torres de Satelite, Naucalpan de Juarez.

3064	**1375** 6p.50 multicoloured	3·75	3·00

1376 Outflow

2007. Infrastructure. El Cajon Dam. Multicoloured.

3065	7p. Type **1376**	4·00	3·25

3066 13p. Aerial view 7·25 5·75

1377 Hearts enclosing Script

2008. The Letter.
3067 **1377** 6p.50 multicoloured 3·75 3·00

1378 Mother and Child

2008. Mothers' Day.
3068 **1378** 6p.50 multicoloured 3·75 3·00

1379 Miguel Aleman Valdes

2008. Miguel Aleman Valdes (president 1946–1952) Commemoration.
3069 **1379** 6p.50 multicoloured 3·75 3·00

1380 *Los frutos* (Diego Rivera)

2008. Teachers' Day.
3070 **1380** 6p.50 multicoloured 3·75 3·00

1381 Santo

2008. Wrestling Heroes. Rodolfo Guzman Huerta (Santo, el Enmascarado de Plata (Saint, the Silver Masked Man)) (wrestler) Commemoration. Multicoloured.
MS3071 6p.50×6, Type **1381**; In ring; With hands raised; Head and shoulders, looking up; Flying leap; Head and shoulders, facing front 22·00 20·00

A miniature sheet was on sale on 19 June 2008 at 150p., for the same anniversary.

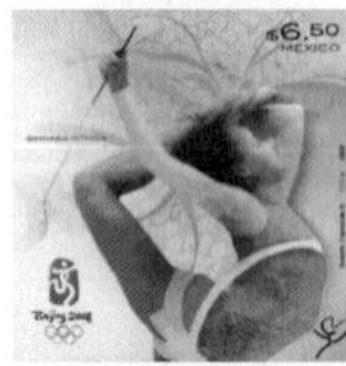

1382 Gymnast

2008. Olympic Games, Beijing. Multicoloured.
3072 6p.50 Type **1382** 3·75 3·00
3073 6p.50 Rower 3·75 3·00
3074 6p.50 Weight lifter 3·75 3·00

1383 Fingerprint, Justice and Raptor

2008. Electoral Justice.
3075 **1383** 6p.50 multicoloured 3·75 3·00

1384 Bird holding Envelope

2008. Mexico Post.
3076 **1384** 6p.50 magenta and green 3·75 3·00

1385 *Ignacio Allende* (Ramon Perez)

2008. Bicentenary of Independence. Multicoloured.
3077 6p.50 Type **1385** 3·75 3·00
3078 6p.50 *Jose Maria Morelos y Pavon (El Mixtequito)* 3·75 3·00
3079 6p.50 *Josefa Ortiz de Dominguez* 3·75 3·00
3080 6p.50 *Batalla del Monte de las Cruces* (47×39 mm) 3·75 3·00
3081 6p.50 *Casa Municipal* and Francisco Primo de Verdad y Ramos (71×30 mm) 3·75 3·00
3082 6p.50 *Meeting of Hidalgo and Morelos* (71×30 mm) 3·75 3·00
3083 6p.50 *Conspiracion de Queretaro* (71×30 mm) 3·75 3·00
3084 6p.50 *Batalla de la Alhondiga de Granaditas* (71×30 mm) 3·75 3·00
MS3085 80×81 mm (a) 10p.50 *Rompiendo Cadenas*. Imperf; (b) 10p.50 *La Almeda de la Ciudad de Mexico en un Domingo Porla Manana*. Imperf 12·00 11·00

1386 *La Historia*

2008. 75th Anniv of Nuevo Leon University. Sheet 157×158 mm containing T **1386** and similar square designs showing stained glass windows by Roberto Montenegro. Multicoloured.
MS3086 6p.50×6, Type **1386**; *La Agricultura; La Ciencia y la Sabiduria; La Historia* lower; *La Agricultura* lower; *La Ciencia y la Sabiduria* lower 22·00 20·00

The stamps of No. **MS**3086 form composite designs of the windows named. The two left hand stamps forming *La Historia*, the centre stamps forming *La Agricultura* and the right hand stamps forming *La Ciencia y la Sabiduria*.

1387 Origami Dove

2008. Stamp Day.
3087 **1387** 10p.50 multicoloured 6·00 4·75

1388 *Hylocereus undatus*

2008. Flora. Multicoloured.
3088 6p.50 Type **1388** 3·75 3·00
3089 6p.50 *Curcubita pepo* 3·75 3·00

1389 Building Facade

2008. 50th Anniv of Juarez Autonoma de Tabasco University.
3090 **1389** 6p.50 multicoloured 3·75 3·00

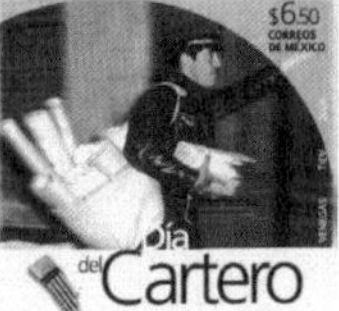

1390 Postman

2008. Day of the Postman. Multicoloured.
3091 6p.50 Type **1390** 3·75 3·00
3092 6p.50 Postman cycling 3·75 3·00
3093 6p.50 Early post motorcycle 3·75 3·00
3094 6p.50 Modern post motorcycle 3·75 3·00
3095 6p.50 Early post vehicle 3·75 3·00
3096 6p.50 Modern post van 3·75 3·00
3097 6p.50 Postmen loading cycles onto van 3·75 3·00
3098 6p.50 Post woman cycling and post van 3·75 3·00

1391 Workers

2008. National Employment Service.
3099 **1391** 6p.50 multicoloured 3·75 3·00

1392 Jose Maria Pino Suarez

2008. Centenary (2010) of Revolution. Multicoloured.
3100 6p.50 Type **1392** (revolutionary leader and Vice Pres. 1911–1913) 3·75 3·00
3101 6p.50 Ricardo Flores Magon and *Regeneracion* (anarchist magazine) 3·75 3·00
3102 6p.50 Aquiles Serdan 3·75 3·00
3103 6p.50 *La Junta Revolucionaria de Puebla* (Daniel Guzman) (72×30 mm) 3·75 3·00
3104 6p.50 Steam locomotive (72×30 mm) 3·75 3·00
3105 6p.50 *Del Porfirismo la Revolucion* (David Alfaro Siqueiros) (72×30 mm) 3·75 3·00
3106 6p.50 Mexican Liberal Party watching soldiers beat demonstrators (72×30 mm) 3·75 3·00
MS3107 81×81 mm. 10p.50 Triumphal entry of Francisco I. Madero (revolutionary and Pres. 1911–1913) Imperf 6·00 5·50
MS3108 81×81 mm. 10p.50 *El Feudalismo Portfirista* (Juan O'Gorman). Imperf 6·00 5·50

1393 Museum Exhibits

2008. 50th Anniv of La Venta Park Museum.
3109 **1393** 6p.50 multicoloured 3·75 3·00

1394 *Adoracion de los Pastores* (Cristobal de Villapando)

2008. Christmas. Multicoloured.
3110 6p.50 Type **1394** 3·75 3·00
3111 10p.50 *Adoracion de los Reyes* (anonymous Flemish painter) 6·00 4·75

1395 Gonzalo Aguirre Beltran

2008. Birth Centenary of Gonzalo Aguirre Beltran (anthropologist).
3112 **1395** 6p.50 multicoloured 3·75 3·00

No. 3113 and Type **1396** have been left for Archaeology, issued on 19 Dec 2008, not yet received.

1397 Trophy

2008. 50th Anniv of Entrega del Ariel (cinematography awards).
3114 **1397** 6p.50 multicoloured 3·75 3·00

1398 Cupid

2009. Day of Love and Friendship.
3115 **1398** 6p.50 multicoloured 3·75 3·00

1399 Mask

2009. Veracruz Carnival.
3116 **1399** 6p.50 multicoloured 3·75 3·00

1400 Jointed Yoke and Eagle-shaped Ax Head

2009. Archaeology. El Tajin. Sheet 161×96 mm containing T **1400** and similar horiz designs. Multicoloured.
MS3117 6p.50 Type **1400**; 6p.50 Carved plaque showing ball game; 10p.50 Teracotta ball player and ball game building; 13p. Carved chest defence and temple to the god Tajin; 13p. Pyramid of Niches and parrot-shaped axe head 28·00 26·00

No. **MS**3117 also contains a stamp size label the whole forming a composite design.

1401 Symbols of Programme Production

2009. 50th Anniv of Canal Once (television channel).
3118 **1401** 6p.50 multicoloured 3·75 3·00

1402 *Construccion de un Nuevo Mundo—La Maestra* (Diego Rivera)

2009. Day of the Teacher.
3119 **1402** 6p.50 multicoloured 3·75 3·00

1403 Palacio de los Condes de San Mateo Valparaiso, Mexico City (c. 1800)

2009. 125th Anniv of National Bank. Sheet 161×96 mm containing T **1403** and similar horiz designs. Multicoloured.
MS3120 6p.50×6, Type **1403**; Principal courtyard, Counts of San Mateo Valparaiso Palace; Details of columns, Palace of Iturbide; Casa Montejo, Fachada, Merida; Casa del Mayorazgo de Canal, San Miguel de Allende; Palacio de los Valle de Suchil, Durango 21·00 19·00

1404 Sea, Globe and Pre-Columbian Bas Relief

2009. World Environment Day.
3121 **1404** 10p.50 multicoloured 6·00 4·75

1405 Central Courtyard

2009. Aguascalientes University.
3122 **1405** 10p.50 multicoloured 6·00 4·75

1406 Californian Condor

2009. Endangered Species. Gymnogyps californianus.
3123 **1406** 10p.50 multicoloured 6·00 4·75

1407 Indigenous Textiles, Pot and Dance

2009. International Day of Indigenous Peoples.
3124 **1407** 6p.50 multicoloured 3·75 3·00

1408 *La Patria* (Jorge Gonzalez Camarena)

2009. 50th Anniv of National Commission for Free Text Books.
3125 **1408** 6p.50 multicoloured 3·75 3·00

1409 Popocatepetel and Iztaccihuatl Mountains

2009. Preserve Polar Regions and Glaciers. Multicoloured.
3126 10p.50 Type **1409** 6·00 4·75
3127 13p. Citlaltepetl mountain 7·75 6·00

Nos. 3126/7 were printed, *se-tenant*, each pair forming a composite design.

1410 Congress of Chilpancingo, 1813

2009. Bicentenary of Independence. Multicoloured.
3128 6p.50 Type **1410** 3·75 3·00
3129 6p.50 Leona Vicario and Andres Quintana Roo (members of Los Guadalupes (independence society)) 3·75 3·00
3130 6p.50 Installation of supreme governing junta 3·75 3·00
3131 6p.50 Execution of Miguel Hidalgo (horiz) 3·75 3·00
3132 6p.50 Execution of Jose María Morelos (horiz) 3·75 3·00
3133 6p.50 Capture of the early leaders (horiz) 3·75 3·00
3134 6p.50 Cuatla, site of battle of War of Independence (72×30 mm) 3·75 3·00
3135 6p.50 Constitution of Apatzingan (72×30 mm) 3·75 3·00
MS3136 81×81 mm. 10p.50 Leaders of the revolution 6·00 5·50
MS3137 81×81 mm. 10p.50 Abolition of slavery 6·00 5·50

1411 Postal Messengers

2009. Americas UNI Post and Logistics Meeting.
3138 **1411** 6p.50 multicoloured 3·75 3·00

1412 Institute Building

2009. 150th Anniv of Literary and Scientific Institute, University of San Luis Potosi.
3139 **1412** 6p.50 multicoloured 3·75 3·00

1413 Envelope as Paper Plane

2009. Stamp Day.
3140 **1413** 10p.50 multicoloured 6·00 4·75

1414 Metropolitan Cathedral of Chihuahua

2009. 300th Anniv of Chihuahua.
3141 **1414** 6p.50 multicoloured 3·75 3·00

1415 Day of the Dead

2009. Traditions. Day of the Dead. Multicoloured.
3142 6p.50 Type **1415** 3·75 3·00
3143 6p.50 Wheel of Fortune 3·75 3·00

1416 Juan Bosch

2009. Birth Centenary of Juan Emilio Bosch Gavino (Juan Bosch) (politician, historian, writer and first freely elected president of Dominican Republic).
3144 **1416** 10p.50 multicoloured 6·00 4·75

1417 El Carmen, Mexico

2009. Wilderness Areas. Multicoloured.
3145 6p.50 Type **1417** 3·75 3·00
3146 10p.50 Nahanni, Canada 6·00 4·75
3147 10p.50 Zion, USA 6·00 4·75
3148 13p. Kronotsky, Russia 7·50 6·00
3149 14p.50 Baviaanskloof, South Africa 8·25 6·50

1418 Postman riding Bicycle

2009. Day of the Postman.
3150 6p.50 black and magenta 3·75 3·00
3151 6p.50 black and apple green 3·75 3·00

Designs:—Type **1418**; Postman riding motorcycle

1419 Revolutionaries (fresco)

2009. Threshold of Centenary of Mexican Revolution. Multicoloured.
3152 6p.50 Type **1419** 3·75 3·00

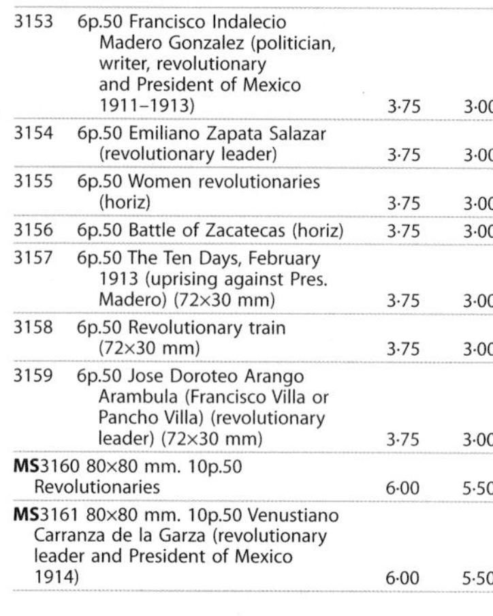
3153 6p.50 Francisco Indalecio Madero Gonzalez (politician, writer, revolutionary and President of Mexico 1911–1913) 3·75 3·00
3154 6p.50 Emiliano Zapata Salazar (revolutionary leader) 3·75 3·00
3155 6p.50 Women revolutionaries (horiz) 3·75 3·00
3156 6p.50 Battle of Zacatecas (horiz) 3·75 3·00
3157 6p.50 The Ten Days, February 1913 (uprising against Pres. Madero) (72×30 mm) 3·75 3·00
3158 6p.50 Revolutionary train (72×30 mm) 3·75 3·00
3159 6p.50 Jose Doroteo Arango Arambula (Francisco Villa or Pancho Villa) (revolutionary leader) (72×30 mm) 3·75 3·00
MS3160 80×80 mm. 10p.50 Revolutionaries 6·00 5·50
MS3161 80×80 mm. 10p.50 Venustiano Carranza de la Garza (revolutionary leader and President of Mexico 1914) 6·00 5·50

1420 Vehicle and Safety Symbols

2009. Road Safety.
3162 **1420** 6p.50 multicoloured 3·75 3·00

1421 Jaime Sabines

2009. Tenth Death Anniv of Jaime Sabines Gutierrez (poet).
3163 **1421** 6p.50 multicoloured 3·75 3·00

1422 Audit Office and Notice

2009. 50th Anniv of Federal Tax Audit.
3164 **1422** 6p.50 multicoloured 3·75 3·00

1423 Balthasar (inscr 'Baltazar')

2009. Christmas.. Multicoloured.
3165 6p.50 Type **1423** 3·75 3·00
3166 6p.50 Melchior (inscr 'Melchor') 3·75 3·00
3167 6p.50 Caspar (inscr 'Gaspar') 3·75 3·00
3168 6p.50 Santa Claus 3·75 3·00

1424 Mother, Children and Symbols of Education and Good Diet

2009. Human Development Programme.
3169 **1424** 6p.50 multicoloured 3·75 3·00

1425 Girl plugging into Sun (Camila Hernandez Sanchez Chavez)

2009. Energy Conservation. Winning Designs in Children's Drawing Competition. Multicoloured.

3170	6p.50 Type **1425**	3·75	3·00
3171	6p.50 Solar powered light bulbs (Luis Javier Alvarez Santoyo)	3·75	3·00
3172	6p.50 Children as light bulbs (Martha Patricia Agundez)	3·75	3·00

Nos. 3170/2 were printed, *se-tenant*, in horizontal strips of three stamps within the sheet.

1426 Agricultural Workers and City Skyline

2009. Civil Programme.

3173	**1426**	6p.50 multicoloured	3·75	3·00

1427 Venustiano Carranza

2009. 150th Birth Anniv of Venustiano Carranza de la Garza (revolutionary leader).

3174	**1427**	6p.50 multicoloured	3·75	3·00

1428 Voisin Aircraft and Alberto Braniff Ricard (first flight in Mexico)

2010. Centenary of Mexican Aviation

3175	**1428**	7p. multicoloured	4·00	3·25

1429 Surgeons and Hospital Interior

2010. 50th Anniv of ISSSTE (Institute of Security and Social Services for State Employees)

3176	**1429**	7p. multicoloured	4·00	3·25

1430 Balloons, Heart, Star and Envelope

2010. Day of Love and Friendship

3177	**1430**	7p. multicoloured	4·00	3·25

1431 Tiger

2010. Chinese New Year. Year of the Tiger

3178	**1431**	7p. multicoloured	4·00	3·25

1432 Luz Gonzalez Cosio de Lopez (founder)

2010. Centenary of Mexican Red Cross

3179	**1432**	10p.50 black and scarlet-vermilion	6·00	4·75

1433 Emblem and Governor's Palace, Uxmal

2010. BIDCII, 2010 (Inter-American Development Bank Board of Governors' Meeting), Cancun, Mexico

3180	**1433**	11p.50 multicoloured	6·50	5·25

1434 Decorated Pot with Legs

2010. Popular Crafts. Multicoloured.

3181	50c. Type **1434**	45	35
3182	1p. Lacquered wooden trunk	55	45
3183	1p.50 Decorative horn comb	75	55
3184	2p. Black clay pitcher	95	65
3185	2p.50 Paper bull within cage of paper flags	1·20	80
3186	5p. Silk shawl	2·30	1·50
3187	7p. Statuette of woman wearing traditional dress (inscr 'Muñeca de plata pella')	3·25	2·10
3188	7p.50 Copper vase	3·50	2·20
3189	11p.50 Bowl shaped basket	5·00	3·25
3190	13p.50 Silver incised pear	5·75	3·75
3191	15p. Marimba	6·50	4·25
3192	30p.50 Obsidian tortoise	13·50	8·75

1435 Jose Luis Sandoval

2010. Baseball in Mexico. Los Diablos Rojos del México. Multicoloured.

MS3211	158×93 mm. 7p.×3, Type **1435**; Miguel Oieda; Roberto Saucedo	12·00	11·00

1436 Gerberas

2010. Mothers' Day

3212	**1436**	7p. multicoloured	4·00	3·25

1437 La Escuela Rural (detail from mural Reconstruccion y la fiesta de la Santa Cruz by Roberto Montenegro Nervo)

2010. Teachers' Day

3213	**1437**	7p. multicoloured	4·00	3·25

1438 Mexican Team (for Mexico versus New Zealand match)

2010. World Cup Football Championships, South Africa. Multicoloured.

3214	7p. Type **1438**	4·00	3·25
3215	7p. Gerardo Torrado (No. 6) and Giovani dos Santos (No. 17)	4·00	3·25
3216	11p.50 Andres Guardado (No. 18) and Guillermo Ochoa (goalkeeper)	6·75	5·50

Nos. 3214/16 were printed, *se-tenant*, froming a composite design.

1439 Profiles and Indigenous Languages

2010. International Day of Indigenous Languages

3217	**1439**	11p.50 multicoloured	6·75	5·50

1440 Adolfo López Mateos

2010. Birth Centenary of Adolfo López Mateos (politician)

3218	**1440**	7p. multicoloured	4·00	3·25

1441 Flower containing Figures

2010. National Commission for Human Rights

3219	**1441**	7p. multicoloured	4·00	3·25

1442 Scouts crossing Forest Bridge

2010. Scouts, Mexico

3220	**1442**	7p. multicoloured	4·00	3·25

1443 Grandparents and Grandchild

2010. Grandparents' Day

3221	**1443**	7p. multicoloured	4·00	3·25

1444 Symbols of Petroleum Production

2010. Mexican Institute of Petroleum

3222	**1444**	7p. multicoloured	4·00	3·25

1445 Pedro Moreno

2010. Bicentenary of Independence. Multicoloured.

3223	7p. Type **1445**	4·00	3·25
3224	7p. José Servando Teresa de Mier Noriega y Guerra (Servando Teresa de Mier)	4·00	3·25
3225	7p. Trigarante Army flag	4·00	3·25
3226	7p. Vicente Ramón Guerrero Saldaña (Vicente Guerrero)	4·00	3·25
3227	7p. José Miguel Ramón Adaucto Fernández y Félix (Guadalupe Victoria)	4·00	3·25
3228	7p. Francisco Javier Mina (Xavier Mina)	4·00	3·25
3229	7p. Interview between Agustín de Iturbide and Juan O'Donojú y O'Rian (Juan O'Donoju) (horiz)	4·00	3·25
3230	7p. Ignacio López Rayón (horiz)	4·00	3·25
3231	7p. Cannon at Celaya battle (horiz)	4·00	3·25
3232	7p. José Manuel Rafael Simeón de Mier y Terán (Manuel de Mier y Terán) (horiz)	4·00	3·25
MS3233	80×80 mm. 11p.50 José Miguel Domínguez Alemán and members of the Independence movement. Imperf	6·50	6·00
MS3233a	80×80 mm. 11p.50 Entry of Trigarante Army. Imperf	6·50	6·00

1446 Justo Sierra Méndez (founder) and Inauguration of UNAM

2010. Centenary of the National University of Mexico. Multicoloured.

MS3234	7p.×6, Type **1446**; National Preparatory School, stained glass window and San Ildefonso College; San Carlos Academy; National Art Studies School; Campus murals; Philharmonic Orchestra and choreography workshop; University Museum of Contemporary Art	25·00	23·00

1447 The Guide Sign

2010. Guides, Mexico

3235	7p. multicoloured	4·00	3·25

1448 Satellites and ITU Emblem

2010. Plenipotentiary Conference of the International Telecommunication Union

3236	**1448**	11p.50 multicoloured	6·50	5·25

1449 Paper as Hand holding Pen and Script

2010. Stamp Day

3237	**1449**	11p.50 multicoloured	6·50	5·25

1449a Pyramid of the Moon, Teotihuacan (Mexico)

2010. Ancient Architecture. Multicoloured.
MS3237a 7p.×2, Type **1449a**; Ateshgah (Temple of fire), Azerbaijan 8·25 7·75

Stamps of a similar design were issued by Azerbaijan.

1450 Dealing with Disaster

2010. 20th Anniv of National Center for Disaster Prevention
3238 **1450** 7p. multicoloured 4·00 3·25

1451 Catrina and Catrin

2010. Mexican Traditions. Day of the Dead
3239 **1451** 7p. multicoloured 4·00 3·25

1452 The Nativity

2010. Christmas. Multicoloured.
3240 7p. Type **1452** 4·00 3·25
3241 7p. Children playing piñata 4·00 3·25
3242 7p. Three Magi 4·00 3·25

1453 Christmas Tree, Santa and Children peeking around Door

2010. Christmas (2nd issue)
3243 **1453** 7p. multicoloured 4·00 3·25

1454 Early Postman and Mail Van

2010. Day of the Postman. Multicoloured.
3245 7p. Type **1454** 4·00 3·25
3246 11p.50 Modern postman riding motorcycle and mail vans 6·50 5·25

1455 Rodolfo Neri Vela and Satellites

2010. 25th Anniversary of the First Mexican in Space. Multicoloured.
3247 7p. Type **1455** 4·00 3·25
3248 7p. Rodolfo Neri Vela, flag and shuttle launch 4·00 3·25

1456 Building Façade

2010. Palace of Arts
3249 **1456** 7p. multicoloured 4·00 3·25

1457 Convention of Aguascalientes

2010. Centenary of Mexican Revolution. Multicoloured.
3250 7p. Type **1457** 4·00 3·25
3251 7p. Revolutionaries fighting at battle of Celaya 4·00 3·25
3252 7p. Crowd (*Constitucion de 1917* (detail) (Jorge Gonzalez Camarena))(vert) 4·00 3·25
3253 7p. Farm Bill and Luis Cabrera (vert) 4·00 3·25
3254 7p. Venustiano Carranza (constitutional president) 4·00 3·25
3255 7p. Venustiano Carranza (*Constitucion de 1917* (detail) (Jorge Gonzalez Camarena)) (vert) 4·00 3·25
3256 7p. Woman and children (*Las Mujeres en la Revolucion Mexicana*) (71×30 mm) 4·00 3·25
3257 7p. Eulalio Gutierrez and Roque Gonzalez Garza (provincila presidents) (71×30 mm) 4·00 3·25
MS3258 80×80mm. 11p.50 Francisco Villa, Emiliano Zapata and Venustiano Carranza on horse back. Imperf 6·50 6·00
MS3259 80×80mm. 11p.50 (*Revolucion de* 1910) (Diego Rivera). Imperf 6·50 6·00

1458 Justice (bronze statue) and Hands

2010. International Day for Eradication of Violence against Women
3260 **1458** 11p.50 multicoloured 6·50 5·25

1458a Clock Tower

2010. Centenary of Monumental Clock of Pachuca Hidalgo
3260a **1458a** 7p. multicoloured 4·00 3·25

1458b Tree and Butterflies (conference emblem)

2010. Climate Change Conferences. COP16 (Conference of Parties to United Nations Framework Convention on Climate Change) and CMP6 (Conference of Parties to Kyoto Protocol), Cancún
3260b **1458b** 7p. multicoloured 4·00 3·25

1459 Symbols of Science and Technology

2010. 40th Anniv of National Council of Science and Technology, CONACYT
3261 **1459** 7p. multicoloured 4·00 3·25

1460 Octavio Paz

2010. 20th Anniv of Octavio Paz's Nobel Prize for Literature
3262 **1460** 7p. multicoloured 4·00 3·25

1461 Men and Women at Work

2010. Week of Small and Medium Enterprises
3263 **1461** 7p. multicoloured 4·00 3·25

1462 Amalia Hernandez's Ballet Folklorico de Mexico

2010. Dance. Multicoloured.
MS3264 7p.×2, Type **1462**; Kalibelia Dance, India 8·25 7·75

1462a Great Blue Heron

2010. Fauna of Gulf of Mexico. Great Blue Heron (*Ardea herodias*)
3264a **1462a** 11p.50 multicoloured 6·50 5·25

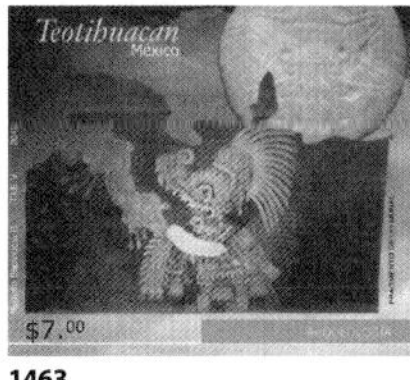

1463

2010. Archaeology. Teotihuacan. Multicoloured.
MS3265 7p. Type **1463**; 7p. Sun enclosing skull and Quetzalpapalotl Palace entrance columns; 11p.50 Stone incense burner and decorated vase; 13p.50 Pyramid of the Moon and Pyramid of the Sun; 13p.50 Steps leading up Pyramid of the Moon 30·00 29·00

The stamps, label and margins of **MS**3265 form a composite design.

1464 *Cypripedium irapeanum*

2010. Orchids. Multicoloured.
MS3266 7p.×6, Type **1464**; *Sobralia macrantha; Prostnechea ionophlebia; Laelia anceps; Trichocentrum oerstedii; Laelia rubescens* 25·00 23·00

1465 Seedling, Electricity Pylon and Anniversary Emblem

2010. 20th Anniv of FIDE (energy saving trust)
3267 **1465** 7p. multicoloured 4·00 3·25

1466 Flowers and Hearts

2011. Day of Love and Friendship. Multicoloured.
3268 7p. Type **1466** 4·00 3·25
3269 7p. Large heart and banner enclosed by flowers 4·00 3·25

1467 Anniversary Emblem

2011. Centenary of UPAEP
3270 **1467** 13p.50 multicoloured 8·00 6·50

1468 Mother and Children

2011. Mothers' Day
3271 **1468** 7p. multicoloured 4·00 3·25

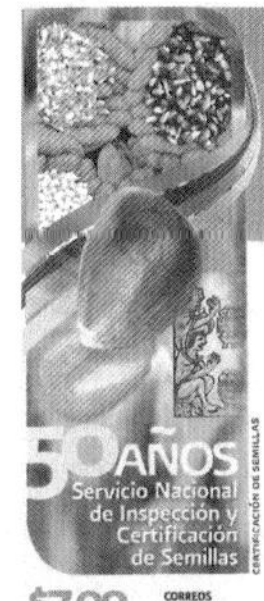

1469 Seeds

2011. 50th Anniv of National Control and Seed Certfication. Multicoloured.
3272 7p. Type **1469** 4·00 3·25
3273 7p. Flowering plants and plant assessment 4·00 3·25
3274 7p. Fruit and flowers 4·00 3·25

1470 Building and Decorative Detail

2011. Postal Palace
3275 **1470** 7p. multicoloured 4·00 3·25

1471 Mil Máscaras

2011. Wrestling Heros. Aaron Rodríguez Arellano (Mil Máscaras (A Thousand Masks)). Multicoloured.

MS3276 7p.×3, Type **1471**; With left hand raised; Posing with other wrestlers in background; Seated head and shoulders, facing front 12·00 11·50

1472 *La Mestra Rural* (fresco, Diego Rivera)

2011. Teachers' Day

3277 **1472** 7p. multicoloured 4·00 3·25

1473 Armillita

2011. Birth Centenary of Fermin Espinosa (Armillita) (bull fighter)

3278 **1473** 7p. multicoloured 4·00 3·25

1474 Trophy and Players tackling for Ball

2011. FIFA U-17 World Cup, Mexico. Multicoloured.

3279 7p. Type **1474** 4·00 3·25

3280 11p.50 Player, goalkeeper and ball in net 6·75 5·50

3281 13p.50 Player, wearing green strip, and ball 7·75 6·50

1475 Grandparents and Grand Children Gardening

2011. Grandparents' Day

3282 **1475** 7p. multicoloured 4·00 3·25

1476 Woodland, Los Troncones, Ciudad Victoria, Tamaulipas

2011. International Year of Forests

3283 **1476** 11p.50 multicoloured 6·75 5·50

1477 Symbols of Stamp Collecting

2011. Philately

3284 **1477** 7p. multicoloured 4·00 3·25

1478 College Building

2011. 30th Anniv of National Defence College

3285 **1478** 7p. multicoloured 4·00 3·25

1479 Cantinflas

2011. Birth Centenary of Fortino Mario Alfonso Moreno Reyes (Cantinflas) (actor, producer and screenwriter). Multicoloured.

3286 7p. Type **1479** 4·00 3·25

3287 11p.50 Cantinflas as drawing and animation figure 6·75 5·50

1480 Adult Students

2011. 30th Anniv of National Institute for Adult Education

3288 **1480** 7p. multicoloured 4·00 3·25

1481 Postman, PC Screen, Parcel and Label

2011. 25th Anniv of Mexican Postal Service

3289 **1481** 7p. multicoloured 4·00 3·25

1482 *Justicia para Todos* (Ariosto Otero (Mexican muralist))

2011. 75th Anniv of Promulgation of the Law on Fiscal Justice

3290 **1482** 7p. multicoloured 4·00 3·25

1483 Quetzalcóatl and Film

2011. Year of Tourism in Mexico

3291 **1483** 11p.50 multicoloured 6·75 5·50

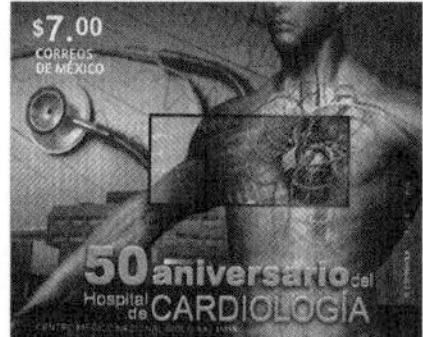

1484 Torso, Heart and Symbols of Cardiovascular Research

2011. 50th Anniv of Cardiology Hospital

3292 **1484** 7p. multicoloured 4·00 3·25

1485 Symbols of Civil Defence

2011. 25th Anniv of National Civil Protection System

3293 **1485** 11p.50 multicoloured 6·75 5·50

1486 Bypass, North of Mexico City

2011. Large Road Infrastructure Works. Multicoloured.

MS3294 7p. Type **1486**; 11p.50 Piedra Colorada Tunnel, Durango Highway; 13p.50 Texcapa Bridge, Mexico Road, Tuxpan 19·00 17·00

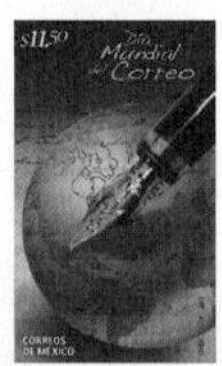

1487 Globe and Pen Nib

2011. Stamp Day

3295 **1487** 11p.50 multicoloured 6·75 5·50

1488 Early Educators

2011. 90th Anniv of Ministry of Education. Multicoloured.

MS3296 7p.×6, Type **1488**; Teacher reading to child; Demonstration; Child holding open book; Office; Mural by Diego Rivera (Ministry of Education, Mexico City) 24·00 22·00

1489 Games Emblem

2011. Pan American Games, Guadalajara. Multicoloured.

3297 7p. Type **1489** 4·00 3·25

3298 11p.50 Mascots 6·75 5·50

3299 13p.50 Emblem and stylized agave 7·75 6·50

1490 '50 ANOS Cinvestav' and Agave

2011. 50th Anniv of Cinvestav (Centre for Research and Advanced Studies, National Polytechnic Institute)

3300 **1490** 7p. multicoloured 4·00 3·25

1491 Alfonso Luis Herrera Lopez (Pioneer of plant health in Mexico)

2011. Health and Safety in Mexico. Multicoloured.

MS3301 7p.×6, Type **1491**; TIF emblem (50 years free of Foot and Mouth disease): Dieter Enkerlin (founding director and dean of Ecological Research Center Southeast (CIES) (sterile insect technique); Side of beef and plantsperson (good practise); Inspection and verification controls; Research and development 24·00 22·00

1492 Gravestone, Flowers and Skeleton

2011. Mexican Traditions. Day of the Dead

3302 **1492** 7p. multicoloured 4·00 3·25

1493 Dancing

2011. 40th Anniv of Educational Development Council (CONAFE)

3303 **1493** 7p. multicoloured 4·00 3·25

1494 Building Façade

2011. 25th Anniv of ISSSTEZAC (Law on Security and Social Services for State Workers' of Zacatecas)

3304 **1494** 7p. multicoloured 4·00 3·25

1495 Sr. Santiago (from cover of the book manuscript from Jiquilpan Post)

2011. Day of the Postman

3305 **1495** 7p. multicoloured 4·00 3·25

1496 German Shepherd

2011. Dog Breeds. Multicoloured.

3306 7p. Type **1496** 4·00 3·25

3307 13p.50 Cocker spaniel 7·75 6·50

1497 Children playing Piñata

2011. Christmas. Multicoloured.
3308 7p. Type **1497** 4·00 3·25
3309 11p.50 The Nativity and table decorations 6·75 5·50
3310 11p.50 Three Magi 6·75 5·50
3311 11p.50 Sant Claus (horiz) 6·75 5·50

1498 Symbols of Social Security

2011. 50th Anniv of IMSS (Mexican Social Security Institute) Delegation in Veracruz
3312 **1498** 7p. multicoloured 4·00 3·25

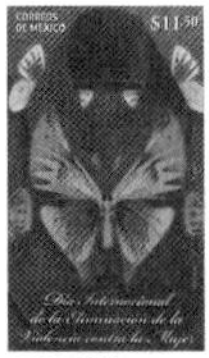
1499 Ribbon and Butterfly

2011. International Day for the Eradication of Violence against Women
3313 **1499** 11p.50 multicoloured 6·75 5·50

1500 Birds

2011. National Award for Voluntary Action and Solidairty
3314 **1500** 11p.50 multicoloured 6·75 5·50

1501 World Heritage Cities

2011. Mexican World Heritage Cities
3315 **1501** 11p.50 multicoloured 6·75 5·50

1502 '50' and Emblem

2011. 50th Anniv of National Medical Centre
3316 **1502** 7p. multicoloured 4·00 3·25

1503 Grey Whale

1504 Grey Whale

2012. 50th Anniv of Mexico – Korea Diplomatic Relations
3317 **1503** 13p.50 multicoloured 7·75 6·50
3318 **1504** 13p.50 multicoloured 7·75 6·50

1505 Watery Heart

2012. Day of Love and Friendship
3319 **1505** 7p. multicoloured 4·00 3·25

1506 Figures and Doves

2012. International Women's Day
3320 **1506** 11p.50 multicoloured 6·75 5·50

1507 Butterfly

2012. World Down's Syndrome Day
3321 **1507** 13p.50 multicoloured 8·00 6·50

1508 Emblem and Building

2012. 20th Anniv of National Commission of Bioethics
3322 **1508** 7p. multicoloured 4·00 3·25

1509 Hand giving Heart

2012. Unite Against Human Trafficking
3323 **1509** 7p. multicoloured 4·00 3·25

1510 Building Façade

2012. 300th Anniv of Nuevo León
3324 **1510** 7p. multicoloured 4·00 3·25

1511 Children surprising Mother

2012. Mothers' Day. Multicoloured.
3325 7p. Type **1511** 4·00 3·25
3326 7p. Children deciding on gifts 4·00 3·25

1512 Interior

2012. Postal Palace
3327 **1512** 7p. multicoloured 4·00 3·25

1513 'Tratados de la Soledad' (Treaties of Soledad)

2012. 150th Anniv of Battle of Puebla. Multicoloured.
MS3328 7p.×3, Type **1513**; General Ignacio Zaragoza; 'Ejercito de Oriente' (The Army of the East) 12·00 11·50

1514 Alfabetizacion (Diego Rivera) (fresco, Bank of Mexico)

2012. Teachers' Day
3329 **1514** 7p. multicoloured 4·00 3·25

1515 Pozole (Mexico)

2012. Mexico - Brazil Diplomatic Relationships. Traditional Foods. Multicoloured.
3330 13p.50 Type **1515** 7·75 6·50
3331 13p.50 Coffee pot, corn products, manioc products and cups (Brazil) 7·75 6·50

1516 Mexican Wolves

2012. Endangered Species. Mexican Wolf (*Canis lupus baileyi*)
3332 **1516** 11p.50 multicoloured 6·75 5·50

1517 Stubbed Cigarette and Butterflies

2012. World No Smoking Day
3333 **1517** 7p. multicoloured 4·00 3·25

1518 School Building and Emilio Rabasa (writer and politician)

2012. Centenary of Escuela Libre de Derecho (Free Law School)
3334 **1518** 7p. multicoloured 4·00 3·25

1519 Grandparents ready for Bed

2012. Grandparents' Day
3335 **1519** 7p. multicoloured 4·00 3·25

1520 El Cajón Dam, Nayarit

2012. 75th Anniv of Federal Electrical Commission. Multicoloured.
MS3336 7p.×6, Type **1520**; Solar farm, Guaycora, Sonara; Wind park, La Venta, Oaxaca; Linesman; National Energy Control Centre; Transmission towers, Colima 24·00 22·00

1521 *Senor de los Mares* Floating Platform

2012. Mexican Petroleum Congress. Multicoloured.
3337 7p. Type **1521** 4·00 3·25
3338 7p. Oil platform complex, Campo Cantarell, Campeche 4·00 3·25

1522 Cloud Gate Dance Theatre of Taiwan

2012. 40th Anniv of Cervantino Festival
3339 **1522** 13p.50 multicoloured 8·00 6·50

1523 Symbols of Cinvestav

2012. 25th Anniv of Cinvestav (Centre for Research and Advanced Studies, National Polytechnic Institute) Saltillo Unit
3340 **1523** 7p. multicoloured 4·00 3·25

1524 University Rectory Façade

2012. 70th Anniv of Sonoro University. Multicoloured.
3341 7p. Type **1524** 4·00 3·25
3342 7p. Don Quixote (stained glass) 4·00 3·25
3343 7p. Library and museum building 4·00 3·25

1525 Globe and Envelopes

2012. International Post Day
3344 **1525** 11p.50 multicoloured 6·75 5·50

1526 Agua Caliente Minaret

2012. Grandezas de México Exhibition, Tijuana
3345 **1526** 11p.50 multicoloured 6·75 5·50

1527 Children, Books and Building Blocks

2012. 20th Anniv of Schools' Councils
3346 **1527** 7p. multicoloured 4·00 3·25

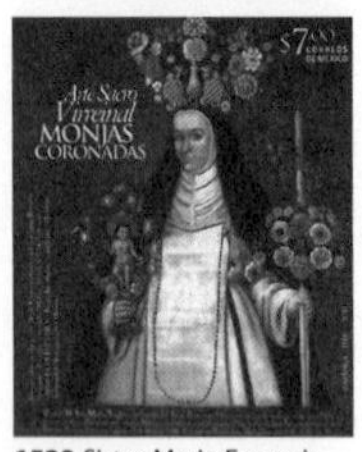

1528 Sister Maria Engracia Josefa

2012. Religious Art. Crowned Nuns. Multicoloured.
3347 7p. Type **1528** 4·00 3·25
3348 7p. Unknown nun 4·00 3·25

1529 Decorated Sugar Skull and Candles

2012. Mexican Traditions. Day of the Dead
3349 **1529** 7p. multicoloured 4·00 3·25

1530 Paintings in the Inner Temple

2012. Archaeology. Mayan Complex, Tulum. Multicoloured.
MS3350 7p. Type **1530**; 7p. Complex on rocky outcrop; 11p.50 'The Castle'; 13p.50 Building containing paintings; 13p.50 Southern corner of complex 30·00 29·00

The stamps, label and margins of **MS**3350 form a composite design.

1531 Elves packing Presents

2012. Christmas. Multicoloured.
3351 11p.50 Type **1531** 6·75 5·50
3352 11p.50 Visiting 6·75 5·50
3353 11p.50 Three Magi 6·75 5·50

1532 Postman

2012. Day of the Postman
3354 **1532** 7p. multicoloured 4·00 3·25

1533 Anniversary Emblem and Centre

2012. 50th Anniv of Lebanese Centre
3355 **1533** 13p.50 multicoloured 8·00 6·50

1534 '40' and Buildings

2012. 40th Anniv of FOVISSSTE (Fund for Public Housing Authority)
3356 **1534** 7p. multicoloured 4·00 3·25

1535 University

2012. 280th Anniv of Guanajuato University
3357 **1535** 7p. multicoloured 4·00 3·25

1536 Justo Sierra

2012. Birth Centenary of Justo Sierra Méndez (writer)
3358 **1536** 7p. multicoloured 4·00 3·25

1537 1537 Canoeists

2012. Sacred Mayan Journey (Xcaret to Cozumel to Playa del Carmen). Multicoloured.
3359 7p.50 Type **1537** 4·25 3·50
3360 11p.50 Canoeists (centre) 6·75 5·50
3361 13p.50 Canoeists (right) 8·00 6·50

1538 Doves

2013. Day of Love and Friendship
3362 **1538** 7p. multicoloured 4·00 3·25

1539 Aircraft, Molino del Rey and Los Pinos, Official Residence

2013. Presidential Day
3363 **1639** 7p. multicoloured 4·00 3·25

1540 Statue

2013. 70th Anniv of Ibero-American University. Multicoloured.
3364 7p. Type **1540** 4·00 3·25
3365 7p. Sports hall 4·00 3·25
3366 7p. Students seated on steps 4·00 3·25

1541 Symbols of Shopping

2013. 30th Anniv of ANTAD - National Association of Supermarkets and Department Stores
3367 **1541** 7p. multicoloured 4·00 3·25

1542 Emblem

2013. International Day of Indigenous Languages
3368 **1542** 11p.50 multicoloured 6·75 5·50

1543 Oil Platform

2013. 75th Anniv of Oil Expropriation
3369 **1543** 7p. multicoloured 4·00 3·25

1544 Guillermo Haro Barraza

2013. Birth Centenary of Guillermo Haro Barraza (astronomer)
3370 **1544** 7p. multicoloured 4·00 3·25

1545 Venustiano Carranza and Riders

2013. Centenary of Promulgation of the Plan of Guadalupe
3371 **1545** 7p. multicoloured 4·00 3·25

1546 *Neofelis diardi borneensis* (Bornean Clouded Leopard)

2013. 60th Anniv of Mexico – Indonesia Diplomatic Relations. Multicoloured.
3372 15p. Type **1546** 8·00 6·50
3373 15p. *Panthers onca* (Jaguar) 8·00 6·50

1547 Soldier (statue) and Anniversary Emblem

2013. Centenary of Mexican Army (1st issue)
3374 **1547** 7p. multicoloured 4·00 3·25

See also Nos. 3379 and 3397.

1548 Ixtliton (Aztec god of medicine and healing)

2013. 70th Anniv of Children's Hospital of Mexico, Federico Gomez
3375 **1548** 7p. multicoloured 4·00 3·25

1549 Bird

2013. Children's Day
3376 **1549** 7p. multicoloured 4·00 3·25

1550 Mother and Children (dolls)

2013. Mothers' Day
3377 **1550** 11p.50 multicoloured 6·75 5·50

1551 *La Importancia de la Educación* (Pablo O'Higgins) (detail)

2013. Teachers' Day
3378 **1551** 7p. multicoloured 4·00 3·25

1552 Anniversary Emblem and Service Personnel

2013. Centenary of Mexican Army (2nd issue)
3379 **1552** 7p. multicoloured 4·00 3·25

1553 Students and Horse

2013. 160th Anniversary of Veterinary Education in Mexico
3380 **1553** 7p. multicoloured 4·00 3·25

1554 Manuel Acuña

2013. 140th Death Anniv of Manuel Acuña (writer)
3381 **1554** 7p. multicoloured 4·00 3·25

1555 Symbols of Grandparents

2013. Grandparents' Day
3382 **1555** 7p. multicoloured 4·00 3·25

1556 *First Congress of Anahuac* (Salvador Tarazona) (detail)

2013. Bicentenary of First Congress of Anáhuac (Chilpancingo)
3383 **1556** 7p. multicoloured 4·00 3·25

1557 Metropolitan Cathedral

2013. Bicentenary of Completion of Metropolitan Cathedral, Mexico City
3384 **1557** 7p. multicoloured 4·00 3·25

1558 Symbols of Industry

2013. 95th Anniv of Confederation of Industrial Chambers (CONCAMIN) of Mexico
3385 **1558** 7p. multicoloured 4·00 3·25

1559 *Los informantes de Sahagun* (base relief) (Federico Cantú) (detail)

2013. 80th Anniv of Nuevo León Autonomous University. Multicoloured.
MS3386 7p.×6, Type **1559**; *Los informantes de Sahagun* (right); *Espejos comunicantes* (Guillermo Ceniceros) (left detail); *Espejos comunicantes* (right detail); *Einstein* (mural) (Sebastián Xavier Treviño) (left detail); *Einstein* (right detail) 24·00 22·00

1560 Stylized Birds, Envelope and Map

2013. World Post Day
3387 **1560** 13p.50 multicoloured 7·25 6·00

1561 Women and Ballot Box

2013. 60th Anniv of Votes for Women in Mexico
3388 **1561** 7p. multicoloured 4·00 3·25

1562 *La Vida y la Salud* (Diego Rivera)

2013. 75th Anniv of Secretariat of Health
3389 **1562** 7p. multicoloured 4·00 3·25

1563 Day of the Dead (image scaled to 48% of original size)

2013. Mexican Traditions. Day of the Dead. Sheet 100×80 mm
MS3390 **1563** 15p. multicoloured 8·00 7·75

1564 Grand Café de la Parroquia

2013. 205th Anniv of Grand Café de la Parroquia, Veracruz
3391 **1564** 7p. multicoloured 4·00 3·25

1565 Nelson Mandela

2013. 20th Anniv of Mexico – South Africa Bilateral Relations
3392 **1565** 15p. multicoloured 8·00 6·50

1566 Symbols of Agriculture

2013. 40th Anniv of National Institute for Capacity Development in the Rural Sector
3393 **1566** 7p. multicoloured 4·00 3·25

1567 Anniversary Emblem

2013. 50th Anniv of Federal Court of Conciliation and Arbitration
3394 **1567** 7p. multicoloured 4·00 3·25

1568 Symbols of Post

2013. Day of the Postman
3395 **1568** 7p. multicoloured 4·00 3·25

1569 Building Façade

2013. 150th Anniv of Casino Español, Mexico City
3396 **1569** 13p.50 multicoloured 7·25 6·00

1570 Anniversary Emblem and Eagle (statue)

2013. Centenary of Mexican Army (3rd issue)
3397 **1570** 7p. multicoloured 4·00 3·25

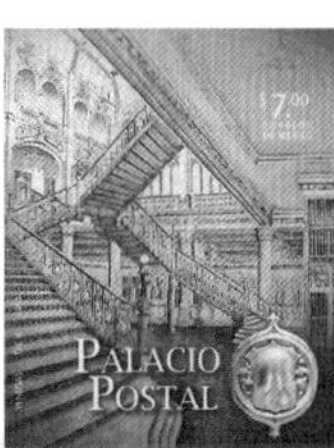

1571 Staircase

2013. Postal Palace
3398 **1571** 7p. multicoloured 4·00 3·25

1572 Oaxaca

2013. World Heritage Site - Oaxaca
3399 **1572** 15p. multicoloured 8·00 6·50

1573 Migrants

2013. Migrant Protection Programme
3400 **1573** 7p. multicoloured 4·00 3·25

1574 Three Kings

2013. Christmas. Multicoloured.

3401	7p. Type **1574**	4·00	3·25
3402	7p. Father Christmas	4·00	3·25
3403	11p.50 Tree and Piñata	6·50	5·25
3404	13p.50 The Holy Family	7·25	6·00

1575 University Buildings

2013. 60th Anniv of Morelos Autonomous University
3405 **1575** 7p. multicoloured 4·00 3·25

1576 Symbols of Education

2013. 70th Anniv of National Union of Education Workers
3406 **1576** 7p. multicoloured 4·00 3·25

1577 Industrial Patent Design

2013. 20th Anniv of Mexican Institute of Industrial Property
3407 **1577** 7p. multicoloured 4·00 3·25

1578 Sports

2013. 25th Anniv of National Commission of Physical Culture and Sports
3408 **1578** 7p. multicoloured 4·00 3·25

1579 *La Danza la Media Luna*

2013. Promotion of Philately. Paintings by Francisco Eppens Helguera. Multicoloured.

3409	7p. Type **1579**	4·00	3·25
3410	7p. *Alcatraces*	4·00	3·25
3411	11p.50 *Cactáceas*	6·50	5·25
3412	13p.50 *Guerrero Águila y Guerero Tigre*	7·25	6·00
3413	15p. *Caballos de Colores*	8·00	6·50

1580 Symbols of Industry

2012. 50th Anniv of Industrial Work Training Centres

3414	**1580**	7p. multicoloured	4·00	3·25

1581 Police Motorcyclist

2013. 85th Anniv of Federal Police

3415	**1581**	7p. multicoloured	4·00	3·25

1582 Organ, Santa Maria Tiltepec Church

2013. Musical Instruments. Church Organs. Multicoloured.

3416	7p. Type **1582**	4·00	3·25
3417	7p. San Jerónimo Tlacochahuaya	4·00	3·25
3418	11p.50 San Andrés Zautla	6·50	5·25
3419	11p.50 Santa María de la Natividad Tamazulapan	6·50	5·25
3420	13p.50 Yanhuitlán Santo Domingo Church	7·25	6·00
3421	13p.50 Catedral de Oaxaca	7·25	6·00

EXPRESS LETTER STAMPS

E55 Express Service Messenger

1919

E445	**E55**	20c. black and red	40	25

E95

1934

E536	**E95**	10c. blue and red	25	50

E121 Indian Archer

1934. New President's Assumption of Office. Imprint "OFICINA IMPRESORA DE HACIENDA–MEXICO".

E581	**E121**	10c. violet	1·60	50

1938. Imprint "TALLERES DE IMP. DE EST. Y VALORES-MEXICO".

E610	**E121**	10c. violet	90	25
E731	**E121**	20c. orange	90	25

1940. Optd 1940.

E665	**E55**	20c. black and red	45	25

E222

1950

E860	**E222**	25c. orange	70	35
E910	-	60c. green	1·10	1·40

Design:—60c. Hands and letter.

E244

E245

1956

E954	**E244**	35c. purple	65	35
E1065	**E244**	50c. green	3·50	80
E956	**E245**	80c. red	70	1·10
E1066	**E245**	1p.20 lilac	4·75	1·60
E1346p	**E244**	2p. orange	4·50	90
E1346q	**E245**	5p. blue	3·25	1·90

E468 Watch Face

1979

E1373	**E468**	2p. black and orange	80	40

INSURED LETTER STAMPS

IN125 Safe

1935. Inscr as in Type **IN125**.

IN583	-	10c. red	2·75	95
IN733	-	50c. blue	2·00	70
IN734	**IN125**	1p. green	1·70	85

Designs:—10c. Bundle of insured letters; 50c. Registered mailbag.

IN222 PO Treasury Vault

1950

IN911	**IN222**	20c. blue	65	35
IN912	**IN222**	40c. purple	65	35
IN913	**IN222**	1p. green	1·70	50
IN914	**IN222**	5p. green and blue	2·30	1·60
IN915	**IN222**	10p. blue and red	6·00	4·00

IN469 Padlock

1976

IN1374	**IN469**	40c. black & turq	50	45
IN1522	**IN469**	1p. black & turq	90	40
IN1376	**IN469**	2p. black and blue	65	45
IN1380	**IN469**	5p. black & turq	2·00	70
IN1524	**IN469**	10p. black & turq	3·25	50
IN1525	**IN469**	20p. black & turq	7·50	2·75
IN1383	**IN469**	50p. black & turq	2·30	1·20
IN1384	**IN469**	100p. black & turq	1·80	1·50

The 5, 10, 20p. exist with the padlock either 31 or 32½ mm high.

OFFICIAL STAMPS

O18 Hidalgo

1884. No value shown.

O156	**O18**	Red	95	70
O157	**O18**	Brown	60	45
O158	**O18**	Orange	1·70	60
O159	**O18**	Green	95	55
O160	**O18**	Blue	2·00	1·90

1894. Stamps of 1895 handstamped **OFICIAL**.

O231	**19**	1c. green	12·00	4·00
O232	**19**	2c. red	13·50	4·00
O233	**19**	3c. brown	12·00	4·00
O234	**20**	4c. orange	18·00	8·00
O235	**21**	5c. blue	24·00	8·00
O236	**22**	10c. purple	22·00	2·00
O237	**20**	12c. olive	47·00	20·00
O238	**22**	15c. blue	29·00	12·00
O239	**22**	20c. red	29·00	12·00
O240	**22**	50c. mauve	60·00	29·00
O241	**23**	1p. brown	£140	60·00
O242	**23**	5p. red	£325	£170
O243	**23**	10p. blue	£500	£350

1899. Stamps of 1899 handstamped **OFICIAL**.

O276	**27**	1c. green	25·00	1·70
O286	**27**	1c. purple	12·50	2·00
O277	**27**	2c. red	34·00	2·75
O287	**27**	2c. green	12·50	2·00
O278	**27**	3c. brown	34·00	1·70
O288	**27**	4c. red	22·00	1·50
O279	**27**	5c. blue	34·00	3·00
O289	**27**	5c. orange	22·00	5·00
O280	**27**	10c. brown and purple	44·00	3·75
O290	**27**	10c. orange and blue	24·00	2·00
O281	**27**	15c. purple and lavender	44·00	3·75
O282	**27**	20c. blue and red	50·00	1·70
O283	**28**	50c. black and purple	£100	17·00
O291	**28**	50c. black and red	65·00	9·25
O284	**29**	1p. black and blue	£200	17·00
O285	**30**	5p. black and red	£400	50·00

1911. Independence stamps optd **OFICIAL**.

O301	**32**	1c. purple	3·50	3·50
O302	-	2c. green	2·50	1·50
O303	-	3c. brown	3·50	1·70
O304	-	4c. red	3·75	1·50
O305	-	5c. orange	8·50	4·75
O306	-	10c. orange and blue	3·75	1·50
O307	-	15c. lake and slate	8·75	5·75
O308	-	20c. blue and lake	6·75	1·70
O309	**40**	50c. black and brown	24·00	10·00
O310	-	1p. black and blue	41·00	17·00
O311	-	5p. black and red	£200	85·00

1915. Stamps of 1915 optd **OFICIAL**.

O321	**43**	1c. violet	70	1·40
O322	**44**	2c. green	70	1·40
O323	**45**	3c. brown	70	1·40
O324	**45**	4c. red	70	1·40
O325	**45**	5c. orange	70	1·40
O326	**45**	10c. blue	70	1·40

1915. Stamps of 1915 optd **OFICIAL**.

O318	**46**	40c. grey	5·50	9·75
O455	**46**	40c. mauve	5·00	3·50
O319	**47**	1p. grey and brown	7·25	9·75
O456	**47**	1p. grey and blue	25·00	17·00
O320	**48**	5p. blue and lake	42·00	40·00
O457	**48**	5p. grey and green	£225	£225

1916. Nos. O301/11 optd with T **49**.

O358	**32**	1c. purple	4·50	
O359	-	2c. green	90	
O360	-	3c. brown	1·20	
O361	-	4c. red	5·00	
O362	-	5c. orange	1·20	
O363	-	10c. orange and blue	1·20	
O364	-	15c. lake and slate	1·20	
O365	-	20c. blue and lake	1·30	
O366	**40**	50c. black and brown	£140	
O367	-	1p. black and blue	7·50	
O368	-	5p. black and red	£3000	

1918. Stamps of 1917 optd **OFICIAL**.

O424	**53**	1c. violet	4·25	4·00
O446	**53**	1c. grey	2·10	1·10
O447	-	2c. green	1·30	45
O448	-	3c. brown	55	45
O449	-	4c. red	13·50	1·70
O450	-	5c. blue	70	45
O451	-	10c. blue	70	45
O452	-	20c. lake	3·75	1·70
O454	-	30c. black	7·50	3·50

1923. No. 416 optd **OFICIAL**.

O485	10p. black and brown	£140	£200

1923. Stamps of 1923 optd **OFICIAL**.

O471	**59**	1c. brown	45	55
O473	**60**	2c. red	45	70
O475	**61**	3c. brown	1·40	1·00
O461	**62**	4c. green	4·25	3·50
O476	**63**	4c. green	1·10	75
O477	**63**	5c. orange	2·75	1·90
O489	**74**	8c. orange	6·75	4·75
O479	**66**	10c. lake	1·60	1·50
O480	**65**	20c. blue	8·50	6·75
O464	**64**	30c. green	1·10	70
O467	**68**	50c. brown	1·10	1·00
O469	**69**	1p. blue and lake	11·00	10·50

1929. Air. Optd **OFICIAL**.

O501	**80**	5c. blue (roul)	1·00	1·00
O502	**81**	20c. violet	1·20	1·90
O490	**58**	25c. sepia and green	4·00	4·25
O492	**58**	25c. sepia and lake	11·00	13·00

1929. Air. As 1926 Postal Congress stamp optd **HABILITADO Servicio Oficial Aereo**.

O493	**70**	2c. black	70·00	80·00
O494	-	4c. black	70·00	80·00
O495	**70**	5c. black	70·00	80·00
O496	-	10c. black	70·00	80·00
O497	**72**	20c. black	70·00	80·00
O498	**72**	30c. black	70·00	80·00
O499	**72**	40c. black	70·00	80·00
O500	**73**	1p. black	£2250	£2000

O85

1930. Air.

O503	**O85**	20c. grey	7·25	7·00
O504	**O85**	35c. violet	1·30	2·20
O505	**O85**	40c. blue and brown	1·50	2·10
O506	**O85**	70c. sepia and violet	1·50	2·20

1931. Air. Surch **HABILITADO Quince centavos**.

O515	**O85**	15c. on 20c. grey	45	55

1932. Air. Optd **SERVICIO OFICIAL** in one line.

O532	**80**	10c. violet (perf or roul)	45	60
O533	**80**	15c. red (perf or roul)	1·50	2·10
O534	**80**	20c. sepia (roul)	1·50	2·10
O531	**58**	50c. red and blue	1·50	1·90

1932. Stamps of 1923 optd **SERVICIO OFICIAL** in two lines.

O535	**59**	1c. brown	45	70
O536	**60**	2c. red	55	60
O537	**61**	3c. brown	2·10	2·00
O538	**63**	4c. green	7·00	5·25
O539	**63**	5c. red	9·50	5·25
O540	**66**	10c. lake	2·40	2·00
O541	**65**	20c. blue	10·50	6·75
O544	**64**	30c. green	5·50	2·00
O545	**46**	40c. mauve	10·50	4·00
O546	**68**	50c. brown	1·80	2·00
O547	**69**	1p. blue and lake	2·00	2·00

1933. Air. Optd **SERVICIO OFICIAL** in two lines.

O553	**58**	50c. red and blue	1·50	2·10

1933. Air. Optd **SERVICIO OFICIAL** in two lines.

O548	**80**	5c. blue (No. 476a)	45	60
O549	**80**	10c. violet (No. 477)	45	35
O550	**80**	20c. sepia (No. 479)	80	1·10
O551	**80**	50c. lake (No. 481)	1·50	2·10

1934. Optd **OFICIAL**.

O565	**92**	15c. blue	70	70

1938. Nos. 561/71 optd **OFICIAL**.

O622	-	1c. orange	1·40	2·75
O623	**101**	2c. green	85	1·40
O624	-	4c. red	85	95
O625	-	10c. violet	85	1·70
O626	-	20c. blue	1·10	1·70
O627	-	30c. red	1·40	2·75
O628	-	40c. brown	1·80	2·75
O629	-	50c. black	2·00	1·90
O630	**101**	1p. red and brown	5·50	8·25

PARCEL POST STAMPS

P167 Steam Mail Train

1941

P732	**P167**	10c. red	2·30	1·30
P733	**P167**	20c. violet	6·75	3·25

P228 Class DE-10 Diesel-electric Locomotive

1951

P916	**P228**	10c. pink	4·25	70
P917	**P228**	20c. violet	4·25	1·80

POSTAGE DUE STAMPS

D32

1908

D282	**D32**	1c. blue	70	1·10
D283	**D32**	2c. blue	70	1·10
D284	**D32**	4c. blue	70	1·10
D285	**D32**	5c. blue	70	1·10
D286	**D32**	10c. blue	70	1·10

MICRONESIA

A group of islands in the Pacific, from 1899 to 1914 part of the German Caroline Islands. Occupied by the Japanese in 1914 the islands were from 1920 a Japanese mandated territory, and from 1947 part of the United States Trust Territory of the Pacific Islands, using United States stamps. Micronesia assumed control of its postal services in 1984.

100 cents = 1 dollar.

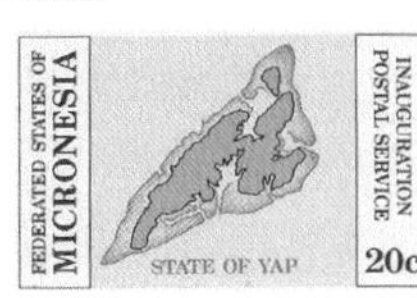
1 Yap

1984. Inauguration of Postal Independence. Maps. Multicoloured.

1	20c. Type **1**	75	70
2	20c. Truk	75	70
3	20c. Pohnpei	75	70
4	20c. Kosrae	75	70

2 Fernandez de Quiros

1984

5	**2**	1c. blue	15	10
6	-	2c. brown	15	10
7	-	3c. blue	15	10
8	-	4c. green	15	10
9	-	5c. brown and olive	20	15
10	-	10c. purple	25	20
11	-	13c. blue	30	25
11a	-	15c. red	45	40
12	-	17c. brown	40	35
13	**2**	19c. purple	50	45
14	-	20c. green	50	45
14a	-	22c. green	65	60
14b	-	25c. orange	75	70
15	-	30c. red	80	70
15a	-	36c. blue	1·00	90
16	-	37c. violet	1·10	1·00
16a	-	45c. green	1·30	1·20
17	-	50c. brown and sepia	1·40	1·30
18	-	$1 olive	2·75	2·50
19	-	$2 blue	5·75	5·25
20	-	$5 brown	13·50	12·50
20a	-	$10 blue	23·00	21·00

Designs:—2, 20c. Louis Duperrey; 3, 30c. Fyodor Lutke; 4, 37c. Jules Dumont d'Urville; 5c. Men's house, Yap; 10, 45c. Sleeping Lady (mountains), Kosrae; 13, 15c. Liduduhriap waterfall, Pohnpei; 17, 25c. Tonachau Peak, Truk; 22, 36c. *Senyavin* (full-rigged sailing ship); 50c. Devil mask, Truk; $1 Sokehs Rock, Pohnpei; $2 Outrigger canoes, Kosrae; $5 Stone money, Yap; $10 Official Seal.

3 Boeing 727-100

1984. Air. Multicoloured.

21	28c. Type **3**	95	85
22	35c. Grumman SA-16 Albatros flying boat	1·30	1·20
23	40c. Consolidated PBY-5A Catalina amphibian	1·60	1·40

4 Truk Post Office

1984. Ausipex 84 International Stamp Exhibition, Melbourne. Multicoloured.

24	20c. Type **4** (postage)	65	60
25	28c. German Caroline Islands 1919 3pf. yacht stamp (air)	90	85
26	35c. German 1900 20pf. stamp optd for Caroline Islands	1·20	1·10
27	40c. German Caroline Islands 1915 5m. yacht stamp	1·60	1·40

5 Baby in Basket

1984. Christmas. Multicoloured.

28	20c. Type **5** (postage)	1·30	1·20
29	28c. Open book showing Christmas scenes (air)	1·20	1·10
30	35c. Palm tree decorated with lights	1·50	1·40
31	40c. Women preparing food	1·80	1·70

6 USS *Jamestown* (warship)

1985. Ships.

32	**6**	22c. black & brown (postage)	80	70
33	-	33c. black and lilac (air)	95	90
34	-	39c. black and green	1·30	1·20
35	-	44c. black and red	1·70	1·60

Designs:—33c. *L'Astrolabe* (D'Urville's ship); 39c. *La Coquille* (Duperrey's ship); 44c. *Shenandoah* (Confederate warship).

7 Lelu Protestant Church, Kosrae

1985. Christmas.

36	**7**	22c. black and orange (postage)	1·00	95
37	-	33c. black and violet (air)	1·30	1·20
38	-	44c. black and green	1·70	1·50

Designs:—33c. Dublon Protestant Church; 44c. Pohnpei Catholic Church.

8 Noddy Tern

1985. Birth Bicentenary of John J. Audubon (ornithologist). Multicoloured.

39	22c. Type **8** (postage)	1·10	1·00
40	22c. Turnstone	1·10	1·00
41	22c. Golden Plover	1·10	1·00
42	22c. Black-bellied Plover	1·10	1·00
43	44c. Sooty Tern (air)	2·00	1·80

9 Land of Sacred Masonry

1985. Nan Madol, Pohnpei. Multicoloured.

44	22c. Type **9** (postage)	75	70
45	33c. Nan Tauas inner courtyard (air)	1·00	90
46	39c. Nan Tauas outer wall	1·10	1·00
47	44c. Nan Tauas burial vault	1·30	1·20

10 Doves, "LOVE" and Hands

1986. Anniversaries and Events. Multicoloured.

48	22c. Type **10** (International Peace Year)	1·00	95
49	44c. Halley's comet	1·90	1·80
50	44c. *Trienza* (cargo liner) arriving at jetty (40th anniv of return of Nauruans from Truk)	2·00	1·80

1986. Nos. 1/4 surch.

51	22c. on 20c. Type **1**	75	70
52	22c. on 20c. Truk	75	70
53	22c. on 20c. Pohnpei	75	70
54	22c. on 20c. Kosrae	75	70

12 Bully Hayes

1986. Ameripex 86 International Stamp Exhibition, Chicago. Bully Hayes (buccaneer). Multicoloured.

55	22c. Type **12** (postage)	80	75
56	33c. Angelo (crew member) forging Hawaii 5c. blue stamp (air)	90	85
57	39c. *Leonora* sinking off Kosrae	1·10	1·00
58	44c. Hayes escaping capture on Kosrae	1·20	1·10
59	75c. Cover of book *Bully Hayes, Buccaneer* by Louis Becke	2·30	2·10
MS60	128×70 mm. $1 Hayes holding Chief to ransom	5·25	4·75

13 *Madonna and Child*

1986. Christmas. "Madonna and Child" Paintings.

61	-	5c. multicoloured (postage)	30	25
62	-	22c. multicoloured	1·00	95
63	-	33c. multicoloured (air)	1·40	1·30
64	**13**	44c. multicoloured	1·90	1·80

14 Passports on Globe

1986. First Micronesian Passport.

65	**14**	22c. blue, black and yellow	90	80

15 Emblem (International Year of Shelter for the Homeless)

1987. Anniversaries and Events.

66	**15**	22c. blue, red and black (postage)	80	75
67	-	33c. green, red and black (air)	1·00	90
68	-	39c. blue, black and red	1·60	1·40
69	-	44c. blue, red and black	1·80	1·60
MS70		85×550 mm. $1 multicoloured	4·75	4·25

Designs:—33c. Dollar sign (bicentenary of dollar currency); 39c. Space capsule (25th Anniv of First American to orbit Earth); 44c. "200 USA" (bicentenary of US consitiution); $1 Micronesian and Canadian flags (Capex '87 International Stamp Exhibition, Toronto).

16 Archangel Gabriel appearing to Mary

1987. Christmas. Multicoloured.

71	22c. Type **16** (postage)	75	70
72	33c. Joseph praying and Mary with baby Jesus (air)	1·00	90
73	39c. Shepherds with their sheep	1·20	1·10
74	44c. Wise men	1·40	1·30

17 Spanish Missionary and Flag

1988. Micronesian History. Multicoloured.

75	22c. Type **17** (postage)	90	80
76	22c. Natives producing copra and German flag	90	80
77	22c. School pupils and Japanese flag	90	80
78	22c. General store and US flag	90	80
79	44c. Traditional boatbuilding and fishing skills (air)	1·60	1·50
80	44c. Welcoming tourists from Douglas DC-10 airliner and divers investigating World War II wreckage	1·60	1·50

18 Ponape White Eye

1988. Birds. Multicoloured.

81	3c. Type **18** (postage)	20	15
82	14c. Truk monarch	45	40
83	22c. Ponape starling	70	65
84	33c. Truk white eye (air)	90	85
85	44c. Blue-faced parrot finch	1·10	1·00
86	$1 Yap monarch	2·75	2·50

19 Marathon

1988. Olympic Games, Seoul. Multicoloured.

87	25c. Type **19**	70	65
88	25c. Hurdling	70	65
89	45c. Basketball	1·10	1·00
90	45c. Volleyball	1·10	1·00

20 Girls decorating Tree

1988. Christmas. Multicoloured.

91	25c. Type **20**	65	60
92	25c. Dove with mistletoe in beak and children holding decorations	65	60
93	25c. Boy in native clothing and girl in floral dress sitting at base of tree	65	60
94	25c. Boy in T-shirt and shorts and girl in native clothing sitting at base of tree	65	60

Nos. 91/4 were printed together in blocks of four, *se-tenant*, forming a composite design.

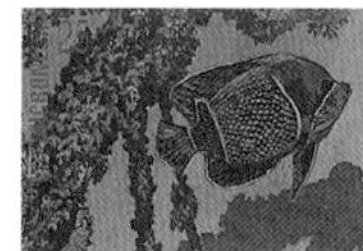
21 Blue-girdled Angelfish

1988. Truk Lagoon, "Micronesia's Living War Memorial". Multicoloured.

95	25c. Type **21**	80	70
96	25c. Jellyfish and shoal of small fish	80	70
97	25c. Snorkel divers	80	70
98	25c. Two golden trevally (black-striped fish facing left)	80	70
99	25c. Blackfinned reef shark	80	70
100	25c. Deck railings of wreck and fish	80	70
101	25c. Soldierfish (red fish) and damselfish	80	70
102	25c. Damselfish, narrow-banded batfish and aircraft cockpit	80	70
103	25c. Three Moorish idols (fish with long dorsal fins)	80	70
104	25c. Four pickhandle barracuda and shoal	80	70

105	25c. Spot-banded butterflyfish and damselfish (facing alternate directions)	80	70
106	25c. Three-spotted dascyllus and aircraft propeller	80	70
107	25c. Fox-faced rabbitfish and shoal	80	70
108	25c. Lionfish (fish with spines)	80	70
109	25c. Scuba diver and white-tailed damselfish	80	70
110	25c. Tubular corals	80	70
111	25c. White-tailed damselfish, ornate butterflyfish and brain coral	80	70
112	25c. Pink anemonefish, giant clam and sea plants	80	70

Nos. 95/112 were printed together, *se-tenant*, in sheetlets of 18 stamps, the backgrounds of the stamps forming an overall design of the remains of a Japanese ship and Zero fighter plane on the Lagoon bed colonized by marine life.

22 Flag of Pohnpei

1989. Air. State Flags. Multicoloured.

113	45c. Type **22**	1·10	1·00
114	45c. Truk	1·10	1·00
115	45c. Kosrae	1·10	1·00
116	45c. Yap	1·10	1·00

23 Plumeria and Headdress

1989. Mwarmwarms (floral decorations). Multicoloured.

117	45c. Type **23**	1·10	1·00
118	45c. Hibiscus and lei	1·10	1·00
119	45c. Jasmine and Yap religious mwarmwarm	1·10	1·00
120	45c. Bougainvillea and Truk dance mwarmwarm	1·10	1·00

24 Whale Shark

1989. Sharks. Multicoloured.

122	25c. Type **24**	95	85
123	25c. Smooth hammerhead	95	85
124	45c. Tiger shark (vert)	1·80	1·70
125	45c. Great white shark (vert)	1·80	1·70

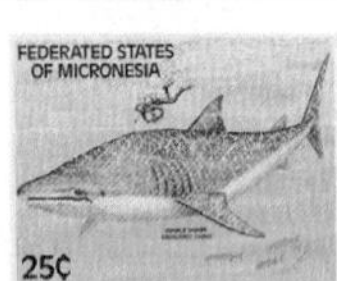

25 "Pheasant and Chrysanthemum" (Ando Hiroshige)

1989. Emperor Hirohito of Japan Commemoration. Sheet 89×1170 mm.
MS121 **25** $1 multicoloured 1·20 1·10

26 *Explorer 1* Satellite over North America

1989. 20th Anniv of First Manned Landing on the Moon. Multicoloured.

126	25c. Bell XS-15 rocket plane	75	70
127	25c. Type **26**	75	70
128	25c. Ed White on space walk during *Gemini 4* mission	75	70
129	25c. *Apollo 18* spacecraft	75	70
130	25c. *Gemini 4* space capsule over South America	75	70
131	25c. Space Shuttle *Challenger*	75	70
132	25c. Italian *San Marco 2* satellite	75	70
133	25c. Russian *Soyuz 19* spacecraft	75	70
134	25c. Neil Armstrong descending ladder to Moon's surface during *Apollo 11* mission	75	70
135	$2.40 Lunar module *Eagle* on Moon (34×46 mm)	6·50	6·00

Nos. 126/34 were printed together in *se-tenant* sheetlets of nine stamps, the backgrounds of the stamps forming an overall design of Earth as viewed from the Moon.

27 Horse's Hoof

1989. Sea Shells. Multicoloured.

136	1c. Type **27**	15	10
137	3c. Rare spotted cowrie	20	15
138	15c. Commercial trochus	30	25
139	20c. General cone	50	45
140	25c. Trumpet triton	65	60
141	30c. Laciniate conch	70	65
142	36c. Red-mouth olive	90	85
143	45c. All-red map cowrie	1·10	1·00
144	50c. Textile cone	1·20	1·10
145	$1 Orange spider conch	2·75	2·40
146	$2 Golden cowrie	5·25	5·00
147	$5 Episcopal mitre	13·00	12·00

28 Oranges

1989. World Stamp Expo '89 International Stamp Exhibition, Washington D.C. "Kosrae–The Garden State". Multicoloured.

155	25c. Type **28**	70	65
156	25c. Limes	70	65
157	25c. Tangerines	70	65
158	25c. Mangoes	70	65
159	25c. Coconuts	70	65
160	25c. Breadfruit	70	65
161	25c. Sugar cane	70	65
162	25c. Kosrae house	70	65
163	25c. Bananas	70	65
164	25c. Children with fruit and flowers	70	65
165	25c. Pineapples	70	65
166	25c. Taro	70	65
167	25c. Hibiscus	70	65
168	25c. Ylang ylang	70	65
169	25c. White ginger	70	65
170	25c. Plumeria	70	65
171	25c. Royal poinciana	70	65
172	25c. Yellow allamanda	70	65

29 Angel over Micronesian Village

1989. Christmas. Multicoloured.

173	25c. Type **29**	65	60
174	45c. Truk children dressed as Three Kings	1·20	1·10

30 Young Kingfisher and Sokehs Rock, Pohnpei

1990. Endangered Species. Micronesian Kingfisher and Micronesian Pigeon.

175	10c. Type **30**	85	80
176	15c. Adult kingfisher and rain forest, Pohnpei	1·30	1·20
177	20c. Pigeon flying over lake at Sleeping Lady, Kosrae	1·80	1·70
178	25c. Pigeon perched on leaf, Tol Island, Truk	2·20	2·00

31 Wooden Whale Stamp and *Lyra*

1990. Stamp World London 90 International Stamp Exhibition. 19th-century British Whaling Ships. Multicoloured.

179	45c. Type **31**	1·30	1·20
180	45c. Harpoon heads and *Prudent*	1·30	1·20
181	45c. Carved whale bone and *Rhone*	1·30	1·20
182	45c. Carved whale tooth and *Sussex*	1·30	1·20

MS183 98×86 mm. $1 Whalers at point of kill (41×28 mm) 3·00 2·75

32 Penny Black

1990. 150th Anniv of Penny Black. Sheet 149×86 mm.
MS184 **32** $1 black, yellow and blue 2·75 2·50

33 Beech 18 over Kosrae Airport

1990. Air. Aircraft. Multicoloured.

185	22c. Type **33**	55	50
186	36c. Boeing 727 landing at Truk	95	90
187	39c. Britten Norman Islander over Pohnpei	1·10	1·00
188	45c. Beech Queen Air over Yap	1·20	1·10

34 School Building

1990. 25th Anniv of Pohnpei Agriculture and Trade School. Multicoloured.

190	25c. Type **34**	70	65
191	25c. Fr. Costigan (founder) and students	70	65
192	25c. Fr. Hugh Costigan	70	65
193	25c. Ispahu Samuel Hadley (Metelanim chief) and Fr. Costigan	70	65
194	25c. Statue of Liberty, New York City Police Department badge and Empire State Building	70	65

35 Flower Bed spelling EXPO '90

1990. Expo 90 International Garden and Greenery Exposition, Osaka. Sheet 115×850 mm.
MS195 **35** $1 multicoloured 2·50 2·30

36 Loading Mail Plane at Pohnpei Airport

1990. Pacific Postal Transport. Multicoloured.

196	25c. Type **36**	75	70
197	45c. Launch meeting *Nantaku* (inter-island freighter) in Truk Lagoon to exchange mail, 1940	1·60	1·50

37 Marshallese Stick Chart, Outrigger Canoe and Flag

1990. Fourth Anniv of Ratification of Micronesia and Marshall Islands Compacts of Free Association. Multicoloured.

198	25c. Type **37**	80	70
199	25c. Great frigate bird, USS *Constitution* (frigate), US flag and American Bald Eagle	80	70
200	25c. Micronesian outrigger canoe and flag	80	70

38 *Caloptilia* sp. and New Moon

1990. Moths. Multicoloured.

201	45c. Type **38**	1·20	1·10
202	45c. *Anticrates* sp. (inscr "Yponomeatidae") and waxing moon	1·20	1·10
203	45c. *Cosmopterigidae* family and full moon	1·20	1·10
204	45c. *Cosmopteridigae* family and waning moon	1·20	1·10

39 Cherub above Roof

1990. Christmas. "Micronesian Holy Night". Multicoloured.

205	25c. Type **39**	70	65
206	25c. Two cherubs and Star of Bethlehem	70	65
207	25c. Cherub blowing horn	70	65
208	25c. Lambs, goat, pig and chickens	70	65
209	25c. Native wise men offering gifts to Child	70	65
210	25c. Children and dog beside lake	70	65
211	25c. Man blowing trumpet triton	70	65
212	25c. Adults and children on path	70	65
213	25c. Man and children carrying gifts	70	65

Nos. 205/13 were printed together, *se-tenant*, forming a composite design.

40 Executive Branch

1991. New Capital, Palikir Valley, Pohnpei. Two sheets, each 121×76 mm containing horiz designs as T **40**.
MS214 Two sheets. (a) 25c. Type **40**; 45c. Legislative and Judiciary Branches; (b) $1 New Capitol 4·75 4·25

41 Hawksbill Turtle returning to Sea

1991. Sea Turtles. Multicoloured.

215	29c. Type **41**	1·40	1·30
216	29c. Green turtles swimming underwater	1·40	1·30
217	50c. Hawksbill turtle swimming underwater	2·00	1·80
218	50c. Leatherback turtle swimming underwater	2·00	1·80

42 Boeing E-3 Sentry

1991. Operations Desert Shield and Desert Storm (liberation of Kuwait). Multicoloured.

219	29c. Type **42**	95	90
220	29c. Grumman F-14 Tomcat fighter	95	90
221	29c. USS *Missouri* (battleship)	95	90
222	29c. Multiple Launch Rocket System	95	90
223	$2.90 Great frigate bird with yellow ribbon and flag of Micronesia (50×37 mm)	8·50	7·75
MS224	127×96 mm. No. 223	8·75	8·25

43 *Evening Flowers, Toloas, Truk*

1991. Phila Nippon '91 International Stamp Exhibition, Tokyo. 90th Birth Anniv (1992) of Paul Jacoulet (artist). Micronesian Ukiyo-e Prints by Jacoulet. Multicoloured.

225	29c. Type **43**	1·00	95
226	29c. *The Chief's Daughter, Mogomog*	1·00	95
227	29c. *Yagourouh and Mio, Yap*	1·00	95
228	50c. *Yap Beauty and Orchids*	1·60	1·50
229	50c. *The Yellow-Eyed Boys, Ohlol*	1·60	1·50
230	50c. *Violet Flowers, Tomil, Yap*	1·60	1·50
MS231	143×790 mm. $1 *First Love, Yap*	3·75	3·50

44 Sheep and Holy Family

1991. Christmas. Shell Cribs. Multicoloured.

232	29c. Type **44**	80	75
233	40c. Three Kings arriving at Bethlehem	1·10	1·00
234	50c. Sheep around manger	1·50	1·40

45 Pohnpei Fruit Bat

1991. Pohnpei Rain Forest. Multicoloured.

235	29c. Type **45**	1·00	95
236	29c. Purple-capped fruit dove	1·00	95
237	29c. Micronesian kingfisher	1·00	95
238	29c. Birdnest fern	1·00	95
239	29c. Caroline swiftlets ("Island Swiftlet")	1·00	95
240	29c. Ponape white-eye ("Long-billed White-eye")	1·00	95
241	29c. Common noddy ("Brown Noddy")	1·00	95
242	29c. Ponape lory ("Pohnpei Lory")	1·00	95
243	29c. Micronesian flycatcher ("Pohnpei Flycatcher")	1·00	95
244	29c. Truk Island ground dove ("Caroline Ground-Dove")	1·00	95
245	29c. White-tailed tropic bird	1·00	95
246	29c. Cardinal honeyeater ("Micronesian Honeyeater")	1·00	95
247	29c. Ixora	1·00	95
248	29c. Rufous fantail ("Pohnpei Fantail")	1·00	95
249	29c. Grey-brown white-eye ("Grey White-eye")	1·00	95
250	29c. Blue-faced parrot finch	1·00	95
251	29c. Common Cicadabird ("Cicadabird")	1·00	95
252	29c. Green skink	1·00	95

Nos. 235/52 were issued together, *se-tenant*, forming a composite design.

46 Britten Norman Islander and Outrigger Canoe

1992. Air. Multicoloured.

253	40c. Type **46**	1·10	1·00
254	50c. Boeing 727-200 airliner and outrigger canoe (different)	1·30	1·20

47 Volunteers learning Crop Planting

1992. 25th Anniv of Presence of United States Peace Corps in Micronesia. Multicoloured.

255	29c. Type **47**	75	70
256	29c. Education	75	70
257	29c. Pres. John Kennedy announcing formation of Peace Corps	75	70
258	29c. Public health nurses	75	70
259	29c. Recreation	75	70

48 Queen Isabella of Spain

1992. 500th Anniv of Discovery of America by Christopher Columbus. Multicoloured.

260	29c. Type **48**	2·20	2·10
261	29c. *Santa Maria*	2·20	2·10
262	29c. Christopher Columbus	2·20	2·10

49 Flags

1992. First Anniv of U.N. Membership.

263	**49**	29c. multicoloured	2·00	1·90
264	**49**	50c. multicoloured	3·25	3·00
MS265		114×73 mm. Nos. 263/4	5·00	4·75

50 Bouquet

1992. Christmas.

266	**50**	29c. multicoloured	2·50	2·40

51 Edward Rickenbacker (fighter pilot)

1993. Pioneers of Flight (1st series). Pioneers and aircraft. Multicoloured.

267	29c. Type **51**	90	80
268	29c. Manfred von Richthofen (fighter pilot)	90	80
269	29c. Andrei Tupolev (aeronautical engineer)	90	80
270	29c. John Macready (first non-stop crossing of USA)	90	80
271	29c. Sir Charles Kingsford-Smith (first trans-Pacific flight)	90	80
272	29c. Igor Sikorsky (aeronautical engineer)	90	80
273	29c. Lord Trenchard ("Father of the Royal Air Force")	90	80
274	29c. Glenn Curtiss (builder of US Navy's first aircraft)	90	80

See also Nos. 322/9, 364/71, 395/402, 418/25, 441/8, 453/60 and 514/21.

52 Big-scaled Soldierfish

1993. Fish. Multicoloured.

275	10c. Type **52**	25	15
276	19c. Bennett's butterflyfish	50	45
277	20c. Peacock hind ("Peacock Grouper")	55	55
278	22c. Great barracuda	70	65
279	23c. Yellow-finned tuna	70	65
280	25c. Coral hind ("Coral Grouper")	75	70
281	29c. Regal angelfish	85	80
282	30c. Bleeker's parrotfish	85	80
283	32c. Saddle butterflyfish (dated "1995")	95	90
284	35c. Picasso triggerfish ("Picassofish")	1·00	90
285	40c. Mandarin fish	1·00	95
286	45c. Clown ("Bluebanded") surgeonfish	1·10	1·00
287	46c. Red-tailed surgeonfish ("Achilles Tang")	1·20	1·20
288	50c. Undulate ("Orange-striped") triggerfish	1·30	1·20
289	52c. Palette surgeonfish	1·40	1·30
290	55c. Moorish idol	1·60	1·40
291	60c. Skipjack tuna	1·70	1·60
292	75c. Oriental sweetlips	2·00	1·90
293	78c. Square-spotted anthias ("Square-spot Fairy Basslet")	2·20	2·00
294	95c. Blue-striped ("Blue-lined") snapper	2·75	2·50
295	$1 Zebra moray	2·75	2·50
296	$2 Fox-faced rabbitfish	5·75	5·25
297	$2.90 Masked ("Orangespine") unicornfish	8·50	7·75
298	$3 Flame angelfish	9·00	8·50
299	$5 Six-blotched hind ("Cave Grouper")	15·00	14·00

See also Nos. 465/89 and 522/5.

53 *Great Republic*

1993. American Clipper Ships. Multicoloured.

301	29c. Type **53**	1·70	1·60
302	29c. *Benjamin F. Packard*	1·70	1·60
303	29c. *Stag Hound*	1·70	1·60
304	29c. *Herald of the Morning*	1·70	1·60
305	29c. *Rainbow* and junk	1·70	1·60
306	29c. *Flying Cloud*	1·70	1·60
307	29c. *Lightning*	1·70	1·60
308	29c. *Sea Witch*	1·70	1·60
309	29c. *Columbia*	1·70	1·60
310	29c. *New World*	1·70	1·60
311	29c. *Young America*	1·70	1·60
312	29c. *Courier*	1·70	1·60

54 Jefferson

1993. 250th Birth Anniv of Thomas Jefferson (U.S. President, 1801–09).

313	**54**	29c. multicoloured	1·10	1·00

55 Yap Outrigger Canoe

1993. Traditional Canoes. Multicoloured.

314	29c. Type **55**	1·10	1·00
315	29c. Kosrae outrigger canoe	1·10	1·00
316	29c. Pohnpei lagoon outrigger canoe	1·10	1·00
317	29c. Chuuk war canoe	1·10	1·00

56 Ambilos Iehsi

1993. Local Leaders (1st series). Multicoloured.

318	29c. Type **56** (Pohnpei)	95	90
319	29c. Andrew Roboman (Yap)	95	90
320	29c. Joab Sigrah (Kosrae)	95	90
321	29c. Petrus Mailo (Chuuk)	95	90

See also Nos. 409/12.

1993. Pioneers of Flight (2nd series). As T **51**. Multicoloured.

322	50c. Lawrence Sperry (inventor of the gyro)	1·40	1·30
323	50c. Alberto Santos-Dumont (first powered flight in Europe)	1·40	1·30
324	50c. Hugh Dryden (developer of first guided missile)	1·40	1·30
325	50c. Theodore von Karman (space pioneer)	1·40	1·30
326	50c. Orville Wright (first powered flight)	1·40	1·30
327	50c. Wilbur Wright (second powered flight)	1·40	1·30
328	50c. Otto Lilienthal (first heavier-than-air flight)	1·40	1·30
329	50c. Sir Thomas Sopwith (aircraft designer)	1·40	1·30

57 Kepirohi Falls

1993. Pohnpei Tourist Sites. Multicoloured.

330	29c. Type **57**	1·20	1·10
331	50c. Spanish Wall	2·10	1·90
MS332	115×870 mm. $1 Sokehs Rock (79×49 mm)	3·00	2·75

See also Nos. 357/9.

58 Female Common ("Great") Eggfly

1993. Butterflies. Multicoloured.

333	29c. Type **58**	1·10	95
334	29c. Female common ("great") eggfly (variant)	1·10	95
335	50c. Male monarch	2·10	1·90
336	50c. Male common ("great") eggfly	2·10	1·90

See also Nos. 360/3.

59 *We Three Kings*

1993. Christmas. Carols. Multicoloured.

337	29c. Type **59**	1·20	1·10
338	50c. *Silent Night, Holy Night*	2·20	1·90

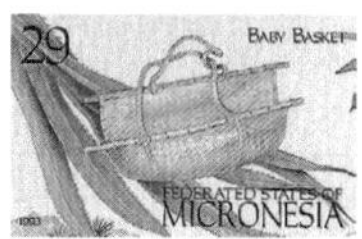

60 Baby Basket

1993. Yap. Multicoloured.

339	29c. Type **60**	1·00	90
340	29c. Bamboo raft	1·00	90
341	29c. Basketry	1·00	90
342	29c. Fruit bat	1·00	90
343	29c. Forest	1·00	90
344	29c. Outrigger canoes	1·00	90
345	29c. Dioscorea yams	1·00	90

346	29c. Mangroves	1·00	90
347	29c. Manta ray	1·00	90
348	29c. *Cyrtosperma taro*	1·00	90
349	29c. Fish weir	1·00	90
350	29c. Seagrass, golden rabbitfish and masked rabbitfish	1·00	90
351	29c. Taro bowl	1·00	90
352	29c. Thatched house	1·00	90
353	29c. Coral reef	1·00	90
354	29c. Lavalava	1·00	90
355	29c. Dancers	1·00	90
356	29c. Stone money	1·00	90

1994. Kosrae Tourist Sites. As T **57** but horiz. Multicoloured.

357	29c. Sleeping Lady (mountains)	90	80
358	40c. Walung	1·20	1·00
359	50c. Lelu Ruins	1·40	1·30

1994. Hong Kong '94 International Stamp Exhibition. Designs as Nos. 333/6 but with inscriptions in brown and additionally inscribed Hong Kong '94 Stamp Exhibition in English (361/2) or Chinese (others).

360	29c. As No. 333	1·40	1·30
361	29c. As No. 334	1·40	1·30
362	50c. As No. 335	2·20	1·90
363	50c. As No. 336	2·20	1·90

1994. Pioneers of Flight (3rd series). As T **51**. Multicoloured.

364	29c. Octave Chanute (early glider designer)	1·00	90
365	29c. T. Claude Ryan (founder of first commercial airline)	1·00	90
366	29c. Edwin (Buzz) Aldrin (*Apollo 11* crew member and second man to step onto moon)	1·00	90
367	29c. Neil Armstrong (commander of *Apollo 11* and first man on moon)	1·00	90
368	29c. Frank Whittle (developer of jet engine)	1·00	90
369	29c. Waldo Waterman (aircraft designer)	1·00	90
370	29c. Michael Collins (*Apollo 11* crew member)	1·00	90
371	29c. Wernher von Braun (rocket designer)	1·00	90

61 Spearfishing

1994. Third Micronesian Games. Multicoloured.

372	29c. Type **61**	1·10	95
373	29c. Basketball	1·10	95
374	29c. Coconut husking	1·10	95
375	29c. Tree climbing	1·10	95

62 Pohnpei

1994. Traditional Costumes. Multicoloured.

376	29c. Type **62**	1·10	95
377	29c. Kosrae	1·10	95
378	29c. Chuuk	1·10	95
379	29c. Yap	1·10	95

63 People

1994. 15th Anniv of Constitution.

380	**63**	29c. multicoloured	2·30	2·10

64 *Fagraea berteriana* (Kosrae)

1994. Native Flowers. Multicoloured.

381	29c. Type **64**	1·10	95
382	29c. *Pangium edule* (Yap)	1·10	95
383	29c. *Pittosporum ferrugineum* (Chuuk)	1·10	95
384	29c. *Sonneratia caseolaris* (Pohnpei)	1·10	95

Nos. 381/4 were issued together, *se-tenant*, forming a composite design.

65 1985 $10 Definitive under Magnifying Glass

1994. Tenth Anniv of Postal Independence. Multicoloured.

385	29c. Type **65**	1·80	1·60
386	29c. 1993 traditional canoes block	1·80	1·60
387	29c. 1984 postal independence block	1·80	1·60
388	29c. 1994 native costumes block	1·80	1·60

Nos. 385/8 were issued together, *se-tenant*, forming a composite design of various Micronesian stamps. Nos. 386/8 are identified by the block in the centre of the design.

66 Players

1994. World Cup Football Championship, U.S.A. Multicoloured.

389	50c. Type **66**	3·25	3·00
390	50c. Ball and players	3·25	3·00

Nos. 389/90 were issued together, *se-tenant*, forming a composite design.

67 United States 1969 10c. Stamp

1994. 25th Anniv of First Manned Moon Landing. Sheet 115×870 mm.

MS391	**67** $2.90 multicoloured	6·50	5·75

68 Iguanodons

1994. Philakorea 1994 International Stamp Exhibition, Seoul. Prehistoric Animals. Multicoloured.

392	29c. Type **68**	1·90	1·70
393	52c. Iguanodons and coelurosaurs	2·30	2·10
394	$1 Camarasaurus	3·25	3·00

Nos. 392/4 were issued together, *se-tenant*, forming a composite design.

1994. Pioneers of Flight (4th series). As T **51**. Multicoloured.

395	50c. Yuri Gagarin (first man in space)	1·40	1·30
396	50c. Alan Shepard Jr. (first American in space)	1·40	1·30
397	50c. William Bishop (fighter pilot)	1·40	1·30
398	50c. Atlas (first US intercontinental ballistic missile) and Karel Bossart (aerospace engineer)	1·40	1·30
399	50c. John Towers (world endurance record, 1912)	1·40	1·30
400	50c. Hermann Oberth (space flight pioneer)	1·40	1·30
401	50c. Marcel Dassault (aircraft producer)	1·40	1·30
402	50c. Geoffrey de Havilland (aircraft designer)	1·40	1·30

69 Oriental Cuckoo

1994. Migratory Birds. Multicoloured.

403	29c. Type **69**	1·20	1·10
404	29c. Long-tailed koel ("Long-tailed Cuckoo")	1·20	1·10
405	29c. Short-eared owl	1·20	1·10
406	29c. Eastern broad-billed roller ("Dollarbird")	1·20	1·10

70 Doves

1994. Christmas. Multicoloured.

407	29c. Type **70**	1·10	95
408	50c. Angels	1·70	1·50

1994. Local Leaders (2nd series). As T **56**. Multicoloured.

409	32c. Anron Ring Buas	95	85
410	32c. Belarmino Hatheylul	95	85
411	32c. Johnny Moses	95	85
412	32c. Paliknoa Sigrah (King John)	95	85

71 Pig

1995. New Year. Year of the Pig. Sheet 115×870 mm.

MS413	**71** 50c. multicoloured	2·00	1·80

72 Diver, Coral, Clown Triggerfish and Black-backed Butterflyfish

1995. Chuuk Lagoon. Multicoloured.

414	32c. Type **72**	1·10	95
415	32c. Black-backed butterflyfish, lionfish, regal angelfish and damselfish	1·10	95
416	32c. Diver, thread-finned butterflyfish and damselfish	1·10	95
417	32c. Pink anemonefish and damselfish amongst anemone tentacles	1·10	95

Nos. 414/17 were issued together, *se-tenant*, forming a composite design.

1995. Pioneers of Flight (5th series). As T **51**. Multicoloured.

418	32c. Robert Goddard (first liquid-fuelled rocket)	95	85
419	32c. Leroy Grumman (first fighter with retractable landing gear)	95	85
420	32c. Louis-Charles Breguet (aeronautics engineer)	95	85
421	32c. Juan de la Cierva (inventor of autogyro)	95	85
422	32c. Hugo Junkers (aircraft engineer)	95	85
423	32c. James Lovell Jr. (astronaut)	95	85
424	32c. Donald Douglas (aircraft designer)	95	85
425	32c. Reginald Mitchell (designer of Spitfire fighter)	95	85

73 West Highland White Terrier

1995. Dogs. Multicoloured.

426	32c. Type **73**	95	85
427	32c. Welsh springer spaniel	95	85
428	32c. Irish setter	95	85
429	32c. Old English sheepdog	95	85

74 *Hibiscus tiliaceus*

1995. Hibiscus. Multicoloured.

430	32c. Type **74**	95	85
431	32c. *Hibiscus huegelii*	95	85
432	32c. *Hibiscus trionum*	95	85
433	32c. *Hibiscus splendens*	95	85

Nos. 430/3 were issued together, *se-tenant*, forming a composite design.

75 UN Flag draped over Girder (new Headquarters, 1949)

1995. 50th Anniv of United Nations Organization. Sheet 82×112 mm.

MS434	**75** $1 multicoloured	3·00	2·75

76 *Paphiopedilum* "Henrietta Fujiwara"

1995. Singapore '95 International Stamp Exhibition. Orchids. Sheet 120×93 mm containing T **76** and similar horiz designs. Multicoloured.

MS435	32c. Type **76**; 32c. *Thunia alba*; 32c. *Lycaste virginalis*; 32c. *Laeliocattleya* Prism Palette	4·00	3·50

77 USS *Portland* (cruiser)

1995. 50th Anniv of End of Second World War. Liberation of Micronesia. Multicoloured.

436	60c. Type **77** (liberation of Chuuk)	1·80	1·60
437	60c. USS *Tillman* (destroyer) (Yap)	1·80	1·60
438	60c. USS *Soley* (destroyer) (Kosrae)	1·80	1·60
439	60c. USS *Hyman* (destroyer) (Pohnpei)	1·80	1·60

78 Temple of Heaven, Peking

1995. Beijing 1995 International Stamp and Coin Exhibition. Sheet 110×870 mm.

MS440	**78** 50c. multicoloured	1·90	1·70

1995. Pioneers of Flight (6th series). As T **51**. Multicoloured.

441	60c. Frederick Rohr (developer of mass-production techniques)	1·80	1·60
442	60c. Juan Trippe (founder of Pan-American Airways)	1·80	1·60
443	60c. Konstantin Tsiolkovsky (rocket pioneer)	1·80	1·60
444	60c. Count Ferdinand von Zeppelin (airship inventor)	1·80	1·60
445	60c. Air Chief Marshal Hugh Dowding (commander of RAF Fighter Command, 1940)	1·80	1·60
446	60c. William Mitchell (pioneer of aerial bombing)	1·80	1·60
447	60c. John Northrop (aircraft designer)	1·80	1·60
448	60c. Frederick Handley Page (producer of first twin-engine bomber)	1·80	1·60

79 Poinsettia

1995. Christmas.

449	**79**	32c. multicoloured	1·00	90
450	**79**	60c. multicoloured	1·90	1·70

80 Rabin

1995. Yitzhak Rabin (Israeli Prime Minister) Commemoration.

451	**80**	32c. multicoloured	1·00	90

81 Rat

1996. New Year. Year of the Rat. Sheet 110×870 mm.

MS452 **81** 50c. multicoloured		1·80	1·60

1995. Pioneers of Flight (7th series). As T **51**. Multicoloured.

453	32c. James Doolittle (leader of America's Second World War bomb raid on Japan)	1·00	90
454	32c. Claude Dornier (aircraft designer)	1·00	90
455	32c. Ira Eaker (leader of air effort against occupied Europe during Second World War)	1·00	90
456	32c. Jacob Ellehammer (first European manned flight)	1·00	90
457	32c. Henry Arnold (Commander of US air operations during Second World War)	1·00	90
458	32c. Louis Bleriot (first flight across the English Channel)	1·00	90
459	32c. William Boeing (founder of Boeing Corporation)	1·00	90
460	32c. Sydney Camm (aircraft designer)	1·00	90

82 Meeting House

1995. Tourism in Yap. Multicoloured.

461	32c. Type **82**	1·00	90
462	32c. Stone money	1·00	90
463	32c. Churu dancing	1·00	90
464	32c. Traditional canoe	1·00	90

1995. Fish. As Nos. 275/95 but face values changed. Multicoloured.

465	32c. Bennett's butterflyfish	1·00	90
466	32c. Regal angelfish	1·00	90
467	32c. Undulate ("Orange-striped") triggerfish	1·00	90
468	32c. Zebra moray	1·00	90
469	32c. Great barracuda	1·00	90
470	32c. Bleeker's parrotfish	1·00	90
471	32c. Mandarin fish	1·00	90
472	32c. Clown ("Blue-banded") surgeonfish	1·00	90
473	32c. Big-scaled soldierfish	1·00	90
474	32c. Peacock hind ("Peacock Grouper")	1·00	90
475	32c. Picasso triggerfish ("Picassofish")	1·00	90
476	32c. Masked ("Orangespine") unicornfish	1·00	90
477	32c. Red-tailed surgeonfish	1·00	90
478	32c. Coral hind ("Coral Grouper")	1·00	90
479	32c. Palette surgeonfish	1·00	90
480	32c. Oriental sweetlips	1·00	90
481	32c. Fox-faced rabbitfish	1·00	90
482	32c. Saddle butterflyfish (dated "1996")	1·00	90
483	32c. Moorish idol	1·00	90
484	32c. Square-spotted anthias ("Square-spot Fairy Basslet")	1·00	90
485	32c. Flame angelfish	1·00	90
486	32c. Yellow-finned tuna	1·00	90
487	32c. Skipjack tuna	1·00	90
488	32c. Blue-striped ("Blue-lined") snapper	1·00	90
489	32c. Six-blotched hind ("Cave Grouper")	1·00	90

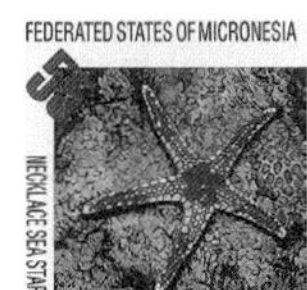

83 Necklace Sea Star

1996. Starfishes. Multicoloured.

490	55c. Type **83**	1·60	1·40
491	55c. Rhinoceros sea star	1·60	1·40
492	55c. Blue sea star	1·60	1·40
493	55c. Thick-skinned sea star	1·60	1·40

Nos. 490/3 were issued together, *se-tenant*, forming a composite design.

84 10l. Stamp

1996. Centenary of Modern Olympic Games. Designs reproducing 1896 Greek Olympic Issue. Multicoloured.

494	60c. Type **84**	1·80	1·60
495	60c. 25l. stamp	1·80	1·60
496	60c. 20l. stamp	1·80	1·60
497	60c. 10d. stamp	1·80	1·60

85 *Palikir*

1996. Patrol Boats. Multicoloured.

498	32c. Type **85**	1·00	90
499	32c. *Micronesia*	1·00	90

Nos. 498/9 were issued together, *se-tenant*, forming a composite design.

86 Gardens of Suzhou, Chins

1996. China 96 International Stamp Exhibition, Peking. Sheet 110×870 mm.

MS500 **86** 50c. multicoloured		1·90	1·70

87 1896 Quadricycle

1996. Centenary of Ford Motor Vehicle Production. Multicoloured.

501	55c. Type **87**	1·60	1·40
502	55c. 1917 Model T Truck	1·60	1·40
503	55c. 1928 Model A Tudor Sedan	1·60	1·40
504	55c. 1932 V-8 Sport Roadster	1·60	1·40
505	55c. 1941 Lincoln Continental	1·60	1·40
506	55c. 1953 F-100 Truck	1·60	1·40
507	55c. 1958 Thunderbird convertible	1·60	1·40
508	55c. 1996 Mercury Sable	1·60	1·40

88 Reza

1996. Reza (National Police Drug Enforcement Unit's dog).

509	**88**	32c. multicoloured	1·00	90

89 Oranges

1996. Citrus Fruits. Multicoloured.

510	50c. Type **89**	1·40	1·30
511	50c. Limes	1·40	1·30
512	50c. Lemons	1·40	1·30
513	50c. Tangerines	1·40	1·30

Nos. 510/13 were issued together, *se-tenant*, forming a composite design.

1996. Pioneers of Flight (8th series). As T **51**. Multicoloured.

514	60c. Curtis LeMay (commander of Strategic Air Command)	2·10	1·90
515	60c. Grover Loening (first American graduate in aeronautical engineering)	2·10	1·90
516	60c. Gianni Caproni (aircraft producer)	2·10	1·90
517	60c. Henri Farman (founder of Farman Airlines)	2·10	1·90
518	60c. Glenn Martin (aircraft producer)	2·10	1·90
519	60c. Alliot Verdon Roe (aircraft designer)	2·10	1·90
520	60c. Sergei Korolyov (rocket scientist)	2·10	1·90
521	60c. Isaac Laddon (aircraft designer)	2·10	1·90

1996. Tenth Asian International Stamp Exhibition, Taipeh. Fishes. As previous designs but additionally inscr for the exhibition in English (522, 525) or Chinese (523/4).

522	32c. As No. 465	1·00	90
523	32c. As No. 468	1·00	90
524	32c. As No. 475	1·00	90
525	32c. As No. 483	1·00	90

90 Wise Men following Star

1996. Christmas.

526	**90**	32c. multicoloured	1·00	90
527	**90**	60c. multicoloured	1·90	1·70

91 Outrigger Canoe and State Flag

1996. Tenth Anniv of Ratification of Compact of Free Association with U.S.A.

528	**91**	$3 multicoloured	8·75	7·75

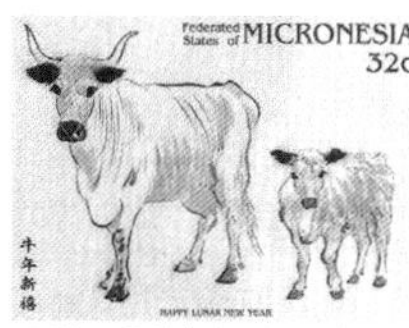

92 Water Buffalo

1997. New Year. Year of the Ox.

529	**92**	32c. multicoloured	1·00	90
MS530 76×106 mm. **92** $2 multicoloured			6·25	5·50

93 Walutahanga, Melanesia

1997. Pacific 97 International Stamp Exhibition, San Francisco. Sea Goddesses of the Pacific. Multicoloured.

531	32c. Type **93**	1·00	90
532	32c. Tien-Hou holding lantern, China	1·00	90
533	32c. Lorop diving in ocean, Micronesia	1·00	90
534	32c. Oto-Hime with fisherman, Japan	1·00	90
535	32c. Nomoi holding shell, Micronesia	1·00	90
536	32c. Junkgowa Sisters in canoe, Australia	1·00	90

94 Deng Xiaoping

1997. Deng Xiaoping (Chinese statesman) Commemoration. Multicoloured.

537	60c. Type **94**	1·80	1·60
538	60c. Facing left (bare-headed)	1·80	1·60
539	60c. Facing right	1·80	1·60
540	60c. Facing left wearing cap	1·80	1·60
MS541 106×76 mm. $3 facing left		9·00	8·25

95 *Melia azedarach*

1997. Return of Hong Kong to China. Multicoloured.

542	60c. Type **95**	1·80	1·60
543	60c. Victoria Peak	1·80	1·60
544	60c. *Dendrobium chrysotoxum*	1·80	1·60
545	60c. *Bauhinia blakeana*	1·80	1·60
546	60c. *Cassia surattensis*	1·80	1·60
547	60c. Sacred lotus (*Nelumbo nucifera*)	1·80	1·60
MS548 Two sheets. (a) 137×950 mm. $2 Central Business District (38½×24½ mm); (b) 63×650 mm. $3 Jade vine (*Strongylodon macrobotrys*) and Hong Kong Tower (27½ ×41 mm)		15·00	13·50

96 Tennis

1997. Second National Games. Multicoloured.

549	32c. Type **96**	1·00	90
550	32c. Throwing the discus	1·00	90
551	32c. Swimming	1·00	90
552	32c. Canoeing	1·00	90

97 Rapids

1997. Birth Bicentenary of Hiroshige Ando (painter). Designs depicting details from "Whirlpools at Naruto in Awa Province" (Nos. 553/5), "Tail of Genji: Viewing the Plum Blossoms" (Nos. 556/8) and "Snow on the Sumida River" (Nos. 559/61). Multicoloured.

553	20c. Type **97**	55	50
554	20c. Whirlpools (rocky island at left)	55	50
555	20c. Whirlpools (rocky island at right)	55	50
556	50c. Woman on stepping stones	1·50	1·40

557	50c. Woman	1·50	1·40
558	50c. Woman on balcony of house	1·50	1·40
559	60c. House and junks	1·80	1·60
560	60c. Two women	1·80	1·60
561	60c. Woman alighting from junk	1·80	1·60
MS562	Two sheets, each 102×130 mm. (a) $2 *Fuji from Satta Point*; (b) $2 *Rapids in Bitchu Province*	12·00	11·00

Nos. 553/5, 556/8 and 559/61 respectively, were issued, *se-tenant*, forming composite designs of the paintings depicted.

98 Presley from High School Graduation Yearbook

1997. 20th Death Anniv of Elvis Presley (entertainer). Multicoloured.

563	50c. Type **98**	1·40	1·30
564	50c. With hound dog Nipper (RCA Records mascot)	1·40	1·30
565	50c. Wearing red striped shirt in publicity photograph for *Loving You* (film), 1957	1·40	1·30
566	50c. Wearing sailor's cap in scene from *Girls, Girls, Girls!* (film), 1963	1·40	1·30
567	50c. Wearing knitted jacket with collar turned up, 1957	1·40	1·30
568	50c. Wearing stetson in scene from *Flaming Star* (film), 1960	1·40	1·30

99 Simon Lake and his Submarine *Argonaut*, 1897

1997. Ocean Exploration: Pioneers of the Deep. Multicoloured.

569	32c. Type **99**	1·00	90
570	32c. William Beebe and Otis Barton's bathysphere (record depth, 1934)	1·00	90
571	32c. Auguste Piccard and his bathyscaphe, 1954	1·00	90
572	32c. Harold Edgerton and his deep sea camera, 1954	1·00	90
573	32c. Jacques Piccard and US Navy bathyscaphe *Trieste* (designed by Auguste Piccard) (record depth with Don Walsh, 1960)	1·00	90
574	32c. Edwin Link and diving chamber ("Man-in-Sea" projects, 1962)	1·00	90
575	32c. Melvin Fisher and diver (discovery of *Atocha* and *Santa Margarita* (Spanish galleons), 1971)	1·00	90
576	32c. Robert Ballard and submersible *Alvin*, 1978	1·00	90
577	32c. Sylvia Earle and submersible *Deep Rover* (record dive in armoured suit, 1979)	1·00	90
MS578	Three sheets, each 111×86 mm. (a) $2 Jacques Yves Cousteau (undersea researcher) (vert); (b) $2 Charles Wyville Thomson and deep sea dredge (vert); (c) $2 *Shinkai 6500* (Japanese submersible) on ocean floor (vert)	34·00	30·00

100 Black-backed Butterflyfish

1997. Butterflyfishes. Multicoloured.

579	50c. Type **100**	2·30	2·10
580	50c. Saddle butterflyfish	2·30	2·10
581	50c. Thread-finned butterflyfish	2·30	2·10
582	50c. Bennett's butterflyfish	2·30	2·10

101 *Christ Glorified in the Court of Heaven* (Fra Angelico) (left detail)

1997. Christmas. Multicoloured.

583	32c. Type **101**	1·00	90
584	32c. *Christ Glorified in the Court of Heaven* (right detail)	1·00	90
585	60c . *A Choir of Angels* (detail, Simon Marmion)	1·80	1·60
586	60c. *A Choir of Angels* (different detail)	1·80	1·60

102 Diana, Princess of Wales

1997. Diana, Princess of Wales Commemoration.

587	**102** 60c. multicoloured	1·90	1·70

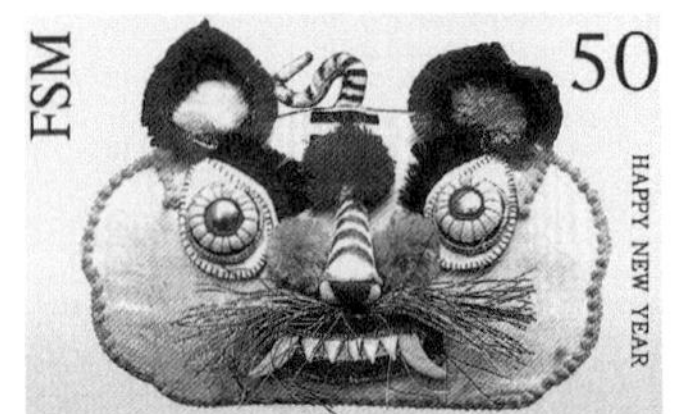

103 Tiger

1998. New Year. Year of the Tiger, Two sheets, each 117×92 mm containing T **103** or similar horiz design.

MS588	Two sheets. (a) 50c. multicoloured (Type **103**); 50c. scarlet, emerald and lemon (paper cut-outs of tigers)	3·50	3·25

104 UN Building, New York, and Flags

1998. Seventh Anniv of Admission to United Nations Organization. Sheet 65×80 mm.

MS589	**104** $1 multicoloured	3·00	2·75

105 Rabbit

1998. Children's Libraries. The Hundred Acre Wood. Featuring characters from the Winnie the Pooh children's books. Multicoloured.

590	32c. Type **105**	1·00	90
591	32c. Owl	1·00	90
592	32c. Eeyore	1·00	90
593	32c. Kanga and Roo	1·00	90
594	32c. Piglet	1·00	90
595	32c. Tigger	1·00	90
596	32c. Pooh	1·00	90
597	32c. Christopher Robin	1·00	90
MS598	Two sheets, each 130×106 mm. (a) $2 Tigger pulling Pooh from Rabbit's hole; (b) $2 Rabbit pushing Pooh out of hole	13·50	12·00

Nos. 590/7 were issued together, *se-tenant*, forming a composite design.

106 Player celebrating Goal

1998. World Cup Football Championship, France. Multicoloured.

599	32c. Type **106**	1·00	90
600	32c. Player in green shirt kicking ball	1·00	90
601	32c. Player in yellow shirt tackling another player	1·00	90
602	32c. Goalkeeper throwing ball	1·00	90
603	32c. Player in yellow shirt kicking ball overhead	1·00	90
604	32c. Goalkeeper in red shirt	1·00	90
605	32c. Player in yellow shirt with ball between legs	1·00	90
606	32c. Player in red shirt and player on ground	1·00	90
MS607	Two sheets, each 70×100 mm. (a) $2 Player in green shirt; (b) $2 Player in striped shirt	12·50	11·50

Nos. 599/606 were issued together, *se-tenant*, forming a composite design of a pitch.

107 Athlete with Torch

1998. Recognition of Micronesia by International Olympic Committee. Sheet 75×100 mm.

MS608	**107** $3 multicoloured	9·00	8·25

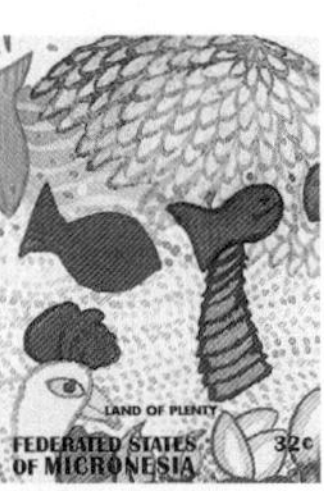

108 Land of Plenty

1998. Old Testament Stories. Multicoloured.

609	32c. Type **108**	1·00	90
610	32c. Adam and Eve	1·00	90
611	32c. Serpent of Temptation	1·00	90
612	40c. Three of Joseph's brothers	1·30	1·10
613	40c. Joseph and merchants	1·30	1·10
614	40c. Ishmaelites	1·30	1·10
615	60c. Rebekah in front of well	1·80	1·60
616	60c. Eliezer, Abraham's servant	1·80	1·60
617	60c. Angel	1·80	1·60
MS618	Three sheets, each 100×1280 mm. (a) $2 Adam and Eve banished from Paradise; (b) $2 Joseph forgiving his brothers; (c) $2 Isaac and Rebekah	19·00	17·00

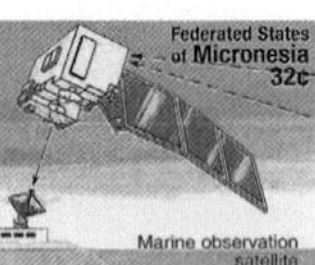

109 Marine Observation Satellite

1998. International Year of the Ocean. Deep Sea Research. Multicoloured.

619	32c. Type **109**	1·00	90
620	32c. *Natsushima* (support vessel)	1·00	90
621	32c. *Kaiyo* (research vessel)	1·00	90
622	32c. Anemone	1·00	90
623	32c. *Shinkai 2000* (deep-sea research vessel)	1·00	90
624	32c. Deep-towed research vessel	1·00	90
625	32c. Tripod fish	1·00	90
626	32c. Towed deep-survey system	1·00	90
627	32c. Black smokers	1·00	90
MS628	Three sheets. (a) 80×110 mm. $2 Weather satellite (vert); (b) 80×110 mm. $2 Ocean observation buoy (vert); (c) 110×80 mm. $2 Communications satellite	19·00	17·00

Nos. 619/27 were issued together, *se-tenant*, forming a composite design.

110 Grey-brown White-Eye ("Kosrae White-eye")

1998. Birds. Multicoloured.

629	50c. Type **110**	1·40	1·30
630	50c. Truk monarch ("Chuuk Monarch")	1·40	1·30
631	50c. Yap monarch	1·40	1·30
632	50c. Pohnpei starling	1·40	1·30
MS633	114×950 mm. $3 Pohnpei starling	9·75	8·75

111 Ribbon-striped ("White-tipped") Soldierfish

1998. Fish. Multicoloured.

634	1c. Type **111**	15	15
635	2c. Red-breasted wrasse	15	15
636	3c. Bicoloured ("Bicolor") angelfish	15	15
637	4c. Falco hawkfish	20	15
638	5c. Convict tang	25	20
639	10c. Square-spotted anthias ("Square-spot Fairy Basslet")	30	25
640	13c. Orange-spotted ("Orangeband") surgeonfish	40	35
641	15c. Multibarred goatfish	45	40
642	17c. Masked rabbitfish	55	45
643	20c. White-spotted surgeonfish	65	55
644	22c. Blue-girdled angelfish	70	65
645	32c. Rectangle triggerfish ("Wedge Picassofish")	95	85
646	33c. Black jack	95	85
647	39c. Red parrotfish	1·10	1·00
648	40c. Lemon-peel angelfish	1·20	1·00
649	50c. White-cheeked ("Whitecheek") surgeonfish	1·40	1·30
650	55c. Scarlet-finned ("Long-jawed") squirrelfish	1·60	1·40
651	60c. Hump-headed ("Humphead") wrasse	1·80	1·60
652	77c. Onespot snapper	2·40	2·10
653	78c. Blue ("Sapphire") damselfish	2·40	2·10
654	$1 Blue-finned ("Bluefin") trevally	3·25	2·75
655	$3 Whitespot hawkfish	9·50	8·50
656	$3.20 Tan-faced parrotfish	9·75	8·75
657	$5 Spotted boxfish ("Trunkfish")	16·00	14·50
658	$10.75 Pink-tailed ("Pinktail") triggerfish	30·00	27·00
659	$11.75 Yellow-faced angelfish (48×25 mm)	34·00	30·00

112 Fala being stroked

1998. Fala (Scottish terrier owned by Franklin D. Roosevelt). Multicoloured.

665	32c. Type **112**	1·00	90
666	32c. Fala and left half of wireless	1·00	90
667	32c. Fala and right half of wireless	1·00	90
668	32c. Fala and Roosevelt in car	1·00	90
669	32c. Fala's seal	1·00	90
670	32c. Fala	1·00	90

113 *Eskimo Madonna* (Claire Fejes)

1998. Christmas. Works of Art. Multicoloured.

671	32c. Type **113**	1·00	90
672	32c. *Madonna* (Man Ray)	1·00	90
673	32c. *Peasant Mother* (David Siquerios)	1·00	90
674	60c. *Mother and Child* (Pablo Picasso)	1·80	1·60

675	60c. *Gypsy Woman with Baby* (Amedeo Modigliani)	1·80	1·60
676	60c. *Mother and Child* (Jose Orozco)	1·80	1·60

MS677 97×121 mm. $2 *The Family* (Marisol) (horiz) 6·25 5·75

114 Glenn

1998. John Glenn's (first American to orbit Earth) Return to Space. Multicoloured.

678	60c. Type **114**	1·80	1·60
679	60c. Launch of *Friendship 7*	1·80	1·60
680	60c. Glenn (bare-headed and in spacesuit) and United States flag on spaceship	1·80	1·60
681	60c. Glenn (in spacesuit) and Friendship space capsule	1·80	1·60
682	60c. Glenn (in spacesuit) and United States flag on pole	1·80	1·60
683	60c. Head and shoulders of Glenn in civilian clothes and stars (dated "1992")	1·80	1·60
684	60c. *Friendship 7*	1·80	1·60
685	60c. John Glenn with President Kennedy	1·80	1·60
686	60c. Glenn in overalls	1·80	1·60
687	60c. Launch of *Discovery* (space shuttle)	1·80	1·60
688	60c. Glenn in cockpit	1·80	1·60
689	60c. Head of Glenn in civilian suit	1·80	1·60
690	60c. Glenn fastening inner helmet	1·80	1·60
691	60c. Glenn with full helmet on	1·80	1·60
692	60c. Model of *Discovery*	1·80	1·60
693	60c. Head of Glenn smiling (bare-headed) in spacesuit	1·80	1·60

MS694 Two sheets, each 110×90 mm. (a) $2 Launch of *Friendship 7* (28×42 mm); (b) $2 John Glenn, 1988 (28×42 mm) 12·50 11·00

115 *Sputnik 1*

1999. Exploration of the Solar System. Multicoloured. (a) Space Achievements of Russia.

695	33c. Type **115** (first artificial satellite, 1957)	1·00	90
696	33c. Space dog Laika (first animal in space, 1957) (wrongly inscr "Leika")	1·00	90
697	33c. *Luna 1*, 1959	1·00	90
698	33c. *Luna 3*, 1959	1·00	90
699	33c. Yuri Gagarin (first man in space, 1961)	1·00	90
700	33c. *Venera 1* probe, 1961	1·00	90
701	33c. *Mars 1* probe, 1962	1·00	90
702	33c. Valentina Tereshkova (first woman in space, 1963)	1·00	90
703	33c. *Voskhod 1*, 1964	1·00	90
704	33c. Aleksei Leonov and *Voskhod 2* (first space walk, 1965)	1·00	90
705	33c. *Venera 3* probe, 1966	1·00	90
706	33c. *Luna 10*, 1966	1·00	90
707	33c. *Luna 9* (first landing on moon, 1966)	1·00	90
708	33c. *Lunokhod 1* moon-vehicle from *Luna 17* (first roving vehicle on Moon, 1970) (wrongly inscr "First robot mission ... *Luna 16*")	1·00	90
709	33c. *Luna 16* on Moon's surface (first robot mission, 1970) (wrongly inscr "First roving vehicle ... *Luna 17*")	1·00	90
710	33c. *Mars 3*, 1971	1·00	90
711	33c. Leonid Popov, *Soyuz 35* and Valery Ryumin (first long manned space mission, 1980)	1·00	90
712	33c. Balloon (*Vega 1* Venus-Halley's Comet probe, 1985–86)	1·00	90
713	33c. *Vega 1* and Halley's Comet, 1986	1·00	90
714	33c. *Mir* space station	1·00	90

(b) Achievements of the United States of America.

715	33c. *Explorer 1*, 1958	1·00	90
716	33c. Space observatory *OSO-1*, 1962	1·00	90
717	33c. *Mariner 2* Venus probe, 1962 (first scientifically successful planetary mission)	1·00	90
718	33c. *Mariner 2* Venus probe, 1962 (first scientific interplanetary space discovery)	1·00	90
719	33c. *Apollo 8* above Moon's surface	1·00	90
720	33c. Astronaut descending ladder on *Apollo 11* mission (first manned Moon landing, 1969)	1·00	90
721	33c. Astronaut taking Moon samples, 1969	1·00	90
722	33c. Lunar Rover of *Apollo 15*, 1971	1·00	90
723	33c. *Mariner 9* Mars probe, 1971	1·00	90
724	33c. *Pioneer 10* passing Jupiter, 1973	1·00	90
725	33c. *Mariner 10* passing Mercury, 1974	1·00	90
726	33c. *Viking 1* on Mars, 1976	1·00	90
727	33c. *Pioneer 11* passing Saturn, 1979	1·00	90
728	33c. STS-1 (first re-usable spacecraft, 1981)	1·00	90
729	33c. *Pioneer 10* (first man-made object to leave solar system, 1983)	1·00	90
730	33c. Solar Maximum Mission, 1984	1·00	90
731	33c. *Cometary Explorer*, 1985	1·00	90
732	33c. *Voyager 2* passing Neptune, 1989	1·00	90
733	33c. *Galileo* space probe, 1992	1·00	90
734	33c. *Sojourner* (Mars rover), 1997	1·00	90

MS735 Four sheets, each 116×86 mm. (a) $2 *Soyuz 19* and *Apollo 18* docking (horiz); (b) $2 Astronaut repairing Hubble space telescope, 1993 (horiz); (c) $2 *Mir* space station, 1998; (d) $2 International space station (horiz) 25·00 23·00

116 Map of the Pacific Ocean

1999. Voyages of the Pacific. Multicoloured.

736	33c. Type **116**	1·00	90
737	33c. Black-fronted parakeet	1·00	90
738	33c. Red-tailed tropic bird	1·00	90
739	33c. Plan of ship's hull	1·00	90
740	33c. Sketches of winches	1·00	90
741	33c. Yellow flowers	1·00	90
742	33c. Full-rigged sailing ship	1·00	90
743	33c. Three flowers growing from seeds and top of compass rose	1·00	90
744	33c. Fish (background of ship's planking)	1·00	90
745	33c. Flag of Yap	1·00	90
746	33c. Flag of Truk (palm tree)	1·00	90
747	33c. Flag of Kosrae (four stars) and bottom of compass rose	1·00	90
748	33c. Sketches of fruit	1·00	90
749	33c. Three plants and leaves	1·00	90
750	33c. Fish (leaves at left)	1·00	90
751	33c. Flag of Pohnpei and equator	1·00	90
752	33c. Sextant	1·00	90
753	33c. Red plant	1·00	90
754	33c. Fish and left side of compass rose	1·00	90
755	33c. Right side of compass rose and full-rigged sailing ship	1·00	90

Nos. 736/55 were issued together, *se-tenant*, forming a composite design.

117 Couple Meeting

1999. *Romance of the Three Kingdoms* (Chinese novel by Luo Guanzhong). Multicoloured.

756	33c. Type **117**	1·00	90
757	33c. Four men (one with lance) in room	1·00	90
758	33c. Two riders in combat	1·00	90
759	33c. Four men watching fifth man walking through room	1·00	90
760	33c. Captives before man on wheeled throne	1·00	90
761	50c. Riders approaching castle	1·50	1·40
762	50c. Warrior pointing at fire	1·50	1·40
763	50c. Opposing warriors riding through thick smoke	1·50	1·40
764	50c. Couple kneeling before man on dais	1·50	1·40
765	50c. Cauldron on fire	1·50	1·40

MS766 77×110 mm. $2 Archers on boat shooting flaming arrows (51×78 mm) 6·25 5·75

118 Carriage of Leipzig–Dresden Railway and Caroline Islands 1900 20pf. Stamp

1999. iBRA International Stamp Fair, Nuremberg, Germany. Multicoloured.

767	55c. Type **118**	1·80	1·60
768	55c. Golsdorf steam railway locomotive and Caroline Islands 1m. "Yacht" stamp	1·80	1·60

MS769 160×106 mm. $2 Caroline Islands 1900 50pf. stamp and exhibition emblem (39×59 mm) 6·75 6·00

119 Black Rhinoceros

1999. Earth Day. Multicoloured.

770	33c. Type **119**	1·00	90
771	33c. Cheetah	1·00	90
772	33c. Jackass penguin	1·00	90
773	33c. Blue whale	1·00	90
774	33c. Red-headed woodpecker	1·00	90
775	33c. African elephant	1·00	90
776	33c. Aurochs	1·00	90
777	33c. Dodo	1·00	90
778	33c. Tasmanian wolf	1·00	90
779	33c. Giant lemur	1·00	90
780	33c. Quagga	1·00	90
781	33c. Steller's sea cow	1·00	90
782	33c. Pteranodon	1·00	90
783	33c. Shonisaurus	1·00	90
784	33c. Stegosaurus	1·00	90
785	33c. Gallimimus	1·00	90
786	33c. Tyrannosaurus	1·00	90
787	33c. Archelon	1·00	90
788	33c. Brachiosaurus	1·00	90
789	33c. Triceratops	1·00	90

MS790 Two sheets, each 86×1050 mm. (a) $2 Moa (37×50 mm); (b) $2 Suchominus tenerensis (50×37 mm) 12·00 11·00

120 *Ghost of O-Iwa*

1999. 150th Death Anniv of Hokusai Katsushika (Japanese artist). Multicoloured.

791	33c. Type **120**	1·00	90
792	33c. Spotted horse with head lowered	1·00	90
793	33c. *Abe Nakamaro*	1·00	90
794	33c. *Ghost of Kasane*	1·00	90
795	33c. Bay horse with head held up	1·00	90
796	33c. *The Ghost of Kiku and the Priest Mitazuki*	1·00	90
797	33c. *Belly Band Float*	1·00	90
798	33c. Woman washing herself	1·00	90
799	33c. *Swimmers*	1·00	90
800	33c. *Eel Climb*	1·00	90
801	33c. Woman playing lute	1·00	90
802	33c. *Kimo Ga Imo ni Naru*	1·00	90

MS803 Two sheets, each 102×72 mm. (a) $2 *Whaling off Goto*; (b) $2 *Fishing by Torchlight* 12·50 11·50

Nos. 792 and 795 are inscribed "Horse Drawings" and No. **MS**803b "Fishing by Torchlight".

121 Deep-drilling for Brine Salt

1999. New Millennium. Multicoloured. (a) Science and Technology of Ancient China.

804	33c. Type **121**	1·00	90
805	33c. Chain pump	1·00	90
806	33c. Magic lantern	1·00	90
807	33c. Chang Heng's seismograph	1·00	90
808	33c. Dial and pointer devices	1·00	90
809	33c. Page of Lui Hui's mathematics treatise (value of Pi)	1·00	90
810	33c. Porcelain production	1·00	90
811	33c. Water mill	1·00	90
812	33c. Relief of horse from tomb of Tang Tai-Tsung (the stirrup)	1·00	90
813	33c. Page of Lu Yu's tea treatise and detail of Liu Songnian's painting of tea-making	1·00	90
814	33c. Umbrella	1·00	90
815	33c. Brandy and whisky production	1·00	90
816	33c. Page from oldest surviving printed book, woodblock and its print (printing)	1·00	90
817	33c. Copper plate and its print (paper money)	1·00	90
818	33c. Woodcut showing gunpowder demonstration	1·00	90
819	33c. Anji Bridge (segmented arch) (56½×36 mm)	1·00	90
820	33c. Mercator's star map and star diagram on bronze mirror	1·00	90

(b) People and Events of the 12-Century (1100–1150).

821	20c. Holy Roman Emperor Henry IV (death, 1106)	65	55
822	20c. Chastisement of monks of Enryakuji Temple, Kyoto, 1108	65	55
823	20c. Founding of Knights of the Hospital of St. John, 1113	65	55
824	20c. Invention of nautical compass, 1117	65	55
825	20c. Drowning of Prince William, heir of King Henry I of England, 1120	65	55
826	20c. Pope Callixtus II (Treaty of Worms, 1122, between Papacy and Holy Roman Emperor Henry V)	65	55
827	20c. Death of Omar Khayyam (Persian poet), 1126	65	55
828	20c. Death of Duke Guilhem IX, Count of Poitiers and Duke of Aquitaine (earliest known troubadour, 1127)	65	55
829	20c. Coronation of King Roger II of Sicily, 1130	65	55
830	20c. King Stephen and Queen Matilda (start of English civil war, 1135)	65	55
831	20c. Moses Maimonides (philosopher, birth, 1138)	65	55
832	20c. Abelard and Heloise (Church's censure of Abelard, 1140)	65	55
833	20c. Defeat of French and German crusaders at Damascus, 1148	65	55
834	20c. Fall of Mexican city of Tula, 1150s	65	55
835	20c. Completion of Angkor Vat, Cambodia, 1150	65	55
836	20c. Rise of Kingdom of Chimu, Peru, 1150s (56½×36 mm)	65	55
837	20c. Honen (Buddhist monk) becomes hermit, 1150	65	55

122 Flowers

1999. Faces of the Millennium: Diana, Princess of Wales. Showing collage of miniature flower photographs. Multicoloured, country panel at left (a) or right (b).

838	50c. Deep red shades (a)	1·40	1·30
839	50c. Deep red shades (b)	1·40	1·30
840	50c. Deep red shades with violet shades at bottom left (a)	1·40	1·30

841 50c. Blackish shades in bottom left corner (b) 1·40 1·30
842 50c. Violet shades at left and bottom, pinkish shades at right (a) 1·40 1·30
843 50c. Lemon and pink shades (b) 1·40 1·30
844 50c. Violet shades (a) 1·40 1·30
845 50c. Type **122** (rose in bottom row) (b) 1·40 1·30

Nos. 838/45 were issued together, *se-tenant*, and when viewed as a whole, form a portrait of Diana, Princess of Wales.

123 Face of Woman

1999. Costumes of the World. Multicoloured.
846 33c. Type **123** 1·00 90
847 33c. Tools for fabric making 1·00 90
848 33c. Head of African Masai warrior and textile pattern 1·00 90
849 33c. Head of woman and textile pattern (inscr "French Renaissance costume") 1·00 90
850 33c. Head of woman in hat with black feathers ("French princess gown 1900–1910") 1·00 90
851 33c. Head of Micronesian woman in wedding costume 1·00 90
852 33c. Body of African Masai warrior and head of woman 1·00 90
853 33c. Body of woman ("Textile patterns of French Renaissance costume") 1·00 90
854 33c. Body of woman ("1900–1910 French princess gown") 1·00 90
855 33c. Body and head of two Micronesian women in wedding costumes 1·00 90
856 33c. Hem of costume and body of woman ("Details of woman costume from African fabrics") 1·00 90
857 33c. Lower part of dress and head of woman ("French Renaissance costume") 1·00 90
858 33c. Hem of dress and furled umbrella 1·00 90
859 33c. Body and legs of two Micronesian women in wedding costumes 1·00 90
860 33c. Head of woman in Japanese Kabuki costume 1·00 90
861 33c. Rulers for tailoring 1·00 90
862 33c. Scissors 1·00 90
863 33c. Japanese fabrics 1·00 90
864 33c. Head and body of two women in Japanese Kabuki costumes 1·00 90
865 33c. Iron 1·00 90

Nos. 846/65 were issued together, *se-tenant*, forming several composite designs.

124 *Holy Family with St. John*

1999. Christmas. Paintings by Anthony van Dyck. Multicoloured.
866 33c. Type **124** 1·20 1·00
867 60c. *Madonna and Child* 2·20 1·90
868 $2 *Virgin and Child with Two Donors* (detail) 7·25 6·25
MS869 102×127 mm. $2 *Adoration of the Shepherds* 7·50 6·75

125 *Wright Flyer I*

1999. Man's First Century of Flight. Multicoloured.
870 33c. Type **125** 1·20 1·00
871 33c. Bleriot XI and Notre Dame Cathedral, Paris 1·20 1·00
872 33c. Fokker D.VII biplane and Brandenburg Gate, Berlin 1·20 1·00
873 33c. Dornier Komet I (numbered B 240) and Amsterdam 1·20 1·00
874 33c. Charles Lindbergh's Ryan NYP Special *Spirit of St. Louis* and steeple 1·20 1·00
875 33c. Mitsubishi A6M Zero-Sen fighter and Mt. Fuji 1·20 1·00
876 33c. Boeing B-29 Superfortress bomber and roof of building 1·20 1·00
877 33c. Messerschmitt Me 262A jet fighter (swastika on tail) 1·20 1·00
878 33c. Chuck Yeager's Bell X-1 rocket plane and Grand Canyon 1·20 1·00
879 33c. Mikoyan Gurevich MiG-19 over Russian church 1·20 1·00
880 33c. Lockheed U-2 reconnaissance plane over building at night 1·20 1·00
881 33c. Boeing 707 jetliner and head of Statue of Liberty, New York 1·20 1·00
882 33c. British Aerospace/Aerospatiale Concorde supersonic jetliner and top of Eiffel Tower, Paris 1·20 1·00
883 33c. McDonnell Douglas DC-10 jetliner and Sydney Opera House 1·20 1·00
884 33c. B-2 Spirit stealth bomber and globe 1·20 1·00
MS885 Two sheets, each 108×108 mm. (a) $2 Dornier Do-X flying boat (47×31 mm); (b) $2 P38 (31×47 mm) 14·50 12·50

Nos. 870/84 were issued together, *se-tenant*, forming a composite design of the globe.

126 *Oncidium obryzatum*

2000. Orchids. Multicoloured.
886 33c. Type **126** 1·20 1·00
887 33c. *Oncidium phalaenopsis* 1·20 1·00
888 33c. *Oncidium pulvinatum* 1·20 1·00
889 33c. *Paphiodedilum armeniacum* 1·20 1·00
890 33c. *Paphiopedilum dayanum* 1·20 1·00
891 33c. *Paphiopedilum druryi* 1·20 1·00
892 33c. *Baptistonia echinata* 1·20 1·00
893 33c. *Bulbophyllum lobbii* 1·20 1·00
894 33c. *Cattleya bicolor* 1·20 1·00
895 33c. *Cischweinfia dasyandra* 1·20 1·00
896 33c. *Cochleanthes discolor* 1·20 1·00
897 33c. *Dendrobium bellatulum* 1·20 1·00
898 33c. *Esmeralda clarkei* 1·20 1·00
899 33c. *Gomesa crispa* 1·20 1·00
900 33c. *Masdevallia elephanticeps* 1·20 1·00
901 33c. *Maxillaria variabilis* 1·20 1·00
902 33c. *Mitoniopsis roezlii* 1·20 1·00
903 33c. *Oncidium cavendishianum* 1·20 1·00
MS904 Two sheets, each 98×70 mm. (a) $1 *Ticoglossum oerstedii* (31×53 mm); (b) $2 *Paphiopedilum hirutissimum* (31×53 mm) 7·25 6·25

127 Martin Luther King (civil rights leader)

2000. Personalities of the Twentieth Century. Multicoloured.
905 33c. Type **127** 1·20 1·00
906 33c. Dr. Albert Schweitzer (philosopher and missionary) 1·20 1·00
907 33c. Pope John Paul II 1·20 1·00
908 33c. Sarvepalli Radhakrishnan (philosopher and Indian statesman) 1·20 1·00
909 33c. Toyohiko Kagawa (social reformer) 1·20 1·00
910 33c. Mahatma Gandhi (Indian leader) 1·20 1·00
911 33c. Mother Teresa (nun and missionary) 1·20 1·00
912 33c. Khyentse Rinpoche (poet and philosopher) 1·20 1·00
913 33c. Desmond Tutu (religious leader) 1·20 1·00
914 33c. Chiara Lubich (founder of Focolare movement) 1·20 1·00
915 33c. Dalai Lama (religious leader) 1·20 1·00
916 33c. Abraham Heschel (theologian) 1·20 1·00

128 Dragon

2000. New Year. Year of the Dragon. 80×6 mm.
MS917 **128** $2 multicoloured 7·25 6·25

129 Mother-of-Pearl (*Salamis parhassus*)

2000. Butterflies. Multicoloured.
918 20c. Type **129** 70 65
919 20c. Blue morpho (*Morpho rhetenor*) 70 65
920 20c. Monarch (*Danaus plexippus*) 70 65
921 20c. *Phyciodes actinote* 70 65
922 20c. *Idea leuconoe* 70 65
923 20c. *Actinote negra sobrina* 70 65
924 55c. Blue triangle (*Graphium sarpedon*) 1·90 1·70
925 55c. Swallowtail (*Papilio machaon*) 1·90 1·70
926 55c. Cairn's birdwing (*Ornithoptera priamus*) 1·90 1·70
927 55c. *Ornithoptera chimaera* 1·90 1·70
928 55c. Five-bar swallowtail (*Graphium antiphates*) 1·90 1·70
929 55c. *Pachliopta aristolochiae* 1·90 1·70
MS930 Three sheets, each 95×132 mm. (a) $2 King cracker (*Hamadryas amphinome*) (vert); (b) $2 Man with butterfly wing (vert); (c) $2 Clouded yellow (*Colias crocea*) (wrongly inscr "croceus") (vert) 22·00 19·00

130 Mahatma Gandhi (Indian leader)

2000. New Millennium. Multicoloured.
931 20c. Type **130** 70 65
932 20c. Poster (Dada Art fair, Berlin, 1920) 70 65
933 20c. Women with American flags (female suffrage, 1930) 70 65
934 20c. Nicola Sacco and Bartolomeo Vanzetti (anarchists) (international controversy over murder conviction, 1921) 70 65
935 20c. Hermann Rorschach (psychiatrist and neurologist) (developed inkblot test, 1921) 70 65
936 20c. George W. Watson (incorporation of IBM, 1924) 70 65
937 20c. Leica camera (first commercial 35 mm camera, 1925) 70 65
938 20c. Scientists and John Thomas Scopes (brought to trial for teaching Darwin's theory of evolution, 1925) 70 65
939 20c. Charles Lindbergh (aviator) and Ryan NYP Special *Spirit of St. Louis* (first solo transatlantic flight, 1927) 70 65
940 20c. *Big Bang* (George Henri Lemaître) (astrophysicist and cosmologist) (formulated *Big Bang theory*, 1927) 70 65
941 20c. Chiang Kai-Shek (Chinese nationalist leader) 70 65
942 20c. Werner Heisenberg (theoretical physicist) developed *Uncertainty Principle*, 1927 70 65
943 20c. Sir Alexander Fleming (bacteriologist) and microscope (discovery of penicillin, 1928) 70 65
944 20c. Emperor Hirohito of Japan 70 65
945 20c. Car and man (US Stock Market crash causes Great Depression) 70 65
946 20c. Douglas World Cruiser seaplanes and men (round-the-world formation flight, 1924) (59×39 mm) 70 65

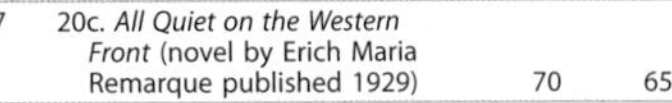
947 20c. *All Quiet on the Western Front* (novel by Erich Maria Remarque published 1929) 70 65

131 Mikhail Gorbachev (statesman)

2000. International Relations in the Twentieth Century. Multicoloured.
948 33c. Type **131** 1·20 1·00
949 33c. USSR and US flags, Gorbachev and Reagan (end of Cold War) 1·20 1·00
950 33c. Ronald Reagan (US President, 1980–88) 1·20 1·00
951 33c. Le Duc Tho (Vietnamese politician) 1·20 1·00
952 33c. Le Duc Tho and Henry Kissinger (resolution to Vietnam conflict) 1·20 1·00
953 33c. Henry Kissinger (US Secretary of State) 1·20 1·00
954 33c. Linus Pauling (chemist) 1·20 1·00
955 33c. Pauling at protest against nuclear weapons 1·20 1·00
956 33c. Peter Benenson (founder of Amnesty International, 1961) 1·20 1·00
957 33c. Amnesty International emblem and prisoners 1·20 1·00
958 33c. Mahatma Gandhi (Indian leader) 1·20 1·00
959 33c. Gandhi fasting 1·20 1·00
960 33c. John F. Kennedy (US President, 1960–3) making speech initiating Peace Corps 1·20 1·00
961 33c. President Kennedy 1·20 1·00
962 33c. Dalai Lama (Tibetan religious leader) praying 1·20 1·00
963 33c. Dalai Lama 1·20 1·00
964 33c. United Nations Headquarters, New York 1·20 1·00
965 33c. Cordell Hull (US Secretary of State 1933–44) (active in creation of United Nations) 1·20 1·00
966 33c. Frederick Willem de Klerk (South African politician) 1·20 1·00
967 33c. De Klerk and Nelson Mandela (end of Apartheid) 1·20 1·00
968 33c. Nelson Mandela 1·20 1·00
969 33c. Franklin D. Roosevelt (US President) 1·20 1·00
970 33c. Winston Churchill, Roosevelt and Josef Stalin (Soviet leader) (Yalta Conference, 1945) 1·20 1·00
971 33c. Winston Churchill (British Prime Minister) 1·20 1·00

132 Andrew Carnegie (industrialist)

2000. Philanthropists of the Twentieth Century. Multicoloured.
972 33c. Type **132** 1·20 1·00
973 33c. John D. Rockefeller (oil magnate) 1·20 1·00
974 33c. Henry Ford (motor manufacturer) 1·20 1·00
975 33c. C. J. Walker 1·20 1·00
976 33c. James B. Duke 1·20 1·00
977 33c. Andrew Mellon (financier) 1·20 1·00
978 33c. Charles F. Kettering (engineer) 1·20 1·00
979 33c. R. W. Woodruff 1·20 1·00
980 33c. Brooke Astor 1·20 1·00
981 33c. Howard Hughes (businessman and aviator) 1·20 1·00
982 33c. Jesse H. Jones 1·20 1·00
983 33c. Paul Mellon 1·20 1·00
984 33c. Jean Paul Getty (oil exectutive) 1·20 1·00
985 33c. George Soros 1·20 1·00
986 33c. Phyllis Wattis 1·20 1·00
987 33c. Ted (Robert Edward) Turner (entrepreneur) 1·20 1·00

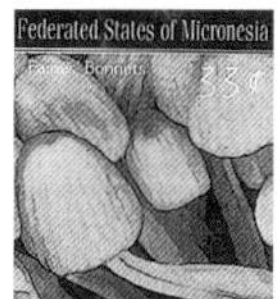

133 Fairies' Bonnets (*Coprinus disseminatus*)

2000. Fungi. Multicoloured.

988	33c. Type **133**	1·20	1·00
989	33c. Black Bulgar (*Bulgaria inquinans*)	1·20	1·00
990	33c. Amethyst deceiver (*Laccaria amethystina*) (inscr "amethystea")	1·20	1·00
991	33c. Common morel (*Morchella esculenta*)	1·20	1·00
992	33c. Common bird's nest (*Crucibulum laeve*)	1·20	1·00
993	33c. Trumpet agaric (*Clitocybe geotropa*)	1·20	1·00
994	33c. Bonnet mycena (*Mycena galericulata*)	1·20	1·00
995	33c. Underside of horse mushroom (*Agaricus arvensis*)	1·20	1·00
996	33c. Part of *Boletus subtomento*	1·20	1·00
997	33c. Oyster mushroom (*Pleurotus ostreatus*)	1·20	1·00
998	33c. Fly agaric (*Amanita muscaria*)	1·20	1·00
999	33c. Aztec mushroom mandala design	1·20	1·00
MS1000	Two sheets, each 100×100 mm. (a) $2 Toad on brown birch bolete; (b) $2 Magpie ink cap	15·00	12·50

134 *Freycinetia arborea*

2000. Flowers. Multicoloured.

1001	33c. Type **134**	1·20	1·00
1002	33c. Mount Cook lily (*Ranunculus lyallii*) (inscr "lyalli")	1·20	1·00
1003	33c. Sun orchid (*Thelymitra nuda*)	1·20	1·00
1004	33c. *Bossiaea ensata*	1·20	1·00
1005	33c. Swamp hibiscus (*Hibiscus diversifolius*)	1·20	1·00
1006	33c. *Gardenia brighamii*	1·20	1·00
1007	33c. Elegant brodiaea (Brodiaea elegans)	1·20	1·00
1008	33c. Skyrocket (*Ipomopsis aggregata*)	1·20	1·00
1009	33c. Hedge bindweed (*Convovulus sepium*)	1·20	1·00
1010	33c. Woods' rose (*Rosa woodsii*)	1·20	1·00
1011	33c. Swamp rose (*Rosa palustris*)	1·20	1·00
1012	33c. Wake robin (*Trillium erectum*)	1·20	1·00
MS1013	Two sheets. (a) 95×80 mm. $2 Black-eyed susan (*Tetratheca juncea*). (b) 108×80 mm. $2 Yellow meadow lily (*Lilium canadense*) Set of 2 sheets	15·00	12·50

135 Two Siamese Cats

2000. Cats and Dogs. Multicoloured.

1014	33c. Type **135**	1·20	1·00
1015	33c. Red mackerel tabbies	1·20	1·00
1016	33c. British shorthair	1·20	1·00
1017	33c. Red Persian	1·20	1·00
1018	33c. Turkish angora	1·20	1·00
1019	33c. Calico	1·20	1·00
1020	33c. Afghan hounds	1·20	1·00
1021	33c. Yellow labrador retriever	1·20	1·00
1022	33c. Greyhound	1·20	1·00
1023	33c. German shepherd	1·20	1·00
1024	33c. King Charles spaniel	1·20	1·00
1025	33c. Jack Russell terrier	1·20	1·00
MS1026	Two sheets, each 85×110 mm. (a) $2 Tortoiseshell and white cat watching bird. (b) $2 Setter and trees Set of 2 sheets	15·00	12·50

Nos. 1014/19 (cats) and 1020/5 (dogs) respectively were issued together, *se-tenant*, each sheetlet forming a composite design.

136 Henry Taylor (Great Britain) preparing to Dive, 1908, London

2000. Olympic Games, Sydney. Multicoloured.

1027	33c. Type **136**	1·20	1·00
1028	33c. Cyclist	1·20	1·00
1029	33c. Munich stadium and flag, West Germany	1·20	1·00
1030	33c. Ancient Greek wrestlers	1·20	1·00

137 Zodiac Airship *Capitaine Ferber*

2000. Centenary of First Zeppelin Flight and Airship Development. Multicoloured.

1031	33c. Type **137**	1·20	1·00
1032	33c. Astra airship *Adjutant Reau*	1·20	1·00
1033	33c. Airship 1A, Italy	1·20	1·00
1034	33c. Astra-Torres No. 14	1·20	1·00
1035	33c. Front of Astra-Torres No. 14, Schutte-Lanz SL3 and front of Siemens-Schukert airship	1·20	1·00
1036	33c. Siemens-Schukert airship	1·20	1·00
MS1037	Two sheets, each 110×85 mm. (a) $2 LZ-130 *Graf Zeppelin II*. (b) $2 Dupuy de Lome airship Set of 2 sheets	15·00	12·50

Nos. 1031/6 were issued together, *se-tenant*, forming a composite design.

138 Top of Head

2000. 100th Birthday of Queen Elizabeth the Queen Mother. T **138** and similar vert designs showing collage of miniature flower photographs. Multicoloured, country inscription and face value at left (a) or right (b).

1038	33c. Type **138**	1·20	1·00
1039	33c. Top of head (b)	1·20	1·00
1040	33c. Eye and temple (a)	1·20	1·00
1041	33c. Temple (b)	1·20	1·00
1042	33c. Cheek (a)	1·20	1·00
1043	33c. Cheek (b)	1·20	1·00
1044	33c. Chin (a)	1·20	1·00
1045	33c. Chin and neck (b)	1·20	1·00

Nos. 1038/45 were issued together in *se-tenant* sheetlets of eight with the stamps arranged in two vertical columns separated by a gutter also containing miniature photographs. When viewed as a whole, the sheetlet forms a portrait of Queen Elizabeth the Queen Mother.

139 Woman Weightlifter and Traditional Cloth

2000. OLYMPHILEX 2000 International Olympic Stamp Exhibition, Sydney. Sheet 137× 82 mm, containing T **139** and similar vert designs. Multicoloured.

MS1046	33c. Type **139**; 33c. Woman playing basketball; $1 Male weightlifter	6·50	5·25

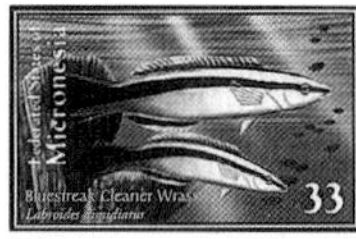

140 Blue-streaked Cleaner Wrasse (*Labroides dimidiatus*)

2000. Coral Reef. Multicoloured.

1047	33c. Type **140**	1·20	1·00
1048	33c. Pennant coralfish (*Heniochus acuminatus*)	1·20	1·00
1049	33c. Chevron butterflyfish (*Chaetodon trifascialis*)	1·20	1·00
1050	33c. Rock beauty (*Holacanthus tricolor*)	1·20	1·00
1051	33c. Mandarin fish (*Synchiropus splendidus*)	1·20	1·00
1052	33c. Emperor snapper (*Lutjanus sebae*) (wrongly inscr "timorensis")	1·20	1·00
1053	33c. Copper-banded butterflyfish (*rostratus*)	1·20	1·00
1054	33c. Chevron butterflyfish (*Chaetodon trifascialis*) (different)	1·20	1·00
1055	33c. Lemon-peel angelfish (*Centropyge flavissimus*)	1·20	1·00
1056	33c. Lemon-peel angelfish and harlequin tuskfish (*Choerodon fasciatus*)	1·20	1·00
1057	33c. Crown triggerfish (*Balistoides conspicillum*)	1·20	1·00
1058	33c. Coral hind (*Cephalopholis miniata*)	1·20	1·00
1059	33c. Pennant coralfish (*Heniochus acuminatus*) (different)	1·20	1·00
1060	33c. Scuba diver and six-blotched hind (*Cephalopholis sexmaculata*)	1·20	1·00
1061	33c. Common jellyfish (*Aurelia aurita*)	1·20	1·00
1062	33c. Palette surgeonfish (*Paracanthurus hepatus*) and common jellyfish	1·20	1·00
1063	33c. Bicoloured angelfish (*Centropyge bicolor*)	1·20	1·00
1064	33c. Thread-finned butterflyfish (*Chaetodon auriga*) and clown anemonefish	1·20	1·00
1065	33c. Clown anemonefish (*Amphiprion percula*)	1·20	1·00
1066	33c. Three-banded damselfish (*Chrysiptera tricincta*)	1·20	1·00
1067	33c. Three-banded damselfish and grey reef shark (*Carcharhinus amblyrhynchs*) (inscr "amblyrhynchos")	1·20	1·00
1068	33c. Tail of grey reef shark and starfish (*Luidia ciliaris*)	1·20	1·00
MS1069	Two sheets, each 98×68 mm. (a) $2 Forceps butterflyfish (*Forcipiger flavissimus*). (b) $2 Emperor angelfish (*Pomacanthus imperator*) Set of 2 sheets	15·00	12·50

Nos. 1051/59 and 1060/8 respectively were issued, *se-tenant*, forming a composite design.

141 Back of Head

2000. 80th Birthday of Pope John Paul II. T 141 and similar vert designs showing collage of miniature religious photographs. Multicoloured, country inscription and face value at left (a) or right (b).

1070	50c. Type **141**	1·90	1·60
1071	50c. Forehead (b)	1·90	1·60
1072	50c. Ear (a)	1·90	1·60
1073	50c. Forehead and eye (b)	1·90	1·60
1074	50c. Neck and collar (a)	1·90	1·60
1075	50c. Nose and cheek (b)	1·90	1·60
1076	50c. Shoulder (a)	1·90	1·60
1077	50c. Hands (b)	1·90	1·60

Nos. 1070/7 were issued together in *se-tenant* sheetlets of eight with the stamps arranged in two vertical columns separated by a gutter also containing miniature photographs. When viewed as a whole, the sheetlet forms a portrait of Pope John Paul II.

142 *The Holy Trinity* (Titian)

2000. Christmas. Multicoloured.

1078	20c. Type **142**	75	65
1079	33c. *Adoration of the Magi* (Diego de Silva y Velasquez)	1·20	1·00
1080	60c. *Holy Nereus* (Peter Paul Rubens)	2·30	1·90
1081	$3.20 *St. Gregory, St. Maurus, St. Papianus and St. Domitilla* (Rubens)	12·00	10·00

143 Snake

2001. New Year. Year of the Snake. Two sheets, each 72×101 mm, containing horiz design as T **143**. Multicoloured.

MS1082	(a) 60c. Type **143**. (b) 60c. Brown snake	4·75	4·00

144 Weepinbell

2001. Pokemon (children's computer game). Showing various Pokemon characters. Mult.

1083	50c. Type **144**	1·90	1·60
1084	50c. Snorlax	1·90	1·60
1085	50c. Seel	1·90	1·60
1086	50c. Hitmonchan	1·90	1·60
1087	50c. Jynx	1·90	1·60
1088	50c. Pontya	1·90	1·60
MS1089	74×114 mm. $2 Farfetch'd (37×50 mm)	7·50	6·25

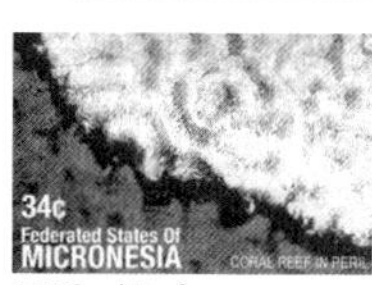

145 Coral Reef

2001. Environmental Protection. Multicoloured.

1090	34c. Type **145**	1·40	1·10
1091	34c. Galapagos turtle	1·40	1·10
1092	34c. Tasmanian tiger	1·40	1·10
1093	34c. Yanomami	1·40	1·10
1094	34c. Pelican and Florida Keys	1·40	1·10
1095	34c. Bird of prey	1·40	1·10
1096	60c. Factory chimneys (Pollution)	2·30	1·90
1097	60c. Desert and tree stump (Deforestation)	2·30	1·90
1098	60c. Forest (Acid rain)	2·30	1·90
1099	60c. Horse, mother and child, tree and Globe (Greenhouse effect)	2·30	1·90
MS1100	Two sheets each 110×77 mm. (a) $2 Sea bird (visit by Jacques Cousteau); (b) $2 Chimpanzee (Jane Goodall Institute) Set of 2 sheets	15·00	12·50

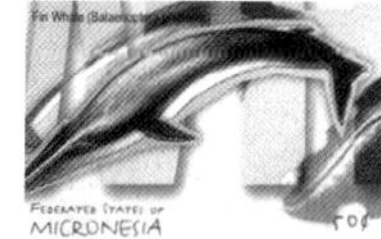

146 Fin Whale (*Balaenoptera physalus*)

2001. Whales of the Pacific. Multicoloured.

1101	50c. Type **146**	1·90	1·60
1102	50c. Right whale (*Balaena galacials*)	1·90	1·60
1103	50c. Pygmy right whale (*Caperea marginata*)	1·90	1·60
1104	50c. Humpback whale (*Megaptera novaeangliae*) (inscr "novaengliae")	1·90	1·60
1105	50c. Blue whale (*Balaenoptera musculus*)	1·90	1·60
1106	50c. Bowhead whale (*Balaena mysticetus*)	1·90	1·60
1107	60c. True's beaked whale (*Mesoplodon mirus*)	2·30	1·90
1108	60c. Cuvier's beaked whale (*Ziphius cavirostris*)	2·30	1·90
1109	60c. Shepherd's beaked whale (*Tasmacetus shepherdi*)	2·30	1·90
1110	60c. Baird's beaked whale (*Berardius bairdii*)	2·30	1·90
1111	60c. Northern bottlenose whale (*Hyperodon ampullatus*)	2·30	1·90
1112	60c. Pygmy sperm whale (*Kogia breviceps*)	2·30	1·90
MS1113	Two sheets each 100×70 mm. (a) $2 Killer whale (*Orcinus orca*); (b) $2 Sperm whale (*Physeter macrocephalus*) Set of 2 sheets	15·00	12·50

Nos. 1101/6 and 1107/12 respectively were issued together, *se-tenant*, forming a composite design.

147 Three-spotted ("Yellow") Damselfish (*Stegastes planifrons*)

2001. Fish. Multicoloured.

1114	11c. Type **147**	50	40
1115	34c. Rainbow runner (*Elegatis bipinnulatus*)	1·40	1·10
1116	70c. Whitelined grouper (*Anyperodon leucogrammicus*)	2·75	2·30
1117	80c. Purple queen anthias (*Pseudanthias pascalus*)	3·00	2·50
1118	$3.50 Eibl's angelfish (*Centropye eibli*)	13·00	11·00
1119	$12.25 Spotted ("Blue-spotted") boxfish (*Ostracion meleagris*)	49·00	41·00

148 *The Courtesan Hinazuru of the Choji-ya* (Chokosai Eisho)

2001. PHILANIPPON '01 International Stamp Exhibition, Tokyo. Japanese Art. Multicoloured.

1130	34c. Type **148**	1·40	1·10
1131	34c. *The Iris Garden* (Torii Kiyonaga)	1·40	1·10
1132	34c. *Girl tying her Hair Ribbon* (Tori Kiyomine)	1·40	1·10
1133	34c. *The Courtesan of the Mayuzumi of the Daimonji-ya* (Katsukawa Shuncho)	1·40	1·10
1134	34c. *Parody of the Allegory of the Sage Chin Kao Riding a Carp* (Suzuki Harunobo)	1·40	1·10
1135	34c. *Bath-house Scene* (Utagawa Toyokuni)	1·40	1·10
1136	34c. *Dance of Kamisha* (Kitagawa Utamaro)	1·40	1·10
1137	34c. *The Courtesan Hinazura at the Keizetsuro* (Kitagawa Utamaro)	1·40	1·10
1138	34c. *Toilet Scene* (Kitagawa Utamaro)	1·40	1·10
1139	34c. *Applying Lip Rouge* (Kitagawa Utamaro)	1·40	1·10
1140	34c. *Beauty reading a Letter* (Kitagawa Utamaro)	1·40	1·10
1141	34c. *The Geisha Kamekichi* (Kitagawa Utamaro)	1·40	1·10
MS1142	Two sheets each 118×88 mm. (a) $2 *Girl seated by a Brook at Sunset* (Suzuki Harunobu). Imperf; (b) $2 *Allegory of Ariwara No Narihira* (Kikugawa Eizan). Imperf Set of 2 shets	15·00	12·50

149 *Oscar Wilde*

2001. Death Centenary of Henri de Toulouse-Lautrec (artist). Multicoloured.

1143	60c. Type **149**	2·30	1·90
1144	60c. *Doctor Tapié in a Theatre Corridor*	2·30	1·90
1145	60c. *Monsieur Delaporte*	2·30	1·90
MS1146	54×84 mm. $2 *The Clowness Cha-U-Kao*	7·50	6·25

150 Queen Victoria

2001. Death Centenary of Queen Victoria. Each black (except **MS**1151 multicoloured).

1147	60c. Type **150**	2·30	1·90
1148	60c. Facing right	2·30	1·90
1149	60c. Facing left wearing black decorated hat	2·30	1·90
1150	60c. Facing forwards	2·30	1·90
1151	60c. Holding baby	2·30	1·90
1152	60c. Facing left wearing lace headdress	2·30	1·90
MS1153	84×110 mm. $2 Queen Victoria (37×50 mm)	7·50	6·25

151 Queen Elizabeth

2001. 75th Birthday of Queen Elizabeth II. Each black (except No. 1153 and **MS**1158 multicoloured).

1154	60c. Type **151**	2·30	1·90
1155	60c. Wearing blue jacket	2·30	1·90
1156	60c. As young girl	2·30	1·90
1157	60c. As infant	2·30	1·90
1158	60c. With dog	2·30	1·90
1159	60c. In profile	2·30	1·90
MS1160	78×108 mm. $2 Princess Elizabeth	7·50	6·25

152 Striped Dolphin

2001. Marine Life. Four sheets containing T **152** and similar multicoloured designs.

MS1161	(a) 162×153 mm. 60c.×6, Type **152**; Olive Ridley turtle; Goldrim tang; Blue shark; Picasso triggerfish; Polkadot grouper; (b) 152×164 mm. 60c.×6, Loggerhead turtle; Striped marlin; Bicolor cherub; Clown wrasse (*Coris gaimard*) (inscr "gaimardi"); Clown triggerfish; Japanese tang; (c) 96×68 mm. $2 Harlequin tusk (50×38 mm); (d) 70×100 mm. $2 Emperor angelfish (38×50 mm)	41·00	34·00

153 Triceratops

2001. Dinosaurs. Multicoloured.

1162	60c. Type **153**	2·30	1·90
1163	60c. Psittacosaurus	2·30	1·90
1164	60c. Two Archaeopteryx	2·30	1·90
1165	60c. Head of Allosaurus	2·30	1·90
MS1166	Four sheets (a) 103×124 mm. 60c.×6, Tyrannosaurus; Pteranodon; Brachiosaurus; Spinosaurus; Deinonychus; Teratosaurus; (b) 104×123 mm. 60c.×6, Parasaurolophus; Plateosaurus; Archaeopteryx in flight; Allosaurus (different); Torosaurus; Euoplocephalus; (c) 68×98 mm. $2 Tyrannosaurus (different); (d) 68×98 mm. $2 Parasaurolophus (different) (horiz)	43·00	36·00

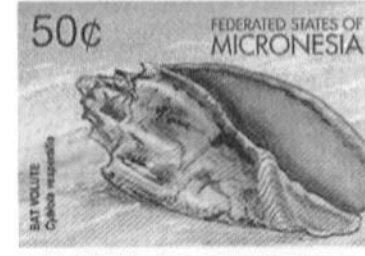

154 *Cymbiola vespertilio* (inscr "Cybiola")

2001. Shells. Four sheets containing T **154** and similar multicoloured designs.

MS1167	(a) 152×107 mm. 50c.×6, Type **154**; *Cassis cornuta*; *Murex trocheli*; *Cymatium lotorium* (incr "lortrium"); *Oliva sericea*; *Phos senticosus*; (b) 111×145 mm. 50c.×6; *Oblique nutmeg* (vert); *Cymbiola imperialis* (vert); Pontifical mitre (vert); *Conus eburneus Hwass in Bruguiere* (vert); *Heliacus areola* (inscr "variegated gmelin") (vert); *Corculum cardissa* (vert); (c) 76×59 mm. $2 *Eyed auger*; (d) 76×59 mm. $2 Geography cone	40·00	33·00

155 Malleefowl

2001. Birds. Multicoloured.

1168	5c. Type **155**	25	20
1169	22c. Corncrake	85	70
1170	23c. Hooded merganser	85	70
1171	$2.10 Purple gallinule	8·00	6·50
MS1172	Four sheets. (a) 146×167 mm. 60c.×6, Fairy wren; Golden crowned kinglet (*Regulus satrapa*) (inscr " Bebrornis rodericanus"); Flame tempered babbler; Golden headed cisticola (*Cisticola exilis*) (inscr " Orthotomus moreauii"); White browed babbler; White throated dipper (inscr "breasted"); (b) 146×167 mm. Logrunner; Common tree creeper (inscr "Eurasian"); Chaffinch (inscr "Goldfinch"); Rufous fantail; Orange bellied flower pecker (inscr "billed"); Goldfinch (inscr "American goldfinch"); (c) 79×109 mm. $2 Emperor bird of paradise; (d) 79×109 mm. $2 Yellow eyed cuckoo shrike (vert) Set of 4 sheets	43·00	36·00

156 Alexis Carrel (Physiology and Medicine, 1912)

2001. Centenary of First Nobel Prize. Four sheets containing T **156** and similar vert designs. Multicoloured.

MS1173	(a) 183× 29 mm. 60c.×6, Type **156**; Max Theiler, 1951 (Physiology and Medicine); Niels Finsen, 1903 (Physiology and Medicine); Philip S. Hench, 1950 (Physiology and Medicine); Sune Bergstrom, 1982 (Physiology and Medicine); JohnVane, 1982 (Physiology and Medicine) (b) 183×129 mm. 60c.×6, Bengt Samuelsson, 1982 (Physiology and Medicine); Johannes Fibiger, 1926 (Physiology and Medicine); Theodore Richards, 1914 (Chemistry); Tadeus Reichstein, 1950 (Physiology and Medicine); Frederick Soddy, 1921 (Chemistry); Albert Szent-Gyorgi von Nagyrapolt, 1937 (Physiology and Medicine) (c) 106 × 75 mm. Irving Langmuir, 1932 (Chemistry); (d) 106×75 mm. Artturi Ilmari Virtanen, 1945 (Chemistry)	43·00	36·00

157 Sinking of USS *Oklahoma*

2001. 60th Anniv of Attack on Pearl Harbour. Four sheets containing T **157** and similar horiz designs. Multicoloured.

MS1174	(a) 149×161 mm. 60c.×6, Type **157**; Attack on Wheeler airfield; Japanese bomber; USS *Ward* sinking submarine; Bombing of USS *Arizona*; Attack on EWA marine base (b) 149×161 mm. 60c.×6, "Remember Pearl Harbour" poster; Hideki Tojo (Japanese prime minister); Rescuing wounded, Bellows Field; Rescuing crew of USS *Arizona*; Isoroku Yamamoto (Japanese admiral); "Remember Pearl Harbour" poster (different) (c) 80×110 mm.; USS *Arizona Memorial*, Hawaii (d) 80×110 mm. President F. D. Roosevelt	43·00	36·00

158 Santa Claus riding Cat

2001. Christmas. Santa Claus. Multicoloured.

1175	22c. Type **158**	85	70
1176	34c. Between decorated trees	1·40	1·10
1177	60c. Flying in sleigh	2·40	2·00
1178	$1 Riding dog	4·00	3·25
MS1179	78×111 mm. $2 Climbing into chimney (vert)	8·00	6·50

159 Horse

2002. Year of the Horse. Sheet containing T **159** and similar vert designs. Each black.

MS1180	60c.×6, Type **159**; Two horses; Two horses (different); Two horses' heads; Galloping horse	11·50	9·75

No. **MS**1180 forms a composite design of a herd of horses.

160 Queen Elizabeth II

2002. Golden Jubilee. 50th Anniv of Queen Elizabeth II's Accession to the Throne. Two sheets containing T **160** and similar square designs. Multicoloured.

MS1181	(a) 132×100 mm. 80c.×4, Type **160**; Prince Phillip; Queen Elizabeth wearing white hat; Queen Elizabeth and children; (b) 76×109 mm. $2 Queen Elizabeth wearing headscarf	20·00	17·00

161 Statue of Liberty and American Flag

2002. United We Stand.

1182	**161**	$1 multicoloured	4·00	3·25

162 Luge Racer

2002. Winter Olympic Games, Salt Lake City (1st issue). Multicoloured.

1183	$1 Type **162**	4·00	3·25
1184	$1 Ice hockey player	4·00	3·25
MS1185	88×119 mm. Nos. 1183/4	8·00	6·50

See also Nos. 1191/**MS**1193.

163 Sun, Bird and Flowering Tree (January)

2002. Japanese Art. "Birds and Flowers of Months of Year" (Nos. **MS**1186a/b). Four sheets containing T **163** and similar vert designs. Multicoloured.

MS1186 Two sheets (a/b), each 135×210 mm. (a) 60c.×6, Type **163**; February; March; April; May; June. (b) 60c.×6, July; August; September; October; November; December. Two sheets (c/d), each 100×69 mm. (c) $2 *Seashells and Plums* (Suzuki Kitsu). Imperf. (d) *Peacock and Peonies* (Nagasawa Rosetsu). Imperf Set of 4 sheets 44·00 37·00

164 John F. Kennedy

2002. 85th Birth Anniv of John Fitzgerald Kennedy (USA president 1961–3) (**MS**1187a/b). Fifth Death Anniv of Diana, Princess of Wales (**MS**1187b/c). Four sheets containing T **164** and similar vert designs. Multicoloured.

MS1187 (a) 132×136 mm. 60c.×4, Type **164**; Facing left; Looking left; Facing front. (b) 80×112 mm. $2 Facing right. (c) 114×133 mm. 60c.×6, Princess Diana as bride; Wearing tiara; Wearing hat; Wearing scarf; Wearing pearl earrings; Wearing tiara facing left. (d) 87×60 mm. $2 Wearing wide-brimmed hat Set of 4 sheets 38·00 32·00

165 The Matterhorn, Switzerland

2002. International Year of Mountains. Two sheets containing T **165** and similar vert designs.

MS1188 (a) 136×95 mm. 80c.×4, Type **165**; Maroon Bells, USA; Wetterhorn, Switzerland; Mount Tasaranoro, Africa (inscr "Tasaranora"). (b) 96×62 mm. $2 Cerro Fitzroy, South America 20·00 16·00

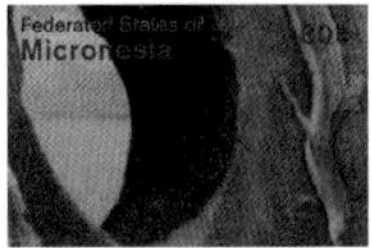

166 Money Rock and Gecko

2002. International Year of Eco Tourism. Two sheets containing T **166** and similar horiz designs. Multicoloured.

MS1189 (a) 138×99 mm. 80c.×6, Type **166**; Outrigger canoe; Tribal meeting house; Children wearing ceremonial costumes; Girl wearing lei; Two boys. (b) 85×55 mm. $2 Fishermen 25·00 21·00

167 Pagoda

2002. World Scout Jamboree, Thailand. Multicoloured.

MS1190 (a) 161×68 mm. $1×3, Type **167**; American eagle; Scout cap. (b) 97×67 mm. $2 Scout badges 18·00 14·50

168 Luge Racer

2002. Winter Olympic Games, Salt Lake City (2nd issue). Multicoloured.

1191	$1 Type **168**	3·50	3·00
1192	$1 Ice hockey player	3·50	3·00
MS1193	88×119 mm. Nos. 1191/2	7·25	6·00

Nos. 1191/**MS**1193 differ from the issue of 18 March in the design of the Olympic rings.

169 School Buildings

2002. 50th Anniv of Xavier High School, Sapwuk, Weno Island.

1194	**169**	37c. multicoloured	1·40	1·20

170 Elizabeth Bowes-Lyon riding Pony

2002. Queen Elizabeth the Queen Mother Commemoration. Two sheets containing T **170** and similar multicoloured designs.

MS1195 (a) 176×126 mm. 80c.×4, Type **170**; Wedding of Duke and Duchess of York; Holding Princess Elizabeth; Coronation of George VI and Queen Elizabeth. (b) 76×106 mm. $2 Queen Elizabeth the Queen Mother wearing hat with veil (vert) 20·00 16·00

171 Teddy Bear dressed as Burglar

2002. Centenary of the Teddy Bear. Sheet 141×145 mm containing T **171** and similar vert designs. Multicoloured.

MS1196 80c.×4, Type **171**; Girl bear holding heart; Blue bear holding flowers; Boy bear holding heart 12·00 10·00

172 Elvis Presley

2002. 25th Death Anniv of Elvis Presley (entertainer). Sheet 214×163 mm containing T **172** and similar vert designs. Multicoloured.

MS1197 37c.×6, Type **172**; Kissing guitar; Wearing hat; Wearing checked shirt; With raised arms; Holding microphone 8·25 7·00

173 *Madonna and Child* (detail) (Agnolo Bronzino)

2002. Christmas. Multicoloured.

1198	21c. Type **173**	75	65
1199	37c. *Madonna And Child* (Giovanni Bellini)	1·30	1·10
1200	70c. *Madonna and Child between St. Stephen and St. Ladislaus* (Simone Martini) (horiz)	2·50	2·10
1201	80c. *Holy Family* (Angola Bronzino)	2·75	2·40
1202	$2 *Holy Family* (Simone Martini)	7·25	6·00
MS1203	102×76 mm. $2 *Sacred Conversation* (Giovanni Bellini) (inscr "Giovanna")	7·25	6·00

174 *Hyles lineate*

2002. Flora and Fauna. Ten sheets containing T **174** and similar multicoloured designs.

MS1204 Five sheets (a/e), each 127×157 mm. (a) Moths. 37c.×6, Type **174**; *Othreis fullonia*; Inscr "Dysphania cuprina"; *Agarista agricola*; *Actias elene*; Inscr "Rhodogastria crokeri". (b) Fungi. 55c.×6, *Phellinus robustus*; Inscr "Collybia iocephala"; *Leucocoprinus rachodes*; *Boletus edulis*; *Boletus crocipodius*; *Lepiota acutesquamosa*. (c) Butterflies. 60c.×6, *Junonia villida*; *Ornithoptera priamus*; *Danis danis*; *Libythea geoffroyi*; Inscr "Elyminas agondas"; *Eurema brigitta*. (d) Orchids. 60c.×6, *Eria javanica*; *Cymbidium finlaysonianum*; *Coelogyne asperata*; *Spathoglottis affinis*; *Vanda tricolour*; *Calanthe rosea*. (e) Insects. Inscr "Pseudolucanus capreolus"; Honey bee (*Apis mellifera*); Black widow spider (*Latrodectus mactans*); Mosquito (*Anopheles*); Black ant (*Monomorium minimum*); Cicada (*Tibicen septendecim*). Five sheets (f/j), each 82×113 mm. (f) $2 *Alcides zodiaca*. (g) $2 *Lepiota acutesquamosa*. (h) $2 *Loxura atymnus*. (i) $2 *Dendrobium phalaenopsis*. (j) $2 *Anax junius* (horiz) 95·00 80·00

The stamps and margins of **MS**1204a/j form composite designs.

175 Greater Flame-backed Woodpecker (*Chrysocolaptes lucidus*)

2002. Birds. Multicoloured.

1204a	2c. Blue-grey gnatcatcher (*Polioptila caeralea*)	15	15
1205	3c. Type **175**	20	15
1206	5c. Red-tailed tropicbird (*Phaethon rubricauda*)	25	20
1206a	10c. Clapper rail (*Rallus longirostris*)	40	30
1207	21c. Hair-crested drongo (*Dicrurus hottentottus*) (inscr "forficatus")	75	65
1208	22c. *Zosterops citronella*	80	65
1209	23c. *Lonchura striata*	80	65
1209a	24c. Slaty-headed parakeet *Psittacula himalayana*	85	70
1210	37c. Yap monarch (*Monarcha godeffroyi*)	1·30	1·10
1210a	39c. Purple sunbird *Nectarinia asiatica*	1·40	1·10
1211	60c. Eclectus parrot (*Eclectus roratus*)	2·10	1·80
1212	70c. Sulphur-crested cockatoo (*Cacatua galerita*)	2·50	2·10
1212a	75c. Plum-headed parakeet (*Psittacula cyanocephala*)	2·50	2·10
1213	80c. Inscr "Magazosterops palauensis"	2·75	2·40
1214	$2 Green magpie (*Cissa chinensis*)	7·25	6·00
1215	$3.85 Eastern broad-billed roller (inscr "Dollarbird") (*Eurystomus orientalis*)	13·50	11·00
1215a	$4.05 Eurasian collared dove (*Streptopelia decaocto*) (horiz)	14·50	12·00
1216	$5 Great frigate bird (*Fregata minor*)	18·00	15·00
1217	$13.65 Micronesian pigeon (*Ducula oceanica*)	49·00	41·00

176 Charles Lindbergh, Donald Hall and *Spirit of St. Louis*

2003. 75th Anniv of First Transatlantic Flight. Sheet 135×118 mm containing T **176** and similar horiz designs. Multicoloured.

MS1218 60c.×6, Type **176**; *Spirit of St. Louis*; *Spirit of St. Louis* on Curtis Field; *Spirit of St. Louis* airborne; Arriving in Paris; Ticker tape parade, New York 12·50 10·50

177 Long-haired Goat

2003. New Year. "Year of the Ram" (stamps show goats). Sheet 110×121 mm containing T **177** and similar vert designs. Multicoloured.

MS1219 37c.×6, Type **177**×2; Angora goat×2; Dark-coloured goat×2 7·25 6·00

178 David Brown

2003. Colombia Space Shuttle Disaster, 1 February 2003. Crew Members. Sheet 184×146 mm containing T **178** and similar vert designs. Multicoloured.

MS1220 37c.×7, Type **178**; Rick Husband; Laurel Blair; Kalpana Chawla; Michael Anderson; William McCool; Ilan Ramon 9·25 7·75

179 Princess Elizabeth

2003. 50th Anniv (2002) of Coronation of Queen Elizabeth. Two sheets containing T **179** and similar vert designs. Multicoloured.

MS1221 (a) 147×85 mm. $1×3, Type **179**; Wearing tiara; Wearing robe. (b) 68×98 mm. $2 Wearing state crown 17·00 14·00

180 Boeing B-52 Bomber

2003. Military Operations in Iraq. Two sheets, each 136×136 mm containing T **180** and similar horiz designs. Multicoloured.

MS1222 (a) 37c.×5, Type **180**; General Dynamics F-16 Fighting Falcon; Bell Cobra helicopter; Hughes AH Apache helicopter; T8,000 Tow missile; US M3A2 Bradley tank. (b) 37c.×6, Stealth aircraft; Lockheed AC-130; Sikorsky MH-53J Pave Low II helicopter; General Atomics RQ-1 Predator; Vickers Challenger Two tank; Aegis cruiser 16·00 13·00

181 Prince William as Small Boy

2003. 21st Birthday of Prince William. Two sheets containing T **181** and similar vert designs. Multicoloured.

MS1223 (a) 148×78 mm. $1×3, Type **181**; As schoolboy; As young man. (b) 98×68 mm. $2 As boy 17·00 14·00

182 Greg Lemond (1990)

2003. Centenary of Tour de France Cycle Race. Two sheets containing T **182** and similar vert designs. Multicoloured. Litho.
MS1224 (a) 161×100 mm. 60c.×4, Type **182**; Miguel Indurain (1991); Miguel Indurain (1992); Miguel Indurain (1993). (b) 101×70 mm. $2 Marco Pantani (1998) 15·00 12·50

183 Kosrae Mangroves

2003. International Year of Freshwater. Two sheets containing T **183** and similar vert designs. Multicoloured.
MS1225 (a) 150×88 mm. $1×3, Type **183**; Chuuk lagoon; Pohnpei waterfalls. (b) 101×70 mm. $2 Pohnpei lagoon 17·00 14·00

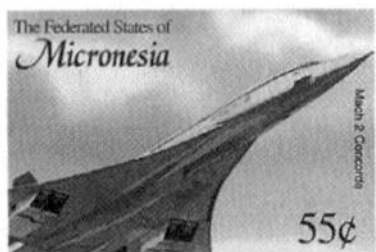

184 Concorde

2003. Centenary of Powered Flight. Two sheets containing T **184** and similar horiz designs. Multicoloured.
MS1226 (a) 117×175 mm. 55c.×6, Type **184**; Boeing 757; Junkers F13a; Martin M-130 China Clipper; Handley Page HP 42W; *Wright Flyer II*. (b) 106×76 mm. $2 Boeing 747 18·00 15·00

185 Glen Little

2003. Centenary of Circus. Two sheets containing T **185** and similar vert designs. Multicoloured.
MS1227 (a) 118×200 mm. Clowns. 80c.×4, Type **185**; Joseph Grimaldi; Beverley Rebo Bergerson; Coco Michael Polakov. (b) 146×219 mm. Performers. 80c.×4, Jane Mandana (animal entertainer); Maxim Papazov (acrobat); Harry Keaton (illusionist); Giraffe 22·00 18·00

186 Scout wearing Tartan Scarf

2003. 25th Death Anniv of Norman Rockwell (illustrator). Two sheets containing T **186** and similar vert designs. Multicoloured.
MS1228 (a) 152×190 mm. 80c.×4, Type **186**; Scout carrying child; Scoutmaster. (b) 66×84 mm. $2 Boys and dog running away ("No Swimming"). Imperf 15·00 12·50

187 *Vahine No Te Tiare*

2003. Death Centenary of Paul Gauguin (artist). Two sheets containing T **187** and similar horiz designs. Multicoloured.
MS1229 (a) 140×127 mm. 80c.×4, Type **187**; *Les Amants; Trois Tahitiens Conversation; Arearea*. (b) 79×64 mm. $2 *Ta Matete*. Imperf 15·00 12·50

188 *Blue and Silver Blue Wave, Biaritz*

2003. Death Centenary of James Whistler (artist). Multicoloured.

1230	37c. Type **188**	1·20	1·00
1231	55c. *Brown and Silver: Old Battersea Bridge*	1·80	1·50
1232	60c. *Nocturne in Blue and Silver: The Lagoon, Venice*	2·00	1·60
1233	80c. *Crepuscule In Flesh Colour and Green: Valparaiso*	2·40	2·00

MS1234 (a) 193×117 mm. $1×3, *Symphony in White No. 2: The Little White Girl* (38×51 mm); *At the Piano* (76×51 mm); *Symphony in White No. 1: The White Girl* (38×51 mm). (b) 83×104 mm. $2 *Portrait of Thomas Carlyle* Imperf 18·00 14·50

189 *Madonna of the Carnation* (Leonardo da Vinci)

2003. Christmas. Multicoloured.

1235	37c. Type **189**	1·20	1·00
1236	60c. *Madonna with Yarn Winder*	2·00	1·60
1237	80c. *Litta Madonna*	2·75	2·20
1238	$1 *Madonna of the grand Duke* (Raphael)	3·25	2·75

MS1239 78×103 mm. $2 *The Adoration of the Magi* (Giambattista Tiepolo) 6·50 5·50

190 Green-winged Macaw

2003. Birds. Two sheets containing T **190** and similar multicoloured designs.
MS1240 (a) 179×155 mm. 80c.×4, Type **190**; Greater flamingo (inscr "American flamingo"); Blue and gold macaw; Abyssinian ground hornbill. (b) 62×76 mm. $2 Greater flamingo (inscr "American flamingo") (vert) 18·00 14·50

191 Leopard gecko

2003. Reptiles. Two sheets containing T **191** and similar horiz designs. Multicoloured.
MS1241 (a) 103×81 mm. 80c.×4, Type **191**; Red-eyed tree frog; Panther chameleon; Green and black poison frog. (b) 96×66 mm. $2 Madagascan chameleon 18·00 14·50

192 Australian Shepherd Dog

2003. Dogs and Cats. Four sheets containing T **192** and similar vert designs. Multicoloured.
MS1242 (a) 89×120 mm. 80c.×4, Type **192**; Greyhound; Bulldog; Schnauzer. (b) 96×67 mm. $2 Poodle. (c) 140×164 mm. 80c.×4, Ragdoll; Calico shorthair; Exotic shorthair; Dilute calico. (d) 66×96 mm. $2 Colour point shorthair 35·00 29·00

193 *Moonstruck Gibbon* (Gao Qi-Feng)

2004. New Year. Year of the Monkey. Multicoloured.

1243	50c. Type **193**	1·80	1·50

MS1244 70×101 mm. $1 *Moonstruck Gibbon* (detail) (30×40 mm) 3·50 2·75

194 Bailey Olter

2004. Bailey Olter (president 1991—1996) Commemoration.

1245	**194**	37c. multicoloured	1·20	1·00

195 Luke Walton

2004. Basketball Players. Multicoloured.

1246	20c. Type **195**	70	55
1247	20c. Dirk Nowitzki	70	55
1248	20c. Vince Carter	70	55

196 *A Young Lady in a Theatrical Costume* (Alexis Grimou)

2004. 300th Anniv of St. Petersburg. Paintings from Hermitage Museum. Multicoloured.

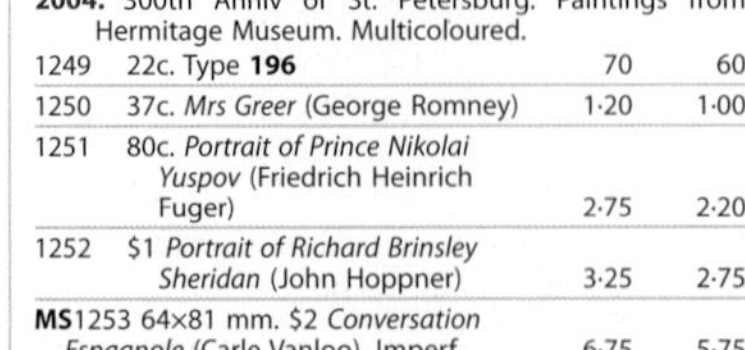

1249	22c. Type **196**	70	60
1250	37c. *Mrs Greer* (George Romney)	1·20	1·00
1251	80c. *Portrait of Prince Nikolai Yuspov* (Friedrich Heinrich Fuger)	2·75	2·20
1252	$1 *Portrait of Richard Brinsley Sheridan* (John Hoppner)	3·25	2·75

MS1253 64×81 mm. $2 *Conversation Espagnole* (Carle Vanloo). Imperf 6·75 5·75

197 *Marie Therese leaning on One Elbow*

2004. 30th Death Anniv (2003) of Pablo Picasso (artist). Multicoloured.

1254-1257	80c.×4, Type **197**; *Portrait of Jaime Sabartes; Portrait of Emmilie Marguerite Walter; Bust of a Woman leaning on One Elbow*	10·00	8·00

MS1258 62×78 mm. $2 *Seated Bather*. Imperf 6·75 5·75

198 Landing Craft

2004. 60th Anniv of D-Day (the Normandy invasion). Multicoloured.

1259-1264	50c.×6, Type **198**; Thompson (destroyer); Vehicles disembarking; Rhino ferry 2 and Rhino tug 3; HMS *Mauritius*; *Arkansas* (battleship)	9·25	7·50

MS1265 97×77 mm. $2 Soldiers seated in landing craft 6·75 5·75

199 Pope John Paul II

2004. 25th Anniv of Pontificate of Pope John Paul II (2003). Sheet 95×117 mm containing T **199** and similar horiz designs. Multicoloured.
MS1266 80c.×4, Type **199** (visit to Mexico); With President and Mrs Clinton; Wearing mitre (visit to Ukraine); Praying (visit to Spain) 10·50 8·75

200 Lars Olsen

2004. European Football Championships, Portugal. Two sheets containing T **200** and similar multicoloured designs.
MS1267 (a) 148×86 mm. 80c.×4, Type **200**; Jurgen Klinsmann; Peter Schmeichel: Nya Ullevi Stadium, Goteburg. (b) 98×85 mm. Denmark team, 1992 Cup Winners (horiz) 14·00 11·50

The stamps and margin of No. **MS**1267a form a composite design.

201 Locomotive RS122

2004. Bicentenary of Steam Locomotives. Multicoloured.

1268-1271	80c.×4, Type **201**; Diesel locomotive class 630; Hitachi monorail, Okinawa; Eurostar	10·00	8·00
1272-1275	80c.×4, Locomotive CFL N5520; inscr "Inter region trains"; Locomotive SW 600; Locomotive WSOR 3801	10·00	8·00
1276-1279	80c.×4, Locomotive Baldwin 280;: Diesel locomotive F 1011114;: inscr "Okinawa Hitachi trains"; Shinkansen (Japanese high-speed train)	10·00	8·00

MS1280 Three sheets. (a) 93×67 mm. $2 Michigan Central locomotive. (b) 93×67 mm. $2 Locomotive 231 065. (c) 66×91 mm. $2 Eurostar (different) 20·00 17·00

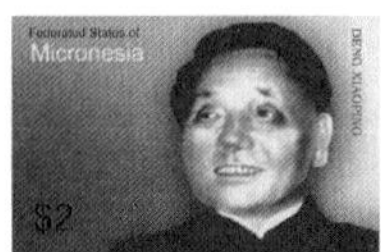

202 Deng Xiaoping

2004. Birth Centenary of Deng Xiaoping (leader of China, 1978—89). Sheet 97×67 mm.

MS1281	**202** $2 multicoloured	6·50	5·50

203 Horseman (bronze statue)

2004. Olympic Games, Athens. Multicoloured.

1282	37c. Type **203**	1·20	95
1283	55c. Athlete (Olympic pin, Stockholm, 1912) (vert)	1·70	1·40
1284	80c. Pierre de Coubertin (founder modern Olympic Games) (vert)	2·50	2·10
1285	$1 Olympic poster, Mexico, 1968 (vert)	3·25	2·75

204 *Aeschnanthus*

2004. Flora and Fauna. Eight sheets containing T **204** and similar multicoloured designs.

MS1286 (a) 100×142 mm. Flowers. 55c.×6, Type **204**; *Darwinia collina*; *Rhododendron*; *Rhododendron retusum*; *Eucryphia lucida*; *Microporus xanthopus*. (b) 136×96 mm. Fish and Coral. 55c.×6, Clown triggerfish (*Balistoides conspicillum*); Masked unicornfish (*Naso lituratus*); *Nemateleotris magnifica*; Longnosed hawkfish (*Oxycirrhites typus*); *Annella mollis*; *Dendronephthya*. (c) 96×137 mm. Reptiles and amphibians. 55c.×6, *Maticora bivirgata*; *Ceratobatrachus guentheri*; *Sphenodon punctatus*; *Draco volans*; *Platymantis vitiensis*; *Candoia carinata*. (d) 94×126 mm. Birds. 55c.×6, *Artamus cinereus* (vert); Brown booby (*Sula leucogaster*) (vert); Rainbow lorry (*Trichoglossus haematodus*) (vert); Wandering albatross (*Diomedea exulans*) (vert); Kagu (*Rhynochetos jubatus*) (vert); Great frigate bird (*Fregata minor*) (vert). (e) 67×93 mm. Flowers. $2 Grevillea. (f) 97×67 mm. Fish. Great barracuda (*Sphyrna barracuda*). (g) 68×94 mm. Reptiles. $2 *Caretta caretta*. (h) 64×92 mm. Birds. $2 Golden whistler (*Pachycephala pectoralis*) 65·00 55·00

The stamps and margins of **MS**1286a/h, respectively, form composite designs.

205 Nelson Mandela

2004. United Nations International Year of Peace. Multicoloured.

1287-1289	80c.×3, Type **205**; Dalai Lama; Pope John Paul II	7·50	6·00

206 Elvis Presley

2004. 50th Anniv of "That's alright Mama" (record by Elvis Presley). Showing Elvis Presley. Multicoloured.

1290-1293	80c.×4, Type **206**; Wearing dark shirt; Smiling; Facing left	10·00	8·00
MS1294	112×148 mm. 80c.×4, Bearded (*Charro*) (horiz); Wearing boxing gloves (*Kid Galaghad*) (horiz); Wearing Arab headdress (*Harum Scarum*) (horiz); Wearing hat	10·00	8·50

The stamps and margin of No. **MS**1294 form a composite design.

207 Herman Crespo (Argentina) (image scaled to 56% of original size)

2004. Centenary of FIFA (Federation Internationale de Football Association). Two sheets containing T **207** and similar horiz designs showing players. Multicoloured.

MS1295	(a) 193×97 mm. 80c.×4, Type **207**; Peter Shilton (England); Klaus Augenthaler (Germany); Bryan Robson (England). (b) 108×87 mm. $2 Ruud Gullit (Holland)	17·00	14·00

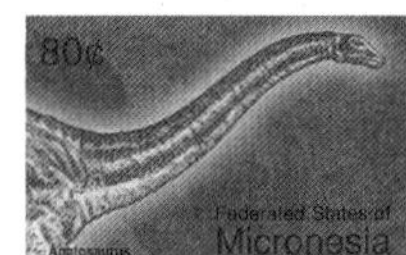

208 Apatosaurus

2004. Prehistoric Animals. Six sheets containing T **208** and similar multicoloured designs.

MS1296	(a) 143×113 mm. 80c.×4, Type **208**; Pachyrinosaurus; Kentosaurus; Saltosaurus. (b) 112×144 mm. 80c.×4, Allosaurus (vert); Tyrannosaurus (vert); Troodon (vert); Carnotaurus (vert). (c) 113×128 mm. 80×4, Indricotheres; Hyaenodons; Deinotherium; Chalicotheres. (d) 102×71 mm. $2 Deinonychus. (e) 103×71 mm. $2 Coelophysis. (f) 71×102 mm. $2 Moeritherium	50·00	41·00

209 *Madonna of the Goldfinch* (Giovanni Battista Tiepolo)

2004. Christmas. Multicoloured.

1297	37c. Type **209**	1·20	95
1298	60c. *Madonna and Child* (Raphael)	1·90	1·60
1299	80c. *Madonna and Child* (Jan Gossaert de Mabuse) (inscr "Gossart")	2·50	2·10
1300	$1 *Madonna and Child with Angels* (Fra Filippo Lippi)	3·25	2·75
MS1301	76×107 mm. $2 *Madonna and child* (modern painting)	6·50	5·25

210 Rooster

2005. New Year. Year of the Rooster.

1302	**210** 50c. multicoloured	1·70	1·40

211 Ronald Reagan and Prime Minister Margaret Thatcher

2005. Ronald Reagan (USA president) Commemoration. Multicoloured.

1303	55c. Type **211**	1·70	1·40
1304	55c. Ronald Reagan and Israeli Prime Minister Yitzchak Shamir	1·70	1·40

212 Elvis Presley

2005. 70th Birth Anniv of Elvis Presley (entertainer). Multicoloured.

1305	60c. Type **212**	1·90	1·60
1306	60c. With backing singers	1·90	1·60
1307	60c. With arm outstretched	1·90	1·60
1308	60c. Seated with guitar	1·90	1·60
1309	60c. Facing right	1·90	1·60
1310	60c. Facing left	1·90	1·60
1311	60c. Holding acoustic guitar	1·90	1·60
1311b	60c. Wearing army uniform	1·90	1·60
1311c	60c. In swimming pool	1·90	1·60
1311d	60c. With guitar facing left	1·90	1·60
1311e	60c. Wearing flying helmet	1·90	1·60
1311f	60c. Wearing suit and hat	1·90	1·60

213 *Evening of Battle* (W. J. Huggins)

2005. Bicentenary of Battle of Trafalgar. Multicoloured.

1312	37c. Type **213**	1·20	95
1313	55c. *Destruction of L' Orient* (George Arnauld)	1·70	1·40
1314	80c. *Surrender of Santissima Trinidad* (painting)	2·50	2·10
1315	$1 *Captain attacking Spanish Ship* (Sir William Allan)	3·25	2·75
MS1316	86×122 mm. $2 *Death of Nelson* (painting)	6·50	5·50

214 US Soldiers in Ireland

2005. 60th Anniv of End of World War II. Multicoloured.

1317-1321	60c.×5, Type **214**; British troops, Italy (1943); Hawker Typhoon, Rhine (1944); Aftermath of Remagen Bridge, Germany attack (1944); Russian and American soldiers, Germany (1945) (VE day—8 May 1945)	8·00	8·00
1322-1326	60c.×5, "These Colours won't Run" (poster); Chula beach; Paul Tibbets and Enola Gay (aircraft); Atomic cloud (Hiroshima); "PEACE" (headline) (VJ day—15 August 1945)	8·00	8·00

215 Friedrich Von Schiller

2005. Death Bicentenary of Friedrich Von Schiller (writer). Multicoloured.

1327-1329	$1×3, Type **215**; Friedrich Von Schiller (statue); With head resting on hand	8·75	7·50
MS1330	53×76 mm. $2 Facing right margin	6·50	5·50

216 Air Balloon (*Around the World in Eighty Days*)

2005. Death Centenary of Jules Verne (writer). Two sheets containing T **216** and similar multicoloured designs.

MS1331	105×133 mm. $1×3, Type **216**; Phileas (inscr "Phineas") Fogg in India; Phileas (inscr "Phineas") Fogg	9·50	7·75
MS1332	108×101 mm. $2 *Nautilus* (*20000 Leagues under the Sea*) (horiz)	6·50	5·50

217 Papyrus Boat

2005. Boats. Two sheets containing T **217** and similar horiz designs. Multicoloured.

MS1333	203×173 mm. 37c. Type **217**; 55c. Outrigger canoe; 80c. Papyrus sail boat; $1 Dhow	8·75	7·25
MS1334	89×101 mm. $2 Nile riverboat	6·50	5·50

218 Grey Nurse Shark

2005. EXPO 2005, Aichi, Japan. Multicoloured.

1335-1338	80c.×4, Type **218**; Surfer; Volcano; Coral	9·00	7·50

219 Pope John Paul II

2005. Pope John Paul II Commemoration.

1339	**219** $1 multicoloured	3·25	2·75

220 Building Entrance

2005. Government Building, Kosrae. Multicoloured.

1340	4c. Type **220**	25	15
1341	10c. Rear of building	40	30
1342	22c. Type **220**	80	65
1343	37c. As No. 1341	1·20	1·00

221 Child

2005. Centenary of Rotary International. Two sheets containing T **221** and similar multicoloured designs.

MS1344	139×110 mm. $1×3, Type **221**; Emblem; Glenn Estess (president 2004—5)	9·50	8·00
MS1345	100×70 mm. $2 Bhicai Rattakul (president 2002—3) (horiz)	6·50	5·50

222 1939 75c. Vatican City Stamp

2005. Vacant See.

1346	**222** 37c. multicoloured	1·20	1·00

223 *Dichrometra flagellate*

2005. Corals. Multicoloured.

1347-1350	50c.×4, Type **223**; *Alloecocomatella polycladia*; *Oxycomanthus bennetti*; *Stephanometra echinus*	5·75	4·75

2005. 50th Death Anniv of Albert Einstein (physicist). Multicoloured.

1351-1354	$1×4 Type **224**; In middle age; In front of blackboard; As older man	11·50	10·00

225 Mother feeding Child

2005. Karat Banana. Multicoloured.

1355	4c. Type **225**	25	15
1356	10c. Different varieties	40	30
1357	22c. Bunch	80	65
1358	37c. Growing on plant	1·20	1·00

226 *Tecoma stans*

2005. Flowers. Multicoloured.

1359	4c. *Tecoma stans*	25	15
1360	10c. *Ipomoea fistulosa*	40	30
1361	22c. *Hibiscus rosa-sinensis*	80	65
1362	37c. *Gerbera jamesonii*	1·20	1·00
1363	80c. *Helianthus annuus*	1·70	1·40
1364	80c. *Tapeinochilos ananassae*	2·75	2·30
1365	80c. *Bauhinia monandra*	2·75	2·30
1366	80c. *Galphima gracilis*	2·75	2·30
1367	80c. *Hibiscus rosa-sinensis*	2·75	2·30
1368	$1 *Ixora casei*	3·25	2·75
MS1369	60×54 mm. $2 *Helianthus annuus*	6·75	5·75
MS1369a	60×54 mm. $2 *Phinia variegata*	6·75	5·75

227 Hans Christian Andersen

2005. Birth Bicentenary of Hans Christian Andersen. Multicoloured.

1370	80c. Type **227**	2·75	2·30
1371	80c. Statue	2·75	2·30
1372	80c. Bust	2·75	2·30
MS1373	70×100 mm. $2 Statue (different)	6·75	5·75

228 Pope Benedict XVI

2005. Pope Benedict XVI.

1374	**228**	80c. multicoloured	2·75	2·30

229 *Kanigani Madonna* (Raphael)

2005. Christmas. Multicoloured.

1375	37c. Type **229**	1·30	1·10
1376	60c. *Madonna with the Fish* (detail) (Raphael)	2·00	1·70
1377	80c. *The Holy Family* (Bartolome Esteban Murillo)	2·75	2·30
1378	$1 *Madonna with the Book* (detail) (Raphael) (inscr "Rapha")	3·25	2·75
MS1379	66×96 mm. $2 *The Holy Family* (Bartolome Esteban Murillo) (different)	6·75	5·75

230 *Wolf Dog* (sitting) (Liu Jiyou)

2006. New Year. Year of the Dog. Multicoloured.

1380	50c. Type **230**	1·70	1·40
MS1381	100×70 mm. $1 *Wolf Dog* (lying down) (Liu Jiyou) (51×37 mm.)	3·50	3·00

231 Petrus Tun

2006. Petrus Tun (vice-president) Commemoration.

1382	**231**	39c. multicoloured	1·40	1·10

233 *Saskia as Flora* (detail)

2006. 400th Birth Anniv of Rembrandt Harmenszoon van Rijn. Multicoloured.

1388	$1 Type **233**	3·25	2·75
1389	$1 *Girl with Broom* (detail)	3·25	2·75
1390	$1 *Young Girl at Window* (detail)	3·25	2·75
1391	$1 *Prodigal Son at the Tavern* (detail)	3·25	2·75
MS1392	70×100 mm. $2 *Man in Oriental Costume* (detail). Imperf	6·50	5·50

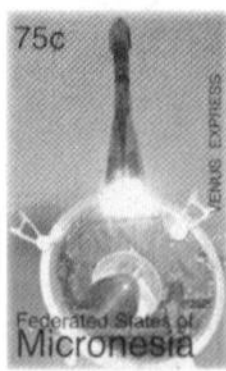

234 Rocket (Venus Express mission)

2006. Space Exploration. Multicoloured. (a) Venus Express Mission.

1393	75c. Type **234**	2·50	2·10
1394	75c. Probe in orbit (blue fins)	2·50	2·10
1395	75c. Probe above Venus (red fins)	2·50	2·10
1396	75c. Probe above Venus	2·50	2·10
1397	75c. Probe (soft focus)	2·50	2·10
1398	75c. Probe (vertical)	2·50	2·10

(b) Return of Space Shuttle *Discovery*.

1399	$1 *Discovery* (horiz)	3·25	2·75
1400	$1 Earth from space (horiz)	3·25	2·75
1401	$1 Shuttle showing solar array (horiz)	3·25	2·75
1402	$1 Shuttle fins (horiz)	3·25	2·75

(c) Project Prometheus.

1403	$1 Spacecraft (Future trip to the Moon) (horiz)	3·25	2·75
1404	$1 Moon and spacecraft (Future trip to the Moon) (horiz)	3·25	2·75
1405	$1 Projectile (Future trip to Mars) (horiz)	3·25	2·75
1406	$1 Spacecraft (Future trip to Mars) (horiz)	3·25	2·75
MS1407	68×98 mm. $2 Space walk (Return of Space Shuttle *Discovery*)	6·50	5·50
MS1408	Two sheets, each 98×68 mm. (a) $2 Mars Reconnaissance Orbiter. (b) $2 *Stardust* Spacecraft	13·00	11·00

Nos. 1405/6 were issued together, *se-tenant*, forming a composite design.

235 *Papilio euchenor*

2006. Butterflies. Multicoloured.

1409	1c. Type **235**	15	15
1410	2c. *Troides aeacus*	15	15
1411	4c. *Delias henningia*	20	15
1412	5c. *Bassarona duda*	25	15
1413	10c. *Graphium sarpedon*	40	30
1414	19c. *Arhopala cleander*	70	55
1415	20c. *Arhopala argentea*	75	65
1416	22c. *Danaus aspasia*	1·10	90
1417	75c. *Arhopala aurea*	2·50	2·10
1418	84c. *Caleta mindarus*	2·75	2·40
1419	$1 *Hyplycaena danis*	3·25	2·75
1420	$4.05 *Jacona amrita*	13·50	11·00
1420a	$5 *Jamides abdul*	17·00	14·00
1420b	$10 Inscr *Para lascita lacoon*	33·00	28·00

236 Tree

2006. Christmas. Multicoloured.

1421	22c. Type **236**	80	65
1422	24c. Stocking	85	70
1423	39c. Snowman	1·30	1·10
1424	75c. Candle	2·50	2·10
1425	84c. Bauble	2·75	2·30

237 In Flight

2006. Concorde. Multicoloured.

1426	75c. Type **237**	2·50	2·10
1427	75c. On ground	2·50	2·10

238 Marilyn Monroe

2007. 80th Birth Anniv of Marilyn Monroe. Multicoloured.

1428	$1 Type **238**	3·25	2·75
1429	$1 Blowing kiss	3·25	2·75
1430	$1 Wearing beret	3·25	2·75
1431	$1 Facing left	3·25	2·75

239 '100'

2007. Centenary of Scouting. Multicoloured.

1432	$1 Type **239**	3·25	2·75
MS1433	80×110 mm. $2 Scouts and flag (37×51 mm)	6·50	5·50

240 Wolfgang Mozart

2007. 250th Birth Anniv of Wolfgang Amadeus Mozart (composer). Sheet 100×70 mm.

MS1434	$2 multicoloured	6·50	5·50

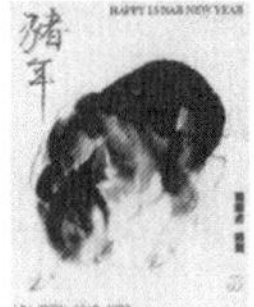

241 Pig (painting by Liu Jiyou)

2007. New Year. Year of the Pig.

1435	**241**	75c. multicoloured	2·75	2·20

242 Pope Benedict XVI

2007. 80th Birth Anniv of Pope Benedict XVI.

1436	**242**	50c. multicloured	1·70	1·40

243 Diana, Princess of Wales

2007. Diana, Princess of Wales Commemoration. Multicoloured.

1437	90c. Type **243**	3·00	2·50
1438	90c. Wearing blue ruffled dress	3·00	2·50
1439	90c. Wearing gold dress and jacket	3·00	2·50
1440	90c. Wearing tiara and yellow dress	3·00	2·50
MS1441	100×70 mm. $3 Diana, Princess of Wales	6·50	5·50

244 Queen Elizabeth II and Prince Philip on Maundy Thursday

2007. 60th Wedding Anniversary of Queen Elizabeth II and Prince Philip. Multicoloured.

1442	60c. Type **244**	2·00	1·70
1443	60c. At state opening of Parliament	2·00	1·70
1444	60c. As Type **244** (white border)	2·00	1·70
1445	60c. As No. 1443 (white border)	2·00	1·70
1446	60c. As Type **244** (violet border)	2·00	1·70
1447	60c. As No. 1443 (violet border)	2·00	1·70

245 Utim was

2007. Bananas. Multicoloured.

1448	22c. Type **245**	70	60
1449	26c. Utin lap	85	70
1450	41c. Mangat	1·40	1·10
1451	58c. Ipali	2·00	1·60
1452	80c. Daiwang	2·75	2·30
1453	90c. Akadhn Weitahta (horiz)	3·00	2·50
1454	$1.14 Peleu	3·75	3·25
1455	$4.60 Utin Kerenis	15·00	12·50

246 Elvis Presley

2007. 30th Death Anniv of Elvis Presley. Multicoloured.

1456	75c. Type **246**	2·50	2·10
1457	75c. Wearing short sleeved shirt	2·50	2·10
1458	75c. Wearing striped jacket	2·50	2·10
1459	75c. Wearing brown shirt	2·50	2·10
1460	75c. Wearing collarless jacket	2·50	2·10
1461	75c. Wearing light grey jacket	2·50	2·10
1462	75c. Wearing check shirt (38×50 mm)	2·50	2·10
1463	75c. Seated with guitar facing left (38×50 mm)	2·50	2·10
1464	75c. Seated with guitar facing right (38×50 mm)	2·50	2·10
1465	75c. As No. 1464 (green) (38×50 mm)	2·50	2·10
1466	75c. As No. 1463 (brown) (38×50 mm)	2·50	2·10
1467	75c. As No. 1462 (lilac) (38×50 mm)	2·50	2·10

247 *Oxycirrhites typus*

2007. Fish. Two sheets containing T **247** and similar vert designs. Multicoloured.

MS1468	131×108 mm. 90c.×4, Type **247**; *Canthigaster compressa*; *Chaetodon ornatissimus*; *Oxymonacanthus longirostris*	12·00	10·00
MS1469	70×100 mm. $2 *Parupeneus multifasciatus*	6·50	5·50

247a *Plumeria rubra*

2007. Flowers. Two sheets containing T **247a** and similar vert designs. Multicoloured.

MS1470	132×98 mm. 90c.×4, Type **247a**; *Plumeria rubra; Lilium candidum; Hedychium flavescens*	12·00	10·00
MS1471	100×70 mm. $2 *Bouganvillea glabra*	10·50	8·75

248 Yap State Peace Corps Emblem

2007. 40th Anniv of Peace Corps in Micronesia. Sheet 108×131 mm containing T **248** and similar horiz designs. Multicoloured.

MS1472	90c.×4, Type **248**; Kosrae State emblem; Volunteer and students, Pohnpei State; Stick fighting, Chuuk State	12·00	10·00

249 African Penguin

2007. International Polar Year. Penguins. Two sheets containing T **249** and similar vert designs showing penguins. Multicoloured.

MS1473	178×126 mm. 75c.×6, Type **249**; Emperor; Galapagos; Humboldt; Magellanic; Rockhopper	17·00	14·00
MS1474	100×70 mm. $3.50 Gentoo	12·00	9·75

250 Gerald Ford

2007. Gerald Ford Commemoration. Sheet 170×100 mm containing T **250** and similar vert designs. Multicoloured.

MS1475	$1×6, Type **250**; Seated reading; As Vice President with Richard Nixon, standing; In conversation with Richard Nixon; With Mrs Betty Ford; Signing Richard Nixon's pardon	11·00	9·00

251 Red Cross Workers

2007. Ninth Anniv of Micronesia Red Cross Society. Sheet 131×108 mm containing T **251** and similar horiz designs. Multicoloured.

MS1476	90c×4, Type **251**; Women and damaged house; Teaching resuscitation techniques; Distributing aid	7·00	5·75

252 Scottish Fold Cat

2007. Cats. Multicoloured.

1477	22c. Type **252**	1·10	90
1478	26c. Inscr 'Munchkin'	1·90	1·60
1479	41c. Inscr 'Abyssinian'	2·10	1·80
1480	90c. Somali (horiz)	4·75	4·00
MS1481	70×100 mm. $2 Inscr 'Blue Silver Shaded Tiffanie' (28×43 mm)	6·50	5·50

253a Mother Church, Pohnpei

2007. Churches. Multicoloured.

1481a	22c. Type **253a**	80	65
1481b	26c. St Mary's church, Yap (horiz)	90	75
1481c	41c. Sapore Bethesda Church, Fefan, Chuuk (horiz)	3·00	2·50
1481d	90c. Lelu Congregational Church, Kosrae (horiz)	3·00	2·50

It has been reported that stamps were issued on:
11 January 2007 for Ludwig Durr Commemoraton.
12 June 2008 for Elvis Presley Commemoration.

254 FA 223 Drache Transport Helicopter

2007. Centenary of First Helicopter Flight. Sheet 100×70 mm.

MS1482	**254** $2.50 multicoloured	8·25	7·00

255 Yacht

2007. Valencia, 32nd Americas Cup. Designs showing yacht sails. Multicoloured, country name panel colour given.

1483	26c. Type **255**	90	75
1484	80c. Sails (vermilion)	2·75	2·30
1485	$1.14 Sails (yellow)	3·75	3·25
1486	$2 Sails (orange)	6·50	5·50

256 John F. Kennedy

2008. John F. Kennedy (president, 1961–1963) Commemoration. Multicoloured.

1487	90c. Type **256**	3·00	2·50
1488	90c. Facing front head raised	3·00	2·50
1489	90c. Facing front	3·00	2·50
1490	90c. At microphone facing left	3·00	2·50

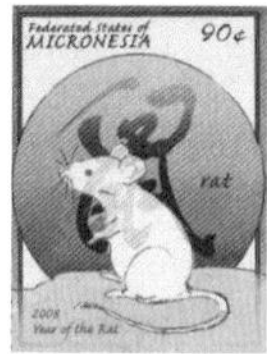
256a Rat

2008. Chinese New Year. Year of the Rat.

1490a	**256a** 90c. multicoloured	3·00	2·50

256b 1904 St Louis World Fair Poster

2008. History of the Olympic Games. St Louis-1904. Sheet 178×102 mm containing T **256b** and similar vert designs. Multicoloured.

MS1490b	50c.×4, Type **256b**; 1904 Olympic Games World Fair poster; Jim Lightbody-track gold medalist; Martin Sheridan-discus gold medalist	6·50	5·50

257 Woman (As USA Type **2342**)

2008. Breast Cancer Awareness Campaign. Sheet 100×70 mm.

MS1491	**257** $2 multicoloured	6·50	5·50

258 Panavia Tornado

2008. 90th Anniv of Royal Air Force. Sheet 136×110 mm containing T **258** and similar horiz designs. Multicoloured.

MS1492	90c.×4, Type **258**; Hawker Siddley Harrier; Eurofighter EF-2000 Typhoon; British Aerospace Hawk	12·00	10·00

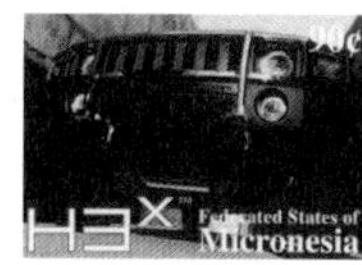
259 Hummer

2008. Hummer H3. Design showing vehicles. Multicoloured.

1493	90c. Type **259**	3·00	2·50
1494	90c. Side view	3·00	2·50
1495	90c. Front grill	3·00	2·50
1496	90c. Rear view	3·00	2·50
MS1497	100×70 mm. $2 On track	6·50	5·50

260 Entrance to the City of David (image scaled to 44% of original size)

2008. World Stamp Championship, Israel. Sheet 110×100 mm.

MS1498	**260** $3 multicoloured	10·00	8·25

260a Amare Stoudemire

2008. Baseball. Phoenix Suns. Designs showing players. Multicoloured.

1498a	42c. Type **260a**	1·30	1·10
1498b	42c. Boris Diaw	1·30	1·10
1498c	42c. Brian Skinner	1·30	1·10
1498d	42c. D. J. Strawberry	1·30	1·10
1498e	42c. Shaquille O'Neal	1·30	1·10
1498f	42c. Grant Hill	1·30	1·10
1498g	42c. Leandro Barbosa	1·30	1·10
1498h	42c. Raja Bell	1·30	1·10
1498i	42c. Steve Nash	1·30	1·10

261 USS *Enterprise*

2008. Star Trek (television series). Multicoloured.

1499	75c. Type **261**	2·50	2·10
1500	75c. Spock (Leonard Nimoy)	2·50	2·10
1501	75c. Captain Kirk (William Shatner)	2·50	2·10
1502	75c. Uhuru (Nichelle Nichols) and Chekov (Walter Koenig)	2·50	2·10
1503	75c. Starbase II	2·50	2·10
1504	75c. Dr. McCoy (DeForest Kelley)	2·50	2·10
MS1505	178×127 mm. Size 37×51 mm. 94c.×4, Scotty (James Doohan); Captain Kirk; Dr. McCoy and Uhuru; Chekov	12·50	10·50

The stamps and margins of No. **MS**1505 form a composite design.

262 Muhammad Ali

2008. Muhammad Ali. Two sheets, each 179×126 mm, containing T **262** and similar multicoloured designs showing Muhammad Ali.

MS1506	75c.×6, Type **262**; Adjusting helmet; Facing right; Facing right, head lowered; Facing left; Bandaging hands	15·00	12·50
MS1507	Size 37×51 mm. 94c.×4, Left hook; Left hook facing opponent; Facing left showing gum shield; Receiving punch to abdomen	12·50	10·50

The stamps of Nos. **MS**1507 share a common background.

263 Pope Benedict XVI and Papal Arms

2008. Pope Benedict XVI's visit to USA. Sheet 178×127 mm containing T **263** and similar vert designs. Multicoloured.

MS1508	94c.×4, Type **263**; As Type **263**, arms lower left; As Type **263**, arms upper right; As Type **263**, arms upper left	12·50	10·50

The stamps of No. **MS**1508 form a composite design.

264 Ioanis Artui

2008. Leaders of Micronesia. Multicoloured.

1509	94c. Type **264**	3·25	2·75
1510	94c. Eluel K. Pretrick	3·25	2·75

265 Angel

2008. Christmas. Tree decorations. Multicoloured.

1511	22c. Type **265**	70	60
1512	27c. Star	90	75
1513	42c. Cross	1·40	1·10
1514	94c. Mobile	3·25	2·75

266 Barack Obama

2009. Inauguration of Barack Hussein Obama as President of USA. Sheet 178×126 containing T **266** and similar vert designs showing President Obama. Multicoloured.

MS1515	42c. Type **266**; 42c. Facing left; 42c. Smiling facing left; 75c. Smiling facing left; 75c. Facing left; 75c. As Type **266**	11·50	9·75

Nos. 1516/19 and Type **267** are left for Marilyn Monroe issued on 22 January 2009 not yet received.

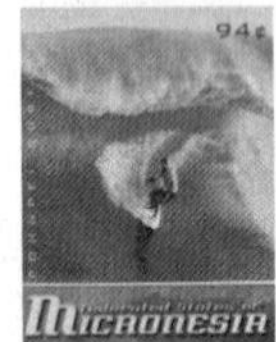

268 Surfer

2009. Surfing. Designs showing surfers. Multicoloured.

1520	94c. Type **268**	3·25	2·75
1521	$1.17 Surfer wearing white t-shirt	3·75	3·25
1522	$4.80 Surfer wearing dark long sleeved t-shirt	16·00	13·00

Nos. 1523/34 are left for additions to this set.

Nos. 1535/6 and Type **269** are left for Year of the Ox issued on 26 January 2009 not yet received.

Nos. 1537 and Type **270** are left for Paeony issued on 10 April 2009 not yet received.

Nos. 1538/41 and Type **271** are left for China 2009 (1st issue) issued on 10 April 2009 not yet received.

272 Emperor Taizong

2009. China 2009 International Stamp Exhibition, Luoyang. Emperor Taizong–Second Tang Dynasty. Multicoloured.

1542	59c. Type **272**	2·00	1·60
1543	59c. With wives	2·00	1·60
1544	59c. Calligraphy	2·00	1·60
1545	59c. Emperor Taizong (mural, Dunhuang)	2·00	1·60

273 Elvis Presley

2009. 40th Anniv of *Change of Habit* (film starring Elvis Presley). Four sheets containing vert designs as T **273** showing Elvis Presley. Multicoloured.

MS1546	125×90 mm. $2.50 Type **273**	8·25	7·00
MS1547	91×126 mm. $2.50 Wearing open necked shirt	8·25	7·00
MS1548	90×125 mm. $2.50 As doctor	8·25	7·00
MS1549	125×90 mm. $2.50 Poster for film	8·25	7·00

2009. Michael Jackson Commemoration. Multicoloured.

MS1549a	160×116 mm. 28c.×2, Wearing gold, facing right; Wearing jacket with epaulettes. 75c.×2, Wearing gold, facing right; Wearing jacket with epaulettes	6·50	5·25
MS1549b	120×160 mm. 28c.×2, Wearing gold, facing left; Wearing white, facing right. 75c.×2, Wearing gold, facing left; Wearing white, facing right	6·50	5·25

2009. 40th Anniv of Manned Moon Landing. Multicoloured.

MS1549c	175×120 mm. 75c.×6, *Apollo 11* and flag; Neil Armstrong; Bust of Neil Armstrong (Paula Slater); *Apollo 11* command module; *Apollo 11* in flight; Buzz Aldrin moonwalk	13·50	11·50
MS1549d	150×110 mm. 98c.×4, *Apollo 11*, command and lunar modules; *Apollo 11* command module; Neil Armstrong, head and shoulders; Silicon disc	12·00	10·00

2009. Fish. Multicoloured.

1549e	22c. *Acanthurus leucosternon*	70	55
1549f	28c. *Premnas biaculeatus*	90	75
1549g	61c. *Centropyge loriculus*	1·80	1·50
1549h	78c. *Thalassoma lunare*	2·50	2·10
1549i	$1.24 *Pygoplites diacanthus*	3·25	2·75
1549j	$2.30 *Nemateleotris magnifica*	6·50	5·25
MS1549k	120×150 mm. 94c.×4, *Balistoides conspicillum; Polyprionidae; Nemateleotris decora; Paracanthurus hepatus*	11·50	9·75

2009. Dolphins. Multicoloured.

1549l	22c. Indo-Pacific Bottle-nose Dolphin (*Tursiops aduncus*)	70	55
1549m	88c. Chinese White Dolphin (*Sousa chinensis chinensis*)	2·40	2·00
1549n	95c. Southern Right Whale Dolphin (*Lissodelphis peronii*)	2·75	2·30
1549o	$2.80 Northern Right Whale Dolphin (*Lissodelphis borealis*)	8·75	7·25
MS1549p	115×145 mm. Vert. 75c.×6, Bottle-nose Dolphin (*Tursiops truncatus*); Costero (*Sotalia guianensis*); Tucuxi (*Sotalia fluviatilis*); Short-beaked Dolphin (*Delphinus delphis*); Long-beaked Dolphin (*Delphinus capensis*); Indo-Pacific Humpbacked Dolphin (*Sousa chinensis*)	13·50	11·50

2009. Seashells. Multicoloured.

1549q	22c. *Clea nigericans*	70	55
1549r	79c. *Achatina fulica*	2·40	2·00
1549s	$1.39 *Panamacea canaliculata*	4·25	3·50
1549t	$1.56 *Cyclophorus diplochilus*	4·75	4·00
MS1549u	160×120 mm. 75c.×6, *Thais bitubercularis; Conus caracteristicus; Amphidromus glaucolarynx; Anadara pilula; Cypraea erronea pyriformis; Thais aculeata*	13·50	11·50

2009. Butterflies. Multicoloured.

1549v	28c. *Hebomoia glaucippe*	90	75
1549w	44c. *Talicada nyseus*	1·40	1·10
1549x	98c. *Chilades pandava*	2·75	2·40
1549y	$1.05 *Kaniska canace*	3·25	2·75
MS1549z	160×150 mm. 75c.×6, *Idea iasonia; Papilio memnon; Graphium agamemnon; Papilio polymnestor; Nissanga patnia; Pachliopta jophon*	13·50	11·50

2009. Coral. Multicoloured.

1549za	27c. *Sinularia dura*	90	75
1549zb	55c. *Scleronephthya*	1·80	1·50
1549zc	83c. *Discosoma*	2·40	2·00
1549zd	$1.14 *Oxypora lacera*	2·00	1·60
MS1549ze	160×150 mm. Vert. 98c.×4, *Lobophytum; Nara nematifera; Leuconia palaoensis; Dendronephthya*	12·00	10·00
MS1549zf	102×72 mm. Vert. 98c.×2, *Sarcophyton; Echinopora lamellosa*	6·00	5·00

274 Brown Booby (*Sula leucogaster*)

2009. Birds of the Pacific. Multicoloured.

1550	28c. Type **274**	1·00	80
1551	44c. Sacred kingfisher (*Todirampus sanctus*)	1·50	1·20
1552	98c. White faced heron (*Egretta novaelhollandiae*)	3·25	2·75
1553	$1.05 Rainbow lorikeet (*Trichoglossus haematodus*)	3·50	3·00
MS1554	100×130 mm. All horiz. 98c.×4, Brandt's cormorant (*Phalacrocorax pencillatus*); Red footed booby (*Sula sula*); Beach thick knee (*Esacus giganteus*); Common (brown) noddy (*Anous stolidus*)	13·00	11·00
MS1555	100×70 mm. All horiz. $1.56×2, Blue footed booby (*Sula nebouxii*); Australian pelican (*Pelecanus conspicillatus*)	10·50	8·50

275 Hawksbill Turtle (*Eretmochelys imbricata*)

2009. Turtles of the Pacific. Multicoloured.

1556	22c. Type **275**	80	65
1557	88c. Australian flat back turtle (*Natator depresus*)	3·00	2·40
1558	95c. Loggerhead turtle (*Caretta caretta*)	3·25	2·75
1559	$2.80 Green sea turtle (*Celonia mydas*)	9·25	7·75
MS1560	100×130 mm. 98c.×4, Kemp's Ridley turtle (*Lepidochelys kempi*); Leatherback turtle (*Dermochelys coriacea*); Loggerhead turtle (different); Olive Ridley turtle (*Lepidochelys olivacea*)	13·00	11·00
MS1561	100×70 mm. $1.56×2, Green sea turtle (different); Hawksbill turtle (different)	10·50	8·50

2009. Birth Bicentenary of Abraham Lincoln. Multicoloured.

MS1561a	98c.×4, As young man without beard, facing right; As young man with partial beard, facing left; Older with beard, facing right; Facing left in profile	11·50	9·75

2009. Centenary of Chinese Aviation. Multicoloured.

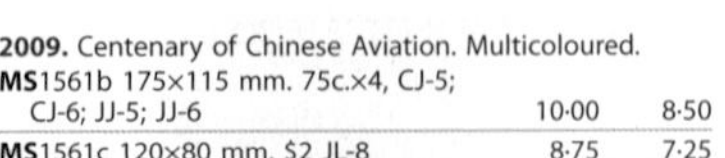

MS1561b	175×115 mm. 75c.×4, CJ-5; CJ-6; JJ-5; JJ-6	10·00	8·50
MS1561c	120×80 mm. $2 JL-8	8·75	7·25

276 Santa and Stylized Palm Tree

2009. Christmas. Multicoloured.

1562	22c. Type **276**	80	65
1563	44c. Baubles	1·50	1·20
1564	98c. Christmas stockings	3·25	2·75
1565	$4.80 Arms of Micronesia and other baubles on tree	16·00	13·50

277 Pope Benedict XVI and Vaclav Klaus (Czech president)

2009. Visit of Pope Benedict XVI to Czech Republic. Sheet 150×100 mm containing T **276** and similar horiz designs. Multicoloured.

MS1566	98c.×4, Type **276**; Pope Bendict XVI; Pope Benedict XVI and Miroslav Vik (Czech cardinal); Pope Benedict XVI wearing green	13·00	11·00

2010. Chinese New Year. Year of the Tiger. Multicoloured.

MS1567	$2×2, Tiger, head; Script	12·00	10·00

279 Charles Darwin

2010. Birth Bicentenary of Charles Darwin. Multicoloured.

MS1569	75c.×6, Type **279**; Modern and early human skulls; Gorilla; The ascent of man from apes; Script; Birds, showing beaks	13·50	11·50

2010. Fifth Death Anniv of Pope John Paul II

1570	75c. Pope John Paul II	2·30	1·90

281 *Galerina decipens*

2010. Fungi. 'Mushrooms of the Micronesia'. Multicoloured.

1571	28c. Type **281**	90	75
1572	44c. *Amanita pekeoides*	1·40	1·10
1573	75c. *Rhodocollybia laulaha*	2·30	1·90
1574	98c. *Amanita nothofagi*	2·75	2·40
MS1575	170×135 mm. 75c.×6, *Hygrocybe minutula; Hygrocybe pakela; Amanita nehuta; Amanita muscaria; Amanita australis; Hygrocybe constrictospara*	13·50	11·50

2010. Tosiwo Nakayama (Founder of the Federated States of Micronesia) Commemoration. Multicoloured.

MS1576	115×150 mm. 80c.×4, Tosiwo Nakayama; Writing wearing spectacles; Wearing short-sleeved shirt; Smiling facing right	9·75	8·25
MS1577	70×100 mm. $2 Wearing dark suit facing left	6·00	5·00

283 Guides

2010. Centenary of Girlguiding. Multicoloured.

MS1578	160×115 mm. Horiz. 94c.×4, Two guides; Two gides, head and shoulders; Three guides wearing red cloaks; Three guides	11·50	9·75
MS1579	70×100 mm. Vert. $2.50 Type **283**	7·50	6·25

2010. Flowers and Fruit. Multicoloured.

1580	1c. Bougainvillea	15	15
1581	2c. Yellow pulmeria	15	15
1582	4c. White ginger	25	20
1583	5c. *Guettardia speciosa*	30	25
1584	10c. Mangat bananas	40	30
1585	19c. Akadahn Weltahta bananas	60	50
1586	20c. Peleu bananas	60	50
1587	22c. Coconuts	70	55
1588	28c. Utin Kerenis bananas	90	75
1589	40c. Coconut	1·20	1·00
1590	44c. Peeled coconut	1·40	1·10
1591	70c. Coconut pieces	2·10	1·80
1592	$1 Cracked coconut	3·00	2·50
1593	$3.85 Cracked coconut (different)	11·50	9·75
1594	$4.60 Soursop	14·00	11·50

1595 $4.80 Soursop (different) 14·50 12·00

2010. British Monarchs. Centenary of Coronation of King George V. Multicoloured.

MS1596 75c.×6, Queen Anne; George I; George II; George III; George IV; George V 13·50 11·50

2010. 500th Death Anniv of Sandro Botticelli. Multicoloured.

MS1597 75c.×6, *Madonna, Child and Two Angels* (detail); *Pallas and Centaur*; *Man with Medallion*; *St Augustine in his Cell*; *Scenes from the Life of Moses* (detail); *Adoration of the Magi* 13·50 11·50

2010. Diana, Princess of Wales Commemoration. Multicoloured.

MS1598 75c.×4, Kissing boy's head; Crouched talking to small girl; Crouched, talking to children; Wearing pink suit 9·00 7·50

2010. Death Centenary of Henri Dunant. Multicoloured.

MS1599 175×120 mm. 94c.×4, Battle and grey-green portrait; Battle and red-brown portrait; Battle and reddish violet portrait; Battle and steel-blue portrait 11·50 9·75

MS1600 70×100 mm. $2.50 Napoleon III 7·50 6·25

2010. 170th Anniv of First Postage Stamp. Multicoloured.

MS1601 $2×2, Victorian One Penny stamp; Map of Micronesia 12·00 10·00

290 *Adoration of the Magi* (Corrado Giaquinto)

2010. Christmas. Multicoloured.

1602 22c. Type **290** 70 55

1603 28c. Polyptych with the Nativity (Rogier van der Weiden) 90 75

1604 44c. *The Nativity* (Federico Barocci) 1·40 1·10

1605 98c. *The New-born Christ* (Georges la Tour) 2·75 2·40

1606 $4.95 *Flight into Egypt* (Giotto de Bondone) 15·00 12·50

291 Pope John Paul II

2010. Fifth Death Anniv of Pope John Paul II

1607 **291** 75c. black 2·30 2·30

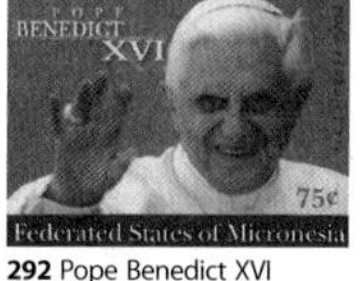

292 Pope Benedict XVI

2010. Fifth Anniv of Pope Benedict XVI's Papacy. Multicoloured.

MS1608 75c.×4, Type **292** and three stamps as Type **292** 10·00 8·25

293 Giving Gettysburg Address

2010. President Abraham Lincoln Commemoration. Multicoloured.

MS1609 75c.×4, Type **293**; With his wife, Mary; Reading draft of Emancipation Proclamation (painting); Seated in tent with General George McCellan at Antietam 10·00 8·25

294 Diego Perez

2010. World Cup Football Championships, South Africa. Multicoloured.

MS1610 Uruguay v Ghana. 61c.×6, Type **294**; Isaac Vorsah; Edigo Arevalo; Kevin-Prince Boateng; Luis Suarez; Kwadwo Asamoah 12·50 10·50

MS1611 Netherlands v Brazil. 61c.×6, Dani Alvez; Dirk Kuyt; Lucio; Gregory Van der Wiel; Robinho; Mark Van Bommel 12·50 10·50

2011. 50th Anniv of Inauguration of President John F Kennedy. Multicoloured.

MS1612 75c.×4, Taking the oath; With hand raised; Standing on podium; With Jaqueline Kennedy 9·00 7·50

2011. Elvis Presley Commemoration. Multicoloured.

MS1613 75c.×4, Smiling; Playing guitar, wearing white; Seated, head and shoulders, holding guitar upright; Standing head and shoulders, playing guitar 9·00 7·50

2011. World Expo 2010, Beijing. Multicoloured.

MS1614 170×100 mm. Three Gorges Dam. 75c.×4, Reservoir; Fountain; Aerial view; Boats and towers 9·00 7·50

MS1615 100×70 mm. Terracotta Warriors. $2 Head of warrior 6·00 5·00

298 Waving

2011. Travels of President Obama. G20 Summit, South Korea. Multicoloured.

MS1616 170×130 mm. Vert. 75c.×4, Type **298**; With Pres. Sarkozy of France; With Pres. Lee Myung-bak of South Korea; With Pres. Medvedev of Russia 10·00 8·25

MS1617 130×170 mm. Horiz. 75c.×4, Pres. Obama; Pres. Lee Myung-bak; Group including Pres. Obama holding certificate; Speaking with flags behind 10·00 8·25

MS1618 is left for sheet not yet received.

2011. Royal Engagement of Prince William to Miss Catherine Middleton. Multicoloured.

MS1619 140×140 mm. 94c.×4, Royal couple, official engagement photographs×2; Coat of Arms×2 11·50 9·75

MS1620 140×140 mm. 94c.×4, Royal couple, Miss Middleton wearing hat, Prince William wearing morning suit×2; Coat of Arms×2 11·50 9·75

MS1621 125×125 mm. $1.50×2, Royal couple, official engagement photographs (different); Coat of Arms 9·00 7·50

MS1622 125×125 mm. $1.50×2, Coat of Arms; Prince William 9·00 7·50

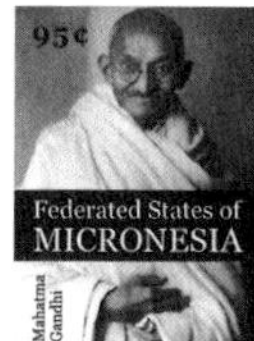

300 Mahatma Gandhi

2011. Mahatma Gandhi, 1869-1948 - International Stamp Exhibition INDIPEX 2011 - New Delhi, India. Each black.

1623 95c. Type **300** 2·75 2·40

MS1624 120×120 mm. $2.50 Praying 7·50 6·25

301 Rabbit

2011. Chinese New Year. Year of the Rabbit. Multicoloured.

MS1625 $1.50×2. Type **301**×2 9·00 7·50

302 Lake Fryxell, Antarctica

2011. Centenary of Roald Admundsen's Expedition to South Pole. Multicoloured.

MS1626 98c.×4, Type **302**; Roald Admundsen; Emperor Penguins; Aurora Australis over Amundsen-Scott Research Station 13·00 11·00

303 CSS *Manassas* attacks USS *Richmond*

2011. 150th Anniv of American Civil War. Multicoloured.

MS1627 Head of Passes, 1861. Commodore G. N. Hollins and Captain John Pope. 98c.×4, Type **303**; USS *Richmond*; CSS *Manassas*; USS *Water Witch* 13·00 11·00

MS1628 Balls Bluff, 1861. Colonel N. G. Evans and General C. P. Stone. 98c.×4, General Stone's forces; Union artillery firing across Potomac River; Battle map; Death of Colonel E. D. Baker 13·00 11·00

304 Abraham Lincoln

2011. 150th Anniv of Civil War. Abraham Lincoln. Multicoloured.

1629 75c. Type **304** 2·50 2·10

MS1630 100×70 mm. Size 38×51 mm. $2.50 Abraham Lincoln seated 8·25 7·00

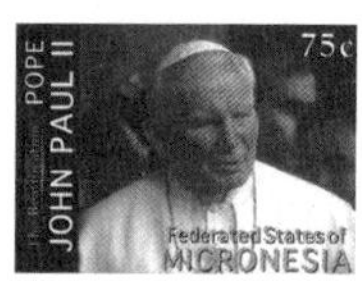

305 Pope John Paul II

2011. Beatification of Pope John Paul II. Multicoloured.

MS1631 180×120 mm. Horiz. 75c.×4, Type **305**; Waving; Pensive; Holding child 10·00 8·25

MS1632 70×100 mm. Vert. $2.50 Giving blessing 8·25 7·00

306 Elvis Presley

2011. Elvis Presley Commemoration. Multicoloured.

MS1633 180×135 mm. Vert. 75c.×6, Type **306**; Head on hand, facing right; With upswept hair, facing left; With sideburns and ornate collar, facing left; As young performer, at microphone, facing right; Older, wearing white and holding microphone, facing left 14·50 12·00

MS1634 180×135 mm. Vert. 75c.×6, Older, with sideburns and ornate jacket, holding acoustic guitar, facing right; Younger, holding acoustic guitar, facing front; Holding twin-necked electric guitar, facing front; Older, wearing white and holding acoustic guitar and microphone, facing left; Younger, holding electric guitar, facing right; Older, wearing white holding microphone with guitar to one side, facing left 14·50 12·00

MS1635 90×125 mm. *Paradise Hawaiian Style*. $2.50 Smiling, face and hands (horiz) 8·25 7·00

MS1636 90×125 mm. *Paradise Hawaiian Style*. $2.50 With Hawaiian girl (vert) 8·25 7·00

MS1637 125×90 mm. *Paradise Hawaiian Style*. $2.50 Poster for *Paradise Hawaiian Style* (vert) 8·25 7·00

MS1638 125×90 mm. *Paradise Hawaiian Style*. $2.50 Serious, face (horiz) 8·25 7·00

307 Princess Diana as Small Child

2011. 50th Birth Anniv of Diana, Princess of Wales. Multicoloured.

MS1639 75c.×4, Type **207**; Wearing pearls and dress with sailor collar, facing left; Wearing red hat and coat, facing right; Wearing beige coat and tam o'shanter, facing front 12·00 10·00

MS1640 75c.×4, Wearing sleeveless blue dress and holding clutch bag, facing right; Wearing white, facing left; Wearing pearls and silver strapeless dress, facing right; Wearing pearl choker and high-necked purple dress, facing left 12·00 10·00

308 Stripe-necked Turtle

2011. Reptiles of Micronesia. Multicoloured.

MS1641 140×110 mm. 50c.×5, Type **308**; Oceanis Gecko; Tropical Gecko; Four-clawed Gecko; Mourning Gecko 8·25 7·00

MS1642 100×70 mm. $1.25×2, Marians Blue-tailed Skink; Green Sea Turtle 8·25 7·00

309 Prince William, Duke of Cambridge

2011. Royal Wedding of Prince William to Miss Catherine Middleton. Multicoloured.

MS1643 175×120 mm. 98c.×4, Type **309**; Duchess of Cambridge, each×2 13·00 11·00

MS1644 175×120 mm. 98c.×4, Kissing×4 13·00 11·00

MS1645 102×70 mm. $2.50 Holding hands 8·25 7·00

310 The Pentagon

2011. Tenth Anniv of '9/11' Terrorist Attacks. Multicoloured.

MS1646 170×110 mm. Vert. 98c.×4, Type **310**; World Trade Centre (left); World Trade Centre (right); Stonycreek TWP, Pennsylvania 13·00 11·00

MS1647 110×70 mm. Horiz. $2.50 World Trade Centre (different) 8·25 7·00

311 Two Team Japan Members

312 Team Japan (image scaled to 32% of original size)

2011. Women's Football World Cup Final, 2011. Multicoloured.

MS1648	150×100 mm. Horiz. 50c.×8, Type **311** forming the overall design Type **312**	13·00	11·00
MS1649	100×150 mm. Vert. 98c.×4, Ayumi Kaihori (goalkeeper, Japan); Team Japan; Team USA; Hope Solo (goalkeeper, USA)	13·00	11·00

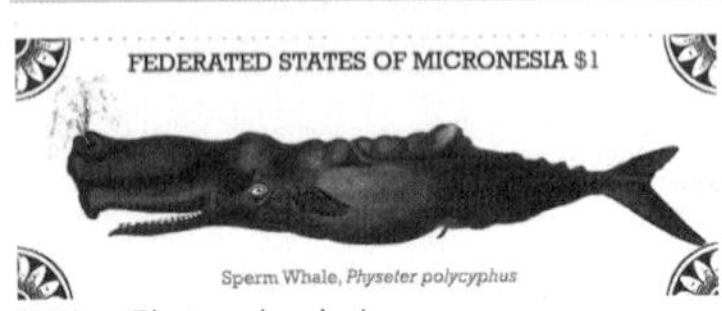

313 Inscr 'Physter polycyphus'

2011. Whales and Whale Watching. Multicoloured.

MS1650	100×160 mm. Horiz. $1×3, Type **313**; Sperm Whale; Sei Whale	10·00	8·50
MS1651	120×100 mm. Size 35×35 mm (circular). $1.25×2, Sperm Whale (tail); Sperm Whale (head)	8·25	7·00

314 Sun Yat-Sen

2011. China 2011, International Stamp Exhibition. Sun Yat-Sen Commemoration. Multicoloured.

MS1652	150×100 mm. 63c.×4, Type **314**; Facing left, each×2	8·50	7·25
MS1653	150×115 mm.63c.×6, As Type **314**, but full size in shades of grey; As 'Facing left', but full size in shades of grey, each×3	13·00	11·00

315 Sharpnose Sevengill Shark

2011. Sharks. Multicoloured.

MS1654	100×170 mm. 75c.×4, Type **315**; Basking Shark; Porbeagle; Bluntnose Sixgill Shark;	10·00	8·50
MS1655	120×80 mm. $2.50 Sand Tiger Shark	8·25	7·00

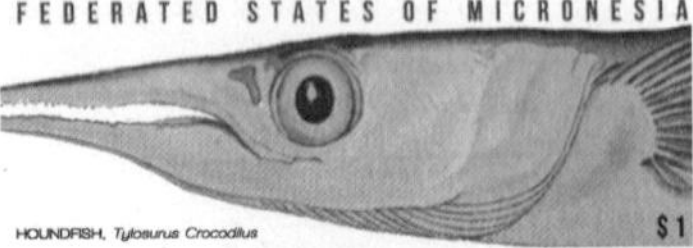

316 Houndfish

2011. Gamefish. Multicoloured.

MS1656	180×120 mm. $1×3, Type **316**; Pacific Agujon Needlefish; Keeltail Needlefish	10·00	8·50
MS1657	120×80 mm. $2.50 Swordfish	8·25	7·00
MS1658	120×80 mm. $2.50 Rainbow Runner	8·25	7·00

317 Pink Anemonefish

2011. Christmas. Multicoloured.

1659	22c. Type **317**	75	65
1660	44c. Perume flower tree (*Fragraea berteriana*)	1·50	1·30
1661	98c. Palm tree and beach	3·25	2·75
1662	$4.95 Conch shell	17·00	14·00

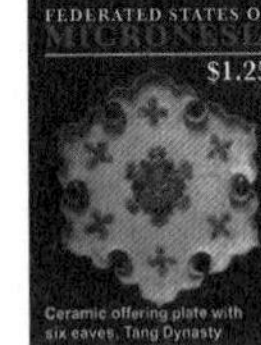

318 Tang Ceramic Offering Plate

2011. Chinese Pottery. Multicoloured.

MS1663	160×100 mm. $1.25×4, Type **318**; Song Dynasty Celadon vase; Ming dynasty porcelain plate; Qing Dynasty porcelain jug	17·00	14·00
MS1664	100×70 mm. $3.50 Ming dynasty blue and white porcelain plate	11·50	9·75

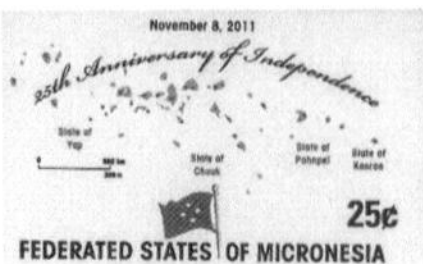

319 Anniversary Emblem

2011. 25th Anniv of Independence

1665	**319** 25c. multicoloured	75	65

320 *Outrigger Canoe* (Arvin Helgenberger)

2011. 50th Anniv of USA Peace Corps. Winning Designs in Children's 'Peace through Friendship' Drawing Competition. Multicoloured.

MS1666	44c.×4, Type **320**; Young couple holding 'Peace through Friendship' poster (Alex Alexander); Landscape with children and 'Peace through Friendship' (Ashly-Ann Alfons); Ship and flag contained in roundel (Leonard Klingen)	6·25	5·25

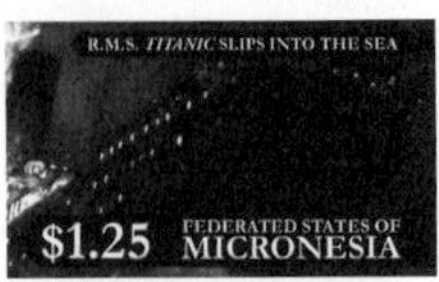

322 *Titanic* slips into the Sea

2012. Centenary of Sinking of *Titanic*. Multicoloured.

MS1668	100×170 mm. $1.25×3, Type **322**; Waiting for survivors; Last known photograph	12·50	10·50
MS1669	70×100 mm. $3.50 Illustration of passengers (vert)	11·50	9·75

323 Princess Elizabeth

2012. 60th Anniv of Accession of Queen Elizabeth II. Multicoloured.

MS1670	180×120 mm. $1.25×4, Type **323**; As girl guide; Working on engine; Wearing ATS uniform facing left	17·00	14·00
MS1671	70×100 mm. $3.50 Wearing uniform head and shoulders (vert)	11·50	9·75

324 Pope Benedict XVI

2012. Pope Benedict XVI. Multicoloured.

MS1672	150×100 mm. $1.25×4, Type **324**×2; Giving blessing×2	17·00	14·00
MS1673	100×70 mm. $3.50 Head and shoulders (vert)	11·50	9·75

325 Ronald Reagan

2012. Birth Centenary (2011) of Ronald Reagan. Multicoloured.

1674	$1.25 Type **325**	4·25	3·50
MS1675	100×100 mm. $3.50 Ronald Reagan (different)	11·50	9·75

326 Mal-shi

2012. Hybrid Dogs. Multicoloured.

MS1676	90×120 mm. $1.25×4, Type **326**; Puggle; Labradoodle; Chiweenie	17·00	14·00
MS1677	100×70 mm. $3.50 Schnoodle	11·50	9·75

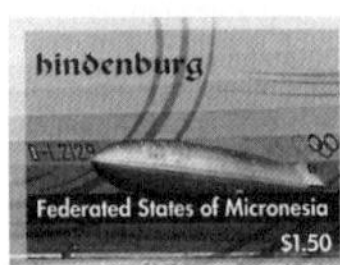

327 *Hindenburg*

2012. 75th Anniv of Hindenburg Disaster. Multicoloured.

MS1678	150×100 mm. Horiz. $1.50 Type **327**; As Type **327**, 'hindenburg' in background; As Type **327**, tower in background	15·00	12·50
MS1679	100×70 mm. $3.50 As Type **327**, nose of airship in background	11·50	9·75

328 Mother Teresa

2012. 15th Death Anniv of Mother Teresa. Multicoloured.

1680	$1.25 Type **328**	4·25	3·50
MS1681	70×100 mm. $3.50 Mother Teresa holding baby	11·50	9·75

329 Sean Hayes as Larry

2012. *The Three Stooges* (film). Multicoloured.

MS1682	100×150 mm. $1×5, Type **329**; Chris Diamantopoulos as Moe; Will Sasso as Curly; Three Stooges; Three Stooges riding tandem	17·00	14·00
MS1683	100×70 mm. $3.50 Threes Stooges, each with left hand to face (horiz)	11·50	9·75

330 Weightlifting

2012. Olympic Games, London. Multicoloured.

MS1684	80c.×4, Type **330**; Archery; Tennis; Equestrian	10·50	9·00

331 Hawksbill Turtle (*Eretmochelys imbricata*)

2012. Endangered Species. Turtles. Multicoloured.

MS1685	105×130 mm. $1.25×4, Type **331**; Leatherback (*Dermochelys coriacea*); Green Sea turtle (*Chelonia mydas*); Olive Ridley (*Lepidochelys olivacea*)	17·00	14·00
MS1686	90×110 mm. $1.25×2, Loggerhead (*Caretta caretta*); Flatback (*Natator depressus*)	8·25	7·00

332 Elvis Presley (*Don't Cry Daddy*)

2012. Elvis Presley - Classic Hits. Multicoloured.

MS1687	$3.50 Type **332**	11·50	9·75
MS1688	$3.50 Elvis holding guitar (*Flaming Star*)	11·50	9·75
MS1689	$3.50 *Heartbreak Hotel*	11·50	9·75
MS1690	$3.50 *Hound Dog*	11·50	9·75
MS1691	$3.50 *Teddy Bear*	11·50	9·75

333 Pitcher Plant (*Nepnthes viellardii*)

2012. Carnivorous Plants. Multicoloured.

MS1692	160×110 mm. Horiz. $1.25×4 Type **333**; Fairy Apron (*Utricularia dichotoma*); Spoon-leaved Sundew (*Drosera spatulata*); Tropical Sundew (*Drosera burmannii*)	17·00	14·00
MS1693	100×70 mm. $1.25×2, Bladderwort (*Utricularia bifida*); Common Swamp Pitcher Plant (*Nepenthes mirabilis*)	8·25	7·00

334 Astronaut walking on Moon

2012. Space Anniversaries. 50th Anniv of President Kennedy announcing 'Man on the Moon' Project (**MS**1694, **MS**1695) or 50th Anniv of Ranger Moon Programme (**MS**1696, **MS**1697). Multicoloured.

MS1694	$1.25×4, Type **334**; John F Kennedy; Mercury; Gemini	17·00	14·00
MS1695	$1.25×4, Lunar Module; Apollo; On the moon; John F Kennedy in close-up	17·00	14·00
MS1696	$1.25×4, Atlas-Agena; Moon targets; *Lander*; *Ranger 3*	17·00	14·00
MS1697	$1.25×4, *Ranger 3* (different); *Ranger 7*; *Lander* (different); *Ranger 4*	17·00	14·00

335 Pope Benedict XVI

2012. 85th Birthday of Pope Benedict XVI. Multicoloured.

MS1698	$1.25×4, Type **335**; With hand raised; Wearing zucchetto; Wearing cappello romano	17·00	14·00
MS1699	$1.25×4, Holding bible aloft; Speaking into microphone; In close-up; Head and shoulders	17·00	14·00

336 Script enclosing Koi Carp

2012. Chinese New Year. Year of the Snake. Multicoloured.

1700	18c. Type **336**	65	55
1701	18c. Stylized snake	65	55
1702	18c. Script enclosing reindeer	65	55
1703	18c. Script enclosing cranes	65	55
1704	18c. Script enclosing magpie	65	55

337 Star and Three Pirogues at Sunset ('Kosrae')

2012. Christmas. Multicoloured.

1705	25c. Type **337**	75	65
1706	25c. The Nativity ('Yap, Stone Money') (vert)	75	65
1707	45c. Pirogue, star and island ('Chuuk')	1·70	1·40
1708	45c. Joseph steering boat containing Mother and Child ('Pohnpei') (vert)	1·70	1·40

338 *St John in the Wilderness*

2012. Paintings by Raphael. Multicoloured.

MS1709 160×90 mm. $1×4, Type **338**; *The Sistene Madonna; Cardinal Bernardo da Bibbiena; The Madonna dell'Impannata*	13·00	11·00
MS1710 80×100 mm. $3.50 *The Transfiguration*	11·50	9·75

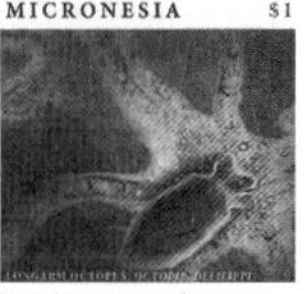

339 Long-arm Octopus (*Octopus defilippi*)

2012. Octopi. Multicoloured.

MS1711 $1×5, Type **339**; Common Octopus (*Octopus vulgaris*); Giant Octopus (*Enteroctopus dofleini*); Red Octopus (*Octopus rubescens*); Day Octopus (*Octopus cyanea*)	17·00	14·00

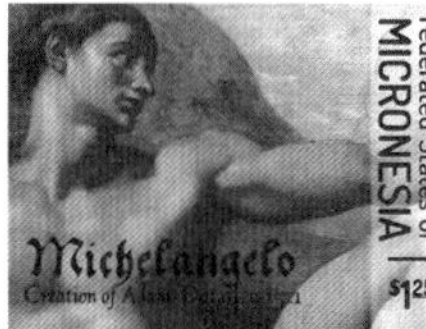

340 Adam (detail, *Creation of Adam*)

2012. 500th Anniv of Completion of Sistine Chapel Ceiling by Michelangelo. Multicoloured.

MS1712 213×115 mm. $1.25×4, Type **340**; Adam's and God's hands; God; The righteous	17·00	14·00
MS1713 80×150 mm. $1.25×3, 'Separation of Land and Water'; 'Creation of Sun, Moon and Earth'; 'Separation of Light and Darkness'	12·50	10·50

341 Anderson Alternator

2013. World Radio Day. Multicoloured.

MS1714 160×140 mm. Vert. $1.25×4, Type **341**; Brant Rock radio tower; Vacuum tube; Crystal radio receiver	17·00	14·00
MS1715 100×70 mm. Circular.$3.50 *Telstar* satellite (38×38 mm)	11·50	9·75

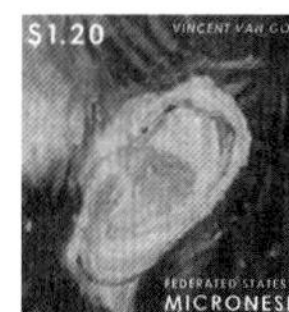

342 Ear (detail from *Self-portrait*)

2013. Paintings by Vicent van Gogh. Multicoloured.

MS1716 120×170 mm. $1.20×4, Type **342**; *Starry Night; Irises; Willows in Sunset*	16·00	13·50
MS1717 180×90 mm. 37×51 mm. $1.20×4, *Entrance Hall of Saint Paul Hospital; Cafe Terrace at Night; Oranges, Lemons and Blue Gloves; Bedroom in Arles*	16·00	13·50
MS1718 70×90 mm. 37×51 mm. $3.50 *Painter on his Way to Work*	11·50	9·75

343 Sarah Bernhardt

2013. 90th Death Anniv of Sarah Bernhardt. Illustrations by Alfred Mucha. Multicoloured.

MS1719 140×140 mm. $1.20×4, Type **343**; From *La Tosca*; From *Medee*; From *Bernhardt*	16·00	13·50
MS1720 100×100 mm. $3.50 From *Sarah Bernhardt* (40×50 mm)	11·50	9·75

344 President Kennedy

2013. 50th Death Anniv of John F Kennedy. Multicoloured.

MS1721 130×105 mm. $1.20×4, Type **344**; Pointing; Facing left; Head and shoulders	16·00	13·50
MS1722 100×70 mm. $3.50 Close-up	11·50	9·75

345 Stained Glass Design

2013. 80th Death Anniv of Louis Comfort Tiffany. Multicoloured.

MS1723 100×100 mm. $1.20×4, Type **345**; Pink; Greens; Purples	16·00	13·50
MS1724 70×100 mm. $3.50 Tulips (40×50 mm)	11·50	9·75

346 *Nanna* (Anslem Feuerbach)

2013. History of Art. Neoclassicism (**MS**1725/**MS**1726) or Romanticism (**MS**1727/**MS**1728). Multicoloured.

MS1725 140×140 mm. $1.50×3, Type **346**; *Portrait of Madame de Verninac* (Jaques-Louis David); *François Marius Granet* (Jean Auguste Dominique Ingres)	15·00	12·50
MS1726 140×140 mm. $1.50×3, *The Daughter of Jephthah* (Alexandre Cabanel); *Raphael and the Fornarina* (Jean Auguste Dominique Ingres); *Portrait of Cornelia Knott Mittenberger* (Jaques Amans)	15·00	12·50
MS1727 100×130 mm. $3.50, *Wanderer above the Sea of Fog* (Caspar David Friedrich)	11·50	9·75
MS1728 100×130 mm. $3.50, *Caspar David Friedrich in his Studio* (Georg Friedrich Kersting) (horiz)	11·50	9·75

347 Pope Benedict XVI

2013. Resignation of Pope Benedict XVI. Multicoloured.

MS1729 100×175 mm. $1.20×4, Type **347**; With right hand raised; Kissing infant; Wearing overcoat	16·00	13·50
MS1730 100×175 mm. $1.20×4, Seated reading from script; Head and shoulders; Waving, head and shoulders; With right hand raised, wind blowing hair	16·00	13·50
MS1731 70×125 mm. $3.50, With raised arms	11·50	9·75
MS1732 70×125 mm. $3.50, With right hand raised, facing right	11·50	9·75

348 Long-beaked Common Dolphin (*Delphinus capensis*)

2013. Dolphins. Multicoloured.

MS1733 150×150 mm. $1.20×4, Type **348**; Short-beaked Common Dolphin (*Delphinus delphis*); Pygmy Killer Whale (*Feresa attenuata*); Short-finned Pilot Whale (*Globicephala macrorhynchus*)	16·00	13·50
MS1734 150×150 mm. $1.20×4, Dusky Dolphin (*Lagenorhynchus obscurus*); Hector's Dolphin (*Cephalorhynchus hectori*); Bottlenose Dolphin (*Tursiops truncatus*); Pantropical Spotted Dolphin (*Stenella attenuata*)	16·00	13·50
MS1735 100×100 mm. $3.50, Spinner Dolphin (*Stenella longirostris*) (50×38 mm)	11·50	9·75
MS1736 100×100 mm. $3.50, Rough-toothed Dolphin (*Steno bredanensis*) (50×38 mm)	11·50	9·75

349 *Synchiropus splendidus*

2013. Fish. Multicoloured.

MS1737 135×100 mm. $1.20×4, Type **349**; *Pomacentrus coelestis; Nomeus gronovii; Pterapogon kauderni*	16·00	13·50
MS1738 135×100 mm. $1.20×4, *Pagrus auratus; Arripis georgianus; Epinephelus daemelii; Asapasmogaster tasmaniensis*	16·00	13·50
MS1739 94×64 mm. $3.50, *Diodon nichthemerus*	11·50	9·75
MS1740 64×94 mm. $3.50, *Amphiprion ocellaris*	11·50	9·75

350 Lois Englberger

2013. Lois Englberger Commemoration. Multicoloured.

1741 **350** $1.20 multicoloured	4·00	3·25
MS1742 100×65 mm. $3.50 As Type **350**	11·50	9·75

351 *Psilocybe aucklandii*

2013. Fungi. 'Mushrooms of the Pacific'. Multicoloured.

MS1743 135×100 mm. $1.25×4, Type **351**; *Entoloma hochstetteri; Amanta citrina; Agaricus bernardii*	17·00	14·00
MS1744 135×100 mm. $1.25×4, *Psilocybe subaeruginosa; Gymnopilus luteofolius; Gymnopilus junonius; Panaeolus cyanescens*	17·00	14·00
MS1745 65×95 mm. $3.50, *Weraroa novae* (vert)	11·50	9·75
MS1746 95×65 mm. $3.50, *Panaeolus subbalteatus*	11·50	9·75

352 John Mengefel

2013. John de Avila Mengefel (first governor of Yap) Comemoration

1747 **352** 46c. multicoloured	1·60	1·30

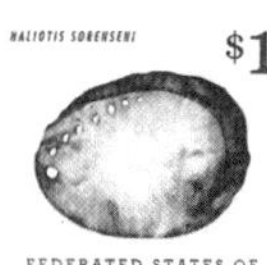

353 *Haliotis sorenseni*

2013. Seashells. Multicoloured.

MS1748 140×100 mm. $1×6, Type **353**; *Melogena corona; Lyropecten nodosus; Pleurotomaria rumphii; Lioconcha castrensis; Conus ammiralis*	20·00	17·00
MS1749 70×100 mm. $3.50 *Echinus melo* (30×50 mm)	11·50	9·75

354 Banded Pitta (*Pitta guajana*)

2013. Wildlife of Thailand. Multicoloured.

MS1750 160×180 mm. 75c.×8, Type **354**; Dhole (*Cuon alpinus*); Wrinkled Hornbill (*Aceros corrugatus*); Nicobar Pigeon (*Caldenas nicobarica*); Lar Gibbon (*Hylobates lar*); Leopard (*Panthera pardus*); Malayan Tapir (*Tapirus indicus*); Red-footed Booby (*Sula sula*)	20·00	17·00
MS1751 100×120 mm. 30×50 mm. $1.75×2, Dugong (*Dugong dugon*); Red-breasted Parrakeet (*Psittacula alexandri*)	11·50	9·75

APPENDIX

The following stamps have either been issued in excess of postal needs, or have not been available to the public in reasonable quantities at face value. Such stamps may later be given full listings if there is evidence of regular postal use. Miniature sheets and imperforate stamps are excluded from this listing.

2007

Diana, Princess of Wales Commemoration. $8 (gold)

MIDDLE CONGO

One of three colonies into which Fr. Congo was divided in 1906. Became part of Fr. Equatorial Africa in 1937. Became part of the Congo Republic within the French Community on 28 November 1958.

100 centimes = 1 franc.

1 Leopard in Ambush

2 Bakalois Woman

3 Coconut Palms, Libreville

1907

1	1	1c. olive and brown	55	65
2	1	2c. violet and brown	1·40	75
3	1	4c. blue and brown	1·60	1·30
4	1	5c. green and blue	2·00	1·50
21	1	5c. yellow and blue	2·20	4·25
5	1	10c. red and blue	2·75	95
22	1	10c. green and light green	5·50	9·00
6	1	15c. purple and pink	3·50	3·25
7	1	20c. brown and blue	6·25	8·50
8	2	25c. blue and green	4·00	1·70
23	2	25c. green and grey	3·25	4·50
9	2	30c. pink and green	3·50	4·75
24	2	30c. red	3·00	5·75
10	2	35c. brown and blue	3·25	3·25
11	2	40c. green and brown	4·00	4·00
12	2	45c. violet and orange	8·75	7·25
25	2	50c. blue and green	3·00	5·75
13	2	50c. green and orange	5·00	6·50
14	2	75c. brown and blue	14·50	10·50
15	3	1f. green and violet	21·00	21·00
16	3	2f. violet and green	21·00	19·00
17	3	5f. blue and pink	65·00	65·00

1916. Surch **5c** and red cross.

20	1	10c.+5c. red and blue	2·10	4·00

1924. Surch **AFRIQUE EQUATORIALE FRANCAISE** and new value.

26	3	25c. on 2f. green and violet	1·90	5·00
27	3	25c. on 5f. pink and blue	1·90	1·90
28	3	65 on 1f. brown and orange	1·90	5·25
29	3	85 on 1f. brown and orange	1·90	5·25
30	2	90 on 75c. scarlet and red	3·25	3·75
31	2	1f.25 on 1f. ultramarine & bl	1·90	2·50
32	2	1f.50 on 1f. blue & ultram	3·00	3·00
33	2	3f. on 5f. pink and brown	6·25	5·50
34	2	10f. on 5f. green and red	17·00	19·00
35	2	20f. on 5f. purple and brown	18·00	19·00

1924. Optd **AFRIQUE EQUATORIALE FRANCAISE**.

36	1	1c. olive and brown	50	3·00
37	1	2c. violet and brown	50	3·00
38	1	4c. blue and brown	50	1·80
39	1	5c. yellow and blue	75	1·90
40	1	10c. green and light green	1·60	4·00
41	1	10c. red and grey	1·40	2·20
42	1	15c. purple and pink	1·60	2·10
43	1	20c. brown and blue	1·10	4·00
44	1	20c. green and light green	1·00	3·25
45	1	20c. brown and mauve	3·50	4·50
46	2	25c. green and grey	1·50	65
47	2	30c. red	2·30	4·25
48	2	30c. grey and mauve	1·10	1·40
49	2	30c. deep green and green	3·25	5·75
50	2	35c. brown and blue	1·30	5·00
51	2	40c. green and brown	2·40	2·50
52	2	45c. violet and orange	2·30	4·25
53	2	50c. blue and green	2·30	2·40
54	2	50c. yellow and black	1·30	1·00
55	2	65c. brown and blue	4·50	7·25
56	2	75c. brown and blue	2·10	3·25
57	2	90c. red and pink	7·00	10·50
58	3	1f. green and violet	2·50	2·10
59	3	1f.10 mauve and brown	6·00	11·50
60	3	1f.50 ultramarine and blue	12·00	12·00
61	3	2f. violet and green	3·00	2·50
62	3	3f. mauve on pink	15·00	13·00
63	3	5f. blue and pink	8·25	6·75

1931. "Colonial Exhibition" key-types inscr "MOYEN CONGO".

65	**E**	40c. green and black	7·00	8·50
66	**F**	50c. mauve and black	6·50	6·25
67	**G**	90c. red and black	6·50	7·25
68	**H**	1f.50 blue and black	8·25	7·75

15 Mindouli Viaduct

1933

69	**15**	1c. brown	40	3·00
70	**15**	2c. blue	40	5·00
71	**15**	4c. olive	50	1·50
72	**15**	5c. red	90	2·50
73	**15**	10c. green	2·50	3·75
74	**15**	15c. purple	3·75	6·00
75	**15**	20c. red on rose	15·00	17·00
76	**15**	25c. orange	3·50	3·00
77	**15**	30c. green	4·50	5·25
78	-	40c. brown	4·50	5·75
79	-	45c. black on green	4·50	5·25
80	-	50c. purple	2·50	1·10
81	-	65c. red on green	4·50	7·00
82	-	75c. black on red	21·00	18·00
83	-	90c. red	4·50	7·25
84	-	1f. red	2·50	1·60
85	-	1f.25 green	4·50	4·00
86	-	1f.50 blue	19·00	8·75
87	-	1f.75 violet	4·75	2·50
88	-	2f. olive	3·75	3·25
89	-	3f. black on red	9·50	6·25
90	-	5f. grey	44·00	41·00
91	-	10f. black	80·00	55·00
92	-	20f. brown	55·00	43·00

Designs:—40c. to 1f.50 Pasteur Institute, Brazzaville; 1f.75 to 20f. Government Building, Brazzaville.

POSTAGE DUE STAMPS

1928. Postage Due type of France optd **MOYEN-CONGO A. E. F.**

D64	**D11**	5c. blue	65	4·25
D65	**D11**	10c. brown	1·00	3·50
D66	**D11**	20c. olive	1·60	5·25
D67	**D11**	25c. red	2·10	6·25
D68	**D11**	30c. red	2·20	5·75
D69	**D11**	45c. green	2·20	5·75
D70	**D11**	50c. purple	2·30	6·50
D71	**D11**	60c. brown on cream	3·50	8·25
D72	**D11**	1f. red on cream	3·75	7·25
D73	**D11**	2f. red	5·50	10·50
D74	**D11**	3f. violet	8·00	19·00

D13 Village

1930

D75	**D13**	5c. olive and blue	1·30	5·00
D76	**D13**	10c. brown and red	1·90	5·25
D77	**D13**	20c. brown and green	4·00	8·50
D78	**D13**	25c. brown and blue	5·50	9·25
D79	**D13**	30c. green and brown	7·50	15·00
D80	**D13**	45c. olive and green	9·25	14·50
D81	**D13**	50c. brown and mauve	8·75	16·00
D82	**D13**	60c. black and violet	11·50	19·00
D83	-	1f. black and brown	17·00	36·00
D84	-	2f. brown and mauve	20·00	41·00
D85	-	3f. brown and red	19·00	44·00

Design:—1 to 3f. *William Guinet* (steamer) on the River Congo.

D17 "Le Djoue"

1933

D93	**D17**	5c. green	1·10	4·75
D94	**D17**	10c. blue on blue	2·10	4·75
D95	**D17**	20c. red on yellow	3·50	5·50
D96	**D17**	25c. red	3·50	5·75
D97	**D17**	30c. red	3·25	6·50
D98	**D17**	45c. purple	4·50	7·00
D99	**D17**	50c. black	5·50	8·50
D100	**D17**	60c. black on red	7·00	11·50
D101	**D17**	1f. red	9·00	16·00
D102	**D17**	2f. orange	11·50	23·00
D103	**D17**	3f. blue	21·00	31·00

For later issues see **FRENCH EQUATORIAL AFRICA**.

MODENA

A state in Upper Italy, formerly a duchy and now part of Italy. Used stamps of Sardinia after the cessation of its own issues in 1860. Now uses Italian stamps.

100 centesimi = 1 lira.

1 Arms of Este

1852. Imperf.

9	**1**	5c. black on green	60·00	65·00
3	**1**	10c. black on pink	£750	£110
4	**1**	15c. black on yellow	£110	43·00
5	**1**	25c. black on buff	£170	65·00
12	**1**	40c. black on blue	65·00	£150
13	**1**	1l. black on white	80·00	£2500

5 Cross of Savoy

1859. Imperf.

18a	**5**	5c. green	£1700	£850
19	**5**	15c. brown	£2750	£4000
20	**5**	15c. grey	£400	
21	**5**	20c. black	£2750	£190
22	**5**	20c. lilac	85·00	£1500
23	**5**	40c. red	£225	£1600
24	**5**	80c. brown	£225	£26000

NEWSPAPER STAMPS

1853. As T **1** but in the value tablet inscr "B.G. CEN" and value. Imperf.

N15	**1**	9c. black on mauve	£950	£100
N16	**1**	10c. black on lilac	£100	£350

N4

1859. Imperf.

N17	**N4**	10c. black	£1300	£2750

MOHELI

An island in the Comoro Archipelago adjacent to Madagascar. A separate French dependency until 1914 when the whole archipelago was placed under Madagascar whose stamps were used until 1950. Now part of the Comoro Islands.

100 centimes = 1 franc.

1906. "Tablet" key-type inscr "MOHELI" in blue (2, 4, 10, 20, 30, 40c., 5f.) or red (others).

1	**D**	1c. black on blue	4·75	3·00
2	**D**	2c. brown on buff	1·90	2·50
3	**D**	4c. brown on grey	3·25	3·75
4	**D**	5c. green	4·75	3·00
5	**D**	10c. red	5·75	3·00
6	**D**	20c. red on green	16·00	19·00
7	**D**	25c. blue	18·00	8·50
8	**D**	30c. brown on drab	23·00	33·00
9	**D**	35c. black on yellow	12·50	5·00
10	**D**	40c. red on yellow	19·00	23·00
11	**D**	45c. black on green	95·00	90·00
12	**D**	50c. brown on blue	25·00	24·00
13	**D**	75c. brown on orange	48·00	60·00
14	**D**	1f. green	26·00	50·00
15	**D**	2f. violet on pink	50·00	75·00
16	**D**	5f. mauve on lilac	£190	£190

1912. Surch in figures.

17A	05 on 4c. brown & bl on grey	3·00	7·25
18A	05 on 20c. red & blue on grn	3·75	11·50
19A	05 on 30c. brn & bl on drab	3·25	8·75
20A	10 on 40c. red & blue on yell	3·50	8·25
21A	10 on 45c. blk & red on grn	2·75	3·00
22A	10 on 50c. brown & red on bl	4·50	7·25

MOLDOVA

Formerly Moldavia, a constituent republic of the Soviet Union. Moldova declared its sovereignty within the Union in 1990 and became independent in 1991.

1991. 100 kopeks = 1 rouble.
1993. Kupon (temporary currency).
1993. 100 bani = 1 leu.

1 Arms

1991. First Anniv of Declaration of Sovereignty. Multicoloured. Imperf.

1	7k. Type **1**	15	15
2	13k. Type **1**	50	40
3	30k. Flag (35×23 mm)	95	85

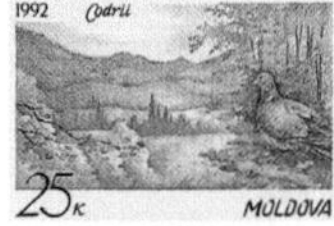
2 Codrii Nature Reserve

1992

4	**2**	25k. multicoloured	80	70

3 Arms

1992

5	**3**	35k. green	30	15
6	**3**	50k. red	50	40
7	**3**	65k. brown	65	55
8	**3**	1r. purple	80	70
9	**3**	1r.50 blue	95	85

4 Tupolev Tu-144

1992. Air.

15	**4**	1r.75 red	80	70
16	**4**	2r.50 mauve	95	85
17	**4**	7r.75 violet	1·60	1·40
18	**4**	8r.50 green	2·40	2·10

See also Nos. 70/3.

5 European Bee-eater

1992. Birds. Multicoloured.

19	50k. Type **5**	70	65
20	65k. Golden oriole	80	70
21	2r.50 Green woodpecker	95	85
22	6r. European roller	1·60	1·40
23	7r.50 Hoopoe	2·10	1·80
24	15r. European cuckoo	4·75	4·25

See also Nos. 63/9.

6 St. Panteleimon's Church

1992. Centenary (1991) of St. Panteleimon's Church, Chisinau.

25	**6**	1r.50 multicoloured	80	70

7 Wolf suckling Romulus and Remus

1992. Trajan Memorial, Chisinau.

26	**7**	5r. multicoloured	1·30	1·10

1992. Various stamps of Russia surch **MOLDOVA** and value.

27	2r.50 on 4k. red (No. 4672)	50	40
28	6r. on 3k. red (No. 4671)	65	55
29	8r.50 on 4k. red (No. 4672)	95	85
30	10r. on 3k. green (No. 6074)	1·30	1·10

9 High Jumping

1992. Olympic Games, Barcelona. Multicoloured.

31	35k. Type **9**	30	30
32	65k. Wrestling	40	35
33	1r. Archery	50	40
34	2r.50 Swimming	80	70
35	10r. Show jumping	4·75	4·25
MS36	147×110 mm. Nos. 31/5 plus label	6·50	6·00

1992. Nos. 4669/71 of Russia surch **MOLDOVA**, new value and bunch of grapes.

37	45k. on 2k. mauve	50	40
38	46k. on 2k. mauve	50	40
39	63k. on 1k. green	50	40
40	63k. on 3k. red	80	70
41	70k. on 1k. green	50	40
42	4r. on 1k. green	80	70

(**11**) **12** Tudor Casapu (gold medal, weightlifting)

1992. Moldovan Olympic Games Medal Winners. Nos. 33/4 optd with Type **11**.

(a) Nos. 33/4 optd with T **11** or similar

43	1r. Archery (optd **NATALIA VALEEVbronz** and emblem)	1·10	1·00
44	2r.50 Swimming (optd **IURIE BASCATOVargint** and emblem)	2·10	1·80

(b) Miniature sheet 69x69 mm

MS45 **12**	25r. multicoloured	7·25	6·50

13 Moldovan Flag, Statue of Liberty and UN Emblem and Building

1992. Admission of Moldova to U.N.O. Multicoloured.

46	1r.30 Type **13**	80	70
47	12r. As Type **13** but with motifs differently arranged	1·60	1·40

14 Moldovan Flag and Prague Castle

1992. Admission of Moldova to European Security and Co-operation Conference. Multicoloured.

48	2r.50 Type **14**	80	70
49	25r. Helsinki Cathedral and Moldovan flag	2·40	2·10

15 Carpet and Pottery

1992. Folk Art.

50	**15**	7r.50 multicoloured	1·60	70

16 Galleon

1992. 500th Anniv of Discovery of America by Columbus. Multicoloured.

51	1r. Type **16**	65	30
52	6r. Carrack	2·00	1·30
53	6r. Caravel	2·00	1·30
MS54	89×69 mm. 25r. Christopher Columbus	8·75	8·75

17 Letter Sorter, Diesel Train, State Flag and UPU Emblem

1992. Admission to U.P.U. Multicoloured.

55	5r. Type **17**	1·30	70
56	10r. Douglas DC-10 jetliner, computerized letter sorting equipment, state flag and UPU emblem	1·60	1·00

18 Aesculapius Snake

1993. Protected Animals. Snakes. Multicoloured.

57	3r. Type **18**	80	70
58	3r. Aesculapius in tree	80	70
59	3r. Aesculapius on path	80	70
60	3r. Aesculapius on rock	80	70
61	15r. Grass snake	2·40	2·10
62	25r. Adder	4·00	3·50

Nos. 57/60 were issued together, *se-tenant*, forming a composite design.

1993. Birds. As Nos. 19/24 but with values changed and additional design. Multicoloured.

63	2r. Type **5**	15	15
64	3r. As No. 20	30	30
65	5r. As No. 21	50	40
66	10r. As No. 22	65	55
67	15r. As No. 23	80	70
68	50r. As No. 24	1·60	1·40
69	100r. Barn swallow	4·00	3·50

1993. Air.

70	**4**	25r. red	65	55
71	**4**	45r. brown	95	85
72	**4**	50r. green	1·10	1·00
73	**4**	90r. blue	2·40	2·10

19 Arms **20** Arms

1993

74	**19**	2k. blue	40	35
75	**19**	3k. purple	40	35
76	**19**	6k. green	40	35
77	-	10k. violet and green	40	35
78	-	15k. violet and green	50	40
79	-	20k. violet and grey	65	55
80	-	30k. violet and yellow	65	55
81	-	50k. violet and red	80	70
82	**20**	100k. multicoloured	1·60	1·40
83	**20**	250k. multicoloured	3·25	2·75

Design:—10 to 50k. Similar to Type **19** but with inscription and value at foot differently arranged.

21 Red Admiral

1993. Butterflies and Moths. Multicoloured.

94	6b. Type **21**	65	55
95	10b. Swallowtail	80	70
96	50b. Peacock	1·60	1·40
97	250b. Emperor moth	6·50	5·50

22 *Tulipa bibersteiniana*

1993. Flowers. Multicoloured.

98	6b. Type **22**	30	30
99	15b. Lily of the valley	50	40
100	25b. Snowdrop	65	55
101	30b. Peony	80	70
102	50b. Snowdrop	1·60	1·40
103	90b. Pasque flower	3·25	2·75
MS104	88×68 mm. 250b. Lady's Slipper (*Cypripedium caleolus*) (44×29 mm)	6·50	6·25

23 Dragos Voda (1352–53)

1993. 14th-century Princes of Moldavia. Multicoloured.

105	6b. Type **23**	25	20
106	25b. Bogdan Voda I (1359–65)	30	30
107	50b. Latcu Voda (1365–75)	50	40
108	100b. Petru I Musat (1375–91)	80	70
109	150b. Roman Voda Musat (1391–94)	1·00	90
110	200b. Stefan I (1394–99)	4·00	3·50

24 *Story of One Life* (M. Grecu)

1993. Europa. Contemporary Art. Multicoloured.

111	3b. Type **24**	1·60	1·40
112	150b. *Coming of Spring* (I. Vieru)	3·25	2·75

25 Biathletes

1994. Winter Olympic Games, Lillehammer, Norway Multicoloured.

113	3b. Type **25**	1·60	1·40
114	150b. Close-up of biathlete shooting	2·40	2·10

1994. No. 4669 of Russia surch **MOLDOVA**, grapes and value.

115	3b. on 1k. green	65	55
116	25b. on 1k. green	80	70
117	50b. on 1k. green	95	85

27 State Arms

1994

118	**27**	1b. multicoloured	15	15
119	**27**	10b. multicoloured	25	20
120	**27**	30b. multicoloured	30	30
121	**27**	38b. multicoloured	40	35
122	**27**	45b. multicoloured	50	40
123	**27**	75b. multicoloured	65	55
124	**27**	1l.50 multicoloured	1·60	1·40
125	**27**	1l.80 multicoloured	2·10	1·80
126	**27**	2l.50 mult (24×29 mm)	2·40	2·10
127	**27**	4l.50 multicoloured	4·00	3·50
128	**27**	5l.40 multicoloured	5·25	4·50
129	**27**	6l.90 multicoloured	6·00	5·25
130	**27**	7l.20 mult (24×29 mm)	6·50	5·50
131	**27**	13l. mult (24×29 mm)	11·00	9·75
132	**27**	24l. mult (24×29 mm)	22·00	20·00

28 Launch of Titan II Rocket

1994. Europa. Inventions and Discoveries. 25th Anniv of First Manned Moon Landing. Multicoloured.

136	1b. Type **28**	80	70
137	45b. Ed White (astronaut) on space walk (*Gemini 4* flight, 1965)	4·75	4·25
138	2l.50 Lunar module landing, 1969	11·00	9·75

29 Maria Cibotari (singer)

1994. Entertainers' Death Anniversaries. Multicoloured.

139	3b. Type **29** (45th)	50	40
140	90b. Dumitru Caraciobanu (actor, 14th)	65	55
141	150b. Eugeniu Coca (composer, 40th)	1·40	1·30
142	250b. Igor Vieru (actor, 11th)	3·50	3·00

30 Preparing Stamp Design

1994. Stamp Day.

143	**30**	10b. black, blue and mauve	50	40
144	-	45b. black, mauve and yellow	65	55
145	-	2l. multicoloured	3·50	3·00

Designs:—45b. Printing stamps; 2l. Checking finished sheets.

31 Pierre de Coubertin (founder)

1994. Centenary of International Olympic Committee. Multicoloured.

146	60b. Type **31**	1·10	1·00
147	1l.50 Rings and Paris 1994 centenary congress emblem	3·00	2·50

32 Map

1994. Partnership for Peace Programme (co-operation of N.A.T.O. and Warsaw Pact members).

148	-	60b. black, ultram and bl	1·90	1·70
149	**32**	2l.50 multicoloured	6·00	5·25

Design:—60b. Manfred Worner (Secretary-General of NATO) and President Mircea Snegur of Moldova.

34 Map (image scaled to 57% of original size)

1994. Air. Self-adhesive. Roul.

152	**34**	1l.50 multicoloured	1·30	1·10
153	**34**	4l.50 multicoloured	3·50	3·00

The individual stamps are peeled directly from the card backing. Each card contains six different designs with the same face value forming the composite design illustrated. Each stamp is a horizontal strip with a label indicating the main class of mail covered by the rate at the left, separated by a vertical line of rouletting. The outer edges of the cards are imperforate.

35 Family

1994. International Year of the Family. Multicoloured.

154	30b. Type **35**	65	55
155	60b. Mother breast-feeding baby	95	85
156	1l.50 Child drawing	3·00	2·50

36 Handshake

1994. Preliminary Rounds of European Football Championship, England (1996). Multicoloured.

157	10b. Type **36**	50	40
158	40b. Players competing for ball	95	85
159	2l.40 Goalkeeper making save	4·75	4·25
MS160	140×105 mm. 1l.10 Moldovan and German pennants; 2l.20, German and Moldovan shields on ball; 2l.40, Players	12·00	10·50

37 *Birth of Jesus Christ* (anon)

1994. Christmas. Multicoloured.

161	20b. Type **37**	80	70
162	3l.60 *Birth of Jesus Christ* (Gherasim)	6·50	5·50

38 Cracked Green Russula

1995. Fungi. Multicoloured.

163	4b. Type **38**	50	40
164	10b. Oak mushroom	80	70
165	20b. Chanterelle	3·25	2·75
166	90b. Red-capped scaber stalk	8·00	7·00
167	1l.80 *Leccinum duriusculum*	19·00	17·00

39 Booted Eagle

1995. European Nature Conservation Year. Multicoloured.

168	4b. Type **39**	80	70
169	45b. Roe deer	4·75	4·25
170	90b. Wild boar	9·50	8·50

40 Earthenware Urns and Necklace

1995. National Museum Exhibits. Multicoloured.

171	4b. Type **40**	80	70
172	10b.+2b. Representation and skeleton of Dinotherium gigantissimum	2·40	2·10
173	1l.80+30b. Silver coins	11·00	9·75

41 *May 1945* (Igor Vieru)

1995. Europa. Peace and Freedom. Paintings. Multicoloured.

174	10b. Type **41**	55	50
175	40b. *Peace* (Sergiu Cuciuc)	2·40	2·10
176	2l.20 *Spring 1944* (Cuciuc)	9·50	8·50

42 Constantin Stere (writer, 130th birth)

1995. Anniversaries.

177	**42**	9b. brown and grey	80	70
178	-	10b. purple and grey	80	70
179	-	40b. lilac and grey	2·40	2·10
180	-	1l.80 green and grey	8·75	7·75

Designs:—10b. Tamara Ceban (singer, fifth death); 40b. Alexandru Plamadeala (sculptor, 55th death); 1l.80, Lucian Blaga (philosopher, birth centenary).

43 Alexandru cel Bun (1400–32)

1995. 15th and 16th-century Princes of Moldavia. Multicoloured.

181	10b. Type **43**	50	40
182	10b. Petru Aron (1451–52 and 1454–57)	50	40
183	10b. Stefan cel Mare (1457–1504)	50	40
184	45b. Petru Rares (1527–38 and 1541–46)	1·60	1·40
185	90b. Alexandru Lapusneanu (1552–61 and 1564–68)	3·25	2·75
186	1l.80 Ioan Voda cel Cumplit (1572–74)	13·50	12·00
MS187	83×66 mm. 5l. Stefan del Mare (1457–1504) (24×29 mm)	3·25	2·75

44 Soroca Castle

1995. Castles. Multicoloured.

188	10b. Type **44**	50	40
189	20b. Tighina Castle	1·10	1·00
190	60b. Alba Castle	3·00	2·50
191	1l.30 Hotin Castle	4·75	4·25

45 Seal in Eye

46 "50" and Emblem

1995. 50th Anniv of U.N.O. Multicoloured. (a) Ordinary gum. Perf.

192	10b. Type **45**	50	40
193	10b. Airplane in eye	50	40
194	1l.50 Child's face and barbed wire in eye	10·50	9·00

(b) Self-adhesive. Rouletted.

195	90b. Type **46**	80	70
196	1l.50 Type **46**	1·60	1·40

47 *Last Moon of Autumn*

1995. Centenary of Motion Pictures.

197	**47**	10b. red and black	50	40
198	-	40b. green and black	1·30	1·10
199	-	2l.40 blue and black	11·00	9·75

Designs:—40b. *Lautarii*; 2l.40, *Dimitrie Cantemir*.

48 Fly Agaric

1996. Fungi. Multicoloured.

200	10b. Type **48**	80	70
201	10b. Satan's mushroom	80	70
202	65b. Death cap	2·40	2·10
203	1l.30 Clustered woodlover	3·25	2·75
204	2l.40 Destroying angel	7·25	6·25

49 Weightlifting

1996. Olympic Games, Atlanta, U.S.A. Multicoloured.

205	10b. Type **49**	50	40
206	20b.+5b. Judo	65	55
207	45b.+10b. Running	1·30	1·10
208	2l.40+30b. Canoeing	8·75	7·75
MS209	123×75 mm. 2l.20 Archery (horiz)	4·00	3·75

50 Rudi Monastery

1996. Monasteries. Multicoloured.

210	10b. Type **50**	30	30
211	90b. Japca	1·30	1·10
212	1l.30 Curchi	1·90	1·70
213	2l.80 Saharna	3·75	3·25
214	4l.40 Capriana	7·25	6·25

51 Moorhens

1996. Birds. Multicoloured.

215	9b. Type **51**	45	40
216	10b. Greylag geese	45	40
217	2l.20 Turtle doves	4·25	3·75
218	4l.40 Mallard	12·50	10·50
MS219	82×65 mm. 2l.20 Ring-necked pheasant (*Phasianus colchicus*)	3·75	3·50

52 Elena Alistar (president of Women's League)

1996. Europa. Famous Women. Multicoloured.

220	10b. Type **52**	60	50
221	3l.70 Marie Sklodowska-Curie (physicist)	6·50	5·50
MS222	94×104 mm. 2l.20 Iulia Hasdeu (writer)	9·50	8·25

53 Mihail Eminescu (poet) (146th birth anniv)

1996. Birth Anniversaries.

223	**53**	10b. brown and deep brown	45	40
224	-	10b. sepia and brown	45	40
225	-	2l.20 green and brown	2·20	1·90
226	-	3l.30 green and deep brown	3·75	3·25
227	-	5l.40 brown and deep brown	6·50	5·75
MS228		96×66 mm. 1l.80 brown	3·00	2·75

Designs:—Horiz: 10b. Gavriil Banulescu-Bodoni (Metropolitan of Chisinau, 250th); 2l.20, Ion Creanga (writer, 159th); 3l.30, Vasile Alecsandri (writer, 172nd); 5l.40, Petru Movila and printing press (400th). Vert—1l.80, Mihail Eminesai (different).

54 Town Hall

1996. 560th Anniv of Chisinau. Multicoloured.

229	10b. Type **54**	30	25
230	1l.30 Cultural Palace	1·20	1·00
231	2l.40 Mazarache Church	8·75	7·50

55 Carol Singers with Star

1996. Christmas. Multicoloured.

232	10b. Type **55**	30	25
233	2l.20+30b. Mother and child at centre of star	2·50	2·30
234	2l.80+50b. Children decorating Christmas tree	3·75	3·25

1996. Moldovan Olympic Games Medal Winners. No. **MS**209 optd **Nicolae JURAVSCHI Victor RENEISCHI – canoe, argint -, Serghei MUREICO – lupt Greco-romame, bronz.**

MS235	123×75 mm. 2l.20 multicoloured	6·50	6·25

57 Feteasca

1997. Moldovan Wines. Each showing a grape variety and bottle of wine. Multicoloured.

236	10b. Type **57**	35	30
237	45b. Cabernet Sauvignon	95	80
238	65b. Sauvignon	1·20	1·00
239	3l.70 Rara Neagra	5·00	4·50

58 Franz Schubert

1997. Composers. Each green and grey.

240	10b. Type **58** (birth bicentenary)	40	35
241	10b. Gavriil Musicescu (150th birth anniv)	40	35
242	45b. Sergei Rachmaninov	65	55
243	4l.40 Georges Enesco	6·50	5·50

59 Girl with Eggs

1997. Easter. Multicoloured.

244	10b. Type **59**	40	35
245	3l.30 Easter dish	5·50	4·75
MS246	87×70 mm. 5l. Easter basket with bread and eggs	8·00	7·75

60 White Stork flying over Battlements

1997. Europa. Tales and Legends. Multicoloured.

247	10b. Type **60**	1·60	1·40
248	2l.80 Master Manole	16·00	14·00

MS249		90×70 mm. 5l. The Spring Fairy	24·00	22·00

61 Praying Mantis

1997. Insects in the Red Book. Multicoloured.

250		25b. Type **61**	80	70
251		80b. *Ascalaphus macaronius* (Owl-fly)	1·60	1·40
252		1l. Searcher	2·40	2·10
253		2l.20 *Liometopum microcephalum* (Ant)	5·50	5·00
MS254		84×67 mm. 5l. *Scolia maculata* (Dagger Wasp)	8·75	8·50

62 Post Office No. 12, Chisinau

1997. World Post Day.

255	**62**	10b. green and olive	40	35
256	-	2l.20 green and brown	3·00	2·50
257	-	3l.30 olive and green	6·50	5·50

Designs:—Horiz: 2l.20, District Head Post and Telegraph Office, Chisinau. Vert: 3l.30, Heinrich von Stephan (founder of UPU) (death centenary).

63 Nicolai Zelinski School, Tiraspol

1997. Protection of Buildings.

258	**63**	7b. black and violet	30	30
259	-	10b. black and purple	40	35
260	-	10b. black and blue	40	35
261	-	90b. black and yellow	95	85
262	-	1l.30 black and blue	1·60	1·40
263	-	3l.30 black and grey	6·50	5·50

Designs:—No. 259, Railway station, Tighina; 260, Sts. Constantine and Elena Cathedral, Balti; 261, Church, Causeni; 262, Archangel Michael Cathedral, Cahul; 263, Academy of Art, Chisinau.

64 Noul Neamt Monastery, Chitcani

1997. Christmas. Multicoloured.

264		10b. Type **64**	40	40
265		45b. *Birth of Our Lord Jesus Christ*	65	60
266		5l. *Birth of Jesus Christ* (different)	7·25	6·75

65 Petru Schiopul (1574–77, 1578–79 and 1582–91)

1997. 16th and 17th-century Princes of Moldavia. Multicoloured.

267		10b. Type **65**	40	40
268		10b. Ieremia Movila (1595–1606)	40	40
269		45b. Stefan Tomsa (1611–15 and 1621–23)	80	75
270		1l.80 Radu Mihnea (1616–19 and 1623–26)	2·40	2·30
271		2l.20 Miron Barnovschi Movila (1626–29 and 1633)	3·50	3·25
272		2l.80 Bogdan Orbul (1504–1517)	4·00	3·75
MS273		93×75 mm. 5l. Mihai Viteazul (May–Sept 1600) (25×30 mm)	8·00	7·75

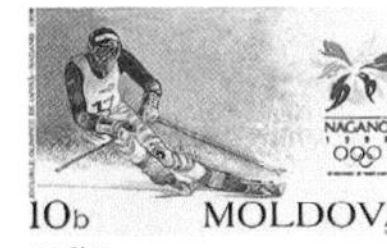

66 Skiing

1998. Winter Olympic Games, Nagano, Japan. Multicoloured.

274		10b. Type **66**	50	45
275		45b. Pairs figure skating	2·40	2·30
276		2l.20 Biathlon	4·00	3·75

67 Alexei Mateeici

1998. Anniversaries. Multicoloured.

277		10b. Type **67** (110th birth anniv)	30	30
278		40b. Pantelimon Halippa (115th birth anniv)	80	75
279		60b. Stefan Ciobanu (115th birth anniv)	1·10	1·10
280		2l. Constantin Stamati-Ciurea (death centenary)	4·50	4·25
MS281		100×80 mm. 5l. Nicolae Milescu-Spatarul (290th death anniv)	9·50	9·25

68 Statue of Stefan cel Mare (Alexandru Plamadeala), Chisinau

1998. Art. Multicoloured.

282		10b. Type **68**	40	40
283		60b. *The Resurrection of Christ* (icon)	65	60
284		1l. Modern sculpture (Constantin Brancusi), Targu-Jiu	1·60	1·50
285		2l.60 Trajan's Column, Rome	5·50	5·25

69 Masks and Eye

1998. Europa. National Festivals. Multicoloured.

286		10b. Type **69** (Eugene Ionescu Theatre Festival)	80	75
287		2l.20 Medallion showing potter (Cermanics Fair)	5·50	5·25
MS288		70×58 mm. 5l. Bar of music (Martisor International Music Festival)	11·00	10·50

70 Cherries

1998. Fruits. Multicoloured.

289		7b. Type **70**	30	30
290		10b. Plums	80	75
291		1l. Apples	1·10	1·10
292		2l. Pears	4·00	3·75

71 Diana, Princess of Wales

1998. Diana, Princess of Wales Commemoration. Sheet 144×116 mm containing T **71** and similar horiz designs. Multicoloured.

MS293		10d. Type **71**; 90b. Wearing orange jacket; 1l.80, Wearing burgundy jacket; 2l.20 Wearing jacket with white collar; 5l. Wearing jacket with velvet collar	12·00	11·50

72 Chilia

1998. Medieval Towns.

294	**72**	10b. grey and black	50	45
295	-	60b. brown and black	95	90
296	-	1l. red and black	1·60	1·50
297	-	2l. blue and black	4·75	4·50

Designs:—60b. Orhei; 1l. Suceava; 2l. Ismail.

73 1858 Moldavia Stamps

1998. 140th Anniv of Stamp Issues for Moldavia. Multicoloured.

298		10b. Type **73**	40	40
299		90b. 1858 Moldavia 54p. and 1928 Rumania 1 and 5l. stamps	65	60
300		2l.20 1858 Moldavia 81p. and Russian stamps	4·00	3·75
301		2l.40 1858 Moldavia 108p. and Moldova 1996 10b. and 1994 45b. stamps	4·75	4·50

74 Northern Eagle Owl

1998. Birds. Multicoloured.

302		25b. Type **74**	65	60
303		2l. Demoiselle crane (horiz)	3·25	3·00

75 Couple from Vara

1998. Regional Costumes. Multicoloured.

304		25b. Type **75**	50	45
305		90b. Couple from Vara (different)	1·30	1·20
306		1l.80 Couple from Iarna	3·75	3·50
307		2l. Couple from Iarna (different)	4·00	3·75

76 Anniversary Emblem and *Proportions of Man* (Leonardo da Vinci)

1998. 50th Anniv of Universal Declaration of Human Rights.

308	**76**	2l.40 multicoloured	4·75	4·50

77 Conference Members

1998. 80th Anniv of Union of Bessarabia and Rumania.

309	**77**	90b. brown, blue and black	1·10	1·10

78 Mail Coach

1999. Anniversaries. Multicoloured.

310		25b. Type **78** (125th anniv of UPU)	80	75
311		2l.20 Map of Europe and Council of Europe emblem (50th anniv)	4·00	3·75

79 Prutul de Jos Park

1999. Europa. Parks and Gardens. Multicoloured.

312		25b. Type **79**	80	75
313		2l.40 Padurea Domneasca Park	6·50	6·00
MS314		84×65 mm. 5l. Codru Park	13·00	12·50

80 Balzac

1999. Birth Bicent of Honore de Balzac (writer).

315	**80**	90b. multicoloured	1·60	1·50

81 *Aleksandr Pushkin and Constantin Stamati* (B. Lebedev)

1999. Birth Bicentenary of Aleksandr Pushkin (poet).

316	**81**	65b. brown, deep brown and black	1·30	1·20

82 Tranta

1999. National Sports.

317	**82**	25b. green and light green	50	45
318	-	1l.80 green and yellow	3·00	2·75

Design:—1l.80, Oina.

83 Neil Armstrong (first man on Moon)

1999. 30th Anniv of First Manned Moon Landing. Multicoloured.

319		25b. Type **83**	50	45
320		25b. Michael Collins (pilot of Command Module)	50	45
321		5l. Edwin Aldrin (pilot of Lunar Module)	7·25	6·75

84 Military Merit

1999. Orders and Medals. Multicoloured.

322		25b. Type **84**	50	45
323		25b. For Valour	50	45
324		25b. Civil Merit	50	45
325		90b. Mihai Eminescu Medal	1·30	1·20
326		1l.10 Order of Gloria Muncii	1·60	1·50
327		2l.40 Order of Stefan al Mare	4·00	3·75
MS328		70×50 mm. 5l. Order of the Republic	8·00	7·75

85 Embroidered Shirt

1999. Crafts. Multicoloured.

329		5b. Inlaid wine flask	25	25
330		25b. Type **85**	40	40
331		95b. Ceramic jugs	95	90
332		1l.80 Wicker table and chairs	3·25	3·00

86 Goethe

1999. 250th Birth Anniv of Johann Wolfgang von Goethe (poet).

333	**86**	1l.10 multicoloured	2·40	2·30

87 Emblem

1999. Tenth Anniv of Adoption of Latin Alphabet.

334	**87**	25b. multicoloured	80	75

88 Metropolitan Varlaam

1999. Patriarchs of the Orthodox Church. Multicoloured.

335	25b. Type **88**	50	45
336	2l.40 Metropolitan Gurie Grosu	4·50	4·25

89 Bogdan II (1449–51)

1999. 15th to 17th-century Princes of Moldavia. Multicoloured.

337	25b. Type **89**	40	40
338	25b. Bogdan IV (1568–72)	40	40
339	25b. Constantin Cantemir (1685–93)	40	40
340	1l.50 Simon Movila (1606–07)	1·60	1·50
341	3l. Gheorghe III Duca (1665–66, 1668–72 and 1678–84)	4·00	3·75
342	3l.90 Ilias Alexandru (1666–68)	7·25	6·75
MS343	97×78 mm. 5l. Vasile Lupu (1634–53) (25×30 mm)	8·00	7·75

90 European Otter (*Lutra lutra*)

1999. Animals in the Red Book. Multicoloured.

344	25b. Type **90**	80	75
345	1l.80 Beluga (*Huso huso*)	2·40	2·30
346	3l.60 Greater horseshoe bat (*Rhinolophus ferrumequinum*)	4·75	4·50

91 Player and Chessboard

1999. World Women's Chess Championship, Chisinau. Multicoloured.

347	25b. Type **91**	50	45
348	2l.20+30b. Championship venue and emblem	4·50	4·25

92 4th-century BC Bronze Helmet and Candle Holder

1999. National History Museum Exhibits. Multicoloured.

349	25b. Type **92**	80	75
350	1l.80 10th-century BC ceramic pot	2·40	2·30
351	3l.60 Gospel, 1855	6·50	6·00

93 Raluca Eminovici

2000. 150th Birth Anniv of Mihail Eminescu (poet). Sheet 141×111 mm containing T **93** and similar vert designs. Multicoloured.

MS352	20b. Type **93**; 25b. Gheorghe Eminovici; 1l.50 Iosif Vulcan; 3l. Veronica Micle; 5l. Mihail Eminescu	13·00	12·50

94 Ileana Cosinzeana

2000. Folk Heroes. Multicoloured.

353	25b. Type **94**	80	75
354	1l.50 Fat-Frumos	2·40	2·30
355	1l.80 Harap Alb	3·25	3·00

95 Henri Coanda (aeronautical engineer)

2000. Birth Anniversaries. Each pink and black.

356	25b. Type **95** (114th anniv)	50	45
357	25b. Toma Ciorba (physician, 136th)	50	45
358	2l. Guglielmo Marconi (physicist, 126th)	2·40	2·30
359	3l.60 Norbert Wiener (mathematician, 106th)	5·50	5·25

96 Globe in Palm and Astronaut on Moon

2000. The Twentieth Century. Multicoloured.

360	25b. Type **96** (first manned moon landing, 1969)	40	40
361	1l. Model of nuclear fission and hand (use of nuclear energy)	2·10	2·00
362	3l. Computer and mouse (development of electronic data processing)	4·00	3·75
363	3l.90 P. F. Teoctist (patriarch) and Pope John Paul II (consultation between Eastern and Roman churches) (horiz)	6·00	5·75

97 *Resurrection* (anon)

2000. Easter. Paintings in the National Gallery. Multicoloured.

364	25b. Type **97**	40	40
365	3l. *Resurrection* (anon)	5·50	5·00

98 "Building Europe"

2000. Europa.

366	**98**	3l. multicoloured	5·50	5·25

99 Emblem and Profiles

2000. EXPO 2000 World's Fair, Hanover, Germany (367) and WIPA 2000 International Stamp Exhibition, Vienna, Austria (368). Multicoloured.

367	25b. Type **99**	80	75
368	3l.60+30b. Hands holding tweezers and 1994 1b. State Arms stamp	5·50	5·25

100 Monastery, Tipova

2000. Churches and Monasteries. Multicoloured.

369	25b. Type **100**	80	75
370	1l.50 St. Nicolas's Church (vert)	1·60	1·50
371	1l.80 Palanca Church (vert)	2·40	2·30
372	3l. Butucheni Monastery	4·75	4·50

101 Judo

2000. Olympic Games, Sydney. Multicoloured.

373	25b. Type **101**	80	75
374	1l.80 Wrestling	2·40	2·30
375	5l. Weightlifting	7·25	6·75

102 Child and Schoolroom

2000. International Teachers' Day.

376	**102**	25b. grey and green	80	75
377	-	3l.60 blue and lilac	5·50	5·25

Design:—3l.60, Teacher holding book.

103 Adoration of the Shepherds (icon)

2000. Christmas. Multicoloured.

378	25b. Type **103**	80	75
379	1l.50 The Nativity (icon)	2·40	2·30
MS380	84×66 mm. 5l. Mary and Baby Jesus (icon) (27×32 mm)	7·25	7·00

104 Mother and Child

2001. 50th Anniv of United Nations High Commissioner for Refugees.

381	**104**	3l. multicoloured	3·00	2·75

105 Corncrake

2001. Endangered Species. The Corncrake. Multicoloured.

382	3l. Type **105**	3·25	3·00
383	3l. Singing	3·25	3·00
384	3l. In reeds	3·25	3·00
385	3l. With chicks	3·25	3·00

Nos. 382/5 were issued together, *se-tenant*, forming a composite design.

106 Yuri Gagarin and Vostok (spacecraft)

2001. 40th Anniv of First Manned Space Flight.

386	**106**	1l.80 multicoloured	2·40	2·30

107 Maria Dragan

2001. Anniversaries. Multicoloured.

387	25b. Type **107** (singer, 15th death anniv)	65	60
388	1l. Marlene Dietrich (actress, birth centenary)	1·30	1·20
389	2l. Ruxandra Lupu (314th death anniv)	2·75	2·50
390	3l. Lidia Lipkovski (opera singer, 43rd death anniv)	3·25	3·00

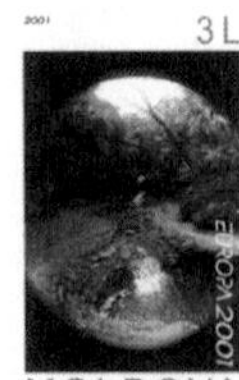

108 Waterfall

2001. Europa. Water Resources.

391	**108**	3l. multicoloured	4·00	3·75

109 Prunariu

2001. 20th Anniv of Space Flight by Dumitru Prunariu (first Rumanian cosmonaut).

392	**109**	1l.80 multicoloured	2·40	2·30

110 Stylized Humans (Aliona Valeria Samburic)

2001. Winning Entries in Children's Painting Competition. Designs by named artist. Multicoloured.

393	25b. Type **110**	40	40
394	25b. Cars inside house and sun (Ion Sestacovschi)	40	40
395	25b. House, balloons and sun (Cristina Mereacre)	40	40
396	1l.80 Abstract painting (Andrei Sestacovschi)	3·25	3·00

111 1991 7k. Arms Stamp

2001. Tenth Anniv of First Moldovan Stamps. Sheet 100×74 mm, containing T **111** and similar multicoloured designs.

MS397	40b. Type **111**; 2l. 1991 13k. Arms stamp; 3l. 30k. 1991 Flag stamp (42×25 mm)	5·50	5·50

112 Tiger (*Panthera tigris*)

2001. Chisinau Zoo. Multicoloured.

398	40b. Type **112**	50	45

399 1l. Quagga (*Equus quagga*) 1·10 1·10
400 1l.50 Brown bear (*Ursus arctos*) 1·60 1·50
401 3l.+30b. *Antilopa nilgau* 4·00 3·75
MS402 84×70 mm. 5l. Lion (*Panthera leo*) 6·50 6·25

113 Flag and Buildings

2001. Tenth Anniv of Independence.
403 **113** 1l. multicoloured 1·60 1·50

114 Cimpoi

2001. Musical Instruments. Multicoloured.
404 40b. Type **114** 80 75
405 1l. Fluier 1·60 1·50
406 1l.80 Nai 2·40 2·30
407 3l. Tar'agot 4·75 4·50

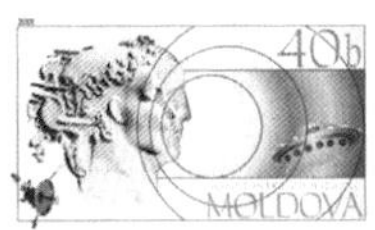

115 Women's Profiles and Space Ship

2001. United Nations Year of Dialogue among Civilizations. Multicoloured.
408 40b. Type **115** 80 75
409 3l.60 Children encircling globe (vert) 6·00 5·75

116 Nicolai Mavrocordat (1711–15)

2001. Rulers. Multicoloured (except **MS**416).
410 40b. Type **116** 80 75
411 40b. Mihai Racovita (1716–26) 80 75
412 40b. Constantin Mavrocordat (1748–49) 80 75
413 40b. Grigore Callimachi (1767–69) 80 75
414 1l. Grigore Alexandru Gnica (1774–77) 1·60 1·50
415 3l. Anton Cantemir (1705–7) 4·75 4·50
MS416 61×88 mm. 5l. Dimitrie Cantemir (1710–11) (black, yellow and red) (horiz) 7·25 7·00

117 St. Treime Basilica, Manastirea Saharna

2001. Christmas. Multicoloured.
417 40b. Type **117** 80 75
418 1l. Adormirea Maicii Domnului Basilica, Manastirea Hancu 1·60 1·50
419 3l. St. Dumitru Basilica, Orhei 4·00 3·75
420 3l.90 Nasterea Domnului Cathedral, Chisinau 6·50 6·00

118 Emblem

2001. Tenth Anniv of Union of Independent States.
421 **118** 1l.50 multicoloured 2·40 2·30

119 Cross Country Skiing

2002. Winter Olympic Games, Salt Lake City. Multicoloured.
422 40b. Type **119** 80 75
423 5l. Biathlon 5·50 5·25

120 Hora

2002. Traditional Dances. Multicoloured.
424 40b. Type **120** 80 75
425 1l.50 Sirba 2·40 2·30

121 *Fetele din Ceadir-lunga* (Mihai Grecu)

2002. Art. Multicoloured.
426 40b. Type **121** 90 80
427 40b. *Meleag Natal* (Eleonora Romanescu) 90 80
428 1l.50 *Fata la Fereastra* (Valentina Rusu-Ciobanu) 2·75 2·40
429 3l. *In Doi* (Igor Vieru) 4·50 4·00

122 Entrance to Kishinev Circus

2002. Europa. Circus.
430 **122** 3l. multicoloured 6·25 6·00

123 Rose

2002. Botanical Gardens, Kishinev. Sheet 130×85 mm containing T **123** and similar vert designs. Multicoloured.
MS431 40b. Type **123**; 40b. Peony; 1l.50 Aster; 3l. Iris 9·00 8·75

124 *Portrait of Cecilia Gallerani*

2002. 550th Birth Anniv of Leonardo da Vinci (artist). Sheet 129×85 mm containing T **124** and similar vert designs. Multicoloured.
MS432 40b. Type **124**; 1l.50 *The Virgin and Child with St. Anne*; 3l. *Mona Lisa* (*La Gioconda*) 8·00 7·75

125 Ion Neculce (chronicler) (Lady with an Ermine)

2002. Personalities. All sepia.
433 40b. Type **125** 90 85
434 40b. Nicolae Costin (chronicler) 90 85
435 40b. Grigore Ureche (chronicler) 90 85
436 40b. Nicolae Testemiteanu (rector, Faculty of Medicine, Chisnau University) 90 85
437 1l.50 Sergiu Radautan (rector, Technical Faculty, Chisnau University) 3·50 3·50
438 3l.90 Alexandre Dumas (writer) 4·50 4·25

126 Vladimir Horse

2002. Horses. Showing horse breeds. Multicoloured.
439 40b. Type **126** 35 35
440 1l.50 Orlov 2·30 2·20
441 3l. Arab 6·25 6·00

127 Stork, Houses and Man carrying Grapes (Alexandru Catranji)

2002. Children's Paintings. The Post. Multicoloured.
442 40b. Type **127** 90 85
443 1l.50 Birds, flower and globe 2·75 2·50
444 2l. Postman and globe 3·50 3·50

128 Union Emblem, Member States Presidents and Flags

2002. Union of Independent States Conference, Chisnau. Multicoloured.
445 1l.50 Type **128** 2·75 2·50
446 3l.60 Emblem and handshake 5·50 5·00

129 Entrance to Underground Warehouse

2002. 50th Anniv of Cricova Wine Factory. Multicoloured.
447 40b. Type **129** 55 50
448 40b. Barrels in warehouse 55 50
449 1l.50 Dining hall (vert) 2·20 2·00
450 2l. Interior of warehouse 2·75 2·50
451 3l.60 Glasses and bottles of wine (vert) 5·50 5·00

130 Tissandier Brothers' Airship (1883)

2003. Airships. Multicoloured.
452 40b. Type **130** 90 85
453 2l. *Uchebny* (Training Craft) (1908) 3·50 3·50
454 5l. LZ 127 *Graf Zeppelin* (1928) (inscr 'Count Zeppelin') 11·00 10·00

131 Scarce Swallowtail (*Iphiclides podalirius*)

2003. Butterflies and Moths. Multicoloured.
455 40b. Type **131** 90 85
456 2l. Jersey tiger moth (*Callimorpha quadripunctaria*) 1·80 1·70
457 3l. Oak hawk moth (*Marumba quercus*) 3·50 3·50
458 5l. Meleager's Blue (*Polyommatus daphnis*) 9·00 8·50
MS459 127×82 mm. Nos. 455/8 22·00 21·00

132 Rural Landscape

2003. Tenth Anniv of Europa Stamps. Sheet 130×85 mm containing T **132** and similar horiz design. Multicoloured.
MS460 1l.50 Type **132**; 5l. Chisinau 9·00 8·75

133 Folk Ensemble "JOC"

2003. Europa. Poster Art. Multicoloured.
461 3l. Type **133** 3·50 3·50
462 5l. Exhibition poster (Mihai Eminescu, 150th birth anniv (Rumanian writer)) 5·50 5·00

134 Emblem and Flag

2003. Red Cross Society of Moldova. Multicoloured.
463 40b. Type **134** 90 85
464 5l. Damaged buildings and Red Cross workers 4·50 4·25

135 Runner

2003. European Youth Olympics Festival, Paris. Multicoloured.
465 40b. Type **135** 90 85
466 3l. Cyclists 2·75 2·50
467 5l. Gymnast 6·25 6·00

136 *Luminari* (A. Akhlupin)

2003. World without Terror. Multicoloured.
468 40b. Type **136** 90 85
469 3l.90 *Pax Cultura* (N. Roerich) 5·50 5·00

137 Dimitrie Cantemir

2003. 340th Birth Anniv of Dimitrie Cantemir (linguist and scholar).
470 **137** 3l.60 multicoloured 5·50 5·00

138 Vladimir Voronin (president of Moldova)

2003. Moldova—Chairman, Council of Europe Committee of Ministers, May–November 2003.
471 **138** 3l. multicoloured 5·00 4·75

139 Nicolae Donici

2003. Personalities. Multicoloured.

472	40b. Type **139** (astronomer)	90	85
473	1l.50 Nicolae Dimo (soil scientist)	2·20	2·00
474	2l. Nicolai Costenco (writer)	2·75	2·50
475	3l.90 Milestone Lewis (Lev Milstein) (film director)	4·50	4·25
476	5l. Vincent van Gogh (artist)	7·25	6·75

140 Mute Swan (*Cygnus olor*)

2003. Birds. Multicoloured.

477	40b. Type **140**	90	85
478	2l. Great egret (*Egretta alba*)	2·75	2·50
479	3l. Tawny eagle (*Aquila rapax*) (vert)	4·50	4·25
480	5l. Little bustard (*Tetrax tetrax*) (vert)	7·25	6·75
MS481	131×86 mm. Nos. 477/80	15·00	14·50

141 Natalie Gheorghiu

2004. Personalities. Multicoloured.

482	40b. Type **141** (doctor)	55	50
483	1l.50 Metropolitan Dosoftei (scholar)	2·20	2·00

142 Archaeological Dig

2004. Europa. Holidays. Multicoloured.

484	40b. Type **142**	90	85
485	4l.40 Winemaking	6·25	6·00

143 Stefan III holding Sword

2004. 500th Death Anniv of Stefan III (Stefan cel Mare) (Moldavian ruler). Multicoloured.

486	40b. Type **143**	90	85
487	2l. Kneeling holding church	2·75	2·50
MS488	110×92 mm. 4l.40 Head and shoulders of Stefan III	7·25	7·00

144 Goalkeeper and Ball

2004. Centenary of FIFA (Federation Internationale de Football Association). Multicoloured.

489	2l. Type **144**	2·75	2·50
490	4l.40 Player and ball	5·00	4·75

145 Memorial

2004. 60th Anniv of Iasi-Chisinau Battle. Sheet 81×62 mm.

MS491	2l. multicoloured	3·50	3·25

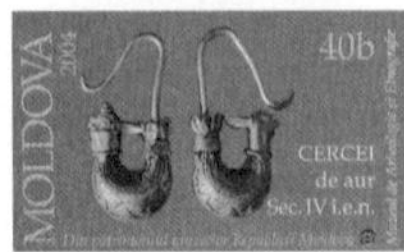
146 Gold Earrings

2004. Ancient Jewellery. Multicoloured.

492	40b. Type **146**	55	50
493	1l. Gold torque	1·40	1·40
494	1l.50 Silver earrings	2·20	2·00
495	2l. Bronze bracelet	3·00	3·00

147 Boxers

2004. Olympic Games, Athens. Multicoloured.

496	40b. Type **147**	90	85
497	4l.40 Weightlifter	6·25	6·00

148 *Ephedra distachya*

2004. Plants. Multicoloured.

498	40b. Type **148**	45	40
499	1l.50 *Pyrus elaeagrifolia*	1·80	1·70
500	2l. *Padus avium*	2·75	2·50
501	2l. *Crataegus pentagyna*	2·75	2·50

149 Locomotive ER

2005. Railways. Multicoloured.

502	60b. Type **149**	75	70
503	1l. Locomotive ChME3	1·20	1·10
504	1l.50 Diesel locomotive D777-3	1·80	1·70
505	4l.40 Locomotive 3TE10M	5·25	5·00

150 Building Facade

2005. Centenary of St. George's Church, Capriana Monastery.

506	**150**	40b. multicoloured	75	70

151 Memorial Monument

2005. 60th Anniv of End of World War II.

507	**151**	1l.50 multicoloured	2·30	2·10

152 Cheese, Bowls, Jug and Cup

2005. Europa. Gastronomy. Multicoloured.

508	1l.50 Type **152**	2·10	2·00
509	4l.40 Pastries, flask and mug	5·50	5·00

153 Pawn and Championship Emblem

2005. European Women's Chess Championship, Chisinau.

510	**153**	4l.40 multicoloured	6·00	5·50

154 Serghi Lunchevici

2005. Composers. Multicoloured.

511	40b. Type **154**	30	30
512	1l. Valeriu Cupcea	1·50	1·40
513	2l. Anton Rubenstein	2·75	2·50

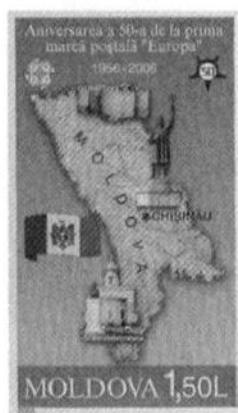
155 Map and National Symbols

2005. 50th Anniv of Europa Stamps. Multicoloured.

514	1l.50 Type **155**	1·10	1·00
515	15l. First Europa stamp	11·50	10·50
MS516	83×70 mm. Nos. 514/15	12·00	11·50

156 Emblem and Globe

2005. World Information Society Summit, Tunis.

517	**156**	4l.40 multicoloured	5·25	5·00

157 Passport Pages

2005. Tenth Anniv of National Passport. Sheet 109×68 mm containing T **157** and similar vert designs. Multicoloured.

MS518	40b. Type **157**; 1l.50 Passport covers; 4l.40 Two passport pages	7·50	7·25

158 *Emys orbicularis*

2005. Reptiles and Amphibians. Multicoloured.

519	40b. Type **158**	60	55
520	1l. *Eremias arguta*	1·50	1·40
521	1l.50 *Pelobates fuscus*	2·10	2·00
522	2l. *Vipera ursinii* (inscr "ursine")	2·75	2·50
MS523	114×109 mm. Nos. 519/22	6·75	6·50

159 St. Nicolae Church (1937)

2005

524	**159**	40b. multicoloured	75	70

160 St. Nicolae Church, Falesti (1795)

2005. Christmas. Multicoloured.

525	40b. Type **160**	45	40
526	1l. Varzharesti monastery (1420)	6·00	5·50

161 Newspapers

2006. 15th Anniv of Makler Newspaper.

527	**161**	60b. emerald and black	75	70

162 Luge

2006. Winter Olympic Games, Turin. Multicoloured.

528	60b. Type **162**	75	70
529	6l.20 Skier	6·75	6·25

163 Postal Building, Balti

2006. Architecture.

530	**163**	22b. ultramarine	15	15
531	-	40b. chocolate	30	30
532	-	53b. blue	45	40
533	-	57b. green	55	50
534	-	60b. green	75	70
535	-	3l.50 claret	4·50	4·25

Designs:—22b. Type **163**; 40b. Monument, Chisinau; 53b. Single storey building, Cahul; 57b. Post and Telegraph building, Soroca; 60b. Biserica Adormirea Maicii Domnului, Copceac; 3l.50 Museum, Chisinau.

164 Lace

2006. Costumes and Textiles. Multicoloured.

536	40b. Type **164**	45	40
537	60b. Woman's costume (vert)	60	55
538	3l. Man's costume (vert)	3·75	3·50
539	4l.50 Embroidery	4·50	4·25

165 Gheorghe Mustea

2006. Gheorghe Mustea (composer and conductor).

540	**165**	60b. multicoloured	75	70

166 Globe as Street of Flags

2006. Europa. Integration. Multicoloured.

541	60b. Type **166**	75	70
542	4l.50 Artist and musicians (vert)	5·25	5·00

167 Chess Board and clocks

2006. 37th Chess Olympiad, Turin.

543	**167** 4l.50 multicoloured	6·00	5·50

168 Trophy and Two Players

2006. World Cup Football Championship, Germany. Multicoloured.

544	2l. Type **168**	2·30	2·10
545	3l. Goleo VI and Pille (mascots)	3·75	3·50
546	4l.50 Two players and high ball	4·50	4·25

169 Ion Halippa (historian) (135th birth anniv)

2006. Personalities. Multicoloured.

547	40b. Type **169**	60	55
548	1l. Eufrosinia (Valentina) Cuza (opera singer) (150th birth anniv)	1·20	1·10
549	2l. Petre Stefanuca (ethnographer) (birth centenary)	2·00	1·80
550	4l.50 Wolfgang Amadeus Mozart (composer) (250th birth anniv)	3·50	3·25

170 *Martes martes*

2006. Animals. Multicoloured.

551	60b. Type **170**	60	55
552	1l. *Mustela erminea*	1·10	1·00
553	2l. *Mustela lutrola*	2·30	2·10
554	3l. *Mustela eversmanni*	3·00	2·75
MS555	81×67 mm. 6l.20 *Felis silvestris* (vert)	7·50	7·00

171 Flag and Government Building

2006. 15th Anniv of Republic.

556	**171** 2l.60 multicoloured	2·50	2·40

172 German Shepherd

2006. Dogs. Multicoloured.

557	40b. Type **172**	40	35
558	60b. Collie	50	50
559	2l. Poodle	2·00	1·80
560	6l.20 Magyar Agar (Hungarian sight-hound)	5·75	5·50

173 Grapes, Glass and Vineyard

2006. Wine.

561	**173** 60b. multicoloured	65	60

174 *Landscape* (Valerii Metleaev)

2006. Christmas. Multicoloured.

562	40b. Type **174**	40	35
563	3l. *Mummers* (Elena Bontea)	2·75	2·75
564	6l.20 *Mummers* (Mihail Statnii) (vert)	5·75	5·50

No. 565 and Type **175** have been left for 'Surcharge', not yet received.

176 *Francesco Petrarca* (Raphael Morghen)

2007. National Art Museum. Multicoloured.

566	65b. Type **176**	65	60
567	85b. *Napoleon Bonaparte*	80	70
568	2l. *Friedrich von Schiller*	2·00	1·80
569	4l.50 *Johann Wolfgang von Goethe*	5·25	4·75

177 *Morchella steppicola*

2007. Fungi. Multicoloured.

570	65b. Type **177**	65	60
571	85b. *Phylloporus rhodoxantus*	80	70
572	2l. *Amanita solitaria*	2·00	1·80
573	6l.20 *Boletus aereus*	5·75	5·50

178 Scouts

2007. Europa. Centenary of Scouting. Multicoloured.

574	2l.85 Type **178**	2·50	2·40
575	4l.50 Scouts examining flowers and butterfly	4·50	4·25

2007. Nos. 85 and No. 75 surch.

576	**19** 25b. on 3k. deep reddish purple	40	35
577	**19** 85b. on 3k. purple	90	85

180 Tabby Cat

2007. Cats. Multicoloured.

578	65b. Type **180**	65	60
579	1l. Siamese (vert)	1·00	95
580	1l.50 Birman (vert)	1·60	1·40
581	6l.20 Persian	5·75	5·50

181 *Otis tarda* (Great Bustard)

2007. Birds. Multicoloured.

582	75b. Type **181**	65	60
583	1l. *Neophron percnopterus* (Egyptian Vulture)	1·30	1·20
584	2l.50 *Lyrurus tetrix* (Black Grouse)	3·25	3·00
585	5l. *Gyps fulvus* (Griffon Vulture)	5·25	4·75
MS586	67×81 mm. 6l.20 *Tetrao urogallus* (Capercaillie)	6·50	6·25

No. **MS**586 also contains a stamp size label which, with the stamp and margins form a composite design of Capercaille cock, hen and chicks.

182 *Acipenser gueldenstaedtii*

2007. Preservation of Dniestr Fauna. Fish. Multicoloured.

587	1l. Type **182**	1·00	95
588	3l. *Zingel zingel*	3·25	3·00

183 Ion Luca Caragiale (Romanian playwright and short story writer)

2007. Personalities. Multicoloured.

589	75b. Type **183** (155th birth anniv)	50	50
590	1l. Anastasia Dicescu (opera singer) (120th birth anniv)	1·00	95
591	3l. Mircea Eliade (Romanian historian, writer and philosopher) (birth centenary)	3·25	3·00
MS592	80×67 mm. 6l.20 Maria Bieshu (singer) (vert)	6·50	6·25

No. **MS**592 also contains a stamp size label which, with the stamp and margins form a composite design.

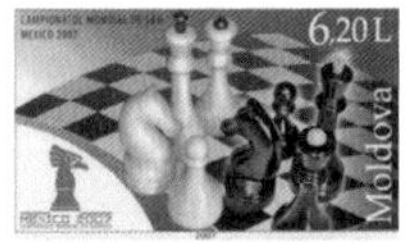
184 Chess Pieces

2007. Chess Championship, Mexico

593	**184** 6l.20 multicoloured	6·25	5·75

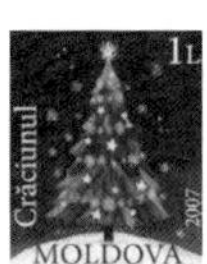
185 Christmas Tree

2007. Christmas. Multicoloured.

594	1l. Type **185**	90	85
595	4l.50 Santa Claus (46×27 mm)	4·25	4·00

186 Peresecina, Orhei

2008. Wells. Multicoloured.

596	10b. blue	25	25
597	75b. green	65	60
598	1l. purple (vert)	90	85
599	3l. brown (vert)	2·50	2·40

Designs:—10b. Type **186**; 75b. Duruitoarea, Riscani; 1l. Ciripcau, Floresti; 3l. Ocnita.

187 Cycling

2008. Olympic Games, Beijing. Multicoloured.

600	1l. Type **187**	65	60
601	6l.20 Boxing	3·75	3·25
602	15l. Weightlifting	8·75	8·25

188 Early Messenger

2008. Europa. The Letter. Multicoloured.

603	3l.50 Type **188**	3·25	3·00
604	4l.50 VDU, '@' and envelopes	4·00	3·50

189 1858 27p. and 54p. Stamps of Moldavia (As Type **1**) and (No. 2)

2008. 150th Anniv of First Moldavian Stamps. Multicoloured.

605	1l. Type **189**	1·30	1·20
606	3l. 1858 81p. and 108p. stamps of Moldavia (As No. 3) and (No. 4)	3·25	3·00

190 Football and Stadium

2008. European Football Championship–Euro 2008.

607	**190** 4l.50 multicoloured	6·50	6·00

191 *Maianthemum bifolium*

2008. Flora. Multicoloured.

608	1l. Type **191**	1·10	1·10
609	3l. *Hepatica nobilis*	3·25	3·00
610	5l. *Nymphaea alba*	5·50	5·25
MS611	160×83 mm. As Nos. 608/10	10·00	9·50

The stamps, margins and labels of **MS**611 form a composite design of a pond.

192 Onisifor Ghibu (politician)

2008. Personalities. Multicoloured.

612	1l.20 Type **192**	1·30	1·20
613	1l.50 Ciprian Porumbescu (composer)	1·60	1·50
614	3l. Lev Tolstoi (Leo Tolstoy) (writer)	3·25	3·00
615	4l.50 Maria Tanase (singer)	5·00	4·75

193 *Cervus nippon* (Sika Deer)

2008. Fauna. Multicoloured.

616	3l. Type **193**	3·25	3·00
617	3l. *Cervus elaphus* (Red Deer)	3·25	3·00

Stamps of the same design were issued by Kazakhstan.

194 Early Town

2008. 600th Anniv of Bender. Sheet 113×81 mm.

MS618	**194** 4l.20 multicoloured	5·50	5·25

195 Antioh Cantemir (Antiochus Kantemir) (diplomat)

2008. Cantemir Dynasty. Each red-brown.

619	1l.20 Type **195**	1·60	1·50
MS620	81×67 mm. 3l. Dimitri Cantemir (Prince of Moldova)	4·00	3·75

196 Mikhail Grigory Sutu

2008. Princes of Moldova. Multicoloured.

621	85b. Type **196**	95	90
622	1l.20 Grigory Alexandru Ghica	1·30	1·20
623	1l.50 Mikhail Sturza	1·60	1·50
624	2l. Alexandru Ipsilanti	1·90	1·80
625	3l. Ioan Sandu Sturza	3·25	3·00
626	4l.50 Scarlat Callimachi	4·75	4·50
MS627	108×113 mm. 6l.20 Alexandru Ioan Cuza	7·25	7·00

2008. Vyacheslav Gozhan, Boxing Bronze Medalist, Olympic Games, Beijing. No. 601 optd **Veaceslav GOJAN Box–Bronz**.

628	6l.20 As No. 601	7·00	6·50

198 Emblem and Globe

2008. Moldovan Presidency of Central European Initiative Organization. Sheet 82×68 mm containing T **198** and similar vert design. Multicoloured.

MS629	1l.20 Type **198**; 4l.50 Emblem and globe (different)	7·25	7·00

199 Christmas Goat

2008. Christmas. Multicoloured.

630	1l.20 Type **199**	1·60	1·50
MS631	90×53 mm. 6l.20 Children carolling (46×27 mm)	7·25	7·00

200 Emblem and Open Book

2008. 60th Anniv of Universal Declaration of Human Rights.

632	**200**	4l.50 multicoloured	5·00	4·75

201 Symbols of Moldova

2009. 650th Anniv of State. Multicoloured.

633	1l.20 Type **201**	1·60	1·50
MS634	69×83 mm. 6l.20 Bogdan Voda (Bogdan I of Moldavia) on horseback	7·25	7·00

202 Weapons (10th/14th-century)

2009. Ancient Weapons. Multicoloured.

635	1l.20 Type **202**	1·40	1·40
636	4l.50 Weapons (8th/13th-century)	5·25	5·00

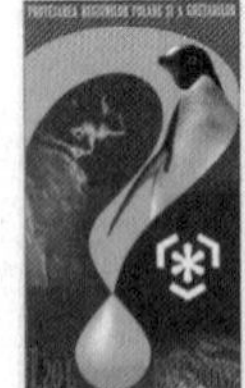
203 Penguin

2009. Preserve Polar Regions and Glaciers. Multicoloured.

637	1l.20 Type **203**	1·60	1·50
638	6l.20 Polar bear	6·50	6·00

204 Decorated Eggs

2009. Easter. Multicoloured.

639	1l.20 Type **204**	1·60	1·50
640	3l. Decorated eggs on plate	4·00	3·75

205 Emblems

2009. 60th Anniv of Council of Europe.

641	**205**	4l.50 multicoloured	5·25	5·00

206 Nicolae Donici (astrophysicist)

2009. Europa. Astronomy. Multicoloured.

642	4l.20 Type **206**	5·00	4·75
643	4l.50 Galileo Galilei (astronomer)	5·50	5·00

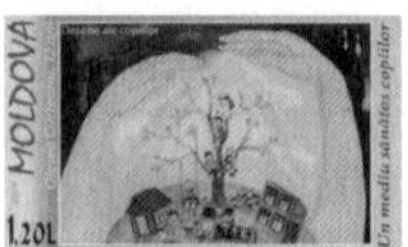

207 Children in Tree (Olesya Curtyanu)

2009. Winning Designs in Children's Drawing Competition 'A Healthy Child'. Multicoloured.

644	1l.20 Type **207**	1·30	1·20
645	1l.50 Child sleeping in bird's nest (Yulia Strutsa) (vert)	1·60	1·50
646	5l.+20b. Child kneeling in diseased world (Irina Simion) (vert)	6·00	5·75

208 *Viola suavis* (Russian violet)

2009. Flora. Multicoloured.

647	1l.20 Type **208**	1·30	1·20
648	1l.50 *Adonis vernalis* (Pheasant's Eye)	1·60	1·50
649	3l. *Campanula persicifolia* (Bellflower)	3·50	3·25
MS650	100×65mm. 4l.50 *Papaver rhoeas* (Poppy)	4·75	4·50
MS651	134×100 mm. 1l.20 As Type **208**; 1l.50 As No. 648; 3l. As No. 649; 4l.50 Poppy	11·00	10·50

209 *Bombus paradoxus*

2009. Insects. Multicoloured.

652	1l.20 Type **209**	1·30	1·20
653	1l.50 *Xylocopa valga*	1·60	1·50
654	3l. *Carabus clathratus*	3·25	3·00
655	4l.50 *Coenagrion lindeni*	5·00	4·75

210 Post Horn

2009. Personal Stamps. Multicoloured.

656	1l.20 Type **210**	4·00	3·75
657	1l.20 Post Horn (blue frame)	4·00	3·75
658	1l.20 Stefan Cel Mare monument	4·00	3·75
659	1l.20 Cathedral	4·00	3·75
660	1l.20 Bouquet of flowers	4·00	3·75
661	1l.20 Wedding bouquet and rings	4·00	3·75

211 Walnut

2009. Fruit and Nut. Multicoloured.

662	50b. Type **211**	65	60
663	85b. Mulberry (*Morus nigra*)	95	90
664	1l.20 Pears	1·40	1·40
665	5l. Apricots (*Prunus armeniaca*)	6·00	5·50

212 Corjeuti, Briceni

2009. Rural Houses. Houses. Multicoloured.

666	1l.20 Type **212**	1·40	1·40
667	4l.50 Chirsova, Comrat	5·25	5·00
668	7l. Batuceni, Orhei	8·00	7·50

213 'Moldova' Grape

2009

669	**213**	4l.50 multicoloured	5·25	5·00

214 Face and Web

2009. European Day Against Human Trafficking.

670	**214**	4l.50 multicoloured	5·25	5·00

215 Eufrosinia Antonovna Kersnovskaya (Gulag camp survivor and memoir writer)

2009. Personalities. Multicoloured.

671	1l.20 Type **215**	1·40	1·40
672	1l.20 Eugène Ionesco (Romanian playwright and dramatist)	1·40	1·40
673	4l.50 Nicolai Gogol (writer)	5·25	5·00
674	7l. Charles Robert Darwin (naturalist and evolutionary theorist)	8·00	7·50

216 *Capra*

2009. Christmas. Showing scenes from Christmas by Vasily Movilyanu. Multicoloured.

675	1l.20 Type **216**	1·40	1·40
676	4l.50 *Plugusorul*	5·25	5·00

217 Natalia Dadiani (educationalist) (145th birth anniv)

2010. Personalities. Multicoloured.

677	1l.20 Type **217**	1·30	1·20
678	1l.20 Grigore Vieru (poet and writer) (85th birth anniv)	1·30	1·20
679	5l.40 Ivan Zaikin (wrestler and aviator) (130th birth anniv)	5·75	5·50
680	7l. Maria Cebotari (soprano and actress) (birth centenary)	7·75	7·25
MS681	115×165 mm. 4l.50 Mihai Eminescu (poet, novelist and journalist) (160th birth anniv) (vert)	4·75	4·50

218 Alpine Skiing

2010. Olympic Winter Games. Vancouver. Multicoloured.

682	1l.20 Type **218**	1·30	1·20
683	8l.50 Biathlon (vert)	8·25	7·75

219 Necklace of Shells

2010. National Museum of Archaeology and History. Multicoloured.

684	1l.20 Type **219**	1·30	1·20
685	7l. Circular and perforated pendants	7·50	7·00

220 Frederic Chopin

2010. Birth Bicentenary of Fryderyk Franciszek Chopin

686	**220**	5l.40 multicoloured	5·50	5·25

221 *Lactarius piperatus*

2010. Fungi. Multicoloured.

687	1l.20 Type **221**	1·30	1·20
688	2l. *Amanita pantherina*	2·10	2·00
689	5l.40 *Russula sanguinea*	5·50	5·25
690	7l. *Coprinus picaceus*	7·25	6·75
MS691	136×67 mm. Nos. 687/90	16·00	15·00

222 *Carduelis carduelis* (Goldfinch)

2010. Birds. Multicoloured.

692	85b. Type **222**	95	90
693	1l. *Passer domesticus* (House Sparrow)	1·10	1·10
694	1l.20 *Strix uralensis Pallas* (Ural Owl)	1·30	1·20
695	4l.50 *Pica pica* (Eurasian Magpie)	4·75	4·25
MS696	101×66 mm. 8l.50 *Columba livia* (Pigeon)	8·75	8·25

223 *Pungata cu Doi Bani*

2010. Europa. Childrens' Books. Multicoloured.

697	1l.20 Type **223**	1·30	1·20
698	5l.40 *Guguta si Prietenii*	5·50	5·25

224 Victory Monument

2010. 65th Anniv of End of World War II

699	**224**	4l.50 multicoloured	4·75	4·50

225 Player and Ball

2010. World Football Championship, South Africa. Multicoloured.

700	1l.20 Type **225**	1·30	1·20
701	8l.50 Goalkeeper making save (vert)	9·00	8·50

226 Broken Heart and Syringe

2010. AIDS Awareness Campaign

702	**226**	1l.20 multicoloured	1·30	1·20

227 *Flowers* (Ion Tabirta)

2010. Flower Paintings. Multicoloured.

703	1l. Type **227**	1·10	1·10
704	1l.20 *Bouquet of Poppies* (Oleg Cojocaru)	1·30	1·20
705	2l. *Flowers* (Mikhail Statnii)	2·10	2·00
706	5l.40 *Chrysanthemums* (Leonid Grigorasenko)	5·75	5·50

228 Flood Victims

2010. Support for Flood Victims of July 2010

707	**228**	1l.20 +50b. multicoloured	1·80	1·70

229 Moldovenesca

2010. Traditional Dances. Multicoloured.

708	85b. Type **229**	95	90
709	5l.40 Calusharii (vert)	5·75	5·50

230 Feteasca Grapes

2010. Grapes

710	**230**	4l.50 multicoloured	4·75	4·50

231 Arms of Moldova

2010. State Symbols. Multicoloured.

711	1l.20 Type **231**	1·30	1·20
712	4l.50 National Flag	4·75	4·50
MS713	135×100 mm. Nos. 711/12, each×3	19·00	18·00

232 Mammoth

2010. Prehistoric Animals. Multicoloured (grey tone).

714	85b. Type **232**	95	90
715	1l. Ursus spelaeus	1·10	1·10
716	1l.20 Panthera leo spelaea	1·30	1·20
717	4l.20 Bison	4·50	4·25
MS718	114×108 mm. 1l.20 Pontoceros; 1l.50 Anancus; 5l.40 Stephanorhinus; 8l.50 Homotherium	18·00	17·00

233 Angel carrying Gift and Child at Window

2010. Christmas and New Year. Multicoloured.

719	1l.20 Type **233**	1·30	1·20
MS720	102×203 mm. 5l.40 Cathedral Church and Bell Tower, Chisinau	5·75	5·50

2011. National Museum of Archaeology and History. Multicoloured.

721	85b. Anthropomorphic amphora with lid	50	45
722	1l.20 Biconical vessel with zoomorphic designs	80	75
723	8l.50 Taller biconical vessel with handles anthropomorphic designs	5·00	4·75
MS724	136×102 mm. Nos. 721, 722×2 and 723	7·25	7·00

234 Ralli Mansion (now Museum), Dolna, Străşeni

2011. Architecture

725	10b. red brown	15	15
726	25b. deep ultramarine	30	30
727	85b. deep turquoise-green	80	75
728	1l. deep claret	95	90
729	1l.20 dark steel blue	1·10	1·10
730	1l.50 deep green	1·40	1·40

Designs:—10b. Type **234**; 25b. Mirzoian Mansion, Hinceşti; 85b. Balioz Mansion, Ivancea; 1l. Secondary School for Girls, Soroca; 1l.20 Pommer Mansion and Park, Ţaul, Donduşeni; 1l.50 Hasnaş Mansion, Soha, Drochia

235 Mărţişor (Ludmila Berezin)

2011. Handicraft Art. Multicoloured.

731	1l.20 Type **235**	1·10	1·10
732	4l.20 Portrait (Natalia Cangea)	4·00	3·75
733	7l. Carpet (Ecaterina Popescu)	6·50	6·00

236 Eugenia Maleşevschi

2011. Art. Self-portraits. Multicoloured.

734	85b. Type **236**	80	75
735	1l.20 Nikolae Grigorescu	1·10	1·10
736	2l. Alexandru Plămădeală	1·90	1·80
737	5l.40 Mihail Grecu	5·00	4·75

237 Yuri Gagarin

2011. 50th Anniversary of First Manned Space Flight. Multicoloured.

MS738	1l.20 Type **237**; 5l.40 Gherman Titov; 7l. Virgil I. Grissom; 8l.50 Alan B. Shepard	21·00	20·00

238 Leaf, Fire, Deer and Forest

2011. Europa. Forests. Multicoloured.

739	4l.20 Type **238**	4·00	3·75
740	5l.40 Forest, owl and slice through tree	5·00	4·75
MS741	134×100 mm. Nos. 739/70, each×3	29·00	28·00

239 Hyacinth

2011. Flowers. Multicoloured.

742	70b. Type **239**	65	60
743	85b. Tulips	80	75
744	1l.20. Narcissi	1·10	1·10
745	2l. Pansies	1·90	1·80

240 Candles on Rail Track

2011. 70th Anniv of Deportation 12-14th June 1941

746	**240**	1l.20 multicoloured	1·10	1·10

241 1991 7c. Stamp (As Type **1**)

2011. 20th Anniv of First Moldovan Stamp. Multicoloured.

MS747	85b. As Type **1**; 1l.20 As No. 2; 4l.20 As No.3	6·00	5·75

242 *Meles meles* (Badger)

2011. Fauna. Multicoloured.

748	85b. Type **242**	80	75
749	1l.20 *Erinaceus europaeus* (Hedgehog)	1·10	1·10
750	3l. *Canis lupus* (Wolf)	3·00	2·75
751	4l.20 *Vulpes vulpes* (Fox)	4·00	3·75
MS752	135×100 mm. 85b. *Plegadis falcinellus* (Glossy Ibis); 1l.20 *Pelicanus onocrotalus* (Great White Pelican); 5l.40 *Platalea leucorodia* (Eurasian Spoonbill); 8l.50 *Aythya nyroca* (Ferruginous Duck)	15·00	14·50

243 Monument and Flag

2011. 20th Anniversary of Independence. Sheet 110×92 mm

MS753	**243** 4l.20 multicoloured	4·00	3·75

244 Cigarette and Lungs

2011. Smoking Awareness Campaign

754	**244**	1l.20 multicoloured	1·10	1·10

245 Holy Gates of Chişinău

2011. 20th Anniv of Moldova - Romania Diplomatic Relations. Multicoloured.

755	1l.20 Type **245**	1·10	1·10
756	4l.50 Arch of Triumph, Bucharest	4·50	4·25
MS757	135×100 mm. As Nos. 755/6	5·50	5·25

246 Palace of Culture

2011. 575th Anniv of Chişinău. Multicoloured.

MS758	85b. Type **246**; 1l.20 National Opera and Ballet Theatre; 2l.' Mihai Emenescu' National Theatre; 3l.85 National Palace; 5l.40 'Patria' Cinema	13·00	12·50

247 Hands enclosing Stylized Figures

2011. 60th Anniv of UNHCR (United Nations High Commissioner for Refugees)

759	**247**	1l.20 multicoloured	1·10	1·10

248 Horn Blower

2011. Christmas and New Year. Multicoloured.

760	1l.20 Type **248**	1·10	1·10
MS761	90×53 mm. 4l.50 Mummers (46×28 mm)	4·50	4·25

249 Magda Isanos (writer)

2011. Personalities. Multicoloured.

762	85b. Type **249**	80	75
763	1l.20 Nicolae Sulac (singer)	1·10	1·10
764	3l. Cleopatra Hrzhanovschi (teacher and composer)	3·00	2·75

765 4l.50 Franz Liszt (composer) 4·50 4·25

250 *Boy of Pokrovca* (Igor Vieru)

2012. Art. Children. Multicoloured.

766 85b. Type **250** 80 75
767 1l.20 *Orphan* (Pavel Piscariov) 1·10 1·10
768 2l.85 *Portrait of a Child* (Lidia Arionescu-Baillayre) 2·75 2·50
769 4l.50 *Boy with Hat* (Constantin Kitaika) 4·50 4·25

251 Ion and Doina Aldea Teodorovichi

2011. 20th Death Anniv of Ion and Doina Aldea Teodorovichi (musicians) in Road Traffic Accident. Sheet 67×80 mm

MS770 **251** 7l. multicoloured 7·00 6·75

252 Mihail Dolgan

2012. 70th Birth Anniv of Mihai Dolgan (singer, composer and founder of Noroc (band)). Sheet 81×67 mm

MS771 **252** 4l.50 multicoloured 4·50 4·25

253 Woman, Colţişor

2012. Traditional Costumes. Regional Cooperation in the Field of Communication. Multicoloured.

772 85b. Type **253** 80 75
773 1l.20 Man, Pălărie 1·10 1·10
774 3l. Woman, Năframă 3·00 2·75
MS775 80×67 mm. 8l.50 Wedding couple 8·00 7·75

254 Monastery Church

2012. Europa. Visit Moldova. Multicoloured.

776 4l.20 Type **254** 4·00 3·75
777 5l.40 'Mileştii Mici' Wine Factory 5·50 5·25

255 Siege Battering Ram

2012. Ancient Weapons. Multicoloured.

778 85b. Type **255** 80 75
779 1l.20 Soldier (vert) 1·10 1·10
780 1l.50 Army Commander (vert) 1·60 1·50
781 5l.40 Siege catapult 5·25 5·00

256 Jucător de Chişinău

2012. Pigeons. Multicoloured.

782 85b. Type **256** 90 85
783 1l.20 Jucător de Balti 1·20 1·10
784 3l. Jucător basarabean 2·90 2·75
785 4l.20 Roller de Chişinău 4·00 3·75

257 Wrestling

2012. Olympic Games, London. Multicoloured.

786 4l.50 Type **257** 4·50 4·25
787 5l.40 Mountain biking 5·25 5·00

258 Mildred Scheel

2012. Roses. Multicoloured.

788 85b. Type **258** 90 85
789 1l.20 Friesia 1·20 1·10
790 3l. Priscilla 2·90 2·75
791 4l.20 Caribia 4·00 3·75
MS791a 134×101 mm. Nos. 788/91 8·00 7·50

259 Eugeny Ureche

2012. Personalities. Multicoloured.

792 85b. Type **259** 90 85
793 1l.20 Spiridon Mocanu (performer) 1·20 1·10
794 4l.50 George Emil Palade (Romanian cell biologist) 4·50 4·25
795 8l.50 Jean-Jacques Rousseau (philosopher and writer) 8·25 8·00

260 Maria Bieshu

2012. Maria Bieşu (opera singer) Commemoration

796 **260** 1l.20 multicoloured 1·20 1·10

261 Chiele Buteşti Canyon

2012. Natural Monuments of Moldova. Multicoloured.

797 1l.20 Type **261** 1·20 1·10
798 4l.20 Preserved landscape Suta de movile nature reserve near Prut River 4·00 3·75
799 7l. Emil Rakovitsa caves 7·00 6·25

262 The Nativity

2012. Christmas. Icons from the National Museum of History and Archaeology. Multicoloured.

800 1l.75 Type **262** 1·80 1·70
801 5l.40 The Nativity (19th-century) 5·25 5·00

263 Kilometer Zero, Chisenau

2012. Kilometre Zero

802 **263** 1l.75 multicoloured 1·80 1·70

264 *Mihai Eminescu* (Emil Cheldescu)

2013. Paintings. Multicoloured.

803 1l.75 Type **264** 1·80 1·70
804 5l.75 *Fidelity* (Vasily Nascu) 5·50 5·25

265 Transmitter and Emblem

2013. Regional Commonwealth in Field of Communications

805 **265** 4l.50 multicoloured 4·50 4·25

266 *Ribes uva-crispa* (gooseberry)

2013. Berries. Multicoloured.

806 55b. Type **265** 45 40
807 1l.50 *Vaccinium myrtillus* (Bilberry) 1·50 1·40
808 1l.75 *Viburnum opulus* (Guelder Rose) 1·80 1·70
809 1l.75 *Rubus idaeus* (Raspberry) 1·80 1·70
810 2l. *Hippophae rhamnoides* (Sea Buckthorn) 2·00 1·80
811 4l. *Ribes rubrum* (Redcurrant) 4·00 3·90

267 Post Van

2013. Europa. Postal Transport. Multicoloured.

812 4l.50 Type **267** 4·50 4·25
813 5l.75 Early horse-drawn mail cart 5·50 5·25

268 *Panthera uncial* (Snow Leopard)

2013. 35th Anniv of Chisinau Zoo. Multicoloured.

814 1l.75 Type **268** 1·80 1·70
815 2l. *Macropus rufogriseus* (Bennett's Wallaby) 1·90 1·80
MS816 67×80 mm. 5l.75 *Pavo cristatus* (Peacock) 6·00 5·75

269 Illustration From *Cuşma lui Guguţă* by Octavia Ţarălungă

2013. Year of Spiridon Vangheli. Multicoloured.

817 1l.75 Type **269** 1·80 1·70
818 1l.75 Illustration from *Datoria lui Guguţă* by Igor Vieru 1·80 1·70

270 *Thysania agrippina*

2013. Butterflies and Moths. Multicoloured.

819 1l. Type **270** 95 90
820 1l.75 *Papilio blumei* 1·80 1·70
821 1l.75 *Salamis temora* 1·80 1·70
822 5l.75 *Cymothoe excelsa* 5·50 5·25

271 Adrian Paunescu (poet)

2013. Personalities. Multicoloured.

823 1l.75 Type **271** 1·80 1·70
824 1l.75 Anton Crihan (politician) 1·80 1·70

272 Ion Bass (folk singer)

2013. Personalities. Multicoloured.

825 1l.75 Type **272** 30 25
826 1l.75 Angela Paduraru (folk singer) 55 50
827 4l.50 Giuseppe Verdi (composer) 1·75 3·00
828 5l.40 Richard Wagner (composer) 2·00 1·80

273 Alexei Mateevici

2013. 125th Birth Anniv of Alexei Mateevici (poet). Sheet 81×67 mm

MS829 **273** 5l.75 multicoloured 5·50 5·25

274 Grapes 'Muscat Timpuriu'

2013. Grapes

830 **274** 1l.75 multicoloured 1·80 1·70

275 Bus

2013. City Transport. Multicoloured.

831 1l.75 Type **275** 1·80 1·70
832 3l. Trolley bus 2·90 2·75
MS833 67×81 mm. 5l.75 Tram 5·50 5·25

276 Carollers

2013. Traditional Rituals. Multicoloured.

834 **276** 1l.75 multicoloured 1·00 80

277 Embroidered Flowers

2013. My Stamp. Multicoloured.

835 1l.75 Type **277** 1·00 80
836 1l.75 Bouquet ('Flori de 'Nu-mă-uita') 1·00 80
837 1l.75 Post horn (34×34 mm) 1·00 80
838 1l.75 Post horn, country inscription different (34×34 mm) 1·00 80

278 Pottery

2014. Crafts. Multicoloured.

839 1l.20 Type **278** 55 50
840 1l.75 Basket weaving 1·00 80
841 5l.75 Carpet weaving 2·25 2·00

279 Skier

2014. Winter Olympic Games, Sochi. Multicoloured.

842 4l.50 Type **279** 2·00 1·80
843 5l.40 Ice hockey goal keeper 2·25 2·00

280 Cimbalom

2014. Europa. Musical Instruments. Multicoloured.

844 3l. Type **280** 3·00 2·75
845 5l.75 Cobza 5·00 4·75

281 Symbols of Easter

2014. Easter.

846 **281** 1l.75 multicoloured 1·50 1·00

282 Ethnographic Museum

2014. Museums of Moldova. Multicoloured.

847 1l.20 Type **282** 1·20 1·10
848 2l. National History Museum 1·90 1·80
849 4l. National Art Museum 4·00 3·75

283 Haymaking

2014. Bicentenary of German Settlement in Bessarabia.

850 **283** 1l.75 multicoloured 1·50 1·40

284 Tamara Cheban (singer)

2014. Personalities. Multicoloured.

851 1l.20 Type **284** (birth centenary) 1·20 1·10
852 1l.75 Dmitry Matcovschi (writer) (75th birth anniv) 1·50 1·40
853 3l. Toma Ciorba (Bessarabian-born Romanian physician and hospital director) (150th birth anniv) 3·00 2·75
854 8l.50 Maria Cebotari (singer) (90th birth anniv) 8·00 7·75

285 *Ion Kryange and Mihai Eminescu* (Mihai Grecu)

2014. Art. Sheet 66×66 mm.

MS855 **285** 5l.75 multicoloured 6·00 6·00

286 *Trenul durerii* (The Train of Pain) (Iurie Platon)

2014. 65th Anniv of Bessarabia Deportation.

856 **286** 1l.75 multicoloured 1·50 4·00

287 Flags

2014. Signing of the Association Agreement with European Union.

857 **287** 1l.75 multicoloured 1·50 1·40

288 Caracul Ewe and Lamb

2014. Sheep Breeds. Multicoloured.

858 1l.20 Type **288** 1·20 1·10
859 5l.75 Tigale ewe and lambs 5·25 5·00

289 Fried Fish with Garlic Sauce

2014. Traditional Food and Culinary Herbs. Multicoloured.

860 1l. Type **289** 95 90
861 1l.20 Bean soup with thyme 1·20 1·10
862 4l. Pies with cheese and dill 4·25 3·75
863 7l. Lemon chicken with parsley 7·00 6·75

290 Burgundy Snail (*Helix pomatia*)

2014. Fauna. Multicoloured.

864 1l.20 Type **290** 1·20 1·10
865 1l.50 White Stork (*Ciconia ciconia*) (46×28 mm) 1·40 1·25
866 1l.75 Zander (*Stizostedion lucioperca*) (46×28 mm) 1·50 1·40
867 2l. Common Carp (*Cyprinus carpio*) (46×28 mm) 1·90 1·80
868 3l. River Snail (*Viviparus viviparus*) 3·00 2·75
869 8l.50 Western Yellow Wagtail (*Motacilla flava*) (46×28 mm) 8·00 7·85
MS870 136×81 mm. As Nos. 864/9 15·00 14·50

291 Dimitrie Bogos

2014. Bessarabian Soldiers of the First World War. Multicoloured.

871 1l.75 Type **291** 1·50 1·40
872 4l. Constantin Brăescu 4·25 4·00
873 5l.75 Aleksandru Averescu 5·25 5·00

292 Snowman

2014. Christmas and New Year. Multicoloured.

874 1l.75 Type **292** 1·50 1·40
875 5l.75 Santa and sleigh 5·25 5·00

293 Grigore Vieru

2015. 80th Birth Anniv of Grigore Vieru (writer). Sheet 81×67 mm.

MS876 **293** 5l.75 multicoloured 5·50 5·50

294 Tree, Roots and Soil

2015. International Year of Soil (877) and International Year of Light (878). Multicoloured.

877 1l.75 Type **294** 1·50 1·40
878 4l.50 Symbols of light 4·75 4·50

295 Egon Doga, Score and Dancers

2015. Musical Masterpiece of the Century - *Gingasa si Tandra mea Hara* composed by Egon Doga.

879 **295** 1l.75 multicoloured 1·50 1·40

2015. Cities' Coats of Arms. Multicoloured.

880 10b. Cauşeni City Arms 15 10·15
881 25b. Hinceşti 30 30
882 1l. Ungheni 95 90
883 1l.20 Orhei 1·20 1·10
884 3l. Balti 3·00 2·75
885 5l. Chishinau 4·75 4·50

297 Rocking Horse

2015. Europa. Old Toys. Multicoloured.

886 5l.75 Type **297** 5·25 5·00
887 11l. Terracotta bird and goat 10·50 10·00
MS888 130×78 mm. As Nos. 886/7, each×2 16·00 16·00

298 Telecommunications

2015. 150th Anniv of ITU (International Telecommunication Union).

889 **298** 1l.75 multicoloured 1·50 1·40

299 Capul de Pod Şerpeni Memorial Complex

2015. 70th Anniv of End of World War II.

890 **299** 1l.75 multicoloured 1·50 1·40

2015. International Childrens Day. Multicoloured.

891 1l.20 Couple playing with baby and pram (Catalina Munteanu) 1·20 1·10
892 1l.75 Swan, fish and waterlilies on pond (Cristina Isakov) 1·50 1·40
893 5l.75 Birds in tree (Ana Vlas) (vert) 5·25 5·00

2015. Traditional Costumes. Multicoloured.

894 1l.75 Blouse with heavily embroidered sleeves (20th century) 1·50 1·40
895 11l. Blouse with strip embroidery (1925) 10·50 10·00

2015. Personalities. Multicoloured.

896 1l.20 Constanta Tirtau (actress and TV presenter) 1·20 1·10
897 1l.75 Gica Petrescu (singer) 1·50 1·40
898 4l. Nicolae Corlateanu (writer) (birth centenary) 3·75 3·50
899 11l. Piotr Chaikovsk (composer) (175th birth anniv) 10·50 10·00
MS900 68×688 mm. 5l.75 Alexandru Cristea (125th birth anniv) 5·25 5·00

2015. 40th Anniv of Signing of the Helsinki Final Act of the Conference on Security and Co-operation in Europe (CSCE) (since 1995, Organization for Security and Co-operation in Europe, OSCE). Multicoloured.

901 11l. '40' Helsinki Final Act and signatories seated at table 10·50 10·00

304 *Rocks* (Veniamin Slobodzinschi)

2015. Art. Landscapes. Multicoloured.

902 1l.75 Type **304** 1·50 1·40
903 3l. *Evening in the Field* (Eleonara Romanescu) 3·00 2·75
904 5l.75 *On the Outskirts of the Village of Dolna* (Dmitrie Peicev) 5·50 5·00
905 9l.50 *Landscape* (Vasile Nascu) 9·00 8·75

305 *Sturnus vulgaris* (Starling)

2015. Birds. Multicoloured.

906 1l.20 Type **305** 1·20 1·10
907 1l.75 *Pyrrhula pyrrhula* (Bullfinch) 1·50 1·40
908 4l. *Cyanistes caeruleus* (Blue Tit) 4·25 2·50
909 5l.75 *Bombycilla garrulus* (Waxwing) 4·25 4·00
MS910 90×53 mm. 5l.75 *Alauda arvensis* (Skylark) 6·00 6·00

306 Moldovenyaska, Moldova

2015. Folk Dances. Multicoloured.

911 1l.75 Type **306** 1·50 1·40
912 11l. Yalli, Azerbaijan 10·50 10·00

307 Mihai Volontir

2015. Mihai Volonti (actor) Commemoration.

913 **307** 1l.75 multicoloured 1·50 1·40

308 Anniversary Emblem

2015. 70th Anniv of United Nations.

914 **308** 15l.50 blue, new blue and silver 12·50 12·00

2015. Personalised Stamps.

915	1l.75 Posthorn, scarlet side panel	1·50	1·40
916	1l.75 Posthorn, ultramarine side panel	1·50	1·40
917	1l.75 Posthorn, emerald side panel	1·50	1·40
918	1l.75 Posthorn, orange lower panel (34×34 mm)	1·50	1·40
919	1l.75 Posthorn, turquoise-green lower panel (34×34 mm)	1·50	1·40
920	1l.75 Posthorn, green lower panel (34×34 mm)	1·50	1·40
921	1l.75 Posthorn, blue lower panel (34×34 mm)	1·50	1·40

310 Motocross

2015. Sport. Motorsport. Multicoloured.

922	1l.20 Type **310**	1·20	1·10
923	5l.75 Autocross race car	5·25	5·00

311 Children and 'Star'

2015. Winter Traditions. Multicoloured.

923a	1l.75 Type **311**	1·50	1·40
923b	9l.50 Tradition of Plugușorul	9·00	8·75

312 Droplet

2016. Blood Donation Campaign

924	**312**	1l.75 multicoloured	1·50	1·40

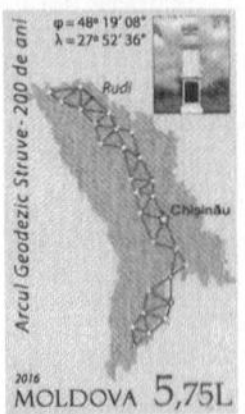

313 Map and Points on Ark

2016. Bicentenary of Struve Geodetic Arc. UNESCO World Heritage Site. Sheet 83×69 mm.

MS925 **313** 5l.75 multicoloured	6·00	6·00

314 Snowdrops

2016. Mertishor Music Festival. Multicoloured.

926	1l.20 Type **314**	1·20	1·10
927	5l.75 Wild Rose flowers and tassels	5·25	5·00

315 Deportation

2016. 65th Anniv of Mass Deportations

928	**315**	1l.75 multicoloured	1·50	1·40

316 Green

2016. Europa. Think Green. Multicoloured.

929	5l.75 Type **316**	5·25	5·00
930	9l.50 Roller painting contaminated landscape green	9·00	8·75
MS931 134×100 mm. Nos. 929/30, each×3		29·00	28·00

11 L

12 APRILIE 2016 - 55 DE ANI DE LA PRIMUL ZBOR AL OMULUI ÎN SPAȚIU

(317)

2016. No. 386 surch and overprinted as T **317**. 55th Anniv of First Manned Space Flight by Yuri Gagarin.

932	11l. on 1l.80 multicoloured	10·50	10·00

318 *Xeranthemum annuum*

2016. Flowers. Multicoloured.

933	10b. Type **318**	15	15
934	25b. *Matricaria recutita*	30	30
935	1l. *Cichorium intybus*	95	90
936	2l. *Taraxacum officinale*	1·90	1·80
937	3l. *Achillea millefolium*	3·00	2·75
938	5l. *Salvia nemorosa*	4·75	4·50
MS939 65×113 mm. Nos. 933/8		15·00	15·00

319 Jesus entering Jerusalem

2016. Palm Sunday

940	**319**	1l.75 multicoloured	1·50	1·40

320 Gladioli

2016. Endangered Species. Turkish Marsh Gladioli (*Gladiolus imbricatus*). Multicoloured.

941	11l. Type **320**	10·50	10·00
942	11l. One spray facing right	10·50	10·00
943	11l. Stem with several blooms	10·50	10·00
944	11l. Two large blooms	10·50	10·00

321 Plants, Dove and Gateway

2016. Christian Holidays - White Sunday.

945	**321**	1l.75 multicoloured	1·50	1·40

322 Carol Schmidt (politician)

2016. Personalities. Multicoloured.

946	1l.20 Type **322** (170th birth anniv)	1·20	1·10
947	1l.20 Nocolae Anestiadi (surgeon) (birth centenary)	1·20	1·10
948	1l.75 Grigore Grigoriu (actor) (75th birth anniv)	1·50	1·40
949	5l.75 Emil Loteanu (film director) (80th birth anniv)	5·25	5·00

323 Putna Monastery

2016. 550th Anniv of Putna Monastery. Sheet 67×67 mm.

MS950 **323** 5l.75 multicoloured	6·00	6·00

324 Girls weaving Crowns of Flowers

2016. Christian Festival - Sanziana.

951	**324**	1l.75 multicoloured	1·50	1·40

325 Women Athletes

2016. Olympic Games - Rio 2016. Multicoloured.

952	5l.75 Type **325**	5·25	5·00
953	15l.50 Canoeing	15·50	15·00

POSTAGE DUE STAMPS

D33 Postal Emblems

1994

D150	**D33**	30b. brown and green	1·30	1·10
D151	**D33**	40b. green and lilac	1·90	1·70

One stamp in the pair was put on insufficiently franked mail, the other stamp on associated documents.

MONACO

A principality on the S. coast of France including the town of Monte Carlo.

1885. 100 centimes = 1 French franc.
2002. 100 cents = 1 euro.

1 Prince Charles III

1885

1	1	1c. olive	33·00	24·00
2	1	2c. lilac	75·00	39·00
3	1	5c. blue	95·00	50·00
4	1	10c. brown on yellow	£120	55·00
5	1	15c. red	£500	33·00
6	1	25c. green	£900	£100
7	1	40c. blue on red	£110	60·00
8	1	75c. black on red	£375	£170
9	1	1f. black on yellow	£2250	£700
10	1	5f. red on green	£4250	£2750

2 Prince Albert

1891

11	2	1c. green	1·10	90
12	2	2c. purple	1·10	90
13	2	5c. blue	65·00	8·75
22	2	5c. green	65	55
14	2	10c. brown on yellow	£140	24·00
23	2	10c. red	4·50	90
15	2	15c. pink	£250	14·50
24	2	15c. brown on yellow	5·00	1·10
25	2	15c. green	2·40	3·25
16	2	25c. green	£375	50·00
26	2	25c. blue	20·00	7·25
17	2	40c. black on pink	4·50	3·75
18	2	50c. brown on orange	10·00	7·25
19	2	75c. brown on buff	36·00	28·00
20	2	1f. black on yellow	25·00	17·00

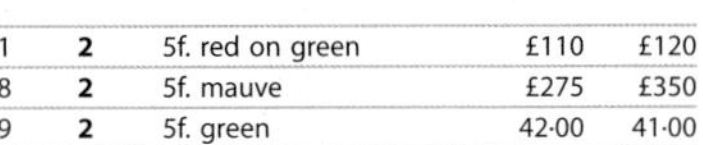

21	2	5f. red on green	£110	£120
28	2	5f. mauve	£275	£350
29	2	5f. green	42·00	41·00

1914. Surcharged **+5c.**

30	2	10c.+5c. red	12·00	11·00

4 War Widow and Monaco

1919. War Orphans Fund.

31	4	2c.+3c. mauve	50·00	55·00
32	4	5c.+5c. green	30·00	30·00
33	4	15c.+10c. red	31·00	31·00
34	4	25c.+15c. blue	55·00	55·00
35	4	50c.+50c. brown on orange	£275	£250
36	4	1f.+1f. black on yellow	£450	£550
37	4	5f.+5f. red	£1500	£1700

1920. Princess Charlotte's Marriage. Nos. 33/7 optd **20 mars 1920** or surch also.

38	4	2c.+3c. on 15c.+10c. red	60·00	65·00
39	4	2c.+3c. on 25c.+15c. blue	60·00	65·00
40	4	2c.+3c. on 50c.+50c. brown on orange	60·00	65·00
41	4	5c.+5c. on 1f.+1f. black on yellow	60·00	65·00
42	4	5c.+5c.on 5f.+5f. red	60·00	65·00
43	4	15c.+10c. red	36·00	36·00
44	4	25c.+15c. blue	24·00	24·00
45	4	50c.+50c. brown on orange	70·00	90·00
46	4	1f.+1f. black on yellow	£110	£120
47	4	5f.+5f. red	£9500	£10000

1921. Princess Antoinette's Baptism. Optd **28 DECEMBRE 1920** or surch also.

48	2	5c. green	1·20	1·20
49	2	75c. brown on buff	7·25	11·00
50	2	2f. on 5f. mauve	50·00	70·00

1922. Surch.

51	2	20c. on 15c. green	1·80	2·40
52	2	25c. on 10c. red	1·20	1·60
53	2	50c. on 1f. black on yellow	7·25	11·00

8 Prince Albert I

9 St. Devote Viaduct

1922

54	8	25c. brown	5·50	6·50
55	-	30c. green	1·20	2·40
56	-	30c. red	60	70
57	9	40c. brown	1·20	1·20
58	-	50c. blue	6·50	7·25
59	-	60c. grey	60	50
60	-	1f. black on yellow	60	35
61	-	2f. red	70	60
62	-	5f. brown	55·00	60·00
63	-	5f. green on blue	17·00	18·00
64	-	10f. red	20·00	30·00

Designs:—As Type **9**: 30, 50c. Oceanographic Museum; 60c., 1, 2f. The Rock; 5, 10f. Prince's Palace, Monaco.

12 Prince Louis

13 Prince Louis and Palace

1923

65	12	10c. green	35	50
66	12	15c. red	60	95
67	12	20c. brown	60	50
68	12	25c. purple	35	35
69	13	50c. blue	50	70

1924. Surch with new value and bars.

70	2	45c. on 50c. brown on orange	70	1·20
71	2	75c. on 1f. black on yellow	85	1·20
72	2	85c. on 5f. green	85	1·20

14

15

16

17 St. Devote Viaduct

1924

73	**14**	1c. grey	10	25
74	**14**	2c. brown	10	25
75	**14**	3c. mauve	4·25	3·50
76	**14**	5c. orange	35	50
77	**14**	10c. blue	25	25
78	**15**	15c. green	25	25
79	**15**	15c. violet	4·75	2·75
80	**15**	20c. mauve	25	25
81	**15**	20c. pink	50	35
82	**15**	25c. pink	25	25
83	**15**	25c. red on yellow	25	25
84	**15**	30c. orange	25	25
85	**15**	40c. brown	25	25
86	**15**	40c. blue on blue	25	35
87	**15**	45c. black	1·60	1·10
88	**16**	50c. green	25	35
89	**15**	50c. brown on yellow	25	25
90	**16**	60c. brown	25	35
91	**15**	60c. green on green	25	35
92	**15**	75c. green on green	1·10	60
93	**15**	75c. red on yellow	35	25
94	**15**	75c. black	1·30	85
95	**15**	80c. red on yellow	60	35
96	**15**	90c. red on yellow	3·00	2·40
97	**17**	1f. black on yellow	35	60
98	**17**	1f.05 mauve	60	1·20
99	**17**	1f.10 green	13·00	9·00
100	**15**	1f.25 blue on blue	35	35
101	**15**	1f.50 blue on blue	5·75	3·50
102	-	2f. brown and mauve	3·00	1·80
103	-	3f. lilac and red on yellow	36·00	19·00
104	-	5f. red and green	12·00	9·50
105	-	10f. blue and brown	32·00	26·00

Design:—As Type **17**: 2f. to 10f. Monaco.

1926. Surch.

106	**15**	30c. on 25c. pink	50	30
107	**15**	50c. on 60c. green on green	2·20	50
108	**17**	50c. on 1f.05 mauve	1·60	95
109	**17**	50c. on 1f.10 green	19·00	13·00
110	**15**	50c. on 1f.25 blue on blue	2·20	95
111	**15**	1f.25 on 1f. blue on blue	1·20	60
112	-	1f.50 on 2f. brown and mauve (No. 102)	9·25	9·00

20 Prince Charles III, Louis II and Albert I

1928. International Philatelic Exn, Monte Carlo.

113	**20**	50c. red	3·50	7·25
114	**20**	1f.50 blue	3·50	7·25
115	**20**	3f. violet	3·50	7·25

20a

21 Palace Entrance

22 St. Devote's Church

23 Prince Louis II

1933

116	**20a**	1c. plum	20	30
117	**20a**	2c. green	20	30
118	**20a**	3c. purple	20	30
119	**20a**	5c. red	20	30
120	**20a**	10c. blue	25	35
121	**20a**	15c. violet	3·00	2·75
122	**21**	15c. red	1·20	35
123	**21**	20c. brown	1·20	35
124	**A**	25c. sepia	1·20	50
125	**22**	30c. green	1·80	50
126	**23**	40c. sepia	4·75	3·00
127	**B**	45c. brown	5·50	2·75
128	**23**	50c. violet	4·75	1·80
129	**C**	65c. green	5·50	1·70
130	**D**	75c. blue	6·00	2·75
131	**23**	90c. red	14·50	5·00
132	**22**	1f. brown	42·00	12·00
133	**D**	1f.25 red	10·00	7·25
134	**23**	1f.50 blue	60·00	17·00
135	**A**	1f.75 claret	55·00	16·00
136	**A**	1f.75 carmine	37·00	19·00
137	**B**	2f. blue	22·00	7·25
138	**21**	3f. violet	32·00	14·50
139	**A**	3f.50 orange	70·00	60·00
140	**22**	5f. purple	44·00	48·00
141	**A**	10f. blue	£180	£110
142	**C**	20f. black	£250	£225

Designs:—Horiz (as Type **21**): A, The Prince's Residence; B, The Rock of Monaco; C, Palace Gardens; D, Fortifications and Harbour.

For other stamps in Type **20a** see Nos. 249, etc.

1933. Air. Surch with Bleriot XI aircraft and 1f50.

143	1f.50 on 5f. red & grn (No. 104)	42·00	42·00

28 Palace Gardens

1937. Charity.

144	**28**	50c.+50c. green	5·00	4·75
145	-	90c.+90c. red	5·00	4·75
146	-	1f.50+1f.50 blue	10·00	9·50
147	-	2f.+2f. violet	17·00	17·00
148	-	5f.+5f. red	£170	£180

Designs:—Horiz: 90c. Exotic gardens; 1f.50, The Bay of Monaco. Vert: 2, 5f. Prince Louis II.

1937. Postage Due stamps optd **POSTES** or surch also.

149	**D18**	5 on 10c. violet	1·60	1·60
150	**D18**	10c. violet	1·60	1·60
151	**D18**	15 on 30c. bistre	1·60	1·60
152	**D18**	20 on 30c. bistre	1·60	1·60
153	**D18**	25 on 60c. red	2·50	2·50
154	**D18**	30c. bistre	3·50	3·50
155	**D18**	40 on 60c. red	3·50	3·50
156	**D18**	50 on 60c. red	3·50	4·25
157	**D18**	65 on 1f. blue	3·25	2·75
158	**D18**	85 on 1f. blue	7·75	7·25
159	**D18**	1f. blue	12·00	12·00
160	**D18**	2f.15 on 2f. red	12·00	13·00
161	**D18**	2f.25 on 2f. red	30·00	31·00
162	**D18**	2f.50 on 2f. red	42·00	42·00

30a Prince Louis II

1938. National Fete Day. Sheet 100×120 mm.

MS163 **30a**	10f. purple	£100	£130

31

1938

164	**31**	55c. brown	10·00	4·00
165	**31**	65c. violet	40·00	30·00
166	**31**	70c. brown	35	40
167	**31**	90c. violet	50	50
168	**31**	1f. red	24·00	15·00
169	**31**	1f.25 red	50	50
170	**31**	1f.75 blue	24·00	14·50
171	**31**	2f.25 blue	50	50

33 Monaco Hospital

1938. Anti-cancer Fund. 40th Anniv of Discovery of Radium.

172	-	65c.+25c. green	16·00	18·00
173	**33**	1f.75+50c. blue	17·00	20·00

Design:—Vert: 65c. Pierre and Marie Curie.

34 The Cathedral

38 Monaco Harbour

1939

174	**34**	20c. mauve	35	50
175	-	25c. brown	70	50
176	-	30c. green	60	50
177	-	40c. red	1·10	70
178	-	45c. purple	1·10	70
179	-	50c. green	70	50
180	-	60c. red	95	50
181	-	60c. green	2·40	1·40
182	**38**	70c. lilac	60	50
183	**38**	75c. green	60	50
184	-	1f. black	60	50
185	-	1f.30 brown	60	50
186	-	2f. purple	70	55
187	-	2f.50 red	36·00	30·00
188	-	2f.50 blue	3·00	2·50
189	**38**	3f. red	85	50
190	**34**	5f. blue	7·75	6·00
191	-	10f. green	2·20	2·40
192	-	20f. blue	2·20	2·40

Designs:—Vert: 25, 40c., 2f. Place St. Nicholas; 30, 60c., 20f. Palace Gateway; 50c., 1f., 1f.30, Palace of Monaco. Horiz: 45c., 2f.50, 10f. Aerial view of Monaco.

40 Louis II Stadium

1939. Inauguration of Louis II Stadium, Monaco.

198	**40**	10f. green	£150	£170

41 Lucien

1939. National Relief. 16th–18th-century portrait designs and view.

199	**41**	5c.+5c. black	3·00	3·00
200	-	10c.+10c. purple	3·00	3·00
201	-	45c.+15c. green	11·00	11·00
202	-	70c.+30c. mauve	17·00	18·00
203	-	90c.+35c. violet	17·00	18·00
204	-	1f.+1f. blue	36·00	38·00
205	-	2f.+2f. red	47·00	42·00
206	-	2f.25+1f.25 blue	55·00	55·00
207	-	3f.+3f. red	65·00	80·00
208	-	5f.+5f. red	£110	£140

Designs:—Vert: 10c. Honore II; 45c. Louis I; 70c. Charlotte de Gramont; 90c. Antoine I; 1f. Marie de Lorraine; 2f. Jacques I; 2f.25, Louise-Hippolyte; 3f. Honore III. Horiz: 5f. The Rock of Monaco.

1939. Eighth International University Games. As T **40** but inscr "VIIIeme JEUX UNIVERSITAIRES INTERNATIONAUX 1939".

209	40c. green	1·80	1·80
210	70c. brown	2·40	2·40
211	90c. violet	3·25	3·25
212	1f.25 red	4·50	5·25
213	2f.25 blue	6·00	6·50

1940. Red Cross Ambulance Fund. As Nos. 174/92 in new colours surch with Red Cross and premium.

214	**34**	20c.+1f. violet	5·50	6·00
215	-	25c.+1f. green	5·50	6·00
216	-	30c.+1f. red	5·50	6·00
217	-	40c.+1f. blue	5·50	6·00
218	-	45c.+1f. red	5·50	6·00
219	-	50c.+1f. brown	5·50	6·00
220	-	60c.+1f. green	6·00	7·25
221	**38**	75c.+1f. black	6·00	7·25
222	-	1f.+1f. red	6·50	7·25
223	-	2f.+1f. slate	6·50	7·25
224	-	2f.50+1f. green	20·00	20·00
225	**38**	3f.+1f. blue	20·00	20·00
226	**34**	5f.+1f. black	30·00	30·00
227	-	10f.+5f. blue	48·00	50·00
228	-	20f.+5f. purple	50·00	55·00

44 Prince Louis II

1941

229	**44**	40c. red	60	85
230	**44**	80c. green	60	85
231	**44**	1f. violet	20	30
232	**44**	1f.20 green	25	30
233	**44**	1f.50 red	25	30
234	**44**	1f.50 violet	25	25
235	**44**	2f. green	70	60
236	**44**	2f.40 red	35	50
237	**44**	2f.50 blue	85	1·40
238	**44**	4f. blue	35	35

45

46

1941. National Relief Fund.

239	**45**	25c.+25c. purple	2·75	2·75
240	**46**	50c.+25c. brown	2·75	2·75
241	**46**	75c.+50c. purple	4·00	4·00
242	**45**	1f.+1f. blue	4·00	4·00
243	**46**	1f.50+1f.50 red	5·50	5·50
244	**45**	2f.+2f. green	5·50	5·50
245	**46**	2f.50+2f. blue	7·75	7·75
246	**45**	3f.+3f. brown	9·00	9·00
247	**46**	5f.+5f. green	12·00	12·00
248	**45**	10f.+8f. sepia	19·00	19·00

1941. New values and colours.

249	**20a**	10c. black	20	30
250	-	30c. red (as No. 176)	60	30
251	**20a**	30c. green	20	30
252	**20a**	40c. red	25	30
253	**20a**	50c. violet	25	30
362	**34**	50c. brown	50	30
254	**20a**	60c. blue	25	30
363	-	60c. pink (as No. 175)	50	30
255	**20a**	70c. brown	25	30
256	**34**	80c. green	20	30
257	-	1f. brown (as Nos. 178)	20	30
258	**38**	1f.20 blue	95	50
259	-	1f.50 blue (as Nos. 175)	95	35
260	**38**	2f. blue	20	30
261	-	2f. green (as No. 179)	1·10	50
262	-	3f. black (as No. 175)	30	30
364	-	3f. purple (as No. 176)	1·70	35
391	-	3f. green (as No. 175)	4·75	1·20
263	**34**	4f. purple	3·50	1·00
365	-	4f. green (as No. 175)	1·60	30
264	-	4f.50 violet (as No. 179)	20	30
265	-	5f. green (as No. 176)	25	30
392	-	5f. green (as No. 178)	1·20	55
393	-	5f. red (as No. 176)	1·80	1·60
266	-	6f. violet (as No. 179)	2·40	1·00
368	-	8f. brown (as No. 179)	5·50	2·40
267	**34**	10f. blue	50	60
370	-	10f. brown (as No. 179)	6·50	2·75
394	**38**	10f. yellow	2·40	95
268	**38**	15f. red	50	60
269	-	20f. brown (as No. 178)	50	60
373	-	20f. red (as No. 178)	2·40	95
270	**38**	25f. green	4·25	1·90
374	**38**	25f. black	43·00	24·00
397	-	25f. blue (as No. 176)	70·00	24·00
398	-	25f. red (as No. 179)	6·00	1·20
399	-	30f. blue (as No. 176)	16·00	5·50
400	-	35f. blue (as No. 179)	15·00	7·25
401	**34**	40f. red	12·50	7·50
402	**34**	50f. violet	7·75	1·60
403	-	65f. violet (as No. 178)	18·00	12·00
404	**34**	70f. yellow	14·50	11·00
405	-	75f. green (as No. 175)	38·00	14·50
406	-	85f. red (as No. 175)	24·00	12·00
407	-	100f. turquoise (as No. 178)	24·00	12·00

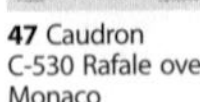
47 Caudron C-530 Rafale over Monaco

48 Propeller and Palace

49 Arms, Aeroplane and Globe

1942. Air.

271	**47**	5f. green	10	50
272	**47**	10f. blue	25	50
273	**48**	15f. brown	60	1·10
274	-	20f. brown	85	1·60
275	-	50f. purple	4·25	6·00
276	**49**	100f. red and purple	4·75	6·00

Designs:—Vert: 20f. Pegasus. Horiz: 50f. Mew gull over Bay of Monaco.

50 Charles II

1942. National Relief Fund. Royal Personages.

277	-	2c.+3c. blue	35	50
278	**50**	5c.+5c. red	35	50
279	-	10c.+5c. black	35	50
280	-	20c.+10c. green	35	50
281	-	30c.+30c. purple	35	50
282	-	40c.+40c. red	35	50
283	-	50c.+50c. violet	35	50
284	-	75c.+75c. purple	35	50
285	-	1f.+1f. green	35	50
286	-	1f.50+1f. red	35	50
287	-	2f.50+2f.50 violet	4·25	7·25
288	-	3f.+3f. blue	4·25	7·25
289	-	5f.+5f. sepia	4·75	9·50
290	-	10f.+5f. purple	5·50	11·00
291	-	20f.+5f. blue	6·50	12·00

Portraits:—2c. Rainier Grimaldi; 10c. Jeanne Grimaldi; 20c. Charles Auguste, Goyon de Matignon; 30c. Jacques I; 40c. Louise-Hippolyte; 50c. Charlotte Grimaldi; 75c. Marie Charles Grimaldi; 1f. Honore III; 1f.50, Honore IV; 2f.50, Honore V; 3f. Florestan I; 5f. Charles III; 10f. Albert I; 20f. Princess Marie-Victoire.

52 Prince Louis II

1943

292	**52**	50f. violet	1·30	1·90

53 St. Devote

54 Blessing the Sea

55 Arrival of St. Devote at Monaco

1944. Charity. Festival of St. Devote.

293	**53**	50c.+50c. brown	10	30
294	-	70c.+80c. blue	10	30
295	-	80c.+70c. green	10	30
296	-	1f.+1f. purple	10	30
297	-	1f.50+1f.50 red	50	50
298	**54**	2f.+2f. purple	85	95
299	-	5f.+2f. violet	95	95
300	-	10f.+40f. blue	95	95
301	**55**	20f.+60f. blue	4·75	9·25

Designs:—Vert: 70c., 1f. Various processional scenes; 1f.50, Burning the boat; 10f. Trial scene. Horiz: 80c. Procession; 5f. St. Devote's Church.

1945. Air. For War Dead and Deported Workers. As Nos. 272/6 (colours changed) surch.

302	1f.+4f. on 10f. red	50	70
303	1f.+4f. on 15f. brown	50	70
304	1f.+4f. on 20f. brown	50	70
305	1f.+4f. on 50f. blue	50	70
306	1f.+4f. on 100f. purple	50	70

57 Prince Louis II

58 Prince Louis II

1946

361	**57**	30c. black	35	30
389	**57**	50c. olive	30	25
390	**57**	1f. violet	35	30
307	**57**	2f.50 green	95	40
308	**57**	3f. mauve	70	40
366	**57**	5f. brown	60	40
309	**57**	6f. red	70	40
367	**57**	6f. purple	6·75	3·25
310	**57**	10f. blue	70	40
369	**57**	10f. orange	60	30
371	**57**	12f. red	8·00	4·25
395	**57**	12f. slate	11·50	9·00
396	**57**	15f. lake	11·50	6·50
372	**57**	18f. blue	13·00	9·50
311	**58**	50f. grey	5·50	3·00
312	**58**	100f. red	7·50	4·25

59 Child Praying

1946. Child Welfare Fund.

313	**59**	1f.+3f. green	50	50
314	**59**	2f.+4f. red	50	50
315	**59**	4f.+6f. blue	50	50
316	**59**	5f.+40f. mauve	1·80	1·40
317	**59**	10f.+60f. red	1·80	1·40
318	**59**	15f.+100f. blue	2·50	2·00

60 Nurse and Baby

1946. Anti-tuberculosis Fund.

319	**60**	2f.+8f. blue	1·10	1·10

1946. Air. Optd **POSTE AERIENNE** over Sud Ouest SO.95 Corse II aircraft.

320	**58**	50f. grey	7·25	6·50
321	**58**	100f. red	7·25	6·50

62 Steamship and Chart

1946. Stamp Day.

322	**62**	3f.+2f. blue	70	70

63

1946. Air.

323	**63**	40f. red	1·80	1·30
324	**63**	50f. brown	3·00	2·40
325	**63**	100f. green	4·50	3·50
326	**63**	200f. violet	5·00	4·25
326a	**63**	300f. blue and ultramarine	£110	£110
326b	**63**	500f. green and deep green	70·00	70·00
326c	**63**	1000f. violet and brown	£120	£110

64 Pres. Roosevelt and Palace of Monaco

66 Pres. Roosevelt

1946. President Roosevelt Commemoration.

327	**66**	10c. mauve (postage)	70	50
328	-	30c. blue	70	50
329	**64**	60c. green	70	50
330	-	1f. sepia	2·20	1·60
331	-	2f.+3f. green	2·30	1·30
332	-	3f. violet	3·50	2·00
333	-	5f. red (air)	1·10	1·10
334	-	10f. black	1·30	1·10
335	**66**	15f.+10f. orange	3·50	2·75

Designs:—Horiz: 30c., 5f. Rock of Monaco; 2f. Viaduct and St. Devote. Vert: 1, 3, 10f. Map of Monaco.

67 Prince Louis II

1947. Participation in the Centenary International Philatelic Exhibition, New York. (a) Postage.

336	**67**	10f. blue	6·00	6·00

68 Pres. Roosevelt as a Philatelist

69 Statue of Liberty, New York Harbour and Sud Ouest SO.95 Corse II

(b) Air. Dated '1847 1947'.

337	**68**	50c. violet	1·80	1·80
338	-	1f.50 mauve	60	85
339	-	3f. orange	60	85
340	-	10f. blue	6·00	6·00
341	**69**	15f. red	11·50	11·50

Designs:—Horiz: As Type **68**: 1f.50, GPO, New York; 3f. Oceanographic Museum, Monte Carlo. As Type **69**: 10f. Bay of Monaco and Sud Ouest SO.95 Corse II.

1947. Twenty-fifth Year of Reign of Prince Louis II. Sheet 85×98 mm.

MS341a 200f.+300f. brown	60·00	36·00

70 Prince Charles III

1948. Stamp Day.

342	**70**	6f.+4f. green on blue	60	60

71 Diving

72 Tennis

1948. Olympic Games, Wembley. Inscr "JEUX OLYMPIQUES 1948".

343	-	50c. green (postage)	35	30
344	-	1f. red	35	40
345	-	2f. blue	1·80	1·20
346	-	2f.50 red	5·25	3·75
347	**71**	4f. slate	6·00	5·00
348	-	5f.+5f. brown (air)	18·00	17·00
349	-	6f.+9f. violet	24·00	23·00
350	**72**	10f.+15f. red	36·00	34·00
351	-	15f.+25f. blue	55·00	50·00

Designs:—Horiz: 50c. Hurdling; 15f. Yachting. Vert: 1f. Running; 2f. Throwing the discus; 2f.50, Basketball; 5f. Rowing; 6f. Skiing.

75 The Salmacis Nymph

77 F. J. Bosio (wrongly inscr "J. F.")

1948. Death Centenary of Francois Joseph Bosio (sculptor).

352	**75**	50c. green (postage)	95	60
353	-	1f. red	1·10	60
354	-	2f. blue	2·75	1·80
355	-	2f.50 violet	6·50	3·50
356	**77**	4f. mauve	6·00	3·50
357	-	5f.+5f. blue (air)	34·00	31·00
358	-	6f.+9f. green	34·00	32·00
359	-	10f.+15f. red	34·00	32·00
360	-	15f.+25f. brown	42·00	42·00

Designs:—Vert: 1, 5f. Hercules struggling with Achelous; 2, 6f. Aristaeus (Garden God); 15f. The Salmacis Nymph (36×48 mm). Horiz: 2f.50, 10f. Hyacinthus awaiting his turn to throw a quoit.

79 Exotic Gardens

80 *Princess Alice II*

1949. Birth Centenary of Prince Albert I.

375		2f. blue (postage)	35	30
376	**79**	3f. green	35	25
377	-	4f. brown and blue	35	25
378	**80**	5f. red	1·20	1·20
379	-	6f. violet	1·40	1·20
380	-	10f. sepia	1·80	1·80
381	-	12f. pink	4·00	3·25
382	-	18f. orange and brown	6·00	5·00
383	-	20f. brown (air)	1·40	1·30
384	-	25f. blue	1·40	1·30
385	-	40f. green	3·00	3·00
386	-	50f. green, brown and black	4·25	4·00
387	-	100f. red	14·50	13·00
388	-	200f. orange	24·00	23·00

Designs:—Horiz: 2f. Yacht *Hirondelle I* (1870); 4f. Oceanographic Museum, Monaco; 10f. *Hirondelle II* (1914); 12f. Albert harpooning whale; 18f. Buffalo (Palaeolithic mural); 20f. Constitution Day, 1911; 25f. Paris Institute of Palaeontology; 200f. Coin with effigy of Albert. Vert: 6f. Statue of Albert at tiller; 40f. Anthropological Museum; 50f. Prince Albert I; 100f. Oceanographic Institute, Paris.

82a Princess Charlotte

1949. Red Cross Fund. Sheet 150×172½ mm, containing vert portraits as T **82a**.

MS408 10f.+5f. brown and red; 40f.+5f. green and red; 15f.+5f. red and 25f.+5f. blue and red. Each ×4	£600	£650
MS409 As **MS**408 but imperf	£600	£650

Designs:—10, 40f. T **82a**; 15, 25f, Prince Rainier.

83 Palace of Monaco and Globe

1949. 75th Anniv of U.P.U.

410	**83**	5f. green (postage)	1·10	95
411	**83**	10f. orange	10·50	8·50
412	**83**	15f. red	1·10	95
413	**83**	25f. blue (air)	1·10	95
414	**83**	40f. sepia and brown	4·25	3·75
415	**83**	50f. blue and green	5·50	5·50
416	**83**	100f. blue and red	9·50	9·00

84 Prince Rainier III and Monaco Palace

1950. Accession of Prince Rainier III.

417	**84**	10c. purple & red (postage)	20	20
418	**84**	50c. brown, lt brn & orge	20	20
419	**84**	1f. violet	60	35
420	**84**	5f. deep green and green	5·25	3·00
421	**84**	15f. carmine and red	8·50	7·25
422	**84**	25f. blue, green & ultram	8·50	7·25
423	**84**	50f. brown and black (air)	12·00	9·50
424	**84**	100f. blue, dp brn & brn	18·00	16·00

85 Prince Rainier III

1950

425	**85**	50c. violet	50	25
426	**85**	1f. brown	50	25
434	**85**	5f. green	19·00	7·25
427	**85**	6f. green	3·00	1·20
428	**85**	8f. green	13·00	3·50
429	**85**	8f. orange	3·00	1·20
435	**85**	10f. orange	32·00	12·50
430	**85**	12f. blue	3·50	60
431	**85**	15f. red	6·00	95
432	**85**	15f. blue	3·50	60
433	**85**	18f. red	11·00	3·50

86 Prince Albert I

1951. Unveiling of Prince Albert Statue.

436	**86**	15f. blue	17·00	9·50

87 Edmond and Jules de Goncourt

1951. 50th Anniv of Goncourt Academy.

437	**87**	15f. purple	17·00	9·50

88 St. Vincent de Paul

89 Judgement of St. Devote

90 St. Peter's Keys and Papal Bull

1951. Holy Year.

438	**88**	10c. blue, ultramarine & red	35	30
439	-	50c. violet and red	35	30
440	**89**	1f. green and brown	35	30
441	**90**	2f. red and purple	50	50
442	-	5f. green	50	55
443	-	12f. violet	85	70
444	-	15f. red	8·25	7·75
445	-	20f. brown	12·00	11·00
446	-	25f. blue	16·00	13·00
447	-	40f. violet and mauve	18·00	14·50
448	-	50f. brown and olive	25·00	18·00
449	-	100f. brown	48·00	42·00

Designs:—Triangular: 50c. Pope Pius XII. Horiz (as Type **90**): 5f. Mosaic. Vert (as Type **90**): 12f. Prince Rainier III in St. Peter's; 15f. St. Nicholas of Patara; 20f. St. Romain; 25f. St. Charles Borromeo; 40f. Coliseum; 50f. Chapel of St. Devote. Vert (as Type **89**): 100f. Rainier of Westphalia.

93 Wireless Mast and Monaco

1951. Monte Carlo Radio Station.

450	**93**	1f. orange, red and blue	1·20	60
451	**93**	15f. purple, red and violet	6·00	2·00
452	**93**	30f. brown and blue	38·00	11·00

94 Seal of Prince Rainier III

1951

453	**94**	1f. violet	1·20	70
454	**94**	5f. black	6·00	3·75
512	**94**	5f. violet	6·00	2·40
513	**94**	6f. red	11·00	4·25
455	**94**	8f. red	13·00	6·25
514	**94**	8f. brown	11·50	6·00
456	**94**	15f. green	24·00	12·00
515	**94**	15f. blue	26·00	10·00
457	**94**	30f. blue	36·00	30·00
516	**94**	30f. green	41·00	30·00

1951. Nos. **MS**408/9 surch **1f. on 10f.+5f., 3f. on 15f.+5f., 5f. on 25f. + 5f., 6f. on 40f.+5f.**

MS458 As above	£650	£650
MS459 As above imperf	£650	£650

95 Gallery of Hercules

1952. Monaco Postal Museum.

460	**95**	5f. chestnut and brown	3·50	95
461	**95**	15f. violet and purple	4·75	1·20
462	**95**	30f. indigo and blue	6·00	1·70

96 Football

1953. 15th Olympic Games, Helsinki. Inscr "HELSINKI 1952".

463	-	1f. mauve & violet (postage)	25	30
464	**96**	2f. blue and green	25	30
465	-	3f. pale and deep blue	25	30
466	-	5f. green and brown	1·40	60
467	-	8f. red and lake	3·75	2·00
468	-	15f. brown, green and blue	1·80	1·40
469	-	40f. black (air)	18·00	16·00
470	-	50f. violet	24·00	16·00
471	-	100f. green	30·00	24·00
472	-	200f. red	42·00	30·00

Designs:—1f. Basketball; 3f. Sailing; 5f. Cycling; 8f. Gymnastics; 15f. Louis II Stadium, Monaco; 40f. Running; 50f. Fencing; 100f. Rifle target and Arms of Monaco; 200f. Olympic torch.

97 *Journal Inedit*

1953. Centenary of Publication of Journal by E. and J. de Goncourt.

473	**97**	5f. green	1·20	60
474	**97**	15f. brown	7·25	1·80

98 Physalia, Yacht *Princess Alice*, Prince Albert, Richet and Portier

1953. 50th Anniv of Discovery of Anaphylaxis.

475	**98**	2f. violet, green and brown	40	10
476	**98**	5f. red, lake and green	1·40	70
477	**98**	15f. lilac, blue and green	6·00	3·50

99 F. Ozanam

1954. Death Centenary of Ozanam (founder of St. Vincent de Paul Conferences).

478	**99**	1f. red	35	35
479	-	5f. blue	80	80
480	**99**	15f. black	3·00	3·00

Design:—5f. Outline drawing of Sister of Charity.

100 St. Jean-Baptiste de la Salle

1954. St. J.-B. de la Salle (educationist).

481	**100**	1f. red	35	35
482	-	5f. sepia	80	80
483	**100**	15f. blue	3·00	3·00

Design:—5f. Outline drawing of De la Salle and two children.

101 **102** **103**

1954. Arms.

484	-	50c. red, black and mauve	20	20
485	-	70c. red, black and blue	20	20
486	**101**	80c. red, black and green	20	20
487	-	1f. red, black and blue	25	20
488	**102**	2f. red, black and orange	25	25
489	-	3f. red, black and green	35	25
490	**103**	5f. multicoloured	60	50

Designs:—Horiz: 50c. as Type **101**. Vert: 70c., 1, 3f. as Type **102**.

104 Seal of Prince Rainier III

1954. Precancelled.

491	**104**	4f. red	2·40	1·00
492	**104**	5f. blue	60	40
493	**104**	8f. green	2·40	1·20
494	**104**	8f. purple	1·20	70
495	**104**	10f. green	50	40
496	**104**	12f. violet	9·50	3·25
497	**104**	15f. orange	1·80	1·00
498	**104**	20f. green	2·40	1·30
499	**104**	24f. brown	16·00	7·25
500	**104**	30f. blue	2·40	1·50
501	**104**	40f. brown	4·75	2·50
502	**104**	45f. red	3·25	2·30
503	**104**	55f. blue	11·00	4·50

See also Nos. 680/3.

105 Lambarene **106** Dr. Albert Schweitzer

1955. 80th Birthday of Dr. Schweitzer (humanitarian).

504	**105**	2f. grn, turq & bl (postage)	50	40
505	**106**	5f. blue and green	2·00	1·70
506	-	15f. purple, black and green	5·50	3·50
507	-	200f. slate, grn & bl (air)	70·00	55·00

Designs:—As Type **106**: 15f. Lambarene Hospital. Horiz (48×27 mm): 200f. Schweitzer and jungle scene.

107 Great Cormorants

1955. Air.

508		100f. indigo and blue	44·00	20·00
509		200f. black and blue	46·00	22·00
510		500f. grey and green	70·00	48·00
511a	**107**	1,000f. black, turq & grn	£150	£100

Designs:—As Type **107**: 100f. Roseate Tern; 200f. Herring Gull; 500f. Wandering Albatrosses.

108 Eight Starting Points

1955. 25th Monte Carlo Car Rally.

517	**108**	100f. red and brown	£130	95·00

109 Prince Rainier III

1955

518	**109**	6f. purple and green	1·20	50
519	**109**	8f. violet and red	1·20	50
520	**109**	12f. green and red	1·20	50
521	**109**	15f. blue and purple	2·30	60
522	**109**	18f. blue and orange	8·50	1·10
523	**109**	20f. turquoise	4·25	1·10
524	**109**	25f. black and orange	1·80	95
525	**109**	30f. black and blue	25·00	12·00

No.	Type	Description	Mint	Used
526	**109**	30f. violet	7·75	4·25
527	**109**	35f. brown	7·25	4·25
528	**109**	50f. lake and green	11·00	5·75

See also Nos. 627/41.

110 "La Maison a Vapeur"

111 "The 500 Millions of the Begum"

112 "Round the World in Eighty Days"

113 USS *Nautilus*

1955. 50th Death Anniv of Jules Verne (author). Designs illustrating his works.

No.	Type	Description	Mint	Used
529	-	1f. blue & brown (postage)	20	20
530	-	2f. sepia, indigo and blue	20	20
531	**110**	3f. blue, black and brown	25	20
532	-	5f. sepia and red	25	30
533	**111**	6f. grey and sepia	70	50
534	-	8f. turquoise and olive	70	60
535	-	10f. sepia, turquoise & ind	1·90	1·40
536	**112**	15f. red and brown	1·40	95
537	-	25f. black and green	4·00	2·75
538	**113**	30f. black, purple & turq	9·75	9·00
539	-	200f. indigo and blue (air)	48·00	42·00

Designs:—Vert (as Type **111**): 1f. *Five Weeks in a Balloon*. Horiz (as Type **110**): 2f. *A Floating Island*; 10f. *Journey to the Centre of the Earth*; 25f. *20,000 Leagues under the Sea*; 200f. *From the Earth to the Moon*. (as Type **111**): 5f. *Michael Strogoff*; 8f. *Le Superbe Orenoque*.

114 *The Immaculate Virgin* (F. Brea)

1955. Marian Year.

No.	Type	Description	Mint	Used
540	**114**	5f. green, grey and brown	30	30
541	-	10f. green, grey and brown	40	40
542	-	15f. brown and sepia	1·20	1·20

Designs:—As Type **114**: 10f. *Madonna* (L. Brea). As Type **113**: 15f. Bienheureux Rainier.

115 Rotary Emblem

1955. 50th Anniv of Rotary International.

No.	Type	Description	Mint	Used
543	**115**	30f. blue and yellow	2·40	2·40

116 George Washington

118 President Eisenhower

117 Abraham Lincoln

1956. Fifth International Stamp Exhibition, New York.

No.	Type	Description	Mint	Used
544	**116**	1f. violet and lilac	20	20
545	-	2f. lilac and purple	20	20
546	**117**	3f. blue and violet	20	20
547	**118**	5f. red	25	30
548	-	15f. brown and chocolate	1·20	80
549	-	30f. black, indigo and blue	6·00	4·00
550	-	40f. brown	9·25	5·50
551	-	50f. red	9·25	5·50
552	-	100f. green	9·25	5·50

Designs:—As Type **117**: 2f. F. D. Roosevelt. Horiz (as Type **116**): 15f. Monaco Palace in the 18th-century; 30f. Landing of Columbus. (48×36 mm): 50f. Aerial view of Monaco Palace in the 18th-century; 100f. Louisiana landscape in 18th-century. Vert (as Type **118**): 40f. Prince Rainier III.

120

1956. Seventh Winter Olympic Games, Cortina d'Ampezzo and 16th Olympic Games, Melbourne.

No.	Type	Description	Mint	Used
553		15f. brown, green & pur	1·80	1·00
554	**120**	30f. red	4·25	2·75

Design:—15f. "Italia" ski-jump.

1956. Nos. D482/95 with "TIMBRE TAXE" barred out and some surch also. (a) Postage.

No.	Description	Mint	Used
555	2f. on 4f. slate and brown	70	70
556	2f. on 4f. brown and slate	70	70
557	3f. lake and green	70	70
558	3f. green and lake	70	70
559	5f. on 4f. slate and brown	1·20	1·20
560	5f. on 4f. brown and slate	1·20	1·20
561	10f. on 4f. slate and brown	2·20	2·20
562	10f. on 4f. brown and slate	2·20	2·20
563	15f. on 5f. violet and blue	3·00	3·00
564	15f. on 5f. blue and violet	3·00	3·00
565	20f. violet and blue	4·75	4·75
566	20f. blue and violet	4·75	4·75
567	25f. on 20f. violet and blue	7·75	7·75
568	25f. on 20f. blue and violet	7·75	7·75
569	30f. on 10f. indigo and blue	14·50	14·50
570	30f. on 10f. blue and indigo	14·50	14·50
571	40f. on 50f. brown and red	20·00	20·00
572	40f. on 50f. red and brown	20·00	20·00
573	50f. on 100f. green and purple	24·00	24·00
574	50f. on 100f. purple and green	24·00	24·00

(b) Air. Optd **POSTE AERIENNE** also.

No.	Description	Mint	Used
575	100f. on 20f. violet and blue	17·00	17·00
576	100f. on 20f. blue and violet	17·00	17·00

121 Route Map from Glasgow

1956. 26th Monte Carlo Car Rally.

No.	Type	Description	Mint	Used
577	**121**	100f. brown and red	42·00	38·00

122 Princess Grace and Prince Rainier III

1956. Royal Wedding.

No.	Type	Description	Mint	Used
578	**122**	1f. black & grn (postage)	20	20
579	**122**	2f. black and red	35	30
580	**122**	3f. black and blue	60	50
581	**122**	5f. black and green	1·30	1·00
582	**122**	15f. black and brown	2·40	1·40
583	**122**	100f. brown & purple (air)	1·80	1·80
584	**122**	200f. brown and red	3·00	3·00
585	**122**	500f. brown and grey	6·00	6·00

123 Princess Grace

1957. Birth of Princess Caroline.

No.	Type	Description	Mint	Used
586	**123**	1f. grey	20	20
587	**123**	2f. olive	20	20
588	**123**	3f. brown	25	20
589	**123**	5f. red	35	30
590	**123**	15f. pink	35	30
591	**123**	25f. blue	1·40	1·20
592	**123**	30f. violet	1·60	1·20
593	**123**	50f. red	3·00	1·40
594	**123**	75f. orange	4·75	4·00

124 Princess Grace with Princess Caroline

1958. Birth of Prince Albert.

No.	Type	Description	Mint	Used
595	**124**	100f. black	14·50	9·50

125 Order of St. Charles

1958. Centenary of Creation of National Order of St. Charles.

No.	Type	Description	Mint	Used
596	**125**	100f. multicoloured	4·75	3·50

126 Route Map from Munich

1958. 27th Monte Carlo Rally.

No.	Type	Description	Mint	Used
597	**126**	100f. multicoloured	12·00	12·00

127 Statue of the Holy Virgin and Popes Pius IX and Pius XII

1958. Centenary of Apparition of Virgin Mary at Lourdes.

No.	Type	Description	Mint	Used
598	**127**	1f. grey & brown (postage)	20	20
599	-	2f. violet and blue	20	20
600	-	3f. sepia and green	25	20
601	-	5f. blue and sepia	30	20
602	-	8f. multicoloured	35	25
603	-	10f. multicoloured	35	35
604	-	12f. multicoloured	60	50
605	-	20f. myrtle and purple	70	55
606	-	35f. myrtle, bistre and brown	85	60
607	-	50f. blue, green and lake	1·40	1·00
608	-	65f. turquoise and blue	1·90	1·60
609	-	100f. grey, myrtle and blue (air)	3·00	2·40
610	-	200f. brown and chestnut	4·25	3·50

Designs:—Vert (26½×36 mm): 2f. St. Bernadette; 3f. St. Bernadette at Bartres; 5f. The Miracle of Bourriette; 20f. St. Bernadette at prayer; 35f. St. Bernadette's canonization. (22×36 mm): 8f. Stained-glass window. As Type **127**: 50f. St. Bernadette, Pope Pius XI, Mgr. Laurence and Abbe Peyramale. Horiz (48×36 mm): 10f. Lourdes grotto; 12f. Interior of Lourdes grotto. (36×26½ mm): 65f. Shrine of St. Bernadette; (48×27 mm): 100f. Lourdes Basilica; 200f. Pope Pius X and subterranean interior of Basilica.

128 Princess Grace and Clinic

1959. Opening of new Hospital Block in "Princess Grace" Clinic, Monaco.

No.	Type	Description	Mint	Used
611	**128**	100f. grey, brown & green	7·50	4·25

129 UNESCO Headquarters, Paris, and Cultural Emblems

1959. Inaug of UNESCO Headquarters Building.

No.	Type	Description	Mint	Used
612	**129**	25f. multicoloured	35	30
613	-	50f. turquoise, black & ol	60	50

Design:—50f. As Type **129** but with heads of children and letters of various alphabets in place of the emblems.

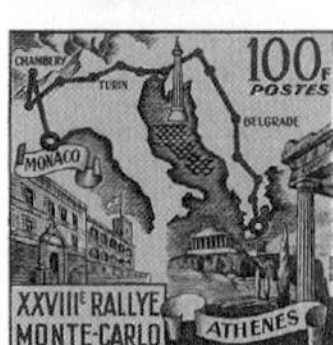

130 Route Map from Athens

1959. 28th Monte Carlo Rally.

No.	Type	Description	Mint	Used
614	**130**	100f. blue, red & grn on bl	12·00	9·50

131 Prince Rainier and Princess Grace

1959. Air.

No.	Type	Description	Mint	Used
615	**131**	300f. violet	26·00	17·00
616	**131**	500f. blue	36·00	30·00

See also Nos. 642/3.

132 "Princess Caroline" Carnation

1959. Flowers.

No.	Type	Description	Mint	Used
617	**132**	5f. mauve, green & brown	25	10
618	-	10f. on 3f. pink, green and brown	60	25

619	-	15f. on 1f. yellow & green	60	40
620	-	20f. purple and green	1·20	85
621	-	25f. on 6f. red, yellow and green	1·80	1·30
622	-	35f. pink and green	3·75	2·75
623	-	50f. green and sepia	5·50	3·50
624	-	85f. on 65f. lavender, bronze and green	6·00	4·75
625	-	100f. red and green	9·00	7·75

Flowers:—As Type **132**: 10f. "Princess Grace" carnation; 100f. "Grace of Monaco" rose. Vert (22×36 mm): 15f. Mimosa; 25f. Geranium. Horiz (36×22 mm): 20f. Bougainvillea; 35f. "Laurier" rose; 50f. Jasmine; 85f. Lavender.

133 "Uprooted Tree"

1960. World Refugee Year.

626	**133**	25c. green, blue and black	50	30

1960. Prince Rainier types with values in new currency.

627	**109**	25c. blk & orge (postage)	95	60
628	**109**	30c. violet	95	70
629	**109**	40c. red and brown	1·20	60
630	**109**	45c. brown and grey	1·20	60
631	**109**	50c. red and green	4·25	70
632	**109**	50c. red and brown	1·20	70
633	**109**	60c. brown and green	3·00	1·30
634	**109**	60c. brown and purple	4·25	3·00
635	**109**	65c. blue and brown	26·00	8·50
636	**109**	70c. blue and plum	2·40	1·20
637	**109**	85c. green and violet	3·50	2·75
638	**109**	95c. blue	1·20	1·40
639	**109**	1f.10 blue and brown	4·75	3·25
640	**109**	1f.30 brown and red	3·25	3·00
641	**109**	2f.30 purple and orange	4·75	1·70
642	**131**	3f. violet (air)	70·00	32·00
643	**131**	5f. blue	70·00	42·00

134 Oceanographic Museum

1960

644	-	5c. green, black and blue	25	20
645	**134**	10c. brown and blue	85	50
646	-	10c. blue, violet and green	60	25
647	-	40c. purple, grn & dp grn	1·20	50
648	-	45c. brown, green and blue	12·00	1·30
649	-	70c. brown, red and green	1·20	70
650	-	80c. red, green and blue	3·00	1·10
651	-	85c. black, brown and grey	16·00	5·50
652	-	90c. red, blue and black	4·75	2·00
653	-	1f. multicoloured	2·00	70
654	-	1f.15 black, red and blue	4·75	3·25
655	-	1f.30 brown, green & blue	1·80	1·20
656	-	1f.40 orange, green & vio	5·50	4·25

Designs:—Horiz: 5c. Palace of Monaco; 10c. (No. 646), Aquatic Stadium; 40, 45, 80c., 1f.40, Aerial view of Palace; 70, 85, 90c., 1f.15, 1f.30, Court of Honour, Monaco Palace; 1f. Palace floodlit.

134a St. Devote

1960. Air.

668	**134a**	2f. violet, blue and green	2·00	1·60
669	**134a**	3f. brown, green and blue	3·50	2·00
670	**134a**	5f. red	6·50	4·00
671	**134a**	10f. brown, grey and green	11·00	6·50

135 Long-snouted Seahorse

1960. Marine Life and Plants. (a) Marine Life.

672	-	1c. red and turquoise	20	20
673	-	12c. brown and blue	35	20
674	**135**	15c. green and red	85	50
675	-	20c. multicoloured	1·10	50

Designs:—Horiz: 1c. *Macrocheira kampferi* (crab); 20c. Lionfish. Vert: 12c. Trapezium horse conch.

(b) Plants.

676	2c. multicoloured	20	20
677	15c. orange, brown and olive	95	50
678	18c. multicoloured	85	30
679	20c. red, olive and brown	95	50

Plants:—Vert: 2c. *Selenicereus* sp.; 15c. *Cereus* sp.; 18c. *Aloe ciliaris*; 20c. *Nopalea dejecta*.

1960. Prince Rainier Seal type with values in new currency. Precancelled.

680	**104**	8c. purple	2·40	1·70
681	**104**	20c. green	3·50	2·40
682	**104**	40c. brown	5·50	3·00
683	**104**	55c. blue	10·00	4·75

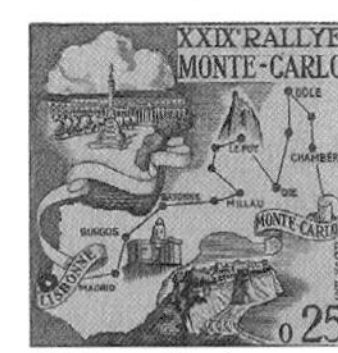

136 Route Map from Lisbon

1960. 29th Monte Carlo Rally.

684	**136**	25c. black, red & bl on bl	4·75	3·50

137 Stamps of Monaco 1885, France and Sardinia, 1860

1960. 75th Anniv of First Monaco Stamp.

685	**137**	25c. bistre, blue and violet	1·30	95

138 Aquarium

1960. 50th Anniv of Oceanographic Museum, Monaco.

686	-	5c. black, blue and purple	85	40
687	**138**	10c. grey, brown and green	95	50
688	-	15c. black, bistre and blue	95	50
689	-	20c. black, blue and mauve	1·80	95
690	-	25c. turquoise	3·50	2·40
691	-	50c. brown and blue	4·50	3·00

Designs:—Vert: 5c. Oceanographic Museum (similar to Type **134**). Horiz: 15c. Conference Hall; 20c. Hauling-in catch; 25c. Museum, aquarium and underwater research equipment; 50c. Prince Albert, *Hirondelle I* (schooner) and *Princess Alice* (steam yacht).

139 Horse-jumping

1960. Olympic Games.

692	**139**	5c. brown, red and green	25	25
693	-	10c. brown, blue and green	35	35
694	-	15c. red, brown and purple	60	60
695	-	20c. black, blue and green	4·75	4·75
696	-	25c. purple, turq & grn	1·20	1·20
697	-	50c. purple, blue & turq	1·80	1·80

Designs:—10c. Swimming; 15c. Long-jumping; 20c. Throwing the javelin; 25c. Free-skating; 50c. Skiing.

140 Rally Badge, Old and Modern Cars

1961. 50th Anniv of Monte Carlo Rally.

698	**140**	1f. violet, red and brown	3·00	3·00

141 Route Map from Stockholm

1961. 30th Monte Carlo Rally.

699	**141**	1f. multicoloured	2·40	2·40

142 Marine Life

1961. World Aquariological Congress. Orange network background.

700	**142**	25c. red, sepia and violet	35	35

143 Leper in Town of Middle Ages

1961. Sovereign Order of Malta.

701	**143**	25c. black, red and brown	35	35

144 Semi-submerged Sphinx of Ouadi-es-Saboua

1961. UNESCO Campaign for Preservation of Nubian Monuments.

702	**144**	50c. purple, blue & brown	1·70	1·70

145 Insect within Protective Hand

1962. Nature Preservation.

703	**145**	25c. mauve and purple	60	60

146 Chevrolet, 1912

1961. Veteran Motor Cars.

704	**146**	1c. brown, green and chestnut	25	25
705	-	2c. blue, purple and red	25	25
706	-	3c. purple, black and mauve	25	25
707	-	4c. blue, brown and violet	25	25
708	-	5c. green, red and olive	25	25
709	-	10c. brown, red and blue	25	25
710	-	15c. green and turquoise	25	30
711	-	20c. brown, red and violet	35	50
712	-	25c. violet, red and brown	60	60
713	-	30c. lilac and green	2·00	2·00
714	-	45c. green, purple and brown	3·50	3·50
715	-	50c. blue, red and brown	4·25	4·25
716	-	65c. brown, red and grey	5·50	5·50
717	-	1f. blue, red and violet	7·25	7·25

Motor Cars:—2c. Peugeot, 1898; 3c. Fiat, 1901; 4c. Mercedes, 1901; 5c. Rolls Royce, 1903;. 10c. Panhard-Lavassor, 1899; 15c. Renault, 1898; 20c. Ford N, 1906 (wrongly inscr "FORD-S-1908"); 25c. Rochet-Schneider, 1894; 30c. FN-Herstal, 1901; 45c. De Dion Bouton, 1900; 50c. Buick, 1910; 65c. Delahaye, 1901; 1f. Cadillac, 1906.

147 Racing Car and Race Route

1962. 20th Monaco Motor Grand Prix.

718	**147**	1f. purple	3·00	3·00

148 Route Map from Oslo

1962. 31st Monte Carlo Rally.

719	**148**	1f. multicoloured	2·20	2·20

149 Louis XII and Lucien Grimaldi

1962. 450th Anniv of Recognition of Monegasque Sovereignty by Louis XII.

720	**149**	25c. black, red and blue	35	35
721	-	50c. brown, lake and blue	85	70
722	-	1f. red, green and brown	1·20	1·10

Designs:—50c. Parchment bearing declaration of sovereignty; 1f. Seals of two Sovereigns.

150 Mosquito and Swamp

1962. Malaria Eradication.

723	**150**	1f. green and olive	85	85

151 Sun, Bouquet and "Hope Chest"

1962. National Multiple Sclerosis Society, New York.

724	**151**	20c. multicoloured	35	35

152 Harvest Scene

1962. Europa.

725	**152**	25c. brown, green and blue (postage)	1·20	70
726	**152**	50c. olive and turquoise	1·20	95
727	**152**	1f. olive and purple	1·80	1·20

728	-	2f. slate, brown & green (air)	2·40	2·40

Design:—2f. Mercury in flight over Europe.

153 Atomic Symbol and Scientific Centre, Monaco

1962. Air. Scientific Centre, Monaco.

729	**153**	10f. violet, brown and blue	7·75	7·25

154 Yellow Wagtails

1962. Protection of Birds useful to Agriculture.

730	**154**	5c. yellow, brown & green	25	25
731	-	10c. red, bistre and purple	25	25
732	-	15c. multicoloured	35	35
733	-	20c. sepia, green & mauve	60	60
734	-	25c. multicoloured	85	85
735	-	30c. brown, blue & myrtle	1·30	95
736	-	45c. brown and violet	2·40	1·90
737	-	50c. black, olive & turq	3·50	2·75
738	-	85c. multicoloured	4·75	3·00
739	-	1f. sepia, red and green	5·50	3·75

Birds:—10c. European Robins; 15c. Eurasian Goldfinches; 20c. Blackcaps; 25c. Greater Spotted Woodpeckers; 30c. Nightingale; 45c. Barn Owls; 50c. Common Starlings; 85c. Red Crossbills; 1f. White Storks.

155 Galeazzi's Diving Turret

1962. Underwater Exploration.

740		5c. black, violet and blue	10	10
741	**155**	10c. blue, violet and brown	25	25
742	-	25c. bistre, green and blue	35	35
743	-	45c. black, blue and green	60	60
744	-	50c. green, bistre and blue	85	85
745	-	85c. blue and turquoise	1·80	1·70
746	-	1f. brown, green and blue	3·00	1·80

Designs:—Horiz: 5c. Divers; 25c. Williamson's photosphere (1914) and bathyscaphe *Trieste*; 45c. Klingert's diving-suit (1797) and modern diving-suit; 50c. Diving saucer; 85c. Fulton's *Nautilus* (1800) and modern submarine; 1f. Alexander the Great's diving bell and Beebe's bathysphere.

156 Donor's Arm and Globe

1962. Third Int Blood Donors' Congress Monaco.

747	**156**	1f. red, sepia and orange	1·20	1·20

157 "Ring-a-ring o' Roses"

158 Feeding Chicks in Nest

1963. U.N. Children's Charter.

748	**157**	5c. red, blue and ochre	25	20
749	**158**	10c. green, sepia and blue	25	20
750	-	15c. blue, red and green	25	30
751	-	20c. multicoloured	25	30
752	-	25c. blue, purple & brown	35	30
753	-	50c. multicoloured	95	60
754	-	95c. multicoloured	2·40	1·10
755	-	1f. purple, red & turquoise	3·00	2·00

Designs:—As Type **157**: 1f. Prince Albert and Princess Caroline; Children's paintings as Type **158**: Horiz: 15c. Children on scales; 50c. House and child. Vert: 20c. Sun's rays and children of three races; 25c. Mother and child; 95c. Negress and child.

159 Ship's Figurehead

1963. International Red Cross Centenary.

756	**159**	50c. red, brown & turquoise	60	60
757	-	1f. multicoloured	1·20	1·20

Design:—Horiz: 1f. Moynier, Dunant and Dufour.

160 Racing Cars

1963. European Motor Grand Prix.

758	**160**	50c. multicoloured	95	95

161 Emblem and Charter

1963. Founding of Lions Club of Monaco.

759	**161**	50c. blue, bistre and violet	95	95

162 Hotel des Postes and UPU Monument, Berne

1963. Paris Postal Conference Centenary.

760	**162**	50c. lake, green and yellow	70	70

163 *Telstar* Satellite and Globe

1963. First Link Trans-Atlantic T.V. Satellite.

761	**163**	50c. brown, green & purple	95	95

164 Route Map from Warsaw

1963. 32nd Monte Carlo Rally.

762	**164**	1f. multicoloured	1·80	1·80

165 Feeding Chicks

1963. Freedom from Hunger.

763	**165**	1f. multicoloured	95	95

166 Allegory

1963. Second Ecumenical Council, Vatican City.

764	**166**	1f. turquoise, green and red	95	95

167 Henry Ford and Ford A Car of 1903

1963. Birth Centenary of Henry Ford (motor pioneer).

765	**167**	20c. green and purple	50	50

168 H. Garin (winner of 1903 race) cycling through Village

1963. 50th "Tour de France" Cycle Race.

766	**168**	25c. green, brown and blue	60	60
767	-	50c. sepia, green and blue	85	85

Design:—50c. Cyclist passing Desgrange Monument, Col du Galibier, 1963.

169 P. de Coubertin and Discus-thrower

1963. Birth Centenary of Pierre de Coubertin (reviver of Olympic Games).

768	**169**	1f. brown, red and lake	1·20	1·20

170 Roland Garros and Morane Saulnier Type I

1963. Air. 50th Anniv of First Aerial Crossing of Mediterranean Sea.

769	**170**	2f. sepia and blue	1·80	1·20

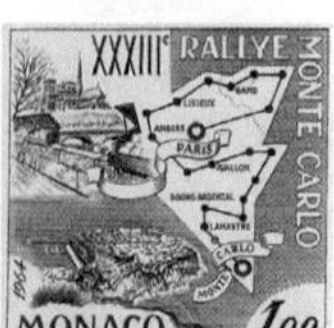

171 Route Map from Paris

1963. 33rd Monte Carlo Rally.

770	**171**	1f. red, turquoise and blue	1·80	1·80

172 Children with Stamp Album

1963. Scolatex International Stamp Exn, Monaco.

771	**172**	50c. blue, violet and red	50	50

173 "Europa"

1963. Europa.

772	**173**	25c. brown, red and green	1·20	60
773	**173**	50c. sepia, red and blue	1·80	1·20

174 Wembley Stadium

1963. Cent of (English) Football Association.

774	**174**	1c. violet, green and red	20	20
775	-	2c. red, black and green	20	20
776	-	3c. orange, olive and red	20	20
777	-	4c. multicoloured	20	20

Multicoloured horiz designs depicting (a) "Football through the Centuries".

778	10c. "Calcio", Florence (16th-cent)	20	20
779	15c. "Soule", Brittany (19th-cent)	20	20
780	20c. English military college (after Cruickshank, 1827)	25	25
781	25c. English game (after Overend, 1890)	25	25

(b) "Modern Football".

782	30c. Tackling	50	50
783	50c. Saving goal	95	95
784	95c. Heading ball	1·70	1·70
785	1f. Corner kick	2·30	1·80

DESIGNS:—As Type **174**: 4c. Louis II Stadium, Monaco. This stamp is optd in commemoration of the Association Sportive de Monaco football teams in the French Championships and in the Coupe de France, 1962–63. HORIZ (36×22 mm): 2c. Footballer making return kick; 3c. Goalkeeper saving ball.

Nos. 778/81 and 782/5 were respectively issued together in sheets and arranged in blocks of 4 with a football in the centre of each block.

175 Communications in Ancient Egypt, and Rocket

1964. PHILATEC 1964 Int Stamp Exn, Paris.

786	**175**	1f. brown, indigo and blue	85	85

176 Reproduction of Rally Postcard Design and Deperdussin Monocoque Racer

1964. 50th Anniv of First Aerial Rally, Monte Carlo.

787	**176**	1c. olive, blue & grn (postage)	20	20
788	-	2c. bistre, brown and blue	20	20
789	-	3c. brown, blue and green	20	20

790	-	4c. red, turquoise and blue	20	20
791	-	5c. brown, red and violet	20	20
792	-	10c. violet, brown and blue	25	25
793	-	15c. orange, brown and blue	35	35
794	-	20c. sepia, green and blue	40	40
795	-	25c. brown, blue and red	50	50
796	-	30c. myrtle, purple and blue	70	70
797	-	45c. sepia, turquoise and brown	1·20	95
798	-	50c. ochre, olive and violet	1·30	1·10
799	-	65c. red, slate and turquoise	2·40	1·80
800	-	95c. turquoise, red and bistre	3·00	2·75
801	-	1f. brown, blue and turquoise	4·00	3·25
802	-	5f. sepia, blue and brown (air)	8·50	7·75

Designs:—48x27 mm—Rally planes: 2c. Renaux's Farman M.F.7 floatplane; 3c. Espanet's Nieuport 4 seaplane; 4c. Moineau's Breguet HU-3 seaplane; 5c. Roland Garros' Morane Saulnier Type I seaplane; 10c. Hirth's WDD Albatros seaplane; 15c. Prevost's Deperdussin Monocoque Racer. Famous planes and flights: 20c. Vickers-Vimy G-EAOU (Ross Smith: London–Port Darwin, 1919); 25c. Douglas World Cruiser seaplane (US World Flight, 1924); 30c. Savoia Marchetti S-55M flying boat *Santa Maria* (De Pinedo's World Flight, 1925); 45c. Fokker F. VIIa/3m *Josephine Ford* (Flight over North Pole, Byrd and Bennett, 1925); 50c. Ryan NYP Special *Spirit of St. Louis* (1st solo crossing of N. Atlantic, Lindbergh, 1927); 65c. Breguet 19 Super Bidon TR *Point d'Interrogation* (Paris–New York, Coste and Bellonte, 1930); 95c. Latecoere 28-3 seaplane F-AJNQ *Comte de la Vaulx* (Dakar–Natal, first S. Atlantic airmail flight, Mermoz, 1930); 1f. Dornier Do-X flying boat (Germany–Rio de Janeiro, Christiansen, 1930); 5f. Convair B-58 Hustler (New York–Paris in 3 hours, 19'41' Major Payne, USAF, 1961).

177 Aquatic Stadium

1964. Precancelled.

803	**177**	10c. multicoloured	3·00	2·40
803a	**177**	15c. multicoloured	1·20	1·20
804	**177**	25c. turquoise, blue & blk	1·20	1·20
805	**177**	50c. violet, turq & blk	2·40	2·40

The '1962' date has been obliterated with two bars.
See also Nos. 949/51a and 1227/30.

178 Europa "Flower"

1964. Europa.

806	**178**	25c. red, green and blue	1·20	60
807	**178**	50c. brown, bistre and blue	2·40	1·80

179 Weightlifting

1964. Olympic Games, Tokyo and Innsbruck.

808	**179**	1c. red, brown and blue (postage)	10	10
809	-	2c. red, green and olive	10	10
810	-	3c. blue, brown and red	10	10
811	-	4c. green, olive and red	10	10
812	-	5f. red, brown and blue (air)	3·50	3·50

Designs:—2c. Judo; 3c. Pole vaulting; 4c. Archery; 5f. Bobsleighing.

180 Pres. Kennedy and Space Capsule

1964. Pres. Kennedy Commemoration.

813	**180**	50c. indigo and blue	85	85

181 Monaco and Television Set

1964. Fifth Int Television Festival, Monte Carlo.

814	**181**	50c. brown, blue and red	70	70

182 F. Mistral and Statue

1964. 50th Death Anniv of Frederic Mistral (poet).

815	**182**	1f. brown and olive	85	85

183 Scales of Justice

1964. 15th Anniv of Declaration of Human Rights.

816	**183**	1f. green and brown	85	85

184 Route Map from Minsk

1964. 34th Monte Carlo Rally.

817	**184**	1f. brown, turq & ochre	2·00	2·00

185 FIFA Emblem

1964. 60th Anniv of Federation Internationale de Football Association (FIFA).

818	**185**	1f. bistre, blue and red	1·40	1·40

186 *Syncom 2* and Globe

1965. Centenary of I.T.U.

819	**186**	5c. grn & ultram (postage)	20	20
820	-	10c. chestnut, brown & bl	20	20
821	-	12c. purple, red and grey	20	20
822	-	18c. blue, red and purple	25	25
823	-	25c. violet, bistre & purple	35	35
824	-	30c. bistre, brown & sepia	40	40
825	-	50c. blue and green	50	50
826	-	60c. blue and brown	1·40	1·30
827	-	70c. sepia, orange and blue	1·60	1·40
828	-	95c. black, indigo and blue	1·90	1·80
829	-	1f. brown and blue	2·75	2·50
830	-	10f. green, bl & brn (air)	7·25	7·00

Designs:—Horiz (as Type **186**): 10c. *Echo 2*; 18c. *Lunik 3*; 30c. A. G. Bell and telephone; 50c. S. Morse and telegraph; 60c. E. Belin and belinograph. (48½x27 mm): 25c. *Telstar* and Pleumeur-Bodou Station; 70c. Roman beacon and Chappe's telegraph; 95c. Cable ships *Great Eastern* and *Alsace*; 1f. E. Branly, G. Marconi and English Channel. Vert (as Type **186**): 12c. *Relay*; 10f. Monte Carlo television transmitter.

187 Europa "Sprig"

1965. Europa.

831	**187**	30c. brown and green	3·00	1·20
832	**187**	60c. violet and red	4·25	1·80

188 Monaco Palace (18th-cent)

1966. 750th Anniv of Monaco Palace.

833	**188**	10c. violet, green and blue	20	20
834	-	12c. bistre, blue and black	20	20
835	-	18c. green, black and blue	30	30
836	-	30c. brown, black and blue	35	35
837	-	60c. green, blue and bistre	1·20	1·20
838	-	1f.30 brown and green	2·40	2·40

Designs:—(Different views of Palace): 12c. 17th-century; 18c. 18th-century; 30c. 19th-century; 60c. 19th-century; 1f.30, 20th-century.

189 Dante

1966. 700th Anniv of Dante's Birth.

839	**189**	30c. green, deep green and red	45	40
840	-	60c. blue, turquoise & grn	90	85
841	-	70c. black, green and red	1·00	95
842	-	95c. blue, violet and purple	1·30	1·20
843	-	1f. turquoise, blue & dp bl	1·40	1·30

Designs:—Scenes from Dante's works: 60c. Dante harassed by the panther (envy); 70c. Crossing the 5th circle; 95c. Punishment of the arrogant; 1f. Invocation of St. Bernard.

190 *The Nativity*

1966. World Association of Children's Friends (A.M.A.D.E.).

844	**190**	30c. brown	40	35

191 Route Map from London

1966. 35th Monte Carlo Rally.

845	**191**	1f. blue, purple and red	1·90	1·80

192 Princess Grace with Children

1966. Air. Princess Stephanie's 1st Birthday.

846	**192**	3f. brown, blue and violet	3·25	2·40

193 Casino in 19th-Century

1966. Centenary of Monte Carlo.

847	-	12c. black, red and blue (postage)	15	10
848	**193**	25c. multicoloured	20	20
849	-	30c. multicoloured	25	25
850	-	40c. multicoloured	35	30
851	-	60c. multicoloured	60	55
852	-	70c. blue and lake	65	60
853	-	95c. black and purple	1·80	1·70
854	-	1f.30 purple, brown and chestnut	2·00	1·80
855	-	5f. lake, ochre and blue (air)	4·00	3·50

Designs:—Vert: 12c. Prince Charles III. Horiz (as Type **143**): 40c. Charles III Monument; 95c. Massenet and Saint-Saens; 1f.30, Faure and Ravel. (48x27 mm): 30c. F. Blanc, originator of Monte Carlo, and view of 1860; 60c. Prince Rainier III and projected esplanade; 70c. Rene Blum and Diaghilev, ballet character from *Petrouchka*. (36x36 mm): 5f. Interior of Opera House, 1879.

194 Europa "Ship"

1966. Europa.

856	**194**	30c. orange	1·30	60
857	**194**	60c. green	2·50	1·80

195 Prince Rainier and Princess Grace

1966. Air.

858	**195**	2f. slate and red	2·00	1·20
859	**195**	3f. slate and green	4·00	2·20
860	**195**	5f. slate and blue	5·25	2·75
860a	**195**	10f. slate and bistre	9·00	4·75
860b	**195**	20f. brown and orange	85·00	55·00

196 Prince Albert I and Yachts *Hirondelle I* and *Princess Alice*

1966. First International Oceanographic History Congress, Monaco.

861	**196**	1f. lilac and blue	1·30	1·20

197 "Learning to Write"

1966. 20th Anniv of UNESCO.

862	**197**	30c. purple and mauve	25	25
863	**197**	60c. brown and blue	50	50

198 TV Screen, Cross and Monaco Harbour

1966. Tenth Meeting of International Catholic Television Association (U.N.D.A.), Monaco.

864	**198**	60c. red, purple & crimson	50	35

199 *Precontinent III*

1966. First Anniv of Underwater Research Craft "Precontinent III".

865	**199**	1f. yellow, brown and blue	90	60

200 WHO Building

1966. Inaug of W.H.O. Headquarters, Geneva.

866	**200**	30c. brown, green and blue	25	25
867	**200**	60c. brown, red and green	50	50

201 Bugatti, 1931

1967. 25th Motor Grand Prix, Monaco. Multicoloured. (a) Postage.

868	1c. Type **201**	20	20
869	2c. Alfa-Romeo, 1932	20	20
870	5c. Mercedes, 1936	20	20
871	10c. Maserati, 1948	20	20
872	18c. Ferrari, 1955	1·00	60
873	20c. Alfa-Romeo, 1950	25	25
874	25c. Maserati, 1957	40	30
875	30c. Cooper-Climax, 1958	65	35
876	40c. Lotus-Climax, 1960	1·00	70
877	50c. Lotus-Climax, 1961	1·30	95
878	60c. Cooper-Climax, 1962	2·00	1·30
879	70c. B.R.M., 1963–6	2·50	2·00
880	1f. Walter Christie, 1907	3·25	2·40
881	2f.30 Peugeot, 1910	5·25	3·75

(b) Air. Diamond. 50×50 mm.

882	3f. black and blue	4·50	4·25

Design:—3f. Panhard-Phenix, 1895.

202 Dog (Egyptian bronze)

1967. Int Cynological Federation Congress, Monaco.

883	**202**	30c. black, purple & green	65	60

203 View of Monte Carlo

1967. International Tourist Year.

884	**203**	30c. brown, green and blue	65	60

204 Pieces on Chessboard

1967. Int Chess Grand Prix, Monaco.

885	**204**	60c. black, plum and blue	1·30	1·20

205 Melvin Jones (founder), Lions Emblem and Monte Carlo

1967. 50th Anniv of Lions International.

886	**205**	60c. blue, ultramarine and brown	90	85

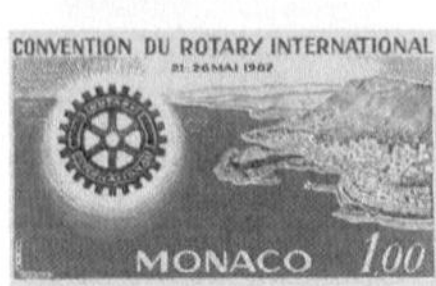

206 Rotary Emblem and Monte Carlo

1967. Rotary International Convention.

887	**206**	1f. bistre, blue and green	1·30	1·20

207 Fair Buildings

1967. World Fair, Montreal.

888	**207**	1f. red, slate and blue	90	85

208 Squiggle on Map of Europe

1967. European Migration Committee (C.I.M.E.).

889	**208**	1f. brown, bistre and blue	90	85

209 Cogwheels

1967. Europa.

890	**209**	30c. violet, purple and red	1·30	60
891	**209**	60c. green, turq & emer	2·50	1·20

210 Dredger and Coastal Chart

1967. Ninth International Hydrographic Congress, Monaco.

892	**210**	1f. brown, blue and green	90	85

211 Marie Curie and Scientific Equipment

1967. Birth Centenary of Marie Curie.

893	**211**	1f. blue, olive and brown	90	85

212 Skiing

1967. Winter Olympic Games, Grenoble.

894	**212**	2f.30 brown, blue & slate	2·50	1·80

213 *Prince Rainier I* (E. Charpentier)

1967. Paintings. "Princes and Princesses of Monaco". Multicoloured.

895	1f. Type **213**	1·00	95
896	1f. *Lucien Grimaldi* (A. di Predis)	1·00	95

See also Nos. 932/3, 958/9, 1005/6, 1023/4, 1070/1, 1108/9, 1213/14, 1271/2, 1325, 1380/1, 1405/6, 1460/1 and 1531/2.

214 Putting the Shot

1968. Olympic Games, Mexico.

897	**214**	20c. blue, brown and green (postage)	25	25
898	-	30c. brown, blue and plum	40	35
899	-	60c. blue, purple and red	50	50
900	-	70c. red, blue and ochre	65	60
901	-	1f. blue, brown and orange	1·00	95
902	-	2f.30 olive, blue and lake	2·75	2·50
903	-	3f. blue, violet & grn (air)	2·00	1·80

Designs:—30c. High-jumping; 60c. Gymnastics; 70c. Water-polo; 1f. Greco-Roman wrestling; 2f.30, Gymnastics (different); 3f. Hockey.

215 "St. Martin"

1968. 20th Anniv of Monaco Red Cross.

904	**215**	2f.30 blue and brown	2·00	1·60

216 *Anemones* (after Raoul Dufy)

1968. Monte Carlo Floral Exhibitions.

905	**216**	1f. multicoloured	1·60	1·20

217 Insignia of Prince Charles III and Pope Pius IX

1968. Centenary of "Nullius Diocesis" Abbey.

906	**217**	10c. brown and red	20	20
907	-	20c. red, green and brown	25	25
908	-	30c. brown and blue	40	35
909	-	60c. brown, blue and green	50	50
910	-	1f. indigo, bistre and blue	90	85

Designs:—Vert: 20c. *St. Nicholas* (after Louis Brea); 30c. *St. Benedict* (after Simone Martini); 60c. Subiaco Abbey. Horiz: 1f. Old St. Nicholas' Church (on site of present cathedral).

218 Europa "Key"

1968. Europa.

911	**218**	30c. red and orange	2·00	1·20
912	**218**	60c. blue and red	3·25	1·80
913	**218**	1f. brown and green	4·50	3·00

219 First Locomotive on Monaco Line, 1868

1968. Centenary of Nice–Monaco Railway.

914	**219**	20c. black, blue and purple	1·00	60
915	-	30c. black, blue and olive	1·30	95
916	-	60c. black, blue and ochre	2·20	1·80
917	-	70c. black, violet & brown	4·00	2·75
918	-	1f. black, blue and red	6·00	4·00
919	-	2f.30 blue, black and red	9·25	7·50

Designs:—30c. Class 220-C steam locomotive, 1898; 60c. Class 230-C steam locomotive, 1910; 70c. Class 231-F steam locomotive, 1925; 1f. Class 241-A steam locomotive, 1932; 2f.30, Class BB 25200 electric locomotive, 1968.

220 Chateaubriand and Combourg Castle

1968. Birth Centenary of Chateaubriand (novelist).

920	**220**	10c. plum, green & myrtle	15	15
921	-	20c. violet, purple and blue	20	20
922	-	25c. brown, violet and blue	30	25
923	-	30c. violet, choc & brn	35	35
924	-	60c. brown, green and red	70	50
925	-	2f.30 brown, mauve & bl	2·75	2·20

Scenes from Chateaubriand's novels: 20c. *Le Genie du Christianisme*; 25c. *Rene*; 30c. *Le Dernier Abencerage*; 60c. *Les Martyrs*; 2f.30, *Atala*.

221 Law Courts, Paris, and statues–"La France et la Fidelite"

1968. Birth Centenary of J. F. Bosio (Monegasque sculptor).

926	**221**	20c. brown and purple	30	20
927	-	25c. brown and red	35	25
928	-	30c. blue and green	40	35
929	-	60c. green and myrtle	1·00	65
930	-	2f.30 black and slate	2·10	1·30

Designs:—Vert (26×36 mm): 25c. "Henry IV as a Child"; 30c. "J. F. Bosio" (lithograph); 60c. "Louis XIV". Horiz (as Type **221**): 2f.30, "Napoleon I, Louis XVIII and Charles X".

222 W.H.O. Emblem

1968. 20th Anniv of W.H.O.

931	**222**	60c. multicoloured	40	35

1968. Paintings. "Princes and Princesses of Monaco". As T **213**. Multicoloured.

932	1f. *Prince Charles II* (Mimault)	1·10	1·00
933	2f.30 *Princess Jeanne Grimaldi* (Mimault)	2·40	2·10

223 The Hungarian March

1969. Death Centenary of Hector Berlioz (composer).

934	**223**	10c. brown, violet and green (postage)	15	20
935	-	20c. brown, olive & mauve	20	20
936	-	25c. brown, blue & mauve	30	25
937	-	30c. black, green and blue	40	35
938	-	40c. red, black and slate	50	40
939	-	50c. brown, slate & purple	55	45
940	-	70c. brown, slate and green	65	60
941	-	1f. black, mauve & brown	70	65
942	-	1f.15 black, blue & turq	1·40	1·30
943	-	2f. black, blue & grn (air)	2·10	2·00

Designs:—Horiz: 20c. Mephistopheles appears to Faust; 25c. Auerbach's tavern; 30c. Sylphs' ballet; 40c. Minuet of the goblins; 50c. Marguerite's bedroom; 70c. "Forests and caverns"; 1f. The journey to Hell; 1f.15, Heaven; All scenes from Berlioz's "The Damnation of Faust". Vert: 2f. Bust of Berlioz.

224 "St. Elisabeth of Hungary"

1969. Monaco Red Cross.

944	**224**	3f. blue, brown and red	2·75	2·30

225 *Napoleon I* (P. Delaroche)

1969. Birth Bicentenary of Napoleon Bonaparte.

945	**225**	3f. multicoloured	2·75	2·50

226 Colonnade

1969. Europa.

946	**226**	40c. red and purple	2·10	1·30
947	**226**	70c. blue, brown and black	4·25	2·50
948	**226**	1f. ochre, brown and blue	7·00	4·00

1969. Precancelled. As T **177**. No date.

949	22c. brown, blue and black	55	50
949a	26c. violet, blue and black	55	50
949b	30c. multicoloured	65	60
950	35c. multicoloured	70	65
950a	45c. multicoloured	1·10	1·00
951	70c. black and blue	1·40	1·30
951a	90c. green, blue and black	2·75	2·50

227 *Head of Woman* (Da Vinci)

1969. 450th Death Anniv of Leonardo da Vinci.

952	**227**	30c. brown	40	35
953	-	40c. red and brown	55	40
954	-	70c. green	65	45
955	-	80c. sepia	70	50
956	-	1f.15 brown	1·50	1·00
957	-	3f. brown	3·50	2·75

Drawings:—40c. *Self-portrait*; 70c. *Head of an Old Man*; 80c. *Head of St. Madeleine*; 1f.15, *Man's Head*; 3f. *The Condottiere*.

1969. Paintings. "Princes and Princesses of Monaco". As T **213**. Multicoloured.

958	1f. *Prince Honore II* (Champaigne)	1·10	1·00
959	3f. *Princess Louise-Hippolyte* (Champaigne)	2·50	2·10

228 Marine Fauna, King Alfonso XIII of Spain and Prince Albert I of Monaco

1969. 50th Anniv of Int Commission for Scientific Exploration of the Mediterranean, Madrid.

960	**228**	40c. blue and black	70	65

229 ILO Emblem

1969. 50th Anniv of I.L.O.

961	**229**	40c. multicoloured	70	65

230 Aerial View of Monaco and TV Camera

1969. Tenth International Television Festival.

962	**230**	40c. purple, lake and blue	70	65

231 JCC Emblem

1969. 25th Anniv of Junior Chamber of Commerce.

963	**231**	40c. violet, bistre and blue	70	65

232 Alphonse Daudet and Scenes from *Lettres*

1969. Centenary of Daudet's "Lettres de Mon Moulin".

964	**232**	30c. lake, violet and green	30	25
965	-	40c. green, brown and blue	40	40
966	-	70c. multicoloured	1·00	90
967	-	80c. violet, brown & green	1·10	1·00
968	-	1f.15 brown, orange & bl	1·40	1·30

Designs: (Scenes from the book): 40c. *Installation* (Daudet writing); 70c. *Mule, Goat and Wolf*; 80c. *Gaucher's Elixir* and *The Three Low Masses*; 1f.15, Daudet drinking, *The Old Man* and *The Country Sub-Prefect*.

233 Conference Building, Albert I and Rainier III

1970. Interparliamentary Union's Spring Meeting, Monaco.

969	**233**	40c. black, red and purple	40	40

234 Baby Common Seal

1970. Protection of Baby Seals.

970	**234**	40c. drab, blue and purple	1·40	1·30

235 Japanese Print

1970. Expo 70.

971	**235**	20c. brown, green and red	30	25
972	-	30c. brown, buff and green	35	35
973	-	40c. bistre and violet	40	40
974	-	70c. grey and red	1·10	1·00
975	-	1f.15 red, green & purple	1·40	1·30

Designs:—Vert: 30c. Manchurian Cranes (birds); 40c. Shinto temple gateway. Horiz: 70c. Cherry blossom; 1f.15, Monaco Palace and Osaka Castle.

236 Dobermann

1970. International Dog Show, Monte Carlo.

976	**236**	40c. black and brown	2·50	1·70

237 Apollo

1970. 20th Anniv of World Federation for Protection of Animals.

977	**237**	30c. black, red and blue	55	55
978	-	40c. brown, blue and green	1·10	65
979	-	50c. brown, ochre and blue	1·50	80
980	-	80c. brown, blue and green	3·50	2·30
981	-	1f. brown, bistre and slate	4·50	4·25
982	-	1f.15 brown, green & blue	5·50	4·00

Designs:—Horiz: 40c. Basque ponies; 50c. Common seal. Vert: 80c. Chamois; 1f. White-tailed sea eagles; 1f.15, European otter.

238 "St. Louis" (King of France)

1970. Monaco Red Cross.

983	**238**	3f. green, brown and slate	2·75	2·75

See also Nos. 1022, 1041, **MS**1073, 1114, 1189 and 1270.

239 *Roses and Anemones* (Van Gogh)

1970. Monte Carlo Flower Show.

984	**239**	3f. multicoloured	4·50	4·00

See also Nos. 1042, 1073, 1105/7, 1143/4, 1225/6, 1244, 1282/3 and 1316/7.

240 Moon Plaque, Presidents Kennedy and Nixon

1970. First Man on the Moon (1969). Multicoloured.

985	40c. Type **240**	1·00	80
986	80c. Astronauts on Moon	1·40	1·20

241 New UPU Building and Monument

1970. New U.P.U. Headquarters Building.

987	**241**	40c. brown, black & green	40	40

242 "Flaming Sun"

1970. Europa.

988	**242**	40c. purple	2·10	1·30
989	**242**	80c. green	4·25	2·50
990	**242**	1f. blue	7·00	4·00

243 Camargue Horse

1970. Horses.

991	**243**	10c. slate, olive and blue (postage)	30	20
992	-	20c. brown, olive and blue	40	35
993	-	30c. brown, green and blue	1·10	90
994	-	40c. grey, brown and slate	2·40	1·60
995	-	50c. brown, olive and blue	3·50	2·00
996	-	70c. brown, orange & grn	5·50	3·75
997	-	85c. blue, green and olive	6·00	4·00
998	-	1f.15 black, green & blue	6·25	4·25
999	-	3f. multicoloured (air)	3·50	3·25

Horses:—Horiz: 20c. Anglo-Arab; 30c. French saddle-horse; 40c. Lippizaner; 50c. Trotter; 70c. English thoroughbred; 85c. Arab; 1f.15, Barbary. DIAMOND (50×50 mm): 3f. Rock-drawings of horses in Lascaux grotto.

244 Dumas, D'Artagnan and the Three Musketeers

1970. Death Centenary of Alexandre Dumas (pere) (author).

1000 **244** 30c. slate, brown and blue 40 25

245 Henri Rougier and Voisin "Boxkite"

1970. 60th Anniv of First Mediterranean Flight.

1001 **245** 40c. brown, blue and slate 50 25

246 De Lamartine and scene from *Meditations Poetiques*

1970. 150th Anniv of "Meditations Poetiques" by Alphonse de Lamartine (writer).

1002 **246** 80c. brown, blue & turq 70 50

247 Beethoven

1970. Birth Bicentenary of Beethoven.

1003 **247** 1f.30 brown and red 4·25 2·50

1970. 50th Death Anniv of Modigliani. Vert Painting as T **213**. Multicoloured.

1004 3f. *Portrait of Dedie* 5·50 4·00

1970. Paintings. "Princes and Princesses of Monaco". As T **213**.

1005 1f. red and black 1·10 1·00

1006 3f. multicoloured 2·75 2·50

Portraits:—1f. *Prince Louis I* (F. de Troy); 3f. *Princess Charlotte de Gramont* (S. Bourdon).

248 Cocker Spaniel

1971. International Dog Show, Monte Carlo.

1007 **248** 50c. multicoloured 5·00 3·75

See also Nos. 1036, 1082, 1119, 1218 and 1239.

249 Razorbill

1971. Campaign Against Pollution of the Sea.

1008 **249** 50c. indigo and blue 1·00 90

250 Hand holding Emblem

1971. Seventh Int Blood Donors Federation Congress.

1009 **250** 80c. red, violet and grey 70 65

251 Sextant, Scroll and Underwater Scene

1971. 50th Anniv of Int Hydrographic Bureau.

1010 **251** 80c. brown, green & slate 1·00 90

252 Detail of Michelangelo Painting ("The Arts")

1971. 25th Anniv of UNESCO.

1011 **252** 30c. brown, blue & violet 35 35

1012 - 50c. blue and brown 40 35

1013 - 80c. brown and green 55 45

1014 - 1f.30 green 1·40 90

Designs:—Vert: 50c. Alchemist and dish aerial ("Sciences"); 1f.30, Prince Pierre of Monaco (National UNESCO Commission). Horiz: 80c. Ancient scribe, book and TV screen ("Culture").

253 Europa Chain

1971. Europa.

1015 **253** 50c. red 2·75 2·00

1016 **253** 80c. blue 5·00 2·50

1017 **253** 1f.30 green 9·00 4·50

254 Old Bridge, Sospel

1971. Protection of Historic Monuments.

1018 **254** 50c. brown, blue & green 40 40

1019 - 80c. brown, green & grey 70 50

1020 - 1f.30 red, green & brown 1·10 1·00

1021 - 3f. slate, blue and olive 2·75 2·00

Designs:—Horiz: 80c. Roquebrune Chateau; 1f.30, Grimaldi Chateau, Cagnes-sur-Mer. Vert: 3f. Roman "Trophy of the Alps", La Turbie.

1971. Monaco Red Cross. As T **238**.

1022 3f. brown, olive and green 2·75 2·50

Design: 3f. St. Vincent de Paul.

1972. Paintings. "Princes and Princesses of Monaco". As T **213**. Multicoloured.

1023 1f. *Prince Antoine I* (Rigaud) 1·10 1·00

1024 3f. *Princess Marie de Lorraine* (18th-century French School) 2·75 2·30

255 La Fontaine and Animal Fables (350th)

1972. Birth Anniversaries (1971).

1025 **255** 50c. brown, emer & grn 1·10 65

1026 - 1f.30 purple, black & red 1·70 1·30

Design:—1f.30, Baudelaire, nudes and cats (150th).

256 Saint-Saens and scene from Opera, *Samson and Delilah*

1972. 50th Death Anniv (1971) of Camile Saint-Saens.

1027 **256** 90c. brown and sepia 1·00 80

257 Battle Scene

1972. 400th Anniv (1971) of Battle of Lepanto.

1028 **257** 1f. blue, brown and red 1·10 80

258 *Christ before Pilate* (engraving by Durer)

1972. 500th Birth Anniv (1971) of Albrecht Durer.

1029 **258** 2f. black and brown 2·75 2·40

259 *The Cradle* (B. Morisot)

1972. 25th Anniv (1971) of UNICEF.

1030 **259** 2f. multicoloured 3·25 3·00

260 *Gilles* (Watteau)

1972. 250th Death Anniv (1971) of Watteau.

1031 **260** 3f. multicoloured 4·50 3·50

261 Santa Claus

1972. Christmas (1971).

1032 **261** 30c. red, blue and brown 35 35

1033 **261** 50c. red, green & orange 40 35

1034 **261** 90c. red, blue and brown 85 70

262 Class 743 Steam Locomotive, Italy, and TGV 001 Turbotrain, France

1972. 50th Anniv of International Railway Union.

1035 **262** 50c. purple, lilac and red 1·80 1·60

1972. Int Dog Show, Monte Carlo. As T **248**.

1036 60c. multicoloured 5·00 4·25

Design:—60c. Great Dane.

263 "Pollution Kills"

1972. Anti-pollution Campaign.

1037 **263** 90c. brown, green & black 1·30 1·10

264 Ski-jumping

1972. Winter Olympic Games, Sapporo, Japan.

1038 **264** 90c. black, red and green 1·30 1·10

1972. Europa.

1039 **265** 50c. blue and orange 4·25 3·50

1040 **265** 90c. blue and green 6·25 5·50

265 "Communications"

1972. Monaco Red Cross. As T **238**.

1041 3f. brown and purple 2·75 2·40

Design: 3f. St. Francis of Assisi.

1972. Monte Carlo Flower Show. As T **239**.

1042 3f. multicoloured 7·75 6·50

Design:—3f. *Vase of Flowers* (Cezanne).

266 *SS Giovanni e Paolo* (detail, Canaletto)

1972. UNESCO "Save Venice" Campaign.

1043 **266** 30c. red 40 35

1044 - 60c. violet 85 70

1045 - 2f. blue 2·40 2·00

Designs:—27×48 mm: 60c. *S. Pietro di Castello* (F. Guradi). As Type **266**: 2f. *Piazzetta S. Marco* (B. Bellotto).

267 Dressage

1972. Olympic Games, Munich. Equestrian Events.

1046 **267** 60c. brown, blue and lake 1·40 1·20

1047 - 90c. lake, brown and blue 1·80 1·60

1048 - 1f.10 blue, lake & brown 2·75 2·40

1049 - 1f.40 brown, lake & blue 4·50 3·75

Designs:—90c. Cross country; 1f.10, Show jumping (wall); 1f.40, Show jumping (parallel bars).

268 Escoffier and Birthplace

1972. 125th Birth Anniv of Auguste Escoffier (master chef).

1050 **268** 45c. black and brown 65 55

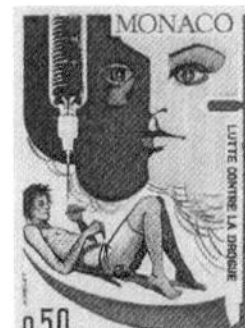

269 Drug Addiction

1972. Campaign Against Drugs.

1051	**269**	50c. red, brown & orange	85	70
1052	**269**	90c. green, brown & blue	1·10	95

See also Nos. 1088/91, 1280/1 and 1318.

270 Globe, Birds and Animals

1972. 17th International Congress of Zoology, Monaco.

1053	**270**	30c. green, brown and red	30	25
1054	-	50c. brown, purple and red	40	35
1055	-	90c. blue, brown and red	85	70

Designs:—Horiz: 50c. Vert: 90c. Similar symbolic design.

271 Bouquet

1972. Monte Carlo Flower Show, 1973 (1st issue). Multicoloured.

1056	30c. Lilies in vase	1·40	1·20
1057	50c. Type **271**	1·80	1·60
1058	90c. Flowers in vase	3·50	3·00

See also Nos. 1073.

272 The Nativity and Child's face

1972. Christmas.

1059	**272**	30c. grey, blue and purple	30	25
1060	**272**	50c. red, purple & brown	35	30
1061	**272**	90c. violet, plum & pur	85	70

273 Louis Bleriot and Bleriot XI (Birth cent)

1972. Birth Anniversaries.

1062	**273**	30c. blue and brown	40	35
1063	-	50c. blue, turq & new blue	1·80	1·60
1064	-	90c. brown and buff	1·40	1·20

Designs and Anniversaries:—50c. Amundsen and polar scene (birth centenary); 90c. Pasteur and laboratory scene (150th birth anniv).

274 *Gethsemane*

1972. Protection of Historical Monuments. Frescoes by J. Canavesio, Chapel of Notre-Dame des Fontaines, La Brigue.

1065	**274**	30c. red	30	25
1066	-	50c. grey	55	50
1067	-	90c. green	70	60
1068	-	1f.40 red	1·30	1·10
1069	-	2f. purple	2·10	1·80

Designs:—50c. *Christ Outraged*; 90c. *Ascent to Calvary*; 1f.40, *The Resurrection*; 2f. *The Crucifixion*.

1972. Paintings. "Princes and Princesses of Monaco". As T **213**. Multicoloured.

1070	1f. *Prince Jacques I* (N. Largilliere)	1·10	95
1071	3f. *Princess Louise-Hippolyte* (J. B. Vanloo)	2·75	2·40

275 "St. Devote" (triptych by Louis Brea)

1973. 25th Anniv of Monaco Red Cross. Sheet 100×130 mm.

MS1072	**275** 5f. red	29·00	28·00

1973. Monte Carlo Flower Show (2nd issue). As T **239**.

1073	3f.50 multicoloured	9·75	8·50

Design:—3f.50, Bouquet of Flowers.

276 Europa "Posthorn"

1973. Europa.

1074	**276**	50c. orange	7·00	6·00
1075	**276**	90c. green	10·50	9·00

277 Moliere and Characters from *Le Malade Imaginaire*

1973. 300th Death Anniv of Moliere.

1076	**277**	20c. red, brown and blue	70	60

278 Colette, Cat and Books

1973. Birth Anniversaries.

1077	**278**	30c. black, blue and red	1·40	1·20
1078	-	45c. multicoloured	3·50	3·00
1079	-	50c. lilac, purple and blue	55	50
1080	-	90c. multicoloured	85	70

Designs and Anniversaries:—Horiz: 30c., Type **278** (nature writer, birth cent); 45c. J.-H. Fabre and insects (entomologists, 150th birth anniv); 90c. Sir George Cayley and his "convertiplane" (aviation pioneer, birth bicent). Vert: 50c. Blaise Pascal (philosopher and writer, 350th birth anniv).

279 E. Ducretet, Panthéon and Eiffel Tower

1973. 75th Anniv of Eugene Ducretet's First Hertzian Radio Link.

1081	**279**	30c. purple and brown	55	50

1973. International Dog Show, Monte Carlo. As T **248**. Inscr "1973". Multicoloured.

1082	45c. Alsatian	20·00	18·00

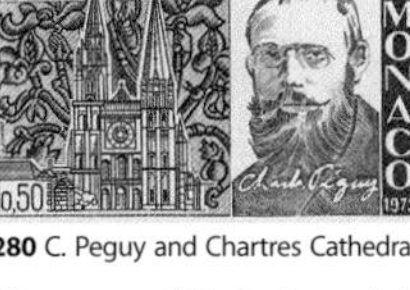

280 C. Peguy and Chartres Cathedral

1973. Birth Bicentenary of Charles Peguy (writer).

1083	**280**	50c. brown, mauve & grey	40	40

281 Telecommunications Equipment

1973. Fifth World Telecommunications Day.

1084	**281**	60c. violet, blue & brown	55	50

282 Stage Characters

1973. Fifth World Amateur Theatre Festival.

1085	**282**	60c. lilac, blue and red	70	65

283 Ellis and Rugby Tackle

1973. 150th Anniv of Founding of Rugby Football by William Webb Ellis.

1086	**283**	90c. red, lake and brown	85	80

284 St. Theresa

1973. Birth Centenary of St. Theresa of Lisieux.

1087	**284**	1f.40 multicoloured	1·10	1·00

285 Drug Addiction

1973. Campaign Against Drugs.

1088	**285**	50c. red, green and blue	40	40
1089	-	50c. multicoloured	40	40
1090	**285**	90c. violet, green and red	1·00	90
1091	-	90c. multicoloured	1·00	90

Design:—Nos. 1089, 1091, Children, syringes and addicts.

286 *Institution of the Creche* (Giotto)

1973. 750th Anniv of St. Francis of Assisi Creche.

1092	**286**	30c. purple (postage)	70	65
1093	-	45c. red	1·10	1·00
1094	-	50c. brown	1·70	1·60
1095	-	1f. green	3·50	3·25
1096	-	2f. brown	6·25	5·75
1097	-	3f. blue (air)	4·25	4·00

Design:—Horiz: 45c. *The Nativity* (School of F. Lippi); 50c. *The Birth of Jesus Christ* (Giotto). Vert: 1f. *The Nativity* (15th-century miniature); 2f. *The Birth of Jesus* (Fra Angelico); 3f. *The Nativity* (Flemish school).

287 Country Picnic

1973. 50th Anniv of National Committee for Monegasque Traditions.

1098	**287**	10c. blue, green & brown	15	15
1099	-	20c. violet, blue and green	30	25
1100	-	30c. sepia, brown & green	40	40
1101	-	45c. red, violet and purple	1·00	90
1102	-	50c. black, red and brown	1·30	1·20
1103	-	60c. red, violet and blue	1·40	1·30
1104	-	1f. violet, blue and brown	2·50	2·30

Designs:—Vert: 20c. Maypole dance. Horiz: 30c. "U Bradi" (local dance); 45c. St. Jean fire-dance; 50c. Blessing the Christmas loaf; 60c. Blessing the sea, Festival of St. Devote; 1f. Corpus Christi procession.

1973. Monte Carlo Flower Show, 1974. As T **271**. Multicoloured.

1105	45c. Roses and Strelitzia	2·75	2·50
1106	60c. Mimosa and myosotis	3·50	3·25
1107	1f. *Vase of Flowers* (Odilon Redon)	7·00	6·50

1973. Paintings. "Princes and Princesses of Monaco". As T **213**. Multicoloured.

1108	2f. *Charlotte Grimaldi* (in day dress, P. Gobert)	3·50	3·25
1109	2f. *Charlotte Grimaldi* (in evening dress, P. Gobert)	3·50	3·25

288 Prince Rainier

1974. 25th Anniv of Prince Rainer's Accession. Sheet 100×130 mm.

MS1110	**288** 10f. black	14·00	13·00

289 UPU Emblem and Symbolic Heads

1974. Centenary of Universal Postal Union.

1111	**289**	50c. purple and brown	40	40
1112	-	70c. multicoloured	70	65
1113	-	1f.10 multicoloured	1·40	1·30

Designs:—70c. Hands holding letters; 1f.10, "Countries of the World" (famous buildings).

1974. Monaco Red Cross. As T **238**.

1114	3f. blue, green and purple	2·75	2·50

Design:—3f. St. Bernard of Menthon.

290 Farman, Farman F.60 Goliath and Farman H.F.III

1974. Birth Centenary of Henry Farman (aviation pioneer).

1115	**290**	30c. brown, purple & blue	40	40

291 Marconi, Circuit Plan and Destroyer

1974. Birth Centenary of Guglielmo Marconi (radio pioneer).

1116	**291**	40c. red, deep blue & blue	70	65

292 Duchesne and "Penicillium glaucum"

1974. Birth Centenary of Ernest Duchesne (microbiologist).

1117	**292**	45c. black, blue & purple	70	65

293 Forest and Engine

1974. 60th Death Anniv of Fernand Forest (motor engineer and inventor).

1118	**293**	50c. purple, red and black	70	65

1974. International Dog Show, Monte Carlo. As T **248**, inscr "1974".

1119	60c. multicoloured	9·00	8·50

Design:—60c. Schnauzer.

294 Ronsard and Characters from *Sonnet to Helene*

1974. 450th Birth Anniv of Pierre de Ronsard (poet).

1120	**294**	70c. brown and red	70	65

295 Sir Winston Churchill (after bust by O. Nemon)

1974. Birth Centenary of Sir Winston Churchill.

1121	**295**	1f. brown and grey	85	80

296 Interpol Emblem, and Views of Monaco and Vienna

1974. 60th Anniv of First International Police Judiciary Congress and 50th Anniv of International Criminal Police Organization (Interpol).

1122	**296**	2f. blue, brown and green	1·80	1·70

297 *The King of Rome* (Bosio)

1974. Europa. Sculptures by J. F. Bosio.

1123	**297**	45c. green and brown	2·75	2·50
1124	-	1f.10 bistre and brown	5·00	4·50
MS1125		170×140 mm. Nos. 1123/5×5	70·00	65·00

Design:—1f.10, *Madame Elizabeth*.

298 *The Box* (A. Renoir)

1974. The Impressionists. Multicoloured.

1126	1f. Type **298**	3·50	3·25
1127	1f. *The Dance Class* (E. Degas)	3·50	3·25
1128	2f. *Impression-Sunrise* (C. Monet) (horiz)	7·75	7·25
1129	2f. *Entrance to Voisins Village* (C. Pissarro) (horiz)	7·75	7·25
1130	2f. *The Hanged Man's House* (P. Cezanne) (horiz)	7·75	7·25
1131	2f. *Floods at Port Marly* (A. Sisley) (horiz)	7·75	7·25

299 Tigers and Trainer

1974. First International Circus Festival, Monaco.

1132	**299**	2c. brown, green and blue	15	15
1133	-	3c. brown and purple	20	20
1134	-	5c. blue, brown and red	30	25
1135	-	45c. brown, black and red	1·00	90
1136	-	70c. multicoloured	1·50	1·40
1137	-	1f.10 brown, green and red	2·50	2·30
1138	-	5f. green, blue and brown	10·50	9·75

Designs:—Vert: 3c. Performing horse; 45c. Equestrian act; 1f.10, Acrobats; 5f. Trapeze act. Horiz: 5c. Performing Elephants; 70c. Clowns.

300 Honore II on Medal

1974. 350th Anniv of Monegasque Numismatic Art.

1139	**300**	60c. green and red	70	65

301 Marine Flora and Fauna

1974. 24th Congress of the International Commission for the Scientific Exploration of the Mediterranean. Multicoloured.

1140	45c. Type **301**	2·10	2·00
1141	70c. Sea-bed flora and fauna	3·50	3·25
1142	1f.10 Sea-bed flora and fauna (different)	4·75	4·50

Nos. 1141/2 are larger, size 52×31 mm.

1974. Monte Carlo Flower Show. As T **271**. Multicoloured.

1143	70c. Honeysuckle and violets	2·10	2·00
1144	1f.10 Iris and chrysanthemums	3·50	3·25

302 Prince Rainier III (F. Messina)

303

1974

1145	**302**	60c. green (postage)	2·40	2·20
1146	**302**	80c. red	2·50	2·30
1147	**302**	80c. green	85	80
1148	**302**	1f. brown	5·00	4·50
1149	**302**	1f. red	1·30	1·20
1149a	**302**	1f. green	85	80
1149b	**302**	1f.10 green	1·30	1·20
1150	**302**	1f.20 violet	14·50	10·50
1150a	**302**	1f.20 red	1·30	1·20
1150b	**302**	1f.20 green	1·40	1·30
1151	**302**	1f.25 blue	3·00	2·75
1151a	**302**	1f.30 red	1·40	1·30
1152	**302**	1f.40 red	1·50	1·40
1152a	**302**	1f.50 black	1·70	1·60
1153	**302**	1f.60 grey	2·10	2·00
1153a	**302**	1f.70 blue	2·00	1·80
1153b	**302**	1f.80 blue	3·50	3·25
1154	**302**	2f. mauve	5·00	4·50
1154a	**302**	2f.10 brown	2·75	2·50
1155	**302**	2f.30 violet	5·00	4·50
1156	**302**	2f.50 black	4·25	4·00
1157	**302**	9f. violet	12·00	9·00
1158	**303**	10f. violet (air)	12·00	9·00
1159	**303**	15f. red	15·00	10·50
1160	**303**	20f. blue	24·00	18·00

304 Coastline, Monte Carlo

1974

1161	**304**	25c. blue, green & brown	5·00	2·30
1162	-	25c. brown, green & blue	40	40
1163	-	50c. brown and blue	5·00	2·30
1164	**304**	65c. blue, brown & green	70	65
1165	-	70c. multicoloured	1·10	1·00
1166	**304**	1f.10 brown, green & bl	4·25	3·25
1167	-	1f.10 black, brown & bl	1·40	1·30
1168	-	1f.30 brown, green & bl	1·50	1·40
1169	-	1f.40 green, grey & brn	5·00	2·50
1170	-	1f.50 green, blue & black	2·75	2·00
1171	-	1f.70 brown, green & bl	8·50	5·25
1172	-	1f.80 brown, green & bl	3·00	2·75
1173	-	2f.30 brown, grey & blue	5·00	3·25
1174	-	3f. brown, grey and green	12·00	7·75
1175	-	5f.50 brown, green & blue	20·00	14·50
1176	-	6f.50 brown, blue & grn	7·75	5·75

Designs:—Vert: 50c. Palace clock tower; 70c. Botanical gardens; 1f.30, Monaco Cathedral; 1f.40, 1f.50, Prince Albert I statue and Museum; 3f. Fort Antoine. Horiz: 25c. (1162), 1f.70, "All Saints" Tower; 1f.10 (1167), Palais de Justice; 1f.80, 5f.50, La Condamine; 2f.30, North Galleries of Palace; 6f.50, Aerial view of hotels and harbour.

305 *Haagocereus chosicensis*

1975. Plants. Multicoloured.

1180	10c. Type **305**	30	25
1181	20c. *Matucana madisoniarum*	35	35
1182	30c. *Parodia scopaioides*	85	80
1183	85c. *Mediolobivia arachnacantha*	5·00	4·50
1184	1f.90 *Matucana yanganucensis*	7·75	7·25
1185	4f. *Echinocereus marksianus*	11·00	10·50

306 *Portrait of a Sailor* (P. Florence)

1975. Europa.

1186	**306**	80c. purple	4·25	4·00
1187	-	1f.20 blue	5·50	5·25
MS1188		170×130 mm. Nos. 1186/7×5	70·00	65·00

Design:—1f.20, *St. Devote* (Ludovic Brea).

307 *St. Bernardin de Sienne*

1975. Monaco Red Cross.

1189	**307**	4f. blue and purple	4·25	4·00

308 Prologue

1975. Centenary of "Carmen" (opera by Georges Bizet).

1190	**308**	30c. violet, brown & blk	30	25
1191	-	60c. grey, green and red	40	40
1192	-	80c. green, brown & blk	1·10	1·00
1193	-	1f.40 purple, brn & ochre	1·70	1·60

Designs:—Horiz: 60c. Lilla Pastia's tavern; 80c. The Smuggler's Den; 1f.40, Confrontation at Seville.

309 Saint-Simon

1975. 300th Birth Anniv of Louis de Saint-Simon (writer).

1194	**309**	40c. blue	40	40

310 Dr. Albert Schweitzer

1975. Birth Centenary of Dr. Schweitzer (Nobel Peace Prize Winner).

1195	**310**	60c. red and brown	1·00	90

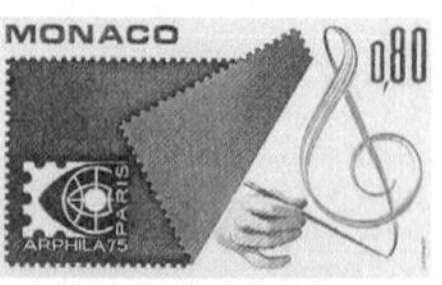

311 "Stamp" and Calligraphy

1975. Arphila 75 International Stamp Exhibition, Paris.

1196	**311**	80c. brown and orange	1·10	1·00

312 Seagull and Sunrise

1975. International Exposition, Okinawa.

1197	**312**	85c. blue, green & orange	1·40	1·30

313 Pike smashing Crab

1975. Anti-cancer Campaign.

1198	**313**	1f. multicoloured	1·40	1·30

314 Christ with Crown of Thorns

1975. Holy Year.

1199	**314**	1f.15 black, brn & pur	1·40	1·30

315 Villa Sauber, Monte Carlo

1975. European Architectural Heritage Year.

1200	**315**	1f.20 green, brown & bl	1·40	1·30

316 Woman's Head and Globe

1975. International Women's Year.

1201	**316**	1f.20 multicoloured	1·40	1·30

317 Rolls-Royce Silver Ghost (1907)

1975. History of the Motor Car.

1202	**317**	5c. blue, green and brown	15	15
1203	-	10c. indigo and blue	20	20
1204	-	20c. blue, ultram & black	30	25
1205	-	30c. purple and mauve	40	40
1206	-	50c. blue, purple & mauve	1·40	1·30
1207	-	60c. red and green	2·10	2·00
1208	-	80c. indigo and blue	3·25	3·00
1209	-	85c. brown, orange & grn	5·00	4·50
1210	-	1f.20 blue, red and green	5·50	5·25
1211	-	1f.40 green and blue	8·50	7·25
1212	-	5f.50 blue, emerald and green	28·00	23·00

Designs:—10c. Hispano-Suiza H.6B (1926); 20c. Isotta Fraschini 8A (1928); 30c. Cord L.29; 50c. Voisin V12 (1930); 60c. Duesenberg SJ (1933); 80c. Bugatti 57 C (1938); 85c. Delahaye 135 M (1940); 1f.20, Cisitalia Pininfarina (1945); 1f.40, Mercedes-Benz 300 SL (1955); 5f.50, Lamborghini Countach (1974).

1975. Paintings. "Princes and Princesses of Monaco". As T 213. Multicoloured.

1213	2f. *Prince Honore III*	3·50	3·25
1214	4f. *Princess Catherine de Brignole*	6·25	5·75

318 Dog behind Bars

1975. 125th Birth Anniv of Gen. J. P. Delmas de Grammont (author of Animal Protection Code).

1215	**318**	60c. black and brown	2·10	2·00
1216	-	80c. black and brown	3·50	3·25
1217	-	1f.20 green and purple	5·00	4·50

Designs:—Vert: 80c. Cat chased up tree. Horiz: 1f.20, Horse being ill-treated.

1975. International Dog Show, Monte Carlo. As T **248**, but inscr "1975". Multicoloured.

1218	60c. black and purple	9·00	8·50

Design:—60c. French poodle.

319 Maurice Ravel

1975. Birth Centenaries of Musicians.

1219	**319**	60c. brown and purple	1·40	1·30
1220	-	1f.20 black and purple	4·25	4·00

Design:—1f.20, Johann Strauss (the younger).

320 Circus Clown

1975. Second International Circus Festival.

1221	**320**	80c. multicoloured	2·10	2·00

321 Monaco Florin Coin, 1640

1975. Monaco Numismatics.

1222	**321**	80c. brown and blue	1·10	1·00

See also Nos. 1275, 1320 and 1448.

322 Andre Ampere with Electrical Meter

1975. Birth Centenary of Andre Ampere (physicist).

1223	**322**	85c. indigo and blue	1·40	1·30

323 *Lamentations for the Dead Christ*

1975. 500th Birth Anniv of Michelangelo.

1224	**323**	1f.40 olive and black	2·10	2·00

1975. Monte Carlo Flower Show (1976). As T **271**. Multicoloured.

1225	60c. Bouquet of wild flowers	2·10	2·00
1226	80c. Ikebana flower arrangement	2·75	2·50

1975. Precancelled. Surch.

1227	42c. on 26c. violet, blue and black (No. 949a)	4·50	4·25
1228	48c. on 30c. multicoloured (No. 949b)	5·50	5·25
1229	70c. on 45c. multicoloured (No. 950a)	7·50	7·00
1230	1f.35 on 90c. green, blue and black (No. 951a)	9·00	8·50

325 Prince Pierre de Monaco

1976. 25th Anniv of Literary Council of Monaco.

1231	**325**	10c. black	30	25
1232	-	20c. blue and red	35	35
1233	-	25c. blue and red	40	40
1234	-	30c. brown	70	65
1235	-	50c. blue, red and purple	85	80
1236	-	60c. brown, grn & lt brn	1·10	1·00
1237	-	80c. purple and blue	2·10	2·00
1238	-	1f.20 violet, blue & mve	4·25	4·00

Council Members:—Horiz: 20c. A. Maurois and Colette; 25c. Jean and Jerome Tharaud; 30c. E. Henriot, M. Pagnol and G. Duhamel; 50c. Ph. Heriat, J. Supervielle and L. Pierard; 60c. R. Dorgeles, M. Achard and G. Bauer; 80c. F. Hellens, A. Billy and Mgr. Grente; 1f.20, J. Giono, L. Pasteur Vallery-Radot and M. Garcon.

326 Dachshunds

1976. International Dog Show, Monte Carlo.

1239	**326**	60c. multicoloured	12·50	10·50

327 Bridge Table and Monte Carlo Coast

1976. Fifth Bridge Olympiad, Monte Carlo.

1240	**327**	60c. brown, green and red	85	80

328 Alexander Graham Bell and Early Telephone

1976. Telephone Centenary.

1241	**328**	80c. brown, light brown and grey	85	80

329 Federation Emblem on Globe

1976. 50th Anniv of International Philatelic Federation.

1242	**329**	1f.20 red, blue and green	1·10	1·00

330 USA 2c. Stamp, 1926

1976. Bicent of American Revolution.

1243	**330**	1f.70 black and purple	1·40	1·30

331 *The Fritillaries* (Van Gogh)

1976. Monte Carlo Flower Show.

1244	**331**	3f. multicoloured	21·00	17·00

332 Diving

1976. Olympic Games, Montreal.

1245	**332**	60c. brown and blue	50	45
1246	-	80c. blue, brown & green	70	65
1247	-	85c. blue, green & brown	85	80
1248	-	1f.20 brown, green & bl	1·40	1·30
1249	-	1f.70 brown, blue & grn	2·10	2·00
MS1250		150×145 mm. Nos. 1245/9	8·50	8·25

Designs:—Vert: 80c. Gymnastics; 85c. Hammer-throwing. Horiz: 1f.20, Rowing; 1f.70, Boxing.

333 Decorative Plate

1976. Europa. Monegasque Ceramics. Multicoloured.

1251	80c. Type **333**	2·75	2·50
1252	1f.20 Grape-harvester (statuette)	5·00	4·50
MS1253	170×140 mm. Nos. 1251/2×5	70·00	65·00

334 Palace Clock Tower

1976. Precancelled.

1254	**334**	50c. red	85	80
1255	**334**	52c. orange	85	80
1256	**334**	54c. green	85	80
1257	**334**	60c. green	85	80
1258	**334**	62c. mauve	85	80
1259	**334**	68c. yellow	85	80
1260	**334**	90c. violet	2·10	2·00
1261	**334**	95c. red	2·10	2·00
1262	**334**	1f.05 brown	2·10	2·00
1263	**334**	1f.60 blue	3·25	3·00
1264	**334**	1f.70 turquoise	3·25	3·00
1265	**334**	1f.85 brown	3·25	3·00

335 *St. Louise de Marillac* (altar painting)

1976. Monaco Red Cross.

1270	**335**	4f. black, purple & green	4·25	4·00

1976. Paintings. "Princes and Princesses of Monaco". As T **213**.

1271	2f. purple	4·25	4·00
1272	4f. multicoloured	7·75	7·25

Designs:—2f. *Prince Honore IV*; 4f. *Princess Louise d'Aumont-Mazarin*.

336 St. Vincent-de-Paul

1976. Centenary of St. Vincent-de-Paul Conference, Monaco.

1273	**336**	60c. black, brown & blue	70	65

337 Marie de Rabutin Chantal

1976. 350th Birth Anniv of Marquise de Sevigne (writer).

1274	**337**	80c. black, violet and red	85	80

338 Monaco 2g. "Honore II" Coin, 1640

1976. Monaco Numismatics.

1275	**338**	80c. blue and green	85	80

339 Richard Byrd, *Josephine Ford*, Airship *Norge* and Roald Amundsen

1976. 50th Anniv of First Flights over North Pole.

1276	**339**	85c. black, blue and green	3·25	2·75

340 Gulliver and Lilliputians

1976. 250th Anniv of Jonathan Swift's "Gulliver's Travels".

1277	**340**	1f.20 multicoloured	1·60	1·40

341 Girl's Head and Christmas Decorations

1976. Christmas.

1278	**341**	60c. multicoloured	65	55
1279	**341**	1f.20 green, orge & pur	1·60	1·40

342 "Drug" Dagger piercing Man and Woman

1976. Campaign against Drug Abuse.

1280	**342**	80c. blue, orge & bronze	95	85
1281	**342**	1f.20 lilac, purple & brn	1·60	1·40

1976. Monte Carlo Flower Show (1977). As T **271**. Multicoloured.

1282	80c. Flower arrangement	3·25	2·75
1283	1f. Bouquet of flowers	4·75	4·25

343 Circus Clown

1976. Third International Circus Festival, Monte Carlo.

1284	**343**	1f. multicoloured	3·75	3·25

344 Schooner *Hirondelle I*

1977. 75th Anniv of Publication of "Career of a Navigator" by Prince Albert I (1st issue). Illustrations by L. Tinayre.

1285	**344**	10c. brown, blue & turq	15	15
1286	-	20c. black, brown & lake	30	30
1287	-	30c. green, blue & orange	65	55
1288	-	80c. black, blue and red	95	85
1289	-	1f. black and brown	1·60	1·40
1290	-	1f.25 olive, green & violet	2·10	1·80
1291	-	1f.40 brown, olive & grn	3·25	2·75
1292	-	1f.90 blue, lt blue & red	6·50	5·50
1293	-	2f.50 brown, blue and turquoise	8·75	7·75

Designs:—Vert: 20c. Prince Albert I; 1f. Helmsman; 1f.90, Bringing in the trawl. Horiz: 30c. Crew-members; 80c. *Hirondelle* in a gale; 1f.25, Securing the lifeboat; 1f.40, Shrimp fishing; 2f.50, Capture of an oceanic sunfish.

See also Nos. 1305/13.

345 Pyrenean Sheep and Mountain Dogs

1977. International Dog Show, Monte Carlo.

1294	**345**	80c. multicoloured	13·50	11·00

346 *Maternity* (M. Cassatt)

1977. World Association of the "Friends of Children".

1295	**346**	80c. deep brown, brown and black	2·40	2·10

347 Archers

1977. Tenth International Archery Championships.

1296	**347**	1f.10 black, brown & bl	1·60	1·40

348 Charles Lindbergh and Ryan NYP *Spirit of St. Louis*

1977. 50th Anniv of Lindbergh's Transatlantic Flight.

1297	**348**	1f.90 light blue, blue and brown	3·25	2·75

349 *Harbour, Deauville*

1977. Birth Centenary of Raoul Dufy (painter).

1298	**349**	2f. multicoloured	9·50	8·50

350 *Portrait of a Young Girl*

1977. 400th Birth Anniv of Peter Paul Rubens (painter).

1299	**350**	80c. orange, brown & blk	1·60	1·40
1300	-	1f. red	2·10	1·80
1301	-	1f.40 orange and red	4·00	3·50

Designs:—1f. *Duke of Buckingham*; 1f.40, *Portrait of a Child*.

351 L'Oreillon Tower

1977. Europa. Views.

1302	**351**	1f. brown and blue	3·25	2·75
1303	-	1f.40 blue, brown and bistre	4·75	4·25
MS1304		169×130 mm. Nos. 1302/3 ×5	70·00	65·00

Design:—1f.40, St. Michael's Church, Menton.

1977. 75th Anniv of Publication of "Career of a Navigator" by Prince Albert I (2nd issue). Illustrations by L. Tinayre. As T **344**.

1305	10c. black and blue	15	15
1306	20c. blue	30	30
1307	30c. blue, light blue and green	50	40
1308	80c. brown, black and green	1·10	1·00
1309	1f. grey and green	1·40	1·30
1310	1f.25 black, brown and lilac	2·10	1·80
1311	1f.40 purple, blue and brown	3·50	3·00
1312	1f.90 black, blue and light blue	6·75	6·00
1313	3f. blue, brown and green	8·00	7·00

Designs:—Horiz: 10c. *Princess Alice* (steam yacht) at Kiel; 20c. Ship's laboratory; 30c. *Princess Alice* in ice floes; 1f. Polar scene; 1f.25, Bridge of *Princess Alice* during snow-storm; 1f.40, Arctic camp; 1f.90, Ship's steam launch in floating ice; 3f. *Princess Alice* passing iceberg. Vert: 80c. Crewmen in Arctic dress.

352 Santa Claus and Sledge

1977. Christmas.

1314	**352**	80c. red, green and blue	1·10	1·00
1315	**352**	1f.40 multicoloured	1·60	1·40

1977. Monte Carlo Flower Show. As T **271**. Mult.

1316	80c. Snapdragons and campanula	2·50	2·20
1317	1f. Ikebana	4·00	3·50

353 Face, Poppy and Syringe

1977. Campaign Against Drug Abuse.

1318	**353**	1f. black, red and violet	1·30	1·10

354 Clown and Flags

1977. Fourth International Festival of Circus, Monaco.

1319	**354**	1f. multicoloured	4·00	3·50

355 Gold Coin of Honore II

1977. Monaco Numismatics.

1320	**355**	80c. brown and red	1·30	1·10

356 Mediterranean divided by Industry

1977. Protection of the Mediterranean Environment.

1321	**356**	1f. black, green and blue	1·30	1·10

357 Dr. Guglielminetti and Road Tarrers

1977. 75th Anniv of First Experiments at Road Tarring in Monaco.

1322	**357**	1f.10 black, bistre and brown	1·40	1·30

358 FMLT Badge and Monte Carlo

1977. 50th Anniv of Monaco Lawn Tennis Federation.

1323	**358**	1f. blue, red and brown	2·40	2·10

359 Wimbledon and First Championships

1977. Centenary of Wimbledon Lawn Tennis Championships.

1324	**359**	1f.40 grey, green & brown	3·25	2·75

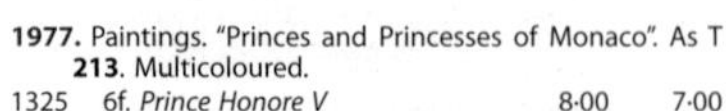

1977. Paintings. "Princes and Princesses of Monaco". As T **213**. Multicoloured.

1325	6f. *Prince Honore V*	8·00	7·00

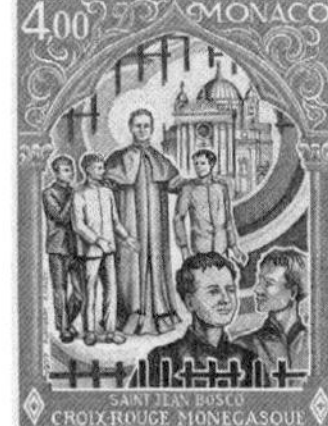

360 St. Jean Bosco

1977. Monaco Red Cross. Monegasque Art.

1326	**360**	4f. green, brown and blue	4·75	4·25

1978. Precancelled. Surch.

1327	**334**	58c. on 54c. green	1·10	1·00
1328	**334**	73c. on 68c. yellow	1·80	1·50
1329	**334**	1f.15 on 1f.05 brown	3·50	3·00
1330	**334**	2f. on 1f.85 brown	4·00	3·50

362 Aerial Shipwreck from *L'Ile Mysterieuse*

1978. 150th Birth Anniv of Jules Verne.

1331	**362**	5c. brown, red and olive	15	15
1332	-	25c. turquoise, blue & red	25	20
1333	-	30c. blue, brown & lt blue	30	30
1334	-	80c. black, green & orge	80	70
1335	-	1f. brown, lake and blue	1·40	1·30
1336	-	1f.40 bistre, brown and green	1·80	1·50
1337	-	1f.70 brown, light blue and blue	3·25	2·75
1338	-	5f.50 violet and blue	8·75	7·75

Designs:—25c. The abandoned ship from *L'Ile Mysterieuse*; 30c. The secret of the island from *L'Ile Mysterieuse*; 80c. *Robur the Conqueror*; 1f. *Master Zacharius*; 1f.40, *The Castle in the Carpathians*; 1f.70, *The Children of Captain Grant*; 5f.50, Jules Verne and allegories.

363 Aerial View of Congress Centre

1978. Inauguration of Monaco Congress Centre.

1339	**363**	1f. brown, blue and green	95	85
1340	-	1f.40 blue, brown & grn	1·30	1·10

Design:—1f.40, View of Congress Centre from sea.

364 Footballers and Globe

1978. World Cup Football Championship, Argentina.

1341	**364**	1f. blue, slate and green	95	85

365 Antonio Vivaldi

1978. 300th Birth Anniv of Antonio Vivaldi (composer).

1342	**365**	1f. brown and red	1·40	1·30

366 *Ramoge* (research vessel) and Grimaldi Palace

1978. Environment Protection. "RAMOGE" Agreement.

1343	**366**	80c. multicoloured	80	70
1344	-	1f. red, blue and green	95	85

Design:—Horiz (48×27 mm): 1f. Map of coastline between St. Raphael and Genes.

367 Monaco Cathedral

1978. Europa. Monaco Views.

1345	**367**	1f. green, brown and blue	3·25	2·75
1346	-	1f.40 brown, green & bl	4·00	3·50
MS1347 170×143 mm. Nos. 1345/6×5			70·00	65·00

Design:—1f.40, View of Monaco from the east.

368 Monaco Congress Centre

1978. Precancelled.

1348	**368**	61c. orange	80	70
1349	**368**	64c. green	80	70
1350	**368**	68c. blue	80	70
1351	**368**	78c. purple	80	70
1352	**368**	83c. violet	80	70
1353	**368**	88c. orange	80	70
1354	**368**	1f.25 brown	1·90	1·70
1355	**368**	1f.30 red	1·90	1·70
1356	**368**	1f.40 green	1·90	1·70
1357	**368**	2f.10 blue	2·75	2·40
1358	**368**	2f.25 orange	2·75	2·40
1359	**368**	2f.35 mauve	2·75	2·40

369 *Cinderella*

1978. 350th Birth Anniv of Charles Perrault (writer).

1360	**369**	5c. red, olive and violet	25	20
1361	-	25c. black, brown & mve	30	30
1362	-	30c. green, lake & brown	30	30
1363	-	80c. multicoloured	95	85
1364	-	1f. red, brown and olive	1·30	1·10
1365	-	1f.40 mauve, ultramarine and blue	1·60	1·40
1366	-	1f.70 green, blue & grey	2·40	2·10
1367	-	1f.90 multicoloured	3·25	2·75
1368	-	2f.50 blue, orange & grn	4·75	4·25

Designs:—25c. *Puss in Boots*; 30c. *The Sleeping Beauty*; 80c. *Donkey's Skin*; 1f. *Little Red Riding Hood*; 1f.40, *Bluebeard*; 1f.70, *Tom Thumb*; 1f.90, *Riquet with a Tuft*; 2f.50, *The Fairies*.

370 *The Sunflowers* (Van Gogh)

1978. Monte Carlo Flower Show (1979) and 125th Birth Anniv of Vincent Van Gogh. Multicoloured.

1369	1f. Type **370**	7·25	6·25
1370	1f.70 *The Iris* (Van Gogh)	9·50	8·50

371 Afghan Hound

1978. International Dog Show, Monte Carlo. Multicoloured.

1371	1f. Type **371**	7·25	6·25
1372	1f.20 Borzoi	9·50	8·50

372 Girl with Letter

1978. Christmas.

1373	**372**	1f. brown, blue and red	1·10	1·00

373 Catherine and William Booth

1978. Centenary of Salvation Army.

1374	**373**	1f.70 multicoloured	2·20	2·00

374 Juggling Seals

1978. Fifth International Circus Festival, Monaco.

1375	**374**	80c. orange, black & blue	95	85
1376	-	1f. multicoloured	1·60	1·40
1377	-	1f.40 brown, mauve and bistre	2·50	2·20
1378	-	1f.90 blue, lilac and mauve	3·75	3·25
1379	-	2f.40 multicoloured	6·00	5·25

Designs:—Horiz: 1f.40, Horseback acrobatics; 1f.90, Musical Monkeys; 2f.40, Trapeze. Vert: 1f. Lion tamer.

1978. Paintings. "Princes and Princesses of Monaco". As T **213**. Multicoloured.

1380	2f. *Prince Florestan I* (G. Dauphin)	4·75	4·25
1381	4f. *Princess Caroline Gilbert de la Metz* (Marie Verrousť)	8·75	7·75

375

1978. 150th Anniv of Henri Dunant (founder of Red Cross). Sheet 100×130 mm.

MS1382 **375** 5f. chocolate, crimson and red	9·50	9·00

376

1979. 21st Birthday of Prince Albert. Sheet 80×105 mm.

MS1383 **376** 10f. green and brown	16·00	15·00

377 *Jongleur de Notre-Dame* (Massenet)

1979. Centenary of "Salle Garnier" (Opera House) (1st issue).

1384	**377**	1f. blue, orange & mauve	95	85
1385	-	1f.20 violet, black & turq	1·60	1·40
1386	-	1f.50 maroon, grn & turq	2·40	2·10
1387	-	1f.70 multicoloured	2·50	2·20
1388	-	2f.10 turquoise and violet	4·50	3·75
1389	-	3f. multicoloured	6·00	5·25

Designs:—Horiz: 1f.20, *Hans the Flute Player* (L. Ganne); 1f.50, *Don Quixote* (J. Massenet); 2f.10, *The Child and the Sorcerer* (M. Ravel); 3f. Charles Garnier (architect) and south facade of Opera House. Vert: 1f.70, *L'Aiglon* (A. Honegger and J. Ibert).

See also Nos. 1399/1404.

378 Flower, Bird and Butterfly

1979. International Year of the Child. Children's Paintings.

1390	**378**	50c. pink, green and black	30	30
1391	-	1f. slate, green and orange	95	85
1392	-	1f.20 slate, orange & mve	1·60	1·40
1393	-	1f.50 yellow, brown & bl	2·75	2·40
1394	-	1f.70 multicoloured	3·25	3·00

Designs:—1f. Horse and Child; 1f.20, The Gift of Love; 1f.50, Peace in the World; 1f.70, Down with Pollution.

379 Armed Foot Messenger

1979. Europa.

1395	**379**	1f.20 brown, green & bl	2·40	2·10
1396	-	1f.50 brown, turq & bl	3·25	2·75
1397	-	1f.70 brown, green & bl	4·75	4·25
MS1398 129×149 mm. Nos. 1395/7, each ×2			48·00	42·00

Designs:—1f.50, 18th-century felucca; 1f.70, Arrival of first train at Monaco.

380 *Instrumental Music* (G. Boulanger) (detail of Opera House interior)

1979. Centenary of "Salle Garnier" (Opera House) (2nd issue).

1399		1f. brown, orange & turq	1·10	1·00
1400		1f.20 multicoloured	1·60	1·40
1401		1f.50 multicoloured	2·40	2·10
1402		1f.70 blue, brown and red	3·25	2·75
1403		2f.10 red, violet & black	4·75	4·25
1404	**380**	3f. green, brown and light green	6·50	5·50

Designs:—(as Type **377**) Horiz: 1f. *Les Biches* (F. Poulenc); 1f.20, *The Sailors* (G. Auric); 1f.70, *Gaiete Parisienne* (J. Offenbach). Vert: 1f.50, *La Spectre de la Rose* (C. M. Weber) (after poster by Jean Cocteau); 2f.10, *Salome* (R. Strauss).

1979. Paintings. "Princes and Princesses of Monaco". As T **213**. Multicoloured.

1405	3f. *Prince Charles III* (B. Biard)	4·00	3·50
1406	4f. *Antoinette de Merode*	6·50	5·50

381 St. Pierre Claver

1979. Monaco Red Cross.

1407	**381**	5f. multicoloured	5·50	5·00

382 "Princess Grace" Orchid

1979. Monte Carlo Flora 1980.

1408	**382**	1f. multicoloured	5·50	5·00

383 "Princess Grace" Rose

1979. Monte Carlo Flower Show.

1409	**383**	1f.20 multicoloured	6·50	5·50

384 Clown balancing on Ball

1979. Sixth International Circus Festival.

1410	**384**	1f.20 multicoloured	4·00	3·50

385 Sir Rowland Hill and Penny Black

1979. Death Centenary of Sir Rowland Hill.

1411	**385**	1f.70 brown, blue & blk	1·40	1·30

386 Albert Einstein

1979. Birth Centenary of Albert Einstein (physicist).

1412	**386**	1f.70 brown, grey and red	1·60	1·40

387 St. Patrick's Cathedral

1979. Centenary of St. Patrick's Cathedral, New York.

1413	**387**	2f.10 black, blue & brn	2·40	2·10

388 Nativity Scene

1979. Christmas.

1414	**388**	1f.20 blue, orange & mve	1·30	1·10

389 Early Racing Cars

1979. 50th Anniv of Grand Prix Motor Racing.

1415	**389**	1f. multicoloured	2·40	2·10

390 Arms of Charles V and Monaco

1979. 450th Anniv of Visit of Emperor Charles V.

1416	**390**	1f.50 brown, blue & blk	1·30	1·10

391 Setter and Pointer

1979. International Dog Show, Monte Carlo.

1417	**391**	1f.20 multicoloured	10·50	9·00

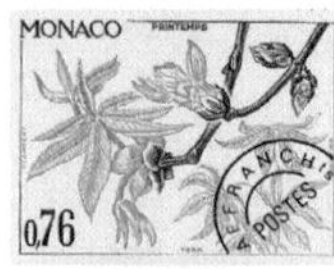

392 Spring

1980. Precancels. The Seasons.

1418	**392**	76c. brown and green	80	70
1419	**392**	88c. olive, emerald & grn	90	75
1420	-	99c. green and brown	1·10	1·00
1421	-	1f.14 green, emer & brn	1·20	1·10
1422	-	1f.60 brown, grey and deep brown	1·60	1·40
1423	-	1f.84 lake, grey & brown	1·90	1·70
1424	-	2f.65 brown, lt blue & bl	3·25	3·00
1425	-	3f.05 brown, bl & slate	4·00	3·50

Designs:—99c., 1f.14, Summer; 1f.60, 1f.84, Autumn; 2f.65, 3f.05, Winter.

394 Paul P. Harris (founder) and View of Chicago

1980. 75th Anniv of Rotary International.

1434	**394**	1f.80 olive, blue & turq	1·60	1·40

395 Gymnastics

1980. Olympic Games, Moscow and Lake Placid.

1435	**395**	1f.10 blue, brown & grey	80	70
1436	-	1f.30 red, brown & blue	95	85
1437	-	1f.60 red, blue & brown	1·40	1·30
1438	-	1f.80 brown, bis & grn	1·60	1·40
1439	-	2f.30 grey, violet & mve	2·10	1·80
1440	-	4f. green, blue and brown	3·25	2·75

Designs:—1f.30, Handball; 1f.60, Pistol-shooting; 1f.80, Volleyball; 2f.30, Ice hockey; 4f. Skiing.

396 Colette (novelist)

1980. Europa. Each black, green and red.

1441	1f.30 Type **396**	1·60	1·40
1442	1f.80 Marcel Pagnol (writer)	2·40	2·10
MS1443	171×143 mm. Nos. 1441/2, each×5	32·00	28·00

397 *La Source*

1980. Birth Bicentenary of Jean Ingres (artist).

1444	**397**	4f. multicoloured	17·00	14·50

398 Montaigne

1980. 400th Anniv of Publication of Montaigne's "Essays".

1445	**398**	1f.30 black, red and blue	1·30	1·10

399 Guillaume Apollinaire (after G. Pieret)

1980. Birth Centenary of Guillaume Apollinaire (poet).

1446	**399**	1f.10 brown	1·10	1·00

400 Congress Centre

1980. Kiwanis International European Convention.

1447	**400**	1f.30 black, blue and red	1·30	1·10

401 Honore II Silver Ecu, 1649

1980. Numismatics.

1448	**401**	1f.50 black and blue	1·60	1·40

402 Lhassa Apso and Shih Tzu

1980. International Dog Show, Monte Carlo.

1449	**402**	1f.30 multicoloured	11·00	9·75

403 *The Princess and the Pea*

1980. 175th Birth Anniv of Hans Christian Andersen.

1450	**403**	70c. sepia, red and brown	50	40
1451	-	1f.30 blue, turq & red	95	85
1452	-	1f.50 black, blue & turq	1·40	1·30
1453	-	1f.60 red, black & brown	2·10	1·80
1454	-	1f.80 yellow, brn & turq	2·40	2·10
1455	-	2f.30 brown, pur & vio	3·25	2·75

Designs:—1f.30, *The Little Mermaid*; 1f.50, *The Chimney-sweep and Shepherdess*; 1f.60, *The Brave Little Lead Soldier*; 1f.80, *The Little Match Girl*; 2f.30, *The Nightingale*.

404 *The Road* (M. Vlaminck)

1980. 75th Anniv of 1905 Autumn Art Exhibition. Multicoloured.

1456	2f. Type **404**	4·75	4·25
1457	3f. *Woman at Balustrade* (Van Dongen)	6·50	5·50
1458	4f. *The Reader* (Henri Matisse)	8·50	7·25
1459	5f. *Three Figures in a Meadow* (A. Derain)	10·50	9·00

1980. Paintings. "Princes and Princesses of Monaco". As T **213**. Multicoloured.

1460	4f. *Prince Albert I* (L. Bonnat)	4·75	4·25
1461	4f. *Princess Marie Alice Heine* (L. Maeterlinck)	4·75	4·25

405 "Sunbirds"

1980. Monaco Red Cross.

1462	**405**	6f. red, bistre and brown	6·50	5·50

406 "MONACO" balanced on Tightrope

1980. Seventh International Circus Festival, Monaco.

1463	**406**	1f.30 red, turquoise & blue	3·00	2·75

407 Children and Nativity

1980. Christmas.

1464	**407**	1f.10 blue, carmine and red	80	70
1465	**407**	2f.30 violet, orange and pink	1·60	1·40

1980. Monte Carlo Flower Show, 1981. As T **383**. Multicoloured.

1466	1f.30 "Princess Stephanie" rose	1·90	1·70
1467	1f.80 Ikebana	3·00	2·50

408 *Alcyonium*

1980. Marine Fauna. Multicoloured.

1468	5c. *Spirographis spallanzanli*	15	15
1469	10c. *Anemonia sulcata*	15	15
1470	15c. *Leptopsammia pruvoit*	25	20
1471	20c. *Pteroides*	30	30
1472	30c. *Paramuricea clavata* (horiz)	40	35
1473	40c. Type **408**	55	50
1474	50c. *Corallium rubrum*	80	70
1475	60c. Trunculus murex (*Calliactis parasitica*) (horiz)	1·60	1·40
1476	70c. *Cerianthus membranaceus* (horiz)	1·90	1·70
1477	1f. *Actinia equina* (horiz)	2·40	2·10
1478	2f. *Protula* (horiz)	4·75	4·25

409 Fish with Hand for Tail

1981. Respect the Sea.

1479	**409**	1f.20 multicoloured	1·60	1·40

410 Prince Rainier and Princess Grace

1981. Royal Silver Wedding.

1480	**410**	1f.20 black and green	2·40	2·10
1481	**410**	1f.40 black and red	3·25	2·75
1482	**410**	1f.70 black and green	4·00	3·50
1483	**410**	1f.80 black and brown	4·75	4·25
1484	**410**	2f. black and blue	6·50	5·50

411 Mozart (after Lorenz Vogel)

1981. 225th Birth Anniv of Wolfgang Amadeus Mozart (composer).

1485	**411**	2f. brown, dp brown & bl	3·00	2·50
1486	-	2f.50 blue, brn & dp brn	4·25	3·75
1487	-	3f.50 dp brown, bl & brn	6·75	6·00

Designs:—Horiz: 2f.50, *Mozart at 7 with his Father and Sister* (engraving by Delafoose after drawing by Carmontelle); 3f.50 *Mozart directing Requiem two Days before his Death* (painting by Baude).

412 Palm Cross

1981. Europa. Multicoloured.

1488	**412**	1f.40 green, brown & red	2·40	2·10
1489	-	2f. multicoloured	3·25	2·75
MS1490		171×143 mm. Nos. 1488/9, each ×5	35·00	31·00

Design:—2f. Children carrying palm crosses.

413 Paris Football Stadium, Cup and Footballer

1981. 25th Anniv of European Football Cup.

1491	**413**	2f. black and blue	1·90	1·70

414 IYDP Emblem and Girl in Wheelchair

1981. International Year of Disabled Persons.

1492	**414**	1f.40 blue and green	1·60	1·40

415 Palace flying Old Flag, National Flag and Monte Carlo

1981. Centenary of National Flag.

1493	**415**	2f. red, blue and brown	1·90	1·70

416 Oceanographic Institute, Paris and Oceanographic Museum, Monaco

1981. 75th Anniv of Oceanographic Institute.

1494	**416**	1f.20 blue, black & brn	1·30	1·10

417 Bureau Building and *Faddey Bellingshausen* (hydrographic research ship)

1981. 50th Anniv of Int Hydrographic Bureau.

1495	**417**	2f.50 sepia, brown and light brown	2·40	2·10

418 Rough Collies and Shetland Sheepdogs

1981. International Dog Show, Monte Carlo.

1496	**418**	1f.40 multicoloured	9·50	8·50

419 Rainier III and Prince Albert

1981. (a) 23×28 mm.

1497	**419**	1f.40 green (postage)	1·60	1·40
1498	**419**	1f.60 red	2·40	2·10
1499	**419**	1f.60 green	1·60	1·40
1500	**419**	1f.70 green	1·60	1·40
1501	**419**	1f.80 red	1·90	1·70
1502	**419**	1f.80 green	1·90	1·70
1503	**419**	1f.90 green	3·25	2·75
1504	**419**	2f. red	2·40	2·10
1505	**419**	2f. green	3·25	2·75
1506	**419**	2f.10 red	2·40	2·10
1507	**419**	2f.20 red	2·20	2·00
1508	**419**	2f.30 blue	6·50	5·50
1509	**419**	2f.50 brown	2·75	2·40
1510	**419**	2f.60 blue	4·00	3·50
1511	**419**	2f.80 blue	4·00	3·50
1512	**419**	3f. blue	4·75	4·25
1513	**419**	3f.20 blue	4·75	4·25
1514	**419**	3f.40 blue	6·50	5·50
1515	**419**	3f.60 blue	4·75	4·25
1516	**419**	4f. brown	3·75	3·25
1517	**419**	5f.50 black	4·75	4·25
1518	**419**	10f. purple	5·50	49·00
1519	**419**	15f. green	15·00	13·50
1520	**419**	20f. blue	16·00	14·00

(b) 36×27 mm.

1521	5f. violet (air)	3·25	2·75
1522	10f. red	8·00	7·00
1523	15f. green	9·50	8·50
1524	20f. blue	14·50	12·50
1525	30f. brown	19·00	17·00

Design:—Nos. 1521/5, Double portrait and monograms.

421 Arctic Scene and Map

1981. First International Congress on Discovery and History of Northern Polar Regions, Rome.

1530	**421**	1f.50 multicoloured	2·40	2·10

1981. Paintings. "Princes and Princesses of Monaco". Vert designs as T **213**. Multicoloured.

1531	3f. *Prince Louis II* (P-A. de Laszlo)	4·75	4·25
1532	5f. *Princess Charlotte* (P.-A. de Laszlo)	6·50	5·50

422 Hercules fighting the Nemean Lion

1981. Monaco Red Cross. The Twelve Labours of Hercules (1st series).

1533	**422**	2f.50+50c. green, brown and red	2·40	2·10
1534	-	3f.50+50c. blue, green and red	3·25	2·75

Design:—3f.50, Slaying the Hydra of Lerna.

See also Nos. 1584/5, 1631/2, 1699/1700, 1761/2 and 1794/5.

423 Ettore Bugatti (racing car designer) (Cent)

1981. Birth Anniversaries.

1535	**423**	1f. indigo, blue and red	1·60	1·40
1536	-	2f. black, blue and brown	2·40	2·10
1537	-	2f.50 brown, black and red	3·25	2·75
1538	-	4f. multicoloured	5·50	5·00
1539	-	4f. multicoloured	5·50	5·00

Designs:—No. 1536, George Bernard Shaw (dramatist, 125th anniv); 1537, Fernand Leger (painter, centenary). Larger: (37×48 mm): 1538, Pablo Picasso (self-portrait) (centenary); 1539, Rembrandt (self-portrait) (375th anniv).

424 Eglantines and Morning Glory

1981. Monte Carlo Flower Show (1982). Mult.

1540	1f.40 Type **424**	3·25	2·75
1541	2f. *Ikebana* (painting by Ikenobo)	4·75	4·25

425 "Catherine Deneuve"

1981. First International Rose Show, Monte Carlo.

1542	**425**	1f.80 multicoloured	6·50	5·50

426 Tiger, Clown, Acrobat and Elephants

1981. Eighth International Circus Festival, Monaco.

1543	**426**	1f.40 violet, mauve & blk	4·75	4·25

427 Praying Children and Nativity

1981. Christmas.

1544	**427**	1f.20 blue, mauve & brn	1·10	1·00

428 Lancia-Stratos Rally Car

1981. 50th Monte Carlo Rally (1982).

1545	**428**	1f. blue, red & turquoise	3·25	2·75

429 Spring

1981. Seasons of the Persimmon Tree. Sheet 143×100 mm containing T 429 and similar horiz designs.

MS1546 1f. green, yellow and blue (T **429**); 2f. green and blue (Summer); 3f. red, brown and yellow (Autumn); 4f. brown and red (Winter) 14·50 12·50

430 *Hoya bella*

1981. Plants in Exotic Garden. Multicoloured.

1547	1f.40 Type **430**	4·75	4·25
1548	1f.60 *Bolivicereus samaipatanus*	4·00	3·50
1549	1f.80 *Trichocereus grandiflorus* (horiz)	4·50	3·75
1550	2f. *Argyroderma roseum*	2·75	2·40
1551	2f.30 *Euphorbia milii*	4·50	3·75
1552	2f.60 *Echinocereus fitchii* (horiz)	4·75	4·25
1553	2f.90 *Rebutia heliosa* (horiz)	4·75	4·25
1554	4f.10 *Echinopsis multiplex cristata* (horiz)	6·50	5·50

431 Spring

1982. Precancels. The Seasons of the Peach Tree.

1555	**431**	97c. mauve and green	80	70
1556	-	1f.25 green, orge & mve	1·10	1·00
1557	-	2f.03 brown	1·80	1·50
1558	-	3f.36 brown and blue	3·25	2·75

Designs:—1f.25, Summer; 2f.03, Autumn; 3f.36, Winter.

432 Common Nutcracker

1982. Birds from Mercantour National Park.

1559	**432**	60c. black, brown & grn	2·20	2·00
1560	-	70c. black and mauve	2·40	2·10
1561	-	80c. red, black & orange	3·00	2·50
1562	-	90c. black, red and blue	4·00	3·50
1563	-	1f.40 brown, black & red	4·50	3·75
1564	-	1f.60 brown, black & blue	5·50	5·00

Designs:—Vert: 70c. Black grouse; 80c. Rock partridge; 1f.60, Golden eagle. Horiz: 90c. Wallcreeper; 1f.40, Rock ptarmigan.

433 Capture of Monaco Fortress, 1297

1982. Europa.

1565	**433**	1f.60 blue, brown and red	1·90	1·70
1566	-	2f.30 blue, brown and red	2·40	2·10

MS1567 173×143 mm. Nos. 1565/6, each ×5 32·00 28·00

Design:—2f.30, Signing the Treaty of Peronne, 1641.

434 Old Quarter

1982. Fontvieille.

1568	**434**	1f.40 blue, brown & grn	1·60	1·40
1569	-	1f.60 light brown, brown and red	1·90	1·70
1570	-	2f.30 purple	2·40	2·10

Designs:—1f.60, Land reclamation; 2f.30, Urban development.

435 Stadium

1982. Fontvieille Sports Stadium (1st series).

1571	**435**	2f.30 green, brown & blue	2·40	2·10

See also No. 1617.

436 Arms of Paris

1982. Philexfrance International Stamp Exhibition, Paris.

1572	**436**	1f.40 red, grey and deep red	1·40	1·30

437 Old English Sheepdog

1982. International Dog Show, Monte Carlo. Multicoloured.

1573	60c. Type **437**	4·75	4·25
1574	1f. Briard	6·50	5·50

438 Monaco Cathedral and Arms

1982. Creation of Archbishopric of Monaco (1981).

1575	**438**	1f.60 black, blue and red	1·40	1·30

439 St. Francis of Assisi

1982. 800th Birth Anniv of St. Francis of Assisi.

1576	**439**	1f.40 grey and light grey	1·30	1·10

440 Dr. Robert Koch

1982. Centenary of Discovery of Tubercle Bacillus.

1577	**440**	1f.40 purple and lilac	1·90	1·70

441 Lord Baden-Powell

1982. 125th Birth Anniv of Lord Baden-Powell (founder of Boy Scout Movement).

1578	**441**	1f.60 brown and black	2·40	2·10

442 Running for Ball

1982. World Cup Football Championship, Spain. Sheet 143×120 mm containing T **442** and similar square designs, each brown, blue and green.

MS1579 1f. Type **442**; 2f. Kicking ball; 3f. Heading ball; 4f. Goalkeeper 13·50 12·00

443 St. Hubert (18th-century medallion)

1982. 29th Meeting of International Hunting Council, Monte Carlo.

1580	**443**	1f.60 multicoloured	1·80	1·50

444 Books, Reader and Globe

1982. International Bibliophile Association General Assembly, Monte Carlo.

1581	**444**	1f.60 blue, purple & red	1·40	1·30

445 *Casino, 1870*

1982. Monaco in the "Belle Epoque" (1st series). Paintings by Hubert Clerissi. Multicoloured.

1582	3f. Type **445**	4·00	3·50
1583	5f. *Porte d'Honneur, Royal Palace, 1893*	6·00	5·25

See also Nos. 1629/30, 1701/2, 1763/4, 1801/2, 1851/2, 1889/90 and 1965/6.

1982. Monaco Red Cross. The Twelve Labours of Hercules (2nd series). As T **422**.

1584	2f.50+50c. green, red and bright red	2·40	2·10
1585	3f.50+50c. brown, blue and red	3·25	2·75

Designs:—2f.50, Capturing the Erymanthine Boar; 3f.50, Shooting the Stymphalian Birds.

446 Nicolo Paganini (violinist and composer, bicent)

1982. Birth Anniversaries.

1586	**446**	1f.60 brown and purple	1·90	1·70
1587	-	1f.80 red, mauve & brn	3·00	2·50
1588	-	2f.60 green and red	3·75	3·25
1589	-	4f. multicoloured	6·50	5·50
1590	-	4f. multicoloured	6·50	5·50

Designs:—Vert: No. 1587, Anna Pavlova (ballerina, centenary); 1588, Igor Stravinsky (composer, centenary). Horiz (47×36 mm): 1589, *In a Boat* (Edouard Manet, 150th anniv); 1590, *The Black Fish* (Georges Braque, centenary).

447 Vase of Flowers

1982. Monte Carlo Flower Show (1983). Mult.

1591	1f.60 Type **447**	3·25	2·75
1592	2f.60 Ikebana arrangement	4·00	3·50

448 Bowl of Flowers

1982

1593	**448**	1f.60 multicoloured	3·25	2·75

449 The Three Kings

1982. Christmas.

1594	**449**	1f.60 green, blue & orge	1·30	1·10
1595	-	1f.80 green, blue & orge	1·40	1·30
1596	-	2f.60 green, blue & orge	2·50	2·20
MS1597		143×105 mm. Nos. 1594/6	5·50	5·00

Designs:—1f.80, The Holy Family; 2f.60, Shepherds and angels.

450 Prince Albert I and Polar Scene

1982. Centenary of First International Polar Year.

1598	**450**	1f.60 brown, green & bl	4·00	3·50

451 Viking Longships off Greenland

1982. Millenary of Discovery of Greenland by Erik the Red.

1599	**451**	1f.60 blue, brown & blk	4·00	3·50

452 Julius Caesar in the Port of Monaco (*Aeneid*, Book VI)

1982. 2000th Death Anniv of Virgil (poet).

1600	**452**	1f.80 deep blue, blue and brown	4·00	3·50

453 Spring

1983. Precancels. The Seasons of the Apple Tree.

1601	**453**	1f.05 purple, green and yellow	1·30	1·10
1602	-	1f.35 light green, deep green and turquoise	1·40	1·30
1603	-	2f.19 red, brown & grey	2·50	2·20
1604	-	3f.63 yellow and brown	3·25	2·75

Designs:—1f.35, Summer; 2f.19, Autumn; 3f.63, Winter.

454 Tourism

1983. 50th Anniv of Exotic Garden. Mult.

1605	1f.80 Type **454**	2·40	2·10
1606	2f. Cactus plants (botanical collections)	3·00	2·75
1607	2f.30 Cactus plants (international flower shows)	3·50	3·00
1608	2f.60 Observatory grotto (horiz)	4·00	3·50
1609	3f.30 Museum of Prehistoric Anthropology (horiz)	4·75	4·25

455 Alaskan Malamute

1983. International Dog Show, Monte Carlo.

1610	**455**	1f.80 multicoloured	13·50	12·00

456 Princess Grace

1983. Princess Grace Commemoration. Sheet 105×143 mm.

MS1611	**456**	10f. black	19·00	18·00

457 St. Charles Borromee and Church

1983. Centenary of St. Charles Church, Monte Carlo.

1612	**457**	2f.60 deep blue, blue and green	1·60	1·40

458 Montgolfier Balloon, 1783

1983. Europa.

1613	**458**	1f.80 blue, brown & grey	2·40	2·10
1614	-	2f.60 grey, blue & brown	2·40	2·10
MS1615		170×143 mm. Nos. 1613/14, each×5	40·00	38·00

Design:—2f.60, Space shuttle.

459 Franciscan College

1983. Centenary of Franciscan College, Monte Carlo.

1616	**459**	2f. grey, brown and red	1·60	1·40

460 Stadium

1983. Fontvieille Sports Stadium (2nd series).

1617	**460**	2f. green, blue and brown	1·60	1·40

461 Early and Modern Cars

1983. Centenary of Petrol-driven Motor Car.

1618	**461**	2f.90 blue, brown & green	4·75	4·25

462 Blue Whale

1983. International Commission for the Protection of Whales.

1619	**462**	3f.30 blue, light blue and grey	5·75	5·00

463 Dish Aerial, Pigeon, WCY Emblem and Satellite

1983. World Communications Year.

1620	**463**	4f. lilac and mauve	2·40	2·10

464 Smoking Moor

1983. Nineteenth Century Automata from the Galea Collection. Multicoloured.

1621	50c. Type **464**	40	35
1622	60c. Clown with diabolo	50	40
1623	70c. Smoking monkey	55	50
1624	80c. Peasant with pig	65	55
1625	90c. Buffalo Bill smoking	80	70
1626	1f. Snake charmer	95	85
1627	1f.50 Pianist	1·90	1·70
1628	2f. Young girl powdering herself	2·40	2·10

1983. Monaco in the "Belle Epoque" (2nd series). As T **445**. Multicoloured.

1629	3f. *The Beach, 1902*	4·75	4·25
1630	5f. *Cafe de Paris, 1905*	6·50	5·50

1983. Monaco Red Cross. The Twelve Labours of Hercules (3rd series). As T **422**.

1631	2f.50+50c. brn, bl & red	2·40	2·10
1632	3f.50+50c. violet, mve & red	3·25	2·75

Designs:—2f.50, Capturing the Hind of Ceryneia; 3f.50, Cleaning the Augean stables.

465 Johannes Brahms (composer)

1983. Birth Anniversaries.

1633	**465**	3f. deep brown, brown and green	2·40	2·10
1634	-	3f. black, brown and red	2·40	2·10
1635	-	4f. multicoloured	4·75	4·25
1636	-	4f. multicoloured	4·75	4·25

Designs:—Horiz: No. 1633, Type **465** (150th anniv); 1634, Giacomo Puccini (composer) and scene from *Madame Butterfly* (125th anniv). Vert (37×48 mm): 1635, *Portrait of a Young Man* (Raphael (artist), 500th anniv); 1636, *Cottin Passage* (Utrillo (artist), centenary).

466 Circus Performers

1983. Ninth International Circus Festival, Monaco.

1637	**466**	2f. blue, red and green	2·40	2·10

467 Bouquet

1983. Monte Carlo Flower Show (1984). Mult.

1638	1f.60 Type **467**	2·20	2·00
1639	2f.60 Arrangement of poppies	3·50	3·00

468 Provencale Creche

1983. Christmas.

1640	**468**	2f. multicoloured	2·40	2·10

469 Nobel Literature Prize Medal

1983. 150th Birth Anniv of Alfred Nobel (inventor of dynamite and founder of Nobel Prizes).
1641 **469** 2f. black, grey and red 1·60 1·40

470 O. F. Ozanam (founder) and Paris Headquarters

1983. 150th Anniv of Society of St. Vincent de Paul.
1642 **470** 1f.80 violet and purple 1·60 1·40

471 *Tazerka* (oil rig)

1983. Oil Industry.
1643 **471** 5f. blue, brown & turq 3·50 3·00

472 Spring

1983. Seasons of the Fig. Sheet 143×100 mm containing T **472** and similar horiz designs.
MS1644 1f. green (Type **472**); 2f. green, yellow and red (Summer); 3f. green and (Autumn); 4f. green and red (Winter) 14·50 13·50

473 Gymnast with Ball

1984. Olympic Games, Los Angeles. Sheet 161×143 mm containing T **473** and similar vert designs, each brown, slate and red.
MS1645 2f. Type **473**; 3f. Gymnast with clubs; 4f. Gymnast with ribbon; 5f. Gymnast with hoop 13·00 12·00

474 Skater and Stadium

1984. Winter Olympic Games, Sarajevo.
1646 **474** 2f. blue, green and turquoise 1·60 1·40
1647 - 4f. blue, violet and purple 3·25 2·75
Design:—4f. Skater and snowflake.

475 Bridge

1984. Europa. 25th Anniv of European Post and Telecommunications Conference.
1648 **475** 2f. blue 2·40 2·10
1649 **475** 3f. green 3·25 2·75
MS1650 143×170 mm. Nos. 1648/9, each×4 40·00 38·00

476 Balkan Fritillary

1984. Butterflies and Moths in Mercantour National Park. Multicoloured.
1651 1f.60 Type **476** 3·25 2·75
1652 2f. *Zygaena vesubiana* 4·25 3·75
1653 2f.80 False mnestra ringlet 5·00 4·50
1654 3f. Small apollo (horiz) 5·50 5·00
1655 3f.60 Southern swallowtail (horiz) 6·50 5·50

477 Auvergne Pointer

1984. International Dog Show, Monte Carlo.
1656 **477** 1f.60 multicoloured 7·25 6·25

478 Sanctuary and Statue of Virgin

1984. Our Lady of Laghet Sanctuary.
1657 **478** 2f. blue, brown and green 1·60 1·40

479 Piccard's Stratosphere Balloon *FNRS*

1984. Birth Centenary of Auguste Piccard (physicist).
1658 **479** 2f.80 black, green & blue 1·60 1·40
1659 - 4f. blue, green & turq 2·40 2·10
Design:—4f. Bathyscaphe.

480 Concert

1984. 25th Anniv of Palace Concerts.
1660 **480** 3f.60 blue and deep blue 2·40 2·10

481 Place de la Visitation

1984. Bygone Monaco (1st series). Paintings by Hubert Clerissi.
1661 **481** 5c. brown 15 15
1662 - 10c. red 25 20
1663 - 15c. violet 30 30
1664 - 20c. blue 40 35
1665 - 30c. blue 50 40
1666 - 40c. green 1·30 1·10
1667 - 50c. red 50 40
1668 - 60c. blue 65 55
1669 - 70c. orange 80 70
1670 - 80c. green 80 70
1671 - 90c. mauve 80 70
1672 - 1f. blue 80 70
1673 - 2f. black 1·60 1·40
1674 - 3f. red 4·00 3·50
1675 - 4f. blue 2·40 2·10
1676 - 5f. green 3·25 2·75
1677 - 6f. green 4·75 4·25
Designs:—10c. Town Hall; 15c. Rue Basse; 20c. Place Saint-Nicolas; 30c. Quai du Commerce; 40c. Rue des Iris; 50c. Ships in harbour; 60c. St. Charles's Church; 70c. Religious procession; 80c. Olive tree overlooking harbour; 90c. Quayside; 1f. Palace Square; 2f. Fishing boats in harbour; 3f. Bandstand; 4f. Railway station; 5f. Mail coach; 6f. Monte Carlo Opera House.
See also Nos. 2012/22.

482 Spring

1984. Precancels. The Seasons of the Quince.
1678 **482** 1f.14 red and green 95 85
1679 - 1f.47 deep green & green 1·00 90
1680 - 2f.38 olive, turquoise and green 1·90 1·70
1681 - 3f.95 green 2·75 2·40
Designs:—1f.47, Summer; 2f.38, Autumn; 3f.95, Winter.

483 Shepherd

1984. Christmas. Crib Figures from Provence. Multicoloured.
1682 70c. Type **483** 80 70
1683 1f. Blind man 95 85
1684 1f.70 Happy man 1·90 1·70
1685 2f. Spinner 2·40 2·10
1686 2f.10 Angel playing trumpet 2·50 2·20
1687 2f.40 Garlic seller 2·75 2·50
1688 3f. Drummer 3·25 2·75
1689 3f.70 Knife grinder 4·00 3·50
1690 4f. Elderly couple 4·75 4·25

484 Gargantua and Cattle

1984. 450th Anniv of First Edition of "Gargantua" by Francois Rabelais.
1691 **484** 2f. black, red and brown 2·40 2·10
1692 - 2f. black, red and blue 2·40 2·10
1693 - 4f. green 4·00 3·50
Designs:—As T **484**: No. 1692, Panurge's sheep. 36×48 mm: 1693, Francois Rabelais.

485 Bowl of Mixed Flowers

1984. Monte Carlo Flower Show (1985). Mult.
1694 2f.10 Type **485** 2·40 2·10
1695 3f. Ikebana arrangement 4·00 3·50

486 Television Lights and Emblem

1984. 25th Int Television Festival, Monte Carlo.
1696 **486** 2f.10 blue, grey and mauve 1·60 1·40
1697 - 3f. grey, blue and red 2·50 2·20
Design:—3f. "Golden Nymph" (Grand Prix).

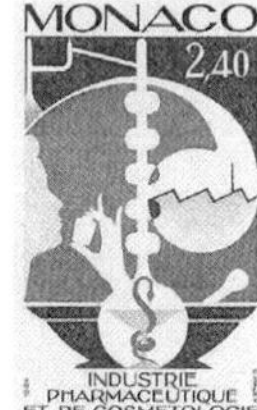

487 Chemical Equipment

1984. Pharmaceutical and Cosmetics Industry.
1698 **487** 2f.40 blue, deep blue and green 1·60 1·40

1984. Monaco Red Cross. The Twelve Labours of Hercules (4th series). As T **422**.
1699 3f.+50c. brown, light brown and red 2·40 2·10
1700 4f.+50c. green, brown and red 3·25 2·75
Designs:—3f. Killing the Cretan bull; 4f. Capturing the Mares of Diomedes.

1984. Monaco in the "Belle Epoque" (3rd series). Paintings by Hubert Clerissi. As T **445**. Mult.

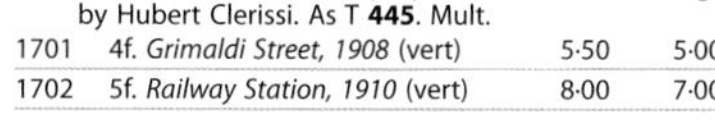
1701 4f. *Grimaldi Street, 1908* (vert) 5·50 5·00
1702 5f. *Railway Station, 1910* (vert) 8·00 7·00

488 Clown

1984. Tenth International Circus Festival, Monaco. Sheet 88 x 72 mm.
MS1703 **488** 5f. multicoloured 9·50 9·00

489 *Woman with Chinese Vase*

1984. 150th Birth Anniv of Edgar Degas (artist).
1704 **489** 6f. multicoloured 8·00 7·00

490 Spring

1985. Precancels. Seasons of the Cherry.
1705 **490** 1f.22 olive, green and blue 1·30 1·10
1706 - 1f.57 red, green and yellow 1·40 1·30
1707 - 2f.55 orange and brown 1·80 1·50
1708 - 4f.23 purple, green and blue 3·25 2·75
Designs:—1f.57, Summer; 2f.55, Autumn; 4f.23, Winter.

491 First Stamp

1985. Centenary of First Monaco Stamps.
1709 **491** 1f.70 green 1·10 1·00
1710 **491** 2f.10 red 1·40 1·30
1711 **491** 3f. blue 2·20 2·00
See also No. **MS**1765.

493 *Berardia subacaulis*

1985. Flowers in Mercantour National Park. Mult.
1724 1f.70 Type **493** 1·60 1·40

1725	2f.10 *Saxifraga florulenta* (vert)	1·90	1·70
1726	2f.40 *Fritillaria moggridgei* (vert)	2·20	2·00
1727	3f. *Sempervivum allionii* (vert)	3·00	2·50
1728	3f.60 *Silene cordifolia* (vert)	3·50	3·00
1729	4f. *Primula allionii*	4·00	3·50

494 Spring

1985. Seasons of the Japanese Medlar. Sheet 144×100 mm containing T **494** and similar horiz designs.
MS1730 1f. olive and deep olive (Type **494**); 2f. olive, yellow and deep olive (Summer); 3f. olive and deep olive (Autumn); 4f. orange, yellow and olive (Winter) 11·00 10·50

495 Nadia Boulanger (composer)

1985. 25th Anniv of First Musical Composition Competition.
1731 **495** 1f.70 brown 1·40 1·30
1732 - 2f.10 blue 2·10 1·80
Design: 2f.10, Georges Auric (composer).

496 Stadium and Runners

1985. Inauguration of Louis II Stadium, Fontvieille, and Athletics and Swimming Championships.
1733 **496** 1f.70 brown, red and violet 1·40 1·30
1734 - 2f.10 blue, brown and green 2·10 1·80
Design:—2f.10, Stadium and swimmers.

497 Prince Antoine I

1985. Europa.
1735 **497** 2f.10 blue 2·40 2·10
1736 - 3f. red 3·25 2·75
MS1737 170×143 mm. Nos. 1735/6, each×5 48·00 46·00
Design:—3f. John-Baptiste Lully (composer).

498 Museum, *Hirondelle I* (schooner) and *Denise* (midget submarine)

1985. 75th Anniv of Oceanographic Museum.
1738 **498** 2f.10 black, green and blue 1·80 1·50

499 Boxer

1985. International Dog Show, Monte Carlo.
1739 **499** 2f.10 multicoloured 4·75 4·25

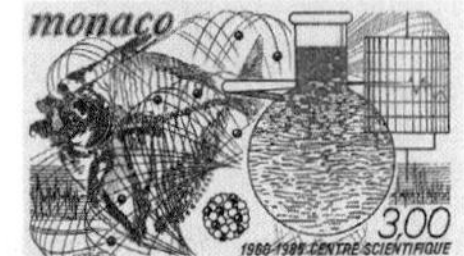

500 Scientific Motifs

1985. 25th Anniv of Scientific Centre.
1740 **500** 3f. blue, black and violet 2·40 2·10

501 Children and Hands holding Seedling and Emblem

1985. International Youth Year.
1741 **501** 3f. brown, green and light brown 2·40 2·10

502 Regal Angelfish

1985. Fishes in Oceanographic Museum Aquarium (1st series). Multicoloured.
1742 1f.80 Type **502** 2·50 2·20
1743 1f.90 Type **502** 4·00 3·50
1744 2f.20 Powder blue surgeonfish 2·75 2·40
1745 3f.20 Red-tailed butterflyfish 3·50 3·00
1746 3f.40 As No. 1745 7·25 6·25
1747 3f.90 Clown triggerfish 4·25 3·75
1748 7f. Fishes in aquarium (36×48 mm) 6·75 6·00
See also Nos. 1857/62.

503 Catamaran

1985. Monaco–New York Sailing Race. Sheet 143×105 mm containing T **503** and similar vert designs. Each black, blue and turquoise.
MS1749 4f. Type **503**; 4f. Single hull yacht; 4f. Trimaran 10·50 9·75

504 Rome Buildings and Emblem

1985. Italia '85 International Stamp Exhibition, Rome.
1750 **504** 4f. black, green and red 2·50 2·20

505 Clown

1985. 11th International Circus Festival, Monaco.
1751 **505** 1f.80 multicoloured 2·40 2·10

506 Decorations

1985. Christmas.
1752 **506** 2f.20 multicoloured 1·90 1·70

507 Ship and Marine Life

1985. Fish Processing Industry.
1753 **507** 2f.20 blue, turquoise and brown 1·40 1·30

508 Arrangement of Roses, Tulips and Jonquil

1985. Monte Carlo Flower Show (1986). Mult.
1754 2f.20 Type **508** 2·40 2·10
1755 3f.20 Arrangement of chrysanthemums and heather 3·50 3·00

509 Globe and Satellite

1985. European Telecommunications Satellite Organization.
1756 **509** 3f. black, blue and violet 2·40 2·10

510 Sacha Guitry (actor, centenary)

1985. Birth Anniversaries.
1757 **510** 3f. orange and brown 2·40 2·10
1758 - 4f. blue, brown and mauve 3·00 2·50
1759 - 5f. turquoise, blue and grey 3·75 3·25
1760 - 6f. blue, brown and black 4·75 4·25
Designs:—4f. Wilhelm and Jacob Grimm (folklorists, bicentenaries); 5f. Frederic Chopin and Robert Schumann (composers, 175th annivs); 6f. Johann Sebastian Bach and Georg Friedrich Handel (composers, 300th annivs).

1985. Monaco Red Cross. The Twelve Labours of Hercules (5th series). As T **422**.
1761 3f.+70c. green, deep red and red 2·40 2·10
1762 4f.+80c. brown, blue & red 2·75 2·40
Designs:—3f. The Cattle of Geryon; 4f. The Girdle of Hippolyte.

1985. Monaco in the "Belle Epoque" (4th series). As T **445**, showing paintings by Hubert Clerissi. Multicoloured.
1763 4f. *Port of Monaco, 1912* 4·75 4·25
1764 6f. *Avenue de la Gare 1920* 6·50 5·50

511 Prince Charles III

1985. Centenary of First Monaco Stamps (2nd issue). Sheet 142×71 mm containing T 511 and similar vert designs. Each blue and black.
MS1765 5f. Type **511**; 5f. Prince Albert I; 5f. Prince Louis II; 5f. Prince Rainier III 13·50 12·50

512 Spring

1986. Precancels. Seasons of the Hazel Tree.
1766 **512** 1f.28 brown, green & bl 95 85
1767 - 1f.65 green, brown & yell 1·00 90
1768 - 2f.67 grey, brown and deep brown 1·90 1·70
1769 - 4f.44 green and brown 3·25 2·75
Designs:—1f.65, Summer; 2f.67, Autumn; 4f.44, Winter.

513 Ancient Monaco

1986. Tenth Anniv of "Annales Monegasques" (historical review).
1770 **513** 2f.20 grey, blue and brown 1·60 1·40

514 Scotch Terriers

1986. International Dog Show, Monte Carlo.
1771 **514** 1f.80 multicoloured 8·75 7·75

515 Mouflon

1986. Mammals in Mercantour National Park. Multicoloured.
1772 2f.20 Type **515** 1·80 1·50
1773 2f.50 Ibex 2·40 2·10
1774 3f.20 Chamois 3·00 2·50
1775 3f.90 Alpine marmot (vert) 3·75 3·25
1776 5f. Arctic hare (vert) 4·75 4·25
1777 7f.20 Stoat (vert) 6·50 5·50

516 Research Vessel *Ramoge*

1986. Europa. Each green, blue and red.
1778 2f.20 Type **516** 3·25 2·75
1779 3f.20 Underwater nature reserve, Larvotto beach 4·75 4·25
MS1780 171×144 mm. Nos. 1778/79, each×5 48·00 46·00

517 Prince Albert I and National Council Building

1986. Anniversaries and Events.
1781 **517** 2f.50 brown and green 1·60 1·40
1782 - 3f.20 brown, red and black 3·00 2·50
1783 - 3f.90 purple and red 4·00 3·50
1784 - 5f. green, red and blue 4·75 4·25
Designs:—Horiz: 2f.50, Type **517** (75th anniv of First Constitution); 3f.20, Serge Diaghilev and dancers (creation of new Monte Carlo ballet company); 3f.90, Henri Rougier and Turcat-Mery car (75th Anniv of first Monte Carlo Rally). Vert: 5f. Flags and Statue of Liberty (centenary).

518 Chicago and Flags

1986. Ameripex '86 International Stamp Exhibition, Chicago.
1785 **518** 5f. black, red and blue 3·25 2·75

519 Player and Mayan Figure

1986. World Cup Football Championship, Mexico. Sheet 100×143 mm containing T **519** and similar vert design. Each black, red and blue.
MS1786 5f. Type **519**; 7f. Goalkeeper and Mayan figures 12·00 11·00

520 Comet, Telescopes and 1532 Chart by Apian

1986. Appearance of Halley's Comet.
1787 **520** 10f. blue, brown & green 6·50 5·50

521 Monte Carlo and Congress Centre

1986. 30th International Insurance Congress.
1788 **521** 3f.20 blue, brown & grn 2·20 2·00

522 Christmas Tree Branch and Holly

1986. Christmas. Multicoloured.
1789 1f.80 Type **522** 1·30 1·10
1790 2f.50 Christmas tree branch and poinsettia 1·90 1·70

523 Clown's Face and Elephant on Ball

1986. 12th International Circus Festival, Monaco.
1791 **523** 2f.20 multicoloured 3·00 2·50

524 Posy of Roses and Acidanthera

1986. Monte Carlo Flower Show (1987). Mult.
1792 2f.20 Type **524** 2·50 2·20
1793 3f.90 Lilies and beech in vase 4·00 3·50

1986. Monaco Red Cross. The Twelve Labours of Hercules (6th series). As T **422**.
1794 3f.+70c. green, yell & red 2·40 2·10
1795 4f.+80c. blue, brown & red 3·25 2·75
Designs:—3f. The Golden Apples of the Hesperides; 4f. Capturing Cerberus.

525 Making Plastic Mouldings for Car Bodies

1986. Plastics Industry.
1796 **525** 3f.90 turquoise, red and grey 2·50 2·20

526 Scenes from *Le Cid* (Pierre Corneille)

1986. Anniversaries.
1797 **526** 4f. deep brown & brown 2·50 2·20
1798 - 5f. brown and blue 3·25 2·75
Designs:—4f. Type **526** (350th anniv of first performance); 5f. Franz Liszt (composer) and bible (175th birth anniv).

527 Horace de Saussure, Mont Blanc and Climbers

1986. Bicentenary of First Ascent of Mont Blanc by Dr. Paccard and Jacques Balmat.
1799 **527** 5f.80 blue, red and black 3·75 3·25

528 *The Olympic Diver* (Emma de Sigaldi)

1986. 25th Anniv of Unveiling of "The Olympic Diver" (statue).
1800 **528** 6f. multicoloured 4·00 3·50

1986. Monaco in the "Belle Epoque" (5th series). Paintings by Hubert Clerissi. As T **445**. Mult.
1801 6f. *Bandstand and Casino, 1920* (vert) 6·50 5·50
1802 7f. *Avenue du Beau Rivage, 1925* (vert) 8·00 7·00

1986. Seasons of the Strawberry Tree. Sheet 143×100 mm containing T **529** and similar horiz designs.
MS1803 3f. red and olive (T **529**); 4f. olive, lake and red (Summer); 5f. lake, olive and brown-red (Autumn); 6f. olive and red (Winter) 16·00 15·00

530 Spring

1987. Precancels. Seasons of the Chestnut.
1804 **530** 1f.31 green, yellow & brn 95 85
1805 - 1f.69 green and brown 1·30 1·10
1806 - 2f.74 brown, yellow & bl 2·10 1·80
1807 - 4f.56 brown, grn & grey 3·25 2·75
Designs:—1f.69, Summer; 2f.74, Autumn; 4f.56, Winter.

531 Golden Hunter

1987. Insects in Mercantour National Park. Multicoloured.
1808 1f. Type **531** 95 85
1809 1f.90 Golden wasp (vert) 1·60 1·40
1810 2f. Green tiger beetle 1·80 1·50
1811 2f.20 Brown aeshna (vert) 2·40 2·10
1812 3f. Leaf beetle 4·00 3·50
1813 3f.40 Grasshopper (vert) 5·00 4·50

532 St. Devote Church

1987. Centenary of St. Devote Parish Church.
1814 **532** 1f.90 brown 1·30 1·10

533 Dogs

1987. International Dog Show, Monte Carlo.
1815 **533** 1f.90 grey, black & brn 3·25 2·75
1816 - 2f.70 black and green 5·00 4·50
Design:—2f.70, Poodle.

534 Stamp Album

1987. Stamp Day.
1817 **534** 2f.20 red, purple and mauve 1·60 1·40

535 Louis II Stadium, Fontvieille

1987. Europa. Each blue, green and red.
1818 2f.20 Type **535** 3·25 2·75
1819 3f.40 Crown Prince Albert Olympic swimming pool 4·00 3·50
MS1820 143×71 mm. Nos. 1818/19, each×5 48·00 46·00

536 Cathedral

1987. Centenary of Monaco Diocese.
1821 **536** 2f.50 green 1·90 1·70

537 Spring

1987. Seasons of the Vine. Sheet 142×100 mm containing T **537** and similar horiz designs.
MS1822 3f. green and brown (Type **537**); 4f. green and brown (Summer); 5f. violet, brown and green (Autumn); 6f. orange-brown (Winter) 26·00 24·00

538 Lawn Tennis

1987. Second European Small States Games, Monaco.
1823 **538** 3f. black, red and purple 3·50 3·00
1824 - 5f. blue and black 4·50 4·00
Design:—5f. Sailing dinghies and windsurfer.

539 *Red Curly Tail* (Alexander Calder)

1987. Monte Carlo Sculpture 1987 Exhibition.
1825 **539** 3f.70 multicoloured 2·50 2·20

540 Prince Rainier III

1987. 50th Anniv of Monaco Stamp Issuing Office.
1826 **540** 4f. blue 3·00 2·50
1827 - 4f. red 3·00 2·50
1828 - 8f. black 5·75 5·00
Designs:—No. 1827, Prince Louis II. (47×37 mm): 1828, Villa Miraflores.
See also No. **MS**1841.

541 Swallowtail on Stamp

1987. International Stamp Exhibition.
1829 **541** 1f.90 deep green and green 1·10 1·00
1830 **541** 2f.20 purple and red 1·60 1·40
1831 **541** 2f.50 purple and mauve 1·80 1·50
1832 **541** 3f.40 deep blue and blue 2·50 2·20

542 Festival Poster (J. Ramel)

1987. 13th International Circus Festival, Monaco (1988).
1833 **542** 2f.20 multicoloured 3·25 2·75

543 Christmas Scenes

1987. Christmas.
1834 **543** 2f.20 red 1·60 1·40

544 Strawberry Plants and Campanulas in Bowl

1987. Monte Carlo Flower Show (1988). Mult.
1835 2f.20 Type **544** 2·20 2·00
1836 3f.40 Ikebana arrangement of water lilies and dog roses (horiz) 2·75 2·40

545 Obverse and Reverse of Honore V 5f. Silver Coin

1987. 150th Anniv of Revival of Monaco Coinage.
1837 **545** 2f.50 black and red 1·60 1·40

546 Graph, Factory, Electron Microscope and Printed Circuit

1987. Electro-Mechanical Industry.
1838 **546** 2f.50 blue, green and red 1·60 1·40

547 St. Devote

1987. Monaco Red Cross. St. Devote, Patron Saint of Monaco (1st series). Multicoloured.
1839 4f. Type **547** 3·00 2·50
1840 5f. St. Devote and her nurse 3·50 3·00
See also Nos. 1898/9, 1956/7, 1980/1, 2062/3 and 2101/2.

1987. 50th Anniv of Monaco Stamp Issuing Office (2nd issue). Sheet 140×70 mm containing T **540** and other designs. Each purple.
MS1841 4f. Type **540**; 4f. As No. 1827; 8f. As No. 1828 12·00 11·00

548 Oceanographic Museum and IAEA Headquarters, Vienna

1987. 25th Anniv of International Marine Radioactivity Laboratory, Monaco.
1842 **548** 5f. black, brown and blue 3·25 2·75

549 Jouvet

1987. Birth Centenary of Louis Jouvet (actor).
1843 **549** 3f. black 1·90 1·70

550 River Crossing

1987. Bicentenary of First Edition of "Paul and Virginia" by Bernardin de Saint-Pierre.
1844 **550** 3f. green, orange and blue 1·90 1·70

551 Marc Chagall (painter)

1987. Anniversaries.
1845 **551** 4f. black and red 2·75 2·40
1846 - 4f. purple, red and brown 2·75 2·40
1847 - 4f. red, blue and brown 2·75 2·40
1848 - 4f. green, brown & purple 2·75 2·40
1849 - 5f. blue, brown and green 4·00 3·50
1850 - 5f. brown, green and blue 4·00 3·50
Designs:—No. 1845, Type **551** (birth centenary); 1846, Chapel of Ronchamp and Charles Edouard Jeanneret (Le Corbusier) (architect, birth centenary); 1847, Sir Isaac Newton (mathematician) and diagram (300th anniv of publication of *Principia Mathematica*); 1848, Key and Samuel Morse (inventor, 150th Anniv of Morse telegraph); 1849, Wolfgang Amadeus Mozart and scene from *Don Juan* (opera, bicentenary of composition); 1850, Hector Berlioz (composer) and scene from *Mass for the Dead* (150th anniv of composition).

1987. Monaco in the "Belle Epoque" (6th series). As T **445** showing paintings by Hubert Clerissi. Multicoloured.
1851 6f. *Main Ramp to Palace Square, 1925* (vert) 6·50 5·50
1852 7f. *Monte Carlo Railway Station, 1925* (vert) 7·25 6·25

552 Coat of Arms

1987
1853 **552** 2f. multicoloured 1·40 1·30
1854 **552** 2f.20 multicoloured 1·30 1·10

553 Spanish Hogfish

1988. Fish in Oceanographic Museum Aquarium (2nd series). Multicoloured.
1857 2f. Type **553** 1·60 1·40
1858 2f.20 Copper-banded butterflyfish 1·90 1·70
1859 2f.50 Harlequin filefish 2·50 2·20
1860 3f. Blue boxfish 3·00 2·50
1861 3f.70 Lionfish 4·00 3·50
1862 7f. Moon wrasse (horiz) 6·50 5·50

554 Spring

1988. Precancels. Seasons of the Pear Tree. Multicoloured.
1863 1f.36 Type **554** 95 85
1864 1f.75 Summer 1·10 1·00
1865 2f.83 Autumn 2·40 2·10
1866 4f.72 Winter 4·00 3·50
See also Nos. 1952/5.

555 Cross-country Skiing

1988. Winter Olympic Games, Calgary. Sheet 143×93 mm containing T **555** and similar horiz design. Each black, lilac and blue.
MS1867 4f. Type **555**; 6f. Shooting 32·00 31·00

556 Dachshunds

1988. European Dachshunds Show, Monte Carlo.
1868 **556** 3f. multicoloured 4·75 4·25

557 Children of different Races around Globe

1988. 25th Anniv of World Association of Friends of Children.
1869 **557** 5f. green, brown and blue 4·00 3·50

558 Satellite Camera above Man with World as Brain

1988. Europa. Transport and Communications. Each black, brown and red.
1870 2f.20 Type **558** 3·25 2·75
1871 3f.60 Atlantique high speed mail train and aircraft propeller 4·75 4·25
MS1872 170×143 mm. Nos. 1870/1, each×5 48·00 46·00

559 Coxless Four

1988. Centenary of Monaco Nautical Society (formerly Regatta Society).
1873 **559** 2f. blue, green and red 1·90 1·70

560 Jean Monnet (statesman)

1988. Birth Centenaries.
1874 **560** 2f. black, brown and blue 4·75 4·25
1875 - 2f. black and blue 4·75 4·25
Design:—No. 1875, Maurice Chevalier (entertainer).

561 "Leccinum rotundifoliae"

1988. Fungi in Mercantour National Park. Multicoloured.
1876 2f. Type **561** 1·90 1·70
1877 2f.20 Crimson wax cap 2·40 2·10
1878 2f.50 *Pholiota flammans* 3·00 2·50
1879 2f.70 *Lactarius lignyotus* 3·50 3·00
1880 3f. Goaty smell (vert) 4·00 3·50
1881 7f. *Russula olivacea* (vert) 6·75 6·00

562 Nansen

1988. Centenary of First Crossing of Greenland by Fridtjof Nansen (Norwegian explorer).
1882 **562** 4f. violet 3·75 3·25

563 Church and "Miraculous Virgin"

1988. Restoration of Sanctuary of Our Lady of Laghet.
1883 **563** 5f. multicoloured 3·25 2·75

564 Anniversary Emblem

1988. 40th Anniv of W.H.O.
1884 **564** 6f. red and blue 4·25 3·75

565 Anniversary Emblem

1988. 125th Anniv of Red Cross.
1885 **565** 6f. red, grey and black 4·25 3·75

566 Congress Centre

1988. Tenth Anniv of Monte Carlo Congress Centre.
1886 **566** 2f. green 1·60 1·40
1887 - 3f. red 1·90 1·70
Design:—3f. Auditorium.

567 Tennis

1988. Olympic Games, Seoul. New Women's Disciplines. Sheet 143×100 mm containing T **567** and similar horiz designs. Each brown, black and blue.
MS1888 2f. Type **567**; 3f. Table tennis; 5f. 470 dinghy; 7f. Cycling 16·00 15·00

1988. Monaco in the "Belle Epoque" (7th series). Paintings by Hubert Clerissi. As T **445**. Mult.
1889 6f. *Steam packet in Monte Carlo Harbour, 1910* 6·50 5·50
1890 7f. *Place de la Gare, 1910* 8·00 7·00

568 Festival Poster (J. Ramel)

1988. 14th International Circus Festival, Monaco (1989).
1891 **568** 2f. multicoloured 2·40 2·10

569 Star Decoration

1988. Christmas.
1892 **569** 2f. multicoloured 1·80 1·50

570 Arrangement of Fuchsias, Irises, Roses and Petunias

1988. Monte Carlo Flower Show (1989).
1893 **570** 3f. multicoloured 3·00 2·50

571 Models

1988. Ready-to-Wear Clothing Industry.
1894 **571** 3f. green, orange & black 2·40 2·10

572 Lord Byron (bicentenary)

1988. Writers' Birth Anniversaries.

1895	**572**	3f. black, brown and blue	2·40	2·10
1896	-	3f. purple and blue	2·40	2·10

Design:—No. 1896, Pierre de Marivaux (300th anniv).

573 Spring

1988. Seasons of the Olive Tree. Sheet 143×100 mm containing T **573** and similar horiz designs.

MS1897 3f. deep olive, yellow and olive (Type **573**); 4f. deep olive and olive (Summer); 5f. deep olive and olive (Autumn); 6f. deep olive and olive (Winter)	22·00	21·00

1988. Monaco Red Cross. St. Devote, Patron Saint of Monaco (2nd series). As T **547**. Multicoloured.

1898	4f. Roman governor Barbarus arriving at Corsica	3·00	2·75
1899	5f. St. Devote at the Roman senator Eutychius's house	4·00	3·50

574 *Le Nain and his Brothers* (Antoine Le Nain)

1988. Artists' Birth Anniversaries.

1900	**574**	5f. brown, olive and red	4·50	4·00
1901	-	5f. black, green and blue	4·50	4·00

Designs:—No. 1900, Type **574** (400th anniv): 1901, *The Great Archaeologists* (bronze statue, Giorgio de Chirico) (centenary).

575 Sorcerer

1989. Rock Carvings in Mercantour National Park. Multicoloured.

1902	2f. Type **575**	1·40	1·30
1903	2f.20 Oxen in yoke	1·60	1·40
1904	3f. Hunting implements	2·40	2·10
1905	3f.60 Tribal chief	3·25	2·75
1906	4f. Puppet (vert)	4·00	3·50
1907	5f. Jesus Christ (vert)	4·75	4·25

576 *Rue des Spelugues*

1989. Old Monaco (1st series). Multicoloured.

1908	2f. Type **576**	1·40	1·30
1909	2f.20 *Place Saint Nicolas*	1·80	1·50

See also Nos. 1969/70 and 2090/1.

577 Prince Rainier

1989

1910	**577**	2f. blue and azure	1·00	65
1911	**577**	2f.10 blue and azure	1·10	45
1912	**577**	2f.20 brown and pink	1·20	75
1913	**577**	2f.20 blue and azure	1·20	65
1914	**577**	2f.30 brown and pink	1·20	65
1915	**577**	2f.40 blue and azure	1·20	65
1916	**577**	2f.50 brown and pink	1·20	90
1917	**577**	2f.70 blue	1·00	55
1918	**577**	2f.80 brown and pink	1·50	75
1919	**577**	3f. brown and pink	1·10	85
1920	**577**	3f.20 blue and cobalt	1·90	1·40
1921	**577**	3f.40 blue and cobalt	2·00	1·50
1922	**577**	3f.60 blue and cobalt	2·10	1·60
1923	**577**	3f.70 blue and cobalt	2·50	1·00
1924	**577**	3f.80 purple and lilac	2·50	1·80
1925	**577**	3f.80 blue and cobalt	1·40	90
1926	**577**	4f. purple and lilac	2·50	1·80
1927	**577**	5f. brown and pink	2·50	1·70
1928	**577**	10f. deep green and green	4·00	2·30
1929	**577**	15f. blue and grey	7·50	5·00
1930	**577**	20f. red and pink	8·00	5·00
1931	**577**	25f. black and grey	10·00	6·50
1932	**577**	40f. brown and pink	15·00	9·25

See also Nos. 2388/90.

578 Yorkshire Terrier

1989. International Dog Show, Monte Carlo.

1941	**578**	2f.20 multicoloured	2·40	2·10

579 Magician, Dove and Cards

1989. Fifth Grand Prix of Magic, Monte Carlo.

1942	**579**	2f.20 black, blue and red	1·90	1·70

580 Nuns and Monks around "Our Lady of Misericorde"

1989. 350th Anniv of Archiconfrerie de la Misericorde.

1943	**580**	3f. brown, black and red	2·20	2·00

581 Charlie Chaplin (actor) and Film Scenes

1989. Birth Centenaries.

1944	-	3f. green, blue and mauve	2·20	2·00
1945	**581**	4f. purple, green and red	3·25	2·75

Design:—3f. Jean Cocteau (writer and painter), scene from *The Double-headed Eagle* and frescoes in Villefranche-sur-Mer chapel.

582 Spring

1989. Seasons of the Pomegranate. Sheet 144×100 mm containing T **582** and similar horiz designs.

MS1946 3f. red, green and (Type **582**); 4f. brown, green and red (Summer); 5f. green, red and brown (Autumn); 6f. brown and green (Winter)	16·00	15·00

583 Boys playing Marbles

1989. Europa. Children's Games. Each mauve, brown and grey.

1947	2f.20 Type **583**	2·40	2·10
1948	3f.60 Girls skipping	4·00	3·50
MS1949 171×143 mm. Nos. 1947/8, each×5		40·00	38·00

584 Prince Rainier

1989. 40th Anniv of Reign of Prince Rainier. Sheet 100×130 mm.

MS1950 **584** 20f. lilac	18·00	17·00

585 "Liberty"

1989. Philexfrance 89 International Stamp Exhibition, Paris. Sheet 143×105 mm containing T **585** and similar vert designs.

MS1951 5f. blue (Type **585**); 5f. black ("Equality"); 5f. red ("Fraternity")	11·00	10·50

1989. Precancels. As Nos. 1863/6 but values changed. Multicoloured.

1952	1f.39 Type **554**	95	85
1953	1f.79 Summer	1·00	90
1954	2f.90 Autumn	1·90	1·70
1955	4f.84 Winter	3·50	3·00

1989. Monaco Red Cross. St. Devote, Patron Saint of Monaco (3rd series). As T **547**. Multicoloured.

1956	4f. St. Devote beside the dying Eutychius	2·75	2·40
1957	5f. St. Barbarus condemns St. Devote to torture for refusing to make a sacrifice to the gods	4·00	3·50

586 "Artist's Mother" (Philibert Florence)

1989. Artists' 150th Birth Anniversaries.

1958	**586**	4f. brown	4·00	3·50
1959	-	6f. multicoloured	4·75	4·25
1960	-	8f. multicoloured	6·50	5·50

Designs:—Horiz: 6f. *Molesey Regatta* (Alfred Sisley). Vert: 8f. *Farmyard at Auvers* (Paul Cezanne).

587 Poinsettia, Christmas Roses and Holly

1989. Christmas.

1961	**587**	2f. multicoloured	3·50	3·00

588 Map and Emblem

1989. Centenary of Interparliamentary Union.

1962	**588**	4f. black, green and red	3·25	2·75

589 Princess Grace (founder)

1989. 25th Anniv of Princess Grace Foundation. Sheet 133×104 mm containing T 589 and similar vert design. Each blue.

MS1963 5f. Type **589**; 5f. Princess Caroline (Foundation president)	14·50	13·50

590 Monaco Palace, White House, Washington, and Emblem

1989. 20th U.P.U. Congress, Washington D.C.

1964	**590**	6f. blue, brown and black	4·00	3·50

1989. Monaco in the "Belle Epoque" (8th series). Paintings by Hubert Clerissi. As T **445**. Mult.

1965	7f. *Barque in Monte Carlo Harbour, 1915* (vert)	5·50	4·75
1966	8f. *Gaming Tables, Casino, 1915* (vert)	6·75	6·00

591 World Map

1989. Tenth Anniv of Monaco Aide et Presence (welfare organization).

1967	**591**	2f.20 brown and red	4·00	3·50

592 Clown and Horses

1989. 15th International Circus Festival, Monte Carlo.

1968	**592**	2f.20 multicoloured	5·50	5·00

1990. Old Monaco (2nd series). Paintings by Claude Rosticher. As T **576**. Multicoloured.

1969	2f.10 *La Rampe Major*	1·30	1·10
1970	2f.30 *Town Hall Courtyard*	1·40	1·30

593 *Phalaenopsis* "Princess Grace"

1990. International Garden and Greenery Exposition, Osaka, Japan. Multicoloured.

1971	2f. Type **593**	1·60	1·40
1972	3f. Iris "Grace Patricia"	2·40	2·10
1973	3f. *Paphiopedilum* "Prince Rainier III"	2·40	2·10
1974	4f. *Cattleya* "Principessa Grace"	3·25	2·75
1975	5f. Rose "Caroline of Monaco"	4·00	3·50

594 Bearded Collie

1990. International Dog Show, Monte Carlo.

1976	**594**	2f.30 multicoloured	3·00	2·50

595 Noghes and Racing Car

1990. Birth Centenary of Antony Noghes (founder of Monaco Grand Prix and Monte Carlo Rally).

1977	**595**	3f. red, lilac and black	2·10	1·80

596 Cyclist and Lancia Rally Car

1990. Centenary of Automobile Club of Monaco (founded as Cycling Racing Club).

1978	**596**	4f. blue, brown & purple	3·00	2·50

597 Telephone, Satellite and Dish Aerial

1990. 125th Anniv of I.T.U.

1979	**597**	4f. lilac, mauve and blue	3·00	2·50

1990. Monaco Red Cross. St. Devote, Patron Saint of Monaco (4th series). As T **547**. Multicoloured.

1980	4f. St. Devote being flogged	3·00	2·50
1981	5f. Placing body of St. Devote in fishing boat	3·75	3·25

598 Sir Rowland Hill and Penny Black

1990. 150th Anniv of Penny Black.

1982	**598**	5f. blue and black	4·00	3·50

599 *Post Office, Place de la Mairie*

1990. Europa. Post Office Buildings. Paintings by Hubert Clerissi. Multicoloured.

1983	2f.30 Type **599**	2·40	2·10
1984	3f.70 *Post Office, Avenue d'Ostende*	4·00	3·50
MS1985	170×145 mm. Nos. 1983/4, each×4	48·00	46·00

600 Ball, Player and Trophy

1990. World Cup Football Championship, Italy. Sheet 142×100 mm containing T **600** and similar horiz designs.

MS1986	5f. green, black and red; (Type **600**); 5f. black, red and green (Players); 5f. black and green (Pitch, ball and map of Italy); 5f. red, green and black (Pitch, players and stadium)	22·00	21·00

601 Anatase

1990. Minerals in Mercantour National Park. Mult.

1987	2f.10 Type **601**	1·60	1·40
1988	2f.30 Albite	1·80	1·50
1989	3f.20 Rutile	2·40	2·10
1990	3f.80 Chlorite	3·25	2·75
1991	4f. Brookite (vert)	3·50	3·00
1992	6f. Quartz (vert)	5·50	5·00

602 Powerboat

1990. World Offshore Powerboat Racing Championship.

1993	**602**	2f.30 brown, red & blue	1·90	1·70

603 Pierrot writing (mechanical toy)

1990. Philatelic Round Table.

1994	**603**	3f. blue	2·20	2·00

604 Christian Samuel Hahnemann (founding of homeopathy)

1990. Bicentenaries.

1995	**604**	3f. purple, green & black	2·20	2·00
1996	-	5f. chestnut, brown & bl	3·50	3·00

Design:—5f. Jean-Francois Champollion (Egyptologist) and hieroglyphics (birth bicentenary).

605 Bell 206B Jet-Ranger III Helicopters at Monaco Heliport, Fontvieille

1990. 30th International Civil Airports Association Congress, Monte Carlo.

1997	**605**	3f. black, red and brown	2·40	2·10
1998	-	5f. black, blue and brown	4·00	3·50

Design:—5f. Aerospatiale AS-350 Ecureuil helicopters over Monte Carlo Congress Centre.

606 Petanque Player

1990. 26th World Petanque Championship.

1999	**606**	6f. blue, brown & orange	4·75	4·25

607 Spring

1990. Precancels. Seasons of the Plum Tree. Multicoloured.

2000	1f.46 Type **607**	1·10	1·00
2001	1f.89 Summer	1·30	1·10
2002	3f.06 Autumn	2·10	1·80
2003	5f.10 Winter	3·50	3·00

608 Miller on Donkey

1990. Christmas. Crib figures from Provence. Multicoloured.

2004	2f.30 Type **608**	1·60	1·40
2005	3f.20 Woman carrying faggots	2·40	2·10
2006	3f.80 Baker	3·25	2·75

See also Nos. 2052/4, 2097/9, 2146/8 and 2191/3.

609 Spring

1990. Seasons of the Lemon Tree. Sheet 143×100 mm containing T **609** and similar horiz designs. Multicoloured.

MS2007	3f. Type **609**; 4f. Summer; 5f. Autumn; 6f. Winter	18·00	17·00

610 Pyotr Ilich Tchaikovsky (composer)

1990. 150th Birth Anniversaries.

2008	**610**	5f. blue and green	3·50	3·00
2009	-	5f. bistre and blue	3·50	3·00
2010	-	7f. multicoloured	7·25	6·25

Designs:—As T **610**: No. 2009, *Cathedral* (Auguste Rodin, sculptor). 48×37 mm: *The Magpie* (Claude Monet, painter).

611 Clown playing Concertina

1991. 16th International Circus Festival, Monte Carlo.

2011	**611**	2f.30 multicoloured	2·20	2·00

See also No. 2069.

1991. Bygone Monaco (2nd series). Paintings by Hubert Clerissi. As T **481**.

2012	20c. purple	25	20
2013	40c. green	30	30
2014	50c. red	30	30
2015	60c. blue	35	30
2016	70c. green	40	35
2017	80c. blue	45	40
2018	90c. lilac	50	40
2019	1f. blue	65	55
2020	2f. red	95	85
2021	3f. black	1·60	1·40
2022	7f. grey and black	4·00	3·50

Designs:—20c. Rock of Monaco and Fontvieille; 40c. Place du Casino; 50c. Place de la Cremaillere and railway station; 60c. National Council building; 70c. Palace and Rampe Major; 80c. Avenue du Beau Rivage; 90c. Fishing boats, Fontvieille; 1f. Place d'Armes; 2f. Marche de la Condamine; 3f. Yacht; 7f. Oceanographic Museum.

612 Abdim's Stork

1991. International Symposium on Bird Migration. Multicoloured.

2029	2f. Type **612**	1·60	1·40
2030	3f. Broad-tailed hummingbirds	2·40	2·10
2031	4f. Garganeys	3·25	2·75
2032	5f. Eastern broad-billed roller	4·00	3·50
2033	6f. European bee eaters	4·75	4·25

613 Phytoplankton

1991. Oceanographic Museum (1st series).

2034	**613**	2f.10 multicoloured	1·90	1·70

See also Nos. 2095/6.

614 Schnauzer

1991. International Dog Show, Monte Carlo.

2035	**614**	2f.50 multicoloured	3·25	2·75

615 Cyclamen, Lily-of-the-Valley and Pine Twig in Fir-cone

1991. Monte Carlo Flower Show.

2036	**615**	3f. multicoloured	2·20	2·00

616 Corals

1991. Joys of the Sea Exhibition. Multicoloured.

2037	2f.20 Type **616**	1·60	1·40
2038	2f.40 Coral necklace	2·40	2·10

617 Control Room, *Eutelsat* Satellite and Globe

1991. Europa. Europe in Space. Each blue, black and green.

2039	2f.30 Type **617**	3·25	2·75
2040	3f.20 Computer terminal, *Inmarsat* satellite, research ship transmitting signal and man with receiving equipment	4·75	4·25
MS2041	143×171 mm. Nos. 2039/40, each×5	45·00	42·00

618 Cross-country Skiers and Statue of Skiers by Emma de Sigaldi

1991. 1992 Olympic Games. (a) Winter Olympics, Albertville.

2042	**618**	3f. green, blue and olive	2·20	2·00
2043	-	4f. green, blue and olive	3·00	2·50

(b) Olympic Games, Barcelona.

2044	3f. green, lt brown & brown	2·20	2·00
2045	5f. black, brown and green	3·75	3·25

Designs:—No. 2043, Right-hand part of statue and cross-country skiers; 2044, Track, relay runners and left part of statue of relay runners by Emma de Sigaldi; 2045, Right part of statue, view of Barcelona and track.

619 Head of *David* (Michelangelo), Computer Image and Artist at Work

1991. 25th International Contemporary Art Prize.

2046	**619**	4f. green, dp green & lilac	3·25	2·75

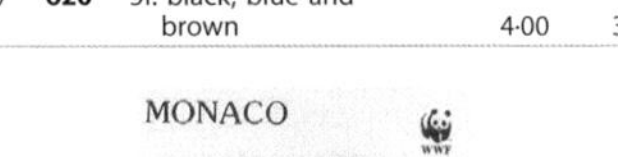

620 Prince Pierre, Open Book and Lyre

1991. 25th Anniv of Prince Pierre Foundation.

2047	**620**	5f. black, blue and brown	4·00	3·50

621 Tortoises

1991. Endangered Species. Hermann's Tortoise. Multicoloured.

2048	1f.25 Type **621**	1·90	1·70
2049	1f.25 Head of tortoise	1·90	1·70
2050	1f.25 Tortoise in grass	1·90	1·70
2051	1f.25 Tortoise emerging from among plants	1·90	1·70

1991. Christmas. As T **608** showing crib figures from Provence. Multicoloured.

2052	2f.50 Consul	2·10	1·80
2053	3f.50 Arlesian woman	3·25	2·75
2054	4f. Mayor	3·50	3·00

622 Norway Spruce

1991. Conifers in Mercantour National Park. Multicoloured.

2055	2f.50 Type **622**	1·60	1·40
2056	3f.50 Silver fir	2·40	2·10
2057	4f. *Pinus uncinata*	2·75	2·50
2058	5f. Scots pine (vert)	3·25	2·75
2059	6f. Arolla pine	4·00	3·50
2060	7f. European larch (vert)	4·75	4·25

623 Spring

1991. Seasons of the Orange Tree. Sheet 142×101 mm containing T **623** and similar horiz designs.

MS2061 3f. orange, green and brown (Type **623**); 4d. green and brown (Summer); 5f. green, orange and brown (Autumn); 6f. green and olive-brown (Winter)	16·00	15·00

1991. Monaco Red Cross. St. Devote, Patron Saint of Monaco (5th series). As T **547**. Multicoloured.

2062	4f.50 Fishing boat carrying body caught in storm	3·25	2·75
2063	5f.50 Dove guiding boatman to port of Monaco	3·50	3·00

624 *Portrait of Claude Monet*

1991. 150th Birth Anniv of Auguste Renoir (painter).

2064	**624**	5f. multicoloured	4·00	3·50

625 Prince Honore II of Monaco

1991. 350th Anniv of Treaty of Peronne (giving French recognition of sovereignty of Monaco). Paintings by Philippe de Champaigne. Mult.

2065	6f. Type **625**	4·75	4·25
2066	7f. King Louis XIII of France	6·50	5·50

626 Princess Grace (after R. Samini)

1991. Tenth Anniv of Princess Grace Theatre.

2067	**626**	8f. multicoloured	6·75	6·00

627 1891 Stamp Design

1991. Centenary of Prince Albert Stamps. Sheet 114×72 mm.

MS2068 **627** 10f. red; 10f. green; 10f. lilac	21·00	20·00

1992. 16th International Circus Festival, Monte Carlo. As No. 2011 but value and dates changed.

2069	**611**	2f.50 multicoloured	2·10	1·80

The 1991 Festival was cancelled.

628 Two-man Bobsleighs

1992. Winter Olympic Games, Albertville (7f.), and Summer Games, Barcelona (8f.).

2070	**628**	7f. blue, turquoise & blk	4·75	4·25
2071	-	8f. purple, blue and green	5·25	4·50

Design:—8f. Football.

629 Spring

1992. Exotic Gardens. Seasons of the Prickly Pear. Sheet 142×100 mm containing T **629** and similar horiz designs. Multicoloured.

MS2072 3f. Type **629**; 4f. Summer; 5f. Autumn; 6f. Winter	16·00	15·00

630 Spring

1992. Precancels. Seasons of the Walnut Tree. Mult.

2073	1f.60 Type **630**	1·30	1·10
2074	2f.08 Summer	1·60	1·40
2075	2f.98 Autumn	1·90	1·70
2076	5f.28 Winter	3·25	2·75

631 Golden Labrador

1992. International Dog Show, Monte Carlo.

2077	**631**	2f.20 multicoloured	3·50	3·00

632 Racing along Seafront

1992. 50th Monaco Grand Prix.

2078	**632**	2f.50 black, purple & bl	1·90	1·70

633 Mixed Bouquet

1992. 25th Monte Carlo Flower Show.

2079	**633**	3f.40 multicoloured	3·25	2·75

634 Ford Sierra Rally Car

1992. 60th Monte Carlo Car Rally.

2080	**634**	4f. black, green and red	3·50	3·00

635 Rough-toothed Dolphin (*Steno bredanensis*)

1992. Mediterranean Dolphins. Sheet 142×100 mm containing T **635** and similar horiz designs. Multicoloured.

MS2081 4f. Type **635** 5f. Common dolphin (*Delphinus delphis*); 6f. Bottle-nosed dolphin (*Tursiops truncates*); 7f. Striped dolphin (*Stenella coeruleoalba*)	19·00	18·00

636 *Pinta* off Palos

1992. Europa. 500th Anniv of Discovery of America by Columbus. Multicoloured.

2082	2f.50 Type **636**	2·40	2·10
2083	3f.40 *Santa Maria* in the Antilles	4·00	3·50
2084	4f. *Nina* off Lisbon	5·25	4·50
MS2085	140×170 mm. Nos. 2082/4, each×2	40·00	38·00

637 Produce

1992. Ameriflora Horticultural Show, Columbus, Ohio. Multicoloured.

2086	4f. Type **637**	3·25	2·75
2087	5f. Vase of mixed flowers	4·00	3·50

638 Prince Rainier I and Fleet (detail of fresco by E. Charpentier, Spinola Palace, Genoa)

1992. Columbus Exhibition, Genoa (6f.), and "Expo '92" World's Fair, Seville (7f.).

2088	**638**	6f. brown, red and blue	4·00	3·50
2089	-	7f. brown, red and blue	4·75	4·25

Design:—7f. Monaco pavilion.

1992. Old Monaco (3rd series). Paintings by Claude Rosticher. As T **576**. Multicoloured.

2090	2f.20 La Porte Neuve (horiz)	1·60	1·40
2091	2f.50 La Placette Bosio (horiz)	2·10	1·80

639 "Christopher Columbus"

1992. Genova '92 International Thematic Stamp Exhibition. Roses. Multicoloured.

2092	3f. Type **639**	3·00	2·50
2093	4f. "Prince of Monaco"	3·50	3·00

640 Lammergeier

1992

2094	**640**	2f.20 orange, blk & grn	2·40	2·10

1992. Oceanographic Museum (2nd series). As T **613**. Multicoloured.

2095	2f.20 *Ceratium ranipes*	2·40	2·10
2096	2f.50 *Ceratium hexacanthum*	2·50	2·20

1992. Christmas. As T **608** showing crib figures from Provence. Multicoloured.

2097	2f.50 Basket-maker	2·40	2·10
2098	3f.40 Fishwife	3·00	2·50
2099	5f. Rural constable	3·50	3·00

641 *Seabus* (projected tourist submarine)

1992

2100	**641**	4f. blue, red and brown	3·00	2·50

642 Burning Boat Ceremony, St. Devote's Eve

1992. Monaco Red Cross. St. Devote, Patron Saint of Monaco (6th series).

2101	**642**	6f. red, blue and brown	4·00	3·50
2102	-	8f. purple, orange and red	4·75	4·25

Design:—8f. Procession of reliquary, St. Devote's Day.

643 Athletes, Sorbonne University and Coubertin

1992. Centenary of Pierre de Coubertin's Proposal for Revival of Olympic Games.

2103	**643**	10f. blue	6·75	6·00

644 Baux de Provence and St. Catherine's Chapel

1992. Titles of Princes of Monaco. Marquis of Baux de Provence.

2104	**644**	15f. multicoloured	8·75	7·75

645 1856 40c. Sardinian Stamp

1992. Stamp Museum. Sheet 115×72 mm containing T **645** and similar vert design.

MS2105 10f. red and black (Type **645**); 10f. green and black (1860 1c. French stamp) 14·50 13·50

646 Clown and Tiger

1993. 17th International Circus Festival, Monte Carlo.

2106	**646**	2f.50 multicoloured	1·90	1·70

647 Short-toed Eagles

1993. Birds of Prey in Mercantour National Park.

2107	**647**	2f. chestnut, brown and orange	1·60	1·40
2108	-	3f. indigo, orange & blue	2·40	2·10
2109	-	4f. brown, ochre and blue	3·25	2·75
2110	-	5f. brown, chestnut and green	3·50	3·00
2111	-	6f. brown, mauve & grn	4·75	4·25

Designs:—Horiz: 3f. Peregrine falcon. Vert: 4f. Eagle owl; 5f. Western honey buzzard; 6f. Tengmalm's owl.

648 Fin Wale (*Balaenoptera physalus*)

1993. Mediterranean Whales. Sheet 143×100 mm containing T **648** and similar horiz designs. Multicoloured.

MS2112 4f. Type **648**; 5f. Minke whale (*Balaenoptera acutorostrata*); 6f. Sperm whale (*Physeter catodon*); 7f. Cuvier's beaked whale (*Ziphius cavirostris*) 19·00 18·00

649 Spring

1993. Seasons of the Almond. Sheet 142×100 mm containing T **649** and similar horiz designs. Multicoloured.

MS2113 5f. Type **649**; 5f. Summer; 5f. Autumn; 5f. Winter 16·00 15·00

650 Mixed Bouquet

1993. Monte Carlo Flower Show.

2114	**650**	3f.40 multicoloured	2·20	2·00

651 Pennants, Auditorium and Masks

1993. Tenth International Amateur Theatre Festival.

2115	**651**	4f.20 multicoloured	3·00	2·50

652 Fire Fighting and Rescue

1993. World Civil Protection Day.

2116	**652**	6f. black, red and green	4·75	4·25

653 Newfoundland

1993. International Dog Show, Monte Carlo.

2117	**653**	2f.20 multicoloured	2·10	1·80

654 Golfer

1993. Tenth Monte Carlo Open Golf Tournament.

2118	**654**	2f.20 multicoloured	1·60	1·40

655 Princess Grace

1993. Tenth Death Anniv (1992) of Princess Grace.

2119	**655**	5f. blue	2·75	2·40

656 Mirror and Candelabra

1993. Tenth Antiques Biennale.

2120	**656**	7f. multicoloured	4·25	3·75

657 *Echinopsis multiplex*

1993. Cacti.

2121	**657**	2f.50 green, purple & yell	1·40	1·30
2122	-	2f.50 green and purple	1·40	1·30
2123	-	2f.50 green, purple & yell	1·40	1·30
2124	-	2f.50 green and yellow	1·40	1·30

Designs:—No. 2122, *Zygocactus truncatus*; 2123, *Echinocereus procumbens*; 2124, *Euphorbia virosa*.

See also Nos. 2154/66.

658 Monte Carlo Ballets

1993. Europa. Contemporary Art.

2125	**658**	2f.50 black, brn & pink	2·40	2·10
2126	-	4f.20 grey and brown	3·25	2·75

MS2127 143×172 mm. Nos. 2125/6, each ×3 18·00 17·00

Design:—4f.20, *Evolution* (sculpture, Emma de Sigaldi).

659

1993. Admission to United Nations Organization. Sheet 115×72 mm.

MS2128 10f. blue (T **659**); 10f. brown (T **577**); 10f. red and brown (State Arms) 19·00 18·00

660 State Arms and Olympic Rings

1993. 110th International Olympic Committee Session, Monaco.

2129	**660**	2f.80 red, brown & blue	1·30	1·10
2130	-	2f.80 blue, lt blue & red	1·30	1·10
2131	-	2f.80 brown, blue & red	1·30	1·10
2132	-	2f.80 blue, lt blue & red	1·30	1·10
2133	-	2f.80 brown, blue & red	1·30	1·10
2134	-	2f.80 blue, lt blue & red	1·30	1·10
2135	-	2f.80 brown, blue & red	1·30	1·10
2136	**660**	2f.80 blue, lt blue & red	1·30	1·10
2137	-	4f.50 multicoloured	2·40	2·10
2138	-	4f.50 black, yellow & bl	2·40	2·10
2139	-	4f.50 red, yellow & blue	2·40	2·10
2140	-	4f.50 black, yellow & bl	2·40	2·10
2141	-	4f.50 red, yellow & blue	2·40	2·10
2142	-	4f.50 black, yellow & bl	2·40	2·10
2143	-	4f.50 red, yellow & blue	2·40	2·10
2144	-	4f.50 red, yellow & blue	2·40	2·10

Designs:—2130, Bobsleighing; 2131, Skiing; 2132, Yachting; 2133, Rowing; 2134, Swimming; 2135, Cycling; 2136, 2144, Commemorative inscription; 2138, Gymnastics (rings exercise); 2139, Judo; 2140, Fencing; 2141, Hurdling; 2142, Archery; 2143, Weightlifting.

661 Examining 1891 1c. Stamp

1993. Centenary of Monaco Philatelic Union.

2145	**661**	2f.40 multicoloured	1·60	1·40

1993. Christmas. Crib figures from Provence. As T **608**. Multicoloured.

2146	2f.80 Donkey	1·60	1·40
2147	3f.70 Shepherd holding lamb	2·40	2·10
2148	4f.40 Ox lying down in barn	3·00	2·50

662 Grieg, Music and Trolls

1993. 150th Birth Anniv of Edvard Grieg (composer).

2149	**662**	4f. blue	4·00	3·50

663 Abstract Lithograph

1993. Birth Centenary of Joan Miro (painter and sculptor).

2150	**663**	5f. multicoloured	4·00	3·50

664 Monaco Red Cross Emblem

1993. Monaco Red Cross.

2151	**664**	5f. red, yellow and black	3·25	2·75
2152	-	6f. red and black	3·50	3·00

Design:—6f. Crosses inscribed with fundamental principles of the International Red Cross.

665 *St. Joseph the Carpenter*

1993. 400th Birth Anniv of Georges de la Tour (painter).

2153	**665**	6f. multicoloured	4·00	3·50

1994. Cacti. As Nos. 2121/4 but values changed and additional designs.

2153a	-	10c. green, orange and red	25	20
2154	**657**	20c. green, purple and yellow	30	30
2155	-	30c. green and purple	30	30
2156	-	40c. green and yellow	30	30
2157	-	50c. green, red and olive	35	30
2158	-	60c. green, red and yellow	40	35
2159	-	70c. green, red and blue	50	40
2160	-	80c. green, orange and red	50	40
2161	-	1f. green, brown and yellow	55	50
2162	-	2f. green, red and yellow	95	85
2163	-	2f.70 green, red and yellow	1·30	1·10
2164	-	4f. green, purple and yellow	1·80	1·50
2165	-	4f. green, red and yellow	2·40	2·10
2166	-	5f. green, mauve and brown	2·50	2·20
2167	-	6f. brown, green and red	3·00	2·50
2167a	-	7f. green, brown and red	3·25	2·75

Designs:—10c. *Bromelia brevifolia*; 30c. *Zygocactus truncatus*; 40c. *Euphorbia virosa*; 50c. *Selenicereus grandiflorus*; 60c. *Opuntia basilaris*; 70c. *Aloe plicatilis*; 80c. *Opuntia hybride*; 1f. *Stapelia flavirostris*; 2f. *Aporocactus flagelliformis*; 2f.70, *Opuntia dejecta*; 4f. (2164), *Echinocereus procumbens*; 4f. (2165), *Echinocereus blanckii*; 5f. *Cereus peruvianus*; 6f. *Euphorbia milii* 7f. *Stapelia variegata*.

666 Festival Poster

1994. 18th Int Circus Festival, Monte Carlo.

2168	**666**	2f.80 multicoloured	1·90	1·70

667 Artist/Poet

1994. Mechanical Toys.

2169	**667**	2f.80 blue	1·40	1·30
2170	-	2f.80 red	1·40	1·30
2171	-	2f.80 purple	1·40	1·30
2172	-	2f.80 green	1·40	1·30

Designs:—No. 2170, Bust of Japanese woman; 2171, Shepherdess with sheep; 2172, Young Parisienne.

1994. Mediterranean Whales and Dolphins. Sheet 143×100 mm containing horiz designs as T **648**. Multicoloured.

MS2173 4f. Killer whale (*Orcimus orca*); 5f. Risso's dolphin (*Grampus griseus*); 6f. False killer whale (*Pseudorca crassidens*); 7f. Long-finned pilot whale (*Globicephala melas*) 19·00 18·00

668

1994. Winter Olympic Games, Lillehammer, Norway. Sheet 123×80 mm containing T **668** and similar horiz design. Each blue and red.

MS2174 10f. Type **668**; 10f. Bobsleighing 14·50 13·50

669 King Charles Spaniels

1994. International Dog Show, Monte Carlo.

2175 **669** 2f.40 multicoloured 2·20 2·00

670 Couple, Leaves and Pollution

1994. Monaco Committee of Anti-tuberculosis and Respiratory Diseases Campaign.

2176 **670** 2f.40+60c. multicoloured 1·90 1·70

671 Iris

1994. Monte Carlo Flower Show.

2177 **671** 4f.40 multicoloured 3·25 2·75

672 Levitation Trick

1994. Tenth Monte Carlo Magic Grand Prix.

2178 **672** 5f. blue, black and red 3·25 2·75

673 Ingredients and Dining Table overlooking Harbour

1994. 35th Anniv of Brotherhood of Cordon d'Or French Chefs.

2179 **673** 6f. multicoloured 4·00 3·50

674 Isfjord, Prince Albert I, Map of Spitzbergen and *Princess Alice II*

1994. Europa. Discoveries made by Prince Albert I. Each black, blue and red.

2180 2f.80 Type **674** 2·40 2·10

2181 4f.50 Oceanographic Museum, Grimaldi's spookfish and *Eryoneicus alberti* (crustacean) 3·25 2·75

MS2182 155×130 mm. Nos. 2180/1, each×3 19·00 18·00

675 Olympic Flag and Sorbonne University

1994. Centenary of International Olympic Committee.

2183 **675** 3f. multicoloured 1·90 1·70

676 Dolphins through Porthole

1994. Economic Institute of the Rights of the Sea Conference, Monaco.

2184 **676** 6f. multicoloured 4·00 3·50

677 Family around Tree of Hearts

1994. International Year of the Family.

2185 **677** 7f. green, orange and blue 4·25 3·75

678 Footballer's Legs and Ball

1994. World Cup Football Championship, U.S.A.

2186 **678** 8f. red and black 4·75 4·25

679 Athletes and Villa Miraflores

1994. Inauguration of New Seat of International Amateur Athletics Federation.

2187 **679** 8f. blue, purple and bistre 4·75 4·25

680 De Dion Bouton, 1903

1994. Vintage Car Collection of Prince Rainier III.

2188 **680** 2f.80 black, brown and mauve 1·90 1·70

681 Emblem and Monte Carlo

1994. First Association of Postage Stamp Catalogue Editors and Philatelic Publications Grand Prix.

2189 **681** 3f. multicoloured 2·10 1·80

682 Emblem and Korean Scene

1994. 21st Universal Postal Union Congress, Seoul.

2190 **682** 4f.40 black, blue and red 3·50 3·00

1994. Christmas. As T **608** showing crib figures from Provence. Multicoloured.

2191	2f.80 Virgin Mary	1·80	1·50
2192	4f.50 Baby Jesus	2·75	2·40
2193	6f. Joseph	3·50	3·00

683 Prince Albert I

1994. Inaug of Stamp and Coin Museum (1st issue). Coins.

2194	**683**	3f. stone, brown and red	1·60	1·40
2195	-	4f. grey, brown and red	2·40	2·10
2196	-	7f. stone, brown and red	4·75	4·25

MS2197 115×73 mm. 10f.×3, As Nos. 2194/6 21·00 20·00

Designs: —4f. Arms of House of Grimaldi; 7f. Prince Rainier III.

See also Nos. **MS**2225; 2265/7 and 2283/**MS**2286.

684 Three Ages of Voltaire (writer, 300th anniv)

1994. Birth Anniversaries.

2198	**684**	5f. green	3·25	2·75
2199	-	6f. brown and purple	4·00	3·50

Design:—Horiz: 6f. Sarah Bernhardt (actress, 150th anniv).

685 Heliport and Bell 206 Helicopter

1994. 50th Anniv of International Civil Aviation Organization.

2200	**685**	5f. green, black and blue	3·25	2·75
2201	-	7f. brown, black and red	4·25	3·75

Design:—7f. Harbour and Eurocopter AS365 Dauphin 2 helicopter.

686 Spring

1994. First European Stamp Salon, Flower Gardens, Paris. Seasons of the Apricot. Sheet 142×100 mm containing T **686** and similar horiz designs. Multicoloured.

MS2202 6f. Type **686**; 7f. Summer; 8f. Autumn; 9f. Winter 21·00 20·00

687 Blood Vessels on Woman (anti-cancer)

1994. Monaco Red Cross. Health Campaigns.

2203	**687**	6f. blue, black and red	3·25	2·75
2204	-	8f. green, black and red	4·75	4·25

Design:—8f. Tree and woman (anti-AIDS).

688 Robinson Crusoe and Friday

1994. Anniversaries. Multicoloured.

2205 7f. Type **688** (275th anniv of publication of *Robinson Crusoe* by Daniel Defoe) 4·75 4·25

2206 9f. *The Snake Charmer* (150th birth anniv of Henri Rousseau, painter) 5·75 5·00

689 Clown playing Trombone

1995. 19th Int Circus Festival, Monte Carlo.

2207 **689** 2f.80 multicoloured 1·90 1·70

690 Crown Prince Albert

1995. 35th Television Festival, Monte Carlo.

2208 **690** 8f. brown 4·75 4·25

691 Fontvieille

1995. European Nature Conservation Year.

2209 **691** 2f.40 multicoloured 2·40 1·50

692 American Cocker Spaniel

1995. International Dog Show, Monte Carlo.

2210 **692** 4f. multicoloured 2·75 2·50

693 Parrot Tulips

1995. Monte Carlo Flower Show.

2211 **693** 5f. multicoloured 3·00 2·50

694 *Acer palmatum*

1995. European Bonsai Congress.

2212 **694** 6f. multicoloured 3·50 3·00

695 Alfred Nobel (founder of Nobel Prizes) and Dove

1995. Europa. Peace and Freedom. Multicoloured.

2213 2f.80 Type **695** 3·25 2·75

2214 5f. Roses, broken chain and watchtower 4·00 3·50

696 Emblem of Monagasque Disabled Children Association

1995. Int Special Olympics, New Haven, U.S.A.
2215 **696** 3f. multicoloured 1·40 1·30

697 Emblem

1995. Rotary International Convention, Nice.
2216 **697** 4f. blue 2·20 2·00

699 Jean Giono

1995. Writers' Birth Centenaries.
2218 **699** 5f. lilac, brown and green 3·00 2·50
2219 - 6f. brown, violet and green 3·50 3·00
Design:—6f. Marcel Pagnol.

700 Saint Hubert (patron saint of hunting)

1995. General Assembly of International Council for Hunting and Conservation of Game.
2220 **700** 6f. blue 3·50 3·00

701 Princess Caroline (President)

1995. World Association of Friends of Children General Assembly, Monaco.
2221 **701** 7f. blue 4·25 3·75

702 Athletes and Medal

1995. International Amateur Athletics Federation Grand Prix, Monaco.
2222 **702** 7f. mauve, purple and grey 4·25 3·75

703 *Trophee des Alpes* (Hubert Clerissi)

1995. 2000th Anniv of Emperor Augustus Monument, La Turbie.
2223 **703** 8f. multicoloured 4·75 4·25

704 Prince Pierre (after Philip Laszlo de Lombos)

1995. Birth Centenary of Prince Pierre of Monaco.
2224 **704** 10f. purple 5·75 5·00

705 1974 60c. Honore II Stamp

1995. Inauguration of Stamp and Coin Museum (2nd issue). Sheet 135×89 mm containing T **705** and similar designs.
MS2225 10f. red, brown and blue (T **706**); 10f. blue and brown (entrance of museum) (*vert*); 10f. blue (1951 30f. first museum stamp) 18·00 17·00

706 St. Antony (wooden statue)

1995. 800th Birth Anniv of St. Antony of Padua.
2226 **706** 2f.80 multicoloured 1·30 1·10

707 United Nations Charter and Peacekeeping Soldiers

1995. 50th Anniv of U.N.O.
2227 **707** 2f.50 multicoloured 1·60 1·40
2228 - 2f.50 multicoloured 1·60 1·40
2229 - 2f.50 multicoloured 1·60 1·40
2230 - 2f.50 blue, black and brown 1·60 1·40
2231 - 3f. black, brown and blue 1·90 1·70
2232 - 3f. multicoloured 1·90 1·70
2233 - 3f. multicoloured 1·90 1·70
2234 - 3f. multicoloured 1·90 1·70
MS2235 112×151 mm. 3f. As No. 2227; 3f. As No. 2228; 3f. As No. 2229; 3f. As No. 2230; 4f.50, As No. 2231; 4f.50, As No. 2232; 4f.50, As No. 2233; 4f.50, As No. 2234 24·00 22·00

Designs:—No. 2228, Wheat ears, boy and arid ground; 2229, Children from different nationalities; 2230, Head of Colossus, Abu Simbel Temple; 2231, United Nations meeting; 2232, Growing crops and hand holding seeds; 2233, Figures and alphabetic characters; 2234, Lute and UNESCO head-quarters, Paris.

Nos. 2228 and 2232 commemorate the FAO, Nos. 2229 and 2233 International Year of Tolerance, Nos. 2230 and 2234 UNESCO.

708 Rose "Grace de Monaco"

1995. Flowers. Multicoloured.
2236 3f. Type **708** 1·80 1·50
2237 3f. Fuchsia "Lakeland Princess" 1·80 1·50
2238 3f. Carnation "Centenaire de Monte-Carlo" 1·80 1·50
2239 3f. Fuchsia "Grace" 1·80 1·50
2240 3f. Rose "Princesse de Monaco" 1·80 1·50
2241 3f. Alstroemeria "Gracia" 1·80 1·50
2242 3f. Lily "Princess Gracia" 1·80 1·50
2243 3f. Carnation "Princesse Caroline" 1·80 1·50
2244 3f. Rose "Stephanie de Monaco" 1·80 1·50
2245 3f. Carnation "Prince Albert" 1·80 1·50
2246 3f. Sweet pea "Grace de Monaco" 1·80 1·50
2247 3f. Gerbera "Gracia" 1·80 1·50

709 Balthazar

1995. Christmas. Crib Figures from Provence of the Three Wise Men. Multicoloured.
2248 3f. Type **709** 1·30 1·10
2249 5f. Gaspard 2·20 2·00
2250 6f. Melchior 3·00 2·50

710 Tree, Bird, Seahorse and Association Emblem

1995. 20th Anniv of Monaco Association for Nature Protection.
2251 **710** 4f. green, black and red 2·20 2·00

711 Rontgen and X-Ray of Hand

1995. Centenary of Discovery of X-Rays by Wilhelm Rontgen.
2252 **711** 6f. black, yellow and green 3·50 3·00

712 First Screening to Paying Public, Paris, December 1895

1995. Centenary of Motion Pictures.
2253 **712** 7f. blue 4·25 3·75

713 Allegory of Anti-leprosy Campaign

1995. Monaco Red Cross. Multicoloured.
2254 7f. Type **713** 4·00 3·50
2255 8f. Doctors Prakash and Mandakini Amte (anti-leprosy campaign in India) 4·75 4·25

714 First Car with Tyres

1995. Centenary of Invention of Inflatable Tyres.
2256 **714** 8f. purple and claret 4·75 4·25

715 "Spring"

1995. 550th Birth Anniv of Sandro Botticelli (artist).
2257 **715** 15f. blue 12·00 10·50

716 Poster

1996. 20th International Circus Festival, Monte Carlo.
2258 **716** 2f.40 multicoloured 1·60 1·40

717 Illusion

1996. Magic Festival, Monte Carlo.
2259 **717** 2f.80 black 1·80 1·50

718 Rhododendron

1996. Monte Carlo Flower Show.
2260 **718** 3f. multicoloured 1·90 1·70

719 Wire-haired Fox Terrier

1996. International Dog Show, Monte Carlo.
2261 **719** 4f. multicoloured 2·50 2·20

720 *Chapel* (Hubert Clerissi)

1996. 300th Anniv of Chapel of Our Lady of Mercy.
2262 **720** 6f. multicoloured 3·50 3·00

721 Prince Albert I of Monaco

1996. Centenary of Oceanographic Expeditions. Multicoloured.

2263 3f. Type **721** 1·90 1·70
2264 4f.50 King Carlos I of Portugal 3·00 2·50

722 Prince Rainier III (after F. Messina)

1996. Inauguration of Stamp and Coin Museum (2nd issue). 1974 Prince Rainier design.

2265 **722** 10f. violet 4·75 3·25
2266 **722** 15f. brown 7·25 5·00
2267 **722** 20f. blue 9·50 6·50

723 Princess Grace

1996. Europa. Famous Women.

2268 **723** 3f. brown and red 4·75 4·25

724 Fish, Sea and Coastline

1996. 20th Anniv of Ramoge Agreement on Environmental Protection of Mediterranean.

2269 **724** 3f. multicoloured 1·90 1·70

725 Saint Nicolas (detail of altarpiece by Louis Brea)

1996. 20th Anniv of Annales Monegasques (historical review). Sheet 180×100 mm containing T **725**. and similar vert designs. Each brown.

MS2270 3f. Type **725**; 3f. hector Berlioz (composer); 4f. Guillaume Apollinaire (poet and art critic); 4f. Niccolo Machiavelli (statesman); 5f. Jean-Baptiste Bosio (painter); 5f. Sidonie Colette (writer); 6f. Francois-Joseph Bosio (sculptor); 6f. Michel Eyqúem de Montaigne (writer and philosopher) 29·00 27·00

726 Chinese Acrobatics Group in Monaco

1996. Monaco–Chinese Diplomatic Relations. Sheet 100×60 mm containing T **726** and similar horiz design. Multicoloured.

MS2271 5f. Type **726**; 5f. Fuling Tomg, Peking 7·00 6·75

727 Code and Monaco

1996. Introduction of International Dialling Code "377".

2272 **727** 3f. blue 2·00 1·80
2273 **727** 3f.80 red 2·40 2·10

728 Throwing the Javelin

1996. Olympic Games, Atlanta. Multicoloured.

2274 3f. Type **728** 1·90 1·70
2275 3f. Baseball 1·90 1·70
2276 4f.50 Running 3·00 2·50
2277 4f.50 Cycling 3·00 2·50

729 Children of Different Races with Balloon

1996. 50th Anniv of UNICEF.

2278 **729** 3f. brown, blue and lilac 1·90 1·70

730 Angel and Star

1996. Christmas. Multicoloured.

2279 3f. Type **730** 1·70 1·50
2280 6f. Angels heralding 3·75 3·25

731 Planet and Neptune, God of the Sea (after Roman mosaic, Sousse)

1996. Anniversaries.

2281 **731** 4f. red, blue and black 2·40 2·10
2282 - 5f. blue and red 3·00 2·75

Designs:—4f. Type **731** (150th anniv of discovery of planet Neptune by Johann Galle); 5f. Rene Descartes (after Franz Hals) (philosopher and scientist, 400th birth anniv).

732 Coins and Press

1996. Inauguaration of Stamp and Coin Museum (3rd issue).

2283 **732** 5f. brown and blue 3·00 2·75
2284 - 5f. brown and purple 3·00 2·75
2285 - 10f. blue and brown 6·00 5·25
MS2286 130×80 mm. Nos. 2283/5 12·00 11·50

Designs:—As T **733**: 5f. Stamp press and engraver. 48×37 mm: 10f. Museum entrance.

733 *Camille Corot* (bicentenary)

1996. Artists' Birth Anniversaries. Self-portraits. Multicoloured.

2287 6f. Type **733** 3·75 3·25
2288 7f. *Francisco Goya* (250th anniv) 4·50 4·00

734 Allegory

1996. Monaco Red Cross. Anti-tuberculosis Campaign. Multicoloured.

2289 7f. Type **734** 4·50 4·00
2290 8f. Camille Guerin and Albert Calmette (developers of vaccine) 5·00 4·50

735 Spring

1996. Seasons of the Blackberry. Sheet 143×100 mm containing T **735** and similar horiz designs. Multicoloured.

MS2291 4f. Type **735**; 5f. Summer; 6f. Autumn; 7f. Winter 14·50 14·00

736 *Gloria* (cadet barque), Club, Motorboat and *Tuiga* (royal yacht)

1996. Monaco Yacht Club.

2292 **736** 3f. multicoloured 2·00 1·80

737 Seal of Prince Rainier III

1996. 700th Anniv of Grimaldi Dynasty (1st issue).

2293 **737** 2f.70 red, brown and blue 1·70 1·50

See also Nos. 2302/**MS**2315, 2326/38 and **MS**2243.

738 Clown

1996. 21st International Circus Festival, Monte Carlo (1997).

2294 **738** 3f. multicoloured 1·90 1·70

739 Old and New Racing and Rally Cars

1996. Motor Sport.

2295 **739** 3f. multicoloured 2·20 2·00

740 Pictures, Engraving Tools and "Stamps"

1996. 60th Anniv of Stamp Issuing Office (2296) and Monaco 97 International Stamp Exhibition, Monte Carlo (2297). Each brown, mauve and blue.

2296 3f. Type **740** 3·50 3·00
2297 3f. Stamp, magnifying glass and letters 3·50 3·00

Nos. 2296/7 were issued together, *se-tenant*, forming a composite design featuring the Grand Staircase of the Prince's Palace.

741 Double Red Camellia

1996. Monte Carlo Flower Show (1997).

2298 **741** 3f.80 multicoloured 2·50 2·30

742 Afghan Hound

1996. International Dog Show, Monte Carlo.

2299 **742** 4f.40 multicoloured 4·00 3·50

743 Award

1996. 37th Television Festival, Monte Carlo (1997).

2300 **743** 4f.90 multicoloured 3·00 2·75

744 Giant Bellflower and Carob Pods and Leaves

1996

2301 **744** 5f. multicoloured 3·00 2·75

745 Rainier I, Battle of Zerikzee, Arms of his wife Andriola Grillo and Chateau de Cagnes

1997. 700th Anniv of Grimaldi Dynasty (2nd issue). The Seigneurs. Multicoloured.

2302 1f. Type **745** 50 45
2303 1f. Seal of Charles I, Battle of Crecy, Chateau de Roquebrune and Rocher fortifications 50 45
2304 1f. Siege of Rocher by Boccanegra, Seal of Rainier II, Arms of his two wives Ilaria del Caretto and Isabelle Asinari, Vatican and Papal Palace, Avignon 50 45
2305 2f. Defeat of combined fleets of Venice and Florence and Jean I on horseback and with his wife Pomelline Fregoso 1·20 1·10
2306 2f. Claudine, acclamation by crowd of her husband Lambert, Seals of Lambert and his father Nicolas and strengthening of Monaco Castle 1·20 1·10
2307 7f. Statue of Francois Grimaldi disguised as Franciscan monk and clashes between Ghibellines and Guelphs at Genoa 4·25 3·75
2308 7f. Honore I flanked by Pope Paul III and Duke of Savoy and Battle of Lepanto 4·25 3·75
2309 7f. Charles II, flags of Genoa and Savoy and attack on Rocher by Capt. Cartier 4·25 3·75
2310 7f. Hercule I, flags of Savoy, Nice and Provence, assassination of Hercule and acclamation of his infant son Honore II 4·25 3·75
2311 9f. Catalan aiding Doge of Venice in war against Aragon, exercising "Right of the Sea" and entrusting education of his heiress Claudine to his wife Pomelline 5·50 4·75
2312 9f. Jean II with his wife Antoinette of Savoy, retable in Chapel of St. Nicholas and assassination of Jean by his brother Lucien 5·50 4·75
2313 9f. Lucien and siege of Monaco by Genoa 5·50 4·75
2314 9f. Seal of Augustin, Treaty of Tordesillas, visit by King Charles V and Augustin as bishop with his nephew and heir Honore 5·50 4·75

MS2315 **737** 150×80 mm. 2×2f.70 red; 2×2f.70 brown; 2×2f.70 blue; 2×2f.70 red, brown and blue 14·50 14·00

746 Tennis Match and Players

1997. Centenary of Monaco Tennis Championships.

2316	**746**	4f.60 multicoloured	3·00	2·75

747 Prince Rainier, Trophy and Stamp and Coin Museum

1997. Award to Prince Rainier of International Philately Grand Prix (made to "Person who has Contributed Most to Philately") by Association of Catalogue Editors.

2317	**747**	4f.60 multicoloured	3·00	2·75

748 Images of St.Devote (patron saint)

1997. Europa. Tales and Legends.

2318	**748**	3f. orange and brown	3·50	3·00
2319	-	3f. blue	3·50	3·00

Design:—No. 2319, Hercules.

749 Syringe and Drug Addicts

1997. Monaco Red Cross. Anti-drugs Campaign.

2320	**749**	7f. black, blue and red	4·25	3·75

750 First Stamps of United States and Monaco 1996 15f. Stamp

1997. Pacific 97 International Stamp Exhibiton, San Francisco. 150th Anniv of First United States Stamps.

2321	**750**	4f.90 multicoloured	3·00	2·75

751 Winter and Summer Uniforms, 1997

1997. The Palace Guard. Multicoloured.

2322	3f. Type **751**	2·00	1·80
2323	3f.50 Uniforms of 1750, 1815, 1818, 1830 and 1853	2·50	2·30
2324	5f.20 Uniforms of 1865, 1870, 1904, 1916 and 1935	3·00	2·75

1997. Victory of Marcelo M. Rios at Monaco Tennis Championships. No. 2316 optd M. RIOS.

2325	**746**	4f.60 multicoloured	3·00	2·75

1997. 700th Anniv of Grimaldi Dynasty (3rd issue). The Princes. As T **745**. Multicoloured.

2326	1f. Honore II	50	45
2327	1f. Louis I	50	45
2328	1f. Antoine I	50	45
2329	2f. Jacques I	1·00	90
2330	7f. Charles III	3·75	3·25
2331	7f. Albert I	3·75	3·25
2332	7f. Louis II	3·75	3·25
2333	7f. Rainier III	3·75	3·25
2334	9f. Louise-Hippolyte	5·00	4·50
2335	9f. Honore IV (wrongly inscr "Honore III")	5·00	4·50
2336	9f. Honore III (wrongly inscr "Honore IV")	5·00	4·50
2337	9f. Honore V	5·00	4·50
2338	9f. Florestan I	5·00	4·50

753 Club Badge, Ball as Globe and Stadium

1997. Monaco, Football Champion of France, 1996–97.

2339	**753**	3f. multicoloured	1·50	1·40

754 Magic Wand, Hands and Stars

1997. 13th Magic Grand Prix, Monte Carlo.

2340	**754**	4f.40 black and gold	2·20	2·00

755 *Francois Grimaldi* (Ernando Venanzi)

1997. Paintings. Multicoloured.

2341	8f. Type **755**	4·00	3·50
2342	9f. *St. Peter and St. Paul* (Peter Paul Rubens)	4·50	4·00

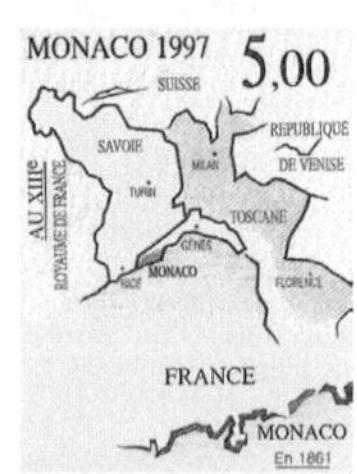

756 Monaco in 13th-Century and 1861

1997. 700th Anniv of Grimaldi Dynasty (4th issue). Geographical Evolution of Monaco. Sheet 120×145 mm containing T **756** and similar vert designs. Multicoloured.

MS2343 5f. Type **756**; 5f. Monaco from 15th/19th-centuries; 5f. Left half of Monaco; 5f. Right half of Monaco 10·00 9·75

The bottom two stamps of the miniature sheet form a composite design of present-day Monaco with a map showing dates at which the territory was expanded.

757 Map of Europe and Blue Whales

1997. 49th Session of International Whaling Commission, Monaco.

2344	**757**	6f.70 multicoloured	3·50	3·00

1997. Election of 1995 Botticelli Stamp as Most Beautiful Stamp in the World. Sheet 115×100 mm.

MS2345 **715** 15f. blue 11·00 10·50

758 Princess Charlotte

1997. 20th Death Anniv of Princess Charlotte.

2346	**758**	3f.80 brown	1·90	1·70

759 Dancer of Russian Ballet and Kremlin, Moscow

1997. Moskva 97 International Stamp Exhbition, Moscow.

2347	**759**	5f. multicoloured	2·50	2·30

760 Trees in Monaco

1997. Tenth Anniv of Marcel Korenlein Arboretum.

2348	**760**	9f. multicoloured	4·50	4·00

761 Diamond-Man (Ribeiro)

1997. Winning Entries in Schoolchildren's Drawing Competition.

2349	**761**	4f. multicoloured	2·00	1·80
2350	-	4f.50 blue, ultramarine and red	2·20	2·00

Design:—Horiz: 4f.50, Flying diamonds (Testa).

762 Four-man Bobsleighing, Speed and Figure Skating and Ice Hockey

1997. Winter Olympic Games, Nagano, Japan (1998). Multicoloured.

2351	4f.90 Type **762**	2·50	2·30
2352	4f.90 Alpine skiing, biathlon, two-man bobsleighing and ski-jumping	2·50	2·30

Nos. 2351/2 were issued together, *se-tenant*, forming a composite design.

763 Albert I (statue)

1997. 150th Birth Anniv of Prince Albert I (1st issue).

2353	**763**	8f. multicoloured	4·25	3·50

See also No. 2368.

764 Clown and Horse

1997. 22nd International Circus Festival, Monte Carlo (1998).

2354	**764**	3f. multicoloured	1·60	1·40

765 Pink Campanula and Carob Plant

1997. Monte Carlo Flower Show (1998).

2355	**765**	4f.40 multicoloured	2·30	2·00

766 *The Departure of Marcus Attilius Regulus for Carthage*

1997. 250th Birth Anniv of Louis David (painter).

2356	**766**	5f.20 green and red	2·75	2·30

767 Pope Innocent IV

1997. 750th Anniv of Creation of Parish of Monaco by Papal Bull.

2357	**767**	7f.50 brown and blue	3·75	3·25

768 Baseball Hat, Television Controller, Ballet Shoe and Football Boot

1998. 38th Television Festival.

2358	**768**	4f.50 multicoloured	2·30	2·00

769 Past and Present Presidents

1998. 50th Anniv of Monaco Red Cross.

2359	**769**	5f. brown and red	2·75	2·30

770 Boxer and Dobermann

1998. International Dog Show, Monte Carlo.

2360	**770**	2f.70 multicoloured	1·40	1·20

771 White Doves and Laurel Wreath

1998. 30th Meeting of Academy of Peace and International Security.

2361	**771**	3f. green and blue	1·60	1·40

772 Ballet Dancer, Piano Keys, Music Score and Violin

1998. 15th Spring Arts Festival.
2362 **772** 4f. multicoloured 2·10 1·80

773 Pierre and Marie Curie

1998. Centenary of Discovery of Radium.
2363 **773** 6f. blue and mauve 3·25 2·75

774 Caravel and Globe

1998. Expo '98 World's Fair, Lisbon. International Year of the Ocean.
2364 **774** 2f.70 multicoloured 1·40 1·20

775 St. Devote (stained glass window, Palace Chapel)

1998. Europa (1st issue). National Festivals.
2365 **775** 3f. multicoloured 2·75 2·30
See also No. 2372.

776 Monte Carlo

1998. Junior Chamber of Commerce European Conference, Monte Carlo.
2366 **776** 3f. multicoloured 1·60 1·40

777 Kessel

1998. Birth Centenary of Joseph Kessel (writer).
2367 **777** 3f.90 multicoloured 1·90 1·70

778 Prince Albert I at different Ages

1998. 150th Birth Anniv of Prince Albert I (2nd issue).
2368 **778** 7f. brown 3·50 3·00

779 Garnier and Monte Carlo Casino

1998. Death Centenary of Charles Garnier (architect).
2369 **779** 10f. multicoloured 5·25 4·50

780 Trophy and Monte Carlo

1998. Tenth World Music Awards, Monte Carlo.
2370 **780** 10f. multicoloured 5·25 4·50

781 Racing Cars

1998. First Formula 3000 Grand Prix, Monte Carlo.
2371 **781** 3f. red and black 1·60 1·40

782x Prince Rainier III, Prince Albert and Royal Palace

1998. Europa (2nd issue). National Festivals.
2372 **782** 3f. multicoloured 2·75 2·30

783 Porcelain Teapot and Figure of Francois Grimaldi

1998. Fine Arts. Multicoloured.
2373 8f. Type **783** 4·25 3·50
2374 9f. Fine-bound books and illustration 4·50 4·00

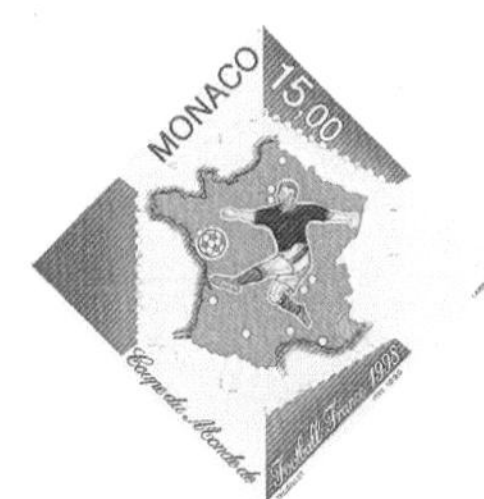

784 Player on Map of France

1998. World Cup Football Championship, France.
2375 **784** 15f. multicoloured 9·25 8·00

785 Modern and Old Motor Cars and Ferrari

1998. Birth Centenary of Enzio Ferrari (motor manufacturer).
2376 **785** 7f. multicoloured 3·50 3·00

786 Gershwin, Trumpeter, Dancers and Opening Bars of *Rhapsody in Blue*

1998. Birth Cent of George Gershwin (composer).
2377 **786** 7f.50 ultramarine, blue and black 3·75 3·25

787 Int Marine Pollution College and Marine Environment Laboratory

1998. Int Marine Pollution Conference, Monaco.
2378 **787** 4f.50 multicoloured 2·30 2·00

788 Venue

1998. Post Europ (successor to C.E.P.T.) Plenary Assembly, Monaco.
2379 **788** 5f. multicoloured 2·75 2·30

789 Belem Tower, Lisbon, and Palace, Monaco

1998. Expo '98 World's Fair and Stamp Exhibition, Lisbon.
2380 **789** 6f.70 multicoloured 3·50 3·00

790 Sportsmen

1998. 30th Anniv of International Association against Violence in Sport.
2381 **790** 4f.20 multicoloured 2·10 1·80

791 Magician

1998. "Magic Stars" Magic Festival, Monte Carlo.
2382 **791** 3f.50 gold and red 1·80 1·50

792 Statue and Vatican Colonnade

1998. 400th Birth Anniv of Giovanni Lorenzo Bernini (architect and sculptor).
2383 **792** 11f.50 blue and brown 6·25 5·25

793 Milan Cathedral

1998. Italia 98 International Stamp Exhibition, Milan.
2384 **793** 4f.90 green and red 2·75 2·30

794 Christmas Tree Decoration

1998. Christmas. Multicoloured.
2385 3f. Type **794** 1·60 1·40
2386 6f.70 *The Nativity* (detail of icon) (horiz) 3·50 3·00

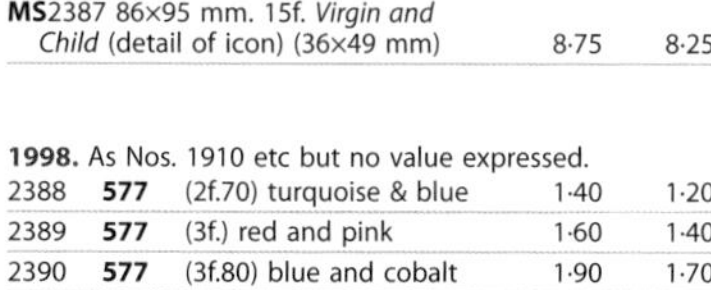

MS2387 86×95 mm. 15f. *Virgin and Child* (detail of icon) (36×49 mm) 8·75 8·25

1998. As Nos. 1910 etc but no value expressed.
2388 **577** (2f.70) turquoise & blue 1·40 1·20
2389 **577** (3f.) red and pink 1·60 1·40
2390 **577** (3f.80) blue and cobalt 1·90 1·70

795 Lion

1998. 23rd International Circus Festival, Monte Carlo (1999).
2391 **795** 2f.70 multicoloured 1·40 1·20

796 Map and Elevation of Seamounts

1998. Grimaldi Seamounts.
2392 **796** 10f. multicoloured 5·25 4·50

797 Prince's Arms and Monogram

1998. 50th Anniv (1999) of Accession of Prince Rainier III (1st issue). Sheet 100×130 mm.
MS2393 **797** 25f. gold and red 16·00 15·00
See also No. **MS**2417.

798 1860 Cover and Stamp and Coin Museum

1999. Monaco 99 International Stamp Exhibition.
2394 **798** 3f. multicoloured 1·80 1·50
MS2395 160×111 mm. No. 2394×4 8·75 8·25

799 Festival Poster

1999. 39th Television Festival.
2396 **799** 3f.80 multicoloured 2·75 2·30

800 Cocker Spaniel and American Cocker

1999. International Dog Show, Fontvieille.
2397 **800** 4f. multicoloured 2·75 2·30

801 World Map

1999. 50th Anniv of Geneva Conventions.
2398 **801** 4f.40 red, brown and black 2·75 2·30

802 Arrangement of Flowers named after Grimaldi Family Members

1999. Monte Carlo Flower Show.
2399 **802** 4f.50 multicoloured 2·75 2·30

803 Children and Heart

1999. 20th Anniv of Monaco Aid and Presence.
2400 **803** 6f.70 multicoloured 5·25 4·50
No. 2400 is also denominated in euros.

804 Palace and Centre

1999. 20th Anniv of Congress Centre Auditorium.
2401 **804** 2f.70 multicoloured 1·80 1·50

DENOMINATION. From No. 2402 Monaco stamps are denominated both in francs and in euros. As no cash for the latter was in circulation until 2002, the catalogue continues to use the franc value.

805 Globe and Piano Keys

1999. Tenth Piano Masters, Monte Carlo.
2402 **805** 4f.60 multicoloured 2·75 2·30

806 Rose "Jubile du Prince de Monaco"

1999. Flowers. Multicoloured.
2403 4f.90 Type **806** 2·75 2·30
2404 6f. Rose "Prince de Monaco", rose "Grimaldi" and orchid "Prince Rainier III" 3·50 3·00

807 Williams's Bugatti (winner of first race) and Michael Schumacher's Car (winner of 1999 race)

1999. 70th Anniv of Monaco Motor Racing Grand Prix.
2405 **807** 3f. multicoloured 1·80 1·50

808 Olympic Rings and Trophy

1999. Third Association of Postage Stamp Catalogue Editors and Philatelic Publications Grand Prix.
2406 **808** 4f.40 multicoloured 2·75 2·30

809 Riders jumping over Monte Carlo

1999. Fifth International Show Jumping Competition, Monte Carlo.
2407 **809** 5f.20 red, black and blue 3·25 2·75

810 Footballer, Runner and Palace

1999. 75th Anniv of Monaco Sports Association. Multicoloured.
2408 7f. Type **810** 3·50 3·00
2409 7f. Boxer, footballer, harbour, runner and handballer 3·50 3·00

811 Architect's Drawing of Forum

1999. Construction of Grimaldi Forum (congress and exhibition centre).
2410 **811** 3f. multicoloured 1·80 1·50

812 Facade and Construction

1999. Centenary of Laying of First Stone of Oceanographic Museum.
2411 **812** 5f. multicoloured 3·25 2·75

813 Eiffel Tower on Map of France, 1849 20c. "Ceres" Stamp and Emblem

1999. Philexfrance 99 International Stamp Exhibition, Paris (1st issue). 150th Anniv of First French Stamps.
2412 **813** 2f.70 multicoloured 1·80 1·50
See also No. 2423.

814 Casino and Rock

1999. Europa. Parks and Gardens. Multicoloured.
2413 3f. Type **814** 2·10 1·80
2414 3f. Fontvieille (48×27 mm) 2·10 1·80

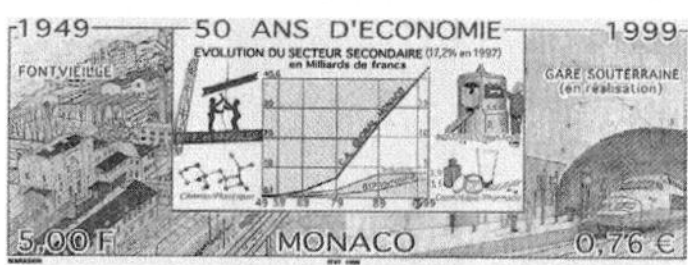
815 Fontvieille in 1949, Line Graph and Underground Station in 1999

1999. 50 Years of the Economy. Multicoloured.
2415 5f. Type **815** (second sector) 2·75 2·30
2416 5f. Le Larvotto in 1949, line graph and Grimaldi Forum in 1999 (third sector) 2·75 2·30

816 Definitive Stamps, 1950–89

1999. 50th Anniv of Accession of Prince Rainier III (2nd issue). Two sheets, 100×130 mm (a) or 119×145 mm (b).
MS2417 Two sheets. (a) 20f. blue and gold (as Type **584** but with monogram superimposed); (b) 30f. multicoloured (Type **816**) 28·00 27·00

817 Honore de Balzac

1999. Writers' Birth Bicentenaries.
2418 **817** 4f.50 blue and scarlet 2·75 2·30
2419 - 5f.20 brown, blue and red 3·50 3·00
Design:—5f.20, Sophie Rostopchine, Comtesse de Segur.

818 Emblem and Chinese Drawing

1999. 125th Anniv of Universal Postal Union.
2420 **818** 3f. blue, red and yellow 1·90 1·70

819 Iris "Rainier III" and Rose "Rainier III"

1999. Flowers.
2421 **819** 4f. multicoloured 2·50 2·10

820 Anniversary Emblem

1999. 50th Anniv of Monaco's Admission to United Nations Educational, Scientific and Educational Organization.
2422 **820** 4f.20 multicoloured 2·75 2·30

821 Emblem and Monaco 1885 and French 1878 Stamps

1999. Philexfrance 99 International Stamp Exhibition, Paris (2nd issue).
2423 **821** 7f. black, blue and mauve 3·75 3·25

822 Athletes

1999. Tenth Sportel (sport and television) Congress, Fontvieille.
2424 **822** 10f. multicoloured 6·25 5·25

823 Maltese Cross, Knights and Valletta

1999. 900th Anniv of Sovereign Military Order of Malta and 25th Anniv of National Association of the Order.
2425 **823** 11f.50 red, brown and blue 7·00 6·00

824 1999 Postcard of Monaco, 1989 Definitive Design and Obverse of Jubilee Coin

1999. Postcard, Coin and Stamp Exhibition, Fontvieille (1st issue).
2426 **824** 3f. multicoloured 1·80 1·50
See also No. 2429.

1999. "Magic Stars" Magic Festival, Monte Carlo. As No. 2382 but face value and date changed.
2427 **791** 4f.50 gold and red 2·75 2·30

825 Fontvieille Project, Stage 2

1999. Achievements and Projects. Sheet 150×100 mm containing T **825** and similar multicoloured designs.
MS2428 4f. Type **825**; 9f. New harbour mole; 9f. Grimaldi Forum (congress centre); 19f. Underground train, harbour and station (76×36 mm) 25·00 24·00

826 1949 Postcard of Monaco, Reverse of Jubilee Coin and 1950 Definitive

1999. Postcard, Coin and Stamp Exhibition, Fontvieille (2nd issue).
2429 **826** 6f.50 multicoloured 3·75 3·25

827 Pierrot juggling "2000"

1999. 24th International Circus Festival, Monte Carlo (2000).
2430 **827** 2f.70 multicoloured 2·10 1·80

828 *Madonna and Child* (Simone Cantarini)

1999. Christmas.
2431 **828** 3f. multicoloured 1·80 1·50

829 Blessing and Holy Door, St. Peter's Cathedral, Rome

1999. Holy Year 2000.
2432 **829** 3f.50 multicoloured 2·20 1·80

830 Mixed Arrangement

1999. 33rd Monte Carlo Flower Show.
2433 **830** 4f.50 multicoloured 2·75 2·30

831 Emblem

1999. Monaco 2000 International Stamp Exhibitions.
2434 **831** 3f. multicoloured 1·80 1·50

832 Bust of Napoleon (Antonio Canova)

2000. 30th Anniv of Napoleonic Museum.
2435 **832** 4f.20 multicoloured 2·75 2·30

833 Festival Emblem

2000. 40th Television Festival, Monte Carlo.
2436 **833** 4f.90 multicoloured 3·25 2·75

834 St. Peter and St. James the Major

2000. The Twelve Apostles. Multicoloured.

2437	**834**	4f. blue, orange and gold	1·80	1·50
2438	-	5f. red and gold	2·75	2·30
2439	-	6f. violet and gold	3·50	3·00
2440	-	7f. brown and gold	4·50	3·75
2441	-	8f. green and gold	5·50	4·50
2442	-	9f. red, orange and gold	6·25	5·25

Designs:—5f. St. John and St. Andrew; 6f. St. Philip and St. Bartholomew; 7f. St. Matthew and St. Thomas; 8f. St. James the Minor and St. Jude; 9f. St. Simon and St. Mathias.

835 Golden Labrador and Golden Retriever

2000. International Dog Show, Monte Carlo.
2443 **835** 6f.50 multicoloured 4·00 3·25

836 Man's Head, Drawings and Key (Adami)

2000. Monaco and the Sea. Multicoloured.

2444	6f.55 Type **836**	4·00	3·25
2445	6f.55 "Monaco" above sea (Arman)	4·00	3·25
2446	6f.55 Abstract designs (Cane)	4·00	3·25
2447	6f.55 Hand touching sun in sky (Folon)	4·00	3·25
2448	6f.55 Angel sleeping and boats (Fuchs)	4·00	3·25
2449	6f.55 Harbour (E. de Sigaldi)	4·00	3·25
2450	6f.55 Views of harbour on silhouettes of yachts (Sosno)	4·00	3·25
2451	6f.55 Waves and floating ball (Verkade)	4·00	3·25

837 Olympic Rings on Globe and Flags

2000. Olympic Games, Sydney, Australia.
2452 **837** 7f. multicoloured 4·00 3·25

838 "Building Europe"

2000. Europa. Multicoloured.

2453	3f. Type **838**	3·50	3·00
2454	3f. Map of Europe and Post Europ member countries' flags (56×37 mm)	3·50	3·00

839 Racing Cars

2000. Second Historic Vehicles Grand Prix.
2455 **839** 4f.40 multicoloured 2·75 2·30

840 Monaco Pavilion and Emblem

2000. EXPO 2000 World's Fair, Hanover.
2456 **840** 5f. multicoloured 3·25 2·75

841 Sts. Mark, Matthew, John and Luke

2000. The Four Evangelists.
2457 **841** 20f. black, flesh and green 12·50 12·00

842 St. Stephen and Emblem

2000. WIPA 2000 International Stamp Exhibition, Vienna.
2458 **842** 4f.50 black, blue and red 2·75 2·30

843 Golfer

2000. Pro-celebrity Golf Tournament, Monte Carlo.
2459 **843** 4f.40 multicoloured 2·75 2·30

844 Fencing

2000. Olympic Games, Sydney. Multicoloured.

2460	2f.70 Type **844**	1·80	1·50
2461	4f.50 Rowing	2·75	2·30

845 Humber Beeston and Woman with Parasol, 1911

2000. Motor Cars and Fashion. Motor cars from the Royal Collection. Multicoloured.

2462	3f. Type **845**	2·75	2·30
2463	6f.70 Jaguar 4-cylinder and woman, 1947	4·50	3·75
2464	10f. Rolls Royce Silver Cloud and woman wearing swing coat, 1956	6·25	5·25
2465	15f. Lamborghini Countach and woman wearing large hat, 1986	10·00	8·25

See also Nos. 2479/81.

846 Entrance to Museum

2000. Philatelic Rarities Exhibition (1999), Stamp and Coin Museum, Monte Carlo.
2466 **846** 3f.50 multicoloured 2·30 2·00

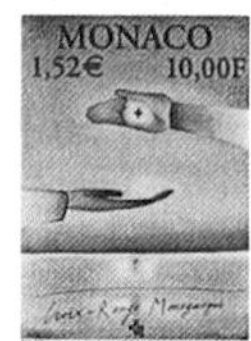
847 Open Hands and Emblem

2000. Monaco Red Cross.
2467 **847** 10f. multicoloured 6·25 5·25

848 Magnifying Glass, Stamps and Exhibition Hall

2000. WORLD STAMP USA International Exhibition, Anaheim, California.
2468 **848** 4f.40 multicoloured 2·75 2·30

849 Magician

2000. Magic Stars Magic Festival, Monte Carlo.
2469 **849** 4f.60 multicoloured 2·75 2·30

850 Da Vinci's Man and Mathematical Symbols

2000. World Mathematics Year.
2470 **850** 6f.50 brown 4·00 3·25

851 Right-hand Section of Screen

2000. Holy Year. Restoration of Altar Screen, Monaco Cathedral. Sheet 120×100 mm containing T **851** and similar design.
MS2471 10f. Type **851**; 20f. Left-hand and central sections (53×52 mm) 20·00 18·00

852 Shark and Museum Facade

2000. Opening of New Aquarium, Oceanographical Museum.
2472 **852** 3f. multicoloured 1·80 1·50

853 Cathedral and Statue of Bear

2000. ESPANA 2000 International Stamp Exhibition, Madrid.
2473 **853** 3f.80 multicoloured 2·75 2·30

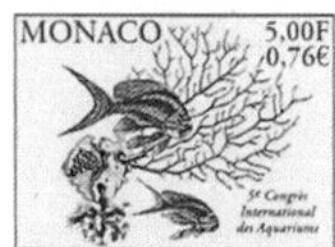

854 Fish and Corals

2000. Fifth International Congress on Aquaria (5f.) and 25th Anniv of Monaco Nature Protection Association (9f.). Multicoloured.
2474 5f. Type **854** 3·25 2·75
2475 9f. Starfish, water plant and fish 5·50 4·50

855 Museum Facade and Plants

2000. 50th Anniv of Observatory Cave and 40th Anniv of Anthropological Museum.
2476 **855** 5f.20 purple, green and brown 3·50 3·00

856x Fresco, Oceanography Museum

2000. International Aquariological Congress.
2477 **856** 7f. multicoloured 4·00 3·25

857 18th-century Crib

2000. Christmas.
2478 **857** 3f. multicoloured 2·75 2·30

2000. Motor Cars and Fashion. Motor cars from the Royal Collection. As T **845**. Multicoloured.
2479 5f. Ferrari Formula 1 racing car and woman in racing clothes, 1989 3·50 3·00
2480 6f. Fiat 600 Jolly and woman wearing swimming costume, 1955 4·50 3·75
2481 8f. Citroen C4F Autochenille and woman wearing coat and hat, 1929 5·50 4·50

858 Princess Stephanie (President)

2000. Association for Help and Protection of Disabled Children (A.M.A.P.E.I.).
2482 **858** 11f.50 blue and red 7·25 6·00

859 Exhibition Poster

2000. Monaco 2000 Stamp Exhibition, Sheet 150×90 mm containing two examples of T 859.
MS2483 20f.×2 multicoloured 27·00 26·00

860 Warrior kneeling

2000. Terracotta Warrior Exhibition, Grimaldi Forum (2001).
2484 **860** 2f.70 black and red 1·80 1·50

861 Museum Building

2000. 50th Anniv of Postal Museum.
2485 **861** 3f. multicoloured 2·00 1·70

862 Arms

2000. Self-adhesive.
2486 **862** (3f.) black and red 2·00 1·70

863 Iris "Princess Caroline of Monaco"

2000. 34th Monte Carlo Flower Show.
2487 **863** 3f.80 multicoloured 2·30 2·00

864 Sardinian 1851 5c., 20c. and 40c. Stamps

2000. 150th Anniv (2001) of First Sardinian Stamp.
2488 **864** 6f.50 blue, red and black 4·00 3·25

865 Seahorse, Marine Life and Life Belt

2000. 25th Anniv (2001) of the Ramoge Agreement on Environmental Protection of Mediterranean.
2489 **865** 6f.70 multicoloured 4·00 3·25

866 *Breitling Orbiter* and 1984 2f.80 Stamp

2000. First Non-Stop Balloon Circumnavigation of Globe (1999). Award to Bertrand Picard of International Philately Grand Prix by Association of Catalogue Editors.
2490 **866** 9f. multicoloured 5·50 4·50

867 Clown with Seal balancing Ball

2000. 25th International Circus Festival, Monte Carlo (2001). Different poster designs by artist named. Multicoloured (except No. 2492).
2491 2f.70 Type **867** 2·20 1·80
2492 6f. Clown playing guitar (Hodge) (black, red and blue) 3·50 3·00
2493 6f. Clown resting head (Knie) 3·50 3·00
2494 6f. Tiger and circus tent (P. Merot) 3·50 3·00
2495 6f. Lions, horses and trapeze artists (Poulet) 3·50 3·00
2496 6f. Monkey and circus tents (T. Mordant) 3·50 3·00

868 Player kicking Ball

2000. Monaco, Football Champion of France, 1999–2000.
2497 **868** 4f.50 multicoloured 2·75 2·30

869 Sea Mammals and Mediterranean Sea

2000. Mediterranean Sea Marine Mammals Sanctuary.
2498 **869** 5f.20 multicoloured 3·50 3·00

870 Nativity Scene

2000. Christmas.
2499 **870** 10f. multicoloured 6·25 5·25

871 Poster

2001. 41st Television Festival, Monte Carlo.
2500 **871** 3f.50 multicoloured 2·20 1·80

872 Leonberger and Newfoundland Dogs

2001. International Dog Show, Monte Carlo.
2501 **872** 6f.50 multicoloured 4·00 3·25

873 Flower Arrangement

2001. Flower Show, Genoa.
2502 **873** 6f.70 multicoloured 4·00 3·25

874 Monaco Palace

2001. Europa. Water Resources. Multicoloured.
2503 3f. Type **874** 3·25 2·75
2504 3f. Undercover washing area 3·25 2·75

875 Princess Caroline and Portrait of Prince Pierre of Monaco (founder)

2001. 50th Anniv of Literary Council of Monaco.
2505 **875** 2f.70 black, brown and green 1·80 1·50

876 Malraux

2001. Birth Centenary of Andre Malraux (writer).
2506 **876** 10f. black and red 6·25 5·25

877 Town Hall

2001. BELGICA 2001 International Stamp Exhibition, Brussels.
2507 **877** 4f. blue and red 2·75 2·30

878 Coins, Stamp and Book

2001. Postcard, Coin and Stamp Exhibition, Fontvielle.
2508 **878** 2f.70 multicoloured 1·80 1·50

879 Princess Grace and Ballet Dancer

2001. 25th Anniv of Princess Grace Dance Academy.
2509 **879** 4f.40 multicoloured 2·75 2·30

880 Model

2001. Naval Museum, Fontvielle.
2510 **880** 4f.50 multicoloured 2·75 2·30

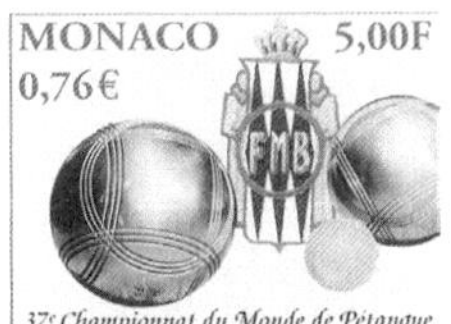
881 Petanque Balls

2001. World Petanque Championships.

2511	**881**	5f. multicoloured	3·25	2·75

882 Fireplace, Throne Room

2001. Royal Palace (1st series). Multicoloured.

2512	3f. Type **882**	1·80	1·50
2513	4f.50 Blue Room	2·75	2·30
2514	6f.70 York Chamber	4·50	3·75
2515	15f. Throne room ceiling fresco	9·00	7·50

See also Nos. 2541/3 and **MS**2582.

883 Littre and Diderot

2001. 250th Anniv of Encyclopaedia or Critical Dictionary of Sciences, Arts and Trades (Denis Diderot) and Birth Bicentenary of Emile Littre (compiler of Dictionary of the French Language).

2516	**883**	4f.20 black, blue and green	2·75	2·30

884 Medal and Steam Yacht

2001. 30th Anniv of Prince Albert Oceanography Prize.

2517	**884**	9f. blue	5·50	4·50

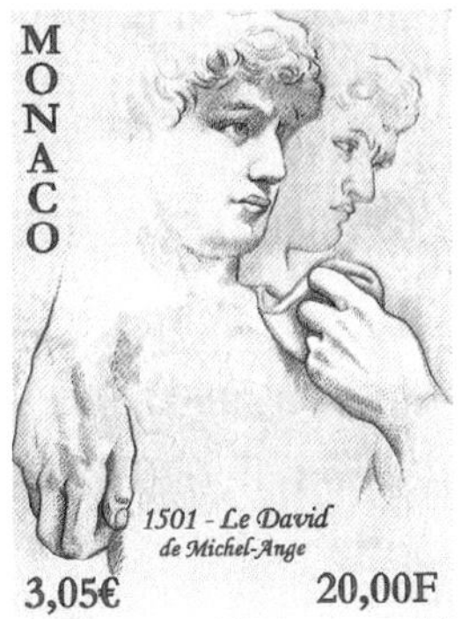
885 Drawings

2001. 500th Anniv of David (sculpture, Michaelangelo).

2518	**885**	20f. multicoloured	12·50	12·00

886 Alfred Nobel (prize fund founder)

2001. Centenary of the Nobel Prize. Multicoloured.

2519	5f. Type **886**	3·50	3·00
2520	8f. Henri Dunant (founder of Red Cross and winner of Peace Prize, 1901)	5·50	4·50
2521	11f.50 Enrico Fermi (physicist and winner of Physics Prize, 1938)	7·25	6·00

887 Prince Rainier, Prince Albert, Map, Satellite, Ship, and Submarine

2001. 36th International Commission for Scientific Exploration of the Mediterranean Meeting.

2522	**887**	3f. multicoloured	2·20	1·80

888 Virgin and Child

2001. Christmas.

2523	**888**	3f. multicoloured	2·20	1·80

889 Garden Tiger Moth (*Artica caja*)

2002. Flora and Fauna.

2524	**889**	1c. black, red and sepia	20	15
2525	-	2c. multicoloured	20	15
2526	-	5c. multicoloured	25	25
2527	-	10c. black, green and yellow	35	30
2528	-	20c. red, yellow and black	55	45
2529	-	41c. multicoloured	1·40	1·20
2530	-	50c. multicoloured	1·80	1·50
2531	-	€1 multicoloured	2·75	2·30
2532	-	€2 multicoloured	3·50	3·00
2533	-	€5 brown, green and black	7·25	6·00
2534	-	€10 green, red and black	16·00	13·50

Designs:—Vert: 5c. Blue trumpet vine (*Thunbergia grandiflora*); 41c. *Helix aspera*; 50c. Foxy charaxes (*Charaxes jasius*); €2 Red thorn apple (*Datura sanguinea*); €5 Crested tit (*Parus crisatus*). Horiz: 2c. *Luria lurida*; 10c. Great tit (*Parus major*); 20c. Common barberfish (*Anthias anthias*); €1 Zoned mitre (*Mitra zonata*); €10 Common snipefish (*Macroramphosus scolopax*).

890 Lion and Ringmaster

2002. 26th International Circus Festival, Monte Carlo.

2540	**890**	41c. multicoloured	1·40	1·20

891 Crystal Gallery

2002. Royal Palace (2nd series). Multicoloured.

2541	41c. Type **891**	1·40	1·20
2542	46c. Throne room (horiz)	1·80	1·50
2543	58c. Landscape painting in Crystal Gallery (horiz)	2·20	1·80

892 Rocking Horse of Flowers

2002. 35th Monte Carlo Flower Show.

2544	**892**	53c. multicoloured	2·00	1·70

893 Old and Modern Rally Cars

2002. Motoring Events in Monaco. Sheet 124×95 mm, containing T **893** and similar vert design. Multicoloured.

MS2545	€1.07, Type **893** (70th Monte Carlo car rally); €1.22, Old racing car (Historic Vehicles third Grand Prix) and modern Formula 1 racing car (60th Monaco Grand Prix)	8·50	8·25

894 Skiers, Ice Skater and Ice Hockey Player

2002. Winter Olympic Games, Salt Lake City, U.S.A. Multicoloured.

2546	23c. Type **894**	90	75
2547	23c. Bobsleigh, luge and skiers (face value, emblem and country inscription at right)	90	75

Nos. 2446/7 were issued together, *se-tenant*, forming a composite design.

895 Exhibition Cases and Prince Albert I

2002. Anniversaries. Multicoloured.

2548	64c. Type **895** (centenary of Prehistoric Anthropology Museum)	2·30	2·00
2549	67c. Title page, Prince Albert I and ship (centenary of publication of *La Carriere d'un Navigateur* (memoirs) by Prince Albert I)	2·50	2·10

896 *Mazarin* (painting, Phillippe de Champaigne)

2002. 400th Birth Anniv of Jules Mazarin (cardinal to Louis XIV).

2550	**896**	69c. multicoloured	2·75	2·30

897 Bust of Napoleon Bonaparte and Medal

2002. Bicentenary of Legion d'Honneur.

2551	**897**	70c. multicoloured	3·00	2·40

898 Whales and Dolphins

2002. First Meeting of Signatories to Agreement on the Conservation of Cetaceans of the Black Sea, Mediterranean Sea and Contiguous Atlantic Area (ACCOBAMS), Monaco.

2552	**898**	75c. multicoloured	3·00	2·50

899 Da Vinci

2002. 550th Birth Anniv of Leonardo da Vinci (artist).

2553	**899**	76c. multicoloured	3·00	2·50

900 St. Bernard and Bouvier

2002. International Dog Show, Monte Carlo.

2554	**900**	99c. multicoloured	3·50	3·00

901 Police Officers and Badge

2002. Centenary of Police Force.

2555	**901**	53c. multicoloured	2·00	1·70

902 Map of Europe and Flag

2002. 25th Anniv of European Academy of Postal Studies.

2556	**902**	58c. multicoloured	2·20	1·80

903 Circus and Globe

2002. Europa. Circus. Multicoloured.

2557	46c. Type **903**	2·30	2·00
2558	46c. "JOURS DE CIRQUE" and performers	2·30	2·00

904 Emblem

2002. 20th International Swimming Competition.

2559	**904**	64c. multicoloured	2·30	2·00

905 Tarmac Roads

2002. Centenary of First Tarmac Roads.

2560	**905**	41c. red, black and brown	1·60	1·40

906 Exhibition Hall and Displays

2002. Monacophil 2002 International Stamp Exhibition.

2561	**906**	46c. green, violet and red	1·80	1·50

See also No. **MS**2584.

907 Emblem

2002. 42nd Television Festival, Monte Carlo.

2562	**907**	70c. multicoloured	2·50	2·10

908 Footballers and Globe

2002. World Cup Football Championship, Japan and South Korea.

2563	**908**	75c. green, blue and red	2·75	2·30

909 Obverse of 1, 2 and 5 cent Coins and Reverse

2002. Coins.

2564	**909**	46c. copper, red and black	1·80	1·50
2565	-	46c. gold, red and black	1·80	1·50
2566	-	€1.50 multicoloured	6·25	5·25
2567	-	€1.50 multicoloured	6·25	5·25

Designs:—Type **909**; 46c. Obverse of 10, 20 and 50 cent coins and reverse; €1.50, Obverse and reverse of 1 euro coin; €1.50, Obverse and reverse of 2 euro coin.

910 Debussy, Pelleas and Melisande

2002. Centenary of First Performance of Claude Debussy's Opera "Pelleas and Melisande".

2568	**910**	69c. green, blue and red	2·50	2·10

911 Saint Devote, Boat and Dove

2002. Monaco Red Cross.

2569	**911**	€1.02 red, greenish blue and black	3·50	3·00

912 Aerial View of Monaco

2002. International Year of Mountains.

2570	**912**	€1.37 multicoloured	5·00	4·25

913 Hugo

2002. Birth Bicentenary of Victor Hugo (writer). Each blue, brown and red.

2571	50c. Type **913**	1·80	1·50
2572	57c. Scenes from his books	2·20	1·80

Nos. 2571/2 were issued together, *se-tenant*, forming a composite design.

914 Dumas

2002. Birth Bicentenary of Alexandre Dumas (writer). Multicoloured.

2573	61c. Type **914**	2·30	2·00
2574	61c. Scenes from his books	2·30	2·00

Nos. 2573/4 were issued together, *se-tenant*, forming a composite design.

915 Princess Grace

2002. 26th Publication of "Annales Monegasques" (archives).

2575	**915**	€1.75 multicoloured	6·25	5·25

916 Star-shaped Flower

2002. Christmas.

2576	**916**	50c. multicoloured	1·80	1·50

917 Frame from Film and Melies

2002. Centenary of "Le Voyage dans la Lune" (film by Georges Melies).

2577	**917**	76c. multicoloured	2·75	2·30

918 Magician

2002. Magic Stars Magic Festival, Monte Carlo.

2578	**918**	€1.52 multicoloured	5·50	4·50

919 1949 Mercedes 220A Cabriolet

2002. Motor Cars from the Royal Collection. Multicoloured.

2579	46c. Type **919**	1·60	1·40
2580	69c. 1956 Rolls Royce Silver Cloud	2·50	2·10
2581	€1.40 1974 Citroen DS 21	5·00	4·25

920 Spring

2002. Royal Palace (3rd series). Frescoes. Sheet 120×100 mm containing T **920** and similar horiz designs showing the Four Seasons. Multicoloured.

MS2582 50c. Type **920**; €1 Summer; €1.50, Autumn; €2 Winter	19·00	18·00

921 Footballer and Golden Ball

2002. Award of International Philatelic Grand Prix to Luis Figo (footballer and 2001 Golden Ball winner). Centenary of Real Madrid Football Club.

2583	**921**	91c. multicoloured	3·25	2·75

922 Exhibition Poster

2002. MonacoPhil 2002 Stamp Exhibition (2nd issue). Sheet 120×82 mm, containing T **922** and similar vert design. Multicoloured. Imperf.

MS2584 €3 Type **922**; €3 Exhibition emblem	23·00	22·00

923 Flower Arrangement

2002. 36th Monte Carlo Flower Show.

2585	**923**	67c. multicoloured	2·50	2·10

924 Princesses Caroline and Stephanie (presidents)

2002. 40th Anniv of "Association Mondiale des Amis de l'Enfance" (children's society).

2586	**924**	€1.25 multicoloured	4·50	3·75

925 St. George (statue)

2002. 1700th Anniv of St. George's Martyrdom.

2587	**925**	53c. multicoloured	2·00	1·70

926 Prince Louis II, Flag, Arch and Building

2002. Bicentenary of Saint-Cyr Imperial Military School.

2588	**926**	61c. multicoloured	2·20	1·80

927 Clown

2003. 27th International Circus Festival, Monte Carlo.

2589	**927**	59c. multicoloured	2·20	1·80

928 Crossed Pennants and Part of Yacht and Crew

2003. 50th Anniv of Monaco Yacht Club.

2590	**928**	46c. multicoloured	1·80	1·50

929 Children

2003. 15th Premiere Rampe (children's circus) Festival.

2591	**929**	€2.82 multicoloured	10·50	8·75

930 Team Members pushing Bobsleigh

2003. Tenth World Bobsleigh Pushing Championship.

2592	**930**	80c. multicoloured	3·00	2·40

931 Dove, Globe and Prince Albert I

2003. Centenary of Monaco International Peace Institute.

2593	**931**	€1.19 multicoloured	4·25	3·50

932 Leaves, Spectator, Tennis Court and Player

2003. Tennis Masters Championship, Monte Carlo.

2594	**932**	€1.30 multicoloured	4·75	4·00

933 Rough Collie

2003. International Dog Show, Monte Carlo.

2595	**933**	79c. multicoloured	3·25	2·75

934 Anniversary Emblem

2003. 40th Anniv of Monaco Junior Chamber of Commerce.

2596	**934**	41c. multicoloured	1·40	1·20

935 Club Grounds

2003. 75th Anniv of Monte Carlo Country Club.

2597	**935**	46c. multicoloured	1·60	1·40

936 Prince Albert I, Sextant, Maps and Emblem

2003. Centenary of First General Bathymetric Chart of the Oceans. Multicoloured.

2598	€1.25 Type **936**	4·50	3·75
2599	€1.25, Buildings and maps	4·50	3·75

Nos. 2598/9 were issued together, *se-tenant*, forming a composite design.

937 Girl on Diving Board (Jean-Gabriel Domergue)

2003. Europa. Poster Art. Multicoloured.

2600	50c. Type **937**	2·30	2·00
2601	50c. Monte-Carlo (Alphonse Mucha)	2·30	2·00

938 Castle, Coin and Ship

2003. Postcard Coin and Stamp Exhibition, Fontvielle.

2602	**938**	45c. multicoloured	1·80	1·50

939 Face

2003. 43rd International Television Festival.

2603	**939**	90c. multicoloured	3·25	2·75

940 Bronze Statuette

2003. 15th Biannual Antique Dealers Meeting.

2604	**940**	€1.80 multicoloured	6·50	5·50

941 Roald Amundsen and Polar Scene

2003. Centenaries. Multicoloured.

2605	90c. Type **941** (First crossing of North Pole)	3·25	2·75
2606	€1.80 Wright brothers and *Flyer 1*	6·50	5·50

942 Hector Berlioz

2003. Composers Birth Anniversaries.

2607	**942**	75c. black and red	2·75	2·30
2608	-	€1.60 blue, sepia and red	5·75	4·75

Designs:—Vert: Type **942** (bicentenary). Horiz: €1.60 Aram Khatchaturian (centenary).

943 Woman's Head (Francois Boucher) (300th anniv)

2003. Artists' Birth Anniversaries.

2609	**943**	€1.30 multicoloured	4·75	4·00
2610	-	€3 mauve and black	11·00	9·00
2611	-	€3.60 brown and black	13·50	11·00

Designs:—€1.30, Type **943**; €3 Vincent Van Gogh (150th anniv); €3.60, Girolamo Francesco Maria Mazzola (Le Parmigianino) (500th anniv).

944 Hand holding Pipette and DNA Double Helix (50th anniv of discovery)

2003. Scientific Anniversaries.

2612	**944**	58c. black, blue and red	2·20	1·80
2613	-	€1.11 chestnut, blue and red	4·00	3·25

Designs:—Type **944**; Alexander Fleming (75th anniv of discovery of penicillin).

945 Nostradamus

2003. 500th Birth Anniv of Michel de Nostre-Dame (Nostradamus) (astrologer).

2614	**945**	70c. multicoloured	2·50	2·10

946 Magician

2003. Magic Stars Magic Festival, Monte Carlo.

2615	**946**	75c. multicoloured	2·75	2·30

947 Marie and Pierre Curie

2003. Centenary of Award of Nobel Prize for Physics to Antoine Henri Becquerel and Pierre and Marie Curie.

2616	**947**	€1.20 multicoloured	4·25	3·50

948 St. Devote kneeling before Cross

2003. 1700th (2004) Anniv of Arrival of St. Devote (patron saint) in Monaco (1st series). Each blue, black and red.

2617	45c. Type **948**	1·60	1·40
2618	45c. St. Devote facing Barbarus	1·60	1·40
2619	45c. Boat carrying St. Devote's body	1·60	1·40
2620	45c. St. Devote (statue)	1·60	1·40

See also No. 2626/30.

949 Edmund Hilary and Mount Everest

2003. 50th Anniv of First Ascent of Mount Everest.

2621	**949**	€1 multicoloured	3·75	3·25

950 Star-shaped Flower

2003. Christmas.

2622	**950**	50c. multicoloured	1·90	1·60

951 Exhibition Poster

2003. MonacoPhil 2004 Stamp Exhibition (December 2004).

2623	**951**	50c. multicoloured	1·90	1·60

952 Lion and Lion Tamer

2003. 28th International Circus Festival (January 2004), Monte Carlo.

2624	**952**	70c. multicoloured	2·50	2·20

953 Tram and Buildings

2004. Centenary of Beausoleil Municipality.

2625	**953**	75c. multicoloured	2·75	2·40

954 St. Devote kneeling before Alta

2004. 1700th Anniv of St. Devote's Arrival (2nd series).

2626	**954**	50c. red and brown	1·90	1·60
2627	-	75c. orange and brown (horiz)	2·75	2·40
2628	-	90c. brown and deep brown (horiz)	3·25	3·00
2629	-	€1 brown and deep brown	3·75	3·25
2630	-	€4 purple and brown (horiz)	15·00	13·00

Designs:—75c. Before Barbarus; 90c. Martyrdom; €1 Boat carrying St. Devote's body; €4 Arrival in Monaco.

955 Princesses Grace and Caroline

2004. 40th Anniv of Princess Grace Foundation.

2640	**955**	50c. multicoloured	1·90	1·60

956 *Hyla meridionalis*

2004. Amphibians.

2641	**956**	75c. green, yellow and black	2·40	1·70
2642	-	€4.50 green, blue and black	14·50	10·00

Design:—Type **956**; €4.50, *Lacerte viridis*.

957 Princess Grace and Shamrock Leaf

2004. 20th Anniv of Princess Grace Irish Library.

2643	**957**	€1.11 green and brown	4·00	3·50

958 Hands

2004. Sixth Biennial Oncological Meeting.

2644	**958**	€1.11 multicoloured	4·00	3·50

959 Princess Grace (statue) (Daphne du Barry)

2004

2645	**959**	€1.45 multicoloured	5·25	4·75

960 Garden

2004. 20th Anniv of Princess Grace Rose Garden.

2646	**960**	€1.90 multicoloured	7·25	6·25

961 Mask, Musical Instruments, Dancer and Actor

2004. Spring Arts Festival.

2647	**961**	€1 brown, scarlet and green	3·75	3·25

962 Cathedral Facade, Choirboy and Emblem

2004. Centenary of Cathedral Choir.

2648	**962**	45c. multicoloured	1·70	1·40

963 Flower Arrangement

2004. 37th Monte Carlo Flower Show.
2649 **963** 58c. multicoloured 2·20 1·90

964 Cavalier King Charles Spaniels

2004. International Dog Show, Monte Carlo.
2650 **964** 90c. multicoloured 3·25 3·00

965 Antony Noghes, King Louis II and Bugatti 35B Race Car driven by William Grover-Williams

2004. 75th Anniv of First Monaco Motor Racing Grand Prix.
2651 **965** €1.20 multicoloured 4·50 3·75

966 Hands enclosing Children

2004. Monaco International School.
2652 **966** 50c. multicoloured 1·90 1·60

967 Athens Stadium (1896) and Modern Runners

2004. Olympic Games, Athens. Multicoloured.
2653 45c. Type **967** 1·70 1·40
2654 45c. Classical Greek runners and Athens stadium (2004) 1·70 1·40

Nos. 2653/4 were issued together, *se-tenant*, forming a composite design.

968 Women wearing Swimsuits ("What Joy to Live the Summer in Monte Carlo") (poster, 1948)

2004. Europa. Holidays. Multicoloured.
2655 50c. Type **968** 2·40 2·10
2656 50c. Frontier sign ("The border of your dreams") (poster, 1951) 2·40 2·10

969 Medal

2004. 50th Anniv of Order of Grimaldi (medal).
2657 **969** 90c. multicoloured 3·25 3·00

970 Napoleon, Crown Prince Honore-Gabriel and Prince Joseph (officers in Napoleon's army)

2004. Bicentenary of Coronation of Emperor Napoleon I. Multicoloured.
2658 58c. Type **970** 2·20 1·90
2659 75c. Eagle and bees (imperial insignia) (horiz) 2·75 2·40
2660 €1.90 Stephanie de Beauharnais (Napoleon's niece and adopted daughter) 7·00 6·00
2661 €2.40 Napoleon I wearing coronation robes 9·25 8·00

971 George Balanchine (choreographer) and Serge Diaghilev (ballet impresario)

2004. First Production of Russian Ballet in Monaco.
2662 **971** €1.60 multicoloured 6·00 5·00

972 Eye enclosing Globe

2004. 44th International Television Festival.
2663 **972** €1.80 multicoloured 6·75 5·75

973 Frederic Mistral

2004. Centenary of Frederic Mistral's Nobel Prize for Literature.
2664 **973** 45c. vermilion, brown and green 1·70 1·40

974 Bird holding Envelope and Globe

2004. 23rd UPU Conference, Bucharest.
2665 **974** 50c. multicoloured 1·90 1·60

975 Chinese Landscape and Marco Polo

2004. 750th Birth Anniv of Marco Polo (traveller).
2666 **975** 50c. multicoloured 1·90 1·60

976 Stamps and Park

2004. Salon de Timbre International Stamp Exhibition, Paris.
2667 **976** 75c. brown, green and vermilion 2·75 2·40

977 Scenes from the Stories

2004. 300th Anniv of French Translation of "One Thousand and One Nights" (collection of stories).
2668 **977** €1 indigo 3·75 3·25

978 Hotel Complex

2004. 75th Anniv of Monte Carlo Beach Hotel.
2669 **978** 45c. multicoloured 1·70 1·40

979 Anniversary Emblem

2004. Centenary of FIFA (Federation Internationale de Football Association).
2670 **979** €1.60 multicoloured 6·00 5·00

980 Female Magician

2004. Magic Stars Magic Festival.
2671 **980** 45c. multicoloured 1·70 1·40

981 Cacti and Presents

2004. Christmas.
2672 **981** 50c. multicoloured 1·90 1·60

982 Princess Grace

2004. 75th Birth Anniv of Princess Grace (**MS**2673a). MonacoPhil 2004 (**MS**2673b). Two sheets, each 141×75 mm containing T **982** and similar vert designs. Each ultramarine and green.
MS2673 (a) 75c. Type **982**; €1.75 Wearing tiara; €3.50 Wearing earrings. (b) As No. **MS**2673a but with colours reversed. Imperf Set of 2 sheets 44·00 43·00

983 Monte Carlo and Emblem

2004. Monaco's Accession to the Council of Europe.
2674 **983** 50c. blue and vermilion 1·90 1·60

984 Equestrian Performer

2004. 29th International Circus Festival (January 2005), Monte Carlo.
2675 **984** 70c. multicoloured 1·70 1·40

985 Stadium Building, Pool and Court

2004. 20th Anniv of Louis II Stadium, Monte Carlo.
2676 **985** 50c. ultramarine, brown and vermilion 1·90 1·60

986 Prince Rainier III

2004. Monaco Prince's Palace. Each salmon, deep green and green.
2677 50c. Type **986** 1·90 1·60
2678 50c. Palace facade (60×27 mm) 1·90 1·60
2679 50c. Prince Albert 1·90 1·60

Nos. 2677/9 were issued together, *se-tenant*, forming a composite design.

987 Entrance

2004. 70th Anniv of Foundation of Monaco Hall of Residence, Cité University, Paris.
2680 **987** 58c. brown, black and vermilion 2·30 1·90

988 Building Facade

2004. 75th Anniv of Law Courts.
2681 **988** 75c. multicoloured 2·75 2·40

989 Artistic and Cultural Symbols

2004. 25th Anniv of "Alliance Francaise" (French language and culture promotion organization).
2682 **989** 75c. multicoloured 2·75 2·40

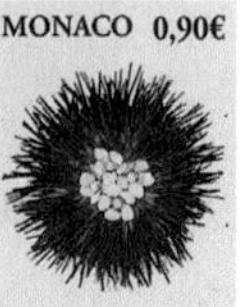

990 Flower Arrangement

2004. 38th Monte Carlo Flower Show (2005).
2683 **990** 90c. multicoloured 3·50 3·00

991 Luigi Valentino Brugnatelli (inventor)

2004. Bicentenary of Electroplating.
2684 **991** €1 brown and black 3·75 3·25

992 Goalkeeper's Hands holding Ball

2004. 75th Anniv of First Football World Cup Championship. Multicoloured.
2685 €1 Type **992** 3·75 3·25
2686 €1 Players' legs and ball 3·75 3·25

993 Jean-Paul Sartre

2004. Birth Centenary of Jean-Paul Sartre (writer).
2687 **993** €1.11 multicoloured 4·25 3·50

994 Johan Edvard Lundstrom (Swedish inventor)

2004. 150th Anniv of Safety Matches.
2688 **994** €1.20 multicoloured 4·50 3·75

995 Don Quixote and Sancho Panza

2004. 400th Anniv of *Don Quixote de la Mancha* (novel by Miguel de Cervantes Saavedra).
2689 **995** €1.20 black, brown and vermilion 4·50 3·75

996 Leo Ferre

2004. Leo Ferre (songwriter, singer and poet) Commemoration.
2690 **996** €1.40 multicoloured 5·25 4·50

997 Hand holding Hypodermic

2004. 150th Anniv of Invention of Hypodermic Syringe by Alexander Wood.
2691 **997** €1.60 purple, black and vermilion 6·00 5·00

998 Frank Libby

2004. 25th Death Anniv of Frank Willard Libby (inventor of Carbon 14 dating and winner of Nobel Prize for Chemistry, 1960).
2692 **998** €1.80 multicoloured 6·75 5·75

999 Emblem and Founder Members (Rotary Club, Chicago)

2005. Centenary of Rotary International (charitable organization). Multicoloured.
2693 55c. Type **999** 2·10 1·80
2694 70c. Emblem and "100 ans" (vert) 2·75 2·20

1000 Artist and Castle

2005. 50th Anniv of Fine Arts Committee Exhibition.
2695 **1000** 48c. multicoloured 1·90 1·60

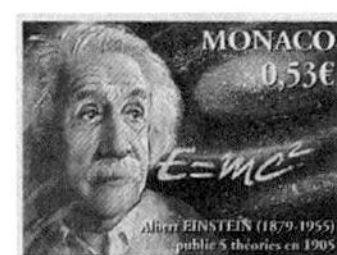

1001 Albert Einstein

2005. Centenary of Publication of Five Papers by Albert Einstein.
2696 **1001** 53c. multicoloured 2·10 1·80

1002 Emblem

2005. Granting of University Diploma to Bosio Pavilion Fine Arts School.
2697 **1002** 64c. vermilion and black 2·50 2·10

1003 Dachshund

2005. International Dog Show, Monte Carlo.
2698 **1003** 82c. multicoloured 3·25 2·75

1004 Centenary Emblem and Race Cars

2005. Centenary of FIA (Federation Internationale de L'Automobile).
2699 **1004** 55c. multicoloured 2·10 1·80

1005 Venturi Fetish

2005. 21st Electric Car Congress (EVS 21), Monaco. Multicoloured.
2700 75c. Type **1005** 2·75 2·40
2701 €1.30 Car enclosing exhibition centre 5·00 4·25

1006 Show Jumper

2005. Tenth International Show Jumping Competition, Monaco.
2702 **1006** 90c. green and vermilion 3·50 3·00

1007 Pissaladiere (pizza)

2005. Europa. Gastronomy. Multicoloured.
2703 53c. Type **1007** 2·10 1·80
2704 53c. Barbagiuans 2·10 1·80
2705 55c. Pastries 2·10 1·80
2706 55c. Chard pie 2·10 1·80

1008 Louis II Stadium and Emblem

2005. 25th Anniv of Monaco Special Olympics.
2707 **1008** €1.20 multicoloured 4·50 3·75

1009 Poster

2005. Centenary of First Industries. Advertising posters. Multicoloured.
2708 77c. Type **1009** (tourism) 3·25 2·75
2709 €2.50 Woman and bath (sanitary ware) 9·50 8·00
2710 €3.10 Harlequin and biscuits (biscuit making) 12·50 10·50

1010 Yachts in Berth

2005. Yacht Show.
2711 **1010** 82c. multicoloured 3·25 2·75

1011 Edmond Halley (predicted the continuing return of Halley's comet)

2005. Astronomers.
2712 **1011** €1.22 violet, vermilion and green 4·75 4·00
2713 - €1.98 deep green, vermilion and green 7·50 6·50
2714 - €3.80 brown, vermilion and green 14·50 12·00

Designs:—€1.22 Type **1011**; €1.98 Gerald Kuiper (discovered Kuiper's belt) (birth centenary); €3.80 Clyde Tombaugh (75th anniv of discovery of Pluto).

1012 Emblem

2005. 50th Anniv of Universal Postal Union Membership.
2715 **1012** €3.03 ultramarine, purple and vermilion 11·50 9·50

1013 Arms

2005. Self-adhesive.
2716 **1013** (48c.) emerald, black and vermilion 1·90 1·60

No. 2716 was for use on mail up to 20 grammes within Monaco and France.

1014 Emblem

2005. Tenth "Journee du Patrimoine" (culture day).
2717 **1014** 48c. multicoloured 1·90 1·60

1015 Emblem

2005. Magic Stars Magic Festival.
2718 **1015** €1.45 scarlet and gold 5·75 4·75

1016 Virgin and Child

2005. Christmas.
2719 **1016** 53c. black and vermilion 2·10 1·80

1017 Monte-Carlo Bay Hotel

2005
2720 **1017** 55c. multicoloured 2·10 1·80

1018 Nadia and Lili Boulanger

2005. 25th Anniv of Nadia and Lili Boulanger Music Competition.
2721 **1018** 90c. indigo, vermilion and green 3·50 3·00

1019 Singer (Le Chant)

2005. 180th Birth Anniv of Charles Garnier (architect).
2722 **1019** 82c. claret and vermilion 3·00 2·50

2723	-	82c. claret and vermilion	3·00	2·50
2724	-	82c. claret and vermilion	3·00	2·50
2725	-	82c. claret and vermilion	3·00	2·50
2726	-	82c. green and vermilion	3·00	2·50
2727	-	82c. claret and vermilion	3·00	2·50

Designs:—82c.×6, Type **1019**; Casino (Salle Garnier); Three figures (La Comedie); Two figures (La Danse); Charles Garnier; Musicians (La Musique).

1020 Prince Albert II

2005. No value expressed.

2728	**1020**	(48c.) green	1·90	1·60
2729	**1020**	(53c.) carmine	2·10	1·80
2730	**1020**	(75c.) blue	2·75	2·40

1021 Monte Carlo

2005. National Day. Multicoloured.

2731	€1.01 Type **1021**	3·75	3·25
2732	€1.01 Palace facade (60×32 mm)	3·75	3·25
2733	€1.01 Fontvielle	3·75	3·25

Nos. 2731/3 were issued together, *se-tenant*, forming a composite design.

1022 Prince Rainier III

2005. Prince Rainier III Commemoration. Sheet 101×130 mm.

MS2734	**1022** €4 black	16·00	15·00

1023 Stamp Museum

2005. MonacoPhil 2006 International Stamp Exhibition.

2735	**1023**	55c. multicoloured	2·10	1·80

1024 Clown

2005. 30th International Circus Festival (January 2006), Monte Carlo. Multicoloured.

2736	64c. Type **1024**	2·50	2·10
2737	75c. Charlie Rivel — Clown d'Or 1974	2·75	2·40
2738	75c. Fredy Knie — Clown d'Or 1977	2·75	2·40
2739	75c. Alexis Gruss Senior — Clown d'Or 1975	2·75	2·40
2740	75c. Clown d'Or statue	2·75	2·40
2741	75c. Georges Carl — Clown d'Or 19791	2·75	2·40

1025 Neve (mascot)

2006. Winter Olympic Games, Turin. Multicoloured.

2742	55c. Type **1025**	2·10	1·80
2743	55c. Gliz	2·10	1·80
2744	82c. Bobsleigh and skier (40×30 mm)	3·50	2·75

Nos. 2742/3 were issued together, *se-tenant*, forming a composite design.

1026 Stamps, Coins and Printing Press

2006. Centenary of Stamp and Coin Museum.

2745	**1026**	53c. black, vermilion and brown	2·10	1·80

1027 Book as Clapperboard

2006. Cinema and Literature Forum.

2746	**1027**	82c. multicoloured	3·25	2·75

1028 Leopold Senghor

2006. Birth Centenary of Leopold Sedar Senghor (writer and politician). Organisation Internationale de la Francophonie.

2747	**1028**	€1.45 multicoloured	5·50	4·75

1029 Player and Emblem

2006. Centenary of Masters Tennis Tournament.

2748	**1029**	55c. multicoloured	2·10	1·80

1030 Grimaldi Arms

2006. Self-adhesive.

2749	**1030**	A (55c.) black and vermilion	2·10	1·80

1031 Conductors and Musical Instruments

2006. 150th Anniv of Philharmonic Orchestra.

2750	**1031**	64c. multicoloured	2·50	2·10

1032 Map and Ship

2006. Centenary of Prince Albert I's Arctic Expeditions.

2751	**1032**	€1.60 multicoloured	6·75	5·50

1033 Schnauzer

2006. International Dog Show, Monte Carlo.

2752	**1033**	64c. multicoloured	2·50	2·10

1034 Blooms

2006. 39th Monte Carlo Flower Show.

2753	**1034**	77c. multicoloured	3·00	2·50

1035 1035 Trophy and Stadium

2006. World Cup Football Championship, Germany. Multicoloured.

2754	90c. Type **1035**	3·75	3·25
2755	90c. Stadium and emblem	3·75	3·25

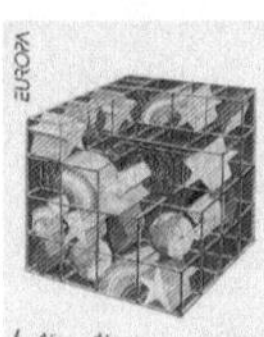

1036 Boxes enclosing Shapes

2006. Europa. Integration. Multicoloured.

2756	53c. Type **1036**	2·10	1·80
2757	55c. Globe containing face, and microchip (horiz)	2·10	1·80

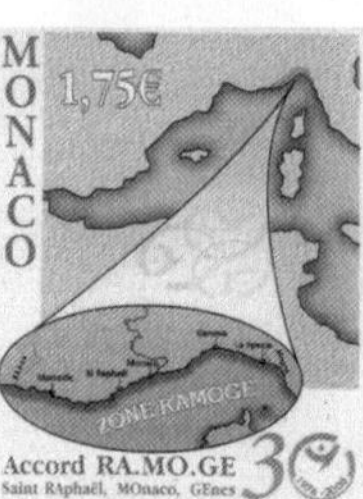

1037 Mediterranean Coastline

2006. 30th Anniv of RAMOGE (Monaco, France and Italy accord to combat coastal and maritime pollution).

2758	**1037**	€1.75 multicoloured	6·75	5·50

1038 Capitol

2006. Washington 2006 International Stamp Exhibition.

2759	**1038**	90c. ultramarine and vermilion	3·50	3·00

1039 John Huston

2006. Birth Centenary of John Huston (actor and director).

2760	**1039**	90c. slate and red	6·75	5·75

1040 Prince Albert and Fencers

2006. 20th Prince Albert Challenge Fencing Competition.

2761	**1040**	48c. multicoloured	1·90	1·60

1041 Pierre Corneille

2006. 400th Birth Anniv of Pierre Corneille (dramatist).

2762	**1041**	53c. multicoloured	2·10	1·80

1042 Hand and TV Screen

2006. 46th International Television Festival.

2763	**1042**	82c. multicoloured	3·25	2·75

1043 Mozart and Scenes from his Operas

2006. 250th Birth Anniv of Wolfgang Amadeus Mozart.

2764	**1043**	€1.22 blue and vermilion	4·75	4·00

1044 Prince Pierre and Cultural Symbols

2006. 40th Anniv of Prince Pierre Foundation (art and culture).

2765	**1044**	€2.50 lilac, blue and vermilion	10·50	8·75

1045 Dino Buzzati

2006. Birth Centenary of Dino Buzzati (writer).

2766	**1045**	55c. multicoloured	2·10	1·80

1046 Cetaceans

2006. 10th Anniv of ACCOBAMS.

2767	90c. multicoloured	3·50	3·00

1047 Luchino Visconti

2006. Birth Centenary of Luchino Visconti (film director).
2768 **1047** €1.75 Indian red 6·75 5·50

1048 Rolls Royce Motor Car

2006. Centenary of Rolls Royce (car manufacturer).
2769 **1048** 64c. multicoloured 2·50 2·10

1049 Hand and Cards

2006. Magic Stars Magic Festival.
2770 **1049** 77c. multicoloured 3·00 2·50

1050 Heads

2006. Red Cross.
2771 **1050** 48c. multicoloured 1·90 1·60

1051 Virgin and Child

2006. Christmas.
2772 **1051** 53c. multicoloured 2·10 1·80

1052 Josephine Baker

2006. Birth Centenary of Josephine Baker (entertainer). 25th Anniv of Princess Grace Theatre.
2773 **1052** 49c. multicoloured 1·90 1·60

1053 Emblems

2006. Tenth Anniv of AIDS Awareness Campaign.
2774 **1053** 49c. multicoloured 1·90 1·60

1054 Prince Albert II

2006. No value expressed.
2775 **1054** (49c.) green 1·90 1·60
2776 **1054** (54c.) scarlet 2·30 1·90
2777 **1054** (85c.) blue 3·50 3·00

1055 Emblems, Envelopes and Stamps

2006. 70th Anniv of Stamp Issuing Office. 20th Anniv of Consultative Committee to the Prince of Monaco's Philatelic Collection.
2778 **1055** 54c. multicoloured 2·10 1·80

1056 Clown and Elephant

2006. 31st International Circus Festival (January 2007), Monte Carlo. Multicoloured.
2779 60c. Type **1056** 2·30 1·90
2780 84c. Poster 3·25 2·75

1057 Prince Albert II

2006. Official Photographic Portrait.
2781 **1057** 60c. multicoloured 2·30 1·90

1058 Formula 1 Race Car

2006. 65th Anniv of Monte Carlo Formula 1 Grand Prix (2782). 75th Anniv of Monte Carlo Rally (2783). Multicoloured.
2782 60c. Type **1058** 2·75 2·20
2783 60c. Rally race car 2·75 2·20

1059 Face

2006. Tenth Anniv of Les Enfants de Frankie (children's charitable association).
2784 **1059** 70c. multicoloured 2·75 2·20

1060 Albert Camus

2006. 50th Anniv of Albert Camus's Nobel Prize for Literature.
2785 **1060** 84c. black, blue and vermilion 3·25 2·75

1061 Auguste Escoffier

2006. 160th Birth Anniv of Auguste Escoffier (chef).
2786 **1061** 85c. chestnut, vermilion and ultramarine 3·25 2·75

1062 Daniel Bovet and Alfred Nobel

2006. Red Cross. Birth Centenary (2007) of Daniel Bovet—Winner of 1957 Nobel Prize for Medicine.
2787 **1062** 86c. lilac and vermilion 3·25 2·75

1063 Blue and Pink Bouquet

2006. 40th Anniv of International Flower Competition. Sheet 110×130 mm containing T **1063** and similar diamond-shaped designs. Multicoloured.
MS2788 €1.30 Type **1063**; €1.30 Tall arrangement; €1.30 Gergeras; €1.30 Two orange flowers and thin leaves 25·00 24·00

Nos. 2789/91 are vacant.

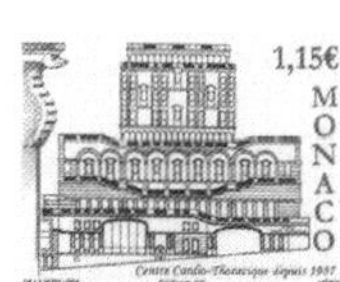

1064 Cardio-Thoracic Centre Building

2006. 20th Anniv of Cardio Thoracic Centre (2792). Opening of Institute of Medicine and Sports Surgery (2793).
2792 **1064** €1.15 ultramarine, vermilion and black 4·75 4·00
2793 - €1.70 vermilion, black and cinnamon 6·50 5·50
Designs:—€1.15 Type **1064**; €1.70 Institute building.

1065 Frontispiece and Rudyard Kipling

2006. Centenary of Rudyard Kipling's Nobel Prize for Literature.
2794 **1065** €1.57 green, vermilion and black 6·00 5·00

1066 Prince Albert II and Pope Benedict XVI

2006. Prince Albert II's Official Visit to the Vatican.
2795 **1066** €1.70 multicoloured 7·50 6·50

1067 *Sunrise*

2006. Grimaldi Forum. Paintings by Nall. Multicoloured.
2796 €1.70 Type **1067** 6·75 5·50
2797 €1.70 *Sunset* 6·75 5·50

1068 Paul-Emile Victor and dog

2006. Birth Centenary of Paul-Emile Victor (explorer).
2798 **1068** €2.11 blue, black and vermilion 8·50 7·25

1069 Flags as Map of Europe

2006. 30th Anniv of European Academy of Philately.
2799 **1069** €2.30 multicoloured 9·50 8·00

1070 Trophy

2006. Alexander Kroo—ASCAT 2006 Philatelic Grand Prix Winner.
2800 **1070** €3 multicoloured 12·50 10·50

1071 Prince Albert II

2006. MonacoPhil (2006). Sheet 101×126 mm.
MS2801 **1071** €6 multicoloured 27·00 26·00

1072 *Stenella coeruleoalba*

2007. Pre-cancelled. No value expressed.
2802 **1072** (36c.) multicoloured 1·50 1·30

No. 2802 was for mass mailing within France weighing less than 35g.

1073 Guiseppe Garibaldi

2007. Birth Bicentenary of Guiseppe Garibaldi (soldier).
2803 **1073** €1.40 sepia and vermilion 6·00 5·00

1074 Carlo Goldoni

2007. 300th Birth Anniv of Carlo Goldoni (playwright).
2804 **1074** €4.54 multicoloured 17·00 14·50

1075 Albert Gautier-Vignal and Committee Emblem

2007. Centenary of Monaco Olympic Committee.
2805 **1075** 60c. multicoloured 2·30 1·90

1076 Dalmatian

2007. International Dog Show, Monte Carlo.
2806 **1076** 70c. multicoloured 2·75 2·20

1077 Members' Flags and Emblem

2007. Small European States' Games.
2807 **1077** 86c. multicoloured 3·50 3·00

1078 Grace Kelly

2007. 25th Death Anniv of Princess Grace. "The Grace Kelly Years" Exhibition, Grimaldi Forum.
2808 **1078** 85c. black and vermilion 3·25 2·75

1079 Leger and Modern Helicopter

2007. Centenary of First Flight of Leger Helicopter (created by Maurice Stanislas Leger).
2809 **1079** €1.15 violet, ultramarine and vermilion 4·50 3·75

1080 Scouts and Campfire

2007. Europa. Centenary of Scouting. Multicoloured.

2810	60c. Type **1080**	3·00	2·40
2811	60c. Robert Baden-Powell (founder)	3·00	2·40

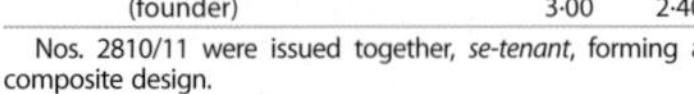
Nos. 2810/11 were issued together, *se-tenant*, forming a composite design.

1081 Lights

2007. 47th International Television Festival.
2812 **1081** €2.90 multicoloured 12·00 9·50

1082 Postcard, Coin and Stamp

2007. Postcard Coin and Stamp Exhibition.
2813 **1082** 49c. multicoloured 2·10 1·70

1083 Magician

2007. 'Magic Stars' Magic Festival.
2814 **1083** €1.30 vermilion and black 5·50 4·25

1084 Virgin Mary

2007. Christmas (Visions of Virgin Mary by Bernadette Soubirous at Lourdes, 1858).
2815 **1084** 54c. multicoloured 2·30 1·80

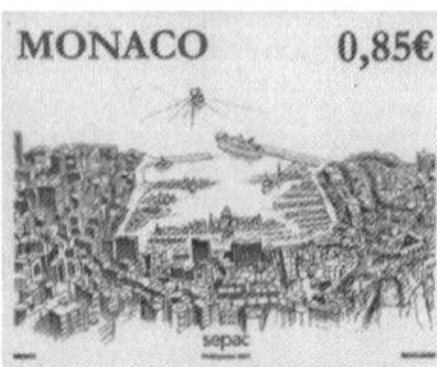

1085 Bay

2007. SEPAC (small European mail services).
2816 **1085** 85c. brown, blue and red 3·50 2·75

1086 Ringmaster

2007. 32nd International Circus Festival (January 2008), Monte Carlo.
2817 **1086** 60c. multicoloured 2·50 2·00

1087 Giacomo Puccini

2007. 140th Birth Anniv of Giacomo Puccini (composer).
2818 **1087** €1.40 blue and vermilion 6·00 4·50

1088 Church Building

2008. 50th Anniv of Reformed Church.
2819 **1088** 49c. brown and blue 2·10 1·70

1089 Flower Arrangement

2008. 41st International Flower Competition.
2820 **1089** 49c. multicoloured 2·10 1·70

1090 Church Building

2008. 125th Anniv of Consecration of St Charles Church.
2821 **1090** 54c. slate and vermilion 2·30 1·80

1091 *Quadriga* and Arc de Triomphe du Carrousel

2008. Bicentenary of Francois Bosio's Quadriga (statue of chariot drawn by four horses).
2822 **1091** 54c. brown, vermilion and carmine 2·30 1·80

1092 Andrea Palladio

2008. 500th Birth Anniv of Andrea Palladio (architect).
2823 **1092** 60c. multicoloured 2·50 2·00

1093 Monte Carlo Country Club

2008. Posters of 1932 by Raymond Gid. Multicoloured.

2824	70c. Type **1093**	3·00	2·30
2825	85c. Monte Carlo Beach Hotel	3·50	2·75
2826	€1.15 Monte Carlo Golf Club	4·75	3·75

1094 Hands enclosing Emblem

2008. Tenth Special Session of United Nations Environment Programme Forum.
2827 **1094** 85c. multicoloured 3·50 2·75

1095 Johannes Brahms

2008. 175th Birth Anniv of Johannes Brahms (composer and pianist).
2828 **1095** €1.15 green and vermilion 4·75 3·75

1096 Comet and Castle

2008. 250th Anniv of First Recorded Appearance of Halley's Comet.
2829 **1096** €1.57 multicoloured 6·75 5·25

1097 Leaves and Cones

2008. 20th Anniv of Marcel Kronenlein's Arboretum.
2830 **1097** €2.11 olive, ultramarine and vermilion 8·75 7·00

1098 'Monte Carlo, Pole d'Attraction' (1948)

2008. Poster by Louis Rue.
2831 **1098** €2.90 multicoloured 12·00 9·50

1099 Andre Massena

2008. 250th Birth Anniv of Andre Massena (Marshal of France).
2832 **1099** 86c. green and brown 3·50 2·75

1100 Bernadette Soubirous

2008. 150th Anniv of Apparition at Lourdes.
2833 **1100** €1.30 ultramarine and blue 5·50 4·25

1101 Henry Ford and Model T Ford Car

2008. Anniversaries.

2834	**1101**	€1.70 brown, green and vermilion	7·25	5·50
2835	-	€2.30 indigo, vermilion and ultramarine	9·75	7·50
2836	-	€4 brown and red	17·00	13·00

Designs:—€1.70 Type **1101** (centenary); €2.30 Apollo, Atlantis and *Mercury* spacecraft (50th anniv of NASA); €4 Alfred Nobel and nitroglycerine (175th birth anniv).

1102 Van Gogh (greyhound)

2008. International Dog Show, Monte Carlo.
2837 **1102** 88c. multicoloured 3·75 3·00

1103 Water Droplet

2008. Zaragoza 2008 International Water and Sustainable Development Exhibition.
2838 **1103** 65c. multicoloured 2·75 2·30

1104 Arms and Map

2008. Centenary of Cap d'Ail.
2839 **1104** 55c. black, brown and vermilion 2·30 1·90

1105 Heart enclosing Children and Flowers

2008. Mothers' Day.
2840 **1105** 55c. multicoloured 2·30 1·90

1106 Pagoda and Stylized Athletes

2008. Olympic Games, Beijing. Each vermilion and black.
2841 55c. Type **1106** 2·30 1·90
2842 85c. Athletes and games emblem 3·50 3·00

1107 Stendhal and Scenes from his Novels

2008. 225th Birth Anniv of Henri Beyle (Stendhal) (writer).
2843 **1107** €1.33 blue, lilac and vermilion 5·75 4·75

1108 Boris Pasternak and Scene from *Dr. Zhivago*

2008. 50th Anniv of Boris Pasternak's Nobel Prize for Literature.
2844 **1108** €2.18 vermilion and green 9·25 7·75

1109 Plants and Monaco

2008. 75th Anniv of Jardin Exotique (garden created by Prince Albert I).
2845 **1109** 50c. olive, purple and vermilion 2·30 1·80

1110 Globe circled by Mail

2008. Europa. The Letter.
2846 55c. brown, orange and vermilion 2·50 1·90
2847 65c. light brown, brown and vermilion 3·00 2·30
Designs:—55c. Type **1110**; 65c. Symbols of transport.

1111 Magician

2008. Magic Stars Festival, Monte-Carlo.
2848 **1111** 72c. multicoloured 3·50 2·75

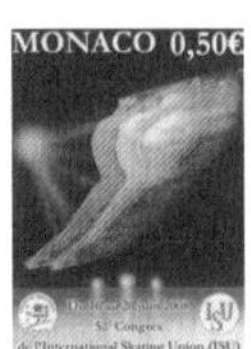

1112 Skater

2008. International Skating Union Congress.
2849 **1112** 50c. multicoloured 2·30 1·80

1113 *Gypaetus barbatus* (Bearded Vulture), Emblem and *Hieraaetus fasciatus* (Bonelli's Eagle)

2008. Prince Albert II Foundation.
2850 **1113** 88c. multicoloured 4·25 3·25

1114 Face, Hand and Colours

2008. 48th International Television Festival.
2851 **1114** €2.80 multicoloured 12·50 9·75

1115 School Children

2008. International Co-operation.
2852 65c. black and vermilion 3·00 2·30
2853 €1 agate and vermilion 4·50 3·50
2854 €1.25 blue and vermilion 5·75 4·50
2855 €1.70 green and vermilion 7·75 6·00
Designs:—65c. Type **1115** (campaign for education); €1 Health worker (health—Monegasque Red Cross); €1.25 Women (campaign against poverty); €1.70 Oasis and desert dwellers (campaign against desertification).

1116 Honore II Pistole (1648) and Monegasque Euro

2008. Monaco Numismatique 2008 Exhibition.
2856 **1116** 65c. multicoloured 3·00 2·30

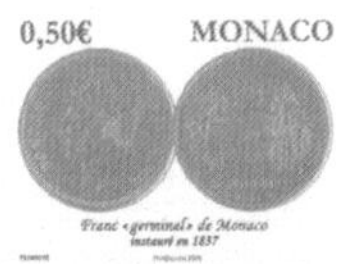

1117 Franc 'Germinal', 1837

2008. Coins. Multicoloured.
2857 50c. Type **1117** 2·40 1·80
2858 55c. Franc, 1943 2·75 1·90
2859 72c. Franc 'Rainier III', 1950 3·50 2·75
2860 €1.25 Franc 'Rainier III', 1960 6·00 4·50
2861 €1.64 Euro coins, 1999 8·00 5·75
2862 €1.72 Euro coins, 2006 8·25 6·00

1118 Schonbrunn Palace

2008. WIPA 2008 International Stamp Exhibition, Vienna.
2863 **1118** 65c. multicoloured 3·00 2·30

1119 Order

2008. 150th Anniv of Order of St Charles
2864 **1119** €1.50 multicoloured 7·25 5·25

1120 Sleigh and Globe

2008. Christmas.
2865 **1120** 55c. multicoloured 2·75 1·90

1121 Symbols of Festival

2008. 33rd International Circus Festival.
2866 **1121** 85c. multicoloured 4·50 3·50

1122 Prince Albert I

2008. International Polar Year. Multicoloured.
2867 85c. Type **1122** 4·50 3·50
2868 85c. Flag of Monaco (41×41 mm) 4·50 3·50
2869 85c. Prince Albert II 4·50 3·50

1123 Robert Peary

2008. Centenary of Robert Peary's Expedition to North Pole. Multicoloured.
2870 87c. Type **1123** 4·75 3·50
2871 87c. USA flag and North Pole (41×41 mm) 4·75 3·50
2872 87c. Matthew Henson and *Theodore Roosevelt* (expedition ship) 4·75 3·50

1124 Railway and Road Emergency Vehicle

2009. Centenary of Monaco Firefighters. Multicoloured.
2873 50c. Type **1124** 2·50 2·00
2874 72c. Emergency vehicle, 1909 4·00 3·00
2875 87c. Long ladder emergency vehicle 4·75 3·50

1125 Rose Garden

2009. 25th Anniv of Princess Grace Rose Garden.
2876 **1125** €1.25 multicoloured 6·50 5·00

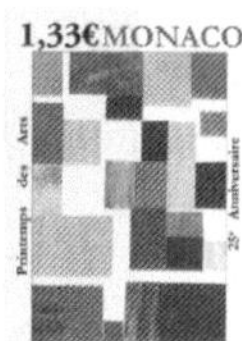

1126 Abstract

2009. 25th Anniv of Spring Arts Festival.
2877 **1126** €1.33 multicoloured 7·00 5·50

1127 Louis Bleriot and *Bleriot XI*

2009. Centenary of First Flight over English Channel.
2878 **1127** 87c. multicoloured 4·75 3·50

1128 Felix Mendelssohn

2009. Birth Bicentenary of Jakob Ludwig Felix Mendelssohn Bartholdy (composer).
2879 **1128** €1.50 indigo and olive 7·75 6·00

1129 Joan of Arc

2009. Centenary of Beatification of Joan of Arc.
2880 **1129** €2.22 scarlet, black and green 11·50 9·00

1130 Stamps and Building

2009. MonacoPhil 2009 International Stamp Exhibition.
2881 **1130** 56c. multicoloured 3·00 2·40

1131 Chihuahua and Cavalier King Charles Spaniel

2009. International Dog Show, Monte Carlo.
2882 **1131** 72c. multicoloured 4·00 3·00

1132 Blue-point Birman

2009. Second International Cat Show.
2883 **1132** 88c. multicoloured 5·00 4·00

1133 Palms and Map

2009. World Conference of Order of Academic Palms Association Members.
2884 **1133** 88c. violet, brown and scarlet 5·00 4·00

1134 Barbie

2009. 50th Anniv of Barbie Doll.
2885 **1134** 88c. multicoloured 5·00 4·00

1135 Flowers

2009. 42nd International Flower Exhibition.
2886 **1135** 89c. multicoloured 5·00 4·00

1136 Fencer and Arms

2009. Centenary of Monaco Fencing and Handgun Club.
2887 **1136** 55c. black, scarlet and lemon 3·00 2·40

1137 Race Winner and Map of Italy

2009. Centenary of Tour of Italy (Giro) Cycle Race.
2888 **1137** 70c. multicoloured 3·75 3·00

1138 Arthur Conan Doyle and Outline of Sherlock Holmes (character)

2009. 150th Birth Anniv of Arthur Conan Doyle (writer).
2889 **1138** 85c. purple, scarlet and vermilion 4·75 3·75

1139 Edgar Allen Poe and Death

2009. Birth Bicentenary of Edgar Allen Poe (writer).
2890 **1139** €1.70 green and scarlet 9·25 7·50

1140 Arms

2009. Booklet Stamp. Self-adhesive.
2891 **1140** (70c.) multicoloured 3·75 3·00

No. 2891 was issued in single sided booklets of ten stamps for use on mail up to 20g. within Zone 1 (EU and Switzerland).

1141 Louis Notari and Script

2009. Centenary of Louis Notari Library.
2892 **1141** 51c. scarlet vermilion and bright violet 2·75 2·20

1142 Early and Modern Race Cars

2009. Centenary of First Formula I Grand Prix.
2893 **1142** 70c. multicoloured 3·75 3·00

1143 Flags of Members

2009. 60th Anniv of Monaco's Membership of UNESCO.
2894 **1143** €1.70 multicoloured 9·25 7·50

1144 Louis Braille

2009. Birth Bicentenary of Louis Braille (inventor of Braille writing for the blind).
2895 **1144** €3.80 indigo, scarlet and bistre 21·00 17·00

1145 Orchestra

2009. 50th Anniv of Princes's Palace Summer Concerts.
2896 **1145** 51c. bright violet and black 2·75 2·20

1146 Francesco Maria Grimaldi

2009. Europa. Astronomy.
2897 56c. deep brown, deep blue and scarlet 3·00 2·40
2898 70c. deep brown, turquoise blue and scarlet 3·75 3·00
Designs:—56c. Type **1146**; 70c. Galileo.

1147 Dancer

2009. Ballet. Multicoloured.
2899 73c. Type **1147** (Ballet de Monte-Carlo) 4·25 3·25
2900 89c. Early dancers and audience (centenary of Ballets Russe) 5·00 4·00
2901 €1.35 Modern dancers (centenary of Ballets Russe) 7·50 6·00

1148 Georges Seurat

2009. 150th Birth Anniv of Georges Seurat (artist)
2902 **1148** 73c. multicoloured 4·25 3·25

1149 Pope Innocent III and Francis of Assisi

2009. 800th Anniv of Franciscan Order.
2903 **1149** 90c. new blue and black 5·00 4·00

1150 John Calvin

2009. 500th Birth Anniv of John Calvin (religious reformer).
2904 **1150** €1.67 black, scarlet and pale orange 9·25 7·50

1151 'Waves'

2009. 49th International Television Festival.
2905 **1151** €1.60 multicoloured 8·75 7·00

1152 Niccolo Machiavelli

2009. 30th Anniv of Dante Alighieri Society (for the promulgation of Italian language and culture).
2906 70c. slate grey, scarlet and orange-brown 3·75 3·00
2907 85c. orange, scarlet and yellow-brown 4·75 3·75
2908 €1.30 new blue, scarlet and bright orange-brown 7·25 5·75
Designs:—70c. Type **1152**; 85c. Giovanni Boccaccio; €1.30 Francesco Petrarca.

1153 Cornucopia

2009. Postcard, Coin and Stamp Exhibition.
2909 **1153** 51c. multicoloured 2·75 2·20

1154 Emblem and Young People

2009. Centenary of Youth Hostels.
2910 **1154** 90c. multicoloured 5·00 4·00

1155 *Tuiga*

2009. Centenary of Tuiga (racing yacht).
2911 **1155** 70c. multicoloured 3·75 3·00

1156 Cyclist

2009. Start of Tour de France Cycle Race in Monaco.
2912 **1156** 56c. multicoloured 3·00 2·40

1157 Pig as Magician

2009. Magic Stars Festival.
2913 **1157** 73c. multicoloured 4·25 3·25

1158 Place de la Marie

2009. SEPAC (small European mail services).
2914 **1158** 85c. multicoloured 4·75 3·75

1159 Big Ben

2009. 150th Anniv of Big Ben Clock, Palace of Westminster.
2915 **1159** €1 black, lemon and scarlet-vermilion 5·50 4·50

1160 Symbols of Christmas

2009. Christmas.
2916 **1160** 56c. new blue, light green and scarlet-vermilion 3·25 2·75

1161 Inscr 'Bengal' (name–Junglewhisper Elia)

2009. International Cat Show, 2010, Rainer III Auditorium.
2917 **1161** 56c. multicoloured 3·25 2·75

1162 Ayrton Senna

2009. 50th Birth Anniv of Ayrton Senna da Silva (racing driver).
2918 **1162** 73c. purple-brown, green and scarlet-vermilion 4·25 3·25

No. 2919 and Type **1163** are left for Birth Centenary of Jean Anouilth, not yet received.

1164 Auguste Rodin and *Le Baiser* (sculpture)

2009. 170th (2010) Birth Anniv of Auguste Rodin (sculptor).
2920 **1164** 85c. blue-black and scarlet-vermilion 4·75 3·75

1165 Grace Kelly receiving Oscar for Best Actress, 1955

2009. 80th Birth Anniv of Grace Kelly (actress and Princess Grace of Monaco).
2921 **1165** 89c. black and scarlet-vermilion 5·00 4·00

1166 Gustav Mahler

2009. 150th (2010) Birth Anniv of Gustav Mahler (composer).
2922 **1166** 90c. deep dull purple and new blue 5·00 4·00

1167 Skier

2009. Winter Olympic Games, Vancouver.
2923 90c. turquoise-green, scarlet-vermilion and deep blue 5·00 4·00
2924 90c. deep blue, scarlet-vermilion and dull orange 5·00 4·00
Designs:—Type **1167**; 2924 Snowboarder.

1168 *Monte Carlo vu de Roquebrune*

2009. 170th (2010) Birth Anniv of Oscar Claude Monet (Claude Monet) (artist).
2925 **1168** €1.30 multicoloured 7·25 5·75

1169 USA 1868 1c. (Z grill) Stamp and Association Emblem

2009. 2009 ASCAT Grand Prix to William H. Gross (for complete 19th-century USA collection).
2926 **1169** €1.35 multicoloured 7·50 6·00

1170 *La Naissance de Venus* (William Bougureau)

2009. Art.
2927 **1170** €1.60 multicoloured 8·75 7·00

1171 Anton Chekov and Scenes from *Three Sisters, The Cherry Orchard* and *The Seagull*

2009. 150th (2010) Birth Anniv of Anton Pavlovich Chekhov (dramatist).
2928 **1171** €1.67 indigo, brown-olive and scarlet-vermilion 9·25 7·50

1172 Rally Race Car

2009. 120th Anniv of Automobile Club de Monaco. Sheet 123×94 mm containing T **1172** and similar horiz design. Multicoloured.
MS2929 €1.30 Type **1172**; €1.70 Formula I race car 17·00 15·00

1173 Prince Albert II

2009. MonacoPhil 2009 International Stamp Exhibition. Sheet 120×100 mm.
MS2930 **1173** €4 black and scarlet-vermilion 23·00 22·00
The margins of No. **MS**2930 were printed in multicoloured offset.

1174 Big Top and Performers

2009. 34th International Circus Festival.
2931 **1174** 70c. multicoloured 3·75 3·00

1175 Crystal Blue Velvet (Australian shepherd dog)

2010. International Dog Show, Monte Carlo
2932 **1175** 51c. multicoloured 2·75 2·20

1176 Scenes from *Seven Samurai*

2010. Birth Centenary of Akira Kurosawa (film director, producer, screenwriter and editor)
2933 **1176** 51c. blackish purple and greenish yellow 2·75 2·20

1177 Players

2010. Centenary of First Five Nations Rugby Championship
2934 **1177** 70c. multicoloured 3·75 3·00

1178 Firebird

2010. 43rd International Flower Exhibition
2935 **1178** 70c. multicoloured 3·75 3·00

1179 Centre Court

2010. Monte-Carlo Rolex Masters Tennis Tournament
2936 **1179** 85c. multicoloured 4·75 3·75

1180 Albert II

2010. Expo 2010, Shanghai. Sheet 114×95 mm
MS2937 **1180** €1 multicoloured 5·75 5·50

1181 Player and Ball

2010. World Cup Football Championships, South Africa. Multicoloured.
2938 89c. Type **1181** 5·00 4·00
2939 89c. Player wearing red 5·00 4·00
Nos. 2938/9 were printed, *se-tenant*, each pair forming a composite design of the South African flag, stadium, two players and ball.

1182 Prince Albert I

2010. Centenary of Oceanographic Museum. Multicoloured.
MS2940 51c. Type **1182**; 56c. *Ursus maritimus* (Polar Bear); 73c. *Pterapogon kauderni* (Banggai Cardinalfish) (horiz); 90c. Hands and Starfish (horiz) 16·00 15·00

1183 Comte de Thann

2010. Former Grimaldi Family Fiefdoms. Multicoloured.
MS2941 €1×4, Type **1183**; Barony of Altkirch; Comte de Rosemont; Comte de Ferrette 23·00 22·00

1184 *Pinna nobilis*

2010. Larvotto Submarine Reserve
2942 **1184** 2c. multicoloured 85 65

1185 Mother Teresa carrying Child

2010. Birth Centenary of Mother Teresa (founder of Missionaries of Charity)
2943 **1185** multicoloured 9·25 7·50

1186 *Lilium martagon* (inscr 'Lis martagon')

2010. Mercantour National Park
2944 **1186** €2 multicoloured 10·00 8·25

1187 Children and Books

2010. Europa. Multicoloured.
2945 56c. Type **1187** 3·00 2·40
2946 70c. Boy reading, open book and pages 3·75 3·00

1188 Anniversary Emblem

2010. 15th Anniv of United Nations AIDS Programme
2947 **1188** 89c. multicoloured 5·00 4·00

1189 Tower Bridge

2010. London 2010 Festival of Stamps. London 2010 International Stamp Exhibition
2948 **1189** €1.30 scarlet vermilion and indigo 7·25 5·75

1190 Emblem

2010. 50th International Television Festival
2949 **1190** €2.80 multicoloured 15·00 12·00

1191 Abbe Breuil, Prince Albert I, Institute Building and Grimaldi Caves

2010. Centenary of Institute of Human Paleontology, Paris
2950 56c. multcoloured 3·25 2·75

1192 Forum Building Façade

2010. Tenth Anniv of Grimaldi Forum
2951 **1192** 75c. multicoloured 4·25 3·25

1193 Singapore Skyline and Athletes

2010. Youth Olympic Games, Singapore
2952 **1193** 87c. multicoloured 5·00 4·00

1194 *Vigilante* (police launch)

2010. 50th Anniv of Maritime and Airport Police Division
2953 **1194** 53c. multicoloured 3·00 2·40

1195 Nicolas Appert

2010. Bicentenary of Canning. Nicolas Appert (French chef and discoverer of method of conserving food by enclosing in hermetically sealed containers) Commemoration
2954 **1195** 95c. brownish maroon and scarlet-vermilion 5·25 4·25

1196 Jean-Joseph Etienne Lenoir

2010. 150th Anniv of First Gas Engine. Jean-Joseph Etienne Lenoir (first to successfully develop an engine functioning in accordance with principle of internal combustion) Commemoration
2955 **1196** €1.75 brown-olive, brownish black and scarlet-vermilion 9·75 7·75

1197 'Little Africa' Garden

2010. 'Little Africa' Garden
2956 **1197** €2.30 multicoloured 12·50 10·00

1198 MC30E LSA

2010. First International Electrically Propelled Mail Flight
2957 **1198** 95c. multicoloured 5·25 4·25

1199 *Stylophora pistillata*

2010. 50th Anniv of Monaco Scientific Centre
2958 **1199** 58c. multicoloured 3·25 2·75

1200 Train in Station

2010. TER Monaco
2959 **1200** €1.35 black, scarlet-vermilion and ochre 7·50 6·00

1201 Anniversary Poster

2010. 25th Anniv of 'Magic Stars' Magic Festival
2960 **1201** €1.40 multicoloured 7·75 6·25

1202 Santa riding Reindeer

2010. Christmas
2961 **1202** 58c. multicoloured 3·25 2·75

1203 Building Façade

2010. Centenary of Albert I Lycee
2962 **1203** 75c. multicoloured 4·25 3·25

1204 2011 Poster

2010. 35th International Circus Festival
2963 **1204** 75c. multicoloured 4·25 3·25

1205 Monaco Castle and Constitution

2011. Centenary of Constitution
2964 **1205** 53c. multicoloured 3·00 2·40

1206 Egyptian Mau

2011. International Cat Show
2965 **1206** 87c. multicoloured 5·00 4·00

No. 2966 and Type **1207** are left for Birth Centenary of Fangio, not yet received

No. 2967 and Type **1208** are left for Indianapolis, not yet received

No. 2968 and Type **1209** are left for Centenary of Monte Carlo Rally, not yet received.

1210 Sea Floor

2011. 50th Anniv of Monaco in International Atomic Energy Agency (IAEA). 50th Anniv of AIEA's Marine Environment Laboratory
2969 **1210** 87c. multicoloured 5·00 4·00

1211 Symbols of Solar, Wind, Geothermal, Hydro and Biomass Power

2011. Renewable Energy
2970 **1211** €1.80 multicoloured 10·00 8·00

1212 Children and 'MISSION enfance 20 ans!'

2011. 20th Anniv of Mission Enfance Association (educational aid and assistance to children in need)
2971 **1212** 53c. multicoloured 3·00 2·40

1213 Labrador Retriever

2011. International Dog Show, Monte Carlo
2972 **1213** 53c. multicoloured 3·00 2·40

1214 Émile Antoine Bourdelle

2011. 150th Birth Anniversaries. Sculptors
2973 75c. black and scarlet-vermilion 4·25 3·25
2974 75c. chocolate and scarlet-vermilion 4·25 3·25
2975 95c. indigo and scarlet-vermilion 5·25 4·25
2976 95c. deep lilac and scarlet-vermilion 5·25 4·25

Designs:—75c. Type **1214**; 75c. Horse for 'Alvear' Monument (detail); 95c. Aristide Maillol; 95c. *La Nuit*.

1215 Irish Coast and Arms of Monaco and Ireland

2011. Visit of Prince Albert II to Ireland
2977 **1215** €1.40 multicoloured 7·75 6·25

1216 Match on Court

2011. Monte-Carlo Rolex Masters Tennis Tournament
2978 **1216** 75c. multicoloured 4·25 3·25

1217 Napoleon II as Child and as Young Man

2011. Birth Bicentenary of Napoléon François Joseph Charles Bonaparte (Napoléon II)
2979 **1217** €1 deep blue and brown 5·50 4·50

1218 Ocean Currents Class Bouquet

2011. 44th International Flower Exhibition

2980	**1218**	95c. multicoloured	5·25	4·25

1219 Big Ben, Houses of Parliament and GB Flag

2011. Royal Horticultural Society Chelsea Flower Show, London

2981	**1219**	€1.75 multicoloured	9·75	7·75

1220 Japanese Garden

2011. Japanese Garden of Monaco (designed by Yasuo Beppu, based on the principals of Zen)

2982	**1220**	€2.35 multicoloured	13·00	10·50

1221 Cathedral Façade

2011. Centenary of Consecration of Cathedral of Our Lady of the Immaculate Conception (Saint Nicholas Cathedral) (Monaco Cathedral)

2983	**1221**	58c. black and scarlet-vermilion	3·25	2·75

1222 Lions International Emblem

2011. 50th Anniv of Lions Club de Monaco

2984	**1222**	75c. multicoloured	4·25	3·25

1223 Saint-Rémy-de-Provence

2011. Former Grimaldi Family Fiefdoms. Multicoloured.

MS2985	€1.75 Type **1223**; €1.80 Les Baux-de-Provence	20·00	19·00

1224 *Aqulegia bertolonii*

2011. Mercantour National Park. Columbine

2986	**1224**	3c. multicoloured	85	65

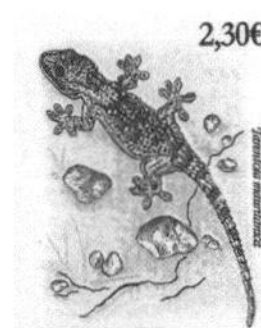

1225 *Tarentola mauritanica*

2011. Wall Gecko (*Tarentola mauritanica*)

2987	**1225**	€2.30 multicoloured	12·00	9·75

1226 Alpine Forest

2011. Europa. Forests. Multicoloured.

2988	58c. Type **1226**	3·25	2·75
2989	75c. Mediterranean forest	4·25	3·25

1227 Stop Pollution (Anaïs Aziadjonou)

2011. Children's Drawing Competition. Environment and Ecology in Monaco

2990	**1227**	53c. multicoloured	3·00	2·40

1228 Prince Albert II and Miss Charlene Wittstock

2011. Royal Wedding of Prince Albert II to Miss Charlene Wittstock

2991	**1228**	55c. black and light green	3·00	2·40
2992	**1228**	60c. black, vermilion and carmine-red	3·25	2·75
2993	**1228**	77c. black, reddish violet and bright violet	4·50	3·50
2994	**1228**	89c. black, new blue and bright ultramarine	5·00	4·00
2995	**1228**	€4.10 agate, carmine-red and gold	23·00	18·00

1229 Prince Albert II and Miss Charlene Wittstock

2011. Royal Wedding of Prince Albert II to Miss Charlene Wittstock. Sheet 110×120 mm

MS2996	**1229** €5 multicoloured	29·00	28·00

No. 2997 and Type **1230** are left for La Compagnie des Carabiniers du Prince de Monaco - The Palace Guard, not yet received.

1231 Lady Golfer

2011. Centenary of Monte Carlo Golf Club

2998	**1231**	60c. multicoloured	3·25	2·75

1233 Fish

2011. Pre-cancelled. No value expressed

3000	**1233**	(39c.) multicoloured	2·20	1·80

1234 Symbols of Exhibition

2011. Postcard, Coin and Stamp Exhibition, 2011

3001	**1234**	60c. multicoloured	3·25	2·75

1235 Monaco decorated with Stamps

2011. MonacoPhil 2011 International Stamp Exhibition

3002	**1235**	55c. multicoloured	3·00	2·40

See also No. **MS**3014.

1236 Symbols of Institute

2011. Centenary of Paris Institute of Oceanography

3003	**1236**	77c. indigo and turquoise-blue	4·50	3·50

1237 Monaco Landscape

2011. SEPAC (small European mail services)

3004	**1237**	75c. multicoloured	4·25	3·25

1238 Georges Méliès

2011. 150th Birth Anniv of Marie-Georges-Jean Méliès (Georges Méliès) (filmmaker)

3005	**1238**	€1.45 slate-lilac and yellow	8·00	6·50

1239 Man and Moon

2011. 50th Anniv of First Manned Space Flight

3006	**1239**	€2.78 dull ultramarine	15·00	12·50

1240 Franz Liszt

2011. Birth Bicentenary of Franz Liszt

3007	**1240**	€1 deep purple and greenish blue	5·50	4·50

1248 Théophile Gautier

2011. Birth Bicentenary of Théophile Gautier (writer and journalist)

3008	**1241**	€1.75 multicoloured	9·75	7·75

1242 Prince Antoine I

2011. 350th Birth Anniv of Prince Antoine I

3009	**1242**	€1.80 multicoloured	10·00	8·00

1243 Henri Troyat

2011. Birth Centenary of Henri Troyat (writer)

3010	**1243**	€2.40 multicoloured	13·00	10·50

1244 The Nativity

2011. Christmas

3011	**1244**	60c. multicoloured	3·25	2·75

1245 Anniversary Emblem

2011. 25th Telethon

3012	**1245**	60c. multicoloured	3·25	2·75

1246 Award

2011. Prince Albert II -ASCAT 2011 Philatelic Grand Prix Winner

3013	**1246**	78c. multicoloured	4·50	3·50

1247 Prince Albert II and Princess Charlene

2011. MonacoPhil 2011 International Stamp Exhibition (2nd issue). Sheet 100×120 mm

MS3014	**1247** €5 multicoloured	28·00	26·00

1248 Lion and Clown

2011. 36th International Circus Festival
3015 **1248** 77c. multicoloured 4·50 3·50

1249 Bouquet

2012. 45th International Flower Exhibition
3016 **1249** 55c. multicoloured 3·00 2·40

1250 Russian Blue

2012. International Cat Show
3017 **1250** 77c. multicoloured 4·50 3·50

1251 Saint Martin Gardens

2012. Saint Martin Gardens
3018 **1251** 89c. multicoloured 5·00 4·00

1252 *La Comedie*

2012. Frescoes of the Salle Garnier, Monte Carlo Opera. Multicoloured.
MS3019 €1.45×4, Type **1252**; *La Musique*; *La Danse*; *Le Chant et l'Eloquence* 32·00 31·00

1253 'Colley'

2012. International Dog Show, Monte Carlo
3020 **1253** 89c. multicoloured 5·00 4·00

1254 Tennis Court

2012. Monte-Carlo Rolex Masters Tennis Tournament
3021 **1254** 89c. multicoloured 5·00 4·00

1255 Louis XII of France and Lucien Grimaldi

2012. 500th Anniv of France's Recognition of Monaco's Independence and Sovereignty
3022 **1255** 55c. black and scarlet-vermilion 3·00 2·40

1256 Symbols of Theatre

2012. 25th Anniv of Florestan Theatrical Company
3023 **1256** 55c. multicoloured 3·00 2·40

1257 Club Members, 1912 and 2012

2012. Centenary of La Carabine de Monaco (Monaco Rifle Shooting Club)
3024 **1257** €1.35 vermilion, red-brown and deep violet-blue 7·50 6·00

1258 Emblem

2012. 75th Bazaar for L'Oeuvre De Soeur Marie (Work of Sister Marie) (association for the assistance of the elderly poor)
3025 **1258** 60c. multicoloured 3·25 2·75

1259 Race Car

2012. 70th Anniv of Monaco Grand Prix
3026 **1259** 77c. bright royal blue, scarlet-vermilion and deep brown 4·50 3·50

1260 Henri Farman Pusher Bi-plane

2012. Centenary of First Seaplane Competition
3027 **1260** €1.80 multicoloured 10·00 8·00

1261 *Tûranor PlanetSolar*

2012. Arrival of *Tûranor PlanetSolar* (largest solar-powered boat) in Monaco after Circumnavigating the Globe
3028 **1261** 77c. bright royal blue, deep brown and scarlet-vermilion 4·50 3·50

1262 Expo 2012

2012. Expo 2012, Yeosu, South Korea
3029 **1262** 78c. multicoloured 4·50 3·50

1263 Arms

2012. Coat of Arms
3030 **1263** (55c.) multicoloured 3·00 2·40

1264 'Chambre Louis XV' (bedroom)

2012. Europa. Visit Monaco. Rooms in Royal Palace. Multicoloured.
3031 60c. Type **1264** 3·25 2·75
3032 77c. Salon Mazarin 4·50 3·50

1265 Hands holding Emblem

2012. 75th Anniv of Rotary Club of Monaco
3033 **1265** 77c. multicoloured 4·50 3·50

1266 World Map, Water and Conference Emblem

2012. RIO+20 United Nations Conference on Sustainable Development, Rio de Janeiro, Brazil
3034 **1266** 78c. multicoloured 4·50 3·50

1267 Giant Antarctic Petrel

2012. Biodiversity. Multicoloured.
MS3035 €1×2, Type **1267**; Prince of Monaco Islands, Kerguelen Islands 11·00 10·50

1268 *Cabaret au Bord de la Riviére* (detail) (Jan Breughel)

2012. Exhibition of Philatelic Collection of HSH Prince Albert II. Sheet 100×120 mm
MS3036 **1268** €3 multicoloured 17·00 16·00

1269 Matignon Castle

2012. Former Grimaldi Family Fiefdoms. Visit of HSH Prince Albert II to Pays de Matignon
3037 **1269** €1.75 multicoloured 9·75 7·75

1270 Anniversary Emblem

2012. Centenary of IAAF - International Association of Athletics Federations
3038 **1270** 89c. gold and scarlet-vermilion 5·00 4·00

1271 Symbols of London and the Games

2012. Olympic Games, London
3039 **1271** €1.35 multicoloured 7·50 6·00

1272 Globe

2012. 30th Anniv of FICAC (World Federation of Consuls). World Congress, Monaco
3040 **1272** 55c. multicoloured 3·00 2·40

1273 Claude Debussy

2012. 150th Birth Anniv of Claude Debussy
3041 **1273** €1 black and scarlet-vermilion 5·50 4·50

1274 *Crucifixion* (Louis Brea)

2012. Religious Art - *Crucifixion* by Louis Brea
3042 **1274** €1.35 multicoloured 7·50 6·00

1275 *Lanius senator* (Woodchat Shrike)

2012. Centenary of LPO (League for the Protection of Birds)
3043 **1275** €1 multicoloured 5·50 4·50

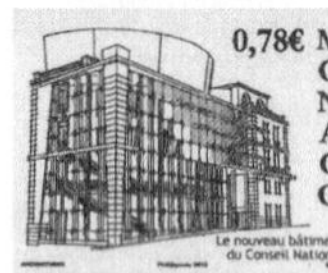

1276 Council Building

2012. New Building of Conseil National
3044 **1276** 78c. brown-purple and black 4·50 3·50

1277 Organ

2012. Grand Organ of Cathedral of Monaco
3045 **1277** €1.80 multicoloured 10·00 8·00

1278 Arms of State and Arms of Prince

2012. 400th Anniv of First Prince of Monaco, Honoré II
3046 **1278** €2.40 ultramarine, vermilion and scarlet-vermilion 13·00 10·50

1279 St Charles Church

2012. Centenary of Consecration of St. Charles' Church
3047 **1279** €1.45 black and scarlet-vermilion 8·00 6·50

1280 Auguste Lumière in Film Strip

2012. 150th Birth Anniv of Auguste Lumière (medical professional, photographer, inventor, chemist, scientist and maker of first film)
3048 **1280** €2.35 salmon, black and scarlet-vermilion 13·00 10·50

1281 Nefertiti

2012. Centenary of Discovery of Bust of Nefertiti
3049 **1281** €3.78 sepia, yellow-ochre and black 21·00 17·00

1282 Louise d'Aumont Mazarin

2012. Former Grimaldi Family Fiefdoms - Belfort. Timbres Passion, 2012. Multicoloured.
3050 55c. Type **1282** 3·00 2·40
3051 55c. Prince Honoré 3·00 2·40

1283 *The Nativity* (detail) (Giotto)

2012. Christmas
3052 **1283** 60c. multicoloured 3·25 2·75

1284 Tintin and Captain Haddock

2012. Publication of Third Volume of *Tintin* in Monegasque Language. *U Tesoru de Rakamu u Russu* (*Red Rackham's Treasure*)
3053 **1284** 77c. multicoloured 4·50 3·50

1285 Prince Albert II

2012. Prince Albert II

3054	**1285**	(56c.) new blue	3·00	2·40
3055		(63c.) bright emerald	3·25	2·75
3056		(80c.) bright rose-red	4·50	3·50
3057		(80c.) deep magenta	4·50	3·50
3058		(€1.05) black	5·50	4·50

1286 Blue

2012. Centre Speranza-Albert II (theraputic day care for Alzheimer's Disease sufferers)
3059 **1286** €1.35 multicoloured 7·50 6·00

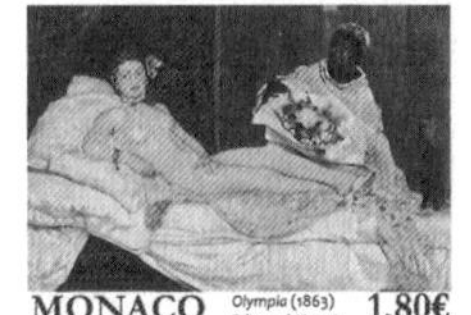

1287 *Olympia* (Edouard Manet)

2012. Paintings - The Nude in Art
3060 **1287** €1.80 multicoloured 10·00 8·00

1288 Elephant, Clown and Horses in Big Top

2013. 37th International Circus Festival
3061 **1288** 63c. multicoloured 3·50 2·75

1289 Pierre de Coubertin

2013. 50th Birth Anniv of Pierre de Coubertin
3062 **1289** €2.55 agate, brown-olive and scarlet-vermilion 14·00 11·00

1290 Turkish Angora Tortoiseshell

2013. International Cat Show
3063 **1290** 56c. multicoloured 3·25 2·75

1291 Rowers

2013. 125th Anniv of Société Nautique du Monaco
3064 **1291** 95c. multicoloured 5·25 4·25

1292 Bouquet

2013. 46th International Flower Exhibition
3065 **1292** €1.75 multicoloured 9·75 7·75

1293 Casino and Garden

2013. Terraces of Monte Carlo Casino
3066 **1293** 80c. multicoloured 4·50 3·50

1294 French Bulldog

2013. International Dog Show, Monte Carlo
3067 **1294** 80c. black, scarlet-vermilion and agate 4·50 3·50

1295 Serve

2013. Monte-Carlo Rolex Masters Tennis Tournament
3068 **1295** €1.05 multicoloured 5·75 4·50

1296 Children

2013. 50th Anniv of l'Amade Mondiale (World Association of Children's Friends)
3069 **1296** €1.55 multicoloured 8·50 6·75

1297 Henry Dunant

2013. 150th Anniv of Red Cross International
3070 **1297** €4.10 black and scarlet-vermilion 23·00 18·00

1298 Maserati 250F

2013. Classic Race Cars. Multicoloured.
3071 €1.05 Type **1298** 5·75 4·50
3072 €1.75 Tyrell P34 9·75 10·00

1299 Solar-Electric Waterbus

2013. Ecological Transportation. Clean Transport in Monaco. Multicoloured.
3073 €1.85 Type **1299** 10·00 8·25
3074 €1.85 Electric cycle 10·00 8·25

1300 Mosaic, Virgin of Mercy Chapel, Monaco-Ville (Ernesto Sprega)

2013. Bicentenary of Venerable Brotherhood of Mercy
3075 **1300** 80c. multicoloured 4·50 3·50

1301 Electric Post Van

2013. Europa. Postal Transport
3076 **1301** 63c. multicoloured 3·50 2·75

1302 Business People

2013. 50th Anniv of Junior Economic Chamber of Monaco
3077 **1302** 56c. multicoloured 3·25 2·75

1303 Arms and Castle

2013. Former Grimaldi Family Fiefdoms - Duchy of Valentinois
3078 **1303** €1.05 multicoloured 5·75 4·50

1304 Giuseppe Verdi and Scene from *La Traviata*

2013. Composers' Birth Bicentenaries
3079 €1.55 slate-black, bluish violet and scarlet-vermilion 8·50 6·75
3080 €1.85 new blue, scarlet-vermilion and gold 10·00 8·25

Design:—€1.55 Type **1304**; €1.85 Richard Wagner and images from *Der Ring des Nibelungen*.

1305 Scene from *Rite of Spring*

2013. Centenary of First Performance of *Rite of Spring* by Igor Stravinsky
3081 **1305** €2.55 multicoloured 14·50 11·50

1306 Monte-Carlo Harbour and UN Emblem

2013. 20th Anniv of Monaco's Membership of the United Nations
3082 **1306** 80c. multicoloured 4·50 3·50

1307 Emblems

2013. 15th World Festival of Amateur Theatre

3083	**1307**	63c. multicoloured	3·50	2·75

1308 *Larus michahellis* (Yellow-legged Gull)

2013. SEPAC (small European mail services)

3084	**1308**	80c. multicoloured	4·50	3·50

1309 *Otiorhynchus monoecirpis*

2013. *Otiorhynchus monoecirpis* (Monegasque Weevil). 'Beetles of Monaco and other Insects' Exhibition, Marcel Kroenlein Room, Exotic Garden, Monaco

3085	**1309**	€1 multicoloured	5·50	4·50

1310 Blacktip Shark

2013. Oceanographic Museum of Monaco - Sharks. World Oceans Day. Multicoloured.

MS3086 63c. Type **1310**; 63c. Tiger Shark; €1.05 Baleen Shark; €1.05 Great White Shark 19·00 18·00

1311 Monte-Carlo Casino

2013. 150th Anniv of SBM. Multicoloured.

MS3087 80c. Type **1311**; 80c. Buff background; €1.05 Multicoloured building, black background; €1.35 Floodlit 22·00 21·00

1312 Harbour, Stamps, Coins and Postcards

2013. Postcard Coin and Stamp Exhibition 2013

3088	**1312**	63c. multicoloured	3·50	2·75

1313 Emblem

2013. MonacoPhil 2013 International Stamp Exhibition

3089	**1313**	80c. multicoloured	4·50	3·50

See also No. **MS**3100.

1314 Roland Garros and Aircraft

2013. Centenary of First Non-Stop Flight across Mediterranean by Roland Garros

3090	**1314**	€1.35 multicoloured	7·50	6·00

1315 Pleasure Cruiser

2013. Yachts. Multicoloured.

3091	€1 Type **1315**	5·50	4·50
3092	€1.55 Sailing yacht	8·75	7·00

1316 Jules Richard

2013. 150th Birth Anniversaries

3093	€1 agate, new blue and scarlet-vermilion	5·50	4·50
3094	€1.85 slate-black and deep claret	10·00	8·25

Design:—€1 Type **1316** (marine scientist and director of Monaco Oceanographic Museum); €1.85 Charles Pathe and film reel.

1317 Crossword Puzzle

2013. Centenary of the Crossword Puzzle

3095	**1317**	€2.78 black, grey and scarlet-vermilion	15·00	12·50

1318 The Nativity

2013. Christmas

3096	**1318**	63c. multicoloured	3·50	2·75

1319 Prince Rainier, Prince Albert II and Venue

2013. Count Jacques Rogge - Winner of ASCAT 2013 Philatelic Grand Prix

3097	**1319**	95c. multicoloured	5·25	4·25

1320 Sunbeam Alpine

2013. History of Automobile Production. Multicoloured.

3098	95c. Type **1320**	5·25	4·25
3099	95c. ZIL 111V	5·25	4·25

1321 Prince Albert II

2013. MonacoPhil International Stamp Exhibition (2nd issue). Slate-grey and bright scarlet (a/c) or multicoloured (d).

MS3100 €1×4, Type **1321**; Prince Albert II, facing front; Prince Albert II, facing right; Crest 22·00 21·00

1322 Tiger

2014. 38th International Circus Festival

3101	**1322**	83c. multicoloured	5·00	4·00

2014. Grace Kelly Movies. Multicoloured.

3102	€1.38 'Une Fille de la Province' (*The Country Girl*)	8·50	6·75
3103	€2.40 'Le Crime était presque parfait' (*Dial M for Murder*)	15·00	12·00

1324 'British Shorthair'

2014. International Cat Show

3104	**1324**	61c. multicoloured	3·75	3·00

1325 Athletes

2014. Winter Olympic Games, Sochi

3105	**1325**	€1.78 multicoloured	11·00	8·75

1326 Trees and Court

2014. Monte-Carlo Rolex Masters Tennis Tournament

3106	**1326**	€1.10 multicoloured	7·00	5·50

1327 'Bull Terrier'

2014. International Dog Show, Monte Carlo

3107	**1327**	87c. multicoloured	5·50	4·50

1328 Modern Bouquet

2014. 47th International Flower Exhibition

3108	**1328**	€2.10 multicoloured	13·00	10·50

1329 Gilles Villeneuve

2014. Formula One Legends. Multicoloured.

3109	66c. Type **1329**	4·25	3·25
3110	66c. Racing (52×30 mm)	4·25	3·25
3111	83c. Ayrton Senna	5·25	4·25
3112	83c. Racing (52×30 mm)	5·25	4·25

1330 Princess Grace

2014. 50th Anniv of Princess Grace of Monaco Foundation

3113	**1330**	66c. multicoloured	4·25	3·25

1331 '30'

2014. 30th Anniv of Monte-Carlo Spring Arts Festival

3114	**1331**	€1.20 multicoloured	7·75	6·25

1332 *Diane au Bain* (Carlo Maratti) (sketch)

2014. Paintings - The Nude in Art

3115	€1.65 sepia	9·00	7·25
3116	€1.65 multicoloured	9·00	7·25

Designs:—Type **1332**; *Diane au Bain* (Pietro Antonio de' Pietri) (painting after Maratti).

1333 Aircraft and Route

2014. Centenary of First Monaco Air Rally

3117	**1333**	€2.65 multicoloured	15·00	5·75

1334 Tram and Modern Coach

2014. Evolution of Monaco's Transport - Buses

3118	**1334**	59c. multicoloured	3·50	2·75

1335 Marsupilami Family

2014. *Marsupilami* (comic book and video game)

3119	**1335**	83c. multicoloured	5·00	4·00

1336 Mandolin

2014. Europa. Musical Instruments

3120	**1336**	83c. multicoloured	5·00	4·00

1337 House of Princes of Monaco at Vic-sur-Cère

2014. Former Grimaldi Family Fiefdoms. Visit of HSH Prince Albert II and Princess Charlene to Carlades Area of Cantal. Multicoloured.

MS3121 €1.65 Rocher de Carlat; €2.10 Type **1337** 21·00 20·00

1338 Flags and Players

2014. World Cup Football Championships, Brazil

3122 **1338** 95c. multicoloured 5·25 4·25

1339 Honoré IV

2014. Bicentenary of Treaty of Paris

3123 **1339** €2.10 multicoloured 13·00 10·50

1340 Black Tip Shark

2014. Oceanographic Museum of Monaco - Sharks. Multicoloured.

MS3124 66c. Type **1340**; €1.10 Hammerhead Shark (horiz); €1.65 Grey Reef Shark 20·00 19·00

1341 Bouquet of Roses

2014. 30th Anniv of Princess Grace Rose Garden

3125 **1341** 66c. multicoloured 4·25 3·25

1342 Protea Blooms

2014. SEPAC (small European mail services)

3126 **1342** 83c. multicoloured 5·25 4·25

1343 Club House and Yachts

2014. Yacht Club of Monaco's New Club House

3127 **1343** 83c. multicoloured 5·25 4·25

1344 Red Scorpion Fish

2014. Pre-cancelled. No value expressed

3128 **1344** (40c.) multicoloured 2·50 2·00

1345 Tree, Leaves and Pod

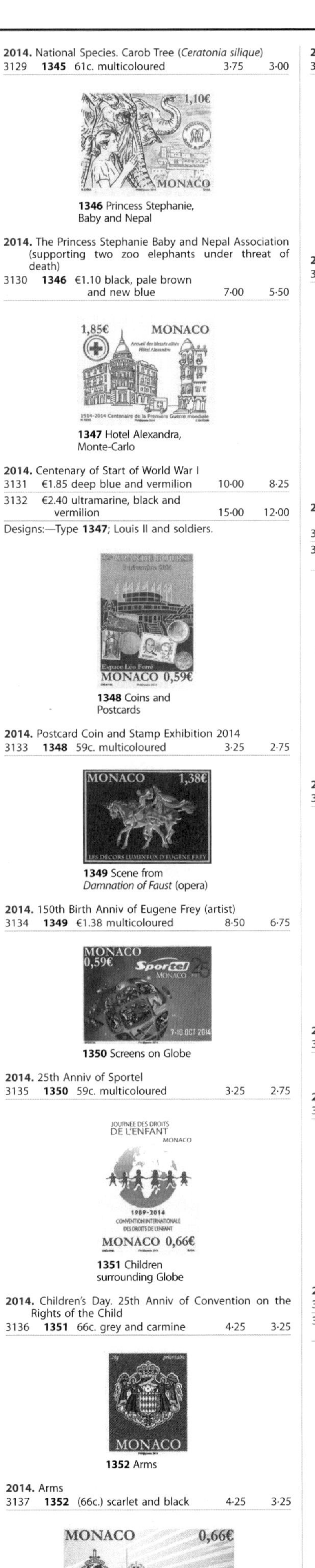

2014. National Species. Carob Tree (*Ceratonia silique*)

3129 **1345** 61c. multicoloured 3·75 3·00

1346 Princess Stephanie, Baby and Nepal

2014. The Princess Stephanie Baby and Nepal Association (supporting two zoo elephants under threat of death)

3130 **1346** €1.10 black, pale brown and new blue 7·00 5·50

1347 Hotel Alexandra, Monte-Carlo

2014. Centenary of Start of World War I

3131 €1.85 deep blue and vermilion 10·00 8·25

3132 €2.40 ultramarine, black and vermilion 15·00 12·00

Designs:—Type **1347**; Louis II and soldiers.

1348 Coins and Postcards

2014. Postcard Coin and Stamp Exhibition 2014

3133 **1348** 59c. multicoloured 3·25 2·75

1349 Scene from *Damnation of Faust* (opera)

2014. 150th Birth Anniv of Eugene Frey (artist)

3134 **1349** €1.38 multicoloured 8·50 6·75

1350 Screens on Globe

2014. 25th Anniv of Sportel

3135 **1350** 59c. multicoloured 3·25 2·75

1351 Children surrounding Globe

2014. Children's Day. 25th Anniv of Convention on the Rights of the Child

3136 **1351** 66c. grey and carmine 4·25 3·25

1352 Arms

2014. Arms

3137 **1352** (66c.) scarlet and black 4·25 3·25

1353 Emblem

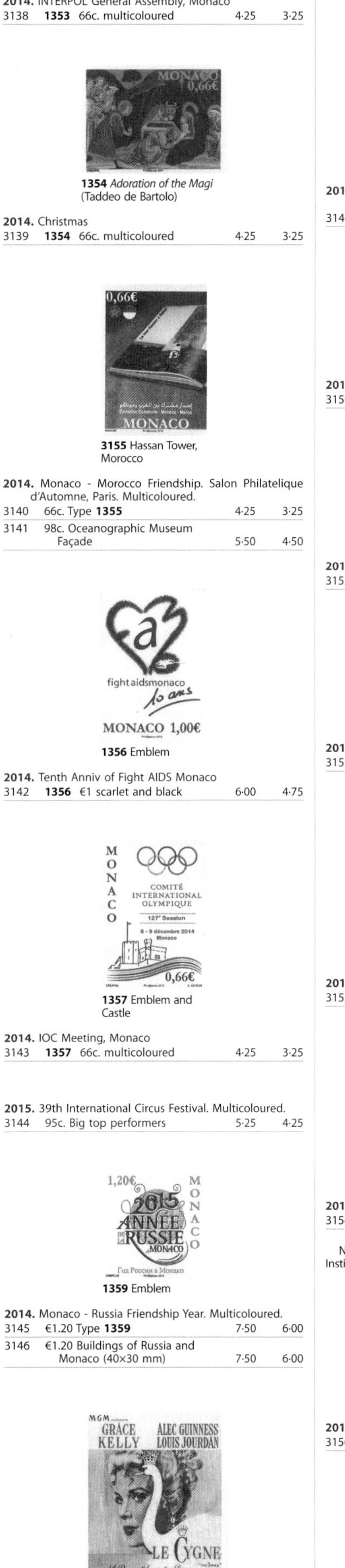

2014. INTERPOL General Assembly, Monaco

3138 **1353** 66c. multicoloured 4·25 3·25

1354 *Adoration of the Magi* (Taddeo de Bartolo)

2014. Christmas

3139 **1354** 66c. multicoloured 4·25 3·25

3155 Hassan Tower, Morocco

2014. Monaco - Morocco Friendship. Salon Philatelique d'Automne, Paris. Multicoloured.

3140 66c. Type **1355** 4·25 3·25

3141 98c. Oceanographic Museum Façade 5·50 4·50

1356 Emblem

2014. Tenth Anniv of Fight AIDS Monaco

3142 **1356** €1 scarlet and black 6·00 4·75

1357 Emblem and Castle

2014. IOC Meeting, Monaco

3143 **1357** 66c. multicoloured 4·25 3·25

2015. 39th International Circus Festival. Multicoloured.

3144 95c. Big top performers 5·25 4·25

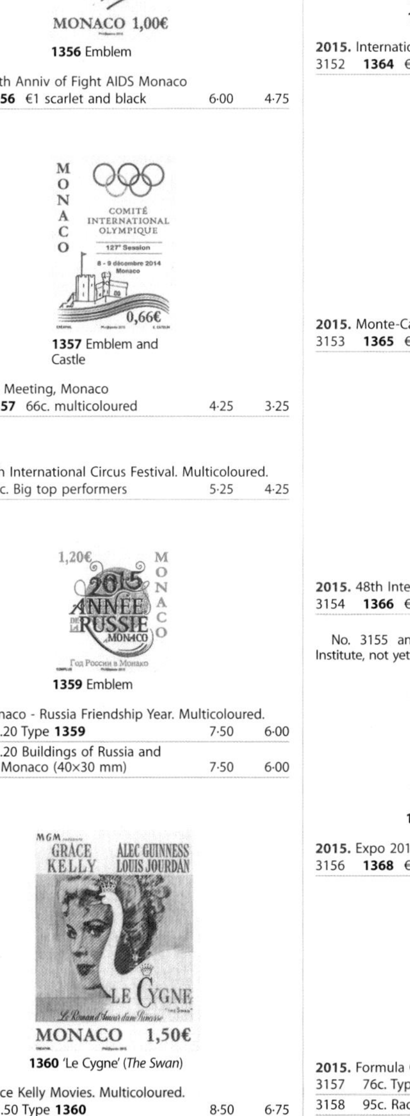

1359 Emblem

2014. Monaco - Russia Friendship Year. Multicoloured.

3145 €1.20 Type **1359** 7·50 6·00

3146 €1.20 Buildings of Russia and Monaco (40×30 mm) 7·50 6·00

1360 'Le Cygne' (*The Swan*)

2015. Grace Kelly Movies. Multicoloured.

3147 €1.50 Type **1360** 8·50 6·75

3148 €2 'La Main au Collet' (*To Catch a Thief*) 12·50 10·00

1361 Neptune Grass and Fish

2015. National Species. Neptune Grass (*Posidonia oceanica*)

3149 **1361** 68c. multicoloured 4·50 3·50

1362 Children

2015. Centenary of Kiwanis (children's charity)

3150 **1362** 95c. multicoloured 5·25 4·25

1363 Flower Borders

2015. Princess Antoinette Park

3151 **1363** €1.45 multicoloured 8·25 6·50

1364 German Pointer

2015. International Dog Show, Monte Carlo

3152 **1364** €1.05 multicoloured 5·75 4·50

1365 Spectators and Court

2015. Monte-Carlo Rolex Masters Tennis Tournament

3153 **1365** €1.25 multicoloured 7·00 5·50

1366 Yellow Bouquet

2015. 48th International Flower Exhibition

3154 **1366** €1.45 multicoloured 8·25 6·50

No. 3155 and Type **1367** are left for Oceanography Institute, not yet received.

1368 Pavilion and Emblem

2015. Expo 2012, Milan

3156 **1368** €1 multicoloured 5·50 5·00

1369 Michele Alboreto

2015. Formula One Legends. Multicoloured.

3157 76c. Type **1369** 3·00 2·50

3158 95c. Racing (52×30 mm) 5·00 4·50

3159 95c. Graham Hill 5·00 4·50

3160 €1.50 Racing (52×30 mm) 7·25 5·25

POSTAGE DUE STAMPS

D3

1906

D29a	**D3**	1c. green	55	65
D30	**D3**	5c. green	65	1·00
D31	**D3**	10c. red	65	1·00
D32	**D3**	10c. brown	£600	£180
D33	**D3**	15c. purple on cream	3·25	2·20
D113	**D3**	20c. bistre on buff	50	50
D34	**D3**	30c. blue	65	1·00
D114	**D3**	40c. mauve	60	50
D35	**D3**	50c. brown on buff	6·50	6·25
D115	**D3**	50c. green	50	50
D116	**D3**	60c. black	50	85
D117	**D3**	60c. mauve	31·00	42·00
D118	**D3**	1f. purple on cream	60	50
D119	**D3**	2f. red	1·40	1·80
D120	**D3**	3f. red	1·40	1·80
D121	**D3**	5f. blue	1·70	1·90

D4

1910

D36	**D4**	1c. olive	35	55
D37	**D4**	10c. lilac	75	1·10
D38	**D4**	30c. bistre	£275	£275

1919. Surch.

D39	**D4**	20c. on 10c. lilac	5·50	11·00
D40	**D4**	40c. on 30c. bistre	6·50	13·00

D18

1925

D106	**D18**	1c. olive	50	70
D107	**D18**	10c. violet	50	70
D108	**D18**	30c. bistre	70	1·20
D109	**D18**	60c. red	70	1·60
D110	**D18**	1f. blue	£130	£130
D111	**D18**	2f. red	£130	£130

1925. Surch 1 franc a percevoir.

D112	**D3**	1f. on 50c. brown on buff	1·20	1·30

D64 D65

1946

D327	**D64**	10c. black	20	25
D328	**D64**	30c. violet	20	25
D329	**D64**	50c. blue	20	25
D330	**D64**	1f. green	20	35
D331	**D64**	2f. brown	20	35
D332	**D64**	3f. mauve	25	40
D333	**D64**	4f. red	70	85
D334	**D65**	5f. brown	70	85
D335	**D65**	10f. blue	95	85
D336	**D65**	20f. turquoise	1·20	1·30
D337	**D65**	50f. red and mauve	80·00	70·00
D338	**D65**	100f. red and green	18·00	18·00

D99 Buddicom Locomotive, 1843

1953

D478	-	1f. red and green	20	20
D479	-	1f. green and red	20	20
D480	-	2f. turquoise and blue	20	20
D481	-	2f. blue and turquoise	20	20
D482	**D99**	3f. lake and green	20	30
D483	-	3f. green and lake	20	30
D484	-	4f. slate and brown	20	30
D485	-	4f. brown and slate	20	30
D486	-	5f. violet and blue	70	70
D487	-	5f. blue and violet	70	70
D488	-	10f. indigo and blue	14·50	14·50
D489	-	10f. blue and indigo	14·50	14·50
D490	-	20f. violet and blue	9·00	9·00
D491	-	20f. blue and violet	9·00	9·00
D492	-	50f. brown and red	18·00	18·00
D493	-	50f. red and brown	18·00	18·00
D494	-	100f. green and purple	31·00	31·00
D495	-	100f. purple and green	31·00	31·00

Triangular Designs:—Nos. D478, Pigeons released from mobile loft; D479, Sikorsky S-51 helicopter; D480, Brig; D481, *United States* (liner); D483, Streamlined steam locomotive; D484, Santos-Dumont's monoplane No. 20 *Demoiselle*; D485, de Havilland Comet 1 airliner; D486, Old motor car; D487, Sabre racing-car; D488, Leonardo da Vinci's drawing of *flying machine*; D489, Postal rocket; D490, Mail balloon, Paris, 1870; D491, Airship LZ-127 *Graf Zeppelin*; D492, Postilion; D493, Motorcycle messenger; D494, Mail coach; D495, Railway mail van.

D140 18th-century Felucca

1960

D698	**D140**	1c. brown, green & bl	20	20
D699	-	2c. sepia, blue & grn	20	20
D700	-	5c. purple, blk & turq	25	25
D701	-	10c. black, green & bl	25	40
D702	-	20c. purple, grn & bl	1·30	1·30
D703	-	30c. brown, bl & grn	2·40	2·40
D704	-	50c. blue, brn & myrtle	3·00	3·00
D705	-	1f. brown, myrtle & bl	3·50	3·50

Designs:—2c. Paddle-steamer *La Palmaria*; 5c. Arrival of first railway train at Monaco; 10c. 15th/16th-century armed messenger; 20c. 18th-century postman; 30c. *Charles III* (paddle-steamer); 50c. 17th-century courier; 1f. Mail coach (19th-century).

D393 Prince's Seal

1980

D1426	**D393**	5c. red and brown	15	20
D1427	**D393**	10c. orange and red	15	20
D1428	**D393**	15c. violet and red	25	20
D1429	**D393**	20c. green and red	30	30
D1430	**D393**	30c. blue and red	40	35
D1431	**D393**	40c. bistre and red	50	40
D1432	**D393**	50c. violet and red	65	55
D1433	**D393**	1f. grey and blue	1·10	1·00
D1434	**D393**	2f. brown and black	1·30	1·10
D1435	**D393**	3f. red and green	3·00	2·50
D1436	**D393**	4f. green and red	4·00	3·50
D1437	**D393**	5f. brown and mauve	4·50	4·00

D492 Coat of Arms

1985

D1712	**D492**	5c. multicoloured	15	15
D1713	**D492**	10c. multicoloured	20	15
D1714	**D492**	15c. multicoloured	20	15
D1715	**D492**	20c. multicoloured	25	20
D1716	**D492**	30c. multicoloured	25	20
D1717	**D492**	40c. multicoloured	30	30
D1718	**D492**	50c. multicoloured	30	30
D1719	**D492**	1f. multicoloured	65	55
D1720	**D492**	2f. multicoloured	1·30	1·10
D1721	**D492**	3f. multicoloured	2·40	2·10
D1722	**D492**	4f. multicoloured	3·00	2·50
D1723	**D492**	5f. multicoloured	3·25	2·75

STANLEY GIBBONS
LONDON 1856

DETECTAMARK

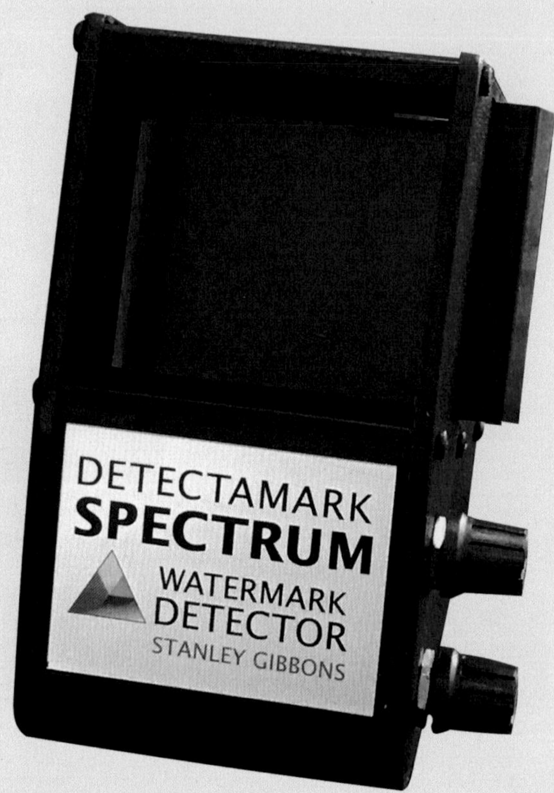

The Stanley Gibbons Detectamark Spectrum makes it even easier to discover the hidden rarities in your collection. It is simplicity itself to use and the multiple colour settings and adjustable light source, unique to the Detectamark Spectrum, provide additional help when identifying more difficult watermarks.

The Detectamark is constructed from durable lightweight plastic and operates with batteries.

R2570 £149

To order, call **01425 472 363**
email **orders@stanleygibbons.com**
or visit **stanleygibbons.com**

MONGOLIA

A republic in Central Asia between China and Russia, independent since 1921.

1924. 100 cents = 1 dollar (Chinese).
1926. 100 mung = 1 tugrik.

1 Eldev-Otchir Symbol

1924. Inscr in black.

1A	1	1c. brown, pink and grey on bistre	18·00	19·00
2B	1	2c. brown, blue and red on brown	16·00	8·75
3A	1	5c. grey, red and yellow	60·00	38·00
4A	1	10c. blue and brown on blue	30·00	25·00
5B	1	20c. grey, blue and white on blue	42·00	28·00
6A	1	50c. red and orange on pink	60·00	38·00
7A	1	$1 bistre, red and white on yellow	85·00	65·00

Stamps vary in size according to the face value.

2 Soyombo Symbol

1926. Fiscal stamps as T **2** optd POSTAGE in frame in English and Mongolian.

8A	2	1c. blue	18·00	19·00
9A	2	2c. buff	24·00	16·00
10A	2	5c. purple	24·00	15·00
11A	2	10c. green	24·00	25·00
12A	2	20c. brown	36·00	31·00
13A	2	50c. brown and yellow	£250	£225
14B	2	$1 brown and pink	£900	£550
15A	2	$5 red and olive	£900	

Stamps vary in size according to the face value.

4 State Emblem: Soyombo Symbol

1926. New Currency.

16	4	5m. black and lilac	18·00	19·00
17	4	20m. black and blue	30·00	38·00

5 State Emblem: Soyombo Symbol

1926

18	5	1m. black and yellow	4·75	5·00
19	5	2m. black and brown	6·00	5·00
20	5	5m. black and lilac (A)	7·25	6·25
28	5	5m. black and lilac (B)	26·00	20·00
21	5	10m. black and blue	6·00	3·25
30	5	20m. black and blue	48·00	44·00
22	5	25m. black and green	12·00	6·25
23	5	40m. black and yellow	17·00	7·50
24	5	50m. black and brown	24·00	10·00
25	5	1t. black, green and brown	48·00	19·00
26	5	3t. black, yellow and red	£110	75·00
27	5	5t. black, red and purple	£140	95·00

In (A) the Mongolian numerals are in the upper and in (B) in the lower value tablets.
These stamps vary in size according to the face value.

(6)

1930. Surch as T **6**.

32	10m. on 1m. black & yellow	48·00	50·00
33	20m. on 2m. black & brown	65·00	65·00
34	25m. on 40m. black & yellow	80·00	75·00

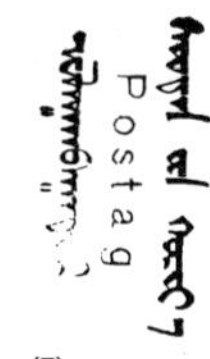

(7)

1931. Optd with T **7**

35A	2	1c. blue	36·00	19·00
36A	2	2c. buff	42·00	15·00
37A	2	5c. purple	55·00	15·00
38A	2	10c. green	48·00	15·00
39A	2	20c. brown	70·00	19·00
40A	2	50c. brown and yellow	£190	£190
41A	2	$1 brown and pink	£300	£250

1931. Surch Postage and value in menge.

43	5m. on 5c. purple	60·00	25·00
44	10m. on 10c. green	85·00	44·00
45	20m. on 20c. brown	95·00	55·00

9 Govt Building, Ulan Bator

11 Sukhe Bator

12 Lake and Mountain Scenery

1932

46	-	1m. brown	4·75	2·50
47	-	2m. red	4·75	2·50
48	-	5m. blue	3·00	1·30
49	9	10m. green	3·00	1·30
50	-	15m. brown	3·00	1·30
51	-	20m. red	3·00	1·30
52	-	25m. violet	3·50	1·30
53	11	40m. black	3·50	1·90
54	-	50m. blue	3·00	1·30
55	12	1t. green	4·25	1·90
56	-	3t. violet	8·50	3·25
57	-	5t. brown	29·00	19·00
58	-	10t. blue	60·00	31·00

Designs:—As Type **9**: 1m. Weavers; 5m. Machinist. As Type **11**: 2m. Telegraphist; 15m. Revolutionary soldier carrying flag; 20m. Mongols learning Latin alphabet; 25m. Soldier; 50m. Sukhe Bator's monument. As Type **12**: 3t. Sheep-shearing; 5t. Camel caravan; 10t. Lassoing wild horses (after painting by Sampilon).

13 Mongol Man

14 Camel Caravan

1943. Network background in similar colour to stamps.

59	13	5m. green	12·00	8·75
60	-	10m. blue	18·00	9·50
61	-	15m. red	20·00	12·50
62	14	20m. brown	30·00	23·00
63	-	25m. brown	30·00	28·00
64	-	30m. red	36·00	31·00
65	-	45m. purple	48·00	44·00
66	-	60m. green	85·00	75·00

Designs:—Vert: 10m. Mongol woman; 15m. Soldier; 30m. Arms of the Republic; 45m. Portrait of Sukhe Bator, dated 1894–1923. Horiz: 25m. Secondary school; 60m. Pastoral scene.

15 Marshal Kharloin Choibalsan

1945. 50th Birthday of Choibalsan.

67	15	1t. black	95·00	£110

16 Choibalsan and Sukhe Bator

17 Victory Medal

1946. 25th Anniv of Independence. Surch as T **16/17**

68	-	30m. bistre	9·00	9·50
69	16	50m. purple	11·00	11·50
70	-	60m. brown	12·00	12·50
71	-	60m. black	22·00	23·00
72	17	80m. brown	20·00	21·00
73	-	1t. blue	24·00	25·00
74	-	2t. brown	36·00	38·00

Designs:—Vert: (21½×32 mm): 30m. Choibalsan, aged four. As Type **17**: 60m. (No. 71), Choibalsan when young man; 1t. 25th Anniversary Medal; 2t. Sukhe Bator. Horiz: As Type **16**: 60m. (No. 70), Choibalsan University.

17a Flags of Communist Bloc

1951. Struggle for Peace.

75	17a	1t. multicoloured	18·00	19·00

17b Lenin (after P. Vasilev)

1951. Honouring Lenin.

76	17b	3t. multicoloured	36·00	38·00

18 State Shop

19 Sukhe Bator

1951. 30th Anniv of Independence.

77	-	15m. green on azure	7·25	7·50
78	18	20m. orange	7·25	7·50
79	-	20m. multicoloured	8·50	8·75
80	-	25m. blue on azure	8·50	8·75
81	-	30m. multicoloured	9·50	10·00
82	-	40m. violet on pink	11·00	11·50
83	-	50m. brown on azure	20·00	21·00
84	-	60m. black on pink	19·00	20·00
85	19	2t. brown	36·00	38·00

Designs:—Horiz: (As Type **18**): 15m. Alti Hotel; 40m. State Theatre, Ulan Bator; 50m. Pedagogical Institute. 55½×26 mm: 25m. Choibalsan University. Vert: (As Type **19**): 20m. (No. 79); 30m. Arms and flag; 60m. Sukhe Bator Monument.

20 Schoolchildren

1952. Culture.

86	-	5m. brown on pink	7·25	7·50
87	20	10m. blue on pink	7·75	8·25

Design:—5m. New houses.

21 Choibalsan in National Costume

22 Choibalsan and Farm Worker

1953. First Death Anniv of Marshal Choibalsan. As T **21/22**.

88	21	15m. blue	6·00	5·00
89	22	15m. green	6·00	5·00
90	21	20m. green	12·00	11·50
91	22	20m. sepia	6·00	5·00
92	-	20m. blue	6·00	5·00
93	-	30m. sepia	9·00	7·50
94	-	50m. brown	9·00	7·50
95	-	1t. red	9·50	8·75
96	-	1t. purple	9·50	8·75
97	-	2t. red	14·50	12·50
98	-	3t. purple	22·00	19·00
99	-	5t. red	42·00	38·00

Designs:—As Type **21**: 1t. (96); 2t. Choibalsan in uniform. 33×48 mm: 3, 5t. Busts of Choibalsan and Sukhe Bator. 33×46 mm: 50m., 1t. (95), Choibalsan and young pioneer. 48×33 mm: 20m. (92); 30m. Choibalsan and factory hand.

23 Arms of the Republic

1954

100	23	10m. red	12·00	7·50
101	23	20m. red	24·00	10·00
102	23	30m. red	12·00	8·75
103	23	40m. red	14·50	15·00
104	23	60m. red	12·00	12·50

23a Lenin

1955. 85th Birth Anniv of Lenin.

105	23a	2t. blue	9·50	4·50

23b Flags of the Communist Bloc

1955. Struggle for Peace.

106	23b	60m. multicoloured	3·00	1·90

24 Sukhe Bator and Choibalsan

1955

107	24	30m. green	1·20	1·30
108	-	30m. blue	1·80	1·90
109	-	30m. red	1·20	1·30
110	-	40m. purple	3·50	5·00
111	-	50m. brown	3·50	5·00
112	-	1t. multicoloured	7·25	7·50

Designs:—Horiz: 30m. blue, Lake Khobsogol; 50m. Choibalsan University. Vert: 30m. red, Lenin Statue, Ulan Bator; 40m. Sukhe Bator and dog; 1t. Arms and flag of the Republic.

24a Steam Train linking Ulan Bator and Moscow

1956. Mongol-Soviet Friendship. Multicoloured.

113	1t. Type **24a**	42·00	25·00

114		2t. Flags of Mongolia and Russia	9·00	6·25

25 Arms of the Republic

1956

115	**25**	20m. brown	1·20	1·30
116	**25**	30m. brown	1·40	1·50
117	**25**	40m. blue	1·90	2·00
118	**25**	60m. green	2·40	2·50
119	**25**	1t. red	3·75	4·00

26 Hunter and Golden Eagle **27** Arms

27a Wrestlers

1956. 35th Anniv of Independence.

120	**26**	30m. brown	60·00	31·00
121	**27**	30m. blue	9·00	7·50
122	**27a**	60m. green	30·00	31·00
123	-	60m. orange	30·00	31·00

Design:—As Type **26**: 60m. (No. 123), Children. Also inscr 'xxxv'.

28

1958. With or without gum.

124	**28**	20m. red	3·50	2·50

29

1958. 13th Mongol People's Revolutionary Party Congress. With or without gum.

125	**29**	30m. red and salmon	6·00	5·00

1958. As T **27a** but without "xxxv". With or without gum.

126		50m. brown on pink	11·00	10·00

30 Dove and Globe

1958. Fourth Congress of International Women's Federation, Vienna. With or without gum.

127	**30**	60m. blue	7·25	5·75

31 Ibex **32** Yak

1958. Mongolian Animals. As T **31/2**.

128	-	30m. pale blue	24·00	5·00
129	-	30m. turquoise	24·00	5·00
130	**31**	30m. green	6·00	3·75
131	**31**	30m. turquoise	6·00	3·75
132	**32**	60m. bistre	6·00	3·75
133	**32**	60m. orange	6·00	2·50
134	-	1t. blue	9·00	5·75
135	-	1t. light blue	7·25	3·75
136	-	1t. red	9·00	6·25
137	-	1t. red	7·25	3·75

Designs:—Vert: 30m. (Nos. 128/9), Dalmatian pelicans. Horiz: 1t. (Nos. 134/5), Yak, facing right; 1t. (Nos. 136/7), Bactrian camels.

33 Goat

1958. Mongolian Animals.

138	**33**	5m. sepia and yellow	25	15
139	-	10m. sepia and green	25	15
140	-	15m. sepia and lilac	50	15
141	-	20m. sepia and blue	50	15
142	-	25m. sepia and red	65	15
143	-	30m. purple and mauve	80	15
144	**33**	40m. green	80	25
145	-	50m. brown and salmon	90	40
146	-	60m. blue	1·60	40
147	-	1t. bistre and yellow	2·75	80

Animals:—10, 30m. Ram; 15, 60m. Stallion; 20, 50m. Bull; 25m., 1t. Bactrian camel.

34 "Tulaga"

1959

148	**34**	1t. multicoloured	7·75	5·75

35 Taming a Wild Horse

1959. Mongolian Sports. Centres and inscriptions multicoloured: frame colours given below.

149	**35**	5m. yellow and orange	25	15
150	-	10m. purple	25	15
151	-	15m. yellow and green	25	15
152	-	20m. lake and red	40	15
153	-	25m. blue	65	25
154	-	30m. yellow, green & turq	90	25
155	-	70m. red and yellow	1·20	40
156	-	80m. purple	1·80	90

Designs:—10m. Wrestlers; 15m. Introducing young rider; 20m. Archer; 25m. Galloping horseman; 30m. Archery contest; 70m. Hunting a wild horse; 80m. Proclaiming a champion.

36 Child Musician

1959. Mongolian Youth Festival (1st issue).

157	**36**	5m. purple and blue	25	15
158	-	10m. brown and green	40	15
159	-	20m. green and purple	40	15
160	-	25m. blue and green	65	25
161	-	40m. violet and myrtle	2·00	90

Designs:—Vert: 10m. Young wrestlers; 20m. Youth on horse; 25m. Artists in National Costume. Horiz: 40m. Festival parade.

37 Festival Badge

1959. Mongolian Youth Festival (2nd issue).

162	**37**	30m. purple and blue	65	40

38 Kalmuck Script

1959. Mongolists' Congress. Designs as T **38** incorporating "MONGOL" in various scripts.

163	-	30m. multicoloured	10·00	9·75
164	-	40m. red, blue and yellow	10·00	9·75
165	**38**	50m. multicoloured	13·50	13·00
166	-	60m. red, blue and yellow	22·00	21·00
167	-	1t. yellow, turquoise & orge	27·00	26·00

Scripts (29½×42½ mm): 30m. Stylized Ulghur; 40m. Soyombo; 60m. Square (Pagspa). (21½×31 mm): 1t. Cyrillic.

39 Military Monument

1959. 20th Anniv of Battle of Khalka River.

168		40m. red, brown and yellow	95	25
169	**39**	50m. multicoloured	95	25

Design:—40m. Mounted horseman with flag (emblem), inscr 'AUGUST 1959 HALHIN GOL'.

40 Herdswoman and Lamb

1959. Second Meeting of Rural Economy Co-operatives.

170	**40**	30m. green	6·75	6·50

41 Sable

1959. Mongolian Fauna.

171	**41**	5m. purple, yellow and blue	25	15
172	-	10m. multicoloured	1·40	15
173	-	15m. black, green and red	70	15
174	-	20m. purple, blue and red	70	15
175	-	30m. myrtle, purple & grn	80	25
176	-	50m. black, blue and green	1·80	55
177	-	1t. black, green and red	2·75	70

Animals:—Horiz: (58×21 mm): 10m. Common pheasants; 20m. European otter; 50m. Saiga; 1t. Siberian musk deer. As Type **41**: 15m. Muskrat; 30m. Argali.

42 *Lunik 3* in Flight

1959. Launching of "Lunik 3" Rocket.

178	**42**	30m. yellow and violet	1·40	1·40
179	-	50m. red, green and blue	2·20	2·20

Design:—Horiz: 50m. Trajectory of *Lunik 3* around the Moon.

43 Motherhood Badge

44 "Flower" Emblem

1960. International Women's Day.

180	**43**	40m. bistre and blue	1·20	25
181	**44**	50m. yellow, green and blue	1·80	70

45 Lenin

1960. 90th Birth Anniv of Lenin.

182	**45**	40m. red	95	25
183	**45**	50m. violet	1·40	55

46 Larkspur

1960. Flowers.

184	**46**	5m. blue, green and bistre	15	15
185	-	10m. red, green and orange	15	15
186	-	15m. violet, green and bistre	25	15
187	-	20m. yellow, green and olive	40	15
188	-	30m. violet, green & emer	55	25
189	-	40m. orange, green & violet	1·10	35
190	-	50m. violet, green and blue	1·50	55
191	-	1t. mauve, green & lt green	2·20	1·40

Flowers:—10m. Tulip; 15m. Jacob's ladder; 20m. Asiatic globe flower; 30m. Clustered bellflower; 40m. Grass of Parnassus; 50m. Meadow cranesbill; 1t. *Begonia vansiana*.

47 Horse-jumping

1960. Olympic Games. Inscr "ROMA 1960" or "ROMA MCMLX". Centres in greenish grey.

192	**47**	5m. red, black & turquoise	15	15
193	-	10m. violet and yellow	15	15
194	-	15m. turquoise, black & red	25	15
195	-	20m. red and blue	40	20
196	-	30m. ochre, black and green	70	25
197	-	50m. blue and turquoise	80	40
198	-	70m. green, black and violet	1·10	55
199	-	1t. mauve and green	1·60	70

Designs:—Diamond Shaped: 10m. Running; 20m. Wrestling; 50m. Gymnastics; 1t. Throwing the discus. As Type **47**: 15m. Diving; 30m. Hurdling; 70m. High-jumping.

48

1960. Red Cross.

200	**48**	20m. red, yellow and blue	1·40	70

49 Newspapers

1960. 40th Anniv of Mongolian Newspaper "Unen" ("Truth").

201	**49**	20m. buff, green and red	55	25
202	**49**	30m. red, yellow and green	70	40

50 Hoopoe

1961. Mongolian Songbirds.

203	-	5m. mauve, black and green	95	25
204	**50**	10m. red, black and green	1·10	25
205	-	15m. yellow, black & green	1·40	40
206	-	20m. green, black and bistre	1·60	40
207	-	50m. blue, black and red	2·30	80
208	-	70m. yellow, black & mauve	3·00	1·10
209	-	1t. mauve, orange and black	3·50	1·50

Birds:—As Type **50**: 15m. Golden oriole; 20m. Black-billed capercaillie. Inverted triangulars: 5m. Rose-coloured starling; 50m. Eastern broad-billed roller; 70m. Tibetan sandgrouse; 1t. Mandarin.

51 Foundry Worker

1961. 15th Anniv of World Federation of Trade Unions.

210	**51**	30m. red and black	55	15
211	-	50m. red and violet	70	25

Design:—Horiz: 50m. Hemispheres.

52 Patrice Lumumba

1961. Patrice Lumumba (Congolese politician) Commemoration.

212	**52**	30m. brown	3·50	2·00
213	**52**	50m. purple	4·00	2·75

53 Bridge

1961. 40th Anniv of Independence (1st issue). Mongolian Modernization.

214	**53**	5m. green	15	15
215	-	10m. blue	20	15
216	-	15m. red	25	15
217	-	20m. brown	25	15
218	-	30m. blue	40	25
219	-	50m. green	55	40
220	-	1t. violet	95	55

Designs:—10m. Shoe-maker; 15m. Store at Ulan Bator; 30m. Government Building, Ulan Bator; 50m. Machinist; 1t. Ancient and modern houses. (59×20½ mm): 20m. Choibalsan University.

See also Nos. 225/**MS**232a, 233/**MS**241c, **MS**241d, 242/8 and 249/56.

54 Yuri Gagarin with Capsule

1961. World's First Manned Space Flight. Multicoloured

221	20m. Type **54**	70	25
222	30m. Gagarin and globe (horiz)	1·10	55
223	50m. Gagarin in capsule making parachute descent	1·40	80
224	1t. Globe and Gagarin (horiz)	2·00	1·10

55 Postman with Reindeer

1961. 40th Anniv of Independence (2nd issue). Mongolian Postal Service.

225	**55**	5m. red, brown and blue (postage)	25	15
226	-	15m. violet, brown & bistre	35	15
227	-	20m. blue, black and green	40	20
228	-	25m. violet, bistre and green	40	25
229	-	30m. green, black & lav	6·75	1·40
MS229a		115×90 mm. 5, 10, 15 and 50m. in designs of Nos. 226/9 but new colours	9·50	7·50
230		10m. orange, black and green (air)	55	15
231		50m. black, pink and green	1·10	25
232		1t. multicoloured	2·00	55
MS232a		115×90 mm. 20, 25, 30m., 1t. in designs of Nos. 225, 230/2 but new colours	5·50	5·50

Designs:—Postman with—10m. Horses; 15m. Camels; 20m. Yaks; 25m. *Sukhe Bator* (lake steamer); 30m. Diesel mail train; 50m. Ilyushin Il-14M mail plane over map; 1t. Postal emblem.

56 Rams

1961. 40th Anniv of Independence (3rd issue). Animal Husbandry.

233	**56**	5m. black, red and blue	15	15
234	-	10m. black, green & purple	20	15
235	-	15m. black, red and green	25	15
236	-	20m. sepia, blue and brown	40	15
237	-	25m. black, yellow & green	40	20
238	-	30m. black, red and violet	55	25
239	-	40m. black, green and red	70	25
240	-	50m. black, brown and blue	95	40
241	-	1t. black, violet and olive	1·40	95
MS241a		105×150 mm. 5, 15 and 40m. in designs of Nos. 241, 237 and 234 but new colours	4·00	2·00
MS241b		105×150 mm. 25, 50m. and 1t. in designs of Nos. 236, 239 and 240, but new colours	5·50	2·75
MS241c		105×150 mm. 25, 50m. and 1t. in designs of Nos. 235, 239 and 233 but new colours	6·75	3·50

Designs: 10m. Oxen; 15m. Camels; 20m. Pigs and poultry; 25m. Angora goats; 30m. Mongolian horses; 40m. Ewes; 50m. Cows; 1t. Combine-harvester.

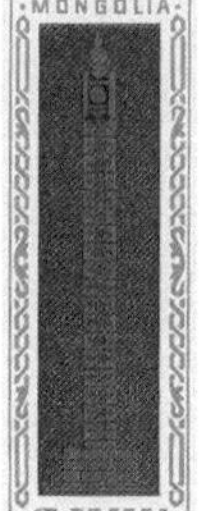

56a

1961. 40th Anniv of Independence (4th issue). Sheet 118×128 mm. Imperf.

MS241d	2t. gold, red and blue (pair separated by label)	11·00	11·00

57 Children Wrestling

1961. 40th Anniv of Independence (5th issue). Mongolian Sports.

242	**57**	5m. multicoloured	25	15
243	-	10m. sepia, red and green	25	15
244	-	15m. purple blue and yellow	25	15
245	-	20m. red, black and green	1·40	40
246	-	30m. purple, green & lav	55	55
247	-	50m. indigo, orange & blue	70	55
248	-	1t. purple, blue and grey	1·10	80

Designs:—10m. Horse-riding; 15m. Children on camel and pony; 20m. Falconry; 30m. Skiing; 50m. Archery; 1t. Dancing.

58 Young Mongol

1961. 40th Anniv of Independence (6th issue). Mongolian Culture.

249	**58**	5m. purple and green	15	15
250	-	10m. blue and red	20	15
251	-	15m. brown and blue	25	15
252	-	20m. green and violet	35	15
253	-	30m. red and blue	40	20
254	-	50m. violet and bistre	80	25
255	-	70m. green and mauve	95	55
256	-	1t. red and blue	1·80	1·40

Designs:—Horiz: 10m. Mongol chief; 70m. Orchestra; 1t. Gymnast. Vert: 15m. Sukhe Bator Monument; 20m. Young singer; 30m. Young dancer; 50m. Dombra-player.

59 Mongol Arms

1961. Arms multicoloured; inscr in blue; background colours given.

257	**59**	5m. salmon	25	15
258	**59**	10m. lilac	20	15
259	**59**	15m. brown	25	15
260	**59**	20m. turquoise	35	20
261	**59**	30m. ochre	40	25
262	**59**	50m. mauve	55	40
263	**59**	70m. olive	70	55
264	**59**	1t. orange	80	70

60 Congress Emblem

1961. Fifth World Federation of Trade Unions Congress, Moscow.

265	**60**	30m. red, yellow and blue	40	25
266	**60**	50m. red, yellow and sepia	55	40

61 Dove, Map and Globe

1962. Admission of Mongolia to U.N.O.

267	**61**	10m. multicoloured	15	15
268	-	30m. multicoloured	40	25
269	-	50m. multicoloured	80	45
270	-	60m. multicoloured	95	55
271	-	70m. multicoloured	1·10	70

Designs:—30m. UN Emblem and Mongol Arms; 50m. UN and Mongol flags; 60m. UN Headquarters and Mongolian Parliament building; 70m. UN and Mongol flags, and Assembly.

62 Football, Globe and Flags

1962. World Cup Football Championship, Chile. Multicoloured.

272	10m. Type **62**	15	15
273	30m. Footballers, globe and ball	40	25
274	50m. Footballers playing in stadium	55	40
275	60m. Goalkeeper saving goal	70	55
276	70m. Stadium	95	55

63 D. Natsagdorj

1962. Third Congress of Mongolian Writers.

277	**63**	30m. brown	40	20
278	**63**	50m. green	55	25

64 Torch and Handclasp

1962. Afro-Asian People's Solidarity.

279	**64**	20m. multicoloured	25	20
280	**64**	30m. multicoloured	40	25

65 Flags of Mongolia and USSR

1962. Mongol-Soviet Friendship.

281	**65**	30m. multicoloured	40	25
282	**65**	50m. multicoloured	70	40

1962. Malaria Eradication. Nos. 184/91 optd with Campaign emblem and **LUTTE CONTRE LE PALUDISME**.

283	**46**	5m.	55	25
284	-	10m.	60	35
285	-	15m.	70	40
286	-	20m.	70	40

287	-	30m.	80	55
288	-	40m.	1·00	80
289	-	50m.	1·40	95
290	-	1t.	2·75	1·70

67 Victory Banner

1962. 800th Birth Anniv of Genghis Khan.

291	**67**	20m. multicoloured	11·00	11·00
292	-	30m. multicoloured	20·00	20·00
293	-	50m. black, brown and red	13·50	13·50
294	-	60m. buff, blue and brown	27·00	27·00

Designs:—30m. Engraved lacquer tablets; 50m. Obelisk; 60m. Genghis Khan.

68 Eurasian Perch

1962. Fish. Multicoloured.

295	5m. Type **68**	25	15
296	10m. Burbot	35	15
297	15m. Arctic grayling	40	15
298	20m. Short-spined seascorpion	70	25
299	30m. Estuarine zander	95	40
300	50m. Siberian sturgeon	1·40	55
301	70m. Waleck's dace	2·00	95
302	1t.50 Yellow-winged bullhead	3·50	1·50

69 Sukhe Bator

1963. 70th Birth Anniv of Sukhe Bator.

303	**69**	30m. blue	25	15
304	**69**	60m. lake	70	40

70 Dog Laika and *Sputnik 2*

1963. Space Flights. Multicoloured.

305	5m. Type **70**	15	15
306	15m. Rocket blasting off	25	15
307	25m. *Lunik 2* (1959)	55	25
308	70m. Nikolaev and Popovich	1·10	55
309	1t. Rocket *Mars 1* (1962)	1·40	80

Sizes:—As Type **70**: 70m., 1t. Vert: (21×70 mm): 15m., 25m.

71 Children packing Red Cross Parcels

1963. Red Cross Centenary Multicoloured.

310	20m. Type **71**	25	15
311	30m. Blood transfusion	40	25
312	50m. Doctor treating child	70	40
313	60m. Ambulance at street accident	80	55
314	1t.30 Centenary emblem	1·20	70

72 Karl Marx

1963. 145th Birth Anniv of Karl Marx.

315	**72**	30m. blue	40	25
316	**72**	60m. lake	55	40

73 Woman

1963. Fifth World Congress of Democratic Women, Moscow.

317	**73**	30m. multicoloured	40	25

74 Peacock

1963. Mongolian Butterflies. Multicoloured.

318	5m. Type **74**	80	15
319	10m. Brimstone	95	20
320	15m. Small tortoiseshell	1·20	25
321	20m. Apollo	1·40	40
322	30m. Swallowtail	2·00	55
323	60m. Damon blue	3·00	95
324	1t. Poplar admiral	4·00	1·20

75 Globe and Scales of Justice

1963. 15th Anniv of Declaration of Human Rights.

325	**75**	30m. red, blue and brown	40	30
326	**75**	60m. black, blue and yellow	55	45

76 Shaggy Ink Cap

1964. Fungi. Multicoloured.

327	5m. Type **76**	70	30
328	10m. Woolly milk cap	95	45
329	15m. Field mushroom	1·10	50
330	20m. Milk-white russula	1·40	60
331	30m. Granulated boletus	2·00	85
332	50m. *Lactarius scrobiculatus*	2·40	1·20
333	70m. Saffron milk cap	3·50	1·50
334	1t. Variegated boletus	5·75	2·20

77 Lenin when a Young Man

1964. 60th Anniv of London Bolshevik (Communist) Party.

335	**77**	30m. red and brown	80	45
336	**77**	50m. ultramarine and blue	1·10	75

77a Cross-country Skier

1964. Ninth Winter Olympic Games, Innsbruck. Sheet 86×72 mm.

MS336a **77a** 4t. black		4·00	3·75

78 Gymnastics

1964. Olympic Games, Tokyo. Multicoloured.

337	5m. Type **78**	15	15
338	10m. Throwing the javelin	25	15
339	15m. Wrestling	35	15
340	20m. Running	40	20
341	30m. Horse-jumping	55	30
342	50m. High-diving	80	45
343	60m. Cycling	1·10	60
344	1t. Emblem of Tokyo Games	1·40	1·00
MS344a 87×77 mm. 4t. black, green and red (Wrestlers–Horiz 38×28 mm)		4·75	4·50

79 Congress Emblem

1964. Fourth Mongolian Women's Congress.

345	**79**	30m. multicoloured	40	30

80 *Lunik 1*

1964. Space Research. Multicoloured.

346	5m. Type **80**	15	15
347	10m. *Vostoks 1* and *2*	20	15
348	15m. *Tiros* (vert)	25	15
349	20m. *Cosmos* (vert)	20	15
350	30m. *Mars Probe* (vert)	40	20
351	60m. *Luna 4* (vert)	55	30
352	80m. *Echo 2*	70	60
353	1t. Radio telescope	1·10	85

81 Horseman and Flag

1964. 40th Anniv of Mongolian Constitution.

354	**81**	25m. multicoloured	55	30
355	**81**	50m. multicoloured	70	15

81a Austrian and Mongolian stamps encircling Globe

1965. WIPA Stamp Exhibition, Vienna. Sheet 90×130 mm.

MS355a **81a** 4t. red		4·75	4·50

82 Marine Exploration

1965. International Quiet Sun Year. Multicoloured.

356	5m. Type **82** (postage)	25	15
357	10m. Weather balloon	35	20
358	60m. Northern Lights	1·20	45
359	80m. Geomagnetic emblems	1·50	60
360	1t. Globe and IQSY emblem	2·30	1·00
361	15m. Weather satellite (air)	80	30
362	20m. Antarctic exploration	4·75	1·00
363	30m. Space exploration	1·10	30

83 Horses Grazing

1965. Mongolian Horses. Multicoloured.

364	5m. Type **83**	25	15
365	10m. Hunting with golden eagles	2·00	30
366	15m. Breaking-in wild horse	40	30
367	20m. Horses racing	45	30
368	30m. Horses jumping	55	35
369	60m. Hunting wolves	70	45
370	80m. Milking a mare	80	60
371	1t. Mare and colt	1·90	75

84 Farm Girl with Lambs

1965. 40th Anniv of Mongolian Youth Movement.

372	**84**	5m. orange, bistre and green	15	15
373	-	10m. bistre, blue and red	25	20
374	-	20m. ochre, red and violet	40	30
375	-	30m. lilac, brown and green	55	45
376	-	50m. orange, buff and blue	95	75

Designs:—10m. Young drummers; 20m. Children around campfire; 30m. Young wrestlers; 50m. Emblem.

85 Chinese Perch

1965. Mongolian Fish. Multicoloured.

377	5m. Type **85**	35	15
378	10m. Lenok	40	15
379	15m. Siberian sturgeon	45	20
380	20m. Taimen	70	30
381	30m. Banded catfish	1·10	45
382	60m. Amur catfish	1·80	60
383	80m. Northern pike	2·00	85
384	1t. Eurasian perch	2·75	1·30

86 Marx and Lenin

1965. Organization of Socialist Countries' Postal Administrations Conference, Peking.

385	**86**	10m. black and red	25	15

87 ITU Emblem and Symbols

1965. Air. I.T.U. Centenary.

386	**87**	30m. blue and bistre	70	30
387	**87**	50m. red, bistre and blue	1·10	45
MS387a 86×130 mm. 4t. blue, black and gold (Communications satellite, 38×51 mm)			6·75	6·50

88 Sable

1966. Mongolian Fur Industry.

388	**88**	5m. purple, black & yellow	25	15
389	-	10m. brown, black and grey	35	15
390	-	15m. brown, black and blue	40	15
391	-	20m. multicoloured	45	20
392	-	30m. brown, black & mauve	55	30
393	-	60m. brown, black & green	80	45
394	-	80m. multicoloured	1·10	60
395	-	1t. blue, black and olive	2·00	1·00

Designs:—(Fur animals): Horiz: 10m. Red fox; 30m. Pallas's cat; 60m. Beech marten. Vert: 15m. European otter; 20m. Cheetah; 80m. Stoat; 1t. Woman in fur coat.

89 WHO Building

1966. Inauguration of W.H.O. Headquarters, Geneva.

396	**89**	30m. blue, gold and green	45	30
397	**89**	50m. blue, gold and red	75	45

90 Footballers

91

1966. World Cup Football Championship. Multicoloured.

398	10m. Type **90**	15	15
399	30m. Footballers (different)	45	30
400	60m. Goalkeeper saving goal	60	45
401	80m. Footballers (different)	90	60
402	1t. World Cup flag	1·20	80
MS403 **91** 4t. brown and grey		7·50	7·25

92 Sukhe Bator and Parliament Buildings, Ulan Bator

1966. 15th Mongolian Communist Party Congress.

404	**92**	30m. multicoloured	45	15

93 Wrestling

1966. World Wrestling Championships, Toledo (Spain). Similar wrestling designs.

405	**93**	10m. black, mauve & purple	15	15
406	-	30m. black, mauve and grey	45	25
407	-	60m. black, mauve & brown	75	30
408	-	80m. black, mauve and lilac	90	45
409	-	1t. black, mauve & turq	1·20	60

94 *Luna 10*, Globe and Moon

1966. Air. "Luna 10" Commemoration. Sheet 84×130 mm.

MS410 **94**	4t. multicoloured	5·25	5·00

95 State Emblem

1966. 45th Anniv of Independence. Multicoloured

411	30m. Type **95**	2·30	1·20
412	50m. Sukhe Bator, emblems of agriculture and industry (horiz)	4·50	1·60

96 *Physochlaena physaloides*

1966. Flowers. Multicoloured.

413	5m. Type **96**	30	15
414	10m. Onion	45	15
415	15m. Red lily	60	15
416	20m. *Thermopsis lanceolata*	90	25
417	30m. *Amygdalus mongolica*	1·40	45
418	60m. Bluebeard	1·50	60
419	80m. *Piptanthus mongolicus*	2·00	95
420	1t. *"ris bungei*	2·40	1·20

1966. 60th Birth Anniv of D. Natsagdorj. Nos. 277/8 optd 1906 1966.

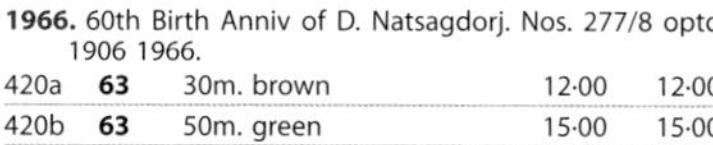

420a	**63**	30m. brown	12·00	12·00
420b	**63**	50m. green	15·00	15·00

97 Child with Dove

1966. Children's Day. Multicoloured.

421	10m. Type **97**	30	15
422	15m. Children with reindeer (horiz)	40	15
423	20m. Boys wrestling	45	25
424	30m. Boy riding horse (horiz)	60	30
425	60m. Children on camel	90	45
426	80m. Shepherd boy with sheep (horiz)	1·20	60
427	1t. Boy archer	1·50	80

98 *Proton 1*

1966. Space Satellites. Multicoloured.

428	5m. *Vostok 2* (vert)	15	15
429	10m. Type **98**	25	15
430	15m. *Telstar 1* (vert)	30	15
431	20m. *Molniya 1* (vert)	45	25
432	30m. *Syncom 3* (vert)	60	30
433	60m. *Luna 9* (vert)	75	45
434	80m. *Luna 12* (vert)	90	60
435	1t. Mars and photographs taken by *Mariner 4*	1·20	80

99 Tarbosaurus

1966. Prehistoric Animals. Multicoloured.

436	5m. Type **99**	60	15
437	10m. Talararus	75	25
438	15m. Protoceratops	85	30
439	20m. Indricotherium	90	40
440	30m. Saurolophus	1·40	45
441	60m. Mastodon	2·75	60
442	80m. Mongolotherium	3·00	1·10
443	1t. Mammuthus	3·25	1·60

100 Congress Emblem

1967. Ninth International Students' Union Congress.

444	**100**	30m. ultramarine and blue	45	30
445	**100**	50m. blue and pink	75	45

101 Sukhe Bator and Mongolian and Soviet Soldiers

1967. 50th Anniv of October Revolution.

446	**101**	40m. multicoloured	60	45
447	-	60m. multicoloured	90	60

Design:—60m. Lenin, and soldiers with sword.

102 Vietnamese Mother and Child

1967. Help for Vietnam.

448	**102**	30m.+20m. brown, red and blue	60	45
449	**102**	50m.+30m. brown, blue and red	1·10	80

103 Figure Skating

1967. Winter Olympic Games, Grenoble. Multicoloured

450	5m. Type **103**	15	15
451	10m. Speed skating	30	15
452	15m. Ice hockey	45	25

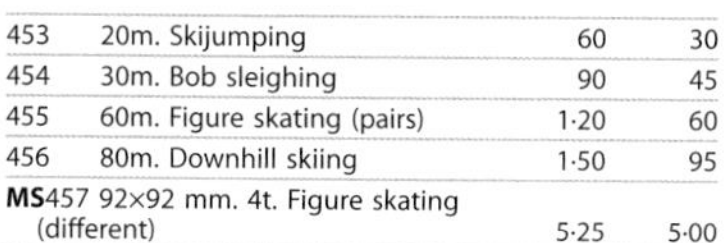

453	20m. Skijumping	60	30
454	30m. Bob sleighing	90	45
455	60m. Figure skating (pairs)	1·20	60
456	80m. Downhill skiing	1·50	95
MS457 92×92 mm. 4t. Figure skating (different)		5·25	5·00

104 Bactrian Camel and Calf

1968. Young Animals. Multicoloured.

458	5m. Type **104**	30	15
459	10m. Yak	45	15
460	15m. Lamb	60	15
461	20m. Foal	75	15
462	30m. Calf	90	25
463	60m. Bison	1·20	30
464	80m. Roe deer	1·80	60
465	1t. Reindeer	3·00	95

105 Prickly Rose

1968. Mongolian Berries.

466	**105**	5m. ultramarine on blue	15	15
467	-	10m. brown on buff	30	15
468	-	15m. emerald on green	40	15
469	-	20m. red on cream	45	15
470	-	30m. red on pink	75	25
471	-	60m. brown on orange	90	45
472	-	80m. turquoise on blue	1·50	60
473	-	1t. red on cream	1·80	95

Designs:—10m. Blackcurrant; 15m. Gooseberry; 20m. Crab-apple; 30m. Strawberry; 60m. Redcurrant; 80m. Cowberry; 1t. Sea buckthorn.

ЛЭХБ
20 ЖИЛ
WHO
(106)

1968. 20th Anniv of World Health Organization. Nos. 396/7 optd with T **106**.

474	**89**	30m. blue, gold and green	9·00	6·25
475	**89**	50m. blue, gold and red	9·00	6·25

107 Human Rights Emblem

1968. Human Rights Year.

476	**107**	30m. green and blue	45	30

108 *Das Kapital*

1968. 150th Birth Anniv of Karl Marx. Multicoloured.

477	30m. Type **108**	45	30
478	50m. Karl Marx	75	45

109 *Portrait of Artist Sharab* (A. Sangatzohyo)

1968. Mongolian Paintings. Multicoloured.

479	5m. Type **109**	30	15

480 10m. *On Remote Roads* (A. Sangatzohyo) 40 15
481 15m. *Camel Calf* (B. Avarzad) 45 25
482 20m. *The Milk* (B. Avarzad) 75 45
483 30m. *The Bowman* (B. Gombosuren) 1·10 60
484 80m. *Girl Sitting on a Yak* (A. Sangatzohyo) 2·10 1·10
485 1t.40 *Cagan Dara Ekke* (Janaivajara) 4·00 2·00
MS486 120×86 mm. 4t. *Meeting* (A. Sangatzohyo) (horiz) 9·00 8·75

110 Volleyball

1968. Olympic Games, Mexico. Multicoloured.
487 5m. Type **110** 15 15
488 10m. Wrestling 15 15
489 15m. Cycling 25 15
490 20m. Throwing the javelin 30 25
491 30m. Football 45 30
492 60m. Running 60 45
493 80m. Gymnastics 90 60
494 1t. Weightlifting 1·20 80
MS495 92×92 mm. 4t. Horse-jumping 4·50 4·25

111 Hammer and Spade

1968. Seventh Anniv of Darkhan Town.
496 **111** 50m. orange and blue 45 15

112 Gorky

1968. Birth Centenary of Maksim Gorky (writer).
497 **112** 60m. ochre and blue 45 30

113 *Madonna and Child* (Boltraffio)

1968. 20th Anniv (1966) of UNESCO. Paintings by European Masters in National Gallery, Budapest. Multicoloured.
498 5m. Type **113** 30 15
499 10m. *St. Roch healed by an Angel* (Moretto of Brescia) 45 25
500 15m. *Madonna and Child with St. Anne* (Macchietti) 60 30
501 20m. *St. John on Patmos* (Cano) 75 40
502 30m. *Young lady with viola da gamba* (Kupetzky) 90 45
503 80m. *Study of a head* (Amerling) 1·80 80
504 1t.40 *The death of Adonis* (Furini) 2·75 1·40
MS505 80×120 mm. 4t. *Portrait of a Lady* (Renoir) 9·00 8·75

114 Paavo Nurmi (running)

1969. Olympic Games' Gold-medal Winners. Multicoloured.
506 5m. Type **114** 15 15
507 10m. Jesse Owens (running) 15 15
508 15m. F. Blankers-Koen (hurdling) 25 15
509 20m. Laszlo Papp (boxing) 30 25
510 30m. Wilma Rudolph (running) 45 30
511 60m. Boris Sahlin (gymnastics) 75 45
512 80m. D. Schollander (swimming) 1·10 80
513 1t. A. Nakayama (ring exercises) 1·50 95
MS514 118x80 mm. 4t. J. Munhbat (wrestling) 7·50 7·25

115 Bayit Costume (woman)

1969. Mongolian Costumes. Multicoloured.
515 5m. Type **115** 30 15
516 10m. Torgut (man) 40 15
517 15m. Sakhchin (woman) 45 15
518 20m. Khalka (woman) 70 25
519 30m. Daringanga (woman) 75 30
520 60m. Mingat (woman) 1·10 40
521 80m. Khalka (man) 1·50 45
522 1t. Barga (woman) 2·40 95

116 Emblem and Helicopter Rescue

1969. 30th Anniv of Mongolian Red Cross.
523 **116** 30m. red and blue 1·50 30
524 - 50m. red and violet 1·20 45
Design:—50m. Shepherd and ambulance.

117 Yellow Lion's-foot

1969. Landscapes and Flowers. Multicoloured.
525 5m. Type **117** 25 20
526 10m. Variegated pink 35 20
527 15m. Superb pink 45 20
528 20m. Meadow cranesbill 50 25
529 30m. Mongolian pink 1·00 35
530 60m. Asiatic globe flower 1·20 55
531 80m. Long-lipped larkspur 1·70 90
532 1t. Saxaul 2·00 1·10

118 *Bullfight* (O. Tsewegdjaw)

1969. Tenth Anniv of Co-operative Movement. Paintings in National Gallery, Ulan Bator. Multicoloured
533 5m. Type **118** 15 20
534 10m. *Colts Fighting* (O. Tsewegdjaw) 15 20
535 15m. *Horse-herd* (A. Sengetsohyo) 25 20
536 20m. *Camel Caravan* (D. Damdinsuren) 35 25
537 30m. *On the Steppe* (N. Tsultem) 50 35
538 60m. *Milking Mares* (O. Tsewegdjaw) 1·00 55
539 80m. *Off to School* (B. Avarzad) 1·40 90
540 1t. *After Work* (G. Odon) 2·20 1·10
MS541 121×85 mm. 4t. *Horse-herd* (D. Damdinsuren) (60×40 mm) 6·75 6·50

119 Astronaut and Module on Moon

1969. Air. First Man on the Moon. Sheet 86×121 mm.
MS542 **119** 4t. multicoloured 7·75 7·50

120 Army Crest

1969. 30th Anniv of Battle of Khalka River.
543 **120** 50m. multicoloured 70 35

БНМАУ-ыг
тунхагласны
45
жилийн ой
1969—XI—26
(121)

1969. 45th Anniv of Mongolian People's Republic. Nos. 411/12 optd with T **121**.
544 **95** 30m. multicoloured 10·00 9·75
545 - 50m. multicoloured 13·50 13·00

122 *Sputnik 3*

1969. Exploration of Space. Multicoloured.
546 5m. Type **122** 15 20
547 10m. *Vostok 1* 25 20
548 15m. *Mercury 7* 35 20
549 20m. Space-walk from *Voskhod 2* 45 25
550 30m. *Apollo 8* in Moon orbit 50 35
551 60m. Space-walk from *Soyuz 5* 1·00 70
552 80m. *Apollo 12* and Moon landing 1·40 90
MS553 108×77 mm. 4t. *Apollo 12* 6·00 5·75

123 Wolf

1970. Wild Animals. Multicoloured.
554 5m. Type **123** 35 20
555 10m. Brown bear 50 20
556 15m. Lynx 70 20
557 20m. Wild boar 1·00 25
558 30m. Elk 1·20 35
559 60m. Bobak marmot 1·40 70
560 80m. Argali 2·00 1·10
561 1t. "Hun Hunter and Hound" (tapestry) 3·00 1·40

124 "Lenin Centenary" (silk panel, Cerenhuu)

1970. Birth Centenary of Lenin. Multicoloured.
562 20m. Type **124** 35 20
563 50m. *Mongolians meeting Lenin* (Sangatzohyo) (horiz) 70 35

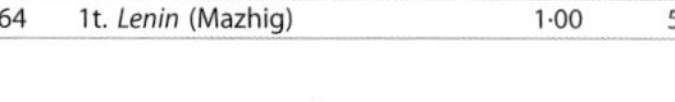
564 1t. *Lenin* (Mazhig) 1·00 55

125 "Fairy Tale" Pavilion

1970. EXPO 70 World Trade Fair, Osaka, Japan. Multicoloured.
565 1t.50 Type **125** 1·40 1·10
MS566 111×81 mm. 4t. Matsushita Pavilion and "Time Capsule" (51×38 mm) 9·25 9·00

126 Footballers

1970. World Cup Football Championship, Mexico.
567 **126** 10m. multicoloured 35 20
568 - 20m. multicoloured 45 20
569 - 30m. multicoloured 50 20
570 - 50m. multicoloured 85 25
571 - 60m. multicoloured 1·00 35
572 - 1t. multicoloured 1·70 45
573 - 1t.30 multicoloured 2·00 90
MS574 122×95 mm 4t. multicoloured (50×37 mm) 6·00 5·75
Designs:—Nos. 568/**MS**574, Different football scenes.

127 Common Buzzard

1970. Birds of Prey. Multicoloured.
575 10m. Type **127** 1·50 20
576 20m. Tawny owls 2·00 35
577 30m. Northern goshawk 2·40 45
578 50m. White-tailed sea eagle 2·50 55
579 60m. Peregrine falcon 3·50 90
580 1t. Common kestrels 4·25 1·10
581 1t.30 Black kite 4·75 1·40

128 Soviet Memorial, Berlin-Treptow

1970. 25th Anniv of Victory in Second World War.
582 **128** 60m. multicoloured 85 55

129 Mongol Archery

1970. Mongolian Traditional Life. Multicoloured.
583 10m. Type **129** 70 35
584 20m. Bodg-gegeen's Palace, Ulan Bator 70 35
585 30m. Mongol horsemen 70 35
586 40m. "The White Goddess-Mother" 70 55
587 50m. Girl in National costume 1·50 1·20
588 60m. "Lion's Head" (statue) 1·70 1·40
589 70m. Dancer's mask 2·00 1·60
590 80m. Gateway, Bogd-gegeen's Palace 2·40 2·10

130 Frogmen boarding *Apollo 13*

1970. Safe Return of Apollo 13 Spacecraft. Sheet 110×80 mm.
MS591 **130** 4t. multicoloured 10·00 9·75

131 IEY and UN Emblems with Flag

1970. International Education Year.
592 **131** 60m. multicoloured 1·00 55

132 Horseman, "50" and Sunrise

1970. 50th Anniv of National Press.
593 **132** 30m. multicoloured 85 55

133 *Vostok 3* and *4*

1971. Space Research. Multicoloured.
594 10m. Type **133** 15 20
595 20m. Space-walk from *Voskhod 2* 25 20
596 30m. *Gemini 6* and *7* 35 25
597 50m. Docking of *Soyuz 4* and *5* 50 35
598 60m. *Soyuz 6*, *7* and *8* 70 45
599 80m. *Apollo 11* and lunar module 85 55
600 1t. *Apollo 13* damaged 1·00 70
601 1t.30 *Luna 16* 1·40 90
MS602 120×90 mm. 4t. Satellite communications station, Ulan Bator 6·00 5·75

No. 594 is incorrectly inscribed '*Vostok 2-3*'. The date refers to flight of *Vostoks 3* and *4*".

134 Sukhe Bator addressing Meeting

1971. 50th Anniv of Revolutionary Party. Multicoloured
603 30m. Type **134** 50 20
604 60m. Horseman with flag 70 25
605 90m. Sukhe Bator with Lenin 85 35
606 1t.20 Mongolians with banner 1·00 70

135 *Lunokhod 1*

1971. Exploration of the Moon. Sheet 114×95 mm containing T **135** and similar vert design. Multicoloured.
MS607 2t.×2 (a) Type **135**; (b) *Apollo 14* module on Moon 6·00 5·75

136 Tsam Mask

1971. Mongol Tsam Masks.
608 **136** 10m. multicoloured 35 20
609 - 20m. multicoloured 50 20
610 - 30m. multicoloured 70 25
611 - 50m. multicoloured 85 35
612 - 60m. multicoloured 1·00 55
613 - 1t. multicoloured 1·90 90
614 - 1t.30 multicoloured 2·20 1·20

Designs:—Nos. 609/14, Different dance masks.

137 Banner and Party Emblems

1971. 16th Revolutionary Party Congress.
615 **137** 60m. multicoloured 50 35

138 Steam Locomotive

1971. 50 Years of Transport Development. Multicoloured.
616 20m. Type **138** 1·20 35
617 30m. Diesel locomotive 1·40 35
618 40m. Russian Urals lorry 1·50 35
619 50m. Russian Moskovich 412 car 1·70 45
620 60m. Polikarpov Po-2 biplane 2·00 55
621 80m. Antonov An-24B airliner 2·40 90
622 1t. Lake steamer *Sukhe Bator* 4·25 1·80

139 Soldier

1971. 50th Anniv of People's Army and Police. Multicoloured.
623 60m. Type **139** 1·00 20
624 1t.50 Policeman and child 1·40 55

140 Emblem and Red Flag

1971. 50th Anniv of Revolutionary Youth Organization.
625 **140** 60m. multicoloured 70 35

141 Mongolian Flag and Year Emblem

1971. Racial Equality Year.
626 **141** 60m. multicoloured 50 35

142 *The Old Man and the Tiger*

1971. Mongolian Folk Tales. Multicoloured.
627 10m. Type **142** 35 20
628 20m. *The Boy Giant-killer* 25 20
629 30m. Cat and mice 50 25
630 50m. Mongolians riding on eagle 70 35
631 60m. Girl on horseback (*The Wise Bride*) 1·00 45
632 80m. King and courtiers with donkey 1·40 55
633 1t. Couple kneeling before empty throne (*Story of the Throne*) 1·90 70
634 1t.30 *The Wise Bird* 2·40 1·10

143 Yaks

1971. Livestock Breeding. Multicoloured.
635 20m. Type **143** 35 20
636 30m. Bactrian camels 45 25
637 40m. Sheep 50 35
638 50m. Goats 85 45
639 60m. Cattle 1·20 60
640 80m. Horses 1·40 70
641 1t. Pony 2·20 1·10

144 Cross-country Skiing

1972. Winter Olympic Games, Sapporo, Japan. Multicoloured.
642 10m. Type **144** 35 20
643 20m. Bobsleighing 45 20
644 30m. Figure skating 50 20
645 50m. Slalom skiing 70 25
646 60m. Speed skating 85 35
647 80m. Downhill skiing 1·00 45
648 1t. Ice hockey 1·40 55
649 1t.30 Pairs figure skating 1·70 70
MS650 110×90 mm. 4t. Ski jumping (50×38 mm) 4·25 4·00

145 *Horse-breaking* (A. Sengatzohyo)

1972. Paintings by Contemporary Artists from the National Gallery, Ulan Bator. Multicoloured.
651 10m. Type **145** 35 20
652 20m. *Black Camel* (A. Sengatzohyo) 45 20
653 30m. *Jousting* (A. Sengatzohyo) 50 20
654 50m. *Wrestling Match* (A. Sengatzohyo) 70 25
655 60m. *Waterfall* (A. Sengatzohyo) 85 35
656 80m. *Old Musician* (U. Yadamsuren) 1·40 60
657 1t. *Young Musician* (U. Yadamsuren) 1·50 70
658 1t.30 *Ancient Prophet* (B. Avarzad) 2·00 90

146 *Apollo 16*

1972. Air. "Co-operation in Space Exploration". Sheet 111×90 mm.
MS659 **146** 4t. multicoloured 7·75 7·50

147 *Calosoma fischeri* (ground beetle)

1972. Beetles. Multicoloured.
660 10m. Type **147** 35 20
661 20m. *Mylabris mongolica* (blister beetle) 50 20
662 30m. *Sternoplax zichyi* (mealworm beetle) 70 20
663 50m. *Rhaebus komarovi* (snout weevil) 85 25
664 60m. *Meloe centripubens* (oil beetle) 1·20 35
665 80m. *Eodorcadion mongolicum* (longhorn beetle) 1·90 55
666 1t. *Platyope maongolica* (mealworm beetle) 2·20 90
667 1t.30 *Lixus nigrolineatus* (weevil) 3·50 1·20

148 Przewalski's Wild Horse

1972. Air. Centenary of Discovery of Wild Horse Species by Nikolai Przewalski. Sheet 115×90 mm.
MS668 **148** 4t. multicoloured 19·00 18·00

149 Satellite and Dish Aerial ("Telecommunications")

1972. Air. National Achievements. Multicoloured.
669 20m. Type **149** 50 20
670 30m. Horse-herd ("Livestock Breeding") 85 20
671 40m. Diesel train and Tupolev Tu-144 jetliner ("Transport") 2·50 45
672 50m. Corncob and farm ("Agriculture") 1·00 35
673 60m. Ambulance and hospital ("Public Health") 1·40 55
674 80m. Actors ("Culture") 1·70 70
675 1t. Factory ("Industry") 2·00 90

150 Globe, Flag and Dish Aerial

1972. Air. World Telecommunications Day.
676 **150** 60m. multicoloured 85 55

151 Running

1972. Olympic Games, Munich. Multicoloured.

677	10m. Type **151**	15	20
678	15m. Boxing	25	20
679	20m. Judo	35	20
680	25m. High jumping	45	25
681	30m. Rifle-shooting	50	35
682	60m. Wrestling	70	55
683	80m. Weightlifting	85	70
684	1t. Mongolian flag and Olympic emblems	1·00	90
MS685	90×110 mm. 4t. Archery (vert)	5·00	4·75

152 ECAFE Emblem

1972. 25th Anniv of E.C.A.F.E.

686	**152** 60m. blue, gold and red	70	35

153 Mongolian Racerunner

1972. Reptiles. Multicoloured.

687	10m. Type **153**	35	20
688	15m. Radde's toad	25	20
689	20m. Halys viper	50	20
690	25m. Toad-headed agama	85	25
691	30m. Asiatic grass frog	1·00	35
692	60m. Plate-tailed gecko	1·40	70
693	80m. Steppe ribbon snake	2·20	1·10
694	1t. Mongolian agama	3·50	1·20

154 "Technical Knowledge"

1972. 30th Anniv of Mongolian State University. Multicoloured.

695	50m. Type **154**	70	20
696	60m. University building	85	35

155 *Madonna and Child with St. John the Baptist and a Holy Woman* (Bellini)

1972. Air. UNESCO "Save Venice" Campaign. Paintings. Multicoloured.

697	10m. Type **155**	35	20
698	20m. *The Transfiguration* (Bellini) (vert)	45	20
699	30m. *Blessed Virgin with the Child* (Bellini) (vert)	50	25
700	50m. *Presentation of the Christ in the Temple* (Bellini)	85	35
701	60m. *St. George* (Bellini) (vert)	1·20	45
702	80m. *Departure of Ursula* (detail, Carpaccio) (vert)	1·40	70
703	1t. *Departure of Ursula* (different detail, Carpaccio)	1·90	1·20
MS704	90×111 mm. 3t.+1t. As No. 703	8·50	8·25

156 Manlay-Bator Damdinsuren

1972. National Heroes. Multicoloured.

705	10m. Type **156**	35	20
706	20m. Ard Ayus in chains (horiz)	50	25
707	50m. Hatan-Bator Magsarzhav	70	35
708	60m. Has-Bator on the march (horiz)	85	55
709	1t. Sukhe Bator	1·70	70

157 Spassky Tower, Moscow Kremlin

1972. 50th Anniv of U.S.S.R.

710	**157** 60m. multicoloured	85	35

158 Snake and *Mars 1*

1972. Air. Animal Signs of the Mongolian Calendar and Progress in Space Exploration. Multicoloured.

711	60m. Type **158**	1·50	70
712	60m. Horse and *Apollo 8* (square)	1·50	70
713	60m. Sheep and *Electron 2* (square)	1·50	70
714	60m. Monkey and *Explorer 6*	1·50	70
715	60m. Dragon and *Mariner 2*	1·50	70
716	60m. Pig and *Cosmos 110* (square)	1·50	70
717	60m. Dog and *Ariel 2* (square)	1·50	70
718	60m. Cockerel and *Venus 1*	1·50	70
719	60m. Hare and *Soyuz 5*	1·50	70
720	60m. Tiger and *Gemini 7* (square)	1·50	70
721	60m. Ox and *Venus 4* (square)	1·50	70
722	60m. Rat and *Apollo 15* lunar rover	1·50	70

The square designs are size 40×40 mm.

159 Swimming Gold Medal (Mark Spitz, USA)

1972. Gold Medal Winners, Munich Olympic Games. Multicoloured.

723	5m. Type **159**	15	20
724	10m. High jumping (Ulrike Meyfarth, West Germany)	35	20
725	20m. Gymnastics (Savao Kato, Japan)	45	20
726	30m. Show jumping (Andras Balczo, Hungary)	50	25
727	60m. Running (Lasse Viren, Finland)	85	35
728	80m. Swimming (Shane Gould, Australia)	1·20	55
729	1t. Putting the shot (Anatoli Bondarchuk, USSR)	1·50	70
MS730	111×91 mm. 4t. Wrestling silver medal (Khorloo Baianmunk, Mongolia)	5·00	4·75

160 Monkey on Cycle

1973. Mongolian Circus (1st series). Multicoloured

731	5m. Type **160**	15	20
732	10m. Seal with ball	35	20
733	15m. Bear on mono-wheel	50	20
734	20m. Acrobat on camel	70	25
735	30m. Acrobat on horse	85	35
736	50m. Clown playing flute	1·00	45
737	60m. Contortionist	1·40	70
738	1t. New Circus Hall, Ulan Bator	1·90	1·20

See also Nos. 824/30.

161 Mounted Postman

1973

739	**161** 50m. brown (postage)	1·40	20
740	- 60m. green	5·00	55
741	- 1t. purple	2·50	70
742	- 1t.50 blue (air)	4·25	90

Designs:—60m. Diesel train; 1t. Mail truck; 1t.50, Antonov An-24 airliner.

162 Sukhe Bator receiving Traditional Gifts

1973. 80th Birth Anniv of Sukhe Bator. Multicoloured

743	10m. Type **162**	15	20
744	20m. Holding reception	35	20
745	50m. Leading army	70	25
746	60m. Addressing council	85	35
747	1t. Giving audience (horiz)	1·40	55

163 W.M.O. Emblem and Meteorological Symbols

1973. Air. Centenary of World Meteorological Organization.

748	**163** 60m. multicoloured	85	55

164 *Copernicus* (anon)

1973. 500th Birth Anniv of Nicholas Copernicus (astronomer). Multicoloured.

749	50m. Type **164**	85	35
750	60m. *Copernicus in his Observatory* (J. Matejko) (55×35 mm)	1·00	55
751	1t. *Copernicus* (Jan Matejko)	1·70	70
MS752	151×115 mm. As Nos. 749/51 but face values 1, 2 and 1t. respectively	6·75	6·50

165 "Tulaga" Stamp of 1959

1973. IBRA 73 International Stamp Exhibition, Munich. Sheet 81×116 mm.

MS753	**165** 4t. multicoloured	6·75	6·50

Нэгдлийн Холбооны IV Их
Хурал 1973—6—11

(166)

1973. Fourth Agricultural Co-operative Congress, Ulan Bator. No. 538 optd with T **166**.

754	60m. multicoloured	17·00	18·00

167 Marx and Lenin

1973. Ninth Organization of Socialist States Postal Ministers Congress, Ulan Bator.

755	**167** 60m. multicoloured	85	35

168 Russian Stamp and Emblems

1973. Air. Council for Mutual Economic Aid Posts and Telecommunications Conference, Ulan Bator. Multicoloured.

756	30m. Type **168**	1·40	55
757	30m. Mongolia	1·40	55
758	30m. Bulgaria	1·40	55
759	30m. Hungary	1·40	55
760	30m. Czechoslovakia	1·40	55
761	30m. German Democratic Republic	1·40	55
762	30m. Cuba	1·40	55
763	30m. Rumania	1·40	55
764	30m. Poland	1·40	55

169 Common Shelduck

1973. Aquatic Birds. Multicoloured.

765	5m. Type **169**	1·00	35
766	10m. Black-throated diver	1·40	35
767	15m. Bar-headed geese	2·20	45
768	30m. Great crested grebe	2·75	55
769	50m. Mallard	3·75	90
770	60m. Mute swan	4·50	1·10
771	1t. Greater scaups	5·00	1·40

170 Siberian Weasel

1973. Small Fur Animals. Multicoloured.

772	5m. Type **170**	25	20
773	10m. Siberian chipmunk	35	20
774	15m. Siberian flying squirrel	50	20
775	20m. Eurasian badger	70	25

776	30m. Eurasian red squirrel	1·00	35
777	60m. Wolverine	1·70	70
778	80m. American mink	2·00	1·10
779	1t. Arctic hare	3·00	1·40

171 Launching Soyuz Spacecraft

1973. Air. Apollo and Soyuz Space Programmes. Multicoloured.

780	5m. Type **171**	15	20
781	10m. *Apollo 8*	15	20
782	15m. *Soyuz 4* and *5* linked	15	20
783	20m. *Apollo 11* module on Moon	35	20
784	30m. *Apollo 14* after splashdown	50	25
785	50m. Triple flight by *Soyuz 6, 7* and *8*	70	35
786	60m. *Apollo 16* lunar rover	85	55
787	1t. *Lunokhod 1*	1·00	70
MS788	110×91 mm. 4t. Proposed Soyuz and Apollo link-up	4·25	4·00

172 Global Emblem

1973. 15th Anniv of Review "Problems of Peace and Socialism".

789	**172**	60m. red, gold and blue	70	35

173 Alpine Aster

1973. Mongolian Flowers. Multicoloured.

790	5m. Type **173**	35	20
791	10m. Mongolian catchfly	50	20
792	15m. *Rosa davurica*	70	20
793	20m. Mongolian dandelion	85	25
794	30m. *Rhododendron dahuricum*	1·00	35
795	50m. *Clematis tangutica*	1·40	70
796	60m. Siberian primrose	1·70	1·40
797	1t. Pasque flower	2·00	1·60

174 Poplar Admiral

1974. Butterflies and Moths. Multicoloured.

798	5m. Type **174**	70	20
799	10m. Hebe tiger moth	75	20
800	15m. Purple tiger moth	85	20
801	20m. Rosy underwing	1·20	25
802	30m. *Isoceras kaszabi* (moth)	1·70	35
803	50m. Spurge hawk moth	2·40	70
804	60m. Garden tiger moth	2·75	90
805	1t. Clouded buff	3·50	1·20

175 *Hebe Namshil* (L. Merdorsh)

1974. Mongolian Opera and Drama. Multicoloured.

806	15m. Type **175**	35	20
807	20m. *Sive Hiagt* (D. Luvsansharav) (horiz)	50	20
808	25m. *Edre* (D. Namdag)	70	20
809	30m. *The Three Khans of Sara-gol* (horiz)	85	25
810	60m. *Amarsana* (B. Damdinsuren)	1·00	35
811	80m. *Edre* (different scene)	1·40	55
812	1t. *Edre* (different scene)	1·70	1·40

176 Comecon Headquarters, Moscow

1974. Air. 25th Anniv of Communist Council for Mutual Economic Aid ("Comecon").

813	**176**	60m. multicoloured	85	55

177 Government Building and Sukhe Bator Monument, Ulan Bator

1974. 50th Anniv of Renaming of Capital as Ulan Bator.

814	**177**	60m. multicoloured	85	55

178 Mongolian 10c. Stamp of 1924

1974. Air. 50th Anniv of First Mongolian Stamps. Sheet 130×85 mm.

MS815	**178** 4t. multicoloured	8·50	8·25

179 Mounted Courier

1974. Air. Centenary of U.P.U (1st issue). Multicoloured.

816	50m. Type **179**	3·00	90
817	50m. Reindeer mail sledge	3·00	90
818	50m. Mail coach	3·00	90
819	50m. Balloon post	3·50	90
820	50m. Lake steamer *Sukhe Bator* and Polikarpov Po-2 biplane	4·25	90
821	50m. Diesel train and PO truck	4·25	90
822	50m. Rocket in orbit	3·50	90
MS823	100×90 mm. 4t. 'UPU' over globe (24×45 mm)	37·00	36·00

See also 883/**MS**890.

180 Performing Horses

1974. Mongolian Circus (2nd series). Multicoloured.

824	10m. Type **180** (postage)	35	20
825	20m. Juggler (vert)	70	25
826	30m. Elephant on ball (vert)	85	35
827	40m. Performing yak	1·40	55
828	60m. Acrobats (vert)	1·70	60
829	80m. Trick cyclist (vert)	2·00	1·10
830	1t. Contortionist (vert) (air)	2·50	1·40

181 *Training a Young Horse*

1974. International Children's Day. Drawings by Lhamsurem. Multicoloured.

831	10m. Type **181**	15	20
832	20m. *Boy with Calf*	35	20
833	30m. *Riding untamed Horse*	50	20
834	40m. *Boy with Foal*	70	25
835	60m. *Girl dancing with Doves*	1·00	35
836	80m. *Wrestling*	1·40	70
837	1t. *Hobby-horse Dance*	1·70	1·10

182 Archer on Foot

1974. Nadam Sports Festival. Multicoloured.

838	10m. Type **182**	15	20
839	20m. "Kazlodanie" (Kazakh mounted game)	35	20
840	30m. Mounted archer	50	20
841	40m. Horse-racing	70	25
842	60m. Bucking horse-riding	1·00	35
843	80m. Capturing wild horse	1·40	70
844	1t. Wrestling	1·70	1·10

183 Giant Panda

1974. Bears. Multicoloured.

845	10m. Brown bear	35	20
846	20m. Type **183**	50	20
847	30m. Giant Panda	85	35
848	40m. Brown bear	1·00	55
849	60m. Sloth bear	1·70	70
850	80m. Asiatic black bear	1·90	1·20
851	1t. Brown bear	3·50	1·60

184 Red Deer

1974. Games Reserves. Fauna. Multicoloured.

852	10m. Type **184**	35	20
853	20m. Eurasian beaver	70	25
854	30m. Leopard	1·00	35
855	40m. Herring gull	2·75	70
856	60m. Roe deer	2·00	60
857	80m. Argali	2·40	1·10
858	1t. Siberian musk deer	2·75	1·20

185 Detail of Buddhist Temple, Palace of Bogdo Gegen

1974. Mongolian Architecture. Multicoloured.

859	10m. Type **185**	35	20
860	15m. Buddhist temple (now museum)	45	20
861	30m. "Charity" Temple, Ulan Bator	50	35
862	50m. Yurt (tent)	85	55
863	80m. Arbour in court-yard	1·40	70

186 Spassky Tower, Moscow, and Sukhe Bator Statue, Ulan Bator

1974. Brezhnev's Visit to Mongolia.

864	**186**	60m. multicoloured	85	35

187 Proclamation of the Republic

1974. 50th Anniv of Mongolian People's Republic. Multicoloured.

865	60m. Type **187**	85	35
866	60m. *First Constitution* (embroidery)	85	35
867	60m. Mongolian flag	85	35

188 Gold Decanter

1974. Goldsmiths' Treasures of the 19th Century. Multicoloured.

868	10m. Type **188**	35	20
869	20m. Silver jug	50	20
870	30m. Night lamp	70	25
871	40m. Tea jug	85	35
872	60m. Candelabra	1·00	45
873	80m. Teapot	1·40	70
874	1t. Silver bowl on stand	1·70	1·10

189 Northern Lapwing

1974. Protection of Water and Nature Conservation. Multicoloured.

875	10m. Type **189** (postage)	85	20
876	20m. Lenok (fish)	1·00	20
877	30m. Marsh marigolds	1·20	35
878	40m. Dalmatian pelican	1·50	35

879	60m. Eurasian perch	1·70	70
880	80m. Sable	2·00	90
881	1t. Hydrologist with jar of water (air)	2·50	1·20
MS882	83×117 mm. 4t. Wild roses (60×60 mm)	8·50	8·25

190 US Mail Coach

1974. Centenary of U.P.U. Multicoloured.

883	10m. Type **190**	35	20
884	20m. French postal cart	50	20
885	30m. Changing horses, Russian mail and passenger carriage	70	35
886	40m. Swedish postal coach with caterpillar tracks	85	55
887	50m. First Hungarian mail van	1·40	70
888	60m. German Daimler-Benz mail van and trailer	1·70	90
889	1t. Mongolian postal courier	2·20	1·40
MS890	111×90 mm. 4t. UPU emblem	13·50	13·00

191 Red Flag

1975. 30th Anniv of Victory.

891	**191**	60m. multicoloured	85	55

192 *Zygophyllum xanthoxylon (image scaled to 57% of original size)*

1975. 12th International Botanical Conference. Rare Medicinal Plants. Multicoloured.

892	10m. Type **192**	35	20
893	20m. *Incarvillea potaninii*	70	20
894	30m. *Lancea tibetica*	1·00	25
895	40m. *Jurinea mongolica*	1·40	35
896	50m. *Saussurea involucrata*	1·50	55
897	60m. *Allium mongolicum*	2·00	70
898	1t. *Adonis mongolica*	3·50	1·20

193 Mongolian Woman

1975. International Women's Year.

899	**193**	60m. multicoloured	85	55

194 Soyuz on Launch-pad

1975. Air. Joint Soviet–American Space Project. Multicoloured.

900	10m. Type **194**	15	20
901	20m. Launch of Apollo	35	20
902	30m. Apollo and Soyuz spacecraft	50	35
903	40m. Docking manoeuvre	85	55
904	50m. Spacecraft docked together	1·20	70
905	60m. Soyuz in orbit	1·50	70
906	1t. Apollo and Soyuz spacecraft and communications satellite	2·20	1·40
MS907	102×83 mm. 4t. Soyuz and Apollo crewmen	7·75	7·50

195 Child and Lamb

1975. International Children's Day. Multicoloured.

908	10m. Type **195**	35	20
909	20m. Child riding horse	50	20
910	30m. Child with calf	70	25
911	40m. Child and orphan camel	1·00	35
912	50m. The Obedient Yak	1·20	55
913	60m. Child riding on swan	1·40	70
914	1t. Two children singing	2·20	1·10

See also Nos. 979/85.

196 Pioneers tending Tree

1975. 50th Anniv of Mongolian Pioneer Organization. Multicoloured.

915	50m. Type **196**	70	35
916	60m. Children's study circle	85	45
917	1t. New emblem of Mongolian pioneers	1·20	70

Тээвэр—50
1975—7—15.
(197)

1975. 50th Anniv of Public Transport. Nos. 616/22 optd with T **197**.

918	**138**	20m. multicoloured	6·00	5·75
919	-	30m. multicoloured	6·00	5·75
920	-	40m. multicoloured	4·25	4·00
921	-	50m. multicoloured	4·25	4·00
922	-	60m. multicoloured	6·00	5·75
923	-	80m. multicoloured	7·75	7·50
924	-	1t. multicoloured	10·00	9·75

198 Argali

1975. Air. South Asia Tourist Year.

925	**198**	1t.50 multicoloured	2·50	1·40

199 Golden Eagle attacking Red Fox

1975. Hunting Scenes. Multicoloured.

926	10m. Type **199**	1·00	20
927	20m. Lynx-hunting (vert)	1·20	35
928	30m. Hunter stalking bobak marmots	1·40	45
929	40m. Hunter riding on reindeer (vert)	1·50	55
930	50m. Shooting wild boar	1·70	70
931	60m. Wolf in trap (vert)	1·90	90
932	1t. Hunters with brown bear	2·40	1·40

200 Haite`s Bullhead

1975. Fish. Multicoloured.

933	10m. Type **200**	35	20
934	20m. Flat-headed asp	70	25
935	30m. Altai osman	1·00	35
936	40m. Tench	1·40	55
937	50m. Hump-backed whitefish	1·70	70
938	60m. Mongolian redfin	2·00	90
939	1t. Goldfish	3·50	1·40

201 "Morin Hur" (musical instrument)

1975. Mongolian Handicrafts. Multicoloured.

940	10m. Type **201**	15	20
941	20m. Saddle	35	20
942	30m. Headdress	50	25
943	40m. Boots	70	35
944	50m. Cap	85	45
945	60m. Pipe and tobacco pouch	1·00	55
946	1t. Fur hat	1·70	1·10

202 Revolutionary with Banner

1975. 70th Anniv of 1905 Russian Revolution.

947	**202**	60m. multicoloured	70	35

203 *Taming a Wild Horse*

1975. Mongolian Paintings. Multicoloured.

948	10m. Type **203**	15	20
949	20m. *Camel Caravan* (horiz)	50	20
950	30m. *Man playing Lute*	70	25
951	40m. *Woman adjusting Headdress* (horiz)	85	35
952	50m. *Woman in ceremonial Costume*	1·00	45
953	60m. *Woman fetching Water*	1·20	55
954	1t. *Woman playing Yaga* (musical instrument)	2·00	1·10
MS955	110×90 mm. 4t. *Warrior on horse-back*	7·75	7·50

204 Ski Jumping

1975. Winter Olympic Games, Innsbruck. Multicoloured.

956	10m. Type **204**	15	20
957	20m. Ice hockey	35	20
958	30m. Slalom skiing	50	25
959	40m. Bobsleighing	70	35
960	50m. Rifle shooting (biathlon)	85	45
961	60m. Speed skating	1·00	55
962	1t. Figure skating	1·70	70
MS963	110×70 mm. 4t. Skier carrying torch	5·00	4·75

205 "House of Young Technicians"

1975. Public Buildings.

964	**205**	50m. blue	85	20
965	-	60m. green	1·00	35
966	-	1t. brown	1·70	70

Designs:—60m. Hotel, Ulan Bator; 1t. "Museum of the Revolution".

206 *Molniya* Satellite

1976. Air. 40th Anniv of Mongolian Meteorological Office.

967	**206**	60m. blue and yellow	1·00	55

207 Mongolian Girl

1976. Air. 30th Anniv of United Nations Educational, Scientific and Cultural Organization. Sheet 100× 86 mm.

MS968	**207**	4t. multicoloured	8·50	8·00

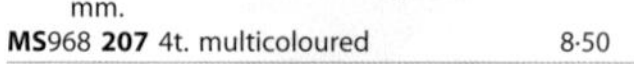

208 *The Wise Musician* (Sharav)

1976. Air. Interphil 76 International Stamp Exhibition, Philadelphia. Sheet 97×70 mm.

MS969	**208**	4t. multicoloured	7·75	7·00

209 "National Economy" Star

1976. 17th Mongolian People's Revolutionary Party Congress, Ulan Bator.

970	**209**	60m. multicoloured	85	35

210 Archery

1976. Olympic Games, Montreal. Multicoloured.

971	10m. Type **210**	15	20
972	20m. Judo	35	20
973	30m. Boxing	50	25
974	40m. Gymnastics	85	35
975	60m. Weightlifting	1·20	55
976	80m. High jumping	1·70	70
977	1t. Rifle shooting	2·20	1·10
MS978	105×78 mm. 4t. Wrestling	4·25	4·00

1976. Int Children's Day. As T **195**. Mult.

979	10m. Gobi Desert landscape	35	20
980	20m. Horse-taming	50	20

981	30m. Horse-riding	70	25
982	40m. Pioneers' camp	85	35
983	60m. Young musician	1·00	45
984	80m. Children's party	1·50	70
985	1t. Mongolian wrestling	1·90	1·10

211 Cavalry Charge

1976. 55th Anniv of Revolution. Multicoloured.

986	60m. Type **211** (postage)	1·00	55
987	60m. Man and emblem (vert)	1·00	55
988	60m. "Industry and Agriculture" (air)	1·00	55

212 "Sukhe Bator" Star

1976. Mongolian Orders and Awards. Sheet 116× 77 mm.
MS989 **212** 4t. multicoloured 4·25 4·00

213 Osprey

1976. Protected Birds. Multicoloured.

990	10m. Type **213**	1·40	35
991	20m. Griffon vulture	2·00	45
992	30m. Lammergeier	2·50	55
993	40m. Marsh harrier	3·00	70
994	60m. Cinerous vulture	3·75	90
995	80m. Golden eagle	4·25	1·20
996	1t. Tawny eagle	5·00	1·40

214 *Rider on Wild Horse*

1976. Paintings by O. Tsewegdjaw. Multicoloured.

997	10m. Type **214**	35	20
998	20m. *The First Nadam* (game on horse-back) (horiz)	50	20
999	30m. *Harbour on Khobsogol Lake* (horiz)	70	25
1000	40m. *Awakening the Steppe* (horiz)	85	35
1001	80m. *Wrestling* (horiz)	1·50	70
1002	1t. *The Descent* (yak hauling timber)	3·00	1·60

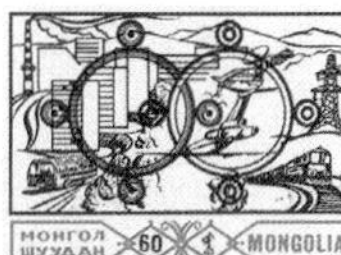

215 "Industrial Development"

1976. Mongolian–Soviet Friendship.
1003 **215** 60m. multicoloured 4·25 55

216 John Naber of USA (Swimming)

1976. Olympic Games, Montreal. Gold Medal Winners. Multicoloured.

1004	10m. Type **216** (postage)	15	20
1005	20m. Nadia Comaneci of Rumania (gymnastics)	25	20
1006	30m. Kornelia Ender of East Germany (swimming)	35	25
1007	40m. Mitsuo Tsukahara of Japan (gymnastics)	50	35
1008	60m. Gregor Braun of West Germany (cycling)	85	55
1009	80m. Lasse Viren of Finland (running)	1·20	70
1010	1t. Nikolai Andrianov of USSR (gymnastics)	1·50	1·10

MS1011 103×78 mm. 4t. Zeveg Oidov of Mongolia (wrestling) (air) 4·25 4·00

217 Tablet on Tortoise

1976. Archaeology.

1012	**217**	50m. brown and blue	1·40	35
1013	-	60m. black and green	1·70	55

Design:—60m. 6th-century stele.

218 R-1 Biplane

1976. Aircraft. Multicoloured.

1014	10m. Type **218**	35	20
1015	20m. Polikarpov R-5 biplane	50	20
1016	30m. Kalinin K-5 monoplane	70	25
1017	40m. Polikarpov Po-2 biplane	85	35
1018	60m. Polikarpov I-16 jet fighter	1·20	55
1019	80m. Yakovlev Ya-6 Air 6 monoplane	1·50	70
1020	1t. Junkers F-13 monoplane	1·90	1·10

219 Dancers in Folk Costume

1977. Mongolian Folk Dances. Multicoloured.

1021	10m. Type **219**	50	20
1022	20m. Dancing girls in 13th-century costume	70	25
1023	30m. West Mongolian dance	1·00	35
1024	40m. "Ekachi" dance	1·40	45
1025	60m. "Bielge" ("Trunk") dance	1·90	55
1026	80m. "Hodak" dance	2·20	70
1027	1t. "Dojarka" dance	2·50	1·10

220 Gravitational Effects on *Pioneer*

1977. 250th Death Anniv of Sir Isaac Newton (mathematician). Multicoloured.

1028	60m. Type **220** (postage)	70	45
1029	60m. Apple tree (25×32 mm)	70	35
1030	60m. Planetary motion and sextant	70	35
1031	60m. Sir Isaac Newton (25×32 mm)	70	35
1032	60m. Spectrum of light	70	35
1033	60m. Attraction of Earth	70	35
1034	60m. Laws of motion of celestial bodies (25×32 mm)	70	35
1035	60m. Space-walking (air)	70	35
1036	60m. *Pioneer 10* and Jupiter	70	35

221 Natsagdorj, Mongolian Scenes and Extract from poem "Mother"

1977. Natsagdorj (poet) Commemoration. Multicoloured

1037	60m. Type **221**	1·00	55
1038	60m. Border stone, landscape and extract from poem "My Homeland"	1·00	55

222 Horse Race

1977. Horses. Multicoloured.

1039	10m. Type **222**	50	20
1040	20m. Girl on white horse	70	20
1041	30m. Rangeman on brown horse	85	25
1042	40m. Tethered horses	1·00	35
1043	60m. White mare with foal	1·40	55
1044	80m. Brown horse with shepherd	1·90	70
1045	1t. White horse	2·20	1·10

223 'Mongolemys elegans'

1977. Prehistoric Animals. Multicoloured.

1046	10m. Type **223**	70	20
1047	20m. 'Embolotherium ergiliense'	1·00	25
1048	30m. 'Psittacosaurus mongoliensis'	1·20	35
1049	40m. "Enthelodon'	1·50	55
1050	60m. 'Spirocerus kiakhtensis'	2·40	70
1051	80m. 'Hipparion'	3·25	90
1052	1t. 'Bos primigenius'	3·75	1·20

224 Netherlands 5c. Stamp, 1852, and Mongolian $1 Fiscal Stamp, 1926

1977. Amphilx 77 International Stamp Exhibition, Amsterdam. Sheet 100×76 mm.
MS1053 **224** 4t. multicoloured 4·25 4·00

225 Child feeding Lambs

1977. Children's Day and First Balloon Flight in Mongolia. Multicoloured.

1054	10m.+5m. Type **225** (postage)	35	20
1055	20m.+5m. Boy playing flute and girl dancing	70	25
1056	30m.+5m. Girl chasing butterflies	85	35
1057	40m.+5m. Girl with ribbon	1·20	55
1058	60m.+5m. Girl with flowers	1·70	70
1059	80m.+5m. Girl with bucket	2·20	90
1060	1t.+5m. Boy going to school	3·00	1·20

MS1061 83×72 mm. 4t.+50m. Children in balloon (air) 13·00 12·50

226 Industrial Plant and Transport

1977. Erdenet (New Town).
1062 **226** 60m. multicoloured 2·50 55

227 Trade Unions Emblem

1977. Air. 11th Mongolian Trade Unions Congress.
1063 **227** 60m. multicoloured 2·00 55

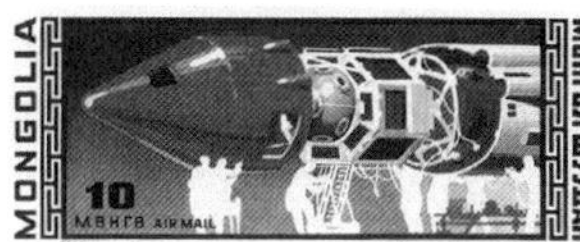

228 Mounting Bell-shaped Gear on Rocket

1977. Air. 11th Anniv of "Intercosmos" Co-operation. Multicoloured.

1064	10m. Type **228**	15	20
1065	20m. Launch of *Intercosmos 3*	35	25
1066	30m. Research ship *Kosmonavt Yury Gargarin*	50	35
1067	40m. Observation of lunar eclipse	70	55
1068	60m. Earth station's multiple antennae	1·00	70
1069	80m. Magnetosphere examination, Van Allen Zone	1·40	90
1070	1t. Meteorological satellites	1·70	1·10

MS1071 126×90 mm. 4t. Satellite linked to Intercosmos countries on globe (58×36 mm) 4·25 4·00

229 Fire-fighters' Bucket Chain

1977. Mongolian Fire-fighting Services. Multicoloured.

1072	10m. Type **229**	35	20
1073	20m. Horse-drawn hand pump	70	25
1074	30m. Horse-drawn steam pump	1·00	35
1075	40m. Fighting forest fire	1·40	45
1076	60m. Mobile foam extinguisher	1·70	55
1077	80m. Modern fire engine	2·20	70
1078	1t. Mil Mi-8 helicopter spraying fire	3·00	90

230 *Molniya* Satellite and Dish Aerial on TV Screen

1977. 40th Anniv of Technical Institute.
1079 **230** 60m. blue, black and grey 85 55

231 Black-veined White

1977. Butterflies and Moths. Multicoloured.

1080	10m. Type **231**	50	20
1081	20m. Lappet moth	1·00	25
1082	30m. Lesser clouded yellow	1·40	35
1083	40m. Dark tussock moth	2·00	45
1084	60m. Lackey moth	2·75	55

1085	80m. Clouded buff	3·50	90
1086	1t. Scarce copper	4·25	1·20

232 Lenin Museum

1977. Inauguration of Lenin Museum, Ulan Bator.

1087	**232**	60m. multicoloured	1·00	55

233 Cruiser *Aurora* and Soviet Flag

1977. 60th Anniv of Russian Revolution. Multicoloured.

1088	50m. Type **233**	1·20	35
1089	60m. Dove and globe (horiz)	1·40	55
1090	1t.50 Freedom banner around the globe (horiz)	2·20	1·10

234 Giant Pandas

1977. Giant Pandas. Multicoloured.

1091	10m. Eating bamboo shoot (vert)	35	20
1092	20m. Type **234**	70	25
1093	30m. Female and cub in washtub (vert)	1·00	35
1094	40m. Male and cub with bamboo shoot	1·40	55
1095	60m. Female and cub (vert)	2·00	70
1096	80m. Family (horiz)	3·50	1·20
1097	1t. Male on hind legs (vert)	4·00	1·60

235 *Helene Fourment and her Chilldren*

1977. 400th Birth Anniv of Peter Paul Rubens (artist). Sheet 78×104 mm.

MS1098	**235**	4t. multicoloured	8·50	8·25

236 Montgolfier Brothers' Balloon

1977. Air. Airships and Balloons. Multicoloured.

1099	20m. Type **236**	35	20
1100	30m. Airship *Graf Zeppelin* over North Pole	45	25
1101	40m. Airship *Osoaviakhim* over the Arctic	50	35
1102	50m. Soviet Airship *Sever*	70	55
1103	60m. Aereon 340 airship	1·00	70
1104	80m. Nestrenko's planned airship	1·40	90
1105	1t.20 *Flying Crane* airship	2·00	1·10
MS1106	104×75 mm. 4t. Russian Zeppelin stamp of 1931 and statue of Sukhe Bator (46×31 mm)	5·00	4·75

237 Ferrari 312-T2

1978. Racing Cars. Multicoloured.

1107	20m. Type **237**	50	20
1108	30m. Ford McLaren M-23	70	25
1109	40m. Soviet experimental car	85	35
1110	50m. Japanese Mazda	1·20	55
1111	60m. Porsche 936-Turbo	1·40	60
1112	80m. Model of Soviet car	1·70	70
1113	1t.20 American rocket car *Blue Flame*	2·20	90

238 Variegated Boletus (image scaled to 59% of original size)

1978. Mushrooms. Multicoloured.

1114	20m. Type **238**	85	20
1115	30m. The charcoal burner	1·40	35
1116	40m. Red cap	1·90	55
1117	50m. Brown birch bolete	2·40	70
1118	60m. Yellow swamp russula	3·00	90
1119	80m. *Lactarius resimus*	4·25	1·10
1120	1t.20 *Flammula spumosa*	6·00	1·60

239 Aleksandr Mozhaisky and his Monoplane, 1884

1978. Air. History of Aviation. Multicoloured.

1121	20m. Type **239**	35	20
1122	30m. Henri Farman and Farman H.F.III biplane	50	25
1123	40m. Geoffrey de Havilland and de Havilland FE-1 biplane	70	35
1124	50m. Charles Lindbergh and *Spirit of St. Louis*	85	45
1125	60m. Shagdarsuren, Demberel, biplane and glider	1·00	55
1126	80m. Chkalov, Baidukov, Belyakov and Tupolev ANT-25 airliner	1·40	70
1127	1t.20 A. N. Tupolev and Tupolev Tu-154 jetliner	2·00	1·10
MS1128	110×75 mm. 4t. Wright Brothers and *Wright Flyer III*	6·00	5·75

240 Footballers and View of Rio de Janeiro

1978. World Cup Football Championship, Argentina. Multicoloured.

1129	20m. Type **240** (postage)	35	20
1130	30m. Footballers and Old Town Tower, Berne	50	25
1131	40m. Footballers and Stockholm Town Hall	70	35
1132	50m. Footballers and University of Chile	85	45
1133	60m. Footballers, Houses of Parliament and Tower of London	1·00	55
1134	80m. Footballers and Theatre Degolladeo of Guadalajara, Mexico	1·40	70
1135	1t.20 Footballers and Munich Town Hall	2·00	1·10
MS1136	105×70 mm. 4t. Footballers (44×38 mm) (air)	6·75	6·50

241 Mongolian Youth and Girl

1978. Mongolian Youth Congress, Ulan Bator.

1137	**241**	60m. multicoloured	1·00	55

242 Eurasian Beaver and 1954 Canadian Beaver Stamp

1978. CAPEX '78 International Stamp Exhibition, Toronto. Multicoloured.

1138	20m. Type **242** (postage)	50	20
1139	30m. Tibetan sandgrouse and Canada S.G. 620	85	35
1140	40m. Black-throated diver and Canada S.G. 495	1·20	55
1141	50m. Argali and Canada S.G. 449	1·70	70
1142	60m. Brown bear and Canada S.G. 447	2·00	90
1143	80m. Elk and Canada S.G. 448	2·20	1·10
1144	1t.20 Herring gull and Canada S.G. 474	3·50	1·60
MS1145	100×80 mm. 4t. Mongolian 1969 stamp and Canadian 1971 stamp depicting paintings (58×36 mm) (air)	8·50	8·25

243 Marx, Engels and Lenin

1978. 20th Anniv of Review "Problems of Peace and Socialism".

1146	**243**	60m. red, gold and black	1·00	55

244 Map of Cuba, Liner, Tupolev Tu-134 Jetliner and Emblem

1978. Air. 11th World Youth Festival, Havana.

1147	**244**	1t. multicoloured	2·40	70

245 *Open-air Repose*

1978. 20th Anniv of Philatelic Co-operation between Mongolia and Hungary. Paintings by P. Angalan. Multicoloured.

1148	1t.50 Type **245**	2·50	1·80
1149	1t.50 *Winter Night*	2·50	1·80
1150	1t.50 *Saddling*	2·50	1·80

246 A. Gubarev, V. Remek and Exhibition Emblem

1978. Air. PRAGA 1978 International Stamp Exhibition, Prague. Sheet 103×88 mm.

MS1151	**246**	4t. multicoloured	6·00	5·75

247 Butterfly Dog

1978. Dogs. Multicoloured.

1152	10m. Type **247**	35	20
1153	20m. Black Mongolian sheepdog	50	25
1154	30m. Puli (Hungarian sheepdog)	85	35
1155	40m. St. Bernard	1·00	45
1156	50m. German shepherd dog	1·40	55
1157	60m. Mongolian watchdog	1·50	60
1158	70m. Semoyedic spitz	1·70	70
1159	80m. Laika (space dog)	2·00	90

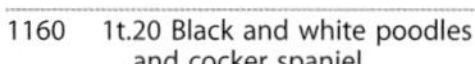

1160	1t.20 Black and white poodles and cocker spaniel	2·50	1·40

248 Open Book showing Scenes from Mongolian Literary Works

1978. 50th Anniv of Mongolian Writers' Association.

1161	**248**	60m. blue and red	85	55

249 *Dressed Maja* (Goya, 150th death anniv)

1978. Painters' Anniversaries.

1162	**249**	1t.50 multicoloured	3·00	3·00
1163	-	1t.50 multicoloured	3·00	3·00
1164	-	1t.50 multicoloured	3·00	3·00
MS1165		105×132 mm. 4t. black and stone	8·50	8·25

Designs:—As T **249**—No. 1163, *Ta Matete* (Gauguin, 75th death Anniv); 1164, *Bridge at Arles* (Van Gogh, 125th birth anniv). 49×49 mm—4t. *Melancholy* (Durer, 450th death anniv).

250 Young Bactrian Camel

1978. Bactrian Camels. Multicoloured.

1166	20m. Camel with Foal	50	25
1167	30m. Type **250**	70	35
1168	40m. Two camels	1·00	45
1169	50m. Woman leading loaded camel	1·40	55
1170	60m. Camel in winter coat	1·70	70
1171	80m. Camel-drawn water waggon	2·20	1·10
1172	1t.20 Camel racing	3·00	1·40

251 Flags of COMECON Countries

1979. 30th Anniv of Council of Mutual Economic Assistance.

1173	**251**	60m. multicoloured	85	55

252 Children riding Camel

1979. International Year of the Child. Multicoloured.

1174	10m.+5m. Type **252**	50	20
1175	30m.+5m. Children feeding chickens	70	35
1176	50m.+5m. Children with deer	85	45
1177	60m.+5m. Children picking flowers	1·20	60
1178	70m.+5m. Children watering tree	1·50	70
1179	80m.+5m. Young scientists	1·70	90
1180	1t.+5m. Making music and dancing	2·00	1·10

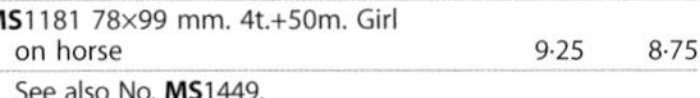

MS1181	78×99 mm. 4t.+50m. Girl on horse	9·25	8·75

See also No. **MS**1449.

253 Silver Tabby

1978. Domestic Cats. Multicoloured.

1182	10m. Type **253**	50	20
1183	30m. White Persian	85	25
1184	50m. Red Persian	1·20	35
1185	60m. Blue-cream Persian	1·70	55
1186	70m. Siamese	2·00	70
1187	80m. Smoke Persian	2·20	90
1188	1t. Birman	2·50	1·20

254 *Potaninia mongolica*

1979. Flowers. Multicoloured.

1189	10m. Type **254**	50	20
1190	30m. *Sophora alopecuroides*	85	25
1191	50m. *Halimodendron halodendron*	1·00	35
1192	60m. *Myosotis asiatica*	1·20	55
1193	70m. *Scabiosa comosa*	1·40	70
1194	80m. *Leucanthemum sibiricum*	1·50	90
1195	1t. *Leontopodium ochroleucum*	1·70	1·20

255 Finland v. Czechoslovakia

1979. World Ice Hockey Championships, Moscow. Multicoloured.

1196	10m. Type **255**	15	20
1197	30m. West Germany v. Sweden	35	25
1198	50m. USA v. Canada	50	35
1199	60m. Russia v. Sweden	70	45
1200	70m. Canada v. Russia	85	55
1201	80m. Swedish goalkeeper	1·00	70
1202	1t. Czechoslovakia v. Russia	1·40	90

256 *Lambs* (Sanzhid)

1979. Agriculture Paintings. Multicoloured.

1203	10m. Type **256**	15	20
1204	30m. *Milking camels* (Budbazar)	50	25
1205	50m. *Aircraft bringing help* (Radnabazar)	85	35
1206	60m. *Herdsmen* (Budbazar)	1·00	55
1207	70m. *Milkmaids* (Nanzadsguren) (vert)	1·20	60
1208	80m. *Summer Evening* (Sanzhid)	1·70	70
1209	1t. *Country Landscape* (Tserendondog)	2·20	90
MS1210	86×70 mm. 4t. *After Rain* (Khaidav)	8·50	8·25

257 First Mongolian and Bulgarian Stamps

1979. Death Centenary of Sir Rowland Hill, and Philaserdica 79 International Stamp Exhibition, Sofia. Each black, grey and brown.

1211	1t. Type **257**	3·50	2·30
1212	1t. American mail coach	3·50	2·30
1213	1t. Travelling post office, London–Birmingham railway	3·50	2·30
1214	1t. Paddle-steamer *Hindoostan*	3·50	2·30

258 Stephenson's *Rocket*

1979. Development of Railways. Multicoloured.

1215	10m. Type **258**	35	20
1216	20m. Locomotive *Adler*, 1835, Germany	70	20
1217	30m. Steam locomotive, 1860, USA	1·00	25
1218	40m. Class KB4 steam locomotive, 1931, Mongolia	1·20	35
1219	50m. Class Er steam locomotive, 1936, Mongolia	1·40	55
1220	60m. Diesel train, 1970, Mongolia	1·50	60
1221	70m. Hikari express train, 1963, Japan	2·00	70
1222	80m. Monorail aerotrain *Orleans*, France	2·20	1·10
1223	1t.20 Experimental jet train *Rapidity*, Russia	2·40	1·40

259 Flags of Mongolia and Russia

1979. 40th Anniv of Battle of Khalka River.

1224	**259**	60m. gold, red and yellow	1·00	55
1225	-	60m. red, yellow and blue	1·00	55

Design:—No. 1225, Ribbons, badge and military scene.

260 Pallas's Cat

1979. Wild Cats. Multicoloured.

1226	10m. Type **260**	35	20
1227	30m. Lynx	85	35
1228	50m. Tiger	1·40	45
1229	60m. Snow leopard	1·50	55
1230	70m. Leopard	1·90	70
1231	80m. Cheetah	2·00	90
1232	1t. Lion	3·00	1·20

262 East German Flag, Berlin Buildings and *Soyuz 31*

1979. 30th Anniv of German Democratic Republic (East Germany).

1234	**262**	60m. multicoloured	1·00	55

263 Demoiselle Crane

1979. Air. Protected Birds. Multicoloured.

1235	10m. Type **263**	70	25
1236	30m. Barred warbler	1·00	35
1237	50m. Ruddy shelduck	1·40	45
1238	60m. Azure-winged magpie	1·70	55
1239	70m. Goldfinch	2·00	60
1240	80m. Great tit	2·40	70
1241	1t. Golden oriole	2·75	90

264 *Venus 5* and *6*

1979. Air. Space Research. Multicoloured.

1242	10m. Type **264**	15	20
1243	30m. *Mariner 5*	35	25
1244	50m. *Mars 3*	50	35
1245	60m. *Viking 1* and *2*	70	45
1246	70m. *Luna 1, 2* and *3*	85	55
1247	80m. *Lunokhod 2*	1·00	60
1248	1t. *Apollo 15* Moon-rover	1·20	70
MS1249	83×77 mm. 4t. Armstrong and Aldrin on Moon	4·25	4·00

265 Cross-country Skiing

1980. Winter Olympic Games, Lake Placid. Multicoloured.

1250	20m. Type **265**	15	20
1251	30m. Biathlon	35	20
1252	40m. Ice hockey	50	25
1253	50m. Ski jumping	70	35
1254	60m. Slalom	85	55
1255	80m. Speed skating	1·00	70
1256	1t.20 Four-man bobsleigh	1·20	90
MS1257	90×105 mm. 4t. Ice skating	4·25	4·00

266 *Andrena scita* (mining bee)

1980. Air. Wasps and Bees. Multicoloured.

1258	20m. Type **266**	50	20
1259	30m. *Paravespula germanica* (wasp)	70	35
1260	40m. *Perilampus ruficornis* (parasitic wasp)	85	55
1261	50m. Buff-tailed bumble bee	1·00	60
1262	60m. Honey bee	1·20	70
1263	80m. *Stilbum cyanurum* (large cuckoo wasp)	1·50	90
1264	1t.20 *Parnopes grandior* (cuckoo wasp)	2·40	1·10

1980. London 1980 International Stamp Exhibition. Sheet 95×64 mm.

MS1265	**117**	4t. multicoloured	4·25	4·00

267 Weightlifting

1980. Olympic Games, Moscow. Multicoloured.

1266	20m. Type **267**	15	20
1267	30m. Archery	35	25
1268	40m. Gymnastics	50	35
1269	50m. Running	70	45
1270	60m. Boxing	85	55
1271	80m. Judo	1·00	60
1272	1t.20 Cycling	1·20	90
MS1273	91×84 mm. 4t. Wrestling	4·25	4·00

268 Zlin Z-526 AFs Akrobat Special

1980. Air. World Acrobatic Championship, Oshkosh, Wisconsin. Multicoloured.

1274	20m. Type **268**	15	20
1275	30m. Socata RF-6B Sportsman (inscr "RS-180")	35	25
1276	40m. Grumman A-1 Yankee	50	35
1277	50m. MJ-2 Tempete	70	45
1278	60m. Pitts S-2A biplane (inscr "Pits")	85	55
1279	80m. Hirth Acrostar	1·00	70
1280	1t.20 Yakovlev Yak-50	1·50	90
MS1281	89×68 mm. 4t. Yakolev Yak-52 (49×42 mm)	5·00	4·75

269 Swimming

1980. Olympic Medal Winners. Multicoloured.

1282	20m. Type **269** (postage)	15	20
1283	30m. Fencing	35	25
1284	50m. Judo	50	35
1285	60m. Athletics	70	45
1286	80m. Boxing	85	55
1287	1t. Weightlifting	1·20	70
1288	1t.20 Kayak-canoe	1·50	90
MS1289	112×95 mm. 4t. Wrestling (silver medal, J. Davaazhav of Mongolia) (air)	4·25	4·00

270 Sukhe Bator

1980. Mongolian Politicians.

1290	**270**	60m. brown	50	35
1291	-	60m. blue	50	35
1292	-	60m. turquoise	50	35
1293	-	60m. bronze	50	35
1294	-	60m. green	50	35
1295	-	60m. red	50	35
1296	-	60m. brown	50	35

Designs:—Vert: No. 1291, Marshal Choibalsan; 1292, Yu. Tsedenbal aged 13; 1293, Tsedenbal as soldier, 1941; 1294, Pres. Tsedenbal in 1979; 1295, Tsedenbal with children. Horiz: No. 1296, Tsedenbal and President Brezhnev of Russia.

See also **MS**1522.

271 Gubarev

1980. Intercosmos Space Programme. Multicoloured.

1297	40m. Type **271**	50	35
1298	40m. Czechoslovak stamp showing Gubarev and Remek	50	35
1299	40m. P. Klimuk	50	35
1300	40m. Polish stamp showing M. Hermaszewski	50	35
1301	40m. V. Bykovsky	50	35
1302	40m. East German stamp showing S. Jahn	50	35
1303	40m. N. Rukavishnikov	50	35
1304	40m. Bulgarian stamp showing G. Ivanov	50	35
1305	40m. V. Kubasov	50	35
1306	40m. Hungarian stamp showing Kubasov and B. Farkas	50	35

272 Benz, 1885

1980. Classic Cars. Multicoloured.

1307	20m. Type **272**	35	20
1308	30m. President Czechoslovakia, 1897	50	25
1309	40m. Armstrong Siddeley, 1904	85	35
1310	50m. Russo-Balt, 1909	1·00	55
1311	60m. Packard, 1909	1·20	70
1312	80m. Lancia, 1911	1·70	90
1313	1t.60 Marne taxi, 1914	3·75	1·60
MS1314	70×90 mm. 4t. NAMI-1, Russia, 1927	10·00	9·75

273 Adelie Penguin

1980. Antarctic Exploration. Multicoloured.

1315	20m. Type **273**	1·40	35
1316	30m. Blue whales	2·00	55
1317	40m. Wandering albatross and Jacques Cousteau's ship *Calypso* and bathysphere	2·50	70
1318	50m. Weddell seals and mobile research station	3·00	80
1319	60m. Emperor penguins	3·75	90
1320	70m. Great skuas	4·25	1·20
1321	80m. Killer whales	5·00	1·40
1322	1t.20 Adelie penguins, research station, Ilyushin Il-18B airplane and tracked vehicle	6·75	2·10
MS1323	90×120 mm. 4t. Map of Antarctica during carbon age (*circular*, 43 mm diameter)	17·00	16·00

274 Kepler

1980. Air. 350th Death Anniv of Johannes Kepler (astronomer). Sheet 98×78 mm.

MS1324	**274** 4t. black and yellow	6·00	5·75

275 *Yurta Picture*

1980. 50th Anniv of Gombosuren (painter). Sheet 80×98 mm containing T **275** and similar horiz design. Multicoloured.

MS1325	2t. Type **275**; 2t. *Old-time Market*	4·25	4·00

276 *The Shepherd speaking the Truth*

1980. Nursery Tales. Multicoloured.

1326	20m. Type **276**	15	20
1327	30m. Children under umbrella and rainbow (*Above them the Sky is always clear*)	35	20
1328	40m. Children on sledge and skis (*Winter's Joys*)	50	25
1329	50m. Girl watching boy playing flute (*Little Musicians*)	70	35
1330	60m. Boys giving girl leaves (*Happy Birthday*)	85	55
1331	80m. Children with flowers and briefcase (*First Schoolday*)	1·00	70
1332	1t.20 Girls dancing (*May Day*)	1·20	90
MS1333	79×89 mm. Children and squirrels (*The Wonder-working Squirrels*)	5·00	4·75

277 Soldier

1981. 60th Anniv of Mongolian People's Army.

1334	**277** 60m. multicoloured	1·00	55

278 Economy Emblems within Party Initials

1981. 60th Anniv of Mongolian Revolutionary People's Party.

1335	**278** 60m. gold, red and black	1·00	55

See also No. **MS**1358.

279 Motocross

1981. Motor Cycle Sports. Multicoloured.

1336	10m. Type **279**	15	20
1337	20m. Tour racing	35	20
1338	30m. Ice racing	50	20
1339	40m. Road racing	60	20
1340	50m. Motocross (different)	70	25
1341	60m. Road racing (different)	75	25
1342	70m. Speedway	85	35
1343	80m. Sidecar racing	95	45
1344	1t.20 Road racing (different)	1·00	55

280 Cosmonauts entering Space Capsule

1981. Soviet–Mongolian Space Flight. Multicoloured

1345	20m. Type **280**	35	20
1346	30m. Rocket and designer S. P. Korolev	45	25
1347	40m. *Vostok 1* and Yuri Gagarin	50	35
1348	50m. Soyuz–Salyut space station	60	45
1349	60m. Spectral photography	70	55
1350	80m. Crystal and space station	1·00	70
1351	1t.20 Space complex, Moscow Kremlin and Sukhe Bator statue, Ulan Bator	1·40	1·10
MS1352	70×80 mm. 4t. Cosmonauts Dzhanibekov and Gurragchaa (31×42 mm)	4·25	4·00

281 Ulan Bator Buildings and 1961 Mongolian Stamp

1981. Stamp Exhibitions.

1353	**281**	1t. multicoloured	4·25	2·10
1354	-	1t. multicoloured	4·25	2·10
1355	-	1t. black, blue and magenta	4·25	2·10
1356	-	1t. multicoloured	4·25	2·10

Designs:—No. 1353, Type **281** (Mongolian stamp exhibition); 1354, Wurttemberg stamps of 1947 and 1949 and view of Old Stuttgart (Naposta '81 exhibition); 1355, Parliament building and sculpture, Vienna, and Austrian stamp of 1933 (WIPA 1981 exhibition); 1356, Japanese stamp of 1964, cherry blossom and girls in Japanese costume (Japex '81 exhibition, Tokyo).

282 Star and Industrial and Agricultural Scenes

1981. 18th Mongolian Revolutionary People's Party Congress.

1357	**282** 60m. multicoloured	85	55

283 Sukhe Bator Statue, Ulan Bator

1981. 60th Anniv of Mongolian Revolutionary People's Party (2nd issue). Sheet 70×90 mm.

MS1358	**283** 4t. multicoloured	5·00	4·75

284 Sheep Farming

1981. Results of the People's Economy. Multicoloured.

1359	20m. Type **284**	35	20
1360	30m. Transport	50	25
1361	40m. Telecommunications	70	35
1362	50m. Public health service	85	45
1363	60m. Agriculture	1·00	55
1364	80m. Electrical industry	1·40	70
1365	1t.20 Housing	2·00	1·10

285 UN Emblem

1981. 20th Anniv of United Nations Membership. Sheet 70×90 mm.

MS1366	**285** 4t. multicoloured	4·25	4·00

286 Pharaonic Ship (15th-century BC)

1981. Sailing Ships. Multicoloured.

1367	10m. Type **286**	35	20
1368	20m. Mediterranean sailing ship (9th-century)	50	25
1369	40m. Hanse kogge (12th-century) (vert)	70	35
1370	50m. Venetian felucca (13th-century) (vert)	1·00	55
1371	60m. Columbus's *Santa Maria* (vert)	1·20	60
1372	80m. Cook's HMS *Endeavour* (vert)	1·40	70
1373	1t. *Poltava* (Russian ship of the line) (vert)	1·70	90
1374	1t.20 American schooner (19th-century) (vert)	2·00	1·10

287 Arms of Mongolia and Russia

1981. Soviet–Mongolian Friendship Pact.

1375	**287** 60m. red, blue and gold	1·00	55

288 *Hendrickje in Bed*

1981. 375th Birth Anniv of Rembrandt (artist). Multicoloured.

1376	20m. *Flora*	35	20
1377	30m. Type **288**	50	25
1378	40m. *Young Woman with Earrings*	85	35
1379	50m. *Young girl in the Window*	1·00	45
1380	60m. *Hendrickje like Flora*	1·40	55
1381	80m. *Saskia with Red Flower*	1·90	70
1382	1t.20 *The Holy Family with Drape* (detail)	2·50	90
MS1383	68×85 mm. 4t. *Self-portrait with Saskia*	8·50	8·25

289 Billy Goat (pawn)

1981. Mongolian Chess Pieces. Multicoloured.

1384	20m. Type **289**	50	20
1385	40m. Horse-drawn cart (rook)	1·00	35
1386	50m. Camel (bishop)	1·20	55
1387	60m. Horse (knight)	1·40	70
1388	80m. Lion (queen)	1·90	90
1389	1t.20 Man with dog (king)	2·50	1·40
MS1390	90×70 mm. 4t. Chess game (illustration of Mongolian folk tale)	8·50	8·25

290 White-tailed Sea Eagle and German 1m. Zeppelin Stamp

1981. Air. 50th Anniv of "Graf Zeppelin" Polar Flight. Multicoloured.

1391	20m. Type **290**	70	35
1392	30m. Arctic fox and German 2m. Zeppelin stamp	85	45
1393	40m. Walrus and German 4m. Zeppelin stamp	1·00	55
1394	50m. Polar bear and Russian 30k. Zeppelin stamp	1·20	60
1395	60m. Snowy owl and Russian 35k. Zeppelin stamp	1·90	70
1396	80m. Atlantic puffin and Russian 1r. Zeppelin stamp	2·20	1·10
1397	1t.20 Northern sealion and Russian 2r. Zeppelin stamp	2·50	1·20
MS1398	93×77 mm. 4t. *Graf Zeppelin* and Russian ice-breaker *Malygin* (36×51 mm)	8·50	8·25

291 Circus Camel and Circus Building, Ulan Bator

1981. Mongolian Sport and Art. Multicoloured.

1399	10m. Type **291**	15	20
1400	20m. Horsemen and stadium (National holiday cavalcade)	35	25
1401	40m. Wrestling and Ulan Bator stadium	70	35
1402	50m. Archers and stadium	85	45
1403	60m. Folk singer-dancer and House of Culture	1·00	55
1404	80m. Girl playing jatga (folk instrument) and Ulan Bator Drama Theatre	1·40	70
1405	1t. Ballet dancers and Opera House	1·90	1·10
1406	1t.20 Exhibition Hall and statue of man on bucking horse	2·20	1·20

292 Mozart and scene from *The Magic Flute*

1981. Composers. Multicoloured.

1407	20m. Type **292**	50	20
1408	30m. Beethoven and scene from *Fidelio*	60	25
1409	40m. Bartok and scene from *The Miraculous Mandarin*	70	35
1410	50m. Verdi and scene from *Aida*	85	45
1411	60m. Tchaikovsky and scene from *The Sleeping Beauty*	1·00	60
1412	80m. Dvorak and score of *New World* symphony	1·40	70
1413	1t.20 Chopin, piano, score and quill pens	2·00	1·10

293 *Mongolian Women in Everyday Life* (detail, Davaakhuu)

1981. International Decade for Women. Multicoloured

1414	20m. Type **293**	50	20
1415	30m. *Mongolian Women in Everyday Life* (different detail)	70	35
1416	40m. *National Day* (detail, Khishigbaiar)	85	45
1417	50m. *National Day* (detail) (different)	1·00	55
1418	60m. *National Day* (detail) (different)	1·20	90
1419	80m. *Ribbon Weaver* (Ts. Baidi)	1·70	1·10
1420	1t.20 *Expectant Mother* (Senghesokhio)	2·50	1·80

294 Gorbatko

1981. Intercosmos Space Programme. Multicoloured

1422	50m. Type **294**	70	35
1423	50m. Vietnam stamp showing Gorbatko and Pham Tuan	70	35
1424	50m. Romanenko	70	35
1425	50m. Cuban stamp showing Tamayo	70	35
1426	50m. Dzhanibekov	70	35
1427	50m. Mongolian stamp showing Dzhanibekov and Gurrugchaa	70	35
1428	50m. Popov	70	35
1429	50m. Rumanian stamp showing Salyut space station and Soyuz space ship	70	35

295 Karl von Drais Bicycle, 1816

1982. History of the Bicycle. Multicoloured.

1430	10m. Type **295**	15	20
1431	20m. Macmillan bicycle, 1838	35	20
1432	40m. First American pedal bicycle by Pierre Lallament, 1866	50	25
1433	50m. First European pedal bicycle by Ernest Michaux	70	35
1434	60m. "Kangaroo" bicycle, 1877	85	45
1435	80m. Coventry Rotary Tandem, 1870s	1·00	55
1436	1t. Chain-driven bicycle, 1878	1·20	60
1437	1t.20 Modern bicycle	1·40	70
MS1438	95×90 mm. 4t. Modern road racers (43×43 mm)	5·00	4·75

296 Footballers (Brazil, 1950)

1982. World Cup Football Championship, Spain. Multicoloured.

1439	10m. Type **296** (postage)	15	20
1440	20m. Switzerland, 1954	35	20
1441	40m. Sweden, 1958	50	25
1442	50m. Chile, 1962	70	35
1443	60m. England, 1966	85	45
1444	80m. Mexico, 1970	1·00	55
1445	1t. West Germany, 1974	1·20	60
1446	1t.20 Argentina, 1978	1·40	70
MS1447	90×70 mm. 4t. Spain, 1982 (44×44 mm) (air)	5·00	4·75

297 Trade Union Emblem and Economic Symbols

1982. 12th Mongolian Trade Unions Congress.

1448	**297**	60m. multicoloured	2·50	90

298 Children with Deer

1982. Philefrance 82 International Stamp Exhibition, Paris. Sheet 105×68 mm.

MS1449	**298**	4t. multicoloured	5·00	4·75

For 50m.+5m. as Type **298** but larger, see No. 1176.

299 Dimitrov

1982. Birth Centenary of Georgi Dimitrov (Bulgarian statesman).

1450	**299**	60m. black, grey and gold	1·00	55

300 Chicks

1982. Young Animals. Multicoloured.

1451	10m. Type **300**	15	20
1452	20m. Colt	35	20
1453	30m. Lamb	45	20
1454	40m. Roe deer fawn	50	20
1455	50m. Bactrian camel	70	25
1456	60m. Kid	85	35
1457	70m. Calf	1·00	45
1458	1t.20 Wild piglet	1·20	55

301 Coal-fired Industry

1982. Coal Mining.

1459	**301**	60m. multicoloured	1·00	55

302 Emblem

1982. 18th Revsomol Youth Congress.

1460	**302**	60m. multicoloured	1·00	55

303 Siberian Pine

1982. Trees. Multicoloured.

1461	20m. Type **303**	15	20
1462	30m. Siberian fir	35	20
1463	40m. Poplar	50	25
1464	50m. Siberian larch	70	45
1465	60m. Scots pine	85	55
1466	80m. Birch	1·00	60
1467	1t.20 Spruce	1·50	70

304 Revsomol Emblem within "Flower"

1982. 60th Anniv of Revsomol Youth Organization.

1468	**304**	60m. multicoloured	1·00	55

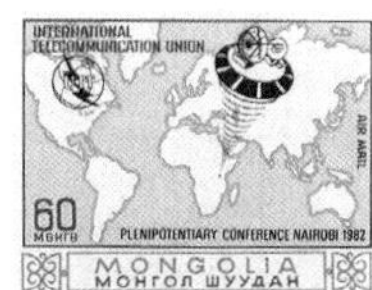

305 World Map and Satellite

1982. Air. I.T.U. Delegates' Conference, Nairobi.

1469	**305**	60m. multicoloured	1·20	70

306 Japanese Iseki-6500 Tractor

1982. Tractors. Multicoloured.

1470	10m. Type **306**	15	20
1471	20m. West German Deutz-DX230	35	20
1472	40m. British Bonser	50	25
1473	50m. American International-884	70	35
1474	60m. French Renault TX 145-14	85	45
1475	80m. Russian Belarus-611	1·00	55
1476	1t. Russian K-7100	1·20	60
1477	1t.20 Russian DT-75	1·40	70

307 Hump-backed Whitefish and Lake Hevsgel

1982. Landscapes and Animals. Multicoloured.

1478	20m. Type **307**	35	20
1479	30m. Zavkhan Highlands and sheep	45	25
1480	40m. Lake Hovd and Eurasian beaver	50	35
1481	50m. Lake Uvs and horses	70	55
1482	60m. Bajankhongor Steppe and goitred gazelle	85	60
1483	80m. Bajan-Elgii Highlands and rider with golden eagle	3·50	70
1484	1t.20 Gobi Desert and bactrian camels	2·50	90

308 *Sputnik 1*

1982. Air. Second U.N. Conference on the Exploration and Peaceful Uses of Outer Space. Multicoloured.

1485	60m. Type **308**	70	35
1486	60m. *Sputnik 2* and Laika (first dog in space)	70	35
1487	60m. *Vostok 1* and Yuri Gagarin (first man in space)	70	35
1488	60m. *Venera 8*	70	35
1489	60m. *Vostok 6* and V. Tereshkova (first woman in space)	70	35
1490	60m. Aleksei Leonov and space walker	70	35
1491	60m. Neil Armstrong and astronaut on Moon's surface	70	35
1492	60m. V. Dzhanibekov, Jean-Loup Chretien and *Soyuz T-6*	70	35
MS1493	88×70 mm. 4t. Soyuz and Salyut coupling (49×33 mm)	5·00	4·75

309 Montgolfier Brothers' Balloon, 1783

1982. Air. Bicentenary of Manned Flight. Multicoloured

1494	20m. Type **309**	15	20
1495	30m. Jean-Pierre Blanchard and John Jeffries crossing the channel, 1785	35	20
1496	40m. Charles Green's flight to Germany in balloon *Royal Vauxhall*, 1836	50	25

1497	50m. Salomon Andree's North Pole flight in balloon *Ornen*, 1897	70	35
1498	60m. First Gordon Bennett balloon race, Paris, 1906	85	45
1499	80m. First stratosphere flight by Auguste Piccard in balloon *FNRS*, Switzerland, 1931	1·00	55
1500	1t.20 Stratosphere balloon USSR-VR-62 flight, 1933	1·70	70
MS1501	78×98 mm. 4t. First Mongolian balloon flight, 1977	5·00	4·75

310 Sorcerer tells Mickey Mouse to clean up Quarters

1983. Drawings from "The Sorcerer's Apprentice" (section of Walt Disney's film "Fantasia"). Multicoloured

1502	25m. Type **310**	35	20
1503	35m. Mickey notices Sorcerer has left his cap behind	50	35
1504	45m. Mickey puts cap on and commands broom to fetch water	70	45
1505	55m. Broom carrying water	85	55
1506	65m. Mickey sleeps while broom continues to fetch water, flooding the room	1·00	70
1507	75m. Mickey uses axe on broom to try to stop it	1·20	80
1508	85m. Each splinter becomes a broom which continues to fetch water	1·50	90
1509	1t.40 Mickey, clinging to Sorcerer's Book of Spells, caught in whirlpool	2·40	1·20
1510	2t. Mickey handing cap back to Sorcerer	3·50	1·80
MS1511	127×102 mm. 7t. Mickey dreaming himself to be Master of the Universe	13·00	12·50

311 Foal with Mother

1983. The Foal and the Hare (folk tale). Multicoloured

1512	10m. Type **311**	15	20
1513	20m. Foal wanders off alone	35	25
1514	30m. Foal finds sack	50	35
1515	40m. Foal unties sack	70	45
1516	50m. Wolf jumps out of sack	85	55
1517	60m. Hare appears as wolf is about to eat foal	1·00	70
1518	70m. Hare tricks wolf into re-entering sack	1·70	80
1519	80m. Hare ties up sack with wolf inside	1·90	90
1520	1t.20 Hare and foal look for foal's mother	2·40	1·10
MS1521	121×94 mm. 7t. Boy with foal (58×58 mm). Imperf	13·00	12·50

311a Tank Monument, Ulan Bator

1983. Air. 40th Anniv of Formation of "Revolutionary Mongolia" Tank Regiment of Soviet Army. Sheet 110×75 mm.

MS1522	**311a** 4t. multicoloured	5·00	4·75

1983. 90th Birth Anniv of Sukhe Bator. Sheet 65×72 mm containing designs as T **270** but smaller, 25×32 mm.

MS1523	**270** 4t. purple	5·00	4·75

312 Antonov An-24B Aircraft

1983. Tourism. Multicoloured.

1524	20m. Type **312**	50	20
1525	30m. Skin tent	70	25
1526	40m. Roe deer	85	35
1527	50m. Argali	1·20	55
1528	60m. Imperial eagle	3·50	90
1529	80m. Khan Museum, Ulan Bator	2·00	70
1530	1t.20 Sukhe Bator statue, Ulan Bator	2·40	90

313 Rose

1983. Flowers. Multicoloured.

1531	20m. Type **313**	35	20
1532	30m. Dahlia	45	20
1533	40m. Marigold	50	25
1534	50m. Narcissus	70	35
1535	60m. Viola	85	45
1536	80m. Tulip	1·00	55
1537	1t.20 Sunflower	1·20	70

314 Border Guard

1983. 50th Anniv of Border Guards.

1538	**314** 60m. multicoloured	1·00	55

315 Boy riding Buffalo (image scaled to 38% of original size)

1983. Brasiliana 83 International Stamp Exhibition, Rio de Janeiro. Sheet 135×88 mm.

MS1539	**325** 4t. multicoloured	5·00	4·75

316 Karl Marx

1983. Death Centenary of Karl Marx.

1540	**316** 60m. red, gold and blue	1·00	55

317 Agriculture

1983. 18th Communist Party Congress Five Year Plan. Multicoloured.

1541	10m. Type **317**	25	20
1542	20m. Power industry	35	25
1543	30m. Textile industry	50	35
1544	40m. Science in industry and agriculture	70	45
1545	60m. Improvement of living standards	1·00	55
1546	80m. Communications	4·25	1·10
1547	1t. Children (education)	1·70	90

318 Young Inventors

1983. Children's Year. Multicoloured.

1548	10m. Type **318**	35	20
1549	20m. In school	50	25
1550	30m. Archery	70	35
1551	40m. Shepherdess playing flute	1·20	55
1552	50m. Girl with deer	1·70	70
1553	70m. Collecting rocks and mushrooms	4·50	1·10
1554	1t.20 Girl playing lute and boy singing	3·00	1·40

319 Skating

1983. Tenth Anniv of Children's Fund. Multicoloured

1555	20m. Type **319**	35	20
1556	30m. Shepherds	45	20
1557	40m. Tree-planting	50	25
1558	50m. Playing by the sea	70	35
1559	60m. Carrying water	85	55
1560	80m. Folk dancing	1·00	60
1561	1t.20 Ballet	1·70	70
MS1562	93×110 mm. 4t. Christmas	5·00	4·75

320 Pallas's Pika

1983. Small Mammals. Multicoloured.

1563	20m. Type **320**	70	35
1564	30m. Long-eared jerboa	1·20	55
1565	40m. Eurasian red squirrel	1·50	70
1566	50m. Daurian hedgehog	1·90	90
1567	60m. Harvest mouse	2·40	1·10
1568	80m. Eurasian water shrew	3·00	1·60
1569	1t.20 Siberian chipmunk	4·00	2·30

321 *Sistine Madonna*

1983. 500th Birth Anniv of Raphael (artist). Sheet 102×138 mm.

MS1570	**321** 4t. multicoloured	8·50	8·25

322 Bobsleighing

1984. Winter Olympic Games, Sarajevo. Multicoloured

1571	20m. Type **322**	25	20
1572	30m. Cross-country skiing	35	20
1573	40m. Ice hockey	45	25
1574	50m. Speed skating	50	35
1575	60m. Ski jumping	70	45
1576	80m. Ice dancing	85	55
1577	1t.20 Biathlon (horiz)	1·00	70
MS1578	133×105 mm. 4t. Ski jumping (horiz)	4·75	4·50

323 Mail Van

1984. World Communications Year. Multicoloured.

1579	10m. Type **323**	35	20
1580	20m. Earth receiving station	50	35
1581	40m. Airliner	70	55
1582	50m. Central Post Office, Ulan Bator	85	70
1583	1t. Transmitter	1·90	90
1584	1t.20 Diesel train	5·00	2·30
MS1585	90×110 mm. 4t. Aerials (41×22 mm)	5·00	4·75

324 Ausipex 84 Emblem and Tupolev Tu-154

1984. Espana 84, Madrid and Ausipex 84, Melbourne, International Stamp Exhibitions. Sheet 104×90 mm.

MS1586	**324** 4t. multicoloured	6·75	6·50

325 Cycling

1984. Olympic Games, Los Angeles. Multicoloured.

1587	20m. Gymnastics (horiz)	25	20
1588	30m. Type **325**	35	20
1589	40m. Weightlifting	45	25
1590	50m. Judo	50	35
1591	60m. Archery	60	45
1592	80m. Boxing	70	55
1593	1t.20 High jumping (horiz)	85	70
MS1594	105×85 mm. 4t. Wrestling (horiz)	5·00	4·75

326 Flag, Rocket and Coastal Scene

1984. 25th Anniv of Cuban Revolution.

1595	**326** 60m. multicoloured	1·00	55

327 1924 1c. Stamp

1984. 60th Anniv of Mongolian Stamps. Sheet 90×110 mm.

MS1596	**327** 4t. multicoloured	5·00	4·75

328 Douglas DC-10

1984. Air. Civil Aviation. Multicoloured.

1597	20m. Type **328**	35	20
1598	30m. Airbus Industrie A300B2	50	35
1599	40m. Concorde supersonic jetliner	70	55
1600	50m. Boeing 747-200	85	60
1601	60m. Ilyushin Il-62M	1·00	70
1602	80m. Tupolev Tu-154	1·40	90
1603	1t.20 Ilyushin Il-86	2·00	1·10
MS1604 110×90 mm. 4t. Yakovlev Yak-42		6·75	6·50

329 Speaker, Radio and Transmitter

1984. 50th Anniv of Mongolian Broadcasting.

1605	**329**	60m. multicoloured	1·40	70

330 Silver and Gold Coins

1984. 60th Anniv of State Bank.

1606	**330**	60m. multicoloured	85	55

331 Donshy Mask

1984. Traditional Masks. Multicoloured.

1607	20m. Type **331**	50	20
1608	30m. Zamandi	70	35
1609	40m. Ulaan-Yadam	85	55
1610	50m. Lkham	1·00	60
1611	60m. Damdinchoizhoo	1·20	70
1612	80m. Ochirvaan	1·50	80
1613	1t.20 Namsrai	2·40	90
MS1614 90×110 mm. 4t. Ulaanzhamsran		8·50	8·25

332 Golden Harp

1984. Scenes from Walt Disney's *Mickey and the Beanstalk* (cartoon film). Multicoloured.

1615	25m. Type **332**	50	20
1616	35m. Mickey holding box of magic beans	70	35
1617	45m. Mickey about to eat bean	1·00	45
1618	55m. Mickey looking for magic bean	1·20	55
1619	65m. Goofy, Mickey and Donald at top of beanstalk	1·40	70
1620	75m. Giant holding Mickey	1·70	90
1621	85m. Giant threatening Mickey	1·90	1·10
1622	140m. Goofy, Mickey and Donald cutting down beanstalk	2·75	1·40
1623	2t. Goofy and Donald rescuing golden harp	4·25	1·80
MS1624 126×101 mm. 7t. Mickey, Goofy, Donald and giant plants (50×37 mm)		15·00	14·50

333 Sukhe Bator Statue

1984. 60th Anniv of Ulan Bator City.

1625	**333**	60m. multicoloured	1·40	70

334 Arms, Flag and Landscape

1984. 60th Anniv of Mongolian People's Republic.

1626	**334**	60m. multicoloured	1·40	70

335 Rider carrying Flag

1984. 60th Anniv of Mongolian People's Revolutionary Party.

1627	**335**	60m. multicoloured	1·00	55

336 Collie

1984. Dogs. Multicoloured.

1628	20m. Type **336**	35	20
1629	30m. German shepherd	50	35
1630	40m. Papillon	70	45
1631	50m. Cocker spaniel	1·00	55
1632	60m. Terrier puppy (diamond-shaped)	1·20	60
1633	80m. Dalmatians (diamond-shaped)	1·50	70
1634	1t.20 Mongolian shepherd	2·40	1·10

337 Gaetan Boucher (speed skating)

1984. Winter Olympic Gold Medal Winners. Multicoloured.

1635	20m. Type **337**	35	20
1636	30m. Eirik Kvalfoss (biathlon)	50	35
1637	40m. Marja-Liisa Hamalainen (cross-country skiing)	70	55
1638	50m. Max Julen (slalom)	85	60
1639	60m. Jens Weissflog (ski jumping) (vert)	1·00	70
1640	80m. W. Hoppe and D. Schauerhammer (two-man bobsleigh) (vert)	1·20	90
1641	1t.20 J. Valova and O. Vassiliev (pairs figure skating) (vert)	1·40	1·10
MS1642 110×90 mm. 4t. Russia (ice hockey)		5·00	4·75

338 Four Animals and Tree

1984. *The Four Friendly Animals* (fairy tale). Multicoloured.

1643	10m. Type **338**	15	20
1644	20m. Animals discussing who was the oldest	35	20
1645	30m. Monkey and elephant beside tree	50	25
1646	40m. Elephant as calf and young tree	70	35
1647	50m. Monkey and young tree	85	45
1648	60m. Hare and young tree	1·00	55
1649	70m. Dove and sapling	1·20	70
1650	80m. Animals around mature tree	1·50	90
1651	1t.20 Animals supporting each other so that dove could reach fruit	2·20	1·20
MS1652 103×84 mm. 4t. Dove passing fruit to other animals (vert)		9·25	9·00

339 Fawn

1984. Red Deer. Multicoloured.

1653	50m. Type **339**	1·50	70
1654	50m. Stag	1·50	70
1655	50m. Adults and fawn by river	1·50	70
1656	50m. Doe in woodland	1·50	70

340 Flag and Pioneers

1985. 60th Anniv of Mongolian Pioneer Organization.

1657	**340**	60m. multicoloured	1·00	55

341 Shar Tarlan

1985. Cattle. Multicoloured.

1658	20m. Type **341**	50	20
1659	30m. Bor khalium	70	35
1660	40m. Sarlag	85	45
1661	50m. Dornod talin bukh	1·00	55
1662	60m. Char tarlan	1·20	60
1663	80m. Nutgiin uulderiin unee	1·50	70
1664	1t.20 Tsagaan tolgoit	1·90	70
MS1665 90×110 mm. 4t. Girl with calf (vert)		8·50	8·25

342 Black Stork

1985. Birds. Multicoloured.

1666	20m. Type **342**	35	20
1667	30m. White-tailed sea eagle	50	35
1668	40m. Great white crane	85	55
1669	50m. Heude's parrotbill	1·00	60
1670	60m. Hooded crane	1·40	70
1671	80m. Japanese white-naped crane	1·70	90
1672	1t.20 Rough-legged buzzard	2·75	1·10
MS1673 125×70 mm. 4t. Brandt's cormorant (*Phalacrocorax penicillatus*) (47×39 mm)		10·00	9·75

343 Footballers

1985. World Junior Football Championship, U.S.S.R.

1674	**343**	20m. multicoloured	25	20
1675	-	30m. multicoloured	35	20
1676	-	40m. multicoloured	50	20
1677	-	50m. multicoloured	70	25
1678	-	60m. multicoloured	85	35
1679	-	80m. multicoloured	1·00	45
1680	-	1t.20 multicoloured	1·20	55
MS1681 110×90 mm. 4t. multicoloured (horiz)			5·00	4·75

Designs:—30m. to 4t., Different footballing scenes.

344 Monument

1985. 40th Anniv of Victory in Europe.

1682	**344**	60m. multicoloured	1·00	55

345 Snow Leopards

1985. The Snow Leopard. Multicoloured.

1683	50m. Type **345**	1·00	70
1684	50m. Leopard	1·00	70
1685	50m. Leopard on cliff ledge	1·00	70
1686	50m. Mother and cubs	1·00	70

346 Moscow Kremlin and Girls of Different Races

1985. 12th World Youth and Students' Festival, Moscow.

1687	**346**	60m. multicoloured	1·00	55

347 Monument

1985. 40th Anniv of Victory in Asia.

1688	**347**	60m. multicoloured	1·20	60

348 *Rosa dahurica*

1985. Plants. Multicoloured.

1689	20m. Type **348**	35	20
1690	30m. False chamomile	50	35
1691	40m. Dandelion	85	45

1692	50m. *Saxzitraga nirculus*	1·00	55
1693	60m. Cowberry	1·20	60
1694	80m. *Sanguisorba officinalis*	1·50	70
1695	1t.20 *Plantago major*	2·20	90
MS1696	90×110 mm. 4t. Sea buckthorn (*Hippophae rhamnoides*) (wrongly inscr 'Hippopae thamnoides')	8·50	8·25

See also Nos. 1719/25.

349 Camel

1985. The Bactrian Camel. Multicoloured.

1697	50m. Type **349**	2·40	1·10
1698	50m. Adults and calf	2·40	1·10
1699	50m. Calf	2·40	1·10
1700	50m. Adult	2·40	1·10

350 Soyuz Spacecraft

1985. Space. Multicoloured.

1701	20m. Type **350**	15	20
1702	30m. *Kosmos* satellite	35	20
1703	40m. *Venera-9* satellite	50	25
1704	50m. Salyut space station	70	35
1705	60m. *Luna-9* landing vehicle	85	55
1706	80m. Soyuz rocket on transporter	2·50	1·20
1707	1t.20 Dish aerial receiving transmission from Soyuz	1·70	55
MS1708	110×90 mm. 4t. Cosmonauts on space walk	4·50	4·25

351 Horseman

1985. Italia '85 International Stamp Exhibition, Rome. Sheet 110×90 mm.

MS1709	**351** 4t. multicoloured	4·50	4·25

352 UN and Mongolian Flags and UN Headquarters, New York

1985. 40th Anniv of U.N.O.

1710	**352**	60m. multicoloured	1·00	55

353 *Tricholoma mongolica*

1985. Fungi. Multicoloured.

1711	20m. Type **353**	50	20
1712	30m. Chanterelle	85	35
1713	40m. Honey fungus	1·00	45
1714	50m. Caesar's mushroom	1·20	55
1715	70m. Chestnut mushroom	1·50	70
1716	80m. Red-staining mushroom	2·00	80
1717	1t.20 Cep	3·00	90

354 Congress Emblem

1986. 19th Mongolian Revolutionary People's Party Congress.

1718	**354**	60m. multicoloured	1·00	55

1986. Plants. As T **348**. Multicoloured.

1719	20m. *Valeriana officinalis*	50	20
1720	30m. *Hyoscymus niger*	70	20
1721	40m. *Ephedra sinica*	85	35
1722	50m. *Thymus gobica*	1·00	45
1723	60m. *Paeonia anomalia*	1·40	55
1724	80m. *Achilea millefolium*	1·70	70
1725	1t.20 *Rhododendron adamsii*	2·40	90

355 Scene from Play

1986. 80th Birth Anniv of D. Natsagdorj (writer).

1726	**355**	60m. multicoloured	1·40	70

356 Thalmann

1986. Birth Centenary of Ernst Thalmann (German politician).

1727	**356**	60m. multicoloured	1·00	55

357 Man wearing Patterned Robe

1986. Costumes. Multicoloured.

1728	60m. Type **357**	85	35
1729	60m. Man in blue robe and fur-lined hat with ear flaps	85	35
1730	60m. Woman in black and yellow dress and bolero	85	35
1731	60m. Woman in pink dress patterned with stars	85	35
1732	60m. Man in cream robe with fur cuffs	85	35
1733	60m. Man in brown robe and mauve and yellow tunic	85	35
1734	60m. Woman in blue dress with black, yellow and red overtunic	85	35

358 Footballers

1986. World Cup Football Championship, Mexico.

1735	**358**	20m. multicoloured	15	20
1736	-	30m. multicoloured	35	20
1737	-	40m. multicoloured	50	25
1738	-	50m. multicoloured	70	35
1739	-	60m. multicoloured	85	45
1740	-	80m. multicoloured	1·00	55
1741	-	1t.20 multicoloured	1·50	70
MS1742		110×90 mm. 4t. multicoloured (horiz)	6·75	6·50

Designs:—30m. to 4t., Different footballing scenes.

359 Mink

1986. Mink. Multicoloured.

1743	60m. Type **359**	1·50	55
1744	60m. Mink on rock	1·50	55
1745	60m. Mink on snow-covered branch	1·50	55
1746	60m. Two mink	1·50	55

See also Nos. 1771/4, 1800/3, 1804/7, 1840/3, 1844/7 and 3268/71.

360 *Neptis coenobita*

1986. Butterflies and Moths. Multicoloured.

1747	20m. Type **360**	35	20
1748	30m. *Colias tycha*	50	25
1749	40m. *Leptidea amurensis*	70	35
1750	50m. *Oeneis tarpenledevi*	85	45
1751	60m. *Mesoacidalia charlotta*	1·00	55
1752	80m. Eyed hawk moth	1·40	70
1753	1t.20 Large tiger moth	2·00	90

361 Sukhe Bator Statue

1986. 65th Anniv of Independence.

1754	**361**	60m. multicoloured	1·00	55

362 Yak and Goats Act

1986. Circus. Multicoloured.

1755	20m. Type **362**	35	20
1756	30m. Acrobat	50	20
1757	40m. Yak act	70	25
1758	50m. Acrobats (vert)	85	35
1759	60m. High wire act (vert)	1·00	45
1760	80m. Fire juggler on camel (vert)	1·20	55
1761	1t.20 Acrobats on camel-drawn cart (vert)	1·90	70

363 Morin Khuur

1986. Musical Instruments. Multicoloured.

1762	20m. Type **363**	35	20
1763	30m. Bishguur (wind instrument)	50	25
1764	40m. Ever buree (wind)	85	35
1765	50m. Shudarga (string)	1·00	45
1766	60m. Khiil (string)	1·20	55
1767	80m. Janchir (string) (horiz)	1·50	65
1768	1t.20 Jatga (string) (horiz)	2·20	70

364 Flag and Emblem

1986. International Peace Year.

1770	**364**	10m. multicoloured	1·20	55

1986. Przewalski's Horse. As T **359**. Mult.

1771	50m. Horses grazing on sparsely grassed plain	1·50	55
1772	50m. Horses grazing on grassy plain	1·50	55
1773	50m. Adults with foal	1·50	55
1774	50m. Horses in snow	1·50	55

365 Temple

1986. Ancient Buildings. Multicoloured.

1775	60m. Type **365**	1·50	55
1776	60m. Temple with light green roof and white doors	1·50	55
1777	60m. Temple with porch	1·50	55
1778	60m. White building with three porches	1·50	55

366 Redhead (*Aythya americana*)

1986. Birds. Multicoloured.

1779	60m. Type **366**	2·00	70
1780	60m. Ruffed grouse (*Bonasa umbellus*)	2·00	70
1781	60m. Tundra swan (*Olor columbianus*)	2·00	70
1782	60m. Water pipit (*Anthus spinoletta*)	2·00	70

367 Alfa Romeo RL Sport, 1922

1986. Cars. Multicoloured.

1783	20m. Type **367**	15	20
1784	30m. Stutz Bearcat, 1912	35	20
1785	40m. Mercedes Simplex, 1902	50	25
1786	50m. Tatra 11, 1923	70	35
1787	60m. Ford Model T, 1908	85	55
1788	80m. Vauxhall, 1905	1·20	70
1789	1t.20 Russo-Balt K, 1913	1·70	90
MS1790	110×90 mm. 4t. As No. 1789	6·00	5·75

368 Wilhelm Steinitz and Curt von Bardeleben Game, 1895

1986. World Chess Champions. Multicoloured.

1791	20m. Type **368**	25	20
1792	30m. Emanuel Lasker and Harry Pilsberi game, 1895	35	20
1793	40m. Alexander Alekhine and Richard Retti game, 1925	50	25
1794	50m. Mikhail Botvinnik and Capablanca game, 1938	70	35
1795	60m. Anatoly Karpov and Wolfgang Untsiker game, 1975	85	45
1796	80m. Nona Gaprindashvili and Lasarevich game, 1961	1·00	55
1797	1t.20 Maia Chirburdanidze and Irina Levitina game, 1984	1·70	70
MS1798	110×100 mm. 4t. Players around International Chess Federation emblem	6·75	6·50

369 *Vega 2* Spacecraft and Comet

1986. Appearance of Halley's Comet. Sheet 110×90 mm.

MS1799	**369** 4t. multicoloured	6·75	6·50

1986. Saiga Antelope. As T **359**. Multicoloured.

1800	60m. Male	1·50	55
1801	60m. Female with calf	1·50	55
1802	60m. Male and female	1·50	55
1803	60m. Male and female in snow	1·50	55

1986. Pelicans. As T **359**. Multicoloured.

1804	60m. Dalmatian pelican (*Pelecanus crispus*)	2·20	70
1805	60m. Dalmatian pelican preening	2·20	70
1806	60m. Eastern white pelican (*Pelecanus onocrotalus*)	2·20	70
1807	60m. Eastern white pelicans in flight	2·20	70

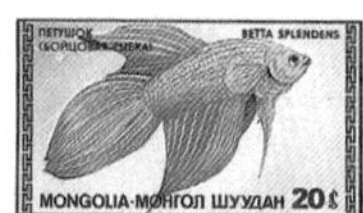

370 Siamese Fighting Fish

1987. Aquarium Fishes. Multicoloured.

1808	20m. Type **370**	35	20
1809	30m. Goldfish	50	20
1810	40m. Glowlight rasbora	70	35
1811	50m. Acara	85	45
1812	60m. Platy	1·00	55
1813	80m. Green swordtail	1·20	65
1814	1t.20 Freshwater angelfish (vert)	1·40	70
MS1815	111×91 mm. 4t. Sail-finned tetra (*Crenuchus spilurus*) (53×32 mm)	8·50	8·25

371 Lassoing Horse

1987. Traditional Equestrian Sports. Multicoloured

1816	20m. Type **371**	35	20
1817	30m. Breaking horse	50	20
1818	40m. Mounted archer	50	35
1819	50m. Race	70	45
1820	60m. Horseman snatching flag from ground	75	55
1821	80m. Tug of war	85	65
1822	1t.20 Racing wolf	1·20	70

372 Grey-headed Woodpecker

1987. Woodpeckers. Multicoloured.

1823	20m. Type **372**	15	20
1824	30m. Wryneck	35	20
1825	40m. Great spotted woodpecker	50	35
1826	50m. White-backed woodpecker	70	45
1827	60m. Lesser spotted woodpecker	1·00	55
1828	80m. Black woodpecker	1·40	70
1829	1t.20 Three-toed woodpecker	2·00	90
MS1830	85×105 mm. 4t. Pryer's woodpecker (*Saphopipo noguchi*)	7·75	7·50

373 Butterfly Hunting

1987. Children's Activities. Multicoloured.

1831	20m. Type **373**	15	20
1832	30m. Feeding calves	35	20
1833	40m. Drawing on ground in chalk	50	35
1834	50m. Football	70	45
1835	60m. Go-carting	75	55
1836	80m. Growing vegetables	85	65
1837	1t.20 Playing string instrument	1·20	70

374 Industry and Agriculture

1987. 13th Congress and 60th Anniv of Mongolian Trade Union.

1838	**374** 60m. multicoloured	3·00	90

375 Women in Traditional Costume

1987. 40th Anniv of Mongol–Soviet Friendship.

1839	**375** 60m. multicoloured	1·00	55

1987. Argali. As T **359**. Multicoloured.

1840	60m. On grassy rock (full face)	1·50	55
1841	60m. On rock (three-quarter face)	1·50	55
1842	60m. Family	1·50	55
1843	60m. Close-up of head and upper body	1·50	55

1987. Swans. As T **359**. Multicoloured.

1844	60m. Mute Swan (*Cygnus olor*) in water	1·50	55
1845	60m. Mute swan on land	1·50	55
1846	60m. Tundra swan (*Cygnus bewickii*)	1·50	55
1847	60m. Tundra swan, (*Cygnus gunus*) and mute swan	1·50	55

376 Flags of Member Countries

1987. 25th Anniv of Membership of Council for Mutual Economic Aid.

1848	**376** 60m. multicoloured	1·00	55

377 Sea Buckthorn

1987. Fruits. Multicoloured.

1849	20m. Type **377**	35	20
1850	30m. Blackcurrants	50	20
1851	40m. Redcurrants	70	35
1852	50m. Redcurrants	75	45
1853	60m. Raspberries	85	55
1854	80m. *Padus asiatica*	1·00	65
1855	1t.20 Strawberries	1·20	70

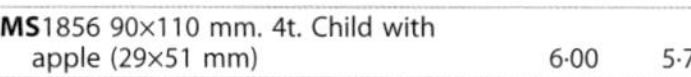

MS1856	90×110 mm. 4t. Child with apple (29×51 mm)	6·00	5·75

378 Couple in Traditional Costume

1987. Folk Art. Multicoloured.

1857	20m. Type **378**	15	20
1858	30m. Gold-inlaid baton and pouch	35	20
1859	40m. Gold and jewelled ornaments	50	25
1860	50m. Bag and dish	70	35
1861	60m. Earrings	85	45
1862	80m. Pipe, pouch and bottle	1·00	55
1863	1t.20 Decorative headdress	1·20	70

379 Dancer

1987. Dances.

1864	**379** 20m. multicoloured	15	20
1865	- 30m. multicoloured	35	20
1866	- 40m. multicoloured	50	25
1867	- 50m. multicoloured	70	35
1868	- 60m. multicoloured	85	45
1869	- 80m. multicoloured	1·00	55
1870	- 1t.20 multicoloured	1·20	70

Designs:—30m. to 1t.20, Different dances.

380 Lute Player

1987. Hafnia 87 International Stamp Exhibition, Copenhagen. Sheet 90×114 mm.

MS1871	**380** 4t. multicoloured	6·00	5·75

381 Scottish Fold

1987. Cats. Multicoloured.

1872	20m. Type **381**	15	20
1873	30m. Grey	35	25
1874	40m. Oriental	50	35
1875	50m. Abyssinian (horiz)	70	45
1876	60m. Manx (horiz)	85	55
1877	80m. Black shorthair (horiz)	1·20	65
1878	1t.20 Spotted (horiz)	1·40	70
MS1879	91×111 mm. 4t. Tabby shorthair	6·00	5·75

382 Mil Mi-V12

1987. Helicopters. Multicoloured.

1880	20m. Type **382**	15	20
1881	30m. Westland WG-30	35	25
1882	40m. Bell 206L LongRanger II	50	35
1883	50m. Kawasaki-Hughes 369HS	70	45
1884	60m. Kamov Ka-32	85	55
1885	80m. Mil Mi-17	1·20	65
1886	1t.20 Mil Mi-10K	1·40	70

383 City Scene

1987. 19th Mongolian People's Revolutionary Party Congress. Multicoloured.

1887	60m. Type **383**	1·00	35
1888	60m. Clothing and mining industries	1·00	35
1889	60m. Agriculture	1·00	35
1890	60m. Family	1·00	35
1891	60m. Workers, factories and fields	1·00	35
1892	60m. Building construction	1·00	35
1893	60m. Scientist	1·00	35

384 Kremlin, Lenin and Revolutionaries

1987. 70th Anniv of Russian October Revolution.

1894	**384** 60m. multicoloured	1·00	55

385 Seven with One Blow

1987. Walt Disney Cartoons. Multicoloured (a) "The Brave Little Tailor" (Grimm Brothers).

1895	25m. Type **385**	35	20
1896	35m. Brought before the King	50	20
1897	45m. Rewards for bravery	70	25
1898	55m. Fight between Mickey and the giant	85	35
1899	2t. Happy ending	2·00	1·60
MS1900	126×102 mm. 7t. Mickey victorious	8·50	8·25

(b) *The Celebrated Jumping Frog of Calaveras County* (Mark Twain).

1901	65m. 'He'd bet on anything'	1·00	45
1902	75m. 'He never done nothing but ... learn that frog to jump'	1·20	55
1903	85m. 'What might it be that you've got in that box?'	1·40	65
1904	1t. '40 He got the frog out and filled him full of quail shot'	1·50	70
MS1905	12×102 mm. 7t. 'He set the frog down and took after that feller'	8·50	8·25

386 Head

1987. The Red Fox. Multicoloured.

1906	60m. Type **386**	1·50	55
1907	60m. Vixen and cubs	1·50	55
1908	60m. Stalking	1·50	55
1909	60m. In the snow	1·50	55

387 *Mir* Space Station

1987. Intercosmos XX. Sheet 118×97 mm.

MS1910	**387** 4t. multicoloured	5·00	4·75

388 Bobsleighing

1988. Air. Winter Olympic Games, Calgary. Multicoloured

1911	20m. Type **388**	15	20
1912	30m. Ski jumping	35	20
1913	40m. Skiing	50	25
1914	50m. Biathlon	70	35
1915	60m. Speed skating	85	45
1916	80m. Figure skating	1·00	55
1917	1t.20 Ice hockey	1·20	70
MS1918	91×110 mm. 4t. Cross-country skiing	6·00	5·75

389 Sukhe Bator

1988. 95th Birth Anniv of Sukhe Bator.

1919	**389**	60m. multicoloured	1·00	55

390 "Invitation"

1988. Roses. Multicoloured.

1920	20m. Type **390**	35	20
1921	30m. "Meilland"	50	20
1922	40m. "Pascali"	70	25
1923	50m. "Tropicana"	85	35
1924	60m. "Wendy Cussons"	1·00	45
1925	80m. *Rosa* sp. (wrongly inscr 'Blue Moon')	1·20	55
1926	1t.20 "Diorama"	1·40	70
MS1927	97×117 mm. 4t. Red rose	6·00	5·75

391 "Ukhaant Ekhner"

1988. Puppets. Multicoloured.

1928	20m. Type **391**	35	20
1929	30m. "Altan Everte Mungun Turuut"	50	20
1930	40m. "Aduuchyn Khuu"	70	25
1931	50m. "Suulenkhuu"	85	35
1932	60m. "Khonchyn Khuu"	1·00	45
1933	80m. "Argat Byatskhan Baatar"	1·20	55
1934	1t.20 "Botgochyn Khuu"	1·40	70

392 Tatra 11 Car, 1923

1988. Praga 88 International Stamp Exhibition, Prague. Sheet 110×90 mm.

MS1935	**392** 4t. multicoloured	6·00	5·75

393 Judo

1988. Olympic Games, Seoul. Multicoloured.

1936	20m. Type **393**	35	20
1937	30m. Archery	50	20
1938	40m. Weightlifting	70	25
1939	50m. Gymnastics	85	35
1940	60m. Cycling	1·00	45
1941	80m. Running	1·20	55
1942	1t.20 Wrestling	1·40	70
MS1943	90×110 mm. 4t. Boxing	6·00	5·75

394 Marx

1988. 170th Birth Anniv of Karl Marx.

1944	**394**	60m. multicoloured	1·40	70

395 Couple and Congress Banner

1988. 19th Revsomol Youth Congress.

1945	**395**	60m. multicoloured	2·00	90

396 *Kosmos*

1988. Spacecraft and Satellites. Multicoloured.

1946	20m. Type **396**	35	20
1947	30m. *Meteor*	50	20
1948	40m. Salyut–Soyuz space complex	70	20
1949	50m. *Prognoz-6*	85	20
1950	60m. *Molniya-1*	1·00	25
1951	80m. Soyuz	1·20	45
1952	1t.20 Vostok	1·40	55
MS1953	96×115 mm. 4t. Satellite scanning areas of Earth	7·75	7·50

397 Buddha

1988. Religious Sculptures.

1954	**397**	20m. multicoloured	15	20
1955	-	30m. multicoloured	35	20
1956	-	40m. multicoloured	50	25
1957	-	50m. multicoloured	70	35
1958	-	60m. multicoloured	85	45
1959	-	70m. multicoloured	1·00	55
1960	-	80m. multicoloured	1·20	65
1961	-	1t.20 multicoloured	1·40	70

Designs:—30m. to 1t.20, Different Buddhas.

398 Emblem

1988. 30th Anniv of Problems of "Peace and Socialism" (magazine).

1962	**398**	60m. multicoloured	1·40	55

399 Eagle

1988. White-tailed Sea Eagle. Multicoloured.

1963	60m. Type **399**	1·70	55
1964	60m. Eagle on fallen branch and eagle landing	1·70	55
1965	60m. Eagle on rock	1·70	55
1966	60m. Eagle (horiz)	1·70	55

400 Ass

1988. Asiatic Wild Ass. Multicoloured.

1967	60m. Type **400**	1·50	55
1968	60m. Head of ass	1·50	55
1969	60m. Two adults	1·50	55
1970	60m. Mare and foal	1·50	55

401 Athlete

1988. Traditional Sports. Multicoloured.

1971	10m. Type **401**	35	20
1972	20m. Horseman	50	20
1973	30m. Archery	70	25
1974	40m. Wrestling	85	35
1975	50m. Archery (different)	1·00	45
1976	70m. Horsemen (national holiday cavalcade)	1·20	55
1977	1t.20 Horsemen, wrestlers and archers	1·40	70

402 "Mongolian Camp" (H. Jargalsuren)

1988. Childrens' Fund. Sheet 115×95 mm.

MS1978	**402** 4t. multicoloured	6·75	6·50

403 USSR (ice hockey)

1988. Winter Olympic Games Gold Medal Winners. Multicoloured.

1979	1t.50 Type **403**	1·20	55
1980	1t.50 Bonnie Blair (speed skating)	1·20	55
1981	1t.50 Alberto Tomba (slalom)	1·20	55
1982	1t.50 Matti Nykanen (ski jumping) (horiz)	1·20	55
MS1983	110×87 mm. 4t. Katarina Witt (figure skating) (horiz)	5·00	4·75

404 Brown Goat

1988. Goats. Multicoloured.

1984	20m. Type **404**	50	20
1985	30m. Black goat	70	20
1986	40m. White long-haired goats	85	25
1987	50m. Black long-haired goat	1·00	35
1988	60m. White goat	1·40	45
1989	80m. Black short-haired goat	1·50	55
1990	1t.20 Nanny and kid	2·50	70
MS1991	95×116 mm. 4t. Head of goat (vert)	5·00	4·75

405 Emblem

1989. 60th Anniv of Mongolian Writers' Association.

1992	**405**	60m. multicoloured	1·20	55

406 Beaver gnawing Trees

1989. Eurasian Beaver. Multicoloured.

1993	60m. Type **406**	1·40	55
1994	60m. Beaver with young	1·40	55
1995	60m. Beavers beside tree stump and in water	1·40	55
1996	60m. Beaver rolling log	1·40	55

407 Dancers

1989. Ballet.

1997	**407**	20m. multicoloured	35	20
1998	-	30m. multicoloured	50	20
1999	-	40m. multicoloured (vert)	70	25
2000	-	50m. multicoloured	85	35
2001	-	60m. multicoloured	1·00	45
2002	-	80m. multicoloured (vert)	1·40	55
2003	-	1t.20 multicoloured (vert)	1·70	70

Designs:—30m. to 1t.20, Different dancing scenes.

408 *Ursus pruinosis*

1989. Bears. Multicoloured.

2004	20m. Type **408**	85	20
2005	30m. Brown bear	1·00	35
2006	40m. Asiatic black bear	1·20	45
2007	50m. Polar bear	1·40	55
2008	60m. Brown bear	1·70	70
2009	80m. Giant panda	2·00	90
2010	1t.20 Brown bear	3·00	1·10
MS2011	110×90 mm. 4t. Giant panda (different)	11·00	10·50

409 Soyuz Spacecraft

1989. Space. Multicoloured.

2012	20m. Type **409**	35	20
2013	30m. Apollo–Soyuz link	50	35
2014	40m. *Columbia* space shuttle (vert)	70	45
2015	50m. Hermes spacecraft	85	55
2016	60m. Nippon spacecraft (vert)	1·00	65
2017	80m. Energy rocket (vert)	1·40	70
2018	1t.20 *Buran* space shuttle (vert)	2·00	90
MS2019	110×88 mm. 4t. German Sanger project	6·75	6·50

410 Tupolev Tu-154

1989. Philexfrance 89, Paris (1st issue). and Bulgaria '89, Sofia, International Stamp Exhibitions. Sheet 90×110 mm.

MS2020	**410** 4t. multicoloured	6·75	6·50

See also **MS**2034.

411 Nehru

1989. Birth Centenary of Jawaharial Nehru (Indian statesman).

2021	**411**	10m. multicoloured	1·40	70

412 *Opuntia microdasys*

1989. Cacti. Multicoloured.

2022	20m. Type **412**	35	20
2023	30m. *Echinopsis multipiex*	50	20
2024	40m. *Rebutia tephracanthus*	70	25
2025	50m. *Brasilicactus haselbergii*	85	35
2026	60m. *Gymnocalycium mihanovichii*	1·00	45
2027	80m. *Cleistocactus strausii*	1·40	55
2028	1t.20 *Horridocactus tuberisvicatus*	1·70	70
MS2029	90×110 mm. 4t. *Astrophytum ornatum*	6·00	6·25

1989. 800th Anniv of Coronation of Genghis Khan. Nos. 291/4 optd **CHINGGIS KHAN CROWNATION 1189**.

2030	**67**	20m. multicoloured	8·50	9·00
2031	-	30m. multicoloured	13·50	14·50
2032	-	50m. black, brown and red	20·00	22·00
2033	-	60m. buff, blue and brown	29·00	31·00

See also No. **MS**2106.

414 Concorde

1989. Philexfrance 89 International Stamp Exhibition, Paris (2nd issue). Sheet 130×55 mm containing T **414** and similar horiz designs. Multicoloured.

MS2034	20m. Type **414**; 60m. French TGV express train; 1t.20, Sukhe Bator statue	13·00	12·50

415 Citroen BX

1989. Motor Cars. Multicoloured.

2035	20m. Type **415**	50	20
2036	30m. Volvo 760 GLF	70	20
2037	40m. Honda Civic	85	25
2038	50m. Volga	1·00	35
2039	60m. Ford Granada	1·20	45
2040	80m. Baz 21099	1·40	55
2041	1t.20 Mercedes 190	2·00	70
MS2042	110×90 mm. 4t. As No. 2038	7·75	7·50

416 Monument

1989. 50th Anniv of Battle of Khalka River.

2043	**416**	60m. multicoloured	1·40	70

417 Florence Griffith-Joyner (running)

1989. Olympic Games Medal Winners. Multicoloured

2044	60m. Type **417** (wrongly inscr "Joyner-Griffith")	1·00	55
2045	60m. Stefano Cerioni (fencing)	1·00	55
2046	60m. Gintautas Umaras (cycling)	1·00	55
2047	60m. Kristin Otto (swimming)	1·00	55
MS2048	90×110 mm. 4t. N. Enkhbat (boxing)	6·00	5·75

418 *Malchin Zaluus* (N. Sandagsuren)

1989. 30th Anniv of Co-operative Movement. Paintings. Multicoloured.

2049	20m. Type **418**	35	20
2050	30m. *Tsaatny Tukhai Dursamkh* (N. Sandagsuren) (vert)	50	35
2051	40m. *Uul Shig Tushigtei* (D. Amgalan)	85	55
2052	50m. *Goviin Egshig* (D. Amgalan)	1·00	70
2053	60m. *Tsagaan Sar* (Ts. Dagvanyam)	1·20	90
2054	80m. *Tumen Aduuny Bayar* (M. Butemkh) (vert)	1·50	1·10
2055	1t.20 *Bilcheer Deer* (N. Tsultem)	2·40	1·30
MS2056	110×90 mm. 4t. *Naadam* (detail, Ts. Dagvanyam)	10·00	9·75

419 Four-man Bobsleighing

1989. Ice Sports. Multicoloured.

2057	20m. Type **419**	35	20
2058	30m. Luge	50	20
2059	40m. Figure skating	70	25
2060	50m. Two-man bobsleighing	85	35
2061	60m. Ice dancing	1·00	45
2062	80m. Speed skating	1·40	55
2063	1t.20 Ice speedway	2·00	70
MS2064	90×110 mm. 4t. Ice hockey	6·75	6·50

420 Victory Medal

1989. Orders. Designs showing different badges and medals. Multicoloured, background colour given.

2065	**420**	60m. blue	1·00	55
2066	-	60m. orange	1·00	55
2067	-	60m. mauve	1·00	55
2068	-	60m. violet	1·00	55
2069	-	60m. green	1·00	55
2070	-	60m. blue	1·00	55
2071	-	60m. red	1·00	55

1989. World Stamp Expo 89 International Stamp Exhibition, Washington D.C. No. **MS**2034 optd **WORLD STAMP EXPO'89, WASHINGTON DC, WASHINGTON DC** and logo on the margin.

MS2072	130× 55 mm. 20m. multicoloured; 60m. multicoloured; 1t.20, multicoloured	13·50	13·00

422 Chu Lha

1989. Buddhas. Multicoloured.

2073	20m. Damdin Sandub	35	20
2074	30m. Pagwa Lama	50	35
2075	40m. Type **422**	70	55
2076	50m. Agwanglobsan	1·00	65
2077	60m. Dorje Dags Dan	1·20	70
2078	80m. Wangchikdorje	1·50	90
2079	1t.20 Buddha	2·20	1·10
MS2080	74×89 mm. 4t. Migjid Jang-Rasek	10·00	9·75

423 Sukhe Bator Statue

1990. New Year.

2081	**423**	10m. multicoloured	1·70	90

424 Newspapers and City

1990. 70th Anniv of "Khuvisgalt Khevlel" (newspaper).

2082	**424**	60m. multicoloured	1·50	90

425 Emblem

1990. 20th Mongolian People's Revolutionary Party Congress.

2083	**425**	60m. multicoloured	2·00	70

426 Male Character

1990. Mandukhai the Wise (film).

2084	**426**	20m. multicoloured	50	35
2085	-	30m. multicoloured	70	55
2086	-	40m. multicoloured	1·00	70
2087	-	50m. multicoloured	1·40	80
2088	-	60m. multicoloured	1·70	1·10
2089	-	80m. multicoloured	2·20	1·40
2090	-	1t.20 multicoloured	3·00	2·20
MS2091		83×105 mm. 4t. multicoloured (vert)	8·50	8·25

Designs:—30m. to 4t., Different characters from the film.

427 Trophy and Players

1990. World Cup Football Championship, Italy.

2092	**427**	20m. multicoloured	35	20
2093	-	30m. multicoloured	50	20
2094	-	40m. multicoloured	70	20
2095	-	50m. multicoloured	85	20
2096	-	60m. multicoloured	1·00	25
2097	-	80m. multicoloured	1·40	35
2098	-	1t.20 multicoloured	2·00	55
MS2099		89×110 mm. 4t. multicoloured (Trophy) (vert)	6·75	6·50

Designs:—30m. to 4t., Trophy and different players.

428 Lenin

1990. 120th Birth Anniv of Lenin.

2100	**428**	60m. black, red and gold	1·50	1·10

429 Mother with Fawn

1990. Siberian Musk Deer. Multicoloured.

2101	60m. Type **429**	1·50	1·10

2102 60m. Deer in wood 1·50 1·10
2103 60m. Deer on river bank 1·50 1·10
2104 60m. Deer in winter landscape 1·50 1·10

430 Clock Tower, Houses of Parliament, London

1990. Stamp World London '90 International Stamp Exhibition (1st issue) Sheet 91×105 mm.
MS2105 **430** 4t. multicoloured 6·75 6·50

See also Nos. **MS**2107 and 2191/**MS**2200.

431 Genghis Khan

1990. 800th Anniv (1989) of Coronation of Genghis Khan (2nd issue). Sheet 116×142 mm.
MS2106 **431** 7t. multicoloured 8·50 8·25

1990. Stamp World London '90 International Stamp Exhibition (2nd issue). No. **MS**2106 optd with Penny Black and Stamp World London 90 in margin.
MS2107 **431** 7t. multicoloured 13·50 13·00

433 Russian Victory Medal

1990. 45th Anniv of End of Second World War.
2108 **433** 60m. multicoloured 1·50 1·10

434 Crane

1990. The Japanese White-naped Crane. Multicoloured
2109 60m. Type **434** 1·50 90
2110 60m. Crane feeding (horiz) 1·50 90
2111 60m. Cranes flying (horiz) 1·50 90
2112 60m. Crane on river bank 1·50 90

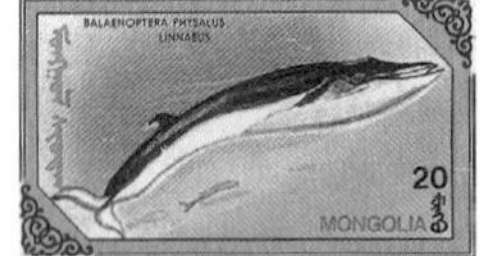

435 Fin Whale

1990. Marine Mammals. Multicoloured.
2113 20m. Type **435** 35 20
2114 30m. Humpback whale 70 35
2115 40m. Narwhal 1·00 55
2116 50m. Risso's dolphin 1·40 70
2117 60m. Bottle-nosed dolphin 1·70 90
2118 80m. Atlantic white-sided dolphin 2·00 1·10
2119 1t.20 Bowhead whale 2·40 1·30
MS2120 90×110 mm. 4t. Dall's porpoise (vert) 9·25 9·00

436 Weapons and Black Standard

1990. 750th Anniv of "Secret History of the Mongols" (book). Multicoloured.
2121 10m. Type **436** 35 20
2122 10m. Weapons and white standard 35 20
2123 40m. Brazier (17½×22 mm) 1·00 35
2124 60m. Genghis Khan (17½×22 mm) 1·50 55
2125 60m. Horses galloping 1·50 55
2126 60m. Tartar camp 1·50 55
2127 80m. Men kneeling to ruler 2·20 90
2128 80m. Court 2·20 90

437 Panda

1990. The Giant Panda. Multicoloured.
2129 10m. Type **437** 50 20
2130 20m. Panda eating bamboo 70 35
2131 30m. Adult eating bamboo, and cub 85 55
2132 40m. Panda on tree branch (horiz) 1·00 70
2133 50m. Adult and cub resting (horiz) 1·40 90
2134 60m. Panda and mountains (horiz) 1·50 1·10
2135 80m. Adult and cub playing (horiz) 2·00 1·40
2136 1t.20 Panda on snow-covered river bank (horiz) 3·00 2·20
MS2137 94×114 mm. 4t. Panda holding bamboo shoots (vert) 11·00 10·50

438 Chasmosaurus

1990. Prehistoric Animals. Multicoloured.
2138 20m. Type **438** 35 20
2139 30m. Stegosaurus 70 35
2140 40m. Probactrosaurus 1·00 55
2141 50m. Opisthocoelicaudia 1·40 70
2142 60m. Iguanodon (vert) 1·70 90
2143 80m. Tarbosaurus 2·00 1·10
2144 1t.20 Mamenchisaurus (after Mark Hallett) (60×22 mm) 3·00 1·30
MS2145 110×90 mm. 4t. Allosaurus attacking herd of Brachiosaurus (after John Gurche) 9·25 9·00

439 Lighthouse, Alexandria, Egypt

1990. Seven Wonders of the World. Multicoloured
2146 20m. Type **439** 85 20
2147 30m. Pyramids of Egypt (horiz) 1·00 25
2148 40m. Statue of Zeus, Olympia 1·20 35
2149 50m. Colossus of Rhodes 1·40 45
2150 60m. Mausoleum, Halicarnassus 1·50 55
2151 80m. Temple of Artemis, Ephesus (horiz) 1·90 90
2152 1t.20 Hanging Gardens of Babylon 2·50 1·40
MS2153 89×110 mm. 4t. Map and pyramids 10·00 9·75

440 Kea

1990. Parrots. Multicoloured.
2154 20m. Type **440** 35 20
2155 30m. Hyacinth macaw 50 35
2156 40m. Australian king parrot 85 55
2157 50m. Grey parrot 1·20 70
2158 60m. Kakapo 1·50 90
2159 80m. Alexandrine parakeet 2·00 1·10
2160 1t.20 Scarlet macaw 3·00 1·30
MS2161 84×104 mm. 4t. Electus parrot 9·25 9·00

441 Purple Tiger Moth

1990. Moths and Butterflies. Multicoloured.
2162 20m. Type **441** 50 20
2163 30m. Viennese emperor moth 70 35
2164 40m. Comma 1·00 55
2165 50m. Magpie moth 1·40 70
2166 60m. Chequered moth 1·50 90
2167 80m. Swallowtail 1·90 1·10
2168 1t.20 Orange-tip 2·50 1·30
MS2169 90×110 mm. 4t. Striped hawk moth (vert). Perf or imperf 9·25 9·00

442 Jetsons in Flying Saucer

1991. The Jetsons (cartoon characters). Multicoloured
2170 20m. Type **442** 50 20
2171 25m. Family walking on planet, and dragon (horiz) 70 25
2172 30m. Jane, George, Elroy and dog Astro 85 35
2173 40m. George, Judy, Elroy and Astro crossing river 1·00 45
2174 50m. Flying in saucer (horiz) 1·20 55
2175 60m. Jetsons and Cosmo Spacely (horiz) 1·40 65
2176 70m. George and Elroy flying with jetpacks 1·50 70
2177 80m. Elroy (horiz) 1·70 80
2178 1t.20 Judy and Astro watching Elroy doing acrobatics on tree 2·50 90
MS2179 Two sheets, each 102×127 mm. (a) 7t. Elroy with hands in pocket; (b) 7t. Elroy jumping 19·00 18·00

443 Dino and Bam-Bam meeting Mongolian Boy with Camel

1991. The Flintstones (cartoon characters). Multicoloured
2180 25m. Type **443** 70 20
2181 35m. Bam-Bam and Dino posing with boy (vert) 85 35
2182 45m. Mongolian mother greeting Betty Rubble, Wilma Flintstone and children 1·00 45
2183 55m. Barney Rubble and Fred riding dinosaurs 1·20 55
2184 65m. Flintstones and Rubbles by river 1·50 65
2185 75m. Bam-Bam and Dino racing boy on camel 1·70 70
2186 85m. Fred, Barney and Bam-Bam with Mongolian boy 2·00 80
2187 1t.40 Flintstones and Rubbles in car 3·00 1·10
2188 2t. Fred and Barney taking refreshments with Mongolian 4·25 1·80
MS2189 Two sheets, each 126×101 mm. (a) 7t. Wilma, Betty and Bam-Bam; (b) 7t. Bam-Bam and Pebbles riding Dino 19·00 18·00

444 Party Emblem

1991. 70th Anniv of Mongolian People's Revolutionary Party.
2190 **444** 60m. multicoloured 1·40 70

445 Black-capped Chickadee

1991. Stamp World London 90 International Stamp Exhibition. Multicoloured.
2191 25m. Type **445** 70 20
2192 35m. Common cardinal 85 25
2193 45m. Crested shelduck 1·00 35
2194 55m. Mountain bluebird 1·20 45
2195 65m. Northern oriole 1·40 55
2196 75m. Bluethroat (horiz) 1·50 70
2197 85m. Eastern bluebird 1·70 90
2198 1t.40 Great reed warbler 2·40 1·10
2199 2t. Golden eagle 3·00 1·30
MS2200 Two sheets. (a) 94×76 mm. 7t. Ring-necked pheasant (*horiz*); (b) 76 x 94 mm. 7t. Great scaup 22·00 21·00

446 Black Grouse

1991. Birds. Multicoloured.
2201 20m. Type **446** 50 20
2202 30m. Common shelduck 85 35
2203 40m. Common pheasant 1·00 55
2204 50m. Long-tailed duck 1·40 70
2205 60m. Hazel grouse 1·70 90
2206 80m. Red-breasted merganser 2·50 1·10
2207 1t.20 Goldeneye 3·00 1·60
MS2208 96×115 mm. 4t. Green-winged teal (*Anas crecca*) (vert) 10·00 9·75

447 Emblem

1991. 70th Anniv of Mongolian People's Army.
2209 **447** 60m. multicoloured 1·40 70

448 Superb Pink

1991. Flowers. Multicoloured.
2210 20m. Type **448** 35 20
2211 30m. *Gentiana pneumonanthe* (wrongly inscr "puenmonanthe") 70 35
2212 40m. Dandelion 1·00 55
2213 50m. Siberian iris 1·40 70
2214 60m. Turk's-cap lily 1·40 90
2215 80m. *Aster amellus* 1·90 1·10
2216 1t.20 Thistle 2·75 1·30

MS2217	95×115 mm. 4t. Bellflower (*Campanula persicifolia*)	9·25	9·00

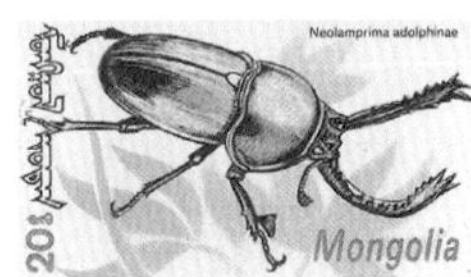

449 Stag Beetle

1991. Beetles. Multicoloured.

2218	20m. Type **449**	50	20
2219	30m. *Chelorrhina polyphemus*	70	35
2220	40m. *Coptolabrus coelestis*	1·00	55
2221	50m. *Epepeotes togatus*	1·40	70
2222	60m. Tiger beetle	1·50	90
2223	80m. *Macrodontia cervicornis*	1·90	1·10
2224	1t.20 Hercules beetle	2·50	1·30
MS2225	95×115 mm. 4t. *Cercopis sanguinolenta* (vert)	9·25	9·00

450 Defend

1991. Buddhas. Multicoloured.

2226	20m. Type **450**	35	20
2227	30m. Badmasanhava	50	35
2228	40m. Avalokitecvara	85	55
2229	50m. Buddha	1·20	70
2230	60m. Mintugwa	1·40	90
2231	80m. Shyamatara	1·90	1·10
2232	1t.20 Samvara	2·00	1·30
MS2233	95×116 mm. 4t. Lamidhatara	8·50	8·25

451 Zebras

1991. African Wildlife. Multicoloured.

2234	20m. Type **451**	50	20
2235	30m. Cheetah (wrongly inscr "Cheetan")	70	35
2236	40m. Black rhinoceros	1·00	55
2237	50m. Giraffe (vert)	1·40	70
2238	60m. Gorilla	1·50	90
2239	80m. Elephants	1·90	1·10
2240	1t.20 Lion (vert)	2·50	1·30
MS2241	95×116 mm. 4t. Gazelle (vert)	9·25	9·00

452 Communications

1991. Meiso Mizuhara Stamp Exhibition, Ulan Bator.

2242	**452**	1t.20 multicoloured	5·00	1·80

453 Scotch Bonnet

1991. Fungi. Multicoloured.

2243	20m. Type **453**	50	25
2244	30m. Oak mushroom	70	35
2245	40m. *Hygrophorus marzuelus*	1·00	45
2246	50m. Chanterelle	1·20	55
2247	60m. Field mushroom	1·40	70
2248	80m. Bronze boletus	1·70	90
2249	1t.20 Caesar's mushroom	2·50	1·30
2250	2t. *Tricholoma terreum*	3·75	1·80
MS2251	95×80 mm. 4t. *Mitrophora hybrida* (31×39 mm)	13·00	12·50

454 Emblem

1991. 70th Anniv of Revolution. Sheet 84×109 mm.

MS2252	**454**	4t. multicoloured	6·75	6·50

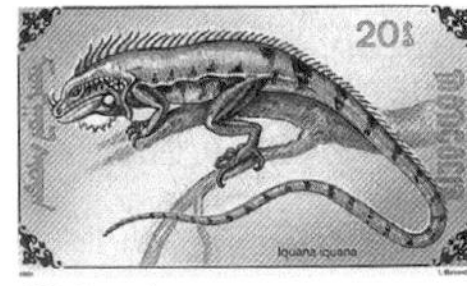

455 Green Iguana

1991. Reptiles. Multicoloured.

2253	20m. Type **455**	35	20
2254	30m. Flying gecko	70	35
2255	40m. Frilled lizard	1·00	55
2256	50m. Common cape lizard	1·40	70
2257	60m. Common basilisk	1·70	90
2258	80m. Common tegu	2·00	1·10
2259	1t.20 Marine iguana	3·00	1·30
MS2260	75×96 mm. 4t. Bengal monitor lizard (*Varanus bengalensis*) (32×54 mm)	9·25	9·00

456 Warrior

1991. Masked Costumes. Multicoloured.

2261	35m. Type **456**	85	35
2262	45m. Mask with fangs	1·00	45
2263	55m. Bull mask	1·20	55
2264	65m. Dragon mask	1·40	70
2265	85m. Mask with beak	1·90	1·10
2266	1t.40 Old man	2·75	1·80
2267	2t. Gold mask with earrings	3·75	2·20
MS2268	90×110 mm. 4t. Lion mask	10·00	9·75

457 German Shepherd

1991. Dogs. Multicoloured.

2269	20m. Type **457**	35	20
2270	30m. Dachshund (vert)	70	35
2271	40m. Yorkshire terrier (vert)	1·00	55
2272	50m. Standard poodle	1·40	70
2273	60m. Springer spaniel	1·70	90
2274	80m. Norfolk terrier	2·00	1·10
2275	1t.20 Keeshund	3·00	1·60
MS2276	110×90 mm. 4t. Herding dog (54×32 mm)	9·25	9·00

458 Siamese

1991. Cats. Multicoloured.

2277	20m. Type **458**	35	20
2278	30m. Black and white longhaired (vert)	70	35
2279	40m. Ginger red	1·00	55
2280	50m. Tabby (vert)	1·40	70
2281	60m. Red and white (vert)	1·70	90
2282	80m. Maine coon (vert)	2·00	1·10
2283	1t.20 Blue-eyed white persian (vert)	3·00	1·60
MS2284	101×91 mm. 4t. Tortoiseshell and white	9·25	9·00

459 Pagoda

1991. Phila Nippon '91 International Stamp Exhibition, Tokyo. Multicoloured.

2285	1t. Type **459**	1·20	55
2286	2t. Japanese woman	1·70	1·10
2287	3t. Mongolian woman	2·40	1·40
2288	4t. Temple	3·75	2·30

(b) No. **MS**2233 optd **PHILA NIPPON'91** and logos in the margin.

MS2288a	95×115 mm. 4t. multicoloured	7·75	7·50

460 *Zegris fausti*

1991. Butterflies and Flowers. Multicoloured.

2289	20m. Type **460**	70	20
2290	25m. Yellow roses	85	20
2291	30m. Apollo	1·00	25
2292	40m. Purple tiger moth	1·40	35
2293	50m. *Pseudochazara regeli*	1·70	45
2294	60m. "Colotis fausta"	2·00	55
2295	70m. Red rose	2·40	70
2296	80m. Margueritas	2·75	80
2297	1t.20 Lily	4·25	90

1991. Expo '90 International Garden and Greenery Exhibition, Osaka. Nos. 2289/97 optd EXPO '90 and symbol.

2298	20m. multicoloured	70	20
2299	25m. multicoloured	85	20
2300	30m. multicoloured	1·00	25
2301	40m. multicoloured	1·40	35
2302	50m. multicoloured	1·70	45
2303	60m. multicoloured	2·00	55
2304	70m. multicoloured	2·40	70
2305	80m. multicoloured	2·75	80
2306	1t.20 multicoloured	4·25	90

(b) Two sheets, each 94×77 mm, containing horiz design as T **460**. Multicoloured.

MS2307	Two sheets. (a) 7t. Cactus; (b) 7t. Butterfly	29·00	28·00

462 Poster for 1985 Digital Stereo Re-issue

1991. 50th Anniv (1990) of Original Release of Walt Disney's *Fantasia* (cartoon film). Multicoloured.

2308	1t.70 Type **462**	50	20
2309	2t. 1940 poster for original release	70	35
2310	2t.30 Poster for 1982 digital re-issue	85	45
2311	2t.60 Poster for 1981 stereo re-issue	1·20	55
2312	4t.20 Poster for 1969 "Psychedelic Sixties" release	1·70	90
2313	10t. 1941 poster for original release	3·00	1·40
2314	15t. Mlle. Upanova (sketch by Campbell Grant)	5·00	2·30
2315	16t. Mickey as the Sorcerer's Apprentice (original sketch)	5·00	2·75
MS2316	Four sheets, each 127×102 mm. (a) 30t. "Russian Dance" (50×37 mm); (b) 30t. Stravinsky's "Rite of Spring" (48×35 mm); (c) 30t. "The Sorcerer's Apprentice"; (d) 30t. "Chinese Dance" (50×36 mm)	41·00	40·00

463 Speed Skating

1992. Winter Olympic Games, Albertville. Multicoloured

2317	60m. Type **463**	50	20
2318	80m. Ski jumping	70	20
2319	1t. Ice hockey	85	20
2320	1t.20 Ice skating	1·00	20
2321	1t.50 Biathlon (horiz)	1·40	35
2322	2t. Skiing (horiz)	1·90	45
2323	2t.40 Two-man bobsleigh (horiz)	2·20	55
MS2324	90×110 mm. 8t. Four-man bobsleigh (32×54 mm)	6·75	6·50

464 Zeppelin

1992. 75th Death Anniv of Count Ferdinand von Zeppelin (airship pioneer). Sheet 78×102 mm.

MS2325	**464**	16t. multicoloured	7·75	7·50

465 Elk

1992. The Elk. Multicoloured.

2326	3t. Type **465**	1·70	90
2327	3t. Female with young (horiz)	1·70	90
2328	3t. Adult male (horiz)	1·70	90
2329	3t. Female	1·70	90

466 Steam Locomotive, Darjeeling–Himalaya Railway, India

1992. Multicoloured. (a) Railways of the World.

2330	3t. Type **466**	1·00	70
2331	3t. The *Royal Scot*, Great Britain	1·00	70
2332	6t. Steam train on bridge over River Kwai, Burma–Siam Railway	2·00	1·60
2333	6t. Baltic steam locomotive No. 767, Burma	2·00	1·60
2334	8t. Baldwin steam locomotive, Thailand	3·00	2·20
2335	8t. Western Railways steam locomotive, Pakistan	3·00	2·20
2336	16t. Class P36 locomotive, Russia	9·25	4·50
2337	16t. Shanghai–Peking express, China	9·25	4·50
MS2338	Two sheets, each 112×83 mm. (a) 30t. Hikari express train, Japan (56×41 mm); (b) 30t. TGV express train, France (56×41 mm)	20·00	19·00

(b) *Orient Express*. Black and gold (**MS**2347a) or multicoloured (others).

2339	3t. 1931 advertising poster	1·00	70
2340	3t. 1928 advertising poster	1·00	70
2341	6t. Dawn departure	2·00	1·60
2342	6t. The *Golden Arrow* leaving Victoria Station, London	2·00	1·60
2343	8t. Standing in station, Yugoslavia	3·00	2·20
2344	8t. Train passing through mountainous landcape, early 1900s	3·00	2·20
2345	16t. *Fleche d'Or* approaching Etaples	9·25	4·50

2346	16t. Arrival in Istanbul	9·25	4·50

MS2347 Two sheets, each 113×84 mm. (a) 30t. Crowded railway platform; (b) 30t. Pullman Car Company Arms; 30t. Compagnie Internationale des Wogons-Lits et des Grands Express Europeens Arms 27·00 26·00

467 Columbus

1992. 500th Anniv of Discovery of America by Columbus (1st issue). World Columbian Stamp Expo '92, Chicago and Genova '92 International Thematic Stamp Exhibition. Sheet 100 x 70 mm containing T **467** and similar vert design. Multicoloured.

MS2348 30t. Type **467**; 30t. *Santa Maria* 17·00 16·00

See also Nos. 2370/**MS**2377.

468 Black-billed Magpie

1992. Multicoloured. (a) Birds.

2349	3t. Type **468**	85	70
2350	3t. Northern eagle owl	85	70
2351	6t. Relict gull (horiz)	1·70	1·60
2352	6t. Redstart (horiz)	1·70	1·60
2353	8t. Demoiselle crane	2·50	2·20
2354	8t. Black stork (horiz)	2·50	2·20
2355	16t. Rough-legged buzzard	5·00	4·50
2356	16t. Golden eagle (horiz)	5·00	4·50

MS2357 Two sheets, each 115×90 mm. (a) 30t. Mallards swimming and in flight (50×37); (b) 30t. Red-breasted goose (50×37 mm) 19·00 18·00

(b) Butterflies and Moths.

2358	3t. Scarce swallowtail (horiz)	85	70
2359	3t. Small tortoiseshell	85	70
2360	6t. *Thyria jacobaeae* (value at right) (horiz)	1·70	1·60
2361	6t. Peacock (value at left) (horiz)	1·70	1·60
2362	8t. Camberwell beauty (value at left) (horiz)	2·50	2·20
2363	8t. Red admiral (value at right) (horiz)	2·50	2·20
2364	16t. *Hyporhaia audica* (horiz)	5·00	4·50
2365	16t. Large tortoiseshell (flying over river) (horiz)	5·00	4·50

MS2366 Two sheets. (a) 114×90 mm. 30t. Swallowtail (50×37 mm); (b) 113×90 mm. 30t. Purple tiger moth (50×37 mm) 19·00 18·00

469 Bugler

1992. Celebrities and Events. Five sheets containing T **469** and similar horiz designs. Multicoloured.

MS2367 Five sheets (a) 120×80 mm. 30t. Mother Teresa of Calcutta (winner of Nobel Peace Prize, 1979); (b) 120×80 mm. 30t. Pope John Paul II celebrating Mass; (c) 115×89 mm. 30t. President Punsalmaagiyn Ochirbat of Mongolia and President George Bush of USA; (d) 120 ×80 mm. 30t. Type **469** (17th World Scout Jamboree, Korea (1991)); (e) 120×80 mm. 30t. Type **469** (18th World Scout Jamboree, Netherlands (1995)) 45·00 44·00

470 Genghis Khan

1992. 830th Birth Anniv of Genghis Khan. Sheet 100×120 mm.

MS2368 **470** 16t. multicoloured 37·00 36·00

471 Gold Medal

1992. Olympic Games, Barcelona (1st issue), Granada '92 International Thematic Stamp Exhibition and Expo '92 World's Fair, Seville. Sheet 100×70 mm containing T **471** and similar vert design. Multicoloured.

MS2369 30t. Type **471**; 30t. Olympic torch 20·00 19·00

See also Nos. 2379/**MS**2388.

472 Fleet

1992. 500th Anniv of Discovery of America by Columbus (2nd issue). Multicoloured.

2370	3t. Type **472**	25	20
2371	7t. Amerindians' canoe approaching *Santa Maria*	50	35
2372	10t. *Pinta*	85	55
2373	16t. *Santa Maria* in open sea (vert)	1·40	70
2374	30t. *Santa Maria* passing coastline	2·75	1·80
2375	40t. Dolphins and *Santa Maria*	3·75	3·25
2376	50t. *Nina*	4·25	4·00

MS2377 Two sheets, each 94×115 mm. (a) 80t. Christopher Columbus (37×49 mm); (b) 80t. *Santa Maria* (37×49 mm) 15·00 14·50

1992. Mongolian Stamp Exhibition, Taiwan. No. **MS**1449 optd **MONGOLIAN STAMP EXHIBTION 1992 – TAIWAN** in margin.

MS2378 105×68 mm. **298** 4t. multicoloured 8·50 8·25

474 Long Jumping

1992. Olympic Games, Barcelona (2nd issue). Multicoloured.

2379	3t. Type **474**	15	20
2380	6t. Gymnastics (pommel exercise)	35	20
2381	8t. Boxing	70	25
2382	16t. Wrestling	85	35
2383	20t. Archery (vert)	1·00	45
2384	30t. Cycling	1·20	55
2385	40t. Show jumping	1·40	65
2386	50t. High jumping	1·70	70
2387	60t. Weightlifting	2·00	90

MS2388 Two sheets, each 100×82 mm. (a) 80t. Throwing the javelin (38×26 mm); (b) 80t. Judo (38×26 mm) 13·50 13·00

1993. Birth Centenary of Sukhe Bator. No. **MS**1523 optd 1893 – 1993 in the margin.

MS2389 65×72 mm. **270** 4t. purple 10·00 9·75

Eight designs, each 200t. and embossed on both gold and silver foil and accompanied by matching miniature sheets, were issued in 1993 in limited printings, depicting animals, sports or transport.

476 Black Grouse

1993. Birds. Multicoloured.

2390	3t. Type **476**	15	15
2391	8t. Moorhen	70	50
2392	10t. Golden-crowned kinglet	85	70
2393	16t. River kingfisher	1·40	1·20
2394	30t. Red-throated diver	2·75	2·40
2395	40t. Grey heron	3·50	3·00
2396	50t. Hoopoe	4·50	4·25
2397	60t. Blue-throated niltava	5·00	4·75

MS2398 Two sheets, each 115×90 mm. (a) 80t. Great crested grebe (*Podiceps cristatus*) (45×35 mm); (b) 80t. Griffon vulture (*Gyps fulvus*) (48×35 mm) 15·00 14·50

477 Orange-tip

1993. Butterflies and Moths. Multicoloured.

2399	3t. Type **477**	15	15
2400	8t. Peacock	70	50
2401	10t. High brown fritillary	85	65
2402	16t. *Limenitis reducta*	1·40	1·10
2403	30t. Common burnet	2·50	2·20
2404	40t. Common blue	3·50	3·00
2405	50t. Apollo	4·25	4·00
2406	60t. Great peacock	5·00	4·50

MS2407 Two sheets, each 115×90 mm. (a) 80t. Poplar admiral (*Limenitis populi*) (49×37 mm); (b) 80t. Scarce copper (*Heodes virgaureae*) (49×37 mm) 13·50 13·00

1993. No. 1221 surch **XXX 15Ter**.

2408	15t. on 70m. multicoloured	24·00	21·00

479 Nicolas Copernicus (astronomer)

1993. Polska'93 International Stamp Exhibition, Poznan. Multicoloured.

2409	30t. Type **479** (520th birth anniv)	4·25	3·25
2410	30t. Frederic Chopin (composer)	4·25	3·25
2411	30t. Pope John Paul II	4·25	3·25

MS2412 Two sheets, each 98×122 mm. (a) 80t. Type **479**; (b) 80t. As No. 2411 26·00 25·00

1993. No. 263 surch **8-Ter**.

2413	8t. on 70m. multicoloured	12·00	11·00

481 Sun Yat-sen (Chinese statesman)

1993. Taipei '93 International Stamp Exhibition. Two sheets each containing vert design as T **481**. Multicoloured.

MS2414 Two sheets, each 100×124 mm. (a) 80t. Type **481**; (b) 80t. Genghis Khan (portrait as in Type **431**) 60·00 55·00

482 Hologram of Airship

1993. Airship Flight over Ulan Bator.

2415	**482** 80t. multicoloured	5·00	4·75

483 Buddha

1993. Bangkok 1993 International Stamp Exhibition. Multicoloured.

2416	50t. Buddha on throne	70	30
2417	100t. Buddha (different)	1·20	65
2418	150t. Type **483**	1·70	95
2419	200t. Multi-armed Buddha	2·40	1·30

MS2420 90×125 mm. 300t. Buddha with right hand raised 3·50 3·25

484 Clouds, Mountains and Dog

1994. New Year. Year of the Dog. Multicoloured.

2421	60t. Type **484**	2·50	1·30
2422	60t. Dog reclining between mountains and waves (horiz)	2·50	1·30

485 Uruguay (1930, 1950)

1994. World Cup Football Championship, U.S.A. Previous Winners. Multicoloured.

2423	150t. Type **485**	1·70	50
2424	150t. Italy (1934)	1·70	50
2425	150t. German Federal Republic (1954)	1·70	50
2426	150t. Brazil (1958)	1·70	50
2427	150t. Argentina (1978, 1986)	1·70	50
2428	200t. Italy (1938)	2·20	80
2429	200t. Brazil (1962)	2·20	80
2430	200t. German Federal Republic (1974)	2·20	80
2431	250t. Brazil (1970)	3·00	1·10
2432	250t. Italy (1982)	3·00	1·10
2433	250t. German Federal Republic (1990)	3·00	1·10

MS2434 Five sheets. (a) 167×120 mm. Nos. 2427 and 2431/3; (b) 118×93 mm. Nos. 2423 and 2427; (c) 118×93 mm. Nos. 2424, 2428 and 2432; (d) 118×93 mm. Nos. 2425, 2430 and 2433; (e) 118×93 mm. Nos. 2426, 2429 and 2431 37·00 36·00

486 Boeing 727

1994. Air. Hong Kong '94 International Stamp Exhibition. Sheet 96×69 mm.

MS2435 **486** 600t. multicoloured 6·75 6·50

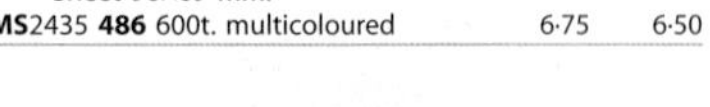

487 Pres. Punsalmaagiin Ochirbat

1994. First Direct Presidential Election. Sheet 86×91 mm.

MS2436 **487** 150t. multicoloured 4·25 4·00

488 Biathlon

1994. Winter Olympic Games, Lillehammer, Norway. Multicoloured.

2437	50t. Type **488**	70	30
2438	60t. Two-man bobsleigh	85	50
2439	80t. Skiing	1·20	80
2440	100t. Ski jumping	1·40	95
2441	120t. Ice skating	1·50	1·10
2442	200t. Speed skating	2·20	1·80

MS2443 100×125 mm. 400t. Ice hockey 7·75 7·50

489 Dalai Lama

1994. Award of Nobel Peace Prize to Dalai Lama. Sheet 85×104 mm.

MS2444	**489** 400t. multicoloured	48·00	48·00

490 Lammergeier

1994. Wildlife. Multicoloured.

2445	60t. Type **490**	1·00	65
2446	60t. Grey-headed woodpecker on tree trunk	1·00	65
2447	60t. Japanese white-naped cranes	1·00	65
2448	60t. Western marsh harrier	1·00	65
2449	60t. Golden oriole on branch	1·00	65
2450	60t. Bank swallows	1·00	65
2451	60t. Montagu's harrier perched on rock	1·00	65
2452	60t. Pallid harriers in flight	1·00	65
2453	60t. Squirrel on branch	1·00	65
2454	60t. Dragonfly	1·00	65
2455	60t. Black stork	1·00	65
2456	60t. Northern pintail	1·00	65
2457	60t. Spotted nutcracker standing on rock	1·00	65
2458	60t. Marmot	1·00	65
2459	60t. Ladybird on flower	1·00	65
2460	60t. Clutch of eggs in ground nest	1·00	65
2461	60t. Grasshopper	1·00	65
2462	60t. Butterfly	1·00	65

Nos. 2445/62 were issued together, *se-tenant*, forming a composite design.

491 Command Module

1994. 25th Anniv of First Manned Moon Landing. Multicoloured.

2463	200t. Type **491**	2·50	95
2464	200t. Earth, astronaut in chair and shuttle wing	2·50	95
2465	200t. Shuttle approaching Earth	2·50	95
2466	200t. Astronaut on Moon	2·50	95
MS2467	105×130 mm. Nos. 2463/6	10·00	9·75

492 Flowers

1994

2468	**492**	10t. green and black	3·50	30
2469	-	18t. purple and black	3·50	30
2470	-	22t. blue and black	3·50	50
2471	-	44t. purple and black	3·50	50

Designs:—18, 44t. Argali; 22t. Aircraft.

493 Korean Empire 1884 5m. Stamp

1994. Philakorea 1994 International Stamp Exhibition, Seoul. Multicoloured.

2472	600t. Type **493**	4·75	1·60
2473	600t. Mongolia 1924 1c. stamp	4·75	1·60
2474	600t. Mongolia 1966 Children's Day 15 m. stamp (47×34 mm)	4·75	1·60
2475	600t. South Korea 1993 New Year 110 w. stamp (47×34 mm)	4·75	1·60
MS2476	94×76 mm. 600t. Korean man in traditional dress (34×47 mm)	7·75	7·50

494 Butterfly

1994. Singpex '94 National Stamp Exhibtion, Singapore. Year of the Dog. Multicoloured.

2477	300t. Type **494**	2·50	1·60
MS2478	105×78 mm. 400t. Dog	7·75	7·50

495 1924 20c. Stamp

1994. 70th Anniv of First Mongolian Stamp. Sheet 91×111 mm.

MS2479	**495** 400t. multicoloured	7·75	7·50

496 Mammoth

1994. Prehistoric Animals. Multicoloured.

2480	60t. Type **496**	85	50
2481	80t. Stegosaurus	1·00	65
2482	100t. Talararus (horiz)	1·20	80
2483	120t. Gorythosaurus (horiz)	1·50	1·10
2484	200t. Tyrannosaurus (horiz)	2·20	1·80
MS2485	124×99 mm. 400t. Triceratops (horiz)	6·00	5·75

497 National Flags

1994. Mongolia–Japan Friendship and Co-operation.

2486	**497**	20t. multicoloured	85	80

498 Boar and Mountains

1995. New Year. Year of the Pig. Multicoloured.

2487	200t. Type **498**	1·00	65
2488	200t. Boar reclining amongst clouds (vert)	1·00	65

499 Dancer

1995. Tsam Religious Mask Dance.

2489	**499**	20t. multicoloured	50	15
2490	-	50t. multicoloured	70	30
2491	-	60t. multicoloured	85	50
2492	-	100t. multicoloured	1·00	55
2493	-	120t. multicoloured	1·20	65
2494	-	150t. multicoloured	1·50	80
2495	-	200t. multicoloured	1·90	95
MS2496		92×133 mm. 400t. multicoloured	7·75	7·50

Designs:—50t. to 400t. Different masked characters.

500 Saiga

1995. The Saiga. Multicoloured.

2497	40t. Type **500**	70	30
2498	50t. Male and female	85	50
2499	70t. Male running	1·20	65
2500	200t. Head and neck of male	3·50	1·60

501 Garden Tiger Moth

1995. Hong Kong '95 Stamp and Collecting Fair. Sheet 104×100 mm containing T **501** and similar square design plus two labels. Multicoloured.

MS2501	200t. Type **501**; 200t. Dandelion and anemone	8·50	8·25

502 Yellow Oranda

1995. Goldfish. Multicoloured.

2502	20t. Type **502**	50	15
2503	50t. Red and white veil-tailed wen-yu	70	30
2504	60t. Brown oranda red-head	1·00	50
2505	100t. Pearl-scaled	1·20	80
2506	120t. Red lion-head	1·50	95
2507	150t. Brown oranda	1·90	1·10
2508	200t. Red and white oranda with narial	2·50	1·60
MS2509	136×110 mm. 400t. Red and white goldfish (49×37 mm)	9·25	9·00

See also No. **MS**2510.

1995. Singapore '95 International Stamp Exhibition. As No. **MS**2509 but with exhibition embelm in the margin.

MS2510	136×110 mm. 400t. multicoloured	9·25	9·00

503 Bishop

1995. X-Men (comic strip). Designs showing characters. Multicoloured.

2511	30t. Type **503**	35	15
2512	50t. Beast	45	25
2513	60t. Rogue	50	30
2514	70t. Gambit	60	40
2515	80t. Cyclops	70	50
2516	100t. Storm	1·20	65
2517	200t. Professor X	1·70	1·40
2518	250t. Wolverine	2·00	1·80
MS2519	168×171 mm. 250t. Wolverine (horiz); 250t. Magneto (horiz)	8·50	8·25

504 Trygve Lie (1946—52)

1995. 50th Anniv of United Nations Organization. Sheet 125×115 mm containing T **504** and similar vert designs showing Secretaries-General and various views of the New York Headquarters complex. Multicoloured.

MS2520	60t. Type **504**; 60t. Dag Hammarskjold (1953–61); 60t. U. Thant (1961–71); 60t. Kurt Waldheim (1972–81); 60t. Javier Perez de Cuellar (1982–91); 60t. Boutros Boutros Ghali (1992-96)	8·50	8·25

505 Presley

1995. 60th Birth Anniv of Elvis Presley (entertainer). Multicoloured.

2521	60t. Type **505**	70	30
2522	80t. Wearing cap	85	50
2523	100t. Holding microphone	1·00	65
2524	120t. Wearing blue and white striped T-shirt	1·20	80
2525	150t. With guitar and microphone	1·40	95
2526	200t. On motor bike with girl	1·70	1·40
2527	250t. On surfboard	2·00	1·80
2528	300t. Pointing with left hand	2·50	2·20
2529	350t. Playing guitar and girl clapping	3·00	2·50
MS2530	Two sheets. (a) 139×91 mm. 400t. Playing guitar; (b) 139×94 mm. 400t. Wearing army uniform with Priscilla Presley	20·00	19·00

Nos. 2521/9 were issued together, *se-tenant*, forming a composite design.

See also No. **MS**2543.

506 Monroe smiling

1995. 70th Birth Anniv (1996) of Marilyn Monroe (actress). Multicoloured.

2531	60t. Type **506**	70	30
2532	80t. Wearing white dress	85	50
2533	100t. Pouting	1·00	65
2534	120t. With naval officer and cello player	1·20	80
2535	150t. Wearing off-the-shoulder blouse	1·40	95
2536	200t. Using telephone and wearing magenta dress	1·70	1·40
2537	250t. Man kissing Monroe's shoulder	2·00	1·80
2538	300t. With white fur collar	2·50	2·20
2539	350t. With Clark Gable	3·00	2·50
MS2540	Two sheets. (a) 139×90 mm. 300t. Wearing black lace dress; (b) 137×106 mm. 300t. Lying on tiger skin rug	20·00	19·00

Nos. 2531/9 were issued together, *se-tenant*, forming a composite design.

Seel also No. **MS**2544.

507 Rat sitting between Mountains

1996. New Year. Year of the Rat. Multicoloured.

2541	150t. Type **507**	1·40	95
2542	200t. Rat crouching between mountains and waves (horiz)	2·00	1·30

1996. 70th Birth Anniv of Marilyn Monroe (actress) (2nd issue). Two sheets containing vert designs as T **506**.

MS2544	Two sheets. (a) 100×136 mm. 200t. Close-up of Monroe; (b) 146×112 mm. 300t. Close-up of Monroe and in scene from *Niagara*	20·00	19·00

1996. Mongolian–Chinese Friendship. Sheet 97×133 mm containing T **508** and similar vert designs. Multicoloured.

MS2545	65t. Type **508**; 65t. Temple of Heaven, Peking; 65t. Migjed Jang-Rasek; 65t. The Great Wall of China	15·00	14·50

1996. China '96 International Stamp Exhibition, Peking. As No. **MS**2545 but with each stamp additionally bearing either the exhibition emblem or a mascot holding the emblem.

MS2546	65t.×4 multicoloured	15·00	14·50

509 Mongolian 1924 2c. Stamp

1996. Capex '96 International Stamp Exhibition, Toronto. Sheet 116×90 mm containing T **509** and similar design. Multicoloured.

MS2547	350t. Type **509**; 400t. Canadian 1851 3d. stamp (36×26 mm)	16·00	15·00

510 Cycling

1996. Olympic Games, Atlanta, U.S.A. Multicoloured

2548	30t. Type **510**	15	15
2549	60t. Shooting	25	15
2550	80t. Weightlifting	35	15
2551	100t. Boxing	45	25
2552	120t. Archery (vert)	50	30
2553	150t. Rhythmic gymnastics (vert)	70	50
2554	200t. Hurdling (vert)	85	65
2555	350t. Show jumping	1·70	1·40
2556	400t. Wrestling	1·90	1·60
MS2557	Two sheets, each 130×93 mm. (a) 500t. Basketball (37×53 mm); (b) 600t. Judo (51×39 mm)	12·00	11·50
MS2558	Two sheets. As No. **MS**2557 but additionally inscr in top margin 'Centenary International Olympic Games 1896—1996'	12·00	11·50

511 Genghis Khan

1996. Genghis Khan Commemoration. Self-adhesive gum.

2559	**511**	10000t. gold	£100	95·00

PHILA SEOUL (512a)

1996. Phila Seoul '96 International Stamp Exhibition. Nos. 2472/5 optd with T **512a** for the exhibition.

2560	600t. 1884 Korean Empire 5m. Stamp	4·25	3·00
2561	600t. 1924 Mongolia 1c. stamp	4·25	3·00
2562	600t. 1966 Mongolia Children's Day stamp (47×34 mm)	4·25	3·00
2563	600t. 1993 South Korea New Year stamp (47×34 mm)	4·25	3·00
MS2564	95×77 mm. 600t. Korean man wearing traditional dress	8·50	8·25

513 Emblems

1996. Seventh Anniv of Democratic Union Coalition.

2565	**513**	100t. multicoloured	85	50

514 Pagoda

1996. TAIPEI '96. Sheet 73×67 mm.

MS2566	**514** 750t. multicoloured	8·50	8·25

515 Girl and Mongolian Flag

1996. 50th Anniv of United Nations Children's Fund. Multicoloured.

2566a	250t. Type **515**	2·75	80
2566b	250t. Dutch girl	2·75	80
2566c	250t. Japanese girl	2·75	80
2566d	250t. German girl in traditional dress	2·75	80
2566e	250t. Chinese girls dancing	2·75	80
2566f	250t. Two American girls	2·75	80
MS2567	107×83 mm. 700t. Mongolian boy	8·50	8·25

250₮
(516)

1996. No. 543 surch as T **516**.

2568	**516**	250t. on 50m. multicoloured	14·50	13·50

518 Ox

1997. New Year. "Year of the Ox". Multicoloured.

2570	300t. Type **518**	1·90	1·80
2571	350t. Ox (horiz)	2·20	2·10

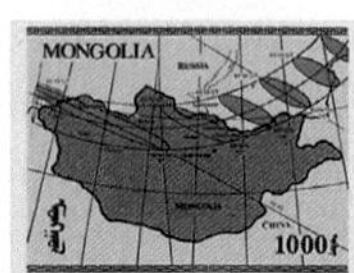
519 Map showing Path of Eclipse

1997. Total Eclipse of the Sun, 9 March 1997. Sheet 83×115 mm.

MS2572	**519** 1000t. multicoloured	9·25	9·00

520 Deng Xiaoping (Chinese leader) and Queen Elizabeth

1997. Return of Hong Kong to China. Multicoloured.

2573	200t. Type **520**	1·90	1·60
2574	250t. Tung Chee-hwa (head of government) and Jiang Zemin (Chinese president)	2·20	1·90

521 Painting and Oil Lamp

1997. Memorial for Victims of Political Oppression.

2575	**521**	150t. black	2·00	1·40

522 Adelie Penguin

1997. 25th Anniv of Greenpeace (ecological organization). Multicoloured.

2576	200t. Type **522**	1·30	1·10
2577	400t. Six Adelie penguins	2·30	2·10
2578	500t. Two Adelie penguins	3·00	2·50
2579	800t. Colony of Emperor penguins	4·75	4·25
MS2580	Two sheets. (a) 120×85 mm. 1000t. *Greenpeace* (ship) amongst icebergs. (b) 183×116 mm. Nos. 2576/9 and **MS**2580a	26·00	25·00

523 Dharma Wheel

1997. Religious Symbols. Multicoloured.

2581	200t. Type **523**	1·60	1·40
2582	200t. Precious Jewels	1·60	1·40
2583	200t. Precious Minister	1·60	1·40
2584	200t. Precious Queen	1·60	1·40
2585	200t. Precious Elephant	1·60	1·40
2586	200t. Precious Horse	1·60	1·40
2587	200t. Precious General	1·60	1·40

524 1961 15m. Stamp (Damdiny Sukhbaatar Monument)

1997. MOCKBA '97 International Stamp Exhibition. Sheet 115×80 mm.

MS2588	**524** 1000t. multicoloured	8·00	7·75

525 Electric Locomotive LV-80

1997. Trains. Multicoloured.

2589	20t. Type **525**	1·10	15
2590	40t. Japanese high-speed electric train	1·30	25
2591	120t. Diesel locomotive BL-80	1·40	30
2592	200t. Steam locomotive	1·60	50
2593	300t. FDP steam locomotive *Lass*	2·00	80
2594	350t. 0-6-0 tank locomotive *Arima*	2·30	95
2595	400t. Diesel locomotive 216	3·00	1·10
2596	500t. Diesel locomotive T6-106	3·25	1·30
2597	600t. Monorail *Europa*	4·00	1·60
MS2598	Two sheets. (a) 133×112 mm. 800t. Eurostar locomotive (57×44 mm). (b) 137×112 mm. 800t. R. and G. Stephenson's locomotive *Rocket* (57×44 mm)	22·00	21·00

526 *Dendrobium cunninghamii* and Adonis blue

1997. Orchids and Butterflies. Multicoloured.

2599	100t. Type **526**	70	15
2600	150t. Brown hairstreak and *Oncidium ampliatum*	90	25
2601	200t. *Maxillaria triloris* and large skipper	1·10	50
2602	250t. *Calypso bulbosa* and orange tip	1·30	65
2603	300t. Painted lady and *Catasetum pileatum*	1·40	70
2604	350t. Purple hairstreak and *Epidedrum fimbratum*	1·60	80
2605	400t. Red admiral and *Celeistes rosea*	1·80	95
2606	450t. Small copper and *Pontheiva maculate*	2·00	1·10
2607	500t. Small tortoiseshell and *Cypripeium calceolus*	2·20	1·30
MS2608	Two sheets, each 150×113 mm. (a) 800t. Red admiral and *Macranthum*. (b) Adonis blue and *Guttatum*	22·00	21·00

527 Princess Diana as Child

1997. Diana, Princess of Wales Commemoration. Six sheets containing T **527** and similar vert designs. Multicoloured.

MS2609	Six sheets. (a) 149×193 mm. 50t. Type **527**; 100t. Wearing high-necked blouse; 150t. As teenager; 200t. Wearing drop earrings and evening gown; 250t. Wearing tiara; 300t. Wearing pink outfit and pearl necklace; 350t. Wearing white outfit with gold frogging; 400t. Wearing black sweater; 450t. Wearing halter-necked dress. (b) 149×193 mm. 50t. As young girl; 100t. Wearing checked coat; 150t. As bride; 200t. With Princes William and Harry; 250t. Wearing red dress and tiara; 300t. Wearing black high-necked blouse; 350t. Wearing white blouse; 400t. Wearing pearl necklace and earrings; 450t. Wearing black outfit and pearl necklace. (c) 125×90 mm. 1000t. Wearing pink outfit. (d) 125×90 mm. 1000t. Wearing white dress. (e) 125×90 mm. 1000t. Holding baby Prince Harry. (f) 125×90 mm. 1000t. Wearing tiara Set of 6 sheets	65·00	60·00

528 Soldier

1997. Soldiers of Chingis Khan. Multicoloured.

2610	100t. Type **528**	90	50
2611	150t. Riding galloping horse	1·60	80
2612	200t. Wearing winged helmet, armour and sword	2·20	95
2613	250t. Riding horse and holding flag	3·00	1·30
2614	300t. Wearing armour and holding two swords	3·25	1·60
2615	350t. Archer	3·50	1·80
2616	400t. Wearing mailed visor and carrying spear and shield	4·25	2·10
2617	600t. Riding horse and leading cheetah	5·00	3·00
MS2618	175×110 mm. 600t. Three riders; 600t. Two foot soldiers with cheetahs; 1000t. Riders carrying standards (65×60 mm)	13·50	13·00

529 Genghis Khan

1997. Khans of the Mongolian Empire. Multicoloured.

2619	1000t. Type **529**	6·00	5·00
2620	1000t. Ogodei	6·00	5·00
2621	1000t. Guyuk	6·00	5·00
2622	1000t. Mongke	6·00	5·00
2623	1000t. Kubilai (Hubilai)	6·00	5·00
MS2624	Four sheets, each 95×131 mm. (a) As Type **529** (22×32 mm). (b) As No. 2620 (22×32 mm). (c) As Nos. 2621/2 (22×32 mm). (d) As No. 2623 (22×32 mm). Set of 4 sheets	31·00	30·00

530 National Emblem

1998. National Symbols. Multicoloured.

2625	300t. Type **530**	2·20	1·90
2626	300t. Flag (horiz)	2·20	1·90

531 Crouching Tiger

1998. New Year. "Year of the Tiger". Multicoloured.

2627	150t. Type **531**	1·80	1·10
2628	200t. Tiger facing right	2·75	1·60
2629	300t. Two tigers (triangle inverted)	3·50	2·40

532 Speed Skating

1998. Winter Olympic Games, Nagano. Multicoloured.

2630	150t.+15t. Type **532**	1·30	80
2631	200t.+20t. Ski jump	1·40	95
2632	300t.+30t. Skateboard	2·30	1·60
2633	600t.+60t. Skiing	4·00	3·00

533 Three Yaks

1998. The Mongolian Yak. Multicoloured.

2634	20t. Type **533**	20	15
2635	30t. White yak	25	25
2636	50t. Yurt, cart and black yak	35	30
2637	100t. White-faced yak with horns	90	80
2638	150t. Mother and calf	1·30	1·10
2639	200t. Tethered yak and milking buckets	1·80	1·60
2640	300t. Large grey yak with horns (53×39 mm)	2·50	2·20
2641	400t. Brown yak with raised tail (53×39 mm)	3·50	3·00

MS2642 95×126 mm. 800t. Yak carrying children and furniture (60×47 mm) 11·00 10·50

534 Players and Competition Emblem

1998. World Cup Football Championship, France. Sheet 121×88 mm.

MS2643 **534** 1000t. multicoloured 10·00 9·75

535 Natsagyn Bagabandi

1998. President Natsagyn Bagabandi. Sheet 70×107 mm.

MS2644 **535** 1000t. multicoloured 9·00 8·75

536 *Lebistes reticulates*

1998. Fish. Multicoloured.

2645	20t. Type **536**	20	15
2646	30t. Inscr 'Goldfish'	25	25
2647	50t. *Balistes conspcillum*	35	30
2648	100t. Inscr 'Goldfish'	55	50
2649	150t. *Synchirops splendidus*	90	80
2650	200t. Inscr 'C. auratus'	1·30	1·10
2651	300t. *Xiphophorus helleri*	1·80	1·60
2652	400t. *Pygoplites diacanthus*	2·50	2·20
2653	600t. *Chaetodon auriga*	3·50	3·25

MS2654 Two sheets, each 141×86 mm. (a) 800t. Fish (105×49 mm). (b) 800t. Fish (different) (105×49 mm). Set of 2 sheets 22·00 21·00

537 Bear

1998. Gobi Bear (*Ursus arctos gobiensis*). Multicoloured.

2655	100t. Type **537**	2·20	80
2656	150t. Facing left	3·00	1·30
2657	200t. Two bears	3·50	1·80
2658	250t. Mother and cubs	4·25	2·20

MS2659 Two sheets, each 111×70 mm. (a) 100t. Type **537**; 200t. No. 2657. (b) 150t. No. 2656; 250t. No. 2658 16·00 15·00

538 Brown Cat (inscr 'Red Persian')

1998. Cats. Multicoloured.

2660	50t. Type **538**	35	30
2661	100t. Blue shorthair (inscr 'Man Cat')	90	80
2662	150t. Smoke Persian	1·30	1·10
2663	200t. Cream Persian (inscr 'Long hairedwhite Persian')	1·80	1·60
2664	250t. Two silver tabbies	2·20	1·90
2665	300t. Two Siamese	2·50	2·20

MS2666 106×73 mm. 1000t. Two kittens and basket 8·00 7·75

539 Jerry Garcia

1998. American Musicians. Multicoloured.

2667	100t. Type **539**	90	80
2668	200t. Jerry Garcia wearing grey T-shirt	2·00	1·30
2669	200t. Bob Marley	2·00	1·30
2670	200t. Carlos Santana	2·00	1·30

MS2671 Five sheets (a) 127×165 mm *Grateful Dead*. 50t. Bear as cyclist; 100t. Bear as footballer; 150t. Bear as basketball player; 200t. Bear as golfer; 250t. Bear as baseball player; 300t. Bear as skater; 350t. Bear as ice hockey player; 400t. Bear as American footballer; 450t. Bear as skier. (b) 127×165 mm. *Jerry Garcia*. 50t. Wearing blue T-shirt; 100t. Wearing jacket; 150t. Wearing dark T-shirt, shorter hair; 200t. Microphone, wearing black T-shirt; 250t. Wearing brown T-shirt; 300t. Wearing dark T-shirt; 350t. Wearing grey T-shirt; 400t. Wearing orange T-shirt; 450t. Wearing black T-shirt. (c) 152×102 mm. Jerry Garcia wearing blue T-shirt (51×77 mm). (d) 102×152 mm. 1000t. Jerry Garcia wearing orange T-shirt (51×77 mm). (e) 152×102 mm. 1000t. Bob Marley (51×77 mm). Set of 5 sheets 65·00 60·00

540 Building

1998. Communications and Transport. Multicoloured background colour given.

2672	100t. Type **540** (brown)	70	65
2673	100t. Computer screen (ultramarine)	70	65
2674	100t. Car (green)	70	65
2675	100t. Locomotive (mauve)	70	65
2676	100t. Aeroplane (violet)	70	65
2677	200t. As No. 2672 (ultramarine)	1·40	1·30
2678	200t. As No. 2673 (green)	1·40	1·30
2679	200t. As No. 2674 (mauve)	1·40	1·30
2680	200t. As No. 2675 (violet)	1·40	1·30
2681	200t. As No. 2676 (brown)	1·40	1·30
2682	200t. As No. 2672 (green)	1·40	1·30
2683	200t. As No. 2673 (mauve)	1·40	1·30
2684	200t. As No. 2674 (violet)	1·40	1·30
2685	200t. As No. 2675 (brown)	1·40	1·30
2686	200t. As No. 2676 (ultramarine)	1·40	1·30
2687	400t. As No. 2672 (mauve)	3·00	2·50
2688	400t. As No. 2673 (violet)	3·00	2·50
2689	400t. As No. 2674 (brown)	3·00	2·50
2690	400t. As No. 2675 (ultramarine)	3·00	2·50
2691	400t. As No. 2676 (green)	3·00	2·50
2692	400t. As No. 2672 (violet)	3·00	2·50
2693	400t. As No. 2673 (brown)	3·00	2·50
2694	400t. As No. 2674 (ultramarine)	3·00	2·50
2695	400t. As No. 2675 (green)	3·00	2·50
2696	400t. As No. 2676 (mauve)	3·00	2·50

541 Three Stooges

1998. "The Three Stooges" (comedy series starring Moe Howard, Larry Fine and Curly Howard). T **541** and similar multicoloured designs.

MS2697 Six sheets (a) 177×143 mm. 50t. Type **541**; 100t. With mandolin, saw and guitar; 150t. Curly with head in trouser press; 200t. Curly using shower head as microphone; 250t. Curly with head in wooden vice; 300t. Curly having dental treatment with percussion drill; 350t. Curly having dental treatment with pliers; 400t. Stuffing turkey; 450t. Curly with head in door jamb. (b) 177×143 mm. 50t. With pistols and cigars; 100t. Wearing pith helmets; 150t. Curly holding dynamite; 200t. As golfers; 250t. With right hands above heads; 300t. Curly holding bird; 350t. Holding bouquets; 400t. Pulling Moe's ears; 450t. Dressing Curly. (c) 176×130 mm. 50t. Wearing civil war uniforms; 100t. As foreign legionnaires; 150t. With two women; 200t. With horse; 250t. Wearing military uniforms, Curly holding candle; 300t. With anti-aircraft gun; 350t. With laughing general; 400t. With British soldier; 450t. Curly with straw beard. (d) 140×89 mm. 800t. Curly with head in trouser press (42×60 mm). (e) 90×137 mm. 800t. Wearing pith helmets (51×42 mm). (f) 101×127 mm. 800t. Playing football (60×51 mm). Set of 6 sheets 60·00 55·00

542 T. Namnansuren

1998. Prime Ministers. Multicoloured.

2698-2715 200t.×18, Type **542**; Badamdorj; D. Chagdarjav; D. Bodoo; S. Damdinbazar; B. Tserendorj; A. Amar; Ts. Jigjidjav; P. Genden; Kh. Ghoibalsan; Yu. Tsedenbal; J. Batmunkh; D. Sodnom; Sh. Gungaadorj; D. Byambasuren; P. Jasrai; M. Enkhsaikhan; Ts. Elbegdorj 26·00 23·00

543 Conch Shell

1998. Buddhist Symbols. Multicoloured.

2716	200t. Type **543**	1·60	1·40
2717	200t. Precious umbrella	1·60	1·40
2718	200t. Victory banner	1·60	1·40
2719	200t. Golden fish	1·60	1·40
2720	200t. Dharma wheel	1·60	1·40
2721	200t. Auspicious drawing	1·60	1·40
2722	200t. Lotus flower	1·60	1·40
2723	200t. Treasure vase	1·60	1·40

544 People of Many Races and Rainbow

1998. 50th Anniv of Declaration of Human Rights.

2724	**544**	450t. multicoloured	3·25	3·00

545 D. Damien

1998. National Wrestling Champions. Sheet 170×120 mm containing T **545** and similar diamond shaped designs. Multicoloured.

MS2725 200t.×7, Type **545**; B. Batsuury; J. Munkhbat; H. Bakanmunkh; B. Tubdendorj; D. Tserentogtokh; B. Bat-Erdre 12·50 12·00

The stamps and margin of No. **MS**2725 form a composite design of bird and animals.

546 *Mercury 6* Space Capsule and Earth

1998. John Glenn's Return to Space. Two sheets, each 125×170 mm containing T **546** and similar vert designs. Multicoloured.

MS2726 (a) 50t. Type **546**; 100t. NASA emblem and earth; 150t. *Friendship 7* mission emblem and earth; 150t. Rocket lift off; 200t. John Glenn as young man; 250t. Capsule floating in sea; 250t. Capsule; 450t. Moon; 450t. Nebula and star. (b) 50t. NASA emblem and earth; 100t. John Glenn wearing space suit; 150t. *Discovery 7* mission emblem and earth; 150t. Shuttle space craft; 200t. John Glenn as older man; 250t. *Discovery 7* landing; 250t. Space craft, shuttle and moon's surface; 450t. Super nova and moon's surface; 450t. NASA 40th anniversary emblem and moon's surface 32·00 31·00

547 Rabbit

1999. New Year. "Year of the Rabbit". Multicoloured.

2727	250t. Type **547**	2·50	1·60
2728	300t. Rabbit facing right (horiz)	3·00	1·90

548 Eastern Red-footed Falcon (*Falco amurensis*)

1999. Raptors. Sheet 140×140 mm containing T **548** and similar vert designs. Multicoloured.

MS2729 30t. Type **548**; 50t. Saker falcon (*Falco cherrug*); 100t. Western red-footed falcon (*Falco vespertinus*); 150t. Merlin (*Falco columbarius*); 170t. Peregrine falcon (*Falco peregrinus*); 200t. Common kestrel (*Falco tinnunculus*); 250t. Lesser kestrel (*Falco naumanni*); 300t. Northern hobby (*Falco subbuteo*); 350t. Barbary falcon (*Falco pelegrinoides*); 400t. Barbary falcon with wings spread; 600t. Gyr falcon (*Falco rusticolus*) in flight; 800t Gyr falcon on nest 22·00 21·00

549 Chief Thunderthud

1999. "Howdy Doody" (children's television programme). Four sheets containing T **549** and similar multicoloured designs.

MS2730 131×176 mm. 50t. Type **549**; 100t. Princess Summerfall Winterspring; 150t. Howdy Doody wearing Mexican dress; 150t. Buffalo Bob and Howdy Doody facing each other; 200t. Howdy Doody sitting on Buffalo Bob's lap; 250t. Buffalo Bob and Howdy Doody rubbing noses; 250t. Clarabell the clown; 450t. Howdy Doody as Mountie; 450t. Howdy Doody 14·50 14·00

MS2731 Two sheets, each 140×90 mm. (a) 800t. Howdy Doody. (b) 800t. Buffalo Bob and Howdy Doody (horiz) 14·50 14·00

MS2732 90×140 mm. 800t. Howdy Doody and Buffalo Bob (48×61 mm) 7·25 7·00

550 Gandan Monastery

1999. Migjid Janraisig (Buddha) (statue). Multicoloured

2733	200t. Type **550**	1·80	1·10
2734	400t. Buddha	3·25	2·40

MS2735 Two sheets, each 97×145 mm. (a) 1000t. Buddha and building (49×105 mm). (b) 1000t. Buddha and script (49×105 mm) 12·50 12·00

551 Man chasing Demons

1999. Folktales. Multicoloured.

2736	50t. Type **551**	55	30
2737	150t. Chess match	1·30	95
2738	200t. Man leading lion carrying wood	1·80	1·30
2739	250t. Flying horse	2·20	1·60
2740	300t. Archer	2·50	1·90
2741	450t. Birds attacking mare and foal	3·50	3·00

MS2742 110×70 mm. 1000t. Camel on bird's back 11·50 11·00

552 Lucy and Ethel

1999. "I Love Lucy" (television programme). Three sheets containing T **552** and similar vert designs. Multicoloured.

MS2743 137×182 mm. 50t. Type **552**; 100t. Desi, Ethel, Fred and Lucy wrapped in blanket; 150t. Lucy talking; 150t. Lucy pushing buggy through doorway; 200t. Lucy behind window; 250t. Lucy carrying packages; 250t. Desi serenading Ethel; 450t. Lucy and Ethel seated; 450t. Desi, Lucy behind window and Ethel 16·00 15·00

MS2744 89×120 mm. 800t. Lucy behind window and Ethel (detail) (38×51 mm) 8·00 7·75

MS2745 93×144 mm. 800t. Lucy talking (detail) (38×51 mm) 8·00 7·75

553 Betty Boop

1999. Betty Boop (cartoon character). Three sheets containing T **553** and similar multicoloured designs.

MS2746 138×182 mm. 50t. Type **553**; 100t. Wearing torn off shorts and walking boots; 150t. Standing on scales; 150t. Wearing short blue skirt and sandals; 200t. Wearing cap, leggings and leg warmers; 250t. Wearing blue jeans and high heeled shoes; 250t. Wearing striped jersey; 450t. Wearing beach outfit; 450t. Wearing scarf, dress and long white socks 14·50 14·00

MS2747 Two sheets, each 125×93 mm. (a) 800t. Dog's eyes containing Betty (51×48 mm). (b) 800t. Betty Boop (51×48 mm) 14·50 14·00

810₮

(554)

1999. 800th Anniv of Temujin as Chinggis Khan. No. 294 surch as T **554**.

2748	810t. on 60m. buff, ultramarine and brown	31·00	27·00

555 Argali Sheep

1999. China 99 International Stamp Exhibition, Beijing.

2749	**555**	250t. multicoloured	1·80	1·30
2750	**555**	450t. multicoloured	3·00	2·20

556 Zanabazar (city founder)

1999. 360th Anniv of Ulaanbaatar (1st issue). Multicoloured.

2751	300t.+30t. Type **556**	1·40	1·10
2752	300t.+30t. City Arms	1·40	1·10
2753	300t.+30t. City and country flags	1·40	1·10

See also **MS**2762.

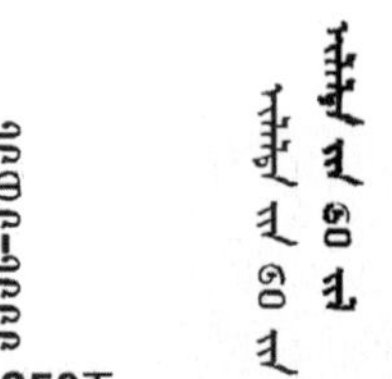

(557) **(557a)**

1999. 60th Anniv of Kalkha River Battle. No. 543 surch as T **557** and No. 2043 as T **557a**.

2754	250t. on 50m. multicoloured	14·50	11·00
2755	250t. on 60m. multicoloured	14·50	13·00

558 Genghis Khan

1999. Genghis Khan Commemoration. Self-adhesive gum.

2756	**558**	15000t. gold and silver	£130	£110

559 Early Document and Rider with Two Horses

1999. 125th Anniv of Universal Postal Union. Multicoloured.

2757	250t. Type **559**	1·40	1·30
2758	250t. Early postal cover and rider	1·40	1·30
2759	250t. Modern envelope, train and truck	1·40	1·30
2760	250t. Computer and airplane	1·40	1·30

MS2761 80×115 mm. 800t. Ogodei Khan (founder of postal relay) (32×41 mm) 7·25 7·00

560 Summer Palace

1999. 360th Anniv of Ulaanbaatar (2nd issue). Sheet 155×103 mm containing T **560** and similar horiz designs. Multicoloured.

MS2762 200t.+20t.×9, Type **560**; Parliament building and Sukhbaatar Square; Summer Palace entrance; City Bank; Urga (*circa* 1900); Opera House; Apartment block; Memorial stone; Aerial view of city 13·50 13·00

561 T. Damdinsuren

1999. World Education Day.

2763	**561**	250t. black and ultramarine	1·30	95
2764	-	250t. black and green	1·30	95
2765	-	450t. black and claret	2·00	1·60
2766	-	450t. black and lake	2·00	1·60
2767	-	600t. multicoloured (56×37 mm)	2·50	1·90

Designs:—250t. Type **561**; 250t. B. Rinchin; 450t. No. 2763; 450t. No. 2764; 600t. Teacher and pupils in Ger.

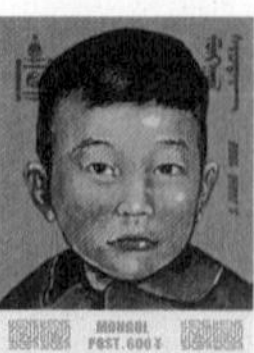

562 Sanjassurengiin Zorig as Child

1999. First Death Anniv of Sanjassurengiin Zorig (politician). Sheet 150×118 mm containing T **562** and similar multicoloured designs.

MS2768 600t. Type **562**; 600t. As adult; 1000t. At political rally (60×40 mm) 13·50 13·00

563 Inscribed Stele

1999. Cultural Heritage. Stone Carvings. Multicoloured.

2769	50t. Type **563**	35	30
2770	150t. 13th-century turtle (horiz)	90	80
2771	200t. Kul Tegin's burial site	1·10	95
2772	250t. 8th-century carving of Kul Tegin	1·40	1·30
2773	300t. 8th/9th-century dragon (horiz)	1·80	1·60
2774	450t. 5th/7th-century figure	2·50	2·20

564 Wolves

1999. Wolves. Multicoloured.

2775	150t. Type **564**	90	65
2776	250t. Wolves feeding	1·60	1·30
2777	300t. Mother and cubs	2·00	1·60
2778	450t. Snarling wolf	2·75	2·20

MS2779 90×60 mm. 800t. Wolves howling (50×30 mm) 7·25 7·00

565 Sunbar Lambs

1999. Mongolian Sheep Breeds. Multicoloured.

2780	50t. Type **565**	55	30
2781	100t. Orkhon	70	50
2782	150t. Baidrag	90	65
2783	250t. Barga	1·30	95
2784	400t. Uzemchin	2·30	1·90
2785	450t. Bayad	2·75	2·20

MS2786 110×75 mm. 800t. Govi-Altai 7·25 7·00

566 *A Day in the Life of Mongolia*

1999. 130th Birth Anniv of Balduugiin Sharav (artist). Sheet 202×159 mm containing T **566** and similar horiz designs showing parts of the painting "A Day in the Life of Mongolia". Multicoloured.

MS2787 50t. Type **566**; 100t. Ger, horsemen and trees; 150t. People seated around fire and workers in fields; 200t. Loaded camels at rest and wrestlers; 250t. Shaman, horse and wrestlers; 300t. Horsemen; 350t. Camels; 450t. Caravan of camels; 600t. Loaded camels and outdoor meal 16·00 15·00

567 Satellite and Aeroplane

1999. 20th Anniv of World Intellectual Property Organization. Sheet 172×112 mm containing T **567** and similar horiz designs. Multicoloured.

MS2788 250t. Type **567**; 250t. Bronze bowl, toy and train; 250t. Printer, stamps and statue; 250t. Racquet, car, bottles and buildings; 250t. Car bonnet, decorated bottles and mobile phones; 250t. Cigarette packet, stereo and boots; 450t. Television, headdress and statue; 450t. Camera, ger and couple; 450t. Perfume bottles 23·00 22·00

568 Prehistoric Ger

1999. Development of the Ger (dwelling). Multicoloured

2789	50t. Type **568**	55	30
2790	100t. Woman, child, dog, horses and early ger	90	65
2791	150t. Woman with elaborate headdress, child, dog and ger	1·30	95
2792	250t. Windmill, ger and motorbike	2·00	1·60

2793 450t. Constructing ger 3·50 3·00

MS2794 Two sheets, each 115×80 mm. (a) 800t. Cart carrying ger. (b) 800t. Men seated inside ger 16·00 15·00

569 Dragon

2000. Chinese New Year. Year of the Dragon. Multicoloured.

2795 250t. Type **569** 1·80 1·10
2796 450t. Dragon (vert) 3·00 2·20

570 Wrestler

2000. Mongolia—Japan Friendship. Sheet 149×115 mm containing T **570** and similar vert design. Multicoloured.

MS2797 450t.×2, Type **570**; Emblem 7·25 7·00

1000₮
(571)

2000. Nos. 739/42 surch as T **571**.

2798 1000t. on 50m. brown (postage) 12·50 5·50
2799 2000t. on 60m. green 18·00 8·00
2800 5000t. on 1t. purple 27·00 11·00
2801 10000t. on 1t.50 blue (air) 41·00 16·00

572 Jerry Garcia

2000. Jerry Garcia (musician) Commemoration. Multicoloured.

2802 50t. Type **572** 35 30
2803 50t. With longer grey hair and sunglasses facing left 35 30
2804 100t. With shorter grey hair facing left 55 50
2805 100t. With shorter grey hair wearing pale t-shirt 55 50
2806 100t. With dark hair and blue guitar 55 50
2807 100t. With longer grey hair facing left 55 50
2808 150t. With dark hair facing left 90 80
2809 150t. With longer grey hair wearing red-tinted glasses 90 80
2810 150t. With dark hair, blue guitar and microphone 90 80
2811 150t. With shorter grey hair, sunglasses and lowered head 90 80
2812 150t. With dark hair and pink and yellow guitar 90 80
2813 150t. With dark hair and pale green guitar 90 80
2814 150t. With shorter grey hair facing left 90 80
2815 150t. With shorter grey hair facing right 90 80
2816 200t. With dark hair wearing green t-shirt 1·10 95
2817 200t. With longer grey hair and guitar raised 1·10 95
2818 200t. With dark hair and purple t-shirt facing left 1·10 95
2819 200t. With dark hair, red t-shirt and yellow guitar 1·10 95
2820 200t. With shorter grey hair and sunglasses facing left 1·10 95
2821 200t. With shorter grey hair leaning left 1·10 95
2822 250t. With dark hair and red and yellow guitar facing right 1·40 1·30
2823 250t. With dark hair, purple shirt and pale green guitar facing right 1·40 1·30
2824 250t. With shorter grey hair and raised head facing left 1·40 1·30
2825 250t. With shorter grey hair tinged with blue 1·40 1·30
2826 250t. With shorter grey hair, blue t-shirt facing right 1·40 1·30
2827 250t. With longer grey hair and closed eyes facing right 1·40 1·30
2828 300t. With shorter grey hair and green t-shirt 1·60 1·40
2829 300t. With longer grey hair facing left 1·60 1·40
2830 350t. With shorter grey hair and purple t-shirt facing left 2·00 1·80
2831 350t. With longer grey hair and sunglasses facing left 2·00 1·80

573 Charles Darwin

2000. New Millennium. Sheet 160×230 mm containing T **573** and similar multicoloured designs.

MS2832 100t. Type **573**; 100t. Clematis; 100t. Down House; 100t. Chimpanzee; 200t. Shell (inscr 'Mollusk'); 200t. Orchid; 200t. Insect (inscr 'Reduviid bug'); 300t. HMS *Beagle*; 300t. Giant tortoise; 300t. *Larus relictus* (inscr 'Duck'); 300t. Turkey; 400t. Peacock; 400t. Dinosaur; 400t. *Vormela peregusna* (inscr 'peregugna'); 550t. Man and woman; 550t. *Equus hemionus*; 600t. Ram (59×48 mm) 32·00 31·00

574 High Speed Locomotive (France)

2000. Trains (1st issue). Eight sheets containing T **574** and similar horiz designs. Multicoloured.

MS2833 Two sheets, each 150×113 mm. (a) 200t. Type **574**; 200t. C38 class Pacific (USA); 200t. Inscr 'Bo-Bo Electric locomotive' (New Zealand); 300t. Inscr 'ALG Bo-Bo electric locomotive' (Britain); 300t. Inscr 'E-10 Bo-Bo electric locomotive' (Germany); 300t. 46 Class electric locomotive (USA); 400t. 2-10-0 *Austerity* (Britain); 400t. Diesel-electric locomotive (Australia); 400t. Inscr 'Bo-Bo electric locomotive' (Netherlands). (b) 200t. Stephenson 2-2-2 (Russia); 200t. 2-2-2 Walt locomotive (USA); 200t. Ross Winans mud digger (USA); 300t. Italian carriage (1840); 300t. *The General* (USA); 300t. Inscr '4-4-0 Ramopo' (USA); 400t. Carriage (Bodmin & Wadebridge railway); 400t. 4-4-0 Washington (USA); 400t. Braithwaite 0-4-0 29·00 28·00

MS2834 Two sheets, each 169×120 mm. (a) 350t.×6, As **MS**3833a. (b) 350t.×6, As **MS**2833b 11·00 10·50

MS2835 Two sheets, each 97×71 mm. (a) 800t. Electric Deltic locomotive (Britain). (b) 800t. Inscr 'The Ringmaster locomotive' (USA) 18·00 17·00

MS2836 Two sheets, each 110×86 mm. (a) 2000t. As **MS**2835a. (b) 2000t. As **MS**2835b 29·00 28·00

See also Nos. **MS**2923/**MS**2924.

575 Emblem

2000. Tenth Anniv of Production and Service Cooperatives.

2837 **575** 300t. indigo 2·20 1·90
2838 **575** 450t. green 3·25 3·00

576 Man's Costume

2000. Traditional Costumes. Multicoloured.

2839 550t. Type **576** 2·50 1·80
2840 550t. Man, closed black top, gold skirt and extended sleeves 2·50 1·80
2841 550t. Man, necklace, gold robe with turned cuffs 2·50 1·80
2842 550t. Man, side fastening, red and gold robe with turned cuffs 2·50 1·80
2843 550t. Man, gold robe, fur cuffs and fur hat with feather 2·50 1·80
2844 550t. Man, crossed white robe under short sleeved gold robe and metal headdress 2·50 1·80
2845 550t. Woman, tall headdress, pink under robe and gold over robe 2·50 1·80
2846 550t. Woman, elaborate furred headdress and blue robe 2·50 1·80

577 Yamantaka

2000. Aspects of Buddha. Multicoloured.

2847 550t. Type **577** 2·50 1·80
2848 550t. Mahakala 2·50 1·80
2849 550t. Inscr 'Esura' 2·50 1·80
2850 550t. Begze 2·50 1·80
2851 550t. Shridevi 2·50 1·80
2852 550t. Vajrapani 2·50 1·80
2853 550t. Kubera 2·50 1·80
2854 550t. Siti Mahakala 2·50 1·80
2855 550t. Yama 2·50 1·80
2856 550t. Inscr 'Sritzaturtuka' 2·50 1·80

578 Two Horses Grazing

2000. Przewalski Horse (*Equus przewalskii*). Multicoloured.

(a) 51×36 mm.

2857 50t. Two colts 70 65
2858 100t. Mare and foal 1·40 1·30
2859 200t. Two horses grazing 3·00 2·75
2860 250t. Two horses galloping 3·75 3·25

(b) 42×28 mm.

2861 100t. Type **578** 90 80
2862 150t. Two horses 1·30 1·10
2863 200t. Two colts 1·80 1·60
2864 300t. Mare and foal 2·30 2·10

579 Ferrari 312 T (1975)

2000. Ferrari Race Cars. Multicoloured.

2865–2870 300t.×6, Type **579**; 156 F1 (1961); 312 T4 (1979); 158 F1 (1964); 126 CK (1981); 312 B3 (1974) 12·50 11·00

2871–2876 350t.×6, As Nos. 2865/70 13·50 12·00

580 Boxing

2000. Olympic Games, Sydney. Multicoloured.

2877 100t. Type **580** 90 50
2878 200t. Wrestling 1·40 95
2879 300t. Judo 2·00 1·40
2880 400t. Shooting 2·50 1·90

581 Lucy (Lucille Ball) and Ethel Mertz (Vivian Vance)

2000. "I Love Lucy" (television comedy series). Four sheets containing T **581** and similar multicoloured designs.

MS2881 133×172 mm. 100t. Type **581**; 100t. Lucy with chin on hands; 100t. Lucy and Ethel with arms raised; 200t. Lucy serving Fred Mertz (William Fawley); 200t. Lucy holding telephone; 300t. Lucy laughing; 300t. Lucy and Ethel; 400t. Ethel and Lucy reading letter; 550t. Lucy holding bowl and Ethel 17·00 16·00

MS2882 Two sheets, each 96×121 mm. (a) 800t. Lucy wearing glasses and Ethel (horiz) (b) 800t. Lucy wearing checked shirt and Ethel (horiz) 18·00 17·00

582 Moe and Larry

2000. "The Three Stooges" (comedy series starring Moe Howard, Larry Fine and Shemp Howard). Three sheets containing T **582** and similar multicoloured designs.

MS2884 172×134 mm. 100t. Type **582**; 100t. Dentist, Shemp, Moe and Larry; 100t. Larry and Shemp fighting with spoons; 200t. Three Stooges as musicians; 200t. Cooking; 300t. Moe spraying Shemp's mouth, Larry holding Shemp's arm; 300t. Heads together; 400t. Behind bars; 550t. Moe, Shemp and Larry holding spanner 17·00 16·00

MS2885 Two sheets, each 122×96 mm. (a) 800t. Shemp and Larry as soldiers (vert). (b) 800t. Moe and Shemp as musicians 18·00 17·00

583 Bogd Khaan (Independence) (1911)

2000. 20th-Century Events. Multicoloured.

2886–2895 300t.×10, Type **583**; National revolution (1921); Declaration of MPR (1924); Political repression (1937); War years (1939–45); Voting for Independence (1945); Agricultural reform (1959); UN membership (1961); Space flight (1981); Democratic revolution (1990) 14·50 11·50

584 Marmot

2000. Marmots (*Marmota sibirica* (inscr "sidisica")). Multicoloured.

2896 100t. Type **584** 90 65
2897 200t. Three marmots 1·80 1·30
2898 300t. Two marmots 2·75 1·90
2899 400t. Three marmots, two fighting 3·50 3·00

MS2900 90×60 mm. 800t. Marmot head (horiz) 12·50 11·50

585 Albert Einstein

2000. Albert Einstein (physicist) Commemoration. Sheet 115×153 mm containing T **585** and similar vert designs. Multicoloured.

MS2901	100t. Type **585**; 100t. As young man reading; 100t. As older man seated holding pipe; 200t. As older man with clasped hands; 200t. Holding violin; 300t. Wearing hat and coat; 300t. Holding clock; 400t. Receiving award; 550t. Head and shoulders	15·00	14·50

586 Traditional Design

2000. Traditional Designs. Multicoloured.

2902	50t. Type **586**	1·10	30
2903	200t. Blue background, central oval design (vert)	1·80	1·10
2904	250t. Red background, green border	2·20	1·30
2905	300t. Red background, central vase shape and corner decoration (vert)	2·75	1·60
2906	400t. Soyombo (national symbol) (vert)	3·25	2·20
2907	550t. Violet background, blue vertical border and diamond shaped central design	4·25	3·00

587 John Fitzgerald Kennedy Jr.

2000. First Death Anniv of John Fitzgerald Kennedy Junior.

2908	**587**	300t. multicoloured	2·75	1·60

588 Precious Umbrella

2000. National Symbols. Multicoloured.

2909	300t. Type **588**	2·50	1·30
2910	300t. Bishguur (trumpet)	2·50	1·30
2911	300t. Bow, arrows and quiver	2·50	1·30
2912	300t. Treasure vase	2·50	1·30
2913	300t. Flaming swords	2·50	1·30
2914	300t. Saddle	2·50	1·30
2915	300t. Belt	2·50	1·30
2916	300t. Seated Khan	2·50	1·30
2917	300t. Throne	2·50	1·30

589 Queen Oulen

2000. Queens. Multicoloured.

2918	300t. Type **589**	2·50	1·30
2919	300t. Queen Borteujin	2·50	1·30
2920	300t. Queen Turakana	2·50	1·30
2921	300t. Queen Caymish	2·50	1·30
2922	300t. Queen Chinbay	2·50	1·30

2000. Trains (2nd issue). Four sheets containing multicoloured designs as T **573**.

MS2923	Two sheets, each 158×121 mm. (a) 100t. Class GS-4 4-8-4 (USA); 100t. Class G85 2-6-2 (Italy); 100t. Class 3700 (Netherlands); 200t. Class 18 4-6-2 (Germany); 200t. Class SY 2-8-2 (China); 200t. Class 231C 4-6-2 (France); 300t. Class 25 4-8-4 (South Africa); 300t. Class HP (India); 300t. LNR A3 Pacific (Britain). (b) 100t. X200 (Sweden); 100t. Deltic (Britain); 100t. GM F7 Warbonnet (USA); 200t. TGV (France); 200t. ICE (Germany); 200t. Class E444 (Italy); 300t. Regio runner (inscr 'Holland'); 300t. Type M**1200** (Burma); 300t. G class (Australia)	22·00	21·00
MS2924	Two sheets, each 85×110 mm. (a) 800t. Inscr 'Rocket 0-2-2' (Britain) (57×43 mm). (b) 800t. Eurostar (France/Britain) (43×57 mm)	18·00	17·00

590 *Scarabaeus typhoon*

2000. Endangered Species. Sheet 215×115 mm containing T **590** and similar multicoloured designs.

MS2925	100t. Type **590** 100t. *Phrynosephalus helioscopus*; 200t. *Coliber spinalus*; 200t. *Euchoreutes paso*; 300t. *Camelus bactrianus ferus* (40×40 mm); 300t. *Saiga mongolica* (40×40 mm); 300t. *Chlamydotis undulate* (40×40 mm); 400t. *Ursus arctos gobiensis* (40×40 mm); 550t. *Ovis ammon* (40×40 mm); 550t. *Unicia unicia* (40×40 mm)	25·00	24·00

591 Elephant, Monkey, Rabbit and Bird

2001. New Millennium. Sheet 120×140 mm.

MS2926	**591**	5000t. multicoloured	36·00	35·00

592 Snake

2001. Chinese New Year. Year of the Snake. Multicoloured.

2927	300t. Type **592**	2·75	1·30
2928	400t. Snake (vert)	3·50	1·90

593 World War I (1914)

2001. 20th Century. Multicoloured.

2929	300t. Type **593**	1·60	1·10
2930	300t. Lenin (October Revolution) (1917)	1·60	1·10
2931	300t. Adolf Hitler (rise of Fascism) (1933)	1·60	1·10
2932	300t. Russian, American and British leaders (World War II) (1939)	1·60	1·10
2933	300t. Albert Einstein (Nuclear weapons) (1945)	1·60	1·10
2934	300t. Emblem and members flags (United Nations) (1945)	1·60	1·10
2935	300t. Hand holding torch (end of colonialism) (1940)	1·60	1·10
2936	300t. Astronaut (space exploration) (1961)	1·60	1·10
2937	300t. Mikhael Gorbachev (end of socialism) (1989)	1·60	1·10
2938	300t. Horses and yurts (New Mongolia) (1911)	1·60	1·10

594 Soldier (statue)

2001. 80th Anniv of Armed Forces. Multicoloured.

2939	300t. Type **594**	2·00	1·10
2940	300t. Soldier with scabbard	2·00	1·10
2941	300t. Mounted soldier	2·00	1·10

595 Mountaineer

2001. Mongolian Mountaineers. Sheet 115×80 mm containing T **595** and similar vert design. Multicoloured.

MS2942	400t.×2, Type **595**; Everest	9·00	8·75

596 Lucy and Desi

2001. "I Love Lucy" (television comedy series). Three sheets containing T **596** and similar multicoloured designs.

MS2943	172×140 mm. 100t. Type **596**; 100t. Lucy smearing woman with chocolate; 100t. Woman smearing Lucy with chocolate; 200t. Cake making; 200t Lucy and Ethel; 300t. Receiving instruction in cake making; 300t. Lucy with arms raised; 400t. Desi and Fred; 550t. Desi holding stocking and Fred	17·00	16·00
MS2944	Two sheets, each 127×102 mm. (a) 800t. Lucy (vert). (b) 800t. Fred and Desi (vert)	18·00	17·00

597 Larry

2001. "The Three Stooges" (comedy series starring Moe Howard, Larry Fine and Shemp Howard). Three sheets containing T **597** and similar multicoloured designs.

MS2945	172×140 mm. 100t. Type **597**; 100t. Moe; 100t. Mo, Larry and Shemp; 200t. Moe, Larry and Shemp using telephones; 200t. Mo with mallet and man using telephone; 300t. Moe and Shemp surprised; 300t. Three Stooges as chefs; 400t. Larry and Shemp as dentists; 550t. Moe, Shemp and Larry and woman	17·00	16·00
MS2946	128×102 mm. 800t. Shemp and Larry	9·00	8·75
MS2947	102×128 mm. 800t. Shemp as Angel (vert)	9·00	8·75

598 Hong Kong 2001 Emblem and *Nomading* (T. S. Minjuur)

2001. International Stamp Exhibitions. Sheet 175×132 mm containing T **598** and similar horiz designs showing painting "Nomading" by T. S. Minjuur and exhibition emblem.

MS2948	400t.×4, Type **598**; Hafnia 01, Denmark; PhilaNippon '01; Belgica 2001	11·00	10·50

599 Roses

2001. Japan EXPO 2001, Kitakyushu. Sheet 120×180 mm containing T **599** and similar multicoloured designs. Self-adhesive.

MS2949	500t.×5, Type **599**; Woman (32×42 mm); Tarbosaurus (48×25 mm); Iguanodon (25×48 mm); Triceratops (48×25 mm)	18·00	18·00

600 Butterfly

2001. Scouting and Nature. Three sheets containing T **600** and similar multicoloured designs.

MS2950	Two sheets, each 172×95 mm. (a) 50t. Type **600**; 100t. Bat; 200t. Butterfly (different); 300t. Fungi; 400t. Dinosaur; 450t. Puffin. (b) 100t. *Salpingotus*; 200t. *Unica unica*; 300t. *Haliaeetus* (inscr 'Haleaeetus') *albicilla*; 400t. *Pandion haliaetus* (inscr 'haliatus'); 450t. *Phasianus* (inscr 'Panciawus') *colchicus*	23·00	22·00
MS2951	134×172 mm. Size 38×51 mm. 50t. Penguins; 100t. Frog; 150t. Seashell; 200t. Elephant; 250t. Butterfly; 300t. Owl; 350t. Whale; 400t. Orchid; 450t. Sea turtle	18·00	17·00

601 Zeppelin Airship

2001. Transport. Sheet 172×134 mm containing T **601** and similar horiz designs. Multicoloured.

MS2952	50t. Type **601**; 100t. Air balloon; 150t. Apollo command module; 200t. *Apollo II* lunar module; 250t. Concorde; 300t. Steam locomotive; 350t. Motorcycle; 400t. Race car; 450t. Yacht	20·00	19·00

602 Flag

2001. 40th Anniv of United Nations Membership. Multicoloured.

2953	400t. Type **602**	2·75	2·40
2954	400t. Dove	2·75	2·40

Nos. 2953/4 were issued together, *se-tenant*, forming a composite design.

603 World Trade Centre and Statue of Liberty

2001. Unite against Terror.

2955	**603**	300t.+50t. multicoloured	2·30	2·10
2956	**603**	400t.+50t. multicoloured	3·00	2·75

604 Children encircling Globe

2001. United Nations Year of Dialogue among Civilizations.

2957	**604**	300t. multicoloured	2·50	1·60

605 Symbols of Italy

2001. History. Sheet 260×186 mm containing T **605** and similar horiz designs. Multicoloured.
MS2958 200t.×10, Type **605**; Roman senators and centurion; Statue and dancers; Mosque, decoration and mounted soldier; Celtic warrior and decoration; *Mona Lisa* and European art; Polynesian mask, stone heads and musician; Astronomy; Symbols of French revolution; Symbols of space exploration; 300t.×10, Greek statue, Parthenon and vase; Temple, Angkor Wat and statue; Mongolian statue, fountain and masked dancer; Genghis Khan; Yurt; Russian church and icons; Globe and Christopher Columbus; Symbols of America; Early printing press and Albrecht Durer; Symbols of United Kingdom 34·00 33·00

606 *Gazella subgutturosa*

2001. Endangered Species. Sheet 219×116 mm containing T **606** and similar multicoloured designs.
MS2959 100t.×2, Type **606**; *Rana chensinensis*; 200t.×2, *Podoces hendersoni*; *Papilio machaon*; 300t.×3, *Vespertilio superans* (40×40 mm); *Capra sibirica* (40×40 mm); *Equus hemionus hemionus* (40×40 mm); 400t. *Equus przewalskii* (40×40 mm); 550t.×2, *Erinaceus dauricus*; *Vormela peregusna* 22·00 21·00

The stamps and margins of **MS**2959 form a composite design.

607 Horse

2002. Chinese New Year. Year of the Horse. Multicoloured.

2960	300t. Type **607**	3·25	1·60
2961	400t. Galloping horse (horiz)	4·00	2·20

(608)

2002. 20th Anniv of Mongolia—USSR Space Flight. No. **MS**1352 surch as T **608**.
MS2962 400t. on 4t. multicoloured 27·00 26·00

609 *Gyps himalayensis*

2002. Vultures. Multicoloured.

2963	100t. Type **609**	90	65
2964	150t. *Gyps fulvus*	1·10	80
2965	300t. *Neophron percnopterus*	2·00	1·60
2966	400t. *Aegypius monachus*	2·75	2·20
2967	550t. *Gypaetus barbatus*	4·00	3·25

610 Horse Rider

2002. 30th Anniv of Mongolia—Japan Diplomatic Relations. Two sheets, each 110×85 mm, containing T **610** and similar multicoloured designs.
MS2968 (a) 550t.×2, Type **610**; Girl's face. (b) 550t.×2, Camel (40×30 mm); Ass (40×30 mm) 16·00 15·00

The stamps and margins of **MS**2968a form a composite design.

611 Dog

2002. The Mongolian Dog. Multicoloured.

2969	100t. Type **611**	70	65
2970	200t. With cattle	1·40	1·30
2971	300t. Two puppies	2·20	1·90
2972	400t. With camels	3·00	2·50

MS2973 105×70 mm. 800t. Dog facing right 6·25 6·00

612 Seoul Stadium

2002. World Cup Football Championship. Sheet 120×95 mm containing T **612** and similar horiz designs. Multicoloured.
MS2974 300t.×2, Type **612**; Yokohama stadium; 400t.×2, French team (1998); English team (1966) 11·00 10·50

613 Ikeguchi Ekan

2002. Mongolia—Japan Diplomatic Relations. Two sheets containing T **613** and similar vert designs. Multicoloured.
MS2975 150×90 mm. 150t. Type **613** 90 80
MS2976 110×90 mm. 1500t. Tomoyoshi Wada 7·25 7·00

614 *Thermopsis*

2002. Medicinal Plants. Multicoloured.

2977	100t. Type **614**	70	65
2978	150t. *Chelidonium*	1·10	95
2979	150t. *Hypericum*	1·10	95
2980	200t. *Plantago*	1·40	1·30
2981	250t. *Saussurea*	1·80	1·60
2982	300t. *Rosa acicularis*	2·20	1·90
2983	450t. *Lilium*	3·50	3·00

615 Horse-drawn Vehicle

2002. Rock Drawings. Multicoloured.

2984	50t. Type **615**	45	40
2985	100t. Deer	90	80
2986	150t. Horseman	1·40	1·20
2987	200t. Horseman (different)	1·80	1·60
2988	300t. Chariot	2·75	2·40
2989	400t. Camel	3·50	3·25

MS2990 97×77 mm. 800t. Stag's head 7·25 7·00

616 Children on Horseback

2002. Children and Sport. Multicoloured.

2991	500t. Boy cycling	3·50	3·25
2992	500t. Boy holding baseball bat	3·50	3·25
2993	500t. Boy playing chess	3·50	3·25

MS2994 134×172 mm. 100t. Type **616**; 150t. Two girls playing football; 200t. Four horses' heads and two riders; 250t. Boys playing golf; 300t. Girl rider and prayer flags; 350t. Ice hockey player; 400t. Horse's head and three riders; 450t. Girl playing football; 500t. Three horses' heads, one rider and flag 27·00 26·00

617 Ram

2003. Chinese New Year. Year of the Sheep (Goat). Multicoloured.

2995	300t. Type **617**	3·00	1·90
2996	400t. Ram, laying down (horiz)	4·25	2·50

618 *Russula aeruginosa* and *Coccothraustes coccothraustes*

2003. Birds and Fungi. Multicoloured.

2997	50t. Type **618**	55	30
2998	100t. *Boletus edulis* and *Loxia curvirostra*	1·10	65
2999	150t. *Boletus badius* and *Carpodacus erythrinus*	1·60	95
3000	200t. *Agaricus campester* and *Garrulus glandarius*	2·20	1·30
3001	250t. *Marasmius oreades* and *Luscinia megarhyuchos*	2·75	1·60
3002	300t. *Cantharellus cibarius* and *Locustella certhiola*	3·25	1·90
3003	400t. *Amanita phalloides* and *Ardea cinerea*	4·25	2·50
3004	550t. *Suillus granulatus* and *Accipiter gentilis*	6·00	3·50

MS3005 Two sheets, each 105×70 mm. (a) 800t. *Tricholoma pertentosum* and *Lanius collurio* (60×40 mm). (b) 800t. *Lactarius tormmosus* and *Aeqithalos caudatus* (60×40 mm) 20·00 19·00

619 Damdin Sukhbaatur (statue)

2003. Tourism. Two sheets, each 151×80 mm containing T **619** and similar horiz designs. Multicoloured.
MS3006 (a) 100t. Type **619**; 200t. Kharakhorum Monastery; 300t. Turtle rock, Terelj; 400t. Yurts. (b) 100t. Camels; 200t. Yaks; 300t. Falconer; 400t. Snow leopard 14·50 14·00

620 Takumi Ueda

2003. Mongolia—Japan Diplomatic Relations. Sheet 110×90 mm.
MS3007 **620** 300t. multicoloured 3·50 3·25

2003. Endangered Species. Sheet 222×121 mm containing multicoloured designs as T **606**.
MS3008 100t.×2, *Moschus moschiferus* (40×40 mm); *Castor fiber birula* (40×30 mm); 200t.×2, *Dryomys nitedula* (40×30 mm); *Lutra lutra* (40×30 mm); 300t.×3, *Rangifer tarandus* (40×40 mm); *Pandion haliaetus* (40×30 mm); *Sus scrofa nigripes* (40×40 mm); 400t. *Alces alces cameloides* (40×40 mm); 550t.×2, *Alces alces pfizenmayen* (40×40 mm); *Phasianus colchicus* (40×30 mm) 18·00 17·00

The stamps and margins of **MS**3008 form a composite design.

621 Common Bush Tanager

2003. Flora and Fauna. Eight sheets, containing T **621** and similar multicoloured designs.
MS3009 138×98 mm. Birds. 800t.×4, Type **621**; Black-headed hemispingus; Scarlet-rumped tanager; Band-tailed seedeater 14·50 14·00
MS3010 Three sheets, each 139×118 mm. (a) Fungi. 800t.×4, *Hypholoma fasciculare*; *Marasmiellus ramealis*; *Collybia fusipes*; *Kuchneromyces mutabilis*. (b) Orchids. 800t.×4, *Vanda Rothchildiana*; *Paphiopedilum parishii*; *Dendrobium nobile*; *Cattleya loddigesii*. (c) Butterflies. 800t.×4, *Thecla teresina*; *Theritas cypria*; *Theritas coronata*; *Thecla phaleros* 43·00 42·00
MS3011 Four sheets, each 99×69 mm. (a) Birds. 2500t. Andean hillstar. (b) Fungi. 2500t. *Psathyrella multipedata* (vert). (c) Orchids. 2500t. *Barkeria skinneri* (inscr 'skinnerii'). (d) Butterflies. 2500t. *Thecla pedusa*. 50·00 49·00

622 Yang Liwei

2003. First Chinese Astronaut. Sheet 80×61 mm.
MS3012 **622** 800t. multicoloured 7·50 7·25

623 Monkey

2004. Chinese New Year. Year of the Monkey. Multicoloured.

3013	300t. Type **623**	3·00	1·90
3014	400t. Monkey facing right	4·00	2·50

624 Heaven

2004. Peace Mandala (patchwork quilt). Two sheets containing T **624** and similar multicoloured designs showing life of Buddha. Self-adhesive.
MS3015 200×290 mm. 50t. Type **624**; 100t. Journey on elephant to birth mother; 150t. Birth from mother's armpit; 200t. Life as prince; 250t. Shaving his hair; 300t. Seated fighting devil; 400t. Seated with hand raised; 550t. Attaining Nirvana; 5000t. Life of Buddha (135×185 mm) 36·00 35·00
MS3016 81×105 mm. 5000t. Seated Buddha (62×78 mm) 34·00 33·00

625 *Equus przewalskii*

2004. Animals. Value expressed as letter. Multicoloured

3017	(A) Type **625**	1·40	1·30
3018	(?) *Ovis ammon*	2·20	1·90
3019	(B) *Camelus bactrianus ferus*	3·50	3·25
3020	(?) *Capra sibirica*	4·50	4·00

626 Genghis Khan

2004. 840th Birth Anniv of Chinggis Khan (leader). 800th Anniv of Mongolian State. Multicoloured.

3021	200t. Type **626**	1·10	95
3022	300t. Facing right (horiz)	1·60	1·40
3023	350t. Statue	2·00	1·80
3024	550t. On horseback	3·00	2·75

627 Judo

2004. Olympic Games, Athens. Multicoloured.

3025	100t. Type **627**	90	50
3026	200t. Wrestling (horiz)	1·40	95
3027	300t. Boxing	1·80	1·40
3028	400t. Shooting (horiz)	2·30	1·90

628 Emblem

2004. 130th Anniv of Universal Postal Union (UPU).

3029	**628**	300t. multicoloured	3·00	1·60

629 Early Team Members

2004. Juventus Football Club. Multicoloured.

3030	50t. Type **629**	55	30
3031	50t. Team members (different)	55	30
3032	100t. Player and ball	70	50
3033	100t. Goalkeeper	70	50
3034	150t. Player heading ball into goal	90	65
3035	150t. Three players	90	65
3036	200t. Players tackling	1·10	95
3037	200t. Juventus player preparing to kick ball	1·10	95

630 1924 $1 Stamp (First Mongolian stamp)

2004. 80th Anniv of First Mongolian Stamp. Sheet 80×60 mm.

MS3038 **630** 800t. multicoloured	6·25	6·00

631 *Lytta caragana* (inscr 'caraganae')

2004. Insects and Flowers. Two sheets, each 120×80 mm containing T **631** and similar horiz designs. Multicoloured.

MS3039 (a) 100t.×2, Type **631**; *Rosa acicularis*; 200t.×2, *Aquilegia sibirica*; *Tabanus bivinus*; 300t.×2, *Corizus hyoscyami*; *Lilium pumilum*. (b) 100t.×2, *Mantis religiosa*; *Aster alpinus*; 200t.×2, *Echinops bumilis*; *Apis mellifera*; 300t.×2, *Angaracris barabensis*; *Nymphaea candida* 16·00 15·00

632 Woman's Headdress, Kazakhstan

2004. Women's Headdresses. Multicoloured.

3040	550t. Type **632**	4·50	4·00
3041	550t. Mongolian headdress	4·50	4·00

Stamps of the same design were issued by Kazakhstan.

633 Rooster

2005. Chinese New Year. Year of the Rooster. Mult.

3042	300t. Type **633**	2·50	1·40
3043	400t. Rooster facing right (vert)	3·25	1·80

634 Butterfly

2005. EXPO 2005, Aichi, Japan. Sheet 161×91 mm containing T **634** and similar vert designs. Multicoloured.

MS3044 100t. Type **634**; 150t. Flower; 200t.; Puppy; 550t. Kitten 8·75 8·50

The stamps and margins of **MS**3044 form a composite design.

635 Two Children

2005. World Vision (charitable organization) (1st issue).

3045	**635**	550t. multicoloured	5·50	2·50

See also No. 3058.

636 Woman's Costume

2005. Traditional Costumes. Multicoloured, background colour given.

3046	200t. Type **636**	1·40	1·30
3047	200t. Man's costume (pink)	1·40	1·30
3048	200t. Woman's costume (green)	1·40	1·30
3049	200t. Man's costume (green)	1·40	1·30
3050	200t. Woman's costume (blue)	1·40	1·30
3051	200t. Man's costume (blue)	1·40	1·30

637 Guardian

2005. Buddhist Guardians. Multicoloured.

3052	400t. Type **637**	2·20	1·90
3053	400t. Guardian holding sword	2·20	1·90
3054	400t. Guardian holding snake	2·20	1·90
3055	400t. Guardian holding pig and umbrella	2·20	1·90

638 Asashoryu

2005. Asashoryu—Mongolian Sumo Wrestler. Sheet 135×106 mm containing T **638** and similar multicoloured designs.

MS3056 600t. Type **638**; 700t. Asashoryu on horseback (vert); 800t. Asashoryu wearing fight costume (vert) 11·50 11·00

2005. TAIPEI 2005. Sheet 73×67 mm.

MS3057 750t. As No. **MS**2566	11·50	11·00

No. **MS**3057 was overprinted in the margin for the exhibition.

640 Child riding Camel

2005. World Vision (charitable organization) (2nd issue).

3058	**640**	550t. multicoloured	5·00	2·75

641 Woman's Headdress

2005. Traditional Headdresses. Multicoloured.

3059	50t. Type **641**	55	30
3060	100t. Woman's with conical centre and train	70	50
3061	150t. Man's with central feather	1·10	80
3062	200t. Man's with fur rim and tassel	1·30	95
3063	250t. Woman's with fur trim	1·60	1·30
3064	300t. Man's with conical centre and long tassel	1·80	1·40

MS3065 100×120 mm. 800t. Fur hat with conical centre and streamers (40×60 mm) 6·25 6·00

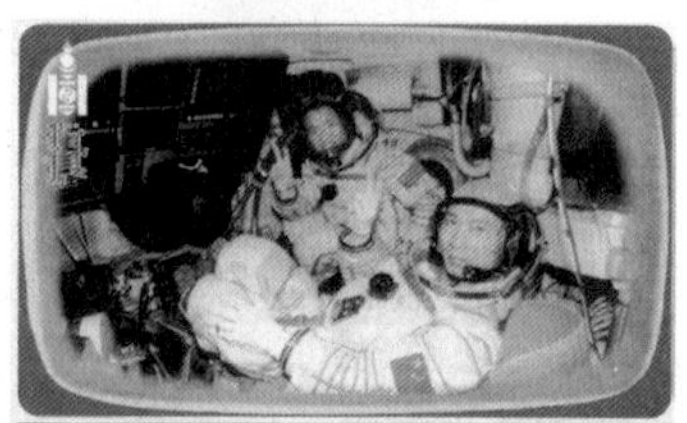

642 Astronauts in Flight

2005. Shenzhou VI Manned Space Flight. Two sheets, each 100×100 mm containing T **642** and similar horiz design. Multicoloured.

MS3066 (a) 800t. Type **642**. (b) 800t. Astronauts waving 12·50 12·00

643 Gold Coin

2006. 800th Anniv of Mongolia. Ancient coins. Multicoloured.

3067-3069 550t.×3, Type **643**; Silver coin; Copper coin 8·00 7·50

644 Dog

2006. Chinese New Year. Year of the Dog. Multicoloured.

3070	300t. Type **644**	2·75	1·40
3071	400t. Dog (different)	3·50	1·90

645 Archer

2006. 50th Anniv of Europa Stamps. Multicoloured.

3072-3083 200t.×12, Type **645**; Camels and dunes; Shepherds and flocks; Horse; Turtle rock; Mosque; Dinosaur skeleton; Gymnasts; Yurt; Wrestlers; Aircraft; Yak 10·50 8·50

MS3084 Six sheets, each 104×50 mm. (a) As Nos. 3072/3. (b) As Nos. 3074/5. (c) As Nos. 3076/7. (d) As Nos. 3078/9. (e) As Nos. 3080/1. (f) As Nos. 3082/3 Set of 6 sheets 34·00 33·00

646 Horse-head Violin

2006. National Symbols. Morin Khuur. Sheet 83×116 mm.

MS3085 **646** 550t. multicoloured	5·25	5·00

647 President Enkhbayar

2006. Nambaryn Enkhbayar, President of Mongolia. Sheet 91×120 mm.

MS3086 **647** 800t. multicoloured	6·75	6·50

648 Two Stylized Players and Goalkeeper

2006. World Cup Football Championship, Germany. Sheet 130×80 mm containing T **648** and similar horiz designs. Multicoloured.

MS3087 200t. Type **648**; 250t. One player; 300t. Two players; 400t. Three players 10·00 9·75

649 Presidents George Bush and Nambaryn Enkhbayar

2006. First Official visit of USA President to Mongolia. Sheet 100×60 mm Multicoloured.

MS3088 **649** 600t. multicoloured	5·25	5·00

650 Armoured Man and Cheetah

2006. 800th Anniv of Mongolia. Sheet 185×80 mm containing T **650** and similar multicoloured designs.

MS3089 50t. Type **650**; 100t. Woman with falcon and cheetah; 300t. Genghis Khan; 400t. Couple with two cheetahs 500t. Army (80×56 mm) 10·50 10·00

651 Early 20th-century Bronze Replica of Equestrian Deity Rao Dev from Bastar, Madhya Pradesh

2006. Art. Sheet 110×60 mm containing T **651** and similar horiz design. Multicoloured.

MS3090 300t. Type **651**; 400t. Ancient bronze horse statue, from Murun city, Mongolia 6·25 6·00

The stamps of **MS**3090 form a composite background design.

Stamps in similar designs were issued by India.

652 Children riding Ox

2006. World Vision. Multicoloured.
3091 550t. Type **652** 3·50 2·75
3092 550t. Boy riding horse 3·50 2·75

653 Genghis Khan

2006. Sheet 100×80 mm. Multicoloured. Silk paper.
MS3093 **653** 3800t. multicoloured 21·00 20·00

654 Building

2006. Mongolia—China Philatelic Exhibition. Sheet 151×58 mm containing T 654 and similar horiz design. Multicoloured.
MS3094 150t. Type **654**; 200t. Waterfall; 250t. Street at night 4·75 4·50

655 Taimen

2006. Hucho Taimen (Taimen). Multicoloured.
3095 100t. Type **655** 55 50
3096 200t. Facing left 1·10 95
3097 300t. Facing right 1·70 1·40
3098 400t. Head facing left and two smaller fish 2·30 1·90

656 Pig

2006. Chinese New Year. Year of the Pig. Multicoloured.
3099 300t. Type **656** 1·90 1·60
3100 400t. Facing left with lowered head 2·50 2·10

657 Prince Willem-Alexander

2007. State Visit of Prince Willem-Alexander and Princess Maxima of the Netherlands. Multicoloured.
3101 700t. Type **657** 3·75 3·25
3102 700t. Prince Willem-Alexander and Princess Maxima 3·75 3·25
3103 700t. Princess Maxima 3·75 3·25

658 Betty Boop

2007. Betty Boop. Two sheets containing T **658** and similar vert designs. Multicoloured.
MS3104 127×178 mm. 700t.×6, Type **658**; With arms and knee raised; With hands clasped; With left arm raised; With leg raised; With left arm raised and right leg bent 23·00 22·00
MS3105 100×70 mm. 1500t.×2, Wearing red dress; Wearing red dress with additional partial heart on left 15·00 14·50

Nos. **MS**3104 and **MS**3105 each form a composite background design.

659 Pope John Paul II

2007. Pope John Paul II.
3106 **659** 880t. multicoloured 4·75 4·00

660 Marilyn Monroe

2007. Marilyn Monroe. Sheet 130×108 mm containing T **660** and similar vert designs. Multicoloured.
MS3107 1050t.×4, Type **660**; Looking over left shoulder; Head only; Wearing red dress 23·00 22·00

The stamps of No. **MS**3107 share a composite background design.

661 Elvis Presley

2007. 30th Death Anniv of Elvis Presley. Multicoloured.
3108 1050t. Type **661** 5·75 4·75
3109 1050t. With right arm raised 5·75 4·75
3110 1050t. Wearing decorative belt 5·75 4·75
3111 1050t. With longer hair 5·75 4·75

662 Lama Tsongkhapa

2007. 650th Death Anniv of Lama Tsongkhapa (Buddhist teacher and reformer).
3112 **662** 100t. multicoloured 8·50 7·25

663 Genghis Khan (statue)

2007. 20th Anniv of Mongolia—USA Diplomatic Relations. Sheet 120×80 mm containing T **663** and similar square design. Multicoloured.
MS3113 400t. Type **663**; 550t. Abraham Lincoln (statue) 7·50 7·25

The stamps and margins of No. **MS**3113 form a composite background design.

664 Mount Fuji, Japan

2007. 35th Anniv of Mongolia—Japan Diplomatic Relations. Sheet 120×60 mm containing T **664** and similar horiz design. Multicoloured.
MS3114 550t. Type **664**; 700t. Mount Otgontenger, Mongolia 7·50 7·25

The stamps and margins of No. **MS**3114 form a composite background design.

2007. Irkutsk 2007 Philatelic Exhibition. No. **MS**2588 inscr 'MOCKBA '97' on sheet margin. Sheet 115×80 mm.
MS3115 1000t. multicoloured 6·75 6·50

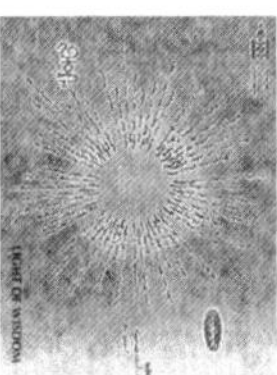

665 'Light of Wisdom'

2007. Mongolian Calligraphy. Multicoloured.
3116 50t. Type **665** 40 30
3117 100t. 'Butterfly' 75 65
3118 150t. 'Flower' 1·10 95
3119 200t. 'Horse' 1·50 1·30
3120 250t. 'Spring' 1·90 1·60
3121 300t. 'Leaves' 2·30 1·90
3122 400t. 'Wow' 2·75 2·40
3123 550t. 'Wild Camel' 3·75 3·25
MS3124 96×121 mm. 800t. 'Sky' 6·75 6·50

666 *Woman as Waterfall* (Ts. Tsegmid)

2007. Modern Art. Five sheets containing T **666** and similar multicoloured designs.
MS3125 Three sheets 62×78 mm. (a) 400t. Type **666**. (b) 400t. *Mountain with face* (S. Sarantsatsralt). (c) 400t. *Woman enclosed in man's outline* (Ts. Enkhjin). Two sheets 78×62 mm. (d) 400t. *Mare and foal* (Sh. Chimeddorj). (e) 400t. *Abstract* (Do. Bold) 14·50 14·00

667 Naotoshi Yamada (Olympic cheerleader) and Wrestler

2007. 35th Anniv of Mongolia—Japan Friendship. Sheet 171×228 mm containing T **667** and similar horiz designs. Multicoloured. Self-adhesive gum.
MS3126 6 stamps (500t.×2, 600t.×2, 700t.×2) showing Naotoshi Yamada and Sumo wrestlers 17·00 16·00

668 Genghis Khan

2007. 780th Death Anniv of Ghengis Khan.
3127 **668** 230t. multicoloured 1·10 95
3128 **668** 400t. multicoloured 1·90 1·60
3129 **668** 650t. multicoloured 2·75 2·40
3130 **668** 800t. multicoloured 3·75 3·25
3131 **668** 1000t. multicoloured 4·75 4·00

669 Rat

2008. Chinese New Year. Year of the Rat. Multicoloured.
3132 800t. Type **669** 3·75 3·25
3134 800t. Rat looking up 6·75 6·50

No. 3132/3 were issued together, *se-tenant*, forming a composite design.

2008. No. 1559 surch **1000t.**
3135 1000t. on 60m. multicoloured 3·75 3·25

2008. Taipei 2008 International Stamp Exhibition. No. 2228 surch **TAIPEI 2008 250t.** and emblem.
3136 250t. on 40m. multicoloured 2·30 1·90

672 Ribbon

2008. AIDS Awareness Campaign.
3137 **672** 500t. multicoloured 2·75 2·20

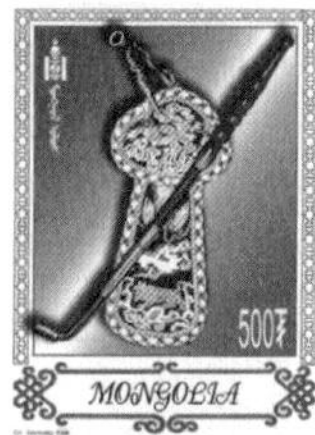

673 Pipe and Pouch

2008. Decorative Arts. Multicoloured.
3138 500t. Type **673** 2·50 2·10
3139 500t. Stone bottle 2·50 2·10
3140 500t. Sword and accoutrements 2·50 2·10
3141 500t. Saddle 2·50 2·10
3142 500t. Decorative metal bowls 2·50 2·10

674 Canoeing

2008. Olympic Games, Beijing. Multicoloured.
3143 600t. Type **674** 2·30 1·90
3144 600t. Fencing 2·30 1·90
3145 600t. Handball 2·30 1·90
3146 600t. Modern Pentathlon 2·30 1·90

675 Boar

2008. Wild Boar. Multicoloured.
3147 800t. Type **675** 3·50 3·00
3148 800t. Mother and piglets 3·50 3·00
3149 800t. Boar facing right 3·50 3·00
3150 800t. Two boar 3·50 3·00

Nos. 3147/50 were issued in together, *se-tenant*, forming a composite design.

676 Ox

2009. Chinese New Year. Year of the Ox. Multicoloured.
3151 200t. Type **676** 1·30 1·10
3152 300t. Ox (different) 2·75 2·30

677 State Arms

2009. State Symbols. Multicoloured.
3153 400t. Type **677** 1·80 1·50
3154 500t. Flame of prosperity 2·20 1·90
3155 800t. State flag 3·25 2·75
3156 1000t. Soyonbo 4·50 3·75

678 Greeting

2009. Hospitality.

3157	**678**	1000t. multicoloured	4·50	3·75

679 Giant Panda

2009. China 2009–International Stamp Exhibition, Luoyang. Multicoloured.

3158	300t. Type **679**	2·00	1·70
3159	300t. *Ursus arctos gobiensis* (Gobi bear)	2·00	1·70

800₮
(680)

2009. Nos. 1524/5 surch as T **680**.

3160	800t. on 30m. multicoloured (Skin tent)	4·00	3·50
3161	1000t. on 20m. multicoloured (Antonov An–24B)	6·00	5·25

681 Tree Peonies

2009

3162	**681**	700t. multicoloured	3·75	3·25

682 Earrings

2009. Jewellery.

3162	**683**	800t. multicoloured	3·75	3·25

684 Parliament Building and Government House, Sukhbaatar Square, Ulaanbaatar

2009. 60th Anniv of Mongolia - China Diplomatic Relations. Multicoloured.

3164	1000t. Type **684**	4·50	3·75
3165	1000t. Great Hall of the People, Tiananmen Square, Beijing	4·50	3·75

Nos. 3166/7 and Type **685** are left for Year of the Tiger, issued on 14 February 2010, not yet received.

Nos. 3168/9 and Type **686** are left for Childeren, issued on 24 April 2010, not yet received.

Nos. 3170/7 and Type **687** are left for Mountains, issued on 15 June 2010, not yet received.

No. 3178 and Type **688** are left for Flag, issued on 15 June 2010, not yet received.

Nos. 3179/80 and Type **689** are left for Football World Cup, issued on 19 July 2010, not yet received.

No. 3181 and Type **690** are left for Personalities, issued on 27 July 2010, not yet received.

No. 3182 and Type **691** are left for President, issued on 22 October 2010, not yet received.

692 *Ornitoptera croesus*

2010. Butterflies. Multicoloured.

3183	100t. Type **692**	65	55
3184	200t. *Papilio antimachus*	1·10	95
3185	400t. *Ornitoptera priamus*	2·20	1·90
3186	500t. *Papilio zalmoxis*	2·75	2·50
3187	800t. *Troides rhadamantus*	4·50	3·75
3188	1000t. *Ornitoptera victoriae epiphanes*	5·50	4·75

Nos. 3189/90 and Type **693** are left for Tara, issued on 8 December 2010, not yet received.

694 Rabbit

2011. Chinese New Year. Year of the Rabbit

3191	**694**	1000t. multicoloured	5·50	4·75

695 Globe and Yuri Gagarin holding Dove

2011. 50th Anniv of First Manned Space Flight

3192	**695**	500t. multicoloured	2·75	2·50

696 Genghis Khan

2011. *The Secret History of the Mongols* (The life of Temujin (Genghis Khan))

3193	1000t. Type **696**	5·50	4·75
3194	1000t. Mounted facing bound prisoners	5·50	4·75
3195	1000t. Mounted heavily armoured	5·50	4·75
3196	1000t. Firing arrows whilst riding at speed	5·50	4·75
3197	1000t. Seated	5·50	4·75
3198	1000t. In battle	5·50	4·75
MS3199	105×145 mm 1500t. Seal (30×40 mm)	6·50	6·25
MS3200	105×145 mm 1500t. Banner (30×40 mm)	6·50	6·25

697 Yak

2011. Domestic Animals. Multicoloured.

3201	1000t. Type **698**	5·50	4·75
3202	1000t. Camel	5·50	4·75
3203	1200t. Horse	6·00	5·25
3204	1200t. Reindeer	6·00	5·25

698 Rally Trucks

2011. Motorsport. Mongolian Automobile and Motorcycle Sports Federation. Multicoloured.

MS3205	300t. Type **698**; 400t. Motorcycle; 600t. Rally car	7·00	7·00

699 K. Choibalsan

2011. 90th Anniv of Revolution. Multicoloured.

MS3206	600t. Type **699**; 600t. D. Chagdarjav; 600t. D. Bodoo; 600t. D. Dogsom; 600t. S. S. Danzan; 600t. D. Losol; 1200t. D. Sukhbaatar (30×40 mm)	26·00	25·00

700 Genghis Khan

2011. 805th Anniv of 'The Great Mongolian State'. Multicoloured.

MS3207	2000t. Type **700**	11·00	10·50
MS3208	2000t. Order of Genghis Khan	11·00	10·50

701 Teapot and Vessel

2011. Hunnu Empire. Multicoloured.

MS3209	170×65 mm. 1000t.×5, Type **701**; Buckle; Bangle; Griffin attacking deer (brooch); Arrow heads	26·00	25·00
MS3210	85×100 mm. 5000t. Modun Chanyu (inscr 'Shanyu') (60×65 mm)	26·00	25·00

702 Polar Bears and Fauna of Antarctica

2011. Fauna. Multicoloured.

3211	400t. Type **702**	2·50	2·20
3212	600t. Deer and fauna of Mongolia	3·75	3·25
3213	1000t. Kangaroos and fauna of Australia	6·25	5·50
3214	1200t. Water buffalo and fauna of Africa	7·50	6·50

703 Mother and Child

2011. Philanippon 2011 International Stamp Exhibition. Sheet 70×90 mm

MS3215	**703** 800t. multicoloured	5·25	5·00

704 Duke and Duchess of Cambridge

2011. Royal Wedding of Prince William of Wales and Miss Catherine Middleton. Multicoloured.

3216	1200t. Type **704**	7·50	6·50
MS3217	76×101 mm. 1500t.×2, Prince William; Catherine Middleton	16·00	15·00

705 Early Students and Parliament Building

2011. 90th Anniv of Education. Multicoloured.

MS3218	1200t. Type **705**; Bell, girl and pupils; Graduating students	7·75	7·50

(706)

2011. China 2011 Asian International Stamp Exhibition. Nos. 2795/6 overprinted as T **706**. Multicoloured.

3219	250t. As Type **569**	1·50	1·30
3220	450t. As No. 2796	2·75	2·40

707 Ban Ki-Moon (UN General Secretary) and Sukhbaatar Batbold (Mongolian Prime Minister)

2011. 50th Anniv of Mongolian Admission to United Nations (1st issue). Sheet 72×69 mm

MS3221	**707** 500t. multicoloured	3·50	3·25

See also No. **MS**3223.

708 M. Khanddorj (First Foreign Minister)

2011. Centenary of Mongolian Diplomatic Service. Multicoloured.

MS3222	600t.×3, Type **708**; Mongolian flag at UN headquarters and dove (50×38 mm); 'Golden Gerege' (tablet of authority for officials and envoys)	14·00	13·50

709 Horse Rider, Ger and Damdin Sukhbaatar Statue, Ulaanbaatar

2011. 50th Anniv of Mongolian Admission to United Nations (2nd issue). Sheet 130×95 mm

MS3223	**709** 1000t. multicoloured	6·50	6·25

710 Parliament Building

2011. Centenary (2012) of Independent Government in Mongolia. Sheet 111×84 mm

MS3224	**710** 1000t. multicoloured	6·50	6·25

711 Eighth Jebtsundamba Khutuktu (Bogd Khan) (spiritual and secular head of Mongolia)

2011. Centenary of Revolution of National Freedom. Multicoloured.

MS3225	1000t.×2, Type **711**; Sain Noyon Khan T. Namnansuren (prime minister)	13·00	12·50

712 Dragon

2012. Chinese New Year. Year of the Dragon

3226	**712**	600t. multicoloured	3·75	3·25

713 Kublai Khan

2012. Kublai Khan's Fleet. Multicoloured.

MS3227 1000t. Type **713**; 1200t. Warship 14·50 14·00

714 Mongolian Doll

2012. 40th Anniv of Mongolia - Japan Diplomatic Relations. Multicoloured.

MS3228 600t.×2, Type **714**; Japanese doll 8·00 7·75

715 Dragon

2012. Mythical Animals of Power. Multicoloured.

3229 100t. Type **715** 75 65

3230 200t. Lion (35×35 mm (square)) 1·30 1·10

3231 400t. Tiger (35×35 mm (square)) 2·50 2·20

3232 600t. Garuda 3·75 3·25

716 Fabian Gottlieb Thaddeus Bellingshausen

2012. Antarctic Research. Multicoloured.

MS3233 800t.×2, Type **716** ((Faddey Faddeyevich Bellinsgauzen) leader of expedition which discovered the continent of Antarctica and Commander of *Vostok*); Mikhail Petrovich Lazarev (second in command and Commander of *Mirny*) 10·50 10·00

717 Symbols of London

2012. Olympic Games, London. Multicoloured.

3234 700t. Type **717** 4·50 4·00

3235 800t. Athletes 5·00 4·50

718 White Costume

2012. Costumes. Multicoloured.

3236 100t. Type **718** 75 65

3237 200t. Magenta costume with frilled sleeves and wide circular hem 1·30 1·10

3238 300t. Bronze coloured costume with raised front hem, leggings and tall headdress with green stones surmounted by three skull-like heads 2·00 1·80

3239 400t. Yellow fitted dress with large cuffs to sleeves and fish-tail hem 2·50 2·20

3240 500t. Blue fitted dress with frogging, green border and complex headdress 3·25 2·75

3241 600t. Blue fitted dress with white coat and complex hairstyle 3·75 3·25

MS3242 140×140 mm. Size 38×50 mm: 700t. Blue and green costume with large sleeves and tall gold headdress; 800t. Slim-fitting costume with gold frogging down the centre, blue and red sleeves and a circular gold headdress 8·00 7·75

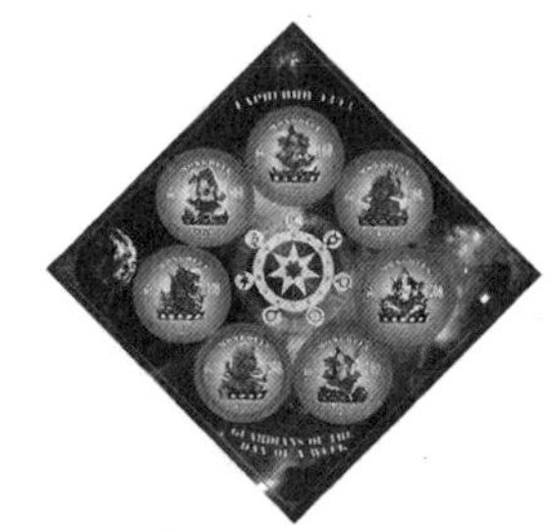

719 Guardians

2012. Guardians. Multicoloured.

MS3243 100t. Moon; 200t. Mars; 300t. Mercury; 400t. Jupiter; 500t. Venus; 600t. Saturn; 700t. Sun 19·00 18·00

720 Customs Officers and Search Dog

2012. Centenary of Customs Department. Multicoloured.

MS3244 800t. Early officers; 1000t. Modern custom officers (horiz); 1200t. German shepherd drug sniffer dog 8·25 8·00

721 Horse

2012. 850th Birth Anniv of Genghis Khan. Multicoloured.

MS3245 350t. Type **721**; 850t. Genghis Khan 8·25 8·00

722 *Ara chloroptera* and *Ara ararauna* (Green-winged Macaw and Blue-and-Yellow Macaw)

2012. Birds. Multicoloured.

3246 100t. Type **722** 75 65

3247 200t. *Paradisaea raggiana* and *Paradisaea rudolphi* (Bird-of-paradise and Blue Bird-of-paradise) 1·30 1·10

3248 300t. *Oygnus aratus* and *Cygnus olor* (Black Swan and Mute Swan) 2·00 1·80

3249 400t. *Aix galericulata* and *Aix sponsa* (Mandarin Duck and Wood Duck) 2·50 2·20

3250 800t. *Eyrthrura gouldiae, Pteridophora albertus* and *Euplectes orix* (Gouldian Finch, King of Saxony Bird-of-paradise and Southern Red Bishop) 5·00 4·50

3251 1000t. *Pavo cristaus* and *Chrysolophus pictus* (Indian Peafowl and Golden Pheasant) 6·25 5·50

723 Flag and Arms

2012. National Symbols

3252 **723** 1200t. multicoloured 7·50 7·25

1893
2013 500₮

(724)

2013. 120th Birth Anniv of Damdin Sükhbaatar (founding member of Mongolian People's Party and leader of Mongolian partisan army). No. 1919 surch as T **724**

3253 500t. on 60m. multicoloured 3·75 3·25

725 Snake

2013. Chinese New Year. Year of the Snake

3254 **725** 600t. multicoloured 3·75 3·25

Nos. 3255/**MS**3259 and Type **726** are left for Gazelle, not yet received.

727 Saker Falcon

2013. National Bird. Saker Falcon (*Falco cherrug*). Multicoloured.

MS3260 100t. Type **727**; 200t. In flight; 300t. Chicks in nest; 400t. Adult perched on rock; 800t. With wings spread, arms as background; 1000t. Being flown by mounted horseman 18·00 17·00

728 The Four Harmonious Brothers

2013. National Symbols. Multicoloured.

3261 1000t. Type **728** 6·25 5·50

3262 1000t. Yurt 6·25 5·50

3263 1000t. Woman wearing traditional dress 6·25 5·50

3264 1000t. Musician 6·25 5·50

(729)

2013. Thailand 2013 International Stamp Exhibition. No. **MS**2735b surch as T **729**. Sheet 97×145 mm. Multicoloured.

MS3265 1500t. on 1000t. (Buddha (Migjed Janraisig), Gandantegchinlen Monastery, Ulaanbaatar)

730 Bat Khaan

2013. Bat (Batu) Khaan Commemoration. Sheet 145×110 mm

MS3266 **730** 1000t. multicoloured 7·00 6·75

No. 3267 and Type **731** are left for Year of the Horse, not yet received.

1300₮

(732)

2014. Nos. 1840/3 surch as T **732.** Argali Sheep Overprints. Multicoloured.

3268 1300t. on 60m. (No. 1840) 4·00 3·75

3269 1300t. on 60m. (No. 1841) 4·00 3·75

3270 1300t. on 60m. (No. 1842) 4·00 3·75

3271 1300t. on 60m. (No. 1843) 4·00 3·75

733 *Lilium dahuricum* and *Cypripedium calceolus*

2014. Flowers. Multicoloured.

3272 200t. Type **733** 1·00 90

3273 300t. *Saussurea involucrata* 1·10 1·00

3274 400t. *Iris sibirica* and *Lilium pumilum* 1·30 1·20

3275 900t. *Cypripedium macranthum* and *Adonis sibirica* 3·00 2·40

3276 1000t. *Trollius asiaticus* and *Tulipa uniflora* 3·75 3·00

734 Albert Einstein

2014. Scientists. Multicoloured.

3277 100t. Type **734** 80 65

3278 100t. Charles Darwin 80 65

3279 300t. Leonardo da Vinci 1·10 1·00

3280 300t. Isaac Newton 1·10 1·00

3281 500t. Niels Bohr 1·50 1·20

3282 500t. Galileo Galilei 1·50 1·20

735 *Lynx pardinus* (Iberian Lynx)

2014. Fauna. Mongolian Red Book. Multicoloured.

3283 200t. Type **735** 5·50 4·75

3284 300t. *Podeces hendersoni* (Henderson's Ground Jay) 5·50 4·75

3285 400t. *Phasianus colchicus* (Pheasant) 5·50 4·75

3286 500t. *Vormela peregusna* (Marbled Polecat) 6·00 5·25

MS3287 160100 mm. Nos. 3277/80 6·00 5·25

No. 3288 and Type **736** are left for 90th Anniv of Mongol Stamps, not yet received.

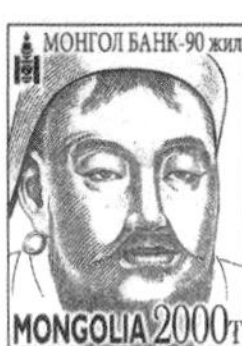

737 Genghis Khan

2014. 90th Anniv of Mongolbank. Multicoloured.

MS3289 2000t.×2, Type **737**; Emblem

738 Museum Gate

2014. Bogd Khan Winter Museum. Multicoloured.

3290 1000t. Type **738** 5·50 4·75

3291 1000t. Large copper container 5·50 4·75

3292 1000t. Tsendiin Dondogdulam (wife) 5·50 4·75

3293 1000t. Two thrones 5·50 4·75

3294 1000t. Hats 5·50 4·75

3295 1000t. Bronze statuettes of Zanzibar and Green Tara 6·00 5·25

3296 1000t. Ceramics 6·00 5·25

3297 1000t. Coach and saddle 6·00 5·25

MS3298 84×102 mm. Bogdo Jebtsundamba Khutuktu (Bogd Khan) (38×58 mm) 6·00 5·25

APPENDIX

The following stamps have either been issued in excess of postal needs, or have not been available to the public in reasonable quantities at face value. Such stamps may later be given full listings if there is evidence of regular postal use. Miniature sheets and imperforate stamps are excluded from this listing.

2007

Diana, Princess of Wales Commemoration. 1150t.×4
60th Wedding Anniv of Queen Elizabeth II and Prince Philip. 400t.×2
Helicopters. 1150t.×4,
Muhammad Ali. 1150t.×4, 1150t.×4

EVERYTHING FOR
THE STAMP COLLECTOR

- ALBUMS
  - Peg-fitting • Springback • Ring-fitting
  - Luxury • One-Country
  - First Day Cover • Postcard • Junior
- CATALOGUES
  - Great Britain • Commonwealth
  - Foreign • Specialised
- ACCESSORIES
  - Microscopes • Watermark Detectors
  - Ultraviolet Lamps • Tweezers
  - Magnifying Glasses • Colour Keys
- STOCKBOOKS
  - Wide range of colours and sizes
- MOUNTS AND HINGES
  - Huge Selection
- GIBBONS STAMP MONTHLY
- SELECTION OF CHILDREN'S STARTER KITS

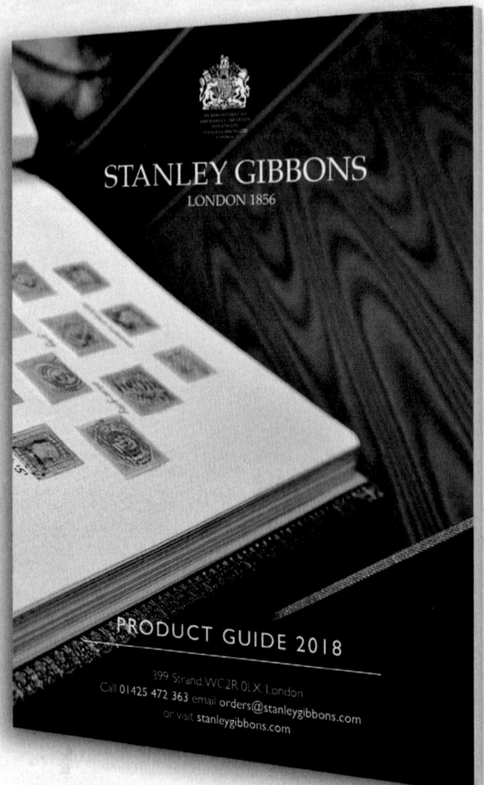

To order, call **01425 472 363**
email **orders@stanleygibbons.com**
or visit **stanleygibbons.com**

MONG-TSEU (MENGTSZ)

An Indo-Chinese P.O. in Yunnan province, China, closed in 1922.

1903. 100 centimes = 1 franc. 1919 100 cents = 1 piastre.

Stamps of Indo-China surcharged.

1903. "Tablet" key-type surch **MONGTZE** and value in Chinese.

1	D	1c. black and red on buff	12·00	23·00
2	D	2c. brown and blue on buff	8·50	16·00
3	D	4c. brown and blue on grey	11·50	13·00
4	D	5c. green and red	7·50	8·25
5	D	10c. red and blue	10·00	13·00
6	D	15c. grey and red	13·00	12·50
7	D	20c. red and blue on green	20·00	33·00
8	D	25c. blue and red	16·00	14·00
9	D	25c. black and red on pink	£900	£900
10	D	30c. brown & blue on drab	17·00	31·00
11	D	40c. red and blue on yellow	£110	£110
12	D	50c. red and blue on pink	£450	£425
13	D	50c. brown and red on blue	£160	£160
14	D	75c. brown and red on orge	£170	£160
15	D	1f. green and red	£170	£150
16	D	5f. mauve and blue on lilac	£180	£160

1906. Surch **Mong-Tseu** and value in Chinese.

17	8	1c. green	2·00	4·50
18	8	2c. purple on yellow	2·00	9·50
19	8	4c. mauve on blue	2·30	4·50
20	8	5c. green	3·50	10·50
21	8	10c. pink	2·75	12·00
22	8	15c. brown on blue	4·00	18·00
23	8	20c. red on green	7·25	12·50
24	8	25c. blue	14·50	18·00
25	8	30c. brown on cream	9·50	30·00
26	8	35c. black on yellow	7·50	22·00
27	8	40c. black on grey	11·00	24·00
28	8	50c. brown	20·00	50·00
29	D	75c. brown & red on orange	90·00	85·00
30	8	1f. green	40·00	45·00
31	8	2f. brown on yellow	80·00	85·00
32	D	5f. mauve and blue on lilac	£170	£170
34	8	10f. red on green	£170	£170

1908. Surch **MONGTSEU** and value in Chinese.

35	10	1c. black and brown	1·50	1·50
36	10	2c. black and brown	1·60	1·60
37	10	4c. black and blue	2·30	2·20
38	10	5c. black and green	2·10	1·40
39	10	10c. black and red	2·75	3·50
40	10	15c. black and violet	4·50	4·50
41	11	20c. black and violet	7·25	10·50
42	11	25c. black and blue	19·00	19·00
43	11	30c. black and brown	7·75	12·50
44	11	35c. black and green	9·50	10·00
45	11	40c. black and brown	6·50	11·50
46	11	50c. black and red	8·00	15·00
47	12	75c. black and orange	20·00	36·00
48	-	1f. black and red	29·00	41·00
49	-	2f. black and green	43·00	60·00
50	-	5f. black and blue	£150	£150
51	-	10f. black and violet	£180	£180

1919. Nos. 35/51 further surch in figures and words.

52	10	$^{2}/_{5}$c. on 1c. black and brown	1·90	5·00
53	10	$^{4}/_{5}$c. on 2c. black and brown	1·90	8·50
54	10	1$^{3}/_{5}$c. on 4c. black and blue	2·10	4·00
55	10	2c. on 5c. black and green	2·50	4·00
56	10	4c. on 10c. black and red	7·00	3·75
57	10	6c. on 15c. black and violet	3·75	4·25
58	11	8c. on 20c. black and violet	9·50	11·50
59	11	10c. on 25c. black and blue	8·50	7·75
60	11	12c. on 30c. black & brown	5·00	8·75
61	11	14c. on 35c. black & green	4·75	5·25
62	11	16c. on 40c. black & brown	4·00	7·00
63	11	20c. on 50c. black and red	5·75	5·75
64	12	30c. on 75c. black & orange	7·25	14·00
65	-	40c. on 1f. black and red	15·00	18·00
66	-	80c. on 2f. black and green	12·50	12·50
67	-	2p. on 5f. black and blue	£190	£190
68	-	4p. on 10f. black and violet	36·00	70·00

MONTENEGRO

Formerly a monarchy on the Adriatic Sea, part of Yugoslavia 1918-2006. In Italian and German occupation during 1939–45 war. An independent state since May 2006.

1874. 100 novcic = 1 florin.
1902. 100 heller = 1 krone.
1907. 100 para = 1 krone (1910 = 1 perper).
2003. 100 cents = 1 euro.

1 Prince Nicholas

1874

45C	1	1n. blue	55	80
38A	1	2n. yellow	4·50	4·25
51A	1	2n. green	55	55
39A	1	3n. green	1·10	1·10
52A	1	3n. red	55	55
40A	1	5n. red	1·10	1·10
53B	1	5n. orange	1·30	75
19	1	7n. mauve	90·00	65·00
41A	1	7n. pink	1·10	1·10
54A	1	7n. grey	65	1·10
42A	1	10n. blue	1·10	1·10
55A	1	10n. purple	80	1·10
56A	1	15n. brown	55	75
46C	1	20n. brown	55	80
7	1	25n. purple	£400	£275
44B	1	25n. brown	1·20	6·50
57A	1	25n. blue	55	75
47C	1	30n. brown	55	80
48A	1	50n. blue	80	80
49B	1	1f. green	2·20	5·50
50B	1	2f. red	2·20	16·00

Прослава
1493 1893
Штампарије
(2)

1893. 400th Anniv of Introduction of Printing into Montenegro. Optd with T **2**.

81A		2n. yellow	43·00	3·75
82A		3n. green	4·50	2·75
83A		5n. red	3·25	2·20
84A		7n. pink	4·50	2·75
85A		10n. blue	5·50	4·25
87A		15n. bistre	6·25	4·25
88A		25n. brown	5·50	3·25

3 Monastery near Cetinje, Royal Mausoleum

1896. Bicentenary of Petrovich Niegush Dynasty.

90A	3	1n. brown and blue	55	1·60
91A	3	2n. yellow and purple	55	1·60
92A	3	3n. green and brown	55	1·60
93A	3	5n. brown and green	55	1·60
94A	3	10n. blue and yellow	55	1·60
95A	3	15n. green and blue	55	1·60
96A	3	20n. blue and green	65	1·80
97A	3	25n. yellow and blue	65	1·80
98A	3	30n. brown and purple	80	1·80
99A	3	50n. blue and red	80	1·80
100	3	1f. blue and pink	1·30	2·20
101	3	2f. black and brown	1·90	2·75

4

1902

102	4	1h. blue	55	55
103	4	2h. mauve	55	55
104	4	5h. green	55	55
105	4	10h. red	55	55
106	4	25h. blue	1·10	1·30
107	4	50h. green	1·10	1·30
108	4	1k. brown	1·10	1·10
109	4	2k. brown	1·10	1·30
110	4	5k. brown	1·30	3·25

УСТАВ
Constitution 1905 Никољдан
(5)

1905. Granting of Constitution. Optd with T **5**.

111		1h. blue	55	55
112		2h. mauve	55	55
113		5h. green	1·10	1·10
114		10h. red	1·70	1·30
124a		25h. blue	80	75
125a		50h. green	80	75
126a		1k. brown	80	75
127a		2k. brown	1·10	1·10
119		5k. orange	1·70	1·60

7

1907. New Currency.

129	7	1pa. yellow	45	30
130	7	2pa. black	45	30
131	7	5pa. green	1·90	20
132	7	10pa. red	3·25	20
133	7	15pa. blue	55	55
134	7	20pa. orange	55	55
135	7	25pa. blue	55	55
136	7	35pa. brown	80	55
137	7	50pa. lilac	80	75
138	7	1k. red	80	75
139	7	2k. green	80	75
140	7	5k. red	1·70	1·30

9 King Nicholas when a Youth

10 King Nicholas and Queen Milena

11 Prince Nicholas

1910. Proclamation of Kingdom and 50th Anniv of Reign of Prince Nicholas.

141	9	1pa. black	90	55
142	10	2pa. purple	90	55
143	-	5pa. green	90	55
144	-	10pa. red	90	55
145	-	15pa. blue	90	55
146	10	20pa. olive	1·10	75
147	-	25pa. blue	1·10	75
148	-	35pa. brown	1·70	1·10
149	-	50pa. violet	1·70	1·10
150	-	1per. lake	1·70	1·10
151	-	2per. green	2·00	1·30
152	11	5per. blue	2·20	1·60

Designs:—As Type **9**: 5, 10, 25, 35pa. Nicholas I in 1910; 15pa. Nicholas I in 1878; 50pa., 1, 2per. Nicholas I in 1890.

12 Nicholas I

1913

153	12	1pa. orange	55	75
154	12	2pa. purple	55	75
155	12	5pa. green	60	75
156	12	10pa. red	60	75
157	12	15pa. blue	65	75
158	12	20pa. brown	65	75
159	12	25pa. blue	1·10	1·10
160	12	35pa. red	80	75
161	12	50pa. blue	55	1·10
162	12	1per. brown	1·10	1·60
163	12	2per. purple	1·10	1·60
164	12	5per. green	1·10	1·60

These issues were only for sale within Montenegro.

M14 Quay, Budva, Montenegro

2003. Tourism. Multicoloured.

M170		25c. Type **M14**	90	85
M171		40c. Durmitor national park (vert)	1·30	1·30

M15 Candle and Baubles

2003. Christmas.

M172	M15	25c. multicoloured	90	85

M16 Map of Montenegro

2005. State Symbols. Multicoloured.

M173		25c. Type **M16**	90	85
M174		40c. First Houses of Parliament	1·30	1·30
M175		50c. State Emblem	1·70	1·60
M176		60c. State Flag	2·75	2·75

M17 Shellfish

2005. Europa. Gastronomy. Multicoloured.

M177		25c. Type **M17**	3·25	3·25
M178		50c. Smoked ham and olives	6·75	6·50
MSM179		110×50 mm. 25c. Bee and honey; 50c. Wine and grapes	22·00	22·00

M18 Montenegro 1913 2pa. Stamp (No. 154) and Emblem

2006. 50th Anniv of Europa Stamps. Multicoloured.

M180		50c. Type **M18**	1·10	1·10
M181		€1 Montenegro 1913 5pa. Stamp (No. 155) and doves	2·20	2·20
M182		€2 Montenegro 1913 10pa. Stamp (No. 156) and bee	4·50	4·25
M183		€2 Montenegro 1913 25pa. Stamp (No. 159) and Europa emblem	4·50	4·25
MSM184		107×92 mm. Nos. M180/3	22·00	22·00
MSM185		103×76 mm. €5.50 Map of Europe highlighting Montenegro. Imperf	22·00	22·00

M19 Figure Skater

2006. Winter Olympic Games, Turin. Multicoloured.

M186		60c. Type **M19**	1·30	1·30
M187		90c. Ski jumper	2·00	1·90

M20 *Petteria ramentacea*

2006. Flora. Multicoloured.

M188		25c. Type **M20**	55	55
M189		50c. *Viola nikolai*	1·10	1·10

M21 1 para Coin and Central Bank

2006. Coins. Multicoloured.

M190 40c. Type **M21** 90 85
M191 50c. 20 para coin and bank 1·10 1·10

M22 Player

2006. World Cup Football Championship, Germany. Multicoloured.

M192 60c. Type **M22** 1·30 1·30
M193 90c. Player wearing short-sleeved jersey 2·00 1·90
MSM194 100×72 mm. 60c. Player leaning right; 90c. Player facing left 3·25 3·25

M23 Durmitor

2006. Tourism. Multicoloured.

M195 25c. Type **M23** 55 55
M196 50c. Sveti Stefan 1·10 1·10

M24 Bird and Map

2006. Independence Referendum 21 May

M197 **M24** 50c. multicoloured 1·10 1·10

M25 Boy holding Case

2006. Europa. Integration. Multicoloured.

M198 60c. Two figures reaching to each other 1·30 1·30
M199 90c. Stylized figures and flowers (horiz) 2·00 2·00
MSM200 100×72 mm. 60c. Type **M25**; 90c. Young people of different nations 3·50 3·50

M26 *Splendido* and Ivo Visin

2006. Birth Bicentenary of Ivan (Ivo) Vizin (circumnavigated globe)

M201 **M26** 40c. multicoloured 90 90

M27 Philatelic Accessories

2006. Stamp Day

M202 **M27** 25c. multicoloured 55 55

M28 Mona Lisa as Child

2006. Joy in Europe Meeting. Children's Day.

M203 **M28** 50c. multicoloured 1·40 1·40

M29 Ruins, Dukla

2006. Cultural and Historical Heritage. Dukla Archeological Site. Multicoloured.

M204 25c. Type **M29** 55 55
M205 25c. Glassware 55 55

M30 Tara River

2006. Environmental Protection

M206 **M30** 40c. multicoloured 90 90

M31 Timepiece

2007. 425th Anniv of Gregorian Calendar

M207 **M31** 50c. multicoloured 1·10 1·10

M32 Pelican

2007. Wildlife Protection

M208 **M32** 50c. multicoloured 1·10 1·10

M33 Emblem (image scaled to 58% of original size)

2007. Europa. Centenary of Scouting. Multicoloured.

M209 60c. Emblem (vert) 1·30 1·30
M210 90c. Tent and fire (vert) 2·00 2·00
MSM211 109×63 mm. 60c.+90c. Type **M33** 1·60 1·60

M34 Black-headed Gull

2007. Fauna. Birds. Multicoloured.

M212 25c. Type **M34** 55 55
M213 50c. Stone Eagle 55 55

M35 Tower

2007. 350th Anniv of Montenegrin Refugees Settlement in Istra

M214 **M35** 60c. multicoloured 1·50 1·50

M36 Fingerprint

2007. Postal History

M215 **M36** 25c. multicoloured 65 65

M37 Text

2007. Cultural and Historical Heritage. Glagolithic Language

M216 **M37** 40c. multicoloured 1·00 1·00

M38 Mountain Landscape

2007. Tourism. Pejaž

M217 **M38** 50c. multicoloured 1·30 1·30

M39 Europe as Butterfly

2007. Together with Europe

M218 **M39** 60c. multicoloured 1·50 1·50

M 40 Petar Lubarda

2007. Birth Centenary of Petar Lubarda (artist).

M219 **M40** 40c. multicoloured 1·10 1·10

M41 *Jadran*

2007. Sailing Ships.

M220 **M41** 60c. multicoloured 1·60 1·60

M42 Children enclosing Dove

2007. Joy in Europe Meeting. Children's Day.

M221 **M42** 50c. multicoloured 1·40 1·40

M43 Dial and Map

2007. Centenary of Interregional Telephone. Multicoloured.

M222 25c. Type **M43** 70 70
M223 50c. Dial and map (different) 1·40 1·40

M44 Ribbon

2007. Christmas and New Year. Multicoloured.

M224 25c. Type **M44** 70 70
M225 25c. Bauble 70 70
M226 50c. Wreath 1·40 1·40
M227 €1 Candle 2·75 2·75

M45 Montenegro Arms as Jigsaw

2008. Montenegro–European Union Stabilization and Association Aggreement. Multicoloured.

M228 60c. Type **M45** 1·60 1·60
MSM229 90×71 mm. 40c. Arms of Montenegro (different); 50c. Arms of EU 1·75 1·75

M46 *Draba bertiscea*

2008. Flora. Multicoloured.

M230 25c. Type **M46** 1·10 1·10
M231 40c. *Edraianthus wettsteinii* 1·20 1·20
M232 50c. *Protoedriantus tarae* 1·30 1·30
M233 60c. *Dianthus nitidus* 1·50 1·50

M47 Stylized Athletes

2008. Olympic Games, Beijing. Multicoloured.

M234 60c. Type **M47** 2·00 2·00
M235 90c. Arms 2·50 2·50

M48 Boy and Envelope

2008. Europa. The Letter. Multicoloured.

MSM238 109×63 mm. 60c. Type **M48**; 90c. Girl holding envelope 4·50 4·50

Nos. M236/7 have been left for single stamps not yet received.

The stamps and margins of No. **MS**M238 form a composite design.

M49 Marko Miljanov

2008. 175th Birth Anniv of Marko Miljanov Popovic Kuc (writer and Kuci clan leader).

M239 **M49**	60c. multicoloured	1·75	1·75

M50 Arms

2008. 150th Anniv of Battle of Grahovac.

M240 **M50**	25c. multicoloured	1·10	1·10

M51 Alpine Hut

2008. Tourism. Sheet 104×90 mm containing Type **M51** and similar horiz designs. Multicoloured.

MSM241	25c. Type **M51**; 40c. River; 50c. Beach; 60c. Lake	3·50	3·50

M52 Chessboard

2008. Chess Olympics, Dresden

M242 **M52**	60c. multicoloured	1·60	1·60

M53 *Jadran*

2008. 75th Anniv of *Jadran* Sail Training Ship

M243 **M53**	50c. multicoloured	1·40	1·40

M54 Emblem

2008. European Water Polo Championship, Malaga 2008

M244 **M54**	50c. multicoloured	1·40	1·40

M55 Faces

2008. Art in Montenegro through Centuries. Frescoes. Multicoloured.

M245	25c. Type **M55**	70	70
M246	50c. Reclining Angel	1·40	1·40

M56 Stamps as House

2008. Stamp Day

M247 **M56**	60c. multicoloured	1·60	1·60

M56a Early Mail Van

2008. Postal History

M248 **M56a**	40c. multicoloured	1·10	1·10

M56b Hourglass containing Map of Montenegro and EU Stars

2008. Together with Europe

M248a **M56b**	50c. multicoloured	1·40	1·40

M56c Eagle and Angel

2008. Cultural and Historical Heritage

M248b **M56c**	60c. multicoloured	1·60	1·60

M56d Nobel Medal

2008. 175th Birth Anniv of Alfred Nobel

M248c **M56d**	50c. multicoloured	1·40	1·40

M57 Lovcen Steam Locomotive

2008. Centenary of Montenegrin Railways. Multicoloured.

M249	25c. Type **M57**	1·10	1·10
M250	25c. First locomotive and crowd	1·10	1·10
M251	25c. Lovcen steam locomotive at Virpazar station	1·10	1·10
M252	25c. Departure of steam locomotive for Virpazar	1·10	1·10
M253	25c. Rail track	1·10	1·10
M254	25c. Port railway, 1910	1·10	1·10

M58 Tower, Birds and Girl

2008. Joy in Europe Meeting. Children's Day

M255	25c. Type **M58**	70	70
M255a	40c. Towers	1·10	1·10

M59 Declaration

2008. 60th Anniv of Universal Declaration of Human Rights

M256 **M59**	50c. multicoloured	1·40	1·40

M60 Louis Braille

2009. Birth Bicentenary of Louis Braille

M257 **M60**	60c. multicoloured	1·60	1·60

M61 St Tryphon

2009. 1200th Anniv of St. Tryphon Cathedral, Kotor

M258	50c. Type **M61**	1·40	1·40
M259	50c. St Tryphon (different)	1·40	1·40

M62 Building Façade

2009. 125th Anniv of First Theatre Performance in Niksic

M260 **M62**	25c. multicoloured	70	70

M63 Vita Nikolić

2009. 75th Birth Anniv of Vita Nikolić (writer)

M261 **M63**	40c. multicoloured	1·10	1·10

M64 Play

2009. 125th Anniv of Zetski Dom Theatre, Cetinje

M262 **M64**	50c. multicoloured	1·40	1·40

M65 Saints

2009. 525th Anniv of Crnojevic Monastery

M263 **M65**	60c. multicoloured	1·60	1·60

M66 *Alburnus scoranza*

2009. Fauna. Fish. Multicoloured.

M264	25c. Type **M66**	70	70
M265	40c. *Thymallus thymallus*	1·10	1·10
M266	50c. *Salmothymus obfusirostris*	1·40	1·40
M267	60c. *Cyprinus carpio*	1·60	1·60

M67 Children, Comet and Planets

2009. Europa. Astronomy. Multicoloured.

M268	60c. Type **M67**	1·60	1·60
M269	90c. Stylized telescope, asteroid and planets	2·40	2·40
MSM69a	109×63 mm. 60c. Planets and constellation; 90c. Comet, asteroid and constellation	3·25	3·25

M68 Waterskiing

2009. Tourism. Multicoloured.

M270	25c. Type **M68**	70	70
M271	40c. Rock climbing	1·10	1·10
M272	50c. Paragliding	1·40	1·40
M273	60c. Rafting	1·60	1·60
MSM273a	104×90 mm. Nos. M270/3	5·00	5·00

M69 Vasilija Petrovica Njegosa

2009. 300th Birth Anniv of Vasilija Petrovica Njegosa (Metropolitan Bishop of Cetinje and Prince - Bishop of Montenegro)

M274 **M69**	40c. multicoloured	1·10	1·10

M70 Students

2009. 25th Universiade, Belgrade

M275 **M70**	50c. multicoloured	1·40	1·40

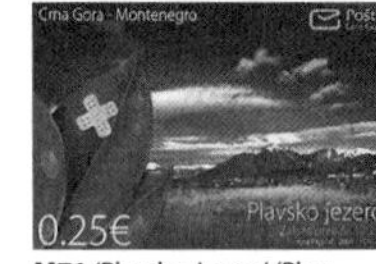

M71 'Plavsko Jezero' (Plav Lake)

2009. Environmental Protection. Multicoloured.

M276	25c. Type **M71**	70	70
M277	50c. Crno Jezero (Black Lake)	1·40	1·40

M72 Vicko Bujović and Ship

2009. 300th Death Anniv of Vicko Bujović (military commander)

M278 **M72**	60c. multicoloured	1·60	1·60

M73 Stamps as Flowers

2009. Stamp Day

M279 **M73**	25c. multicoloured	70	70

M74 Girl and Boy

2009. Joy in Europe Meeting. Children's Day

M280	40c. Type **M74**	1·10	1·10
M281	50c. Boy wearing striped jumper	1·40	1·40

M75 Valtazara Bogišić

2009. 175th Birth Anniv of Valtazara Bogišić (sociology pioneer)

M282	**M75**	50c. multicoloured	1·40	1·40

M75a Document

2009. 700th Anniversary of the Oldest Document in Kotor Archive

M283	**M75a**	25c. multicoloured	70	70

M75b Head (Dado Đurić)

2010. Art in Montenegro through the Centuries. Multicoloured.

M284	50c. Type **M75b**	1·40	1·40
M285	50c. St Elias, fresco, Moraca Monastery	1·40	1·40

M76 Speed Skater

2010. Winter Olympic Games, Vancouver. Multicoloured.

M288	€1 Type **M76**	4·50	4·50
M289	€1.50 Snow boarder	7·50	7·50

M77 Danilo Kis

2010. 75th Birth Anniv of Danilo Kis (writer and poet)

M290	**M77**	50c. multicoloured	2·50	2·50

M78 *Salvia officinalis* (sage)

2010. Flowering Plants. Multicoloured.

M291	25c. Type **M78**	1·20	1·20
M292	50c. *Satureja subspicata*	2·50	2·50
M293	60c. *Tilia tomentosa* (lime tree)	3·00	3·00
M294	€1 *Epilobium angustifolium* (fireweed)	4·74	4·75

M79 Girl, Pile of Books and Symbols of Stories

2010. Europa. Multicoloured.

M295	60c. Type **M79**	3·50	3·50
M296	90c. Boy standing on pile of books surrounded by symbols of stories	3·75	3·75
MSM297	78×62 mm. 60c. Crown, fairy and dress on bridge of books; 90c. Sword, dragon's tail and ship on bridge of books	7·25	7·25

M80 St Vasilije Ostroški

2010. 400th Birth Anniv of St Vasilije Ostroški

M298	**M80**	50c. multicoloured	75	75

M81 Football

2010. Sport. World Cup Football Championships, South Africa

M299	**M81**	€1.50 multicoloured	2·50	2·50

M82 Boat and Trees

2010. Tourism. Multicoloured.

M300	25c. Type **M82**	70	70
M301	50c. Lake and mountain	1·40	1·40
M302	60c. Straw hut on lake edge	1·60	1·60
M303	€1 Beach	2·75	2·75

M83 Steam Ship

2010. The Sea

M304	**M83**	25c. multicoloured	50	50

See also Nos. M340, M368/9 and M400.

M84 Castle

2010. 650th Anniv of Balsic Dynasty

M305	**M84**	25c. multicoloured	50	50

M85 Power Plant

2010. Centenary of First Power Plant

M306	**M85**	25c. multicoloured	50	50

M86 Day of Proclamation of the Kingdom of Montenegro

2010. Centenary of Kingdom of Montenegro Revival

M307	**M86**	50c. multicoloured	75	75

M87 Božidar Vuković Podgoričanin

2010. 500th Birth Anniv of Božidar Vuković Podgoričanin (one of first printers of Serb books and founded Venetian Printing House)

M308	**M87**	50c. multicoloured	75	75

No. M309 and Type **M88** have been left for Stamp Day, not yet received

M89 Children

2010. Joy in Europe Meeting. Children's Day

M310	**M89**	90c. multicoloured	1·50	1·50

Nos. M311/14 and Type **M90** have been left for Cultural Heritage, not yet received.

Nos. M315/16 and Type **M91** have been left for Environmental Protection, not yet received.

M92 Painting (Vojo Stanić)

2011. Art in Montenegro through the Centuries. Multicoloured.

M317	30c. Type **M92**	50	50
M318	40c. Jovan Đurov Ivanišević (composer)	75	75

M93 Bust of Tripo Kokolja, Perast

2011. 350th Birth Anniv of Tripo Kokolja (artist)

M319	**M93**	30c. multicoloured	50	50

M94 Vuk Vrčević

2011. Birth Bicentenary of Vuk Vrčević (translator, collector of lyric poetry and companion of Vuk Karadžić (linguist and reformer of the Serbian language))

M320	**M94**	30c. multicoloured	50	50

Nos. M321/4 and Type **M95** have been left for Fauna, not yet received.

M96 Leaves as 'EU'

2011. Europa. Forests

M325	90c. Type **M96**	1·50	1·50
M326	90c. Leaf as map of Europe	1·50	1·50
MSM327	78×64 mm. 90c.×2 Designs as M325/M326 but vert	4·00	4·00

M97 Lake in Hills

2011. Tourism. Multicoloured.

M328	30c. Type **M97**	50	50
M329	30c. Cliff face, mountains and walkers	50	50
M330	40c. Wooded river valley	50	50
M331	90c. Sand and surf	1·50	1·50

No. M332 is left for stamp not received.

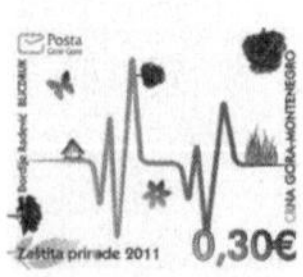

M98 Growth as Heart Monitor Reading

2011. Environmental Protection. Multicoloured.

M333	30c. Type **M98**	50	50
M334	40c. Growth as 'Smiley'	50	50

Nos. M335/6 and Type **M99** have been left for Architecture, not yet received

M100 Volleyball

2011. Sport. Games of Small States of Europe. Multicoloured.

M337	30c. Type **M100**	50	50
M338	90c. Tennis ball	1·50	1·50

M101 Members of the Demonstration

2011. 75th Anniv of Belvederskih Protests

M339	**M101**	30c. multicoloured	50	50

M102 *Brindizi*

2011. The Sea

M340	**M102**	40c. multicoloured	50	50

M103 Clasped Hands

2011. 125th Anniv of Montenegro - Holy See Concordat

M341	**M103**	30c. multicoloured	50	50

M104 House, Mother and Child

2011. Joy in Europe Meeting. Children's Day

M342	**M104**	90c. multicoloured	1·50	1·50

M105 King Mihaila (fresco)

2011. Cultural and Historical Heritage. Multicoloured.

M343	30c. Type **M105**	50	50
M344	40c. *Crnogorac* (first newspaper)	75	75
M345	50c. Zabljak Crnojevića (medieval fortress)	75	75
M346	90c. Josip Slade (architect and engineer)	1·50	1·50

M106 Early Post Van

2011. Stamp Day

M347	**M106**	40c. multicoloured	75	75

M107 *Women* (sculpture) (Risto Stijović)

2012. Art in Montenegro through the Centuries. Multicoloured.

M348	30c. Type **M107**	50	50
M349	40c. *Man with pipe* (woodcut) (Ilija Šobajić)	75	75
M350	80c. *Landscape* (Nikola Vujošević)	1·20	1·20
M351	95c. Early Montenegrin military music corps	1·50	1·50

M108 Nomocanon (detail)

2012. 750th Anniv of Nomocanon of Saint Sava (Ilovička krmčija)

M352	**M108**	30c. multicoloured	50	50

M109 Arms and Coin

2012. 650th Anniv of Enthronement of Đurađ Balšić

M353	**M109** 30c. multicoloured	50	50

M110 'Kopriva' (nettle)

2012. Flora. Multicoloured.

M354	30c. Type **M110**	50	50
M355	90c. Grapes 'Vranac'	1·50	1·50

M111 Matija Zmajević

2012. 275th Anniv of Recognition of Matija Zmajević (Admiral of Baltic Fleet)

M356	**M111** 30c. multicoloured	50	50

M112 Montenegrin Destinations

2012. Tourism. Multicoloured.

M357	30c. Type **M112**	50	50
M358	30c. 'Turizam 2012'	50	50
M359	80c. Symbols of winter holiday pursuits	1·20	1·20
M360	95c. Symbols of summer holiday pursuits	1·50	1·50

M113 Duck in Lifebelt

2012. Environmental Protection. Multicoloured.

M361	30c. Type **M113**	50	50
M362	95c. Frog in lifebelt	1·50	1·50

M114 Rhythmic Gymnast

2012. Sport. Olympic Games, London. Multicoloured.

M363	90c. Type **M114**	1·50	1·50
M364	95c. Discus	1·50	1·50
MSM365	104×48 mm. 90c.As Type **M114**; 95c. As No. M364	4·00	4·00

M115 Monument

2012. 300th Anniv of the Battle of Carev Laz

M366	**M115** 30c. multicoloured	50	50

M116 EU Stars and Flag as Ribbons

2012. Opening of Accession Negotiations with EU

M367	**M116** 95c. multicoloured	1·50	

M117 Volujica Lighthouse

2012. The Sea. Lighthouses. Multicoloured.

M368	30c. Type **M117**	50	50
M369	30c. Verige	50	50

M118 Player

2012. Women's European Handball Championships, Serbia

M370	**M118** 30c. multicoloured	50	50

M119 Map showing Demarcation and Flags of Austria and Montenegro

2012. 175th Anniv of Demarcation of Austria and Montenegro Borders

M371	**M119** 30c. multicoloured	50	50

M120 River Canyon

2012. Europa. Visit Montenegro. Multicoloured.

M372	80c. Type **M120**	1·20	1·20
M373	95c. Kotor	1·50	1·50
MSM374	105×48mm. 80c. As Type **M120**; 95c. As No. M373	4·00	4·00

M121 Stars

2012. Joy in Europe Meeting. Children's Day

M375	**M121** 90c. multicoloured	1·50	1·50

M122 Fresco, Piva Monastery

2012. Cultural and Historical Heritage. Multicoloured.

M376	30c. Type **M122**	50	50
M377	30c. Page from *Oktoih provglasnik* (first book in Cyrillic), printing press and Makarije (monk, first Serbian printer)	50	50
M378	40c. Pava and Ahmet (legendary lovers)	75	75
M379	95c. Map of Battle of Tuđemila	1·50	1·50

M123 Stamps as Kites

2012. Stamp Day

M380	**M123** 30c. multicoloured	50	50

M124 European Championship Teams (winner)

2012. Montenegrin Women's Handball Team Successes in 2012. Multicoloured.

M381	30c. Type **M124**	50	50
M382	30c. Silver medallists Olympic Games, London	50	50

M125 Camil Sijarić (birth centenary)

2013. Art in Montenegro through the Centuries. Multicoloured.

M383	30c. Type **M125**	50	50
M384	40c. Pero Poček (50th death anniv)	75	75
M385	80c. Embroidered cloth (part of traditional costume)	1·20	1·20
M386	95c. *Bogorodice Filermose* (Virgin Filermosa) (icon)	1·50	1·50

M126 Petar II Petrovic Njegosa

2013. Birth Bicentenary of Petar II Petrovic Njegosa (prince-bishop and writer)

M387	**M126** 30c. multicoloured	50	50

M127 Fort

2013. Bicentenary of Unification of Montenegro and Boka

M388	**M127** 30c. multicoloured	50	50

M128 *Apollo Parnassius* (Inscr 'Pamassius')

2013. Fauna and Flora. Multicoloured.

M389	80c. Type **M128**	1·20	1·20
M390	95c. *Scabiosa ochroleuca*	1·50	1·50

M129 Early Post Van

2013. Europa. Postal Transport

M391	**M129** 95c. multicoloured	1·50	1·50

M130 Valtazar Bogisic (creator) and Frontispiece of Code

2013. 125th Anniv of General Property Code

M392	**M130** 30c. multicoloured	50	50

M131 Hikers

2013. Tourism. Multicoloured.

M393	30c. Type **M131**	50	50
M394	40c. Cyclist holding cycle aloft	60	60

M132 'The Old Olive', Mirovica (more than 2000 years old)

2013. Environmental Protection

M395	**M132** 30c. multicoloured	50	50

M133 Basketball (Eurobasket, Slovenia 2013)

2013. Sport. Multicoloured.

M396	80c. Type **M133**	1·20	1·20
M397	95c. Centenary emblem (FK Lovcen Cetinje)	1·50	1·50
MSM398	90×48 mm. 80c. As Type **M133**; 95c. As No. M397	4·00	4·00

M134 Roman Emperor Constantine

2013. 1700th Anniv of Edict of Milan (decreed religious tolerance throughout the empire)

M399	**M134** 30c. multicoloured	50	50

M135 Marka Martinovića

2013. The Sea. 350th Birth Anniv of Marka Martinovića (mathematician, seaman and ship builder)

M400	**M135** 30c. multicoloured	50	50

M136 Bleriot Bi-plane

2013. Centenary of Aviation in Montenegro

M401	**M136** 30c. black, scarlet-vermilion and ochre	50	50

M137 Ljubo Čupić

2013. Birth Centenary of Ljubo Čupić (resistance fighter)

M402	**M137** 30c. multicoloured	50	50

M138 Aeroplanes

2013. Joy in Europe Meeting. Children's Day

M403	**M138** 95c. multicoloured	1·50	1·50

M139 Princess Elena Petrović-Njegoš of Montenegro (140th birth anniv)

2013. Cultural and Historical Heritage. Multicoloured.

M404		30c. Type **M139**	50	50
M405		40c. Ancient map of Stari Bar (horiz)	50	50

M140 Rose

2013. Stamp Day

M406	**M140**	30c. multicoloured	50	50

M141 Lacework

2014. Art in Montenegro through the Centuries. Multicoloured.

M407		30c. Type **M141**	50	50
M408		95c. Stećci (tombstones) (UNESCO World Heritage Site)	1·50	1·50

M142 Skier

2014. Sport. Winter Olympic Games, Sochi

M409	**M142**	95c. multicoloured	1·50	1·50

M143 Episcopal Seal

2014. 925th Anniv of Archdiocese of Bar

M410	**M143**	30c. multicoloured	50	50

ITALIAN OCCUPATION

Montenegro
Црна Гора
17-IV-41-XIX
(1)

1941. Stamps of Yugoslavia optd with T **1**. (a) Postage. On Nos. 414, etc.

1	**99**	25p. black	1·10	1·80
2	**99**	1d. green	1·10	1·80
3	**99**	1d.50 red	1·10	1·80
4	**99**	2d. mauve	1·10	1·80
5	**99**	3d. brown	1·10	1·80
6	**99**	4d. blue	1·10	1·80
7	**99**	5d. blue	4·50	5·50
8	**99**	5d.50 violet	4·50	5·50
9	**99**	6d. blue	4·50	5·50
10	**99**	8d. brown	4·50	6·50
11	**99**	12d. violet	4·50	5·50
12	**99**	16d. purple	4·50	5·50
13	**99**	20d. blue	£275	£325
14	**99**	30d. pink	£110	£130

(b) Air. On Nos. 360/7.

15	**80**	50p. brown	11·00	11·00
16	-	1d. green	8·50	11·00
17	-	2d. blue	8·50	11·00
18	-	2d.50 red	11·00	11·00
19	**80**	5d. violet	65·00	80·00
20	-	10d. red	65·00	80·00
21	-	20d. green	£140	£150
22	-	30d. blue	80·00	80·00

ЦРНА ГОРА
(2)

1941. Stamps of Italy optd with T **2**. (a) On Postage stamps of 1929.

28	**98**	5c. brown	90	1·30
29	-	10c. brown	90	1·30
30	-	15c. green	90	1·30
31	**99**	20c. red	90	1·30
32	-	25c. green	90	1·30
33	**103**	30c. brown	90	1·30
34	**103**	50c. violet	90	1·30
35	-	75c. red	90	1·30
36	-	1l.25 blue	90	1·30

(b) On Air stamp of 1930.

37	**110**	50c. brown	90	1·30

1942. Nos. 416 etc of Yugoslavia optd **Governatorato del Montenegro Valore LIRE.**

43	**99**	1d. green	2·75	3·75
44	**99**	1d.50 red	£130	85·00
45	**99**	3d. brown	2·75	3·75
46	**99**	4d. blue	2·75	3·75
47	**99**	5d.50 violet	2·75	3·75
48	**99**	6d. blue	2·75	3·75
49	**99**	8d. brown	2·75	3·75
50	**99**	12d. violet	2·75	3·75
51	**99**	16d. purple	2·75	3·75

1942. Air. Nos. 360/7 of Yugoslavia optd **Governatorato del Montenegro Valore in Lire.**

52	**80**	0.50l. brown	7·75	8·75
53	-	1l. green	7·75	8·75
54	-	2l. blue	7·75	8·75
55	-	2.50l. red	7·75	8·75
56	**80**	5l. violet	7·75	8·75
57	-	10l. brown	7·75	8·75
58	-	20l. green	£225	£250
59	-	30l. blue	60·00	70·00

4 Prince Bishop Peter Njegos and View

1943. National Poem Commemoratives. Each stamp has fragment of poetry inscr at back.

60	**4**	5c. violet	3·25	5·50
61	-	10c. green	3·25	5·50
62	-	15c. brown	3·25	5·50
63	-	20c. orange	3·25	5·50
64	-	25c. green	3·25	5·50
65	-	50c. mauve	3·25	5·50
66	-	1l.25 blue	3·25	5·50
67	-	2l. green	5·00	8·00
68	-	5l. red on buff	11·00	14·00
69	-	20l. purple on grey	22·00	30·00

Designs:—Horiz: 10c. Meadow near Mt. Lovcen; 15c. Country Chapel; 20c. Chiefs Meeting; 25, 50c. Folk Dancing; 1l.25, Taking the Oath; 2l. Moslem wedding procession; 5l. Watch over wounded standard-bearer. Vert: 20l. Portrait of Prince Bishop Peter Njegos.

1943. Air. With Junkers G31 aircraft (2, 20l.) or Fokker F.VIIa/3m aircraft (others).

70	**5**	50c. brown	1·70	3·50
71	-	1l. blue	1·70	3·50
72	-	2l. mauve	2·20	3·50
73	-	5l. green	2·75	4·25
74	-	10l. purple on buff	14·50	20·00
75	-	20l. blue on pink	34·00	43·00

Designs:—Horiz: 1l. Coastline; 2l. Budva; 5l. Mt. Lovcen; 10l. Lake of Scutari. Vert: 20l. Mt. Durmitor.

GERMAN OCCUPATION

1943. Nos. 419/20 of Yugoslavia surch Deutsche Militaer-Verwaltung Montenegro and new value in lire.

76	**99**	50c. on 3d. brown	8·75	44·00
77	**99**	1l. on 3d. brown	8·75	44·00
78	**99**	1l.50 on 3d. brown	8·75	44·00
79	**99**	2l. on 3d. brown	15·00	90·00
80	**99**	4l. on 3d. brown	15·00	90·00
81	**99**	5l. on 4d. blue	15·00	90·00
82	**99**	8l. on 4d. blue	38·00	£180
83	**99**	10l. on 4d. blue	50·00	£275
84	**99**	20l. on 4d. blue	£100	£650

1943. Appointment of National Administrative Committee. Optd **Nationaler Verwaltungsausschuss 10.XI.1943.** (a) Postage. On Nos. 64/8.

85		25c. green	28·00	£300
86		50c. mauve	28·00	£300
87		1l.25 blue	28·00	£300
88		2l. green	28·00	£300
89		5l. red on buff	£375	£3750

(b) Air. On Nos. 70/4.

90	**5**	50c. brown	28·00	£300
91	**5**	1l. blue	28·00	£300
92	**5**	2l. mauve	28·00	£300
93	**5**	5l. green	28·00	£300
94	**5**	10l. purple on buff	£4500	£33000

1944. Refugees Fund. Surch Fluchtlingshilfe Montenegro and new value in German currency. (a) On Nos. 419/20 of Yugoslavia.

95	**99**	0.15+0.85Rm. on 3d.	29·00	£300
96	**99**	0.15+0.85Rm. on 4d.	29·00	£300

(b) On Nos. 46/9.

97		0.15+0.85Rm. on 25c.	29·00	£300
98		0.15+1.35Rm. on 50c.	29·00	£300
99		0.25+1.75Rm. on 1l.25	29·00	£300
100		0.25+1.75Rm. on 2l.	29·00	£300

5 Cetinje

(c) Air. On Nos. A52/4.

101	**5**	0.15+0.85Rm. on 50c.	29·00	£300
102	-	0.25+1.25Rm. on 1l.	29·00	£300
103	-	0.50+1.50Rm. on 2l.	29·00	£300

1944. Red Cross. Surch +Crveni krst Montenegro and new value in German currency. (a) On Nos. 419/20 of Yugoslavia.

104	**99**	0.50+2.50Rm. on 3d.	28·00	£275
105	**99**	0.50+2.50Rm. on 4d.	28·00	£275

(b) On Nos. 64/5.

106		0.15+0.85Rm. on 25c.	28·00	£275
107		0.15+1.35Rm. on 50c.	28·00	£275

(c) Air. On Nos. 70/2.

108	**5**	0.25+1.75Rm. on 50c.	28·00	£275
109	-	0.25+2.75Rm. on 1l.	28·00	£275
110	-	0.50+2Rm. on 2l.	28·00	£275

ACKNOWLEDGEMENT OF RECEIPT STAMPS

A3

1895

A90	**A3**	10n. blue and red	1·30	1·30

A4

1902

A111	**A4**	25h. orange and red	1·30	1·30

1905. Optd with T **5**.

A120		25h. orange and red	1·30	1·30

1907. As T **7**, but letters "A" and "R" in top corners.

A141	**7**	25p. olive	1·10	1·60

1913. As T **12**, but letters "A" and "R" in top corners.

A169	**12**	25p. olive	1·10	4·00

POSTAGE DUE STAMPS

D3

1894

D90	**D3**	1n. red	4·50	4·25
D91	**D3**	2n. green	1·70	1·60
D92	**D3**	3n. orange	1·10	1·10
D93	**D3**	5n. green	80	75
D94	**D3**	10n. purple	80	75
D95	**D3**	20n. blue	80	75
D96	**D3**	30n. green	80	75
D97	**D3**	50n. pale green	80	75

D4

1902

D111	**D4**	5h. orange	55	75
D112	**D4**	10h. green	55	75
D113	**D4**	25h. purple	55	75
D114	**D4**	50h. green	55	75
D115	**D4**	1k. grey	1·10	1·80

1905. Optd with T **5**.

D120		5h. orange	80	1·60
D121		10h. olive	1·10	3·25
D122		25h. purple	80	1·60
D123		50h. green	80	1·60
D124		1k. pale green	1·10	2·20

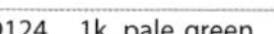

D8

1907

D141	**D8**	5p. brown	55	1·60
D142	**D8**	10p. violet	55	1·60
D143	**D8**	25p. red	55	1·60
D144	**D8**	50p. green	55	1·60

1913. As T **12** but inscr "HOPTOMAPKA" at top.

D165		5p. grey	1·70	2·20
D166		10p. lilac	1·10	1·60
D167		25p. blue	1·10	1·60
D168		50p. red	1·70	2·20

ITALIAN OCCUPATION

1941. Postage Due stamps of Yugoslavia optd **Montenegro Upha 17-IV-41-XIX.**

D23	**D56**	50p. violet	1·90	2·75
D24	**D56**	1d. mauve	1·90	2·75
D25	**D56**	2d. blue	1·90	2·75
D26	**D56**	5d. orange	£130	£140
D27	**D56**	10d. brown	11·00	14·00

1942. Postage Due stamps of Italy optd **UPHATOPA**.

D38	**D141**	10c. blue	2·20	3·25
D39	**D141**	20c. red	2·20	3·25
D40	**D141**	30c. orange	2·20	3·25
D41	**D141**	50c. violet	2·20	3·25
D42	**D141**	1l. orange	2·20	3·25

MONTSERRAT

One of the Leeward Is., Br. W. Indies. Used general issues for Leeward Is. concurrently with Montserrat stamps until 1 July 1956, when Leeward Is. stamps were withdrawn.

1876. 12 pence = 1 shilling; 20 shillings = 1 pound.
1951. 100 cents = 1 West Indian dollar.

1876. Stamps of Antigua as T **1** optd **MONTSERRAT**.

8c		1d. red	32·00	13·00
2		6d. green	70·00	40·00

3

1880

7	**3**	½d. green	1·00	11·00
9	**3**	2½d. brown	£275	65·00
10	**3**	2½d. blue	30·00	21·00
12	**3**	4d. mauve	5·50	3·00
5	**3**	4d. blue	£150	30·00

4 Device of the Colony

1903

24a	**4**	½d. green	1·00	1·25
15	**4**	1d. grey and red	75	40
26a	**4**	2d. grey and brown	2·25	1·25
17	**4**	2½d. grey and blue	1·50	1·75
28a	**4**	3d. orange and purple	12·00	2·50
29a	**4**	6d. purple and olive	16·00	6·50
30	**4**	1s. green and purple	12·00	7·00
21	**4**	2s. green and orange	42·00	27·00
22	**4**	2s.6d. green and black	28·00	60·00
33	**5**	5s. black and red	£160	£190

5

1908

36	**4**	1d. red	1·40	30
38	**4**	2d. grey	1·75	21·00
39	**4**	2½d. blue	2·25	3·50
40	**4**	3d. purple on yellow	1·00	18·00
43	**4**	6d. purple	12·00	55·00
44	**4**	1s. black on green	9·00	45·00
45	**4**	2s. purple and blue on blue	50·00	60·00

46	**4**	2s.6d. black and red on blue	48·00	80·00
47	**5**	5s. red and green on yellow	65·00	85·00

1914. As T **5**, but portrait of King George V.

48	5s. red and green on yellow	90·00	£160

8

1916

63	**8**	¼d. brown	15	5·50
64	**8**	½d. green	30	30
50	**8**	1d. red	3·25	75
65	**8**	1d. violet	30	60
67	**8**	1½d. yellow	1·75	9·50
68	**8**	1½d. red	45	6·00
69	**8**	1½d. brown	3·50	50
70	**8**	2d. grey	50	2·00
71*a*	**8**	2½d. blue	70	90
72	**8**	2½d. yellow	1·25	19·00
73	**8**	3d. blue	75	16·00
74	**8**	3d. purple on yellow	1·10	8·50
75	**8**	4d. black and red on yellow	75	13·00
76	**8**	5d. purple and olive	6·50	10·00
77	**8**	6d. purple	3·00	7·50
78	**8**	1s. black on green	3·00	7·00
79	**8**	2s. purple and blue on blue	7·00	24·00
80	**8**	2s.6d. black and red on blue	12·00	65·00
81	**8**	3s. green and violet	12·00	24·00
82	**8**	4s. black and red	15·00	50·00
83	**8**	5s. green and red on yellow	38·00	65·00

1917. Optd **WAR STAMP**.

60	**8**	½d. green	10	1·50
62	**8**	1½d. black and orange	20	30

10 Plymouth

1932. 300th Anniv of Settlement of Montserrat.

84	**10**	½d. green	1·75	16·00
85	**10**	1d. red	1·75	5·50
86	**10**	1½d. brown	1·75	3·75
87	**10**	2d. grey	2·00	23·00
88	**10**	2½d. blue	2·00	21·00
89	**10**	3d. orange	1·75	21·00
90	**10**	6d. violet	2·25	38·00
91	**10**	1s. olive	12·00	50·00
92	**10**	2s.6d. purple	48·00	85·00
93	**10**	5s. brown	£110	£190

1935. Silver Jubilee. As T **50a** of Mauritius.

94	1d. blue and red	1·00	3·25
95	1½d. blue and grey	2·25	3·50
96	2½d. brown and blue	2·25	4·50
97	1s. grey and purple	6·50	19·00

1937. Coronation. As T **50b** of Mauritius.

98	1d. red	35	1·75
99	1½d. brown	1·00	40
100	2½d. blue	60	1·75

11 Carr's Bay

1938. King George VI.

101a	**11**	½d. green	15	20
102a	-	1d. red	1·75	30
103a	-	1½d. purple	1·75	50
104a	-	2d. orange	2·00	70
105a	-	2½d. blue	50	30
106a	**11**	3d. brown	3·50	40
107a	-	6d. violet	4·25	60
108a	**11**	1s. red	2·50	30
109a	-	2s.6d. blue	27·00	4·25
110a	**11**	5s. red	30·00	4·00
111	-	10s. blue	23·00	24·00
112	**11**	£1 black	30·00	45·00

Designs:—1d., 1½d., 2½d. Sea Island cotton; 2d., 6d., 2s.6d., 10s. Botanic station.

1946. Victory. As T **8a** of Pitcairn Islands.

113	1½d. purple	15	15
114	3d. brown	15	15

1949. Silver Wedding. As T **8b/c** of Pitcairn Islands.

115	2½d. blue	10	10
116	5s. red	7·00	16·00

1949. U.P.U. As T **8d/g** of Pitcairn Islands.

117	2½d. blue	15	1·25
118	3d. brown	2·25	2·00
119	6d. purple	30	3·00
120	1s. purple	30	2·50

13a Arms of University

13b Princess Alice

1951. Inauguration of B.W.I. University College.

121	**13a**	3c. black and purple	20	1·25
122	**13b**	12c. black and violet	20	1·25

14 Government House

1951

123	**14**	1c. black	10	2·75
124	-	2c. green	15	1·25
125	-	3c. brown	40	70
126	-	4c. red	30	2·75
127	-	5c. violet	30	1·50
128	-	6c. brown	30	30
129	-	8c. blue	2·75	20
130	-	12c. blue and brown	1·00	30
131	-	24c. red and green	1·25	1·00
132	-	60c. black and red	11·00	6·00
133	-	$1.20 green and blue	9·00	8·50
134	-	$2.40 black and green	18·00	23·00
135	-	$4.80 black and purple	30·00	32·00

Designs:—2c., $1.20, Sea Island cotton: cultivation; 3c. Map; 4c., 24c. Picking tomatoes; 5c., 12c. St. Anthony's Church; 6c., $4.80, Badge; 8c., 60c. Sea Island cotton: ginning; $2.40, Government House (portrait on right).

1953. Coronation. As T **8i** of Pitcairn Islands.

136	2c. black and green	60	40

1953. As 1951 but portrait of Queen Elizabeth II.

136a	½c. violet (As 3c.) (I)	50	10
136b	½c. violet (II)	80	10
137	1c. black	10	10
138	2c. green	15	10
139	3c. brown (I)	50	10
139a	3c. brown (II)	1·00	2·00
140	4c. red	30	20
141	5c. violet	30	1·00
142	6c. brown (I)	30	10
142a	6c. brown (II)	55	15
143	8c. blue	1·00	10
144	12c. blue and brown	1·50	10
145	24c. red and green	1·50	20
145a	48c. olive and purple (As 2c.)	17·00	7·50
146	60c. black and red	10·00	2·25
147	$1.20 green and blue	19·00	13·00
148	$2.40 black and green	27·00	27·00
149	$4.80 black and purple (I)	6·50	10·00
149a	$4.80 black and purple (II)	30·00	15·00

I. Inscr 'Presidency'. II. Inscr 'Colony'.

18a Federation Map

1958. Inauguration of British Caribbean Federation.

150	**18a**	3c. green	1·00	20
151	**18a**	6c. blue	1·00	75
152	**18a**	12c. red	1·10	15

1963. Freedom from Hunger. As T **20a** of Pitcairn Islands.

153	12c. violet	30	15

1963. Cent of Red Cross. As T **20b** of Pitcairn Islands.

154	4c. red and black	25	20
155	12c. red and blue	45	50

20 Shakespeare and Memorial Theatre, Stratford-upon-Avon

1964. 400th Birth Anniv of Shakespeare.

156	**20**	12c. blue	35	10

1965. Cent of I.T.U. As T **24a** of Pitcairn Islands.

158	4c. red and violet	15	10
159	48c. green and red	40	20

21 Pineapple

1965. Multicoloured

160	1c. Type **21**	10	10
161	2c. Avocado	10	10
162	3c. Soursop	10	10
163	4c. Pepper	10	10
164	5c. Mango	10	10
165	6c. Tomato	10	10
166	8c. Guava	10	10
167	10c. Ochro	10	10
168	12c. Lime	50	75
169	20c. Orange	30	10
170	24c. Banana	20	10
171	42c. Onion	75	60
172	48c. Cabbage	2·00	75
173	60c. Pawpaw	3·00	1·10
174	$1.20 Pumpkin	2·00	6·00
175	$2.40 Sweet potato	8·00	8·50
176	$4.80 Egg plant	8·00	12·00

1965. I.C.Y. As T **24b** of Pitcairn Islands.

177	2c. purple and turquoise	10	20
178	12c. green and lavender	25	10

1966. Churchill Commemoration. As T **24c** of Pitcairn Islands.

179	1c. blue	10	2·50
180	2c. green	30	20
181	24c. brown	1·00	10
182	42c. violet	1·10	1·25

23 Queen Elizabeth II and Duke of Edinburgh

1966. Royal Visit.

183	**23**	14c. black and blue	1·00	15
184	**23**	24c. black and mauve	1·50	15

24 WHO Building

1966. Inauguration of W.H.O. Headquarters, Geneva.

185	**24**	12c. black, green and blue	20	25
186	**24**	60c. black, pur & ochre	55	75

1966. 20th Anniv of UNESCO. As T **25b/d** of Pitcairn Islands.

187	4c. multicoloured	10	10
188	60c. yellow, violet and olive	70	20
189	$1.80 black, purple and orange	2·25	85

25 Sailing Dinghies

1967. International Tourist Year. Multicoloured.

190	5c. Type **25**	10	10
191	15c. Waterfall near Chance Mountain (vert)	15	10
192	16c. Fishing, skin diving and swimming	20	70
193	24c. Playing golf	1·00	45

1968. Nos. 168, 170, 172, 174/6 surch.

194	15c. on 12c. Lime	20	15
195	25c. on 24c. Banana	25	15
196	50c. on 48c. Cabbage	45	15
197	$1 on $1.20 Pumpkin	1·10	40
198	$2.50 on $2.40 Sweet potato	1·10	4·25
199	$5 on $4.80 Egg plant	1·10	4·25

27 Sprinting

1968. Olympic Games, Mexico.

200	**27**	15c. mauve, green and gold	10	10
201	-	25c. blue, orange and gold	15	10
202	-	50c. green, red and gold	25	15
203	-	$1 multicoloured	35	30

Designs:—Horiz: 25c. Weightlifting; 50c. Gymnastics. Vert: $1 Sprinting and Aztec pillars.

31 Alexander Hamilton

1968. Human Rights Year. Multicoloured.

204	5c. Type **31**	10	10
205	15c. Albert T. Marryshow	10	10
206	25c. William Wilberforce	10	10
207	50c. Dag Hammarskjold	10	15
208	$1 Dr. Martin Luther King	25	30

32 *The Two Trinities* (Murillo)

1968. Christmas.

209	**32**	5c. multicoloured	10	10
210	-	15c. multicoloured	10	10
211	**32**	25c. multicoloured	10	10
212	-	50c. multicoloured	25	25

Design:—15, 50c. *The Adoration of the Kings* (detail, Botticelli).

34 Map showing CARIFTA Countries

1969. First Anniv of CARIFTA (Caribbean Free Trade Area). Multicoloured.

223	15c. Type **34**	10	10
224	20c. Type **34**	10	10
225	35c. "Strength in Unity" (horiz)	10	20
226	50c. As 35c. (horiz)	15	20

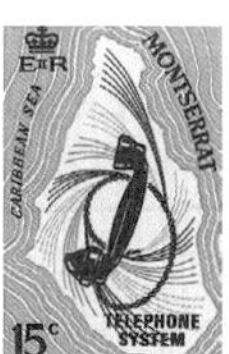

36 Telephone Receiver and Map of Montserrat

1969. Development Projects. Multicoloured.

227	15c. Type **36**	10	10
228	25c. School symbols and map	10	10
229	50c. Hawker Siddeley H.S.748 aircraft and map	15	20
230	$1 Electricity pylon and map	25	75

40 Dolphinfish

1969. Game Fish. Multicoloured.

231	5c. Type **40**	25	10
232	15c. Atlantic sailfish	30	10
233	25c. Blackfin tuna	35	10
234	40c. Spanish mackerel	45	55

41 King Caspar before the Virgin and Child (detail) (Norman 16th-cent stained glass window)

1969. Christmas. Paintings. Multicoloured, frame colours given.

235	**41**	15c. black, gold and violet	10	10
236	**41**	25c. black and red	10	10
237	-	50c. black, blue and orange	15	15

Design:—Horiz: 50c. *Nativity* (Leonard Limosin).

43 "Red Cross Sale"

1970. Centenary of British Red Cross. Multicoloured

238	3c. Type **43**	15	25
239	4c. School for deaf children	15	25
240	15c. Transport services for disabled	20	20
241	20c. Workshop	20	60

44 Red-footed Booby

1970. Birds. Multicoloured.

242	1c. Type **44**	10	10
243	2c. American kestrel (vert)	15	15
244	3c. Magnificent frigate bird (vert)	15	15
245	4c. Great egret (vert)	2·00	15
299a	5c. Brown Pelican (vert)	75	55
247	10c. Bananaquit (vert)	40	60
248	15c. Smooth-billed ani	30	15
249	20c. Red-billed tropic bird	35	15
250	25c. Montserrat oriole	50	50
251	50c. Green-throated carib (vert)	11·00	1·50
252	$1 Antillean crested hummingbird	13·00	1·00
253	$2.50 Little blue heron (vert)	5·50	12·00
254	$5 Purple-throated carib	7·50	20·00
254c	$10 Forest thrush	18·00	24·00

45 *Madonna and Child with Animals* (Brueghel the Elder, after Durer)

1970. Christmas. Multicoloured.

255	5c. Type **45**	10	10
256	15c. *The Adoration of the Shepherds* (Domenichino)	10	10
257	20c. Type **45**	10	10
258	$1 As 15c.	35	1·50

46 War Memorial

1970. Tourism. Multicoloured.

259	5c. Type **46**	10	10
260	15c. Plymouth from Fort St. George	10	10
261	25c. Carr's Bay	15	15
262	50c. Golf Fairway	1·00	2·25
MS263	135×109 mm. Nos. 259/62	3·25	2·25

47 Girl Guide and Badge

1970. Diamond Jubilee of Montserrat Girl Guides. Multicoloured.

264	10c. Type **47**	10	10
265	15c. Brownie and badge	10	10
266	25c. As 15c.	15	15
267	40c. Type **47**	20	80

48 *Descent from the Cross* (Van Hemessen)

1971. Easter. Multicoloured.

268	5c. Type **48**	10	10
269	15c. *Noli me tangere* (Orcagna)	10	10
270	20c. Type **48**	10	10
271	40c. As 15c.	15	85

49 DFC and DFM in Searchlights

1971. Golden Jubilee of Commonwealth Ex-Services League. Multicoloured.

272	10c. Type **49**	15	10
273	20c. MC, MM and jungle patrol	20	10
274	40c. DSC, DSM and submarine action	20	15
275	$1 VC and soldier attacking bunker	30	80

50 *The Nativity with Saints* (Romanino)

1971. Christmas. Multicoloured.

276	5c. Type **50**	10	10
277	15c. *Choir of Angels* (Simon Marmion)	10	10
278	20c. Type **50**	10	10
279	$1 As 15c.	35	40

51 Piper Apache

1971. 14th Anniv of Inauguration of L.I.A.T. (Leeward Islands Air Transport). Multicoloured.

280	5c. Type **51**	10	10
281	10c. Beech 50 Twin Bonanza	15	15
282	15c. de Havilland Heron	30	15
283	20c. Britten Norman Islander	35	15
284	40c. de Havilland Twin Otter 100	50	45
285	75c. Hawker Siddeley H.S.748	1·40	2·25
MS286	203×102 mm. Nos. 280/5	7·00	13·00

52 "Chapel of Christ in Gethsemane", Coventry Cathedral

1972. Easter. Multicoloured.

287	5c. Type **52**	10	10
288	10c. *The Agony in the Garden* (Bellini)	10	10
289	20c. Type **52**	10	10
290	75c. As 10c.	35	1·25

53 Lizard

1972. Reptiles. Multicoloured.

291	15c. Type **53**	15	10
292	20c. Mountain chicken (frog)	20	10
293	40c. Iguana (horiz)	35	20
294	$1 Tortoise (horiz)	1·00	1·00

54 *Madonna of the Chair* (Raphael)

1972. Christmas. Multicoloured.

303	10c. Type **54**	10	10
304	35c. *Virgin and Child with Cherub* (Fungai)	15	10
305	50c. *Madonna of the Magnificat* (Botticelli)	20	30
306	$1 *Virgin and Child with St. John and an Angel* (Botticelli)	30	65

55 Lime, Tomatoes and Pawpaw

1972. Royal Silver Wedding. Multicoloured, background colour given.

307	**55**	35c. pink	10	10
308	**55**	$1 blue	20	20

56 *Passiflora herbertiana*

1973. Easter. Passion Flowers. Multicoloured.

309	20c. Type **56**	20	10
310	35c. *Passiflora vitifolia*	25	10
311	75c. *Passiflora amabilis*	35	75
312	$1 *Passiflora alata-caerulea*	50	80

57 Montserrat Monastery, Spain

1973. 480th Anniv of Columbus's Discovery of Montserrat. Multicoloured.

313	10c. Type **57**	15	10
314	35c. Columbus sighting Montserrat	25	15
315	60c. *Santa Maria* off Montserrat	60	45
316	$1 Island badge and map of voyage	65	55
MS317	126×134 mm. Nos. 313/16	8·00	13·00

58 *Virgin and Child* (School of Gerard David)

1973. Christmas. Multicoloured.

318	20c. Type **58**	15	10
319	35c. *The Holy Family with St. John* (Jordaens)	20	10
320	50c. *Virgin and Child* (Bellini)	25	30
321	90c. *Virgin and Child with Flowers* (Dolci)	50	70

58a Princess Anne and Captain Mark Phillips

1973. Royal Wedding. Multicoloured, background colour given.

322	**58a**	35c. green	10	10
323	**58a**	$1 blue	20	20

59 Steel Band

1974. 25th Anniv of University of West Indies. Multicoloured.

324	20c. Type **59**	15	10
325	35c. Masqueraders (vert)	15	10
326	60c. Student weaving (vert)	25	45
327	$1 University Centre, Montserrat	30	55
MS328	130×89 mm. Nos. 324/7	1·25	5·00

60 Hands with Letters

1974. Centenary of U.P.U.

329	**60**	1c. multicoloured	10	10
330	-	2c. red, orange and black	10	10
331	**60**	3c. multicoloured	10	10
332	-	5c. orange, red and black	10	10
333	**60**	50c. multicoloured	20	20
334	-	$1 blue, green and black	40	65

Design:—2, 5c., $1 Figures from UPU Monument.

1974. Various stamps surch.

335	2c. on $1 mult (No. 252)	1·00	3·25
336	5c. on 50c. mult (No. 333)	30	60
337	10c. on 60c. mult (No. 326)	65	1·75
338	20c. on $1 mult (No. 252)	30	2·50
339	35c. on $1 blue, green and black (No. 334)	40	1·25

62 Churchill and Houses of Parliament

1974. Birth Centenary of Sir Winston Churchill. Multicoloured

340	35c. Type **62**	15	10
341	70c. Churchill and Blenheim Palace	20	20
MS342	81×85 mm. Nos. 340/1	50	70

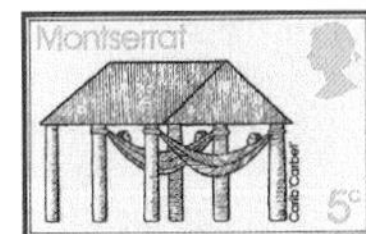
63 Carib "Carbet"

1975. Carib Artefacts. Self-adhesive or ordinary gum.

No.	Type	Description		
343	**63**	5c. brown, yellow and black	10	10
344	-	20c. black, brown & yellow	10	10
345	-	35c. black, yellow & brown	15	10
346	-	70c. yellow, brown & black	45	40

Designs:—20c. "Caracoli"; 35c. Club or mace; 70c. Carib canoe.

64 One-Bitt Coin

1975. Local Coinage, 1785–1801.

No.	Type	Description		
351	**64**	5c. black, blue and silver	10	10
352	-	10c. black, pink and silver	15	10
353	-	35c. black, green and silver	20	15
354	-	$2 black, red and silver	70	1·50
MS355		142×142 mm. Nos. 351/4	1·00	2·25

Designs:—10c. Eighth dollar; 35c. Quarter dollar; $2 One dollar.

65 1d. and 6d. Stamps of 1876

1976. Centenary of First Montserrat Postage Stamp.

No.	Type	Description		
356	**65**	5c. red, green and black	15	10
357	-	10c. yellow, red and black	20	10
358	-	40c. multicoloured	40	40
359	-	55c. mauve, green and black	50	50
360	-	70c. multicoloured	60	70
361	-	$1.10 green, blue and black	80	1·00
MS362		170×159 mm. Nos. 356/61	2·50	5·50

Designs:—10c. GPO and bisected 1d. stamp; 40c. Bisects on cover; 55c. GB 6d. used in Montserrat and local 6d. of 1876; 70c. Stamps for 2½d. rate, 1876; $1.10, Packet boat *Antelope* and 6d. stamp.

66 *The Trinity*

1976. Easter. Paintings by Orcagna. Multicoloured.

No.	Description		
363	15c. on 5c. Type **66**	10	10
364	40c. on 35c. *The Resurrection*	20	15
365	55c. on 70c. *The Ascension*	20	15
366	$1.10 on $1 *Pentecost*	35	40
MS367	160×142 mm. Nos. 363/6	1·50	2·25

1976. Nos. 244, 246 and 247 surch.

No.	Description		
368	2c. on 5c. multicoloured	10	1·25
369	30c. on 10c. multicoloured	30	30
370	45c. on 3c. multicoloured	40	50

68 White Frangipani

1976. Flowering Trees. Multicoloured.

No.	Description		
371	1c. Type **68**	10	40
372	2c. Cannon-ball tree	10	40
373	3c. Lignum vitae	10	40
374	5c. Malay apple	15	10
375	10c. Jacaranda	30	10
376	15c. Orchid tree	70	10
377	20c. Manjak	30	10
378	25c. Tamarind	70	85
379	40c. Flame of the forest	30	30
380	55c. Pink cassia	55	40
381	70c. Long john	40	30
382	$1 Saman	50	80
383	$2.50 Immortelle	75	1·50
384	$5 Yellow poui	1·10	2·25
385	$10 Flamboyant	1·75	4·25

69 Mary and Joseph

1976. Christmas. Multicoloured.

No.	Description		
386	5c. Type **69**	10	15
387	20c. The Shepherds	10	15
388	55c. Mary and Jesus	15	15
389	$1.10 The Magi	30	70
MS390	95×135 mm. Nos. 386/9	60	2·25

70 Hudson River Review, 1976

1976. Bicentenary of American Revolution. Multicoloured.

No.	Description		
391	15c. Type **70**	50	50
392	40c. *Raleigh* (American frigate), 1777*	50	70
393	75c. HMS *Druid* (frigate), 1777*	60	70
394	$1.25 Hudson River Review (different detail)	60	90
MS395	95×145 mm. Nos. 391/4	2·00	2·50

*The date is wrongly given on the stamps as "1776".

Nos. 391 and 394 and 392/3 respectively were issued in *se-tenant* pairs, each pair forming a composite design.

71 The Crowning

1977. Silver Jubilee. Multicoloured.

No.	Description		
396	30c. Royal Visit, 1966	10	10
397	45c. Cannons firing salute	15	10
398	$1 Type **71**	25	50

72 *Ipomoea alba*

1977. Flowers of the Night. Multicoloured.

No.	Description		
399	15c. Type **72**	15	10
400	40c. *Epiphyllum hookeri* (horiz)	25	30
401	55c. *Cereus hexagonus* (horiz)	25	30
402	$1.50 *Cestrum nocturnum*	60	1·40
MS403	126×130 mm. Nos. 399/402	1·00	2·75

73 Princess Anne laying Foundation Stone of Glendon Hospital

1977. Development. Multicoloured.

No.	Description		
404	20c. Type **73**	30	10
405	40c. *Statesman* (freighter) in Plymouth Port	30	15
406	55c. Glendon Hospital	30	20
407	$1.50 Jetty at Plymouth Port	75	1·50
MS408	146×105 mm. Nos. 404/7	1·50	2·50

1977. Royal Visit. Nos. 380/1 and 383 surch **$1.00 SILVER JUBILEE 1977 ROYAL VISIT TO THE CARIBBEAN.**

No.	Description		
409	$1 on 55c. Pink cassia	25	45
410	$1 on 70c. Long john	25	45
411	$1 on $2.50 Immortelle	25	45

75 The Stable at Bethlehem

1977. Christmas. Multicoloured.

No.	Description		
412	5c. Type **75**	10	10
413	40c. The Three Kings	10	10
414	55c. Three Ships	15	10
415	$2 Three Angels	40	2·00
MS416	119×115 mm. Nos. 412/15	1·00	2·25

76 Four-eyed Butterflyfish

1978. Fish. Multicoloured.

No.	Description		
417	30c. Type **76**	35	10
418	40c. French angelfish	40	15
419	55c. Blue tang	50	15
420	$1.50 Queen triggerfish	70	1·25
MS421	152×102 mm. Nos. 417/20	2·75	3·00

77 St. Paul's Cathedral

1978. 25th Anniv of Coronation. Multicoloured.

No.	Description		
422	40c. Type **77**	10	10
423	55c. Chichester Cathedral	10	10
424	$1 Lincoln Cathedral	20	25
425	$2.50 Llandaff Cathedral	40	50
MS426	130×102 mm. Nos. 422/5	70	1·25

78 *Alpinia speciosa*

1978. Flowers. Multicoloured.

No.	Description		
427	40c. Type **78**	20	10
428	55c. *Allamanda cathartica*	20	15
429	$1 *Petrea volubilis*	35	45
430	$2 *Hippeastrum puniceum*	55	80

79 Private, 21st (Royal North British Fusiliers), 1786

1978. Military Uniforms (1st series). British Infantry Regiments. Multicoloured.

No.	Description		
431	30c. Type **79**	15	15
432	40c. Corporal, 86th (Royal County Down), 1831	20	15
433	55c. Sergeant, 14th (Buckinghamshire), 1837	25	15
434	$1.50 Officer, 55th (Westmorland), 1784	50	80
MS435	140×89 mm. Nos. 431/4	1·50	2·75

See also Nos. 441/**MS**445.

80 Cub Scouts

1979. 50th Anniv of Boy Scout Movement on Montserrat. Multicoloured.

No.	Description		
436	40c. Type **80**	20	10
437	55c. Scouts with signalling equipment	20	15
438	$1.25 Camp fire (vert)	35	60
439	$2 Oath ceremony (vert)	45	1·00
MS440	120×110 mm. Nos. 436/9	1·25	2·25

1979. Military Uniforms (2nd series). As T **79**. Multicoloured.

No.	Description		
441	30c. Private, 60th (Royal American), 1783	20	15
442	40c. Private, 1st West India, 1819	25	15
443	55c. Officer, 5th (Northumberland), 1819	25	15
444	$2.50 Officer, 93rd (Sutherland Highlanders), 1830	70	1·25
MS445	139×89 mm. Nos. 441/4	1·25	2·50

81 Child reaching out to Adult

1979. International Year of the Child.

No.	Type	Description		
446	**81**	$2 black, brown and flesh	50	55
MS447		85×99 mm. No. 446	50	1·10

82 Sir Rowland Hill with Penny Black and Montserrat 1876 1d. Stamp

1979. Death Cent of Sir Rowland Hill and Cent of U.P.U. Membership. Multicoloured.

No.	Description		
448	40c. Type **82**	20	10
449	55c. UPU emblem and notice announcing Leeward Islands entry into Union	20	15
450	$1 1883 letter following UPU membership	30	50
451	$2 Great Britain Post Office Regulations Notice and Sir Rowland Hill	40	1·50
MS452	135×154 mm. Nos. 448/51	1·00	2·25

83 Plume Worm

1979. Marine Life. Multicoloured.

No.	Description		
453	40c. Type **83**	25	15
454	55c. Sea fans	30	20
455	$2 Sponge and coral	75	2·25

84 Tree Frog

1980. Reptiles and Amphibians. Multicoloured

No.	Description		
456	40c. Type **84**	15	15
457	55c. Tree lizard	15	15
458	$1 Crapaud	30	50
459	$2 Wood slave	50	1·00

85 *Marquess of Salisbury* and 1838 Handstamps

1980. London 1980 International Stamp Exhibition. Multicoloured

No.	Description		
460	40c. Type **85**	20	15
461	55c. Hawker Siddeley H.S.748 aircraft and 1976 55c. definitive	25	25
462	$1.20 *La Plata* (liner) and 1903 5s. stamp	30	55
463	$1.20 *Lady Hawkins* (packet steamer) and 1932 Tercentenary 5s. commemorative	30	55

464	$1.20 *Avon I* (paddle-steamer) and Penny Red stamp with "A 08" postmark	30	55
465	$1.20 Aeronca Champion 17 airplane and 1953 $1.20 definitive	30	55
MS466	115×110 mm. Nos. 460/5	1·25	2·25

1980. 75th Anniv of Rotary International. No. 383 optd 75th Anniversary of Rotary International.

467	$2.50 Immortelle	55	85

87 Greek, French and USA Flags

1980. Olympic Games, Moscow. Multicoloured.

468	40c. Type **87**	20	60
469	55c. Union, Swedish and Belgian flags	20	60
470	70c. French, Dutch and USA flags	25	75
471	$1 German, Union and Finnish flags	30	75
472	$1.50 Australian, Italian and Japanese flags	35	1·00
473	$2 Mexican, West German and Canadian flags	40	1·00
474	$2.50 *The Discus Thrower* (sculpture, Miron)	40	1·10
MS475	150×100 mm. Nos. 468/74	1·50	3·50

1980. Nos. 371, 373, 376 and 379 surch.

476	5c. on 3c. Lignum vitae	10	10
477	35c. on 1c. Type **68**	15	15
478	35c. on 3c. Lignum vitae	15	15
479	35c. on 15c. Orchid tree	15	15
480	55c. on 40c. Flame of the forest	15	15
481	$5 on 40c. Flame of the forest	60	2·00

89 *Lady Nelson*, 1928

1980. Mail Packet Boats (1st series). Multicoloured

482	40c. Type **89**	30	15
483	55c. *Chignecto*, 1913	30	15
484	$1 *Solent II*, 1878	50	65
485	$2 *Dee*, 1841	70	1·25

See also Nos. 615/**MS**619.

90 *Heliconius charithonia*

1981. Butterflies. Multicoloured.

486	50c. Type **90**	50	40
487	65c. *Pyrgus oileus*	60	45
488	$1.50 *Phoebis agarithe*	70	1·00
489	$2.50 *Danaus plexippus*	1·00	1·50

91 Atlantic Spadefish

1981. Fish. Multicoloured.

555	5c. Type **91**	20	10
556	10c. Hogfish and neon goby	25	10
492	15c. Creole wrasse	80	30
493	20c. Three-spotted damselfish	1·00	30
559	25c. Sergeant major	35	20
560	35c. Fin-spot wrasse	45	30
496	45c. Schoolmaster	80	40
497	55c. Striped parrotfish	1·10	45
498	65c. Bigeye	80	60
564	75c. French grunt	75	55
565	$1 Rock beauty	85	65
501	$2 Blue chromis	1·50	1·10
502	$3 Royal gramma ('Fairy basslet') and blueheads	1·50	1·75
503	$5 Cherub angelfish	1·50	2·75
504	$7.50 Long-jawed squirrelfish	2·00	4·75
570	$10 Caribbean long-nosed butterflyfish	2·00	6·00

92 Fort St. George

1981. Montserrat National Trust. Multicoloured.

506	50c. Type **92**	25	20
507	65c. Bird sanctuary, Fox's Bay	45	35
508	$1.50 Museum	50	65
509	$2.50 Bransby Point Battery, *c.* 1780	60	1·10

92a *Charlotte (image scaled to NaN% of original size)*

92b Prince Charles and Lady Diana Spencer (image scaled to 59% of original size)

1981. Royal Wedding. Royal Yachts. Multicoloured.

510	90c. Type **92a**	20	25
511	90c. Type **92b**	75	85
512	$3 *Portsmouth*	50	60
513	$3 As No. 511	1·25	1·50
514	$4 *Britannia*	60	75
515	$4 As No. 511	1·50	1·75
MS516	120×109 mm. $5 As No. 511	1·00	1·00

93 HMS *Dorsetshire* and Fairey Firefly Seaplane

1981. 50th Anniv of Montserrat Airmail Service. Multicoloured.

519	50c. Type **93**	30	30
520	65c. Beech 50 Twin Bonanza	40	30
521	$1.50 de Havilland Dragon Rapide *Lord Shaftesbury*	60	1·75
522	$2.50 Hawker Siddeley H.S.748 and maps of Montserrat and Antigua	80	3·00

94 Methodist Church, Bethel

1981. Christmas. Churches. Multicoloured.

523	50c. Type **94**	15	15
524	65c. St. George's Anglican Church, Harris	15	15
525	$1.50 St. Peter's Anglican Church, St. Peter's	30	60
526	$2.50 St. Patrick's R.C. Church, Plymouth	50	1·00
MS527	176×120 mm. Nos. 523/6	1·40	3·00

95 Rubiaceae (*Rondeletia buxifolia*)

1982. Plant Life. Multicoloured.

528	50c. Type **95**	20	30
529	65c. Boraginaceae (*Heliotropium ternatum*) (horiz)	20	40
530	$1.50 Simarubaceae (*Picramnia pentandra*)	40	85
531	$2.50 Ebenaceae (*Diospyrus revoluta*) (horiz)	55	1·25

96 Plymouth

1982. 350th Anniv of Settlement of Montserrat by Sir Thomas Warner.

532	**96** 40c. green	20	30
533	**96** 55c. red	20	35
534	**96** 65c. brown	20	50
535	**96** 75c. grey	20	60
536	**96** 85c. blue	20	75
537	**96** 95c. orange	20	80
538	**96** $1 violet	20	80
539	**96** $1.50 olive	25	1·25
540	**96** $2 claret	30	1·50
541	**96** $2.50 brown	35	1·50

The design of Nos. 532/41 is based on the 1932 Tercentenary set.

97 Catherine of Aragon, Princess of Wales, 1501

1982. 21st Birthday of Princess of Wales. Multicoloured

542	75c. Type **97**	15	15
543	$1 Coat of Arms of Catherine of Aragon	15	15
544	$5 Diana, Princess of Wales	80	1·25

98 Local Scout

1982. 75th Anniv of Boy Scout Movement. Multicoloured

545	$1.50 Type **98**	50	50
546	$2.20 Lord Baden-Powell	60	75

99 Annunciation

1982. Christmas. Multicoloured.

547	35c. Type **99**	15	15
548	75c. Shepherds' Vision	25	35
549	$1.50 The Stable	45	85
550	$2.50 Flight into Egypt	55	1·10

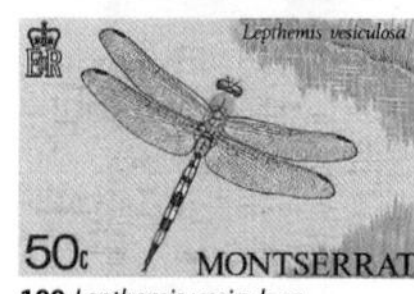

100 *Lepthemis vesiculosa*

1983. Dragonflies. Multicoloured.

551	50c. Type **100**	65	20
552	65c. *Orthemis ferruginea*	75	25
553	$1.50 *Triacanthagyna trifida*	1·40	1·75
554	$2.50 *Erythrodiplax umbrata*	1·90	3·25

101 Blue-headed Hummingbird

1983. Hummingbirds. Multicoloured.

571	35c. Type **101**	1·50	35
572	75c. Green-throated carib	1·75	85
573	$2 Antilean crested hummingbird	2·75	2·75
574	$3 Purple-throated carib	3·00	3·75

102 Montserrat Emblem

1983

575	**102** $12 blue and red	2·50	5·00
576	**102** $30 red and blue	4·75	12·00

1983. Various stamps surch

(a) Nos. 498, 501, 556, 559 and 564

577	40c. on 25c. Sergeant major (No. 559)	30	35
578	70c. on 10c. Hogfish and neon goby (No. 556)	45	50
579	90c. on 65c. Bigeye (No. 498)	55	70
580	$1.15 on 75c. French grunt (No. 564)	65	80
581	$1.50 on $2 Blue chromis (No. 501)	85	1·00

(b) Nos. 512/15.

582	70c. on $3 *Portsmouth*	50	1·00
583	70c. on $3 Prince Charles and Lady Diana Spencer	1·50	2·75
584	$1.15 on $4 *Britannia*	65	1·50
585	$1.15 on $4 As No. 583	1·75	3·25

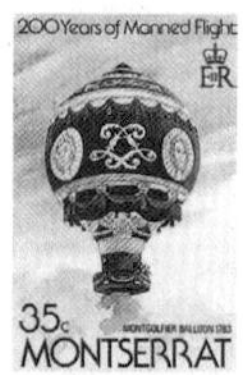

104 Montgolfier Balloon, 1783

1983. Bicentenary of Manned Flight. Multicoloured

586	35c. Type **104**	15	15
587	75c. de Havilland Twin Otter 200/300 (horiz)	25	30
588	$1.50 Lockheed Vega V (horiz)	40	75
589	$2 Beardmore airship R.34 (horiz)	60	1·25
MS590	109×145 mm. Nos. 586/9	1·25	2·75

105 Boys dressed as Clowns

1983. Christmas. Carnival. Multicoloured.

591	55c. Type **105**	10	10
592	90c. Girls dressed as silver star bursts	15	20
593	$1.15 Flower girls	20	35
594	$2 Masqueraders	35	1·25

106 Statue of Discus Thrower

1984. Olympic Games, Los Angeles. Multicoloured

595	90c. Type **106**	30	35
596	$1 Olympic torch	35	45
597	$1.25 Los Angeles Olympic stadium	40	50
598	$2.50 Olympic and American flags	65	1·00
MS599	110×110 mm. Nos. 595/8	1·50	2·25

107 Cattle Egret

1984. Birds of Montserrat. Multicoloured.

600	5c. Type **107**	30	60
601	10c. Carib grackle	30	60
602	15c. Moorhen ('Common Gallinule')	30	60
603	20c. Brown booby	40	60

604	25c. Black-whiskered vireo	40	60
605	40c. Scaly-breasted thrasher	60	60
606	55c. Laughing gull	75	40
607	70c. Glossy ibis	90	45
608	90c. Green-backed heron ('Green Heron')	1·00	60
609	$1 Belted kingfisher (vert)	1·25	70
610	$1.15 Bananaquit (vert)	1·50	1·40
611	$3 American kestrel ('Sparrow Hawk') (vert)	3·25	5·50
612	$5 Forest thrush (vert)	4·50	7·50
613	$7.50 Black-crowned night heron (vert)	5·00	13·00
614	$10 Bridled quail dove (vert)	5·50	13·00

1984. Mail Packet Boats (2nd series). As T **89**. Multicoloured.

615	55c. *Tagus II*, 1907	20	40
616	90c. *Cobequid*, 1913	30	50
617	$1.15 *Lady Drake*, 1942	40	70
618	$2 *Factor*, 1948	60	1·75
MS619	152×100 mm. Nos. 615/18	1·50	5·00

No. **MS**619 also commemorates the 250th anniversary of *Lloyd's List* (newspaper).

108 Hermit Crab and West Indian Top Shell

1984. Marine Life. Multicoloured.

620	90c. Type **108**	1·50	1·00
621	$1.15 Rough file shell	1·75	1·40
622	$1.50 True tulip	2·50	3·25
623	$2.50 Queen or pink conch	3·25	5·00

109 "Bull Man"

1984. Christmas. Carnival Costumes. Mult.

624	55c. Type **109**	50	25
625	$1.15 Masquerader Captain	1·50	1·25
626	$1.50 "Fantasy" Carnival Queen	1·75	2·50
627	$2.30 "Ebony and Ivory" Carnival Queen	2·50	4·25

110 Mango

1985. National Emblems. Multicoloured.

628	$1.15 Type **110**	30	60
629	$1.50 Lobster claw	40	1·00
630	$3 Montserrat oriole	60	3·75

111 *Oncidium urophyllum*

1985. Orchids of Montserrat. Multicoloured.

631	90c. Type **111**	40	55
632	$1.15 *Epidendrum difforme*	40	80
633	$1.50 *Epidendrum ciliare*	45	1·25
634	$2.50 *Brassavola cucullata*	55	2·75
MS635	120×140 mm. Nos. 631/4	3·75	7·50

112 Queen Elizabeth the Queen Mother

1985. Life and Times of Queen Elizabeth the Queen Mother. Various vertical portraits.

636	112	55c. multicoloured	25	45
637	-	55c. multicoloured	25	45
638	-	90c. multicoloured	25	55
639	-	90c. multicoloured	25	55
640	-	$1.15 multicoloured	25	60
641	-	$1.15 multicoloured	25	60
642	-	$1.50 multicoloured	30	70
643	-	$1.50 multicoloured	30	70
MS644		85×113 mm. $2 multicoloured; $2 multicoloured	65	1·90

Each value was issued in pairs showing a floral pattern across the bottom of the portraits which stops short of the left-hand edge on the first stamp and of the right-hand edge on the second.

113 Cotton Plants

1985. Montserrat Sea Island Cotton Industry. Multicoloured.

645	90c. Type **113**	25	45
646	$1 Operator at carding machine	25	50
647	$1.15 Threading loom	25	65
648	$2.50 Weaving with hand loom	50	2·75
MS649	148×103 mm. Nos. 645/8	3·00	3·75

1985. Royal Visit. Nos. 514/15, 543, 587/8 and 640/1 optd CARIBBEAN ROYAL VISIT 1985 or surch also.

650	75c. multicoloured (No. 587)	3·00	2·50
651	$1 multicoloured (No. 543)	4·50	3·50
652	$1.15 multicoloured (No. 640)	4·25	6·50
653	$1.15 multicoloured (No. 641)	4·25	6·50
654	$1.50 multicoloured (No. 588)	7·00	7·00
655	$1.60 on $4 on $4 mult (No. 514)	2·00	4·25
656	$1.60 on $4 on $4 mult (No. 515)	20·00	25·00

No. 656 shows a new face value only, **CARIBBEAN ROYAL VISIT 1985** being omitted from the surcharge.

115 Black-throated Blue Warbler

1985. Leaders of the World. Birth Bicentenary of John J. Audubon (ornithologist). Designs showing original paintings. Multicoloured.

657	15c. Type **115**	15	40
658	15c. Palm warbler	15	40
659	30c. Bobolink	15	40
660	30c. Lark sparrow	15	40
661	55c. Chipping sparrow	20	40
662	55c. Northern oriole	20	40
663	$2.50 American goldfinch	40	1·40
664	$2.50 Blue grosbeak	40	1·40

116 Herald Angel appearing to Goatherds

1985. Christmas. Designs showing Caribbean Nativity. Multicoloured.

665	70c. Type **116**	20	15
666	$1.15 Three Wise Men following Star	30	40
667	$1.50 Carol singing around War Memorial, Plymouth	40	85
668	$2.30 Praying to "Our Lady of Montserrat", Church of Our Lady, St. Patrick's Village	50	2·00

117 Lord Baden-Powell

1986. 50th Anniv of Montserrat Girl Guide Movement. Multicoloured.

669	20c. Type **117**	15	60
670	20c. Girl Guide saluting	15	60
671	75c. Lady Baden-Powell	25	75
672	75c. Guide assisting in old people's home	25	75
673	90c. Lord and Lady Baden-Powell	30	75
674	90c. Guides serving meal in old people's home	30	75
675	$1.15 Girl Guides of 1936	40	80
676	$1.15 Two guides saluting	40	80

117a Queen Elizabeth II

1986. 60th Birthday of Queen Elizabeth II. Multicoloured.

677	10c. Type **117a**	10	10
678	$1.50 Princess Elizabeth in 1928	25	50
679	$3 In Antigua, 1977	40	1·25
680	$6 In Canberra, 1982 (vert)	65	2·25
MS681	85×115 mm. $8 Queen with bouquet	2·50	4·75

118 King Harold and Halley's Comet, 1066 (from Bayeux Tapestry)

1986. Appearance of Halley's Comet. Multicoloured

682	35c. Type **118**	20	25
683	50c. Comet of 1301 (from Giotto's *Adoration of the Magi*)	25	30
684	70c. Edmond Halley and Comet of 1531	25	40
685	$1 Comets of 1066 and 1910	25	40
686	$1.15 Comet of 1910	30	50
687	$1.50 ESA *Giotto* spacecraft and Comet	30	80
688	$2.30 US space telescope and Comet	40	1·75
689	$4 Computer reconstruction of 1910 Comet	50	3·25
MS690	Two sheets, each 140×115 mm. (a) 40c. Type **118**; $1.75, As No. 683; $2 As No. 684; $3 As No. 685. (b) 55c. As No. 686; 60c. As No. 687; 80c. As No. 688; $5 As No. 689 Set of 2 sheets	3·00	9·00

118a Prince Andrew

1986. Royal Wedding (1st issue). Multicoloured.

691	70c. Type **118a**	25	40
692	70c. Miss Sarah Ferguson	25	40
693	$2 Prince Andrew wearing stetson (horiz)	40	90
694	$2 Miss Sarah Ferguson on skiing holiday (horiz)	40	90
MS695	115×85 mm. $10 Duke and Duchess of York on Palace balcony after wedding (horiz)	2·75	5·50

See also Nos. 705/8.

119 *Antelope* being attacked by *L'Atalante*

1986. Mail Packet Sailing Ships. Multicoloured

696	90c. Type **119**	2·00	1·50
697	$1.15 *Montagu* (1810)	2·25	2·00
698	$1.50 *Little Catherine* being pursued by *L'Etoile* (1813)	2·75	2·75
699	$2.30 *Hinchingbrook I* (1813)	3·50	5·00
MS700	165×123 mm. Nos. 696/9	10·00	11·00

120 Radio Montserrat Building, Dagenham

1986. Communications. Multicoloured.

701	70c. Type **120**	1·00	70
702	$1.15 Radio Gem dish aerial, Plymouth	1·00	1·50
703	$1.50 Radio Antilles studio, O'Garro's	1·75	2·25
704	$2.30 Cable and Wireless building, Plymouth	2·25	4·25

1986. Royal Wedding (2nd issue). Nos. 691/4 optd **Congratulations to T.R.H. The Duke & Duchess of York**.

705	70c. Prince Andrew	90	1·50
706	70c. Miss Sarah Ferguson	90	1·50
707	$2 Prince Andrew wearing stetson (horiz)	1·25	2·00
708	$2 Miss Sarah Ferguson on skiing holiday (horiz)	1·25	2·00

121a Statue of Liberty

1986. Centenary of Statue of Liberty. Vert views of Statue as T **121a** in separate miniature sheets. Multicoloured.

MS709	Three sheets, each 85×115 mm. $3; $4.50; $5 Set of 3 sheets	3·75	9·00

122 Sailing and Windsurfing

1986. Tourism. Multicoloured.

710	70c. Type **122**	40	70
711	$1.15 Golf	70	1·50
712	$1.50 Plymouth market	70	2·00
713	$2.30 Air Recording Studios	80	3·00

123 Christmas Rose

1986. Christmas. Flowering Shrubs. Multicoloured

714	70c. Type **123**	70	40
715	$1.15 Candle flower	95	85
716	$1.50 Christmas tree kalanchoe	1·50	1·50
717	$2.30 Snow on the mountain	2·00	4·50
MS718	150×110 mm. Nos. 714/17	8·00	10·00

124 Tiger Shark

1987. Sharks. Multicoloured.

719	40c. Type **124**	1·25	55
720	90c. Lemon shark	2·00	1·50
721	$1.15 Great white shark	2·25	2·00
722	$3.50 Whale shark	4·50	8·00
MS723	150×102 mm. Nos. 719/22	12·00	15·00

1987. Nos. 601, 603, 607/8 and 611 surch.

724	5c. on 70c. Glossy ibis	75	4·00
725	$1 on 20c. Brown booby	2·25	1·50
726	$1.15 on 10c. Carib grackle	2·50	1·50
727	$1.50 on 90c. Green-backed heron	2·50	2·75
728	$2.30 on $3 American kestrel (vert)	3·50	9·00

1987. Capex '87 International Stamp Exhibition, Toronto. No. **MS**690 optd with CAPEX 87 logo.

MS729	Two sheets. As No. **MS**690 Set of 2 sheets	4·00	10·00

No. **MS**729 also carries an overprint commemorating the exhibition on the lower sheet margins.

127 *Phoebis trite*

1987. Butterflies. Multicoloured.

730	90c. Type **127**	2·00	1·10

731	$1.15 *Biblis hyperia*	2·50	1·60
732	$1.50 *Polygonus leo*	3·00	2·50
733	$2.50 *Hypolimnas misippus*	4·50	6·50

128 *Oncidium variegatum*

1987. Christmas. Orchids. Multicoloured.

734	90c. Type **128**	60	45
735	$1.15 *Vanilla planifolia* (horiz)	85	55
736	$1.50 *Gongora quinquenervis*	1·10	1·10
737	$3.50 *Brassavola nodosa* (horiz)	2·00	5·00
MS738	100×75 mm. $5 *Oncidium lanceanum* (horiz)	12·00	14·00

1987. Royal Ruby Wedding. Nos. 601, 604/5 and 608 surch **40th Wedding Anniversary HM Queen Elizabeth II HRH Duke of Edinburgh. November 1987** and value.

739B	5c. on 90c. Green-backed heron	30	1·00
740B	$1.15 on 10c. Carib grackle	1·00	1·00
741B	$2.30 on 25c. Black-whiskered vireo	1·75	2·25
742B	$5 on 40c. Scaly-breasted thrasher	3·50	5·50

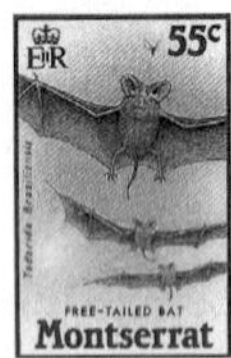

130 Free-tailed Bat

1988. Bats. Multicoloured.

743	55c. Type **130**	80	40
744	90c. *Chiroderma improvisum* (fruit bat)	1·25	90
745	$1.15 Fisherman bat	1·60	1·50
746	$2.30 *Brachyphylla cavernarum* (fruit bat)	3·00	5·50
MS747	133×110 mm. $2.50 Funnel-eared bat	6·50	8·00

131 Magnificent Frigate Bird

1988. Easter. Birds. Multicoloured.

748	90c. Type **131**	60	45
749	$1.15 Caribbean elaenia	80	75
750	$1.50 Glossy ibis	1·00	1·50
751	$3.50 Purple-throated carib	2·00	4·00
MS752	100×75 mm. $5 Brown pelican	2·50	3·50

132 Discus throwing

1988. Olympic Games, Seoul. Multicoloured.

753	90c. Type **132**	80	50
754	$1.15 High jumping	90	55
755	$3.50 Athletics	2·25	3·25
MS756	103×77 mm. $5 Rowing	3·00	3·00

133 Golden Tulip

1988. Sea Shells. Multicoloured.

757	5c. Type **133**	45	75
758	10c. Little knobbed scallop	60	75
759	15c. Sozoni's cone	60	75
760	20c. Globular coral shell	70	40
761	25c. American or common sundial	70	50
762	40c. King helmet	85	50
763	55c. Channelled turban	1·00	50
764	70c. True tulip	1·25	75
765	90c. Music volute	1·50	75
766	$1 Flame auger	1·60	80
767	$1.15 Rooster-tail conch	1·75	90
768	$1.50 Queen or pink conch	1·75	1·40
769	$3 Teramachi's slit shell	2·75	4·50
770	$5 Common or Florida crown conch	3·50	7·00
771	$7.50 Beau's murex	4·25	12·00
772	$10 Atlantic trumpet triton	4·50	12·00

134 University Crest

1988. 40th Anniv of University of West Indies.

773	**134** $5 multicoloured	3·00	3·50

1988. Princess Alexandra's Visit. Nos. 763, 766 and 769/70 surch HRH PRINCESS ALEXANDRA'S VISIT NOVEMBER 1988 and new value.

774	40c. on 55c. Channelled turban	75	45
775	90c. on $1 Flame auger	1·25	80
776	$1.15 on $3 Teramachi's slit shell	1·50	95
777	$1.50 on $5 Common or Florida crown conch	1·75	1·75

136 Spotted Sandpiper

1988. Christmas. Sea Birds. Multicoloured.

778	90c. Type **136**	70	55
779	$1.15 Ruddy turnstone	85	70
780	$3.50 Red-footed booby	2·00	3·75
MS781	105×79 mm. $5 Audubon's shearwater	2·75	4·00

137 Disabled Children in Classroom

1988. 125th Anniv of International Red Cross.

782	**137** $3.50 multicoloured	1·50	2·25

138 Drum Major in Ceremonial Uniform

1989. 75th Anniv (1986) of Montserrat Defence Force. Uniforms. Multicoloured.

783	90c. Type **138**	90	50
784	$1.15 Field training uniform	1·00	75
785	$1.50 Cadet in ceremonial uniform	1·50	2·00
786	$3.50 Gazetted Police Officer in ceremonial uniform	4·00	4·50
MS787	102×76 mm. $5 Island Girl Guide Commissioner and brownie	3·50	4·25

139 Amazon Lily

1989. Easter. Lilies. Multicoloured.

788	90c. Type **139**	50	50
789	$1.15 Salmon blood lily (vert)	70	70
790	$1.50 Amaryllis (vert)	85	1·25
791	$3.50 Amaryllis (vert)	1·90	3·00
MS792	103×77 mm. $5 Resurrection lily (vert)	4·75	7·00

140 *Morning Prince* (schooner), 1942

1989. Shipbuilding in Montserrat. Multicoloured

793	90c. Type **140**	1·40	60
794	$1.15 *Western Sun* (inter-island freighter)	1·90	1·10
795	$1.50 *Kim G* (inter-island freighter) under construction	2·25	2·25
796	$3.50 *Romaris* (inter-island ferry), *c.* 1942	3·50	5·50

141 The Scarecrow

1989. 50th Anniv of *The Wizard of Oz* (film). Multicoloured.

797	90c. Type **141**	50	45
798	$1.15 The Lion	65	60
799	$1.50 The Tin Man	90	85
800	$3.50 Dorothy	1·75	2·50
MS801	113×84 mm. $5 Characters from film (horiz)	2·40	3·75

1989. Hurricane Hugo Relief Fund. Nos. 795/6 surch Hurricane Hugo Relief Surcharge $2.50.

802	$1.50 +$2.50 *Kim G* (inter-island freighter under construction)	2·25	4·00
803	$3.50 +$2.50 *Romaris* (inter-island ferry), *c.* 1942	2·50	5·00

143 *Apollo 11* above Lunar Surface

1989. 20th Anniv of First Manned Landing on Moon. Multicoloured.

804	90c. Type **143**	45	40
805	$1.15 Astronaut alighting from lunar module *Eagle*	55	50
806	$1.50 *Eagle* and astronaut conducting experiment	75	80
807	$3.50 Opening *Apollo 11* hatch after splashdown	1·60	2·50
MS808	101×76 mm. $5 Astronaut on Moon	5·50	6·50

144 *Yamato* (Japanese battleship)

1990. World War II Capital Ships. Multicoloured.

809	70c. Type **144**	3·25	70
810	$1.15 USS *Arizona* at Pearl Harbor	3·75	95
811	$1.50 *Bismarck* (German battleship) in action	4·75	2·75
812	$3.50 HMS *Hood* (battle cruiser)	7·00	10·00
MS813	118×90 mm. $5 *Bismarck* and map of North Atlantic	16·00	16·00

145 The Empty Tomb

1990. Easter. Stained glass windows from St. Michael's Parish Church, Bray, Berkshire. Multicoloured.

814	$1.15 Type **145**	2·25	2·50
815	$1.50 The Ascension	2·25	2·50
816	$3.50 The Risen Christ with Disciples	2·75	3·25
MS817	65×103 mm. $5 The Crucifixion	5·00	6·50

1990. Stamp World London '90 International Stamp Exhibition. Nos. 460/4 surch Stamp World London 90, emblem and value.

818	70c. on 40c. Type **85**	80	80
819	90c. on 55c. Hawker Siddeley H.S.748 aircraft and 1976 55c. definitive	1·00	1·00
820	$1 on $1.20 *La Plata* (liner) and 1903 5s. stamp	1·25	1·40
821	$1.15 on $1.20 *Lady Hawkins* (packet steamer) and 1932 Tercentenary 5s. commemorative	1·40	1·50
822	$1.50 on $1.20 *Avon I* (paddle-steamer) and Penny Red stamp with "A 08" postmark	1·75	2·00

147 General Office, Montserrat and 1884 ½d. Stamp

1990. 150th Anniv of the Penny Black. Multicoloured

823	90c. Type **147**	65	65
824	$1.15 Sorting letters and Montserrat 1d. stamp of 1876 (vert)	85	90
825	$1.50 Posting letters and Penny Black (vert)	1·25	1·75
826	$3.50 Postman delivering letters and 1840 Twopence Blue	3·00	4·50
MS827	102×75 mm. $5 Montserrat soldier's letter of 1836 and Penny Black	8·50	10·00

148 Montserrat v. Antigua Match

1990. World Cup Football Championship, Italy. Multicoloured.

828	90c. Type **148**	65	55
829	$1.15 USA v. Trinidad match	85	75
830	$1.50 Montserrat team	1·25	1·50
831	$3.50 West Germany v. Wales match	2·25	3·50
MS832	77×101 mm. $5 World Cup trophy (vert)	6·00	7·50

149 Spinner Dolphin

1990. Dolphins. Multicoloured.

833	90c. Type **149**	1·50	85
834	$1.15 Common dolphin	1·75	1·25
835	$1.50 Striped dolphin	2·50	2·50
836	$3.50 Atlantic spotted dolphin	3·75	5·00
MS837	103×76 mm. $5 Atlantic white-sided dolphin	8·50	9·50

150 Spotted Goatfish

1991. Tropical Fish. Multicoloured.

838	90c. Type **150**	1·50	95
839	$1.15 Cushion star	1·75	1·25
840	$1.50 Rock beauty	2·50	2·75
841	$3.50 French grunt	3·75	5·50
MS842	103×76 mm. $5 Buffalo trunkfish	6·50	8·00

1991. Nos. 760/1, 768 and 771 surch.

843	5c. on 20c. Globular coral shell	65	2·25
844	5c. on 25c. American or common sundial	65	2·25
845	$1.15 on $1.50 Queen or pink conch	2·75	3·25
846	$1.15 on $7.50 Beau's murex	2·75	3·25

152 Duck

1991. Domestic Birds. Multicoloured.

847	90c. Type **152**	60	60
848	$1.15 Hen and chicks	80	90
849	$1.50 Red junglefowl ('Rooster')	1·10	1·50

850	$3.50 Helmeted guineafowl	2·40	3·50

153 *Panaeolus antillarum*

1991. Fungi.

851	**153**	90c. grey	1·50	1·00
852	-	$1.15 red	1·75	1·25
853	-	$1.50 brown	2·50	2·25
854	-	$2 purple	2·75	3·50
855	-	$3.50 blue	4·00	6·00

Designs:—$1.15, *Cantharellus cinnabarinus*; $1.50, *Gymnopilus chrysopellus*; $2 *Psilocybe cubensis*; $3.50, *Leptonia caeruleocapitata*.

154 Red Water Lily

1991. Lilies. Multicoloured.

856	90c. Type **154**	65	65
857	$1.15 Shell ginger	75	85
858	$1.50 Early day lily	1·00	1·60
859	$3.50 Anthurium	2·50	4·25

155 Tree Frog

1991. Frogs and Toad. Multicoloured.

860	$1.15 Type **155**	3·75	1·25
861	$2 Crapaud toad	5·00	5·00
862	$3.50 Mountain chicken (frog)	8·50	9·50
MS863	110×110 mm. $5 Tree frog, crapaud toad and mountain chicken (76½×44 mm)	13·00	14·00

156 Black British Shorthair Cat

1991. Cats. Multicoloured.

864	90c. Type **156**	2·00	90
865	$1.15 Seal point Siamese	2·25	1·10
866	$1.50 Silver tabby Persian	2·75	2·25
867	$2.50 Birman temple cat	3·50	4·50
868	$3.50 Egyptain mau	5·00	7·00

157 Navigational Instruments

1992. 500th Anniv of Discovery of America by Columbus. Multicoloured.

869	$1.50 Type **157**	1·75	1·90
870	$1.50 Columbus and Coat of Arms	1·75	1·90
871	$1.50 Landfall on the Bahamas	1·75	1·90
872	$1.50 Petitioning Queen Isabella	1·75	1·90
873	$1.50 Tropical birds	1·75	1·90
874	$1.50 Tropical fruits	1·75	1·90
875	$3 Ships of Columbus (81×26 mm)	2·00	2·25

158 Runner with Olympic Flame

1992. Olympic Games, Barcelona. Multicoloured.

876	$1 Type **158**	1·25	60
877	$1.15 Montserrat, Olympic and Spanish flags	2·50	1·00
878	$2.30 Olympic flame on map of Montserrat	3·50	3·50
879	$3.60 Olympic events	3·50	6·00

159 Tyrannosaurus

1992. Death Centenary of Sir Richard Owen (zoologist). Multicoloured.

880	$1 Type **159**	2·00	1·25
881	$1.15 Diplodocus	2·25	1·40
882	$1.50 Apatosaurus	2·75	2·75
883	$3.45 Dimetrodon	5·50	8·00
MS884	114×84 mm. $4.60, Sir Richard Owen and dinosaur bone (vert)	8·50	10·00

160 Male Montserrat Oriole

1992. Montserrat Oriole. Multicoloured.

885	$1 Type **160**	1·10	1·10
886	$1.15 Male and female orioles	1·40	1·40
887	$1.50 Female oriole with chicks	1·75	2·00
888	$3.60 Map of Montserrat and male oriole	3·50	5·00

161 *Psophus stridulus* (grasshopper)

1992. Insects. Multicoloured.

889	5c. Type **161**	40	1·00
890	10c. *Gryllus campestris* (field cricket)	50	1·00
891	15c. *Lepthemis vesiculosa* (dragonfly)	60	1·00
892	20c. *Orthemis ferruginea* (red skimmer)	65	1·00
893	25c. *Gerris lacustris* (pond skater)	65	1·00
894	40c. *Byctiscus betulae* (leaf weevil)	80	1·00
895	55c. *Atta texana* (leaf-cutter ants)	85	40
896	70c. *Polistes fuscatus* (paper wasp)	1·00	60
897	90c. *Sparmopolius fulvus* (bee fly)	1·25	60
898	$1 *Chrysopa carnea* (lace wing)	1·75	65
899	$1.15 *Phoebis philea* (butterfly)	3·00	90
900	$1.50 *Cynthia cardui* (butterfly)	3·25	1·75
901	$3 *Utetheisa bella* (moth)	3·50	4·75
902	$5 *Alucita pentadactyla* (moth)	5·00	7·00
903	$7.50 *Anartia jatropha* (butterfly)	8·00	11·00
904	$10 *Heliconius melpomene* (butterfly)	8·00	11·00

162 Adoration of the Magi

1992. Christmas. Multicoloured.

905	$1.15 Type **162**	2·00	75
906	$4.60 Appearance of Angel to shepherds	4·50	6·50

163 $1 Coin and $20 Banknote

1993. East Caribbean Currency. Multicoloured.

907	$1 Type **163**	90	70
908	$1.15 10c. and 25c. coins with $10 banknote	1·25	85
909	$1.50 5c. coin and $5 banknote	1·75	2·00
910	$3.60 1c. and 2c. coins with $1 banknote	4·00	6·00

164 Columbus meeting Amerindians

1993. Organization of East Caribbean States. 500th Anniv of Discovery of America by Columbus. Multicoloured.

911	$1 Type **164**	1·25	1·00
912	$2 Ships approaching island	2·25	3·00

165 Queen Elizabeth II on Montserrat with Chief Minister W. H. Bramble, 1966

1993. 40th Anniv of Coronation. Multicoloured.

913	$1.15 Type **165**	1·50	75
914	$4.60 Queen Elizabeth II in State Coach, 1953	4·00	5·00

1993. 500th Anniv of Discovery of Montserrat. As Nos. 869/75, some with new values, each showing "500th ANNIVERSARY DISCOVERY OF MONTSERRAT" at foot and with additional historical inscr across the centre.

915	$1.15 mult (As Type **157**)	2·25	2·50
916	$1.15 multicoloured (As No. 870)	2·25	2·50
917	$1.15 multicoloured (As No. 871)	2·25	2·50
918	$1.50 multicoloured (As No. 872)	2·50	2·75
919	$1.50 multicoloured (As No. 873)	2·50	2·75
920	$1.50 multicoloured (As No. 874)	2·50	2·75
921	$3.45 multicoloured (As No. 875)	3·75	4·25

Additional inscriptions: No. 915, 'PRE-COLUMBUS CARIB NAME OF ISLAND ALLIOUGANA'; 916, 'COLUMBUS NAMED ISLAND SANTA MARIA DE MONTSERRATE'; 917, 'COLUMBUS SAILED ALONG COASTLINE 11th NOV. 1493'; 918, 'ISLAND OCCUPIED BY FRENCH BRIEFLY IN 1667'; 919, 'ISLAND DECLARED ENGLISH BY TREATY OF BREDA 1667'; 920, 'AFRICAN SLAVES BROUGHT IN DURING 1600's'; 921, 'IRISH CATHOLICS FROM ST. KITTS AND VIRGINIA SETTLED ON ISLAND BETWEEN 1628–1634'.

166 Boeing Sentry, 1993

1993. 75th Anniv of Royal Air Force. Multicoloured

922	15c. Type **166**	55	20
923	55c. Vickers Valiant B Mk 1, 1962	75	40
924	$1.15 Handley Page Hastings C Mk 2, 1958	1·25	75
925	$3 Lockheed Ventura, 1943	2·50	4·25
MS926	117×78 mm. $1.50 Felixstowe F5, 1921; $1.50 Armstrong Whitworth Atlas, 1934; $1.50 Fairey Gordon, 1935; $1.50 Boulton & Paul Overstrand, 1936	4·50	6·00

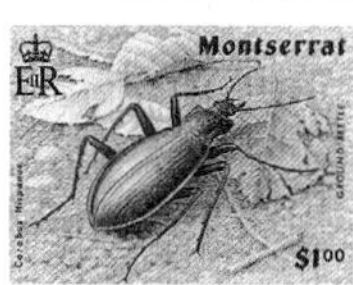

167 Ground Beetle

1994. Beetles. Multicoloured.

927	$1 Type **167**	65	65
928	$1.15 Click beetle	80	80
929	$1.50 Harlequin beetle	1·00	1·25
930	$3.45 Leaf beetle	2·50	4·00
MS931	68×85 mm. $4.50 Scarab beetle	3·50	4·00

168 *Gossypium barbadense*

1994. Flowers. Multicoloured.

932	90c. Type **168**	1·25	80
933	$1.15 *Hibiscus sabdariffa*	1·50	1·00
934	$1.50 *Hibiscus esculentus*	1·75	1·75
935	$3.50 *Hibiscus rosa-sinensis*	3·75	6·00

169 Coaching Young Players and Logo

1994. World Cup Football Championship, U.S.A. Multicoloured.

936	90c. Type **169**	1·60	3·00
937	$1 United States scoring against England, 1950	1·60	2·00
938	$1.15 Rose Bowl stadium, Los Angeles, and trophy	1·60	2·00
939	$3.45 German players celebrating with trophy, 1990	2·25	3·50
MS940	114×85 mm. $2 Jules Rimet (founder) and Jules Rimet Trophy; $2 Bobby Moore (England) holding trophy, 1966; $2 Lew Jaschin (USSR); $2 Sepp Herberger (Germany) and German players celebrating, 1990	5·00	7·50

170 Elasmosaurus

1994. Aquatic Dinosaurs. Multicoloured.

941	$1 Type **170**	2·25	2·25
942	$1.15 Plesiosaurus	2·25	2·25
943	$1.50 Nothosaurus	2·75	2·75
944	$3.45 Mosasaurus	3·50	4·25

1994. Space Anniversaries. Nos. 804/7 variously surch or optd, each including Space Anniversaries.

945	40c. on 90c. Type **143**	1·75	80
946	$1.15 Astronaut alighting from lunar module *Eagle*	2·50	1·50
947	$1.50 *Eagle* and astronaut conducting experiment	3·00	3·00
948	$2.30 on $3.50 Opening *Apollo 11* hatch after splashdown	4·75	7·00

Surcharges and overprints: No. 945, **Juri Gagarin First man in space April 12, 1961**; 946, **First Joint US Soviet Mission July 15, 1975**; 947 **25th Anniversary First Moon Landing Apollo XI – July 20, 1994**; 948, **Columbia First Space Shuttle April 12, 1981**.

172 1969 Festival Logo

1994. 25th Anniv of Woodstock Music Festival. Multicoloured.

949	$1.15 Type **172**	1·00	1·00
950	$1.50 1994 anniversary festival logo	1·25	1·25

173 Sea Fan

1995. Marine Life. Multicoloured.

951	$1 Type **173**	60	50
952	$1.15 Sea lily	70	60
953	$1.50 Sea pen	90	1·00
954	$3.45 Sea fern	2·00	3·00
MS955	88×96 mm. $4.50 Sea rose	3·00	4·00

174 Marilyn Monroe

1995. Centenary of Cinema. Portraits of Marilyn Monroe (film star). Multicoloured.

956	$1.15 Type **174**	60	85
957	$1.15 Puckering lips	60	85
958	$1.15 Laughing in brown evening dress and earrings	60	85
959	$1.15 Wearing red earrings	60	85
960	$1.15 In brown dress without earrings	60	85
961	$1.15 With white boa	60	85
962	$1.15 In red dress	60	85
963	$1.15 Wearing white jumper	60	85
964	$1.15 Looking over left shoulder	60	85
MS965	102×132 mm. $6 With Elvis Presley (50×56 mm)	3·25	5·00

175 Jesse Owens (USA)

1995. Fifth International Amateur Athletic Federation Games, Göteborg. Sheet 181×103 mm, containing T **175** and similar vert designs.

MS966	$1.50 black and pink (Type **175**); $1.50 black and orange (Eric Lemming (Sweden)); $1.50 black and yellow (Rudolf Harbig (Germany)); $1.50 black and green (young Montserrat athletes)	4·50	6·00

176 Atmospheric Sounding Experiments using V2 Rockets

1995. 50th Anniv of End of Second World War. Scientific Achievements. Multicoloured.

967	$1.15 Type **176**	1·00	1·25
968	$1.15 American space shuttle *Challenger*	1·00	1·25
969	$1.15 Nuclear experiment, Chicago, 1942	1·00	1·25
970	$1.15 Calder Hall Atomic Power Station, 1956	1·00	1·25
971	$1.50 Radar-equipped Ju 88G 7a nightfighter	1·90	2·00
972	$1.50 Boeing E6 AWACS aircraft	1·90	2·00
973	$1.50 Gloster G.41 Meteor Mk III jet fighter	1·90	2·00
974	$1.50 Concorde (airliner)	1·90	2·00

177 Ears of Wheat ("Food")

1995. 50th Anniv of United Nations. Multicoloured.

975	$1.15 Type **177**	90	75
976	$1.50 Open book ("Education")	1·25	1·00
977	$2.30 P.T. class ("Health")	1·75	2·25
978	$3 Dove ("Peace")	2·25	3·50
MS979	105×75 mm. $6 Scales ("Justice")	3·75	6·00

178 Headquarters Building

1995. 25th Anniv of Montserrat National Trust. Multicoloured.

980	$1.15 Type **178**	80	75
981	$1.50 17th-century cannon, Bransby Point	1·25	1·00
982	$2.30 Impression of Galways Sugar Mill (vert)	2·25	2·50
983	$3 Great Alps Falls (vert)	5·00	6·00

1995. 25th Anniv of Air Recording Studios. No. 713 surch **air 25TH ANNIVERSARY 1970 - 1995.**

984	$2.30+$5 Air Recording Studios	3·00	5·00

The $5 premium on No. 984 was for relief following a volcanic eruption.

180 Bull Shark

1996. Scavengers of the Sea. Multicoloured.

985	$1 Type **180**	80	70
986	$1.15 Sea mouse	90	80
987	$1.50 Bristleworm	1·25	1·50
988	$3.45 Prawn *Xiphocaris*	2·50	3·50
MS989	69×95 mm. $4.50 Man of war fish	3·00	4·00

181 Marconi and Radio Equipment, 1901

1996. Centenary of Radio. Multicoloured.

990	$1.15 Type **181**	90	80
991	$1.50 Marconi's steam yacht *Elettra*	1·25	1·00
992	$2.30 Receiving first Transatlantic radio message, Newfoundland, 1901	1·75	2·25
993	$3 Imperial Airways airplane at Croydon Airport, 1920	2·25	3·50
MS994	74×105 mm. $4.50 Radio telescope, Jodrell Bank	3·00	4·00

182 Paul Masson (France) (Cycling)

1996. Olympic Games, Atlanta. Gold Medal Winners of 1896. Multicoloured.

995	$1.15 Type **182**	1·25	80
996	$1.50 Robert Garrett (USA) (Discus)	1·25	1·00
997	$2.30 Spyridon Louis (Greece) (Marathon)	1·50	1·75
998	$3 John Boland (Great Britain) (Tennis)	2·00	3·25

183 James Dean

1996. James Dean (film star) Commemoration. Multicoloured.

999	$1.15 Type **183**	50	70
1000	$1.15 Wearing stetson facing right	50	70
1001	$1.15 Wearing blue sweater	50	70
1002	$1.15 Wearing black sweater	50	70
1003	$1.15 Full face portrait wearing stetson	50	70
1004	$1.15 Wearing fawn jacket	50	70
1005	$1.15 Wearing red wind-cheater	50	70
1006	$1.15 Smoking a cigarette	50	70
1007	$1.15 In open-necked shirt and green jumper	50	70
MS1008	169×133 mm. $6 As No. 1000 (51×57 mm)	3·25	5·00

184 Leprechaun

1996. Mythical Creatures. Multicoloured.

1009	5c. Type **184**	10	50
1010	10c. Pegasus	10	50
1011	15c. Griffin	15	50
1012	20c. Unicorn	20	50
1013	25c. Gnomes	25	50
1014	40c. Mermaid	40	60
1015	55c. Cockatrice	50	30
1016	70c. Fairy	65	40
1017	90c. Goblin	80	50
1018	$1 Faun	90	55
1019	$1.15 Dragon	1·00	65
1020	$1.50 Giant	1·25	85
1021	$3 Elves	2·00	2·50
1022	$5 Centaur	3·25	4·00
1023	$7.50 Phoenix	4·75	7·00
1024	$10 Erin	5·50	7·50

185 Blue and Green Teddybears

1996. Jerry Garcia of the Grateful Dead (rock group) Commemoration. Multicoloured.

1025	$1.15 Type **185**	1·00	1·00
1026	$1.15 Green and yellow teddybears	1·00	1·00
1027	$1.15 Brown and pink teddybears	1·00	1·00
1028	$6 Jerry Garcia (37×50 mm)	5·50	5·50

Nos. 1025/7 were printed together, *se-tenant*, forming a composite design.

186 Turkey Vulture

1997. Scavengers of the Sky. Multicoloured.

1029	$1 Type **186**	85	70
1030	$1.15 American crow	1·00	70
1031	$1.50 Great skua	1·50	1·50
1032	$3.45 Black-legged kittiwake ('Kittiwake')	2·50	4·00
MS1033	74×95 mm. $4.50 King vulture	3·50	4·50

1997. HONG KONG '97 International Stamp Exhibition. Nos. 1025/7 optd HONG KONG '97.

1034	$1.15 Type **185**	70	1·00
1035	$1.15 Green and yellow teddybears	70	1·00
1036	$1.15 Brown and pink teddybears	70	1·00

1997. PACIFIC '97 International Stamp Exhibition, San Francisco. Nos. 999/1007 optd **PACIFIC 97 World Philatelic Exhibition San Francisco, California 29 May - 8 June.**

1037	$1.15 Type **183**	60	80
1038	$1.15 Wearing stetson facing right	60	80
1039	$1.15 Wearing blue sweater	60	80
1040	$1.15 Wearing black sweater	60	80
1041	$1.15 Full-face portrait wearing stetson	60	80
1042	$1.15 Wearing fawn jacket	60	80
1043	$1.15 Wearing red wind-cheater	60	80
1044	$1.15 Smoking a cigarette	60	80
1045	$1.15 In open-necked shirt and green jumper	60	80

189 Heavy Ash Eruption over Plymouth, 1995

1997. Eruption of Soufriere Volcano. Multicoloured.

1046	$1.50 Type **189**	1·40	1·60
1047	$1.50 Burning rock flow entering sea	1·40	1·60
1048	$1.50 Double venting at Castle Peak	1·40	1·60
1049	$1.50 Mangrove cuckoo	1·40	1·60
1050	$1.50 Lava flow at night, 1996	1·40	1·60
1051	$1.50 Antillean crested hummingbird	1·40	1·60
1052	$1.50 Ash cloud over Plymouth	1·40	1·60
1053	$1.50 Lava spine, 1996	1·40	1·60
1054	$1.50 Burning rock flows forming new land	1·40	1·60

190 Elvis Presley

1997. Rock Legends. Multicoloured.

1055	$1.15 Type **190**	1·75	1·40
1056	$1.15 Jimi Hendrix	1·75	1·40
1057	$1.15 Jerry Garcia	1·75	1·40
1058	$1.15 Janis Joplin	1·75	1·40

191 Untitled Painting by Frama

1997. Frama Exhibition at Guggenheim Museum, New York.

1059	**191** $1.50 multicoloured	1·00	1·25

1997. No. 1028 surch $1.50.

1060	$1.50 on $6 on $6 Jerry Garcia (37×50 mm)	2·25	2·50

193 Prickly Pear

1998. Medicinal Plants. Multicoloured.

1061	$1 Type **193**	65	50
1062	$1.15 Pomme coolie	70	55
1063	$1.50 Aloe	85	90
1064	$3.45 Bird pepper	1·75	2·50

194 Eva and Juan Peron (Argentine politicians)

1998. Famous People of the 20th Century. Multicoloured

1065	$1.15 Type **194**	1·50	1·50
1066	$1.15 Pablo Picasso (painter)	1·50	1·50
1067	$1.15 Wernher von Braun (space scientist)	1·50	1·50
1068	$1.15 David Ben Gurion (Israeli statesman)	2·25	2·25
1069	$1.15 Jean Henri Dunant (founder of Red Cross)	1·50	1·50
1070	$1.15 Dwight Eisenhower (President of USA)	1·50	1·50
1071	$1.15 Mahatma Gandhi (leader of Indian Independence movement)	2·25	2·25
1072	$1.15 King Leopold III and Queen Astrid of Belgium	1·50	1·50
1073	$1.15 Grand Duchess Charlotte and Prince Felix of Luxembourg	1·50	1·50
1074	$1.50 Charles Augustus Lindbergh (pioneer aviator)	1·50	1·50
1075	$1.50 Mao Tse-tung (Chinese communist leader)	1·50	1·50
1076	$1.50 Earl Mountbatten (last Viceroy of India)	2·25	2·25
1077	$1.50 Konrad Adenauer (German statesman)	1·50	1·50
1078	$1.50 Anne Frank (Holocaust victim)	2·25	2·25
1079	$1.50 Queen Wilhelmina of the Netherlands	1·50	1·50

1080	$1.50 King George VI of Great Britain	1·50	1·50
1081	$1.50 King Christian X of Denmark	1·50	1·50
1082	$1.50 King Haakon VII and Crown Prince Olav of Norway	1·50	1·50
1083	$1.50 King Alfonso XIII of Spain	1·50	1·50
1084	$1.50 King Gustavus V of Sweden	1·50	1·50
MS1085	115×63 mm. $3 John F. Kennedy (Resident of USA) (50×32 mm)	2·00	2·75

195 Jerry Garcia

1998. Rock Music Legends. Multicoloured

(a) Jerry Garcia

1086	$1.15 In long-sleeved blue shirt	1·10	1·25
1087	$1.15 With drum kit in background	1·10	1·25
1088	$1.15 Type **195**	1·10	1·25
1089	$1.15 Wearing long-sleeved black t-shirt	1·10	1·25
1090	$1.15 Close-up with left hand in foreground	1·10	1·25
1091	$1.15 With purple and black background	1·10	1·25
1092	$1.15 Holding microphone	1·10	1·25
1093	$1.15 In short-sleeved blue t-shirt	1·10	1·25
1094	$1.15 In sunglasses with cymbal in background	1·10	1·25
1095	$1.15 Pointing (green)	1·10	1·25

(b) Bob Marley. Predominant colour for each design given.

1096	$1.15 Wearing neck chain (green)	1·10	1·25
1097	$1.15 Singing into microphone (green)	1·10	1·25
1098	$1.15 Singing with eyes closed (yellow)	1·10	1·25
1099	$1.15 Facing audience (yellow)	1·10	1·25
1100	$1.15 In striped t-shirt with fingers on chin (red)	1·10	1·25
1101	$1.15 In Rastafarian hat (red)	1·10	1·25
1102	$1.15 In striped t-shirt with hand closed (red)	1·10	1·25
MS1103	152×101 mm. $5 Jerry Garcia (50×75 mm)	3·00	3·75

196 Ash Eruption from Soufriere Hills Volcano

1998. Total Eclipse of the Sun. Multicoloured.

1104	$1.15 Type **196**	2·00	1·50
1105	$1.15 Volcano emitting black cloud	2·00	1·50
1106	$1.15 Village below volcano	2·00	1·50
1107	$1.15 Lava flow and wrecked house	2·00	1·50
MS1108	152×102 mm. $6 Solar eclipse (vert)	8·00	8·50

197 Princess Diana on Wedding Day, 1981

1998. Diana, Princess of Wales Commemoration. Multicoloured.

1109	$1.15 Type **197**	1·50	70
1110	$1.50 Accepting bouquet from children	1·75	1·10
1111	$3 At Royal Ascot	3·00	4·00
MS1112	133×100 mm. $6 Diana and "Princess of Wales" rose (50×37 mm)	5·50	5·50

1998. 19th World Scout Jamboree, Chile. Nos. 669/72 optd **19th WORLD JAMBOREE MONDIAL CHILE 1999** and emblem.

1113	20c. Type **117**	30	40
1114	20c. Girl Guide saluting	30	40
1115	75c. Lady Baden-Powell	70	1·00
1116	75c. Guide assisting in old people's home	70	1·00

199 Jerry Garcia

1999. Jerry Garcia (rock musician) Commemoration. Multicoloured

1117	$1.15 Type **199**	90	1·00
1118	$1.15 In front of drum kit (violet background)	90	1·00
1119	$1.15 Singing into microphone	90	1·00
1120	$1.15 Playing guitar, facing right (vert)	90	1·00
1121	$1.15 Singing with eyes closed (vert)	90	1·00
1122	$1.15 Singing in white spotlight (vert)	90	1·00
1123	$1.15 In front of drum kit (green background)	90	1·00
1124	$1.15 In long-sleeved black shirt	90	1·00
1125	$1.15 In red shirt	90	1·00
1126	$1.15 In short-sleeved black t-shirt (without frame) (vert)	90	1·00
1127	$1.15 In blue t-shirt (oval frame) (vert)	90	1·00
1128	$1.15 In short-sleeved black t-shirt (oval frame) (vert)	90	1·00
MS1129	Two sheets. (a) 115×153 mm. $6 Jerry Garcia in concert (50×75 mm). (b) 153×115 mm. $6 Singing into microphone (75×50 mm) Set of 2 sheets	8·00	10·00

1999. iBRA '99 International Stamp Exhibition, Nuremberg. Nos. 975/6 optd **iBRA INTERNATIONALE BRIEFMARKEN WELTAUSSTELLUNG NURNBERG 27.4.-4.5.99.**

1130	$1.15 Type **177**	2·25	1·75
1131	$1.50 Open book ("Education")	2·25	2·50

201 Mango

1999. Tropical Caribbean Fruits. Multicoloured.

1132	$1.15 Type **201**	85	70
1133	$1.50 Breadfruit	1·00	85
1134	$2.30 Papaya	1·60	1·60
1135	$3 Lime	2·00	2·50
1136	$6 Akee	3·75	6·00
MS1137	134×95 mm. Nos. 1132/6	10·00	12·00

202 Yorkshire Terrier

1999. Dogs. Each black.

1138	70c. Type **202**	2·00	90
1139	$1 Welsh corgi	2·25	1·00
1140	$1.15 King Charles spaniel	2·50	1·00
1141	$1.50 Poodle	2·75	1·50
1142	$3 Beagle	4·50	8·00
MS1143	133×95 mm. Nos. 1138/42	12·50	13·00

203 Pupil's Equipment and World Map

1999. World Teachers' Day. Multicoloured.

1144	$1 Type **203**	2·00	90
1145	$1.15 Teacher and class	2·00	90
1146	$1.50 Emblems of vocational training	2·25	1·50
1147	$5 Scientific equipment	6·50	9·50

204 Great Hammerhead Shark

1999. Endangered Species. Great Hammerhead Shark. Multicoloured.

1148	50c. Type **204**	85	1·00
1149	50c. Two hammerhead sharks among fish	85	1·00
1150	50c. Two hammerhead sharks on sea-bed	85	1·00
1151	50c. Three hammerhead sharks	85	1·00

205 Flowers

2000. New Millennium.

1152	**205** $1.50 multicoloured	2·75	2·75

206 Alfred Valentine

2000. West Indies Cricket Tour and 100th Test Match at Lord's. Multicoloured.

1153	$1 Type **206**	2·50	1·00
1154	$5 George Headley batting	5·50	6·50
MS1155	119×101 mm. $6 Lord's Cricket Ground (horiz)	8·00	9·00

207 Spitfire Squadron taking-off

2000. The Stamp Show 2000 International Stamp Exhibition, London. 60th Anniv of Battle of Britain. Multicoloured.

1156	70c. Type **207**	1·00	50
1157	$1.15 Overhauling Hurricane Mk I	1·25	65
1158	$1.50 Hurricane MK I attacking	1·50	1·25
1159	$5 Flt. Lt. Frank Howell's Spitfire Mk IA	3·50	5·50
MS1160	110×87 mm. $6 Hawker Hurricane	4·50	5·50

208 Statue of Liberty and Carnival Scene

2000. New Millennium. Landmarks. Each including carnival scene. Multicoloured.

1161	90c. Type **208**	75	50
1162	$1.15 Great Wall of China	95	60
1163	$1.50 Eiffel Tower	1·25	1·25
1164	$3.50 Millennium Dome	2·50	4·00

209 Queen Elizabeth the Queen Mother and W.H. Bramble Airport

2000. Queen Elizabeth the Queen Mother's 100th Birthday. Each showing different portrait. Multicoloured

1165	70c. Type **209**	85	40
1166	$1.15 Government House	1·25	65
1167	$3 Court House	2·50	3·00
1168	$6 War Memorial Clock Tower	4·50	6·00
MS1169	120×75 mm. Nos. 1165/8	8·00	9·50

210 Three Wise Men following Star

2000. Christmas. Multicoloured.

1170	$1 Type **210**	1·00	55
1171	$1.15 Cavalla Hill Methodist Church	1·10	65
1172	$1.50 Shepherds with flocks	1·25	85
1173	$3 Mary and Joseph arriving at Bethlehem	2·25	4·25
MS1174	105×75 mm. $6 As $3	4·50	6·00

211 Golden Swallow

2001. Caribbean Birds. Multicoloured.

1175	$1 Type **211**	1·25	65
1176	$1.15 Crested quail dove (horiz)	1·40	75
1177	$1.50 Red-legged thrush (horiz)	1·50	1·10
1178	$5 Fernandina's flicker	4·25	6·00
MS1179	95×68 mm. $8 St. Vincent amazon (horiz)	9·00	9·50

212 Edward Stanley Gibbons, Charles J. Phillips and 391 Strand Shop

2001. Famous Stamp Personalities. Multicoloured.

1180	$1 Type **212**	1·75	1·00
1181	$1.15 John Lister and Montserrat stamps	1·75	1·00
1182	$1.50 Theodore Champion and French postilion	2·00	1·50
1183	$3 Thomas De La Rue and De La Rue's stand at Great Exhibition, 1851	3·25	5·00
MS1184	95×68 mm. $8 Sir Rowland Hill and Bruce Castle	6·50	8·50

213 Princess Elizabeth at International Horse Show, 1950

2001. Queen Elizabeth II's 75th Birthday. Multicoloured.

1185	90c. Type **213**	1·25	60
1186	$1.15 Queen Elizabeth II, 1986	1·40	75
1187	$1.50 Queen Elizabeth II, 1967	1·60	1·40
1188	$5 Queen Elizabeth, 1976	4·75	5·50
MS1189	90×68 mm. $6 Queen Elizabeth, 2000	7·00	8·00

214 Look Out Village

2001. Reconstruction. Multicoloured.

1190	70c. Type **214**	80	60
1191	$1 St. John's Hospital	1·00	65
1192	$1.15 Tropical Mansions Suites Hotel	1·10	70
1193	$1.50 Montserrat Secondary School	1·40	1·25
1194	$3 Golden Years Care Home	3·00	5·00

215 West Indian Cherry

2001. Caribbean Fruits. Multicoloured.

1195	5c. Type **215**	40	70
1196	10c. Mammee apple	40	70
1197	15c. Lime	45	70
1198	20c. Grapefruit	45	70
1199	25c. Orange	45	70
1200	40c. Passion fruit	60	50

1201	55c. Banana	70	40
1202	70c. Pawpaw	90	50
1203	90c. Pomegranate	1·00	70
1204	$1 Guava	1·10	75
1205	$1.15 Mango	1·25	75
1206	$1.50 Sugar apple	1·50	1·10
1207	$3 Cashew	2·75	3·00
1208	$5 Soursop	4·50	5·50
1209	$7.50 Watermelon	7·00	9·00
1210	$10 Pineapple	8·00	9·50

216 Common Long-tail Skipper (butterfly)

2001. Caribbean Butterflies. Multicoloured.

1211	$1 Type **216**	1·10	60
1212	$1.15 Straight-line sulphur	1·25	70
1213	$1.50 Giant hairstreak	1·50	1·25
1214	$3 Monarch	2·50	4·00
MS1215	115×115 mm. $10 Painted Lady	8·50	11·00

The overall design of No. **MS**1215 is butterfly-shaped.

217 Alpine Skiing

2002. Winter Olympic Games, Salt Lake City. Multicoloured

1216	$3 Type **217**	2·25	2·75
1217	$5 Four man bobsleigh	3·25	4·25

218 Sergeant Major (fish)

2002. Fish of the Caribbean. Multicoloured.

1218	$1 Type **218**	1·25	60
1219	$1.15 Mutton snapper	1·40	70
1220	$1.50 Lantern bass	1·75	1·25
1221	$5 Shy Hamlet	6·00	7·50
MS1222	102×70 mm. $8 Queen angelfish	9·00	10·00

2002. Queen Elizabeth the Queen Mother Commemoration. Nos. 1165/8 optd **Life and Death of Her Majesty Queen Elizabeth The Queen Mother 1900 2002.**

1223	70c. Type **209**	70	55
1224	$1.15 Government House	1·00	70
1225	$3 Court House	2·75	3·00
1226	$6 War Memorial Clock Tower	4·75	6·00

220 *Allamanda cathartica*

2002. Wild Flowers. Multicoloured.

1227	70c. Type **220**	85	55
1228	$1.15 *Lantana camara*	1·25	70
1229	$1.50 *Leonotis nepetifolia*	1·50	1·25
1230	$5 *Plumeria rubra*	5·00	6·50
MS1231	105×75 mm. $8 *Alpinia purpurata*	8·00	9·50

221 Queen Elizabeth II wearing Imperial State

2003. 50th Anniv of Coronation. Two sheets containing vert designs as T **221**. Multicoloured.

MS1232	153×85 mm. $3 Type **221**; $3 St. Edward's Crown; $3 Queen wearing diadem and blue sash	7·00	8·00
MS1233	105×75 mm. $6 Queen wearing Imperial State Crown and Coronation robes	4·50	5·00

222 *Wright Flyer II* (blue)

2003. Centenary of Powered Flight. Multicoloured.

MS1234	116×125 mm. $2 Type **222**; $2 *Wright Flyer II* (brown); $2 Orville and Wilbur Wright; $2 *Wright Flyer I*	6·00	6·50
MS1235	106×76 mm. $6 *Wright Flyer II*	6·00	6·50

223 Prince William Crown and Coronation Robes

2003. 21st Birthday of Prince William of Wales. Different portraits. Multicoloured.

MS1236	155×85 mm. $3 Type **223**; $3 Prince William (frame incomplete at bottom left); $3 Prince William (frame complete at bottom left)	7·00	8·00
MS1237	106×76 mm. $6 Prince William	5·50	6·00

224 Piping Frog

2003. Animals of the Caribbean. Multicoloured.

MS1238	145×90 mm. $1.50 Type **224**; $1.50 Land hermit crab; $1.50 Spix's pinche; $1.50 Dwarf Ggecko; $1.50 Green sea turtle; $1.50 Small Indian mongoose	7·50	8·00
MS1239	92×66 mm. $6 Sally lightfoot crab	7·00	7·00

225 *Lactarius trivialis*

2003. Mushrooms of the World. Multicoloured.

MS1240	145×90 mm. $1.50 Type **225**; $1.50 *Gomphidius roseus*; $1.50 *Lycoperdon pyriforme*; $1.50 *Hygrophorus coccineus*; $1.50 *Russula xerampelina*; $1.50 *Gomphus floccosus*	8·00	9·00
MS1241	92×66 mm. $6 *Amanita muscaria*	5·50	6·00

226 Belted Kingfisher

2003. Birds of the Caribbean. Multicoloured.

1242	90c. Type **226**	1·60	75
1243	$1.15 Yellow warbler	1·75	1·10
1244	$1.50 Hooded warbler	2·25	1·75
1245	$5 Cedar waxwing	7·75	9·00
MS1246	145×90 mm. $1.50 Roseate spoonbill; $1.50 Laughing gull; $1.50 White-tailed tropic bird; $1.50 Bare-eyed thrush; $1.50 Glittering-throated emerald; $1.50 Carib grackle ('Lesser Antillean Grackle')	9·00	9·00
MS1247	92×68 mm. $6 Bananaquit	7·00	7·00

227 Olympic Poster, Los Angeles, 1932

2004. Olympic Games, Athens. Multicoloured.

1248	90c. Type **227**	1·25	70
1249	$1.15 Olympic pin, Munich, 1972	1·50	80
1250	$1.50 Olympic poster, Montreal, 1976	1·75	1·50
1251	$5 Greek art depicting Pankration (horiz)	4·00	6·00

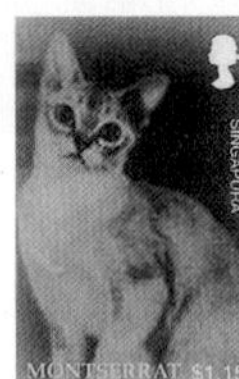
228 Singapura

2004. Cats. Multicoloured.

1252	$1.15 Type **228**	1·50	90
1253	$1.50 Burmese	1·75	1·25
1254	$2 Abyssinian	2·25	2·00
1255	$5 Norwegian	5·50	7·00
MS1256	92×68 mm. $6 Russian blue	6·50	7·50

229 Lace Wing

2004. Butterflies. Multicoloured.

MS1257	125×88 mm. $2.30 Type **229**; $2.30 Swallowtail; $2.30 Shoemaker; $2.30 White peacock	7·00	7·50
MS1258	70×96 mm. $6 Flashing astraptes	5·00	5·50

230 Blue-girdled Angelfish

2004. Fish. Multicoloured.

MS1259	122×93 mm. $2.30 Type **230**; $2.30 Regal angelfish; $2.30 Emperor angelfish; $2.30 Blotch-eye soldierfish	7·50	8·00
MS1260	70×96 mm. $6 Banded butterflyfish	5·00	5·50

231 Austerity Steam Locomotive

2004. Bicentenary of Steam Locomotives. Multicoloured.

MS1261	159×120 mm. $1.50 Type **231**; $1.50 Deli Vasut No. 109.109; $1.50 Class 424 No. 424.247/287; $1.50 L1646; $1.50 No. 324.1564; $1.50 Class 204	7·00	7·50
MS1262	119×159 mm. $2 375.562 Old Class TV; $2 Class Va 7111; $2 Class 424 No. 424.009; $2 Class III No. 269	6·00	6·50
MS1263	92×106 mm. $6 Class QR1 No. 3038	6·00	6·50

232 AIDS Ribbon

2004. World AIDS Day. Sheet 123×95 mm.

MS1264	$3 **232**×4 multicoloured	8·00	10·00

233 National Football Team

2004. Centenary of FIFA (Federation Internationale de Football Association).

1265	**233**	$6 multicoloured	5·00	6·50

234 Start of Air Assault

2004. 60th Anniv of D-Day Landings. Multicoloured.

1266	$1.15 Type **234**	2·00	1·00
1267	$1.50 Soldiers landing on Normandy beaches	2·50	1·50
1268	$2 Field Marshall Montgomery	3·00	3·00
1269	$5 HMS *Belfast*	7·50	9·00

2005. Royal Visit. Nos. 1190/4 optd **THE VISIT OF HRH PRINCESS ROYAL FEBRUARY 2005.**

1270	70c. Look Out Village	1·50	1·00
1271	$1 St John's Hospital	2·00	1·50
1272	$1.15 Tropical Mansions Suites Hotel	2·00	1·50
1273	$1.50 Montserrat Secondary School	2·50	2·00
1274	$3 Golden Years Care Home	4·50	6·00

236 *Cattleya lueddemanniana*

2005. Orchids. Multicoloured.

MS1275	140×105 mm. $2.30×4, Type **236**; *Cattleya luteola*; *Cattleya trianaei*; *Cattleya mossiae*	7·50	8·00
MS1276	100×70 mm. $6 *Cattleya mendelii*	6·00	6·50

237 Brown Pelican

2005. Seabirds. Multicoloured.

MS1277	140×105 mm. $2.30×4, Type **237**; Red-billed tropic bird; Galapagos Island cormorant; Waved albatross	9·00	9·00
MS1278	100×70 mm. $6 Common tern	8·00	8·00

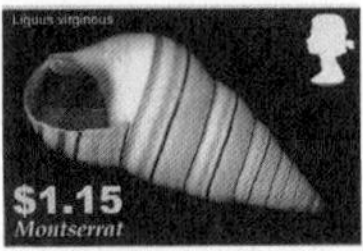

238 *Liguus virgineus*

2005. Molluscs. Multicoloured.

1279	$1.15 Type **238**	2·00	1·00
1280	$1.50 *Liguus fasciatus testudineus*	2·50	1·50
1281	$2 *Liguus fasciatus*	3·00	3·00
1282	$5 *Cerion striatella*	8·00	10·00
MS1283	70×100 mm. $6 *Liguus fasciatus* (vert)	8·00	9·00

239 Soufriere Hills Volcano

2005. Tenth Anniv of the Eruption of Soufrière Hills Volcano. Sheet, 146×116 mm, containing T **239** and similar horiz designs. Multicoloured.

MS1284	$2×9, Type **239**; Explosion; Tar River Delta; Belham River; Montserrat Volcano Observatory building; Pyroclastic flow; Blackburne airport, destroyed in 1997; Maintenance and monitoring helicopter; Instruments used for monitoring volcano	22·00	24·00

240 Shamrock

2005. Centenary of Rotary International. Multicoloured designs.

1285	$1 Type **240**	1·50	90
1286	$1.15 *Heliconia* (National Flower)	1·75	1·00
1287	$1.50 The lady and the harp	2·25	2·00

1288 $5 Map of Montserrat 8·00 9·50
MS1289 100×70 mm. $6 Immunising children (horiz) 6·50 8·50

241 Napoleon Bonaparte

2005. Bicentenary of the Battle of Trafalgar. Multicoloured.

1290	$2 Type **241**	4·00	4·00
1291	$2 Admiral Lord Nelson (seated)	4·00	4·00
1292	$2 Battle of the Nile, 1798	4·00	4·00
1293	$2 Battle of Trafalgar, 1805	4·00	4·00
MS1294	109×70 mm. $6 Admiral Lord Nelson	12·00	12·00

242 Patricia Griffin (voluntary social worker)

2005. Local Personalities. Multicoloured.

1295	$1.15 Type **242**	1·25	1·50
1296	$1.15 Michael Simmons Osborne (merchant/ parliamentarian)	1·25	1·50
1297	$1.15 Lilian Cadogan (nurse)	1·25	1·50
1298	$1.15 Samuel Aymer (folk musician)	1·25	1·50
1299	$1.15 William Henry Bramble (first Chief Minister)	1·25	1·50
1300	$1.15 Robert William Griffith (trade union pioneer)	1·25	1·50
MS1301	100×115 mm. Nos. 1295/1300	6·75	8·00

243 *Thumbelina*

2005. Birth Bicentenary of Hans Christian Andersen (writer). Multicoloured.

1302	$3 Type **243**	2·75	3·50
1303	$3 *The Flying Trunk*	2·75	3·50
1304	$3 *The Buckwheat*	2·75	3·50
MS1305	100×70 mm. $6 *The Little Mermaid* (49×38 mm)	6·00	7·00

2006. 30th Anniv of the Philatelic Bureau. Nos. 1175, 1212/13, 1227 and 1230 optd **30th ANNIVERSARY OF THE PHILATELIC BUREAU 1976–2006.**

1306	70c. Type **220**	75	55
1307	$1 Type **211**	1·00	85
1308	$1.15 Straight-line sulphur	1·25	90
1309	$1.50 Giant hairstreak	1·50	1·50
1310	$5 *Plumeria rubra*	5·00	6·50

245 Cecropia Moth

2006. Moths and Butterflies of the World. Multicoloured.

1311	$2.30 Type **245**	4·00	4·50
1312	$2.30 Madagascan sunset moth	4·00	4·50
1313	$2.30 Peacock butterfly	4·00	4·50
1314	$2.30 Zodiac moth	4·00	4·50
MS1315	96×76 mm. $6 White-lined sphinx moth	7·00	8·00

No. 1313 is wrongly inscr "GREAT PEACOCK MOTH *Saturnia pyri*".

246 Giant Caribbean Anemone

2006. Caribbean "Sea Flowers". Multicoloured.

1316	$2.30 Type **246**	3·00	3·75
1317	$2.30 Beadlet anemone	3·00	3·75
1318	$2.30 Golden crinoid	3·00	3·75
1319	$2.30 Oval cup coral	3·00	3·75
MS1320	96×78 mm. $6 Tube-dwelling anemone	6·50	8·00

247 Doberman (inscr Rottweiller)

2006. Dogs. Multicoloured.

1321	$1.15 Type **247**	2·25	1·25
1322	$1.50 Boxer	2·50	1·75
1323	$2 Corgi	3·25	3·25
1324	$5 Great Dane	7·00	8·50
MS1325	96×78 mm. $6 St. Bernard	8·00	8·50

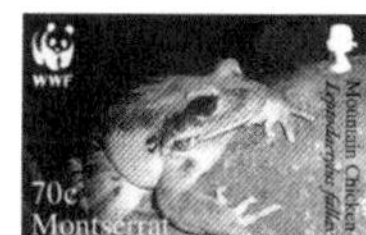

248 "Mountain Chicken"

2006. Endangered Species. "Mountain Chicken" (frog, *Leptodactylus fallax*). Multicoloured.

1326	70c. Type **248**	55	75
1327	$1 In close-up	80	1·00
1328	$1.15 Back view	95	1·25
1329	$1.50 Facing left	1·25	1·40
MS1330	102×152 mm. Nos. 1326/9, each ×2	6·50	8·00

249 World Cup Stadium, Hanover, Germany, 2006

2006. World Cup Football Championship, Germany. Sheet 127×102 mm containing T **249** and similar horiz designs. Multicoloured.
MS1331 $1.15 Type **249**; $1.50 Sir Stanley Matthews; $2 Sir William Ralph "Dixie" Dean; $3 Bobby Moore 8·50 9·50

250 Queen Elizabeth II at Coronation, 1953

2006. 80th Birthday of Queen Elizabeth II. Multicoloured.

1332	$2.30 Type **250**	1·75	2·00
1333	$2.30 Queen Elizabeth wearing crown, *c.* 1977	1·75	2·00
1334	$2.30 Wearing tiara, *c.* 1980	1·75	2·00
1335	$2.30 Wearing tiara, *c.* 2002	1·75	2·00
MS1336	120×120 mm. $8 Wearing tiara and pearl drop earrings, *c.* 2002	6·00	7·50

251 Replica of Columbus's Fleet

2006. 500th Death Anniv of Christopher Columbus. Multicoloured.

1337	$1.15 Type **251**	1·75	1·00
1338	$1.50 Columbus and map showing voyage to New World	2·50	1·50
1339	$2 Sailing ships, globe and Columbus	3·00	3·00
1340	$5 Christopher Columbus (vert)	6·00	8·50
MS1341	100×70 mm. $6 Columbus and his crew in New World (vert)	6·50	7·50

252 Boy Scouts and Bird of Paradise Flower

2007. Centenary of Scouting. Multicoloured.

1342	$2 Type **252**	2·25	2·25
1343	$2 Scouts working in damaged building	2·25	2·25
1344	$2 Scouts sailing dinghy	2·25	2·25
1345	$2 Scout bottle-feeding kid	2·25	2·25
1346	$2 Scout gathering firewood	2·25	2·25
1347	$2 Scouts putting up bird nestbox	2·25	2·25
MS1348	100×70 mm. $6 Lord Baden-Powell (founder) (vert)	6·00	7·00

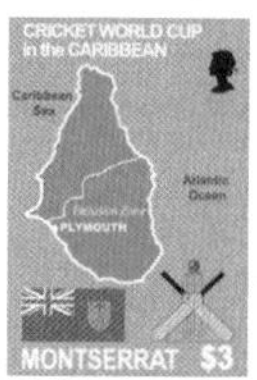

253 Montserrat Flag and Outline Map

2007. World Cup Cricket, West Indies. Multicoloured.

1349	$3 Type **253**	5·00	4·25
1350	$5 Cricket team (horiz)	8·00	9·00
MS1351	117×90 mm. $8 World Cup Cricket emblem	11·00	12·00

254 *Euphorbia pulcherrima* (poinsettia)

2007. Flowers. Multicoloured.

1352	10c. Type **254**	25	50
1353	30c. *Catharanthus roseus* (periwinkle)	60	65
1354	35c. *Bougainvillea glabra*	65	65
1355	50c. *Ixora macrothyrsa*	90	65
1356	70c. *Heliconia humilis*	1·25	75
1357	80c. *Ipomoea learii* (morning glory)	1·25	80
1358	90c. *Delonix regia* (poinciana)	1·25	80
1359	$1 *Solandra nitida* (cup of gold)	1·40	85
1360	$1.10 *Acalypha hispida* (chenille plant)	1·40	90
1361	$1.50 *Nerium oleander*	2·00	1·40
1362	$2.25 *Hibiscus rosa-sinensis*	2·75	2·75
1363	$2.50 *Plumeria acuminata* (frangipani)	2·75	3·00
1364	$2.75 *Strelitzia reginae* (bird of paradise flower)	3·00	3·25
1365	$5 *Stephanotis floribunda* (Madagascar jasmine)	5·50	6·00
1366	$10 *Tabebuia serratifolia* (yellow poui)	9·00	11·00
1367	$20 Rosa 'Bucbi'	15·00	19·00

255 Hawksbill Turtle

2007. Turtles of Montserrat. Multicoloured.
MS1368 130×100 mm. $3.40×4 Type **255**; Green turtle; Leatherback turtle; Loggerhead turtle 10·50 10·50
MS1369 100×70 mm. $7 Kemp's Ridley sea turtle 7·00 7·50

The stamps and margins of No. **MS**1368 form a composite design.

256 Diana, Princess of Wales

2007. Tenth Death Anniv of Diana, Princess of Wales. Multicoloured.

1370	$3.40 Type **256**	3·75	3·75
1371	$3.40 Wearing black dress	3·75	3·75
1372	$3.40 Wearing white dress	3·75	3·75
1373	$3.40 Wearing white jacket with stand-up collar	3·75	3·75
MS1374	100×70 mm. $7 Black/white photograph	7·00	8·00

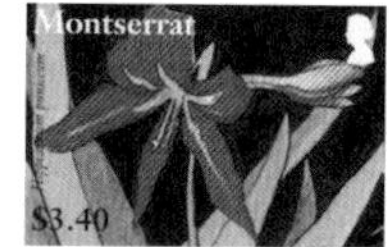

257 *Hippeastrum puniceum*

2007. Lilies of Montserrat. Multicoloured.
MS1375 130×100 mm. $3.40×4 Type **257**; *Hymenocallis caribaea*; *Zephyranthespuertoricensis*; *Belamcanda chinensis* 10·00 11·00
MS1376 100×70 mm. $7 *Crinum erubescens* (vert) 8·00 8·50

The stamps and margins of No. **MS**1375 form a composite background design of Lily foliage.

258 Green-winged Macaw

2007. Parrots of the Caribbean. Multicoloured.

1377	$3.40 Type **258**	3·75	3·75
1378	$3.40 Mitred conure	3·75	3·75
1379	$3.40 Sun conure	3·75	3·75
1380	$3.40 Blue-and-yellow macaw	3·75	3·75
MS1381	100×70 mm. $7 Hyacinth macaw	8·50	8·50

259 Charles Wesley

2007. 300th Birth Anniv of Charles Wesley (founder of Methodism). Multicoloured.

1382	$2.50 Type **259**	2·50	2·75
1383	$2.50 Charles Wesley (hands at left)	2·50	2·75
1384	$2.50 Charles Wesley with Bible	2·50	2·75
1385	$2.50 Bethany Methodist Church	2·50	2·75

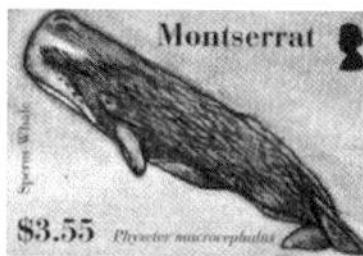

260 Sperm Whale

2008. Whales of the World. Multicoloured.
MS1386 130×100 mm. $3.55×4 Type **260**; Minke whale; Cuvier's beaked whale; Humpback whale 14·00 14·00
MS1387 100×70 mm. $7 Blue whale 9·00 9·00

The stamps and margins of No. **MS**1386 form a composite background design.

261 *Explorer I* atop Launcher *Juno I*, 1958

2008. 50 Years of Space Exploration and Satellites. Multicoloured.

1388	$3.55 Type **261**	3·50	3·75
1389	$3.55 Dr. James Van Allen and *Explorer I*	3·50	3·75
1390	$3.55 *Explorer I*	3·50	3·75
1391	$3.55 Drs. William Pickering, James Van Allen and Wernher von Braun with *Explorer I* model	3·50	3·75

MS1392	100×70 mm. $7 *Explorer I* (horiz)	7·00	8·00

262 African Elephant

2008. Endangered Animals of the World. Multicoloured.

1393	$2.25 Type **262**	3·00	3·00
1394	$2.25 Bald eagle	3·00	3·00
1395	$2.25 Sumatran tiger	3·00	3·00
1396	$2.25 Hawksbill turtle	3·00	3·00
1397	$2.25 Indian rhinoceros	3·00	3·00
1398	$2.25 Western gorilla	3·00	3·00
MS1399	100×70 mm. $7 Rock iguana (horiz)	8·00	8·50

263 First Caribbean Stamp and *Lady McLeod* (early packet ship)

2008. Early Postal History. Multicoloured.

1400	$2.75 Type **263**	3·25	3·25
1401	$2.75 Early Montserrat postcard	3·25	3·25
1402	$2.75 Great Britain Mulready envelopes	3·25	3·25
1403	$2.75 Great Britain Penny Black and Sir Rowland Hill	3·25	3·25
1404	$2.75 Antigua 1d. red and 6d. green stamps overprinted Montserrat, 1876	3·25	3·25
1405	$2.75 Montserrat fleuron and crowned circle handstamps and 'A08' cancellation	3·25	3·25

264 English Electric Lightning F3

2008. 90th Anniv of the Royal Air Force. Multicoloured.

1406	$3.55 Type **264**	4·50	4·50
1407	$3.55 Hurricane IIC	4·50	4·50
1408	$3.55 Jet Provost T3A	4·50	4·50
1409	$3.55 Jaguar TR3A	4·50	4·50
1410	$3.55 Westland Sea King HAR.3 helicopter	4·50	4·50
1411	$3.55 Gloster Javelin FAW9	4·50	4·50
1412	$3.55 P-66 Pembroke C1	4·50	4·50
1413	$3.55 Chinook HC2 helicopter	4·50	4·50

265 University of the West Indies Centre, Montserrat

2008. 60th Anniv of the University of the West Indies. Multicoloured.

1414	$2 Type **265**	4·00	3·00
1415	$5 Scroll	7·00	8·50

266 Common Dolphin

2008. Dolphins of the World. Multicoloured.

1416	$3.55 Type **266**	5·00	5·00
1417	$3.55 Bottlenose dolphin	5·00	5·00
1418	$3.55 Pantropical spotted dolphin	5·00	5·00
1419	$3.55 Long-snouted spinner dolphin	5·00	5·00
MS1420	100×70 mm. $7 Risso's dolphin	8·50	9·00

267 *Cattleya labiata*

2008. Orchids of the Caribbean. Multicoloured.

1421	$2.75 Type **267**	4·00	4·00
1422	$2.75 *Phalaenopsis* cultivar	4·00	4·00
1423	$2.75 *Cymbidium annabelle*	4·00	4·00
1424	$2.75 *Phalaenopsis taisuco*	4·00	4·00
1424a	$2.75 *Phalaenopsis amabilis*	4·00	4·00
1424b	$2.75 *Cattleya aurantiaca*	4·00	4·00
1424c	$2.75 *Phalaenopsis* cultivar	4·00	4·00
1424d	$2.75 *Dendrobium nobile*	4·00	4·00

268 Ox

2009. Chinese New Year (Year of the Ox). Multicoloured, outline colours given.

MS1425	Type **268**; Ox (black) (facing left); Ox (purple-brown); Ox (white) (facing left)	15·00	16·00

269 Martin Luther King

2009. 80th Birth Anniv of Dr. Martin Luther King (civil rights leader). Two sheets, 130×100 mm, containing T **269** and similar multicoloured designs.

MS1426	Type **269**; Sitting in chair; Wearing hat; Mrs. Coretta Scott King	9·00	10·00
MS1427	Crowd of marchers ('March on Washington for Jobs and Freedom'); Martin Luther King meeting Malcolm X, 1964; With Pres. John F. Kennedy and Civil Rights leaders; Waving to crowd ('March on Washington for Jobs and Freedom') (all horiz)	9·00	10·00

270 Smooth-billed Ani (*Crotophaga ani*)

2009. Birds of Montserrat. Multicoloured.

MS1428	100×130 mm. $2.75×4 Type **270**; American kestrel (*Falco sparverius*); Common moorhen (*Gallinula chloropus*); Cattle egret (*Bubulcus ibis*)	19·00	19·00
MS1429	70×100 mm. $7 Male Montserrat oriole (*Icterus oberi*)	12·00	12·00

271 Staghorn Coral (*Actopora cervicornis*)

2009. Coral Reef of the Caribbean. Multicoloured.

1430	$1.10 Type **271**	1·75	1·25
1431	$2.25 Zoanthid coral (*Palythoa caesia*)	2·50	2·50
1432	$2.50 Blade fire coral (*Millepora complanata*)	2·75	3·25
1433	$2.75 Brain coral (*Diploria strigosa*)	3·00	4·00
MS1434	100×70 mm. $7 Orange tube coral (*Tubastrea aurea*)	8·00	8·50

272 Charles Darwin

2009. Birth Bicentenary of Charles Darwin (evolutionary theorist). Multicoloured.

MS1435	$2.75×4 Type **272**; Soldier crab (*Coenobita clypeatus*); Tree lizard (*Anolis lividus*); Endemic orchid (*Epidendrum montserratense*)	17·00	18·00
MS1436	70×100 mm. $7 Charles Darwin and Montserrat Centre Hills Project emblem (horiz)	11·00	12·00

273 Green Iguana (*Iguana iguana*)

2009. Rain Forest Animals of Montserrat. Multicoloured.

MS1437	100×80 mm. $1.10 Type **273**; $2.25 Galliwasp (*Diploglossus montisserrati*); $2.50 Black snake (*Alsophisantillensis manselli*); $2.75 Common agouti (*Dasyprocta leporina*)	15·00	16·00
MS1438	100×70 mm. $5 Yellow-shouldered bat (*Sturnira thomasi vulcanensis*)	8·50	9·00

274 Tamarind Tree (*Tamarindus indica*)

2009. Tropical Trees. Multicoloured.

1439	$1.10 Type **274**	1·75	1·25
1440	$2.25 Dwarf coconut tree (*Cocos nucifera*)	2·50	2·00
1441	$2.50 Breadfruit tree (*Artocarpus altilis*)	2·75	2·50
1442	$2.75 Calabash tree (*Crescentia cujete*)	3·00	3·25
1443	$5 Geiger tree (*Cordia sebestena*)	5·00	7·00

275 HMS *Ark Royal II*

2009. Centenary of Naval Aviation. Aircraft Carriers. Sheet 160×134 mm containing T **275** and similar horiz designs. Multicoloured.

MS1444	70c. Type **275**; $1.10 HMS *Furious*; $2.25 HMS *Argus*; $2.50 HMS *Illustrious*; $2.75 HMS *Ark Royal IV*; $5 HMS *Invincible*	17·00	17·00

276 Snowflake (*Euphorbia leucocephala*)

2009. Christmas. Multicoloured.

1445	$1.10 Type **276**	1·25	70
1446	$2.25 Carnival troupe	1·75	1·25
1447	$2.50 Masquerade	2·00	2·00
1448	$2.75 St. Patrick's Roman Catholic Church	2·25	3·50
MS1449	100×70 mm. $6 Nativity (vert)	5·00	6·00

277 Basket Star

2010. Marine Life. Multicoloured.

1450	$1.10 Type **277**	2·00	1·25
1451	$2.25 Spiny lobster	2·75	2·25
1452	$2.50 Spotted drum	3·00	2·75
1453	$2.75 Sea anemone (vert)	3·25	3·25
1454	$5 Batwing coral crab	5·50	7·00

278 Jin Mao Tower at Night, Shanghai, China

2010. Expo 2010, Shanghai, China. Multicoloured.

MS1455	$1.10 Type **278**; $2.25 Montserrat Cultural Centre, Little Bay; $2.50 Assumption Cathedral, Kremlin, Russia; $2.75 Brooklyn Bridge, New York	9·00	10·00
MS1456	$1.10 Fishing village in Shanghai, Hong Kong Island, China; $2.25 Camelot Villa, Montserrat; $2.50 Zaanse Schans Windmill, Zaandam, Holland; $2.75 Reichstag German Parliament, Berlin, Germany	9·00	10·00

279 Michael Jackson

2010. Michael Jackson Commemoration. Multicoloured.

MS1457	$2.50×4 Type **279**; Wearing red jacket and white T shirt; In close-up, singing, wearing silver jacket; In profile, facing left, wearing red and gold jacket	10·00	11·00
MS1458	$2.50×4 Wearing white jacket and black shirt, in profile facing right; Wearing black jacket, holding microphone, facing left; Wearing white T shirt and black leather jacket; Wearing black shirt and white jacket, facing forwards	10·00	11·00

280 Wild Marigold (*Wedelia calycina*)

2010. Wild Flowers of Montserrat. Multicoloured.

1459	$1.10 Type **280**	1·00	1·00
1460	$2.25 Shrubby toothedthread (*Odontonema nitidum*)	2·10	2·25
1461	$2.50 Wild sweet pea (*Crotalaria retusa*)	2·40	2·75
1462	$2.75 Rosy periwinkle (*Catharanthus roseus*)	3·00	3·25
1463	$5 Measle bush (*Lantana camara*)	6·00	6·50
MS1464	100×70 mm. $7 Pribby (*Rondeletia buxifolia*)	8·00	9·00

281 Reddish Egret

2010. Endangered Species. Reddish Egret (*Egretta rufescens*). Multicoloured.

1465	$1.10 Type **281**	3·25	3·25
1466	$2.25 White phase and dark phase egrets in flight	3·25	3·25
1467	$2.50 Reddish egret (dark phase) preening	3·25	3·25
1468	$2.75 White phase egret taking off from wetland	3·25	3·25
MS1469	100×139 mm. Nos. 1465/8, each×2	19·00	19·00

282 Giant Panda

2010. Beijing 2010 International Stamp and Coin Exhibition. Giant Panda (*Ailuropoda melanoleuca*). Multicoloured.

MS1470	160×95 mm. $2.50×4 Type **282**; Panda laying between rock and tree trunk; Panda eating bamboo; Panda looking down (side view of head, shoulders and foreleg)	9·50	9·50
MS1471	90×62 mm. $7 Panda looking down (side view of head and shoulders)	7·00	7·50

283 Beaded Periwinkle (*Tectarius muricatus*)

2011. Seashells. Multicoloured.

1472	$1.10 Type **283**	1·75	1·25

1473 $2.25 Green star shell (*Astraea tuber*) 2·75 2·50
1474 $2.50 Smooth Scotch bonnet (*Phalium cicatricosum*) 3·00 3·00
1475 $2.75 Calico scallop (*Aequipecten gibbus*) 3·50 3·75
1476 $5 Hawk wing conch (*Strombus raninus*) 5·00 6·50
MS1477 100×80 mm. $7 Atlantic partridge tun (*Tonna maculosa*) (vert) 8·00 9·00

284 Anise (*Pimpinella anisum*)

2011. Medicinal Plants. Multicoloured.
MS1478 $2.25×6 Type **284**; Lemon grass (*Cymbopogon citratus*); Vervain (*Stachytarpheta jamaicenis*); Ram goat bush (*Eryngium foetidum*); Rosemary (*Rosmarinus officinalis*); Inflammation bush (*Peperomia pellucida*) 16·00 16·00

285 Prince William and Miss Catherine Middleton

2011. Royal Engagement. Multicoloured.
MS1479 100×130 mm. $2.75×4 Type **285**; Miss Catherine Middleton waring black hat with white curled feather; Prince William; Prince William and Miss Catherine Middleton (gold framed painting in background) 12·00 12·00
MS1480 80×110 mm. $5 Miss Catherine Middleton; $5 Prince William 10·00 10·00

286 Barbados Black Belly Sheep (*Ovis aries*)

2011. Animals of Montserrat. Multicoloured.
1481 $2.25 Type **286** 3·00 2·50
1482 $2.50 Boer goat (*Capra aegagrus hircus*) 3·25 3·00
1483 $2.75 Black donkey (*Equus africanus asinus*) 3·75 3·75
1484 $5 Red cattle (*Bos primigenius*) 5·50 7·00
MS1485 100×100 mm. $7 Arabian horse (*Equus caballus*) 8·50 8·50

287 Prince William

2011. Royal Wedding. Multicoloured.
MS1486 $2.25×6 Type **287**; Leaving Westminster Abbey after wedding; Duchess of Cambridge; Prince William (no cap); Duke and Duchess of Cambridge in carriage; Duchess of Cambridge (facing right) 16·00 16·00
MS1487 100×70 mm. $7 Duke and Duchess of Cambridge kissing on Buckingham Palace balcony 8·00 8·50

288 Washington Square, New York, 14 September 2001

2011. Tenth Anniv of Attack on World Trade Centre, New York. Multicoloured.
MS1488 100×130 mm. $2.75×4 Type **288**; US flag and 'God Bless the Memory of those Lost' banner; 'Love' and 'No War Peace' messages, Union Square, New York, 13 September 2001; US flag and memorial cross, Stoneycreek township, Pennsylvania 12·00 12·00
MS1489 100×70 mm. $6 Keithroy Maynard, 1971-2001 (Montserrat born New York firefighter) 6·50 7·00

289 Alphonsus Cassell

2011. Alphonsus Cassell 'Mighty Arrow' (soca musician) Commemoration. Multicoloured.
1490 $2.25 Type **289** 2·75 2·50
1491 $2.50 Alphonsus Cassell (wearing red and black jacket) 3·00 3·00
MS1492 130×100 mm. $2.75×4 Alphonsus Cassell (wearing white jacket); Wearing headphones; Wearing tasselled sleeveless top; Wearing patterned V-neck top (all horiz) 12·00 12·00

290 Statue of Liberty

2011. 125th Anniv of Statue of Liberty. Multicoloured.
MS1493 100×131 mm. $1.10 Type **290**; $1.10 Torch; $2.25 Head of Statue of Liberty; $2.25 Book; $2.50 Statue of Liberty; $2.50 Back of Statue's head and book 6·00 6·00
MS1494 70×100 mm. $6 Statue of Liberty and base (30×80 mm) 6·00 6·00

291 Purple Heron (*Ardea purpurea*)

2011. China 2011 27th Asian International Stamp Exhibition, Wuxi. Fauna and Flora of China. Multicoloured.
MS1495 $1.10 Type **291**; $2.25 Indian elephant (*Elephas maximus indicus*); $2.50 Snub-nosed monkey (*Rhinopithecus roxellana*); $2.75 Royal Bengal tiger (*Panthera tigris tigris*) 11·00 11·00
MS1496 $1.10 Chinese plum (*Prunus mume*); $2.25 Opium poppy (*Papaver somniferum*); $2.50 Japanese camellia (*Camellia japonica*); $2.75 Pomegranate (*Punica granatum*) 11·00 11·00

292 The Choral Group Voices

2011. Christmas. Multicoloured.
1497 $2.25 Type **292** 2·50 2·00
1498 $2.50 Emerald Community Singers 2·75 2·50
1499 $2.75 Volpanics Steel Band 3·00 3·00
1500 $5 New Ebenezer SDA Church 5·00 7·00

293 Queen of the Night (*Cereus hildmannianus*)

2012. Cacti of the Caribbean. Multicoloured.
MS1501 150×100 mm. $2.75×4 Type **293**; Old Man's Whiskers (*Opuntia aciculata*); Devil Cholla (*Opuntia stanlyi*); Century Plant (*Agave americana*) 8·00 8·00
MS1502 110×110 mm. $3.50 Prickly pear cactus (*Opuntia ovata*); $3.50 Prickly pear fruit 5·00 5·00

294 Northern Pintail (*Anas acuta*)

2012. Ducks of Montserrat. Multicoloured.
MS1503 130×100 mm. $3.50×4 Type **294**; Green-winged Teal (*Anas carolinensis*); Fulvous Whistling Duck (*Dendrocygna bicolor*); Blue-winged Teal (*Anas discors*) 10·50 10·50
MS1504 101×70 mm. $6 Northern Shoveler (*Anas clypeata*) 4·50 4·50

295 Queen Elizabeth II

2012. Diamond Jubilee. Multicoloured.
MS1505 180×121 mm. $3.50×4 Type **295**; Queen Elizabeth II at Westminster Abbey for her Coronation; Queen Elizabeth II in Coronation chair; Coronation photograph of Queen Elizabeth II and Prince Philip 10·50 10·50
MS1506 69×100 mm. $7 Coronation photograph of Queen Elizabeth II (vert) 5·00 5·00

296 Sydney Harbour Bridge, Australia

2012. Engineering Wonders: Bridges. Multicoloured.
MS1507 110×140 mm. $4×3 Type **296**; Brooklyn Bridge, New York City; Golden Gate Bridge, San Francisco 8·75 8·75
MS1508 80×79 mm. $6 Tower Bridge, London (horiz) 4·50 4·50

297 Yellow Tang (*Zebrasoma flavescens*)

2012. Life in the Sea. Multicoloured.
MS1509 150×100 mm. $3×4 Type **297**; Spotted Dolphin (*Stenella attenuata*); Manatee (*Trichechus manatus*); Green Sea Turtle (*Chelonia mydas*) 8·75 8·75
MS1510 101×70 mm. $6 Blue Spotted Grouper (*Cephalopholis argus*) 4·50 4·50

298 *Argyrochosma jonesii*

2012. Ferns of the Caribbean. Multicoloured.
MS1511 $3×4 Type **298**; *Danaea kalevala*; *Lastreopsis effusa*; *Asplenium serratum* 8·75 8·75

MS1512 is left for a miniature sheet, not yet received.

299 The Great Wall of China

2012. Beijing 2012 International Philatelic Exhibition. Sites and Scenes of China. Multicoloured.
MS1513 80×110 mm. $2.25×4 Type **299**; Section of Great Wall of China with four towers; Close-up of wall; Top of wall 6·00 6·00
MS1514 120×110 mm. $2.50×6 The Gate of Heavenly Peace; The Forbidden City; Top of the Summer Palace; The Summer Palace (different); Skyline of Pudong, Shanghai; Li River, Guangxi Province 10·00 10·00
MS1515 90×91 mm. $5 Sanquingshan National Park (38×51 mm) 3·50 3·50
MS1516 90×91 mm. $5 Dragon carving on temple facade 3·50 3·50

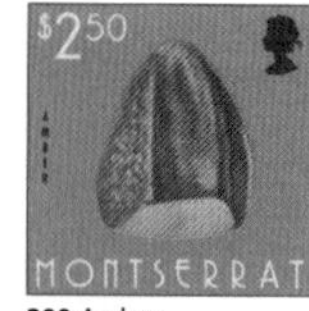

300 Amber

2013. Minerals of the World. Multicoloured.
MS1517 130×101 mm. $2.50×6 Type 300; Chrysoberyl; Garnet; Microcline; Sunstone; Lapis 10·00 10·00
MS1518 61×80 mm. $6 Orpiment (38×51 mm) 4·00 4·00

301 Pigmy Fritillary (*Anaea minor*)

2013. Butterflies. Multicoloured.
1519 10c. Type **301** 10 10
1520 30c. Cloudless Sulphur (*Phoebis senna*) 20 20
1521 35c. Gulf Fritillary (*Dione vanillae*) 25 25
1522 50c. St. Christopher's Hairstreak (*Chlorostrymon simaethis*) 35 35
1523 70c. Nyctelius Skipper (*Nyctelius nyctelius*) 45 45
1524 80c. Cassius Blue (*Leptotes cassius*) 55 55
1525 90c. Antillean Crescent (*Antillea pelops*) 60 60
1526 $1 Polydamas Swallowtail (*Battus polydamas*) 65 65
1527 $1.10 The Flambeau (*Dryas julia warner*) 75 75
1528 $1.50 Bronze Hairstreak (*Electrostrymon angerona*) 1·00 1·00
1529 $2.25 Caribbean Buckeye (*Junonia evarete*) 1·50 1·50
1530 $2.50 The Red Rim (*Biblis hyperia*) 1·75 2·00
1531 $2.75 White Peacock (*Anartia jatrophae*) 1·90 1·90
1532 $5 Stub-tailed Skipper (*Urbanus obscurus*) 3·50 4·00
1533 $10 Zebra (*Heliconius charitonius*) 6·75 7·75
1534 $20 Manuel's Skipper (*Polygonus manueli*) 13·50 14·50

302 *Hamlet*

2013. 400th Anniv of the Globe Theatre Fire. Multicoloured.
MS1535 150×100 mm. $2.75×4 Type **302**; Silhouette holding sword (*Julius Caesar*); Sword dripping blood (*Macbeth*); Male and female silhouettes (*Romeo and Juliet*) 7·50 7·50
MS1536 101×100 mm. $7 William Shakespeare (38×51 mm) 4·75 4·75

303 Grazing Horse

2013. Chinese New Year. Year of the Horse. Multicoloured.
MS1537 164×100 mm. $2.75×4 Type **303**; Horse cantering to left (off foreleg extended); Horse galloping (seen from front); Horse cantering to left (both forelegs off ground) 7·50 7·50

MS1538 100×70 mm. $7 Horse galloping right (drawn Chinese style) 4·75 4·75

304 Coins (Economy)

2013. 40th Anniv of CARICOM. Multicoloured.
MS1539 140×141 mm. $3×4 Type **304**; Handshake (Diplomacy); Pencil (Education); Dripping tap (Conservaton) 8·00 8·00
MS1540 75×75 mm. $7 Emblem 4·75 4·75

305 Peony 'Black Pirate' (*Paeonia lutea* var.)

2013. Blossoming Plants. Multicoloured.
MS1541 110×130 mm. $2.75 Type **305**; $2.75 Cape Blue Water Lily (*Nymphaea capensis*); $3 Angel's Trumpet (*Brugmansia arborea*); $3 Emerald Vine (*Strongylodon macrobotrysc*) 7·75 7·75
MS1542 110×130 mm. $7 Moon Vine (*Ipomoea alba*) 4·75 4·75

306 Coconut Trees

2013. Thailand 2013 World Stamp Exhibition, Bangkok. Sites and Scenes of Thailand. Multicoloured.
MS1543 160×100 mm. $2.75 Type **306**; $2.75 Sanphet Prasat Palace; $3 Buddha Statues; $3 Erawan Waterfall 7·50 7·50
MS1544 100×101 mm. $7 Elephant ride 4·75 4·75

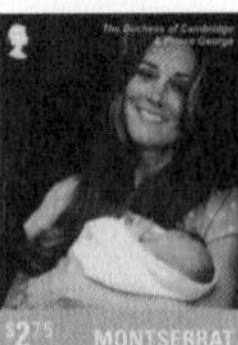

307 Catherine, Duchess of Cambridge holding Prince George

2013. Birth of Prince George. Multicoloured.
MS1545 150×119 mm. $2.75 Type **307**×2; $2.75 Duke and Duchess of Cambridge with Prince George×2 6·50 6·50
MS1546 100×72 mm. $7 Prince William, Duke of Cambridge holding Prince George 8·50 8·50

308 Bicolor Tabby Kitten

2013. Kittens. Multicoloured.
MS1547 80×120 mm. $3×4 Type **308**; Mackeral Tabby (ginger); Calico; Mackeral Tabby (brown) 14·50 14·50
MS1548 75×75 mm. $7 Head of Mackeral Tabby kitten 8·50 8·50

309 Pres. John F. Kennedy

2013. 50th Death Anniv of Pres. John F. Kennedy. Multicoloured.
MS1549 100×100 mm. $2.25×4 Type **309**; John Kennedy (looking to right); Facing camera; At desk, writing 11·00 11·00
MS1550 100×100 mm. $7 John Kennedy behind microphone 8·50 8·50

310 Red-footed Tortoise (*Chelonoidis carbonaria*)

2013. Reptiles of the Caribbean. Multicoloured.
MS1551 133×100 mm. $2.75×4 Type **310**; Iguana (*Iguana iguana*); Brown Anole (*Anolis sagrei*); House Gecko (*Hemidactylus frenatus*) 13·00 13·00
MS1552 70×100 mm. $7 Blue-headed Anole (*Anolis allisoni*) 8·50 8·50

311 Munitions Worker at Work Bench welding in Munitions Factory, 1915

2014. Centenary of World War I. Women's Efforts during the War. Multicoloured.
MS1553 120×110 mm. $2.25×6 Type **311**; Nurse ironing bandages at the British Hospital, 1915; Army Recruiting Office, Southwark Hall, London, 1915; Delivery woman, 1914; Woman cleaning railway car door frames with an electric brush, France, 1914; Miss D. Milman of the Women's Service League, 1918 16·00 16·00
MS1554 69×100 mm. $7 French Red Cross poster, 1915 (38×51 mm) 8·50 8·50

312 Bronze-Tailed Plumeleteer (*Chalybura urochrysia*)

2014. Hummingbirds. Multicoloured.
MS1555 81×96 mm. $3×4 Type **312**; White-bellied Mountaingem (*Oreopyra hemileucus*); Olivaceus Thornbill (*Chalcostigma olivaceum*); White-Bellied Emerald (*Amazilia candida*) 14·50 14·50
MS1556 81×96 mm. $3.50 Chestnut-breasted Coronet (*Boissonneaua matthewsii*); $3.50 Collared Inca (*Coeligena torquata*) 8·50 8·50

313 Illustrated Observation of the Moon by Galileo

2014. 450th Birth Anniv of Galileo Galilei (astronomer). Multicoloured.
MS1557 86×90 mm. $3×4 Galileo Galilei's illustrated observations of the Moon: Type **313**; Shadow at right; Deep shadow at left; Light shadow at left 14·50 14·50
MS1558 86×90 mm. $7 Galileo Galilei 8·50 8·50

314 Lettuce (*Lactuca sativa*)

2014. Vegetables. Multicoloured.
MS1559 80×96 mm. $3 Type **314**; $3 Corn (*Zea mays*); $3 Eggplant (*Solanum melongena*); $3 Sweet potato (*Ipomoea satatas*) 8·75 8·75
MS1560 80×95 mm. $3.50 Cauliflower (*Brassica olenacea*); $3.50 Carrots (*Daucus carota*) 5·25 5·25

315 Stream of Light dispersed into Spectral Colours by Glass Prism

2015. International Year of Light. Multicoloured.
MS1561 80×100 mm. $3.25 Type **315**; $3.25 Sir Isaac Newton, 1643-1727, physicist; $3.25 Spectrum wavelengths in nanometers (blue and green); $3.25 Spectrum wavelengths in nanometers (green, yellow and red) 9·25 9·25
MS1562 80×85 mm. $7 Ultraviolet and infrared (37×47 mm) 5·00 5·00

316 Leatherback Sea Turtle

2015. Leatherback Sea Turtle (*Dermochelys coriacea*). Multicoloured.
MS1563 100×100 mm. $3.25 Type **316**; $3.25 Leatherback Turtle on beach; $3.25 Female returning from beach to sea; $3.25 Female coming ashore 9·25 9·25
MS1564 100×100 mm. $7 Hatchling making its way to the sea 5·00 5·00

317 Longsnout Seahorse (*Hippocampus reidi*)

2015. Seahorses of the Caribbean. Multicoloured.
MS1565 101×100 mm. $3.25 Type **317**; $3.25 Lined Seahorse (*Hippocampus erectus*) in weed; $3.25 Lined Seahorse (*Hippocampus erectus*) (head and upper body); $3.25 Two Longsnout Seahorses (*Hippocampus reidi*) 9·25 9·25
MS1566 100×101 mm. $7 Dwarf Seahorse (*Hippocampus zosterae*) 5·00 5·00

318 Wildfires in Central Chile

2015. Earth from Space. Multicoloured.
MS1567 70×100 mm. $3.25 Type **318**; $3.25 Kavir Desert, Iran; $3.25 Central Saudi Arabia; $3.25 Cancun, Mexico 9·25 9·25
MS1568 70×80 mm. $7 The island of Montserrat 5·00 5·00

319 Queen Elizabeth II

2016. Longest Reigning British Monarch (**MS**1569) and 5th Wedding Anniv of the Duke and Duchess of Cambridge (**MS**1570). Multicoloured.
MS1569 125×110 mm. $3.25 Type **319**; $3.25 Queen Elizabeth II holding bouquet; $3.25 Queen Elizabeth II with horse (white background); $3.25 Queen Elizabeth II with horse (metal mesh pen in background) 9·25 9·25
MS1570 111×91 mm. $7 Prince George and Princess Charlotte (35×47 mm) 5·00 5·00

320 Cricket Ball

2017. Cricket. Multicoloured.
MS1571 120×105 mm. $3.25 Type **320**; $3.25 Glove; $3.25 Bat and wicket; $3.25 Helmet 9·25 9·25
MS1572 79×100 mm. $7 Cricket Ball (different) (37×50 mm) 5·00 5·00

321 Brown Trembler (*Cinclocerthia ruficauda*)

2016. Birds of Montserrat. Multicoloured.
MS1573 110×110 mm. $3.25 Type **321**; $3.25 Black Swift (*Cypseloides niger*); $3.25 Willet (*Tringa semipalmata*); $3.25 Brown Noddy (*Anous stolidus*) 9·25 9·25
MS1574 70×100 mm. $7 Montserrat Oriole (*Icterus oberi*) 5·00 5·00

322 Nassau Grouper

2016. Endangered Species. Nassau Grouper (*Epinephelus striatus*). Multicoloured.

1575	$3.75 Type **322**	2·75	2·75
1576	$3.75 Nassau Grouper (weed at left)	2·75	2·75
1577	$3.75 Nassau Grouper (mouth open)	2·75	2·75
1578	$3.75 Nassau Grouper (on sea bed)	2·75	2·75
MS1579	180×100 mm. Nos. 1575/8, each ×2	21·00	21·00

323 Bigar Waterfall, Caras Severin County, Romania

2016. Waterfalls. Multicoloured.
MS1580 150×110 mm. $3.25 Type **323**; $3.25 Pearl Shoal Waterfall in Jiuzhai Valley National Park, Jiuzhaigou, Sichuan, China; $3.25 Ban Gioc Waterfall, Cao Bang, Vietnam; $3.25 Iguazu Falls, Misiones Province, Argentina 9·25 9·25
MS1581 100×70 mm. $10 Great Alps Waterfall, Montserrat (destroyed by pyroclastic flow, 1997) (37×50 mm) 7·25 7·25

324 Green Sea Turtle (*Chelonia mydas*)

2016. Sea Turtles. Multicoloured.
MS1582 150×110 mm. $3.50 Type **324**; $3.50 Loggerhead Sea Turtle (*Caretta caretta*); $3.50 Olive Ridley Sea Turtle (*Lepidochelys olivacea*); $3.50 Kemp's Ridley Sea Turtle (*Lepidochelys kempii*) 11·50 11·50
MS1583 100×70 mm. $7 Hawksbill Sea Turtle (*Eretmochelys imbricata*) (50×37 mm) 5·75 5·75

325 Ferry *Caribe Sun*

2016. Transportation used in Montserrat. Multicoloured.

MS1584	170×110 mm. $3.50 Type **325**; $3.50 Van – prison conveyance; $3.50 Automobile – state vehicle; $3.50 Motorcycle – police	11·50	11·50
MS1585	100×70 mm. $7 FlyMontserrat Britten-Norman BN-2 Islander Airplane (50×37 mm)	5·75	5·75

326 Baubles

2016. Christmas Ornaments. Multicoloured.

MS1586	100×110 mm. $3.50 Type **326**; $3.50 Christmas tree branches with cones and silver baubles; $3.50 Reindeer tree decoration; $3.50 Gold decorations including baubles and gold-wrapped present	10·50	10·50
MS1587	70×75 mm. $7 Green bauble and silver decorations (50×37 mm)	5·25	5·25

OFFICIAL STAMPS

1976. Various stamps, some already surch, optd **O.H.M.S.**

O1	5c. multicoloured (No. 299a)		70
O2	10c. multicoloured (No. 247)		1·00
O3	30c. on 10c. mult (No. 369)		1·50
O4	45c. on 3c. mult (No. 370)		2·00
O5	$5 multicoloured (No. 254)		£110
O6	$10 multicoloured (No. 254c)		£650

These stamps were issued for use on mail from the Montserrat Philatelic Bureau. They were not sold to the public, either unused or used.

1976. Nos. 372, 374/82, 384/5 and 476 optd **O.H.M.S.** or surch also.

O17	5c. Malay apple	†	10
O28	5c. on 3c. Lignum vitae	†	20
O18	10c. Jacaranda	†	10
O19	15c. Orchid tree	†	10
O20	20c. Manjak	†	10
O21	25c. Tamarind	†	15
O33	30c. on 15c. Orchid tree	†	30
O34	35c. on 2c. Cannon-ball tree	†	30
O35	40c. Flame of the forest	†	40
O22	55c. Pink cassia	†	35
O23	70c. Long john	†	45
O24	$1 Saman	†	60
O39	$2.50 on 40c. Flame of the forest	†	2·00
O25	$5 Yellow poui	†	1·50
O16	$10 Flamboyant	†	3·75

1981. Nos. 490/4, 496, 498, 500, 502/3 and 505 optd **O.H.M.S.**

O42	5c. Type **91**	10	10
O43	10c. Hogfish and neon goby	10	10
O44	15c. Creole wrasse	10	10
O45	20c. Three-spotted damselfish	15	15
O46	25c. Sergeant major	15	15
O47	45c. Schoolmaster	25	20
O48	65c. Bigeye	35	30
O49	$1 Rock beauty	65	65
O50	$3 Royal gramma ("Fairy basslet") and blueheads	1·50	1·75
O51	$5 Cherub angelfish	2·00	2·25
O52	$10 Caribbean long-nosed butterflyfish	3·00	2·25

1983. Nos. 510/15 surch **O.H.M.S.** and value.

O53	45c. on 90c. *Charlotte*	20	30
O54	45c. on 90c. Prince Charles and Lady Diana Spencer	60	1·00
O55	75c. on $3 *Portsmouth*	25	35
O56	75c. on $3 Prince Charles and Lady Diana Spencer	90	1·40
O57	$1 on $4 *Britannia*	35	50
O58	$1 on $4 Prince Charles and Lady Diana Spencer	1·00	1·50

1983. Nos. 542/4 surch **O.H.M.S.**

O59	70c. on 75c. Type **97**	60	40
O60	$1 Coat of Arms of Catherine of Aragon	70	50
O61	$1.50 on $5 Diana, Princess of Wales	1·00	80

1985. Nos. 600/12 and 614 optd **O H M S**.

O62	5c. Type **107**	1·25	1·50
O63	10c. Carib grackle	1·25	1·00
O64	15c. Moorhen	1·50	1·00
O65	20c. Brown booby	1·50	1·00
O66	25c. Black-whiskered vireo	1·50	1·00
O67	40c. Scaly-breasted thrasher	2·00	70
O68	55c. Laughing gull	2·25	70
O69	70c. Glossy ibis	2·50	90
O70	90c. Green-backed heron	2·75	90
O71	$1 Belted kingfisher	2·75	70
O72	$1.15 Bananaquit	3·00	1·25
O73	$3 American kestrel	4·50	2·50
O74	$5 Forest thrush	5·50	2·50
O75	$10 Bridled quail dove	7·00	2·50

1989. Nos. 757/70 and 772 optd **O H M S**.

O76	5c. Type **133**	40	75
O77	10c. Little knobbed scallop	40	75
O78	15c. Sozoni's cone	50	1·00
O79	20c. Globular coral shell	55	1·00
O80	25c. American or common sundial	55	50
O81	40c. King helmet	60	55
O82	55c. Channelled turban	70	1·00
O83	70c. True tulip shell	90	1·25
O84	90c. Music volute	1·00	90
O85	$1 Flame auger	1·00	80
O86	$1.15 Rooster-tail conch	1·25	1·00
O87	$1.50 Queen or pink conch	1·40	1·60
O88	$3 Teramachi's slit shell	2·00	2·50
O89	$5 Common or Florida crown conch	3·25	3·25
O90	$10 Atlantic trumpet triton	5·50	5·50

1989. Nos. 578 and 580/1 surch **OHMS**.

O91	70c. on 10c. Hogfish and neon goby	2·25	1·75
O92	$1.15 on 75c. French grunt	3·00	1·75
O93	$1.50 on $2 Blue chromis	3·00	3·00

1992. Nos. 838/41, 847/50, 856/9 surch or optd **OHMS**.

O94	70c. on 90c. Type **150**	1·40	1·40
O95	70c. on 90c. Type **152**	1·40	1·40
O96	70c. on 90c. Type **154**	1·40	1·40
O97	70c. on $3.50 French grunt	1·40	1·40
O98	$1 on $3.50 Helmeted guineafowl	1·50	1·50
O99	$1 on $3.50 Anthurium	1·50	1·50
O100	$1.15 Cushion star	1·50	2·00
O101	$1.15 Hen and chicks	1·50	1·75
O102	$1.15 Shell ginger	1·50	1·75
O103	$1.50 Rock beauty	1·60	2·25
O104	$1.50 Red junglefowl	1·60	2·25
O105	$1.50 Early day lily	1·60	2·25

1993. Nos. 889/902 and 904 optd **OHMS**.

O106	5c. Type **161**	70	1·25
O107	10c. *Gryllus campestris* (field cricket)	70	1·25
O108	15c. *Lepthemis vesiculosa* (dragonfly)	80	1·25
O109	20c. *Orthemis ferruginea* (red skimmer)	80	1·25
O110	25c. *Gerris lacustris* (pond skater)	80	1·25
O111	40c. *Byctiscus betulae* (leaf weevil)	1·25	60
O112	55c. *Atta texana* (leaf-cutter ants)	1·40	60
O113	70c. *Polistes fuscatus* (paper wasp)	1·60	1·25
O114	90c. *Sparmopolius fulvus* (bee fly)	1·75	1·00
O115	$1 *Chrysopa carnea* (lace wing)	1·75	1·00
O116	$1.15 *Phoebis philea* (butterfly)	2·25	1·75
O117	$1.50 *Cynthia cardui* (butterfly)	2·75	2·50
O118	$3 *Utetheisa bella* (moth)	4·00	4·50
O119	$5 *Alucita pentadactyla* (moth)	5·50	6·00
O120	$10 *Heliconius melpomene* (butterfly)	8·00	9·00

1997. Nos. 1009/22 and 1024 optd **O.H.M.S.**

O121	5c. Type **184**	15	70
O122	10c. Pegasus	25	70
O123	15c. Griffin	35	1·00
O124	20c. Unicorn	35	1·00
O125	25c. Gnomes	35	50
O126	40c. Mermaid	50	70
O127	55c. Cockatrice	60	1·00
O128	70c. Fairy	70	70
O129	90c. Goblin	90	1·25
O130	$1 Faun	1·00	70
O131	$1.15 Dragon	1·25	70
O132	$1.50 Giant	1·40	1·00
O133	$3 Elves	2·50	2·75
O134	$5 Centaur	4·00	4·25
O135	$10 Erin	6·00	6·50

2002. Nos. 1195/1208 and 1210 optd **OHMS**.

O137	5c. Type **215**	25	50
O138	10c. Mammee apple	35	50
O139	15c. Lime	45	50
O140	20c. Grapefruit	50	70
O141	25c. Orange	50	50
O142	40c. Passion fruit	60	50
O143	55c. Banana	70	70
O144	70c. Pawpaw	80	70
O145	90c. Pomegranate	1·00	1·00
O146	$1 Guava	1·25	70
O147	$1.15 Mango	1·50	80
O148	$1.50 Sugar apple	1·75	1·50
O149	$3 Cashew	2·75	3·25
O150	$5 Soursop	5·00	5·50
O151	$10 Pineapple	7·50	8·00

2008. Nos. 1352/65 and 1367 optd **OHMS**.

O152	10c. Type **254**	20	30
O153	30c. *Catharanthus roseus* (periwinkle)	45	50
O154	35c. *Bougainvillea glabra*	50	50
O155	50c. *Ixora macrothyrsa*	70	50
O156	70c. *Heliconia humilis*	90	65
O157	80c. *Ipomoea learii* (morning glory)	1·00	1·00
O158	90c. *Delonix regia* (poinciana)	1·00	1·00
O159	$1 *Solandra nitida* (cup of gold)	1·10	85
O160	$1.10 *Acalypha hispida* (chenille plant)	1·25	90
O161	$1.50 *Nerium oleander*	1·75	1·40
O162	$2.25 *Hibiscus rosa-sinensis*	2·25	2·25
O163	$2.50 *Plumeria acuminata*	2·50	2·75
O164	$2.75 *Strelitzia reginae* (bird of paradise flower)	2·75	3·00
O165	$5 *Stephanotis floribunda*	4·50	4·75
O166	$20 Rosa 'Buchi'	14·00	16·00

POSTAL FISCAL STAMPS

F1 War Memorial, Plymouth

F2 Arms of Montserrat

2014. War Memorial and Arms

F1	**F 1**	$50 multicoloured	35·00	35·00
F2	**F 2**	$100 multicoloured	70·00	70·00

MOROCCO

An independent kingdom, established in 1956, comprising the former French and Spanish International Zones.

A. Northern Zone.
100 centimes = 1 peseta.

B. Southern Zone.
100 centimes = 1 franc.

C. Issues for the Whole of Morocco.
1958. 100 centimes = 1 franc.
1962. 100 francs = 1 dirham.

A. NORTHERN ZONE

1 Sultan of Morocco

2 Polytechnic

1956

1	**1**	10c. brown	30	25
2	-	15c. brown	30	25
3	**2**	25c. violet	10	10
4	-	50c. green	45	45
5	**1**	80c. green	1·10	1·10
6	-	2p. lilac	9·50	9·00
7	**2**	3p. blue	19·00	19·00
8	-	10p. green	42·00	42·00

Designs:—Horiz: 15c., 2p. Villa Sanjurjo harbour. Vert: 50c., 10p. Cultural Delegation building, Tetuan.

3 Lockheed Super Constellation over Lau Dam

1956. Air.

9	**3**	25c. purple	45	45
10	-	1p.40 mauve	1·10	1·10
11	**3**	3p.40 red	2·40	2·40
12	-	4p.80 purple	4·25	4·25

Design:—1p.40, 4p.80, Lockheed Super Constellation over Rio Nekor Bridge.

1957. First Anniv of Independence. As T **7** but with Spanish inscriptions and currency.

13	80c. green	95	90
14	1p.50 olive	2·40	2·30
15	3p. red	5·25	5·00

1957. As T **5** but with Spanish inscriptions and currency.

16	30c. indigo and blue	30	10
17	70c. purple and brown	45	10
18	80c. purple	1·90	45
19	1p.50 lake and green	65	35
20	3p. green	95	80
21	7p. red	6·50	1·80

1957. Investiture of Prince Moulay el Hassan. As T **9** but with Spanish inscriptions and currency.

22	80c. blue	75	45
23	1p.50 green	1·90	1·40
24	3p. red	5·75	4·00

1957. Nos. 17 and 19 surch.

25	15c. on 70c. purple and brown	95	95
26	1p.20 on 1p.50 lake and green	1·60	1·60

1957. 30th Anniv of Coronation of Sultan Sidi Mohammed ben Yusuf. As T **10** but with Spanish inscription and currency.

27	1p.20 green and black	75	65
28	1p.80 red and black	1·10	90
29	3p. violet and black	2·10	1·80

B. SOUTHERN ZONE

5 Sultan of Morocco

1956

30	**5**	5f. indigo and blue	45	10
31	**5**	10f. sepia and brown	35	10
32	**5**	15f. lake and green	45	10
33	**5**	25f. purple	1·50	25
34	**5**	30f. green	3·00	25
35	**5**	50f. red	3·75	25
36	**5**	70f. brown and sepia	5·50	85

6 Classroom

1956. Education Campaign.

37	-	10f. violet and purple	2·20	1·40
38	-	15f. lake and red	3·00	1·80
39	**6**	20f. green and turquoise	3·50	2·75
40	-	30f. red and lake	6·00	3·50
41	-	50f. blue and indigo	9·25	6·00

Designs:—10f. Peasants reading book; 15f. Two girls reading; 30f. Child reading to old man; 50f. Child teaching parents the alphabet.

7 Sultan of Morocco

1957. First Anniv of Independence.

42	**7**	15f. green	2·00	1·40
43	**7**	25f. olive	2·50	1·40
44	**7**	30f. red	4·75	2·10

8 Emblem over Casablanca

1957. Air. International Fair, Casablanca.

45	**8**	15f. green and red	1·70	1·20
46	**8**	25f. turquoise	2·50	1·50
47	**8**	30f. brown	3·50	1·90

9 Crown Prince Moulay el Hassan

1957. Investiture of Crown Prince Moulay el Hassan.

48	**9**	15f. blue	1·80	1·10
49	**9**	25f. green	2·00	1·50
50	**9**	30f. red	3·50	1·90

10 King Mohammed V

1957. 30th Anniv of Coronation of King Mohammed V.

51	**10**	15f. green and black	1·00	80
52	**10**	25f. red and black	1·80	1·10
53	**10**	30f. violet and black	2·10	1·40

C. ISSUES FOR THE WHOLE OF MOROCCO

11 Moroccan Pavilion

1958. Brussels International Exhibition.

54	**11**	15f. turquoise	45	25
55	**11**	25f. red	45	30
56	**11**	30f. blue	75	55

12 King Mohammed V and UNESCO Headquarters, Paris

1958. Inauguration of UNESCO Headquarters Building, Paris.

57	**12**	15f. green	45	25
58	**12**	25f. lake	45	30
59	**12**	30f. blue	75	55

13 Ben-Smine Sanatorium

1959. National Aid.

60	**13**	50f. bistre, green and red	95	55

14 King Mohammed V on Horseback

1959. King Mohammed V's 50th Birthday.

61	**14**	15f. lake	75	45
62	**14**	25f. blue	1·00	50
63	**14**	45f. green	1·20	80

15 Princess Lalla Amina

1959. Children's Week.

64	**15**	15f. blue	45	25
65	**15**	25f. green	50	30
66	**15**	45f. purple	75	55

16

1960. Meeting of U.N. African Economic Commission, Tangier.

67	**16**	45f. green, brown and violet	1·20	70

+10f

اغاثة ضحايا
الزيوت المسممة
اكتوبر 1959

(17)

1960. Adulterated Cooking Oil Victims Relief Fund. Surch as T **17**.

68	**5**	5f.+10f. indigo and blue	55	45
69	**5**	10f.+10f. sepia and brown	95	75
70	**5**	15f.+10f. lake and green	1·50	1·00
71	**5**	25f.+15f. purple	1·80	1·30
72	**5**	30f.+20f. green	2·75	2·40

18 Arab Refugees

1960. World Refugee Year.

73	**18**	15f. black, green and ochre	45	25
74	-	45f. green and black	75	50

Designs:—45f. "Uprooted tree" and Arab refugees.

19 Marrakesh

1960. 900th Anniv of Marrakesh.

75	**19**	100f. green, brown and blue	1·50	1·10

20 Lantern

1960. 1100th Anniv of Karaouiyne University.

76	**20**	15f. purple	75	55
77	-	25f. blue	75	75
78	-	30f. brown	1·50	90
79	-	35f. black	2·00	1·10
80	-	45f. green	2·50	1·70

Designs:—25f. Fountain; 30f. Minaret; 35f. Frescoes; 45f. Courtyard.

21 Arab League Centre and King Mohammed V

1960. Inauguration of Arab League Centre, Cairo.

81	**21**	15f. black and green	45	25

اسبوع التضامن +5f
1380
1960

(22)

1960. Solidarity Fund. Nos. 458/9 (Mahakma, Casablanca) of French Morocco surch as T **22**.

82	**106**	15f.+3f. on 18f. myrtle	95	95
83	**106**	+5f. on 20f. lake	1·30	1·30

23 Wrestling

1960. Olympic Games.

84	**23**	5f. purple, green and violet	10	10
85	-	10f. chocolate, blue & brown	30	25
86	-	15f. brown, blue and green	45	25
87	-	20f. purple, blue and bistre	50	40
88	-	30f. brown, violet and red	55	45
89	-	40f. brown, blue and violet	95	45
90	-	45f. blue, green and purple	1·20	70
91	-	70f. black, blue and brown	1·80	80

Designs:—10f. Gymnastics; 15f. Cycling; 20f. Weightlifting; 30f. Running; 40f. Boxing; 45f. Sailing; 70f. Fencing.

24 Runner

1961. Third Pan-Arab Games, Casablanca.

92	**24**	20f. green	45	25
93	**24**	30f. lake	75	40
94	**24**	50f. blue	80	70

25 Post Office and Letters

1961. African Postal and Telecommunications Conference, Tangier.

95	**25**	20f. purple and mauve	45	40
96	-	30f. turquoise and green	75	45
97	-	90f. ultramarine and blue	1·20	80

Designs:—Vert: 30f. Telephone operator. Horiz: 90f. Sud Aviation Caravelle mail plane over Tangier.

26 King Mohammed V and African Map

1962. First Anniv of African Charter of Casablanca.

98	**26**	20f. purple and buff	35	10
99	**26**	30f. indigo and blue	65	25

27 Lumumba and Congo Map

1962. Patrice Lumumba Commemoration.

100	**27**	20f. black and bistre	30	10
101	**27**	30f. black and brown	50	45

28 King Hassan II

1962. Air.

102	**28**	90f. black	85	10
103	**28**	1d. red	1·30	25
104	**28**	2d. blue	1·50	70
105	**28**	3d. green	2·75	1·30
106	**28**	5d. violet	5·25	1·90

29 "Pupils of the Nation"

1962. Children's Education.

107	**29**	20f. blue, red and green	55	30
108	**29**	30f. sepia, brown and green	60	45
109	**29**	90f. blue, purple and green	1·10	70

1962. Arab League Week. As T **76** of Libya.

110		20f. brown	30	25

30 King Hassan II

1962

111	**30**	1f. olive	10	10
112	**30**	2f. violet	10	10
113	**30**	5f. sepia	10	10
114	**30**	10f. brown	10	10
115	**30**	15f. turquoise	30	10
116	**30**	20f. purple (18×22 mm)	45	10
116a	**30**	20f. purple (17½×23½ mm)	3·00	10
116b	**30**	25f. red	45	10
117	**30**	30f. green	55	10
117a	**30**	35f. slate	70	10
117b	**30**	40f. blue	70	10
118	**30**	50f. purple	95	10
118a	**30**	60f. purple	1·40	25
119	**30**	70f. blue	1·50	40
120	**30**	80f. lake	2·40	40

31 Scout with Banner

1962. Fifth Arab Scout Jamboree, Rabat.

121	**31**	20f. purple and blue	45	25

32 Campaign Emblem and Swamp

1962. Malaria Eradication Campaign.

122	**32**	20f. blue and green	45	10
123	-	50f. lake and green	75	45

Design:—Vert: 50f. Sword piercing mosquito.

33 Aquarium, Brown Trout and Fish

1962. Casablanca Aquarium. Multicoloured.

124		20f. Type **33**	75	40
125		30f. Aquarium and Mediterranean moray	75	40

34 Mounted Postman and 1912 Sherifian Stamp

1962. First National Philatelic Exhibition, Rabat, and Stamp Day.

126	**34**	20f. green and brown	70	35
127	-	30f. black and red	95	55
128	-	50f. bistre and blue	1·60	70

Designs:— 30f. Postman and circular postmark; 50f. Sultan Hassan I and octagonal postmark (both stamps commemorate 70th anniv of Sherifian post).

فيضانات
1
9
6
3
20 + 5

(35)

1963. Flood Relief Fund. Surch as T **35**.

129	**5**	20+5f. on 5f. indigo & bl	95	95

130	5	30+10f. on 50f. red	1·30	95

36 King Moulay Ismail

1963. 300th Anniv of Meknes.

131	36	20f. sepia	75	30

37 Ibn Batota (voyager)

1963. Famous Men of Maghreb.

132	37	20f. purple	65	40
133	-	20f. black	65	40
134	-	20f. myrtle	65	40
134a	37	40f. blue	60	40

Portraits:—No. 133, Ibn Khaldoun (historian); 134, Al Idrissi (geographer).

38 Sugar Beet and Refinery

1963. Freedom from Hunger.

135	38	20f. black, brown and green	75	35
136	-	50f. black, brown and blue	95	45

Design:—Vert: 50f. Fisherman and tuna.

39 Isis (bas relief)

1963. Nubian Monuments Preservation.

137		20f. black and grey	50	40
138	39	30f. violet	60	40
139	-	50f. purple	1·00	55

Designs:—Horiz: 20f. Heads of Colossi, Abu Simbel; 50f. Philae Temple.

40 Agadir before Earthquake

1963. Reconstruction of Agadir.

140	40	20f. red and blue	75	35
141	40	30f. red and blue	95	55
142	-	50f. red and blue	1·20	70

Designs:—30f. is optd with large red cross and date of earthquake, **29th February, 1960**; 50f. Reconstructed Agadir.

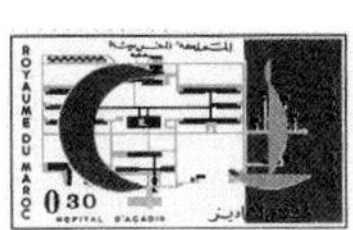
41 Plan of new Agadir Hospital

1963. Centenary of International Red Cross.

143	41	30f. multicoloured	55	40

42 Emblems of Morocco and Rabat

1963. Opening of Parliament.

144	42	20f. multicoloured	55	40

43 Hands breaking Chain

1963. 15th Anniv of Declaration of Human Rights.

145	43	20f. brown, sepia and green	55	40

44 National Flag

1963. Evacuation of Foreign Troops from Morocco.

146	44	20f. red, green and black	65	25

45 *Moulay Abd-er-Rahman* (after Delacroix)

1964. Third Anniv of King Hassan's Coronation.

147	45	1d. multicoloured	3·25	2·10

46 Map, Chart and WMO Emblem

1964. World Meteorological Day. Multicoloured.

148	20f. African weather map (vert) (postage)	50	25
149	30f. Type **46**	75	45
150	90f. Globe and weather vane (vert) (air)	1·00	75

47 Fair Entrance

1964. Air. 20th Anniv of Casablanca Int Fair.

151	47	1d. red, drab and blue	1·20	80

48 Moroccan Pavilion at Fair

1964. Air. New York World's Fair.

152	48	1d. multicoloured	1·30	80

49 Children Playing in the Sun

1964. Postal Employees' Holiday Settlements.

153	49	20f. multicoloured	45	25
154	-	30f. multicoloured	75	45

Design:—30f. Boy, girl and holiday settlement.

50 Olympic Torch

1964. Olympic Games, Tokyo.

155	50	20f. green, violet and red	55	40
156	50	30f. purple, blue and green	75	40
157	50	50f. red, blue and green	95	65

51 Lighthouse and Sultan Mohamed ben Abd-er-Rahman (founder)

1964. Centenary of Cape Spartel Lighthouse.

158	51	25f. multicoloured	75	40

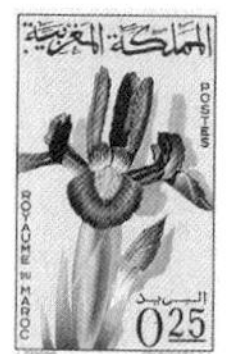
52 Tangier Iris

1965. Flowers. Multicoloured.

159	25f. Type **52**	1·20	75
160	40f. Gladiolus (vert)	1·50	85
161	60f. Caper (horiz)	2·50	1·60

53 Return of King Mohammed

1965. Tenth Anniv of Return of King Mohammed V from Exile.

162	53	25f. green	55	40

54 Early Telegraph Receiver

1965. Centenary of I.T.U. Multicoloured.

163	25f. Type **54**	45	35
164	40f. *TIROS* weather satellite	75	55

55 ICY Emblem

1965. International Co-operation Year.

165	55	25f. black and green	40	25
166	55	60f. lake	55	30

1965. Sea Shells. As T **52**. Mult, background colours given.

167	25f. violet	1·10	50
168	25f. blue	1·10	50
169	25f. yellow	1·10	50

Seashells:—No. 167, Knobbed triton (*Charonia nodifera*); 168, Smooth callista (*Pitaria chione*); 169, *Cymbium tritonis.*

1965. Shellfish. As T **52**. Multicoloured.

170	25f. Helmet crab	1·10	55
171	40f. Mantis shrimp	2·00	1·10
172	1d. Royal prawn (horiz)	2·75	1·60

1965. Orchids. As T **52**. Multicoloured.

173	25f. *Ophrys speculum* (vert)	80	55
174	40f. *Ophrys fusca* (vert)	1·20	55
175	60f. *Ophrys tenthredinifera* (horiz)	2·20	1·40

59 Corn

1966. Agricultural Products (1st issue).

176	59	25f. black and ochre	45	25

See also Nos. 188/9 and 211.

60 Flag, Map and Dove

1966. Tenth Anniv of Independence.

177	60	25f. red and green	45	25

61 King Hassan II and Crown

1966. Fifth Anniv of King Hassan's Coronation.

178	61	25f. blue, green and red	45	20

62 Cross-country Runner

1966. 53rd "Cross des Nations" (Cross-country Race).

179	62	25f. green	55	25

63 WHO Building

1966. Inauguration of W.H.O. Headquarters, Geneva.

180	63	25f. black and purple	40	25
181	-	40f. black and blue	55	25

Design: 40f. WHO Building (different view).

64 King Hassan and Parachutist

1966. Tenth Anniv of Royal Armed Forces.

182	64	25f. black and gold	75	40
183	-	40f. black and gold	70	40

Design:—40f. Crown Prince Hassan kissing hand of King Mohammed.

1966. Palestine Week. As No. 110 but inscr "SEMAINE DE LA PALESTINE" at foot and dated "1966".

184	25f. blue	45	10

65 Brooch

1966. Red Cross Seminar. Moroccan Jewellery. Multicoloured.

185	25f.+5f. Type **65**	1·20	70
186	40f.+10f. Pendant	1·50	90

See also Nos. 203/4, 246/7, 274/5, 287/8, 303/4, 324/5, 370/1, 397/8, 414/15, 450/1 and 493.

66 Rameses II, Abu Simbel

1966. Air. 20th Anniv of UNESCO.

187	**66**	1d. red and yellow	1·50	85

1966. Agricultural Products (2nd and 3rd issue). As T **59**.

188	40f. multicoloured	60	30
189	60f. multicoloured	70	30

Designs:—Vert: 40f. Citrus fruits. Horiz: 60f. Olives.

67 Class XDd Diesel Train

1966. Moroccan Transport. Multicoloured.

190	25f. Type **67** (postage)	1·10	45
191	40f. Liner *Maroc*	1·00	45
192	1d. Tourist coach	1·20	70
193	3d. Sud Aviation Caravelle of Royal Air Maroc (48×27½ mm) (air)	5·00	2·10

68 Twaite Shad

1967. Fish. Multicoloured.

194	25f. Type **68**	1·00	45
195	40f. Plain bonito	1·20	55
196	1d. Bluefish	2·40	1·50

69 Hilton Hotel, Ancient Ruin and Map

1967. Opening of Hilton Hotel, Rabat.

197	**69**	25f. black and blue	45	40
198	**69**	1d. purple and blue	1·00	40

70 Ait Aadel Dam

1967. Inauguration of Ait Aadel Dam.

199	**70**	25f. grey, blue and green	55	45
200	**70**	40f. bistre and blue	95	45

71 Moroccan Scene and Lions Emblem

1967. 50th Anniv of Lions International.

201	**71**	40f. blue and gold	55	35
202	**71**	1d. green and gold	1·30	55

1967. Moroccan Red Cross. As T **65**. Mult.

203	60f.+5f. Necklace	1·20	1·20
204	1d.+10f. Two bracelets	2·30	2·20

72 Three Hands and Pickaxe

1967. Communal Development Campaign.

205	**72**	25f. green	45	15

73 ITY Emblem

1967. International Tourist Year.

206	**73**	1d. blue and cobalt	1·00	55

74 Arrow and Map

1967. Mediterranean Games, Tunis.

207	**74**	25f. multicoloured	45	25
208	**74**	40f. multicoloured	60	25

75 Horse-jumping

1967. International Horse Show.

209	**75**	40f. multicoloured	55	30
210	**75**	1d. multicoloured	95	55

1967. Agricultural Products (4th issue). As T **59**.. Multicoloured.

211	40f. Cotton plant	75	40

76 Human Rights Emblem

1968. Human Rights Year.

212	**76**	25f. slate	45	25
213	**76**	1d. lake	55	40

77 Msouffa Woman

1968. Moroccan Costumes. Multicoloured.

214	10f. Ait Moussa or Ali	75	25
215	15f. Ait Mouhad	95	40
216	25f. Barquemaster of Rabat-Sale	95	55
217	25f. Townsman	1·20	55
218	40f. Townswoman	1·20	70
219	60f. Royal Mokhazni	2·00	90
220	1d. Type **77**	2·00	1·10
221	1d. Riff	1·90	1·10
222	1d. Zemmour woman	2·75	1·30
223	1d. Meknassa	2·50	80

78 King Hassan

1968

224	**78**	1f. multicoloured	10	10
225	**78**	2f. multicoloured	10	10
226	**78**	5f. multicoloured	10	10
227	**78**	10f. multicoloured	30	10
228	**78**	15f. multicoloured	30	10
229	**78**	20f. multicoloured	30	10
230	**78**	25f. multicoloured	30	10
231	**78**	30f. multicoloured	45	10
232	**78**	35f. multicoloured	55	25
233	**78**	40f. multicoloured	55	10
234	**78**	50f. multicoloured	75	10
235	**78**	60f. multicoloured	95	25
236	**78**	70f. multicoloured	4·50	90
237	**78**	75f. multicoloured	1·20	25
238	**78**	80f. multicoloured	1·20	25
239	-	90f. multicoloured	1·80	45
240	-	1d. multicoloured	2·20	25
241	-	2d. multicoloured	3·00	55
242	-	3d. multicoloured	6·00	1·10
243	-	5d. multicoloured	10·00	2·75

Nos. 239/43 bear a similar portrait of King Hassan, but are larger, 26½×40½ mm.

79 Red Crescent Nurse and Child

1968. 20th Anniv of W.H.O.

244	**79**	25f. brown, red and blue	40	10
245	**79**	40f. brown, red and slate	55	20

1968. Red Crescent. Moroccan Jewellery. As T **65**. Multicoloured.

246	25f. Pendant brooch	1·00	55
247	40f. Bracelet	1·50	70

80 Rotary Emblem, Conference Building and Map

1968. Rotary Int District Conf, Casablanca.

248	**80**	40f. gold, blue and green	75	25
249	**80**	1d. gold, ultramarine and blue	1·10	45

81 Belt Pattern

1968. "The Belts of Fez". Designs showing ornamental patterns.

250	**81**	25f. multicoloured	2·30	95
251	-	40f. multicoloured	2·75	1·40
252	-	60f. multicoloured	4·00	2·10
253	-	1d. multicoloured	7·50	4·25

82 Princess Lalla Meryem

1968. World Children's Day. Multicoloured.

254	25f. Type **82**	50	25
255	40f. Princess Lalla Asmaa	75	40
256	1d. Crown Prince Sidi Mohammed	1·50	90

83 Wrestling

1968. Olympic Games, Mexico. Multicoloured.

257	15f. Type **83**	40	25
258	20f. Basketball	45	40
259	25f. Cycling	70	40
260	40f. Boxing	95	45
261	60f. Running	1·50	55
262	1d. Football	1·90	70

84 Silver Crown

1968. Ancient Moroccan Coins.

263	**84**	20f. silver and purple	75	45
264	-	25f. gold and purple	95	55
265	-	40f. silver and green	1·70	80
266	-	60f. gold and red	2·00	90

Coins:—25f. Gold dinar; 40f. Silver dirham; 60f. Gold piece.

See also Nos. 270/1.

85 Costumes of Zagora, South Morocco

1969. Traditional Women's Costumes. Mult.

267	15f. Type **85** (postage)	1·70	90
268	25f. Ait Adidou costumes	2·40	1·10
269	1d. Ait Ouaouzguit costumes (air)	3·25	1·40

1969. Eighth Anniv of Coronation of Hassan II. As T **84** (silver coins).

270	1d. silver and blue	5·25	1·80
271	5d. silver and violet	11·50	6·75

Coins:—1d. One dirham coin of King Mohammed V; 5d. One dirham coin of King Hassan II.

86 Hands "reading" Braille on Map

1969. Protection of the Blind Week.

272	**86**	25f.+10f. multicoloured	55	25

87 "Actor"

1969. World Theatre Day.

273	**87**	1d. multicoloured	60	40

1969. 50th Anniv of League of Red Cross Societies. Moroccan Jewellery as T **65**. Mult.

274	25f.+5f. Bracelets	1·30	70
275	40f.+10f. Pendant	2·00	90

89 King Hassan II

1969. King Hassan's 40th Birthday.

276	**89**	1d. multicoloured	1·50	60
MS277		75×105 mm. **89** 1d. multicoloured (sold at 2d.50)	80·00	65·00

مؤتمر القمة الاسلامى
الرباط 10 رجب 1389

(90)

1969. Islamic Summit Conf, Rabat (1st issue). No. 240 optd with T **90**.

278	1d. multicoloured	5·50	4·00

See also No. 281.

91 Mahatma Gandhi

1969. Birth Centenary of Mahatma Gandhi.

279	**91**	40f. brown and lavender	95	45

92 ILO Emblem

1969. 50th Anniv of I.L.O.

280	**92**	50f. multicoloured	55	40

93 King Hassan on Horseback

1969. Islamic Summit Conference, Rabat (2nd issue).

281	**93**	1d. multicoloured	1·50	60

94 *Spahi Horseman* (Haram al Glaoui)

1970. Moroccan Art.

282	**94**	1d. multicoloured	1·40	60

1970. Flood Victims Relief Fund. Nos. 227/8 surch.

283	**78**	10f.+25f. multicoloured	4·50	4·50
284	**78**	15f.+25f. multicoloured	4·25	4·25

96 Drainage System, Fez

1970. 50th Congress of Public and Municipal Health Officials, Rabat.

285	**96**	60f. multicoloured	55	25

97 *Dance of the Guedra* (P. Beaubrun)

1970. Folklore Festival, Marrakesh.

286	**97**	40f. multicoloured	95	20

1970. Red Crescent. Moroccan Jewellery as T **65**. Multicoloured.

287	25f.+5f. Necklace	1·20	95
288	50f.+10t. Pendant	2·00	1·60

1970. Opening of Moroccan Postal Museum, Rabat. Sheet 244×120 mm containing Nos. 214/23 in *se-tenant* block of 10. Multicoloured.

MS289	Sold at 10d	25·00	25·00

1970. Population Census. No. 189 surch **1970 0,25** and Arabic inscr.

290	25f. on 60f. multicoloured	55	40

99 Dish Aerial, Souk el Arba des Sehoul Communications Station

1970. 17th Anniv of Revolution.

291	**99**	1d. multicoloured	95	55

100 Ruddy Shelduck

1970. Nature Protection. Wild Birds. Multicoloured

292	25f. Type **100**	1·20	50
293	40f. Houbara bustard	1·80	70

101 IEY Emblem and Moroccan with Book

1970. International Education Year.

294	**101**	60f. multicoloured	95	45

102 Symbols of UN

1970. 25th Anniv of U.N.O.

295	**102**	50f. multicoloured	75	40

103 League Emblem, Map and Laurel

1970. 25th Anniv of Arab League.

296	**103**	50f. multicoloured	55	40

104 Olive Grove and Extraction Plant

1970. World Olive-oil Production Year.

297	**104**	50f. black, brown & green	95	45

105 Es Sounna Mosque

1971. Restoration of Es Sounna Mosque, Rabat.

298	**105**	60f. multicoloured	75	40

106 "Heart" within Horse

1971. European and North African Heart Week.

299	**106**	50f. multicoloured	55	25

107 King Hassan II and Dam

1971. Tenth Anniv of King Hassan's Accession.

300	**107**	25f. multicoloured	55	25
MS301		115×100 mm. No. 300×4 (sold at 2d.50)	3·50	3·50

108 Palestine on Globe

1971. Palestine Week.

302	**108**	25f.+10f. multicoloured	55	25

1971. Red Crescent, Moroccan Jewellery. As T **65**. Multicoloured.

303	25f.+5f. "Arrow-head" brooch	1·50	90
304	40f.+10f. Square pendant	2·00	1·10

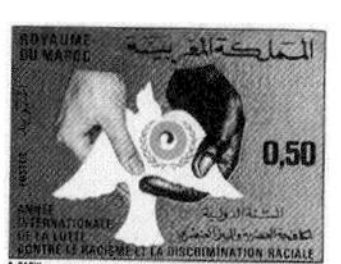

109 Hands holding Peace Dove

1971. Racial Equality Year.

305	**109**	50f. multicoloured	95	35

110 Musical Instrument

1971. Protection of the Blind Week.

306	**110**	40f.+10f. multicoloured	80	40

111 Children at Play

1971. International Children's Day.

307	**111**	40f. multicoloured	55	25

112 Shah Mohammed Reza Pahlavi of Iran

1971. 2,500th Anniv of Persian Empire.

308	**112**	1d. multicoloured	95	55

113 Aerial View of Mausoleum

1971. Mausoleum of Mohammed V. Multicoloured.

309	25f. Type **113**	40	25
310	50f. Tomb of Mohammed V	55	40
311	1d. Interior of Mausoleum (vert)	1·30	70

114 Football and Emblem

1971. Mediterranean Games, Izmir, Turkey. Multicoloured.

312	40f. Type **114**	75	45
313	60f. Athlete and emblem	95	45

115 APU Emblem

1971. 25th Anniv of Founding of Arab Postal Union at Sofar Conference.

314	**115**	25f. red, blue & light blue	45	25

116 Sun and Landscape

1971. 50th Anniv of Sherifian Phosphates Office.

315	**116**	70f. multicoloured	75	40

117 Torch and Book Year Emblem

1972. International Book Year.

316	**117**	1d. multicoloured	1·20	35

118 Lottery Symbol

1972. Creation of National Lottery.

317	**118**	25f. gold, black and brown	30	10

119 Bridge of Sighs

1972. UNESCO "Save Venice" Campaign. Multicoloured.

318	25f. Type **119**	25	20
319	50f. St. Mark's Basilica (horiz)	45	25
320	1d. Lion of St. Marks (horiz)	1·00	50

120 Mizmar (double- horned flute)

1972. Protection of the Blind Week.

321	**120**	25f.+10f. multicoloured	75	75

121 Bridge and Motorway

1972. Second African Highways Conference, Rabat.

322	**121**	75f. multicoloured	95	45

122 Moroccan Stamp of 1969, and Postmark

1972. Stamp Day.

323	**122**	1d. multicoloured	75	40

1972. Red Crescent. Moroccan Jewellery. As T **65**. Multicoloured.

324	25f.+5f. Jewelled bangles	1·20	1·20
325	70f.+10f. Filigree pendant	1·70	1·40

123 *Betrothal of Imilchil* (Tayeb Lahlou)

1972. Folklore Festival, Marrakesh.

326	**123**	60f. multicoloured	1·00	55

124 Dove on African Map

1972. Ninth Organization of African Unity Summit Conference, Rabat.

327	**124**	25f. multicoloured	45	15

125 Polluted Beach

1972. U.N. Environmental Conservation Conference, Stockholm.

328	**125**	50f. multicoloured	55	25

126 Running

1972. Olympic Games, Munich.

329	**126**	25f. red, pink and black	30	25
330	-	50f. violet, lilac and black	45	25
331	-	75f. green, yellow & black	75	40
332	-	1d. blue, lt blue & black	1·00	65

Designs:—50f. Wrestling; 75f. Football; 1d. Cycling.

127 *Sonchus pinnatifidus*

1972. Moroccan Flowers (1st series). Multicoloured

333	25f. Type **127**	65	15
334	40f. *Amberboa crupinoides*	1·00	40

See also Nos. 375/6.

128 Sand Gazelle

1972. Nature Protection. Fauna. Multicoloured.

335	25f. Type **128**	1·50	70
336	40f. Barbary sheep	2·50	90

129 Rabat Carpet

1972. Moroccan Carpets (1st series). Multicoloured

337	50f. Type **129**	1·20	55
338	75f. Rabat carpet with "star-shaped" centre	1·80	80

See also Nos. 380/1, 406/7, 433/4, 485/7 and 513.

130 Mother and Child with UN Emblem

1972. International Children's Day.

339	**130**	75f. blue, yellow and green	55	25

131 "Postman" and "Stamp"

1973. Stamp Day.

340	**131**	25f. multicoloured	45	25

132 Global Weather Map

1973. Centenary of W.M.O.

341	**132**	70f. multicoloured	95	45

133 King Hassan and Arms

1973

342	**133**	1f. multicoloured	10	10
343	**133**	2f. multicoloured	10	10
344	**133**	5f. multicoloured	10	10
345	**133**	10f. multicoloured	10	10
346	**133**	15f. multicoloured	10	10
347	**133**	20f. multicoloured	30	10
348	**133**	25f. multicoloured	30	10
349	**133**	30f. multicoloured	30	10
350	**133**	35f. multicoloured	45	25
351	**133**	40f. multicoloured	6·00	80
352	**133**	50f. multicoloured	55	10
353	**133**	60f. multicoloured	75	10
354	**133**	70f. multicoloured	55	10
355	**133**	75f. multicoloured	70	25
356	**133**	80f. multicoloured	75	55
357	**133**	90f. multicoloured	95	25
358	**133**	1d. multicoloured	2·50	25
359	**133**	2d. multicoloured	5·50	80
360	**133**	3d. multicoloured	7·25	1·40
361	**133**	5d. multicoloured (brown background)	5·25	1·40
361a	**133**	5d. multicoloured (pink background)	5·25	1·40

مناظرة
السياحة
1973

(134)

1973. Nat Tourist Conference. Nos. 324/5 surch with T **134**.

362	25f. on 5f. multicoloured	3·00	3·00
363	70f. on 10f. multicoloured	3·00	3·00

On No. 363 the Arabic text is arranged in one line.

135 Tambours

1973. Protection of the Blind Week.

364	**135**	70f.+10f. multicoloured	95	70

136 Kaaba, Mecca, and Mosque, Rabat

1973. Prophet Mohammed's Birthday.

365	**136**	25f. multicoloured	45	10

137 Roses and M'Gouna

1973. M'Gouna Rose Festival.

366	**137**	25f. multicoloured	75	25

138 Handclasp and Torch

1973. Tenth Anniv of Organization of African Unity.

367	**138**	70f. multicoloured	55	25

139 Folk-dancers

1973. Folklore Festival, Marrakesh. Multicoloured.

368	50f. Type **139**	65	25
369	1d. Folk-musicians	1·00	45

1973. Red Crescent. Moroccan Jewellery. As T **65**. Multicoloured.

370	25f.+5f. Locket	1·60	90
371	70f.+10f. Bracelet inlaid with pearls	1·90	1·10

140 Solar System

1973. 500th Birth Anniv of Nicholas Copernicus.

372	**140**	70f. multicoloured	95	40

141 Microscope

1973. 25th Anniv of W.H.O.

373	**141**	70f. multicoloured	75	25

142 Interpol Emblem and Fingerprint

1973. 50th Anniv of International Criminal Police Organization (Interpol).

374	**142**	70f. multicoloured	55	25

1973. Moroccan Flowers (2nd series). As T **127**. Multicoloured.

375	25f. *Chrysanthemum carinatum* (horiz)	1·10	45
376	1d. *Amberboa muricata*	1·70	70

143 Striped Hyena

1973. Nature Protection. Multicoloured.

377	25f. Type **143**	1·70	45
378	50f. Eleonora's falcon (vert)	4·00	1·10

144 Map and Arrows

1973. Meeting of Maghreb Committee for Co-ordination of Posts and Telecommunications, Tunis.

379	**144**	25f. multicoloured	55	25

1973. Moroccan Carpets (2nd series). As T **129**. Multicoloured.

380	25f. Carpet from the High Atlas	1·20	45
381	70f. Tazenakht carpet	1·80	70

145 Golf Club and Ball

1974. International "Hassan II Trophy" Golf Grand Prix, Rabat.

382	**145**	70f. multicoloured	1·50	70

المؤتمر الاسلامي - لاهور
1394

(146)

1974. Islamic Summit Conference, Lahore, Pakistan. No. 281 optd with T **146**.

383	1d. multicoloured	4·00	2·10

147 Human Rights Emblem

1974. 25th Anniv (1973) of Declaration of Human Rights.

384	**147**	70f. multicoloured	55	25

148 Vanadinite

1974. Moroccan Mineral Sources. Multicoloured.

385	25f. Type **148**	2·75	90
386	70f. Erythrine	4·25	1·40

149 Marrakesh Minaret

1974. 173rd District of Rotary International Annual Conference, Marrakesh.

387	**149**	70f. multicoloured	95	45

150 UPU Emblem and Congress Dates

1974. Centenary of U.P.U.
388 **150** 25f. black, red and green 45 25
389 - 1d. multicoloured 95 45
Design:—Horiz: 1d. Commemorative scroll.

151 Drummers and Dancers

1974. 15th Folklore Festival, Marrakesh. Multicolured
390 25f. Type **151** 75 25
391 70f. Juggler with woman 1·50 65

152 Environmental Emblem and Scenes

1974. World Environmental Day.
392 **152** 25f. multicoloured 45 15

154 Flintlock Pistol

1974. Red Crescent. Moroccan Firearms. Multicoloured
397 25f.+5f. Type **154** 95 90
398 70f.+10f. Gunpowder box 1·50 1·50

155 Stamps, Postmark and Magnifying Glass

1974. Stamp Day.
399 **155** 70f. multicoloured 75 25

الاحصاء الفلاحي

1,00

(156)

1974. No. D393 surch with T **156**.
400 1d. on 5f. orange, green & blk 2·30 1·50

157 World Cup Trophy

1974. World Cup Football Championship, West Germany.
401 **157** 1d. multicoloured 1·50 80

158 Erbab (two-string fiddle)

1974. Blind Week.
402 **158** 70f.+10f. multicoloured 1·50 70
See also No. 423.

1974. Eighth International Blood Donors' Organization Federation Congress. No. **MS**289 optd **8 CONGRES DE LA F.I.O.D.S.**
MS403 244×120 mm. (Sold at 20d.) 35·00 35·00

160 Double-spurred Francolin

1974. Moroccan Animals. Multicoloured.
404 25f. Type **160** 75 35
405 70f. Leopard (horiz) 1·20 55

1974. Moroccan Carpets (3rd series). As T **129**. Multicoloured.
406 25f. Zemmour carpet 75 25
407 1d. Beni M'Guild carpet 1·50 65

162 Jasmine

1975. Flowers (1st series). Multicoloured.
408 25f. Type **162** 70 25
409 35f. Orange lilies 1·00 40
410 70f. Poppies 1·50 55
411 90f. Carnations 2·00 80
See also Nos. 417/20.

163 Aragonite

1975. Minerals. Multicoloured.
412 50f. Type **163** 2·10 70
413 1d. Agate 3·75 1·10
See also Nos. 543 and 563/4.

1975. Red Crescent. Moroccan Jewellery. As T **65**. Multicoloured.
414 25f.+5f. Pendant 95 90
415 70f.+10f. Earring 1·50 1·20

165 *The Water-carrier* (Feu Taieb-Lalou)

1975. Moroccan Painters.
416 **165** 1d. multicoloured 1·40 50

1975. Flowers (2nd series). As T **162**. Mult.
417 10f. Daisies 30 25
418 50f. Pelargoniums 75 25
419 60f. Orange blossom 1·20 60
420 1d. Pansies 1·50 90

166 Collector with Stamp Album

1975. Stamp Day.
421 **166** 40f. multicoloured 45 10

167 Dancer with Rifle

1975. 16th Nat Folklore Festival, Marrakesh.
422 **167** 1d. multicoloured 1·20 45

1975. Blind Week. As T **158**. Multicoloured.
423 1d. Mandolin 45 10

168 Animals in Forest (child's drawing)

1975. Children's Week.
424 **168** 25f. multicoloured 50 20

169 Games Emblem and Athletes

1975. Seventh Mediterranean Games, Algiers.
425 **169** 40f. multicoloured 55 25

170 Waldrapp

1975. Fauna. Multicoloured.
426 40f. Type **170** 2·40 55
427 1d. Caracal (vert) 2·40 85
See also Nos. 470/1.

1975. Green March (1st issue). Nos. 370/1 optd **1975** and Arabic inscr.
428 25f. (+ 5f.) multicoloured 3·00 2·75
429 70f. (+ 10f.) multicoloured 3·00 2·75
The premiums on the stamps are obliterated.
See also No. 435.

172 King Mohammed V greeting Crowd

1975. 20th Anniv of Independence. Mult.
430 40f. Type **172** 55 25
431 1d. King Hassan (vert) 95 55
432 1d. King Hassan V wearing fez (vert) 90 55
MS432a 188×96 mm. Nos. 430/2 22·00 22·00

1975. Moroccan Carpets (4th series). As T **129**. Multicoloured.
433 25f. Ouled Besseba carpet 1·00 55
434 1d. Ait Ouaouzguid carpet 1·80 75

173 Marchers crossing Desert

1975. Green March (2nd issue).
435 **173** 40f. multicoloured 45 25

174 Fez Coin of 1883/4

1976. Moroccan Coins (1st series). Multicoloured.
436 5f. Type **174** 45 40
437 15f. Rabat silver coin 1774/5 65 25
438 35f. Sabta coin, 13/14th-centuries 1·40 55
439 40f. Type **174** 55 25
440 50f. As No. 437 95 45
441 65f. As No. 438 95 55
442 1d. Sabta coin, 12/13th centuries 1·30 70
For Nos. 439/40 in smaller size, see Nos. 520/b.
See also Nos. 458/67a.

175 Interior of Mosque

1976. Millennium of Ibn Zaidoun Mosque. Mult.
443 40f. Type **175** 45 10
444 65f. Interior archways (vert) 75 40

176 Moroccan Family

1976. Family Planning.
445 **176** 40f. multicoloured 45 25

177 Bou Anania College, Fez

1976. Moroccan Architecture.
446 **177** 1d. multicoloured 95 45

178 Temple Sculpture

1976. Borobudur Temple Preservation Campaign. Multicoloured.
447 40f. Type **178** 70 25
448 1d. View of Temple 1·80 35

179 Dome of the Rock, Jerusalem

1976. Sixth Anniv of Islamic Conference.
449 **179** 1d. multicoloured 95 25

1976. Red Crescent. Moroccan Jewellery. As T **65**. Multicoloured.
450 40f. Jewelled purse 95 70
451 1d. Jewelled pectoral 1·50 90

180 George Washington, King Hassan I, Statue of Liberty and Mausoleum of Mohammed V

1976. Bicentenary of American Revolution. Mult.

452	40f. Flags of USA and Morocco (horiz)	75	55
453	1d. Type **180**	1·50	80

181 Wrestling

1976. Olympic Games, Montreal. Multicoloured.

454	35f. Type **181**	45	10
455	40f. Cycling	65	35
456	50f. Boxing	1·10	60
457	1d. Running	1·60	90

1976. Moroccan Coins (2nd series). As T **174**. Multicoloured.

458	5f. Medieval silver mohur	45	10
459	10f. Gold mohur	40	10
460	15f. Gold coin	45	10
461	20f. Gold coin (different)	60	35
461a	25f. As No. 437	5·25	90
462	30f. As No. 459	60	35
463	35f. Silver dinar	1·00	45
464	60f. As No. 458	75	25
465	70f. Copper coin	1·60	75
466	75f. As No. 463	95	30
466a	80f. As No. 460	9·00	1·80
467	2d. As No. 465	2·50	70
467a	3d. As No. 461	14·00	2·30

182 Early and Modern Telephones with Dish Aerial

1976. Telephone Centenary.

468	**182**	1d. multicoloured	95	25

183 Gold Medallion

1976. Blind Week.

469	**183**	50f. multicoloured	55	25

1976. Birds. As T **170**. Multicoloured.

470	40f. Dark chanting goshawk (vert)	2·50	90
471	1d. Purple swamphen (vert)	3·75	1·40

185 King Hassan, Emblems and Map

1976. First Anniv of "Green March".

472	**185**	40f. multicoloured	95	45

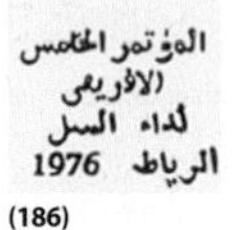

(186)

1976. Fifth African Tuberculosis Conference. Nos. 414/15 optd with T **186**.

473	25f. multicoloured	2·50	2·40
474	70f. multicoloured	3·00	2·75

187 Globe and Peace Dove

1976. Conference of Non-Aligned Countries, Colombo.

475	**187**	1d. red, black and blue	55	25

188 African Nations Cup

1976. African Nations Football Championship.

476	**188**	1d. multicoloured	75	40

189 Letters encircling Globe

1977. Stamp Day.

477	**189**	40f. multicoloured	45	10

190 *Aeonium arboreum*

1977. Flowers. Multicoloured.

478	40f. Type **190**	75	45
479	50f. *Malope trifida* (24×38 mm)	2·75	90
480	1d. *Hesperolaburnum platyclarpum*	1·50	70

191 Ornamental Candle Lamps

1977. Procession of the Candles, Sale.

481	**191**	40f. multicoloured	55	25

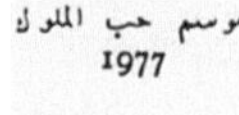

(192)

1977. Cherry Festival. No. D394 surch with T **192**.

482	40f. on 10f. Cherries	95	45

193 Map and Emblem

1977. Fifth Congress. Organization of Arab Towns.

483	**193**	50f. multicoloured	45	10

194 APU Emblem

1977. 25th Anniv of Arab Postal Union.

484	**194**	1d. multicoloured	75	25

1977. Moroccan Carpets (5th series). As T **129**. Multicoloured.

485	35f. Marmoucha carpet	45	25
486	40f. Ait Haddou carpet	75	25
487	1d. Henbel rug, Sale	1·20	55

195 Zither

1977. Blind Week.

488	**195**	1d. multicoloured	1·50	45

196 Mohammed Ali Jinnah

1977. Birth Centenary of Mohammed Ali Jinnah.

489	**196**	70f. multicoloured	55	25

197 Marcher with Flag

1977. Second Anniv of "Green March".

490	**197**	1d. multicoloured	75	25

198 Assembly Hall

1977. Opening of House of Representatives.

491	**198**	1d. multicoloured	75	25
MS492		121×86 mm. No. 491 (sold at 3d.)	3·75	3·75

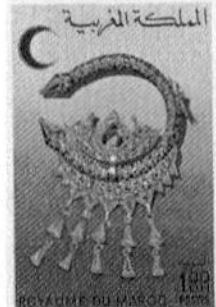
199 Silver Brooch

1977. Red Crescent.

493	**199**	1d. multicoloured	2·75	90

200 Bowl with Funnel

1978. Moroccan Copperware. Multicoloured.

494	40f. Type **200**	45	25
495	1d. Bowl with cover	1·20	55

201 Development Emblem

1978. Sahara Development. Multicoloured.

496	40f. Type **201**	45	25
497	1d. Fish in net and camels at oasis (horiz)	1·00	40

202 Decorative Pot with Lid

1978. Blind Week. Multicoloured.

498	1d. Type **202**	95	40
499	1d. Decorative jar	1·00	40

203 Map and Red Cross within Red Crescent

1978. Tenth Conference of Arab Red Crescent and Red Cross Societies.

500	**203**	1d. red and black	75	40

204 View of Fez

1978. Rotary International Meeting, Fez.

501	**204**	1d. multicoloured	75	40

205 Dome of the Rock

1978. Palestine Welfare.

502	**205**	5f. multicoloured	30	10
503	**205**	10f. multicoloured	30	10

206 Flautist and Folk Dancers

1978. National Folklore Festival, Marrakesh.

504	**206**	1d. multicoloured	2·00	70

207 Sugar Field and Crushing Plant

1978. Sugar Industry.

505	**207**	40f. multicoloured	45	25

208 Yacht

1978. World Sailing Championships.

506	**208**	1d. multicoloured	95	45

209 Tree, Tent and Scout Emblem

1978. Pan-Arab Scout Festival, Rabat.
507 **209** 40f. multicoloured 45 25

210 Moulay Idriss

1978. Moulay Idriss Great Festival.
508 **210** 40f. multicoloured 45 25

211 Human Rights Emblem

1978. 30th Anniv of Declaration of Human Rights.
509 **211** 1d. multicoloured 75 25

212 Houses in Agadir

1979. Southern Moroccan Architecture (1st series). Multicoloured.
510 40f. Type **212** 45 25
511 1d. Old fort at Marrakesh 1·00 25

See also Nos. 536 and 562.

213 Player, Football and Cup

1979. Mohammed V Football Cup.
512 **213** 40f. multicoloured 45 25

1979. Moroccan Carpets (6th series). As T **129**. Multicoloured.
513 40f. Marmoucha carpet 75 25

214 Decorated Pot

1979. Blind Week.
514 **214** 1d. multicoloured 1·50 70

215 *Procession from a Mosque*

1979. Paintings by Mohamed Ben Ali Rbati. Mult.
515 40f. Type **215** 45 25
516 1d. *Religious Ceremony in a Mosque* (horiz) 1·00 40

216 Coffee Pot and Heater

1979. Red Cresent. Brassware. Multicoloured.
517 40f. Engraved circular boxes 45 25
518 1d. Type **216** 1·50 55

217 Costumed Girls

1979. National Folklore Festival, Marrakesh.
519 **217** 40f. multicoloured 45 25

1979. Moroccan Coins. As T **174**, but smaller, 17½×22½ mm.
520 40f. multicoloured 50 10
520b 50f. multicoloured 60 10

218 Curved Dagger in Jewelled Sheath

1979. Ancient Weapons.
521 **218** 1d. black and yellow 95 25

219 King Hassan II

1979. King Hassan's 50th Birthday.
522 **219** 1d. multicoloured 95 25

220 Festival Emblem

1979. Fourth Arab Youth Festival, Rabat.
523 **220** 1d. multicoloured 95 25

221 King Hassan II

1979. 25th Anniv of Revolution of King and People.
524 **221** 1d. multicoloured 55 25

222 World Map superimposed on Open Book

1979. 50th Anniv of Int Bureau of Education.
525 **222** 1d. brown and yellow 75 25

223 Pilgrims in Wuquf, Arafat

1979. Pilgrimage to Mecca.
526 **223** 1d. multicoloured 95 45

استرجاع اقليم وادى الذهب
1979_8_14
(224)

1979. Recovery of Oued Eddahab Province. Design as No. 497, with face value amended (40f.), optd with T **224**.
527 40f. multicoloured 45 10
528 1d. multicoloured 1·00 45

225 *Centaurium*

1979. Flowers. Multicoloured.
529 40f. Type **225** 45 10
530 1d. *Leucanthemum catanance* 1·40 25

226 Children around Globe

1979. International Year of the Child.
531 **226** 40f. multicoloured 1·00 40

227 European Otter

1979. Wildlife. Multicoloured.
532 40f. Type **227** 1·30 55
533 1d. Moussier's redstart 2·50 55

228 Traffic Signs

1980. Road Safety. Multicoloured.
534 40f. Type **228** 30 10
535 1d. Children at crossing 65 25

229 Fortress

1980. South Moroccan Architecture (2nd series).
536 **229** 1d. multicoloured 75 25

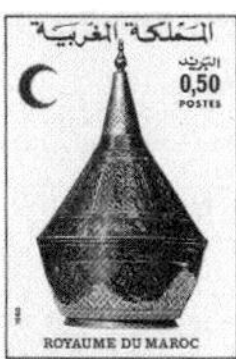

230 Copper Bowl with Lid

1980. Red Crescent. Multicoloured.
537 50f. Type **230** 95 45
538 70f. Copper kettle and brazier 1·50 45

231 Pot

1980. Blind Week.
539 **231** 40f. multicoloured 40 10

232 Mechanized Sorting Office, Rabat

1980. Stamp Day.
540 **232** 40f. multicoloured 45 10

233 World Map and Rotary Emblem

1980. 75th Anniv of Rotary International.
541 **233** 1d. multicoloured 75 25

234 Leather Bag and Cloth

1980. Fourth Textile and Leather Exhibition, Casablanca.
542 **234** 1d. multicoloured 75 25

1980. Minerals (2nd series). As T **163**. Mult.
543 40f. Gypsum 1·90 70

235 Peregrine Falcon

1980. Hunting with Falcon.
544 **235** 40f. multicoloured 1·90 70

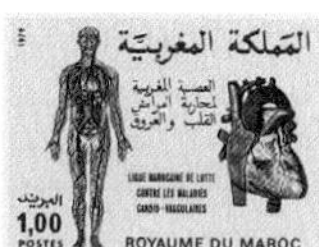

236 Diagram of Blood Circulation and Heart

1980. Campaign against Cardiovascular Diseases.
545 **236** 1d. multicoloured 95 35

237 Decade Emblem and Human Figures

1980. Decade for Women.
546 **237** 40f. mauve and blue 45 10
547 - 1d. multicoloured 1·00 35

Design:—1d. Decade and United Nations emblems.

238 Harnessed Horse

1980. Ornamental Harnesses. Multicoloured.

548		40f. Harnessed horse (different)	45	25
549		1d. Type **238**	1·00	40

239 Satellite orbiting Earth and Dish Aerial

1980. World Meteorological Day.

550	**239**	40f. multicoloured	45	10

240 Light Bulb and Fuel Can

1980. Energy Conservation. Multicoloured.

551		40f. Type **240**	30	10
552		1d. Hand holding petrol pump	1·20	25

241 Conference Emblem

1980. World Tourism Conference, Manila.

553	**241**	40f. multicoloured	30	10

242 Tree bridging Straits of Gibraltar

1980. European–African Liaison over the Straits of Gibraltar.

554	**242**	1d. multicoloured	95	45

243 Flame and Marchers

1980. Fifth Anniv of "The Green March".

555	**243**	1d. multicoloured	95	35

244 Holy Kaaba, Mecca

1980. 1400th Anniv of Hegira. Multicoloured.

556		40f. Type **244**	30	10
557		1d. Mosque, Mecca	75	25
MS557a		137×91 mm. Nos. 555/6	2·50	2·50

245 *Senecio antheuphorbium*

1980. Flowers. Multicoloured.

558		40f. Type **245**	1·30	35
559		1d. *Periploca laevigata*	2·50	65

246 Painting by Aherdan

1980. Paintings.

560	-	40f. bistre and brown	30	10
561	**246**	1d. multicoloured	95	25

Design:—40f. Composition of bird and feathers.

247 Nejjarine Fountain, Fez

1981. Moroccan Architecture (3rd series).

562	**247**	40f. multicoloured	30	10

1981. Minerals (3rd series). Vert designs as T **163**. Multicoloured.

563		40f. Onyx	1·80	45
564		1d. Malachite-azurite	2·50	1·10

248 King Hassan II

1981. 25th Anniv of Independence. Mult.

565		60f. Type **248**	75	25
566		60f. Map, flags, broken chains and "25"	75	25
567		60f. King Mohammed V.	75	25

249 King Hassan II

1981. 20th Anniv of King Hassan's Coronation.

568	**249**	1d.30 multicoloured	95	45

250 *Source* (Jillali Gharbaoul)

1981. Moroccan Painting.

569	**250**	1d.30 multicoloured	95	40

251 *Anagalis monelli*

1981. Flowers. Multicoloured.

570		40f. Type **251**	60	10
571		70f. *Bubonium intricatum*	1·30	45

252 King Hassan as Major General

1981. 25th Anniv of Moroccan Armed Forces.

572	**252**	60f. lilac, gold and green	45	25
573	-	60f. multicoloured	45	25
574	-	60f. lilac, gold and green	45	25

Designs:—No. 573, Army badge; 574, King Mohammed V (founder).

253 Caduceus (Telecommunications and Health)

1981. World Telecommunications Day.

575	**253**	1d.30 multicoloured	95	45

254 Plate with Pattern

1981. Blind Week. Multicoloured.

576		50f. Type **254**	45	10
577		1d.30 Plate with ship pattern	75	40

255 Musicians and Dancers

1981. 22nd National Folklore Festival, Marrakesh.

578	**255**	1d.30 multicoloured	1·20	40

256 "Seboula" Dagger

1981. Ancient Weapons.

579	**256**	1d.30 multicoloured	95	40

257 Pestle and Mortar

1981. Red Crescent. Moroccan Copperware. Mult.

580		60f. Type **257**	45	25
581		1d.30 Tripod brazier	1·00	40

258 Hands holding IYDP Emblem

1981. International Year of Disabled People.

582	**258**	60f. multicoloured	45	15

259 *Iphiclides feisthamelii Lotteri*

1981. Butterflies (1st series). Multicoloured.

583		60f. Type **259**	1·90	60
584		1d.30 *Zerynthina rumina africana*	3·75	1·30

See also Nos. 609/10.

260 King Hassan and Marchers

1981. Sixth Anniv of "Green March".

585	**260**	1d.30 multicoloured	95	45

261 Town Buildings and Congress Emblem

1981. Tenth International Twinned Towns Congress, Casablanca.

586	**261**	1d.30 multicoloured	95	50

262 Dome of the Rock

1981. Palestinian Solidarity Day.

587	**262**	60f. multicoloured	45	10

1981. 12th Arab Summit Conference, Fez. Nos. 502/3 surch **1981 0,40.**

588	**205**	40f. on 5f. multicoloured	6·50	5·00
588a	**205**	40f. on 10f. multicoloured	4·75	3·50

264 Terminal Building and Runway

1981. First Anniv of Mohammed V Airport.

589	**264**	1d.30 multicoloured	95	45

265 Al Massira Dam

1981. Al Massira Dam.

590	**265**	60f. multicoloured	45	20

266 King Hassan II

1981. King Hassan II.

No.	Type	Description	Unused	Used
591	**266**	5f. red, blue and gold	10	10
592	**266**	10f. red, yellow and gold	10	10
593	**266**	15f. red, green and gold	10	10
594	**266**	20f. red, pink and gold	10	10
595	**266**	25f. red, lilac and gold	10	10
596	**266**	30f. blue, lt blue & gold	10	10
597	**266**	35f. blue, yellow and gold	10	10
598	**266**	40f. blue, green and gold	10	10
599	**266**	50f. blue, pink and gold	30	10
600	**266**	60f. blue, lilac and gold	30	10
601	**266**	65f. blue, lilac and gold	30	10
602	**266**	70f. violet, yellow and gold	30	10
603	**266**	75f. violet, green and gold	30	15
604	**266**	80f. violet, pink and gold	30	15
605	**266**	90f. violet, lilac and gold	45	15
605a	**266**	1d.25 red, mauve & gold	45	15
605b	**266**	4d. brown, yell & gold	1·30	55

See also Nos. 624/9, 675a, 718/22, 759/61, 809, 866, 895/6, 930, 940a and 959a/h.

267 Horse Jumping

1981. Equestrian Sports.

No.	Type	Description	Unused	Used
606	**267**	1d.30 multicoloured	1·80	45

268 Ait Quaquzguit

1982. Carpets (1st series). Multicoloured.

No.	Description	Unused	Used
607	50f. Type **268**	30	10
608	1d.30 Ouled Besseba	95	40

See also Nos. 653/4.

1982. Butterflies and Moths (2nd series). As T **259**. Multicoloured.

No.	Description	Unused	Used
609	60f. *Celerio oken lineata*	1·70	55
610	1d.30 *Mesoacidalia aglaja lyauteyi*	3·25	1·10

269 Tree and Emblem

1982. World Forestry Day.

No.	Type	Description	Unused	Used
611	**269**	40f. multicoloured	30	10

270 Jug

1982. Blind Week.

No.	Type	Description	Unused	Used
612	**270**	1d. multicoloured	55	25

271 Dancers

1982. Popular Art.

No.	Type	Description	Unused	Used
613	**271**	1d.40 multicoloured	75	25

272 Candlestick

1982. Red Crescent.

No.	Type	Description	Unused	Used
614	**272**	1d.40 multicoloured	95	35

273 Painting by M. Mezian

1982. Moroccan Painting.

No.	Type	Description	Unused	Used
615	**273**	1d.40 multicoloured	95	45

274 Buildings and People on Graph

1982. Population and Housing Census.

No.	Type	Description	Unused	Used
616	**274**	60f. multicoloured	45	25

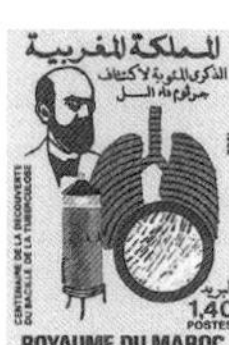
275 Dr. Koch, Lungs and Apparatus

1982. Centenary of Discovery of Tubercle Bacillus.

No.	Type	Description	Unused	Used
617	**275**	1d.40 multicoloured	1·20	55

276 ITU Emblem

1982. I.T.U. Delegates' Conference, Nairobi.

No.	Type	Description	Unused	Used
618	**276**	1d.40 multicoloured	75	25

277 Wheat, Globe, Sea and FAO Emblem

1982. World Food Day.

No.	Type	Description	Unused	Used
619	**277**	60f. multicoloured	45	15

278 Class XDd Diesel Locomotive (1956) and Route Map

1982. Unity Railway.

No.	Type	Description	Unused	Used
620	**278**	1d.40 multicoloured	1·20	40

279 APU Emblem

1982. 30th Anniv of Arab Postal Union.

No.	Type	Description	Unused	Used
621	**279**	1d.40 multicoloured	75	25

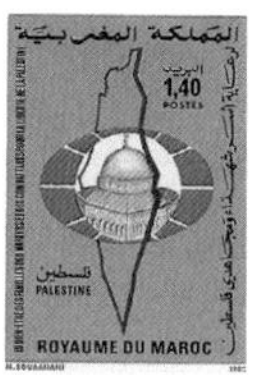
280 Dome of the Rock and Map of Palestine

1982. Palestinian Solidarity.

No.	Type	Description	Unused	Used
622	**280**	1d.40 multicoloured	75	25

281 Red Coral

1982. Red Coral of Al Hoceima.

No.	Type	Description	Unused	Used
623	**281**	1d.40 multicoloured	1·60	55

1983. Size 25×32 mm but inscribed "1982".

No.	Type	Description	Unused	Used
624	**266**	1d. red, blue and gold	45	10
625	**266**	1d.40 brown, lt brown & gold	45	10
626	**266**	2d. red, green and gold	75	25
627	**266**	3d. brown, yellow and gold	1·10	30
628	**266**	5d. brown, green and gold	1·80	70
629	**266**	10d. brown, orange and gold	3·50	1·30

282 Moroccan Stamps

1983. Stamp Day.

No.	Type	Description	Unused	Used
630	**282**	1d.40 multicoloured	75	25

283 King Hassan II

1983

No.	Type	Description	Unused	Used
631	**283**	1d.40 multicoloured	55	15
632	**283**	2d. multicoloured	75	25
633	**283**	3d. multicoloured	1·00	40
634	**283**	5d. multicoloured	1·70	70
635	**283**	10d. multicoloured	3·50	1·30

284 Decorated Pot

1983. Blind Week.

No.	Type	Description	Unused	Used
636	**284**	1d.40 multicoloured	95	35

285 Musicians

1983. Popular Arts.

No.	Type	Description	Unused	Used
637	**285**	1d.40 multicoloured	95	45

286 Ornamental Stand

1983. Red Crescent.

No.	Type	Description	Unused	Used
638	**286**	1d.40 multicoloured	95	45

287 Commission Emblem

1983. 25th Anniv of Economic Commission for Africa.

No.	Type	Description	Unused	Used
639	**287**	1d.40 multicoloured	75	25

288 *Tecoma* sp.

1983. Flowers. Multicoloured.

No.	Description	Unused	Used
640	60c. Type **288**	70	25
641	1d.40 *Strelitzia* sp.	1·80	45

289 King Hassan II, Map and Sultan of Morocco

1983. 30th Anniv of Revolution.

No.	Type	Description	Unused	Used
642	**289**	80c. multicoloured	45	25

290 Games Emblem and Stylized Sports

1983. Ninth Mediterranean Games, Casablanca.

No.	Type	Description	Unused	Used
644	**290**	80c. blue, silver and gold	45	30
645	-	1d. multicoloured	55	35
646	-	2d. multicoloured	1·10	65
MS647		92×151 mm. Nos. 644/6. Imperf. (sold at 5d)	3·50	3·50

Designs:—Vert: 1d. Games emblem. Horiz: 2d. Stylized runner.

291 Ploughing

1983. Touiza.
648 291 80c. multicoloured 45 25

292 Symbol of "Green March"

1983. Eighth Anniv of "Green March".
649 292 80f. multicoloured 45 25

293 Palestinian formed from Map and Globe

1983. Palestinian Welfare.
650 293 80f. multicoloured 45 20

294 Ouzoud Waterfall

1983. Ouzoud Waterfall.
651 294 80f. multicoloured 45 25

295 Children's Emblem

1983. Children's Day. Multicoloured.
652 295 2d. multicoloured 95 25

1983. Carpets (2nd series). As T 268. Mult.
653 60f. Zemmouri 30 10
654 1d.40 Zemmouri (different) 95 35

296 Transport and WCY Emblem

1983. World Communications Year.
655 296 2d. multicoloured 1·20 45

297 Views of Jerusalem and Fez

1984. Twinned Towns.
656 297 2d. multicoloured 1·20 40

298 Fennec Fox

1984. Animals. Multicoloured.
657 80f. Type 298 80 30
658 2d. Lesser Egyptian jerboa 1·80 65

299 Map of League Members and Emblem

1984. 39th Anniv of League of Arab States.
659 299 2d. multicoloured 95 25

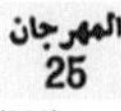
(300)

1984. 25th National Folklore Festival, Marrakesh. No. 578 optd with T 300.
660 255 1d.30 multicoloured 95 45

301 *Metha viridis*

1984. Flowers. Multicoloured.
661 80f. Type 301 45 15
662 2d. Aloe 1·20 50

302 Decorated Bowl

1984. Blind Week.
663 302 80f. multicoloured 45 25

303 Lidded Container

1984. Red Crescent.
664 303 2d. multicoloured 95 45

304 Sports Pictograms

1984. Olympic Games, Los Angeles.
665 304 2d. multicoloured 95 45

305 Dove carrying Children

1984. International Child Victims' Day.
666 305 2d. multicoloured 95 25

306 UPU Emblem and Ribbons

1984. Universal Postal Union Day.
667 306 2d. multicoloured 75 40

307 Hands holding Ears of Wheat

1984. World Food Day.
668 307 80f. multicoloured 70 25

308 Stylized Bird, Aeroplane and Emblem

1984. 40th Anniv of I.C.A.O.
669 308 2d. multicoloured 75 25

309 Inscribed Scroll

1984. Ninth Anniv of "Green March".
670 309 80f. multicoloured 45 10

311 Flag and Dome of the Rock

1984. Palestinian Welfare.
672 311 2d. multicoloured 95 35

312 Emblem and People

1984. 36th Anniv of Human Rights Declaration.
673 312 2d. multicoloured 75 25

313 Aidi

1984. Dogs. Multicoloured.
674 80f. Type 313 1·20 35
675 2d. Sloughi 2·10 75

1984. King Hassan II. Vert design as T 266 inscr '1984'. Size 27×34 mm.
675a 1d.70 lake-brown, azure and gold 60 60

314 Weighing Baby

1985. Infant Survival Campaign.
676 314 80f. multicoloured 45 25

315 Children playing in Garden

1985. First Moroccan S.O.S. Children's Village.
677 315 2d. multicoloured 75 25

316 Sherifian Mail Postal Cancellation, 1892

1985. Stamp Day.
678 316 2d. grey, pink and black 95 25
MS679 148×98 mm. 316 80c.×6, grey, black and (a) emerald; (b) yellow; (c) blue; (d) vermilion; (e) violet; (f) brown (sold at 5d.) 5·00 5·00

See also Nos. 698/9, 715/16, 757/8, 778/9, 796/7, 818/19, 841/2, 877/8, 893/4, 910/11 and 924/5.

317 Emblem, Birds, Landscape and Fish

1985. World Environment Day.
680 317 80f. multicoloured 45 10

318 Musicians

1985. National Folklore Festival, Marrakesh.
681 318 2d. multicoloured 1·20 45

319 Decorated Plate

1985. Blind Week.
682 319 80f. multicoloured 45 25

320 Bougainvillea

1985. Flowers. Multicoloured.
683 80f. Type 320 1·20 55

684 2d. *Hibiscus rosasinensis* 2·50 80

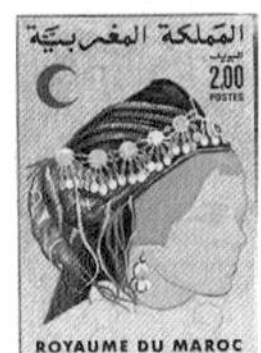

321 Woman in Headdress

1985. Red Crescent.
685 **321** 2d. multicoloured 3·00 90

322 Musicians and Dancers

1985. National Folklore Festival, Marrakesh.
686 **322** 2d. multicoloured 1·50 45

323 Map and Emblem

1985. Sixth Pan-Arab Games.
687 **323** 2d. multicoloured 90 25

324 Emblem on Globe

1985. 40th Anniv of U.N.O.
688 **324** 2d. multicoloured 1·50 35

325 Emblem

1986. International Youth Year.
689 **325** 2d. multicoloured 1·50 35

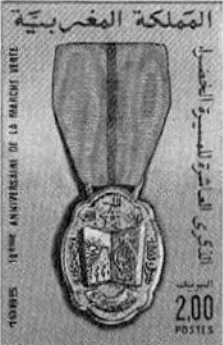

326 Medal

1985. Tenth Anniv of "Green March".
690 **326** 2d. multicoloured 1·20 35

327 Clasped Hands around Flag

1985. Palestinian Welfare.
691 **327** 2d. multicoloured 95 25

328 *Euphydryas desfontainii*

1985. Butterflies (1st series). Multicoloured.
692 80f. Type **328** 1·40 60
693 2d. *Colotis evagore* 3·25 1·40
See also Nos. 713/14.

329 Arms

1986. 25th Anniv of King Hassan's Coronation. Multicoloured.
694 80f. Type **329** 55 10
695 2d. King Hassan II (horiz) 1·10 25
MS696 105×90 mm. Nos. 694/5. Imperf 1·50 1·50

330 Emblem

1986. 26th International Military Medicine Congress.
697 **330** 2d. multicoloured 95 25

1986. Stamp Day. As T **316**.
698 80f. orange and black 45 10
699 2d. green and black 1·20 25
Designs:—80f. Sherifian postal seal of Maghzen-Safi; 2d. Sherifian postal seal of Maghzen-Safi (different).

331 Vase

1986. Blind Week.
700 **331** 1d. multicoloured 95 25

332 Footballer and Emblem

1986. World Cup Football Championship, Mexico. Multicoloured.
701 1d. Type **332** 95 25
702 2d. Cup, pictogram of footballer and emblem 1·50 65

333 Copper Coffee Pot

1986. Red Crescent.
703 **333** 2d. multicoloured 2·00 70

334 *Warionia saharae*

1986. Flowers. Multicoloured.
704 1d. Type **334** 1·50 45
705 2d. *Mandragora autumnalis* 3·50 90

335 Emblem

1986. 18th Parachute Championships.
706 **335** 2d. multicoloured 1·50 45

336 Dove and Olive Branch

1986. International Peace Year.
707 **336** 2d. multicoloured 95 45

337 Horsemen

1986. Horse Week.
708 **337** 1d. light brown, pink and brown 1·40 40

338 Book

1986. 11th Anniv of "Green March".
709 **338** 1d. multicoloured 45 10

339 Stylized People and Wheat

1986. Fight against Hunger.
710 **339** 2d. multicoloured 75 25

340 Marrakesh

1986. Aga Khan Architecture Prize.
711 **340** 2d. multicoloured 2·00 45

341 Hands holding Wheat

1986. 1,000,000 Hectares of Grain.
712 **341** 1d. multicoloured 45 10

1986. Butterflies (2nd series). As T **328**. Mult.
713 1d. "Elphinstonia charlonia" 1·30 50
714 2d. "Anthocharis belia" 3·25 1·20

1987. Stamp Day. As T **316**.
715 1d. blue and black 45 10
716 2d. red and black 75 25
Designs:—1d. Circular postal cancellation of Tetouan; 2d. Octagonal postal cancellation of Tetouan.

الملتقى العالمي الاول
لخطباء الجمعة

(342)

1987. Air. First World Reunion of Friday Preachers. Optd with T **342**.
717 **283** 2d. multicoloured 1·00 70

1987. Size 25×32 mm but inscr "1986".
718 **266** 1d.60 red, brown and gold 50 25
719 **266** 2d.50 red, grey and gold 80 40
720 **266** 6d.50 red, brown and gold 2·10 95
721 **266** 7d. red, brown and gold 2·30 1·00
722 **266** 8d.50 red, lilac and gold 2·75 1·30

343 Sidi Muhammad ben Yusuf addressing Crowd

1987. 40th Anniv of Tangier Conference. Each blue, silver and black.
723 1d. Type **343** 45 25
724 1d. King Hassan II making speech 45 25
MS725 150×100 mm. Nos. 723/4 (sold at 3d.) 1·50 1·50

344 Copper Lamp

1987. Red Crescent.
726 **344** 2d. multicoloured 95 40

345 Woman with Baby and Packet of Salt being emptied into Beaker

1987. UNICEF Child Survival Campaign.
727 **345** 1d. multicoloured 45 10

346 Decorated Pottery Jug

1987. Blind Week.
728 **346** 1d. multicoloured 45 10

347 *Zygophyllum fontanesii*

1987. Flowers. Multicoloured.
729 1d. Type **347** 60 10
730 2d. *Otanthus maritimus* 95 25

348 Arabesque from Door, Dar Batha Palace, Fez

1987. Bicentenary of Diplomatic Relations with United States of America.

731	**348**	1d. blue, red and black	45	10

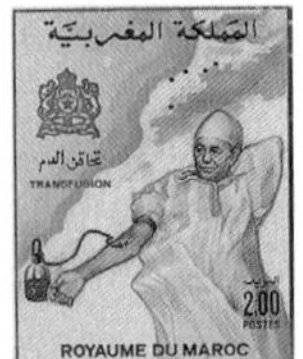

349 Map and King Hassan giving Blood

1987. Blood Transfusion Service.

732	**349**	2d. multicoloured	1·20	45

350 Woman from Melhfa

1987. Sahara Costumes. Multicoloured.

733	1d. Type **350**	65	25
734	2d. Man from Derraa	1·30	40

351 Emblem and Irrigated Field

1987. 13th International Irrigation and Drainage Congress.

735	**351**	1d. multicoloured	45	25

352 Baby on Hand and Syringe

1987. United Nations Children's Fund Child Survival Campaign.

736	**352**	1d. multicoloured	45	10

353 Azurite

1987. Mineral Industries Congress, Marrakesh. Multicoloured.

737	1d. Type **353**	1·50	45
738	2d. Wulfenite	2·75	90

354 "12" on Scroll

1987. 12th Anniv of "Green March".

739	**354**	1d. multicoloured	45	25

355 Activities

1987. Armed Forces Social Services Month.

740	**355**	1d. multicoloured	50	10

356 Desert Sparrow

1987. Birds. Multicoloured.

741	1d. Type **356**	1·20	55
742	2d. Barbary partridge	2·50	80

357 1912 25m. Stamp and Postmark

1987. 75th Anniv of Moroccan Stamps.

743	**357**	3d. mauve, black and green	1·30	55

358 Cetiosaurus mogrebiensis

1988. Dinosaur of Tilougguite.

744	**358**	2d. multicoloured	3·25	90

359 King Mohammed V

1988. International Conf on King Mohammed V, Rabat.

745	**359**	2d. multicoloured	95	25

360 Map and Player in Arabesque Frame

1988. 16th African Nations Cup Football Competition.

746	**360**	3d. multicoloured	1·20	45

361 Boy with Horse

1988. Horse Week.

747	**361**	3d. multicoloured	2·20	70

362 Pottery Flask

1988. Blind Week.

748	**362**	3d. multicoloured	1·20	45

363 Anniversary Emblem

1988. 125th Anniv of Red Cross.

749	**363**	3d. black, red and pink	1·50	55

364 *Citrullus colocynthis*

1988. Flowers. Multicoloured.

750	3d.60 Type **364**	1·90	75
751	3d.60 *Calotropis procera*	1·90	75

365 Breastfeeding Baby

1988. UNICEF Child Survival Campaign.

752	**365**	3d. multicoloured	1·90	45

366 Olympic Medals and Rings

1988. Olympic Games, Seoul.

753	**366**	2d. multicoloured	75	25

367 Great Bustard

1988. Birds. Multicoloured.

754	3d.60 Type **367**	2·40	90
755	3d.60 Greater flamingo	2·40	90

368 "13" on Scroll

1988. 13th Anniv of "Green March".

756	**368**	2d. multicoloured	95	25

1988. Stamp Day. As T **316**.

757	3d. brown and black	1·20	45
758	3d. violet and black	1·20	45

Designs:—No. 757, Octagonal postal cancellation of Maghzen el Jadida; 758, Circular postal cancellation of Maghzen el Jadida.

1988. Size 25×32 mm but inscr "1988".

759	**266**	1d.20 blue, lilac and gold	45	10
760	**266**	3d.60 red and gold	1·20	25
761	**266**	5d.20 brown, bis & gold	1·80	45

369 Housing of the Ksours and Csbaha

1989. Architecture.

762	**369**	2d. multicoloured	75	25

اتحاد المغرب العربى

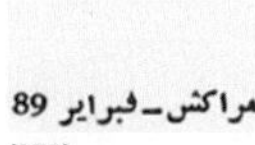
مراكش – فبراير 89

(370)

1989. Union of Arab Maghreb. No. 631 optd with T **370**.

763	**283**	1d.40 multicoloured	55	45

371 King and Bishop with Chess Symbols

1989. 25th Anniv of Royal Moroccan Chess Federation.

764	**371**	2d. multicoloured	1·20	40

372 Copper Vase

1989. Red Crescent.

765	**372**	2d. multicoloured	1·50	35

373 Ceramic Vase

1989. Blind Week.

766	**373**	2d. multicoloured	95	25

374 King Hassan

1989. 60th Birthday of King Hassan II. Mult.

767	2d. Type **374**	95	45
768	2d. King Hassan in robes	1·00	45
MS769	140×105 mm. Nos. 767/8. Imperf. (sold at 5d.)	10·50	10·50

375 *Cerinthe major*

1989. Flowers. Multicoloured.

770	2d. Type **375**	1·20	45
771	2d. *Narcissus papyraceus*	1·20	45

376 Telephone Handset linking Landmarks

1989. World Telecommunications Day.

772	**376**	2d. multicoloured	75	25

377 Gender Symbols forming Globe, Woman and Eggs

1989. First World Fertility and Sterility Congress.

773	**377**	2d. multicoloured	95	45

378 Desert Wheatear

1989. Birds. Multicoloured.

774	2d. Type **378**	1·20	45
775	3d. Shore lark	1·50	90

379 House of Representatives

1989. Centenary of Interparliamentary Union.

776	**379**	2d. multicoloured	75	25

380 Scroll

1989. 14th Anniv of "Green March".

777	**380**	3d. multicoloured	1·20	45

1990. Stamp Day. As T **316**.

778	2d. orange and black	95	45
779	3d. green and black	1·30	45

Designs:—2d. Round postal cancellation of Casablanca; 3d. Octagonal postal cancellation of Casablanca.

381 Flags forming Map

1990. First Anniv of Union of Arab Maghreb.

780	**381**	2d. multicoloured	80	25
MS781		120×85 mm. No. 780 (sold 3d.)	1·60	1·60

382 Oil Press

1990. Third World Olive Year. Multicoloured.

782	2d. Type **382**	80	45
783	3d. King Hassan and olives	1·20	55

383 Decorated Pot

1990. Blind Week.

784	**383**	2d. multicoloured	80	30

384 Silver Teapot

1990. Red Crescent.

785	**384**	2d. multicoloured	80	30

385 Arabic Script and Open Book

1990. International Literacy Year.

786	**385**	3d. green, yellow and black	1·20	50

386 Turtle Dove

1990. Birds. Multicoloured.

787	2d. Type **386**	1·10	45
788	3d. Hoopoe (horiz)	1·70	70

387 "15" on Scroll

1990. 15th Anniv of "Green March".

789	**387**	3d. multicoloured	1·20	40

388 "35", Sun's Rays and Flag

1990. 35th Anniv of Independence.

790	**388**	3d. multicoloured	1·00	40

389 Dam

1990

791	**389**	3d. multicoloured	1·20	40

390 Emblem

1990. Tenth Anniv of Royal Academy of Morocco.

792	**390**	3d. multicoloured	1·00	40

391 Morse Code Apparatus

1990. 20th Anniv of National Postal Museum. Multicoloured.

793		2d. Type **391**	80	45
794		3d. Horse-drawn mail wagon, 1913	1·30	55
MS795		164×94 mm. Nos. 793/4. Imperf. (sold at 6d.)	3·00	3·00

1991. Stamp Day. As T **316**.

796	2d. red and black	80	45
797	3d. blue and black	1·30	45

Designs:—2d. Round postal cancellation of Rabat; 3d. Octagonal postal cancellation of Rabat.

392 Projects and Emblem

1991. 40th Anniv of United Nations Development Programme.

798	**392**	3d. turquoise, yellow & blk	1·00	40

393 King Hassan

1991. 30th Anniv of Enthronement of King Hassan II. Multicoloured.

799	3d. Type **393**	1·90	70
800	3d. King Hassan in robes	1·90	70
MS801	164×101 mm. Nos. 799/80 (sold at 10d.)	4·25	4·25

394 Mining

1991. 70th Anniv of Mineral Exploitation by Sherifian Phosphates Office.

802	**394**	3d. multicoloured	1·00	45

395 Kettle on Stand

1991. Blind Week.

803	**395**	3d. multicoloured	1·00	55

396 Lantern

1991. Red Crescent.

804	**396**	3d. multicoloured	1·20	55

397 *Cynara humilis*

1991. Flowers. Multicoloured.

805	3d. Type **397**	1·20	55
806	3d. *Pyrus mamorensis*	1·30	55

398 Man

1991. Ouarzazate Costumes. Multicoloured.

807	3d. Type **398**	1·30	45
808	3d. Woman	1·30	45

1991. Inscribed "1991".

809	**266**	1d.35 red, green and gold	45	10

399 Road

1991. 19th World Roads Congress, Marrakesh.

810	**399**	3d. multicoloured	1·00	40

400 Members' Flags and Map

1991. Fourth Ordinary Session of Arab Maghreb Union Presidential Council, Casablanca.

811	**400**	3d. multicoloured	1·20	45

401 "16" on Scroll

1991. 16th Anniv of "Green March".

812	**401**	3d. multicoloured	1·20	40

402 White Stork

1991. Birds. Multicoloured.

813	3d. Type **402**	1·90	60
814	3d. European bee-eater	1·90	60

403 Figures and Blood Splash

1991. World AIDS Day.

815	**403**	3d. multicoloured	1·00	40

404 Emblem

1991. 20th Anniv of Islamic Conf Organization.

816	**404**	3d. multicoloured	1·00	40

405 Zebra and Map of Africa

1991. African Tourism Year.

817	**405**	3d. multicoloured	1·20	40

1992. Stamp Day. As T **316**.

818	3d. green and black	1·30	45
819	3d. violet and black	1·30	45

Designs:—No. 818, Circular postal cancellation of Essaouira; No. 819, Octagonal postal cancellation of Essaouira.

406 Satellites around Earth

1992. International Space Year.

820	**406**	3d. multicoloured	1·20	55

407 Bottle

1992. Blind Week.

821	**407**	3d. multicoloured	1·20	55

408 Brass Jug

1992. Red Crescent.

822	**408**	3d. multicoloured	1·20	55

409 Quartz

1992. Minerals. Multicoloured.

823	1d.35 Type **409**	80	45
824	3d.40 Calcite	1·80	90

410 Woman

1992. Tata Costumes. Multicoloured.

825	1d.35 Type **410**	80	25
826	3d.40 Man	1·80	80

411 *Campanula afra*

1992. Flowers. Multicoloured.

827	1d.35 Type **411**	80	25
828	3d.40 *Thymus broussonetii*	1·60	80

412 Olympic Rings and Torch

1992. Olympic Games, Barcelona.

829	**412**	3d.40 multicoloured	1·40	45

413 Map of Africa and Methods of Transport and Communication

1992. Decade of Transport and Communications in Africa.

830	**413**	3d.40 multicoloured	1·60	55

414 La Koutoubia, La Giralda (cathedral bell-tower) and Exhibition Emblem

1992. Expo '92 World's Fair, Seville.

831	**414**	3d.40 multicoloured	1·40	55

415 Columbus's Fleet and Route Map

1992. 500th Anniv of Discovery of America by Columbus.

832	**415**	3d.40 multicoloured	1·80	65

416 Pin-tailed Sandgrouse

1992. Birds. Multicoloured.

833	3d. Type **416**	1·40	65
834	3d. Griffon vulture (*Gyps fulvus*) (vert)	1·40	65

417 "17" on Scroll

1992. 17th Anniv of "Green March".

835	**417**	3d.40 multicoloured	1·60	55

418 Postal Messenger, Route Map and Cancellations

1992. Centenary of Sherifian Post. Multicoloured.

836	1d.35 Type **418**	80	25
837	3d.40 Postal cancellation, "100" on scroll and Sultan Mulay al-Hassan	1·60	65
MS838	165×105 mm. 5d. Postal cancellations, "100" on scroll and Sultan Moulay al-Hassan	2·50	2·50

419 Conference Emblem

1992. International Nutrition Conference, Rome.

839	**419**	3d.40 multicoloured	1·40	75

420 Douglas DC-9 Airliners on Runway

1992. Al Massira Airport, Agadir.

840	**420**	3d.40 multicoloured	1·60	65

1993. Stamp Day. As T **316**.

841	1d.70 green and black	80	30
842	3d.80 orange and black	1·60	80

Designs:—1d.70, Round postal cancellation of Tangier; 3d.80, Octagonal postal cancellation of Tangier.

421 Dishes

1993. Blind Week.

843	**421**	4d.40 multicoloured	1·60	40

422 Satellite orbiting Earth

1993. World Meteorological Day.

844	**422**	4d.40 multicoloured	1·90	55

423 Kettle on Stand

1993. Red Crescent.

845	**423**	4d.40 multicoloured	1·60	40

424 Emblem

1993. World Telecommunications Day.

846	**424**	4d.40 multicoloured	1·60	40

425 Woman extracting Argan Oil

1993. Argan Oil. Multicoloured.

847	1d.70 Type **425**	80	25
848	4d.80 Branch and fruit of argan tree	1·80	65

426 Prince Sidi Mohammed

1993. 30th Birthday of Prince Sidi Mohammed.

849	**426**	4d.80 multicoloured	1·60	35

427 King Hassan and Mosque

1993. Inauguration of King Hassan II Mosque.

850	**427**	4d.80 multicoloured	1·60	40

428 Canopy, Sceptres, Flag and "40" on Sun

1993. 40th Anniv of Revolution.

851	**428**	4d.80 multicoloured	1·60	40

429 Post Box and Globe

1993. World Post Day.

852	**429**	4d.80 multicoloured	1·60	40

430 Emblem

1993. Islamic Summer University.

853	**430**	4d.80 multicoloured	1·60	40

431 "18" on Scroll

1993. 18th Anniv of "Green March".

854	**431**	4d.80 multicoloured	1·90	55

432 Marbled Teal

1993. Waterfowl. Multicoloured.
855 1d.70 Type **432** 95 25
856 4d.80 Red-knobbed coot 2·50 65

433 Flags, Scroll and "50"

1994. 50th Anniv of Istaqlal (Independence) Party.
857 **433** 4d.80 multicoloured 2·10 45

434 House

1994. Signing of Uruguay Round Final Act of General Agreement on Tariffs and Trade, Marrakesh.
858 **434** 1d.70 multicoloured 75 30
859 - 4d.80 multicoloured 2·10 95
MS860 165×105 mm. purple, black and yellow (as Nos. 858/9) (sold at 10d.) 4·75 4·75
Design:—4d.80, Mosque.

435 Decorated Vase

1994. Blind Week.
861 **435** 4d.80 multicoloured 3·75 70

436 Copper Vessel

1994. Red Crescent.
862 **436** 4d.80 multicoloured 2·50 55

437 Couple

1994. National Congress on Children's Rights. Children's Drawings. Multicoloured.
863 1d.70 Type **437** 80 25
864 4d.80 Couple under sun 1·80 65

438 Ball, Moroccan and USA Flags, Pictogram and Trophy

1994. World Cup Football Championship, U.S.A.
865 **438** 4d.80 multicoloured 1·90 55

1994. Size 25×32 mm but inscr "1994".
866 **266** 1d.70 red, blue and gold 1·10 10

439 King Hassan II and Arms

1994. 65th Birthday of King Hassan II. Mult.
867 1d.70 Type **439** 75 25
868 4d.80 King Hassan II (vert) 2·10 65

440 "100" and Rings

1994. Centenary of International Olympic Committee.
869 **440** 4d.80 multicoloured 1·80 55

441 Saint-Exupery, Route Map and Biplane

1994. 50th Death Anniv of Antoine de Saint-Exupery (writer and pilot).
870 **441** 4d.80 multicoloured 2·30 55

442 *Chamaeleon gummifer*

1994. Flowers. Multicoloured.
871 1d.70 Type **442** 75 25
872 4d.80 *Pancratium maritimum* (vert) 2·10 80

443 Slender-billed Curlew

1994. Birds. Multicoloured.
873 1d.70 Type **443** 1·70 25
874 4d.80 Audouin's gull 4·00 80

444 Scroll and March

1994. 19th Anniv of "Green March". Mult.
875 1d.70 Type **444** 65 25
876 4d.80 Marchers and Moroccan coastline 1·90 65

1994. Stamp Day. As T **316**.
877 1d.70 blue and black 65 25
878 4d.80 red and black 1·80 80
Designs:—1d.70, Round postal cancellation of Marrakesh; 4d.80, Octagonal postal cancellation of Marrakesh.

445 Decorated Vase

1995. Blind Week.
879 **445** 4d.80 multicoloured 1·90 55

446 Anniversary Emblem

1995. 50th Anniv of League of Arab States.
880 **446** 4d.80 multicoloured 1·60 40

447 Copper Vessel

1995. Red Crescent.
881 **447** 4d.80 multicoloured 1·70 55

448 *Malva hispanica*

1995. Flowers. Multicoloured.
882 2d. Type **448** 75 25
883 4d.80 *Phlomis crinita* 2·10 65

449 European Roller

1995. Birds. Multicoloured.
884 1d.70 Type **449** 50 25
885 4d.80 Eurasian goldfinch 1·80 80

450 Anniversary Emblem, Building and Map

1995. 50th Anniv of F.A.O.
886 **450** 4d.80 multicoloured 1·50 45

451 "50" and Flags

1995. 50th Anniv of U.N.O. Multicoloured.
887 1d.70 Type **451** 95 25
888 4d.80 UN emblem, doves and map 2·75 55

452 "20" on Scroll

1995. 20th Anniv of "Green March". Mult.
889 1d.70 Type **452** 50 25
890 4d.80 National Flag, book and medal 1·60 40

453 "40", National Flag and Crown

1995. 40th Anniv of Independence. Multicoloured.
891 4d.80 Type **453** 1·50 45
MS892 120×90 mm. 10d. Sultan Mohammed V and King Hassan II. Imperf 3·25 3·25

1995. Stamp Day. As T **316**.
893 1d.70 bistre and black 50 25
894 4d.80 lilac and black 1·60 40
Designs:—1d.70, Round postal cancellation of Meknes; 4d.80, Octagonal cancellation of Meknes.

1996. Size 25×32 mm but inscr "1996".
895 **266** 5d.50 brown, red and gold 1·60 45
896 **266** 20d. brown, blue and gold 6·25 1·80

454 National Arms

1996. 35th Anniv of Enthronement of King Hassan II. Multicoloured.
897 2d. Type **454** 60 25
898 5d.50 King Hassan II 1·80 65
MS899 142×93 mm. 10d. King Hassan II. Imperf 3·75 3·75

455 Decorated Vase

1996
900 **455** 5d.50 multicoloured 1·90 45

456 Leather Flask

1996
901 **456** 5d.50 multicoloured 1·90 45

457 *Cleonia lusitanica*

1996. Flowers. Multicoloured.
902 2d. Type **457** 80 25
903 5d.50 *Tulipa sylvestris* 2·00 80

458 King Hassan II wearing Military Uniform

1996. 40th Anniv of Royal Armed Forces. Mult.
904 2d. Type **458** 60 25
905 5d.50 King Hassan II and globe 1·80 65

459 Emblem and Runners

1996. Centenary of Modern Olympic Games. Olympic Games, Atlanta, U.S.A.
906 **459** 5d.50 multicoloured 2·10 90

460 Osprey

1996. Birds. Multicoloured.
907 2d. Type **460** 1·00 35
908 5d.50 Little egret 2·75 80

461 "21" on Scroll

1996. 21st Anniv of "Green March".
909 **461** 5d.50 multicoloured 1·90 35

1996. Stamp Day. As T **316**.
910 2d. orange and black 60 25
911 5d.50 green and black 1·80 65
Designs:—2d. Round postal cancellation of Maghzen-Fes; 5d.50, Octagonal postal cancellation of Maghzen-Fes.

462 Rainbow and Emblem

1996. 50th Anniv of UNICEF.
912 **462** 5d.50 multicoloured 1·90 55

463 Terracotta Vessel

1997
913 **463** 5d.50 multicoloured 1·90 45

464 Lupin

1997. Flowers. Multicoloured.
914 2d. Type **464** 80 25
915 5d.50 Milk thistle 2·00 80

465 King Mohammed V

1997. 50th Anniv of Tangier Talks (determining future status of Tangier).
916 2d. Type **465** 80 25
917 2d. King Hassan II 80 25

466 Map in Open Book and Quill

1997. World Book Day.
918 **466** 5d.50 multicoloured 2·00 45

467 Ibn Battuta and Globe

1997. International Conference on Ibn Battuta (explorer).
919 **467** 5d.50 multicoloured 1·90 45

468 Copper Door Knocker

1997
920 **468** 5d.50 multicoloured 2·00 45

469 Demoiselle Crane

1997. Birds. Multicoloured.
921 2d. Type **469** 80 35
922 5d.50 Blue tit 2·00 80

470 "22" on Scroll

1997. 22nd Anniv of "Green March".
923 **470** 5d.50 multicoloured 2·00 35

1997. Stamp Day. As T **316**.
924 2d. blue and black 60 25
925 5d.50 red and black 1·80 65
Designs:—2d. Round postal cancellation of Maghzen-Larache; 5d.50, Octagonal postal cancellation of Maghzen-Larache.

471 Flask

1998. Moroccan Pottery.
926 **471** 6d. multicoloured 1·90 45

472 *Rhus pentaphylla*

1998. Plants. Multicoloured.
927 2d.30 Type **472** 80 25
928 6d. *Orchis papilionacea* 2·00 80

473 Route Map and Emblem

1998. 26th International Road Haulage Union Congress, Marrakesh.
929 **473** 6d. multicoloured 2·10 45

1998. Size 25×32 mm but inscr "1998".
930 **266** 2d.30 red, green and gold 80 20

474 Sconce

1998. Moroccan Copperware.
931 **474** 6d. multicoloured 1·90 45

475 Players and Ball

1998. World Cup Football Championship, France.
932 **475** 6d. multicoloured 2·10 55

476 Emblem, Rainbow, World Map and Hands

1998. International Year of the Ocean.
933 **476** 6d. multicoloured 2·10 45

477 King Mohammed V and King Hassan II

1998. 45th Anniv of Revolution.
934 **477** 6d. multicoloured 1·90 35

478 Globe and Letter

1998. World Stamp Day.
935 **478** 6d. multicoloured 1·90 45

479 Nightingale

1998. Birds. Multicoloured.
936 2d.30 Type **479** 80 35
937 6d. Ostrich 2·00 80

480 Scroll

1998. 23rd Anniv of "Green March".
938 **480** 6d. multicoloured 1·90 35

481 Arabic Script

1998. 40th Anniv of Code of Civil Liberties.
939 **481** 6d. multicoloured 1·90 35

482 Anniversary Emblem

1998. 50th Anniv of Universal Declaration of Human Rights.
940 **482** 6d. multicoloured 2·10 45

1998. King Hassen II. Size 27×35 mm.
940a **266** 6d. blue and gold 2·10 45

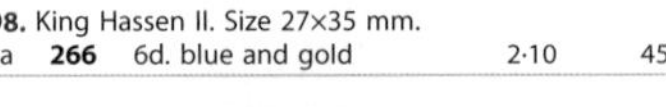

483 Mask and Globe

1999. World Theatre Day.
941 **483** 6d. multicoloured 2·10 45

484 *Eryngium triquetrum*

1999. Flowers. Multicoloured.
942 2d.30 Type **484** 80 25
943 6d. Mistletoe 2·00 80

485 Bab Mansour Laalej

1999
944 **485** 6d. multicoloured 1·90 45

486 King Hassan II on Throne

1999. 70th Birthday of King Hassan II. Mult.
945 2d.30 Type **486** 80 35
946 6d. King Hassan wearing robes 1·80 80
MS947 125×95 mm. Nos. 945/6. Imperf. (sold at 10d) 3·75 3·50

487 Necklace

1999. Moroccan Jewellery.

948	**487**	6d. multicoloured	1·90	45

488 Hands holding Globe and Water falling on Tree

1999. World Environment Day.

949	**488**	6d. multicoloured	2·10	45

489 Emblem

1999. 125th Anniv of Universal Postal Union.

950	**489**	6d. multicoloured	2·10	45

490 Obverse and Reverse of Medal

1999. F.A.O. Agriculture Medal.

951	**490**	6d. multicoloured	2·30	45

491 Stylized People

1999. Solidarity Week.

952	**491**	6d. blue, yellow and black	1·90	35

492 "24" on Scroll

1999. 24th Anniv of "Green March".

953	**492**	6d. multicoloured	1·90	35

493 Zebra Seabream

1999. Fish. Multicoloured.

954	2d.30 Type **493**	80	35
955	6d. Opah	2·20	45

494 *Stork on Nest* (A. Slaoui)

1999. Year of Morocco in France. Paintings. Multicoloured.

956	6d. Type **494**	1·90	70
957	6d. *Women sitting on mat* (Afif Bennani)	1·90	70
958	6d. *Guitar* (Abdelkader Rhorbal)	1·90	70
959	6d. *View of harbour* (A. Slaoui)	1·90	70

1999. King Hassan II. Vert designs as T **266** inscr '1999'.

959a	70f. violet, flesh and gold (24×28 mm)	30	30
959b	80f. violet, pale yellow and gold (24×28 mm)	35	35
959c	2d.30 lake, pale green and gold (27×34 mm)	45	45
959d	2d.50 lake-brown, brownish grey and gold (27×34 mm)	50	50
959e	5d.50 lake-brown, pink and gold (27×34 mm)	1·00	1·00
959f	6d. ultramarine, pale turquoise blue and gold (27×34 mm)	1·10	1·10
959g	6d.50 lake-brown, pale orange and gold (27×34 mm)	1·10	1·10
959h	10d. lake-brown, pale orange-red and gold (27×34 mm)	1·80	1·80

495 Players and Globe

2000. African Nations' Cup Football Championship.

960	**495**	6d. multicoloured	2·10	55

496 Globe and "2000"

2000. New Year.

961	**496**	6d. multicoloured	2·10	55

497 Beach and Calendar

2000. 40th Anniv of the Reconstruction of Agadir.

962	**497**	6d.50 multicoloured	2·10	55

498 Emblem and Building

2000. 25th Anniv of Islamic Development Bank.

963	**498**	6d.50 multicoloured	2·10	55

499 Stylized People

2000. National Disabled Persons Day.

964	**499**	6d.50 multicoloured	2·10	70

500 *Jasione montana*

2000. Flowers. Multicoloured.

965	2d.50 Type **500**	80	35
966	6d.60 *Pistorica breviflora*	2·30	80

501 Emblem

2000. 50th Anniv of World Meteorological Organization.

967	**501**	6d.50 multicoloured	2·10	70

502 People dancing

2000. National Festival of Popular Arts, Marrakesh.

968	**502**	6d.50 multicoloured	2·10	70

503 Open Book and White Dove

2000. International Year of Culture and Peace.

969	**503**	6d.50 multicoloured	2·10	70

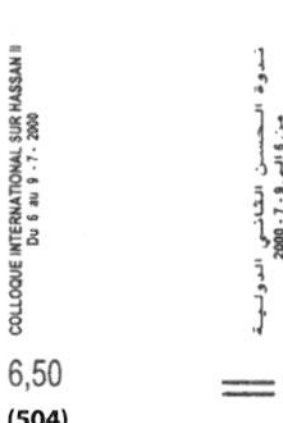

(504)

2000. Air. International Conference on Hassan II. No. 631 optd with T **504**.

970	**283**	6d.50 on 1d.40 multicoloured	2·10	70

505 King Mohammed VI

2000. First Anniv of Enthronement of King Mohammed VI. Multicoloured.

971	2d.50 Type **505**	80	35
972	6d.50 King Mohammed VI	2·00	80
MS973	120×91 mm. Nos. 971/2. Imperf. (sold at 10d.)	3·00	3·00

506 Ruins, Volubis and Performers

2000. Mediterranean Song and Dance Festival.

974	**506**	6d.50 multicoloured	2·10	45

507 Emblem and Olympic Torch

2000. Olympic Games, Sydney.

975	**507**	6d.50 multicoloured	2·10	55

508 Emblem, House and Children

2000. 50th Anniv of S.O.S. Children's Villages.

976	**508**	6d.50 multicoloured	2·10	55

509 Quill, Globe and Emblem

2000. International Teachers' Day.

977	**509**	6d.50 multicoloured	2·10	45

510 Emblem

2000. King Mohammed VI Solidarity Foundation.

978	**510**	6d.50 blue, yellow and black	2·10	70

511 "25" on Scroll

2000. 25th Anniv of "Green March". Mult.

979	2d.50 Type **511**	80	25
980	6d.50 "25" and text	2·00	55

512 St. Exupery and Plane

2000. Birth Centenary of Antonie de Saint.-Exupery (author).

981	**512**	6d.50 multicoloured	2·30	55

513 "45" and National Flag

2000. 45th Anniv of Independence.

982	**513**	6d.50 multicoloured	2·10	45

514 Mediterranean Cardinalfish (*Apogon imberbis*)

2000. Fish. Multicoloured.

983	2d.50 Type **514**	80	35
984	6d.50 Cadenat's rockfish (*Scorpaena loppei*)	2·00	80

515 El Bab el Gharbi

2001

985	**515**	6d.50 multicoloured	2·10	70

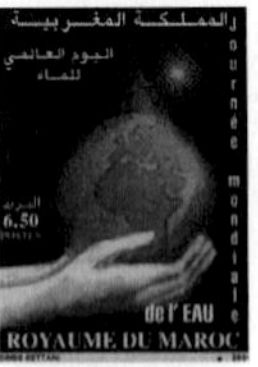
516 Hands holding Globe enclosed in Droplet of Water

2001. International Water Day.

986	**516**	6d.50 multicoloured	2·10	70

517 King Mohammed VI

2001. 45th Anniv of Armed Forces. Multicoloured.

987	2d.50 Type **517**	80	25
988	6d.50 King Mohammed VI (different)	2·00	45

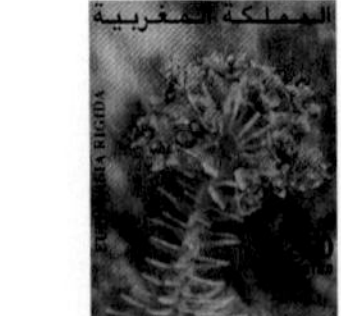
518 Spurge (*Euphorbia rigida*)

2001. Flowers. Multicoloured.

989	2d.50 Type **518**	80	35
990	6d.50 Horned poppy (*Glaucium flavum*)	2·00	80

519 Koekelberg Basilica, Brussels

2001. Religious Buildings.

991	2d.50 Type **519**	80	45
992	6d.50 Hassan II Mosque, Casablanca	2·00	90

Stamps of a similar design were issued by Belgium.

520 Globe and Dove

2001. National Diplomacy Day.

993	**520**	6d.50 multicoloured	1·50	35

521 King Mohammed VI

2001. Second Anniv of Enthronement of King Mohammed VI

994	2d.50 Type **521**	55	10
995	6d. Smiling facing left	1·40	35
996	6d.50 Wearing decorated tie (crown upper left)	1·50	40
997	10d. King Mohammed VI (horiz)	2·40	65

522 Black-bellied Angler (*Lophus budegassa*)

2001. Marine Life. Multicoloured.

998	2d.50 Type **522**	55	25
999	6d.50 Monk seal (*Monachus monachus*) (horiz)	1·50	75

523 Postal Seal, Kasir el Kabir

2001. Stamp Day.

1000	**523**	2d.50 bistre and black	55	25
1001	-	6d.50 lilac and black	1·50	75

Design: 6d.50 Octagonal seal.

524 Hands holding Globe

2001. Seventh Conference Session of Signatory States to United Nations Framework Convention on Climatic Change, Marrakech.

1002	**524**	6d.50 multicoloured	1·50	35

525 Palm Trees

2001. World Day to Combat Desertification.

1003	**525**	6d.50 multicoloured	1·50	35

526 Flags and Marchers

2001. 26th Anniv of "Green March".

1004	**526**	6d.50 multicoloured	1·60	45

527 King Mohammed VI and Children

2001. King Mohammed VI Solidarity Foundation.

1005	**527**	6d.50 multicoloured	1·60	55
1006	-	6d.50 ultramarine, lemon and black (28×28 mm)	1·60	55

Design:—No. 1006 As No. 978 but inscr "2001".

528 Wallace Fountain, Paris

2001. Moroccan—French Cultural Heritage. Fountains. Multicoloured.

1007	2d.50 Type **528**	60	25
1008	6d.50 Nejjarine fountain, Fez	1·60	75

Stamps of the same design were issued by France.

529 Hands holding Globe

2001. United Nations Year of Dialogue among Civilizations.

1009	**529**	6d.50 multicoloured	1·60	45

530 Bab Chellah, Rabat

2002

1010	**530**	6d.50 multicoloured	1·60	45

531 Globe and Woman

2002. International Women's Day.

1011	**531**	6d.50 multicoloured	1·60	75

532 Cedar Tree

2002

1012	**532**	6d.50 multicoloured	1·60	75

533 Baby and Elderly Couple

2002. Second World Assembly on Aging.

1013	**533**	6d.50 multicoloured	1·60	45

534 Emblem

2002. United Nations Special Session for Children (September 2001).

1014	**534**	6d.50 multicoloured	1·60	45

535 *Linaria bipartite*

2002. Flowers. Multicoloured.

1015	2d.50 Type **535**	60	25
1016	6d.50 *Verbascum pseudocreticum*	1·60	75

2002. Third Anniv of Enthronement of King Mohammed VI

1016a	2d.50 As Type **521**	55	25
1016b	6d. As No. 995	1·30	25
1016c	6d.50 As No. 996	1·60	45
1016d	10d. As No. 997 (horiz)	2·10	85

536 Emblem and Map

2002. International Union of Telecommunications Conference, Marrakech. Multicoloured.

1017	6d.50 Type **536**	1·60	45
MS1018	120×90 mm. 10d. As No. 1017 but with design enlarged. Imperf	2·50	2·50

537 Mohamed Dorra, Father and Protestors

2002. Al Aqsa Intifada.

1019	**537**	6d.50 multicoloured	1·60	75

538 Oasis

2002. International Year of EcoTourism.

1020	**538**	6d.50 multicoloured	1·60	45

539 Map and Marchers

2002. 27th Anniv of "Green March".
1021 **539** 6d.50 multicoloured 1·60 45

540 King Mohammed VI

2002. King Mohammed VI Solidarity Foundation.
1022 **540** 6d.50 multicoloured 1·60 55
1023 - 6d.50 lemon and ultramarine (28×28 mm) 1·60 55

Design:—No. 1023 As No. 978 but inscr '2002'.

541 Sultan Moulay Hassan and City

2002. 110th Anniv of Maghzen Post. Multicoloured.
1024 2d.50 Type **541** 60 25
1025 6d.50 Sultan Moulay Hassan and tall building 1·60 75

542 Fortresses, Dune and Coastline

2002. International Year of Cultural Heritage.
1026 **542** 6d.50 nmulticoloured 1·60 45

543 Allis Shad (*Alosa alosa*)

2002. Fish. Multicoloured.
1027 2d.50 Type **543** 60 25
1028 6d.50 *Epinephelus marginatus* 1·60 75

545 Bab El Okla, Tetouan

2003
1032 **545** 6d.50 multicoloured 1·60 45

546 Le Sapin Forest

2003
1033 **546** 6d.50 multicoloured 1·60 75

547 Child and Fountain

2003. International Year of Freshwater.
1034 **547** 6d.50 multicoloured 1·60 55

548 *Limonium sinuatum*

2003. Flora. Multicoloured.
1035 2d.50 Type **548** 60 25
1036 6d.50 *Echinops spinosus* 1·60 75

549 King Mohammed VI

2003
1037 **549** 70f. multicoloured 20 10
1038 **549** 80f. multicoloured 20 10
1039 **549** 5d. multicoloured 1·20 25
1039a **549** 13d. multicoloured 3·00 55
1040 **549** 20d. multicoloured 4·75 1·20

550 Courtyard

2003. Millenary of Grand Mosque, Sale.
1060 **550** 6d.50 multicoloured 1·60 45

551 Stylized Figures and Globe

2003. World Youth Congress, Morocco.
1061 **551** 6d.50 multicoloured 1·60 45

552 Kings Mohammed V, Hassan II and Mohammed VI

2003. 50th Anniv of Revolution of King and People.
1062 **552** 6d.50 multicoloured 1·60 55

553 King Mohammed VI

2003. 40th Birthday of King Mohammed VI. Multicoloured.
1063 2d.50 Type **553** 60 25
1064 6d.50 Wearing traditional dress 1·60 75
MS1065 121×90 mm. Nos. 1063/4 2·50 2·50

2003. As T **521**. Self-adhesive.
1066 2d.50 As No. 994 60 25
1067 6d.50 As No. 1008 1·60 75

554 *Sparisoma cretense*

2003. Fish. Multicoloured.
1068 2d.50 Type **554** 60 25
1069 6d. *Anthias anthias* 1·60 75

555 Satellites circling Globe

2003. World Post Day.
1070 **555** 6d.50 multicoloured 1·60 35

556 King Mohammed VI and Sick Child

2003. King Mohammed VI Solidarity Foundation.
1071 **556** 6d.50 multicoloured 1·60 55
1072 - 6d.50 lemon and ultramarine (28×28 mm) 1·60 55

Design:—No. 1072 As No. 978 but inscr '2003'.

557 "28" and Marchers

2003. 28th Anniv of "Green March".
1073 **557** 6d.50 multicoloured 1·60 35

558 City and Cultural Symbols

2003. Rabat—Arab Cultural Capital, 2003.
1074 **558** 6d.50 multicoloured 1·60 35

559 School Children examining Stamps

2003. Philately in Schools.
1075 **559** 6d.50 multicoloured 1·60 35

560 Sun, Child writing and Clouds

2003. United Nations Decade for Literacy.
1076 **560** 6d.50 multicoloured 1·60 35

561 Chinese and Moroccan Flags as Clasped Hands

2003. 45th Anniv of Morocco—China Diplomatic Relations.
1077 **561** 6d.50 multicoloured 1·60 35

562 Ship and D'Ibn Battutah

2004. 700th Birth Anniv of D'Ibn Battutah (traveller).
1078 **562** 6d.50 multicoloured 1·60 75

563 Bab Agnaou, Marrakech

2004
1079 **563** 6d.50 multicoloured 1·60 55

564 *Linaria gharbensis*

2004. Flowers. Multicoloured.
1080 2d.50 Type **564** 60 25
1081 6d.50 *Nigella damascene* 1·60 75

565 Equestrian, Globe and Emblem

2004. 16th World Military Equestrian Championship, Temara, Morocco.
1082 **565** 6d.50 multicoloured 1·60 75

566 Trophy

2004. 20th Anniv of Hassan II Tennis Grand Prix.
1083 **566** 6d.50 multicoloured 1·60 75

567 Festival Emblem

2004. Tenth World Festival of Sacred Music.
1084 **567** 6d.50 multicoloured 1·60 45

568 Woman wearing Kaftan

2004. Traditional Costume.
1085 **568** 6d.50 multicoloured 1·60 45

569 Tazoudasaurus Naimi

2004. Tazoudasaurus Naimi (dinosaur, newly discovered at Tazouda).
1086 **569** 6d.50 multicoloured 1·60 75

570 Emblem

2004. 30th International Military History Congress, Rabat.
1087 **570** 6d.50 multicoloured 1·60 55

571 King Mohammed VI

2004. Fifth Anniv of Enthronement of King Mohammed VI.
1088 2d.50 Type **571** 95 10
1089 6d. Seated 95 10

572 Dove holding Olive Branch and Globe

2004. International Peace Day.
1090 **572** 6d. multicoloured 1·50 35

573 King Mohammed VI and Sick Woman

2004. King Mohammed VI Solidarity Foundation.
1091 **573** 6d.50 multicoloured 1·60 55
1092 - 6d.50 lemon and deep ultramarine (28×28 mm) 1·60 55
Design:—No. 1092 As No. 978 but inscr '2004'.

574 "29" and Marchers

2004. 29th Anniv of "Green March".
1093 **574** 6d. multicoloured 1·50 35

575 Swordfish (*Xiphias gladius*)

2004. Marine Fauna. Multicoloured.
1094 2d.50 Type **575** 60 25
1095 6d.50 Octopus (*Octopus vulgaris*) 1·60 75

576 Child Holding Globe and Dove

2004. International Day of the Child.
1096 **576** 6d.50 multicoloured 1·60 45

578 Great Bustard (As No. 754)

2005. Birds. Self-adhesive. Multicoloured.

1099	2d.50 Type **578**	55	10
1100	2d.50 As No. 470	55	10
1101	2d.50 As No. 908	55	10
1102	2d.50 As No. 907	55	10
1103	2d.50 As No. 742	55	10
1104	2d.50 As No. 471	55	10
1105	2d.50 As No. 885	55	10
1106	2d.50 As No. 874	55	10
1107	2d.50 As No. 292	55	10
1108	2d.50 As No. 378	55	10

579 Costumes Zagora, South Morocco (As No. 267)

2005. Costumes. Self-adhesive Multicoloured.

1109	6d. Type **579**	1·30	25
1110	6d. As No. 215	1·30	25
1111	6d. As No. 734	1·30	25
1112	6d. As No. 268	1·30	25
1113	6d. As No. 216	1·30	25
1114	6d. As No. 733	1·30	25
1115	6d. As No. 825	1·30	25
1116	6d. As No. 826	1·30	25
1117	6d. As No. 223	1·30	25
1118	6d. As No. 219	1·30	25

580 Arch, Emblem, Globe and Dove

2005. Centenary of Rotary International.
1119 **580** 6d.50 multicoloured 1·50 25

581 Emblem, Flags and Map of Arab Nations

2005. 60th Anniv of Arab League.
1120 **581** 6d.50 multicoloured 1·50 25

582 Bab Boujloud, Fes

2005
1121 **582** 6d.50 multicoloured 1·50 25

583 Dove in Chains and Candle encased in Barbed Wire

2005. Amnesty International.
1122 **583** 6d.50 multicoloured 1·50 25

584 *Erodium sebaceum*

2005. Flowers. Multicoloured.
1123 2d.50 Type **584** 70 10
1124 6d.50 *Linaria ventricosa* 1·30 25

585 Horse (rock carving)

2005. Cultural Heritage.
1125 **585** 6d.50 multicoloured 1·50 25

586 Head and Globe

2005. World Neurosurgery Congress, Marrakesh.
1126 **586** 6d.50 multicoloured 1·50 25

587 Combine Harvester and Ears of Corn

2005. 85th Anniv of OCP Group (Groupe Office Cherifien des Phosphates).
1127 **587** 6d.50 multicoloured 1·50 25

588 Emblem

2005. 60th Anniv of United Nations.
1128 **588** 6d. multicoloured 1·40 25

589 "30", Procession with Flags and Marchers

2005. 30th Anniv of "Green March". Multicoloured.
1129 2d.50 Type **589** 55 10
1130 6d. "30", dunes and marchers 1·30 25

590 King Mohammed VI giving to Woman

2005. King Mohammed VI Solidarity Foundation.
1131 **590** 6d.50 multicoloured 1·40 25
1132 - 6d.50 lemon and ultramarine (28×28 mm) 1·40 25

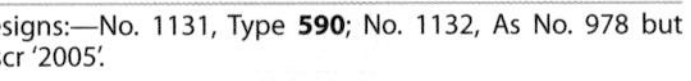
Designs:—No. 1131, Type **590**; No. 1132, As No. 978 but inscr '2005'.

591 Symbols of Morocco and Netherlands

2005. 400th Anniv of Morocco—Netherlands Diplomatic Relations. Multicoloured.
1133 6d.50 Type **591** 1·40 25
1134 6d.50 Moroccan arch enclosing Dutch canal (vert) 1·40 25

592 Couple, Symbols of Information Dissemination and Globe

2005. World Information Society Summit, Tunis.
1135 **592** 6d. multicoloured 1·80 35

593 King Mohammed V

2005. 50th Anniv of the Return of King Mohammed V. Multicoloured.
1136 6d.50 Type **593** 1·50 25
MS1137 120×90 mm. 6d.50×2, No. 1136; As 1136 but with colours of inscriptions reversed 3·25 3·25

594 Children in Circle (Kaoutar Azizi Alaoui)

2005. Children's Paintings. Multicoloured.
1138 2d.50 Type **594** 55 10
1139 2d.50 Dove and girls crying (Sara Bourquiba) 55 10
1140 2d.50 House (Mohcine Kahyouchat) 55 10
1141 2d.50 Hill, sea, sunset and palm tree (Anise Anico) 55 10

595 Emblem

2005. International Year of Microcredit.
1142 **595** 6d.50 multicoloured 1·50 25

596 *Sparus aurata*

2005. Marine Fauna. Multicoloured.
1143 2d.50 Type **596** 55 10
1144 6d. *Sepia officinalis* 1·30 25

597 Dove, Traffic, Emblem and Traffic Control Lights

2006. National Road Safety Day.
1145 **597** 6d.50 multicoloured 1·50 25

598 Ship and Oil Rigs

2006. 30th Anniv of OPEC International Development Fund.
1146 **598** 6d.50 multicoloured 1·50 25

599 Bab Marshan, Tangier

2006
1147 **599** 6d.50 multicoloured 1·50 25

600 World Map and Crowd

2006. 50th Anniv of Ministry of Foreign Affairs.
1148 **600** 6d. multicoloured 1·40 25

601 *Narcissus cantabricus*

2006. Flora. Multicoloured.
1149 2d.50 Type **601** 55 10
1150 6d.50 *Paeonia mascula* 1·50 30

602 King Mohammed VI and Tanks

2006. 50th Anniv of Royal Armed Forces. Multicoloured.
1151 2d.50 Type **602** 55 10
1152 6d.50 King Mohamed VI and ships 1·50 30
MS1153 120×90 mm. Nos. 1151/2 2·30 2·30

2006. King Mohammed VI.
1154 3d.25 As Type **521** 75 15

603 King Mohammed VI

2006. King Mohammed VI.
1155 **603** 7d.80 multicoloured 1·80 35

604 Barbary Macaque

2006. Fauna. Multicoloured.
1156 3d.25 Type **604** 85 20
1157 7d.80 Barbary lion 2·00 40

605 King Mohammed VI

2006. 31st Anniv of "Green March". Multicoloured.
1158 7d.80 Type **605** 1·80 35
1159 7d.80 Mohammed VI a Boujdour Mosque 2·00 40

606 Emblem

2006. King Mohammed VI Solidarity Foundation.
1160 **606** 7d.80 ultramarine, lemon and black 2·00 40

607 Globe

2006. Stamp Day.
1161 **607** 7d.80 multicoloured 2·00 40

608 Emblem, Flag and Assembly

2006. 50th Anniv of Membership of United Nations.
1162 **608** 7d.80 multicoloured 2·00 40

609 Virus and Bleeding Finger

2006. International AIDS Awareness Day.
1163 **609** 7d.80 multicoloured 2·00 40

610 Dove and Flags

2006. 50th Anniv of Morocco—Japan Diplomatic Relations. Multicoloured.
1164 3d.25 Type **610** 95 25
1165 7d.80 Symbols of Morocco and Japan 2·00 40

611 *Thunnus thynnus*

2006. Fish. Multicoloured.
1166 3d.25 Type **611** 95 25
1167 7d.80 *Sardina pilchardus* 2·00 40

612 Emblem

2007. 50th Anniv of Confederation of African Football.
1168 **612** 7d.80 multicoloured 2·00 40

613 Emblem

2007. 50th Anniv of Mohammed V University, Agdal, Rabat.
1169 **613** 3d.25 multicoloured 95 25

614 Ibn Khaldun

2007. 600th Death Anniv of Ibn Khaldun (historian, sociologist and philosopher).
1170 **614** 7d.80 multicoloured 2·00 40

615 Palm

2007. International Agricultural Exhibition, Meknès. Sheet 140×110 mm containing T **615** and similar multicoloured designs.
MS1171 3d.25 Type **615**; 3d.25 Argan tree; 7d.80 Cattle (horiz); 7d.80 Olives (horiz) 3·00 3·00

616 Couscous

2007. Moroccan Cuisine.
1172 **616** 7d.80 multicoloured 1·10 1·10

617 Musicians

2007. Music of Andalusia.
1173 **617** 7d.80 multicoloured 1·10 1·10

618 *Fulgurance* (M. Qotbi)

2007. Art. Sheet 125×135 mm containing T **618** and similar multicoloured designs.
MS1174 3d.25×4, Type **618**; Horsemen (H. Glaoui) (horiz); *Symphonie d'Ete* (M. Qotbi) (horiz); Horses (H. Glaoui) (horiz) 1·90 1·90

619 Scouts

2007. Centenary of Scouting.
1175 **619** 7d.80 multicoloured 1·10 1·10

620 Castelo de Silves, Portugal

2007. Architecture. Multicoloured.
1176 3d.25 Type **620** 1·00 1·00
1177 7d.80 Keep (El Kamara) Tower, Arzila 1·10 1·10

Stamps of a similar design were issued by Portugal.

621 Stamp Outline enclosing UPU Emblem

2007. Stamp Day.
1178 **621** 3d.25 multicoloured 1·00 1·00

622 City Skyline

2007. Fes–Islamic Capital of Culture–2007.
1179 **622** 7d.80 multicoloured 1·10 1·10

623 Marchers

2007. 32nd Anniv of 'Green March'.
1180 **623** 7d.80 multicoloured 1·10 1·10

2007. King Mohammed VI Solidarity Foundation.
1181 7d.80 lemon and ultramarine (28×28 mm) 1·10 1·10

Design:—No. 1181 As No. 1160, but inscr '2007'.

625 Medallion

2007. National Quality Week.
1182 **625** 7d.80 multicoloured 1·10 1·10

626 Child

2007. Children's Day.
1183 **626** 7d.80 multicoloured 1·10 1·10

627 Court Building

2007. 50th Anniv of Supreme Court.

1184	**627**	3d.25 multicoloured	1·00	1·00

628 Bab Lamrissa, Sale

2007

1185	**628**	7d.80 multicoloured	1·10	1·10

629 Mohammed V, Hassan II, Mohammed VI and Aircraft

2007. 50th Anniv of Royal Air Maroc.

1186	**629**	7d.80 multicoloured	1·10	1·10

630 Symbols of Sport

2007. 50th Anniv of Moroccan Sport.

1187	**630**	7d.80 multicoloured	1·10	1·10

631 Symbols of Tourism

2008. International Tourism Exhibition, Marrakech.

1188	**631**	7d.80 multicoloured	1·10	1·10

632 Map of Africa and Football

2008. African Nations Cup.

1189	**632**	7d.80 multicoloured	1·10	1·10

633 Export Trophy

2008

1190	**633**	3d.25 multicoloured	1·00	1·00

634 Emblem

2008. 1200th Anniv of Fez (1st issue).

1191	**634**	3d.25 multicoloured	1·00	1·00

See also No. 1202.

635 *Calendula stellata*

2008. Flora. Multicoloured.

1192	3d.25 Type **635**	1·00	1·00
1193	7d.80 *Convolvulus tricolor*	1·00	1·00

636 Falak Ol Aflak Castle, Iran and Script

2008. Morocco—Iran Issue. Multicoloured.

1194	3d.25 Type **636**	1·00	1·00
1195	3d.25 Flags of Morocco and Iran	1·00	1·00
1196	7d.80 La Kasbah des Oudayas, Morocco and script (different)	1·10	1·10

637 Globe (Narjiss Lasfar) (communications)

2008. Children's Drawings. Multicoloured.

1197	3d.25 Type **637**	1·00	1·00
1198	3d.25 House and trees (Chaimae Abbaich) (my childhood)	1·00	1·00
1199	3d.25 Globe enclosing habitats (our environment) (vert)	1·00	1·00
1200	3d.25 House and sunshine (daily life) (vert)	1·00	1·00

638 Damaged and Healthy Environments

2008. International Day of the Environment.

1201	**638**	7d.80 multicoloured	1·10	1·10

639 City

2008. 1200th Anniv of Fez (2nd issue).

1202	**639**	7d.80 multicoloured	1·10	1·10

640 Symbols of Development

2008. Transport. Agency for Development of Bouregreg Valley. Multicoloured.

1203	3d.25 Type **640**	1·10	1·10
1204	7d.80 Gate, walls and modern locomotive	1·20	1·20

641 Runners

2008. Olympic Games, Beijing. Multicoloured.

1205	3d.25 Type **641**	1·10	1·10
1206	3d.25 Hurdlers	1·10	1·10
1207	3d.25 Boxers	1·10	1·10
1208	3d.25 Runner	1·10	1·10

642 Pigeon

2008. Arab Post Day. Sheet 180×51 mm containing T **642** and similar horiz design. Multicoloured.

MS1209 7d.80 Type **642**; 7d.80 Camels	1·20	1·20

643 *Isurus oxyrinchus* (shortfin mako)

2008. Marine Fauna. Multicoloured.

1210	3d.25 Type **643**	1·10	1·10
1211	7d.80 *Haliotis tuberculata*	1·20	1·20

644 Musicians (La musique)

2008. Art and Culture. Sheet 143×106 mm containing T **644** and similar vert designs.

MS1212 3d.25×4, Type **644**; Zellij, hand cut polychrome tiles (Ezzellij); Woman (El haik); Scholar (l'École Coranique)	4·50	4·50

645 Ceramics

2008. 50th Anniv of Morocco–China Diplomatic Relations. Multicoloured.

1213	3d.25 Type **645**	1·10	1·10
1214	7d.80 Moroccan gateway and Great Wall of China (vert)	1·20	1·20
1215	7d.80 Conjoined Chinese and Moroccan symbols	1·20	1·20
MS1215a	170×110 mm. Nos. 1213/15	3·50	3·50

646 '33'

2008. 33rd Anniv of 'Green March'.

1216	**646**	3d.25 multicoloured	1·10	1·10

2008. King Mohammed VI Solidarity Foundation.

1217	7d.80 ultramarine, lemon and black (28×28 mm)	1·20	1·20

Design:—As No. 1160, but inscr '2008'.

647 Clasped Hands

2008. National Cancer Awareness Day.

1218	**647**	3d.25 multicoloured	1·10	1·10

648 Emblem and Scales

2008. 60th Anniv of Declaration of Human Rights.

1219	**648**	7d.80 multicoloured	1·20	1·20

649 Bab Al Marsa, Essaquira

2008

1220	**649**	7d.80 multicoloured	1·20	1·20

2008. King Mohammed VI.

1221	3d.25 As Type **521**	1·10	1·10

650 Carpet, Hénbale de Salé

2008. Carpets. Multicoloured. Self-adhesive.

1222	7d.80 Type **650**	1·20	1·20
1223	7d.80 Marmoucha	1·20	1·20
1224	7d.80 Ouled Besseba	1·20	1·20
1225	7d.80 Haut Atlas	1·20	1·20
1226	7d.80 Haddou	1·20	1·20
1227	7d.80 Tazenakht	1·20	1·20
1228	7d.80 Marmoucha (different)	1·20	1·20
1229	7d.80 Rabat	1·20	1·20
1230	7d.80 Ouaouzguid	1·20	1·20
1231	7d.80 Rabat (different)	1·20	1·20

651 Louis Braille, Braille Letters and Hands reading

2009. Birth Bicentenary of Louis Braille (inventor of Braille writing for the blind).

1232	**651**	7d.80 multicoloured	1·20	1·20

652 Emblems and Craftsmen

2009. Insurance for Independent Workers and Craftsmen.

1233	**652**	3d.25 multicoloured	1·10	1·10

653 Player

2009. 25th Grand Prix Hassan II Tennis Tournament, Casablanca.

1234	**653**	3d.25 multicoloured	1·10	1·10

654 Emblem

2009. 30th Anniv of Cadi Ayyad University, Marrakesh.

1235	**654**	3d.25 multicoloured	1·10	1·10

655 Sugar Cane

2009. 80th Anniv of Sugar Industry.

1236	**655**	3d.25 multicoloured	1·10	1·10

656 Mask and Script

2009. National Theatre Day.

1237	**656**	3d.25 multicoloured	1·10	1·10

657 Galileo Galilei, Telescope, Satellite and Receiver

2009. International Year of Astronomy.

1238	**657**	7d.80 multicoloured	1·20	1·20

658 Children, PC and Child's Hand holding Adult's Hand

2009. Protection for Children whilst using Internet.

1239	**658**	7d.80 multicoloured	1·20	1·20

659 Stylized Building

2009. 50th Anniv of Al-Maghrib Bank.

1240	**659**	3d.25 chrome yellow, greenish yellow and black	1·10	1·10

660 Mohammed VI

2009. Tenth Anniv of Enthronement of Mohammed VI. Multicoloured. (a) Ordinary gum.

1241		3d.25 Type **660**	1·10	1·10
1242		7d.80 Mohammed VI seated	1·20	1·20
MS1243		144×198 mm. Nos. 1241/2	2·50	2·50

(b) Self-adhesive gum.

1244		15d. Mohammed VI, Hassan II and Mohammed V	3·75	3·75

661 Emblem

2009. al-Quds—2009 Capital of Arab Culture.

1245	**661**	3d.25 multicoloured	1·10	1·10

663 Woman holding Globe

2009. National Women's Day.

1247	**663**	3d.25 multicoloured	1·10	1·10

664 Building Façade

2009. 50th Anniv of Mohammedia School of Engineers.

1248	**664**	3d.25 multicoloured	1·10	1·10

665 Gateway, Mehdia

2009

1249	**665**	7d.80 multicoloured	1·20	1·20

666 Marchers

2009. 34th Anniv of Green March.

1250	**666**	3d.25 multicoloured	1·10	1·10

2009. King Mohammed VI Solidarity Foundation.

1251		7d.80 ultramarine, lemon and black (28×28 mm)	1·20	1·20

Design:—As No. 1160, but inscr '2009'.

667 Oil Rigs, Ship and Symbols of Motion

2009. Morocco in Motion. Tanger-Med Port. Multicoloured.

1252		3d.25 Type **667**	1·10	1·10
1253		7d.80 Port, ship and symbols of motion (different)	1·20	1·20

668 '50'

2009. 50th Anniv of Caisse de Depot et de Gestion (financial institution).

1254	**668**	7d.80 ultramarine and gold	1·20	1·20

669 *Sarda sarda*

2009. Fish. Multicoloured.

1255		7d.80 Type **669**	1·20	1·20
1256		7d.80 *Oblada melanura*	1·20	1·20

670 Horses (Ayoub Elaidi)

2009. Children's Drawings. Multicoloured.

1257		3d.25 Type **670**	1·10	1·10
1258		3d.25 Trees (Yahya Elmhayi)	1·10	1·10
1259		3d.25 Mountain and water (Achraf Moussai)	1·10	1·10
1260		3d.25 Building and chimneys (Mohammed Chater)	1·10	1·10

Nos. 1261/2 and Type **671** are left for Flora,not yet recieved.

No. 1263 and Type **672** are left for 50th Anniv of Rebuilding of Agadir, not yet recieved.

Nos. 1264 and Type **673** are left for Earth Day, not yet recieved.

Nos. 1265 and Type **674** are left for Alfalfa, not yet recieved.

Nos. 1266/9 and Type **675** are left for Art and Culture, not yet recieved.

Nos. 1270 and Type **676** are left for A-Level Qualification, not yet recieved.

Nos. 1271 and Type **677** are left for National Resistance Day, not yet recieved.

Nos. 1272 and Type **678** are left for Bab Al Bahir Asilah, not yet recieved.

Nos. 1273 and Type **679** are left for Year of Biodiversity, not yet recieved.

680 Marchers with Flags

2010. 35th Anniv of Green March. Multicoloured.

MS1274		7d.80×2, Type **680**; Flag and dune	1·30	1·30

681 *Sciaena umbra*

2010. Fish

1275	**681**	7d.80 multicoloured	1·30	1·30

2010. King Mohammed VI Solidarity Foundation.

1276		7d.80 ultramarine, lemon and black (28×28 mm)	1·30	1·30

Design:—As No. 1160, but inscr '2010'.

682 Symbols of Digital Communication

2010. Maroc Numeric 2013 (strategy for internet access and e-government)

1277	**682**	7d.80 multicoloured	1·30	1·30

683 '10' and Festival Emblem enclosed in Film Strip

2010. Tenth Anniv of Marrakech International Film Festival

1278	**683**	7d.80 multicoloured	1·30	1·30

684 ONCF Electric Locomotive

2010. Transport. Trains

1279	**684**	3d.25 multicoloured	1·00	40

685 'Bonheur'

2010. Greetings. Multicoloured.

1280		3d.25 Type **685**	1·00	40
1281		3d.25 'Santé'	1·00	40
1282		3d.25 'Prospéritié'	1·00	40

686 King Mohammed VI

2011. King Mohammed VI

1283		3d.50 Type **686**	1·60	1·40
1284		8d.40 As Type **603**	3·75	3·25
1285		20d. As Type **521** (horiz)	9·00	8·00

687 Cheetah delivering Mail

2011. Priority Mail

1286	**687**	5d.90 multicoloured	2·75	2·40
1287	**687**	6d.40 multicoloured	2·75	2·50

2011. King Mohammed VI. Booklet Stamps. Size 20×22 mm

1288		3d.50 As Type **686**	1·60	1·40

688 Tom and Jerry

2011. Cartoons - *Tom and Jerry*. Multicoloured.

1289		3d.50 Type **688**	1·60	1·40
1290		3d.50 In hammocks betweeen palm trees	1·60	1·40
1291		3d.50 Jerry shooting Tom with ball machine	1·60	1·40
1292		3d.50 Jerry surfing on Tom's stomach	1·60	1·40
1293		3d.50 Playing tennis	1·60	1·40
1294		3d.50 Caught out by large wave	1·60	1·40
1295		3d.50 Jerry holding tennis ball for Tom	1·60	1·40
1296		3d.50 Collecting shells	1·60	1·40
1297		3d.50 Jerry throwing balls causing Tom to fall	1·60	1·40
1298		3d.50 Building sandcastle	1·60	1·40

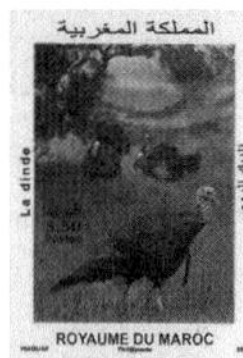

689 *Meleagris gallopavo* (Turkey)

2011. Flora and Fauna. Multicoloured.

1299		3d.50 Type **689**	1·60	1·40
1300		3d.50 *Lawsonia inermis*	1·60	1·40

690 Vessel

2011. Moroccan Copperware. Booklet Stamps. Multicoloured.

1301		8d.40 Type **690** (As Type **303**)	3·75	3·25
1302		8d.40 Vessel with pointed lid (As Type **230**)	3·75	3·25
1303		8d.40 Pestle and mortar (As Type **257**)	3·75	3·25
1304		8d.40 Vase with bulbous base and handles (As Type **436**)	3·75	3·25
1305		8d.40 Tripod brazier (As No. 581)	3·75	3·25
1306		8d.40 Jug	3·75	3·25
1307		8d.40 Kettle and brazier (As No. 538)	3·75	3·25
1308		8d.40 Kettle on stand (As Type **423**)	3·75	3·25
1309		8d.40 Stepped lantern (As Type **396**)	3·75	3·25
1310		8d.40 Coffee pot with heater (As Type **216**)	3·75	3·25

691 Emblem

2011. Al Barid Bank

1311	**691**	3d.50 multicoloured	1·60	1·40

692 Moulay Abderrahmane Ben Zidane

2011. Personalities. Multicoloured.

1312	3d.50 Type **692**	1·60	1·40
1313	3d.50 Abou Chouaib Doukkali Essadiki	1·60	1·40
1314	3d.50 Mohamed Ben Larbi Alaoui Lamdaghri	1·60	1·40
1315	3d.50 Mohamed El Mokhtar Soussi	1·60	1·40
1316	3d.50 Abdellah Ben Abdessamad Guennoune	1·60	1·40

693 AIDS Ribbon

2011. Campaign to Control AIDS

1317	**693**	8d.40 multicoloured	3·75	3·25

694 Symbols of Crafts

2011. National Week of Crafts

1318	**694**	3d.50 multicoloured	1·60	1·40

695 Postmark and Aircraft

2011. Centenary of Airmail

1319	**695**	8d.40 multicoloured	3·75	3·25
1320	**695**	8d.40 black	3·75	3·25

696 Bronze 8 falus, Fâs, 1893

2011. Moroccan Coins. Multicoloured.

1321	3d.50 Type **696**	1·60	1·40
1322	3d.50 Gold dinar, 1609	1·60	1·40
1323	3d.50 Dinar	1·60	1·40
1324	3d.50 Gold dinar, Marrakech, 1145	1·60	1·40
1325	3d.50 Silver dirham, Wallia, 790	1·60	1·40

697 Emblem

2011. National Campaign for the Millennium Development Goals

1326	**697**	8d.40 multicoloured	3·75	3·25

698 Alphabet (Ibtissam Gariate)

2011. Children's Drawings

1327	3d.50 Type **698**	1·60	1·40
1328	3d.50 Green and devastated landscape (Rahma Damach)	1·60	1·40
1329	3d.50 Boy crushing cigarette (Hanane Aliquan)	1·60	1·40
1330	3d.50 Children in the park (Kenza Najdaoui) (horiz)	1·60	1·40

699 '36'

2011. 36th Anniv of Green March

1331	**699**	8d.40 chrome and ultramarine	3·75	3·25

700 Screen, Paula Cardozo

2011. Art and Culture. Screens

MS1332	3d.50 Type **700**; 3d.50 Abdellah Yacoubi; 8d.40 Yakako Fukuda-Ota (vert); 8d.40 Miki Tica (vert)	11·00	10·50

2011. King Mohammed VI Solidarity Foundation

1333	8d.40 ultramarine, lemon and black (28×28 mm)	3·75	3·25

Design:—As No. 1160, but inscr '2011'

701 Symbols of Statistics

2011. 50th Anniv of INSEA (National Institute of Statistics and Applied Economics)

1334	**701**	3d.50 multicoloured	1·60	1·40

702 Oryx

2012. Centenary of Rabat Zoo

1335	3d.50 Type **702**	1·60	1·40
1336	3d.50 Barbary Sheep	1·60	1·40
1337	8d.40 Bald Ibis (vert)	3·75	3·25
1338	8d.40 Barbary Lion	3·75	3·25
MS1339	160×125 mm. 3d.50 As Type **702**; 3d.50 As No. 1336; 8d.40 As No. 1337 (vert); 8d.40 As No. 1338 (vert)	11·00	10·50

703 Symbols of Football

2012. Football - The African Cup of Nations

1340	**703**	3d.50 multicoloured	1·60	1·40

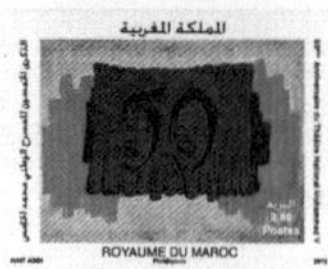

704 '50'

2012. 50th Anniv of National Theatre

1341	**704**	3d.50 multicoloured	1·60	1·40

705 '100'

2012. Centenary of First Moroccan Stamp. Multicoloured.

1342	3d.50 Type **705**	1·60	1·40
1343	8d.40 *Spahi Horsemen* (Haram al Glaoui) (As Type **94**)	3·75	3·25

706 Dove and Map

2012. Arab Post Day

1344	**706**	8d.40 multicoloured	3·75	3·25

707 Runner

2012. London 2012 - Olympic Games, London

1345	**707**	8d.40 multicoloured	3·75	3·25

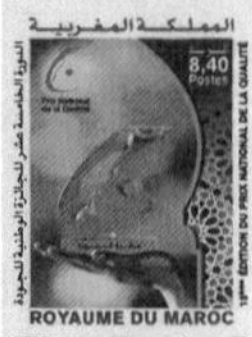

708 Emblem

2012. 15th National Prize for Quality

1346	**708**	8d.40 multicoloured	3·75	3·25

709 'RCAR'

2012. 35th Anniv of Collective Allocation Retirement Plan

1347	**709**	3d.50 multicoloured	1·60	1·40

710 Falcon

2012. Falcon

1348	**710**	8d.40 multicoloured	3·75	3·25

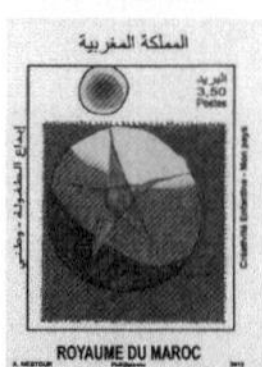

711 Sun and Star (A. Mestour)

2012. Children's Drawings

1349	3d.50 Type **711**	1·60	1·40
1350	3d.50 Trees and pyramids (Z. el Amri) (horiz)	1·60	1·40
1351	3d.50 Woman carrying in shopping (R. Souini) (horiz)	1·60	1·40

712 Horsemen

2012. Fifth Anniv of Salon du Cheval

1352	**712**	8d.40 multicoloured	3·75	3·25

713 Marchers

2012. 37th Anniv of Green March

1353	**713**	3d.50 multicoloured	1·60	1·40

2012. King Mohammed VI Solidarity Foundation

1354	8d.40 ultramarine, lemon and black (28×28 mm)	3·75	3·25

Design:—As No. 1160, but inscr '2012'

714 '100'

2012. Centenary of the Official Bulletin. Multicoloured.

1355	**714**	3d.50 black	1·60	1·40
1356	**714**	8d.40 multicoloured	3·75	3·25

715 Seal

2012. 120th Anniv of Poste Maghzen. Multicoloured.

1357	3d.50 Type **715**	1·60	1·40
1358	3d.50 Octagonal seal, purple ink	1·60	1·40
1359	3d.50 Circular seal, aquamarine ink	1·60	1·40
1360	3d.50 Octaganol seal, aquamarine ink	1·60	1·40
1361	3d.50 Circular seal with ornate handle, ultramarine ink	1·60	1·40
1362	3d.50 Octagonal seal with ornate handle, ultramarine ink	1·60	1·40
1363	3d.50 Circular seal, red ink	1·60	1·40
1364	3d.50 Octagonal seal, red ink	1·60	1·40
1365	3d.50 Circular seal with ornate handle, dark green ink	1·60	1·40
1366	3d.50 Octagonal seal with ornate handle, dark green ink	1·60	1·40
1367	3d.50 Circular seal with ornate handle, orange ink	1·60	1·40
1368	3d.50 Octagonal seal with ornate handle, orange ink	1·60	1·40
MS1368a	154×108 mm. 13d.×2, Octagonal seal, ultramarine ink (25×25 mm (octagonal)); Circular seal, aquamarine ink (27×27 mm (circular))	12·00	11·50

716 Symbols of Renewable Energy

2012. International Renewable Energy Year

1369	**716**	8d.40 multicoloured	3·75	3·25

717 Early and Modern Postal Trains

2012. Centenary of the Post Office in Morocco. Multicoloured.

1370	3d.50 Type **717**	1·60	1·40
1371	3d.50 Development of the post	1·60	1·40

718 Forest

2013. Centenary of the Ministry for Water and Forestry

1372	3d.50 Type **718**	1·60	1·40
1373	8d.40 Anniversary emblem (vert)	3·75	3·25

719 Green Globe

2013. Seventh Environmental Education Congress, Marrakesch
1374 **719** 3d.50 multicoloured 1·60 1·40

720 El Houssaine Slaoui

2013. Personalities. Multicoloured.

1375	3d.50 Type **720**	1·60	1·40
1376	3d.50 Mohammed Ben Ali Rbati	1·60	1·40
1377	3d.50 Abu El Kassem Zayani	1·60	1·40
1378	3d.50 Abu El Hassan Ali El Youssi	1·60	1·40
1379	3d.50 Sidi Mohammed Ben Abdellah	1·60	1·40

721 King Mohammed VI **722** King Mohammed VI

2013. King Mohammed VI

(a) Sheet stamps. Ordinary gum

1380	**721**	3d.50 multicoloured	1·60	1·40
1381	**722**	8d.40 multicoloured	3·75	3·25

(b) Booklet stamps

1381a	3d.50 As Type **721** (15×22 mm)	1·60	1·40
1381b	8d.40 As Type **722** (15×22 mm)	3·75	3·25

723 World and Figures

2013. Tenth Anniv of National Day of Moroccan Community Living Abroad
1382 **723** 8d.40 multicoloured 3·75 3·25

724 Demonstrators

2013. 60th Anniv of King and People's Revolution
1383 **724** 3d.50 multicoloured 1·60 1·40

2013. 50th Birth Anniv of King Mohammed VI. Multicoloured.
MS1384 8d.40×2, As Type **721**; As Type **722** 7·75 7·50

725 Rabat

2013. World Summit of Local and Regional Leaders. Multicoloured.

1385	8d.40 Type **725**	3·75	3·25
1386	8d.40 Regions of Morocco, Rabat	3·75	3·25

726 Monument

2013. 38th Anniv of Green March
1387 **726** 8d.40 multicoloured 3·75 3·25

2013. King Mohammed VI Solidarity Foundation
1388 8d.40 ultramarine, lemon and black (28×28 mm) 3·75 3·25
Design:—As No. 1160, but inscr '2013'

727 Procession

2013. National Day of Les Trois Glorieuses (Three Glorious Events) (return of King Mohammed V from exile, the resurgence of the Moroccan nation and the enthronement of His Majesty King Mohammed V)
1389 **727** 3d.50 sepia and black 1·60 1·40

728 Anniversary Emblem

2013. Centenary of Land Registration
1390 **728** 3d.50 multicoloured 1·60 1·40

729 Odessa Port, Ukraine

2013. Ports. Multicoloured.

1391	3d.50 Type **729**	1·60	1·40
1392	8d.40 Tanger-Med Port, Morocco	3·75	3·25

730 Children

2013. 20th Anniv of Ratification by Morocco of United Nations Convention of the Rights of the Child. Multicoloured.

1393	3d.50 Type **730**	1·60	1·40
1394	8d.40 Children in sunshine	3·75	3·25

731 '50' and Parliament

2013. 50th Anniv of Morocco's Parliament
1395 **731** 3d.50 multicoloured 1·60 1·40

732 Steam Engine

2014. 50th Anniv of National Office of Railways (ONCF)
1396 **732** 3d.50 multicoloured 1·60 1·40

2014. King Mohammed VI

1284	8d.40 As Type **603**	3·75	3·25
1285	20d. As Type **521** (horiz)	9·00	8·00

733 Birds

2014. 20th Sacred Music of the World Festival, Fez, Morocco
1399 **733** 3d.50 multicoloured 1·60 1·40

734 Mediterranean

2014. EUROMED - Euromed 2014 Postal Conference
1400 **734** 8d.40 multicoloured 3·75 3·25

735 Runners

2014. International Association of Athletics Federations Continental Cup, Marrakech

1401	3d.50 Type **735**	1·60	1·40
1402	8d.40 Emblem and athlete (vert)	3·75	3·25

736 Ruddy Shelduck and Lake, Haut Atlas Oriental National Park

2014. Flora and Fauna of Morocco. Multicoloured.

1403	3d.50 Type **736**	1·60	1·40
1404	8d.40 Heron, Lake Tislit	3·75	3·25

2014. Inauguration of Mohammed VI Museum for Modern and Contemporary Art. Multicoloured.
1405 3d.50 'MMVI' and 'Fleur de lys' shapes 1·60 1·40

738 '39'

2014. 39th Anniv of Green March
1406 **738** 8d.40 multicoloured 3·75 3·25

739 Oceanographic Museum Façade

2014. Monaco - Morocco Friendship. Multicoloured.

1407	3d.50 Type **739**	1·60	1·40
1408	8d.40 Hassan Tower, Morocco	3·75	3·25

740 Emblem

2014. World Forum on Human Rights, Marrakech
1409 **740** 8d.40 multicoloured 3·75 3·25

2015. King Mohammed VI Solidarity Foundation
1388 1 20g. (8d.40) ultramarine, lemon and black (28×28 mm) 3·75 3·25
Design:—As No. 1160, but with different face value and inscr '2014'

741 Aguelmam Azegza

2015. Lakes of Morocco. Multicoloured.

1411	N 20g. (3d.75) Type **741**	1·70	1·50
1412	N 20g. (3d.75) Aguelmam Sidi Ali	1·70	1·50
1413	N 20g. (3d.75) Dayet Aoua	1·70	1·50
1414	N 20g. (3d.75) Lake Ifni	1·70	1·50
1415	N 20g. (3d.75) Lake Sidi Boughaba	1·70	1·50

742 Lighthouse

2015. 150th Anniv of Cap Spartel Lighthouse
1416 **742** 9d. multicoloured 4·00 3·50

743 Emblem

2015. Jidar Street Art Festival, Rabat
1417 **743** 9d. multicoloured 4·00 3·50

744 Main Post Office, Rabat

2015. Stamp Day
1417 **744** 3d.75 multicoloured 1·70 1·50

745 *Sparus auratus*

2015. Marine Life. Booklet Stamps. Multicoloured.

1419	9d. Type **745**	4·00	3·50
1420	9d. *Oblada melanura*	4·00	3·50
1421	9d. *Sarda sarda*	4·00	3·50
1422	9d. *Haliotis tuberculata*	4·00	3·50
1423	9d. *Isurus oxyrhynchus*	4·00	3·50
1424	9d. *Sardina pilchardus*	4·00	3·50
1425	9d. *Sparisoma cretense*	4·00	3·50
1426	9d. *Xiphias gladius*	4·00	3·50
1427	9d. *Octopus vulgaris*	4·00	3·50
1428	9d. *Sepia officinalis*	4·00	3·50

2015. EUROMED - Boats of the Mediterranean
1428 9d. *Le Chebec* 4·00 3·50

747 Tower and Oudaia Gate, Rabat

2015. World Tourism Cities Federation (WTCF) Tourism Summit - Rabat - Fez, Morocco
1429 **747** 9d. multicoloured 4·00 3·50

748 Stromatolite of Amane n' Tourhart

2015. Rocks and Fossils of Morocco

1430	3d.50 Type **748**	1·60	1·40
1431	3d.50 Marrellomorphe, Zagora	1·60	1·40
1432	9d. Meteorite, Tissint (horiz)	4·00	3·50
1433	9d. *Aegirocassis benmoulai* fossil (horiz)	4·00	3·50

749 Anniversary Emblem

2015. 70th Anniv of United Nations

1434	**749**	9d. multcoloured	4·00	3·50

750 Marchers

2015. 40th Anniv of Green March

1435	9d. Type **750**	4·00	3·50
1436	9d. Flag	4·00	3·50
MS1437 95×200 mm. 9d.×2, As Type **750**; As No. 1436		8·25	8·00

751 Flag

2015. Centenary of National Flag

1438	**751**	9d. multicoloured	4·00	3·50

752 Symbols of Independence

2015. 60th Anniv of Independence

1439	**752**	9d. multicoloured	4·00	3·50

753 Emblem

2015. 110th Anniv of Rotary International

1440	**753**	9d. multicoloured	4·00	3·50

754 Symbols of Crafts

2015. National Week of Crafts

1441	**754**	3d.75 multicoloured	1·70	1·50

755 Ahmed Balafrej

2015. Personalities. Multicoloured.

1442	3d.75 Type **755**	1·70	1·50
1443	3d.75 Mouha Ou Hammou Zayani	1·70	1·50
1444	3d.75 Abdelkrim El Khatib	1·70	1·50
1445	3d.75 Ahmed Tayeb Laâlej	1·70	1·50
1446	3d.75 Larbi Ben Barek	1·70	1·50

756 Aerial View

2016. Centenary of Urban Planning Law

1447	**756**	3d.75 multicoloured	1·70	1·50

2016. King Mohammed VI Solidarity Foundation

1448		9d. ultramarine, lemon and black (28×28 mm)	4·00	3·50

Design:—As No. 1160, but with different face value and inscr '2016'

757 Women

2016. International Women's Day

1449	**757**	9d. multicoloured	4·00	3·50

758 Emblem

2016. National Civil Society Day

1450	**758**	3d.75 multicoloured	1·70	1·50

759 *The Walking Man*

2016. Albrto Giacometti Retrospective Exhibition, Mohammed VI Museum of Modern and Contemporary Arts, Rabat

1451	**759**	9d. multicoloured	4·00	3·50

760 *Pagrus auriga*

2016. EUROMED - Fish of the Mediterranean

1452	**760**	3d.75 multicoloured	1·70	1·50

761 Map

2016. Africa Philatelic Hub - africaphilatelyshop.post

1453	**761**	9d. multicoloured	4·00	3·50

762 '41'

2016. 41st Anniv of Green March

1454	**762**	9d. multicoloured	4·00	3·50

763 'ACTUEMOS AGISSONS'

2016. COP22 - United Nations Climate Change Conference and CMP12 - Conference of the Parties serving as the meeting of the Parties to the Kyoto Protocol, Marrakech. Multicoloured.

1455	9d. Type **763**	4·00	3·50
1456	9d. 'MARRAKECH 2016'	4·00	3·50

POSTAGE DUE STAMPS

D53

1965

D162	**D53**	5f. green	24·00	9·00
D163	**D53**	10f. brown	95	45
D164	**D53**	20f. red	95	45
D165	**D53**	30f. sepia	2·75	90

D153 Peaches

1974

D393	-	5f. orange, grn & blk	30	25
D394	-	10f. green, red & blk	45	25
D395	-	20f. green and black	70	40
D396	**D153**	30f. orge, grn & blk	1·00	40
D397	-	40f. green and black	95	20
D398	-	60f. orge, grn & blk	1·30	35
D399	-	80f. orge, grn & blk	1·60	35
D399a	-	1d. multicoloured	95	45
D400	-	1d.20 multicoloured	95	70
D401	-	1d.60 multicoloured	45	35
D402	-	2d. multicoloured	45	55
D403	-	5d. multicoloured	2·10	1·40

Designs:—60f., 1d.60, Peaches. Vert: 5f. Oranges; 10f., 1d.20, Cherries; 20f. Raisins; 40f. Grapes; 80f. Oranges; 1, 5d. Apples; 2d. Strawberries.

D544 Strawberries

2003. Multicoloured.. Multicoloured.

D1029	1d.50 Type **D5**44	55	45
D1030	2d. Cherries	75	55
D1031	5d. Apples	2·00	1·50

D577 Peaches

2005. Postage Due.

D1097	**D577**	60f. multicoloured	55	45

2005. Postage Due. As D397. Multicoloured.

D1098	2d. Grapes	75	55

D662 Bananas

2009. Self-adhesive.

D1246	**D662**	3d.25 multicoloured	1·10	1·10

APPENDIX

The following issues for Mozambique have either been issued in excess of postal needs, or have not been made available to the public in reasonable quantities at face value. Such stamps mat later be given full listing if there is evidence of regular postal use. Miniature sheets, imperforate stamps etc are excluded from this section.

2009

Transport with Animals. 33m.×6
Two-wheeled Transport. 33m.×6
Vintage Cars. 33m.×6
Modern Cars. 33m.×6
Modern Electric Cars. 33m.×6
Ancient Sailing Vessels. 33m.×6
Ships and Maps. 33m.×6
Steam-powered Ships. 33m.×6
Warships. 33m.×12
Modern Ships. 33m.×6
Early Locomotives. 33m.×6
Locomotives. 33m.×18
High-speed Trains. 33m.×12
Pioneer Aircraft. 33m.×12
Airplanes. 33m.×6
Military Airplanes. 33m.×12
Supersonic Airplanes. 33m.×6
Fire Vehicles. 33m.×6
Ambulances. 33m.×6
Spacecraft. 33m.×12
Chinese New Year. Year of the Tiger (2010). 8m.×6
500th Death Anniv of Shen Chou (artist). 8m.×6
90th Birth Anniv of John Paul II. 8m.×6
140th Birth Anniv of Mahatma Gandhi. 8m.×6
Chinese Film Stars. 8m.×6
60th Anniv of the People's Republic of China. 8m.×6
120th Birth Anniv of Charlie Chaplin (actor). 20m.×6
20th Death Anniv of Emperor Hirohito of Japan. 20m.×6
Pres. John F. Kennedy Commemoration. 20m.×6
Marilyn Monroe (actress) Commemoration. 20m.×6
Elvis Presley Commemoration. 20m.×6
Michael Jackson (singer) Commemoration. 20m.×6
Pope Benedict XVI. 20m.×6
Expo 2010, Shanghai. 20m.×6
Galileo Galilei (astronomer) Commemoration. 33m.×6
Johannes Kepler (astronomer) Commemoration. 33m.×6
250th Death Anniv of George Frideric Handel (composer). 33m.×6
250th Birth Anniv of William Kirby (entomologist). 33m.×6
240th Birth Anniv of Napolean Bonaparte (emperor of France). 33m.×6
Death Bicentenary of Joseph Haydn (composer). 33m.×6
Birth Bicentenary of Charles Darwin (naturalist). 33m.×6
Birth Bicentenary of Louis Braille (inventor of Braille). 33m.×6
160th Death Anniv of Katsushika Hokusai (artist). 33m.×6
150th Death Anniv of Alexander von Humboldt (naturalist). 33m.×6
150th Birth Anniv of Georges-Pierre Seurat (artist). 33m.×6
Birth Centenary of Sir Peter Scott (founder of Worldwide Fund for Nature). 33m.×6
40th Anniv of the First Man on the Moon. 33m.×6
International Polar Year. 33m.×6

2013

Christmas (2012). Nativity Paintings. 16m.×2, 92m.×2
50th Death Anniversary (2012) of Niels Bohr. 16m.×2, 92m.×2
230th Birth Anniversary (2012) of Niccolo Paganini. 16m.×2, 92m.×2
Nobel Prizes 2012. 16m.×2, 92m.×2
Chinese New Year. Year of the Snake. 16m.×2, 92m.×2
European High Speed Trains. 16m.×2, 92m.×2
Japanese High Speed Trains. 16m.×2, 92m.×2
Japanese Airplanes. 16m.×2, 92m.×2
Unmanned Aerial Vehicles. 16m.×2, 92m.×2
Genoese Medieval Shipbuilders. 16m.×2, 92m.×2
Venetian Medieval Shipbuilders. 16m.×2, 92m.×2
World War II Submarines. 16m.×2, 92m.×2
World War II Tanks. 16m.×2, 92m.×2
Table Tennis. 16m.×2, 92m.×2
Rugby. 16m.×2, 92m.×2
Cricketers. 16m.×2, 92m.×2
Reef Fish. 16m.×2, 92m.×2
Impressionist Painters. 16m.×2, 92m.×2
Hans Werner Henze Commemoration. 16m.×2, 92m.×2
Minerals of Mozambique. 16m.×2, 92m.×2
World Anti Malaria Campaign. 16m.×2, 92m.×2
Alberto Chissano (Mozambican sculptor). 16m.×2, 92m.×2
Aerial Firefighting. 16m.×2, 92m.×2
Domestic Cats. 16m.×2, 92m.×2
Rare and Endangered Orchids. 16m.×2, 92m.×2
20th Death Anniversary (2012) of Gille Villeneuve. 16m.×2, 92m.×2
Golfers. 16m.×2, 92m.×2
Dogs in Art. Paintings. 16m.×2, 92m.×2
Hurricanes. 16m.×2, 92m.×2
WWF. Ground Pangolin. 16m.×2, 92m.×2
Veteran Racing Cars. 16m.×5, 92m.
Mail Transport. 16m.×5, 92m.
Centenary of the London Underground. 16m.×5, 92m.
Horse-drawn Transport. 16m.×6
Jet Airplanes. 16m.×5, 92m.
Popemobiles. 16m.×5, 92m.
Historic Military Vehicles. 16m.×4, 92m.×2
Icebreakers. 16m.×5, 92m.
Motorcycles. 16m.×5, 92m.
Early Aviators. 16m.×5, 92m.
Ice Sailing. 16ml.×5, 92m.
Military Helicopters. 16m.×5, 92m.
25th Death Anniversary of Enzo Ferrari. 16m.×5, 92m.
High Speed Trains. 16m.×5, 92m.
Formula 1 Motor Racing Champions. 16m.×5, 92m.
10th Anniversary of the Last Flight of Concorde. 16m.×5, 92m.
Airships. 16m.×5, 92m.
High Speed Trains of the World. 16m.×5, 92m.
90th Birth Anniversary of Alan Shepard (astronaut). 16m.×5, 92m.
45th Anniversary of Launching of Apollo 8. 16m.×5, 92m.
Drones. 16m.×5, 92m.
Special Transport. 16m.×5, 92m.
Steam Locomotives. 16m.×5, 92m.
Rescue Boats. 16m.×5, 92m.
Fire Engines. 16m.×4, 92m.×2
Centenary of the Tour de France (cycle race). 16m.×6
Sledge Dogs. 16m.×6
10th Anniversary of Yang Liwei's Flight in Shenzhou 5 (first manned Chinese spacecraft). 16m.×6
Vendee Globe Regatta 2012-13. 16m.×5, 92m.
Scouting. 16m.×2, 92m.×2
Women World Chess Champions. 16m.×2, 92m.×2
Model Trains. 16m.×2, 92m.×2
Turtles. 16m.×2, 92m.×2
150th Anniversary of the International Committee of the Red Cross. 16m.×2, 92m.×2
Volcanoes and Minerals. 16m.×2, 92m.×2
160th Birth Anniversary of Vincent van Gogh. 16m.×2, 92m.×2
Prince William, Duke of Cambridge. RAF Rescue Pilot. 16m.×2, 92m.×2
Mozambican Seafood Cuisine. 16m.×2, 92m.×2
Frogs and Snails. 16m.×2, 92m.×2
Pandas. 16m.×2, 92m.×2
Paintings by Ivan Aivazovsky. 16m.×2, 92m.×2
530th Birth Anniversary of Raphael. 16m.×2, 92m.×2
Dinosaurs. 16m.×2, 92m.×2
Bees. 16m.×2, 92m.×2
Pope Benedict XVI. 16m.×2, 92m.×2
Birds of Prey. 16m.×2, 92m.×2
Butterflies and Orchids. 16m.×2, 92m.×2
150th Death Anniversary of Eugene Delacroix. 16m.×2, 92m.×2
Elephants. 16m.×2, 92m.×2
Dolphins. 16m.×2, 92m.×2
Lighthouses and Sea Birds. 16m.×2, 92m.×2
Marilyn Monroe Commemoration. 16m.×2, 92m.×2
Owls and Mushrooms. 16m.×2, 92m.×2
65th Death Anniversary of Mahatma Gandhi. 16m.×2, 92m.×2
Mushrooms and Insects. 16m.×2, 92m.×2
Parrots. 16m.×2, 92m.×2
Pope Francis I. 16m.×2, 92m.×2
120th Birth Anniversary of Mao Tse-tung. 16m.×2, 92m.×2
Winter Olympic Games, Sochi, Russia (2014). 16m.×2, 92m.×2

MOROCCO AGENCIES

Stamps used at British postal agencies in Morocco, N. Africa, the last of which closed on 30 April 1957.

I. GIBRALTAR ISSUES OVERPRINTED

For use at all British Post Offices in Morocco.
All British POs in Morocco were under the control of the Gibraltar PO until 1907 when control was assumed by HM Postmaster-General.

1898. Stamps of Gibraltar (Queen Victoria) optd **Morocco Agencies**.

9	**7**	5c. green	4·00	3·25
10	**7**	10c. red	6·00	3·25
3	**7**	20c. olive and brown	23·00	4·25
11	**7**	20c. olive	15·00	2·75
4	**7**	25c. blue	10·00	2·50
5	**7**	40c. brown	6·50	3·50
14	**7**	50c. lilac	16·00	6·50
7	**7**	1p. brown and blue	21·00	32·00
8	**7**	2p. black and red	35·00	38·00

1903. Stamps of Gibraltar (King Edward VII) optd **Morocco Agencies**.

24	**8**	5c. light green and green	22·00	13·00
18	**8**	10c. purple on red	9·00	40
26	**8**	20c. green and red	9·50	35·00
20	**8**	25c. purple and black on blue	8·00	30
28	**8**	50c. purple and violet	11·00	65·00
29	**8**	1p. black and red	50·00	90·00
30	**8**	2p. black and blue	28·00	38·00

II. BRITISH CURRENCY

On sale at British POs throughout Morocco, including Tangier, until 1937.

PRICES. Our prices for used stamps with these overprints are for examples used in Morocco. These stamps could also be used in the United Kingdom, with official sanction, from the summer of 1950 onwards, and with UK postmarks are worth about 50% less.

Stamps of Great Britain optd **MOROCCO AGENCIES**

1907. King Edward VII.

31	**83**	½d. green	2·25	15·00
32	**83**	1d. red	9·50	9·50
33	-	2d. green and red	10·00	6·00
34	-	4d. green and brown	3·75	4·25
35a	-	4d. orange	10·00	22·00
36	-	6d. purple	15·00	35·00
37	-	1s. green and red	26·00	17·00
38	-	2s.6d. purple	95·00	£170

1914. King George V.

55	**105**	½d. green	3·25	50
43	**104**	1d. red	2·25	20
44	**105**	1½d. brown	8·50	19·00
45	**106**	2d. orange	6·00	60
58	**104**	2½d. blue	9·50	1·50
46	**106**	3d. violet	1·75	35
47	**106**	4d. green	9·50	1·50
60b	**107**	6d. purple	2·00	60
49	**108**	1s. brown	16·00	2·50
53	**109**	2s.6d. brown	50·00	26·00
74	**109**	5s. red	28·00	£140

1935. Silver Jubilee.

62	**123**	½d. green	1·50	6·50
63	**123**	1d. red	1·50	13·00
64	**123**	1½d. brown	7·00	24·00
65	**123**	2½d. blue	8·00	2·50

1935. King George V.

66	**119**	1d. red	3·25	23·00
67	**118**	1½d. brown	6·50	27·00
68	**120**	2d. orange	1·25	16·00
69	**119**	2½d. blue	1·75	4·25
70	**120**	3d. violet	50	30
71	**120**	4d. green	50	30
72	**122**	1s. brown	1·00	9·50

1936. King Edward VIII.

75	**124**	1d. red	10	40
76	**124**	2½d. blue	10	15

In 1937 unoverprinted Great Britain stamps replaced overprinted **MOROCCO AGENCIES** issues as stocks became exhausted. In 1949 overprinted issues reappeared and were in use at Tetuan (Spanish Zone), the only remaining British PO apart from that at Tangier.

1949. King George VI.

77	**128**	½d. green	1·75	8·50
94	**128**	½d. orange	2·00	1·00
78	**128**	1d. red	2·75	11·00
95	**128**	1d. blue	2·00	1·40
79	**128**	1½d. brown	2·75	9·50
96	**128**	1½d. green	2·00	11·00
80	**128**	2d. orange	3·00	14·00
97	**128**	2d. brown	2·25	7·00
81	**128**	2½d. blue	3·25	14·00
98	**128**	2½d. red	2·00	6·50
82	**128**	3d. violet	1·50	3·00
83	**129**	4d. green	50	1·25
84	**129**	5d. brown	3·00	15·00
85	**129**	6d. purple	1·50	2·50
86	**130**	7d. green	50	17·00
87	**130**	8d. red	3·00	7·50
88	**130**	9d. olive	50	13·00
89	**130**	10d. blue	50	11·00
90	**130**	11d. plum	70	12·00
91	**130**	1s. brown	3·00	7·00
92	**131**	2s.6d. green	22·00	48·00
93	**131**	5s. red	42·00	75·00

1951. Pictorials.

99	**147**	2s.6d. green	13·00	21·00
100	-	5s. red (No. 510)	13·00	23·00

1952. Queen Elizabeth II.

101	**154**	½d. orange	10	10
102	**154**	1d. blue	15	1·75
103	**154**	1½d. green	15	20
104	**154**	2d. brown	20	2·50
105	**155**	2½d. red	15	1·25
106	**155**	4d. blue	4·50	5·00
107	**156**	5d. brown	60	1·00
108	**156**	6d. purple	1·25	4·50
109	**158**	8d. mauve	60	1·00
110	**159**	1s. bistre	60	1·50

III. SPANISH CURRENCY

Stamps surcharged in Spanish currency were sold at British POs throughout Morocco until the establishment of the French Zone and the Tangier International Zone, when their use was confined to the Spanish Zone.

Stamps of Great Britain surch **MOROCCO AGENCIES** and value in Spanish currency.

1907. King Edward VII.

112	**83**	5c. on ½d. green	14·00	20
113	**83**	10c. on 1d. red	22·00	10
114a	-	15c. on 1½d. purple and green	9·00	20
115	-	20c. on 2d. green and red	7·00	3·00
116a	**83**	25c. on 2½d. blue	3·00	20
117	-	40c. on 4d. green & brown	3·25	6·50
118a	-	40c. on 4d. orange	1·50	2·00
119a	-	50c. on 5d. purple and blue	12·00	9·00
120a	-	1p. on 10d. purple and red	23·00	24·00
121	-	3p. on 2s.6d. purple	25·00	40·00
122	-	6p. on 5s. red	35·00	45·00
123	-	12p. on 10s. blue	80·00	80·00

1912. King George V.

126	**101**	5c. on ½d. green	4·75	20
127	**102**	10c. on 1d. red	1·25	10

1914. King George V.

128	**105**	3c. on ½d. green	4·00	14·00
129	**105**	5c. on ½d. green	3·00	10
130	**104**	10c. on 1d. red	4·75	10
131	**105**	15c. on 1½d. brown	1·50	10
132	**106**	20c. on 2d. orange	1·50	25
133	**104**	25c. on 2½d. blue	3·50	25
148	**106**	40c. on 4d. green	7·50	2·50
135	**108**	1p. on 10d. blue	9·00	18·00
142	**109**	3p. on 2s.6d. brown	28·00	75·00
136	**109**	6p. on 5s. red	38·00	50·00
138	**109**	12p. on 10s. blue	£110	£200

1935. Silver Jubilee.

149	**123**	5c. on ½d. green	1·00	1·25
150	**123**	10c. on 1d. red	2·75	2·75
151	**123**	15c. on 1½d. brown	7·50	24·00
152	**123**	25c. on 2½d. blue	3·50	2·25

1935. King George V.

153	**118**	5c. on ½d. green	1·50	23·00
154	**119**	10c. on 1d. red	5·00	23·00
155	**118**	15c. on 1½d. brown	13·00	3·25
156	**120**	20c. on 2d. orange	50	35
157	**119**	25c. on 2½d. blue	1·25	12·00
158	**120**	40c. on 4d. green	50	8·50
159	**122**	1p. on 10d. blue	6·00	4·00

1936. King Edward VIII.

160	**124**	5c. on ½d. green	10	10
161	**124**	10c. on 1d. red	50	2·00
162	**124**	15c. on 1½d. brown	10	15
163	**124**	25c. on 2½d. blue	10	10

1937. Coronation.

164	**126**	15c. on 1½d. brown	1·00	70

1937. King George VI.

165	**128**	5c. on ½d. green	1·25	30
182	**128**	5c. on ½d. orange	2·00	7·00
166	**128**	10c. on 1d. red	1·00	10
183	**128**	10c. on 1d. blue	3·25	10·00
167	**128**	15c. on 1½d. brown	3·50	25
184	**128**	15c. on 1½d. green	1·75	26·00
168	**128**	25c. on 2½d. blue	2·00	1·25
185	**128**	25c. on 2½d. red	1·75	24·00
169	**129**	40c. on 4d. green	40·00	17·00
186	**129**	40c. on 4d. blue	1·00	13·00
170	**130**	70c. on 7d. green	3·50	24·00
171	**130**	1p. on 10d. blue	2·25	11·00

1940. Stamp Centenary.

172	**134**	5c. on ½d. green	30	2·75
173	**134**	10c. on 1d. red	3·75	5·50
174	**134**	15c. on 1½d. brown	70	6·50
175	**134**	25c. on 2½d. blue	80	5·50

1948. Silver Wedding.

176	**137**	25c. on 2½d. blue	1·25	1·00
177	**138**	45p. on £1 blue	17·00	23·00

1948. Olympic Games.

178	**139**	25c. on 2½d. blue	50	1·50
179	**140**	30c. on 3d. violet	50	1·50
180	-	60c. on 6d. purple	50	1·50
181	-	1p.20 on 1s. brown	60	1·50

1954. Queen Elizabeth II.

189	**154**	5c. on ½d. orange	15	4·50
188	**154**	10c. on 1d. blue	50	2·75
190	**155**	40c. on 4d. blue	70	4·00

IV. FRENCH CURRENCY

Stamps surch in French currency were sold at British POs in the French Zone.

Stamps of Great Britain surch **MOROCCO AGENCIES** and value in French currency.

1917. King George V.

191	**105**	3c. on ½d. green	3·25	3·00
192	**105**	5c. on ½d. green	75	20
203	**104**	10c. on 1d. red	30	2·00
194	**105**	15c. on 1½d. brown	4·75	20
205	**104**	25c. on 2½d. blue	3·75	50
206	**106**	40c. on 4d. green	75	80
207	**107**	50c. on 5d. brown	1·50	10
198	**108**	75c. on 9d. green	1·00	75
209	**108**	90c. on 9d. green	23·00	15·00
210	**108**	1f. on 10d. blue	1·50	10
211	**108**	1f.50 on 1s. brown	21·00	2·25
200	**109**	3f. on 2s.6d. brown	5·00	1·50
226	**109**	6f. on 5s. red	9·50	23·00

1935. Silver Jubilee.

212	**123**	5c. on ½d. green	20	20
213	**123**	10c. on 1d. red	4·50	70
214	**123**	15c. on 1½d. brown	1·75	2·50
215	**123**	25c. on 2½d. blue	45	25

1935. King George V.

216	**118**	5c. on ½d. green	75	8·50
217	**119**	10c. on 1d. red	35	30
218	**118**	15c. on 1½d. brown	13·00	6·00
219	**119**	25c. on 2½d. blue	30	15
220	**120**	40c. on 4d. green	30	15
221	**121**	50c. on 5d. brown	30	15
222	**122**	90c. on 9d. olive	75	2·00
223	**122**	1f. on 10d. blue	30	30
224	**122**	1f.50 on 1s. brown	75	3·50

1936. King Edward VIII.

227	**124**	5c. on ½d. green	10	15
228	**124**	15c. on 1½d. brown	10	15

1937. Coronation.

229	**126**	15c. on 1½d. brown	50	20

1937. King George VI.

230	**128**	5c. on ½d. green	4·50	4·25

V. TANGIER INTERNATIONAL ZONE.

This Zone was established in 1924 and the first specially overprinted stamps issued in 1927.

PRICES. Our note re UK usage (at beginning of Section II) also applies to **TANGIER** optd stamps.

Stamps of Great Britain optd **TANGIER**.

1927. King George V.

231	**105**	½d. green	7·50	20
232	**104**	1d. red	10·00	25
233	**105**	1½d. brown	8·50	9·00
234	**106**	2d. orange	3·25	20

1934. King George V.

235	**118**	½d. green	1·25	3·00
236	**119**	1d. red	13·00	4·00
237	**118**	1½d. brown	75	20

1935. Silver Jubilee optd **TANGIER TANGIER**.

238	**123**	½d. green	2·75	9·00
239	**123**	1d. red	25·00	22·00
240	**123**	1½d. brown	1·25	2·25

1936. King Edward VIII.

241	**124**	½d. green	10	20
242	**124**	1d. red	10	10
243	**124**	1½d. brown	15	10

1937. Coronation optd **TANGIER TANGIER**.

244	**126**	1½d. brown	1·50	50

1937. King George VI.

245	**128**	½d. green	9·00	1·75
280	**128**	½d. orange	1·00	1·50
246	**128**	1d. red	27·00	1·75
281	**128**	1d. blue	1·25	3·00
247	**128**	1½d. brown	2·75	40
282	**128**	1½d. green	1·25	24·00
261	**128**	2d. orange	8·50	11·00
283	**128**	2d. brown	1·25	5·00
262	**128**	2½d. blue	6·50	11·00
284	**128**	2½d. red	1·25	11·00
263	**128**	3d. violet	70	1·25
264	**129**	4d. green	11·00	17·00
265	**129**	5d. brown	5·50	35·00
285	**129**	4d. blue	4·50	3·00
266	**129**	6d. purple	1·50	30
267	**130**	7d. green	2·50	19·00
268	**130**	8d. red	5·00	17·00
269	**130**	9d. olive	2·50	17·00
270	**130**	10d. blue	2·75	16·00
271	**130**	11d. plum	4·50	25·00
272	**130**	1s. brown	1·50	2·75
273	**131**	2s.6d. green	9·50	28·00
274	**131**	5s. red	21·00	48·00
275	-	10s. blue (No. 478b)	55·00	£140

1940. Stamp Centenary.

248	**134**	½d. green	30	9·00
249	**134**	1d. red	55	1·00
250	**134**	1½d. brown	2·00	13·00

1946. Victory.

253	**135**	2½d. blue	1·00	65
254	-	3d. violet	1·00	2·00

1948. Silver Wedding.

255	**137**	2½d. blue	50	15
256	**138**	£1 blue	20·00	25·00

1948. Olympic Games.

257	**139**	2½d. blue	1·00	2·00
258	**140**	3d. violet	1·00	2·25
259	-	6d. purple	1·00	2·25
260	-	1s. brown	1·00	2·25

1949. U.P.U.

276	**143**	2½d. blue	75	4·50
277	**144**	3d. violet	75	7·50
278	-	6d. purple	75	1·25
279	-	1s. brown	75	3·25

1951. Pictorial stamps.

286	**147**	2s.6d. green	10·00	5·00
287	-	5s. red (No. 510)	17·00	15·00
288	-	10s. blue (No. 511)	32·00	15·00

1952. Queen Elizabeth II.

313	**154**	½d. orange	10	1·00
314	**154**	1d. blue	20	50
291	**154**	1½d. green	10	30
292	**154**	2d. brown	20	1·25
293	**155**	2½d. red	10	1·00
294	**155**	3d. lilac	20	1·25
320	**155**	4d. blue	65	2·00
296	**157**	5d. brown	60	1·00
297	**157**	6d. purple	60	15
298	**157**	7d. green	1·00	4·25
299	**158**	8d. mauve	60	1·50
300	**158**	9d. olive	1·40	1·75
301	**158**	10d. blue	1·40	2·75
302	**158**	11d. purple	1·40	3·25
303	**159**	1s. bistre	60	70
304	**159**	1s.3d. green	1·00	7·50
305	**159**	1s.6d. blue	1·50	2·25

1953. Coronation.

306	**161**	2½d. red	75	50
307	-	4d. blue	2·25	50
308	**163**	1s.3d. green	2·00	1·50
309	-	1s.6d. blue	2·00	2·00

1955. Pictorials.

310	**166**	2s.6d. brown	3·50	10·00
311	-	5s. red	4·50	24·00
312	-	10s. blue	18·00	29·00

1957. Cent of British Post Office in Tangier. Queen Elizabeth II stamps optd **1857-1957 TANGIER**.

323	**154**	½d. orange	10	15
324	**154**	1d. blue	10	15
325	**154**	1½d. green	10	15
326	**154**	2d. brown	10	15
327	**155**	2½d. red	15	1·25
328	**155**	3d. lilac	15	40
329	**155**	4d. blue	30	30
330	**157**	5d. brown	30	35
331	**157**	6d. purple	30	35
332	**157**	7d. green	30	35
333	**158**	8d. mauve	30	1·00
334	**158**	9d. olive	30	30
335	**158**	10d. blue	30	30
336	**158**	11d. plum	30	30
337	**159**	1s. bistre	30	30
338	**159**	1s.3d. green	45	5·00
339	**159**	1s.6d. blue	50	1·60

340	166	2s.6d. brown	2·00	7·00
341	-	5s. red (No. 596a)	2·75	13·00
342	-	10s. blue (No. 597a)	3·75	13·00

MORVI

A state of India, Bombay district. Now uses Indian stamps.

12 pies = 1 anna.

1 Maharaja Lakhdirji

1931

8	1	3p. red	5·00	21·00
9b	1	6p. green	9·00	25·00
5	1	½a. blue	10·00	35·00
6	1	1a. brown	3·50	45·00
10	1	1a. blue	11·00	25·00
7	1	2a. brown	5·00	60·00
11	1	2a. violet	21·00	75·00

3 Maharaja Lakhdirji

1934

16	3	3p. red	3·00	7·50
17	3	6p. green	7·00	8·50
14	3	1a. brown	5·50	24·00
19	3	2a. violet	3·00	25·00

MOSUL

Stamps used by Indian forces in Mesopotamia (now Iraq) at the close of the 1914–18 war.

12 pies = 1 anna; 16 annas = 1 rupee.

1919. Turkish Fiscal stamps surch **POSTAGE I.E.F. 'D'** and value in annas.

1	½a. on 1pi. green and red	2·25	1·90
2	1a. on 20pa. black on red	1·40	1·75
4	2½a. on 1pi. mauve and yellow	1·50	1·50
5	3a. on 20pa. green	1·60	4·00
6	3a. on 20pa. green and orange	£100	£140
7	4a. on 1pi. violet	3·00	3·50
8	8a. on 10pa. red	4·00	5·00

MOZAMBIQUE

Former Overseas Province of Portugal in East Africa, granted independence in 1975. The Republic of Mozambique joined the Commonwealth on 12 November 1995.

1876. 1000 reis = 1 milreis.
1913. 100 centavos = 1 escudo.
1980. 100 centavos = 1 metical.

1876. "Crown" key-type inscr "MOCAMBIQUE".

1	P	5r. black	2·30	1·40
11	P	10r. yellow	13·00	6·50
19	P	10r. green	1·90	1·30
3	P	20r. bistre	2·20	1·20
20	P	20r. red	£1600	£950
4a	P	25r. red	1·20	85
21	P	25r. lilac	6·25	2·50
14	P	40r. blue	40·00	18·00
22	P	40r. buff	5·50	5·00
6	P	50r. green	£325	£160
23	P	50r. blue	1·40	1·20
7	P	100r. lilac	2·20	1·30
8	P	200r. orange	8·50	6·75
9	P	300r. brown	5·25	3·25

1886. "Embossed" key-type inscr "PROVINCIA DE MOCAMBIQUE".

30	Q	5r. black	2·20	1·40
32	Q	10r. green	2·20	1·40
34	Q	20r. red	2·20	1·40
48	Q	25r. lilac	20·00	9·25
37	Q	40r. brown	3·25	2·10
38	Q	50r. blue	3·75	1·40
40	Q	100r. brown	3·75	1·40
42	Q	200r. violet	7·00	4·25
43	Q	300r. orange	9·00	5·75

1893. No. 37 surch **PROVISORIO 5 5.**

53	5 on 40r. brown	£300	£160

1894. "Figures" key-type inscr "MOCAMBIQUE".

56	R	5r. orange	1·00	80
57	R	10r. mauve	1·00	80
58	R	15r. brown	1·50	1·00
59	R	20r. lilac	1·50	1·30
65	R	25r. green	1·00	60
60	R	50r. blue	6·50	1·80
67	R	75r. pink	3·00	2·30
61	R	80r. green	6·50	3·00
62	R	100r. brown on buff	3·25	2·50
68	R	150r. red on pink	23·00	8·25
64	R	200r. blue on blue	7·00	5·75
69	R	300r. blue on brown	11·50	6·50

1895. "Embossed" key-type of Mozambique optd **1195 CENTENARIO ANTONINO 1895.**

71	Q	5r. black	14·00	10·50
72	Q	10r. green	19·00	13·00
73	Q	20r. red	22·00	14·00
74	Q	25r. purple	22·00	14·00
75	Q	40r. brown	23·00	18·00
76	Q	50r. blue	23·00	18·00
77	Q	100r. brown	23·00	18·00
78	Q	200r. lilac	45·00	32·00
79	Q	300r. orange	55·00	35·00

1897. No. 69 surch **50 reis.**

82	R	50r. on 300r. blue on brown	£425	£275

1898. Nos. 34 and 37 surch **MOCAMBIQUE** and value.

84	Q	2½r. on 20r. red	38·00	31·00
85	Q	5r. on 40r. brown	50·00	38·00

1898. "King Carlos" key type inscr "MOCAMBIQUE". Name and value in red (500r.) or black (others).

100	S	700r. mauve on yellow	30·00	13·50
86	S	2½r. grey	65	30
87	S	5r. red	65	35
88	S	10r. green	65	35
89	S	15r. brown	6·25	3·75
138	S	15r. green	2·20	1·70
90	S	20r. lilac	1·70	90
91	S	25r. green	1·80	90
139	S	25r. red	2·20	1·70
92	S	50r. blue	2·10	1·10
140	S	50r. brown	4·50	3·25
141	S	65r. blue	14·00	10·50
93	S	75r. pink	8·00	3·75
142	S	75r. purple	4·50	3·25
94	S	80r. mauve	8·00	3·75
95	S	100r. blue on blue	4·25	2·75
143	S	115r. brown on pink	14·00	8·00
144	S	130r. brown on yellow	14·00	8·50
96	S	150r. brown on yellow	4·25	4·50
97	S	200r. purple on pink	4·00	2·75
98	S	300r. blue on pink	8·75	4·50
145	S	400r. blue on cream	20·00	16·00
99	S	500r. black on blue	18·00	9·50

1902. Various types surch.

146	S	50r. on 65r. blue	5·75	4·75
101	R	65r. on 10r. mauve	4·50	4·25
102	R	65r. on 15r. brown	4·50	4·25
105	Q	65r. on 20r. red	6·00	3·25
106	R	65r. on 20r. lilac	4·50	4·25
108	Q	65r. on 40r. brown	7·00	3·50
110	Q	65r. on 200r. violet	6·00	3·25
111	V	115r. on 2½r. brown	4·50	4·25
113	Q	115r. on 5r. black	2·50	2·10
114	R	115r. on 5r. orange	4·50	4·25
115	R	115r. on 25r. green	4·50	4·25
117	Q	115r. on 50r. blue	2·75	2·10
120	Q	130r. on 25r. mauve	3·50	2·10
121	R	130r. on 75r. red	4·50	4·25
122	R	130r. on 100r. brn on buff	10·00	9·25
123	R	130r. on 150r. red on pink	4·50	4·25
124	R	130r. on 200r. blue on bl	9·00	8·50
126	Q	130r. on 300r. orange	4·00	2·50
128	Q	400r. on 10r. green	7·50	6·50
129	R	400r. on 50r. blue	2·75	2·10
130	R	400r. on 80r. green	2·75	1·80
132	Q	400r. on 100r. brown	60·00	42·00
133	R	400r. on 300r. bl on brn	2·75	2·10

1902. "King Carlos" key-type of Mozambique optd **PROVISORIO.**

134	S	15r. brown	3·50	1·80
135	S	25r. green	3·50	1·80
136	S	50r. blue	7·00	4·00
137	S	75r. pink	10·00	5·25

1911. "King Carlos" key-type of Mozambique optd **REPUBLICA.**

147	S	2½r. grey	55	35
148	S	5r. orange	55	35
149	S	10r. green	1·80	1·10
150	S	15r. green	45	30
151	S	20r. lilac	1·80	45
152	S	25r. red	35	30
153	S	50r. brown	65	45
154	S	75r. purple	1·20	1·10
155	S	100r. blue on blue	1·20	1·10
156	S	115r. brown on pink	1·80	1·10
157	S	130r. brown on yellow	1·80	1·10
158	S	200r. purple on pink	3·75	1·80
159	S	400r. blue on yellow	3·75	1·80
160	S	500r. black on blue	3·75	2·30
161	S	700r. mauve on yellow	3·75	2·30

1912. "King Manoel" key-type inscr "MOCAMBIQUE" with opt REPUBLICA.

162	T	2½r. lilac	50	30
163	T	5r. black	50	35
164	T	10r. green	50	35
165	T	20r. red	1·30	90
166	T	25r. brown	50	35
167	T	50r. blue	1·10	65
168	T	75r. brown	1·10	65
169	T	100r. brown on green	1·10	65
170	T	200r. green on orange	3·25	1·50
171	T	300r. black on blue	2·00	1·50
172	T	500r. brown and green	6·50	3·25

1913. Surch REPUBLICA MOCAMBIQUE and value on "Vasco da Gama" issues. (a) Portuguese Colonies.

173	¼c. on 2½r. green	1·70	1·20
174	½c. on 5r. red	1·70	1·20
175	1c. on 10r. purple	1·70	1·20
176	2½c. on 25r. green	1·70	1·20
177	5c. on 50r. blue	1·80	1·30
178	7½c. on 75r. brown	3·00	2·20
179	10c. on 100r. brown	2·20	1·70
180	15c. on 150r. brown	2·20	1·90

(b) Macao.

181	¼c. on ½a. green	2·30	1·90
182	½c. on 1a. red	2·30	1·90
183	1c. on 2a. purple	2·30	1·90
184	2½c. on 4a. green	2·30	1·90
185	5c. on 8a. blue	6·50	4·50
186	7½c. on 12a. brown	3·50	3·25
187	10c. on 16a. brown	2·50	1·90
188	15c. on 24a. brown	2·50	1·90

(c) Timor.

189	¼c. on ½a. green	2·50	2·00
190	½c. on 1a. red	2·50	2·00
191	1c. on 2a. purple	2·50	2·00
192	2½c. on 4a. green	2·50	2·00
193	5c. on 8a. blue	3·75	2·75
194	7½c. on 12a. brown	3·75	2·75
195	10c. on 16a. brown	2·30	1·50
196	15c. on 24a. brown	2·30	1·50

1914. "Ceres" key-type inscr "MOCAMBIQUE".

264	U	1e. pink	1·90	1·20
197	U	¼c. green	45	30
198	U	½c. black	45	30
199	U	1c. green	45	30
200	U	1½c. brown	45	30
201	U	2c. red	50	30
270	U	2c. grey	35	35
202	U	2½c. violet	50	30
255	U	3c. orange	35	25
256	U	4c. pink	35	25
257	U	4½c. grey	35	25
203	U	5c. blue	50	30
275	U	6c. mauve	35	35
259	U	7c. blue	35	25
260	U	7½c. brown	35	25
278	U	8c. grey	35	25
279	U	10c. red	35	25
280	U	12c. brown	35	35
281	U	12c. green	35	35
283	U	15c. purple	35	25
284	U	20c. green	70	65
285	U	24c. blue	45	35
286	U	25c. brown	55	45
209	U	30c. brown on green	3·50	2·20
287	U	30c. green	50	35
295	U	30c. lilac on pink	2·20	1·80
210	U	40c. brown on pink	3·75	2·30
288	U	40c. turquoise	1·20	45
211	U	50c. orange on orange	6·50	4·75
289	U	50c. mauve	65	45
290	U	60c. blue	1·30	70
291	U	60c. pink	1·90	1·20
297	U	60c. brown on pink	2·30	1·80
293	U	80c. red	1·60	70
298	U	80c. brown on blue	2·00	1·50
299	U	1e. green on blue	4·25	2·50
301	U	1e. blue	1·90	1·40
300	U	2e. mauve on pink	3·00	1·50
302	U	2e. purple	1·60	90
303	U	5e. brown	10·50	6·50
304	U	10e. pink	15·00	7·50
305	U	20e. green	48·00	21·00

1915. Provisional issues of 1902 optd **REPUBLICA.**

226	S	50r. blue (No. 136)	1·40	1·20
227	S	50r. on 65r. blue	1·40	1·20
213	S	75r. pink (No. 137)	3·25	1·80
228	V	115r. on 2½r. brown	1·40	1·20
216	Q	115r. on 5r. black	75·00	60·00
229	R	115r. on 5r. orange	1·40	1·20
230	R	115r. on 25r. green	1·40	1·20
231	R	130r. on 75r. red	1·40	1·20
220	R	130r. on 100r. brown on buff	2·20	1·80
232	R	130r. on 150r. red on pink	1·40	1·20
233	R	130r. on 200r. blue on bl	1·40	1·20
223	R	400r. on 50r. blue	2·75	2·10
224	R	400r. on 80r. green	2·75	2·10
225	R	400r. on 300r. blue on brn	2·75	2·10

1918. Charity Tax stamp surch **2½ CENTAVOS**. Roul or perf.

248	C 16	2½c. on 5c. red	1·40	1·20

1920. Charity Tax stamps surch. (a) CORREIOS and value in figures.

306	C15	1c. on 1c. green	1·30	1·00
307	C16	1½c. on 5c. red	1·30	1·00

(b) **SEIS CENTAVOS.**

308	6c. on 5c. red	1·40	1·20

1921. "Ceres" stamps of 1913 surch.

309	U	10c. on ½c. black	2·75	1·70
310	U	30c. on 1½c. brown	2·75	1·70
316	U	50c. on 4c. pink	2·20	1·10
311	U	60c. on 2½c. violet	4·00	2·20
328	U	70c. on 2e. purple	1·30	70
329	U	1e.40 on 2e. purple	1·60	70

1922. "Ceres" key-type of Lourenco Marques surch.

312	U	10c. on ½c. black	2·75	1·80
314	U	30c. on 1½c. brown	2·75	1·80

1922. Charity Tax stamp surch 2$00.

315	C16	$2 on 5c. red	2·30	1·10

1924. Fourth Death Centenary of Vasco da Gama. "Ceres" key-type of Mozambique optd Vasco da Gama 1924.

317	U	80c. pink	2·20	1·10

1925. Nos. 129 and 130 surch **Republica 40 C.**

318	R	40c. on 400r. on 50r.	1·50	85
319	R	40c. on 400r. on 80r.	1·50	85

1929. "Due" key-type inscr "MOCAMBIQUE" optd CORREIOS.

320	W	50c. lilac	1·90	1·50

23 Mousinho de Albuquerque

1930. Albuquerque's Victories Commemorative. Vignette in grey.

321	23	50c. lake and red (Macontene)	10·50	10·50
322	23	50c. orge & red (Mujenga)	10·50	10·50
323	23	50c. mve & brn (Coolela)	10·50	10·50
324	23	50c. grey and green (Chaimite)	10·50	10·50
325	23	50c. bl & ind (Ibrahimo)	10·50	10·50
326	23	50c. blue and black (Mucuto-muno)	10·50	10·50
327	23	50c. vio & lilac (Naguema)	10·50	10·50

The above were for compulsory use throughout Mozambique in place of ordinary postage stamps on certain days in 1930 and 1931. They are not listed among the Charity Tax stamps as the revenue was not applied to any charitable fund.

25 'Portugal' and Camoens' *The Lusiads*

1938. Value in red (1, 15c., 1e.40) or black (others).

330	25	1c. brown	20	15
331	25	5c. brown	25	20
332	25	10c. purple	25	20
333	25	15c. black	25	20
334	25	20c. grey	25	20
335	25	30c. green	25	20
336	25	35c. green	9·75	3·75
337	25	40c. red	25	20
338	25	45c. blue	45	35
339	25	50c. brown	45	20
340	25	60c. green	65	30

341	**25**	70c. brown	65	30
342	**25**	80c. green	65	30
343	**25**	85c. red	1·70	1·00
344	**25**	1e. purple	1·20	30
345	**25**	1e.40 blue	13·50	3·50
346	**25**	1e.75 blue	8·75	3·25
347	**25**	2e. lilac	3·00	1·30
348	**25**	5e. green	4·75	1·30
349	**25**	10e. brown	11·00	2·75
350	**25**	20e. orange	55·00	7·25

1938. As 1938 issue of Macao. Name and value in black.

351	**54**	1c. green (postage)	25	25
352	**54**	5c. brown	25	25
353	**54**	10c. red	25	25
354	**54**	15c. purple	25	25
355	**54**	20c. grey	25	25
356	-	30c. purple	25	25
357	-	35c. green	50	25
358	-	40c. brown	50	25
359	-	50c. mauve	50	25
360	-	60c. black	50	25
361	-	70c. violet	50	25
362	-	80c. orange	50	25
363	-	1e. red	1·10	50
364	-	1e.75 blue	4·00	85
365	-	2e. red	4·00	1·00
366	-	5e. green	7·50	1·50
367	-	10e. blue	16·00	2·10
368	-	20e. brown	37·00	4·25
369	**56**	10c. red (air)	65	60
370	**56**	20c. violet	65	60
371	**56**	50c. orange	75	65
372	**56**	1e. blue	75	65
373	**56**	2e. red	1·30	65
374	**56**	3e. green	2·75	65
375	**56**	5e. brown	4·50	95
376	**56**	9e. red	8·25	1·70
377	**56**	10e. mauve	14·00	3·25

Designs:—30 to 50c. Mousinho de Albuquerque; 60c. to 1e. Dam; 1e.75 to 5e. Henry the Navigator; 10, 20e. Afonso de Albuquerque.

1938. No. 338 surch **40 centavos.**

378	**25**	40c. on 45c. blue	6·50	4·25

26a Route of President's Tour

1938. President Carmona's Second Colonial Tour.

379	**26a**	80c. violet on mauve	4·75	3·25
380	**26a**	1e.75 blue on blue	16·00	6·75
381	**26a**	3e. green on green	28·00	10·50
382	**26a**	20e. brown on cream	£140	60·00

27 New Cathedral, Lourenco Marques

1944. 400th Anniv of Lourenco Marques.

383	**27**	50c. brown	2·20	80
384	-	50c. green	2·20	80
385	-	1e.75 blue	9·75	2·75
386a	-	20e. black	27·00	2·75

Designs:—Horiz: 1e.75, Lourenco Marques Central Railway Station; 20e. Town Hall, Lourenco Marques.

See also No. 405.

1946. Nos. 354, 364 and 375 surch.

387	**54**	10c. on 15c. purple (postage)	1·30	75
388	-	60c. on 1e.75 blue	2·20	85
389	**56**	3e. on 5e. brown (air)	18·00	17·00

1947. No. 386a surch.

390	2e. on 20e. black	3·50	1·30

30 Lockheed L.18 Lodestar

1946. Air. Values in black.

391	**30**	1e.20 red	3·25	1·70
392	**30**	1e.60 blue	3·25	1·80
393	**30**	1e.70 purple	6·00	2·50
394	**30**	2e.90 brown	9·50	5·00
395	**30**	3e. green	10·50	5·00

1947. Air. Optd Taxe percue. Values in red (50c.) or black (others).

397	50c. black	1·50	95
398	1e. pink	1·50	95
399	3e. green	2·75	1·10
400	4e.50 green	4·50	2·00
401	5e. red	6·50	2·20
402	10e. blue	18·00	5·75
403	20e. violet	47·00	16·00
404	50e. orange	95·00	40·00

1948. As T **27** but without commemorative inscr.

405	4e.50 red	4·25	1·10

31 Antonio Enes

1948. Birth Centenary of Antonio Enes.

406	**31**	50c. black and cream	1·60	75
407	**31**	5e. purple and cream	3·75	2·30

33 Lourenco Marques

1948

408	-	5c. brown	45	25
409	-	10c. purple	45	25
410	-	20c. brown	45	25
411	-	30c. purple	45	25
412	-	40c. green	55	25
413	**33**	50c. grey	55	25
414	-	60c. purple	55	25
415	**33**	80c. violet	55	25
416	-	1e. red	85	45
417	-	1e.20 grey	95	45
418	-	1e.50 violet	1·30	50
419	-	1e.75 blue	1·90	65
420	-	2e. brown	1·70	50
421	-	2e.50 blue	5·75	45
422	-	3e. green	2·75	45
423	-	3e.50 green	3·75	45
424	-	5e. green	3·75	45
425	-	10e. brown	9·00	60
426	-	15e. red	22·00	3·25
427	-	20e. orange	43·00	5·25

Designs:—Vert: 5, 30c. Gogogo Peak; 20, 40c. Zumbo River; 60c., 3e.50, Nhanhangare Waterfall. Horiz: 10c., 1e.20, Railway bridge over River Zambesi at Sena; 1, 5e. Gathering coconuts; 1e.50, 2e. River Pungue at Beira; 1e.75, 3e. Polana beach, Lourenco Marques; 2e.50, 10e. Bird's eye view of Lourenco Marques; 15, 20e. Malema River.

1949. Honouring the Statue of Our Lady of Fatima. As T **62** of Macao.

428	50c. blue	3·75	1·70
429	1e.20 mauve	8·25	3·50
430	4e.50 green	32·00	10·50
431	20e. brown	60·00	16·00

35 Aircraft and Globe

1949. Air.

432	**35**	50c. brown	75	30
433	**35**	1e.20 violet	1·50	70
434	**35**	4e.50 blue	3·50	1·10
435	**35**	5e. green	6·00	1·40
436	**35**	20e. brown	17·00	7·00

1949. 75th Anniv of U.P.U. As T **64** of Macao.

437	4e.50 blue	4·50	1·80

1950. Holy Year. As Nos. 425/6 of Macao.

438	1e.50 orange	1·20	65
439	3e. blue	1·70	95

36 Clown Triggerfish

1951. Fish. Multicoloured.

440	5c. Type **36**	35	15
441	10c. Thread-finned butterflyfish	20	15
442	15c. Racoon butterflyfish	90	45
443	20c. Lionfish	30	15
444	30c. Pearl puffer	25	15
445	40c. Golden filefish	20	15
446	50c. Spot-cheeked surgeonfish	20	15
447	1e. Pennant coralfish (vert)	30	15
448	1e.50 Seagrass wrasse	30	15
449	2e. Sombre sweetlips	30	15
450	2e.50 Blue-striped snapper	1·00	20
451	3e. Convict tang	1·00	20
452	3e.50 Starry triggerfish	1·20	15
453	4e. Cornetfish	1·80	35
454	4e.50 Vagabond butterflyfish	2·75	35
455	5e. Sail-backed mailcheek	2·75	15
456	6e. Dusky batfish (vert)	2·75	15
457	8e. Moorish idol (vert)	4·50	60
458	9e. Triangulate boxfish	4·50	45
459	10e. Eastern flying gurnard	11·00	2·30
460	15e. Red-toothed triggerfish	65·00	19·00
461	20e. Picasso triggerfish	34·00	7·00
462	30e. Long-horned cowfish	41·00	9·50
463	50e. Spotted cowfish	50·00	18·00

1951. Termination of Holy Year. As T **69** of Macao.

464	5e. red and orange	2·75	1·50

37 Victor Cordon (colonist)

1951. Birth Centenary of Cordon.

465	**37**	1e. brown and light brown	2·75	65
466	**37**	5e. black and blue	14·00	1·70

1952. First Tropical Medicine Congress, Lisbon. As T **71** of Macao.

467	3e. orange and blue	1·80	75

Design:—3e. Miguela Bombarda Hospital.

39 Liner and Lockheed Constellation Airliner

1952. Fourth African Tourist Congress.

468	**39**	1e.50 multicoloured	1·00	70

40 Missionary

1953. Missionary Art Exhibition.

469	**40**	10c. red and lilac	20	15
470	**40**	1e. red and green	1·10	30
471	**40**	5e. black and blue	2·75	90

41 Citrus Butterfly

1953. Butterflies and Moths. Multicoloured.

472	10c. Type **41**	15	15
473	15c. *Amphicallia thelwalli*	15	15
474	20c. Forest queen	15	15
475	30c. Western scarlet	15	15
476	40c. Black-barred red-tip	15	15
477	50c. Mocker swallowtail	15	15
478	80c. *Nudaurelia hersilia dido*	20	15
479	1e. African moon moth	20	15
480	1e.50 Large striped swallowtail	25	15
481	2e. *Athletes ethica*	6·50	60
482	2e.30 African monarch	5·25	60
483	2e.50 Green swallowtail	11·50	60
484	3e. *Arniocera ericata*	2·10	20
485	4e. Apollo moth	75	15
486	4e.50 Peach moth	95	15
487	5e. *Metarctica lateritia*	95	15
488	6e. *Xanthospilopteryx mozambica*	1·10	30
489	7e.50 White bear	6·50	60
490	10e. Flame-coloured charaxes	10·50	1·90
491	20e. Fervid tiger moth	18·00	1·90

42 Stamps

1953. Philatelic Exhibition, Lourenco Marques.

492	**42**	1e. multicoloured	1·50	55
493	**42**	3e. multicoloured	5·75	1·40

1953. Portuguese Postage Stamp Centenary. As T **75** of Macao.

494	50c. multicoloured	1·20	75

1954. Fourth Centenary of Sao Paulo. As T **76** of Macao.

495	3e.50 multicoloured	60	30

43 Map of Mozambique

1954. Multicoloured map; Mozambique territory in colours given.

496	**43**	10c. lilac	20	15
497	**43**	20c. yellow	20	15
498	**43**	50c. blue	20	15
499	**43**	1e. yellow	25	15
500	**43**	2e.30 white	85	65
501	**43**	4e. orange	95	50
502	**43**	10e. green	2·50	30
503	**43**	20e. brown	4·25	65

44 Arms of Beira

1954. First Philatelic Exhibition, Manica and Sofala.

504	**44**	1e.50 multicoloured	60	30
505	**44**	3e.50 multicoloured	1·40	60

45 Mousinho de Albuquerque

1955. Birth Centenary of M. de Albuquerque.

506	**45**	2e. brown and grey	85	50
507	-	2e.50 multicoloured	1·70	85

Design:—2e.50, Equestrian statue of Albuquerque.

46 Arms and Inhabitants

1956. Visit of President to Mozambique. Multicoloured. Background in colours given.

508	**46**	1e. cream	60	20
509	**46**	2e.50 blue	1·20	60

47 Beira

1957. 50th Anniv of Beira.

510	**47**	2e.50 multicoloured	1·20	60

1958. Sixth International Congress of Tropical Medicine. As T **79** of Macao.

511	1e.50 multicoloured	3·25	1·40

Design:—1e.50, *Strophanthus grandiflorus* (plant).

1958. Brussels International Exn. As T **78** of Macao.

512	3e.50 multicoloured	50	30

48 Caravel

1960. 500th Death Anniv of Prince Henry the Navigator.

513	**48**	5e. multicoloured	1·00	30

49 "Arts and Crafts"

1960. Tenth Anniv of African Technical Co-operation Commission.

514	**49**	3e. multicoloured	80	50

50 Arms of Lourenco Marques

1961. Arms. Multicoloured.

515	5c. Type **50**	20	15
516	15c. Chibuto	20	15
517	20c. Nampula	20	15
518	30c. Inhambane	20	15
519	50c. Mozambique (city)	20	15
520	1e. Matola	35	15
521	1e.50 Quelimane	35	15
522	2e. Mocuba	65	15
523	2e.50 Antonio Enes	2·00	20
524	3e. Cabral	75	20
525	4e. Manica	75	20
526	4e.50 Pery	75	20
527	5e. St. Tiago de Tete	75	20
528	7e.50 Porto Amelia	1·60	55
529	10e. Chinde	2·40	60
530	20e. Joao Belo	5·25	95
531	50e. Beira	10·50	2·20

1962. Sports. As T **82** of Macao. Multicoloured.

532	50c. Water-skiing	20	15
533	1e. Wrestling	1·30	30
534	1e.50 Gymnastics	60	25
535	2e.50 Hockey	50	25
536	4e.50 Netball	1·40	65
537	15e. Outboard speedboat racing	2·75	1·50

1962. Malaria Eradication. Mosquito design as T **83** of Macao. Multicoloured.

538	2e.50 *Anopheles funestus*	1·90	55

51 Fokker F.27 Friendship and de Havilland DH.89 Dragon Rapide over Route Map

1962. 25th Anniv of D.E.T.A. (Mozambique Airline).

539	**51**	3e. multicoloured	95	30

52 Lourenco Marques in 1887 and 1962

1962. 75th Anniv of Lourenco Marques.

540	**52**	1e. multicoloured	65	30

53 Oil Refinery, Sonarep

1962. Air. Multicoloured.

541	1e.50 Type **53**	85	30
542	2e. Salazar Academy	75	20
543	3e.50 Aerial view of Lourenco Marques Port	75	20
544	4e.50 Salazar Barrage	75	20
545	5e. Trigo de Morais Bridge and Dam	75	20
546	20e. Marcelo Caetano Bridge and Dam	2·75	95

Each design includes an aeroplane in flight.

54 Arms of Mozambique and Statue of Vasco da Gama

1963. Bicentenary of City of Mozambique.

547	**54**	3e. multicoloured	65	30

1963. Tenth Anniv of T.A.P. Airline. As T **52** of Portuguese Guinea.

548	2e.50 multicoloured	60	25

55 Nef, 1430

1963. Evolution of Sailing Ships. Multicoloured.

549	10c. Type **55**	20	15
550	20c. Caravel, 1436 (vert)	20	15
551	30c. Lateen-rigged caravel, 1460 (vert)	20	15
552	50c. Vasco da Gama's ship *Sao Gabriel*, 1497 (vert)	20	15
553	1e. Don Manuel's nau, 1498 (vert)	60	15
554	1e.50 Galleon, 1530 (vert)	60	15
555	2e. Nau *Flor de la Mar*, 1511 (vert)	60	15
556	2e.50 Caravel *Redonda*, 1519	60	15
557	3e.50 Nau, 1520 (vert)	75	20
558	4e. Portuguese Indies galley, 1521	85	25
559	4e.50 Galleon *Santa Tereza*, 1639 (vert)	85	25
560	5e. Nau *N. Senhora da Conceicao*, 1716 (vert)	17·00	45
561	6e. Warship *N. Senhora do Bom Sucesso*, 1764	1·20	45
562	7e.50 Bomb launch, 1788	1·60	55
563	8e. Naval brigantine *Lebre*, 1793	1·60	55
564	10e. Corvette *Andorinha*, 1799	1·60	55
565	12e.50 Naval schooner *Maria Teresa*, 1820	1·80	95
566	15e. Warship *Vasco da Gama*, 1841	2·50	95
567	20e. Sail frigate *Don Fernando II e Gloria*, 1843 (vert)	3·25	1·20
568	30e. Cadet barque *Sagres I*, 1924 (vert)	5·50	2·10

1964. Centenary of National Overseas Bank. As T **84** of Macao but view of Bank building, Lourenco Marques.

569	1e.50 multicoloured	60	20

56 Pres. Tomas

1964. Presidential Visit.

570	**56**	2e.50 multicoloured	60	20

57 State Barge of Joao V, 1728

1964. Portuguese Marine, 18th and 19th Centuries. Multicoloured.

571	15c. Type **57**	20	15
572	35c. State barge of Jose I, 1753	20	15
573	1e. Barge of Alfandega, 1768	55	20
574	1e.50 Oarsman of 1780 (vert)	65	25
575	2e.50 State barge *Pinto da Fonseca*, 1780	35	15
576	5e. State barge of Carlota Joaquina, 1790	65	30
577	9e. Don Miguel's state barge, 1831	1·60	95

1965. I.T.U. Centenary. As T **85** of Macao.

578	1e. multicoloured	60	30

1966. 40th Anniv of Portuguese National Revolution. As T **86** of Macao, but showing different building. Multicoloured.

579	1e. Beira railway station and Antonio Enes Academy	55	30

58 Arquebusier, 1560

1967. Portuguese Military Uniforms. Multicoloured.

580	20c. Type **58**	20	15
581	30c. Arquebusier, 1640	20	15
582	40c. Infantryman, 1777	20	15
583	50c. Infantry officer, 1777	20	15
584	80c. Drummer, 1777	60	25
585	1e. Infantry sergeant, 1777	60	20
586	2e. Infantry major, 1784	65	20
587	2e.50 Colonial officer, 1788	70	25
588	3e. Infantryman, 1789	70	25
589	5e. Colonial bugler, 1801	1·40	45
590	10e. Colonial officer, 1807	1·50	65
591	15e. Infantryman, 1817	2·75	1·70

1967. Centenary of Military Naval Association. As T **88** of Macao. Multicoloured.

592	3e. A. Coutinho and paddle-gunboat *Tete*	45	20
593	10e. J. Roby and paddle-gunboat *Granada*	1·40	65

1967. 50th Anniv of Fatima Apparitions. As T **89** of Macao.

594	50c. Golden Crown	30	20

1968. 500th Birth Anniv of Pedro Cabral (explorer). As T **90** of Macao.

595	1e. Erecting the Cross at Porto Sequro (horiz)	20	15
596	1e.50 First mission service in Brazil (horiz)	50	15
597	3e. Church of Grace, Santarem	95	50

1969. Birth Centenary of Admiral Gago Coutinho. As T **91** of Macao.

598	70c. Admiral Gago Coutinho Airport, Lourenco Marques (horiz)	35	20

59 Luis de Camoens (poet)

1969. 400th Anniv of Camoens' Visit to Mozambique. Multicoloured.

599	15c. Type **59**	20	15
600	50c. Nau of 1553 (horiz)	25	15
601	1e.50 Map of Mozambique, 1554	35	20
602	2e.50 Chapel of Our Lady of Baluarte (horiz)	50	25
603	5e. Part of the "Lusiad" (poem)	70	55

1969. 500th Birth Anniv of Vasco da Gama (explorer). As T **92** of Macao. Multicoloured.

604	1e. Route map of Da Gama's Voyage to India (horiz)	30	20

1969. Centenary of Overseas Administrative Reforms. As T **93** of Macao.

605	1e.50 multicoloured	35	20

1969. 500th Birth Anniv of King Manoel I. As T **95** of Macao. Multicoloured.

606	80c. Illuminated Arms (horiz)	30	20

1970. Birth Centenary of Marshal Carmona. As T **96** of Macao. Multicoloured.

607	5e. Portrait in ceremonial dress	55	30

60 Fossilized Fern

1971. Rocks, Minerals and Fossils. Mult.

608	15c. Type **60**	30	15
609	50c. *Lytodiscoides conduciensis* (fossilized snail)	30	15
610	1e. Stibnite	45	20
611	1e.50 Pink beryl	65	20
612	2e. Endothiodon and fossil skeleton	75	20
613	3e. Tantalocolumbite	1·20	20
614	3e.50 Verdelite	1·60	30
615	4e. Zircon	2·10	45
616	10e. Petrified tree-stump	3·75	1·20

1972. 400th Anniv of Camoens' *The Lusiads* (epic poem). As T **98** of Macao. Multicoloured.

617	4e. Mozambique Island in 16th-century	60	30

1972. Olympic Games, Munich. As T **99** of Macao. Multicoloured.

618	3e. Hurdling and swimming	45	30

1972. 50th Anniv of First Flight, Lisbon–Rio de Janeiro. As T **100** of Macao. Multicoloured.

619	1e. Fairey IIID seaplane "Santa Cruz" at Recife	30	20

61 Racing Dinghies

1973. World Championships for "Vauriens" Class Yachts, Lourenco Marques.

620	**61**	1e. multicoloured	20	15
621	-	1e.50 multicoloured	30	15
622	-	3e. multicoloured	60	30

Designs:—Nos. 621/2 similar to Type **61**.

1973. Centenary of I.M.O./W.M.O. As T **102** of Macao.

623	2e. multicoloured	50	30

62 Dish Aerials

1974. Inauguration of Satellite Communications Station Network.

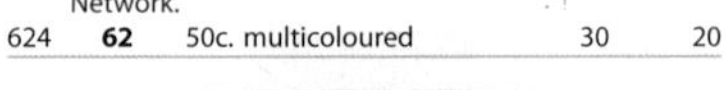

624	**62**	50c. multicoloured	30	20

63 Bird with "Flag" Wings

1975. Implementation of Lusaka Agreement.

625	**63**	1e. multicoloured	20	15
626	**63**	1e.50 multicoloured	25	15
627	**63**	2e. multicoloured	30	20
628	**63**	3e.50 multicoloured	55	45
629	**63**	6e. multicoloured	1·20	50
MS630		150×75 mm. Nos. 625/9. Imperf	7·00	7·00

1975. Independence. Optd **INDEPENDENCIA 25 JUN 75**.

631	**43**	10c. multicoloured (postage)	50	50
632	-	40c. mult (No. 476)	10	10
633	**62**	50c. multicoloured	20	15
634	**61**	1e. multicoloured	30	25
635	-	1e.50 mult (No. 621)	85	75
636	-	2e. multicoloured (No. 623)	2·40	2·40
637	-	2e.50 mult (No. 535)	35	30
638	-	3e. multicoloured (No. 618)	40	35
639	-	3e. multicoloured (No. 622)	45	40
640	-	3e.50 mult (No. 614)	2·40	2·40
641	-	4e.50 mult (No. 536)	2·75	1·50
642	-	7e.50 mult (No. 489)	80	30
643	-	10e. mult (No. 616)	1·40	35
644	-	15e. mult (No. 537)	1·75	1·50
645	**43**	20e. multicoloured	4·75	4·25
646	-	3e.50 multicoloured (No. 543) (air)	35	25
647	-	4e.50 mult (No. 544)	40	25
648	-	5e. multicoloured (No. 545)	1·25	50
649	-	20e. mult (No. 546)	2·00	4·25

66 Workers, Farmers and Children

1975. Vigilance, Unity, Work. Multicoloured.

650	20c. Type **66**	10	10
651	30c. Type **66**	10	10
652	50c. Type **66**	10	10
653	2e.50 Type **66**	15	10

654	4e.50 Armed family, workers and dancers	25	15
655	5e. As No. 654	35	15
656	10e. As No. 654	95	30
657	50e. As No. 654	4·25	2·10
MS658	132×179 mm. Nos. 650/7 (sold for 75e.)	6·25	3·00

67 Farm Worker

1976. Women's Day.

659	**67**	1e. black and green	10	10
660	-	1e.50 black and brown	10	10
661	-	2e.50 black and blue	15	10
662	-	10e. black and red	90	40

Designs:—1e.50, Teaching; 2e.50, Nurse; 10e. Mother.

1976. Pres. Kaunda's First Visit to Mozambique. Optd **PRESIDENTE KENNETH KAUNDA PREMEIRA VISITA 20/4/1976**.

663	**63**	2e. multicoloured	15	10
664	**63**	3e.50 multicoloured	25	15
665	**63**	6e. multicoloured	50	30

69 Arrival of President Machel

1976. First Anniv of Independence. Mult.

666	50c. Type **69**	10	10
667	1e. Proclamation ceremony	10	10
668	2e.50 Signing ceremony	15	10
669	7e.50 Soldiers on parade	40	20
670	20e. Independence flame	1·50	1·10

70 Mozambique Stamp of 1876 and Emblem

1976. Stamp Centenary.

671	**70**	1e.50 multicoloured	10	10
672	**70**	6e. multicoloured	30	20

1976. FACIM Industrial Fair. Optd FACIM 1976.

673	**66**	2e.50 multicoloured	30	15

72 Weapons and Flag

1976. Army Day.

674	**72**	3e. multicoloured	20	10

73 Thick-tailed Bush baby

1977. Animals. Multicoloured.

675	50c. Type **73**	15	10
676	1e. Ratel (horiz)	15	10
677	1e.50 Temminck's ground pangolin	20	10
678	2e. Steenbok (horiz)	20	10
679	2e.50 Diademed monkey	25	10
680	3e. Hunting dog (horiz)	25	10
681	4e. Cheetah (horiz)	35	10
682	5e. Spotted hyena	50	15
683	7e.50 Warthog (horiz)	1·00	25
684	8e. Hippopotamus (horiz)	1·10	30
685	10e. White rhinoceros (horiz)	1·10	30
686	15e. Sable antelope	1·60	65

74 Congress Emblem

1977. Third Frelimo Congress, Maputo. Mult.

687	3e. Type **74**	15	10
688	3e.50 Macheje Monument (site of Second Congress) (34×24 mm)	20	10
689	20e. Maputo Monument (23×34 mm)	1·40	50

75 Women (child's drawing)

1977. Mozambique Women's Day.

690	**75**	5e. multicoloured	25	10
691	**75**	15e. multicoloured	65	25

76 Labourer and Farmer

1977. Labour Day.

692	**76**	5e. multicoloured	25	10

77 Crowd with Arms and Crops

1977. Second Anniv of Independence.

693	**77**	50c. multicoloured	10	10
694	**77**	1e.50 multicoloured	10	10
695	**77**	3e. multicoloured	15	10
696	**77**	15e. multicoloured	60	25

78 *Encephalartos ferox*

1978. Stamp Day. Nature Protection. Mult.

697	1e. Type **78**	10	10
698	10e. Nyala	50	20

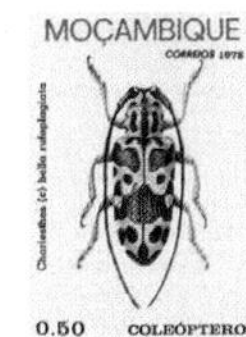

79 *Charriesthes bella*

1978. Beetles. Multicoloured.

699	50c. Type **79**	10	10
700	1e. *Tragocephalus variegata*	10	10
701	1e.50 *Monochamus leuconotus*	10	10
702	3e. *Prosopocera lactator*	25	10
703	5e. *Dinocephalus ornatus*	40	10
704	10e. *Tragiscoschema nigroscriptus*	60	20

80 Violet-crested Turaco

1978. Birds. Multicoloured.

705	50c. Type **80**	35	15
706	1e. Lilac-breasted roller	45	15
707	1e.50 Red-headed weaver	45	15
708	2e.50 Violet starling	50	25
709	3e. Peters's twin-spot	1·00	35
710	15e. European bee-eater	2·50	70

81 Mother and Child

1978. Global Eradication of Smallpox.

711	**81**	15e. multicoloured	45	25

82 *Crinum delagoense*

1978. Flowers. Multicoloured.

712	50c. Type **82**	10	10
713	1e. *Gloriosa superba*	10	10
714	1e.50 *Eulophia speciosa*	10	10
715	3e. *Erithrina humeana*	15	10
716	5e. *Astripomoea malvacea*	80	15
717	10e. *Kigelia africana*	1·00	60

83 First Stamps of Mozambique and Canada

1978. CAPEX '78 International Stamp Exhibition, Toronto.

718	**83**	15e. multicoloured	45	25

84 Mozambique Flag

1978. Third Anniv of Independence. Multicoloured.

719	1e. Type **84**	10	10
720	1e.50 Coat of Arms	10	10
721	7e.50 People and Constitution	25	15
722	10e. Band and National Anthem	30	20
MS723	130×100 mm. Nos. 719/22 (sold at 30e.)	75	55

85 Boy with Books

1978. 11th World Youth Festival, Havana. Mult.

724	2e.50 Type **85**	10	10
725	3e. Soldiers	15	10
726	7e.50 Harvesting wheat	25	20

86 Czechoslovakian 50h. Stamp, 1919

1978. PRAGA '78 International Stamp Exhibition.

727	**86**	15e. blue, ochre and red	45	30
MS728		135×109 mm. No. 727 (sold at 30e.)	45	30

87 Football

1978. Stamp Day. Sports. Multicoloured.

729	50c. Type **87**	10	10
730	1e.50 Putting the shot	10	10
731	3e. Hurdling	15	10
732	7e.50 Basketball	35	20
733	12e.50 Swimming	45	35
734	25e. Roller-skate hockey	1·25	60

88 UPU Emblem and Dove

1979. Membership of U.P.U.

735	**88**	20e. multicoloured	1·00	45

89 Eduardo Mondlane

1979. Tenth Death Anniv of Eduardo Mondlane (founder of FRELIMO). Multicoloured.

736	1e. Soldier handing gourd to woman	10	10
737	3e. FRELIMO soldiers	15	10
738	7e.50 Children learning to write	30	20
739	12e.50 Type **89**	40	30

90 Shaded Silver

1979. Domestic Cats. Multicoloured.

740	50c. Type **90**	10	10
741	1e.50 Manx cat	10	10
742	2e.50 British blue	15	10
743	3e. Turkish cat	20	10
744	12e.50 Long-haired tabby	85	55
745	20e. African wild cat	1·50	90

91 IYC Emblem

1979. Obligatory Tax. International Year of the Child.

746	**91**	50c. red	15	10

92 Wrestling

1979. Olympic Games, Moscow (1980). Mult.

747	1e. Type **92**	10	10
748	2e. Running	10	10
749	3e. Horse jumping	15	10
750	5e. Canoeing	15	10
751	10e. High jump	30	20
752	15e. Archery	50	40
MS753	100×81 mm. 30e. Discus	95	75

93 Flowers

1979. International Year of the Child. Mult.

754	50c. Type **93**	10	10
755	1e.50 Dancers	10	10
756	3e. In the city	15	10
757	5e. Working in the country	15	10
758	7e.50 Houses	25	15
759	12e.50 Transport	1·50	50

94 Flight from Colonialism

1979. Fourth Anniv of Independence. Multicoloured.

760	50c. Type **94**	10	10
761	2e. Eduardo Mondlane (founder of FRELIMO)	10	10
762	3e. Armed struggle, death of Mondlane	15	10
763	7e.50 Final fight for liberation	25	15
764	15e. President Samora Machel proclaims victory	45	35
MS765	92×60 mm. 30e. Liberation	90	65

95 Golden Scorpionfish

1979. Tropical Fish. Multicoloured.

766	50c. Type **95**	10	10
767	1e.50 Golden trevally	15	10
768	2e.50 Brick goby	20	10
769	3e. Clown surgeonfish	25	15
770	10e. Lace goby	60	25
771	12e.50 Yellow-edged lyretail	95	40

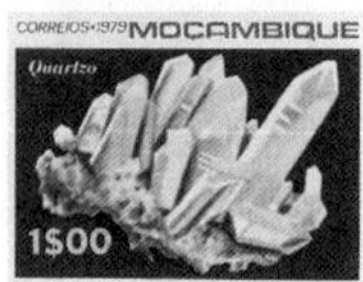

96 Quartz

1979. Minerals. Multicoloured.

772	1e. Type **96**	10	10
773	1e.50 Beryl	10	10
774	2e.50 Magnetite	15	10
775	5e. Tourmaline	30	10
776	10e. Euxenite	60	20
777	20e. Fluorite	1·40	45

97 Soldier handing out Guns

1979. 15th Anniv of Fight for Independence.

778	**97** 5e. multicoloured	25	15

98 Locomotive No. 1, 1914

1979. Early Locomotives. Multicoloured.

779	50c. Type **98**	15	10
780	1e.50 Gaza Railway locomotive No. 1, 1898	20	10
781	3e. Cape Government Railway 1st Class locomotive, 1878	45	10
782	7e.50 Delagoa Bay Railway locomotive No. 9, 1892	75	20
783	12e.50 Locomotive No. 41, 1896	1·25	30
784	15e. Trans Zambesia Railway Class D steam locomotive	1·40	35

99 Dalmatian

1979. Dogs. Multicoloured.

785	50c. Basenji (vert)	10	10
786	1e.50 Type **99**	15	10
787	3e. Boxer	15	10
788	7e.50 Blue gascon pointer	35	15
789	12e.50 English cocker spaniel	85	25
790	15e. Pointer	1·25	30

100 *Papilio nireus*

1979. Stamp Day. Butterflies. Multicoloured.

791	1e. Type **100**	10	10
792	1e.50 *Amauris ochlea*	10	10
793	2e.50 *Pinacopterix eriphia*	15	10
794	5e. *Junonia hierta*	35	10
795	10e. *Nephronia argia*	1·00	20
796	20e. *Catacroptera cloanthe*	2·10	90

101 *Dermacentor circumguttatus cunhasilvai* and African Elephant

1980. Ticks. Multicoloured.

797	50c. Type **101**	20	10
798	1e.50 *Dermacentor rhinocerinos* and black rhinoceros	30	10
799	2e.50 *Amblyomma hebraeum* and giraffe	40	15
800	3e. *Amblyomma pomposum* and eland	50	15
801	5e. *Amblyomma theilerae* and cow	60	15
802	7e.50 *Amblyomma eburneum* and African buffalo	85	30

102 Ford Hercules Bus, 1950

1980. Road Transport. Multicoloured.

803	50c. Type **102**	10	10
804	1e.50 Scania Marco-Polo bus, 1978	10	10
805	3e. Bussing Nag Bus, 1936	15	10
806	5e. Ikarus articulated bus, 1978	20	10
807	7e.50 Ford Taxi, 1929	40	15
808	12e.50 Fiat 131 Taxi, 1978	80	20

103 Soldier and Map of Southern Africa

1980. Zimbabwe Independence.

809	**103** 10e. blue and brown	40	15

104 Marx, Engels and Lenin

1980. International Workers' Day.

810	**104** 10e. multicoloured	40	15

105 *Market* (Moises Simbine)

1980. London 1980 International Stamp Exhibition. Multicoloured.

811	50c. *Heads* (Malangatana)	10	10
812	1e.50 Type **105**	10	10
813	3e. *Heads with Helmets* (Malangatana)	15	10
814	5e. *Women with Goods* (Machiana)	20	10
815	7e.50 *Crowd with Masks* (Malangatana)	25	15
816	12e.50 *Man and Woman with Spear* (Mankeu)	50	25

106 Telephone

1980. World Telecommunications Day.

817	**106** 15e. multicoloured	60	25

107 Mueda Massacre

1980. 20th Anniv of Mueda Massacre.

818	**107** 15e. green, brown and red	60	25

108 Crowd waving Tools

1980. Fifth Anniv of Independence.

819	- 1e. black and red	10	10
820	**108** 2e. multicoloured	10	10
821	- 3e. multicoloured	15	10
822	- 4e. multicoloured	20	10
823	- 5e. black, yellow and red	20	10
824	- 10e. multicoloured	40	15
MS825	140×100 mm. 30e. black, ultramarine and emerald	1·10	45

Designs:—As T **108**: 1e. Crowd, doctor tending patient, soldier and workers tilling land; 3e. Crowd with flags and tools; 4e. Stylized figures raising right hand; 5e. Hand grasping flags, book and plants; 10e. Figures carrying banners each with year date. 55×37 mm: 30e. Soldiers.

109 Gymnastics

1980. Olympic Games, Moscow. Multicoloured.

826	50c. Type **109**	10	10
827	1e.50 Football	10	10
828	2e.50 Running	10	10
829	3e. Volleyball	20	10
830	10e. Cycling	40	15
831	12e.50 Boxing	45	20

110 Narina's Trogon

1980. Birds. Multicoloured.

832	1m. Type **110**	35	10
833	1m.50 South African crowned crane	40	10
834	2m.50 Red-necked spurfowl	45	10
835	5m. Ostrich	85	20
836	7m.50 Spur-winged goose	1·00	25
837	12m.50 African fish eagle	1·40	35

111 Family and Census Officer

1980. First General Census.

838	**111** 3m.50 multicoloured	25	10

112 Animals fleeing from Fire

1980. Campaign against Bush Fires.

839	**112** 3m.50 multicoloured	25	10

113 Common Harp

1980. Stamp Day. Shells. Multicoloured.

840	1m. Type **113**	10	10
841	1m.50 Arthritic spider conch	15	10
842	2m.50 Venus comb murex	20	10
843	5m. Clear sundial	40	15
844	7m.50 Ramose murex	50	20
845	12m.50 Diana conch	1·10	35

114 Pres. Machel, Electricity Pylons, Aircraft and Lorry

1981. Decade for Victory over Underdevelopment.

846	**114** 3m.50 blue and red	2·00	75
847	- 7m.50 brown and green	25	15
848	- 12m.50 mauve and blue	50	30

Designs:—7m.50, Pres. Machel and armed forces on parade; 12m.50, Pres. Machel and classroom scenes.

115 Footballer and Athletic de Bilbao Stadium

1981. World Cup Football Championship, Spain (1982). Multicoloured.

849	1m. Type **115**	10	10
850	1m.50 Valencia, CF	10	10
851	2m.50 Oviedo CF	10	10
852	5m. R. Betis Balompie	20	10
853	7m.50 Real Zaragoza	25	15
854	12m.50 R.C.D. Espanol	50	25

MS855 Three sheets (a) 125×155 mm. Nos. 849/54; (b) 140×110 mm. 20m. FC Barcelona; (c) 105×85 mm. 20m. Atletico de Madrid Set of 3 sheets 2·75 1·60

116 Giraffe

1981. Protected Animals. Multicoloured.

856	50c. Type **116**	10	10
857	1m.50 Topi	10	10
858	2m.50 Aardvark	10	10
859	3m. African python	10	10
860	5m. Loggerhead turtle	20	15
861	10m. Marabou stork	1·10	45
862	12m.50 Saddle-bill stork	1·40	55
863	15m. Kori bustard	1·90	65

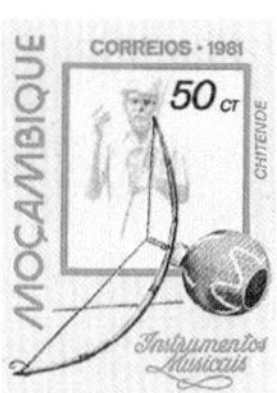

117 Chitende

1981. Musical Instruments. Multicoloured.

864	50c. Type **117**	10	10
865	2m. Pankwe (horiz)	10	10
866	2m.50 Kanyembe	10	10
867	7m. Nyanga (horiz)	30	20
868	10m. Likuti and M'Petheni (horiz)	70	25

118 Disabled Persons making Baskets

1981. International Year of Disabled People.

869	**118**	5m. multicoloured	25	15

119 de Havilland Dragon Rapide

1981. Air. Mozambique Aviation History. Mult.

870	50c. Type **119**	10	10
871	1m.50 Junkers Ju 52/3m	10	10
872	3m. Lockheed Super Electra	20	15
873	7m.50 de Havilland Dove	35	30
874	10m. Douglas DC-3	50	35
875	12m.50 Fokker Friendship	75	50

120 Controlled Killing, Marromeu

1981. World Hunting Exhibition, Plovdiv. Mult.

876	2m. Type **120**	30	15
877	5m. Traditional hunting Cheringoma	20	15
878	6m. Tourist hunting, Save	40	30
879	7m.60 Marksmanship, Gorongosa	40	20
880	12m.50 African elephants, Gorongosa	1·50	60
881	20m. Trap, Cabo Delgado	80	50

MS882 155×100 mm. Nos. 876/81 3·75 2·00

121 50 Centavos Coin

1981. First Anniv of New Currency. Mult.

883	50c. Type **121**	10	10
884	1m. One metical coin	10	10
885	2m.50 Two meticals 50 coin	10	10
886	5m. Five meticals coin	20	15
887	10m. Ten meticals coin	50	25
888	20m. Twenty meticals coin	1·40	50

MS889 121×121 mm. Nos. 883/8 2·40 1·25

122 Sunflower

1981. Agricultural Resources.

890	**122**	50c. orange and red	10	10
891	-	1m. black and red	10	10
892	-	1m.50 blue and red	10	10
893	-	2m.50 yellow and red	10	10
894	-	3m.50 green and red	15	10
895	-	4m.50 grey and red	15	10
896	-	10m. blue and red	40	15
897	-	12m.50 brown and red	50	20
898	-	15m. brown and red	60	25
899	-	25m. green and red	1·40	40
900	-	40m. orange and red	2·00	60
901	-	60m. brown and red	2·75	1·00

Designs:—1m. Cotton; 1m.50, Sisal; 2m.50, Cashew; 3m.50, Tea; 4m.50, Sugar cane; 10m. Castor oil; 12m.50, Coconut; 15m. Tobacco; 25m. Rice; 40m. Maize; 60m. Groundnut.

123 Archaeological Excavation, Manyikeni

1981. Archaeological Excavation. Mult.

902	1m. Type **123**	10	10
903	1m.50 Hand-axe (Massingir Dam)	10	10
904	2m.50 9th-century bowl (Chibuene)	10	10
905	7m.50 9th-century pot (Chibuene)	30	20
906	12m.50 Gold beads (Manyikeni)	50	30
907	20m. Gong (Manyikeni)	80	50

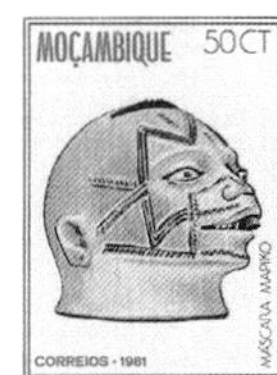

124 Mapiko Mask

1981. Sculptures. Multicoloured.

908	50c. Type **124**	10	10
909	1m. Woman who suffers	10	10
910	2m.50 Woman with a child	10	10
911	3m.50 The man who makes fire	15	10
912	5m. Chietane	20	15
913	12m.50 Chietane (different)	70	30

125 Broken Loaf on Globe

1981. World Food Day.

914	**125**	10m. multicoloured	45	25

126 Tanker *Matchedje*

1981. Mozambique Ships. Multicoloured.

915	50c. Type **126**	15	15
916	1m.50 Tug *Macuti*	15	15
917	3m. Trawler *Vega 7*	25	15
918	5m. Freighter *Linde*	35	25
919	7m.50 Freighter *Pemba*	55	30
920	12m.50 Dredger *Rovuma*	95	55

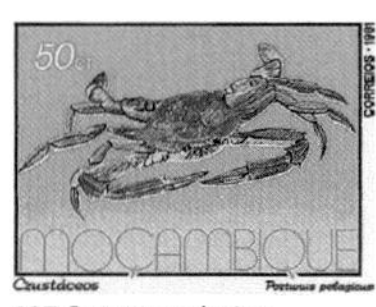

127 *Portunus pelagicus*

1981. Crustaceans. Multicoloured.

921	50c. Type **127**	10	10
922	1m.50 *Scylla serrata*	10	10
923	3m. *Penacus indicus*	15	10
924	7m.50 *Palinurus delagoae*	35	20
925	12m.50 *Lysiosquilla maculata*	55	35
926	15m. *Panulirus ornatus*	80	45

128 *Hypoxis multiceps*

1981. Flowers. Multicoloured.

927	1m. Type **128**	10	10
928	1m.50 *Pelargonium luridun*	10	10
929	2m.50 *Caralluma melanathera*	10	10
930	7m.50 *Ansellia gigantea*	35	20
931	12m.50 *Stapelia leendertsiae*	60	35
932	25m. *Adenium multiflorum*	1·50	70

129 Telex Tape, Telephone and Globe

1982. First Anniv of Mozambique Post and Telecommunications. Multicoloured.

933	6m. Type **129**	35	20
934	15m. Winged envelope and envelope forming railway wagon	3·00	1·50

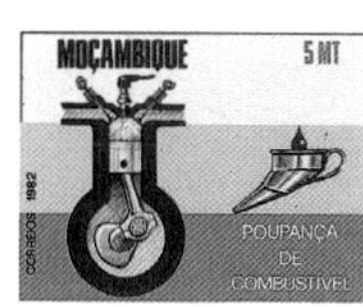

130 Diagram of Petrol Engine

1982. Fuel Saving. Multicoloured.

935	5m. Type **130**	30	15
936	7m.50 Speeding car	45	25
937	10m. Loaded truck	60	35

131 Sea-snake

1982. Reptiles. Multicoloured.

938	50c. Type **131**	20	10
939	1m.50 *Naja mossambica mossambica*	10	10
940	3m. *Thelotornis capensis mossambica*	20	15
941	6m. *Dendroaspis polylepis polylepis*	35	25
942	15m. *Dispholidus typus*	80	50
943	20m. *Bitis arietans arietans*	1·50	75

132 Dr. Robert Koch, Bacillus and X-Ray

1982. Centenary of Discovery of Tubercle Bacillus.

944	**132**	20m. multicoloured	1·75	1·00

133 Telephone Line

1982. International Telecommunications Union. Plenipotentiary Conference.

945	**133**	20m. multicoloured	1·00	75

134 Player with Ball

1982. World Cup Football Championship, Spain. Multicoloured.

946	1m.50 Type **134**	10	10
947	3m.50 Player heading ball	25	15
948	7m. Two players fighting for ball	40	20
949	10m. Player receiving ball	60	30
950	20m. Goalkeeper	1·25	1·00

MS951 84×69 mm. 50m. Footballer. Imperf 3·00 1·50

135 Tahitian Woman (detail from painting by Gauguin)

1982. Philexfrance 82 International Stamp Exhibition, Paris. Sheet 98×92 mm.

MS952 **135** 35m. multicoloured 1·90 1·50

136 Political Rally

1982. 25th Anniv of FRELIMO. Multicoloured.

953	4m. Type **136**	25	15
954	8m. Agriculture	45	25
955	12m. Marching workers	70	35

137 *Vangueria infausta*

1982. Fruits. Multicoloured.

956	1m. Type **137**	10	10
957	2m. *Mimusops caffra*	10	10
958	4m. *Sclerocarya caffra*	25	15
959	8m. *Strychnos spinosa*	45	25
960	12m. *Salacia kraussi*	70	40
961	32m. *Trichilia emetica*	1·90	85

138 *Sputnik I*

1982. 25th Anniv of First Artificial Satellite. Multicoloured.

962	1m. Type **138**	10	10
963	2m. First manned space flight	10	10

964	4m. First walk in space	25	15
965	8m. First manned flight to the Moon	45	25
966	16m. Soyuz–Apollo mission	1·25	70
967	20m. Intercosmos rocket	1·50	70

139 Vigilantes

1982. People's Surveillance Day.

968	**139**	4m. multicoloured	25	15

140 Caique

1982. Traditional Boats. Multicoloured.

969	1m. Type **140**	10	10
970	2m. Machua	15	10
971	4m. Calaua (horiz)	30	15
972	8m. Chitatarro (horiz)	60	25
973	12m. Cangaia (horiz)	80	35
974	16m. Chata (horiz)	1·75	60

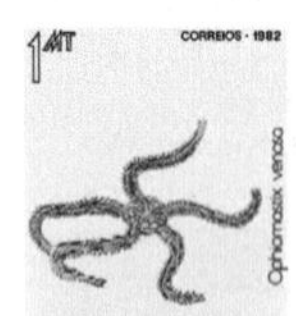
141 *Ophiomostix venosa*

1982. Starfish and Sea Urchins. Multicoloured.

975	1m. Type **141**	10	10
976	2m. *Protoreaster lincki*	10	10
977	4m. *Tropiometra carinata*	15	10
978	8m. *Holothuria scabra*	35	20
979	12m. *Prionocidaris baculosa*	60	35
980	16m. *Colobocentrotus atnatus*	80	40

142 Soldiers defending Mozambique

1983. Fourth Frelimo Party Congress. Multicoloured.

981	4m. Type **142**	15	10
982	8m. Crowd waving voting papers	30	20
983	16m. Agriculture, industry and education	65	40

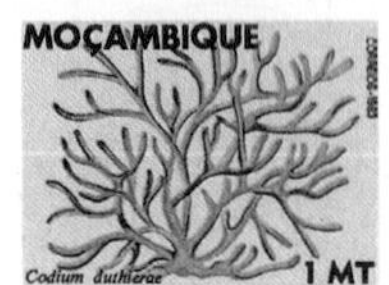
143 *Codium duthierae*

1983. Seaweeds. Multicoloured.

984	1m. Type **143**	10	10
985	2m. *Halimeda cunata*	10	10
986	4m. *Dictyota liturata*	15	10
987	8m. *Endorachne binghamiae*	40	20
988	12m. *Laurencia flexuosa*	60	30
989	20m. *Acrosorium* sp.	1·25	55

144 Diving and Swimming

1983. Olympic Games, Los Angeles (1st issue). Multicoloured.

990	1m. Type **144**	10	10
991	2m. Boxing	10	10
992	4m. Basketball	20	10
993	8m. Handball	35	20
994	12m. Volleyball	55	30
995	16m. Running	65	40
996	20m. Yachting	1·25	65
MS997	120×100 mm. 50m. Discus. Imperf	2·50	1·40

See also Nos. 1029/34.

145 Mallet Type Locomotive

1983. Steam Locomotives. Multicoloured.

998	1m. Type **145**	10	10
999	2m. Baldwin, 1915–45	20	10
1000	4m. Class 141-148, 1950	40	15
1001	8m. Baldwin, 1926	75	25
1002	16m. Henschel Garratt type, 1956	1·40	50
1003	32m. Natal Government Class H, 1899–1903	3·00	1·00

146 OAU Emblem

1983. 20th Anniv of Organization of African Unity.

1004	**146**	4m. multicoloured	20	15

147 Four-toed Elephant-shrew

1983. Mozambique Mammals. Multicoloured.

1005	1m. Type **147**	10	10
1006	2m. Four-striped grass mouse	15	10
1007	4m. Vincent's bush squirrel	25	15
1008	8m. Hottentot mole-rat	50	25
1009	12m. Natal red hare	75	40
1010	16m. Straw-coloured fruit bat	1·25	75

148 Aiding Flood Victims

1983. Second Anniv of Mozambique Red Cross. Multicoloured.

1011	4m. Type **148**	20	10
1012	8m. Red Cross lorry	40	20
1013	16m. First aid demonstration	75	40
1014	32m. Agricultural worker performing first aid	1·90	75

149 Musician

1983. Brasiliana 83 International Stamp Exhibition, Rio de Janeiro. Sheet 102×73 mm.

MS1015	**149** 30m. multicoloured	1·90	1·50

150 "Communications"

1983. World Communications Year.

1016	**150**	8m. multicoloured	1·50	75

151 Line Fishing

1983. Fishery Resources. Multicoloured.

1017	50c. Type **151**	10	10
1018	2m. Chifonho (basket trap)	10	10
1019	4m. Spear fishing	25	15
1020	8m. Gamboa (fence trap)	40	25
1021	16m. Mono (basket trap)	1·50	40
1022	20m. Lema (basket trap)	1·60	55

152 Kudu Horn

1983. Stamp Day. Multicoloured.

1023	50c. Type **152**	10	10
1024	1m. Drum communication	10	10
1025	4m. Postal runners	20	15
1026	8m. Mail canoe	40	40
1027	16m. Mail van	75	40
1028	20m. Steam mail train	3·25	1·50

153 Swimming

1984. Olympic Games, Los Angeles (2nd issue). Multicoloured.

1029	50c. Type **153**	10	10
1030	4m. Football	20	10
1031	8m. Hurdling	35	20
1032	16m. Basketball	90	50
1033	32m. Handball	1·90	80
1034	60m. Boxing	3·00	1·75

154 *Trichilia emetica*

1984. Indigenous Trees. Multicoloured.

1035	50c. Type **154**	10	10
1036	2m. *Brachystegia spiciformis*	10	10
1037	4m. *Androstachys johnsonii*	20	10
1038	8m. *Pterocarpus angolensis*	35	20
1039	16m. *Milletia stuhlmannii*	80	40
1040	50m. *Dalbergia melanoxylon*	2·75	1·75

155 Dove with Olive Sprig

1984. Nkomati South Africa–Mozambique Non-aggression Pact.

1041	**155**	4m. multicoloured	25	10

156 State Arms

1984. Emblems of the Republic. Multicoloured.

1042	4m. Type **156**	20	10
1043	8m. State Flag	40	20

157 Makway Dance

1984. Lubrapex '84 Portuguese–Brazilian Stamp Exhibition, Lisbon. Traditional Mozambican dances. Multicoloured.

1044	4m. Type **157**	20	10
1045	8m. Mapiko dance	40	20
1046	16m. Wadjaba dance	1·40	50

158 Nampula Museum and Statuette of Woman with Water Jug

1984. Museums. Multicoloured.

1047	50c. Type **158**	10	10
1048	4m. Natural History Museum and secretary bird	35	10
1049	8m. Revolution Museum and soldier carrying wounded comrade	35	20
1050	16m. Colonial History Museum and cannon	65	40
1051	20m. National Numismatic Museum and coins	1·25	65
1052	30m. St. Paul's Palace and antique chair	1·50	95

159 Imber's Tetra

1984. Fish. Multicoloured.

1053	50c. Type **159**	10	10
1054	4m. Purple labeo	25	10
1055	12m. Brown squeaker	75	35
1056	16m. Blue-finned notho	95	55
1057	40m. Slender serrate barb	2·50	1·40
1058	60m. Barred minnow	3·75	1·90

160 Badge and Laurels

1984. International Fair, Maputo.

1059	**160**	16m. multicoloured	70	50

161 Rural Landscape and Emblem

1984. 20th Anniv of African Development Bank.

1060	**161**	4m. multicoloured	30	10

162 Knife and Club

1984. Traditional Weapons. Multicoloured.

1061	50c. Type **162**	10	10
1062	4m. Axes	20	10
1063	8m. Spear and shield	35	15
1064	16m. Bow and arrow	75	35
1065	32m. Rifle	1·90	95
1066	50m. Assegai and arrow	2·75	1·90

163 Workers and Emblem

1984. First Anniv of Organization of Mozambican Workers.

1067	**163**	4m. multicoloured	20	10

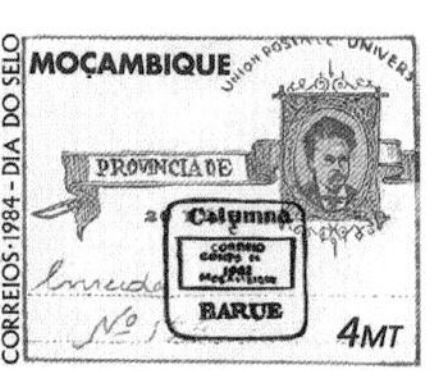

164 Barue 1902 Postmark

1984. Stamp Day. Postmarks. Multicoloured.

1068	4m. Type **164**	15	10
1069	8m. Zumbo postmark and King Carlos 15r. Mozambique "key type" stamp	35	20
1070	12m. Mozambique Company postmark and 1935 airmail stamp	55	30
1071	16m. Macequece postmark and 1937 2e. Mozambique Company stamp	70	40

165 Keeper and Hive

1985. Bee-keeping. Multicoloured.

1072	4m. Type **165**	15	10
1073	8m. Worker bee	45	20
1074	16m. Drone	1·25	40
1075	20m. Queen bee	1·75	60

166 Shot-putter and Emblem

1985. Olymphilex 85 Olympic Stamps Exhibition, Lausanne.

1076	**166**	16m. blue, black and red	75	35

167 Forecasting Equipment and Desert

1985. World Meteorology Day.

1077	**167**	4m. multicoloured	35	10

168 Map

1985. Fifth Anniv of Southern African Development Co-ordination Conference. Multicoloured.

1078	4m. Type **168**	15	10
1079	8m. Map and pylon	45	20
1080	16m. Industry and transport	2·50	1·25
1081	32m. Member states' flags	1·90	95

169 Battle of Mujenga, 1896

1985. Tenth Anniv of Independence. Mult.

1082	1m. Type **169**	10	10
1083	4m. Attack on Barue by Macombe, 1917	25	10
1084	8m. Attack on Massangano, 1868	55	20
1085	16m. Battle of Marracuene, 1895, and Gungunhana	1·50	50

170 UN Building, New York and Flag

1985. 40th Anniv of U.N.O.

1086	**170**	16m. multicoloured	80	50

171 Mathacuzana

1985. Traditional Games and Sports. Multicoloured.

1087	50c. Type **171**	10	10
1088	4m. Mudzobo	20	10
1089	8m. Muravarava (board game)	40	20
1090	16m. N'tshuwa	90	50

172 *Rana angolensis*

1985. Frogs and Toads. Multicoloured.

1091	50c. Type **172**	10	10
1092	1m. *Hyperolius pictus*	10	10
1093	4m. *Ptychadena porosissima*	15	10
1094	8m. *Afrixalus formasinii*	50	20
1095	16m. *Bufo regularis*	95	50
1096	32m. *Hyperolius marmoratus*	2·40	95
MS1097	89×85 mm. 30m. *Ptychadena porosissima* (different). Imperf	2·25	90

173 *Romulus, Remus and Wolf* (detail)

1985. Italia 85 International Stamp Exhibition, Rome. Sheet 90×85 mm. Imperf.

MS1098	**173**	60m. multicoloured	4·00	2·00

174 *Aloe ferox*

1985. Medicinal Plants. Multicoloured.

1099	50c. Type **174**	10	10
1100	1m. *Boophone disticha*	10	10
1101	3m.50 *Gloriosa superba*	15	10
1102	4m. *Cotyledon orbiculata*	15	10
1103	8m. *Homeria breyniana*	55	20
1104	50m. *Haemanthus coccineus*	3·75	1·90

175 Mozambique Company 1918 10c. Stamp

1985. Stamp Day. Multicoloured.

1105	1m. Type **175**	1·25	75
1106	4m. Nyassa Co. 1911 25r. stamp	15	10
1107	8m. Mozambique Co. 1918 ½c. stamp	50	20
1108	16m. Nyassa Co. 1924 1c. Postage Due stamp	1·25	50

176 Comet and *Giotto* Space Probe

1986. Appearance of Halley's Comet.

1109	**176**	4m. blue and light blue	20	10
1110	-	8m. violet and light violet	50	20
1111	-	16m. multicoloured	95	50
1112	-	30m. multicoloured	2·00	95

Designs:—8m. Comet orbits; 16m. Small and large telescopes, comet and space probe; 30m. Comet, stars and globe.

177 Vicente

1986. World Cup Football Championship, Mexico. Multicoloured.

1113	3m. Type **177**	15	10
1114	4m. Coluna	20	10
1115	8m. Costa Pereira	40	20
1116	12m. Hilario	65	35
1117	16m. Matateu	95	50
1118	50m. Eusebio	3·25	1·90

178 Dove and Emblem

1986. International Peace Year.

1119	**178**	16m. multicoloured	85	45

179 *Amanita muscaria*

1986. Fungi. Multicoloured.

1120	4m. Type **179**	50	20
1121	8m. *Lactarius deliciosus*	95	30
1122	16m. *Amanita phaloides*	2·00	65
1123	30m. *Tricholoma nudum*	4·25	1·25

180 Head and Arm of Statue

1986. Ameripex 86 International Stamp Exhibition, Chicago. Centenary of Statue of Liberty. Sheet 77×105 mm. Imperf.

MS1124	**180**	100m. multicoloured	7·50	4·75

181 Spiky Style

1986. Women's Hairstyles. Multicoloured.

1125	1m. Type **181**	10	10
1126	4m. Beaded plaits	25	10
1127	8m. Plaited tightly to head	50	20
1128	16m. Plaited tightly to head with ponytail	1·25	55

182 Dugong

1986. Marine Mammals. Multicoloured.

1129	1m. Type **182**	10	10
1130	8m. Common dolphin	35	20
1131	16m. *Neobalena marginata*	1·25	85
1132	50f. Fin whale	4·25	2·75

183 Children Studying

1986. First Anniv of Continuadores Youth Organization.

1133	**183**	4m. multicoloured	30	15

184 50m. Notes

1986. Savings. Multicoloured.

1134	4m. Type **184**	25	10
1135	8m. 100m. notes	50	20
1136	16m. 500m. notes	1·40	50
1137	30m. 1000m. notes	2·75	1·25

185 Quelimane Post Office

1986. Stamp Day. Post Offices. Multicoloured.

1138	3m. Type **185**	20	10
1139	4m. Maputo	30	10
1140	8m. Beira	65	20
1141	16m. Nampula	1·40	50

186 Pyrite

1987. Minerals. Multicoloured.

1142	4m. Type **186**	30	10
1143	8m. Emerald	60	20

1144	12m. Agate	85	40
1145	16m. Malachite	1·40	50
1146	30m. Garnet	2·50	1·25
1147	50m. Amethyst	4·25	2·00

187 Crowd beneath Flag

1987. Tenth Anniv of Mozambique Liberation Front.

1148	**187**	4m. multicoloured	30	15

188 Little Libombos Dam

1987

1149	**188**	16m. multicoloured	1·40	60

189 Children being Vaccinated

1987. World Health Day. Vaccination Campaign.

1150	**189**	50m. multicoloured	1·90	1·50

190 Common Grenadier

1987. Birds. Multicoloured.

1151	3m. Type **190**	25	15
1152	4m. Woodland kingfisher	30	20
1153	8m. White-fronted bee-eater	65	40
1154	12m. Lesser seedcracker	1·10	60
1155	16m. African broad-billed roller	1·25	90
1156	30m. Neergaard's sunbird	2·50	1·60

191 Football

1987. Olympic Games, Seoul (1988) (1st issue). Multicoloured.

1157	12m.50 Type **191**	10	10
1158	25m. Running	20	10
1159	50m. Handball	40	20
1160	75m. Chess	1·25	30
1161	100m. Basketball	1·25	35
1162	200m. Swimming	2·00	65

See also Nos. 1176/81.

192 Tower and Canadian Flag

1987. Capex 87 International Stamp Exhibition, Toronto. Sheet 70×100 mm. Imperf.

MS1163	**192**	200m. multicoloured	2·00	65

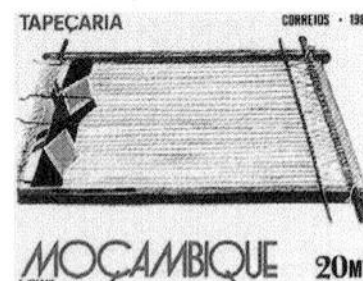

193 Work on Loom

1987. Weaving. Multicoloured.

1164	20m. Type **193**	15	10
1165	40m. Triangle and diamond design	40	10
1166	80m. "Eye" design	70	20
1167	200m. Red carpet	2·00	60

194 Piper Navajo

1987. Air. History of Aviation in Mozambique. Multicoloured.

1168	20m. Type **194**	15	10
1169	40m. de Havilland Hornet moth	25	10
1170	80m. Boeing 737	50	20
1171	120m. Beechcraft King Air	75	20
1172	160m. Piper Aztec	1·00	35
1173	320m. Douglas DC-10	2·00	75

195 Early Plan

1987. Centenary of Maputo as City.

1174	**195**	20m. multicoloured	20	15

1987. No. 895 surch **4,00 MT.**

1175	4m. on 4m.50 grey and red	15	10

197 Javelin throwing

1988. Olympic Games, Seoul (2nd issue). Mult.

1176	10m. Type **197**	10	10
1177	20m. Baseball	10	10
1178	40m. Boxing	10	10
1179	80m. Hockey	40	10
1180	100m. Gymnastics	50	15
1181	400m. Cycling	1·50	75

198 *Boophane disticha*

1988. Flowers. Multicoloured.

1182	10m. *Heamanthus nelsonii*	10	10
1183	20m. *Crinum polyphyllum*	15	10
1184	40m. Type **198**	15	10
1185	80m. *Cyrtanthus contractus*	35	10
1186	100m. *Nerine angustifolia*	50	15
1187	400m. *Cyrtanthus galpinnii*	2·00	75

199 Man refusing Cigarette

1988. 40th Anniv of W.H.O. Anti-smoking Campaign.

1188	**199**	20m. multicoloured	20	10

200 Helsinki Cathedral

1988. Finlandia 88 International Stamp Exhibition, Helsinki. Sheet 70×85 mm. Imperf.

MS1189	**200**	500m. multicoloured	1·90	1·40

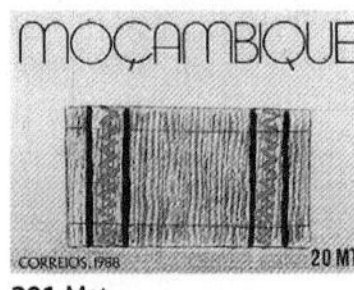

201 Mat

1988. Basketry. Multicoloured.

1190	20m. Type **201**	10	10
1191	25m. Basket with lid	10	10
1192	80m. Basket with handle	20	10
1193	100m. Fan	30	10
1194	400m. Dish	1·50	1·00
1195	500m. Conical basket	1·90	1·40

202 Cathedral Spire

1988. Visit of Pope John Paul II. Sheet 83×103 mm.

MS1196	**202**	500m. blue, red and black	1·90	1·40

203 Percheron

1988. Horses. Multicoloured.

1197	20m. Type **203**	15	10
1198	40m. Arab	20	10
1199	80m. Pure blood	40	10
1200	100m. Pony	50	15

204 Machel

1988. Second Death Anniv of Samora Machel (President 1975–86).

1201	**204**	20m. multicoloured	15	10

205 Inhambane

1988. Ports. Multicoloured.

1202	20m. Type **205**	15	10
1203	50m. Quelimane (vert)	40	10
1204	75m. Pemba	50	10
1205	100m. Beira	55	20
1206	250m. Nacali (vert)	1·10	50
1207	500m. Maputo	2·75	1·25

206 Mobile Post Office

1988. Stamp Day. Multicoloured.

1208	20m. Type **206**	10	10
1209	40m. Posting box (vert)	15	10

207 Maize

1989. Fifth FRELIMO Congress. Multicoloured.

1210	25m. Type **207**	10	10
1211	50m. Hoe	10	10
1212	75m. Abstract	10	10
1213	100m. Cogwheels	20	10
1214	250m. Right-half of cogwheel	50	25

Nos. 1210/14 were printed together, *se-tenant*, forming a composite design.

208 Mondlane

1989. 20th Anniv of Assassination of Pres. Mondlane.

1215	**208**	25m. black, gold and red	15	10

209 *Storming the Bastille* (Thevenin)

1989. Bicentenary of French Revolution. Mult.

1216	100m. Type **209**	25	10
1217	250m. *Liberty guiding the People* (Delacroix)	60	35
MS1218	78×106 mm. 500m. *Declaration of Rights of Man* (detail, Blanchard)	1·20	1·20

No. **MS**1218 also commemorates Philexfrance 89 International Stamp Exhibition.

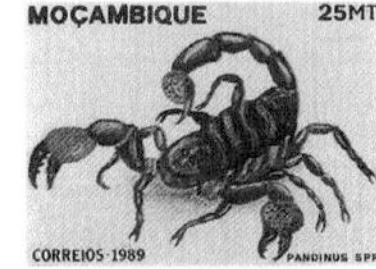

210 *Pandinus* sp.

1989. Venomous Animals. Multicoloured.

1219	25m. Type **210**	10	10
1220	50m. Egyptian cobra	10	10
1221	75m. *Bombus* sp. (bee)	15	10
1222	100m. *Paraphysa* sp. (spider)	25	10
1223	250m. Marble cone	90	40
1224	500m. Lionfish	1·90	70

211 *Acropora pulchra*

1989. Corals. Multicoloured.

1225	25m. Type **211**	10	10
1226	50m. *Eunicella papilosa*	15	10
1227	100m. *Dendrophyla migrantus*	30	10
1228	250m. *Favia fragum*	50	35

212 Footballers

1989. World Cup Football Championship, Italy (1990). Designs showing various footballing scenes.

1229	**212**	30m. multicoloured	10	10
1230	-	60m. multicoloured	15	10
1231	-	125m. multicoloured	30	10
1232	-	200m. multicoloured	50	25
1233	-	250m. multicoloured	65	35
1234	-	500m. multicoloured	1·50	70

213 Macuti Lighthouse

1989. Lighthouses. Multicoloured.

1235	30m. Type **213**	15	10
1236	60m. Pinda	15	10
1237	125m. Cape Delgado	30	10
1238	200m. Goa Island	60	25
1239	250m. Caldeira Point	80	35
1240	500m. Vilhena	1·50	70

214 Bracelet

1989. Silver Filigree Work.

1241	**214**	30m. grey, red and black	10	10
1242	-	60m. grey, blue and black	15	10
1243	-	125m. grey, red and black	25	10
1244	-	200m. grey, blue & black	40	25
1245	-	250m. grey, purple & blk	55	35
1246	-	500m. grey, green & blk	1·25	70

Designs:—60m. Flower belt; 125m. Necklace; 200m. Casket; 250m. Spoons; 500m. Butterfly.

215 Flag and Soldiers

1989. 25th Anniv of Fight for Independence.

1247	**215**	30m. multicoloured	15	10

216 Rain Gauge

1989. Meteorological Instruments. Multicoloured.

1248	30m. Type **216**	10	10
1249	60m. Radar graph	15	10
1250	125m. Sheltered measuring instruments	30	10
1251	200m. Computer terminal	55	25

217 Washington Monument

1989. World Stamp Expo 89 International Stamp Exhibition, Washington D.C. Sheet 78×104 mm.

MS1252 **217**	500m. multicoloured	1·20	1·20

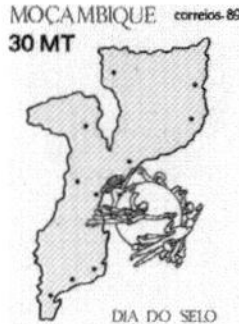

218 Map and UPU Emblem

1989. Stamp Day.

1253	**218**	30m. multicoloured	15	10
1254	-	60m. black, green and red	15	10

Design:—60m. Map and Mozambique postal emblem.

219 Railway Map

1990. Tenth Anniv of Southern Africa Development Coordination Conference.

1255	**219**	35m. multicoloured	1·00	50

220 Cloth and Woman wearing Dress

1990. Traditional Dresses. Designs showing women wearing different dresses and details of cloth used.

1256	**220**	42m. multicoloured	10	10
1257	-	90m. multicoloured	15	10
1258	-	150m. multicoloured	20	10
1259	-	200m. multicoloured	25	15
1260	-	400m. multicoloured	55	40
1261	-	500m. multicoloured	65	50

221 Sena Fortress, Sofala

1990. Fortresses.

1262	**221**	45m. blue and black	10	10
1263	-	90m. blue and black	15	10
1264	-	150m. multicoloured	20	10
1265	-	200m. multicoloured	30	15
1266	-	400m. red and black	55	40
1267	-	500m. red and black	70	40

Designs:—90m. Sto. Antonio, Ibo Island; 150m. S. Sebastiao, Mozambique Island; 200m. S. Caetano, Sofala; 400m. Our Lady of Conception, Maputo; 500m. S. Luis, Tete.

223 Obverse and Reverse of 50m. Coin

1990. 15th Anniv of Bank of Mozambique.

1269	**223**	100m. multicoloured	20	10

224 Statue of Eduardo Mondlane (founder of FRELIMO)

1990. 15th Anniv of Independence. Mult.

1270	42m.50 Type **224**	10	10
1271	150m. Statue of Samora Machel (President, 1975–86)	25	15

225 White Rhinoceros

1990. Endangered Animals. Multicoloured.

1272	42m.50 Type **225**	15	10
1273	100m. Dugong	20	10
1274	150m. African elephant	35	15
1275	200m. Cheetah	40	15
1276	400m. Spotted-necked otter	70	40
1277	500m. Hawksbill turtle	85	50

226 *Dichrostachys cinerea*

1990. Environmental Protection. Plants. Mult.

1278	42m.50 Type **226**	10	10
1279	100m. Forest fire	20	10
1280	150m. Horsetail tree	25	10
1281	200m. Mangrove	30	15
1282	400m. *Estrato herbaceo* (grass)	65	40
1283	500m. Pod mahogany	80	50

227 Pillar Box waving to Kurika

1990. Kurika (post mascot) at Work. Mult.

1284	42m.50 Type **227**	15	10
1285	42m.50 Hand cancelling envelopes	15	10
1286	42m.50 Leaping across hurdles	15	10
1287	42m.50 Delivering post to chicken	15	10

228 "10" and Posts Emblem

1991. Tenth Anniv of National Posts and Telecommunications Enterprises, Mozambique.

1288	**228**	50m. blue, red and black	15	10
1289	-	50m. brown, green & black	15	10

Design:—No. 1289, "10" and telecommunications emblem.

229 Bird-of-Paradise Flower

1991. Flowers. Multicoloured.

1290	50m. Type **229**	15	10
1291	125m. Flamingo lily	25	15
1292	250m. Calla lily	50	30
1293	300m. Canna lily	55	35

230 Two Hartebeest

1991. Lichtenstein's Hartebeest. Multicoloured.

1294	50m. Type **230**	15	10
1295	100m. Alert hartebeest	20	10
1296	250m. Hartebeest grazing	1·50	70
1297	500m. Mother feeding young	2·10	1·40

231 Mpompine

1991. Maputo Drinking Fountains. Mult.

1298	50m. Type **231**	10	10
1299	125m. Chinhambanine	15	10
1300	250m. S. Pedro-Zaza	25	10
1301	300m. Xipamanine	35	15

232 Painting by Samate

1991. Paintings by Mozambican Artists. Mult.

1302	180m. Type **232**	15	10
1303	250m. Malangatana Ngwenya	20	15
1304	560m. Malangatana Ngwenya (different)	40	30

233 Diving

1991. Olympic Games, Barcelona (1992). Mult.

1305	10m. Type **233**	10	10
1306	50m. Roller hockey	15	10
1307	100m. Tennis	20	10
1308	200m. Table tennis	30	10
1309	500m. Running	50	20
1310	1000m. Badminton	1·10	40

234 Proposed Boundaries in 1890 Treaty

1991. Centenary of Settling of Mozambique Borders. Multicoloured.

1311	600m. Type **234**	50	25
1312	800m. Frontiers settled in English–Portuguese 1891 treaty	75	35

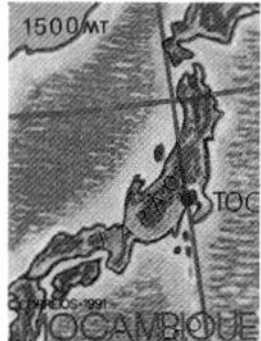

235 Map of Japan

1991. Phila Nippon 91 International Stamp Exhibition, Tokyo. Sheet 102×71 mm.

MS1313 **235**	1500m. multicoloured	1·40	1·40

236 Skipping

1991. Stamp Day. Children's Games. Mult.

1314	40m. Type **236**	10	10
1315	150m. Spinning top	10	10
1316	400m. Marbles	20	10
1317	900m. Hopscotch	45	20

237 "Christ"

1992. Stained Glass Windows. Multicoloured.

1318	40m. Type **237**	10	10
1319	150m. "Faith"	10	10
1320	400m. "IC XC"	20	10
1321	900m. Window in three sections	45	20

238 *Rhisophora mucronata*

1992. Marine Flowers. Multicoloured.

1322	300m. Type **238**	15	10
1323	600m. *Cymodocea ciliata*	30	15
1324	1000m. *Sophora inhambanensis*	85	25

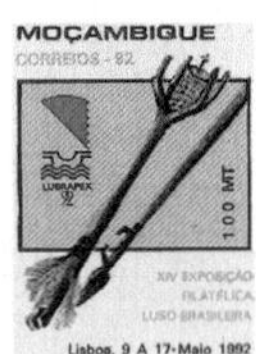
239 Spears

1992. Lubrapex 92 Brazilian–Portuguese Stamp Exhibition, Lisbon. Weapons. Multicoloured.

1325	100m. Type **239**	10	10
1326	300m. Tridents	15	10
1327	500m. Axe	25	10
1328	1000m. Dagger	85	25

240 Amethyst Sunbird

1992. Birds. Multicoloured.

1329	150m. Type **240**	30	30
1330	200m. Mosque swallow	30	30
1331	300m. Red-capped robin chat	45	30
1332	400m. Lesser blue-eared glossy starling	60	30
1333	500m. Grey-headed bush shrike	1·50	30
1334	800m. African golden oriole	2·25	70

241 Emblem

1992. 30th Anniv of Eduardo Mondlane University.

1335	**241**	150m. green and brown	10	10

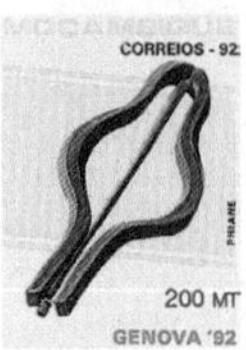
242 Phiane

1992. Genova '9" International Thematic Stamp Exhibition. Musical Instruments. Multicoloured.

1336	200m. Type **242**	10	10
1337	300m. Xirupe (rattle)	15	10
1338	500m. Ngulula (drum)	25	10
1339	1500m. Malimba (drum)	75	35
MS1340	130×100 mm. Nos. 1336/9	1·25	1·25

243 Children Eating

1992. International Nutrition Conference, Rome.

1341	**243**	450m. multicoloured	20	10

244 Parachutist

1992. Parachuting. Multicoloured.

1342	50m. Type **244**	10	10
1343	400m. Parachutist and buildings	20	10
1344	500m. Airplane dropping parachutists	25	10
1345	1500m. Parachutist (different)	1·10	1·10

1992. No. 890 surch **50MT**.

1346	**122**	50m. on 50c. orge & red	10	10

246 Order of Peace and Friendship

1993. Mozambique Decorations. Multicoloured.

1347	400m. Type **246**	20	10
1348	800m. Bagamoyo Medal	40	20
1349	1000m. Order of Eduardo Mondlane	50	25
1350	1500m. Veteran of the Struggle for National Liberation Medal	70	35

247 Tree Stumps and Girl carrying Wood

1993. Pollution. Multicoloured.

1351	200m. Type **247**	10	10
1352	750m. Chimneys smoking	35	15
1353	1000m. Tanker sinking	50	25
1354	1500m. Car exhaust fumes	70	35

248 Lion (Gorongosa Park, Sofala)

1993. National Parks. Multicoloured.

1355	200m. Type **248**	10	10
1356	800m. Giraffes (Banhine Park, Gaza)	40	20
1357	1000m. Dugongs (Bazoruto Park, Inhambane)	50	25
1358	1500m. Ostriches (Zinave Park, Inhambane)	1·75	75

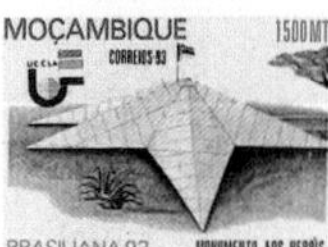
249 Heroes Monument, Maputo

1993. Brasiliana 93 International Stamp Exhibition, Rio de Janeiro.

1359	**249**	1500m. multicoloured	55	25

250 Conference Emblem

1993. National Culture Conference, Maputo.

1360	**250**	200m. multicoloured	10	10

251 *Cycas cercinalis*

1993. Forest Plants. Multicoloured.

1361	200m. Type **251**	10	10
1362	250m. *Cycas revoluta*	10	10
1363	900m. *Encephalartos ferox*	25	10
1364	2000m. *Equisetum ramosissimum*	50	25

252 *Anacardium occidentale*

1994. Medicinal Plants. Multicoloured.

1365	200m. Type **252**	10	10
1366	250m. *Sclerocarya caffra*	10	10
1367	900m. *Annona senegalensis*	25	10
1368	2000m. *Crinum delagoense*	50	25

1994. Various stamps surch.

1369	50m. on 7m.50 mult (No. 905)	10	10
1370	50m. on 7m.50 mult (No. 924)	10	10
1371	50m. on 7m.50 mult (No. 930)	10	10
1372	100m. on 10m. blue and red (No. 896)	10	10
1373	100m. on 12m.50 mult (No. 931)	10	10
1374	200m. on 12m.50 brown and red (No. 897)	10	10
1375	250m. on 12m.50 mult (No. 925)	10	10

254 Mozambique Rough-scaled Sand Lizard

1994. Philakorea 1994 International Stamp Exhibition, Seoul. Reptiles. Multicoloured.

1376	300m. Type **254**	10	10
1377	500m. Olive loggerhead turtle	10	10
1378	2000m. Northern coppery snake	40	20
1379	3500m. Marshall's chameleon	75	35
MS1380	79×70 mm. 4000m. Snake swallowing prey	80	80

255 Crop-spraying

1994. 50th Anniv of I.C.A.O. Multicoloured.

1381	300m. Type **255**	10	10
1382	500m. Airport	10	10
1383	2000m. Air transport	40	20
1384	3500m. Aircraft maintenance	75	35

256 Bean Plant

1994. Lubrapex'94 Portuguese–Brazilian Stamp Exhibition. World Food Day.

1385	**256**	2000m. multicoloured	40	20

257 Queue of Voters

1994. First Multiparty Elections.

1386	**257**	900m. multicoloured	20	10

258 Document and Handshake

1994. 20th Anniv of Lusaka Accord (establishing independence).

1387	**258**	1500m. multicoloured	30	15

259 Couple using Drugs

1994. Anti-drugs Campaign. Multicoloured.

1388	500m. Type **259**	10	10
1389	1000m. Couple, syringe, cigarette and skeleton	20	10
1390	2000m. Addict	40	20
1391	5000m. Sniffer dog capturing man with drugs	1·00	50

260 Basket

1995. Baskets and Bags. Multicoloured.

1392	250m. Type **260**	10	10
1393	300m. Bag with two handles	10	10
1394	1200m. Circular bag with one handle	20	10
1395	5000m. Bag with flap	85	40

261 Dress and Cloak

1995. Women's Costumes. Multicoloured.

1396	250m. Type **261**	10	10
1397	300m. Blouse and calf-length skirt	10	10
1398	1200m. Blouse and ankle-length skirt	20	10
1399	5000m. Strapless top and skirt	85	40

262 State Arms

1995. Investiture (1994) of President Joaquim Chissano. Multicoloured.

1400	900m. Type **262**	15	10
1401	2500m. National Flag	45	20
1402	5000m. Pres. Chissano	85	40

Nos. 1400/2 were issued together, *se-tenant*, the commemorative inscription at the foot extending across the strip.

263 Bushbaby

1995. Mammals. Multicoloured.

1403	500m. Type **263**	10	10
1404	2000m. Greater kudu (horiz)	25	10
1405	3000m. Bush pig (horiz)	40	20
1406	5000m. Bushbuck	65	30

222 GB Unissued "VR" Penny Black and Mozambique 1876 5r. Stamp

1990. Stamp World London 90 International Stamp Exhibition. 150th Anniv of the Penny Black. Sheet 70×100 mm.

MS1268	**222** 1000m. black, blue and red	1·40	1·40

1995. Various stamps surch.

1407	250m. on 12m.50 multicoloured (No. 931)	10	10
1408	300m. on 10m. blue and red (No. 896)	10	10
1409	500m. on 12m.50 multicoloured (No. 925)	10	10
1410	900m. on 12e.50 multicoloured (No. 771)	10	10
1411	1000m. on 12m.50 multicoloured (No. 837)	15	10
1412	1500m. on 16m. multicoloured (No. 1064)	20	10
1413	2000m. on 16m. multicoloured (No. 995)	25	10
1414	2500m. on 12m. multicoloured (No. 880)	35	15

265 Family carrying Foodstuffs

1995. 50th Anniv of F.A.O.

1415	**265** 5000m. multicoloured	65	30

266 Emblem

1995. 50th Anniv of United Nations Organization.

1416	**266** 5000m. blue and black	65	30

267 Child wearing Blue Cloak

1995. 20th Anniv of UNICEF in Mozambique.

1417	**267** 5000m. multicoloured	1·00	1·00

268 Player scoring Goal

1996. Football. Multicoloured.

1418	1000m. Type **268**	35	35
1419	2000m. Goalkeeper holding ball	60	60
1420	4000m. Referee admonishing players	80	80
1421	6000m. Two players tackling for ball	1·10	1·10

269 Mask

1996. Local Masks.

1422	**269** 1000m. multicoloured	35	35
1423	- 2000m. multicoloured	60	60
1424	- 4000m. multicoloured	80	80
1425	- 6000m. multicoloured	1·10	1·10

Designs:—2000 to 6000m. Different masks.

270 *Mae Africa* (De Malangatana)

1996. 15th Anniv of Mozambique Red Cross.

1426	**270** 5000m. multicoloured	1·00	1·00

271 African Elephant

1996. Wild Animals. Multicoloured.

1427	1000m. Type **271**	75	40
1428	2000m. White rhinoceros	1·00	75
1429	4000m. Leopard	1·25	1·00
1430	6000m. Pel's fishing owl	2·00	1·50

272 Mine Field

1996. Land Mine Clearance Campaign. Mult.

1431	2000m. Type **272**	50	35
1432	6000m. Warning sign	1·25	65
1433	8000m. Soldier with mine detector	1·50	1·00
1434	10000m. Soldier lifting mine	2·25	1·50

273 City Street

1996. Keeping the City Clean.

1435	**273** 2000m. multicoloured	50	25

274 5r. Stamp of 1876 and Magnifying Glass

1996. 120th Anniv of Mozambique Stamps.

1436	**274** 2000m. multicoloured	50	25

275 Mitumbui

1997. Local Boats. Multicoloured.

1437	2000m. Type **275**	40	25
1438	6000m. Muterere	1·25	65
1439	8000m. Lancha	1·50	1·00
1440	10000m. Dhow	2·25	2·00

275a Anhinga

1997. First AICEP (Association of Post Office and Telecommunications Operators of Portuguese Speaking Territories) Philatelic Conference, Sao Tome. Sheet 70×91 mm.

MS1440a	5000m. multicoloured	12·00	12·00

276 Village Scene

1997. International Children's Day.

1441	**276** 2000m. multicoloured	50	25

277 *Enaretta conitera*

1997. Beetles. Multicoloured.

1442	2000m. Type **277**	50	25
1443	6000m. *Zographus hieroglyphicus*	1·50	75
1444	8000m. *Tragiscoschema bertolonii*	2·00	1·00
1445	10000m. *Tragocephala ducalis*	2·75	1·50
MS1446	97×105 mm. Nos. 1442/5	6·00	6·00

No. **MS**1446 also commemorates the "LUBRAPEX 97" International Stamp Exhibition, Brazil.

278 Yellow-billed Stork

1997. Aquatic Birds. Multicoloured.

1447	2000m. Type **278**	50	25
1448	4000m. Black-winged stilt	1·50	75
1449	8000m. Long-toed stint (horiz)	2·00	1·00
1450	10000m. Eastern white pelican	2·75	1·50

279 Abstract Patterns

1997. Centenary of Joao Ferreira dos Santos Group.

1451	**279** 2000m. multicoloured	1·00	5·00

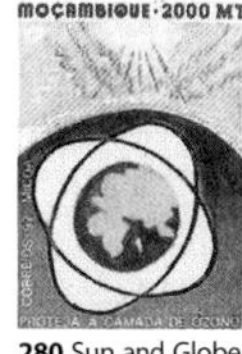

280 Sun and Globe

1997. Protection of Ozone Layer.

1452	**280** 2000m. multicoloured	30	25

281 Gandhi

1997. 50th Anniv of Republic of India

1453	**281** 2000m. multicoloured		

282 Dove holding Olive Branch

1997. Fifth Anniv of Peace Accord

1454	**282** 2000m. multicoloured	50	25

2 000 MT

500.00 MT (283) 1 000 MT (283a) (283b)

8000 MT (283c) 17 000ml (283d)

1997. Nos. 783, 789, 854, 896/7, 920, 925, 930, 1056, 1095, 1108, 1136, 1143, 1145, 1155, 1173, 1298/9, 1305/8, 1310, 1467/9, 1485/90, 1492/4 and 1991 surch as T **283/d**

1455	500m. on 16m. Blue-finned notho (*Notobranchius zachovii*) (1984 Fish) (1056)	25·00	15·00
1456	1000m. on 16m. *Bufo regularis* (frog) (1985 Frogs and Toads) (1095)	30·00	—
1457	2000m. on 12e.50 Locomotive No. 41, 1896 (1979 Early Locomotives) (783)	3·00	2·00
1457*a*	2000m. on 12e.50 English cocker spaniel (1979 Dogs) (789)	3·00	2·00
1457*b*	2000m. on 10m. *Ricinus plant* (castor oil) (1981 Agricultural Resources definitive) (896)	10·00	5·00
1457*c*	2000m. on 16m. African broad-billed roller (1987 Birds) (1155)	50·00	—
1458	3000m. on 4000m. Teacher (1467)	—	—
1458*a*	3000m. on 8000m. Using computer (1468)	—	10·00
1458*b*	3000m. on 10,000m. Woman in field (1469)	—	10·00
1458*c*	3000m. on 2000m. Traditional dwelling (*** oblit) (1485)	—	10·00
1458*d*	3000m. on 6000m. Traditional dwelling (*** oblit) (1487)	—	10·00
1458*e*	3000m. on 8000m. Traditional dwelling (*** oblit) (1488)	—	—
1458*f*	3000m. on 15,000m. Traditional dwelling (*** oblit) (1490)	—	10·00
1458*g*	3000m. on 20,000m. Traditional dwelling (*** oblit) (1491)	—	10·00
1458*h*	3000m. on 30,000m. Traditional dwelling (*** oblit) (1492)	—	—
1458*i*	3000m. on 100,000m. Traditional dwelling (*** oblit) (1494)	—	10·00
1459	4000m. on 12m.50 Coconut (1981 Agricultural Resources definitive) (897)	2·00	1·50
1460	5000m. on 10m. *Ricinus plant* (castor oil) (1981 Agricultural Resources definitive) (with **** oblit) (896)	—	5·00
1461	6000m. on 7m.50 *Ansellia gigantea* (1981 Flowers) (930)	2·00	1·50
1462	7500m. on 16m. 500m. banknotes (1986 Savings) (1136)	3·50	2·50
1463	10,000m. on 12m.50 R.C.D. Espanol (footballer and stadium) (1981 World Cup Football, Spain 1982) (854)	2·50	1·50
1463*a*	10,000m. on 12m.50 *Lysiosquilla maculata* (1981 Crustaceans) (925)	—	—
1463*b*	10,000m. on 16m. Nyassa Co. 1924 1c. Postage Due stamp (1985 Stamp Day) (1108)	15·00	15·00
1463*c*	10,000m. on 320m. Douglas DC-10 (1987 Air. History of Aviation in Mozambique) (1173)	75·00	25·00
1464	12,500m. on 12m.50 Dredger *Rovuma* (1981 Mozambique Ships) (920)	25·00	25·00
1464*a*	12,500m. on 8m. Emerald (1987 Minerals) (1143)	5·00	4·00
1464*b*	12,500m. on 16m. Malachite (1987 Minerals) (1145)	5·00	5·00
1465	17,000m. on 50m. Type **231** Maputo waterpump (1991 Maputo Drinking Fountains) (1298)	—	—

1465*a*	17,000m. on 125m. Chinhambanine (1991 Maputo Drinking Fountains) (1299)	—	10·00
1465*b*	17,000m. on 300m. Xipamanine (1991 Maputo Drinking Fountains) (1301)	—	—
1465*c*	17,000m. on 10m. Type **233** (swimming) (1991 Olympic Games, Barcelona) (1305)	—	25·00
1465*d*	17,000m. on 50m. Roller hockey (1991 Olympic Games, Barcelona) (1306)	—	—
1465*e*	17,000m. on 100m. Tennis (1991 Olympic Games, Barcelona) (1307)	—	25·00
1465*f*	17,000m. on 200m. Table tennis (1991 Olympic Games, Barcelona) (1308)	—	—
1465*g*	17,000m on 1000m. Badminton (1991 Olympic Games, Barcelona) (1310)	—	25·00
1465*h*	17,000m. on 2000m. Traditional dwellings (with *** oblit) (1485)	—	—
1465*i*	17,000m. on 4000m. Traditional dwellings (with *** oblit) (1486)	10·00	10·00
1465*j*	17,000m. on 6000m. Traditional dwellings (with *** oblit) (1487)	10·00	10·00
1465*k*	17,000m. on 8000m. Traditional dwellings (with *** oblit) (1488)	10·00	10·00
1465*l*	17,000m. on 10,000m. Traditional dwellings (with *** oblit) (1489)	—	20·00
1465*m*	17,000m. on 15,000m. Traditional dwellings (with *** oblit) (1490)	10·00	10·00
1465*n*	17,000m. on 30,000m. Traditional dwellings (with *** oblit) (1492)	—	20·00
1465*o*	17,000m. on 50,000m. Traditional dwellings (with *** oblit) (1493)	10·00	10·00
1465*p*	17,000m. on 100,000m. Traditional dwellings (with *** oblit) (1494)	—	—

284 Coelacanth

1998. EXPO '98 International Stamp Exhibition, Lisbon.

1465*q*	**284**	2000m. multicoloured	1·00	50

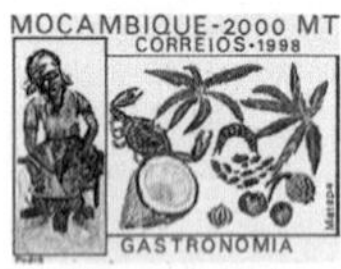

285 Woman with Food Products

1998. Food Production.

1465*r*	**285**	2000m. multicoloured	60	30

286a Breast Feeding

1998. Mothers Day. Multicoloured.

1466	2000m. Type **286a**	1·50	—
1467	4000m. Teacher	1·75	—
1468	8000m. Using computer	2·00	—
1469	10000m. Woman in field	2·50	—

Nos. 1470 to 1472 are vacant.

MOÇAMBIQUE-CORREIOS 1998

2000 MT

287 Diana, Princess of Wales

1998. Diana, Princess of Wales Commemoration (1st issue). T **287** and similar vert designs. Multicoloured.

MS1473	135×189 mm. 2000m. Type **287**; 2000m. Wearing tiara and white dress; 2000m. Wearing black V-neck dress; 2000m. Wearing blue sleeveless dress and choker; 2000m. With Indian woman and baby; 2000m. Wearing black halter-neck dress; 2000m. In RNLI uniform; 2000m. Wearing red dress; 2000m. Wearing Red Cross badge and protective vest	85	90
MS1474	135×189 mm. 5000m. Wearing red and white hat and pearl necklace; 5000m. Wearing pink check hat and dress; 5000m. Wearing red hat and red patterned dress; 5000m. Wearing blue hat and white jacket with blue edging; 5000m. Wearing red and black hat and red and white check jacket; 5000m. Wearing dark blue and white hat and white jacket with dark blue edging; 5000m. Wearing white and grey hat and white dress; 5000m. Turquoise and white hat and dress; 5000m. Wearing blue hat and blue jacket with flower brooch	2·20	2·30
MS1475	135×190 mm. 8000m. Wearing cream embroidered dress and bolero; 8000m. Wearing black dress and choker; 8000m. Wearing red dress; 8000m. Wearing red dress (different); 8000m. Wearing beige embroidered dress and bolero; 8000m. Wearing white dress and choker; 8000m. Wearing pale blue dress and pearl necklace; 8000m. Wearing dark blue dress; 8000m. Wearing white lace dress and carrying clutch bag	3·25	3·50
MS1476	Two sheets, each 130×100 mm. (a) 30000m. Wearing mauve dress (41×59 mm). (b) 30000m. With African child (41×59 mm). Set of 2 sheets	3·00	3·25

See also Nos. **MS**1506/**MS**1507 and **MS**1593/**MS**1594.

288 Breast Feeding

1998. Promotion of Breast Feeding

1477	**288**	2000m. multicoloured	80	25

289 Mother Teresa

1998. Mother Teresa

1478	**289**	2000m. multicoloured	80	25

290 Kudu

1998. 18th Anniv of PAPU

1479	**290**	2000m. multicoloured	80	30

291 *Garcinia livingstonei*

1998. Plants. Wild Fruit. Multicoloured.

1480	2000m. Type **291**	1·50	—
1481	7500m. *Tabernaemontana elegans*	2·50	—
1482	12500m. *Ximenia caffra*	3·00	—
1483	25000m. Syzygium guineense	4·50	—
MS1484	50,000m. *Uapaca kirkiana*		

292 Traditional Dwelling

1998. Traditional Dwellings

1485	**292**	2000m. multicoloured		
1486		4000m. multicoloured		
1487		6000m. multicoloured		
1488		8000m. multicoloured		
1489		10,000m. multicoloured		
1490		15,000m. multicoloured		
1491		20,000m. multicoloured		
1492		30,000m. multicoloured		
1493		50,000m. multicoloured		
1494		100,000m. multicoloured		

Nos. 1495 to 1504 are vacant.

296 Lucy (Lucille Ball) wearing Dark Brown Hat and Coat

1999. Scenes from I Love Lucy (American TV comedy series). Two sheets containing T **296** and similar multicoloured design.

MS1505	(a) 88×121 mm. 35000m. Type **296**; (b) 121×88 mm. 35000m. Lucy as ballet dancer	3·50	3·75

297 Diana, Princess of Wales

1999. Diana, Princess of Wales Commemoration (2nd issue). T **297** and similar vert designs. Stamp colours shown.

MS1506	165×170 mm. 6500m. Type **297** (violet and black); 6500m. In profile, looking left (brown and black); 6500m. Wearing jacket and pearl necklace (chestnut and black); 6500m. Wearing round-collared dress (olive and black); 6500m. Wearing hat with feathers (lilac and black); 6500m. Wearing white blouse with pointed collar, looking to left (brown and black)	1·80	1·90
MS1507	165×170 mm. 6500m. Wearing large white collar (lilac and black); 6500m. Wearing hat (lilac and black); 6500m. Wearing white (brown and black); 6500m. Wearing dress with narrow straps (brown and black); 6500m. Wearing patterned blouse (violet and black); 6500m. In profile, with bouquet of flowers (olive and black)	1·50	1·60

298 Joe Besser, Larry and Moe with Frying Pan

1999. Scenes from "The Three Stooges" (American TV comedy series). T **298** and similar horiz designs. Multicoloured.

MS1508	174×140 mm. 5000m. Type **298**; 5000m. Shemp wearing trilby; 5000m. Moe and Larry putting pan on Joe Besser's head; 5000m. Moe with pipe; 5000m. Larry and Moe pouring drinks on Curly's head; 5000m. Larry wearing straw hat; 5000m. Joe Besser and Larry pulling Moe's tooth; 5000m. Curly wearing mauve shirt; 5000m. Shemp, Larry and Moe behind green sofa	2·20	2·30
MS1509	Two sheets, each 140×89 mm. (a) 35000m. Larry wearing pink shirt. (b) 35000m. Larry holding shovel	3·50	3·75

299 AE-AC Blue Tiger, Germany

1999. Trains. Multicoloured.

1510	2000m. Type **299**	10	15
1511	2500m. DB 218 locomotive, Germany	15	20
1512	3000m. Mt. Pilatus incline railway car, Switzerland	1·20	1·30
1513	3500m. Berlin underground railway train, Germany	1·80	1·90

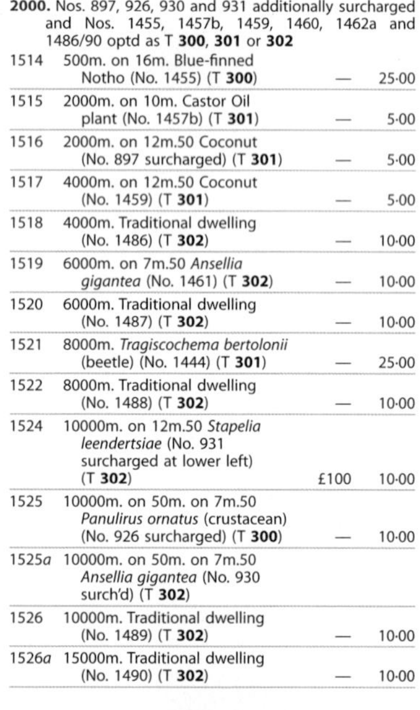

CORREIOS - 2000	2000	✱ 2000
(300)	**(301)**	**(302)**

2000. Nos. 897, 926, 930 and 931 additionally surcharged and Nos. 1455, 1457b, 1459, 1460, 1462a and 1486/90 optd as T **300**, **301** or **302**

1514	500m. on 16m. Blue-finned Notho (No. 1455) (T **300**)	—	25·00
1515	2000m. on 10m. Castor Oil plant (No. 1457b) (T **301**)	—	5·00
1516	2000m. on 12m.50 Coconut (No. 897 surcharged) (T **301**)	—	5·00
1517	4000m. on 12m.50 Coconut (No. 1459) (T **301**)	—	5·00
1518	4000m. Traditional dwelling (No. 1486) (T **302**)	—	10·00
1519	6000m. on 7m.50 *Ansellia gigantea* (No. 1461) (T **302**)	—	10·00
1520	6000m. Traditional dwelling (No. 1487) (T **302**)	—	10·00
1521	8000m. *Tragiscochema bertolonii* (beetle) (No. 1444) (T **301**)	—	25·00
1522	8000m. Traditional dwelling (No. 1488) (T **302**)	—	10·00
1524	10000m. on 12m.50 *Stapelia leendertsiae* (No. 931 surcharged at lower left) (T **302**)	£100	10·00
1525	10000m. on 50m. on 7m.50 *Panulirus ornatus* (crustacean) (No. 926 surcharged) (T **300**)	—	10·00
1525*a*	10000m. on 50m. on 7m.50 *Ansellia gigantea* (No. 930 surch'd) (T **302**)		
1526	10000m. Traditional dwelling (No. 1489) (T **302**)	—	10·00
1526*a*	15000m. Traditional dwelling (No. 1490) (T **302**)	—	10·00

303 *Palla usher*

2000. Butterflies of the World. Multicoloured.

1527	2000m. Type **303**	10	10
1528	2500m. *Euschemon rafflesia*	15	20
1529	3000m. *Buttus philenor*	20	25
1530	3000m. *Hypolimnas bolina*	20	25
1531	3500m. *Lycorea cleobaea*	20	25
1532	4000m. *Dynastor napoleon*	20	25
1533	4500m. *Callimorpha dominula*	25	30
1534	5000m. *Pereute leucodrosime*	25	30
MS1535	95×100 mm. 4500m. *Tisiphone abeone*; 4500m. *Pseudacraea boisduvali*; 4500m. *Mylothris chloris*; 4500m. *Papilio glaucus*; 4500m. *Mimacraea marshalli*; 4500m. *Gonepteryx Cleopatra*	1·20	1·30
MS1536	95×100 mm. 4500m. *Palla ussheri*; 4500m. *Hypolimnas salmacis*; 4500m. *Pereute leucodrosime*; 4500m. *Anteos clorinde*; 4500m. *Colias eurytheme*; 4500m. *Hebomoia glaucippe*	1·20	1·30
MS1537	95×100 mm. 4500m. *Thauria aliris*; 4500m. *Catocala ilia*; 4500m. *Colotis danae*; 4500m. *Agrias Claudia*; 4500m. *Euploe core*; 4500m. *Scoptes alphaeus* (all horiz)	1·20	1·30
MS1538	95×100 mm. 4500m. *Phoebis philea*; 4500m. *Anteos clorinde*; 4500m. *Arhopala amantes*; 4500m. *Mesene phareus*; 4500m. *Euploea mulciber*; 4500m. *Heliconius ricini* (all horiz)	1·20	1·30
MS1539	141×112 mm. 4500m. *Euphaedra neophorn*; 4500m. *Catopsilia florella*; 4500m. *Charaxes bohemani*; 4500m. *Junonia orithya*; 4500m. *Colotis danae*; 4500m. *Eurytela dryope*	1·20	1·30
MS1540	141×112 mm. 4500m. *Papilio demodocus*; 4500m. *Kallimoides rumia*; 4500m. *Danaus chrysippus*; 4500m. *Palla ussheri*; 4500m. *Hypolimnas salmacis*; 4500m. *Zinina otis*	1·20	1·30

MS1541 Six sheets. (a) 85×110 mm. 20000m. *Papilio glaucus*. (b) 85×110 mm. 20000m. *Delias mysis* (horiz). (c) 85×110 mm. 20000m. *Mylothris cloris* (horiz). (d) 20000m. *Loxura atymnus* (horiz). (e) 70×100 mm. 20000m. *Hemiolaus coeculus* (horiz). (f) 73×103 mm. 20000m. *Euxanthe wakefieldii* (horiz). Set of 6 sheets 6·00 6·25

304 Male and Female Blue Wildebeest

2000. Endangered Species. Blue Wildebeest. Multicoloured.

1542	6500m. Type **304**	30	35
1543	6500m. Female and calf	30	35
1544	6500m. Lion catching blue wildebeest	30	35
1545	6500m. Blue wildebeest	30	35

305 *Leptailerus several*

2000. Wild Cats of the World. Multicoloured.

MS1546 134×200 mm. 3000m. Type **305**; 3000m. *Panthera onca*; 3000m. *Panthera tigris corbetti*; 3000m. *Puma concolor*; 3000m. *Panthera leo persica*; 3000m. *Felis pardina*; 3000m. *Lepardus pardalia*; 3000m. *Acinonyx jubatus*; 3000m. *Felis wrangeli* 1·30 1·40

MS1547 134×200 mm. 3000m. *Felis silvestris grampia*; 3000m. *Felis ourata*; 3000m. *Panthera tigris tigris*; 3000m. *Panthera uncial*; 3000m. *Felis caracal*; 3000m. *Panthera pardus*; 3000m. *Panthera tigris amoyensis*; 3000m. *Panthera once*; 3000m. *Neofelis nabuluso* 1·30 1·40

MS1548 Two sheets. (a) 25000m.85×110 mm. *Panthera tigris altaica*. (b) 110×85 mm. 25000m. *Panthera tigris* (horiz). Set of 2 sheets 2·50 2·60

306 *Laetiocottleya*

2000. Exotic Flowers. Multicoloured.

MS1549 137×105 mm. 3000m. Type **306**; 3000m. *Papaver orientale* and *Nomada* (wasp); 3000m. *Anemone blanda*; 3000m. *Ipoema alba* and hawkmoth; 3000m. *Phalaenopsis luma* and *Delta unguiculata* (wasp); 3000m. *Iris ensata* and Colorado beetle; 3000m. *Bomarea caldasil* and *Coenagrion puella* (dragonfly); 3000m. Rosa "Raubritter" and *Bombus hortorum* (bumble bee); 3000m. Iris x daylily hybrid and fly 1·20 1·30

MS1550 137×105 mm. 3000m. *Lilium auratum* and *Tragocephala variegate* (beetle); 3000m. *Oncidim macianthum* and beetle; 3000m. *Dendrobium* and *Agelia petali* (beetle); 3000m. *Cobaea scandens*; 3000m. *Paphiopedium gilda* and *Cotalpa linegera scarabaedae*; 3000m. *Papaver nudicaule* and *Delta unduiculate* (wasp); 3000m. *Colocasia esculenta*; 3000m. *Carinatum tricolor* and butterfly; 3000m. *Phalaenopsis* and locust 1·20 1·30

MS1551 125×103 mm. 3500m. *Euanthe sanderiana* and *Teiraatenia surinama* (grasshopper); 3500m. *Torenia fourleri*; 3500m. Pansies and *Papilio polyxenes* caterpillar; 3500m. *Gladiolus* "Preludio"; 3500m. *Dendrobium primulinum* and beetle; 3500m. *Clematis* "Lasurstern" and carrion beetle; 3500m. *Helianthus annuus* and beetle; 3500m. *Jacinto Grana* (all vert) 1·60 1·70

MS1552 Four sheets, each 100×70 mm. (a) 20000m. *Violaxwittrockiana* (pansies). (b) 20000m. *Nelimbo nucifera*. (c) 20000m. *Gerbera jamesoni*. (d) 20000m. Daffodils and anemones. Set of 4 sheets 4·00 4·25

Nos. 1553 to 1561 are vacant.

311 Cycling

2000. Sports and Chess. Multicoloured.

MS1562 140×115 mm. 6500m. Type **311**; 6500m. Volleyball; 6500m. Boxing; 6500m. Weightlifting; 6500m. Fencing; 6500m. Judo 1·80 1·90

MS1563 140×115 mm. 9000m. Six chess pieces, including red queen and elephant carrying palanquin; 9000m. Six pieces, including ivory bishop and grey bishop; 9000m. Five knights; 9000m. Six rooks, including red elephant and sailing ship; 9000m. Six pawns; 9000m. Six pawns, including soldiers, flute player and spearholder 2·75 2·75

MS1564 140×115 mm. 9500m. Paul Morphy; 9500m. Mikhail Botvinnik; 9500m. Emanuel Lasker; 9500m. Wilhelm Steinitz; 9500m. Jose Raul Capablanca; 9500m. Howard Staunton 2·75 2·75

MS1565 140×115 mm. 12500m. Cricket (batsmen and bowler); 12500m. Cricket (four batsmen and fielder); 12500m. Polo players on horseback and elephant polo; 12500m. Four galloping polo players; 12500m. Golf (two men); 12500m. Man and woman playing golf 3·50 3·75

MS1566 140×115 mm. 14000m. Two tennis players (woman with headband serving at right); 14000m. Table tennis (two men); 14000m. Table tennis (man with pink shirt and woman); 14000m. Three tennis players (two men at left); 14000m. Tennis players (man with cap at left); 14000m. Table tennis (man with red shirt and woman) 3·50 3·75

MS1567 Two sheets, each 110×87 mm. (a) 35000m. Garry Kasparov (chess champion) (50×35 mm). (b) 35000m. Table tennis (50×35 mm). Set of 2 sheets 3·75 4·00

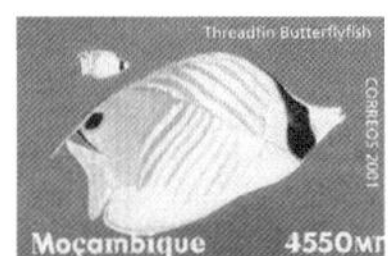

312 Threadfin Butterflyfish

2001. Marine Life. Multicoloured.

MS1568 162×177 mm. 4550m. Type **312**; 4550m. Common clownfish; 4550m. Regal tang; 4550m. Regal angelfish; 4550m. Copperbanded butterflyfish; 4550m. Blue-girdled angelfish; 4550m. Sharpnosed pufferfish; 4550m. Humbug damselfish; 4550m. Tailbar lionfish; 4550m. Forcepsfish; 4550m. Powder blue surgeonfish; 4550m. Moorish idol 2·00 2·10

MS1569 155×117 mm. 9500m. Oceanic whitetip shark; 9500m. Grey reef shark; 9500m. Tiger shark; 9500m. Silky shark; 9500m. Basking shark; 9500m. Epaulette shark 2·75 3·00

MS1570 117×131 mm. 9500m. Sperm whale; 9500m. Giant squid; 9500m. Killer whale; 9500m. Great hite shark; 9500m. Manta ray; 9500m. Octopus 2·75 3·00

MS1571 117×131 mm. 9500m. Blue whale; 9500m. Dolphinfish; 9500m. Hammerhead shark; 9500m. Whale shark; 9500m. Leatherback turtle; 9500m. Porkfish 2·75 3·00

MS1572 Five sheets, each 85×57 mm. (a) 35000m. Wimple fish. (b) 35000m. Queen angelfish. (c) 35000m. *Phryniehthys wedli*. (d) 35000m. Bull shark. (e) 35000m. Spotted trunkfish. Set of 5 sheets 9·00 9·25

313 Luis Figo

2001. European Football Championship, Belgium and The Netherlands (2000). Multicoloured.

MS1573 131×99 mm. 10000m. Type **313**; 10000m. Fernando Couto; 10000m. Luis Figo diving at ball; 10000m. Sergio Conceicao; 10000m. Nuno Gomes; 10000m. Rui Costa 3·00 3·25

MS1574 131×99 mm. 17000m. Nicolas Anelka; 17000m. Didier Deschamps; 17000m. Emmanuel Petit; 17000m. Thierry Henry; 17000m. Marcel Desailly; 17000m. Zinedine Zidane 5·25 5·50

314 Domenico Fivaranti (swimming)

2001. Olympic Games, Sydney (2000). Multicoloured.

MS1575 131×135 mm. 8500m. Type **314**; 8500m. Stacy Dragila (pole vault); 8500m. Pieter van den Hoogenband (swimming); 8500m. David O'Connor (three day eventing); 8500m. Venus Williams (tennis); 8500m. Maurice Greene (athletics); 8500m. Joy Fawcett (football); 8500m. Marion Jones (athletics); 8500m. Patricio Ormazabal and Jeff Agoos (football) 3·75 4·00

MS1576 131×135 mm. 10000m. Agnes Kovacs (swimming); 10000m. Youlia Rasksina (gymnastics); 10000m. Kong Linghui and Lui Guoliang (table tennis); 10000m. Nicolas Gill; 10000m. Anky van Grunsven (dressage); 10000m. Brian Olsen; 10000m. Wang Nan (table tennis); 10000m. Megan Quann (swimming); 10000m. Venus Williams (tennis) 6·25 6·50

MS1577 131×99 mm. 17000m. Vince Carter (basketball); 17000m. Blaine Wilson (gymnastics); 17000m. Steve Keir (handball); 17000m. Wen Xiao Wang and Chris Xu (table tennis); 17000m. Venus and Serena Williams (tennis); 17000m. Gu Jun and Ge Fei (table tennis) 5·25 5·50

MS1578 131×99 mm. 20000m. Clara Hughes (cycling); 20000m. Martina Hingis (tennis); 20000m. Otilla Badescu (table tennis); 20000m. Isabel Fernandez (judo); 20000m. Coralie Simmons (water polo). 20000m. Mia Hamm (football) 6·00 6·25

MS1579 131×99 mm. 28000m. Patrick Rafter (tennis); 28000m. Tadahiro Nomura (judo); 28000m. Seiko Iseki (table tennis); 28000m. Michael Dodge (cycling); 28000m. Ann Dow (water polo); 28000m. David Beckham (football) 8·25 8·50

MS1580 Six sheets, each 95×98 mm. (a) 50000m. Andre Agassi (tennis). (b) 50000m.Chang Jun Gao and Michelle Do (table tennis). (c) 50000m. Kong Linghui (table tennis). (d) 50000m. Michelle Do (table tennis); (e) 100000m. Michelle Do. (f) 100000m. Serena Williams (tennis). (g) 100000m. Christophe Legout and Damien Eldi (table tennis). Set of 6 sheets 12·00 12·50

315 Mikhail Botvinnik

2001. Chess Players. Multicoloured.

MS1581 131×135 mm. 10000m. Type **315**; 10000m. Garry Kasparov; 10000m. Wilhelm Steinitz; 10000m. Emanuel Lasker; 10000m. Paul Morphy; 10000m. Anatoly Karpov; 10000m. Tigran Petrossian; 10000m. Mikhail Tal; 10000m. Jose Raul Capablanca 4·00 4·25

MS1582 131×135 mm. 10000m. Judith Polgar (wearing maroon jumper); 10000m. Xie Jun; 10000m. Zsuza Polgar; 10000m. Nana Ioseliani; 10000m. Alisa Galliamova; 10000m. Judith Polgar (with head in hands); 10000m. Judith Polgar (wearing blouse); 10000m. Monica Calzetta; 10000m. Anjelina Belakovskaia 4·00 4·25

MS1583 Two sheets, each 96×100 mm. (a) 100000m. Garry Kasparov. (b) 100000m. Judith Polgar 5·00 5·25

316 Martin Brodeur (ice hockey goalkeeper)

2001. Winter Olympic Games, Salt Lake City (2002) (1st issue). Multicoloured.

MS1584 131×99 mm. 17000m. Type **316**; 17000m. Svetlana Vysokova (speed skating); 17000m. Ray Bourque and Patrik Elias (ice hockey); 17000m. Rachel Belliveau (cross-country skiing); 17000m. Scott Gomez and Janne Laukkanen (ice hockey); 17000m. Sonja Nef (skiing) 5·00 5·25

MS1585 131×99 mm. 20000m. Rusty Smith (speed skating); 20000m. Sandra Schmirler (curling); Totmianina and Marinin (ice skating); 20000m. Brigitte Obermoser (skiing); 20000m. Roman Turek (ice hockey); 20000m. Jennifer Heil (skiing) 5·00 5·25

MS1586 131×99 mm. 28000m. Kovarikova and Novotny (skating); 28000m. Li Song (speed skating); 28000m. Armin Zoeggeler (bobsleigh); 28000m. Michael von Gruenigen (skiing); 28000m. Tami Bradley (skiing); 28000m. Chris Drury, Turner Stevenson and Greg de Vries (ice hockey) 8·00 8·25

MS1587 Three sheets, each 95×98 mm. (a) 50000m. Armin Zoggeler (toboggan). (b) 75000m. Tommy Salo. (c) 100000m. Jayne Torvill and Christopher Dean (ice dancing) Set of 3 sheets 10·00 10·50

See also 1588/9.

317 Skier

2002. Winter Olympic Games, Salt Lake City, U.S.A. (2nd issue). Multicoloured.

1588	10000m. Type **317**	50	55
1589	17000m. Skier upside down (vert)	85	90

318 Dhow

2002. Ships. Multicoloured.

MS1590 147×105 mm. 13500m. Type **318**; 13500m. Junk; 13500m. Galleon; 13500m. Schooner; 13500m. Full-rigged ship; 13500m. Barque 4·00 4·25

MS1591 147×105 mm. 13500m. Viking Longboat; 13500m. Canoe; 13500m. Gondola; 13500m. Fishing boat; 13500m. Light boat; 13500m. Tug 4·00 4·25

MS1592 Two sheets. (a) 79×60 mm. 40000m. Aircraft carrier; (b) 60×80 mm. 40000m. Figurehead (vert). Set of 2 sheets 4·00 4·25

319 Princess Diana

2002. Diana, Princess of Wales Commemoration (3rd issue). Multicoloured.

MS1593 Three sheets each 132×135 mm. (a) 28000m. Type **319**; 28000m. Wearing feathered hat; 28000m. Wearing pearl necklace; 28000m. Wearing wide brimmed hat. (b) 28000m. Wearing blue top; 28000m. Wearing white top; 28000m. Looking right; 28000m. Holding bouquet. (c) 28000m. Wearing pink outfit; 28000m. Wearing black with drop earrings; 28000m. Looking straight ahead; 28000m. Wearing black and white outfit. Set of 3 sheets 12·00 12·50

MS1594 Three sheets each 81×112 mm. (a) 50000m. Wearing hat and wrap. (b) 50000m. With hand on chin; (c) 50000m. Wearing large stud earrings. Set of 3 sheets 7·50 8·00

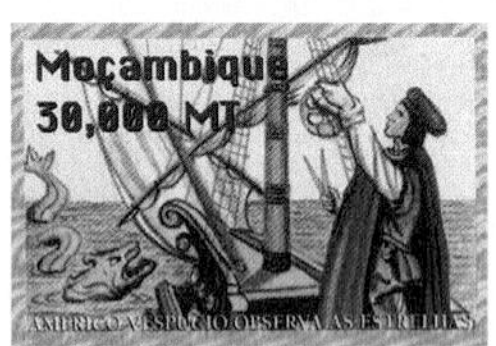

320 Americo Vespucio

2002. 500th Anniv (2001) of Amerigo Vespucci's Third Voyage. Multicoloured.
MS1595 157×117 mm. 30000m. Type **320**; 30000m. Green parrot; 30000m. Homes on stilts and ship 4·50 4·75
MS1596 55×76 mm. 50000m. Outline of Brazil and ship's course 2·50 2·75

321 England World Cup Poster

2002. World Cup Football Championship, Japan and South Korea. Multicoloured.
MS1597 Two sheets each 153×175 mm. (a) 28000m. Type **321**; 28000m. Italian player; 28000m. Danish player (red strip); 28000m. Colombian player; 28000m. Munhak stadium (55×41 mm). (b) 28000m. Brazilian player; 28000m. Swedish poster; 28000m. Nigerian player; 28000m. Danish player (white strip); 28000m. Gwangju stadium (55×41 mm). Set of 2 sheets 12·00 12·50
MS1598 Two sheets. (a) 53×73 mm. 50000m. Pele (Brazilian player). (b) 73×53 mm. 50000m. Max Morlock (German player). Set of 2 sheets 5·00 5·25

322 Horse

2002. Chinese New Year ("Year of the Horse"). Multicoloured.
MS1599 68×58 mm. 11000m. Type **322**; 11000m. Purple and red horse; 11000m. Purple horse; 11000m. Orange and red horse 2·20 2·30
MS1600 100×70 mm. 11000m. Horse cantering (27×41 mm) 55 60

323 Mount Binga, Mozambique

2002. International Year of Mountains. Multicoloured.
1601 17000m. Type **323** 85 90
1602 17000m. Mount Namuli, Mozambique 85 90
MS1603 160×98 mm. 17000m. Mount Kenya, Kenya; 17000m. Mount Cook, New Zealand; 17000m. Mount Ararat, Turkey; 17000m. Mount Paine, Chile; 17000m. Mount Everest, Nepal; 17000m. Mount Kilimanjaro, Tanzania 5·00 5·25
MS1604 72×51 mm. 50000m. Mount Zugspitze, Germany 2·50 3·00

324 *Papilio demoleus*

2002. Butterflies. Multicoloured.
1605 5000m. Type **324** 25 30
1606 10000m. *Euschemon rafflesia* 50 55
1607 17000m. *Liphyra brassolis* 85 90
1608 28000m. *Mimacraea marshalli* 1·40 1·50

MS1609 Two sheets each 112×155 mm. (a) 10000m. *Parides coon*; 10000m. *Delias mysis*; 10000m. *Troides brookiana*; 10000m. *Syrmatia dorilas*; 10000m. *Danis danis*; 10000m. *Lycaena dispar*; 10000m. *Mesene phareus*; 10000m. *Kallima inachus*; 10000m. *Morpho rhetenor*. (b) 10000m. *Eurema brigitta*; 10000m. *Loxura atymunus*; 10000m. *Arhopala amantes*; 10000m. *Junonia coenia*; 10000m. *Eurides isabella*; 10000m. *Heliconius ricini*; 10000m. *Zipaetis xcylax* (scylax); 10000m. *Cepheuptychia cephus*; 10000m. *Philaethria dido*. Set of 2 sheets 9·00 9·25
MS1610 Two sheets each 106×81 mm. (a) 50000m. *Papilio cresphontes*. (b) 50000m. *Ornithoptera alexandrae*. Set of 2 sheets 5·00 5·25

325 *Hemerocallis*

2002. Flowers. Multicoloured.
MS1611 Three sheets. (a) 150×117 mm. 10000m. Type **325**; 10000m. *Nazcissys* (Narcissus); 10000m. Hybrid tea; 10000m. Cayenne capers; 10000m. *Araceae*; 10000m. *Hymenocallis narcissiflora*; 10000m. *Hymenocallis*; 10000m. *Tulipa*; 10000m. *Lachenalia aloides* and *meconopsis poppies*. (b) 150×117 mm. 10000m. Narcissus; 10000m. L. *Bulbiferum var croceum*; 10000m. *Iris purpureobractea* and butterfly; 10000m. *Neomarica caerulea*; 10000m. *Peonia lactiflora, Primula chungensis* and *Viola cornuta*; 10000m. *Cayenne caper* and beetle; 10000m. *Iris purpureobractea*; 10000m. *Tuberous begonia cultivar*; 10000m. Oriental hybrid lily. (c) 108×160 mm. 10000m. *Viola jeannie*; 10000m. Sunflower; 10000m. *Momo botan*; 10000m. *Scho,buzgkia* orchid; 10000m. Dahlia hybrid; 10000m. *Sparaxis elegans harlequin*; 10000m. Dianthus; 10000m. *Tulipa saxatilis* and *camassia leichtlinii*; 10000m. Hybrid ("Hibrid"). Set of 3 sheets 13·00 13·50

326 *Tachymarptis melba*

2002. Birds. Multicoloured.
1612 5000m. Type **326** 25 30
1613 5000m. *Falco tinnunculus* 25 30
1614 10000m. *Ardea cinerea* 50 55
1615 10000m. *Pitta angolensis* 50 55
1616 17000m. *Corythaeola cristata* 85 90
1617 28000m. *Butastur rufipennis* 1·40 1·50
MS1618 Two sheets each 116×116 mm. (a) 17000m. *Coracias garrulous*; 17000m. *Estrilda astrild*; 17000m. *Upupa epops*; 17000m. *Merops apiaster*; 17000m. *Ploceus Cucullatus*; 17000m. *Clamator glandarius*. (b) 17000m. *Psittacus erithacus*; 17000m. *Ficedula hypoleuca*; 17000m. *Tchagra senegala*; 17000m. *Oriolus oriolus*; 17000m. *Luscinia megarhynchos*; 17000m. *Halcyon malimbica*. Set of 12 sheets 10·00 10·50
MS1619 Four sheets. (a) 83×108 mm. 50000m. *Sitrix varia*. (b) 83×108 mm. 50000m. *Falco subbuteo*. (c) 83×108 mm. 50000m. *Butorides striatus*. (d) 108×83 mm 50000m. *Actophilornis Africana* (*africanus*) (horiz). Set of 4 sheets 10·00 10·50

The stamps in No. **MS**1618a/b were printed together, *se-tenant*, with the backgrounds forming composite designs.

327 *Creagrus furcatus*

2002. Sea Birds. Multicoloured.
1620 5000m. Type **327** 25 30
1621 10000m. *Larosterna inca* 50 55
1622 17000m. *Pelecanus crispus* 85 90
1623 28000m. *Morus bassanus* 1·20 1·50

MS1624 110×162 mm. 10000m. *Phaethon aethereus*; 10000m. *Catharacta Maccormicki*; 10000m. *Diomedea bulleri*; 10000m. *Puffinus iherminieri*; 10000m. *Oceanities oceanicus*; 10000m. *Pterodroma hasitata*; 10000m. *Fregata magnificens*; 10000m. *Sula nebouxii*; 10000m. *Uria aagle* 4·50 4·75
MS1625 Two sheets. (a) 98×68 mm. 50000m. *Spheniscus demersus*. (b) 97×68 mm. 50000m. *Rynchops niger* (horiz). Set of 2 sheets 5·00 5·25

The stamps in No. **MS**1624 were printed together, *se-tenant*, with the background forming a composite design.

328 Maine Coon Cat

2002. Cats. Multicoloured.
MS1626 118×91 mm. 17000m. Type **328**; 17000m. Cornish Rex; 17000m. La Perm (Red Tabby); 17000m. Sphynx; 17000m. Siamese; 17000m. Persian 4·25 4·25
MS1627 66×96 mm. 50000m. Chestnut (Oriental Longhair) 2·50 2·75

2002. Dogs. As T **328**. Multicoloured.
MS1628 118×91 mm. 17000m. Labrador; 17000m. Bulldog; 17000m. Cocker spaniel; 17000m. Golden retriever; 17000m. Boxer; 17000m. Bloodhound 5·00 5·25
MS1629 66×96 mm. 40000m. Basset hound 2·00 2·10

2002. Horses. As T **328**. Multicoloured.
MS1630 118×91 mm. 17000m. Hanoverian; 17000m. Haflinger; 17000m. Nonius; 17000m. Belgian Heavy Draughts; 17000m. Australian-bred Arab; 17000m. Thoroughbred 5·00 5·25
MS1631 96×66 mm. 50000m. Two Don horses 2·50 2·75

329 Protosaurus

2002. Prehistoric Animals. Multicoloured.
1632 5000m. Type **329** 25 30
1633 10000m. Psittacosaurus 50 55
1634 17000m. Torosaurus 85 90
1635 28000m. Triceratops 1·40 1·50
MS1636 Two sheets each 180×135 mm. (a) 10000m. Diplodocus; 10000m. Pterosaurs; 10000m. Young diplodocus; 10000m. Afrovenator; 10000m. Parasarolophus; 10000m. Ramphorincus; 10000m. Lambeosaur; 10000m. Euoplocephalus; 10000m. Cynodont. (b) 10000m. Brachiosaur; 10000m. Monoclonius; 10000m. Homalocephale; 10000m. Pterodactyl; 10000m. Deinonychus; 10000m. Archaeopteryx; 10000m. Cretaceous landscape; 10000m. Hypsilophodon; 10000m. Lystrosaur. Set of 2 sheets 9·00 9·25
MS1637 Two sheets. (a) 100×68 mm. 50000m. Baryonyx. (b) 100×70 mm. 50000m. Styracosaurus (vert). Set of 2 sheets 5·00 5·25

The stamps in No. **MS**1636a/b were each printed together, *se-tenant*, plus labels, with the backgrounds forming composite designs.

330 *Heraclides cresphontes*

2002. Woodland Fauna and Flora. Multicoloured.
MS1638 Two sheets each 153×115 mm. (a) 10000m. Type **330**; 10000m. *Tyto alba*; 10000m. *Drocopus pileatus*; 10000m. *Archilochus colobris* (colubris) (Ruby-throated Hummingbird) and *Cypripedium parviflorum*; 10000m. *Vulpes vulpes*; 10000m. *Odocoileus virginianus*; 10000m. *Enallagma* sp.; 10000m. *Amanita muscaria*; 10000m. *Tamiasciurus hudsonicus*. (b) 10000m. *Pandion haliaetus*; 10000m. Flying squirrel; 10000m. Fox squirrel; 10000m. *Agelaius phoeniceus*; 10000m. *Papilio polyxenes*; 10000m. *Didelphus viginiana*; 10000m. *Hyla crucifer*; 10000m. Two *Odocoileus virginianus*; 10000m. *Procyon lotor* Set of 2 sheets 9·00 9·25

The stamps in No. **MS**1638a/b were each printed together, *se-tenant*, with the backgrounds forming composite designs.

331 Scout Badge

2002. World Scout Congress. T **331** and similar multicoloured designs.
MS1639 109×99 mm. 28000m. Type **331**; 28000m. 19th Jamboree badge; 28000m. Tiger mascot; 28000m. 20th Jamboree logo 5·50 5·75
MS1640 111×82 mm. 28000m. Scout (vert) 1·40 1·50

332 African Elephant

2002. Endangered Animals. African Elephant. Multicoloured.
1641 1900m. Type **332** 10 10
1642 1900m. Elephants at waterhole 10 10
1643 1900m. Elephant in swamp 10 10
1644 1900m. Elephant with calf 10 10
MS1645 145×170 mm. Nos. 1641/4 plus four stamp-sized labels, each picturing Prince Bernhard or elephants 45 45

333 Lord Baden-Powell

2002. World Scout Jamboree (2003). T **333** and similar vert designs showing Lord Baden Powell and plants or butterflies. Multicoloured.
MS1646 Two sheets each 133×101 mm. (a) 17000m. Type **333**; 17000m. *Morpho Aega*; 17000m. *Prepona meander*; 17000m. *Charaxes bernardus*; 17000m. *Hypolimnas salmacis*; 17000m. *Morpho rhetenor*. (b) 17000m. Four mushrooms; 17000m. Two pink and white flowers; 17000m. Three orange mushrooms; 17000m. Five purple and red flowers; 17000m. Three brownish white mushrooms; 17000m. Two striped-petal flowers 10·00 10·50
MS1647 98×100 mm. 88000m. Lord Baden Powell with arms crossed 4·25 4·50

2002. Aviation. Sheet 96×100 mm containing vert designs as T **333**. Multicoloured.
MS1648 22000m. Antoine de Saint-Exupery; 22000m. Charles Lindberg and *Spirit of St. Louis*; 22000m. Charles Lindberg and light aircraft; 22000m. Concorde 2·30 2·40

2002. Cinematic Personalities. Sheet 97×101 mm containing vert designs as T **333**. Multicoloured.
MS1649 25000m. Charlie Chaplin; 25000m. Frank Sinatra; 25000m. Alfred Hitchcock; 25000m. Walt Disney 2·50 2·60

2002. John Audubon (ornithologist) Commemoration. Vert designs as T **333**. Multicoloured.
MS1650 97×101 mm. 33000m. John Audubon; 33000m. *Aix sponsa*; 33000m. *Toxostoma rufum* ("Toxastoma montanum") and *Ixoreus naevius*; 33000m. *Loxia Leucoptera* 3·25 3·50
MS1651 Two sheets each 97×101 mm. (a) 11000m. *Quiscalus quiscula*. (b) 11000m. *Columba leucocephala* ("Patagioenas leucocephala"). Set of 2 sheets 60 65

2002. 40th Death Anniv of Marilyn Monroe. Vert designs as T **333**.

MS1652 Two sheets each 133×101 mm. (a) 17000m. Looking at camera; 17000m.Wearing drop earrings; 17000m. Laughing; 17000m. Wearing choker; 17000m. Looking over shoulder; 17000m. Looking surprised. (b) 17000m. Wearing sleeveless top; 17000m. Looking over shoulder (different); 17000m. Beckoning with finger; 17000m. Wearing fur stole and drop earrings; 17000m. With arms folded; 17000m. Smiling with long hair. Set of 2 sheets 10·00 10·50

MS1653 Two sheets each 97×100 mm. (a) 88000m. Wearing crochet top. (b) 88000m. Wearing red top with pearls. Set of 2 sheets 4·50 4·75

2002. Visits of Pope John Paul II. Vert designs as T **333**. Multicoloured.

MS1654 133×100 mm. 15000m. Pope John Paul II waving; 15000m. Wearing red robe; 15000m. Carrying Pastoral staff; 15000m. Wearing mitre; 15000m. Sitting in chair; 15000m. Looking left 4·75 5·00

MS1655 97×100 mm. 20000m. Princess Diana wearing poppy; 20000m. Princess Diana carrying bouquet; 20000m. The Pope looking down; 20000m. The Pope looking up 4·00 4·25

MS1656 Two sheets each 97×100 mm. (a) 88000m. Pope John Paul II. (b) 110000m. Mother Teresa. Set of 2 sheets 5·00 5·25

2002. Egyptian Pharaohs. Vert designs as T **333**. Multicoloured.

MS1657 Two sheets each 133×100 mm. (a) 15000m. Seti I; 15000m. Djedefre; 15000m. Smenkhkare; 15000m. Seti II; 15000m. Senusret III; 15000m. Tutankhamun. (b) 17000m. Netjenkhet Djoser; 17000m. Death mask of Tutankhamun (front); 17000m. Neferefre; 17000m. Amenhotep III; 17000m. Pepi I; 17000m. Amenmesses. Set of 2 sheets 7·25 7·50

MS1658 Three sheets each 98×100 mm. (a) 20000m. Amenhotep II; 20000m. Merenptah; 20000m. Amenophis IV; 20000m. Tuthmosis (stone). (b) 20000m. Nefertiti (profile); 20000m. Cleopatra VII; 20000m. Nefertari (facing left); 20000m. Nefertiti (front). (c) 20000m. Nefertari (facing right); 20000m. Death mask of Tutankhamun (from angle); 20000m. Tuthmosis (black and gold); Nefertiti (from angle). Set of 3 sheets 11·00 11·50

MS1659 Two sheets each 97×101 mm. (a) 110000m. Nefertiti. (b) 110000m. Tutankhamun. Set of 3 sheets 1·00 1·50

2002. Nobel Prize Winners. Vert designs as T **333**. Multicoloured.

MS1660 Two sheets each 133×100 mm. (a) 15000m. Henri ("Hemri") Dunant; 15000m. Theodore Roosevelt; 15000m. Albert Einstein; 15000m. Ernest Hemingway; 15000m. Thomas Nast; 15000m. Albert Camus. (b) 17000m. Albert Einstein with hands clasped; 17000m. Dalai Lama; 17000m. Winston Churchill; 17000m. Hideki Yukawa; 17000m. Albert Schweitzer; 17000m. Linus Pauling 8·25 8·25

Although included in the set, Thomas Nast was not the recipient of a Nobel Prize.

2002. Robert Stephenson Commemoration. Vert designs as T **333**. Multicoloured.

MS1661 97×100 mm. 25000m. Robert Stephenson (black); 25000m. Early US steam locomotive; 25000m. Great Western Railway steam locomotive; 25000m. Early steam locomotive 5·00 5·50

MS1662 Two sheets each 97×101 mm. (a) 110000m. Robert Stephenson (sepia). (b) 110000m. Robert Stephenson (green). Set of 2 stamps 2·75 2·50

2002. Explorers. Vert designs as T **333**. Multicoloured.

MS1663 97×101 mm. 22000m. Vasco de Gama; 22000m. Ferdinand Magellan; 22000m. Christopher Columbus; 22000m. Amerigo Vespucci 1·10 1·20

MS1664 97×101 mm. 110000m. Vasco de Gama 5·50 5·75

2002. Charles Darwin and Alexander Fleming Commemorations. Sheet 97×100 mm containing vert designs as T **333**. Multicoloured.

MS1665 33000m. Charles Darwin and Byronosaurus; 33000m. Alexander Fleming and *Tricholoma terreum*; 33000m. Alexander Fleming and *Boletus edulis*; 33000m. Charles Darwin and Irratator 6·00 6·25

2002. Composers. Vert designs as T **333**. Multicoloured.

MS1666 97×101 mm. 5000m. Antonio Vivaldi; 5000m. Franz Liszt; 5000m. Ludwig van Beethoven; 5000m. Wolfgang Mozart 1·00 1·00

MS1667 97×101 mm. 88000m. Wolfgang Mozart at piano 2·20 2·30

2002. 25th Death Anniv of Elvis Presley (entertainer). Vert designs as T **333**. Multicoloured.

MS1668 133×101 mm. 15000m. Wearing jacket and tie; 15000m. Looking down in cable-knit sweater; 15000m. Wearing white shirt; 15000m. Wearing square checked shirt; 15000m. Reclining in cable-knit sweater; 15000m. Wearing hat 4·50 4·75

MS1669 97×100 mm. 110000m. Wearing blue jacket 5·50 5·75

2002. Personalities. Vert designs as T **333**. Multicoloured.

MS1670 Three sheets each 97×100 mm. (a) 20000m. Che Guevara; 20000m. Pope John Paul II; 20000m. Martin Luther King; 20000m. Mao Zedung. (b) 22000m. Dalai Lama; 22000m. Mother Teresa; 22000m. Pope John Paul II waving; 22000m. Mahatma Gandhi. (c) 33000m. Albert Schweitzer; 33000m. Claude Bernard; 33000m. Henri Dunant; 33000m. Raoul Follerau. Set of 3 sheets 10·00 10·50

2002. Formula 1 Motor Sport. Sheet 97×100 mm containing vert designs as T **333**. Multicoloured.

MS1671 20000m. Ayrton Senna; 20000m. Modern Formula 1 racing car; 20000m. Early Formula 1 racing car; 20000m. Juan Manuel Fangio 4·00 4·25

2002. Birth Centenary of Victor Hugo (author). Sheet 97×101 mm containing vert design as T **333**. Multicoloured.

MS1672 88000m. Victor Hugo 4·25 4·50

2002. John F. Kennedy (President. of U.S.A. 1961–3) Commemoration. Sheet 97×101 mm. Vert design as T **333**. Multicoloured.

MS1673 88000m. John F. Kennedy 4·25 4·50

2002. Political Leaders. Sheet 97×100 mm containing vert designs as T **333**. Multicoloured.

MS1674 25000m. Winston Churchill; 25000m. John F. Kennedy; 25000m. Konrad Adenauer; 25000m. Charles de Gaulle 5·00 5·25

2002. Haroun Tazieff (French vulcanologist and geologist) Commemoration. Sheet 97×100 mm containing vert designs as T **333**. Multicoloured.

MS1675 25000m. Scipionyx and erupting volcano; 25000m. Beipiaosaurus and erupting volcano; 25000m. Haroun Tazieff wearing radiation suit and vanadinite rock; 25000m. Haroun Tazieff and adamite rock 5·00 5·25

2002. Astronauts and Concorde. Vert designs as T **333**. Multicoloured.

MS1676 133×101 mm. 17000m. Michael Collins; 17000m. Concorde taking off to right; 17000m. John Glenn ("Genn"); 17000m. Concorde flying left; 17000m. Neil Armstrong; 17000m. Concorde taking off to left 4·75 5·00

MS1677 97×101 mm. 88000m. John Glenn 4·25 4·50

2002. 180th Birth Anniv of Louis Pasteur (French Chemist). Sheet 97×101 mm containing vert designs as T **333**, each showing Louis Pasteur with a different breed of dog. Multicoloured.

MS1678 25000m. Husky; 25000m. Weimaraner; 25000m. Wolfhound; 25000m. Springer spaniel 5·00 5·25

2002. Fifth Death Anniv of Diana, Princess of Wales. Vert designs as T **333**. Multicoloured.

MS1679 133×100 mm. 15000m. Diana and Pope John Paul II; 15000m. Wearing white halter-neck top; 15000m. Wearing red hat and spotted top; 15000m. Holding award; 15000m. Wearing deep purple dress; 15000m. Wearing blue dress and choker 4·75 5·00

MS1680 97×101 mm. 88000m. Wearing tiara 4·25 4·50

334 Ferdinand von Zeppelin

2002. Ferdinand von Zeppelin (inventor) Commemoration. Multicoloured.

MS1681 Two sheets each 173×120 mm. (a) 28000m. Type **334**; 28000m. LZ 2 airship (1905); 28000m. LZ 10 airship (1911); 28000m. LZ 1 airship (1900). (b) 28000m. LZ 1 airship over water; 28000m. LZ 2 airship over water; 28000m. LZ 10 airship over field of sheep; 28000m. Ferdinand von Zeppelin holding binoculars. Set of 2 sheets 10·00 10·50

MS1682 Two sheets. (a) 106×70 mm. 50000m. Ferdinand von Zeppelin wearing shirt and tie (vert). (b) 70×106 mm. 50000m. Ferdinand von Zeppelin wearing army uniform (vert). Set of 2 sheets 5·00 5·25

335 Mercedes (1906)

2002. Vintage Cars (1st series). Racing Cars. Multicoloured.

MS1683 Two sheets each 172×146 mm. (a) 13000m. Type **335**; 13000m. Morgan (1951); 13000m. Sunbeam (1912); 13000m. Sunbeam (1922); 13000m. Sunbeam Tiger (1925); 13000m. Austin 100 HP (1908). (b) 13000m. Bentley (1912); 13000m. Delage Grand Prix (1914); 13000m. Healey Silverstone (1949); 13000m. Duesenberg (1922); 13000m. Delage 1500cc Grand Prix; 13000m. Ferrari 375 F1 (1961). Set of 2 sheets 8·25 8·50

MS1684 Two sheets. (a) 100×70 mm. 40000m. Marmon Wasp (1911). (b) 70×100 mm. 40000m. Alfa Romeo (1931). Set of 2 sheets 8·00 8·25

336 Austin (1908)

2002. Vintage Cars (2nd series). Multicoloured.

MS1685 Two sheets each 165×102 mm. (a) 17000m. Type 336; 17000m. Studebaker Coupe (1937): 17000m. Type 40GP Bugatti (1930); 17000m. Ford Model A Roadster (1931); 17000m. Alfa Romeo 2900B (1937); 17000m. Cord 812 (1937). (b) 17000m. Type 57 Bugatti Alalanta Coupe (1937); 17000m. Tucker Torpedo (1948); 17000m. Honda S 800M (1966); 17000m. Cisitalia 202 GT (1946): 17000m. Chevy Impala (1958); 17000m. Cadillac LaSalle Convertible (1934). Set of 2 sheets 10·00 10·50

MS1686 Two sheets each 92×60 mm. (a) 50000m. Mercedes Benz SSK (1928). (b) 50000m. Plymouth Fury (1957) Set of 2 sheets 4·75 5·00

337 Western Railway of France

2002. Trains. Multicoloured.

MS1687 Three sheets each 161×114 mm. (a) 17000m. Type **337**; 17000m. Netherlands State Railway (bridge); 17000m. Great Indian Peninsula Railway; 17000m. Paris Orleans Railway; 17000m. Madras and Southern Mahratta Railway of India; 17000m. Netherlands State Railway. (b) 17000m. Great Southern Railway of Spain; 17000m. Shantung Railway of China; 17000m. Shanghai—Nanking Railway of China; 17000m. Austrian State Railway; 17000m. Victorian Government Railways of Australia; 17000m. London and Northwestern Railways. (c) 17000m. London, Midland and Scottish Railway; 17000m. Great Northern Railway of Ireland; 17000m. Southern Railway of England; 17000m. Great Northern Railway of USA; 17000m. Chicago, Milwaukee, St. Paul and Pacific Railroad; 17000m. London and Northeastern Railway. Set of 3 sheets 12·00 12·50

MS1688 Two sheets each 98×67 mm. (a) 50000m. New York Central Lines (vert). (b) 50000m. London, Brighton and South Coast Railway (vert). Set of 2 sheets 4·75 5·00

337a Pote

2002. Pottery. Multicoloured.

1688*a* 1000m. Pote

1688*b* 2000m. Chaleira

1688*c* 4000m. Tacas

1688*d* 5000m. Cantaro

1688*e* 17,000m. Panela

1688*f* 28,000m. Alguidar

1688*g* 50,000m. Jarra

1688*h* 1000,000m. Bihas

337b Justino Chemane

2003. Justino Chemane, composer of national anthem

1688*i* **337b** 6000m. multicoloured

337c Bauxite

2004. Minerals. Multicoloured.

1688*j* 5000m. Bauxite

1688*k* 14,000m. Marble

1688*l* 19,000m.

1688*m* 33,000m. Gold

338 *October* (James Jacques Tissot)

2004. Paintings. Multicoloured.

1689–1694 6500m.×6, Type **338**; *Seaside* (James Jacques Tissot); *The Bunch of Lilacs* (James Jacques Tissot); *The Traveller* (James Jacques Tissot); *Young Lady holding Japanese Objects* (James Jacques Tissot); *Young Lady in a Boat* (James Jacques Tissot) 1·80 1·90

1695–1700 6500m.×6, *Portrait of Madame de Senonnes* (Jean Auguste Ingres); *The Virgin of the Host* (Jean Auguste Ingres); *Portrait of Countess D'Haussonville* (Jean Auguste Ingres); *Paolo and Francesca* (Jean Auguste Ingres); *Portrait of Baroness James de Rothschild* (Jean Auguste Ingres); *Portrait of Madame Moitessier Sitting* (Jean Auguste Ingres) 1·80 1·90

1701–1706 10000m.×6, *The Promenade* (Pierre Auguste Renoir); *Alfred Sisley and His Wife* (Pierre Auguste Renoir); *Little Miss Romaine Lacaux* (Pierre Auguste Renoir); *In the Summer* (Pierre Auguste Renoir); *The Dancer* (Pierre Auguste Renoir); *Bouquet of Chrysanthemums* (Pierre Auguste Renoir) 3·00 3·25

1707–1712 17000m.×6, *Miss La La at the Circus Fernando* (Edgar Degas); *Portrait of Madame Dietz-Monnin* (Edgar Degas); *Woman Ironing* (Edgar Degas); *The Star* (Edgar Degas); *Cafe Concert Singer* (Edgar Degas); *The Dance Examination* (Edgar Degas) 3·00 3·25

MS1713 Three sheets, each 87×133 mm. (a) 6500m. As No. 1693. (b) 35000m. *Madame Monet in Japanese Costume* (Claude Monet). (c) 35000m. *Charlotte Dubourg* (Henri Fantin-Latour) 3·50 3·75

339 National Flags, Buildings, Panda and Giraffe

2005. 30th Anniv of Diplomatic Relations between Mozambique and Republic of China. Multicoloured.

1714 33,000m. Type **339**

1715 33,000m. Arms, Admiral Zheng He and building

340 Emblem and Transport

2005. 25th Anniv of Southern African Development Community

1716	**340**	8000m. multicoloured		

341 Trees

2005. Traditional African Medicine Day

1717	**341**	8000m. multicoloured		

342 Woman and Emblem

2005. World Summit on the Information Society, Tunis

1718	**342**	8000m. multicoloured		

3.000 Mt (**342a**) 6.000 mt (**342b**) 33.000 MT (**342c**) 33.000 MT (**342d**)

Nos. 1478, 1481/2, 1621/2 and 1688b surcharged with new values as T **342a/d**

1719	3000m. on 2000m. Mother Teresa (No. 1478) (T **342a**)		10·00
1720	6000m. on 2000m. Chaleira (pottery) (No. 1688b) (T **342b**)	20·00	10·00
1721	6000m. on 10000m. *Lariosterna inca* (No. 1621) (T **342b**)	20·00	10·00
1722	8000m. on 17000m. *Pelecanus crispus* (No. 1622) (T **342b**)	20·00	10·00
1723	33000m. on 7500m. *Tabernaemontana elegans* (No. 1481) (T **342c**)	20·00	10·00
1724	33000m. on 12500m. *Ximenia caffra* (No. 1482) (T **342c**)	25·00	10·00

On Nos. 1723a and 1724/a the original value is obliterated by a silver block in addition to a row of asterisks.

343 Telephone and Mast

2006. 25th Anniv of Mozambique Telecommunications Company (TDM)

1725	**343**	8000m. multicoloured		

344 Pres. Armando Guebuzza holding Gavel

2006. Presidential Initiative against AIDS. Multicoloured.

1726	8m. Type **344**		
1727	16m. Pres. Guebuza behind microphones		
1728	33m. With arm raised		

2006. Nos. 1621, 1688*j* and 1725 surch as T **344b** (No. 1729b) or **344a** (others)

1729	33000/33m. on 10000m. Larostera inca (No. 1621) (T **344a**)	20·00	10·00
1729*a*	33000/33m. on 5000m. Bauxite (No. 1688*j*) (T **344a**)	50·00	10·00
1729*b*	33000/33m. on 8000m. Telephone and mast (No. 1725) (T **344b**)	50·00	10·00

345 Dam and Reservoir

2007. Cahora Bassa Dam. Multicoloured.

1730	8m. Type **345**	50	50
1731	20m. Dignitaries shaking hands	1·25	1·25
1732	33m. Dam and flag of Mozambique	2·00	2·00

346 Building

2007. 50th Anniv of the Reign of the Aga Khan. Multicoloured.

MS1733	8m. Type **346**; 20m. People on beach; 20m. People under shelter; 33m. Polana Serena Hotel; 33m. Students in classroom (30×40 mm)	7·00	7·00

347 Emblems

2008. Centenary of Minerva Central Publishers (bookshop and publishing house), Maputo

1734	**347**	8m. multicoloured	50	50
1735	**347**	20m. multicoloured	1·25	1·25
1736	**347**	multicoloured	2·00	2·00

348 Emblem

2008. 40th Anniv of Second Frelimo Party Congress, Matchedje

1737	**348**	8m. multicoloured	50	50

349 Football

2008. Olympic Games, Beijing (1st issue). Multicoloured.

1738	8m. Type **349**	50	50
1739	8m. Basketball	50	50
1740	8m. Swimming	50	50
1741	8m. Athletics	50	50

8.00 MT
(**350**)

2008. Olympic Games, Beijing (2nd issue). Nos. 1738/41 surch as Type **350**

1742	8m. Type **349**	50	50
1743	8m. Basketball	50	50
1744	8m. Swimming	50	50
1745	8m. Athletics	50	50

351 Bolode milho (maize cake)

2008. Mozambique Gastronomy. Multicoloured.

1746	8m. Type **351**	50	50
1747	20m. Mathapa com carangueio (cassava with crab, coconut and peanuts)	1·25	1·25
1748	33m. Quiabo com camarao (okra with prawns and coconut)	2·00	2·00

352 Maria de Lurdes Mutola and Mozambique Flag

2009. Maria de Lurdes Mutola (800 metre gold medallist, 2000 Olympics)

1749	**352**	8m. multicoloured	50	50

353 Eduardo Mondlane

2009. Eduardo Chivambo Mondlane (President of Mozambique Liberation Front) Commemoration

1750	**353**	33m. multicoloured		

354 Roan Antelope

2010. Endangered Species. Roan Antelope (*Hippotragus equinus*). Multicoloured.

1751	33m. Type **354**	1·50	1·50
1752	33m. Adult and juvenile	1·50	1·50
1753	33m. Two antelopes at waterhole	1·50	1·50
1754	33m. Roan antelopes in savannah	1·50	1·50
MS1755	83×63 mm. 175m. Roan antelope grazing	8·50	8·50

355 Two Football Players

2010. World Cup Football, South Africa. Multicoloured.

MS1756	33m.×4 Type 355; Players wearing pink (left) and green (right) shirts; Players wearing pale mauve (left) and pale blue (right) shirts; Players wearing pink (left) shirt or white (right)	6·00	6·00

356 Emblem

2010. 30th Anniv of LAM (Linhas Aéreas de Mocambique)

1757	**356**	8m. multicoloured	40	40
1758		20m. multicoloured	90	90
1759		33m. multicoloured	1·50	1·50

357 Emblem

2010. 20th Anniv of AICEP

1760	**357**	33m. multicoloured	50	50

358 Anniversary Emblem

2011. 30th Anniv of TVM

1761	**358**	66m. multicoloured	30	30
1762		92m. multicoloured	50	50

CHARITY TAX STAMPS

The notes under this heading in Portugal also apply here.

C15 Arms of Portugal and Mozambique and Allegorical Figures

C16 Prow of Galley of Discoveries and Symbols of Declaration of War

1916. War Tax Fund. Imperf, roul or perf.

C234	**C15**	1c. green	95	50
C235	**C16**	5c. red	95	50

C18 "Charity"

1920. 280th Anniv of Restoration of Portugal. Wounded Soldiers and Social Assistance Funds.

C309	**C18**	¼c. green	1·60	1·60
C310	**C18**	½c. black	1·60	1·60
C311	**C18**	1c. brown	1·60	1·60
C312	**C18**	2c. brown	1·60	1·60
C313	**C18**	3c. lilac	1·70	1·70
C314	**C18**	4c. green	1·70	1·70
C315	-	5c. green	2·00	1·80
C316	-	6c. blue	2·00	1·80
C317	-	7½c. brown	2·00	1·80
C318	-	8c. yellow	2·00	1·80
C319	-	10c. lilac	2·00	1·80
C320	-	12c. pink	2·00	1·80
C321	-	18c. red	2·00	1·80
C322	-	24c. brown	2·75	2·10
C323	-	30c. green	2·75	2·10
C324	-	40c. red	2·75	2·10
C325	-	50c. yellow	2·75	2·10
C326	-	1e. blue	2·75	2·10

Designs:—5c. to 12c. Wounded soldier and nurse; 18c. to 1e. Family scene.

1925. Marquis de Pombal stamps of Portugal, but inscr "MOCAMBIQUE".

C327	**C73**	15c. brown	40	25
C328	-	15c. brown	40	30
C329	**C75**	15c. brown	40	25

1925. Red Cross. Surch **50 CENTAVOS**.

C330	**C22**	50c. yellow and grey	95	80

C22 Society's Emblem

1926. Surch **CORREIOS** and value.

C337	5c. yellow and red	1·30	1·20
C338	10c. yellow and green	1·30	1·20
C339	20c. yellow and grey	1·50	1·40
C340	30c. yellow and blue	1·50	1·40
C331	40c. yellow and grey	2·10	1·50
C341	40c. yellow and violet	1·50	1·40
C332	50c. yellow and grey	2·10	1·50
C342	50c. yellow and red	1·80	1·60
C333	60c. yellow and grey	2·10	1·50
C343	60c. yellow and brown	1·80	1·60
C334	80c. yellow and grey	2·10	1·50
C344	80c. yellow and blue	1·80	1·60
C335	1e. yellow and grey	2·10	1·50
C345	1e. yellow and green	1·80	1·60
C336	2e. yellow and grey	2·20	2·10
C346	2e. yellow and brown	2·20	2·00

C25

1928. Surch **CORREIOS** and value in black, as in Type **C25**.

C347	**C25**	5c. yellow and green	2·50	2·40
C348	**C25**	10c. yellow and blue	2·50	2·40
C349	**C25**	20c. yellow and black	2·50	2·40
C350	**C25**	30c. yellow and red	2·50	2·40
C351	**C25**	40c. yellow and purple	2·50	2·40
C352	**C25**	50c. yellow and red	2·50	2·40
C353	**C25**	60c. yellow and brown	2·50	2·40
C354	**C25**	80c. yellow and brown	2·50	2·40
C355	**C25**	1e. yellow and grey	2·50	2·40

C356	**C25**	2e. yellow and red	2·50	2·40

C27

1929. Value in black.

C357	**C27**	40c. purple and blue	2·75	2·50
C358	**C27**	40c. violet and red	2·75	2·50
C359	**C27**	40c. violet and green	2·75	2·50
C360	**C27**	40c. red and brown	2·75	2·50
C361	**C27**	(No value) red & green	2·75	2·50
C362	**C27**	40c. blue and orange	4·25	4·00
C363	**C27**	40c. blue and brown	2·75	2·50
C364	**C27**	40c. purple and green	2·75	2·50
C365	**C27**	40c. black and yellow	4·25	4·00
C366	**C27**	40c. black and brown	4·25	4·00

C28 "Charity"

1942

C383	**C28**	50c. pink and black	8·75	2·30

C29 Pelican

1943. Inscr "Colonia de Mocambique". Value in black.

C386	**C29**	50c. violet	9·75	1·30
C387	**C29**	50c. brown	9·75	1·30
C389	**C29**	50c. blue	9·75	1·30
C390	**C29**	50c. red	9·75	1·30
C393	**C29**	50c. green	6·25	1·30

1952. Inscr "Provincia de Mocambique". Value in black.

C469	50c. green	90	65
C470	50c. brown	90	65
C514	30c. yellow	85	65
C515	50c. orange	85	65

1957. No. C470 surch **$30.**

C511	30c. on 50c. brown	65	35

C56 Women and Children

1963

C569	**C56**	30c. black, green & red	35	25
C570	**C56**	50c. black, bistre & red	35	25
C571	**C56**	50c. black, pink & red	35	25
C572	**C56**	50c. black, green & red	35	25
C573	**C56**	50c. black, blue & red	35	25
C574	**C56**	50c. black, buff & red	35	25
C575	**C56**	50c. black, grey & red	35	25
C576	**C56**	50c. black, yell & red	25	15
C577	**C56**	1e. grey, black and red	1·10	45
C578	**C56**	1e. black, buff and red	30	20
C578a	**C56**	1e. black, mauve & red	30	20

C58 Telegraph Poles and Map

1965. Mozambique Telecommunications Improvement.

C579	**C58**	30c. black, pink & vio	20	15
C580	-	50c. black, brown & blue	20	15
C581	-	1e. black, orange & green	25	20

Design:—19½x36 mm: 50c., 1e. Telegraph linesman.

A 2e.50 in Type C **58** was also issued for compulsory use on telegrams.

NEWSPAPER STAMPS

1893. "Embossed" key-type of Mozambique surch. (a) JORNAES 2½ 2½.

N53	**Q**	2½r. on 40r. brown	42·00	23·00

(b) **JORNAES 2½ REIS.**

N54	2½r. on 40r. brown	£170	£120
N57	5r. on 40r. brown	85·00	50·00

1893. "Newspaper" key-type inscribed "MOCAMBIQUE".

N58	**V**	2½r. brown	60	45

POSTAGE DUE STAMPS

1904. "Due" key-type inscr "MOCAMBIQUE".

D146	**W**	5r. green	25	25
D147	**W**	10r. grey	25	25
D148	**W**	20r. brown	35	35
D149	**W**	30r. orange	75	45
D150	**W**	50r. brown	75	45
D151	**W**	60r. brown	2·75	1·70
D152	**W**	100r. mauve	2·75	1·70
D153	**W**	130r. blue	1·70	1·30
D154	**W**	200r. red	2·30	1·30
D155	**W**	500r. violet	3·00	1·50

1911. "Due" key-type of Mozambique optd REPUBLICA.

D162	**W**	5r. green	25	20
D163	**W**	10r. grey	45	20
D164	**W**	20r. brown	45	20
D165	**W**	30r. orange	45	20
D166	**W**	50r. brown	50	30
D167	**W**	60r. brown	70	35
D168	**W**	100r. mauve	90	50
D169	**W**	130r. blue	1·00	70
D170	**W**	200r. red	1·30	1·10
D171	**W**	500r. lilac	1·80	1·30

1917. "Due" key-type of Mozambique, but currency changed.

D246	**W**	½c. green	35	30
D247	**W**	1c. grey	35	30
D248	**W**	2c. brown	35	30
D249	**W**	3c. orange	35	30
D250	**W**	5c. brown	35	30
D251	**W**	6c. brown	35	30
D252	**W**	10c. mauve	35	30
D253	**W**	13c. blue	70	55
D254	**W**	20c. red	70	55
D255	**W**	50c. lilac	70	55

1918. Charity Tax stamps optd PORTEADO.

D256	**C15**	1c. green	1·20	90
D257	**C16**	5c. red	1·20	90

1922. "Ceres" key-type of Lourenco Marques (½, 1½c.) and of Mozambique (1, 2½, 4c.) surch PORTEADO and value and bar.

D316	**U**	5c. on ½c. black	1·20	85
D318	**U**	6c. on 1c. green	1·20	85
D317	**U**	10c. on 1¼c. brown	1·20	85
D319	**U**	20c. on 2½c. violet	1·20	85
D320	**U**	50c. on 4c. pink	1·20	85

1924. "Ceres" key-type of Mozambique surch Porteado and value.

D321	**U**	20c. on 30c. green	75	55
D323	**U**	50c. on 60c. blue	1·20	90

1925. Marquis de Pombal charity tax designs as Nos. C327/9, optd MULTA.

D327	**C73**	30c. brown	30	30
D328	-	30c. brown	30	30
D329	**C 75**	30c. brown	30	30

1952. As Type D 70 of Macao, but inscr "MOCAMBIQUE".

D468	10c. multicoloured	15	15
D469	30c. multicoloured	15	15
D470	50c. multicoloured	20	15
D471	1e. multicoloured	25	20
D472	2e. multicoloured	25	20
D473	5e. multicoloured	65	40

APPENDIX

The following issues for Mozambique have either been issued in excess of postal needs, or have not been made available to the public in reasonable quantities at face value. Such stamps mat later be given full listing if there is evidence of regular postal use. Miniature sheets, imperforate stamps etc are excluded from this section.

1999

Birds and Butterflies. 6000m.x6, 7500m.x6
Minerals. 12500m.x6
Dinosaurs. 9000m.x6
Animals. 6500x6
Mushrooms. 9500m.x6
Locomotives. 2500m.x9, 3000m.x9
Betty Boop. 3500m.x9

2000

Formula 1 Drivers. 6500m.x6
Cats and Dogs of the World. 4000m.x12, 4500m.x12
Dinosaurs. 3000m.x18

2001

Artists. 5000m.x6. 10000m.x87, 12000m.x48, 15000m.x6, 17000m.x6, 28000m.x6
Painters. 28000m.x6
World Cup Football (2002). 5000m.x33, 8500m.x18, 12000m.x6, 17000m.x6, 20000m.x6, 28000m.x6

2002

Nelson Mandela. 20000m.x4
World of the Sea. 5000m.x6, 17000m.x146, 20000m.x6, 33000x6

2007

Wild Cats. 8m.x3, 33m.x3
Elephants. 8m.x3, 33m.x3
Lighthouses and Marine Mammals. 8m.x3, 33m.x3
Birds of Prey 8m.x3, 33m.x3
Hummingbirds and Orchids 8m.x3, 33m.x3
Bees. 8m.x3, 33m.x3
Butterflies. 8m.x3, 33m.x3
Crocodiles. 8m.x3, 33m.x3
Frogs 8m.x3, 33m.x3
Dinosaurs. 8m.x3, 33m.x3
Cacti. 8m.x3, 33m.x3
Fruit. 8m.x3, 33m.x3
Minerals. 8m.x3, 33m.x3
Primates. 20m.x6
Lighthouses and Whales. 20m.x6
Owls. 20m.x6
Parrots. 20m.x6
Butterflies, Moths and Flowers. 20m.x6
Fish. 20m.x6
Marine Life. 20m.x6
Reptiles. 20m.x6
Turtles. 20m.x6
Snakes. 20m.x6
Dinosaurs. 20m.x6
Trees. 20m.x6
Orchids. 20m.x6
Minerals. 20m.x6

2010

Giraffes. 8m.x6
Wild Pigs. 8m.x6
Zebras. 8m.x6
Squirrels. 8m.x6
Elephants. 8m.x6
Peonies. 20m.x6
Tropical Birds and Plants. 20m.x6
Pigeons. 20m.x6
Rabbits and Hares. 20m.x6
Wild Dogs and Hyenas. 20m.x6
Wild Cats. 20m.x6
Aardvarks. 20m.x6
Bats. 20m.x6
Rhinos. 20m.x6
Antelopes and Gazelles. 20m.x6
Marine Birds. 33m.x6
Parrots. 33m.x6
Birds of Prey. 33m.x6
Hippos. 33m.x6
Pangolins. 33m.x6
Seals and Sea Lions. 33m.x6
Dolphins. 33m.x6
Whales. 33m.x6
Monkeys. 33m.x6
Orchids. 33m.x6
Volcanoes. 33m.x6
Global Warming. 33m.x6
World Cup Football Stadiums, South Africa. 33m.x6
Winter Olympic Gold Medallists, Vancouver. 20m.x12, 33m.x12
Table Tennis Players. 20m.x6, 33m.x6
Cyclists. 20m.x6, 33m.x6
Chess Players. 20m.x6, 33m.x6
Golfers. 33m.x6
Tennis Players. 33m.x6
Baseball Players. 33m.x6
Ice Hockey Players. 33m.x6
Judo. 33m.x6
Taekwondo. 33m.x6
Polo Players. 33m.x6
Horse Racing. 33m.x6
Dog Racing. 33m.x6
Rugby Players. 33m.x6
Football Players. 33m.x6
Lionel Messi (football player). 33m.x6
Roger Federer (tennis player). 33m.x6
Alberto Contador (cyclist). 33m.x6
Valentino Rossi (cyclist). 33m.x6
Prehistoric Art. 8m.x6
Architecture of the World. 20m.x24, 33m.x48
Paintings and Museums of the World. 20m.x6, 33m.x12
French Castles and Chateaux. 33m.x6
Bridges of the World. 33m.x6
335th Birth Anniv of Jan Vermeer. 66m.x4
Animals from Ocean Park Zoo, Hong Kong. 16m.x8
19th Commonwealth Games, New Delhi. 16m.x8
Chinese New Year. Year of the Robbit (2011). 16m.x6
400th Death Anniv of Michelangelo Merisi da Caravaggio (artist). 16m.x6, 92m.x2
Tony Curtis (actor) Commemoration. 16m.x6, 92m.x2
Explosion of Deepwater Horizon Oil Platform and Oil Spill, Gulf of Mexico. 16m.x6, 92m.x2
Christmas Paintings. 16m.x6, 92m.x2
90th Death Anniv of Amedeo Modigliani. 16m.x3, 66m.x3
30th Death Anniv of Alfred Hitchcock. 16m.x3, 33m.x3
50th Birth Anniv of Princess Diana. 16m.x3, 33m.x3
Witali Sewastianow (cosmonaut) Commemoration. 16m.x3, 33m.x3
70th Birthday of Pele (footballer). 16m.x3, 33m.x3
Engagement of Prince William and Miss Catherine Middleton. 16m.x3, 66m.x3

2011

International Year of Forests: Birdwing Butterflies. 16m.x4, 66m.x2.
Blue Butterflies. 16m.x4, 66m.x2.
Monarch Butterflies. 16mx4, 92m.x2.
Dragonflies. 16m.x4, 92m.x2.
Piranhas. 16m.x4, 66m.x2.
Tree-frogs. 16m.x4, 66m.x2.
Poison-dart Frogs. 16m.x4, 92m.x2.
Crocodiles. 16m.x4, 66m.x2.
Turtles. 16mx4, 66m.x2.
Parrot Snakes. 16mx4, 66m.x2.
Snakes. Gabon Viper 16m.x4, 92m.x2.
Harpy Eagles. 16m.x4, 66m.x2.
Cassowary. 16m.x4, 92m.x2.
Resplendent Quetzal. 16m.x4, 66m.x2.
Toucans. 16m.x4, 92m.x2.
Great Hornbill. 16m.x4, 92m.x2.
Owls. 16m.x4, 92m.x2.
Parrots. 16m.x4, 92m.x2.
Sumatran Rhinoceros. 16m.x4, 66m.x2.
Vampire Bats. 16m.x4, 66m.x2.
Manatees. 16m.x4, 66m.x2.
Sloths. 16m.x4, 66m.x2.
Jaguars. 16m.x4, 66m.x2.
Lemurs. 16m.x4, 66m.x2.
Monkeys. 16m.x4, 66m.x2.
Bengal Tigers. 16m.x4, 92m.x2.
Jupara. 16m.x3, 92m.x3.
Tarsier. 16m.x4, 92m.x2.
Spider Monkey. 16m.x4, 92m.x2.
Gorillas. 16m.x4, 92m.x2
Human Evolution. 16m.x2, 66m., 92m.
500th Birth Anniv of Giorgio Vasari. 16m.x2, 66m., 92m.
Paintings by Lucas Cranach. 16m.x2, 66m., 92m.
Birth Bicentenary of Franz Liszt. 16m.x2, 66m., 92m.
150th Birth Anniversary of Fridtjof Nansen. 16m., 66m., 92m.
Centenary of Roald Amundsen Expedition reaching the South Pole. 16m.x2, 66m., 92m.
Centenary of the World's First Airmail. 16m.x2, 66m., 92m.
Death Centenary of Gustav Mahler. 16m.x2, 66m., 92m.
Birth Centenary of Andor Lilienthal (chess grandmaster). 16m. x2, 66m., 92m.
50th Birth Anniv of Princess Diana. 16m.x2, 66m., 92m.
50th Birthday of George Clooney. 16m.x2, 66m., 92m.
50th Birthday of Maia Chiburdanidze (chess grandmaster). 16m.x2, 66m., 92m.
25th Death Anniv of Chiune Sugihara (Japanese diplomat, saved Jews from holocaust). 16m.x2, 66m., 92m.
20th Death Anniv of Rajiv Gandhi. 16m.x2, 66m., 92m.
Elizabeth Taylor Commemoration. 16m.x2, 66m., 92m.
Tribute to the Tsunami Victims in Japan. 16m.x2, 66m., 92m.
250th Birth Anniversary of Marie Tussaud. 16m.x4, 66m., 92m.
150th Anniv of the American Civil War. 16m.x4, 66m., 92m.
Centenary of the First Monte Carlo Rally. 16m.x4, 66m., 92m.
Birth Centenary of Ishiro Honda. 16m.x4, 66m., 92m.
Birth Centenary of Juan Manuel Fangio. 16m.x4, 66m., 92m.
Birth Centenary of Joseph Barbera. 16m.x4, 66m., 92m.
The Antarctic Treaty. Wildlife. 16m.x4, 66m., 92m.
50th Anniversary of the First Human in Space. Yuri Gagarin. 16m.x4, 66m., 92m.
50th Anniversary of the First American in Space. Alan B. Shepard Jr. 16m.x4, 66m., 92m.
50th Birthday of James Gandolfini. 16m.x4, 66m., 92m.
25th Anniversary of the Challenger Space Shuttle.. 16m.x4, 66m., 92m.
25th Anniversary of the Launching of Soviet Space Station MIR. 16m.x4, 66m., 92m.
Beatification of Pope John Paul II. 16m.x4, 66m., 92m.
Royal Wedding. Prince William and Miss Kate Middleton. 16m. x4, 66m., 92m.
Twentieth Century Scientists. Alexander Fleming. 16m.x2, 66m., 92m.
Twentieth Century Scientists. Albert Einstein. 16m.x4, 66m., 92m.
Twentieth Century Scientists. International Year of Chemistry. Marie Curie. 16m.x2, 66m., 92m.
Twentieth Century Art. Henri Matisse. 16m.x2, 66m., 92m.
Twentieth Century Art. American Impressionists. 16m.x4, 66m., 92m.
Twentieth Century Art. Rene Magritte. 16m.x2, 66m., 92m.
Twentieth Century Trains. 16m.x2, 66m., 92m.
Legendary Figures of Twentieth Century India. 16m.x2, 66m., 92m.
Legendary Figures of Twentieth Century India. Mohandas Karamchand Gandhi. 16m.x2, 66m., 92m.
Twentieth Century Humanitarians. Pope John Paul il. 16m.x2, 66m., 92m.
Twentieth Century Humanitarians. Diana, Princess of Wales. 16m.x2, 66m., 92m.
Warships of World War II. 16m.x2, 66m., 92m.
Jet Engines (Aircraft). 16m.x2, 66m., 92m.
Twentieth Century Communications. 16m.x4, 66m.,92m.
Twentieth Century Music. 16m.x4, 66m., 92m.
Leaders of the Twentieth Century. 16m.x8, 66m.x2, 92m.x2
Twentieth Century Sporting Icons. 16m.x4, 66m., 92m.
Royal Wedding (Prince William and Miss Kate Middleton). 16m.x4, 66m., 92m.

2012

Explosion of the Airship LZ 129 *Hindenburg*, 1937. 16m.x3, 66m.x3
280th Birth Anniversary of Joseph Haydn. 16m.x3, 66m.x3
Leonardo da Vinci Commemoration. 16m.x3, 66m.x3
Elizabeth Taylor Commemoration. 16m.x3, 66m.x3
185th Death Anniversary of Ludwig van Beethoven. 16m.x3, 66m.x3
Bombardment of Guernica, Spain, 1937. 16m.x3, 66m.x3
Discovery of the Bust of Nefertiti, Egypt. 16mx3, 66m.x3
Whitney Houston Commemoration. 16m.x3, 66m.x3
Pres. John Fitzgerald Kennedy Commemoration. 16mx3, 66m. x3
Milo Forman (film director). 16m.x3, 66m.x3
600th Birth Anniversary of Joan of Arc. 16m.x3, 66m.x3
70th Birthday of Paul McCartney. 16m.x3, 66m.x3
Isaac Newton Commemoration. 16m.x3, 66m.x3
80th Birth Anniversary of Francois Truffaut. 16m.x3, 66m.x3
150th Anniversary of Abolition of Slavery in the USA. 16m. x3, 66m.x3
210th Birth Anniversary of Alexandre Dumas. 16m.x3, 66m.x3
50th Death Anniversary of Marilyn Monroe. 16m.x3, 66m.x3
160th Birth Anniversary of Antoni Gaudi. 16m.x3, 66m.x3
Judy Garland Commemoration. 16m.x3, 66m.x3
Elvis Presley Commemoration. 16m.x3, 66m.x3
Joe Louis (boxer) Commemoration. 16m.x3, 66m.x3
Paintings of Napolean III. 16m.x3, 66m.x3
50th Anniversary of John Glenn's Orbit of Earth in Friendship 7. 16m.x3, 66m.x3
Discoveries. Thomas Edison. 16m.x3, 66m.x3
Discoveries. Jacobus Henricus Van t' Hoff. 16m.x3, 66m.x3
300th Birth Anniversary of Frederick II of Prussia. 16m.x3, 66m.x3
Birth Centenary of Gene Kelly. 16m.x3, 66m.x3
300th Birth Anniversary of Jean-Jacques Rousseau. 16m.x3, 66m.x3
Birth Bicentenary of Charles Dickens. 16m.x3, 66m.x3
Charles Lindbergh's Transatlantic Flight, 1927. 16m.x3, 66m.x3
Extinct Parrots. 66m.x4
Extinct Reptiles. 66m.x4
Extinct Birds. 16m.x18, 66m.x10, 92m.x4
Extinct Animals of the Americas. 16m.x3, 66m.x3
Extinct Animals of Asia. 16m.x6, 92m.x2
Extinct Birds of Africa. 66m.x4
Extinct Animals of Europe. 66m.x4
Extinct Bats. 66m.x4
Extinct Mammals of Africa. 66m.x4

Extinct Marine Animals. 66m.x4
Extinct Animals. 16m.x3, 66m.x3
Extinct Animals of Oceania. 16m.x6, 92m.x2
Extinct Rodents. 16m.x6, 92m.x2
Endangered Species. Birds of Prey. 16m.x3, 66m.x3
Endangered Species. Cockroaches. 16m.x3, 66m.x3
Endangered Species. Monkeys. 16m.x3, 66m.x3
Endangered Species. Butterflies. 16m.x6, 92m.x2
Endangered Species. Dolphins. 16m.x3, 66m.x3
Endangered Species. Snakes. 16m.x3, 66m.x3
Endangered Species. Sea Birds. 16m.x3, 66m.x3
Endangered Species. Reptiles. 16m.x3, 66m.x3
Endangered Species. Ungulates. 16m.x6, 92m.x2
Endangered Species. Turtles. 16m.x6, 92m.x2
Endangered Species. Marine Life. 16m.x3, 66m.x3
Endangered Species. Wild Cats. 16m.x3, 66m.x3
Endangered Species. Carnivores. 16m.x3, 66m.x3
Centenary of Sinking of the *Titanic*. 16m.x3, 66m.x3
Birth Centenary of Dean Arthur Amadon (ornithologist). 16m.x3, 66m.x3
Os Cinco Moguchaya Kuchka (Russian composer) Commemoration. 16m.x3, 66m.x3
150th Birth Anniversary of Achille-Claude Debussy. 16m.x3, 66m.x3
Charles Darwin and Dinosaurs. 16m.x3, 66m.x3
Centenary of the State Museum of Fine Arts. Alexander Pushkin Commemoration. 16m.x3, 66m.x3
20th Anniversary of the Catechism of the Catholic Church. Pope John Paul II Commemoration. 16m.x3, 66m.x3
Airbus A380 World's Biggest Commercial Plane. 16m.x3, 66m.x3
Volcanoes and Vulcanologists. 16m.x3, 66m.x3
Death Centenary of Wilbur Wright (aviation pioneer). 16m.x3, 66m.x3
Birth Centenary of Byron Nelson (golfer). 16m.x3, 66m.x3

MOZAMBIQUE COMPANY

The Mozambique Company was responsible from 1891 until 1942 for the administration of Manica and Sofala territory in Portuguese East Africa. Now part of Mozambique.

1899. 1000 reis = 1 milreis.
1913. 100 centavos = 1 escudo.

1892. "Embossed" key-type inscr "PROVINCA DE MOCAMBIQUE" optd COMPA. DE MOCAMBIQUE.

10	**Q**	5r. black	1·30	75
2	**Q**	10r. green	1·40	1·10
3	**Q**	20r. red	1·80	1·10
4	**Q**	25r. mauve	1·40	1·10
5	**Q**	40r. brown	1·40	1·10
6	**Q**	50r. blue	1·90	1·30
7	**Q**	100r. brown	1·90	1·30
8	**Q**	200r. violet	2·30	1·80
9	**Q**	300r. orange	3·25	1·90

2

1895. Value in black or red (500, 1000r.).

112	**2**	400r. black on blue	3·00	2·30
33	**2**	2½r. yellow	55	50
114	**2**	2½r. grey	1·90	1·10
17	**2**	5r. orange	55	50
36	**2**	10r. mauve	80	55
115	**2**	10r. green	1·40	1·10
39	**2**	15r. brown	80	55
116	**2**	15r. green	1·90	1·10
20	**2**	20r. lilac	60	50
45	**2**	25r. green	70	65
117	**2**	25r. red	1·90	1·10
46	**2**	50r. blue	80	55
118	**2**	50r. brown	1·90	1·40
109	**2**	65r. blue	1·10	85
48	**2**	75r. red	80	55
119	**2**	75r. mauve	3·75	2·10
50	**2**	80r. green	80	55
120	**2**	100r. blue on blue	3·75	2·75
52	**2**	100r. brown on buff	2·20	1·30
110	**2**	115r. pink on pink	3·00	2·30
121	**2**	115r. brown on pink	5·00	3·50
111	**2**	130r. green on pink	3·00	2·30
122	**2**	130r. brown on yellow	5·25	3·50
54	**2**	150r. orange on pink	2·20	1·30
55	**2**	200r. blue on blue	1·80	1·60
123	**2**	200r. lilac on pink	5·25	3·50
56	**2**	300r. blue on brown	2·10	1·60
124	**2**	400r. blue on yellow	7·00	5·75
58	**2**	500r. black	1·80	1·30
125	**2**	500r. black on blue	7·00	5·75
126	**2**	700r. mauve on buff	7·00	6·50
59	**2**	1000r. mauve	2·30	1·60

1895. Surch **PROVISORIO 25**.

77	**2**	25 on 80r. green	38·00	29·00

1895. No. 6 optd **PROVISORIO**.

78	**Q**	50r. blue	7·50	6·50

1898. Vasco da Gama. Optd 1498 Centenario da India 1898.

80	**2**	2½r. yellow	2·20	1·80
81	**2**	5r. orange	3·00	2·10
82	**2**	10r. mauve	3·00	2·00
84	**2**	15r. brown	3·75	3·25
86	**2**	20r. lilac	5·25	3·50
87	**2**	25r. green	5·75	3·50
99	**2**	50r. blue	3·75	3·25
89	**2**	75r. red	10·00	6·50
91	**2**	80r. green	7·00	5·00
101	**2**	100r. brown on buff	7·50	6·50
102	**2**	150r. orange on pink	7·50	6·50
94	**2**	200r. blue on blue	11·50	7·50
104	**2**	300r. blue on brown	14·00	9·25

1899. Surch **25 PROVISORIO**.

105	**2**	25 on 75r. red	6·00	5·00

1900. Surch **25 Reis** and bar.

106	**2**	25r. on 5r. orange	4·75	2·75

1900. Perforated through centre and surch **50 REIS**.

108	**2**	50r. on half of 20r. lilac	2·20	1·80

1911. Optd **REPUBLICA**.

145	**2**	2½r. grey	70	65
147	**2**	5r. orange	70	65
148	**2**	10r. green	70	65
150	**2**	15r. green	45	35
151	**2**	20r. lilac	70	65
153	**2**	25r. red	70	65
155	**2**	50r. brown	70	65
156	**2**	75r. mauve	70	65
157	**2**	100r. blue on blue	70	65
159	**2**	115r. brown on pink	1·40	95
160	**2**	130r. brown on yellow	1·40	95
161	**2**	200r. lilac on pink	1·40	95
162	**2**	400r. blue on yellow	1·40	95
163	**2**	500r. black on blue	1·40	95
164	**2**	700r. mauve on yellow	2·10	1·30

1916. Surch **REPUBLICA** and value in figures.

166	**2**	¼c. on 2½r. grey	45	35
168	**2**	½c. on 5r. orange	45	35
170	**2**	1c. on 10r. green	70	55
173	**2**	1½c. on 15r. green	60	55
175	**2**	2c. on 20r. lilac	70	55
178	**2**	2½c. on 25r. red	60	55
180	**2**	5c. on 50r. brown	60	55
181	**2**	7½c. on 75r. mauve	1·10	80
182	**2**	10c. on 100r. blue on blue	1·10	60
183	**2**	11½c. on 115r. brown on pink	2·50	1·20
184	**2**	13c. on 130r. brown on yell	2·50	1·20
185	**2**	20c. on 200r. lilac on pink	2·75	1·10
186	**2**	40c. on 400r. blue on yellow	2·75	1·10
187	**2**	50c. on 500r. black on blue	3·00	1·40
188	**2**	70c. on 700r. mauve on yell	3·00	1·70

1917. Red Cross Fund. Stamps of 1911 (optd **REPUBLICA**) optd with red cross and **31.7.17**.

189	**2**	2½r. grey	10·00	8·00
190	**2**	10r. green	10·00	8·00
191	**2**	20r. lilac	12·00	10·00
192	**2**	50r. brown	40·00	32·00
193	**2**	75r. mauve	90·00	85·00
194	**2**	100r. blue on blue	£100	£100
195	**2**	700r. mauve on yellow	£250	£250

1918. Stamps of 1911 (optd **REPUBLICA**) surch with new value.

196	**2**	½c. on 700r. mauve on yellow	3·25	2·50
197	**2**	2½c. on 500r. black on blue	3·25	2·50
198	**2**	5c. on 400r. blue on yellow	3·25	2·50

14 Native Village **15** Ivory

1918

199A	**14**	¼c. green and brown	55	35
233	**14**	¼c. black and green	45	35
200A	**15**	½c. black	55	35
201A	-	1c. black and green	55	35
202A	-	1½c. green and black	55	35
203A	-	2c. black and red	55	35
235	-	2c. black and grey	45	45
204A	-	2½c. black and lilac	55	35
236	-	3c. black and orange	55	50
205A	-	4c. brown and green	55	35
237	-	4c. black and red	55	50
227A	**14**	4½c. black and grey	55	35
206A	-	5c. black and blue	55	55
207A	-	6c. blue and purple	55	35
238	-	6c. black and mauve	65	50
228A	-	7c. black and blue	55	35
208A	-	7½c. green and orange	1·40	70
239	-	8c. black and lilac	1·30	1·00
210A	-	10c. black and red	1·40	95
229A	-	12c. black and brown	1·90	1·40
241	-	12c. black and green	1·10	75
242	-	15c. black and red	1·10	95
212A	-	20c. black and green	1·40	55
213A	-	30c. black and brown	1·40	95
244	-	30c. black and green	1·30	1·10
214A	-	40c. black and green	1·40	95
246	-	40c. black and blue	1·70	1·30
215A	-	50c. black and orange	1·40	95
247	-	50c. black and mauve	2·10	1·70
230A	-	60c. brown and red	2·20	1·50
231A	-	80c. brown and blue	2·20	1·50
248	-	80c. black and red	2·10	1·70
216A	-	1e. black and green	2·75	2·10
249	-	1e. black and blue	2·10	1·70
232A	-	2e. violet and red	3·25	2·50
250	-	2e. black and lilac	3·75	2·20

Designs:—Horiz: 1, 3c. Maize field; 2c. Sugar factory; 5c., 2e. Beira; 20c. Law Court; 40c. Mangrove swamp. Vert: 1½c. India-rubber; 2½c. River Buzi; 4c. Tobacco bushes; 6c. Coffee bushes; 7, 15c. Steam train, Amatongas Forest; 7½c. Orange tree; 8, 12c. Cotton plants; 10, 80c. Sisal plantation; 30c. Coconut palm; 50, 60c. Cattle breeding; 1e. Mozambique Co's Arms.

1920. Pictorial issue surch in words.

217	½c. on 30c. (No. 213)	6·50	5·75
218	½c. on 1e. (No. 216)	6·50	5·75
219	1½c. on 2½c. (No. 204)	4·75	2·75
220	1½c. on 5c. (No. 206)	4·75	2·75
221	2c. on 2½c. (No. 204)	4·75	2·75
222	4c. on 20c. (No. 212)	5·25	4·00
223	4c. on 40c. (No. 214)	5·25	4·00
224	6c. on 8c. (No. 239)	6·75	4·00
225	6c. on 50c. (No. 215)	6·75	4·00

33

36 Tea

1925

251	**33**	24c. black and blue	2·75	2·00
252	-	25c. blue and brown	2·75	2·00
253	**33**	85c. black and red	2·10	1·50
254	-	1e.40 black and blue	2·10	1·50
255	-	5e. blue and brown	3·25	1·30
256	**36**	10e. black and red	5·75	1·70
257	-	20e. black and green	7·00	2·50

Designs:—Vert: 25c., 1e.40, Beira; 5e. Tapping rubber. Horiz: 20e. River Zambesi.

38 Ivory

1931

258	**38**	45c. blue	4·25	2·40
259	-	70c. brown	2·10	1·50

Design:—Vert: 70c. Gold mining.

40 Zambesi Bridge

1935. Opening of River Zambesi Railway Bridge at Sena.

260	**40**	1e. black and blue	6·50	3·25

41 Armstrong-Whitworth Atalanta Airliner over Beira

1935. Inauguration of Blantyre–Beira–Salisbury Air Route.

261	**41**	5c. black and blue	1·30	85
262	**41**	10c. black and red	1·30	85
263	**41**	15c. black and red	1·30	85
264	**41**	20c. black and green	1·30	85
265	**41**	30c. black and green	1·30	85
266	**41**	40c. black and blue	1·70	1·10
267	**41**	45c. black and blue	1·70	1·10
268	**41**	50c. black and purple	1·70	1·10
269	**41**	60c. brown and red	2·75	1·70
270	**41**	80c. black and red	2·75	1·70

42 Armstrong-Whitworth Atalanta Airliner over Beira

1935. Air.

271	**42**	5c. black and blue	35	30
272	**42**	10c. black and red	35	30
273	**42**	15c. black and red	35	30
274	**42**	20c. black and green	35	30
275	**42**	30c. black and green	35	30
276	**42**	40c. black and green	35	30
277	**42**	45c. black and blue	35	30
278	**42**	50c. black and purple	35	30
279	**42**	60c. brown and red	35	30
280	**42**	80c. black and red	35	30
281	**42**	1e. black and blue	35	30
282	**42**	2e. black and lilac	85	75
283	**42**	5e. blue and brown	1·40	1·20
284	**42**	10e. black and red	1·90	1·40
285	**42**	20e. black and green	3·75	1·80

43 Coastal Dhow **45** Crocodile

46 Palms at Beira

1937

286	-	1c. lilac and green	35	30
287	-	5c. green and blue	35	30
288	**43**	10c. blue and red	35	30
289	-	15c. black and red	45	30
290	-	20c. blue and green	45	30
291	-	30c. blue and green	45	30
292	-	40c. black and blue	45	30
293	-	45c. brown and blue	45	30
294	**45**	50c. green and violet	45	30
295	-	60c. blue and red	45	30
296	-	70c. green and brown	45	30
297	-	80c. green and red	55	45
298	-	85c. black and red	65	50
299	-	1e. black and blue	65	50
300	**46**	1e.40 green and blue	1·30	50
301	-	2e. brown and lilac	2·10	60
302	-	5e. blue and brown	1·30	60
303	-	10e. black and red	2·10	1·00
304	-	20e. purple and green	3·25	1·90

Designs:—Vert: 21×29 mm—1c. Giraffe; 20c. Common zebra; 70c. Native woman. 23×31 mm—10e. Old Portuguese gate, Sena; 20e. Arms. Horiz: 29×21 mm—5c. Native huts; 15c. S. Caetano fortress, Sofala; 60c. Leopard; 80c. Hippopotami. 37×22 mm—5e. Railway bridge over River Zambesi. Triangular: 30c. Python; 40c. White rhinoceros; 45c. Lion; 85c. Vasco da Gama's flagship *Sao Gabriel*; 1e. Native in dugout canoe; 2e. Greater kudu.

1939. President Carmona's Colonial Tour. Optd **28-VII-1939 Visita Presidencial.**

305	-	30c. (No. 291)	1·90	1·50
306	-	40c. (No. 292)	1·90	1·50
307	-	45c. (No. 293)	1·90	1·50
308	**45**	50c. green and violet	1·90	1·50
309	-	85c. (No. 298)	1·90	1·50
310	-	1e. (No. 299)	3·50	1·80
311	-	2e. (No. 301)	4·25	3·25

49 King Afonso Henriques

1940. 800th Anniv of Portuguese Independence.

312	**49**	1e.75 light blue and blue	3·25	1·50

51 *Don John IV after Alberto de Souza*

1940. Tercentenary of Restoration of Independence.

313	**51**	40c. black and blue	85	65
314	**51**	50c. green and violet	85	65
315	**51**	60c. blue and red	85	65
316	**51**	70c. green and brown	85	65
317	**51**	80c. green and red	85	65
318	**51**	1e. black and blue	85	65

CHARITY TAX STAMPS

The notes under this heading in Portugal also apply here.

1932. No. 236 surch **Assistencia Publica 2 Ctvos. 2**.

C260	2c. on 3c. black and orange	1·50	1·10

C41 "Charity"

1934

C261	**C41**	2c. black and mauve	1·60	1·10

C50

1940

C313	**C50**	2c. blue and black	8·00	5·25

C52

1941

C319	**C52**	2c. red and black	8·00	5·25

NEWSPAPER STAMPS

1894. "Newspaper" key-type inscr "MOCAMBIQUE" optd **COMPA. DE MOCAMBIQUE**.

N15	**V**	2½r. brown	75	60

POSTAGE DUE STAMPS

D9

1906

D114	**D9**	5r. green	50	40
D115	**D9**	10r. grey	50	40
D116	**D9**	20r. brown	50	40
D117	**D9**	30r. orange	80	60
D118	**D9**	50r. brown	80	60
D119	**D9**	60r. brown	3·50	3·50
D120	**D9**	100r. mauve	1·10	1·00
D121	**D9**	130r. blue	7·00	3·75
D122	**D9**	200r. red	1·80	1·30
D123	**D9**	500r. lilac	3·00	2·40

1911. Optd **REPUBLICA**.

D166	**D9**	5r. green	25	25
D167	**D9**	10r. grey	30	30
D168	**D9**	20r. brown	30	30
D169	**D9**	30r. orange	30	30
D170	**D9**	50r. brown	30	30
D171	**D9**	60r. brown	60	45
D172	**D9**	100r. mauve	60	45
D173	**D9**	130r. blue	1·30	1·20
D174	**D9**	200r. red	1·60	1·30
D175	**D9**	500r. lilac	1·90	1·60

1916. Currency changed.

D189	**D9**	½c. green	25	25
D190	**D9**	1c. grey	25	25
D191	**D9**	2c. brown	25	25
D192	**D9**	3c. orange	25	25
D193	**D9**	5c. brown	25	25
D194	**D9**	6c. brown	40	40
D195	**D9**	10c. mauve	70	70
D196	**D9**	13c. blue	1·30	1·30
D197	**D9**	20c. red	1·30	1·30
D198	**D9**	50c. lilac	2·00	2·00

D32

1919

D217	**D32**	½c. green	10	10
D218	**D32**	1c. black	10	10
D219	**D32**	2c. brown	10	10
D220	**D32**	3c. orange	10	10
D221	**D32**	5c. brown	15	10
D222	**D32**	6c. brown	20	20
D223	**D32**	10c. red	20	20
D224	**D32**	13c. blue	25	25
D225	**D32**	20c. red	25	20
D226	**D32**	50c. grey	30	30

MUSCAT

Independent Sultanate of Eastern Arabia with Indian and, subsequently, British postal administration.

12 pies = 1 anna; 16 annas = 1 rupee

(2)

1944. Bicentenary of Al-Busaid Dynasty. Stamps of India (King George VI) optd as T **2**.

1	**100a**	3p. slate	50	8·50
2	**100a**	½a. mauve	50	8·50
3	**100a**	9p. green	50	8·50
4	**100a**	1a. red	50	8·50
5	**101**	1½a. plum	50	8·50
6	**101**	2a. red	50	8·50
7	**101**	3a. violet	1·00	8·50
8	**101**	3½a. blue	1·00	8·50
9	**102**	4a. brown	1·25	8·50
10	**102**	6a. green	1·25	8·50
11	**102**	8a. violet	1·50	8·50
12	**102**	12a. red	2·00	8·50
13	-	14a. purple (No. 277)	4·00	14·00
14	**93**	1r. slate and brown	5·00	13·00
15	**93**	2r. purple and brown	12·00	22·00

OFFICIAL STAMPS

1944. Bicentenary of Al-Busaid Dynasty. Official stamps of India optd as T **2**.

O1	**O20**	3p. slate	60	16·00
O2	**O20**	½a. purple	1·50	16·00
O3	**O20**	9p. green	1·00	16·00
O4	**O20**	1a. red	1·00	16·00
O5	**O20**	1½a. violet	1·50	16·00
O6	**O20**	2a. orange	1·50	16·00
O7	**O20**	2½a. violet	7·50	16·00
O8	**O20**	4a. brown	2·75	16·00
O9	**O20**	8a. violet	5·00	18·00
O10	**93**	1r. slate and brown (No. O138)	10·00	30·00

For later issues see **BRITISH POSTAL AGENCIES IN EASTERN ARABIA**.

MUSCAT AND OMAN

Independent Sultanate in Eastern Arabia. The title of the Sultanate was changed in 1971 to Oman.

1966. 64 baizas = 1 rupee.
1970. 1000 baizas = 1 rial saidi.

12 Sultan's Crest

14 Nakhal Fort

1966

94	**12**	3b. purple	30	25
95	**12**	5b. brown	30	25
96	**12**	10b. brown	30	25
97	**A**	15b. black and violet	1·20	30
98	**A**	20b. black and blue	1·80	30
99	**A**	25b. black and orange	2·50	75
100	**14**	30b. mauve and blue	3·25	80
101	**B**	50b. green and brown	4·25	1·90
102	**C**	1r. blue and orange	8·50	2·00
103	**D**	2r. brown and green	16·00	6·00
104	**E**	5r. violet and red	34·00	20·00
105	**F**	10r. red and violet	70·00	42·00

Designs:—Vert: 21½×25½ mm: A, Crest and Muscat harbour. Horiz (as Type **14**): B, Samail Fort; C, Sohar Fort; D, Nizwa Fort; E, Matrah Fort; F, Mirani Fort.

15 Mina el Fahal

1969. First Oil Shipment (July 1967). Multicoloured.

106	20b. Type **15**	5·75	1·20
107	25b. Storage tanks	8·25	1·80
108	40b. Desert oil-rig	11·50	2·75
109	1r. Aerial view from *Gemini 4*	30·00	8·00

1970. Designs as issue of 1966, but inscribed in new currency.

110	**12**	5b. purple	1·10	25
111	**12**	10b. brown	2·20	50
112	**12**	20b. brown	2·50	55
113	**A**	25b. black and violet	4·50	70
114	**A**	30b. black and blue	5·25	1·20
115	**A**	40b. black and orange	6·25	1·50
116	**14**	50b. mauve and blue	8·75	1·80
117	**B**	75b. green and brown	11·00	3·00
118	**C**	100b. blue and orange	13·00	3·25
119	**D**	¼r. brown and green	33·00	8·00
120	**E**	½r. violet and red	65·00	25·00
121	**F**	1r. red and violet	£110	44·00

For later issues see **OMAN**.

MYANMAR

Formerly known as Burma.

100 pyas = 1 kyat.

81 Fountain, National Assembly Park (image scaled to 60% of original size)

1990. State Law and Order Restoration Council.

312	**81**	1k. multicoloured	1·80	1·10

1990. As Nos. 258/61 of Burma but inscr "UNION OF MYANMAR".

313	**62**	15p. deep green and green	40	25
314	**63**	20p. black, brown and blue	70·00	†
315	-	50p. violet and brown	1·20	40
316	-	1k. violet, mauve and black	2·50	1·10

82 Map and Emblem

1990. 40th Anniv of United Nations Development Programme.

322	**82**	2k. blue, yellow and black	7·00	2·10

83 Nawata Ruby

1991. Gem Emporium.

323	**83**	50p. multicoloured	2·75	1·10

84 *Grandfather giving Sword to Grandson* (statuette, Nan Win)

1992. 44th Anniv of Independence. Multicoloured.

324	50p. Warrior defending personification of Myanmar and map (poster, Khin Thein)	1·40	65
325	2k. Type **84**	4·75	2·75

85 Emblem

1992. National Sports Festival.

326	**85**	50p. multicoloured	2·30	65

86 Campaign Emblem

1992. Anti-AIDS Campaign.

327	**86**	50p. red	3·25	65

87 Fish, Water Droplet and Leaf

1992. International Nutrition Conference, Rome.

328	**87**	50p. multicoloured	85	25
329	**87**	1k. multicoloured	1·70	65
330	**87**	3k. multicoloured	4·50	2·00
331	**87**	5k. multicoloured	7·00	3·25

88 Statue

1993. National Convention for Drafting of New Constitution.

332	**88**	50p. multicoloured	70	25
333	**88**	3k. multicoloured	4·75	2·00

89 Hintha (legendary bird)

1993. Statuettes. Multicoloured.

334	5k. Type **89**	8·25	3·50
335	10k. Lawkanat	17·00	7·25

90 Horseman aiming Spear at Target

1993. Festival of Traditional Equestrian Sports, Sittwe.

336	**90**	3k. multicoloured	7·00	2·00

91 Tree, Globe and Figures

1994. World Environment Day.

337	**91**	4k. multicoloured	7·50	2·75

92 Association Emblem

1994. First Anniv of Union Solidarity and Development Association.

338	**92**	3k. multicoloured	7·50	2·30

93 City and Emblem

1995. 50th Anniv of Armed Forces Day.

339	**93**	50p. multicoloured	1·70	80

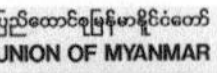

94 Cross through Poppy Head

1995. International Day against Drug Abuse.

340	**94**	2k. multicoloured	4·25	2·40

95 Camera and Film

1995. 60th Anniv of Myanmar Film Industry.

341	**95**	50p. multicoloured	2·30	80

96 Figures around Emblem

1995. 50th Anniv of United Nations Organization.

342	**96**	4k. multicoloured	7·00	4·75

97 Convocation Hall

1995. 60th Anniv of Yangon University.

343	**97**	50p. multicoloured	1·40	65
344	**97**	2k. multicoloured	3·50	2·30

98 Punt

1996. Visit Myanmar Year. Multicoloured.

345	50p. Type **98**	1·40	55
346	4k. Karaweik Hall	7·00	4·25
347	5k. Mandalay Palace	8·25	5·25

99 Four-man Canoe

1996. International Letter Writing Week. "Unity equals Success". Multicoloured.

348	2k. Type **99**	3·50	2·10
349	5k. Human pyramid holding flag aloft (vert)	8·25	5·25

100 Breastfeeding

1996. 50th Anniv of UNICEF. Multicoloured.

350	1k. Type **100**	2·10	1·10
351	2k. Nurse inoculating child	3·50	2·10
352	4k. Children outside school	7·00	4·25

101 Emblem and Map of Myanmar

1997. 30th Anniv of Association of South-East Asian Nations.

353	**101**	1k. multicoloured	2·10	1·30
354	**101**	2k. multicoloured	3·50	2·75

102 Throne

1998. 50th Anniv of Independence.

355	**102**	2k. multicoloured	3·50	2·40

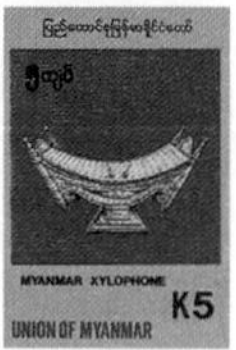

103 Xylophone

1998. Musical Instruments. Multicoloured.

356	5k. Type **103**	6·25	6·25
357	10k. Mon brass gongs	12·50	12·50
358	20k. Rakhine auspicious drum	21·00	21·00
359	30k. Myanmar harp	28·00	28·00
360	50k. Shan pot drum	43·00	43·00
361	100k. Kachin brass gong	60·00	60·00

104 Emblem

1999. Asian and Pacific Decade of Disabled Persons. Seventh Far East and South Pacific Region Disabled Games.

365	**104**	2k. multicoloured	4·25	2·75
366	**104**	5k. multicoloured	7·50	5·25

105 Dove and UPU Emblem

1999. 125th Anniv of Universal Postal Union.

367	**105**	2k. multicoloured	4·00	3·50
368	**105**	5k. multicoloured	8·75	7·50

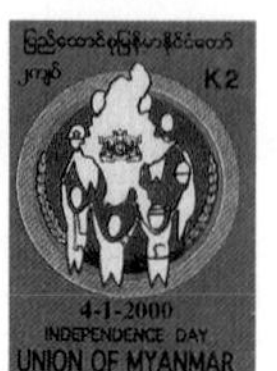

106 People linking Hands around Map of Myanmar

2000. 52nd Anniv of Independence.

369	**106**	2k. multicoloured	4·00	3·50

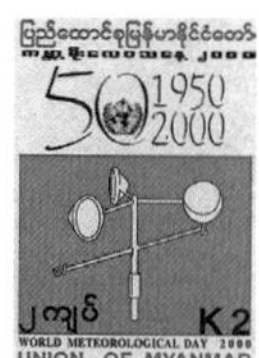

107 Weathervane

2000. World Meteorological Day. 50th Anniv of World Meteorological Organization.

370	**107**	2k. black and blue	3·25	2·75
371	-	5k. multicoloured	7·25	6·25
372	-	10k. multicoloured	13·50	11·50

Designs:—Horiz: 5k. Emblem and globe; 10k. Emblem and symbols for rain and sunshine.

108 Royal Palace Gate, Burma and Great Wall of China (image scaled to 58% of original size)

2000. 50th Anniv of Burma–China Relations.

373	**108**	5k. multicoloured	11·00	9·75

109 Burning Poppy Heads and Needles

2000. Anti-drugs Campaign.

374	**109**	2k. multicoloured	4·75	4·25

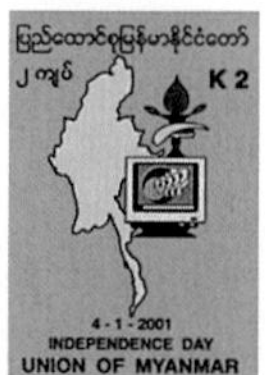

110 Television Set and Map of Myanmar

2001. 53rd Anniv of Independence.

375	**110**	2k. multicoloured	5·50	4·75

111 National Flag and Globe

2002. 54th Anniv of Independence. Multicoloured.

376	2k. Type **111**	1·60	1·40
377	30k. As No. 376 but inscriptions and face value in English	17·00	15·00

112 Flag and Statue

2003. 55th Anniv of Independence. Multicoloured.

378	2k. Type **112**	1·60	1·40
379	30k. As No. 378 but inscriptions and face value in English	17·00	15·00

113 Black Orchid

2004. Flora. Multicoloured.

380	30k. Type **113**	12·50	11·00
381	30k. Mango	12·50	11·00

114 Trophies and Football

2004. Centenary of FIFA (Federation Internationale de Football Association).

382	**114**	2k. multicoloured	8·00	7·00

115 Stupas (image scaled to 58% of original size)

2004. World Buddhist Summit, Yangon, Myanmar. Multicoloured.

383	5k. Type **115**	2·40	2·10
384	30k. Stupas (different)	10·50	9·00

116 Flag and Statues

2007. 59th Independence Day. Multicoloured.

385	(2k.) Type **116**	1·60	1·40
386	5k. Map and statues	4·00	3·50

Nos. 387/9 and Type **117** have been left for 'National Convention', issued on 13 August 2007, not yet received.

118 Secretariat Building, Bandar Seri Begawan, Brunei Darussalam

2007. Architecture. 40th Anniv of ASEAN (Association of South-East Asian Nations). Multicoloured.

390	50k. Type **118**	4·75	4·25
391	50k. National Museum, Cambodia	4·75	4·25
392	50k. Fatahillah Museum, Jakarta	4·75	4·25

393	50k. Traditional house, Laos	4·75	4·25
394	50k. Railway Headquarters Building, Malaysia	4·75	4·25
395	50k. Yangon Post Office, Union of Myanmar	4·75	4·25
396	50k. Malacanang Palace, Manila	4·75	4·25
397	50k. National Museum, Singapore	4·75	4·25
398	50k. Vimanmek Mansion, Bangkok, Thailand	4·75	4·25
399	50k. Presidential Palace, Hanoi, Vietnam	4·75	4·25

Stamps of a similar design were issued by all member countries.

119 Assembly and Crowd

2008. Referendum. Multicoloured.

400	100k. Type **119**	3·25	2·75
401	100k. Assembly	3·25	2·75
402	200k. Assembly, warriors, map and ballot box (*vert*)	6·25	5·50

120 Fountains

2009. 61st Anniv of Independence Day. Multicoloured.

403	200k. Type **120**	4·75	4·25
404	300k. Symbols of Myanmar	7·25	6·25

121 Parliament, Map and Figures

2010. 62nd Anniv of Independence Day. Multicoloured.

405	100k. Type **121**	2·40	2·10
406	200k. Parliament, map and figures (different)	4·75	4·25

122 Parliament, Myanmar and Tiananmen Gate, China (image scaled to 59% of original size)

2010. 60th Anniv of Myanmar - China Diplomatic Relations

407	**122** 100k. multicoloured	4·00	4·00

123 Elephants, Stars and Parliament (image scaled to 59% of original size)

2010. Multi-Party Elections

408	**123** 50k. multicoloured	2·00	2·00

124 Children and Plant growing from Globe (image scaled to 58% of original size)

2010. 25th Anniv of Vienna Convention for Protection of Ozone Layer. Sheet 132×90 mm

MS409	**124** 100k. multicoloured	5·00	5·00

2011. 63rd Anniv of Independence Day

410	100k. Figures, map and parliament	4·00	4·00

2011. Republic of Myanmar. Multicoloured.

411	500k. Parliament	12·50	12·50
412	500k. Parliament (different)	12·50	12·50

2012. 64th Anniv of Independence Day. Multicoloured.

413	500k. Independence Monument, Yangon and Lotus Fountain	12·50	12·50
414	1200k. Parliament, bridge, satellite dish and dam (80×26 mm)	18·00	18·00

2012. 11th ASEAN TELMIN (Telecommunications and Information Ministers Meeting) and 12th ASEAN TELSOM (Telecommunications Senior Officials Meeting), Myanmar International Convention Centre. Multicoloured.

415	100k. Members' flags and emblem	4·00	4·00
416	100k. Flags surrounding emblem	4·00	4·00
417	100k. Emblem and centre	4·00	4·00
418	300k. As No. 415	8·00	8·00
419	300k. As No. 416	8·00	8·00
420	300k. As No. 417	8·00	8·00

2012. Second TELSOM - ATRC Leaders Retreat. MUlticoloured.

421	500k. Dhammayangyi Temple	12·50	12·50
422	500k. Htilominlo Temple	12·50	12·50

2013. 65th Anniv of Independence Day. Multicoloured.

423	100k. Temple, map and monument	4·00	4·00
424	100k. Parliament (80×26 mm)	4·00	4·00

2013. 65th Anniv of Myanmar - Russia Diplomatic Relations

425	500k. Temple, Myanmar and St. Basil's Cathedral, Russia	12·50	12·50

125 Emblem

2013. 27th SEA (South East Asian) Games, Myanmar. Multicoloured.

426	100k. Type **132**	4·00	4·00
427	100k. Mascot holding torch	4·00	4·00
428	100k. Shwe Yoe and Ma Moe, official mascots	4·00	4·00
429	100k. Emblem and mascots	4·00	4·00
430	500k. As No. 426	12·50	12·50
431	500k. As No. 427	12·50	12·50
432	500k. As No. 428	12·50	12·50
433	500k. As No. 429	12·50	12·50

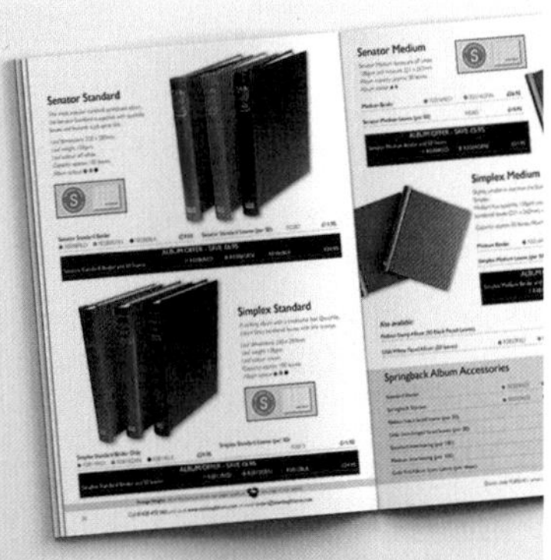
EVERYTHING FOR THE STAMP COLLECTOR

For your copy of the Stanley Gibbons 2018 Product Guide, call 01425 472 363
email orders@stanleygibbons.com
or visit stanleygibbons.com

Gibbons Stamp Monthly

FIRST CHOICE FOR STAMP COLLECTORS SINCE 1890

SUBSCRIBE AND GET £££S OFF THE COVER PRICE

SUBSCRIBE TODAY
Visit **stanleygibbons.com/gsm**
or call **01425 472 363**
overseas **+44 1425 472 363**

399 Strand, WC2R 0LX, London
Phone: **+44 1425 472 363** | Email: gsm@stanleygibbons.com
www.stanleygibbons.com

*T&Cs apply. *Saving based on a 12-month UK print subscription.*

NABHA

A "Convention" state in the Punjab, India.

12 pies = 1 anna; 16 annas = 1 rupee.

Stamps of India optd NABHA STATE.

1885. Queen Victoria. Vert opt.

1	**23**	½a. turquoise	8·00	13·00
2	-	1a. purple	95·00	£375
3	-	2a. blue	45·00	£100
4	-	4a. green (No. 96)	£140	£400
5	-	8a. mauve	£600	
6	-	1r. grey (No. 79)	£600	

1885. Queen Victoria. Horiz opt.

36	**40**	3p. red	30	20
14	**23**	½a. turquoise	1·50	10
15	**24**	9p. red	3·50	7·50
16	**25**	1a. purple	5·50	1·00
18	**26**	1a.6p. brown	4·25	8·50
11		2a. blue	6·00	5·00
22		3a. orange	10·00	3·50
12		4a. green (No. 69)	80·00	£425
24		4a. green (No. 96)	11·00	5·50
26		6a. brown (No. 80)	4·50	7·50
27	**31**	8a. mauve	6·50	7·00
28	**32**	12a. purple on red	6·00	10·00
29	**33**	1r. grey (No. 101)	24·00	90·00
30	**37**	1r. green and red	27·00	22·00
31	**38**	2r. red and orange	£250	£425
32		3r. brown and green	£275	£650
33		5r. blue and violet	£275	£1000

1903. King Edward VII.

37	**38**	3p. grey	75	15
38	**38**	½a. green (No. 122)	1·10	70
39	**38**	1a. red (No. 123)	3·00	2·00
40*a*	**38**	2a. lilac	7·00	35
40*b*	**38**	2½a. blue	19·00	£120
41	**38**	3a. orange	2·75	40
42	**38**	4a. olive	10·00	3·25
43	**38**	6a. bistre	11·00	40·00
44	**38**	8a. mauve	12·00	50·00
45	**38**	12a. purple on red	10·00	50·00
46	**38**	1r. green and red	12·00	32·00

1907. As last, but inscr "INDIA POSTAGE & REVENUE".

47	½a. green (No. 149)	1·50	1·75
48	1a. red (No. 150)	2·25	70

1913. King George V. Optd in two lines.

49*a*	**55**	3p. grey	1·75	40
50	**56**	½a. green	2·50	1·75
51	**57**	1a. red	1·10	10
59	**57**	1a. brown	16·00	9·00
52	**59**	2a. lilac	2·75	3·25
53	**62**	3a. orange	2·75	75
54	**63**	4a. olive	2·75	4·75
55	**64**	6a. bistre	6·00	9·00
57	**66**	12a. red	11·00	45·00
58	**67**	1r. brown and green	23·00	25·00

1928. King George V. Optd in one line.

60	**55**	3p. grey	1·75	15
61	**56**	½a. green	2·50	30
73	**79**	½a. green	1·25	50
61*b*	**80**	9p. green	6·00	1·40
62	**57**	1a. brown	2·25	15
74	**81**	1a. brown	1·00	50
63	**82**	1¼a. mauve	5·00	7·50
64	**70**	2a. lilac	2·75	35
65	**61**	2½a. orange	4·00	17·00
66	**62**	3a. blue	7·00	3·50
75	**57**	3a. red	4·25	23·00
67	**71**	4a. green	10·00	4·75
76	**63**	4a. olive	12·00	6·00
71	**67**	2r. red and orange	60·00	£300
72	**67**	5r. blue and purple	£110	£800

1938. King George VI. Nos. 247/63.

77	**91**	3p. slate	13·00	2·75
78	**91**	½a. brown	7·50	2·00
79	**91**	9p. green	18·00	5·50
80	**91**	1a. red	6·00	2·25
81	**92**	2a. red	2·50	16·00
82	-	2a.6p. violet	3·50	22·00
83	-	3a. green	2·50	10·00
84	-	3a.6p. blue	7·50	48·00
85	-	4a. brown	13·00	8·00
86	-	6a. green	7·00	50·00
87	-	8a. violet	4·25	48·00
88	-	12a. red	3·00	35·00
89	**93**	1r. slate and brown	16·00	50·00
90	**93**	2r. purple and brown	38·00	£200
91	**93**	5r. green and blue	48·00	£450
92	**93**	10r. purple and red	65·00	£900
93	**93**	15r. brown and green	£375	£1800
94	**93**	25r. slate and purple	£200	£1800

1942. King George VI. Optd **NABHA** only.

95	**91**	3p. slate	50·00	9·50
105	**100a**	3p. slate	1·25	1·25
96	**91**	½a. brown	90·00	10·00
106	**100a**	½a. mauve	1·00	2·50
97	**91**	9p. green	12·00	17·00
107	**100a**	9p. green	1·00	2·75
98	**91**	1a. red	15·00	6·50
108	**100a**	1a. red	1·00	5·00
109	**101**	1a.3p. brown	1·00	4·50
110	**101**	1½a. violet	2·50	3·25
111	**101**	2a. red	2·00	4·50
112	**101**	3a. violet	2·00	7·50
113	**101**	3½a. blue	10·00	£100
114	**102**	4a. brown	1·00	1·00
115	**102**	6a. green	18·00	70·00
116	**102**	8a. violet	17·00	60·00
117	**102**	12a. purple	16·00	90·00

OFFICIAL STAMPS

Stamps of Nabha optd SERVICE.

1885. Nos. 1/3 (Queen Victoria).

O1	½a. turquoise	12·00	3·00
O2	1a. purple	70	20
O3	2a. blue	£140	£275

1885. Nos. 14/30 (Queen Victoria).

O6	½a. turquoise	40	10
O7	1a. purple	4·00	60
O5	2a. blue	2·75	55
O11	3a. orange	32·00	£160
O13	4a. green (No. 4)	8·00	2·50
O15	6a. brown	32·00	55·00
O17	8a. mauve	7·50	3·00
O18	12a. purple on red	9·00	30·00
O19	1r. grey	75·00	£600
O20	1r. green and red	45·00	£130

1903. Nos. 37/46 (King Edward VII).

O25	3p. grey	7·00	28·00
O26	½a. green	1·00	50
O27	1a. red	80	10
O29	2a. lilac	6·00	40
O30	4a. olive	3·50	50
O32	8a. mauve	3·75	1·50
O34	1r. green and red	3·75	3·75

1907. Nos. 47/8 (King Edward VII inscr "INDIA POSTAGE & REVENUE").

O35	½a. green	2·75	50
O36	1a. red	1·50	30

1913. Nos. 54 and 58 (King George V).

O37	**63**	4a. olive	10·00	80·00
O38	**67**	1r. brown and green	85·00	£600

1913. Official stamps of India (King George V) optd **NABHA STATE**.

O39*a*	**55**	3p. grey	2·25	11·00
O40	**56**	½a. green	1·00	50
O41	**57**	1a. red	1·50	20
O42	**59**	2a. purple	2·50	1·75
O43	**63**	4a. olive	2·00	1·00
O44	**65**	8a. mauve	4·50	2·25
O46	**67**	1r. brown and green	11·00	8·00

1932. Stamps of India (King George V) optd **NABHA STATE SERVICE**

O47	**55**	3p. grey	10	15
O48	**81**	1a. brown	35	15
O49	**63**	4a. olive	29·00	2·50
O50	**65**	8a. mauve	1·00	3·25

1938. Stamps of India (King George VI) optd **NABHA STATE SERVICE**

O53	**91**	9p. green	12·00	4·00
O54	**91**	1a. red	18·00	1·10

1943. Stamps of India (King George VI) optd **NABHA**

(a) Stamps of India (King George V) optd **NABHA**

O55	**O20**	3p. slate	1·25	3·00
O56	**O20**	½a. brown	1·10	30
O57	**O20**	½a. purple	7·00	2·50
O58	**O20**	9p. green	1·25	50
O59	**O20**	1a. red	2·00	20
O61	**O20**	1½a. violet	70	40
O62	**O20**	2a. orange	2·25	1·50
O64	**O20**	4a. brown	3·00	4·25
O65	**O20**	8a. violet	5·00	27·00

(b) Stamps of India (KingGeorge V) optd **NABHA SERVICE**

O66	**93**	1r. slate and brown	12·00	55·00
O67	**93**	2r. purple and brown	50·00	£450
O68	**93**	5r. green and blue	£275	£1000

NAGORNO-KARABAKH

The mountainous area of Nagorno-Karabakh, mainly populated by Armenians, was declared an Autonomous Region within the Azerbaijan Soviet Socialist Republic in 1923.

Following agitation for union with Armenia in 1998 Nagorno-Karabakh was placed under U.S.S.R. rule in 1989. On 2 September 1991 the Regional Societ declared its independence and this was confirmed by popular vote on 10 December. By 1993 fighting between Azerbaijan forces and those of Nagorno-Karabakh, supported by Armenia, led to the occupation of all Azerbaijan territory separating Nagorno-Karabakh from the border with Armenia. A ceasefire under Russian auspices was signed on 18 February 1994.

1993. 100 kopeks = 1 rouble.
1995. 100 louma = 1 dram

1 National Flag

1993. Inscr "REPUBLIC OF MOUNTAINOUS KARABAKH".

1	**1**	1r. multicoloured	2·10	2·00
2	-	3r. blue, purple and brown	5·00	4·50
3	-	15r. red and blue	24·00	22·00
MS4		80×80 mm. 20r. brown, ultramarine and red	7·00	6·50
MS5		60×80 mm. 20r. brown, ultramarine and red (imperf)	7·00	6·50

Designs:—3r. President Arthur Mkrtchian; 15r. "We are Our Mountains" (sculpture of man and woman); 20r. Gandzasar Monastery.

ա 2 "A" բ 2a "P" գ 2b "K"

1995. Nos. 1 and 3 surch in Armenian script as T **2/2b**.

6	**2**	(50d.) on 1r. multicoloured	14·00	13·00
7	**2a**	(100d.) on 15r. red and blue	21·00	20·00
8	**2b**	(200d.) on 15r. red and blue	35·00	33·00

3 Dadiwank Monastery

1996. Fifth Anniversary of Independence. Multicoloured.

9	50d. Type **3**	70	65
10	100d. Parliament Building, Stepanakert	1·40	1·30
11	200d. "We are Our Mountains" (sculpture of man and woman)	2·10	2·00
MS12	110×82 mm. 50d. Map and flag; 100d. As No. 10; 200d. As No. 11; 500d. Republic Coat of Arms (colours of National Flag extend diagonally across the miniature sheet from bottom left to top right with the order incorrectly shown as orange, blue and red)	7·00	6·50

4 Boy playing Drum and Fawn (Erna Arshakyan)

1997. Festivals. Multicoloured.

13	50d. Type **4** (New Year)	2·75	2·50
14	200d. Madonna and Child with Angels (Mihran Akopyan) (Christmas) (vert)	4·25	4·00

5 Eagle and Demonstrator with Flag

1998. Tenth Anniversary of Karabakh Movement.

15	**5**	250d. multicoloured	5·50	5·25

6 Parliament Summer Palace

1998. Fifth Anniversary of Liberation of Shushi. Multicoloured.

16	100d. Type **6**	1·70	1·60
17	250d. Church of the Saviour (vert)	2·50	1·00
MS18	124×92 mm. 750d. Type **6**	7·00	1·00

NAKHICHEVAN

An autonomous province of Azerbaijan, separated from the remainder of the republic by Armenian territory. Nos. 1 and 2 were issued during a period when the administration of Nakhichevan was in dispute with the central government.

100 qopik = 1 manat.

1 President Aliev

1993. 70th Birthday of President H. Aliev of Nakhichevan.

1	**1**	5m. black and red	9·50	9·50
2	-	5m. multicoloured	9·50	9·50
MS3		110×90 mm. Nos. 1/2	£250	£250

Design:—No. 2, Map of Nakhichevan.

NAMIBIA

Formerly South West Africa, which became independent on 21 March 1990.

1990. 100 cents = 1 rand.
1993. 100 cents = 1 Namibia dollar.

141 Pres. Sam Nujoma, Map of Namibia and National Flag

1990. Independence. Multicoloured.

538	18c. Type **141**	20	15
539	45c. Hands releasing dove and map of Namibia (vert)	50	75
540	60c. National Flag and map of Africa	1·00	1·50

142 Fish River Canyon

1990. Namibia Landscapes. Multicoloured.

541	18c. Type **142**	25	20
542	35c. Quiver-tree forest, Keetmanshoop	50	35
543	45c. Tsaris Mountains	60	55
544	60c. Dolerite boulders, Keetmanshoop	70	65

143 Stores on Kaiser Street, c. 1899

1990. Centenary of Windhoek. Multicoloured.

545	18c. Type **143**	20	20
546	35c. Kaiser Street, 1990	30	35
547	45c. City Hall, 1914	40	65
548	60c. City Hall, 1990	50	1·00

144 Maizefields

1990. Farming. Multicoloured.

549	20c. Type **144**	15	20
550	35c. Sanga bull	30	35
551	50c. Damara ram	40	45
552	65c. Irrigation in Okavango	50	60

145 Gypsum

1991. Minerals. As Nos. 519/21 and 523/33 of South West Africa, some with values changed and new design (5r.), inscr "Namibia" as T **145**. Multicoloured.

553	1c. Type **145**	15	30
554	2c. Fluorite	25	30
555	5c. Mimetite	35	30
556	10c. Azurite	50	30
557	20c. Dioptase	65	10
558	25c. Type **139**	1·00	20
559	30c. Tsumeb lead and copper complex	85	20
560	35c. Rosh Pinah zinc mine	85	20
561	40c. Diamonds	1·50	25
562	50c. Uis tin mine	1·00	25
563	65c. Boltwoodite	90	35
564	1r. Rossing uranium mine	1·25	50
565	1r.50 Wulfenite	1·40	70
566	2r. Gold	2·00	1·10
567	5r. Willemite (vert as T **145**)	3·00	2·75

146 Radiosonde Weather Balloon

1991. Centenary of Weather Service. Mult.

568	20c. Type **146**	20	20
569	35c. Sunshine recorder	35	30
570	50c. Measuring equipment	45	50
571	65c. Meteorological station, Gobabeb	50	60

147 Herd of Zebras

1991. Endangered Species. Mountain Zebra. Mult.

572	20c. Type **147**	1·00	60
573	25c. Mare and foal	1·10	70
574	45c. Zebras and foal	1·50	1·75
575	60c. Two zebras	1·75	3·00

148 Karas Mountains

1991. Mountains of Namibia. Multicoloured.

576	20c. Type **148**	20	20
577	25c. Gamsberg Mountains	30	30
578	45c. Mount Brukkaros	45	70
579	60c. Erongo Mountains	65	1·00

149 Bernabe de la Bat Camp

1991. Tourist Camps. Multicoloured.

580	20c. Type **149**	45	30
581	25c. Von Bach Dam Recreation Resort	55	45
582	45c. Gross Barmen Hot Springs	85	65
583	60c. Namutoni Rest Camp	1·00	1·00

150 Artist's Pallet

1992. 21st Anniv of Windhoek Conservatoire. Multicoloured.

584	20c. Type **150**	20	15
585	25c. French horn and cello	25	20
586	45c. Theatrical masks	50	60
587	60c. Ballet dancers	65	1·25

151 Mozambique Mouthbrooder

1992. Freshwater Angling. Multicoloured.

588	20c. Type **151**	40	20
589	25c. Large-mouthed yellowfish	45	20
590	45c. Common carp	85	50
591	60c. Sharp-toothed catfish	95	65

152 Old Jetty

1992. Centenary of Swakopmund. Mult.

592	20c. Type **152**	25	25
593	25c. Recreation centre	25	25
594	45c. State House and lighthouse	80	60
595	60c. Sea front	85	75
MS596	118×93 mm. Nos. 592/5	3·50	4·00

153 Running

1992. Olympic Games, Barcelona. Mult.

597	20c. Type **153**	25	20
598	25c. Map of Namibia, Namibian flag and Olympic rings	30	20
599	45c. Swimming	50	40
600	60c. Olympic Stadium, Barcelona	65	55
MS601	115×75 mm. Nos. 597/600 (sold at 2r.)	2·25	3·50

154 Wrapping English Cucumbers

1992. Integration of the Disabled. Mult.

602	20c. Type **154**	20	15
603	25c. Weaving mats	20	15
604	45c. Spinning thread	40	30
605	60c. Preparing pot plants	55	50

155 Elephants in Desert

1993. Namibia Nature Foundation. Rare and Endangered Species. Multicoloured.

606	20c. Type **155**	60	20
607	25c. Sitatunga in swamp	30	20
608	45c. Black rhinoceros	90	50
609	60c. Hunting dogs	65	60
MS610	217×59 mm. Nos. 606/9 (sold at 2r.50)	3·75	3·50

156 Herd of Simmentaler Cattle

1993. Centenary of Simmentalar Cattle in Namibia. Multicoloured.

611	20c. Type **156**	30	10
612	25c. Cow and calf	30	15
613	45c. Bull	60	40
614	60c. Cattle on barge	85	75

157 Sand Dunes, Sossusvlei

1993. Namib Desert Scenery. Multicoloured.

615	30c. Type **157**	25	20
616	40c. Blutkuppe	25	20
617	65c. River Kuiseb, Homeb	40	45

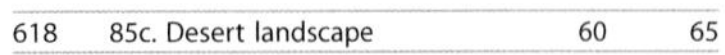

618	85c. Desert landscape	60	65

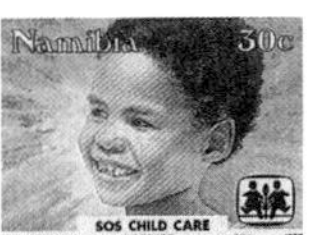

158 Smiling Child

1993. S.O.S. Child Care in Namibia. Mult.

619	30c. Type **158**	20	20
620	40c. Family	25	20
621	65c. Modern house	45	55
622	85c. Young artist with mural	65	80

159 *Charaxes jasius*

1993. Butterflies. Multicoloured.

623	5c. Type **159**	20	50
624	10c. *Acraea anemosa*	20	50
625	20c. *Papilio nireus*	30	30
626	30c. *Junonia octavia*	30	10
627	40c. *Hypolimnus misippus*	30	10
628	50c. *Physcaeneura panda*	40	20
629	65c. *Charaxes candiope*	40	30
630	85c. *Junonia hierta*	50	40
631	90c. *Colotis cellmene*	50	40
632	$1 *Cacyreus dicksoni*	55	35
633	$2 *Charaxes bohemani*	80	1·00
634	$2.50 *Stugeta bowkeri*	1·00	1·25
635	$5 *Byblia anvatara*	1·50	2·00

See also No. 648.

160 White Seabream

1994. Coastal Angling. Multicoloured.

636	30c. Type **160**	25	25
637	40c. Kob	25	25
638	65c. West coast steenbras	40	40
639	85c. Galjoen	60	60
MS640	134×89 mm. Nos. 636/9 (sold at $2.50)	2·00	2·50

161 Container Ship at Wharf

1994. Incorporation of Walvis Bay Territory into Namibia. Multicoloured.

641	30c. Type **161**	40	60
642	65c. Aerial view of Walvis Bay	60	90
643	85c. Map of Namibia	95	1·50

162 *Adenolobus pechuelii*

1994. Flowers. Multicoloured.

644	35c. Type **162**	25	25
645	40c. *Hibiscus elliottiae*	25	25
646	65c. *Pelargonium cortusifolium*	40	40
647	85c. *Hoodia macrantha*	50	60

1994. Butterflies. As T **159**, but inscr "STANDARDISED MAIL". Multicoloured.

648	(–) *Graphium antheus*	40	20

No. 648 was initially sold at 35c., but this was subsequently increased to reflect changes in postal rates.

163 Yellow-billed Stork

1994. Storks. Multicoloured.

649	35c. Type **163**	60	30
650	40c. Abdim's stork	60	40
651	80c. African open-bill stork	80	80
652	$1.10 White stork	1·00	1·25

164 Steam Railcar, 1908

1994. Steam Locomotives. Multicoloured.

653	35c. Type **164**	45	30
654	70c. Krauss side-tank locomotive No. 106, 1904	70	50
655	80c. Class 24 locomotive, 1948	75	55
656	$1.10 Class 7C locomotive, 1914	1·10	80

165 Cape Cross Locomotive No. 84 *Prince Edward*, 1895

1995. Cent of Railways in Namibia. Mult.

657	35c. Type **165**	45	25
658	70c. Steam locomotive, German South West Africa	70	35
659	80c. South African Railways Class 8 steam locomotive	75	40
660	$1.10 Trans-Namib Class 33-400 diesel-electric locomotive	1·10	55
MS661	101×94 mm. Nos. 657/60	2·75	2·50

166 National Arms

1995. Fifth Anniv of Independence.

662	**166**	(–) multicoloured	45	30

No. 662 is inscribed "STANDARDISED MAIL" and was initially sold for 35c., but this was subsequently increased to reflect changes in postal rates.

167 Living Tortoise and 'Geochelone stromeri' (fossil)

1995. Fossils. Multicoloured.

663	40c. Type **167**	65	25
664	80c. Ward's diamond bird and 'Diamantornis wardi' (fossil eggs)	1·00	70
665	90c. Hyraxes and 'Prohyrax hendeyi' skull	1·10	1·00
666	$1.20 Crocodiles and 'Crocodylus lloydi' skull	1·40	2·00

168 Martii Rautanen and Church

1995. 125th Anniv of Finnish Missionaries in Namibia. Multicoloured.

667	40c. Type **168**	25	20
668	80c. Albin Savola and hand printing press	50	50
669	90c. Karl Weikkolin and wagon	60	65
670	$1.20 Dr. Selma Rainio and Onandjokwe Hospital	85	95

169 Ivory Buttons

1995. Personal Ornaments. Multicoloured.

671	40c. Type **169**	20	20
672	80c. Conus shell pendant	45	45
673	90c. Cowrie shell headdress	55	55
674	$1.20 Shell button pendant	85	95

169a Warthog

1995. Singapore '95 International Stamp Exhibition. Sheet 110×52 mm, containing design as No. 359b of South West Africa.

MS675 **169a** $1.20 multicoloured 1·10 1·40

170 UN Flag

1995. 50th Anniv of the United Nations.

676 **170** 40c. blue and black 25 30

171 Bogenfels Arch

1996. Tourism. Multicoloured.

677	(–) Type **171**	15	15
678	90c. Ruacana Falls	30	30
679	$1 Epupa Falls	30	30
680	$1.30 Herd of wild horses	35	50

No. 677 is inscribed "Standardised Mail" and was initially sold at 45c.

172 Sister Leoni Kreitmeier and Dobra Education and Training Centre

1996. Centenary of Catholic Missions in Namibia. Multicoloured.

681	50c. Type **172**	20	20
682	95c. Father Johann Malinowski and Heirachabis Mission	30	40
683	$1 St. Mary's Cathedral, Windhoek	30	40
684	$1.30 Archbishop Joseph Gotthardt and early church, Ovamboland	35	80

172a Caracal

1996. CAPEX '96 International Stamp Exhibition, Toronto. Sheet 105×45 mm, containing design as No. 358c of South West Africa.

MS685 **172a** $1.30 multicoloured 1·00 1·40

173 Children and UNICEF Volunteer

1996. 50th Anniv of UNICEF. Multicoloured.

686	(–) Type **173**	15	15
687	$1.30 Girls in school	60	60

No. 686 is inscribed "STANDARD POSTAGE" and was initially sold at 50c.

174 Boxing

1996. Centennial Olympic Games, Atlanta. Mult.

688	(–) Type **174**	15	15
689	90c. Cycling	50	40
690	$1 Swimming	30	40
691	$1.30 Running	30	55

No. 688 is inscribed "Standard Postage" and was initially sold at 50c.

175 Scorpius

1996. Stars in the Namibian Sky. Multicoloured.

692	(–) Type **175**	15	15
693	90c. Sagittarius	25	30
694	$1 Southern Cross	30	30
695	$1.30 Orion	40	50
MS696	100×80 mm. No. 694	1·50	1·75

No. 692 is inscribed "Standard Postage" and was initially sold at 50c.

See also No. **MS**706.

176 Urn-shaped Pot

1996. Early Pottery. Multicoloured.

697	(–) Type **176**	15	15
698	90c. Decorated storage pot	30	40
699	$1 Reconstructed cooking pot	30	40
700	$1.30 Storage pot	35	70

No. 697 is inscribed "Standard Postage" and was initially sold at 50c.

177 Khauxanas Ruins

1997. Khaux!nas Ruins.

701	**177**	(–) multicoloured	35	20
702	-	$1 multicoloured	75	55
703	-	$1.10 multicoloured	85	75
704	-	$1.50 multicoloured	1·40	2·00

Designs:—$1 to $1.50, Different views.

No. 701 is inscribed "Standard postage" and was initially sold at 50c.

178 Ox

1997. HONG KONG '97 International Stamp Exhibition and Chinese New Year ("Year of the Ox"). Sheet 103×67 mm.

MS705 **178** $1.30 multicoloured 1·10 1·40

1997. Support for Organised Philately. No. **MS**696 with margin additionally inscr "Reprint February 17 1997. Sold in aid of organised philately N$3.50".

MS706 $1 Southern Cross (sold at $3.50) 2·00 2·25

179 Heinrich von Stephan

1997. Death Centenary of Heinrich von Stephan (founder of U.P.U.).

709 **179** $2 multicoloured 1·25 1·40

180 Cinderella Waxbill

1997. Waxbills. Multicoloured.

710	50c. Type **180**	50	40
711	60c. Black-cheeked waxbill	50	60

181 Helmeted Guineafowl

1997. Greetings Stamp.

712 **181** $1.20 multicoloured 1·00 1·00

For similar designs see Nos. 728/32 and 744/**MS**748.

182 Jackass Penguins Calling

1997. Endangered Species. Jackass Penguin. Mult.

713	(–) Type **182**	35	30
714	$1 Incubating egg	55	40
715	$1.10 Adult with chick	60	50
716	$1.50 Penguins swimming	75	60
MS717	101×92 mm. As Nos. 713/16, but without WWF symbol (sold at $5)	1·90	1·50

No. 713 is inscribed "STANDARD POSTAGE" and was initially sold at 50c.

183 Caracal

1997. Wildcats. Multicoloured.

718	(–) Type **183**	20	20
719	$1 *Felis lybic*	40	30
720	$1.10 Serval	50	40
721	$1.50 Black-footed cat	60	55
MS722	100×80 mm. $5 As No. 721	2·00	2·25

No. **MS**722 was sold in aid of organised philately in Southern Africa.

No. 718 is inscribed "STANDARD POSTAGE" and was initially sold at 50c.

184 *Catophractes alexandri*

1997. Greeting Stamps. Flowers and Helmeted Guineafowl. Multicoloured.

723	(–) Type **184**	35	45
724	(–) *Crinum paludosum*	35	45
725	(–) *Gloriosa superba*	35	45
726	(–) *Tribulus zeyheri*	35	45
727	(–) *Aptosimum pubescens*	35	45
728	50c. Helmeted guineafowl raising hat	35	45
729	50c. Holding bouquet	35	45
730	50c. Ill in bed	35	45
731	$1 With heart round neck	65	75
732	$1 With suitcase and backpack	65	75

Nos. 723/7 are inscribed "Standard Postage" and were initially sold at 50c. each.

185 Collecting Bag

1997. Basket Work. Multicoloured.

733	50c. Type **185**	20	20
734	90c. Powder basket	30	30
735	$1.20 Fruit basket	35	35
736	$2 Grain basket	70	75

186 Veterinary Association Coat of Arms

1997. 50th Anniv of Namibian Veterinary Association.

737 **186** $1.50 multicoloured 50 50

187 Head of Triceratops

1997. Youth Philately. Dinosaurs. Sheet 82×56 mm.

MS738 **187** $5 multicoloured 1·50 1·75

188 German South West Africa Postman

1997. World Post Day.

739 **188** (–) multicoloured 30 30

No. 739 is inscribed "STANDARD POSTAGE" and was initially sold at 50c.

189 False Mopane

1997. Trees. Multicoloured.

740	(–) Type **189**	15	20
741	$1 Ana tree	30	40
742	$1.10 Shepherd's tree	35	55
743	$1.50 Kiaat	50	70

No. 740 is inscribed "STANDARD POSTAGE" and was initially sold at 50c.

1997. Christmas. As T **181**, showing Helmeted Guineafowl, each with festive frame. Mult.

744	(–) Guineafowl facing right	20	20
745	$1 Guineafowl in grass	35	30
746	$1.10 Guineafowl on rock	35	40
747	$1.50 Guineafowl in desert	50	55
MS748	110×80 mm. $5 Helmeted guineafowl (vert)	3·00	3·25

No. 744 is inscribed "standard postage" and was initially sold at 50c.

190 Flame Lily

1997. Flora and Fauna. Multicoloured.

749	5c. Type **190**	10	50
750	10c. Bushman poison	10	50
751	20c. Camel's foot	10	50
752	30c. Western rhigozum	50	50
753	40c. Blue-cheeked bee-eater	50	50
754	50c. Laughing dove	50	20
755a	(–) Peach-faced lovebird ("Roseyfaced Lovebird")	35	30
756	60c. Lappet-faced vulture	60	25
757	90c. Southern yellow-billed hornbill ("Yellow-billed Hornbill")	60	25
758	$1 Lilac-breasted roller	60	30
759	$1.10 Hippopotamus	1·00	40
760	$1.20 Giraffe	1·00	40
761a	(–) Leopard	60	60
762	$1.50 Elephant	1·25	45
763	$2 Lion	75	45
764	$4 Buffalo	1·25	85
765	$5 Black rhinoceros	2·00	1·25
766	$10 Cheetah	2·50	2·25

No. 755a is inscribed "standard postage" and was initially sold at 50c.; No. 761a is inscribed "postcard rate" and was initially sold at $1.20.

Nos. 755a, 758 and 761a exist with ordinary or self-adhesive gum.

191 John Muafangejo

1997. Tenth Death Anniv of John Muafangejo (artist).

770	**191**	(–) multicoloured	60	50

No. 770 is inscribed "STANDARD POSTAGE" and was initially sold at 50c.

192 Gabriel B. Taapopi

1998. Gabriel B. Taapopi (writer) Commemoration.

771	**192**	(–) silver and brown	40	40

No. 771 is inscribed "STANDARD POSTAGE" and was initially sold at 50c.

193 Year of the Tiger

1998. International Stamp and Coin Exhibition, 1997, Shanghai. Sheets 165×125 mm or 97×85 mm, containing multicoloured designs as T **193**. (a) Lunar New Year.

MS772	165×125 mm. $2.50×6. Type **193**; Light green tiger and circular symbol; Yellow tiger and head symbol; Blue tiger and square symbol; Emerald tiger and square symbol; Mauve tiger and triangular symbol (61×29 mm)	2·50	3·25
MS773	97×85 mm. $6 Symbolic tiger designs (71×40 mm)	1·25	1·40

(b) Chinese Calendar.

MS774	165×125 mm. $2.50×6. Various calendar symbols (24×80 mm)	2·50	3·25
MS775	97×85 mm. $6 Soft toy tigers (71×36 mm)	1·25	1·40

(c) 25th Anniv of Shanghai Communique.

MS776	165×125 mm. $3.50×4. Pres. Nixon's visit to China, 1972; Vice Premier Deng Xiaoping's visit to USA, 1979; Pres. Reagan's visit to China, 1984; Pres. Bush's visit to China, 1989 (61×32 mm)	2·00	3·00
MS777	97×85 mm. $6 China–U.S.A. Communique, 1972 (69×36 mm)	1·25	1·40

(d) Pres. Deng Xiaoping's Project for Unification of China.

MS778	165×125 mm. $3.50×4. Beijing as National Capital; Return of Hong Kong; Return of Macao; Links with Taiwan (37×65 mm)	2·00	3·00
MS779	97×85 mm. $6 Reunified China (71×41 mm)	1·25	1·40

(e) Return of Macao to China, 1999.

MS780	Two sheets, each 165×120 mm. (a) $4.50×3 Carnival dragon and modern Macao (44×33 mm). (b) $4.50×3 Ruins of St. Paul's Church, Macao (62×29 mm) Set of 2 sheets	2·50	4·75
MS781	Two sheets, each 97×85 mm. (a) $6 Carnival dragon and modern Macao (62×32 mm). (b) $6 Deng Xiaoping and ruins of St. Paul's Church, Macao (71×36 mm) Set of 2 sheets	1·75	2·75

194 Leopard

1998. Large Wild Cats. Multicoloured.

782	$1.20 Type **194**	60	40
783	$1.90 Lioness and cub	80	65
784	$2 Lion	80	1·25
785	$2.50 Cheetah	95	1·50
MS786	112×98 mm. Nos. 782/5	3·50	3·50

195 Narra Plant

1998. Narra Cultivation.

787	**195**	$2.40 multicoloured	55	65

196 Collecting Rain Water

1998. World Water Day.

788	**196**	(–) multicoloured	50	40

No. 788 is inscribed "STANDARD POSTAGE" and was initially sold at 50c. On 1 April 1998 the standard postage rate was increased to 55c.

1998. Diana, Princess of Wales Commemoration. Sheet 145×70 mm, containing vert designs as T **91** of Kiribati. Multicoloured.

MS789	$1 Princess Diana wearing protective mask; $1 Wearing Red Cross badge; $1 Wearing white shirt; $1 Comforting crippled child	1·60	1·75

197 White-faced Scops Owl ("Whitefaced Owl")

1998. Owls of Namibia. Multicoloured.

790	55c. Black-tailed tree rat (20×24 mm)	50	50
791	$1.50 Type **197**	1·00	1·10
792	$1.50 African barred owl ("Barred Owl")	1·00	1·10
793	$1.90 Spotted eagle owl	1·10	1·40
794	$1.90 Barn owl (61×24 mm)	1·10	1·40

See also No. **MS**850.

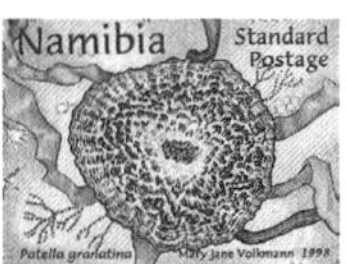

198 *Patella ganatina* (Limpet)

1998. Shells. Multicoloured.

795	(–) Type **198**	30	10
796	$1.10 *Cymatium cutaceum africanum* (Triton)	65	30
797	$1.50 *Conus mozambicus* (Cone)	85	65
798	$6 *Venus verrucosa* (Venus clam)	2·75	3·75
MS799	109×84 mm. Nos. 795/8	4·50	5·50

No. 795 is inscribed "Standard Postage" and was initially sold at 55c.

199 Underwater Diamond Excavator

1998. Marine Technology. Sheet 70×90 mm.

MS800	**199** $2.50 multicoloured	2·50	2·50

200 "Chinga" (cheetah)

1998. Wildlife Conservation. "Racing for Survival" (Olympic sprinter Frank Frederiks v cheetah). Sheet 108×80 mm.

MS801	**200** $5 multicoloured	1·75	2·25

201 Namibian Beach

1998. World Environment Day. Multicoloured.

802	(–) Type **201**	25	10
803	$1.10 Okavango sunset	50	30
804	$1.50 Sossusvlei	65	60
805	$1.90 African Moringo tree	90	1·00

No. 802 is inscribed "STANDARD POSTAGE" and was initially sold at 55c.

202 Two Footballers

1998. World Cup Football Championship, France. Sheet 80×56 mm.

MS806	**202** $5 multicoloured	1·25	1·75

203 Chacma Baboon

1998. Animals with their Young. Sheet 176×60 mm, containing T **203** and similar vert designs.

MS807	$1.50, Type **203**; $1.50, Blue Wildebeest; $1.50, Meercat (suricate); $1.50, African Elephant; $1.50, Burchell's Zebra	1·75	2·50

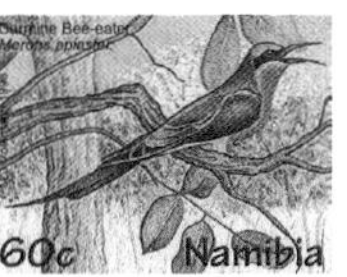

204 Carmine Bee-eater

1998. Wildlife of the Caprivi Strip. Multicoloured.

808	60c. Type **204**	80	80
809	60c. Sable antelope (40×40 mm)	80	80
810	60c. Lechwe (40×40 mm)	80	80
811	60c. Woodland waterberry	80	80
812	60c. Nile monitor (40×40 mm)	80	80
813	60c. African jacana	80	80
814	60c. African fish eagle	80	80
815	60c. Woodland kingfisher	80	80
816	60c. Nile crocodile (55×30 mm)	80	80
817	60c. Black mamba (32×30 mm)	80	80

Nos. 808/17 were printed together, *se-tenant*, with the backgrounds forming a composite design.

205 Black Rhinoceros and Calf

1998. ILSAPEX '98 International Stamp Exhibition, Johannesburg. Sheet 103×68 mm.

MS818	**205** $5 multicoloured	1·75	2·25

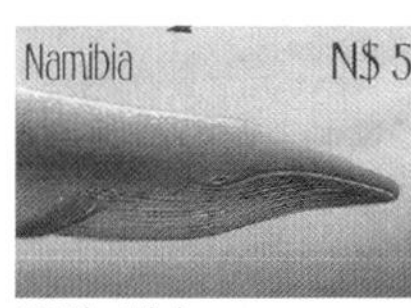

206 Blue Whale

1998. Whales of the Southern Oceans (joint issue with Norfolk Island and South Africa). Sheet 103×70 mm.

MS819	**206** $5 multicoloured	1·75	2·25

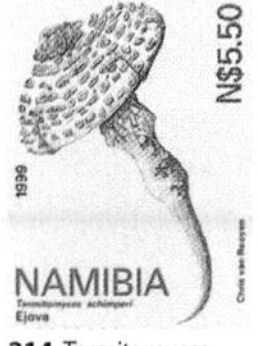

207 Damara Dik-dik

1999. "Fun Stamps for Children". Animals. Mult.

820	$1.80 Type **207**	2·25	1·50
821	$2.65 Striped tree squirrel (26×36 mm)	3·75	4·00

208 Yoka perplexed

1999. Yoka the Snake (cartoon). Multicoloured. Self-adhesive.

822	$1.60 Type **208**	35	40
823	$1.60 Yoka under attack (33×27 mm)	35	40
824	$1.60 Yoka caught on branch	35	40
825	$1.60 Yoka and wasps (33×27 mm)	35	40
826	$1.60 Yoka and footprint	35	40
827	$1.60 Yoka and tail of red and white snake	35	40
828	$1.60 Mouse hunt (33×27 mm)	35	40
829	$1.60 Snakes entwined	35	40
830	$1.60 Red and white snake singing	35	40
831	$1.60 Yoka sulking (33×27 mm)	35	40

See also Nos.**MS**835, and **MS**877.

209 *Windhuk* (liner)

1999. *Windhuk* (liner) Commemoration. Sheet 110×90 mm.

MS832	**209** $5.50 multicoloured	1·50	2·00

210 Zogling Glider, 1928

1999. Gliding in Namibia. Multicoloured.

833	$1.60 Type **210**	40	50
834	$1.80 Schleicher glider, 1998	60	75

211 Yoka the Snake with Toy Zebra

1999. iBRA '99 International Stamp Exhibition, Nuremberg. Sheet 110×84 mm.

MS835	**211** $5.50 multicoloured	1·25	1·75

212 Greater Kestrel

1999. Birds of Prey. Multicoloured.

836	60c. Type **212**	75	45
837	$1.60 Common kestrel ("Rock Kestrel")	1·25	90
838	$1.80 Red-headed falcon ("Red-necked Falcon")	1·25	1·00
839	$2.65 Lanner falcon	2·00	3·00

213 Wattled Crane

1999. Wetland Birds. Multicoloured.

840	$1.60 Type **213**	1·10	70
841	$1.80 Variegated sandgrouse ("Burchell's Sandgrouse")	1·25	1·00
842	$1.90 White-collared pratincole ("Rock Pratincole")	1·25	1·00
843	$2.65 Eastern white pelican	1·90	3·00

214 *Termitomyces schimperi* (fungus)

1999. PhilexFrance '99 International Stamp Exhibition, Paris. Sheet 79×54 mm.

MS844 **214**	$5.50 multicoloured	1·75	2·25

215 *Eulophia hereroensis* (orchid)

1999. China '99 International Philatelic Exhibition, Beijing. Orchids. Multicoloured.

845	$1.60 Type **215**	80	65
846	$1.80 *Ansellia africana*	90	75
847	$2.65 *Eulophia leachii*	1·40	1·75
848	$3.90 *Eulophia speciosa*	2·00	2·50
MS849	72×72 mm. $5.50 *Eulophia walleri*	2·00	2·50

1999. Winning entry in 5th Stamp World Cup, France. Sheet 120×67 mm, design as No. 794, but with changed face value. Multicoloured.

MS850	$11 Barn owl (61×24 mm)	7·50	7·50

216 Johanna Gertze

1999. Johanna Gertze Commemoration.

851 **216**	$20 red, pink and blue	4·00	5·00

217 Sunset over Namibia

1999. New Millennium. Multicoloured.

852	$2.20 Type **217**	1·10	1·10
853	$2.40 Sunrise over Namibia	1·25	1·40
MS854	77×54 mm. $9 Globe (hologram) (37×44 mm)	3·50	4·00

218 South African Shelduck

2000. Ducks of Namibia. Multicoloured.

855	$2 Type **218**	1·00	60
856	$2.40 White-faced whistling duck	1·25	75
857	$3 Comb duck ("Knobbilled duck")	1·60	1·40
858	$7 Cape shoveler	3·25	4·50

No. 858 is inscribed "Cape shoveller" in error.

2000. Nos. 749/52 surch with standard postage (859) or new values (others).

859	(–) on 5c. Type **190**	50	15
860	$1.80 on 30c. Western rhigozum	90	40
861	$3 on 10c. Bushman poison	1·25	1·25
862	$6 on 20c. Camel's foot	2·00	2·50

No. 859 was initially sold at 65c. The other surcharges show face values.

220 Namibian Children

2000. Tenth Anniv of Independence. Multicoloured.

863	65c. Type **220**	50	15
864	$3 Namibian flag	1·75	1·75

221 Actor playing Jesus wearing Crown of Thorns

2000. Easter Passion Play. Multicoloured.

865	$2.10 Type **221**	70	70
866	$2.40 On the way to Calvary	80	80

222 Tenebrionid Beetle

2000. The Stamp Show 2000 International Stamp Exhibition, London. Wildlife of Namibian Dunes. Sheet 165×73 mm, containing T **222** and similar multicoloured designs.

MS867	$2 Type **222**; $2 Namib golden mole; $2 Brown hyena; $2 Shovel-snouted lizard (49×30 mm); $2 Dune lark (25×36 mm); $6 Namib side-winding adder (25×36 mm)	8·50	9·00

223 *Welwitschia mirabilis*

2000. Welwitschia mirabilis (prehistoric plant). Multicoloured.

868	(–) Type **223**	55	20
869	$2.20 *Welwitschia mirabilis* from above	1·25	70
870	$3 Seed pods	1·75	1·75
871	$4 Flats covered by *Welwitschia mirabilis*	2·00	2·50

No. 868 is inscribed "Standard inland mail" and was originally sold for 65c.

224 High Energy Stereoscopic System Telescopes

2000. High Energy Stereoscopic System Telescopes Project. Namibian Khomas Highlands. Sheet 100×70 mm.

MS872 **224**	$11 multicoloured	5·50	7·00

225 Jackal-berry Tree

2000. Trees with Nutritional Value. Multicoloured.

873	(–) Type **225**	45	25
874	$2 Sycamore fig	1·00	1·00
875	$2.20 Bird plum	1·10	1·00
876	$7 Marula	3·25	4·50

No. 873 is inscribed "Standard inland mail" and was originally sold for 65c.

226 Yoka and Nero the Elephant

2000. "Yoka the Snake" (cartoon) (2nd series). Sheet 103×68 mm.

MS877 **226**	$11 multicoloured	5·00	6·00

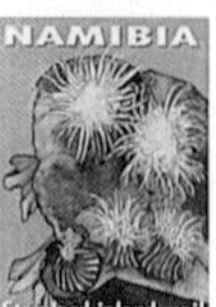

227 Striped Anemone

2001. Sea Anemone. Multicoloured.

878	(–) Type **227**	60	20
879	$2.45 Violet-spotted anemone	1·25	80
880	$3.50 Knobbly anemone	1·75	1·75
881	$6.60 False plum anemone	3·00	4·00

No. 878 is inscribed "Standard inland mail" and was originally sold for 70c.

228 Cessna 210 Turbo Aircraft

2001. Civil Aviation. Multicoloured.

882	(–) Type **228**	90	25
883	$2.20 Douglas DC-6B airliner	1·75	85
884	$2.50 Pitts S2A bi-plane	1·75	1·00
885	$13.20 Bell 407 helicopter	7·00	8·50

No. 882 is inscribed "Standard inland mail" and was originally sold for 70c.

229 Wood-burning Stove

2001. Renewable Energy Sources. Multicoloured.

886	(–) Type **229**	90	90
887	(–) Biogas digester	90	90
888	(–) Solar cooker	90	90
889	(–) Re-cycled tyre	90	90
890	(–) Solar water pump	90	90
891	$3.50 Solar panel above traditional hut	1·25	1·50
892	$3.50 Solar street light	1·25	1·50
893	$3.50 Solar panels on hospital building	1·25	1·50
894	$3.50 Solar telephone	1·25	1·50
895	$3.50 Wind pump	1·25	1·50

Nos. 886/95 were printed together, *se-tenant*, with the backgrounds forming a composite design.

Nos. 886/90 are inscribed "Standard Mail" and were originally sold for $1 each.

230 Ruppell's Parrot

2001. Flora and Fauna from the Central Highlands. Multicoloured.

896	(–) Type **230**	1·25	1·25
897	(–) Flap-necked chameleon (40×30 mm)	1·25	1·25
898	(–) Klipspringer (40×30 mm)	1·25	1·25
899	(–) Rockrunner (40×30 mm)	1·25	1·25
900	(–) Pangolin (40×40 mm)	1·25	1·25
901	$3.50 Camel thorn (55×30 mm)	1·60	1·75
902	$3.50 Berg aloe (40×30 mm)	1·60	1·75
903	$3.50 Kudu (40×40 mm)	1·60	1·75
904	$3.50 Rock agama (40×40 mm)	1·60	1·75
905	$3.50 Armoured ground cricket (40×30 mm)	1·60	1·75

Nos. 896/905 were printed together, *se-tenant*, with the backgrounds forming a composite design.

Nos. 896/900 are inscribed "Standard Mail" and were originally sold for $1 each.

231 Plaited Hair, Mbalantu

2002. Traditional Women's Hairstyles and Headdresses. Multicoloured.

906	(–) Type **231**	2·50	2·50
907	(–) Cloth headdress, Damara	2·50	2·50
908	(–) Beaded hair ornaments, San	2·50	2·50
909	(–) Leather ekori headdress, Herero	2·50	2·50
910	(–) Bonnet, Baster	2·50	2·50
911	(–) Seed necklaces, Mafue	2·50	2·50
912	(–) Thihukeka hairstyle, Mbukushu	2·75	2·75
913	(–) Triangular cloth headdress, Herero	2·75	2·75
914	(–) Goat-skin headdress, Himba	2·75	2·75
915	(–) Horned headdress, Kwanyama	2·75	2·75
916	(–) Headscarf, Nama	2·75	2·75
917	(–) Plaits and oshikoma, Ngandjera/Kwaluudhi	2·75	2·75

Nos. 906/17 are inscribed "STANDARD MAIL" and were originally sold for $1 each.

232 African Hoopoe

2002. Birds. Multicoloured.

918	(–) Type **232**	1·50	75
919	$2.20 Paradise flycatcher	2·00	1·00
920	$2.60 Swallowtailed bee-eater	2·25	2·00
921	$2.80 Malachite kingfisher	2·50	2·75

No. 918 is inscribed "Standard Mail" and was originally sold for $1.

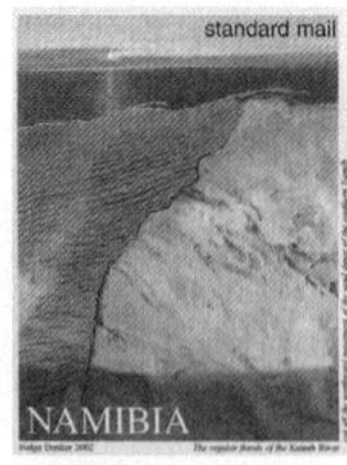

233 The Regular Floods of Kuiseb River

2002. Ephemeral Rivers. Multicoloured.

922	(–) Type **233**	90	25
923	$2.20 Tsauchab River after heavy rainfall (39×31 mm)	1·40	60
924	$2.60 Elephants in the sandbed of the Hoarusib River (89×24 mm)	2·25	1·75
925	$2.80 Nossob River after heavy rainfall (39×32 mm)	1·75	2·00
926	$3.50 Fish River and birds (23×57 mm)	3·00	4·00

No. 922 is inscribed "standard mail" and was initially sold for $1.30.

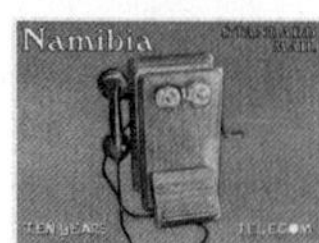

234 Wall Mounted Telephone, 1958

2002. Tenth Anniv of Nampost and Telecommunication. Multicoloured.

MS927	102×171 mm. ($1.30) Type **234**; ($1.30) Courier van; ($1.30) Black wall mounted phone; ($1.30) Pillar box and envelope; ($1.30) Black desk top phone; ($1.30) Computer; ($1.30) Unplugged phone; ($1.30) Dolphin carrying envelope; ($1.30) Modern multi-function phone; ($1.30) Aeroplane and envelopes	6·00	7·00
MS928	102×171 mm. ($1.30) Type **234**×2; ($1.30) Black wall mounted phone; ($1.30) Black desk top phone×2; ($1.30) Unplugged phone×2; ($1.30) Modern multi-function phone×2	6·00	7·00
MS929	102×171 mm. ($1.30) Courier van×2; ($1.30) Pillar box and envelope×2; ($1.30) Computer×2; ($1.30) Dolphin carrying envelope×2; ($1.30) Aeroplane and envelopes×2	6·00	7·00

The stamps in Nos. **MS**927/9 were all inscribed "Standard Mail" and were initially sold for $1.30.

2002. Nos. 749/50 optd standard postage.

930	(–) Type **190**	65	40
931	(–) Bushman poison	65	40

Nos. 930/1 were initially sold for $1.30.

235 Black Cross

2002. Health Care. AIDS Awareness. Multicoloured.

932	(–) Type **235**	45	25
933	$2.45 Blood cell	85	45
934	$2.85 Hand reaching to seated man	90	65
935	$11.50 Three test tubes	4·50	6·50

No. 932 was inscribed "Standard Mail" was initially sold for $1.30.

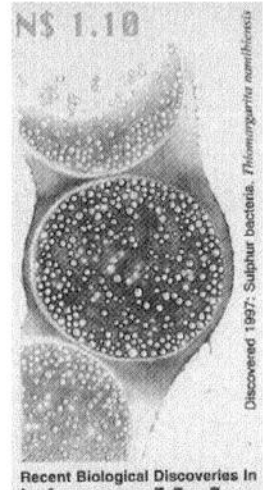

236 Sulphur Bacteria

2003. New Discoveries in Namibia. Multicoloured.

936	$1.10 Type **236**	50	20
937	$2.45 *Whiteheadia etesionamibensis*	1·00	45
938	$2.85 Cunene Flathead (horiz)	1·25	65
939	$3.85 Zebra Racer (horiz)	1·50	1·25
940	$20 Gladiator	7·00	9·00

237 Water and electricity supply

2003. Rural Development. Multicoloured.

941	$1.45 Type **237**	50	30
942	(–) Conservancy formation and land use diversification	70	50
943	$4.40 Education and health services	1·75	1·40
944	(–) Communication and road infrastructure	4·50	6·00

Nos. 942 and 944 were inscribed "Postcard Rate" (942) "Registered Mail" (944) were initially sold at $2.85 and $11.50 respectively.

238 Cattle Grazing and People Fishing at an Oshana

2003. Cuvelai Drainage System. Multicoloured.

945	$1.10 Type **238**	60	25
946	$2.85 Omadhiya Lakes	1·75	1·25
947	(–) Aerial view of Oshanas	2·25	3·00

No. 947 was inscribed "Non Standard Mail" and initially sold for $3.85.

239 Statue of Soldier and Obelisk

2003. National Monuments, Heroes Acre, Windhoek. Multicoloured.

948	(–) Type **239**	75	1·00
949	(–) Statue of woman	1·40	1·75
950	(–) Stone monument	1·75	2·50

No. 948 was inscribed "Standard Mail" and sold for $1.45. No. 949 was inscribed "Postcard Rate" and sold for $2.75. No. 950 was inscribed "Non Standard Mail" and sold for $3.85.

240 Namibian Flag

2003. 25th Anniv of the Windhoek Philatelic Society. Sheet 67×57 mm.

MS951	$10 multicoloured	6·50	7·50

241 Surveying Equipment

2003. Centenary of Geological Survey. Sheet 67×57 mm.

MS952	$10 multicoloured	6·50	7·50

2003. Winning Stamp of the Eighth Stamp World Cup. Sheet 140×80 mm. Multicoloured.

MS953	$3.15 As No. 924	3·75	4·00

242 Vervet Monkey

2004. Vervet Monkeys. Multicoloured.

954	$1.60 Type **242**	75	30
955	$3.15 Two monkeys in tree	1·40	1·00
956	$3.40 Adult monkey with offspring	1·60	1·00
957	(–) Monkey chewing twig	6·00	7·50
MS958	80×60 mm. $4.85 As No. 957	2·50	3·00

No. 957 was inscribed "Inland Registered Mail Paid" and was initially sold for $14.25.

243 Honey Bees on Sickle Bush

2004. Honey Bees. Multicoloured.

959	(–) Type **243**	65	30
960	$2.70 Bee on daisy	1·00	75
961	(–) Bee on aloe	1·10	80
962	$3.15 Bee on cats claw	1·10	1·00
963	(–) Bees on edging senecio	5·00	7·00
MS964	75×55 mm. $4.85 Bee on pretty lady (flower)	2·50	3·00

Nos. 959, 961 and 963 were each inscribed "standard mail" (959), "postcard rate" (961) "inland registered mail paid" (963) and were initially sold for $1.60, $3.05 and $14.25 respectively.

244 Dove

2004. Centenary of the War of Anti-Colonial Resistance.

965	(–) Type **244**	1·00	60
MS966	105×70 mm. $5 As No. 965	2·25	2·75

No. 965 was inscribed "Standard Mail" and sold for $1.60 initially.

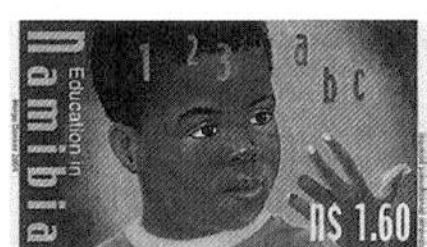

245 Boy and Pre-school Lessons

2004. Education. Multicoloured.

967	$1.60 Type **245**	60	30
968	$2.75 Teacher and primary and secondary school lessons	90	75
969	$4.40 Teacher and vocational lessons	1·25	1·25
970	(–) Teacher and life skill lessons	4·00	6·00

No. 970 was inscribed "Registered Mail" and sold for $12.65.

246 Loading Fish on Dockside

2004. Fishing Industry. Multicoloured.

971	$1.60 Type **246**	1·00	40
972	$2.75 Ship at dockside	1·60	1·00
973	$4.85 Preparing fish	2·50	3·75

247 Joseph Fredericks House

2004. Historical Buildings of Bethanie. Multicoloured.

974	(–) Type **247**	60	30
975	(–) Schmelen House	90	75
976	(–) Rhenish Mission Church	1·10	1·25
977	(–) Stone Church	4·00	6·00

No. 974 was inscribed "Standard Mail" and sold for $1.60. No. 975 was inscribed "Postcard Rate" and sold for $3.05. No. 976 was inscribed "Non Standard Mail" and sold for $4.40. No 977 was inscribed "Registered Mail" and sold for $12.65.

248 Wrestling

2004. Olympic Games, Athens. Multicoloured.

978	(–) Type **248**	60	30
979	$2.90 Boxing (vert)	1·10	90
980	$3.40 Shooting	1·40	1·50
981	$3.70 Mountain biking (vert)	1·50	2·00

No. 978 was inscribed "Standard Mail" and sold for $1.60.
No. 981 was also issued incorrectly inscribed "XVIII Olympiad".

248a African Fish Eagle (Namibia)

2004. First Joint Issue of Southern Africa Postal Operators Association Members. Sheet 170×95 mm containing T **248a** and similar hexagonal designs showing national birds of Association members. Multicoloured.

MS982	$3.40 Type **248a**; $3.40 Two African fish eagles perched (Zimbabwe); $3.40 Peregrine falcon (Angola); $3.40 Cattle egret (Botswana); $3.40 Purple-crested turaco ("Lourie") (Swaziland); $3.40 Stanley ("Blue") Crane (South Africa); $3.40 Bar-tailed trogon (Malawi) (inscribed "apaloderma vittatum"); $3.40 Two African fish eagles in flight (Zambia)	15·00	16·00

The stamp depicting the Bar-tailed trogon is not inscribed with the country of which the bird is a National Symbol.
Miniature sheets of similar designs were also issued by Angola, Botswana, Malawi, South Africa, Swaziland, Zambia and Zimbabwe.

249 Gemsbok

2005. Centenary of Rotary International.

983	**249** $3.70 multicoloured	2·00	2·25

250 President Hifikepunye Pohamba

2005. Inauguration of Pres. Hifikepunye Pohamba.

984	**250** (–) multicoloured	1·00	45

No. 984 was inscribed "Standard Mail" and initially sold for $1.70.

251 Mariqua ("Marico") Sunbird

2005. Sunbirds. Multicoloured.

985	$2.90 Type **251**	1·50	80
986	$3.40 Dusky sunbird	1·75	1·10
987	(–) White-breasted ("bellied") sunbird	2·00	1·90
988	(–) Scarlet-chested sunbird	6·50	7·50
MS989	100×70 mm. $10 Amethyst sunbird	4·50	4·75

No. 987 was inscribed "Non Standard Mail" and No. 988 "Registered Inland Postage Paid" and sold for $4.80 and $15.40 respectively.

2005. Nos. 750/1, 754, 757/8, 762 and 764/6 surch.

990	(–) on 10c. Bushman poison flower (surch **Standard Mail 10c.**)	£140	50·00
991	(–) on 20c. Camel's foot (flower) (surch **Standard Mail 20c.**)	60	30
993	(–) on 50c. Laughing dove (surch **Standard Mail 50c.**)	75	30

994	(–) on 90c. Yellow-billed hornbill (surch **Standard Mail 90c.**)	75	30
995	(–) on $1 Lilac-breasted roller (surch **Standard Mail 90c.**)	75	30
996	$2.90 on 20c. Camel's foot (surch **$2.90 on 20c.**)	30·00	6·00
997	$2.90 on 20c. Camel's foot (surch **$2.90 on 20c.**)	2·50	75
998	$2.90 on 90c. Yellow-billed hornbill (surch **$2.90 on 90c.**)	2·50	1·00
999	(–) on $1.50 Elephant as T **253** (surch in two lines **Standard Mail 90c.**)	1·75	90
1000	(–) on $4 Buffalo (surch **Standard Mail 50c.**)	1·50	1·25
1001	$5.20 on 20c. Camel's foot (surch **$2.90 on 20c.**)	2·50	1·50
1002	$5.20 on 90c. Yellow-billed hornbill (surch **$2.90 on 20c.**)	2·75	1·50
1003	(–) on $4 Buffalo (surch **Registered Standard Mail**)	3·25	2·50
1004	(–) on $10 Cheetah (surch **Registered Standard Mail**)	4·50	4·00
1005	$25 on $5 Black rhinoceros (surch **$2.90 on 20c.**)	9·50	5·00
1006	$50 on $10 Cheetah (surch **$50 on $10**)	14·00	7·00

Nos. 990/5 are inscribed "Standard Mail" and were originally sold for $1.70. Nos. 999/1000 are inscribed "Non Standard Mail" and was originally sold for $4.80. No. 1003 is inscribed "Registered Standard Mail" and was originally sold for $15.40. No. 1004 is inscribed "Registered Non Standard Mail" and was originally sold for $18.50.

261 Nara (*Acanthosicyos horridus*)

2005. Plants with Medicinal Value. Multicoloured.

1013	(–) Type **261**	65	30
1014	$2.90 Devil's claw	1·10	80
1015	(–) *Hoodia gordonii*	1·25	1·00
1016	(–) *Tsamma*	1·75	2·50

No. 1013 is inscribed "Standard Mail", 1015 "Postcard Rate" and 1016 "Non Standard Mail" and they were originally sold for $1.70, $3.10 and $4.80 respectively.

262 Vegetables

2005. Crop Production in Namibia. Multicoloured.

1017	$2.90 Type **262**	1·10	60
1018	$3.40 Pearl millet	1·25	70
1019	(–) Maize	5·00	6·50

No. 1019 is inscribed "Registered Mail" and was originally sold for $13.70.

263 Cape Gull

2006. Seagulls of Namibia. Multicoloured.

1020	$3.10 Type **263**	1·60	70
1021	$4 Hartlaub's gull	1·75	1·25
1022	$5.50 Sabine's gull	2·00	1·75
1023	(–) Grey-headed gull	6·00	7·50

No. 1023 is inscribed "Inland Registered Mail Paid" and was originally sold for $16.20.

2006. Nos. 933, 960 and 972 surch.

1024	$3.10 on $2.45 Blood cell	1·75	1·00
1025	$3.10 on $2.70 Bee on daisy	1·75	1·00
1026	$3.10 on $2.75 Ship at dockside	1·75	1·00

267 Risso's Dolphin

2006. Dolphins. Multicoloured.

1027	(–) Type **267**	65	20
1028	$3.10 Southern right-whale dolphin	1·25	65
1029	$3.70 Benguela dolphin	1·40	1·25
1030	$4 Common dolphin	1·50	1·75
1031	$5.50 Bottlenose dolphin	2·00	2·75

No. 1027 is inscribed "Standard Mail" and was originally sold for $1.80.

268 Father with Young Child

2006. Traditional Role of Men in Namibia. Multicoloured.

1032	(-) Type **268**	50	50
1033	(-) Musicians	50	50
1034	(-) Wood carver	50	50
1035	(-) Shaman and rock painting	50	50
1036	(-) Planter with ox-drawn plough	50	50
1037	(-) Hunter with bow and arrow	50	50
1038	(-) Leader speaking	50	50
1039	(-) Blacksmith	50	50
1040	(-) Warrior guarding houses ("protector")	50	50
1041	(-) Pastoralist and cattle	50	50
1042	(-) Trader	50	50
1043	(-) Storyteller	50	50

Nos. 1032/43 are all inscribed "standard mail" and were originally sold for $1.80 each.

2006. Nos. 758 and 760 surch.

1044	($3.30) on $1 Lilac-breasted roller	2·50	1·25
1045	($3.30) on $1.20 Giraffe	2·50	1·25

Nos. 1044/5 are surch "Postcard Rate" and were sold for $3.30 each.

270 Orange River in the Southern Namib

2006. Perennial Rivers of Namibia. Multicoloured.

1046	$3.10 Type **270**	1·75	60
1047	$5.50 Kunene River, northern Namib (24×58 mm)	2·25	1·50
1048	(-) Zambezi River and African fish eagle (90×25 mm)	7·50	10·00

No. 1048 is inscribed "Registered Non Standard Mail" and sold for $19.90 each.

271 Construction of OMEG Railway Line

2006. Centenary of OMEG Railway Line. Multicoloured.

1049	$3.10 Type **271**	1·75	65
1050	$3.70 Henschel Class NG15 locomotive No. 41	1·90	1·10
1051	$5.50 Narrow gauge Class Jung tank locomotive No. 9 pulling iron ore train	3·00	4·00

272 Centenary Emblem and Cheetah

2006. Centenary of Otjiwarongo.

1052	**272**	$1.90 multicoloured	1·00	1·00

273 Bullfrog (*Pyxicephalus adspersus*) and River

2007. Biodiversity. Multicoloured.

1053	5c. Type **273**	10	10
1054	10c. Mesemb (*Namibia cinerea*) and desert landscape	10	10
1055	30c. Solifuge (*Ceroma inerme*) and seashore with shell, plover and seal	10	10
1056	40c. Jewel beetle (*Julodis egho*) and antelopes in desert	15	10
1057	60c. Compass jellyfish (*Chrysaora hysoscella*), turtle and seabirds	20	10
1058	(-) Web-footed gecko (*Palmatogecko rangei*) and sand dunes	60	20
1059	$2 Otjikoto tilapia (*Tilapia guinasana*)	70	30
1059a	$4.10 Thrimble grass (*Fingerhuthia africana*)	1·00	45
1059b	$4.60 Bronze whaler shark (*Carchahinus brachyurus*)	1·10	50
1059c	$5.30 Deep sea red crab (*Chaceon maritae*)	1·50	1·10
1060	$6 Milkbush (*Euphorbia damarana*) and zebras in desert	1·75	70
1061	(-) African Hawk-eagle with prey and landscape with trees	1·75	70
1062	$10 Black-faced impala and sandy river-bed	2·50	1·50
1062a	(-) False ink cap (*Podxis Pistillaris*)	5·00	4·00
1063	$25 Lichens (*Santessonia* and *Xanthorea*sp.) on seashore rocks	5·50	4·50
1064	$50 Baobab, elephant and antelopes in bushveldt	9·00	9·00

No. 1058 is inscr "Standard Mail" and sold for $1.90.
No. 1061 is inscr "Non-Standard Mail" and sold for $6.
No. 1062a was inscr "Registered Mail" and originally sold for $18.20.

274 Caracal, Snake and Zebras, Otjovasandu Wilderness Area ("Conservation")

275 Red-billed Quelea

2007. Centenary of Etosha National Park. Multicoloured.

(a) As T **274**.

1065	(-) Type **274**	1·50	55
1066	$3.40 Lions, elephants and gemsbok, Okaukuejo Waterhole and Resort ("Tourism")	3·00	1·50
1067	(-) Researcher and elephant herd ("Anthrax Research")	9·00	11·00

(b) As T **275**.

MS1068 172×112 mm. ($2.25)×10 Gabar goshawk (29×29 mm); *Acacia tortillis* (umbrella thorn) (49×29 mm); Type **275**; Burchell's zebra; Elephant; Blue Wildebeest; *Salvadora persica* (mustard tree); *Anax tristis* (black emperor dragonfly) (39×40 mm); Springbok (39×40 mm); *Agama aculeata* (ground agama) (39×40 mm) 12·00 13·00

No. 1065 is inscr "Standard Mail" and sold for $1.90.
No. 1067 is inscr "Inland Registered Mail Paid" and sold for $17.20.
The stamps within **MS**1068 are all inscr "Postcard Rate", and the miniature sheet sold for $22.50.
The stamps and margins of **MS**1068 form a composite design showing wildlife at the Salvadora Waterhole.

276 *Anax imperator* (blue emperor)

2007. Dragonflies of Namibia. Multicoloured.

1069	(-) Type **276**	1·00	25
1070	$3.90 *Trithemis kirbyi ardens* (rock dropwing)	2·00	1·00
1071	$4.40 *Trithemis arteriosa* (red-veined dropwing)	2·25	2·50
1072	(-) *Trithemis stictica* (jaunty dropwing)	2·75	3·50

MS1073 75×54 mm. $6 *Urothemis edwardsii* (blue basker) 2·50 3·00

No. 1069 is inscr "Standard Mail" and sold for $1.90.
No. 1072 is inscr "Non Standard Mail Paid" and sold for $6.

277 *Commiphora kraeuseliana*

2007. Commiphora (corkwood) Trees of Namibia. Multicoloured.

1074	(-) Type **277**	70	20
1075	$3.40 *Commiphora wildii*	1·25	75
1076	$3.90 *Commiphora glaucescens*	1·50	1·25
1077	(-) *Commiphora dinteri*	2·50	3·50

No. 1074 is inscr 'Standard Mail' and sold for $1.90.
No. 1077 is inscr 'Non-standard Mail' and sold for $6.

278 *Cheiridopsis caroli-schmidtii*

2007. Indigenous Flowers of Namibia. Multicoloured.

1078	(-) Type **278**	1·00	20
1079	(-) *Namibia ponderosa*	2·50	2·50
1080	(-) *Fenestraria rhopalophylla*	6·50	8·50

No. 1078 is inscr 'STANDARD MAIL' and sold for $1.90. No. 1079 is inscr 'NON-STANDARD MAIL' and sold for $6. No. 1080 is inscr 'INLAND REGISTERED MAIL PAID' and sold for $17.20.

2007. Nos. 757, 760, 762 and 764 surch.

1081	($2) on 90c. Yellow-billed hornbill	1·50	60
1082	($2) on $1.20 Giraffe	1·50	60
1083	($2) on $1.50 Elephant	1·50	60
1084	($2) on $4 Buffalo	1·50	60
1085	$3.70 on $1.20 Giraffe	2·00	1·25
1086	$4.20 on $1.20 Giraffe	2·50	2·00
1087	$4.85 on $1.20 Giraffe	2·50	2·00
1088	($6.50) on $1.20 Giffe	3·50	3·00
1089	($16.45) on $1.20 Giraffe	9·00	11·00

Nos. 1081/4 are surch 'Standard Mail' and sold for $2, No. 1088 is surch 'Non Standard Mail' and sold for $6.50 and No. 1089 is surch 'Registered Mail' and sold for $16.45.

285 Nyala (Malawi)

2007. Second Joint Issue of Southern Africa Postal Operators Association Members. Sheet 135×170 mm containing T **285** and similar square designs showing national mammals of Association members. Multicoloured.

MS1090 ($2) Type **285**; ($2) Nyala (Zimbabwe); ($2) Burchell's zebra (Botswana); ($2) Oryx (Namibia); ($2) Buffalo (Zambia) 6·00 6·50

The stamps within **MS**1090 are all inscr 'Standard mail'. Miniature sheets of similar designs were also issued by Botswana, Malawi, Zambia and Zimbabwe. Botswana and Zambia also issued sheet stamps.

286 Southern Masked-weaver (*Ploceus velatus*)

2008. Weaver Birds of Namibia. Multicoloured.

1091	(-) Type **286**	90	30
1092	$3.70 Red-headed weaver (*Anaplectes rubriceps*)	1·40	60
1093	(-) White-browed sparrow-weaver (*Plocepasser mahali*)	1·40	60
1094	$4.20 Sociable weaver (*Philetarius socius*)	1·50	1·25
1095	(-) Thick-billed weaver (*Amblyospiza albifrons*)	7·00	9·00

No. 1091 is inscr 'Standard Mail' and sold for $2, No. 1093 is inscr 'Postcard Rate' and sold for $3.90 and No. 1095 is inscr 'Inland Registered Mail Paid' and sold for $18.45.

287 *Euphorbia virosa*

2008. Euphorbias of Namibia. Multicoloured.

1096	(-) Type **287**	1·25	25
1097	$6.45 *Euphorbia dregeana*	2·00	2·00
1098	(-) *Euphorbia damarana*	5·50	8·00

No. 1096 is inscr 'Postcard Rate' and sold for $3.90 and No. 1098 is inscr 'Registered Non Standard Mail' and sold for $22.95.

288 Uncut Diamonds

2008. Centenary of the Discovery of Diamonds in Namibia. Sheet 128×91 mm containing T **288** and similar diamond-shaped designs. Multicoloured.

MS1099 Type **288**; Land mining; Marine mining; Diamond jewellery 4·00 4·00

No. **MS**1099 is an irregular diamond-shape with the top point missing. The stamps are printed in a block of four within the sheet, with the land mining and marine mining designs oriented with the top of the stamp facing left (land) or right (marine) within the block.

289 Herero

2008. Traditional Houses of Namibia. Multicoloured.

1100	(-) Type **289**	75	75
1101	(-) Kavango	75	75
1102	(-) Owambo	75	75
1103	(-) Nama	75	75
1104	(-) Caprivi	75	75
1105	(-) San	75	75

Nos. 1100/5 are all inscr 'standard mail' and sold for $2 each.

290 The Lion-Man

2008. Petroglyphs at Twyfelfontein World Heritage Site. Multicoloured.

1106	(-) Type **290**	2·25	2·25
1107	(-) The Giraffe and the Dancing Kudu	2·25	2·25
1108	(-) The Elephant	2·25	2·25

MS1109 105×70 mm. (2r.)×3 As Nos. 1106/8 2·25 2·25

Nos. 1106/8 were inscr 'Non Standard Mail' and sold for $6.50.
The stamps within **MS**1109 were inscr 'Standard Mail' and were valid for 2r. each.

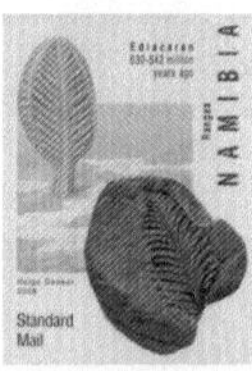

291 Rangea

2008. Ediacaran Fossils. Multicoloured.

1110	(-) Type **291**	55	55
1111	(-) Swartpuntia	1·00	30
1112	(-) Pteridinium	5·25	5·50
1113	(-) Ernietta	6·25	5·75

No. 1110 is inscr 'Standard Mail' and sold for $2, 1111 is inscr 'Postcard Rate' and sold for $3.90, 1112 is inscr 'Registered Non-Standard Mail' and sold for $18.45, and 1113 is inscr 'Registered Inland Mail Paid' and sold for $22.95.

292 Athlete and Globe

2008. Olympic Games, Beijing. Multicoloured.

1114	$2 Type **292**	55	55
1115	$3.70 Athlete with fist raised and bronze medal	1·00	30
1116	$3.90 Athlete with arms raised in triumph and gold medal	1·00	30
1117	$4.20 Athlete and silver medal	1·60	2·00

293 Martial Eagle (*Polemaetus bellicosus*)

2009. Eagles of Namibia. Multicoloured.

No.	Description		
1118	$4.10 Type **293**	1·75	75
1119	(–) Bateleur (*Terathopius ecaudatus*)	1·75	85
1120	$4.60 Verreaux's eagle (*Aquila verreauxii*)	1·75	1·25
1121	(–) Tawny eagle (*Aquila rapax*)	7·50	10·00

No. 1119 was inscr 'Postcard Rate' and sold for $4.30.

No. 1121 was inscr 'Registered Non-Standard Mail' and sold for $25.40.

294 Ox

2009. Chinese New Year. Year of the Ox.

No.	Description		
1122	**294** $2.20 multicoloured	1·00	1·00

295 Augur Buzzard (*Buteo augur*)

2009. The Brandberg. Sheet 172×112 mm containing T **295** and similar multicoloured designs.

No.	Description		
MS1123	($4.30)×10 Type **295**; Numasfels peak (49×29 mm); Quiver tree (*Aloe dichotoma*) (39×29 mm); CMR beetle (*Mylabrisoculata*) (39×29 mm); Leopard (*Panthera pardus*) (39×29 mm); Kobas tree (*Cyphostemma curiorii*) (39×29 mm); Bokmakiri (*Telophorus zeylonus*) (39×29 mm); Jameson's red rock rabbit (*Pronolagus randensis*) (39×39 mm); Brandberg halfmens (*Euphorbia monteiri* ssp. *brandbergensis*) (39×39 mm); Jordan's girdled lizard (*Cordylus jordani*) (39×39 mm)	14·00	15·00

The stamps within **MS**1123 are all inscr 'Postcard Rate', and the miniature sheet sold for $43.

The stamps and margins of **MS**1123 form a composite design showing wildlife in a view towards Wasserfallfläche and Numasfels.

296 Paul Graetz and his Team in their Special Vehicle, 1909

2009. Centenary of First Africa Crossing (from Dar es Salaam to Swakopmund) by Car. Sheet 67×56 mm.

No.	Description		
MS1124	**296** $7.10 multicoloured	2·50	2·75

297 Stallions fighting

2009. Wild Horses of Namibia. Multicoloured.

No.	Description		
1124a	(–) Four Horses and rocky background	1·00	50
1125	$5.30 Type **297**	1·75	70
1126	$8 Bay horses in a rocky landscape	2·50	1·75
1127	(–) Chestnut stallion and mares with foal grazing	6·00	8·50

No. 1124a was inscr 'Postcard Rate' and originally sold for 4r.60.

No. 1127 was inscr 'Inland Registered Mail Paid' and initially sold for $20.40. The rate increased to $22.20 from 1 October 2009.

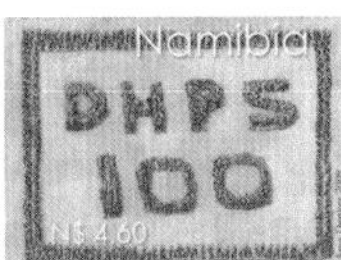

298 Children as Centenary Emblem

2009. Centenary of DHPS (Deutsche Höhere Privatschule), Windhoek. Sheet 75×55 mm.

No.	Description		
MS1128	**298** $4.60 multicoloured	2·00	2·25

299 Festive Gecko (*Narudasia festiva*)

2009. Geckos. Multicoloured.

No.	Description		
1129	$4.40 Type **299**	1·10	1·10
1130	$5 Koch's barking gecko (*Ptenopus kochi*)	1·25	1·25
1131	$6 Giant ground gecko (*Chondrodactylus angulifer namibensis*)	1·50	1·50
1132	$7.70 Velvety thick-toed gecko (*Pachydactylus bicolor*)	1·90	1·90
1133	(–) Bradfield's namib day gecko (*Rhoptropus bradfieldi*)	5·25	5·25

No. 1133 was inscr 'Registered Mail' and originally sold for $20.40.

300 Wattled Crane (*Grus carunculatus*)

2010. Endangered Species. Multicoloured.

No.	Description		
1134	(–) Type **300**	2·50	2·50
1135	(–) *Gazania thermalis*	2·50	2·50
1136	(–) Leatherback turtle (*Dermochelys coriacea*) and jellyfish	2·50	2·50
1137	(–) Giant quiver tree (*Aloe pillansii*)	2·50	2·50
1138	(–) Cape vulture (*Gyps coprotheres*)	2·50	2·50
1139	(–) White Namib toktokkie (*Cauricara eburnea*)	2·50	2·50
1140	(–) Two cheetahs (*Acinonyx jubatus*)	2·50	2·50
1141	(–) Hook-lipped rhinoceros (*Diceros bicornis*)	2·50	2·50
1142	(–) Wild dog (*Lycaon pictus*)	2·50	2·50
1143	(–) Nama-padloper tortoise (*Homopus solus*)	2·50	2·50

Nos. 1134/43 were inscr 'Postcard Rate' and were initially valid for $4.60.

301 Map and Flag of Namiibia

2010. 20th Anniv of Independence

No.	Description		
1144	**301** (–) multicoloured	1·00	85

No. 1144 was inscr 'Standard Mail' and originally sold for $2.50.

2010. Third Joint Issue of Southern Africa Postal Operators Association Members. World Cup Football Championship, South Africa. Multicoloured.

No.	Description		
MS1145	(4r.60)×9 Namibia; South Africa; Zimbabwe; Malawi; Swaziland; Botswana, Mauritius; Lesotho; Zambia	14·00	14·00

The stamps within **MS**1145 were each inscr 'postcard rate' and were originally valid for $4.60 each.

Similar designs were issued by Botswana, Lesotho, Malawi, Mauritius, South Africa, Swaziland, Zambia and Zimbabwe.

302 Northern Black Korhaan (*Eupodotis afraoides*)

2010. Bustards and Korhaans. Multicoloured.

No.	Description		
1146	(–) Type **302**	2·50	2·50
1147	(–) Red-crested korhaan (*Eupodotis ruficrista*)	2·50	2·50
1148	(–) Black-bellied bustard (*Eupodotis melanogaster*)	2·50	2·50
1149	(–) Rüppell's korhaan (*Eupodotis rueppellii*)	2·50	2·50
1150	(–) Ludwig's bustard (*Neotis ludwigii*)	2·50	2·50
1151	(–) Kori bustard (*Ardeotis kori*)	2·50	2·50

Nos. 1146/51 were all inscr 'postcard rate' and originally sold for $4.60 each.

303 Swakopmund Lighthouse

2010. Lighthouses. Multicoloured.

No.	Description		
1152	$4.40 Type **303**	2·00	1·25
1153	(–) Diaz Point Lighthouse, Lüderitzbucht	4·00	4·00
1154	(–) Pelican Point Lighthouse, Walvis Bay	7·00	8·00

No. 1153 was inscr 'Non Standard Mail' and originally sold for $9.50.

No. 1154 was inscr 'Registered Mail' and originally sold for $18.20.

304 Christuskirche, Windhoek

2010. Centenary of the Christuskirche, Windhoek. Sheet 76×56 mm

No.	Description		
MS1155	**304** $5 multicoloured	2·00	2·50

305 Stylized Figures and Globe

2010. World Standards Day. Sheet 75×55 mm

No.	Description		
MS1156	**305** $5.30 multicoloured	2·00	2·50

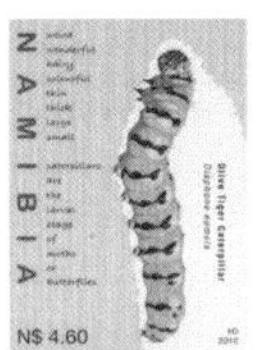

306 Olive Tiger Caterpillar (*Diaphone eumela*)

2010. Caterpillars. Multicoloured.

No.	Description		
1157	$4.60 Type **306**	2·00	1·75
1158	$5.30 African armyworms (*Spodoptera exempta*)	2·50	2·50
1159	$6.40 Wild Silk Caterpillar (*Gonometa postica*)	2·75	2·75
1160	(–) Mopane caterpillar (*Imbrasia belina*)	10·00	12·00

No. 1160 was inscr 'Registered Non-Standard Mail' and originally sold for $29.40.

307 Leopard (*Panthera pardus*)

2011. The Big Five (animals). Multicoloured.

No.	Description		
1161	$4.60 Type **307**	1·50	1·75
1162	(–) African elephant (*Loxodonta africana*) (vert)	2·25	2·25
1163	$5.30 Black rhino (*Diceros bicornis*)	2·25	2·25
1164	$6.40 African buffalo (*Syncerus caffer*)	2·25	2·50
1165	(–) Lion (*Panthera leo*) (vert)	2·50	2·75

No. 1162 was inscr 'Postcard Rate' and originally sold for $5.

No. 1165 was inscr 'Non Standard Mail' and originally sold for $8.50.

308 Long Reed Frog (*Hyperolius nasutus*)

2011. Frogs. Multicoloured.

No.	Description		
MS1166	($5)×4 Type **308**; Bubbling kassina (*Kassina senegalensis*); Tandy's sand frog (*Tomopterna tandyi*); Angolan reed frog (*Hyperolius parallelus*)	7·75	7·75

The stamps within **MS**1166 were all inscr 'Postcard Rate' and were originally valid for $5.

No. **MS**1166 was cut around in the shape of a giant bullfrog.

309 Eye and Desert Road

2011. Decade of Action for Road Safety 20112020. Sheet 75×55 mm

No.	Description		
MS1167	**309** $5.30 multicoloured	10·75	10·75

310 Cape Gannet (*Morus capensis*)

2011. Endangered Marine Life. Multicoloured.

No.	Description		
MS1168	$4.60×8 Type **310**; Atlantic yellow-nosed albatross (*Thalassarche chlororhynchos*) (50×30 mm); African penguin (*Spheniscus demersus*) (40×30 mm); Southern right whale (*Eubalaena australis*) (40×30 mm); Bank cormorant (*Phalacrocorax neglectus*) (40×30 mm); Westcoast steenbras (fish) (*Lithognathus aureti*) (40×30 mm); Split-fan kelp (*Laminaria pallida*) (40×40 mm); Cape rock lobster (*Jasus lalandii*) (40×40 mm)	12·00	12·00

The stamps and margins of **MS**1168 form a composite design showing rocks and ocean.

311 *Aloe gariepensis*

2011. Aloes. Multicoloured.

No.	Description		
1169	(–) Type **311**	2·00	1·90
1170	(–) *Aloe variegata*	3·00	2·75
1171	(–) *Aloe striata* sp. *Karasbergensis*	6·00	7·00

No. 1169 was inscr 'Postcard Rate' and originally sold for $5.

No. 1170 was inscr 'Non Standard Mail' and originally sold for $8.50.

No. 1171 was inscr 'Registered Mail' and originally sold for $20.90.

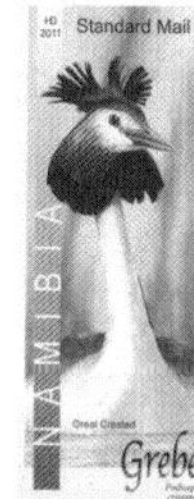

312 Great Crested Grebe (*Podiceps cristatus*)

2011. Grebes of Namibia. Multicoloured.

No.	Description		
1172	(–) Type **312**	1·00	85
1173	(–) Little grebe (*Tachybaptus ruficollis*)	1·00	85
1174	(–) Black-necked grebe (*Podiceps nigricollis*) (horiz)	6·00	7·00

Nos. 1172/3 were each inscr 'Standard Mail' and originally sold for $2.70.

No. 1174 was inscr 'Inland Registered Mail' and initially sold for $20.90.

313 Natal Red Top Grass

2011. Grasses. Multicoloured.

No.	Description		
1175	(–) Type **313**	95	85
1176	$4.80 Feather-top Chloris	1·75	1·60
1177	$5.40 *Urochloa brachyuran*	1·90	1·75
1178	$6.50 Nine-awned Grass	2·25	2·10
1179	(–) Foxtail Buffalo Grass	3·00	3·00

No. 1175 was inscr 'Standard Mail' and originally sold for $2.70.

No. 1179 was inscr 'Non Standard Mail' and originally sold for $8.50.

314 Carp's Tit (*Parus carpi*)

2012. Endemic Birds. Multicoloured.

1180	5c. Type **314**	10	10
1181	10c. Hartlaub's Spurfowl (*Pternis hartlaubi*)	10	10
1182	20c. Herero Chat (*Namibornis herero*)	10	10
1183	30c. Rüppell's Parrot (*Poicephalus rueppellii*)	15	10
1184	50c. Rüppell's Korhaan (*Eupodotis rueppellii*)	20	10
1185	90c. Benguela Long-billed Lark (*Certhilauda benguelensis*)	40	20
1186	$1 Barlow's Lark (*Calendulauda barlowi*)	40	20
1187	(–) White-tailed Shrike (*Lanioturdus torquatus*)	1·10	50
1188	$3 Rosy-faced Lovebird (*Agapornis roseicollis*)	1·25	60
1189	$5 Rockrunner (*Achaetops pycnopygius*)	2·00	1·00
1190	(–) Dune Lark (*Calendulauda erythrochlamys*)	2·25	1·10
1191	(–) Damara Hornbill (*Tockus damarensis*)	3·50	1·75
1192	$10 Gray's Lark (*Ammomanopsis grayi*)	4·00	2·00
1193	$12 Monteiro's Hornbill (*Tockus monteiri*)	4·50	2·00
1194	$20 Damara Tern (*Sterna balaenarum*)	5·50	6·00
1195	(–) Violet Wood-Hoopoe (*Phoeniculus damarensis*)	6·50	7·00
1196	$100 Bare-cheeked Babbler (*Turdoides gymnogenys*)	20·00	20·00

No. 1187 was inscr 'Standard Mail', No. 1190 'Postcard Rate', No. 1191 'Non-Standard Mail' and No. 1195 'Registered Mail' and they were originally sold for $2.90, $5.30, $8.90 and $21.90 respectively.

315 Straw-coloured Fruit-bat (*Eidolom helvum*)

2012. Bats. Multicoloured.

1197	(–) Type **315**	2·25	2·00
1198	(–) Egyptian Slit-faced Bat (*Nycteris thebaica*)	2·25	2·00
1199	(–) Angolan Epauletted Fruit-Bat (*Epomophorus angolensis*)	2·25	2·00

Nos. 1197/9 were inscr 'Postcard Rate' and originally sold for $5.30 each.

316 Shooting ('Getting There')

2012. Olympic and Paralympic Games, London. Multicoloured.

1200	$2.90 Type **316**	1·10	95
1201	$4.80 Athlete running ('For Our Country') (vert)	1·90	1·75
1202	$5.40 Three cyclists ('Competing with the Best')	2·10	2·00
1203	$6.50 Wheelchair athlete ('Paralympic Glory') (vert)	2·50	2·40

317 *Parabuthus villosus*

2012. Scorpions of Namibia. Multicoloured.

1204	$4.80 Type **317**	1·90	1·75
1205	(–) *Parabuthus namibensis*	2·25	2·00
1206	$5.40 *Opistophthalmus carinatus*	2·10	2·00
1207	$6.50 *Hottentotta arenaceus*	2·50	2·40

No. 1205 was inscr 'Postcard Rate' and originally sold for $5.30.

318 Mail Carrier in the Bush

2012. 20th Anniv of NamPost. Multicoloured.

MS1208	$2.90 Type **318**; $2.90 Modern NamPost mail lorry	2·40	2·40

319 Satellite Dishes

2012. 20th Anniv of Telecom Namibia. Multicoloured.

MS1209	$2.90 Type **319**; $2.90 Fibre-optic cable strands	2·40	2·40

320 Namaqua Chameleon (*Chameleo namaquensis*)

2012. 50th Anniv of Gobabeb Research and Training Centre. Multicoloured.

MS1210	($3.10) Type **320**; $5.10 Dune Grass (*Stipagrostis sabulicola*); $5.80 Flying Saucer Beetle (*Lepidochora discoidalis*)	5·50	5·50

321 Black Mongoose (*Galerella nigrata*)

2012. Mongooses. Multicoloured.

1211	$5.10 Type **321**	2·00	1·90
1212	(–) Yellow Mongoose (*Cynictis penicillata*) (vert)	2·25	2·00
1213	$5.80 Banded Mongoose (*Mungos mungo*)	2·40	2·25
1214	$6.90 Dwarf Mongoose (*Helogale parvula*)	2·75	2·50

No. 1212 was inscr 'Postcard Rate' and originally sold for $5.60.

322 Glittering Jewel Beetle

2013. Beetles. Multicoloured.

1215	(–) Type **322**	1·10	1·00
1216	$5.10 Red-spotted Lily Weevil	1·75	1·60
1217	$5.80 Garden Fruit Chafer	2·00	1·90
1218	$6.90 Lunate Ladybird	2·40	2·25
1219	(–) Two-spotted Ground Beetle	9·25	9·75

Nos. 1215 and 1219 were inscr 'Standard mail' and 'Inland registered mail' and originally sold for $3.10 and $26.50.

323 Boy

2013. Children of Namibia. Multicoloured.

MS1220	($5.10)×6 Type **323** ('Right to early development support, education & information'); Girl with hand on chin ('aspirations & dreams'); Boy ('Right to special care & support'); Four girls of different races ('Freedom of expression, association & participation'); Girl with painted face and hands ('play & creativity'); Girl ('Freedom from discrimination & exploitation')	8·50	8·50
MS1221	($5.10)×6 Four children ('Right to family, shelter & a healthy environment'); Boy in water ('faith & joy'); Child receiving oral vaccine ('Right to health, nutrition & safety'); Girl held by adult ('Freedom from neglect, fear, abuse & violence'); Child's hand in adult's ('love & trust'); Girl with braided hair ('Freedom of identity, traditions & beliefs')	8·50	8·50

The stamps within **MS**1220/1 were all inscr 'standard mail' and were originally valid for $5.10 each.

324 Desert Landscape

2013. Environmental Education. Sheet 100×100 mm with semi-circular lower right corner

MS1222	**324** $5.10 multicoloured	2·00	1·90

325 Couple in Donkey Cart

2013. Transport by Donkey Cart. Sheet 75×60 mm

MS1223	**325** (–) multicoloured	2·00	2·00

No. **MS**1223 was inscr 'Postcard Rate' and originally sold for $5.80.

326 Johanna Benson

2013. Johanna Benson's 200 Metres Gold Medal in Paralympic Games, London, 2012

1224	**326** (–) multicoloured	1·10	1·00

No. 1224 was inscr 'Standard Mail' and originally sold for $3.10.

We believe that a postcard rate stamp perforated 13½×13 was only issued in personalised sheetlets sold at a premium.

327 Greater Kudu

2013. Large Antelopes of Namibia. Multicoloured.

1225	(–) Type **327**	2·00	1·75
1226	(–) Gemsbok	2·00	1·75
1227	$5.40 Eland	1·90	1·75
1228	$6.20 Sable Antelope	2·25	2·10
1229	$7.30 Blue Wildebeest	2·50	2·40

Nos. 1225/6 were inscr 'Postcard Rate' and originally sold for $5.60.

328 Ha Mbukushu

2014. Traditional Wooden Vessels. Multicoloured.

1230	(–) Type **328**	1·10	1·00
1231	$5.40 Ba Subiva	1·90	1·75
1232	(–) Naman	2·10	2·00
1233	$6.20 Aa Wambo	2·25	2·10
1234	$7.30 Ova Herero	2·50	2·40

No. 1230 was inscr 'Standard Mail' and was originally sold for $3.30.

No. 1232 was inscr 'Postcard Rate' and originally sold for $6.

329 Southern Lesser Galago (*Galago moholi*)

2014. Nocturnal Animals of Namibia. Multicoloured.

MS1235	($3.30)×6 Type **329**; Cape Porcupine (*Hystrix africaeaustralis*); Small-spotted Genet (*Genetta genetta*); Ground Pangolin (*Manis temminckii*); Aardvark (*Orycteropus afer*); Aardwolf (*Proteles cristatus*)	7·00	7·50

The stamps within **MS**1235 were all inscr 'Standard Mail' and were originally valid for $3.30 each.

330 Namibia Flag on Map of Country

2014. 'My Namibia My Country My Pride'

1236	**330** (–) multicoloured	1·10	1·00
MS1237	100×60 mm. **330** (–) multicoloured	8·25	8·75

No. 1236 was inscr 'Standard Mail' and was originally sold for $3.30.

No. **MS**1237 was inscr 'Inland Registered Mail' and was originally sold for $23.40.

331 Red Hartebeest (*Alcelaphus buselaphus*)

2014. Medium-sized Antelopes of Namibia. Multicoloured.

1238	(–) Type **331**	2·10	2·00
1239	(–) Springbok (*Antidorcas marsupialis*)	2·10	2·00
1240	(–) Bushbuck (*Tragelaphus scriptus*)	2·10	2·00
1241	(–) Red Lechwe (*Kobus leche*)	2·10	2·00

Nos. 1238/41 were all inscr 'Postcard Rate' and originally sold for $6.

332 Black Mamba (*Dendroaspis polylepis*)

2014. Poisonous Snakes. Multicoloured.

1242	$5.40 Type **332**	1·90	1·75
1243	(–) Boomslang (*Dispholidus typus*)	2·10	2·00
1244	$6.20 Puff Adder (*Bitis arietans*)	2·25	2·10
1245	$7.30 Zebra Snake (*Naja nigricollis nigricincta*)	2·50	2·40

No. 1243 was inscr 'Postcard Rate' and originally sold for $6.

333 *Taihu* (supply ship)

2014. Chinese Navy's First Visit to Namibia. Multicoloured.

1246	$3.30 Type **333**	1·10	1·00
1247	$3.30 *Yancheng* (missile frigate)	1·10	1·00
MS1248	114×60 mm. $3.30 Walvis Bay port; $3.30 *Luoyang* (missile frigate)	2·40	2·40

334 Peregrine Falcon (*Falco peregrinus*)

2014. The Kalahari. Multicoloured.

MS1249	($6)×10 Type **334**; Pair of Cape Turtle-Doves (*Streptopelia capicola*) (80×48 mm); Shepherd's Tree (*Boscia albitrunca*) (65×49 mm); Giraffe (*Giraffa camelopardalis*) (65×49 mm); African Monarch Butterfly (*Danaus chrysippus*) (65×49 mm); Cheetah (*Acinonyx jubatus*) (65×49 mm); Gemsbok Cucumber (*Acanthosicyos naudinianus*) (65×49 mm); Suricate (*Suricata suricatta*) (65×65 mm); Trumpet-Thorn (*Catophractes alexandri*) (65×65 mm); Spotted Sandveld Lizard (*Nucras intertexta*) (65×65 mm)	21·00	23·00

The stamps within **MS**1249 were all inscr 'Postcard Rate' and were originally valid for $6 each.

The stamps and margins of **MS**1249 form a composite design showing wildlife in the Kalahari

335 Pied Kingfisher (*Ceryle rudis*)

2014. Kingfishers. Multicoloured.

No.	Description	Mint	Used
1250	(-) Type **335**	2·00	1·75
1251	(-) Half-collared Kingfisher (*Alcedo semitorquata*)	2·25	2·10
1252	(-) Woodland Kingfisher (*Halcyon senegalensis*)	2·40	2·25
1253	(-) Malachite Kingfisher (*Corythornis cristatus longirostris*)	2·75	2·50
1254	(-) Giant Kingfisher (*Megaceryle maximus*)	9·25	9·75

No. 1250 was inscr 'Zone A' and originally sold for $5.70.
No. 1251 was inscr 'Postcard Rate' and originally sold for $6.40.
No. 1252 was inscr 'Zone B' and originally sold for $6.60.
No. 1253 was inscr 'Zone C' and originally sold for $7.70.
No. 1254 was inscr 'Inland Registered Mail' and originally sold for $26.50.

336 Sossusvlei/Deadvlei

2015. UNESCO World Heritage Site - Namib Sand Sea. Multicoloured.

No.	Description	Mint	Used
MS1255	($6.40) Type **336**; ($6.40) *Comicus* spp. (Dune Cricket) (Biodiversity/Endemism); ($6.40) Sandwich Harbour	2·75	3·25

The stamps within **MS**1255 were all inscr 'Postcard Rate' and were each originally valid for $6.40. The miniature sheet was originally sold for $19.20.

337 Dr. Sam Nujoma (founding President), Dr. Hifikepunye Pohamba (second President) and Dr. Hage Geingob (third President)

2015. 25th Anniv of Independence. Sheet 115×65 mm

No.	Description	Mint	Used
MS1256	**337** $30 multicoloured	4·25	4·75

338 Dr. Hage Geingob

2015. Inauguration of Third President of Namibia, Dr. Hage Geingob

No.	Description	Mint	Used
1257	**338** (-) multicoloured	85	80

No. 1257 was inscr 'Standard Mail' and was originally valid for $3.50.

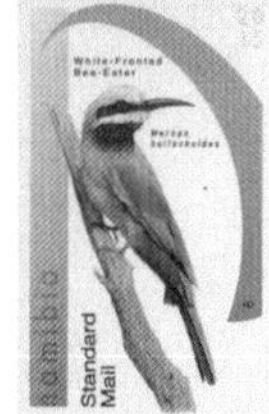

339 White-fronted Bee-eater (*Merops bullockoides*)

2015. Bee-eaters of Namibia. Multicoloured.

No.	Description	Mint	Used
1258	(-) Type **339**	50	45
1259	$5.70 Southern Carmine Bee-eater (*Merops nubicoides*) (horiz)	85	80
1260	$6.60 Swallow-tailed Bee-eater (*Merops hirundineus*) (horiz)	95	90
1261	$7.70 Little Bee-eater (*Merops pusilllus*) (horiz)	1·10	1·00
1262	(-) European Bee-eater (*Merops apiaster*)	4·00	4·25

No. 1258 was inscr 'Standard Mail' and was originally valid for $3.50.
No. 1262 was inscr 'Inland Registered Mail' and was originally valid for $28.30.

340 Damara Dik-Dik (*Madoqua kirkii*)

2015. Small Antelopes of Namibia. Multicoloured.

No.	Description	Mint	Used
1263	(-) Type **340**	95	90
1264	(-) Klipspringer (*Oreotragus oreotragus*)	95	90
1265	(-) Common Duiker (*Sylvicapra grimmia*)	95	90
1266	(-) Steenbok (*Raphicerus campestris*)	95	90

Nos. 1263/6 were each inscr 'Postcard Rate' and originally sold for $6.40.

341 Leopard (*Panthera pardus*)

2015. Baby Big Five. Multicoloured.

No.	Description	Mint	Used
1267	(-) Type **341**	50	45
1268	$5.70 African Elephant (*Loxodonta africana*)	85	80
1269	$6.60 Black Rhino (*Diceros bicornis*)	95	90
1270	$7.70 African Buffalo (*Syncerus caffer*)	1·10	1·00
1271	(-) Lion (*Panthera leo*)	5·25	5·75

No. 1267 was inscr 'Standard mail' and originally sold for $3.50.
No. 1271 was inscr 'Non-standard registered mail' and originally sold for $35.50.

342 Bronze Whaler (*Carcharhinus brachyurus*)

2015. Sharks. Multicoloured.

No.	Description	Mint	Used
1272	$5.70 Type **342**	85	80
1273	(-) Broadnose Sevengill Shark (*Notorynchus cepedianus*)	95	90
1274	$6.60 Great White Shark (*Carcharodon carcharias*)	95	90
1275	$7.70 Smooth Hammerhead (*Sphyrna zygaena*)	1·10	1·00

No. 1273 was inscr 'Postcard Rate' and originally sold for $6.40.
Nos. 1276/9, Type **343** are left for Coursers, not yet received.

344 Rhinoceros and Calf ('rhinos forever')

2015. Hong Kong 2015 International Stamp Exhibition. Multicoloured.

No.	Description	Mint	Used
MS1280	135×85 mm. ($6.80) Type **344**; ($6.80) Globe and 'one world no wildlife crime'; ($6.80) Two elephants with calf ('elephants forever')	3·00	3·50

The stamps within **MS**1280 were each inscr 'Postcard Rate' and were originally valid for $6.80 each.
No. **MS**1280 has a wavy line sheet edge perf 7½ all round with one elliptical hole in each vertical side.

345 *Allgemeine Zeitung*, 1919

2016. Centenary of *Allgemeine Zeitung* (newspaper). Multicoloured.

No.	Description	Mint	Used
1281	(-) Centenary Issue of *Allgemeine Zeitung*, 2016	55	50
1282	(-) Type **345**	1·00	95
MS1283	Nos. 1281/2	1·60	1·50

No. 1281 was inscr 'Standard MAIL' and originally sold for $3.70.
No. 1282 was inscr 'Postcard RATE' and originally sold for $6.80.

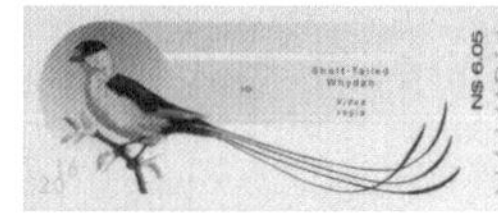

346 Shaft-Tailed Whydah (*Vidua regia*)

2016. Whydahs. Multicoloured.

No.	Description	Mint	Used
1284	$6.05 Type **346**	90	85
1285	$7 Long-Tailed Paradise-Whydah (*Vidua paradisaea*) (vert)	1·10	1·00
1286	(-) Pin-Tailed Whydah (*Vidua macroura*) (vert)	4·50	5·00

No. 1286 was inscr 'INLAND REGISTERED MAIL' and originally sold for $30.

347 Speke's Hinged Tortoise (*Kinixys spekii*)

2016. Tortoises of Namibia. Multicoloured.

No.	Description	Mint	Used
MS1287	165×104 mm. ($3.70) Type **347**; ($3.70) Namaqualand Tent Tortoise (*Psammobates tentorius trimeni*); ($3.70) Nama Padloper (*Homopus solus*); ($3.70) Angulate Tortoise (*Chersina angulata*)	2·25	2·50

The stamps within **MS**1287 were each inscr 'STANDARD MAIL' and were originally valid for $3.70 each.
No. **MS**1287 was cut in the shape of a Leopard Tortoise (*Geochelone pardalis*).

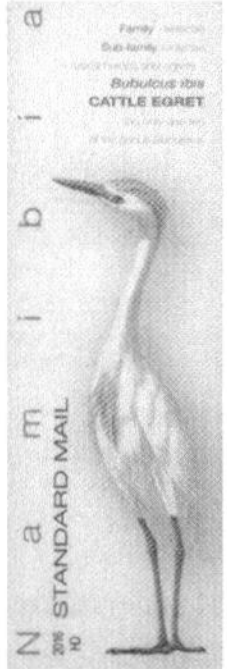

348 Cattle Egret (*Bubulcus ibis*)

2016. Herons. Multicoloured.

No.	Description	Mint	Used
1288	($3.70) Type **348**	55	50
1289	$6.05 Green-backed Heron (*Butorides striata*)	90	85
1290	($6.80) Goliath Heron (*Ardea goliath*) (horiz)	1·00	95
1291	$7 Squacco Heron (*Ardeola ralloides*) (horiz)	1·10	1·00
1292	$8.20 Black Heron (*Egretta ardesiaca*) (horiz)	1·25	1·10

No. 1288 was inscr 'STANDARD MAIL' and originally sold for $3.70.
No. 1289 was inscr 'POST CARD RATE' and originally sold for $6.80.

349 Commercial and Home Building Materials, Arts and Crafts and Household Utensils ('Timber resources')

2016. Forestry in Namibia. Multicoloured.

No.	Description	Mint	Used
MS1293	140×80 mm. ($6.80) Type **349**; ($6.80) Elephant and trees ('Resources for all great or small') (vert); ($6.80) Marula fruit, Namibian myrrh essential oil (from *Commiphora wildii* tree resin), marula oil and marula soap ('Non-timber resources')	3·00	3·50

The stamps within **MS**1293 were all inscr 'POSTCARD RATE' and were originally valid for $6.80 each.

350 African Wild Dog (*Lycaon pictus*)

2016. Large Canines of Namibia. Multicoloured.

No.	Description	Mint	Used
1294	($6.10) Type **350**	90	85
1295	($7) Spotted Hyaena (*Crocuta crocuta*)	1·10	1·00

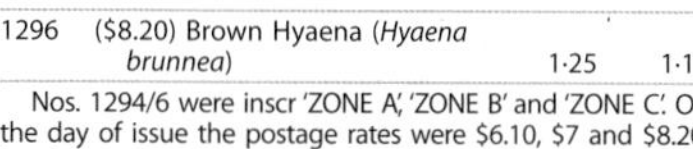

No.	Description	Mint	Used
1296	($8.20) Brown Hyaena (*Hyaena brunnea*)	1·25	1·10

Nos. 1294/6 were inscr 'ZONE A', 'ZONE B' and 'ZONE C'. On the day of issue the postage rates were $6.10, $7 and $8.20, but from 1 October 2016 they were increased to $6.60, $7.50 and $8.80.

2016. As Nos. 1125/7 but inscr. 'Postcard Rate'

No.	Description	Mint	Used
1297	($7.30) As Type **297**	1·10	1·00
1298	($7.30) Bay horses in a rocky landscape	1·10	1·00
1299	($7.30) Chestnut stallion and mares with foal grazing	1·10	1·00

Nos. 1297/9 were all inscr' 'Postcard Rate' and were originally sold for $7.30 each.

351 Mandume ya Ndemufayo

2017. Namibian Heroes. Mandume ya Ndemufayo (1894-1917, King of the Oukwanyama 1911-17 and anti-colonial leader)

No.	Description	Mint	Used
MS1300	70×90 mm. **351** ($7.30) multicoloured	1·10	1·00

No. **MS**1300 was inscr 'Post Card Rate' and originally sold for $7.30.

352 Boy Scout and Girl Scout

2017. Centenary of Scouting in Namibia

No.	Description	Mint	Used
MS1301	108×90 mm. **352** ($4) multicoloured	60	55

No. **MS**1301 was inscr. 'STANDARD MAIL' and originally sold for $4.

353 Emblem and 'LIBERATED BY GOD'S GRACE'

2017. Twelfth Assembly of the Lutheran World Federation, Windhoek and 500th Anniv of the Lutheran Reformation

No.	Description	Mint	Used
MS1302	90×90 mm. **353** ($7.30) multicoloured	1·10	1·00

No. **MS**1302 was inscr. 'Postcard Rate' and originally sold for $7.30.

354 Black-collared Barbet (*Lybius torquatus*)

2017. Barbets. Multicoloured.

No.	Description	Mint	Used
1303	($6.60) Type **354**	1·00	95
1304	($7.50) Crested Barbet (*Trachyphonus vaillantii*) (horiz)	1·10	1·00
1305	($8.80) Acacia Pied Barbet (*Tricholaema leucomelas*)	1·25	1·10

No. 1303 was inscr 'ZONE A' and originally sold for $6.60.
No. 1304 was inscr 'ZONE B' and originally sold for $7.50.
No. 1305 was inscr 'ZONE C' and originally sold for $8.80.

355 Jameson's Red Rock Rabbit (*Pronolagus randensis*)

2017. Hares and Rabbits of Namibia. Multicoloured.

No.	Description	Mint	Used
1306	($7.30) Type **355**	1·10	1·00
1307	($7.30) Scrub Hare (*Lepus saxatilis*)	1·10	1·00

Nos. 1306/7 were both inscr. 'postcard rate' and originally sold for $7.30 each.

356 Limestone Lily (*Ornithoglossum calcicola*)

2017. Flame Lilies. Multicoloured.

1308	($6.60) Type **356**	1·00	95
1309	($7.50) Flame Lily (*Gloriosa superba*)	1·10	1·00
1310	($8.80) Namib Lily (*Hexacyrtis dickiana*) (vert)	1·25	1·10

No. 1308 was inscr. 'ZONE A' and originally sold for $6.60.
No. 1309 was inscr. 'ZONE B' and originally sold for $7.50.
No. 1310 was inscr. 'ZONE C' and originally sold for $8.80.

357 Bo'Bo' Benzol-Electric Locomotive C.D.M. No. 40

2017. Diamond Trains of Namibia. Multicoloured.

1311	($7.30) Type **357**	1·10	1·00
1312	($7.30) Bo'Bo' electric locomotive K.B.G.	1·10	1·00
1313	($7.30) (1AO)'Bo' Benzol-electric locomotive	1·10	1·00
1314	($7.30) Railcar No. 3 Kolmanskop	1·10	1·00

Nos. 1311/14 were inscr. 'Postcard Rate' and originally sold for $7.30 each.

358 Racket-tailed Roller (*Coracias spatulatus*)

2017. Rollers. Multicoloured.

1315	($7.30) Type **358**	1·10	1·00
1316	($7.30) Lilac-breasted Roller (*Coracias caudatus*)	1·10	1·00
1317	($7.30) Purple Roller (*Coracias naevius*)	1·10	1·00
1318	($7.30) Broad-billed Roller (*Eurystomus glaucurus*)	1·10	1·00
1319	($7.30) European Roller (*Coracius garrulus*)	1·10	1·00

Nos. 1315/19 were inscr. 'Post Card Rate' and sold for $7.30 each.

359 Bat-eared Fox (*Otocyon megalotis*)

2017. Small Canines of Namibia. Multicoloured.

1320	($4) Type **359**	60	55
1321	($6.60) Black-backed Jackal (*Canis mesomelas*)	1·00	95
1322	($7.50) Side-striped Jackal (*Canis adustus*)	1·10	1·00
1323	($8.80) Aardwolf (*Proteles cristata*)	1·25	1·10
1324	($28.10) Cape Fox (*Vulpes chama*)	4·25	4·75

No. 1320 was inscr. 'Standard Mail' and originally sold for $4.
No. 1321 was inscr. 'Zone A' and originally sold for $6.60.
No. 1322 was inscr. 'Zone B' and originally sold for $7.50.
No. 1323 was inscr. 'Zone C' and originally sold for $8.80.
No. 1324 was inscr. 'Inland Registered Mail' and originally sold for $28.10.
On 1 October 2017 these prices were increased to $4.30, $7.10, $8.10, $9.50 and $30.10.

NANDGAON

A state of central India. Now uses Indian stamps.

12 pies = 1 anna; 16 annas = 1 rupee.

GUM. The stamps of Nandgaon were issued without gum.

1

2 (½a.)

1891

1	1	½a. blue	11·00	£250
2	1	2a. pink	38·00	£750

2 (½a.)

1893. Imperf.

5	2	½a. green	45·00	£110
6	2	1a. red	£100	£180
4	2	2a. red	20·00	£140

OFFICIAL STAMPS

1893. Optd **M.B.D.** in oval.

O1	1	½a. blue	£550	
O4	2	½a. green	10·00	20·00
O5	2	1a. red	22·00	60·00
O6	2	2a. red	18·00	48·00

NAPLES

A state on the S.W. coast of Central Italy, formerly part of the Kingdom of Sicily, but now part of Italy.

200 tornesi = 100 grano = 1 ducato.

1 Arms under Bourbon Dynasty

1858. The frames differ in each value. Imperf.

8	1	½t. blue	£241000	£13000
1A	1	½g. red	£2500	£400
2	1	1g. red	£750	65·00
3	1	2g. red	£550	27·00
4A	1	5g. red	£3250	85·00
5A	1	10g. red	£7000	£325
6A	1	20g. red	£7500	£1500
7A	1	50g. red	£15000	£3500

4 Cross of Savoy

1860. Imperf.

9	4	½t. blue	£54000	£4250

NATAL

On the east coast of S. Africa. Formerly a British Colony, later a province of the Union of S. Africa.

12 pence = 1 shilling; 20 shillings = 1 pound.

1

1857. Embossed stamps. Various designs.

1	1	1d. blue		£1200
2	1	1d. red		£1900
3	1	1d. buff		£1400
4	-	3d. red		£400
5	-	6d. green		£1100
6	-	9d. blue		£7500
7	-	1s. buff		£5500

The 3d., 6d., 9d. and 1s. are larger. Beware of reprints.

6

7

1859

19	6	1d. red	£130	29·00
12	6	3d. blue	£170	40·00
13	6	6d. grey	£275	70·00
24	6	6d. violet	90·00	35·00

1867

25	7	1s. green	£250	50·00

1869. Variously optd **POSTAGE** or **Postage**.

50	6	1d. red	£150	50·00
82	6	1d. yellow	90·00	90·00
53	6	3d. blue	£225	50·00
83	6	6d. violet	85·00	8·00
84	7	1s. green	£140	7·50

1870. Optd **POSTAGE** in a curve.

59	7	1s. green	£150	10·00
108	7	1s. orange	10·00	1·75

1870. Optd **POSTAGE** twice, reading up and down.

60	6	1d. red	£120	13·00
61	6	3d. blue	£130	13·00
62	6	6d. violet	£250	48·00

1873. Optd **POSTAGE** once, reading up.

63	7	1s. brown	£425	35·00

23 28

16

1874. Queen Victoria. Various frames.

97a	23	½d. green	6·50	1·25
99	-	1d. red	8·00	25
107	-	2d. olive	5·50	1·40
113	28	2½d. blue	10·00	1·50
100	-	3d. blue	£160	17·00
101	-	3d. grey	12·00	5·50
102	-	4d. brown	17·00	1·75
103	-	6d. lilac	14·00	2·50
73	16	5s. red	£110	38·00

1877. No. 99 surch ½ **HALF.**

85	16	½d. on 1d. red	48·00	75·00

POSTAGE

Half-penny

(21)

1877. Surch as T **21**.

91	6	½d. on 1d. yellow	13·00	25·00
92	6	1d. on 6d. violet	75·00	11·00
93	6	1d. on 6d. red	£140	55·00

1885. Surch in words.

104	½d. on 1d. red (No. 99)	25·00	15·00
105	2d. on 3d. grey (No. 101)	42·00	5·50
109	2½d. on 4d. brown (No. 102)	16·00	18·00

POSTAGE.

Half-Penny

(29)

1895. No. 23 surch with T **29**.

114	½d. on 6d. violet	3·00	10·00

1895. No. 99 surch **HALF**.

125	HALF on 1d. red	3·00	2·25

31

32

1902

127	31	½d. green	7·50	50
147	31	1d. red	12·00	15
129	31	1½d. green and black	4·00	7·00
130	31	2d. red and olive	6·50	40
131	31	2½d. blue	2·00	5·50
132	31	3d. purple and grey	1·50	2·50
152	31	4d. red and brown	3·00	1·25
134	31	5d. black and orange	4·75	3·75
135	31	6d. green and purple	4·75	4·50
136	31	1s. red and blue	6·00	4·75
137	31	2s. green and violet	55·00	9·00
138	31	2s.6d. purple	50·00	12·00
139	31	4s. red and yellow	95·00	95·00
140	32	5s. blue and red	65·00	12·00
141	32	10s. red and purple	£130	50·00
142	32	£1 black and blue	£350	80·00
143	32	£1.10s. green and violet	£600	£130
162	32	£1.10s. orange and purple	£1800	£4750
144	32	£5 mauve and black	£5500	£1500
145	32	£10 green and orange	£14000	£6500
145b	32	£20 red and green	£28000	£19000

1908. As T **31/2** but inscr "POSTAGE POSTAGE".

165	31	6d. purple	5·00	3·00
166	31	1s. black on green	6·00	3·00
167	31	2s. purple and blue on blue	15·00	3·00
168	31	2s.6d. black and red on blue	25·00	3·00
169	32	5s. green and red on yellow	30·00	50·00
170	32	10s. green and red on green	£130	£130
171	32	£1 purple and black on red	£425	£375

OFFICIAL STAMPS

1904. Optd **OFFICIAL**.

O1	31	½d. green	3·50	1·00
O2	31	1d. red	15·00	1·25
O3	31	2d. red and olive	48·00	22·00
O4	31	3d. purple and grey	27·00	7·00
O5	31	6d. green and purple	85·00	80·00
O6	31	1s. red and blue	£250	£275

NAURU

An island in the W. Pacific Ocean, formerly a German possession and then administered by Australia under trusteeship. Became a republic on 31 January 1968.

1916. 12 pence = 1 shilling; 20 shillings = 1 pound.
1966. 100 cents = 1 Australian dollar.

1916. Stamps of Gt. Britain (King George V) optd **NAURU**.

1	105	½d. green	2·25	11·00
2	104	1d. red	2·50	14·00
4	106	2d. orange	2·00	13·00
6	104	2½d. blue	2·75	7·00
7	106	3d. violet	2·00	6·00
8	106	4d. green	2·00	8·50
9	107	5d. brown	2·25	14·00
10	107	6d. purple	7·50	10·00
11	108	9d. black	8·50	23·00
12	108	1s. brown	7·00	19·00
15	105	1½d. brown	28·00	55·00
20	109	2s.6d. brown	70·00	£120
22	109	5s. red	£100	£150
23	109	10s. blue	£250	£350

4

1924

26A	4	½d. brown	3·00	2·75
27B	4	1d. green	2·50	3·00
28B	4	1½d. red	1·00	1·50
29B	4	2d. orange	6·50	8·00
30B	4	2½d. blue	5·00	4·00
31A	4	3d. blue	4·00	13·00
32B	4	4d. green	7·50	13·00
33B	4	5d. brown	12·00	4·00
34B	4	6d. violet	11·00	5·00
35A	4	9d. olive	9·50	19·00
36B	4	1s. red	14·00	2·75
37B	4	2s.6d. green	32·00	35·00
38B	4	5s. purple	38·00	50·00
39B	4	10s. yellow	85·00	£100

1935. Silver Jubilee. Optd **HIS MAJESTY'S JUBILEE. 1910-1935.**

40	1½d. red	75	80
41	2d. orange	1·50	4·25
42	2½d. blue	1·50	1·50
43	1s. red	7·25	3·50

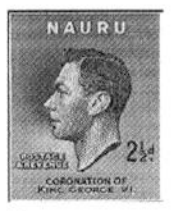

6

1937. Coronation.

44	**6**	1½d. red	45	1·75
45	**6**	2d. orange	45	2·75
46	**6**	2½d. blue	45	1·75
47	**6**	1s. purple	65	2·00

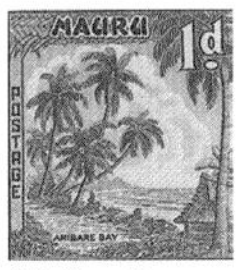

8 Anibare Bay

1954

48*a*	-	½d. violet	20	80
49a	**8**	1d. green	1·00	55
50	-	3½d. red	1·75	1·00
51	-	4d. blue	3·00	2·00
52	-	6d. orange	70	20
53	-	9d. red	60	20
54	-	1s. purple	30	30
55	-	2s.6d. green	2·75	1·00
56	-	5s. mauve	8·00	2·25

Designs:—Horiz: ½d. Nauruan netting fish; 3½d. Loading phosphate from cantilever; 4d. Great frigate bird; 6d. Canoe; 9d. Domaneab (meeting house); 2s.6d. Buada Lagoon. Vert: 1s. Palm trees; 5s. Map of Nauru.

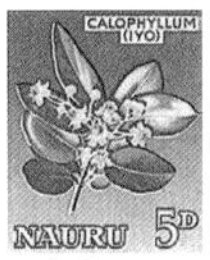

18 'Iyo' (*calophyllum*)

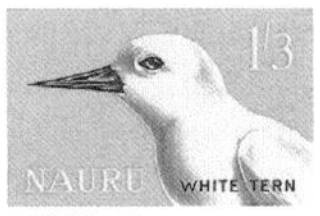

21 White Tern

1963

57	-	2d. multicoloured	75	2·25
58	-	3d. multicoloured	40	35
59	**18**	5d. multicoloured	40	75
60	-	8d. black and green	1·75	80
61	-	10d. black	40	30
62	**21**	1s.3d. blue, black and green	1·00	4·75
63	-	2s.3d. blue	2·00	55
64	-	3s.3d. multicoloured	1·00	3·75

Designs—Vert (As Type **21**): 2d. Micronesian pigeon. (26×29 mm): 10d. Capparis (flower). Horiz (As Type **18**): 3d. Poison nut (flower); 8d. Black lizard; 2s.3d. Coral pinnacles; 3s.3d. Nightingale reed warbler ("Red Warbler").

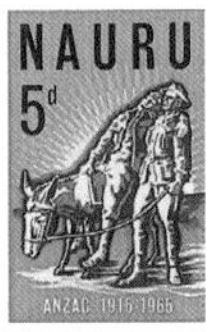

22 Simpson and his Donkey

1965. 50th Anniv of Gallipoli Landing.

65	**22**	5d. sepia, black and green	15	10

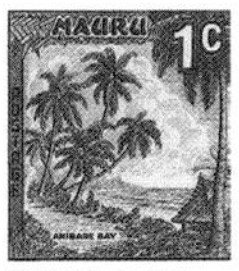

24 Anibare Bay

1966. Decimal Currency. As earlier issues but with values in cents and dollars as in T **24**. Some colours changed.

66	**24**	1c. blue	15	10
67	-	2c. purple (as No. 48)	15	50
68	-	3c. green (as No. 50)	30	2·25
69	-	4c. multicoloured (as T **18**)	20	10
70	-	5c. blue (as No. 54)	25	60
71	-	7c. black & brn (as No. 60)	30	10
72	-	8c. green (as No. 61)	20	10
73	-	10c. red (as No. 51)	40	10
74	-	15c. bl, blk and grn (as T **21**)	60	3·25
75	-	25c. brown (as No. 63)	30	1·25
76	-	30c. mult (as No. 58)	45	30
77	-	35c. mult (as No. 64)	75	35
78	-	50c. mult (as No. 57)	1·50	80
79	-	$1 mauve (as No. 56)	75	1·00

The 25c. is as No. 63 but larger, 27½×25 mm.

1968. Nos. 66/79 optd **REPUBLIC OF NAURU**.

80	**24**	1c. blue	10	30
81	-	2c. purple	10	10
82	-	3c. green	15	10
83	-	4c. multicoloured	10	10
84	-	5c. blue	10	10
85	-	7c. black and brown	25	10
86	-	8c. green	10	10
87	-	10c. red	50	15
88	-	15c. blue, black and green	1·00	2·75
89	-	25c. brown	15	15
90	-	30c. multicoloured	40	15
91	-	35c. multicoloured	1·25	30
92	-	50c. multicoloured	1·00	35
93	-	$1 purple	75	50

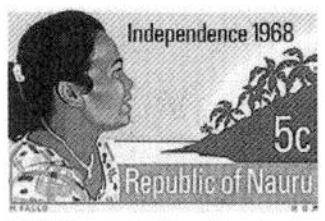

27 "Towards the Sunrise"

1968. Independence.

94	**27**	5c. multicoloured	10	10
95	-	10c. black, green and blue	10	10

Design:—10c. Planting seedling, and map.

29 Flag of Independent Nauru

1969

96	**29**	15c. yellow, orange and blue	65	15

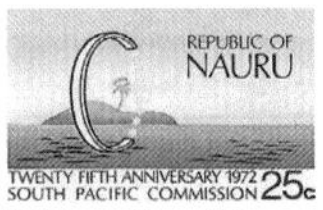

30 Island, "C" and Stars

1972. 25th Anniv of South Pacific Commission.

97	**30**	25c. multicoloured	30	30

1973. Fifth Anniv of Independence. No. 96 optd **Independence 1968-1973**.

98	**29**	15c. yellow, orange and blue	20	30

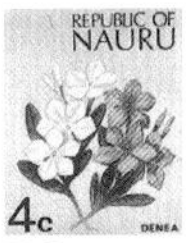

32 Denea

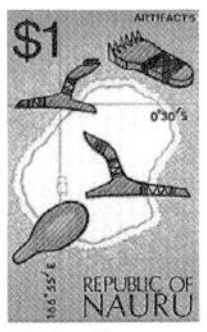

33 Artefacts and Map

1973. Multicoloured.

99	1c. Ekwenababae	30	20
100	2c. Kauwe iud	35	20
101	3c. Rimone	35	20
102	4c. Type **32**	35	40
103	5c. Erekogo	35	40
104	7c. Racoon butterflyfish ("Ikimago") (horiz)	40	1·00
105	8c. Catching flying fish (horiz)	20	20
106	10c. Itsibweb (ball game) (horiz)	20	20
107	15c. Nauruan wrestling	25	20
108	20c. Snaring great frigate birds ("Frigate Birds")	70	1·00
109	25c. Nauruan girl	25	30
110	30c. Catching common noddy birds ("Noddy Birds") (horiz)	60	40
111	50c. Great frigate birds ("Frigate Birds") (horiz)	70	75
112	$1 Type **33**	70	75

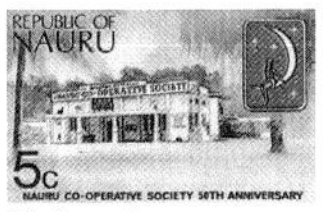

34 Co-op Store

1973. 50th Anniv of Nauru Co-operative Society. Multicoloured.

113	5c. Type **34**	15	30
114	25c. Timothy Detudamo (founder)	15	15
115	50c. NCS trademark (vert)	35	55

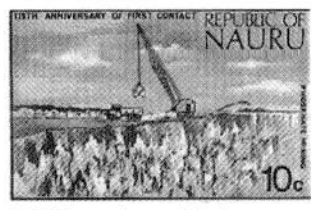

35 Phosphate Mining

1974. 175th Anniv of First Contact with the Outside World. Multicoloured.

116	7c. MV *Eigamoiya* (bulk carrier)	55	90
117	10c. Type **35**	40	25
118	15c. Fokker Fellowship *Nauru Chief*	55	30
119	25c. Nauruan chief in early times	40	35
120	35c. Capt. Fearn and 18th-century frigate (70×22 mm)	2·00	2·50
121	50c. 18th-century frigate off Nauru (70×22 mm)	1·00	1·40

The ship on the 35c. and 50c. is wrongly identified as the "Hunter" (snow).

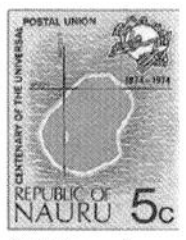

36 Map of Nauru

1974. Centenary of U.P.U. Multicoloured.

122	5c. Type **36**	15	20
123	8c. Nauru Post Office	15	20
124	20c. Nauruan postman	15	10
125	$1 UPU Building and Nauruan flag	40	60
MS126	157×105 mm. Nos. 122/5. Imperf	1·50	4·50

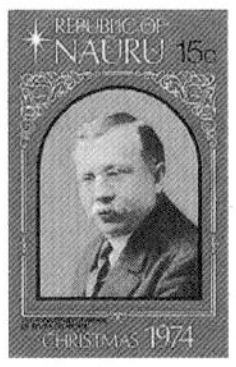

37 Rev. P. A. Delaporte

1974. Christmas and 75th Anniv of Rev. Delaporte's Arrival.

127	**37**	15c. multicoloured	20	20
128	**37**	20c. multicoloured	30	30

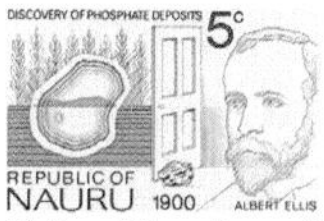

38 Map of Nauru, Lump of Phosphate Rock and Albert Ellis

1975. Phosphate Mining Anniversaries. Mult.

129	5c. Type **38**	25	40
130	7c. Coolies and mine	25	40
131	15c. Electric phosphate train, barges and ship	75	1·00
132	25c. Modern ore extraction	1·00	1·10

Anniversaries:—5c. 75th anniv of discovery; 7c. 70th anniv of Mining Agreement; 15c. 55th anniv of British Phosphate Commissioners; 25c. Fifth anniv of Nauru Phosphate Corporation.

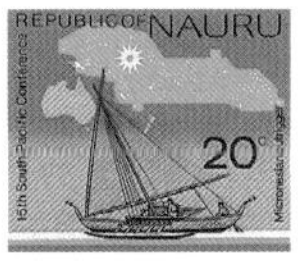

39 Micronesian Outrigger

1975. South Pacific Commission Conf, Nauru (1st issue). Multicoloured.

133	20c. Type **39**	55	75
134	20c. Polynesian double-hull	55	75
135	20c. Melanesian outrigger	55	75
136	20c. Polynesian outrigger	55	75

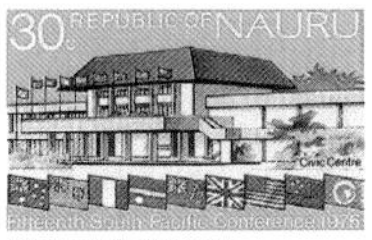

40 New Civic Centre

1975. South Pacific Commission Conf, Nauru (2nd issue). Multicoloured.

137	30c. Type **40**	15	15
138	50c. Domaneab (meeting-house)	30	30

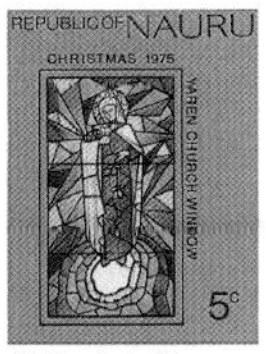

41 *Our Lady* (Yaren Church)

1975. Christmas. Stained-glass Windows. Mult.

139	5c. Type **41**	15	30
140	7c. *Suffer little children* (Orro Church)	15	30
141	15c. As 7c.	20	60
142	25c. Type **41**	25	80

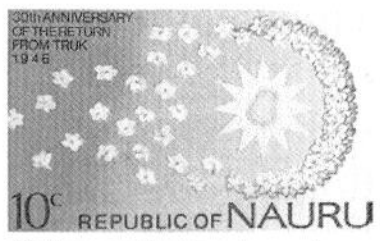

42 Flowers floating towards Nauru

1976. 30th Anniv of Islanders' Return from Truk. Multicoloured.

143	10c. Type **42**	10	15
144	14c. Nauru encircled by garland	15	20
145	25c. Nightingale reed warbler and maps	70	30
146	40c. Return of the islanders	30	45

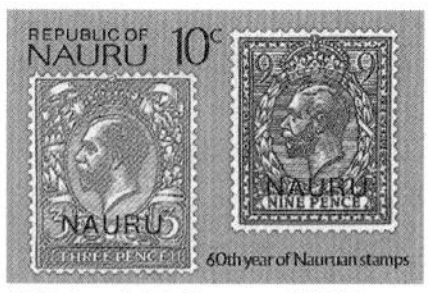

43 3d. and 9d. Stamps of 1916

1976. 60th Anniv of Nauruan Stamps. Mult.

147	10c. Type **43**	15	15
148	15c. 6d. and 1s. stamps	15	15
149	25c. 2s.6d. stamp	20	25
150	50c. 5s. "Specimen" stamp	25	35

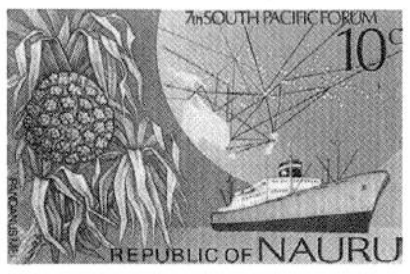

44 *Pandanus mei* and *Enna G* (cargo liner)

1976. South Pacific Forum, Nauru. Mult.

151	10c. Type **44**	30	30
152	20c. *Tournefortia argentea* with Boeing 737 and Fokker Fellowship aircraft	45	40
153	30c. *Thespesia populnea* and Nauru Tracking Station	25	40
154	40c. *Cordia subcordata* and produce	25	40

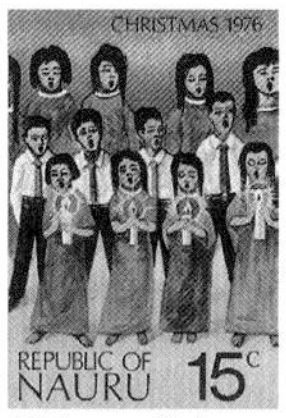

45 Nauruan Choir

1976. Christmas. Multicoloured.

155	15c. Type **45**	10	10
156	15c. Nauruan choir	10	10
157	20c. Angel in white dress	15	15
158	20c. Angel in red dress	15	15

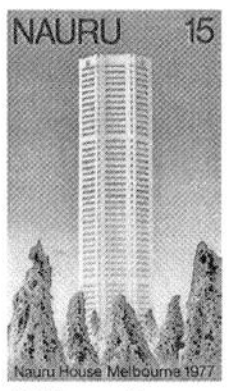

46 Nauru House and Coral Pinnacles

1977. Opening of Nauru House, Melbourne. Mult.

159	15c. Type **46**	15	15
160	30c. Nauru House and Melbourne skyline	25	25

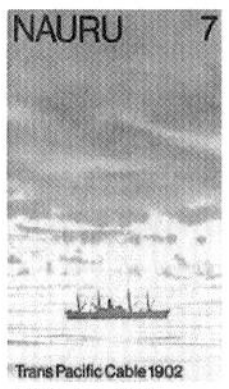

47 Cable Ship *Anglia*

1977. 75th Anniv of First Trans-Pacific Cable and 20th Anniv of First Artificial Earth Satellite.

161	**47**	7c. multicoloured	20	10
162	-	15c. blue, grey and black	30	15
163	-	20c. blue, grey and black	30	20
164	-	25c. multicoloured	30	20

Designs:—15c. Tracking station, Nauru; 20c. Stern of *Anglia*; 25c. Dish aerial.

48 Father Kayser and First Catholic Church

1977. Christmas. Multicoloured.

165		15c. Type **48**	10	10
166		25c. Congregational Church, Orro	15	15
167		30c. Catholic Church, Arubo	15	15

49 Arms of Nauru

1978. Tenth Anniv of Independence.

168	**49**	15c. multicoloured	20	15
169	**49**	60c. multicoloured	35	30

1978. Nos. 159/60 surch.

170	**46**	4c. on 15c. multicoloured	45	1·25
171	**46**	5c. on 15c. multicoloured	45	1·25
172	-	8c. on 30c. multicoloured	45	1·25
173	-	10c. on 30c. multicoloured	45	1·25

51 Collecting Shellfish

1978

174	**51**	1c. multicoloured	35	30
175	-	2c. multicoloured	35	30
176	-	3c. multicoloured	2·00	1·00
177	-	4c. brown, blue and black	35	30
178	-	5c. multicoloured	2·25	1·00
179	-	7c. multicoloured	20	1·50
180	-	10c. multicoloured	20	20
181	-	15c. multicoloured	20	30
182	-	20c. grey, black and blue	20	30
183	-	25c. multicoloured	20	30
184	-	30c. multicoloured	1·75	45
185	-	32c. multicoloured	2·50	1·25
186	-	40c. multicoloured	1·75	2·25
187	-	50c. multicoloured	1·50	1·25
188	-	$1 multicoloured	40	1·00
189	-	$2 multicoloured	60	1·10
190	-	$5 grey, black and blue	1·10	2·25

Designs:—2c. Coral outcrop; 3c. Reef scene; 4c. Girl with fish; 5c. Reef heron; 7c. Catching fish, Buada Lagoon; 10c. Ijuw Lagoon; 15c. Girl framed by coral; 20c. Pinnacles, Anibare Bay reef; 25c. Pinnacle at Meneng; 30c. Head of great frigate bird; 32c. White-capped noddy birds in coconut palm; 40c. Wandering tattler; 50c. Great frigate birds on perch; $1 Old coral pinnacles at Topside; $2 New pinnacles at Topside; $5 Blackened pinnacles at Topside.

52 APU Emblem

1978. 14th General Assembly of Asian Parliamentarians' Union. Nauru.

191	**52**	15c. multicoloured	20	25
192	-	20c. black, blue and gold	20	25

Design:—20c. As Type **52**, but with different background.

53 Virgin and Child

1978. Christmas. Multicoloured.

193		7c. Type **53**	10	10
194		15c. Angel in sunrise scene (horiz)	10	10
195		20c. As 15c.	15	15
196		30c. Type **53**	20	20

54 Baden-Powell and Cub Scout

1978. 70th Anniv of Boy Scout Movement. Mult.

197		20c. Type **54**	20	15
198		30c. Scout	25	20
199		50c. Rover Scout	35	30

55 *Wright Flyer I* over Nauru

1979. Flight Anniversaries. Multicoloured.

200		10c. Type **55**	25	15
201		15c. Fokker F.VIIa/3m *Southern Cross* superimposed on nose of Boeing 737	35	20
202		15c. *Southern Cross* and Boeing 737 (front view)	35	20
203		30c. *Wright Flyer I* over Nauru airfield	60	30

Anniversaries:—Nos. 200, 203, 75th anniv of powered flight; 201/2, 50th anniv of Kingsford-Smith's Pacific flight.

56 Sir Rowland Hill and Marshall Islands 10pf. stamp of 1901

1979. Death Cent of Sir Rowland Hill. Mult.

204		5c. Type **56**	15	10
205		15c. Sir Rowland Hill and **Nauru** opt on G.B. 10s. "Seahorse" stamp of 1916–23	25	20
206		60c. Sir Rowland Hill and Nauru 60c. Tenth anniv of Independence stamp, 1978	55	40
MS207		159×101 mm. Nos. 204/6	85	1·25

57 Dish Antenna, Transmitting Station and Radio Mast

1979. 50th Anniv of International Consultative Radio Committee. Multicoloured.

208		7c. Type **57**	15	10
209		32c. Telex operator	35	25
210		40c. Radio operator	40	25

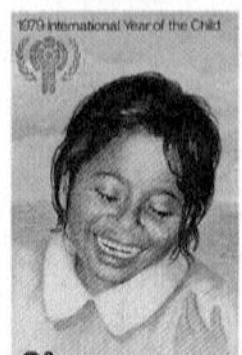

58 Smiling Child

1979. International Year of the Child.

211	**58**	8c. multicoloured	10	10
212	-	15c. multicoloured	15	15
213	-	25c. multicoloured	20	20
214	-	32c. multicoloured	20	20
215	-	50c. multicoloured	25	25

Designs:—15c. to 50c. Smiling children.

59 Ekwenababae (flower), Scroll inscribed "Peace on Earth" and Star

1979. Christmas. Multicoloured.

216		7c. Type **59**	10	10
217		15c. *Thespia populnea* (flower), scroll inscribed "Goodwill towards Men" and star	10	10
218		20c. Denea (flower), scroll inscribed "Peace on Earth" and star	10	10
219		30c. Erekogo (flower), scroll inscribed "Goodwill toward Men" and star	20	20

60 Dassault Bregeut Mystere Falcon 50 over Melbourne

1980. Tenth Anniv of Air Nauru. Multicoloured.

220		15c. Type **60**	40	15
221		20c. Fokker F.28 Fellowship over Tarawa	45	15
222		25c. Boeing 727-100 over Hong Kong	45	15
223		30c. Boeing 737 over Auckland	45	15

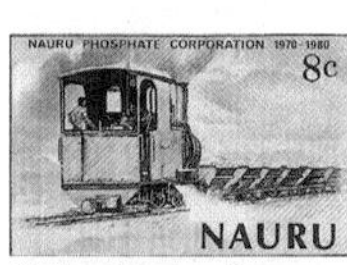

61 Steam Locomotive

1980. Tenth Anniv of Nauru Phosphate Corporation. Multicoloured.

224		8c. Type **61**	10	10
225		32c. Electric locomotive	20	20
226		60c. Diesel-hydraulic locomotive	35	35
MS227		168×118 mm. Nos. 224/6	1·00	2·50

No. **MS**227 also commemorates the "London 1980" International Stamp Exhibition.

62 Verse 10 from Luke, Chapter 2 in English

1980. Christmas. Verses from Luke, Chapter 2. Multicoloured.

228		20c. Type **62**	10	10
229		20c. Verse 10 in Nauruan	10	10
230		30c. Verse 14 in English	15	15
231		30c. Verse 14 in Nauruan	15	15

See also Nos. 248/51.

63 Nauruan, Australia, Union and New Zealand Flags on Aerial View of Nauru

1980. 20th Anniv of U.N. Declaration on the Granting of Independence to Colonial Countries and Peoples. Multicoloured.

232		25c. Type **63**	15	15
233		50c. UN Trusteeship Council (72×23 mm)	15	15
234		50c. Nauru independence ceremony, 1968 (72×23 mm)	25	25

64 Timothy Detudamo

1981. 30th Anniv of Nauru Local Government Council. Head Chiefs. Multicoloured.

235		20c. Type **64**	15	15
236		30c. Raymond Gadabu	15	15
237		50c. Hammer DeRoburt	25	25

65 Casting Net by Hand

1981. Fishing. Multicoloured.

238		8c. Type **65**	15	10
239		20c. Outrigger canoe	25	15
240		32c. Outboard motor boat	35	20
241		40c. Trawler	35	25
MS242		167×116 mm. No. 241×4	1·40	2·00

No. **MS**242 was issued to commemorate the "WIPA 1981" International Stamp Exhibition, Vienna.

66 Bank of Nauru Emblem and Building

1981. Fifth Anniv of Bank of Nauru.

243	**66**	$1 multicoloured	60	60

67 Inaugural Speech

1981. U.N. Day. E.S.C.A.P. (United Nations Economic and Social Commission for Asia and the Pacific) Events. Multicoloured.

244		15c. Type **67**	15	15
245		20c. Presenting credentials	15	15
246		25c. Unveiling plaque	20	20
247		30c. Raising UN flag	25	25

1981. Christmas. Bible Verses. Designs as T **62**. Multicoloured.

248		20c. Matthew 1, 23 in English	15	15
249		20c. Matthew 1, 23 in Nauruan	15	15
250		30c. Luke 2, 11 in English	20	20
251		30c. Luke 2, 11 in Nauruan	20	20

68 Earth Satellite Station

1981. Tenth Anniv of South Pacific Forum. Mult.

252		10c. Type **68**	20	15
253		20c. "Enna G" (cargo liner)	25	20
254		30c. Boeing 737 airliner	25	25
255		40c. Local produce	25	30

69 Nauru Scouts leaving for 1935 Frankston Scout Jamboree

1982. 75th Anniv of Boy Scout Movement. Mult.

256		7c. Type **69**	15	15
257		8c. Two Nauru scouts on *Nauru Chief*, 1935 (vert)	15	15
258		15c. Nauru scouts making pottery, 1935 (vert)	15	20
259		20c. Lord Huntingfield addressing Nauru scouts, Frankston Jamboree, 1935	20	25
260		25c. Nauru cub and scout, 1982	20	30
261		40c. Nauru cubs, scouts and scouters, 1982	30	45
MS262		152×114 mm. Nos. 256/61. Imperf	1·00	2·25

No. **MS**262 also commemorates Nauru's participation in the "Stampex" National Stamp Exhibition, London.

70 100 kw Electricity Generating Plant under Construction (left side)

1982. Ocean Thermal Energy Conversion. Mult.

263		25c. Type **70**	60	30
264		25c. 100 kw Electricity Generating Plant under construction (right side)	60	30
265		40c. Completed plant (left)	80	40
266		40c. Completed plant (right)	80	40

Nos. 263/4 and 265/6 were each issued as horizontal *se-tenant* pairs, forming composite designs.

71 SS *Fido*

1982. 75th Anniv of Phosphate Shipments. Mult.

267	5c. Type **71**	40	10
268	10c. Steam locomotive *Nellie*	50	20
269	30c. Class *Clyde* diesel locomotive	60	50
270	60c. MV *Eigamoiya* (bulk carrier)	65	80
MS271	165×107 mm. $1 *Eigamoiya*, *Rosie-D* and *Kolle-D* (bulk carriers) (67×27 mm)	1·25	2·25

No. **MS**271 was issued to commemorate ANPEX 82 National Stamp Exhibition, Brisbane.

72 Queen Elizabeth II on Horseback

1982. Royal Visit. Multicoloured.

272	20c. Type **72**	30	20
273	50c. Prince Philip, Duke of Edinburgh	40	45
274	$1 Queen Elizabeth II and Prince Philip (horiz)	45	1·00

73 Father Bernard Lahn

1982. Christmas. Multicoloured.

275	10c. Type **73**	20	35
276	30c. Reverend Itubwa Amram	20	50
277	40c. Pastor James Aingimen	25	80
278	50c. Bishop Paul Mea	30	1·10

74 Speaker of the Nauruan Parliament

75 Nauru Satellite Earth Station

1983. 15th Anniv of Independence. Mult.

279	15c. Type **74**	20	20
280	20c. Family Court in session	25	25
281	30c. Law Courts building (horiz)	25	25
282	50c. Parliamentary chamber (horiz)	40	40

1983. World Communications Year. Mult.

283	5c. Type **75**	20	10
284	10c. Omni-directional range installation	20	15
285	20c. Emergency short-wave radio	25	25
286	25c. Radio Nauru control room	40	30
287	40c. Unloading air mail	90	45

76 Return of Exiles from Truk on MV *Trienza*, 1946

1983. Angam Day. Multicoloured.

288	15c. Type **76**	20	25
289	20c. Mrs. Elsie Agio (exile community leader) (vert) (25×41 mm)	20	25
290	30c. Child on scales (vert) (25×41 mm)	35	40
291	40c. Nauruan children (vert) (25×41 mm)	45	50

77 The Holy Virgin, Holy Child and St. John (School of Raphael)

1983. Christmas. Multicoloured.

292	5c. Type **77**	10	10
293	15c. *Madonna on the Throne, surrounded by Angels* (School of Sevilla)	20	15
294	50c. *The Mystical Betrothal of St. Catherine with Jesus* (School of Veronese) (horiz)	60	40

78 SS *Ocean Queen*

1984. 250th Anniv of "Lloyd's List" (newspaper). Multicoloured.

295	20c. Type **78**	30	20
296	25c. MV *Enna G*	35	25
297	30c. MV *Baron Minto*	40	30
298	40c. Sinking of MV *Triadic*, 1940	50	45

79 1974 UPU $1 Stamp

1984. Universal Postal Union Congress, Hamburg.

299	**79** $1 multicoloured	70	1·25

80 *Hypolimnas bolina* (female)

1984. Butterflies. Multicoloured.

300	25c. Type **80**	35	40
301	30c. *Hypolimnas bolina* (male)	35	55
302	50c. *Danaus plexippus*	40	85

81 Coastal Scene

1984. Life in Nauru. Multicoloured.

303	1c. Type **81**	10	60
304	3c. Nauruan woman (vert)	15	75
305	5c. Modern trawler	40	75
306	10c. Golfer on the links	90	75
307	15c. Excavating phosphate (vert)	90	75
308	20c. Surveyor (vert)	65	55
309	25c. Air Nauru Boeing 727 airliner	80	55
310	30c. Elderly Nauruan (vert)	50	50
311	40c. Loading hospital patient onto Boeing 727 aircraft	90	55
312	50c. Skin-diver with fish (vert)	1·00	80
313	$1 Tennis player (vert)	2·50	3·25
314	$2 Anabar Lagoon	2·50	3·75

82 Buada Chapel

1984. Christmas. Multicoloured.

315	30c. Type **82**	30	50
316	40c. Detudamo Memorial Church	40	65
317	50c. Candle-light service, Kayser College (horiz)	40	70

83 Air Nauru Boeing 737 Jet on Tarmac

1985. 15th Anniv of Air Nauru. Multicoloured.

318	20c. Type **83**	50	35
319	30c. Stewardesses on Boeing 737 aircraft steps (vert)	60	60
320	40c. Fokker F.28 Fellowship over Nauru	75	75
321	50c. Freight being loaded onto Boeing 727 (vert)	85	85

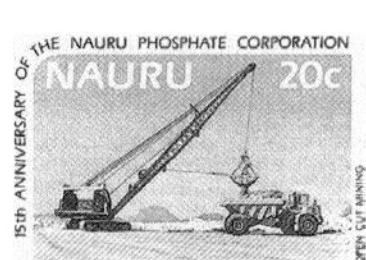

84 Open Cut Mining

1985. 15th Anniv of Nauru Phosphate Corporation. Multicoloured.

322	20c. Type **84**	1·00	60
323	25c. Diesel locomotive hauling crushed ore	2·00	1·00
324	30c. Phosphate drying plant	1·75	1·00
325	50c. Early steam locomotive	2·50	1·75

85 Mother and Baby on Beach

1985. Christmas. Multicoloured.

326	50c. Beach scene	1·50	2·25
327	50c. Type **85**	1·50	2·25

Nos. 326/7 were printed together, *se-tenant*, forming a composite design.

86 Adult Common Noddy with Juvenile

1985. Birth Bicentenary of John J. Audubon (ornithologist). Common ("Brown") Noddy. Mult.

328	10c. Type **86**	35	35
329	20c. Adult and immature birds in flight	50	70
330	30c. Adults in flight	65	85
331	50c. *Brown Noddy* (John J. Audubon)	80	1·10

87 Douglas Motor Cycle

1986. Early Transport on Nauru. Multicoloured.

332	15c. Type **87**	1·00	70
333	20c. Primitive lorry	1·25	95
334	30c. German-built steam locomotive, 1910	1·50	1·50
335	40c. Baby Austin car	1·75	1·75

88 Island and Bank of Nauru

1986. Tenth Anniv of Bank of Nauru. Children's Paintings. Multicoloured.

336	20c. Type **88**	20	30
337	25c. Borrower with notes and coins	25	35
338	30c. Savers	30	40
339	40c. Customers at bank counter	35	55

89 *Plumeria rubra*

1986. Flowers. Multicoloured.

340	20c. Type **89**	30	70
341	25c. *Tristellateia australis*	40	85
342	30c. *Bougainvillea cultivar*	50	1·00
343	40c. *Delonix regia*	60	1·25

90 Carol Singers

1986. Christmas. Multicoloured.

344	20c. Type **90**	40	30
345	$1 Carol singers and hospital patient	1·60	3·50

91 Young Girls Dancing

1987. Nauruan Dancers. Multicoloured.

346	20c. Type **91**	65	80
347	30c. Stick dance	80	1·25
348	50c. Boy doing war dance (vert)	1·25	2·50

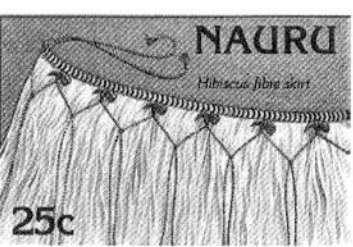

92 Hibiscus Fibre Skirt

1987. Personal Artefacts. Multicoloured.

349	25c. Type **92**	60	75
350	30c. Headband and necklets	65	85
351	45c. Decorative necklets	75	1·10
352	60c. Pandanus leaf fan	1·10	1·60

93 UPU Emblem and Air Mail Label

1987. World Post Day.

353	**93** 40c. multicoloured	1·50	1·25
MS354	122×82 mm. $1 UPU emblem and map of Pacific showing mail routes (114×74 mm)	3·25	4·25

94 Open Bible

1987. Centenary of Nauru Congregational Church.

355	**94** 40c. multicoloured	1·50	1·75

95 Nauruan Children's Party

1987. Christmas. Multicoloured.

356	20c. Type **95**	50	50
357	$1 Nauruan Christmas dinner	1·75	3·25

96 Loading Phosphate on Ship

1988. 20th Anniv of Independence. Mult.

358	25c. Type **96**	1·00	1·00
359	40c. Tomano flower (vert)	1·25	1·25
360	55c. Great frigate bird (vert)	2·00	2·00
361	$1 Arms of Republic (35×35 mm)	2·00	3·50

97 Map of German Marshall Is. and 1901 5m. Yacht Definitive

1988. 80th Anniv of Nauru Post Office. Mult.

362	30c. Type **97**	60	75
363	50c. Letter and post office of 1908	70	1·25
364	70c. Nauru Post Office and airmail letter	80	1·50

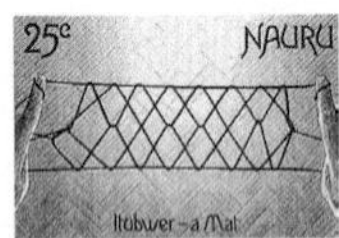

98 "Itubwer" (mat)

1988. String Figures. Multicoloured.

365	25c. Type **98**	30	35
366	40c. "Etegerer – the Pursuer"	40	60
367	55c. "Holding up the Sky"	45	70
368	80c. "Manujie's Sword"	70	1·75

99 UPU Emblem and National Flag

1988. Cent of Nauru's Membership of U.P.U.

369	**99**	$1 multicoloured	1·00	1·25

100 *Hark the Herald Angels*

1988. Christmas. Designs showing words and music from "Hark the Herald Angels Sing".

370	**100**	20c. black, red and yellow	60	30
371	-	60c. black, red and mauve	1·40	1·25
372	-	$1 black, red and green	2·25	2·25

101 Logo (15th anniv of Nauru Insurance Corporation)

1989. Anniversaries and Events. Multicoloured.

373	15c. Type **101**	25	30
374	50c. Logos (World Telecommunications Day and Tenth anniv of Asian-Pacific Telecommunity)	60	85
375	$1 Photograph of island scene (150 years of photography)	1·40	2·00
376	$2 Capitol and U.P.U. emblem (20th UPU Congress, Washington)	2·25	4·50

102 Mother and Baby

1989. Christmas. Multicoloured.

377	20c. Type **102**	40	30
378	$1 Children opening presents	1·50	3·25

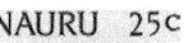

103 Eigigu working while Sisters play

1989. 20th Anniv of First Manned Landing on Moon. Legend of "Eigigu, the Girl in the Moon". Multicoloured.

379	25c. Type **103**	3·00	2·75
380	30c. Eigigu climbing tree	3·25	3·00
381	50c. Eigigu stealing toddy from blind woman	6·00	5·50
382	$1 Eigigu on Moon	8·00	7·50

104 Early Mining by Hand

1990. 20th Anniv of Nauru Phosphate Corporation. Multicoloured.

383	50c. Type **104**	1·00	1·00
384	$1 Modern mining by excavator	1·50	2·00

105 Sunday School Class

1990. Christmas. Multicoloured.

385	25c. Type **105**	90	1·25
386	25c. Teacher telling Christmas story	90	1·25

Nos. 385/6 were printed together, *se-tenant*, forming a composite design.

106 Eoiyepiang laying Baby on Mat

1990. Legend of "Eoiyepiang, the Daughter of Thunder and Lightning". Multicoloured.

387	25c. Type **106**	1·50	60
388	30c. Eoiyepiang making floral decoration	1·75	70
389	50c. Eoiyepiang left on snow-covered mountain	2·25	2·00
390	$1 Eoiyepiang and warrior	3·25	3·50

107 Oleander

1991. Flowers. Multicoloured.

391	15c. Type **107**	15	60
392	20c. Lily	15	60
393	25c. Passion flower	20	45
394	30c. Lily (different)	25	40
395	35c. Caesalpinia	30	45
396	40c. Clerodendron	35	50
397	45c. *Baubina pinnata*	40	50
398	50c. Hibiscus (vert)	40	50
399	75c. Apocymaceae	65	70
400	$1 Bindweed (vert)	85	1·00
401	$2 Tristellateia (vert)	1·75	2·25
402	$3 Impala lily (vert)	2·50	3·75

108 Jesus Christ and Children (stained glass window)

1991. Christmas. Sheet 124×82 mm.

MS403	**108** $2 multicoloured	4·25	5·00

109 Star and Symbol of Asian Development Bank

1992. 25th Annual Meeting of Asian Development Bank.

404	**109**	$1.50 multicoloured	2·00	2·50

110 Gifts under Christmas Tree

1992. Christmas. Children's Paintings. Mult.

405	45c. Type **110**	75	75
406	60c. Father Christmas in sleigh	1·00	1·50

111 Hammer DeRoburt

1993. 25th Anniv of Independence and Hammer DeRoburt (former President) Commemoration.

407	**111**	$1 multicoloured	2·00	3·00

112 Running, Constitution Day Sports

1993. 15th Anniv of Constitution Day. Mult.

408	70c. Type **112**	1·00	1·40
409	80c. Part of Independence Proclamation	1·00	1·40

113 Great Frigate Birds, Flying Fish and Island

1993. 24th South Pacific Forum Meeting, Nauru. Multicoloured.

410	60c. Type **113**	1·40	1·75
411	60c. Red-tailed tropic bird, great frigate bird, dolphin and island	1·40	1·75
412	60c. Racoon butterflyfish ("Ikimago"), coral and sea urchins	1·40	1·75
413	60c. Three different types of fish with corals	1·40	1·75
MS414	140×130 mm. Nos. 410/13	6·00	8·00

Nos. 410/13 were printed together, *se-tenant*, forming a composite design.

114 "Peace on Earth, Goodwill to Men" and Star

1993. Christmas. Multicoloured.

415	55c. Type **114**	60	85
416	65c. "Hark the Herald Angels Sing" and star	65	90

115 Girls with Dogs

1994. Hong Kong '94 International Stamp Exhibition. Chinese New Year ("Year of the Dog"). Multicoloured.

417	$1 Type **115**	1·25	2·00
418	$1 Boys with dogs	1·25	2·00
MS419	100×75 mm. Nos. 417/18	3·50	4·25

1994. Singpex '94 National Stamp Exhibition, Singapore. No. MS419 optd "SINGPEX '94" and emblem in gold on sheet margin.

MS420	100×75 mm. Nos. 417/18	2·50	3·50

116 Weightlifting

1994. 15th Commonwealth Games, Victoria, Canada.

421	**116**	$1.50 multicoloured	1·40	2·00

117 Peace Dove and Star over Island

1994. Christmas. Multicoloured.

422	65c. Type **117**	90	90
423	75c. Star over Bethlehem	1·00	1·00

118 Air Nauru Airliner and Emblems

1994. 50th Anniv of I.C.A.O. Multicoloured.

424	55c. Type **118**	50	55
425	65c. Control tower, Nauru International Airport	60	65
426	80c. DVOR equipment	70	1·00
427	$1 Crash tenders	90	1·10
MS428	165×127 mm. Nos. 424/7	4·00	4·50

119 Emblem and Olympic Rings

1994. Nauru's Entry into Int Olympic Committee.

429	**119**	50c. multicoloured	50	50

120 Nauruan Flag

1995. 50th Anniv of United Nations (1st issue). Multicoloured.

430	75c. Type **120**	1·40	1·75
431	75c. Arms of Nauru	1·40	1·75
432	75c. Outrigger canoe on coastline	1·40	1·75
433	75c. Airliner over phosphate freighter	1·40	1·75

MS434 110×85 mm. Nos. 430/3 5·50 6·50

Nos. 430/3 were printed together, *se-tenant*, forming a composite design.

See also Nos. 444/5.

121 Signing Phosphate Agreement, 1967

1995. 25th Anniv of Nauru Phosphate Corporation. Multicoloured.

435	60c. Type **121**	80	1·00
436	60c. Pres. Bernard Dowiyogo and Prime Minister Keating of Australia shaking hands	80	1·00
MS437	120×80 mm. $2 Excavating phosphate	2·75	3·25

1995. International Stamp Exhibitions. No. 309 surch.

438	50c. on 25c. multicoloured (surch **at Beijing**)	1·75	2·00
439	$1 on 25c. multicoloured (surch **at Jakarta**)	1·75	2·00
440	$1 on 25c. multicoloured (surch **at Singapore**)	1·75	2·00

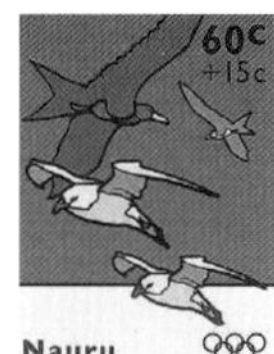

123 Sea Birds (face value at top right)

1995. Olympic Games, Atlanta. Sheet 140×121 mm, containing T **123** and similar vert designs. Multicoloured.

MS441 60c.+15c. Type **123**; 60c.+15c. Sea brids (face value at top left); 60c.+15c. Four dolphins; 60c.+15c. Pair of dolphins 4·50 5·50

The premiums on No. **MS**441 were for Nauru sport development.

124 Children playing on Gun

1995. 50th Anniv of Peace. Multicoloured.

442	75c. Type **124**	1·75	2·00
443	$1.50 Children making floral garlands	1·75	2·00

125 Nauru Crest, Coastline and UN Anniversary Emblem

1995. 50th Anniv of United Nations (2nd issue). Multicoloured.

444	75c. Type **125**	80	1·00
445	$1.50 Aerial view of Nauru and UN Headquarters, New York	1·25	2·00

126 Young Girl praying

1995. Christmas. Multicoloured.

446	60c. Type **126**	90	1·00
447	70c. Man praying	90	1·00

127 Returning Refugees and Head Chief Timothy Detudamo

1996. 50th Anniv of Nauruans' Return from Truk.

448	**127**	75c. multicoloured	90	1·00
449	**127**	$1.25 multicoloured	1·60	2·00
MS450		120×80 mm. Nos. 448/9	3·50	4·25

128 Nanjing Stone Lion

1996. CHINA '96 Ninth Asian International Stamp Exhibition, Peking. Sheet 130×110 mm.

MS451 **128** 45c. multicoloured 1·00 1·25

129 Symbolic Athlete

1996. Centenary of Modern Olympic Games. Mult.

452	40c. Type **129**	1·00	80
453	50c. Symbolic weightlifter	1·25	1·00
454	60c. Weightlifter (horiz)	1·25	1·10
455	$1 Athlete (horiz)	1·75	2·25

130 The Nativity and Angel

1996. Christmas. Multicoloured.

456	50c. Type **130**	60	60
457	70c. Angel, world map and wild animals	80	1·00

131 Dolphinfish

1997. Endangered Species. Fish. Multicoloured.

458	20c. Type **131**	1·10	1·10
459	30c. Wahoo	1·25	1·25
460	40c. Sailfish	1·40	1·40
461	50c. Yellow-finned tuna	1·50	1·50

132 Statue of Worshipper with Offering

1997. HONG KONG '97 International Stamp Exhibition. Statues of different worshippers (1c. to 15c.) or Giant Buddha of Hong Kong (25c.).

462	**132**	1c. multicoloured	20	30
463	-	2c. multicoloured	20	30
464	-	5c. multicoloured	25	35
465	-	10c. multicoloured	30	40
466	-	12c. multicoloured	30	40
467	-	15c. multicoloured	30	40
468	-	25c. multicoloured	40	45

133 Princess Elizabeth and Lieut. Philip Mountbatten, 1947

1997. Golden Wedding of Queen Elizabeth and Prince Philip.

469	**133**	80c. black and gold	75	1·00
470	-	$1.20 multicoloured	1·00	1·40

MS471 150×110 mm. Nos. 469/70 (sold at $3) 2·50 3·25

Design:—$1.20, Queen Elizabeth and Prince Philip, 1997.

134 Conference Building

1997. 28th Parliamentary Conference of Presiding Officers and Clerks. Sheet 150×100 mm.

MS472 **134** $2 multicoloured 1·50 2·25

135 Commemorative Pillar

1997. Christmas. 110th Anniv of Nauru Congregational Church. Multicoloured.

473	60c. Type **135**	60	55
474	80c. Congregational Church	80	90

136 Weightlifter

1998. Commonwealth, Oceania and South Pacific Weightlifting Championships, Nauru. Sheet 180×100 mm, containing T **136** and similar vert designs showing weightlifters.

MS475 40c., 60c., 80c., $1.20 multicoloured 1·75 2·50

137 Juan Antonio Samaranch and Aerial View

1998. Visit of International Olympic Committee President.

476	**137**	$2 multicoloured	1·40	2·00

138 Diana, Princess of Wales

1998. Diana, Princess of Wales Commemoration. Multicoloured.

477	70c. Type **138**	35	50
478	70c. Wearing white shirt	35	50
479	70c. With tiara	35	50
480	70c. In white jacket	35	50
481	70c. Wearing pink hat	35	50
482	70c. In white suit	35	50

139 Gymnastics

1998. 16th Commonwealth Games, Kuala Lumpur, Malaysia. Multicoloured.

483	40c. Type **139**	30	40
484	60c. Athletics	45	60
485	70c. Sprinting	55	70
486	80c. Weightlifting	60	80
MS487	153×130 mm. Nos. 483/6	1·60	2·40

140 Sqn. Ldr. Hicks (Composer of Nauru's National Anthem) conducting

1998. 30th Anniv of Independence. Multicoloured.

488	$1 Type **140**	85	80
489	$2 Sqn. Ldr. Hicks and score	1·75	2·25
MS490	175×110 mm. Nos. 488/9	2·75	3·50

141 Palm Trees, Fish, Festive Candle and Flower

1998. Christmas. Multicoloured.

491	85c. Type **141**	80	1·00
492	95c. Flower, present, fruit and island scene	85	1·00

142 18th-century Frigate

1998. Bicentenary of First Contact with the Outside World. Multicoloured.

493	$1.50 Type **142**	1·50	1·75
494	$1.50 Capt. John Fearn	1·50	1·75
MS495	173×131 mm. Nos. 493/4	3·00	3·50

No. 493 is wrongly identified as "Hunter" (snow).

143 HMAS *Melbourne* (cruiser)

1999. Australia '99 World Stamp Exhibition, Melbourne. Ships. Sheet 101×120 mm, containing T **143** and similar multicoloured designs.

MS496 70c. Type **143**; 80c. HMAS *D'Amantina* (frigate); 90c. *Alcyone* (experimental ship); $1 *Rosie-D* (bulk carrier); $1.10 Outrigger canoe (80×30 mm) 4·25 4·75

1999. 30th Anniv of First Manned Landing on Moon. As T **98a** of Kiribati. Multicoloured.

497	70c. Neil Armstrong (astronaut)	55	70
498	80c. Service and lunar module on way to Moon	60	80
499	90c. Aldrin and *Eagle* on Moon's surface	70	1·00
500	$1 Command module entering Earth's atmosphere	80	1·25
MS501	90×80 mm. $2 Earth as seen from Moon (circular, 40 mm diam)	1·90	2·40

144 Emblem and Forms of Transport

1999. 125th Anniv of Universal Postal Union.

502	**144**	$1 multicoloured	1·00	1·25

145 Killer Whale

1999. China '99 International Philatelic Exhibition, Beijing. Sheet 185×85 mm, containing T **145** and similar vert design. Multicoloured.

MS503 50c. Type **145**; 50c. Swordfish 2·50 3·00

146 Girl holding Candle

1999. Christmas. Multicoloured.

504	65c. Type **146**	70	75
505	70c. Candle and Christmas tree	80	85

147 Nauruan Woman in Traditional Dress and Canoes

2000. New Millennium. Multicoloured.

506	70c. Type **147**	1·75	1·75
507	$1.10 Aspects of modern Nauru	2·50	2·50
508	$1.20 Woman holding globe and man at computer	2·50	2·50
MS509 149×88 mm. Nos. 506/8		6·00	7·00

148 Power Plant

2000. Centenary of Phosphate Discovery. Mult.

510	$1.20 Type **148**	1·25	1·25
511	$1.80 Phosphate train	2·00	2·00
512	$2 Albert Ellis and phosphate sample	2·00	2·25
MS513 79×131 mm. Nos. 510/12		4·50	5·50

149 Queen Mother in Royal Blue Hat and Coat

2000. 100th Birthday of Queen Elizabeth the Queen Mother. Sheet 150×106 mm, containing T **149** and similar horiz designs, each including photograph of Queen Mother as a child. Multicoloured.

MS514 150×106 mm. $1 Type **149**; $1.10 In lilac hat and coat; $1.20 In turquoise hat and coat; $1.40 In greenish blue hat and coat with maple leaf brooch		4·50	5·50

150 Running and Sydney Opera House

2000. Olympic Games, Sydney. Multicoloured.

515	90c. Type **150**	2·25	1·40
516	$l Basketball	2·25	1·60
517	$1.10 Weightlifting and cycling	2·25	2·00
518	$1.20 Running and Olympic Torch	2·25	2·25

151 Flower, Christmas Tree and Star

2000. Christmas. Multicoloured.

519	65c. Type **151**	1·25	1·25
520	75c. Decorations, toy engine and palm tree	1·50	1·50
MS521 134×95 mm. Nos. 519/20		4·00	4·25

152 Noddy and Part of Island

2001. 32nd Pacific Islands Forum, Nauru. Multicoloured.

522	90c. Type **152**	2·25	2·25
523	$1 Frigate bird in flight and part of island	2·40	2·40
524	$1.10 Two frigate birds and part of island	2·40	2·40
525	$2 Frigate bird and Nauru airport	3·00	3·00
MS526 145×130 mm. Nos. 522/5		9·00	9·50

Nos. 522/5 were printed together, *se-tenant*, forming a composite view of Nauru.

153 Princess Elizabeth in ATS Uniform, 1946

2002. Golden Jubilee.

527	**153**	70c. black, mauve and gold	1·50	1·75
528	-	80c. multicoloured	1·50	1·75
529	-	90c. black, mauve and gold	1·50	1·75
530	-	$1 multicoloured	1·50	1·90
MS531 162×95 mm. Nos. 527/30 and $4 multicoloured			8·00	8·50

Designs:—Horiz: 80c. Queen Elizabeth in multicoloured hat; 90c. Princess Elizabeth at Cheltenham Races, 1951; $1 Queen Elizabeth in evening dress, 1997. Vert (38x51 mm)—$4 Queen Elizabeth after Annigoni.

Designs as Nos. 527/30 in No. **MS**531 omit the gold frame around each stamp and the "Golden Jubilee 1952–2002" inscription.

154 Statue of Liberty with US and Nauru Flags

2002. In Remembrance. Victims of Terrorist Attacks on U.S.A. (11 September 2001).

532	**154**	90c. multicoloured	1·40	1·40
533	**154**	$1 multicoloured	1·50	1·50
534	**154**	$1.10 multicoloured	1·60	1·60
535	**154**	$2 multicoloured	2·25	2·25

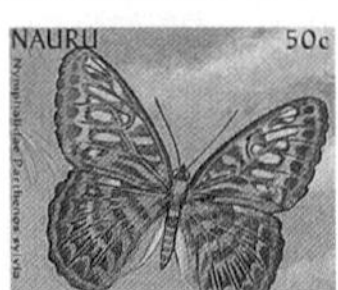

155 *Parthenos sylvia*

2002. Butterflies of the Pacific. Multicoloured.

536	50c. Type **155**	1·00	1·00
537	50c. *Delias madetes*	1·00	1·00
538	50c. *Danaus philene*	1·00	1·00
539	50c. *Arhopala hercules*	1·00	1·00
540	50c. *Paipilio canopus*	1·00	1·00
541	50c. *Danaus schenkii*	1·00	1·00
542	50c. *Pairthenos tigrina*	1·00	1·00
543	50c. *Mycalesis phidon*	1·00	1·00
544	50c. *Vindula sapor*	1·00	1·00
MS545 85×60 mm. $2 *Graphium agamemnon*		3·25	3·75

Nos. 536/44 were printed together, *se-tenant*, forming a composite design.

156 Queen Elizabeth in London, 1940

2002. Queen Elizabeth the Queen Mother Commemoration.

546	**156**	$1.50 black, gold and purple	2·25	2·75
547	-	$1.50 multicoloured	2·25	2·75
MS548 145×70 mm. Nos. 546/7			5·50	7·00

Designs:—No. 547, Queen Mother in Norwich, 1990.

Designs as Nos. 546/7 in No. **MS**548 omit the "1900–2002" inscription and the coloured frame.

157 Turntable Ladder and Burning Building

2002. International Firefighters. Multicoloured.

549	20c. Type **157**	80	65
550	50c. Firefighting tug and burning ship	1·50	75
551	90c. Fighting a forest fire	2·00	1·25
552	$1 Old and new helmets	2·00	1·40
553	$1.10 Steam-driven pump and modern fire engine	2·25	1·50
554	$2 19th-century and present day hose teams	3·75	5·00
MS555 110×90 mm. $5 Airport fire engine		14·00	13·00

158 First Catholic Church, Arubo

2002. Centenary of Catholic Church on Nauru.

556	**158**	$1.50 brown and black	2·50	2·50
557	-	$1.50 violet and black	2·50	2·50
558	-	$1.50 blue and black	2·50	2·50
559	-	$1.50 green and black	2·50	2·50
560	-	$1.50 blue and black	2·50	2·50
561	-	$1.50 red and black	2·50	2·50

Designs:—No. 557, Father Friedrich Gründl (first missionary); 558, Sister Stanisla; 559, Second Catholic church, Ibwenape; 560, Brother Kalixtus Bader (lay brother); 561, Father Alois Kayser (missionary).

159 *Holy Family with dancing Angels* (Van Dyck)

2002. Christmas. Religious Art. Multicoloured.

562	15c. Type **159**	60	45
563	$1 *Holy Virgin with Child* (Cornelis Bloemaert after Lucas Cangiasius)	2·00	1·10
564	$1.20 *Holy Family with Cat* (Rembrandt)	2·25	1·40
565	$3 *Holy Family with St. John* (Pierre Brebiette after Raphael)	5·00	7·00

160 Bubble Tentacle Sea Anemone and Fire Anemonefish ("Red-and-Black Anemone Fish")

2003. Endangered Species. Sea Anemones and Anemonefish. Multicoloured.

566	15c. Type **160**	75	80
567	$1 Leathery sea anemone and orange-finned anemonefish	1·75	1·75
568	$1.20 Magnificent sea anemone and pink anemonefish	2·00	2·00
569	$3 Merten's sea anemone and yellow-tailed anemonefish ("Clark's Anemone Fish")	4·00	5·00

161 Santos-Dumont's *Ballon No. 6* flying around Eiffel Tower, 1901

2003. Centenary of Powered Flight. Airships. Multicoloured.

570	50c. Type **161**	1·50	1·50
571	50c. USS *Shenandoah*	1·50	1·50
572	50c. Airship R101, 1929	1·50	1·50
573	50c. British Beardmore Airship R34, 1919 (first double crossing of North Atlantic)	1·50	1·50
574	50c. Zeppelin LZ-1 (first flight, 1900)	1·50	1·50
575	50c. Airship USS *Los Angeles* moored to airship tender USS *Patoka*	1·50	1·50
576	50c. Goodyear C-71 airship	1·50	1·50
577	50c. LZ-130 *Graf Zeppelin II*	1·50	1·50
578	50c. Zeppelin airship over Alps	1·50	1·50
MS579 150×100 mm. $2 LZ-127 *Graf Zeppelin* over Mount Fuji; $2 LZ-127 *Graf Zeppelin* over San Francisco; $2 LZ-127 *Graf Zeppelin* exchanging mail with Soviet ice breaker over Franz Josef Land		14·00	15·00

162 Nightingale Reed Warbler

2003. Bird Life International. Nightingale Reed Warbler ("Nauru Reed Warbler"). Multicoloured.

580	$1.50 Type **162**	4·50	4·50
581	$1.50 Nightingale reed warbler on reeds (horiz)	4·50	4·50
MS582 175×80 mm. $1.50 Head (horiz); Type **162**; $1.50 Singing; $1.50 No. 581; $1.50 Adult and nestlings (horiz)		14·00	14·00

163 *The Aigle* and HMS *Defiance*

2005. Bicentenary of the Battle of Trafalgar (1st issue). Multicoloured.

583	25c. Type **163**	90	70
584	50c. French *Eprouvette*	1·10	90
585	75c. *The Santissima Trinidad* and HMS *Africa*	1·50	1·40
586	$1 Emperor Napoleon Bonaparte (vert)	1·60	1·60
587	$1.50 HMS *Victory*	3·00	3·25
588	$2.50 Vice-Admiral Sir Horatio Nelson (vert)	4·00	4·50
MS589 120×79 mm. $2.50 Admiral Villeneuve (vert); $2.50 *Formidable* (vert)		9·00	9·50

No. 587 contains traces of powdered wood from HMS *Victory*.

See also Nos. 604/6.

164 *Komet* (German raider)

2005. 60th Anniv of the End of World War II. Pacific Explorer World Stamp Exhibition (**MS**600). Multicoloured.

590	75c. Type **164**	1·60	1·60
591	75c. *Le Triomphant* (French warship)	1·60	1·60
592	75c. Type 97 Te-Ke (Japanese tank)	1·60	1·60
593	75c. USAF B-24 Liberator aircraft	1·60	1·60
594	75c. USS *Paddle* (US submarine)	1·60	1·60
595	75c. *Coral Princess* (B-25G Mitchell aircraft)	1·60	1·60
596	75c. Spitfires	1·60	1·60
597	75c. HMAS *Diamantina* (River Class Frigate)	1·60	1·60
598	75c. D-Day Landings	1·60	1·60
599	75c. Crowds gathered and Union Jack flag	1·60	1·60
MS600 90×60 mm. $5 HMAS *Manoora* (Australian troop ship)		10·00	11·00

165 Pope John Paul II

2005. Commemoration of Pope John Paul II.

601	**165**	$1 multicoloured	1·60	1·60

166 Rotary Emblem

2005. Centenary of Rotary International.

602	**166**	$2.50 multicoloured	2·25	3·00

167 Rota Bridled White-Eye

2005. Birdlife International. Multicoloured.

MS603	Three sheets each 170×85 mm. (a) 25c.×6, Type **167**; Truk ("Faichuk") White-eye; Savaii ("Samoan") White-eye; Bridled white-eye; Ponape ("Long-billed") White-eye; Golden white-eye. (b) 50c.×6, Kuhl's ("Lorikeet") Lory; Masked shining parrot; Kandavu ("Crimson") shining parrot; Tahitian lorikeet ("Blue Lory"); Stephen's lory ("Henderson Lorikeet"); Ultramarine ("Lorikeet") lory. (c) $1×6, Atoll fruit dove; Henderson Island fruit dove; Rarotongan ("Cook Islands") fruit dove; Rapa Island fruit dove; Whistling dove; Mariana fruit dove	23·00	26·00

The backgrounds of Nos. **MS**603a/c form composite designs.

168 HMS *Victory*

2005. Bicentenary of the Battle of Trafalgar (2nd issue). Multicoloured.

604	50c. Type **168**	1·50	85
605	$1 Ships engaged in battle (horiz)	2·00	1·60
606	$5 Admiral Lord Nelson	7·00	8·00

169 *The Little Fir Tree*

2005. Christmas and Birth Bicentenary of Hans Christian Andersen (writer). Multicoloured.

607	25c. Type **169**	40	30
608	50c. *The Wild Swans*	70	60
609	75c. *The Farmyard Cock and the Weather Cock*	1·00	1·00
610	$1 *The Storks*	1·25	1·25
611	$2.50 *The Toad*	3·00	3·50
612	$5 *The Ice Maiden*	5·00	6·50

170 Wolfgang Amadeus Mozart (composer, 250th birth anniv)

2006. Exploration and Innovation. Anniversaries. Multicoloured.

613	25c. Type **170**	1·50	1·50
614	25c. Violin heads and piano keyboards	1·50	1·50
615	50c. Isambard Kingdom Brunel (engineer, birth bicentenary)	1·50	1·50
616	50c. Cogwheels	1·50	1·50
617	75c. Edmund Halley (astronomer, 350th birth anniv)	1·75	1·75
618	75c. Halley's quadrant	1·75	1·75
619	$1 Charles Darwin (originator of *Theory of Evolution*, 175th anniv of voyage on *Beagle*)	1·75	1·75
620	$1 Early microscope	1·75	1·75
621	$1.25 Thomas Edison (inventor and physicist, 75th death anniv)	1·75	1·75
622	$1.25 Edison's lightbulb	1·75	1·75
623	$1.50 Christopher Columbus (discoverer of New World, 500th death anniv)	2·25	2·25
624	$1.50 Astrolabe	2·25	2·25

Nos. 613/14, 615/16, 617/18, 619/20, 621/2 and 623/4 were each printed together, *se-tenant*, each pair forming a composite background design.

171 Uruguay (winners) v. Brazil, 1950

2006. World Cup Football Championship, Germany. showing scenes from previous World Cup finals. Multicoloured.

625	$1 Type **171**	1·50	1·50
626	$1.50 Argentina (winners) v. Netherlands, 1978	2·50	2·75
627	$2 Italy (winners) v. West Germany, 1982	3·00	3·25
628	$3 Brazil (winners) v. Germany, 2002	4·00	4·50

172 Parasaurolophus

2006. Dinosaurs. Multicoloured.

629	10c. Type **172**	50	70
630	25c. Quetzalcoatlus	90	60
631	50c. Spinosaurus	1·25	85
632	75c. Triceratops	1·50	1·25
633	$1 Tyrannosaurus rex	1·75	1·50
634	$1.50 Euoplocephalus	2·75	2·75
635	$2 Velociraptor	3·25	3·50
636	$2.50 Protoceratops	3·25	4·25

173 Lieut. Gerald Graham bringing in Wounded Man

2006. 150th Anniv of the Victoria Cross. Designs showing Victoria Cross recipients of Crimean War. Multicoloured.

637	$1.50 Type **173**	3·00	3·00
638	$1.50 Private MacGregor driving Russians from rifle pits	3·00	3·00
639	$1.50 Private Alexander Wright repelling a sortie	3·00	3·00
640	$1.50 Corporal John Ross ascertaining the evacuation of the Redan	3·00	3·00
641	$1.50 Sgt McWheeney digging cover with bayonet for wounded Corporal Courtney	3·00	3·00
642	$1.50 Brevet Major G. L. Goodlake surprising the enemy's picket at Windmill Ravine	3·00	3·00

174 British Airways Concorde G-BOAF

2006. 30th Anniv of Inaugural Flight of Concorde. Multicoloured.

643	$1 Type **174**	2·50	2·50
644	$1 First flight of Concorde 002, 9 April 1969	2·50	2·50
645	$1 Concorde at take-off	2·50	2·50
646	$1 Concorde and Red Arrows in Golden Jubilee Flypast, 4 June 2002	2·50	2·50
647	$1 Concorde and Spitfire, Battle of Britain 50th anniversary, 6 June 1990	2·50	2·50
648	$1 Concorde at 60000 feet at Mach 2	2·50	2·50
649	$1 Extreme condition testing	2·50	2·50
650	$1 Concorde on runway	2·50	2·50
651	$1 First commercial flight, 21 January 1976	2·50	2·50
652	$1 Concorde above Earth	2·50	2·50
653	$1 British Airways Concorde G-BOAF at take-off	2·50	2·50
654	$1 Two Concordes on ground	2·50	2·50

175 Queen Elizabeth II

2006. 50th Anniv of the Year of Three Kings. Multicoloured.

655	**175**	$1.50 multicoloured	3·00	3·00
656	-	$1.50 black and grey	3·00	3·00
657	-	$1.50 black and grey	3·00	3·00
658	-	$1.50 black and grey	3·00	3·00

Designs: No. 656, King George V and Princess Elizabeth; 657, King Edward VIII and Princess Elizabeth; 658, King George VI and Princess Elizabeth.

176 Princess Elizabeth and Lt. Philip Mountbatten, 1947

2007. Diamond Wedding of Queen Elizabeth II and Prince Philip. Multicoloured.

659	$1 Type **176**	1·50	1·50
660	$1.50 Princess Elizabeth and Prince Philip on wedding day	2·50	2·50
661	$2 Wedding ceremony	3·00	3·25
662	$3 Princess Elizabeth and Prince Philip walking in the countryside, c. 1947	4·00	4·50
MS663	125×85 mm. $5 Wedding portrait of Princess Elizabeth (42×56 mm)	8·00	9·00

177 Air Vice Marshal 'Johnnie' Johnson (fighter ace)

2008. 90th Anniv of the Royal Air Force. Multicoloured.

664	70c. Type **177**	2·00	2·00
665	70c. R. J. Mitchell (Spitfire designer)	2·00	2·00
666	70c. Sir Sydney Camm (Hawker Hurricane designer)	2·00	2·00
667	70c. Sir Frank Whittle (inventor of the jet engine)	2·00	2·00
668	70c. Sir Douglas Bader ('flying legend')	2·00	2·00
MS669	110×70 mm. $3 Avro Vulcan	8·00	8·00

178 Badminton

2008. Olympic Games, Beijing. Multicoloured.

670	15c. Type **178**	50	70
671	25c. Archery	70	80
672	75c. Weightlifting	1·25	1·40
673	$1 Diving	1·50	1·60

179 Pride of Lions ('THE EMPIRE NEEDS MEN!')

2008. 90th Anniv of the End of World War I. Designs showing recruitment posters. Multicoloured.

674	$1 Type **179**	2·25	2·25
675	$1 Column of soldiers marching into sunrise ('VICTORY JOIN NOW')	2·25	2·25
676	$1 Officer beckoning ('AN APPEAL TO YOU')	2·25	2·25
677	$1 Proud soldier with old man ('YOUR KING & COUNTRY NEED YOU')	2·25	2·25
678	$1 Officer calling ('SOUTH AUSTRALIANS COME AND HELP')	2·25	2·25
679	$1 Lord Kitchener pointing ('BRITONS JOIN YOUR COUNTRY'S ARMY')	2·25	2·25
MS680	110×70 mm. $2 The Queen's Wreath of Remembrance	4·75	4·75

180 Frigate Bird on Nest with Chick

2008. Endangered Species. Greater Frigate Bird (*Fregata minor*). Multicoloured.

681	25c. Type **180**	70	65
682	75c. Two frigate birds in flight	1·60	1·40
683	$1 Frigate bird landing on branch	1·75	1·75

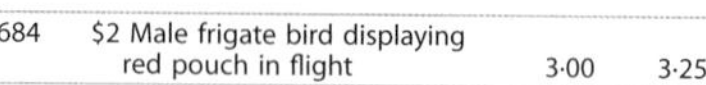

684	$2 Male frigate bird displaying red pouch in flight	3·00	3·25

181 Avro 504C

2009. Centenary of Naval Aviation. Multicoloured.

685	$1.50 Type **181**	3·75	3·75
686	$1.50 Fairey Flycatcher	3·75	3·75
687	$1.50 de Havilland Sea Vixen	3·75	3·75
688	$1.50 Short Folder seaplane	3·75	3·75
MS689	110×70 mm. $3 Grumman Avenger, Operation Meridian, 1945	7·50	7·50

182 *Sputnik 1* Satellite, 1957

2011. Russia's Space Programme. Multicoloured.

690	60c. Type **182**	2·00	2·00
691	60c. Cosmonaut Yuri Gagarin (first man in space, 12 April 1961)	2·00	2·00
692	$1.20 Nauru Island seen from space	3·00	3·00
693	$2.25 Launch of *Vostok 1*, 12 April 1961	5·50	5·50
694	$3 International Space Station	7·50	7·50

183 Prince William and Miss Catherine Middleton

2011. Royal Wedding. Sheet 118×90 mm. Multicoloured.

MS695	**183**	$5 multicoloured	10·00	11·00

184 Transformation of Aiwo Boat Harbour into Nauru's Port

2018. 50th Anniversary of Independence. Port Development Project

696	**184**	50c. multicoloured	1·25	1·25

NAWANAGAR

A state of India, Bombay District. Now uses Indian stamps.

6 docra = 1 anna.

1 (1 docra)

1877. Imperf or perf.

1	**1**	1doc. blue	1·50	35·00

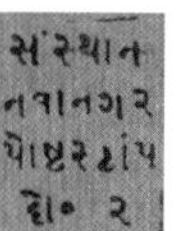
2 (2 docra)

1880. Imperf.

6ab	**2**	1doc. lilac	6·00	20·00
8c	**2**	2doc. green	6·00	20·00
9b	**2**	3doc. yellow	7·00	17·00

4 (1 docra)

1893. Imperf or perf.

13	**4**	1doc. black	2·75	13·00
14	**4**	2doc. green	4·50	20·00
15*b*	**4**	3doc. yellow	4·50	23·00

NEAPOLITAN PROVINCES

Temporary issues for Naples and other parts of S. Italy which adhered to the new Kingdom of Italy in 1860.

200 tornesi = 100 grano = 1 ducato.

1

1861. Embossed. Imperf.

2	**1**	½t. green	21·00	£325
5	**1**	½g. brown	£275	£375
9	**1**	1g. black	£475	55·00
10	**1**	2g. blue	£170	21·00
15	**1**	5g. red	£160	£110
18	**1**	10g. orange	£130	£190
19	**1**	20g. yellow	£600	£3250
23	**1**	50g. slate	75·00	£9000

NEGRI SEMBILAN

A state of the Federation of Malaya, incorporated in Malaysia in 1963.

100 cents = 1 dollar (Straits or Malayan).

1891. Stamp of Straits Settlements optd Negri Sembilan.

1	**5**	2c. red	3·00	14·00

2 Tiger

1891

2	**2**	1c. green	3·25	1·00
3	**2**	2c. red	3·25	19·00
4	**2**	5c. blue	30·00	48·00

3

1896

5	**3**	1c. purple and green	27·00	15·00
6	**3**	2c. purple and brown	35·00	£130
7	**3**	3c. purple and red	18·00	3·75
8	**3**	5c. purple and yellow	18·00	20·00
9	**3**	8c. purple and blue	29·00	27·00
10	**3**	10c. purple and orange	27·00	14·00
11	**3**	15c. green and violet	50·00	90·00
12	**3**	20c. green and olive	75·00	40·00
13	**3**	25c. green and red	80·00	£100
14	**3**	50c. green and black	95·00	70·00

1898. Surch in words and bar.

15	**3**	1c. on 15c. green and violet	£110	£300
16	**2**	4c. on 1c. green	3·50	27·00
17	**3**	4c. on 3c. purple and red	7·50	29·00
18	**2**	4c. on 5c. blue	1·50	15·00

1898. Surch in words only.

19	**3**	4c. on 8c. purple and blue	16·00	4·25

6 Arms of Negri Sembilan

1935

21	**6**	1c. black	1·00	20
22	**6**	2c. green	1·00	20
23	**6**	2c. orange	4·25	75·00
24a	**6**	3c. green	8·00	25·00
25	**6**	4c. orange	2·00	10
26	**6**	5c. brown	2·00	10
27	**6**	6c. red	18·00	4·25
28	**6**	6c. grey	4·75	£130
29	**6**	8c. grey	2·00	10
30	**6**	10c. purple	1·25	10
31	**6**	12c. blue	3·25	50
32	**6**	15c. blue	11·00	60·00
33	**6**	25c. purple and red	1·50	70
34	**6**	30c. purple and orange	3·50	3·25
35	**6**	40c. red and purple	3·75	2·00
36	**6**	50c. black on green	6·50	2·25
37	**6**	$1 black and red on blue	5·00	7·50
38	**6**	$2 green and red	60·00	22·00
39	**6**	$5 green and red on green	45·00	£130

1948. Silver Wedding. As T **8b/c** of Pitcairn Islands.

40	10c. violet	40	50
41	$5 green	23·00	32·00

7 Arms of Negri Sembilan

1949

42	**7**	1c. black	1·25	10
43	**7**	2c. orange	1·25	10
44	**7**	3c. green	60	30
45	**7**	4c. brown	30	10
46a	**7**	5c. purple	4·25	45
47	**7**	6c. grey	2·75	10
48	**7**	8c. red	1·00	75
49	**7**	8c. green	8·00	1·60
50	**7**	10c. mauve	40	10
51	**7**	12c. red	8·00	3·25
52	**7**	15c. blue	5·00	10
53	**7**	20c. black and green	3·75	4·25
54	**7**	20c. blue	4·00	10
55	**7**	25c. purple and orange	1·25	10
56	**7**	30c. red and purple	1·25	2·50
57	**7**	35c. red and purple	7·00	1·00
58	**7**	40c. red and purple	7·00	4·75
59	**7**	50c. black and blue	7·00	20
60	**7**	$1 blue and purple	7·50	2·50
61	**7**	$2 green and red	25·00	48·00
62	**7**	$5 green and brown	55·00	£120

1949. U.P.U. As T **8d/g** of Pitcairn Islands.

63	10c. purple	20	20
64	15c. blue	1·40	3·50
65	25c. orange	30	3·00
66	50c. black	60	3·25

1953. Coronation. As T **8h** of Pitcairn Islands.

67	10c. black and purple	1·50	50

1957. As Nos. 92/102 of Kedah but inset Arms of Negri Sembilan.

68	1c. black	10	10
69	2c. red	10	10
70	4c. sepia	10	10
71	5c. lake	10	10
72	8c. green	3·00	1·40
73	10c. sepia	2·00	10
74	10c. purple	14·00	10
75	20c. blue	1·00	10
76	50c. black and blue	75	10
77	$1 blue and purple	10·00	2·00
78	$2 green and red	18·00	20·00
79	$5 brown and green	20·00	32·00

8 Tuanku Munawir

1961. Installation of Tuanku Munawir as Yang di-Pertuan Besar of Negri Sembilan.

80	**8**	10c. multicoloured	30	70

9 *Vanda hookeriana*

1965. As Nos. 115/21 of Kedah but with Arms of Negri Sembilan inset and inscr "NEGERI SEMBILAN" as in T **6**.

81	**9**	1c. multicoloured	10	1·60
82	-	2c. multicoloured	10	1·60
83	-	5c. multicoloured	1·75	10
84	-	6c. multicoloured	40	60
85	-	10c. multicoloured	1·00	10
86	-	15c. multicoloured	80	10
87	-	20c. multicoloured	2·25	1·00

The higher values used in Negri Sembilan were Nos. 20/7 of Malaysia (National Issues).

10 Negri Sembilan Crest and Tuanku Ja'afar

1968. Installation of Tuanku Ja'afar as Yang di-Pertuan Besar of Negri Sembilan.

88	**10**	15c. multicoloured	20	1·40
89	**10**	50c. multicoloured	40	1·40

11 *Hebomoia glaucippe*

1971. Butterflies. As Nos. 124/30 of Kedah but with Arms of Negri Sembilan inset as T **11** and inscr "negeri sembilan".

91	-	1c. multicoloured	40	2·00
92	-	2c. multicoloured	70	2·00
93	-	5c. multicoloured	1·00	20
94	-	6c. multicoloured	1·00	2·00
95	**11**	10c. multicoloured	1·00	10
96	-	15c. multicoloured	1·40	10
97	-	20c. multicoloured	1·40	50

The higher values in use with this issue were Nos. 64/71 of Malaysia (National Issues).

12 *Hibiscus rosa-sinensis*

1979. Flowers. As Nos. 135/41 of Kedah but with Arms of Negri Sembilan and inscr "negeri sembilan" as in T **12**.

103	1c. *Rafflesia hasseltii*	10	1·25
104	2c. *Pterocarpus indicus*	10	1·25
105	5c. *Lagerstroemia speciosa*	15	40
106	10c. *Durio zibethinus*	20	10
107	15c. Type **12**	20	10
108	20c. *Rhododendron scortechinii*	25	10
109	25c. *Etlingera elatior* (inscr '*Phaeomeria speciosa*')	45	25

13 Oil Palm

1986. As Nos. 152/8 of Kedah but with Arms of Negri Sembilan and inscr "NEGERI SEMBILAN" as T **13**.

117	1c. Coffee	10	50
118	2c. Coconuts	10	50
119	5c. Cocoa	15	15
120	10c. Black pepper	20	10
121	15c. Rubber	40	10
122	20c. Type **13**	40	10
123	30c. Rice	40	10

14 *Nelumbium nelumbo* (sacred lotus)

2007. Garden Flowers. As Nos. 210/15 of Johore, but with portrait of Sultan Tuanku Ja'afar and Arms of Negri Sembilan as in T **14**. Multicoloured.

124	5s. Type **14**	10	10
125	10s. *Hydrangea macrophylla*	15	10
126	20s. *Hippeastrum reticulatum*	25	15
127	30s. *Bougainvillea*	40	20
128	40s. *Ipomoea indica*	50	30
129	50s. *Hibiscus rosa-sinensis*	65	35

15 Tuanku Muhriz Ibni Almarhum

2009. Coronation of Tuanku Muhriz Ibni Almarhum. Multicoloured.

130	30s. Type **15**	60	40
131	50s. Tuanku Muhriz Ibni Almarhum (wearing black hat)	1·00	75
132	1r. Tuanku Muhriz Ibni Almarhum and Tuanku Aishah Rohani (58×34 mm)	1·75	2·25

2009. Garden Flowers. Sheet 100x85mm.

MS133	5s. *Nelumbium nelumbo* (sacred lotus); 10s. *Hydrangea macrophylla*; 20s. *Hippeastrum reticulatum*; 30s. *Bougainvillea*; 40s. *Ipomoea indica*; 50s. *Hibiscus rosa-sinensis*	2·75	3·00

NEPAL

An independent kingdom in the Himalayas N. of India.

1861. 16 annas = 1 rupee.
1907. 64 pice = 1 rupee.
1954. 100 paisa = 1 rupee.

1 (1a.) Crown and Kukris

2 (½a.) Bow and Arrow and Kukris

1881. Imperf or pin-perf.

34	**2**	½a. black	11·50	8·25
35	**2**	½a. orange	£1200	£350
14	**1**	1a. green	75·00	75·00
42	**1**	1a. blue	11·50	4·25
16c	**1**	2a. violet	60·00	60·00
40	**1**	2a. brown	23·00	12·00
41	**1**	4a. green	26·00	27·00

3 Siva Mahadeva (2p.)

1907. Various sizes.

57	**3**	2p. brown	85	60
58	**3**	4p. green	2·00	1·20
59	**3**	8p. red	2·30	80
60	**3**	16p. purple	19·00	4·25
61	**3**	24p. orange	18·00	3·00
62	**3**	32p. blue	23·00	3·50
63	**3**	1r. red	47·00	29·00
50	**3**	5r. black and brown	41·00	27·00

5 Swayambhunath Temple, Katmandu

7 Guheswari Temple, Patan

8 Sri Pashupati (Siva Mahadeva)

1949

64	**5**	2p. brown	1·60	1·20
65	-	4p. green	1·60	1·20
66	-	6p. pink	3·25	1·20
67	-	8p. red	3·50	1·80
68	-	16p. purple	3·50	1·80
69	-	20p. blue	7·00	3·00
70	**7**	24p. red	6·50	1·80
71	-	32p. blue	11·00	3·00
72	**8**	1r. orange	50·00	29·00

Designs:—As Type **5**: 4p. Pashupatinath Temple, Katmandu; 6p. Tri-Chundra College; 8p. Mahabuddha Temple. 26×30 mm: 16p. Krishna Mandir Temple, Patan. As Type **7**: 20p. View of Katmandu; 32p. The twenty-two fountains, Balaju.

9 King Tribhuvana

10 Map of Nepal

1954. (a) Size 18×22 mm.

73	**9**	2p. brown	3·00	60
74	**9**	4p. green	9·25	1·80
75	**9**	6p. red	2·30	60
76	**9**	8p. lilac	1·80	60
77	**9**	12p. orange	18·00	3·00

(b) Size 25½×29½ mm.

78	**9**	16p. brown	2·30	60
79	**9**	20p. red	4·75	1·80
80	**9**	24p. purple	4·00	1·80
81	**9**	32p. blue	5·75	1·80
82	**9**	50p. mauve	47·00	8·75
83	**9**	1r. red	70·00	14·00
84	**9**	2r. orange	60·00	11·50

(c) Size 30×18 mm.

85	**10**	2p. brown	2·30	1·20
86	**10**	4p. green	9·25	1·80
87	**10**	6p. red	23·00	3·00
88	**10**	8p. lilac	1·80	1·20
89	**10**	12p. orange	23·00	3·00

(d) Size 38×21½ mm.

90	**10**	16p. brown	3·00	1·20
91	**10**	20p. red	4·75	1·20
92	**10**	24p. purple	3·50	1·20
93	**10**	32p. blue	8·75	2·30
94	**10**	50p. mauve	47·00	8·75
95	**10**	1r. red	75·00	11·50
96	**10**	2r. orange	60·00	11·50

11 Mechanization of Agriculture

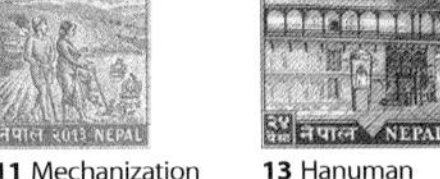
13 Hanuman Dhoka, Katmandu

1956. Coronation.

97	**11**	4p. green	9·25	8·75
98	-	6p. red and yellow	5·75	4·75
99	-	8p. violet	4·75	2·30
100	**13**	24p. red	9·25	8·75
101	-	1r. red	£180	£150

Designs:—As Type **11**: 8p. Processional elephant. As Type **13**: 6p. Throne; 1r. King and Queen and mountains.

15 UN Emblem and Nepalese Landscape

1956. First Anniv of Admission into U.N.O.

102	**15**	12p. blue and brown	11·50	9·25

16 Nepalese Crown

1957. (a) Size 18×22 mm.

103	**16**	2p. brown	1·20	1·10
104	**16**	4p. green	1·80	1·10
105	**16**	6p. red	1·20	1·10
106	**16**	8p. violet	1·20	1·10
107	**16**	12p. red	6·75	1·70

(b) Size 25½×29½ mm.

108	**16**	16p. brown	9·00	2·75
109	**16**	20p. red	14·50	4·00
110	**16**	24p. mauve	9·00	3·50
111	**16**	32p. blue	12·00	4·00
112	**16**	50p. pink	24·00	8·50
113	**16**	1r. salmon	60·00	17·00
114	**16**	2r. orange	36·00	11·50

17 Gaunthali carrying Letter

1958. Air. Inauguration of Nepalese Internal Airmail Service.

115	**17**	10p. blue	3·75	3·00

18 Temple of Lumbini

1958. Human Rights Day.

116	**18**	6p. yellow	2·40	2·30

19 Nepalese Map and Flag

1959. First Nepalese Elections.

117	**19**	6p. red and green	85	70

20 Spinning Wheel

1959. Cottage Industries.

118	**20**	2p. brown	75	70

21 King Mahendra

1959. Admission of Nepal to U.P.U.

119	**21**	12p. blue	85	70

22 Vishnu

23 Nyatopol Temple, Bhaktapur

1959

120	**22**	1p. brown	20	15
121	-	2p. violet	25	20
122	-	4p. blue	85	55
123	-	6p. pink	85	25
124	-	8p. brown	60	25
125	-	12p. grey	85	25
126	**23**	16p. violet and brown	85	25
127	**23**	20p. red and blue	3·00	1·10
128	**23**	24p. red and green	3·00	1·10
129	**23**	32p. blue and lilac	1·80	1·10
130	**23**	50p. green and red	3·00	1·10
131	-	1r. blue and brown	36·00	9·00
132	-	2r. blue and purple	24·00	9·50
133	-	5r. red and violet	£130	£110

Designs:—As Type **22**. Horiz: 2p. Krishna; 8p. Siberian musk deer; 12p. Indian rhinoceros. Vert: 4p. Himalayas; 6p. Gateway, Bhaktapur Palace. As Type **23**. Vert: 1r., 2r. Himalayan monal pheasant; 5r. Satyr tragopan.

24 King Mahendra opening Parliament

1959. Opening of First Nepalese Parliament.

134	**24**	6p. red	1·80	1·70

25 Sri Pashupatinath

1959. Renovation of Sri Pashupatinath Temple, Katmandu.

135	**25**	4p. green (18×25 mm)	1·20	1·00
136	**25**	8p. red (21×28½ mm)	2·40	1·20
137	**25**	1r. blue (24½×33½ mm)	14·50	9·00

26 Children, Pagoda and Mt. Everest

1960. Children's Day.

137a	**26**	6p. blue	24·00	17·00

27 King Mahendra

1960. King Mahendra's 41st Birthday.

138	**27**	1r. purple	2·75	1·70

See also Nos. 163/4a.

28 Mt. Everest

1960. Mountain Views.

139	-	5p. brown and purple	60	25
140	**28**	10p. purple and blue	95	35
141	-	40p. brown and violet	2·40	1·20

Designs:—5p. Machha Puchhre; 40p. Manaslu (wrongly inscr "MANSALU").

29 King Tribhuvana

1961. Tenth Democracy Day.

142	**29**	10p. orange and brown	50	20

30 Prince Gyanendra cancelling Children's Day Stamps of 1960

1961. Children's Day.

143	**30**	12p. orange	60·00	55·00

31 King Mahendra

1961. King Mahendra's 42nd Birthday.

144	**31**	6p. green	60	55
145	**31**	12p. blue	85	80
146	**31**	50p. red	1·80	1·70
147	**31**	1r. brown	3·00	2·75

32 Campaign Emblem and House

1962. Malaria Eradication.

148	**32**	12p. blue	60	55
149	-	1r. orange and red	1·80	1·70

Design:—1r. Emblem and Nepalese flag.

33 King Mahendra on Horseback

1962. King Mahendra's 43rd Birthday.

150	**33**	10p. blue	35	25
151	**33**	15p. brown	60	55
152	**33**	45p. brown	1·20	1·10
153	**33**	1r. grey	1·80	1·70

34 Bhana Bhakta Acharya

1962. Nepalese Poets.

154	**34**	5p. brown	50	45
155	-	10p. turquoise	60	55
156	-	40p. green	85	80

Portraits:—10p. Moti Ram Bhakta; 40p. Sambhu Prasad.

35 King Mahendra

36 King Mahendra

1962

157	**35**	1p. red	20	10
158	**35**	2p. blue	25	15
158a	**35**	3p. grey	1·20	55
159	**35**	5p. brown	30	20
160	**36**	10p. purple	60	55
161	**36**	40p. brown	18·00	17·00
162	**36**	75p. green	2·40	1·10
162a	**35**	75p. green	2·40	2·30
163	**27**	2r. red	2·40	2·30
164	**27**	5r. green	4·75	4·50
164a	**27**	10r. violet	17·00	13·50

No. 162a is smaller, 17½×20 mm.

37 Emblems of Learning

1963. UNESCO "Education for All" Campaign.

165	**37**	10p. black	75	25
166	**37**	15p. brown	95	55
167	**37**	50p. blue	1·60	1·10

38 Hands holding Lamps

1963. National Day.

168	**38**	5p. blue	25	15
169	**38**	10p. brown	35	25
170	**38**	50p. purple	1·30	80
171	**38**	1r. green	2·75	1·10

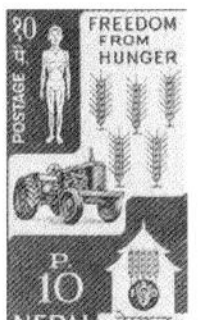
39 Campaign Symbols

1963. Freedom from Hunger.

172	**39**	10p. orange	85	25
173	**39**	15p. blue	1·20	55
174	**39**	50p. green	2·75	1·10
175	**39**	1r. brown	3·75	1·90

40 Map of Nepal and Open Hand

1963. Rastruya Panchayat.

176	**40**	10p. green	60	25
177	**40**	15p. purple	1·20	55
178	**40**	50p. grey	2·75	80
179	**40**	1r. blue	3·75	1·40

41 King Mahendra

1963. King Mahendra's 44th Birthday.

180	**41**	5p. violet	35	20
181	**41**	10p. brown	75	25
182	**41**	15p. green	95	55

42 King Mahendra and Highway Map

1964. Inauguration of East–West Highway.

183	**42**	10p. orange and blue	50	20
184	**42**	15p. orange and blue	85	35
185	**42**	50p. brown and green	1·50	55

43 King Mahendra at Microphone

1964. King Mahendra's 45th Birthday.

186	**43**	1p. brown	35	20
187	**43**	2p. grey	60	35
188	**43**	2r. brown	2·75	1·70

44 Crown Prince Birendra

1964. Crown Prince's 19th Birthday.

189	**44**	10p. green	1·70	1·20
190	**44**	15p. brown	1·30	1·20

45 Flag, Kukris, Rings and Torch

1964. Olympic Games, Tokyo.

191	**45**	10p. blue, red and pink	2·10	1·10

46 Nepalese Family

1965. Land Reform.

192	-	2p. black and green	40	40
193	-	5p. brown and green	50	45
194	-	10p. purple and grey	60	55
195	**46**	15p. brown and yellow	85	80

Designs:—2p. Farmer ploughing; 5p. Ears of wheat; 10p. Grain elevator.

47 Globe and Letters

1965. Introduction of International Insured and Parcel Service.

196	**47**	15p. violet	75	60

48 King Mahendra

1965. King Mahendra's 46th Birthday.

197	**48**	50p. purple	1·50	1·20

49 Four Martyrs

1965. Nepalese Martyrs.

198	**49**	15p. green	75	60

50 ITU Emblem

1965. I.T.U. Centenary.

199	**50**	15p. black and purple	85	60

51 ICY Emblem

1965. International Co-operation Year.

200	**51**	1r. multicoloured	1·80	1·40

52 Devkota (poet)

1965. Devkota Commemoration.

201	**52**	15p. brown	60	45

54 Flag and King Mahendra

1966. Democracy Day.

202	**54**	15p. red and blue	1·20	80

55 Siva Parvati and Pashuvati Temple

1966. Maha Siva-Ratri Festival.

203	**55**	15p. violet	75	60

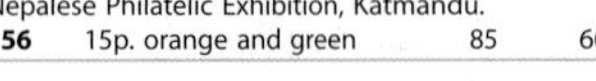
56 "Stamp" Emblem

1966. Nepalese Philatelic Exhibition, Katmandu.

204	**56**	15p. orange and green	85	60

57 King Mahendra

1966. King Mahendra's 47th Birthday.

205	**57**	15p. brown and yellow	75	45

58 Queen Mother

1966. Queen Mother's 60th Birthday.

206	**58**	15p. brown	60	55

59 Queen Ratna

1966. Children's Day.

207	**59**	15p. brown and yellow	75	60

60 Flute-player and Dancer

1966. Krishna Anniv.

208	**60**	15p. violet and yellow	75	60

61 "To render service..."

1966. First Anniv of Nepalese Red Cross.

209	**61**	50p. red and green	7·25	2·30

62 W.H.O. Building on Flag

1966. Inaug of W.H.O. Headquarters, Geneva.

210	**62**	1r. violet	3·75	2·30

63 Paudyal

1966. Leknath Paudyal (poet) Commemoration.

211	**63**	15p. blue	75	60

64 Rama and Sita

1967. Rama Navami, 2024, birthday of Rama.

212	**64**	15p. brown and yellow	75	60

65 Buddha

1967. Buddha Jayanti, birthday of Buddha.

213	**65**	75p. purple and orange	1·50	1·30

66 King Mahendra addressing Nepalese

1967. King Mahendra's 48th Birthday.

214	**66**	15p. brown and blue	75	60

67 Queen Ratna and Children

1967. Children's Day.

215	**67**	15p. brown and cream	75	60

68 Ama Dablam (mountain)

1967. International Tourist Year.

216	**68**	5p. violet (postage)	65	60
217	-	65p. brown	90	80
218	-	1r.80 red and blue (air)	1·90	1·60

Designs:—38×20 mm: 65p. Bhaktapur Durbar Square. 35½×25½ mm: 1r.80, Plane over Katmandu.

69 Open-air Class

1967. Constitution Day. "Go to the Village" Educational Campaign.

219	**69**	15p. multicoloured	75	60

70 Crown Prince Birendra, Campfire and Scout Emblem

1967. Diamond Jubilee of World Scouting.

220	**70**	15p. blue	1·30	80

71 Prithvi Narayan Shah (founder of Kingdom)

1968. Bicentenary of the Kingdom.

221	**71**	15p. blue and red	1·30	80

72 Arms of Nepal

1968. National Day.

222	**72**	15p. blue and red	1·30	80

73 WHO Emblem and Nepalese Flag

1968. 20th Anniv of W.H.O.

223	**73**	1r.20 blue, red and yellow	5·25	3·50

74 Sita and Janaki Temple

1968. Sita Jayanti.
224 **74** 15p. brown and violet 90 60

75 King Mahendra, Mountains and Himalayan Monal Pheasant

1968. King Mahendra's 49th Birthday.
225 **75** 15p. multicoloured 90 60

76 Garuda and Airline Emblem

1968. Air. Tenth Anniv of Royal Nepalese Airlines.
226 **76** 15p. brown and blue 65 60
227 - 65p. blue 1·30 1·20
228 - 2r.50 blue and orange 4·50 3·50

Designs:—Diamond (25½×25½ mm): 65p. Route-map. As Type **76**: 2r.50, Convair Metropolitan airliner over Mount Dhaulagiri.

77 Flag, Queen Ratna and Children

1968. Children's Day and Queen Ratna's 41st Birthday.
229 **77** 5p. red, yellow and green 65 45

78 Human Rights Emblem and Buddha

1968. Human Rights Year.
230 **78** 1r. red and green 5·00 3·50

79 Crown Prince Birendra and Dancers

1968. Crown Prince Birendra's 24th Birthday, and National Youth Festival.
231 **79** 25p. blue 1·30 80

80 King Mahendra, Flags and UN Building, New York

1969. Nepal's Election to U.N. Security Council.
232 **80** 1r. multicoloured 1·90 1·40

81 Amsu Varma (7th-century ruler)

1969. Famous Nepalese.
233 **81** 15p. violet and green 90 80
234 - 25p. turquoise 1·30 1·20
235 - 50p. brown 1·60 1·50
236 - 1r. purple and brown 1·90 1·40

Designs:—Vert: 25p. Ram Shah (17th-century King of Gurkha); 50p. Bhimsen Thapa (19th-century Prime Minister). Horiz: 1r. Bal Bhadra Kunwar (19th-century warrior).

82 ILO Emblem

1969. 50th Anniv of I.L.O.
237 **82** 1r. brown and mauve 8·75 5·75

83 King Mahendra

1969. King Mahendra's 50th Birthday.
238 **83** 25p. multicoloured 90 70

84 King Tribhuvana and Queens

1969. 64th Birth Anniv of King Tribhuvana.
239 **84** 25p. brown and yellow 90 70

1969. National Children's Day.
240 **85** 25p. mauve and brown 90 70

86 Rhododendron

1969. Flowers. Multicoloured.
241 25p. Type **86** 1·00 80
242 25p. Narcissus 1·00 80
243 25p. Marigold 1·00 80
244 25p. Poinsettia 1·00 80

87 Durga, Goddess of Victory

1969. Durga Pooja Festival.
245 **87** 15p. black and orange 65 55
246 **87** 50p. violet and brown 1·40 1·20

88 Crown Prince Birendra and Princess Aishwarya

1970. Royal Wedding.
247 **88** 25p. multicoloured 75 60

89 Produce, Cow and Landscape

1970. Agricultural Year.
248 **89** 25p. multicoloured 75 60

90 King Mahendra, Mt. Everest and Nepalese Crown

1970. King Mahendra's 51st Birthday.
249 **90** 50p. multicoloured 1·30 80

91 Lake Gosainkunda

1970. Nepalese Lakes. Multicoloured.
250 5p. Type **91** 65 60
251 25p. Lake Phewa Tal 90 80
252 1r. Lake Rara Daha 1·80 1·60

92 APY Emblem

1970. Asian Productivity Year.
253 **92** 1r. blue 1·50 1·20

93 Queen Ratna and Children's Palace, Taulihawa

1970. National Children's Day.
254 **93** 25p. grey and brown 75 60

94 New Headquarters Building

1970. New U.P.U. Headquarters, Berne.
255 **94** 2r.50 grey and brown 3·25 2·30

95 UN Flag

1970. 25th Anniv of United Nations.
256 **95** 25p. blue and purple 75 60

96 Durbar Square, Patan

1970. Tourism. Multicoloured.
257 15p. Type **96** 75 25
258 25p. Boudhanath Stupa (temple) (vert) 1·10 60
259 1r. Mt. Gauri Shankar 1·90 1·20

97 Statue of Harihar, Valmiki Ashram

1971. Nepalese Religious Art.
260 **97** 25p. black and brown 75 45

98 Torch within Spiral

1971. Racial Equality Year.
261 **98** 1r. red and blue 1·90 1·30

99 King Mahendra taking Salute

1971. King Mahendra's 52nd Birthday.
262 **99** 15p. purple and blue 75 45

100 Sweta Bhairab

1971. Bhairab Statues of Shiva.
263 **100** 15p. brown and chestnut 75 45
264 - 25p. brown and green 90 60
265 - 50p. brown and blue 1·60 1·20

Designs:—25p. Mahankal Bhairab; 50p. Kal Bhairab.

101 Child presenting Queen Ratna with Garland

1971. National Children's Day.
266 **101** 25p. multicoloured 75 45

102 Iranian and Nepalese Flags on Map of Iran

1971. 2,500th Anniv of Persian Empire.
267 **102** 1r. multicoloured 1·90 1·20

103 Mother and Child

1971. 25th Anniv of UNICEF.
268 **103** 1r. blue 1·90 1·20

104 Mt. Everest

1971. Tourism. Himalayan Peaks.
269 **104** 25p. dp brown, brn and bl 65 25
270 - 1r. black, brown and blue 1·40 80
271 - 1r.80 green, brown & blue 2·50 1·60

Designs:—1r. Mt. Kanchenjunga; 1r.80, Mt. Annapurna I.

105 Royal Standard

1972. National Day.
272 **105** 25p. black and red 75 45

106 Araniko and White Dagoba, Peking

1972. Araniko (13th-century architect) Commem.
273 **106** 15p. brown and blue 40 35

107 Open Book

1972. International Book Year.
274 **107** 2p. brown and buff 20 15
275 **107** 5p. black and brown 25 25
276 **107** 1r. black and blue 1·50 1·20

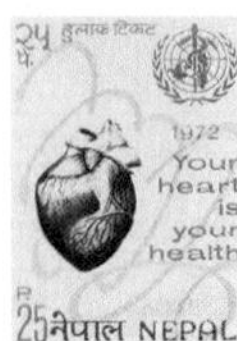
108 Human Heart

1972. World Heart Month.

277	**108**	25p. red and green	75	60

109 King Mahendra

1972. First Death Anniv of King Mahendra.

278	**109**	25p. brown and black	75	45

110 King Birendra

1972. King Birendra's 28th Birthday.

279	**110**	50p. purple and brown	90	70

111 Northern Border Costumes

1973. National Costumes. Multicoloured.

280	25p. Type **111**	65	25
281	50p. Hill-dwellers	75	60
282	75p. Katmandu Valley	1·00	70
283	1r. Inner Terai	1·50	95

112 Sri Baburam Acharya

1973. 85th Birth Anniv of Sri Baburam Acharya (historian).

284	**112**	25p. grey and red	65	35

113 Nepalese Family

1973. 25th Anniv of W.H.O.

285	**113**	1r. blue and orange	1·50	1·20

114 Birthplace of Buddha, Lumbini

1973. Tourism. Multicoloured.

286	25p. Type **114**	65	25
287	75p. Mt. Makalu	90	60
288	1r. Castle, Gurkha	1·40	1·30

115 Transplanting Rice

1973. Tenth Anniv of World Food Programme.

289	**115**	10p. brown and violet	50	25

116 Interpol HQ, Paris

1973. 50th Anniv of International Criminal Police Organization (Interpol).

290	**116**	25p. blue and brown	65	35

117 Shri Shom Nath Sigdyal

1973. First Death Anniv of Shri Shom Nath Sigdyal (scholar).

291	**117**	1r.25 violet	1·50	1·20

118 Cow

1973. Domestic Animals. Multicoloured.

292	2p. Type **118**	25	20
293	3r.25 Yak	2·75	1·80

119 King Birendra

1974. King Birendra's 29th Birthday.

294	**119**	5p. brown and black	25	20
295	**119**	15p. brown and black	40	25
296	**119**	1r. brown and black	1·30	80

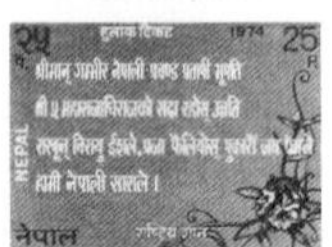
120 Text of National Anthem

1974. National Day.

297	**120**	25p. purple	65	25
298	-	1r. green	90	70

Design:—1r. Anthem musical score.

121 King Janak seated on Throne

1974. King Janak Commemoration.

299	**121**	2r.50 multicoloured	3·25	2·30

122 Emblem and Village

1974. 25th Anniv of SOS Children's Village International.

300	**122**	25p. blue and red	65	60

123 Football

1974. Nepalese Games. Multicoloured.

301	2p. Type **123**	25	20
302	2r.75 Baghchal (diagram)	1·90	1·40

124 WPY Emblem

1974. World Population Year.

303	**124**	5p. blue and brown	40	25

125 UPU Monument, Berne

1974. Centenary of U.P.U.

304	**125**	1r. black and green	1·30	80

126 Red Lacewing

1974. Nepalese Butterflies. Multicoloured.

305	10p. Type **126**	25	20
306	15p. Leaf butterfly	75	35
307	1r.25 Leaf butterfly (underside)	1·90	1·20
308	1r.75 Red-breasted jezebel	2·30	1·80

127 King Birendra

1974. King Birendra's 30th Birthday.

309	**127**	25p. black and green	40	35

128 Muktinath

1974. Visit Nepal Tourism. Multicoloured.

310	25p. Type **128**	65	25
311	1r. Peacock window, Bhaktapur (horiz)	1·30	70

129 Guheswari Temple

1975. Coronation of King Birendra. Multicoloured.

312	25p. Type **129**	50	20
313	50p. Lake Rara (37×30 mm)	65	25
314	1r. Throne and sceptre (46×26 mm)	90	60
315	1r.25 Royal Palace, Katmandu (46×26 mm)	1·90	80
316	1r.75 Pashupatinath Temple (25×31 mm)	1·30	1·20
317	2r.75 King Birendra and Queen Aishwarya (46×25 mm)	1·90	1·40
MS318	143×105 mm. Nos. 314/15 and 317. Imperf	7·00	6·75

130 Tourism Year Emblem

1975. South Asia Tourism Year. Multicoloured.

319	2p. Type **130**	25	20
320	25p. Temple stupa (vert)	65	60

131 Tiger

1975. Wildlife Conservation. Multicoloured.

321	2p. Type **131**	50	45
322	5p. Swamp deer (vert)	65	60
323	1r. Lesser panda	1·30	1·20

132 Queen Aishwarya and IWY Emblem

1975. International Women's Year.

324	**132**	1r. multicoloured	90	60

133 Rupse Falls

1975. Tourism. Multicoloured.

325	2p. Mt. Ganesh Himal (horiz)	25	20
326	25p. Type **133**	40	25
327	50p. Kumari ("Living Goddess")	1·10	60

134 King Birendra

1975. King Birendra's 31st Birthday.

328	**134**	25p. violet and mauve	45	25

136 Flag and Map

1976. Silver Jubilee of National Democracy Day.

330	**136**	2r.50 red and blue	1·70	1·20

137 Transplanting Rice

1976. Agriculture Year.

331	**137**	25p. multicoloured	45	25

138 Flags of Nepal and Colombo Plan

1976. 25th Anniv of Colombo Plan.

332	**138**	1r. multicoloured	1·00	70

139 Running

1976. Olympic Games, Montreal.

333	**139**	3r.25 black and blue	2·75	1·80

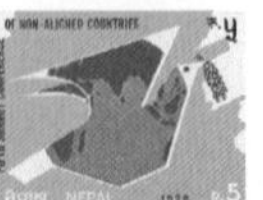
140 "Dove of Peace"

1976. Fifth Non-aligned Countries' Summit Conf.

334	**140**	5r. blue, yellow and black	3·75	2·00

141 Lakhe Dance

1976. Nepalese Dances. Multicoloured.

335	10p. Type **141**	25	20
336	15p. Maruni dance	30	25
337	30p. Jhangad dance	70	35
338	1r. Sebru dance	1·00	60

142 Nepalese Lily

1976. Flowers. Multicoloured.

339	30p. Type **142**	1·00	25
340	30p. *Meconopsis grandis*	1·00	25
341	30p. *Cardiocrinum giganteum* (horiz)	1·00	25
342	30p. *Megacodon stylophorus* (horiz)	1·00	25

143 King Birendra

1976. King Birendra's 32nd Birthday.

343	**143**	5p. green	30	10
344	**143**	30p. dp brown, brn & yell	45	25

144 Liberty Bell

1976. Bicentenary of American Revolution.

345	**144**	10r. multicoloured	5·00	3·75

145 Kaji Amarsingh Thapa

1977. Kaji Amarsingh Thapa (19th-century warrior) Commemoration.

346	**145**	10p. green and brown	55	25

146 Terracotta Figurine and Kapilavastu

1977. Tourism.

347	**146**	30p. violet	30	20
348	-	5r. green and brown	2·75	1·80

Design:—5r. Ashokan pillar, Lumbini.

147 Great Indian Hornbill

1977. Birds. Multicoloured.

349	5p. Type **147**	1·00	35
350	15p. Cheer pheasant (horiz)	1·70	45
351	1r. Green magpie (horiz)	2·75	80
352	2r.30 Spiny babbler	5·00	1·20

148 Tukuche Himal and Police Flag

1977. First Anniv of Ascent of Tukuche Himal by Police Team.

353	**148**	1r.25 multicoloured	1·00	60

149 Map of Nepal and Scout Emblem

1977. 25th Anniv of Scouting in Nepal.

354	**149**	3r.50 multicoloured	2·10	1·20

150 Dhanwantari, the Health-giver

1977. Health Day.

355	**150**	30p. green	45	25

151 Map of Nepal and Flags

1977. 26th Consultative Committee Meeting of Colombo Plan, Katmandu.

356	**151**	1r. multicoloured	70	35

152 King Birendra

1977. King Birendra's 33rd Birthday.

357	**152**	5p. brown	30	20
358	**152**	1r. brown	70	60

153 General Post Office, Katmandu, and Seal

1978. Centenary of Nepalese Post Office.

359	**153**	25p. brown and agate	30	20
360	-	75p. brown and agate	70	60

Design:—75p. General Post Office, Katmandu, and early postmark.

154 South-west Face of Mt. Everest

1978. 25th Anniv of First Ascent of Mt. Everest.

361	**154**	2r.30 grey and brown	1·70	80
362	-	4r. blue and green	2·50	1·80

Design:—4r. South face of Mt. Everest.

155 Sun, Ankh and Landscape

1978. World Environment Day.

363	**155**	1r. green and orange	70	35

156 Queen Mother Ratna

1978. Queen Mother's 50th Birthday.

364	**156**	2r.30 green	1·40	80

157 Rapids, Tripsuli River

1978. Tourism. Multicoloured.

365	10p. Type **157**	45	15
366	50p. Window, Nara Devi, Katmandu	55	25
367	1r. Mahakali dance (vert)	1·00	60

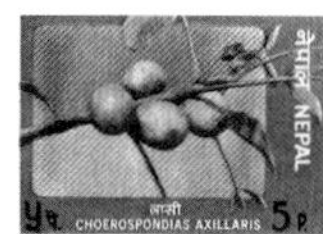

158 Lapsi (*Choerospondias axillaris*)

1978. Fruits. Multicoloured.

368	5p. Type **158**	45	15
369	1r. Katus (vert)	1·00	60
370	1r.25 Rudrakshya	1·40	70

159 Lamp and UN Emblem

1978. 30th Anniv of Human Rights Declaration.

371	**159**	25p. brown and red	30	10
372	**159**	1r. blue and red	70	35

160 *Wright Flyer I* and Boeing 727-100

1978. Air. 75th Anniv of First Powered Flight.

373	**160**	2r.30 blue and brown	1·70	1·20

161 King Birendra

1978. King Birendra's 34th Birthday.

374	**161**	30p. blue and brown	30	10
375	**161**	2r. brown and violet	1·10	70

162 Red Machchhindranath and Kamroop and Patan Temples

1979. Red Machchhindranath (guardian deity) Festival.

376	**162**	75p. brown and green	70	35

163 *Buddha's Birth* (carving, Maya Devi Temple)

1979. Lumbini Year.

377	**163**	1r. yellow and brown	70	35

164 Planting a Sapling

1979. Tree Planting Festival.

378	**164**	2r.30 brown, green & yellow	1·70	1·20

165 Chariot of Red Machchhindranath

1979. Bhoto Jatra (Vest Exhibition) Festival.

379	**165**	1r.25 multicoloured	85	60

166 Nepalese Scouts and Guides

1979. International Year of the Child.

380	**166**	1r. brown	85	60

167 Mount Pabil

1979. Tourism.

381	**167**	30p. green	20	20
382	-	50p. red and blue	30	25
383	-	1r.25 multicoloured	85	70

Designs:—50p. Yajnashala, Swargadwari. 1r.25, Shiva-Parbati (wood carving, Gaddi Baithak Temple).

168 Great Grey Shrike

1979. International World Pheasant Association Symposium, Katmandu. Multicoloured.

384	10p. Type **168** (postage)	45	25
385	10r. Fire-tailed sunbird	10·50	5·25
386	3r.50 Himalayan monal pheasant (horiz) (air)	3·75	2·50

169 Lichchhavi Coin (obverse)

1979. Coins.

387	**169**	5p. orange and brown	25	20
388	-	5p. orange and brown	25	20
389	-	15p. blue and indigo	30	25
390	-	15p. blue and indigo	30	25
391	-	1r. blue and deep blue	85	70
392	-	1r. blue and deep blue	85	70

Designs:—No. 388, Lichchhavi coin (reverse); No. 389, Malla coin (obverse); No. 390, Malla coin (reverse); No. 391, Prithvi Narayan Shah coin (obverse); No. 392, Prithvi Narayan Shah coin (reverse).

170 King Birendra

1979. King Birendra's 35th Birthday. Mult.

393	25p. Type **170**	30	10
394	2r.30 Reservoir	1·40	80

171 Samyak Pooja Festival

1980. Samyak Pooja Festival, Katmandu.

395	**171**	30p. brown, grey & purple	55	25

172 Sacred Basil

1980. Herbs. Multicoloured.

396	5p. Type **172**	30	10
397	30p. Valerian	45	20
398	1r. Nepalese pepper	70	35
399	2r.30 Himalayan rhubarb	1·40	80

173 Gyandil Das

1980. Nepalese Writers.

400	**173**	5p. lilac and brown	20	10
401	-	30p. purple and brown	30	20
402	-	1r. green and blue	55	35
403	-	2r.30 blue and green	1·10	80

Designs:—30p. Siddhidas Amatya; 1r. Pahalman Singh Swanr; 2r.30, Jay Prithvi Bahadur Singh.

174 Everlasting Flame and Temple, Shirsasthan

1980. Tourism. Multicoloured.

404	10p. Type **174**	30	20
405	1r. Godavari Pond	70	35
406	5r. Mount Dhaulagiri	2·50	1·50

175 Bhairab Dancer

1980. World Tourism Conf, Manila, Philippines.

407	**175**	25r. multicoloured	10·00	6·50

176 King Birendra

1980. King Birendra's 36th Birthday.

408	**176**	1r. multicoloured	70	35

177 IYDP Emblem and Nepalese Flag

1981. International Year of Disabled Persons.

409	**177**	5r. multicoloured	2·75	1·80

178 Nepal Rastra Bank

1981. 25th Anniv of Nepal Rastra Bank.

410	**178**	1r.75 multicoloured	85	60

179 One Anna Stamp of 1881

1981. Nepalese Postage Stamp Centenary.

411	**179**	10p. blue, brown and black	20	10
412	-	40p. purple, brown & blk	30	20
413	-	3r.40 green, brown & blk	1·70	1·20

MS414 117×77 mm. Nos. 411/13 (sold at 5r.) 4·25 4·00

Designs:—40p. 2a. stamp of 1881; 3r.40, 4a. stamp of 1881.

180 Nepalese Flag and Association Emblem

1981. 70th Council Meeting of International Hotel Association, Katmandu.

415	**180**	1r.75 multicoloured	85	60

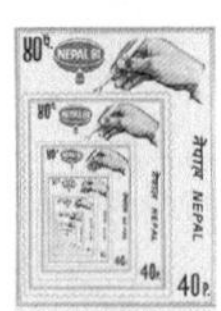

181 Hand holding Stamp

1981. Nepal 81 Stamp Exhibition, Katmandu.

416	**181**	40p. multicoloured	45	20

182 King Birendra

1981. King Birendra's 37th Birthday.

417	**182**	1r. multicoloured	55	35

183 Image of Hrishikesh, Ridi

1981. Tourism. Multicoloured.

418	5p. Type **183**	20	15
419	25p. Tripura Sundari Temple, Baitadi	30	25
420	2r. Mt. Langtang Lirung	1·00	35

184 Academy Building

1982. 25th Anniv of Royal Nepal Academy.

421	**184**	40p. multicoloured	35	25

185 Balakrishna Sama

1982. First Death Anniv of Balakrishna Sama (writer).

422	**185**	1r. multicoloured	45	35

186 "Intelsat V" and Dish Aerial

1982. Sagarmatha Satellite Earth Station, Balambu.

423	**186**	5r. multicoloured	2·50	1·20

187 Mount Nuptse

1982. 50th Anniv of Union of International Alpinist Associations. Multicoloured.

424	25p. Type **187**	30	20
425	2r. Mount Lhotse (31×31 mm)	1·00	60
426	3r. Mount Everest (39×31 mm)	2·10	80

Nos. 424/6 were issued together, *se-tenant*, forming a composite design.

188 Games Emblem and Weights

1982. Ninth Asian Games, New Delhi.

427	**188**	3r.40 multicoloured	1·70	1·20

189 Indra Sarobar Lake

1982. Kulekhani Hydro-electric Project.

428	**189**	2r. multicoloured	1·00	60

190 King Birendra

1982. King Birendra's 38th Birthday.

429	**190**	5p. multicoloured	45	25

191 NIDC Emblem

1983. 25th Anniv (1984) of Nepal Industrial Development Corporation.

430	**191**	50p. multicoloured	45	25

192 Boeing 727 over Himalayas

1983. 25th Anniv of Royal Nepal Airlines.

431	**192**	1r. multicoloured	85	35

193 WCY Emblem and Nepalese Flag

1983. World Communications Year.

432	**193**	10p. multicoloured	70	25

194 Sarangi

1983. Musical Instruments. Multicoloured.

433	5p. Type **194**	15	10
434	10p. Kwota (drum)	20	15
435	50p. Narashinga (horn)	45	35
436	1r. Murchunga	70	60

195 Chakrapani Chalise

1983. Birth Centenary of Chakrapani Chalise (poet).

437	**195**	4r.50 multicoloured	2·10	1·30

196 King Birendra and Doves

1983. King Birendra's 39th Birthday.

438	**196**	5r. multicoloured	2·40	1·40

197 Barahkshetra Temple and Image of Barah

1983. Tourism. Multicoloured.

439	1r. Type **197**	45	25
440	2r.20 Temple, Triveni	85	60
441	6r. Mount Cho-oyu	2·40	1·50

198 Auditing Accounts

1984. 25th Anniv of Auditor General.

442	**198**	25p. multicoloured	1·00	80

199 Antenna and Emblem

1984. 20th Anniv of Asia-Pacific Broadcasting Union.

443	**199**	5r. multicoloured	2·40	1·80

200 University Emblem

1984. 25th Anniv of Tribhuvan University.

444	**200**	50p. multicoloured	45	25

201 Boxing

1984. Olympic Games, Los Angeles.

445	**201**	10r. multicoloured	4·25	2·30

202 Family and Emblem

1984. 25th Anniv of Nepal Family Planning Association.

446	**202**	1r. multicoloured	45	25

203 National Flag and Emblem

1984. Social Service Day.

447	**203**	5p. multicoloured	30	20

204 Gharial

1984. Wildlife. Multicoloured.

448	10p. Type **204**	55	25
449	25p. Snow leopard	70	35
450	50p. Blackbuck	1·30	60

205 Vishnu as Giant (stone carving)

1984. Tourism. Multicoloured.

451	10p. Type **205**	15	10
452	1r. Temple of Chhinna Masta Bhagavati and sculpture (horiz)	45	25
453	5r. Mount Api	2·50	1·30

206 King Birendra

1984. King Birendra's 40th Birthday.

454	**206**	1r. multicoloured	20	15

207 Animals and Mountains

1985. Sagarmatha (Mt. Everest) National Park.

455	**207**	10r. multicoloured	4·00	1·50

208 Shiva

1985. Traditional Paintings. Details of cover of "Shiva Dharma Purana". Multicoloured.

456	50p. Type **208**	20	20
457	50p. Multi-headed Shiva talking to woman	45	35
458	50p. Brahma and Vishnu making offering (15×22 mm)	45	35
459	50p. Shiva in single- and multi-headed forms	45	35
460	50p. Shiva talking to woman	45	35

Nos. 456/60 were printed together, *se-tenant*, forming a composite design.

209 UN Flag

1985. 40th Anniv of U.N.O.

461	**209**	5r. multicoloured	2·10	1·20

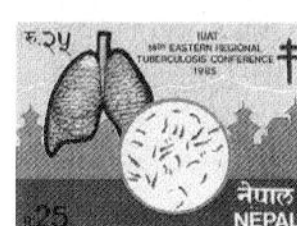
210 Lungs and Bacilli

1985. 14th Eastern Regional Tuberculosis Conf, Katmandu.

462	**210**	25r. multicoloured	10·00	5·75

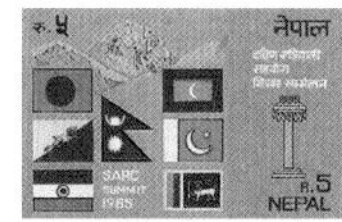
211 Flags of Member Countries

1985. First South Asian Association for Regional Co-operation Summit.

463	**211**	5r. multicoloured	2·10	1·20

212 Jaleshwar Temple

1985. Tourism. Multicoloured.

464	10p. Type **212**	15	10
465	1r. Temple of Goddess Shaileshwari, Silgadi	45	25
466	2r. Phoksundo Lake	85	35

213 IYY Emblem

1985. International Youth Year.

467	**213**	1r. multicoloured	45	25

214 King Birendra

1985. King Birendra's 41st Birthday.

468	**214**	50p. multicoloured	30	25

215 Devi Ghat Hydro-electric Project

1985

469	**215**	2r. multicoloured	1·00	60

216 Emblem

1986. 25th Anniv of Panchayat System (partyless government).

470	**216**	4r. multicoloured	1·70	1·20

217 Royal Crown

1986

471	**217**	5p. brown and deep brown	30	10
472	-	10p. blue	35	20
473	-	50p. blue	45	25
474	-	1r. brown and ochre	55	35

Designs:—10p. Mayadevi Temple of Lumbini (Buddha's birthplace); 50p. Pashupati Temple; 1r. Royal Crown.

218 Pharping Hydro-electric Station

1986. 75th Anniv of Pharping Hydro-electric Power Station.

480	**218**	15p. multicoloured	55	25

219 Emblem and Map

1986. 25th Anniv of Asian Productivity Organization.

481	**219**	1r. multicoloured	45	25

220 Mt. Pumori, Himalayas (35×22 mm)

1986. Tourism. Multicoloured.

482	60p. Type **220**	30	20
483	8r. *Budhanilkantha* (sculpture of reclining Vishnu), Katmandu Valley	3·00	1·90

221 King Birendra

1986. King Birendra's 42nd Birthday.

484	**221**	1r. multicoloured	45	25

222 IPY Emblem

1986. International Peace Year.

485	**222**	10r. multicoloured	3·00	2·00

223 National Flag and Council Emblem

1987. Tenth Anniv of National Social Service Co-ordination Council.

486	**223**	1r. multicoloured	45	25

224 Emblem and Forest

1987. First Nepal Scout Jamboree, Katmandu.

487	**224**	1r. brown, orange and blue	85	25

225 Ashokan Pillar and Maya Devi

1987. Lumbini (Buddha's Birthplace) Development Project.

488	**225**	4r. multicoloured	1·40	80

226 Emblem

1987. Third South Asian Association for Regional Co-operation Summit, Katmandu.

489	**226**	60p. gold and red	30	20

227 Emblem

1987. 25th Anniv of Rastriya Samachar Samiti (news service).

490	**227**	4r. purple, blue and red	1·40	80

228 Kashthamandap, Katmandu

1987

491	**228**	25p. multicoloured	30	20

229 Gyawali

1987. 89th Birth Anniv of Surya Bikram Gyawali.

492	**229**	60p. multicoloured	30	20

230 Emblem

1987. International Year of Shelter for the Homeless.

493	**230**	5r. multicoloured	1·70	1·20

231 King Birendra

1987. King Birendra's 43rd Birthday.

494	**231**	25p. multicoloured	30	20

232 Mt. Kanjiroba

1987

495	**232**	10r. multicoloured	3·00	1·80

233 Crown Prince Dipendra

1988. Crown Prince Dipendra's 17th Birthday.

496	**233**	1r. multicoloured	45	25

234 Baby in Incubator

1988. 25th Anniv of Kanti Children's Hospital, Katmandu.
497 **234** 60p. multicoloured 30 20

235 Swamp Deer

1988. 12th Anniv of Royal Shukla Phanta Wildlife Reserve.
498 **235** 60p. multicoloured 1·40 25

236 Laxmi, Goddess of Wealth

1988. 50th Anniv of Nepal Bank Ltd.
499 **236** 2r. multicoloured 70 35

237 Queen Mother

1988. 60th Birthday of Queen Mother.
500 **237** 5r. multicoloured 1·70 1·20

238 Hands protecting Blood Droplet

1988. 25th Anniv of Nepal Red Cross Society.
501 **238** 1r. red and brown 45 25

239 Temple and Statue

1988. Temple of Goddess Bindhyabasini, Pokhara.
502 **239** 15p. multicoloured 30 20

240 King Birendra

1988. King Birendra's 44th Birthday.
503 **240** 4r. multicoloured 1·40 70

241 Temple

1989. Pashupati Area Development Trust.
504 **241** 1r. multicoloured 45 25

242 Emblem

1989. Tenth Anniv of Asia-Pacific Telecommunity.
505 **242** 4r. green, black and violet 85 45

243 SAARC Emblem

1989. South Asian Association for Regional Co-operation Year against Drug Abuse and Trafficking.
506 **243** 60p. multicoloured 30 20

244 King Birendra

1989. King Birendra's 45th Birthday.
507 **244** 2r. multicoloured 70 25

245 Child Survival Measures

1989. Child Survival Campaign.
508 **245** 1r. multicoloured 30 20

246 Lake Rara

1989. Rara National Park.
509 **246** 4r. multicoloured 85 45

247 Mt. Amadablam

1989
510 **247** 5r. multicoloured 1·40 60

248 Crown Prince Dipendra

1989. Crown Prince Dipendra's Coming-of-Age.
511 **248** 1r. multicoloured 30 20

249 Temple of Manakamana, Gorkha

1990
512 **249** 60p. black and violet 30 20

250 Emblem and Children

1990. 25th Anniv of Nepal Children's Organization.
513 **250** 1r. multicoloured 30 20

251 Emblem

1990. Centenary of Bir Hospital.
514 **251** 60p. red, blue and yellow 30 20

252 Emblem

1990. 20th Anniv of Asian–Pacific Postal Training Centre, Bangkok.
515 **252** 4r. multicoloured 1·10 50

253 Goddess and Bageshwori Temple, Nepalgunj

1990. Tourism. Multicoloured.
516 1r. Type **253** 30 20
517 5r. Mt. Saipal (36×27 mm) 1·50 65

254 Leisure Activities

1990. South Asian Association for Regional Co-operation Girls' Year.
518 **254** 4r.60 multicoloured 1·40 65

255 King Birendra

1990. King Birendra's 46th Birthday.
519 **255** 2r. multicoloured 45 25

256 Koirala

1990. 76th Birth Anniv of Bisweswar Prasad Koirala (Prime Minister, 1959–60).
520 **256** 60p. black, orange and red 30 20

257 Indian Rhinoceros and Lake

1991. Royal Chitwan National Park.
521 **257** 4r. multicoloured 1·80 65

258 Flower and Crowd

1991. First Anniv of Abrogation of Ban on Political Parties.
522 **258** 1r. multicoloured 30 20

259 Official and Villagers

1991. National Population Census.
523 **259** 60p. multicoloured 30 20

260 Federation and Jubilee Emblems

1991. 25th Anniv of Federation of Nepalese Chambers of Commerce and Industry.
524 **260** 3r. multicoloured 75 40

261 Crosses

1991. 25th Anniv (1990) of Nepal Junior Red Cross.
525 **261** 60p. red and grey 30 15

262 Delegates

1991. First Session of Revived Parliament.
526 **262** 1r. multicoloured 30 20

263 King Birendra making Speech

1991. Constitution Day.
527 **263** 50p. multicoloured 30 20

264 Rama and Janaki (statues) and Vivaha Mandap

1991. Fifth Anniv of Rebuilt Vivaha Mandap Pavilion, Janaki Temple.
528 **264** 1r. multicoloured 30 20

265 Mt. Kumbhakarna

1991. Tourism.
529 **265** 4r.60 multicoloured 1·10 50

266 King Birendra

1991. King Birendra's 47th Birthday.

530	**266**	8r. multicoloured	1·80	90

267 Houses

1991. South Asian Association for Regional Co-operation Year of Shelter.

531	**267**	9r. multicoloured	2·00	1·00

268 Glass magnifying Society Emblem

1992. 25th Anniv (1991) of Nepal Philatelic Society.

532	**268**	4r. multicoloured	90	50

269 Rainbow over River and Trees

1992. Environmental Protection.

533	**269**	60p. multicoloured	30	20

270 Nutrition, Education and Health Care

1992. Rights of the Child.

534	**270**	1r. multicoloured	30	20

271 Thakurdwara Temple, Bardiya

1992. Temples. Multicoloured.

535	75p. Type **271** (postage)	15	10
536	1r. Namo Buddha Temple, Kavre	30	15
537	2r. Narijhowa Temple, Mustang	45	20
538	11r. Dantakali Temple, Bijayapur (air)	2·30	1·10

272 Bank Emblem

1992. 25th Anniv of Agricultural Development Bank.

539	**272**	40p. brown and green	30	20

273 Pin-tailed Green Pigeon

1992. Birds. Multicoloured.

540	1r. Type **273**	30	15
541	3r. Bohemian waxwing	75	25
542	25r. Rufous-tailed desert (inscr "Finch") lark	5·50	2·75

274 King Birendra exchanging Swords with Goddess Sree Bhadrakali

1992. King Birendra's 48th Birthday.

543	**274**	7r. multicoloured	1·20	65

275 Pandit Kulchandra Gautam

1992. Poets. Multicoloured, frame colour given in brackets.

544	1r. Type **275**	45	15
545	1r. Chittadhar Hridaya (drab)	45	15
546	1r. Vidyapati (stone)	45	15
547	1r. Teongsi Sirijunga (grey)	45	15

276 Shooting and Marathon

1992. Olympic Games, Barcelona.

548	**276**	25r. multicoloured	4·50	2·50

277 Golden Mahseer

1993. Fish. Multicoloured.

549	25p. Type **277**	30	15
550	1r. Marinka	75	25
551	5r. Indian eel	1·40	50
552	10r. False loach	2·40	1·00
MS553	90×70 mm. Nos. 549/52	7·50	7·25

278 Antibodies attacking Globe

1993. World AIDS Day.

554	**278**	1r. multicoloured	30	20

279 Tanka Prasad Acharya (Prime Minister, 1956–57)

1993. Death Anniversaries. Multicoloured.

555	25p. Type **279** (First anniv)	15	10
556	1r. Sungdare Sherpa (mountaineer) (Fourth anniv)	30	15
557	7r. Siddhi Charan Shrestha (poet) (First anniv)	1·10	50
558	15r. Falgunanda (religious leader) (44th anniv)	2·30	1·30

280 Bagh Bairab Temple, Kirtipur

1993. Holy Places. Multicoloured.

559	1r.50 Type **280**	15	10
560	5r. Devghat (gods' bathing place), Tanahun	75	40
561	8r. Halesi Mahadev Cave (hiding place of Shiva), Khotang	1·20	65

281 Tushahiti Fountain, Sundari Chowk, Patan

1993. Tourism. Multicoloured.

562	5r. Type **281**	90	40
563	8r. White-water rafting	1·40	65

282 King Birendra

1993. King Birendra's 49th Birthday.

564	**282**	10r. multicoloured	1·50	75

283 Monument

284 Mt. Everest

1994

565	**283**	20p. brown	10	10
566	-	25p. red	10	10
567	-	30p. green	15	10
568	**284**	1r. multicoloured	30	20
569	-	5r. multicoloured	75	40

Designs:—20×22 mm: 25p. State Arms. 22×20 mm: 30p. Lumbini. 25×15 mm: 5r. Map of Nepal, crown and State Arms and flag.

285 Pasang Sherpa

1994. First Death Anniv of Pasang Sherpa (mountaineer).

570	**285**	10r. multicoloured	1·50	75

286 Cigarette, Lungs and Crab's Claws

1994. Anti-smoking Campaign.

571	**286**	1r. multicoloured	30	20

287 Postal Delivery

1994

572	**287**	1r.50 multicoloured	30	20

288 Khuda

1994. Weapons. Multicoloured.

573	5r. Kukris (three swords and two scabbards)	75	40
574	5r. Type **288**	75	40
575	5r. Dhaal (swords and shield)	75	40
576	5r. Katari (two daggers)	75	40

289 Workers and Emblem

1994. 75th Anniv of I.L.O.

577	**289**	15r. gold, blue & ultram	2·30	1·30

290 Landscape

1994. World Food Day.

578	**290**	25r. multicoloured	3·75	2·00

291 *Dendrobium densiflorum*

1994. Orchids. Multicoloured.

579	10r. Type **291**	1·50	75
580	10r. *Coelogyne flaccida*	1·50	75
581	10r. *Cymbidium devonianum*	1·50	75
582	10r. *Coelogyne corymbosa*	1·50	75

292 Family

1994. International Year of the Family.

583	**292**	9r. emerald, green and red	1·40	75

293 Emblem and Aeroplane

1994. 50th Anniv of I.C.A.O.

584	**293**	11r. blue, gold and deep blue	1·70	90

294 *Russula nepalensis*

1994. Fungi. Multicoloured.

585	7r. Type **294**	1·10	50
586	7r. Morels (*Morchella conica*)	1·10	50
587	7r. Caesar's mushroom (*Amanita caesarea*)	1·10	50
588	7r. *Cordyceps sinensis*	1·10	50

295 Dharanidhar Koirala (poet)

1994. Celebrities. Multicoloured.

589	1r. Type **295**	15	10
590	2r. Narayan Gopal Guruwacharya (singer)	30	15
591	6r. Bahadur Shah (vert)	90	40
592	7r. Balaguru Shadananda	1·10	50

296 King Birendra, Flag, Map and Crown

1994. King Birendra's 50th Birthday (1st issue).

593	**296**	9r. multicoloured	1·40	75

See also No. 621.

297 Lake Tilicho, Manang

1994. Tourism. Multicoloured.

594	9r. Type **297**	1·40	75
595	11r. Taleju Temple, Katmandu (vert)	1·70	90

298 Health Care

1994. Children's Activities. Multicoloured.

596	1r. Type **298**	25	15
597	1r. Classroom	25	10
598	1r. Playground equipment	25	10
599	1r. Stamp collecting	25	10

299 Singhaduarbar

1995

600	**299**	10p. green	15	10
601	-	50p. blue	25	10

Design:—Vert: 50p. Pashupati.

300 Crab on Lungs

1995. Anti-cancer Campaign.

602	**300**	2r. multicoloured	30	20

301 Chandra Man Singh Maskey (artist)

1995. Celebrities. Multicoloured.

603	3r. Type **301**	45	25
604	3r. Parijat (writer)	45	25
605	3r. Bhim Nidhi Tiwari (writer)	45	25
606	3r. Yuddha Prasad Mishra (writer)	45	25

302 Bhakti Thapa (soldier)

1995. Celebrities. Multicoloured.

607	15p. Type **302**	25	10
608	1r. Madan Bhandari (politician)	30	15
609	4r. Prakash Raj Kaphley (human rights activist)	60	25

303 Gaur (*Bos gaurus*)

1995. Singapore '95 International Stamp Exhibition. Mammals. Multicoloured.

610	10r. Type **303**	1·50	70
611	10r. Lynx (*Felis lynx*)	1·50	70
612	10r. Assam macaque (*Macaca assamensis*)	1·50	70
613	10r. Striped hyena (*Hyaena hyaena*)	1·50	70

304 Anniversary Emblem

1995. 50th Anniv of F.A.O.

614	**304**	7r. multicoloured	1·10	45

305 Figures around Emblem

1995. 50th Anniv of U.N.O.

615	**305**	50r. multicoloured	7·50	3·75

306 Bhimeswor Temple, Dolakha

1995. Tourism. Multicoloured.

616	1r. Type **306**	15	10
617	5r. Ugra Tara Temple, Dadeldhura (horiz)	75	35
618	7r. Mt. Nampa (horiz)	1·10	45
619	18r. Nrity Aswora (traditional Pauba painting) (27×39 mm)	2·75	1·40
620	20r. Lumbini (Buddha's birthplace) (28×28 mm)	3·00	1·50

307 King Birendra

1995. King Birendra's 50th Birthday (1994) (2nd issue).

621	**307**	1r. multicoloured	30	20

308 Anniversary Emblem

1995. Tenth Anniv of South Asian Association for Regional Co-operation.

622	**308**	10r. multicoloured	1·50	70

309 King Birendra

1995. King Birendra's 51st Birthday.

623	**309**	12r. multicoloured	1·80	95

310 Karnali Bridge

1996

624	**310**	7r. multicoloured	1·10	45

311 State Arms

1996

625	**311**	25p. red	30	20

312 Kaji Kalu Pande (soldier and royal adviser)

1996. Political Figures. Multicoloured.

626	75p. Type **312**	10	10
627	1r. Pushpa Lal Shrestha (Nepal Communist Party General-Secretary)	15	10
628	5r. Suvarna Shamsher Rana (founder of Nepal Democratic Congress Party)	75	35

313 Hem Raj Sharma (grammarian)

1996. Writers. Multicoloured.

629	1r. Type **313**	15	10
630	3r. Padma Prasad Bhattarai (Sanskrit scholar)	45	25
631	5r. Bhawani Bhikshu (novelist)	75	35

314 Runner and Track

1996. Olympic Games, Atlanta.

632	**314**	7r. multicoloured	1·10	45

315 Kasthamandap, Katmandu

1996. Temples.

633	**315**	10p. red and black	10	10
634	**315**	50p. black and red	10	10
635	-	1r. red and blue	15	10

Design:—Vert: 1r. Nyata Pola temple, Bhaktapur.

316 Hindu Temple, Arjundhara

1996. Tourism. Multicoloured.

636	1r. Type **316**	15	10
637	2r. Durbar, Nuwakot	30	10
638	8r. Gaijatra Festival, Bhaktapur	1·40	70
639	10r. Lake Beganas, Kaski	1·80	95

317 Krishna Peacock

1996. Butterflies and Birds. Multicoloured.

640	5r. Type **317**	90	45
641	5r. Great barbet ("Great Himalayan Barbet")	90	45
642	5r. Sarus crane	90	45
643	5r. Northern jungle queen	90	45

Nos. 640/3 were issued together, *se-tenant*, forming a composite design.

318 Ashoka Pillar

1996. Centenary of Rediscovery of Ashoka Pillar, Lumbini (birthplace of Buddha).

644	**318**	12r. multicoloured	2·75	1·10

319 King Birendra

1996. King Birendra's 52nd Birthday.

645	**319**	10r. multicoloured	1·20	75

320 Mt. Annapurna South and Mt. Annapurna I

1996. The Himalayas. Multicoloured.

646	18r. Type **320**	2·30	1·20
647	18r. Mt. Machhapuchhre and Mt. Annapurna III	2·30	1·20
648	18r. Mt. Annapurna IV and Mt. Annapurna II	2·30	1·20

Nos. 646/8 were issued together, *se-tenant*, forming a composite design.

321 King Birendra before Throne

1997. Silver Jubilee of King Birendra's Accession.

649	**321**	2r. multicoloured	30	20

322 Mountains and National Flags

1997. 40th Anniv of Nepal–Japan Diplomatic Relations.

650	**322**	18r. multicoloured	2·75	1·40

323 Postal Emblem

1997

651	**323**	2r. red and brown	30	20

324 Campaign Emblem

1997. National Tourism Year.

652	**324**	2r. red and blue	30	20
653	-	10r. multicoloured	1·50	70
654	-	18r. multicoloured	2·75	1·40
655	-	20r. multicoloured	3·00	1·50

Designs—Horiz: 10r. Upper Mustang mountain peak; 18r. Rafting, River Sunkoshi. Vert: 20r. Changunarayan.

325 Chepang Couple

1997. Ethnic Groups. Multicoloured.

656	5r. Type **325**	75	35
657	5r. Gurung couple	75	35
658	5r. Rana Tharu couple	75	35

326 National Flags and Handshake

1997. 50th Anniv of Nepal United States Diplomatic Relations.

659	**326**	20r. multicoloured	3·00	1·70

327 Riddhi Bahadur Malla (writer)

1997. Celebrities. Multicoloured.

660	2r. Type **327**	40	15
661	2r. Dr. K. I. Singh (politician)	40	15

328 *Jasminum gracile*

1997. Flowers. Multicoloured.

662	40p. Type **328**	10	10
663	1r. China aster	15	10
664	2r. *Manglietia insignis*	45	25
665	15r. *Luculia gratissima*	2·40	1·30

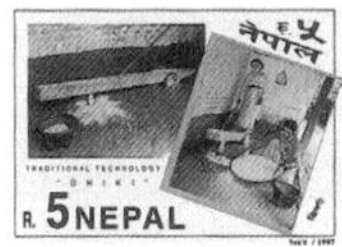
329 Dhiki (corn crusher)

1997. Traditional Technology. Multicoloured.

666	5r. Type **329**	75	40
667	5r. Janto (mill stone)	75	40
668	5r. Kol (oil mill) (vert)	75	40
669	5r. Okhal (implement for pounding rice) (vert)	75	40

330 King Birendra

1997. King Birendra's 53rd Birthday.

670	**330**	10r. multicoloured	1·50	85

331 Sunrise, Shree Antudanda, Ilam

1998. Tourism. Multicoloured.

671	2r. Type **331**	30	15
672	10r. Maitidevi Temple, Katmandu	1·50	85
673	18r. Great Renunciation Gate, Kapilavastu	2·75	1·50
674	20r. Mt. Cholatse, Solukhumbu (vert)	3·00	1·70

332 Ram Prasad Rai (nationalist)

1998. Personalities.

675	**332**	75p. black and brown	15	10
676	-	1r. black and mauve	30	15
677	-	2r. black and green	45	25
678	-	2r. black and blue	45	25
679	-	5r.40 black and red	75	40

Designs:—No. 676, Imansing Chemjong (Kiranti language specialist); No. 677, Tulsi Meher Shrestha (social worker); No. 678, Maha Pundit Dadhi Ram Marasini (poet); No. 679, Mahananda Sapkota (educationalist and writer).

333 Match Scenes

1998. World Cup Football Championship, France.

680	**333**	12r. multicoloured	1·80	1·00

334 Ganesh Man Singh

1998. First Death Anniv of Ganesh Man Singh (politician).

681	**334**	5r. multicoloured	75	40

335 World Map and Nepalese Soldiers

1998. 40 Years of Nepalese Army Involvement in United Nations Peace Keeping Missions.

682	**335**	10r. multicoloured	1·50	85

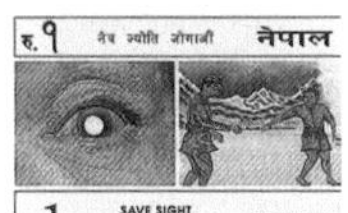
336 Cataract and Guiding of Blind Man

1998. Cataract Awareness Campaign.

683	**336**	1r. multicoloured	30	15

337 King Cobra

1998. Snakes. Multicoloured.

684	1r.70 Type **337**	30	15
685	2r. Golden tree snake	45	25
686	5r. Asiatic rock python	1·10	60
687	10r. Karan's pit viper	2·10	1·20

338 Dove and Profile

1998. 50th Anniv of Universal Declaration of Human Rights.

688	**338**	10r. multicoloured	1·50	85

339 Disabled Persons

1998. Asian and Pacific Decade of Disabled Persons.

689	**339**	10r. multicoloured	1·50	85

340 King Birendra

1998. King Birendra's 54th Birthday.

690	**340**	2r. multicoloured	30	15

341 Dam and Power House

1998. River Marsyangdi Hydro-electric Power Station.

691	**341**	12r. multicoloured	1·80	1·00

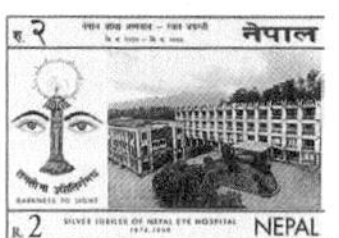
342 Hospital and Emblem

1999. 25th Anniv of Nepal Eye Hospital.

692	**342**	2r. multicoloured	30	15

343 Kalika Bhagawati Temple, Baglung

1999. Tourism. Multicoloured.

693	2r. Type **343**	30	15
694	2r. Chandan Nath Temple, Jumla (vert)	30	15
695	12r. Bajrayogini Temple, Sankhu (vert)	2·30	1·30
696	15r. Mt. Everest	2·75	1·50
697	15r. Ashokan Pillar, Lumbini, and English translation of its inscription (39×27 mm)	2·75	1·50

344 Four-horned Antelope

1999. Mammals. Multicoloured.

698	10r. Type **344**	1·80	1·00
699	10r. Argali (*Ovis ammon*)	1·80	1·00

345 Him Kanchha (mascot) and Games Emblem

1999. Eighth South Asian Sports Federation Games, Katmandu.

700	**345**	10r. multicoloured	1·80	1·00

346 UPU Emblem and Cockerel

1999. 125th Anniv of Universal Postal Union.

701	**346**	15r. multicoloured	2·75	1·50

347 Ramnarayan Mishra (revolutionary, 1922–67)

1999. Personalities.

702	**347**	1r. green and black	30	15
703	-	1r. brown and black	30	15
704	-	1r. blue and black	30	15
705	-	2r. red and black	40	20
706	-	2r. blue and black	40	20
707	-	2r. buff and black	40	20

Designs:—No. 703, Master Mitrasen (writer, 1895–1946); No. 704, Bhupi Sherchan (poet, 1935–89); No. 705, Rudraraj Pandey (writer, 1901–87); No. 706, Gopalprasad Rimal (writer, 1917–73); No. 707, Mangaladevi Singh (revolutionary, 1924–96).

348 Sorathi Dance

1999. Local Dances. Multicoloured.

708	5r. Type **348**	1·10	60
709	5r. Bhairav dance	1·10	60
710	5r. Jhijhiya dance	1·10	60

349 Children working and writing

1999. Nepal's involvement in International Programme on the Elimination of Child Labour.

711	**349**	12r. multicoloured	2·30	1·40

350 King Birendra

1999. King Birendra's 55th Birthday.

712	**350**	5r. multicoloured	90	55

351 Headquarters

2000. 60th Anniv of Radio Nepal.

713	**351**	2r. multicoloured	30	20

352 Queen Aishwarya

2000. Queen Aishwarya's 50th Birthday.

714	**352**	15r. multicoloured	2·50	1·80

353 Front Page of Newspaper and Emblem

2000. Centenary of Gorkhapatra (newspaper).

715	**353**	10r. multicoloured	1·70	1·20

354 Tchorolpa Glacial Lake, Dolakha

2000. Tourist Sights. Multicoloured.

716	12r. Type **354**	2·10	1·50
717	15r. Dakshinkali Temple, Kathmandu	2·50	1·80
718	18r. Mount Annapurna (50th anniv of first ascent)	3·00	2·20

355 Ranipokhari Pagoda, Kathmandu

2000

719	**355**	50p. black and orange	15	10
720	**355**	1r. black and blue	25	15
721	**355**	2r. black and brown	30	20

356 Soldier and Child

2000. 50th Anniv of Geneva Convention.

725	**356**	5r. multicoloured	1·10	75

357 Runners

2000. Olympic Games, Sydney.

726	**357**	25r. multicoloured	5·00	3·75

358 Hridayachandra Singh Pradhan (writer)

2000. Personalities.

727	**358**	2r. black and yellow	30	20
728	-	2r. black and brown	30	20
729	-	5r. black and blue	90	65
730	-	5r. black and red	90	65

Designs:—No. 728, Thir Barn Malla (revolutionary); No. 729, Krishna Prasad Koirala (social reformer); No. 730, Manamohan Adhikari (politician).

359 Indian Rhinoceros (male)

2000. Wildlife. Multicoloured.

731	10r. Type **359**	1·80	1·30
732	10r. Indian rhinoceros (*Rhinoceros unicornis*) (female)	1·80	1·30
733	10r. Lesser adjutant stork (*Leptoptilos javanicus*)	1·80	1·30
734	10r. Bengal florican (*Houbaropsis bengalensis*)	1·80	1·30

360 Orchid (*Dactylorhiza hatagirea*)

2000. Flowers. Multicoloured.

735	5r. Type **360**	1·10	80
736	5r. *Mahonia napaulensis* (horiz)	1·10	80
737	5r. *Talauma hodgsonii* (horiz)	1·10	80

361 King Birendra

2000. King Birendra's 56th Birthday.

738	**361**	5r. multicoloured	90	70

362 King Tribhuvana and Crowd

2001. 50th Anniv of Constitutional Monarchy.

739	**362**	5r. multicoloured	90	70

363 Crowd and Emblem

2001. Population Census.

740	**363**	2r. multicoloured	30	20

364 Khaptad Baba (religious leader)

2001. Personalities.

741	**364**	2r. pink and black	30	20
742	-	2r. mauve and black	30	20
743	-	2r. magenta and black	30	20
744	-	2r. red and black	30	20
745	-	2r. blue and black	30	20

Designs:—No. 742, Bhikkhu Pragyananda Mahathera (Buddhist writer and teacher); No. 743, Guru Prasad Mainali (author); No. 744, Tulsi Lal Amatya Politician); No. 745, Madan Lal Agrawal (industrialist).

365 Asiatic Coinwort (*Centella asiatica*)

2001. Plants. Multicoloured.

746	5r. Type **365**	90	70
747	15r. *Bergenia ciliata*	3·00	2·30
748	30r. Himalayan yew (*Taxus baccata wallichania*)	5·75	4·50

366 Pipal Tree (*Ficus religiosa*)

2001

749	**366**	10r. multicoloured	1·80	1·40

367 Tents

2001. 50th Anniv of United Nations High Commissioner for Refugees.

750	**367**	20r. multicoloured	3·50	2·75

368 National Flag

2001

751	**368**	10p. red and blue	30	20

369 Amargadi Fort

2001. Tourism. Multicoloured.

752	2r. Type **369**	30	20
753	5r. Hiranyavarna Mahavihar (Golden Temple) (vert)	90	70
754	15r. Jugal mountain range	2·75	2·10

370 King Birendra

2001. 57th Birth Anniv of King Birendra.

755	**370**	15r. multicoloured	2·75	2·10

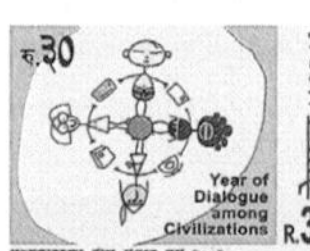
371 Children encircling Globe

2001. United Nations Year of Dialogue among Civilizations.

756	**371**	30r. multicoloured	5·25	4·00

372 Scout Emblem

2002. 50th Anniv of Nepalese Scouts.

757	**372**	2r. chestnut and olive	45	35

373 World Cup Emblem and Footballer

2002. World Cup Football Championships, Japan and South Korea.

758	**373**	15r. multicoloured	2·75	2·10

374 King Gyanendra

2002. First Anniv of Accession of King Gyanendra.

759	**374**	5r. multicoloured	90	70

375 King Birendra and Queen Aishwarya

2002. King Birendra and Queen Aishwarya Commemoration.

760	**375**	10r. multicoloured	90	70

376 *Aryabalokiteshwor*

2002. Paintings. Multicoloured.

761	5r. Type **376**	90	70
762	5r. *Moti (pearl)*, (King Birendra) (horiz)	90	70

377 Family encircled by Barbed Wire (Siddhimuni Shakya)

2002. Social Awareness.

763	**377**	1r. black and brown	30	20
764	-	2r. black and lilac	45	35

Designs:—Type **377** (integration of untouchables); 2r. Children leaving for school (treatment of girls).

378 Leaf Beetle

2002. Insects. Multicoloured.

765	3r. Type **378**	60	45
766	5r. Short horn grasshopper	90	70

379 Valley and Mountains

2002. International Year of Mountains.

767	**379**	5r. multicoloured	1·10	80

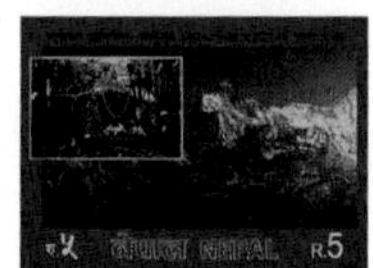
380 Pathibhara Devisthan, Taplejung

2002. Tourism. Multicoloured.

768	5r. Type **380**	1·10	80
769	5r. Galeshwor Mahadevsthan, Myagdi	1·10	80
770	5r. Ramgram Stupa, Nawalparasi	1·10	80
771	5r. Mt. Nilgiri, Mustang	1·10	80

381 Dayabor Singh Kansakar (philanthropist)

2002. Personalities. Multicoloured.

772	2r. Type **381**	30	20
773	25r. Ekai Kawaguchi (first Japanese to visit Nepal)	4·50	3·50

382 Members Flags and Organization Emblem

2002. South Asian Association for Regional Co-operation (SAARC) Charter Day.

774	**382**	15r. multicoloured	2·75	2·10

383 Anniversary Emblem

2003. 50th Anniv of Chamber of Commerce.

775 **383** 5r. multicoloured 75 60

384 FNCCI Emblem

2003. Industry and Commerce Day.

776 **384** 5r. multicoloured 75 60

385 Mt. Everest

2003. 50th Anniv of the First Ascent of Mount Everest.

777 **385** 25r. multicoloured 4·25 3·25

386 Babu Chiri Sherpa

2003. Babu Chiri Sherpa (mountaineer) Commemoration.

778 **386** 5r. multicoloured 75 60

387 King Gyanendra

2003. 57th Birth Anniv of King Gyanendra.

779 **387** 5r. multicoloured 75 60

388 Tea Garden

2003. Eastern Nepal Tea Gardens.

780 **388** 25r. multicoloured 4·25 3·25

389 Dilli Raman Regmi

2003. Second Death Anniv of Dilli Raman Regmi (politician and historian).

781 **389** 5r. brown and black 75 60

390 Gopal Das Shrestha

2003. Fifth Death Anniv of Gopal Das Shrestha (journalist).

782 **390** 5r. green and black 75 60

391 Container, Crane and Emblem

2003. Export Year.

783 **391** 25r. multicoloured 3·75 3·00

392 Sankhadhar Sakhwaa (statue) and Celebrating Crowd

2003. Sankhadhar Sakhwaa (founder of Nepal calender).

784 **392** 5r. multicoloured 75 60

393 Ganesh (statue), Kageshwar

2003. Tourist Sights. Multicoloured.

785	5r. Type **393**	75	60
786	5r. Hydroelectric dam on Kali Gandaki river (horiz)	75	60
787	30r. Buddha (statue), Swayambhu (horiz)	4·50	3·50

394 Lotus

2003. Flowers. Multicoloured.

788	10r. Type **394**	1·50	1·20
789	10r. Picrorhiza	1·50	1·20
790	10r. Himalayan rhubarb	1·50	1·20
791	10r. Jasmine	1·50	1·20

395 Emblem and Symbols of Social Work

2004. 50th Anniv of Social Services of United Mission to Nepal.

792 **395** 5r. multicoloured 85 70

396 NNJS Emblem

2004. 25th Anniv of Nepal Netra Jyoti Sangh (NNJS) (eye care organization).

793 **396** 5r. multicoloured 85 70

397 Society Emblem

2004. 50th Anniv of Marwadi Sewa Samiti, Nepal (charitable organization).

794 **397** 5r. multicoloured 85 70

398 King Gyanendra

2004. 58th Birth Anniv of King Gyanendra.

795 **398** 5r. multicoloured 85 70

399 APT Emblem

2004. 25th Anniv of Asia—Pacific Tele-Community (APT).

796 **399** 5r. multicoloured 85 70

400 Anniversary Emblem

2004. 50th Anniv of Management Education.

797 **400** 5r. multicoloured 85 70

401 Anniversary Emblem

2004. Centenary of FIFA (Fedération Internationale de Football Association).

798 **401** 20r. multicoloured 3·00 2·50

402 Mt. Lhotse

2004. 50th Anniv of Assent Mt Cho Oyu. Multicoloured.

799	10r. Type **402**	1·50	1·30
800	10r. Makalu	1·50	1·30
801	10r. Manasalu	1·50	1·30
802	10r. Annapurna	1·50	1·30
803	10r. Everest	1·50	1·30
804	10r. Kanchenjunga main peak	1·50	1·30
805	10r. Cho Oyu	1·50	1·30
806	10r. Dhaulagiri	1·50	1·30

403 Narahari Nath

2004. Personalities. Multicoloured.

807	5r. Type **403** (religious scholar)	85	70
808	5r. Nayaraj Panta (historian)	85	70

404 *Sasia ochracea* Hodgson (inscr "Rufous piculet" woodpecker)

2004. Biodiversity. Multicoloured.

809	10r. Type **404**	1·50	1·30
810	10r. Atlas moth (*Attacus atlas*)	1·50	1·30
811	10r. *Swertia multicaulis*	1·50	1·30
812	10r. High altitude rice (*Oryza sativa*)	1·50	1·30

405 Mayadevi Temple, Lumbini

2004. Tourism. Multicoloured.

813	10r. Type **405**	1·50	1·30
814	10r. Gadhimai, Bara	1·50	1·30

406 Writer and Emblem

2004. 50th Anniv of Madan Puraskar (language and literature prize).

815 **406** 5r. multicoloured 85 70

407 Jayavarma

2004. Sculpture. Multicoloured.

816	10r. Type **407** (National museum, Kathmandu)	1·50	1·30
817	10r. Umamaheswar (Kathmandu)	1·50	1·30
818	10r. Vishwarupa (Bhaktapur)	1·50	1·30
819	10r. Krishna playing flute (Makawanpur)	1·50	1·30

408 Building Facade

2005. 50th Anniv of Nepal Rasta Bank.

820 **408** 2r. multicoloured 35 30

409 Mt. Makalu

2005. 50th Anniv of First Ascent of Mt. Makalu.

821 **409** 10r. multicoloured 1·50 1·30

410 Mt. Kanchanjunga

2005. 50th Anniv of First Ascent of Mt. Kanchanjunga.

822 **410** 12r. multicoloured 1·80 1·60

411 King Gyanendra

2005. 59th Birth Anniv of King Gyanendra.

823 **411** 5r. multicoloured 85 70

412 Birth of Buddha

2005. Buddha. Showing the life of Buddha. Multicoloured border given.

824	10r. Type **412**	1·50	1·30
825	10r. Enlightenment	1·50	1·30
826	10r. First sermon	1·50	1·30
827	10r. Mahaparinirvana	1·50	1·30
828	10r. Type **412** (green)	1·50	1·30
829	10r. As No. 825 (green)	1·50	1·30
830	10r. As No. 826 (green)	1·50	1·30
831	10r. As No. 827 (green)	1·50	1·30
832	10r. Type **412** (vermilion)	1·50	1·30
833	10r. As No. 825 (vermilion)	1·50	1·30
834	10r. As No. 826 (vermilion)	1·50	1·30
835	10r. As No. 827 (vermilion)	1·50	1·30
836	10r. Type **412** (violet)	1·50	1·30
837	10r. As No. 825 (violet)	1·50	1·30
838	10r. As No. 826 (violet)	1·50	1·30
839	10r. As No. 827 (violet)	1·50	1·30

413 *Phyllanthus emblica*

2005. Fruit. Multicoloured.

840	10r. Type **413**	1·50	1·30
841	10r. *Juglans regia*	1·50	1·30
842	10r. *Aegle marmelos*	1·50	1·30
843	10r. *Rubus ellipticus*	1·50	1·30

414 Queen Mother Ratna Rajya Laxmi Devi Shah

2005. 77th Birth Anniv of Queen Mother Ratna Rajya Laxmi Devi Shah.

844	**414**	20r. multicoloured	3·00	2·50

415 Asian Elephant

2005. Endangered Species. Mammals. Multicoloured border colour given.

845	10r. Type **415**	1·50	1·30
846	10r. Clouded leopard	1·50	1·30
847	10r. Gangetic dolphin	1·50	1·30
848	10r. Indian pangolin	1·50	1·30
849	10r. Type **415** (green)	1·50	1·30
850	10r. As No. 846 (green)	1·50	1·30
851	10r. As No. 847 (green)	1·50	1·30
852	10r. As No. 848 (green)	1·50	1·30
853	10r. Type **415** (vermilion)	1·50	1·30
854	10r. As No. 846 (vermilion)	1·50	1·30
855	10r. As No. 847 (vermilion)	1·50	1·30
856	10r. As No. 848 (vermilion)	1·50	1·30
857	10r. Type **415** (violet)	1·50	1·30
858	10r. As No. 846 (violet)	1·50	1·30
859	10r. As No. 847 (violet)	1·50	1·30
860	10r. As No. 848 (violet)	1·50	1·30

416 Bhupalmansingh Karki

2005. Bhupalmansingh Karki (politician) Commemoration.

861	**416**	2r. multicoloured	35	30

417 Kalinchok Bhagawati, Dolakha

2005. Tourism. Multicoloured.

862	5r. Type **417**	85	70
863	5r. Panauti City, Kabhrepalanchok	85	70
864	5r. Ghodaghodi Lake, Kailali	85	70
865	5r. Budhasubba, Sunasari	85	70

418 Sherpa Jewellery

2005. Tribal Jewellery. Multicoloured.

866	25r. Type **418**	3·75	3·25
867	25r. Newar	3·75	3·25
868	25r. Tharu	3·75	3·25
869	25r. Limbu	3·75	3·25

419 Stupa and Chinese and Nepalese Flags

2005. 50th Anniv of Nepal–China Diplomatic Relations.

870	**419**	30r. multicoloured	4·50	3·75

420 Flags

2005. 50th Anniv of United Nations Membership.

871	**420**	50r. multicoloured	7·50	6·50

421 King Tribhuvan

2006. King Tribhuvan Bir Bikram Shah Dev Commemoration. 55th National Democracy Day.

872	**421**	5r. multicoloured	85	70

422 Queen Komal Rajya Laxmi Devi Shah

2006. Queen Komal Rajya Laxmi Devi Shah. 30th Anniv (2005) of International Women's Day.

873	**422**	5r. multicoloured	85	70

423 Emblem

2006. 25th Anniv of World Hindu Federation.

874	**423**	2r. multicoloured	50	45

424 Mt. Lohtse

2006. 50th Anniv of Mountain Ascents. Multicoloured.

875	25r. Type **424**	3·75	3·00
876	25r. Mt. Manaslu	3·75	3·00

425 Court Building

2006. 50th Anniv of Supreme Court.

877	**425**	5r. multicoloured	85	70

426 *Primula sharmae*

2006. Flora and Fauna. Multicoloured.

878	10r. Type **426**	1·50	1·30
879	10r. *Amolops formosus*	1·50	1·30
880	10r. *Dicranocephalus wallichi*	1·50	1·30
881	10r. *Russula kathmanduensis*	1·50	1·30
882	10r. *Teinopalpus imperialis*	1·50	1·30

427 Sandal Buddha, Burytiya, Russia and Swayamobhunath, Kathmandu

2006. 50th Anniv of Nepal—Russia Diplomatic Relations.

883	**427**	30r. multicoloured	2·50	2·10

428 Nyatapole Temple, Bhaktapur, Nepal

2006. 50th Anniv of Nepal—Japan Diplomatic Relations.

884	**428**	30r. multicoloured	2·50	2·10

429 Changtse and Everest and Horyuji Temple, Nara, Japan

2006. Mount Everest. Multicoloured.

885	1r. Type **429**	35	30
886	5r. Changtse and Everest (32×27 mm)	85	55

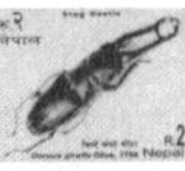

430 *Dorcus giraffe*

2006

887	**430**	2r. multicoloured	50	45

431 Envelope with 1881 1 anna Stamp (Type **1**)

2006. 125th Anniv of First Stamp. Showing first stamps issued by Nepal. Multicoloured.

888	5r. Type **431**	50	45
889	20r. Envelope with 2 anna stamp	1·70	1·40
890	100r. Envelope with 3 anna stamp	8·25	7·00
MS891	91×75 mm. 125r. First stamps and technical details. Imperf	10·00	9·25

No. **MS**891 has perforations surrounding the three stamp images.

432 Emblems

2006. 50th Anniv of UPU Membership.

892	**432**	15r. multicoloured	1·30	1·10

433 Buddha descending

2006. 2550th Anniv of Buddha.

893	**433**	30r. multicoloured	2·50	2·10

434 Dentistry and Examinations

2007. 50th Anniv of Chhatrapati Free Clinic.

894	**434**	2r. multicoloured	35	30

435 Mount Everest

2007

895	**435**	5r. multicoloured	50	45

436 *Satyrium nepalense*

2007. Orchids. Multicoloured.

896	10r. Type **436**	85	70
897	10r. *Dendrobium heterocarpum*	85	70
898	10r. *Pelatantheria insectifera*	85	70
899	10r. *Coelogyne ovalis*	85	70
900	10r. *Coelogyne cristata*	85	70
901	10r. *Dendrobium chrysanthum*	85	70
902	10r. *Phaleneopsis mannii*	85	70
903	10r. *Dendrobium densiflorum*	85	70
904	10r. *Esmeralda clarkei*	85	70
905	10r. *Acampe rigida*	85	70
906	10r. *Bulbophyllum leopardinum*	85	70
907	10r. *Dendrobium fimbriatum*	85	70
908	10r. *Arundina graminifolia*	85	70
909	10r. *Dendrobium moschatum*	85	70
910	10r. *Rhynchostylis retusa*	85	70
911	10r. *Cymbidium devonianum*	85	70

437 Competitors

2007. Taekwondo.

912	**437**	5r. multicoloured	50	45

438 Batsman and Fielders

2007. Cricket.

913	**438**	5r. multicoloured	50	45

439 Setu BK

2007. Democratic Movement (Jana Aandolan) Martyrs. Multicoloured.

914	2r. Type **439**	35	30
915	2r. Tulasi Chhetri	35	30
916	2r. Anil Lama	35	30
917	2r. Umesh Chandra Thapa	35	30
918	2r. Chakraraj Joshi	35	30
919	2r. Chandra Bayalkoti	35	30
920	2r. Devilal Poudel	35	30
921	2r. Govindanath Sharma	35	30
922	2r. Hari Raj Adhikari	35	30
923	2r. Horilal Rana Tharu	35	30
924	2r. Lai Bahadur Bista	35	30
925	2r. Mohamad Jahangir	35	30
926	2r. Pradhumna Khadka	35	30
927	2r. Rajan Giri	35	30
928	2r. Suraj Bishwas	35	30
929	2r. Sagun Tamrakar	35	30
930	2r. Bhimsen Dahal	35	30
931	2r. Shivahari Kunwar	35	30
932	2r. Basudev Ghimire	35	30
933	2r. Bishnu Prasad Panday	35	30
934	2r. Yamlal Lamichhane	35	30
935	2r. Deepak Kami	35	30
936	2r. Darshanlal Yadab	35	30
937	2r. Tahir Hussain Ansari	35	30
938	2r. Hiralal Gautam	35	30

440 Symbols of Nepal and Sri Lanka

2007. 50th Anniv of Nepal–Sri Lanka Diplomatic Relations.

939	**440**	5r. multicoloured	50	45

441 Symbols of Nepal and Egypt

2007. 50th Anniv of Nepal–Egypt Diplomatic Relations.

940	**441**	5r. multicoloured	50	45

441a Robert Baden-Powell (founder) and Baden-Powell Scout Peak (Urkema mountain)

2007. Centenary of Scouting.

941	**441a**	2r. multicoloured	35	30

442 Emblem

2007. 25th Anniv of Cancer Relief Society.

942	**442**	1r. multicoloured	35	30

443 House of Parliament

2007. Re-instatement of Parliament. Multicoloured.

943	1r. Type **443**	35	30
944	1r. Building and document 'Interim Constitution of Nepal'	35	30
945	1r. As Type **443** but inscr 'The re-instatement of The House of Representatives'	35	30
946	1r. As No. 944 but different document inscr 'The Proclamation of The House of Representatives'	35	30

444 Chaya Devi Parajuli

2007. Chaya Devi Parajuli (activist) Commem.

947	**444**	2r. multicoloured	35	30

445 Mount Abi

2007. Tourism. Multicoloured.

948	5r. Type **445**	50	45
949	5r. Shree Bhageshwor, Dadeldhura	50	45
950	5r. Shree Shaillya Malikarjun, Darchula	50	45
951	5r. Shiddhakali, Bhojpur	50	45
952	5r. Buddha (victory over the mali of Siddhartha Gautam)	50	45

446 Shree Govindananda Bharati (Shivapuri Baba) (Hindi saint)

2007. Personalities. Multicoloured.

953	5r. Type **446**	50	45
954	5r. Mahesh Chandra Regmi (historian)	50	45
955	5r. Bhrikuti Devi (first wife of Songtsan Gampo (emperor of Tibet)) (statue)	50	45
956	5r. Pt. Udayananda Arijyal (writer)	50	45
957	5r. Ganesh Lal Shrestha (musician)	50	45
958	5r. Tara Devi (singer)	50	45

447 Dattatreya Temple, Bhaktapur, Nepal and Cologne Cathedral, Germany

2008. 50th Anniv of Nepal–Germany Diplomatic Relations.

959	**447**	25r. multicoloured	2·00	1·70

448 Buddha's Birth at Lumbini

2008

960	**448**	2r. multicoloured	35	30

449 National Arms

2008

961	**449**	1r. multicoloured	35	30

450 Athletes and Emblem

2008. Olympic Games, Beijing.

962	**450**	15r. multicoloured	1·50	1·30

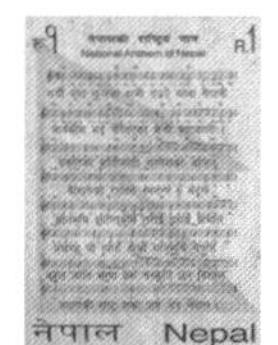

451 Script

2008. National Anthem.

963	**451**	1r. multicoloured	35	30

452 Interior

2008. Centenary of Kaiser Library.

964	**452**	5r. multicoloured	50	45

453 Harka Gurung and Mountain

2008. Renaming of Mt. Nagdi Chuli to Mt. Harka Gurung Chuli.

965	**453**	5r. multicoloured	50	45

454 *Rauvolfia serpentina*

2008. Bio-Diversity. Multicoloured.

966	5r. Type **454**	50	45
967	5r. *Demonax bicincta*	50	45
968	5r. *Russula chloroides*	50	45
969	5r. *Varanus flavescens*	50	45

455 Mustang Village

2008. Tourism. Multicoloured.

970	5r. Type **455**	50	45
971	5r. Syarpu Lake	50	45
972	5r. Jal Jala Hill	50	45
973	5r. Pindeshwor Babadham Shrine	50	45
974	5r. Shree Kumari Chariot Festival	50	45

456 Emblems

2009. 50th Anniv of National Family Planning Association.

975	**456**	1r. multicoloured	35	30

457 Emblem and University Building

2009. 50th Anniv of Tribhuvan University.

976	**457**	5r. multicoloured	50	45

458 Emblem and Book of Records

2009. 50th Anniv of Auditor General's Office.

977	**458**	5r. multicoloured	50	45

459 Marker Stone and Nativity Sculpture

2009. World Heritage Site. Buddha's Birthplace, Lumbini. Multicoloured.

978	10r. Type **459**	1·00	85
979	10r. Puskarini (holy pond)	1·00	85
980	10r. Ashokan Pillar	1·00	85
981	10r. Ruins of stupas and viharas	1·00	85
982	10r. Mayadevi Temple	1·00	85

460 Map of Nepal containing Flag and Arms

2009. Federal Democratic Republic.

983	**460**	2r. multicoloured	35	30

461 *Parnassius hardwickei*

2009. Butterflies. Multicoloured.

984	10r. Type **461**	1·00	85
985	10r. *Euploea mulciber*	1·00	85
986	10r. *Papilio machaon*	1·00	85
987	10r. *Polyura athamus*	1·00	85
988	10r. *Aulocera swaha* (inscr '*Aulocera padma*')	1·00	85
989	10r. *Pieris brassicae nepalensis*	1·00	85
990	10r. *Danaus genutia*	1·00	85
991	10r. *Gonepteryx rhammni*	1·00	85
992	10r. *Ixias pyrene*	1·00	85
993	10r. *Graphium cloanthus* (inscr '*Idaides cloanthus*')	1·00	85
994	10r. *Parnassius acdestis*	1·00	85
995	10r. *Kaniska canace*	1·00	85
996	10r. *Papilio demoleus*	1·00	85
997	10r. *Menelaides helenus*	1·00	85
998	10r. *Pathysa nomius* (inscr '*Deoris nomius*')	1·00	85
999	10r. *Heliophorus androcles*	1·00	85

462 Govinda Biyogi

2009. 80th Birth Anniv of Govinda Biyogi (journalist).

1000	**462**	5r. multicoloured	50	45

463 Guru Mangal Das

2009. Guru Mangal Das (religious philanthropist and writer) Commemoration.

1001	**463**	5r. multicoloured	50	45

464 Tej Bahadur Chitrakar

2009. Tej Bahadur Chitrakar (artist) Commemoration.. Multicoloured.

1002	5r. Type **464**	50	45
1003	5r. *Tribute to Forefathers*	50	45

465 Rameshwor Sharma Chalise

2009. Rameshwor Sharma Chalise (Ramesh Vikal) (writer) Commemoration.

1004	**465**	2r. multicoloured	35	30

466 Krishna Sen

2009. Krishna Sen (Ichhuk) (writer) Commemoration.

1006	**466**	5r. multicoloured	50	45

467 L. P. Devkota

2009. Birth Centenary of Laxmi Prasad Devkota (writer)

1006	**467**	1r. multicoloured	35	30

468 Lahurya Folk Dance

2009. Cultural Heritage. Multicoloured.

1007	5r. Type **468**	50	45
1008	5r. Chhath Festival	50	45

469 Mountain Biking

2009. Sport. Multicoloured.

1009	10r. Type **469**	1·00	85
1010	10r. Kayaking	1·00	85

470 Stupa

2010. 25th Anniv of Television Broadcasting

1011	**470**	2r. multicoloured	35	30

471 Tiger

2010. Chinese New Year

1012	**471**	5r. multicoloured	50	45

472 Pemba Doma Sherpa

2010. 40th Birth Anniv of Pemba Doma Sherpa (mountaineer)

1013	**472**	25r. multicoloured	2·00	1·70

473 Mountain Peak

2010. 50th Anniv of First Ascent of Mt. Dhaulagiri

1014	**473**	25r. multicoloured	2·00	1·70

474 Temple Entrance and Ganesh

2010. Maru Ganesh Shrine, Kathmandu

1015	**474**	2r. multicoloured	35	30

475 Kankalini Mai and Temple Building

2010. Kankalini Mai Temple of Bhardah, Saptari

1016	**475**	2r. multicoloured	35	30

476 Bhairav Aryal

2010. Bhairav Aryal (writer) Commemoration

1017	**476**	5r. multicoloured	50	45

477 Nati Kaji Shrestha

2010. Nati Kaji Shrestha (musician and singer) Commemoration

1018	**477**	5r. multicoloured	50	45

478 Jibraj Ashrit

2010. Jibraj Ashrit (politician) Commemoration

1019	**478**	5r. multicoloured	50	45

479 Bhikkchu Amritananda

2010. 20th Death Anniv of Bhikkchu Amritananda (Buddhist monk)

1020	**479**	5r. multicoloured	50	45

480 Bhagat Sarbjit Bishwakarma (inscr 'Bhagat Sarbajit Biswokarma')

2010. Bhagat Sarbjit Bishwakarma (social reformer) Commemoration

1021	**480**	5r. multicoloured	50	45

481 Sadhana Adhikari

2010. Sadhana Adhikari (politician) Commemoration

1022	**481**	5r. multicoloured	50	45

482 Mai Pokhari

2010. Mai Pokhari, Illam (ponds and place of pilgrimage)

1023	**482**	2r. multicoloured	35	30

483 Washing Hands

2010. Hand Washing and Health Campaign

1024	**483**	2r. multicoloured	35	30

484 'NEPAL TOURISM YEAR' and '2011'

2010. 2011–Nepal Tourism Year

1025	**484**	5r. multicoloured	50	45

Nos. 1026/7 and Type **485** are left for Cricket World Cup, issued on 2 april 2011, not yet received.

No. 1028 and Type **486** are left for Mount Everest Day, issued on 29 May 2011, not yet received.

487 Kathmandu, 1881

2011. Native Postmarks of Nepal. Multicoloured.

1029	1r. Type **487**	20	15
1030	1r. Birgani, 1910	20	15
1031	2r. Kanchanpur, 1934	35	30
1032	2r. Bethani, 1915	35	30
1033	3r. Tamghas, Gulmi, 1952	40	35

488 Ganges Softshell Turtle (*Aspideretes gangeticus*)

2011. Turtles and Tortoise. Multicoloured.

1034	10r. Type **488**	1·00	85
1035	10r. Elongated tortoise (*Indorestudo elongata*)	1·00	85
1036	10r. Tricarinate hill turtle (*Melanochelys tricarinata*)	1·00	85
1037	10r. Common roofed turtle (*Pangshura tecta*) (inscr 'Pangshura tectum')	1·00	85

489 Mohan Gopal Khetan

2011. Mohan Gopal Khetan (industrialist) Commemoration

1038	**489**	5r. multicoloured	50	45

490 Ekdav Aale

2011. Personalities

1039	10r. Type **490** (politician)	1·00	85
1040	10r. Yagyaraj Sharma Ariyal (musician) (horiz)	1·00	85
1041	10r. Motidevi Shrestha (politician)	1·00	85
1042	10r. Shankar Lamichhane (writer)	1·00	85

No. 1043 and Type **491** are left for Rishikesh Shaha, not yet received.

492 Badmalika, Bajura

2011. Religious Sites. Multicoloured.

1044	1r. Type **492**	20	15
1045	2r. Bhat Bhateni Mai, Kathmandu	35	30
1046	2r. Tansen Bhagawati, Palpa	35	30
1047	2r. Siddha Ratannath Temple, Dang	35	30
1048	2r. Deuti Bajai, Surkhet	35	30
1049	2r. Shree Arryavalokiteswora, Seto Machhindranath, Kathmandu (vert)	35	30
1050	2r. Seto Machhindranath, Kathmandu (vert)	35	30
1051	5r. Gajurmukhi Dham, Ilam	50	45
1052	5r. Shree Baidhyanath Temple, Achham	50	45
1053	25r. Yetser Jangchubling Monastery, Upper Dolpa	2·50	2·00

493 Panch Pokhari, Sindhupalchok

2011. Tourism. Landscapes. Multicoloured.

1054	10r. Type **493**	1·00	85
1055	10r. Badaiya Taal, Bardiya	1·00	85
1056	10r. Mt Mera Peak	1·00	85

494 Phodaling Cave, Upper Mustang

2011. Mural Paintings, Phodaling Cave, Upper Mustang. Multicoloured.

1057	10r. Type **494**	1·00	85
1058	10r. Flute player	1·00	85
1059	10r. Male figure	1·00	85
1060	10r. Budhist deity	1·00	85

Nos. 1061/2 and Type **495** are left for Personalities, not yet received.

496 Girja Prasad Koirala

2012. Girja Prasad Koirala (Prime Minister) Commemoration

1063	**496**	10r. multicoloured	1·00	85

497 Anniversary Emblem

2012. 50th Anniv of National News Agency (RSS)

1064	**497**	10r. multicoloured	1·00	85

498 Anniversary Emblem

2012. 60th Anniv (2011) of Nepali Shikshya Parishad (language and literature initiative)

1065	**498**	5r. new blue and ultramarine	50	45

499 *Delphinium himalayai*

2012. Biodiversity. Multicoloured.

1066		10r. Type **499**	1·00	85
1067		10r. *Dendrobium eriiflorum*	1·00	85
1068		10r. *Podophyllum hexandrum*	1·00	85
1069		10r. *Ganoderma lucidum*	1·00	85
1070		10r. *Prinia burnesii nepalicola* (Nepal Rufous-vented Prinia)	1·00	85
1071		10r. *Gyps bengalensis* (White-rumped vulture)	1·00	85
1072		10r. *Caprolagus hispidus* (Hispid Hare)	1·00	85
1073		10r. *Cyrtopodion markuscombaii* (Comba's Gecko)	1·00	85

500 Mount Everest and Dead Sea

2012. Highest and Lowest Places on Earth.

1074	**500**	35r. multicoloured	3·50	3·00
MS1075		79×123 mm. 50r. As Type **500**	5·00	4·75

501 Museum Building

2012. B P Museum, Sundarijal, Kathmandu

1076	**501**	10r. multicoloured	1·00	85

502 Eye

2012. Lions Club Blindness Prevention Campaign

1077	**502**	5r. multicoloured	50	45

503 AIDS Ribbon

2012. World AIDS Day

1078	**503**	5r. multicoloured	50	45

504 Mt Everest and Emblem

2012. Mt Everest. Nepal Civil Service Employee's First Mt. Everest Expedition 2011

1079	**504**	10r. multicoloured	1·00	85

505 Anniversary Emblem

2012. 50th Anniv of Asian - Pacific Postal Union

1080	**505**	35r. multicoloured	3·50	3·00

506 Krishna Prasad Bhattarai

2012. Krishna Prasad Bhattarai (Prime Minister) Commemoration

1081	**506**	10r. multicoloured	1·00	85

507 Group Meeting and Emblem

2012. International Year of Cooperatives

1082	**507**	20r. multicoloured	2·00	1·75

508 Elephant Football

2012. Sports

1083		25r. Type **508**	2·50	2·00
1084		25r. Bungee jumping (vert)	2·50	2·00

509 Bhikshu Sudarshan (monk)

2012. Personalities. Multicoloured.

1085		5r. Type **509**	50	45
1086		5r. Basudev Luintel (writer)	50	45
1087		10r. Ali Miyan (writer)	1·00	85
1088		10r. Ramniwas Pandeya (educator)	1·00	85
1089		10r. Bhuvaneswor Patheya (writer)	1·00	85
1090		10r. Khagendra Bahadur Basnet (disabled rights activist)	1·00	85
1091		10r. Kishore and Kumar Narsingh Rama (architects)	1·00	85
1092		10r. Karuna and Lupau Ratna Tuladhar (first public bus service operators)	1·00	85

510 Monastery of World Peace

2012. Visit Lumbini (Birth Place of Buddha) Year

1093	**510**	20r. multicoloured	2·00	1·75

511 Portrait and Antelopes

2012. Raj Man Singh Chitraker (artist) Commemoration. Multicoloured.

1094		10r. Type **511**	1·00	85
1095		10r. Portrait and birds	1·00	85

512 Pandit Ramakanta Jha

2013. Pandit Ramakanta Jha (politician) Commemoration

1096	**512**	10r. brownish black	1·00	85

513 Bridge and Emblems

2013. 50th Anniv of Nepal - World Bank Partnership

1097	**513**	10r. multicoloured	1·00	85

514 Melwa Devi Gurung and Disc

2013. Melwa Devi Gurung (singer) Commemoration

1098	**514**	5r. multicoloured	50	45

515 Salpa Pokhari, Bholpur

2013. Tourism. Multicoloured.

1099		10r. Type **515**	1·00	85
1100		10r. Lomanthang Durbar	1·00	85
1101		10r. Lok Nayak Raja Salhes, Salhes Gardens	1·00	85
1102		10r. Sahashra Dhara Jatra Festival, Dolakha (vert)	1·00	85

516 Ramaja Prasad Singh (politician)

2013. Personalities. Multicoloured.

1103		10r. Type **516**	1·00	85
1104		10r. Moti Kaji Shakya (sculptor)	1·00	85
1105		10r. Bhimbahadur Tamang (politician)	1·00	85
1106		10r. Basudev Prasad Dhungana (senior advocate)	1·00	85
1107		10r. Harihar Gautam (social worker) (vert)	1·00	85
1108		10r. Gopal Pande 'Aseem (writer) (vert)	1·00	85

517 Anniversary Emblem

2013. 50th Anniv of Nepalese Red Cross Society

1109	**517**	50r. multicoloured	5·00	4·75

518 Batsaladevi Bhagawati

2013. Batsaladevi Bhagawati, Dhadhing

1110	**518**	1r. multicoloured	20	15

519 Rupchandra Bista (politician)

2013. Personalities. Multicoloured.

1111		5r. Type **519**	50	45
1112		5r. Kewalpure Kisan (writer)	50	45
1113		10r. Rupak Raj Sharma (footballer)	1·00	85
1114		10r. Ram Sharan Darnal (music researcher)	1·00	85
1115		20r. Diamond Shumsher Rana (writer)	2·00	1·75

520 Rajdevi Temple, Saptari

2013. Tourism. Multicoloured.

1116		1r. Type **520**	20	15
1117		1r. Bagalamukhi Devi, Lalitpur (vert)	20	15
1118		5r. Argha Bhagwati, Arghkhanchi	50	45
1119		5r. Ivory window, Hanumandhoka Palace, Kathmandu	50	45
1120		5r. Kakre Bihar, Surkhet	50	45
1121		40r. RaraLake, Muga	4·25	4·00

521 Ramhari Sharma (nationalist)

2013. Personalities. Multicoloured.

1122		3r. Type **521**	40	35
1123		3r. Shankar Koirala (politician)	40	35
1124		10r. Dilliraman Regmi (historian and politician) (horiz)	1·00	85
1125		10r. Bhanubhakta Acharya (writer)	1·00	85

522 Patan Museum

2013. Tourism. Museums. Multicoloured.

1126		20r. Type **522**	2·00	1·75
1127		20r. National Art Museum, Bhaktapur	2·00	1·75
1128		20r. International Mountain Museum, Kaski	2·00	1·75
1129		35r. National Museum, Chhauni	3·50	3·00

523 Bauddhanath Monument

2013. UNESCO World Heritage Site. Multicoloured.

1130		25r. Type **523**	2·50	2·00
1131		25r. Changu Narayan Monument	2·50	2·00
1132		25r. Bhaktapur Durbar Square	2·50	2·00
1133		30r. Swayambhu Monument	3·00	2·75
1134		30r. Hanumandhoks Durbar Square	3·00	2·75
1135		30r. Pashupati Monument	3·00	2·75
1136		30r. Patan Durbar Square	3·00	2·75

524 *Piper longum*

2013. Flora. Multicoloured.

1137		40r. Type **524**	4·25	4·00
1138		40r. *Swertia chirayita*	4·25	4·00
1139		40r. *Asparagus racemosus*	4·25	4·00
1140		40r. *Gaulthera fragrantissima*	4·25	4·00

525 Giraffa punjabiensis

2013. Fossils. Multicoloured.

1141		50r. Type **525**	5·00	4·75
1142		50r. Archidiskidon planifrons	5·00	4·75
1143		50r. Hexaprotodon sivalensis	5·00	4·75
1144		50r. Ramapithecus sivalensis	5·00	4·75

526 Mount Everest

2013. 60th Anniv of Ascent of Mount Everest.

1145	**526**	100r. multicoloured	8·50	8·00

527 Rishkesh Temple, Ridi

2014. Tourism. Multicoloured.

1146	5r. Type **527**	50	45
1147	20r. Narayanhiti Palace Museum	2·00	1·75
1148	50r. Manakamana Cable Car	5·00	4·75

528 Emblem

2014. 60th Anniv of Nepal Scouts.

1149	**528**	30r. multicoloured	3·00	2·75

529 Mount Cho-Oyu

2014. 60th Anniv of Ascent of Mount Cho-Oyu.

1150	**529**	100r. multicoloured	8·50	8·00

530 Skiers

2014. Winter Olympic Games, Sochi.

1151	**530**	2r. multicoloured	35	30

531 Emblem

2014. 50th Anniv of JCI Kathmandu Nepal (Kathmandu Jaycees) (Worldwide Federation of Young Leaders and Entrepreneurs).

1152	**531**	10r. multicoloured	1·00	85

532 Aadeshwor Mahadev, Kathmandu

2014. Tourism. Multicoloured.

1153	1r. Type **532**	20	15
1154	1r. Shivaparbati Temple, Kathmandu	20	15
1155	1r. Natural History Museum, Kathmandu	20	15
1156	2r. Kumari Ghar, Basantpur, Kathmandu	35	30
1157	4r. Koteshwor Mahadev, Kathmandu	45	40

533 Batsman

2014. ICC World Twenty20, Bangladesh.

1158	**533**	2r. multicoloured	35	30

534 National Health Women Volunteer

2014. 25th Anniv (2013) of FCHV Programme.

1159	**534**	3r. multicoloured	40	35

535 Prem Bahadur Kansakar

2014. Prem Bahadur Kansakar (democracy and linguistic rights campaigner) Commemoration.

1160	**535**	5r. multicoloured	50	45

536 Paraglider

2014. Sports.

1161	**536**	10r. multicoloured	1·00	85

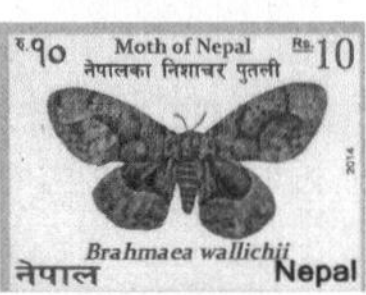

537 *Brahmaea wallichii*

2014. Moths. Multicoloured.

MS1164	10r.×4, *Acherontia lachesis; Asota producta; Argina argus; Biston contectaria*	4·50	4·50
MS1162	10r.×4, Type **537**; *Campylotes histrionicus; Dermaleipa juno; Episteme adulatrix*	4·50	4·50
MS1163	10r.×4, *Erasmia pulchella; Eterrusia aedea; Eudocima salaminia; Gynautocera papilionaria*	4·50	4·50

538 Birthplace of Buddha, Lumbini

2014. Birthplace of Buddha. Multicoloured.

MS1165	20r.×4, Type **538**; Ashoka Pillar; Ramagrama, Nawalparasi; Tilaurakpot, Kapilavastu	8·00	8·00

539 Competitors

2014. 18th Tenzing-Hillary Everest Marathon.

1166	**539**	3r. multicoloured	40	35

540 Bishweshwar Prasad Koirala

2014. Birth Centenary of Bishweshwar Prasad Koirala (politician).

1167	**540**	10r. multicoloured	1·00	85

541 Dwarika Bhakta Mathema

2015. Dwarika Bhakta Mathema (musician) Commemoration.

1168	**541**	1r. multicoloured	20	15

542 Chandeswori Temple, Banepa

2015. Tourism. Multicoloured.

1169	1r. Type **542**	20	15
1170	1r. Makwanpur Gadhi Fort, Makwanpur	20	15
1171	2r. Lamjung Durbar, Lamjung	35	30
1172	2r. Siddha Pokhari, Bhaktapur	35	30
1173	5r. Doleshwor Mahadev, Bhaktapur	50	45
1174	5r. Sindhuli Gadhi Fort, Sindhuli	50	45
1175	8r. Mohankali Dhungedhara, Hanumandhoka	75	50
1176	10r. Bulbule Lake, Surkhet	1·00	85
1177	10r. Taleju Temple, Nuwakot	1·00	85

543 Kaliyadaman, Hanumandhoka

2015. Cultural Heritage. Kaliyadaman, Hanumandhoka.

1178	**543**	5r. multicoloured	50	45

544 Roads and Terraces

2015. Nepal-Japan Co-operation. B P Koirala Highway. Multicoloured.

1179	10r. Type **544**	1·00	85
1180	10r. Road and river	1·00	85
1181	10r. Two roads on forested hillside	1·00	85
1182	10r. Jeep travelling over viaduct	1·00	85

545 Fewa Lake and Machhapuchchhre, Kaski

2015. Tourism.

1183	**545**	60r. multicoloured	5·25	5·00

546 Deinotherium indicum

2015. Pre-historic Elephants. Multicoloured.

1184	10r. Type **546**	1·00	85
1185	10r. Stegodon ganesa	1·00	85
1186	10r. Elephas namadicus	1·00	85
1187	10r. Comphotherium	1·00	85
1188	10r. Stegadon bombifrons	1·00	85
1189	10r. Elephas hysudricus	1·00	85

547 Flags and Mountains

2015. 50th Anniv of Nepal-China Diplomatic Relations.

1190	**547**	20r. multicoloured	2·00	1·75

548 Sunlight on Mountains

2015. 60th Anniv of First Successful Ascent of Mt. Kanchenjunga and Mt. Makalu. Multicoloured.

MS1191	10r.×6, Type **548**; Mount Makalu; Flight over mountains (left); Flight over mountains (right); Hilary Peak; Tenzing Peak	5·50	5·50

549 Nautale Durbar

2015. UNESCO World Heritage Site. Durbar Square Area, Hanumandhoka. Multicoloured.

1192	10r. Type **549**	1·00	85
1193	10r. Narashimha (vert)	1·00	85
1194	35r. Gaddhi Baithak	3·50	3·00

550 Rani Mahal, Palpa

2015. Architecture - Rani Mahal, Palpa.

1195	**550**	25r. multicoloured	2·50	2·00

551 Dove of Peace

2015. Nonviolence, Harmony, Morality and Non-Addiction.

1196	**551**	25r. multicoloured	2·50	2·00

552 Koshi Tappu Wildlife Reserve

2015. National Parks and Wildlife Reserves. Multicoloured.

1197	1r. Type **552**	20	15
1198	2r. Chitwan National Park	35	30
1199	2r. Sagarmatha National Park	35	30
1200	5r. Lamtang National Park	50	45
1201	5r. Shuklaphanta Wildlife Reserve	50	45

553 *Paris polyphylla*

2015. Flora. Multicoloured.

1202	10r. Type **553**	1·00	85
1203	10r. *Maharanga emodi*	1·00	85
1204	10r. *Abies spectabilis*	1·00	85
1205	10r. *Lilium nepalense*	1·00	85
1206	10r. *Gentiana robusta*	1·00	85
1207	10r. *Saussurea gossipiphora*	1·00	85

554 Sarbeshwor Mahadev, Lalitpur

2015. Tourism.

1208	**554**	3r. multicoloured	40	35

555 Survival Advice

2015. Earthquake Emergency.

1209	**555**	5r. multicoloured	50	45

556 Nagendra Prasad Rijal

2015. Personalities. Multicoloured.

1210	8r. Type **556**	85	75
1211	8r. Deviprasad Uprety	85	75
1212	8r. Yadav Prasad Pant	85	75
1213	8r. Siddhi Charan Shrestha (vert)	85	75
1214	8r. Shreeprasad Parajuli	85	75
1215	8r. Ganeshman Singh	85	75

557 Emblem

2015. SAARC (South Asian Association for Regional Cooperation) Summit, Kathmandu.

1216	**557**	10r. multicoloured	10·85	

OFFICIAL STAMPS

O25 Nepalese Arms and Soldiers

1960. (a) Size 30×18 mm.

O135	**O25**	2p. brown	10	10
O136	**O25**	4p. green	15	10
O137	**O25**	6p. red	15	10
O138	**O25**	8p. violet	15	15
O139	**O25**	12p. orange	20	20

(b) Size 38×27 mm.

O140	**O25**	16p. brown	35	30
O141	**O25**	24p. red	50	45
O142	**O25**	32p. purple	60	60
O143	**O25**	50p. blue	1·10	1·00
O144	**O25**	1r. red	2·20	1·90
O145	**O25**	2r. orange	4·50	4·00

काज सरकारी

(O28)

1960. Optd as Type **O28**.

O146	**27**	1r. purple	90	

1961. Optd with Type **O28**.

O148	**35**	1p. red	15	15
O149	**35**	2p. blue	15	15
O150	**35**	5p. brown	20	20
O151	**36**	10p. purple	10	10
O152	**36**	40p. brown	15	15
O153	**36**	75p. green	20	20
O154	**27**	2r. red	60	60
O155	**27**	5r. green	1·60	1·60

NETHERLANDS

A kingdom in the N.W. of Europe on the North Sea.

1852. 100 cents = 1 gulden (florin).
2002. 100 cents = 1 euro.

1

1852. Imperf.

1	**1**	5c. blue	£700	55·00
2	**1**	10c. red	£700	44·00
3b	**1**	15c. orange	£1400	£225

3 King William III

1864. Perf.

8	**3**	5c. blue	£450	25·00
9	**3**	10c. red	£650	12·50
10	**3**	15c. orange	£1600	£140

4

1867

17b	**4**	5c. blue	£225	4·50
18c	**4**	10c. red	£325	4·75
19c	**4**	15c. brown	£1200	47·00
20	**4**	20c. green	£1200	36·00
15	**4**	25c. purple	£3500	£150
16	**4**	50c. gold	£3750	£250

5

1869

58	**5**	½c. brown	44·00	5·25
53	**5**	1c. black	£350	£110
59	**5**	1c. green	38·00	3·75
55a	**5**	1½c. red	£225	£120
56	**5**	2c. yellow	90·00	22·00
62	**5**	2½c. mauve	£800	£110

6

1872

80	**6**	5c. blue	50·00	2·50
81	**6**	7½c. brown	£100	28·00
100	**6**	10c. red	£180	2·50
83	**6**	12½c. grey	£190	3·75
102	**6**	15c. brown	£750	8·50
85	**6**	20c. green	£900	8·75
86	**6**	22½c. green	£225	70·00
87	**6**	25c. lilac	£1100	6·25
97	**6**	50c. bistre	£1300	18·00
90	**6**	1g. violet	£950	65·00
75	-	2g.50 blue and red	£1500	£180

No. 75 is similar to Type **6** but larger and with value and country scrolls transposed.

8

1876

133	**8**	½c. red	5·00	40
134	**8**	1c. green	12·50	40
137	**8**	2c. yellow	50·00	4·50
139	**8**	2½c. mauve	23·00	50

9 Queen Wilhelmina

1891

147a	**9**	3c. orange	16·00	3·50
148a	**9**	5c. blue	9·50	40
149b	**9**	7½c. brown	33·00	12·50
150b	**9**	10c. red	47·00	2·50
151b	**9**	12½c. grey	47·00	2·50
152a	**9**	15c. brown	£110	8·75
153b	**9**	20c. green	£130	5·00
154a	**9**	22½c. green	65·00	22·00
155	**9**	25c. mauve	£190	9·75
156a	**9**	50c. bistre	£950	31·00
159	-	50c. brown and green	£180	25·00
157	**9**	1g. violet	£1100	£120
160	-	1g. green and brown	£325	38·00
161	-	2g.50 blue and red	£700	£225
165	-	5g. red and green	£1200	£700

Nos. 159, 160, 161 and 165 are as Type **9** but larger and with value and country scrolls transposed.

11

12

13

1898. Nos. 174 and 176 also exist imperf.

167	**12**	½c. lilac	75	40
168	**12**	1c. red	1·50	30
170	**12**	1½c. blue	4·50	50
171	**12**	2c. brown	6·25	40
172	**12**	2½c. green	5·00	40
173	**13**	3c. orange	27·00	5·75
174	**13**	3c. green	1·90	40
175	**13**	4c. purple	3·50	1·90
176	**13**	4½c. mauve	5·25	5·25
177	**13**	5c. red	2·40	40
178	**13**	7½c. brown	1·10	40
179	**13**	10c. grey	10·00	40
180	**13**	12½c. blue	5·25	50
181	**13**	15c. brown	£180	5·75
182	**13**	15c. red and blue	9·50	40
183	**13**	17½c. mauve	80·00	20·00
184	**13**	17½c. brown and blue	25·00	1·50
185	**13**	20c. green	£250	1·30
186	**13**	20c. grey and green	16·00	90
187	**13**	22½c. green and brown	15·00	1·00
188	**13**	25c. blue and pink	15·00	75
189	**13**	30c. purple and mauve	39·00	90
190	**13**	40c. orange and green	55·00	1·90
191	**13**	50c. red and green	£190	1·90
192	**13**	50c. violet and grey	£100	1·90
193	**13**	60c. green and olive	55·00	1·90
194b	**11**	1g. green	85·00	1·30
195c	**11**	2½g. lilac	£140	4·50
196b	**11**	5g. red	£325	10·00
197	**11**	10g. red	£1200	£1000

14

1906. Society for the Prevention of Tuberculosis.

208	**14**	1c. (+1c.) red	34·00	19·00
209	**14**	3c. (+3c.) green	55·00	44·00
210	**14**	5c. (+5c.) violet	55·00	25·00

15 Admiral M. A. de Ruyter

1907. Birth Tercentenary of Admiral de Ruyter.

211	**15**	½c. blue	3·25	2·20
212	**15**	1c. red	5·75	3·75
213	**15**	2½c. red	9·75	3·75

16 William I

1913. Independence Centenary.

214	**16**	2½c. green on green	1·90	1·30
215	-	3c. yellow on cream	3·25	2·50
216	-	5c. red on buff	2·50	1·30
217	-	10c. grey	6·25	5·00
218	**16**	12½c. blue on blue	5·00	3·75
219	-	20c. brown	19·00	19·00
220	-	25c. blue	24·00	12·50
221	-	50c. green	50·00	50·00
222	**16**	1g. red	90·00	31·00
223	-	2½g. lilac	£180	65·00
224	-	5g. yellow on cream	£375	55·00
225	-	10g. orange	£1200	£1100

Designs:—3c., 20c., 2½g. William II; 5c., 25c., 5g. William III; 10c., 50c., 10g. Queen Wilhelmina.

1919. Surch Veertig Cent (40c.) or Zestig Cent (60c.).

234	**13**	40c. on 30c. purple & mve	44·00	8·75
235	**13**	60c. on 30c. purple & mve	44·00	8·75

1920. Surch in figures.

236	**11**	2.50 on 10g. red	£225	£170
237	-	2.50 on 10g. red (No. 225)	£225	£170
238	**13**	4c. on 4½c. mauve	6·25	2·50

23

1921. Air.

239	**23**	10c. red	3·75	1·90
240	**23**	15c. green	10·00	3·25
241	**23**	60c. blue	35·00	65

24

1921

242	**24**	5c. green	19·00	40
243	**24**	12½c. red	31·00	3·00
244	**24**	20c. blue	49·00	40

25 Lion in Dutch Garden and Orange Tree (emblematic of Netherlands)

26

27

1923

248	**25**	1c. violet	90	90
249	**25**	2c. orange	8·50	40
250	**26**	2½c. green	2·50	1·00
251	**27**	4c. blue	2·00	90

1923. Surch.

252	**12**	2c. on 1c. red	80	40
253	**12**	2c. on 1½c. blue	80	50
254	**13**	10c. on 3c. green	7·25	40
255	**13**	10c. on 5c. red	14·00	90
256	**13**	10c. on 12½c. blue	11·50	1·30
257a	**13**	10c. on 17½c. brown & blue	4·75	5·25
258a	**13**	10c. on 22½c. olive & brown	4·75	5·25

30

31

1923. 25th Anniv of Queen's Accession.

259b	**31**	2c. green	35	40
260a	**30**	5c. green	65	50
261b	**31**	7½c. red	1·00	50
262b	**31**	10c. red	65	40
263	**31**	20c. blue	6·50	1·70
264a	**31**	25c. yellow	13·00	2·50
265	**31**	35c. orange	9·00	5·25
266a	**31**	50c. black	26·00	2·00
267	**30**	1g. red	50·00	13·00
268	**30**	2½g. black	£325	£350
269	**30**	5g. blue	£300	£300

1923. Surch **DIENST ZEGEL PORTEN AAN TEEKEN RECHT** and value.

270	**13**	10c. on 3c. green	2·00	2·00
271	**13**	1g. on 17½c. brown & blue	£110	33·00

33

1923. Culture Fund.

272 **33** 2c. (+5c.) blue on pink 29·00 33·00
273 - 10c. (+5c.) red on pink 29·00 33·00

Design:—10c. Two women.

35 Carrier Pigeon

36 Queen Wilhelmina

1924

304C **35** ½c. grey 65 65
305A **35** 1c. red 40 25
306C **35** 1½c. mauve 65 65
424a **35** 1½c. grey 40 25
425 **35** 2c. orange 40 25
426a **35** 2½c. green 3·00 40
427 **35** 3c. green 40 25
427a **35** 4c. blue 40 25
428 **36** 5c. green 40 25
429 **36** 6c. brown 40 15
279A **36** 7½c. yellow 65 40
313A **36** 7½c. violet 5·25 25
314A **36** 7½c. red 50 25
279cA **36** 9c. red and black 2·50 2·00
281A **36** 10c. red 2·50 40
317A **36** 10c. blue 4·50 25
282A **36** 12½c. red 2·50 65
319A **36** 12½c. blue 65 25
320A **36** 15c. blue 11·50 40
321C **36** 15c. yellow 1·30 1·00
322C **36** 20c. blue 8·50 4·50
434 **36** 21c. brown 39·00 1·30
324B **36** 22½c. brown 10·50 4·00
434a **36** 22½c. orange 26·00 29·00
435 **36** 25c. green 6·50 40
326A **36** 27½c. grey 6·50 1·30
286cA **36** 35c. brown 60·00 16·00
437 **36** 30c. violet 9·00 65
437a **36** 40c. brown 20·00 40
330A **36** 50c. green 9·00 40
289A **36** 60c. violet 50·00 1·30
331A **36** 60c. black 46·00 1·70
301 **36** 1g. blue (23×29 mm) 13·00 1·30
302 **36** 2½g. red (23×29 mm) £160 9·00
303 **36** 5g. black (23×29 mm) £300 4·50

For further stamps in Type **35**, see Nos. 522/39 and 546/57.

1924. International Philatelic Exn, The Hague.

290 10c. green 65·00 65·00
291 15c. black 80·00 80·00
292 35c. red 65·00 65·00

37

38

1924. Dutch Lifeboat Centenary.

293 **37** 2c. brown 5·75 4·25
294 **38** 10c. brown on yellow 10·50 3·50

39

1924. Child Welfare.

295 **39** 2c. (+2c.) green 3·25 3·25
296 **39** 7½c. (+3½c.) brown 11·50 14·50
297 **39** 10c. (+2½c.) red 7·25 3·25

40 Arms of South Holland

1925. Child Welfare. Arms as T **40**.

298A - 2c. (+2c.) green and yellow 1·30 1·30
299A - 7½c. (+3½c.) violet and blue 6·50 7·75
300A **40** 10c. (+2½c.) red and yellow 5·25 65

Arms:—2c. North Brabant; 7½c. Gelderland.
See also Nos. 350/3A and 359/62A.

1926. Child Welfare. Arms as T **40**.

350A 2c. (+2c.) red and silver 1·30 65
351A 5c. (+3c.) green and blue 2·50 2·50
352A 10c. (+3c.) red and green 4·00 65
353A 15c. (+3c.) yellow and blue 11·50 10·50

Arms:—2c. Utrecht; 5c. Zeeland; 10c. North Holland; 15c. Friesland.

46 Queen Wilhelmina

47 Red Cross Allegory

1927. 60th Anniv of Dutch Red Cross Society.

354 **46** 2c. (+2c.) red 6·50 5·75
355 - 3c. (+2c.) green 13·00 16·00
356 - 5c. (+3c.) blue 2·50 2·50
357 - 7½c. (+3½c.) blue 8·50 3·25
358 **47** 15c. (+5c.) red and blue 18·00 18·00

Portraits:—2c. King William III; 3c. Queen Emma; 5c. Henry, Prince Consort.

1927. Child Welfare. Arms as T **40**.

359A 2c. (+2c.) red and lilac 1·30 1·30
360A 5c. (+3c.) green and yellow 2·50 2·50
361A 7½c. (+3½c.) red and black 6·50 65
362A 15c. (+3c.) blue and brown 9·00 8·50

Arms:—2c. Drente; 5c. Groningen; 7½c. Limburg; 15c. Overyssel.

48 Sculler

49 Footballer

1928. Olympic Games, Amsterdam.

363 **48** 1½c.+1c. green 5·25 5·25
364 - 2c.+1c. purple 5·25 6·50
365 **49** 3c.+1c. green 7·75 7·75
366 - 5c.+1c. blue 6·50 4·00
367 - 7½c.+2½c. orange 6·50 4·00
368 - 10c.+2c. red 11·50 9·00
369 - 15c.+2c. blue 16·00 9·00
370 - 30c.+3c. sepia 33·00 33·00

Designs:—Horiz: 2c. Fencing. Vert: 5c. Sailing; 7½c. Putting the shot; 10c. Running; 15c. Show-jumping; 30c. Boxing.

50 Lieut. Koppen

1928. Air.

371 **50** 40c. red 65 65
372 - 75c. green 65 65

Design:—75c. Van der Hoop.

52 J. P. Minckelers

1928. Child Welfare.

373 **52** 1½c.+1½c. violet 90 80
374 - 5c.+3c. green 3·00 1·30
375a - 7½c.+2½c. red 5·75 50
376a - 12½c.+3½c. blue 16·00 14·50

Portraits:—5c. Boerhaave; 7½c. H. A. Lorentz; 12½c. G. Huygens.

53 Mercury

1929. Air.

377 **53** 1½g. black 4·00 2·50
378 **53** 4½g. red 4·00 7·75
379 **53** 7½g. green 44·00 7·75

1929. Surch 21.

380 **36** 21c. on 22½c. brown 33·00 2·50

55 "Friendship and Security"

1929. Child Welfare.

381A **55** 1½c. (+1½c.) grey 3·50 90
382A **55** 5c. (+3c.) green 6·00 1·40
383A **55** 6c. (+4c.) red 3·50 65
384A **55** 12½c. (+3½c.) blue 20·00 20·00

56 Rembrandt and *De Staalmeesters*

1930. Rembrandt Society.

385 **56** 5c. (+5c.) green 11·50 11·50
386 **56** 6c. (+5c.) black 9·00 9·00
387 **56** 12½c. (+5c.) blue 18·00 18·00

57 Spring

1930. Child Welfare.

388A **57** 1½c. (+1½c.) red 2·50 90
389A - 5c. (+3c.) green 4·00 1·30
390A - 6c. (+4c.) purple 3·25 1·00
391A - 12½c. (+3½c.) blue 26·00 20·00

Designs:—(allegorical): 5c. Summer; 6c. Autumn; 12½c. Winter.

58

1931. Gouda Church Restoration Fund.

392 **58** 1½c.+1½c. green 30·00 29·00
393 - 6c.+4c. red 35·00 33·00

Design:—No. 393, Church facade.

59 Queen Wilhelmina and Fokker F.XII Monoplanes

1931

394 **59** 36c. red and blue (air) 23·00 1·30
395 - 70c. blue and red (postage) 49·00 1·30
395b - 80c. green and red £180 5·25

Designs:—70c. Portrait and factory; 80c. Portrait and shipyard.

61 Mentally Handicapped Child

1931. Child Welfare.

396A 1½c. (+1½c.) red and blue 2·50 2·50
397A **61** 5c. (+3c.) green and purple 9·00 2·50
398A - 6c. (+4c.) purple and green 10·50 2·50
399B - 12½c. (+3½c.) blue and red 46·00 33·00

Designs:—1½c. Deaf mute; 6c. Blind girl; 12½c. Sick child.

62 Windmill and Dykes, Kinderdijk

1932. Tourist Propaganda.

400 **62** 2½c.+1½c. green and black 13·00 10·50
401 - 6c.+4c. grey and black 18·00 10·50
402 - 7½c.+3½c. red and black 50·00 29·00
403 - 12½c.+2½c. blue and black 55·00 34·00

Designs:—6c. Aerial view of Town Hall, Zierikzee; 7½c. Bridges at Schipluiden and Moerdijk; 12½c. Tulips.

63 Gorse (Spring)

1932. Child Welfare.

404A **63** 1½c. (+1½c.) brown & yell 3·50 90
405A - 5c. (+3c.) blue and red 4·75 1·60
406A - 6c. (+4c.) green and orange 3·50 80
407A - 12½c. (+3½c.) blue & orange 47·00 39·00

Designs:—Child and: 5c. Cornflower (Summer); 6c. Sunflower (Autumn); 12½c. Christmas rose (Winter).

64 Arms of House of Orange

65 Portrait by Goltzius

1933. Fourth Birth Centenary of William I of Orange. T **64** and portraits of William I inscr "1533", as T 65.

408 **64** 1½c. black 90 65
409 **65** 5c. green 3·00 65
410 - 6c. purple 4·50 50
411 - 12½c. blue 27·00 5·75

Designs:—6c. Portrait by Key; 12½c. Portrait attributed to Moro.

68 Dove of Peace

1933. Peace Propaganda.

412 **68** 12½c. blue 15·00 65

69 Projected Monument at Den Helder

70 *De Hoop* (hospital ship)

1933. Seamen's Fund.

413 **69** 1½c. (+1½c.) red 6·50 5·75
414 **70** 5c. (+3c.) green and red 20·00 9·75
415 - 6c. (+4c.) green 29·00 7·25
416 - 12½c. (+3½c.) blue 42·00 36·00

Designs:—6c. Lifeboat; 12½c. Seaman and Seamen's Home.

73 Pander S.4 Postjager

1933. Air. Special Flights.

417 **73** 30c. green 1·30 1·30

74 Child and Star of Epiphany

1933. Child Welfare.

418A **74** 1½c. (+1½c.) orange and grey 2·50 1·00
419A **74** 5c. (+3c.) yellow and brown 3·50 1·20
420A **74** 6c. (+4c.) gold and green 4·25 1·00
421A **74** 12½c. (+3½c.) silver and blue 42·00 36·00

75 Princess Juliana

1934. Crisis stamps.

438	-	5c. (+4c.) purple	21·00	5·75
439	**75**	6c. (+5c.) blue	18·00	7·25

Design:—5c. Queen Wilhelmina.

76 Dutch Warship

1934. Tercentenary of Curacao.

440	-	6c. black	5·75	35
441	**76**	12½c. blue	35·00	5·00

Design:—6c. Willemstad Harbour.

77 Dowager Queen Emma

1934. Anti-T.B. Fund.

442	**77**	6c. (+2c.) blue	21·00	2·50

78 Destitute child

1934. Child Welfare.

443	**78**	1½c. (+1½c.) brown	2·50	1·30
444	**78**	5c. (+3c.) red	4·50	2·00
445	**78**	6c. (+4c.) green	4·50	65
446	**78**	12½c. (+3½c.) blue	40·00	29·00

79 H. D. Guyot

1935. Cultural and Social Relief Fund.

447	**79**	1½c. (+1½c.) red	3·25	3·25
448	-	5c. (+3c.) brown	7·75	8·50
449	-	6c. (+4c.) green	9·00	1·30
450	-	12½c. (+3½c.) blue	45·00	13·00

Portraits:—5c. A. J. M. Diepenbrock; 6c. F. C. Donders; 12½c. J. P. Sweelinck.

See also Nos. 456/9, 469/72, 478/82 and 492/6.

80 Aerial Map of Netherlands

1935. Air Fund.

451	**80**	6c. (+4c.) brown	47·00	17·00

81 Child picking Fruit

1935. Child Welfare.

452	**81**	1½c. (+1½c.) red	1·00	65
453	**81**	5c. (+3c.) green	2·50	2·00
454	**81**	6c. (+4c.) brown	2·30	65
455	**81**	12½c. (+3½c.) blue	36·00	16·00

1936. Cultural and Social Relief Fund. As T **79**.

456	1½c. (+1½c.) sepia	1·30	1·30
457	5c. (+3c.) green	7·75	5·75
458	6c. (+4c.) red	6·50	1·30
459	12½c. (+3½c.) blue	23·00	4·50

Portraits:—1½c. H. Kamerlingh Onnes; 5c. Dr. A. S. Talma; 6c. Mgr. Dr. H. J. A. M. Schaepman; 12½c. Desiderius Erasmus.

83 Pallas Athene

1936. Tercentenary of Utrecht University Foundation.

460	**83**	6c. red	2·50	65
461	-	12½c. blue	9·00	8·50

Design:—12½c. Gisbertus Voetius.

84 Child Herald

1936. Child Welfare.

462	**84**	1½c. (+1½c.) slate	65	65
463	**84**	5c. (+3c.) green	4·00	1·30
464	**84**	6c. (+4c.) brown	3·25	65
465	**84**	12½c. (+3½c.) blue	25·00	7·75

85 Scout Movement

1937. Scout Jamboree.

466	-	1½c. black and green	65	40
467	**85**	6c. brown and black	2·00	40
468	-	12½c. black and blue	6·50	2·50

Designs:—1½c. Scout Tenderfoot Badge; 12½c. Hermes.

1937. Cultural and Social Relief Fund. Portraits as T **79**.

469	1½c.+1½c. sepia	65	65
470	5c.+3c. green	7·25	5·75
471	6c.+4c. purple	2·00	65
472	12½c.+3½c. blue	13·00	4·00

Portraits:—1½c. Jacob Maris; 5c. F. de la B. Sylvius; 6c. J. van den Vondel; 12½c. A. van Leeuwenhoek.

86 *Laughing Child* by Frans Hals

1937. Child Welfare.

473	**86**	1½c. (+1½c.) black	35	35
474	**86**	3c. (+2c.) green	2·50	2·00
475	**86**	4c. (+2c.) red	1·00	65
476	**86**	5c. (+3c.) green	90	35
477	**86**	12½c. (+3½c.) blue	11·50	3·25

1938. Cultural and Social Relief Fund. As T **79**.

478	1½c.+1½c. sepia	60	1·00
479	3c.+2c. green	1·00	65
480	4c.+2c. red	3·25	3·50
481	5c.+3c. green	4·25	65
482	12½c.+3½c. blue	14·50	2·00

Portraits:—1½c. M. van St. Aldegonde; 3c. O. G. Heldring; 4c. Maria Tesselschade; 5c. Rembrandt; 12½c. H. Boerhaave.

87 Queen Wilhelmina

1938. 40th Anniv of Coronation.

483	**87**	1½c. black	35	35
484	**87**	5c. red	45	35
485	**87**	12½c. blue	6·25	2·50

88 Carrion Crow

1938. Air. Special Flights.

486	**88**	12½c. blue and grey	80	65
790a	**88**	25c. blue and grey	5·75	2·50

89 Boy with Flute

1938. Child Welfare.

487	**89**	1½c.+1½c. black	35	35
488	**89**	3c.+2c. brown	80	65
489	**89**	4c.+2c. green	1·60	1·30
490	**89**	5c.+3c. red	60	35
491	**89**	12½c.+3½c. blue	14·50	3·25

1939. Cultural and Social Relief Fund. As T **79**.

492	1½c.+1½c. brown	1·30	65
493	2½c.+2½c. green	5·75	4·00
494	3c.+3c. red	1·30	2·00
495	5c.+3c. green	4·50	65
496	12½c.+3½c. blue	10·50	2·00

Portraits:—1½c. M. Maris; 2½c. Anton Mauve; 3c. Gerardus van Swieten; 5c. Nicolas Beets; 12½c. Pieter Stuyvesant.

91 St. Willibrord's landing in the Netherlands

1939. 12th Death Centenary of St. Willibrord.

497	**91**	5c. green	1·00	35
498	-	12½c. blue	8·75	4·50

Design:—12½c. St. Willibrord as Bishop of Utrecht.

92 Replica of Locomotive *De Arend*

1939. Centenary of Netherlands Railway.

499	**92**	5c. green	1·30	35
500	-	12½c. blue	13·00	6·50

Design:—12½c. Electric railcar.

93 Child and Cornucopia

1939. Child Welfare.

501	**93**	1½c.+1½c. black	40	65
502	**93**	2½c.+2½c. green	7·75	4·00
503	**93**	3c.+3c. red	90	65
504	**93**	5c.+3c. green	2·00	65
505	**93**	12½c.+3½c. blue	6·50	2·50

94 Queen Wilhelmina

1940

506	**94**	5c. green	40	15
506a	**94**	6c. brown	90	35
507	**94**	7½c. red	40	15
508	**94**	10c. purple	40	15
509	**94**	12½c. blue	40	35
510	**94**	15c. blue	40	35
510a	**94**	17½c. blue	2·10	1·30
511	**94**	20c. violet	95	35
512	**94**	22½c. olive	3·50	3·25
513	**94**	25c. red	70	35
514	**94**	30c. ochre	1·60	65
515	**94**	40c. green	3·00	1·30
515a	**94**	50c. orange	13·00	1·30
515b	**94**	60c. purple	13·00	4·25

95 Vincent Van Gogh

1940. Cultural and Social Relief Fund.

516	**95**	1½c.+1½c. brown	4·00	90
517	-	2½c.+2½c. green	6·50	1·80
518	-	3c.+3c. red	4·00	1·80
519	-	5c.+3c. green	9·75	80
520	-	12½c.+3½c. blue	7·75	3·00

Portraits:—1½c. E. J. Potgieter; 3c. Petrus Camper; 5c. Jan Steen; 12½c. Joseph Scaliger.

See also Nos. 558/62 and 656/60.

1940. As No. 519, colour changed. Surch.

521	7½c.+2½c. on 5c.+3c. red	65	65

1940. Surch with large figures and network.

522	**35**	2½ on 3c. red	7·00	40
523	**35**	5 on 3c. green	40	40
524	**35**	7½ on 3c. red	40	15
525	**35**	10 on 3c. green	40	40
526	**35**	12½ on 3c. blue	65	65
527	**35**	17½ on 3c. green	2·00	65
528	**35**	20 on 3c. green	1·30	40
529	**35**	22½ on 3c. green	5·75	7·75
530	**35**	25 on 3c. green	2·30	65
531	**35**	30 on 3c. green	2·00	80
532	**35**	40 on 3c. green	4·75	3·75
533	**35**	50 on 3c. green	2·30	1·00
534	**35**	60 on 3c. green	3·50	2·10
535	**35**	70 on 3c. green	15·00	6·50
536	**35**	80 on 3c. green	19·00	10·50
537	**35**	100 on 3c. green	55·00	60·00
538	**35**	250 on 3c. green	65·00	70·00
539	**35**	500 on 3c. green	60·00	65·00

98 Girl with Dandelion

1940. Child Welfare.

540	**98**	1½c.+1½c. violet	1·40	40
541	**98**	2½c.+2½c. olive	4·75	1·60
542	**98**	4c.+3c. blue	5·75	1·60
543	**98**	5c.+3c. green	6·00	40
544	**98**	7½c.+3½c. red	1·70	40

1941

546	**35**	5c. green	15	15
547	**35**	7½c. red	15	15
548	**35**	10c. violet	1·50	40
549	**35**	12½c. blue	60	50
550	**35**	15c. blue	1·50	65
551	**35**	17½c. red	35	40
552	**35**	20c. violet	1·50	40
553	**35**	22½c. olive	35	65
554	**35**	25c. lake	60	50
555	**35**	30c. brown	5·25	50
556	**35**	40c. green	35	50
557	**35**	50c. brown	35	40

1941. Cultural and Social Relief Fund. As T **95** but inscr "ZOMERZEGEL 31.12.46".

558	1½c.+1½c. brown	1·40	50
559	2½c.+2½c. green	1·40	50
560	4c.+3c. red	1·40	50
561	5c.+3c. green	1·40	50
562	7½c.+3½c. purple	1·40	50

Portraits:—1½c. Dr. A. Mathijsen; 2½c. J. Ingenhousz; 4c. Aagje Deken; 5c. Johan Bosboom; 7½c. A. C. W. Staring.

100 *Titus Rembrandt*

1941. Child Welfare.

563	**100**	1½c.+1½c. black	70	50
564	**100**	2½c.+2½c. olive	70	50
565	**100**	4c.+3c. blue	70	50
566	**100**	5c.+3c. green	70	50
567	**100**	7½c.+3½c. red	70	50

101 Legionary

1942. Netherlands Legion Fund.

568	**101**	7½c.+2½c. red	1·70	1·20
569	-	12½c.+87½c. blue	13·50	14·50

MS569a 155×110 mm. No. 568 (block of ten) £190 £150

MS569b 96×97 mm. No. 569 (block of ten) £150 £160

Design:—Horiz: 12½c. Legionary with similar inscription.

1943. First European Postal Congress. As T **26** but larger (21×27½ mm) surch **EUROPEESCHE P T T VEREENIGING 19 OCTOBER 1942 10 CENT.**

570	**26**	10c. on 2½c. yellow	1·00	50

103 Seahorse

1943. Old Germanic Symbols.

571	**103**	1c. black	15	25
572	-	1½c. red	15	25
573	-	2c. blue	15	25
574	-	2½c. green	15	25
575	-	3c. red	15	25
576	-	4c. brown	15	25
577	-	5c. olive	15	25

Designs:—Vert: 1½c. Triple crowned tree; 2½c. Birds in ornamental tree; 4c. Horse and rider. Horiz: 2c. Swans; 3c. Trees and serpentine roots; 5c. Prancing horses.

104 Michiel A. de Ruyter

1943. Dutch Naval Heroes.

578	**104**	7½c. red	20	25
579	-	10c. green	20	25
580	-	12½c. blue	20	40
581	-	15c. violet	35	50
582	-	17½c. grey	20	50
583	-	20c. brown	20	50
584	-	22½c. red	20	65
585	-	25c. purple	70	1·00
586	-	30c. blue	20	50
587	-	40c. grey	20	65

Portraits:—10c. Johan Evertsen; 12½c. Maarten H. Tromp; 15c. Piet Hein; 17½c. Wilhelm Joseph van Gent; 20c. Witte de With; 22½c. Cornelis Evertsen; 25c. Tjerk Hiddes de Fries; 30c. Cornelis Tromp; 40c. Cornelis Evertsen the younger.

105 Mail Cart

1943. Stamp Day.

589	**105**	7½c.+7½c. red	25	40

106 Child and Doll's House

1944. Child Welfare and Winter Help Funds. Inscr "WINTERHULP" (1½c. and 7½c.) or "VOLKSDIENST" (others).

590	**106**	1½c.+3½c. black	35	50
591	-	4c.+3½c. brown	35	50
592	-	5c.+5c. green	35	50
593	-	7½c.+7½c. red	35	50
594	-	10c.+40c. blue	35	50

Designs:—4c. Mother and child; 5c., 10c. Mother and children; 7½c. Child and wheatsheaf.

107 Infantryman

111 Queen Wilhelmina

1944

595	**107**	1½c. black	20	25
596	-	2½c. green	20	25
597	-	3c. brown	20	25
598	-	5c. blue	20	25
599	**111**	7½c. red	20	25
600	**111**	10c. orange	20	25
601	**111**	12½c. blue	20	25
602	**111**	15c. red	2·50	2·50
603	**111**	17½c. green	1·80	1·80
604	**111**	20c. violet	70	50
605	**111**	22½c. red	2·00	2·10
606	**111**	25c. brown	3·00	2·30
607	**111**	30c. green	45	50
608	**111**	40c. purple	4·00	4·00
609	**111**	50c. mauve	2·75	1·80

The above set was originally for use on Netherlands warships serving with the Allied Fleet, and was used after liberation in the Netherlands.

112 Lion and Dragon

1945. Liberation.

610	**112**	7½c. orange	25	25

113

1945. Child Welfare.

611	**113**	1½c.+2½c. grey	45	50
612	**113**	2½c.+3½c. green	45	50
613	**113**	5c.+5c. brown	45	50
614	**113**	7½c.+4½c. red	45	50
615	**113**	12½c.+5½c. blue	45	50

114 Queen Wilhelmina

1946

616	**114**	1g. blue	5·25	1·60
617	**114**	2½g. red	£250	26·00
618	**114**	5g. green	£250	60·00
619	**114**	10g. violet	£250	60·00

115 Emblem of Abundance

1946. War Victims' Relief Fund.

620	**115**	1½c.+3½c. black	80	50
621	**115**	2½c.+5c. green	90	90
622	**115**	5c.+10c. violet	90	90
623	**115**	7½c.+15c. red	80	50
624	**115**	12½c.+37½c. blue	1·60	1·00

116 Princess Irene

1946. Child Welfare.

625	**116**	1½c.+1½c. brown	90	90
626	-	2½c.+1½c. green	90	90
627	**116**	4c.+2c. red	1·20	90
628	-	5c.+2c. brown	1·20	90
629	-	7½c.+2½c. red	90	40
630	-	12½c.+7½c. blue	90	1·30

Portraits:—2½c., 5c. Princess Margriet; 7½c., 12½c. Princess Beatrix.

117 Boy on Roundabout

1946. Child Welfare.

631	**117**	2c.+2c. violet	80	70
632	**117**	4c.+2c. green	80	70
633	**117**	7½c.+2½c. red	80	70
634	**117**	10c.+5c. purple	1·00	40
635	**117**	20c.+5c. blue	1·40	95

118 Numeral

1946

636	**118**	1c. red	20	20
637	**118**	2c. blue	20	20
638	**118**	2½c. orange	7·75	2·50
638a	**118**	3c. brown	20	20
639	**118**	4c. green	50	25
639a	**118**	5c. orange	20	20
639c	**118**	6c. grey	60	40
639d	**118**	7c. red	40	20
639f	**118**	8c. mauve	40	20

119 Queen Wilhelmina

1947

640	**119**	5c. green	1·80	25
641	**119**	6c. black	50	25
642	**119**	6c. blue	90	25
643	**119**	7½c. red	65	25
644	**119**	10c. purple	1·30	25
645	**119**	12½c. red	1·30	65
646	**119**	15c. violet	15·00	25
647	**119**	20c. blue	16·00	25
648	**119**	22½c. green	1·30	1·30
649	**119**	25c. blue	31·00	25
650	**119**	30c. orange	30·00	50
651	**119**	35c. blue	29·00	90
652	**119**	40c. brown	34·00	90
653	-	45c. blue	36·00	20·00
654	-	50c. brown	24·00	65
655	-	60c. red	31·00	4·00

Nos. 653/5 are as Type **119** but have the inscriptions in colour on white ground.

1947. Cultural and Social Relief Fund. As T **95** but inscr "ZOMERZEGEL ... 13.12.48".

656	2c.+2c. red	1·40	80
657	4c.+2c. green	2·00	1·00
658	7½c.+2½c. violet	3·00	1·30
659	10c.+5c. brown	2·75	65
660	20c.+5c. blue	2·20	1·00

Portraits:—2c. H. van Deventer; 4c. P. C. Hooft; 7½c. Johan de Witt; 10c. J. F. van Royen; 20c. Hugo Grotius.

122 Children

1947. Child Welfare.

661	**122**	2c.+2c. brown	40	40
662	-	4c.+2c. green	1·60	1·00
663	-	7½c.+2½c. brown	1·60	1·30
664	-	10c.+5c. lake	1·90	40
665	**122**	20c.+5c. blue	2·10	1·60

Design:—4c. to 10c. Baby.

124 Ridderzaal, The Hague

1948. Cultural and Social Relief Fund.

666	**124**	2c.+2c. brown	2·75	1·00
667	-	6c.+4c. green	3·25	1·00
668	-	10c.+5c. red	2·10	65
669	-	20c.+5c. blue	3·25	1·80

Buildings:—6c. Palace on the Dam; 10c. Kneuterdijk Palace; 20c. Nieuwe Kerk, Amsterdam.

125 Queen Wilhelmina

1948. Queen Wilhelmina's Golden Jubilee.

670	**125**	10c. red	40	25
671	**125**	20c. blue	3·25	2·75

126 Queen Juliana

1948. Coronation.

672	**126**	10c. brown	2·50	25
673	**126**	20c. blue	3·25	80

127 Boy in Canoe

1948. Child Welfare.

674	**127**	2c.+2c. green	40	25
675	-	5c.+3c. green	3·50	1·20
676	-	6c.+4c. grey	1·90	50
677	-	10c.+5c. red	70	25
678	-	20c.+8c. blue	3·50	2·10

Designs:—5c. Girl swimming; 6c. Boy on toboggan; 10c. Girl on swing; 20c. Boy skating.

128 Terrace near Beach

1949. Cultural and Social Relief Fund.

679	**128**	2c.+2c. yellow and blue	3·00	25
680	-	5c.+3c. yellow and blue	5·25	3·00
681	-	6c.+4c. green	4·25	80
682	-	10c.+5c. yellow and blue	5·00	25
683	-	20c.+5c. blue	5·25	3·00

Designs:—5c. Hikers in cornfield; 6c. Campers by fire; 10c. Gathering wheat; 20c. Yachts.

129 Queen Juliana

130 Queen Juliana

1949

684	**129**	5c. green	1·30	25
685	**129**	6c. blue	65	25
686	**129**	10c. orange	65	25
687	**129**	12c. red	4·00	5·25
688	**129**	15c. green	7·75	25
689	**129**	20c. blue	6·50	25
690	**129**	25c. brown	24·00	25
691	**129**	30c. violet	16·00	25
692	**129**	35c. blue	44·00	40
693	**129**	40c. purple	75·00	50
694	**129**	45c. orange	3·25	1·60
695	**129**	45c. violet	90·00	90
696	**129**	50c. green	21·00	50
697	**129**	60c. brown	33·00	50
697a	**129**	75c. red	£130	4·00
698	**130**	1g. red	6·50	65
699	**130**	2½g. brown	£350	6·50
700a	**130**	5g. brown	£800	9·00
701	**130**	10g. violet	£550	29·00

131 Hands reaching for Sunflower

1949. Red Cross and Indonesian Relief Fund.

702	**131**	2c.+3c. yellow and grey	2·00	50
703	**131**	6c.+4c. yellow and red	3·25	65
704	**131**	10c.+5c. yellow and blue	6·50	40
705	**131**	30c.+10c. yellow & brn	14·00	5·50

132 Posthorns and Globe

1949. 75th Anniv of U.P.U.

706	132	10c. lake	1·30	25
707	132	20c. blue	13·00	3·75

133 "Autumn"

1949. Child Welfare Fund. Inscr "VOOR HET KIND".

708	133	2c.+3c. brown	60	25
709	-	5c.+3c. red	11·50	3·00
710	-	6c.+4c. green	7·00	60
711	-	10c.+5c. grey	60	25
712	-	20c.+7c. blue	10·50	3·00

Designs:—5c. "Summer"; 6c. "Spring"; 10c. "Winter"; 20c. "New Year".

134 Resistance Monument

135 Section of Moerdijk Bridge

1950. Cultural and Social Relief Fund. Inscr "ZOMERZEGEL 1950".

713	134	2c.+2c. brown	5·25	2·00
714	-	4c.+2c. green	19·00	17·00
715	-	5c.+3c. grey	15·00	9·00
716	-	6c.+4c. violet	8·25	1·30
717	135	10c.+5c. slate	10·50	65
718	-	20c.+5c. blue	24·00	23·00

Designs:—Vert: 4c. Sealing dykes; 5c. Rotterdam skyscraper. Horiz: 6c. Harvesting; 20c. *Overijssel* (canal freighter).

1950. Surch with bold figure 6.

719	119	6c. on 7½c. red	2·50	40

137 Good Samaritan and Bombed Church

1950. Bombed Churches Rebuilding Fund.

720	137	2c.+2c. olive	15·00	5·25
721	137	5c.+3c. brown	20·00	17·00
722	137	6c.+4c. green	13·00	7·00
723	137	10c.+5c. red	38·00	1·30
724	137	20c.+5c. blue	50·00	42·00

138 Janus Dousa

1950. 375th Anniv of Leyden University.

725	138	10c. olive	7·25	40
726	-	20c. blue	7·25	2·30

Portrait:—20c. Jan van Hout.

139 Baby and Bees

1950. Child Welfare. Inscr "VOOR HET KIND".

727	139	2c.+3c. red	65	40
728	-	5c.+3c. olive	20·00	8·75
729	-	6c.+4c. green	6·50	1·20
730	-	10c.+5c. purple	65	40
731	-	20c.+7c. blue	21·00	16·00

Designs:—5c. Boy and fowl; 6c. Girl and birds; 10c. Boy and fish; 20c. Girl, butterfly and frog.

140 Bergh Castle

1951. Cultural and Social Relief Fund. Castles.

732		2c.+2c. violet	5·75	2·10
733	140	5c.+3c. red	16·00	11·50
734	-	6c.+4c. sepia	7·00	2·00
735	-	10c.+5c. green	10·50	50
736	-	20c.+5c. blue	16·00	12·00

Designs:—Horiz: 2c. Hillenraad; 6c. Hernen. Vert: 10c. Rechteren; 20c. Moermond.

141 Girl and Windmill

1951. Child Welfare.

737	141	2c.+3c. green	1·30	40
738	-	5c.+3c. blue	14·50	7·25
739	-	6c.+4c. brown	9·00	1·20
740	-	10c.+5c. lake	65	40
741	-	20c.+7c. blue	14·50	13·00

Designs:—Each shows boy or girl: 5c. Crane; 6c. Fishing nets; 10c. Factory chimneys; 20c. Flats.

142 Gull

1951. Air.

742	142	15g. brown	£450	£200
743	142	25g. black	£450	£200

143 Jan van Riebeeck

1952. Tercentenary of Landing in South Africa and Van Riebeeck Monument Fund.

744	143	2c.+3c. violet	7·50	5·75
745	143	6c.+4c. green	9·25	7·00
746	143	10c.+5c. red	10·50	5·75
747	143	20c.+5c. blue	7·50	7·00

144 Miner

1952. 50th Anniv of State Mines, Limburg.

748	144	10c. blue	3·00	40

145 Wild Rose

1952. Cultural and Social Relief Fund. Floral designs inscr "ZOMERZEGEL 1952".

749	145	2c.+2c. green and red	1·40	90
750	-	5c.+3c. yellow and green	6·75	5·75
751	-	6c.+4c. green and red	3·50	1·80
752	-	10c.+5c. green & orange	3·00	50
753	-	20c.+5c. green and blue	16·00	11·50

Flowers:—5c. Marsh marigold; 6c. Tulip; 10c. Marguerite; 20c. Cornflower.

146 Radio Masts

1952. Netherlands Stamp Centenary and Centenary of Telegraph Service.

754		2c. violet	80	25
755	146	6c. red	90	40
756	-	10c. green	90	25
757	-	20c. slate	11·50	3·00

Designs:—2c. Telegraph poles and steam train; 10c. Postman delivering letters, 1852; 20c. Postman delivering letters, 1952.

1952. International Postage Stamp Exn, Utrecht ("ITEP"). Nos. 754/7 but colours changed.

757a		2c. brown	37·00	20·00
757b	146	6c. blue	37·00	20·00
757c	-	10c. lake	37·00	20·00
757d	-	20c. blue	37·00	20·00

Nos. 757a/d were sold only in sets at the Exhibition at face plus 1g. entrance fee.

147 Boy feeding Goat

1952. Child Welfare.

758	147	2c.+3c. black and olive	35	40
759	-	5c.+3c. black and pink	4·75	3·00
760	-	6c.+4c. black and green	3·75	80
761	-	10c.+5c. black & orange	35	40
762	-	20c.+7c. black and blue	11·00	9·00

Designs:—5c. Girl riding donkey; 6c. Girl playing with dog; 10c. Boy and cat; 20c. Boy and rabbit.

1953. Flood Relief Fund. Surch 19 53 10c +10 WATERSNOOD.

763	129	10c.+10c. orange	95	40

149 Hyacinth

1953. Cultural and Social Relief Fund.

764	149	2c.+2c. green and violet	1·30	65
765	-	5c.+3c. green & orange	7·00	6·50
766	-	6c.+4c. yellow and green	3·50	1·30
767	-	10c.+5c. green and red	6·50	65
768	-	20c.+5c. green and blue	21·00	17·00

Flowers:—5c. African marigold; 6c. Daffodil; 10c. Anemone; 20c. Dutch iris.

150 Red Cross

1953. Red Cross Fund. Inscr "RODE KRUIS".

769	150	2c.+3c. red and sepia	1·70	90
770	-	6c.+4c. red and brown	8·50	5·75
771	-	7c.+5c. red and olive	2·00	90
772	-	10c.+5c. red	1·30	40
773	-	25c.+8c. red and blue	12·50	8·75

Designs:—6c. Man with lamp; 7c. Rescue worker in flooded area; 10c. Nurse giving blood transfusion; 25c. Red Cross flags.

151 Queen Juliana

152 Queen Juliana

1953

775	151	10c. brown	25	25
776	151	12c. turquoise	25	25
777	151	15c. red	25	25
777b	151	18c. turquoise	25	25
778	151	20c. purple	25	25
778b	151	24c. olive	50	25
779	151	25c. blue	2·10	25
780	151	30c. orange	65	25
781	151	35c. brown	1·30	25
781a	151	37c. turquoise	65	25
782	151	40c. slate	65	25
783	151	45c. red	50	25
784	151	50c. green	1·00	25
785	151	60c. brown	1·30	25
785a	151	62c. red	3·50	3·50
785b	151	70c. blue	1·60	25
786	151	75c. purple	1·60	25
786a	151	80c. violet	1·60	25
786b	151	85c. green	2·10	25
786c	151	95c. brown	2·10	50
787	152	1g. red	3·00	25
788	152	2½g. green	13·50	35
789	152	5g. black	5·50	50
790	152	10g. blue	25·00	3·00

153 Girl with Pigeon

1953. Child Welfare. Inscr "VOOR HET KIND".

791	-	2c.+3c. blue and yellow	40	40
792	-	5c.+3c. lake and green	8·25	6·50
793	153	7c.+5c. brown and blue	5·25	1·80
794	-	10c.+5c. lilac and bistre	40	40
795	-	25c.+8c. turq & pink	16·00	14·50

Designs:—2c. Girl, bucket and spade; 5c. Boy and apple; 10c. Boy and tjalk (sailing boat); 25c. Girl and tulip.

154 M. Nijhoff (poet)

1954. Cultural and Social Relief Fund.

796	154	2c.+3c. blue	4·00	3·00
797	-	5c.+3c. brown	6·50	5·25
798	-	7c.+5c. red	6·75	2·30
799	-	10c.+5c. green	13·00	1·20
800	-	25c.+8c. purple	17·00	17·00

Portraits:—5c. W. Pijper (composer); 7c. H. P. Berlage (architect); 10c. J. Huizinga (historian); 25c. Vincent van Gogh (painter).

155 St. Boniface

1954. 1200th Anniv of Martyrdom of St. Boniface.

801	155	10c. blue	3·00	40

156 Boy and Model Glider

1954. National Aviation Fund.

802	156	2c.+2c. green	1·70	1·30
803	-	10c.+4c. blue	4·25	1·30

Portrait:—10c. Dr. A. Plesman (aeronautical pioneer).

157 Making Paperchains

1954. Child Welfare.

804	157	2c.+3c. brown	35	35
805	-	5c.+3c. olive	6·50	6·25
806	-	7c.+5c. blue	3·00	90
807	-	10c.+5c. red	40	35
808	-	25c.+8c. blue	14·50	9·50

Designs:—Vert: 5c. Girl brushing her teeth; 7c. Boy and toy boat; 10c. Nurse and child. Horiz: 25c. Invalid boy drawing in bed.

158 Queen Juliana

1954. Ratification of Statute for the Kingdom.

809	158	10c. red	1·30	40

159 Factory, Rotterdam

1955. Cultural and Social Relief Fund.

810	159	2c.+3c. brown	2·50	2·10
811	-	5c.+3c. green	5·75	5·25
812	-	7c.+5c. red	2·50	1·80
813	-	10c.+5c. blue	4·50	40
814	-	25c.+8c. brown	19·00	14·50

Designs:—Horiz: 5c. Post Office, The Hague; 10c. Town Hall, Hilversum; 25c. Office Building, The Hague. Vert: 7c. Stock Exchange, Amsterdam.

160 "The Victory of Peace"

1955. Tenth Anniv of Liberation.

815	**160**	10c. red	1·70	40

161 Microscope and Emblem of Cancer

1955. Queen Wilhelmina Anti-cancer Fund.

816	**161**	2c.+3c. black and red	1·40	90
817	**161**	5c.+3c. green and red	4·75	3·50
818	**161**	7c.+5c. purple and red	2·75	1·20
819	**161**	10c.+5c. blue and red	2·10	40
820	**161**	25c.+8c. olive and red	10·00	8·25

162 *Willem van Loon* (D. Dircks)

1955. Child Welfare Fund.

821	**162**	2c.+3c. green	65	40
822	-	5c.+3c. red	5·75	4·50
823	-	7c.+5c. brown	5·75	1·30
824	-	10c.+5c. blue	65	40
825	-	25c.+8c. lilac	14·00	12·50

Portraits:—5c. *Portrait of a Boy* (J. A. Backer); 7c. *Portrait of a Girl* (unknown); 10c. *Philips Huygens* (A. Hanneman); 25c. *Constantin Huygens* (A. Hanneman).

163 *Farmer*

1956. Cultural and Social Relief Fund and 350th Birth Anniv of Rembrandt. Details from Rembrandt's paintings.

826	**163**	2c.+3c. slate	4·75	4·00
827	-	5c.+3c. olive	5·00	4·50
828	-	7c.+5c. brown	7·00	7·00
829	-	10c.+5c. green	17·00	65
830	-	25c.+8c. brown	24·00	22·00

Paintings:—5c. *Young Tobias with Angel*; 7c. *Persian wearing Fur Cap*; 10c. *Old Blind Tobias*; 25c. *Self-portrait*, 1639.

164 Yacht

165 Amphora

1956. 16th Olympic Games, Melbourne.

831	**164**	2c.+3c. black and blue	1·40	1·30
832	-	5c.+3c. black and yellow	2·10	2·00
833	**165**	7c.+5c. black and brown	2·30	2·00
834	-	10c.+5c. black and grey	3·50	1·00
835	-	25c.+8c. black and green	7·25	7·25

Designs:—As Type **164**: 5c. Runner; 10c. Hockey player; 25c. Water polo player.

1956. Europa. As T **110** of Luxembourg.

836	10c. black and lake	5·75	40
837	25c. black and blue	70·00	2·75

167 *Portrait of a Boy* (Van Scorel)

1956. Child Welfare Fund. 16th-century Dutch Paintings.

838	**167**	2c.+3c. grey and cream	65	40
839	-	5c.+3c. olive and cream	2·10	2·00
840	-	7c.+5c. purple & cream	5·25	2·50
841	-	10c.+5c. red and cream	50	40
842	-	25c.+8c. blue and cream	9·25	6·75

Paintings:—5c. *Portrait of a Boy*; 7c. *Portrait of a Girl*; 10c. *Portrait of a Girl*; 25c. *Portrait of Eechie Pieters*.

168 *Curacao* (trawler) and Fish Barrels

1957. Cultural and Social Relief Fund. Ships.

843		4c.+3c. blue	2·20	2·10
844		6c.+4c. lilac	5·50	5·25
845		7c.+5c. red	3·25	2·10
846	**168**	10c.+8c. green	6·00	70
847	-	30c.+8c. brown	8·00	7·00

Designs:—4c. *Gaasterland* (freighter); 6c. Coaster; 7c. *Willem Barendsz* (whale factory ship) and whale; 30c. *Nieuw Amsterdam* (liner).

169 Admiral M. A. de Ruyter

1957. 350th Birth Anniv of M. A. de Ruyter.

848	**169**	10c. orange	1·10	40
849	-	30c. blue	6·25	2·10

Design:—30c. De Ruyter's flagship, *De Zeven Provincien*.

170 Blood Donors' Emblem

1957. 90th Anniv of Netherlands Red Cross Society and Red Cross Fund.

850	**170**	4c.+3c. blue and red	1·60	1·60
851	-	6c.+4c. green and red	2·10	1·90
852	-	7c.+5c. red and green	2·10	1·90
853	-	10c.+8c. red and ochre	1·90	40
854	-	30c.+8c. red and blue	4·25	3·75

Designs:—6c. *J. Henry Dunant* (hospital ship); 7c. Red Cross; 10c. Red Cross emblem; 30c. Red Cross on globe.

171 "Europa" Star

1957. Europa.

855	**171**	10c. black and blue	2·20	40
856	**171**	30c. green and blue	9·50	2·75

172 Portrait by B. J. Blommers

1957. Child Fund Welfare. 19th- and 20th-Century Paintings by Dutch Masters.

857	**172**	4c.+4c. red	75	40
858	-	6c.+4c. green	5·50	5·25
859	-	8c.+4c. sepia	5·00	3·50
860	-	12c.+9c. purple	60	40
861	-	30c.+9c. blue	12·00	9·75

Portraits:—Child paintings by: W. B. Tholen (6c.); J. Sluyters (8c.); M. Maris (12c.); C. Kruseman (30c.).

173 Walcheren Costume

1958. Cultural and Social Relief Fund. Provincial Costumes.

862	**173**	4c.+4c. blue	2·30	1·00
863	-	6c.+4c. ochre	5·25	4·00
864	-	8c.+4c. red	8·25	2·75
865	-	12c.+9c. brown	3·75	40
866	-	30c.+9c. lilac	13·00	10·50

Costumes:—6c. Marken; 8c. Scheveningen; 12c. Friesland; 30c. Volendam.

1958. Surch 12 C.

867	**151**	12c. on 10c. brown	1·80	30

1958. Europa. As T **119a** of Luxembourg.

868	12c. blue and red	65	40
869	30c. red and blue	2·30	1·00

176 Girl on Stilts and Boy on Tricycle

1958. Child Welfare Fund. Children's Games.

870	**176**	4c.+4c. blue	45	40
871	-	6c.+4c. red	4·75	4·00
872	-	8c.+4c. green	3·25	1·70
873	-	12c.+9c. red	35	40
874	-	30c.+9c. blue	9·25	7·00

Designs:—6c. Boy and girl on scooter; 8c. Boys playing leap-frog; 12c. Boys on roller-skates; 30c. Girl skipping and boy in toy car.

1959. Tenth Anniv of N.A.T.O. As T **123** of Luxembourg (N.A.T.O. emblem).

875	12c. blue and yellow	45	40
876	30c. blue and red	1·40	85

177 Cranes

1959. Cultural and Social Relief Fund. Prevention of Sea Encroachment.

877	-	4c.+4c. blue on green	2·40	2·30
878	-	6c.+4c. brown on grey	3·50	3·00
879	-	8c.+4c. violet on blue	3·50	2·50
880	**177**	12c.+9c. green on yell	5·75	45
881	-	30c.+9c. black on red	9·50	9·25

Designs:—4c. Tugs and caisson; 6c. Dredger; 8c. Labourers making fascine mattresses; 30c. Sand-spouter and scoop.

1959. Europa. As T **123a** of Luxembourg.

882	12c. red	1·70	45
883	30c. green	6·00	3·00

178 Silhouette of Douglas DC-8 Airliner and World Map

1959. 40th Anniv of K.L.M. (Royal Dutch Airlines).

884	**178**	12c. blue and red	50	45
885	-	30c. blue and green	2·30	1·80

Design:—30c. Silhouette of Douglas DC-8 airliner.

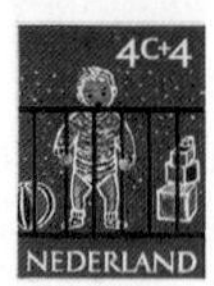

179 Child in Play-pen

1959. Child Welfare Fund.

886	**179**	4c.+4c. blue and brown	50	45
887	-	6c.+4c. brown and green	2·75	2·30
888	-	8c.+4c. blue and red	4·75	3·00
889	-	12c.+9c. red, black and blue	50	45
890	-	30c.+9c. turquoise and yellow	7·00	6·75

Designs:—6c. Boy as 'Red Indian' with bow and arrow; 8c. Boy feeding geese; 12c. Traffic warden escorting children; 30c. Girl doing homework.

180 Refugee Woman

1960. World Refugee Year.

891	**180**	12c.+8c. purple	80	45
892	**180**	30c.+10c. green	5·25	3·75

181 White Water-lily

1960. Cultural and Social Relief Fund. Flowers.

893	-	4c.+4c. red, green and grey	2·40	1·20
894	-	6c.+4c. yellow, green and salmon	3·50	3·50
895	**181**	8c.+4c. multicoloured	5·75	3·50
896	-	12c.+8c. red, green and buff	4·75	45
897	-	30c.+10c. blue, green and yellow	9·50	7·75

Flowers:—Vert: 4c. "The Princess" tulip; 6c. Gorse; 12c. Poppy; 30c. Blue sea-holly.

182 J. van der Kolk

1960. World Mental Health Year.

898	**182**	12c. red	1·40	45
899	-	30c. blue (J. Wier)	8·50	2·75

1960. Europa. As T **113a** of Norway.

900	12c. yellow and red	80	45
901	30c. yellow and blue	4·75	2·30

183 Marken Costume

1960. Child Welfare Fund. Costumes. Mult portraits.

902	**183**	4c.+4c. slate	80	45
903	-	6c.+4c. ochre	4·75	4·25
904	-	8c.+4c. turquoise	8·50	4·50
905	-	12c.+9c. violet	80	45
906	-	30c.+9c. grey	9·50	9·25

Designs:—Costumes of: 6c. Volendam; 8c. Bunschoten; 12c. Hindeloopen; 30c. Huizen.

184 Herring Gull

1961. Cultural and Social Relief Fund. Beach and Meadow Birds.

907	**184**	4c.+4c. slate and yellow	2·20	1·90
908	-	6c.+4c. sepia and brown	3·25	3·00
909	-	8c.+4c. brown and olive	2·00	1·70
910	-	12c.+8c. black and blue	4·00	80
911	-	30c.+10c. black & green	4·75	4·50

Birds:—Horiz: 6c. Oystercatcher; 12c. Pied avocet. Vert: 8c. Curlew; 30c. Northern lapwing.

185 Doves

1961. Europa.

912	**185**	12c. brown	30	30
913	**185**	30c. turquoise	50	45

186 St. Nicholas

1961. Child Welfare.

914	**186**	4c.+4c. red	50	45
915	-	6c.+4c. blue	2·10	1·60
916	-	8c.+4c. bistre	1·90	1·60
917	-	12c.+9c. green	50	45
918	-	30c.+9c. orange	5·50	5·25

Designs:—6c. Epiphany; 8c. Palm Sunday; 12c. Whitsuntide; 30c. Martinmas.

187 Queen Juliana and Prince Bernhard

1962. Silver Wedding.

919	**187**	12c. red	50	45
920	**187**	30c. green	2·20	1·20

188 Detail of *The Repast of the Officers of the St. Jorisdoelen* after Frans Hals

1962. Cultural, Health and Social Welfare Funds.

921	-	4c.+4c. green	1·90	1·60
922	-	6c.+4c. black	1·60	1·60
923	-	8c.+4c. purple	2·50	2·30
924	-	12c.+8c. bistre	2·50	70
925	**188**	30c.+10c. blue	2·50	2·50

Designs:—Horiz: 4c. Roman cat (sculpture). Vert: 6c. Pleuroceras spinatus (ammonite); 8c. Pendulum clock (after principle of Huygens); 12c. Ship's figurehead.

189 Telephone Dial

1962. Completion of Netherlands Automatic Telephone System. Inscr "1962".

926	**189**	4c. red and black	50	45
927	-	12c. drab and black	1·20	45
928	-	30c. ochre, blue and black	3·25	2·20

Designs:—Vert: 12c. Diagram of telephone network. Horiz: 30c. Arch and telephone dial.

190 Europa "Tree"

1962. Europa.

929	**190**	12c. black, yellow & bistre	50	30
930	**190**	30c. black, yellow and blue	1·90	1·20

191 Polder Landscape (reclaimed area)

1962

935	-	4c. deep blue and blue	30	30
937	**191**	6c. deep green and green	65	30
938	-	10c. deep purple and purple	30	30

Designs:—4c. Cooling towers, State mines, Limburg; 10c. Delta excavation works.

192 Children cooking Meal

1962. Child Welfare.

940	**192**	4c.+4c. red	50	45
941	-	6c.+4c. bistre	1·60	1·10
942	-	8c.+4c. blue	2·30	2·20
943	-	12c.+9c. green	50	45
944	-	30c.+9c. lake	4·50	4·25

Designs:—Children: 6c. Cycling; 8c. Watering flowers; 12c. Feeding poultry; 30c. Making music.

193 Ears of Wheat

1963. Freedom from Hunger.

945	**193**	12c. ochre and blue	50	45
946	**193**	30c. ochre and red	1·80	1·70

194 Gallery Windmill

1963. Cultural, Health and Social Welfare Funds. Windmill types.

947	**194**	4c.+4c. blue	2·10	1·90
948	-	6c.+4c. violet	2·10	1·90
949	-	8c.+4c. green	2·50	2·20
950	-	12c.+8c. brown	2·50	55
951	-	30c.+10c. red	3·50	3·50

Windmills:—Vert: 6c. North Holland polder; 12c. Post; 30c. Wip. Horiz: 8c. South Holland polder.

195

1963. Paris Postal Conference Centenary.

952	**195**	30c. blue, green & blk	2·30	1·90

196 Wayside First Aid Post

1963. Red Cross Fund and Centenary (8c.).

953	**196**	4c.+4c. blue and red	70	70
954	-	6c.+4c. violet and red	95	95
955	-	8c.+4c. red and black	1·60	1·30
956	-	12c.+9c. brown and red	50	45
957	-	30c.+9c. green and red	2·75	2·75

Designs:—6c. Books collection-box; 8c. Crosses; 12c. 'International Aid' (Children at meal); 30c. First aid party tending casualty.

197 "Co-operation"

1963. Europa.

958	**197**	12c. orange and brown	50	30
959	**197**	30c. orange and green	2·40	1·60

198 "Auntie Luce sat on a goose ..."

1963. Child Welfare.

960	**198**	4c.+4c. ultramarine & bl	40	45
961	-	6c.+4c. green and red	1·80	1·20
962	-	8c.+4c. brown & green	2·40	1·20
963	-	12c.+9c. violet & yellow	40	45
964	-	30c.+8c. blue and pink	3·25	3·00

Designs:—(Nursery rhymes): 6c. "In the Hague there lives a count ..."; 8c. "One day I passed a puppet's fair ..."; 12c. "Storky, storky, Billy Spoon ..."; 30c. "Ride on a little pram ...".

199 William, Prince of Orange, landing at Scheveningen

1963. 150th Anniv of Kingdom of the Netherlands.

965	**199**	4c. black, bistre and blue	40	40
966	**199**	5c. black, red and green	40	40
967	-	12c. bistre, blue and black	40	40
968	-	30c. red and black	1·10	1·10

Designs:—12c. Triumvirate: Van Hogendorp, Van Limburg, and Van der Duyn van Maasdam; 30c. William I taking oath of allegiance.

200 Knights' Hall, The Hague

1964. 500th Anniv of First States-General Meeting.

969	**200**	12c. black and olive	50	40

201 Guide Dog for the Blind

1964. Cultural, Health and Social Welfare Funds. Animals.

970	**201**	5c.+5c. red, black and olive	95	80
971	-	8c.+5c. brown, black and red	65	55
972	-	12c.+9c. black, grey and bistre	95	45
973	-	30c.+9c. multicoloured	1·10	1·10

Designs:—8c. Three red deer; 12c. Three kittens; 30c. European bison and calf.

202 University Arms

1964. 350th Anniv of Groningen University.

974	**202**	12c. slate	50	40
975	-	30c. brown	65	60

Design:—30c. "AG" monogram.

203 Signal No. 144, Amersfoort Station

1964. 125th Anniv of Netherlands Railways.

976	**203**	15c. black and green	50	40
977	-	40c. black and yellow	1·40	1·30

Design:—40c. Class ELD-4 electric train.

204 Bible and Dove

1964. 150th Anniv of Netherlands Bible Society.

978	**204**	15c. brown	50	40

205 Europa "Flower"

1964. Europa.

979	**205**	15c. green	50	40
980	**205**	20c. brown	1·30	80

1964. 20th Anniv of "BENELUX". As T **150a** of Luxembourg, but smaller 35×22 mm.

981		15c. violet and flesh	50	40

206 Young Artist

1964. Child Welfare.

982	**206**	7c.+3c. blue and green	1·00	95
983	-	10c.+5c. red, pink and green	80	80
984	-	15c.+10c. yellow, black and bistre	50	45
985	-	20c.+10c. red, sepia and mauve	1·20	95
986	-	40c.+15c. green & blue	1·80	1·60

Designs:—10c. Ballet-dancing; 15c. Playing the recorder; 20c. Masquerading; 40c. Toy-making.

207 Queen Juliana

1964. Tenth Anniv of Statute for the Kingdom.

987	**207**	15c. green	50	30

208 *Killed in Action* (Waalwijk) and *Destroyed Town* (Rotterdam) (monuments)

1965. Resistance Commemoration.

988	**208**	7c. black and red	50	45
989	-	15c. black and olive	50	45
990	-	40c. black and red	1·40	1·30

Monuments: —15c. *Docker* (Amsterdam) and *Killed in Action* (Waalwijk); 40c. *Destroyed Town* (Rotterdam) and *Docker* (Amsterdam).

209 Medal of Knight (Class IV)

1965. 150th Anniv of Military William Order.

991	**209**	1g. grey	1·90	1·80

210 ITU Emblem and "Lines of Communication"

1965. Centenary of I.T.U.

992	**210**	20c. blue and drab	50	45
993	**210**	40c. brown and blue	90	70

211 Veere

1965. Cultural, Health and Social Welfare Funds.

994	**211**	8c.+6c. black and yellow	50	45
995	-	10c.+6c. black & turq	80	60
996	-	18c.+12c. black & brn	65	45
997	-	20c.+10c. black & blue	80	60
998	-	40c.+10c. black & green	95	80

Designs:—(Dutch towns): 10c. Thorn; 18c. Dordrecht; 20c. Staveren; 40c. Medemblik.

212 Europa "Sprig"

1965. Europa.

999	**212**	18c. black, red and brown	50	30
1000	**212**	20c. black, red and blue	65	45

213 Girl's Head

1965. Child Welfare. Multicoloured.

1001	8c.+6c. Type **213**	50	45
1002	10c.+6c. Ship	1·30	95
1003	18c.+12c. Boy (vert)	50	45
1004	20c.+10c. Duck-pond	1·70	1·10
1005	40c.+10c. Tractor	2·20	1·60
MS1006	143×124 mm. Nos. 1001x5 and 1003x6	44·00	39·00

214 Marines of 1665 and 1965

1965. Tercentenary of Marine Corps.

1007	**214**	18c. blue and red	50	30

215 "Help them to a safe Haven" (Queen Juliana)

1966. Intergovernmental Committee for European Migration (I.C.E.M.) Fund.

1008	**215**	18c.+7c. yellow & blk	80	45
1009	**215**	40c.+20c. red & black	50	45
MS1010		117×44 mm. Nos. 1008 and 1009x2	4·75	1·90

216 Writing Materials

1966. Cultural, Health and Social Welfare Funds. Gysbert Japicx Commem and 200th Anniv of Netherlands Literary Society. Multicoloured.

1011	10c.+5c. Type **216**	65	60
1012	12c.+8c. Part of MS, Japicx's poem *Wobbelke*	65	60
1013	20c.+10c. Part of miniature, *Knight Walewein*	95	60
1014	25c.+10c. Initial "D" and part of MS, novel, *Ferguut*	1·30	95
1015	40c.+20c. 16th-century printery (woodcut)	95	95

217 Aircraft in Flight

1966. Air (Special Flights).

1016	**217**	25c. multicoloured	40	80

218 Europa "Ship"

1966. Europa.

1017	**218**	20c. green and yellow	50	30
1018	**218**	40c. deep blue and blue	1·40	45

219 Infant

1966. Child Welfare.

1019	**219**	10c.+5c. red and blue	50	45
1020	-	12c.+8c. green and red	50	45
1021	-	20c.+10c. blue and red	50	45
1022	-	25c.+10c. purple & bl	1·30	1·20
1023	-	40c.+20c. red & green	1·30	1·20
MS1024		132×125 mm. Nos. 1019×4, 1020×5, 1021×3	4·25	4·00

Designs:—12c. Young girl; 20c. Boy in water; 25c. Girl with moped; 40c. Young man with horse.

220 Assembly Hall

1967. 125th Anniv of Delft Technological University.

1025	**220**	20c. sepia and yellow	50	30

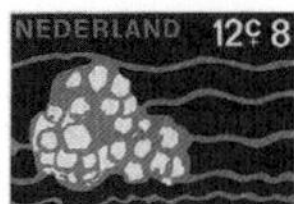

221 Common Northern Whelk Eggs

1967. Cultural, Health and Social Welfare Funds. Marine Fauna.

1026	**221**	12c.+8c. brown & grn	50	45
1027	-	15c.+10c. blue, light blue and deep blue	50	45
1028	-	20c.+10c. multicoloured	50	45
1029	-	25c.+10c. brown, purple and bistre	95	95
1030	-	45c.+20c. mult	1·40	1·20

Designs:—15c. Common northern whelk; 20c. Common blue mussel; 25c. Jellyfish; 45c. Crab.

222 Cogwheels

1967. Europa.

1031	**222**	20c. blue and light blue	80	45
1032	**222**	45c. purple & light purple	1·90	1·20

223 Netherlands 5c. Stamp of 1852

1967. "Amphilex 67" Stamp Exn, Amsterdam.

1035	**223**	20c. blue and black	5·25	4·00
1036	-	25c. red and black	5·25	4·00
1037	-	75c. green and black	5·25	4·00

Designs:—25c. Netherlands 10c. stamp of 1864; 75c. Netherlands 20c. stamp of 1867.

Nos. 1035/7 were sold at the exhibition and at post offices at 3g.70, which included entrance fee to the exhibition.

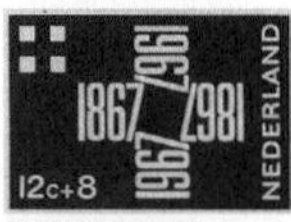

224 "1867–1967"

1967. Centenary of Dutch Red Cross.

1038	12c.+8c. blue and red	55	50
1039	15c.+10c. red	70	65
1040	20c.+10c. olive and red	55	50
1041	25c.+10c. green and red	90	80
1042	45c.+20c. grey and red	1·40	1·30

Designs: —12c. Type **224**; 15c. Red crosses; 20c. "NRK" ("Nederlandsche Rood Kruis") in the form of a cross; 25c. Maltese cross and "red" crosses; 45c. "100" in the form of a cross.

225 Porcupine Lullaby

1967. Child Welfare. Multicoloured.

1043	12c.+8c. Type **225**	55	50
1044	15c.+10c. The Whistling Kettle	55	50
1045	20c.+10c. Dikkertje Dap (giraffe)	55	50
1046	25c.+10c. The Flower-seller	2·40	1·60
1047	45c.+20c. Pippeloentje (bear)	2·50	1·80
MS1048	150×108 mm. Nos. 1043x3, 1044x4 1045x3	8·25	7·50

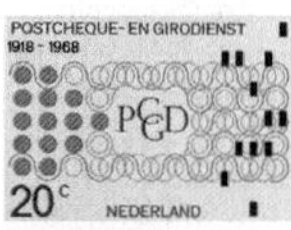

226 "Financial Automation"

1968. 50th Anniv of Netherlands Postal Cheque and Clearing Service.

1049	**226**	20c. red, black and yellow	55	30

227 St. Servatius' Bridge, Maastricht

1968. Cultural, Health and Social Welfare Funds. Dutch Bridges.

1050	**227**	12c.+8c. green	90	80
1051	-	15c.+10c. brown	1·20	1·10
1052	-	20c.+10c. red	70	50
1053	-	25c.+10c. blue	90	80
1054	-	45c.+20c. blue	1·60	1·40

Bridges:—15c. Magere ("Narrow"), Amsterdam; 20c. Railway, Culemborg; 25c. Van Brienenoord, Rotterdam; 45c. Oosterschelde, Zeeland.

228 Europa "Key"

1968. Europa.

1055	**228**	20c. blue	70	65
1056	**228**	45c. red	1·80	1·30

229 *Wilhelmus van Nassouwe*

1968. 400th Anniv of Dutch National Anthem, "Wilhelmus".

1057	**229**	20c. multicoloured	55	30

230 Wright Type A and Cessna 150F

1968. Dutch Aviation Anniversaries.

1058	12c. black, red and mauve	55	30
1059	20c. black, emerald and green	55	30
1060	45c. black, blue and green	2·30	2·20

Designs and Events:—12c. T **230** (60th anniv (1967) of Royal Netherlands Aeronautical Assn); 20c. Fokker F.II H-NABC and Fokker F.28 Fellowship aircraft (50th anniv (1969) of Royal Netherlands Aircraft Factories Fokker); 45c. Airco de Havilland D.H.9B biplane H-NABE and Douglas DC-9 airliner (50th anniv (1969) of Royal Dutch Airlines KLM).

231 Goblin

1968. Child Welfare.

1061	**231**	12c.+8c. pink, black and green	55	50
1062	-	15c.+10c. pink, blue and black	55	50
1063	-	20c.+10c. blue, green and black	55	50
1064	-	25c.+10c. red, yellow and black	3·50	3·25
1065	-	45c.+20c. yellow, orange and black	3·50	3·25
MS1066		106½×151 mm. Nos. 1061 (3), 1062 (2), 1063 (3)	9·75	8·75

Designs:—15c. Giant; 20c. Witch; 25c. Dragon; 45c. Sorcerer.

232 "I A O" (Internationale Arbeidsorganisatie)

1969. 50th Anniv of I.L.O.

1067	**232**	25c. red and black	70	30
1068	**232**	45c. blue and black	1·40	1·10

233 Queen Juliana

1969. (a) Type **233**.

1069	**233**	25c. red	1·10	30
1069b	**233**	30c. brown	55	30
1070	**233**	35c. blue	55	30
1071	**233**	40c. red	70	30
1072	**233**	45c. blue	70	30
1073	**233**	50c. purple	90	30
1073bc	**233**	55c. red	90	30
1074a	**233**	60c. blue	1·10	30
1075	**233**	70c. brown	1·20	30
1076	**233**	75c. green	1·20	30
1077	**233**	80c. red	1·40	30
1077a	**233**	90c. grey	1·40	30

(b) Size 22×33 mm.

1078	1g. green	1·60	30
1079	1g.25 lake	1·90	30
1080	1g.50 brown	2·50	30
1081	2g. mauve	3·25	30
1082	2g.50 blue	4·00	30
1083	5g. grey	8·00	30
1084	10g. blue	16·00	1·60

DESIGN: 1g.to 10g. similar to Type **233**.

234 Villa, Huis ter Heide (1915)

1969. Cultural, Health and Social Welfare Funds. 20th-century Dutch Architecture.

1085	**234**	12c.+8c. black & brn	1·40	1·30
1086	-	15c.+10c. black, red and blue	1·40	1·30
1087	-	20c.+10c. black & vio	1·40	1·30
1088	-	25c.+10c. brown & grn	1·40	50
1089	-	45c.+20c. black, blue and yellow	1·40	1·30

Designs:—15c. Private House, Utrecht (1924); 20c. Open-air School, Amsterdam (1930); 25c. Orphanage, Amsterdam (1960); 45c. Congress Building, The Hague (1969).

235 Colonnade

1969. Europa.

1090	**235**	25c. blue	55	50
1091	**235**	45c. red	2·10	1·90

236 Stylized Crab (of Cancer)

1969. 20th Anniv of Queen Wilhelmina Cancer Fund.

1092	**236**	12c.+8c. violet	90	80
1093	**236**	25c.+10c. orange	1·80	50
1094	**236**	45c.+20c. green	2·75	2·40

1969. 25th Anniv of "BENELUX" Customs Union. As T **186** of Luxembourg.

1095 25c. multicoloured 55 30

238 Erasmus

1969. 500th Birth Anniv of Desiderius Erasmus.

1096	**238**	25c. purple on green	55	30

239 Child with Violin

1969. Child Welfare.

1097	-	12c.+8c. black, yellow and blue	55	50
1098	**239**	15c.+10c. black and red	55	50
1099	-	20c.+10c. black, yellow and red	3·25	3·00
1100	-	25c.+10c. black, red and yellow	55	50

1101	-	45c.+20c. black, red and green	3·25	3·00
MS1102 150×99 mm. Nos. 1097x4, 1098x4, 1100x2			14·00	13·00

Designs:—Vert: 12c. Child with recorder; 20c. Child with drum. Horiz: 25c. Three choristers; 45c. Two dancers.

240 Queen Juliana and "Sunlit Road"

1969. 25th Anniv of Statute for the Kingdom.

1103	**240**	25c. multicoloured	55	30

241 Prof. E. M. Meijers (author of *Burgerlijk Wetboek*)

1970. Introduction of New Netherlands Civil Code ("Burgerlijk Wetboek").

1104	**241**	25c. ultramarine, green and blue	55	30

242 Netherlands Pavilion

1970. Expo 70 World Fair, Osaka, Japan.

1105	**242**	25c. grey, blue and red	55	30

243 Circle to Square

1970. Cultural, Health and Social Welfare Funds.

1106	**243**	12c.+8c. black on yell	1·80	1·60
1107	-	15c.+10c. black on silver	1·80	1·60
1108	-	20c.+10c. black	1·80	1·60
1109	-	25c.+10c. black on bl	1·80	1·40
1110	-	45c.+20c. white on grey	1·80	1·60

Designs:—15c. Parallel planes in cube; 20c. Overlapping scales; 25c. Concentric circles in transition; 45c. Spirals.

244 "V" Symbol

1970. 25th Anniv of Liberation.

1111	**244**	12c. red, blue and brown	55	30

245 "Flaming Sun"

1970. Europa.

1112	**245**	25c. red	90	30
1113	**245**	45c. blue	1·80	1·60

246 "Work and Co-operation"

1970. Inter-Parliamentary Union Conference.

1114	**246**	25c. green, black and grey	90	30

247 Globe on Plinth

1970. 25th Anniv of United Nations.

1115	**247**	45c. black, violet & blue	1·80	1·30

248 Human Heart

1970. Netherlands Heart Foundation.

1116	**248**	12c.+8c. red, black and yellow	1·20	1·10
1117	**248**	25c.+10c. red, black and mauve	1·20	80
1118	**248**	45c.+20c. red, black and green	1·20	1·10

249 Toy Block

1970. Child Welfare. "The Child and the Cube".

1119	**249**	12c.+8c. blue, violet and green	55	50
1120	-	15c.+10c. green, blue and yellow	2·75	1·90
1121	**249**	20c.+10c. mauve, red and violet	2·75	1·90
1122	-	25c.+10c. red, yellow and mauve	55	50
1123	**249**	45c.+20c. grey, cream and black	3·00	2·50
MS1124 126×145 mm. Nos. 1119x9, 1122x2			24·00	22·00

Design:—15c., 25c. As Type **249**, but showing underside of block.

250 "Fourteenth Census 1971"

1971. 14th Netherlands Census.

1125	**250**	15c. purple	55	30

251 "50 years of Adult University Education"

1971. Cultural, Health and Social Welfare Funds. Other designs show 15th-century wooden statues by unknown artists.

1126	**251**	15c.+10c. black, red and yellow	1·90	1·60
1127	-	20c.+10c. black and green on green	1·90	1·60
1128	-	25c.+10c. black and orange on orange	1·90	80
1129	-	30c.+15c. black and blue on blue	1·90	1·60
1130	-	45c.+20c. black and red on pink	1·90	1·60

Statues:—20c. *Apostle Paul*; 25c. *Joachim and Ann*; 30c. *John the Baptist and Scribes*; 45c. *Ann, Mary and Christ-Child* (detail).

252 Europa Chain

1971. Europa.

1131	**252**	25c. yellow, red and black	90	30
1132	**252**	45c. yellow, blue & black	1·80	1·30

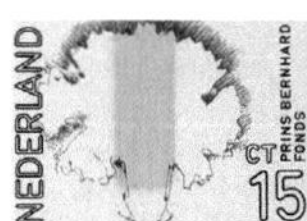

253 Carnation Symbol of Prince Bernhard Fund

1971. Prince Bernhard's 60th Birthday.

1133	**253**	15c. yellow, grey & black	55	30
1134	-	20c. multicoloured	1·40	50
1135	-	25c. multicoloured	55	30
1136	-	45c.+20c. black, purple and yellow	3·25	3·00

Designs:—Horiz: 20c. Panda symbol of World Wildlife Fund. Vert: 25c. Prince Bernhard, Boeing 747 and Fokker F.27 Friendship; 45c. Statue, Borobudur Temple, Indonesia.

254 "The Good Earth"

1971. Child Welfare.

1137	**254**	15c.+10c. red, purple and black	55	50
1138	-	20c.+10c. mult	55	50
1139	-	25c.+10c. mult	55	50
1140	-	30c.+15c. blue, violet and black	2·30	1·30
1141	-	45c.+20c. blue, green and black	3·25	2·40
MS1142 100×145 mm. Nos. 1137x6, 1138 and 1139x2			12·50	11·00

Designs:—Vert: 20c. Butterfly; 45c. Reflecting water. Horiz: 25c. Sun waving; 30c. Moon winking.

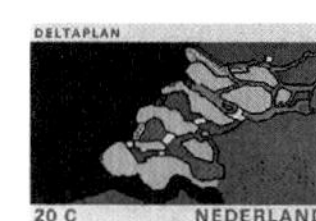

255 Delta Map

1972. Delta Sea-Defences Plan.

1143	**255**	20c. multicoloured	55	30

256 Fruits

1972. Cultural, Health and Social Welfare Funds. "Floriade Flower Show" (20c., 25c.) and "Holland Arts Festival" (30c., 45c.). Multicoloured.

1144		20c.+10c. Type **256**	1·80	1·60
1145		25c.+10c. Flower	1·80	1·60
1146		30c.+15c. Sunlit Landscape	1·80	80
1147		45c.+25c. Music	1·80	1·60

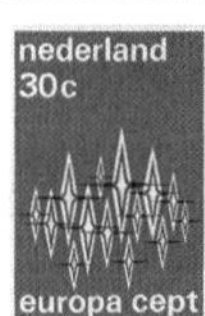

257 "Communications"

1972. Europa.

1148	**257**	30c. brown and blue	90	30
1149	**257**	45c. brown and orange	1·80	1·30

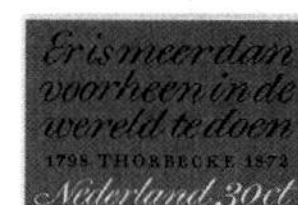

258 "There is more to be done in the world than ever before" (Thorbecke)

1972. Death Centenary of J. R. Thorbecke (statesman).

1150	**258**	30c. black and blue	90	50

259 Netherlands Flag

1972. 400th Anniv of Netherlands Flag.

1151	**259**	20c. multicoloured	90	30
1152	**259**	25c. multicoloured	1·30	30

260 Hurdling

1972. Olympic Games, Munich. Multicoloured.

1153		20c. Type **260**	55	50
1154		30c. Diving	55	50
1155		45c. Cycling	1·60	1·40

261 Red Cross

1972. Netherlands Red Cross.

1156	**261**	5c. red	55	30
1157	-	20c.+10c. red and pink	90	80
1158	-	25c.+10c. red & orange	1·80	1·60
1159	-	30c.+15c. red & black	1·20	65
1160	-	45c.+25c. red and blue	1·80	1·60

Designs:—20c. Accident services; 25c. Blood transfusion; 30c. Refugee relief; 45c. Child care.

262 Prince Willem-Alexander

1972. Child Welfare. Multicoloured.

1161		25c.+15c. Type **262**	55	50
1162		30c.+10c. Prince Johan Friso (horiz)	1·60	95
1163		35c.+15c. Prince Constantin (horiz)	1·40	50
1164		50c.+20c. The Three Princes (horiz)	5·25	4·00
MS1165 126×109 mm. Nos. 1161×4 and 1163×3			12·50	11·00

263 Tulips in Bloom

1973. Tulip Exports.

1166	**263**	25c. multicoloured	70	30

264 *De Zeven Provincien* (De Ruyter's flagship)

1973. Cultural, Health and Social Welfare Funds. Dutch Ships. Multicoloured.

1167		25c.+15c. Type **264**	1·80	1·60
1168		30c.+10c. *W.A. Scholten* (steamship) (horiz)	1·80	1·60
1169		35c.+15c. *Veendam* (liner) (horiz)	1·80	80
1170		50c.+20c. Fishing boat (from etching by R. Nooms)	1·80	1·60

265 Europa "Posthorn"

1973. Europa.

1171	**265**	35c. light blue and blue	90	30
1172	**265**	50c. blue and violet	1·80	1·30

266 Hockey-players

1973. Events and Anniversaries. Multicoloured.

1173	25c. Type **266**	70	30
1174	30c. Gymnastics	1·80	80
1175	35c. Dish aerial (vert)	1·10	50
1176	50c. Rainbow	1·80	1·10

Events:—Vert: 25c. 75th anniv of Royal Netherlands Hockey Association; 30c. World Gymnastics Championships, Rotterdam. Horiz: 35c. Opening of Satellite Station, Burum; 50c. Centenary of World Meteorological Organization.

267 Queen Juliana

1973. Silver Jubilee of Queen Juliana's Accession.

1177	**267**	40c. multicoloured	70	50

268 "Co-operation"

1973. International Development Co-operation.

1178	**268**	40c. multicoloured	70	50

269 Chess

1973. Child Welfare.

1179	**269**	25c.+15c. red, yellow and black	55	50
1180	-	30c.+10c. green, mauve and black	1·20	80
1181	-	40c.+20c. yellow, green and black	55	50
1182	-	50c.+20c. blue, yellow and black	3·75	3·25
MS1183		74×144 mm. Nos. 1179×2, 1180 and 1181×3	12·50	11·00

Designs: 30c. Noughts and crosses; 40c. Maze; 50c. Dominoes.

270 Northern Goshawk

1974. "Nature and Environment". Multicoloured.

1184	25c. Type **270**	1·20	80
1185	25c. Tree	1·20	80
1186	25c. Fisherman and frog	1·20	80

Nos. 1184/6 were issued together, *se-tenant*, forming a composite design.

271 Bandsmen (World Band Contest, Kerkrade)

1974. Cultural, Health and Social Welfare Funds.

1187	**271**	25c.+15c. multicoloured	1·80	1·60
1188	-	30c.+10c. multicoloured	1·80	1·60
1189	-	40c.+20c. brown, black and red	1·80	80
1190	-	50c.+20c. purple, black and red	1·80	1·60

Designs:—30c. Dancers and traffic-lights (Modern Ballet); 40c. Herman Heijermans; 50c. Kniertje (character from Heijermans' play *Op hoop van zegan*). The 40c. and 50c. commemorate the 50th death anniv of the playwright.

272 Football on Pitch

1974. Sporting Events.

1191	**272**	25c. multicoloured	90	50
1192	-	40c. yellow, red & mauve	90	50

Designs and Events:—Horiz: 25c. (World Cup Football Championship, West Germany). Vert: 40c. Hand holding tennis ball (75th anniv of Royal Dutch Lawn Tennis Association).

273 Netherlands Cattle

1974. Anniversaries. Multicoloured.

1193	25c. Type **273**	10·00	2·40
1194	25c. Cancer	2·75	50
1195	40c. *Suzanna* (lifeboat) seen through binoculars	2·75	50

Events and Anniversaries:—No. 1193, Cent of Netherlands Cattle Herdbook Society; No. 1194, 25th anniv of Queen Wilhelmina Cancer Research Fund; No. 1195, 150th anniv of Dutch Lifeboat Service.

274 "BENELUX" (30th Anniv of Benelux (Customs Union))

1974. International Anniversaries.

1196	**274**	30c. green, turquoise & blue	90	50
1197	-	45c. deep blue, silver & blue	90	50
1198	-	45c. yellow, blue & black	90	50

Designs:—Vert: No. 1197, NATO emblem (25th anniv); 1198, Council of Europe emblem (25th anniv).

275 Hands with Letters

1974. Centenary of Universal Postal Union.

1199	**275**	60c. multicoloured	90	65

276 Boy with Hoop

1974. 50th Anniv of Child Welfare Issues. Early Photographs.

1200	**276**	30c.+15c. brown & blk	55	50
1201	-	35c.+20c. brown	1·20	80
1202	-	45c.+20c. black	1·20	50
1203	-	60c.+20c. black	3·25	2·40
MS1204		75×145 mm. Nos. 1200×4 and 1201/2	7·00	6·50

Designs:—35c. Child and baby; 45c. Two young girls; 60c. Girl sitting on balustrade.

277 Amsterdam

1975. Anniversaries. Multicoloured.

1205	30c. Type **277**	90	50
1206	30c. Synagogue and map	90	65
1207	35c. Type **277**	90	50
1208	45c. "Window" in human brain	1·10	50

Anniversaries: Nos. 1205, 1207, Amsterdam (700th anniv); No. 1206, Portuguese-Israelite Synagogue, Amsterdam (300th anniv); No. 1208, Leyden University and university education (400th anniv).

278 St. Hubertus Hunting Lodge, De Hoge Veluwe National Park

1975. Cultural, Health and Social Welfare Funds. National Monument Year. Preserved Monuments. Multicoloured.

1209	35c.+20c. Type **278**	1·20	1·10
1210	40c.+15c. Bergijnhof (Beguinage), Amsterdam (vert)	1·20	1·10
1211	50c.+20c. "Kuiperspoort" (Cooper's gate), Middelburg (vert)	1·60	1·10
1212	60c.+20c. Orvelte village, Drenthe	2·10	1·90

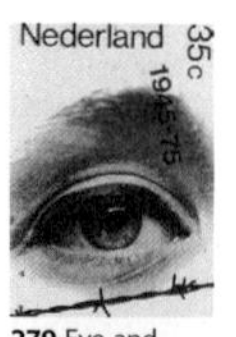

279 Eye and Barbed Wire

1975. 30th Anniv of Liberation.

1213	**279**	35c. black and red	90	50

280 Company Emblem and *Stad Middelburg* (schooner)

1975. Centenary of Zeeland Shipping Company.

1214	**280**	35c. multicoloured	1·10	50

281 Dr. Albert Schweitzer crossing Lambarene River

1975. Birth Centenary of Dr. Schweitzer (medical missionary).

1215	**281**	50c. multicoloured	1·10	50

282 Man and Woman on "Playing-card"

1975. International Events. Multicoloured.

1216	35c. Type **282** (Int Women's Year)	1·10	50
1217	50c. Metric scale (Metre Convention cent) (horiz)	1·10	50

283 Braille Reading

1975. 150th Anniv of Invention of Braille.

1218	**283**	35c. multicoloured	1·10	50

284 Dutch 25c. Coins

1975. Savings Campaign.

1219	**284**	50c. grey, green and blue	1·10	50

285 *Four Orphans* (C. Simons), Torenstraat Orphanage, Medemblik

1975. Child Welfare. Historic Ornamental Stones. Multicoloured.

1220	35c.+15c. Type **285**	55	50
1221	40c.+15c. *Milkmaid* Kooltuin Alkmaar	1·80	95
1222	50c.+25c. *Four Sons of Aymon seated on Beyaert*, Herengracht	90	50
1223	60c.+25c. *Life at the Orphanage*, Molenstraat Orphanage, Gorinchem	2·75	1·80
MS1224	145×75 mm. Nos. 1220×3 and 1222×2	6·25	5·50

286 18th-century Lottery Ticket

1976. 250th Anniv of National Lottery.

1225	**286**	35c. multicoloured	70	50

287 Numeral

1976. (a) Ordinary gum.

1226	**287**	5c. grey	20	15
1227	**287**	10c. blue	35	25
1228	**287**	25c. violet	55	30
1229	**287**	40c. brown	90	30
1230	**287**	45c. blue	90	30
1231	**287**	50c. mauve	1·10	30
1232	**287**	55c. green	1·40	30
1233	**287**	60c. yellow	1·60	30
1234	**287**	65c. brown	2·75	30
1235	**287**	70c. violet	2·75	30
1236	**287**	80c. mauve	3·50	30

(b) Self-adhesive gum.

1237	**287**	5c. grey	35	15
1238	**287**	10c. blue	55	25
1239	**287**	25c. violet	70	30

288 West European Hedgehog

1976. Cultural, Health and Social Welfare Funds. Nature Protection (40, 75c.) and Anniversaries. Multicoloured.

1241	40c.+20c. Type **288**	1·80	1·10
1242	45c.+20c. Open book (vert)	1·60	1·10
1243	55c.+20c. People and organization initials	1·60	50
1244	75c.+25c. Frog and spawn (vert)	2·10	1·60

Anniversaries:—No. 1242, 175th anniv of Primary education and centenary of Agricultural education; No. 1243, 75th anniv of Social Security Bank and legislation.

289 Admiral Michiel de Ruyter (statue)

1976. 300th Death Anniv of Admiral Michiel de Ruyter.

1245	**289**	55c. multicoloured	90	30

290 Guillaume Groen van Prinsterer

1976. Death Centenary of Guillaume Groen van Prinsterer (statesman).

1246	**290**	55c. multicoloured	90	30

291 Detail of 18th-century Calendar

1976. Bicentenary of American Revolution.

1247	**291**	75c. multicoloured	1·20	65

292 Long-distance Marchers

1976. Sport and Recreation Anniversaries. Mult.

1248	40c. Type **292**	90	50
1249	55c. Runners "photo-finish"	90	50

Anniversaries:—40c. 60th Nijmegen Long-distance March; 55c. Royal Dutch Athletics Society (75th anniv).

293 The Art of Printing

1976. Anniversaries.

1250	**293**	45c. red and blue	1·20	50
1251	-	55c.+25c. mult	1·40	95

Designs and Events:—45c. Type **293** (75th anniv of Netherlands Printers' organization); 55c. Rheumatic patient "Within Care" (50th anniv of Dutch Anti-Rheumatism Association).

294 Dutch Tjalk and Reclaimed Land

1976. Zuider Zee Project—Reclamation and Urbanization. Multicoloured.

1252	**294**	40c. blue, olive and red	1·20	50
1253	-	75c. yellow, red and blue	1·80	95

Design:—75c. Duck flying over reclaimed land.

295 Queen Wilhelmina 4½c. Stamp, 1919

1976. Amphilex '77 International Stamp Exhibition, Amsterdam (1977) (1st series). Stamp Portraits of Queen Wilhelmina. Multicoloured.

1254		55c.+55c. blue, deep grey and grey	1·90	1·60
1255	**295**	55c.+55c. purple, deep grey and grey	1·90	1·60
1256	-	55c.+55c. brown, deep grey and grey	1·90	1·60
1257	-	75c.+75c. turquoise, deep grey and grey	1·90	1·60
1258	-	75c.+75c. blue, deep grey and grey	1·90	1·60

Designs:—No. 1254, 5c. stamp, 1891; No. 1256, 25c. stamp, 1924; No. 1257, 15c. stamp, 1940; No. 1258, 25c. stamp, 1947.

See also Nos. 1273/**MS**1277.

296 *Football* (J. Raats)

1976. Child Welfare. Children's Paintings. Mult.

1259	40c.+20c. Type **296**	90	50
1260	45c.+20c. *Boat* (L. Jacobs)	1·10	50
1261	55c.+20c. *Elephant* (M. Lugtenburg)	1·20	50
1262	75c.+25c. *Caravan* (A. Seeleman)	3·75	1·60
MS1263	145×75 mm. Nos. 1259/61×2	7·00	4·00

297 Ballot-paper and Pencil

1977. National Events. Multicoloured.

1264	40c. "Energy" (vert)	90	50
1265	45c. Type **297**	90	50

Events:—40c. "Be wise with energy" campaign; 45c. Elections to Lower House of States-General.

See also No. 1268.

298 Spinoza

1977. 300th Death Anniv of Barach (Benedictus) de Spinoza (philosopher).

1266	**298**	75c. multicoloured	1·60	65

299 Early Type Faces and "a" on Bible Script

1977. 500th Anniv of Printing of "Delft Bible".

1267	**299**	55c. multicoloured	1·10	80

1977. Elections to Lower House of States-General. As T **297** but also inscribed "**25 MEI '77**".

1268	45c. multicoloured	90	50

300 Altar of Goddess Nehalennia

1977. Cultural, Health and Social Welfare Funds. Roman Archaeological Discoveries.

1269	-	40c.+20c. mult	1·20	65
1270	**300**	45c.+20c. black, stone and green	1·40	65
1271	-	55c.+20c. black, blue and red	1·40	65
1272	-	75c.+25c. black, grey and yellow	1·80	1·10

Designs:—40c. Baths, Heerlen; 55c. Remains of Zwammerdam ship; 75c. Parade helmet.

1977. Amphilex 1977 International Stamp Exhibition, Amsterdam (2nd series). As T **295**.

1273	55c.+45c. grn, brn & grey	1·10	50
1274	55c.+45c. blue, brn & grey	1·10	50
1275	55c.+45c. blue, brn & grey	1·10	50
1276	55c.+45c. red, brn & grey	1·10	50
MS1277	100×72 mm. Nos. 1273 and 1276	2·75	1·60

Designs:—No. 1273, Queen Wilhelmina 1g. stamp, 1898; No. 1274, Queen Wilhelmina 20c. stamp, 1923; No. 1275, Queen Wilhelmina 12½c. stamp, 1938; No. 1276, Queen Wilhelmina 10c. stamp, 1948.

301 "Kaleidoscope"

1977. Bicentenary of Netherlands Society for Industry and Commerce.

1278	**301**	55c. multicoloured	90	30

302 Man in Wheelchair and Maze of Steps

1977. Anniversaries.

1279	**302**	40c. brown, green & blue	90	50
1280	-	45c. multicoloured	90	50
1281	-	55c. multicoloured	90	50

Designs:—Horiz: 40c. Type **302** (50th anniv of AVO Nederland); 45c. Diagram of water current (50th anniv of Delft Hydraulic Laboratory). Vert: 55c. Teeth (centenary of dentists' training in Netherlands).

303 Risk of Drowning

1977. Child Welfare. Dangers to Children. Mult.

1282	40c.+20c. Type **303**	90	50
1283	45c.+20c. Medicine cabinet (poisons)	90	50
1284	55c.+20c. Balls in road (traffic)	90	50
1285	75c.+25c. Matches (fire)	1·80	1·30
MS1286	75×144 mm. Nos. 1282/4×2	5·50	4·00

304 "Postcode"

1978. Introduction of Postcodes.

1287	**304**	40c. red and blue	90	30
1288	**304**	45c. red and blue	1·10	30

305 Makkum Dish

1978. Cultural, Health and Social Welfare Funds. Multicoloured.

1289	40c.+20c. Anna Maria van Schurman (writer)	1·10	65
1290	45c.+20c. Passage from letter by Belle de Zuylen (Mme. de Charriere)	1·20	65
1291	55c.+20c. Delft dish	1·40	65
1292	75c.+25c. Type **305**	1·60	95

306 "Human Rights" Treaty

1978. European Series.

1293	**306**	45c. grey, black and blue	90	50
1294	-	55c. black, stone and orange	90	50

Design:—55c. Haarlem Town Hall (Europa).

307 Chess

1978. Sports.

1295	**307**	40c. multicoloured	90	50
1296	-	45c. red and blue	1·10	50

Design:—45c. The word "Korfbal".

308 Kidney Donor

1978. Health Care. Multicoloured.

1297	**308**	40c. black, blue and red	90	50
1298	-	45c. multicoloured	90	50
1299	-	55c.+25c. red, grey and black	90	65
MS1300		144×50 mm. No. 1299×3	3·00	2·75

Designs:—Vert: 45c. Heart and torch. Horiz: 55c. Red crosses on world map.

309 Epaulettes

1978. 150th Anniv of Royal Military Academy, Breda.

1301	**309**	55c. multicoloured	90	50

310 Verkade as Hamlet

1978. Birth Centenary of Eduard Rutger Verkade (actor and producer).

1302	**310**	45c. multicoloured	90	50

311 Boy ringing Doorbell

1978. Child Welfare. Multicoloured.

1303	40c.+20c. Type **311**	90	50
1304	45c.+20c. Child reading	95	55
1305	55c.+20c. Boy writing (vert)	95	55
1306	75c.+25c. Girl and blackboard	1·80	1·30

MS1307	144×75 mm. Nos. 1303/5×2	5·50	4·00

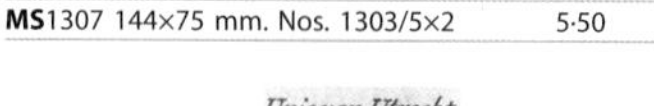

312 Clasped Hands and Arrows

1979. 400th Anniv of Treaty of Utrecht.

1308	**312**	55c. blue	1·10	50

313 Names of European Community Members

1979. First Direct Elections to European Assembly.

1309	**313**	45c. red, blue and black	90	50

314 Queen Juliana

1979. Queen Juliana's 70th Birthday.

1310	**314**	55c. multicoloured	1·10	50

315 Fragment of *Psalmen Trilogie* (J. Andriessen)

1979. Cultural, Health and Social Welfare Funds.

1311	**315**	40c.+20c. grey and red	1·10	65
1312	-	45c.+20c. grey and red	1·20	65
1313	-	55c.+20c. mult	1·40	50
1314	-	75c.+25c. mult	1·60	95

Designs and Events:—150th anniv of Musical Society; 45c. Choir. Restoration of St. John's Church, Gouda (stained glass windows); 55c. Mary (detail, *Birth of Christ*); 75c. William of Orange (detail, *Relief of Leyden*).

316 Netherlands Stamps and Magnifying Glass

1979. Europa and 75th Anniv of Scheveningen Radio. Multicoloured.

1315	55c. Type **316**	90	30
1316	75c. Liner and Morse Key	1·40	65

317 Map of Chambers of Commerce

1979. 175th Anniv of First Dutch Chamber of Commerce, Maastricht.

1317	**317**	45c. multicoloured	90	50

318 Action Shot of Football Match

1979. Anniversaries. Multicoloured.

1318	45c. Type **318** (centenary of organized football)	90	30
1319	55c. Women's suffrage meeting (60th anniv of Women's suffrage) (vert)	1·10	30

319 Porch of Old Amsterdam Theatre

1979. 300th Death Annivs of Joost van den Vondel (poet) and Jan Steen (painter). Multicoloured.

1320		40c. Type **319**	90	30
1321		45c. *Gay Company* (detail) (Jan Steen)	90	30

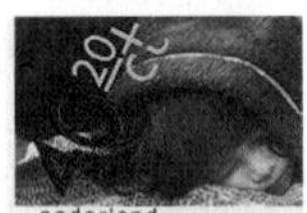

320 Hindustani Girl on Father's Shoulder (The Right to Love)

1979. Child Welfare. International Year of the Child.

1322	**320**	40c.+20c. grey, red and yellow	90	50
1323	-	45c.+20c. grey, red and black	95	55
1324	-	55c.+20c. grey, black and yellow	95	55
1325	-	75c.+25c. black, blue and red	1·80	95
MS1326		144×75 mm. Nos. 1322/4, each×2	5·50	4·00

Designs:—Horiz: 45c. Chilean child from refugee camp (The Right to Medical Care). Vert: 55c. Senegalese boy from Sahel area (The Right to Food); 75c. Class from Albert Cuyp School, Amsterdam (The Right to Education).

321 A. F. de Savornin Lohman

1980. Dutch Politicians. Multicoloured.

1327		45c. Type **321** (Christian Historical Union)	90	30
1328		50c. P. J. Troelstra (Socialist Party)	1·10	30
1329		60c. P. J. Oud (Liberal Party)	1·20	30

322 Dunes

1980. Cultural, Health and Social Welfare Funds. Multicoloured.

1330		45c.+20c. Type **322**	1·10	65
1331		50c.+20c. Country estate (vert)	1·10	65
1332		60c.+25c. Lake District	1·10	65
1333		80c.+35c. Moorland	1·50	95

323 Avro Type 683 Lancaster dropping Food Parcels

1980. 35th Anniv of Liberation. Multicoloured.

1334		45c. Type **323**	1·20	30
1335		60c. Anne Frank (horiz)	1·40	30

324 Queen Beatrix and New Church, Amsterdam

1980. Installation of Queen Beatrix.

1336	**324**	60c. blue, red and yellow	1·10	15
1337	**324**	65c. blue, red and yellow	1·20	15

325 Young Stamp Collectors

1980. Jupostex 1980 Stamp Exhibition, Eindhoven, and Dutch Society of Stamp Dealers Show, The Hague.

1338	**325**	50c. multicoloured	90	50

326 "Flight"

1980. Air. (Special Flights).

1339	**326**	1g. blue and black	1·80	1·60

327 Bridge Players and Cards

1980. Sports Events. Multicoloured.

1340		50c. Type **327** (Bridge Olympiad, Valkenburg)	1·10	30
1341		60c.+25c. Sportswoman in wheelchair (Olympics for the Disabled, Arnhem and Veenendaal)	1·40	65

328 Road Haulage

1980. Transport.

1342	**328**	50c. multicoloured	90	30
1343	-	60c. blue, brown & black	1·10	30
1344	-	80c. multicoloured	1·40	50

Designs:—60c. Rail transport; 80c. Motorized canal barge.

329 Queen Wilhelmina

1980. Europa.

1345	**329**	60c. black, red and blue	1·20	30
1346	-	80c. black, red and blue	1·60	50

Design:—80c. Sir Winston Churchill.

330 Abraham Kuyper (first rector) and University Seal

1980. Centenary of Amsterdam Free University.

1347	**330**	50c. multicoloured	90	30

331 "Pop-up" Book

1980. Child Welfare. Multicoloured.

1348		45c.+20c. Type **331**	90	50
1349		50c.+20c. Child flying on a book (vert)	1·10	65
1350		60c.+30c. Boy reading *Kikkerkoning* (vert)	1·10	50
1351		80c.+30c. Dreaming in a book	1·80	1·30
MS1352		144×75 mm. Nos. 1348×2 and 1350×3	5·50	3·75

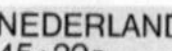

332 Saltmarsh

1981. Cultural, Health and Social Welfare Funds. Multicoloured.

1353		45c.+20c. Type **332**	1·10	50
1354		55c.+25c. Dyke	1·20	50
1355		60c.+25c. Drain	1·40	50
1356		65c.+30c. Cultivated land	1·60	50

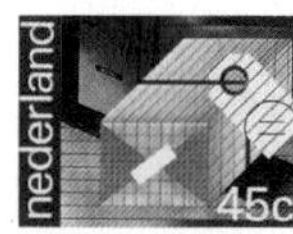

333 Parcel (Parcel Post)

1981. P.T.T. Centenaries. Multicoloured.

1357		45c. Type **333**	80	30
1358		55c. Telephone, dish aerial and telephone directory page (public telephone service)	90	30
1359		65c. Savings bank books, deposit transfer card and savings bank stamps (National Savings Bank)	95	30
MS1360		145×75 mm. Nos. 1357/9	2·75	1·90

334 Huis ten Bosch Royal Palace, The Hague

1981

1361	**334**	55c. multicoloured	1·10	50

335 Carillon

1981. Europa. Multicoloured.

1362		45c. Type **335**	1·10	30
1363		65c. Barrel organ	1·60	30

336 Council of State Emblem and Maps of 1531 and 1981

1981. 450th Anniv of Council of State.

1364	**336**	65c. orange, deep orange and red	1·20	30

337 Marshalling Yard, Excavator and Ship's Screw

1981. Industrial and Agricultural Exports. Mult.

1365		45c. Type **337**	90	30
1366		55c. Inner port, cast-iron component and weighing machine	1·10	30
1367		60c. Airport, tomato and lettuce	1·20	65
1368		65c. Motorway interchange, egg and cheese	1·40	30

338 "Integration in Society"

1981. Child Welfare. Integration of Disabled Children. Multicoloured.

1369		45c.+25c. Type **338**	90	30
1370		55c.+20c. "Integration in the Family" (vert)	1·10	80
1371		60c.+25c. Child vaccinated against polio (Upper Volta project) (vert)	1·20	80
1372		65c.+30c. "Integration among Friends"	1·40	30
MS1373		144×76 mm. Nos. 1369×3 and 1372×2	6·25	3·25

339 Queen Beatrix

1981

1374	**339**	65c. brown and black	1·20	25
1375	**339**	70c. lilac and black	1·60	25
1376	**339**	75c. pink and black	1·60	25
1377	**339**	90c. green and black	1·60	25
1378	**339**	1g. lilac and black	1·60	30
1379	**339**	1g.20 bistre and black	2·75	30
1380	**339**	1g.40 green and black	2·75	50
1381	**339**	1g.50 lilac and black	2·50	50
1382	**339**	2g. bistre and black	3·25	30
1383	**339**	2g.50 orange and black	4·00	50
1384	**339**	3g. blue and black	5·00	50
1385	**339**	4g. green and black	6·25	50
1386	**339**	5g. blue and black	8·00	50
1387	**339**	6g.50 lilac and black	10·50	65
1388	**339**	7g. blue and black	12·50	80
1389	**339**	7g.50 green and black	18·00	4·00

For this design but on uncoloured background see Nos. 1594/1609a.

340 Agnieten Chapel and Banners

1982. 350th Anniv of University of Amsterdam.

1395	**340**	65c. multicoloured	1·10	30

341 Skater

1982. Centenary of Royal Dutch Skating Association.

1396	**341**	45c. multicoloured	90	30

342 Apple Blossom

1982. Cultural, Health and Social Welfare Funds. Multicoloured.

1397		50c.+20c. Type **342**	1·20	65
1398		60c.+25c. Anemones	1·20	65
1399		65c.+25c. Roses	1·20	65
1400		70c.+30c. African violets	1·20	95

343 Stripes in National Colours

1982. Bicentenary of Netherlands–United States Diplomatic Relations.

1401	**343**	50c. red, blue and black	90	30
1402	**343**	65c. red, blue and black	1·20	30

344 Sandwich Tern and Eider

1982. Waddenzee. Multicoloured.

1403		50c. Type **344**	1·10	30
1404		70c. Barnacle Geese	1·40	30

345 Zebra Crossing

1982. 50th Anniv of Dutch Road Safety Organization.

1405	**345**	60c. multicoloured	90	30

346 Ground Plan of Enkhuizen Fortifications

1982. Europa. Multicoloured.

1406		50c. Type **346**	1·10	30
1407		70c. Part of ground plan of Coevorden fortifications	1·40	30

347 Aerial view of Palace and Liberation Monument

1982. Royal Palace, Dam Square, Amsterdam. Mult.

1408		50c. Facade, ground plan and cross-section of palace	90	30
1409		60c. Type **347**	1·10	30

348 Great Tits and Child

1982. Child Welfare. Child and Animal. Mult.

1410		50c.+30c. Type **348**	90	50
1411		60c.+20c. Child arm-in-arm with cat	1·20	50
1412		65c.+20c. Child with drawing of rabbit	1·90	1·30
1413		70c.+30c. Child with palm cockatoo	2·30	1·30
MS1414		75×144 mm. Nos. 1410×4 and 1411	6·25	3·50

349 Touring Club Activities

1983. Centenary of Royal Dutch Touring Club.

1415	**349**	70c. multicoloured	1·20	30

350 Johan van Oldenbarnevelt (statesman) (after J. Houbraken)

1983. Cultural, Health and Social Welfare Funds.

1416	**350**	50c.+20c. pink, blue and black	1·40	85
1417	-	60c.+25c. mult	1·40	85
1418	-	65c.+25c. mult	1·40	1·20
1419	-	70c.+30c. grey, black and gold	1·40	1·20

Designs:—60c. Willem Jansz Blaeu (cartographer) (after Thomas de Keijser); 65c. Hugo de Groot (statesman) (after J. van Ravesteyn); 70c. *Saskia van Uylenburch* (portrait of his wife by Rembrandt).

351 Newspaper

1983. Europa. Multicoloured.

1420		50c. Type **351** (75th anniv of Netherlands Newspaper Publishers Association)	90	35
1421		70c. European Communications Satellite and European Telecommunication Satellites Organization members' flags	1·30	35

352 *Composition 1922* (P. Mondriaan)

1983. De Stijl Art Movement. Multicoloured.

1422		50c. Type **352**	90	35
1423		65c. Contra construction from *Maison Particuliere* (C. van Eesteren and T. van Doesburg)	1·30	50

353 "Geneva Conventions"

1983. Red Cross.

1424	**353**	50c.+25c. mult	1·40	85
1425	-	60c.+20c. mult	1·40	85
1426	-	65c.+25c. mult	1·40	85
1427	-	70c.+30c. grey, black and red	1·40	85

Designs:—60c. Red Cross and text "charity, independence, impartiality"; 65c. "Socio-medical work"; 70c. Red Cross and text "For Peace".

354 Luther's Signature

1983. 500th Birth Anniv of Martin Luther (Protestant Reformer).

1428	**354**	70c. multicoloured	1·30	35

355 Child looking at Donkey and Ox through Window

1983. Child Welfare. Child and Christmas. Mult.

1429		50c.+10c. Type **355**	1·40	1·00
1430		50c.+25c. Child riding flying snowman	1·10	50
1431		60c.+30c. Child in bed and star	1·70	1·30
1432		70c.+30c. Children dressed as the three kings	1·60	60
MS1433		144×75 mm. Nos. 1430×4 and 1432×2	7·75	6·50

356 Parliament

1984. Second Elections to European Parliament.

1434	**356**	70c. multicoloured	1·30	35

357 Northern Lapwings

1984. Cultural, Health and Social Welfare Funds. Pasture Birds. Multicoloured.

1435		50c.+20c. Type **357**	2·00	70
1436		60c.+25c. Ruffs	2·00	70
1437		65c.+25c. Redshanks (vert)	2·00	70
1438		70c.+30c. Black-tailed godwits (vert)	2·00	70

358 St. Servaas

1984. 1600th Death Anniv of St. Servaas (Bishop of Tongeren and Maastricht).

1439	**358**	60c. multicoloured	1·10	35

359 Bridge

1984. Europa. 25th Anniv of European Post and Telecommunications Conference.

1440	**359**	50c. deep blue and blue	90	35
1441	**359**	70c. green and light green	1·30	35

360 Eye and Magnifying Glass

1984. Centenary of Organized Philately in the Netherlands and "Filacento" International Stamp Exhibition, The Hague. Multicoloured.

1442		50c.+20c. Type **360**	1·20	95
1443		60c.+25c. 1909 cover	1·30	1·00
1444		70c.+30c. Stamp club meeting, 1949	1·40	1·20
MS1445		144×50 mm. Nos. 1442/4	4·50	4·00

361 William of Orange (after Adriaen Thomaszoon Key)

1984. 400th Death Anniv of William of Orange.

1446	**361**	70c. multicoloured	1·30	35

362 Giant Pandas and Globe

1984. World Wildlife Fund.

1447	**362**	70c. multicoloured	1·80	35

363 Graph and Leaf

1984. 11th International Small Business Congress, Amsterdam.

1448	**363**	60c. multicoloured	1·10	35

364 Violin Lesson

1984. Child Welfare. Strip Cartoons. Mult.

1449		50c.+25c. Type **364**	90	50
1450		60c.+20c. At the dentist	1·80	1·20
1451		65c.+20c. The plumber	2·20	1·50
1452		70c.+30c. The king and money chest	1·40	50
MS1453		75×144 mm. Nos. 1449×4 and 1452×2	7·25	6·00

365 Sunny, First Dutch Guide-Dog

1985. 50th Anniv of Royal Dutch Guide-Dog Fund.

1454	**365**	60c. black, ochre and red	1·10	35

366 Plates and Cutlery on Place-mat

1985. Tourism. Multicoloured.

1455		50c. Type **366** (centenary of Travel and Holidays Association)	90	35
1456		70c. Kroller-Muller museum emblem, antlers and landscape (50th anniv of De Hoge Veluwe National Park)	1·30	35

367 Saint Martin's Church, Zaltbommel

1985. Cultural, Health and Social Welfare Funds. Religious Buildings. Multicoloured.

1457a		50c.+20c. Type **367**	1·40	1·00
1458		60c.+25c. Winterswijk synagogue and Holy Ark (horiz)	1·40	1·20
1459		65c.+25c. Bolsward Baptist church	1·40	1·20
1460		70c.+30c. Saint John's Cathedral, 's-Hertogen-bosch (horiz)	1·40	85

368 Star of David, Illegal Newspapers and Rifle Practice (Resistance Movement)

1985. 40th Anniv of Liberation.

1461	**368**	50c. black, stone and red	90	35
1462	-	60c. black, stone and blue	1·10	35
1463	-	65c. black, stone & orge	1·30	85
1464	-	70c. black, stone & green	1·40	35

Designs:—60c. Fighters over houses, *De Vliegende Hollander* (newspaper) and soldier (Allied Forces); 65c. Soldiers and civilians, *Parool* (newspaper) and American war cemetery, Margraten (Liberation); 70c. Women prisoners, prison money and Burma Railway (Dutch East Indies).

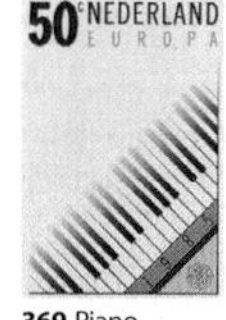

369 Piano Keyboard

1985. Europa. Music Year. Multicoloured.

1465		50c. Type **369**	90	35
1466		70c. Organ	1·30	50

370 National Museum, Amsterdam (centenary)

1985. Anniversaries and Events. Multicoloured.

1467		50c. Type **370**	90	35
1468		60c. Teacher with students (bicentenary of Amsterdam Nautical College)	9·00	3·50
1469		70c. Ship's mast and rigging ("Sail '85", Amsterdam)	1·30	35

371 Porpoise and Graph

1985. Endangered Animals.

1470	**371**	50c. black, blue and red	1·10	50
1471	-	70c. black, blue and red	1·40	50

Design:—70c. Seal and PCB molecule structure.

372 Ignition Key and Framed Photograph ("Think of Me")

1985. Child Welfare. Road Safety. Multicoloured.

1472		50c.+25c. Type **372**	90	50

1473	60c.+20c. Child holding target showing speeds	1·40	1·00
1474	65c.+20c. Girl holding red warning triangle	1·40	1·00
1475	70c.+30c. Boy holding "Children Crossing" sign	1·60	50
MS1476	132×80 mm. Nos. 1472×4 and 1475×2	7·75	6·50

373 Penal Code Extract

1986. Centenary of Penal Code.

1477	**373**	50c. black, yellow & purple	90	50

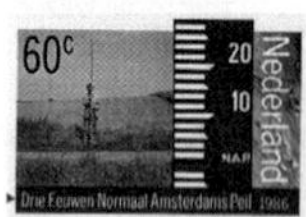

374 Surveyor with Pole and NAP Water Gauge

1986. 300th Anniv of Height Gauging Marks at Amsterdam.

1478	**374**	60c. multicoloured	1·10	35

375 Windmill, Graph and Cloudy Sky

1986. Inaug of Windmill Test Station, Sexbierum.

1479	**375**	70c. multicoloured	1·30	35

376 Scales

1986. Cultural, Health and Social Welfare Funds. Antique Measuring Instruments. Multicoloured.

1480a	50c.+20c. Type **376**	1·40	70
1481	60c.+25c. Clock (vert)	1·40	70
1482	65c.+25c. Barometer (vert)	1·40	70
1483	70c.+30c. Jacob's staff	1·40	70

377 Het Loo Palace Garden, Apeldoorn

1986. Europa. Multicoloured.

1484	50c. Type **377**	90	50
1485	70c. Tree with discoloured crown	1·30	35

378 Cathedral

1986. Utrecht Events.

1486	**378**	50c. multicoloured	90	50
1487	-	60c. blue, pink and black	1·10	50
1488	-	70c. multicoloured	1·30	50

Designs:—Vert: 50c. Type **378** (completion of interior restoration); 60c. German House (75th anniv of Heemschut Conservation Society). Horiz: 70c. Extract from foundation document (350th anniv of Utrecht University).

379 Drees at Binnenhof, 1947

1986. Birth Centenary of Dr. Willem Drees (politician).

1489	**379**	55c. multicoloured	90	35

380 Draughts as Biscuits in Saucer

1986. 75th Anniversary of Royal Dutch Draughts Association (1490) and Royal Dutch Billiards Association (1491). Multicoloured.

1490	75c. Type **380**	1·40	50
1491	75c. Player in ball preparing to play	1·40	50

381 Map of Flood Barrier

1986. Delta Project Completion. Multicoloured.

1492	65c. Type **381**	1·30	35
1493	75c. Flood barrier	1·40	50

382 Children listening to Music (experiencing)

1986. Child Welfare. Child and Culture.

1494	55c.+25c. Type **382**	1·40	1·20
1495	65c.+35c. Boy drawing (achieving)	1·80	75
1496	75c.+35c. Children at theatre (understanding)	1·80	50
MS1497	150×72 mm. Nos. 1494, 1495×2 and 1496×2	6·50	5·00

383 Engagement Picture

1987. Golden Wedding of Princess Juliana and Prince Bernhard.

1498	**383**	75c. orange, black and gold	1·60	35

384 Block of Flats and Hut

1987. International Year of Shelter for the Homeless (65c.) and Centenary of Netherlands Salvation Army (75c.). Multicoloured.

1499	65c. Type **384**	1·30	50
1500	75c. Army officer, meeting and tramp	1·40	50

385 Eduard Douwes Dekker (Multatuli) and De Harmonie Club

1987. Writers' Death Annivs. Multicoloured.

1501	55c. Type **385** (centenary)	1·30	35
1502	75c. Constantijn Huygens and Scheveningseweg, The Hague (300th anniv)	1·40	35

386 Steam Pumping Station, Nijerk

1987. Cultural Health and Social Welfare Funds. Industrial Buildings.

1503a	**386**	55c.+30c. red, grey and black	1·40	1·40
1504	-	65c.+35c. grey, black and blue	1·80	1·40
1505	-	75c.+35c. grey, yellow and black	1·90	1·40

Designs:—65c. Water tower, Deventer; 75c. Brass foundry, Joure.

387 Dance Theatre, Scheveningen (Rem Koolhaas)

1987. Europa. Architecture. Multicoloured.

1506	55c. Type **387**	90	35
1507	75c. Montessori School, Amsterdam (Herman Hertzberger)	1·30	35

388 Auction at Broek op Langedijk

1987. Centenary of Auction Sales (55, 75c.) and 150th Anniv of Groningen Agricultural Society (65c.). Multicoloured.

1508	55c. Type **388**	90	35
1509	65c. Groningen landscape and founders' signatures	1·10	35
1510	75c. Auction sale and clock	1·30	35

389 Telephone Care Circles

1987. Dutch Red Cross. Multicoloured.

1511a	55c.+30c. Type **389**	1·40	1·10
1512	65c.+35c. Red cross and hands (Welfare work)	1·50	1·20
1513	75c.+35c. Red cross and drip (Blood transfusion)	1·60	1·00

390 Map of Holland

1987. 75th Anniv of Netherlands Municipalities Union.

1514	**390**	75c. multicoloured	1·40	35

391 Noordeinde Palace, The Hague

1987

1515	**391**	65c. multicoloured	1·30	35

392 Woodcutter

1987. Child Welfare. Child and Profession. Mult.

1516	55c.+25c. Type **392**	1·40	85
1517	65c.+35c. Woman sailor	1·50	70
1518	75c.+35c. Woman pilot	1·60	35
MS1519	150×72 mm. Nos. 1516, 1517×2 and 1518×2	7·25	6·50

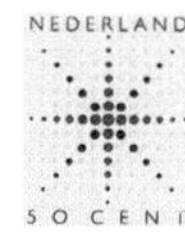

393 Star

1987. Christmas.

1520	**393**	50c. red, blue and green	1·30	50
1521	**393**	50c. yellow, red and blue	1·30	50
1522	**393**	50c. red, blue and yellow	1·30	50
1523	**393**	50c. yellow, red and green	1·30	50
1524	**393**	50c. blue, green and red	1·30	50

The first colour described is that of the St. George's Cross.

394 *Narcissus cyclamineus* "Peeping Tom" and Extract from *I Call You Flowers* (Jan Hanlo)

1988. Filacept European Stamp Exhibition, The Hague (1st issue). Flowers. Multicoloured.

1525	55c.+55c. Type **394**	1·80	1·70
1526	75c.+70c. *Rosa gallica* Versicolor and Roses (Daan van Golden)	1·80	1·70
1527	75c.+70c. Sea holly and 1270 map of The Hague	1·80	1·70

See also No. **MS**1542.

395 Quagga

1988. Cultural, Health and Social Welfare Funds. 150th Anniv of Natura Artis Magistra Zoological Society. Multicoloured.

1528a	55c.+30c. Type **395**	1·80	1·50
1529	65c.+35c. American manatee	1·80	1·70
1530	75c.+35c. Orang-utan (vert)	1·80	1·40

396 Man's Shoulder

1988. 75th Anniv of Netherlands Cancer Institute.

1531	**396**	75c. multicoloured	1·40	35

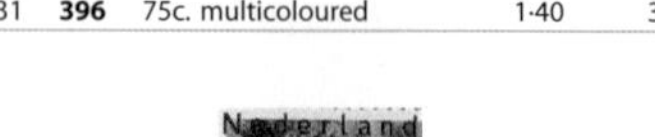

397 Traffic Scene with Lead Symbol crossed Through

1988. Europa. Transport. Multicoloured.

1532	55c. Type **397** (lead-free petrol)	1·30	50
1533	75c. Cyclists reflected in car wing mirror (horiz)	1·60	50

398 Pendulum, Prism and Saturn

1988. 300th Anniv of England's Glorious Revolution. Multicoloured.

1534	65c. Type **398**	1·30	35
1535	75c. Queen Mary, King William III and 17th-century warship	1·40	35

399 *Cobra Cat* (Appel)

1988. 40th Anniv of Founding of Cobra Painters Group. Multicoloured.

1536	55c. Type **399**	1·10	85
1537	65c. *Kite* (Corneille)	1·30	85
1538	75c. *Stumbling Horse* (Constant)	1·40	50

400 Sailing Ship and Map of Australia

1988. Bicentenary of Australian Settlement.

1539	**400**	75c. multicoloured	1·60	35

401 Statue of Erasmus, Rotterdam

1988. 75th Anniv of Erasmus University, Rotterdam (1540) and Centenary of Concertgebouw Concert Hall and Orchestra (1541).

1540	**401**	75c. deep green and green	1·60	35
1541	-	75c. violet	1·60	35

Design:—No. 1541, Violin and Concertgebouw concert hall.

1988. Filacept European Stamp Exhibition, The Hague (2nd issue). Flowers. Sheet 144×62 mm.

MS1542	Nos. 1525/7	7·00	6·25

402 Rain

1988. Child Welfare. Centenary of Royal Netherlands Swimming Federation. Children's drawings. Multicoloured.

1543	55c.+25c. Type **402**	1·30	1·10
1544	65c.+35c. Getting Ready for the Race	1·50	1·00
1545	75c.+35c. Swimming Test	1·60	60
MS1546	150×72 mm. Nos. 1543, 1544×2 and 1545×2	7·75	6·50

403 Stars

1988. Christmas.

1547	**403**	50c. multicoloured	90	35

404 Postal and Telecommunications Services

1989. Privatization of Netherlands PTT.

1548	**404**	75c. multicoloured	1·60	35

405 "Solidarity"

1989. Trade Unions. Multicoloured.

1549	55c. Type **405**	1·10	50
1550	75c. Talking mouths on hands	1·40	50

406 Members' Flags

1989. 40th Anniv of NATO.

1551	**406**	75c. multicoloured	1·40	35

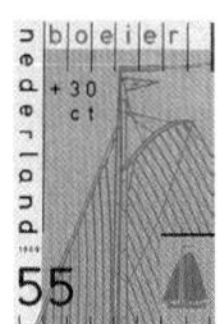

407 Boier

1989. Cultural, Health and Social Welfare Funds. Old Sailing Vessels.

1552a	**407**	55c.+30c. green & blk	1·80	1·40
1553	-	65c.+35c. blue & black	1·80	1·40
1554	-	75c.+35c. brown & blk	1·80	1·40

Designs:—65c. Fishing smack; 75c. Clipper.

408 Boy with Homemade Telephone

1989. Europa. Children's Games. Multicoloured.

1555	55c. Type **408**	90	35
1556	75c. Girl with homemade telephone	1·30	35

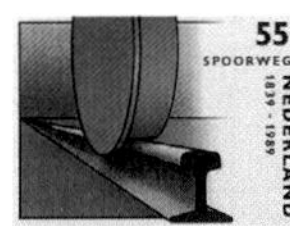

409 Wheel on Rail

1989. 150th Anniv of Netherlands' Railways. Mult.

1557	55c. Type **409**	1·10	35
1558	65c. Steam, electric and diesel locomotives	1·30	45
1559	75c. Diesel train, station clock and *The Kiss* (sculpture by Rodin)	1·60	50

410 Boy with Ball and Diagram of Goal Scored in European Championship

1989. Centenary of Royal Dutch Football Assn.

1560	**410**	75c. multicoloured	1·30	45

411 Map

1989. 150th Anniv of Division of Limburg between Netherlands and Belgium.

1561	**411**	75c. multicoloured	1·30	45

412 Right to Housing

1989. Child Welfare. 30th Anniv of Declaration of Rights of the Child. Multicoloured.

1562	55c.+25c. Type **412**	1·20	1·10
1563	65c.+35c. Right to food	1·40	95
1564	75c.+35c. Right to education	1·50	75
MS1565	150×72 mm. Nos. 1562, 1563×2 and 1564×2	7·25	6·00

413 Candle

1989. Christmas.

1566	**413**	50c. multicoloured	1·10	35

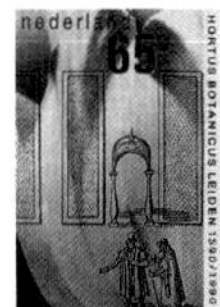

414 "Arms of Leiden" (tulip) and Plan of Gardens in 1601

1990. 400th Anniv of Hortus Botanicus (botanical gardens), Leiden.

1567	**414**	65c. multicoloured	1·30	45

415 Pointer on Graduated Scale

1990. Centenary of Labour Inspectorate.

1568	**415**	75c. multicoloured	1·40	45

416 *Self-portrait* (detail)

1990. Death Centenary of Vincent van Gogh (painter). Multicoloured.

1569	55c. Type **416**	1·30	45
1570	75c. *Green Vineyard* (detail)	1·60	45

417 Summer's Day

1990. Cultural, Health and Social Welfare Funds. The Weather. Multicoloured.

1571a	55c.+30c. Type **417**	1·80	1·40
1572	65c.+35c. Clouds and isobars (vert)	1·80	1·50
1573a	75c.+35c. Satellite weather picture (vert)	1·80	1·40

418 Zuiderkerk Ruins

1990. 50th Anniv of German Bombing of Rotterdam.

1574	**418**	55c. deep brown, brown and black	1·10	35
1575	-	65c. multicoloured	1·30	45
1576	-	75c. multicoloured	1·40	50

Designs:—65c. City plan as stage; 75c. Girder and plans for future construction.

419 Postal Headquarters, Groningen, and Veere Post Office

1990. Europa. Post Office Buildings.

1577	-	55c. grey, mauve & brn	1·40	60
1578	**419**	75c. blue, green and grey	1·60	60

Design:—55c. As Type **419** but inscr "Postkantoor Veere".

420 Construction of Indiaman and Wreck of *Amsterdam*

1990. Third Anniv of Dutch East India Company Ships Association (replica ship project) (1579) and "Sail 90", Amsterdam (1580). Multicoloured.

1579	65c. Type **420**	1·30	45
1580	75c. Crew manning yards on sailing ship	1·40	45

421 Queens Emma, Wilhelmina, Juliana and Beatrix

1990. Netherlands Queens of the House of Orange.

1581	**421**	150c. multicoloured	3·25	1·60

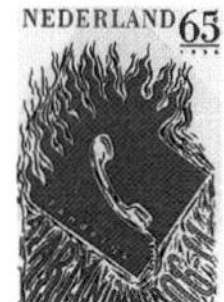

422 Flames, Telephone Handset and Number

1990. Introduction of National Emergency Number.

1582	**422**	65c. multicoloured	1·30	45

423 Girl riding Horse

1990. Child Welfare. Hobbies. Multicoloured.

1583	55c.+25c. Type **423**	1·60	1·20
1584	65c.+35c. Girl at computer	1·70	1·00
1585	75c.+35c. Young philatelist	1·80	65
MS1586	150×71 mm. Nos. 1583, 1584×2 and 1585×2	8·50	6·75

424 Falling Snow

1990. Christmas.

1587	**424**	50c. multicoloured	1·10	35

425 Industrial Chimneys, Exhaust Pipes and Aerosol Can (Air Pollution)

1991. Environmental Protection. Multicoloured.

1588	55c. Type **425**	1·20	35
1589	65c. Outfall pipes and chemicals (sea pollution)	1·40	35
1590	75c. Agricultural chemicals, leaking drums and household landfill waste (soil pollution)	1·60	35

426 German Raid on Amsterdam Jewish Quarter and Open Hand

1991. 50th Anniv of Amsterdam General Strike.

1591	**426**	75c. multicoloured	1·60	45

427 Princess Beatrix and Prince Claus on Wedding Day

1991. Royal Silver Wedding Anniversary. Mult.

1592	75c. Type **427**	1·80	55
1593	75c. Queen Beatrix and Prince Claus on horseback	1·80	55

428 Queen Beatrix

1991. (a) Ordinary gum.

1594	**428**	75c. deep green & green	2·00	35
1595	**428**	80c. brown & lt brown	2·00	20
1597	**428**	90c. blue	2·00	2·75
1598	**428**	1g. violet	2·00	90
1599	**428**	1g.10 blue	3·00	2·75
1600	**428**	1g.30 blue and violet	2·50	55
1601	**428**	1g.40 green and olive	2·75	55
1601a	**428**	1g.50 green	4·00	3·50
1602	**428**	1g.60 purple and mauve	3·25	35
1603	**428**	2g. brown	4·00	1·80
1603a	**428**	2g.50 purple	5·00	3·50
1604	**428**	3g. blue	6·00	2·75
1605	**428**	5g. red	10·00	2·75

1706	**428**	7g.50 violet	20·00	9·00
1707	**428**	10g. green	12·00	2·30

(b) Self-adhesive gum.

1606	**428**	1g. violet	3·00	1·80
1607	**428**	1g.10 blue	3·50	3·00
1608	**428**	1g.45 green	3·50	3·25
1609	**428**	2g.50 purple	7·00	5·50
1609a	**428**	5g. red	36·00	†

429 Meadow Farm, Wartena, Friesland

1991. Cultural, Health and Social Welfare Funds. Traditional Farmhouses. Multicoloured.

1611	65c.+35c. T-house farm, Kesteren, Gelderland	2·00	1·60
1613	55c.+30c. Type **429**	1·40	55
1614	75c.+35c. Courtyard farm, Nuth, Limburg	1·40	55

430 Gerard Philips's Experiments with Carbon Filaments

1991. 75th Anniv of Netherlands Standards Institute (65c.) and Centenary of Philips Organization (others). Multicoloured.

1615	55c. Type **430**	1·20	70
1616	65c. Wiring to Standard NEN 1010 (horiz)	1·40	35
1617	75c. Laser beams reading video disc	1·60	35

431 Man raising Hat to Space

1991. Europa. Europe in Space. Multicoloured.

1618	55c. Type **431**	1·40	55
1619	75c. Ladders stretching into space	1·80	55

432 Sticking Plaster over Medal

1991. 75th Anniv of Nijmegen International Four Day Marches.

1620	**432**	80c. multicoloured	1·60	35

433 Jacobus Hendericus van't Hoff

1991. Dutch Nobel Prize Winners (1st series). Multicoloured.

1621	60c. Type **433** (chemistry, 1901)	1·20	35
1622	70c. Pieter Zeeman (physics, 1902)	1·40	35
1623	80c. Tobias Michael Carel Asser (peace, 1911)	1·60	35

See also Nos. 1690/2 and 1773/5.

434 Children and Open Book

1991. Centenary (1992) of Public Libraries in the Netherlands.

1624	**434**	70c. drab, black & mauve	1·60	35
1625	-	80c. multicoloured	1·80	35

Design:—80c. Books on shelf.

435 Girls with Doll and Robot

1991. Child Welfare. Outdoor Play. Multicoloured.

1626	60c.+30c. Type **435**	1·40	70
1627	70c.+35c. Bicycle race	1·90	1·40
1628	80c.+40c. Hide and seek	2·30	80
MS1629	144×75 mm. Nos. 1626×4 and 1638×2	10·00	7·25

436 "Greetings Cards keep People in Touch"

1991. Christmas.

1630	**436**	55c. multicoloured	1·10	35

437 Artificial Lightning, Microchip and Oscilloscope

1992. 150th Anniv of Delft University of Technology.

1631	**437**	60c. multicoloured	1·40	45

438 Extract from Code

1992. Implementation of Property Provisions of New Civil Code.

1632	**438**	80c. multicoloured	1·80	45

439 Volleyball

1992. Winter Olympic Games, Albertville and Summer Games, Barcelona. Sheet 125×72 mm containing T **439** and similar vert designs. Multicoloured.

MS1633	80c. Type **439**; 80c. Putting the shot and rowing; 80c. Speed skating and rowing; 80c. Hockey	8·00	6·25

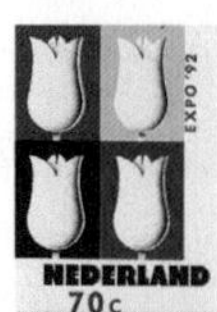

440 Tulips ("Mondrian does not like Green")

1992. Expo '92 World's Fair, Seville. Mult.

1634	70c. Type **440**	1·60	45
1635	80c. "Netherland Expo '92"	1·80	45

441 Tasman's Map of Staete Landt (New Zealand)

1992. 350th Anniv of Discovery of Tasmania and New Zealand by Abel Tasman.

1636	**441**	70c. multicoloured	1·60	45

442 Yellow and Purple Flowers

1992. Cultural, Health and Social Welfare Funds. "Floriade" Flower Show, Zoetermeer. Mult.

1639	80c.+40c. Type **442**	2·50	1·80
1640	60c.+30c. Water lilies	1·70	1·30
1641	70c.+35c. Orange and purple flowers	1·80	1·50

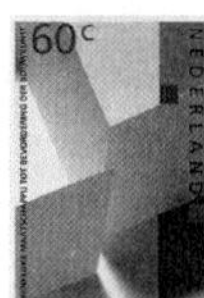

443 Geometric Planes

1992. 150th Anniv of Royal Association of Netherlands Architects (60c.) and Inauguration of New States General Lower House (80c.). Mult.

1643	60c. Type **443**	1·40	55
1644	80c. Atrium and blue sky (symbolizing sending of information into society)	1·80	55

444 Globe and Columbus

1992. Europa. 500th Anniv of Discovery of America by Columbus.

1645	**444**	60c. multicoloured	1·70	1·00
1646	-	80c. black, mauve & yellow	2·00	1·00

Design:—Vert: 80c. Galleon.

445 Moneta (Goddess of Money)

1992. Centenary of Royal Netherlands Numismatics Society.

1647	**445**	70c. multicoloured	1·60	45

446 Teddy Bear wearing Stethoscope

1992. Centenary of Netherlands Paediatrics Society.

1648	**446**	80c. multicoloured	2·00	45

447 List of Relatives and Friends

1992. 50th Anniv of Departure of First Deportation Train from Westerbork Concentration Camp.

1649	**447**	70c. multicoloured	1·60	45

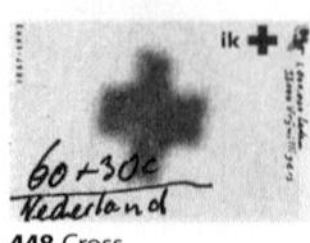

448 Cross

1992. 125th Anniv of Netherlands Red Cross. Multicoloured.

1652	80c.+40c. Red cross on dirty bandage	2·50	1·80
1653	60c.+30c. Type **448**	1·40	80
1654	70c.+35c. Supporting injured person	1·60	1·30

449 "United Europe" and European Community Flag

1992. European Single Market.

1656	**449**	80c. multicoloured	1·60	35

450 Queen Beatrix on Official Birthday, 1992, and at Investiture

1992. 12½ Years since Accession to the Throne of Queen Beatrix.

1657	**450**	80c. multicoloured	1·60	35

451 Saxophone Player

1992. Child Welfare. Child and Music. Mult.

1658	60c.+30c. Type **451**	1·80	90
1659	70c.+35c. Piano player	2·10	1·20
1660	80c.+40c. Double bass player	2·30	1·60
MS1661	144×75 mm. Nos. 1658×3, 1659×2 and 1660	11·00	8·00

452 Poinsettia

1992. Christmas.

1662	**452**	55c. multicoloured (centre of flower silver)	1·20	35
1663	**452**	55c. multicoloured (centre red)	1·20	35

453 Cycling

1993. Centenary of Netherlands Cycle and Motor Industry Association.

1664	**453**	70c. multicoloured	1·80	45
1665	-	80c. brown, grey & yell	2·00	45

Design:—80c. Car.

454 Collages

1993. Greetings Stamps. Multicoloured.

1666	70c. Type **454**	1·40	45
1667	70c. Collages (different)	1·40	45

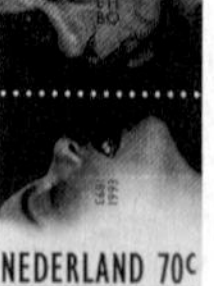

455 Mouth to Mouth Resuscitation

1993. Anniversaries. Multicoloured.

1668	70c. Type **455** (centenary of Royal Netherlands First Aid Association)	1·60	35
1669	80c. Pests on leaf (75th anniv of Wageningen University of Agriculture)	1·70	35
1670	80c. Lead driver and horses (bicentenary of Royal Horse Artillery)	1·70	35

456 Emblems

1993. 150th Anniv of Royal Dutch Notaries Association. Each red and violet.

1671	80c. Type **456** ("150 Jaar" reading up)	2·00	35

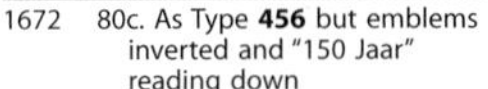

1672	80c. As Type **456** but emblems inverted and "150 Jaar" reading down	2·00	35

Nos. 1671/2 were issued together in horizontal *tête-bêche* pairs, each pair forming a composite design.

457 Large White

1993. Butterflies. Multicoloured.

1673	70c. Pearl-bordered fritillary	1·80	90
1674	80c. Large tortoiseshell	2·00	55
1675	90c. Type **457**	2·20	2·00
MS1676	104×71 mm. 160c. Common blue	6·00	5·00

458 Elderly Couple

1993. Cultural, Health and Social Welfare Funds. Senior Citizens' Independence.

1677	70c.+35c. Type **458**	2·20	2·00
1681	70c.+35c. Elderly man	7·00	6·25
1682	80c.+40c. Elderly woman with dog	1·60	1·10

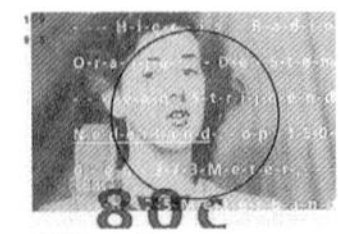

459 Broadcaster

1993. Radio Orange (Dutch broadcasts from London during Second World War). Mult.

1683	80c. Type **459**	2·00	35
1684	80c. Man listening to radio in secret	2·00	35

460 Sports Pictograms

1993. Second European Youth Olympic Days. Mult.

1685	70c. Type **460**	1·70	35
1686	80c. Sports pictograms (different)	1·80	35

461 *The Embodiment of Unity* (Wessel Couzijn)

1993. Europa. Contemporary Art. Multicoloured.

1687	70c. Type **461**	2·00	1·10
1688	80c. Architectonic sculpture (Per Kirkeby)	2·20	70
1689	160c. Sculpture (Naum Gabo) (vert)	3·75	3·25

462 Johannes Diderik van der Waals (Physics, 1910)

1993. Dutch Nobel Prize Winners (2nd series).

1690	**462**	70c. blue, black and red	1·40	80
1691	-	80c. mauve, black & red	1·60	70
1692	-	90c. multicoloured	2·00	2·20

Designs:—80c. Willem Einthoven (medicine, 1924); 90c. Christiaan Eijkman (medicine, 1929).

463 Pen and Pencils

1993. Letter Writing Campaign. Multicoloured.

1693	80c. Type **463**	1·70	45
1694	80c. Envelope	1·70	45

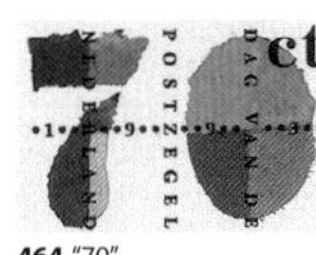

464 "70"

1993. Stamp Day (70c.) and Netherlands PTT (80c.). Multicoloured.

1695	70c. Type **464**	1·40	55
1696	80c. Dish aerial and dove carrying letter	1·60	55

465 Child in Newspaper Hat

1993. Child Welfare. Child and the Media. Mult.

1697	70c.+35c. Type **465**	2·10	1·10
1698	70c.+35c. Elephant using headphones	2·10	1·10
1699	80c.+40c. Television	2·30	1·10
MS1700	143×75 mm. Nos. 1697/99, each×2	13·00	10·00

466 Candle

1993. Christmas. Multicoloured.

1711	55c. Type **466**	1·10	45
1712	55c. Fireworks	1·10	45

Both designs have a number of punched holes.

467 *Composition*

1994. 50th Death Anniv of Piet Mondriaan (artist). Multicoloured.

1713	70c. *The Red Mill* (detail)	1·60	70
1714	80c. Type **467**	1·80	55
1715	90c. *Broadway Boogie Woogie* (detail)	2·00	1·80

468 Barnacle Goose

1994. Fepapost 94 European Stamp Exhibition, The Hague. Multicoloured.

1716	70c.+60c. Type **468**	2·75	2·30
1717	80c.+70c. Bluethroat	2·75	2·30
1718	90c.+80c. Garganey	2·75	2·30

See also No. **MS**1743.

469 Downy Rose

1994. Wild Flowers. Multicoloured.

1719	70c. Type **469**	1·60	90
1720	80c. Daisies	1·80	80
1721	90c. Wood forgetmenot	2·00	2·20
MS1722	71×50 mm. 160c. Orange lily	6·00	5·50

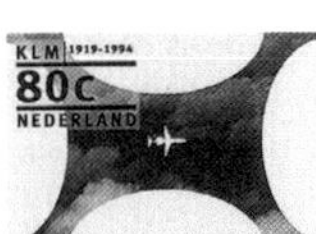

470 Fokker F.28 Airliner

1994. 75th Aircraft Industry Anniversaries.

1723	**470**	80c. blue and black	1·80	45
1724	-	80c. grey, red and black	1·80	45
1725	-	80c. multicoloured	1·80	45

Designs:—No. 1723, Type **470** (KLM (Royal Dutch Airlines)); No. 1724, Plan and outline of aircraft and clouds (Royal Netherlands Fokker Aircraft Industries); No. 1725, Aircraft and clouds (National Aerospace Laboratory).

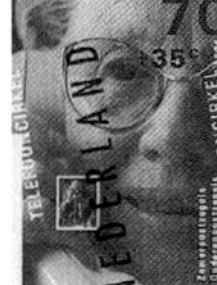

471 Woman using Telephone

1994. Cultural, Health and Social Welfare Funds. Senior Citizens' Security. Multicoloured.

1727	80c.+40c. Man using telephone	2·50	1·90
1728	90c.+35c. Man using telephone (different)	2·75	2·40
1729	70c.+35c. Type **471**	1·60	1·30

472 Eisinga's Planetarium

1994. Anniversaries. Multicoloured.

1732	80c. Type **472** (250th birth anniv of Eise Eisinga)	1·80	45
1733	90c. Astronaut and boot print on Moon surface (25th anniv of first manned Moon landing)	2·20	1·60

473 Players Celebrating

1994. World Cup Football Championship, U.S.A.

1734	**473**	80c. multicoloured	2·00	1·40

474 Stock Exchange

1994. Quotation of Netherlands PTT (KPN) on Stock Exchange.

1735	**474**	80c. multicoloured	1·80	45

475 Road Sign, Car and Bicycle

1994. Anniversaries and Events. Multicoloured.

1736	70c. Type **475** (centenary of provision of road signs by Netherlands Motoring Association)	1·80	45
1737	80c. Equestrian sports (World Equestrian Games, The Hague)	2·00	45

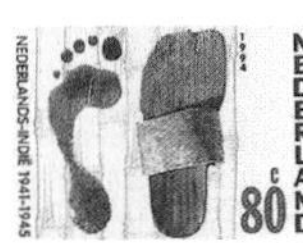

476 Footprint and Sandal

1994. Second World War. Multicoloured.

1738	80c. Type **476** (war in Netherlands Indies, 1941–45)	1·80	45
1739	90c. Soldier, children and Douglas C-47 dropping paratroops (50th anniv of Operation Market Garden (Battle of Arnhem)) (vert)	2·00	1·80

477 Brandaris Lighthouse, Terschelling

1994. Lighthouses. Multicoloured.

1740	70c. Type **477**	2·00	90
1741	80c. Ameland (vert)	2·00	70
1742	90c. Vlieland (vert)	2·00	2·20

1994. Fepapost '94 European Stamp Exhibition, The Hague (2nd issue). Sheet 144×62 mm.

MS1743	Nos. 1716/18 plus 3 labels	9·00	7·25

478 Decorating

1994. Child Welfare. "Together". Multicoloured.

1744	70c.+35c. Type **478**	2·20	1·10
1745	80c.+40c. Girl on swing knocking fruit off tree (vert)	2·30	1·10
1746	90c.+35c. Girl helping boy onto playhouse roof (vert)	2·50	2·75
MS1747	144×75 mm. No. 1744×2, 1745×3 and 1746	13·00	11·00

479 Star and Christmas Tree

1994. Christmas. Multicoloured.

1748	55c. Type **479**	1·00	35
1749	55c. Candle and star	1·00	35

480 Flying Cow

1995

1750	**480**	100c. multicoloured	2·50	70

481 "Prayer" (detail)

1995. Anniversary and Events.

1751	**481**	80c. multicoloured	2·00	70
1752	-	80c. multicoloured	2·00	70
1753	-	80c. black and red	2·00	70

Designs:—Vert: No. 1751, Type **481** (50th death anniv of Hendrik Werkman (graphic designer); No. 1752, *Mesdag Panorama* (detail) (re-opening of Mesdag Museum). Horiz: No. 1753, Mauritius 1847 2d. "POST OFFICE" stamp (purchase of remaining mint example in private hands by PTT Museum).

482 Joriz Ivens (documentary maker)

1995. Year of the Film (centenary of motion pictures). Multicoloured.

1754	70c. Type **482**	1·80	45
1755	80c. Scene from *Turkish Delight*	2·00	45

483 Mahler and Score of 7th Symphony

1995. Mahler Festival, Amsterdam.

1756	**483**	80c. black and blue	1·90	45

484 Dates and Acronym

1995. Centenaries. Multicoloured.

1757	80c. Type **484** (Netherlands Institute of Chartered Accountants)	2·00	55
1758	80c. Builders, bricklayer's trowel and saw (Netherlands Association of Building Contractors)	2·00	55

485 Postcard from Indonesia

1995. Cultural, Health and Social Welfare Funds. Mobility of the Elderly. Multicoloured.

1759	70c.+35c. Type **485**	2·00	1·80
1760	80c.+40c. Couple reflected in mirror	2·50	1·20
1761	100c.+45c. Couple with granddaughter at zoo	2·50	2·30
MS1762	144×75 mm. Nos. 1759×2, 1760×3 and 1761	16·00	11·50

486 "40 45"

1995. 50th Anniversaries. Multicoloured.

1763	80c. Type **486** (end of Second World War)	2·00	65
1764	80c. "45 95" (liberation)	2·00	65
1765	80c. "50" (UNO)	2·00	65

487 Birthday Cake and Signs of the Zodiac

1995. Birthday Greetings.

1766	**487**	70c. multicoloured	1·80	55

488 Scout

1995. Events. Multicoloured.

1767	70c. Type **488** (World Scout Jamboree, Dronten)	1·70	70
1768	80c. Amsterdam harbour ("Sail '95" and finish of Tall Ships Race) (horiz)	1·80	55

489 Common Kestrel

1995. Birds of Prey. Multicoloured.

1769	70c. Type **489**	2·00	1·20
1770	80c. Face of hen harrier (horiz)	2·00	1·10
1771	100c. Red kite (horiz)	3·00	2·75
MS1772	72×50 mm. 160c. Honey buzzard	6·00	5·50

490 Petrus Debye (Chemistry, 1936)

1995. Dutch Nobel Prize Winners (3rd series). Multicoloured.

1773	80c. Type **490**	1·70	55
1774	80c. Frederik Zernike (Physics, 1953)	1·70	55
1775	80c. Jan Tinbergen (Economics, 1969)	1·70	55

491 Eduard Jacobs and Jean-Louis Pisuisse

1995. Centenary of Dutch Cabaret. Multicoloured.

1776	70c. Type **491**	1·40	55
1777	80c. Wim Kan and Freek de Jonge	1·70	55

492 *The Schoolteacher* (Leonie Ensing)

1995. Child Welfare. "Children and Fantasy". Children's Computer Drawings. Multicoloured.

1778	70c.+35c. *Dino* (Sjoerd Stegeman) (horiz)	2·00	1·20
1779	80c.+40c. Type **492**	2·40	90
1780	100c.+50c. *Children and Colours* (Marcel Jansen) (horiz)	2·75	2·30
MS1781	144×74 mm. Nos. 1778×2, 1779×3 and 1780	13·50	11·50

493 Children with Stars

1995. Christmas. Self-adhesive.

1782	**493**	55c. red, yellow and black	1·40	35
1783	-	55c. blue, yellow and black	1·40	35

Design:—No. 1783, Children looking at star through window.

494 *Woman in Blue reading a Letter*

1996. Johannes Vermeer Exhibition, Washington and The Hague. Details of his Paintings. Mult.

1784	70c. *Lady writing a Letter with her Maid*	2·40	90
1785	80c. *The Love Letter*	2·50	55
1786	100c. Type **494**	3·00	2·50
MS1787	144×75 mm. Nos. 1784/6	9·00	7·25

495 Trowel, Daffodil Bulb and Glove

1996. Spring Flowers. Multicoloured.

1788	70c. Type **495**	2·40	70
1789	80c. Tulips "kissing" woman	2·50	55
1790	100c. Snake's-head fritillary (detail of painting, Charles Mackintosh)	3·00	2·50
MS1791	72×50 mm. 160c. Crocuses	6·00	5·50

496 Putting up "MOVED" sign

1996. Change of Address Stamp.

1792	**496**	70c. multicoloured	1·90	70

For 80c. self-adhesive version of this design see No. 1826.

497 Swimming

1996. Cultural, Health and Social Welfare Funds. The Elderly in the Community. Multicoloured.

1793	70c.+35c. Type **497**	2·00	1·30
1794	80c.+40c. Grandad bottle-feeding baby	2·40	1·40
1795	100c.+50c. Playing piano	4·00	3·00
MS1796	144×75 mm. Nos. 1793×2, 1794×3 and 1795	16·00	14·50

498 Beside Car

1996. Heer Bommel (cartoon character). Sheet 108×50 mm containing T 498 and similar horiz design. Multicoloured.

MS1797	70c. Type **498**; 80c. Reading letter	6·00	5·50

499 Cycling

1996. Tourism. Multicoloured.

1798	70c. Type **499**	2·00	70
1799	70c. Paddling in sea	2·00	90
1800	80c. Traditional architecture, Amsterdam	2·00	70
1801	100c. Windmills, Zaanse Schand Open-Air Museum	2·00	90

500 Parade in Traditional Costumes

1996. Bicentenary of Province of North Brabant.

1802	**500**	80c. multicoloured	1·90	55

501 Lighting Olympic Torch

1996. Sporting Events. Multicoloured.

1803	70c. Type **501** (Olympic Games, Atlanta)	2·00	70
1804	80c. Flag and cyclists (Tour de France cycling championship)	2·00	55
1805	100c. Player, ball and Wembley Stadium (European Football Championship, England)	2·40	2·00
1806	160c. Olympic rings and athlete on starting block (Olympic Games, Atlanta)	3·50	2·20

502 Erasmus Bridge

1996. Bridges and Tunnels. Multicoloured.

1807	80c. Type **502**	2·00	65
1808	80c. Wijker Tunnel (horiz)	2·00	65
1809	80c. Martinus Nijhoff Bridge (horiz)	2·00	65

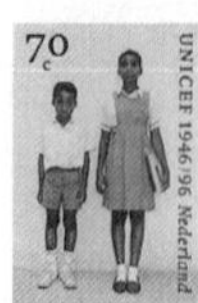

503 Children in School Uniforms

1996. 50th Anniv of UNICEF. Multicoloured.

1810	70c. Type **503**	1·60	55
1811	80c. Girl carrying platter on head	1·80	55

504 Bert and Ernie

1996. Sesame Street (children's television programme). Multicoloured.

1812	70c. Type **504**	1·90	55
1813	80c. Bears holding Big Bird's foot	1·90	55

505 Petrus Plancius

1996. 16th-century Voyages of Discovery.

1814	**505**	70c. black, yellow and red	2·20	70
1815	-	80c. multicoloured	2·20	55
1816	-	80c. multicoloured	2·20	55
1817	-	100c. multicoloured	3·50	2·20

Designs:—No. 1815, Cornelis de Houtman; 1816, Willem Barentsz; 1817, Mahu en De Cordes.

506 Books and Baby

1996. Child Welfare. Multicoloured.

1818	70c.+35c. Type **506**	2·10	1·10
1819	80c.+40c. Animals and boy	2·20	1·10
1820	80c.+40c. Tools and girl	2·20	1·10
MS1821	75×144 mm. Nos. 1818/20, each×2	13·50	11·50

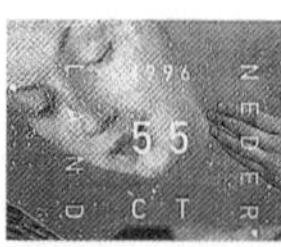

507 Woman's Face and Hand

1996. Christmas. Multicoloured. Self-adhesive.

1822	55c. Type **507**	1·20	55
1823	55c. Woman's eyes and man shouting	1·20	55
1824	55c. Bird's wing, hands and detail of man's face	1·20	55
1825	55c. Men's faces and bird's wing	1·20	55

Nos. 1822/5 were issued together, *se-tenant*, forming a composite design.

1997. Change of Address Stamp. Self-adhesive.

1826	**496**	80c. multicoloured	1·80	90

No. 1826 was intended for use by people moving house.

508 Numeral on Envelope with Top Flap

1997. Business Stamps. Multicoloured. Self-adhesive.

1827	80c. Type **508**	1·50	35
1828	160c. Numeral on envelope with side flap	3·00	35

509 Skaters

1997. 15th Eleven Cities Skating Race.

1829	**509**	80c. multicoloured	1·90	55

510 Heart

1997. Greetings Stamps.

1830	**510**	80c. multicoloured	1·70	1·10

The price quoted for No. 1830 is for an example with the heart intact. The heart can be scratched away to reveal different messages.

511 Pony

1997. Nature and the Environment. Multicoloured.

1831	80c. Type **511**	2·20	55
1832	100c. Cow	2·75	2·10
MS1833	72×50 mm. 160c. Sheep	6·00	5·75

512 Suske, Wiske, Lambik and Aunt Sidonia

1997. Suske and Wiske (cartoon by Willy Vandersteen). Multicoloured.

1834	80c. Type **512**	1·80	50
MS1835	108×50 mm. 80c. Wilbur; 80c. Type **512**	8·00	6·75

513 Rosebud

1997. Cultural, Health and Social Welfare Funds. The Elderly and their Image. Multicoloured.

1836	80c.+40c. Type **513**	2·40	2·30
1837	80c.+40c. Rose stem	2·40	2·30
1838	80c.+40c. Rose	2·40	2·30
MS1839	144×75 mm. Nos. 1836/8, each×2	14·50	13·50

514 Birthday Cake

1997. Greetings Stamps. Multicoloured.

1840	80c. Type **514**	1·60	50
1841	80c. Cup of coffee, glasses of wine, candles, writing letter, and amaryllis	1·60	50

See also No. 1959.

515 "REKENKAMER ..." (550th anniv of Court of Audit)

1997. Anniversaries.

1842	**515**	80c. multicoloured	2·20	55
1843	-	80c. red, yellow and black	2·20	55
1844	-	80c. red, black and blue	2·20	55

Designs:—50th anniv of Marshall Plan (post-war American aid for Europe): No. 1843, Map of Europe; 1844, Star and stripes.

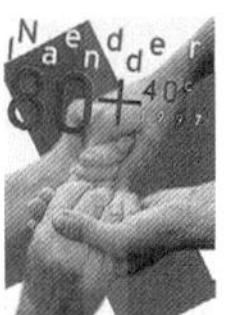

516 Clasped Hands over Red Cross

1997. Red Cross.

1845	**516**	80c.+40c. multicoloured	2·75	2·10

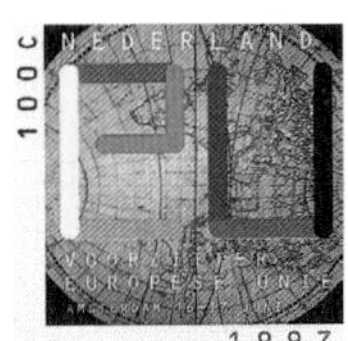

517 "eu" and Globe

1997. European Council of Ministers' Summit, Amsterdam.

1846	**517**	100c. multicoloured	2·50	1·60

518 Children playing in Boat

1997. Water Activities. Multicoloured.

1847	80c. Type **518**	1·80	55
1848	1g. Skutsje (sailing barges) race, Friesland	2·40	1·50

519 "vernuft"

1997. Anniversaries. Multicoloured.

1849	**519**	80c. ultramarine and blue	2·00	65
1850	-	80c. ultramarine and blue	2·00	65
1851	-	80c. multicoloured	2·00	65
1852	-	80c. multicoloured	2·00	65

Designs:—No. 1849, Type **519** (150th anniv of Royal Institute of Engineers); No. 1850, "adem" (centenary of Netherlands Asthma Centre, Davos, Switzerland); No. 1851, Flower (centenary of Florens College (horticultural college) and 125th anniv of Royal Botanical and Horticultural Society); No. 1852, Pianist accompanying singer (birth bicentenary of Franz Schubert (composer)).

520 "Nederland80"

1997. Youth. Multicoloured.

1853	**520**	80c. red and blue	1·60	55
1854	-	80c. multicoloured	1·60	55

Design:—No. 1854, "NEDERLAND80" in style of computer games giving appearance of three-dimensional block on race track.

521 Stork with Bundle

1997. New Baby Stamp. Self-adhesive gum.

1855	**521**	80c. multicoloured	1·80	50

See also Nos. 1960, 2120, 2201 and 2776.

522 *Little Red Riding Hood*

1997. Child Welfare. Fairy Tales. Multicoloured.

1856	80c.+40c. Type **522**	2·40	95
1857	80c.+40c. Man laying loaves on ground (*Tom Thumb*)	2·40	95
1858	80c.+40c. Woodman with bottle (*Genie in the Bottle*)	2·40	95
MS1859	144×75 mm. Nos. 1856/8, each×2	14·50	14·00

523 Heads and Star

1997. Christmas. Multicoloured, colour of background given.

1860	**523**	55c. yellow	1·30	50
1861	**523**	55c. blue	1·30	50
1862	-	55c. orange	1·30	50
1863	-	55c. red	1·30	50
1864	-	55c. green	1·30	50
1865	**523**	55c. green	1·30	50

Design:—Nos. 1862/4, Heads and heart.

524 Light across Darkness

1998. Bereavement Stamp.

1866	**524**	80c. blue	1·80	50

See also No. 2051 and 2777.

525 Cow and Ship Tiles

1998. Delft Faience.

1867	**525**	100c. multicoloured	2·00	95
1868	-	160c. blue	3·25	1·90

Design:—160c. Ceramic tile showing boy standing on head.

526 Strawberries in Bloom (Spring)

1998. The Four Seasons. Multicoloured.

1869	80c. Type **526**	2·00	1·90
1870	80c. Strawberry, flan and strawberry plants (Summer)	2·00	1·90
1871	80c. Bare trees and pruning diagram (Winter)	2·00	1·90
1872	80c. Orchard and apple (Autumn)	2·00	1·90

527 Handshake

1998. Anniversaries. Multicoloured.

1873	80c. Type **527** (350th anniv of Treaty of Munster)	1·60	65
1874	80c. Statue of Johan Thorbecke (politician) (150th anniv of Constitution)	1·60	65
1875	80c. Child on swing (50th anniv of Declaration of Human Rights)	1·60	65

528 Bride and Groom

1998. Wedding Stamp. Self-adhesive gum.

1876	**528**	80c. multicoloured	1·80	50

See also No. 1961.

529 Shopping List

1998. Cultural, Health and Social Welfare Funds. Care and the Elderly.

1877	80c.+40c. Type **529**	2·40	2·10
1878	80c.+40c. Sweet	2·40	2·10
1879	80c.+40c. Training shoe	2·40	2·10
MS1880	144×75 mm. Nos. 1877/9, each×2	14·50	13·50

530 Letters blowing in Wind

1998. Letters to the Future.

1881	**530**	80c. multicoloured	1·80	50

531 Customers

1998. Centenary of Rabobank.

1882	**531**	80c. yellow, green and blue	1·80	50

532 Goalkeeper catching Boot

1998. Sport. Multicoloured.

1883	80c. Type **532** (World Cup Football Championship, France)	1·80	50
1884	80c. Family hockey team (centenary of Royal Netherlands Hockey Federation) (35×24 mm)	1·80	50

533 Map of Friesland, *c.* 1600

1998. 500th Anniv of Central Administration of Friesland.

1885	**533**	80c. multicoloured	1·80	50

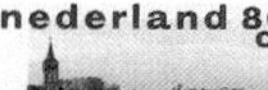

534 River Defences

1998. Bicentenary of Directorate-General of Public Works and Water Management. Multicoloured.

1886	80c. Type **534**	1·60	50
1887	1g. Sea defences	2·00	1·40

535 "tnt post groep"

1998. Separation of Royal Netherlands PTT into TNT Post Groep and KPN NV (telecommunications).

1888	**535**	80c. black, blue and red	1·60	85
1889	-	80c. black, blue and green	1·60	85

Design:—No. 1889, "kpn nv".

Nos. 1888/9 were issued together, *se-tenant*, forming a composite design of the complete "160".

536 Books and Keyboard

1998. Cultural Anniversaries. Multicoloured.

1890	80c. Type **536** (bicentenary of National Library)	1·70	55
1891	80c. Maurits Escher (graphic artist, birth centenary) looking at his mural *Metamorphose* in The Hague Post Office (vert)	1·70	75
1892	80c. Simon Vestdijk (writer, birth centenary) and page from *Fantoches* (vert)	1·70	75

537 Queen Wilhelmina

1998. Royal Centenaries. Sheet 144×75 mm containing T **537** and similar vert design. Multicoloured.

MS1893	80c. Type **537** (coronation); 80c. Gilded Coach	7·00	5·75

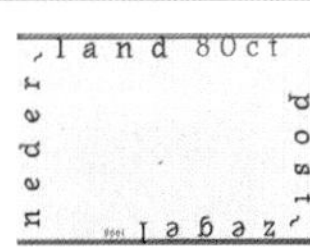

538 "land 80 ct"

1998. Greetings Stamps. Multicoloured. Self-adhesive.

1894	80c. Type **538** (top of frame red)	2·00	95
1895	80c. "80 ct post" (top of frame mauve)	2·00	95
1896	80c. Type **538** (top of frame orange)	2·00	95
1897	80c. "80 ct post" (top of frame orange)	2·00	95
1898	80c. Type **538** (top of frame yellow)	2·00	95

The part of the frame used for identification purposes is above the face value.

Nos. 1894/8 were only available in sheetlets of ten stamps and 20 labels (five stamps and ten labels on each side of the card). It was intended that the sender should insert the appropriate greetings label into the rectangular space on each stamp before use.

539 Rabbits

1998. Domestic Pets. Multicoloured.

1899	80c. Type **539**	2·00	75

1900	80c. Drent partridge dog	2·00	75
1901	80c. Kittens	2·00	75

540 Cathy and Jeremy writing a Letter

1998. 25th Anniv of Jack, Jacky and the Juniors (comic strip characters).

1902	80c. Type **540**	1·80	55
MS1903 108×50 mm. 80c. Type **540**; 80c. Posting letter		7·00	5·75

541 St. Nicholas on Horseback

1998. Child Welfare. Celebrations. Multicoloured.

1904	80c.+40c. Type **541**	3·00	95
1905	80c.+40c. Making birthday cake	3·00	95
1906	80c.+40c. Carnival parade	3·00	95
MS1907 144×75 mm. Nos. 1904/6, each×2		18·00	14·50

542 Hare and Snowball

1998. Christmas. Self-adhesive.

1908	**542**	55c. blue, red and black	1·20	55
1909	-	55c. multicoloured	1·20	55
1910	-	55c. blue, red and black	1·20	55
1911	-	55c. multicoloured	1·20	55
1912	-	55c. blue, red and black	1·20	55
1913	-	55c. green, blue and red	1·20	55
1914	-	55c. green, blue and red	1·20	55
1915	-	55c. green, blue and red	1·20	55
1916	-	55c. green, blue and red	1·20	55
1917	-	55c. green, blue and red	1·20	55
1918	-	55c. blue, green and red	1·20	55
1919	-	55c. red, green and black	1·20	55
1920	-	55c. blue, green and red	1·20	55
1921	-	55c. green, red and black	1·20	55
1922	-	55c. blue, green and red	1·20	55
1923	-	55c. blue, green and red	1·20	55
1924	-	55c. blue, green and red	1·20	55
1925	-	55c. blue, green and red	1·20	55
1926	-	55c. blue, green and red	1·20	55
1927	-	55c. blue, green and red	1·20	55

Designs:—No. 1909, House and snowball; No. 1910, Dove and snowball; No. 1911, Christmas tree and snowball; No. 1912, Reindeer and snowball; No. 1913, Hare; No. 1914, House; No. 1915, Dove; No. 1916, Christmas tree; No. 1917, Reindeer; No. 1918, House and hare; No. 1919, House and heart; No. 1920, Dove and house; No. 1921, Christmas tree and house; No. 1922, House and reindeer; No. 1923, Christmas tree and hare; No. 1924, Christmas tree and house; No. 1925, Christmas tree and dove; No. 1926, Christmas tree and heart; No. 1927, Christmas tree and reindeer.

543 House and Tree on Snowball

1999. Make-up Rate Stamp.

1928	**543**	25c. red and black	60	50

544 Euro Coin

1999. Introduction of the Euro (European currency).

1929	**544**	80c. multicoloured	1·80	1·20

545 Pillar Box, 1850

1999. Bicentenary of Netherlands Postal Service.

1930	**545**	80c. multicoloured	2·00	1·50

See also No. **MS**1965.

546 Richard Krajicek serving

1999. Centenary of Royal Dutch Lawn Tennis Federation.

1931	**546**	80c. multicoloured	1·80	55

547 White Spoonbill

1999. Protection of Bird and Migrating Waterfowl. Multicoloured.

1932	80c. Type **547** (centenary of Dutch Bird Protection Society)	1·60	55
1933	80c. Section of globe and arctic terns (African–Eurasian Waterbird Agreement)	1·60	55

548 Haarlemmerhout in Autumn

1999. Parks during the Seasons. Multicoloured.

1934	80c. Type **548**	2·00	1·90
1935	80c. Sonsbeek in winter	2·00	1·90
1936	80c. Weerribben in summer	2·00	1·90
1937	80c. Keukenhof in spring	2·00	1·90

549 Woman

1999. Cultural, Health and Social Welfare Funds. International Year of the Elderly. Multicoloured.

1938	80c.+40c. Type **549**	2·50	2·50
1939	80c.+40c. Man (green background)	2·50	2·50
1940	80c.+40c. Man (blue background)	2·50	2·50
MS1941 144×75 mm. Nos. 1938/40, each×2		16·00	14·50

550 Lifeboats on Rough Sea

1999. Water Anniversaries. Multicoloured.

1942	80c. Type **550** (175th Anniv of Royal Netherlands Lifeboat Association)	1·60	55
1943	80c. Freighters in canal (150th Anniv of Royal Association of Ships' Masters "Schuttevaer")	1·60	55

551 "I Love Stamps"

1999

1944	**551**	80c. blue and red	1·80	75
1945	-	80c. red and blue	2·40	1·90

Design:—No. 1945, "Stamps love Me".

552 *The Goldfinch* (Carel Fabritius)

1999. 17th-century Dutch Art. Multicoloured. Self-adhesive gum (1g.).

1946	80c. Type **552**	2·00	1·80
1947	80c. *Self-portrait* (Rembrandt)	2·00	1·80
1948	80c. *Self-portrait* (Judith Leyster)	2·00	1·80
1949	80c. *St. Sebastian* (Hendrick ter Brugghen)	2·00	1·80
1950	80c. *Beware of Luxury* (Jan Steen)	2·00	1·80
1951	80c. *The Sick Child* (Gabriel Metsu)	2·00	1·80
1952	80c. *Gooseberries* (Adriaen Coorte)	2·00	1·80
1953	80c. *View of Haarlem* (Jacob van Ruisdael)	2·00	1·80
1954	80c. *Mariaplaats, Utrecht* (Pieter Saenredam)	2·00	1·80
1955	80c. *Danae* (Rembrandt)	2·00	1·80
1956	1g. *The Jewish Bride* (Rembrandt)	2·20	1·90

553 "80" on Computer Screen

1999. Ordinary or self-adhesive gum.

1957	**553**	80c. multicoloured	1·80	50

554 Amaryllis, Coffee Cup, Candles, Letter Writing and Wine Glasses

1999. Greetings Stamp. Self-adhesive.

1959	**554**	80c. multicoloured	2·75	1·40

1999. New Baby Stamp. As No. 1855 but ordinary gum.

1960	**521**	80c. multicoloured	2·00	75

1999. Wedding Stamp. As No. 1876 but ordinary gum.

1961	**528**	80c. multicoloured	2·00	95

555 Victorian Heavy Machinery and Modern Computer

1999. Centenary of Confederation of Netherlands Industry and Employers.

1962	**555**	80c. multicoloured	1·80	50

556 Tintin and Snowy wearing Space Suits

1999. 70th Anniv of Tintin (comic strip character by Herge). Scenes from "Explorers on the Moon". Multicoloured.

1963	80c. Type **556**	2·00	50
MS1964 108×50 mm. 80c. Tintin, Snowy and Captain Haddock in moon buggy; 80c. Type **556**		8·50	7·50

557 Pillar Box, 1850

1999. Bicentenary of Netherlands Postal Service (2nd issue). Sheet 144×75 mm.

MS1965 **557** 5g. red, black and blue	10·50	10·00

558 Digger (completion of Afsluitdijk, 1932)

1999. The Twentieth Century. Multicoloured.

1966	80c. Type **558**	2·50	2·20
1967	80c. Space satellite	2·50	2·20
1968	80c. Berlage Commodity Exchange, Amsterdam (inauguration, 1903)	2·50	2·20
1969	80c. Empty motorway (car-free Sundays during oil crisis, 1973–74)	2·50	2·20
1970	80c. Old man (Old Age Pensions Act, 1947)	2·50	2·20
1971	80c. Delta Flood Project, 1953–97	2·50	2·20
1972	80c. Players celebrating (victory of Netherlands in European Cup Football Championship, 1998)	2·50	2·20
1973	80c. Four riders on one motorcycle (liberation and end of Second World War, 1945)	2·50	2·20
1974	80c. Woman posting vote (Women's Franchise, 1919)	2·50	2·20
1975	80c. Ice skaters (11 cities race)	2·50	2·20

559 Pluk van de Pettevlet on Fire Engine

1999. Child Welfare. Characters created by Fiep Westendorp. Multicoloured.

1976	80c.+40c. Type **559**	3·00	1·10
1977	80c.+40c. Otje drinking through straw	3·00	1·10
1978	80c.+40c. Jip and Janneke with cat	3·00	1·10
MS1979 144×75 mm. Nos. 1976/8, each×2		18·00	14·50

560 Father Christmas (Robin Knegt)

1999. Christmas. Winning entries in design competition. Multicoloured.

1980	55c. Type **560**	1·20	55
1981	55c. Angel singing (Davinia Bovenlander) (vert)	1·20	55
1982	55c. Dutch doughnuts in box (Henk Drenth)	1·20	55
1983	55c. Moon wearing Christmas hat (Lizet van den Berg) (vert)	1·20	55
1984	55c. Father Christmas carrying sacks (Noortje Kruse)	1·20	55
1985	55c. Clock striking midnight (Hucky de Haas) (vert)	1·20	55
1986	55c. Ice skater (Marleen Bos)	1·20	55
1987	55c. Human Christmas tree (Mariette Strik) (vert)	1·20	55
1988	55c. Woman wearing Christmas tree earrings (Saskia van Oversteeg)	1·20	55
1989	55c. Woman vacuuming pine needles (Frans Koenis) (vert)	1·20	55
1990	55c. Angel with harp and music score (Evelyn de Zeeuw)	1·20	55
1991	55c. Hand balancing candle, star, hot drink, hat and Christmas tree on fingers (Aafke van Ewijk) (vert)	1·20	55
1992	55c. Christmas tree (Daan Roepman) (vert)	1·20	55
1993	55c. Cat wearing crown (Sjoerd van der Zee) (vert)	1·20	55
1994	55c. Bird flying over house (Barbara Vollers)	1·20	55
1995	55c. Baby with angel wings (Rosmarijn Schmink) (vert)	1·20	55
1996	55c. Dog wearing Christmas hat (Casper Heijstek and Mirjam Cnosser)	1·20	55
1997	55c. Angel flying (Patricia van der Neut) (vert)	1·20	55
1998	55c. Nativity (Marco Cockx)	1·20	55
1999	55c. Christmas tree with decorations (Matthias Meiling) (vert)	1·20	55

561 "25"

2000. Make-up Rate Stamp.

2000	**561**	25c. red, blue and yellow	60	50

562 1 Guilder Coin, Margaret of Austria (Regent of Netherlands) (after Bernard van Orley) and *Coronation of Charles V* (Juan de la Coate)

2000. 500th Birth Anniv of Charles V, Holy Roman Emperor. Multicoloured.

2001 80c. Type **562** 2·40 1·90
2002 80c. Map of the 17 Provinces, *Charles V after the Battle of Muehlberg* (Titian) and Margaret of Parma (Regent of Netherlands) (after Antonius Mohr) 2·40 1·90

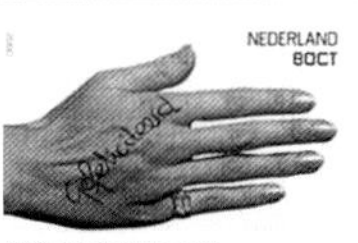

563 "Gefeliciteerd" ("Congratulations")

2000. Greetings stamps. Showing greetings messages on hands. Multicoloured.

2003 80c. Type **563** 1·90 1·60
2004 80c. "Succes met je nieuwe baan" ("Good luck with your new job") 1·90 1·60
2005 80c. "gefeliciteerd met je huis" ("Congratulations on your new home") 1·90 1·60
2006 80c. "PROFICIAT" ("Congratulations") 1·90 1·60
2007 80c. "Succes" ("Hope you have success") 1·90 1·60
2008 80c. "Veel geluk samen" ("Good luck together") 1·90 1·60
2009 80c. "Proficiat met je diploma" ("Congratulations on passing your exam") 1·90 1·60
2010 80c. "Geluk" ("Good luck") 1·90 1·60
2011 80c. "Van Harte" ("Cordially") 1·90 1·60
2012 80c. "GEFELICITEERD MET JE RUBEWIUS!" ("Congratulations on passing your driving test!") 1·90 1·60

564 Players celebrating

2000. European Football Championship, Netherlands and Belgium. Multicoloured.

2013 80c. Type **564** 1·50 55
2014 80c. Football 1·90 1·40

565 Man and Woman passing Ball

2000. Cultural, Health and Social Welfare Funds. Senior Citizens. Multicoloured.

2015 80c.+40c. Type **565** 2·75 2·30
2016 80c.+40c. Woman picking apples 2·75 2·30
2017 80c.+40c. Woman wearing swimming costume 2·75 2·30
MS2018 144×74 mm. Nos. 2015/17, each×2 16·00 14·00

566 *Feigned Sadness* (C. Troost)

2000. Bicentenary of the Rijksmuseum, Amsterdam. Multicoloured. (a) Ordinary gum.

2019 80c. Type **566** 2·20 2·00
2020 80c. *Harlequin and Columbine* (porcelain figurine) (J. J. Kandler) 2·20 2·00
2021 80c. *Ichikawa Ebizo IV* (woodcut) (T. Sharaku) 2·20 2·00
2022 80c. *Heavenly Beauty* (sandstone sculpture) 2·20 2·00
2023 80c. *St. Vitus* (wood sculpture) 2·20 2·00
2024 80c. *Woman in Turkish Costume* (J. E. Liotard) 2·20 2·00
2025 80c. *J. van Speyk* (J. Schoemaker Doyer) 2·20 2·00
2026 80c. *King Saul* (engraving) (L. van Leyden) 2·20 2·00
2027 80c. *L'Amour Menacant* (marble sculpture) (E. M. Falconet) 2·20 2·00
2028 80c. *Sunday* (photograph) (C. Ariens) 2·20 2·00

(b) Self-adhesive.

2029 100c. *The Nightwatch* (Rembrandt) 2·75 2·00

567 "80" and "Doe Maar" Record Cover

2000. Doe Maar (Dutch pop group). Multicoloured.

2030 80c. Type **567** 1·60 95
2031 80c. "80" and song titles 2·40 1·90

568 *Dutch Landscape* (Jeroen Krabb)

2000. Priority Mail. Contemporary Art. Self-adhesive.

2033 **568** 110c. multicoloured 3·00 2·50

569 *The Nightwatch* (Rembrandt)

2000. Priority Mail. Self-adhesive.

2034 **569** 110c. multicoloured 3·00 2·50

570 *Libertad* (full-rigged cadet ship)

2000. Sail Amsterdam 2000. Sailing Ships. Multicoloured.

2036 80c. Type **570** 2·20 2·00
2037 80c. *Amerigo Vespucci* (cadet ship) and figurehead 2·20 2·00
2038 80c. *Dar Mlodziezy* (full-rigged cadet ship) and sail 2·20 2·00
2039 80c. *Europa* (cadet ship) and wheel 2·20 2·00
2040 80c. *Kruzenshtern* (cadet barque) and bell 2·20 2·00
2041 80c. *Sagres II* (cadet barque) and sail 2·20 2·00
2042 80c. *Alexander von Humboldt* (barque) and sail 2·20 2·00
2043 80c. *Sedov* (cadet barque) and sailors dropping sail 2·20 2·00
2044 80c. *Mir* (square-rigged training ship) 2·20 2·00
2045 80c. *Oosterschelde* (schooner) and rope 2·20 2·00

571 Roller Skating

2000. Sjors and Sjimmie (comic strip characters by Frans Piet). Multicoloured.

2046 80c. Type **571** 2·50 1·70
2047 80c. In car 2·50 1·70
MS2048 108×50 mm. 80c. As No. 2049; 80c. As No. 2047 7·00 5·75
2049 80c. Listening to radio 2·50 1·70
2050 80c. Swinging on rope 2·50 1·70

2000. Bereavement Stamp. As No. 1866 but self-adhesive.

2051 **524** 80c. blue 2·50 1·40

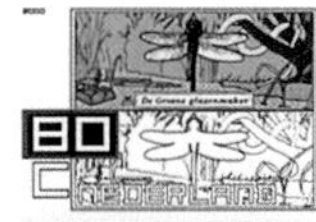

572 Green Dragonfly

2000. Endangered Species. Multicoloured.

2052 80c. Type **572** 1·70 55
2053 80c. Weather loach 2·10 1·40

573 Canal Boat

2000. 150th Anniv (2002) of Netherlands Stamps (1st issue). Sheet 108×50 mm containing T **573** and similar horiz design. Multicoloured.

MS2054 80c. Type **573**; 80c. Mail carriage 4·50 3·75

See also Nos. **MS**2138 and **MS**2250.

574 Children wearing Monster Hats

2000. Child Welfare. Multicoloured. (a) Self-adhesive gum.

2055 80c.+40c. Type **574** 3·50 3·25
2056 80c.+40c. Boy sailing bath-tub 3·50 3·25
2057 80c.+40c. Children brewing magical stew 3·50 3·25

(b) Ordinary gum.

MS2058 80c.+40c. Type **574**; 80c.+40c. Ghostly games; 80c.+40c. Girl riding crocodile; 80c.+40c. As No. 2056; 80c.+40c. As No. 2057; 80c.+40c. Children playing dragon 16·00 13·50

575 Couple with Christmas Tree

2000. Christmas. Multicoloured.

2059 60c. Type **575** 1·50 55
2060 60c. Children making snow balls 1·50 55
2061 60c. Couple dancing 1·50 55
2062 60c. Man playing French horn 1·50 55
2063 60c. Man carrying Christmas tree 1·50 55
2064 60c. Man carrying young child 1·50 55
2065 60c. Woman reading book 1·50 55
2066 60c. Couple kissing 1·50 55
2067 60c. Man playing piano 1·50 55
2068 60c. Woman watching from window 1·50 55
2069 60c. Woman sitting in chair 1·50 55
2070 60c. Man sitting beside fire 1·50 55
2071 60c. Snowman flying 1·50 55
2072 60c. Couple in street 1·50 55
2073 60c. Child playing violin 1·50 55
2074 60c. Children on sledge 1·50 55
2075 60c. Man writing letter 1·50 55
2076 60c. Woman carrying plate of food 1·50 55
2077 60c. Family 1·50 55
2078 60c. Woman sleeping 1·50 55

576 Moon

2001. Make-up Rate Stamp.

2079 **576** 20c. multicoloured 60 55

577 Whinchat

2001. Centenary of Royal Dutch Nature Society. Multicoloured.

2080 80c. Type **577** 1·90 1·70
2081 80c. Family in rowing boat 1·90 1·70
2082 80c. Fox 1·90 1·70
2083 80c. Couple bird watching 1·90 1·70
2084 80c. Flowers 1·90 1·70

578 Poem (by E. du Perron)

2001. Between Two Cultures. National Book Week. Multicoloured.

2085 80c. Type **578** 2·00 1·80
2086 80c. Men in street 2·00 1·80
2087 80c. Poem (by Hafid Bouazza) 2·00 1·80
2088 80c. Woman and young men 2·00 1·80
2089 80c. Poem (by Adriaan van Dis) 2·00 1·80
2090 80c. Profiles of two women 2·00 1·80
2091 80c. Poem (by Kader Abdolah) 2·00 1·80
2092 80c. Two young girls 2·00 1·80
2093 80c. Poem (by Ellen Ombre) 2·00 1·80
2094 80c. Boy carrying map 2·00 1·80

579 Rotterdam Bridge

2001. Priority Mail. Rotterdam, European City of Culture. Self-adhesive gum.

2095 **579** 110c. multicoloured 2·50 2·10

580 Emergency Rescuers

2001. International Year of Volunteers. Sheet 108×50 mm. containing T **580** and similar horiz design. Multicoloured.

MS2096 80c. Type **508**, 80c. Animal rescuers 5·00 4·75

581 Chess Board

2001. Birth Centenary of Machgielis "Professor Max" Euwe (chess player). Sheet 108×50 mm containing T **581** and similar horiz design. Multicoloured.

MS2097 80c. Type **581**; 80c. Euwe and chess pieces 5·00 4·75

582 Helen's Flower (*Helenium rubinzwerg*)

2001. Flowers. Multicoloured. (a) Self-adhesive gum.

2098 80c.+40c. Type **582** 4·00 3·75
2099 80c.+40c. Russian hollyhock (*Alcea rugosa*) 4·00 3·75
2100 80c.+40c. Persian cornflower (*Centaurea dealbata*) 4·00 3·75

(b) Ordinary gum.

MS2101 144×75 mm. 80c.+40c. *Caryopteris* "Heavenly Blue"; 80c.+40c. Type **582**; 80c.+40c. As No. 2099; 80c.+40c. Spurge (*Euphorbia schillingii*); 80c.+40c. As No. 2100; 80c.+40c. Hooker inula (*Inula hookeri*) 17·00 13·50

583 *Autumn* (detail) (L. Gestel)

2001. Art Nouveau. Multicoloured.

2102 80c. Type **583** 2·00 1·90
2103 80c. Book cover by C. Lebeau for *De Stille Kracht* 2·00 1·90
2104 80c. Burcht Federal Council Hall, Amsterdam (R. N. Roland Holst and H. P. Berlage) 2·00 1·90
2105 80c. *O Grave Where is Thy Victory* (painting) (J. Throop) 2·00 1·90
2106 80c. Vases by C. J. van der Hoef from Amphora factory 2·00 1·90
2107 80c. Capital from staircase of Utrecht building (J. Mendes da Costa) 2·00 1·90
2108 80c. Illustration of common peafowl from *The Happy Owls* (T. van Hoytema) 2·00 1·90
2109 80c. *The Bride* (detail) (painting) (J. Thorn Prikker) 2·00 1·90
2110 80c. Factory-printed cotton fabric (M. Duco Crop) 2·00 1·90
2111 80c. Dentz van Schaik room (L. Zyl) 2·00 1·90

2001. As T **428** but with face value expressed in euros and cents. Self-adhesive gum.

2112	85c. blue	2·30	50

584 Sky and Landscape

2001. Self-adhesive gum.

2113	**584**	85c. multicoloured	2·00	55

585 Arrows

2001. Business Coil Stamp. Self-adhesive gum.

2114	**585**	85c. purple and silver	2·00	50

586 Reclaimed Land

2001. Multicoloured. Self-adhesive gum.

2115	85c. Type **586** (postage)	2·30	75
2116	1g.20 Beach (priority mail)	3·00	2·10
2117	1g.65 Town and canal	4·00	3·25

587 House carrying Suitcase

2001. Greetings Stamps. Self-adhesive gum.

2118	**587**	85c. black and yellow	2·10	1·70
2119	-	85c. red, yellow and gold	2·20	1·70
2120	-	85c. multicoloured	2·00	1·40
2121	-	85c. multicoloured	3·25	2·00

Designs:— No. 2118, Type **587** (change of address stamp); No. 2119, Couple (wedding stamp); No. 2120, As Type **521** (new baby); No. 2121, As Type **524** (bereavement stamp).

588 Tom and Jerry

2001. Cartoon Characters. Multicoloured.

2122	85c. Type **588**	2·20	1·90
2123	85c. Fred Flintstone and Barney Rubble	2·20	1·90
2124	85c. Johnny Bravo	2·20	1·90
2125	85c. Dexter posting letter	2·20	1·90
2126	85c. Powerpuff Girls	2·20	1·90

589 "Veel Geluk" ("Good Luck")

2001. Greetings Stamps. Multicoloured. Self-adhesive gum.

2127	85c. Type **589**	2·20	1·90
2128	85c. "Gefeliciteerd!" ("Congratulations!")	2·20	1·90
2129	85c. "Veel Geluk" with envelope flap (horiz)	2·20	1·90
2130	85c. "Gefeliciteerd!" with envelope flap (horiz)	2·20	1·90
2131	85c. "Proficiat" ("Congratulations")	2·20	1·90
2132	85c. "Succes !" ("Success")	2·20	1·90
2133	85c. "Van Harte ..." ("Cordially ...")	2·20	1·90
2134	85c. "Proficiat" with envelope flap (horiz)	2·20	1·90
2135	85c. "Succes !" with envelope flap (horiz)	2·20	1·90
2136	85c. "Van Harte ..." with envelope flap (horiz)	2·20	1·90

590 Guilder Coins

2001. Replacement of the Guilder. Self-adhesive.

2137	**590**	12g.75 silver	28·00	21·00

591 Waaigat Canal and Williamstad, Curacao (J. E. Heemskerk after G. C. W. Voorduin)

2001. 150th Annivs of Netherlands Stamps (2002) (2nd issue) and of Royal Institute foe Linguistics and Anthropology. Sheet 108×50 mm containing T **591** and similar horiz design. Multicoloured.

MS2138 39c. Type **591**; 39c. Pangka sugar refinery, Java (J.C. Grieve after A. Salm) 4·50 3·75

592 Magnifier, Target Mark and Dots

2001. Centenary of Royal Dutch Printers' Association. Sheet 108×50 mm containing T **592** and similar horiz design. Multicoloured.

MS2139 39c. Type **592**; 39c. Magnifier, computer zoom symbol and colour palette 4·50 3·75

593 Computer Figure and River

2001. Child Welfare. Multicoloured. (a) Self-adhesive gum.

2140	85c.+40c. Type **593**	5·00	4·25

(b) Ordinary gum.

MS2141 146×76 mm. 85c.+40c. Figure and printer; 85c.+40c. Road, car and figure; 85c.+40c. Post box, blocks and droplets; 85c.+40c. Post box, figure and stairs; 85c.+40c. Type **593**; 85c.+40c. Figure swinging on rope and log in river 16·00 14·00

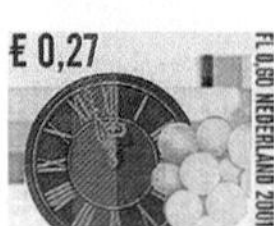

594 Clock and Grapes

2001. Christmas. Multicoloured. Self-adhesive gum.

2142	27c. Type **594**	1·20	55
2143	27c. Stars and bun	1·20	55
2144	27c. Steeple and buns	1·20	55
2145	27c. Cherub and coins	1·20	55
2146	27c. Champagne bottle	1·20	55
2147	27c. Wreath around chimney	1·20	55
2148	27c. Tower	1·20	55
2149	27c. Christmas tree bauble	1·20	55
2150	27c. Playing card with Christmas tree as sign	1·20	55
2151	27c. Cake seen through window	1·20	55
2152	27c. Decorated Christmas tree	1·20	55
2153	27c. Father Christmas	1·20	55
2154	27c. Sign displaying hot drink	1·20	55
2155	27c. Candles seen through window	1·20	55
2156	27c. Illuminated roof-tops	1·20	55
2157	27c. Reindeer	1·20	55
2158	27c. Snowman	1·20	55
2159	27c. Parcel	1·20	55
2160	27c. Bonfire	1·20	55
2161	27c. Children on toboggan	1·20	55

595 "12"

2002. Make-up Rate Stamp. (a) Self-adhesive gum.

2162	**595**	2c. red	50	50
2166	**595**	12c. green	60	50

(b) Ordinary gum.

2169	**595**	2c. red	40	40
2170	**595**	3c. agate	60	55
2171	**595**	5c. mauve	40	40
2172	**595**	10c. blue	40	40

596 Queen Beatrix

2002. Queen Beatrix

2175	**596**	25c. brown and green	1·00	55
2176	**596**	39c. blue and pink	1·60	50
2177	**596**	40c. blue and brown	1·60	1·00
2178	**596**	44c. rose and olive	1·70	1·10
2179	**596**	1 (46c.) blue and reddish lilac	2·30	1·00
2180	**596**	50c. pink and green	2·10	1·00
2181	**596**	55c. mauve and brown	4·00	3·00
2182	**596**	57c. blue and purple	4·25	2·75
2183	**596**	61c. violet and brown	4·25	3·00
2184	**596**	65c. green and violet	3·25	2·20
2185	**596**	67c. rose and olive	4·50	2·30
2186	**596**	70c. deep green and green	4·50	3·25
2187	**596**	72c. ochre and blue	4·75	3·25
2187b	**596**	74c. olive-green and violet-blue	3·50	2·75
2188	**596**	76c. ochre and green	4·50	3·25
2189	**596**	78c. blue and brown	3·50	75
2190	**596**	80c. blue and purple	3·50	2·50
2191	**596**	88c. violet and green	3·50	2·00
2192	**596**	2 (92c.) gold and dull green	4·50	1·90
2193	**596**	€1 green and blue	4·00	75
2194	**596**	€3 mauve and green	12·00	1·30

597 Arrows

2002. Business Coil Stamps. Self-adhesive gum.

2195	**597**	39c. purple and silver	1·50	50
2196	**597**	78c. blue and gold	3·00	75

598 Prince Willem-Alexander and Máxima Zorreguieta

2002. Marriage of Prince Willem-Alexander and Maxima Zorreguieta. Sheet 145×75 mm, containing T **598** and similar horiz design.

MS2197 **598** 39c. black, silver and orange; 39c. multicoloured 4·50 4·25

Design:—39c. "Willem-Alexander Maxima" and "222".

599 Sky and Landscape

2002. Self-adhesive gum.

2198	**599**	39c. multicoloured	1·50	50

600 Couple

2002. Greetings Stamps. Face values in euros. Self-adhesive gum.

2199	-	39c. black and yellow	1·80	75
2200	**600**	39c. red, yellow and gold	1·80	75
2201	-	39c. multicoloured	1·60	75
2202	-	39c. blue	1·60	75

Designs:—No. 2199, As Type **587** (change of address stamp); No. 2200, Type **600** (wedding stamp); No. 2201, As Type **521** (new baby); No. 2202, As Type **524** (bereavement stamp).

601 "Veel Geluk" ("Good Luck")

2001. Greetings Stamps. Face values in euros. Multicoloured. Self-adhesive gum.

2203	39c. Type **601**	2·00	1·40
2204	39c. "Gefeliciteerd!" ("Congratulations!")	2·00	1·40
2205	39c. "Veel Geluk" ("Good Luck") (horiz)	2·00	1·40
2206	39c. "Gefeliciteerd!" with envelope flap (horiz)	2·00	1·40
2207	39c. "Proficiat" ("Congratulations")	2·00	1·40
2208	39c. "Succes !" ("Success")	2·00	1·40
2209	39c. "Van Harte..." ("Cordially ...")	2·00	1·40
2210	39c. "Proficiat" with envelope flap (horiz)	2·00	1·40
2211	39c. "Succes !" with envelope flap (horiz)	2·00	1·40
2212	39c. "Van Harte..." with envelope flap (horiz)	2·00	1·40

602 Reclaimed Land

2002. Landscapes. Face values in euros. Multicoloured. Self-adhesive gum.

2213	39c. Type **602** (postage)	1·40	40
2214	54c. Beach (priority mail)	2·00	1·70
2215	75c. Town and canal	2·75	2·50

603 Water Lily

2002. Floriade 2002 International Horticultural Exhibition, Harlemmermeer. Flowers. Multicoloured.

2216	39c. + 19c. Type **603**	2·20	1·70
2217	39c. + 19c. Dahlia	2·20	1·70
2218	39c. + 19c. Japanese cherry blossom	2·20	1·70
2219	39c. + 19c. Rose	2·20	1·70
2220	39c. + 19c. Orchid	2·20	1·70
2221	39c. + 19c. Tulip	2·20	1·70

Nos. 2216/21 were printed on paper impregnated with perfume which was released when the stamps were scratched.

604 Flowers and Red Crosses

2002. Red Cross. Tenth Annual Blossom Walk.

2222	**604**	39c. + 19c. multicoloured	2·40	2·10

605 Langnek

2002. 50th Anniv of Efteling Theme Park. Multicoloured. Self-adhesive gum.

2223	39c. Type **605**	1·70	85
2224	39c. Pardoes de Tovernar	1·70	85
2225	39c. Droomvlucht Elfje	1·70	85
2226	39c. Kleine Boodschap	1·70	85
2227	39c. Holle Bolle Gijs	1·70	85

606 *West Indies Landscape* (Jan Mostaert)

2002. Landscape Paintings. Showing paintings and enlarged detail in foreground. Multicoloured.

2228	39c. Type **606**	1·80	1·70
2229	39c. *Riverbank with Cows* (Aelbert Cuyp)	1·80	1·70
2230	39c. *Cornfield* (Jacob van Ruisdael)	1·80	1·70
2231	39c. *Avenue at Middelharnis* (Meindert Hobbema)	1·80	1·70
2232	39c. *Italian Landscape with Umbrella Pines* (Hendrik Voogd)	1·80	1·70
2233	39c. *Landscape in Normandy* (Andreas Schelfhout)	1·80	1·70
2234	39c. *Landscape with Waterway* (Jan Toorop)	1·80	1·70
2235	39c. *Landscape* (Jan Sluijters)	1·80	1·70
2236	39c. *Kismet* (Michael Raedecker)	1·80	1·70
2237	39c. *Untitled* (Robert Zandvliet)	1·80	1·70

607 Circus Performers

2002. Priority Mail. Europa. Circus. Multicoloured.

No.	Description	Unused	Used
2238	54c. Type **607**	3·00	2·40
2239	54c. Lions and Big Top	3·00	2·40

608 Circles

2002. Business Coil Stamp. Self-adhesive gum.

No.	Description	Unused	Used
2240	**608** 39c. deep blue, blue and red	1·60	95
2241	**608** 78c. green, light green and red	3·25	1·70

609 Dutch East Indiaman and 1852 Stamps

2002. 150th Anniv of Netherlands Stamps. 400th Anniv of Dutch East India Company (V. O. C.). Sheet 108×50 mm, containing T **609** and similar horiz design. Multicoloured.

MS2250 39c. Type **609**; 39c. Two Dutch East Indiamen and and stamps of 1852 4·50 4·25

610 Boatyard, Spakenburg

2002. Industrial Heritage. Multicoloured.

No.	Description	Unused	Used
2251	39c. Type **610**	1·80	1·70
2252	39c. Limekiln, Dedemsvaart	1·80	1·70
2253	39c. Steam-driven pumping station, Cruquius	1·80	1·70
2254	39c. Mine-shaft winding gear, Heerlen	1·80	1·70
2255	39c. Salt drilling tower, Hengelo	1·80	1·70
2256	39c. Windmill, Weidum	1·80	1·70
2257	39c. Brick-works, Zevenaar	1·80	1·70
2258	39c. "Drie Hoefijzers" brewery, Breda	1·80	1·70
2259	39c. Water-treatment plant, Tilburg	1·80	1·70
2260	39c. "Nodding-donkey" oil pump, Schoonebeck	1·80	1·70

611 Cat and Child

2002. Child Welfare. Sheet 147×76 mm, containing T **611** and similar horiz designs. Multicoloured.

MS2261 Type **611**, 39c.+19c. Blue figure and upper part of child with green head; 39c.+19c. Child and ball; 39c.+19c. Child with yellow head and raised arms; 39c.+19c. Child with brown head and left arm raised; 39c.+19c. Dog and child 15·00 13·50

612 Woman and Child

2002. Christmas. Multicoloured. Self-adhesive gum.

No.	Description	Unused	Used
2262	29c. Type **612**	1·20	85
2263	29c. Seated man facing left	1·20	85
2264	29c. Profile with raised collar	1·20	85
2265	29c. Stream and figure wearing scarf	1·20	85
2266	29c. Woman, tree and snowflakes	1·20	85
2267	29c. Snowflakes and man wearing knee-length coat beside grasses	1·20	85
2268	29c. Snowflakes, man, and gate and stream	1·20	85
2269	29c. Snowflakes, windmill, stream and woman	1·20	85
2270	29c. Seated man facing right	1·20	85
2271	29c. Willow tree and profile of child facing left	1·20	85
2272	29c. Man leaning against tree	1·20	85
2273	29c. Man with hands in pockets	1·20	85
2274	29c. Seated couple	1·20	85
2275	29c. Fir tree and man's profile facing left	1·20	85
2276	29c. Man carrying child on shoulders	1·20	85
2277	29c. Profile of boy facing right	1·20	85
2278	29c. Standing child facing left	1·20	85
2279	29c. Snowflakes, sea and upper part of man with raised collar	1·20	85
2280	29c. Sea behind man wearing hat and glasses	1·20	85
2281	29c. Figure with out-stretched arms	1·20	85

Nos. 2262/81 were issued together, *se-tenant*, the stamps arranged in strips of five, each strip forming a composite design.

613 *Landscape with Four Trees*

614 *Self-portrait with Straw Hat*

2003. 150th Birth Anniv of Vincent Van Gogh (artist). Multicoloured. (a) Ordinary gum.

No.	Description	Unused	Used
2282	39c. Type **613**	2·00	1·80
2283	39c. *The Potato Eaters*	2·00	1·80
2284	39c. *Four Cut Sunflowers*	2·00	1·80
2285	39c. *Self-portrait with Grey Felt Hat*	2·00	1·80
2286	39c. *The Zouave*	2·00	1·80
2287	39c. *Place Du Forum Cafe Terrace by Night, Arles*	2·00	1·80
2288	39c. *Tree Trunks in Long Grass*	2·00	1·80
2289	39c. *Almond Blossom*	2·00	1·80
2290	39c. *Auvers-sur-Oise*	2·00	1·80
2291	39c. *Wheatfield with Crows, Auvers-sur-Oise*	2·00	1·80

(b) Self-adhesive.

No.	Description	Unused	Used
2292	39c. Type **614**	1·80	1·10
2293	59c. *Vase with Sunflowers*	2·40	2·20
2294	75c. *The Sower*	3·50	3·25

615 North Pier, Ijmuiden

2003. 50th Anniv of Floods in Zeeland, North Brabant and South Holland. Designs showing photographs from national archives. Each grey and black.

No.	Description	Unused	Used
2295	39c. Type **615**	1·90	1·70
2296	39c. Hansweert Lock	1·90	1·70
2297	39c. Building dam, Wieringermeer	1·90	1·70
2298	39c. Ijsselmeer Dam	1·90	1·70
2299	39c. Breached dyke, Willemstad	1·90	1·70
2300	39c. Repairing dyke, Stavenisse	1·90	1·70
2301	39c. Building dam, Zandkreek	1·90	1·70
2302	39c. Building dam, Grevelingen	1·90	1·70
2303	39c. Flood barrier, Oosterschelde	1·90	1·70
2304	39c. Floods, Roermond	1·90	1·70

616 See-through Register (security feature)

2003. 300th Anniv of Joh. Enschede (printers). Multicoloured.

No.	Description	Unused	Used
2305	39c. Type **616**	1·70	1·00
2306	39c. Fleischman's musical notation	1·70	1·00

No. 2305 has the remaining symbols of the see-through register printed on the back over the gum. This forms a complete design when held up to the light.

No. 2305 was embossed with a notional barcode and No. 2306 with a security device.

617 Alstroemeria

2003. Flower Paintings. Multicoloured.

No.	Description	Unused	Used
2307	39c.+19c. Type **617**	2·10	1·50
2308	39c.+19c. Sweet pea	2·10	1·50
2309	39c.+19c. Pansies	2·10	1·50
2310	39c.+19c. Trumpet vine	2·10	1·50
2311	39c.+19c. Lychnis	2·10	1·50
2312	39c.+19c. Irises	2·10	1·50

618 Oystercatcher

2003. Fauna of the Dutch Shallows. Winning Entry in Stamp Design Competition. Multicoloured.

MS2313 Two sheets, each 140×82 mm. (a) 39c.×4, Type **618**; Spoonbill (horiz); Eider duck: Grey seal (horiz) (b) 59c.×4, Herring gull; Curlew (horiz); Seals and gull; Crab (horiz) 18·00 16·00

MS2313 (b) were issued with "PRIORITY/Prioritaire" label attached at either upper or lower edge.

619 "39"

2003. Greetings Stamps. Two sheets, each 122×170 mm, containing T **619** and similar vert designs. Multicoloured.

MS2314 (a) 39c.×10, Type **619** (blue) (green) (purple) (pink) (orange) (yellow) (olive) (turquoise) (red) (brown); (b) 39c.×10, Flowers; Flag; Present; Champagne glass; Medal; Guitar; Balloons; Cut-out figures; Slice of cake; Garland 36·00 32·00

Nos. **MS**2314a/b were each issued with a *se-tenant* label attached at left showing either Marjolein Bastin (artist); *Paint tubes and splashes* (painting, Marjolein Bastin); Humberto Tan (television presenter); Figures symbolising Red Cross; Daphne Deckers (presenter and actress); Fan-mail; Prime Minister Jan Balkenende; Palm top computer; Sien Diels (*Sesame Street* presenter); Tommie (character from *Sesame Street*) (**MS**2314a) or a girl (**MS**2314b). The labels could be personalised by the addition of a photograph for an inclusive fee of €12 for the first sheet and €5.95 for subsequent sheets bearing the same design.

620 Coffee Cup

2003. 250th Anniv of Douwe Egberts (coffee and tea retailers). Multicoloured.

No.	Description	Unused	Used
2315	39c. Type **620**	1·70	1·00
2316	39c. As No. 2315 but with colours reversed	1·70	1·00

Nos. 2315/16 were impregnated with the scent of coffee which was released when the stamps were rubbed.

621 Aeroplane, Ship and Trucks

2003. Land, Air and Water. Winning Entry in Stamp Design Competition. Multicoloured.

No.	Description	Unused	Used
2317	39c. Type **621**	1·70	1·00
2318	39c. Cat, bird, fish and envelope	1·70	1·00

622 Nelson Mandela and Child

2003. 85th Birth Anniv of Nelson Mandela (President of South Africa). Multicoloured.

No.	Description	Unused	Used
2319	39c. Type **622**	1·70	1·00
2320	39c. Children (Nelson Mandela's Children's Fund)	1·70	1·00

623 "For You from Me"

2003. Self-adhesive gum.

No.	Description	Unused	Used
2321	**623** 39c. multicoloured	1·70	1·00

624 Children Kissing

2003. Winning Entries in Stamp Design Competition. Sheet 108×151 mm containing T **624** and similar horiz designs. Multicoloured.

MS2322 39c.×10, Type **624**; Traditional costume; Cat; Puppies; Child; Bride and groom; 2CV cars; Motorcycle; Peacock butterfly; Flowers 21·00 18·00

625 "39"

2003. Company Stamp. Self-adhesive.

No.	Description	Unused	Used
2323	**625** 39c. multicoloured	2·10	1·90

626 Coloured Squares

2003. Stamp Day. 75th Anniv of Netherlands Association of Stamp Dealers (NVPH).

No.	Description	Unused	Used
2324	**626** 39c. multicoloured	1·70	95

627 Notepad, Radio and Ballet Shoes

2003. Child Welfare. Sheet 147×76 mm containing T **627** and similar horiz designs. Multicoloured.

MS2325 39c.+19c.×6, Type **627**; Masks and open book; Microphone, music notation and paint brush; Violin, pencil, football and television; Drum and light bulbs; Trumpet, light bulbs, hat and earphones 14·50 13·50

628 Star

2003. Greetings Stamp.

No.	Description	Unused	Used
2326	**628** 29c. multicoloured	1·30	1·00

629 Family

2003. Christmas. Multicoloured. Self-adhesive.

No.	Description	Unused	Used
2327	29c. Type **629**	1·30	85
2328	29c. Parcel	1·30	85
2329	29c. Cat and dog	1·30	85
2330	29c. Tree	1·30	85
2331	29c. Hands holding glasses	1·30	85
2332	29c. Bell	1·30	85
2333	29c. Hand holding pen	1·30	85
2334	29c. Stag's head	1·30	85
2335	29c. Hand holding toy windmill	1·30	85
2336	29c. Holly leaf	1·30	85
2337	29c. Candle flame	1·30	85
2338	29c. Star	1·30	85
2339	29c. Couple	1·30	85
2340	29c. Snowman	1·30	85
2341	29c. Fireplace and fire	1·30	85
2342	29c. Angel	1·30	85
2343	29c. Couple dancing	1·30	85
2344	29c. Round bauble	1·30	85
2345	29c. Mother and child	1·30	85
2346	29c. Pointed bauble	1·30	85

630 Queen Beatrix as Baby

2003. The Royal Family. Queen Beatrix. Sheet 123×168 mm containing T **630** and similar horiz designs. Multicoloured.

MS2347 39c.×10, Type **630**; Sitting on swing as small child; As young girl leading pony; Reading magazine; With Claus von Amsberg on their engagement; Holding baby Prince Willem-Alexander; Royal family when young; Queen Beatrix and Prince Claus dancing; Prince Willem-Alexander, Prince Johan Friso, Prince Claus, Queen Beatrix and Prince Constantijn, Queen Beatrix viewing painting in art gallery 21·00 18·00

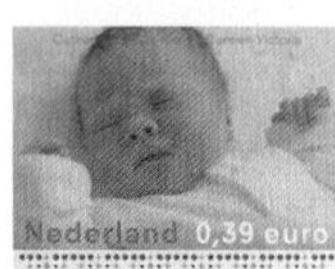

631 Princess Amalia

2003. Birth of Princess Amalia of Netherlands. Sheet 104×71 mm.

MS2348 39c. **631** multicoloured 3·75 3·25

632 *Woman Reading a Letter* (Gabriel Metsu) (detail)

2004. Art. Multicoloured. Self-adhesive.

2349 61c. Type **632** 2·75 1·60
2350 77c. *The Love Letter* (Jan Vermeer) (detail) 3·25 2·40

633 Water, Buildings and Rainbow

2004. 150th Anniv of Royal Netherlands Meteorological Institute (KNMI). Multicoloured.

2351 39c. Type **633** 1·70 1·20
2352 39c. Water, buildings and rainbow (different) 1·70 1·20

Nos. 2351/2 were issued together, *se-tenant*, forming a composite design.

634 Patchwork

2004. Business Stamp. Self-adhesive.

2353 **634** 39c. multicoloured 1·90 95
2354 **634** 78c. multicoloured 3·75 1·80

See also No. 2791.

635 Iris

2004. Flower Paintings. Multicoloured.

2355 39c.+19c. Type **635** 2·30 1·80
2356 39c.+19c. Lily 2·30 1·80
2357 39c.+19c. Poppy 2·30 1·80
2358 39c.+19c. Tulips 2·30 1·80
2359 39c.+19c. Orange flower 2·30 1·80
2360 39c.+19c. Thistle 2·30 1·80

636 Spiker C4 (1922)

2004. 50th Anniv of Dutch Youth Philately Association.

2361 **636** 39c. multicoloured 1·80 1·60
2362 - 39c. orange and black 1·80 1·60

Designs: No. 2361, Type **636**; nO. 2362, Spiker C8 Double12 R (2003).

637 Czech Republic Flag, Stamp, Map and Country Identification Code

2004. Enlargement of European Union. Sheet 108×150 mm containing T **637** and similar horiz designs showing the flag, stamp, map and country identification code of the new member states. Multicoloured.

MS2363 39c.×10, Type **637**; Lithuania; Estonia; Poland; Malta; Hungary. Latvia; Slovakia; Cyprus; Slovenia 20·00 18·00

638 "39" and Rays

2004. Greetings Stamp.

2364 **638** 39c. multicoloured 1·70 1·40

2004. Company Stamp. Self-adhesive.

2365 **625** 39c. multicoloured 2·10 1·90

639 Prince Willem-Alexander and Máxima Zorreguieta on their Engagement

2004. The Royal Family. Prince Willem-Alexander. Sheet 123×168 mm containing T **639** and similar horiz designs. Multicoloured.

MS2366 39c.×10, Type **639**; Máxima Zorreguieta showing engagement ring; Facing each other on their wedding day; Facing left; Kissing; Princess Máxima leaning towards Prince Willem-Alexander; Royal couple with Princess Amalia; With Princess Amalia and reading book; Princess Máxima holding Princess Amalia at christening font; At font Princess Amalia looking upwards 20·00 17·00

640 Red Squirrel

2004. Veluwe Nature Reserve. Two sheets, each 144×81 mm containing T **640** and similar horiz designs. Multicoloured.

MS2367 (a) 39c.×4, Type **640**; Hoopoe; Deer; Wild boar (b) 61c.×4, Fox; Woodpecker; Stag and hind; Mouflon sheep 22·00 20·00

641 Pen Nib

2004. Greetings Stamps. Sheet 144×75 mm containing T **641** and similar square designs.

MS2368 39c. light orange and orange; 39c. multicoloured; 39c. blue and red 5·25 4·75

Designs:—39c.Type **641**; 39c. Hand; 39c. Profiles.

642 *Mercury and Argus*

2004. 350th Death Anniv of Carel Fabritius (artist). Paintings. Multicoloured.

2369 39c. Type **642** 1·80 1·60
2370 39c. *Self Portrait* (wearing large hat) 1·80 1·60
2371 39c. *Mercury and Aglauros* 1·80 1·60
2372 39c. *Abraham de Potter* 1·80 1·60
2373 39c. *Hagar and the Angel* 1·80 1·60
2374 39c. *The Sentry* 1·80 1·60
2375 78c. *Hera* 3·25 2·75
2376 78c. *Self Portrait* (wearing small-brimmed hat) 3·25 2·75
2377 78c. *Self Portrait* (hatless) 3·25 2·75
2378 78c. *The Goldfinch* 3·25 2·75

643 Pumpkin and Football

2004. Child Welfare. 80th Anniv of Foundation for Children's Welfare Stamps. Sheet 144×75 mm containing T **643** and similar horiz designs. Multicoloured.

MS2379 39c.+19c.×6, Type **643**; Lemon skipping; Orange cycling; Pear skateboarding; Banana doing sit-ups; Strawberry weightlifting 14·50 13·50

644 Snowman

2004. Greetings Stamp.

2380 **644** 29c. multicoloured 1·70 1·50

645 Family as Shadows

2004. Christmas. Multicoloured.

2381 29c. Type **645** 1·30 1·10
2382 29c. Girls holding parcels 1·30 1·10
2383 29c. Girl and dog 1·30 1·10
2384 29c. Two children 1·30 1·10
2385 29c. Sheep 1·30 1·10
2386 29c. Two polar bears 1·30 1·10
2387 29c. Children making snowman 1·30 1·10
2388 29c. Couple pulling tree 1·30 1·10
2389 29c. Couple swimming 1·30 1·10
2390 29c. Three people wearing fur hats 1·30 1·10

646 Woman (NOVIB)

2004. Christmas. Charity Stamps. Multicoloured. Self-adhesive.

2401 29c.+10c. Type **646** 1·80 1·60
2402 29c.+10c. Children (Stop AIDS Now) 1·80 1·60
2403 29c.+10c. Deer (Natuurmonumenten) 1·80 1·60
2404 29c.+10c. Two boys (KWF Kankerbestrijding) 1·80 1·60
2405 29c.+10c. Girl holding baby (UNICEF) 1·80 1·60
2406 29c.+10c. Two boys writing (Plan Nederland) 1·80 1·60
2407 29c.+10c. Bauble containing mother and child (Tros Helpt) 1·80 1·60
2408 29c.+10c. Canoeist and snow covered mountains (Greenpeace) 1·80 1·60
2409 29c.+10c. Woman and child (Artsen Zonder Grenzen) 1·80 1·60
2410 29c.+10c. Girl feeding toddler (World Food Programme) 1·80 1·60

647 Two Hearts

2005. Greetings Stamp. Self-adhesive.

2411 **647** 39c. multicoloured 1·70 1·50

See also No. 2775.

648 Traditional and Modern Windmills

2005. Dutch Buildings. Multicoloured. Self-adhesive gum.

2412 39c. Type **648** 1·70 1·50
2413 65c. Canal-side house and modern housing 2·75 2·50
2414 81c. Farmhouse and greenhouse 3·25 3·00

651 Nijmegen

2005. Tourism. Multicoloured.

2415 39c. Type **651** 1·70 1·50
2416 39c. Rotterdam 1·70 1·50
2417 39c. Amsterdam 1·70 1·50
2418 39c. Roermond 1·70 1·50
2419 39c. Goer 1·70 1·50
2420 39c. Boalsert 1·70 1·50
2421 39c. Monnickendam 1·70 1·50
2422 39c. Netherland 1·70 1·50
2423 39c. Weesp 1·70 1·50
2424 39c. Papendrecht 1·70 1·50

652 *Trying* (Liza May Post)

2005. Art. Multicoloured.

2425 39c. Type **652** 1·70 1·50
2426 39c. *Emilie* (Sidi el Karchi) 1·70 1·50
2427 39c. *ZT* (Koen Vermeule) 1·70 1·50
2428 39c. *Het Bedrijf* (Atelier van Lieshout) 1·70 1·50
2429 39c. *Me kissing Vinoodh* (Inez van Lamsweerde) 1·70 1·50
2430 39c. *Lena* (Carla van de Puttelaar) 1·70 1·50
2431 39c. *NR. 13* (Tom Claassen) 1·70 1·50
2432 39c. *Zonder Titel* (Pieter Kusters) 1·70 1·50
2433 39c. *Witte Roos* (Ed van der Kooy) 1·70 1·50
2434 39c. *Portrait of a Boy* (Tiong Ang) 1·70 1·50

653 Symbols of Industry

2005. Business Stamps. Entrepreneur Week. Self-adhesive.

2435 **653** 39c. multicoloured 2·10 1·90

654 Cormorant

2005. Centenary of Vereniging Natuurmonumenten (Nature preservation society). Multicoloured.

2436 39c. Type **654** 4·00 3·75
2437 39c. Pike 4·00 3·75
2438 39c. Blue-tailed damsel fly 4·00 3·75
2439 39c. Water lily 4·00 3·75
2440 65c. Hawfinch 5·25 4·75
2441 65c. Sconebeeker sheep 5·25 4·75
2442 65c. Sand lizard 5·25 4·75
2443 65c. Common blue butterfly 5·25 4·75

MS2444 Two sheets, each 144×81 mm. (a) 39c.×4, As Nos. 2436/9 (b) 65c.×4, As Nos.2440/3 19·00 17·00

Nos. 2430/3 and the stamps of **MS**2434b, each have a Priority label attached at left.

655 "Who is the Wisest"

2005. Birth Centenary of Cornelis Jetses (children's reading book illustrator). Showing illustrations from "Ot en Sien". Multicoloured.

2445 39c.+19c. Type **655** 2·50 2·30
2446 39c.+19c. "Two old chums" 2·50 2·30
2447 39c.+19c. "His own fault" 2·50 2·30
2448 39c.+19c. "What does Puss think?" 2·50 2·30
2449 39c.+19c. "Nothing forgotten" 2·50 2·30
2450 39c.+19c. "Two bright things" 2·50 2·30

Nos. 2435/7 and 2438/40, each had a *se-tenant* label at head and foot, the upper inscribed with text from the book, the lower showing a modern photograph on the same theme.

656 Queen Beatrix and Prince Claus (Coronation, 1980)

2005. 25th Anniv of Coronation of Queen Beatrix. Multicoloured.

No.	Description	Mint	Used
2451	39c. Type **656**	1·70	1·50
2452	78c. Seated (Queen's speech, 1991)	3·25	3·00
2453	117c. With Nelson Mandela (state visit, 1999)	5·00	4·50
2454	156c. Wearing glasses (visit to Netherlands Antilles, 1999)	6·75	6·00
2455	225c. Wearing hat (speech to European Parliament, 2004)	9·50	8·50
MS2456	144×75 mm. 39c. Type **655**; 78c. As No. 2442; 117c. As No. 2443; 156c. As No. 2444; 225c. As No. 2445	26·00	29·00

657 Circles

2005. Business Coil Stamps.

No.	Description	Mint	Used
2457	**657** 39c. copper	1·70	1·50
2458	**656** 78c. silver	3·25	3·00

658 Thought Bubble

2005. Greetings Stamps. Sheet 144×75 mm containing T **657** and similar square designs. Two phosphor bands. Multicoloured background colour given.

No.	Description	Mint	Used
MS2461	39c.×3, Type **658**; Thought bubble (yellow); Thought bubble (blue)	5·00	4·50

659 Windmill, Netherlands

2005. Waterwheels and Windmills. Multicoloured.

No.	Description	Mint	Used
2462	81c. Type **659**	3·25	3·00
2463	81c. Waterwheel, China	3·25	3·00

Stamps of the same design were issued by China.

660 Dorothy Counts (black student) (Douglas Martin, 1957)

2005. 50th Anniv of World Press Photo (photojournalism competition). Multicoloured.

No.	Description	Mint	Used
2464	39c. Type **660**	1·70	1·50
2465	39c. Chaplin Luis Padillo with wounded soldier (Hector Rondon Lovera, 1962)	1·70	1·50
2466	39c. Tank commander, Vietnam (Co Rentmeester, 1967)	1·70	1·50
2467	39c. Catholic graffiti (Hans-Jorg Anders, 1969)	1·70	1·50
2468	39c. Niger drought victims (Ovie Cartor, 1974)	1·70	1·50
2469	39c. Cambodian famine victim (Devid Burnett, 1979)	1·70	1·50
2470	39c. South Korea soldiers and mother (Anthony Suau, 1987)	1·70	1·50
2471	39c. Mourners at deathbed of Elshani Nashim (Georges Merillon, 1990)	1·70	1·50
2472	39c. Wounded man, Kukes (Claus Bjorn Larsen, 1999)	1·70	1·50
2473	39c. Woman mourns tsunami victims (Arko Datta, 2004)	1·70	1·50

661 *Blauwe Engel*

2005. Trains. Multicoloured.

No.	Description	Mint	Used
2474	39c. Type **661**	1·70	1·50
2475	39c. Steam locomotive 3737	1·70	1·50
2476	39c. Intercity Express (ICE)	2·40	2·20
2477	39c. *Koploper*	2·40	2·20

662 Miffy and Snuffy

2005. Child Welfare. Miffy created by Dick Bruna. Sheet 144×75 mm containing T **662** and similar horiz designs. Multicoloured.

No.	Description	Mint	Used
MS2478	39c.+19c.×6, Type **662**; Miffy and friends; Miffy and bear; Miffy writing; Miffy and Nina; Miffy at school	14·50	13·50

663 Bells

2005. Personal Stamps.

No.	Description	Mint	Used
2479	**663** 29c. multicoloured	1·30	1·10

664 Flames

2005. Christmas. Multicoloured. Self-adhesive.

No.	Description	Mint	Used
2480	29c. Type **664**	1·30	1·10
2481	29c. Parcel	1·30	1·10
2482	29c. Stars	1·30	1·10
2483	29c. Bells	1·30	1·10
2484	29c. Doves	1·30	1·10
2485	29c. Snowmen hugging	1·30	1·10
2486	29c. Balloons	1·30	1·10
2487	29c. Ice skates	1·30	1·10
2488	29c. Trees	1·30	1·10
2489	29c. Glasses	1·30	1·10

665 The Annunciation

2005. Christmas. Charity Stamps. Multicoloured. Self-adhesive.

No.	Description	Mint	Used
2490	29c.+10c. Type **665**	1·50	1·30
2491	29c.+10c. Mary and Jesus	1·50	1·30
2492	29c.+10c. Adoration of the shepherds	1·50	1·30
2493	29c.+10c. Adoration of the Magi	1·50	1·30
2494	29c.+10c. Journey to Bethlehem	1·50	1·30
2495	29c.+10c. The Annunciation (different)	1·50	1·30
2496	29c.+10c. Mary and Jesus (different)	1·50	1·30
2497	29c.+10c. Adoration of the shepherds (different)	1·50	1·30
2498	29c.+10c. Adoration of the Magi (different)	1·50	1·30
2499	29c.+10c. Journey to Bethlehem (different)	1·50	1·30

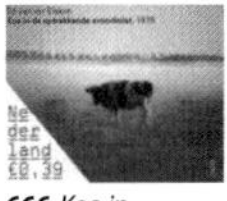

666 *Koe in optrekkende avondmist* (Ed van der Elsken)

2006. Contemporary Art. Multicoloured. Self-adhesive.

No.	Description	Mint	Used
2500	39c. Type **666**	1·70	1·50
2501	39c. *Double Dutch* (Berend Strik)	1·70	1·50
2502	39c. *Hollandese Velden* (Hans van der Meer)	1·70	1·50
2503	39c. *Tomorrow* (Marijke van Warmerdam)	1·70	1·50
2504	39c. *A Day in Holland/Holland in a Day* (Barbara Visser)	1·70	1·50
2505	39c. *Compositie met rode ruit* (Daan van Golden)	1·70	1·50
2506	39c. *Untitled* (JCJ Vanderheyden)	1·70	1·50
2507	39c. *De Goene Kathedraal* (Marinus Boezem)	1·70	1·50
2508	39c. *Hollandpan* (John Kormeling)	1·70	1·50
2509	39c. *Drijftbeeld* (Atelier Van Lieshout)	1·70	1·50
2510	69c. *Study for the horizon* (Sigurdur Gudmundsson)	3·00	2·75
2511	69c. *Lost luggage depot* (Jeff Wall)	3·00	2·75
2512	69c. *11000 Tulips* (Daniel Buren)	3·00	2·75
2513	69c. *Fiets & Stal* (FAT)	3·00	2·75
2514	69c. *Double sunset* (Olafur Eliasson)	3·00	2·75
2515	85c. *Untitled* (Dustin Larson)	3·50	3·25
2516	85c. *Working Progress* (Tadshi Kawamata)	3·50	3·25
2517	85c. *Boerderligezichten* (Sean Snyder)	3·50	3·25
2518	85c. *Toc Toc* (Amalie Pica)	3·50	3·25
2519	85c. *Freude* (Rosemarie Trockel)	3·50	3·25

Nos. 2500/9 were for use on mail within Netherlands, Nos. 2510/14 were for use within Europe and Nos. 2515/19 were for use worldwide.

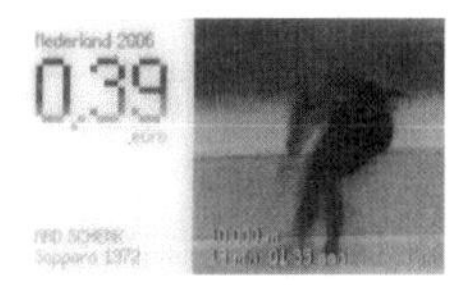

667 Ard Schenk (10000 metres, Sapporo (1972))

2006. Winter Olympic Gold Medal Winners. Sheet 141×102 mm containing T **667** and similar horiz design. Multicoloured.

No.	Description	Mint	Used
MS2520	39c.×2, Type **667**; Yvonne van Gennip (3000 metres, Calgary (1988))	12·50	11·50

2006. Tourism. As T **660**. Multicoloured.

No.	Description	Mint	Used
2521	39c. Sittard	1·10	95
2522	39c. Leiden	1·10	95
2523	39c. Woudrichem	1·10	95
2524	39c. Vlieland	1·10	95
2525	39c. Enkhuizen	1·10	95
2526	39c. Zutphen	1·10	95
2527	39c. Schoonhoven	1·10	95
2528	39c. Deventer	1·10	95
2529	39c. Zwolle	1·10	95
2530	39c. Kampen	1·10	95

668 Monkey

2006. Summer Charity Stamps. Designs showing traditional reading boards. Multicoloured.

No.	Description	Mint	Used
2531	39c.+19c. Type **668**	1·70	1·40
2532	39c.+19c. Nut	1·70	1·40
2533	39c.+19c. Cat	1·70	1·40
2534	39c.+19c. Boy and puzzle	1·70	1·40
2535	39c.+19c. Toddler	1·70	1·40
2536	39c.+19c. Girl and doll	1·70	1·40

The premium was for the benefit of Nationaal Fonds Ouderenhulp (for the assistance of vulnerable seniors).

669 Dirk Kuyt

2006. Personal Stamp.

No.	Description	Mint	Used
2537	**669** 39c. multicoloured	1·10	95

670 Elvis Presley (50th anniv of *Heartbreak Hotel* (record))

2006. The Dutch Choice. Winning Designs in Stamp of your Choice Competition. Multicoloured.

No.	Description	Mint	Used
2538	39c. Type **670**	1·10	95
2539	39c. Square and compass (250th anniv of Masons in Netherlands)	1·10	95
2540	39c. Purk and Pino (30th anniv of *Sesame Street* (children's TV programme))	1·10	95
2541	39c. Sampler (regional languages)	1·10	95
2542	39c. Multatuli (creator of Max Havelaar (Dutch fictional character))	1·10	95

671 *Bearded Man in Oriental Cap*

2006. 400th Birth Anniv of Rembrandt Harmenszoon van Rijn (artist). Multicoloured.

No.	Description	Mint	Used
2543	39c. Type **671**	1·10	95
2544	39c. *Old Woman seated at a Table*	1·10	95
2545	39c. *Saskia*	1·10	95
2546	39c. *Titus*	1·10	95
2547	39c. *Woman at Window*	1·10	95
MS2548	104×71 mm. €6.45 *Self-portrait with Saskia*	27·00	25·00

672 Figure

2006. Greetings Stamp.

No.	Description	Mint	Used
2549	**672** 39c. multicoloured	1·10	95

673 Reticulated Giraffe

2006. World Animal Day. Endangered Species. Sheet 135×170 mm containing T **673** and similar square designs. Multicoloured.

No.	Description	Mint	Used
MS2550	39c×12, Type **673**; Tropical butterfly; Manchurian crane; Francois's leaf monkey; Blue poison dart frog; Red panda; Lowland gorilla; Sumatran tiger; Asiatic lion; Indian rhinoceros; Asian elephant; Pygmy hippopotamus	21·00	19·00

The stamps and margins of No. **MS**2540 form a composite design of a forest.

674 Bands

2006. Change of Postal Service Name from TPG Post to Royal TNT Post.

No.	Description	Mint	Used
2551	**674** 39c. multicoloured	1·70	1·50

675 Children

2006. Child Welfare. Sheet 144×75 mm containing T **675** and similar horiz designs. Multicoloured.

No.	Description	Mint	Used
MS2552	39c.+19c.×6, Type **675**; Children, boy wearing green jumper looking up; Children, boy riding bicycle facing right; Children, boy wearing orange jumper with football; Children, girl wearing purple jumper nursing baby; Children, girl seated holding teddy bear	14·50	13·50

The stamps of No. **MS**2552 were laid in two strips of three, each strip forming a composite design.

676 Snowflakes

2006. Christmas. Sheet 143×80 mm containing T **676** and similar vert designs showing snowflakes, colours given. Multicoloured. Self-adhesive.

No.	Description	Mint	Used
MS2553	29c.×10, Type **676**; Small orange and large magenta; Large brown and small orange; Large blue and small orange; Large brown and small blue; Large orange and small blue; Large blue and brown; Small blue and large magenta; Small brown and large orange; Large blue and small magenta	12·50	11·50

677 Boy as Angel

2006. Christmas. Charity Stamps. Designs showing children as angels. Multicoloured. Self-adhesive.

2554	29c.+10c. Type **677**	1·70	1·50
2555	29c.+10c. Girl with dark hair	1·70	1·50
2556	29c.+10c. Girl lying	1·70	1·50
2557	29c.+10c. Boy with blonde hair standing	1·70	1·50
2558	29c.+10c. Boy with blonde hair facing right	1·70	1·50
2559	29c.+10c. Child with brown hair facing left	1·70	1·50
2560	29c.+10c. Girl with long hair seated	1·70	1·50
2561	29c.+10c. Boy with curly hair facing left	1·70	1·50
2562	29c.+10c. Angel wearing blue	1·70	1·50
2563	29c.+10c. Girl with blonde hair standing	1·70	1·50

2006. Greetings Stamps. As T **521**, **524** and **647**. Self-adhesive gum.

2564	44c. multicoloured	1·90	1·70
2565	44c. multicoloured	1·90	1·70
2566	44c. multicoloured	1·90	1·70

Designs:—No. 2564, As Type **521** (new baby); No. 2565 As Type **524** (bereavement stamp); No. 2566 As Type **647** (Valentine's Day).

678 Glass ('Glidglas')

2006. Dutch Manufacture. Multicoloured. Self-adhesive.

2567	44c. Type **678**	1·50	1·20
2568	44c. Chair ('Revolt Stoel')	1·50	1·20
2569	44c. Beer bottle ('Heineken Longneck')	1·50	1·20
2570	44c. Child's buggy ('Bugaboo')	1·50	1·20
2571	44c. Kettle ('Fluitketel')	1·50	1·20
2572	44c. Lamp ('Flessenlamp')	1·50	1·20
2573	44c. Cargo bicycle ('Bakfiets')	1·50	1·20
2574	44c. Light bulb ('Spaarlamp')	1·50	1·20
2575	44c. Sausage ('Unox Rookworst')	1·50	1·20
2576	44c. Tulip ('Tulp')	1·50	1·20
2577	72c. Ice skate ('Klapschaats')	2·50	1·90
2578	89c. Cheese slice ('Kaasschaaf')	3·75	3·50

2006. Business Stamps. Self-adhesive.

2579	**634**	44c. multicoloured	1·90	1·70
2580	**634**	88c. multicoloured	3·75	3·50

679 '44' **680** '88'

2006. Business Stamps.

2581	**679**	44c. multicoloured	1·90	1·70
2582	**680**	88c. multicoloured	3·75	3·50

See also Nos. 2792/3

2007. As Type **679**. Self-adhesive gum.

2583	**679**	44c. multicoloured	1·90	1·70

See also No. 2794.

681 Royal Dutch Mint, Utrecht

2007. Personal Stamp. Bicentenary of Royal Dutch Mint.

2584	**681**	44c. multicoloured	1·90	1·70

2007. Tourism. As T **660**. Multicoloured.

2585	44c. Groningen	1·90	1·70
2586	44c. Gouda	1·90	1·70

682 Lime Tree

2007. Trees (1st issue). Spring. 50th Anniv of National Tree Planting Committee. Multicoloured. Self-adhesive.

2587	44c. Type **682**	1·90	1·70
2588	44c. Chestnut flower bud	1·90	1·70

See also Nos. 2594/5, 2605/6 and 2611/12.

2007. Tourism. As T **660**. Multicoloured.

2589	44c. Hoorn	1·90	1·70
2590	44c. Vissingen	1·90	1·70

683 Children (*c.* 2000) playing and Group (*c.* 1920)

2007. Summer Charity Stamps. Two sheets, each 145×76 mm containing T **683** and similar horiz designs showing beach holiday photographs. Multicoloured.

MS2591 (a) 44c.+22c. Type **683**; 44c.+22c. Three women in cane seat; 44c.+22c. Sand yacht. (b) 44c.+22c. Woman wearing traditional dress paddling; 44c.+22c. Woman (*c.* 1910) in sea and children (*c.* 1950) riding donkeys; 44c.+22c. Children riding donkeys and children (*c.* 2000) playing — 17·00 15·00

The stamps and margins of **MS**2591a/b each form a composite design. The premium was for the benefit of Nationaal Fonds Ouderenhulp (for the assistance of vulnerable seniors).

Nos. 2592 has been left for 'Tourism. Schone (as T **660**), issued on 13 April 2007, respectively, not yet received.

684 Snapdragons

2007. Flowers. Sheet 107×150 mm containing T **684** and similar horiz designs. Multicoloured.

MS2593 44c.×8, Type **684**; Blue lobelia; Snapdragons and red dianthus; White petunias; Arabis; Red and white petunias; Arabis and sweet peas; Pink flox and red and white petunias; 88c.×2, Red and white dianthus and sweet peas; Pink flox — 23·00 21·00

The stamps of **MS**2593 form a composite design and each contain a small amount of seeds placed centrally.

2007. Trees. Summer. 50th Anniv of National Tree Planting Committee (2nd issue). As T **682**. Multicoloured.

2594	44c. Plane tree bark (detail)	1·90	1·70
2595	44c. Oak	1·90	1·70

685 'JIJ' (you)

2007. 140th Anniv of Dutch Red Cross.

2596	**685**	44c.+22c. multicoloured	2·75	2·50

2007. Tourism. As T **660**. Multicoloured.

2597	44c. Den Helder	1·90	1·70

686 Knot, Globe and Sun

2007. Centenary of Scouting. Multicoloured.

2598	72c. Type **686**	3·25	3·00
2599	72c. Moon, globe and knot	3·25	3·00

2007. Tourism. As T **660**. Multicoloured.

2600	44c. Lelystad	1·90	1·70
2601	44c. The Hague	1·90	1·70

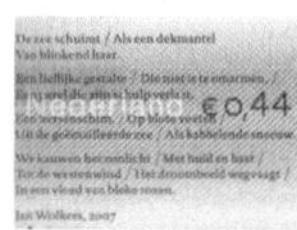

687 'De zee schuimt/Al seen?' and *Snow* (detail, paintings) (Jan Wolkers)

2007. Greetings Stamp.

2602	**687**	44c. multicoloured	1·90	1·70

688 Crown

2007. Bicentenary of Dutch Monarchy and Royal Designation of Products. Sheet 104×71 mm.

MS2603 **688** €6.45 multicoloured — 27·00 25·00

The stamp and margins of **MS**2603 form a composite design.

689 L. E. J. Brouwer

2007. Personal Stamp. Centenary of Publication of Mathematic Dissertation by L. E. J. Brouwer. Self-adhesive.

2604	**689**	44c. multicoloured	1·90	1·70

2007. Trees. Autumn. 50th Anniv of National Tree Planting Committee (3rd issue). As T **682**. Multicoloured.

2605	44c. Norway maple seeds	1·90	1·70
2606	44c. Purple beech trunk and branches	1·90	1·70

2007. Tourism. As T **660**. Multicoloured.

2607	44c. Utrecht	1·90	1·70
2608	44c. Edam	1·90	1·70

2007. Tourism. Two sheets each 144×75 mm containing vert designs as T **660** Multicoloured.

MS2609 (a) 44c.×5, Den Helder; Lelystad; Hoorn; The Hague; Vissingen. (b) 44c.×5, Gouda; Edam; Leerdam; Groningen; Utrecht — 19·00 17·00

The stamps and margins of **MS**2609a/b, respectively, each form a composite design.

690 Child watching Television

2007. Child Welfare. Sheet 144×75 mm containing T **690** and similar horiz designs. Multicoloured.

MS2610 44c.+22c.×6, Type **690**; Girl looking through window at tall building; Child in bed playing with flashlight; Girl using computer; Boy holding cat; Girl reading — 17·00 15·00

The stamps of No. **MS**2610 share a common background.

2007. Trees. Winter. 50th Anniv of National Tree Planting Committee (4th issue). As T **682**. Multicoloured.

2611	44c. Black alder	1·90	1·70
2612	44c. Willows in water	1·90	1·70

691 Firework

2007. December Lottery Stamps (scratch stamps). Sheet 141×79 mm containing T **691** and similar vert designs showing fireworks, colours given. Multicoloured. Self-adhesive.

2613	29c. Type **691**	1·30	1·10
2614	29c. Pink with green edges	1·30	1·10
2615	29c. Green with pink tips	1·30	1·10
2616	29c. Orange with pale centre	1·30	1·10
2617	29c. Pink with multicoloured centre	1·30	1·10
2618	29c. Orange with lavender centre	1·30	1·10
2619	29c. Green with pink and yellow centre	1·30	1·10
2620	29c. Purplish blue with multicoloured centre	1·30	1·10
2621	29c. Blue with pink centre	1·30	1·10
2622	29c. Large pink with dark centre	1·30	1·10

692 Tree and Snow

2007. Christmas. Sheet 143×79 mm containing T **692** and similar vert designs showing trees in snow. Multicoloured. Self-adhesive.

2623	29c. Type **692**	1·30	1·10
2624	29c. Branches to left and falling snow	1·30	1·10
2625	29c. Outline of snow covered tree	1·30	1·10
2626	29c. Large central snow flake and falling snow	1·30	1·10
2627	29c. Falling snow and outline of buildings	1·30	1·10
2628	29c. Falling snow	1·30	1·10
2629	29c. Trunk, branches and falling snow	1·30	1·10
2630	29c. Conifer	1·30	1·10
2631	29c. Copse	1·30	1·10
2632	29c. Snow covered trunk and branches	1·30	1·10

693 Heart, '80' and Stamps

2008. Personal Stamps. Multicoloured.

2633	44c. Type **693** (80th anniv of NVPH (Netherlands Association of Stamp Dealers))	1·90	1·70
2634	44c. Pigeons in flight (centenary of NBFV (Netherlands Federation of Philatelic Associations))	1·90	1·70

694 Hybrid Fuel Car

2008. Think Green, Act Green. Multicoloured. Self-adhesive.

2635	44c. Type **694**	1·90	1·70
2636	44c. House and sun (solar power)	1·90	1·70
2637	44c. Cow (methane—bio-fuel)	1·90	1·70
2638	44c. Wind turbines	1·90	1·70
2639	44c. Trees (CO2 offsetting)	1·90	1·70
2640	44c. Car sharing	1·90	1·70
2641	44c. Plug with leaves (green energy)	1·90	1·70
2642	44c. Lorry with soot filter (pollution control)	1·90	1·70
2643	44c. Envelope (greener postal service)	1·90	1·70
2644	44c. House enclosed (home insulation)	1·90	1·70
2645	75c. Cycle with globes as wheels (25×30 mm)	3·25	2·75
2646	92c. Globe as heart (25×30 mm)	4·00	3·50

Nos. 2645/6 each include a label inscribed 'PRIORITY' attached at top.

Nos. 2635/44 were for use on domestic mail.

No. 2645 was for use on mail within Europe.

No. 2646 was for use on mail for rest of the world.

See also Nos. 2698/9 and 2778/89.

695 Book Pages as Heart (Bart Kuipers)

2008. Winning Designs in Design a Stamp Competition. Multicoloured.

2647	44c. Type **695**	1·90	1·70
2648	44c. Man, woman and 'heart' tree (Ramona)	1·90	1·70
2649	44c. Love	1·90	1·70
2650	44c. Stylized red heart (Palle van der Lijke)	1·90	1·70
2651	44c. Heart in checkerboard (Jasper)	1·90	1·70

2008. Tourism. As T **660**. Multicoloured.
2652 44c. Cow, rowing boat and Coevorden Castle enclosed in goose silhouette (Coevorden) 1·90 1·70
2653 44c. Sküsje boat, Water Gate and peppermints enclosed in silhouette of Pieter Gerbrandy (prime minister during WW II) (Sneek) 1·90 1·70

696 Stylized Forget-me-not

2008. Summer Charity Stamps. Two sheets, each 144×75 mm containing T **696** and similar horiz designs. Multicoloured.
MS2654 (a) 44c.+22c.×3, Type **696**; Blue flower (crane's bill); Pink flower (larkspur). (b) 44c.+22c.×3, Japanese anemone; Globe thistle; Stylized forget-me-not (different) 17·00 15·00

The stamps and margins of **MS**2654a/b each form a composite design and, if the sheets are laid horizontally together, they also form a continuous composite design.
The premium was for the benefit of Nationaal Fonds Ouderenhulp (for the assistance of vulnerable seniors).

2008. Tourism. As T **660**. Multicoloured.
2655 44c. Heiligenbergbeek, blue butterfly, Amersfoort boulder and Tower of Our Lady enclosed in silhouette of Piet Mondriaan (artist) (Amersfoort) 1·90 1·70
2656 44c. Windmill, St George and dragon enclosed in silhouette of Gisbertus Voetius (theologian) (Heusden) 1·90 1·70

697 Book, Cells, Tweezers, Moon and Ladder

2008. Anniversaries. Multicoloured.
2657 44c. Type **697** (bicentenary of KNAW (Royal Netherlands Academy of Arts and Science)) 1·90 1·70
2658 44c. Bridge, map, currency symbols and De Nederlandsche Bank building (tenth anniv of European Central Bank) 1·90 1·70
2659 44c. Amsterdam skyline, Beurs van Berlage tower, share price graph, trader and market (25th anniv of AEX (Amsterdam Exchanges)) 1·90 1·70
2660 44c. Girl reading, book piles, bookshelves and elderly man reading (140th anniv of Bruna (bookshop)) 1·90 1·70
2661 44c. Tent and symbols of tourism (125th anniv of ANWB (Royal Dutch Tourist Board)) 1·90 1·70

698 Envelope and Smiley

2008. Europa. The Letter.
2662 **698** 75c. multicoloured 3·75 3·50

No. 2657 was issued with a *se-tenant* label inscribed 'PRIORITY'.

2008. Tourism. As T **660**. Multicoloured.
2663 44c. De Nieuwe Polder pumping station, Old Church, snow boarder and snow crystal enclosed in silhouette of Dappere Dirk (Zoetermeer) 1·90 1·70

2008. Tourism. Sheet 144×75 mm containing vert designs as T **660**. Multicoloured.
MS2664 44c.×5, Sneek; Zoetermeer; Heusden; Amersfoort; Coevorden 9·50 8·50

The stamps and margins of **MS**2664 form a composite design.

699 Artists' Signatures and Coils

2008. 125th Anniv of Vereniging Rembrandt (Rembrandt Association). Sheet 104×71 mm.
MS2665 **699** €6.65 multicoloured 28·00 26·00

700 Chillies and Cheese (food)

2008. Netherlands and Beyond. Sheet 145×75 mm containing T **700** and similar multicoloured.
MS2666 92c.×3, Type **700**; Peas, condensed milk and papaya (vert); Ham, plantain and Ponche Pistachio (vert) 12·00 10·50

No. **MS**2666 also includes Netherlands Antilles 5c. stamp (Houses (architecture)) and Aruba 240c. stamp (Script (poem by Frederico Oduber)).
The 'foreign' stamps could only be used in their country of origin.

701 Heart and Pen Nib

2008. Greetings Stamp.
2667 **701** 44c. multicoloured 1·90 1·70

702 Aries

2008. Constellations. Signs of the Zodiac. Multicoloured.

2668	44c. Type **702**	1·90	1·70
2669	44c. Taurus	1·90	1·70
2670	44c. Gemini	1·90	1·70
2671	44c. Cancer	1·90	1·70
2672	44c. Leo	1·90	1·70
2673	44c. Virgo	1·90	1·70
2674	44c. Libra	1·90	1·70
2675	44c. Scorpio	1·90	1·70
2676	44c. Sagittarius	1·90	1·70
2677	44c. Capricorn	1·90	1·70
2678	44c. Pisces	1·90	1·70
2679	44c. Aquarius	1·90	1·70

703 Squid-shaped Fungi

2008. Centenary of Mycological Society. Showing fungi. Multicoloured.

2680	44c. Type **703**	1·90	1·70
2681	44c. Star-shaped	1·90	1·70
2682	44c. Fly agaric	1·90	1·70
2683	44c. Nest-shaped	1·90	1·70
2684	44c. Ink cap	1·90	1·70
2685	44c. Squid-shaped decaying	1·90	1·70
2686	44c. Star-shaped decaying	1·90	1·70
2687	44c. Fly agaric (different)	1·90	1·70
2688	44c. Nest-shaped decaying	1·90	1·70
2689	44c. Ink cap decaying	1·90	1·70

704 Pinkeltje (Dick Laan)

2008. Gnomes from Dutch Literature. Multicoloured.

2690	75c. blue, orange and bright violet	3·25	2·75
2691	75c. bistre, new blue and blue	3·25	2·75
2692	75c. orange, blue and new blue	3·25	2·75
2693	75c. blue, violet and bistre	3·25	2·75
2694	75c. violet, bistre and orange	3·25	2·75

DESIGNS:—No. 2690 Type **704**; No. 2691 Wipneus en Pim (Leonardus van der Made); No. 2692 Piggelmee (L. C. Steenhuizen); No. 2693 Paulus de boskabouter (Jean Dulieu); No. 2694 de Kabouter (Rien Poorlvliet).
Nos. 2690/4 were issued each with a label inscribed 'Priority' attached at left.

705 'O'

2008. Child Welfare. Sheet 144×75 mm containing T **705** and similar horiz designs. Multicoloured.
MS2695 44c.+22c.×6,Type **705**; 'N' and 'D'; 'E' and 'R'; 'W'; 'I' and 'J'; 'S' 17·00 15·00

The stamps of **MS**2695 share a common background, and spell out 'ONDERWIJS' (education).

706 Walkers in Snowy Landscape

2008. Personal Stamp. Self-adhesive.
2696 **706** 34c. multicoloured 1·50 1·30

707 Clock Tower and Present

2008. Christmas. Sheet 144×75 mm containing vert designs as T **707**. Multicoloured. Self-adhesive.
MS2697 34c.×10, Type **707**; Envelopes and Christmas tree in glass box; Christmas tree in glass box and rockets; Bell, Christmas tree and three-storied building; Three-storied building and pile of presents; Christmas tree and three-storied building with narrow windows; Three-storied building with narrow windows and candle; Snow-covered house; Envelope and left-side of fireplace; Fireplace as building 14·50 13·50

The stamps and margins of **MS**2697 form a composite design of a stylized townscape.

2009. Think Green, Act Green. As T **694**. Self-adhesive gum.
2698 77c. Cycle with globes as wheels (As No. 2645) (25×30 mm) 3·25 3·00
2699 95c. Globe as heart (As No. 2646) (25×30 mm) 4·00 3·50

Nos. 2698/9 each include a label inscribed 'PRIORITY' attached at top.
Designs as Nos. 2635/44 were re-issued on the same date.
No. 2698 was for use on mail within Europe, No. 2699 was for use on mail for rest of the world.

NEDERLAND
H LD
BRAILLESCHRIFT
OE
1829 · 2009
MY H
44 EUROCENT

708 'H LD OE MY H

2009. Birth Bicentenary of Louis Braille (inventor of Braille writing for the blind). Sheet 135×170 mm containing T **708** and similar vert designs. Multicoloured.
MS2700 44c.×12, Type **708**; 'DR K MS T UI'; 'NI K Z LF AN'; 'S PE O R AD U'; 'EV G DW S N IE'; 'M D XTR KA S'; ' EG N M RG XA T'; ' FI N B AF K S'; 'GE U W S RAV'; 'F BE CR O L FS'; 'Q A I N TS PHE'; 'RI F VU G H RT' 23·00 21·00

The letters missing from the front of the stamps of No. **MS**2700 are printed on the back.
The stamps are also embossed with Braille letters.

709 Golfer

2009. Personal Stamps. 125th Anniv of NVPV (philatelic society) (2702). Multicoloured. Self-adhesive.
2701 44c. Type **709** 1·90 1·70
2702 44c. Young stamp collector 1·90 1·70

2009. Tourism. As T **660**. Multicoloured.
2703 44c. Spinner, ferris wheel and buildings (Tilburg) 1·90 1·70
2704 44c. Barje (character created by Anne de Vries) (statue), Pedal cars and motorcycles (Assen) 1·90 1·70

710 Couple ('DANSJE?)

2009. Summer Charity Stamps. Multicoloured.

2705	44c.+22c. Type **710**	2·75	2·50
2706	44c.+22c. Woman ('ER-OP-UIT!')	2·75	2·50
2707	44c.+22c. Ballet dancer ('JONG GELLEERD OUD GEDAAN')	2·75	2·50
2708	44c.+22c. Woman and dog ('VERGEET ME NIET')	2·75	2·50
2709	44c.+22c. Trumpeter ('LET'S TWIST AGAIN!')	2·75	2·50
2710	44c.+22c. Woman holding diploma ('CHATTEN?')	2·75	2·50

The premium was for the benefit of Nationaal Fonds Ouderenhulp (for the assistance of vulnerable seniors).

711 Christian Huygens' Lens and Sketch of Saturn and Titan

2009. Europa. Astronomy. Multicoloured.
2711 77c. Type **711** 3·75 3·50
2712 77c. Locations of LOFAR (Low frequency Array) radio telescope antennae 3·75 3·50

Nos. 2711/12, respectively, have a label inscribed 'PRIORITY' attached at left, with the face value of the stamps leaching into the label.

2009. Tourism. As T **660**. Multicoloured.
2713 44c. Pheasant, locomotive and stylized roses (Roosendaal) 1·90 1·70
2714 44c. Antenna, entertainers and St. Driehoek Church (Oosterhout) 1·90 1·70

712 Queens Wilhelmina Heleana Pauline Maria, Juliana Louise Emma Marie Wilhelmina and Beatrix Wilhelmina Armgard

2009. Three Queens. Sheet 104×71 mm.
MS2715 **712** €7 multicoloured 29·00 27·00

713 Books, Wooden Figure and Bottles

2009. Charities' Anniversaries. Multicoloured.
2716 44c. Type **713** (60th anniv of Cancer Support Fund) 1·90 1·70
2717 44c. Swallow, binoculars and egg (110th anniv of Bird Protection League) 1·90 1·70
2718 44c. Figures sheltered by book (95th anniv of Cordaid–People in need charity) 1·90 1·70
2719 44c. Pouring coffee (60th anniv of The Sunflower Care Association) 1·90 1·70
2720 44c. Children's building blocks as house (60th anniv of SOS Childrens' Villages) 1·90 1·70

2009. Tourism. As T **660**. Multicoloured.
2721 44c. Sail ship, Maigret and container ship (Delfzijl) 1·90 1·70
MS2722 144×75 mm. As Nos. 2703/4; 2713/14; 2721 9·50 8·50

714 Tubas in Brass Band

2009. Music. World Music and Europa Cantat 2009 Competitions, Netherlands. Multicoloured.
2723 77c. Type **714** 3·25 3·00

2724	77c. WHEN YOU SING YOU BEGIN WITH DO RE MI	3·25	3·00
2725	77c. Drum majorettes	3·25	3·00
2726	77c. JAUCHZET FROH-LOCKET	3·25	3·00
2727	77c. Tubas in military band	3·25	3·00
2728	77c. para bailar la bamba	3·25	3·00

Nos. 2723/4×2, 2725/6×2 and 2727/8 were printed, each stamp having a label inscribed 'PRIORITY', attached at left or right.

715 Aboriginal Dancers (detail of painting by Albert Eckhout)

2009. Netherlands and Beyond. Netherlands and Brazil. Sheet 108×150 mm containing T **715** and similar horiz designs. Multicoloured.

MS2729 95c.×6, Type **915**; Capoeira dancers and aboriginal warrior; Passion fruit (extract from *Historia Naturalis Brasiliae*); Cashew nut (extract from *Historia Naturalis Brasiliae*); Farmer and sugar plantation (detail of painting by Frans Post); Church ruins, Olinda (detail of painting by Frans Post) 24·00 22·00

The stamps of **MS**2729 were laid in pairs within the sheet, each stamp having a label inscribed 'PRIORITY', attached at either left or right.

716 Anthony van Assiche (gymnast) and Jochem Uyldehaage (mentor)

2009. Sport. Stichting Sporttop-Mentoring for Olympic Athletes. Multicoloured.

2730	44c. Type **716**	1·90	1·70
2731	44c. Leon Commandeur (cyclist) and Johan Kenkhuis (mentor)	1·90	1·70
2732	44c. Mike Marissen (swimmer) and Bas van de Goor (mentor)	1·90	1·70
2733	44c. Maureen Groefsema (judo) and Lobke Berkhout (mentor)	1·90	1·70
2734	44c. Aniek van Koot (wheelchair tennis player) and Marko Koers (mentor)	1·90	1·70

717 Parcel Ribbon and Bow

2009. Greetings Stamp.

2735	**717**	44c. multicoloured	1·90	1·70

718 '88' and 'GEFELICITEERD!'
719 '88' and 'VAN HARTE!'

2009. Greetings Stamps. Birthdays. (a) Ordinary gum.

2736	44c. bright ultramarine and black	1·90	1·70
2737	44c. bright scarlet and black	1·90	1·70
2738	44c. bright emerald and black	1·90	1·70
2739	44c. bright ultramarine and black	1·90	1·70
2740	44c. bright scarlet and black	1·90	1·70

(b) Size 21×26 mm. Self-adhesive.

2741	44c. bright scarlet and black	1·90	1·70
2742	44c. bright emerald and black	1·90	1·70
2743	44c. bright ultramarine and black	1·90	1·70
2744	44c. bright ultramarine and black	1·90	1·70
2745	44c. bright scarlet and black	1·90	1·70

DESIGNS: No. 2736 Type **718**; No. 2737 '88' and 'HOERA!'; No. 2738 '88' and 'PROFICIAT!'; No. 2739 '88' and 'NOG VELE JAREN!'; No. 2740 '88' and 'VAN HARTE!'; No. 2741 Type **719**; No. 2742 As No. 2737; No. 2743 As No. 2738; No. 2744 As No. 2739; No. 2745 As Type **718**.

The phosphor bands were laid at right-angles along the left and bottom edge of the stamps.

The numerals on the stamps could be altered with a ballpoint pen to show the age of the recipient.

720 1905 10g. Stamp (As Type **11**)

2009. Stamp Day. Personal Stamp.

2746	**720**	44c. multicoloured	2·10	1·90

721 Trauma Helicopter, 1995

2009. Centenary of Powered Flight in the Netherlands. Sheet 108×150 mm containing T **721** and similar horiz designs. Multicoloured.

MS2747 44c.×10, Type **721**; Boeing 747, 1971; Apache helicopter, 1998; Schipol airport (opened 1967); Fokker F-27 Friendship, 1955; Lockheed Super Constellation, 1953; Fokker F-18 Pelican and crew (flew Christmas post to Jakarta in record time of four days); Douglas DC-2 Univer (handicap class winner and second overall in London to Melbourne air race, 1934); *Wright Flyer*, 1909; Anthony Fokker piloting *Spin*, 1911 19·00 18·00

722 Blue Stripe as Figure holding Pencil

2009. Child Welfare. Sheet 145×75 mm containing T **722** and similar horiz designs showing stripes as figures. Multicoloured.

MS2748 44c.+22c.×6,Type **722**; Turquoise stripe holding magnifying glass; Six stripe figures watching falling star; Blue stripe curved around red stripe; Eight stripe figures reading; Three stripe figures leaning to right watching pegasus figure 17·00 15·00

723 Parcel

2009. Christmas. Christmas rate stamps. Multicoloured. Self-adhesive.

2749	34c. Type **723**	1·50	1·30
2750	34c. Candlestick in window	1·50	1·30
2751	34c. Christmas tree on parcel (green background)	1·50	1·30
2752	34c. Pink parcel	1·50	1·30
2753	34c. Woman holding glass in window	1·50	1·30
2754	34c. Man holding glass in window	1·50	1·30
2755	34c. Christmas tree on parcel (pink background)	1·50	1·30
2756	34c. Tall magenta parcel	1·50	1·30
2757	34c. Christmas tree on parcel (blue background)	1·50	1·30
2758	34c. Blue parcel with white ribbon and Christmas tree	1·50	1·30

724 Silhouettes of Wildlife

2010. Personal Stamp

2759	**724**	44c. rosine, blue-black and indigo	2·10	1·90

2010. Tourism. Multicoloured.

2760	44c. Silhouette of Vleeshal, Frans Hals, De Adriaan windmill, St. Bavo church, Toneelschuur and city seal (Haarlem)	1·90	1·70
2761	44c. City Hall, Abbey, Veersepoort district building and Hans Lipperhey (Middelburg)	1·90	1·70

725 Submarine (invented by Cornelis Drebbel (1620))

2010. Centenary of Patents Act. Multicoloured.

MS2762 44c.×10, Type **725**; LED light (Philips (2007)); Artificial kidney (Willem Kolff (1943)); Wine bottle vacuum valve (Bernd Schneider (1987)); Milking machine robot (Van der Lely (1987)); Bicycle chain casing (Wilhelmine J. van der Woerd (1974)); TNT Post's automated handwriting recognition (1980); Solar vehicle (Solar Team Twente (University of Twente and Saxion University of Applied Sciences, Twente) (2009)); Dyneema fibre, world's strongest fibre (DSM (1979); Telescope (Hans Lipperhey (1608)) 19·00 18·00

726 'BOEKENWEEK'

2010. 75th Anniv of Book Week

2763	**726**	€2.20 multicoloured	9·50	8·50

727 VVV (Tourist Information Office of the Netherlands (125th anniv))

2010. Tourism and Environmental Anniversaries. Multicoloured.

2764	44c. Type **727**	1·90	1·70
2765	44c. Silhouettes of Africa (Royal Tropical Institute (centenary))	1·90	1·70
2766	44c. Duinrell, Wassenaar (holiday and amusement park) (75th anniv)	1·90	1·70
2767	44c. Euromast Tower, Rotterdam (50th anniv)	1·90	1·70
2768	44c. Pyramids of Giza, Sphinx and camels (Djoser (tour organization) (25th anniv))	1·90	1·70

728 Four-leafed Clover

2010. Greetings Stamp

2769	**728**	44c. multicoloured	1·90	1·70

2010. Tourism. Multicoloured.

2770	44c. Basilica of Saint Servatius, Helspoort gate, St Servatius Bridge, Church of St John, Bonnefanten Museum, fool's cap (reference to the Carnival festivities held annually in Maastricht) and André Rieu playing violin (Maastricht)	1·90	1·70
2771	44c. St Eusebius Church tower, City Hall, John Frost Bridge, the Rhine, ArtEZ Institute of Arts, sculpture by French artist François Pompon, Le grand cerf (big deer), Sonsbeek Park and Dutch singer-songwriter Ilse DeLange (Arnhem)	1·90	1·70

729 Ramses Shaffy

2010. 75th Anniv of Summer Stamps

MS2772 44c.+22c.×6, olive-bistre and black; orange and black; reddish purple and black; grey-blue and black; deep yellow-brown and black; dull yellow-green and black 17·00 15·00

Designs:—Type **729** (songwriter); Fanny Blankers-Koen (female athlete); Mies Bouwman (children's author and TV personality); Willy Alberti (singer); Dick Bruna (children's author); Annie M. G. Schmidt (children's author)

730 Breskens Lighthouse

2010. Lighthouses

MS2773 **730** €7 multicoloured 30·00 28·00

No. **MS**2773 was for use on domestic registered mail.

2010. Tourism. Multicoloured.

2774	44c. Oldehove Tower, the Chancellery, Church of St Boniface, Achmea Tower, Harmonie Municipal Theatre, golden skate (reference to Elfstedentocht) and Jan Jacob Slauerhoff (poet) (Leeuwarden)	1·90	1·70

731 Two Hearts

2010. Greetings Stamp

2775	**731**	1 (46c.) multicoloured	2·10	1·90

732 Stork carrying Bundle

2010. Greetings Stamp

2776	**732**	1 (46c.) multicoloured	2·10	1·90

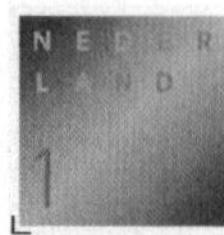
733 Light across Darkness

2010. Beareavement Stamp

2777	**733**	1 (46c.) deep turquoise	2·10	1·90

734 Hybrid Car

2010. Think Green, Act Green. Multicoloured.

2778	1 (46c.) Type **734**	2·10	1·90
2779	1 (46c.) House and sun (solar power)	2·10	1·90
2780	1 (46c.) Cow (methane—bio-fuel)	2·10	1·90
2781	1 (46c.) Wind turbines	2·10	1·90
2782	1 (46c.) Trees (CO^2 offsetting)	2·10	1·90
2783	1 (46c.) Car sharing	2·10	1·90
2784	1 (46c.) Plug with leaves (green energy)	2·10	1·90
2785	1 (46c.) Lorry with soot filter (pollution control)	2·10	1·90
2786	1 (46c.) Envelope (greener postal service)	2·10	1·90
2787	1 (46c.) House enclosed (home insulation)	2·10	1·90
2788	1 EUROPA (79c.) Cycle with globes as wheels (25×30 mm)	3·25	3·00
2789	1 WERELD (95c.) Globe as heart (25×30 mm)	4·00	3·50

Nos. 2788/9 each include a label inscribed 'PRIORITY' attached at top, separated from the design by a line of rouletting.

735 Children (painting)

2010. Personal Stamp

2790	**735**	1 (46c.) multicoloured	2·10	1·90

736 Patchwork

2010. Business Stamp

2791	**736** 1 (46c.) multicoloured	2·10	1·90

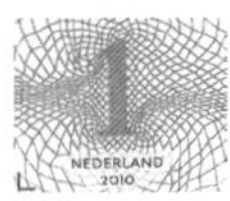

737 '1'

2010. Business Stamps. Multicoloured.

2792	1 (46c.) Type **737**	2·10	1·90
2793	2 (92c.) As Type **737**	4·25	3·75

2010. Horiz design as Type **737**

2794	1 (46c.) multicoloured	2·10	1·90

738 'GRAND DEPART ROTTERDAM'

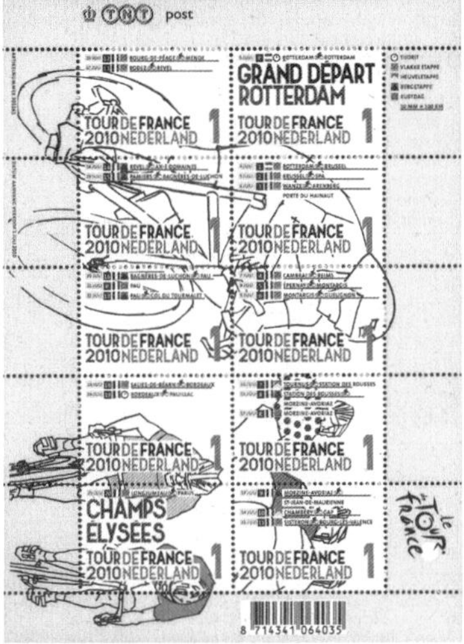

739 Tour de France (image scaled to 45% of original size)

2010. Tour de France. Multicoloured.

MS2795 1 (46c.)×10, Type **738**; Stages 1-3; Stages 4-6; Stages 7-R; Stages 9-11; Stages 12-13; Stages 14-15; Stages 16-17; Stages 18-19; Stage 20, 'CHAMPS ELYSEES' 22·00 20·00

740 Maple Leaves

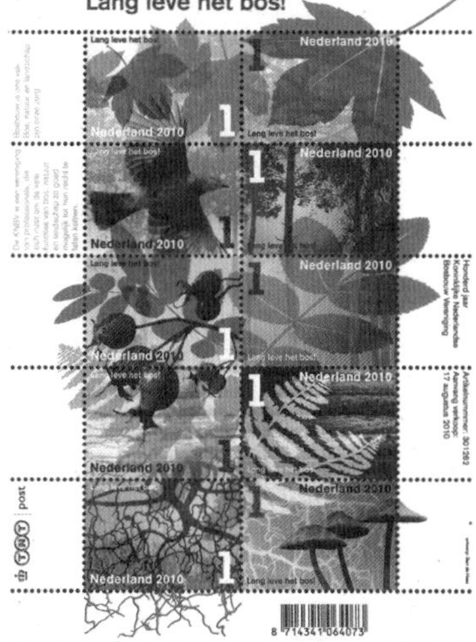

741 Forests (image scaled to 48% of original size)

2010. Centenary of Royal Dutch Forestry Association. Multicoloured.

MS2796 1 (46c.)×10, Type **740**; Maple leaf (different); Jay; Pine trees; Rose hips; Rose leaves; Rose hips and fern; Ferns and logs; Tree roots; Fungi 22·00 20·00

742 Plantation House and Lamp

2010. Netherlands and Beyond. Netherlands and Surinam. Multicoloured.

MS2797 1 WERELD (95c.)×6, Type **742**; Handrail and building; Suriname and Dutch costume; Suriname and Dutch caps; Coloured feathers; Fruit 25·00 23·00

The stamps of **MS**2797 have a label inscribed 'PRIORITY', attached at either left or right.

743 1923 10c. Stamp

2010. Stamp Day

2798	**743** 1 (46c.) multicoloured	2·10	1·90

744 Carice van Houten and Windmill (scene from *Kleinste Kortste Film* (Tiniest, shortest film) directed by Anton Corbijn)

2010. 30th Anniv of Netherlands Film Festival

2799	**744** 5 (€2.30) muluticoloured	10·50	9·50

745 Poster on Woman's Head

2010. AIDS Awareness Campaign. Each scarlet, black and bright lemon.

2800	1 (46c.) Type **745**	2·10	1·90
2801	1 (46c.) AIDS emblem as woman's skirt	2·10	1·90
2802	1 (46c.) Hand holding pill	2·10	1·90
2803	1 (46c.) Woman wearing sari teaching	2·10	1·90
2804	1 (46c.) Mother and child	2·10	1·90
2805	1 (46c.) Woman with eyes downcast	2·10	1·90

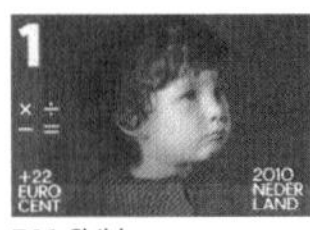

746 Child

2010. Child Welfare. Multicoloured.

MS2806 1 (46c.)+22c.×6, Type **746**; Boy with hand to his head; Boy with dark curly hair; Girl looking up, facing right; Child with hands behind head; Child with left hand raised 17·00 16·00

Nos. 2807/8 are vacant.

747 Snoopy

2010. 60th Anniv of *Peanuts* (comic strip)

2809	**747** (32c.) multicoloured	1·50	1·30

No. 2809 Inscr 'DECEMBER'.

748 Child carrying Christmas Tree

2010. Christmas. Multicoloured.

2810	(32c.) Type **748**	1·50	1·30
2811	(32c.) Bell	1·50	1·30
2812	(32c.) Rocking horse	1·50	1·30
2813	(32c.) Embroidered heart-shaped cushion	1·50	1·30
2814	(32c.) Candle	1·50	1·30
2815	(32c.) Deer wearing ribbon	1·50	1·30
2816	(32c.) Santa enclosed in roundel	1·50	1·30
2817	(32c.) Clasped hands and roses (old-style Christmas card)	1·50	1·30
2818	(32c.) Angel kneeling	1·50	1·30
2819	(32c.) Gingerbread house	1·50	1·30

Nos. 2810/9 Inscr 'DECEMBER'.

749 St Jan's Cathedral, Hertogenbosch

2011. Personal Stamp

2820	**749** 1 (46c.) multicoloured	2·10	1·90

2011. Tourism. Multicoloured.

2821	1 (46c.) Waterside buildings, City Centre, Almere and map	2·10	1·90
2822	1 (46c.) Skyscraper, Einhoven and map	2·10	1·90

750 Great Tit

2011. Personal Stamp

2823	**750** 1 (46c.) multicoloured	2·10	1·90

751 Brain (90th Anniv of Psychology Studies)

2011. 375th Anniv of Utrecht University. Multicoloured.

2824	1 (46c.) Type **751**	2·10	1·90
2825	1 (46c.) Owl (centenary of UNITAS)	2·10	1·90
2826	1 (46c.) Gerard't Hooft (65th anniv of Nobel Prize for Physics)	2·10	1·90
2827	1 (46c.) Globe (125th anniv of University Funding)	2·10	1·90
2828	1 (46c.) Stylised building plans (50th anniv of Utrecht Science Park)	2·10	1·90
2829	1 (46c.) Horse (190th anniv of Animal Medicine)	2·10	1·90
2830	1 (46c.) Spotlight (45th anniv of Drama Institute)	2·10	1·90
2831	1 (46c.) Petrus van Musschenbroek (250th death anniv)	2·10	1·90
2832	1 (46c.) Partial DNA (25th anniv of M.B.V. Mebiose)	2·10	1·90
2833	1 (46c.) Buildings (325th anniv of Portrait Gallery)	2·10	1·90

752 Map of Netherlands (Netherlands Architectural Institute)

2011. Construction Projects. Multicoloured.

2834	1 (46c.) Type **752**	2·10	1·90
2835	1 (46c.) Floor plan (Kennisclusster, Arnhem)	2·10	1·90
2836	1 (46c.) Building projection (Kennisclusster, Arnhem)	2·10	1·90
2837	1 (46c.) Floor plan (Parkeertoren (parking tower))	2·10	1·90
2838	1 (46c.) Building projection (Parkeertoren (parking tower))	2·10	1·90
2839	1 (46c.) Stylised stepped mountain (Boekenberg (book mountain) Library, Spijkenisse)	2·10	1·90
2840	1 (46c.) Skytower, Amsterdam	2·10	1·90
2841	1 (46c.) Floor plan (Skytower, Amsterdam)	2·10	1·90
2842	1 (46c.) Boekenberg Library building, Spijkenisse	2·10	1·90
2843	1 (46c.) Stylised tower (Windpost, Maasvlakte, Rotterdam)	2·10	1·90
2844	1 (46c.) Windpost building, Maasvlakte, Rotterdam	2·10	1·90

2011. Tourism. Multicoloured.

2845	1 (46c.) Apartment Buildings, Plantsoen Welgelegen and map	2·10	1·90
2846	1 (46c.) Onze-Lieve-Vrouwe Church, Breda and map	2·10	1·90

753 Kaleidoscope

2011. Publicity Campaign. 'Now that deserves a card!'

2847	**753** 1 (46c.) multicoloured	2·10	1·90

See also No. 2945.

754 '50 JAAR OESO (OECD)'

2011. Anniversaries. Multicoloured.

2848	1 (46c.) Type **754**	2·10	1·90
2849	1 (46c.) '100 JAAR KONINKLIJKE NEDERLANDSE BILJARTBOND' (Royal Dutch Billiards Association centenary)	2·10	1·90
2850	1 (46c.) '100 JAAR KONINKLIJKE NEDERLANDSE DAMBOND' (Royal Dutch Chess Association centenary)	2·10	1·90
2851	1 (46c.) '650 JAAR SLOT LOEVESTEIN' (650th anniv of Loevestein Castle)	2·10	1·90
2852	1 (46c.) '100 JAAR GENOOTSCHAP NEDERLANDSE COMPONISTEN' (Dutch Composers' Society centenary)	2·10	1·90

755 Child holding Doll

2011. 60th Anniv of UNICEF. Multicoloured.

2853	1 (46c.) Type **755**	2·10	1·90
2854	1 (46c.) Children using globe	2·10	1·90
2855	1 (46c.) Child holding envelope addressed to 'Bryan'	2·10	1·90
2856	1 (46c.) Child carrying load on head	2·10	1·90
2857	1 (46c.) Child looking through broken window	2·10	1·90
2858	1 (46c.) Child playing violin	2·10	1·90
2859	1 (46c.) Mother and baby	2·10	1·90
2860	1 (46c.) Giving toddler drops on tongue	2·10	1·90
2861	1 (46c.) Child using bag as rain shield	2·10	1·90
2862	1 (46c.) Child blowing bubbles	2·10	1·90

756 'WIJN' (wine) (*Sacharmyces cerevisiae*)

2011. Centenary of Society for Microbiology. Multicoloured.

2863	1 (46c.) Type **756**	2·10	1·90
2864	1 (46c.) 'PENICILLIN'	2·10	1·90
2865	1 (46c.) 'KAAS' (cheese)	2·10	1·90
2866	1 (46c.) 'BIOGAS'	2·10	1·90
2867	1 (46c.) 'GROENBEMESTING' (green fertilization)	2·10	1·90
2868	1 (46c.) 'BIODIESEL'	2·10	1·90
2869	1 (46c.) 'AFVALWATERZUIVERING' (sanitation)	2·10	1·90
2870	1 (46c.) 'COMPOST'	2·10	1·90
2871	1 (46c.) 'DESINFECTIE' (disinfection)	2·10	1·90
2872	1 (46c.) 'ZELFHELEND BETON' (self setting concrete)	2·10	1·90

No. 2873 is left for Post, issued on 31 May 2011, not yet received.

Nos. 2874/9 and Type **757** are left for Netherlands and Beyond, issued on 25 July 2011, not yet received.

Nos. 2880/5 and Type **758** are left for Centenary Heemschut, issued on 22 August 2011, not yet received.

Nos. 2886/97 and Type **759** are left for Green Initiatives, issued on 1 September 2011, not yet received.

Nos. 2898/2907 and Type **760** are left for Centenary of Circus, issued on 19 September 2011, not yet received.

No. 2908 and Type **761** is left for Personal Stamp, issued on 10 October 2011, not yet received.

Nos. 2909/14 and Type **762** are left for Post Crossing Initiative, issued on 14 October 2011, not yet received.

No. 2915 and Type **763** are left for Stamp Day, issued on 14 October 2011, not yet received.

No. **MS**2916 and Type **764** are left for 'For Children', issued on 29 October 2011, not yet received.

Nos. 2917/26 and Type **765** are left for Christmas, issued on 22 November 2011, not yet received.

2011. Re-branding and Initial Public Offering of Royal Dutch Post. Multicoloured.

2873	1 (46c.) Symbols of internet, post and parcels services	2·40	2·20

2011. Netherlands and Beyond. Netherlands and South Africa. Multicoloured.

MS2874 1 WERELD (95c.)×6, Elephant; Leopard; Buffalo; Rhinoceros; Lion; African Penguin 29·00 26·00

2011. Centenary of Association for the Protection of Cultural Heritage - Bond Heemschut. Multicoloured.

2880	1 (46c.) American Embassy, The Hague	2·40	2·20
2881	1 (46c.) House, Amerongen	2·40	2·20
2882	1 (46c.) Factory, Winterswijk	2·40	2·20
2883	1 (46c.) North Zuidhollandsch Coffee House, Amsterdam	2·40	2·20
2884	1 (46c.) Basilica of Saint Servatius, Maastricht	2·40	2·20
2885	1 (46c.) Synogogue, Gronigen	2·40	2·20

2011. Green Initiatives. Multicoloured.

2886	1 (46c.) T-shirt (clean with less water and power)	2·40	2·20
2887	1 (46c.) Heart (Netherlands builds sustainable future)	2·40	2·20
2888	1 (46c.) Bird (green post, good message)	2·40	2·20
2889	1 (46c.) Hen (human and animal happy with biology)	2·40	2·20
2890	1 (46c.) Kite (green energy, wind power)	2·40	2·20
2891	1 (46c.) 'KLIMAAT' (preliminary energy label initiative)	2·40	2·20
2892	1 (46c.) Laptop (new working, green profit)	2·40	2·20
2893	1 (46c.) Suitcase (concious travel, climate neutral)	2·40	2·20
2894	1 (46c.) 'Recycling' (gives new life)	2·40	2·20
2895	1 (46c.) 'Snel Vooruit' (fast forward with electric vehicles)	2·40	2·20
2896	EUROPA (79c.) Brain	3·75	3·50
2897	WERELD (96c.) Tree	4·50	4·25

2011. Centenary of Circus Renz. Multicoloured.

2898	1 (46c.) Fire eater	2·40	2·20
2899	1 (46c.) Snake charmer	2·40	2·20
2900	1 (46c.) Clown	2·40	2·20
2901	1 (46c.) Prancing horse	2·40	2·20
2902	1 (46c.) Head balancing hat on nose	2·40	2·20
2903	1 (46c.) Trapeze artists	2·40	2·20
2904	1 (46c.) Lion	2·40	2·20
2905	1 (46c.) Acrobats	2·40	2·20
2906	1 (46c.) Elephant	2·40	2·20
2907	1 (46c.) High-wire cyclist	2·40	2·20

2011. Postcrossing (people from many countries sending each other traditional postcards). Multicoloured.

2909	Europa (79c.) Matryoshka nesting dolls	3·75	3·50
2910	Europa (79c.) Bull fighter	3·75	3·50
2911	Europa (79c.) Taj Mahal	3·75	3·50
2912	Wereld (96c.) Geisha	4·50	4·25
2913	Wereld (96c.) Big Ben, London	4·50	4·25
2914	Wereld (96c.) Windmill	4·50	4·25

2011. Stamp Day. Multicoloured.

2915	1 (46c.) Queen Wilhelmina in profile	2·40	2·20

2010. Child Welfare. Multicoloured.

MS2916 1 (46c.)+23c.×6, Boy wearing orange; Boy wearing light green; Girl wearing pink; Girl seated with green triangle; Boy wearing darker green; Child wearing white 21·00 19·00

2011. Christmas. Multicoloured.

2917	(36c.) Snowman	1·90	1·80
2918	(36c.) Squirrel	1·90	1·80
2919	(36c.) Angel	1·90	1·80
2920	(36c.) Bird	1·90	1·80
2921	(36c.) Bird and heart	1·90	1·80
2922	(36c.) Baubles	1·90	1·80
2923	(36c.) Church	1·90	1·80
2924	(36c.) Reindeer with decorated antlers	1·90	1·80
2925	(36c.) Candle	1·90	1·80
2926	(36c.) Reindeer	1·90	1·80

Nos. 2917/26 inscr 'DECEMBER'.

766 De Drie Haringen (Three Herrings) House, Deventer

2012. Personal Stamps. KLM Delftware Houses. Multicoloured.

2927	1 (85c.) Type **766**	4·00	3·75
2928	1 (95c.) Rembrandt's House, Amsterdam	4·50	4·25

767 Red Cross 'Eerste Hulp Bij Ongelukken' (first aid)

2012. Red Cross. First Aid. Multicoloured.

2929	1 (50c.)+25c. Type **767**	3·50	3·25
2930	1 (50c.)+25c. White cross enclosing face *Eerste Hulp dóór iedereen* (first aid by all)	3·50	3·25
2931	1 (50c.)+25c. White cross enclosing hand *Eerste Hulp vóór iedereen* (first aid for all)	3·50	3·25

2012. Tourism. Historic Country Houses. Multicoloured.

2932	1 (50c.) David (statue), Mattemburgh	2·40	2·20
2933	1 (50c.) Amstenrade House	2·40	2·20

2012. Tourism. Historic Country Houses. Multicoloured.

2934	1 (50c.) Vollenhoven House	2·40	2·20
2935	1 (50c.) Trompenburg House	2·40	2·20

768 Outline of Albert Heijn Store over Photo of First Grocery Delivery Bicycle

2012. 125th Anniv of Albert Heijn (food retailer). Multicoloured.

2936	1 (50c.) Type **768**	2·40	2·20
2937	1 (50c.) Coffee beans over photo of women working in coffee production	2·40	2·20
2938	1 (50c.) Hamster over poster advertising first 'Stock-up Week'	2·40	2·20
2939	1 (50c.) Father pushing trolley over photo of modern employees	2·40	2·20

769 Salvationist giving Homeless Man Bowl of Soup

2012. 125th Anniv of Dutch Salvation Army

2940	**769**	1 (50c.) multicoloured	2·40	2·20

770 *De Amsterdam* (Dutch East Indiaman), National Maritime Museum, Oosterdok

2012. Visit Amsterdam. Multicoloured.

2941	1 (50c.) Type **770**	3·00	2·75
2942	1 (50c.) Muziekgebouw aan 't IJ Concert Hall, Bimhuis Jazz Hall and *Lirica* cruise ship alongside.	3·00	2·75
2943	1 (85c.) *De bocht van de Herengracht* (Gerrit Berckheyde)	4·75	4·50
2944	1 (85c.) Magere Brug (skinny bridge) over River Amstel	4·75	4·50

Nos. 2941/2 and 2943/4, respectively were printed, *se-tenant*, in pairs within sheets of six stamps, Nos. 2943/4 with alternate designs reversed. All the stamps have various design elements refering to the waterways of the Netherlands and were also issued in booklets.

Nos. 2943/4 were inscribed for 'Europa Stamps', were for use on mail within Europe and each issued with a *se-tenant* label inscribed 'PRIORITY' at left.

The phosphor bands were laid at right-angles along the left and bottom edge of the stamps.

771 Pigeon and Flowers

2012. Publicity Campaign. 'Now that deserves a card!'

2945	**771**	1 (50c.) multicoloured	3·00	2·75

772 Women cleaning Courtyard

2012. Centenary of Netherlands Open Air Museum. Colours given in text.

MS2946 1 (50c.)×10, Type **772** (emerald and black); Women at market (black and bright mauve); Children and smart phone (black, magenta and new blue); Children playing *c.* 1940 (new blue and black); Migrant worker in his room (new blue, black and bright mauve); Women and sod hut (bright mauve, black and magenta); Camper van and occupants (bright mauve, black and emerald); Children with tablet device and camping lamp (emerald, black and new blue); Boarding aircraft *c.* 1960 (black and magenta); Petrol station (magenta, black and emerald) 30·00 28·00

2012. Tourism. Historic Country Houses. Multicoloured.

2947	1 (50c.) Middachten House	3·00	2·75

MS2948 144×75 mm. 1 (50c.)×5, Nos. 2932/3, 2934/5 and 2947 15·00 14·00

773 *De Amsterdam* (Dutch East Indiaman)

2012. 60th Anniv of Madurodam (miniature city). Multicoloured.

2949	1 (50c.) Type **755**	3·00	2·75
2950	1 (50c.) Windmill in a polder near Zaanse Schans	3·00	2·75
2951	1 (50c.) Alkmaar cheese market	3·00	2·75
2952	1 (50c.) Port of Rotterdam	3·00	2·75
2953	1 (50c.) Bulbfields in South Holland	3·00	2·75
2954	1 (50c.) Rijksmuseum, Amsterdam	3·00	2·75
2955	1 (50c.) KLM aircraft at Schiphol Airport	3·00	2·75
2956	1 (50c.) Maeslantkering storm surge barrier, Nieuwe Waterweg ship canal	3·00	2·75
2957	1 (50c.) Dredger in Maasvlakte 2 harbour, Rotterdam	3·00	2·75
2958	1 (50c.) Prinsjesdag, Queen's speech day, Binnenhof, The Hague	3·00	2·75

1 NEDERLAND 2012

774 Page from 1877 Edition of *De Grote Bosatlas* (detail)

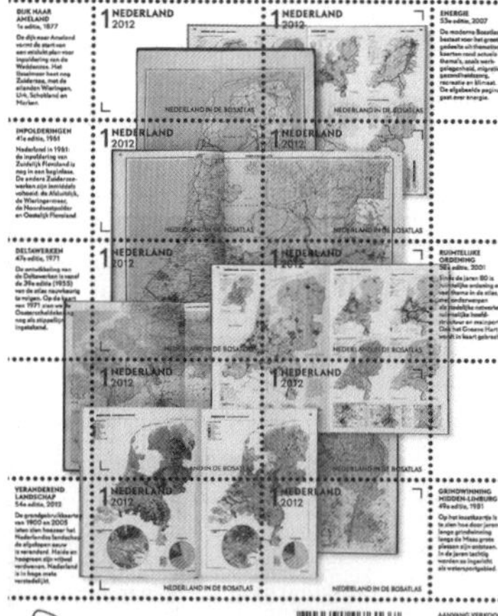

775 Pages from *De Grote Bosatlas* (image scaled to 45% of original size)

2012. 135th Anniv of *De Grote Bosatlas* (atlas). Multicoloured.

MS2959 1 (50c.)×10, Type **774**; Pages from 2007 edition; Page from 1961 edition; Page from 1961 edition (different); Page from 1971 edition; Pages from 2001 edition; Pages from 2102 edition; Pages from 2001 edition (different); Pages from 2102 edition (different); Page from 1981 edition 30·00 28·00

775a Sjoukje Dijkstra, Figure Skating, Innsbruck 1964

2012. Centenary of National Olympic Committee. Gold Medal Winners. Multicoloured.

MS2960 1 (50c.)×10, Type **775a**; Anton Geesink, Judo, Tokyo 1964; Nico Rienks, Rowing, Seoul 1988; Ellen van Langen, 800 metres, Barcelona 1992; Men's Hockey Team, Atlanta 1996; Leontien Zijlaard-van-Moorsel, Cycling, Sydney 2000; Esther Vergeer, Wheelchair Tennis, Athens 2004; Maarten van der Weijden, Men's Marathon 10 kilometre Swimming, Beijing 2008; Anky van Grunsven, Equestrian Dressage, Beijing 2008; Nicolien Saurbreij, Women's Parallel Giant Slalom Snowboard, Vancouver 2010 30·00 28·00

776 Maple Leaves

2012. 20th Anniv of Lifestyle Magazine, *Seasons*. Multicoloured.

MS2961 1 (50c.)×10, Type **776**; Ice bloom; Bundle of pea pods; Dahlia; Green Fritillary flowers; Frozen Rowan berries; Coneflower; Rose, Rose hips and Geranium; Tulip; Blueberries 30·00 28·00

777 Hella Haase (writer)

2012. Netherlands and Beyond. Netherlands and Indonesia. Multicoloured.

MS2962 WERELD 1 (95c.)×6, Type **777**; Hendrick Petrius Beriage (architect); Andy Tielman (Eurasian rock artist); Kantjil (Mouse Deer); Charles Prosper Wolff Schoemaker (architect); Jan Boon (Tim Robinson (writer and journalist)) 29·00 26·00

778 Maas-Rijn-IJsselvee (Meuse-Rhine-Yessel)

2012. Dutch Cattle Breeds. Multicoloured.

2963	1 (50c.) Type **778**	3·00	2·75
2964	1 (50c.) Blaarkop	3·00	2·75
2965	1 (50c.) Fries-Hollands (Friesian)	3·00	2·75
2966	1 (50c.) Lakenvelder (Dutch Belted)	3·00	2·75
2967	1 (50c.) Brandrode Rund	3·00	2·75
2968	1 (50c.) Witrik	3·00	2·75

779 Theatre Building

2012. 125th Anniv of Carré Theatre. Multicoloured.
MS2969 1 (50c.)×10, Type **779**; Toon Hermans (comedian), 1963; Circus horses (Oscar Carré, founder, was previously circus artist); Modern ballet dancers, (Hans van Manen) 1979; Musician; Dancers (*Cats*), 1987; Uni-cyclist highwire artist (Louis and Heintje Davids), 1893; Classical ballerina; Elephant (World Christmas Circus); Anniversary emblem 30·00 28·00

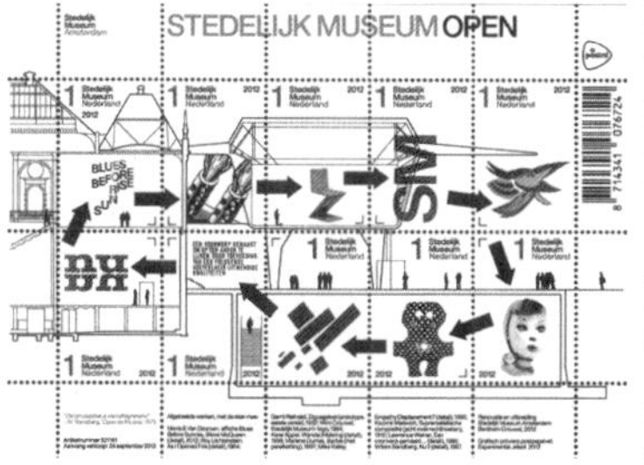

780 'Blues before Sunrise' (image scaled to 32% of original size)

2012. Stedelijk Museum Open. Sheet 150×108 mm
MS2970 **780** 1 (50c.)×10 multicoloured 30·00 28·00

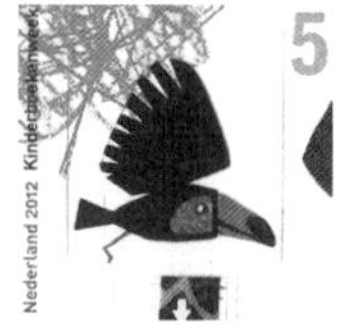
781 Toucan

2012. Children's Book Week. Multicoloured.
MS2971 5 (€2.50)×2, Type **781**; Butterfly 25·00 23·00

782 Queen Julianna 1949 10g. Stamp (as No. 701)

2012. Stamp Day

2972	**782**	1 (50c.) multicoloured	3·00	2·75

783 Catharina-Amalia, Princess of Orange

2012. Child Welfare. Multicoloured.
MS2973 1 (50c.)+25c.×6, Type **783**; Princess Alexia, Princess Ariane and Princess Catharina-Amalia; Princess Ariane; Princess Catharina, Princess Alexia and Princess Ariane; Princess Alexia; Princess Alexia; Princess Ariane and Princess Catharina-Amaila 28·00 25·00

784 Fair Isle Knitting Patterns

2012. Christmas. December rate stamps. Multicoloured.

2974	(40C.) Type **784**	2·40	2·20
2975	(40c.) Two angels blowing trumpets	2·40	2·20
2976	(40c.) Two red reindeer	2·40	2·20
2977	(40c.) Three angels	2·40	2·20
2978	(40c.) Three candles	2·40	2·20
2979	(40c.) Trees and snowflakes, narrow patterns	2·40	2·20
2980	(40c.) Baubles and snowflakes	2·40	2·20
2981	(40c.) Trees and snowflakes, wider patterns	2·40	2·20
2982	(40c.) Three snowmen	2·40	2·20
2983	(40c.) Two reinder, blue background	2·40	2·20

Nos. 2974/83 inscr 'DECEMBER'.

785 Red Squirrel

2013. Personal Stamps. Multicoloured.

2984	1 (50c.) Type **785**	3·25	3·00
2985	1 (50c.) Reinier Paping (long track speed skater) winner Elfstedentocht (Eleven Cities) Skating Competition, 1963	3·25	3·00

786 Headdress, Bunschoten-Spakenburg

2013. Tourism. Headdresses. Streekdrachten. Multicoloured.

2986	1 (50c.) Type **786**	3·25	3·00
2987	1 (50c.) Staphorst	3·25	3·00

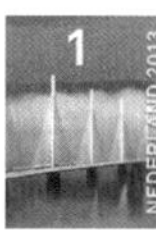
787 Millau Viaduct

2013. 125th Anniv of ARCADIS (engineering and consultancy organisation) and KNHM (non-profit organisation). Multicoloured.
MS2988 1 (50c.)×10, Type **787**; Nature Bridge, Zanderij Crailoo (800m long and 50m wide, the largest wildlife crossing in the world); Corn field (improving sea defences); Floriade 2012 Park; Olympic Stadium, London; Storm defences, New Orleans; Allotments, Lake; Amsterdam Bijlmer Arena; 'Artcadia bruist' 35·00 31·00

2013. Tourism. Headdresses. Streekdrachten. Multicoloured.

2989	1 (50c.) Marken	3·25	3·00
2990	1 (50c.) Walcheren	3·25	3·00

788 Leopards

2013. Centenary of Burger's Zoo, Arnhem. Multicoloured.
MS2991 1 (50c.)×10, Type **788**; Giraffes; Rhinoceros; Yellow-cheeked Baboon; African Penguin; Chimpanzees; Iguanas; Zebras; Hyacinth Parrots; Banggai Cardinalfish 35·00 31·00

789 King Willem-Alexander

2013. Succession to the Throne by King Willem-Alexander

2992	1 (50c.) vermilion	3·25	3·00
2993	1 (50c.) new blue	3·25	3·00

Design:—No. 2992 Type **789**; No. 2993 Queen Beatrix

790 Alexandrine Tinné (explorer)

2013. 1001 Women in Dutch History Exhibition

2994	1 (50c.) pale red-brown and black	3·25	3·00
2995	1 (50c.) salmon and black	3·25	3·00
2996	1 (50c.) brown and black	3·25	3·00
2997	1 (50c.) slate-lilac and black	3·25	3·00
2998	1 (50c.) orange-brown and black	3·25	3·00
2999	1 (50c.) pale greenish slate and black	3·25	3·00

Designs:—No. 2994 Type **790**; No. 2995 Belle van Zuylen, 1740-1805 (writer); No. 2996 Trijn van Leemput, 1530-1607 (Utrecht heroine); No. 2997 Maria van Oosterwijck, 1630-1693 (artist); No. 2998 Queen Mary of Burgundy, 1457-1482; No. 2999Anna Zernike, 1887-1972 (theologian)

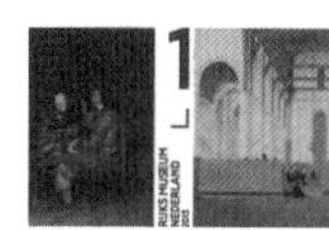
791 *The Paternal Admontion* (Gerard ter Borch) and *Interior of St Odulphus Church in Assendelft* (Pieter Janaz. Saenredam)

792 Rijksmuseum (image scaled to 45% of original size)

2013. Art. Inauguration of Rijksmuseum. Multicoloured.
MS3000 1 (50c.)×10, Type **791** and other designs as Type **792** 35·00 31·00

793 Renault Kangoo, Fiat Florino, Simca 1100 and Daf 33

2013. Europa. Postal Vehicles. Multicoloured.

3001	1 (90c.) Type **793**	6·50	6·00
3002	1 (90c.) Bedford CA, Opel Blitz, Opel P4 and GMC 2.5	6·50	6·00

794 'WA'

2013. Inauguration of King Willem-Alexander. Multicoloured.

3003	1 (54c.) As Type **794**	3·25	3·00
3004	2 (€1.08) Type **794**	6·50	6·00

2013. Tourism. Headdresses. Streekdrachten. Multicoloured.

3005	1 (54c.) Noordwest-Veluwe	3·25	3·00

795 Louis Couperus, 1863-1923

2013. Dutch Writers

3006	1 (54c.) sage-green and black	3·25	3·00
3007	1 (54c.) bistre and black	3·25	3·00
3008	1 (54c.) carmine-rose and black	3·25	3·00
3009	1 (54c.) turquoise-blue and black	3·25	3·00
3010	1 (54c.) orange-brown and black	3·25	3·00

Designs:—No. 3006 Type **795**; Adriaan Roland Holst, 1888-1976; No. 3007 Godfried Bomans, 1913-1971; No. 3009 Simon Carmiggelt, 1913-1987; No. 3010 Gerrit Kouwenaar, 1923

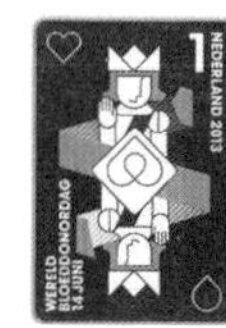
796 King of Hearts

2013. World Blood Donor Day. Each scarlet-vermilion and gold.

3011	1 (50c.) Type **796**	3·25	3·00
3012	1 (50c.) Queen of Hearts	3·25	3·00

797 Binnenkruier

2013. Dutch Windmills. Multicoloured.

3013	1 (60c.) Type **797**	3·50	3·25
3014	1 (60c.) Spinnenkop	3·50	3·25
3015	1 (60c.) Watervluchtmolen	3·50	3·25
3016	1 (60c.) Wipmolen	3·50	3·25
3017	1 (60c.) Paltrokmolen	3·50	3·25
3018	1 (60c.) Ronde Stellingmolen	3·50	3·25
3019	1 (60c.) Standermolen	3·50	3·25
3020	1 (60c.) Torenmolen	3·50	3·25
3021	1 (60c.) Ronde Grondzeiler	3·50	3·25
3022	1 (60c.) Achtkante Stellingmolen	3·50	3·25

798 Bathers

2013. 125th Anniv Royal Dutch Swimming Association. Multicoloured.
MS3023 1 (60c.)×10, Type **798**; Two divers; Swimmer holding pool edge; Diving from the right; Swimmers on diving board; Two synchronised swimmers; Swimmer swimming to the left; Several swimmers standing in water; Swimmer with head raised; Preparing to dive 38·00 28·00

799 Museum aan de Stroom (MAS) (Neutelings Riedijk Architects)

2013. Netherlands and Beyond. Netherlands and Belgium. Multicoloured.
MS3024 WERELD 1×6, Type **799**; Hoenderloo Museum (Henry van de Velde); Books (left); Books (right); *Après-midi à Amsterdam* (Rik Wouters); *De vlakte* (Jacob Smits) 38·00 34·00

800 Numbers

2013. Greetings Stamp

3025	**800**	1 (60c.) multicoloured	3·50	3·25

801 Glazed Wall Tile (Leon Senf)

2013. Centenary of Peace Palace, the Hague. Multicoloured.

3026	1 (60c.) Type **801**	3·50	3·25
3027	1 (60c.) Friendship (detail) bronze medallion, entrance (Bruno Möhring)	3·50	3·25
3028	1 (60c.) Lead windows, central hall (Adolf le Compte)	3·50	3·25
3029	1 (60c.) *Hugo Grotius* (Michiel Jansz)	3·50	3·25
3030	1 (60c.) Mosaic floor, entrance hall (Hendrik Wijdeveld)	3·50	3·25
3031	1 (60c.) *Veritas* (relief), grand courtroom (Toon Dupuis)	3·50	3·25
3032	1 (60c.) Tapestry, small courtroom (Luc-Olivier Merson)	3·50	3·25
3033	1 (60c.) Tile picture (detail) (Herman Rosse)	3·50	3·25
3034	1 (60c.) Mother and child, central hall (Herman Rosse)	3·50	3·25
3035	1 (60c.) Locomotive, leaded light, party room (Herman Rosse)	3·50	3·25

802 Queen Wilhelmina, As 1933 36c. Stamp (Type **59**)

2013. Stamp Day

3036	**802**	1 (60c.) multicoloured	3·50	3·25

803 Boy and Maths Tables

2013. Child Welfare. 'Let Children Learn', Ethiopia. Multicoloured.

3037	1 (60c.)+30c. Type **803**	5·50	4·75
3038	1 (60c.)+30c. Boy carrying sticks	5·50	4·75
3039	1 (60c.)+30c. Girl carrying baby on her back	5·50	4·75
3040	1 (60c.)+30c. Boy and alphabet	5·50	4·75
3041	1 (60c.)+30c. Boy and descriptive poster	5·50	4·75
3042	1 (60c.)+30c. Boy carrying lamb	5·50	4·75

804 St Nicholas and Pageboy

2013. Christmas. Santa Claus. Multicoloured.

3043	1 (60c.) Type **804**	3·50	3·25
3044	1 (60c.) Pageboy holding present	3·50	3·25
3045	1 (60c.) Moon 'caught' in tree	3·50	3·25
3046	1 (60c.) St Nicholas	3·50	3·25
3047	1 (60c.) Stocking full of presents	3·50	3·25

805 Houses and Star

2013. Christmas. December rate stamps. Multicoloured.

3048	(40c.) Type **805**	3·25	3·00
3049	(40c.) Houses, right	3·25	3·00
3050	(40c.) House and fireworks	3·25	3·00
3051	(40c.) Houses, star, moon and weather vane	3·25	3·00
3052	(40c.) Houses and large Christmas tree, left	3·25	3·00
3053	(40c.) Houses and large Christmas tree, right	3·25	3·00
3054	(40c.) Houses, running man and larger Christmas tree	3·25	3·00
3055	(40c.) Detached house and clock	3·25	3·00
3056	(40c.) Robin and woman pulling sledge	3·25	3·00
3057	(40c.) Sledge and man skating	3·25	3·00
3058	(40c.) Two skaters pulling sledge	3·25	3·00
3059	(40c.) Child in sledge and windows	3·25	3·00
3060	(40c.) Snowman	3·25	3·00
3061	(40c.) Man pulling Christmas tree	3·25	3·00
3062	(40c.) Postman on bicycle and dog	3·25	3·00
3063	(40c.) Woman holding dog lead and hanging wreath	3·25	3·00
3064	(40c.) Couple under misteltoe	3·25	3·00
3065	(40c.) Bridge and two seagulls wearing Santa hats	3·25	3·00
3066	(40c.) Large Christmas tree	3·25	3·00
3067	(40c.) Doorway of tall building	3·25	3·00

Nos.3048/67 inscr 'DECEMBER'.

806 List of rulers

2013. Bicentenary of Monarchy of the Netherlands. Each vermilion, new blue and black.

3068	2 (€1.28) Type **806**	7·25	6·50
3069	2 (€1.28) King Willem I returning, eyes and Dutch flag	7·25	6·50

807 King Willem-Alexander

2014. King Willem-Alexander

3070	**807**	1 (64c.) new blue	4·50	4·00
3071		1 (€1.05) grey and ultramarine	7·25	6·50
3072		2 (€1.28) rose	9·00	8·00

808 '1'

2014. Business Stamps

3073	1 (64c.) Type **808**	4·50	4·00
3074	2 (€1.28) '2'	9·00	8·00

809 Dutch Sailboat

2014. Dutch Icons. Each ultramarine and scarlet.

3075	1 (64c.) Type **809**	4·50	4·00
3076	1 (64c.) Windmill	4·50	4·00
3077	1 (64c.) Gouda cheese	4·50	4·00
3078	1 (64c.) Dutch house	4·50	4·00
3079	1 (64c.) Dutch dolls kissing	4·50	4·00
3080	1 (64c.) Bicycle	4·50	4·00
3081	1 (64c.) Friesian cow	4·50	4·00
3082	1 (64c.) Tulip	4·50	4·00
3083	1 (64c.) Skate	4·50	4·00
3084	1 (64c.) Wooden clog	4·50	4·00

810 Windmill

2014. Dutch Icons (2nd issue). Each ultramarine and scarlet.

3085	1 (€1.05) Type **810**	7·25	6·50
3086	1 (€1.05) Bicycle	7·25	6·50
3087	1 (€1.05) Freisian cow	7·25	6·50
3088	1 (€1.05) Dutch house	7·25	6·50
3089	1 (€1.05) Tulip	7·25	6·50

811 Loosdrecht

2014. Tourism. Ceramics. Loosdrecht and Tegelen. Multicoloured.

3090	1 (64c.) Type **811**	4·50	4·00
3091	1 (64c.) Tegelen	4·50	4·00

812 De Dion ET Trépardoux

2014. Classic Cars from Louwman Museum. Multicoloured.

3092	1 (64c.) Type **812**	4·50	4·00
3093	1 (64c.) Brooke	4·50	4·00
3094	1 (64c.) Eysink	4·50	4·00
3095	1 (64c.) Spyker	4·50	4·00
3096	1 (64c.) Bugatti	4·50	4·00
3097	1 (64c.) Duesenberg	4·50	4·00
3098	1 (64c.) Toyota	4·50	4·00
3099	1 (64c.) Porsche	4·50	4·00
3100	1 (64c.) Aston Martin	4·50	4·00
3101	1 (64c.) Ferrari	4·50	4·00

2014. Tourism. Ceramics. Harlingen and Makkum. Multicoloured.

3102	1 (64c.) Harlingen	4·50	4·00
3103	1 (64c.) Makkum	4·50	4·00

813 Post Pigeon

2014. Day of Youth Philately

3104	1 (64c.) bright mauve, turquoise-green and black	4·50	4·00
3105	1 (64c.) bright mauve, orange and black	4·50	4·00

Designs:—No. 3104 Type **813**; No. 3105 Post Hedgehog

814 Inauguration of King Willem I (statue)

2014. Bicentenary of Kingdom of the Netherlands. Multicoloured.

3106	2 (€1.28) Type **814**	9·00	8·00
3107	2 (€1.28) Inauguration of King Willem-Alexander	9·00	8·00

815 Back of The Three Wigs Barrel Organ

2014. Europa. Musical Instruments. Multicoloured.

3108	1 (€1.05) Type **815**	7·25	6·50
3109	1 (€1.05) Front of The Three Wigs barrel organ	7·25	6·50

816 *Gymnadenia conopsea*

2014. Orchids of Gerendal Nature Reserve, Limburg. Multicoloured.

3110	1 (64c.) Type **816**	4·50	4·00
3111	1 (64c.) *Orchis militaris*	4·50	4·00
3112	1 (64c.) *Orchis anthropophora*	4·50	4·00
3113	1 (64c.) *Anacamtis pyramidalis*	4·50	4·00
3114	1 (64c.) *Dactylorhiza maculata*	4·50	4·00
3115	1 (64c.) *Orchis purpurea*	4·50	4·00
3116	1 (64c.) *Plantanthera bifolia*	4·50	4·00
3117	1 (64c.) *Orchis mascula*	4·50	4·00
3118	1 (64c.) *Coeloglossum viride*	4·50	4·00
3119	1 (64c.) *Orchis simia*	4·50	4·00

2014. Tourism. Ceramics. Delft. Multicoloured.

3120	1 (64c.) Delft	4·50	4·00
MS3121	144×75 mm. 1 (64c.)×5, Nos. 3090/1, 3102/3 and 3120	23·00	21·00

817 Italy, 1934

2014. 'Orange at the World Cup'. Multicoloured.

3122	1 (64c.) Type **817**	4·50	4·00
3123	1 (64c.) France, 1938	4·50	4·00
3124	1 (64c.) West Germany, 1974	4·50	4·00
3125	1 (64c.) Argentina, 1978	4·50	4·00
3126	1 (64c.) Italy, 1990	4·50	4·00
3127	1 (64c.) USA, 1994	4·50	4·00
3128	1 (64c.) France, 1998	4·50	4·00
3129	1 (64c.) Germany, 2006	4·50	4·00
3130	1 (64c.) South Africa, 2010	4·50	4·00
3131	1 (64c.) Brazil, 2014	4·50	4·00

818 *Girl with a Pearl Earring* (Johannes Vermeer)

2014. Personal Stamps

3132	**818**	(€1.05) multicoloured	7·25	6·50

819 Otsuki Gentaku

2014. Netherlands and Beyond. Netherlands and Japan. Multicoloured.

MS3133	INTERNATIONAL 1 (€1.05)×6, Type **819**; Philipp Franz von Siebold; *The Courtesan* (Vincent van Gogh); *The Red Kimono* (George Hendrik Breitner); *De Liefde* (ship); Dejima, (small fan-shaped artificial island); Nagasaki	45·00	41·00

820 The Royal Family

2014. 12½th Anniv of Wedding of King Willem-Alexander and Queen Máxima. Multicoloured.

3134	1 (64c.) Type **820**	4·50	4·00
3135	1 (64c.) Wearing orange, 2014	4·50	4·00
3136	1 (64c.) Wearing evening dress	4·50	4·00
3137	1 (64c.) Engagement, 2001	4·50	4·00
3138	1 (64c.) Amalia, Alexia, Ariane wearing blue gowns, and Royal couple	4·50	4·00

821 Droogmakerij de Beemster, 1999

2014. World Heritage Sites. Multicoloured.

MS3139	1 (64c.)×6, Type **821**; Waddenzee, 2009; Schokland en Omgeving, 1995; Molencomplex Kinderijk, Elshout, 1997; Reitveld Schröderhuis, 2000; Ir. D.F. Woudagemaal; Grachtengodel Amsterdam; Willemstad Curaçao; De Stelling van Amsterdam (Fort bij Spijkerboor); De Stelling van Amsterdam (Forteiland Pampus)	48·00	43·00

822 NS-LOC Series 2200

2014. 175th Anniv of Railways in Netherland. Multicoloured.

MS3140 1 (64c.)×6, Type **822**; Station clock and stairway; Haarlem Station; Nieuwbouw Station, Arnhem; Bridge, station platform and go lights; 'TIENER TOER' and winged wheel; Intercity Materieel and stop lights; Clock and Central Station; Emblems; 1939 12½ cent stamp and Sprinter Lighttrain 48·00 43·00

823 Afrojack

2014. Dutch DJs. Multicoloured.

3141	1 (64c.) Type **823**	4·50	4·00
3142	1 (64c.) Armin Van Buuren	4·50	4·00
3143	1 (64c.) Dash Berlin	4·50	4·00
3144	1 (64c.) Hardwell	4·50	4·00
3145	1 (64c.) Tiësto	4·50	4·00

824 Netherlands and Overseas Stamps

2014. Stamp Day

3146	**824** 1 (64c.) multicoloured	4·50	4·00

825 Children on Beach

2014. Child Welfare. 'Let Children Learn'. Children and Rijksmuseum, Amsterdam. Multicoloured.

MS3147 1 (64c.)+32c.×6, Type **825**; Donkey rides; Skateboarder (33×46 mm); Girl reclining wearing kimono; Girl at piano with two small boys 36·00 32·00

826 Mittens

2014. Christmas. December rate stamps. Multicoloured.

3148	(59c.) Type **826**	4·25	3·75
3149	(59c.) Baubles	4·25	3·75
3150	(59c.) Owl and Santa and sleigh	4·25	3·75
3151	(59c.) Kiss under mistletoe	4·25	3·75
3152	(59c.) Champagne flutes	4·25	3·75
3153	(59c.) Doughnuts and sparklers	4·25	3·75
3154	(59c.) Snowman	4·25	3·75
3155	(59c.) Snow covered Christmas tree	4·25	3·75
3156	(59c.) Arm placing present on tree	4·25	3·75
3157	(59c.) Envelope and post box	4·25	3·75
3158	(59c.) Fondue	4·25	3·75
3159	(59c.) Bells	4·25	3·75
3160	(59c.) Baubles and candle	4·25	3·75
3161	(59c.) Candy cane and bauble	4·25	3·75
3162	(59c.) Sleigh	4·25	3·75
3163	(59c.) Ice skates	4·25	3·75
3164	(59c.) Stockings	4·25	3·75
3165	(59c.) Birds	4·25	3·75
3166	(59c.) Presents	4·25	3·75
3167	(59c.) Fireworks	4·25	3·75

Nos. 3148/67 inscr 'DECEMBER'.

827 *Golden Earring* (Radar Love)

2015. 50th Anniv of Dutch Top 40 Chart. Multicoloured.

3168	1 (68c.) Type **827**	4·75	4·25
3169	1 (68c.) The Cats (*One Way Wind*)	4·75	4·25
3170	1 (68c.) André van Duin (*Willempie*)	4·75	4·25
3171	1 (68c.) MWN (*Mon Amour*)	4·75	4·25
3172	1 (68c.) 2 Unlimited (*No Limit*)	4·75	4·25
3173	1 (68c.) Paul de Leeuw (*Fly with Me*)	4·75	4·25
3174	1 (68c.) Marco Borsato (*Dreams are Cheating*)	4·75	4·25
3175	1 (68c.) Vengaboys (*We're Going to Ibiza*)	4·75	4·25
3176	1 (68c.) Jan Smit (*Cupid*)	4·75	4·25
3177	1 (68c.) Anouk (*Birds*)	4·75	4·25

828 King Willem-Alexander

2015. King Willem-Alexander

3178	**828** 1 (69c.) new blue, silver and black	4·75	4·25

829 Elburg

2015. Tourism. Fortified Towns. Multicoloured.

3179	1 (69c.) Type **829**	4·75	4·25
3180	1 (69c.) Bourtange	4·75	4·25
3181	1 (69c.) Naarden	4·75	4·25

830 Symbols of Childhood

2015. Greetings Stamp. Birth

3182	**830** 1 (69c.) multicoloured	4·75	4·25

2015. King Willem-Alexander

3183	**828** 1 (€1.25) grey and ultramarine	7·75	7·00
3184	**828** 2 (€1.38) rose	9·50	8·75

831 Map and Seal

2015. Bicentenary of Kingdom of the Netherlands. Multicoloured.

3185	2 (€1.38) Type **831**	9·50	8·75
3186	2 (€1.38) King Willem 1, 1815	9·50	8·75

832 HSL Bridge Moerdijk, 2006

2015. Bridges in Netherlands. Multicoloured.

MS3187 1 (69c.)×6, Type **832**; Ehzerbrug, Almen, 1946; Coal Harbour Bridge, Delft, 2004; Cable-stayed bridge, Heusden, 1989; Zouthaven, Amsterdam, 2005; Jan Waaijer Bridge, Zoetermeer, 2013; Crossing, Nijmegen, 2013; Zeeland Bridge over the Oosterschelde, 1965; Hanseatic Arch, Zwolle, 2011; Nesciobrug, Amsterdam, 2006 50·00 46·00

833 *Alnus glutinosa*

2015. Flora and Fauna of Naardermeer. Multicoloured.

3188	1 (69c.) Type **833**	4·75	4·25
3189	1 (69c.) *Phalacrocorax carbo* (Great Cormorant)	4·75	4·25
3190	1 (69c.) *Phragmites australis*	4·75	4·25
3191	1 (69c.) *Acrocephalus scirpaceus* (Eurasian Reed Warbler)	4·75	4·25
3192	1 (69c.) *Dactylorhiza majalis*	4·75	4·25
3193	1 (69c.) *Natrix natrix* (Grass Snake)	4·75	4·25
3194	1 (69c.) *Nymphaea alba*	4·75	4·25
3195	1 (69c.) *Podiceps cristatus* (Great Crested Grebe)	4·75	4·25
3196	1 (69c.) *Nymphoides peltata*	4·75	4·25
3197	1 (69c.) *Esox lucius*	4·75	4·25

Nos. 3188/9, 3190/1, 3192/3, 3194/5 and 3196/7, respectively were printed, *se-tenant*, in horizontal pairs within sheets of ten stamps, each pair forming a composite design

The phosphor bands were laid at right-angles along the left and bottom edge of the stamps.

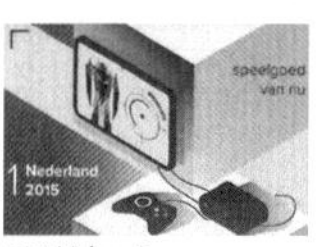

834 Video Game

2015. Europa. Old Toys (Nos. 3200/1) or Toys of Today (Nos. 3198/9). Multicoloured.

3198	1 (69c.) Type **834**	4·75	4·25
3199	1 (69c.) Rubik's cube	4·75	4·25
3200	(€1.15) Wind up robot	7·75	7·00
3201	(€1.15) Ludo	7·75	7·00

835 Heart

2015. Greetings Stamp. Love

3202	**835** 1 (69c.) multicoloured	4·75	4·25

2015. Tourism. Fortified Towns. Multicoloured.

3203	1 (69c.) Hulst	4·75	4·25
3204	1 (69c.) Willemstad	4·75	4·25

MS3205 144×75 mm. 1 (69c.)×5, Nos. 3179/81 and 3203/4 25·00 22·00

836 On Deck

2015. Volvo Ocean Race Pitstop, The Hague, 2015. Multicoloured.

3206	1 (69c.) Type **836**	4·75	4·25
3207	1 (69c.) Tacking	4·75	4·25
3208	1 (69c.) Start	4·75	4·25
3209	1 (69c.) Team on deck (different)	4·75	4·25
3210	1 (69c.) Aerial view of deck	4·75	4·25
3211	1 (69c.) Team Vestas	4·75	4·25

837 Prince of Orange (King Willem II)

2015. Bicentenary of Battle of Waterloo

3212	**837** (€1.15) multicoloured	7·75	7·00

838 Vacuum

2015. Nemo Science Centre. Explore Science. Multicoloured.

3213	1 (69c.) Type **838**	4·75	4·25
3214	1 (69c.) Conduction	4·75	4·25
3215	1 (69c.) Electricity	4·75	4·25
3216	1 (69c.) Refraction of light	4·75	4·25
3217	1 (69c.) Static charge	4·75	4·25

839 Vincent van Gogh

2015. Letter Writing. Multicoloured.

MS3218 1 (69c.)×10, Type **839**; 'Waarde Theo...'; 'Komte, oude lieden...'; Leo Vroman; Rembrandt van Rijn; '..deesen twee sijnt....'; 'Des te belangrijker......'; Desiderius Erasmus; Christiaan Huygens; 'Ik zal u een.....' 50·00 46·00

840 Baseball Shirt inscribed 'Jankees' (Yankees)

2015. Netherlands and Beyond. Netherlands and USA. Multicoloured.

MS3219 1 INTERNATIONAL (€1.15)×6, Type **840**; 'Uptown & Haarlem...'; High Line in New York; City Hall, The Hague, designed by American architect Richard Meier; Park designed by Dutch landscape architect Piet Oudolf; Hot Dog USA (Jan Cremer); Carrying 'Ghetto Blaster' 50·00 46·00

841 Guinness (Retrieved, 2011)

2015. Animal Portraits by Charlotte Dumas. Multicoloured.

3220	1 (69c.) Type **840**	4·75	4·25
3221	1 (69c.) Isolde (Day is Done, 2004) (Horse)	4·75	4·25
3222	1 (69c.) Taza (Reverie, 2005) (Wolf)	4·75	4·25
3223	1 (69c.) Zeus (Tiger, Tiger, 2007)	4·75	4·25
3224	1 (69c.) Tom Tom (Heart-shaped Hole, 2008) (Collie)	4·75	4·25
3225	1 (69c.) Moxie (Retrieved, 2011)	4·75	4·25
3226	1 (69c.) Zonder Titel (untitled, stray Dog) (Randagi, 2006)	4·75	4·25
3227	1 (69c.) Ringo (Anima, 2012) (Horse)	4·75	4·25
3228	1 (69c.) Rocky Road (The Wildest Prairies, 2013) (Horse)	4·75	4·25
3229	1 (69c.) Kat (Rabat, 2012)	4·75	4·25

842 Archipelago (image scaled to NaN% of original size)

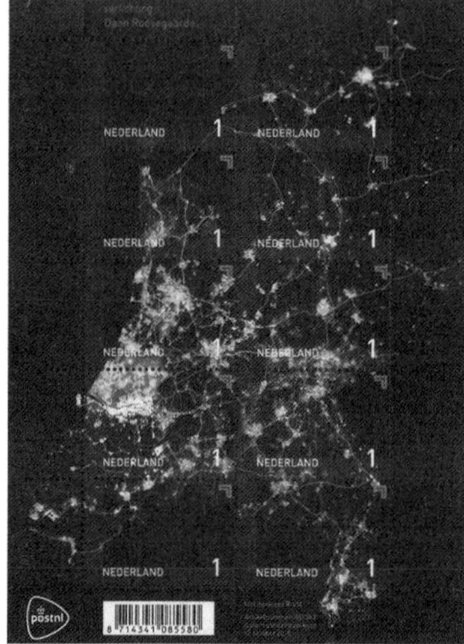

843 Lights in Netherlands (image scaled to 45% of original size)

2015. Netherlands Seen from Space. Multicoloured.

MS3230 1 (69c.)×10, Type **842**; Lights in Netherlands as Type **843** 50·00 46·00

844 *Aegir*

2015. Ship Models at Maritime Museum. Multicoloured.

3231	1 (69c.) Type **844**	4·75	4·25
3232	1 (69c.) *Bomschuit*	4·75	4·25
3233	1 (69c.) *Trio*	4·75	4·25
3234	1 (69c.) *Sindoro*	4·75	4·25
3235	1 (69c.) *Sultan van Koetei*	4·75	4·25
3236	1 (69c.) *Fairmount Expedition*	4·75	4·25
3237	1 (69c.) *Matarómodel*	4·75	4·25
3238	1 (69c.) *Assahan*	4·75	4·25
3239	1 (69c.) *Nedlloyd Houtman*	4·75	4·25
3240	1 (69c.) *Padmos/Blijdorp*	4·75	4·25

845 1944 7½ cent Stamp

2015. Stamp Day

3241	**845** 1 (69c.) multicoloured	4·75	4·25

846 *Kiki at Home*

2015. Child Welfare. Multicoloured.

MS3242	1 (69c.)+32c.×6, Type **846**; Bird, nest and cat in tree (*Poes Pinkie*); Child pulling toy train (*Kiki at Home*); Ducks, house and garden (*Kippetje Tok*); Cat on mitten (*Poes Pinkie*); Duck and other animals in gardening clothes (*Kippetje Tok*)	39·00	35·00

847 Woman playing with Dog

2015. Christmas. December rate stamps. Multicoloured.

3243	(59c.) Type **847**	4·25	3·75
3244	(59c.) Phoenix and Bluebird	4·25	3·75
3245	(59c.) Squirrels	4·25	3·75
3246	(59c.) Woman feeding Stag	4·25	3·75
3247	(59c.) Fox in earth	4·25	3·75
3248	(59c.) Swans	4·25	3·75
3249	(59c.) Fawn and Rabbit	4·25	3·75
3250	(59c.) Woman feeding bird	4·25	3·75
3251	(59c.) Rabbits	4·25	3·75
3252	(59c.) Envelope and post box	4·25	3·75

Nos. 3243/52 inscr 'DECEMBER'.

848 Mother holding Child and Men Fighting (left)

2016. 500th Death Anniv of Jhieronymus Bosch. Multicoloured.

MS3253	1 (73c.)×10, Type **848**; Men fighting (right) and waggon wheel (left); People fallen under cart; Waggon wheel (right); Fish-headed man carrying fish and fantastical animals; Man and boy; Two women; Dentist and patient; Man playing bagpipes; Sacks of corn	55·00	49·00

849 Sail Boat, Volendam

2016. Tourism. Fishing Towns. Multicoloured.

3254	1 (73c.) Type **849**	5·00	4·50
3255	1 (73c.) Urk	5·00	4·50
3256	1 (73c.) Zoutkamp	5·00	4·50

850 Delta Works

2016. Postcrossing (people from many countries sending each other traditional postcards). Multicoloured.

3257	1 (€1.25) Type **850**	8·75	7·75
3258	1 (€1.25) Wetlands	8·75	7·75
3259	1 (€1.25) Hoge Veluwe National Park	8·75	7·75
3260	1 (€1.25) Binnenhof government buildings	8·75	7·75
3261	1 (€1.25) Alkmaar Cheese Market	8·75	7·75
3262	1 (€1.25) Tulip fields	8·75	7·75
3263	1 (€1.25) Glethoorn	8·75	7·75
3264	1 (€1.25) Marken	8·75	7·75
3265	1 (€1.25) Zaanse Schans	8·75	7·75
3266	1 (€1.25) *The Night Watch* (detail), Rembrandt	8·75	7·75

851 Sandwich Tern

2016. Birds of Griend Island, Wadden Sea. Multicoloured.

MS3267	1 (73c.)×10, Type **851**; Oystercatcher; Shelduck; Bar-tailed Godwit; Dunlin; Grey Plover; Ringed Plover; Common Tern; Knot; Eider Duck	55·00	49·00

852 Roller painting Contaminated Landscape Green

2016. Europa. Think Green. Multicoloured.

3268	1 (€1.25) Type **852**	8·75	7·75
3269	1 (€1.25) Bicycle	8·75	7·75

853 Women on the Street

2016. Netherlands Photograph Museum - Ed van der Elsken (photgrapher) Commemoration. Multicoloured.

3270	1 (73c.) Type **853**	5·00	4·50
3271	1 (73c.) Couple laying on grass and mother riding bicycle with two children on parcel carrier	5·00	4·50
3272	1 (73c.) Man lighting cigarette and mother cycling with child in rear carrier	5·00	4·50
3273	1 (73c.) Passionate embrace	5·00	4·50
3274	1 (73c.) Women in swimsuits and men on motorcycles	5·00	4·50
3275	1 (73c.) Man with long hair and young family	5·00	4·50
3276	1 (73c.) Men carrying tools and women with pram	5·00	4·50
3277	1 (73c.) Couple walking and woman adjusting shoe	5·00	4·50
3278	1 (73c.) Woman wearing shorts and young people standing on jeep	5·00	4·50
3279	1 (73c.) Mixed race couple and woman wearing fringed jacket	5·00	4·50

2016. Tourism. Fishing Towns. Multicoloured.

3280	1 (73c.) Sheveningen	5·00	4·50
3281	1 (73c.) Arnemuiden	5·00	4·50
MS3282	144×75 mm. 1 (73c.)×5, Nos. 3254/6 and 3280/1	26·00	24·00

854 Mozart and Score

2016. Mozart in the Netherlands 1765-1766. Multicoloured.

3283	1 (73c.) Type **854**	5·00	4·50
3284	1 (73c.) Mozart and Müller organ, Grote Kerk, Haarlem	5·00	4·50

855 Oliver B. Bumble

2016. 75th Anniv of *Tom Poes* (cartoon) by Maarten Toonder. Multicoloured.

3285	1 (73c.) Type **855**	5·00	4·50
3286	1 (73c.) Tom Puss (Tom Poes)	5·00	4·50

856 Silver

2016. Olympic Games - Rio 2016

MS3287	1 (78c.)×3, Type **856**; Gold (36×50 mm); Bronze	8·00	8·00

857 Female Figure

2016. Europride Amsterdam 2016. Multicoloured.

3288	1 (78c.) Type **857**	2·75	2·50
3289	1 (78c.) Male figure	2·75	2·50

858 Cox's Orange Pippin

2016. Apple and Pear Varieties in Netherlands. Multicoloured.

3290	1 (78c.) Type **858**	2·75	2·50
3291	1 (78c.) Brielsche Calville	2·75	2·50
3292	1 (78c.) Bezy Van Schonauwen	2·75	2·50
3293	1 (78c.) Ananas Reinette	2·75	2·50
3294	1 (78c.) William	2·75	2·50
3295	1 (78c.) Pondspeer	2·75	2·50
3296	1 (78c.) Schone Van Boskoop	2·75	2·50
3297	1 (78c.) Zoete Ermgaard	2·75	2·50
3298	1 (78c.) *Coeloglossum viride*	2·75	2·50
3299	1 (78c.) *Orchis simia*	2·75	2·50

859 Dutch Emigrant Ship in Sydney Harbour

2016. Netherlands and Beyond. Netherlands and Australia. Multicoloured.

MS3300	INTERNATIONAL 1 (€1.33)×6, Type **859**; 100,000th emmigrant family on wharf in Amsterdam; SKA radio telescope with Dutch antennae; Dutch designed water treatment plant; Dutch map, 1753, showing Dirk Hartog Island; *Duyfken* (first European vessel to chart the north coast of Australia)	22·00	22·00

860 Doutzen Kroes

2016. Doutzen Kroes - Dutch Model and Actress. Multicoloured.

3301	1 (78c.) Type **860**	2·75	2·50
3302	1 (78c.) Hands clasped, facing left, looking over right shoulder	2·75	2·50
3303	1 (78c.) Head and shoulders, hair loose, two circles covering eyes	2·75	2·50
3304	1 (78c.) Wearing black swimsuit, facing front, left hand touching hair	2·75	2·50
3305	1 (78c.) Head and shoulders, facing right, hair up	2·75	2·50
3306	1 (78c.) Head and shoulders, facing left, hair down	2·75	2·50
3307	1 (78c.) Wearing white swimsuit, left hand clasping right arm	2·75	2·50
3308	1 (78c.) Upper torso, arms crossed	2·75	2·50
3309	1 (78c.) Upper torso, facing left, wearing white swimsuit	2·75	2·50
3310	1 (78c.) Wearing black swimsuit, body facing left, looking over right shoulder	2·75	2·50

861 *Chassidischw legenden* (H N Werkman)

2016. Year of the Book. Multicoloured.

3311	1 (78c.) Type **861**	2·75	2·50
3312	1 (78c.) *Turks Fruit* (Jan Wolkers)	2·75	2·50
3313	1 (78c.) *Het Achterhuis* (Anne Frank)	2·75	2·50
3314	1 (78c.) *Het Schilder-Broek* (Karel van Mander)	2·75	2·50
3315	1 (78c.) *Mei* (Herman Gorter)	2·75	2·50
3316	1 (78c.) *De Schippers van de Kameleon* (H de Roos)	2·75	2·50
3317	1 (78c.) *Zomer* (Jac P Thijsse)	2·75	2·50
3318	1 (78c.) *Opera Posthuma* (*Ethica*) (Spinoza)	2·75	2·50
3319	1 (78c.) *Oom Jan Leert Zjn Neefje Schaken* (Max Euwe and Albert Loon)	2·75	2·50
3320	1 (78c.) *Der Naturen Bloeme* (Jacob van Maerlant)	2·75	2·50

862 Early Concourse

2016. Centenary of Schiphol Airport. Multicoloured.

3321	1 (78c.) Type **862**	2·75	2·50
3322	1 (78c.) Rear of aircraft and boarding steps	2·75	2·50
3323	1 (78c.) Early concourse	2·75	2·50
3324	1 (78c.) Modern concourse	2·75	2·50
3325	1 (78c.) Schiphol at night	2·75	2·50

863 Kings Willem I, Willem II, Willem III and Queen Wilhelmina

2016. Stamp Day.

3326	**863** 1 (78c.) multicoloured	2·75	2·50

864 Fiep Westendorp Characters

865 Bus containing Fiep Westendorp Characters (image scaled to 33% of original size)

2016. Child Welfare. Birth Centenary of Sophia Maria 'Fiep' Westendorp. Multicoloured.

MS3327	1 (78c.)+36c.×6, Type **864**; Characters including cat; Characters including chef; Musicians; Children; Two cats and bus driver	18·00	18·00

866 Parcels on Sleigh

2016. Christmas. December rate stamps. Multicoloured.

3328	(65c.) Type **866**	2·20	1·80
3329	(65c.) Ice skate	2·20	1·80
3330	(65c.) Snow globe	2·20	1·80
3331	(65c.) Squirrels	2·20	1·80
3332	(65c.) Christmas biscuits	2·20	1·80
3333	(65c.) Bicycle carrying Christmas tree	2·20	1·80
3334	(65c.) Baubles and mulled wine	2·20	1·80
3335	(65c.) Champagne glasses	2·20	1·80
3336	(65c.) Figure wearing hat and scarf	2·20	1·80
3337	(65c.) Bells and turn-table	2·20	1·80
3338	(65c.) Fingers making star (for the person forgotten)	2·20	1·80

Nos. 3328/38 inscr 'DECEMBER'.

867 Twents Hoen

2017. Dutch Chicken Breeds. Multicoloured.

3339	1 (76c.) Type **867**	5·25	5·00
3340	1 (76c.) Lakenvelder	5·25	5·00
3341	1 (76c.) Hollands kuifhoen (Poland)	5·25	5·00
3342	1 (76c.) Kraaikop (Kraienkopp)	5·25	5·00
3343	1 (76c.) Nederlandse Uilebaard (Dutch Owlbeard)	5·25	5·00
3344	1 (76c.) Noord-Hollandse Hoen (North Holland Blue)	5·25	5·00
3345	1 (76c.) Hollandse Kriel (Dutch Bantam)	5·25	5·00
3346	1 (76c.) Fries Hoen (Friesian)	5·25	5·00
3347	1 (76c.) Barnevelder	5·25	5·00
3348	1 (76c.) Welsumer	5·25	5·00

868 Old Church Avereest, near Reest River

2017. Tourism. River Valleys. Multicoloured.

3349	1 (78c.) Type **868**	5·50	5·00
3350	1 (78c.) Saxon farmhouse, near Drensche Aa river	5·50	5·00
3351	1 (78c.) Fort Asperen, near Linge river	5·50	5·00

869 Doornenburg Castle

2017. Europa. Castles. Multicoloured.

3352	1 (€1.33) Type **869**	9·25	8·75
3353	1 (€1.33) Ammersoyen Castle	9·25	8·75

870 'Gefelici Teerd'

2017. Greeting Stamps. Special Moments

3354	1 (78c.) Type **870**	5·50	5·00
3355	1 (78c.) 'Liefs' ()	5·50	5·00
3356	1 (78c.) 'Veel Geluk'	5·50	5·00
3357	1 (78c.) 'Sterkte' (30×30 mm)	5·50	5·00
3358	1 (78c.) 'Succes' (30×30 mm)	5·50	5·00
3359	1 (78c.) 'Hoera' (30×30 mm)	5·50	5·00
3360	1 (78c.) 'Fijne Dag' (30×30 mm)	5·50	5·00
3361	1 (78c.) 'Proficiat'	5·50	5·00
3362	1 (78c.) 'Voor Jou'	5·50	5·00
3363	1 (78c.) 'Beterschap'	5·50	5·00

871 Architectural Analysis by Theo van Doesburg (founder of *De Stijl*) (image scaled to NaN% of original size)

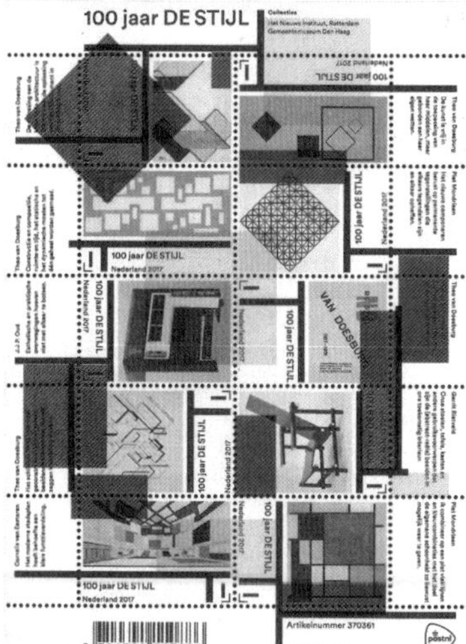

871a Architectural Analysis (image scaled to 45% of original size)

2017. Centenary of *De Stijl* Magazine. Multicoloured.
MS3364 1 (78c.)×10, Type **871**; Painting by Theo van Doesburg; Painting by Theo van Doesburg (different); Painting by Piet Mondrian; Model of restaurant 'De Unie' in Rotterdam (J.J.P. Oud); 'Van Doesburg 1917-1931' (*De Stijl*); Architectural drawing by Theo van Doesburg (different); Slatted chair (Gerrit Rietveld); Design by Cornelis van Eesteren; Painting by Piet Mondrian (different) 60·00 55·00

872 Willem-Alexander

2017. 50th Birth Anniv of King Willem-Alexander. Multicoloured.

3365	1 (78c.) Type **872**	5·50	5·00
3366	1 (78c.) Standing on stairs, wearing suit	5·50	5·00
3367	1 (78c.) On board yacht	5·50	5·00
3368	1 (78c.) Wearing striped top	5·50	5·00
3369	1 (78c.) As King Willem-Alexander	5·50	5·00
3370	1 (78c.) Prince Willem-Alexander and Princess Maxima	5·50	5·00

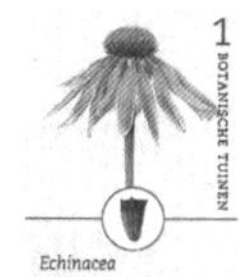

873 *Echinacea purpurea*

2017. Botanical Gardens in Netherlands. Multicoloured.
MS3371 1 (78c.)×10, Type **873**; *Metasequoia glyptostroboides*; *Pyrostegia venusta*; *Sarracena flava*; *Veratrum nigrum*; *Ginkgo biloba*; *Arum italicum*; *Vanilla planifolia*; *Clerodenrum trichotomum*; *Atropa bella-donna* 60·00 55·00

874 Children and Women in Warzone

2017. 150th Anniv of Red Cross in Netherlands. Multicoloured.

3372	1 (78c.) Type **874**	5·50	5·00
3373	1 (78c.) Dressing woman's arm	5·50	5·00
3374	1 (78c.) Hugging elderly woman	5·50	5·00

2017. Tourism. River Valleys. Multicoloured.

3375	1 (78c.) Ferryhouse 't Vaantje in Sint-Michielsgestel, near Dommel river	5·50	5·00
3376	1 (78c.) Timbered house, near Trench river	5·50	5·00

MS3377 144×75 mm. 1 (78c.)×5, Nos. 33349/51 and 3375/6 28·00 27·00

875 'Bossche Bol'

2017. Dutch Treats. Multicoloured.

3378	1 (78c.) Type **875**	5·50	5·00
3379	1 (78c.) 'Limburgse Vlaai'	5·50	5·00
3380	1 (78c.) 'Drents Kniepertie'	5·50	5·00
3381	1 (78c.) 'Fries Suikerbrood'	5·50	5·00
3382	1 (78c.) 'Zwolse Balletjes'	5·50	5·00
3383	1 (78c.) 'Goudes Stroopwafel'	5·50	5·00
3384	1 (78c.) 'Zeeuwse Bolus'	5·50	5·00
3385	1 (78c.) 'Groningse Eirbal'	5·50	5·00
3386	1 (78c.) 'Amsterdamse Ui'	5·50	5·00
3387	1 (78c.) 'Tielse Kermiskoek'	5·50	5·00

876 *Marus bassanus* (Northern Gannet)

2017. Living in the North Sea. Multicoloured.

3388	1 (83c.) Type **876**	5·75	5·50
3389	1 (83c.) *Chelidonichthys lucerna* (Tub Gunnard)	5·75	5·50
3390	1 (83c.) *Cancer pagurus* (Edible Crab)	5·75	5·50
3391	1 (83c.) *Fucus vesiculosus* (Bladderwrack)	5·75	5·50
3392	1 (83c.) *Limecola balthica* (Baltic Macoma)	5·75	5·50

877 *Couple under an Umbrella* (Ron Mueck)

2017. Voorlinden Museum. Multicoloured.
MS3393 1 (83c.)×10, Type **877**; *r81-4* (Jan Schoonhaven); Garden flowers; *Casserole des Moules Noire* (Marcel Broodthaers); *Tuinen* (Piet Oudolf) and *The Performance* (Esther Tielemans); Museum building; *California* (Etel Adnan) and *Swimming Pool* (Leandro Erlich); *2×7×7* (Sol Lewitt); *Untitled* (Zonder titel) (Robert Zandvilet); *Lames de Verre* (Man Ray) 65·00 60·00

878 Philharmonie Luxembourg and Golden Lady Statue

2017. Multilaterale Hertogpost 2017 Stamp Exhibition. Multicoloured.
MS3394 1 (83c.)×2 Type **878**; St John's Cathedral 12·00 11·50

879 Flower

880 Fashion (image scaled to 32% of original size)

2017. 25th Anniv of Viktor & Rolf, Fashion Designers. Multicoloured.
MS3395 1 (83c.)×10, Type **879**; Shoe and eye; Woman's face behind hair; Bow and frock; Eye and profile; Woman's face; Frock design; Shoe; Seal; Ram's head 65·00 60·00

881 Velsertunnel (Velsen, 1957)

2017. Post-war Architectural Reconstruction. Multicoloured.
MS3396 1 (83c.)×10 Type **881**; Petrol Station Purfina (Arnhem, 1957); Industrial building (Rotterdam, 1951); Van Leer's Vatenfabriek (Amstelveen, 1958); Soesterkwartier residential area (Amersfoort, 1957); Gemeenteflat (Maastricht, 1950); Weverij de Ploeg (Bergeijk, 1958); Hoogovens (IJmuiden, 1951); Faculty of Geodesy (Wageningen, 1953); Second Vrijzinnig-Christelijk Lyceum (The Hague, 1954) 65·00 60·00

882 Dad and Baby

883 *Jan, Jans and Children (image scaled to 33% of original size)*

2017. Child Welfare. *Jan, Jans and the Children* - Jan Kruis Commemoration. Multicoloured.
MS3397 1 (83c.)+38c.×6, Type **882**; Drinking milk, pouring coffee into cereal; Cat and grandpa; Child and dog; Child and envelope; Cat 55·00 50·00

884 Queen Wilhelmina

2017. Stamp Day.

3398	**884**	1 (83c.) multicoloured	5·75	5·50

885 George Michael

2017. Christmas December Rate Stamps - Christmas Remembered. Multicoloured.

3399	(73c.) Type **885**	5·00	4·75
3400	(73c.) Fairy lights	5·00	4·75
3401	(73c.) Candle flame	5·00	4·75
3402	(73c.) Woman	5·00	4·75
3403	(73c.) Symbols of music	5·00	4·75
3404	(73c.) Christmas bell	5·00	4·75
3405	(73c.) Turkey	5·00	4·75
3406	(73c.) Pyramid, with hands playing accordion	5·00	4·75
3407	(73c.) Champaigne glasses and painting	5·00	4·75
3408	(73c.) Christmas pudding	5·00	4·75

MARINE INSURANCE STAMPS

M22

1921

M238	**M22**	15c. green	19·00	£130
M239	**M22**	60c. red	25·00	£130
M240	**M22**	75c. brown	31·00	£130
M241	-	1g.50 blue	£110	£950
M242	-	2g.25 brown	£170	£1300
M243	-	4½g. black	£275	£1600
M244	-	7½g. red	£400	£2250

Designs:—(inscr 'DRIJVENDE BRANDKAST'): 1g.50, 2g.25, 'Explosion'; 4½g., 7½g. Lifebelt.

OFFICIAL STAMPS

1913. Stamps of 1898 optd **ARMENWET**.

O214	**12**	1c. red	5·75	4·50
O215	**12**	1½c. blue	1·30	3·75
O216	**12**	2c. brown	10·00	11·50
O217	**12**	2½c. green	25·00	20·00
O218	**13**	3c. green	5·75	2·50
O219	**13**	5c. red	5·75	8·25
O220	**13**	10c. grey	55·00	65·00

POSTAGE DUE STAMPS

D8

1870

D76	**D8**	5c. brown on yellow	£120	19·00
D77	**D8**	10c. purple on blue	£450	25·00

For same stamps in other colours, see Netherlands Indies, Nos. D1/5.

D9

1881

D174	**D9**	½c. black and blue	£550	80·00
D175	**D9**	1c. black and blue	1·90	55
D176	**D9**	1½c. black and blue	1·10	70
D177	**D9**	2½c. black and blue	2·50	90
D178	**D9**	3c. black and blue	2·50	1·70
D179	**D9**	4c. black and blue	2·50	2·50
D180	**D9**	5c. black and blue	20·00	55
D181	**D9**	6½c. black and blue	50·00	55·00
D182	**D9**	7½c. black and blue	4·50	90
D183	**D9**	10c. black and blue	50·00	90
D184	**D9**	12½c. black and blue	44·00	1·80
D185	**D9**	15c. black and blue	50·00	1·30
D186	**D9**	20c. black and blue	35·00	10·00
D187	**D9**	25c. black and blue	60·00	75
D173b	**D9**	1g. red and blue	£140	39·00

No. D173b is inscribed "EEN GULDEN".

1906. Surch.

D213b	**D9**	3c. on 1g. red and blue	44·00	44·00
D215	**D9**	4 on 6½c. black and blue	6·50	8·50
D216	**D9**	6½ on 20c. black & blue	6·00	7·25
D214b	**D9**	50c. on 1g. red & blue	£200	£200

1907. De Ruyter Commemoration. **PORTZEGEL** and value.

			stamps	surch
D217A	**15**	½c. on 1c. red	1·90	2·50
D218A	**15**	1c. on 1c. red	1·30	1·30
D219A	**15**	1½c. on 1c. red	1·30	1·30
D220A	**15**	2½c. on 1c. red	3·75	3·75
D221A	**15**	5c. on 2½c. red	2·50	1·30
D222A	**15**	6½c. on 2½c. red	4·50	5·00
D223A	**15**	7½c. on ½c. blue	3·00	2·50
D224A	**15**	10c. on ½c. blue	3·00	1·90
D225A	**15**	12½c. on ½c. blue	6·25	7·00
D226A	**15**	15c. on 2½c. red	9·75	6·25
D227A	**15**	25c. on ½c. blue	12·50	11·50
D228A	**15**	50c. on ½c. blue	70·00	60·00
D229A	**15**	1g. on ½c. blue	£100	90·00

1912. Re-issue of Type **D9** in one colour.

D230	**D9**	½c. blue	65	65
D231	**D9**	1c. blue	65	65
D232	**D9**	1½c. blue	3·25	2·50
D233	**D9**	2½c. blue	1·00	65
D234	**D9**	3c. blue	1·40	1·00
D235	**D9**	4c. blue	75	75
D236	**D9**	4½c. blue	7·75	7·50
D237	**D9**	5c. blue	65	65
D238	**D9**	5½c. blue	8·25	7·25
D239	**D9**	7c. blue	3·75	3·75
D240	**D9**	7½c. blue	5·00	2·50
D241	**D9**	10c. blue	1·00	1·00
D242	**D9**	12½c. blue	1·00	1·00
D453	**D9**	15c. blue	1·00	1·00
D244	**D9**	20c. blue	1·00	65
D245	**D9**	25c. blue	£110	1·30
D246	**D9**	50c. blue	1·00	65

D25

1921

D442	**D25**	3c. blue	50	50
D445	**D25**	6c. blue	50	50
D446	**D25**	7c. blue	1·00	1·00
D447	**D25**	7½c. blue	1·00	1·00
D448	**D25**	8c. blue	1·00	1·00
D449	**D25**	9c. blue	1·20	1·00
D247	**D25**	11c. blue	16·00	5·00
D451	**D25**	12c. blue	1·00	65
D455	**D25**	25c. blue	1·00	65
D456	**D25**	30c. blue	1·00	65
D458	**D25**	1g. red	1·30	65

1923. Surch in white figures in black circle.

D272	**D9**	1c. on 3c. blue	1·30	1·20
D273	**D9**	2½c. on 7c. blue	2·00	1·00
D274	**D9**	25c. on 1½c. blue	13·00	1·20
D275	**D9**	25c. on 7½c. blue	16·00	1·00

1924. Stamps of 1898 surch **TE BETALEN PORT** and value in white figures in black circle.

D295	**13**	4c. on 3c. green	2·30	1·80
D296	**12**	5c. on 1c. red	1·30	65
D297	**12**	10c. on 1½c. blue	2·00	1·00
D298	**13**	12½c. on 5c. red	2·40	1·00

D121

1947

D656	**D121**	1c. blue	35	35
D657	**D121**	3c. blue	35	45
D658	**D121**	4c. blue	16·00	1·50
D659	**D121**	5c. blue	35	35
D660	**D121**	6c. blue	60	60
D661	**D121**	7c. blue	45	45
D662	**D121**	8c. blue	45	45
D663	**D121**	10c. blue	45	35
D664	**D121**	11c. blue	80	80
D665	**D121**	12c. blue	1·50	1·50
D666	**D121**	14c. blue	1·50	1·20
D667	**D121**	15c. blue	60	35
D668	**D121**	16c. blue	1·30	1·40
D669	**D121**	20c. blue	60	45
D670	**D121**	24c. blue	1·80	2·10
D671	**D121**	25c. blue	60	45
D672	**D121**	26c. blue	3·75	4·00
D673	**D121**	30c. blue	90	35
D674	**D121**	35c. blue	1·20	35
D675	**D121**	40c. blue	1·20	35
D676	**D121**	50c. blue	1·50	45
D677	**D121**	60c. blue	1·60	80
D678	**D121**	85c. blue	25·00	90
D679	**D121**	90c. blue	4·50	1·00
D680	**D121**	95c. blue	4·50	1·00
D681	**D121**	1g. red	3·75	35
D682	**D121**	1g.75 red	8·75	60

For stamps as Types **D121**, but in violet, see under Suriname.

INTERNATIONAL COURT OF JUSTICE

Stamps specially issued for use by the Headquarters of the Court of International Justice.

1934. Optd COUR PER- MANENTE DE JUSTICE INTER- NATIONALE.

J1	**35**	1½c. mauve	†	3·75
J2	**35**	2½c. green	†	3·75
J3	**36**	7½c. red	†	5·00
J4	**68**	12½c. blue	†	41·00
J7	**36**	12½c. blue	†	25·00
J5	**36**	15c. yellow	†	4·50
J6	**36**	30c. purple	†	5·00
J8	**36**	30c. purple	†	5·00

1940. Optd COUR PER- MANANTE DE JUSTICE INTER- NATIONALE.

J9	**94**	7½c. red	†	14·00
J10	**94**	12½c. blue	†	14·00
J11	**94**	15c. blue	†	14·00
J12	**94**	30c. bistre	†	14·00

1947. Optd COUR INTERNATIONALE DE JUSTICE.

J13	**94**	7½c. red	†	1·80
J14	**94**	10c. purple	†	1·80
J15	**94**	12½c. blue	†	1·80
J16	**94**	20c. violet	†	1·80
J17	**94**	25c. red	†	1·80

J3

1950

J18	**J3**	2c. blue	†	12·50
J19	**J3**	4c. green	†	12·50

J4 Peace Palace, The Hague

J5 Queen Juliana

1951

J20	**J4**	2c. lake	†	1·00
J21	**J4**	3c. blue	†	1·00
J22	**J4**	4c. green	†	1·00
J23	**J4**	5c. brown	†	1·00
J24	**J5**	6c. mauve	†	3·00
J25	**J4**	6c. green	†	1·30
J26	**J4**	7c. red	†	1·30
J27	**J5**	10c. green	†	40
J28	**J5**	12c. red	†	3·00
J29	**J5**	15c. red	†	65
J30	**J5**	20c. blue	†	65
J31	**J5**	25c. brown	†	65
J32	**J5**	30c. purple	†	65
J33	**J4**	40c. blue	†	65
J34	**J4**	45c. red	†	65
J35	**J4**	50c. mauve	†	95
J36	**J5**	1g. grey	†	1·30

J6 Olive Branch and Peace Palace, The Hague

1989

J37	**J6**	5c. black and yellow	35	35
J38	**J6**	10c. black and blue	35	35
J39	**J6**	25c. black and red	35	35
J41	**J6**	50c. black and green	65	65
J42	**J6**	55c. black and mauve	65	65
J43	**J6**	60c. black and bistre	65	65
J44	**J6**	65c. black and green	65	65
J45	**J6**	70c. black and blue	70	70
J46	**J6**	75c. black and yellow	65	65
J47	**J6**	80c. black and green	80	80
J49	**J6**	1g. black and orange	95	95
J50	**J6**	1g.50 black and blue	1·40	1·40
J51	**J6**	1g.60 black and brown	3·25	3·25
J54	-	5g. multicoloured	5·25	5·25
J56	-	7g. multicoloured	7·25	7·00

Designs: 5, 7g. Olive branch and column.

J7 Peace Palace, The Haag

2004

J57	**J7**	39c. blue, green and black	1·00	1·00
J58	-	61c. blue, azure and black	1·50	1·50

Designs: 39c. Type **J7**; 61c. Seal.

J* Peace Palace, the Haig

2016. 70th Anniv of International Court of Justice

J62	**J8**	1 (€1.25) multicoloured	3·75	3·75

PROVINCIAL STAMPS

The following stamps, although valid for postage throughout Netherlands, were only available from Post Offices within the province depicted and from the Philatelic Bureau.

V1 Freisland

2002. Multicoloured.

V1	39c. Type **V1**	1·60	1·10
V2	39c. Drenthe	1·60	1·10
V3	39c. North Holland	1·60	1·10
V4	39c. Gelderland	1·60	1·10
V5	39c. North Brabant	1·60	1·10
V6	39c. Groningen	1·60	1·10
V7	39c. South Holland	1·60	1·10
V8	39c. Utrecht	1·60	1·10
V9	39c. Limburg	1·60	1·10
V10	39c. Zeeland	1·60	1·10
V11	39c. Flevoland	1·60	1·10
V12	39c. Overijssel	1·60	1·10

V2 Nijmegen

2005. Multicoloured.

V13	39c. Type **V2**	65	55
V14	39c. Nederland, Overjissel	65	55
V15	39c. Rotterdam	65	55
V16	39c. Weesp	65	55
V17	39c. Monnickendam	65	55
V18	39c. Goes	65	55

NETHERLANDS ANTILLES

Curacao and other Netherlands islands in the Caribbean Sea. In December 1954 these were placed on an equal footing with Netherlands under the Crown.

100 cents = 1 gulden.

48 Spanish Galleon

49 Alonso de Ojeda

1949. 450th Anniv of Discovery of Curacao.

306	**48**	6c. green	7·25	4·50
307	**49**	12½c. red	7·75	5·75
308	**48**	15c. blue	8·50	6·50

50 Posthorns and Globe

1949. 75th Anniv of U.P.U.

309	**50**	6c. red	7·75	5·25
310	**50**	25c. blue	7·75	2·50

1950. As numeral and portrait types of Netherlands but inscr "NED. ANTILLEN".

325	**118**	1c. brown	40	25
326	**118**	1½c. blue	40	25
327	**118**	2c. orange	40	25
328	**118**	2½c. green	2·00	40
329	**118**	3c. violet	50	25
329a	**118**	4c. green	1·60	65
310a	**129**	5c. yellow	40	40
330	**118**	5c. red	40	25
311	**129**	6c. purple	2·50	25
311a	**129**	7½c. brown	9·00	25
312a	**129**	10c. red	2·75	2·50
313	**129**	12½c. green	4·50	40
314a	**129**	15c. blue	40	40
315a	**129**	20c. orange	40	40
316	**129**	21c. black	6·50	4·00
316a	**129**	22½c. green	10·50	25
317a	**129**	25c. violet	40	40
318	**129**	27½c. brown	13·50	3·25
319a	**129**	30c. sepia	2·00	2·00
319b	**129**	40c. blue	65	65
320	**129**	50c. olive	21·00	25
321	**130**	1½g. green	65·00	65
322	**130**	2½g. brown	65·00	3·25
323	**130**	5g. red	£100	29·00
324	**130**	10g. purple	£325	£110

51 Leap-frog

1951. Child Welfare.

331	**51**	1½c.+1c. violet	17·00	9·00
332	-	5c.+2½c. brown	17·00	9·00
333	-	6c.+2½c. blue	17·00	9·00
334	-	12½c.+5c. red	17·00	9·00
335	-	25c.+10c. turquoise	17·00	9·00

Designs:—5c. Kite-flying; 6c. Girl on swing; 12½c. Girls playing "Oranges and Lemons"; 25c. Bowling hoops.

52 Gull over Ship

1952. Seamen's Welfare Fund. Inscr "ZEEMANSWELVAREN".

336	**52**	1½c.+1c. green	14·50	3·25
337	-	6c.+4c. brown	25·00	7·25
338	-	12½c.+7c. mauve	18·00	7·25
339	-	15c.+10c. blue	21·00	8·50
340	-	25c.+15c. red	20·00	6·50

Designs:—6c. Sailor and lighthouse; 12½c. Sailor on ship's prow; 15c. Tanker in harbour; 25c. Anchor and compass.

1953. Netherlands Flood Relief Fund. No. 321 surch **22½ Ct. +7½ Ct. WATERSNOOD NEDERLAND 1953.**

341	**130**	22½c.+7½c. on 1½g. green	3·25	2·50

54 Fort Beekenburg

1953. 250th Anniv of Fort Beekenburg.

342	**54**	22½c. brown	11·00	1·30

55 Aruba Beach

1954. Third Caribbean Tourist Assn Meeting.

343	**55**	15c. blue and buff	10·50	5·25

1954. Ratification of Statute of the Kingdom. As No. 809 of Netherlands.

344	**158**	7½c. green	2·50	2·00

56 "Anglo" Flower

1955. Child Welfare.

345	**56**	1½c.+1c. bl, yell & turq	5·75	2·00
346	-	7½c.+5c. red, yellow & vio	7·75	4·00
347	-	15c.+5c. red, grn & olive	7·75	4·50
348	-	22½c.+7½c. red, yell & bl	7·75	4·00
349	-	25c.+10c. red, yell & grey	7·75	4·00

Flowers: 7½c. White Cayenne; 15c. "French" flower; 22½c. Cactus; 25c. Red Cayenne.

57 Prince Bernhard and Queen Juliana

1955. Royal Visit.

350	**57**	7½c.+2½c. red	65	65
351	**57**	22½c.+7½c. blue	2·00	2·00

59 Oil Refinery

1955. 21st Meeting of Caribbean Commission.

352	-	15c. blue, green and brown	5·50	4·50
353	**59**	25c. blue, green and brown	7·25	5·25

Design:—(rectangle, 36×25 mm): 15c. Aruba Beach.

60 St. Anne Bay

1956. Tenth Anniv of Caribbean Commission.

354	**60**	15c. blue, red and black	80	65

61 Lord Baden-Powell

1957. 50th Anniv of Boy Scout Movement.

355	**61**	6c.+1½c. yellow	1·60	1·00
356	**61**	7½c.+2½c. green	1·60	1·00
357	**61**	15c.+5c. red	1·60	1·00

62 "Dawn of Health"

1957. First Caribbean Mental Health Congress, Aruba.

358	**62**	15c. black and yellow	70	65

63 Saba

1957. Tourist Publicity. Multicoloured.

359	7½c. Type **63**	1·30	80
360	15c. St. Maarten	1·30	80
361	25c. St. Eustatius	1·30	80

64 Footballer

1957. Eighth Central American and Caribbean Football Championships.

362	**64**	6c.+2½c. orange	3·25	1·30
363	-	7½c.+5c. red	3·25	2·00
364	-	15c.+5c. green	3·25	2·00
365	-	22½c.+7½c. blue	3·25	2·00

Designs:—Horiz: 7½c. Caribbean map. Vert: 15c. Goalkeeper saving ball; 22½c. Footballers with ball.

65 Curacao Intercontinental Hotel

1957. Opening of Curacao Intercontinental Hotel.

366	**65**	15c. blue	65	65

66 Map of Curacao

1957. International Geophysical Year.

367	**66**	15c. deep blue and blue	1·30	1·20

67 American Kestrel

1958. Child Welfare. Bird design inscr "VOOR HET KIND". Multicoloured.

368	2½c.+1c. Type **67**	2·50	2·00
369	7½c.+1½c. Yellow oriole	2·50	2·00
370	15c.+2½c. Scaly-breasted ground doves	2·50	2·00
371	22½c.+2½c. Brown-throated conure	2·50	2·00

68 Greater Flamingoes (Bonaire)

1958. Size 33½×22 mm.

372	**68**	6c. pink and green	4·00	25
373	**A**	7½c. yellow and brown	40	25
374	**A**	8c. yellow and blue	40	25
375	**B**	10c. yellow and grey	40	25
376	**C**	12c. grey and green	40	25
377	**D**	15c. blue and green	40	25
377a	**D**	15c. lilac and green	40	25
378	**E**	20c. grey and red	40	25
379	**A**	25c. green and blue	50	25
380	**D**	30c. green and brown	50	25
381	**E**	35c. pink and grey	65	25
382	**C**	40c. green and mauve	80	25
383	**B**	45c. blue and violet	80	25
384	**68**	50c. pink and brown	80	25
385	**E**	55c. green and red	90	40
386	**68**	65c. pink and green	1·30	50
387	**D**	70c. orange and purple	2·20	90
388	**68**	75c. pink and violet	1·20	90
389	**B**	85c. green and brown	1·30	1·20
390	**E**	90c. orange and blue	1·60	1·40
391	**C**	95c. yellow and orange	1·80	1·60
392	**D**	1g. grey and red	1·70	25
393	**A**	1½g. brown and violet	2·30	25
394	**C**	2½g. yellow and blue	4·50	65
395	**B**	5g. mauve and brown	8·50	1·20
396	**68**	10g. pink and blue	15·00	8·50

Designs:—A. Dutch Colonial houses (Curacao); B. Mountain and palms (Saba); C. Town Hall (St. Maarten); D. Church tower (Aruba); E. Memorial obelisk (St. Eustatius).

For larger versions of some values see Nos. 653/6.

69

1958. 50th Anniv of Netherlands Antilles Radio and Telegraph Administration.

397	**69**	7½c. lake and blue	40	40
398	**69**	15c. blue and red	65	65

70 Red Cross Flag and Antilles Map

1958. Neth. Antilles Red Cross Fund. Cross in red.

399	**70**	6c.+2c. brown	1·60	1·00
400	**70**	7½c.+2½c. green	1·60	1·00
401	**70**	15c.+5c. yellow	1·60	1·00
402	**70**	22½c.+7½c. blue	1·60	1·00

71 Aruba Caribbean Hotel

1959. Opening of Aruba Caribbean Hotel.

403	**71**	15c. multicoloured	65	65

72 Zeeland

1959. Curacao Monuments Preservation Fund. Multicoloured.

404	6c.+1½c. Type **72**	2·50	2·00
405	7½c.+2½c. Saba Island	2·50	2·00
406	15c.+5c. Molenplein (vert)	2·50	2·00
407	22½c.+7½c. Scharloobrug	2·50	2·00
408	25c.+7½c. Brievengat	2·50	2·00

73 Water-distillation Plant

1959. Inauguration of Aruba Water-distillation Plant.

409	**73**	20c. light blue and blue	80	80

74 Antilles Flag

1959. Fifth Anniv of Ratification of Statute of the Kingdom.

410	**74**	10c. red, blue and light blue	80	65
411	**74**	20c. red, blue and yellow	80	65
412	**74**	25c. red, blue and green	80	65

75 Fokker F.XVIII *De Snip* over Caribbean

1959. 25th Anniv of K.L.M. Netherlands–Curacao Air Service. Each yellow, deep blue and blue.

413	10c. Type **75**	1·30	65
414	20c. Fokker F.XVIII *De Snip* over globe	1·30	65
415	25c. Douglas DC-7C *Seven Seas* over Handelskade (bridge), Willemstad	1·30	40
416	35c. Douglas DC-8 at Aruba Airport	1·30	1·00

76 Mgr. Niewindt

1960. Death Centenary of Mgr. M. J. Niewindt.

417	**76**	10c. purple	1·60	80
418	**76**	20c. violet	1·60	90
419	**76**	25c. olive	1·60	90

77 Flag and Oil-worker

1960. Labour Day.

420	**77**	20c. multicoloured	80	80

78 Frogman

1960. Princess Wilhelmina Cancer Relief Fund. Inscr "KANKERBESTRIJDING".

421	**78**	10c.+2c. blue	2·75	2·00
422	-	20c.+3c. multicoloured	2·75	2·50
423	-	25c.+5c. red, blue & blk	2·75	2·50

Designs:—Horiz: 20c. Queen angelfish; 25c. Big-scaled soldierfish.

79 Child on Bed

1961. Child Welfare. Inscr "voor het kind".

424		6c.+2c. black and green	90	50
425		10c.+3c. black and red	90	50
426		20c.+6c. black and yellow	90	50
427		25c.+8c. black and orange	90	50

Designs: 6c. Type **79**; 10c. Girl with doll; 20c. Boy with bucket; 25c. Children in classroom.

80 Governor's Salute to the American Naval Brig *Andrew Doria* at St. Eustatius

1961. 185th Anniv of First Salute to the American Flag.

428	**80**	20c. multicoloured	1·30	1·00

See also **MS**996.

1962. Royal Silver Wedding. As T **187** of Netherlands.

429	10c. orange	80	50
430	25c. blue	80	50

81 Jaja (nursemaid) and Child

1962. Cultural Series.

431	-	6c. brown and yellow	65	65
432	-	10c. multicoloured	65	65
433	-	20c. multicoloured	65	65
434	**81**	25c. brown, green and black	65	65
MS435		108×134 mm. Nos. 431/4	4·00	4·00

Designs:—6c. Corn-masher; 10c. Benta player; 20c. Petji kerchief.

82 Knight and World Map

1962. Fifth International Candidates Chess Tournament, Curacao.

436	**82**	10c.+5c. green	2·00	1·30
437	**82**	20c.+10c. red	2·00	1·30
438	**82**	25c.+10c. blue	2·00	1·30

1963. Freedom from Hunger. No. 378 surch **TEGEN DE HONGER** wheat sprig and +10c.

439	20c.+10c. grey and red	90	90

84 Family Group

1963. Fourth Caribbean Mental Health Congress, Curacao.

440	**84**	20c. buff and blue	65	65
441	-	25c. red and blue	65	65

Design:—25c. Egyptian Cross emblem.

85 "Freedom"

1963. Centenary of Abolition of Slavery in Dutch West Indies.

442	**85**	25c. brown and yellow	65	50

86 Hotel Bonaire

1963. Opening of Hotel Bonaire.

443	**86**	20c. brown	65	50

87 Child and Flowers

1963. Child Welfare. Child Art. Multicoloured.

444	5c.+2c. Type **87**	65	50
445	6c.+3c. Children and flowers (horiz)	65	50
446	10c.+5c. Girl with ball (horiz)	65	50
447	20c.+10c. Men with flags (horiz)	65	50
448	25c.+12c. Schoolboy	65	50

1963. 150th Anniv of Kingdom of the Netherlands. As No. 968 of Netherlands, but smaller, 26×27 mm.

449	25c. green, red and black	65	50

88 Test-tube and Flask

1963. Chemical Industry, Aruba.

450	**88**	20c. red, light green and green	80	80

89 Winged Letter

1964. 35th Anniv of First U.S.–Curacao Flight. Multicoloured.

451	20c. Type **89**	65	65
452	25c. Route map, Sikorsky S-38 flying boat and Boeing 707	65	65

90 Trinitaria

1964. Child Welfare. Multicoloured.

453	6c.+3c. Type **90**	65	50
454	10c.+5c. Magdalena	65	50
455	20c.+10c. Yellow keiki	65	50
456	25c.+11c. Bellisima	65	50

91 Caribbean Map

1964. Fifth Caribbean Council Assembly.

457	**91**	20c. yellow, red and blue	65	50

92 "Six Islands"

1964. Tenth Anniv of Statute for the Kingdom.

458	**92**	25c. multicoloured	65	50

93 Princess Beatrix

1965. Visit of Princess Beatrix.

459	**93**	25c. red	65	65

94 ITU Emblem and Symbols

1965. Centenary of I.T.U.

460	**94**	10c. deep blue and blue	45	40

95 *Asperalla* (tanker) at Curacao

1965. 50th Anniv of Curacao's Oil Industry. Multicoloured.

461	10c. Catalytic cracking plant (vert)	65	50
462	20c. Type **95**	65	50
463	25c. Super fractionating plant (vert)	65	50

96 Flag and Fruit Market, Curacao

1965

464	**96**	1c. blue, red and green	40	25
465	-	2c. blue, red and yellow	40	25
466	-	3c. blue, red and cobalt	40	25
467	-	4c. blue, red and orange	40	25
468	-	5c. blue, red and blue	40	25
469	-	6c. blue, red and pink	40	25

Designs:—(Flag and): 2c. Divi-divi tree; 3c. Lace; 4c. Greater flamingoes; 5c. Church; 6c. Lobster.

Each is inscr with a different place-name.

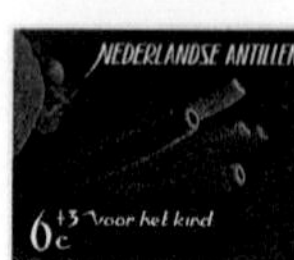

97 Cup Sponges

1965. Child Welfare. Marine Life. Multicoloured.

470	6c.+3c. Type **97**	55	40
471	10c.+5c. Cup sponges (diff)	55	40
472	20c.+10c. Sea anemones on star coral	70	40
473	25c.+11c. Basket sponge, blue chromis and *Brain coral*	70	55

98 Marine and Seascape

1965. Tercentenary of Marine Corps.

474	**98**	25c. multicoloured	55	40

1966. Intergovernmental Committee for European Migration (I.C.E.M.) Fund. As T **215** of Netherlands.

475	35c.+15c. bistre and brown	55	55

99 Budgerigars and Wedding Rings

1966. Marriage of Crown Princess Beatrix and Herr Claus von Amsberg.

476	**99**	25c. multicoloured	70	40

100 Admiral de Ruyter and Map

1966. 300th Anniv of Admiral de Ruyter's Visit to St. Eustatius.

477	**100**	25c. ochre, violet and blue	55	40

101 "Grammar"

1966. 25 Years of Secondary Education.

478	**101**	6c. black, blue and yellow	40	40
479	-	10c. black, red and green	40	40
480	-	20c. black, blue and yellow	55	40
481	-	25c. black, red and green	55	40

Designs:—The "Free Arts", figures representing: 10c. "Rhetoric" and "Dialect"; 20c. "Arithmetic" and "Geometry"; 25c. "Astronomy" and "Music".

102 Cooking

1966. Child Welfare. Multicoloured.

482	6c.+3c. Type **102**	55	40
483	10c.+5c. Nursing	55	40
484	20c.+10c. Metal-work fitting	55	40
485	25c.+11c. Ironing	55	40

103 *Gelderland* (cruiser)

1967. 60th Anniv of Royal Netherlands Navy League.

486	**103**	6c. bronze and green	55	40
487	-	10c. ochre and yellow	55	40
488	-	20c. brown and sepia	55	40
489	-	25c. blue and indigo	55	40

Ships:—10c. *Pioneer* (schooner); 20c. *Oscilla* (tanker); 25c. *Santa Rosa* (liner).

104 M. C. Piar

1967. 150th Death Anniv of Manuel Piar (patriot).

490	**104**	20c. brown and red	55	40

105 "Heads in Hands"

1967. Cultural and Social Relief Funds.

491	**105**	6c.+3c. black and blue	55	40
492	**105**	10c.+5c. black & mauve	55	40
493	**105**	20c.+10c. purple	55	40
494	**105**	25c.+11c. blue	55	40

106 *The Turtle and the Monkey*

1967. Child Welfare. "Nanzi" Fairy Tales. Mult.

495	6c.+3c. *Princess Long Nose* (vert)	40	40
496	10c.+5c. Type **106**	40	40
497	20c.+10c. *Nanzi (spider) and the Tiger*	55	40
498	25c.+11c. *Shon Arey's Balloon* (vert)	55	40

107 Olympic Flame and Rings

1968. Olympic Games, Mexico. Multicoloured.

499	10c. Type **107**	70	55
500	20c. *Throwing the discus* (statue)	70	55
501	25c. Stadium and doves	70	55

108 "Dance of the Ribbons"

1968. Cultural and Social Relief Funds.

502	**108**	10c.+5c. multicoloured	55	40
503	**108**	15c.+5c. multicoloured	55	40
504	**108**	20c.+10c. multicoloured	55	40
505	**108**	25c.+10c. multicoloured	55	40

109 Boy with Goat

1968. Child Welfare Fund. Multicoloured.

506	6c.+3c. Type **109**	55	40
507	10c.+5c. Girl with dog	55	40
508	20c.+10c. Boy with cat	55	40
509	25c.+11c. Girl with duck	55	40

110 Fokker Friendship 500

1968. Dutch Antillean Airlines.

510	**110**	10c. blue, black and yellow	70	55
511	-	20c. blue, black and brown	70	55
512	-	25c. blue, black and pink	70	55

Designs:—20c. Douglas DC-9; 25c. Fokker Friendship 500 in flight and Douglas DC-9 on ground.

111 Radio Pylon, "Waves" and Map

1969. Opening of Broadcast Relay Station, Bonaire.

513	**111**	25c. green, dp blue & blue	55	55

112 "Code of Laws"

1969. Centenary of Netherlands Antilles Court of Justice.

514	**112**	20c. green, gold & lt green	55	55
515	-	25c. multicoloured	55	55

Design:—25c. "Scales of Justice".

113 "Carnival"

1969. Cultural and Social Relief Funds. Antilles' Festivals. Multicoloured.

516		10c.+5c. Type **113**	75	70
517		15c.+5c. "Harvest Festival"	75	70
518		20c.+10c. "San Juan Day"	75	70
519		25c.+10c. "New Years' Day"	75	70

114 ILO Emblem, "Koenoekoe" House and Cacti

1969. 50th Anniv of I.L.O.

520	**114**	10c. black and blue	60	40
521	**114**	25c. black and red	60	40

115 Boy playing Guitar

1969. Child Welfare.

522	**115**	6c.+3c. violet & orange	75	70
523	-	10c.+5c. green & yellow	75	70
524	-	20c.+10c. red and blue	75	70
525	-	25c.+11c. brown & pink	75	70

Designs:—10c. Girl playing recorder; 20c. Boy playing "marimula"; 25c. Girl playing piano.

1969. 15th Anniv of Statute of the Kingdom. As T **240** of the Netherlands, but inscr "NEDER-LANDSE ANTILLEN".

526		25c. multicoloured	75	55

117 Radio Station, Bonaire

1970. Fifth Anniv of Trans-World Religious Radio Station, Bonaire. Multicoloured.

527		10c. Type **117**	45	40
528		15c. Trans-World Radio emblem	45	40

118 St. Anna Church, Otrabanda, Curacao

1970. Churches of the Netherlands Antilles. Mult.

529		10c. Type **118**	75	55
530		20c. "Mikve Israel-Emanuel" Synagogue, Punda, Curacao (horiz)	75	55
531		25c. Pulpit Fort Church Curacao	75	55

119 "The Press"

1970. Cultural and Social Relief Funds. "Mass-media". Multicoloured.

532		10c.+5c. Type **119**	1·00	90
533		15c.+5c. "Films"	1·00	90
534		20c.+10c. "Radio"	1·00	90
535		25c.+10c. "Television"	1·00	90

120 Mother and Child

1970. Child Welfare. Multicoloured.

536		6c.+3c. Type **120**	1·00	90
537		10c.+5c. Child with piggy-bank	1·00	90
538		20c.+10c. Children's Judo	1·00	90
539		25c.+11c. "Pick-a-back"	1·00	90

121 St. Theresia's Church, St. Nicolaas, Aruba

1971. 40th Anniv of St. Theresia Parish, Aruba.

540	**121**	20c. multicoloured	60	55

122 Lions Emblem

1971. 25th Anniv of Curacao Lions Club.

541	**122**	25c. multicoloured	75	70

123 Charcoal Stove

1971. Cultural and Social Relief Funds. Household Utensils. Multicoloured.

542		10c.+5c. Type **123**	1·10	1·10
543		15c.+5c. Earthenware water vessel	1·10	1·10
544		20c.+10c. Baking oven	1·10	1·10
545		25c.+10c. Kitchen implements	1·10	1·10

1971. Prince Bernhard's 60th Birthday. Design as No. 1135 of Netherlands.

546		45c. multicoloured	1·50	1·10

125 Admiral Brion

1971. 150th Death Anniv of Admiral Pedro Luis Brion.

547	**125**	40c. multicoloured	75	70

126 Bottle Doll

1971. Child Welfare. Home-made Toys. Mult.

548		15c.+5c. Type **126**	1·30	1·20
549		20c.+10c. Simple cart	1·30	1·20
550		30c.+15c. Spinning-tops	1·30	1·20

127 Queen Emma Bridge, Curacao

1971. Views of the Islands. Multicoloured.

551		1c. Type **127**	45	30
552		2c. The Bottom, Saba	45	30
553		3c. Greater flamingoes, Bonaire	45	30
554		4c. Distillation plant, Aruba	45	30
555		5c. Fort Amsterdam, St. Maarten	45	30
556		6c. Fort Oranje, St. Eustatius	45	30

128 Ship in Dock

1972. Inauguration of New Dry Dock Complex, Willemstad, Curacao.

557	**128**	30c. multicoloured	75	70

129 Steel Band

1972. Cultural and Social Relief Funds. Folklore. Multicoloured.

558		15c.+5c. Type **129**	1·50	1·40
559		20c.+10c. "Seu" festival	1·50	1·40
560		30c.+15c. "Tambu" dance	1·50	1·40

130 J. E. Irausquin

1972. Tenth Death Anniv of Juan Enrique Irausquin (Antilles statesman).

561	**130**	30c. red	75	60

131 Dr. M. F. da Costa Gomez

1972. 65th Birth Anniv of Moises F. da Costa Gomez (statesman).

562	**131**	30c. black and green	75	70

132 Child playing with Earth

1972. Child Welfare. Multicoloured.

563		15c.+5c. Type **132**	1·40	1·30
564		20c.+10c. Child playing in water	1·40	1·30
565		30c.+15c. Child throwing ball into the air	1·40	1·30

133 Pedestrian Crossing

1973. Cultural and Social Relief Funds. Road Safety.

566	**133**	12c.+6c. multicoloured	1·50	1·40
567	-	15c.+7c. grn, orge & red	1·50	1·40
568	-	40c.+20c. multicoloured	1·50	1·40

Designs:—15c. Road-crossing patrol; 40c. Traffic lights.

134 William III (portrait from stamp of 1873)

1973. Stamp Centenary.

569	**134**	15c. violet, mauve and gold	75	55
570	-	20c. multicoloured	90	70
571	-	30c. multicoloured	90	70

Designs:—20c. Antilles postman; 30c. Postal Service emblem.

135 Map of Aruba, Curacao and Bonaire

1973. Inauguration of Submarine Cable and Microwave Telecommunications Link. Multicoloured.

572		15c. Type **135**	90	85
573		30c. Six stars ("The Antilles")	90	85
574		45c. Map of Saba, St. Maarten and St. Eustatius	90	85
MS575		145×50 mm. Nos. 572/4	4·75	4·00

136 Queen Juliana

1973. Silver Jubilee of Queen Juliana's Reign.

576	**136**	15c. multicoloured	1·10	1·00

137 Jan Eman

1973. 16th Death Anniv of Jan Eman (Aruba statesman).

577	**137**	30c. black and green	75	70

138 "1948–1973"

1973. Child Welfare Fund. 25th Anniv of 1st Child Welfare Stamps.

578	**138**	15c.+5c. light green, green and blue	1·30	1·20
579	-	20c.+10c. brown, green and blue	1·30	1·20
580	-	30c.+15c. violet, blue and light blue	1·40	1·30
MS581		108×75 mm. Nos. 578 ×2, 579 ×2	6·00	5·25

Designs:—No. 579, Three Children; No. 580, Mother and child.

139 L. B. Scott

1974. Eighth Death Anniv of Lionel B. Scott (St. Maarten statesman).

582	**139**	30c. multicoloured	75	70

140 Family Meal

1974. Family Planning Campaign. Multicoloured.

583		6c. Type **140**	75	55
584		12c. Family at home	75	55

585 15c. Family in garden 75 55

141 Girl combing Hair

1974. Cultural and Social Relief Funds. "The Younger Generation". Multicoloured.
586 12c.+6c. Type **141** 2·10 1·80
587 15c.+7c. "Pop dancers" 2·10 1·80
588 40c.+20c. Group drummer 2·10 1·80

142 Desulphurisation Plant

1974. 50th Anniv of Lago Oil Co, Aruba. Mult.
589 15c. Type **142** 60 55
590 30c. Fractionating towers 75 70
591 45c. Lago refinery at night 1·10 1·00

143 UPU Emblem

1974. Centenary of Universal Postal Union.
592 **143** 15c. gold, green and black 90 85
593 **143** 30c. gold, blue and black 90 85

144 *A Carpenter outranks a King*

1974. Child Welfare. Children's Songs. Mult.
594 15c.+5c. Type **144** 1·60 1·50
595 20c.+10c. Footprints (*Let's Do a Ring-dance*) 1·60 1·50
596 30c.+15c. *Moon and Sun* 1·60 1·50

145 Queen Emma Bridge

1975. Antillean Bridges. Multicoloured.
597 20c. Type **145** 90 85
598 30c. Queen Juliana Bridge 90 85
599 40c. Queen Wilhelmina Bridge 1·10 1·00

146 Ornamental Ventilation Grid

1975. Cultural and Social Welfare Funds.
600 **146** 12c.+6c. multicoloured 1·70 1·40
601 - 15c.+7c. brown & stone 1·70 1·40
602 - 40c.+20c. multicoloured 1·70 1·40
Designs:—15c. Knight accompanied by buglers (tomb-stone detail); 40c. Foundation stone.

147 Sodium Chloride Molecules

1975. Bonaire Salt Industry. Multicoloured.
603 15c. Type **147** 1·10 70
604 20c. Salt incrustation and blocks 1·10 85
605 40c. Map of salt area (vert) 1·20 85

148 Fokker F.XVIII *De Snip* and Old Control Tower

1975. 40th Anniv of Aruba Airport. Mult.
606 15c. Type **148** 90 70
607 30c. Douglas DC-9-30 and modern control tower 90 70
608 40c. Tail of Boeing 727-200 and "Princess Beatrix" Airport buildings 90 85

149 IWY Emblem

1975. International Women's Year. Multicoloured.
609 6c. Type **149** 65 45
610 12c. "Social Development" 80 60
611 20c. "Equality of Sexes" 95 75

150 Children making Windmill

1975. Child Welfare. Multicoloured.
612 15c.+5c. Type **150** 1·60 1·50
613 20c.+10c. Child modelling clay 1·60 1·50
614 30c.+15c. Children drawing pictures 1·60 1·50

151 Beach, Aruba

1976. Tourism. Multicoloured.
615 40c. Type **151** 1·20 1·10
616 40c. Fish Kiosk, Bonaire 1·20 1·10
617 40c. Table Mountain, Curacao 1·20 1·10

152 J. A. Abraham (statesman)

1976. Abraham Commemoration.
618 **152** 30c. purple on brown 1·30 90

153 Dyke Produce

1976. Agriculture, Animal Husbandry and Fisheries. Multicoloured.
619 15c. Type **153** 95 75
620 35c. Cattle 1·10 90
621 45c. Fishes 1·10 1·10

154 Arm holding Child

1976. Child Welfare. "Carrying the Child".
622 **154** 20c.+10c. multicoloured 1·60 1·50
623 - 25c.+12c. multicoloured 1·60 1·50
624 - 40c.+18c. multicoloured 1·60 1·50
Designs:—Horiz: 25c. Vert: 40c. Both similar to Type **154** showing arm holding child.

155 *Andrew Doria* (naval brig) receiving Salute

1976. Bicentenary of American Revolution. Multicoloured.
625 25c. Flags and plaque, Fort Oranje 1·60 90
626 40c. Type **155** 1·60 90
627 55c. Johannes de Graaff, Governor of St. Eustatius 1·60 1·40
See also No. **MS**996.

156 Carnival Costume

1977. Carnival.
628 - 25c. multicoloured 1·30 1·10
629 **156** 35c. multicoloured 1·30 1·10
630 - 40c. multicoloured 1·30 1·10
Designs:—25c., 40c. Women in Carnival costumes.

157 Tortoise (Bonaire)

1977. Rock Paintings. Multicoloured.
631 25c. Bird (Aruba) 1·30 90
632 35c. Abstract (Curaca) 1·30 90
633 40c. Type **157** 1·30 90

158 "Ace" Playing Card

1977. Sixth Central American and Caribbean Bridge Championships. Multicoloured.
634 **158** 20c.+10c. red and black 1·10 90
635 - 25c.+12c. multicoloured 1·10 1·10
636 - 40c.+18c. multicoloured 1·40 1·40
MS637 75×108 mm. Nos. 634/5×2 4·75 3·75
Designs:—Vert: 25c. "King" playing card. Horiz: 40c. Bridge hand.

1977. Amphilex 77 International Stamp Exhibition, Amsterdam. Sheet 175×105 mm.
MS638 Nos. 634/6 but with green backgrounds 8·00 7·50

159 *Cordia sebestena*

1977. Flowers. Multicoloured.
639 25c. Type **159** 1·10 90
640 40c. *Albizzia lebbeck* (vert) 1·30 90
641 55c. *Tamarindus indica* 1·40 1·20

160 Bells outside Main Store

1977. 50th Anniv of Spritzer and Fuhrmann (jewellers). Multicoloured.
642 20c. Type **160** 1·10 90
643 40c. Globe basking in sun 1·30 90
644 55c. Antillean flag and diamond ring 1·40 1·20

161 Children with Toy Animal

1977. Child Welfare. Multicoloured.
645 15c.+15c. Type **161** 95 75
646 20c.+10c. Children with toy rabbit 1·10 90
647 25c.+12c. Children with toy cat 1·30 1·10
648 40c.+18c. Children with toy beetle 1·40 1·20
MS649 108×75 mm. Nos. 646×2, 648×2 5·00 4·75

162 "The Unspoiled Queen" (Saba)

1977. Tourism. Multicoloured.
650 25c. Type **162** 65 45
651 35c. "The Golden Rock" (St. Eustatius) 80 60
652 40c. "The Friendly Island" (St. Maarten) 80 75

1977. As Nos. 378, 381/2 and 385, but larger, (39×22 mm).
653 **E** 20c. grey and red 3·25 3·00
654 **E** 35c. pink and brown 8·50 6·00
655 **C** 40c. green and mauve 1·10 1·10
656 **E** 55c. green and red 1·60 1·50

163 19th-century Chest

1978. 150th Anniv of Netherlands Antilles' Bank. Multicoloured.
657 **163** 15c. blue and light blue 65 45
658 - 20c. orange and gold 65 45
659 - 40c. green and deep green 65 45
Designs:—20c. Bank emblem; 40c. Strong-room door.

164 Water-skiing

1978. Sports Funds. Multicoloured.
660 15c.+5c. Type **164** 80 45
661 20c.+10c. Yachting 80 45
662 25c.+12c. Football 90 45
663 40c.+18c. Baseball 1·00 75

165 *Erythrina velutina*

1978. Flora of Netherlands Antilles. Multicoloured.
664 15c. *Delconix regia* 80 60
665 25c. Type **165** 80 60
666 50c. *Gualacum officinale* (horiz) 1·00 75
667 55c. *Gilricidia sepium* (horiz) 1·40 1·10

166 *Polythysana rubrescens*

1978. Butterflies. Multicoloured.
668 15c. Type **166** 95 60
669 25c. *Caligo* sp. 95 60
670 35c. *Prepona praeneste* 1·10 75
671 40c. *Morpho* sp. 1·50 90

167 "Conserve Energy" (English)

1978. Energy Conservation.
672 **167** 15c. orange and black 65 60
673 - 20c. green and black 80 60
674 - 40c. red and black 1·00 75
Designs:—As No. 672 but text in Dutch (20c.) or in Papiamento (40c.).

168 Red Cross

1978. 150th Birth Anniv of Henri Dunant (founder of Red Cross).

675	**168**	55c.+25c. red and blue	80	75
MS676		144×50 mm. No. 675×3	4·00	3·75

169 Curacao from Sea, and Punched Tape

1978. 70th Anniv of Antilles Telecommunications Corporation (Landsradio). Multicoloured.

677	20c. Type **169**	80	60
678	40c. Ship's bridge, punched tape and radio mast	95	75
679	55c. Satellite and aerial (vert)	1·10	1·10

170 Boy Rollerskating

1978. Child Welfare. Multicoloured.

680	15c.+5c. Type **170**	95	90
681	20c.+10c. Boy and girl flying kite	1·10	90
682	25c.+12c. Boy and girl playing marbles	1·10	1·10
683	40c.+18c. Girl riding bicycle	1·40	1·10
MS684	75×108 mm. Nos. 680/1×2	4·75	3·75

171 Caï Awa (pumping station)

1978. 80th Death Anniv of Leonard Burlington Smith (entrepreneur and U.S. Consul).

685	**171**	25c. multicoloured	65	45
686	-	35c. black, greenish yellow and yellow	80	60
687	-	40c. multicoloured	95	75

Designs:—Vert: 35c. Leonard Burlington Smith. Horiz: 40c. Opening ceremony of Queen Emma Bridge, 1888.

172 Aruba Coat of Arms (float)

1979. 25th Aruba Carnival. Multicoloured.

688	40c.+10c. Float representing heraldic fantasy	1·10	90
689	75c.+20c. Type **172**	1·60	1·40

173 Goat and PAHO Emblem

1979. 12th Inter-American Ministerial Meeting on Foot and Mouth Disease and Zoonosis Control, Curacao. Multicoloured.

690	50c. Type **173**	95	75
691	75c. Horse and conference emblem	1·30	1·10
692	150c. Cows, flag and Pan-American Health Organization (PAHO) and WHO emblems	2·20	2·10
MS693	143×50 mm. As Nos. 690/2 but background colours changed	5·50	4·50

174 Yacht and Sun

1979. 12th International Sailing Regatta, Bonaire. Multicoloured.

694	15c.+5c. Type **174**	65	45
695	35c.+25c. Yachts	80	75
696	40c.+15c. Yacht and globe (horiz)	1·10	90
697	55c.+25c. Yacht, sun and flamingo	1·40	1·10
MS698	124×72 mm. Nos. 694/7	4·00	3·75

175 Corps Members

1979. 50th Anniv of Curacao Volunteer Corps.

699	**175**	15c.+10c. blue, red and ultramarine	80	75
700	-	40c.+20c. blue, violet and gold	1·10	1·10
701	-	1g. multicoloured	1·40	1·20

Designs:—40c. Sentry in battle dress and emblem; 1g. Corps emblem, flag and soldier in ceremonial uniform.

176 *Melochia tomentosa*

1979. Flowers. Multicoloured.

702	25c. *Casearia tremula*	95	60
703	40c. *Cordia cylindrostachya*	1·30	90
704	1g.50 Type **176**	2·50	2·20

177 Girls reading Book

1979. International Year of the Child.

705	**177**	20c.+10c. multicoloured	85	75
706	-	25c.+12c. multicoloured	1·00	75
707	-	35c.+15c. violet, brown and black	1·30	90
708	-	50c.+20c. multicoloured	1·50	1·40
MS709		75×108 mm. Nos. 705 and 707, each×2	5·00	4·25

Designs:—25c. Toddler and cat; 35c. Girls carrying basket; 50c. Boy and girl dressing-up.

178 Dove and Netherlands Flag

1979. 25th Anniv of Statute of the Kingdom. Multicoloured.

710	65c. Type **178**	1·30	1·10
711	1g.50 Dove and Netherlands Antilles flag	2·50	2·30

179 Map of Aruba and Foundation Emblem

1979. 30th Anniv of Aruba Cultural Centre Foundation. Multicoloured.

712	95c. Type **179**	1·70	1·60
713	1g. Foundation headquarters	2·00	1·80

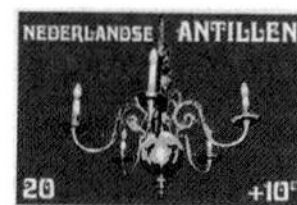
180 Brass Chandelier

1980. 210th Anniv of Fort Church, Curacao.

714	**180**	20c.+10c. yellow, black and brown	85	75
715	-	50c.+25c. multicoloured	1·20	1·10
716	-	100c. multicoloured	2·00	1·60

Designs:—50c. Pipe organ; 100c. Cupola tower, 1910.

181 Rotary Emblem and Cogwheel

1980. 75th Anniv of Rotary International. Multicoloured.

717	45c. Rotary emblem	1·00	75
718	50c. Globe and cogwheels	1·00	75
719	85c. Type **181**	1·30	1·20
MS720	120×75 mm. Nos. 717/19	4·25	4·00

182 Savings Box

1980. 75th Anniv of Post Office Savings Bank. Multicoloured.

721	25c. Type **182**	85	75
722	150c. Savings box (different)	2·50	2·30

183 Queen Juliana Accession Stamp

1980. Accession of Queen Beatrix.

723	**183**	25c. red, green and gold	65	60
724	-	60c. green, red and gold	1·10	90

Design:—60c. 1965 Royal Visit stamp.

184 Sir Rowland Hill

1980. London 1980 International Stamp Exhibition.

725	**184**	45c. black and green	1·00	90
726	-	60c. black and red	1·20	1·10
727	-	1g. red, black and blue	2·00	1·80
MS728		160×90 mm. 45c. black and red; 60c. black and blue; 1g. red, black and green	5·00	4·75

Designs:—60c. "London 1980" logo; 1g. Airmail label.

185 Gymnastics (beam exercise)

1980. Sports Funds.

729	**185**	25c.+10c. red and black	85	75
730	-	30c.+15c. yellow & blk	1·00	90
731	-	45c.+20c. light green, green and black	1·30	1·10
732	-	60c.+25c. pink, orange and black	1·50	1·20
MS733		75×144 mm. Nos. 729 and 732, each×3	7·50	6·50

Designs:—30c. Gymnastics (horse vaulting); 45c. Volleyball; 60c. Basketball.

186 White-fronted Dove

1980. Birds. Multicoloured.

734	25c. Type **186**	1·70	60
735	60c. Tropical mockingbird	2·00	1·10
736	85c. Bananaquit	2·50	1·40

187 *St. Maarten Landscape*

1980. Child Welfare. Children's Drawings. Multicoloured.

737	25c.+10c. Type **187**	1·00	60
738	30c.+15c. *Bonaire House*	1·20	1·10
739	40c.+20c. *Child writing on Board*	1·30	1·20
740	60c.+25c. *Dancing Couple* (vert)	1·60	1·30
MS741	149×108 mm. Nos. 737 and 740, each×3 plus four labels	7·50	6·50

188 Rudolf Theodorus Palm

1981. Birth Centenary (1980) of Rudolf Theodorus Palm (musician).

742	**188**	60c. brown and yellow	1·30	1·20
743	-	1g. buff and blue	2·20	1·80

Design:—1g. Musical score and hands playing piano.

189 Map of Aruba and TEAM Emblem

1981. 50th Anniv of Evangelical Alliance Mission (TEAM) in Antilles. Multicoloured.

744	30c. Type **189**	85	75
745	50c. Map of Curacao and emblem	1·30	1·00
746	1g. Map of Bonaire and emblem	2·10	1·80

190 Boy in Wheelchair

1981. International Year of Disabled Persons. Multicoloured.

747	25c.+10c. Blind woman	1·00	90
748	30c.+15c. Type **190**	1·20	1·10
749	45c.+20c. Child in walking frame	1·50	1·40
750	60c.+25c. Deaf girl	1·80	1·70

191 Tennis

1981. Sports Funds. Multicoloured.

751	30c.+15c. Type **191**	1·30	1·10
752	50c.+20c. Swimming	1·70	1·40
753	70c.+25c. Boxing	2·10	1·90
MS754	100×72 mm. Nos. 751/3	5·75	5·50

192 Gateway

1981. 125th Anniv of St. Elisabeth's Hospital. Multicoloured.

755	60c. Type **192**	1·20	1·10
756	1g.50 St. Elisabeth's Hospital	2·75	2·50

193 Marinus van der Maarel (promoter)

1981. 50th Anniv (1980) of Antillean Boy Scouts Association. Multicoloured.

757	45c.+20c. Wolf Cub and leader	2·10	1·80
758	70c.+25c. Type **193**	2·50	2·30

759	1g.+50c. Headquarters, Ronde Klip	3·50	3·25
MS760	144×50 mm. Nos. 757/9	8·25	7·75

194 Mother and Child

1981. Child Welfare. Multicoloured.

761	35c.+15c. Type **194**	1·20	1·10
762	45c.+20c. Boy and girl	1·30	1·20
763	55c.+25c. Child with cat	1·70	1·50
764	85c.+40c. Girl with teddy bear	2·50	2·30
MS765	75×108 mm. Nos. 761 and 763, each×2	5·75	5·50

195 *Jatropha gossypifolia*

1981. Flowers. Multicoloured.

766	45c. *Cordia globosa*	1·00	90
767	70c. Type **195**	1·70	1·50
768	100c. *Croton flavens*	2·10	1·80

196 Pilot Gig approaching Ship

1982. Centenary of Pilotage Service. Mult.

769	70c. Type **196**	2·10	1·90
770	85c. Modern liner and map of Antilles	2·30	2·00
771	1g. Pilot boarding ship	2·50	2·10

197 Fencing

1982. Sports Funds.

772	**197**	35c.+15c. mauve and violet	1·70	1·40
773	-	45c.+20c. blue and deep blue	2·10	1·70
774	-	70c.+35c. multicoloured	2·75	2·50
775	-	85c.+40c. brown and deep brown	3·25	2·75
MS776		144×50 mm. No. 774×2 plus label	6·50	5·75

Designs:—45c. Judo; 70c. Football; 85c. Cycling.

198 Holy Ark

1982. 250th Anniv of Dedication of Mikve Israel-Emanuel Synagogue, Curacao. Mult.

777	75c. Type **198**	2·10	1·50
778	85c. Synagogue facade	2·30	1·50
779	150c. Tebah (raised platform)	3·50	2·75

199 Peter Stuyvesant (Governor) and Flags of Netherlands, Netherlands Antilles and United States

1982. Bicentenary of Netherlands–United States Diplomatic Relations.

780	**199**	75c. multicoloured	2·50	1·80
MS781		101×70 mm. No. 780	3·25	3·00

See also No. **MS**996.

200 Airport Control Tower

1982. International Federation of Air Traffic Controllers.

782	-	35c. black, ultramarine and blue	1·30	90
783	**200**	75c. black, green and light green	2·10	1·60
784	-	150c. black, orange and salmon	3·25	2·50

Designs:—35c. Radar plot trace; 150c. Radar aerials.

201 Mail Bag

1982. Philexfrance 82 International Stamp Exhibition, Paris. Multicoloured.

785	45c. Exhibition emblem	1·50	1·10
786	85c. Type **201**	2·10	1·70
787	150c. Netherlands Antilles and French flags	3·50	2·75
MS788	125×64 mm. Nos. 785/7	7·50	6·75

202 Brown Chromis

1982. Fish. Multicoloured.

789	35c. Type **202**	2·00	1·10
790	75c. Spotted trunkfish	2·75	1·80
791	85c. Blue tang	3·00	2·30
792	100c. French angelfish	3·25	2·40

203 Girl playing Accordion

1982. Child Welfare. Multicoloured.

793	35c.+15c. Type **203**	1·80	1·20
794	75c.+35c. Boy playing guitar	3·25	2·50
795	85c.+40c. Boy playing violin	3·50	2·75
MS796	144×50 mm. Nos. 793/5	9·00	8·25

204 Saba House

1982. Cultural and Social Relief Funds. Local Houses. Multicoloured.

797	35c.+15c. Type **204**	1·90	1·50
798	75c.+35c. Aruba House	3·00	2·40
799	85c.+40c. Curacao House	3·25	2·75
MS800	72×100 mm. Nos. 797/9	8·25	7·75

205 High Jumping

1983. Sports Funds. Multicoloured.

801	35c.+15c. Type **205**	1·70	1·40
802	45c.+20c. Weightlifting	2·40	1·80
803	85c.+40c. Wind-surfing	3·50	3·00

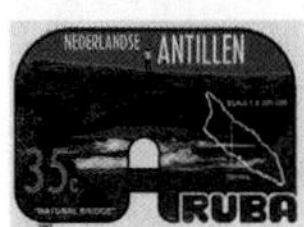

206 Natural Bridge, Aruba

1983. Tourism. Multicoloured.

804	35c. Type **206**	1·30	1·10
805	45c. Lac Bay, Bonaire	1·60	1·20
806	100c. Willemstad, Curacao	2·75	2·50

207 WCY Emblem and Means of Communication

1983. World Communications Year.

807	**207**	1g. multicoloured	3·00	2·50
MS808		100×72 mm. No. 807	3·50	3·25

208 *Curacao* (paddle-steamer) and Post Office Building

1983. Brasiliana 83 International Stamp Exhibition, Rio de Janeiro. Multicoloured.

809	45c. Type **208**	2·00	1·50
810	55c. Brazil flag, exhibition emblem and Netherlands Antilles flag and postal service emblem	2·10	1·70
811	100c. Governor's Palace, Netherlands Antilles, and Sugarloaf Mountain, Rio de Janeiro	3·25	2·50
MS812	100×72 mm. Nos. 809/11	7·50	6·75

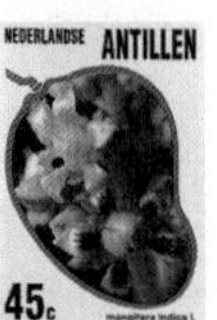

209 Mango (*Mangifera indica*)

1983. Flowers. Multicoloured.

813	45c. Type **209**	2·00	1·50
814	55c. *Malpighia punicifolia*	2·10	1·70
815	100c. *Citrus aurantifolia*	3·25	2·75

210 Boy and Lizard

1983. Child Welfare. Multicoloured.

816	45c.+20c. Type **210**	2·30	1·80
817	55c.+25c. Girl watching ants	2·75	2·10
818	100c.+50c. Girl feeding donkey	4·25	3·75
MS819	100×72 mm. Nos. 816/18	10·00	9·50

211 Aruba Water Jar

1983. Cultural and Social Relief Funds. Pre-Columbian Pottery.

820	**211**	45c.+20c. light blue, blue and black	2·50	2·20
821	-	55c.+25c. pink, red and black	3·00	2·30
822	-	85c.+40c. stone, green and black	3·50	2·75
823	-	100c.+50c. light brown, brown and black	4·75	4·00

Designs:—55c. Aruba decorated bowl; 85c. Curacao human figurine; 100c. Fragment of Curacao female figurine.

212 Saba

1983. Local Government Buildings. Multicoloured.

824	20c. Type **212**	65	45
825	25c. St. Eustatius	65	45
826	30c. St. Maarten	85	75
827	35c. Aruba	5·00	90
828	45c. Bonaire	1·20	1·10
829	55c. Curacao	1·70	1·20
830	60c. Type **212**	1·30	1·20
831	65c. As No. 825	1·50	1·40
832	70c. Type **212**	2·00	90
833	75c. As No. 826	2·00	1·80
834	85c. As No. 827	6·00	2·10
835	85c. As No. 828	2·30	1·10
836	90c. As No. 828	2·30	2·10
837	95c. As No. 829	2·50	2·30
838	1g. Type **212**	2·75	2·10
839	1g.50 As No. 825	3·50	2·75
840	2g.50 As No. 826	4·25	3·75
841	5g. As No. 828	8·25	6·75
842	10g. As No. 829	17·00	11·50
843	15g. Type **212**	25·00	18·00

213 Note-taking, Typesetting and Front Page of *Amigoe*

1984. Centenary of "Amigoe de Curacao" (newspaper). Multicoloured.

845	45c. Type **213**	1·70	1·40
846	55c. Printing press and newspapers	1·90	1·50
847	85c. Reading newspaper	3·00	2·50

214 WIA and ICAO Emblems

1984. 40th Anniv of I.C.A.O.

848	**214**	25c. multicoloured	1·30	85
849	-	45c. violet, blue and black	2·00	1·40
850	-	55c. multicoloured	2·10	1·50
851	-	100c. multicoloured	3·25	2·50

Designs:—45c. ICAO anniversary emblem; 55c. ALM and ICAO emblems; 100c. Fokker F.XIII aeroplane *De Snip*.

215 Fielder

1984. Sports Funds. 50th Anniv of Curacao Baseball Federation. Multicoloured.

852	25c.+10c. Type **215**	2·00	1·20
853	45c.+20c. Batter	3·00	2·10
854	55c.+25c. Pitcher	3·50	2·50
855	85c.+40c. Running for base	4·25	3·50
MS856	144×50 mm. Nos. 853/5	13·00	11·00

216 Microphones and Radio

1984. Cultural and Social Relief Funds. Radio and Gramophone. Multicoloured.

857	45c.+20c. Type **216**	3·25	2·10
858	55c.+25c. Gramophones and record	4·00	2·75
859	100c.+50c. Gramophone with horn	4·75	4·25

217 Bonnet-maker

1984. Centenary of Curacao Chamber of Commerce and Industry. Multicoloured.

860	45c. Type **217**	2·50	1·80
861	55c. Chamber emblem	2·75	1·80
862	1g. *Southward* (liner) passing under bridge	3·75	2·75

No. 861 is an inverted triangle.

218 Black-faced Grassquit

1984. Birds. Multicoloured.

863	45c. Type **218**	2·40	1·70
864	55c. Rufous-collared sparrow	2·75	2·10
865	150c. Blue-tailed emerald	5·00	4·00

219 Eleanor Roosevelt and Val-Kill, Hyde Park, New York

1984. Birth Centenary of Eleanor Roosevelt.

866	**219**	45c. multicoloured	1·70	1·40
867	-	85c. black, gold and bistre	2·75	2·10
868	-	100c. black, yellow and red	3·00	2·40

Designs:—85c. Portrait in oval frame; 100c. Eleanor Roosevelt with children.

220 Child Reading

1984. Child Welfare. Multicoloured.

869	45c.+20c. Type **220**	2·30	2·10
870	55c.+25c. Family reading	3·00	2·75
871	100c.+50c. Family in church	4·00	3·50
MS872	100x72 mm. Nos. 869/71	9·75	9·25

221 Adult Flamingo and Chicks

1985. Greater Flamingoes. Multicoloured.

873	25c. Type **221**	1·80	1·20
874	45c. Young flamingoes	2·50	1·60
875	55c. Adult flamingoes	2·75	1·90
876	100c. Flamingoes in various flight positions	4·00	3·00

222 Symbols of Entered Apprentice

1985. Bicentenary of De Vergenoeging Masonic Lodge, Curacao. Multicoloured.

877	45c. Type **222**	2·50	1·60
878	55c. Symbols of the Fellow Craft	2·75	2·00
879	100c. Symbols of the Master Mason	4·25	3·50

223 Players with Ball

1985. Sports Funds. Football. Multicoloured.

880	10c.+5c. Type **223**	1·20	75
881	15c.+5c. Dribbling ball	1·30	90
882	45c.+20c. Running with ball	2·40	2·00
883	55c.+25c. Tackling	3·00	2·50
884	85c.+40c. Marking player with ball	4·25	3·50

224 Boy using Computer

1985. Cultural and Social Welfare Funds. International Youth Year. Multicoloured.

885	45c.+20c. Type **224**	2·50	2·10
886	55c.+25c. Girl listening to records	3·50	2·75
887	100c.+50c. Boy break-dancing	5·00	4·25

225 UN Emblem

1985. 40th Anniv of U.N.O.

888	**225**	55c. multicoloured	2·10	1·70
889	**225**	1g. multicoloured	3·25	2·75

226 Pierre Lauffer and Poem

1985. Papiamentu (Creole language). Multicoloured.

890	45c. Type **226**	1·30	1·20
891	55c. Wave inscribed "Papiamentu"	1·70	1·50

227 Eskimo

1985. Child Welfare. Multicoloured.

892	5c.+5c. Type **227**	85	45
893	10c.+5c. African child	1·00	60
894	25c.+10c. Chinese girl	1·50	1·10
895	45c.+20c. Dutch girl	2·50	2·00
896	55c.+25c. Red Indian girl	2·75	2·40
MS897	100x72 mm. Nos. 894/6	7·50	6·50

228 *Calotropis procera*

1985. Flowers. Multicoloured.

898	5c. Type **228**	1·00	45
899	10c. *Capparis flexuosa*	1·00	45
900	20c. *Mimosa distachya*	1·50	75
901	45c. *Ipomoea nil*	2·10	1·30
902	55c. *Heliotropium ternatum*	2·50	1·60
903	150c. *Ipomoea incarnata*	4·25	3·50

229 Courthouse

1986. 125th Anniv of Curacao Courthouse. Multicoloured.

904	5c. Type **229**	65	45
905	15c. States room (vert)	85	45
906	25c. Court room	1·20	75
907	55c. Entrance (vert)	2·00	1·50

230 Sprinting

1986. Sports Funds. Multicoloured.

908	15c.+5c. Type **230**	2·00	1·10
909	25c.+10c. Horse racing	2·30	1·50
910	45c.+20c. Motor racing	3·00	2·00
911	55c.+25c. Football	3·50	2·50

231 Girls watching Artist at work

1986. Curacao Youth Care Foundation. Multicoloured.

912	30c.+15c. Type **231**	2·00	1·40
913	45c.+20c. Children watching sculptor at work	2·30	1·60
914	55c.+25c. Children watching potter at work	3·00	2·10

232 Chained Man

1986. 25th Anniv of Amnesty International. Multicoloured.

915	45c. Type **232**	1·90	1·20
916	55c. Dove behind bars	2·10	1·40
917	100c. Man behind bars	3·00	2·20

233 Post Office Mail Box

1986. Mail Boxes. Multicoloured.

918	10c. Type **233**	50	45
919	25c. Street mail box on pole	85	45
920	45c. Street mail box in brick column	1·30	1·10
921	55c. Street mail box	1·70	1·20

234 Boy playing Football

1986. Child Welfare. Multicoloured.

922	20c.+10c. Type **234**	1·30	90
923	25c.+15c. Girl playing tennis	1·70	1·10
924	45c.+20c. Boy practising judo	2·00	1·60
925	55c.+25c. Boy playing baseball	2·40	2·00
MS926	75x72 mm. Nos. 924/5	5·00	4·25

235 Brothers' First House and Mauritius Vliegendehond

1986. Centenary of Friars of Tilburg Mission. Multicoloured.

927	10c. Type **235**	65	40
928	45c. St. Thomas College and Mgr. Ferdinand E. C. Kieckens	1·60	1·10
929	55c. St. Thomas College courtyard and Fr. F. S. de Beer	1·80	1·40

236 Engagement Picture

1987. Golden Wedding of Princess Juliana and Prince Bernhard.

930	**236**	1g.35 orange, blk & gold	4·75	3·00
MS931		50x72 mm. No. 930	7·75	6·50

237 Map

1987. 150th Anniv of Maduro Holding Inc. Multicoloured.

932	70c. Type **237**	1·70	1·20
933	85c. Group activities	2·10	1·70
934	1g.55 Saloman Elias Levy Maduro (founder)	3·50	3·00

238 Girls playing Instruments

1987. Cultural and Social Relief Funds.

935	**238**	35c.+15c. multicoloured	1·50	1·20
936	-	45c.+25c. light green, green and blue	2·30	1·50
937	-	85c.+40c. multicoloured	3·25	2·75

Designs:—45c. Woman pushing man in wheelchair. 85c. Bandstand.

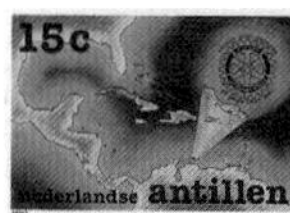

239 Map and Emblem

1987. 50th Anniv of Curacao Rotary Club. Multicoloured.

938	15c. Type **239**	85	45
939	50c. Zeelandia country house (meeting venue)	1·70	1·20
940	65c. Emblem on map of Curacao	2·10	1·50

240 Octagon (house where Bolivar's sisters lived)

1987. 175th Anniv of Simon Bolivar's Exile on Curacao (60, 80c.) and 50th Anniv of Bolivarian Society (70, 90c.). Multicoloured.

941	60c. Type **240**	1·50	1·30
942	70c. Society headquarters, Willemstad, Curacao	1·70	1·60
943	80c. Room in Octagon	2·10	1·90
944	90c. Portraits of Manuel Carlos Piar, Simon Bolivar and Pedro Luis Brion	2·30	2·10

241 Baby

1987. Child Welfare. Multicoloured.

945	40c.+15c. Type **241**	2·10	1·60
946	55c.+25c. Child	2·75	2·00
947	115c.+50c. Youth	4·00	3·25
MS948	144x 50 mm. Nos. 945/7	9·00	7·75

242 White-tailed Tropic Birds

1987. 25th Anniv of Netherlands Antilles National Parks Foundation. Multicoloured.

949	70c. Type **242**	1·70	1·20
950	85c. White-tailed deer	2·00	1·70
951	155c. Iguana	3·50	3·00

243 Printing Press and Type

1987. 175th Anniv of "De Curacaosche Courant" (periodical and printing shop). Multicoloured.

952	55c. Type **243**	1·50	1·20

953	70c. Keyboard and modern printing press	1·70	1·50

244 William Godden (founder)

1988. 75th Anniv of Curacao Mining Company. Multicoloured.

954	40c. Type **244**	1·30	95
955	105c. Phosphate processing plant	2·50	2·20
956	155c. Tafelberg (source of phosphate)	3·50	3·00

245 Flags, Minutes and John Horris Sprockel (first President)

1988. 50th Anniv of Netherlands Antilles Staten (legislative body). Multicoloured.

957	65c. Type **245**	1·70	1·40
958	70c. Ballot paper and schematic representation of extension of voting rights	2·00	1·50
959	155c. Antilles and Netherlands flags and birds representing five Antilles islands and Aruba	3·50	3·00

246 Bridge through "100"

1988. Cultural and Social Relief Funds. Centenary of Queen Emma Bridge, Curacao. Mult.

960	55c.+25c. Type **246**	2·40	1·50
961	115c.+55c. Willemstad harbour (horiz)	3·75	2·75
962	190c.+60c. Leonard B. Smith (engineer) and flags (horiz)	6·00	5·25

247 Broken Chain

1988. 125th Anniv of Abolition of Slavery. Mult.

963	155c. Type **247**	3·25	2·50
964	190c. Breach in slave wall	3·75	3·00

248 Flags and Map

1988. Third Inter-American Foundation of Cities "Let us Build Bridges" Conference, Curacao. Multicoloured.

965	80c. Type **248**	2·00	1·40
966	155c. Bridge and globe	3·25	2·50

249 Charles Hellmund (Bonaire councillor)

1988. Celebrities. Multicoloured.

967	55c. Type **249**	1·30	1·00
968	65c. Atthelo Maud Edwards-Jackson (founder of Saba Electric Company)	1·60	1·20
969	90c. Nicolaas Debrot (Governor of Antilles, 1962–69)	2·30	1·70
970	120c. William Charles de la Try Ellis (lawyer and politician)	2·75	2·30

250 Child watching Television

1988. Child Welfare. Multicoloured.

971	55c.+25c. Type **250**	2·10	1·60
972	65c.+30c. Boy with radio	2·30	1·90
973	115c.+55c. Girl using computer	3·50	3·00
MS974	118×67 mm. Nos. 971/3	10·50	8·50

251 *Cereus hexagonus*

1988. Cacti. Multicoloured.

975	55c. Type **251**	1·70	1·10
976	115c. *Melocactus*	2·75	1·90
977	125c. *Opuntia wentiana*	3·25	2·20

252 Magnifying Glass over 1936 and 1980 Stamps

1989. Cultural and Social Relief Funds. 50th Anniv of Curacao Stamp Association. Multicoloured.

978	30c.+10c. Type **252**	2·10	1·20
979	55c.+20c. Picking up stamp with tweezers (winning design by X. Rico in drawing competition)	2·50	2·00
980	80c.+30c. Barn owl and stamp album	2·75	2·30

Nos. 978/80 were printed together, *se-tenant*, forming a composite design.

253 Crested Bobwhite

1989. 40th Anniv of Curacao Foundation for Prevention of Cruelty to Animals. Multicoloured.

981	65c. Type **253**	2·50	1·50
982	115c. Dogs and cats	3·00	2·20

254 *Sun Viking* in Great Bay Harbour, St. Maarten

1989. Tourism. Cruise Liners. Multicoloured.

983	70c. Type **254**	2·00	1·50
984	155c. *Eugenio C* entering harbour, St. Annabay, Curacao	3·50	3·00

255 Paula Clementina Dorner (teacher)

1989. Celebrities. Multicoloured.

985	40c. Type **255**	1·30	95
986	55c. John Aniseto de Jongh (pharmacist and politician)	1·50	1·20
987	90c. Jacobo Jesus Maria Palm (musician)	2·20	1·90
988	120c. Abraham Mendes Chumaceiro (lawyer and social campaigner)	2·75	2·50

256 Boy and Girl under Tree

1989. Child Welfare. Multicoloured.

989	40c.+15c. Type **256**	2·00	1·20
990	65c.+30c. Two children playing on shore	2·30	1·90
991	115c.+35c. Adult carrying child	4·00	3·50
MS992	92×62 mm. 155c.+75c. Children playing on shore	7·50	6·00

257 Hand holding "7"

1989. 40th Anniv of Queen Wilhelmina Foundation for Cancer Care. Multicoloured.

993	30c. Type **257**	1·20	95
994	60c. Seated figure and figure receiving radiation treatment	1·80	1·50
995	80c. Figure exercising and Foundation emblem	2·10	1·70

1989. World Stamp Expo '89 International Stamp Exhibition, Washington, D.C. Sheet 112×65 mm containing multicoloured designs as previous issues but with changed values.

MS996	70c. As No. 625; 155c. Type **199**; 250c. Type **80**	11·00	9·75

258 Fireworks

1989. Christmas. Multicoloured.

997	30c. Type **258**	1·20	80
998	100c. Christmas tree decorations	2·50	2·00

259 *Tephrosia cinerea*

1990. Flowers. Multicoloured.

999	30c. Type **259**	85	75
1000	55c. *Erithalis fruticosa*	1·50	1·20
1001	65c. *Evolvulus antillanus*	1·70	1·40
1002	70c. *Jacquinia arborea*	1·80	1·50
1003	125c. *Tournefortia onaphalodes*	3·25	2·75
1004	155c. *Sesuvium portulacastrum*	4·25	3·25

260 Girl Guides

1990. Cultural and Social Relief Funds. Mult.

1005	30c.+10c. Type **260** (60th anniv)	1·60	1·00
1006	40c.+15c. Totolika (care of mentally disabled organization) (17th anniv)	1·90	1·50
1007	155c.+65c. Boy scout (60th anniv)	5·50	5·25

261 Nun with Child, Flag and Map

1990. Centenary of Arrival of Dominican Nuns in Netherlands Antilles. Multicoloured.

1008	10c. Type **261**	45	40
1009	55c. St. Rose Hospital and St. Martin's Home, St. Maarten	1·30	1·10
1010	60c. St. Joseph School, St. Maarten	1·60	1·20

262 Goal Net, Ball and Shield

1990. Multicoloured.

1011	65c.+30c. Type **262** (65th anniv of Sport Unie Brion Trappers football club)	2·30	2·10
1012	115c.+55c. Guiding addict from darkness towards sun (anti-drugs campaign)	3·75	3·50

263 Carlos Nicolaas-Perez (philologist and poet)

1990. Meritorious Antilleans. Multicoloured.

1013	40c. Type **263**	1·10	90
1014	60c. Evert Kruythoff (writer)	1·50	1·30
1015	80c. John de Pool (writer)	1·90	1·70
1016	150c. Joseph Sickman Corsen (poet and composer)	3·50	3·25

264 Queen Emma

1990. Dutch Queens of the House of Orange. Multicoloured.

1017	100c. Type **264**	3·00	2·20
1018	100c. Queen Wilhelmina	3·00	2·20
1019	100c. Queen Juliana	3·00	2·20
1020	100c. Queen Beatrix	3·00	2·20
MS1021	77×64 mm. 250c. Queens Emma, Wilhelmina, Juliana and Beatrix (35×24 mm)	14·00	13·00

265 Isla Refinery

1990. 75th Anniv of Oil Refining on Curacao.

1022	**265** 100c. multicoloured	2·75	2·30

266 Flower and Bees

1990. Child Welfare. International Literacy Year. Designs illustrating letters of alphabet. Multicoloured.

1023	30c.+5c. Type **266**	1·30	90
1024	55c.+10c. Dolphins and sun	2·10	1·50
1025	65c.+15c. Donkey with bicycle	2·40	1·80
1026	100c.+20c. Goat dreaming of house	3·50	2·75
1027	115c.+25c. Rabbit carrying food on yoke	4·00	3·00
1028	155c.+55c. Lizard, moon and cactus	6·50	5·25

267 Parcels

1990. Christmas. Multicoloured.

1029	30c. Type **267** (25th anniv of Curacao Lions Club's Good Neighbour project)	1·20	75
1030	100c. Mother and child	3·25	2·20

268 Flag, Map and Distribution of Mail

1991. Sixth Anniv of Express Mail Service.
1031 **268** 20g. multicoloured 41·00 39·00

269 Scuba Diver and French Grunt

1991. Fish. Multicoloured.
1032 10c. Type **269** 90 40
1033 40c. Spotted trunkfish 1·60 95
1034 55c. Copper sweepers 1·90 1·50
1035 75c. Skindiver and yellow goatfish 2·40 1·90
1036 100c. Black-barred soldierfish 3·50 2·40

270 Children and Stamps

1991. Cultural and Social Relief Funds. Mult.
1037 30c.+10c. Type **270** (12th anniv of Philatelic Club of Curacao) 1·70 1·20
1038 65c.+25c. St. Vincentius Brass Band (50th anniv) 2·75 2·20
1039 155c.+55c. Games and leisure pursuits (30th anniv of FESEBAKO) (Curacao community centres) 5·75 5·25

271 "Good Luck"

1991. Greetings Stamps. Multicoloured.
1040 30c. Type **271** 85 80
1041 30c. "Thank You" 85 80
1042 30c. Couple and family ("Love You") 85 80
1043 30c. Song birds ("Happy Day") 85 80
1044 30c. Greater flamingo and medicines ("Get Well Soon") 85 80
1045 30c. Flowers and balloons ("Happy Birthday") 85 80

272 Westpoint Lighthouse, Curacao

1991. Lighthouses. Multicoloured.
1046 30c. Type **272** 2·75 1·60
1047 70c. Willems Toren, Bonaire 3·00 2·00
1048 115c. Klein Curacao lighthouse 4·25 2·75

273 Peter Stuyvesant College

1991. 50th Anniv of Secondary Education in Netherlands Antilles (65c.) and Espamer '91 Spain–Latin America Stamp Exhibition, Buenos Aires (125c.). Multicoloured.
1049 65c. Type **273** 1·70 1·60
1050 125c. Dancers of Netherlands Antilles, Argentina and Portugal (vert) 3·25 3·00

274 Octopus with Letters and Numbers

1991. Child Welfare. Multicoloured.
1051 40c.+15c. Type **274** 2·10 1·50
1052 65c.+30c. Parents teaching arithmetic 3·00 2·40
1053 155c.+65c. Bird and tortoise with clock 5·50 5·25
MS1054 118×67 mm. 55c.+25c. Owl with letters and National Flag; 100c.+35c. Books and bookworms; 115c.+50c. Dragon, ice-cream cone and icicles. Imperf 12·50 11·00

275 Nativity

1991. Christmas. Multicoloured.
1055 30c. Type **275** 75 70
1056 100c. Angel appearing to shepherds 2·40 2·30

276 Joseph Alvarez Correa (founder) and Headquarters of SEL Maduro and Sons

1991. 75th Anniv of Maduro and Curiel's Bank. Multicoloured.
1057 30c. Type **276** 1·70 95
1058 70c. Lion rampant (bank's emblem) and "75" 2·75 1·90
1059 155c. Isaac Haim Capriles (Managing Director, 1954–74) and Scharloo bank branch 4·00 3·50

277 Fawn

1992. The White-tailed Deer. Multicoloured.
1060 5c. Type **277** (postage) 1·80 1·60
1061 10c. Young adults 1·80 1·60
1062 30c. Stag 1·80 1·60
1063 40c. Stag and hind in water 1·80 1·60
1064 200c. Stag drinking (air) 7·50 5·25
1065 355c. Stag calling 10·50 8·50

278 Windsurfer

1992. Cultural and Social Relief Funds. Olympic Games, Barcelona. Multicoloured.
1066 30c.+10c. Type **278** (award of silver medal to Jan Boersma, 1988 Games) 1·70 1·10
1067 55c.+25c. Globe, National Flag and Olympic rings 2·40 1·80
1068 115c.+55c. Emblem of National Olympic Committee (60th anniv) 4·75 4·00

Nos. 1066/8 were issued together, *se-tenant*, forming a composite design.

279 The Alhambra, Grenada

1992. Granada '92 International Stamp Exhibition (250c.) and Expo '92 World's Fair, Seville (500c.). Sheet 92×52 mm containing T **279** and similar horiz design. Multicoloured.
MS1069 250c. Type **279**; 500c. Carthusian Monastery, Seville, and Columbus 21·00 20·00

280 *Santa Maria*

1992. World Columbian Stamp Expo '92, Chicago. Multicoloured.
1070 250c. Type **280** 6·50 5·50
1071 500c. Chart and Columbus 13·00 11·00

281 View of Dock and Town

1992. Curacao Port Container Terminal. Mult.
1072 80c. Type **281** 2·10 1·90
1073 125c. Crane and ship 3·25 2·75

282 Angela de Lannoy-Willems

1992. Celebrities.
1074 **282** 30c. black, brown & grn 1·00 80
1075 - 40c. black, brown & blue 1·30 95
1076 - 55c. black, brown & orge 1·70 1·20
1077 - 70c. black, brown and red 1·80 1·50
1078 - 100c. black, brown & blue 2·50 2·30

Designs:—30c. Type **282** (first woman Member of Parliament); 40c. Lodewijk Daniel Gerharts (entrepreneur on Bonaire); 55c. Cyrus Wilberforce Wathey (entrepreneur on St. Maarten); 70c. Christian Winkel (Deputy Governor of Antilles); 100c. Mother Joseph (founder of Roosendaal Congregation (Franciscan welfare sisterhood)).

283 Spaceship

1992. Child Welfare. Multicoloured.
1079 30c.+10c. Type **283** 1·30 95
1080 70c.+30c. Robot 2·40 2·20
1081 100c.+40c. Extra-terrestrial being 3·50 3·00
MS1082 94×54 mm. 155c.+70c. Martian 7·50 7·00

284 Queen Beatrix and Prince Claus

1992. 12½ Years since Accession to the Throne of Queen Beatrix (100c.) and Royal Visit to Netherlands Antilles (others). Designs showing photos of previous visits to the Antilles. Mult.
1083 70c. Type **284** 1·80 1·60
1084 100c. Queen Beatrix signing book 2·50 2·20
1085 175c. Queen Beatrix and Prince Claus with girl 4·25 3·75

285 Crib

1992. Christmas. Multicoloured.
1086 30c. Type **285** 1·00 80
1087 100c. Mary and Joseph searching for lodgings (vert) 3·00 2·20

286 Hibiscus

1993. Flowers. Multicoloured.
1088 75c. Type **286** 2·00 1·60
1089 90c. Sunflower 2·30 2·00
1090 175c. Ixora 4·25 3·75
1091 195c. Rose 4·75 4·50

287 de Havilland Twin Otter and Flight Paths

1993. Anniversaries. Multicoloured.
1092 65c. Type **287** (50th anniv of Princess Juliana International Airport, St. Maarten) 1·70 1·40
1093 75c. Laboratory worker and National Health Laboratory (75th anniv) 1·80 1·60
1094 90c. de Havilland Twin Otter on runway at Princess Juliana International Airport 2·10 2·00
1095 175c. White and yellow cross (50th anniv of Princess Margriet White and Yellow Cross Foundation for District Nursing) 4·00 3·75

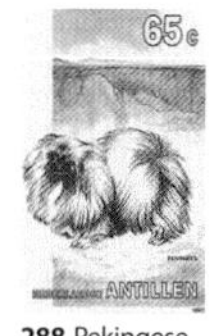

288 Pekingese

1993. Dogs. Multicoloured.
1096 65c. Type **288** 2·00 1·70
1097 90c. Standard poodle 2·75 2·30
1098 100c. Pomeranian 3·00 2·50
1099 175c. Papillon 5·00 4·25

289 Cave Painting, Bonaire

1993. Brasiliana '93 International Stamp Exhibition, Rio de Janeiro, and Admittance of Antilles to Postal Union of the Americas, Spain and Portugal. Multicoloured.
1100 150c. Type **289** 5·00 3·50
1101 200c. Exhibition emblem and Antilles flag 5·75 4·50
1102 250c. Globe and hand signing UPAEP agreement 6·50 5·50

290 *Sun and Sea*

1993. Carib-Art Exhibition, Curacao. Multicoloured.
1103 90c. Type **290** 2·10 2·00
1104 150c. *Heaven and Earth* 3·50 3·25

291 "Safety in the Home"

1993. Child Welfare. Child and Danger. Mult.
1105 65c.+25c. Type **291** 2·50 2·00
1106 90c.+35c. Child using seat belt ("Safety in the Car") (vert) 3·00 2·75
1107 175c.+75c. Child wearing armbands ("Safety in the Water") 5·75 5·50
MS1108 168×79 mm. 35c.+15c.×5, Child writing in exercise book ("Danger of Failing at School") 11·50 11·00

292 Consulate, Curacao

1993. Bicentenary of United States Consul General to the Antilles. Multicoloured.
1109 65c. Type **292** 1·70 1·40
1110 90c. Arms of Netherlands Antilles and USA 2·50 2·00
1111 175c. American bald eagle 4·25 3·75

293 *Mother and Child* (mosaic)

1993. Christmas. Works by Lucila Engels-Boskaljon. Multicoloured.

1112	30c. Type **293**	1·00	60
1113	115c. *Madonna and Christ* (painting)	2·75	2·50

294 Basset Hound

1994. Dogs. Multicoloured.

1114	65c. Type **294**	2·10	1·70
1115	75c. Pit bull terrier	2·50	1·90
1116	90c. Cocker spaniel	3·00	2·20
1117	175c. Chow-chow	5·00	4·25

295 Common Caracara

1994. Birds. Multicoloured.

1118	50c. Type **295**	3·25	1·30
1119	95c. Green peafowl	3·50	2·50
1120	100c. Scarlet macaw	3·50	2·75
1121	125c. Troupial	4·25	3·25

296 Joseph Husurell Lake

1994. Celebrities. Multicoloured.

1122	65c. Type **296** (founder of United People's Liberation Front)	1·70	1·60
1123	75c. Efrain Jonckheer (politician and diplomat)	1·90	1·80
1124	100c. Michiel Martinus Romer (teacher)	2·75	2·40
1125	175c. Carel Nicolaas Winkel (social reformer)	4·25	4·00

297 Players' Legs

1994. World Cup Football Championship, U.S.A. Multicoloured.

1126	90c. Type **297**	2·50	2·00
1127	150c. Foot and ball	3·75	3·25
1128	175c. Referee's whistle and cards	4·25	4·00

298 Chair and Hammer

1994. 75th Anniv of International Labour Organization. Multicoloured.

1129	90c. Type **298**	2·50	2·20
1130	110c. Heart and "75"	2·75	2·50
1131	200c. Tree	5·50	5·25

299 Birds and Dolphin

1994. Nature Protection. Multicoloured.

1132	10c. Type **299**	1·00	60
1133	35c. Dolphin, magnificent frigate bird, brown pelican and troupial	1·30	1·00
1134	50c. Coral, iguana, lobster and fish	1·50	1·30
1135	125c. Fish, turtle, queen conch, greater flamingoes and American wigeons	3·50	3·25
MS1136	84×70 mm. Nos. 1132/5	10·00	9·25

300 1945 7½c. Netherlands Stamp

1994. Fepapost '94 European Stamp Exhibition, The Hague. Multicoloured.

1137	2g.50 Type **300**	6·25	5·75
1138	5g. Curacao 1933 6c. stamp	12·50	11·50
MS1139	96×55 mm. Nos. 1137/8	20·00	19·00

301 Mother and Child

1994. Child Welfare. International Year of the Family. Multicoloured.

1140	35c.+15c. Type **301**	1·30	1·20
1141	65c.+25c. Father and daughter reading together	2·50	2·30
1142	90c.+35c. Grandparents	4·75	4·25
MS1143	86×51 mm. 175c.+75c. IYF emblem	7·75	7·50

302 Dove in Hands

1994. Christmas. Multicoloured.

1144	30c. Type **302**	1·70	80
1145	115c. Globe and planets in hands	3·25	2·50

303 Carnival and Houses

1995. Carnival. Multicoloured.

1146	125c. Type **303**	3·25	2·75
1147	175c. Carnival and harbour	4·50	3·75
1148	250c. Carnival and rural house	6·50	5·50

304 Disabled and Able-bodied Children

1995. 50th Anniv of Mgr. Verriet Institute (for the physically handicapped). Multicoloured.

1149	65c. Type **304**	1·70	1·40
1150	90c. Cedric Virginie (wheelchair-bound bookbinder)	2·40	2·00

305 Dobermann

1995. Dogs. Multicoloured.

1151	75c. Type **305**	2·50	1·70
1152	85c. German shepherd	3·00	2·00
1153	100c. Bouvier	3·25	2·20
1154	175c. St. Bernard	5·50	3·75

306 Bonaire

1995. Flags and Arms of the Constituent Islands of the Netherlands Antilles. Multicoloured.

1155	10c. Type **306**	50	45
1156	35c. Curacao	1·20	80
1157	50c. St. Maarten	1·50	1·10
1158	65c. Saba	1·80	1·50
1159	75c. St. Eustatius (also State Flag and Arms)	2·10	1·60
1160	90c. Island Flags and State Arms	2·50	2·00

307 Monument to Slave Revolt of 1795

1995. Cultural and Social Relief Funds. Bicentenary of Abolition of Slavery in the Antilles (1161/2) and Children's Drawings on Philately (1163/4). Multicoloured.

1161	30c.+10c. Type **307**	1·70	1·20
1162	45c.+15c. Magnificent frigate bird and slave bell	2·50	1·90
1163	65c.+25c. "Stamps" from Curacao and Bonaire (Nicole Wever and Sabine Anthonio)	2·75	2·00
1164	75c.+35c. "Stamps" from St. Maarten, St. Eustatius and Saba (Chad Jacobs, Martha Hassell and Dion Humphreys)	3·00	2·40

1995. Hurricane Relief Fund. Nos. 831, 833 and 838 surch ORKAAN LUIS and premium.

1165	65c.+65c. multicoloured	3·75	3·00
1166	75c.+75c. multicoloured	4·00	3·50
1167	1g.+1g. multicoloured	5·00	4·50

309 Sealpoint Siamese

1995. Cats. Multicoloured.

1168	25c. Type **309**	1·70	60
1169	60c. Maine coon	2·50	1·20
1170	65c. Silver Egyptian mau	2·75	1·50
1171	90c. Angora	3·25	2·00
1172	150c. Blue smoke Persian	5·00	3·25

310 Helping Elderly Woman across Road

1995. Child Welfare. Children and Good Deeds. Multicoloured.

1173	35c.+15c. Type **310**	1·30	1·10
1174	65c.+25c. Reading newspaper to blind person	2·30	2·00
1175	90c.+35c. Helping younger brother	3·00	2·75
1176	175c.+75c. Giving flowers to the sick	6·00	5·25

311 Wise Men on Camels

1995. Christmas. Multicoloured.

1177	30c. Type **311**	1·20	80
1178	115c. Fireworks over houses	3·25	2·50

312 Serving the Community

1996. 50th Anniv of Curacao Lions Club. Multicoloured.

1179	75c. Type **312**	2·50	1·60
1180	105c. Anniversary emblem	3·00	2·30
1181	250c. Handshake	6·50	5·50

313 Disease on Half of Leaf

1996. 60th Anniv of Capriles Psychiatric Clinic, Otrabanda on Rif. Multicoloured.

1182	60c. Type **313**	1·70	1·20
1183	75c. Tornado and sun over house	2·50	1·60

314 Dish Aerial and Face

1996. Centenary of Guglielmo Marconi's Patented Wireless Telegraph. Multicoloured.

1184	85c. Type **314**	2·30	2·00
1185	175c. Dish aerial and morse transmitter	4·25	3·75

315 Letters and Buildings

1996. Translation of Bible into Papiamentu (Creole language). Multicoloured.

1186	85c. Type **315**	2·30	2·00
1187	225c. Bible and alphabets	6·00	5·00

316 Gulf Fritillary

1996. Capex '96 International Stamp Exhibition, Toronto, Canada. Butterflies. Multicoloured.

1188	5c. Type **316**	1·20	45
1189	110c. *Callithea philotima*	3·25	2·50
1190	300c. Clipper	8·25	6·50
1191	750c. *Euphaedra francina*	19·00	17·00
MS1192	132×75 mm. Nos. 1189/90	14·00	13·00

317 Mary Johnson-Hassell (introducer of drawn-thread work to Saba, 57th death)

1996. Anniversaries.

1193	**317**	40c. orange and black on grey	1·30	95
1194	-	50c. green and black on grey	1·60	1·10
1195	-	75c. red and black on grey	2·10	1·60
1196	-	80c. blue and black on grey	2·30	2·00

Designs:—40c. Type **317** (introducer of drawn-thread work to Saba); 50c. Cornelius Marten (Papa Cornes) (pastor to Bonaire); 75c. Phelippi Chakutoe (union leader); 85c. Chris Engels (physician, artist, author and fencing champion).

318 Shire

1996. Horses. Multicoloured.

1197	110c. Type **318**	3·50	2·50
1198	225c. Shetland ponies	6·50	5·00
1199	275c. British thoroughbred	7·50	6·00
1200	350c. Przewalski mare and foal	10·00	8·25

319 Street Child and Shanty Town

1996. Child Welfare. 50th Anniv of UNICEF. Multicoloured.

1201	40c.+15c. Type **319**	1·50	1·30
1202	75c.+25c. Asian child weaver	2·75	2·40
1203	110c.+45c. Child in war zone of former Yugoslavia (vert)	4·00	3·75
1204	225c.+100c. Impoverished Caribbean mother and child (vert)	7·75	7·25

320 Straw Hat with Poinsettias and Gifts

1996. Christmas. Multicoloured. Self-adhesive.

1205	35c. Type **320**	1·70	80
1206	150c. Father Christmas	4·25	3·25

321 Emblem

1997. Cultural and Social Relief Funds.

1207	**321**	40c.+15c. black and yellow	1·80	1·20
1208	-	75c.+30c. blue, mauve and black	2·75	2·40
1209	-	85c.+40c. red and black	3·50	3·00
1210	-	110c.+50c. black, green and red	4·00	3·75

Designs:—40c. Type **321** (50th anniv of Curacao Foundation for Care and Resettlement of Ex-prisoners); 75c. Emblem (60th anniv (1996) of General Union of Public Servants (ABVO)); 85c. Flag of Red Cross (65th anniv of Curacao division); 110c. National Red Cross emblem (65th anniv of Curacao division).

322 Deadly Galerina

1997. Fungi. Multicoloured.

1211	40c. Type **322**	1·70	95
1212	50c. Destroying angel	2·00	1·10
1213	75c. Cep	3·00	1·60
1214	175c. Fly agaric	5·00	4·00

323 Budgerigars

1997. Birds. Multicoloured.

1215	5c. Type **323**	1·20	55
1216	25c. Sulphur-crested cockatoo	2·10	60
1217	50c. Yellow-shouldered Amazon	2·50	1·10
1218	75c. Purple heron	3·25	1·60
1219	85c. Ruby topaz hummingbird	3·50	1·90
1220	100c. South African crowned crane	4·00	2·30
1221	110c. Vermilion flycatcher	4·00	2·30
1222	125c. Greater flamingo	4·25	2·75
1223	200c. Osprey	5·75	4·25
1224	225c. Keel-billed toucan	6·75	5·00

324 Parrots ("Love")

325 "Correspondence"

1997. Greetings Stamps. Multicoloured. (a) As T **324**.

1225	40c. Type **324**	1·20	95
1226	75c. Waterfall ("Positivism")	2·00	1·60
1227	85c. Roses ("Mothers' Day")	2·30	2·00
1228	100c. Quill pen ("Correspondence")	2·50	2·20
1229	110c. Leaves, rainbow and heart ("Success")	2·75	2·50
1230	225c. Ant on flower ("Congratulations")	5·75	5·25

(b) As T **325**.

1231	40c. Motif as in Type **324**	1·70	1·60
1232	40c. Type **325**	1·70	1·60
1233	75c. Petals and moon ("Positivism")	2·50	2·30
1234	75c. Motif as No. 1226	2·50	2·30
1235	75c. Sun and moon ("Success")	2·50	2·30
1236	85c. Motif as No. 1227	2·50	2·30
1237	100c. Motif as No. 1228	3·25	3·00
1238	110c. Motif as No. 1229	3·25	3·00
1239	110c. Heart between couple ("Love")	3·25	3·00
1240	225c. Motif as No. 1230	6·50	6·25

326 Rat

1997. Pacific '97 International Stamp Exhibition, San Francisco. Chinese Zodiac. Designs showing Tangram (puzzle) representations and Chinese symbols for each animal. Multicoloured.

1241	5c. Type **326**	50	45
1242	5c. Ox	50	45
1243	5c. Tiger	50	45
1244	40c. Rabbit	1·30	95
1245	40c. Dragon	1·30	95
1246	40c. Snake	1·30	95
1247	75c. Horse	2·20	1·60
1248	75c. Goat	2·20	1·60
1249	75c. Monkey	2·20	1·60
1250	100c. Rooster	2·75	2·20
1251	100c. Dog	2·75	2·20
1252	100c. Pig	2·75	2·20
MS1253	145×150 mm. Nos. 1241/52	21·00	20·00

327 2½ Cent Coin (Plaka)

1997. Coins. Obverse and reverse of coins. Multicoloured.

1254	85c. Type **327**	2·50	2·00
1255	175c. 5 cent (Stuiver)	5·00	4·00
1256	225c. 2½ gulden (Fuerte)	6·75	5·00

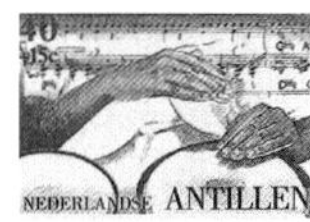
328 Score of *Atras de Nos* and Salsa Drummer

1997. Child Welfare. The Child and Music. Multicoloured.

1257	40c.+15c. Type **328**	1·70	1·20
1258	75c.+25c. Score of *For Elise* and pianist	2·50	2·20
1259	110c.+45c. Score of *Blues for Alice* and flautist	4·25	3·50
1260	225c.+100c. Score of *Yesterday* and guitarist	6·50	6·00

329 Nampu Grand Bridge, Shanghai

1997. Shanghai 1997 International Stamp and Coin Exhibition, China. Multicoloured.

1261	15c. Type **329**	1·70	80
1262	40c. Giant panda	2·50	1·60
1263	75c. Tiger (New Year) (vert)	3·25	2·30
MS1264	108×78 mm. 90c. The Bund, Shanghai	5·75	5·50

330 Worshippers (detail of mural by Marcolino Maas in Church of the Holy Family, Willemstad, Curacao)

1997. Christmas and New Year. Multicoloured.

1265	35c. Type **330**	1·70	80
1266	150c. Popping champagne cork and calendar (New Year)	4·25	3·25

331 Partial Eclipse

1998. Total Solar Eclipse, Curacao. Multicoloured.

1267	85c. Type **331**	2·75	2·20
1268	110c. Close-up of sun in total eclipse	3·75	2·50
1269	225c. Total eclipse	6·50	5·50
MS1270	85×52 mm. 750c. Hologram of stages of the eclipse	25·00	24·00

332 Camera and Painting

1998. Cultural and Social Relief Funds. Mult.

1271	40c.+15c. Type **332** (50th anniv of Curacao Museum)	1·70	1·20
1272	40c.+15c. Desalination plant and drinking water (70 years of seawater desalination)	1·70	1·20
1273	75c.+25c. Mangrove roots and shells (Lac Cai wetlands, Bonaire) (vert)	3·00	2·40
1274	85c.+40c. Lake and underwater marine life (Little Bonaire wetlands) (vert)	4·00	3·25

333 Salt Deposit, Dead Sea

1998. Israel 98 International Stamp Exhibition, Tel Aviv. Multicoloured.

1275	40c. Type **333**	1·70	1·10
1276	75c. Zion Gate, Jerusalem	2·00	1·60
1277	110c. Masada	3·00	2·40
MS1278	58×91 mm. 225c. Mikve Israel-Emanuel Synagogue, Curacao	7·50	7·00

334 Superior, 1923, and Elias Moreno Brandao

1998. 75th Anniv of E. Moreno Brandao and Sons (car dealers). Chevrolet Motor Cars. Multicoloured.

1279	40c. Type **334**	2·10	1·00
1280	55c. Roadster, 1934	2·30	1·50
1281	75c. Styleline deluxe sedan, 1949	2·75	1·70
1282	110c. Bel Air convertible, 1957	3·75	2·50
1283	225c. Corvette Stingray coupe, 1963	6·25	5·25
1284	500c. Chevelle SS-454 2-door hardtop, 1970	14·50	11·50

335 State Flag and Arms

1998. 50th Anniv of Netherlands Antilles Advisory Council. Multicoloured.

1285	75c. Type **335**	2·00	1·60
1286	85c. Gavel	2·30	1·90

336 Christina Flanders (philanthropic worker)

1998. Death Anniversaries. Multicoloured.

1287	40c. Type **336** (second anniv)	1·20	95
1288	75c. Abraham Jesurun (writer and first president of Curacao Chamber of Commerce, 80th anniv)	2·00	1·60
1289	85c. Capt. Gerrit Newton (seaman and shipyard manager, 50th anniv (1999))	2·10	1·90
1290	110c. Eduardo Adriana (sportsman, first anniv)	3·00	2·40

337 Ireland Pillar Box

1998. Postboxes (1st series). Multicoloured.

1291	15c. Type **337**	65	45
1292	40c. Nepal postbox	1·30	95
1293	75c. Uruguay postbox	2·10	1·60
1294	85c. Curacao postbox	2·30	2·00

See also Nos. 1413/16.

338 Globe and New Post Emblem

1998. Privatization of Postal Services.

1295	**338**	75c. black, blue and red	2·00	1·60
1296	-	110c. multicoloured	3·00	2·40
1297	-	225c. multicoloured	5·50	5·00

Designs:—Vert: 110c. Tree and binary code. Horiz: 225c. 1949 25c. UPU stamp, reproduction of No. 1296 and binary code.

339 Black Rhinoceros

1998. Endangered Species. Multicoloured.

1298	5c. Type **339**	2·50	1·60
1299	75c. White-tailed hawk (vert)	3·25	2·30
1300	125c. White-tailed deer	5·00	3·00
1301	250c. Tiger ("Tigris") (vert)	7·50	5·50

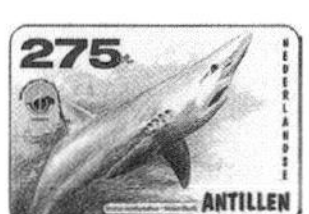
340 Short-finned Mako ("Mako Shark")

1998. Fish. Multicoloured.

1302	275c. Type **340**	10·00	6·25
1303	350c. Manta ray	11·50	7·75

341 1950 5c. Stamp

1998. 70th Anniv of Dutch Stamp Dealers Club Stamp Exhibition, The Hague. Multicoloured.

1304	225c. Type **341**	5·75	5·50
1305	500c. 1950 Queen Juliana 15c. stamp	11·50	11·00
MS1306	72×50 mm. 500c. Curacao 1922 12½c. stamp	13·00	12·50

342 Child with Family Paper Chain

1998. Child Welfare. Universal Rights of the Child. Multicoloured.

1307	40c.+15c. Type **342** (right to name and nationality)	1·70	1·20
1308	75c.+25c. Children eating water melons (right to health care)	2·50	2·20
1309	110c.+45c. Children painting (right of disabled children to special care)	4·00	3·50
1310	225c.+100c. Children playing with can telephones (right to freedom of expression)	8·00	7·00

343 Former Office, Curacao

1998. 60th Anniv of PriceWaterhouseCoopers (accountancy firm). Multicoloured.

1311	75c. Type **343**	3·75	3·00
1312	225c. Modern office, Curacao	6·50	4·75

344 *Christmas Tree* (Theodora van Ierland)

1998. Christmas. Children's Paintings. Multicoloured.

1313	35c. Type **344**	1·20	1·10
1314	150c. *Post in mail box* (Anna Sordam)	4·00	3·25

345 Avila Beach Hotel and Dr. Pieter Maal (founder)

1999. 50th Anniv of Avila Beach Hotel. Mult.

1315	75c. Type **345**	2·20	1·60
1316	110c. Beach and flamboyant tree	3·25	2·30
1317	225c. Mesquite tree	5·75	4·75

346 Rabbit and Great Wall of China

1999. China 1999 International Stamp Exhibition, Peking. Year of the Rabbit. Multicoloured.

1318	75c. Type **346**	3·00	1·60
1319	225c. Rabbit and Jade Pagoda (vert)	7·00	4·75
MS1320	88×53 mm. 225c. Rabbit (vert)	8·25	7·75

347 Girls hugging and Wiri

1999. 50th Anniv of Government Correctional Institute. Musical instruments. Multicoloured.

1321	40c. Type **347**	1·30	1·00
1322	75c. Institute building and bamba	2·10	1·60
1323	85c. Boy at lathe and triangle (horiz)	2·50	1·90

348 Launch of Ship

1999. 500th Anniv of First Written Record (by Amerigo Vespucci) of Curacao. Multicoloured.

1324	75c. Type **348**	2·50	1·60
1325	110c. Otrobanda, 1906	3·25	2·40
1326	175c. Nos. 1324/5 and anniversary emblem	4·75	4·00
1327	225c. Fort Beeckenburg, Caracasbaai	6·00	4·75
1328	500c. 1949 12½c. stamp and sailing ship	12·00	11·00

349 Godett

1999. Fourth Death Anniv of Wilson Godett (politician).

1329	**349** 75c. multicoloured	2·40	1·60

350 Amerindians and Old Map

1999. The Millennium. Multicoloured. (a) Size 35½×35½ mm. Ordinary gum.

1330	5c. Type **350** (arrival of Alonso de Ojeda, Amerigo Vespucci and Juan de la Cosa, 1499)	85	80
1331	10c. Dutch ship, indian and soldier on horseback (Dutch conquest, 1634)	85	80
1332	40c. Flags of constituent islands of Netherlands Antilles, Autonomy Monument in Curacao and document granting autonomy, 1954	1·70	1·20
1333	75c. Telephone and Curacao 1873 25c. King William III stamp (installation of telephones on Curacao, 1892)	2·50	2·00
1334	85c. Fokker F.XVIII airplane *De Snip* (first Amsterdam–Curacao flight, 1934)	2·50	2·30
1335	100c. Oil refinery, Curacao (inauguration, 1915)	2·50	2·30
1336	110c. Dish aerial, undersea fibre optic cable and dolphins (telecommunications)	3·25	2·75
1337	125c. Curacao harbour, bridge and bow of cruise liner (tourism)	4·25	3·50
1338	225c. Ka'i orgel (musical instrument) and couple in folk costume (culture)	5·75	5·50
1339	350c. Brown-throated conure, common caracara, yellow-shouldered amazon and greater flamingoes (nature)	9·00	8·50

(b) Size 29×29 mm. Self-adhesive.

1340	5c. Type **350**	85	80
1341	10c. As No. 1331	85	80
1342	40c. As No. 1332	1·70	1·20
1343	75c. As No. 1333	2·50	2·00
1344	85c. As No. 1334	2·50	2·30
1345	100c. As No. 1335	2·50	2·30
1346	110c. As No. 1336	3·25	2·75
1347	125c. As No. 1337	4·25	3·50
1348	225c. As No. 1338	5·75	5·50
1349	350c. As No. 1339	9·00	8·50

351 Ijzerstraat, Otrobanda

1999. Cultural and Social Relief Funds. Willemstad, World Heritage Site. Multicoloured.

1350	40c.+15c. Type **351**	1·50	1·20
1351	75c.+30c. Oldest house in Punda (now Postal Museum) (vert)	3·00	2·40
1352	110c.+50c. "The Bridal Cake" (now Central National Archives), Scharloo	4·25	3·50

352 St. Paul's Roman Catholic Church, Saba

1999. Tourist Attractions. Multicoloured.

1357	150c. Type **352**	5·75	3·25
1359	250c. Greater flamingoes, Bonaire	7·50	5·50
1361	500c. Courthouse, St. Maarten	13·00	11·00

353 Basketball

1999. Child Welfare. Sports. Multicoloured.

1370	40c.+15c. Type **353**	2·50	1·40
1371	75c.+25c. Golf	3·75	2·30
1372	110c.+45c. Fencing	5·00	3·50
1373	225c.+100c. Tennis	9·50	7·50

354 *Saintpaulia ionantha*

1999. Flowers. Multicoloured.

1374	40c. Type **354**	2·30	1·60
1375	40c. *Gardenia jasminioides*	2·30	1·60
1376	40c. Allamanda	2·30	1·60
1377	40c. Bougainvillea	2·30	1·60
1378	75c. Strelitzia	2·75	2·30
1379	75c. Cymbidium	2·75	2·30
1380	75c. Phalaenopsis	2·75	2·30
1381	75c. *Cassia fistula*	2·75	2·30
1382	110c. Doritaenopsis	4·25	3·00
1383	110c. Guzmania	4·25	3·00
1384	225c. *Catharanthus roseus*	6·50	5·50
1385	225c. *Caralluma hexagona*	6·50	5·50

355 Children wearing Hats

1999. Christmas. Multicoloured.

1386	35c. Type **355**	1·70	80
1387	150c. Clock face and islands	4·25	3·25

356 Man, Baby and Building Blocks (Fathers' Day)

2000. Greetings Stamps. Multicoloured.

1388	40c. Type **356**	1·20	95
1389	40c. Women and globe (Mothers' Day)	1·20	95
1390	40c. Hearts and flowers (Valentine's Day)	1·20	95
1391	75c. Puppy and present ("Thank You")	2·10	1·90
1392	110c. Butterfly and vase of flowers (Special Occasions)	3·25	2·75
1393	150c. As No. 1389	4·50	4·25
1394	150c. As No. 1390	4·50	4·25
1395	225c. Hands and wedding rings (Anniversary)	6·25	6·00

357 Dragon

2000. Chinese Year of the Dragon. Multicoloured.

1396	110c. Type **357**	4·25	3·00
MS1397	50×85 mm. 225c. Chinese dragons	8·25	7·75

358 Red Eyed Tree Frog

2000. Endangered Animals. Multicoloured.

1398	40c. Type **358**	3·25	2·30
1399	75c. King penguin (vert)	4·25	3·00
1400	85c. Killer whale (vert)	4·25	3·00
1401	100c. African elephant (vert)	4·25	3·00
1402	110c. Chimpanzee (vert)	4·25	3·00
1403	225c. Tiger	6·50	6·25

359 Children playing

2000. Cultural and Social Relief Funds. Mult.

1404	75c.+30c. Type **359**	3·00	2·50
1405	110c.+50c. Schoolchildren performing science experiments	5·00	4·50
1406	225c.+100c. Teacher giving lesson (vert)	9·50	8·50

360 Space Shuttle Launch

2000. World Stamp Expo 2000, Anaheim, California. Space Exploration. Multicoloured.

1407	75c. Type **360**	4·25	2·30
1408	225c. Astronaut, Moon and space station	7·50	6·50
MS1409	100×70 mm. 225c. Futuristic space station	8·25	7·75

361 Cycling

2000. Olympic Games, Sydney. Multicoloured.

1410	75c. Type **361**	3·25	2·30
1411	225c. Athletics	7·50	6·50
MS1412	50×72 mm. 225c. Swimming	8·25	7·75

2000. Postboxes (2nd series). As T **337**. Multicoloured.

1413	110c. Mexico postbox	3·25	3·00
1414	175c. Dubai postbox	5·25	5·00
1415	350c. Great Britain postbox	10·00	9·50
1416	500c. United States of America postbox	14·50	13·50

362 People

2000. Social Insurance Bank. Multicoloured.

1417	75c. Type **362**	2·50	2·30
1418	110c. Adult holding child's hand (horiz)	3·50	3·25
1419	225c. Anniversary emblem	7·00	6·50

363 Child reaching towards Night Sky

2000. Child Welfare. Multicoloured.

1420	40c.+15c. Type **363**	2·10	2·00
1421	75c.+25c. Children using Internet (horiz)	3·50	3·25
1422	110c.+45c. Children playing with toy boat (horiz)	5·00	4·75
1423	225c.+100c. Children consulting map	9·00	8·50

364 Angels and Score of *Jingle Bells* (carol)

2000. Christmas. Multicoloured.

1424	40c. Type **364**	1·70	1·60
1425	150c. Seasonal messages in different languages (horiz)	5·00	4·75

365 Red King Snake

2001. Chinese Year of the Snake. Multicoloured.

1426	110c. Type **365**	4·25	3·00
MS1427	87×53 mm. 225c. Indian cobra (*Naja naja*) (vert)	9·00	8·50

366 Forest

2001. HONG KONG 2001 World Stamp Exhibition. Landscapes. Multicoloured.

1428	25c. Type **366**	1·50	1·10
1429	40c. Palm trees and waterfall	1·80	1·60
1430	110c. Spinner dolphins (*Stenella longirostris*)	4·25	2·75

367 Persian Shaded Golden Cat

2001. Cats and Dogs. Multicoloured.

1431	55c. Type **367**	3·25	2·00
1432	75c. Burmese bluepoint cat and kittens	4·25	2·75
1433	110c. American wirehair	4·25	3·50
1434	175c. Golden retriever dog	5·75	4·50
1435	225c. German shepherd dog	7·50	6·25
1436	750c. British shorthair silver tabby	21·00	20·00

368 *Mars* (Dutch ship of the line)

2001. Ships. Multicoloured.

1437	110c. Type **368**	4·25	3·00
1438	275c. *Alphen* (frigate)	8·25	7·25
1439	350c. *Curacao* (paddle-steamer) (horiz)	10·50	9·50
1440	500c. *Pioneer* (schooner) (horiz)	16·00	13·00

369 Pen and Emblem

2001. Fifth Anniv of Caribbean Postal Union. Multicoloured.

1441	75c.+25c. Type **369**	3·25	2·75
1442	110c.+45c. Emblem	5·00	4·25
1443	225c. + 100c. Silhouettes encircling globe	10·00	9·00

370 Fedjai riding Bicycle

2001. Fedjai (cartoon postman) (1st series). Multicoloured.

1444	5c. Type **370**	1·20	45
1445	40c. Fedjai and children	1·40	1·10
1446	75c. Fedjai and post box containing bird's nest and chicks	2·50	2·10
1447	85c. Fedjai and elderly woman	3·00	2·30
1448	100c. Barking dog and Fedjai sitting on postbox	3·25	2·75
1449	110c. Fedjai and boy reading comic	4·25	3·00

See also Nos. 1487/90 and **MS**1538.

371 Cave Entrance and Area Map

2001. Kueba Boza (Muzzle Cave). Multicoloured.

1450	85c. Type **371**	3·00	2·30
1451	110c. *Leptonycteris nivalis cursoae* (bat)	3·50	3·00
1452	225c. *Glosophaga elongata* (bat)	7·25	6·25

372 Streamertail (*Trochilus polytmus*)

2001. Birds. Multicoloured.

1453	10c. Type **372**	1·30	80
1454	85c. Eastern white pelican (*Pelecanus onocrotalus*)	3·75	2·50
1455	110c. Gouldian finch (*Erythrura gouldiae*)	4·25	3·00
1456	175c. Painted bunting (*Passerina ciris*)	5·50	4·75
1457	250c. Atlantic puffin (*Fratercula artica*)	7·75	6·75
1458	350c. American darter (*Anhinga anhinga*)	12·00	10·00

373 Chapel Facade and Map of St. Maarten Island

2001. 150th Anniv of Philipsburg Methodist Chapel. Multicoloured.

1459	75c. Type **373**	2·50	2·10
1460	110c. Rainbow, open Bible and map of St. Maarten	3·75	3·00

374 Boy feeding Toddler

2001. Child Welfare. Youth Volunteers. Multicoloured.

1461	40c.+15c. Type **374**	2·75	1·70
1462	75c.+25c. Girls dancing (vert)	3·25	3·00
1463	110c.+45c. Boy and elderly woman (vert)	5·50	4·50

375 Children of Different Nations

2001. Christmas. Multicoloured.

1464	40c. Type **375**	1·70	1·20
1465	150c. Children and Infant Jesus (vert)	5·00	4·00

376 Prince Willem-Alexander

2002. Wedding of Crown Prince Willem-Alexander to Maxima Zorreguieta. Multicoloured.

1466	75c. Type **376**	2·50	2·00
1467	110c. Princess Máxima	3·75	3·00
MS1468	75×72 mm. 2g.25, Prince Willem-Alexander facing left; 2g.75, Princess Máxima facing left	17·00	16·00

377 Horse

2002. Chinese New Year. Year of the Horse. Multicoloured.

1469	25c. Type **377**	2·00	1·60
MS1470	52×86 mm. 95c. Horse's head	5·00	4·75

378 Blue-tailed Emerald (*Chlorostilbon mellisugus*) and Passion Flower (*Passiflora foetida*)

2002. Flora and Fauna. Multicoloured.

1471	50c. Type **378**	1·70	1·40
1472	95c. Lineated anole (*Anolis lineatus*) and *Cordia sebestena* (flower) (horiz)	3·25	2·75
1473	120c. Dragonfly (*Odonata*) (horiz)	4·00	3·25
1474	145c. Hermit crab (*Coenobita clypeatus*) (horiz)	4·75	4·00
1475	285c. Paper wasp (*Polistes versicolor*)	8·75	7·50

379 Flambeau (*Dryas julia*)

2002. Butterflies. Multicoloured.

1400	25c. Type **379**	1·70	80
1481	145c. Monarch (*Danaus plexippus*) (horiz)	5·00	3·75
1482	400c. *Mechanitis polymnia* (horiz)	12·50	11·00
1483	500c. *Pyrrhopygopsis socrates* (wrongly inscr "Pyrhapygopsis socrates") (horiz)	15·00	13·50

380 Flags as Football

2002. World Cup Football Championship, Japan and South Korea. Multicoloured.

1484	95c.+35c. Type **380**	4·25	3·50
1485	145c.+55c. Player and globe as football	6·00	5·25
1486	240c.+110c. Player and ball	10·50	9·25

381 Fedjai skipping

2002. Fedjai (cartoon postman) (2nd series). Multicoloured.

1487	10c. Type **381**	1·70	60
1488	55c. Fedjai and dog in rubbish bin (vert)	2·50	1·70
1489	95c. Fedjai presenting envelope on tray (vert)	3·25	2·75
1490	240c. Fedjai helping elderly woman across road (vert)	7·50	6·50

382 Man

2002. The Potato Eaters (Vincent Van Gogh). Amphilex 2002 International Stamp Exhibition, Amsterdam. Designs showing parts of painting. Multicoloured.

1491	70c. Type **382**	2·50	2·00
1492	95c. Man (different)	3·25	2·75
1493	145c. Woman facing front	5·00	4·00
1494	240c. Woman facing left	7·50	6·75
MS1495	98×75 mm. 550c. As No. 1494 but design enlarged (horiz)	17·00	16·00

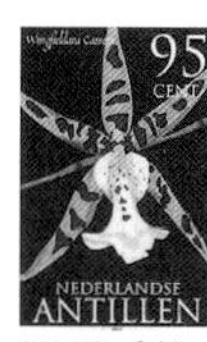

383 *Wingfieldara casseta*

2002. Orchids. Multicoloured.

1496	95c. Type **383**	3·75	3·25
1497	285c. *Cymbidium Magna Charta*	8·25	7·75
1498	380c. *Brassolaeliocattleya*	11·50	10·50
1499	750c. *Miltonia spectabilis*	21·00	20·00

384 Lion wearing Snorkel

2001. Child Welfare. Multicoloured.

1500	50c.+15c. Type **384**	2·10	1·90
1501	95c.+35c. Kangaroo	4·25	3·50
1502	145c.+55c. Goat and penguin	6·25	5·50
1503	240c.+100c. Lizard and toucan	10·50	9·75

385 Christmas Trees

2002. Christmas. Multicoloured.

1504	95c. Type **385**	3·00	2·75
1505	240c. Lanterns	7·50	6·75

386 Savanna Hawk (*Buteogallus meridionalis*)

2002. Birds. Multicoloured.

1506	5c. Type **386**	85	60
1507	20c. Black-spotted barbet (*Capito niger*)	1·00	80
1508	30c. Scarlet macaw (*Ara macao*)	1·20	95
1509	35c. Great jacamar (*Jacamerops aurea*)	1·30	1·10
1510	70c. White-necked jacobin (*Florisuga mellivora*)	2·10	1·90
1511	85c. Crimson fruit-crow (*Haematoderis militaris*) (inscr "Heamatoderus")	2·50	2·20
1512	90c. Peach-fronted conure (*Aratinga aurea*)	2·75	2·30
1513	95c. Green oropendula (*Psarocolius viridis*)	2·75	2·50
1514	100c. Eastern meadowlark (*Stumella magna*) (horiz)	3·00	2·75
1515	145c. Sun conure (*Aratinga solstitalis*) (horiz)	4·25	4·00
1516	240c. White-tailed toucan (*Trogon virdis*)	7·00	6·50
1517	285c. Red-billed toucan (*Ramphastos tucanus*)	8·25	7·75

387 Goat's Head

2003. New Year. Year of the Goat.

1518	**387**	25c. multicoloured	2·00	1·60
MS1519 86×52 mm. 96c. black, red and grey			4·25	4·00

Design:—95c. Rearing goat.

388 Leeward Islands

2003. Cultural and Social Relief Funds. Sheet 150× 61 mm containing T **388** and similar multicoloured designs showing maps.

MS1520 25c.+10c. Type **388**; 30c.+15c. Windward Islands (vert); 55c.+25c. Curacao and Bonaire; 85c.+35c. St. Marten, Saba and St. Eustatius (vert); 95c +40c. Caribbean	13·00	12·50

389 *Rhetus arcius*

2003. Butterflies. Multicoloured.

1521	5c. Type **389**	65	45
1522	10c. *Evenus teresina* (horiz)	85	60
1523	25c. *Bhutanitis thaidina* (horiz)	1·00	80
1524	30c. *Semomesia capanea* (horiz)	1·20	95
1525	45c. *Papilio machaon* (horiz)	1·30	1·10
1526	55c. *Papilio multicaudata*	1·80	1·40
1527	65c. *Graphium weiskei*	2·10	1·90
1528	95c. *Aneyluris formosissima venahalis*	2·75	2·50
1529	100c. *Euphaedra neophron* (horiz)	3·00	2·75
1530	145c. *Ornithoptera goliath Samson* (horiz)	4·25	4·00
1531	275c. *Aneyluris colubra*	8·00	7·25
1532	350c. *Papilio lorquinianus*	10·00	9·00

390 Trumpet

2003. Musical Instruments. Sheet 125×61 mm containing T **390** and similar vert designs. Multicoloured.

MS1533 20c. Type **390**; 75c. Drums; 145c. Tenor saxophone; 285c. Double bass	15·00	14·50

391 Early Banknote

2003. 300th Anniv of Joh. Enschede (printers). Two sheets containing T **391** and similar vert designs. Multicoloured.

MS1534 (a) 120×61 mm. 70c. Type **391**; 95c. 1873 stamp; 145c. Revenue stamp; 240c. 1967 banknote (b) 85×52 mm. 550c. Johan Enschede building, Haarlem	31·00	29·00

392 10 Gilder Banknote

2003. 175th Anniv of Central Bank. Multicoloured.

1535	95c. Type **392**	2·75	2·75
1536	145c. Street map and bank building	4·25	4·00
1537	285c. "First Instructions of the Bank of Curacao" (vert)	7·00	6·75

393 Fedjai proposing to Angelina

2003. Fedjai (cartoon postman) (3rd series). Sheet 120×61 mm containing T **393** and similar multicoloured designs.

MS1538 30c. Type **393**; 95c. Married couple; 145c. Taking Angelina to maternity hospital (horiz); 240c. With baby in post bag	15·00	14·50

394 15th-century Egyptian Boat

2003. Watercraft.

1539	**394**	5c. multicoloured	1·00	80
1540	-	5c. multicoloured	1·00	80
1541	-	35c. reddish orange and black	1·30	95
1542	-	35c. multicoloured	1·30	95
1543	-	40c. multicoloured	1·50	1·10
1544	-	40c. multicoloured	1·50	1·10
1545	-	60c. multicoloured	1·70	1·40
1546	-	60c. orange and black	1·70	1·40
1547	-	75c. multicoloured	2·00	1·70
1548	-	75c. multicoloured	2·00	1·70
1549	-	85c. multicoloured (horiz)	2·30	2·00
1550	-	85c. multicoloured (horiz)	2·30	2·00

Designs:—5c. Type **394**; 5c. Model boat from Tutankhamen's tomb; 35c. Ulysseus and the Sirens (vase decoration); 35c .Egyptian river craft; 40c. Greek dromon (galley); 40c. Illustration from *Vergilius Aenes* (15th-century book); 60c. Javanese fusta (galley); 60c. Greek trading ship; 75c. 16th-century Venetian; 75c. Mora (Bayeux tapestry); 85c. Captain Cook's *Earl of Pembroke*; 85c. *Savannah* (transatlantic steamship).

2003. Greetings Stamps. Personnal Stamps. Multicoloured.

1550a	95c. Parcel	2·50	2·20
1550b	95c. Rocking Horse	2·50	2·20
1550c	95c. Drums	2·50	2·20
1550d	95c. Bells	2·50	2·20
1550e	95c. Palm Tree	2·50	2·20
1550f	95c. Sunflower	2·50	2·20
1550g	145c. Parcel	3·75	3·25
1550g	145c. Rocking Horse	3·75	3·25
1550i	145c. Drums	3·75	3·25
1550j	145c. Bells	3·75	3·25
1550k	145c. Palm Tree	3·75	3·25
1550l	145c. Sunflower	3·75	3·25

395 Bombay Cat

2003. Cats. Multicoloured.

1551	5c. Type **395**	65	45
1552	20c. Persian seal point	85	60
1553	25c. British shorthair	90	80
1554	50c. British blue	1·70	1·40
1555	65c. Persian chinchilla	1·80	1·60
1556	75c. Tonkinese red point	2·00	1·70
1557	85c. Balinese lilac tabby point	2·10	1·90
1558	95c. Persian shaded cameo	2·50	2·20
1559	100c. Burmilla	2·75	2·30
1560	145c. Chocolate tortie shaded silver eastern shorthair	3·75	3·25
1561	150c. Devon rex	3·75	3·50
1562	285c. Persian black tabby	7·25	6·50

396 Child under Shower

2003. Child Welfare. Sheet 125×61 mm containing T **396** and similar vert designs. Multicoloured.

MS1563 50c.+15c. Type **396**; 95c.+35c. Girl holding umbrella; 145c.+55c. Boy watering plants; 240c.+110c. Hands under water tap	19·00	18·00

397 Cacti hung with Baubles

2003. Christmas. Multicoloured.

1564	75c. Type **397**	2·00	1·90
1565	240c. Cacti as figures holding fairy lights and clock	5·00	4·75

398 "BON" (Bonaire)

2003. Tourism. Multicoloured.

1566	50c. Type **398**	1·20	1·10
1567	75c. "CUR" (Curaçao)	1·80	1·70
1568	95c. "SAB" (Saba)	2·10	2·00
1569	120c. "EUX" (St. Eustatius)	2·75	2·50
1570	145c. "SXM" (Saint Maartin)	3·00	2·75
1571	240c. "CUR" (Curaçao)	5·00	4·75
1572	285c. "SXM" (Saint Maartin)	5·75	5·50
1573	380c. Emblem	7·50	7·00

399 Princess Amalia

2004. Birth of Princess Amalia of Netherlands. Two sheets containing T **399** and similar square design. Multicoloured.

MS1574 (a) 120×61 mm. 145c. Type **399**; 380c. Crown Prince Willem Alexander holding Princess Amalia (b) 90×120 mm. No. **MS**1574×2	35·00	33·00

400 Monkey

2004. New Year. Year of the Monkey. Multicoloured.

1575	95c. Type **400**	4·25	4·00
MS1576 100×72 mm. 145c. Monkey and fan		5·00	4·75

401 Belevedere (inscr "L.B. Smithplein 3)

2004. Houses. Multicoloured.

1577	10c. Type **401**	85	80
1578	25c. Hoogstraat 27	1·20	1·10
1579	35c. Landhuis, Brievengat	1·50	1·40
1580	65c. Scharlooweg 102	2·00	1·90
1581	95c. Hoogstrat 21-25	2·10	2·00
1582	145c. Villa Maria	3·00	2·75
1583	275c. Werfstraat 6	5·75	5·50
1584	350c. Landhuis, Ronde Klip	7·50	7·00

402 Elephant

2004. Fauna. Multicoloured.

1585	5c. Type **402**	25	25
1586	10c. Elephant facing left	50	45
1587	25c. Elephant amongst trees	90	85
1588	35c. Chimpanzee	1·10	1·00
1589	45c. Chimpanzee holding stick	1·20	1·20
1590	55c. Head of chimpanzee	1·40	1·30
1591	65c. Polar bear and cub	1·60	1·50
1592	95c. Polar bear facing left	2·00	1·90
1593	100c. Polar bear and cub (different)	2·10	2·00
1594	145c. Lion facing right	3·00	2·75
1595	275c. Lion facing left	5·75	5·50
1596	350c. Head of lion	6·50	6·25

403 Diesel Locomotive (1977)

2004. Transport. Multicoloured.

1597	10c. Type **403**	50	30
1598	55c. Water-carrier (1900)	1·70	1·60
1599	75c. Ford Model A (1903)	2·10	2·00
1600	85c. Tanker (2004)	2·30	2·20
1601	95c. *Wright Flyer* (1903)	2·75	2·50
1602	145c. Penny Farthing bicycle (1871)	3·25	3·00

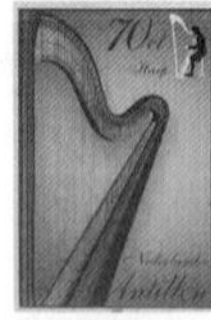

404 Harp

2004. Musical Instruments. Multicoloured.

1603	70c. Type **404**	1·70	1·60
1604	95c. Lute	2·30	2·20
1605	145c. Violin (horiz)	3·25	3·00
1606	240c. Zither (horiz)	5·25	5·00

405 Miniature Pinscher

2004. Dogs. Multicoloured.

1607	5c. Type **405**	50	30
1608	5c. Pomeranian	50	30
1609	35c. Longhaired Teckel (dachshund)	1·20	1·10
1610	35c. Shih Tzu	1·20	1·10
1611	40c. Boxer puppy	1·30	1·20
1612	40c. Jack Russell terrier	1·30	1·20
1613	60c. Basset hound	1·80	1·70
1614	60c. Braque de l'Ariege	1·80	1·70
1615	75c. Afghan hound	2·10	2·00
1616	75c. Old English sheepdog	2·10	2·00
1617	85c. Entlebucher Sennen	2·30	2·20
1618	85c. Mastiff	2·30	2·20

406 Dragon and Curacao Harbour

2004. International Stamp Exhibition, Singapore. Multicoloured.

1619	95c. Type **406**	2·30	2·20
1620	95c. Merlion and flags	2·30	2·20
1621	145c. Dragon and Brion Plaza, Otrobanda	3·25	3·00
1622	145c. Dr. A. C. Wathey Cruise and Cargo Facility, St. Maarten	3·25	3·00
MS1623 106×72 mm. 500c. As No. 1620		10·50	10·00

407 *Pomacanthus paru*

2004. Fish and Ducks. Multicoloured.

1624	30c. Type **407**	65	60
1625	65c. *Epinephelus guttatus*	1·20	1·10
1626	70c. *Mycteroperca interstitialis*	1·60	1·50
1627	75c. *Holacanthus isabelita*	1·70	1·60
1628	85c. *Epinephelus itajara*	1·80	1·70
1629	95c. *Holacanthus ciliaris*	2·00	1·90
1630	100c. American widgeon (*Anas Americana*) and *Sphyraena barracuda* (inscr "Sphyreana")	2·10	2·00
1631	145c. Blue-winged teal (*Anas discors*)	3·25	3·00

1632 250c. Bahama pintail (*Anas bahamensis*) 5·50 5·00
1633 285c. Lesser scaup (*Aythya affinis*) 6·00 5·75

2004. Maps and Flags. Personal Stamps. Multicoloured.
1634 95c. Bonaire 2·10 2·00
1635 95c. Curaçao 2·10 2·00
1636 95c. Saba 2·10 2·00
1637 95c. St Eustatius 2·10 2·00
1638 95c. St Maarten 2·10 2·00
1639 95c. Netherlands Antilles 2·10 2·00
1640 145c. Bonaire 3·25 3·00
1641 145c. Curaçao 3·25 3·00
1642 145c. Saba 3·25 3·00
1643 145c. St Eustatius 3·25 3·00
1644 145c. St Maarten 3·25 3·00
1645 145c. Netherlands Antilles 3·25 3·00

408 *Icterus icterus* (troupial)

2004. Birds. Multicoloured.
1646 10c. Type **408** 65 60
1647 95c. *Coereba flaveola* (bananaquit) 2·10 2·00
1648 100c. *Zonotrichia capensis* (rufous-collared sparrow) 2·30 2·20
1649 145c. *Sterna hirundo* (common tern) 3·25 3·00
1650 250c. *Phoenicopterus ruber* (greater flamingo) 5·75 5·50
1651 500c. *Buteo albicaudatus* (white-tailed hawk) 11·00 10·00

409 Lulu, Basje and Slave Huts, Bonaire

2004. Child Welfare. Multicoloured.
1652 50c. +15c. Type **409** 1·50 1·40
1653 95c. +35c. Lulu and Autonomy Monument 3·00 2·75
1654 95c. +35c. Visiting slave houses on Curçao 3·00 2·75
1655 145c. +55c. Visiting Kenepa plantation house 4·25 4·00
1656 145c. +55c. Basje and part of Constitution document 4·25 4·00

410 *Caretta caretta* (loggerhead turtle)

2004. Turtles. Multicoloured.
1657 100c. Type **410** 2·30 2·20
1658 145c. *Lepidochelys kempii* (Kemp's Ridley) 3·25 3·00
1659 240c. *Chelonia mydas* (Green) 5·50 5·00
1660 285c. *Lepidochelys olivacea* (Olive Ridley) 6·25 6·00
1661 380c. *Eretmochelys imbricata* (Hawksbill) 8·25 7·75
1662 500c. *Dermochelys coriacea* (Leatherback) 10·50 10·00

413 *Hibiscus rosa-sinensis*

2005. Flowers. Multicoloured.
1663 65c. Type **413** 1·70 1·60
1664 76c. *Plumbago auriculata* 1·80 1·70
1665 97c. *Tecoma stans* 2·10 2·00
1666 100c. *Ixora coccinea* 1·90 1·80
1667 122c. *Catharanthus roseus* 2·75 2·50
1668 148c. *Lantana camara* 3·25 3·00
1669 240c. *Tradescantia pallida* 5·00 4·75
1670 270c. *Nerium oleander* 5·75 5·50
1671 285c. *Plumeria obtusa* 6·00 5·75
1672 350c. *Bougainvillea spectabilis* 7·50 7·25

2005. Chinese New Year. Year of the Rooster. Multicoloured.
1673 145c. Golden rooster 3·75 3·50
MS1674 53×85 mm. 500c. Rooster (different) 12·00 11·00

2005. 25th Anniv of Coronation of Queen Beatrix. Multicoloured.
MS1675 50c. Coronation; 97c. Seated; 145c. With Nelson Mandela; 285c. Wearing glasses; 550c. Wearing hat 28·00 26·00

2005. Houses. Curaçao. Multicoloured.
1676 10c. Scharlooweg 86 35 35
1677 21c. Landhuis, Zeelandia 85 75
1678 25c. Berg Altena 95 70
1679 35c. Landhuis, Dokterstuin 1·10 1·00
1680 97c. Landhuis, Santa Martha 2·40 2·20
1681 148c. Landhuis, Seri Papaya 3·75 3·50
1682 270c. Landhuis, Rooi Katootje 6·50 6·00
1683 300c. Plase Horacio Hoyer 19 7·25 6·75

2005. Art. Paintings by Vincent van Gogh. Multicoloured.
1684 10c. *Vase of Fifteen Sunflowers* (detail, left of vase) 35 35
1685 65c. *Sunflowers* (detail, two sunflowers) 2·00 1·90
1686 80c. *Self Portrait* 2·50 2·40
1687 120c. *Sunflowers* (detail, single sunflower) 3·25 3·00
1688 150c. *Vase of Fifteen Sunflowers* 3·75 3·50
1689 175c. *Portrait of Joseph Roulin* 4·25 4·00
MS1690 145×72 mm. 500c. *Four Cut Sunflowers* (detail) 14·00 13·00

2005. 300th Anniv Otrobanda (1st issue). Multicoloured.
1691 100c. Early street scene 2·75 2·50
1692 150c. Stonemason's yard ('Werf') 3·75 3·50
1693 285c. Rifwater 6·75 6·25
1694 500c. Bus station, Brion Square 12·00 11·00
See also Nos. 1756/9 and 1852/5.

2005. Fruit. Multicoloured.
1695 25c. Papaya 55 50
1696 45c. Pomegranite 95 85
1697 70c. Mango 1·50 1·40
1698 75c. Banana 1·70 1·50
1699 85c. Cashews 1·90 1·70
1700 97c. Soursop 2·20 2·00
1701 145c. Tamarind 3·25 3·00
1702 193c. Watermelon 4·25 4·00
1703 270c. Genip 6·00 5·50
1704 300c. Seagrape 6·50 6·00
See also Nos. 2072/81.

2005. Corals. Multicoloured.
1705 51c. *Stephanocoenia intersepta* 1·10 1·00
1706 148c. *Manicina areolata* 3·25 3·00
1707 270c. *Eusmilia fastigiata* 6·00 5·50
1708 750c. *Diploria strigosa* 16·00 14·50

2005. Child Welfare. International Year of Sport and Sports Education. Multicoloured.
1709 55c. +20c. Football 1·90 1·70
1710 97c. +36c. Table tennis 3·25 3·00
1711 148c. +56c. Tennis 5·00 4·50
1712 240c. +110c. Baseball 8·50 7·75

2005. Musical Instruments. Multicoloured.
1713 55c. Accordian 1·30 1·20
1714 97c. Bagpipes (vert) 2·20 2·00
1715 145c. Veena (inscr 'Fina') 3·25 3·00
1716 195c. Shamisen (vert) 4·25 4·00
1717 240c. Shofar (musical Ram's horn) (vert) 5·25 4·75
1718 285c. Organ (vert) 6·00 5·50

2005. Christmas
1719 10c. Santa Claus 35 35
1720 97c. Santa and children (horiz) 2·75 2·50
1721 148c. Santa holding '2006' (horiz) 3·75 3·50
1722 580c. Santa asleep wearing striped socks 14·00 13·00

2005. 150th Anniv of St. Elisabeth Hospital, Otrobanda. Multicoloured.
1723 97c. Projected new buildings 2·75 2·50
1724 145c Stained glass window 3·75 3·50
1725 300c Entrance to first hospital at Yzerstraat 68 8·25 7·75

2006. Chinese New Year. Year of the Dog. Multicoloured.
1726 100c. Chinese ceramic dog 2·75 2·50
1727 149c Six dogs 3·75 3·50
MS1728 46×76 mm. 500c. Outline of dog and detail of Chinese zodiac 12·00 11·00

2006. Equine Animals. Multicoloured.
1729 50c. Asiatic Wild Ass and foal 1·50 1·40
1730 100c. Rhenish German Coldblood 2·40 2·20
1731 149c. Donkey and foal 3·75 3·50
1732 285c. Mule 6·75 6·25
1733 550c. Hanoverian 13·50 12·00

2006. Frogs. Multicoloured.
1734 55c. *Hyla cinerea* 1·70 1·50
1735 100c. *Dendrobates tinctorius* 2·40 2·20
1736 149c. *Dendrobates azureus* 3·75 3·50
1737 405c. *Epipedobates tricolor* 9·75 9·00

2006. Butterflies. Multicoloured.
1738 24c. *Danaus chrysippus* 95 85
1739 53c. *Prepona praeneste* 1·90 1·70
1740 100c. *Caligo uranus* 2·50 2·40
1741 149c. *Ituna lamirus* 3·75 3·50
1741a 285c. *Euphaedra gausape* 6·75 6·25
1741b 385c. *Morpho secuba* 8·25 7·50

2006. Orchids. Multicoloured.
1742 153c. *Brassoaelio cattleya* 4·50 4·00
1743 240c. *Miltonipsis* 6·00 5·50
1744 285c. *Promenaea xanthina* 7·00 6·50
1745 295c. *Paphiopedilum streathamense* (vert) 7·50 6·75
1745a 380c. *Cattleya chocensis* (vert) 9·25 8·50
1745b 500c. *Disa kewensis* (vert) 12·00 11·00

2006. Classic Cars. Multicoloured.
1746 5c. MGB, 1976 1·30 1·20
1747 10c. Studebaker Avanti, 1963 2·20 2·00
1748 25c. Pegaso Cabriolet, 1953 3·25 3·00
1749 30c. Delage Aerosport. 1939 3·50 3·25
1750 45c. Hispano Suiza, 1924 4·25 4·00
1751 55c. Pierce Arrow Motorette, 1903 16·00 14·50

2006. Washington 2006 International Philatelic Exhibition. Multicoloured.
1752 100c. Post boxes, USA and Netherlands Antilles 2·20 2·00
1753 100c. Queen Emma Bridge, Curacao and George Washington Bridge, New York 2·20 2·00
1754 149c. UPU emblem 3·25 3·00
1755 149c. Fokker F18 and F4 aircraft 3·25 3·00
MS1755a 86×57 mm. 405c. Capitol, Washington and Government Building, Willemstad, Curaçao 9·25 8·50

2006. 300th Anniv Otrobanda (2nd issue). Multicoloured.
1756 100c. Hoogstraat 2·00 1·90
1757 149c. Emmabrug 3·00 2·75
1758 500c. Zeeman's Hius 6·50 6·00
1759 335c. Pasakontrami 9·25 8·50

2006. Greetings Stamps. Multicoloured.
1760 52c. 'BLESS YOU' 1·10 1·00
1761 55c. 'LOVE' 1·20 1·10
1762 77c. 'ALL THE BEST' 1·70 1·50
1763 95c. 'REGARDS' 2·00 1·90
1764 1g. 'GO FOR IT' 2·20 2·00
1765 1g.49 'TOLERANCE' 3·25 3·00
1766 1g.53 POSITIVISM 3·25 3·00
1767 2g.85 'KEEP ON GOING' 5·50 5·00
1768 3g.35 'SUCCESS' 6·75 6·00
1769 4g.05 'BE GOOD' 8·25 7·50

2006. Birds. Multicoloured.
1770 5c. *Taeniopygia guttata* (Zebra Finch) 20 15
1771 5c. *Parus caeruleus* (Blue Tit) (vert) 20 15
1772 35c. *Pitta moluccensis* (Blue-winged Pitta) 75 70
1773 35c. *Pyrrhula pyrrhula* (Bullfinch) (vert) 75 70
1774 60c. *Calospiza fastuosa* (Blue-necked Tanager) 1·30 1·20
1775 60c. *Cosmopsarus regius* (Golden-breasted Starling) 1·30 1·20
1776 75c. *Coracias caudatus* (Lilac-breasted Roller) (vert) 1·50 1·40
1777 75c. *Merops apiaster* (European Bee-eater) (vert) 1·50 1·40
1778 85c. *Icterus nigrogularis* (Yellow Oriole) 1·70 1·50
1779 85c. *Dendrocopos major* (Great Spotted Woodpecker) (vert) 1·70 1·50
1780 100c. *Amazona barbadensis* (Yellow-shouldered Amazon) 2·10 1·90
1781 100c. *Alcedo atthis* (Kingfisher) (vert) 2·10 1·90

2006. Greetings Stamps. Personal Stamps. Multicoloured.
1781a Local Mail (1g.) Puppy and 'Thank You' 3·25 3·00
1781b Local Mail (1g.) Two hearts and 'Love You' 3·25 3·00
1781c Local Mail (1g.) Teddy Bear and 'Hugs and Kisses' 3·25 3·00
1781d Local Mail (1g.) Bougainvillea and 'Missing You' 3·25 3·00
1781e Local Mail (1g.) Kitten and 'Hello' 3·25 3·00
1781f Local Mail (1g.) Dolphin and 'Wish You were Here' 3·25 3·00
1781g International Mail (1g.49) Puppy and 'Thank You' 5·75 5·00
1781g International Mail (1g.49) Two hearts and 'Love You' 5·75 5·00
1781i International Mail (1g.49) Teddy Bear and 'Hugs and Kisses' 5·75 5·00
1781j International Mail (1g.49) Bougainvillea and 'Missing You' 5·75 5·00
1781k International Mail (1g.49) Kitten and 'Hello' 5·75 5·00
1781l International Mail (1g.49) Dolphin and 'Wish You were Here' 5·75 5·00

2006. Art. 400th Birth Anniv of Rembrandt van Rijn. Multicoloured.
1782 70c. *The Vigil* 1·70 1·50
1783 100c. *The Sampling Officials* (datail) 2·75 2·40
1784 153c. *The Jewish Bride* 3·50 3·00
1785 285c. *Self-Portrait* 6·00 5·50
MS1786 57×86 mm. 550c. *Night Watch* 13·00 11·50

2006. Child Welfare. International Year of Planet Earth. Multicoloured.
1787 55c. +20c. Straw hat (America) 1·70 1·50
1788 100c. +45c. Fez (Africa) 3·25 3·00
1789 149c. +61c. Dutch cap (Europe) 5·25 4·50
1790 285c. +125c. Coolie hat (Asia) 9·00 8·00

2006. Royal Visit. Multicoloured.
MS1791 149c. Wearing yellow, red background; 285c. Wearing red hat, blue background; 335c. Wearing small red hat, yellow background; 750c. Wearing large brimmed hat, orange background 35·00 31·00

2006. Christmas. Multicoloured.
1792 45c. Candles 1·10 1·00
1793 100c. Bells 2·10 1·90
1794 149c. As No. 1792 3·00 2·75
1795 215c. As No. 1793 4·50 4·00
1796 285c. Lines 6·00 5·25
1797 380c. Poinsettia flowers 8·00 7·25

2007. Greetings Stamps. Multicoloured.
1798 32c. 'BLESS YOU' 1·10 1·00
1799 60c. 'LOVE' 1·70 1·50
1800 81c. 'ALL THE BEST' 2·30 2·00
1801 87c. 'REGARDS' 2·50 2·20
1802 106c. 'GO FOR IT' 2·75 2·50
1803 157c. 'TOLERANCE' 3·50 3·25
1804 161c. POSITIVISM 3·75 3·50

2007. Fauna. Multicoloured.
1805 3c. *Cacatua leadbeateri* (Major Mitchell's Cockatoo) (As No. 1216) 20 15
1806 25c. King Penguins (As No. 1399) 75 70
1807 53c. Chimpanzee (As No. 1402) 1·30 1·20
1808 60c. Spinner Dolphins (As No. 1430) 1·50 1·40
1809 80c. *Anolis lineatus* (As No. 1472) (horiz) 1·90 1·70
1810 81c. *Passerina ciris* (Painted Bunting) (As No. 1456) 1·90 1·70
1811 95c. *Dryas julia* (Flambeau) 2·30 2·00
1812 106c. Bombay Cat (As Type **395**) 2·50 2·20
1813 145c. *Epinephelus guttatus* (As No. 1625) (horiz) 3·25 3·00
1814 157c. Lion (As No. 1596) (horiz) 3·50 3·00
1815 161c. Pomeranian (As No. 1608) 3·50 3·25
1816 240c. *Eretmochelys imbricata* (Hawksbill Sea Turtle) (As No. 1661) (horiz) 5·25 4·75

2007. Chinese New Year. Year of the Pig. Multicoloured.
1817 104c. Berkshire Pig 2·30 2·00
1818 155c. Warthog 3·50 3·00
MS1819 85×57 mm. 500c. Pig, head and shoulders (vert) 12·00 10·50

2007. Islands of the Netherlands Antilles. Multicoloured.
1820 1c. Bonaire 20 15
1821 2c. Curaçao 20 15
1822 3c. Saba 20 15
1823 4c. Statia 20 15
1823a 5c. St Maarten 20 15
1823b 104c. Bonaire (different) (horiz) 2·50 2·20
1823c 285c. Curaçao (different) (horiz) 6·50 5·75
1823d 335c. Saba (different) (horiz) 7·50 6·75
1823e 405c. Statia (different) (horiz) 9·00 8·25
1823f 500c. St Maarten (different) (horiz) 11·50 10·00

443 Nanzi and Turtle

2007. Cartoons. Nanzi. Multicoloured.
1824 104c. Type **443** 2·40 2·20
1825 104c. Nanzi and shark 2·40 2·20
1826 104c. Nanzi and bird 2·40 2·20
1827 104c. Nanzi and cow 2·40 2·20
1828 104c. Nanzi and dog 2·40 2·20
1829 104c. Nanzi and goat 2·40 2·20
1830 104c. Nanzi and chicken 2·40 2·20
1831 104c. Nanzi and donkey 2·40 2·20

444 Double Bee (Wilda Johnson)

2007. Saba Lacework. Designs showing lacework crafted by women of Saba Island. Multicoloured.

1832	59c. Type **444**	1·30	1·20
1833	80c. The Cross	1·90	1·70
1834	95c. The Leaf	2·20	2·00
1835	104c. The Cross	2·40	2·20
1836	155c. Wallamina	3·50	3·25
1837	159c. The Ada	3·75	3·50

445 School of Fish

2007. Marine Fauna. Multicoloured.

1838	104c. Type **445**	2·00	1·90
1839	155c. Jellyfish	3·00	2·75
1840	195c. Coral reef	3·75	3·50
1841	335c. Turtle	6·25	5·75
1842	405c. Pink coral	7·50	6·75
1843	525c. Three fish	9·50	8·75

446 Grapes, Tomatoes, Bananas, Sprouts and Peppers

2007. Fruit and Vegetables. Multicoloured.

1844	10c. Type **446**	35	35
1845	25c. Pumpkin	55	50
1846	35c. Cucumber, tomato, leek and sweetcorn	75	70
1847	65c. Pear, pineapple, strawberry and orange	1·30	1·20
1848	95c. Avocado (*horiz*)	1·90	1·70
1849	145c. Lemon (*horiz*)	2·75	2·50
1850	275c. Peppers, mushrooms, potato, sweetcorn and tomato (*horiz*)	5·00	4·50
1851	350c. Mangoes (*horiz*)	6·25	5·75

447 Brionplein Square, Willemstad

2007. 300th Anniv Otrobanda (3rd issue). Multicoloured.

1852	104c. Type **447**	2·00	1·90
1853	155c. Jopi building and Hotel Otrobanda	3·00	2·75
1854	285c. Kura Hulanda Hotel	5·25	4·75
1855	380c. Luna Blou Theatre	7·00	6·50

Stamps were issued in both 2005 and 2006 for this celebration.

448 Shell

2007. Natural World. Multicoloured.

1856	30c. Type **448**	55	50
1857	65c. Young turtles crossing beach	1·30	1·20
1858	70c. Cricket	1·40	1·30
1859	75c. Cacti in flower	1·50	1·40
1860	85c. River edge	1·70	1·50
1861	95c. Woodpecker on cacti	1·90	1·70
1862	104c. Waves breaking against rocks	2·00	1·90
1863	145c. Shoreline	2·75	2·50
1864	250c. Rainforest	4·75	4·25
1865	285c. Sunset	5·25	4·75

449 *Portrait of a Man*

2007. Art. Paintings by Frans Hals. Multicoloured.

1866	104c. Type **449**	2·00	1·90
1867	104c. *Marriage*	2·00	1·90
1868	155c. *The Merry Drinker*	3·00	2·75
1869	155c. *Judith Leyster, The Serenade*	3·00	2·75
MS1870	130×65 mm. 550c. *De Magere Compagnie* (detail) (*horiz*)	12·50	11·50

450 Emma (second wife of Willem III)

2007. Women of the Royal Family. Multicoloured.

1871	50c. Type **450**	95	85
1872	104c. Queen Wilhelmina (1890–1948 (abdicated))	2·00	1·90
1873	155c. Queen Juliana (1840–1980 (abdicated))	3·00	2·75
1874	285c. Queen Beatrix	5·25	4·75
1875	380c. Princess Maxima (wife of Crown Prince Willem Alexander)	6·75	6·25
1876	550c. Princess Amalia (daughter of Crown Prince Willem Alexander)	9·75	9·00

451 Family saying Grace at Table (giving thanks)

2007. Child Welfare. Multicoloured.

1877	59c.+26c. Type **451**	1·70	1·50
1878	104c.+46c. Raising flag (respect)	2·75	2·50
1879	155c.+65c. Baseball team members (Team spirit)	4·00	3·75
1880	285c.+125c. Teacher and pupils (education)	7·50	7·00

452 Candle and 'Merry Christmas'

2007. December Stamps. Multicoloured.

1881	48c. Type **452**	95	85
1882	104c. Tree, presents and 'Merry Christmas'	2·00	1·90
1883	155c. Notes of song and 'Happy New Year' (*horiz*)	3·00	2·75
1884	215c. 2008–2007	4·00	3·50

453 Early Mailbox

2007. Mailboxes. Multicoloured.

1885	20c. Type **453**	55	50
1886	104c. Modern mailbox	2·00	1·90
1887	240c. Mailbox with postal emblem	4·50	4·00
1888	285c. Early box with postal emblem	5·25	4·75
1889	380c. Tall decorative mailbox	6·75	6·25
1890	500c. Decorative mailbox on stand	8·75	8·00

454 Malmok Lighthouse, Bonaire

2008. Lighthouses. Designs showing lighthouses. Multicoloured.

1891	158c. Type **454**	3·25	3·00
1892	158c. Fort Oranje, Bonaire	3·25	3·00
1893	158c. Klein, Curacao	3·25	3·00
1894	158c. Noordpunt, Curacao	3·25	3·00
1895	158c. Bullenbaai, Curacao	3·25	3·00
1896	158c. Willemstoren, Bonaire	3·25	3·00

455 Stylized Rat

2008. Chinese New Year. Year of the Rat. Multicoloured.

1897	106c. Type **455**	2·40	2·20
1898	158c. White rat	3·25	3·00
MS1899	44×70 mm. 500c. Rat on twig (horiz)	10·00	9·25

456 Pollution ('One of the Causes')

2008. Global Warming. Multicoloured.

1900	50c. Type **456**	95	85
1901	75c. Polar bear ('One of the Victims')	1·40	1·30
1902	125c. Wind farm ('One of the Solutions')	2·30	2·10
1903	250c. Beach ('One of the Hopes')	4·75	4·25

457 Princess Catharina Amelia

2008. Heirs to the Throne of the Netherlands. Multicoloured.

1904	75c. Type **457**	1·40	1·30
1905	100c. Princess Catharina Amelia wearing white	1·90	1·70
1906	125c. Prince Willem Alexander	2·30	2·10
1907	250c. Prince Willem Alexander, head and shoulders	4·75	4·25
1908	375c. Queen Beatrix wearing court dress	7·00	6·50
1909	500c. Queen Beatrix wearing evening coat	9·25	8·50

458 Athletics

2008. Olympic Games, Beijing. Multicoloured.

1910	25c. Type **458**	45	45
1911	35c. Gymnastics	65	60
1912	75c. Swimming	1·40	1·30
1913	215c. Cycling	4·00	3·75

459 Curacao 1931 70c. Stamp (No. 132)

2008. Stamp Passion 2008 Exhibition. Designs showing early stamps. Multicoloured.

1914	75c. Type **459**	1·40	1·30
1915	100c. Netherlands 1901 12½c. stamp optd **Curacao** (No. 51 of Curacao)	1·90	1·70
1916	125c. Curaçao 1944 40c.+50c. Red Cross stamp (No. 230)	2·30	2·10
1917	250c. Netherlands 1951 7c. International Court of Justice stamp (No. J26)	4·75	4·25
1918	375c. Netherland 1923 5g. stamp (No. 269)	7·00	6·50
1919	500c. Curacao 1946 10g. stamp (No. 261)	9·25	8·50

460 Alto Vista Chapel, Aruba

2008. 50th Anniv of Diocese of Aruba and Netherlands Antilles. Multicoloured.

1920	59c. Type **460**	1·10	1·00
1921	106c. Cross, Seru Larga, Bonaire	2·00	1·80
1922	158c. St. Ana Basilica, Curacao	3·00	2·75
1923	240c. Sacred Heart Church, Saba	4·50	4·00
1924	285c. Roman Catholic Church, Oranjestad, St. Eustatius	5·25	4·75
1925	335c. May Star of the Sea Church, St. Maarten	6·25	5·75

461 Pounding Corn

2008. Women's Work. Designs showing dolls as women working. Multicoloured.

1926	145c. Type **461**	2·75	2·50
1927	145c. Fishmonger	2·75	2·50
1928	145c. Frying mackerel	2·75	2·50
1929	145c. Grinding coffee	2·75	2·50
1930	155c. Laundress washing clothes	3·00	2·75
1931	155c. Ironing clothes	3·00	2·75
1932	155c. Grinding corn	3·00	2·75
1933	155c. Weaving straw hat	3·00	2·75

462 *Little Street*

2008. Art. Paintings by Johannes (Jan) Vermeer. Two sheets containing T **462** and similar vert designs. Multicoloured.

MS1934	105×103 mm. 145c. Type **462**; 145c. *Girl with a Pearl Earring*; 155c. *Woman in Blue reading Letter*; 155c. *The Love Letter*	12·00	10·50
MS1935	65×123 mm. 500c. *The Milkmaid* (detail)	10·00	9·00

463 Houses (architecture)

2008. Netherlands and Beyond. Sheet 145×75 mm containing T **463** and similar multicoloured designs.

MS1936	5c. Type **463**; 106c. White and blue building (vert); 285c. Roofs (vert)	8·00	7·25

No. **MS**1936 also includes Netherlands 90c. stamps (Chillies and cheese (food)) and Aruba 240c. stamp (Script (poem by Frederico Oduber)).

The 'foreign' stamps could only be used in their country of origin.

464 *Cypraea zebra*

2008. Shells. Multicoloured.

1937	20c. Type **464**	40	35
1938	40c. *Charonia varigata Lamarck*	75	70

1939	65c. *Callistoma armillata*	1·20	1·10
1940	106c. *Strombus gigas Linne*	4·75	4·25
1941	158c. *Pina carnea*	3·00	2·75
1942	285c. *Olivia sayana Ravenel*	5·50	4·75
1943	335c. *Natica canrena Linne*	6·25	5·75
1944	405c. *Voluta musica*	7·75	7·00

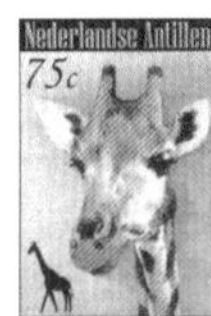

465 Giraffe

2008. African Fauna. Multicoloured.

1945	75c. Type **465**	1·40	1·30
1946	150c. Elephants (horiz)	2·75	2·50
1947	175c. Cheetah (horiz)	3·25	3·00
1948	250c. Zebra (horiz)	4·75	4·25
MS1949	90×62 mm. 250c. Impala	5·25	4·75

466 Potato as Peruvian Farmer

2008. Child Welfare. International Year of the Potato. Multicoloured.

1950	59c.+26c. Type **466**	1·60	1·40
1951	106c.+46c. Potato preparing potatoes	3·00	2·50
1952	158c.+65c. Potato as Belgian girl eating chips	4·25	3·75
1953	285c.+125c. Potatoes as Irish family	7·75	7·00

467 Leaves and 'We wish you a healthy Christmas'

2008. December Stamps. Multicoloured.

1954	50c. Type **467**	95	85
1955	106c. Ponsettias and 'We wish you a merry Christmas'	2·00	1·80
1956	158c. Boat and 'We wish you a prosperous New Year'	3·00	2·75
1957	215c. Dock and 'We wish you a peaceful New Year'	4·00	3·75

468 Girl wearing Seu Festival Clothes, Papiamentu

2008. Traditional Costumes. Multicoloured.

1958	100c. Type **468**	1·90	1·70
1959	104c. Boy wearing Dutch costume	2·00	1·80
1960	155c. Girl wearing kimono	3·00	2·75

469 Ostrich

2008. Birds. Multicoloured.

1961	158c. Type **469**	3·00	2·75
1962	158c. Wild turkey	3·00	2·75
1963	158c. Mandarin duck (horiz)	3·00	2·75
1964	158c. Green heron (horiz)	3·00	2·75
1965	158c. Cassowary	3·00	2·75
1966	158c. Penguin	3·00	2·75
1967	158c. Cormorant (horiz)	3·00	2·75
1968	158c. Goldfinch (horiz)	3·00	2·75

470 'Fria'

2008. 70th Anniv of Coca Cola in Curaçao. Three sheets, each 170×130 mm containing T **470** and similar multicoloured designs.

MS1969	106c.×8, Type **470**; Fria bottle, bronze contents; Fria bottle, purple contents; Fria bottle, yellow contents; Fria bottle, orange-yellow contents; Fria bottle, pink contents; Fria bottle, pale green contents; Fria bottle, pale green contents	17·00	15·00
MS1970	106c. Coca-Cola bottle, 1899; 106c. Coca-Cola bottle, 1900; 158c. Coca-Cola bottle, 1905; 158c. Coca-Cola bottle, 1913; 158c. Coca-Cola bottle, 1915; 285c. Girl with striped umbrella; 285c. Girl with yellow umbrella; 285c. Coca-Cola bottle, 1923	30·00	27·00
MS1971	158c.×8, 'WELCOME TO CURACAO' (horiz); Early Coca-Cola advertising promotion (horiz); Coca-Cola building (horiz); Early advertising hoarding; Two men holding Coca-Cola bottles (horiz); 1950's bar serving Coca-Cola (horiz); Man smoking cigar holding advertising poster (horiz); Early delivery lorry (horiz)	25·00	22·00

471 Divers, Bonaire

2009. Islands. Multicoloured.

1972	30c. Type **471** (As Type **442a**)	55	50
1973	59c. Oil storage tanks, Statia (As No. 1822)	1·10	1·00
1974	110c. Flowers, Curacao (As No. 1815) (vert)	2·10	1·90
1975	164c. Cruise ship and pier (As No. 1818) (vert)	3·00	2·75
1976	168c. Flamingoes, Bonaire (As No. 1819)	3·25	2·75
1977	285c. Houses, Saba (As No. 1821)	5·50	4·75

472 *Nelumbo nucifera*

2009. Flowers. Multicoloured.

1978	75c. Type **472**	1·40	1·30
1979	150c. *Chrysanthemum leucanthemum*	2·75	2·50
1980	200c. *Hepatica nobilis*	3·75	3·50
1981	225c. *Cistus incanus*	4·25	3·75
1982	350c. Alamanda flower	6·75	6·00
1983	500c. Rose 'Wise portia'	9·50	8·50

Nos. 1978-1983 were printed *se-tenant*, in blocks of six stamps within the sheet.

473 Symbol

2009. Year of Ox. Multicoloured.

1984	110c. Type **473**	2·10	1·90
1985	168c. Ox (horiz)	3·25	2·75

474 *Lycaena Phlaeas*

2009. Butterflies. Multicoloured.

1986	25c. Type **474**	50	45
1987	35c. *Danus plexippus*	65	60
1988	50c. *Nymphalis antiopa*	95	85
1989	105c. *Carterocephalus palaemon*	2·00	1·80
1990	115c. *Inachis io*	2·20	2·00
1991	115c. *Phyciodes tharos*	3·00	2·75
1992	185c. *Papilio glaucus*	3·50	3·25
1993	240c. *Dryas julia*	4·50	4·00
1994	315c. *Libytheana carinenta*	6·00	5·25
1995	375c. *Melanis pixe*	7·25	6·50
1996	400c. *Astrocampa celtis*	7·50	6·75
1997	1000c. *Historis acheronta*	19·00	17·00

Nos. 1986-1997x2 were printed *se-tenant*, in blocks of 12 stamps within the sheet.

475 *Daptrius americanus* (Red-throated Caracara)

2009. Birds. Multicoloured.

1998	10c. Type **475**	30	25
1999	45c. *Amazona amazonica* (Orange-winged Amazon)	85	75
2000	80c. *Querula purpurata* (Purple-throated Fruitcrow)	1·50	1·40
2001	145c. *Aratinga leucophthalmus* (White-eyed Parakeet)	2·75	2·50
2002	190c. *Xipholena punicea* (Pompadour Cotinga)	3·50	3·25
2003	235c. *Celeus torquatus* (Ringed Woodpecker)	4·50	4·00
2004	285c. *Lamprospiza melanoleuca* (Red-billed Pied Tanager)	5·50	4·75
2005	300c. *Selenidera culik* (Guianan Toucanet)	5·75	5·00
2006	335c. *Amazila viridigaster* (Green-bellied Hummingbird)	6·25	5·75
2007	425c. *Tangara gyrola* (Bay-headed Tanager)	8·00	7·25
2008	450c. *Nyctibius grandis* (Great Potoo)	8·50	7·75
2009	500c. *Galbula leucogastra* (Bronzy Jacamar)	9·50	8·50

Nos. 1998-2009x2 were printed *se-tenant*, in blocks of 12 stamps within the sheet.

476 Telegraph Operator

2009. Centenary of Post and Telecommunications. Multicoloured.

2010	59c. Type **476**	1·10	1·00
2011	110c. Telephone user and living room	2·10	1·90
2012	164c. Laptop user and symbols of modern communications	3·00	2·75

477 Piano, J.B. & Sons, 1796

2009. 300th Anniv of Pianos. Multicoloured designs showing pianos, maker given.

2013	175c. Type **477**	3·25	3·00
2014	225c. J. Schantz, 1818 (vert)	4·25	3·75
2015	250c. Steinway-Welt, 1927 (vert)	4·75	4·25
2016	350c. Yamaha, 2007	6·75	6·00

No. 2017 is vacant.

478 *Celeus elegans* (Chestnut Woodpecker)

2009. Birds. Multicoloured.

MS2018	5g. Type **478**; 10g. *Iodopleura fusca* (Dusky Purpletuft)	30·00	27·00

479 Merchantman, 200 AD

2009. Ships. Multicoloured.

2019	1c. Type **479**	20	15
2020	2c. Caravel, 1490	40	35
2021	3c. Inscr 'Naos, 1492'	55	50
2022	4c. *Constant*, 1605	75	70
2023	5c. Merchant ship, 1620	95	85
2024	80c. *Vasa*, 1628	1·50	1·40
2025	220c. Hoy, 1730	4·25	3·75
2026	275c. Bark, 1750	5·25	4·75
2027	385c. Schooner, 1838	7·25	6·50
2028	475c. Sailing rig, 1884	9·00	8·00
2029	500c. Inscr 'Fifie, 1903'	9·50	8·50
2030	750c. Junk, 1938	14·50	13·00

Nos. 2019-2030 were printed, *se-tenant* in blocks of 12 stamps within the sheet.

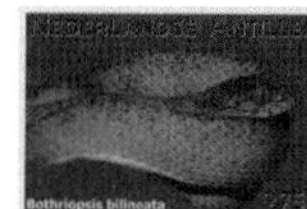

480 *Bothriopsis bilineata*

2009. Snakes. Multicoloured.

2031	275c. Type **480**	5·25	4·75
2032	325c. *Bothriechis schlegelii*	6·25	5·50
2033	340c. *Agkistrodon piscivorus* (inscr 'Agkistrodeon piscivorous')	6·50	5·75
2034	390c. *Erythrolamprus aesculapii*	7·50	6·75
2035	420c. *Atropoides mexicanus*	8·00	7·25
2036	450c. *Bothriechis nigroviridis*	8·50	7·75

Nos. 2031-2036 were printed, *se-tenant*, in blocks of six stamps within the sheet.

481 Galileo Galilei

2009. Child Welfare. Multicoloured.

2037	59c.+26c. Type **481**	1·60	1·40
2038	110c.+45c. Family and telescope	3·00	2·75
2039	168c.+75c. Children and Space Shuttle	4·50	4·25
2040	285c.+125c. Astronaut walking on moon	7·75	7·00

482 Walter Frederick Martinus (Freddy) Johnson

2009. Aviation Pioneers. Multicoloured.

2041	59c. Type **482**	1·10	1·00
2042	110c. Norman Chester Wathey	2·10	1·90
2043	164c. José (Pipe) Domoy	3·00	2·75

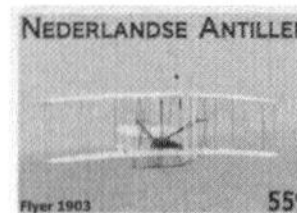

483 *Wright Flyer I*, 1903

2009. Aircraft. Multicoloured.

2044	55c. Type **483**	1·00	95
2045	100c. Douglas DC 3 (inscr 'DST Skysleeper'), 1935	1·90	1·70
2046	205c. Cesna 170, 1948	4·00	3·50
2047	395c. Lockheed Constellation, 1943	7·50	6·75
2048	645c. de Havilland Comet I (inscr 'Havilland Comet'), 1949	12·50	11·00
2049	800c. Vickers (insc 'BAC') Super VC10, 1962	15·00	13·50

484 Family and Menorah (Hanukkah)

2009. December Stamps. Multicoloured.

2050	50c. Type **484**	95	85
2051	110c. Family and decorated tree (Christmas)	2·10	1·90
2052	168c. Family wearing traditional dress and candles (Kwanza)	3·25	2·75
2053	215c. Analogue clock, digital clock and fireworks (New Year)	4·00	3·75

485 Sapodilla

2009. Fruit. Multicoloured.

2054	20c. Type **485**	40	35
2055	45c. Pineapple	85	75
2056	125c. Mamey sapote	2·40	2·10
2057	145c. Avocado	2·75	2·50
2058	160c. Mangosteen	3·00	2·75
2059	210c. Rambutan	4·00	3·50
2060	295c. Pomelo	5·50	5·00
2061	1000c. Watermelon	19·00	17·00

Nos. 2062/71 and Type **486** are left for stamps not yet received.

487 Papaya

2010. Fruits. Multicoloured.

2072	1c. Type **487**	20	15
2073	5c. Pomegranate	40	35
2074	30c. Mango	55	50
2075	59c. Bananas	1·10	1·00
2076	79c. Cashews	1·50	1·30
2077	111c. Soursop	2·10	1·90
2078	164c. Tamarind	3·00	2·75
2079	170c. Watermelon	3·25	3·00
2080	199c. Gennip	3·75	3·50
2081	285c. Seagrape	5·50	4·75

Nos. 2072/81 are as those issued in 2005, with new face values.

488 Tiger Cub

2010. Chinese New Year. Multicoloured.

2082	111c. Type **488**	2·75	2·50
2083	164c. Mother and cub	3·00	2·75
2084	170c. White tiger	3·25	3·00

489 *Thersamonia thersamon*

2010. Butterflies. Multicoloured.

2085	20c. Type **489**	40	35
2086	50c. *Acrea natalica*	95	85
2087	80c. *Vanessa carye*	1·50	1·40
2088	100c. *Apodemia mormo*	1·90	1·70
2089	125c. *Siproeta stelenes meridionalis*	2·40	2·10
2090	175c. *Anartia amathea*	3·25	3·00
2091	200c. *Doxocopa laure*	3·75	3·50
2092	250c. *Euphaedra uganda*	4·75	4·25
2093	350c. *Precis westermanni* (inscr 'Precis westermannii')	6·75	6·00
2094	450c. *Precis octavia*	8·50	7·75
2095	500c. *Euphaedra neophron*	9·50	8·50
2096	700c. *Vanessa cardui*	13·50	12·00

490 *Self-Portrait*

2010. Paintings by Vincent van Gogh. Multicoloured.

2097	200c. Type **490**	3·75	3·50
2098	400c. *Agostina Segatori*	7·50	6·75
2099	500c. *L'Arlesienne Woman*	9·50	8·50
2100	700c. *Emperor Moth*	13·50	12·00

491 *Pipra aureola* (crimson-hooded manakin)

2010. Birds. Multicoloured.

2101	75c. Type **491**	1·40	1·30
2102	150c. *Neopelma chrysocephalum* (Saffron-crested Tyrant-manakin)	2·75	2·50
2103	200c. *Pipra aureola* (Crimson-hooded Manakin) (inscr '*Oxyruncus cristatus*' (sharpbill))	3·75	3·50
2104	225c. *Automolus rufipileatus* (Chestnut-crowned Foliage-gleaner)	4·25	3·75
2105	350c. *Empidonomus varius* (Variegated Flycatcher)	6·75	6·00
2106	500c. *Venilornis sanquineus* (Blood-coloured Woodpecker)	9·50	8·50

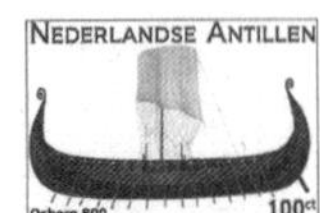

492 Oseberg (inscr 'Osberg'), 800

2010. Ships. Multicoloured.

2107	100c. Type **492**	1·90	1·70
2108	125c. *Dromon*, 910	2·40	2·10
2109	175c. *Cocca*, 1500	3·25	3·00
2110	200c. *Mary*, 1661	3·75	3·50
2111	250c. *Houtport*, 1700	4·75	4·25
2112	300c. *Santissima Trinidad*, 1769	5·75	5·00
2113	350c. Cargo ship (inscr 'Vrachtschip'), 1800	6·75	6·00
2114	400c *Amistad*, 1839	7·50	6·75
2115	450c. Two masted warship (inscr 'Oorlogsschip'), 1840	8·50	7·75
2116	650c. Inscr 'Netherlands schip', 1850	12·50	11·00

493 1933 Curacao 6c. Stamp (As Type **24a**)

2010. Stamp on Stamp. Multicoloured.

2117	25c. Type **493**	50	45
2118	50c. 1933 Curaçao 30c. Stamp (As No. 168)	95	85
2119	100c. 1923 Curaçao 6c. Stamp (As No. 100)	1·90	1·70
2120	250c. 1938 Curaçao 1½c. Stamp (As Type **29**)	4·75	4·25
2121	275c. Netherlands Antilles 25c. Stamp (As Type **93**)	5·25	4·75
2122	300c. 1923 Curaçao 5c. Stamp (As Type **17**)	5·75	5·00
2123	400c. 1947 Curaçao 15c. AIR Stamp (As No. 265)	7·50	6·75
2124	600c. 1948 Curaçao 6c. Stamp (As No. 297)	11·50	10·00
MS2125	75×72mm. 700c. 1949 Curaçao 12½c. Stamp (As Type **49**) 800c. 1936 Curaçao 50c. Stamp (As No. 169)	30·00	27·00

494 Early TV Set

2010. 50th Anniv of TeleCuraçao. Multicoloured.

2126	59c. Type **494**	1·10	1·00
2127	111c. TV set showing transmitter	2·10	1·90
2128	164c. Modern TV showing anniversary emblem	3·00	2·75

495 Ulysse, 1890

2010. Pocket Watches. Multicoloured.

2129	125c. Type **495**	2·40	2·10
2130	175c. Hampden, 1910	3·25	3·00
2131	250c. Elgin, 1924	4·75	4·25
2132	300c. Illinois, 1928	5·75	5·00
2133	350c. Vacheron, 1955	6·75	6·00

POSTAGE DUE STAMPS

1952. As Type **D121** of Netherlands but inscr "NEDERLANDSE ANTILLEN".

D336	1c. green	40	65
D337	2½c. green	1·00	1·30
D338	5c. green	40	65
D339	6c. green	1·30	1·60
D340	7c. green	1·30	1·60
D341	8c. green	1·30	1·60
D342	9c. green	1·30	1·60
D343	10c. green	50	65
D344	12½c. green	50	65
D345	15c. green	1·30	1·60
D346	20c. green	1·30	1·60
D347	25c. green	1·00	40
D348	30c. green	2·50	3·25
D349	35c. green	2·50	3·25
D350	40c. green	2·50	3·25
D351	45c. green	2·50	3·25
D352	50c. green	2·50	3·25

NETHERLANDS INDIES

A former Dutch colony, consisting of numerous settlements in the East Indies, of which the islands of Java and Sumatra and parts of Borneo and New Guinea are the most important. Renamed Indonesia in 1948, Independence was granted during 1949. Netherlands New Guinea remained a Dutch possession until 1962 when it was placed under UN control, being incorporated with Indonesia in 1963.

100 cents = 1 gulden.

1 King William III

1864. Imperf.

1	**1**	10c. red	£550	£170

1868. Perf.

2	**1**	10c. red	£2000	£300

2

1870. Perf.

27	**2**	1c. green	16·00	6·50
28	**2**	2c. purple	£160	£200
29	**2**	2c. brown	21·00	7·75
30	**2**	2½c. buff	£100	49·00
12	**2**	5c. green	£180	13·00
32	**2**	10c. brown	65·00	2·00
40	**2**	12½c. drab	16·00	5·25
34	**2**	15c. brown	65·00	4·50
5	**2**	20c. blue	£200	7·25
36	**2**	25c. purple	80·00	2·50
44	**2**	30c. green	£100	7·75
17	**2**	50c. red	80·00	5·25
38	**2**	2g.50 green and purple	£180	42·00

5

1883

87	**5**	1c. green	2·00	65
88	**5**	2c. brown	2·00	65
89	**5**	2½c. buff	2·00	1·30
90	**5**	3c. purple	3·25	65
86	**5**	5c. green	£100	42·00
91	**5**	5c. blue	23·00	65

6 Queen Wilhelmina

1892

94	**6**	10c. brown	13·00	65
95	**6**	12½c. grey	20·00	50·00
96	**6**	15c. brown	33·00	4·00
97	**6**	20c. blue	£100	2·50
98	**6**	25c. purple	60·00	3·25
99	**6**	30c. green	80·00	5·75
100	**6**	50c. red	65·00	3·25
101	**6**	2g.50 blue and brown	£225	70·00

1900. Netherlands stamps of 1898 surch **NED.-INDIE** and value.

111	**13**	10c. on 10c. lilac	7·75	70
112	**13**	12½c. on 12½c. blue	7·75	1·20
113	**13**	15c. on 15c. brown	7·75	1·20
114	**13**	20c. on 20c. green	35·00	1·20
115	**13**	25c. on 25c. blue and pink	27·00	1·20
116	**13**	50c. on 50c. red and green	60·00	2·10
117	**11**	2½g. on 2½g. lilac	£110	35·00

1902. Surch.

118	**5**	½ on 2c. brown	80	70
119	**5**	2½ on 3c. purple	90	85

11

12

13

1902

120	**11**	½c. lilac	1·40	70
121	**11**	1c. olive	1·40	70
122	**11**	2c. brown	6·75	70
123	**11**	2½c. green	4·00	70
124	**11**	3c. orange	6·75	2·10
125	**11**	4c. blue	24·00	14·50
126	**11**	5c. red	10·00	70
127	**11**	7½c. grey	6·75	70
128	**12**	10c. slate	8·00	70
129	**12**	12½c. blue	4·00	70
130	**12**	15c. brown	17·00	3·50
131	**12**	17½c. bistre	6·75	70
132	**12**	20c. grey	4·00	2·75
133	**12**	20c. olive	55·00	1·40
134	**12**	22½c. olive and brown	6·75	70
135	**12**	25c. mauve	27·00	70
136	**12**	30c. brown	60·00	70
137	**12**	50c. red	55·00	70
138	**13**	1g. lilac	£110	70
206	**13**	1g. lilac on blue	£100	14·00
139	**13**	2½g. grey	£130	3·50
207	**13**	2½g. grey on blue	£200	70·00

1902. No. 130 optd with horiz bars.

140	**12**	15c. brown	3·50	1·40

1905. No. 132 surch 10 cent.

141	**12**	10c. on 20c. grey	4·75	2·75

1908. Stamps of 1902 optd **JAVA**.

142	**11**	½c. lilac	70	70
143	**11**	1c. olive	1·00	70
144	**11**	2c. brown	4·00	4·50
145	**11**	2½c. green	2·75	40
146	**11**	3c. orange	2·00	1·70
147	**11**	5c. red	4·00	40
148	**11**	7½c. grey	3·50	3·00
149	**12**	10c. slate	2·40	40
150	**12**	12½c. blue	3·50	1·40
151	**12**	15c. brown	6·00	6·25
152	**12**	17½c. bistre	3·50	1·40
153	**12**	20c. olive	17·00	1·40
154	**12**	22½c. olive and brown	8·75	5·00
155	**12**	25c. mauve	8·75	70
156	**12**	30c. brown	47·00	5·00
157	**12**	50c. red	34·00	1·40
158	**13**	1g. lilac	80·00	5·50
159	**13**	2½g. grey	£120	£100

1908. Stamps of 1902 optd **BUITEN BEZIT**.

160	**11**	½c. lilac	1·00	70
161	**11**	1c. olive	1·00	70
162	**11**	2c. brown	3·50	5·25
163	**11**	2½c. green	2·00	70
164	**11**	3c. orange	2·00	2·10
165	**11**	5c. red	5·50	70
166	**11**	7½c. grey	5·00	5·25
167	**12**	10c. slate	2·00	35
168	**12**	12½c. blue	17·00	4·25
169	**12**	15c. brown	8·00	7·00
170	**12**	17½c. bistre	3·75	3·50
171	**12**	20c. olive	17·00	4·25
172	**12**	22½c. olive and brown	13·50	12·00
173	**12**	25c. mauve	13·50	70
174	**12**	30c. brown	27·00	3·75
175	**12**	50c. red	13·50	1·40
176	**13**	1g. lilac	£100	10·50
177	**13**	2½g. grey	£170	£110

19

20

1912

208	**19**	½c. lilac	40	40
209	**19**	1c. green	35	40
210	**19**	2c. brown	1·00	40
264	**19**	2c. grey	1·20	45
211	**19**	2½c. green	2·40	40
265	**19**	2½c. pink	1·40	45
212	**19**	3c. brown	1·00	40
266	**19**	3c. green	2·10	45
213	**19**	4c. blue	2·00	40
267	**19**	4c. green	2·10	45
268	**19**	4c. bistre	16·00	8·75
214	**19**	5c. pink	2·10	40
269	**19**	5c. green	2·10	45
270	**19**	5c. blue	1·40	45
215	**19**	7½c. brown	1·40	40
271	**19**	7½c. bistre	1·40	45
216	**20**	10c. red	2·00	40
272	**19**	10c. lilac	3·50	45
217	**20**	12½c. blue	2·10	40
273	**20**	12½c. red	2·30	75
274	**20**	15c. blue	15·00	45
218	**20**	17½c. brown	2·10	40
219	**20**	20c. green	3·50	40
275	**20**	20c. blue	3·75	45
276	**20**	20c. orange	26·00	45
220	**20**	22½c. orange	3·50	1·40
221	**20**	25c. mauve	3·50	40
222	**20**	30c. grey	3·50	40
277	**20**	32½c. violet and orange	3·75	45
278	**20**	35c. brown	15·00	1·00
279	**20**	40c. green	7·00	45

21

1913

223	**21**	50c. green	10·50	45
280	**21**	60c. blue	10·50	45
281	**21**	80c. orange	10·50	75
224	**21**	1g. brown	10·50	45
283	**21**	1g.75 lilac	35·00	3·75
225	**21**	2½g. pink	28·00	75

1915. Red Cross. Stamps of 1912 surch **+5 cts.** and red cross.

243	**19**	1c.+5c. green	10·50	14·50
244	**19**	5c.+5c. pink	10·50	14·50
245	**20**	10c.+5c. red	14·00	18·00

1917. Stamps of 1902, 1912 and 1913 surch.

246	**19**	½c. on 2½c. (No. 211)	70	75
247	**19**	1c. on 4c. (No. 213)	70	1·10
250	**20**	12½c. on 17½c. (No. 218)	1·40	45
251	**20**	12½c. on 22½c. (No. 220)	1·40	45
248	**12**	17½c. on 22½c. (No. 134)	3·50	1·50
252	**20**	20c. on 22½c. (No. 220)	1·40	75
249	**13**	30c. on 1g. (No. 138)	11·00	3·25
253	**21**	32½c. on 50c. (No. 223)	2·75	45
254	**21**	40c. on 50c. (No. 223)	7·00	75
255	**21**	60c. on 1g. (No. 224)	11·00	75
256	**21**	80c. on 1g. (No. 224)	14·00	2·20

1922. Bandoeng Industrial Fair. Stamps of 1912 and 1917 optd **3de N. I. JAARBEURS BANDOENG 1922.**

285	**19**	1c. green	14·00	14·50
286	**19**	2c. brown	14·00	14·50
287	**19**	2½c. pink	£100	£110
288	**19**	3c. yellow	14·00	14·50
289	**19**	4c. blue	55·00	70·00
290	**19**	5c. green	21·00	16·00
291	**19**	7½c. brown	14·00	14·50
292	**19**	10c. lilac	£110	£160
293	**20**	12½c. on 22½c. orge (No. 251)	18·00	16·00
294	**20**	17½c. brown	14·00	14·50
295	**20**	20c. blue	18·00	14·50

Nos. 285/95 were sold at a premium for 3, 4, 5, 6, 8, 9, 10, 12½, 15, 20 and 22c. respectively.

33

1923. Queen's Silver Jubilee.

296	**33**	5c. green	75	75
297	**33**	12½c. red	75	75
298	**33**	20c. blue	1·50	75
299	**33**	50c. orange	3·75	1·50
300	**33**	1g. purple	8·00	1·50
301	**33**	2½g. grey	75·00	75·00
302	**33**	5g. brown	£225	£250

1928. Air. Stamps of 1912 and 1913 surch **LUCHTPOST,** Fokker F.VII aircraft and value.

303	**20**	10c. on 12½c. red	2·20	2·20
304	**20**	20c. on 25c. mauve	5·00	5·00
305	**21**	40c. on 80c. orange	5·00	5·00
306	**21**	75c. on 1g. sepia	2·20	2·20
307	**21**	1½g. on 2½g. red	14·50	14·50

36 Fokker F.VIIa

1928. Air.

308	**36**	10c. purple	75	75
309	**36**	20c. brown	1·80	1·50
310	**36**	40c. red	2·20	1·50
311	**36**	75c. green	5·00	75
312	**36**	1g.50 orange	9·50	1·50

1930. Air. Surch **30** between bars.

313	**36**	30c. on 40c. red	3·25	75

38 Watch-tower

1930. Child Welfare. Centres in brown.

315	-	2c. (+1c.) mauve	2·20	2·20
316	**38**	5c. (+2½c.) green	8·75	6·50
317	-	12½c. (+2½c.) red	5·75	1·50
318	-	15c. (+5c.) blue	8·75	11·50

Designs:—Vert: 2c. Bali Temple. Horiz: 12½c. Minangkabau Compound; 15c. Buddhist Temple, Borobudur.

1930. No. 275 surch **12½.**

319	**20**	12½c. on 20c. blue	1·50	45

40 M. P. Pattist in Flight

1931. Air. First Java–Australia Mail.

320	**40**	1g. brown and blue	29·00	33·00

41

1931. Air.

321	**41**	30c. red	5·75	75
322	**41**	4½g. blue	16·00	5·75
323	**41**	7½g. green	22·00	8·00

42 Ploughing

1931. Lepers' Colony.

324	**42**	2c. (+1c.) brown	5·00	3·75
325	-	5c. (+2½c.) green	7·25	7·25
326	-	12½c. (+2½c.) red	5·75	1·50
327	-	15c. (+5c.) blue	14·50	14·50

Designs:—5c. Fishing; 12½c. Native actors; 15c. Native musicians.

1932. Air. Surch **50** on Fokker F.VIIa/3m aircraft.

328	**36**	50c. on 1g.50 orange	5·75	1·10

44 Plaiting Rattan

1932. Salvation Army. Centres in brown.

329	-	2c. (+1c.) purple	1·10	1·10
330	**44**	5c. (+2½c.) green	5·75	4·25
331	-	12½c. (+2½c.) red	1·80	75
332	-	15c. (+5c.) blue	8·00	7·00

Designs:—2c. Weaving; 12½c. Textile worker; 15c. Metal worker.

45 William of Orange

1933. 400th Birth Anniv of William I of Orange.

333	**45**	12½c. red	3·00	75

46 Rice Cultivation

47 Queen Wilhelmina

1933

335	**46**	1c. violet	45	45
397	**46**	2c. purple	75	75
337	**46**	2½c. bistre	45	45
338	**46**	3c. green	45	45
339	**46**	3½c. grey	45	45
340	**46**	4c. green	1·70	45
401	**46**	5c. blue	75	75
342	**46**	7½c. violet	1·70	45
343	**46**	10c. red	3·25	45
403	**47**	10c. red	35	75
334	**47**	12½c. brown	14·50	75
345	**47**	12½c. red	1·10	45
404	**47**	15c. blue	35	75
405	**47**	20c. purple	75	75
348	**47**	25c. green	4·00	45
349	**47**	30c. blue	6·50	45
350	**47**	32½c. bistre	14·50	14·50
408	**47**	35c. violet	10·00	3·00
352	**47**	40c. green	5·00	45
353	**47**	42½c. yellow	5·00	2·20
354	**47**	50c. blue	11·00	75
355	**47**	60c. blue	11·00	1·50
356	**47**	80c. red	14·50	2·20
357	**47**	1g. violet	14·50	75
358	**47**	1g.75 green	36·00	24·00
414	**47**	2g. green	47·00	25·00
359	**47**	2g.50 purple	36·00	3·75
415	**47**	5g. bistre	44·00	25·00

The 50c. to 5g. are larger, 30×30 mm.

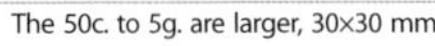

48 Pander S.4 Postjager

1933. Air. Special Flights.

360	**48**	30c. blue	3·75	3·00

49 Woman and Lotus Blossom

1933. Y.M.C.A. Charity.

361	**49**	2c. (+1c.) brown & purple	1·50	75
362	-	5c. (+2½c.) brown and green	4·25	3·75
363	-	12½c. (+2½c.) brown & orge	4·25	45
364	-	15c. (+5c.) brown and blue	5·75	4·75

Designs:—5c. Symbolizing the sea of life; 12½c. YMCA emblem; 15c. Unemployed man.

1934. Surch.

365	**36**	2c. on 10c. purple	1·50	75
366	**36**	2c. on 20c. brown	1·50	75
367	**41**	2c. on 30c. red	1·50	2·20
368	**36**	42½c. on 75c. green	11·00	75
369	**36**	42½c. on 1g.50 orange	11·00	75

1934. Anti-tuberculosis Fund. As T **77** of Netherlands.

370		12½c. (+2½c.) brown	3·25	1·10

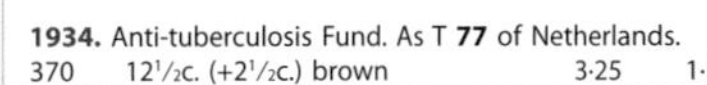

53 Cavalryman and Wounded Soldier

1935. Christian Military Home.

371	-	2c. (+1c.) brown and purple	3·75	3·00
372	**53**	5c. (+2½c.) brown and green	6·50	6·50
373	-	12½c. (+2½c.) brown & orange	6·50	75
374	-	15c. (+5c.) brown and blue	9·50	9·50

Designs:—2c. Engineer chopping wood; 12½c. Artilleryman and volcano victim; 15c. Infantry bugler.

54 Dinner-time

1936. Salvation Army.

375	**54**	2c. (+1c.) purple	2·50	1·50
376	**54**	5c. (+2½c.) blue	3·00	2·20
377	**54**	7½c. (+2½c.) violet	3·00	3·00
378	**54**	12½c. (+2½c.) orange	3·25	75
379	**54**	15c. (+5c.) blue	5·75	4·25

Nos. 376/9 are larger, 30×27 mm.

55 Boy Scouts

1937. Scouts' Jamboree.

380	**55**	7½c. (+2½c.) green	1·80	1·60
381	**55**	12½c. (+2½c.) red	1·80	1·50

1937. Nos. 222 and 277 surch in figures.

382	**20**	10c. on 30c. slate	5·00	75
383	**20**	10c. on 32½c. violet and orange	5·00	75

59 Sifting Rice

1937. Relief Fund. Inscr "A.S.I.B.".

385	**59**	2c. (+1c.) sepia and orange	2·75	1·50
386	-	3½c. (+1½c.) grey	3·00	1·60
387	-	7½c. (+2½c.) green & orange	3·00	2·20
388	-	10c. (+2½c.) red and orange	3·25	50
389	-	20c. (+5c.) blue	3·00	2·50

Designs:—3½c. Mother and children; 7½c. Ox-team ploughing rice-field; 10c. Ox-team and cart; 20c. Man and woman.

1938. 40th Anniv of Coronation. As T **87** of Netherlands.

390		2c. violet	45	50
391		10c. red	50	60
392		15c. blue	2·50	2·20
393		20c. red	1·50	75

62 Douglas DC-2 Airliner

1938. Air Service Fund. Tenth Anniv of Royal Netherlands Indies Air Lines.

394	**62**	17½c. (+5c.) brown	1·80	1·60
395	-	20c. (+5c.) slate	2·20	1·50

Design:—20c. As Type **62**, but reverse side of airliner.

63 Nurse and Child

1938. Child Welfare. Inscr "CENTRAAL MISSIE-BUREAU".

416	**63**	2c. (+1c.) violet	1·50	1·00
417	-	3½c. (+1½c.) green	2·20	2·20

418	-	7½c. (+2½c.) red	1·80	1·50
419	-	10c. (+2½c.) red	1·80	75
420	-	20c. (+5c.) blue	2·20	1·80

Designs:—(23×23 mm): Nurse with child suffering from injuries to eye (3½c.), arm (7½c.), head (20c.) and nurse bathing a baby (10c.).

63a Group of Natives

64 European Nurse and Patient

1939. Netherlands Indies Social Bureau and Protestant Church Funds.

421	-	2c. (+1c.) violet	45	45
422	-	3½c. (+1½c.) green	75	45
423	**63a**	7½c. (+2½c.) brown	45	45
424	-	10c. (+2½c.) red	3·00	1·70
425	**64**	10c. (+2½c.) red	3·00	1·70
426	**64**	20c. (+5c.) blue	1·30	1·00

Designs: Vert: 2c. as Type **63a** but group in European clothes. Horiz: 3½c., 10c. (No. 424) as Type **64**, but Native nurse and patient.

1940. Red Cross Fund. No. 345 surch 10+5 ct and cross.

428	**47**	10c.+5c. on 12½c. red	6·50	1·00

68 Queen Wilhelmina

1941. As T **94** of Netherlands but inscr "NED. INDIE" and T **68**.

429	-	10c. red	1·50	75
430	-	15c. blue	6·00	6·00
431	-	17½c. orange	2·75	2·75
432	-	20c. mauve	65·00	£110
433	-	25c. green	80·00	£170
434	-	30c. brown	21·00	18·00
435	-	35c. purple	£250	£750
436	-	40c. green	28·00	14·50
437	-	50c. red	9·75	5·75
438	-	60c. blue	8·75	3·00
439	-	80c. red	8·75	3·00
440	-	1g. violet	9·50	4·25
441	-	2g. green	36·00	4·25
442	-	5g. bistre	£600	£2500
443	-	10g. green	75·00	44·00
444	**68**	25g. orange	£475	£275

Nos 429/36 measure 18×23 mm, Nos. 431/43 20½×26 mm.

69 Netherlands Coat of Arms

1941. Prince Bernhard Fund for Dutch Forces.

453	**69**	5c.+5c. blue and orange	2·20	75
454	**69**	10c.+10c. blue and red	2·20	75
455	**69**	1g.+1g. blue and grey	29·00	28·00

70 Doctor and Child

1941. Indigent Mohammedans' Relief Fund.

456	**70**	2c. (+1c.) green	2·00	2·00
457	-	3½c. (+1½c.) brown	9·75	9·75
458	-	7½c. (+2½c.) violet	8·25	8·25
459	-	10c. (+2½c.) red	3·25	75
460	-	15c. (+5c.) blue	24·00	24·00

Designs:—3½c. Native eating rice; 7½c. Nurse and patient; 10c. Nurse and children; 15c. Basket-weaver.

71 Wayangwong Dancer

1941

461	-	2c. red	75	45
462	-	2½c. purple	1·00	1·50
463	-	3c. green	1·00	1·50
464	**71**	4c. green	85	1·50
465	-	5c. blue	45	45
466	-	7½c. violet	1·00	60

Designs (dancers): 2c. Menari; 2½c. Nias; 3c. Legon; 5c. Padjoge; 7½c. Dyak.

See also Nos. 514/16.

72 Paddyfield

73 Queen Wilhelmina

1945

467	**72**	1c. green	1·00	45
468	-	2c. mauve	1·00	60
469	-	2½c. purple	1·00	45
470	-	5c. blue	75	45
471	-	7½c. olive	1·50	45
472	**73**	10c. brown	75	45
473	**73**	15c. blue	75	45
474	**73**	17½c. red	75	45
475	**73**	20c. purple	75	45
476	**73**	30c. grey	75	45
477	-	60c. grey	1·50	45
478	-	1g. green	2·20	45
479	-	2½g. orange	6·50	1·30

Designs:—As Type **72**: 2c. Lake in W. Java; 2½c. Medical School, Batavia; 5c. Seashore; 7½c. Douglas DC-2 airplane over Bromo Volcano. (30×30 mm): 60c. to 2½g. Portrait as Type **73** but different frame.

76 Railway Viaduct near Soekaboemi

1946

484	**76**	1c. green	60	45
485	-	2c. brown	60	45
486	-	2½c. red	60	45
487	-	5c. blue	60	45
488	-	7½c. blue	60	45

Designs:—2c. Power station; 3c. Minangkabau house; 5c. Tondano scene (Celebes); 7½c. Buddhist Stupas, Java.

1947. Surch in figures.

502	-	3c. on 2½c. red (No. 486)	60	45
503	-	3c. on 7½c. blue (No. 488)	60	45
504	**76**	4c. on 1c. green	60	45
505	**47**	45c. on 60c. blue (No. 355)	2·50	1·70

No. 505 has three bars.

1947. Optd 1947.

506	**47**	12½c. red	75	45
507	**47**	25c. green	75	45
508	-	40c. green (No. 436)	1·50	45
509	**47**	50c. blue	1·50	60
510	**47**	80c. red	2·20	2·20
511	-	2g. green (No. 441)	7·25	2·50
512	-	5g. brown (No. 442)	20·00	17·00

1948. Relief for Victims of the Terror. Surch PELITA 15+10 Ct. and lamp.

513	**47**	15c.+10c. on 10c. red	60	60

1948. Dancers. As T **71**.

514		3c. red (Menari)	75	45
515		4c. green (Legon)	75	45
516		7½c. brown (Dyak)	1·50	1·30

81 Queen Wilhelmina

1948

517	**81**	15c. orange	1·50	3·75
518	**81**	20c. blue	75	75
519	**81**	25c. green	75	75
520	**81**	40c. green	75	75
521	**81**	45c. mauve	1·00	1·50
522	**81**	50c. lake	85	75
523	**81**	80c. red	1·00	1·00
524	**81**	1g. violet	75	75
525	**81**	10g. green	60·00	28·00
526	**81**	25g. orange	£110	£110

Nos. 524-526 are larger, 21×26 mm.

1948. Queen Wilhelmina's Golden Jubilee. As T **81** but inscr "1898 1948".

528	15c. orange	75	75
529	20c. blue	75	50

1948. As T **126** of Netherlands.

530	15c. red	85	75
531	20c. blue	85	75

MARINE INSURANCE STAMPS

1921. As Type **M22** of the Netherlands, but inscribed "NED. INDIE".

M257	15c. green	18·00	85·00
M258	60c. red	18·00	£130
M259	75c. brown	18·00	£170
M260	1g.50 blue	55·00	£425
M261	2g.25 brown	65·00	£375
M262	4½g. black	£110	£950
M263	7½g. red	£140	£1100

OFFICIAL STAMPS

1911. Stamps of 1892 optd D in white on a black circle.

O178	**6**	10c. brown	4·00	2·75
O179	**6**	12½c. grey	6·75	14·00
O180	**6**	15c. bistre	6·75	7·00
O181	**6**	20c. blue	6·75	4·25
O182	**6**	25c. mauve	27·00	18·00
O183	**6**	50c. red	6·75	3·50
O184	**6**	2g.50 blue and brown	£110	£110

1911. Stamps of 1902 (except No. O185) optd **DIENST**.

O186	**11**	½c. lilac	70	1·40
O187	**11**	1c. olive	70	70
O188	**11**	2c. brown	70	70
O185	**5**	2½c. yellow (No. 91)	1·60	3·50
O189	**11**	2½c. green	3·50	3·50
O190	**11**	3c. orange	1·10	1·10
O191	**11**	4c. blue	70	70
O192	**11**	5c. red	2·00	1·70
O193	**11**	7½c. grey	4·75	5·00
O194	**12**	10c. slate	70	70
O195	**12**	12½c. blue	4·75	5·00
O196	**12**	15c. brown	1·80	1·70
O197	**12**	15c. brown (No. 140)	70·00	†
O198	**12**	17½c. bistre	6·75	5·00
O199	**12**	20c. olive	1·60	1·10
O200	**12**	22½c. olive and brown	6·75	7·00
O201	**12**	25c. mauve	4·00	3·50
O202	**12**	30c. brown	2·00	1·40
O203	**12**	50c. red	27·00	18·00
O204	**13**	1g. lilac	6·75	3·50
O205	**13**	2½g. grey	55·00	60·00

POSTAGE DUE STAMPS

1874. As Postage Due stamps of Netherlands. Colours changed.

D56	**D8**	5c. yellow	£500	£450
D57	**D8**	10c. green on yellow	£300	£250
D59	**D8**	15c. orange on yellow	60·00	39·00
D60	**D8**	20c. green on blue	£100	39·00

1882. As Type **D10** of Netherlands.

D63b	2½c. black and red	1·30	2·00
D64b	5c. black and red	1·30	2·00
D65b	10c. black and red	6·50	6·50
D70c	15c. black and red	6·50	5·25
D71c	20c. black and red	£160	1·30
D76b	30c. black and red	5·75	7·25
D72	40c. black and red	4·00	5·25
D73b	50c. black and pink	2·00	2·50
D67a	75c. black and red	2·00	4·00

1892. As Type **D9** of Netherlands.

D102	2½c. black and pink	2·50	50
D103	5c. black and pink	7·75	40
D104	10c. black and pink	4·00	65
D105	15c. black and pink	35·00	4·50
D106b	20c. black and pink	90·00	65·00
D107	30c. black and pink	49·00	16·00
D108	40c. black and pink	43·00	5·25
D109	50c. black and pink	29·00	2·50
D110	75c. black and pink	55·00	8·50

1913. As Type **D9** of Netherlands.

D226	1c. orange	40	3·75
D489	1c. violet	1·50	2·20
D227	2½c. orange	40	45
D527	2½c. brown	2·20	3·75
D228	3½c. orange	40	4·75
D491	3½c. blue	1·50	2·20
D229	5c. orange	40	45
D230	7½c. orange	40	45
D493	7½c. green	1·50	2·20
D231	10c. orange	40	45
D494	10c. mauve	1·50	2·20
D232	12½c. orange	7·00	75
D448	15c. orange	3·75	6·75
D234	20c. orange	40	45
D495	20c. blue	1·50	2·20
D235	25c. orange	40	45
D496	25c. yellow	1·50	2·20
D236	30c. orange	40	45
D497	30c. brown	2·20	3·00
D237	37½c. orange	35·00	36·00
D238	40c. orange	40	45
D498	40c. green	2·20	3·00
D239	50c. orange	4·25	45
D499	50c. yellow	3·00	3·00
D240	75c. orange	5·50	45
D500	75c. blue	3·00	3·00
D501	100c. green	3·00	3·00
D241	1g. orange	10·50	14·50
D452	1g. blue	3·00	6·75

1937. Surch 20.

D384	**D7**	20c. on 37½c. red	1·60	80

1946. Optd TE BETALEN PORT or surch also.

D480	2½c. on 10c. red (No. 429)	2·20	2·20
D481	10c. red (No. 429)	3·75	3·75
D482	20c. mauve (No. 432)	11·00	11·00
D483	40c. green (No. 436)	80·00	80·00

For later issues see **INDONESIA**.

NETHERLANDS NEW GUINEA

The Western half of the island of New Guinea was governed by the Netherlands until 1962, when control was transferred to the UN (see West New Guinea). The territory later became part of Indonesia as West Irian (q.v.).

100 cents = 1 gulden.

1950. As numeral and portrait types of Netherlands but inscr "NIEUW GUINEA".

1	**118**	1c. grey	50	40
2	**118**	2c. orange	50	40
3	**118**	2½c. olive	80	40
4	**118**	3c. mauve	3·25	2·50
5	**118**	4c. green	3·25	2·10
6	**118**	5c. blue	5·50	40
7	**118**	7½c. brown	90	40
8	**118**	10c. violet	3·00	40
9	**118**	12½c. red	3·00	2·75
10	**129**	15c. brown	4·50	1·30
11	**129**	20c. blue	2·00	40
12	**129**	25c. red	2·00	40
13	**129**	30c. blue	20·00	65
14	**129**	40c. green	3·25	40
15	**129**	45c. brown	9·75	1·30
16	**129**	50c. orange	2·50	40
17	**129**	55c. grey	19·00	90
18	**129**	80c. purple	21·00	5·25
19	**130**	1g. red	23·00	65
20	**130**	2g. brown	20·00	2·30
21	**130**	5g. green	26·00	2·20

1953. Netherlands Flood Relief Fund. Nos. 6, 10 and 12 surch hulp nederland 1953 and premium.

22	**118**	5c.+5c. blue	20·00	20·00
23	**129**	15c.+10c. brown	20·00	20·00
24	**129**	25c.+10c. red	20·00	20·00

5 Lesser Bird of Paradise

1954

25	**5**	1c. yellow and red	40	40
26	**5**	5c. yellow and brown	65	40
27	-	10c. brown and blue	65	40
28	-	15c. brown and yellow	65	40
29	-	20c. brown and green	2·00	1·00

Design:—10, 15, 20c. Greater bird of paradise.

6 Queen Juliana

1954

30	**6**	25c. red	65	40
31	**6**	30c. blue	90	50
32	**6**	40c. orange	4·25	4·00
33	**6**	45c. green	2·00	2·30
34	**6**	55c. turquoise	1·30	40
35	**6**	80c. grey	2·50	65
36	**6**	85c. brown	3·25	90
37	**6**	1g. purple	8·50	4·00

1955. Red Cross. Nos. 26/8 surch with cross and premium.

38	**5**	5c.+5c. yellow and sepia	2·75	2·75
39	-	10c.+10c. brown and blue	2·75	2·75
40	-	15c.+10c. brown and lemon	2·75	2·75

8 Child and Native Hut

1956. Anti-leprosy Fund.

41	-	5c.+5c. green	2·00	2·00
42	**8**	10c.+5c. purple	2·00	2·00
43	-	25c.+10c. blue	2·00	2·00
44	**8**	30c.+10c. buff	2·00	2·00

Design:—5c., 25c. Palm-trees and native hut.

10 Papuan Girl and Beach Scene

1957. Child Welfare Fund.

51	**10**	5c.+5c. lake	2·00	2·00
52	-	10c.+5c. green	2·00	2·00
53	**10**	25c.+10c. brown	2·00	2·00
54	-	30c.+10c. blue	2·00	2·00

Design:—10c., 30c. Papuan child and native hut.

11 Red Cross and Idol

1958. Red Cross Fund.

55	**11**	5c.+5c. multicoloured	2·00	2·00
56	-	10c.+5c. multicoloured	2·00	2·00
57	**11**	25c.+10c. multicoloured	2·00	2·00
58	-	30c.+10c. multicoloured	2·00	2·00

Design:—10c., 30c. Red Cross and Asman-Papuan bowl in form of human figure.

12 Papuan and Helicopter

1959. Stars Mountains Expedition, 1959.

59	**12**	55c. brown and blue	2·30	1·60

13 Blue-crowned Pigeon

1959

60	**13**	7c. purple, blue and brown	90	60
61	**13**	12c. purple, blue and green	90	60
62	**13**	17c. purple and blue	90	45

14 *Tecomanthe dendrophila*

1959. Social Welfare. Inscr "SOCIALE ZORG".

63	**14**	5c.+5c. red and green	1·30	1·30
64	-	10c.+5c. purple, yellow and olive	1·30	1·30
65	-	25c.+10c. yellow, green and red	1·30	1·30
66	-	30c.+10c. green and violet	1·30	1·30

Designs:—10c. *Dendrobium attennatum Lindley*; 25c. *Rhododendron zoelleri Warburg*; 30c. *Boea cf. urvillei*.

1960. World Refugee Year. As T **180** of Netherlands.

67	25c. blue	1·00	1·00
68	30c. ochre	1·00	1·00

16 Paradise Birdwing

1960. Social Welfare Funds. Butterflies.

69	**16**	5c.+5c. multicoloured	2·00	2·00
70	-	10c.+5c. bl, blk & salmon	2·00	2·00
71	-	25c.+10c. red, sepia & yell	2·00	2·00
72	-	30c.+10c. multicoloured	2·00	2·00

Butterflies:—10c. Large green-banded blue; 25c. Red lacewing; 30c. Catops owl butterfly.

17 Council Building, Hollandia

1961. Opening of Netherlands New Guinea Council.

73	**17**	25c. turquoise	50	65
74	**17**	30c. red	50	65

18 *Scapanes australis*

1961. Social Welfare Funds. Beetles.

75	**18**	5c.+5c. multicoloured	1·30	1·30
76	-	10c.+5c. multicoloured	1·30	1·30
77	-	25c.+10c. multicoloured	1·30	1·30
78	-	30c.+10c. multicoloured	1·30	1·30

Beetles:—10c. Brenthid weevil; 25c. *Neolamprima adolphinae* (Stag Beetle); 30c. *Aspidomorpha aurata* (Leaf Beetle).

19 Children's Road Crossing

1962. Road Safety Campaign. Triangle in red.

79	**19**	25c. blue	65	65
80	-	30c. green (Adults at road crossing)	65	65

1962. Silver Wedding of Queen Juliana and Prince Bernhard. As T **187** of Netherlands.

81	55c. brown	65	80

21 Shadow of Palm on Beach

1962. Fifth South Pacific Conference, Pago Pago. Multicoloured.

82	25c. Type **21**	50	65
83	30c. Palms on beach	50	65

22 Lobster

1962. Social Welfare Funds. Shellfish. Multicoloured.

84	5c.+5c. Crab (horiz)	50	50
85	10c.+5c. Type **22**	50	50
86	25c.+10c. Spiny lobster	50	50
87	30c.+10c. Shrimp (horiz)	50	50

POSTAGE DUE STAMPS

1957. As Type **D121** of Netherlands but inscr "NEDERLANDS NIEUW GUINEA".

D45	1c. red	80	80
D46	5c. red	2·30	2·30
D47	10c. red	4·75	4·75
D48	25c. red	5·50	5·50
D49	40c. red	5·50	5·50
D50	1g. blue	8·50	8·50

For later issues see **WEST NEW GUINEA** and **WEST IRIAN**.

NEVIS

One of the Leeward Islands, Br. W. Indies. Used stamps of St. Kitts-Nevis from 1903 until June 1980 when Nevis, although remaining part of St. Kitts-Nevis, had a separate postal administration.

1861. 12 pence = 1 shilling; 20 shillings = 1 pound.
1980. 100 cents = 1 dollar.

1

2

1862. Various frames.

15	**1**	1d. red	32·00	25·00
2	**2**	4d. red	£160	75·00
12	**2**	4d. orange	£150	23·00
3	-	6d. lilac	£170	60·00
20	-	1s. green	90·00	£110

5

1879

25	**5**	½d. green	14·00	27·00
23	**5**	1d. mauve	80·00	50·00
27*a*	**5**	1d. red	20·00	20·00
28	**5**	2½d. brown	£120	50·00
29	**5**	2½d. blue	23·00	27·00
30	**5**	4d. blue	£350	50·00
31	**5**	4d. grey	24·00	8·00
32	**5**	6d. green	£450	£350
33	**5**	6d. brown	24·00	75·00
34	**5**	1s. violet	£110	£200

1883. Half of No. 23 surch **NEVIS. ½d.**

35	**5**	½d. on half 1d. mauve	£1100	55·00

1980. Nos. 394/406 of St. Christopher, Nevis and Anguilla with "St. Christopher" and "Anguilla" obliterated.

37	5c. Radio and TV station	10	10
38	10c. Technical college	10	10
39	12c. TV assembly plant	10	30
40	15c. Sugar cane harvesting	10	10
41	25c. Crafthouse (craft centre)	10	10
42	30c. *Europa* (liner)	20	15
43	40c. Lobster and sea crab	20	40
44	45c. Royal St. Kitts Hotel and golf course	80	70
45	50c. Pinney's Beach, Nevis	20	30
46	55c. New runway at Golden Rock	40	15
47	$1 Picking cotton	15	30
48	$5 Brewery	30	75
49	$10 Pineapples and peanuts	40	1·00

7a Queen Elizabeth the Queen Mother

1980. 80th Birthday of Queen Elizabeth the Queen Mother.

50	**7a**	$2 multicoloured	20	30

8 Nevis Lighter

1980. Boats. Multicoloured.

51	5c. Type **8**	10	10
52	30c. Local fishing boat	15	10
53	55c. *Caona* (catamaran)	15	10
54	$3 *Polynesia* (cruise schooner) (39×53 mm)	40	40

9 Virgin and Child

1980. Christmas. Multicoloured.

55	5c. Type **9**	10	10
56	30c. Angel	10	10
57	$2.50 The Wise Men	20	30

10 Charlestown Pier **11** New River Mill

1981. Multicoloured.

58A	5c. Type **10**	10	10
59A	10c. Court House and Library	10	10
60A	15c. Type **11**	10	10
61A	20c. Nelson Museum	10	10
62A	25c. St. James' Parish Church	15	15
63A	30c. Nevis Lane	15	15
64A	40c. Zetland Plantation	20	20
65A	45c. Nisbet Plantation	20	25
66A	50c. Pinney's Beach	25	25
67A	55c. Eva Wilkin's Studio	25	30
68A	$1 Nevis at dawn	30	45
69A	$2.50 Ruins of Fort Charles	35	80
70A	$5 Old Bath House	40	1·00
71A	$10 Beach at Nisbet's	50	1·50

11a *Royal Caroline*

11b Prince Charles and Lady Diana Spencer (image scaled to 59% of original size)

1981. Royal Wedding. Royal Yachts. Multicoloured.

72	55c. Type **11a**	15	15
73	55c. Type **11b**	40	40
74	$2 *Royal Sovereign*	20	30
75	$2 As No. 73	70	1·25
76	$5 *Britannia*	35	65
77	$5 As No. 73	80	1·75
MS78	120×109 mm. $4.50 As No. 73	1·10	1·25

12 *Heliconius charithonia*

1982. Butterflies (1st series). Multicoloured.

81	5c. Type **12**	10	10
82	30c. *Siproeta stelenes*	20	10
83	55c. *Marpesia petreus*	25	15
84	$2 *Phoebis agarithe*	60	80

See also Nos. 105/8.

13 Caroline of Brunswick, Princess of Wales, 1793

1982. 21st Birthday of Princess of Wales. Mult.

85	30c. Type **13**	10	10
86	55c. Coat of Arms of Caroline of Brunswick	15	15
87	$5 Diana, Princess of Wales	60	1·00

1982. Birth of Prince William of Wales. Nos. 85/7 optd ROYAL BABY.

88	30c. As Type **13**	10	10
89	55c. Coat of Arms of Caroline of Brunswick	15	15
90	$5 Diana, Princess of Wales	60	1·00

14 Cyclist

1982. 75th Anniv of Boy Scout Movement. Multicoloured.

91	5c. Type **14**	20	10
92	30c. Athlete	20	10
93	$2.50 Camp cook	30	65

15 Santa Claus

1982. Christmas. Children's Paintings. Mult.

94	15c. Type **15**	10	10
95	30c. Carollers	10	10
96	$1.50 Decorated house and local band (horiz)	15	25
97	$2.50 Adoration of the Shepherds (horiz)	25	40

16 Tube Sponge

1983. Corals (1st series). Multicoloured.

98	15c. Type **16**	10	10
99	30c. Stinging coral	15	10
100	55c. Flower coral	15	10
101	$3 Sea rod and red fire sponge	50	90
MS102	82×115 mm. Nos. 98/101	1·60	3·00

See also Nos. 423/6.

17 HMS *Boreas* off Nevis

1983. Commonwealth Day. Multicoloured.

103	55c. Type **17**	15	10
104	$2 Capt. Horatio Nelson and HMS *Boreas* at anchor	45	60

1983. Butterflies (2nd series). As T **12**. Mult.

105	30c. *Pyrgus oileus*	25	10
106	55c. *Junonia evarete* (vert)	25	10
107	$1.10 *Urbanus proteus* (vert)	40	40
108	$2 *Hypolimnas misippus*	50	75

1983. Nos. 58 and 60/71 optd **INDEPENDENCE 1983**.

109B	5c. Type **10**	10	10
110B	15c. Type **11**	10	10
111B	20c. Nelson Museum	10	10
112B	25c. St. James' Parish Church	10	15
113B	30c. Nevis Lane	15	15
114B	40c. Zetland Plantation	15	20
115B	45c. Nisbet Plantation	15	25
116B	50c. Pinney's Beach	15	25
117B	55c. Eva Wilkin's Studio	15	30
118B	$1 Nevis at dawn	15	30
119B	$2.50 Ruins of Fort Charles	25	45
120B	$5 Old Bath House	30	55
121B	$10 Beach at Nisbet's	40	70

19 Montgolfier Balloon, 1783

1983. Bicentenary of Manned Flight. Mult.

122	10c. Type **19**	10	10
123	45c. Sikorsky S-38 flying boat (horiz)	25	10
124	50c. Beech 50 Twin Bonanza (horiz)	25	10
125	$2.50 Hawker Siddeley Sea Harrier (horiz)	55	1·25
MS126	118×145 mm. Nos. 122/5	75	1·25

20 Mary praying over Holy Child

1983. Christmas. Multicoloured.

127	5c. Type **20**	10	10
128	30c. Shepherds with flock	10	10
129	55c. Three Angels	10	10
130	$3 Boy with two girls	30	60
MS131	135×149 mm. Nos. 127/30	85	2·00

21 *County of Oxford* (1945)

1983. Leaders of the World. Railway Locomotives (1st series). The first in each pair shows technical drawings and the second the locomotive at work.

132	**21**	55c. multicoloured	10	20
133	-	55c. multicoloured	10	20
134	-	$1 red, blue and black	10	20
135	-	$1 multicoloured	10	20
136	-	$1 purple, blue and black	10	20
137	-	$1 multicoloured	10	20
138	-	$1 red, black and yellow	10	20
139	-	$1 multicoloured	10	20
140	-	$1 multicoloured	10	20
141	-	$1 multicoloured	10	20
142	-	$1 yellow, black and blue	10	20
143	-	$1 multicoloured	10	20
144	-	$1 yellow, black and purple	10	20
145	-	$1 multicoloured	10	20
146	-	$1 multicoloured	10	20
147	-	$1 multicoloured	10	20

Designs:—Nos. 132/3, *County of Oxford*, Great Britain (1945); 134/5, *Evening Star*, Great Britain (1960); 136/7, Stanier Class 5 No. 44806, Great Britain (1934); 138/9, *Pendennis Castle*, Great Britain (1924); 140/1, *Winston Churchill*, Great Britain (1946); 142/3, *Mallard*, Great Britain (1938) (inscr "1935" in error); 144/5, *Britannia*, Great Britain (1951); 146/7, *King George V*, Great Britain.

See also Nos. 219/26, 277/84, 297/308, 352/9 and 427/42.

22 Boer War

1984. Leaders of the World. British Monarchs (1st series). Multicoloured.

148	5c. Type **22**	10	10
149	5c. Queen Victoria	10	10
150	50c. Queen Victoria at Osborne House	10	30
151	50c. Osborne House	10	30
152	60c. Battle of Dettingen	10	30
153	60c. George II	10	30
154	75c. George II at the Bank of England	10	30
155	75c. Bank of England	10	30
156	$1 Coat of Arms of George II	10	30
157	$1 George II (different)	10	30
158	$3 Coat of Arms of Queen Victoria	20	50
159	$3 Queen Victoria (different)	20	50

See also Nos. 231/6.

23 Golden Rock Inn

1984. Tourism (1st series). Multicoloured.

160	55c. Type **23**	25	20
161	55c. Rest Haven Inn	25	20
162	55c. Cliffdwellers Hotel	25	20
163	55c. Pinney's Beach Hotel	25	20

See also Nos. 245/8.

24 Early Seal of Colony

1984

164	**24**	$15 red	1·10	4·00

25 Cadillac

1984. Leaders of the World Automobiles (1st series). As T **25**. The first design in each pair shows technical drawings and the second paintings.

165	1c. yellow, black and mauve	10	10
166	1c. multicoloured	10	10
167	5c. blue, mauve and black	10	10
168	5c. multicoloured	10	10
169	15c. multicoloured	10	15
170	15c. multicoloured	10	15
171	35c. mauve, yellow and black	10	25
172	35c. multicoloured	10	25
173	45c. blue, mauve and black	10	25
174	45c. multicoloured	10	25
175	55c. multicoloured	10	25
176	55c. multicoloured	10	25
177	$2.50 mauve, black and yellow	20	40
178	$2.50 multicoloured	20	40
179	$3 blue, yellow and black	20	40
180	$3 multicoloured	20	40

Designs:—No. 165/6, Cadillac V16 Fleetwood Convertible (1932); 167/8, Packard Twin Six Touring Car (1916); 169/70, Daimler 2 Cylinder (1886); 171/2, Porsche 911 S Targa (1970); 173/4, Benz Three Wheeler (1885); 175/6, M.G. TC (1947); 177/8, Cobra Roadster 289 (1966); 179/80, Aston Martin DB6 Hardtop (1966).

See also Nos. 203/10, 249/64, 326/37, 360/371 and 411/22.

26 Carpentry

1984. Tenth Anniv of Culturama Celebrations. Multicoloured.

181	30c. Type **26**	10	10
182	55c. Grass mat and basket making	10	10
183	$1 Pottery firing	15	25
184	$3 Culturama Queen and dancers	40	55

27 Yellow Bell

1984. Flowers. Multicoloured.

185A	5c. Type **27**	10	10
186A	10c. Plumbago	10	10
187A	15c. Flamboyant	10	10
189A	30c. Bougainvillea	10	15
191A	50c. Night-blooming cereus	10	20
192A	55c. Yellow mahoe	10	25
193A	60c. Spider-lily	10	25
194A	75c. Scarlet cordia	15	30
195A	$1 Shell-ginger	15	40
196A	$3 Blue petrea	20	1·10
197A	$5 Coral hibiscus	40	2·00
198A	$10 Passion flower	70	3·50

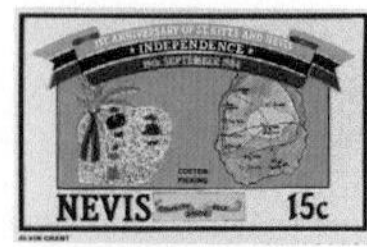
28 Cotton-picking and Map

1984. First Anniv of Independence of St. Kitts-Nevis. Multicoloured.

199	15c. Type **28**	10	10
200	55c. Alexander Hamilton's birthplace	10	10
201	$1.10 Local agricultural produce	20	40
202	$3 Nevis Peak and Pinney's Beach	50	1·00

1984. Leaders of the World. Automobiles (2nd series). As T **25**. The first in each pair shows technical drawings and the second paintings.

203	5c. black, blue and brown	10	10
204	5c. multicoloured	10	10
205	30c. black, turquoise and brown	15	15
206	30c. multicoloured	15	15
207	50c. black, drab and brown	15	15
208	50c. multicoloured	15	15
209	$3 black, brown and green	30	45
210	$3 multicoloured	30	45

Designs:—Nos. 203/4, Lagonda Speed Model touring car (1929); 205/6, Jaguar E-Type 4.2 litre (1967); 207/8, Volkswagen Beetle (1947); 209/10, Pierce Arrow V12 (1932).

29 C. P. Mead

1984. Leaders of the World. Cricketers (1st series). As T **29**. The first in each pair shows a head portrait and the second the cricketer in action. Multicoloured.

211	5c. Type **29**	10	10
212	5c. C. P. Mead	10	10
213	25c. J. B. Statham	20	30
214	25c. J. B. Statham	20	30
215	55c. Sir Learie Constantine	30	40
216	55c. Sir Learie Constantine	30	40
217	$2.50 Sir Leonard Hutton	50	1·25
218	$2.50 Sir Leonard Hutton	50	1·25

See also Nos. 237/44.

1984. Leaders of the World. Railway Locomotives (2nd series). As T **21**. The first in each pair shows technical drawings and the second the locomotive at work.

219	5c. multicoloured	10	10
220	5c. multicoloured	10	10
221	10c. multicoloured	10	10
222	10c. multicoloured	10	10
223	60c. multicoloured	15	25
224	60c. multicoloured	15	25
225	$2.50 multicoloured	50	70
226	$2.50 multicoloured	50	70

Designs:—Nos. 219/20, Class EF81 electric locomotive, Japan (1968); 221/22, Class 5500 electric locomotive, France (1927); 223/4, Class 240P, France (1940); 225/6, Hikari express train, Japan (1964).

30 Fifer and Drummer from Honeybees Band

1984. Christmas. Local Music. Multicoloured.

227	15c. Type **30**	15	10
228	40c. Guitar and "barhow" players from Canary Birds Band	25	10
229	60c. Shell All Stars steel band	30	10
230	$3 Organ and choir, St. John's Church, Fig Tree	1·25	1·00

1984. Leaders of the World. British Monarchs (2nd series). As T **22**. Multicoloured.

231	5c. King John and *Magna Carta*	10	10
232	5c. Barons and King John	10	10
233	55c. King John	10	15
234	55c. Newark Castle	10	15
235	$2 Coat of Arms	25	40
236	$2 King John (different)	25	40

1984. Leaders of the World. Cricketers (2nd series). As T **29**. The first in each pair listed shows a head portrait and the second the cricketer in action. Multicoloured.

237	5c. J. D. Love	10	10
238	5c. J. D. Love	10	10
239	15c. S. J. Dennis	10	15
240	15c. S. J. Dennis	10	15
241	55c. B. W. Luckhurst	15	20
242	55c. B. W. Luckhurst	15	20
243	$2.50 B. L. D'Oliveira	40	60
244	$2.50 B. L. D'Oliveira	40	60

1984. Tourism (2nd series). As T **23**. Multicoloured.

245	$1.20 Croney's Old Manor Hotel	15	25
246	$1.20 Montpelier Plantation Inn	15	25
247	$1.20 Nisbet's Plantation Inn	15	25
248	$1.20 Zetland Plantation Inn	15	25

1985. Leaders of the World. Automobiles (3rd series). As T **25**. The first in each pair shows technical drawings and the second paintings.

249	1c. black, green and light green	10	10
250	1c. multicoloured	10	10
251	5c. black, blue and light blue	10	10

No.	Description	Unused	Used
252	5c. multicoloured	10	10
253	10c. black, green and light green	10	10
254	10c. multicoloured	10	10
255	50c. black, green and brown	10	10
256	50c. multicoloured	10	10
257	60c. black, green and blue	10	10
258	60c. multicoloured	10	10
259	75c. black, red and orange	10	10
260	75c. multicoloured	10	10
261	$2.50 black, green and blue	20	30
262	$2.50 multicoloured	20	30
263	$3 black, green and light green	20	30
264	$3 multicoloured	20	30

Designs:—Nos. 249/50, Delahaye Type 35 Cabriolet (1935); 251/2, Ferrari Testa Rossa (1958); 253/4, Voisin Aerodyne (1934); 255/6, Buick Riviera (1963); 257/8, Cooper Climax (1960); 259/60, Ford 999 (1904); 261/2, MG M-Type Midget (1930); 263/4, Rolls- Royce Corniche (1971).

31 Broad-winged Hawk

1985. Local Hawks and Herons. Multicoloured.

No.	Description	Unused	Used
265	20c. Type **31**	1·25	20
266	40c. Red-tailed hawk	1·40	30
267	60c. Little blue heron	1·40	40
268	$3 Great blue heron (white phase)	2·75	1·90

32 Eastern Bluebird

1985. Leaders of the World. Birth Bicentenary of John J. Audubon (ornithologist) (1st issue). Multicoloured.

No.	Description	Unused	Used
269	5c. Type **32**	10	10
270	5c. Common cardinal	10	10
271	55c. Belted kingfisher	20	55
272	55c. Mangrove cuckoo	20	55
273	60c. Yellow warbler	20	55
274	60c. Cerulean warbler	20	55
275	$2 Burrowing owl	60	1·25
276	$2 Long-eared owl	60	1·25

See also Nos. 285/92.

1985. Leaders of the World. Railway Locomotives (3rd series). As T **21**. The first in each pair showing technical drawings and the second the locomotive at work.

No.	Description	Unused	Used
277	1c. multicoloured	10	10
278	1c. multicoloured	10	10
279	60c. multicoloured	20	20
280	60c. multicoloured	20	20
281	90c. multicoloured	25	25
282	90c. multicoloured	25	25
283	$2 multicoloured	40	60
284	$2 multicoloured	40	60

Designs:—Nos. 277/8, Class Wee Bogie, Great Britain (1882); 279/80, *Comet*, Great Britain (1851); 281/2, Class 8H No. 6173, Great Britain (1908); 283/4, Class A No. 23, Great Britain (1866).

1985. Leaders of the World. Birth Bicentenary of John J. Audubon (ornithologist) (2nd issue). As T **32**. Multicoloured.

No.	Description	Unused	Used
285	1c. Painted bunting	10	10
286	1c. Golden-crowned kinglet	10	10
287	40c. Common flicker	25	40
288	40c. Western tanager	25	40
289	60c. Varied thrush	25	45
290	60c. Evening grosbeak	25	45
291	$2.50 Blackburnian warbler	50	80
292	$2.50 Northern oriole	50	80

33 Guides and Guide Headquarters

1985. 75th Anniv of Girl Guide Movement. Multicoloured.

No.	Description	Unused	Used
293	15c. Type **33**	10	10
294	60c. Girl Guide uniforms of 1910 and 1985 (vert)	15	25
295	$1 Lord and Lady Baden-Powell (vert)	20	40
296	$3 Princess Margaret in Guide uniform (vert)	50	1·25

1985. Leaders of the World. Railway Locomotives (4th series). As T **21**. The first in each pair shows technical drawings and the second the locomotive at work.

No.	Description	Unused	Used
297	5c. multicoloured	10	10
298	5c. multicoloured	10	10
299	30c. multicoloured	10	15
300	30c. multicoloured	10	15
301	60c. multicoloured	10	20
302	60c. multicoloured	10	20
303	75c. multicoloured	10	25
304	75c. multicoloured	10	25
305	$1 multicoloured	10	25
306	$1 multicoloured	10	25
307	$2.50 multicoloured	20	60
308	$2.50 multicoloured	20	60

Designs: Nos. 297/8, *Snowdon Ranger* (1878); 299/300, Large Belpaire locomotive, Great Britain (1904); 301/2, Class County No. 3821, Great Britain (1904); 303/4, *L'Outrance*, France (1877); 305/6, Class PB-15, Australia (1899); 307/8, Class 64, Germany (1928).

34 The Queen Mother at Garter Ceremony

1985. Leaders of the World. Life and Times of Queen Elizabeth the Queen Mother. Various vertical portraits.

No.	Type	Description	Unused	Used
309	**34**	45c. multicoloured	10	15
310	-	45c. multicoloured	10	15
311	-	75c. multicoloured	10	20
312	-	75c. multicoloured	10	20
313	-	$1.20 multicoloured	15	35
314	-	$1.20 multicoloured	15	35
315	-	$1.50 multicoloured	20	40
316	-	$1.50 multicoloured	20	40
MS317		85×114 mm. $2 multicoloured; $2 multicoloured	50	1·40

Each value was issued in pairs showing a floral pattern across the bottom of the portraits which stops short of the left-hand edge on the first stamp and of the right-hand edge on the second.

35 Isambard Kingdom Brunel

1985. 150th Anniv of Great Western Railway. Designs showing railway engineers and their achievements. Multicoloured.

No.	Description	Unused	Used
318	25c. Type **35**	15	35
319	25c. Royal Albert Bridge, 1859	15	35
320	50c. William Dean	20	45
321	50c. Locomotive *Lord of the Isles*, 1895	20	45
322	$1 Locomotive *Lode Star*, 1907	20	65
323	$1 G. J. Churchward	20	65
324	$2.50 Locomotive *Pendennis Castle*, 1924	30	80
325	$2.50 C. B. Collett	30	80

Nos. 318/19, 320/1, 322/3 and 324/5 were printed together se-tenant, each pair forming a composite design.

1985. Leaders of the World. Automobiles (4th series). As T **25**. The first in each pair shows technical drawings and the second paintings.

No.	Description	Unused	Used
326	10c. black, blue and red	10	10
327	10c. multicoloured	10	10
328	35c. black, turquoise and blue	10	25
329	35c. multicoloured	10	25
330	75c. black, green and brown	10	40
331	75c. multicoloured	10	40
332	$1.15 black, brown and green	15	45
333	$1.15 multicoloured	15	45
334	$1.50 black, blue and red	15	50
335	$1.50 multicoloured	15	50
336	$2 black, lilac and violet	20	60
337	$2 multicoloured	20	60

Designs:—Nos. 326/7, Sunbeam Coupe de l'Auto (1912); 328/9, Cisitalia Pininfarina Coupe (1948); 330/1, Porsche 928S (1980); 332/3, MG K3 Magnette (1933); 334/5, Lincoln Zephyr (1937); 336/7, Pontiac 2 Door (1926).

1985. Royal Visit. Nos. 76/7, 83, 86, 92/3, 98/9 and 309/10 optd **CARIBBEAN ROYAL VISIT 1985** or surch also.

No.	Type	Description	Unused	Used
338	**16**	15c. multicoloured	75	1·25
339	-	30c. multicoloured (No. 92)	2·25	2·25
340	-	30c. multicoloured (No. 99)	75	1·25
341	-	40c. on 55c. mult (No. 86)	2·25	3·50
342	**34**	45c. multicoloured	1·50	3·50
343	-	45c. multicoloured (No. 310)	1·50	3·50
344	-	55c. multicoloured (No. 83)	1·75	1·25
345	-	$1.50 on $5 multicoloured (No. 76)	2·25	3·50
346	-	$1.50 on $5 multicoloured (No. 77)	13·00	19·00
347	-	$2.50 mult (No. 93)	2·50	4·00

36 St. Paul's Anglican Church, Charlestown

1985. Christmas. Churches of Nevis (1st series). Multicoloured.

No.	Description	Unused	Used
348	10c. Type **36**	15	10
349	40c. St. Theresa Catholic Church, Charlestown	35	30
350	60c. Methodist Church, Gingerland	40	50
351	$3 St. Thomas Anglican Church, Lowland	80	2·75

See also Nos. 462/5.

1986. Leaders of the World. Railway Locomotives (5th series). As T **21**. The first in each pair shows technical drawings and the second the locomotive at work.

No.	Description	Unused	Used
352	30c. multicoloured	15	25
353	30c. multicoloured	15	25
354	75c. multicoloured	25	50
355	75c. multicoloured	25	50
356	$1.50 multicoloured	40	70
357	$1.50 multicoloured	40	70
358	$2 multicoloured	50	80
359	$2 multicoloured	50	80

Designs:—Nos. 352/3, *Stourbridge Lion*, USA (1829); 354/5, EP-2 Bi-Polar electric locomotive, USA (1919); 356/7, Gas turbine No. 59, USA (1953); 358/9 Class FL9 diesel locomotive No. 2039, USA (1955).

1986. Leaders of the World. Automobiles (5th series). As T **25**. The first in each pair showing technical drawings and the second paintings.

No.	Description	Unused	Used
360	10c. black, brown and green	10	10
361	10c. multicoloured	10	10
362	60c. black, orange and red	15	25
363	60c. multicoloured	15	25
364	75c. black, light brown and brown	15	25
365	75c. multicoloured	15	25
366	$1 black, light grey and grey	15	30
367	$1 multicoloured	15	30
368	$1.50 black, yellow and green	15	35
369	$1.50 multicoloured	15	35
370	$3 black, light blue and blue	20	65
371	$3 multicoloured	20	65

Designs:—Nos. 360/1, Adler Trumpf (1936); 362/3, Maserati Tipo 250F (1957); 364/5, Oldsmobile Limited (1910); 366/7, Jaguar C-Type (1951); 368/9, ERA 1.5L B Type (1937); 370/1, Chevrolet Corvette (1953).

37 Supermarine Spitfire Prototype, 1936

1986. 50th Anniv of Spitfire (fighter aircraft). Multicoloured.

No.	Description	Unused	Used
372	$1 Type **37**	30	50
373	$2.50 Supermarine Spitfire Mk 1A in Battle of Britain, 1940	35	90
374	$3 Supermarine Spitfire Mk XII over convoy, 1944	35	90
375	$4 Supermarine Spitfire Mk XXIV, 1948	35	1·40
MS376	114×86 mm. $6 Supermarine Seafire Mk III on escort carrier HMS *Hunter*	1·10	3·75

38 Head of Amerindian

1986. 500th Anniv (1992) of Discovery of America by Columbus (1st issue). Multicoloured.

No.	Description	Unused	Used
377	85c. Type **38**	85	1·00
378	85c. Exchanging gifts for food from Amerindians	85	1·00
379	$1.75 Columbus's Coat of Arms	1·40	2·00
380	$1.75 Breadfruit plant	1·40	2·00
381	$2.50 Columbus's fleet	1·40	2·25
382	$2.50 Christopher Columbus	1·40	2·25
MS383	95×84 mm. $6 Christopher Columbus (different)	5·50	10·00

The two designs of each value were printed together, *se-tenant*, each pair forming a composite design showing charts of Columbus's route in the background.

See also Nos. 546/**MS**554, 592/**MS**600, 678/**MS**684 and 685/6.

38a Queen Elizabeth in 1976

1986. 60th Birthday of Queen Elizabeth II. Multicoloured.

No.	Description	Unused	Used
384	5c. Type **38a**	10	10
385	75c. Queen Elizabeth in 1953	15	25
386	$2 In Australia	20	60
387	$8 In Canberra, 1982 (vert)	75	2·00
MS388	85×115 mm. $10 Queen Elizabeth II	4·00	7·50

39 Brazilian Player

1986. World Cup Football Championship, Mexico. Multicoloured.

No.	Description	Unused	Used
389	1c. Official World Cup mascot (horiz)	10	10
390	2c. Type **39**	10	10
391	5c. Danish player	10	10
392	10c. Brazilian player (different)	10	10
393	20c. Denmark v Spain	15	20
394	30c. Paraguay v Chile	20	30
395	60c. Italy v West Germany	25	55
396	75c. Danish team (56×36 mm)	25	65
397	$1 Paraguayan team (56×36 mm)	25	70
398	$1.75 Brazilian team (56×36 mm)	35	1·00
399	$3 Italy v England	50	1·60
400	$6 Italian team (56×36 mm)	70	2·25
MS401	Five sheets, each 85×115 mm. (a) $1.50 As No. 398. (b) $2 As No. 393. (c) $2 As No. 400. (d) $2.50 As No. 395. (e) $4 As No. 394 Set of 5 sheets	10·00	15·00

40 Clothing Machinist

1986. Local Industries. Multicoloured.

No.	Description	Unused	Used
402	15c. Type **40**	20	15
403	40c. Carpentry/joinery workshop	45	30
404	$1.20 Agricultural produce market	1·25	1·60
405	$3 Fishing boats landing catch	2·50	3·50

40a Prince Andrew in Midshipman's Uniform

1986. Royal Wedding. Multicoloured.

No.	Description	Unused	Used
406	60c. Type **40a**	15	25
407	60c. Miss Sarah Ferguson	15	25
408	$2 Prince Andrew on safari in Africa (horiz)	40	60
409	$2 Prince Andrew at the races (horiz)	40	60

MS410	115×85 mm. $10 Duke and Duchess of York on Palace balcony after wedding (horiz)	2·50	5·00

See also Nos. 454/7.

1986. Automobiles (6th series). As T **25**. The first in each pair showing technical drawings and the second paintings.

411	15c. multicoloured	10	10
412	15c. multicoloured	10	10
413	45c. black, light blue and blue	15	25
414	45c. multicoloured	15	25
415	60c. multicoloured	15	30
416	60c. multicoloured	15	30
417	$1 black, light green and green	20	40
418	$1 multicoloured	20	40
419	$1.75 black, lilac and deep lilac	20	50
420	$1.75 multicoloured	20	50
421	$3 multicoloured	35	70
422	$3 multicoloured	35	70

Designs:—Nos. 411/12, Riley Brooklands Nine (1930); 413/14, Alfa Romeo GTA (1966); 415/16, Pierce Arrow Type 66 (1913); 417/18, Willys-Knight 66A (1928); 419/20, Studebaker Starliner (1953); 421/2, Cunningham V-8 (1919).

41 Gorgonia

1986. Corals (2nd series). Multicoloured.

423	15c. Type **41**	20	15
424	60c. Fire coral	35	40
425	$2 Elkhorn coral	50	1·75
426	$3 Vase sponge and feather star	60	2·25

1986. Railway Locomotives (6th series). As T **21**. The first in each pair showing technical drawings and the second the locomotive at work.

427	15c. multicoloured	10	10
428	15c. multicoloured	10	10
429	45c. multicoloured	15	25
430	45c. multicoloured	15	25
431	60c. multicoloured	20	30
432	60c. multicoloured	20	30
433	75c. multicoloured	20	40
434	75c. multicoloured	20	40
435	$1 multicoloured	20	50
436	$1 multicoloured	20	50
437	$1.50 multicoloured	25	60
438	$1.50 multicoloured	25	60
439	$2 multicoloured	30	65
440	$2 multicoloured	30	65
441	$3 multicoloured	35	80
442	$3 multicoloured	35	80

Designs:—Nos. 427/8, Connor Single Class, Great Britain (1859); 429/30, Class P2 *Cock o' the North*, Great Britain (1934); 431/2, Class 7000 electric locomotive, Japan (1926); 433/4, Class P3, Germany (1897); 435/6, *Dorchester*, Canada (1836); 436/7, Class Centennial diesel locomotive, USA (1969); 439/40, *Lafayette*, USA (1837); 441/2, Class C-16 No. 222, USA (1882).

41a Statue of Liberty and World Trade Centre, Manhattan

1986. Centenary of Statue of Liberty. Multicoloured.

443	15c. Type **41a**	20	15
444	25c. Sailing ship passing statue	30	20
445	40c. Statue in scaffolding	30	25
446	60c. Statue (side view) and scaffolding	30	30
447	75c. Statue and regatta	40	40
448	$1 Tall Ships parade passing statue (horiz)	40	45
449	$1.50 Head and arm of statue above scaffolding	40	60
450	$2 Ships with souvenir flags (horiz)	55	80
451	$2.50 Statue and New York waterfront	60	90
452	$3 Restoring statue	80	1·25
MS453	Four sheets, each 85×115 mm. (a) $3.50 Statue at dusk. (b) $4 Head of Statue. (c) $4.50 Statue and lightning. (d) $5 Head and torch at sunset Set of 4 sheets	3·00	11·00

1986. Royal Wedding (2nd issue). Nos. 406/9 optd Congratulations to T.R.H. The Duke & Duchess of York.

454	60c. Prince Andrew in midshipman's uniform	15	40
455	60c. Miss Sarah Ferguson	15	40
456	$2 Prince Andrew on safari in Africa (horiz)	40	1·00
457	$2 Prince Andrew at the races (horiz)	40	1·00

42 Dinghy sailing

1986. Sports. Multicoloured.

458	10c. Type **42**	20	10
459	25c. Netball	35	15
460	$2 Cricket	3·50	2·75
461	$3 Basketball	4·25	3·25

43 St. George's Anglican Church, Gingerland

1986. Christmas. Churches of Nevis (2nd series). Multicoloured.

462	10c. Type **43**	15	10
463	40c. Trinity Methodist Church, Fountain	30	25
464	$1 Charlestown Methodist Church	60	65
465	$5 Wesleyan Holiness Church, Brown Hill	2·75	4·00

44 Constitution Document, Quill and Inkwell

1987. Bicentenary of U.S. Constitution and 230th Birth Anniv of Alexander Hamilton (U.S. statesman). Multicoloured.

466	15c. Type **44**	10	10
467	40c. Alexander Hamilton and Hamilton House	20	25
468	60c. Alexander Hamilton	25	35
469	$2 Washington and his Cabinet	90	1·40
MS470	70×82 mm. $5 Model ship *Hamilton* on float, 1788	6·50	8·00

1987. Victory of "Stars and Stripes" in America's Cup Yachting Championship. No. 54 optd America's Cup 1987 Winners 'Stars & Stripes'.

471	$3 Windjammer SV *Polynesia*	1·10	1·60

46 Fig Tree Church

1987. Bicentenary of Marriage of Horatio Nelson and Frances Nisbet. Multicoloured.

472	15c. Type **46**	20	10
473	60c. Frances Nisbet	50	30
474	$1 HMS *Boreas* (frigate)	1·90	1·25
475	$3 Captain Horatio Nelson	3·00	4·00
MS476	102×82 mm. $3 As No. 473; $3 No. 475	5·00	6·50

47 Queen Angelfish

1987. Coral Reef Fish. Multicoloured.

477	60c. Type **47**	30	60
478	60c. Blue angelfish	30	60
479	$1 Stoplight parrotfish (male)	30	80
480	$1 Stoplight parrotfish (female)	30	80
481	$1.50 Red hind	35	90
482	$1.50 Rock hind	35	90
483	$2.50 Coney (bicoloured phase)	35	1·50
484	$2.50 Coney (red-brown phase)	35	1·50

Nos. 478, 480, 482 and 484 are inverted triangles.

48 *Panaeolus antillarum*

1987. Fungi (1st series). Multicoloured.

485	15c. Type **48**	50	30
486	50c. *Pycnoporus sanguineus*	1·00	55
487	$2 *Gymnopilus chrysopellus*	1·50	2·75
488	$3 *Cantharellus cinnabarinus*	1·75	4·00

See also Nos. 646/**MS**654.

49 Rag Doll

1987. Christmas. Toys. Multicoloured.

489	10c. Type **49**	10	10
490	40c. Coconut boat	15	15
491	$1.20 Sandbox cart	40	50
492	$5 Two-wheeled cart	1·40	3·75

50 Hawk-wing Conch

1988. Sea Shells and Pearls. Multicoloured.

493	15c. Type **50**	20	15
494	40c. Rooster-tail conch	30	20
495	60c. Emperor helmet	40	40
496	$2 Queen or pink conch	1·10	1·75
497	$3 King helmet	1·25	2·00

51 Visiting Pensioners at Christmas

1988. 125th Anniv of International Red Cross. Multicoloured.

498	15c. Type **51**	10	10
499	40c. Teaching children first aid	15	20
500	60c. Providing wheelchairs for the disabled	25	35
501	$5 Helping cyclone victim	2·10	3·50

52 Athlete on Starting Blocks

1988. Olympic Games, Seoul. Multicoloured.

502	10c. Type **52**	10	35
503	$1.20 At start	50	85
504	$2 During race	85	1·25
505	$3 At finish	1·25	1·50
MS506	137×80 mm. As Nos. 502/5, but each size 24×36 mm	2·50	3·75

Nos. 502/5 were printed together, *se-tenant*, each strip forming a composite design showing an athlete from start to finish of race.

53 Outline Map and Arms of St. Kitts–Nevis

1988. Fifth Anniv of Independence.

507	**53**	$5 multicoloured	2·10	3·00

53a House of Commons passing Lloyd's Bill, 1871

1988. 300th Anniv of Lloyd's of London. Multicoloured.

508	15c. Type **53a**	25	10
509	60c. *Cunard Countess* (liner) (horiz)	1·75	65
510	$2.50 Space shuttle deploying satellite (horiz)	2·75	3·00
511	$3 *Viking Princess* (cargo liner) on fire, 1966	3·50	3·00

54 Poinsettia

1988. Christmas. Flowers. Multicoloured.

512	15c. Type **54**	10	10
513	40c. Tiger claws	15	15
514	60c. Sorrel flower	25	25
515	$1 Christmas candle	40	45
516	$5 Snow bush	1·25	3·50

55 British Fleet off St. Kitts

1989. Philexfrance 89 International Stamp Exhibition, Paris. Battle of Frigate Bay, 1782. Multicoloured.

517	50c. Type **55**	1·40	1·75
518	$1.20 Battle off Nevis	1·60	2·25
519	$2 British and French fleets exchanging broadsides	2·00	2·50
520	$3 French map of Nevis, 1764	2·50	3·00

Nos. 517/19 were printed together, *se-tenant*, forming a composite design.

56 Cicada

1989. Sounds of the Night. Multicoloured.

521	10c. Type **56**	20	15
522	40c. Grasshopper	40	35
523	60c. Cricket	55	50
524	$5 Tree frog	3·75	5·50
MS525	135×81 mm. Nos. 521/4	5·50	7·00

56a Vehicle Assembly Building, Kennedy Space Centre

1989. 20th Anniv of First Manned Landing on Moon. Multicoloured.

526	15c. Type **56a**	15	10
527	40c. Crew of *Apollo 12* (30×30 mm)	20	20
528	$2 *Apollo 12* emblem (30×30 mm)	1·00	1·75
529	$3 *Apollo 12* astronaut on Moon	1·40	2·00
MS530	100×83 mm. $6 Aldrin undertaking lunar seismic experiment	2·50	3·50

57 Queen or Pink Conch feeding

1990. Queen or Pink Conch. Multicoloured.

531	10c. Type **57**	40	30
532	40c. Queen or pink conch from front	60	40
533	60c. Side view of shell	85	90
534	$1 Black and flare	1·25	2·00
MS535	72×103 mm. $5 Underwater habitat	3·00	4·50

58 Wyon Medal Portrait

1990. 150th Anniv of the Penny Black.

536	**58**	15c. black and brown	20	10
537	-	40c. black and green	40	25
538	-	60c. black	55	55
539	-	$4 black and blue	2·50	3·25
MS540		114×84 mm. $5 black, red and brown	4·00	5·00

Designs:—40c. Engine-turned background; 60c. Heath's engraving of portrait; $4 Essay with inscriptions; $5 Penny Black.

No. **MS**540 also commemorates "Stamp World London 90" International Stamp Exhibition.

59

1990. 500th Anniv of Regular European Postal Services.

541	**59**	15c. brown	20	15
542	-	40c. green	35	25
543	-	60c. violet	55	65
544	-	$4 blue	2·75	3·75
MS545		110×82 mm. $5 red, brown and grey	4·00	5·00

Nos. 541/5 commemorate the Thurn and Taxis postal service and the designs are loosely based on those of the initial 1852–58 series.

60 Sand Fiddler

1990. 500th Anniv (1992) of Discovery of America by Columbus (2nd issue). New World Natural History—Crabs. Multicoloured.

546	5c. Type **60**	10	10
547	15c. Great land crab	15	15
548	20c. Blue crab	15	15
549	40c. Stone crab	30	30
550	60c. Mountain crab	45	45
551	$2 Sargassum crab	1·40	1·75
552	$3 Yellow box crab	1·75	2·25
553	$4 Spiny spider crab	2·25	3·00
MS554	Two sheets, each 101×70 mm. (a) $5 Sally Lightfoot. (b) $5 Wharf crab Set of 2 sheets	9·50	11·00

60a Duchess of York with Corgi

1990. 90th Birthday of Queen Elizabeth the Queen Mother.

555	**60a**	$2 black, mauve and buff	1·40	1·60
556	-	$2 black, mauve and buff	1·40	1·60
557	-	$2 black, mauve and buff	1·40	1·60
MS558		90×75 mm. $6 brown, mauve and black	3·50	4·25

Designs:—No. 556, Queen Elizabeth in Coronation robes, 1937; 557, Duchess of York in garden; **MS**558, Queen Elizabeth in Coronation robes, 1937 (different).

61 MaKanaky, Cameroons

1990. World Cup Football Championship, Italy. Star Players. Multicoloured.

559	10c. Type **61**	40	10
560	25c. Chovanec, Czechoslovakia	45	15
561	$2.50 Robson, England	2·00	2·75
562	$5 Voller, West Germany	3·25	4·50
MS563	Two sheets, each 90×75 mm. (a) $5 Maradona, Argentina. (b) $5 Gordillo, Spain Set of 2 sheets	6·00	7·50

62 *Cattleya deckeri*

1990. Christmas. Native Orchids. Mult.

564	10c. Type **62**	55	20
565	15c. *Epidendrum ciliare*	55	20
566	20c. *Epidendrum fragrans*	65	20
567	40c. *Epidendrum ibaguense*	85	25
568	60c. *Epidendrum latifolium*	1·10	50
569	$1.20 *Maxillaria conferta*	1·40	1·75
570	$2 *Epidendrum strobiliferum*	1·75	2·75
571	$3 *Brassavola cucullata*	2·00	3·00
MS572	102×71 mm. $5 *Rodriguezia lanceolata*	7·00	8·00

62a Two Jugs

1991. 350th Death Anniv of Rubens. Details from "The Feast of Achelous". Multicoloured.

573	10c. Type **62a**	55	15
574	40c. Woman at table	1·00	30
575	60c. Two servants with fruit	1·25	45
576	$4 Achelous	3·25	6·00
MS577	101×71 mm. $5 *The Feast of Achelous*	4·50	6·00

63 *Agraulis vanillae*

1991. Butterflies. Multicoloured.

578B	5c. Type **63**	40	60
579A	10c. *Historis odius*	40	50
580B	15c. *Marpesia corinna*	50	20
581B	20c. *Anartia amathea*	60	30
582B	25c. *Junonia evarete*	60	30
583B	40c. *Heliconius charithonia*	70	30
584B	50c. *Marpesia petreus*	70	35
585A	60c. *Dione juno*	75	50
586B	75c. *Heliconius doris*	80	60
586cB	80c. As 60c.	80	60
587A	$1 *Hypolimnas misippus*	90	80
588A	$3 *Danaus plexippus*	2·00	2·75
589A	$5 *Heliconius sara*	2·75	4·00
590A	$10 *Tithorea harmonia*	5·00	8·00
591A	$20 *Dryas julia*	9·50	13·00

64 *Viking Mars Lander*, 1976

1991. 500th Anniv of Discovery of America by Columbus (1992) (3rd issue). History of Exploration. Multicoloured.

592	15c. Type **64**	20	20
593	40c. *Apollo 11*, 1969	30	25
594	60c. *Skylab*, 1973	45	45
595	75c. *Salyut 6*, 1977	55	55
596	$1 *Voyager 1*, 1977	65	65
597	$2 *Venera 7*, 1970	1·25	1·60
598	$4 *Gemini 4* , 1965	2·50	3·25
599	$5 *Luna 3*, 1959	2·75	3·25
MS600	Two sheets, each 105×76 mm. (a) $6 Bow of *Santa Maria* (vert). (b) $6 Christopher Columbus (vert) Set of 2 sheets	8·00	9·00

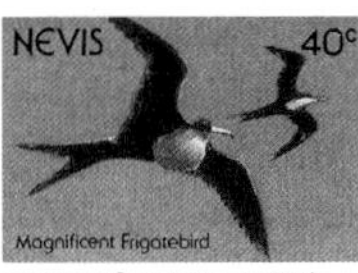

65 Magnificent Frigate Bird

1991. Island Birds. Multicoloured.

601	40c. Type **65**	90	75
602	40c. Roseate tern	90	75
603	40c. Red-tailed hawk	90	75
604	40c. Zenaida dove	90	75
605	40c. Bananaquit	90	75
606	40c. American kestrel	90	75
607	40c. Grey kingbird	90	75
608	40c. Prothonotary warbler	90	75
609	40c. Blue-hooded euphonia	90	75
610	40c. Antillean crested hummingbird	90	75
611	40c. White-tailed tropic bird	90	75
612	40c. Yellow-bellied sapsucker	90	75
613	40c. Green-throated carib	90	75
614	40c. Purple-throated carib	90	75
615	40c. Red-billed whistling duck ("Black-bellied tree-duck")	90	75
616	40c. Ringed kingfisher	90	75
617	40c. Burrowing owl	90	75
618	40c. Ruddy turnstone	90	75
619	40c. Great blue heron	90	75
620	40c. Yellow-crowned night-heron	90	75
MS621	76×59 mm. $6 Great egret	11·00	12·00

Nos. 601/20 were printed together, *se-tenant*, forming a composite design.

65a Queen Elizabeth at Polo Match with Prince Charles

1991. 65th Birthday of Queen Elizabeth II. Multicoloured.

622	15c. Type **65a**	40	20
623	40c. Queen and Prince Philip on Buckingham Palace balcony	50	35
624	$2 In carriage at Ascot, 1986	1·75	1·75
625	$4 Queen Elizabeth II at Windsor polo match, 1989	3·00	3·75
MS626	68×90 mm. $5 Queen Elizabeth and Prince Philip	4·25	5·00

1991. Tenth Wedding Anniv of Prince and Princess of Wales. As T **65a**. Multicoloured.

627	10c. Prince Charles and Princess Diana	85	20
628	50c. Prince of Wales and family	90	30
629	$1 Prince William and Prince Harry	1·40	1·00
630	$5 Prince and Princess of Wales	4·50	4·00
MS631	68×90 mm. $5 Prince and Princess of Wales in Hungary, and young princes at Christmas	6·00	6·00

65b Class C62 Steam Locomotive

1991. Phila Nippon '91 International Stamp Exhibition, Tokyo. Japanese Railway Locomotives. Multicoloured.

632	10c. Type **65b**	90	30
633	15c. Class C56 steam locomotive (horiz)	1·00	30
634	40c. Class C55 streamlined steam locomotive (horiz)	1·50	50
635	60c. Class 1400 steam locomotive (horiz)	1·60	80
636	$1 Class 485 diesel rail car	1·90	1·00
637	$2 Class C61 steam locomotive	3·00	2·50
638	$3 Class 485 diesel train (horiz)	3·25	3·00
639	$4 Class 7000 electric train (horiz)	3·50	3·75
MS640	Two sheets, each 108×72 mm. (a) $5 Class D51 steam locomotive (horiz). (b) $5 Hikari express train (horiz) Set of 2 sheets	8·50	9·00

65c *Mary being Crownd by an Angel*

1991. Christmas. Drawings by Albrecht Durer.

641	**65c**	10c. black and green	15	10
642	-	40c. black and orange	30	25
643	-	60c. black and blue	35	30
644	-	$3 black and mauve	1·40	3·00
MS645		Two sheets, each 96×124 mm. (a) $6 black. (b) $6 black Set of 2 sheets	5·50	6·25

Designs:—40c. *Mary with the Pear*; 60c. *Mary in a Halo*; $3 *Mary with Crown of Stars and Sceptre*; $6 (**MS**645a) *The Holy Family* (detail); $6 (**MS**645b) *Mary at the Yard Gate* (detail).

66 *Marasmius haemtocephalus*

1991. Fungi (2nd series). Multicoloured.

646	15c. Type **66**	25	20
647	40c. *Psilocybe cubensis*	35	30
648	60c. *Hygrocybe acutoconica*	40	40
649	75c. *Hygrocybe occidentalis*	50	60
650	$1 *Boletellus cubensis*	60	70
651	$2 *Gymnopilus chrysopellus*	80	1·25
652	$4 *Cantharellus cinnabarinus*	1·75	2·50
653	$5 *Chlorophyllum molybdites*	1·75	2·50
MS654	Two sheets, each 70×58 mm. (a) $6 *Psilocybe cubensis, Hygrocybe acutoconica* and *Boletellus cubensis* (horiz). (b) $6 *Hygrocybe occidentalis, Marasmius haematocephalus* and *Gymnopilus chrysopellus* (horiz) Set of 2 sheets	9·00	9·50

66a Charlestown from the Sea

1992. 40th Anniv of Queen Elizabeth II's Accession. Multicoloured.

655	10c. Type **66a**	40	10
656	40c. Charlestown square	60	25
657	$1 Mountain scenery	1·00	60
658	$5 Early cottage	3·00	3·75
MS659	Two sheets, each 74×97 mm. (a) $6 Queen or pink conch on beach. (b) $6 Nevis sunset Set of 2 sheets	9·50	9·00

67 Monique Knol (cycling), Netherlands

1992. Olympic Games, Barcelona. Gold Medal Winners of 1988. Multicoloured.

660	20c. Type **67**	1·25	50
661	25c. Roger Kingdom (hurdles), USA	60	40
662	50c. Yugoslavia (men's waterpolo)	1·00	50
663	80c. Anja Fichtel (foil), West Germany	1·10	70
664	$1 Said Aouita (mid-distance running), Morocco	1·25	80

665	$1.50 Yuri Sedykh (hammer throw), USSR	1·40	1·60
666	$3 Shushunova (women's gymnastics), USSR	2·50	3·00
667	$5 Valimir Artemov (men's gymnastics), USSR	2·75	3·50
MS668	Two sheets, each 103×73 mm. (a) $6 Niam Suleymanoglu (weightlifting), Turkey. (b) $6 Florence Griffith-Joyner (women's 100 metres), USA Set of 2 sheets	4·75	7·00

No. 660 is inscribed "France" in error.

68 *Landscape* (Mariano Fortuny i Marsal)

1992. Granada '92 International Stamp Exhibition, Spain. Spanish Paintings. Multicoloured.

669	20c. Type **68**	40	30
670	25c. *Dona Juana la Loca* (Francisco Pradilla Ortiz) (horiz)	40	30
671	50c. *Idyll* (Fortuny i Marsal)	60	50
672	80c. *Old Man Naked in the Sun* (Fortuny i Marsal)	80	70
673	$1 *The Painter's Children in the Japanese Salon* (detail) (Fortuny i Marsal)	90	80
674	$2 *The Painter's Children in the Japanese Salon* (different detail) (Fortuny i Marsal)	1·40	1·40
675	$3 *Still Life: Sea Bream and Oranges* (Luis Eugenio Melendez) (horiz)	2·25	2·75
676	$5 *Still Life: Box of Sweets, Pastry and Other Objects* (Melendez)	2·75	3·50
MS677	Two sheets, each 121×95 mm. (a) $6 *Bullfight* (Fortuny i Marsal) (111×86 mm). (b) $6 *Moroccans* (Fortuny i Marsal) (111×86 mm). Imperf Set of 2 sheets	5·50	6·50

69 Early Compass and Ship

1992. 500th Anniv of Discovery of America by Columbus (4th issue) and "World Columbian Stamp Expo '92", Chicago. Multicoloured.

678	20c. Type **69**	75	25
679	50c. Manatee and fleet	1·25	50
680	80c. Green turtle and *Santa Maria*	1·50	80
681	$1.50 *Santa Maria* and Arms	2·25	1·75
682	$3 Queen Isabella of Spain and commission	2·50	3·25
683	$5 Pineapple and colonists	3·00	4·50
MS684	Two sheets, each 101×70 mm. (a) $6 British storm petrel and town (horiz). (b) $6 Peppers and carib canoe (horiz) Set of 2 sheets	12·00	13·00

1992. 500th Anniv of Discovery of America by Columbus (5th issue). Organization of East Caribbean States. As Nos. 911/12 of Montserrat. Multicoloured.

685	$1 Columbus meeting Amerindians	50	50
686	$2 Ships approaching island	1·25	1·40

69a Empire state Building

1992. Postage Stamp Mega Event, New York. Sheet 100×70 mm.

MS687	**69a** $6 multicolured	5·00	5·50

70 Minnie Mouse

1992. Mickey's Portrait Gallery. Mult.

688	10c. Type **70**	50	20
689	15c. Mickey Mouse	50	20
690	40c. Donald Duck	70	30
691	80c. Mickey Mouse, 1930	90	70
692	$1 Daisy Duck	1·00	80
693	$2 Pluto	1·75	1·50
694	$4 Goofy	2·75	3·00
695	$5 Goofy, 1932	2·75	3·00
MS696	Two sheets. (a) 102×128 mm. $6 Mickey in armchair (horiz). (b) 128×102 mm. $6 Mickey and Minnie in airplane (horiz) Set of 2 sheets	10·00	11·00

70a *The Virgin and Child between Two Saints* (Giovanni Bellini)

1992. Christmas. Religious Paintings. Mult.

697	20c. Type **70a**	65	20
698	40c. *The Virgin and Child surrounded by Four Angels* (Master of the Castello Nativity)	80	25
699	50c. *Virgin and Child surrounded by Angels with St. Frediano and St. Augustine* (detail) (Filippo Lippi)	85	30
700	80c. *The Virgin and Child between St. Peter and St. Sebastian* (Bellini)	1·25	70
701	$1 *The Virgin and Child with St. Julian and St. Nicholas of Myra* (Lorenzo di Credi)	1·50	80
702	$2 *St. Bernadino and a Female Saint presenting a Donor to Virgin and Child* (Francesco Bissolo)	2·50	1·75
703	$4 *Madonna and Child with Four Cherubs* (ascr Barthel Bruyn)	3·50	4·00
704	$5 *The Virgin and Child* (Quentin Metsys)	3·75	4·00
MS705	Two sheets, each 76×102 mm. (a) $6 *Virgin and Child surrounded by Two Angels* (detail) (Perugino). (b) $6 *Madonna and Child with the Infant, St. John and Archangel Gabriel* (Sandro Botticelli) Set of 2 sheets	8·00	10·00

No. 699 is inscribed "Fillipo Lippi" in error.

71 Care Bear and Butterfly

1993. Ecology. Multicoloured.

706	80c. Type **71**	60	60
MS707	71×101 mm. $2 Care Bear on beach	2·50	3·75

71a *The Card Cheat* (left detail) (La Tour)

1993. Bicentenary of the Louvre, Paris. Multicoloured.

708	$1 Type **71a**	85	85
709	$1 *The Card Cheat* (centre detail) (La Tour)	85	85
710	$1 *The Card Cheat* (right detail) (La Tour)	85	85
711	$1 *St. Joseph, the Carpenter* (La Tour)	85	85
712	$1 *St. Thomas* (La Tour)	85	85
713	$1 *Adoration of the Shepherds* (left detail) (La Tour)	85	85
714	$1 *Adoration of the Shepherds* (right detail) (La Tour)	85	85
715	$1 *Mary Magdalene with a Candle* (La Tour)	85	85
MS716	70×100 mm. $6 *Archangel Raphael leaving the Family of Tobius* (Rembrandt) (52×85 mm)	4·25	4·75

71b Elvis Presley

1993. 15th Death Anniv of Elvis Presley (singer). Multicoloured.

717	$1 Type **71b**	1·40	1·00
718	$1 Elvis with guitar	1·40	1·00
719	$1 Elvis with microphone	1·40	1·00

72 Japanese Launch Vehicle H-11

1993. Anniversaries and Events. Mult.

720	15c. Type **72**	75	30
721	50c. Airship *Hindenburg* on fire, 1937 (horiz)	1·50	65
722	75c. Konrad Adenauer and Charles de Gaulle (horiz)	1·00	65
723	80c. Red Cross emblem and map of Nevis (horiz)	2·25	1·25
724	80c. *Resolute* (yacht), 1920	1·50	1·25
725	80c. Nelson Museum and map of Nevis (horiz)	2·25	1·25
726	80c. St. Thomas's Church (horiz)	1·00	1·25
727	$1 Blue whale (horiz)	2·75	1·50
728	$3 Mozart	4·00	3·25
729	$3 Graph and UN emblems (horiz)	1·75	2·75
730	$3 Lions Club emblem	1·75	2·75
731	$5 Soviet Energia launch vehicle SL-17	3·50	4·25
732	$5 Lebaudy-Juillot airship No. 1 *La Jaune* (horiz)	3·50	4·25
733	$5 Adenauer and Pres. Kennedy (horiz)	3·50	4·25
MS734	Five sheets. (a) 104×71 mm. $6 Astronaut. (b) 104×71 mm. $6 Zeppelin LZ-5, 1909 (horiz). (c) 100×70 mm. $6 Konrad Adenauer (horiz). (d) 75×103 mm. $6 *America 3* (yacht), 1992 (horiz). (e) 98×66 mm. $6 Masked reveller from *Don Giovanni* (horiz) Set of 5 sheets	19·00	20·00

Anniversaries and Events—Nos. 720, 731, **MS**734a, International Space Year; 721, 732, **MS**734b, 75th death anniv of Count Ferdinand von Zeppelin (airship pioneer); 722, 733, **MS**734c, 25th death anniv of Konrad Adenauer (German statesman); 723, 50th anniv of St. Kitts–Nevis Red Cross; 724, **MS**734d, Americas Cup Yachting Championship; 725, Opening of Nelson Museum; 726, 150th anniv of Anglican Diocese of North-eastern Caribbean and Aruba; 727, Earth Summit '92, Rio; 728, **MS**734e, Death bicentenary of Mozart; 729, International Conference on Nutrition, Rome; 730, 75th anniv of International Association of Lions Clubs.

73 *Plumeria rubra*

1993. West Indian Flowers. Multicoloured.

735	10c. Type **73**	75	30
736	25c. *Bougainvillea*	95	30
737	50c. *Allamanda cathartica*	1·10	50
738	80c. *Anthurium andraeanum*	1·50	70
739	$1 *Ixora coccinea*	1·75	75
740	$2 *Hibiscus rosa-sinensis*	2·75	2·25
741	$4 *Justicia brandegeeana*	4·00	4·75
742	$5 *Antigonon leptopus*	4·00	4·75
MS743	Two sheets, each 100×70 mm. (a) $6 *Lantana camara*. (b) $6 *Petrea volubilis* Set of 2 sheets	7·50	8·50

74 Antillean Blue (male)

1993. Butterflies. Multicoloured.

744	10c. Type **74**	60	40
745	25c. Cuban crescentspot (female)	75	40
746	50c. Ruddy daggerwing	1·00	50
747	80c. Little yellow (male)	1·25	75
748	$1 Atala	1·25	90
749	$1.50 Orange-barred giant sulphur	2·00	2·25
750	$4 Tropic queen (male)	3·25	4·50
751	$5 Malachite	3·25	4·50
MS752	Two sheets, each 76×105 mm. (a) $6 Polydamus swallowtail (male). (b) $6 West Indian buckeye Set of 2 sheets	10·00	11·00

74a 10c. Queen Elizabeth II at Coronation (photograph by Cecil Beaton)

1993. 40th Anniv of Coronation.

753	**74a**	10c. multicoloured	15	20
754	-	80c. brown and black	45	55
755	-	$2 multicoloured	80	1·25
756	-	$4 multicoloured	1·50	1·75
MS757		71×101 mm. $6 multicoloured	2·50	3·00

Designs:—38×47 mm: 80c. Queen wearing Imperial State Crown; $2 Crowning of Queen Elizabeth II; $4 Queen and Prince Charles at polo match. 28½×42½ mm: $6 *Queen Elizabeth II, 1977* (detail) (Susan Crawford).

75 Flag and National Anthem

1993. Tenth Anniv of Independence of St. Kitts–Nevis. Multicoloured.

758	25c. Type **75**	1·75	50
759	80c. Brown pelican and map of St. Kitts–Nevis	2·00	1·50

75a Imre Garaba (Hungary) and Michel Platini (France) (horiz)

1993. World Cup Football Championship 1994, U.S.A. Multicoloured.

760	10c. Type **75a**	70	30
761	25c. Diego Maradona (Argentina) and Giuseppe Bergomi (Italy)	85	30
762	50c. Luis Fernandez (France) and Vasily Rats (Russia)	1·10	45
763	80c. Victor Munez (Spain)	1·50	65
764	$1 Preben Elkjaer (Denmark) and Andoni Goicoechea (Spain)	1·75	85
765	$2 Elzo Coelho (Brazil) and Jean Tigana (France)	2·75	2·25
766	$3 Pedro Troglio (Argentina) and Sergei Alejnikov (Russia)	3·00	3·25
767	$5 Jan Karas (Poland) and Antonio Luiz Costa (Brazil)	3·75	4·75
MS768	Two sheets. (a) 100×70 mm. $5 Belloumi (Algeria) (horiz). (b) 70×100 mm. $5 Trevor Steven (England) Set of 2 sheets	9·00	11·00

76 *Annunciation of Mary*

1993. Christmas. Religious Paintings by Durer. Black, yellow and red (Nos. 769/73 and 776) or multicoloured (others).

769	20c. Type **76**	50	15
770	40c. *The Nativity* (drawing)	70	30
771	50c. *Holy Family on a Grassy Bank*	80	30
772	80c. *The Presentation of Christ in the Temple*	1·00	55
773	$1 *Virgin in Glory on the Crescent*	1·25	70
774	$1.60 *The Nativity* (painting)	2·00	2·25
775	$3 *Madonna and Child*	2·50	3·25
776	$5 *The Presentation of Christ in the Temple* (detail)	3·25	4·75
MS777	Two sheets, each 105×130 mm. (a) $6 *Mary, Child and the Long-tailed Monkey* (detail) (Durer). (b) $6 *The Rest on the Flight into Egypt* (detail) (Jean-Honure Fragonard) (horiz) Set of 2 sheets	8·50	9·50

77 Mickey Mouse playing Basketball

1994. Sports and Pastimes. Walt Disney cartoon characters. Multicoloured (except No. MS786a).

778	10c. Type **77**	40	30
779	25c. Minnie Mouse sunbathing (vert)	50	20
780	50c. Mickey playing volleyball	70	40
781	80c. Minnie dancing (vert)	80	60
782	$1 Mickey playing football	1·00	70
783	$1.50 Minnie hula hooping (vert)	1·75	2·00
784	$4 Minnie skipping (vert)	2·75	3·50
785	$5 Mickey wrestling Big Pete	2·75	3·50
MS786	Two sheets. (a) 127×102 mm. $6 Mickey, Donald Duck and Goofy in tug of war (black, red and green). (b) 102×127 mm. $6 Mickey using Test your Strength machine Set of 2 sheets	8·00	10·00

1994. Hong Kong '94 International Stamp Exhibition. No. **MS**752 optd with "HONG KONG '94" logo on sheet margins.

MS787	Two sheets, each 76×105 mm. (a) $6 Polydamas swallowtail (male). (b) $6 West Indian buckeye Set of 2 sheets	6·00	8·00

77a Girl with Umbrella

1994. Hummel Figurines. Multicoloured.

788	5c. Type **77a**	15	40
789	25c. Boy holding beer mug and parsnips	45	15
790	50c. Girl sitting in tree	65	35
791	80c. Boy in hat and scarf	85	60
792	$1 Boy with umbrella	1·00	70
793	$1.60 Girl with bird	1·75	1·75
794	$2 Boy on sledge	2·00	2·00
795	$5 Boy sitting in apple tree	2·75	3·75
MS796	Two sheets, each 94×125 mm. (a) Nos. 788 and 792/4. (b) Nos. 789/91 and 795 Set of 2 sheets	6·50	7·50

79 Beekeeper collecting Wild Nest

1994. Beekeeping. Multicoloured.

797	50c. Type **79**	65	30
798	80c. Beekeeping club	90	40
799	$1.60 Extracting honey from frames	1·75	1·75
800	$3 Keepers placing queen in hive	2·75	3·75
MS801	100×70 mm. $6 Queen and workers in hive and mechanical honey extractor	5·00	5·50

80 Blue Point Himalayan

1994. Persian Cats. Multicoloured.

802	80c. Type **80**	1·10	90
803	80c. Black and white Persian	1·10	90
804	80c. Cream Persian	1·10	90
805	80c. Red Persian	1·10	90
806	80c. Persian	1·10	90
807	80c. Persian black smoke	1·10	90
808	80c. Chocolate smoke Persian	1·10	90
809	80c. Black Persian	1·10	90
MS810	Two sheets, each 100×70 mm. (a) $6 Silver tabby Persian. (B) $6 Brown tabby Persian Set of 2 sheets	12·00	12·00

81 Black Coral

1994. Endangered Species. Black Coral.

811	**81**	25c. multicoloured	60	75
812	-	40c. multicoloured	70	80
813	-	50c. multicoloured	70	80
814	-	80c. multicoloured	80	90

Designs:—40c. to 80c. Different forms of coral.

82 Striped Burrfish

1994. Fish. Multicoloured.

815	10c. Type **82**	50	50
816	50c. Flame-backed angelfish	3·50	55
817	50c. Reef bass	50	55
818	50c. Long-finned damselfish ("Honey Gregory")	50	55
819	50c. Saddle squirrelfish	50	55
820	50c. Cobalt chromis	50	55
821	50c. Genie's neon goby	50	55
822	50c. Slender-tailed cardinalfish	50	55
823	50c. Royal gramma	50	55
824	$1 Blue-striped grunt	65	75
825	$1.60 Blue angelfish	80	1·25
826	$3 Cocoa damselfish	1·25	1·75
MS827	Two sheets, each 100×70 mm. (a) $6 Blue marlin. (b) $6 Sailfish (vert) Set of 2 sheets	8·00	8·50

Nos. 816/23 were printed together, *se-tenant*, forming a composite design.

No. 824 is inscribed "BLUESRIPED GRUNT" in error.

83 Symbol 1. Turtles and Cloud

1994. "Philakorea '94" International Stamp Exhibition, Seoul. Longevity symbols. Multicoloured.

828	50c. Type **83**	45	50
829	50c. Symbol 2. Manchurian cranes and bamboo	45	50
830	50c. Symbol 3. Deer and bamboo	45	50
831	50c. Symbol 4. Turtles and Sun	45	50
832	50c. Symbol 5. Manchurian cranes under tree	45	50
833	50c. Symbol 6. Deer and tree	45	50
834	50c. Symbol 7. Turtles and rock	45	50
835	50c. Symbol 8. Manchurian cranes above tree	45	50

84 Twin-roofed House with Veranda

1994. Island Architecture. Multicoloured.

836	25c. Type **84**	70	20
837	50c. Two-storey house with outside staircase	95	30
838	$1 Government Treasury	1·40	1·10
839	$5 Two-storey house with red roof	4·00	6·00
MS840	102×72 mm. $6 Raised bungalow with veranda	3·75	5·00

85 William Demas

1994. First Recipients of Order of Caribbean Community. Multicoloured.

841	25c. Type **85**	30	10
842	50c. Sir Shridath Ramphal	50	45
843	$1 Derek Walcott	2·50	1·50

86 *The Virgin Mary as Queen of Heaven* (detail) (Jan Provost)

1994. Christmas. Religious Paintings. Multicoloured.

844	20c. Type **86**	20	10
845	40c. *The Virgin Mary as Queen of Heaven* (different detail) (Provost)	35	25
846	50c. *The Virgin Mary as Queen of Heaven* (different detail) (Provost)	40	30
847	80c. *Adoration of the Magi* (detail) (Circle of Van der Goes)	60	40
848	$1 *Adoration of the Magi* (different detail) (Circle of Van der Goes)	70	50
849	$1.60 *Adoration of the Magi* (different detail) (Circle of Van der Goes)	1·25	1·50
850	$3 *Adoration of the Magi* (different detail) (Circle of Van der Goes)	1·75	2·50
851	$5 *The Virgin Mary as Queen of Heaven* (different detail) (Provost)	2·50	3·75
MS852	Two sheets, each 96×117 mm. (a) $5 *The Virgin Mary as Queen of Heaven* (different detail) (Provost). (b) $6 *Adoration of the Magi* (different detail) (Circle of Van der Goes) Set of 2 sheets	7·50	8·50

87 Mickey and Minnie Mouse

1995. Disney Sweethearts (1st series). Walt Disney Cartoon Characters. Multicoloured.

853	10c. Type **87**	20	20
854	25c. Donald and Daisy Duck	35	20
855	50c. Pluto and Fifi	50	35
856	80c. Clarabelle Cow and Horace Horsecollar	70	50
857	$1 Pluto and Figaro	85	65
858	$1.50 Polly and Peter Penguin	1·25	1·50
859	$4 Prunella Pullet and Hick Rooster	2·00	3·25
860	$5 Jenny Wren and Cock Robin	2·00	3·25
MS861	Two sheets, each 133×107 mm. (a) $6 Daisy Duck (vert). (b) $6 Minnie Mouse (vert) Set of 2 sheets	6·50	8·50

See also Nos. 998/**MS**1007.

88 Rufous-breasted Hermit

1995. Birds. Multicoloured.

862	50c. Type **88**	60	50
863	50c. Purple-throated carib	60	50
864	50c. Green mango	60	50
865	50c. Bahama woodstar	60	50
866	50c. Hispaniolan emerald	60	50
867	50c. Antillean crested hummingbird	60	50
868	50c. Green-throated carib	60	50
869	50c. Antillean mango	60	50
870	50c. Vervain hummingbird	60	50
871	50c. Jamaican mango	60	50
872	50c. Cuban emerald	60	50
873	50c. Blue-headed hummingbird	60	50
874	50c. Hooded merganser	60	50
875	80c. Green-backed heron	80	50
876	$2 Double-crested cormorant	1·40	1·40
877	$3 Ruddy duck	1·60	1·75
MS878	Two sheets, each 100×70 mm. (a) $6 Black skimmer. (b) $6 Snowy plover Set of 2 sheets	8·00	8·50

No. 870 is inscribed "VERVIAN" in error.

89 Pointer

1995. Dogs. Multicoloured.

879	25c. Type **89**	30	20
880	50c. Old Danish pointer	50	50
881	80c. Irish setter	65	65
882	80c. Weimaraner	65	65
883	80c. Gordon setter	65	65
884	80c. Brittany spaniel	65	65
885	80c. American cocker spaniel	65	65
886	80c. English cocker spaniel	65	65
887	80c. Labrador retriever	65	65
888	80c. Golden retriever	65	65
889	80c. Flat-coated retriever	65	65
890	$1 German short-haired pointer	75	75
891	$2 English setter	1·40	1·40
MS892	Two sheets, each 72×58 mm. (a) $6 German shepherds. (b) $6 Bloodhounds Set of 2 sheets	8·00	8·50

"POINTER" is omitted from the inscription on No. 890. No. **MS**892a is incorrectly inscribed "SHEPHARD".

90 *Schulumbergera truncata*

1995. Cacti. Multicoloured.

893	40c. Type **90**	30	20
894	50c. *Echinocereus pectinatus*	40	25
895	80c. *Mammillaria zeilmanniana alba*	65	40
896	$1.60 *Lobivia hertriehiana*	1·10	1·25
897	$2 *Hammatocactus setispinus*	1·40	1·50
898	$3 *Astrophytum myriostigma*	1·60	2·00
MS899	Two sheets, each 106×76 mm. (a) $6 *Opuntia robusta*. (b) $6 *Rhipsalidopsis gaertneri* Set of 2 sheets	7·00	7·50

91 Scouts backpacking

1995. 18th World Scout Jamboree, Netherlands. Multicoloured.

900	$1 Type **91**	1·00	1·10
901	$2 Scouts building aerial rope way	1·50	1·75
902	$4 Scout map reading	2·00	2·25
MS903	101×71 mm. $6 Scout in canoe (vert)	4·00	4·50

Nos. 900/2 were printed together, *se-tenant*, forming a composite design.

91a Clark Gable and Aircraft

1995. 50th Anniv of End of Second World War in Europe. Multicoloured.

904	$1.25 Type **91a**	1·00	1·00
905	$1.25 Audie Murphy and machine-gunner	1·00	1·00
906	$1.25 Glenn Miller playing trombone	1·00	1·00
907	$1.25 Joe Louis and infantry	1·00	1·00
908	$1.25 Jimmy Doolittle and USS *Hornet* (aircraft carrier)	1·00	1·00
909	$1.25 John Hersey and jungle patrol	1·00	1·00
910	$1.25 John F. Kennedy in patrol boat	1·00	1·00
911	$1.25 James Stewart and bombers	1·00	1·00
MS912	101×71 mm. $6 Jimmy Doolittle (vert)	4·00	4·50

92 Oriental and African People

1995. 50th Anniv of United Nations. Each lilac and black.

913	$1.25 Type **92**	55	80
914	$1.60 Asian people	75	1·10
915	$3 American and European people	1·40	1·60
MS916	105×75 mm. $6 Pres. Nelson Mandela of South Africa	2·75	3·25

Nos. 913/15 were printed together, *se-tenant*, forming a composite design.

1995. 50th Anniv of F.A.O. As T **92**. Multicoloured.

917	40c. Woman wearing yellow headdress	15	60
918	$2 Babies and emblem	85	1·25
919	$3 Woman wearing blue headdress	1·25	1·60
MS920	105×80 mm. $6 Man carrying hoe	2·75	3·75

Nos. 917/19 were printed together, *se-tenant*, forming a composite design.

No. **MS**920 is inscribed "1945–1955" in error.

93 Rotary Emblem on Nevis Flag

1995. 90th Anniv of Rotary International. Multicoloured.

921	$5 Type **93**	2·00	3·25
MS922	95×66 mm. $6 Rotary emblem and beach	2·75	3·75

93a Queen Elizabeth the Queen Mother (pastel drawing)

1995. 95th Birthday of Queen Elizabeth the Queen Mother.

923	**93a**	$1.50 brown, light brown and black	2·00	1·75
924	-	$1.50 multicoloured	2·00	1·75
925	-	$1.50 multicoloured	2·00	1·75
926	-	$1.50 multicoloured	2·00	1·75
MS927		102×127 mm. $6 multicoloured	4·75	5·00

Designs:—No. 924, Wearing pink hat; 925, At desk (oil painting); 926, Wearing blue hat; **MS**927, Wearing tiara.

No. **MS**927 was also issued additionally inscribed "IN MEMORIAM 1900–2002" on margin.

93b Grumman F4F Wildcat

1995. 50th Anniv of End of Second World War in the Pacific. United States Aircraft. Multicoloured.

928	$2 Type **93a**	1·40	1·40
929	$2 Chance Vought F4U-1A Corsair	1·40	1·40
930	$2 Vought SB2U Vindicator	1·40	1·40
931	$2 Grumman F6F Hellcat	1·40	1·40
932	$2 Douglas SDB Dauntless	1·40	1·40
933	$2 Grumman TBF-1 Avenger	1·40	1·40
MS934	108×76 mm. $6 Chance Vought F4U-1A Corsair on carrier flight deck	5·50	6·50

94 Emil von Behring (1901 Medicine)

1995. Centenary of Nobel Trust Fund. Past Prize Winners. Multicoloured.

935	$1.25 Type **94**	75	85
936	$1.25 Wilhelm Rontgen (1901 Physics)	75	85
937	$1.25 Paul Heyse (1910 Literature)	75	85
938	$1.25 Le Duc Tho (1973 Peace)	75	85
939	$1.25 Yasunari Kawabata (1968 Literature)	75	85
940	$1.25 Tsung-dao Lee (1957 Physics)	75	85
941	$1.25 Werner Heisenberg (1932 Physics)	75	85
942	$1.25 Johannes Stark (1919 Physics)	75	85
943	$1.25 Wilhelm Wien (1911 Physics)	75	85
MS944	101×71 mm. $6 Kenzaburo Oe (1994 Literature)	3·25	3·75

95 American Eagle Presidents' Club Logo

1995. Tenth Anniv of American Eagle Air Services to the Caribbean. Sheet 70×100 mm, containing T **95** and similar horiz design. Multicoloured.

MS945	80c. Type **95**; $3 Aircraft over Nevis beach	2·40	2·50

96 Great Egrets

1995. Marine Life. Multicoloured.

946	50c. Type **96**	55	55
947	50c. 17th-century galleon	55	55
948	50c. Galleon and marlin	55	55
949	50c. Herring gulls	55	55
950	50c. Nassau groupers	55	55
951	50c. Spotted eagleray	55	55
952	50c. Leopard shark and hammerhead	55	55
953	50c. Hourglass dolphins	55	55
954	50c. Spanish hogfish	55	55
955	50c. Jellyfish and seahorses	55	55
956	50c. Angelfish and buried treasure	55	55
957	50c. Hawksbill turtle	55	55
958	50c. Common octopus	55	55
959	50c. Moray eel	55	55
960	50c. Queen angelfish and butterflyfish	55	55
961	50c. Ghost crab and sea star	55	55
MS962	Two sheets. (a) 106×76 mm. $5 Nassau grouper. (b) 76×106 mm. $5 Queen angelfish (vert) Set of 2 sheeets	7·00	7·00

No. **MS**962 also commemorates the "Singapore '95" International Stamp Exhibition.

Nos. 946/61 were printed together, *se-tenant*, forming a composite design.

97 SKANTEL Engineer

1995. Tenth Anniv of SKANTEL (telecommunications company). Multicoloured.

963	$1 Type **97**	60	50
964	$1.50 SKANTEL sign outside Nevis office	80	1·25
MS965	76×106 mm. $5 St. Kitts SKANTEL office (horiz)	3·00	3·50

98 *Rucellai Madonna and Child* (detail) (Duccio)

1995. Christmas. Religious Paintings by Duccio di Buoninsegna. Multicoloured.

966	20c. Type **98**	20	15
967	50c. *Angel from the Rucellai Madonna* (detail)	40	25
968	80c. *Madonna and Child* (different)	60	40
969	$1 *Angel from the Annunciation* (detail)	75	60
970	$1.60 *Madonna and Child* (different)	1·25	1·50
971	$3 *Angel from the Rucellai Madonna* (different)	1·90	2·75
MS972	Two sheets, each 102×127 mm. (a) $5 *Nativity with the Prophets Isaiah and Ezekiel* (detail). (b) $6 *The Crevole Madonna* (detail) Set of 2 sheets	6·50	7·50

99 View of Nevis Four Seasons Resort

1996. Fifth Anniv of Four Seasons Resort, Nevis. Multicoloured.

973	25c. Type **99**	15	20
974	50c. Catamarans, Pinney's Beach	25	30
975	80c. Robert Trent Jones II Golf Course	40	45
976	$2 Prime Minister Simeon Daniel laying foundation stone	1·00	1·40
MS977	76×106 mm. $6 Sunset over resort	3·00	3·50

100 Rat, Plant and Butterfly

1996. Chinese New Year ("Year of the Rat"). Multicoloured.

978	$1 Type **100**	60	60
979	$1 Rat with prickly plant	60	60
980	$1 Rat and bee	60	60
981	$1 Rat and dragonfly	60	60
MS982	74×104 mm. Nos. 978/81	2·25	2·50
MS983	74×104 mm. $3 Rat eating	2·25	2·50

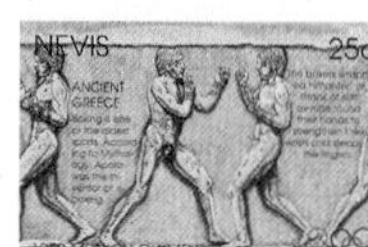
101 Ancient Greek Boxers

1996. Olympic Games, Atlanta. Previous Medal Winners. Multicoloured.

984	25c. Type **101**	30	20
985	50c. Mark Spitz (USA) (Gold – swimming, 1972)	40	30
986	80c. Siegbert Horn (East Germany) (Gold – single kayak slalom, 1972)	60	45
987	$1 Jim Thorpe on medal (USA), 1912 (vert)	65	70
988	$1 Glenn Morris on medal (USA), 1936 (vert)	65	70
989	$1 Bob Mathias on medal (USA), 1948 and 1952 (vert)	65	70
990	$1 Rafer Johnson on medal (USA), 1960 (vert)	65	70
991	$1 Bill Toomey (USA), 1968 (vert)	65	70
992	$1 Nikolay Avilov (Russia), 1972 (vert)	65	70
993	$1 Bruce Jenner (USA), 1976 (vert)	65	70
994	$1 Daley Thompson (Great Britain), 1980 and 1984 (vert)	65	70
995	$1 Christian Schenk (East Germany), 1988 (vert)	65	70
996	$3 Olympic Stadium and Siegestor Arch, Munich (vert)	1·75	2·00
MS997	Two sheets, each 105×75 mm. (a) $5 Willi Holdorf (West Germany) (Gold – decathlon, 1964) (vert). (b) $5 Hans-Joachim Walde (West Germany) (Silver – decathlon, 1968) (vert) Set of 2 sheets	6·50	7·00

1996. Disney Sweethearts (2nd series). As T 87. Walt Disney Cartoon Characters. Multicoloured.

998	$2 Pocahontas and John Smith	2·00	1·50
999	$2 Mowgli and the Girl	2·00	1·50
1000	$2 Belle and the Beast	2·00	1·50
1001	$2 Cinderella and Prince Charming	2·00	1·50
1002	$2 Pinocchio and the Dutch Girl	2·00	1·50
1003	$2 Grace Martin and Henry Coy	2·00	1·50
1004	$2 Snow White and the Prince	2·00	1·50
1005	$2 Aladdin and Jasmine	2·00	1·50
1006	$2 Pecos Bill and Slue Foot Sue	2·00	1·50
MS1007	Two sheets, each 110×130 mm. (a) $6 Sleeping Beauty and Prince Phillip (vert). (b) $6 Ariel and Eric Set of 2 sheets	10·00	11·00

102 Qian Qing Gong, Peking

1996. CHINA '96 Ninth Asian International Stamp Exhibition, Peking. Peking Pagodas. Multicoloured.

1008	$1 Type **102**	60	70
1009	$1 Temple of Heaven	60	70
1010	$1 Zhongnanhai	60	70
1011	$1 Da Zing Hall, Shehyang Palace	60	70
1012	$1 Temple of the Sleeping Buddha	60	70
1013	$1 Huang Qiong Yu, Altar of Heaven	60	70
1014	$1 The Grand Bell Temple	60	70
1015	$1 Imperial Palace	60	70
1016	$1 Pu Tuo Temple	60	70
MS1017	104×74 mm. $6 Summer Palace of Emperor Wan Yen-liang (vert)	3·00	3·50

102a Queen Elizabeth II

1996. 70th Birthday of Queen Elizabeth II. Multicoloured.

1018	$2 Type **102a**	1·25	1·40
1019	$2 Wearing evening dress	1·25	1·40
1020	$2 In purple hat and coat	1·25	1·40
MS1021	125×103 mm. $6 Taking the salute at Tropping the Colour	4·25	4·50

103 Children reading Book

1996. 50th Anniv of UNICEF. Multicoloured.

1022	25c. Type **103**	40	20
1023	50c. Doctor and child	70	30
1024	$4 Children	2·75	3·75

MS1025	75×105 mm. $6 Young girl (vert)	3·00	3·50

104 Cave Paintings, Tassili n'Ajjer, Algeria

1996. 50th Anniv of UNESCO. Multicoloured.

1026	25c. Type **104**	1·00	40
1027	$2 Temple, Tikai National Park, Guatemala (vert)	1·50	1·75
1028	$3 Temple of Hera, Samos, Greece	2·00	2·75
MS1029	106×76 mm. $6 Pueblo, Taos, USA	3·00	3·50

105 American Academy of Ophthalmology Logo

1996. Centenary of American Academy of Ophthalmology.

1030	**105** $5 multicoloured	5·00	5·00

106 *Rothmannia longiflora*

1996. Flowers. Multicoloured.

1031	25c. Type **106**	35	20
1032	50c. *Gloriosa simplex*	50	30
1033	$1 *Monodora myristica*	70	70
1034	$1 *Giraffa camelopardalis* (Giraffe)	70	70
1035	$1 *Adansonia digitata*	70	70
1036	$1 *Ansellia gigantea*	70	70
1037	$1 *Geissorhiza rochensis*	70	70
1038	$1 *Arctotis venusta*	70	70
1039	$1 *Gladiotus cardinalis*	70	70
1040	$1 *Eucomis bicolor*	70	70
1041	$1 *Protea obtusifolia*	70	70
1042	$2 *Catharanthus roseus*	1·10	1·25
1043	$3 *Plumbago auriculata*	1·60	1·90
MS1044	75×105 mm. $5 *Strelitzia reginae*	2·50	3·00

107 Western Meadowlark on Decoration

1996. Christmas. Birds. Multicoloured.

1045	25c. Type **107**	30	20
1046	50c. Bird (incorrectly inscr as "American goldfinch") with decorations (horiz)	45	30
1047	80c. Santa Claus, sleigh and reindeer (horiz)	60	45
1048	$1 American goldfinch on stocking	70	55
1049	$1.60 Northern mockingbird ("Mockingbird") with snowman decoration	1·00	1·10
1050	$5 Yellow-rumped cacique and bauble	2·75	4·00
MS1051	Two sheets. (a) 106×76 mm. $6 Blue and yellow macaw ("Macaw") (horiz). (b) 76×106 mm. $6 Vermilion flycatcher (horiz) Set of 2 sheets	7·00	8·00

No. 1048 is inscribed "WESTERN MEADOWLARK" and No. 1050 "YELLOW-RUMPED CAIEQUE", both in error.

108 Ox (from *Five Oxen* by Han Huang)

1997. Chinese New Year ("Year of the Ox"). T 108 and similar oxen from the painting by Han Huang. Sheet 230×93 mm.

MS1052	50c., 80c., $1.60, $2 multicoloured	3·50	3·75

The fifth ox appears on a small central label.

109 Giant Panda eating Bamboo Shoots

1997. HONG KONG '97 International Stamp Exhibition. Giant Pandas. Multicoloured.

1053	$1.60 Type **109**	1·50	1·50
1054	$1.60 Head of panda	1·50	1·50
1055	$1.60 Panda with new-born cub	1·50	1·50
1056	$1.60 Panda hanging from branch	1·50	1·50
1057	$1.60 Panda asleep on tree	1·50	1·50
1058	$1.60 Panda climbing trunk	1·50	1·50
MS1059	73×103 mm. $5 Panda with cub	2·50	3·00

110 Elquemedo Willett

1997. Nevis Cricketers. Multicoloured.

1060	25c. Type **110**	45	25
1061	80c. Stuart Williams	80	50
1062	$2 Keith Arthurton	1·25	1·50
MS1063	Two sheets, each 106×76 mm. (a) $5 Willett, Arthurton and Williams as part of the 1990 Nevis team (horiz). (b) $5 Williams and Arthurton as part of the 1994 West Indies team Set of 2 sheets	6·00	7·00

111 Crimson-speckled Moth

1997. Butterflies and Moths. Multicoloured.

1064	10c. Type **111**	20	30
1065	25c. Purple emperor	35	20
1066	50c. Regent skipper	45	30
1067	80c. Provence burnet moth	70	45
1068	$1 Common wall butterfly	70	80
1069	$1 Red-lined geometrid	70	80
1070	$1 Boisduval's autumnal moth	70	80
1071	$1 Blue pansy	70	80
1072	$1 Common clubtail	70	80
1073	$1 Tufted jungle king	70	80
1074	$1 Lesser marbled fritillary	70	80
1075	$1 Peacock royal	70	80
1076	$1 Emperor gum moth	70	80
1077	$1 Orange swallow-tailed moth	70	80
1078	$4 Cruiser butterfly	2·25	2·75
MS1079	Two sheets. (a) 103×73 mm. $5 Great purple. (b) 73×103 mm. $5 Jersey tiger moth Set of 2 sheets	5·50	6·50

No. 1073 is inscribed "TUFTED JUNGLE QUEEN" in error.

112 Boy with Two Pigeons

1997. 300th Anniv of Mother Goose Nursery Rhymes. Sheet 72×102 mm.

MS1080	**112** $5 multicoloured	2·75	3·50

113 Paul Harris and Literacy Class

1997. 50th Death Anniv of Paul Harris (founder of Rotary International). Multicoloured.

1081	$2 Type **113**	1·00	1·25
MS1082	78×108 mm. $5 Football coaching session, Chile	2·50	3·00

113a Queen Elizabeth II

1997. Golden Wedding of Queen Elizabeth and Prince Philip. Multicoloured.

1083	$1 Type **113a**	95	95
1084	$1 Royal Coat of Arms	95	95
1085	$1 Queen Elizabeth wearing red hat and coat with Prince Philip	95	95
1086	$1 Queen Elizabeth in blue coat and Prince Philip	95	95
1087	$1 Caernarvon Castle	95	95
1088	$1 Prince Philip in RAF uniform	95	95
MS1089	100×70 mm. $5 Queen Elizabeth at Coronation	3·00	3·50

113b Russian reindeer post, 1859

1997. Pacific '97 International Stamp Exhibition, San Francisco. Death Centenary of Heinrich von Stephan.

1090	**113b** $1.60 green	90	1·10
1091	- $1.60 brown	90	1·10
1092	- $1.60 blue	90	1·10
MS1093	82×118 mm. $5 sepia	2·50	3·00

Designs:—No. 1091, Von Stephan and Mercury; No. 1092, *City of Cairo* (paddle-steamer), Mississippi, 1800s; **MS**1093, Von Stephan and Bavarian postal messenger, 1640.

113c *Scattered Pines, Tone River*

1997. Birth Bicentenary of Hiroshige (Japanese painter). "One Hundred Famous Views of Edo". Multicoloured.

1094	$1.60 Type **113c**	1·25	1·25
1095	$1.60 *Mouth of Nakagawa River*	1·25	1·25
1096	$1.60 *Niijuku Ferry*	1·25	1·25
1097	$1.60 *Horie and Nekozane*	1·25	1·25
1098	$1.60 *Konodai and the Tone River*	1·25	1·25
1099	$1.60 *Maple Trees, Tekona Shrine and Bridge, Mama*	1·25	1·25
MS1100	Two sheets, each 102×127 mm. (a) $6 *Mitsumata Wakarenofuchi*. (b) $6 *Moto-Hachiman Shrine, Sunamura* Set of 2 sheets	7·00	7·50

114 Augusta National Course, USA

1997. Golf Courses of the World. Multicoloured.

1101	$1 Type **114**	80	80
1102	$1 Cabo del Sol, Mexico	80	80
1103	$1 Cypress Point, USA	80	80
1104	$1 Lost City, South Africa	80	80
1105	$1 Moscow Country Club, Russia	80	80
1106	$1 New South Wales, Australia	80	80
1107	$1 Royal Montreal, Canada	80	80
1108	$1 St. Andrews, Scotland	80	80
1109	$1 Four Seasons Resort, Nevis	80	80

115 *Cantharellus cibarius*

1997. Fungi. Multicoloured.

1110	25c. Type **115**	30	20
1111	50c. *Stropharia aeruginosa*	40	30
1112	80c. *Suillus hiteus*	60	65
1113	80c. *Amanita muscaria*	60	65
1114	80c. *Lactarius rufus*	60	65
1115	80c. *Amanita rubescens*	60	65
1116	80c. *Armillaria mellea*	60	65
1117	80c. *Russula sardonia*	60	65
1118	$1 *Boletus edulis*	65	70
1119	$1 *Pholiota lenta*	65	70
1120	$1 *Cortinarius bolaris*	65	70
1121	$1 *Coprinus picaceus*	65	70
1122	$1 *Amanita phalloides*	65	70
1123	$1 *Cystolepiota aspera*	65	70
1124	$3 *Lactarius turpis*	1·75	2·00
1125	$4 *Entoloma clypeatum*	2·25	2·50
MS1126	Two sheets, each 98×68 mm. (a) $5 *Galerina mutabilis*. (b) $5 *Gymnopilus junonius* Set of 2 sheets	6·00	6·50

Nos. 1112/17 and 1118/23 respectively were printed together, *se-tenant*, with the backgrounds forming composite designs.

116 Diana, Princess of Wales

1997. Diana, Princess of Wales Commemoration. Multicoloured.

1127	$1 Type **116**	1·00	90
1128	$1 Wearing white blouse	1·00	90
1129	$1 In wedding dress, 1981	1·00	90
1130	$1 Wearing turquoise blouse	1·00	90
1131	$1 Wearing tiara	1·00	90
1132	$1 Wearing blue blouse	1·00	90
1133	$1 Wearing pearl necklace	1·00	90
1134	$1 Wearing diamond drop earrings	1·00	90
1135	$1 Wearing sapphire necklace and earrings	1·00	90

117 Victoria Govt Class S Pacific Locomotive, Australia

1997. Trains of the World. Multicoloured.

1136	10c. Type **117**	35	20
1137	50c. Express steam locomotive, Japan	55	30
1138	80c. LMS steam-turbine locomotive, Great Britain	75	45
1139	$1 Electric locomotive, Switzerland	90	55
1140	$1.50 Mikado steam locomotive, Sudan	1·25	1·40
1141	$1.50 *Mohammed Ali el Kebir* steam locomotive, Egypt	1·25	1·40
1142	$1.50 Southern Region steam locomotive *Leatherhead*	1·25	1·40
1143	$1.50 Great Southern Railway Drumm battery-powered railcar, Ireland	1·25	1·40
1144	$1.50 Pacific locomotive, Germany	1·25	1·40
1145	$1.50 Canton–Hankow Railway Pacific locomotive, China	1·25	1·40
1146	$2 LMS high-pressure locomotive, Great Britain	1·60	1·75
1147	$3 Great Northern Railway *Kestrel*, Ireland	2·00	2·25
MS1148	Two sheets, each 71×48 mm. (a) $5 LMS high-pressure locomotive. (b) $5 GWR *King George V* Set of 2 sheets	7·00	7·50

118 *Selection of Angels* (detail) (Durer)

1997. Christmas. Paintings. Multicoloured.

1149	20c. Type **118**	30	15
1150	25c. *Selection of Angels* (different detail) (Durer)	35	20
1151	50c. *Andromeda and Perseus* (Rubens)	55	30
1152	80c. *Harmony* (detail) (Raphael)	75	45
1153	$1.60 *Harmony* (different detail) (Raphael)	1·40	1·50
1154	$5 *Holy Trinity* (Raphael)	3·50	4·50
MS1155	Two sheets, each 114×104 mm. (a) $5 *Study Muse* (Raphael) (horiz). (b) $5 *Ezekiel's Vision* (Raphael) (horiz) Set of 2 sheets	6·50	7·00

119 Tiger (semi-circular character at top left)

1998. Chinese New Year ("Year of the Tiger"). Multicoloured.

1156	80c. Type **119**	60	65
1157	80c. Oblong character at bottom right	60	65
1158	80c. Circular character at top left	60	65
1159	80c. Square character at bottom right	60	65
MS1160	67×97 mm. $2 Tiger (vert)	1·40	1·60

120 Social Security Board Emblem

1998. 20th Anniv of Social Security Board. Multicoloured.

1161	30c. Type **120**	20	15
1162	$1.20 Opening of Social Security building, Charlestown (horiz)	80	1·00
MS1163	100×70 mm. $6 Social Security staff (59×39 mm)	3·50	4·00

121 Soursop

1998. Fruits. Multicoloured.

1164A	5c. Type **121**	10	30
1165B	10c. Carambola	20	40
1166A	25c. Guava	25	15
1167B	30c. Papaya	40	30
1168A	50c. Mango	35	25
1169A	60c. Golden apple	40	30
1170A	80c. Pineapple	50	35
1171A	90c. Watermelon	60	40
1172A	$1 Bananas	70	50
1173B	$1.80 Orange	1·75	2·00
1174A	$3 Honeydew	1·75	2·25
1175B	$5 Canteloupe	4·50	6·00
1176B	$10 Pomegranate	8·00	10·00
1177A	$20 Cashew	9·50	13·00

122 African Fish Eagle ("Fish Eagle")

1998. Endangered Species. Multicoloured.

1178	30c. Type **122**	65	30
1179	80c. Summer tanager at nest	1·00	55
1180	90c. Orang-Utan and young	1·00	70
1181	$1 Young chimpanzee	80	90
1182	$1 Keel-billed toucan	80	90
1183	$1 Chaco peccary	80	90
1184	$1 Spadefoot toad and insect	80	90
1185	$1 Howler monkey	80	90
1186	$1 Alaskan brown bear	80	90
1187	$1 Koala bears	80	90
1188	$1 Brown pelican	80	90
1189	$1 Iguana	80	90
1190	$1.20 Tiger cub	1·25	1·00
1191	$2 Cape pangolin	1·40	1·75
1192	$3 Hoatzin	1·75	2·25
MS1193	Two sheets, each 69×99 mm. (a) $5 Young mandrill. (b) $5 Polar bear cub Set of 2 sheets	7·00	7·50

No. 1185 is inscribed "MOWLER MONKEY" and No. 1192 "MOATZIN", both in error.

123 Chaim Topol (Israeli actor)

1998. Israel 98 International Stamp Exn, Tel-Aviv.

1194	**123**	$1.60 multicoloured	2·00	1·75

124 Boeing 747 200B (USA)

1998. Aircraft. Multicoloured.

1195	10c. Type **124**	40	40
1196	90c. Cessna 185 Skywagon (USA)	80	55
1197	$1 Northrop B-2 A (USA)	80	90
1198	$1 Lockheed SR-71A (USA)	80	90
1199	$1 Beechcraft T-44A (USA)	80	90
1200	$1 Sukhoi Su-27UB (USSR)	80	90
1201	$1 Hawker Siddeley Harrier GR. Mk1 (Great Britain)	80	90
1202	$1 Boeing E-3A Sentry (USA)	80	90
1203	$1 Convair B-36H (USA)	80	90
1204	$1 IAI KFIR C2 (Israel)	80	90
1205	$1.80 McDonnell Douglas DC-9 SO (USA)	1·75	1·75
1206	$5 Airbus A-300 B4 (USA)	3·75	4·50
MS1207	Two sheets, each 76×106 mm. (a) $5 Lockheed F-117A (USA) (56×42 mm). (b) $5 Concorde (Great Britain) (56×42 mm) Set of 2 sheets	7·50	7·50

125 Anniversary Logo

1998. Tenth Anniv of "Voice of Nevis" Radio.

1208	**125**	20c. vio, lt vio & blk	40	35
1209	-	30c. multicoloured	40	25
1210	-	$1.20 multicoloured	1·40	1·60
MS1211		110×85 mm. $5 multicoloured	3·25	3·50

Designs:—30c. Evered Herbert (Station Manager); $1.20, V.O.N. studio; $5 Merritt Herbert (Managing Director).

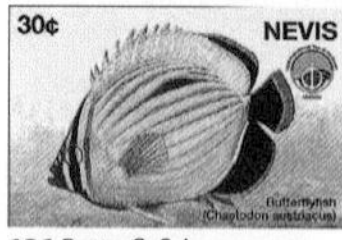

126 Butterflyfish

1998. International Year of the Ocean. Multicoloured.

1212	30c. Type **126**	30	15
1213	80c. Bicolor cherub	65	35
1214	90c. Copperbanded butterflyfish (vert)	70	80
1215	90c. Forcepsfish (vert)	70	80
1216	90c. Double-saddled butterflyfish (vert)	70	80
1217	90c. Blue surgeonfish (vert)	70	80
1218	90c. Orbiculate batfish (vert)	70	80
1219	90c. Undulated triggerfish (vert)	70	80
1220	90c. Rock beauty (vert)	70	80
1221	90c. Flamefish (vert)	70	80
1222	90c. Queen angelfish (vert)	70	80
1223	$1 Pyjama cardinal fish	70	80
1224	$1 Wimplefish	70	80
1225	$1 Long-nosed filefish	70	80
1226	$1 Oriental sweetlips	70	80
1227	$1 Blue-spotted boxfish	70	80
1228	$1 Blue-stripe angelfish	70	80
1229	$1 Goldrim tang	70	80
1230	$1 Blue chromis	70	80
1231	$1 Common clownfish	70	80
1232	$1.20 Silver badgerfish	80	80
1233	$2 Asfur angelfish	1·40	1·50
MS1234	Two sheets. (a) 76×106 mm. $5 Red-faced batfish (vert). (b) 106×76 mm. $5 Longhorned cowfish (vert) Set of 2 sheets	8·50	9·00

Nos. 1214/22 and 1223/31 respectively were printed together, *se-tenant*, with the backgrounds forming composite designs.

No. 1223 is inscribed "Pygama" in error.

127 Prime Minister Kennedy Simmonds receiving Constitutional Instruments from Princess Margaret, 1983

1998. 15th Anniv of Independence.

1235	**127**	$1 multicoloured	85	1·00

128 Stylized "50"

1998. 50th Anniv of Organization of American States.

1236	**128**	$1 blue, light blue and black	75	1·00

129 365 California

1998. Birth Centenary of Enzo Ferrari (car manufacturer). Multicoloured.

1237	$2 Type **129**	1·60	1·60
1238	$2 Pininfarina's P6	1·60	1·60
1239	$2 250 LM	1·60	1·60
MS1240	104×70 mm. $5 212 "Export Spyder" (91×34 mm)	4·50	4·75

130 Scouts of Different Nationalities

1998. 19th World Scout Jamboree, Chile. Multicoloured.

1241	$3 Type **130**	2·00	2·25
1242	$3 Scout and Gettysburg veterans, 1913	2·00	2·25
1243	$3 First black scout troop, Virginia, 1928	2·00	2·25

131 Gandhi in South Africa, 1914

1998. 50th Death Anniv of Mahatma Gandhi. Multicoloured.

1244	$1 Type **131**	1·25	1·00
1245	$1 Gandhi in Downing Street, London	1·25	1·00

132 Panavia Tornado F3

1998. 80th Anniv of Royal Air Force. Multicoloured.

1246	$2 Type **132**	2·00	2·00
1247	$2 Panavia Tornado F3 firing Skyflash missile	2·00	2·00
1248	$2 Tristar Mk1 Tanker refuelling Tornado GR1	2·00	2·00
1249	$2 Panavia Tornado GR1 firing AIM-9L missile	2·00	2·00
MS1250	Two sheets, each 91×68 mm. (a) $5 Bristol F2B Fighter and two peregrine falcons (birds). (b) $5 Wessex helicopter and EF-2000 Eurofighter Set of 2 sheets	9·50	9·00

133 Princess Diana

1998. First Death Anniv of Diana, Princess of Wales.

1251	**133**	$1 multicoloured	60	75

134 Kitten and Santa Claus Decoration

1998. Christmas. Multicoloured.

1252	25c. Type **134**	25	15
1253	60c. Kitten playing with bauble	40	30
1254	80c. Kitten in Christmas stocking (vert)	50	35
1255	90c. Fox Terrier puppy and presents	60	40
1256	$1 Angel with swallows	70	45
1257	$3 Boy wearing Santa hat (vert)	2·00	3·00
MS1258	Two sheets. (a) 71×102 mm. $5 Two dogs. (b) 102×71 mm. $5 Family with dog (vert) Set of 2 sheets	8·00	8·00

135 Mickey Mouse

1998. 70th Birthday of Mickey Mouse. Walt Disney cartoon characters playing basketball. Mult.

1259	$1 Type **135**	95	85
1260	$1 Donald Duck bouncing ball	95	85
1261	$1 Minnie Mouse in green kit	95	85
1262	$1 Goofy wearing purple	95	85
1263	$1 Huey in green baseball cap	95	85
1264	$1 Goofy and Mickey	95	85
1265	$1 Mickey bouncing ball	95	85
1266	$1 Huey, Dewey and Louie	95	85
1267	$1 Mickey, in purple, shooting ball	95	85
1268	$1 Goofy in yellow shorts and vest	95	85
1269	$1 Minnie in purple	95	85
1270	$1 Mickey in yellow vest and blue shorts	95	85
1271	$1 Minnie in yellow	95	85
1272	$1 Donald spinning ball on finger	95	85
1273	$1 Donald and Mickey	95	85
1274	$1 Dewey shooting for goal	95	85
MS1275	Four sheets. (a) 127×105 mm. $5 Minnie wearing purple bow (horiz). (b) 105×127 mm. $5 Minnie wearing green bow (horiz). (c) 105×127 mm. $6 Mickey in yellow vest (horiz). (d) 105×127 mm. $6 Mickey in purple vest (horiz) Set of 4 sheets	15·00	15·00

136 Black Silver Fox Rabbits

1999. Chinese New Year ("Year of the Rabbit"). Multicoloured.

1276	$1.60 Type **136**	1·50	1·50
1277	$1.60 Dutch rabbits (brown with white "collar")	1·50	1·50
1278	$1.60 Dwarf rabbits (brown)	1·50	1·50
1279	$1.60 Netherlands Dwarf rabbits (white with brown markings)	1·50	1·50
MS1280	106×76 mm. $5 Dwarf albino rabbit and young (57×46 mm)	4·00	4·25

137 Laurent Blanc (France)

1999. Leading Players of 1998 World Cup Football Championship, France. Multicoloured.

1281	$1 Type **137**	60	70
1282	$1 Dennis Bergkamp (Holland)	60	70
1283	$1 Davor Sukor (Croatia)	60	70
1284	$1 Ronaldo (Brazil)	60	70
1285	$1 Didier Deschamps (France)	60	70
1286	$1 Patrick Kluivert (Holland)	60	70
1287	$1 Rivaldo (Brazil)	60	70
1288	$1 Zinedine Zidane (France)	60	70
MS1289	121×96 mm. $5 Zinedine Zidane (France)	3·25	3·50

Nos. 1281/8 were printed together, *se-tenant*, with the backgrounds forming a composite design.

138 Kritosaurus

1999. Australia '99 World Stamp Exhibition, Melbourne. Prehistoric Animals. Multicoloured.

1290	30c. Type **138**	40	30
1291	60c. Oviraptor	50	45
1292	80c. Eustreptospondylus	60	50
1293	$1.20 Tenontosaurus	80	85
1294	$1.20 Edmontosaurus	80	85
1295	$1.20 Avimimus	80	85
1296	$1.20 Minmi	80	85
1297	$1.20 Segnosaurus	80	85
1298	$1.20 Kentrosaurus	80	85
1299	$1.20 Deinonychus	80	85
1300	$1.20 Saltasaurus	80	85
1301	$1.20 Compsoganthus	80	85
1302	$1.20 Hadrosaurus	80	85
1303	$1.20 Tuojiangosaurus	80	85
1304	$1.20 Euoplocephalus	80	85
1305	$1.20 Anchisaurus	80	85
1306	$2 Ouranosaurus	1·40	1·75
1307	$3 Muttaburrasaurus	1·75	2·00
MS1308	Two sheets, each 110×85 mm. (a) $5 Triceratops. (b) $5 Stegosaurus Set of 2 sheets	7·00	7·50

Nos. 1294/9 and 1300/5 respectively were printed together, *se-tenant*, with the backgrounds forming composite designs.

139 Emperor Haile Selassie of Ethiopia

1999. Millennium Series. Famous People of the Twentieth Century. World Leaders. Multicoloured.

1309	90c. Type **139**	1·25	1·00
1310	90c. Haile Selassie and Ethiopian warriors (56×41 mm)	1·25	1·00
1311	90c. David Ben-Gurion, woman soldier and ancient Jewish prophet (56×41 mm)	1·25	1·00
1312	90c. David Ben-Gurion (Prime Minister of Israel)	1·25	1·00
1313	90c. President Franklin D. Roosevelt of USA and Mrs. Roosevelt	1·25	1·00
1314	90c. Franklin and Eleanor Roosevelt campaigning (56×41 mm)	1·25	1·00
1315	90c. Mao Tse-tung and the Long March, 1934 (56×41 mm)	1·25	1·00
1316	90c. Poster of Mao Tse-tung (founder of People's Republic of China)	1·25	1·00
MS1317	Two sheets. (a) 76×105 mm. $5 President Nelson Mandela of South Africa. (b) 105×76 mm. $5 Mahatma Gandhi (leader of Indian Independence movement) Set of 2 sheets	8·00	8·50

140 Malachite Kingfisher

1999. Birds. Multicoloured.

1318	$1.60 Type **140**	1·00	1·10
1319	$1.60 Lilac-breasted roller	1·00	1·10
1320	$1.60 Swallow-tailed bee-eater	1·00	1·10
1321	$1.60 Jay ("Eurasian Jay")	1·00	1·10
1322	$1.60 Black-collared apalis	1·00	1·10
1323	$1.60 Grey-backed camaroptera	1·00	1·10
1324	$1.60 Yellow warbler	1·00	1·10
1325	$1.60 Common yellowthroat	1·00	1·10
1326	$1.60 Painted bunting	1·00	1·10
1327	$1.60 Belted kingfisher	1·00	1·10
1328	$1.60 American kestrel	1·00	1·10
1329	$1.60 Northern oriole	1·00	1·10
MS1330	Two sheets, each 76×106 mm. (a) $5 Bananaquit. (b) $5 Groundscraper thrush (vert) Set of 2 sheets	7·50	8·00

141 *Phaius* hybrid

1999. Orchids. Multicoloured.

1331	20c. Type **141**	30	30
1332	25c. *Cuitlauzina pendula*	30	30
1333	50c. *Bletilla striata*	45	40
1334	80c. *Cymbidium* 'Showgirl'	60	55
1335	$1 *Cattleya intermedia*	70	75
1336	$1 *Cattleya* 'Sophia Martin'	70	75
1337	$1 *Phalaenopsis* 'Little Hal'	70	75
1338	$1 *Laeliocattleya alisal* 'Rodeo'	70	75
1339	$1 *Laelia lucasiana fournieri*	70	75
1340	$1 *Cymbidium* 'Red Beauty'	70	75
1341	$1 *Sobralia* sp.	70	75
1342	$1 *Promenaea xanthina*	70	75
1343	$1 *Cattleya pumpernickel*	70	75
1344	$1 *Odontocidium artur elle*	70	75
1345	$1 *Neostylis lou sneary*	70	75
1346	$1 *Phalaenopsis aphrodite*	70	75
1347	$1 *Arkundina graminieolia*	70	75
1348	$1 *Cymbidium* 'Hunter's Point'	70	75
1349	$1 *Rhynchostylis coelestis*	70	75
1350	$1 *Cymbidium* 'Elf's Castle'	70	75
1351	$1.60 *Zygopetalum crinitium* (horiz)	1·00	1·00
1352	$3 *Dendrobium nobile* (horiz)	1·90	2·50
MS1353	Two sheets, each 106×81 mm. (a) $5 *Spathoglottis plicata* (horiz). (b) $5 *Arethusa bulbosa* Set of 2 sheets	9·00	9·00

142 Miss Sophie Rhys-Jones and Prince Edward

1999. Royal Wedding. Multicoloured.

1354	$2 Type **142**	1·40	1·40
1355	$2 Miss Sophie Rhys-Jones at Ascot	1·40	1·40
1356	$2 Miss Sophie Rhys-Jones smiling	1·40	1·40
1357	$2 Prince Edward smiling	1·40	1·40
1358	$2 Miss Sophie Rhys-Jones wearing black and white checked jacket	1·40	1·40
1359	$2 Prince Edward and Miss Sophie Rhys-Jones wearing sunglasses	1·40	1·40
1360	$2 Miss Sophie Rhys-Jones wearing black hat and jacket	1·40	1·40
1361	$2 Prince Edward wearing red-striped tie	1·40	1·40
MS1362	Two sheets, each 83×66 mm. (a) $5 Prince Edward and Miss Sophie Rhys-Jones smiling (horiz). (b) $5 Prince Edward kissing Miss Sophie Rhys-Jones (horiz) Set of 2 sheets	6·00	7·00

142a *Beuth* (railway locomotive) and Baden 1851 1k. stamp

1999. iBRA '99 International Stamp Exhibition, Nuremberg. Multicoloured.

1363	30c. Type **142a**	30	25
1364	80c. *Beuth* and Brunswick 1852 1sgr. stamp	50	45
1365	90c. *Kruzenshtern* (cadet barque) and Bergedorf 1861 ½s. and 1s. stamps	60	50
1366	$1 *Kruzenshtern* and Bremen 1855 3gr. stamp	70	70
MS1367	134×90 mm. $5 1912 First Bavarian air flight label	3·25	3·50

142b *Women returning Home at Sunset* (women by lake)

1999. 150th Death Anniv of Katsushika Hokusai (Japanese artist). Multicoloured.

1368	$1 Type 142a	70	80
1369	$1 Blind Man (without beard)	70	80
1370	$1 *Women returning Home at Sunset* (women descending hill)	70	80
1371	$1 Young Man on a White Horse	70	80
1372	$1 Blind Man (with beard)	70	80
1373	$1 Peasant crossing a Bridge	70	80
1374	$1.60 *Poppies* (one flower)	1·00	1·10
1375	$1.60 Blind Man (with beard)	1·00	1·10
1376	$1.60 *Poppies* (two flowers)	1·00	1·10
1377	$1.60 *Abe No Nakamaro gazing at the Moon from a Terrace*	1·00	1·10
1378	$1.60 Blind Man (without beard)	1·00	1·10
1379	$1.60 *Cranes on a Snowy Pine*	1·00	1·10
MS1380	Two sheets, each 74×103 mm. (a) $5 *Carp in a Waterfall*. (b) $5 *Rider in the Snow* Set of 2 sheets	7·00	7·50

142c First Class carriage, 1837.

1999. PhilexFrance '99 International Stamp Exhibition, Paris. Two sheets, each 106×81 mm, containing horiz designs. Multicoloured.

MS1381	(a) $5 Type **142c**. (b) $5 141.R Mixed Traffic steam locomotive Set of 2 sheets	9·00	9·00

143 Steelband

1999. 25th Culturama Festival. Multicoloured.

1382	30c. Type **143**	30	15
1383	80c. Clowns	60	35
1384	$1.80 Masqueraders with band	1·40	1·10
1385	$5 Local string band	3·25	4·00
MS1386	91×105 mm. $5 Carnival dancers (50×37 mm)	3·25	3·75

143a Lady Elizabeth Bowes-Lyon on Wedding Day, 1923

1999. Queen Elizabeth the Queen Mother's Century.

1387	**143a** $2 black and gold	1·40	1·50
1388	- $2 multicoloured	1·40	1·50
1389	- $2 black and gold	1·40	1·50
1390	- $2 multicoloured	1·40	1·50
MS1391	153×157 mm. $6 multicoloured	3·25	4·00

Designs:—No. 1388, Duchess of York with Princess Elizabeth, 1926; No. 1389, King George VI and Queen Elizabeth during Second World War; No. 1390, Queen Mother in 1983. 37×49 mm: No. **MS**1391, Queen Mother in 1957.

No. **MS**1391 was also issued with the embossed gold coat of arms at bottom left replaced by the inscription "Good Health and Happiness to Her Majesty the Queen Mother on her 101st Birthday".

144 *The Adoration of the Magi* (Durer)

1999. Christmas. Religious Paintings. Multicoloured.

1392	30c. Type **144**	35	15
1393	90c. *Canigiani Holy Family* (Raphael)	70	40
1394	$1.20 *The Nativity* (Durer)	1·10	80
1395	$1.80 *Madonna and Child surrounded by Angels* (Rubens)	1·40	1·40
1396	$3 *Madonna and Child surrounded by Saints* (Rubens)	2·50	4·00
MS1397	76×106 mm. $5 *Madonna and Child by a Window* (Durer) (horiz)	3·25	3·75

145 Flowers forming Top of Head

1999. Faces of the Millennium: Diana, Princess of Wales. Showing collage of miniature flower photographs. Multicoloured.

1398	$1 Type **145** (face value at left)	75	75
1399	$1 Top of head (face value at right)	75	75
1400	$1 Ear (face value at left)	75	75
1401	$1 Eye and temple (face value at right)	75	75
1402	$1 Cheek (face value at left)	75	75
1403	$1 Cheek (face value at right)	75	75
1404	$1 Blue background (face value at left)	75	75
1405	$1 Chin (face value at right)	75	75

Nos. 1398/1405 were printed together, *se-tenant*, and when viewed as a sheetlet, forms a portrait of Diana, Princess of Wales.

145a Jonathan Swift (*Gulliver's Travels*, 1726)

2000. New Millennium. People and Events of Eighteenth Century (1700–49). Multicoloured.

1406	30c. Type **145a**	50	40
1407	30c. Emperor Kangxi of China	50	40
1408	30c. Bartolommeo Cristofori (invention of piano, 1709)	50	40
1409	30c. Captain William Kidd hanging on gibbet, 1701	50	40
1410	30c. William Herschel (astronomer)	50	40
1411	30c. King George I of Great Britain, 1714	50	40
1412	30c. Peter the Great of Russia (trade treaty with China, 1720)	50	40
1413	30c. "Death" (bubonic plague in Austria and Germany, 1711)	50	40
1414	30c. *Standing Woman* (Kaigetsudo Dohan (Japanese artist))	50	40
1415	30c. Queen Anne of England, 1707	50	40
1416	30c. Anders Celcius (invention of centigrade thermometer, 1742)	50	40

1417 30c. Vitus Bering (discovery of Alaska and Aleutian Islands, 1741) 50 40
1418 30c. Edmund Halley (calculation of Halley's Comet, 1705) 50 40
1419 30c. John Wesley (founder of Methodist Church, 1729) 50 40
1420 30c. Sir Isaac Newton (publication of *Optick Treatise*, 1704) 50 40
1421 30c. Queen Anne (Act of Union between England and Scotland, 1707) (59×39 mm) 50 40
1422 30c. Johann Sebastian Bach (composition of *The Well-tempered Klavier*, 1722) 50 40

No. 1418 is inscribed "cometis" in error.

146 Boris Yeltsin (President of Russian Federation, 1991)

2000. New Millennium. People and Events of Twentieth Century (1990–99). Multicoloured.

1423 50c. Type **146** 65 50
1424 50c. American soldiers and burning oil wells (Gulf War, 1991) 65 50
1425 50c. Soldiers (Bosnian Civil War, 1992) 65 50
1426 50c. Pres. Clinton, Yitzchak Rabin and Yasser Arafat (Oslo Accords, 1993) 65 50
1427 50c. Prime Ministers John Major and Albert Reynolds (Joint Declaration on Northern Ireland, 1993) 65 50
1428 50c. Frederik de Klerk and Nelson Mandela (end of Apartheid, South Africa, 1994) 65 50
1429 50c. Cal Ripkin (record number of consecutive baseball games, 1995) 65 50
1430 50c. Kobe from air (earthquake, 1995) 65 50
1431 50c. Mummified Inca girl preserved in ice, 1995 65 50
1432 50c. NASA's *Sojourner* on Mars, 1997 65 50
1433 50c. Dr. Ian Wilmat and cloned sheep, 1997 65 50
1434 50c. Death of Princess Diana, 1997 65 50
1435 50c. Fireworks over Hong Kong on its return to China, 1997 65 50
1436 50c. Mother with septuplets, 1998 65 50
1437 50c. Guggenheim Museum, Bilbao, 1998 65 50
1438 50c. "2000" and solar eclipse, 1999 (59×39 mm) 65 50
1439 50c. Pres. Clinton (impeachment in 1999) 65 50

No. 1423 incorrectly identifies his office as "Prime Minister".

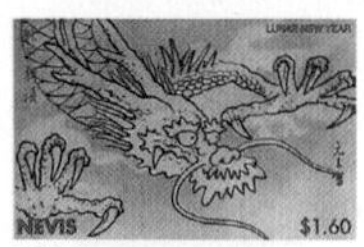

147 Dragon

2000. Chinese New Year ("Year of the Dragon"). Multicoloured.

1440 $1.60 Type **147** 1·10 1·10
1441 $1.60 Dragon with open claws (face value bottom left) 1·10 1·10
1442 $1.60 Dragon holding sphere (face value bottom right) 1·10 1·10
1443 $1.60 Dragon looking up (face value bottom left) 1·10 1·10
MS1444 76×106 mm. $5 Dragon (37×50 mm) 3·50 4·00

148 Spotted Scat

2000. Tropical Fish. Showing fish in spotlight. Multicoloured.

1445 30c. Type **148** 50 20
1446 80c. Delta topsail platy ("Platy Variatus") 75 45
1447 90c. Emerald betta 80 50
1448 $1 Sail-finned tang 90 90
1449 $1 Black-capped basslet ("Black-capped Gramma") 90 90
1450 $1 Sail-finned snapper ("Majestic Snapper") 90 90
1451 $1 Purple fire goby 90 90
1452 $1 Clown triggerfish 90 90
1453 $1 Forceps butterflyfish ("Yellow Long-nose") 90 90
1454 $1 Clown wrasse 90 90
1455 $1 Yellow-headed jawfish 90 90
1456 $1 Oriental sweetlips 90 90
1457 $1 Royal gramma 90 90
1458 $1 Thread-finned butterflyfish 90 90
1459 $1 Yellow tang 90 90
1460 $1 Bicoloured angelfish 90 90
1461 $1 Catalina goby 90 90
1462 $1 Striped mimic blenny ("False Cleanerfish") 90 90
1463 $1 Powder-blue surgeonfish 90 90
1464 $4 Long-horned cowfish 2·75 3·25
MS1465 Two sheets, each 97×68 mm. (a) $5 Clown killifish. (b) $5 Twin-spotted wrasse ("Clown Coris") Set of 2 sheets 7·00 7·50

Nos. 1448/55 and 1456/63 were each printed together, *se-tenant*, the backgrounds forming composite designs.

149 Miniature Pinscher

2000. Dogs of the World. Multicoloured.

1466 10c. Type **149** 20 30
1467 20c. Pyrenean mountain dog 25 30
1468 30c. Welsh springer spaniel 30 20
1469 80c. Alaskan malamute 65 40
1470 90c. Beagle (horiz) 75 80
1471 90c. Bassett hound (horiz) 75 80
1472 90c. St. Bernard (horiz) 75 80
1473 90c. Rough collie (horiz) 75 80
1474 90c. Shih tzu (horiz) 75 80
1475 90c. American bulldog (horiz) 75 80
1476 $1 Irish red and white setter (horiz) 75 80
1477 $1 Dalmatian (horiz) 75 80
1478 $1 Pomeranian (horiz) 75 80
1479 $1 Chihuahua (horiz) 75 80
1480 $1 English sheepdog (horiz) 75 80
1481 $1 Samoyed (horiz) 75 80
1482 $2 Bearded collie 1·40 1·50
1483 $3 American cocker spaniel 1·90 2·25
MS1484 Two sheets. (a) 76×106 mm. $5 Leonberger dog. (b) 106×76 mm. $5 Longhaired miniature dachshund (horiz) Set of 2 sheets 7·50 8·00

149a Prince William shaking hands

2000. 18th Birthday of Prince William. Mult.

1485 $1.60 Type **149a** 1·10 1·10
1486 $1.60 Wearing ski outfit 1·10 1·10
1487 $1.60 At airport 1·10 1·10
1488 $1.60 Wearing blue shirt and jumper 1·10 1·10
MS1489 100×80 mm. $5 At official engagement (38×50 mm) 3·75 4·00

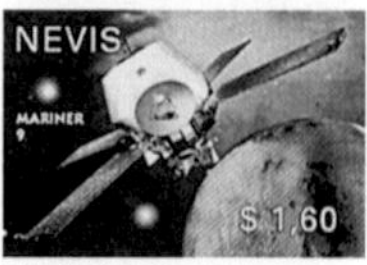

150 *Mariner 9*

2000. EXPO 2000 World Stamp Exhibition, Anaheim, U.S.A. Exploration of Mars. Multicoloured.

1490 $1.60 Type **150** 1·10 1·10
1491 $1.60 *Mars 3* 1·10 1·10
1492 $1.60 *Mariner 4* 1·10 1·10
1493 $1.60 *Planet B* 1·10 1·10
1494 $1.60 *Mars Express Lander* 1·10 1·10
1495 $1.60 *Mars Express* 1·10 1·10
1496 $1.60 *Mars 4* 1·10 1·10
1497 $1.60 *Mars Water* 1·10 1·10
1498 $1.60 *Mars 1* 1·10 1·10
1499 $1.60 *Viking* 1·10 1·10
1500 $1.60 *Mariner 7* 1·10 1·10
1501 $1.60 *Mars Surveyor* 1·10 1·10
MS1502 Two sheets, each 106×76 mm. (a) $5 *Mars Observe*" (horiz). (b) $5 *Mars Climate Orbiter* Set of 2 sheets 7·50 8·00

Nos. 1490/5 and 1496/1501 were each printed together, *se-tenant*, with the backgrounds forming composite designs.

150b *Rani Radovi*, 1969

2000. 50th Anniv of Berlin Film Festival. Showing actors, directors and film scenes with awards. Multicoloured.

1503 $1.60 Type **150b** 1·10 1·10
1504 $1.60 Salvatore Giuliano (director), 1962 1·10 1·10
1505 $1.60 *Schonzeit fur Fuches*, 1966 1·10 1·10
1506 $1.60 Shirley Maclaine (actress), 1971 1·10 1·10
1507 $1.60 Simone Signoret (actress), 1971 1·10 1·10
1508 $1.60 Tabejad Bijad (director), 1974 1·10 1·10
MS1509 97×103 mm. $5 *Komissar*, 1988 3·50 4·00

150c *Locomotion No. 1*, 1875, and George Stephenson

2000. 175th Anniv of Stockton and Darlington Line (first public railway). Multicoloured.

1510 $3 Type**150b** 2·25 2·25
1511 $3 Original drawing of Richard Trevithick's locomotive, 1804 2·25 2·25

150d Johann Sebastian Bach

2000. 250th Death Anniv of Johann Sebastian Bach (German composer). Sheet 76×88 mm, containing vert design.

MS1512 $5 multicoloured 3·75 4·00

151 Albert Einstein

2000. Election of Albert Einstein (mathematical physicist) as Time Magazine "Man of the Century". Showing portraits with photographs in background. Multicoloured.

1513 $2 Type **151** 2·50 2·25
1514 $2 Riding bicycle 2·50 2·25
1515 $2 Standing on beach 2·50 2·25

151a LZ-129 *Hindenburg*, 1929

2000. Centenary of First Zeppelin Flight.

1516 **151a** $3 green, purple and black 2·50 2·50
1517 - $3 green, purple and black 2·50 2·50
1518 - $3 green, purple and black 2·50 2·50
MS1519 116×76 mm. $5 green, mauve and black 3·75 4·00

Designs:—(38×24 mm)—No. 1517, LZ-1, 1900; No. 1518, LZ-11 *Viktoria Luise*. (50×37 mm)—No. **MS**1519, LZ-127 *Graf Zeppelin*, 1928.

No. 1516 is inscribed "Hindenberg" in error.

151b Gisela Mauermeyer (discus), Berlin (1936)

2000. Olympic Games, Sydney. Multicoloured.

1520 $2 Type **151b** 1·50 1·50
1521 $2 Gymnast on uneven bars 1·50 1·50
1522 $2 Wembley Stadium, London (1948) and Union Jack 1·50 1·50
1523 $2 Ancient Greek horseman 1·50 1·50

151c Elquemeda Willett

2000. West Indies Cricket Tour and 100th Test Match at Lord's. Multicoloured.

1524 $2 Type **151c** 2·50 1·75
1525 $3 Keith Arthurton 3·25 3·00
MS1526 121×104 mm. $5 Lord's Cricket Ground (horiz) 4·00 4·50

152 King Edward III of England

2000. Monarchs of the Millennium.

1527 **152** $1.60 black, stone and brown 1·25 1·25
1528 - $1.60 multicoloured 1·25 1·25
1529 - $1.60 multicoloured 1·25 1·25
1530 - $1.60 black, stone and brown 1·25 1·25
1531 - $1.60 black, stone and brown 1·25 1·25
1532 - $1.60 purple, stone and brown 1·25 1·25
MS1533 115×135 mm. $5 multicoloured 3·75 4·00

Designs:—No. 1528, Emperor Charles V (of Spain); No. 1529, King Joseph II of Hungary; No. 1530, Emperor Henry II of Germany; No. 1531, King Louis IV of France; No. 1532, King Ludwig II of Bavaria; **MS**1533, King Louis IX of France.

153 Member of *The Angels*

2000. Famous Girl Pop Groups. Multicoloured.

1534 90c. Type **153** 65 65
1535 90c. Member of *The Angels* with long hair 65 65
1536 90c. Member of *The Angels* with chin on hand 65 65
1537 90c. Member of *The Dixie Cups* (record at left) 65 65
1538 90c. Member of *The Dixie Cups* with shoulder-length hair 65 65
1539 90c. Member of *The Dixie Cups* with short hair and slide 65 65
1540 90c. Member of *The Vandellas* (record at left) 65 65
1541 90c. Member of *The Vandellas* ("Nevis" clear of hair) 65 65
1542 90c. Member of *The Vandellas* ("is" of "Nevis" on hair) 65 65

Each horizontal row depicts a different group with Nos. 1534/6 having green backgrounds, Nos. 1537/9 yellow and Nos. 1540/2 mauve.

154 Bob Hope in Ranger Uniform, Vietnam

2000. Bob Hope (American entertainer).

1543	**154**	$1 black, grey and mauve	1·00	85
1544	-	$1 Indian red, grey and mauve	1·00	85
1545	-	$1 black, grey and mauve	1·00	85
1546	-	$1 multicoloured	1·00	85
1547	-	$1 black, grey and mauve	1·00	85
1548	-	$1 multicoloured	1·00	85

Designs:—No. 1544, On stage with Sammy Davis Jnr.; No. 1545, With wife Dolores; No. 1546, Playing golf; No. 1547, Making radio broadcast; No. 1548, Visiting Great Wall of China.

155 David Copperfield

2000. David Copperfield (conjurer).

1549	**155**	$1.60 multicoloured	1·25	1·50

156 Mike Wallace

2000. Mike Wallace (television journalist). Sheet 120×112 mm.

MS1550 **156**	$5 multicoloured	3·25	3·50

2000. Second Caribbean Beekeeping Congress. No. **MS**801 optd 2nd Caribbean Beekeeping Congress August 14–18, 2000 on top margin.

MS1551 100×70 mm. $6 Queen and workers in hive and mechanical honey extractor	3·75	4·00

157 Beach Scene and Logo

2000. Carifesta VII Arts Festival. Multicoloured.

1552	30c. Type **157**	30	20
1553	90c. Carnival scenes	65	55
1554	$1.20 Stylized dancer with streamers	90	1·25

158 Golden Elegance Oriental Lily

2000. Caribbean Flowers. Multicoloured.

1555	30c. Type **158**	40	20
1556	80c. Frangipani	70	35
1557	90c. Star of the March	70	75
1558	90c. Tiger lily	70	75
1559	90c. Mont Blanc lily	70	75
1560	90c. Torch ginger	70	75
1561	90c. Cattleya orchid	70	75
1562	90c. St. John's wort	70	75
1563	$1 Culebra	70	75
1564	$1 Rubellum lily	70	75
1565	$1 Silver elegance oriental lily	70	75
1566	$1 Chinese hibiscus	70	75
1567	$1 Tiger lily (different)	70	75
1568	$1 Royal poincia	70	75
1569	$1.60 Epiphyte	70	75
1570	$1.60 Enchantment lily	1·00	1·10
1571	$1.60 Glory lily	1·00	1·10
1572	$1.60 Purple granadilla	1·00	1·10
1573	$1.60 Jacaranda	1·00	1·10
1574	$1.60 Shrimp plant	1·00	1·10
1575	$1.60 Garden zinnia	1·00	1·10
1576	$5 Rose elegance lily	3·00	3·25
MS1577	Two sheets. (a) 75×90 mm. $5 Bird of paradise (plant). (b) 90×75 mm. $5 Dahlia Set of 2 sheets	7·00	8·00

Nos. 1557/62, 1563/8 and 1569/74 were each printed together, *se-tenant*, with the backgrounds forming composite designs.

159 Aerial View of Resort

2000. Re-opening of Four Seasons Resort. Mult.

1578	30c. Type **159**	65	65
1579	30c. Palm trees on beach	65	65
1580	30c. Golf course	65	65
1581	30c. Couple at water's edge	65	65

160 *The Coronation of the Virgin* (Velazquez)

2000. Christmas. Religious Paintings. Multicoloured.

1582	30c. Type **160**	60	30
1583	80c. *The Immaculate Conception* (Velazquez)	1·25	70
1584	90c. *Madonna and Child* (Titian) (horiz)	1·25	80
1585	$1.20 *Madonna and Child with St. John the Baptist and St. Catherine* (Titian) (horiz)	1·50	2·00
MS1586	108×108 mm. $6 *Madonna and Child with St. Catherine* (Titian) (horiz)	4·50	5·00

Nos. 1584/5 are both inscribed "Titien" in error.

161 Snake coiled around Branch

2001. Chinese New Year. "Year of the Snake". Multicoloured.

1587	$1.60 Type **161**	1·10	1·10
1588	$1.60 Snake in tree	1·10	1·10
1589	$1.60 Snake on path	1·10	1·10
1590	$1.60 Snake by rocks	1·10	1·10
MS1591	70×100 mm. $5 Cobra at foot of cliff	3·25	3·50

162 Charlestown Methodist Church

2001. Leeward Islands District Methodist Church Conference. Multicoloured.

1592	50c. Type **162**	35	40
1593	50c. Jessups Methodist Church	35	40
1594	50c. Clifton Methodist Church	35	40
1595	50c. Trinity Methodist Church	35	40
1596	50c. Combermere Methodist Church	35	40
1597	50c. New River Methodist Church	35	40
1598	50c. Gingerland Methodist Church	35	40

163 Two Giraffes

2001. Wildlife from "The Garden of Eden". Multicoloured.

1599	$1.60 Type **163**	1·10	1·10
1600	$1.60 Rainbow boa constrictor	1·10	1·10
1601	$1.60 Suffolk sheep and mountain cottontail hare	1·10	1·10
1602	$1.60 Bluebuck antelope	1·10	1·10
1603	$1.60 Fox	1·10	1·10
1604	$1.60 Box turtle	1·10	1·10
1605	$1.60 Pileated woodpecker ("Red-crested Woodpecker") and unicorn	1·10	1·10
1606	$1.60 African elephant	1·10	1·10
1607	$1.60 Siberian tiger	1·10	1·10
1608	$1.60 Greater flamingo and Adam and Eve	1·10	1·10
1609	$1.60 Hippopotamus	1·10	1·10
1610	$1.60 Harlequin frog	1·10	1·10
MS1611	Four sheets, each 84×69 mm. (a) $5 Keel-billed toucan ("Toucan") (vert). (b) $5 American bald eagle. (c) $5 Koala bear (vert). (d) $5 Blue and yellow macaw (vert) Set of 4 sheets	14·00	15·00

Nos. 1599/1604 and 1605/10 were each printed together, *se-tenant*, with the backgrounds forming composite designs.

164 Zebra

2001. Butterflies of Nevis. Multicoloured.

1612	30c. Type **164**	50	20
1613	80c. Julia	85	55
1614	$1 Ruddy dagger	90	90
1615	$1 Common morpho	90	90
1616	$1 Banded king shoemaker	90	90
1617	$1 Figure of eight	90	90
1618	$1 Grecian shoemaker	90	90
1619	$1 Mosaic	90	90
1620	$1 White peacock	90	90
1621	$1 Hewitson's blue hairstreak	90	90
1622	$1 Tiger pierid	90	90
1623	$1 Gold drop helicopsis	90	90
1624	$1 Cramer's mesene	90	90
1625	$1 Red-banded pereute	90	90
1626	$1.60 Small flambeau	1·40	1·40
1627	$5 Purple mort bleu	3·25	3·75
MS1628	Two sheets, each 72×100 mm. (a) $5 Common mechanitis. (b) $5 Hewitson's pierella Set of 2 sheets	7·50	8·00

165 *Clavulinopsis corniculata*

2001. Caribbean Fungi. Multicoloured.

1629	20c. Type **165**	60	35
1630	25c. *Cantharellus cibarius*	60	35
1631	50c. *Chlorociboria aeruginascens*	80	45
1632	80c. *Auricularia auricula-judae*	1·00	55
1633	$1 *Entoloma incanum*	1·00	1·00
1634	$1 *Entoloma nitidum*	1·00	1·00
1635	$1 *Stropharia cyanea*	1·00	1·00
1636	$1 *Otidea onotica*	1·00	1·00
1637	$1 *Aleuria aurantia*	1·00	1·00
1638	$1 *Mitrula paludosa*	1·00	1·00
1639	$1 *Gyromitra esculenta*	1·00	1·00
1640	$1 *Helvella crispa*	1·00	1·00
1641	$1 *Morcella semilibera*	1·00	1·00
1642	$2 *Peziza vesiculosa*	1·75	2·00
1643	$3 *Mycena acicula*	2·50	3·00
MS1644	Two sheets, each 110×85 mm. (a) $5 *Russula sardonia*. (b) $5 *Omphalotus olearius* Set of 2 sheets	7·50	8·00

166 Early Life of Prince Shotoku

2001. Philanippon 01 International Stamp Exhibition, Tokyo. Prince Shotoku Pictorial Scroll. Multicoloured.

1645	$2 Type **166**	1·40	1·40
1646	$2 With priests and nuns, and preaching	1·40	1·40
1647	$2 Subduing the Ezo	1·40	1·40
1648	$2 Playing with children	1·40	1·40
1649	$2 Passing through gate	1·40	1·40
1650	$2 Battle against Mononobe-no-Moriya	1·40	1·40
1651	$2 Yumedono Hall	1·40	1·40
1652	$2 Watching dog and deer	1·40	1·40

167 Prince Albert

2001. Death Centenary of Queen Victoria. Multicoloured.

1653	$1.20 Type **167**	90	90
1654	$1.20 Queen Victoria at accession	90	90
1655	$1.20 Queen Victoria as a young girl	90	90
1656	$1.20 Victoria Mary Louisa, Duchess of Kent (Queen Victoria's mother)	90	90
1657	$1.20 Queen Victoria in old age	90	90
1658	$1.20 Albert Edward, Prince of Wales as a boy	90	90
MS1659	97×70 mm. $5 Queen Victoria at accession	3·25	3·75

168 Queen Elizabeth II wearing Blue Hat

2001. Queen Elizabeth II's 75th Birthday. Multicoloured.

1660	90c. Type **168**	80	80
1661	90c. Wearing tiara	80	80
1662	90c. Wearing yellow hat	80	80
1663	90c. Wearing grey hat	80	80
1664	90c. Wearing red hat	80	80
1665	90c. Bare-headed and wearing pearl necklace	80	80
MS1666	95×107 mm. $5 Wearing blue hat	4·00	4·25

169 Christmas Candle (flower)

2001. Christmas. Flowers. Multicoloured.

1667	30c. Type **169**	35	15
1668	90c. Poinsettia (horiz)	70	40
1669	$1.20 Snowbush (horiz)	1·10	1·00
1670	$3 Tiger claw	2·25	3·00

NEVIS 90¢ ANTIGUA & BARBUDA

170 Flag of Antigua and Barbuda

2001. Flags of the Caribbean Community. Multicoloured.

1671	90c. Type **170**	1·25	1·10
1672	90c. Bahamas	1·25	1·10
1673	90c. Barbados	1·25	1·10
1674	90c. Belize	1·25	1·10
1675	90c. Dominica	1·25	1·10
1676	90c. Grenada	1·25	1·10
1677	90c. Guyana	1·25	1·10
1678	90c. Jamaica	1·25	1·10
1679	90c. Montserrat	1·25	1·10
1680	90c. St. Kitts & Nevis	1·25	1·10
1681	90c. St. Lucia	1·25	1·10
1682	90c. Suriname	1·25	1·10
1683	90c. St. Vincent and the Grenadines	1·25	1·10
1684	90c. Trinidad & Tobago	1·25	1·10

No. 1675 shows the former flag of Dominica, superseded in 1990.

171 Maracana Football Stadium, Brazil 1950

2001. World Cup Football Championship, Japan and Korea (2002). Multicoloured.

1685	$1.60 Type **171**	1·10	1·10
1686	$1.60 Ferenc Puskas (Hungary), Switzerland 1954	1·10	1·10
1687	$1.60 Luiz Bellini (Brazil), Sweden 1958	1·10	1·10
1688	$1.60 Mauro (Brazil), Chile 1962	1·10	1·10
1689	$1.60 West German cap, England 1966	1·10	1·10
1690	$1.60 Pennant, Mexico 1970	1·10	1·10
1691	$1.60 Passarella (Argentina), Argentina 1978	1·10	1·10
1692	$1.60 Dino Zoff (Italy), Spain 1982	1·10	1·10
1693	$1.60 Azteca Stadium, Mexico 1986	1·10	1·10
1694	$1.60 San Siro Stadium, Italy 1990	1·10	1·10
1695	$1.60 Dennis Bergkamp (Holland), USA 1994	1·10	1·10
1696	$1.60 Stade de France, France 1998	1·10	1·10
MS1697	Two sheets, each 88×75 mm. (a) $5 Detail of Jules Rimet Trophy, Uruguay 1930. (b) $5 Detail of World Cup Trophy, Japan/Korea 2002 Set of 2 sheets	7·00	7·50

Nos. 1685 and 1687 are inscribed "Morocana" and "Luis" respectively, both in error.

172 Queen Elizabeth and Duke of Edinburgh in reviewing Car

2002. Golden Jubilee. Multicoloured.

1698	$2 Type **172**	1·75	1·75
1699	$2 Prince Philip	1·75	1·75
1700	$2 Queen Elizabeth wearing yellow coat and hat	1·75	1·75
1701	$2 Queen Elizabeth and horse at polo match	1·75	1·75
MS1702	76×108 mm. $5 Queen Elizabeth with Prince Philip in naval uniform	5·00	5·00

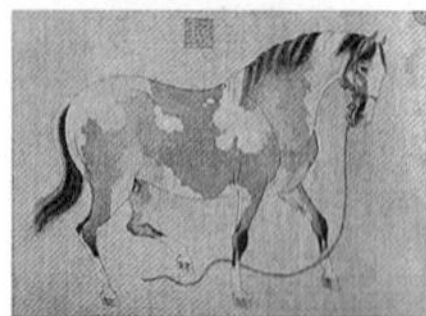

173 Chestnut and White Horse

2002. Chinese New Year ("Year of the Horse"). Paintings by Ren Renfa. Multicoloured.

1703	$1.60 Type **173**	1·10	1·10
1704	$1.60 Bay horse	1·10	1·10
1705	$1.60 Brown horse	1·10	1·10
1706	$1.60 Dappled grey horse	1·10	1·10

174 Beechey's Bee

2002. Fauna. Multicoloured.

1707	$1.20 Type **174**	1·25	1·25
1708	$1.20 Banded king shoemaker butterfly	1·25	1·25
1709	$1.20 Streaked sphinx caterpillar	1·25	1·25
1710	$1.20 Hercules beetle	1·25	1·25
1711	$1.20 South American palm weevil	1·25	1·25
1712	$1.20 Giant katydid	1·25	1·25
1713	$1.60 Roseate spoonbill	1·25	1·25
1714	$1.60 White-tailed tropicbird	1·25	1·25
1715	$1.60 Ruby-throated tropicbird	1·25	1·25
1716	$1.60 Black skimmer	1·25	1·25
1717	$1.60 Black-necked stilt	1·25	1·25
1718	$1.60 Mourning dove	1·25	1·25
1719	$1.60 Sperm whale and calf	1·25	1·25
1720	$1.60 Killer whale	1·25	1·25
1721	$1.60 Minke whales	1·25	1·25
1722	$1.60 Fin whale	1·25	1·25
1723	$1.60 Blaineville's beaked whale	1·25	1·25
1724	$1.60 Pygmy sperm whale	1·25	1·25
MS1725	Three sheets, each 105×78 mm. (a) $5 Click beetle. (b) $5 Royal tern. (c) $5 Humpback whale (vert)	11·00	12·00

Nos. 1707/12 (insects), 1713/18 (birds) and 1719/24 (whales) were each printed together, *se-tenant*, with the backgrounds forming composite designs.

175 Mount Assiniboine, Canada

2002. International Year of Mountains. Multicoloured.

1726	$2 Type **175**	1·40	1·40
1727	$2 Mount Atitlan, Guatemala	1·40	1·40
1728	$2 Mount Adams, USA	1·40	1·40
1729	$2 The Matterhorn, Switzerland	1·40	1·40
1730	$2 Mount Dhaulagiri, Nepal	1·40	1·40
1731	$2 Mount Chamlang, Nepal	1·40	1·40
MS1732	106×125 mm. $5 Mount Kvaenangen, Norway	3·25	3·75

Nos. 1727 and 1729 are inscribed "ATAILAN" and "MATTHERORN", both in error.

176 Horse-riders on Beach

2002. Year of Eco Tourism. Multicoloured.

1733	$1.60 Type **176**	1·75	1·75
1734	$1.60 Windsurfing	1·75	1·75
1735	$1.60 Pinney's Beach	1·75	1·75
1736	$1.60 Hikers by beach	1·75	1·75
1737	$1.60 Robert T. Jones Golf Course	1·75	1·75
1738	$1.60 Scuba diver and fish	1·75	1·75
MS1739	115×90 mm. $5 Snorkel diver on reef	3·50	3·75

177 Women's Figure Skating

2002. Winter Olympic Games, Salt Lake City. Multicoloured.

1740	$2 Type **177**	1·40	1·50
1741	$2 Aerial skiing	1·40	1·50
MS1742	88×119 mm. Nos. 1740/1	2·75	3·00

178 Two Scout Canoes in Mist

2002. 20th World Scout Jamboree, Thailand. Multicoloured.

1743	$2 Type **178**	1·40	1·40
1744	$2 Canoe in jungle	1·40	1·40
1745	$2 Scout on rope-ladder	1·40	1·40
1746	$2 Scouts with inflatable boats	1·40	1·40
MS1747	105×125 mm. $5 Scout painting	3·25	3·50

179 US Flag as Statue of Liberty with Nevis Flag

2002. United We Stand. Support for Victims of 11 September 2001 Terrorist Attacks.

1748	**179**	$2 multicoloured	1·40	1·40

180 *Nevis Peak with Windmill* (Eva Wilkin)

2002. Art. Mmulticoloured (except Nos. 1750/1).

1749	$1.20 Type **180**	1·00	1·00
1750	$1.20 *Nevis Peak with ruined Windmill* (Eva Wilkin) (brown and black)	1·00	1·00
1751	$1.20 *Fig Tree Church* (Eva Wilkin) (brown and black)	1·00	1·00
1752	$1.20 *Nevis Peak with Blossom* (Eva Wilkin)	1·00	1·00
1753	$2 *Golden Pheasants and Loquat* (Kano Shoei) (30×80 mm)	1·50	1·50
1754	$2 *Flowers and Birds of the Four Seasons* (Winter) (Ikeda Koson) (30×80 mm)	1·50	1·50
1755	$2 *Pheasants and Azaleas* (Kano Shoei) (30×80 mm)	1·50	1·50
1756	$2 *Flowers and Birds of the Four Seasons* (Spring) (Ikeda Koson) (different) (30×80 mm)	1·50	1·50
1757	$3 *White Blossom* (Shikibu Terutada) (38×62 mm)	1·75	1·90
1758	$3 *Bird and Flowers* (Shikibu Terutada) (38×62 mm)	1·75	1·90
1759	$3 *Bird and Leaves* (Shikibu Terutada) (38×62 mm)	1·75	1·90
1760	$3 *Red and White Flowers* (Shikibu Terutada) (38×62 mm)	1·75	1·90
1761	$3 *Bird on Willow Tree* (Yosa Buson) (62×38 mm)	1·75	1·90
1762	$3 *Bird on Peach Tree* (Yosa Buson) (62×38 mm)	1·75	1·90
MS1763	Two sheets, each 105×105 mm. (a) $5 *Golden Pheasants among Rhododendrons* (Yamamoto Baiitsu) (38×62 mm). (b) $5 *Musk Cat and Camellias* (Uto Gyoshi) (62×38 mm)	7·50	8·00

Nos. 1757/62 were printed together, *se-tenant*, with the backgrounds forming a composite design.

181 *Madonna and Child Enthroned with Saints* (Pietro Perugino)

2002. Christmas. Religious Art. Multicoloured.

1764	30c. Type **181**	35	15
1765	80c. *Adoration of the Magi* (Domenico Ghirlandaio)	70	35
1766	90c. *San Zaccaria Altarpiece* (Giovanni Bellini)	80	40
1767	$1.20 *Presentation at the Temple* (Bellini)	1·10	90
1768	$5 *Madonna and Child* (Simone Martini)	3·75	5·50
MS1769	102×76 mm. $6 *Maesa* (Martini)	3·50	4·00

182 Claudio Reyna (USA) and Torsten Frings (Germany)

2002. World Cup Football Championship, Japan and Korea. Multicoloured.

1770	$1.20 Type **182**	95	95
1771	$1.20 Michael Ballack (Germany) and Eddie Pope (USA)	95	95
1772	$1.20 Sebastian Kehl (Germany) and Brian McBride (USA)	95	95
1773	$1.20 Carlos Puyol (Spain) and Eul Yong Lee (South Korea)	95	95
1774	$1.20 Jin Cheul Choi (South Korea) and Gaizka Mendieta (Spain)	95	95
1775	$1.20 Juan Valeron (Spain) and Jin Cheul Choi (South Korea)	95	95
1776	$1.60 Emile Heskey (England) and Edmilson (Brazil)	1·10	1·10
1777	$1.60 Rivaldo (Brazil) and Sol Campbell (England)	1·10	1·10
1778	$1.60 Ronaldinho (Brazil) and Nicky Butt (England)	1·10	1·10
1779	$1.60 Ilhan Mansiz (Turkey) and Omar Daf (Senegal)	1·10	1·10
1780	$1.60 Hasan Sas (Turkey) and Pape Bouba Diop (Senegal)	1·10	1·10
1781	$1.60 Lamine Diata (Senegal) and Hakan Sukur (Turkey)	1·10	1·10
MS1782	Four sheets, each 82×82 mm. (a) $3 Sebastian Kehl (Germany); $3 Frankie Hejduk (USA). (b) $3 Hong Myung Bo (South Korea); $3 Gaizka Mendieta (Spain). (c) $3 David Beckham (England) and Roque Junior (Brazil); $3 Paul Scholes (England) and Rivaldo (Brazil). (d) $3 Alpay Ozalan (Turkey); $3 Khalilou Fadiga (Senegal)	13·00	15·00

No. 1780 is inscribed "Papa" in error.

183 Ram and Two Ewes

2003. Chinese New Year ("Year of the Ram").

1783	**183**	$2 multicoloured	1·75	1·75

184 Marlene Dietrich

2003. Famous People of the 20th Century

(a) Tenth Death Anniv of Marlene Dietrich. Multicoloured

MS1784	127×165 mm. $1.60×2 Type **184**; $1.60×2 Wearing white coat and black hat; $1.60×2 Holding cigarette	5·50	6·00
MS1785	76×51 mm. $5 Marlene Dietrich	3·50	3·75

(b) 25th Death Anniv of Elvis Presley. Sheet 154×151 mm. Multicoloured.

MS1786	$1.60×6 Elvis Presley	7·00	7·50

(c) Life and Times of President John F. Kennedy. Two sheets, each 126×141 mm.

MS1787	$2 Taking Oath of Office, 1961 (black, brown and rose); $2 Watching swearing in of Cabinet Officers (black, brown and rose); $2 With Andrei Gromyko (Soviet Foreign Minister), 1963 (multicoloured); $2 Making speech during Cuban Missile Crisis, 1962 (black, violet and rose)	6·00	6·50

MS1788 $2 Robert and Ted Kennedy (brothers) (slate, violet and rose); $2 John F. Kennedy (slate, violet and rose); $2 John as boy with brother Joe Jnr (maroon, black and rose); $2 With Robert Kennedy in Rose Garden of White House (multicoloured) 6·00 6·50

(d) 75th Anniv of First Solo Transatlantic Flight. Two sheets, each 142×126 mm. Multicoloured.

MS1789 $2 Ryan Airlines crew attaching wing to fuselage of NYP Special *Spirit of St. Louis*; $2 Charles Lindbergh with Donald Hall and Mr. Mahoney (president of Ryan Airlines); $2 Lindbergh planning flight; $2 Donald Hall (chief engineer of Ryan Airlines) working on plans of aircraft 6·00 6·50

MS1790 $2 Donald Hall and drawing of *Spirit of St. Louis*; $2 Charles Lindbergh; $2 *Spirit of St. Louis* being towed from factory; $2 *Spirit of St. Louis* at Curtis Field before flight 6·00 6·50

185 Princess Diana

2003. Fifth Death Anniv of Diana, Princess of Wales. Multicoloured.

MS1791 203×150 mm. $2 Type **185**; $2 Wearing white dress and four strings of pearls; $2 Wearing black sleeveless dress; $2 Wearing black and white hat 6·00 6·50

MS1792 95×116 mm. $5 Wearing pearl and sapphire choker 3·75 4·00

186 Abraham Lincoln Bear

2003. Centenary of the Teddy Bear. Multicoloured.

MS1793 137×152 mm. $2 Type **186**; $2 Napolean bear; $2 Henry VIII bear; $2 Charlie Chaplin bear 3·75 4·25

MS1794 100×70 mm. $5 Baseball bear 3·25 3·75

186a Gustave Garrigou (1911)

2003. Centenary of Tour de France Cycle Race. Showing past winners. Multicoloured.

MS1795 160×100 mm. $2 Type **186a**; $2 Odile Defraye (1912); $2 Philippe Thys (1913); $2 Philippe Thys (1914) 7·00 7·00

MS1796 100×70 mm. $5 Francois Faber 6·00 6·00

187 Cadillac 355-C V8 Sedan (1933)

2003. Centenary of General Motors Cadillac. Multicoloured.

MS1797 120×170 mm. $2 Type **187**; $2 Eldorado (1953); $2 Coupe Deville (1977); $2 Seville Elegante (1980) 6·00 6·50

MS1798 84×120 mm. $5 Cadillac (1954) 3·75 4·00

188 Corvette (1970)

2003. 50th Anniv of General Motors Chevrolet Corvette. Multicoloured.

MS1799 120×140 mm. $2 Type **188**; $2 Corvette (1974); $2 Corvette (1971); $2 Corvette (1973) 6·00 6·50

MS1800 120×85 mm. $5 C5 Corvette (1997) 3·75 4·00

189 Queen Elizabeth II on Coronation Day

2003. 50th Anniv of Coronation. Multicoloured.

MS1801 156×93 mm. $3 Type **189**; $3 Queen wearing Imperial State Crown (red background); $3 Wearing Imperial State Crown (in recent years) 8·50 8·50

MS1802 106×76 mm. $5 Wearing tiara and blue sash 6·00 6·00

190 Prince William

2003. 21st Birthday of Prince William of Wales. Multicoloured.

MS1803 147×86 mm. $3 Type **190**; $3 Wearing jacket and blue and gold patterned tie; $3 Wearing fawn jumper 8·50 8·50

MS1804 98×68 mm. $5 Prince William 6·00 6·00

190a A. V. Roe's Triplane I, 1909

2003. Centenary of Powered Flight. A. V. Roe (aircraft designer) Commemoration. Multicoloured.

MS1805 177×96 mm. $1.80 Type **190a**; $1.80 Avro Type D biplane, 1911; $1.80 Avro Type F, 1912; $1.80 Avro 504 7·00 7·00

MS1806 106×76 mm. $5 Avro No. 561, 1924 5·00 5·00

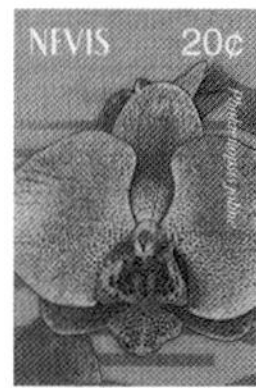

191 *Phalaenopsis joline*

2003. Orchids, Marine Life and Butterflies. Multicoloured.

1807	20c. Type **191**	45	35
1808	30c. Nassau grouper (fish)	50	40
1809	30c. *Perisama bonplandii* (butterfly) (horiz)	50	40
1810	80c. Acropora (coral)	70	45
1811	90c. Doubletooth soldierfish (horiz)	80	75
1812	90c. *Danaus Formosa* (butterfly) (horiz)	80	75
1813	$1 *Amauris vasati* (butterfly) (horiz)	90	75
1814	$1.20 Vanda thonglor (orchid)	1·10	80
1815	$2 Potinara (orchid) (horiz)	1·90	1·90
1816	$3 *Lycaste aquila* (orchid) (horiz)	2·75	3·25
1817	$3 *Lycorea ceres* (butterfly) (horiz)	2·75	3·25
1818	$5 American manatee (horiz)	3·50	4·00

MS1819 136×116 mm. $2 *Brassolaelia cattleya*; $2 *Cymbidium claricon*; $2 *Calanthe restita*; $2 *Odontoglossum crispum* (orchids) (all horiz) 6·50 7·00

MS1820 116×136 mm. $2 Lionfish; $2 Copper-banded butterflyfish; $2 Honeycomb grouper; $2 Blue tang (all horiz) 6·50 7·00

MS1821 136×116 mm. $2 *Kallima rumia*; $2 *Nessaea ancaeus*; $2 *Callicore cajetani*; $2 *Hamadryas guatemalena* (butterflies) (all horiz) 6·50 7·00

MS1822 Three sheets, each 96×66 mm. (a) $5 *Odontioda brocade* (orchid). (b) $5 Blue-striped grunt (fish). (c) $5 *Euphaedra medon* (butterfly) (all horiz) 11·00 12·00

192 *Madonna of the Magnificat* (Botticelli)

2003. Christmas. Multicoloured.

1823	30c. Type **192**	35	20
1824	90c. *Madonna with the Long Neck* (detail) (Parmigianino)	70	45
1825	$1.20 *Virgin and Child with St. Anne* (detail) (Da Vinci)	1·10	70
1826	$5 *Madonna and Child and Scenes from the Life of St. Anne* (detail) (Filippo Lippi)	3·50	4·25

MS1827 96×113 mm. $6 *The Conestabile Madonna* (Raphael) 3·75 4·25

193 Two Stylised Men and AIDS Ribbon

2003. World AIDS Awareness Day. Multicoloured.

1828	90c. Type **193**	1·25	75
1829	$1.20 Nevis flag and map and ribbon	2·00	1·75

194 Monkey King

2004. Chinese New Year ("Year of the Monkey"). Grey, black and brown (MS1830) or multicoloured (MS1831).

MS1830 Sheet 102×130 mm. $1.60 Type **194**×4 4·50 4·75

MS1831 Sheet 70×100 mm. $3 Monkey King (29×39 mm) 2·75 3·00

195 Guide Badges

2004. 50th Anniv of Nevis Girl Guides. Multicoloured.

1832	30c. Type **195**	35	15
1833	90c. Mrs Gwendolyn Douglas-Jones and Miss Bridget Hunkins (past and present Commissioners) (horiz)	75	40
1834	$1.20 Lady Olave Baden-Powell	1·00	90
1835	$5 Photographs of Girl Guides	3·50	4·50

196 *The Morning After* (1945)

2004. 25th Death Anniv of Norman Rockwell (artist) (2003). Multicoloured.

MS1836 150×180 mm. $2 Type **196**; $2 *Solitaire* (1950); $2 *Easter Morning* (1959); $2 *Walking to Church* (1953) 6·00 7·00

MS1837 90×98 mm. $5 *The Graduate* (1959) (horiz) 4·00 4·25

197 *Woman with a Hat* (1935)

2004. 30th Death Anniv of Pablo Picasso (2003) (artist). Multicoloured.

MS1838 Two sheets each 133×168 mm. (a) $2 Type **197**; $2 *Seated Woman* (1937); $2 *Portrait of Nusch Eluard* (1937); $2 *Woman in a Straw Hat* (1936). (b) $2 *L'Arlesienne* (1937); $2 *The Mirror* (1932); $2 *Repose* (1932); $2 *Portrait of Paul Eluard* (1937). Set of 2 sheets 11·00 12·00

MS1839 Two sheets. (a) 75×100 mm. $5 *Portrait of Nusch Eluard* (with green ribbon in hair) (1937). (b) 100×75 mm. $5 *Reclining Woman with a Book* (1939). Imperf. Set of 2 sheets 8·00 8·50

198 *Still Life with a Drapery* (1899)

2004. 300th Anniv of St. Petersburg. "Treasures of the Hermitage". Multicoloured.

1840	30c. Type **198**	25	15
1841	90c. *The Smoker* (1895) (vert)	60	40
1842	$2 *Girl with a Fan* (1881) (vert)	1·40	1·40
1843	$5 *Grove* (1912) (vert)	3·25	5·00

MS1844 94×74 mm. $5 *Lady in the Garden* (1867). Imperf 3·25 3·75

199 John Denver

2004. John Denver (musician) Commemoration. Sheet 127×107 mm containing T **199** and similar vert designs. Multicoloured.

MS1845 $1.20 Type **199**; $1.20 Wearing patterned shirt; $1.20 Wearing dark shirt; $1.20 Wearing white shirt 3·50 3·75

200 Marilyn Monroe

2004. Marilyn Monroe Commemoration. Multicoloured.

1846	60c. Type **200**	1·00	75

MS1847 175×125 mm. $2 Pouting; $2 Laughing and looking left; $2 Laughing with head tilted back; $2 Smiling wearing drop earrings (37×50 mm) 5·00 6·00

201 Brain

2004. Arthur the Aardvark and Friends. Multicoloured.

MS1848	Three sheets, each 152×185. (a) $1×6, Type **201**; Sue Ellen; Buster; Francine; Muffy; Binky. (b) $2×4, Binky inside heart; Sue Ellen inside heart; Brain inside heart; Francine inside heart wearing red top. (c) $2×4, Arthur inside heart; D.W. inside heart; Francine inside heart wearing pink top; Buster inside heart	12·00	13·00

202 HMCS *Penetang*

2004. 60th Anniv of D-Day Landings. Multicoloured.

MS1849	Two sheets. (a) 136×122 mm. $1.20×6 Type **202**; Infantry disembarking from landing craft; Landing craft tank from above; Two landing craft tanks; Landing barge kitchen; Battleship *Texas*. (b) 96×76 mm. $6 HMS *Scorpion*	16·00	16·00

203 Medal (Mexico City, 1968)

2004. Olympic Games, Athens. Multicoloured.

1850	30c. Type **203**	40	20
1851	90c. Pentathlon (Greek art)	75	60
1852	$1.80 Avery Brundage (International Olympic Committee, 1952–1972)	1·50	1·75
1853	$3 Tennis (Antwerp, 1920) (horiz)	2·25	3·25

204 Deng Xiaoping

2004. Birth Centenary of Deng Xiaoping (leader of China, 1978–89). Sheet 96×66 mm.

MS1854	**204** $5 multicoloured	3·25	3·50

205 Peace Dove carrying Olive Branch

2004. United Nations International Year of Peace. Sheet 142×82 mm containing horiz designs as T **205**. Multicoloured.

MS1855	$3×3, Type **205**; Dove from front; Dove angled left	5·50	6·50

206 Elvis Presley

2004. Elvis Presley (entertainer) Commemoration. Multicoloured.

MS1856	Two sheets, each 146×103 mm. (a) $1.20×6, Type **206**×3; magenta background×3. (b) $1.20×6, scarlet jumper; yellow jumper; blue jumper; turquoise jumper; purple jumper; green jumper	11·00	10·00

207 Nery Pumpido (Argentina)

2004. Centenary of FIFA (Federation Internationale de Football Association). Multicoloured

MS1857	192×96 mm. $2×4, Type **207**; Gary Lineker (England); Thomas Hassler (Germany); Sol Campbell (England)	5·50	6·00

2004. World Cup Football Championship, Germany

MS1858	90×115 mm. $5 Jason Berkley Joseph (Nevis)	4·50	5·00

208 *Santa's Good Boys*

2004. Christmas. Paintings by Norman Rockwell. Multicoloured.

1859	25c. Type **208**	35	20
1860	30c. *Ride 'em Cowboy*	40	20
1861	90c. *Christmas Sing Merrillie*	85	60
1862	$5 *The Christmas Newsstand*	3·50	5·00
MS1863	63×72 mm. $5 *Is He Coming*. Imperf	3·50	4·00

209 Steam Idyll, Indonesia

2004. Bicentenary of Steam Trains. Multicoloured.

1864	$3 Type **209**	3·25	3·25
1865	$3 2-8-2, Syria	3·25	3·25
1866	$3 Narrow Gauge Mallet 0-4-4-0, Portugal	3·25	3·25
1867	$3 Western Pacific Bo Bo Road Switcher, USA	3·25	3·25
MS1868	100×70 mm. $5 LMS 5305, Great Britain	6·00	6·00

210 Gekko Gecko

2005. Reptiles and Amphibians. Multicoloured.

1869	$1.20 Type **210**	1·25	1·40
1870	$1.20 Eyelash viper	1·25	1·40
1871	$1.20 Green iguana	1·25	1·40
1872	$1.20 Whistling frog	1·25	1·40
MS1873	96×67 mm. $5 Hawksbill turtle	4·50	5·00

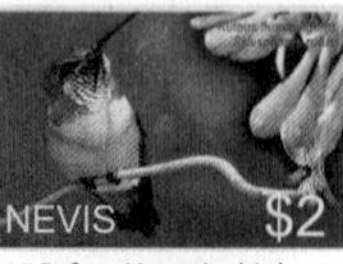

211 Rufous Hummingbird

2005. Hummingbirds. Multicoloured.

1874	$2 Type **211**	3·50	3·00
1875	$2 Green-crowned brilliant	3·50	3·00
1876	$2 Ruby-throated hummingbird	3·50	3·00
1877	$2 Purple-throated carib	3·50	3·00
MS1878	79×108 mm. $5 Rivoli's ("Magnificent") Hummingbird	7·00	7·00

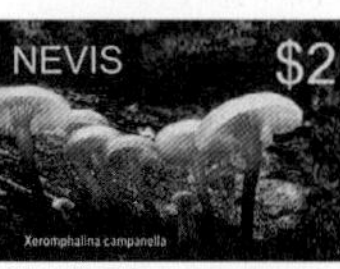

212 *Xeromphalina campanella*

2005. Mushrooms. Multicoloured.

MS1879	137×127 mm. $2×4, Type **212**; *Calvatia sculpta; Mitrula elegans; Aleuria aurantia*	7·00	7·50
MS1880	97×68 mm. $5 *iSarcoscypha coccinea*	5·00	5·50

213 Hawksbill Turtle (Leon Silcott)

2005. Hawksbill Turtle. Children's Drawings. Multicoloured.

1881	30c. Type **213**	35	20
1882	90c. Hawksbill turtle on sand (Kris Liburd)	85	40
1883	$1.20 Spotted hawksbill turtle (Alice Webber)	1·10	90
1884	$5 Hawksbill turtle in water (Jeuaunito Huggins)	3·75	4·50

214 Zebra Shark

2005. Sharks. Multicoloured.

MS1885	99×137 mm. $2×4, Type **214**; Caribbean reef shark; Blue shark; Bronze whaler	6·00	6·50
MS1886	96×67 mm. $5 Blacktip reef shark	4·00	4·25

215 Rooster

2005. Chinese New Year ("Year of the Rooster"). Multicoloured.

1887	75c. Type **215**	70	70
1888	75c. Pink silhouette of rooster	70	70
1889	75c. Grey silhouette of rooster	70	70
1890	75c. Rooster on rose-lilac background	70	70

216 *Enola Gay* and Flight Crew

2005. 60th Anniv of Victory in Japan. Multicoloured.

1891	$2 Type **216**	2·50	2·50
1892	$2 Bomb exploding over Hiroshima	2·50	2·50
1893	$2 Souvenir of Japanese Surrender Ceremony	2·50	2·50
1894	$2 Japanese Delegation aboard USS *Missouri*	2·50	2·50
1895	$2 General Macarthur speaking	2·50	2·50

217 Brazil Team, 1958

2005. 75th Anniv of First World Cup Football Championship. Multicoloured.

1896	$2 Type **217**	1·40	1·40
1897	$2 Brazil and Sweden	1·40	1·40
1898	$2 Rasunda Stadium, Stockholm	1·40	1·40
1899	$2 Edson Arantes do Nascimento (Pele)	1·40	1·40
MS1900	115×89 mm. $5 Brazil celebrating with Swedish flag	3·25	3·50

218 Friedrich von Schiller

2005. Death Bicentenary of Friedrich von Schiller (poet and dramatist). Multicoloured.

1901	$3 Type **218**	1·75	1·90
1902	$3 Friedrich von Schiller (black and white portrait)	1·75	1·90
1903	$3 Birthplace of Friedrich von Schiller	1·75	1·90
MS1904	100×70 mm. $5 Friedrich von Schiller statue, Chicago	3·25	3·50

219 Young Boy

2005. Centenary of Rotary International (humanitarian organisation). Multicoloured.

1905	$3 Type **219**	1·75	1·90
1906	$3 Immunising child	1·75	1·90
1907	$3 Boy with leg braces and crutches	1·75	1·90
MS1908	103×70 mm. $5 Two children and adult (horiz)	3·25	3·50

220 Admiral Sir William Cornwallis

2005. Bicentenary of the Battle of Trafalgar. Multicoloured.

1909	30c. Type **220**	70	30
1910	90c. Captain Maurice Suckling (Comptroller of the Navy)	1·25	70
1911	$1.20 Richard Earl Howe (First Lord of the Admiralty)	1·60	1·25
1912	$3 Sir John Jervis (First Earl of St Vincent)	3·75	4·25
MS1913	83×119 mm. $5 Richard Earl Howe on quarterdeck of *Queen Charlotte*	6·00	6·50

221 General Charles de Gaulle

2005. 60th Anniv of Victory in Europe.

1914	**221**	$2 multicoloured	2·50	2·50
1915	**221**	$2 sepia and pink	2·50	2·50
1916	**221**	$2 black and yellow	2·50	2·50
1917	**221**	$2 brown, stone and blue	2·50	2·50
1918	**221**	$2 multicoloured	2·50	2·50

Designs:—No. 1914, Type **221**; 1915, General George S. Patton; 1916, Field Marshall Bernhard Montgomery; 1917, Prisoners of War; 1918, "Germany Defeated!".

222 *The Little Mermaid* (sculpture)

2005. Birth Bicentenary of Hans Christian Andersen (writer). Multicoloured.

1919	$2 Type **222**	1·40	1·40
1920	$2 *Thumbelina*	1·40	1·40
1921	$2 *The Snow Queen*	1·40	1·40
1922	$2 *The Emperor's New Clothes*	1·40	1·40
MS1923	100×75 mm. $6 Hans Christian Andersen	3·50	3·75

223 Tyrannosaurus Rex

2005. Prehistoric Animals. Multicoloured.

1924	30c. Type **223**	1·25	75

1925	$5 Hadrosaur	4·50	5·00
MS1926	Three sheets. (a) 104×128 mm. $1.20×6, Apatosaurus; Camarasaurus; Iguanodon; Edmontosaurus; Centrosaurus; Euoplocephalus. (b) 128×104 mm. $1.20×6 (vert), Deinotherium; Platybelodon; Palaeoloxodon; Arsinoitherium; Procoptodon; Macrauchenia; (c) 104×128 mm. $1.20×6, Ouranosaurus; Parasaurolophus; Psittacosaurus; Stegasaurus; Scelidosaurus; Hypsilophodon	16·00	17·00
MS1927	Three sheets. (a) 97×77 mm. $5 Brontotherium. (b) 98×87 mm. $5 Daspletosaurus; (c) 98×92 mm. $5 Pliosaur	14·00	15·00

The backgrounds of Nos. **MS**1926a/c form a composite design which bleeds onto the sheet margins.

224 Captain Nemo (*20,000 Leagues under the Sea*)

2005. Death Centenary of Jules Verne (writer). Multicoloured.

1928	$2 Type **224**	2·25	2·25
1929	$2 Michael Strogoff	2·25	2·25
1930	$2 Phileas Fogg (*Around the World in 80 Days*)	2·25	2·25
1931	$2 Captain Cyrus Smith (*Mysterious Island*)	2·25	2·25
MS1932	78×100 mm. $5 Pat Boone (*Journey to the Centre of the Earth*)	4·50	4·75

No. 1930 is inscribed "Phinias Fogg".

225 No. SG69 of Vatican City

2005. Pope John Paul II Commemoration. Multicoloured.

1933	90c. Type **225**	1·75	1·00
1934	$4 Pope John Paul II (28×42 mm)	6·00	6·00

226 Shareef Abdur-Rahim (Portland Trail Blazers)

2005. National Basketball Association. Multicoloured.

1935	$1 Type **226**	1·00	90
1936	$1 Vince Carter (New Jersey Nets)	1·00	90
1937	$1 Shaun Livingston (Los Angeles Clippers)	1·00	90
1938	$1 Theo Ratliff (Portland Trail Blazers)	1·00	90
1938b	$1 Portland Trail Blazers emblem	1·00	90
1939	$1 Rasheed Wallace (Detroit Pistons)	1·00	90

227 Dr Sun Yat-Sen

2005. TAIPEI 2005 International Stamp Exhibition. 80th Death Anniv of Dr Sun Yat-Sen (Chinese revolutionary leader). Multicoloured.

1940	$2 Type **227**	1·40	1·40
1941	$2 Wearing jacket and tie	1·40	1·40
1942	$2 In front of statue	1·40	1·40
1943	$2 In front of building	1·40	1·40

228 *Madonna and the Angels* (detail) (Fra Angelico)

2005. Christmas. Multicoloured.

1944	25c. Type **228**	45	20
1945	30c. *Madonna and the Child* (detail) (Filippo Lippi)	50	20
1946	90c. *Madonna and Child* (detail) (Giotto)	1·10	60
1947	$4 *Madonna of the Chair* (detail) (Raphael)	3·50	4·50
MS1948	67×97 mm. $5 *Adoration of the Magi* (Giovanni Batista Tiepolo) (horiz)	4·00	4·50

229 "A Dog" (Ren Xun)

2006. Chinese New Year ("Year of the Dog").

1949 **229**	75c. multicoloured	1·25	1·25

230 Eldorado National Forest, California

2006. Centenary of United States Forest Service (2005). Multicoloured.

1950	$1.60 Type **230**	1·75	1·75
1951	$1.60 Pisgah National Forest, North Carolina	1·75	1·75
1952	$1.60 Chattahoochee-Oconee National Forests, Georgia	1·75	1·75
1953	$1.60 Nantahala National Forest, North Carolina	1·75	1·75
1954	$1.60 Bridger-Teton National Forest, Wyoming	1·75	1·75
1955	$1.60 Mount Hood National Forest, Oregon	1·75	1·75
MS1956	Two sheets, each 104×70 mm. (a) $6 Klamath National Forest, California (horiz). (b) $6 The Source Rain Forest Walk, Nevis	9·00	10·00

231 Queen Elizabeth II wearing Garter Robes

2006. 80th Birthday of Queen Elizabeth II. Multicoloured.

1957	$2 Type **231**	2·00	2·00
1958	$2 Wearing white dress	2·00	2·00
1959	$2 Wearing tiara and evening dress	2·00	2·00
1960	$2 Waving, wearing white hat and gloves	2·00	2·00
MS1961	120×120 mm. $5 Queen Elizabeth II, *c.* 1955	4·75	4·75

232 Italy 1956 Winter Olympics 10l. Ski-jump Stamp

2006. Winter Olympic Games, Turin. Multicoloured.

1962	25c. USA 1980 Winter Olympics 15c.downhill skiing stamp	35	25
1963	30c. Type **232**	35	25
1964	90c. Italy 1956 Winter Olympics 25l. ice stadium stamp	85	55
1965	$1.20 Emblem of Winter Olympic Games, Lake Placid, USA, 1980 (vert)	1·60	1·25
1966	$4 Italy 1956 Winter Olympics 60l. skating arena stamp	3·00	3·75
1967	$5 Emblem of Winter Olympic Games, Cortina d'Ampezzo, 1956 (vert)	3·25	4·00

233 Mahatma Gandhi

2006. Washington 2006 International Stamp Exhibition. Sheet 140×152 mm.

1968 **233**	$3 multicoloured	4·50	4·50

234 *The Anatomy Lesson of Dr. Tulp* (detail)

2006. 400th Birth Anniv of Rembrandt Harmenszoon van Rijn (artist). Multicoloured.

1969	$2 Type **234**	1·50	1·50
1970	$2 *The Anatomy Lesson of Dr. Tulp* (detail of man leaning forward)	1·50	1·50
1971	$2 *The Anatomy Lesson of Dr. Tulp* (detail of man seen in profile)	1·50	1·50
1972	$2 *The Anatomy Lesson of Dr. Tulp* (detail)	1·50	1·50
MS1973	70×100 mm. $6 *Bald-headed Old Man*. Imperf	4·00	4·50

235 Saturn 1B Launch KSC's from Launch Complex 39B

2006. Space Anniversaries. Multicoloured

(a) 30th Anniv (2005) of Apollo Soyuz Test Project

1974	$2 Type **235**	2·25	2·25
1975	$2 Astronaut Donald Slayton and cosmonaut Aleksey Leonov	2·25	2·25
1976	$2 Liftoff of *Soyuz 19* from Baikonur Cosmodrome	2·25	2·25
1977	$2 Soyuz spacecraft seen from Apollo CM	2·25	2·25
1978	$2 American and Soviet crewmen	2·25	2·25
1979	$2 Apollo CSM with docking adapter seen from Soyuz	2·25	2·25

(b) 30th Anniv of *Viking 1* Landing on Mars.

1980	$3 Titan/Centaur rocket lifting off from Cape Canaveral	3·25	3·25
1981	$3 *Viking 1*	3·25	3·25
1982	$3 *Viking Lander*	3·25	3·25
1983	$3 Global view of Mars taken from *Viking 1*	3·25	3·25

236 Christmas Tree, Charlestown, Nevis

2006. Christmas. Multicoloured.

1984	25c. Type **236**	50	25
1985	30c. Snowman and other decorations, Bath, Nevis	50	25
1986	90c. Three white reindeer and other decorations, Bath, Nevis	1·25	60
1987	$4 Decorated Christmas tree (vert)	4·50	5·50
MS1988	100×70 mm. $6 Children meeting Santa	6·00	6·50

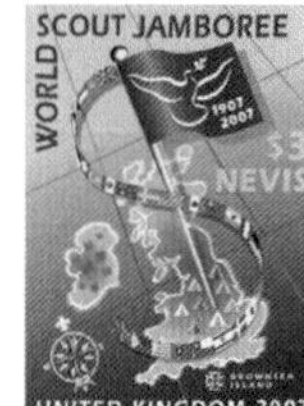

237 Map of United Kingdom and Centenary Flag

2007. Centenary of World Scout Movement and 21st World Scout Jamboree, Chelmsford, England. Multicoloured.

1989	$3 Type **237**	2·25	2·50
MS1990	80×111 mm. $5 Centenary flag and streamer of National Flags (horiz)	3·75	4·25

238 Marilyn Monroe

2007. 80th Birth Anniv (2006) of Marilyn Monroe (actress). Multicoloured.

1991	$2 Type **238**	1·40	1·50
1992	$2 Wearing necklace	1·40	1·50
1993	$2 Wearing pearl earrings	1·40	1·50
1994	$2 Wearing white dress	1·40	1·50

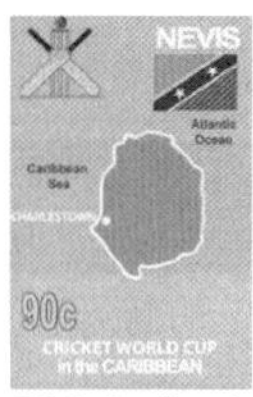

239 Outline Map of Nevis and Flag of St. Kitts and Nevis

2007. World Cup Cricket, West Indies. Multicoloured.

1995	90c. Type **239**	1·50	1·00
1996	$2 Runako Morton	3·00	3·25
MS1997	120×93 mm. $6 World Cup Cricket emblem	5·50	5·50

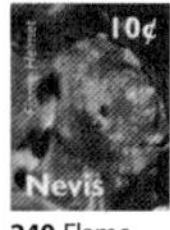

240 Flame Helmet

2007. Shells. Multicoloured.

1998	10c. Type **240**	15	40
1999	25c. Rooster tail conch	30	30
2000	30c. Three beaded periwinkles	30	30
2001	60c. Emperor helmet	55	45
2002	80c. Scotch bonnet	70	60
2003	90c. Milk conch	80	60
2004	$1 Beaded periwinkle	90	75
2005	$1.20 Alphabet cone	1·10	75
2006	$1.80 Measled cowrie	1·60	1·60
2007	$3 King helmet	2·75	2·75
2008	$5 Atlantic hairy triton	4·00	4·50
2009	$10 White lined mitre	7·50	8·50
2010	$20 Reticulated cowrie shell	15·00	17·00

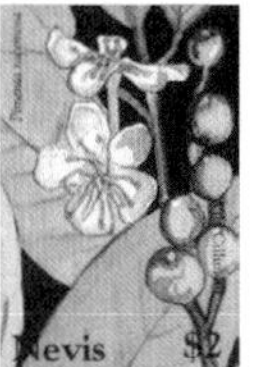

241 *Pimenta racemosa* (wild cilliment)

2007. Flowers of Nevis. Multicoloured.

MS2011	108×131 mm. $2×4 Type **241**; *Abrus precatorius* (jumbie beads); *Lantanacamara* (wild sage); *Asclepias curassavica* (blood flower/milky-milky)	5·50	6·00
MS2012	70×100 mm. $6 *Tabebuia heterophylla* (pink trumpet)	4·00	4·25

The stamps and margins of No. **MS**2011 form a composite background design.

242 *Battus zetides* (Zetides swallowtail)

2007. Butterflies of Nevis. Multicoloured.

MS2013	131×108 mm. $2×4 Type **242**; *Parides hahnell* (Hahnel's amazon swallowtail); *Dismorphia spio* (Haitian mimic); *Hesperocharis graphites* (Marbled white)	6·00	6·50
MS2014	100×70 mm. $6 *Papilio multicaudata* (Three-tailed tiger swallowtail)	4·50	4·75

The stamps and margins of No. **MS**2013 form a composite background design.

243 Rainbow Parrotfish

2007. Endangered Species. Rainbow Parrotfish (Scarus guacamaia). Multicoloured.

2015	$1.20 Type **243**	90	1·00
2016	$1.20 Pair	90	1·00
2017	$1.20 In close-up, facing to left	90	1·00
2018	$1.20 Facing to right	90	1·00
MS2019	115×168 mm. Nos. 2015/18, each×2	5·50	6·50

244 Elvis Presley

2007. 30th Death Anniv of Elvis Presley. Multicoloured.

2020	$1.20 Type **244**	90	90
2021	$1.20 Wearing white jumpsuit, playing guitar	90	90
2022	$1.20 As No. 2021, but seen three-quarter length, spotlight at top right	90	90
2023	$1.20 Wearing black leather jacket	90	90
2024	$1.20 As No. 2023, seen three-quarter length	90	90
2025	$1.20 As Type **244**, seen in close-up	90	90

245 Concorde 02 on Ground

2007. Concorde. Multicoloured.

2026	$1.20 Type **245**	1·40	1·40
2027	$1.20 Concorde 02 flying over snowy mountains (blue inscriptions)	1·40	1·40
2028	$1.20 As Type **245** (lemon inscriptions)	1·40	1·40
2029	$1.20 As No. 2027 (lemon inscriptions)	1·40	1·40
2030	$1.20 As Type **245** (blue inscriptions)	1·40	1·40
2031	$1.20 As No. 2027 (white inscriptions)	1·40	1·40
MS2032	150×100 mm. $1.20×6 Concorde F-BTSD: Flying to right, dark blue background (over upper left part of globe); Flying to left, azure background (over map 'MERICA'); Flying right, dark blue background (over upper right part of globe); Flying left, azure background (over equator line); Flying right, dark blue background (over map of islands); Flying left, azure background (equator line at lower right)	8·00	8·00

Nos. 2026/31 commemorate the Washington to Paris record flight of Concorde 02, the second pre-production aircraft, on September 26 1973.

The stamps and margins of No. **MS**2032 form a composite background design showing a globe. **MS**2032 commemorates the eastbound round the world record of Concorde F-BTSD on August 15–16 1995.

246 Diana, Princess of Wales

2007. Tenth Death Anniv of Diana, Princess of Wales. Multicoloured.

2033	$2 Type **246**	1·50	1·50
2034	$2 Wearing black evening dress and choker	1·50	1·50
2035	$2 Wearing pale jacket and pearl necklace	1·50	1·50
2036	$2 Wearing white dress with narrow shoulder straps	1·50	1·50
MS2037	70×100 mm. $6 Wearing blue and white jacket and hat	4·00	4·25

247 Pope Benedict XVI

2007. 80th Birthday of Pope Benedict XVI.

2038	**247**	$1 multicoloured	1·75	1·75

248 Queen Elizabeth II and Prince Philip

2007. Diamond Wedding of Queen Elizabeth II and Prince Philip. Multicoloured.

2039	$1.20 Type **248**	2·00	2·00
2040	$1.20 Queen Elizabeth and Prince Philip waving	2·00	2·00
2041	$1.20 In Garter robes	2·00	2·00
2042	$1.20 Waving from Coronation coach at Golden Jubilee	2·00	2·00
2043	$1.20 Waving from carriage at Ascot	2·00	2·00
2044	$1.20 Waving from balcony	2·00	2·00

249 *Begonias and Rock*

2007. 50th Death Anniv of Qi Baishi (artist). Designs showing paintings. Multicoloured.

2045	$3 Type **249**	2·00	2·25
2046	$3 *Mother and Child*	2·00	2·25
2047	$3 *Fish and Bait*	2·00	2·25
2048	$3 *Solitary Hero* (bird)	2·00	2·25
MS2049	100×70 mm. $6 *Chrysanthemums and Insects* (28×42 mm)	3·75	4·00

250 Westland Sea King Naval Helicopter

2007. Centenary of the First Helicopter Flight. Multicoloured.

MS2050	$3×4 Type **250**; Schweizer N330TT light utility helicopter; Sikorsky R-4/R-5 first production helicopter; PZL Swidnik W-3 Sokol	13·00	13·00
MS2051	100×70 mm. $6 MIL V-12 heavy transport helicopter	9·50	9·50

251 Jacqueline Kennedy

2007. 90th Birth Anniv of John F. Kennedy (US President 1960–3). Multicoloured.

2052	$3 Type **251**	2·25	2·25
2053	$3 John F. Kennedy (in library)	2·25	2·25
2054	$3 John F. Kennedy (clapping)	2·25	2·25
2055	$3 Vice President Lyndon B. Johnson	2·25	2·25

252 *The Rest on the Flight into Egypt* (Federico Barocci)

2007. Christmas. Paintings. Multicoloured.

2056	25c. Type **252**	40	30
2057	30c. *The Annunciation* (detail) (Federico Barocci)	40	30
2058	90c. *The Annunciation* (Cavalier d'Arpino)	1·10	70
2059	$4 *The Rest on the Flight into Egypt* (Francesco Mancini)	3·75	4·50
MS2060	100×70 mm. $5 *The Virgin and Child between Saints Peter and Paul and the Twelve Magistrates of the Rota* (Antoniazzo Romano)	4·00	4·25

253 F 355 F1 GTS, 1997

2007. 60th Anniv of Ferrari. Multicoloured.

2061	$1 Type **253**	80	80
2062	$1 412, 1985	80	80
2063	$1 158 F1, 1964	80	80
2064	$1 375 MM, 1953	80	80
2065	$1 330 P4, 1967	80	80
2066	$1 512 BB LM, 1978	80	80
2067	$1 312 B3-74, 1974	80	80
2068	$1 308 GTB Quattrovalvole, 1982	80	80

254 Yacht

2007. 32nd Americas Cup Yachting Championship, Valencia, Spain. Multicoloured.

2069	$1.20 Type **254**	1·50	1·75
2070	$1.80 White-hulled yacht	2·00	2·25
2071	$3 Yacht, 'T Systems' on sail	2·50	2·75
2072	$5 Yachts, sail with orange stripes in foreground	3·50	3·75

255 Cycling

2008. Olympic Games, Beijing. Multicoloured.

2073	$2 Type **255**	2·50	2·50
2074	$2 Kayaking	2·50	2·50
2075	$2 Yachting	2·50	2·50
2076	$2 Three-day eventing	2·50	2·50

256 Mt. Masada

2008. Israel 2008 World Stamp Championship, Tel-Aviv. Natural Sites and Scenes of Israel. Multicoloured.

2077	$1.50 Type **256**	2·25	2·25
2078	$1.50 Red Sea and desert mountains	2·25	2·25
2079	$1.50 Dead Sea	2·25	2·25
2080	$1.50 Sea of Galilee	2·25	2·25
MS2081	100×70 mm. $5 Mt. Hermon	7·00	7·00

257 Elvis Presley

2008. 40th Anniv of Elvis Presley's '68 Special'. Multicoloured.

2082	$1.80 Type **257**	1·40	1·50
2083	$1.80 Wearing black leather, facing forward	1·40	1·50
2084	$1.80 Standing, seen three-quarter length (red background)	1·40	1·50
2085	$1.80 Wearing black leather, facing left	1·40	1·50
2086	$1.80 Wearing blue shirt	1·40	1·50
2087	$1.80 Wearing black leather, facing right	1·40	1·50

258 Muhammad Ali and Opponent

2008. Muhammad Ali (world heavyweight boxing champion, 1964, 1974–8). Multicoloured.

2088	$1.80 Type **258**	1·40	1·50
2089	$1.80 In ring with fists raised, opponent at right	1·40	1·50
2090	$1.80 Punched by opponent	1·40	1·50
2091	$1.80 Seated by ring ropes	1·40	1·50
2092	$1.80 With arms raised in victory	1·40	1·50
2093	$1.80 Muhammad Ali and trophy	1·40	1·50
2094	$2 In profile, speaking (37×50 mm)	1·50	1·75
2095	$2 Seen full face, speaking (37×50 mm)	1·50	1·75
2096	$2 Looking towards left (37×50 mm)	1·50	1·75
2097	$2 Eyes looking to right, speaking (37×50 mm)	1·50	1·75

259 Pope Benedict XVI

2008. First Visit of Pope Benedict XVI to the United States. Sheet 178×127 mm containing T 259 and similar vert designs.

MS2098	multicoloured	7·25	7·25

The four stamps within **MS**2103 are as Type **259** but have slightly different backgrounds at the foot of the stamps, the middle two showing parts of the UN emblem.

260 Geothermal Well, Spring Hill, discovered June 2008

2008. 25th Anniv of Independence.

2099	**260**	$5 multicoloured	4·50	5·00

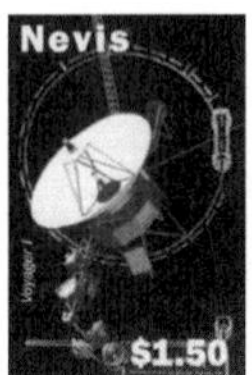

261 *Voyager I*

2008. 50 Years of Space Exploration and Satellites. Multicoloured.

2100	$1.50 Type **261**	1·75	1·75
2101	$1.50 *Voyager I*, Io, and part of Ganymede and Callisto	1·75	1·75
2102	$1.50 *Voyager I*, Europa and part of Ganymede and Callisto	1·75	1·75
2103	$1.50 *Voyager I*	1·75	1·75
2104	$1.50 *Voyager I*, Dione and part of Titan	1·75	1·75
2105	$1.50 *Voyager I*, Enceladus and part of Titan	1·75	1·75
2106	$1.50 *Galileo* spacecraft	1·75	1·75
2107	$1.50 *Galileo* (without sun shields)	1·75	1·75
2108	$1.50 *Galileo* Probe	1·75	1·75
2109	$1.50 Technical drawing of *Galileo* Probe	1·75	1·75
2110	$1.50 *Galileo* passing Io	1·75	1·75
2111	$1.50 Technical drawing of *Galileo*	1·75	1·75
2112	$2 Van Allen radiation belt	2·25	2·25
2113	$2 Technical drawing of *Explorer I*	2·25	2·25
2114	$2 James Van Allen	2·25	2·25
2115	$2 *Explorer I* above Earth	2·25	2·25
2116	$2 Technical drawing of *Apollo 11* Command Module	2·25	2·25
2117	$2 Saturn V Apollo Programme Launcher	2·25	2·25
2118	$2 Edwin 'Buzz' Aldrin Jr. walking on Moon, 1969	2·25	2·25
2119	$2 Technical drawing of *Apollo 11* Lunar Module	2·25	2·25

262 Roast Pork

2008. Christmas. Multicoloured.

2120	25c. Type **262**	30	20
2121	30c. Fruit-topped sponge cake	30	20
2122	80c. Pumpkin pie	90	60
2123	90c. Sorrel drink	1·00	60
2124	$2 Fruit cake	2·25	3·00
MS2125	100×70 mm. $6 Baked ham and turkey (vert)	5·50	6·00

263 Pres. Barack Obama

2009. Inauguration of President Barack Obama. Sheet 180×100 mm containing T **263** and similar horiz designs showing Pres. Obama. Multicoloured.

MS2126	$3×4 Type **263**; US flag in background; White House garden in background; Black background	5·50	6·00

264 Processed Agricultural Products

2009. 15th Anniv of Agriculture Open Day. Multicoloured.

2127	25c. Type **264**	25	20
2128	30c. Fruits	30	20
2129	90c. Goats	80	60
2130	$5 Plant propagation	4·50	5·00
MS2131	100×70 mm. $6 Entertainment	5·00	5·50

265 Kangxi, Second Emperor of the Qing Dynasty (image scaled to 33% of original size)

2009. China 2009 World Stamp Exhibition, Luoyang (1st issue). Kangxi, Second Emperor of the Qing Dynasty (1654–1722). Multicoloured. .

MS2132	146×100 mm. $1.40×4 Type **265**; Wearing gold with blue armlets; Wearing gold with gold armlets; At desk writing	5·25	5·75

266 Shooting (image scaled to 35% of original size)

2009. China 2009 World Stamp Exhibition, Luoyang (2nd issue). Sports of the Summer Games.. Multicoloured.

MS2133	137×98 mm. $1.40×4 Type **266**; Field hockey; Taekwondo; Softball	5·25	5·75

267 Marine Iguana (*Amblyrhynchus cristatus*)

2009. Birth Bicentenary of Charles Darwin (naturalist and evolutionary theorist). Multicoloured.

MS2134	Type **267**; Statue of Charles Darwin, Shrewsbury, England; Platypus (*Ornithorhynchus anatinus*); Vampire bat (*Desmodus rotundus* incorrectly inscr '*Desmodus d'Orbignyi*'); Portrait of Charles Darwin in late 1830s by George Richmond; Large ground-finch (*Geospiza magnirostris*)	11·00	11·00
MS2135	100×70 mm. $6 Charles Darwin (photograph), 1881 (37×50 mm)	6·00	6·00

268 Amazon River Dolphin (*Inia geoffrensis*)

2009. Dolphins and Whales. Multicoloured.

MS2136	140×116 mm. $2×6 Type **268**; Indus river dolphin (*Platanista minor*); Atlantic white-sided dolphin (*Lagenorhynchus acutus*); La Plata dolphin; Peale's dolphin (*Lagenorhynchus australis*); White-beaked dolphin (*Lagenorhynchus albirostris*)	10·00	11·00
MS2137	100×70 mm. $3×3 Killer whale (*Orcinus orca*); Pygmy killer whale (*Feresa attenuata*)	6·00	6·00
MS2138	100×70 mm. $3×2 Long-finned pilot whale (*Globicephala melas*); Short-finned pilot whale (*Globicephalamacrorhynchus*)	6·00	6·00

269 Film Poster for *Clambake*

2009. Elvis Presley in Film Clambake

MS2139	125×90 mm. $6 Type **269**	4·50	4·50
MS2140	90×125 mm. $6 Wearing black stetson and white jacket	4·50	4·50
MS2141	90×125 mm. $6 On motorcycle	4·50	4·50
MS2142	125×90 mm. $6 Wearing white jacket	4·50	4·50

270 Michael Jackson

2009. Michael Jackson Commemoration. Two sheets, each 178×127 mm, containing T **270** and similar multicoloured designs.

MS2143	Wearing black: Type **270** (pale blue inscr); Three-quarter length (yellow inscr); Type **270** (lavender inscr); Three-quarter length (red inscr)	5·75	5·75
MS2144	Wearing white: With both hands raised to face; In profile; With microphone; With both arms raised	6·50	6·50

On No. **MS**2143 the colours givan are for the country inscription 'NEVIS'.

271 Lincoln Memorial

2009. Birth Bicentenary of Abraham Lincoln (US President 1861–5). Sheet 175×136 mm containing T **271** and similar vert designs. Multicoloured.

MS2145	Type **271**; Statue of Abraham Lincoln; Head and upper body of statue; Lincoln Memorial from air	6·25	6·25

272 Moe, Curly and Larry

2009. The Three Stooges. Sheet 130×150 mm containing T **272** and similar vert designs. Multicoloured.

MS2146	Type **272**; Curly; Moe; Larry	6·25	6·25

273 Pope Benedict XVI wearing Mitre

2009. Visit of Pope Benedict XVI to Israel. Sheet 100×150 mm containing T **273** and similar horiz designs. Multicoloured.

MS2147	Type **273**; As Type **273** (gold frame); Pope Benedict XVI wearing skull cap (brown frame); Pope wearing skull cap (gold frame)	9·00	9·00

274 *Genipa americana*

2009. Flowers of the Caribbean. Multicoloured.

2148	25c. Type **274**	40	25
2149	30c. *Clusia rosea*	40	25
2150	80c. *Browallia americana*	1·00	70
2151	90c. *Bidens alba*	1·10	75
2152	$1 *Begonia odorata*	1·25	1·25
2153	$5 *Jatropha gossypiifolia*	5·00	6·00
MS2154	150×100 mm. $2.50×4 *Crantzia cristata*; *Selaginella flabellata*; *Hibiscus tiliaceus*; *Heliconia psittacorum*	9·00	9·00

275 Caribbean Reef Squid

2009. Endangered Species. Caribbean Reef Squid (*Sepioteuthis sepioidea*). Multicoloured.

2155	$2 Type **275**	1·75	1·75
2156	$2 One squid	1·75	1·75
2157	$2 One squid (body bent showing head and tail)	1·75	1·75
2158	$2 Two squid (foreground squid swimming to left)	1·75	1·75
MS2159	112×165 mm. Nos. 2155/8, each×2	11·00	11·00

276 Journey of the Magi

2009. Christmas. Multicoloured.

2160	25c. Type **276**	35	25
2161	30c. Nativity with magi on star	35	25
2162	90c. Magi and camel in stars	1·10	80
2163	$5 Nativity with angels	5·00	6·00

277 Neil Armstrong and Saturn 5 Rocket

2009. 40th Anniv of First Manned Moon Landing. International Year of Astronomy. T **277** and similar horiz designs. Multicoloured.

MS2164	150×100 mm. $2.50×4 Type **277**; Lunar Module, Buzz Aldrin and Michael Collins; Command Module in Moon orbit; Lunar Module leaving the Moon	8·50	8·50
MS2165	100×70 mm. $6 Neil Armstrong and Lunar Module taking off	6·50	6·50

278 Engine of DINO 156 F2, 1957

2010. Ferrari Cars. Multicoloured.

2166	$1.25 Type **278**	1·25	1·25
2167	$1.25 DINO 156 F2, 1957 (car no. 122)	1·25	1·25
2168	$1.25 Diagram of engine and chassis of 125 S, 1947	1·25	1·25
2169	$1.25 125 S, 1947 (car no. 56)	1·25	1·25
2170	$1.25 Exhaust pipes of 553 F2, 1953	1·25	1·25
2171	$1.25 553 F2, 1953	1·25	1·25
2172	$1.25 Engine of 500 F2, 1951	1·25	1·25
2173	$1.25 500 F2, 1951 (car no. 15)	1·25	1·25

279 Elvis Presley

2010. 75th Birth Anniv of Elvis Presley. Multicoloured.

MS2174	$2.50x4 Type **279**; Wearing brown jacket and tie; Wearing cream jacket; Wearing pale grey shirt	6·50	6·50

280 *Psilocybe guilartensis*

2010. Fungi. Multicoloured.

2175	25c. Type **280**	40	20
2176	80c. *Alboleptonia flavifolia*	1·10	75
2177	$1 *Agaricus* sp.	1·25	1·50

2178	$5 *Psilocybe caerulescens*	1·25	1·50
MS2179	125×158 mm. $1.50×6 *Psilocybe portoricensis*; *Boletus ruborculus*; *Psilocybe plutonia* (one mushroom); *Alboleptonia largentii*; *Psilocybe plutonia* (three mushrooms); *Collybia aurea*	7·00	7·00

The stamps and margins of **MS**2179 form a composite background design.

MS2179 is inscr 'MUSHROOMS' on the sheet margin.

281 Great Blue Heron (*Ardea herodias*)

2010. Birds of Nevis. Multicoloured.

2180	30c. Type **281**	65	30
2181	90c. Magnificent frigatebird (*Fregata magnificens*)	1·50	1·00
2182	$1 Masked booby (*Sula dactylatra*)	1·75	1·25
2183	$5 Great egret (*Ardea alba*)	5·50	6·50
MS2184	150×110 mm. $2×4 White-tailed tropicbird (*Phaethon lepturus*); Audubon's shearwater (*Puffinus lherminieri*); Red-billed tropicbird (*Phaethon aethereus*); Leach's storm-petrel (*Oceanodroma leucorhoa*) (all vert)	9·00	9·00
MS2185	120×80 mm. $3 Brown pelican (*Pelecanus occidentalis*); $3 Brown booby (*Sula leucogaster*)	9·00	9·00

The stamps and margins of **MS**2184 form a composite background design of grassland.

The stamps and margins of **MS**2185 form a composite background design of trees at sunset.

282 John F. Kennedy

2010. 50th Anniv of Election of Pres. John F. Kennedy (1st issue). Multicoloured.

MS2186	$3×4 Type **282**; Nikita Khrushchev; Nikita Khrushchev seated; Pres. Kennedy seated	6·50	6·50
MS2187	$3×4 Richard NIxon (Republican Candidate); John F. Kennedy (Democratic Candidate); John F. Kennedy (Democratic Candidate) (black/white photo); Richard Nixon (Republican Candidate) (black/white photo)	6·50	6·50

The two lower stamps within **MS**2187 form a composite design.

See also No. **MS**2196.

283 Four Brownies and Leader

2010. Centenary of Girlguiding. Mutlicoloured.

MS2188	150×100 mm. $3×4 Type **283**; Four guides; Guide abseiling; Three guides	7·00	7·00
MS2189	70×100 mm. $6 Four guides (vert)	5·00	5·00

284 Minke Whale (*Balaenoptera acutorostrata*)

2010. Sea Mammals of the Caribbean. Multicoloured.

2190	$1.20 Type **284**	2·00	1·25
2191	$1.80 Northern right whale (*Eubalaena glacialis*)	2·50	1·75
2192	$3 Fin whale (*Balaenoptera physalus*)	4·50	5·00
2193	$5 Sei whale (*Balaenoptera borealis*)	4·50	5·00
MS2194	101×70 mm. $3 Caribbean monk seal (*Monachus tropicalis*); $3 West Indian manatee (*Trichechus manatus*)	7·00	7·00
MS2195	99×70 mm. $6 Blue whale (*Balaenoptera musculus*)	7·00	7·00

285 'VOTE KENNEDY FOR PRESIDENT' Badge

2010. 50th Anniv of Election of Pres. John F. Kennedy (2nd issue). Campaign Badges. Sheet 182×122 mm. Multicoloured.

MS2196	$2×4 Type **285**; Portrait and 'FOR PRESIDENT JOHN F. KENNEDY'; 'KENNEDY JOHNSON'; Portraits and 'AMERICA NEEDS KENNEDY JOHNSON'	7·00	7·00

286 Heart-lipped Brassavola (*Brassavola venosa*)

2010. Orchids of the Caribbean. Multicoloured.

MS2197	150×100 mm. $2×6 Type **286**; Waunakee Sunset (*Phragmepidium* Jason Fisher); Moss-loving Cranichis (*Cranichis muscosa*); Longclaw orchid (*Eltroplectris calcarata*); Golden yellow cattleya (*Cattleya aurea*); Fat cat (*Zygoneria* Adelaide Meadows)	11·00	11·00
MS2198	100×70 mm. $6 Von Martin's Brassavola (*Brassavola martiana*) (vert)	7·00	7·00

287 Bertha Von Suttner and Henri Dunant

2010. Death Centenary of Henri Dunant (founder of Red Cross). Multicoloured.

MS2199	151×100 mm. Type **287**; Victor Hugo; Charles Dickens; Harriet Beecher Stowe	9·00	9·00
MS2200	71×101 mm. $6 Abolition of slavery, Washington DC, 1862	6·00	6·00

288 *Annunciation* (Paolo Uccello), *c.* 1420

2010. Christmas. Multicoloured.

2201	30c. Type **288**	40	20
2202	90c. *The Altarpiece of the Rose Garlands* (Albrecht Dürer)	1·10	50
2203	$1.80 As 30c.	2·00	1·75
2204	$2 *Sistine Madonna* (Raffaello Sanzlo da Urbino), *c.* 1513	2·25	2·00
2205	$2.30 As $2	2·25	2·50
2206	$3 *The Adoration of the Magi* (Giotto di Bondone), *c.* 1305	3·00	4·00

289 Princess Diana

2010. Princess Diana Commemoration. Multicoloured.

MS2207	130×150 mm. $2×6 Type **289**×2; Wearing white jacket and tiara; Wearing white hat and jacket×2	9·50	9·50
MS2208	140×100 mm. $3 Wearing white sleeveless dress×4	3·00	3·00

290 Bank of Nevis Building, Charlestown

2010. 25th Anniv of the Bank of Nevis. Multicoloured.

2209	30c. Type **290**	40	20
2210	$5 Projected new Bank of Nevis building	4·50	5·50

291 Marek Hamsik (Slovakia)

2010. World Cup Football Championship, South Africa. Multicoloured.

MS2211	131×155 mm. $1.50×6 Netherlands vs. Slovakia: Type **291**; Giovanni Van Bronckhorst (Netherlands); Robert Vittek (Slovakia); Eljero Elia (Netherlands); Miroslav Stoch (Slovakia); Dirk Kuyt (Netherlands)	6·50	6·50
MS2212	130×155 mm. $1.50×6 Brazil vs. Chile: Lucio (Brazil); Alexis Sanchez (Chile); Dani Alves (Brazil); Arturo Vidal (Chile); Gilberto Silva (Brazil); Rodrigo Tello (Chile)	6·50	6·50
MS2213	130×155 mm. $1.50×6 Paraguay vs. Japan: Paulo Da Silva (Paraguay); Yoshito Okubo (Japan); Edgar Barreto (Paraguay); Yuichi Komano (Japan); Cristian Riveros (Paraguay); Yasuhito Endo (Japan)	6·50	6·50
MS2214	130×155 mm. $1.50×6 Spain vs. Portugal: Liedson (Portugal); Xavi Hernandez (Spain); Simao (Portugal); Jasper Juinen (Spain); Cristiano Ronaldo (Portugal); David Villa (Spain)	6·50	6·50
MS2215	85×90 mm. $1.50 Bert van Marwijk (Netherlands); $1.50 Joris Mathijsen	3·00	3·00
MS2216	85×90 mm. $1.50 Dunga (coach, Brazil); Kaka (Brazil)	3·00	3·00
MS2217	85×90 mm. $1.50 Gerardo Martino (coach, Paraguay); $1.50 Roque Santa Cruz	3·00	3·00
MS2218	85×90 mm. $1.50 Vicente del Bosque (coach, Spain); Sergio Ramos (Spain)	3·00	3·00

292 Abraham Lincoln

2011. Birth Bicentenary (2009) of Abraham Lincoln (US President, 18615). Multicoloured.

MS2219	100×150 mm. $2 Type **292**×4	6·00	6·00
MS2220	110×150 mm. $2×4 Abraham Lincoln portraits: With sepia background; With grey background; Oval portrait with white background but facing forwards; Black background	6·00	6·00

293 Elvis Presley

2011. Elvis Presley Commemoration. Multicoloured.

MS2221	100×168 mm. $3 Type **293**×4	2·50	2·50
MS2222	167×100 mm. $3 Elvis Presley (wearing black jacket)×4	2·50	2·50

294 Buckingham Palace (image scaled to 57% of original size)

2010. Royal Engagement. Multicoloured.

MS2223	130×140 mm. $3×4 Type **294**; Miss Catherine Middleton (black/white photo); Coat of Arms of Prince William of Wales (circular 38 mm diameter); Prince William (black/white photo)	10·00	10·00
MS2224	130×140 mm. $3×4 Prince William and Miss Catherine Middleton; Miss Catherine Middleton (wearing red jacket and black hat); Coat of Arms of Prince William of Wales (circular 38 mm diameter); Prince William (colour photo)	10·00	10·00
MS2225	70×120 mm. $6 Prince William and Miss Catherine Middleton (40×30 mm)	6·00	6·00

Nos. **MS**2223/4 each contain a central circular stamp surrounded by three semi-circular stamps as T **294**.

295 Pres. Barack Obama and Mrs. Michelle Obama

2011. Visit of President Barack Obama to India. Multicoloured.

MS2226	157×100 mm. $3×4 Type **295**; Pres. Obama addressing Inidan students in Mumbai; Pres. Obama signing condolence book for Mumbai terror attack; Pres. Obama with Indian Prime Minister Singh	9·00	10·50
MS2227	70×100 mm. $6 Pres. Obama addressing Indian students in Mumbai (horiz)	4·75	5·00

296 Pope John Paul II

2011. Fifth Death Anniv of Pope John Paul II. Multicoloured.

MS2228	110×170 mm. $3 Type **296**×4	10·00	10·00
MS2229	110×170 mm. $4 Pope John Paul II wearing red brimmed hat×3	4·50	4·50

297 Mahatma Gandhi

2011. Indipex 2011 International Stamp Exhibition, Delhi. Mahatma Gandhi. Multicoloured.

MS2230	$3 Type **297**×4	12·00	12·00
MS2231	$3 Mahatma Gandhi (facing left)×4	12·00	12·00

298 Elvis Presley

2011. Elvis Presley Commemoration. Multicoloured.

MS2232	$3×4 Type **298**; Elvis Presley wearing cap; Head tilted to left; In profile	10·00	10·00
MS2233	$3×4 Elvis Presley smiling, wearing dark jacket; Singing, wearing white jacket and bow tie; Singing, wearing dark shirt; Smiling, wearing white (all vert)	10·00	10·00

299 Pope Benedict XVI

2011. Pope Benedict XVI. Multicoloured.

MS2234	109×173 mm. $3×4 As Type **299** but with different backgrounds showing interior of Basilica: Type **299** (windows in dome); Top of pillar at bottom left; Pillars; Statue with cross at foot	12·00	12·00
MS2235	180×140 mm. $3 Pope Benedict XVI (in profile) (vert)×4	12·00	12·00

300 Elvis Presley as Guy Lambert in *Double Trouble*, 1967

2011. Elvis Presley in *Double Trouble*. Multicoloured.

MS2236	90×125 mm. $6 Type **300**	5·00	5·00
MS2237	125×90 mm. $6 Poster for *Double Trouble*	5·00	5·00
MS2238	90×125 mm. $6 Elvis Presley (wearing grey jacket and bow tie) (horiz)	5·00	5·00
MS2239	125×90 mm. $6 Elvis Presley playing guitar	5·00	5·00

301 Queen Elizabeth II

2011. 85th Birthday of Queen Elizabeth II and 90th Birthday of Prince Philip. Multicoloured.

MS2240	$2 Type **301**×2 $2 Queen Elizabeth II (wearing mauve)×2	7·00	7·00
MS2241	$2 Prince Philip×4	7·00	7·00

302 Meadow Argus (*Junonia villida*)

2011. Butterflies of the World. Multicoloured.

MS2242	104×150 mm. $2×6 Type **302**; Gulf fritillary (*Agraulis vanillae*); Eastern tiger swallowtail (*Papilio glaucus*); Gabb's checkerspot (*Chlosyne gabbii*); Indian leafwing (*Kallima paralekta*); Blue diadem (*Hypolimnas salmacis*)	12·00	12·00
MS2243	70×100 mm. $6 Monarch (*Danaus plexippus*)	7·00	7·00

303 Maine Coon

2011. Cats of the World. Multicoloured.

MS2244	$2.50×4 Type **303**; Norwegian forest cat; Ragdoll; Turkish angora	10·00	10·00
MS2245	$2.50×4 Russian blue; Siamese; Abyssinian; Bombay	10·00	10·00

304 King George V

2011. Centenary of the Coronation of King George V. Sheet 150×101 mm. Multicoloured.

MS2246	$3 Type **304**×4	11·00	11·00

305 King George VI

2011. 75th Anniv of the Accession of King George VI. Sheet 150×100 mm. Multicoloured.

MS2247	$3 Type **305**×4	11·00	11·00

306 Shoaib Akhtar (Pakistan)

2011. Cricket World Cup, India, Sri Lanka and Bangladesh. Multicoloured.

MS2248	$3×4 Type **306**; Shoaib Akhtar (head and shoulders); Pakistan team; Emblem (all with yellow-olive background)	12·00	12·00
MS2249	$3×4 A. B. De Villiers batting; A. B. De Villiers; South Africa team; Emblem (all with orange-yellow backgrounds)	12·00	12·00
MS2250	$3×4 A. B. De Villiers batting; A. B. De Villiers; South Africa team celebrating; Emblem (all with pale orange background)	12·00	12·00
MS2251	$3×4 Chris Gayle on pitch; Chris Gayle; West Indies team; Emblem (all with brown-red background)	12·00	12·00
MS2252	$3×4 Kumar Sangakkara on pitch; Kumar Sangakkara; Sri Lanka team; Emblem (all with reddish-orange background)	12·00	12·00

307 Miss Catherine Middleton on Wedding Day

2011. Royal Wedding. Multicoloured.

MS2253	100×150 mm. $3 Type **307**×2; $3 Prince William (in profile)×2	10·00	10·00
MS2254	100×150 mm. $3 Duke and Duchess of Cambridge in carriage×2; $3 Duchess of Cambridge; $3 Prince William	10·00	10·00
MS2255	100×90 mm. $6 Duke and Duchess of Cambridge; $6 Duke and Duchess of Cambridge riding in carriage	10·00	10·00

308 Princess Diana

2011. 50th Birth Anniv of Princess Diana. Multicoloured.

MS2256	150×130 mm. $2×4 Type **308**; Wearing cap; Waving, in profile; Wearing dark purple and maroon hat	6·50	6·50
MS2257	160×125 mm. $2×4 Princess Diana wearing bright mauve jacket; Wearing black and white hat and jacket; Wearing navy blue jacket and white top; Wearing red dress	6·50	6·50

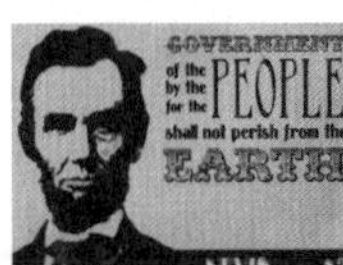

309 Pres. Abraham Lincoln and 'Government of the People by the People for the People shall not perish from the Earth'

2011. 150th Anniv of the American Civil War. Multicoloured.

MS2258	$2×4 all showing Pres. Abraham Lincoln and quotation: Type **309**; 'The best way to destroy an enemy is to make him a friend'; 'A house divided against itself cannot stand'; 'Avoid popularity if you would have peace'	8·00	8·00
MS2259	$2×4 Union Army soldier; Shield and Constitution ('The American Civil War'); Union Army soldiers in trenches; Pres. Abraham Lincoln	8·00	8·00

310 Blue Stripe Grunt (*Haemulon sciurus*)

2011. Tropical Fish of the Caribbean. Multicoloured.

2260	10c. Type **310**	20	30
2261	30c. Red hind (*Cephalopholis miniatus*)	45	30
2262	40c. Red snapper (*Lutjanus campechanus*)	55	30
2263	$5 Old wife (*Enoplosus armatus*)	5·00	6·00
MS2264	102×123 mm. $2×6 Spotfin butterflyfish (*Chaetodon ocellatus*); Caribbean reef squid (*Sepioteuthis sepioidea*); Chubs (*Kyphosus bigibbus*); Surgeonfish (*Acanthuroidei olivaceus*); Blue-headed wrasse (*Thalassoma bifasciatum*); Long-spine porcupinefish (*Diodon holocanthus*) (all horiz)	10·00	10·00
MS2265	100×71 mm. $6 Anemone fish (*Amphiprioninae*) (horiz)	6·00	6·00

311 *Scaphella junonia*

2011. Seashells of the Caribbean. Multicoloured.

2266	20c. Type **311**	30	20
2267	30c. *Strombus gigas*	45	20
2268	$1.80 *Busycon contrarium*	1·75	1·75
2269	$5 *Arca zebra*	4·75	5·50
MS2270	150×101 mm. $2.50×4 *Charonia variegata*; *Cypraea aurantium*; *Cyphoma gibbosa*; *Chicoreus articulatus*	9·00	9·00
MS2271	100×71 mm. $6 *Thais deltoidea*	6·00	6·00
MS2272	100×71 mm. $6 *Cittarium pica*	6·00	6·00

312 Pres. John F. Kennedy

2011. 50th Anniv of the Inauguration of Pres. John F. Kennedy. Multicoloured.

MS2273	120×180 mm. $3×4 Type **312**; Pres. Kennedy in front of microphones; Facing microphones, in profile; Shaking hands	10·00	10·00
MS2274	90×100 mm. $6 Pres. Kennedy	5·50	5·50

313 Memorial, Staten Island, New York

2011. Tenth Anniv of Attack on World Trade Center, New York. Black and turquoise-green.

MS2275	161×100 mm. $2.75×4 Type **313**; Memorial, Bayonne, New Jersey; Memorial, The Pentagon; Memorial, Jerusalem	8·50	8·50
MS2276	100×100 mm. $6 Ground Zero Reflecting Pools	5·50	5·50

314 First Italian League, 1910

2011. Juventus Football Club, Turin, Italy. Multicoloured.

MS2277	$1.50×9 Type **314**; Giorgio Muggiani; Angelo Moratti; Helenio Herrera; Tim Cup, 2011; Giacinto Facchetti; Sandro Mazzola; Mario Corso; Luis Suarez	9·75	9·75

315 Alaskan Malamute

2011. Dogs of the World. Multicoloured.

MS2278	140×100 mm. $2.75×4 Type **315**; Yorkshire terrier; Black labrador; Dachshund	9·50	9·50
MS2279	100×70 mm. $6 Beagle	6·50	6·50

316 *Annunciation*

2011. Christmas. Paintings by Melchior Broederlam. Multicoloured.

2280	25c. Type **316**	30	20
2281	30c. *Visitation*	35	20
2282	90c. *Presentation in the Temple*	1·10	50
2283	$5 *Flight into Egypt*	4·25	4·75

317 Anegada Ground Iguana (*Cyclura pinguis*)

2011. Reptiles of the Caribbean. Multicoloured.

MS2284	150×100 mm. $3×4 Type **317**; Antilles racer (snake) (*Alsophis antillensis*); Brown anole (*Anolis sagrei*); Lesser Antillean iguana (*Iguana delicatissima*)	9·00	9·00
MS2285	70×101 mm. $6 Anegada ground iguana (*Cyclura pinguis*) (51×38 mm)	6·50	6·50

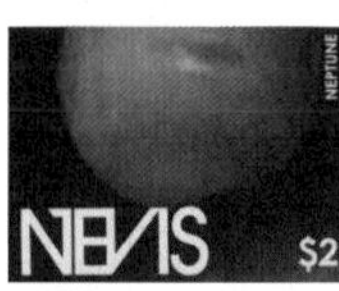

318 Neptune

2011. 50th Anniv of the First Man in Space. Multicoloured.

MS2286	210×140 mm. $2×6 Type **318**; Uranus; Earth and Mars; Venus and Mercury; Jupiter; Saturn	11·00	11·00
MS2287	220×80 mm. $3×4 Full moon; Waxing gibbous moon; First quarter; Waxing crescent moon (all circular 35 mm diameter)	11·00	11·00

319 Queen Elizabeth II

2012. Diamond Jubilee. Multicoloured.

MS2288	113×113 mm. $3×4 Type **319**; Queen Elizabeth II wearing cream; Wearing light blue; Wearing pale turquoise-blue	8·50	8·50
MS2289	75×75 mm. $10 Queen Elizabeth II wearing tiara, *c.* 1952	7·00	7·00

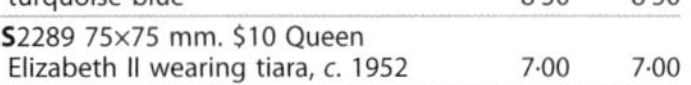

320 Caribbean Whiptail (*Himantura schmardae*)

2012. Stingrays of the Caribbean. Multicoloured.

MS2290 51×180 mm. $3×5 Type **320**; Lesser Electric Ray (*Narcine brasiliensis*); Giant Manta Ray (*Manta birostris*); Southern Stingray (*Dasyatis americana*); Spotted Eagle Ray (*Aetobatus narinari*) 10·50 10·50

321 Charles Dickens

2012. Birth Bicentenary of Charles Dickens (1812-70, writer). Multicoloured.

MS2291 159×70 mm. $3.50 Type **321**×4 9·75 9·75

MS2292 100×70 mm. $4.50 Novels by Charles Dickens; $4.50 Charles Dickens seated in chair, in profile 6·25 6·25

344 Indigo Macaw (*Anodorhynchus leari*)

2014. Macaws. Multicoloured.

MS2365 100×150 mm. $3.25×4 Type **344**; Hyacinth Macaw (*Anodorhynchus hyacinthinus*); Blue-headed Macaw (*Primolius couloni*); Great Green Macaw (*Ara ambiguus*) 9·25 9·25

MS2366 100×150 mm. $3.25×4 Blue-and-yellow Macaw (*Ara ararauna*); Red-shouldered Macaw (*Diopsittaca nobilis*); Red-fronted Macaw (*Ara rubrogenys*); Green-winged Macaw (*Ara chloropterus*) 9·25 9·25

MS2367 100×150 mm. $5 Blue-and-yellow Macaw (*Ara ararauna*); $5 Blue-throated Macaw (*Ara glaucogularis*) 7·25 7·25

MS2368 100×150 mm. $5 Scarlet Macaw (*Ara macao*); $5 Golden-collared Macaw (*Primolius auricollis*) 7·25 7·25

322 *Adoration of the Shepherds*

2012. Christmas. Paintings by Caravaggio. Multicoloured.

2293	25c. Type **322**	20	20
2294	30c. *Annunciation*	20	20
2295	90c. *Holy Family with St. John the Baptist*	65	65
2296	$1 *Nativity with St. Francis and St. Lawrence*	70	70
2297	$3 *Rest on the Flight into Egypt*	2·10	2·10
2298	$5 *Madonna of the Rosary*	3·50	3·50

323 *Hamadryas amphinome*

2012. Butterflies of the Caribbean. Multicoloured.

MS2299 120×140 mm. $2.50×6 Type **323**; *Lycorea halia atergatis*; *Marpesia eleuchea bahamensis*; *Pyrisitia proterpia* (with dark veins on wings); *Pyrisitia proterpia*; *Pyrrhocalles antiqua* 10·50 10·50

324 Coronation of Queen Elizabeth II

2013. 60th Anniv of the Coronation. Multicoloured.

MS2300 100×151 mm. $3.25×4 Type **324**; Queen Elizabeth II wearing blue; Wearing grey and orange; Wearing tiara, *c.* 1952 9·00 9·00

MS2301 71×90 mm. $9 Queen Elizabeth II at Coronation, waving 6·25 6·25

325 Antillean Mango (*Anthracothorax dominicus*)

2013. Hummingbirds of the Caribbean. Multicoloured.

MS2302 100×100 mm. $3.25×4 Type **325**; Ruby-throated Hummingbird (*Archilochus colubris*); Purple-throated Carib (*Eulampis jugularis*); Long-billed Starthroat (*Heliomaster longirostris*) 9·00 9·00

MS2303 100×80 mm. $4.50 Green-throated Carib (*Eulampis holosericeus*); $4.50 Tufted Coquette (*Lophornis ornatus*) 6·25 6·25

326 *Bicyrtes quadrifasciatus*

2013. Bees of the Caribbean. Multicoloured.

MS2304 150×100 mm. $4×4 Type **326**; *Bembix americana*; *Ammophila apicalis*; *Ectemnius continuus* 11·00 11·00

MS2305 100×70 mm. $8 *Bicyrtes quadrifasciatus* (facing left) 5·50 5·50

327 Imperial Amazon (*Amazona imperialis*)

2013. Parrots of the Caribbean. Multicoloured.

MS2306 150×81 mm. $3.25×4 Type **327**; Cuban Amazon (*Amazona leucocephala*); Hispaniolan Parrot (*Amazona ventralis*); St. Vincent Parrot (*Amazona guildingii*) 9·00 9·00

MS2307 80×80 mm. $9 St. Lucia Amazon (*Amazona versicolor*) (38×51 mm) 6·25 6·25

328 Lemon

2013. Fruits. Multicoloured.

MS2308 151×101 mm. $3.25×4 Type **328**; Persimmon; Yellow plum; Orange 9·00 9·00

MS2309 101×100 mm. $9 Peach (38×51 mm) 6·25 6·25

329 Pineapple (*Ananas comosus*)

2013. Thailand 2013 World Stamp Exhibition, Bangkok. Flora of Thailand. Multicoloured.

MS2310 130×100 mm. $2.50×6 Type **329**; Papaya (*Carica papaya*); Red Pineapple (*Ananas V*); Plumeria (*Plumeria rubra*); Magnolia (*Magnoliaceae X*); Camellia (*Camellia reticulata*) 7·25 7·25

MS2311 70×100 mm. $9 Bromeliad (*Guzmannia erythrolepsis*) (36×48 mm) 6·50 6·50

330 Duke and Duchess of Cambridge with Prince George

2013. Birth of Prince George. Multicoloured.

MS2312 100×151 mm. $3.25×4 Type **330**; Prince George; Duchess of Cambridge holding Prince George; Duke of Cambridge holding Prince George 9·00 9·00

MS2313 70×100 mm. $4.75 Duke and Duchess of Cambridge with Prince George; $4.75 Prince George 6·75 6·75

331 Citrus Root Weevil (*Diaprepes abbreviatus*)

2013. Caribbean Insects. Multicoloured.

MS2314 151×80 mm. $3.50×4 Type **331**; West Indian Firetail (*Telebasis dominicana*); Catarina (*Macrohaltica jamaicensis*); Field Cricket (*Gryllus bryanti*) 9·75 9·75

MS2315 $9 Biting Black Fly (*Simulium bipunctatum*) 6·25 6·25

332 Flag Ceremony

2013. 30th Anniv of Independence. Multicoloured.

2316	30c. Type **332**	20	20
2317	$5 Words of National Anthem (30×50 mm)	3·50	3·50
2318	$10 Parade	7·00	7·00
MS2319	74×99 mm. $9 Map of St. Kitts and Nevis (vert)	6·25	6·25

333 Cup of Coffee

2013. Brasiliana 2013 World Stamp Exhibition, Rio de Janeiro, Brazil. Coffee Export of Brazil. Multicoloured.

MS2320 120×140 mm. $3.75 Type **333**; $3.75 Coffee leaves and beans; $3.75 Coffee berries 8·25 8·25

MS2321 70×100 mm. $9 Coffee bean 6·50 6·50

334 *Adoration by the Shepherds*

2013. Christmas. Paintings by Carlo Crivelli. Multicoloured.

2322	30c. Type **334**	20	20
2323	90c. *Montefior Cristo*	65	65
2324	$2 *Immacolata Concezione*	1·40	1·40
2325	$5 *Madonna D'Ancona*	3·50	3·50

335 Barred Hogfish (*Bodianus scrofa*)

2013. Fish. Multicoloured.

2326	10c. Type **335**	10	10
2327	15c. Ray-finned Fish (*Pomacanthus xanthometopon*)	10	10
2328	20c. Comb Grouper (*Mycteroperca fusca*)	15	15
2329	30c. Spotfin Hogfish (*Bodianus pulchellus*)	20	20
2330	90c. Yellow Jack (*Carangoides bartholomaei*)	65	65
2331	$1 Broadbarred Firefish (*Pterois antennata*)	70	70
2332	$1.20 Queen Angelfish (*Holacanthus ciliaris*)	85	85
2333	$2 Stoplight Parrotfish (*Sparisoma viride*)	1·40	1·40
2334	$3 Tiger Grouper (*Mycteroperca tigris*)	2·10	2·10
2335	$5 Titan Triggerfish (*Balistoides viridescens*)	3·50	3·50
2336	$10 Blue Striped Grunt (*Haemulon sciurus*)	7·00	7·00
2337	$20 Flameback Angelfish (*Centropyge aurantonotus*)	14·00	14·00

336 Nelson Mandela

2013. Nelson Mandela (President of South Africa 1994-1999) Commemoration. Multicoloured.

MS2338 150×150 mm. $4 Type **336**; $4 Nelson Mandela (wearing black and white shirt with chevron pattern on collar and shoulders); $4 Nelson Mandela smiling and waving (side view); $4 In close-up, wearing bright blue and white patterned shirt 11·00 11·00

MS2339 150×150 mm. $4 Nelson Mandela waving and smiling (seen from front)×4 11·00 11·00

MS2340 100×100 mm. $14 Nelson Mandela (wearing black jacket and tie) 9·50 9·50

MS2341 100×100 mm. $14 Nelson Mandela (wearing check shirt) 9·50 9·50

337 Cicely Tyson

2014. Cicely Tyson (actress). Black.

MS2342 70×90 mm. $3.25 Type **337**×4 9·00 9·00

338 Alexander Hamilton

2014. 225th Anniv of Alexander Hamilton (1757-1804) as First US Secretary of Treasury (1789-1795). Multicoloured.

2343	30c. Type **338**	20	20
2344	90c. Statue of Alexander Hamilton at US Treasury Building, Washington DC	65	65
2345	$10 Reports on National Bank, Establishing a Mint, Manufactures and Public Credit	7·00	7·00
MS2346	99×70 mm. $9 Nevis Heritage Centre (49×29 mm)	6·25	6·25

339 Caribbean Reef Shark

2014. Endangered Species. Caribbean Reef Shark (*Carcharhinus perezi*). Multicoloured.

2347 $2.50 Type **338** 1·75 1·75
2348 $2.50 Sharks and other fish on reef 1·75 1·75
2349 $2.50 Shark swimming to top left 1·75 1·75
2350 $2.50 Shark swimming to left 1·75 1·75
MS2351 89×149 mm. As Nos. 2347/50 but $2.75, each×2 15·00 15·00

340 Anniversary Emblem

2014. 30th Anniv of Nevis Financial Services Department

2352 **340** 30c. multicoloured 20 20
2353 $2 multicoloured 1·40 1·40
2354 $5 multicoloured 3·50 3·50

341 *Phalaenopsis* Orchid

2014. Orchids of the Caribbean. Multicoloured.

MS2355 99×104 mm. $4 Type **341**; $4 *Sogo yukidian*; $4 *Aerides houlletiana*; $4 *Zygopetalum crinitum* 11·00 11·00
MS2356 99×104 mm. $4 *Laelia gouldiana*; $4 *Miltonia regnellii*; $4 *Epidendrum fulgens*; $4 *Cattleya alaorii* 11·00 11·00
MS2357 99×89 mm. $9 *Phalaenopsis* (pink orchid); $9 *Miltonia* (white and yellow orchid) (both vert) 12·50 12·50
MS2358 99×89 mm. $9 *Phalaenopsis* (yellow orchid); $9 *Miltoniopsis* (both vert) 12·50 12·50

342 Audience watching Culturama, 2014

2014. 40th Anniv of Culturama Festival, Nevis. Multicoloured.

2359 $5 Type **342** 3·50 3·50
2360 $10 Performers in Victorian costume 7·00 7·00
MS2361 100×99 mm. $10 King Meeko and King Dis and Dat 7·00 7·00

343 Prince George

2014. First Birthday of Prince George. Multicoloured.

MS2362 170×150 mm. $3.25 Type **343**×3; $3.25 Prince George (wearing white top with navy around collar, Prince William's collar and tie in background); $3.25 Prince George (wearing white top with navy around collar, black background)×2 9·00 9·00
MS2363 80×100 mm. $9.50 Prince George (looking left, held by Duchess of Cambridge) 6·75 6·75
MS2364 80×100 mm. $9.50 Prince George (looking down, held by Duke of Cambridge) 6·75 6·75

345 Coral Reef

2014. Coral Reefs. Multicoloured.

MS2369 140×130 mm. $3.25 Type **345**; $3.25 Orange corals in foreground, shoal of small fish in background; $3.25 Tube sponges and green soft corals; $3.25 Orange coral surrounded by green soft corals; $3.25 Elkhorn coral; $3.25 White sea fan; $3.25 Butterflyfish and corals; $3.25 Pink coral and black and white fish 18·00 18·00
MS2370 119×80 mm. $5 Coral reef, sheet coral in foreground; $5 Pink bowl-shaped sponge 7·00 7·00

346 *Madonna of Foligno*, 1511-12

2014. Christmas. Paintings by Raphael. Multicoloured.

2371 30c. Type **346** 20 20
2372 90c. *The Transfiguration*, 1516-20 65 65
2373 $2 *Madonna of Loreto*, 1508-9 1·40 1·40
2374 $5 *Madonna del Baldacchino*, 1506-8 3·50 3·50

347 Killer Whale (*Orcinus orca*)

2014. Whales and Dolphins of the Caribbean. Multicoloured.

MS2375 149×149 mm. $3.15 Type **347**; $3.15 Killer Whale (*Orcinus orca*) (facing left, leaping with only tail fin in water); $3.15 Killer Whale (facing right); $3.15 Head of Killer Whale; $3.15 Killer Whale (facing left, back and fin above water); $3.15 Killer Whale (facing left, leaping, with tail in water) 11·00 11·00
MS2376 149×149 mm. $3.25 Humpback Whale (*Megaptera novaeangliae*) (underwater facing left); $3.25 Humpback Whale (leaping to right); $3.25 Humpback Whale (facing left, half of body above water); $3.25 Humpback Whale (leaping to left) 9·00 9·00
MS2377 124×99 mm. $10 Pygmy Killer Whale (*Feresa attenuata*) 7·00 7·00
MS2378 149×99 mm. $10 Sperm Whale (*Physeter macrocephalus*) 7·00 7·00

348 Popocatépetl, Puebla, Mexico

2015. Volcanoes of the World

MS2379 175×130 mm. $3.15 Klyuchevskoy, Kamchatka Peninsula, Russia (79×29 mm); $3.15 Type **348**; $3.15 Kamchatka, Kamchatka Peninsula, Russia (39×59 mm); $3.15 Yasur, Vanuatu; $3.15 Nevis Peak, Nevis; $3.15 Kilauea, Hawaii, USA 13·50 13·50
MS2380 91×120 mm. $10 Mt Fuji, Japan (triangle, 44×44×63 mm) 7·25 7·25

349 Scarlet Ibis (*Eudocimus ruber*)

2015. Pink Birds of the Caribbean. Multicoloured.

MS2381 160×120 mm. $4 Type **349**; $4 Greater Flamingo (*Phoenicopterus roseus*); $4 Scarlet Ibis (*Eudocimus ruber*) (perched on rock, wings outstretched); $4 Roseate Spoonbill (*Platalea ajaja*); $4 Scarlet Ibis (*Eudocimus ruber*) (perched on rock); $4 Caribbean Flamingo (*Phoenicopterus ruber*) 17·00 17·00
MS2382 130×100 mm. $10 Caribbean Flamingo (*Phoenicopterus ruber*) (29×79 mm) 7·25 7·25

350 Loggerhead Sea Turtle

2015. Loggerhead Sea Turtles (*Caretta caretta*). Multicoloured.

MS2383 100×130 mm. $3.15 Type **350**; $3.15 Loggerhead Turtle, facing camera (dark brown background); $3.15 Loggerhead Turtle, swimming to top left (deep turquoise background); $3.15 Loggerhead Turtle, facing camera, mouth open (grey brown background); $3.15 Loggerhead Turtle, swimming left (blue grey background); $3.15 Loggerhead Turtle, swimming left (dark blue background) 13·50 13·50
MS2384 100×100 mm. $10 Loggerhead Sea Turtle (different) 7·25 7·25

351 Roker Pier Lighthouse, Sunderland Harbour

2015. Europhilex Stamp Exhibition, London. Lighthouses of England. Multicoloured.

MS2385 150×110 mm. $3.15 Type **351**; $3.15 Beachy Head Lighthouse, East Sussex; $3.15 New Lighthouse at Dungeness, Kent; $3.15 Smeaton's Tower, Plymouth; $3.15 St. Catherine's Lighthouse, Isle of Wight; $3.15 Flamborough Head Lighthouse, Yorkshire 13·50 13·50
MS2386 105×67 mm. $10 Needles Lighthouse, Isle of Wight 6·00 6·00

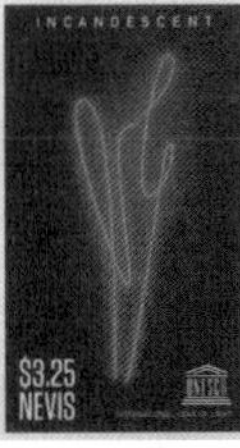

352 Incandescent Light

2015. UNESCO International Year of Light. Artificial Light Sources. Multicoloured.

MS2387 180×80 mm. $3.25 Type **352**; $3.25 Halogen; $3.25 Fluorescent; $3.25 LED; $3.25 Laser 13·50 13·50
MS2388 80×80 mm. $10 Orange, magenta and turquoise lights (37×50 mm) 7·25 7·25

353 Cricket World Cup, Christchurch, New Zealand

2015. Cricket World Cup, Australia and New Zealand. Multicoloured.

2389 $4 Type **353** 2·75 2·75

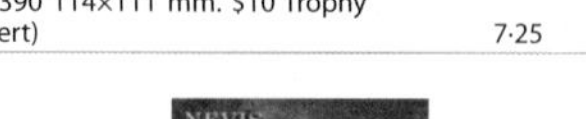

MS2390 114×111 mm. $10 Trophy (vert) 7·25 7·25

354 *The Annunciation*, 1660-1665

2015. Christmas. Paintings by Bartolomé Esteban Murillo. Multicoloured.

2391 30c. Type **354** 25 25
2392 90c. *Nativity*, 1665-1670 75 75
2393 $2 *Madonna and Child*, 1655-1660 1·75 1·75
2394 $5 *Adoration of the Shepherds*, 1668 4·25 4·25

355 Queen Elizabeth II

2015. Queen Elizabeth II Britain's Longest Reigning Monarch. Multicoloured.

MS2395 140×123 mm. $3.15 Type **355**; $3.15 Queen Elizabeth II (wearing pale turquoise); $3.15 Queen Elizabeth II holding bouquet (wearing azure); $3.15 Queen Elizabeth II (wearing pale fawn); $3.15 Queen Elizabeth II waving (wearing navy and white); $3.15 Queen Elizabeth II (wearing pale yellow) 13·50 13·50
MS2396 110×100 mm. $10 Queen Elizabeth II holding papers (38×50 mm) 7·25 7·25

356 Royal Poinciana (*Delonix regia*)

2015. Caribbean Blooms. Multicoloured.

MS2397 101×151 mm. $3.15 Type **356** (inscr 'Poincana') $3.15 Hibiscus (*Hibiscus rosa-sinensis*); $3.15 Bromeliad (*Neoregalia rosea*); $3.15 Paper Flower (*Bougainvillea spectabilis*); $3.15 Moth Orchid (*Phalaenopsis amabilis*); $3.15 Flamingo Flower (*Anthurium andreanum*) 13·50 13·50
MS2398 81×100 mm. $10 Red Palulu (*Heliconia bihai*) (29×49 mm) 7·25 7·25

357 Bank of Nevis Building

2015. 30th Anniv of the Bank of Nevis Limited. Multicoloured.

2399 30c. Type **357** 25 25
2400 90c. Bank of Nevis building (different) 70 70
2401 $5 R. E. Sir Simeon Daniel (vert) 4·00 4·00

358 Belted Kingfisher (*Megaceryle alcyon*)

2015. Central American Kingfishers. Multicoloured.

MS2402 116×101 mm. $3.15 Type **358**; $3.15 Ringed Kingfisher (*Megaceryle torquata*); $3.15 Green and Rufous Kingfisher (*Chloroceryle inda*); $3.15 Green Kingfisher (*Chloroceryle americana septentrionalis*) (seen from front); $3.15 Amazon Kingfisher (*Chloroceryle amazona*); $3.15 Green Kingfisher (*Chloroceryle americana septentrionalis*) (seen from back) 13·50 13·50

MS2403 90×65 mm. $10 Belted Kingfisher (*Megaceryle alcyon*) in flight	7·25	7·25

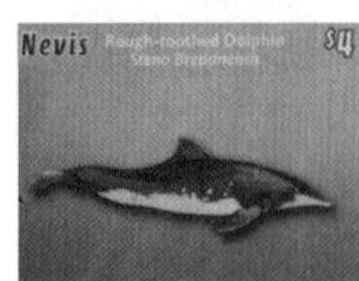

359 Rough-toothed Dolphin (*Steno bredanensis*)

2016. Marine Mammals of Nevis. Dolphins. Multicoloured.

MS2404 90×130 mm. $4 Type **359**; $4 Atlantic Spotted Dolphin (*Stenella frontalis*); $4 Striped Dolphin (*Stenella coeruleoalba*); $4 Common Bottlenose Dolphin (*Tursiops truncatus*); $4 Risso's Dolphin (*Grampus griseus*); $4 Fraser's Dolphin (*Lagenodelphis hosei*)	17·00	17·00
MS2405 95×65 mm. $10 Short-beaked Common Dolphin (*Delphinus delphis*) (79×29 mm)	7·25	7·25

360 King Venus (*Chione paphia*)

2016. Caribbean Seashells. Multicoloured.

MS2406 130×130 mm. $4 Type **360**; $4 Channeled Duck Clam (*Raeta plicatella*); $4 Sunrise Tellin (*Tellina radiata*); $4 Calico Clam (*Macrocallista maculata*)	11·50	11·50
MS2407 100×80 mm. $10 Royal Comb Venus (*Pitar dione*) (50×38 mm)	7·25	7·25

361 Queen Elizabeth II, 1953

2016. 90th Birthday of Queen Elizabeth II. Multicoloured.

MS2408 140×145 mm. $3.25 Type **361**; $3.25 Queen Elizabeth II wearing diadem (in profile), 1953; $3.25 Queen Elizabeth II, 1970 (29×79 mm); $3.25 Queen Elizabeth II wearing diadem and pearl drop earrings, 1953; $3.25 Coronation photograph of Queen Elizabeth II and Prince Philip, 1953	11·50	11·50
MS2409 100×120 mm. $13 Queen Elizabeth II, 1987 (29×49 mm)	9·25	9·25

362 Central Park

2016. NY2016 World Stamp Show, New York. Multicoloured.

MS2410 150×100 mm. $4 Type **362**; $4 Statue of Liberty; $4 Grand Central Terminal; $4 Brooklyn Bridge	11·50	11·50
MS2411 253×178 mm. $8 New York City skyline (59×79 mm)	5·75	5·75

363 Birthplace, Stratford-upon-Avon, England

2016. 400th Death Anniv of William Shakespeare. Multicoloured.

MS2412 180×120 mm. $3.15 Type **363**; $3.15 William Shakespeare; $3.15 *Oberon, Titania and Puck with Fairies Dancing* (Henry Fuseli), 1780; $3.15 *Pity* (William Blake), 1795; $3.15 *Hamlet and His Father's Ghost* (William Blake), 1786; $3.15 *Macbeth Consulting the Vision of the Armed Head* (Henry Fuseli), 1793	13·50	13·50
MS2413 100×100 mm. $12 William Shakespeare (oval 32×42 mm)	8·75	8·75

OFFICIAL STAMPS

1980. Nos. 40/49 optd **OFFICIAL**.

O1	15c. Sugar cane being harvested	10	10
O2	25c. Crafthouse (craft centre)	10	10
O3	30c. *Europa* (liner)	10	10
O4	40c. Lobster and sea crab	15	15
O5	45c. Royal St. Kitts Hotel and golf course	20	20
O6	50c. Pinney's Beach, Nevis	15	20
O7	55c. New runway at Golden Rock	15	20
O8	$1 Picking cotton	15	25
O9	$5 Brewery	45	55
O10	$10 Pineapples and peanuts	70	90

1981. Nos. 60/71 optd **OFFICIAL**.

O11	15c. New River Mill	10	10
O12	20c. Nelson Museum	10	10
O13	25c. St. James' Parish Church	10	15
O14	30c. Nevis Lane	15	15
O15	40c. Zetland Plantation	15	20
O16	45c. Nisbet Plantation	20	25
O17	50c. Pinney's Beach	20	25
O18	55c. Eva Wilkin's Studio	25	30
O19	$1 Nevis at dawn	30	30
O20	$2.50 Ruins of Fort Charles	40	50
O21	$5 Old Bath House	50	65
O22	$10 Beach at Nisbet's	80	1·00

1983. Nos. 72/7 optd or surch **OFFICIAL**.

O23	45c. on $2 *Royal Sovereign*	10	15
O24	45c. on $2 Prince Charles and Lady Diana Spencer	20	25
O25	55c. *Royal Caroline*	10	15
O26	55c. Prince Charles and Lady Diana Spencer	25	25
O27	$1.10 on $5 *Britannia*	20	25
O28	$1.10 on $5 Prince Charles and Lady Diana Spencer	55	60

1985. Nos. 187/98 optd **OFFICIAL**.

O29	15c. Flamboyant	20	20
O30	20c. Eyelash orchid	30	30
O31	30c. Bougainvillea	30	40
O32	40c. Hibiscus sp	30	40
O33	50c. Night-blooming cereus	35	40
O34	55c. Yellow mahoe	35	45
O35	60c. Spider-lily	40	50
O36	75c. Scarlet cordia	45	55
O37	$1 Shell-ginger	60	60
O38	$3 Blue petrea	1·25	1·75
O39	$5 Coral hibiscus	2·00	2·25
O40	$10 Passion flower	3·00	2·50

1993. Nos. 578/91 optd **OFFICIAL**.

O41	5c. Type **63**	45	60
O42	10c. *Historis odius*	50	60
O43	15c. *Marpesia corinna*	60	50
O44	20c. *Anartia amathea*	60	40
O45	25c. *Junonia evarete*	60	40
O46	40c. *Heliconius charithonia*	75	45
O47	50c. *Marpesia petreus*	75	45
O48	75c. *Heliconius doris*	1·00	60
O49	80c. *Dione juno*	1·00	50
O50	$1 *Hypolimnas misippus*	1·00	80
O51	$3 *Danaus plexippus*	2·25	2·75
O52	$5 *Heliconius sara*	3·00	3·50
O53	$10 *Tithorea harmonia*	5·50	6·50
O54	$20 *Dryas julia*	11·00	12·00

1999. Nos. 1166/77 optd **OFFICIAL**.

O55	25c. Guava	20	30
O56	30c. Papaya	20	30
O57	50c. Mango	30	30
O58	60c. Golden apple	40	35
O59	80c. Pineapple	50	45
O60	90c. Watermelon	60	50
O61	$1 Bananas	70	55
O62	$1.80 Orange	1·25	1·00
O63	$3 Honeydew	2·00	3·00
O64	$5 Cantaloupe	2·75	3·00
O65	$10 Pomegranate	5·50	6·00
O66	$20 Cashew	10·00	12·00

POSTAL FISCAL STAMPS

F 3 Medicinal Spring

F 4 Coat of Arms

2012. Postage and Revenue Stamps

F9	**F3**	$100 multicoloured	70·00	70·00
F10	**F4**	$150 multicoloured	£100	£100

APPENDIX

The following stamps have either been issued in excess of postal needs, or have not been made available to the public in reasonable quantities at face value. Miniature sheets, imperforate sheets etc. are excluded from this section.

2012

Centenary of Sinking of the *Titanic*. $3×4
35th Death Anniv of Elvis Presley. $2.50×4
75th Death Anniv of J. M. Barrie (author of *Peter Pan*). $3×4
Beetles $2.50×4; $4×2
500th Anniv of Michelangelo's Sistine Chapel Ceiling. $3.50×4

2013

Centenary of the Crossword Puzzle. $2×18
United Nations World Radio Day. $3×4
Election of Pope Francis I. $3.25×4
Turtles of the World. $3.25×4

2015

Rosetta Mission (landing of *Philae* probe on comet), 12 November 2014 $3.25×4
Prehistoric Mammals $3.25×8
25th Anniv of the Hubble Telescope $1.60×12
Events of the Papacy of Pope Benedict XVI $3.15×6
Famous Battles of World War I. The First Battle of Ypres $3.25×4
Pope Francis visits New York City $3.15×6
The Olympic Champions. 1896 $3.25×4

2016

15th Anniv of 9.11 (11 September 2001 Terrorist Attacks) $3.25×6; $3.50×4

NEW BRUNSWICK

An eastern province of the Dominion of Canada, whose stamps are now used.

1851. 12 pence = 1 shilling; 20 shillings = 1 pound.
1860. 100 cents = 1 dollar.

1 Royal Crown and Heraldic Flowers of the United Kingdom

1851

2	1	3d. red	£3500	£350
4	1	6d. yellow	£5000	£800
5	1	1s. mauve	£18000	£4500

2 Locomotive

3 Queen Victoria

1860

8	**2**	1c. purple	70·00	50·00
10	**3**	2c. orange	35·00	29·00
13	-	5c. brown	£10000	
14	-	5c. green	28·00	18·00
17	-	10c. red	65·00	75·00
18	-	12½c. blue	70·00	42·00
19	-	17c. black	42·00	90·00

Designs:—Vert: 5c. brown, Charles Connell; 5c. green, 10c. Queen Victoria; 17c. King Edward VII when Prince of Wales. Horiz: 12½c. Steamship.

NEW CALEDONIA

A French Overseas Territory in the S. Pacific, E. of Australia, consisting of New Caledonia and a number of smaller islands.

100 centimes = 1 franc.

1 Napoleon III

1860. Imperf.

1	**1**	10c. black	£325	†

1881. "Peace and Commerce" type surch N C E and new value. Imperf.

5	**H**	05 on 40c. red on yellow	36·00	36·00
8a	**H**	5 on 40c. red on yellow	27·00	27·00
9	**H**	5 on 75c. red	65·00	55·00
6	**H**	25 on 35c. black on orange	£325	£325
7	**H**	25 on 75c. red	£400	£400

Nos. 5/30 are stamps of French Colonies optd or surch.

1886. "Peace and Commerce" (imperf) and "Commerce" types surch N.C.E. 5c.

10	**J**	5c. on 1f. green	35·00	35·00
11	**H**	5c. on 1f. green	£12000	£13000

1891. "Peace and Commerce" (imperf) and "Commerce" types surch N.-C.E. 10 c. in ornamental frame.

13		10c. on 40c. red on yellow	46·00	55·00
14	**J**	10c. on 40c. red on yellow	28·00	28·00

1892. "Commerce" type surch N.-C.E. 10 centimes in ornamental frame.

15	10c. on 30c. brown on drab	26·00	23·00

1892. Optd NLLE CALEDONIE. (a) "Peace and Commerce" type. Imperf.

16	**H**	20c. red on green	£350	£400
17	**H**	35c. black on orange	£100	90·00
19	**H**	1f. green	£300	£300

(b) "Commerce" type.

20	**J**	5c. green on green	48·00	19·00
21	**J**	10c. black on lilac	£150	£110
22	**J**	15c. blue	£130	65·00
23	**J**	20c. red on green	£140	85·00
24	**J**	25c. brown on yellow	50·00	17·00
25	**J**	25c. black on pink	£130	24·00
26	**J**	30c. brown on drab	£120	£100
27	**J**	35c. black on orange	£250	£200
29	**J**	75c. red on pink	£225	£190
30	**J**	1f. green	£190	£180

1892. "Tablet" key-type inscr "NLLE CALEDONIE ET DEPENDANCES".

31	**D**	1c. black and red on blue	1·10	85
32	**D**	2c. brown and blue on buff	1·90	1·10
33	**D**	4c. brown and blue on grey	2·30	4·50
55	**D**	5c. green and red	3·50	90
34	**D**	10c. black and blue on lilac	4·50	1·50
56	**D**	10c. red and blue	8·75	1·00
35	**D**	15c. blue and red	8·25	4·00
57	**D**	15c. grey and red	12·50	90
36	**D**	20c. red and blue on green	38·00	2·20
37	**D**	25c. black and red on pink	12·50	9·50
58	**D**	25c. blue and red	16·00	7·25
38	**D**	30c. brown and blue on drab	20·00	4·00
39	**D**	40c. red and blue on yellow	19·00	17·00
40	**D**	50c. red and blue on pink	21·00	10·50
59	**D**	50c. brown and red on blue	90·00	£110
60	**D**	50c. brown and blue on blue	60·00	40·00
41	**D**	75c. brown & red on orange	90·00	35·00
42	**D**	1f. green and red	28·00	28·00

1892. Surch N-C-E in ornamental scroll and new value. (a) "Peace and Commerce" type. Imperf.

44	**H**	10 on 1f. green	£6500	£5000

(b) "Commerce" type.

45	**J**	5 on 20c. red on green	55·00	14·50
46	**J**	5 on 75c. red on pink	26·00	25·00
48	**J**	10 on 1f. green	24·00	15·00

1899. Stamps of 1892 surch (a) N-C-E in ornamental scroll and 5.

50	**D**	5 on 2c. brown & bl on buff	17·00	18·00
51	**D**	5 on 4c. brown & bl on grey	4·00	4·50

(b) **N.C.E.** and **15** in circle.
52 **D** 15 on 30c. brown and blue on drab 4·50 7·00
53 **D** 15 on 75c. brown and red on orange 17·00 23·00
54 **D** 15 on 1f. green and red 60·00 44·00

1902. Surch N.-C.E. and value in figures.
61 **D** 5 on 30c. brown and blue on drab 7·00 9·75
62 **D** 15 on 40c. red and blue on yellow 7·50 9·00

1903. 50th Anniv of French Annexation. Optd CINQUANTENAIRE 24 SEPTEMBRE 1853 1903 and eagle.
63 **D** 1c. black and red on blue 2·75 2·50
64 **D** 2c. brown and blue on buff 4·25 3·75
65 **D** 4c. brown and blue on grey 8·25 6·25
66 **D** 5c. green and red 6·00 4·50
69 **D** 10c. black and blue on lilac 10·50 8·75
70 **D** 15c. grey and red 15·00 5·25
71 **D** 20c. red and blue on green 21·00 28·00
72 **D** 25c. black and red on pink 19·00 20·00
73 **D** 30c. brown and blue on drab 25·00 29·00
74 **D** 40c. red and blue on yellow 55·00 30·00
75 **D** 50c. red and blue on pink 60·00 65·00
76 **D** 75c. brown & blue on orange 80·00 £120
77 **D** 1f. green and red £130 £130

1903. Nos. 64 etc further surch with value in figures within the jubilee opt.
78 **D** 1 on 2c. brown & bl on buff 1·80 1·80
79 **D** 2 on 4c. brown & bl on grey 4·00 5·25
80 **D** 4 on 5c. green and red 2·30 3·00
82 **D** 10 on 15c. grey and red 2·30 3·25
83 **D** 15 on 20c. red and blue on green 3·00 5·50
84 **D** 20 on 25c. black and red on pink 6·50 7·75

15 Kagu **16** **17** *President Felix Faure* (barque)

1905
85 **15** 1c. black on green 30 30
86 **15** 2c. brown 30 65
87 **15** 4c. blue on orange 50 65
88 **15** 5c. green 1·40 55
112 **15** 5c. blue 40 40
113 **15** 10c. green 1·50 85
114 **15** 10c. red 75 70
90 **15** 15c. lilac 1·10 95
91 **16** 20c. brown 75 45
92 **16** 25c. blue on green 1·60 65
115 **16** 25c. red on yellow 75 55
93 **16** 30c. brown on orange 1·40 2·30
116 **16** 30c. red 2·50 3·50
117 **16** 30c. orange 60 1·10
94 **16** 35c. black on yellow 1·50 1·20
95 **16** 40c. red on green 1·70 2·00
96 **16** 45c. red 1·50 2·75
97 **16** 50c. red on orange 5·50 4·00
118 **16** 50c. blue 1·80 1·50
119 **16** 50c. grey 1·20 1·00
120 **16** 65c. blue 1·80 3·25
98 **16** 75c. olive 2·75 3·75
121 **16** 75c. blue 90 1·80
122 **16** 75c. violet 1·20 5·50
99 **17** 1f. blue on green 1·80 2·50
123 **17** 1f. blue 2·75 3·25
100 **17** 2f. red on blue 4·50 5·00
101 **17** 5f. black on orange 9·00 19·00

1912. Stamps of 1892 surch.
102A **D** 05 on 15c. grey and red 1·30 1·50
103A **D** 05 on 20c. red and blue on green 1·40 1·70
104A **D** 05 on 30c. brown and blue on drab 1·90 3·00
105A **D** 10 on 40c. red and blue on yellow 3·00 3·25
106A **D** 10 on 50c. brown and blue on blue 3·25 3·25

1915. Surch NCE 5 and red cross.
107 **15** 10c.+5c. red 2·30 1·70

1915. Surch 5c and red cross.
109 **15** 10c.+5c. red 2·30 6·25
110 **15** 15c.+5c. lilac 1·50 5·00

1918. Surch 5 CENTIMES.
111 **15** 5c. on 15c. lilac 2·50 3·25

1922. Surch 0 05.
124 **15** 0.05 on 15c. lilac 65 2·00

1924. Types **15/17** (some colours changed) surch.
125 **15** 25c. on 15c. lilac 75 4·25
126 **17** 25c. on 2f. red on blue 1·10 4·75
127 **17** 25c. on 5f. black on orange 95 7·25
128 **16** 60 on 75c. green 75 1·80
129 **16** 65 on 45c. purple 1·50 3·50
130 **16** 85 on 45c. purple 2·00 4·00
131 **16** 90 on 75c. red 1·10 3·25
132 **17** 1f.25 on 1f. blue 1·10 7·25
133 **17** 1f.50 on 1f. blue on blue 1·90 3·25
134 **17** 3f. on 5f. mauve 2·50 7·50
135 **17** 10f. on 5f. green on mauve 5·00 25·00
136 **17** 20f. on 5f. red on yellow 17·00 50·00

22 Pointe des Paletuviers **23** Chief's Hut

24 La Perouse, De Bougainville and *L'Astrolabe*

1928
137 **22** 1c. blue and purple 35 2·00
138 **22** 2c. green and brown 30 2·40
139 **22** 3c. blue and red 35 6·25
140 **22** 4c. blue and orange 35 2·50
141 **22** 5c. brown and blue 55 1·40
142 **22** 10c. brown and lilac 35 55
143 **22** 15c. blue and brown 65 65
144 **22** 20c. brown and red 65 1·40
145 **22** 25c. brown and green 75 50
146 **23** 30c. deep green and green 65 80
147 **23** 35c. mauve and black 1·10 65
148 **23** 40c. green and red 65 2·75
149 **23** 45c. red and blue 2·75 7·00
150 **23** 45c. green and deep green 3·00 3·75
151 **23** 50c. brown and mauve 1·00 80
152 **23** 55c. red and blue 4·75 2·30
153 **23** 60c. red and blue 95 7·25
154 **23** 65c. blue and brown 1·70 1·20
155 **23** 70c. brown and mauve 1·80 7·25
156 **23** 75c. drab and blue 2·30 1·80
157 **23** 80c. green and purple 1·50 6·50
158 **23** 85c. brown and green 3·50 3·75
159 **23** 90c. pink and red 2·75 2·50
160 **23** 90c. red and brown 2·00 4·50
161 **24** 1f. pink and drab 7·25 3·25
162 **24** 1f. carmine and red 3·00 1·90
163 **24** 1f. green and red 1·20 4·75
164 **24** 1f.10 brown and green 12·50 38·00
165 **24** 1f.25 green and brown 4·50 7·50
166 **24** 1f.25 carmine and red 1·80 7·75
167 **24** 1f.40 red and blue 2·00 7·25
168 **24** 1f.50 light blue and blue 1·10 2·20
169 **24** 1f.60 brown and green 2·75 8·25
170 **24** 1f.75 orange and blue 4·25 5·00
171 **24** 1f.75 blue and ultramarine 3·75 7·00
172 **24** 2f. brown and orange 1·00 70
173 **24** 2f.25 blue and ultramarine 2·50 6·75
174 **24** 2f.50 brown 2·30 5·50
175 **24** 3f. brown and mauve 90 2·75
176 **24** 5f. brown and blue 1·30 2·40
177 **24** 10f. brown & pur on pink 2·00 6·25
178 **24** 20f. brown & red on yellow 3·25 5·50

1931. "Colonial Exhibition" key-types.
179 **E** 40c. green and black 6·50 13·00
180 **F** 50c. mauve and black 6·50 7·25
181 **G** 90c. red and black 6·50 13·00
182 **H** 1f.50 blue and black 6·50 7·25

1932. Paris–Noumea Flight. Optd with Couzinet 33 aircraft and PARIS-NOUMEA Verneilh-Deve-Munch 5 Avril 1932.
183 **23** 40c. olive and red £500 £550
184 **23** 50c. brown and mauve £500 £550

1933. First Anniv of Paris–Noumea Flight. Optd PARIS-NOUMEA Premiere liaison aerienne 5 Avril 1932 and Couzinet 33 aircraft.
185 **22** 1c. blue and purple 7·25 29·00
186 **22** 2c. green and brown 8·00 26·00
187 **22** 4c. blue and orange 6·75 27·00
188 **22** 5c. brown and blue 7·25 24·00
189 **22** 10c. brown and lilac 9·25 28·00
190 **22** 15c. blue and brown 6·50 27·00
191 **22** 20c. brown and red 6·50 27·00
192 **22** 25c. brown and green 8·25 30·00
193 **23** 30c. deep green and green 7·50 28·00
194 **23** 35c. mauve and black 7·50 28·00
195 **23** 40c. green and red 7·50 19·00
196 **23** 45c. red and blue 9·25 28·00
197 **23** 50c. brown and mauve 6·50 29·00
198 **23** 70c. brown and mauve 7·75 32·00
199 **23** 75c. drab and blue 10·50 24·00
200 **23** 85c. brown and green 7·75 25·00
201 **23** 90c. pink and red 9·00 26·00
202 **24** 1f. pink and drab 10·50 34·00
203 **24** 1f.25 green and brown 10·50 32·00
204 **24** 1f.50 light blue and blue 12·00 34·00
205 **24** 1f.75 orange and blue 8·75 20·00
206 **24** 2f. brown and orange 10·50 38·00
207 **24** 3f. brown and mauve 10·50 38·00
208 **24** 5f. brown and blue 12·00 40·00
209 **24** 10f. brown & pur on pink 9·25 38·00
210 **24** 20f. brown & red on yellow 8·75 38·00

1937. International Exhibition, Paris. As T **4a** of Niger.
211 20c. violet 2·10 5·00
212 30c. green 2·10 7·75
213 40c. red 2·10 3·75
214 50c. brown and blue 2·10 3·75
215 90c. red 2·10 5·25
216 1f.50 blue 2·10 3·75
MS216a 120×100 mm. 3f. sepia 20·00 48·00
Designs:—Horiz: 30c. Sailing ships; 40c. Berber, Negress and Annamite; 90c. France extends torch of civilization; 1f.50, Diane de Poitiers. Vert: 50c. Agriculture.

27 Breguet Saigon Flying Boat over Noumea

1938. Air.
217 **27** 65c. violet 1·60 7·00
218 **27** 4f.50 red 4·00 6·75
219 **27** 7f. green 1·30 6·00
220 **27** 9f. blue 5·50 6·25
221 **27** 20f. orange 3·25 5·00
222 **27** 50f. black 4·25 10·50

1938. Int Anti-cancer Fund. As T **17a** of Oceanic Settlement.
223 1f.75+50c. blue 11·50 46·00

1939. New York World's Fair. As T **17b** of Oceanic Settlement.
224 1f.25 red 1·20 8·50
225 2f.25 blue 1·40 4·25

1939. 150th Anniv of French Revolution. As T **17c** of Oceanic Settlement.
226 45c.+25c. green and black (postage) 15·00 26·00
227 70c.+30c. brown and black 15·00 26·00
228 90c.+35c. orange and black 15·00 26·00
229 1f.25+1f. red and black 15·00 26·00
230 2f.25+2f. blue and black 15·00 26·00
231 4f.50+4f. black and orange (air) 31·00 50·00

1941. Adherence to General de Gaulle. Optd France Libre.
232 **22** 1c. blue and purple 9·25 30·00
233 **22** 2c. green and brown 9·75 32·00
234 **22** 3c. blue and red 9·25 55·00
235 **22** 4c. blue and orange 9·25 24·00
236 **22** 5c. brown and blue 9·00 24·00
237 **22** 10c. brown and lilac 9·00 60·00
238 **22** 15c. blue and brown 21·00 38·00
239 **22** 20c. brown and red 20·00 32·00
240 **22** 25c. brown and green 20·00 38·00
241 **23** 30c. deep green and green 20·00 30·00
242 **23** 35c. mauve and black 20·00 30·00
243 **23** 40c. green and red 21·00 30·00
244 **23** 45c. green and deep green 22·00 34·00
245 **23** 50c. brown and mauve 20·00 29·00
246 **23** 55c. red and blue 22·00 30·00
247 **23** 60c. red and blue 20·00 29·00
248 **23** 65c. blue and brown 25·00 38·00
249 **23** 70c. brown and mauve 17·00 42·00
250 **23** 75c. drab and blue 20·00 30·00
251 **23** 80c. green and purple 20·00 29·00
252 **23** 85c. brown and green 17·00 29·00
253 **23** 90c. pink and red 20·00 38·00
254 **24** 1f. carmine and red 16·00 55·00
255 **24** 1f.25 green and brown 15·00 36·00
256 **24** 1f.40 red and blue 18·00 29·00
257 **24** 1f.50 light blue and blue 16·00 29·00
258 **24** 1f.60 brown and green 17·00 29·00
259 **24** 1f.75 orange and blue 20·00 29·00
260 **24** 2f. brown and orange 20·00 29·00
261 **24** 2f.25 blue and ultramarine 18·00 29·00
262 **24** 2f.50 brown 22·00 33·00
263 **24** 3f. brown and mauve 18·00 33·00
264 **24** 5f. brown and blue 18·00 33·00
265 **24** 10f. brown & pur on pink 20·00 60·00
266 **24** 20f. brown & red on yellow 21·00 65·00

29 Kagu

30 Fairey FC-1 Airliner

1942. Free French Issue. (a) Postage.
267 **29** 5c. brown 35 5·00
268 **29** 10c. blue 40 4·25
269 **29** 25c. green 55 3·00
270 **29** 30c. red 65 3·25
271 **29** 40c. green 65 3·00
272 **29** 80c. purple 75 2·30
273 **29** 1f. mauve 1·00 90
274 **29** 1f.50 red 1·00 85
275 **29** 2f. black 1·40 90
276 **29** 2f.50 blue 1·60 5·00
277 **29** 4f. violet 1·30 1·20
278 **29** 5f. yellow 1·20 95
279 **29** 10f. brown 1·70 1·30
280 **29** 20f. green 2·30 2·75

(b) Air.
281 **30** 1f. orange 85 3·50
282 **30** 1f.50 red 85 6·50
283 **30** 5f. purple 90 3·75
284 **30** 10f. black 1·10 5·00
285 **30** 25f. blue 1·40 2·50
286 **30** 50f. green 1·80 1·90
287 **30** 100f. red 2·30 2·30

1944. Mutual Aid and Red Cross Funds. As T **19b** of Oceanic Settlements.
288 5f.+20f. red 1·70 8·25

1945. Eboue. As T **20a** of Oceanic Settlements.
289 2f. black 1·00 6·00
290 25f. green 2·00 4·00

1945. Surch.
291 **29** 50c. on 5c. brown 1·40 1·10
292 **29** 60c. on 5c. brown 1·40 7·25
293 **29** 70c. on 5c. brown 1·40 7·50
294 **29** 1f.20 on 5c. brown 75 4·25
295 **29** 2f.40 on 25c. green 1·30 8·00
296 **29** 3f. on 25c. green 1·70 2·00
297 **29** 4f.50 on 25c. green 1·90 6·75
298 **29** 15f. on 2f.50 blue 2·10 1·50

1946. Air. Victory. As T **20b** of Oceanic Settlements.
299 8f. blue 1·10 6·00

1946. Air. From Chad to the Rhine. As T **25a** of Madagascar.
300 5f. black 1·50 4·75
301 - 10f. red 1·50 3·00
302 - 15f. blue 1·50 7·50
303 - 20f. brown 1·50 7·50
304 - 25f. green 1·80 7·50
305 - 50f. purple 2·75 8·25
Designs:—5f. Legionaries by Lake Chad; 10f. Battle of Koufra; 15f. Tank Battle, Mareth; 20f. Normandy Landings; 25f. Liberation of Paris; 50f. Liberation of Strasbourg.

36 Two Kagus

37 Sud Est Languedoc Airliners over Landscape

1948. (a) Postage.
306 **36** 10c. purple and yellow 40 3·75
307 **36** 30c. purple and green 40 7·00
308 **36** 40c. purple and brown 45 3·00

309	-	50c. purple and pink	75	55
310	-	60c. brown and yellow	85	3·25
311	-	80c. green and light green	90	4·00
312	-	1f. violet and orange	95	60
313	-	1f.20 brown and blue	1·30	5·00
314	-	1f.50 blue and yellow	1·00	1·00
315	-	2f. brown and green	1·20	60
316	-	2f.40 red and purple	1·40	7·00
317	-	3f. violet and orange	5·00	1·30
318	-	4f. indigo and blue	1·80	75
319	-	5f. violet and red	2·40	90
320	-	6f. brown and yellow	3·00	95
321	-	10f. blue and orange	2·40	80
322	-	15f. red and blue	2·75	1·00
323	-	20f. violet and yellow	2·75	1·10
324	-	25f. blue and orange	4·00	1·90

(b) Air.

325	-	50f. purple and orange	4·75	4·00
326	**37**	100f. blue and green	10·00	4·00
327	-	200f. brown and yellow	12·00	7·75

Designs:—As T **36**: Horiz: 50c. to 80c. Ducos Sanatorium; 1f.50, Porcupine Is; 2f. to 4f. Nickel foundry; 5f. to 10f. "The Towers of Notre Dame" Rocks. Vert: 15f. to 25f. Chief's hut. As T **37**: Horiz: Sud Est Languedoc airliner over- 50f. St. Vincent Bay; 200f. Noumea.

38 People of Five Races, Bomber and Globe

1949. Air. 75th Anniv of U.P.U.

328	**38**	10f. multicoloured	6·00	7·50

39 Doctor and Patient

1950. Colonial Welfare Fund.

329	**39**	10f.+2f. purple & brown	4·50	17·00

40

1952. Military Medal Centenary.

330	**40**	2f. red, yellow and green	5·25	6·25

41 Admiral D'Entrecasteaux

1953. French Administration Centenary. Inscr "1853 1953".

331	**41**	1f.50 lake and brown	5·00	4·00
332	-	2f. blue and turquoise	4·00	2·30
333	-	6f. brown, blue and red	7·50	4·00
334	-	13f. blue and green	8·50	5·00

Designs:—2f. Mgr. Douarre and church; 6f. Admiral D'Urville and map; 13f. Admiral Despointes and view.

42 Normandy Landings, 1944

1954. Air. Tenth Anniv of Liberation.

335	**42**	3f. blue and deep blue	9·50	12·50

43 Towers of Notre-Dame (rocks)

44 Coffee

45 Transporting Nickel

1955

336	**43**	2f.50c. blue, green and sepia (postage)	1·10	1·50
337	**43**	3f. blue, brown and green	5·50	3·75
338	**44**	9f. deep blue and blue	2·00	1·20
339	**45**	14f. blue and brown (air)	3·50	1·70

46 Dumbea Barrage

1956. Economic and Social Development Fund.

340	**46**	3f. green and blue	1·60	1·20

47 *Xanthostemon*

1958. Flowers.

341	**47**	4f. multicoloured	2·10	1·40
342	-	15f. red, yellow and green	4·00	1·90

Design:—15f. Hibiscus.

48 "Human Rights"

1958. Tenth Anniv of Declaration of Human Rights.

343	**48**	7f. red and blue	1·70	1·70

49 Zebra Lionfish

1959

344	**49**	1f. brown and grey	75	70
345	-	2f. blue, purple and green	2·00	1·30
346	-	3f. red, blue and green	1·70	75
347	-	4f. purple, red and green	2·00	3·25
348	-	5f. bistre, blue and green	3·25	2·75
349	-	10f. multicoloured	2·40	1·10
350	-	26f. multicoloured	4·25	5·75

Designs:—Horiz: 2f. Outrigger canoes racing; 3f. Harlequin tuskfish; 5f. Sail Rock, Noumea; 26f. Fluorescent corals. Vert: 4f. Fisherman with spear. 10f. Blue sea lizard and *Spirographe* (coral).

49a The Carved Rock, Bourail

1959. Air.

351		15f. green, brown and red	4·00	3·00
352		20f. brown and green	10·00	5·25
353		25f. black, blue and purple	9·50	4·75
354		50f. brown, green and blue	7·75	4·75
355		50f. brown, green and blue	7·25	3·75
356		100f. brown, green & blue	25·00	11·50
357	**49a**	200f. brown, green & blue	21·00	14·00

Designs:—Horiz: 15f. Fisherman with net; 20f. New Caledonia nautilus; 25f. Underwater swimmer shooting bump-headed unicornfish; 50f. (No. 355), Isle of Pines; 100f. Corbeille de Yate. Vert: 50f. (No. 354), Yate barrage.

49b Napoleon III

49c Port-de-France, 1859

1960. Postal Centenary.

358	**15**	4f. red	65	1·10
359	-	5f. brown and lake	80	1·70
360	-	9f. brown and turquoise	85	2·40
361	-	12f. black and blue	1·00	3·00
362	**49b**	13f. blue	2·50	3·25
363	**49c**	19f. red, green & turquoise	2·50	1·80
364	-	33f. red, green and blue	2·75	3·50
MS364a 150×80 mm. Nos. 358, 362 and 364			13·50	29·00

Designs:—As Type **49c**: Horiz: 5f. Girl operating cheque-writing machine; 12f. Telephone receiver and exchange building; 33f. As Type **49c** but without stamps in upper corners. Vert: 9f. Letter-box on tree.

49d Map of Pacific and Palms

1962. Fifth South Pacific Conference, Pago-Pago.

365	**49d**	15f. multicoloured	3·00	2·75

49e Map and Symbols of Meteorology

1962. Third Regional Assembly of World Meteorological Association, Noumea.

366	**49e**	50f. multicoloured	6·75	11·50

50 *Telstar* Satellite and part of Globe

1962. Air. First Transatlantic TV Satellite Link.

367	**50**	200f. turquoise, brown & bl	21·00	20·00

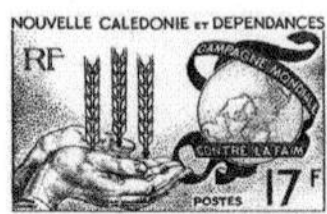

51 Emblem and Globe

1963. Freedom from Hunger.

368	**51**	17f. blue and purple	3·50	3·00

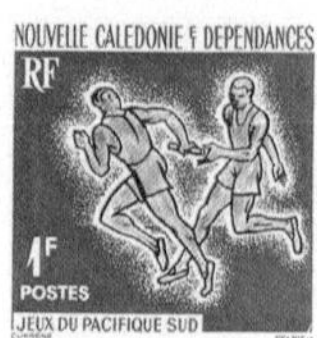

52 Relay-running

1963. First South Pacific Games, Suva, Fiji.

369	**52**	1f. red and green	90	2·50
370	-	7f. brown and blue	1·30	5·25
371	-	10f. brown and green	1·80	3·00
372	-	27f. blue and deep purple	3·25	5·00

Designs:—7f. Tennis; 10f. Football; 27f. Throwing the javelin.

53 Centenary Emblem

1963. Red Cross Centenary.

373	**53**	37f. red, grey and blue	6·50	11·50

54 Globe and Scales of Justice

1963. 15th Anniv of Declaration of Human Rights.

374	**54**	50f. red and blue	6·75	14·00

54a *Bikkia fritillarioides*

1964. Flowers. Multicoloured.

375	1f. *Freycinettia*	85	3·25
376	2f. Type **54a**	85	2·30
377	3f. *Xanthostemon francii*	1·30	3·25
378	4f. *Psidiomyrtus locellatus*	2·40	2·50
379	5f. *Callistemon suberosum*	3·00	2·75
380	7f. *Montrouziera sphaeroidea* (horiz)	3·75	3·25
381	10f. *Ixora collina* (horiz)	4·50	3·25
382	17f. *Deplanchea speciosa*	6·75	5·50

54b *Ascidies polycarpa*

1964. Corals and Marine Animals from Noumea Aquarium.

383	**54b**	7f. red, brown and blue (postage)	1·80	2·20
384	-	10f. red and blue	2·75	2·20
385	-	17f. red, green and blue	4·25	1·80
386	-	27f. multicoloured	5·50	5·00
387	-	37f. multicoloured	7·25	9·00
388	-	13f. bistre, black and orange (air)	4·50	4·75
389	-	15f. green, olive and blue	5·50	4·75
390	-	25f. blue and green	8·00	9·00

Designs:—As T **54b**: Vert: 10f. *Alcyonium catalai* (coral). 17f. *Hymenocera elegans* (crab). Horiz: 48×28 mm: 27f. Palette surgeonfish; 37f. *Phyllobranchus* (sea slug). 48×27 mm: 13f. Twin-spotted wrasse (young); 15f. Twin-spotted wrasse (subadult); 25f. Twin-spotted wrasse (adult).

54c "Philately"

1964. PHILATEC 1964 International Stamp Exhibition, Paris.

391	**54c**	40f. brown, green & violet	6·25	9·50

54d Houailou Mine

1964. Air. Nickel Production at Houailou.

392	**54d**	30f. multicoloured	4·00	10·00

54e Ancient Greek Wrestling

1964. Air. Olympic Games, Tokyo.

393	**54e**	10f. sepia, mauve & green	13·50	18·00

55 Weather Satellite

1965. Air. World Meteorological Day.

394	**55**	9f. multicoloured	4·75	5·00

56 *Syncom* Communications Satellite, Telegraph Poles and Morse Key

1965. Air. Centenary of I.T.U.

395	**56**	40f. purple, brown and blue	9·50	14·00

56a De Gaulle's Appeal of 18 June 1940

1965. 25th Anniv of New Caledonia's Adherence to the Free French.

396	**56a**	20f. black, red and blue	9·00	13·00

56b Amedee Lighthouse

1965. Inauguration of Amedee Lighthouse.

397	**56b**	8f. bistre, blue and green	2·30	2·30

56c Rocket Diamant

1966. Air. Launching of First French Satellite.

398	**56c**	8f. lake, blue and turquoise	3·75	5·00
399	-	12f. lake, blue & turquoise	4·50	5·50

Design: 12f. Satellite *A1*.

56d Games Emblem

1966. Publicity for Second South Pacific Games, Noumea.

400	**56d**	8f. black, red and blue	1·40	2·30

56e Satellite *D1*

1966. Air. Launching of Satellite "D1".

401	**56e**	10f. brown, blue and buff	2·30	4·00

57 Noumea, 1866 (after Lebreton)

1966. Air. Centenary of Renaming of Port-de-France as Noumea.

402	**57**	30f. slate, red and blue	5·25	12·50

58 Red-throated Parrot Finch

1966. Birds. Multicoloured.

403		1f. Type **58** (postage)	3·00	4·00
404		1f. New Caledonian grass warbler	2·00	2·00
405		2f. New Caledonian whistler	2·75	2·00
406		3f. New Caledonian pigeon ("Notou")	4·50	3·00
407		3f. White-throated pigeon ("Collier blanc")	3·00	2·50
408		4f. Kagu	4·75	3·00
409		5f. Horned parakeet	7·00	4·25
410		10f. Red-faced honeyeater	12·50	6·00
411		15f. New Caledonian friarbird	8·75	4·50
412		30f. Sacred kingfisher	13·50	11·00
413		27f. Horned parakeet (diff) (air)	7·25	5·50
414		37f. Scarlet honeyeater	11·00	10·50
415		39f. Emerald dove	21·00	12·50
416		50f. Cloven-feathered dove	15·00	16·00
417		100f. Whistling kite	50·00	34·00

Nos. 413/14 are 26×45½ mm; Nos. 415/17 are 27½×48 mm.

59 UNESCO Allegory

1966. 20th Anniv of UNESCO.

418	**59**	16f. purple, ochre and green	3·25	3·00

60 High Jumping

1966. South Pacific Games, Noumea.

419	**60**	17f. violet, green and lake	3·00	2·00
420	-	20f. green, purple and lake	4·25	3·25
421	-	40f. green, violet and lake	5·50	4·50
422	-	100f. purple, turq & lake	9·50	11·00
MS423		149×99 mm. Nos. 419/22	33·00	70·00

Designs:—20f. Hurdling; 40f. Running; 100f. Swimming.

61 Lekine Cliffs

1967

424	**61**	17f. grey, green and blue	3·00	2·50

62 Ocean Racing Yachts

1967. Air. Second Whangarei–Noumea Yacht Race.

425	**62**	25f. red, blue and green	6·75	5·75

63 Magenta Stadium

1967. Sport Centres. Multicoloured.

426		10f. Type **63**	2·75	2·40
427		20f. Ouen-Toro swimming pool	4·00	2·00

64 New Caledonian Scenery

1967. International Tourist Year.

428	**64**	30f. multicoloured	4·00	4·25

65 19th-century Postman

1967. Stamp Day.

429	**65**	7f. red, green and turquoise	3·00	3·00

66 *Papilio montrouzieri*

1967. Butterflies and Moths.

430	**66**	7f. blue, black and green (postage)	4·00	2·50
431	-	9f. blue, brown and mauve	4·50	2·50
432	-	13f. violet, purple & brown	6·00	7·00
433	-	15f. yellow, purple and blue	8·75	6·25
434	-	19f. orange, brown and green (air)	7·50	5·50
435	-	29f. purple, red and blue	9·25	9·25
436	-	85f. brown, red and yellow	22·00	30·00

Butterflies:—As T **66**: 9f. *Polyura clitarchus*; 13f. Common eggfly (male), and 15f. (female). 48×27 mm: 19f. Orange tiger; 29f. Silver-striped hawk moth; 85f. *Dellas elipsis*.

67 Garnierite (mineral), Factory and Jules Garnier

1967. Air. Centenary of Garnierite Industry.

437	**67**	70f. multicoloured	8·00	20·00

67a Lifou Island

1967. Air.

438	**67a**	200f. multicoloured	12·00	11·50

67b Skier and Snow-crystal

1967. Air. Winter Olympic Games, Grenoble.

439	**67b**	100f. brown, blue & green	13·50	18·00

68 Bouquet, Sun and WHO Emblem

1968. 20th Anniv of W.H.O.

440	**68**	20f. blue, red and violet	3·75	3·50

69 Human Rights Emblem

1968. Human Rights Year.

441	**69**	12f. red, green and yellow	2·75	2·75

70 Ferrying Mail Van across Tontouta River

1968. Stamp Day.

442	**70**	9f. brown, blue and green	4·50	3·25

71 Geography Cone

1968. Sea Shells.

443	-	1f. brn, grey & grn (postage)	2·50	3·00
444	-	1f. purple and violet	2·30	2·50
445	-	2f. purple, red and blue	3·75	3·25
446	-	3f. brown and green	2·40	1·80
447	-	5f. red, brown and violet	3·25	1·70
448	**71**	10f. brown, grey and blue	3·50	3·00
449	-	10f. yellow, brown and red	4·25	3·00
450	-	10f. black, brown & orange	5·00	3·25
451	-	15f. red, grey and green	7·25	5·75
452	-	21f. brown, sepia and green	8·00	5·50
453	-	22f. red, brown & blue (air)	8·00	5·50
454	-	25f. brown and red	5·75	4·75
455	-	33f. brown and blue	8·75	7·75
456	-	34f. violet, brown & orange	9·75	6·00
457	-	39f. brown, grey and green	9·25	9·25
458	-	40f. black, brown and red	9·25	4·50
459	-	50f. red, purple and green	7·75	8·50
460	-	60f. brown and green	19·00	21·00
461	-	70f. brown, grey and violet	14·50	9·75
462	-	100f. brown, black and blue	23·00	26·00

Designs:—Vert: 1f. (No. 443) Swan conch (*Strombus epidromis*); 1f. (No. 444) Scorpion conch (*Lambis scorpius*); 3f. Common spider conch; 10f. (No. 450) Variable conch (*Strombus variabilis*). 27×48 mm: 22f. Laciniate cone; 25f. Orange spider conch; 34f. Vomer conch; 50f. Chiragra spider conch. Horiz: 36×22 mm: 2f. Snipe's-bill murex; 5f. Troschel's murex; 10f. (No. 449) Sieve cowrie; 15f. *Murex* sp.; 21f. Mole cowrie. 48×27 mm: 33f. Eyed cowrie; 39f. Lienardi's cone; 40f. Cabrit's cone; 60f. All-red map cowrie; 70f. Scarlet cone; 100f. Adusta murex.

72 Dancers

1968. Air.

463	**72**	60f. red, blue and green	7·50	11·50

73 Rally Car

1968. Second New Caledonian Motor Safari.

464	**73**	25f. blue, red and green	6·50	5·25

74 Caudron C-60 Aiglon and Route Map

1969. Air. Stamp Day. 30th Anniv of First Noumea–Paris Flight by Martinet and Klein.

465 **74** 29f. red, blue and violet 5·25 3·75

75 Concorde in Flight

1969. Air. First Flight of Concorde.

466 **75** 100f. green and light green 27·00 29·00

76 Cattle-dip

1969. Cattle-breeding in New Caledonia.

467 **76** 9f. brown, green and blue (postage) 2·50 2·40
468 - 25f. violet, brown and green 3·75 4·25
469 - 50f. purple, red & grn (air) 7·00 5·50

Designs:—25f. Branding. LARGER 48×27 mm; 50f. Stockman with herd.

77 Judo

1969. Third South Pacific Games, Port Moresby, Papua New Guinea.

470 **77** 19f. purple, bl & red (post) 3·75 2·75
471 - 20f. black, red and green 3·75 2·75
472 - 30f. black and blue (air) 6·25 6·75
473 - 39f. brown, green and black 9·00 11·00

Designs:—Horiz: 20f. Boxing; 30f. Diving (38×27 mm). Vert: 39f. Putting the shot (27×48 mm).

1969. Air. Birth Bicentenary of Napoleon Bonaparte. As T **114b** of Mauritania. Multicoloured.

474 40f. *Napoleon in Coronation Robes* (Gerard) (vert) 19·00 18·00

78 Douglas DC-4 over Outrigger Canoe

1969. Air. 20th Anniv of Regular Noumea–Paris Air Service.

475 **78** 50f. green, brown and blue 20·00 9·25

79 ILO Building Geneva

1969. 50th Anniv of I.L.O.

476 **79** 12f. brown, violet & salmon 2·75 4·25

80 "French Wings around the World"

1970. Air. Tenth Anniv of French "Around the World" Air Service.

477 **80** 200f. brown, blue and violet 26·00 15·00

81 New UPU Building, Berne

1970. Inauguration of New U.P.U. Headquarters Building, Berne.

478 **81** 12f. red, grey and brown 3·50 2·50

82 Packet Steamer *Natal*, 1883

1970. Stamp Day.

479 **82** 9f. black, green and blue 8·00 2·75

83 Cyclists on Map

1970. Air. Fourth "Tour de Nouvelle Caledonie" Cycle Race.

480 **83** 40f. brown, blue & lt blue 10·00 7·25

84 Mt. Fuji and Japanese Hikari Express Train

1970. Air. EXPO 70 World Fair, Osaka, Japan. Multicoloured.

481 20f. Type **84** 6·00 5·75
482 45f. "EXPO" emblem, map and Buddha 8·50 4·50

85 Racing Yachts

1971. Air. One Ton Cup Yacht Race Auckland, New Zealand.

483 **85** 20f. green, red and black 6·00 2·75

86 Steam Mail Train, Dumbea

1971. Stamp Day.

484 **86** 10f. black, green and red 6·50 6·25

87 Ocean Racing Yachts

1971. Third Whangarei–Noumea Ocean Yacht Race.

485 **87** 16f. turquoise, green and blue 8·75 5·00

88 Lieut.-Col. Broche and Theatre Map

1971. 30th Anniv of French Pacific Battalion's Participation in Second World War Mediterranean Campaign.

486 **88** 60f. multicoloured 11·00 9·00

89 Early Tape Machine

1971. World Telecommunications Day.

487 **89** 19f. orange, purple and red 5·00 4·75

90 Weightlifting

1971. Fourth South Pacific Games, Papeete, French Polynesia

488 **90** 11f. brown & red (postage) 4·25 3·75
489 - 23f. violet, red and blue 5·25 2·75
490 - 25f. green and red (air) 4·75 4·50
491 - 100f. blue, green and red 8·75 6·75

Designs:—Vert: 23f. Basketball. Horiz: 48×27 mm: 25f. Pole-vaulting; 100f. Archery.

91 Port de Plaisance, Noumea

1971. Air.

492 **91** 200f. multicoloured 19·00 16·00

92 De Gaulle as President of French Republic, 1970

1971. First Death Anniv of General De Gaulle.

493 **92** 34f. black and purple 8·50 5·75
494 - 100f. black and purple 15·00 12·50

Design:—100f. De Gaulle in uniform, 1940.

93 Publicity Leaflet showing de Havilland Gipsy Moth *Golden Eagle*

1971. Air. 40th Anniv of First New Caledonia to Australia Flight.

495 **93** 90f. brown, blue and orange 13·00 17·00

94 Downhill Skiing

1972. Air. Winter Olympic Games, Sapporo, Japan.

496 **94** 50f. green, red and blue 9·75 7·00

95 St. Mark's Basilica, Venice

1972. Air. UNESCO "Save Venice" Campaign.

497 **95** 20f. brown, green and blue 6·50 5·75

96 Commission Headquarters, Noumea

1972. Air. 25th Anniv of South Pacific Commission.

498 **96** 18f. multicoloured 3·75 4·75

97 Couzinet 33 *Le Biarritz* and Noumea Monument

1972. Air. 40th Anniv of First Paris–Noumea Flight.

499 **97** 110f. black, purple & green 9·25 8·75

98 Pacific Island Dwelling

1972. Air. South Pacific Arts Festival, Fiji.

500 **98** 24f. brown, blue and orange 5·00 3·00

99 Goa Door-post

1972. Exhibits from Noumea Museum.

501 **99** 1f. red, green & grey (post) 1·90 1·60
502 - 2f. black, green & deep grn 2·20 1·60
503 - 5f. multicoloured 2·75 2·00
504 - 12f. multicoloured 5·25 2·75
505 - 16f. multicoloured (air) 3·75 3·25
506 - 40f. multicoloured 6·50 4·00

Designs:—2f. Carved wooden pillow; 5f. Monstrance; 12f. Tchamba mask; 16f. Ornamental arrowheads; 40f. Portico, chief's house.

100 Hurdling over "H" of "MUNICH"

1972. Air. Olympic Games, Munich.

507 **100** 72f. violet, purple and blue 9·25 10·50

101 New Head Post Office Building, Noumea

1972. Air.

508 **101** 23f. brown, blue and green 4·50 2·75

102 JCI Emblem

1972. Tenth Anniv of New Caledonia Junior Chamber of Commerce.

509	**102**	12f. multicoloured	2·75	2·40

103 Forest Scene

1973. Air. Landscapes of the East Coast. Multicoloured.

510		11f. Type **103**	4·00	2·40
511		18f. Beach and palms (vert)	5·00	5·00
512		21f. Waterfall and inlet (vert)	6·50	7·50

See also Nos. 534/6.

104 Moliere and Characters

1973. Air. 300th Death Anniv of Moliere (playwright).

513	**104**	50f. multicoloured	8·25	4·75

105 Tchamba Mask

1973

514	**105**	12f. purple (postage)	11·00	7·00
515	-	23f. blue (air)	18·00	14·00

Design:—23f. Concorde in flight.

106 Liner *El Kantara* in Panama Canal

1973. 50th Anniv of Marseilles–Noumea Shipping Service via Panama Canal.

516	**106**	60f. black, brown & green	19·00	12·00

107 Globe and Allegory of Weather

1973. Air. Centenary of World Meteorological Organization.

517	**107**	80f. multicoloured	9·50	7·75

108 DC-10 in Flight

1973. Air. Inauguration of Noumea–Paris DC-10 Air Service.

518	**108**	100f. green, brown & blue	24·00	10·50

109 Common Egg Cowrie

1973. Marine Fauna from Noumea Aquarium. Multicoloured.

519		8f. Black-wedged butterflyfish (daylight)	3·25	2·50
520		14f. Black-wedged butterflyfish (nocturnal)	5·00	4·25
521		3f. Type **109** (air)	2·40	2·20
522		32f. Orange-spotted surgeonfish (adult and young)	7·25	5·50
523		32f. Green-lined paper bubble (*Hydatina*)	5·00	5·50
524		37f. Pacific partridge tun (*Dolium perdix*)	5·75	3·50

111 Office Emblem

1973. Tenth Anniv of Central Schools Co-operation Office.

532	**111**	20f. blue, yellow and green	3·00	2·30

112 New Caledonia Mail Coach, 1880

1973. Air. Stamp Day.

533	**112**	15f. multicoloured	4·25	2·10

1974. Air. Landscapes of the West Coast. As T 103. Multicoloured.

534		8f. Beach and palms (vert)	3·25	5·75
535		22f. Trees and mountain	4·00	5·25
536		26f. Trees growing in sea	4·25	3·50

113 Centre Building

1974. Air. Opening of Scientific Studies Centre, Anse-Vata, Noumea.

537	**113**	50f. multicoloured	5·00	4·50

114 "Bird" embracing Flora

1974. Nature Conservation.

538	**114**	7f. multicoloured	1·80	2·20

115 18th-century French Sailor

1974. Air. Discovery and Reconnaissance of New Caledonia and Loyalty Islands.

539	-	20f. violet, red and blue	5·25	4·75
540	-	25f. green, brown and red	5·00	5·25
541	**115**	28f. brown, blue and green	6·00	3·75
542	-	30f. blue, brown and red	8·25	4·25
543	-	36f. red, brown and blue	8·75	9·50

Designs:—Horiz: 20f. Captain Cook, HMS *Endeavour* and map of Grand Terre island; 25f. La Perouse, *L'Astrolabe* and map of Grand Terre island (reconnaissance of west coast); 30f. Entrecasteaux, ship and map of Grand Terre island (reconnaissance of west coast); 36f. Dumont d'Urville, *L'Astrolabe* and map of Loyalty Islands.

116 "Telecommunications"

1974. Air. Centenary of U.P.U.

544	**116**	95f. orange, purple & grey	6·50	10·00

117 "Art"

1974. Air. Arphila 75 International Stamp Exhibition, Paris (1975) (1st issue).

545	**117**	80f. multicoloured	6·50	5·75

See also No. 554.

118 Hotel Chateau-Royal

1974. Air. Inauguration of Hotel Chateau Royal, Noumea.

546	**118**	22f. multicoloured	3·25	2·75

118a Animal Skull, Burnt Tree and Flaming Landscape

1975. Stop Bush Fires.

547	**118a**	20f. multicoloured	2·50	2·20

119 "Cricket"

1975. Air. Tourism. Multicoloured.

548		3f. Type **119**	2·75	2·10
549		25f. "Bougna" ceremony	3·25	4·25
550		31f. "Pilou" native dance	3·75	2·50

120 *Calanthe veratrifolia*

1975. New Caledonian Orchids. Multicoloured.

551		8f. Type **120** (postage)	3·50	2·00
552		11f. *Lyperanthus gigas*	4·25	2·10
553		42f. *Eriaxis rigida* (air)	9·00	4·50

121 Global "Flower"

1975. Air. Arphila 75 International Stamp Exhibition, Paris (2nd issue).

554	**121**	105f. purple, green & blue	10·00	5·50

122 Throwing the Discus

1975. Air. Fifth South Pacific Games, Guam.

555		24f. Type **122**	5·75	4·75
556		50f. Volleyball	6·75	3·50

123 Festival Emblem

1975. Melanesia 2000 Festival, Noumea.

557	**123**	12f. multicoloured	2·75	2·30

124 Birds in Flight

1975. Tenth Anniv of Noumea Ornithological Society.

558	**124**	5f. multicoloured	2·00	1·90

125 Pres. Pompidou

1975. Pompidou Commemoration.

559	**125**	26f. grey and green	3·75	3·25

126 Concordes

1976. Air. First Commercial Flight of Concorde.

560	**126**	147f. blue and red	19·00	20·00

127 Brown Booby

1976. Ocean Birds. Multicoloured.

561		1f. Type **127**	1·60	2·10
562		2f. Blue-faced booby	2·30	2·20
563		8f. Red-footed booby (vert)	4·00	2·75

128 Festival Emblem

1976. South Pacific Festival of Arts, Rotorua, New Zealand.

564	**128**	27f. multicoloured	3·50	4·50

129 Lion and Lions' Emblem

1976. 15th Anniv of Lions Club, Noumea.

565	**129**	49f. multicoloured	6·25	9·00

130 Early and Modern Telephones

1976. Air. Telephone Centenary.

566	**130**	36f. multicoloured	5·50	5·00

131 Capture of Penbosct

1976. Air. Bicent of American Revolution.

567	**131**	24f. purple and brown	3·75	3·00

132 Bandstand

1976. Aspects of Old Noumea. Multicoloured.

568	25f. Type **132**	2·75	3·25
569	30f. Monumental fountain (vert)	3·25	3·00

133 Athletes

1976. Air. Olympic Games, Montreal.

570	**133**	33f. violet, red and purple	3·75	3·50

134 "Chick" with Magnifier

1976. Air. Philately in Schools, Stamp Exhibition, Noumea.

571	**134**	42f. multicoloured	4·50	5·50

135 Dead Bird and Trees

1976. Nature Protection.

572	**135**	20f. multicoloured	3·50	3·00

136 South Pacific Heads

1976. 16th South Pacific Commission Conference.

573	**136**	20f. multicoloured	2·75	2·40

137 Old Town Hall, Noumea

1976. Air. Old and New Town Halls, Noumea. Mult.

574	75f. Type **137**	7·25	5·00
575	125f. New Town Hall	11·00	5·75

138 Water Carnival

1977. Air. Summer Festival, Noumea.

576	**138**	11f. multicoloured	3·00	2·30

139 *Pseudophyllanax imperiali* (cricket)

1977. Insects.

577	**139**	26f. emerald, green & brn	4·50	7·00
578	-	31f. brown, sepia & green	4·75	3·75

Design:—31f. *Agrianome fairmairei* (Long-horn beetle).

140 Miniature Roadway

1977. Air. Road Safety.

579	**140**	50f. multicoloured	4·75	4·25

141 Earth Station

1977. Earth Satellite Station, Noumea.

580	**141**	29f. multicoloured	3·25	3·00

142 *Phajus daenikeri*

1977. Orchids. Multicoloured.

581	22f. Type **142**	4·75	6·00
582	44f. *Dendrobium finetianum*	6·25	7·50

143 Mask and Palms

1977. La Perouse School Philatelic Exn.

583	**143**	35f. multicoloured	2·75	4·25

144 Trees

1977. Nature Protection.

584	**144**	20f. multicoloured	2·10	3·00

145 Palm Tree and Emblem

1977. French Junior Chambers of Commerce Congress.

585	**145**	200f. multicoloured	13·50	12·00

146 Young Bird

1977. Great Frigate Birds. Multicoloured.

586	16f. Type **146** (postage)	5·75	4·75
587	42f. Adult male bird (horiz) (air)	8·00	6·50

147 Magenta Airport and Map of Internal Air Network

1977. Air. Airports. Multicoloured.

588	24f. Type **147**	4·00	4·75
589	57f. La Tontout International Airport, Noumea	6·25	8·50

1977. Air. First Commercial Flight of Concorde, Paris–New York. Optd **22.11.77 PARIS NEW-YORK.**

590	**126**	147f. blue and red	44·00	42·00

149 Horse and Foal

1977. 10th Anniv of S.E.C.C. (Horse-breeding Society).

591	**149**	5f. brown, green and blue	2·75	5·00

150 *Moselle Bay* (H. Didonna)

1977. Air. Views of Old Noumea (1st series).

592	**150**	41f. multicoloured	8·00	8·25
593	-	42f. purple and brown	5·50	6·00

Design:—49×27 mm: 42f. *Settlers Valley* (J. Kreber).
See also No. 607, 615, 644 and 665.

151 Black-naped Tern

1978. Ocean Birds. Multicoloured.

594	22f. Type **151**	3·25	6·00
595	40f. Sooty tern	5·25	4·50

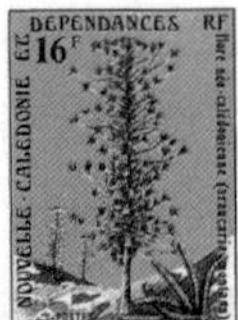
152 *Araucaria montana*

1978. Flora. Multicoloured.

596	16f. Type **152** (postage)	2·20	4·00
597	42f. *Amyema scandens* (horiz) (air)	4·25	3·00

153 *Halityle regularis*

1978. Noumea Aquarium.

598	**153**	10f. multicoloured	2·40	2·40

154 Turtle

1978. Protection of the Turtle.

599	**154**	30f. multicoloured	3·50	6·00

155 New Caledonian Flying Fox

1978. Nature Protection.

600	**155**	20f. multicoloured	4·75	3·00

156 "Underwater Carnival"

1978. Air. Aubusson Tapestry.

601	**156**	105f. multicoloured	7·75	9·75

157 Pastor Maurice Leenhardt

1978. Birth Centenary of Pastor Maurice Leenhardt.

602	**157**	37f. sepia, green & orange	3·75	5·25

158 Hare chasing "Stamp" Tortoise

1978. School Philately (1st series).

603	**158**	35f. multicoloured	6·00	4·50

159 Heads, Map, Magnifying Glass and Cone Shell

1978. Air. Thematic Philately at Bourail.

604	**159**	41f. multicoloured	4·75	6·50

160 Candles

1978. Third New Caledonian Old People's Day.

605	**160**	36f. multicoloured	2·75	5·00

161 Footballer and League Badge

1978. 50th Anniv of New Caledonian Football League.
606 **161** 26f. multicoloured 3·00 4·50

162 *Fauberg Blanchot* (after Lacouture)

1978. Air. Views of Old Noumea.
607 **162** 24f. multicoloured 3·25 5·75

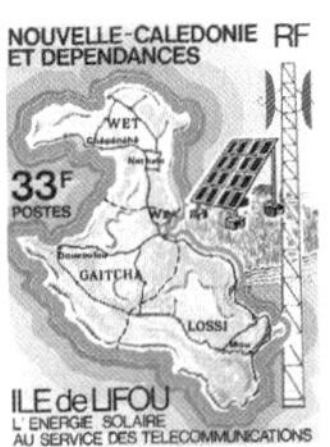

163 Map of Lifou, Solar Energy Panel and Transmitter Mast

1978. Telecommunications through Solar Energy.
608 **163** 33f. multicoloured 4·00 6·50

164 Petroglyph, Mere Region

1979. Archaeological Sites.
609 **164** 10f. red 2·30 1·20

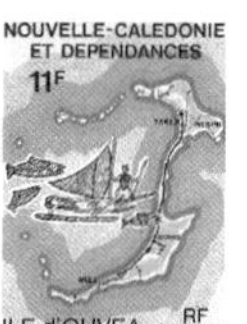

165 Ouvea Island and Outrigger Canoe

1979. Islands. Multicoloured.
610 11f. Type **165** 2·50 4·50
611 31f. Mare Island and ornaments (horiz) 2·10 1·50

See also Nos. 629 and 649.

166 Satellite Orbit of Earth

1979. Air. First World Survey of Global Atmosphere.
612 **166** 53f. multicoloured 4·50 5·00

167 19th-century Barque and Modern Container Ship

1979. Air. Centenary of Chamber of Commerce and Industry.
613 **167** 49f. mauve, blue & brown 4·50 5·75

168 Child's Drawing

1979. Air. International Year of the Child.
614 **168** 35f. multicoloured 3·75 6·25

169 House at Artillery Point

1979. Views of Old Noumea.
615 **169** 20f. multicoloured 2·75 3·50

170 Skipjack Tuna

1979. Air. Sea Fish (1st series). Multicoloured.
616 29f. Type **170** 3·25 5·25
617 30f. Black marlin 3·25 4·50

See also Nos. 632/3 and 647/8.

171 L. Tardy de Montravel (founder) and View of Port-de-France (Noumea)

1979. Air. 125th Anniv of Noumea.
618 **171** 75f. multicoloured 7·50 6·00

172 The Eel Queen (Kanaka legend)

1979. Air. Nature Protection.
619 **172** 42f. multicoloured 4·50 4·25

173 Auguste Escoffier

1979. Auguste Escoffier Hotel School.
620 **173** 24f. brown, green and turquoise 2·50 6·00

174 Games Emblem and Catamarans

1979. Sixth South Pacific Games, Fiji.
621 **174** 16f. multicoloured 2·75 2·75

175 Children of Different Races, Map and Postmark

1979. Air. Youth Philately.
622 **175** 27f. multicoloured 3·00 4·00

176 Aerial View of Centre

1979. Air. Overseas Scientific and Technical Research Office (O.R.S.T.O.M.) Centre, Noumea.
623 **176** 25f. multicoloured 3·25 4·75

177 *Agathis ovata*

1979. Trees. Multicoloured.
624 5f. Type **177** 2·30 2·10
625 34f. *Cyathea intermedia* 3·00 3·25

178 Rodeo Riding

1979. Pouembout Rodeo.
626 **178** 12f. multicoloured 2·75 2·30

179 Hill, 1860 10c. Stamp and Post Office

1979. Air. Death Centenary of Sir Rowland Hill.
627 **179** 150f. black, brown & orge 8·75 8·00

180 *Bantamia merleti*

1980. Noumea Aquarium. Fluorescent Corals (1st issue).
628 **180** 23f. multicoloured 2·75 4·00

See also No. 646.

1980. Islands. As T **165**. Multicoloured.
629 23f. Map of Ile des Pins and ornaments (horiz) 2·30 2·50

181 Outrigger Canoe

1980. Air.
630 **181** 45f. blue, turq & indigo 2·75 3·00

182 Globe, Rotary Emblem, Map and Carving

1980. Air. 75th Anniv of Rotary International.
631 **182** 100f. multicoloured 6·25 4·50

1980. Air. Sea Fish (2nd series). As T **170**. Multicoloured.
632 34f. Angler holding dolphinfish 2·75 4·00
633 39f. Fishermen with sailfish (vert) 3·25 4·00

183 *Hibbertia virotii*

1980. Flowers. Multicoloured.
634 11f. Type **183** 2·10 2·00
635 12f. *Grevillea meisneri* 2·10 2·30

184 High Jumper, Magnifying Glass, Albums and Plimsoll

1980. School Philately.
636 **184** 30f. multicoloured 2·75 3·75

185 Scintex Super Emeraude Aeroplane and Map

1980. Air. Coral Sea Air Rally.
637 **185** 31f. blue, green and brown 3·25 5·25

186 Sailing Canoe

1980. Air. South Pacific Arts Festival, Port Moresby.
638 **186** 27f. multicoloured 2·30 5·00

187 Road Signs as Road-users

1980. Road Safety.
639 **187** 15f. multicoloured 1·90 2·75

188 *Parribacus caledonicus*

1980. Noumea Aquarium. Marine Animals (1st series). Multicoloured.
640 5f. Type **188** 1·10 1·70
641 8f. *Panulirus versicolor* 1·40 2·00

See also Nos. 668/9.

189 Kiwanis Emblem

1980. Air. Tenth Anniv of Noumea Kiwanis Club.
642 **189** 50f. multicoloured 3·25 4·50

190 Sun, Tree and Solar Panel

1980. Nature Protection. Solar Energy.
643 **190** 23f. multicoloured 2·00 3·50

191 Old House, Poulou

1980. Air. Views of Old Noumea (4th series).

644	**191**	33f. multicoloured	2·30	3·25

192 Charles de Gaulle

1980. Air. Tenth Death Anniv of Charles de Gaulle (French statesman).

645	**192**	120f. green, olive and blue	8·75	7·00

1981. Air. Noumea Aquarium. Fluorescent Corals (2nd series). As T **180**. Multicoloured.

646	60f. *Trachyphyllia geoffroyi*	3·75	3·00

193 Manta Ray

1981. Sea Fish (3rd series). Multicoloured.

647	23f. Type **193**	2·50	4·75
648	25f. Grey reef shark	2·50	4·75

1981. Islands. As T **165**. Multicoloured.

649	26f. Map of Belep Archipelago and diver (horiz)	2·75	4·50

194 *Xeronema moorei*

1981. Air. Flowers. Multicoloured.

650	38f. Type **194**	2·30	3·00
651	51f. *Geissois pruinosa*	3·00	3·25

195 Yuri Gagarin and *Vostok 1*

1981. Air. 20th Anniv of First Men in Space. Multicoloured.

652	64f. Type **195**	3·25	4·50
653	155f. Alan Shepard and *Freedom 7*	6·50	6·00
MS654	149×119 mm. As Nos. 652/3 but colours changed (sold at 225f.)	23·00	36·00

196 Liberation Cross, *Zealandia* (troopship) and Badge

1981. Air. 40th Anniv of Departure of Pacific Battalion for Middle East.

655	**196**	29f. multicoloured	5·00	6·00

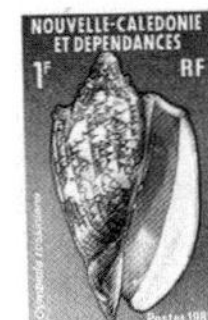
197 Rossini's Volute

1981. Shells. Multicoloured.

656	1f. Type **197**	1·10	2·00
657	2f. Clouded cone	1·20	2·20
658	13f. Stolid cowrie (horiz)	2·10	3·00

198 Sail Corvette *Constantine*

1981. Ships (1st series).

659	**198**	10f. blue, brown and red	2·30	2·75
660	-	25f. blue, brown and red	3·50	4·00

Designs:—25f. Paddle-gunboat *Le Phoque*, 1853.

See also Nos. 680/1 and 725/6.

199 *Echinometra mathaei*

1981. Air. Water Plants. Multicoloured.

661	38f. Type **199**	2·20	4·75
662	51f. *Prionocidaris verticillata*	3·25	3·50

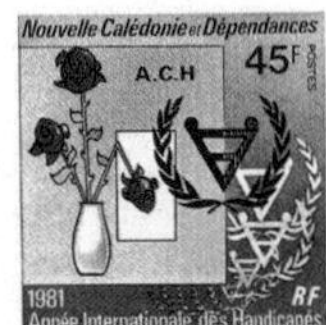
200 Broken-stemmed Rose and IYDP Emblems

1981. International Year of Disabled Persons.

663	**200**	45f. multicoloured	3·00	3·50

201 25c. Surcharged Stamp of 1881

1981. Air. Stamp Day.

664	**201**	41f. multicoloured	3·25	5·00

202 Latin Quarter

1981. Air. Views of Old Noumea.

665	**202**	43f. multicoloured	3·25	5·00

203 Trees and Unicornfish

1981. Nature Protection.

666	**203**	28f. blue, green and brown	2·75	5·00

204 Victor Roffey and "Golden Eagle"

1981. Air. 50th Anniv of First New Caledonia–Australia Airmail Flight.

667	**204**	37f. black, violet and blue	3·25	4·75

1982. Noumea Aquarium. Marine Animals (2nd series). As T **188**. Multicoloured.

668	13f. *Calappa calappa*	1·60	4·25
669	25f. *Etisus splendidus*	2·20	3·25

205 *La Rousette*

1982. Air. New Caledonian Aircraft (1st series).

670	**205**	38f. brown, red and green	3·25	4·25
671	-	51f. brown, orange & grn	3·75	4·25

Design:—51f. *Le Cagou*.

See also Nos. 712/13.

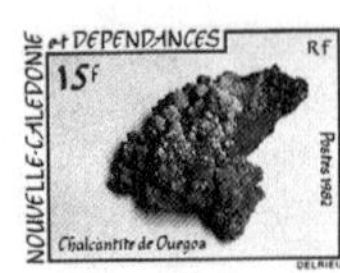
206 Chalcantite, Ouegoa

1982. Rocks and Minerals (1st series). Multicoloured.

672	15f. Type **206**	2·00	4·25
673	30f. Anorthosite, Blue River	2·75	5·00

See also Nos. 688/9.

207 De Verneilh, Deve and Munch (air crew), Couzinet 33 *Le Biarritz* and Route Map

1982. Air. 50th Anniv of First Flight from Paris to Noumea.

674	**207**	250f. mauve, blue and black	17·00	12·50

208 Scout and Guide Badges and Map

1982. Air. 50th Anniv of New Caledonian Scout Movement.

675	**208**	40f. multicoloured	2·10	3·75

209 "The Rat and the Octopus" (Canaque legend)

1982. "Philexfrance 82" International Stamp Exhibition, Paris.

676	**209**	150f. blue, mauve and deep blue	6·00	7·50

210 Footballer, Mascot and Badge

1982. Air. World Cup Football Championship, Spain.

677	**210**	74f. multicoloured	3·00	5·00

211 Savanna Trees at Niaoulis

1982. Flora. Multicoloured.

678	20f. Type **211**	1·90	4·50
679	29f. *Melaleuca quinquenervia* (horiz)	2·20	3·50

1982. Ships (2nd series). As T **198**.

680	44f. blue, purple and brown	3·75	2·75
681	59f. blue, light brown and brown	4·25	4·00

Designs:—44f. Naval transport barque *Le Cher*; 59f. Sloop *Kersaint*, 1902.

212 Islanders, Map and Kagu

1982. Air. Overseas Week.

682	**212**	100f. brown, green & blue	5·00	4·75

213 Ateou Tribal House

1982. Traditional Houses.

683	**213**	52f. multicoloured	3·25	4·00

214 Grey's Fruit Dove

1982. Birds. Multicoloured.

684	32f. Type **214**	2·75	4·75
685	35f. Rainbow lory	3·00	5·25

215 Canoe

1982. Central Education Co-operation Office.

686	**215**	48f. multicoloured	3·25	5·00

216 Bernheim and Library

1982. Bernheim Library, Noumea.

687	**216**	36f. brown, purple & blk	2·10	3·75

1983. Air. Rocks and Minerals (2nd series). As T **206**. Multicoloured.

688	44f. Paya gypsum (vert)	3·25	4·00
689	59f. Kone silica (vert)	4·50	4·50

217 *Dendrobium oppositifolium*

1983. Orchids. Multicoloured.

690	10f. Type **217**	1·30	3·00
691	15f. *Dendrobium munificum*	1·90	2·30

692 29f. *Dendrobium fractiflexum* 2·75 2·40

218 WCY Emblem, Map of New Caledonia and Globe

1983. Air. World Communications Year.
693 **218** 170f. multicoloured 6·00 7·75

219 *Crinum asiaticum*

1983. Flowers. Multicoloured.
694 1f. Type **219** 65 95
695 2f. *Xanthostemon aurantiacum* 65 1·40
696 4f. *Metrosideros demonstrans* (vert) 65 3·50

220 Wall Telephone and Noumea Post Office, 1890

1983. 25th Anniv of Post and Telecommunications Office. Multicoloured.
697 30f. Type **220** 2·10 3·75
698 40f. Telephone and Noumea Post Office, 1936 2·30 4·25
699 50f. Push-button telephone and Noumea Post Office, 1972 2·75 4·50
MS700 114×94 mm. As Nos. 697/9 but colours changed 14·00 30·00

221 *Laticaudata laticaudata*

1983. Noumea Aquarium. Sea Snakes. Multicoloured.
701 31f. Type **221** 2·50 2·75
702 33f. *Laticauda colubrina* 2·75 4·25

1983. Air. New Caledonian Aircraft (2nd series). As T **205**. Each red, mauve & brown.
712 46f. Mignet HM14 *Pou du Ciel* 4·25 5·00
713 61f. Caudron C-600 Aiglon 5·00 4·50

223 Bangkok Temples

1983. Air. Bangkok 1983 International Stamp Exhibition.
714 **223** 47f. multicoloured 2·50 5·50

224 Volleyball

1983. Seventh South Pacific Games, Western Samoa.
715 **224** 16f. purple, blue and red 1·90 4·50

225 Oueholle

1983. Air.
716 **225** 76f. multicoloured 3·75 5·00

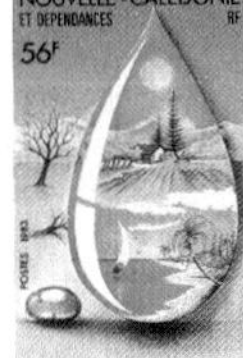

226 Desert and Water Drop showing Fertile Land

1983. Water Resources.
717 **226** 56f. multicoloured 2·75 4·75

227 Barn Owl

1983. Birds of Prey. Multicoloured.
718 34f. Type **227** 3·00 5·25
719 37f. Osprey 3·25 5·50

228 *Young Man on Beach* (R. Mascart)

1983. Air. Paintings. Multicoloured.
720 100f. Type **228** 5·50 5·50
721 350f. *Man with Guitar* (P. Nielly) 14·00 13·50

229 *Conus chenui*

1984. Sea Shells (1st series). Multicoloured.
722 5f. Type **229** 1·60 1·90
723 15f. Molucca cone 1·80 4·00
724 20f. *Conus optimus* 2·30 4·50
See also Nos. 761/2 and 810/11.

230 *St. Joseph* (freighter)

1984. Ships (3rd series). Each black, red and blue.
725 18f. Type **230** 2·30 4·50
726 31f. *Saint Antoine* (freighter) 2·50 3·25

231 Yellow-tailed Anemonefish

1984. Air. Noumea Aquarium. Fish. Multicoloured.
727 46f. Type **231** 3·25 3·25
728 61f. Bicoloured angelfish 4·25 6·00

232 Arms of Noumea

1984
729 **232** 35f. multicoloured 2·30 2·75

233 *Araucaria columnaris*

1984. Air. Trees. Multicoloured.
730 51f. Type **233** 3·25 2·75
731 67f. *Pritchardiopsis jeanneneyi* 4·25 3·75

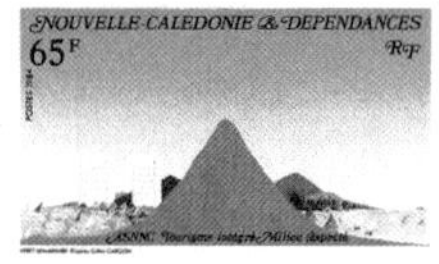

234 Tourist Centres

1984. Nature Protection.
732 **234** 65f. multicoloured 3·25 4·75

235 Swimming

1984. Air. Olympic Games, Los Angeles. Multicoloured.
733 50f. Type **235** 2·50 5·75
734 83f. Windsurfing 5·25 5·25
735 200f. Marathon 9·00 14·00

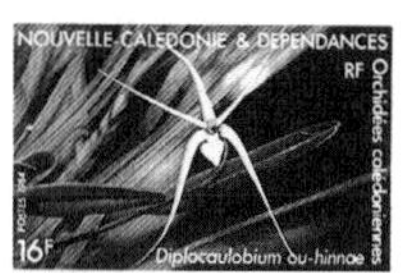

236 *Diplocaulobium ou-hinnae*

1984. Orchids. Multicoloured.
736 16f. Type **236** 1·90 4·50
737 38f. *Acianthus atepalus* 2·75 3·75

237 Royal Exhibition Hall, Melbourne

1984. Air. Ausipex 84 International Stamp Exhibition, Melbourne.
738 **237** 150f. green, brown & mve 6·25 11·50
MS739 143×104 mm. **237** 150f. mauve and violet 10·00 19·00

238 School and Arrow Sign-post

1984. Centenary of Public Education.
740 **238** 59f. multicoloured 2·75 2·50

239 Anchor, Rope and Stars

1984. Air. Armed Forces Day.
741 **239** 51f. multicoloured 2·75 4·50

240 *Women looking for Crabs* (Mme. Bonnet de Larbogne)

1984. Air. Art. Multicoloured.
742 120f. Type **240** 5·25 4·75
743 300f. *Cook discovering New Caledonia* (tapestry by Pilioko) 12·50 19·00

241 Kagu

1985
744 **241** 1f. blue 1·00 2·75
745 **241** 2f. green 1·00 2·00
746 **241** 3f. orange 1·10 2·00
747 **241** 4f. green 1·10 3·50
748 **241** 5f. mauve 1·00 2·75
749 **241** 35f. red 2·10 3·00
750 **241** 38f. red 2·10 3·00
751 **241** 40f. red 2·30 4·25

For similar design but with "& DEPENDANCES" omitted, see Nos. 837/43.

1985. Sea Shells (2nd series). As T **229**. Multicoloured.
761 55f. Bubble cone 2·75 3·50
762 72f. Lambert's cone 3·25 4·50

243 Weather Station transmitting Forecast to Boeing 737 and Trawler

1985. World Meteorology Day.
763 **243** 17f. multicoloured 2·30 3·50

244 Map and Hands holding Red Cross

1985. International Medicines Campaign.
764 **244** 41f. multicoloured 2·75 4·50

245 Electronic Telephone Exchange

1985. Inaug of Electronic Telephone Equipment.
765 **245** 70f. multicoloured 3·25 3·75

246 Marguerite la Foa Suspension Bridge

1985. Protection of Heritage.
766 **246** 44f. brown, red and blue 2·50 4·75

247 Kagu with Magnifying Glass and Stamp

1985. Le Cagou Stamp Club.
767 **247** 220f. multicoloured 8·50 11·50
MS768 120×100 mm. No. 767 (sold at 230f.) 13·00 21·00

248 Festival Emblem

1985. Fourth Pacific Arts Festival, Papeete. Mult.

769	55f. Type **248**		2·10	5·25
770	75f. Girl blowing trumpet triton		3·25	6·00

249 Flowers, Barbed Wire and Starving Child

1985. International Youth Year.

771	**249**	59f. multicoloured	2·75	4·75

250 *Amedee Lighthouse* (M. Hosken)

1985. Electrification of Amedee Lighthouse.

772	**250**	89f. multicoloured	3·25	3·50

251 Tree and Seedling

1985. Planting for the Future.

773	**251**	100f. multicoloured	3·50	4·50

252 de Havilland Dragon Rapide and Route Map

1985. Air. 30th Anniv of First Regular Internal Air Service.

774	**252**	80f. multicoloured	5·25	6·00

253 Hands and UN Emblem

1985. 40th Anniv of U.N.O.

775	**253**	250f. multicoloured	7·75	11·50

254 School, Map and "Nautilus"

1985. Air. Jules Garnier High School.

776	**254**	400f. multicoloured	14·50	15·00

255 Purple Swamphen

1985. Birds. Multicoloured.

777	50f. Type **255**		2·00	5·50
778	60f. Island thrush		2·75	4·75

256 Aircraft Tail Fins and Eiffel Tower

1986. Air. 30th Anniv of Scheduled Paris-Noumea Flights.

779	**256**	72f. multicoloured	3·75	5·75

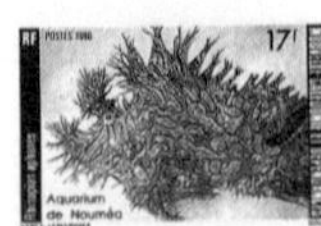
257 Merlet Scorpionfish

1986. Noumea Aquarium. Multicoloured.

780	10f. Emperor angelfish		75	2·30
781	17f. Type **257**		1·00	4·25

258 Kanumera Bay, Isle of Pines

1986. Landscapes (1st series). Multicoloured.

782	50f. Type **258**		1·80	4·75
783	55f. Inland village		2·00	3·00

See also Nos. 795/6 and 864/5.

259 *Bavayia sauvagii*

1986. Geckos. Multicoloured.

784	20f. Type **259**		1·30	3·00
785	45f. *Rhacodactylus leachianus*		2·10	5·00

260 Players and Azteca Stadium

1986. World Cup Football Championship, Mexico.

786	**260**	60f. multicoloured	2·20	5·75

261 Vivarium, Nou Island

1986. Air. Protection of Heritage.

787	**261**	230f. deep brown, blue and brown	7·25	10·50

262 Pharmaceutical Equipment

1986. 120th Anniv of First Pharmacy.

788	**262**	80f. multicoloured	2·75	6·00

263 *Coelogynae licastioides*

1986. Orchids. Multicoloured.

789	44f. Type **263**		2·10	4·75
790	58f. *Calanthe langei*		2·75	3·75

264 Black-backed Magpie

1986. Stampex 86 National Stamp Exhibition, Adelaide.

791	**264**	110f. multicoloured	4·50	9·50

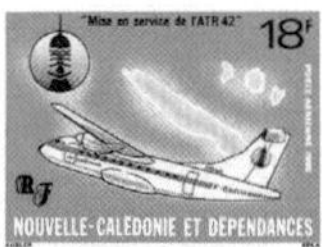
265 Aerospatiale/Aeritalia ATR 42 over New Caledonia

1986. Air. Inaugural Flight of ATR 42.

792	**265**	18f. multicoloured	2·10	4·25

266 Emblem and 1860 Stamp

1986. Air. Stockholmia 86 International Stamp Exhibition.

793	**266**	108f. black, red and lilac	4·25	6·75

267 Arms of Mont Dore

1986

794	**267**	94f. multicoloured	3·75	6·00

1986. Landscapes (2nd series). As T **258**. Multicoloured.

795	40f. West coast (vert)		1·50	2·20
796	76f. South		2·50	3·00

268 Wild Flowers

1986. Association for Nature Protection.

797	**268**	73f. multicoloured	3·50	5·75

269 Club Banner

1986. 25th Anniv of Noumea Lions Club.

798	**269**	350f. multicoloured	9·50	21·00

270 *Moret Bridge* (Alfred Sisley)

1986. Paintings. Multicoloured.

799	74f. Type **270**		3·25	4·00
800	140f. *Hunting Butterflies* (Berthe Morisot)		5·75	4·50

271 Emblem and Sound Waves

1987. Air. 25th Anniv of New Caledonia Amateur Radio Association.

801	**271**	64f. multicoloured	2·30	5·50

272 *Challenge France*

1987. America's Cup Yacht Race. Multicoloured.

802	30f. Type **272**		2·00	4·75
803	70f. *French Kiss*		2·75	6·00

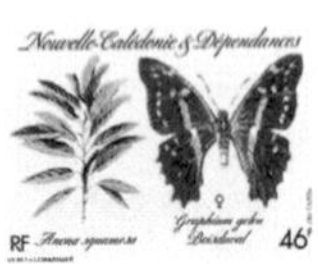
273 *Anona squamosa* and *Graphium gelon*

1987. Plants and Butterflies. Multicoloured.

804	46f. Type **273**		3·25	5·00
805	54f. *Abizzia granulosa* and *Polyura gamma*		3·75	5·50

274 Peaceful Landscape, Earphones and Noisy Equipment

1987. Air. Nature Protection. Campaign against Noise.

806	**274**	150f. multicoloured	5·75	6·25

275 Isle of Pines Canoe

1987. Canoes. Each brown, green and blue.

807	72f. Type **275**		2·50	5·75
808	90f. Ouvea canoe		3·25	4·50

276 Town Hall

1987. New Town Hall, Mont Dore.

809	**276**	92f. multicoloured	3·25	6·00

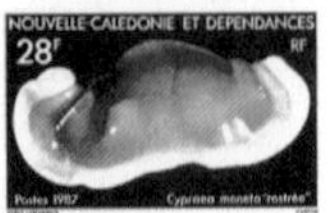
277 Money Cowrie

1987. Sea Shells (3rd series). Multicoloured.

810	28f. Type **277**		1·80	4·50
811	36f. Martin's cone		2·30	4·75

278 Games Emblem

1987. Eighth South Pacific Games. Noumea (1st issue).

812	**278**	40f. multicoloured	1·90	3·00

See also Nos. 819/21.

279 Emblem

1987. 13th Soroptimists International Convention, Melbourne.

813	**279**	270f. multicoloured	8·50	14·50

280 New Caledonia White-Eye

1987. Birds. Multicoloured.

814	18f. Type **280**	1·40	4·25
815	21f. Peregrine falcon (vert)	1·40	4·25

281 Flags on Globe

1987. 40th Anniv of South Pacific Commission.

816	**281**	200f. multicoloured	7·50	10·50

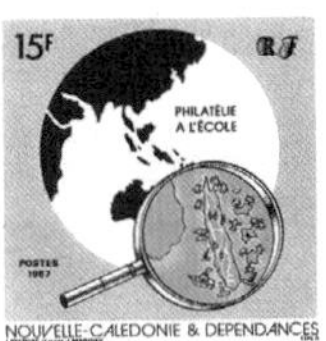

282 Globe and Magnifying Glass on Map of New Caledonia

1987. Schools Philately.

817	**282**	15f. multicoloured	1·40	4·00

283 Cricketers

1987. Air. French Cricket Federation.

818	**283**	94f. multicoloured	4·25	5·75

284 Golf

1987. Eighth South Pacific Games, Noumea (2nd issue). Multicoloured.

819	20f. Type **284**	1·50	4·00
820	30f. Rugby football	2·30	4·25
821	100f. Long jumping	3·75	6·00

285 Arms of Dumbea

1988. Air.

822	**285**	76f. multicoloured	3·25	3·00

286 Route Map, *L'Astrolabe*, *La Boussole* and La Perouse

1988. Bicentenary of Disappearance of La Perouse's Expedition.

823	**286**	36f. blue, brown and red	4·75	3·50

287 University

1988. French University of South Pacific, Noumea and Papeete.

824	**287**	400f. multicoloured	11·50	14·00

288 Semicircle Angelfish

1988. Noumea Aquarium. Fishes. Multicoloured.

825	30f. Type **288**	2·50	4·00
826	46f. Sapphire sergeant major	2·75	4·75

289 Mwaringou House, Canala

1988. Traditional Huts. Each brown, green and blue.

827	19f. Type **289**	1·10	4·00
828	21f. Nathalo house, Lifou (horiz)	1·40	3·75

290 Anniversary Emblem

1988. 125th Anniv of International Red Cross.

829	**290**	300f. blue, green and red	10·50	8·25

291 *Ochrosia elliptica*

1988. Medicinal Plants. Multicoloured.

830	28f. Type **291** (postage)	1·50	4·00
831	64f. *Rauvolfia sevenetii* (air)	3·00	4·75

292 *Gymnocrinus richeri*

1988. Marine Fauna.

832	**292**	51f. multicoloured	3·25	4·50

293 Furnished Room and Building Exterior

1988. Bourail Museum and Historical Association.

833	**293**	120f. multicoloured	4·50	7·50

294 La Perouse sighting Phillip's Fleet in Botany Bay

1988. Sydpex 88 Stamp Exhibition, Sydney. Multicoloured.

834	42f. Type **294**	2·75	5·00
835	42f. Phillip sighting *La Boussole* and *L'Astrolabe*	2·75	5·00

MS836 175×120 mm. Nos. 834/5 (sold at 120f.)	6·25	11·50

295 Kagu

1988

837	**295**	1f. blue	1·80	2·75
838	**295**	2f. green	1·80	3·25
839	**295**	3f. orange	1·80	3·75
840	**295**	4f. green	1·80	2·75
841	**295**	5f. mauve	1·80	3·50
842	**295**	28f. orange	2·40	3·75
843	**295**	40f. red	3·50	4·00

296 Table Tennis

1988. Olympic Games, Seoul.

846	**296**	150f. multicoloured	5·25	6·50

297 Laboratory Assistant, Noumea Institute and Pasteur

1988. Centenary of Pasteur Institute, Paris.

847	**297**	100f. red, black and blue	4·00	5·50

298 Georges Baudoux

1988. Writers.

848	**298**	72f. brown, green and purple (postage)	2·75	4·50
849	-	73f. brown, bl & blk (air)	3·00	4·00

Design:—73f. Jean Mariotti.

299 Map and Emblems

1988. Air. Rotary International Anti-Polio Campaign.

850	**299**	220f. multicoloured	7·75	8·00

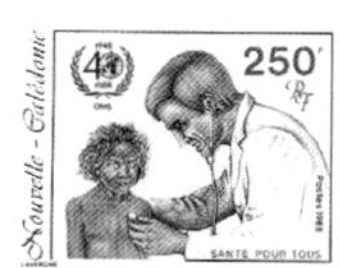

300 Doctor examining Child

1988. 40th Anniv of W.H.O.

851	**300**	250f. multicoloured	9·00	9·75

301 *Terre des Hommes* (L. Bunckley)

1988. Paintings. Multicoloured.

852	54f. Type **301**	3·50	4·75
853	92f. *Latin Quarter* (Marik)	4·50	6·00

302 Arms of Koumac

1989

854	**302**	200f. multicoloured	7·75	10·50

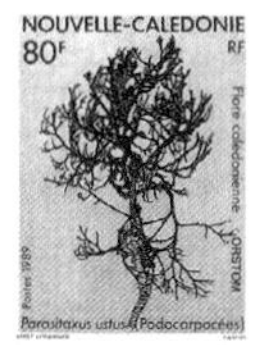

303 *Parasitaxus ustus*

1989. Flowers. Multicoloured.

855	80f. Type **303**	2·75	5·75
856	90f. *Tristaniopsis guillainii* (horiz)	3·75	6·00

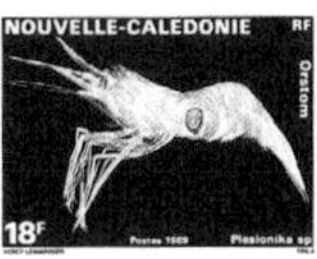

304 *Plesionika* sp.

1989. Marine Life. Multicoloured.

857	18f. Type **304**	1·90	3·75
858	66f. Stoutspine waspfish	3·25	5·50
859	110f. *Cristiate latiaxis*	4·50	4·75

305 "Liberty"

1989. Bicentenary of French Revolution and Philexfrance 89 International Stamp Exhibition, Paris. Multicoloured.

860	40f. Type **305** (postage)	3·25	2·75
861	58f. "Equality" (air)	3·50	3·00
862	76f. "Fraternity"	4·50	3·50

MS863 155×110 mm. 180f. "Liberty" "Equality" and "Fraternity" (92×51 mm)	10·50	15·00

1989. Landscapes (3rd series). As T **258**. Mult.

864	180f. Ouaieme ferry (post)	6·00	6·50
865	64f. 'The Broody Hen' (rocky islet), Hienghene (air)	2·30	5·00

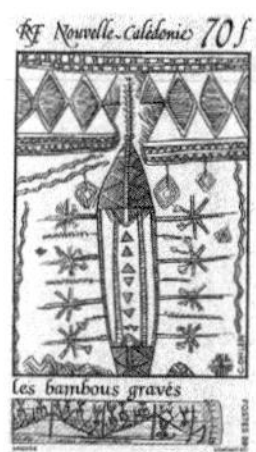

306 Canoe and Diamond Decoration

1989. Bamboo Decorations by C. Ohlen. Each black, bistre and orange.

866	70f. Type **306** (postage)	2·75	4·00
867	44f. Animal design (air)	1·80	4·25

307 Hobie Cat 14 Yachts

1989. Tenth World "Hobie Cat" Class Catamaran Championship, Noumea.

868 **307** 350f. multicoloured 10·50 17·00

308 Book Title Pages and Society Members

1989. 20th Anniv of Historical Studies Society.

869 **308** 74f. black and brown 3·00 2·75

309 Fort Teremba

1989. Protection of Heritage.

870 **309** 100f. green, brown & blue 3·75 6·00

310 *Rochefort's Escape* (Edouard Manet)

1989. Paintings. Multicoloured.

871 130f. Type **310** 4·75 5·25

872 270f. *Self-portrait* (Gustave Courbet) 9·50 14·00

311 Fr. Patrick O'Reilly

1990. Writers.

873 **311** 170f. black and mauve 6·75 8·25

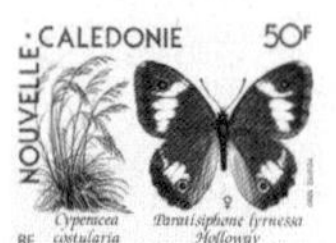

312 Grass and Female Butterfly

1990. "Cyperacea costularia" (grass) and "Paratisiphone lyrnessa" (butterfly). Multicoloured.

874 50f. Type **312** (postage) 3·25 4·75

875 18f. Grass and female butterfly (different) (air) 1·80 2·20

876 94f. Grass and male butterfly 5·00 6·00

313 "Maize" Stem with Face

1990. Kanaka Money.

877 **313** 85f. olive, orange & green 3·00 2·50

878 - 140f. orange, black & grn 5·00 7·00

Design: 140f. "Rope" stem with decorative end.

314 Exhibit

1990. Jade and Mother-of-pearl Exhibition.

879 **314** 230f. multicoloured 7·75 11·00

315 Ocellate Nudibranch

1990. Noumea Aquarium. Sea Slugs. Multicoloured.

880 10f. Type **315** 75 4·00

881 42f. *Chromodoris kuniei* (vert) 1·70 4·50

316 Head of *David* (Michelangelo) and Footballers

1990. World Cup Football Championship, Italy.

882 **316** 240f. multicoloured 9·50 8·50

317 De Gaulle

1990. Air. 50th Anniv of De Gaulle's Call to Resist.

883 **317** 160f. multicoloured 5·00 9·00

318 Neounda Site

1990. Petroglyphs.

884 **318** 40f. brown, green and red (postage) 1·80 3·25

885 - 58f. black, brown and blue (air) 2·50 3·25

Design:—Horiz: 58f. Kassducou site.

319 Map and Pacific International Meeting Centre

1990

886 **319** 320f. multicoloured 8·75 8·50

320 New Zealand Cemetery, Bourail

1990. Air. New Zealand 1990 International Stamp Exhibition, Auckland. Multicoloured.

887 80f. Type **320** 2·75 4·25

888 80f. Brigadier William Walter Dove 2·75 4·25

MS889 140×100 mm. 150f. Kagu, brown kiwi and maps of New Caledonia and New Zealand 7·50 13·00

321 Kagu

1990

890 **321** 1f. blue 2·10 4·00

891 **321** 2f. green 2·10 4·00

892 **321** 3f. yellow 2·10 4·00

893 **321** 4f. green 2·10 4·00

894 **321** 5f. violet 2·10 4·00

895 **321** 9f. grey 2·00 4·00

896 **321** 12f. red 2·30 4·00

897 **321** 40f. mauve 1·90 4·25

898 **321** 50f. red 2·00 4·50

899 **321** 55f. red 3·25 5·50

The 5 and 55f. exist both perforated with ordinary gum and imperforate with self-adhesive gum.

For design with no value expressed see No. 994.

322 *Munidopsis* sp

1990. Air. Deep Sea Animals. Multicoloured.

900 30f. Type **322** 1·40 3·00

901 60f. *Lyreidius tridentatus* 3·00 3·50

323 Emblem

1990. Air. 30th South Pacific Conference, Noumea.

902 **323** 85f. multicoloured 2·75 5·75

324 *Gardenia aubryi*

1990. Flowers. Multicoloured.

903 105f. Type **324** 3·75 6·00

904 130f. *Hibbertia baudouinii* 4·25 7·00

325 De Gaulle

1990. Air. Birth Centenary of Charles de Gaulle (French statesman).

905 **325** 410f. blue 12·50 14·50

326 *Mont Dore, Mountain of Jade* (C. Degroiselle)

1990. Air. Pacific Painters. Multicoloured.

906 365f. Type **326** (postage) 12·00 12·00

907 110f. *The Celieres House* (M. Petron) (air) 4·50 5·50

327 Fayawa-Ouvea Bay

1991. Air. Regional Landscapes. Multicoloured.

908 36f. Type **327** 2·10 3·25

909 90f. Coastline of Mare 3·00 4·00

328 Louise Michel and Classroom

1991. Writers.

910 **328** 125f. mauve and blue 5·25 7·00

911 - 125f. blue and brown 5·25 7·00

Design:—No. 911, Charles B. Nething and photographer.

329 Houailou Hut

1991. Melanesian Huts. Multicoloured.

912 12f. Type **329** 1·80 2·75

913 35f. Hienghene hut 2·40 4·25

330 Northern Province

1991. Provinces. Multicoloured.

914 45f. Type **330** 1·50 3·75

915 45f. Islands Province 1·50 3·75

916 45f. Southern Province 1·50 3·75

331 *Dendrobium biflorum*

1991. Orchids. Multicoloured.

917 55f. Type **331** 2·75 4·75

918 70f. *Dendrobium closterium* 3·00 5·00

332 Japanese Pineconefish

1991. Fish. Multicoloured.

919 60f. Type **332** 3·25 4·75

920 100f. Japanese bigeye 4·00 5·50

333 Research Equipment and Sites

1991. French Scientific Research Institute for Development and Co-operation.

921 **333** 170f. multicoloured 7·25 7·00

334 Emblem

1991. Ninth South Pacific Games, Papua New Guinea.

922 **334** 170f. multicoloured 7·25 7·00

335 Map and Dragon

1991. Centenary of Vietnamese Settlement in New Caledonia.

923 **335** 300f. multicoloured 10·00 13·00

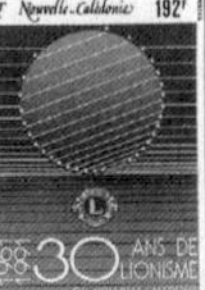

336 Emblems

1991. 30th Anniv of Lions International in New Caledonia.
924 **336** 192f. multicoloured 8·25 8·25

337 Map, *Camden* (missionary brig), Capt. Robert Clark Morgan and Trees

1991. 150th Anniv of Discovery of Sandalwood.
925 **337** 200f. blue, turquoise & grn 8·25 8·25

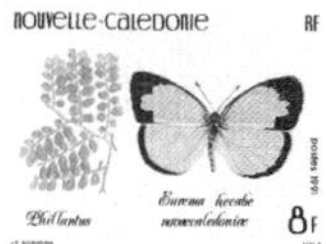

338 *Phillantus* and Common Grass Yellow

1991. Phila Nippon '91 International Stamp Exhibition, Tokyo. Plants and Butterflies. Mult.
926 8f. Type **338** 1·60 3·00
927 15f. *Pipturus incanus* and *Hypolimnas octocula* 1·60 3·00
928 20f. *Stachytarpheta urticaefolia* and meadow argos 1·80 3·25
929 26f. *Malaisia scandens* and *Cyrestis telamon* 1·80 3·25
MS930 100×122 mm. 75f. *Cyrestis telamon*; 75f. *Hypolimnas octocula*; 75f. *Eurema hecabe*; 75f. *Precis villida* (all vert) 16·00 23·00

339 Nickel Processing Plant and Dam

1991. 50th Anniv of Central Economic Co-operation Bank. Multicoloured.
931 76f. Type **339** 3·50 5·25
932 76f. Housing and hotels 3·50 5·25

340 *Caledonian Cricket* (Marcel Moutouh)

1991. Air. Pacific Painters. Multicoloured.
933 130f. Type **340** 5·75 6·25
934 435f. *Saint Louis* (Janine Goetz) 14·50 19·00

341 Blue River

1992. Air. Blue River National Park.
935 **341** 400f. multicoloured 14·00 14·50
MS936 127×91 mm. No. 935 (sold at 450f.) 15·00 20·00

342 La Madeleine Falls

1992. Nature Protection.
937 **342** 15f. multicoloured 1·30 3·25
MS938 122×88 mm. No. 937 (sold at 150f.) 6·25 7·00

343 Lapita Pot

1992. Air. Noumea Museum.
939 **343** 25f. black and orange 1·40 3·25

344 Barqueta Bridge

1992. Air. Expo '92 World's Fair, Seville.
940 **344** 10f. multicoloured 1·20 2·00

345 *Pinta*

1992. Air. World Columbian Stamp Expo '92, Chicago. Multicoloured.
941 80f. Type **345** 3·00 4·25
942 80f. *Santa Maria* 3·00 4·25
943 80f. *Nina* 3·00 4·25
MS944 160×70 mm. 110f. Eric the Red and longship; 110f. Christopher Columbus and Arms; 110f. Amerigo Vespucci (sold at 360f.) 12·50 15·00

346 Manchurian Crane and Kagu within "100"

1992. Centenary of Arrival of First Japanese Immigrants. Multicoloured, background colours given.
945 **346** 95f. yellow 3·75 4·00
946 **346** 95f. grey 3·75 4·00

347 Synchronised Swimming

1992. Olympic Games, Barcelona.
947 **347** 260f. multicoloured 8·50 7·25

348 Bell Airacobra, Grumman F4F Wildcat, Barrage Balloon, Harbour and Nissen Huts

1992. 50th Anniv of Arrival of American Forces in New Caledonia.
948 **348** 50f. multicoloured 3·25 3·50

349 *Wahpa* (Paul Mascart)

1992. Air. Pacific Painters.
949 **349** 205f. multicoloured 6·25 5·50

350 Australian Cattle Dog

1992. Air. Canine World Championships.
950 **350** 175f. multicoloured 5·75 5·25

351 Entrecasteaux and Fleet

1992. Air. Navigators. Bicentenary of Landing of Admiral Bruni d'Entrecasteaux on West Coast of New Caledonia.
951 **351** 110f. orange, blue & green 3·75 4·25

352 *Amalda fuscolingua*

1992. Air. Shells. Multicoloured.
952 30f. Type **352** 1·80 3·25
953 50f. *Cassis abbotti* 2·10 3·50

353 Deole

1992. Air. "La Brousse en Folie" (comic strip) by Bernard Berger. Multicoloured.
954 80f. Type **353** 3·00 3·25
955 80f. Tonton Marcel 3·00 3·25
956 80f. Tathan 3·00 3·25
957 80f. Joinville 3·00 3·25

354 Lagoon

1993. Lagoon Protection.
958 **354** 120f. multicoloured 4·25 4·75

355 *Harbour* (Gaston Roullet)

1993. Air. Pacific Painters.
959 **355** 150f. multicoloured 5·00 5·25

356 Symbols of New Caledonia

1993. School Philately. "Tourism my Friend".
960 **356** 25f. multicoloured 1·60 2·30

357 Still and Plantation

1993. Air. Centenary of Production of Essence of Niaouli.
966 **357** 85f. multicoloured 2·50 2·20

358 Planets and Copernicus

1993. Air. Polska '93 International Stamp Exhibition, Poznan. 450th Death Anniv of Nicolas Copernicus (astronomer).
967 **358** 110f. blue, turquoise & grey 3·75 4·25

359 Noumea Temple

1993. Air. Centenary of First Protestant Church in Noumea.
968 **359** 400f. multicoloured 11·50 10·00

1993. No. 898 surch **55F**.
969 **321** 55f. on 50f. red 1·90 3·50

361 Malabou

1993. Air. Regional Landscapes.
970 **361** 85f. multicoloured 2·75 3·00

362 Locomotive and Bridge

1993. Air. Centenary of Little Train of Thio.
971 **362** 115f. red, green and lilac 3·50 4·25

363 Rochefort

1993. Air. 80th Death Anniv of Henri Rochefort (journalist).
972 **363** 100f. multicoloured 3·25 4·00

364 *Megastylis paradoxa*

1993. Air. Bangkok 1993 International Stamp Exhibition, Thailand. Multicoloured.
973 30f. Type **364** 1·40 3·00
974 30f. *Vanda coerulea* 1·40 3·00
MS975 120×90 mm. 140f. Exhibition centre (51×39 mm) 5·50 6·75

365 Route Map and Boeing 737-300/500

1993. Air. Tenth Anniv of Air Cal (national airline).

976 **365** 85f. multicoloured 3·00 3·25

366 *Francois Arago* (cable ship)

1993. Air. Centenary of New Caledonia–Australia Telecommunications Cable.

977 **366** 200f. purple, blue & turq 5·50 5·75

367 *Oxypleurodon orbiculatus*

1993. Air. Deep-sea Life.

978 **367** 250f. multicoloured 7·00 7·25

368 Aircraft, Engine and Hangar

1993. Air. 25th Anniv of Chamber of Commerce and Industry's Management of La Tontouta Airport, Noumea.

979 **368** 90f. multicoloured 3·25 2·75

369 First Christmas Mass, 1843 (stained glass window, Balade church)

1993. Air. Christmas.

980 **369** 120f. multicoloured 4·00 4·25

370 Bourail

1993. Town Arms. Multicoloured.

981	70f. Type **370**	3·25	4·25
982	70f. Noumea	3·25	4·25
983	70f. Canala	3·25	4·25
984	70f. Kone	3·25	4·25
985	70f. Paita	3·25	4·25
986	70f. Dumbea	3·25	4·25
987	70f. Koumac	3·25	4·25
988	70f. Ponerihouen	3·25	4·25
989	70f. Kaamoo Hyehen	3·25	4·25
990	70f. Mont Dore	3·25	4·25
991	70f. Thio	3·25	4·25
992	70f. Kaala-Gomen	3·25	4·25
993	70f. Touho	3·25	4·25

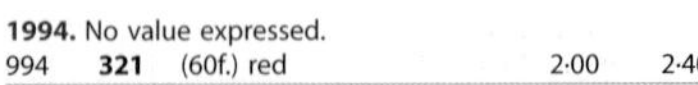

1994. No value expressed.

994 **321** (60f.) red 2·00 2·40

371 Dog, Exhibition Emblem and Chinese Horoscope Signs (New Year)

1994. Air. Hong Kong '94 International Stamp Exhibition. Multicoloured.

995 60f. Type **371** 2·20 3·50

MS996 161×120 mm. 105f. Giant panda (51×39 *mm*); 105f. Kagu (51×39 mm) 8·50 12·00

372 Airbus Industrie A340

1994. Air. First Paris–Noumea Airbus Flight. Self-adhesive.

997 **372** 90f. multicoloured 3·75 4·25

1994. Philexjeunes '94 Youth Stamp Exhibition, Grenoble. No. 960 optd **PHILEXJEUNES'94 GRENOBLE 22–24 AVRIL.**

998 **356** 25f. multicoloured 90 3·00

374 Photograph of Canala Post Office and Post Van

1994. 50th Anniv of Noumea–Canala Postal Service.

999 **374** 15f. brown, green and blue 1·50 3·00

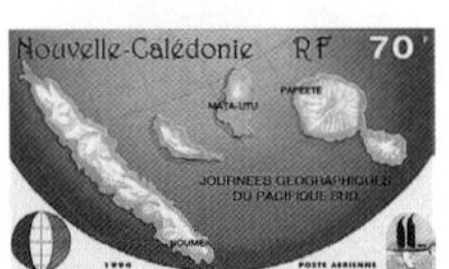

375 Pacific Islands on Globe

1994. Air. South Pacific Geographical Days.

1000 **375** 70f. multicoloured 2·50 3·00

376 Post Office, 1859

1994. Postal Administration Head Offices. Mult.

1001	30f. Type **376**	3·00	3·00
1002	60f. Posts and Telecommunications Office, 1936	4·00	3·25
1003	90f. Ministry of Posts and Telecommunications, 1967	4·75	4·25
1004	120f. Ministry of Posts and Telecommunications, 1993	5·75	5·00

377 *The Mask Wearer*

1994. Pacific Sculpture.

1005 **377** 60f. multicoloured 2·50 3·25

378 *Legend of the Devil Fish* (Micheline Neporon)

1994. Air. Pacific Painters.

1006 **378** 120f. multicoloured 4·00 4·25

379 *Chambeyronia macrocarpa*

1994. Flora

1007 **379** 90f. multicoloured 3·25 3·75

380 Podtanea Pot

1994. Air. Noumea Museum.

1008 **380** 95f. multicoloured 3·50 4·25

381 Trophy, US Flag and Ball

1994. Air. World Cup Football Championship, U.S.A.

1009 **381** 105f. multicoloured 3·50 4·50

1994. No. D707 with "Timbre Taxe" obliterated by black bar.

1010 **D222** 5f. multicoloured 17·00 7·25

382 Timor Deer

1994. Bourail Fair.

1011 **382** 150f. multicoloured 5·00 4·75

383 Korean Family

1994. Air. Philakorea 1994 International Stamp Exhibition, Seoul. Multicoloured.

1012 60f. Type **383** 3·25 2·75

MS1013 110×110 mm. 35f. Containers, peppers and emblem (36×37 mm); 35f. Carafe, celery, cannage and garlic (36×37 mm); 35f. Container and turnips (36×37 mm); 35f. Jug, seafood and lemon (36×37 mm) 8·25 10·50

384 *L'Atalante* (oceanographic research vessel)

1994. Air. ZoNeCo (evaluation programme of Economic Zone).

1014 **384** 120f. multicoloured 3·75 4·75

385 *Nivose*

1994. Attachment of the "Nivose" (French surveillance frigate) to New Caledonia. Multicoloured.

1015	30f. Type **385**	3·25	3·00
1016	30f. Aircraft over frigate	3·25	3·00
1017	30f. Frigate moored at quay	3·25	3·00
1018	60f. Frigate and map of New Caledonia on parchment	4·00	3·50
1019	60f. Ship's bell	4·00	3·50
1020	60f. Frigate and sailor	4·00	3·50

386 Driving Cattle

1994. Air. First European Stamp Salon, Flower Gardens, Paris. Multicoloured.

1021 90f. Aerial view of island 2·75 3·75

1022 90f. Type **386** 2·75 3·75

387 Paper Darts around Girl

1994. School Philately.

1023 **387** 30f. multicoloured 1·40 3·00

388 Jaques Nervat

1994. Writers.

1024 **388** 175f. multicoloured 5·00 5·50

389 Satellite transmitting to Globe and Computer Terminal

1994. Air. 50th Anniv of Overseas Scientific and Technical Research Office.

1025 **389** 95f. multicoloured 3·75 4·25

390 Emblem and Temple

1994. Air. 125th Anniv of Freemasonary in New Caledonia.

1026 **390** 350f. multicoloured 10·00 8·25

391 Thiebaghi Mine

1994. Air.

1027 **391** 90f. multicoloured 3·50 4·25

392 Place des Cocotiers, Noumea

1994. Christmas.

1028 **392** 30f. multicoloured 1·40 3·00

No. 1028 covers any one of five stamps which were issued together in horizontal *se-tenant* strips, the position of the bell, tree and monument differing on each stamp. The strip is stated to produce a three-dimensional image without use of a special viewer.

393 Globe and Newspapers

1994. 50th Anniv of *Le Monde* (newspaper).

1029	**393**	90f. multicoloured	3·25	4·00

394 1988 100f. Pasteur Institute Stamp

1995. Death Centenary of Louis Pasteur (chemist).

1030	**394**	120f. multicoloured	3·50	4·25

395 Pictorial Map

1995. Air. Tourism.

1031	**395**	90f. multicoloured	3·25	4·00

396 Profile of De Gaulle (Santucci) and Cross of Lorraine

1995. 25th Death Anniv of Charles de Gaulle (French President, 1959–69).

1032	**396**	1000f. deep blue, blue and gold	28·00	35·00

397 Emblem

1995. Pacific University Teachers' Training Institute.

1033	**397**	100f. multicoloured	3·50	4·50

398 *Sylviornis neocaledoniae*

1995

1034	**398**	60f. multicoloured	2·30	3·25

399 Swimming, Cycling and Running

1995. Triathlon.

1035	**399**	60f. multicoloured	2·10	3·50

400 Tent and Trees

1995. 50th Anniv of Pacific Franc.

1036	**400**	10f. multicoloured	1·10	2·75

No. 1036 covers any one of four stamps which were issued together in horizontal *se-tenant* strips, the position of the central motif rotating slightly in a clockwise direction from the left to the right-hand stamp. The strip is stated to produce a three-dimensional image without use of a special viewer.

401 Bourbon Palace (Paris), Map of New Caledonia and Chamber

1995. 50th Anniversaries. Multicoloured.

1037		60f. Type **401** (first representation of New Caledonia at French National Assembly)	2·10	3·25
1038		90f. National emblems, De Gaulle and Allied flags (end of Second World War)	3·00	3·75
1039		90f. UN Headquarters, New York (UNO)	2·75	3·75

402 *Sebertia acuminata*

1995

1040	**402**	60f. multicoloured	2·30	3·25

403 Common Noddy

1995. Singapore'95 International Stamp Exhibition. Sea Birds. Multicoloured.

1041	5f. Type **403**	1·00	1·80
1042	10f. Silver gull	1·10	2·00
1043	20f. Roseate tern	1·30	2·50
1044	35f. Osprey	1·60	3·00
1045	65f. Red-footed booby	2·00	3·75
1046	125f. Great frigate bird	4·00	4·50
MS1047	130×100 mm. Nos. 1041/6	12·00	17·00

404 Golf

1995. Tenth South Pacific Games.

1048	**404**	90f. multicoloured	3·25	4·00

405 *The Lizard Man* (Dick Bone)

1995. Pacific Sculpture.

1049	**405**	65f. multicoloured	2·40	3·50

406 Venue

1995. Air. 35th South Pacific Conference.

1050	**406**	500f. multicoloured	12·50	14·00

407 Silhouette of Francis Carco

1995. Writers.

1051	**407**	95f. multicoloured	2·75	4·25

408 Ouare

1995. Air. Kanak Dances. Multicoloured.

1052	95f. Type **408**	2·75	3·75
1053	100f. Pothe	3·25	4·00

409 Saw-headed Crocodilefish

1995. World of the Deep.

1054	**409**	100f. multicoloured	3·25	4·00

410 *Mekosuchus inexpectatus*

1996. Air.

1055	**410**	125f. multicoloured	3·50	4·50

411 Vessel with decorated Rim

1996. Noumea Museum.

1056	**411**	65f. multicoloured	2·00	3·50

412 *Captaincookia margaretae*

1996. Flowers. Multicoloured.

1057	65f. Type **412**	2·00	3·25
1058	95f. *Ixora cauliflora*	2·75	3·75

413 Pirogue on Beach

1996. World Pirogue Championships, Noumea. Multicoloured.

1059	30f. Type **413**	2·00	3·00
1060	65f. Pirogue leaving shore	2·75	3·25
1061	95f. Double-hulled pirogue	3·25	4·00
1062	125f. Sports pirogue	4·00	5·00

Nos. 1059/62 were issued together, *se-tenant*, forming a composite design.

414 Red Batfish

1996. China'96 International Stamp Exhibition, Peking. Deep Sea Life. Multicoloured.

1063	25f. Type **414**	1·20	2·75
1064	40f. *Perotrochus deforgesi* (slit shell)	1·50	3·00
1065	65f. *Mursia musorstomia* (crab)	2·40	3·25
1066	125f. Sea lily	4·00	5·00

415 *Sarcolchilus koghiensis*

1996. Capex'96 International Stamp Exhibition, Toronto, Canada. Orchids. Multicoloured.

1067	5f. Type **415**	40	2·30
1068	10f. *Phaius robertsii*	1·10	2·50
1069	25f. *Megastylis montana*	1·20	2·75
1070	65f. *Dendrobium macrophyllum*	2·10	3·25
1071	95f. *Dendrobium virotii*	3·25	3·75
1072	125f. *Ephemerantha comata*	3·75	4·25

416 Indonesian Couple beneath Tree

1996. Air. Centenary of Arrival of First Indonesian Immigrants.

1073	**416**	130f. multicoloured	4·25	5·25

417 Louis Brauquier

1996. Air. Writers.

1074	**417**	95f. multicoloured	3·00	3·75

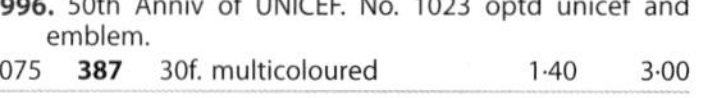

1996. 50th Anniv of UNICEF. No. 1023 optd unicef and emblem.

1075	**387**	30f. multicoloured	1·40	3·00

419 Dish Aerial

1996. Air. Anniversaries. Multicoloured.

1076	95f. Type **419** (20th anniv of New Caledonia's first Earth Station)	3·00	3·75
1077	125f. Guglielmo Marconi (inventor) and telegraph masts (centenary of radio-telegraphy)	4·00	5·00

420 Tribal Dance

1996. Air. Seventh South Pacific Arts Festival.

1078	**420**	100f. multicoloured	3·25	4·25

421 *The Woman* (Elija Trijikone)

1996. Sculptures of the Pacific.

1079	**421**	105f. multicoloured	3·25	4·25

422 Ordination, St. Joseph's Cathedral, Noumea

1996. 50th Anniv of Ordination of First Priests in New Caledonia.

1080 **422** 160f. multicoloured 4·50 5·00

423 *Man* (Paula Boi)

1996. Pacific Painters.

1081 **423** 200f. multicoloured 5·75 6·25

424 Gaica Dance

1996

1082 **424** 500f. multicoloured 14·00 12·00

425 Great Reef

1996. Air. 50th Autumn Stamp Show, Paris. Multicoloured.

1083 95f. Type **425** 3·00 3·75

1084 95f. Mount Koghi 3·00 3·75

426 Decorated Sandman

1996. Christmas.

1085 **426** 95f. multicoloured 3·00 3·50

427 Horned Tortoises

1997. Air.

1086 **427** 95f. multicoloured 3·00 4·25

428 Emblem

1997. Air. 50th Anniv of South Pacific Commission.

1087 **428** 100f. multicoloured 3·00 4·50

429 Junk, Hong Kong, Ox and Flag

1997. Air. Hong Kong '97 International Stamp Exhibiton. Year of the Ox. Multicoloured.

1088 95f. Type **429** 3·25 3·75

MS1089 121×91 mm. 75f. Farmer ploughing with ox (39×29 mm); 75f. Cattle grazing (39×29 mm) 5·25 8·50

430 Mitterrand

1997. First Death Anniv of Francois Mitterrand (French President, 1981–95).

1090 **430** 1000f. multicoloured 25·00 31·00

431 Windmill (*Letters from My Windmill*)

1997. Death Centenary of Alphonse Daudet (writer). Multicoloured.

1091 65f. Type **431** 2·50 2·75

1092 65f. Boy sitting by wall (*The Little Thing*) 2·50 2·75

1093 65f. Hunter in jungle (*Tartarinde Tarascon*) 2·50 2·75

1094 65f. Daudet at work 2·50 2·75

MS1095 100×120 mm. Nos. 1091/4 9·50 12·50

432 Lapita Pot with Geometric Pattern

1997. Air. Melanesian Pottery in Noumea Museum. Multicoloured.

1096 95f. Type **432** 3·00 4·25

1097 95f. Lapita pot with "face" design 3·00 4·25

433 French Parliament Building and Lafleur

1997. Appointment of Henri Lafleur as First New Caledonian Senator in French Parliament.

1098 **433** 105f. multicoloured 3·25 4·50

434 Cotton Harlequin Bug

1997. Insects. Multicoloured.

1099 65f. Type **434** 3·00 3·75

1100 65f. *Kanakia gigas* 3·00 3·75

1101 65f. *Aenetus cohici* (moth) 3·00 3·75

435 Iekawe

1997. Fifth Death Anniv of Jacques Ieneic Iekawe (first Melanesian Prefect).

1102 **435** 250f. multicoloured 7·50 8·25

436 Consolidated Catalina Flying Boat and South Pacific Routes Map

1997. Air. 50th Anniv of Establishment by TRAPAS of First Commercial Air Routes in South Pacific. Multicoloured.

1103 95f. Type **436** 2·75 4·25

1104 95f. TRAPAS emblem, seaplane and New Caledonia domestic flight routes 2·75 4·25

437 Kagu

1997

1105 **437** 5f. violet 1·30 1·30

1106 **437** 30f. orange 1·40 3·00

1107 **437** 95f. blue 3·00 4·25

1108 **437** 100f. blue 3·25 4·00

No. 1008 also comes self-adhesive.
See also No. 1128.

438 Cup and Harness Racing

1997. Equestrian Sports. Multicoloured.

1118 65f. Type **438** 2·40 3·25

1119 65f. Cup and horse racing 2·40 3·25

439 Port de France (engraving)

1997

1120 **439** 95f. multicoloured 3·00 3·75

440 Marianne, Voter and Tiki

1997. 50th Anniv of First Elections of Melanesian Representatives to French Parliament.

1121 **440** 150f. multicoloured 4·25 5·25

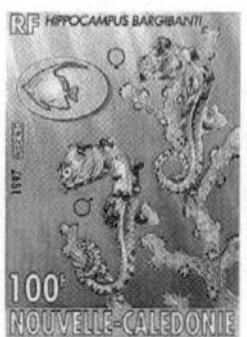

441 Seahorses

1997. Fifth Indo-Pacific Fishes Conference.

1122 **441** 100f. multicoloured 3·75 3·75

442 Hammerhead Shark Dance Mask (Ken Thaiday)

1997. Pacific Art and Culture. Multicoloured.

1123 100f. Type **442** 3·00 4·50

1124 100f. Painting of traditional Melanesian images by Yvette Bouquet 3·00 4·50

1125 100f. *Doka* (figurines by Frank Haikiu) 3·00 4·50

443 Father Christmas surfing to Earth

1997. Christmas. Multicoloured.

1126 95f. Type **443** 3·00 3·50

1127 100f. Dolphin with "Meilleurs Voeux" banner 3·25 3·75

1998. As Nos. 1107/13 but with no value expressed. Ordinary or self-adhesive gum.

1128 **437** (70f.) red 2·50 3·25

444 *Lentinus tuber-regium*

1998. Edible Mushrooms. Multicoloured.

1130 70f. Type **444** 2·00 2·50

1131 70f. *Morchella anteridiformis* 2·00 2·50

1132 70f. *Volvaria bombycina* 2·00 2·50

445 Mask from Northern Region

1998. Territorial Museum. Multicoloured.

1133 105f. Type **445** 3·00 2·75

1134 110f. Section of door frame from Central Region 3·00 2·75

446 Painting by Gauguin

1998. 150th Birth Anniv of Paul Gauguin (painter).

1135 **446** 405f. multicoloured 12·00 8·75

447 Player

1998. World Cup Football Championship, France.

1136 **447** 100f. multicoloured 3·00 3·75

448 *Mitimitia*

1998. Tjibaou Cultural Centre. Multicoloured.

1137	30f. Type **448**	1·60	2·75
1138	70f. Jean-Marie Tjibaou (politician) and Centre	2·10	3·25
1139	70f. Detail of a Centre building (Renzo Piano) (vert)	2·10	3·25
1140	105f. *Man Bird* (Mathias Kauage) (vert)	3·25	3·75

449 Broken Chains and Slaves

1998. 150th Anniv of Abolition of Slavery.

1141	**449**	130f. brown, blue and purple	3·25	3·50

450 Dogs watching Postman delivering Letter

1998. Stamp Day.

1142	**450**	70f. multicoloured	2·30	3·00

451 Vincent Bouquet

1998. 50th Anniv of Election of First President of Commission of Chiefs.

1143	**451**	110f. multicoloured	3·00	3·75

452 Noumea Fantasia, 1903

1998. 100 Years of Arab Presence.

1144	**452**	80f. multicoloured	2·30	2·50

453 Departure

1998. Portugal 98 International Stamp Exhibition, Lisbon. 500th Anniv of Vasco da Gama's Voyage to India via Cape of Good Hope. Multicoloured.

1145	100f. Type **453**	3·00	3·50
1146	100f. Fleet at Cape of Good Hope	3·00	3·50
1147	100f. Vasco da Gama meeting Indian king	3·00	3·50
1148	100f. Vasco da Gama in armorial shield flanked by plants	3·00	3·50
MS1149	160×130 mm. 70f. Route map (39×51 mm); 70f. Vasco da Gama (39×51 mm); 70f. *Sao Gabriel* (flagship) and fleet (39×51 mm)	7·00	9·75

454 Kagu

1998. Endangered Species. The Kagu. Multicoloured.

1150	5f. Type **454**	1·00	85
1151	10f. Kagu by branch	1·10	85
1152	15f. Two kagus	1·20	90
1153	70f. Two kagus, one with wings outspread	2·10	2·50

455 Liberty Trees

1998. 50th Anniv of Universal Declaration of Human Rights.

1154	**455**	70f. green, black and blue	2·40	2·50

456 *Prison, Nou Island* (engraving)

1998

1155	**456**	155f. multicoloured	4·25	4·50

457 View of Island

1998. Regional Scenes. Multicoloured.

1156	100f. Type **457**	3·00	3·50
1157	100f. View of sea	3·00	3·50

458 Switchboard, Post Van, Postman on Bicycle and Post Office (1958)

1998. 40th Anniv of Posts and Telecommunications Office. Multicoloured.

1158	70f. Type **458**	2·75	2·50
1159	70f. Automatic service machine, woman with mobile phone, dish aerial, motorcycle courier and post office (1998)	2·75	2·50

459 Marine Life forming Christmas Tree ("Merry Christmas")

1998. Greetings stamps. Multicoloured.

1160	100f. Type **459**	3·50	3·50
1161	100f. Treasure chest ("Best Wishes")	3·50	3·50
1162	100f. Fish ("Good Holiday")	3·50	3·50
1163	100f. Fish and reefs ("Happy Birthday")	3·50	3·50

460 Map, Memorial and *Monique*

1998. 20th Anniv of Erection of Memorial to the Victims of the "Monique" (inter-island freighter) Disaster.

1164	**460**	130f. multicoloured	4·75	4·50

461 *Argiope aetherea*

1999. Spiders. Multicoloured.

1165	70f. Type **461**	2·75	2·40
1166	70f. *Latrodectus hasselti*	2·75	2·40
1167	70f. *Cyrtophora moluccensis*	2·75	2·40
1168	70f. *Barycheloides alluvviophilus*	2·75	2·40

462 Tooth

1999. Giant-toothed Shark. (Carcharodon megalodon). Multicoloured.

1169	100f. Type **462**	3·50	3·50
MS1170	90×120 mm. 70f. Giant-toothed shark (29×39 mm); 70f. Diver, giant-toothed shark and great white shark (39×29 mm); 70f. Decaying tooth and section of jawbone (triangular, 55×28 mm)	8·25	9·75

463 Athletics

1999. 11th South Pacific Games. Multicoloured.

1171	5f. Type **463**	1·60	70
1172	10f. Tennis	1·70	75
1173	30f. Karate	1·80	2·50
1174	70f. Baseball	3·00	2·75

464 Bwanjep

1999. Traditional Musical Instruments. Mult.

1175	30f. Type **464**	1·70	1·10
1176	70f. Bells	2·40	2·50
1177	100f. Flutes	3·50	3·50

465 Scene from *Les Filles de la Neama* and Bloc

1999. 29th Death Anniv of Paul Bloc (writer).

1178	**465**	105f. blue, green & purple	4·00	3·50

466 School Building and Computer

1999. 20th Anniv of Auguste Escoffier Commercial and Hotelier Professional School. Multicoloured.

1179	70f. Type **466**	2·75	2·50
1180	70f. School building and chef's hat	2·75	2·50

467 Unloading Supplies, Helicopters and Map

1999. Humanitarian Aid.

1181	**467**	135f. multicoloured	5·00	4·50

468 10c. Napoleon III Stamp, 1860

1999. 140th Anniv (2000) of First New Caledonian Stamp and Philexfrance 99 International Stamp Exhibition, Paris.

1182	**468**	70f. multicoloured	2·75	2·50
MS1183		155×110 mm. 100f. black (two 1860 10c. stamps) (recess) (36×29 mm); 100f. multicoloured (1860 10c. stamp) (thermography) (36×29 mm); 100f. Close-up of Napoleon's head (litho) (36×29 mm); 100f. gold and black (1860 10c. stamp) (embossing); 700f. 1997 Kagu design and hologram of Napoleon's head (44×35 mm)	39·00	46·00

469 Food Platter

1999. Hotels and Restaurants. Multicoloured.

1184	5f. Type **469**	45	70
1185	30f. Seafood platter	1·20	90
1186	70f. Hotel cabins by lake	2·30	2·20
1187	100f. Modern hotel and swimming pool	3·50	3·50

470 Eiffel Tower, Lighthouse with 1949 and 1999 Aircraft

1999. Air. 50th Anniv of First Paris–Noumea Scheduled Flight.

1188	**470**	100f. multicoloured	4·00	3·50

471 Paintings

1999

1189	**471**	70f. multicoloured	2·75	2·40

472 Aji Aboro (Kanak dance)

1999

1190	**472**	70f. multicoloured	2·75	2·40

473 Chateau Hagen

1999. Historic Monuments of South Province.

1191	**473**	155f. multicoloured	5·50	4·75

474 Children protecting Tree

1999. Nature Protection: "Don't touch my Tree".

1192	**474**	30f. multicoloured	2·75	1·10

475 Children around Tree

1999. Greetings Stamps. Multicoloured.

1193	100f. Type **475** ("Merry Christmas")	3·75	3·25
1194	100f. Children with flowers and star ("Best Wishes 2000")	3·75	3·25
1195	100f. Children and Year 2000 cake ("Happy Birthday")	3·75	3·25
1196	100f. Children looking in pram ("Congratulations")	3·75	3·25

476 Amedee Lighthouse

2000

1197	**476**	100f. multicoloured	4·50	3·75

477 *L'Emile Renouf* (four-masted steel barque)

2000. Centenary of Loss of Emile Renouf on Durand Reef, Insel Mare.

1198	**477**	135f. multicoloured	5·25	4·50

478 *Painted Shells* (Gilles Subileau)

2000. Pacific Painters.

1199	**478**	155f. multicoloured	6·00	5·00

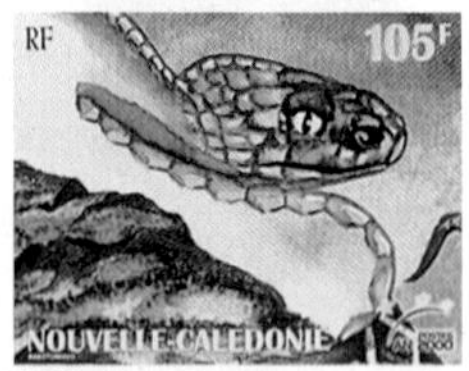

479 Snake

2000. Chinese New Year. Year of the Dragon. Sheet 121×90 mm containing T **479** and similar horiz design. Multicoloured.

MS1200	105f. Type **479**; 105f. Dragon	7·50	8·00

480 Prawn

2000. Noumia Aquarium. Multicoloured.

1201	70f. Type **480**	3·50	2·75
1202	70f. Fluorescent corals	3·50	2·75
1203	70f. Hump-headed wrasse (*Cheilinus undulatus*)	3·50	2·75

481 Lockheed P-38 Lightning Fighter

2000. Air. Birth Centenary of Antoine de Saint-Exupery (writer and pilot).

1204	**481**	130f. multicoloured	5·00	4·50

482 Aerial View

2000. Mangrove Swamp, Voh.

1205	**482**	100f. multicoloured	4·00	3·00

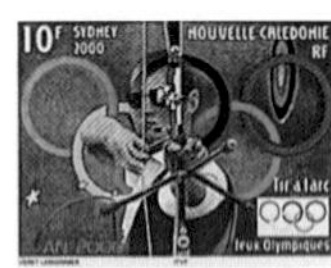

483 Archery

2000. Olympic Games, Sydney. Multicoloured.

1206	10f. Type **483**	2·50	1·80
1207	30f. Boxing	2·75	1·90
1208	80f. Cycling	3·25	3·00
1209	100f. Fencing	3·50	3·50

484 Museum Exhibit

2000. Museum of New Caledonia. Multicoloured.

1210	90f. Type **484**	3·25	3·00
1211	105f. Museum exhibit	4·00	3·50

485 Library Building and Lucien Bernheim

2000. Bernheim Library, Noumea.

1212	**485**	500f. brown, blue and green	17·00	16·00

486 Painting

2000. Eighth Pacific Arts Festival, Kanaky, New Caledonia. Sheet 120×90 mm containing T **486** and similar horiz designs. Multicoloured.

MS1213	70f. Type **486**; 70f. Human figures; 70f. Stylized faces and fish; 70f. Stylized faces and fish on coloured squares	9·75	10·50

487 Henri Dunant (founder), Baby and Patients with Volunteers

2000. Red Cross.

1214	**487**	100f. multicoloured	3·75	3·50

488 Canoeist

2000. Regional Landscapes. Multicoloured.

1215	100f. Type **488**	3·75	3·50
1216	100f. Speedboat near island	3·75	3·50
1217	100f. Sunset and man on raft	3·75	3·50

489 Queen Hortense

2000

1218	**489**	110f. red, green and blue	4·00	3·75

490 Boy on Roller Skates (Kevyn Pamoiloun)

2000. "Philately at School". Entries in Children's Painting Competition. Multicoloured.

1219	70f. Type **490**	2·40	2·20
1220	70f. People using airborne vehicles (Lise-Marie Samanich)	2·40	2·20
1221	70f. Aliens (Alexandre Mandin)	2·40	2·20

491 Kagu Parents ("Congratulations")

2000. Greetings Stamps. Multicoloured.

1222	100f. Type **491**	3·50	3·00
1223	100f. Kagu on deck chair ("Happy Holidays")	3·50	3·00
1224	100f. Kagu with bunch of flowers ("Best Wishes")	3·50	3·00

492 The Nativity

2000. Christmas.

1225	**492**	100f. multicoloured	3·50	3·25

493 Snakes

2001. Chinese New Year. Year of the Snake. Multicoloured.

1226	100f. Type **493**	3·50	3·25
MS1227	130×91 mm. 70f. Snake and Pacific island; 70f. Snake and Chinese symbols	5·25	5·75

494 *France II* (barque)

2001. Reconstruction of France II.

1228	**494**	110f. multicoloured	3·75	3·50

495 Two Nautili

2001. Noumea Aquarium. The New Calendonia Nautilus. Multicoloured.

1229	100f. Type **495**	3·50	3·25
1230	100f. Section through nautilus	3·50	3·25
1231	100f. Two nautili (different)	3·50	3·25

496 New Caledonian Crow, Tools and Emblem

2001. Association for the Protection of New Caledonian Nature (ASNNC).

1232	**496**	70f. multicoloured	2·40	2·20

497 Humpback Whale and Calf

2001. Operation Cetaces (marine mammal South Pacific study programme). Multicoloured.

1233	100f. Type **497**	3·50	3·25
1234	100f. Whales leaping	3·50	3·25

498 *Guards of Gaia* (statue) (I.Waia)

2001. Ko Neva 2000 Prize Winner.

1235	**498**	70f. multicoloured	2·40	2·20

499 *Vision of Oceania* (J. Lebars)

2001

1236	**499**	110f. multicoloured	4·50	4·00

500 Profiles

2001. Year of Communication.

1237	**500**	265f. multicoloured	9·75	9·25

501 Air International Caledonie Airbus A310-300

2001. Air. First Anniv of Noumea–Osaka Passenger Service.

1238	**501**	110f. multicoloured	4·25	4·00

502 *The Solitary Boatman* (Marik)

2001. Pacific Painters.
1239 **502** 110f. multicoloured 4·25 4·00

503 Observation Capsule on Coral Reef

2001
1240 **503** 135f. multicoloured 5·25 5·00

504 Qanono Church, Lifou

2001
1241 **504** 500f. multicoloured 18·00 17·00

505 Fernande Leriche (educator and author)

2001
1242 **505** 155f. brown, red and blue 6·00 5·75

506 Cyclists

2001. First Olympic Gold Medal for New Caledonian Sportsman.
1243 **506** 265f. multicoloured 10·50 9·75

507 Kite Surfer

2001
1244 **507** 100f. multicoloured 4·00 3·75

508 Children on Book

2001. School Philately.
1245 **508** 70f. multicoloured 3·00 2·75

509 Easo

2001. Lifou Island. Multicoloured.
1246 100f. Type **509** 3·75 3·50
1247 100f. Jokin 3·75 3·50

510 Father Christmas

2001. Christmas. Multicoloured.
1248 100f. Type **510** 3·75 3·50
1249 100f. Bat with spotted wings and "Meilleurs Voeux" 3·75 3·50
1250 100f. Bat with party hat and red nose and "Vive la Fete" 3·75 3·50

511 Horse and Sea Horse

2002. Chinese New Year. Year of the Horse. Multicoloured.
1251 100f. Type **511** 4·50 3·75
MS1252 190×30 mm. 70f. Horse's head; 70f. Sea horse 5·25 5·50

512 Two Flying Foxes

2002. St. Valentine's Day.
1253 **512** 100f. multicoloured 4·50 3·75

513 Cricketer in Traditional Dress

2002. Cricket.
1254 **513** 100f. multicoloured 4·50 3·75

514 Ancient Axe

2002
1255 **514** 505f. multicoloured 18·00 17·00

515 Hobie 16 Catamaran

2002. Hobie 16 Catamaran World Championship.
1256 **515** 70f. multicoloured 3·00 2·75

516 Loggerhead Turtle (*Caretta caretta*)

2002. Noumea Aquarium. Sheet 185×120 mm in shape of turtle containing T **516** and similar horiz designs. Multicoloured.
MS1257 30f. Type **516**; 30f. Green sea turtle (*Chelonia mydas*); 70f. Hawksbill turtle (*Eretmochelys imbricata*) (inscr "imbricat"); 70f. Leatherback sea turtle (*Dermochelys coriacea*) 7·25 7·50

517 Player

2002. World Cup Football Championship 2002, Japan and South Korea.
1258 **517** 100f. multicoloured 4·50 3·75

518 Coffee Bean Plant

2002. Coffee Production. Multicoloured.
1259 70f. Type **518** 2·40 2·10
1260 70f. Coffee production process 2·40 2·10
1261 70f. Cafe and cup of coffee 2·40 2·10

519 *Alcmene* (French corvette)

2002. Exploration of Coast of New Caledonia by Alcmene.
1262 **519** 210f. multicoloured 7·50 7·00

520 Emma Piffault (statue)

2002. Emma Piffault Commemoration.
1263 **520** 10f. multicoloured 75 65

521 Circus School

2002
1264 **521** 70f. multicoloured 2·75 2·50

522 Telescope and Caillard

2002. 90th Birth Anniv of Edmond Caillard (astronomer).
1265 **522** 70f. multicoloured 2·75 2·50

523 Face in Landscape, Couple, Ship and Birds

2002. Jean Mariotti (writer).
1266 **523** 70f. multicoloured 2·75 2·50

524 Adult Sperm Whale and Calf

2002. New Caledonia–Norfolk Island Joint Issue. Operation Cetaces (marine mammal study). Multicoloured.
1267 100f. Type **524** 4·50 4·00
1268 100f. Sperm whale attacked by giant squid 4·50 4·00

Stamps of similar designs were issued by Norfolk Islands.

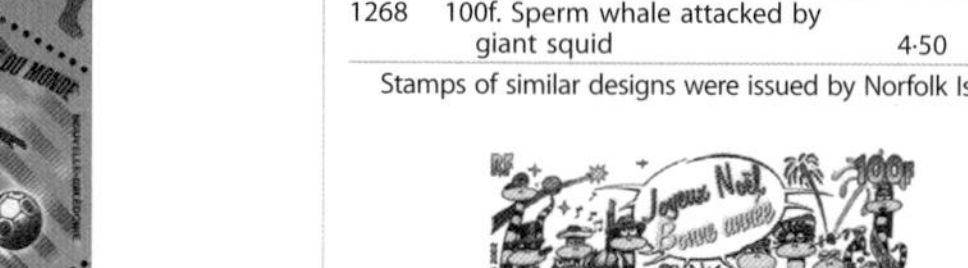

525 Coral Snake Musicians

2002. Christmas.
1269 **525** 100f. multicoloured 3·75 3·50

526 Central Mountain Chain

2002. International Year of Mountains. Litho.
1270 **526** 100f. multicoloured 3·75 3·50

527 Powder Store, Bourail Military Post

2002
1271 **527** 1000f. multicoloured 36·00 35·00

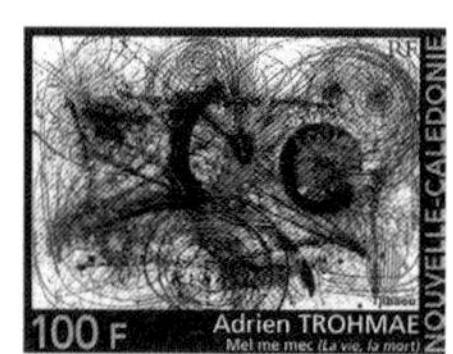

528 *Life and Death* (Adrian Trohmae)

2002. Pacific Painters.
1272 **528** 100f. multicoloured 3·75 3·50

529 Couple enclosed in Heart

2003. St. Valentine's Day.
1273 **529** 100f. multicoloured 3·75 3·50

530 Goat's Head

2003. Chinese New Year. Year of the Goat.
1274 **530** 100f. multicoloured 3·75 3·50

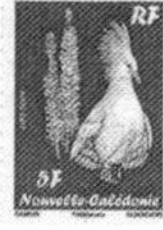
644 Kagu

2003. Kagu

(a) With face value

(i) Sheet stamps
1275 1f. light yellowish green 25 20
1276 3f. light greenish blue 40 35
1277 5f. violet 45 40
1278 10f. myrtle-green 55 45
1279 15f. agate 60 55
1280 30f. bright orange 1·10 90
1281 100f. ultramarine 3·50 3·25
1282 110f. blue-black 4·00 3·75

(ii) Booklet stamps
1283 110f. blue-black 4·00 3·75

(b) No value espressed

(ii) Sheet stamps

1284	(70c.) bright scarlet	2·40	2·10

(ii) Booklet stamps

1285	(70c.) scarlet	2·40	2·10
1286	(70c.) bright scarlet	2·40	2·10

532 1903 Stamp

2003. Centenary of First Kagu Stamp.

1290	**532**	70f. multicoloured	3·00	2·75

533 High-finned Grouper (*Epinephelus maculates*)

2003. Noumea Aquarium. Groupers. Multicoloured.

1291	70f. Type **533**	2·40	2·10
1292	70f. Purple-spotted grouper (*Plectropomus leopardus*)	2·40	2·10
1293	70f. Hump-back grouper (*Cromileptes altivelis*)	2·40	2·10

534 School Building

2003. Grand Noumea High School.

1294	**534**	70f. multicoloured	2·75	2·10

535 Shooting

2003. 12th South Pacific Games, Suva. Multicoloured.

1295	5f. Type **535**	30	25
1296	30f. Rugby	1·20	1·10
1297	70f. Tennis	2·75	2·10

536 Adult Sea Cow and Calf

2003. Sea Cow (*Dugong dugon*). Operation Cetaces (marine mammal study). Multicoloured.

1298	100f. Type **536**	4·00	3·75
1299	100f. Adult and calf grazing (40×30 mm)	4·00	3·75

Nos. 1298/9 were printed together, *se-tenant*, forming a composite design.

537 *The Harvest*

2003. Death Centenary of Paul Gauguin (artist) (1st issue).

1300	**537**	100f. multicoloured	4·00	3·75

See also No. **MS**1303.

538 Governor Feillet

2003. Death Centenary of Governor Feillet (first governor).

1301	**538**	100f. black and green	4·00	3·75

539 Aircalin Airbus A330-200

2003. 20th Anniv of Aircalin.

1302	**539**	100f. multicoloured	4·00	3·75

540 Tahitian Heads (sketch)

2003. Death Centenary of Paul Gauguin (artist) (2nd issue). Sheet 130×90 mm containing T **540** and similar vert design. Multicoloured.

MS1303	100f. Type **540**; 100f. Still-life with Maori statue	8·25	8·25

Stamps of a similar design were issued by Wallis et Futuna.

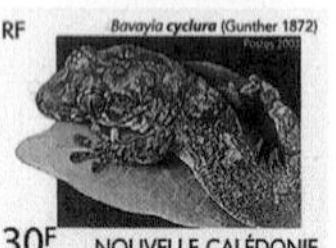

541 *Bavayia cyclura*

2003. Geckos. Sheet 140×110 mm containing T **541** and similar horiz designs. Multicoloured.

MS1304	30f.×2, Type **541**; *Rhacodactylus chahoua*; 70f.×2, *Rhacodactylus ciliatus*; *Eurydactylodes vieillardi*	8·25	8·25

542 German Shepherd Dog

2003

1305	**542**	105f. multicoloured	4·00	3·75

543 Rade de Balade (1853)

2003

1306	**543**	110f. brown, green and blue	4·25	4·00

544 *Men and Women surrounding Port* (painting) (Robert Tatin)

2003. Pacific Painters.

1307	**544**	135f. multicoloured	5·00	4·50

2003. World Cup Football Championships, Japan and South Korea. As No. 1257 but with inscription added to sheet margin.

MS1308	185×120 mm 30f. Type **516**; 30f. Green sea turtle (*Chelonia mydas*); 70f. Hawksbill turtle (*Eretmochelys imbricate*) (inscr "imbricat"); 70f. Leatherback sea turtle (*Dermochelys coriacea*)	7·75	7·75

545 Ouen Island

2003

1309	**545**	100f. multicoloured	3·75	3·25

546 Characters from *Brousse en Folie*

2003. Christmas. "Brousse en Folie" (Bush in Madness) (comic strip created by Bernard Berger).

1310	**546**	100f. multicoloured	3·75	3·25

547 Tiger King

2003. Year of the Monkey (1st issue). Sheet 130×100 mm containing T **547** and similar vert design. Multicoloured.

MS1311	100f.×2 Type **547**; Monkey King on horseback	8·25	8·25

548 Three Monkeys

2004. Year of the Monkey (2nd issue).

1312	**548**	70f. multicoloured	2·75	2·20

549 Cupid enclosed in Heart

2004. St. Valentine's Day.

1313	**549**	100f. multicoloured	3·75	3·50

550 Whale

2004. Blainville's Beaked Whales (*Mesoplodon densirostris*). Operation Cetaces (marine mammal study). Sheet 196×96 mm containing T **550** and similar horiz design. Multicoloured.

MS1314	100f.×2 Type **550**; Head of whale (40×30 mm)	8·50	8·25

The stamps and margin of **MS**1314 form a composite design.

551 Blue-spotted Stingray (*Dasyatis kuhlii*)

2004. Noumea Aquarium. Rays. Multicoloured.

1315	100f. Type **551**	3·75	3·50
1316	100f. Spotted eagle ray (*Aetobatus narinari*)	3·75	3·50
1317	100f. Marbled stingray (*Taeniura meyrni*)	3·75	3·50

552 Postman on Horseback

2004. Postal Service.

1318	**552**	105f. multicoloured	4·00	3·75

553 Decauville C/N 637 Locomotive (1905)

2004. Railways.

1319	**553**	155f. multicoloured	6·00	5·75

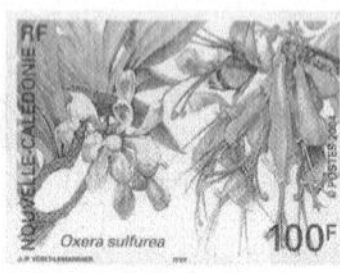

554 *Oxera sulfurea*

2004. Endangered Species. Forest Flowers. Multicoloured.

1320	100f. Type **554**	4·00	3·75
1321	100f. *Turbina inopinata*	4·00	3·75
1322	100f. *Gardenia urvillei*	4·00	3·75

555 Carving, House and Tree

2004. Sandalwood. Multicoloured.

1323	200f. Type **555**	7·75	7·50

(b) Size 40×30 mm.

MS1324	141×110 mm. 100f.×3, Fruit; Distillery; Sandalwood products	11·50	11·50

556 Early and Modern Noumea

2004. 150th Anniv of Noumea.

1325	**556**	70f. multicoloured	2·75	2·20

557 Cat

2004. Cats. Multicoloured.

1326	100f. Type **557**	3·75	3·25
1327	100f. Oriental	3·75	3·25
1328	100f. White Persian	3·75	3·25
1329	100f. Birman	3·75	3·25
1330	100f. European shorthair	3·75	3·25
1331	100f. Abyssinian	3·75	3·25

558 Gymnasts

2004. Olympic Games, Athens. Multicoloured.

1332	70f. Type **558**	2·75	2·20
1333	70f. Women's relay	2·75	2·20
1334	70f. Men's volleyball	2·75	2·20

559 Face, Butterfly, Hut and Trees

2004. French Research in the Pacific. Multicoloured.

1335	100f. Type **559**	3·75	3·50
1336	100f. Palms, dolphin and woman	3·75	3·50

560 Walla Bay, Belep

2004. Tourism.

1337	**560**	100f. multicoloured	3·75	3·50

561 *Tradimodernition* (Nat D.)

2004. Pacific Painters.

1338	**561**	505f. multicoloured	19·00	18·00

562 Nativity

2004. Christmas.

1339	**562**	100f. multicoloured	3·75	3·50

563 Rooster

2005. Chinese New Year. Year of the Rooster

1340	100f. Type **563**	6·00	5·75
MS1340a	130×100 mm. Vert. 100f.×2, Rooster wearing armour; Monkey wearing female dress	12·50	12·50

564 Anniversary Emblem

2005. Centenary of Rotary International.

1341	**564**	110f. multicoloured	4·25	3·75

565 People from Many Nations

2005. French-speaking Culture.

1342	**565**	135f. multicoloured	5·00	4·50

A stamp of similar design was issued by Wallis et Futuna.

566 Swimming, Cycling and Running

2005. International Triathlon Competition, Noumea.

1343	**566**	80f. multicoloured	3·25	3·00

567 Passenger Ship

2005. Coastal Tour.

1344	**567**	75f. multicoloured	2·75	2·50

568 Pan-tropical Spotted Dolphins (*Stenella attenuate*)

2005. Operation Cetaces (marine mammal study). Multicoloured.

1345	100f. Type **568**	3·75	3·50
1346	100f. Bottle-nose dolphin (*Tursiop truncates*) (inscr "Tiurciop")	3·75	3·50
1347	100f. Spinner dolphin (*Stenella longirostris*)	3·75	3·50

569 Corpet et Louvet 0-6-OTs Locomotive

2005. Railways.

1348	**569**	745f. multicoloured	28·00	26·00

570 Black-tip Reef Shark (*Carcharhinus melanopterus*)

2005. Noumea Aquarium. Sheet 140×90 mm containing T **570** and similar horiz design. Multicoloured.

MS1349	110f.×2, Type **551**; Tawny nurse shark (*Nebrius ferrugineus*)	8·25	7·50

The stamps and margin of **MS**1349 form a composite design.

571 *Eunymphicus uvaeensis*

2005. Endangered Species. Birds. Multicoloured.

1350	75f. Type **571**	2·75	2·40
1351	75f. *Eunymphicus cornutus*	2·75	2·40
1352	75f. *Cyanoramphus saisseti*	2·75	2·40

572 Luengoni Beach, Lifou

2005. Tourism.

1353	**572**	85f. multicoloured	3·25	3·00

573 Emblem and People of Many Nations

2005. East Pacific Region IOMS Conference, Noumea.

1354	**573**	150f. multicoloured	5·50	5·00

574 *My Dream of Peace* (Mendoza)

2005. International Day of Peace.

1355	**574**	85f. multicoloured	3·75	3·00

2005. Nos. 1114 and 1277a surch.

1356	110f. on 100f. blue (No. 1108)	4·25	4·00
1357	110f. on 100f. ultramarine (No. 1277)	4·25	4·00

2005. Nos. 1345/7 surch.

1358	110f. on 100f. multicoloured	4·25	4·00
1359	110f. on 100f. multicoloured	4·25	4·00
1360	110f. on 100f. multicoloured	4·25	4·00

577 Ouare

2005. Petroglyphs (rock paintings).

1361	**577**	120f. violet and vermilion	4·50	4·00
1362	-	120f. chocolate and blue	4·50	4·00
1363	-	120f. green and scarlet vermilion	4·50	4·00

Designs:—No. 1361, Type **577**; No. 1362, Balade; No. 1363, Croix enveloppees (wrapped crosses).

578 Marquis du Bouzet

2005. Birth Bicentenary of Marquis du Bouzet (governor).

1364	**578**	500f. black, blue and violet	19·00	17·00

579 Santa sailing Yacht

2005. Christmas.

1365	**579**	110f. multicoloured	4·25	4·00

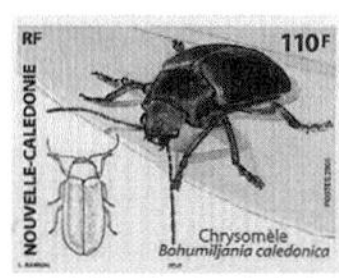

580 *Bohumiljania caledonica*

2005. Insects. Multicoloured.

1366	110f. Type **580**	4·25	4·00
1367	110f. *Bohumiljania humboldti*	4·25	4·00
1368	110f. *Cazeresia Montana*	4·25	4·00

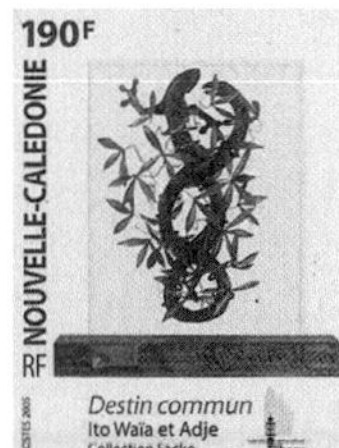

581 Snakes and Twigs

2005. Kanak and Oceanic Art Fund.

1369	**581**	190f. multicoloured	8·00	7·25

582 Nokanhoui Island

2006. Tourism.

1370	**582**	110f. multicoloured	4·25	3·75

583 Georges Richard (1903)

2006. Vintage Cars. Multicoloured.

1371	110f. Type **583**	4·25	3·75
1372	110f. Renault NN 6cv (1925)	4·25	3·75
1373	110f. Citroen Trefle (1926)	4·25	3·75

584 Emblem

2006. 50th Anniv of National Red Cross.

1374	**584**	75f. vermilion and black	2·75	2·50

585 *Conus geographus*

2006. Pain Relief Research. Discovery of Anaesthetic in Cone Shellfish.

1375	**585**	150f. multicoloured	5·25	4·75

586 Colonists and Tractor

2006. 80th Anniv of Arrival of Northern Colonists.

1376	**586**	180f. multicoloured	6·25	5·75

587 *Gallirallus lafresnayanus*

2006. Endangered Species. Birds. Multicoloured.

1377	75f. Type **587**	2·75	2·50
1378	75f. *Charmosyna diadema*	2·75	2·50
1379	75f. *Aegotheles savesi*	2·75	2·50
MS1380	100×130 mm. 110f.×3, *Charmosyna diadema* (52×31 mm); *Aegotheles savesi* (31×52 mm); *Gallirallus lafresnayanus* (52×31 mm)	12·50	12·50

The stamps and margins of **MS**1380 form a composite design of the forest.

588 Players

2006. World Cup Football Championship, Germany.

1381	**588**	110f. multicoloured	4·25	3·75

589 *Artia balansae*

2006. Ornamental Vines. Multicoloured.

1382		110f. Type **589**	4·25	3·75
1383		110f. *Oxera brevicalyx*	4·25	3·75
1384		110f. *Canavalia favieri*	4·25	3·75

590 Aircraft and Route

2006. 25th Anniv of Voluntary Aid to Caledonian Evacuees.

1385	**590**	85f. multicoloured	3·25	3·00

591 Mobile Post Office

2006. Stamp Day.

1386	**591**	75f. chocolate, black and ultramarine	2·75	2·50

592 Turtle, Starfish and Palm Trees

2006. Regional Ocean and Environmental Programme (PROE) Conference.

1387	**592**	190f. multicoloured	7·25	6·75

593 SACM 030T Mining Locomotive Nakale

2006. Railways.

1388	**593**	320f. multicoloured	12·00	11·00

594 Cell Phone and Tower

2006. Tenth Anniv of MobiLis (mobile telephone network).

1389	**594**	75f. multicoloured	3·00	2·75

595 Musicians

2006. 20th Anniv of Kaneka (music style).

1390	**595**	75f. multicoloured	3·00	2·75

596 Animals

2006. Les Comediens de Bois.

1391	**596**	280f. multicoloured	10·50	9·50

597 Madonna and Child

2006. Christmas.

1392	**597**	110f. multicoloured	4·25	3·75

598 *L'homme lezard*

2006

1393	**598**	110f. multicoloured	4·25	3·75

599 Emblem

2007. 60th Anniv of CPS (Secretariat of the Pacific Community).

1394	**599**	120f. multicoloured	4·50	4·25

600 Boar

2007. New Year. Year of the Pig.

1395	**600**	110f. multicoloured	4·25	3·75

601 Building Facade

2007. Bicentenary of Court of Auditors.

1396	**601**	110f. blue and vermilion	4·25	3·75

602 EU Stars and Children

2007. 50th Anniv of Treaty of Rome.

1397	**602**	110f. multicoloured	4·25	3·75

603 *Siganus lineatus*

2007. Fish. Multicoloured.

1398		35f. Type **603**	1·30	1·10
1399		75f. *Lutjanus adetii*	2·75	2·50
1400		110f. *Naso unicornis*	4·25	3·75

604 Swimmer

2007. South Pacific Games.

1401	**604**	75f. multicoloured	4·25	3·75

605 Cable and Ship

2007. Sub-marine Cable Between Sydney and Noumea.

1402	**605**	280f. multicoloured	10·50	9·50

606 Rescue

2007. National Society for Sea Rescue.

1403	**606**	75f. multicoloured	2·75	2·50

607 Post Box

2007. Stamp Day. Letter Boxes. Multicoloured.

1404		75f. Type **607**	2·75	2·50
1405		75f. Thatched roof and open sides	2·75	2·50
1406		75f. Rectangular with square opening, coloured roof and shells	2·75	2·50
1407		75f. Corrugated roof (vert)	2·75	2·50
1408		75f. Red rectangular with white edges (vert)	2·75	2·50
1409		75f. Metal with circular opening	2·75	2·50
1410		75f. Circular with triangular opening	2·75	2·50
1411		75f. House shaped	2·75	2·50
1412		75f. Motorcycle helmet used as post box (vert)	2·75	2·50
1413		75f. Wooden with steep roof (vert)	2·75	2·50

608 *Gymnomyzaaubryana*

2007. Endemic Birds. Multicoloured.

1414		35f. Type **608**	1·30	1·20
1415		75f. *Coracina analis*	2·75	2·50
1416		110f. *Rhynochetos jubatus*	4·50	4·00

609 Magnifier and 1942 4f. Stamp (No. 277)

2007. 60th Anniv of Cagou Philatelic Club. Sheet 90×120 mm containing T **609** and similar horiz design. Multicoloured.

MS1417	110f.×2, Type **609**; Cagou	9·25	9·25

The stamps and margins of **MS**1417 form a composite design.

610 New Caledonian and New Zealand Traditional Dress and Body Decoration

2007. New Caledonia in New Zealand.

1418	**610**	190f. multicoloured	7·50	6·75

611 *Gymnothoraxpolyranodon*

2007. Inauguration of New Aquarium, Noumea. Multicoloured.

1419		110f. Type **611**	5·25	4·75
1420		110f. Aquarium building (80×30 mm)	5·25	4·75
1421		110f. *Monodactylus argenteus*	5·25	4·75
1422		110f. *Negaprion brevirostris*	5·25	4·75
1423		110f. *Pseudanthias bicolour*	5·25	4·75

612 Player

2007. Rugby World Cup Championship, France.

1424	**612**	110f. multicoloured	5·25	4·75

613 Jules Repiquet

2007. Jules Repiquet (governor 1914–23) Commemoration.

1425	**613**	320f. multicoloured	14·50	13·00

614 Bananas and Pomegranate

2007. Fruit. Multicoloured.

1426		35f. Type **614**	1·60	1·40
1427		75f. Vanilla (vert)	3·75	3·25
1428		110f. Pineapple and lychees	5·25	4·75

615 Globe and Couple

2007. Happy New Year.

1429	**615**	110f. multicoloured	5·25	4·75

No. 1430 and Type **616** have been left for 'Arrows (Fleches)', issued on 9 November 2007, not yet received.

617 Cascade de Tao

2007. Waterfalls.

1431	**617**	110f. multicoloured	5·25	4·75

618 Baby in Seashell

2007

1432	**618**	110f. multicoloured	5·25	4·75

619 *Les damnes* (dance by Najib Guerfi Company)

2007. Tjibaou Cultural Centre.

1433	**619**	110f. multicoloured	5·25	4·75

620 *La Montagnarde* Locomotive

2007. Caledonian Railways.

1434	**620**	400f. multicoloured	18·00	17·00

621 Rat

2008. New Year. Year of the Rat.

1435	**621**	110f. multicoloured	5·25	4·75

622 Laurel Wreath

2008. Bicentenary of Palmes Academiques.

1436	**622**	110f. multicoloured	5·25	4·75

623 *Pseudobulweria rostrata* (Tahiti petrel)

2008. Endangered Species. Sea Birds. Multicoloured.

1437	110f. Type **623**	5·25	4·75
1438	110f. *Pterodroma leucoptera* (Gould's petrel)	5·25	4·75
1439	110f. *Nesofregetta fuliginosa* (white-throated storm-petrel)	5·25	4·75

624 Mango

2008. Fruit. Multicoloured.

1440	110f. Type **624**	5·25	4·75
1441	110f. Papaya	5·25	4·75
1442	110f. Mandarin	5·25	4·75

625 Stylized Great House (part of centre complex) (designed by Renzo Piano)

2008. Tenth Anniv of Tjibaou Cultural Centre, Tina Peninsula, Noumea.

1443	**625**	120f. multicoloured	5·75	5·25

626 Symbols of Accord

2008. 20th Anniv of Matignon Accords.

1444	**626**	430f. multicoloured	20·00	18·00

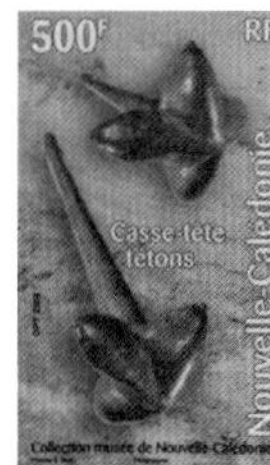
627 Casse-tete Tetons (ceremonial objects)

2008. Museum Exhibits.

1445	**627**	500f. multicoloured	22·00	20·00

628 1960 5f. Stamp (No. 359), Debit Card and Online Banking ('Le financier')

2008. 50th Anniv of OPT (Office des Postes et Telecommunications). Multicoloured.

1446	75f. Type **628**	3·75	3·50
1447	75f. Sorting, 1973 15f. stamp (Type **112**) and mail box ('Le courier')	3·75	3·50
1448	75f. Fibre optic cable, 1960 12f. stamp (No. 359) and satellite dish ('Les Telecommunications')	3·75	3·50

629 Table Tennis

2008. Olympic Games, Beijing. Multicoloured.

1449	75f. Type **629**	3·75	3·50
1450	75f. Taekwondo	3·75	3·50
1451	75f. Weightlifting	3·75	3·50

630 Telegraph

2008. Stamp Day. History of Telecommunications on New Caledonia. Sheet 100×130 mm containing T **630** and similar vert designs. Multicoloured.

MS1452 75f.×4, Type **630**; Radio telephone; Satellite; Fibre optic cable 15·00 15·00

631 Fort de Kone Ancient and Modern

2008. 130th Anniv of Fort de Kone (military installation).

1453	**631**	220f. multicoloured	10·50	10·50

632 General de Gaulle and Michel Debre (first Prime Minister of Fifth Republic)

2008. 50th Anniv of Fifth Republic.

1454	**632**	290f. ultramarine and vermilion	14·00	13·50

633 Symbols of New Caledonia

2008. Christmas.

1455	**633**	110f. multicoloured	6·00	5·50

634 Fields, River and Bridge

2008. River Diahot (Le Fleuve Diahot). Multicoloured.

1456	110f. Type **634**	6·00	5·50
1457	110f. Delta	6·00	5·50

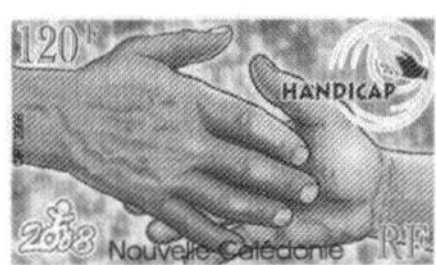
635 Clasped Hands

2008. HANDICAP—Charter for Disabilities.

1458	**635**	120f. multicoloured	6·00	5·50

636 Masked Boobies

2008. World Heritage Site. Caledonia Lagoons. Sheet 184×102 mm containing T **636** and similar multicoloured designs.

MS1459 75f.×6, Type **636**; Sea snake (Tricot raye) (horiz); Marine turtles (horiz); Humphead wrasse; Dugong; Humpback whale (horiz) 24·00 22·00

637 Emblem

2008. Pacific Games.

1460	**637**	110f. multicoloured	6·00	5·50

638 *Lethrinus atkinsoni*

2009. Fish. Multicoloured.

1461	75f. Type **638**	4·00	3·75
1462	75f. *Chlorurus microrhinuos*	4·00	3·75
1463	75f. *Letherinus nebulosus*	4·00	3·75

Nos. 1461/3 were printed, *se-tenant*, forming a composite design.

639 Ox on Lantern

2009. Chinese New Year. Year of the Ox. Multicoloured.

1464	75f. Type **639**	4·00	3·75

MS1465 120×90 mm.110f.×2, Ox amongst flowers; Ox as constellation 13·00 12·00

The stamps and margins of **MS**1469 form a composite design.

640 *Turtle Carrier* (Tein Thavouvace)

2009. Ngan Jila Cultural Centre.

1466	**640**	180f. multicoloured	10·00	9·50

641 *Sterna nereis* (fairy tern)

2009. Terns. Multicoloured.

1467	75f. Type **641**	4·25	4·00
1468	75f. *Sterna sumatrana* (black-naped tern)	4·25	4·00
1469	75f. *Sterna dougallii* (roseate tern) (inscr 'Sterna dougalli')	4·25	4·00

642 Entrance

2009. Tenth Anniv of Cinema de la Foa.

1470	**642**	75f. multicoloured	4·25	4·00

643 Flower containing Globe

2009. Third France–Oceania Summit. Multicoloured.

1471	110f. Type **643**	6·25	5·75
1472	110f. Hands holding globe	6·25	5·75

644 Kagu

2009. Kagu

(a) Ordinary gum

1473	**644**	5f. violet	85	75
1474	**644**	10f. pale green	1·50	1·40
1475	**644**	30f. orange (5.6.12)	1·70	1·50
1476	**644**	(75f.) scarlet-vermilion	4·25	4·00
1477	**644**	110f. blue	6·25	5·75

(b) Self-adhesive. Booklet Stamp

1486	**644**	(75f.) scarlet-vermilion	4·25	4·00

(c) Size 27×37 mm. Self-adhesive

1487	**644**	500f. multicoloured	25·00	24·00

645 Mail Coach

2009. 150th Anniv of Postal Services. Sheet 130×100 mm containing T **645** and similar multicoloured designs.

MS1491 110f.×4, Type **645**; Pony express messenger (vert); Modern mail van; Indigenous messenger (vert) 26·00 23·00

The stamps and margins of **MS**1491 form a composite design.

646 Symbols of Astronomy and Astronaut

2009. International Year of Astronomy.
1492 **646** 110f. multicoloured 6·25 5·75

647 Kagu

2009. Kagu on Stamps. Self-adhesive.
1493 **647** 500f. multicoloured 28·00 26·00

No. 1493 shows five designs of Kagu, and the names of the stamp designers, when tilted.

648 Armand Weneguei, Father Joseph-Marie Dubois and Henry Daly

2009. 40th Anniv of Society for Historical Studies.
1494 **648** 75f. sepia, red-brown and black 4·25 4·00

649 Joemy (games mascot)

2009. Pacific Games 2009, Rarotonga.
1495 **649** 75f. multicoloured 4·25 4·00

650 Museum Buiding and Ships

2009. Tenth Anniv of Maritime Museum. Multicoloured.
1496 75f. Type **650** 4·25 4·00
1497 75f. Symbols of La Perouse's wreck on Vanikoro 4·25 4·00

651 Santa and Reindeer

2009. Christmas.
1498 **651** 110f. multicoloured 6·25 5·75

652 Valley

2009. Tontouta River. Multicoloured.
1499 110f. Type **652** 6·25 5·75
1500 110f. Delta 6·25 5·75

653 Block House

2009. 150th Anniv of Blockhouse, Canala.
1501 **653** 120f. multicoloured 7·25 6·50

654 Dugong Cow and Calf

2009. Coastal Lagoon West–UNESCO World Heritage Site.
1502 **654** 75f. multicoloured 4·25 4·00

655 *Women and Children (Micheline Neporon)*

2010. Art
1502a **655** 110f. multicoloured 6·25 5·75

656 Tiger

2010. Chinese New Year. Year of the Tiger
1503 **656** 110f. multicoloured 6·25 5·75

657 *Acanthocybium solandri*

2010. Fish. Multicoloured.
1504 75c. Type **657** 4·25 4·00
1505 75c. *Thunnus albacares* 4·25 4·00
1506 75c. *Coryphaena hippurus* 4·25 4·00

658 Dumbea River

2010. Tourism. Dumbea River. Multicoloured.
1507 110f. Type **658** 6·25 5·75
1508 110f. Conoeists and bridge 6·25 5·75

659 Figures encircling Tree

2010. 25th Anniv of Alliance Champlain (Francophones in the Pacific)
1509 **659** 110f. multicoloured 6·25 5·75

660 Stylized Canoe

2010. Va'a (canoe) World Championships–2010, New Caledonia
1510 **660** 75f. multicoloured 4·25 4·00

661 Exhibition Site

2010. Expo 2010, Shanghai
1511 **661** 110f. multicoloured 6·50 6·00

662 Young Athletes

2010. Olympic Youth Games, Singapore
1512 **662** 75f. multicoloured 4·25 4·00

663 Flags of Competitors, Games Emblem and Joemy (games mascot)

2010. NC2011–Pacific Games, New Caledonia (1st issue)
1513 **663** 75f. multicoloured 4·25 4·00

See also No. **MS**1540.

664 Early Soldier and Fort Buildings

2010. 150th Anniv of Fort Mueo
1514 **664** 75f. multicoloured 4·25 4·00

665 Extraction

2010. Nickel Production. Multicoloured.
1515 75f. Type **665** 4·25 4·00
1516 75f, Smelting 4·25 4·00
1517 75f. Ship transportation 4·25 4·00

666 *Pteropus ornatus* (Ornate Flying Fox)

2010. Grandes Fougeres Park. Multicoloured.
MS1518 110f.×4, Type **666**; *Ducula goliath* (Goliath Imperial Pigeon); *Cyathea* (fern); *Calanthe langel* (flowering plant) 26·00 23·00

667 Cathedral Facade

2010. 120th Anniv of St. Joseph Cathedral, Noumea
1519 **667** 1000f. multicoloured 55·00 50·00

668 Pirogues

2010. Melanesian Arts Festival–2010, New Caledonia
1520 **668** 180f. multicoloured 10·00 9·00

669 Henri Sautot and Soldiers

2010. 70th Anniv of New Caledonia joining Free French Forces
1521 **669** 250f. multicoloured 14·00 12·50

670 Woman with Pushchair avoiding Speeding Motor Cyclist

2010. Road Safety Awareness Campaign. Multicoloured.
1522 75f. Type **670** 4·25 4·00
1523 75f. Drunken driver 4·25 4·00

671 Wrasse and UNESCO Emblem

2010. World Heritage Site. Lagoons of New Caledonia. Great Northern Lagoon
1524 **671** 75f. multicoloured 4·25 4·00

672 Symbols of New Caledonia on Display

2012. Culture
1525 **672** 110f. multicoloured 6·25 5·75

673 Symbols of Biodiversity erupting from Globe

2010. International Year of Biodiversity
1526 **573** 110f. multicoloured 6·25 5·75

674 Santa's Sleigh drawn by Seahorses

2010. Christmas
1527 **674** 110f. multicoloured 6·25 5·75

No. 1528, T **675** are vacant.

676 Hare and Chinese Symbols

2011. Chinese New Year. Year of the Rabbit
1529 **676** 110f. multicoloured 6·25 5·75

677 Symbols of Communication and New Caledonia

2011. Arrival of TNT Television

1530	**677**	75f. multicoloured	4·25	4·00

678 Pourina River

2011. Tourism. Rivers. Multicoloured.

1531	110f. Type **678**	6·25	5·75
1532	110f. Quinné	6·25	5·75

679 'Pacifique Attitude'

2011. South Pacific Games, New Caledonia

1533	**679**	110f. multicoloured	6·50	6·00

680 Medal and Competitors

2011. 20th Year of Transcalédonienne (Kanak trail race)

1534	**680**	75f. multicoloured	4·25	4·00

681 *Podoserpula miranda*

2011. Fungi

1535	**681**	110f. multicoloured	6·50	6·00

681a Turtle laying Eggs on Beach

2011. World Heritage Site. Lagoons of New Caledonia. Ouvea Lagoon and Beautemps-Beaupre

1535a	**681a**	75f. multicoloured	4·25	4·00

682 *Syzygium acre*

2011. Parc Provincial Rivière Bleue. Multicoloured.

MS1536 110f.×4, Type **682**; *Montrouziera gabriellae*; Grand Cascade; *Rhynochetos jubatus* (Kagu) 26·00 23·00

683 Fort

2011. Fort Ouegoa

1537	**683**	75f. multicoloured	4·25	4·00

684 Forest Canopy

2011. International Year of Forests

1538	**684**	120f. multicoloured	7·00	6·25

685 Athletes

2011. Traditional Kanak Games

1539	**685**	75f. multicoloured	4·25	4·00

686 Medal

2011. NC2011–Pacific Games, New Caledonia (2nd issue). Multicoloured.

MS1540 110f.×3, Type **686**; Torch; Cauldron (inscr 'La vasque') 19·00 17·00

687 Children and Parcel

2011. Christmas

1541	**687**	110f. multicoloured	6·25	5·75

688 Sea Krait

2011. Landscapes and Fauna. Multicoloured.

1542	110f. Type **688**	6·25	5·75
1543	110f. Lindéralique cliffs	6·25	5·75
1544	110f. Ile aux Canards island (inscr 'Flot Canard') (vert)	6·25	5·75
1545	110f. Rusa deer	6·25	5·75

689 Sugar Factory Chimney, Dumbéa

2011. Architectural Heritage

1546	**689**	450f. multicoloured	26·00	23·00

690 Jacques Lafleur

2011. Jaques Lafleur (politician) Commemoration

1547	**690**	1000f. multicoloured	55·00	50·00

691 Dragon

2012. Chinese New Year. Year of the Dragon

1548	**691**	75f. multicoloured	4·25	4·00

692 Fish enclosed in Heart

2012. St Valentine's Day

1549	**692**	110f. multicoloured	6·25	5·75

693 Bungalow, Traditional Sugarcane Extractor and 'Heart'

2011. 120th Anniv of Voh. Multicoloured.

1550	100f. Type **693**	6·25	5·75
1551	110f. 'Heart' and refinery	6·25	5·75

694 Trail

2012. Great South Hiking Trail

1552	**694**	110f. multicoloured	6·25	5·75

695 Sugar Factory Chimney, Ouaménie

2012. Architectural Heritage

1553	**695**	750f. multicoloured	43·00	39·00

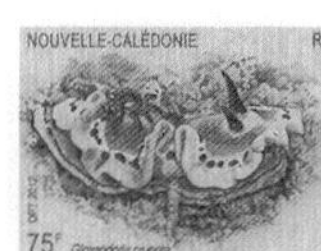

696 *Glossodoris cruenta*

2012. Nudibranches. Multicoloured.

1554	75f. Type **696**	4·25	4·00
1555	85f. *Halgerda* (vert)	5·00	4·50
1556	120f. *Noumea catalai*	7·00	6·25

697 Memorial

2012. 120th Anniv of Japanese Presence in New Caledonia

MS1557 110f.×3, Type **697**; Miner; Wagon filled with spoil 19·00 17·00

698 Koumac River

2012. Landscapes and Fauna. Multicoloured.

1558	110f. Type **698**	6·25	5·75
1559	110f. Snowman (rock formation), Bourail	6·25	5·75
1560	110f. Inscr 'Case à Maré'	6·25	5·75
1561	110f. Stockmen driving cattle	6·25	5·75

699 *Amborella trichopoda*

2012. Endangered Species. *Amborella trichopoda* (unique evergreen shrub)

1562	**699**	180f. multicoloured	10·00	9·00

700 Shot Put

2012. Paralympic Games, London. Multicoloured.

1563	75f. Type **700**	4·25	4·00
1564	75f. Wheelchair racers	4·25	4·00

701 Tree and Figures

2012. One Tree, One Day, One Life (Oceania tree planting initiative to combat effects of global warming)

1565	**701**	75f. multicoloured	4·25	4·00

702 *Rhacodactylus leachianus* (Leach's Giant Gecko)

2012. 50th Anniv of Michel Corbasson Botanical and Wildlife Park. Multicoloured.

MS1566 110f.×3, Type **702**; *Corvus moneduloides* (New Caledonia Crow); *Pittosporum tanianum* 20·00 18·00

703 Symbols of '3G'

2012. 3G - New Technology

1567	**703**	280f. multicoloured	16·00	14·50

704 Mangrove and Inhabitants

2012. Mangrove. Association pour la Sauvegarde de la Nature Néo-Calédonienne (Association for the Protection of New Caledonian Nature)

1568	**704**	75f. multicoloured	4·25	4·00

705 Humpback Whales

2012. World Heritage Site. Lagoons of New Caledonia. Great Southern Lagoon
1569 **705** 75f. multicoloured 4·25 4·00

706 Christmas on New Caledonia

2012. Christmas
1570 **706** 110f. multicoloured 6·25 5·75

707 Snake

2013. Chinese New Year. Year of the Snake
1571 **707** 110f. multicoloured 6·25 5·75

708 Masked Boobys

2013. World Heritage Site. Lagoons of New Caledonia. D'Entrecasteaux Reefs
1572 **708** 110f. multicoloured 6·25 5·75

709 New Buildings and Aircraft

2013. Inauguration of La Tontouta Airport, Noumea
1573 **709** 110f. multicoloured 6·25 5·75

710 Bacouya Sugar Factory Chimney

2013. Architectural Heritage
1574 **710** 120f. multicoloured 7·00 6·25

711 Ti'pwen (mascot)

2013. Red Cross - PIROPS (Regional Intervention Platform South Pacific)
1575 **711** 75f. multicoloured 4·25 4·00

712 'CALEDOSCOPE'

2013. Caledoscope (Philatelic Agency)
1576 **712** 75f. multicoloured 4·25 4·00

713 *Naso unicornis*

2013. Fish
1577 **713** 110f. blue 6·25 5·75

714 *Plectropomus leopardis* and *Epinephelus polyphekadion*

2013. New Caledonian Lagoon. Booklet Stamps. Multicoloured.
1578 110f. Type **714** 6·25 5·75
1579 110f. *Carcharhinus amblyrhynchos* (Grey Reef Shark) 6·25 5·75
1580 110f. *Scomberomorus commerson* (Narrow-barred Spanish Mackerel) 6·25 5·75
1581 110f. *Chelonia mydas* (Green Sea Turtle) 6·25 5·75
1582 110f. *Caranx melampygus* (Bluefin Trevally) 6·25 5·75
1583 110f. *Tridacna maxima* (Maxima Clam) and *Forcipiger flavissimus* (Yellow Longnose Butterflyfish) 6·25 5·75
1584 110f. *Chromis viridis* 6·25 5·75
1585 110f. *Panulirus penicillatus* (Red Spiny Lobster) 6·25 5·75
1586 110f. *Myripristis berndti* (Blotcheye Soldierfish) 6·25 5·75
1587 110f. *Lutjanus kasmira* (Bluestripe Snapper) 6·25 5·75

715 Museum

2013. Re-opening of Maritime Museum
1588 **715** 110f. multicoloured 6·25 5·75

716 Nouville Penal Colony

2013. Architectural Heritage. Nouville Penal Colony Museum
1589 **716** 280f. multicoloured 16·00 14·50

717 Girl

2013. Greetings Stamps. Birth. Multicoloured.
1590 110f. Type **717** 6·25 5·75
1591 110f. Boy 6·25 5·75

718 Swimmers

2013. International Paralympic Committee Swimming World Championship
1592 **718** 120f. multicoloured 7·00 6·25

719 Captaincookia Blooms

2013. Endangered Species. *Captaincookia margaretae* (unique tree)
1593 **719** 85f. multicoloured 5·00 4·50

720 'Le Pigeonnier de Pouembout'

2013. Architectural Heritage. Le Pigeonnier de Pouembout
1594 **720** 180f. multicoloured 10·50 9·50

721 *Eria karicouyensis*

2013. Orchids. Multicoloured.
MS1595 110f.×4, Type **721**; *Earina deplanchei* (vert); *Eriaxis rigida* (vert); *Dendrobium poissonianum* 26·00 24·00

722 Fruit Bat

2013. Landscapes and Fauna. Multicoloured.
1596 85f. Type **722** 5·00 4·50
1597 110f. 'Beach of 500 franc note', Hienghène 6·25 5·75
1598 190f. 'Warrior Jump' near Wakone on Maré Island (vert) 11·00 10·00
1599 250f. Thio and Bota Mere (vert) 14·50 13·00

2013. Christmas. Multicoloured.
1600 110f. 'Joyeux Noel' and postcards 6·25 5·75

724 Honey, Hives and Beekeeper

2013. Honey and Bees. Multicoloured.
1601 110f. Type **724** 6·25 5·75
1602 110f. Bees and wild hives 6·25 5·75

725 500 Franc Banknote

2014. New Banknotes. Multicoloured.
MS1603 75f. Type **725**; 75f. 1000 franc banknote; 110f. 5000 franc banknote; 110f. 10000 franc banknote 22·00 20·00

726 Horse

2014. Chinese New Year. Year of the Horse
1604 **726** 110f. multicoloured 6·25 5·75

2014. 'Kanak, l'art est une parole' Exhibition, Paris, France. Multicoloured.
1605 **5.75** 110f. 'KANAK l'art est une parole' and *flèche faîtière* (carved rooftop finial from Kanak house) 6·25 5·75

728 Fauna and Flora of Zone

2014. World Heritage Site. Lagoons of New Caledonia. Coastal Zone, North and East
1606 **728** 110f. multicoloured 6·25 5·75

729 Fighters' House

2014. 50th Anniv of Fighters' House (Veterans' centre)
1607 **729** 150f. multicoloured 8·50 7·75

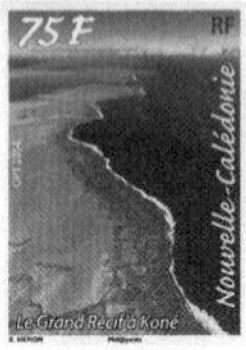

730 La Maison Caujolle

2014. Architectural Heritage. La Maison Caujolle (Pomémie Cultural Centre), Koné
1608 **730** 750f. multicoloured 43·00 39·00

731 Grand Reef, Koné

2014. Landscapes and Fauna. Multicoloured.
1609 75f. Type **731** 4·25 4·00
1610 110f. Lemon Damselfish (horiz) 6·25 5·75
1611 120f. Horned Parakeet (horiz) 7·00 6·25
1612 190f. Drowned Forest 11·00 10·00

732 Exchange of Blood

2014. World Blood Donor Day
1613 **732** 110f. multicoloured 6·25 5·75

733 Search and Rescue

2014. Tenth Anniv of Search and Rescue at Sea Service
1614 **733** 110f. multicoloured 6·25 5·75

734 *Erythrura psittacea* (Red-throated Parrotfinch) (inscr 'Diamant psittaculaire')

2014. Fauna and Flora of 'Le Maquis Minier' (mineral rich - nutrient poor scrubland). Multicoloured.
MS1615 110f.×3, Type **734**; *Grevillea gillivrayi* (vert); *Deplanchea sessilifolia* 20·00 18·00

735 Ile de Pins

2014. Architectural Heritage. Ile des Pins Prison Colony
1616 **735** 280f. multicoloured 16·00 14·50

L'ART DU BONSAÏ
150F
RF
NOUVELLE-CALÉDONIE

736 Bonsai *Murraya paniculata*

2014. Bonsai Trees

1617	**736**	150f. multicoloured	8·50	7·75

737 Horse Riders

2014. Christmas

1618	**737**	110f. multicoloured	6·25	5·75

738 *Papilio montrouzieri*

2014. Butterfly

1619	**738**	180f. multicoloured	10·50	9·50

739 Niaouli

2014. Niaouli (*Melaleuca quinquenervia*)

1620	**739**	190f. multicoloured	11·00	10·00

740 Weaving

2014. Kanak Crafts. Weaving

1621	**740**	250f. multicoloured	14·50	13·00

741 Dick Ukeiwé

2015. Dick Ukeiwé (politician) Commemoration

1622	**741**	500f. sepia and deep ultramarine	29·00	26·00

742 Goat

2015. Chinese New Year. Year of the Goat

1623	**742**	110f. multicoloured	6·25	5·75

743 *Pittosporum tanianum*

2015. Endangered Species. *Pittosporum tanianum*

1624	**743**	120f. multicoloured	7·00	6·25

744 Salt Gathering

2015. Salt from Kô, Poingam

1625	**744**	450f. multicoloured	26·00	24·00

745 Embarkation

2015. New Caledonian Engagement in the Great War (World War I). Multicoloured.

1626	35f. Type **745**	2·00	1·80
1627	35f. Battle	2·00	1·80
1628	35f. Disembarkation	2·00	1·80

Nos. 1629/31 are awaiting stamps.

2015. Philately in School. Multicoloured.

1629	75f. House, tree and sun	3·25	3·00
1630	75f. Hibiscus flower and snake	3·25	3·00
1631	75f. Arms of New Caledonia (vert)	3·25	3·00

747 *Nycticorax caledonicus* (Rufous Night Heron)

2015. Herons of New Caledonia. Multicoloured.
MS1632 110f.×3, Type **747**; *Egretta novaehollandiae* (White-faced Heron); *Egretta sacra* (Pacific Reef Heron) (horiz) 20·00 18·00

2015. The Yam Cycle (Maxat)

1633	110f. Digging and planting	6·25	5·75

2015. Birds - 50th Anniv of Société Calédonienne d'Ornithologie (SCO)

1634	180f. Anniversary emblem and *Ducula goliath* (Goliath Imperial Pigeon)	10·50	9·50

750 Amédée Lighthouse

2015. 150th Anniv of Amédée Lighthouse

1635	**750**	110f. multicoloured	6·25	5·75

751 The Holy Family

2015. Christmas

1636	**751**	110f. multicoloured	6·25	5·75

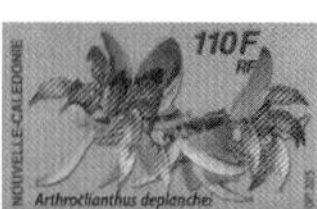

752 *Arthroclianthus depanchei*

2015. New Caledonian Flora. Booklet Stamps. Multicoloured.

1637	110f. Type **752**	6·25	5·75
1638	110f. *Thiollierea campanulata*	6·25	5·75
1639	110f. *Xanthostemon aurantiacus*	6·25	5·75
1640	110f. *Deplanchea speciosa*	6·25	5·75
1641	110f. *Xanthostemon sulfureus*	6·25	5·75
1642	110f. *Deplanchea sessilifolia*	6·25	5·75
1643	110f. *Boronella pancheri*	6·25	5·75
1644	110f. *Artia balansae*	6·25	5·75
1645	110f. *Virotia angustifolia*	6·25	5·75
1646	110f. *Arthroclianthus microbotrys*	6·25	5·75

753 Loggerhead Turtle

2015. New Caledonian Turtles. Multicoloured.
MS1647 110f.×4, Type **753**; Big-headed Turtle; Green Sea Turtle (horiz); Leatherback Turtle (horiz) 26·00 23·00

754 Monkey

2016. Chinese New Year. Year of the Monkey

1648	**754**	110f. multicoloured	6·25	5·75

755 Trees of New Caledonia

2016. Trees of New Caledonia

1649	**755**	120f. multicoloured	6·50	6·00

OFFICIAL STAMPS

O49 Ancestor Pole

1958. Inscr "OFFICIEL".

O344	**O49**	1f. yellow	55	1·00
O345	**O49**	3f. green	60	1·00
O346	**O49**	4f. purple	70	70
O347	**O49**	5f. blue	80	1·30
O348	**O49**	9f. black	95	1·50
O349	**A**	10f. violet	2·40	1·30
O350	**A**	13f. green	1·40	2·75
O351	**A**	15f. blue	2·20	2·10
O352	**A**	24f. mauve	2·75	2·75
O353	**A**	26f. orange	2·20	3·50
O354	**B**	50f. green	3·75	7·25
O355	**B**	100f. brown	8·25	14·00
O356	**B**	200f. red	12·50	29·00

Designs: A, B, Different idols.

O110 Carved Wooden Pillow (Noumea Museum)

1973

O525	**O110**	1f. green, blk & yell	2·30	2·50
O526	**O110**	2f. red, black & grn	2·30	5·25
O527	**O110**	3f. green, blk & brn	2·30	2·75
O528	**O110**	4f. green, black & bl	2·30	3·00
O529	**O110**	5f. green, blk & mve	2·50	2·10
O530	**O110**	9f. green, black & bl	2·50	3·75
O531	**O110**	10f. green, blk & orge	2·75	2·75
O532	**O110**	11f. grn, blk & mve	3·25	5·25
O533	**O110**	12f. green, blk & turq	2·50	4·00
O534	**O110**	15f. green, blk & lt grn	2·20	3·50
O535	**O110**	20f. green, blk & red	3·25	3·50
O536	**O110**	23f. green, blk & red	3·00	5·50
O537	**O110**	24f. green, blk & bl	2·20	5·50
O538	**O110**	25f. green, blk & grey	2·30	4·00
O539	**O110**	26f. green, blk & yell	2·30	5·25
O540	**O110**	29f. red, black & grn	2·20	4·00
O541	**O110**	31f. red, black & yell	2·30	4·75
O542	**O110**	35f. red, black & yell	2·20	2·75
O543	**O110**	36f. green, blk & mve	3·00	5·50
O544	**O110**	38f. red, black & brn	2·30	5·75
O545	**O110**	40f. red, black & bl	2·30	5·75
O546	**O110**	42f. green, blk & brn	3·00	5·25
O547	**O110**	50f. green, blk & bl	2·75	4·50
O548	**O110**	58f. blue, blk & grn	2·75	6·25
O549	**O110**	65f. red, black & mve	2·75	6·25

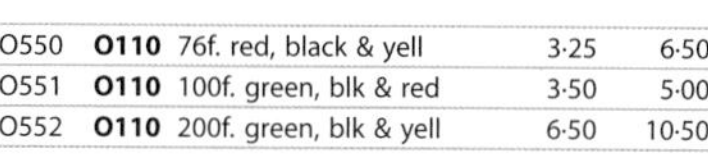

O550	**O110**	76f. red, black & yell	3·25	6·50
O551	**O110**	100f. green, blk & red	3·50	5·00
O552	**O110**	200f. green, blk & yell	6·50	10·50

PARCEL POST STAMPS

1926. Optd Colis Postaux or surch also.

P137	**17**	50c. on 5f. green on mauve	1·10	8·00
P138	**17**	1f. blue	1·50	9·00
P139	**17**	2f. red on blue	1·90	10·00

1930. Optd Colis Postaux.

P179	**23**	50c. brown and mauve	95	3·25
P180	**24**	1f. pink and drab	1·40	7·50
P181	**24**	2f. brown and orange	1·70	8·25

POSTAGE DUE STAMPS

1903. Postage Due stamps of French Colonies optd **CINQUANTENAIRE 24 SEPTEMBRE 1853 1903** and eagle. Imperf.

D78	**U**	5c. blue	3·00	3·00
D79	**U**	10c. brown	13·00	8·00
D80	**U**	15c. green	30·00	5·25
D81	**U**	30c. red	17·00	28·00
D82	**U**	50c. purple	95·00	16·00
D83	**U**	60c. brown on buff	£250	75·00
D84	**U**	1f. pink	34·00	21·00
D85	**U**	2f. brown	£1100	£1100

D18 Outrigger Canoe

1906

D102	**D18**	5c. blue on blue	70	60
D103	**D18**	10c. brown on buff	70	2·75
D104	**D18**	15c. green	1·00	3·00
D105	**D18**	20c. black on yellow	1·00	1·60
D106	**D18**	30c. red	1·50	3·25
D107	**D18**	50c. blue on cream	2·10	8·50
D108	**D18**	60c. green on blue	1·60	7·25
D109	**D18**	1f. green on cream	2·40	8·50

1926. Surch.

D137	2f. on 1f. mauve	5·00	9·25
D138	3f. on 1f. brown	5·75	12·50

D25 Sambar Stag

1928

D179	**D25**	2c. brown and blue	30	2·75
D180	**D25**	4c. green and red	45	3·00
D181	**D25**	5c. grey and orange	55	3·75
D182	**D25**	10c. blue and mauve	55	1·20
D183	**D25**	15c. red and olive	55	2·75
D184	**D25**	20c. olive and red	1·40	6·75
D185	**D25**	25c. blue and brown	60	4·50
D186	**D25**	30c. olive and green	75	5·75
D187	**D25**	50c. red and brown	1·80	4·00
D188	**D25**	60c. red and mauve	2·75	6·25
D189	**D25**	1f. green and blue	2·75	3·00
D190	**D25**	2f. olive and red	3·25	6·25
D191	**D25**	3f. brown and violet	3·00	4·75

D38

1948

D328	**D38**	10c. mauve	30	5·25
D329	**D38**	30c. brown	35	7·50
D330	**D38**	50c. green	60	7·50
D331	**D38**	1f. brown	60	7·50
D332	**D38**	2f. red	85	6·75
D333	**D38**	3f. brown	85	6·75
D334	**D38**	4f. blue	1·20	7·75
D335	**D38**	5f. red	1·20	8·25
D336	**D38**	10f. green	1·90	8·75
D337	**D38**	20f. blue	2·30	7·25

D222 New Caledonian Flying Fox

1983

D703	**D223**	1f. multicoloured	1·10	4·00

D704	D223	2f. multicoloured	1·10	4·00
D705	D223	3f. multicoloured	1·10	4·00
D706	D223	4f. multicoloured	1·30	4·00
D707	D223	5f. multicoloured	1·30	4·00
D708	D223	10f. multicoloured	1·30	4·00
D709	D223	20f. multicoloured	1·50	4·50
D710	D223	40f. multicoloured	2·10	5·50
D711	D223	50f. multicoloured	2·30	5·75

NEWFOUNDLAND

An island off the east coast of Canada. A British Dominion merged since 1949 with Canada, whose stamps it now uses.

1857. 12 pence = 1 shilling; 20 shillings = 1 pound.
1866. 100 cents = 1 dollar.

1

2

3 Royal Crown and Heraldic Flowers of the United Kingdom

1857. Imperf.

1	1	1d. purple	£160	£250
10	2	2d. red	£600	£700
11	3	3d. green	£110	£190
12	2	4d. red	£4500	£1100
13	1	5d. brown	£140	£400
14	2	6d. red	£5000	£800
7	2	6½d. red	£4500	£4750
8	2	8d. red	£400	£950
9	2	1s. red	£27000	£9000

The frame design of Type **2** differs for each value.

1861. Imperf.

16	1	1d. brown	£350	£450
17	2	2d. lake	£300	£500
18	2	4d. lake	50·00	£110
19a	1	5d. brown	90·00	£200
20	2	6d. lake	35·00	£100
21	2	6½d. lake	£100	£450
22	2	8d. lake	£130	£650
23	2	1s. lake	50·00	£300

6 Codfish

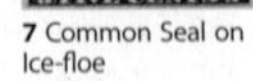
7 Common Seal on Ice-floe

8 Prince Consort

9 Queen Victoria

10 Schooner

11 Queen Victoria

1866. Perf (2c. also roul).

31	6	2c. green	£120	50·00
26	7	5c. brown	£600	£180
32	8	10c. black	£275	48·00
33	9	12c. brown	60·00	48·00
29	10	13c. orange	£120	£140
30	11	24c. blue	50·00	38·00

12 King Edward VII when Prince of Wales

14 Queen Victoria

1868. Perf or roul.

34	12	1c. purple	75·00	60·00
36	14	3c. orange	£300	£100
37	14	3c. blue	£275	27·00
38	7	5c. black	£325	£110
43	7	5c. blue	£200	4·00
39	14	6c. red	17·00	30·00

15 King Edward VII when Prince of Wales

16 Codfish

17

18 Common Seal on Ice-floe

19 Newfoundland Dog

20 Atlantic Brigantine

1880

49	19	½c. red	16·00	11·00
59	19	½c. black	10·00	9·50
44	15	1c. brown	50·00	17·00
50a	15	1c. green	7·00	4·50
46	16	2c. green	60·00	32·00
51	16	2c. orange	27·00	7·50
47a	17	3c. blue	85·00	6·50
52	17	3c. brown	85·00	2·75
59a	18	5c. blue	80·00	5·50
54	20	10c. black	75·00	75·00

21 Queen Victoria

1890

55	21	3c. grey	55·00	3·50

This stamp on pink paper was stained by sea-water.

22 Queen Victoria

23 John Cabot

24 Cape Bonavista

25 Caribou hunting

1897. 400th Anniv of Discovery of Newfoundland and 60th Year of Queen Victoria's Reign. Dated "1497 1897".

66	22	1c. green	8·50	13·00
67	23	2c. red	2·75	2·75
68	24	3c. blue	4·00	1·00
69	25	4c. olive	14·00	9·50
70	-	5c. violet	14·00	4·50
71	-	6c. brown	9·50	3·25
72	-	8c. orange	21·00	9·50
73	-	10c. brown	45·00	15·00
74	-	12c. blue	42·00	12·00
75	-	15c. red	26·00	26·00
76	-	24c. violet	32·00	38·00
77	-	30c. blue	70·00	95·00
78	-	35c. red	65·00	90·00
79	-	60c. black	27·00	22·00

Designs:—As Type **24**: 5c. Mining; 6c. Logging; 8c. Fishing; 10c. Cabot's ship, the *Matthew*; 15c. Seals; 24c. Salmon-fishing; 35c. Iceberg. As Type **23**: 12c. Willow/red grouse; 30c. Seal of the Colony; 60c. Henry VII.

1897. Surch **ONE CENT** and bar.

80	21	1c. on 3c. grey	80·00	40·00

39 Prince Edward, later Duke of Windsor

40 Queen Victoria

1897. Royal portraits.

83	39	½c. olive	2·25	1·50
84	40	1c. red	8·00	9·00
85	-	1c. green	19·00	20
86	-	2c. orange	10·00	10·00
87	-	2c. red	22·00	75
88	-	3c. orange	32·00	30
89	-	4c. violet	35·00	11·00
90	-	5c. blue	50·00	3·00

Designs:—2c. King Edward VII when Prince of Wales; 3c. Queen Alexandra when Princess of Wales; 4c. Queen Mary when Duchess of York; 5c. King George V when Duke of York.

45 Map of Newfoundland

1908

94	45	2c. lake	30·00	1·00

46 King James I

47 Arms of Colonisation Co.

49 *Endeavour* (immigrant ship), 1610

1910. Dated "1610 1910".

109	46	1c. green	3·25	30
107	47	2c. red	9·50	40
97	-	3c. olive	14·00	27·00
98	49	4c. violet	27·00	21·00
108	-	5c. blue	12·00	3·00
111	-	6c. purple	18·00	50·00
112	-	8c. bistre	50·00	80·00
102	-	9c. green	70·00	£110
103	-	10c. grey	75·00	£140
115	-	12c. brown	70·00	70·00
105	-	15c. black	70·00	£130

Designs:—Horiz: 5c. Cupids; 8c. Mosquito; 9c. Logging camp, Red Indian Lake; 10c. Paper mills, Grand Falls. Vert: 3c. John Guy; 6c. Sir Francis Bacon; 12c. King Edward VII; 15c. King George V. (Cupids and Mosquito are places).

57 Queen Mary

58 King George V

67 Seal of Newfoundland

1911. Coronation.

117	57	1c. green	10·00	30
118	58	2c. red	12·00	20
119	-	3c. brown	26·00	50·00
120	-	4c. purple	25·00	45·00
121	-	5c. blue	8·00	2·25
122	-	6c. grey	15·00	27·00
123	-	8c. blue	60·00	85·00
124	-	9c. blue	35·00	55·00
125	-	10c. green	42·00	50·00
126	-	12c. plum	32·00	50·00
127	67	15c. lake	29·00	50·00

Portraits:—Vert (As Type **57/8**): 3c, Duke of Windsor when Prince of Wales; 4c. King George VI when Prince Albert; 5c. Princess Mary, the Princess Royal; 6c. Duke of Gloucester when Prince Henry; 8c. Duke of Kent when Prince George; 9c. Prince John; 10c. Queen Alexandra; 12c. Duke of Connaught.

68 Caribou

1919. Newfoundland Contingent, 1914–18.

130	68	1c. green	3·75	20
131	68	2c. red	3·75	85
132	68	3c. brown	8·50	20
133	68	4c. mauve	13·00	80
134	68	5c. blue	18·00	1·25
135	68	6c. grey	19·00	70·00
136	68	8c. purple	19·00	70·00
137	68	10c. green	9·00	8·00
138	68	12c. orange	22·00	75·00
139	68	15c. blue	17·00	90·00
140	68	24c. brown	32·00	42·00
141	68	36c. olive	24·00	50·00

Designs:—Each inscr with the name of a different action: 1c. Suvla Bay; 3c. Gueudecourt; 4c. Beaumont Hamel; 6c. Monchy; 10c. Steenbeck; 15c. Langemarck; 24c. Cambrai; 36c. Combles. The 2, 5, 8 and 12c. are inscribed "Royal Naval Reserve-Ubique".

1919. Air. Hawker Flight. No. 132a optd **FIRST TRANS-ATLANTIC AIR POST April, 1919.**

142		3c. brown	£22000	£12000

1919. Air. Alcock and Brown Flight. Surch Trans-Atlantic AIR POST, 1919. ONE DOLLAR.

143		$1 on 15c. red (No. 75)	£130	£150

1920. Surch in words between bars.

144		2c. on 30c. blue (No. 77)	8·00	38·00
146		3c. on 15c. red (No. 75)	40·00	42·00
147		3c. on 35c. red (No. 78)	18·00	27·00
148a		35c. red (No. 78)	£130	90·00

73 Twin Hills, Tor's Cove

75 Statue of Fighting Newfoundlander, St. John's

1923

149	73	1c. green	2·25	20
150	-	2c. red	1·00	10
151	75	3c. brown	3·75	10
152	-	4c. purple	1·00	30
153	-	5c. blue	6·50	1·75
154	-	6c. grey	12·00	20·00
155	-	8c. purple	19·00	4·25
156	-	9c. green	21·00	38·00
157	-	10c. violet	17·00	11·00
158	-	11c. olive	7·00	40·00
159	-	12c. lake	8·00	38·00
160	-	15c. blue	8·00	40·00
161	-	20c. brown	32·00	21·00
162	-	24c. brown	70·00	£100

Designs:—Horiz: 2c. South-west Arm, Trinity; 6c. Upper Steadies, Humber River; 8c. Quidi Vidi, near St. John's; 9c. Caribou crossing lake; 11c. Shell Bird Island; 12c. Mount Moriah, Bay of Islands; 20c. Placentia. Vert: 4c. Humber River; 5c. Coast at Trinity; 10c. Humber River Canon; 15c. Humber River, near Little Rapids; 24c. Topsail Falls.

1927. Air. Optd Air Mail **DE PINEDO 1927.**

163		60c. black (No. 79)	£42000	£13000

88 Newfoundland and Labrador

89 SS *Caribou*

90 King George V and Queen Mary

91 Duke of Windsor when Prince of Wales

1928. Publicity issue.

164	88	1c. green	5·00	1·50
180	89	2c. red	1·75	40
181	90	3c. brown	1·00	20
201	91	4c. mauve	8·50	4·25
183	-	5c. grey	13·00	5·00
184a	-	6c. blue	3·50	32·00
170	-	8c. brown	12·00	55·00
171	-	9c. green	3·25	27·00
185	-	10c. violet	10·00	5·50
173	-	12c. lake	3·25	27·00
174a	-	14c. purple	26·00	12·00
175	-	15c. blue	14·00	50·00
176a	-	20c. black	9·50	13·00
177	-	28c. green	28·00	70·00
178	-	30c. brown	8·00	25·00

Designs:—Horiz: 5c. Express train; 6c. Newfoundland Hotel, St. John's; 8c. Heart's Content; 10c. War Memorial, St. John's; 15c. Vickers Vimy aircraft; 20c. Parliament House, St. John's. Vert: 9, 14c. Cabot Tower, St. John's; 12, 28c. GPO, St. John's; 30c. Grand Falls, Labrador.

1929. Surch **THREE CENTS.**

188		3c. on 6c. (No. 154)	3·75	13·00

1930. Air. No. 141 surch Trans-Atlantic AIR MAIL By B. M. "Columbia" September 1930 Fifty Cents.

191	68	50c. on 36c. olive	£6500	£6500

103 Westland Limousine III and Dog-team

104 Vickers Vimy Biplane and early Sailing Packet

105 Routes of historic Trans-Atlantic Flights

1931. Air.

192	**103**	15c. brown	9·00	18·00
193	**104**	50c. green	38·00	55·00
194	**105**	$1 blue	50·00	95·00

107 Codfish

108 King George V

110 Duke of Windsor when Prince of Wales

111 Reindeer

112 Queen Elizabeth II when Princess

121 Corner Brook Paper Mills

1932

209	**107**	1c. green	3·75	30
276	**107**	1c. grey	20	2·75
210	**108**	2c. red	1·50	20
223	**108**	2c. green	2·50	10
211	-	3c. brown	1·50	20
212	**110**	4c. lilac	13·00	2·25
224	**110**	4c. red	6·50	40
213	**111**	5c. purple	10·00	8·00
225c	**111**	5c. violet	1·00	30
214	**112**	6c. blue	4·00	15·00
226	-	7c. lake	3·00	4·25
227	**121**	8c. red	3·75	2·00
215	-	10c. brown	1·00	65
216	-	14c. black	5·50	6·00
217	-	15c. purple	1·25	2·00
218	-	20c. green	1·00	1·00
228	-	24c. blue	1·25	3·25
219	-	25c. grey	2·00	2·50
220	-	30c. blue	55·00	45·00
289	-	48c. brown	5·00	9·50

Designs:—Vert: 3c. Queen Mary; 7c. Queen Mother when Duchess of York. Horiz: 10c. Salmon; 14c. Newfoundland dog; 15c. Harp seal; 20c. Cape Race; 24c. Loading iron ore, Bell Island; 25c. Sealing fleet; 30, 48c. Fishing fleet.

1932. Air. Surch **TRANS-ATLANTIC WEST TO EAST Per Dornier DO-X May, 1932.** One Dollar and Fifty Cents.

221	**105**	$1.50 on $1	£250	£225

1933. Optd L. & S. Post. ("Land and Sea") between bars.

229	**103**	15c. brown	6·50	23·00

124 Put to Flight

1933. Air.

230	**124**	5c. brown	22·00	22·00
231	-	10c. yellow	18·00	35·00
232	-	30c. blue	40·00	50·00
233	-	60c. green	50·00	£120
234	-	75c. brown	50·00	£120

Designs:—10c. Land of Heart's Delight; 30c. Spotting the herd; 60c. News from home; 75c. Labrador.

1933. Air. Balbo Trans-Atlantic Mass Formation Flight. No. 234 surch **1933 GEN. BALBO FLIGHT. $4.50.**

235	$4.50 on 75c. brown	£275	£350

130 Sir Humphrey Gilbert

131 Compton Castle, Devon

1933. 350th Anniv of Annexation. Dated "1583 1933".

236	**130**	1c. black	1·25	1·50
237	**131**	2c. green	2·00	70
238	-	3c. brown	2·50	1·25
239	-	4c. red	1·00	50
240	-	5c. violet	2·00	1·00
241	-	7c. blue	18·00	24·00
242	-	8c. orange	9·50	25·00
243	-	9c. blue	7·50	26·00
244	-	10c. brown	8·50	21·00
245	-	14c. black	22·00	50·00
246w	-	15c. red	9·50	35·00
247	-	20c. green	20·00	25·00
248	-	24c. purple	22·00	35·00
249	-	32c. black	20·00	75·00

Designs:—Vert: 3c. Gilbert Coat of Arms; 5c. Anchor token; 14c. Royal Arms; 15c. Gilbert in the *Squirrel*; 24c. Queen Elizabeth I; 32c. Gilbert's statue at Truro. Horiz: 4c. Eton College; 7c. Gilbert commissioned by Elizabeth; 8c. Fleet leaving Plymouth, 1583; 9c. Arrival at St. John's; 10c. Annexation, 5 August, 1583; 20c. Map of Newfoundland.

143a Windsor Castle

1935. Silver Jubilee.

250	**143a**	4c. red	1·00	1·75
251	**143a**	5c. violet	1·25	4·25
252	**143a**	7c. blue	4·75	7·00
253	**143a**	24c. olive	5·00	28·00

143b King George VI and Queen Elizabeth

1937. Coronation.

254	**143b**	2c. green	1·00	3·00
255	**143b**	4c. red	1·60	4·00
256	**143b**	5c. purple	3·00	4·00

144 Atlantic Cod

1937. Coronation.

257	**144**	1c. grey	3·50	30
258	-	3c. brown	38·00	7·50
258ed	-	3c. brown	9·50	4·75
259	-	7c. blue	4·00	1·25
260	-	8c. red	5·50	4·00
261	-	10c. black	7·50	9·00
262	-	14c. black	3·00	4·00
263	-	15c. red	21·00	9·00
264	-	20c. green	11·00	21·00
265	-	24c. blue	2·75	3·00
266	-	25c. black	5·00	4·50
267	-	48c. purple	11·00	6·50

Designs:—3c. Map of Newfoundland; 7c. Caribou; 8c. Corner Brook Paper Mills; 10c. Atlantic salmon; 14c. Newfoundland dog; 15c. Harp seal; 20c. Transatlantic Beacon; 24c. Bell Island; 25c. Sealing fleet; 48c. The Banks fishing fleet.

155 King George VI

1938

277	**155**	2c. green	40	75
278	-	3c. red	40	30
279	-	4c. blue	4·50	40
271	-	7c. blue	1·50	12·00

Designs:—3c. Queen Mother; 4c. Queen Elizabeth II, aged 12; 7c. Queen Mary.

159 King George VI and Queen Elizabeth

1938. Royal Visit.

272	**159**	5c. blue	4·00	1·00

1939. Surch in figures and triangles.

273	**159**	2c. on 5c. blue	2·50	50
274	**159**	4c. on 5c. blue	2·00	2·25

161 Grenfell on the *Strathcona* (after painting by Gribble)

1941. 50th Anniv of Sir Wilfred Grenfell's Labrador Mission.

275	**161**	5c. blue	30	1·00

162 Memorial University College

1942

290	**162**	30c. red	2·50	5·50

163 St. John's

1943. Air.

291	**163**	7c. blue	50	1·25

1946. Surch **TWO CENTS**.

292	**162**	2c. on 30c. red	30	2·50

165 Queen Elizabeth II when Princess

1947. 21st Birthday of Princess Elizabeth.

293	**165**	4c. blue	40	1·00

166 Cabot off Cape Bonavista

1947. 450th Anniv of Cabot's Discovery of Newfoundland.

294	**166**	5c. violet	50	1·00

POSTAGE DUE STAMPS

D1

1939

D1	**D1**	1c. green	2·25	23·00
D2	**D1**	2c. red	20·00	8·50
D3	**D1**	3c. blue	5·00	40·00
D4	**D1**	4c. orange	9·00	30·00
D5	**D1**	5c. brown	13·00	45·00
D6	**D1**	10c. purple	13·00	30·00

NEW GUINEA

Formerly a German Colony, part of the island of New Guinea. Occupied by Australian forces during the 1914–18 war and subsequently joined with Papua and administered by the Australian Commonwealth under trusteeship. After the Japanese defeat in 1945 Australian stamps were used until 1952 when the combined issue appeared for Papua and New Guinea (q.v.). The stamps overprinted "N.W. PACIFIC ISLANDS" were also used in Nauru and other ex-German islands.

12 pence = 1 shilling; 20 shillings = 1 pound.

1914. "Yacht" key-types of German New Guinea surch **G.R.I.** and value in English currency.

16	**N**	1d. on 3pf. brown	£100	£110
17	**N**	1d. on 5pf. green	35·00	50·00
18	**N**	2d. on 10pf. red	50·00	60·00
19	**N**	2d. on 20pf. blue	50·00	70·00
5	**N**	2½d. on 10pf. red	95·00	£200
6	**N**	2½d. on 20pf. blue	£110	£225
22	**N**	3d. on 25pf. blk & red on yell	£190	£250
23	**N**	3d. on 30pf. blk & orge on buff	£170	£200
24	**N**	4d. on 40pf. black and red	£180	£275
25	**N**	5d. on 50pf. black & pur on buff	£325	£400
26	**N**	8d. on 80pf. blk & red on rose	£425	£600
12	**O**	1s. on 1m. red	£3500	£4250
13	**O**	2s. on 2m. blue	£3250	£4000
14	**O**	3s. on 3m. black	£5500	£7000
15	**O**	5s. on 5m. red and black	£14000	£16000

1915. Nos. 3/4 surch **1**

31	**N**	"1" on 2d. on 10pf. red	£28000	£28000
32	**N**	"1" on 2d. on 20pf. blue	£28000	£17000

4

1914. Registration labels with names of various towns surch **G.R.I. 3d.**

33	**4**	3d. black and red	£275	£325

1914. "Yacht" key-types of German Marshall Islands surch **G.R.I.** and value in English currency.

50	**N**	1d. on 3pf. brown	£110	£170
51	**N**	1d. on 5pf. green	80·00	85·00
52	**N**	2d. on 10pf. red	27·00	50·00
53	**N**	2d. on 20pf. blue	27·00	50·00
64g	**N**	2½d. on 10pf. red	£27000	
64h	**N**	2½d. on 20pf. blue	£40000	
54	**N**	3d. on 25pf. black and red on yellow	£450	£550
55	**N**	3d. on 30pf. black and orange on buff	£475	£600
56	**N**	4d. on 40pf. black and red	£170	£250
57	**N**	5d. on 50pf. black and purple on buff	£300	£375
58	**N**	8d. on 80pf. black and red on rose	£475	£700
59	**O**	1s. on 1m. red	£4000	£5000
60	**O**	2s. on 2m. blue	£1900	£4000
61	**O**	3s. on 3m. black	£6500	£9500
62	**O**	5s. on 5m. red and black	£14000	£15000

1915. Nos. 52 and 53 surch 1.

63	**N**	1d. on 2d. on 10pf. red	£200	£275
64	**N**	1d. on 2d. on 20pf. blue	£4000	£2500

1915. Stamps of Australia optd **N. W. PACIFIC ISLANDS.**

102	**3**	½d. green	1·75	3·50
103	**3**	1d. red	3·75	1·60
120	**3**	1d. violet	2·50	6·50
94	**1**	2d. grey	6·50	32·00
121	**3**	2d. orange	8·50	2·50
122	**3**	2d. red	9·50	2·00
74	**1**	2½d. blue	2·75	16·00
96	**1**	3d. olive	5·50	11·00
70	**3**	4d. orange	4·00	15·00
123	**3**	4d. violet	20·00	40·00
124	**3**	4d. blue	11·00	60·00
105	**3**	5d. brown	4·00	12·00
110	**1**	6d. blue	4·50	14·00
89	**1**	9d. violet	16·00	21·00
90	**1**	1s. green	11·00	24·00
115	**1**	2s. brown	21·00	38·00
116	**1**	5s. grey and yellow	65·00	70·00
84	**1**	10s. grey and pink	£150	£180
99	**1**	£1 brown and blue	£350	£450

1918. Nos. 105 and 90 surch One Penny.

100	**3**	1d. on 5d. brown	90·00	80·00
101	**1**	1d. on 1s. green	£100	80·00

12 Native Village

1925

125	**12**	½d. orange	2·50	7·00
126	**12**	1d. green	2·50	5·50
126a	**12**	1½d. red	3·25	2·75
127	**12**	2d. red	7·00	4·50
128	**12**	3d. blue	8·50	4·00
129	**12**	4d. olive	13·00	26·00
130a	**12**	6d. brown	6·00	50·00
131	**12**	9d. purple	13·00	45·00
132	**12**	1s. green	15·00	27·00
133	**12**	2s. lake	30·00	48·00
134	**12**	5s. brown	50·00	65·00
135	**12**	10s. pink	£120	£180
136	**12**	£1 grey	£190	£300

1931. Air. Optd with biplane and AIR MAIL.

137	**12**	½d. orange	1·50	9·50
138	**12**	1d. green	1·60	5·00
139	**12**	1½d. red	1·25	8·50
140	**12**	2d. red	1·25	7·00
141	**12**	3d. blue	1·75	13·00
142	**12**	4d. olive	1·25	9·00
143	**12**	6d. brown	1·75	14·00
144	**12**	9d. purple	3·00	17·00

145	**12**	1s. green	3·00	17·00
146	**12**	2s. lake	7·00	48·00
147	**12**	5s. brown	20·00	65·00
148	**12**	10s. pink	85·00	£110
149	**12**	£1 grey	£160	£250

14 Raggiana Bird of Paradise (Dates either side of value)

1931. Tenth Anniv of Australian Administration. Dated "1921–1931".

150	**14**	1d. green	4·25	7·50
151	**14**	1½d. red	5·00	10·00
152	**14**	2d. red	5·00	2·25
153	**14**	3d. blue	5·00	4·75
154	**14**	4d. olive	6·50	29·00
155	**14**	5d. green	9·00	24·00
156	**14**	6d. brown	5·00	19·00
157	**14**	9d. violet	8·50	19·00
158	**14**	1s. grey	6·00	15·00
159	**14**	2s. lake	10·00	48·00
160	**14**	5s. brown	42·00	55·00
161	**14**	10s. pink	£120	£140
162	**14**	£1 grey	£250	£275

1931. Air. Optd with biplane and AIR MAIL.

163	**14**	½d. orange	3·25	3·25
164	**14**	1d. green	4·00	7·00
165	**14**	1½d. red	3·75	10·00
166	**14**	2d. red	3·75	3·00
167	**14**	3d. blue	6·00	6·50
168	**14**	4d. olive	6·00	6·00
169	**14**	5d. green	6·00	11·00
170	**14**	6d. brown	7·00	26·00
171	**14**	9d. violet	8·00	15·00
172	**14**	1s. grey	7·50	15·00
173	**14**	2s. lake	16·00	50·00
174	**14**	5s. brown	42·00	70·00
175	**14**	10s. pink	80·00	£120
176	**14**	£1 grey	£150	£250

1932. As T **14**, but without dates.

177	1d. green	7·00	20
178	1½d. red	7·00	21·00
179	2d. red	5·50	20
179a	2½d. green	6·50	28·00
180	3d. blue	7·50	1·25
180a	3½d. red	13·00	23·00
181	4d. olive	6·50	6·50
182	5d. green	7·00	70
183	6d. brown	7·50	5·50
184	9d. violet	9·50	26·00
185	1s. grey	6·50	10·00
186	2s. lake	5·00	17·00
187	5s. brown	32·00	48·00
188	10s. pink	55·00	70·00
189	£1 grey	£120	£100

1932. Air. T **14**, but without dates, optd with biplane and AIR MAIL.

190	½d. orange	60	1·50
191	1d. green	1·25	3·25
192	1½d. mauve	1·75	11·00
193	2d. red	1·75	30
193a	2½d. green	8·50	2·50
194	3d. blue	3·25	3·00
194a	3½d. red	4·75	3·25
195	4d. olive	4·50	10·00
196	5d. green	7·00	7·50
197	6d. brown	4·50	15·00
198	9d. violet	6·00	9·00
199	1s. grey	6·00	12·00
200	2s. lake	15·00	50·00
201	5s. brown	50·00	60·00
202	10s. pink	95·00	85·00
203	£1 grey	85·00	55·00

16 Bulolo Goldfields

1935. Air.

204	**16**	£2 violet	£350	£140
205	**16**	£5 green	£750	£450

1935. Silver Jubilee. Nos. 177 and 179 optd HIS MAJESTY'S JUBILEE. 1910–1935.

206	1d. green	1·00	65
207	2d. red	3·50	65

18 King George VI

1937. Coronation.

208	**18**	2d. red	50	1·50
209	**18**	3d. blue	50	1·75
210	**18**	5d. green	50	1·75
211	**18**	1s. purple	50	2·25

1939. Air. As T **16** but inscr "AIR MAIL POSTAGE".

212	½d. orange	4·00	9·50
213	1d. green	3·25	4·50
214	1½d. purple	4·00	19·00
215	2d. red	9·50	3·00
216	3d. blue	18·00	18·00
217	4d. olive	15·00	8·50
218	5d. green	14·00	4·00
219	6d. brown	45·00	32·00
220	9d. violet	45·00	45·00
221	1s. green	45·00	32·00
222	2s. red	90·00	75·00
223	5s. brown	£190	£160
224	10s. pink	£600	£425
225	£1 olive	£140	£150

OFFICIAL STAMPS

1915. Nos. 16 and 17 optd **O. S.**

O1	**N**	1d. on 3pf. brown	35·00	75·00
O2	**N**	1d. on 5pf. green	£100	£140

1925. Optd **O S.**

O22	**12**	1d. green	5·50	4·50
O23	**12**	1½d. red	5·50	17·00
O24	**12**	2d. red	3·00	3·75
O25	**12**	3d. blue	6·00	10·00
O26	**12**	4d. olive	4·50	8·50
O27a	**12**	6d. brown	7·50	35·00
O28	**12**	9d. purple	4·25	35·00
O29	**12**	1s. green	5·50	35·00
O30	**12**	2s. lake	42·00	65·00

1931. Optd **O S.**

O31	**14**	1d. green	12·00	13·00
O32	**14**	1½d. red	12·00	12·00
O33	**14**	2d. red	12·00	7·00
O34	**14**	3d. blue	7·00	6·00
O35	**14**	4d. olive	7·50	8·50
O36	**14**	5d. green	10·00	12·00
O37	**14**	6d. brown	14·00	17·00
O38	**14**	9d. violet	16·00	28·00
O39	**14**	1s. grey	16·00	28·00
O40	**14**	2s. lake	40·00	70·00
O41	**14**	5s. brown	£110	£180

1932. T **14**, but without dates, optd O S.

O42	1d. green	19·00	21·00
O43	1½d. red	19·00	21·00
O44	2d. red	19·00	3·25
O45	2½d. green	11·00	13·00
O46	3d. blue	11·00	42·00
O47	3½d. red	9·00	9·00
O48	4d. olive	20·00	32·00
O49	5d. green	9·00	30·00
O50	6d. brown	25·00	55·00
O51	9d. violet	15·00	48·00
O52	1s. grey	15·00	30·00
O53	2s. lake	30·00	75·00
O54	5s. brown	£120	£180

For later issues see **PAPUA NEW GUINEA**.

NEW HEBRIDES

A group of islands in the Pacific Ocean, E. of Australia, under joint administration of Gt. Britain and France. The Condominium ended in 1980, when the New Hebrides became independent as the Republic of Vanuatu.

1908. 12 pence = 1 shilling; 20 shillings = 1 pound.
1938. 100 gold centimes = 1 gold franc.
1977. 100 centimes = 1 New Hebrides franc.

BRITISH ADMINISTRATION

1908. Stamps of Fiji optd. (a) NEW HEBRIDES. CONDOMINIUM. (with full points).

1a	**23**	½d. green	40	7·00
2	**23**	1d. red	50	40
5	**23**	2d. purple and orange	60	70
6	**23**	2½d. purple and blue on blue	60	70
7	**23**	5d. purple and green	80	2·00
8	**23**	6d. purple and red	70	1·25
3	**23**	1s. green and red	29·00	3·75

(b) **NEW HEBRIDES CONDOMINIUM** (without full points).

10	**23**	½d. green	3·50	32·00
11	**23**	1d. red	11·00	8·50
12	**23**	2d. grey	70	3·00
13	**23**	2½d. blue	75	8·00
14	**23**	5d. purple and green	2·25	5·50
15	**23**	6d. purple and deep purple	1·50	8·50
16	**23**	1s. black and green	1·50	7·50

3 Weapons and Idols

1911

18	**3**	½d. green	85	1·75
19	**3**	1d. red	5·50	2·00
20	**3**	2d. grey	9·00	3·00
21	**3**	2½d. blue	5·00	5·50
24	**3**	5d. green	4·50	7·00
25	**3**	6d. purple	3·00	5·00
26	**3**	1s. black on green	2·75	13·00
27	**3**	2s. purple on blue	48·00	22·00
28	**3**	5s. green on yellow	48·00	55·00

1920. Surch. (a) On T **3**.

40	**3**	1d. on ½d. green	4·00	24·00
30	**3**	1d. on 5d. green	11·00	65·00
31	**3**	1d. on 1s. black on green	4·25	13·00
32	**3**	1d. on 2s. purple on blue	2·00	10·00
33	**3**	1d. on 5s. green on yellow	1·00	10·00
41	**3**	3d. on 1d. red	4·00	11·00
42	**3**	5d. on 2½d. blue	7·50	29·00

(b) On No. F16 of French New Hebrides.

34	**3**	2d. on 40c. red on yellow	1·00	23·00

5

1925

43	**5**	½d. (5c.) black	1·25	21·00
44	**5**	1d. (10c.) green	1·00	19·00
45	**5**	2d. (20c.) grey	1·75	2·50
46	**5**	2½d. (25c.) brown	1·00	13·00
47	**5**	5d. (50c.) blue	3·00	2·75
48	**5**	6d. (60c.) purple	3·75	18·00
49	**5**	1s. (1f.25) black on green	3·25	19·00
50	**5**	2s. (2f.50) purple on blue	6·00	22·00
51	**5**	5s. (6f.25) green on yellow	6·00	25·00

6 Lopevi Islands and Outrigger Canoe

1938

52	**6**	5c. green	2·50	4·50
53	**6**	10c. orange	3·50	2·25
54	**6**	15c. violet	3·50	4·50
55	**6**	20c. red	4·25	6·50
56	**6**	25c. brown	1·60	3·00
57	**6**	30c. blue	4·50	2·75
58	**6**	40c. olive	4·50	6·50
59	**6**	50c. purple	1·60	2·75
60	**6**	1f. red on green	11·00	9·00
61	**6**	2f. blue on green	30·00	25·00
62	**6**	5f. red on yellow	75·00	55·00
63	**6**	10f. violet on blue	£225	80·00

1949. U.P.U. As T **4d/g** of Pitcairn Islands.

64	10c. orange	30	1·25
65	15c. violet	30	1·25
66	30c. blue	30	1·25
67	50c. purple	40	1·25

7 Outrigger Sailing Canoes

1953

68	**7**	5c. green	1·00	2·25
69	**7**	10c. red	1·50	1·00
70	**7**	15c. yellow	1·50	20
71	**7**	20c. blue	1·50	20
72	-	25c. olive	60	20
73	-	30c. brown	60	20
74	-	40c. sepia	60	20
75	-	50c. violet	1·00	20
76	-	1f. orange	7·00	3·25
77	-	2f. purple	7·00	8·50
78	-	5f. red	8·50	22·00

Designs:—25c. to 50c. Native carving; 1f. to 5f. Two natives outside hut.

1953. Coronation. As T **8a** of Pitcairn Islands.

79	10c. black and red	1·00	50

10 *San Pedro y San Paulo* (Quiros) and Map

1956. 50th Anniv of Condominium. Inscr "1906 1956".

80	**10**	5c. green	15	10
81	**10**	10c. red	40	10
82	-	20c. blue	10	10
83	-	50c. lilac	15	15

Design:—20, 50c. Marianne, Talking Drum and Britannia.

12 Port Vila; Iririki Islet

1957

84	**12**	5c. green	40	1·50
85	**12**	10c. red	30	10
86	**12**	15c. yellow	50	1·50
87	**12**	20c. blue	40	10
88	-	25c. olive	45	10
89	-	30c. brown	45	10
90	-	40c. sepia	45	10
91	-	50c. violet	45	10
92	-	1f. orange	1·00	1·00
93	-	2f. mauve	4·00	2·50
94	-	5f. black	9·00	3·25

Designs:—25c. to 50c. River scene and spear fisherman; 1f. to 5f. Woman drinking from coconut.

1963. Freedom from Hunger. As T **20a** of Pitcairn Islands.

95	60c. green	50	15

1963. Centenary of Red Cross. As T **20b** of Pitcairn Islands, but with British and French cyphers in place of the Queen's portrait.

96	15c. red and black	40	10
97	45c. red and blue	60	20

17 Cocoa Beans

1963

98	-	5c. red, brown and blue	2·00	50
99	**17**	10c. brown, buff and green	15	10
100	-	15c. bistre, brown and violet	15	10
101	-	20c. black, green and blue	55	10
102	-	25c. violet, brown and red	50	70
103	-	30c. brown, bistre and violet	75	10
104	-	40c. red and blue	80	1·40
105	-	50c. green, yellow and blue	60	10
129	-	60c. red and blue	40	15
106	-	1f. red, black and green	2·00	3·00
107	-	2f. black, purple and green	2·00	1·25
108	-	3f. multicoloured	6·00	3·50
109	-	5f. blue, deep blue and black	6·00	19·00

Designs:—5c. Exporting manganese, Forari; 15c. Copra; 20c. Fishing from Palikulo Point; 25c. Picasso triggerfish; 30c. New Caledonian nautilus shell; 40, 60c. Lionfish; 50c. Clown surgeonfish; 1f. Cardinal honeyeater (bird); 2f. Buff-bellied flycatcher; 3f. Thicket warbler; 5f. White-collared kingfisher.

1965. Centenary of I.T.U. As T **24a** of Pitcairn Islands, but with British and French cyphers in place of the Queen's portrait.

110	15c. red and drab	20	10
111	60c. blue and red	35	20

1965. I.C.Y. As T **24b** of Pitcairn Islands, but with British and French cyphers in place of the Queen's portrait.

112	5c. purple and turquoise	15	10
113	55c. green and lavender	20	20

1966. Churchill Commemoration. As T **24c** of Pitcairn Islands, but with British and French cyphers in place of the Queen's portrait.

114	5c. blue	20	15
115	15c. green	70	10
116	25c. brown	80	10
117	30c. violet	80	15

1966. World Cup Football Championship. As T **25** of Pitcairn Islands, but with British and French cyphers in place of the Queen's portrait.

No.	Description		
118	20c. multicoloured	30	15
119	40c. multicoloured	70	15

1966. Inauguration of W.H.O. Headquarters, Geneva. As T **25a** of Pitcairn Islands, but with British and French cyphers in place of the Queen's portrait.

No.	Description		
120	25c. black, green and blue	15	10
121	60c. black, purple and ochre	40	20

1966. 20th Anniv of UNESCO. As T **25b/d** of Pitcairn Islands, but with British and French cyphers in place of the Queen's portrait.

No.	Description		
122	15c. multicoloured	25	10
123	30c. yellow, violet and olive	65	10
124	45c. black, purple and orange	75	15

36 The Coast Watchers

1967. 25th Anniv of Pacific War. Multicoloured.

No.	Description		
125	15c. Type **36**	40	15
126	25c. Map of war zone, US marine and Australian soldier	70	25
127	60c. HMAS *Canberra* (cruiser)	70	40
128	1f. Boeing B-17 Flying Fortress	70	1·25

40 Globe and Hemispheres

1968. Bicent of Bougainville's World Voyage.

No.	Type	Description		
130	**40**	15c. green, violet and red	20	10
131	-	25c. olive, purple and blue	45	15
132	-	60c. brown, purple & green	45	20

Designs:—25c. Ships *La Boudeuse* and *L'Etoile*, and map; 60c. Bougainville, ship's figure-head and bougainvillea flowers.

43 Concorde and Vapour Trails

1968. Anglo-French Concorde Project.

No.	Type	Description		
133	**43**	25c. blue, red and blue	35	30
134	-	60c. red, black and blue	40	45

Design:—60c. Concorde in flight.

45 Kauri Pine

1969. Timber Industry.

No.	Type	Description		
135	**45**	20c. multicoloured	10	10

46 Cyphers, Flags and Relay Runner receiving Baton

1969. Third South Pacific Games, Port Moresby. Multicoloured.

No.	Description		
136	25c. Type **46**	10	10
137	1f. Runner passing baton	20	20

48 Diver on Platform

1969. Pentecost Island Land Divers. Mult.

No.	Description		
138	15c. Type **48**	10	10
139	25c. Diver jumping	10	10
140	1f. Diver at end of fall	20	20

51 UPU Emblem and Headquarters Building

1970. New U.P.U. Headquarters Building.

No.	Type	Description		
141	**51**	1f.05 slate, orange & purple	20	20

52 General Charles de Gaulle

1970. 30th Anniv of New Hebrides' Declaration for the Free French Government.

No.	Type	Description		
142	**52**	65c. multicoloured	35	70
143	**52**	1f.10 multicoloured	45	70

1970. No. 101 surch 35.

No.	Description		
144	35c. on 20c. black, green and blue	30	30

54 *The Virgin and Child* (Bellini)

1970. Christmas. Multicoloured.

No.	Description		
145	15c. Type **54**	10	10
146	50c. *The Virgin and Child* (Cima)	20	20

1971. Death of General Charles de Gaulle. Nos. 142/3 optd 1890-1970 IN MEMORIAM 9-11-70.

No.	Type	Description		
147	**52**	65c. multicoloured	15	10
148	**52**	1f.10 multicoloured	15	20

56 Football

1971. Fourth South Pacific Games, Papeete, French Polynesia.

No.	Description		
149	20c. Type **56**	10	10
150	65c. Basketball (vert)	30	20

57 Kauri Pine, Cone and Arms of Royal Society

1971. Royal Society's Expedition to New Hebrides.

No.	Type	Description		
151	**57**	65c. multicoloured	20	15

58 *The Adoration of the Shepherds* (detail, Louis le Nain)

1971. Christmas. Multicoloured.

No.	Description		
152	25c. Type **58**	10	10
153	50c. *The Adoration of the Shepherds* (detail, Tintoretto)	30	90

59 de Havilland Drover 3

1972. Aircraft. Multicoloured.

No.	Description		
154	20c. Type **59**	30	15
155	25c. Short S25 Sandringham 4 flying boat	30	15
156	30c. de Havilland Dragon Rapide	30	15
157	65c. Sud Aviation SE 210 Caravelle	75	1·25

60 Ceremonial Headdress, South Malekula

1972. Multicoloured.

No.	Description		
158	5c. Type **60**	10	20
159	10c. Baker's pigeon	30	20
160	15c. Gong and carving, North Ambrym	15	20
161	20c. Red-headed parrot finch	50	25
162	25c. Graskoin's cowrie (shell)	40	25
163	30c. Red-lip olive (shell)	50	30
164	35c. Chestnut-bellied kingfisher	80	40
165	65c. Pretty conch (shell)	75	60
166	1f. Gong (North Malekula) and carving (North Ambrym)	50	1·00
167	2f. Palm lorikeet	3·50	4·50
168	3f. Ceremonial headdress, South Malekula (different)	1·50	6·00
169	5f. Great green turban (shell)	4·00	13·00

61 *Adoration of the Kings* (Spranger)

1972. Christmas. Multicoloured.

No.	Description		
170	25c. Type **61**	10	10
171	70c. *The Virgin and Child in a Landscape* (Provoost)	20	20

1972. Royal Silver Wedding. As T **73** of Pitcairn Islands, but with Royal and French cyphers in background.

No.	Description		
172	35c. violet	15	10
173	65c. green	20	10

63 *Dendrobium teretifolium*

1973. Orchids. Multicoloured.

No.	Description		
174	25c. Type **63**	25	10
175	30c. *Ephemerantha comata*	25	10
176	35c. *Spathoglottis petri*	30	10
177	65c. *Dendrobium mohlianum*	60	55

64 New Wharf at Vila

1973. Opening of New Wharf at Villa. Mult.

No.	Description		
178	25c. Type **64**	20	10
179	70c. As Type **64** but horiz	40	30

65 Wild Horses

1973. Tanna Island. Multicoloured.

No.	Description		
180	35c. Type **65**	45	15
181	70c. Yasur Volcano	55	20

66 Mother and Child

1973. Christmas. Multicoloured.

No.	Description		
182	35c. Type **66**	10	10
183	70c. Lagoon scene	20	20

67 Pacific Pigeon

1974. Wild Life. Multicoloured.

No.	Description		
184	25c. Type **67**	60	25
185	35c. *Lyssa curvata* (moth)	60	45
186	70c. Green sea turtle	60	50
187	1f.15 Grey-headed flying fox	80	1·25

1974. Royal Visit. Nos. 164 and 167 optd **ROYAL VISIT 1974.**

No.	Description		
188	35c. multicoloured	40	10
189	2f. multicoloured	60	40

69 Old Post Office

1974. Inaug of New Post Office, Vila. Mult.

No.	Description		
190	35c. Type **69**	15	50
191	70c. New Post Office	15	60

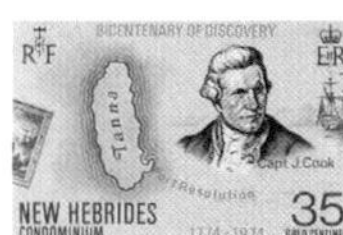

70 Capt. Cook and Map

1974. Bicent of Discovery. Multicoloured.

No.	Description		
192	35c. Type **70**	1·00	1·75
193	35c. William Wales and beach landing	1·00	1·75
194	35c. William Hodges and island scene	1·00	1·75
195	1f.15 Capt. Cook, map and HMS *Resolution* (59×34 mm)	2·25	3·25

71 UPU Emblem and Letters

1974. Centenary of U.P.U.

No.	Type	Description		
196	**71**	70c. multicoloured	30	70

72 *Adoration of the Magi* (Velazquez)

1974. Christmas. Multicoloured.

No.	Description		
197	35c. Type **72**	10	10
198	70c. *The Nativity* (Gerard van Honthorst)	20	20

73 Charolais Bull

1975

199	**73**	10f. brown, green and blue	7·50	18·00

74 Canoeing

1975. World Scout Jamboree, Norway. Mult.

200	25c. Type **74**	15	10
201	35c. Preparing meal	15	10
202	1f. Map-reading	35	15
203	5f. Fishing	1·00	2·50

75 *Pitti Madonna* (Michelangelo)

1975. Christmas. Michelangelo's Sculptures. Mult.

204	35c. Type **75**	10	10
205	70c. *Bruges Madonna*	15	10
206	2f.50 *Taddei Madonna*	70	50

76 Concorde in British Airways Livery

1976. First Commercial Flight of Concorde.

207	**76**	5f. multicoloured	3·00	3·25

77 Telephones of 1876 and 1976

1976. Centenary of Telephone. Multicoloured.

208	25c. Type **77**	15	10
209	70c. Alexander Graham Bell	30	10
210	1f.15 Satellite and Noumea Earth Station	50	50

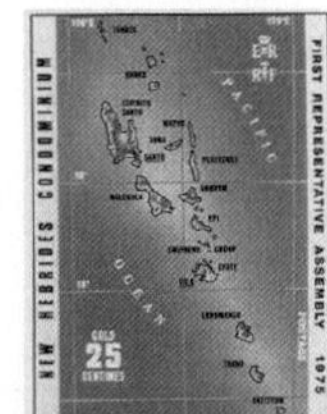

78 Map of the Islands

1976. Constitutional Changes. Multicoloured.

211	25c. Type **78**	40	15
212	1f. View of Santo (horiz)	75	60
213	2f. View of Vila (horiz)	1·10	2·25

Nos. 212/13 are smaller, 36×26 mm.

79 *The Flight into Egypt* (Lusitano)

1976. Christmas. Multicoloured.

214	35c. Type **79**	10	10
215	70c. *Adoration of the Shepherds*	15	10
216	2f.50 *Adoration of the Magi*	45	50

Nos. 215/16 show retables by the Master of Santos-o-Novo.

80 Royal Visit, 1974

1977. Silver Jubilee. Multicoloured.

217	35c. Type **80**	10	10
218	70c. Imperial State Crown	15	10
219	2f. The Blessing	30	65

1977. Currency change. Nos. 158/69 and 199 surch.

233	5f. on 5c. Type **60**	50	15
234	10f. on 10c. Baker's pigeon	1·00	15
222	15f. on 15c. Gong and carving	60	1·50
223	20f. on 20c. Red-headed parrot finch	1·25	55
224	25f. on 25c. Gaskoin's cowrie (shell)	1·75	2·00
225	30f. on 30c. Red-lip olive (shell)	1·75	1·10
226	35f. on 35c. Chestnut-bellied kingfisher	1·75	1·25
239	40f. on 65c. Pretty conch (shell)	1·50	55
228	50f. on 1f. Gong and carving	1·00	1·75
229	70f. on 2f. Palm lorikeet	6·50	75
230	100f. on 3f. Ceremonial headdress	1·00	3·75
231	200f. on 5f. Great green turban (shell)	4·00	14·00
241	500f. on 10f. Type **73**	19·00	14·00

89 Island of Erromango and Kauri Pine

1977. Islands. Multicoloured.

242	5f. Type **89**	30	10
243	10f. Territory map and copra making	40	1·00
244	15f. Espiritu Santo and cattle	30	30
245	20f. Efate and Vila PO	30	25
246	25f. Malekula and headdresses	40	40
247	30f. Aobe, Maewo and pigs' tusks	45	50
248	35f. Pentecost and land diver	50	65
249	40f. Tanna and John Frum Cross	70	60
250	50f. Shepherd Is. and canoe	1·50	40
251	70f. Banks Is. and dancers	1·00	3·50
252	100f. Ambrym and idols	1·00	90
253	200f. Aneityum and baskets	1·00	2·00
254	500f. Torres Is. and archer fisherman	2·25	7·50

90 *Tempi Madonna* (Raphael)

1977. Christmas. Multicoloured.

255	10f. Type **90**	20	45
256	15f. *The Flight into Egypt* (Gerard David)	30	60
257	30f. *Virgin and Child* (Batoni)	40	90

91 Concorde over New York

1978. Concorde Commemoration.

258	10f. Type **91**	60	50
259	20f. Concorde over London	60	50
260	30f. Concorde over Washington	75	75
261	40f. Concorde over Paris	80	80

92 White Horse of Hanover

1978. 25th Anniv of Coronation.

262	**92**	40f. brown, blue and silver	15	30
263	-	40f. multicoloured	15	30
264	-	40f. brown, blue and silver	15	30

Designs:—No. 263, Queen Elizabeth II; 264, Gallic Cock.

93 *Madonna and Child*

1978. Christmas. Paintings by Durer. Mult.

265	10f. Type **93**	10	10
266	15f. *The Virgin and Child with St. Anne*	10	10
267	30f. *Madonna of the Siskin*	15	10
268	40f. *Madonna of the Pear*	20	15

1979. First Anniv of Internal Self-Government. Surch **166°E 11.1.79 FIRST ANNIVERSARY INTERNAL SELF-GOVERNMENT** and new value.

269	**78**	10f. on 25f. multicoloured (blue background)	10	10
270	**78**	40f. on 25f. multicoloured (green background)	20	20

95 1938 5c. Stamp and Sir Rowland Hill

1979. Death Centenary of Sir Rowland Hill. Mult.

271	10f. Type **95**	10	10
272	20f. 1969 25c. Pentecost Island Land Divers commemorative	20	10
273	40f. 1925 2d. (20c.)	25	20
MS274	143×94 mm. Nos. 272 and F286	75	90

96 Chubwan Mask

1979. Arts Festival. Multicoloured.

275	5f. Type **96**	10	10
276	10f. Nal-Nal clubs and spears	10	10
277	20f. Ritual puppet	15	10
278	40f. Neqatmalow headdress	25	15

97 *Native Church* (Metas Masongo)

1979. Christmas and International Year of the Child. Children's Drawings. Multicoloured.

279	5f. Type **97**	10	10
280	10f. *Priest and Candles* (Herve Rutu)	10	10
281	20f. *Cross and Bible* (Mark Deards) (vert)	10	10
282	40f. *Green Candle and Santa Claus* (Dev Raj) (vert)	15	15

98 White-bellied Honeyeater

1980. Birds. Multicoloured.

283	10f. Type **98**	40	15
284	20f. Scarlet robin	60	15
285	30f. Yellow-fronted white-eye	70	50
286	40f. Fan-tailed cuckoo	80	90

POSTAGE DUE STAMPS

1925. Optd **POSTAGE DUE**.

D1	**5**	1d. (10c.) green	30·00	1·00
D2	**5**	2d. (20c.) grey	32·00	1·25
D3	**5**	3d. (30c.) red	32·00	2·75
D4	**5**	5d. (50c.) blue	35·00	4·75
D5	**5**	10d. (1c.) red on blue	40·00	6·00

1938. Optd **POSTAGE DUE**.

D6	**6**	5c. green	35·00	50·00
D7	**6**	10c. orange	35·00	50·00
D8	**6**	20c. red	42·00	75·00
D9	**6**	40c. olive	48·00	85·00
D10	**6**	1f. red on green	48·00	90·00

1953. Nos. 68/9, 71, 74 and 76 optd **POSTAGE DUE**.

D11	**7**	5c. green	5·00	19·00
D12	**7**	10c. red	1·75	16·00
D13	**7**	20c. blue	5·00	25·00
D14	-	40c. sepia (No. 74)	17·00	45·00
D15	-	1f. orange (No. 76)	4·50	45·00

1957. Optd **POSTAGE DUE**.

D16	**12**	5c. green	30	1·50
D17	**12**	10c. red	30	1·50
D18	**12**	20c. blue	75	1·75
D19	-	40c. sepia (No. 90)	1·00	2·50
D20	-	1f. orange (No. 92)	1·25	3·25

FRENCH ADMINISTRATION

1908. Stamps of New Caledonia optd **NOUVELLES HEBRIDES**.

F1	**15**	5c. green	13·00	4·75
F2	**15**	10c. red	13·00	3·50
F3	**16**	25c. blue on green	9·50	2·25
F4	**16**	50c. red on green	8·50	4·75
F5	**17**	1f. blue on green	28·00	20·00

1910. Nos. F1/5 further optd **CONDOMINIUM**.

F6	**15**	5c. green	10·00	3·00
F7	**15**	10c. red	10·00	1·25
F8	**16**	25c. blue on green	3·25	4·50
F9	**16**	50c. red on orange	14·00	38·00
F10	**17**	1f. blue on green	32·00	22·00

The following issues are as stamps of British Administration but are inscr "NOUVELLES HEBRIDES" except where otherwise stated.

1911

F11	**3**	5c. green	1·00	3·00
F12	**3**	10c. red	50	1·00
F13	**3**	20c. grey	1·00	2·25
F25	**3**	25c. blue	1·25	7·50
F15	**3**	30c. brown on yellow	6·50	5·25
F16	**3**	40c. red on yellow	1·40	6·00
F17	**3**	50c. olive	2·00	6·50
F18	**3**	75c. orange	7·00	30·00
F19	**3**	1f. red on blue	7·50	4·50
F20	**3**	2f. violet	12·00	22·00
F21	**3**	5f. red on green	12·00	48·00

1920. Surch in figures.

F34	5c. on 40c. red on yellow (No. F16)	27·00	£100
F32a	5c. on 50c. red on orange (No. F4)	£550	£650
F33	5c. on 50c. red on orange (No. F9)	2·40	22·00
F38	10c. on 5c. green (No. F11)	1·00	11·00
F33a	10c. on 25c. blue on green (No. F8)	50	1·50
F35	20c. on 30c. brown on yellow (No. F15)	15·00	70·00
F39	30c. on 10c. red (No. F12)	1·00	3·00
F41	50c. on 25c. blue (No. F25)	2·50	29·00

1921. Stamp of New Hebrides (British) surch 10c.

F37	10c. on 5d. green (No. 24)	16·00	60·00

1925

F42	**5**	5c. (½d.) black	75	13·00
F43	**5**	10c. (1d.) green	1·00	9·00
F44	**5**	20c. (2d.) grey	3·75	3·00
F45	**5**	25c. (2½d.) brown	1·50	9·00

F46 5 30c. (3d.) red 1·75 18·00
F47 5 40c. (4d.) red on yellow 3·25 16·00
F48 5 50c. (5d.) blue 2·00 1·75
F49 5 75c. (7½d.) brown 1·50 22·00
F50 5 1f. (10d.) red on blue 1·50 2·50
F51 5 2f. (1s.8d.) violet 2·50 38·00
F52 5 5f. (4d.) red on green 3·50 35·00

1938
F53 6 5c. green 6·00 14·00
F54 6 10c. orange 6·50 4·00
F55 6 15c. violet 6·50 10·00
F56 6 20c. red 6·50 7·50
F57 6 25c. brown 13·00 9·50
F58 6 30c. blue 13·00 10·00
F59 6 40c. olive 7·00 18·00
F60 6 50c. purple 7·00 7·00
F61 6 1f. red on green 8·00 11·00
F62 6 2f. blue on green 50·00 50·00
F63 6 5f. red on yellow 75·00 80·00
F64 6 10f. violet and blue £160 £170

1941. Free French Issue. As last, optd France Libre.
F65 6 5c. green 2·00 25·00
F66 6 10c. orange 6·00 24·00
F67 6 15c. violet 9·50 40·00
F68 6 20c. red 26·00 32·00
F69 6 25c. brown 29·00 42·00
F70 6 30c. blue 29·00 38·00
F71 6 40c. olive 29·00 40·00
F72 6 50c. purple 25·00 38·00
F73 6 1f. red on green 25·00 38·00
F74 6 2f. blue on green 24·00 38·00
F75 6 5f. red on yellow 19·00 38·00
F76 6 10f. violet on blue 18·00 38·00

1949. 75th Anniv of U.P.U.
F77 10c. orange 3·50 7·50
F78 15c. violet 4·75 12·00
F79 30c. blue 7·50 16·00
F80 50c. purple 8·50 19·00

1953
F81 7 5c. green 3·25 7·50
F82 7 10c. red 6·00 7·50
F83 7 15c. yellow 6·00 8·00
F84 7 20c. blue 6·00 6·00
F85 - 25c. olive 3·25 6·00
F86 - 30c. brown 1·75 6·00
F87 - 40c. sepia 2·00 6·00
F88 - 50c. violet 2·00 4·50
F89 - 1f. orange 14·00 12·00
F90 - 2f. purple 19·00 50·00
F91 - 5f. red 19·00 85·00

1956. 50th Anniv of Condominium.
F92 10 5c. green 2·00 2·25
F93 10 10c. red 2·25 2·50
F94 - 20c. blue 1·50 2·75
F95 - 50c. violet 1·50 2·75

1957
F96 12 5c. green 1·75 3·00
F97 12 10c. red 2·25 3·00
F98 12 15c. yellow 2·50 3·50
F99 12 20c. blue 2·50 3·00
F100 - 25c. olive 2·25 3·00
F101 - 30c. brown 2·25 1·75
F102 - 40c. sepia 2·25 1·50
F103 - 50c. violet 2·75 1·60
F104 - 1f. orange 9·00 4·00
F105 - 2f. mauve 12·00 21·00
F106 - 5f. black 32·00 35·00

1963. Freedom from Hunger. As T **51** of New Caledonia.
F107 60c. green and brown 19·00 18·00

1963. Centenary of Red Cross. As T **53** of New Caledonia.
F108 15c. red, grey and orange 11·00 11·00
F109 45c. red, grey and bistre 14·00 29·00

1963
F110 - 5c. lake, brown and blue 55 2·00
F111 - 10c. brown, buff and green* 2·00 4·00
F112 17 10c. brown, buff and green 1·00 2·25
F113 - 15c. bistre, brown and violet 6·00 1·25
F114 - 20c. black, green and blue* 2·25 5·50
F115 - 20c. black, green and blue 2·00 2·50
F116 - 25c. violet, brown and red 70 2·00
F117 - 30c. brown, bistre and violet 7·50 1·25
F118 - 40c. red and blue 3·25 9·00
F119 - 50c. green, yellow and turquoise 8·50 2·50
F120 - 60c. red and blue 1·75 3·00
F121 - 1f. red, black and green 2·00 5·00
F122 - 2f. black, brown and olive 17·00 7·00
F123 - 3f. multicoloured* 8·50 23·00
F124 - 3f. multicoloured 8·50 12·00
F125 - 5f. blue, indigo and black 30·00 23·00

The stamps indicated by an asterisk have "RF" wrongly placed on the left.

1965. Centenary of I.T.U. As T **56** of New Caledonia.
F126 15c. blue, green and brown 10·00 9·00
F127 60c. red, grey and green 28·00 35·00

1965. I.C.Y. As Nos. 112/13.
F128 5c. purple and turquoise 3·00 6·00
F129 55c. green and lavender 11·00 12·00

1966. Churchill Commem. As Nos. 114/17.
F130 5c. multicoloured 2·10 8·00
F131 15c. multicoloured 3·00 3·00
F132 25c. multicoloured 4·00 9·00
F133 30c. multicoloured 4·25 10·00

1966. World Cup Football Championship. As Nos. 118/19.
F134 20c. multicoloured 2·75 5·50
F135 40c. multicoloured 4·75 5·50

1966. Inauguration of W.H.O. Headquarters, Geneva. As Nos. 120/1.
F136 25c. black, green and blue 4·00 4·50
F137 60c. black, mauve and ochre 6·00 10·00

1966. 20th Anniv of UNESCO. As Nos. 122/4.
F138 15c. multicoloured 2·50 3·25
F139 30c. yellow, violet and olive 3·50 4·75
F140 45c. black, purple and orange 4·00 6·50

1967. 25th Anniv of Pacific War. As Nos. 125/8.
F141 15c. multicoloured 1·40 1·50
F142 25c. multicoloured 2·00 3·00
F143 60c. multicoloured 2·00 2·50
F144 1f. multicoloured 2·25 2·75

1968. Bicentenary of Bougainville's World Voyage. As Nos. 130/2.
F145 15c. green, violet and red 55 1·10
F146 25c. olive, purple and blue 65 1·25
F147 60c. brown, purple and green 1·10 1·50

1968. Anglo-French Concorde Project. As Nos. 133/4.
F148 25c. blue, red and violet 1·90 2·40
F149 60c. red, black and blue 2·25 4·25

1969. Timber Industry. As No. 135.
F150 20c. multicoloured 45 1·00

1969. Third South Pacific Games, Port Moresby, Papua New Guinea. As Nos. 136/7.
F151 25c. multicoloured 50 1·40
F152 1f. multicoloured 1·50 2·00

1969. Land Divers of Pentecost Island. As Nos. 138/40.
F153 15c. multicoloured 55 1·25
F154 25c. multicoloured 45 1·25
F155 1f. multicoloured 1·10 2·00

1970. Inauguration of New U.P.U. Headquarters Building, Berne. As No. 141.
F156 1f.05 slate, orange & purple 1·00 2·75

1970. New Hebrides' Declaration for the Free French Government. As Nos. 142/3.
F157 65c. multicoloured 2·75 2·00
F158 1f.10 multicoloured 3·00 2·25

1970. No. F115 surch 35.
F159 35c. on 20c. black, green and blue 65 1·75

1970. Christmas. As Nos. 145/6.
F160 15c. multicoloured 25 1·00
F161 50c. multicoloured 45 1·25

1971. Death of General Charles de Gaulle. Nos. F157/8 optd **1890-1970 IN MEMORIAM 9-11-70.**
F162 65c. multicoloured 1·00 1·50
F163 1f.10 multicoloured 1·50 2·00

1971. Fourth South Pacific Games, Papeete, French Polynesia. As Nos. 149/50.
F164 20c. multicoloured 75 1·00
F165 65c. multicoloured 1·00 1·50

1971. Royal Society Expedition to New Hebrides. As No. 151.
F166 65c. multicoloured 1·00 1·50

1971. Christmas. As Nos. 152/3.
F167 25c. multicoloured 50 75
F168 50c. multicoloured 60 1·25

1972. Aircraft. As Nos. 154/7.
F169 20c. multicoloured 1·00 1·60
F170 25c. multicoloured 1·00 1·60
F171 30c. multicoloured 1·10 1·60
F172 65c. multicoloured 2·75 5·00

1972. As Nos. 158/69.
F173 5c. multicoloured 85 1·40
F174 10c. multicoloured 1·90 1·75
F175 15c. multicoloured 90 1·25
F176 20c. multicoloured 2·50 1·50
F177 25c. multicoloured 1·90 1·60
F178 30c. multicoloured 1·90 1·50
F179 35c. multicoloured 3·00 1·50
F180 65c. multicoloured 2·40 2·00
F181 1f. multicoloured 1·75 2·75
F182 2f. multicoloured 15·00 14·00
F183 3f. multicoloured 5·50 16·00
F184 5f. multicoloured 8·50 25·00

1972. Christmas. As Nos. 170/1.
F185 25c. multicoloured 45 1·00
F186 70c. multicoloured 65 1·50

1972. Royal Silver Wedding. As Nos. 172/3.
F187 35c. multicoloured 50 50
F188 65c. multicoloured 60 1·25

1973. Orchids. As Nos. 174/7.
F189 25c. multicoloured 2·75 1·40
F190 30c. multicoloured 2·75 1·60
F191 35c. multicoloured 2·75 1·60
F192 65c. multicoloured 4·75 5·00

1973. Opening of New Wharf at Vila. As Nos. 178/9.
F193 25c. multicoloured 80 1·10
F194 70c. multicoloured 1·10 2·25

1973. Tanna Island. As Nos. 180/1.
F195 35c. multicoloured 2·25 2·25
F196 70c. multicoloured 3·25 3·25

1973. Christmas. As Nos. 182/3.
F197 35c. multicoloured 50 1·00
F198 70c. multicoloured 75 2·75

1974. Wild Life. As Nos. 184/7.
F199 25c. multicoloured 3·50 2·75
F200 35c. multicoloured 4·50 1·75
F201 70c. multicoloured 5·00 4·00
F202 1f.15 multicoloured 5·50 10·00

1974. Royal Visit of Queen Elizabeth II. Nos. F179 and F182 optd **VISITE ROYALE 1974.**
F203 35c. Chestnut-bellied kingfisher 3·00 90
F204 2f. Green palm lorikeet 6·50 8·25

1974. Inauguration of New Post Office, Vila. As Nos. 190/1.
F205 35c. multicoloured 1·00 2·00
F206 70c. multicoloured 1·00 2·00

1974. Bicent of Discovery. As Nos. 192/5.
F207 35c. multicoloured 4·50 5·75
F208 35c. multicoloured 4·50 5·75
F209 35c. multicoloured 4·50 5·75
F210 1f.15 multicoloured 9·00 12·00

1974. Centenary of U.P.U. As No. 196.
F210a 70c. blue, red and black 1·75 3·00

1974. Christmas. As Nos. 197/8.
F211 35c. multicoloured 40 75
F212 70f. multicoloured 60 1·25

1975. Charolais Bull. As No. 199.
F213 10f. brown, green and blue 20·00 40·00

1975. World Scout Jamboree, Norway. As Nos. 200/3.
F214 25c. multicoloured 60 40
F215 35c. multicoloured 60 50
F216 1f. multicoloured 1·00 1·00
F217 5f. multicoloured 1·00 8·50

1975. Christmas. As Nos. 204/6.
F218 35c. multicoloured 35 50
F219 70c. multicoloured 55 90
F220 2f.50 multicoloured 1·90 3·00

1976. First Commercial Flight of Concorde. As No. 207, but Concorde in Air France livery.
F221 5f. multicoloured 7·50 8·50

1976. Centenary of Telephone. As Nos. 208/10.
F222 25c. multicoloured 60 50
F223 70c. multicoloured 1·50 1·50
F224 1f.15 multicoloured 1·75 2·75

1976. Constitutional Changes. As Nos. 211/13.
F225 25c. multicoloured 60 50
F226 1f. multicoloured 1·50 1·25
F227 2f. multicoloured 2·50 2·75

1976. Christmas. Paintings. As Nos. 214/16.
F228 35c. multicoloured 30 30
F229 70c. multicoloured 50 50
F230 2f.50 multicoloured 1·75 3·00

1977. Silver Jubilee. As Nos. F217/9.
F231 35c. multicoloured 30 20
F232 70c. multicoloured 55 35
F233 2f. multicoloured 55 65

1977. Currency change. Nos. F173/84 and F213, surch.
F234 5f. on 5c. multicoloured 1·50 1·50
F235 10f. on 10c. multicoloured 2·50 1·25
F236 15f. on 15c. multicoloured 1·25 1·25
F237 20f. on 20c. multicoloured 3·50 1·50
F238 25f. on 25c. multicoloured 2·50 1·75
F239 30f. on 30c. multicoloured 2·50 2·25
F240 35f. on 35c. multicoloured 4·50 2·25
F241 40f. on 65c. multicoloured 3·25 3·00
F242 50f. on 1f. multicoloured 2·00 3·00
F243 70f. on 2f. multicoloured 7·50 4·00
F244 100f. on 3f. multicoloured 2·75 6·00
F245 200f. on 5f. multicoloured 9·00 25·00
F246 500f. on 10f. multicoloured 16·00 45·00

1977. Islands. As Nos. 242/54.
F256 5f. multicoloured 1·50 1·75
F257 10f. multicoloured 1·50 1·75
F258 15f. multicoloured 2·00 1·75
F259 20f. multicoloured 2·00 1·75
F260 25f. multicoloured 2·00 1·75
F261 30f. multicoloured 2·00 1·75
F262 35f. multicoloured 2·75 1·75
F263 40f. multicoloured 1·50 2·25
F264 50f. multicoloured 2·75 2·25
F265 70f. multicoloured 5·00 4·50
F266 100f. multicoloured 2·75 3·25
F267 200f. multicoloured 3·75 9·00
F268 500f. multicoloured 6·50 17·00

1977. Christmas. As Nos. 255/7.
F269 10f. multicoloured 30 30
F270 15f. multicoloured 50 50
F271 30f. multicoloured 80 1·40

1978. Concorde. As Nos. 258/61.
F272 10f. multicoloured 2·25 1·50
F273 20f. multicoloured 2·50 1·75
F274 30f. multicoloured 3·00 2·25
F275 40f. multicoloured 3·50 3·50

1978. Coronation. As Nos. 262/4.
F276 40f. brown, blue and silver 25 70
F277 40f. multicoloured 25 70
F278 40f. brown, blue and silver 25 70

1978. Christmas. As Nos. 265/8.
F279 10f. multicoloured 20 30
F280 15f. multicoloured 25 35
F281 30f. multicoloured 30 70
F282 40f. multicoloured 35 85

1979. Internal Self-Government. As T **37** surch 166°E PREMIER GOUVERNEMENT AUTONOME 11.1.78. 11.1.79 and new value.
F283 10f. on 25f. multicoloured (blue background) 90 1·00
F284 40f. on 25f. multicoloured (green background) 1·60 1·75

1979. Death Centenary of Sir Rowland Hill. As Nos. 271/3.
F285 10f. multicoloured 35 50
F286 20f. multicoloured 35 60
F287 40f. multicoloured 40 1·00

1979. Arts Festival. As Nos. 275/8.
F288 5f. multicoloured 30 60
F289 10f. multicoloured 30 60
F290 20f. multicoloured 40 80
F291 40f. multicoloured 60 1·25

1979. Christmas and International Year of the Child. As Nos. 279/82.
F292 5f. multicoloured 75 60
F293 10f. multicoloured 85 60
F294 20f. multicoloured 90 80
F295 40f. multicoloured 1·60 2·00

1980. Birds. As Nos. 283/6.
F296 10f. multicoloured 1·10 1·75
F297 20f. multicoloured 1·40 2·00
F298 30f. multicoloured 1·75 2·75
F299 40f. multicoloured 1·90 3·25

POSTAGE DUE STAMPS

1925. Nos. F32 etc, optd CHIFFRE TAXE.
FD53 5 10c. (1d.) green 55·00 4·25
FD54 5 20c. (2d.) grey 55·00 4·25
FD55 5 30c. (3d.) red 55·00 4·25
FD56 5 50c. (5d.) blue 55·00 4·25
FD57 5 1f. (10d.) red on blue 55·00 4·25

1938. Optd CHIFFRE TAXE.
FD65 6 5c. green 20·00 75·00
FD66 6 10c. orange 23·00 75·00
FD67 6 20c. red 29·00 80·00
FD68 6 40c. olive 65·00 £160
FD69 6 1f. red on green 65·00 £160

1941. Free French Issue. As last optd France Libre.
FD77 5c. green 19·00 48·00
FD78 10c. orange 19·00 48·00
FD79 20c. red 19·00 48·00
FD80 40c. olive 24·00 48·00
FD81 1f. red on green 22·00 48·00

1953. Optd TIMBRE TAXE.
FD92 7 5c. green 11·00 25·00
FD93 7 10c. red 10·00 24·00
FD94 7 20c. blue 25·00 40·00
FD95 - 40c. sepia (No. F87) 18·00 38·00

FD96	-	1f. orange (No. F89)	20·00	60·00

1957. Optd TIMBRE-TAXE.

FD107	**12**	5c. green	1·50	9·50
FD108	**12**	10c. red	2·00	9·50
FD109	**12**	20c. blue	3·50	14·00
FD110	-	40c. sepia (No. F102)	8·00	27·00
FD111	-	1f. orange (No. F104)	7·00	35·00

For later issues see **VANUATU**.

NEW REPUBLIC

A Boer republic originally part of Zululand. It was incorporated with the South African Republic in 1888 and annexed to Natal in 1903.

12 pence = 1 shilling;
20 shillings = 1 pound.

1

1886. On yellow or blue paper.

1	**1**	1d. black		£3000
2	**1**	1d. violet	20·00	22·00
73	**1**	2d. violet	18·00	18·00
79	**1**	3d. violet	26·00	26·00
75	**1**	4d. violet	27·00	27·00
81	**1**	6d. violet	17·00	17·00
82	**1**	9d. violet	16·00	19·00
83	**1**	1s. violet	20·00	20·00
84	**1**	1s.6d. violet	55·00	45·00
85	**1**	2s. violet	40·00	42·00
86	**1**	2s.6d. violet	38·00	38·00
87	**1**	3s. violet	65·00	65·00
88b	**1**	4s. violet	65·00	65·00
16	**1**	5s. violet	55·00	65·00
90	**1**	5s.6d. violet	29·00	32·00
91	**1**	7s.6d. violet	35·00	38·00
92	**1**	10s. violet	32·00	35·00
93	**1**	10s.6d. violet	28·00	32·00
44	**1**	12s. violet	£400	
23	**1**	13s. violet	£550	
94	**1**	£1 violet	75·00	80·00
25	**1**	30s. violet	£130	

Some stamps are found with Arms embossed in the paper, and others with the Arms and without a date above "ZUID-AFRIKA".

STANLEY GIBBONS
LONDON 1856

STOCKBOOKS

Deluxe - available in a range of four colours.

A deluxe A4 stock book with padded leather cover. Black pages with 9 clear strips and clear interleaving.

Luxury Leather 64 Page - £49.95
• R2672BLK • R2672BLU • R2672GRN • R2672MAR

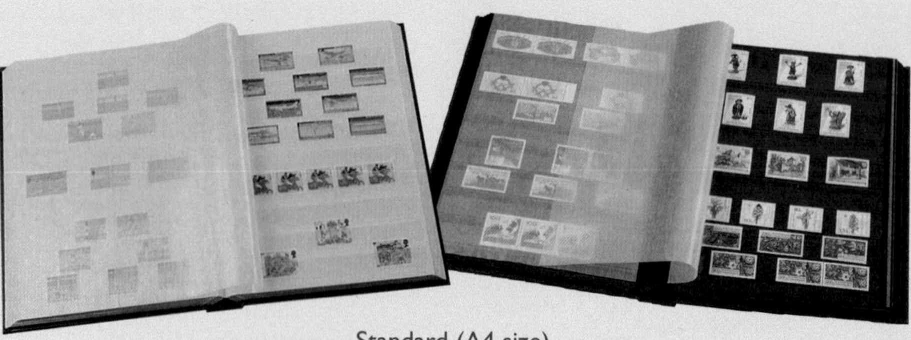

Standard (A4 size)

16 Page (black) with 9 glassine strips and double glassine interleaving

• R2680BLK • R2680BLU • R2680GRN

To order, call **01425 472 363**
email **orders@stanleygibbons.com** or visit **stanleygibbons.com**

Index

Abu Dhabi Vol. 1
Abyssinia (Ethiopia) Vol. 2
Aden Vol. 1
Aden - Kathiri State of Seiyun Vol. 4
Aden - Qu'aiti State of Shihr and Mukalla Vol. 5
Aden - Qu'aiti State in Hadhramaut Vol. 5
Aegean Islands (Dodecanese Islands) Vol. 2
Afghanistan Vol. 1
Africa - *see individual countries or colonies.*
Aitutaki Vol. 1
Aitutaki (New Zealand Dependency) Vol. 1
Aitutaki (Part of Cook Islands) Vol. 1
Ajman Vol. 1
Aland Islands Vol. 1
Alaouites Vol. 1
Albania Vol. 1
Albania (German Occupation 1943) Vol. 1
Albania (Greek Occupation 1940) Vol. 3
Albania (Independent State 1945) Vol. 1
Albania (Italian Occupation 1939-1943) Vol. 1
Albania (People's Republic 1946) Vol. 1
Alderney - *see Guernsey* Vol. 3
Alexandretta Vol. 1
Alexandria Vol. 1
Algeria Vol. 1
Algeria (Independent State 1962) Vol. 1
Allenstein Vol. 1
Alsace (German Occupation 1940) Vol. 3
Alsace and Lorraine Vol. 1
Alwar Vol. 1
Andorra (French) Vol. 1
Andorra (Spanish) Vol. 1
Angola Vol. 1
Angora (Turkey, 1922) Vol. 6
Angra Vol. 1
Anguilla Vol. 1
Anjouan Vol. 1
Ankara (Angora) Vol. 6
Annam and Tongking Vol. 1
Antigua Vol. 1
Antioquia Vol. 1
Arad (French Occupation of Hungary) Vol. 2
Arbe Vol. 1
Argentina Vol. 1
Armenia Vol. 1
Aruba Vol. 1
Arward *(see Rouad Island)* Vol. 5
Ascension Vol. 1
Aunus (Finnish Occupation of) Vol. 2
Australia Vol. 1
Australian Antarctic Territory Vol. 1
Austria Vol. 1
Austrian Territories acquired by Italy Vol. 1
Austro-Hungarian Military Post Vol. 1
Austro-Hungarian Post Offices in the Turkish Empire Vol. 1
Azerbaijan Vol. 1
Azores Vol. 1

Baden Vol. 1
Baghdad Vol. 1
Bahamas Vol. 1
Bahawalpur Vol. 1
Bahrain Vol. 1
Bamra Vol. 1
Bangladesh Vol. 1
Barbados Vol. 1
Barbuda Vol. 1
Barwani Vol. 1
Basutoland Vol. 1
Batum Vol. 1
Bavaria Vol. 1
Bechuanaland Vol. 1
Belarus Vol. 1
Belgian Congo Vol. 1
Belgian Occupation of Germany Vol. 1
Belgium Vol. 1
Belize Vol. 1
Benin Vol. 1
Bergedorf Vol. 1
Bermuda Vol. 1
Bhopal Vol. 1
Bhor Vol. 1
Bhutan Vol. 1
Biafra Vol. 1
Bijawar Vol. 1
Bohemia and Moravia Vol. 1
Bolivar Vol. 1
Bolivia Vol. 1
Bophuthatswana Vol. 1
Bosnia and Herzegovina Vol. 1
Botswana Vol. 1
Boyaca Vol. 1
Brazil Vol. 1
Bremen Vol. 1
British Antarctic Territory Vol. 1
British Central Africa - *see Nyasaland* Vol. 5
British Columbia and Vancouver Island Vol. 1
British Commonwealth Occupation of Japan Vol. 1
British East Africa Vol. 1
British Forces in Egypt Vol. 1
British Guiana Vol. 1
British Honduras Vol. 1
British Indian Ocean Territory Vol. 1
British Levant Vol. 1
British New Guinea - *see Papua* Vol. 5
British Occupation of Italian Colonies Vol. 1
British Post Offices in China Vol. 1
British Post Offices in Crete Vol. 1
British Post Offices in Siam Vol. 1
British Postal Agencies in Eastern Arabia Vol. 1
British Virgin Islands Vol. 1
Brunei Vol. 1
Brunei - Japanese Occupation Vol. 1
Brunswick Vol. 1
Buenos Aires Vol. 1
Bulgaria Vol. 1
Bulgarian Occupation of Romania Vol. 1
Bundi Vol. 1
Burkina Faso Vol. 1
Burma Vol. 1
Burma (Japanese Occupation) Vol. 1
Burundi Vol. 1
Bushire Vol. 1
Bussahir (Bashahr) Vol. 1

Caicos Islands Vol. 1
Cambodia Vol. 1
Cameroon Vol. 1
Cameroun Vol. 1
Canada Vol. 1
Canal Zone Vol. 1
Canton Vol. 1
Cape Juby Vol. 1
Cape of Good Hope Vol. 1
Cape Verde Islands Vol. 1
Caribisch Nederland Vol. 1
Caroline Islands Vol. 1
Castelrosso Vol. 1
Cauca Vol. 1
Cavalla (Kavalla) Vol. 1
Cayes of Belize Vol. 1
Cayman Islands Vol. 1
Central African Empire Vol. 1
Central African Republic Vol. 1
Central Lithuania Vol. 1
Ceylon Vol. 1
Chad Vol. 1
Chamba Vol. 1
Channel Islands - *see Great Britain, or individual islands.* Vol. 3
Charkhari Vol. 1
Chile Vol. 2
China Vol. 2
China - Taiwan (Formosa) Vol. 2
China Expeditionary Force Vol. 2
Christmas Island Vol. 2
Cilicia Vol. 2
Ciskei Vol. 2
Cochin Vol. 2
Cochin-China Vol. 2
Cocos (Keeling) Islands Vol. 2
Colombia Vol. 2
Comoro Islands Vol. 2
Confederate States of America Vol. 2
Congo (Brazzaville) Vol. 2
Congo Democratic Republic (Ex Zaire) Vol. 2
Congo (Kinshasa) Vol. 2
Cook Islands Vol. 2
Costa Rica Vol. 2
Crete Vol. 2
Croatia Vol. 2
Cuba Vol. 2
Cundinamarca Vol. 2
Curacao Vol. 2
Cyprus Vol. 2
Cyprus (Turkish Cypriot Posts) Vol. 2
Cyrenaica Vol. 2
Czech Republic Vol. 2
Czechoslovak Army in Siberia Vol. 2
Czechoslovakia Vol. 2

Dahomey Vol. 2
Danish West Indies Vol. 2
Danzig Vol. 2
Dedeagatz Vol. 2
Denmark Vol. 2
Dhar Vol. 2
Diego-Suarez Vol. 2
Djibouti Vol. 2
Djibouti Republic Vol. 2
Dodecanese Islands Vol. 2
Dominica Vol. 2
Dominican Republic Vol. 2
Dubai Vol. 2
Dungarpur Vol. 2
Duttia (Datia) Vol. 2

East Silesia Vol. 2
East Timor Vol. 2
Eastern Roumelia and South Bulgaria Vol. 2
Ecuador Vol. 2
Egypt Vol. 2
Egypt - Alexandretta Vol. 1
Egypt - British Forces in Vol. 1
Elobey, Annobon and Corisco Vol. 2
El Salvador Vol. 2
England - *see Great Britain* Vol. 3
Equatorial Guinea Vol. 2
Eritrea Vol. 2
Estonia Vol. 2
Ethiopia Vol. 2

Falkland Islands Vol. 2
Falkland Islands Dependencies Vol. 2
Faridkot Vol. 2
Faroe Islands Vol. 2
Federated Malay States Vol. 2
Fernando Poo Vol. 2
Fezzan Vol. 2
Fiji Vol. 2
Finland Vol. 2
Finland - Aland Islands Vol. 1
Finnish Occupation of Aunus Vol. 2
Finnish Occupation of Eastern Karelia Vol. 2
Fiume Vol. 2
Fiume and Kupa Zone Vol. 2
France Vol. 2
Free French Forces in the Levant Vol. 2
French Colonies Vol. 2
French Congo Vol. 2
French Equatorial Africa Vol. 2
French Guiana Vol. 2
French Guinea Vol. 2
French Indian Settlements Vol. 2
French Morocco Vol. 2
French Occupation of Hungary (Arad) Vol. 2
French Polynesia Vol. 2
French Post Offices in China Vol. 2
French Post Offices in Crete Vol. 2
French Post Offices in Ethiopia Vol. 2
French Post Offices in Morocco Vol. 2
French Post Offices in Tangier Vol. 2
French Post Offices in the Turkish Empire Vol. 2
French Post Offices in Zanzibar Vol. 2
French Somali Coast Vol. 2
French Southern and Antarctic Territories Vol. 2
French Sudan Vol. 2
French Territory of the Afars and the Issas Vol. 2

French West Africa Vol. 2
Fujeira Vol. 2
Funchal Vol. 2

Gabon Vol. 2
Galapagos Islands Vol. 2
Gambia Vol. 2
Gaza Vol. 2
Georgia Vol. 2
German Commands Vol. 3
German East Africa Vol. 3
German New Guinea Vol. 3
German Occupation of Alsace Vol. 3
German Occupation of Belgium Vol. 3
German Occupation of Dalmatia Vol. 3
German Occupation of Estonia Vol. 3
German Occupation of Latvia Vol. 3
German Occupation of Lithuania Vol. 3
German Occupation of Lorraine Vol. 3
German Occupation of Poland Vol. 3
German Occupation of Romania Vol. 3
German Occupation of Russia Vol. 3
German Occupation of Zante Vol. 3
German Post Offices in China Vol. 3
German Post Offices in Morocco Vol. 3
German Post Offices in the Turkish Empire Vol. 3
German South West Africa Vol. 3
Germany Vol. 3
Germany (Democratic Republic (East Germany)) Vol. 3
Ghadames Vol. 3
Ghana Vol. 3
Gibraltar Vol. 3
Gilbert and Ellice Islands Vol. 3
Gilbert Islands Vol. 3
Gold Coast Vol. 3
Graham Land (Falkland Islands Dependencies) Vol. 2
Great Britain Vol. 3
Great Britain Regional Issues - Channel Islands Vol. 3
Great Britain Regional Issues - Guernsey Vol. 3
Great Britain Regional Issues - Isle of Man Vol. 3
Great Britain Regional Issues - Jersey Vol. 3
Great Britain Regional Issues - England Vol. 3
Great Britain Regional Issues - Northern Ireland Vol. 3
Great Britain Regional Issues - Scotland Vol. 3
Great Britain Regional Issues - Wales Vol. 3
Great Comoro Vol. 3
Greece Vol. 3
Greek Occupation of Albania Vol. 3
Greenland Vol. 3
Grenada Vol. 3
Grenadines of Grenada (Carriacou and Petite Martinique) Vol. 3
Grenadines of St. Vincent Vol. 3
Griqualand West Vol. 3
Guadeloupe Vol. 3
Guam Vol. 3
Guanacaste Vol. 3
Guatemala Vol. 3
Guernsey Vol. 3
Guernsey (Alderney) Vol. 3
Guinea Vol. 3
Guinea-Bissau Vol. 3
Guyana Vol. 3
Gwalior Vol. 3

Haiti Vol. 3
Hamburg Vol. 3
Hanover Vol. 3
Hatay Vol. 3
Hawaii Vol. 3
Heligoland Vol. 3
Hoi-Hao (Hoihow) Vol. 3
Honduras Vol. 3
Hong Kong (Crown Colony) Vol. 3
Hong Kong (Japanese Occupation) Vol. 3
Hong Kong (Special Administrative Region) Vol. 3
Horta Vol. 3
Hungary Vol. 3
Hyderabad Vol. 3

Iceland Vol. 3
Idar Vol. 3
Ifni Vol. 3
India Vol. 3
Indian Custodian Forces in Korea Vol. 3
Indian Expeditionary Forces Vol. 3
Indian Forces in Indo-China Vol. 3
Indian U.N. Force in Congo Vol. 3
Indian U.N. Force in Gaza (Palestine) Vol. 3
Indo-China Vol. 3
Indo-Chinese Post Offices in China Vol. 3
Indonesia Vol. 3
Indore (Holkar State) Vol. 3
Inhambane Vol. 3
Inini Vol. 3
Ionian Islands Vol. 3
Iran Vol. 3
Iraq Vol. 3
Ireland Vol. 3
Isle Of Man Vol. 3
Israel Vol. 3
Italian Colonies Vol. 3
Italian East Africa Vol. 3
Italian Occupation of Cephalonia and Ithaca Vol. 3
Italian Occupation of Corfu Vol. 3
Italian Occupation of Corfu and Paxos Vol. 3
Italian Occupation of Ionian Islands Vol. 3
Italian Post Offices In China Vol. 3
Italian Post Offices In Crete Vol. 3
Italian Post Offices In the Turkish Empire Vol. 3
Italy Vol. 3
Italy (Italian Social Republic) Vol. 3
Ivory Coast Vol. 3

Jaipur Vol. 3
Jamaica Vol. 3
Jammu and Kashmir Vol. 3
Japan Vol. 3
Japanese Prefecture Stamps Vol. 3
Japanese Taiwan (Formosa) Vol. 3
Japanese Occupation of Brunei Vol. 1
Japanese Occupation of Burma Vol. 1
Japanese Occupation of China (Kwangtung) Vol. 3
Japanese Occupation of China (Mengkiang (Inner Mongolia)) Vol. 3
Japanese Occupation of China (North China) Vol. 3
Japanese Occupation of China (Nanking and Shanghai) Vol. 3
Japanese Occupation of Hong Kong Vol. 3
Japanese Occupation of Malaya Vol. 4
Japanese Occupation of Netherlands Indies Vol. 3
Japanese Occupation of North Borneo Vol. 5
Japanese Occupation of Philippines Vol. 3
Japanese Occupation of Sarawak Vol. 5
Japanese Post Offices in China Vol. 3
Japanese Post Offices in Korea Vol. 3
Jasdan Vol. 3
Jersey Vol. 4
Jhalawar Vol. 4
Jind Vol. 4
Johore Vol. 4
Jordan Vol. 4
Jordanian Occupation of Palestine Vol. 4
Jubaland Vol. 4

Kampuchea Vol. 4
Karelia Vol. 4
Katanga Vol. 4
Kathiri State of Seiyun Vol. 4
Kazakhstan Vol. 4
Kedah Vol. 4
Kelantan Vol. 4
Kenya Vol. 4
Kenya, Uganda and Tanganyika (Tanzania) Vol. 4
Khmer Republic Vol. 4
Khor Fakkan Vol. 4
Kiautschou (Kiaochow) Vol. 4
King Edward VII Land Vol. 4
Kionga Vol. 4
Kiribati Vol. 4
Kishangarh Vol. 4
Korea (Empire of) Vol. 4
Korea (South) Vol. 4
Korea (North Korean Occupation of South Korea) Vol. 4
Korea (North) Vol. 4
Kouang Tcheou (Kwangchow) Vol. 4
Kuwait Vol. 4
Kyrgyzstan Vol. 4

La Aguera Vol. 4
Labuan Vol. 4
Lagos Vol. 4
Laos Vol. 4
Las Bela Vol. 4
Latakia Vol. 4
Latakia - Alaouites Vol. 1
Latvia Vol. 4
Lebanon Vol. 4
Leeward Islands Vol. 4
Lesotho Vol. 4
Liberia Vol. 4
Libya Vol. 4
Liechtenstein Vol. 4
Lithuania Vol. 4
Lombardy and Venetia Vol. 4
Lourenco Marques Vol. 4
Lubeck Vol. 4
Luxembourg Vol. 4

Macao Vol. 4
Macedonia Vol. 4
Madagascar and Dependencies (French Post Offices) Vol. 4
Madagascar (French Colony) Vol. 4
Madagascar Vol. 4
Madeira Vol. 4
Mafeking Vol. 4
Mahra Sultanate of Qishn and Socotra Vol. 4
Malacca Vol. 4
Malagasy Republic Vol. 4
Malawi Vol. 4
Malaya (British Military Administration) Vol. 4
Malaya (Japanese Occupation) Vol. 4
Malaya (Thai Occupation) Vol. 4
Malayan Federation Vol. 4
Malayan Postal Union Vol. 4
Malaysia Vol. 4
Maldive Islands Vol. 4
Mali Vol. 4
Malta Vol. 4
Manama Vol. 4
Manchukuo Vol. 4
Mariana Islands Vol. 4
Marienwerder Vol. 4
Marshall Islands Vol. 4
Martinique Vol. 4
Mauritania Vol. 4
Mauritius Vol. 4
Mayotte Vol. 4
Mecklenburg-Schwerin Vol. 4
Mecklenburg-Strelitz Vol. 4
Memel Vol. 4
Mexico Vol. 4
Micronesia Vol. 4
Middle Congo Vol. 4
Modena Vol. 4
Moheli Vol. 4
Moldova Vol. 4
Monaco Vol. 4
Mongolia Vol. 4
Mong-Tseu (Mengtsz) Vol. 4
Montenegro Vol. 4
Montenegro (German Occupation) Vol. 4
Montenegro (Italian Occupation) Vol. 4
Montserrat Vol. 4
Morocco Vol. 4
Morocco Agencies Vol. 4
Morvi Vol. 4
Mosul Vol. 4
Mozambique Vol. 4
Mozambique Company Vol. 4
Muscat Vol. 4
Muscat and Oman Vol. 4
Myanmar Vol. 4

Nabha Vol. 4
Nagorno-Karabakh Vol. 4
Nakhichevan Vol. 4
Namibia Vol. 4
Nandgaon Vol. 4
Naples Vol. 4
Natal Vol. 4
Nauru Vol. 4
Nawanagar Vol. 4
Neapolitan Provinces Vol. 4
Negri Sembilan Vol. 4
Nepal Vol. 4
Netherlands Vol. 4
Netherlands Antilles Vol. 4
Netherlands Indies Vol. 4
Netherlands Indies (Japanese Occupation) Vol. 3
Netherlands New Guinea Vol. 4
Nevis Vol. 4
New Brunswick Vol. 4
New Caledonia Vol. 4
Newfoundland Vol. 4
New Guinea Vol. 4
New Hebrides Vol. 4
New Republic Vol. 4
New South Wales Vol. 5
New Zealand Vol. 5
Nicaragua Vol. 5
Niger Vol. 5
Niger Coast Protectorate Vol. 5
Nigeria Vol. 5
Niuafo'ou Vol. 5
Niue Vol. 5
Norfolk Island Vol. 5
North Borneo Vol. 5
North Borneo (Japanese Occupation) Vol. 5
North German Confederation Vol. 5
North Ingermanland Vol. 5
North West Russia Vol. 5
Northern Ireland - *see Great Britain* Vol. 3
Northern Nigeria Vol. 5
Northern Rhodesia Vol. 5
Norway Vol. 5
Nossi-Be Vol. 5
Nova Scotia Vol. 5
Nyasaland Protectorate Vol. 5
Nyassa Company Vol. 5

Obock Vol. 5
Oceanic Settlements Vol. 5
Oil Rivers Protectorate - *see Niger Coast* Vol. 5
Oldenburg Vol. 5
Oman (Sultanate) Vol. 5
Orange Free State (Orange River Colony) Vol. 5
Orchha Vol. 5

Pahang Vol. 5
Pakhoi Vol. 5
Pakistan Vol. 5
Palau Vol. 5
Palestine Vol. 5
Palestinian Authority Vol. 5
Panama Vol. 5
Papal States Vol. 5
Papua Vol. 5
Papua New Guinea Vol. 5
Paraguay Vol. 5
Parma Vol. 5
Patiala Vol. 5
Penang Vol. 5
Penrhyn Island Vol. 5
Perak Vol. 5
Perlis Vol. 5
Peru Vol. 5
Phillipines Vol. 5
Philippines (Japanese Occupation) Vol. 3
Pitcairn Islands Vol. 5
Poland Vol. 5
Polish Post in Danzig Vol. 5
Polish Post Office in Turkey Vol. 5
Ponta Delgada Vol. 5
Poonch Vol. 5
Port Lagos Vol. 5
Port Said Vol. 5
Portugal Vol. 5
Portuguese Colonies Vol. 5
Portuguese Congo Vol. 5
Portuguese Guinea Vol. 5
Portuguese India Vol. 5
Portuguese Timor Vol. 5
Prince Edward Island Vol. 5
Prussia Vol. 5
Puerto Rico Vol. 5

Qatar Vol. 5
Qu'aiti State in Hadhramaut Vol. 5
Queensland Vol. 5
Quelimane Vol. 5

Rajasthan Vol. 5
Rajpipla Vol. 5
Ras Al Khaima Vol. 5
Redonda Vol. 5
Reunion Vol. 5
Rhodesia Vol. 5
Rhodesia and Nyasaland Vol. 5
Riau-Lingga Archipelago Vol. 5
Rio de Oro Vol. 5
Rio Muni Vol. 5
Romagna Vol. 5
Romania Vol. 5
Romanian Occupation of Hungary Vol. 5
Romanian Post Offices in the Turkish Empire Vol. 5
Ross Dependency Vol. 5
Rouad Island (Arwad) Vol. 5
Ruanda-Urundi Vol. 5
Russia Vol. 5
Russian Post Offices in China Vol. 5
Russian Post Offices in Crete Vol. 5
Russian Post Offices in Turkish Empire Vol. 5
Rwanda Vol. 5
Ryukyu Islands Vol. 5

Saar Vol. 5
Sabah Vol. 5
St. Christopher Vol. 5
St. Helena Vol. 5
St. Kitts Vol. 5
St. Kitts-Nevis Vol. 5
St. Lucia Vol. 5
Sint. Maaten Vol. 5
Ste. Marie De Madagascar Vol. 5
St. Pierre et Miquelon Vol. 5
St. Thomas and Prince Is. Vol. 5
St. Vincent Vol. 5
Samoa Vol. 5
San Marino Vol. 5
Santander Vol. 5
Sarawak Vol. 5
Sarawak (Japanese Occupation) Vol. 5
Sardinia Vol. 5
Saseno Vol. 5
Saudi Arabia Vol. 5
Saxony Vol. 5
Schleswig-Holstein Vol. 5
Scotland - *see Great Britain* Vol. 3
Selangor Vol. 5
Senegal Vol. 5
Senegambia and Niger Vol. 5
Serbia Vol. 5
Serbia and Montenegro Vol. 5
Serbian Occupation of Hungary Vol. 5
Seychelles Vol. 5
Shahpura Vol. 5
Shanghai Vol. 5
Sharjah Vol. 5
Siberia Vol. 5
Sicily Vol. 5
Sierra Leone Vol. 5
Singapore Vol. 5
Sirmoor Vol. 6
Slesvig Vol. 6
Slovakia Vol. 6
Slovenia Vol. 6
Solomon Islands Vol. 6
Somalia Vol. 6
Somaliland Protectorate Vol. 6
Soruth Vol. 6
South Africa Vol. 6
South Arabian Federation Vol. 6
South Australia Vol. 6
South Georgia (Falkland Islands Dependencies) Vol. 2
South Georgia Vol. 6
South Georgia and the South Sandwich Islands Vol. 6
South Kasai Vol. 6
South Orkneys (Falkland Islands Dependencies) Vol. 2
South Russia Vol. 6
South Shetlands (Falkland Islands Dependencies) Vol. 2
South West Africa Vol. 6
Southern Nigeria Vol. 6
Southern Rhodesia Vol. 6
Southern Yemen Vol. 6
Spain Vol. 6
Spanish Guinea Vol. 6
Spanish Morocco Vol. 6
Spanish Post Offices in Tangier Vol. 6
Spanish Sahara Vol. 6
Spanish West Africa Vol. 6
Sri Lanka Vol. 6
Stellaland Vol. 6
Straits Settlements Vol. 6
Sudan Vol. 6
Sungei Ujong Vol. 6
Surinam Vol. 6
Swaziland Vol. 6
Sweden Vol. 6
Switzerland Vol. 6
Syria Vol. 6
Syria - Alaouites, Latakia Vol. 1

Tahiti Vol. 6
Tajikistan Vol. 6
Tanganyika Vol. 6
Tanzania Vol. 6
Tasmania Vol. 6
Tchongking (Chungking) Vol. 6
Tete Vol. 6
Thailand Vol. 6
Thessaly Vol. 6
Thrace Vol. 6
Thurn and Taxis Vol. 6
Tibet Vol. 6
Tierra Del Fuego Vol. 6
Tobago Vol. 6
Togo Vol. 6
Tokelau Vol. 6
Tolima Vol. 6
Tonga Vol. 6
Transcaucasian Federation Vol. 6
Transkei Vol. 6
Transvaal Vol. 6
Travancore Vol. 6
Travancore-Cochin Vol. 6
Trengganu Vol. 6
Trieste Vol. 6
Trinidad Vol. 6
Trinidad and Tobago Vol. 6
Tripolitania Vol. 6
Tristan da Cunha Vol. 6
Trucial States Vol. 6
Tunisia Vol. 6
Turkey Vol. 6
Turkmenistan Vol. 6
Turks Islands Vol. 6
Turks and Caicos Islands Vol. 6
Tuscany Vol. 6
Tuva Vol. 6
Tuvalu Vol. 6

Ubangi-Shari Vol. 6
Uganda Vol. 6
Ukraine Vol. 6
Umm Al Qiwain Vol. 6
United Arab Emirates Vol. 6
United Nations Vol. 6
United States of America Vol. 6
United States Postal Agency in Shanghai Vol. 6
Upper Senegal and Niger Vol. 6
Upper Silesia Vol. 6
Upper Volta Vol. 6
Upper Yafa Vol. 6
Uruguay Vol. 6
Uzbekistan Vol. 6

Vanuatu Vol. 6
Vathy Vol. 6
Vatican City Vol. 6
Veglia Vol. 6
Venda Vol. 6
Venezia Giulia and Istria Vol. 6
Venezuela Vol. 6
Victoria Vol. 6
Victoria Land Vol. 6
Vietnam (Democratic Republic) Vol. 6
Vietnam (Independent State - South Vietnam Vol. 6
Vietnam (North Vietnam) Vol. 6
Vietnam (Socialist Republic) Vol. 6

Wadhwan Vol. 6
Wales - *see Great Britain* Vol. 3
Wallis and Futuna Islands Vol. 6
Wenden Vol. 6
West Irian Vol. 6
West New Guinea Vol. 6
West Ukraine Vol. 6
Western Australia Vol. 6
Wurttemberg Vol. 6

Yemen Vol. 6
Yemen People's Democratic Republic Vol. 6
Yemen Republic (combined) Vol. 6
Yugoslavia Vol. 6
Yunnanfu Vol. 6

Zaire Vol. 6
Zambezia Vol. 6
Zambia Vol. 6
Zanzibar Vol. 6
Zil Elwannyen Sesel Vol. 6
Zimbabwe Vol. 6
Zululand Vol. 6

STANLEY GIBBONS

LONDON 1856

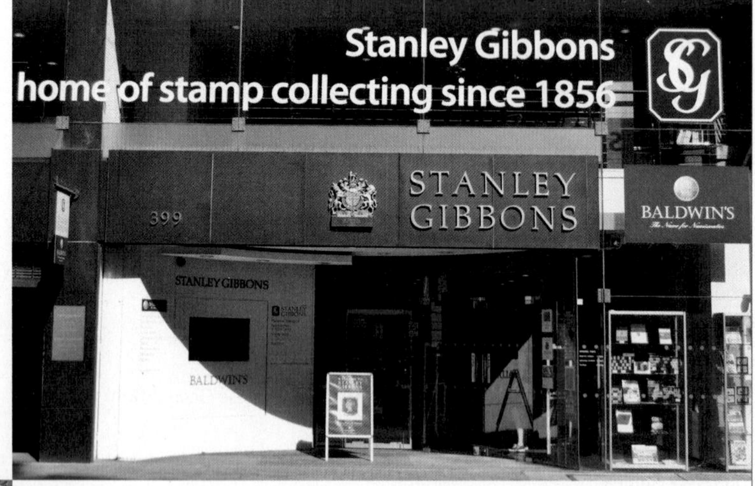

STANLEY GIBBONS - THE HOME OF STAMP COLLECTING FOR OVER 160 YEARS.

Visit our store at 399 Strand
for all your philatelic needs.

EVERYTHING FOR THE STAMP COLLECTOR.

- Great Britain Stamps
- Commonwealth Stamps
- Publications and Accessories
- Auctions

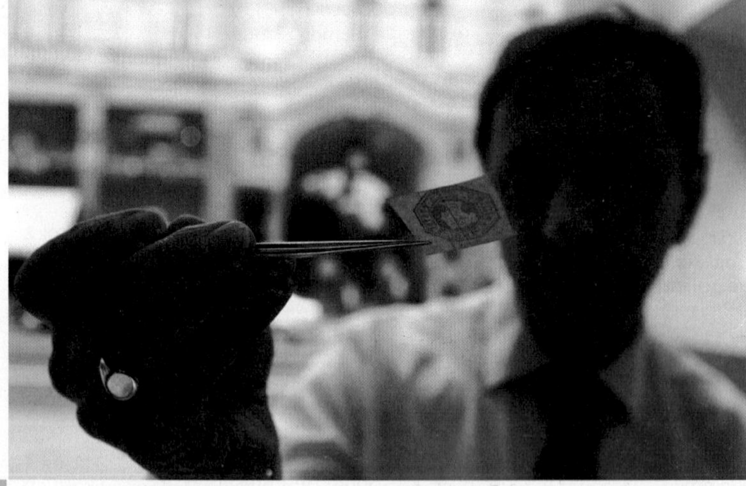

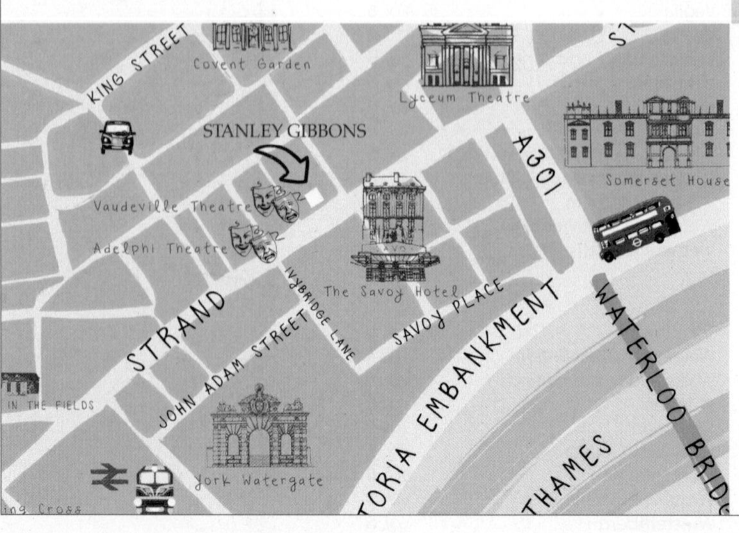

WHERE TO FIND US

STANLEY GIBBONS
399 STRAND
LONDON, WC2R 0LX
UNITED KINGDOM

0207 557 4436

SHOP@STANLEYGIBBONS.COM

OPENING HOURS

Mon - Fri: 9am - 5:30pm | Sat: 9:30 - 5:30pm | Sun: Closed